BENN'S MEDIA 5

WORLD NEWS MEDIA

World News Media
Volume 2
163rd EDITION

The guide to news media and broadcast.

Contents

ISBN: 978-1-906035-72-3 - World News Media (excluding UK & Ireland)

Published by: Cision UK Ltd.
VAT registration number: 553 8580 17
Registered Office: Longbow House, 20 Chiswell Street, London, EC1Y 4TW
Website: www.cision.com
Telephone: 0207 689 1160

E-mail: benns.uk@cision.com
Please send any data amendments or additions to: changes.uk@cision.com

BENN'S MEDIA

2015

WORLD NEWS MEDIA

About Benn's Media

Published in two volumes, Benn's Media aims to provide listings of media which either carry advertising or accept press releases in UK and Ireland (Volume 1) and an overview of world news media, newspapers, news syndicates and broadcast organisations. (Volume 2)

ISBN: 978-1-906035-70-9 - Full Set
ISBN: 978-1-906035-71-6 - UK & Ireland
ISBN: 978-1-906035-72-3 - World News Media (excluding UK & Ireland)

Advertising rates: US/Canada
Newspapers show per-column-inch rate of a full page colour/mono

To update entry details	To contact the Benn's Sales Team
Contact the Research Team	Telephone: 0207 689 1160
Email: changes.uk@cision.com	E-mail: benns.uk@cision.com

When contacting publications, please mention you found them in Benn's Media

AFGHANISTAN Tel: 93

Standard Time: GMT +4.5
Continent: Asia
Capital City: Kabul

NEWSPAPERS & PUBLICATIONS

NEWS SERVICE/SYNDICATE

Associated Press
Editorial: House 1, Street 15, Wazir Akbar Khan, Kabul. **T:** 93 20 230-0335
NEWS SERVICE/SYNDICATE

BROADCASTING

RADIO STATIONS

Arman FM
Editorial: ARMAN FM, PO Box 1045, Kabul
E: info@arman.fm **W:** http://www.arman.fm

ALBANIA Tel: 355

Standard Time: GMT +1
Continent: Europe
Capital City: Tirana

NEWSPAPERS & PUBLICATIONS

NEWSPAPERS

Gazeta e Tiranes
Owner: SHEKULLI MEDIA GROUP
Editorial: Rr. Aleksander Moisiu, Ish-Kinostudio, Tirane. **T:** 355 42 51 422
E: letra@gazetaetiranes.com.al
W: http://www.gazetaetiranes.com.al
Freq: Daily; **Circ:** 10000 Pub Statement
Editor In Chief: Elisabeta Ilnica
Editorial Profile: Daily newspaper covering news and current affairs from Tirana.
Language (s): Albanian
DAILY NEWSPAPER

Gazeta Metropol
Editorial: Rruga Dull Keta, nr.5, Tirane.
T: 355 4 233 991
E: gazetametropol@yahoo.com
W: http://www.gazetametropol.com
Freq: Daily
Editorial Profile: National newspaper covering politics, economics, business, social issues, culture and sports.
Language (s): Albanian
DAILY NEWSPAPER

Integrimi
Editorial: Rruga "Sami Frashëri", Nr. 20/10, Tirane. **T:** 355 4 270 413
E: gazetaintegrimi@lsi.al
W: http://www.integrimi.com
Editorial Profile: Newspaper in Albania covering general news and political events from the socialist party point of views.
Language (s): Albanian
DAILY NEWSPAPER

Panorama
Owner: Panorama Group
Editorial: Rr "Jordan Misja", behind Harry Fulltz School, Palace 1, Shk. 2/2, Tirana.
T: 355 4 273 207 **E:** info@panorama.com.al
W: http://www.panorama.com.al
Freq: Daily; **Circ:** 25000 Pub Statement
Editor In Chief: Robert Rakipllari
Editorial Profile: Daily newspaper covering social, economic, politic and cultural issues.
Language (s): English
DAILY NEWSPAPER

Shekulli
Owner: SHEKULLI MEDIA GROUP
Editorial: Rruga Ismail Qemali, Pallati Abissnet, Tirane. **T:** 355 4 256994
E: komente@shekulli.com.al
W: http://www.shekulli.com.al

Freq: Daily; **Circ:** 25000 Pub Statement
Editorial Profile: Newspaper covering politics, economy, education, health, culture, social events and sport, classified, recruitment, real estates, sell and buy business, travel offers, reportages, letters and comments, investigation.
Language (s): Albanian
DAILY NEWSPAPER

Sporti Shqiptar
Owner: SHEKULLI MEDIA GROUP
Editorial: Rruga Aleksandër Moisiu, ish-Kinostudio, Tirane. **T:** 355 43 68 322
E: www.sportishqiptar@live.com
W: http://www.sportishqiptar.com.al
Freq: Daily; **Circ:** 20000 Not Audited
Publisher: Koço Kokëdhima; **Editor:** Baskhim Tufa
Editorial Profile: Newspaper covering sports news from Albania, especially football, international sport news.
Language (s): Albanian
DAILY NEWSPAPER

Standard
Owner: Standard shpk
Editorial: ad. rruga e Kavajes, nr.67, Tirana.
T: 355 4 2260695 **E:** info@standard.al
W: http://www.standard.al
Freq: Daily Pub Statement
Editor In Chief: Sami Neza
Editorial Profile: Newspaper covering daily news, politics, economics, social issues, culture, sports, with special reports and features. Presents right wing political views.
Language (s): Albanian
DAILY NEWSPAPER

TemA
Owner: Media - Enter Sh. p. k.
Editorial: Zayed Business Center, Rr. Sulejman Delvina, Tirane. **T:** 355 69 20 20 806
E: info@tema.al **W:** http://www.gazetatema.net
Freq: Daily; **Circ:** 10000 Pub Statement
Editor: Enton Palushi
Editorial Profile: Newspaper covering politics, economics, social issues, current affairs, culture, entertainment, sport and general news nationally and internationally.
Language (s): Albanian
DAILY NEWSPAPER

Tirana Observer
Editorial: Rruga "Irfan Tomini", pallati "Biorn", Kati i 2-të, Tirane. **T:** 355 4 2419001
E: tiranaobserver@gmail.com
W: http://www.tiranaobserver.al
Freq: Daily; **Circ:** 10000 Pub Statement
News Editor: Nikoleta Kovaçi; **Editor In Chief:** Altin Sinani; **News Editor:** Elton Tafaruçi
Editorial Profile: Informative daily paper distributed on all the territory of the Albanian Republic and Greece.
Language (s): Albanian
DAILY NEWSPAPER

Tirana Times
Owner: Thnegel
Editorial: Rruga "Dëshmorët e 4 shkurtit" No.7/1, Tirane. **T:** 355 4 274 203
E: editor@tiranatimes.com
W: http://www.tiranatimes.com
Editorial Profile: Weekly newspaper of original news and views devoted to serving the English speaking audience of Albania and abroad.
Language (s): English
DAILY NEWSPAPER

NEWS SERVICE/SYNDICATE

Reuters
Editorial: 1 Nikolla Tupe Street, 2nd Floor, Tirana Unavailable. **T:** 355 4 222-9824
W: http://www.thomsonreuters.com
NEWS SERVICE/SYNDICATE

BROADCASTING

RADIO NETWORKS

Radio Tirana
Editorial: Rr. Ismail Qemali 11, Tirane.
T: 355 4 22 24 81 **E:** edamerepeza@yahoo.it

W: http://rtsh.sil.at

Top Albania Radio
Editorial: QNK, Blv Deshmoret e Kombit, Tirana. **T:** 355 42 247492
E: contact@topalbaniaradio.com
W: http://www.topalbaniaradio.com
Editorial Profile: National radio station in Albania covering general entertainment.

TELEVISION STATIONS

Vizion Plus
Editorial: Rr. Don Bosko Nr.5, Tirane.
T: 355 4 225 84 88 **E:** info@vizionplus.tv
W: http://www.vizionplus.tv
Editorial Profile: A national TV station transmitting news, local production (entertainment, social, political programs, movies, sports, documentaries and series).

ALGERIA Tel: 213

Standard Time: GMT +1
Continent: Africa
Capital City: Algiers

NEWSPAPERS & PUBLICATIONS

NEWSPAPERS

El Ayem El Djazairia
Owner: El Ayem El Djazairia Publishing & Distribution
Editorial: Office 5 & 6, Building 3, Hay 1200 Maskan, Algiers. **T:** 213 21 241343
E: watani_ayem@yahoo.fr
W: http://www.elayem.com
Freq: Daily; **Circ:** 100000 Pub Statement
News Editor: Siham Ain; **Editor In Chief:** Badreddine Chaa
Editorial Profile: El Ayem El Djazairia (Algerian Days) is a newspaper covering national and international news, politics, sport, lifestyle and society. It launched in 2004.
Language (s): Arabic
DAILY NEWSPAPER

Le Buteur
Owner: EXA
Editorial: Maison de la Presse, 1, Rue Bachir Attar, Algiers. **T:** 213 21 731417
E: lebuteur5@yahoo.fr
W: http://www.lebuteur.com
Freq: Daily; **Circ:** 120000 Rate Card
Editor-in-Chief: Mohamed Saad
Editorial Profile: Le Buteur is a daily newspaper covering local and international football. It launched in 2001 and is the French sister title to El Heddaf, which is published in Arabic.
Language (s): French
DAILY NEWSPAPER

Compétition
Owner: Top Sport sarl
Editorial: 17, Rue Reda-Houhou, Algiers.
T: 213 21 747695 **E:** contact@competition.dz
W: http://www.competition.dz
Freq: Daily; **Circ:** 65000 Pub Statement
Editor: Noureddine Boumali
Editorial Profile: Compétition is a daily newspaper covering local and international sport, particularly football. It launched in 1993, and is aimed at sports fans in Algeria.
Language (s): French
DAILY NEWSPAPER

Djazair News
Owner: Eurl Express News
Editorial: Alger Centre, 28, Rue Ahmed Boualem Khelfi, Algiers. **T:** 213 21 637026
E: djazairnews@gmail.com
W: http://www.djazairnews.info
Freq: Daily; **Circ:** 62000 Pub Statement
News Editor: Sara Douifi; **Editor In Chief:** Toufik Sissani
Editorial Profile: Djazair News is a national newspaper focusing on local news and current affairs. It is published daily, except Fridays, and launched in 2004.
Language (s): Arabic
DAILY NEWSPAPER

Ech Chaab
Owner: El Chaab Presse
Editorial: PO Box 59, 39, Boulevard des Martures, Algiers 16000. **T:** 213 21 606783
E: info@ech-chaab.com
W: http://www.ech-chaab.com
Freq: Daily; **Circ:** 55000 Pub Statement
Editorial Profile: Ech Chaab (The People) is a newspaper covering national and international news, politics, business, sport, society, culture and youth issues. It is published daily, except Fridays, and launched in 1962. Sout Al Assir, a supplement covering Palestinian news, history and heritage, is issued with the newspaper on Thursdays.
Language (s): Arabic
DAILY NEWSPAPER

Ech-Chorouk El Yaoumi
Owner: Ech-Chorouk Infed SARL
Editorial: Maison de la Presse, 2, Rue Farid Zaouiouech, Algiers. **T:** 213 21 284784
E: infos@echoroukonline.com
W: http://www.echoroukonline.com
Freq: Daily; **Circ:** 400000 Pub Statement
News Editor: Jamal Alami; **Editor In Chief:** Mohamed Yagoubi
Editorial Profile: Ech-Chorouk El Yaoumi is a newspaper covering local and international news, business, politics and sport. It launched in 2001.
Language (s): Arabic
DAILY NEWSPAPER

Echibek
Owner: Sept Com SARL
Editorial: Maison de la Presse Tahar Djaout, 1, rue Bachir Attar, Algiers. **T:** 213 21 402222
E: echibek@yahoo.fr
W: http://www.echibek.net
Freq: Daily; **Circ:** 87000 Pub Statement
Editor In Chief: Walid Medouar
Editorial Profile: Echibek (The Goal) is a national newspaper focusing on local and international sport, particularly football. The newspaper is published four times a week on Saturdays, Mondays, Tuesdays and Thursdays, and launched in 1993.
Language (s): Arabic
DAILY NEWSPAPER

Ennahar El Djadid
Owner: El Athir Presse sarl
Editorial: PO Box 146, Boulevard Said Hamdine, Algiers. **T:** 213 23 599292
E: wataniennahar@gmail.com
W: http://www.ennaharonline.com
Freq: Daily; **Circ:** 364155 Pub Statement
Editor In Chief: Dalila Belkhir
Editorial Profile: Ennahar El Djadid (The New Day) is a newspaper covering news and sport. It is published daily, except Fridays, and launched in 2007.
Language (s): Arabic
DAILY NEWSPAPER

Al Fadjr
Owner: Erraid Lilialam S.A.R.L
Editorial: Maison de la Presse, 1 Rue Bachir Attar, Place du 1er Mai, Algiers.
T: 213 21 657660 **E:** fadjr@al-fadjr.com
W: http://www.al-fadjr.com
Freq: Daily; **Circ:** 65000 Pub Statement
News Editor: Amine Lounessi; **Editor in Chief:** Malek Reddad
Editorial Profile: Al Fadjr is a national newspaper covering local news, current affairs, business and sport. It is published daily, except Fridays, and launched in 2000.
Language (s): Arabic
DAILY NEWSPAPER

El Heddaf
Owner: EXA
Editorial: Maison De La Presse, 1 Rue Bachir Attar, Place Du 1er Mai, Algiers.
T: 213 21 731417 **E:** redaction3@gmail.com
W: http://www.elheddaf.com
Freq: Daily; **Circ:** 475000 Rate Card
Editor In Chief: Ismail Marazka
Editorial Profile: El Heddaf is a tabloid-sized newspaper covering local and international sport, particularly football. It launched in 1999 and is the Arabic sister title to Le Buteur, which is published in French.
Language (s): Arabic
DAILY NEWSPAPER

El Khabar
Owner: El Khabar Spa
Editorial: PO Box 378, 32 rue Al Fath Ben Khalkan, Algiers 16016. **T:** 213 21 484436
E: redaction@elkhabar.com
W: http://www.elkhabar.com
Freq: Daily; **Circ:** 550000 Pub Statement
Editor In Chief: Mohamed Bghali; **News Editor:** Hacine Djaafar
Editorial Profile: El Khabar (The News) is a 24-page, tabloid-sized newspaper focusing on national and international news. It launched in 1990.
Language (s): Arabic
DAILY NEWSPAPER

El Khabar El Riadi
Owner: El Khabar Spa
Editorial: La Maison de la Presse, Zone Industrielle, Constantine. **T:** 213 31 660587
E: elkhabarerriadhi@gmail.com
W: http://www.elkhabarerriadhi.com
Freq: Daily; **Circ:** 70000 Pub Statement
Editor in Chief: Adlene Hamidechi; **Editor:** Rafik Harich; **Editor:** Tarik Kadri; **Editor:** Chouaib Zouazoui
Editorial Profile: El Khabar El Riadi (Sports News) is a tabloid-sized newspaper covering national and international football. It launched in 2010.
Language (s): Arabic
DAILY NEWSPAPER

Liberté
Owner: SAEC sarl
Editorial: 15, Lottissement Azzitoune, Oued Roumane, Algiers. **T:** 213 21 307884
E: info@liberte-algerie.com
W: http://www.liberte-algerie.com
Freq: Daily; **Circ:** 180000 Pub Statement
Publisher: Abrous Outoudert; **Editor in Chief:** Salim Tamani
Editorial Profile: Liberté (Freedom) is a national newspaper focusing on national and international news, business, culture and sport. It is published daily, except Fridays, and launched in 1992. The newspaper includes football supplement Liberté Foot on Mondays.
Language (s): French
DAILY NEWSPAPER

Maracana
Owner: La Gazette de L'Omnisports
Editorial: 28, Rue Ali Khodja, Bordj El-Kiffan, Algiers 16000. **T:** 213 21 926225
E: maracanalejournal@yahoo.fr
W: http://www.maracanafoot.com
Freq: Daily; **Circ:** 75000
Editor: Djamel Touafek
Editorial Profile: Maracana is a daily newspaper covering national and international sport. It launched in February 2005.
Language (s): French
DAILY NEWSPAPER

El Massa
Owner: El Massa
Editorial: 51, Rue Arbi Ben Mhidi, Algiers.
T: 213 21 745799 **E:** info@el-massa.com
W: http://www.el-massa.com
Freq: Daily; **Circ:** 50000 Pub Statement
News Editor: Malika Khallaf; **Editor In Chief:** Ali Salem
Editorial Profile: El Massa is a newspaper focusing on national and international news, current affairs, politics, sports and entertainment. It is published daily, except Fridays, and launched in 1985.
Language (s): Arabic
DAILY NEWSPAPER

Al Mawîd Alyaoumi
Owner: Dar Alwaâd
Editorial: Maison de la Presse, Place du 1er Mai, Algiers. **T:** 213 21 670716
E: maouidhawa@yahoo.fr
W: http://www.elmaouid.com
Freq: Daily; **Circ:** 50000 Pub Statement
News Editor: Hakim Massoudi
Editorial Profile: Al Mawîd Alyaoumi is a newspaper covering news, culture, society and sport. It is published daily, except Fridays, and launched in 1992.
Language (s): Arabic
DAILY NEWSPAPER

Le Midi Libre
Owner: Midi Libre EURL
Editorial: 26, rue Didouche Mourad, Algiers.
T: 213 21 638082 **E:** redaction@lemidi-dz.com
W: http://www.lemidi-dz.com
Freq: Daily; **Circ:** 50000 Pub Statement
News Editor: Sadek Belhocine; **Editor in Chief:** Sihem Henine
Editorial Profile: Le Midi Libre is a tabloid-sized newspaper covering local and

international news, business and sport. It launched in 2007.
Language (s): French
DAILY NEWSPAPER

El Moudjahid
Owner: SIA
Editorial: 20 rue de la Liberté, Algiers.
T: 213 21 737081
E: elmoudjahid@elmoudjahid.com
W: http://www.elmoudjahid-dz.com
Freq: Daily; **Circ:** 150000 Pub Statement
News Editor: Noura Chargui; **Editor In Chief:** Kamal Oulman
Editorial Profile: El Moudjahid is a newspaper focusing on national and international news, current affairs, politics, sports and entertainment. It is published daily, except Fridays, and launched in 1956.
Language (s): French
DAILY NEWSPAPER

Le Quotidien D'Oran
Owner: SPA Oran Presse
Editorial: PO Box 110, 1, rue Laid Ould Tayeb, Oran. **T:** 213 41 327278
E: lequotidiendoran@yahoo.fr
W: http://www.lequotidien-oran.com
Freq: Daily; **Circ:** 155678 Pub Statement
News Editor: Jamal Belaifa; **Editor In Chief:** Sid Ahmed Mohamed
Editorial Profile: Le Quotidien D'Oran is a newspaper covering national and international news, current affairs, politics, sports and entertainment. It is published daily, except Fridays, and launched in 1994.
Language (s): French
DAILY NEWSPAPER

Le Soir D'Algerie
Owner: Le Soir D'Algerie SARL
Editorial: 1 Rue Bachir Attar, Place du 1er Mai, Algiers 16000. **T:** 213 21 670651
E: info@lesoirdalgerie.com
W: http://www.lesoirdalgerie.com
Freq: Daily; **Circ:** 80000 Pub Statement
News Editor: Abderrahmane Bettache; **Editor In Chief:** Badreddine Manaa
Editorial Profile: Le Soir D'Algerie is a daily newspaper focusing on national and international news, sport and business. It launched in 1991.
Language (s): French
DAILY NEWSPAPER

Le Temps d'Algérie
Owner: Group Media Temps Nouveaux EURL
Editorial: No 8, Lotissement Sylvain Fourastier, El Mouradia, Algiers 9108.
T: 213 21 699635
E: redaction@letempsdz.com
W: http://www.letempsdz.com
Freq: Daily; **Circ:** 100000 Pub Statement
Editor in Chief: Malika Bougherara
Editorial Profile: Le Temps d'Algérie is a tabloid-sized newspaper covering local and international news, culture and sport. It is published daily, except Fridays, and launched in 2009.
Language (s): French
DAILY NEWSPAPER

Transaction d'Algerie
Owner: Sedi Eurl
Editorial: 6, Rue du Centenaire, Ruisseau, Algiers. **T:** 213 21 671966
E: transactiondalgerie@yahoo.fr
W: http://www.transactiondalgerie.com
Freq: Daily; **Circ:** 80000 Pub Statement
News Editor: Hafid Azouz; **Editor in Chief:** Sid-Ahmed Hamache
Editorial Profile: Transaction d'Algerie is a daily newspaper covering business and the economy. It is published daily, except Fridays, and launched in 2004.
Language (s): French
DAILY NEWSPAPER

El Watan
Owner: El Watan Presse
Editorial: Maison de la Presse Tahar Djaout, 1 rue Bachir Attar, Algiers 16000.
T: 213 21 682183 **E:** nationale@elwatan.com
W: http://www.elwatan.com
Freq: Daily; **Circ:** 170000 Pub Statement
Editor In Chief: Ali Benyahia
Editorial Profile: El Watan is a newspaper containing national and international news, business, features and sport. It is published daily, except Fridays when it is replaced by El Watan Week-end. The newspaper includes business supplement El Watan Economie on Mondays, and was first published in 1990.
Language (s): French
DAILY NEWSPAPER

El Watan Week-end
Owner: El Watan Presse
Editorial: Maison de la Presse Tahar Djaout, 1 rue Bachir Attar, Algiers 16000.
T: 213 21 653317 **E:** weekend@elwatan.com
W: http://www.elwatan.com
Freq: Fri; **Circ:** 100000 Pub Statement
Editor In Chief: Adlene Meddi; **News Editor:** Yasmine Said
Editorial Profile: El Watan Week-end is the Friday edition of El Watan newspaper, and covers politics, travel, sport, business and culture. The Friday edition was introduced in 2009.
Language (s): French
NEWSPAPER

El Youm
Owner: Group International de Communication
Editorial: Maison de la Presse Tahar Djaout, Place du 1er Mai, Algiers 16000.
T: 213 21 667085 **E:** elyoum11@yahoo.fr
W: http://www.elyawm.com
Freq: Daily; **Circ:** 150000 Pub Statement
Editorial Profile: El Youm (The Day) is a daily newspaper covering news, current affairs, business, culture and sport. It launched in 1999.
Language (s): Arabic
DAILY NEWSPAPER

NEWS SERVICE/SYNDICATE

Agence France-Presse - Algiers Bureau
Owner: Agence France-Presse
Editorial: 6 rue Abdelkrim El-Khettabi, Algiers 16000. **T:** 213 21 630781
E: amer.ouali@afp.com
W: http://www.afp.com
Bureau Chief: Amer Ouali
Editorial Profile: Algiers bureau of international news agency supplying news - text, graphics, video and pictures - to subscribers around the world.
Language (s): Arabic
NEWS SERVICE/SYNDICATE

Agence Photo Presse
Owner: Agence Photo Presse
Editorial: 9 Rue Rouiba, Delmonte, Oran 31000. **T:** 213 41 496094
E: redaction_app@outlook.com
Editor: Ahmed Ben Mohamed
Editorial Profile: Agence Photo Presse is a press agency covering news and sport.
Language (s): French
NEWS SERVICE/SYNDICATE

Algérie Presse Service
Owner: Algérie Presse Service
Editorial: PO Box 444, Avenue des Frères Bouadou, Algiers. **T:** 213 23 569685
E: dt@aps.dz **W:** http://www.aps.dz
Editor in Chief: Haceni Rabeh
Editorial Profile: Algérie Presse Service is the national news agency of Algeria. It was founded in Tunis on 1 December 1961 during the national liberation war and, after independence, its headquarters was transferred to Algiers. The agency covers news, politics, society, culture, sport, regional news, investigations and business and produces around 600 news dispatches daily in three languages (Arabic, French and English). It has a staff of nearly 460 employees, including 300 reporters, photographers and translators.As well as the headquarters in Algiers, the agency collects news through a network of four regional directorates with offices in Constantine (East), Oran (West), Ouargla (South) and Blida (Central). It also has overseas representation in Washington, Moscow, Paris, London, Brussels, Rome, Madrid, Cairo, Rabat, Tunis, Amman, and Dakar.
Language (s): Arabic
NEWS SERVICE/SYNDICATE

European Pressphoto Agency - Maghreb Bureau
Owner: European Pressphoto Agency
Editorial: 4, Rue Mohamed Idriss Bay, Algiers 16000. **T:** 213 770 563160 **E:** messara@epa.eu
W: http://www.epa.eu
Editorial Profile: Photo agency representing 11 European news agencies (DPA, ANSA, EFE, Belga, APA, Athens News Agency, PAP, ANP, MTI, Keystone and LUSA) - covers news, politics, sports, fashion, economy, conflicts, disasters, features and business.
Language (s): Arabic
NEWS SERVICE/SYNDICATE

New Press Algerie
Owner: New Press Algerie

Editorial: Maison de la Presse, 1 Rue Bachir Attar, Algiers. **T:** 213 21 663317
E: newpress@newpressphoto.com
W: http://www.newpressphoto.com
Editorial Profile: New Press Algerie is an independent Algerian photo agency.
Language (s): French
NEWS SERVICE/SYNDICATE

BROADCASTING

RADIO STATIONS

Radio Algerienne - Chaine 1
Owner: La Radio Algérienne
Editorial: 21 Boulevard des Martyrs, Algiers.
T: 213 21 483790 **E:** chaine1@radioalgerie.dz
W: http://www.radioalgerie.dz
Editorial Profile: Chaine 1 (Channel 1) is a state-owned national radio station broadcasting round the clock in Arabic. Besides four full news bulletins and hourly news summaries, programmes include educational, cultural, information and entertainment broadcasting. It launched in 1986.

Radio Algerienne - Chaine 2
Owner: La Radio Algérienne
Editorial: 21 Boulevard des Martyrs, Algiers.
T: 213 21 483790 **E:** chaine2@radioalgerie.dz
W: http://www.radioalgerie.dz
Editorial Profile: Chaine 2 (Channel 2) is a state-owned national radio station broadcasting round the clock in the Tamazight (Berber) language. The station launched in 1986 and aims to promote Algerian national culture and the people's cultural heritage.

Radio Algerienne - Chaine 3
Owner: La Radio Algérienne
Editorial: 21, Boulevard des Martyrs, Algiers.
T: 213 21 483790 **E:** chaine3@radioalgerie.dz
W: http://www.radioalgerie.dz/fr/chaine3
Editorial Profile: Chaine 3 (Channel 3) is a state-owned national radio station broadcasting for 21-hrs a day in French. The station launched in 1986, and broadcasts music, entertainment and information programmes tackling daily topical issues.

TELEVISION STATIONS

Algérie 1
Owner: L'Enterprise Nationale de Télévision
Editorial: PO Box 184, 21, Boulevard des Martyrs, Algiers 16000. **T:** 213 21 602300
E: dinfo.entv@gmail.com
W: http://www.entv.dz
Editorial Profile: Algérie 1, also known as ENTV, is a state-owned television channel broadcasting entertainment, news and films 24 hours a day. The channel launched in 1962 and broadcasts terrestrially in Algeria.

Algérie 3
Owner: L'Enterprise Nationale de Télévision
Editorial: PO Box 184, 21, Boulevard des Martyrs, Algiers 16000. **T:** 213 21 602300
E: dinfo.entv@gmail.com
W: http://www.entv.dz
Editorial Profile: Algérie 3, also known as Thalitha TV, is a state-owned television station broadcasting entertainment, news and films 24 hours a day. Launched in 2002, the station broadcasts free-to-air on satellite.

Algérie 4
Owner: L'Enterprise Nationale de Télévision
Editorial: PO Box 184, 21, Boulevard des Martyrs, Algiers 16000. **T:** 213 21 239870
E: dinfo.entv@gmail.com
W: http://www.entv.dz
Editorial Profile: Algérie 4 is a state-owned television station broadcasts films, news and general programmes. Launched in 2009, the channel is aimed at the Amazigh population of Algeria.

Algérie 5
Owner: L'Enterprise Nationale de Télévision
Editorial: Centre Club des Pins, Algiers.
T: 213 21 374121 **E:** aouadi@entv.dz
W: http://www.entv.dz
Editorial Profile: Algérie 5 is a state-owned television station broadcasting Islamic programmes presented by Algerian Muslim scholars. Launched in 2009, the channel was formerly called Al Qoran Al Kareem Channel Algérie.

Canal Algérie
Owner: L'Enterprise Nationale de Télévision

Editorial: PO Box 184, 21, Boulevard des Martyrs, Algiers 16000. **T:** 213 21 239919
E: alger-contact@entv.dz
W: http://www.entv.dz
Editorial Profile: Canal Algérie, also known as Algérie 2, is a state-owned television channel broadcasting entertainment, news and films 24-hours a day. The channel launched in 1994 and broadcasts free-to-air on satellite.

AMERICAN SAMOA
Tel: 684

Standard Time: GMT -11
Continent: Oceania
Capital City: Pago Pago

NEWSPAPERS & PUBLICATIONS

NEWSPAPERS

Samoa News
Editorial: PO Box 909, Pago Pago 96799. **T:** 684 6335599
E: news.newsroom@samoatelco.com
W: http://www.samoanews.com
Freq: Daily; **Circ:** 4000 Not Audited
Editor in Chief: Rhonda Annesely-Canales
Editorial Profile: Samoa News is a local, daily newspaper serving residents of Pago Pago, American Samoa. The paper contains local news, politics, business, community issues and sports, as well as U.S. and world news that affects the readership.
Language (s): Samoan
DAILY NEWSPAPER

BROADCASTING

RADIO STATIONS

KKHJ-FM
Owner: South Seas Broadcasting Inc.
T: 684 6337793 **W:** http://www.khjradio.com
Editorial Profile: Provides daily news, sports, and live programs.

WVUV-FM
Owner: Shannon J. Cummings
T: 1 684 633-7793 **W:** http://www.wvuv.com

TELEVISION STATIONS

KVZK-TV
Owner: American Samoa Government
T: 684 6334191
Editorial Profile: Covers socio-economic and entertainment news.

ANDORRA
Tel: 376

Standard Time: GMT +1
Continent: Europe
Capital City: Andorra la Vella

NEWSPAPERS & PUBLICATIONS

NEWSPAPERS

Bondia
Owner: La Veu del Poble S.L.
Editorial: Carre Maria Pla 28, 1ª planta, Andorra La Vella. **T:** 376 80 88 88
E: bondia@bondia.ad
W: http://www.bondia.ad
Freq: Daily; **Circ:** 8000 Pub Statement
Redactora Jefe: Maria Baró
Editorial Profile: Daily newspaper focusing on Andorra general news.
Language (s): Catalan
DAILY NEWSPAPER

Diari d'Andorra
Owner: Premsa Andorrana SA
Editorial: Avda. Riberaygua 39, 5° piso, AD 50500, Andorra La Vella. **T:** 376 87 74 77
E: redaccio@diariandorra.info
W: http://www.diariandorra.info
Freq: Daily; **Circ:** 3200 Pub Statement
Redactor Jefe: David Domingo; **Editor:** Pietat Martín Vivas; **Redactor Jefe:** Toni Solanelles
Language (s): Catalan
DAILY NEWSPAPER

El Periodic d'Andorra
Owner: Andorrana de Publicaciones SA
Editorial: Parc de la Mola, 10 Torre Caldea, Les Escaldes - Engordany. **T:** 376 73 62 00
E: redaccio@andorra.elperiodico.com
W: http://www.elperiodico.com/andorra/default.asp
Freq: Daily; **Circ:** 7700 Pub Statement
Editorial Profile: General news about Andorra.
Language (s): Catalan
DAILY NEWSPAPER

ANGOLA
Tel: 244

Standard Time: GMT +1
Continent: Africa
Capital City: Luanda

NEWSPAPERS & PUBLICATIONS

NEWSPAPERS

Diário da República
Editorial: Cp 1306, Luanda. **T:** 244 22530
Freq: Daily
Editor: Editorial
Language (s): Portuguese
DAILY NEWSPAPER

BROADCASTING

RADIO STATIONS

Radio Ecclesia
Editorial: Street Commander Papal brief, N.° 118, Luanda. **T:** 244 2443041
E: recclesia@recclesia.org
W: http://www.recclesia.org

ANGUILLA
Tel: 1264

Standard Time: GMT -4
Continent: The Americas
Capital City: The Valley

NEWSPAPERS & PUBLICATIONS

NEWSPAPERS

The Anguillian
Owner: Nat Hodge's Public Relations, Information and Consultancy Se
T: 1 264 497-3823
E: theanguillian@anguillanet.com
W: http://www.anguillian.com
Freq: Fri; **Circ:** 1500 Not Audited
Publisher & Editor: A. Nat Hodge
Editorial Profile: The Anguillian is a weekly newspaper providing Local and Community News coverage for the residents of Anguilla.
Language (s): English
NEWSPAPER

BROADCASTING

RADIO NETWORKS

Radio Anguilla
Editorial: PO Box 60, The Valley.
T: 264 4972218 **E:** radioaxa@anguillanet.com
W: http://www.radioaxa.com
Editorial Profile: Provides news and live music, playing country, hip hop, socca, calypso and other rhythms.

ANTIGUA & BARBUDA
Tel: 1268

Standard Time: GMT -4
Continent: The Americas
Capital City: St John's (Antigua), Codrington (Barbuda)

NEWSPAPERS & PUBLICATIONS

NEWSPAPERS

The Daily Observer
Owner: Daily Observer Ltd

Editorial: PO Box 1318, St John's.
T: 1268 48 01 750 **E:** dailyobserver@candw.ag
W: http://www.antiguaobserver.com
Freq: Daily; **Circ:** 4000 Not Audited
Publisher: Winston A. Derrick; **Editor:** Carol Williams
Editorial Profile: Serves residents of St. John's, Antigua. Features national and international news, sports, entertainment and leisure.
Language (s): English
DAILY NEWSPAPER

BROADCASTING

RADIO NETWORKS

Observer Radio 91.1FM
T: 268 4819105
E: voice@antiguaobserver.com
W: http://www.antiguaobserver.com
Editorial Profile: Plays Calipso, Soca, Reggaeton. Provides daily news, sports, radio call-in programs in which the audience interacts.

ARGENTINA
Tel: 54

Standard Time: GMT -3
Continent: The Americas
Capital City: Buenos Aires

NEWSPAPERS & PUBLICATIONS

NEWSPAPERS

Clarín
Editorial: Tacuarí 1842, Capital Federal C1139AAN. **T:** 54 11 43097500
E: lectores@clarin.com
W: http://www.clarin.com
Freq: Daily; **Circ:** 410535 Not Audited
City Editor: Guillermo Allerand; **Editor:** Horacio Convertini; **Architecture Editor:** Humberto González Montaner; **Editor:** Eduardo Menegazzi; **Editor:** Pablo Scholz; **Editor:** Oscar Spinelli; **Editor:** Dolores Vidal; **Editor:** Dora Beatriz Videla
Editorial Profile: Líder en la Argentina y el de mayor circulación en el mundo de habla hispana. Es el diario de mayor influencia por ser el de mayor lectura. Gran variedad de secciones y suplementos y se destaca por su alto número de avisos clasificados. Formato tabloide. Fecha de Aparición: 28 de agosto de 1945
Language (s): Spanish
DAILY NEWSPAPER

Crónica
Editorial: Av. Juan de Garay 140, Capital Federal C1063ABO. **T:** 54 11 43611051
E: cronica@diariocronica.com.ar
W: http://www.diariocronica.com.ar
Freq: Daily; **Circ:** 160000 Not Audited
Editor: Ricardo Filigueras; **Editor in Chief:** Héctor Lorenzo; **Editor:** Eduardo Marrazzi
Editorial Profile: Formato tabloide. No está inscripto al IVC. Es sensacionalista y se destaca por las notas de policiales, de turf y de fútbol. Fecha de Aparición: 29 de julio de 1936
Language (s): Spanish
DAILY NEWSPAPER

Diario del Viajero
Editorial: Av. De Mayo 666, Capital Federal 1084. **T:** 54 11 43315050
E: redaccion@diariodelviajero.com.ar
W: http://www.diariodelviajero.com.ar
Freq: Weekly; **Circ:** 300000 Not Audited
Editor in Chief: Carlos Besanson
Editorial Profile: Publication targeted towards tourists in Argentina featuring museums, cultural centers, hotels, transportation, the Argentine Automobile Club, restaurants, and more.
Language (s): Spanish
NEWSPAPER

Diario Popular
Editorial: Intendente Beguiristain 142, Sarandí B1872CBD. **T:** 54 1142038091
E: redaccion@diariopopular.com.ar
Freq: Daily; **Circ:** 70091 Not Audited
Editor: Alberto Calligari; **Editor in Chief:** José Di Mauro; **Editor:** Hugo Iñiguez; **Editor:** Hugo Martínez; **Editor:** Pablo Quiróz; **Editor:** Claudio Rodríguez; **Editor:** Luly Vitcop; **Editor:** Guillermo Vucetich

Editorial Profile: Formato tabloide. No está inscripto en el IVC es un diario sensacionalista. Fecha de Aparición: 1 de julio de 1974
Language (s): Spanish
DAILY NEWSPAPER

La Nación
Editorial: Bouchard 557, Capital Federal C1106ABG. **T:** 54 11 43191600
E: exterior@lanacion.com.ar
W: http://www.lanacion.com.ar
Freq: Daily; **Circ:** 160000 Not Audited
Editor: Julio Aguirre Chanetón; **Editor:** Daniel Amiano; **Editor:** Carolina Arenes; **Editor:** Nora Bär; **Editor:** José Luis Brea; **Editor:** Hugo Caligaris; **Editor in Chief:** Ricardo Cárpena; **Editor:** Jesús Cornejo; **Editor in Chief:** Luis Cortina; **Editor:** Diego Cúneo; **Editor:** Alicia de Arteaga; **Editor:** Josefina Giglio; **Editor:** Graciela Guadalupe; **Editor:** Catalina Lanús; **Editor:** Graciela Melgarejo; **Editor:** Cristian Mira; **Editor:** Javier Navia; **Editor:** Jorge Oviedo; **Editor:** Jorge Pandini; **Editor:** Nicolás Singer; **Editor:** Ariel Torres; **Editor:** Alberto Wainziger
Editorial Profile: Since 1870 La Nacion covers national and international news.
Language (s): Spanish
DAILY NEWSPAPER

Página 12
Editorial: Solís 1525, Capital Federal C1092AAG. **T:** 54 11 6772-4400
E: redactor@pagina12.com.ar
W: http://www.pagina12.com.ar
Freq: Daily; **Circ:** 125000 Not Audited
Editor: Juan Ignacio Boido; **Editor:** Fernando D'Addario; **Editor:** Eduardo Fabregat; **Editor:** Pedro Lipjobich; **Editor:** Leonardo Moledo; **Editor:** Andrés Osojnik; **Editor:** Nora Veiras; **Editor:** Eduardo Videla; **Editor:** Alfredo Zaiat; **Editor:** Claudio Ariel Zeiger
Editorial Profile: Formato tabloide. No está inscripto en el IVC. Es un diario de izquierda. Presenta las noticias con un estilo de revista y realiza trabajos de investigación periodística de denuncia. Fecha de Aparición: 26 de mayo de 1987
Language (s): Spanish
DAILY NEWSPAPER

Tiempo Argentino
Editorial: Buenos Aires
E: editorial@tiempoargentino.com
W: http://tiempo.infonews.com
Freq: Daily; **Circ:** 50000
Language (s): Spanish
DAILY NEWSPAPER

La Voz del Interior
Editorial: Av. La Voz del Interior 6080, Cordoba 5000. **T:** 54 351 4757100
E: lavoz@lavozdelinterior.com.ar
W: http://www.lavoz.com.ar
Freq: Daily; **Circ:** 80000 Not Audited
Editor: Eduardo Bocco; **Editor:** Javier Candelero; **Editor:** Alejandra Conti; **Editor:** Mariana Grimaldi; **Editor:** Damián Oroz; **Editor:** Carlos Rodríguez; **Editor:** Carlos Schilling; **Editor:** Juan Turello
Editorial Profile: Es el diario de mayor prestigio y tirada en la Provincia de Córdoba. Tiene formato sábana. Fecha de Aparición: La Voz del Interior S.A
Language (s): Spanish
DAILY NEWSPAPER

NEWS SERVICE/SYNDICATE

Agencia Los Diarios
Editorial: Sarmiento 1236, Capital Federal C1041AAZ. **T:** 54 11 43822728
E: losdiarios@losdiarios.com.ar
W: http://www.losdiarios.com.ar
Language (s): Spanish
NEWS SERVICE/SYNDICATE

Agencia Nosis
Editorial: San Martín 365, Capital Federal C1004AAG. **T:** 54 11 63160000
E: info@nosis.com.ar
W: http://www.nosis.com.ar
Editor in Chief: Marcelo Bottini
Language (s): Spanish
NEWS SERVICE/SYNDICATE

Agencia Nova
Editorial: Calle 48 633, 3 307, La Plata 1900
E: noticias@nova.net.com.ar
W: http://www.nova-noticias.com
Editor in Chief: Mario Casalongue
Language (s): Spanish
NEWS SERVICE/SYNDICATE

WORLD NEWS MEDIA

AICA - Agencia Informativa Católica Argentina
Editorial: Bolívar 218, Capital Federal C1066AAF. T: 54 11 43434397
E: info@aica.org W: http://www.aica.org.ar
Language (s): Spanish
NEWS SERVICE/SYNDICATE

APF Agencia Periodística Federal
Editorial: Tucumán 257, 2 3, Paraná 3100.
T: 54 343 4225374
E: direccion@apfdigital.com.ar
W: http://www.agenciapf.com.ar
Language (s): Spanish
NEWS SERVICE/SYNDICATE

Associated Press
Editorial: Leandro N Alem 712 Piso 4 (1101), Buenos Aires C1006ABG. T: 54 11 4311-0081
Bureau Chief: Michael Warren
NEWS SERVICE/SYNDICATE

Bloomberg News
Editorial: Corrientes 485 Piso 9, Buenos Aires C1043AAE. T: 54 11 4321-7738
E: release@bloomberg.net
Bureau Chief: Daniel Cancel; Editor: Robin Saponar
NEWS SERVICE/SYNDICATE

DIB Diarios Bonaerenses
Editorial: Calle 49 535, 1 3, La Plata 1900.
T: 54 221 43313415
E: administracion@dib.com.ar
W: http://www.dib.com.ar
Language (s): Spanish
NEWS SERVICE/SYNDICATE

Dow Jones Newswires
Editorial: Ing. Butty 240 Piso 5, Buenos Aires 1001. T: 54 11 4590-2428
Bureau Chief: Ken Parks
NEWS SERVICE/SYNDICATE

DYN – Diarios y Noticias
Editorial: Julio A. Roca 636, Capital Federal C1067ABO. T: 54 11 43423040
E: editor@dyn.com.ar
W: http://www.dyn.com.ar
Editor: Gabriela Bersier; Editor in Chief: Carmen Coiro; Editor in Chief: José Cutello; Editor: Jorge Neri; Editor in Chief: Mario Poliak; Editor: Miguel Rouco; Editor: Walter Schmidt
Language (s): Spanish
NEWS SERVICE/SYNDICATE

El Consultor
Editorial: Mendoza 3142, Santa Fe S3000FTO.
T: 54 342 4566378
E: correo@elconsultorweb.com
W: http://www.elconsultorweb.com
Editor-in-Charge: José Luis Tepper
Language (s): Spanish
NEWS SERVICE/SYNDICATE

Noticias Argentinas
Editorial: Moreno 769, Capital Federal C1008AAL. T: 54 11 43313850
E: redaccion@noticiasargentinas.com
W: http://www.noticiasargentinas.com
Language (s): Spanish
NEWS SERVICE/SYNDICATE

Reuters
Editorial: Av E Madero 942 - 24 Piso, Buenos Aires C1106ACW. T: 54 11 4318-0600
E: buenosaires.newsroom@thomsonreuters.com
NEWS SERVICE/SYNDICATE

Télam
Editorial: Bolívar 531, Capital Federal C1066AAK. T: 54 11 43390300
E: admperiodistica@telam.com.ar
W: http://www.telam.com.ar
Editor: Marcelo Bianco; Editor: Daniel Casas; Editor: Mora Cordeau; Editor: Eduardo De La Fuente; Editor: Eduardo Duschatzky; Editor: Mariano Fontella
Language (s): Spanish
NEWS SERVICE/SYNDICATE

BROADCASTING

RADIO NETWORKS

La 100 (FM 99.9)
Editorial: Mansilla 2668, Capital Federal C1425BDP. T: 54 11 41260100
E: la100@la100.com.ar
W: http://www.la100.com.ar

Cadena Eco (AM 1220)
Editorial: Av. Rivadavia 10561, Capital Federal 1408. T: 54 11 56311220
W: http://www.cadenaeco.com.ar

Concepto (AM 1050)
Editorial: Maipú 267, Capital Federal 1084.
T: 54 11 41361050
E: opaino@conceptoam.com.ar
W: http://www.conceptoam.com.ar

Continental (AM 590)
Editorial: Rivadavia 835, Capital Federal C1002AAG. T: 54 11 43384250
E: rrpp@continental.com.ar
W: http://www.continental.com.ar

Del Plata (AM 1030)
Editorial: Olleros 3551, Capital Federal C1427BNE. T: 54 11 45357070
E: rrhh@ideasdelsur.com.ar
W: http://www.amdelplata.com

FM Provincia (FM 89.9)
Editorial: Calle 60 826, La Plata 1900.
T: 54 221 4519696
E: direccion@amprovincia.com.ar
W: http://www.amprovincia.com.ar

La Red (AM 910)
Editorial: Av. Paseo Colón 505, Capital Federal C1063ACF. T: 54 11 5032-0400
E: info@radiolared.com.ar
W: http://www.laredonline.com.ar

Lagos (FM 93.5)
Editorial: San Miguel - Gba Oeste
E: jlagos@radiolagos.com
W: http://www.radiolagos.com

Libertad (AM 11240)
Editorial: Capital Federal
E: mensajes@cadenauno.com.ar
W: http://www.cdenauno.com.ar

Los 40 principales (FM 105.5)
Editorial: Rivadavia 835, Capital Federal C1002AAG. T: 54 11 43384250
E: internet@boxpublicidad.es
W: http://www.los40principales.com.ar

LV3 Cadena 3 (FM 106.9)
Editorial: Alvear 139, Cordoba X5000EAC.
T: 54 351 5260597 E: info@cadena3.com.ar
W: http://www.cadena3.com.ar

María (FM 101.5)
Editorial: Cordoba 5000. T: 54 351 4443999
W: http://www.radiomaria.org.ar

Mega (FM 98.3)
Editorial: Uriarte 1899, Buenos Aires C1414DAU. T: 54 11 48338800
E: mega@mega983.com.ar
W: http://www.mega983.com.ar/

Mitre (AM 790)
Editorial: Mansilla 2668, Buenos Aires C1425BDP. T: 54 11 57771500
E: info@radiomitre.com.ar
W: http://www.radiomitre.com.ar

Provincia (AM 1270)
Editorial: Calle 53 810, La Plata 1900.
T: 54 221 4247305
E: direccion@amprovincia.com.ar
W: http://www.amprovincia.com.ar

Radio 10 (AM 710)
Editorial: Uriarte 1899, Capital Federal C1414DAU. T: 54 11 48338800
W: http://www.radio10.com.ar

Radio Nacional Buenos Aires (AM 870)
Editorial: Maipú 555, Capital Federal C1006ACE. T: 54 11 43259100
E: portal@radionacional.gov.ar
W: http://www.radionacional.com.ar/

Radio Nacional Clásica (FM 96.7)
Editorial: Maipú 555, Capital Federal C1006ACE. T: 54 11 43228944
E: clasica@radionacional.gov.ar
W: http://www.radionacional.gov.ar

Radio Nacional Folklórica (FM 98.7)
Editorial: Maipú 555, Capital Federal C1006ACE. T: 54 11 43259100
E: portal@radionacional.gov.ar
W: http://www.radionacional.gov.ar

Rivadavia (AM 630)
Editorial: Arenales 2467, Capital Federal C1124AAM. T: 54 11 5219-4760
E: info@rivadavia.com.ar
W: http://www.rivadavia.com.ar

Rock & Pop (FM 95.9)
Editorial: Gral. Ramón Freire 962, Capital Federal C1426AVT. T: 54 11 40108200
E: valeria.podesta@rpmb.com.ar
W: http://www.fmrockandpop.com

TELEVISION NETWORKS

América 2
Editorial: Fitz Roy 1650, Capital Federal C1414CHX. T: 54 11 50322222
E: americanoticias@america2.com.ar
W: http://www.america2.com.ar

América 24
Editorial: Fitz Roy 1650, Capital Federal C1414CHX. T: 54 11 50322222
E: america24@america2.com.ar

America Sports
Editorial: Honduras 5637, Capital Federal 1414. T: 54 11 47785421
E: americasports@pramer.tv
W: http://www.america-sports.com.ar

Canal 13
Editorial: Lima 1261, Capital Federal C1138ACA. T: 54 11 43050013
E: eltrecetv@artear.com
W: http://www.canaltrece.com.ar

Canal 26
Editorial: Av. Provincias Unidas 2860, San Justo 1754. T: 54 11 44820091
E: canal26@telecentro.com.ar
W: http://www.canal26.com.ar/

Canal 5 Noticias (C5N)
Editorial: Fitz Roy 1940, Capital Federal 1414.
T: 54 11 48993737 E: comercial@c5n.com
W: http://www.infobae.com/c5n/index.html

Canal 7 Argentina
Editorial: Av. Figueroa Alcorta 2977, Capital Federal C1425CKI. T: 54 11 48082500
E: comercial@tvpublica.com.ar
W: http://www.canal7.com.ar/canal7/

Canal 9
Editorial: Dorrego 1782, Capital Federal C1414CKZ. T: 54 11 41199999
E: info@canal9.com.ar
W: http://www.canal9.com.ar

Canal á
Editorial: Bonpland 1745, Capital Federal C1414CMU. T: 54 11 47785427
E: jczulueta@pramer.tv
W: http://www.canalaonline.com

Canal Rural Satelital
Editorial: Honduras 5940, Capital Federal C1414BNL. T: 54 11 47774200
E: elrural@elrural.com
W: http://www.elrural.com/

Cosmopolitan TV
Editorial: Bonpland 1745, Capital Federal C1414CMU. T: 54 11 47785420
E: cosmopolitan@pramer.tv
W: http://www.cosmopolitan.tv

Crónica TV
Editorial: Riobamba 280, Capital Federal C1025ABF. T: 54 11 49530297
E: cronicatv@cronicatv.com.ar
W: http://www.cronicatv.com.ar

El Garage TV
Editorial: Sir Alexander Fleming 2845, Capital Federal. T: 54 11 4836 E: info@elgarage.com
W: http://www.elgarage.com

elgourmet.com
Editorial: Bonpland 1745, Capital Federal C1414CMU. T: 54 11 47785451
E: elgourmet@pramer.tv
W: http://www.elgourmet.com

ESPN
Editorial: Maipú 939, Capital Federal C1006ACM. T: 54 50310800
E: ignacio.x.cabanillas@espn.com
W: http://www.espndeportes.com

FOX Sports
Editorial: Balcarce 510, Capital Federal 1064.
T: 54 11 43494800
E: sdecarolis@fox-sports.com.ar
W: http://www.foxsportsla.com

Magazine
Editorial: Lima 1261, Capital Federal C1138ACA. T: 54 11 43701109
E: infocomercial@artear.com.ar
W: http://www.comercial.artear.com.ar/info/magazine/index.htm

MTV
Editorial: Av. del Libertador 498, Capital Federal C1001ABR. T: 54 11 45100600
W: http://www.mtvla.com

Sólo Tango
Editorial: Pje Carlos Gardel 3200, Capital Federal C1215AAB. T: 54 11 4862
W: http://www.tangocity.com

Telefé
Editorial: Pavón 2444, Capital Federal C1248AAT. T: 54 11 49419331
W: http://www.telefe.com

TN - Todo Noticias
Editorial: Lima 1261, Capital Federal C1138ACA. T: 54 11 43050013
E: mensajes@tn.com.ar
W: http://www.tn.com.ar

TyC Sports
Editorial: Av. San Juan 1132, Capital Federal C1147AAW. T: 54 11 43003800
E: libero@tycsports.com.ar
W: http://www.tycsports.com.ar

Utilísima Satelital
Editorial: Piedras 1080, Capital Federal 1070.
T: 54 11 43005270
E: utilisimasatelital@speedy.com.ar
W: http://www.utilisima.com.ar

Volver
Editorial: Lima 1261, Capital Federal C1138ACA. T: 54 11 43701424
E: correovolver@artear.com.ar
W: http://www.volver.com.ar

CABLE

New Tang Dynasty TV
Editorial: Coronel Diaz 1510, Piso 9, Capital Federal W: http://spanish.ntdtv.com
Editorial Profile: Provides news and entertainment in Mandarin and Cantonese to Chinese Argentinians.

ARMENIA Tel: 374

Standard Time: GMT +4
Continent: Asia
Capital City: Yerevan

NEWSPAPERS & PUBLICATIONS

NEWSPAPERS

168 Hours
Editorial: 3a Pushkin str., Yerevan.
T: 374 10 58 48 31 E: 168@168.r.am
W: http://www.168.am
Freq: 2 Times/Week; Circ: 5000 Pub Statement
Editor-in-Chief: Satik Seyranyan
Editorial Profile: Provides information about politics, economics, social issues and society, culture and health, sports.
Language (s): Armenian
NEWSPAPER

Aravot Daily
Owner: ARAVOT ORATERT Co. Ltd
Editorial: 2 Arshakuniats, 15th floor, Yerevan 375023. T: 374 10 56 89 68
E: aravot@aravot.am
W: http://www.aravot.am
Freq: Daily; Circ: 5000 Pub Statement
Editor: Aram Abramyan
Editorial Profile: Newspaper covering national and regional news, politics, the economy, culture, sport and entertainment.
Language (s): Armenian
DAILY NEWSPAPER

Delovoy Express
Owner: EIS Ltd

Editorial: Tigran Metsi, 67a, Yerevan 5.
T: 374 10 57 33 05 **E:** editor@express.am
W: http://www.express.am
Freq: Weekly; **Circ:** 3000 Not Audited
Editor-in-Chief: Eduard Aykazovich Naghdalyan
Editorial Profile: Newspaper focusing on all aspects of business, finance and banks, real estate market, business investments.
Language (s): Russian
NEWSPAPER

Golos Armenii
Owner: Golos Armenii
Editorial: Arshakuniatz Sq. 2, Floor 7, Yerevan.
T: 374 1 52 89 28
E: gonline@press.arminco.com
W: http://www.golos.am
Freq: 2 Times/Week; **Circ:** 3500 Pub Statement
Editor: Flora Nakhshkaryan
Editorial Profile: Newspaper covering national and international news, economics, politics, entertainment and sport.
Language (s): Russian
NEWSPAPER

Hayastani Hanrapetutiun
Owner: Hanrapetutiun
Editorial: Arshakunyats Ave. 2, 13th and 14th Floors, Yerevan 23. **T:** 374 1 52 57 56
E: hh@press.aic.net
W: http://www.hhpress.am
Freq: Daily; **Circ:** 6000 Pub Statement
Editor: Tigran Syemyon Farmanyan
Editorial Profile: Newspaper covering national and international news, politics, economy and culture.
Language (s): Armenian
DAILY NEWSPAPER

Haykakan zhamanak
Owner: Haykakan zhamanak
Editorial: Israyelyan St. 37, Yerevan 375015.
T: 374 10 58 11 75 **E:** nikol@arminco.com
W: http://www.hzh.am
Freq: Daily; **Circ:** 10000 Pub Statement
Editor: Nikol Pashinyan
Editorial Profile: Newspaper covering national and international news, economics, sport and social events.
Language (s): Armenian
DAILY NEWSPAPER

Hayots Ashkharh
Owner: TIGRAN METS
Editorial: 38/ Apt. 41 Tumanyan St., Yerevan 375002. **T:** 374 10 53 88 65
E: hayashkh@arminco.com
W: http://www.armworld.am
Freq: Daily; **Circ:** 3500 Pub Statement
Editor: Gagik Mkrtchyan
Editorial Profile: Newspaper covering national and regional news, politics, business, culture and social events.
Language (s): Armenian
DAILY NEWSPAPER

Iravunk
Owner: Iravunk
Editorial: Yeznik Koghbatsu St. 50 A, Yerevan 375002. **T:** 374 10 53 27 30
E: iravunk@cornet.am
W: http://www.iravunk.com **Circ:** 60000 Pub Statement
Editorial Profile: Newspaper covering national and international news including features on law and legal issues, business and politics.
Language (s): Armenian
DAILY NEWSPAPER

Novoe Vremia
Owner: Novoe Vremia Ltd
Editorial: Arshakunyats Ave. 2, 3rd Floor, Yerevan 375023. **T:** 374 10 52 69 46
E: nvremya@arminco.com
W: http://www.nv.am
Freq: 2 Times/Week; **Circ:** 5000 Pub Statement
Editor: Ruben A. Satyan
Editorial Profile: Newspaper focusing on national and international news, politics, the economy, culture and social events.
Language (s): Russian
NEWSPAPER

The Noyan Tapan Highlights
Owner: Noyan Tapan
Editorial: 28 Issahakian Street, Yerevan 375009. **T:** 374 10 56 59 65 **E:** contact@nt.am
W: http://www.nt.am **Circ:** 2000 Pub Statement
News Editor: Gayaneh Arakelian;
Editor-in-Chief: Harutyun Khachatryan
Editorial Profile: Newspaper in English language covering politics, economics, society and cultural events in Armenia.

Language (s): English
DAILY NEWSPAPER

Republica Armenia
Owner: Hayastani Hanrapetutiun-Republica Armenia CJSC
Editorial: Arshakunyats Prospekt 2, 9 floor, Yerevan 23. **T:** 374 10 54 57 00
E: ra@arminco.am **W:** http://www.ra.am
Freq: 2 Times/Week; **Circ:** 1500 Pub Statement
Editor In Chief: Yelena Kurdiyan
Editorial Profile: Newspaper focusing on national and international news, politics, economics and current affairs.
Language (s): Russian
NEWSPAPER

Yerkir
Owner: ARF Publication
Editorial: 30 Hanrapetutian Str., Yerevan 10.
T: 374 10 52 15 01 **E:** editor@yerkir.am
W: http://www.yerkir.am **Circ:** 3000 Pub Statement
Editor In Chief: Spartak Seyranyan
Editorial Profile: Official newspaper of the Armenian Revolutionary Federation focusing on national and international news, politics, the economy, society, culture, education and sport.
Language (s): Armenian
DAILY NEWSPAPER

NEWS SERVICE/SYNDICATE

ARKA News Agency
Editorial: 1/3 Pavstos Byuzand St., Yerevan 375010. **T:** 374 10 52 40 80
E: arka@arminco.com **W:** http://www.arka.am
Language (s): Armenian
NEWS SERVICE/SYNDICATE

Armenpress
Editorial: 28 Isahakian Street, 4 floor, Yerevan 375009. **T:** 374 1 52 67 02
E: contact@armenpress.am
W: http://www.armenpress.am
Editor-in-Chief: Satinik Haklbyan
Editorial Profile: Produces home, international, regional news bulletins, photo news and provides a wide range of analytical stories covering politics, economy, culture and other areas. News items are issued on a daily basis in Armenian, Russian and English.
Language (s): Armenian
NEWS SERVICE/SYNDICATE

De facto
Editorial: 2 Arshakuniats, 9 floor, Yerevan.
T: 374 10 54 57 99 **W:** http://www.defacto.am
Editor-in-Chief: Karen Zakharyan
Editorial Profile: Information Analytical News Agency providing political and economics news in Armenian, Russian and English languages.
Language (s): Armenian
NEWS SERVICE/SYNDICATE

Mediamax
Editorial: 1-32 Marshal Baghramian Ave., Yerevan. **T:** 374 10 54 54 31
E: news@mediamax.am
W: http://www.mediamax.am
Editor-in-Chief: David Alaverdyan
Editorial Profile: News from Armenia - 6 times a week on-line, the most important political, economic, public, social and other events - in Russian, English and Armenian languages. Presents qualitative, efficient and reliable source of information about the developments in Armenia and in the region of the South Caucasus.
Language (s): Armenian
NEWS SERVICE/SYNDICATE

News Armenia
T: 374 10 52 40 80 **E:** news@newsarmenia.am
W: http://newsarmenia.ru
Editorial Profile: Provides political news and analysis of the situation in Armenia and the whole territory of the CIC in Russian and Armenian languages.
Language (s): Armenian
NEWS SERVICE/SYNDICATE

NEWS.am
Editorial: 18 Proshyan St., Yerevan.
T: 374 10 22 66 21 **E:** editor@news.am
W: http://news.am/en
Editorial Profile: Independent Armenian information-analytic agency, delivering the regular coverage of analyzed current information about policy, life and culture to the public.
Language (s): Armenian
NEWS SERVICE/SYNDICATE

Language (s): English
DAILY NEWSPAPER

Yerevan Press Club
Editorial: 9B, Ghazar Parpetsi str, Yerevan 375002. **T:** 374 10 53 00 67 **E:** info@ypc.am
W: http://www.ypc.am
Editor: Elina Poghosbekian
Editorial Profile: Informing about the events and the situation of the Armenian media.
Language (s): Armenian
NEWS SERVICE/SYNDICATE

BROADCASTING

RADIO NETWORKS

Impulse
Editorial: 19 Hanjanyana Str., 6 floor, Yerevan 375001. **T:** 374 10 54 12 73
E: impuls@impuls.am
W: http://www.impuls.am
Editorial Profile: Dedicated to analytical, political, social and ethnic issues and broadcasts classical and ethnic Armenian music.

TELEVISION STATIONS

Armenian Second TV Channel
Editorial: G-3 3/1, Achapniak, Yerevan 375088. **T:** 374 10 39 88 31 **E:** h2@tv.am
W: http://www.tv.am
Editorial Profile: Armenian Second TV-Channel is the biggest private TV-Channel in the whole region of Armenia and in Nagorno-Karabakh. Contains informational-analytical programs, talk-shows, entertaining, music, sports programs, soap operas and Hollywood latest films.

Public TV of Armenia
Editorial: 26 Gevorg Hovsepyan St., Nork, Yerevan 47. **T:** 374 10 65 15 00
E: diana@armtv.com **W:** http://www.armtv.com
Editorial Profile: Armenian Public Television has largest coverage in Armenia with a choice of cultural, entertainment, sports programmes, films and documentaries.

ARUBA   Tel: 297

Standard Time: GMT -4
Continent: The Americas
Capital City: Oranjestad

NEWSPAPERS & PUBLICATIONS

NEWSPAPERS

Aruba Today
Owner: Caribbean Speed Printers
Editorial: Weststraat 22, Oranjestad.
T: 297 582-7800
W: http://www.arubatoday.com
Freq: Daily; **Circ:** 15000 Not Audited
Editor in Chief: Julia Renfro
Editorial Profile: Newspaper covering national and international news and current affairs, politics, the economy, culture, sport and health.
Language (s): English
DAILY NEWSPAPER

Bon Dia Aruba
Owner: Caribbean Speed Printers
Editorial: Weststraat 22, Oranjestad.
T: 297 58 27 800 **E:** noticia@bondia.com
W: http://www.bondia.com
Freq: Daily; **Circ:** 25000 Not Audited
Editor: Harold Farro; **Editor:** Benjamin Romero; **Editor:** Oscar Vidal
Editorial Profile: Newspaper covering national and international news and current affairs; includes politics, the economy, sports, culture and health.
Language (s): Dutch
DAILY NEWSPAPER

AUSTRALIA   Tel: 61

Standard Time: GMT +8 (West Coast), GMT +10 (East Coast)
Continent: Oceania
Capital City: Canberra

NEWSPAPERS & PUBLICATIONS

NEWSPAPERS

The Advertiser Adelaide
Owner: News Limited
Editorial: 31 Waymouth Street, Adelaide SA 5000. **T:** 61 1300 130 370
E: tiser@adv.newsltd.com.au
W: http://www.adelaidenow.com.au
Freq: Daily
Racing Editor: Lincoln Moore
Editorial Profile: Metropolitan daily newspaper first established in 1858.
Language (s): English
DAILY NEWSPAPER

The Advertiser Woolgoolga
Owner: Rupak Pty Ltd
Editorial: 7 Market Street, Woolgoolga NSW 2456. **T:** 61 2 6654 2133
E: editorial@woolgoolgaadvertiser.com.au
W: http://apnap.com.au/newspapers
Freq: Weekly
Editor: Graeme Singleton
Editorial Profile: Published each morning Monday - Sunday. Read by 580,000 people Monday - Friday and 740,000 each Saturday.
Language (s): English
NEWSPAPER

The Advocate (Daylesford + Hepburn Shire)
Owner: Rural Press Limited
Editorial: Unit 4, 32 Vincent Street, Daylesford VIC 3460. **T:** 61 3 5348 1028
E: advocateads@thecourier.com.au
W: http://www.hepburnadvocate.com.au
Freq: Weekly
Editorial Profile: Incorporating The Daylesford Advocate and The Creswick Advertiser
Language (s): English
NEWSPAPER

The Advocate TAS (Burnie)
Owner: Rural Press Limited
Editorial: 54-56 Mount Street, Burnie TAS 7320. **T:** 61 3 6440 7409
E: news@theadvocate.com.au
W: http://www.theadvocate.com.au
Circ: 21996
Editor: Jason Purdie
Editorial Profile: Daily newspaper covering news, sport and current affairs.
Language (s): English
DAILY NEWSPAPER

The Age
Owner: Fairfax Media
Editorial: 655 Collins Street, Docklands VIC 3008. **T:** 61 3 8667 2250
E: newsdesk@theage.com.au
W: http://www.theage.com.au
Freq: Daily
City Editor: Jason Dowling; **Drive Editor:** Toby Hagon; **COO:** David Hoath; **Editor-in-Chief:** Andrew Holden
Editorial Profile: Newspaper covering news, finance, sport, business and travel.
Language (s): English
DAILY NEWSPAPER

The Age Money
Owner: The Age
Editorial: 655 Collins Street, Docklands VIC 3008. **T:** 61 2 9282 2976
E: vpalestrant@fairfaxmedia.com.au
W: http://www.moneymanager.com.au
Freq: Weekly
Editorial Profile: Supplement containing personal finance information. Published on Monday. Geographical Focus: Australia Victoria
Language (s): English
NEWSPAPER

The Area News
Owner: Rural Press Limited
Editorial: Cnr Ulong & Olympic Streets, Griffith NSW 2680. **T:** 61 2 6962 1733
E: editor@areanews.com.au
W: http://www.areanews.com.au
Freq: 2 Times/Week
Editorial Profile: Weekly regional newspaper that focuses on local issues.
Language (s): English
NEWSPAPER

The Armidale Express
Owner: Rural Press Limited
Editorial: 115 Faulkner Street, Armidale NSW 2350. **T:** 61 2 6776 0500
E: editor.armexpress@ruralpress.com
W: http://www.armidaleexpress.com.au
Freq: 2 Times/Week
Editor: Lydia Roberts
Editorial Profile: It is a tri-weekly paid newspaper.Established in 1856. It has more than 10,000 readers in Armidale, Uralla, Guyra and Walcha.
Language (s): English
NEWSPAPER

The Australian
Owner: News Limited
Editorial: 2 Holt Street, Surry Hills NSW 2010. **T:** 61 2 9288 2318
E: nsw@theaustralian.com.au
W: http://www.theaustralian.com.au
Freq: Daily
Asia-Pacific Editor: Rowan Callick; **Editor:** Michelle Gunn; **Bureau Chief:** Patricia Karvelas; **Editor at Large:** Paul Kelly; **Editor:** Glenda Korporaal; **Editor:** Clive Mathieson; **Legal Affairs Editor:** Chris Merritt; **Editor-in-Chief:** Chris Mitchell; **Defence Editor:** Brendan Nicholson; **Bureau Chief:** Jamie Walker
Editorial Profile: Metropolitan daily newspaper. Geographical Focus: Australia Metropolitan
Language (s): English
DAILY NEWSPAPER

The Australian Financial Review
Owner: Fairfax Business Media
Editorial: 1 Darling Island Road, Pyrmont NSW 2009. **T:** 61 2 9282 2833
E: afrnewsdesk@afr.com.au
W: http://www.afr.com
Freq: Daily
Editor: Paul Bailey; **Graphic Designer:** Evelyn Barota; **Editor:** Matthew Drummond; **Asia Pacific Editor:** Greg Earl; **Editor:** James Eyers; **Legal Editor:** Hannah Low; **Editor-at-Large:** Pamela Williams
Editorial Profile: National daily paper containing business, finance, international and IT news. Geographical Focus: Australia Metropolitan
Language (s): English
DAILY NEWSPAPER

The Australian Motoring
Owner: The Australian
Editorial: 2 Holt Street, Surry Hills NSW 2010. **T:** 61 2 9288 2357
E: kingp@theaustralian.com.au
Freq: Weekly
Editor: Philip King
Editorial Profile: Weekly motoring section covering motorshows, products and general articles on the motor industry.
Language (s): English
NEWSPAPER

The Avon Valley Advocate
Owner: Rural Press Limited
Editorial: 146 Fitzgerald Street, Northam WA 6401. **T:** 61 8 9622 5500
E: editor.avonadvocate@ruralpress.com
W: http://www.avonadvocate.com.au
Freq: Weekly
Editorial Profile: Focuses on news, sports and events of the region. Weekly newspaper and circulates 2217. Published every Wednesday.
Language (s): English
NEWSPAPER

The Ballarat News
Owner: Victorian Country Press Association
Editorial: 110 Creswick Road, Ballarat VIC 3350. **T:** 61 3 5331 3833
E: ballarat.news@thecourier.com.au
W: http://www.vcpa.com.au
Freq: 2 Times/Week
Editorial Profile: Circulation of 32,586. Published every Wednesday and is distributed free to homes in the region.
Language (s): English
NEWSPAPER

The Border Mail VIC
Owner: Fairfax Media
Editorial: 1 McKoy Street, Wodonga VIC 3690. **T:** 61 2 6024 0555
E: newsroom@bordermail.com.au
W: http://www.bordermail.com.au
Freq: Daily
Editor: Dianne Thomas
Editorial Profile: Regional newspaper.
Language (s): English
DAILY NEWSPAPER

The Border Times
Owner: Pinnaroo Printers & Publishers
Editorial: Ral Ral Avenue, Renmark SA 5341. **T:** 61 8 8586 6603
E: wendy@murraypioneer.com.au
W: http://www.murraypioneer.com.au
Freq: Weekly
Editorial Profile: Regional newspaper with news and issues specific to people living in the Murray Lands SA and the Mallee region in Victoria. Preferred delivery for media releases: fax or email.
Language (s): English
NEWSPAPER

The Bullsbrook Ellenbrook Advocate
Owner: Community Newspaper Group
Editorial: 12 Old Great Northern Highway, Midland WA 6056. **T:** 61 8 9237 1900
E: advocate@communitynews.com.au
W: http://www.communitynews.com.au
Freq: Weekly
Language (s): English
NEWSPAPER

The Bunyip
Owner: Bunyip Press
Editorial: 120-122 Murray Street, Gawler SA 5118. **T:** 61 8 8522 1233
E: editor@bunyippress.com.au
W: www.bunyippress.com.au
Freq: Weekly
Editor: Rob McLean
Editorial Profile: A weekly regional newspaper with news and issues specifically of interest to the local community in the lower north and Barossa Valley regions of NSW. Photographic information: Colour photos, black & white photos. Preferred delivery images: fax or email.
Language (s): English
NEWSPAPER

The Cairns Weekend Post
Owner: The Cairns Post Pty Ltd
Editorial: 22-24 Abbott Street, Cairns QLD 4870. **T:** 61 7 4052 6666
E: editorial@tcp.newsltd.com.au
W: http://www.cairns.com.au
Freq: Weekly
Editor: Andrew van Smeerdijk
Editorial Profile: Regional newspaper covering news and issues that effect the community.
Language (s): English
NEWSPAPER

The Canberra Times
Owner: Fairfax Media
Editorial: 9 Pirie Street, Fyshwick ACT 2609. **T:** 61 2 6280 2122
E: letters.editor@canberratimes.com.au
W: http://www.canberratimes.com.au
Freq: Daily
Editor: Scott Hannaford; **Editor:** Lyn Mills; **Editor-in-Chief:** Rod Quinn; **Editor at Large:** Jack Waterford
Editorial Profile: All the latest national and international news. Featuring segments on lifestyle, health, food, wine, fashion etc.
Language (s): English
DAILY NEWSPAPER

The Cessnock Advertiser
Owner: Rural Press Limited
Editorial: 155 Vincent Street, Cessnock NSW 2325. **T:** 61 2 4990 1244
E: manager.cessadvertiser@ruralpress.com
W: http://www.cessnockadvertiser.com.au
Freq: Weekly
Editor: Krystal Sellars
Editorial Profile: Published each morning Monday- Sunday. Read by over 580,000 people Monday-Friday and 740,00 each Saturday. Geographical Focus: Australia New South Wales
Language (s): English
NEWSPAPER

The Coastal Rag
Editorial: 1 Captain Cook Drive, Agnes Water QLD 4677. **T:** 61 7 4974 7253
E: coastalrag@bigpond.com
Freq: Weekly
Editor: Cheryl Wicks
Editorial Profile: A regional weekly newspaper distributed throughout the Miriam Vale Shire.
Language (s): English
NEWSPAPER

The Colac Herald
Owner: Gannon Newspapers Pty Ltd
Editorial: 37-41 Bromfield Street, Colac VIC 3250. **T:** 61 3 5231 5322
E: news@colacherald.com
W: http://www.colacherald.com
Freq: 2 Times/Week
Editor: Bruce Lawson
Editorial Profile: Regional newspaper. Formats Available: CD-ROM, other online, disk.Photographic Information: B/W Photographs, Colour Photographs Preferred Delivery images: Email or PostPreferred Format: PDF Press Material Accepted in: English
Language (s): English
NEWSPAPER

The Coonabarabran Times
Owner: Warrumbungle Publications Pty Ltd
Editorial: 44 Dalgarno Street, Coonabarabran NSW 2357. **T:** 61 2 6842 1844
E: cbntimes@tpg.com.au
Freq: Weekly
Editor: Richard Duggan
Editorial Profile: Year First Published: 1885 Target Audience: Local Community & Rural Photographic Information: B/W Photographs, Colour Photographs Preferred Delivery images: Email Preferred Format: JPEG
Language (s): English
NEWSPAPER

The Courier Mail
Owner: News Limited
Editorial: 41 Campbell Street, Bowen Hills QLD 4006. **T:** 61 7 3666 6480
E: cos@thecouriermail.com.au
W: http://www.couriermail.com.au
Freq: Daily
News Editor: Anna Caldwell
Editorial Profile: Newspaper covering the latest news issues, sport, food, travel and business.
Language (s): English
DAILY NEWSPAPER

The Daily Telegraph
Owner: The Daily Telegraph
Editorial: 2 Holt Street, Surry Hills NSW 2010. **T:** 61 2 9288 3000
E: news@dailytelegraph.com.au
W: http://www.dailytelegraph.com.au
Freq: Daily
News Editor: Lucy Carne; **News Editor:** Barclay Crawford; **News Editor:** Gemma Jones; **Editor at Large:** John Lehmann; **News Editor:** Clare Masters; **Editor:** Mark Morri; **Editor at Large:** Jeni O'Dowd; **Editor:** Paul Whitaker; **Editor:** James Wigney
Editorial Profile: Daily Metropolitan Newspaper covering News, Weather, Sport Entertainment, Travel, Horoscopes, Business and Finance.
Language (s): English
DAILY NEWSPAPER

The Dimboola Banner
Owner: Victorian Country Press Association
Editorial: 94 Lloyd St, Dimboola VIC 3414. **T:** 61 3 5389 1440 **E:** banner1@iinet.net.au
W: http://www.vcpa.com.au
Freq: Weekly
Editor: David Ward
Language (s): English
NEWSPAPER

The District Reporter- Camden
Editorial: PO Box 116, Camden NSW 2570. **T:** 61 2 4655 1234 **E:** editor@tdr.com.au
W: http://www.tdr.com.au/index
Freq: Weekly
Editor: Lee Abrahams
Language (s): English
NEWSPAPER

The Examiner (TAS)
Owner: Rural Press Limited
Editorial: 71 - 75 Paterson Street, Launceston TAS 7250. **T:** 61 3 6336 7111
E: mail@examiner.com.au
W: http://www.examiner.com.au
Freq: Daily
Editor: Martin Gilmour
Editorial Profile: Regional Daily Newspaper.
Language (s): English
DAILY NEWSPAPER

The Gazette Warragul & Drouin
Owner: Warragul Regional Newspapers Pty Ltd
Editorial: 97-103 Queen Street, Warragul VIC 3820. **T:** 61 3 5623 5666
E: editorial@warragulgazette.com.au
W: http://www.warragulgazette.com.au
Freq: Weekly
Editor: Carolyn Turner
Editorial Profile: Local, community and regional news presented weekly to local residents. Photographic Information: B/W Photographs, Colour Photographs.Preferred Delivery: Post primarily but also Email. Preferred Format: PDF
Language (s): English
NEWSPAPER

Geelong Advertiser
Owner: News Limited
Editorial: 191-195 Ryrie Street, Geelong VIC 3220. **T:** 61 3 5227 4340
E: journo@geelongadvertiser.com.au
W: http://www.geelongadvertiser.com.au
Geelong News Editor: Elise Potter
Editorial Profile: Regional Daily newspaper. he Geelong Advertiser is the voice of Geelong, Bellarine and Surf Coast. First published in 1840.
Language (s): English
DAILY NEWSPAPER

The Gilgandra Weekly
Owner: Rural Press Limited
Editorial: 64 - 66 Miller Street, Gilgandra NSW 2827. **T:** 61 2 6847 2022
E: mail.gilgandraweekly@ruralpress.com
W: http://www.ruralpresssales.com.au
Freq: Weekly
Editor: Marion Ferrier
Editorial Profile: Gilgandra Weekly is the source of local information, news and entertainment.
Language (s): English
NEWSPAPER

The Gold Coast Bulletin
Owner: Gold Coast Publications Pty Ltd
Editorial: 385 Nerang Road, Molendinar QLD 4214. **T:** 61 7 5584 2000
E: editorial@gcb.newsltd.com.au
W: http://www.goldcoast.com.au
Freq: Daily
News Editor: Lendl Ryan; **Editor:** Catherine Webber
Editorial Profile: A newspaper with news and issues relevant to people living on the Gold Coast.
Language (s): English
DAILY NEWSPAPER

The Good Mail
Owner: Sunday Times
Editorial: 41 Campbell St, Bowen Hills QLD 4006. **T:** 61 7 3666 6559
E: collinsmi@qnp.newsltd.com.au
W: http://www.news.com.au/sundaymail
Editor: Michelle Collins
Editorial Profile: Column looks behind the scenes and the lighter side of news.
Language (s): English
DAILY NEWSPAPER

The Good Mail
Owner: Sunday Times
Editorial: 41 Campbell St, Bowen Hills QLD 4006. **T:** 61 7 3666 6559
E: smletters@qnp.newsltd.com.au
W: http://www.news.com.au/sundaymail
Editorial Profile: Column looks behind the scenes and the lighter side of news.
Language (s): English
DAILY NEWSPAPER

The Greater Springfield Times
Owner: Local News Publications
Editorial: 36 Pradella Street, Richlands QLD 4077. **T:** 61 7 3217 0533
E: reporter@lnp.net.au
W: http://www.lnp.net.au
Freq: Monthly
Editor: Susannah Friis
Language (s): English
NEWSPAPER

The Herald Sun
Owner: News Limited
Editorial: HWT Tower, 40 City Road, Southbank VIC 3006. **T:** 61 3 9292 2000
E: news@heraldsun.com.au
W: http://www.heraldsun.com.au
Freq: Daily
Editor: Damon Johnston; **Editor:** Keith Moor
Editorial Profile: Major metropolitan newspaper.
Language (s): English
DAILY NEWSPAPER

The Independent Sydney Bureau
Owner: Independent Newspapers
Editorial: 5 Napier Street, Paddington NSW 2021. **T:** 61 2 9380 4004
W: http://www.independent.co.uk
Freq: Daily
Editorial Profile: A UK publication covering world news topics.
Language (s): English
DAILY NEWSPAPER

The Islander
Owner: Rural Press Limited
Editorial: Dauncey Street, Kingscote, Kangaroo Island SA 5223. **T:** 61 8 8553 2080
E: theislander@ruralpress.com
W: http://www.theislanderonline.com.au

Freq: Weekly
Editorial Profile: Regional weekly newspaper.
Language (s): English
NEWSPAPER

The Kuranda Paper
Editorial: n/a, Kuranda QLD 4881.
T: 61 7 4093 8942
E: kurandamedia@bigpond.com
W: http://www.kurandapaper.com
Freq: Monthly
Language (s): English
NEWSPAPER

The Lake News
Owner: JA Bradley & Sons
Editorial: 193 Hoskins Street, Temora NSW 2666. **T:** 61 2 6977 1077
E: editorial@temoraindependent.com.au
Freq: Weekly
Editor: Andrew Hawksley
Editorial Profile: Regional weekly paper in the central-west region of NSW. Preferred delivery for media releases: Fax or Post.
Language (s): English
NEWSPAPER

The Leader
Owner: Country Press Association of SA Inc.
Editorial: 34 Dean Street, Angaston SA 5353.
T: 61 8 8564 2035
E: leadernewspaper@bigpond.com
W: http://sacountrypress.com.au/newspapers/newspapers/angaston.htm
Freq: Weekly
Editor: Tony Robinson
Editorial Profile: A local regional newspaper with news and issues relevant to local residents living in Barossa Valley, north to Eudunda, south to Mannum, east to Swan Reach, west to Freeling, Gawler, Elizabeth.
Language (s): English
NEWSPAPER

The Lightning Ridge News
Owner: Rural Press Limited
Editorial: 10a Opal Street, Lightning Ridge NSW 2834. **T:** 61 2 6829 2150
E: mail.ridgenews@ruralpress.com
W: http://lightningridge.yourguide.com.au
Freq: Weekly
Editorial Profile: A regional local paper with news and issues relevant to the local community.
Language (s): English
NEWSPAPER

The Loddon Times
Owner: Jenwhit Publishers Pty Ltd
Editorial: 24 Scoresby Street, Kerang VIC 3579. **T:** 61 3 5452 1733
E: editorial@northernnewspapers.com.au
W: http://www.thenortherntimes.com.au
Freq: Weekly
Editorial Profile: Title formed by an amalgamation of the Wedderburn and Inglewood Express with the Boort Standard and Quambatook Times. The Loddon Times embraces the restructured Shire of Loddon in north-central Victoria with offices at Wedderburn and Boort. The southern centres surrounding Wedderburn are part of the rich gold mining "Golden Triangle" area north of Bendigo and farming areas extending from Inglewood in the west to Dingee. The northern area is part of the northern plains irrigation area, extending from the Boort area east through Pyramid Hill.
Language (s): English
NEWSPAPER

The Loxton News
Owner: The Loxton News Pty Ltd
Editorial: 54 East Terrace, Loxton SA 5333.
T: 61 8 8584 7271
E: editor@loxton-news.com.au
W: http://www.loxton-news.com.au
Freq: Weekly
Editor: Paul Mitchell; **Editor:** Paul Mitchell
Editorial Profile: Local and regional newspaper in the Mallee region. First published: 1960Target readership: Local community Regular features: Finance, Home Improvement, sports coverage, agricultural and horticultural newsPhotographic information: Colour photos, black & white photos. Preferred delivery: e-mailPreferred format: TIFF, JPEG
Language (s): English
NEWSPAPER

The Macarthur Chronicle
Owner: Cumberland Newspaper Group
Editorial: Macarthur Place, 1st Floor, Campbelltown NSW 2560. **T:** 61 2 4620 1500
E: editor@macarthurchronicle.com.au
W: http://www.macarthurchronicle.com.au
Freq: Weekly
Editor: Mandy Perrin
Editorial Profile: A regional newspaper with regular features including travel, finance, sport, news, community notices, food guide and entertainment etc.
Language (s): English
NEWSPAPER

The Maitland Mercury Town & Country
Owner: Maitland Mercury
Editorial: 258 High Street, Maitland NSW 2320. **T:** 61 2 4931 0100
E: tandcleader@ruralpress.com
W: http://www.maitlandmercury.com.au
Freq: Bi-Weekly
Editorial Profile: Town and Country supplements, that covers farming and rural issues. Formats Available: CD-ROM, Other Online, Disk.Readership: Farming, Hobby Farms & Vineyards. Photographic Information: No PhotographsGeographical Focus: Australia New South Wales
Language (s): English
NEWSPAPER

The Maitland Mercury Town & Country
Owner: Maitland Mercury
Editorial: 258 High Street, Maitland NSW 2320. **T:** 61 2 4931 0100
E: editor.mercury@ruralpress.com
Editor: Stephen Bissett
Editorial Profile: Town and Country supplements 6 Hunter Valley newspapers, that covers farming and rural issues. Formats Available: CD-ROM, Other Online, Disk. Readership: Farming, Hobby Farms & Vineyards. Photographic Information: No Photographs
Language (s): English
DAILY NEWSPAPER

The Maltese Herald
Owner: The Maltese News & Information Pty Ltd
Editorial: 4/235 Pitt Street, Merrylands NSW 2160. **T:** 61 2 9637 9992
E: tmh@the-vellas.com
W: http://www.crc.nsw.gov.au/ethnic_media
Freq: Weekly
Editorial Profile: Established: 1961.
Language (s): Maltese
NEWSPAPER

The Mercury
Owner: News Limited
Editorial: Level 1, 2 Salamanca Square, Hobart TAS 7000. **T:** 61 3 6230 0760
E: mercury.news@dbl.newsltd.com.au
W: http://www.themercury.com.au
Freq: Daily
Editor-in-Chief: Matt Deighton
Editorial Profile: The Mercury is based in the largest population centre, Hobart, and provides essential reading for Tasmanians. The Mercury features news, sport, business, entertainment and lifestyle.
Language (s): English
DAILY NEWSPAPER

The Mid State Observer
Owner: Rural Press Limited
Editorial: 132 Kite Street, Orange NSW 2800.
T: 61 2 6391 2900
E: editor.cwd@ruralpress.com
W: http://www.centralwesterndaily.com.au
Freq: Weekly
Editor: Tony Rhead
Editorial Profile: Free weekly regional newspaper in the central-western region of NSW. Sister paper: Central Western DailyPhotographic information: Colour photos, black & white photos, colour transparencies Preferred delivery images: e-mail (mail.cwd@ruralpress.com)Preferred format: TIFF, JPEG
Language (s): English
NEWSPAPER

Moe & Narracan News
Owner: Rural Press Limited
Editorial: 44B George Street, Moe VIC 3825.
T: 61 3 5127 6600 **E:** news@moenews.net.au
W: http://www.vcpa.com.au/vic-members/74-moe-a-narracan-news.html **Circ:** 11079
Editorial Profile: Circulates 10,973 in areas including the City of Moe and the townships of Newsborough, Trafalgar, Tallourn North, Thorpdale and surrounding districts.
Language (s): English
DAILY NEWSPAPER

The Monaro Post
Owner: Monaro Media Group Pty Ltd
Editorial: 220-226 Sharp Street, Cooma NSW 2630. **T:** 61 2 6452 0312
E: info@monaropost.com.au
W: http://www.monaropost.com.au
Freq: Weekly
Editor: Gail Eastaway
Language (s): English
NEWSPAPER

The Moorabool News
Owner: Victorian Country Press Association
Editorial: 40 Old Geelong Road, Ballan VIC 3342. **T:** 61 3 5368 1966
E: news@ballannews.com
Freq: Weekly
Editorial Profile: Weekly regional newspaper that caters to Moorabool shire, an area dedicated primarily to farming with a large amount of potato growing land in the west of the Shire.
Language (s): English
NEWSPAPER

Moreton Border News
Owner: Victorian Country Press Association
Editorial: 7 Church Street, Boonah QLD 4310.
T: 61 7 5463 1888
E: info@boonahnewspapers.com.au
W: http://www.vcpa.com.au **Circ:** 4080
Editorial Profile: Year First Published: 1997 Target Audience: Local community.Regular Features: Shows and Special Events. Photographic Information: B/W Photographs, Colour Photographs.Preferred Delivery: Post.
Language (s): English
DAILY NEWSPAPER

The Morning Bulletin
Owner: APN News & Media Limited
Editorial: 162-164 Quay Street, Rockhampton QLD 4700. **T:** 61 7 4930 4222
E: tmbully@capnews.com.au
W: http://www.themorningbulletin.com.au
Freq: Daily
Editor: Frazer Pearce
Editorial Profile: Regular Features: Editorial, National, World, Entertainer, Racing, Weddings/Babies, Business, Classifieds and Television. Saturday cover price $1.35
Language (s): English
DAILY NEWSPAPER

Moruya Examiner
Owner: Rural Press Limited
Editorial: Shop 7, 33 Orient Street, Batemans Bay NSW 2536. **T:** 61 2 4472 6577
E: editor.baypost@ruralpress.com
W: http://www.batemansbaypost.com.au
Freq: 2 Times/Week
Editor: Carmen McIntosh
Editorial Profile: Regional newspaper covering issues and current affairs in Moruya and the surrounding areas.
Language (s): English
NEWSPAPER

The Moyne Gazette
Owner: Fairfax Media
Editorial: 2/10 Bank Street, Port Fairy VIC 3284. **T:** 61 3 5568 1982
E: abrady@standard.fairfax.com.au
W: http://www.vcpa.com.au
Freq: Weekly
Editor: Ian Pech
Editorial Profile: Weekly regional newspaper with issues, sports, gardening etc. news of interest to the wider community. Photographic information: B/W photographs, colour photographs.Geographical Focus: South West England
Language (s): English
NEWSPAPER

Mt Buller News
Owner: Mansfield Newspapers Pty Ltd
Editorial: 96 High Street, Mansfield VIC 3722.
T: 61 3 5775 2115
E: edit.mcourier@nenews.com.au
W: http://www.nenews.com.au
Freq: Bi-Weekly
Editorial Profile: A weekly regional newspaper of particular interest to those living and travelling in the snow region. Distributed through travel and ski outlets on Mountains.Year First Published: 1980 Content Summary: Mount Buller events.Photographic Information: B/W Photographs, Colour Photographs. Preferred Delivery: Email or Post.Preferred Format: TIFF, JPEG, PDF
Language (s): English
NEWSPAPER

Mudgee Guardian
Owner: Rural Press Limited
Editorial: 9 Perry Street, Mudgee NSW 2850.
T: 61 2 6372 1455
E: editor.mguardian@ruralpress.com
W: http://www.mudgeeguardian.com.au
Freq: 2 Times/Week
Editor: Robyn Murray
Editorial Profile: Regional newspaper. Email is preferred form to receive editorial and advertising.
Language (s): English
NEWSPAPER

The Murray Pioneer - Countryside Quarterly
Owner: The Murray Pioneer
Editorial: 78 Ral Ral Avenue, Renmark SA 5341. **T:** 61 8 8586 6603
E: editor@murraypioneer.com.au
Freq: Quarterly
Editor: Paul Mitchell
Editorial Profile: Quarterly supplement of the Murray Pioneer.
Language (s): English
NEWSPAPER

Murray Tourist News
Owner: Sunraysin Newspaper Services Pty Ltd
Editorial: 54 McCallum Street, Swan Hill VIC 3585. **T:** 61 3 5032 2161
E: edit@theguardian.com.au
Freq: Bi-Monthly
Editorial Profile: A weekly newspaper for tourists in the local community. Editorial material accepted: Coming events and trade literature.
Language (s): English
NEWSPAPER

Murray Valley Standard
Owner: Rural Press Limited
Editorial: 110-118 Adelaide Road, Murray Bridge SA 5253. **T:** 61 8 8532 8000
E: editor.mvstandard@ruralpress.com
W: http://www.murrayvalleystandard.com.au
Freq: 2 Times/Week
Editor: Sharon Hansen
Editorial Profile: Regional newspaper with news and issues relevant to people living in the Murray Lands and outer Adelaide. Preferred delivery for media releases: fax
Language (s): English
NEWSPAPER

Musu Pastoge
Owner: Musu Pastoge
Editorial: 16-20 Meredith Street, Bankstown NSW 2200. **T:** 61 2 9782 0080
E: mpastoge@bigpond.com
W: http://www.slic.org.au/Pastoge
Freq: Weekly
Editor: Doniela Dalia
Editorial Profile: Translation: Our Haven Lithuanian newspaper.
Language (s): Lithuanian
NEWSPAPER

mX (Brisbane)
Owner: News Limited
Editorial: 41 Campbell Street, Bowen Hills QLD 4006. **T:** 61 7 3666 6022
E: briseditor@mxnet.com.au
W: http://www.mxnet.com.au
Freq: Daily
Editor: Emma Chalmers
Editorial Profile: mX covers from news, sport and business through to features focusing on lifestyle, popular culture, entertainment, movies, music, gossip, travel and the latest in IT.
Language (s): English
DAILY NEWSPAPER

mX (Melbourne)
Owner: News Limited
Editorial: HWT Tower, Level 10, Southbank VIC 3006. **T:** 61 3 9292 1800
E: acotts@mxnet.com.au
W: http://www.mxnet.com.au
Freq: Daily
City Beat Editor: Andrea Beattie; **Editor:** Anna Brain
Editorial Profile: Free afternoon Newspaper. Contains News and current Affairs, also Including Sport, Health, Travel, Lifestyle & Entertainment.
Language (s): English
DAILY NEWSPAPER

mX (Sydney)
Owner: News Limited
Editorial: Level 3, 2 Holt Street, Surry Hills NSW 2010. **T:** 61 2 9288 2823
W: http://www.mxnet.com.au
Freq: Daily
Editor: Melissa Matheson
Editorial Profile: mX is a free daily metropolitan newspaper, which includes business, sport, news, glamour, gossip, health, travel and entertainment.
Language (s): English

DAILY NEWSPAPER

Namoi Valley Independent
Owner: Gunnedah Publishing Company Pty Ltd
Editorial: 287 Conadilly Street, Gunnedah NSW 2380. **T:** 61 2 6742 0455
E: editorial@nvi.com.au
W: http://www.nvi.com.au
Freq: 2 Times/Week
Editor: Kate Ramien
Editorial Profile: Year First Published: 1876 Target Audience: LocalRegular Features: Lifestyle Page, Schools Pages Copy Deadline: Week PriorPhotographic Information: B/W Photographs, Colour Photographs Preferred Delivery: EmailPreferred Format: JPEG Press Material Accepted in: English
Language (s): English
NEWSPAPER

Naracoorte Herald
Owner: Fairfax Media
Editorial: 93 Smith Street, Naracoorte SA 5271. **T:** 61 8 8762 2555
E: editor.naracoorte@ruralpress.com
W: http://www.naracoorteherald.com.au
Freq: Weekly
Editor: Lee Curnow
Editorial Profile: A weekly regional newspaper with news and stories relevant to the local community. A team of journalists are responsible for gathering news, human interest and sports stories and pictures throughout the circulation area which includes Naracoorte, Lucindale, Padthaway, Penola, Coonawarra and the Victorian border districts.
Language (s): English
NEWSPAPER

Narooma News
Owner: Rural Press Limited
Editorial: Shop 4, Costin Village, Narooma NSW 2546. **T:** 61 2 4476 3024
E: mail.naroomanews@ruralpress.com
W: http://www.naroomanewsonline.com.au
Freq: Weekly
Editor: Stan Gorton
Editorial Profile: The Narooma News covers the local district from Bodalla to Cobargo and includes Bermagui, Tilba, Potato Point, Dalmeny and Kianga. Our focus is on local people, places and events with an emphasis on the community.
Language (s): English
NEWSPAPER

The Narrabri Courier
Owner: The North Western Courier Pty Ltd
Editorial: 60 Maitland Street, Narrabri NSW 2390. **T:** 61 2 6792 1011
E: editorial@nwcourier.com.au
W: http://www.thecourier.net.au
Freq: 2 Times/Week
Editor: Ian Dunnet
Editorial Profile: Regional weekly newspaper. Covers news, sport and community events in and around Narrabri.
Language (s): English
NEWSPAPER

Nea Ellada
Owner: Ethnic Publications Pty Ltd
Editorial: Level 1, 600 Nicholson Street, Fitzroy North VIC 3068. **T:** 61 3 9482 4433
E: editor@neoskosmos.com.au
W: http://www.neoskosmos.com.au
Freq: Weekly
Editorial Profile: Nea Ellada translates as Greek Times. Free translation service offered.
Language (s): Greek
NEWSPAPER

The Newcastle Herald
Owner: Newcastle Newspapers Pty Ltd
Editorial: 28 - 30 Bolton Street, Newcastle NSW 2300. **T:** 61 2 4979 5000
E: news@theherald.com.au
W: http://www.theherald.com.au
Freq: Daily
Editor: Chad Watson
Editorial Profile: Regional daily newspaper for the Newcastle, Hunter valley and Central coast district.
Language (s): English
DAILY NEWSPAPER

The Newcastle Star
Owner: Rural Press Limited
Editorial: 28 Bolton Street, Newcastle NSW 2300. **T:** 61 2 4979 5000
E: thestarnews@newcastle.fairfax.com.au
W: http://www.newcastlestar.com.au
Freq: Weekly
Editor: Kim-Cherie Davidson
Editorial Profile: Regional weekly newspaper.
Language (s): English

NEWSPAPER

North Central News
Owner: Nadalyn Pty Ltd
Editorial: 16-18 Napier Street, St Arnaud VIC 3478. **T:** 61 3 5495 1055 **E:** ncn@iinet.net.au
W: http://www.vcpa.com.au
Freq: Weekly
Editor: Peter Marland
Editorial Profile: A weekly regional paper with news and issues relevant to the local community.
Language (s): English
NEWSPAPER

North West Magazine
Owner: Gunnedah Publishing Company Pty Ltd
Editorial: 287 Conadilly Street, Gunnedah NSW 2380. **T:** 61 2 6742 0204
E: nwmagedit@nvi.com.au
W: http://www.ruralpresssales.com.au
Freq: Weekly
Editor: Keith Milerd
Editorial Profile: A regional newspaper with news and issues. Photographic information: Black & white photosPreferred delivery: e-mail Preferred format: JPEG
Language (s): English
NEWSPAPER

The North Western Courier
Editorial: The North Western Courier, 60 Maitland Street, Narrabri NSW 2390.
T: 61 2 6792 1011
E: editorial@nwcourier.com.au
W: http://www.thecourier.net.au
Freq: 2 Times/Week
Language (s): English
NEWSPAPER

The Northern Argus
Owner: Rural Press Limited
Editorial: 181 Main North Road, Clare SA 5453. **T:** 61 8 8842 2651
E: northernargus@ruralpress.com
W: http://www.northernargus.com.au
Freq: Weekly
Editorial Profile: A regional newspaper with news and issues relevant to the local community in the outer Adelaide and northern region of SA.
Language (s): English
NEWSPAPER

The Northern Daily Leader
Owner: Rural Press Limited
Editorial: 92 Brisbane Street, Tamworth NSW 2340. **T:** 61 2 6768 1200
E: mail.ndl@ruralpress.com
W: http://www.tamworth.yourguide.com.au
Freq: Daily
Editorial Profile: Regional newspaper in the north-West NSW region. Saturday cover price $1.40 Websites: www.localnews.com.au/ndl ; propertyguide.com.au/tamworth ; jobsguide.com.au/tamworth ; autoguide.com.au/tamworth
Language (s): English
DAILY NEWSPAPER

Northern Guardian
Owner: West Australian Newspapers Holdings Ltd
Editorial: 46 Robinson Street, Cnr Egan Street, Carnarvon WA 6701.
T: 61 8 9941 2222
E: news@northernguardian.com.au
W: http://www.newspapers.com.au/carnarvon
Freq: Weekly
Editor: Claire Tyrrell
Editorial Profile: Regional weekly publication with news and local issues for people living in the Carnarvon - North West area. Alternative email address = amrmail@margaret-river.com.au
Language (s): English
NEWSPAPER

The Northern Territory News
Owner: News Limited
Editorial: 1 Printers Place, Darwin NT 0800.
T: 61 8 8944 9900 **E:** news@ntnews.com.au
W: http://www.ntnews.com.au
Editor: Rachel Hancock
Editorial Profile: The Northern Territory News features the latest and local and national news. First published on February 8, 1952. The NT News reaches more than 64,000 people each day Monday – Friday, and the Saturday edition of the NT News is the highest circulating paper of the week. Liftouts in Saturday's NT News such as Property, Career One, Carsguide, Marine Guide and the investigative journalism feature 'Saturday Extra' ensure there is something for everyone.
Language (s): English

DAILY NEWSPAPER

Noticias Y Deportes
Owner: The Hispanoamerican Newspaper
Editorial: PO Box 1376, Green Valley NSW 2168. **T:** 61 2 9608 3158
E: jose@hispanoamerican.com.au
W: http://www.crc.nsw.gov.au/ethnic_media/newspapers
Freq: Weekly
Editorial Profile: Weekly newspaper, published in Spanish, servicing the Hispanic community in Sydney.
Language (s): Spanish
NEWSPAPER

Nova Hrvatska Weekly
Owner: Nova Hrvatska
Editorial: Suite 22, 647 George Street, Sydney NSW 2000. **T:** 61 2 9212 3623
E: franjo@ihug.com.au
W: http://homepages.ihug.com.au
Freq: Weekly
Editorial Profile: Independent Australian-Croatian weekly. Translation: New Croatia Translation service: free Also published in English
Language (s): English
NEWSPAPER

Numurkah Leader
Owner: Jinki Sixteen Pty Ltd
Editorial: 88 Melville Street, Numurkah VIC 3636. **T:** 61 3 5862 1034
E: editorial@leader.net.au
W: http://www.vcpa.com.au/vic-members
Freq: Weekly
Editor: Beverley Hutchins
Editorial Profile: A weekly regional newspaper with issues and news specific to residents in Numurkah, east to Cobram, north to Strathmerton, south to Shepparton, west to Barmah.
Language (s): English
NEWSPAPER

The Oakey Champion
Owner: OurNews Pty Ltd
Editorial: 2A Cherry Street, Oakey QLD 4401. **T:** 61 7 4691 1376
E: editorial@oakeychampion.com.au
W: http://www.themediaworkshop.com.au
Freq: Weekly
Editor: Ted Rogers; **Editor:** John Schmidt
Editorial Profile: A regional newspaper with news and issues relevant to local people and surrounds.
Language (s): English
NEWSPAPER

The Oberon Review
Owner: Rural Press Limited
Editorial: 83 Oberon Street, Oberon NSW 2787. **T:** 61 2 6336 1340
E: julia.kurtz@ruralpress.com
W: http://www.oberonreview.com.au
Freq: Weekly
Editorial Profile: Central-West NSW regional newspaper. Preferred delivery for media releases: Email
Language (s): English
NEWSPAPER

On Our Selection News
Owner: OurNews Pty Ltd
Editorial: 60 Clark Street, Clifton QLD 4361. **T:** 61 7 4697 3603
E: cliftoncourier@redzone.com.au
Freq: Weekly
Editor: Ted Rogers
Editorial Profile: Free weekly paper distributed throughout the cambooya district.
Language (s): English
NEWSPAPER

Parkes Champion-Post
Owner: Rural Press Limited
Editorial: 7-9 Court Street, Parkes NSW 2870. **T:** 61 2 6862 2322
E: mail.championpost@ruralpress.com
W: http://www.parkeschampionpost.com.au
Freq: 2 Times/Week
Editorial Profile: Tri-weekly regional newspaper.
Language (s): English
NEWSPAPER

The Philippine Community Herald
Owner: The Philippine Community Herald
Editorial: 37 Prince Street, Canley Vale NSW 2166. **T:** 61 297257722
E: pcherald@iinet.net.au
Freq: Monthly
Editorial Profile: A national newspaper covering news from the Philippines and Australia. Please send any information via fax

as the managing editor is not very good with email.
Language (s): English
NEWSPAPER

Phillip Island & San Remo Advertiser
Owner: Phillip Island & San Remo Advertiser P/L
Editorial: Suite 2, 60 Chapel Street, Cowes VIC 3922. **T:** 61 3 5952 3248
E: advertiser@waterfront.net.au
W: http://www.vcpa.com.au/vic-members
Freq: 2 Times/Week
Editor: Anne Oswin
Editorial Profile: A local regional newspaper with news and issues relevant to residents and visitors to Phillip Island and San Remo.
Language (s): English
NEWSPAPER

Pilbara News
Owner: Murray Pioneer
Editorial: Murray Pioneer, 78 Ral Ral Avenue, Renmark SA 5341. **T:** 61 8 9185 2666
Editorial Profile: Supplement of the Murray Pioneer
Language (s): English
DAILY NEWSPAPER

Pinjarra Murray Times
Owner: Community Newspaper Group
Editorial: Unit 2, 96 Pinjarra Road, Mandurah WA 6210. **T:** 61 8 9583 1000
E: jill.burgess@communitynews.com.au
W: http://www.communitynews.com.au/OurNewspapers/MandurahCoastalTimes/tabid/65/Defa
Freq: Weekly
Editorial Profile: Formerly the Coastal District Times-it is a local community paper with stories relevant to the local community. It is the same paper as the Mandurah Coastal Times but with a different masthead.
Language (s): English
NEWSPAPER

The Plains Producer
Owner: Papers & Publications Pty Ltd
Editorial: 9 Howe Street, Balaklava SA 5461.
T: 61 8 8862 1977
E: editor@plainsproducer.com.au
W: http://www.plainsproducer.com.au
Freq: Weekly
Editor: Terry Williams
Editorial Profile: National daily newspaper. Any photographic format is accepted.Email is preferred delivery for images Preferred format: JPEG
Language (s): English
NEWSPAPER

Port Macquarie Express
Owner: Rural Press Limited
Editorial: 16-20 Milton Circuit, Port Macquarie NSW 2444. **T:** 61 2 6581 1622
E: editor.portnews@ruralpress.com
W: http://www.portnews.com.au
Freq: Weekly
Editor: Gordon Wiegold
Editorial Profile: Year First Published: 1986 Regional weekly paper in the Mid-North Coast NSW region.Sister paper: The Port Macquarie News Formats Available: CD-ROM, Other Online.Target Audience: Hastings local government area. Photographic Information: B/W Photographs, Colour Photographs, Colour Transparencies.Preferred Delivery: Email Preferred Fomat: JPEG
Language (s): English
NEWSPAPER

Port Macquarie News
Owner: Rural Press Limited
Editorial: 16-20 Milton Circuit, Port Macquarie NSW 2444. **T:** 61 2 6588 6688
E: editor.portnews@ruralpress.com
W: http://www.portnews.com.au
Freq: 2 Times/Week
Editor: Gordon Wiegold
Editorial Profile: Regional newspaper in the Mid-North coast NSW region. Sister paper: Port Macquarie ExpressFormats available: CD-ROM Regular features: Youth, Schools, Finance, Business.Photographic information: Colour photos, black & white photos, colour transparencies. Preferred delivery: e-mailPreferred format: JPEG
Language (s): English
NEWSPAPER

Port Stephens Examiner
Owner: Fairfax Community Newspapers Pty Ltd
Editorial: 10 William Street, Raymond Terrace NSW 2324. **T:** 61 2 4983 8400
E: news@pse.fairfax.com.au

W: http://www.portstephensexaminer.com.au
Freq: Weekly
Editor: Anna Wolf
Editorial Profile: Regional weekly paper in the NSW Hunter region. Preferred delivery for media releases: Fax or Email
Language (s): English
NEWSPAPER

Post Weekly
Owner: Goulburn Post
Editorial: 199 Auburn Street, Goulburn NSW 2580. **T:** 61 2 4827 3500
E: editorial.goulburnpost@ruralpress.com
W: http://www.goulburn.yourguide.com.au
Freq: Weekly
Editorial Profile: Weekly newspaper covering news and issues in Goulburn and surrounding areas.
Language (s): English
NEWSPAPER

Property Week
Owner: Sunshine Coast Daily
Editorial: PO Box 56, Maroochydore QLD 4558. **T:** 61 7 5430 8098
E: property@scnews.com.au
Editorial Profile: Blend of national and regional property trends covering residential, land, commercial/ business, new-homes and developments. 40,000 + copies distributed each Saturday. Known as the "Noosa Property Week" in the Noosa News.
Language (s): English
DAILY NEWSPAPER

Pyrenees Advocate
Owner: Pyrenees Newspapers
Editorial: 32 Willoby Street, Beaufort VIC 3373. **T:** 61 3 5349 2787
E: mail@theadvocate.net.au
W: http://www.theadvocate.net.au
Freq: Weekly
Editorial Profile: Regional weekly newspaper.
Language (s): English
NEWSPAPER

Queensland Newspapers Pty Ltd
Owner: Telstra Corporation Limited
Editorial: 41 Campbell Street, Bowen Hills QLD 4006. **T:** 61 1300 304 020
W: http://www.thecouriermail.com.au
Language (s): English
DAILY NEWSPAPER

Radio National Life Matters
Owner: ABC Radio National
Editorial: Level 1, 700 Harris Street, Ultimo NSW 2007. **T:** 61 283331650
E: armstrong.amanda@abc.net.au
W: http://abc.net.au/rn/lifematters
Editorial Profile: Programme that discusses issues of social change. Guest interviews.Monday Personal Column: Geraldine Doogue takes one of your letters or e-mails describing a personal or ethical dilemma and puts it to our panel for comment or advice.Monday Economics: Peter MartinWednesday Our weekly talkback session. The call-in number is 1800 025 977.Thursday Work Matters: Rebecca GormanFriday Rear View, which debates the story of the week.
Language (s): English
DAILY NEWSPAPER

Rev It Up
Owner: The Longreach Leader
Editorial: Longreach Leader, Magpie Lane, Longreach QLD 4730. **T:** 61 746583855
E: advertising@longreachleader.com.au
Freq: Monthly
Language (s): English
NEWSPAPER

The Riverine Grazier
Owner: The Riverine Grazier Pty Ltd
Editorial: 95 Lachlan Street, Hay NSW 2711. **T:** 61 2 6993 1002
E: riverine_grazier@bigpond.com
W: http://www.vcpa.com.au
Freq: Weekly
Editor: Tertia Butcher
Editorial Profile: Year First Published: 1863 Regional newspaper with regular features: History, Sports Formats Available: CD-ROM, Disk Supplements: 8 per year, various events and issues Photographic Information: B/W Photographs, Colour Photographs Preferred Delivery images: Email Preferred Format: JPEG, EPS Press Material Accepted in: English
Language (s): English
NEWSPAPER

Robina Mail
Editorial: Newspaper Place, Maroochydore QLD 4558. **T:** 61 7 5430 1021
E: ally.elphinstone@apn.com.au
W: http://apnarm.com.au/newspapers/community/4690.html
Freq: Weekly
Editorial Profile: Robina Mail is a new weekly newspaper featuring editorial that is specifically-written for the high-growth Robina micro-community. Robina Mail delivers unparalleled hyper-local coverage across a market that is home to over 62,000 residents and a rapidly-increasing business community. Robina Mail has been developed to target and support the unique Robina market the weekly newspaper delivers localised news, events and opinions that really matter to local residents, not just news from across the Gold Coast region. Robina Mail complements the existing, successful Gold Coast Mail bringing the combined package circulation of the titles to over 52,000 copies per week#.
Language (s): English
NEWSPAPER

The Rural
Owner: Wagga Daily Advertiser Pty Ltd
Editorial: 48 Trail Street, Wagga Wagga NSW 2650. **T:** 61 2 6938 3330
E: tpower@rivmediagroup.com.au
W: http://www.therural.com.au
Freq: Weekly
Editor: Daisy Huntly
Editorial Profile: The Rural is one of the largest circulating rural newspapers in Southern NSW. The paper plays a pivotal role in supplying agricultural and farming news to business, industry and farming communities in this part of the State. The Rural offers advertisers a vehicle to target a range of potential customers in the richest and most heavily populated agricultural and grazing areas of the State. The Rural provides agricultural industry news together with national and international news, lifestyle, weather, sport, automotive and property news.
Language (s): English
NEWSPAPER

Sarina Midweek
Owner: Mackay Printing & Publishing Company Pty Ltd
Editorial: 38 - 40 Wellington Street, Mackay QLD 4740. **T:** 61 7 4957 0444
E: midweek@dailymercury.com.au
W: http://apnap.com.au/newspapers
Freq: Weekly
Editorial Profile: A weekly regional newspaper with news and issues relevant to residents of Sarina & Mackay.
Language (s): English
NEWSPAPER

The Saturday Paper
Editorial: 37-39 Langridge Street, Collingwood 3066 Vic. **T:** 61 3 9486 0288
E: enquiries@thesaturdaypaper.com.au
W: http://www.thesaturdaypaper.com.au
Freq: Weekly
Editor: Erik Jensen; **Publisher:** Morry Schwartz
Editorial Profile: The Saturday Paper is a weekly newspaper covering news, culture, and analysis, with a particular focus on Australia. Launched on 1 March 2014.
Language (s): English
NEWSPAPER

Scone Advocate
Owner: Rural Press Limited
Editorial: 152 Kelly Street, Scone NSW 2337. **T:** 61 2 6545 1155
E: editor.sconeadvocate@ruralpress.com
W: http://www.sconeadvocate.com.au
Freq: Weekly
Editorial Profile: Regional weekly paper in the Hunter region of NSW. Preferred delivery for media releases: Email
Language (s): English
NEWSPAPER

The Shepparton Adviser
Owner: Simtru Pty Ltd
Editorial: Newspaper House, 95-97 Welsford Street, Shepparton VIC 3630. **T:** 61 3 5822 1522
E: editorial@sheppartonadviser.com.au
W: http://www.sheppartonadvisor.com.au
Freq: Weekly
Editor: Julie Moore
Editorial Profile: Weekly regional newspaper with news and issues for the local community. Also distributed in Mooroopna. The Shepparton Car Weekly has combined with the Adviser, they are now a single publication. The car weekly is in the adviser every tuesday.
Language (s): English
NEWSPAPER

The Singleton Argus
Owner: Rural Press Limited
Editorial: 6 Campbell Street, Singleton NSW 2330. **T:** 61 2 6572 2611
E: editor.singletonargus@ruralpress.com
W: http://www.singletonargus.com.au
Freq: 2 Times/Week
Editor: Dianne Sneddon
Editorial Profile: Regional weekly publication with news and local issues for people living in the Singleton area.
Language (s): English
NEWSPAPER

Snowy River Mail
Owner: James Yeates & Sons Pty Ltd
Editorial: 122 Nicholson Street, Orbost VIC 3888. **T:** 61 3 5154 1919
E: srm@eastvicmedia.com.au
W: www.vcpa.com.au/vic-members
Freq: Weekly
Editorial Profile: A weekly regional newspaper with news and issues relevant to people living in the area.
Language (s): English
NEWSPAPER

South Coast Register
Owner: Rural Press Limited
Editorial: 122 Kinghorne Street, Nowra NSW 2541. **T:** 61 2 4421 9123
E: editor.scregister@ruralpress.com
W: http://www.southcoastregister.com.au
Freq: 2 Times/Week
Editor: John Hanscombe
Editorial Profile: Year First Published: 1886 Regional newspaper.Preferred delivery for media releases: Email Target Audience: Residents from Gerringong in the North to Sussex Inlet in the South (South Coast NSW)Regular Features: Property Guide, Auto Guide, Entertainment Photographic Information: AnyPreferred Format: JPEG
Language (s): English
NEWSPAPER

South Gippsland Sentinel Times
Owner: South-Eastern Newspapers Pty Ltd
Editorial: 8 Radovick Street, Korumburra VIC 3950. **T:** 61 3 5655 1422
E: news@sgst.com.au
W: http://www.sgst.com.au
Freq: Weekly
Editor: Nathan Johnston
Editorial Profile: A weekly regional newspaper with news and current issues relevant to the residents of the local community. With coverage north to Warragul, south to Phillip Island, east to Yarram, west to Cranbourne.Formats available: CD-ROM, Disk Photographic information: Colour photos, black & white photosPreferred delivery: e-mail Preferred format: PDF
Language (s): English
NEWSPAPER

South Western Times
Owner: West Australian Newspapers Holdings Ltd
Editorial: 19 Proffit Street, Bunbury WA 6230. **T:** 61 8 9780 0800 **E:** editor@swtimes.com.au
W: http://southwest.thewest.com.au
Freq: Weekly
Editorial Profile: Weekly regional newspaper with news and issues relevant to the local community in south-west WA. Alternative email address for WA subscribers: bunbury@wanews.com.auPress Photos are available for the following types & prices: Laser prints:black and white: A4 $2.20, A3 $3.30 colour: A4 $4.40, A3 $5.50Glossy prints: black & white or colour: A5 $14.50, A4 $22, A3 $33Including postage: A5 $16.15, A4 $23.65, A3 $36.50 Orders can be placed at Proffitt Street or the main Bunbury Herald Office. Newspaper article search also available. Whole back copies of newspapers are not available.
Language (s): English
NEWSPAPER

The Southern Cross (Junee)
Owner: Rural Press Limited
Editorial: 48 Trail Street, Wagga Wagga NSW 2650. **T:** 61 2 6924 3861
E: editorial.southerncross@rivmediagroup.com.au
W: http://www.juneesoutherncross.com.au
Freq: Weekly
Editorial Profile: Published Thursdays, circulates 1,100. The paper offers two sections, special features and business profile. This offers an opportunity for businesses, event organisers, charity groups and industry specific groups, to promote their products and services.
Language (s): English
NEWSPAPER

The Southern Free Times
Owner: The Victorian Country Press
Editorial: Shop 5, 70 Fitzroy Street, Warwick QLD 4370. **T:** 61 7 4661 9800
E: editor@freetimes.com.au
W: http://www.freetimes.com.au
Freq: Weekly
Editor: Janine Crawford
Editorial Profile: The Southern Free Times is a newspaper covering grain, fruit, vegetables, dairy, grazing, food processing, transport & distribution and manufacturing.
Language (s): English
NEWSPAPER

Stockton Messenger - North Of The Harbour
Owner: Peter & Kathy Quinn
Editorial: 72 Newcastle Street, Stockton NSW 2295
Freq: Bi-Weekly
Editorial Profile: Local community paper in the central coast region of NSW. Editorial will only be included if relevant to local community.No email or website. Preferred delivery for media releases: fax or post
Language (s): English
NEWSPAPER

Sunbury Leader
Owner: The Leader Community Newspaper Group
Editorial: 30 Station Street, Sunbury VIC 3429. **T:** 61 3 9744 9303
E: sunbury@leadernewspapers.com.au
W: http://www.sunburyleader.com.au
Freq: Weekly
Editor: Liam McAleer
Language (s): English
NEWSPAPER

Sunbury Weekly
Owner: Fairfax Community Newspapers (Victoria)
Editorial: 12 Howes Street, Airport West VIC 3042. **T:** 61 3 8318 5777
E: avalente@fairfaxmedia.com.au
W: http://www.adcentre.com.au/sunbury-weeklymacedon-ranges-weekly.aspx
Freq: Weekly
Editor: David Bonnici; **Editor:** Stephen Linnell
Editorial Profile: A weekly regional newspaper with news and issues relevant to residents. Linked with Macedon Ranges TelegraphRegular features: Health, Horse, Dine, Vet care, Home decorating. Photographic information: Colour photosPreferred delivery: Post, e-mail (e-mail to dreed@fcnvio.fairfax.com.au)
Language (s): English
NEWSPAPER

Sunday Examiner
Owner: Rural Press Limited
Editorial: 71-75 Paterson Street, Launceston TAS 7250. **T:** 61 3 6336 7111
E: mail@examiner.com.au
W: http://www.examiner.com.au
Freq: Weekly
Editor: Martin Gilmour
Editorial Profile: Regional newspaper covering Launceston and the surrounding Northern ares of Tasmania.
Language (s): English
NEWSPAPER

Sunday Times
Owner: News Limited
Editorial: 34 Stirling Street, Perth WA 6000. **T:** 61 8 9326 9000
E: news@perthnow.newsltd.com.au
W: http://www.perthnow.com.au
Freq: Weekly
News Editor: Anthony DeCeglie; **Editor:** Rod Savage
Editorial Profile: Metropolitan Sunday newspaper circulating in Perth and Western Australia.
Language (s): English
NEWSPAPER

Sunshine Coast Daily
Owner: APN News & Media Limited
Editorial: Newspaper Place & Dalton Drive, Maroochydore QLD 4558. **T:** 61 7 5430 1012
E: editorial@scnews.com.au
W: http://www.sunshinecoastdaily.com.au
Freq: Daily
Editor-in-Chief: Darren Burnett; **Editor at Large:** Bill Hoffman; **Editor:** Erle Levey
Editorial Profile: Regional newspaper in the Sunshine Coast area. Regular Features: Business, Comics, Crosswords, Letters, Sport, TV and Weather.
Language (s): English
DAILY NEWSPAPER

The Sydney Morning Herald
Owner: Fairfax Media
Editorial: 1 Darling Island Road, Pyrmont NSW 2009. **T:** 61 2 9282 2833
E: newsdesk@smh.com.au
W: http://www.smh.com.au
Freq: Daily
Editor: Rick Feneley; **Drive Editor:** Toby Hagon; **Editor:** Peter Hannam
Editorial Profile: Metropolitan Daily Broadsheet Newspaper in Sydney. The Sydney Morning Herald offers independence, authority, integrity, quality and an inquiring, AB readership. Its news pages, analysis and commentary set the standard for journalist excellence, involving the questioning reader in the affairs of Sydney, Australia and the world. The paper features a wide number of weekly and daily sections adn inserts. From food to fashion, from real estate to racing, our modern sections deliver specialised information amid vibrant pages boasting world-class design.
Language (s): English
DAILY NEWSPAPER

The Tablelander
Owner: North Queensland Newspaper Company Limited
Editorial: 53 Mabel Street, Atherton QLD 4883. **T:** 61 7 4091 1977
E: editorial@tablelandnewspapers.com.au
W: http://www.newsspace.com.au/tablelander__atherton_
Freq: Weekly
Editorial Profile: A regional newspaper with news and issues relevant to the local community.
Language (s): English
NEWSPAPER

Tamworth Times
Owner: Rural Press Limited
Editorial: 92 Brisbane Street, Tamworth NSW 2340. **T:** 61 2 6768 1245
E: mail.ndl@ruralpress.com
W: http://www.tamworth.yourguide.com.au
Freq: Weekly
Editorial Profile: Regional paper in the Tamworth region and satellite townships, including a small part of the Parry Shire. Preferred delivery for media releases: Fax or Email
Language (s): English
NEWSPAPER

Temora Independent
Owner: JA Bradley & Sons
Editorial: 193 Hoskins Street, Temora NSW 2666. **T:** 61 2 6977 1077
E: editorial@temoraindependent.com.au
Freq: 2 Times/Week
Editorial Profile: Regional paper in the Murrumbidgee region of NSW. Preferred delivery for media releases: Fax or Post
Language (s): English
NEWSPAPER

Tennant & District Times
Owner: Tennant & District Times
Editorial: Shop 1, 139 Paterson Street, Tennant Creek NT 0860. **T:** 61 8 8962 1040
E: media@tdtimes.com.au
W: http://tennantcreek.yourguide.com.au
Freq: Weekly
Editor: Jasmin Afianos
Editorial Profile: Regional newspaper.
Language (s): English
NEWSPAPER

Terang Express
Owner: Western District Newspapers Pty Ltd
Editorial: 126 Manifold Street, Camperdown VIC 3260. **T:** 61 3 5593 1888
E: terangexpress@wdnews.com.au
W: http://www.wdnews.com.au
Freq: Weekly
Editorial Profile: A weekly regional newspapers with news and issues relevant to people living in Terang, north to Kolora, south to South Ecklin, east to Boorcan, west to Panmure.
Language (s): English
NEWSPAPER

The Queenstowner
T: 61 364711885
E: john.hepher@bigpond.com.au
Freq: Weekly
Publisher: John Hepher
Editorial Profile: Newspaper covering news and information relevant to the residents of Queenstown, Tasmania.
Language (s): English
NEWSPAPER

The Singleton Argus- Upper Hunter TV Guide
Owner: Muswellbrook Chronicle
Editorial: Scone Advocate, 6 Campbell Street, Singleton NSW 2330. **T:** 61 265722611
Editor: Stuart McLagan
Editorial Profile: Television guide.
Language (s): English
DAILY NEWSPAPER

The Times (Victor Harbor)
Owner: Rural Press Limited
Editorial: 13 Coral Street, Victor Harbor SA 5211. **T:** 61 8 8552 1488
E: victortimes@ruralpress.com
W: http://www.victorharbortimes.com.au
Freq: Weekly
Editor: Brooke DuBois
Editorial Profile: Regional newspaper with news and issues relevant to people living in outer Adelaide regions. Preferred delivery for media releases: email
Language (s): English
NEWSPAPER

The Toowoomba Mail
Owner: Toowoomba Newspapers Pty Ltd
Editorial: 618 Ruthven Street, Toowoomba QLD 4350. **T:** 61 7 4690 9394
E: editorial@thechronicle.com.au
W: http://apnarm.com.au/newspapers/community/4647.html
Freq: Weekly
Editor-in-Chief: Steve Etwell
Editorial Profile: A regional newspaper with news and issues for people living in Toowoomba, north to Highfields. (Formerly the Downs Star)
Language (s): English
NEWSPAPER

Top
Owner: Top Newspaper Co Ltd
Editorial: Suite 2B, Level 2, Strathfield NSW 2135. **T:** 61 2 9746 2200
E: marketing@topnews.com.au
W: http://www.topnews.com.au
Freq: Weekly
Editorial Profile: Korean weekly community publication. Includes news, social and cultural reports.
Language (s): Korean
NEWSPAPER

The Townsville Sun
Owner: The North Queensland Newspaper Company Limited
Editorial: 198 Ogden Street, Townsville QLD 4810. **T:** 61 7 4722 4467
E: admin@townsvillesun.com.au
W: http://www.townsvillebulletin.com.au/publications/townsville_sun.html
Freq: Weekly
Editorial Profile: The Sun, a free weekly newspaper, features news and events affecting the communities of Townsville and Thuringowa, Queensland.
Language (s): English
NEWSPAPER

The Transcontinental
Owner: Rural Press Limited
Editorial: 6 Tassie Street, Port Augusta SA 5700. **T:** 61 8 8642 2688
E: editor.trans@ruralpress.com
W: www.transcontinental.com.au
Freq: Weekly
Editor: Seema Sharma
Editorial Profile: Regional weekly newspaper in the Northern region of SA. Preferred delivery for media releases: fax or email
Language (s): English
NEWSPAPER

TV Guide
Owner: The Shepparton News
Editorial: The Shepparton News, Melbourne Road, Kialla VIC 3631. **T:** 61 3 5831 2312
E: editor@sheppnews.com.au
W: http://www.sheppnews.com.au
Freq: Weekly
Editorial Profile: Weekly TV Guide SupplementCirculation Notes: 700,032 (July-December 2001) ABC
Language (s): English
NEWSPAPER

Visitors Guide
Owner: Bombala Times
Editorial: Southern Highland News, 28 Wingecarribee Street, Bowral NSW 2576.
T: 61 2 4861 2333
W: http://www.bowral.yourguide.com.au
Editorial Profile: Local events and entertainment supplement.
Language (s): English
DAILY NEWSPAPER

Wagin Argus
Owner: Rural Press Limited
Editorial: 18 Tavistock Street, Wagin WA 6315. **T:** 61 8 9861 1200
E: waginargus@ruralpress.com
W: http://www.waginargus.com.au
Freq: Weekly
Editor: James Taylor
Editorial Profile: Regional weekly publication with news and local issues for people living in the Margaret River area. Alternative email address = amrmail@margaret-river.com.au
Language (s): English
NEWSPAPER

Walcha News
Owner: Rural Press Limited
Editorial: 16N Derby Street, Walcha NSW 2354. **T:** 61 2 6777 2513
E: walcha.news@ruralpress.com
W: http://walcha.yourguide.com.au
Freq: Weekly
Editor: Stephanie van Eyk
Editorial Profile: Local paper distributed Northern NSW.Preferred delivery of Media releases; fax.
Language (s): English
NEWSPAPER

Wall Street Journal (Australia)
Editorial: Level 10, 56 Pitt Street, Sydney NSW 2000. **T:** 61 2 8272-4600
E: djnews.sydney@dowjones.com
News Editor: Shani Raja; **Bureau Chief:** David Winning
DAILY NEWSPAPER

The Warialda Standard
Owner: DG & PA Wilson
Editorial: 38 Hope Street, Warialda NSW 2402. **T:** 61 2 6729 1460
E: editor@warialdastandard.com.au
W: http://warialdastandard.squarespace.com
Freq: Weekly
Editor: Rachel Sherman
Editorial Profile: Regional paper in the northern NSW region. No email or website.
Language (s): English
NEWSPAPER

Warracknabeal Herald
Owner: Warracknabeal Herald Pty Ltd
Editorial: 89 Scott Street, Warracknabeal VIC 3393. **T:** 61 3 5398 2033
E: wkherald@netconnect.com.au
W: http://www.warrackherald.com.au
Freq: 2 Times/Week
Editorial Profile: A regional twice-weekly newspaper with news and issues relevant to people living in the area.
Language (s): English
NEWSPAPER

Warrego Watchman
Owner: Warrego Watchman Pty Ltd
Editorial: 38 John Street, Cunnamulla QLD 4490. **T:** 61 7 4655 1617
E: editorial@warregowatchmen.com.au
W: http://www.warregowatchman.com.au
Freq: Weekly
Editorial Profile: A weekly regional newspaper with news and issues for people living in Cunnamulla and Charleville.
Language (s): English
NEWSPAPER

Warren Advocate
Owner: Rural Press Limited
Editorial: Burton Street, Warren NSW 2824. **T:** 61 2 6847 4333
E: mail.warrenadvocate@ruralpress.com
W: http://www.warrenadvocate.com.au
Freq: Weekly
Editorial Profile: Local paper for residents of Warren. Colour Photographs.Preferred Delivery: Email. Preferred Format: JPEG
Language (s): English
NEWSPAPER

Warren Weekly
Owner: Warren Weekly Prt Ltd
Editorial: 6a Burton Street, Warren NSW 2824. **T:** 61 2 6847 3044
E: waweekly@bigpond.net.au
Freq: Weekly
Editorial Profile: First published in 1985.Regular Features: Cotton, Wool, Show. Photographic Information: B/W Photographs, Colour Photographs. Preferred Delivery: Post.
Language (s): English
NEWSPAPER

The Warrnambool Standard
Owner: Fairfax Media
Editorial: 575 Raglan Parade, Warrnambool VIC 3280. **T:** 61 3 5563 1800
E: editor@thestandard.net.au
W: http://www.standard.net.au
Freq: Weekly
Editor: Steve Hynes; **Editor-in-Chief:** Steve Kelly
Editorial Profile: A regional daily paper with news, issues and sport relevant to the local community. Saturday cover price $1.30
Language (s): English
NEWSPAPER

Wauchope Gazette
Owner: Rural Press Limited
Editorial: 47 Hasting Street, Wauchope NSW 2446. **T:** 61 2 6585 2355
E: wauchopegazette@ruralpress.com
W: http://www.wauchopegazette.com.au
Freq: Weekly
Editorial Profile: First published: 1907 Regional paper in the mid-north coast region of NSW. Formats available: CD-ROM, Disk Photographic information: Colour photos Preferred delivery: e-mail Preferred format: JPEG
Language (s): English
NEWSPAPER

Wee Waa News
Owner: The North Western Courier Pty Ltd
Editorial: 60 Maitland Street, Narrabri NSW 2390. **T:** 61 2 6792 1011
E: wwnews@nwcourier.com.au
W: http://www.themediaworkshop.com.au
Freq: Weekly
Editorial Profile: Favourite television stars & music stars - posters, interviews, song lyrics.
Language (s): English
NEWSPAPER

The Weekend Australian Editor
Owner: The Weekend Australian
Editorial: 2 Holt Street, Surry Hills NSW 2010. **T:** 61 2 9288 2418
E: wynhausene@theaustralian.com.au
Freq: Weekly
Editorial Profile: "Editor" offers a weekly overview of the week's essential stories and debates and how they were covered in news, editorial and media outlets around the world, together with the hottest in film, books, fashion, art, architecture, music, trends and on stage.
Language (s): English
NEWSPAPER

The Weekend West
Owner: The West Australian
Editorial: 50 Hasler Road, Osborne Park WA 6017. **T:** 61 8 9482 3111
E: westinfo@wanews.com.au
W: http://www.thewest.com.au
Freq: Weekly
Editor: Jenni Garrigan; **Editor:** Brett McCarthy
Editorial Profile: The West Australian's weekend paper.
Language (s): English
NEWSPAPER

The West Australian
Owner: West Australian Newspapers Holdings Ltd
Editorial: 50 Hasler Road, Osborne Park, Perth WA 6017. **T:** 61 8 9482 3111
E: online@thewest.com.au
W: http://au.news.yahoo.com/thewest
Freq: Daily
Editor-in-Chief: Brett McCarthy; **Editor:** Grace Millimaci
Editorial Profile: Newspaper covering news, weather, employment, real estate, cars, boats, shopping, sport and entertainment.
Language (s): English
DAILY NEWSPAPER

West Coast Sentinel
Owner: Rural Press Limited
Editorial: Shop 8, 35 Poynton Street, Ceduna SA 5690. **T:** 61 8 8625 2265
E: westcoastsentinel@ruralpress.com
W: http://www.westcoastsentinel.com.au
Freq: Weekly
Editorial Profile: A regional weekly newspaper in the Eyre region of SA. Preferred delivery for media releases: Email.
Language (s): English
NEWSPAPER

The West Gippsland Trader
Owner: Warragul Regional Newspapers Pty Ltd
Editorial: 97 Queen Street, Warragul VIC 3820. **T:** 61 3 5623 5666
E: editorial@warragulgazette.com.au
W: http://www.warragulgazette.com.au
Freq: Weekly
Editor: Carolyn Turner
Editorial Profile: A regional newspaper with news and issues relevant to the local

community.Photographic information: Colour photos, black & white photos.Preferred delivery: Post
Language (s): English
NEWSPAPER

The West Wyalong Advocate
Owner: West Australian Newspapers Holdings Ltd
Editorial: 140-142 Main Street, West Wyalong NSW 2671. **T:** 61 2 6972 2033
E: wwadvoc@bigpond.net.au
Freq: 2 Times/Week
Editor: Heatherbelle Vearing
Editorial Profile: Regional paper in the central west region of NSW. Preferred delivery for media releases: Fax, as office runs on Macintosh computers. For email Rich Text Format is required.
Language (s): English
NEWSPAPER

The Western Herald (TAS)
Owner: Harris & Co. Ltd
Editorial: 54 - 56 Mount Street, Burnie TAS 7320. **T:** 61 3 6440 7409
E: news@theadvocate.com.au
W: http://www.theadvocate.com.au
Freq: Monthly
Editorial Profile: Regional weekly newspaper
Language (s): English
NEWSPAPER

The Western Herald Bourke
Owner: Navoc
Editorial: 36 Mertin Street, Bourke NSW 2840. **T:** 61 2 6872 2035
E: westernherald@auzzie.net
W: http://www.themediaworkshop.com.au
Freq: Weekly
Editorial Profile: Distributed from Bourke, north to Queensland border, south to Nyngan, east to Brewarrina, west to Tibooburra. NB: Office runs on Macintosh, so emails must be in either plain text format, PDF or pasted into the body of the email.
Language (s): English
NEWSPAPER

The Western Times (NSW)
Owner: Rural Press Limited
Editorial: 163 George Street, Bathurst NSW 2795. **T:** 61 2 6331 2611
E: editor.westernadvocate@ruralpress.com
W: http://www.westernadvocate.com.au
Freq: Weekly
Editorial Profile: Rural weekly newspaper founded in 1891. Circulates in northern and central areas of QLD, NT and the Kimberley.Covers rural commodity and market information.
Language (s): English
NEWSPAPER

The Western Times (QLD)
Owner: Western Times
Editorial: 62 Alfred Street, Charleville QLD 4470. **T:** 61 7 4654 1099
E: editorial@westerntimes.com.au
W: http://apnarm.com.au/newspapers
Freq: Weekly
Editorial Profile: A weekly regional newspaper with news and issues for people living in Western Qld- Charleville, north to Blackall, south to Cunnamulla, east to Mitchell, west to Windorah.
Language (s): English
NEWSPAPER

The Young Witness
Owner: Rural Press Limited
Editorial: 61 Boorowa Street, Young NSW 2594. **T:** 61 2 6382 1477
E: manager.youngwitness@ruralpress.com
W: http://www.youngwitness.com.au
Freq: 2 Times/Week
Editorial Profile: Regional paper in the south-eastern regional paper of NSW. Included in the South West News Pictorial and the Young Times.
Language (s): English
NEWSPAPER

NEWS SERVICE/SYNDICATE

AAP Adelaide
Owner: AAP Information Services Pty Ltd
Editorial: Level 5 West, 50 Grenfell Street, Adelaide SA 5000. **T:** 61 8 8238 4300
E: news.adelaide@aap.com.au
W: http://www.aap.com.au
Bureau Chief: Liza Kappelle
Editorial Profile: AAP provides world news and images to our customers through commercial partnerships with major international agencies like Associated Press,

Reuters, Agence France-Presse, Agencia EFE, Deutsche Presse-Agentur, The Press Association, Kyodo, Knight-Ridder and New Zealand Press Association.
Language (s): English
NEWS SERVICE/SYNDICATE

AAP Brisbane
Owner: AAP Information Services Pty Ltd
Editorial: Level 2, 200 Mary Street, Brisbane QLD 4000. **T:** 61 7 3834 9999
E: news.brisbane@aap.com.au
W: http://www.aap.com.au
Bureau Chief: Tracey Ferrier; **Bureau Chief:** Paul Osbourne
Editorial Profile: AAP provides world news and images to our customers through commercial partnerships with major international agencies like Associated Press, Reuters, Agence France-Presse, Agencia EFE, Deutsche Presse-Agentur, The Press Association, Kyodo, Knight-Ridder and New Zealand Press Association.
Language (s): English
NEWS SERVICE/SYNDICATE

AAP Cairns
Editorial: 127 Abbott St, Cairns Qld 4870, Cairns North QLD 4870. **T:** 61 7 4051 3745
E: news.cairns@aap.com.au
W: aap.com.au/contacts
Bureau Chief: Patrick Caruana
Language (s): English
NEWS SERVICE/SYNDICATE

AAP Darwin
Owner: AAP Information Services Pty Ltd
Editorial: Printers Place, Darwin NT 800. **T:** 61 8 8981 1730
E: news.darwin@aap.com.au
W: http://www.aap.com.au
Bureau Chief: Larine Statham
Editorial Profile: AAP provides world news and images to our customers through commercial partnerships with major international agencies like Associated Press, Reuters, Agence France-Presse, Agencia EFE, Deutsche Presse-Agentur, The Press Association, Kyodo, Knight-Ridder and New Zealand Press Association.
Language (s): English
NEWS SERVICE/SYNDICATE

AAP Hobart
Owner: AAP Information Services Pty Ltd
Editorial: 97 - 93 Macquarie Street, Hobart TAS 7000. **T:** 61 3 6234 5541
E: news.hobart@aap.com.au
W: www.aap.com.au
Bureau Chief: David Beneuk
Editorial Profile: AAP provides world news and images to our customers through commercial partnerships with major international agencies like Associated Press, Reuters, Agence France-Presse, Agencia EFE, Deutsche Presse-Agentur, The Press Association, Kyodo, Knight-Ridder and New Zealand Press Association.
Language (s): English
NEWS SERVICE/SYNDICATE

AAP Melbourne
Owner: AAP Information Services Pty Ltd
Editorial: Level 3, 250 Victoria Parade, East Melbourne VIC 3002. **T:** 61 3 9619 9361
E: news.melbourne@aap.com.au
W: http://www.aap.com.au
Bureau Chief: Paul Mulvey
Editorial Profile: AAP provides world news and images to our customers through commercial partnerships with major international agencies like Associated Press, Reuters, Agence France-Presse, Agencia EFE, Deutsche Presse-Agentur, The Press Association, Kyodo, Knight-Ridder and New Zealand Press Association.
Language (s): English
NEWS SERVICE/SYNDICATE

AAP Perth
Owner: AAP Information Services Pty Ltd
Editorial: Level 7, Septimus Roe Square, 256 Adelaide Terrace, Perth WA 6000.
T: 61 8 9421 2211 **E:** news.perth@aap.com.au
W: http://www.aap.com.au
Bureau Chief: Lloyd Jones
Editorial Profile: AAP provides world news and images to our customers through commercial partnerships with major international agencies like Associated Press, Reuters, Agence France-Presse, Agencia EFE, Deutsche Presse-Agentur, The Press Association, Kyodo, Knight-Ridder and New Zealand Press Association.
Language (s): English
NEWS SERVICE/SYNDICATE

AAP Sydney
Owner: AAP Information Services Pty Ltd
Editorial: 3 Rider Boulevard, Rhodes NSW 2138. **T:** 61 2 9322 8000
E: news.sydney@aap.com.au
W: http://www.aap.com.au
Editor-in-Chief: Tony Gillies; **Editor:** Michael Osborne; **Bureau Editor:** Judy Skatssoon; **News Editor:** Bronwyn Walenkamp; **Racing Editor:** Caryl Williamson
Editorial Profile: AAP provides world news and images to our customers through commercial partnerships with major international agencies like Associated Press, Reuters, Agence France-Presse, Agencia EFE, Deutsche Presse-Agentur, The Press Association, Kyodo, Knight-Ridder and New Zealand Press Association.
Language (s): English
NEWS SERVICE/SYNDICATE

ABC Radio & Television - London Bureau
Owner: ABC Capricornia
Editorial: 4 Millbank Road, London, England. **T:** 44 20 7808 1350
Bureau Chief: Lisa Millar
Editorial Profile: London bureau for ABC Radio & Television.
Language (s): English
NEWS SERVICE/SYNDICATE

Agence France-Presse Sydney Bureau
Owner: Agence France-Presse
Editorial: Level 8, 50 Margaret St, Sydney NSW 2000. **T:** 61 2 9251 1544
E: sydney@afp.com **W:** http://www.afp.com
Editor: Talek Harris
Editorial Profile: Newspaper Service: Wire service for news and photos
Language (s): English
NEWS SERVICE/SYNDICATE

Agencia EFE Australian Bureau
Editorial: 4 Zania Street, Redfern NSW 2016. **T:** 61 438 187 154 **E:** mgarriga1@mac.com
Editorial Profile: Agencia EFE is the largest Spanish-language news agency and the fourth largest world-wide. From its headquarters in Madrid, this Spanish owned and operated entity is committed to keeping the global Hispanic community up-to-date. The Australian Bureau covers the news from Australia and the pacific.
Language (s): Spanish
NEWS SERVICE/SYNDICATE

ANSA News Agency Sydney Bureau
Owner: Italian Associated Press
Editorial: 4/2 Grosvenor Street, Bondi Junction NSW 2022. **T:** 61 2 9369 1427
E: ansasyd@ozemail.com.au
W: http://www.ansa.it
Bureau Chief: Claudio Marcello
Editorial Profile: International wire service
Language (s): English
NEWS SERVICE/SYNDICATE

ANTARA INDONESIAN NEWS
Owner: ANTARA INDONESIAN NEWS - Independent
Editorial: Antara News Agency 105, Press Gallery, Canberra ACT 2600.
T: 62 21 380 2383 **E:** alisvan@antara.net.id
W: http://www.antaranews.com/en
Editorial Profile: ANTARA has been officially serving as a National News Agency since 1962. It was declared as a public corporation in July, 2007. With 32 bureaus nationwide, a number of representative offices and correspondents abroad, ANTARA is now trusted to be the president of the Organization of Asia-Pacific News Agency (OANA) for the 2007-2010 period. As a national information emissary, ANTARA remains on the front line to strive for the national development and maintain the national dignity through dissemination of news on Indonesia throughout the country andabroad. Geographical Focus: Indonesia
Language (s): English
NEWS SERVICE/SYNDICATE

Associated Press Sydney Bureau
Editorial: 309 Kent Street, Suite 1 Level 6, Sydney 2000. **T:** 61 2 8235-2999
Bureau Chief: Kristen Gelineau
NEWS SERVICE/SYNDICATE

Australasian Business Intelligence
Owner: Lexis Nexis
Editorial: Level 10, 461 Bourke Street, Melbourne VIC 3000. **T:** 61 2 9422 2174
W: http://www.lexisnexis.com.au
Editorial Profile: A print media monitoring service on business companies and industry

information, including statistics, profit results and product releases. Australasian Business Intelligence is a magazine specializing in International topics. ABIX is owned by LexisNexis, a division of Reed International Books Australia Pty Ltd.
Language (s): English
NEWS SERVICE/SYNDICATE

Bloomberg (Melbourne)
Editorial: 101 Collins Street, Level 20, Melbourne 3000. **T:** 61 392288700
NEWS SERVICE/SYNDICATE

Bloomberg (Sydney)
Editorial: 1 McQuarie Place, Level 36, Sydney 2000. **T:** 61 2 9777-8601
E: sydnews@bloomberg.net
Stocks Editor: John McCluskey; **Editor:** Garfield Reynolds; **Asia Page One Editor:** Peter Vercoe
NEWS SERVICE/SYNDICATE

Dow Jones Newswires
Editorial: Level 10, 56 Pitt Street, Sydney NSW 2000. **T:** 61 2 8272-4600
E: djnews.sydney@dowjones.com
News Editor: Shani Raja
NEWS SERVICE/SYNDICATE

Dow Jones Newswires
Editorial: Suite 117 Press Gallery, Parliament House, Canberra 2600. **T:** 61 2 6208-0901
NEWS SERVICE/SYNDICATE

DPA - German Press Agency Sydney Bureau
Owner: DPA - German Press Agency
Editorial: 10 Terry Street, Tempe NSW 2044. **T:** 61 2 9558 2261
E: sidastbury@bigpond.com
W: http://www.dpa.de
Editorial Profile: Sydney bureau of the German Press Agency
Language (s): English
NEWS SERVICE/SYNDICATE

ITAR-TASS Sydney Bureau
Editorial: Sydney. **T:** 61 2 9398 2321
E: australiatass@gmail.com
W: http://www.itar-tass.com/en
Editorial Profile: Sydney bureau of the Russian news agency.
Language (s): English
NEWS SERVICE/SYNDICATE

Jewish Telegraph Agency Sydney Bureau
Editorial: 34 Rivers Street, Bellevue Hill NSW 2203. **T:** 61 2 9326 2765
E: dan.goldberg@northonetv.com
W: http://www.jta.org
Editorial Profile: Sydney bureau of a Jewish news agency.
Language (s): English
NEWS SERVICE/SYNDICATE

Jiji Press Sydney Bureau
Owner: Jiji Press (Aust) Pty Ltd
Editorial: Suite 1401, 109 Pitt Street, Sydney NSW 2000. **T:** 61 2 9230 0020
E: sydney@jiji.com.au
Bureau Chief: Naoki Odaira
Editorial Profile: Nationality: Japan Nabutoshi has taken over the position of bureau chief. He was previously stationed at the Tokyo head office. Preferred method of receiving media releases = email.
Language (s): Japanese
NEWS SERVICE/SYNDICATE

Kyodo News Service Sydney Bureau
Owner: Kyodo News Service
Editorial: Level 3, 301B, 46 Market Street, Sydney NSW 2000. **T:** 61 2 9262 5400
E: kyodosyd@bigpond.net.au
W: http://home.kyodo.co.jp
Bureau Chief: Noriko Goi; **Bureau Chief:** Takushi Ohno
Editorial Profile: International wire service. Geographical Focus: Japanese
Language (s): English
NEWS SERVICE/SYNDICATE

My Dr
Owner: MIMS Australia
Editorial: Level 2, 1 Chandos Street, St Leonards NSW 2065. **T:** 61 299027700
E: frances.westwick@mydr.com.au
W: http://www.mydr.com.au
Freq: Daily
Editorial Profile: An online health and medical information site.
Language (s): English
NEWS SERVICE/SYNDICATE

Network TEN News & Stock Footage Library

Editorial: 1 Saunders Street, Pyrmont NSW 2009. **T:** 61 2 9650 1296
Editorial Profile: News and stock footage library.
Language (s): English
NEWS SERVICE/SYNDICATE

News Net Asia Sydney Bureau

Editorial: Suite 8, Level 13, 327 Pitt Street, Sydney NSW 2000. **T:** 61 2 9264 0998
Editorial Profile: Sydney bureau of the Japanese news agency, News Net Asia.
Language (s): Japanese
NEWS SERVICE/SYNDICATE

Press Trust of India Sydney Bureau

Editorial: 6/23 Poate Road, Centennial Park NSW 2021. **T:** 61 293312767
E: neena@india-voice.com
W: http://www.ptinews.com
Editorial Profile: Sydney bureau of the press trust of India.
Language (s): English
NEWS SERVICE/SYNDICATE

Reuters

Editorial: 60 Margaret Street, Sydney NSW 2000. **T:** 61 2 9373-1500
Bureau Chief: Lincoln Feast
NEWS SERVICE/SYNDICATE

RWE Australian Business News

Owner: RWE Australian Business News Pty Ltd
Editorial: 6 Kirpson Street, Berrara NSW 2540. **T:** 61 2 9871 4149
E: brebase@rweabn.com.au
News Editor: Ben Rebase
Editorial Profile: Includes RWE - SNN News Network (video streaming) Distribution: Global
Language (s): English
NEWS SERVICE/SYNDICATE

Xinhua News Agency - Canberra Bureau

Owner: People's Republic of China
Editorial: 50 Russell Street, Hackett ACT 2602. **T:** 61 2 6248 6369
E: canberraxinhua@gmail.com
W: http://www.xinhuanet.com
Bureau Chief: Yaping Jiang
Editorial Profile: Geographical Focus: Chinese
Language (s): English
NEWS SERVICE/SYNDICATE

BROADCASTING

RADIO NETWORKS

101.7 WS-FM Classic Hits

Owner: Australian Radio Network
Editorial: 3 Byfield Street, North Ryde NSW 2113. **T:** 61 2 8899 9888
E: sydnews@arn.com.au
W: http://www.wsfm.com.au
Editorial Profile: Adult classic hits music station.

4KQ

Owner: Australian Radio Network
Editorial: 444 Logan Road, Stones Corner QLD 4151. **T:** 61 7 3394 0693
E: bnenews@arn.com.au
W: http://www.4kq.com.au
Editorial Profile: Weekend programme presenters change frequently- check with station Format: Classic hits from the 60s, 70s, 80s & 90s. Sister Station: Radio 4BH (882 KHz) Editorial material accepted: specialist topics please send to news director. Prefered after hours delivery of news releases is the News fax on 07 3397 4714, the direct newsroom number is 07 3394 2299

612 ABC Brisbane

Owner: Australian Broadcasting Corporation (ABC)
Editorial: 15 Lissner Street, Toowong QLD 4066. **T:** 61 7 3377 5222
E: news.qld@abc.net.au
W: http://www.abc.net.au/brisbane
Editorial Profile: The ABC broadcast in Brisbane. Format: news, talkback and current affairs. Most likely point of contact for after hours is the Newsroom on 07 3377 5244

666 ABC Canberra

Owner: Australian Broadcasting Corporation (ABC)
Editorial: Cnr Northbourne & Wakefield Avenues, Dickson ACT 2602.
T: 61 2 6275 4600 **E:** act.news@abc.net.au

W: http://abc.net.au/canberra
Editorial Profile: Comprehensive what's on listings of live music, film, theatre, nightclubs, and dance parties. Geographical Focus: Australia Circus

702 ABC Sydney

Owner: Australian Broadcasting Corporation (ABC)
Editorial: Level 2, ABC Centre, Ultimo NSW 2007. **T:** 61 2 8333 2138
E: radio.news@abc.net.au
W: http://www.abc.net.au/sydney
Editorial Profile: 702 ABC Sydney offers the latest news and information, views, comedy, music, entertainment, and sport. The station - Sydney's major source of local, national, and international stories - draws on the full resources of ABC News and Current Affairs correspondents worldwide.

720 ABC Perth

Owner: Australian Broadcasting Corporation (ABC)
Editorial: 30 Fielder Street, East Perth WA 6004. **T:** 61 8 9220 2700
E: 720perth@your.abc.net.au
W: http://www.abc.net.au
Editorial Profile: Contemporary radio with news, talk and sport. Editorial material accepted: specialist topics to the Chief of Staff. The News phone is manned nearly 24 hours, 08 9220 2820

891 ABC Adelaide

Owner: Australian Broadcasting Corporation (ABC)
Editorial: 85 North East Road, Collinswood SA 5081. **T:** 61 8 8343 4332
E: sanews@your.abc.net.au
W: http://www.abc.net.au/adelaide
Editorial Profile: Station that provides a mix of news, views, current affairs, talkback, entertainment, sport, music, and rural issues. Preffered method of after hours news releases is via the News room Fax, on 08 8343 4370

936 ABC Hobart

Owner: Australian Broadcasting Corporation (ABC)
Editorial: 1-7 Liverpool Street, Hobart TAS 7000. **T:** 61 3 6235 3217
E: tasmania.news@abc.net.au
W: http://www.abc.net.au/hobart
Editorial Profile: Metropolitan Radio Station. For after hoursa newsreleases, the number for boith the AM and PM Chief of staff is 03 6235 3340, or the general news phone is 03 6235 3341.

96 FM

Owner: Australian Radio Network
Editorial: Level 1, 169 Hay Street, East Perth WA 6004. **T:** 61 8 9220 1400
E: news@6pr.com.au
W: http://www.96fm.com.au
Editorial Profile: Editorial material accepted: specialist topics please send to News Director Frequency: 96.1 MHz

97.3 FM

Owner: Australian Radio Network
Editorial: 444 Logan Road, Stones Corner QLD 4120. **T:** 61 7 3421 4973
E: bnenews@arn.com.au
W: http://www.973fm.com.au
Editorial Profile: Plays popular music from the 80s, 90s, and today aimed at a female audience of 24-44 years old.

ABC Classic FM

Owner: Australian Broadcasting Corporation (ABC)
Editorial: ABC Centre, 700 Harris Street, Ultimo NSW 2007. **T:** 61 2 8333 2800
E: classicfm@your.abc.net.au
W: http://www.abc.net.au/classic
Editorial Profile: Station dedicated to contemporary and classical music. They are not available until 9am.

ABC Local Radio

Owner: Australian Broadcasting Corporation (ABC)
Editorial: 700 Harris Street, Ultimo NSW 2007. **T:** 61 2 8333 2619
E: rasmussen.anthony@abc.net.au
W: http://www.abc.net.au/radio/localradio

ABC News Radio

Owner: Australian Broadcasting Corporation (ABC)
Editorial: 700 Harris Street, Ultimo NSW 2007. **T:** 61 2 8333 5094
E: newsradio.media@your.abc.net.au
W: http://www.abc.net.au/newsradio

Editorial Profile: Rolling format of news, current affairs, finance, business, politics, technology & sport; broadcasts Federal Parliament when its sitting.

ABC Radio National

Owner: Australian Broadcasting Corporation (ABC)
Editorial: Level 1, 700 Harris Street, Ultimo NSW 2007. **T:** 61 2 8333 1500
E: browning.daniel@abc.net.au
W: http://www.abc.net.au
Editorial Profile: National radio network featuring news, arts and music.

Canberra FM RADAR

Owner: Australian Radio Network
Editorial: PO Box 106, Dickson ACT 2602.
T: 61 2 6123 4111
E: eobyrne@canberrafm.com.au
Editorial Profile: Strong focus on Australian local music. Plays music from local bands that have not yet been signed by major comapnies. Seeks to promote up-and-coming groups.

FM 104.7 Canberra

Owner: Australian Radio Network
Editorial: Bellenden Street, Gungahlin ACT 2615. **T:** 61 2 6123 4104
E: news@canberrafm.com.au
W: http://www.fm1047.com.au
Editorial Profile: Contemporary music station, with talk, interviews and competition. Target audience: 18-34 yrs. Editorial material accepted: specialist topics, please send to Production Manager. First broadcast:1988

Gold 104.3 FM

Owner: Australian Radio Network
Editorial: Level 2, 21-31 Goodwood Street, Richmond VIC 3121. **T:** 61 3 9420 1043
E: melnews@arn.com.au
W: http://www.gold1043.com.au
Editorial Profile: Classic hits metropolitan radio station.

Mix 101.1 FM

Owner: Australian Radio Network
Editorial: Level 2, 21-31 Goodwood Street, Richmond VIC 3121. **T:** 61 3 9420 1011
E: melnews@arn.com.au
W: http://www.mix1011.com.au
Editorial Profile: Melbourne's Best Mix of the 80s, 90s & Today . The newsroom is empty from 7pm to 4am, but any after hours newsreleases can be directed to the newsfax at 03 9420 1244. E-mail to melnews@arn.com.au

Mix 102.3

Owner: Australian Radio Network
Editorial: 201 Tynte Street, North Adelaide SA 5006. **T:** 61 8 8300 1000
E: adelaidenews@arn.com.au
W: http://www.5ad1023.com.au
Editorial Profile: A blend of adult contemporary and solid gold music favourites. 24 hour news, contests and on-air personalities. Targets 25-54 year olds with most appeal to 30-49 years and household shoppers.Editorial material accepted: specialist topics please send to producer/ news room Formerly known as Radio 5AD.

Mix 106.3

Owner: Australian Radio Network
Editorial: Bellenden Street, Gungahlin ACT 2912. **T:** 61 2 6242 0860
E: news@canberrafm.com.au
W: http://www.mix106.com.au
Editorial Profile: Adult contemporary, music and entertainment. News via Prime TV local newsroom. Year First Broadcast: 1988 Audience Figure: 106,000 Mon - Sun (Source: AC Neilson Survey 2 2000) Target Audience: 35-49 yrs.The Newroom Phone, 02 6242 0860, is the best point of contact for after hours, it's diverted onto messagebank which is checked frequently.

Mix 106.5 FM

Owner: Australian Radio Network
Editorial: 3 Byfield Street, North Ryde NSW 2113. **T:** 61 2 8899 9777
E: glenndaniel@arn.com.au
W: http://www.mix1065.com.au
Editorial Profile: Adult music station that plays a mix of music from the '70s to the present. Glenn Daniel, News Director, is the best contact for after hours news releases on 02 8899 9615.

Radio Australia

Owner: Australian Broadcasting Corporation (ABC)
Editorial: ABC Southbank Centre, Southbank Boulevard, South Melbourne VIC 3205.

T: 61 3 9626 1500
E: broadbent.roger@abc.net.au
W: http://www.abc.net.au/ra
Editorial Profile: International shortwave, satellite and cable service of the ABC broadcasting in English, Indonesian, Cambodian, Pidgin (PNG), Vietnamese and Mandarin with a focus on Asia and the Pacific. To listen to the programme must have a shortwave radio. Satellite, Internet and Re-broadcast. Year first broadcast: 1940 Target audience: Asia-Pacific. Editorial material accepted in: English. Alternative email: english@ra.abc.net.au

Triple J

Owner: Australian Broadcasting Corporation (ABC)
Editorial: Level 1, 700 Harris Street, Ultimo NSW 2007. **T:** 61 2 8333 2905
E: triplejradio@your.abc.net.au
W: http://www.abc.net.au/triplej
Editorial Profile: National youth radio network. Editorial material accepted: specialist topics please send to News Editor.NOTE: There is no specific Triple J News Director. Preferred format for email: attachments should not exceed 4 meg

TELEVISION STATIONS

ABC 3

Owner: Australian Broadcasting Corporation (ABC)
Editorial: 700 Harris Street, Ultimo NSW 2007. **T:** 61 2 8333 4441
E: tvnews@news.abc.net.au
W: http://www.abc.net.au/tv/meon3
Editorial Profile: ABC3 is the digital TV channel created for young people of Australia, aged 6 to 15 years old.

ABC Australia Network

Owner: Australian Broadcasting Corporation (ABC)
Editorial: 700 Harris Street, Ultimo NSW 2007. **T:** 61 2 8333 5598
E: amy.williams@australianetwork.com
W: http://australianetwork.com
Editorial Profile: ABC Asia Pacific is Australia's international satellite television service telecasting into 30 countries in North and South Asia and the Pacific. The channel is designed to be a window into Australia, reflecting Australian lifestyle and culture.

ABC Channel 2 ACT

Owner: Australian Broadcasting Corporation (ABC)
Editorial: Cnr Northbourne & Wakefield Avenues, Dickson ACT 2602.
T: 61 2 6275 4600 **E:** act.news@abc.net.au
W: http://www.abc.net.au
Editorial Profile: ABC television broadcasting to Canberra and the surrounding region. Geographical Focus: Australia Circus

ABC Channel 2 NSW

Owner: Australian Broadcasting Corporation (ABC)
Editorial: 700 Harris Street, Ultimo NSW 2007. **T:** 61 2 8333 1500
E: tvnews@news.abc.net.au
W: http://www.abc.net.au
Editorial Profile: The ABC's head office is in Sydney. The ABC is a national television service with State news, current affairs and sport, with production and transmission centres in all States and Territories. ABC Health Matters is a page within the ABC website featuring news and health related articles. Any material needing to be mailed to the producers of this page should be sent to: ABC Health Online 4th Floor, ABC Ultimo Centre GPO Box 9994 Sydney NSW 2001 For After Hours news releases, the most likely number to be answered is the Chief of Staff's number; 02 8333 4781 Geographical Focus: Australia Circus

ABC Channel 2 QLD

Owner: Australian Broadcasting Corporation (ABC)
Editorial: GPO Box 9994, Brisbane QLD 4001.
T: 61 7 3377 5222 **E:** news.qld@abc.net.au
W: http://www.abc.net.au
Editorial Profile: National Television Network - QLD, with a local news service and local as well as national programming.

ABC Channel 2 SA

Owner: Australian Broadcasting Corporation (ABC)
Editorial: 85 North East Road, Collinswood SA 5081. **T:** 61 8 8343 4000
E: sanews@your.abc.net.au

W: http://www.abc.net.au
Editorial Profile: National Television Network - SA

ABC Channel 2 TAS
Owner: Australian Broadcasting Corporation (ABC)
Editorial: 1-7 Liverpool Street, Hobart TAS 7000. **T:** 61 3 6235 3333
E: tasmania.news@abc.net.au
W: http://www.abc.net.au
Editorial Profile: It reflects and extends the ABC's commitment to localism through the development of a website

ABC Channel 2 VIC
Owner: Australian Broadcasting Corporation (ABC)
Editorial: Level 3, ABC Southbank Centre, Southbank VIC 3006. **T:** 61 3 9626 1500
E: tvnews.abcvic@abc.net.au
W: http://www.abc.net.au
Editorial Profile: National Television Network - VICFor after hours contacts, 03 9626 1668 is the ABC Radio line. all calls can be diverted from there.

ABC Channel 2 WA
Owner: Australian Broadcasting Corporation (ABC)
Editorial: 30 Fielder Street, East Perth WA 6004. **T:** 61 8 9220 2700
E: tvperth@your.abc.net.au
W: http://www.abc.net.au
Editorial Profile: ABC -National Television Network for WA Please send all news releases to, Chief of Staff.

ABC News 24
Owner: Australian Broadcasting Corporation (ABC)
Editorial: 700 Harris Street, Ultimo NSW 2007. **T:** 61 2 8333 3685
E: abcnews24@your.abc.net.au
W: http://www.abc.net.au/news
Editorial Profile: ABC News 24 is Australia's most watched news channel and provides live, continuous news coverage of breaking stories from Australia and around the world.

ABC Television NT
Owner: Australian Broadcasting Corporation (ABC)
Editorial: 1 Cavenagh Street, Darwin NT 0800. **T:** 61 8 8943 3222 **E:** tlozek.eric@abc.net.au
W: www.abc.net.au/tv
Editorial Profile: It screens repeated ABC news and current affairs programs, ABC news, bulletin stories and some reporting, childrens programming, music documentaries and state football.

NITV (National Indigenous Television)
Owner: NITV (National Indigenous Television) PTY LTD
Editorial: Level 6, 1 James Place, North Sydney NSW 2060. **T:** 61 2 9959 3888
E: abates@skynews.com.au
W: http://www.nitv.org.au
Editorial Profile: Geographical Focus: Aboriginal Affairs

AUSTRIA — Tel: 43
Standard Time: GMT +1
Continent: Europe
Capital City: Vienna

NEWSPAPERS & PUBLICATIONS

NEWSPAPERS

Der Standard
Owner: STANDARD Verlagsgesellschaft m.b.H
Editorial: Vordere Zollamtsstraße 13, Wien 1030. **T:** 43 1 53170 700
E: redaktion@derStandard.at
W: http://derstandard.at/
Freq: Daily; **Circ:** 97399 ÖAK
Chefredaktion: Oscar Bronner; **Chefredaktion:** Alexandra Föderl-Schmid; **Chef vom Dienst:** Eric Frey; **Redakteur:** Bettina Pluger; **Chef vom Dienst:** Otto Ranftl; **Umweltredaktion:** Conrad Seidl; **EDV-Redaktion:** Helmut Spudich; **Chef vom Dienst:** Erhard Stackl; **Chef vom Dienst:** Bettina Stimeder; **Redaktion Beilagen / Sonderseiten:** Bettina Stimeder; **Redakteurin / Editor:** Karin Tzschentke
Editorial Profile: Der Standard is an Austrian newspaper. It is independent of institutions and political parties. Relevant topics of the standard culture, society, economy and politics.
Language (s): German
DAILY NEWSPAPER

Heute
Owner: AHVV Verlags GmbH
Editorial: Heiligenstädter Lände 29/Top 6, Wien 1190. **T:** 43 50 9501 2200
E: redaktion@heute.at **W:** http://www.heute.at
Freq: Daily; **Circ:** 622990
Redaktion Fernsehen / Hörfunk: Mr./Ms. Editor; **stellv. Chefredaktion:** Peter Lattinger; **stellv. Chefredaktion:** Thomas Staisch
Editorial Profile: Heute is a free daily newspaper in Austria, which offers news and reports on culture, lifestyle, celebrities, entertainment, and consumer issues.
Language (s): German
DAILY NEWSPAPER

Kleine Zeitung Kärnten
Owner: Kleine Zeitung GmbH & Co. KG
Editorial: Hasnerstraße 2, Klagenfurt 9020.
T: 43 463 5800 0
E: sekretariat.ktn@kleinezeitung.at
W: http://www.kleinezeitung.at
Freq: Daily; **Circ:** 100646
Redakteur / Editor: Hubert Budai; **Redakteurin / Editor:** Christiane Canori; **Chefredakteurin / Editor in Chief:** Eva Weissenberger
Editorial Profile: The Kleine Zeitung Kärnten is a regional daily newspaper with news from politics, economy, culture, sport and society in Kärnten and the surrounding area. The Kleine Zeitung Kärnten is just one of the regional editions of the Kleine Zeitung.
Language (s): German
DAILY NEWSPAPER

Kleine Zeitung Steiermark
Owner: Kleine Zeitung GmbH & Co. KG
Editorial: Schönaugasse 64, Graz 8010.
T: 43 316 875 0 **E:** redaktion@kleinezeitung.at
W: http://www.kleinezeitung.at
Freq: Daily; **Circ:** 207327
Redakteurin / Editor: Daniela Bachal; **Redakteurin / Editor:** Johanna Birnbaum; **Redakteur / Editor:** Harald Hofer; **Redakteurin / Editor:** Andrea Kratzer; **Redakteurin / Editor:** Bettina Kuzmicki; **Redakteurin / Editor:** Bettina Oberrainer; **Chefredakteur / Editor in Chief:** Hubert Patterer; **Redakteurin / Editor:** Ulla Patz; **Redakteur / Editor:** Franz Pototschnig; **Redakteurin / Editor:** Manuela Swoboda; **Redakteurin / Editor:** Regina Trummer
Editorial Profile: The Kleine Zeitung is a regional daily newspaper for Styria with news from politics, business, culture, sports, travel, technology and other consumer topics.
Language (s): German
DAILY NEWSPAPER

Kronen Zeitung
Owner: Krone-Verlag GmbH & Co. KG
Editorial: Muthgasse 2, Wien 1190.
T: 43 1 360113475
E: redaktion@kronenzeitung.at
W: http://www.krone.at
Freq: Daily; **Circ:** 800031
Chefredaktion: Christoph Dichand; **Chef vom Dienst:** Herold Pearson; **Umweltredaktion:** Mark Perry; **Redaktion Mode:** Michaela Schwarz; **stellv. Chefredaktion:** Georg Wailand; **Redaktion Fernsehen / Hörfunk:** Susanne Zilk
Editorial Profile: The Kronen Zeitung is an Austrian tabloid newspaper with news, sports and society topics. In addition it offers consumer topics, such as leisure and health.
Language (s): German
DAILY NEWSPAPER

KURIER
Owner: Kurier Redaktionsges.m.b.H. & Co.KG
Editorial: Lindengasse 52, Wien 1070.
T: 43 1 521002601 **E:** redaktion@kurier.at
W: http://www.kurier.at
Freq: Daily; **Circ:** 196019
Chefredakteur / Editor in Chief: Helmut Brandstätter; **Chefredakteur / Editor in Chief:** Gerald Reischl; **Redakteurin / Editor:** Barbara Reiter; **Redakteur / Editor:** Patrick Wammerl
Editorial Profile: The KURIER is a tabloid-sized newspaper in Austria, covering national and international news and current affairs. Also provides information concerning politics, economics, culture, sports, travel and technology.
Language (s): German
DAILY NEWSPAPER

Oberösterreichische Nachrichten
Owner: Wimmer Medien GmbH & Co. KG
Editorial: Promenade 23, Linz 4010.
T: 43 732 78050 **E:** redaktion@nachrichten.at
W: http://www.nachrichten.at
Freq: Daily; **Circ:** 105434 ÖAK
Redakteurin / Editor: Sigrid Brandstätter; **Redakteurin / Editor:** Elisabeth Eidenberger; **Redakteurin / Editor:** Julia Evers; **Chef vom Dienst:** Alois Grasböck; **Redaktion Frauen / Mode:** Ulrike Griessl; **Redakteur / Editor:** Peter Grubmüller; **Redakteur / Editor:** Erhard Gstöttner; **Redakteurin / Editor:** Irene Gunnesch; **Redakteurin / Editor:** Karin Haas; **Redaktion Frauen / Mode:** Valerie Hader; **Chefredakteur / Editor in Chief:** Gerald Mandlbauer; **Redakteur / Editor:** Lucian Mayringer; **Editor:** Friedrich Müller; **Redakteurin / Editor:** Silvia Nagl; **Redakteurin / Editor:** Sabine Novak; **Redakteurin / Editor:** Heidi Riepl; **Redakteur / Editor:** Freidrich Salmen; **Redakteurin / Editor:** Renate Schiesser; **Redakteur / Editor:** Herbert Schorn; **Redakteur / Editor:** Clemens Schuhmann; **Redakteur / Editor:** Robert Stammler; **Redakteur / Editor:** Markus Staudinger; **Redakteur / Editor:** Heinz Steinbock; **Redakteur / Editor:** Alexander Zens
Editorial Profile: The Oberösterreichische Nachrichten is a regional daily newspaper for Upper Austria with news from politics, economy, sports, culture, society, and consumer issues.
Language (s): German
DAILY NEWSPAPER

Österreich
Owner: Mediengruppe Österreich GmbH
Editorial: Friedrichstr. 10, Wien 1010.
T: 43 1 58811 1997 **E:** redaktion@oe24.at
W: http://www.oe24.at
Freq: Daily; **Circ:** 628000
Redaktion Fernsehen / Hörfunk: Mr./Ms. Editor; **stellv. Chefredaktion:** Barbara Haas; **Chefredaktion:** Christian Nusser; **Redaktion Medien:** Albert Sachs; **Redaktion Society:** Norman Schenz; **Chefredaktion:** Werner Schima; **Chef vom Dienst:** Trude Schreibershofen; **Redaktion Finanzen:** Angela Sellner; **Chef vom Dienst:** Walter Sohler; **Chef vom Dienst:** Gerhard Torner
Editorial Profile: Österreich is a nationwide Austrian daily newspaper, which is complemented by the online portal Oe24.at. In addition to national news, the newspaper also offers entertainment, sports and consumer topics such as travel or health.
Language (s): German
DAILY NEWSPAPER

Die Presse
Owner: Die Presse Verlagsges. mbH & Co. KG
Editorial: Hainburger Str. 33, Wien 1030.
T: 43 1 514140
E: chefredaktion@diepresse.com
W: http://www.diepresse.com
Freq: Daily; **Circ:** 91363 ÖAK
Chef vom Dienst: Florian Asamer; **Chefredaktion:** Michael Fleischhacker; **Chef vom Dienst:** Benedikt Kommenda; **Umweltredaktion:** Martin Kugler; **Redaktion Wissenschaft:** Jürgen Langenbach; **Redaktion Medien:** Isabella Leitenmüller-Wallnöfer; **Redaktion Beilagen / Sonderseiten:** Sabine Mezler-Andelberg; **Editor-in-Chief:** Rainer Nowak; **Redaktion Frau und Mode:** Petra Percher; **Redakteur / Editor:** Georg Renner; **Unterhaltungsredaktion:** Wilhelm Sinkovicz; **EDV-Redaktion:** Andreas Tanzer; **Chronik Editor:** Ulrike Weiser; **Redaktion Bildung:** Erich Witzmann
Editorial Profile: Tabloid-sized quality newspaper providing national and international news, political and economic information. Covers history, geography, commerce, IT, EU affairs and investment details.Aimed at decision-makers within business and industry, senior management, executives, civil servants and university students.
Language (s): German
DAILY NEWSPAPER

Salzburger Nachrichten
Owner: Salzburger Nachrichten Verlagsges. mbH & Co. KG
Editorial: Karolingerstr. 40, Salzburg 5021.
T: 43 662 8373 301 **E:** redakt@salzburg.com
W: http://www.salzburg.com
Freq: Daily; **Circ:** 88653 ÖAK
Unterhaltungsredaktion: Mr./Ms. Editor; **Redaktion Rock/Pop:** Bernhard Flieher; **Chef vom Dienst:** Hermann Fröschl; **stellv. Chefredaktion:** Viktor Hermann; **Redaktion Mode & Style:** Ines Hinterkörner; **Redaktion Kinderseite:** Trude Kaindl-Hönig; **Umweltredaktion:** Ursula Kastler; **Redaktion Beilagen / Sonderseiten:** Doris Kitzenegger; **stellv. Chefredaktion:** Andreas Koller; **Chefredaktion:** Manfred Perterer; **Chef vom Dienst:** Alfred Pfeiffenberger; **Redaktion Verteidigung / Militär:** Alexander Purger; **Redaktion Beilagen / Sonderseiten:** Michael Roither; **Redaktion Neue Medien:** Robert Rosin; **Redaktion Bildung/Erziehung:** Helmut Schliesselberger; **Redaktion Immobilien:** Bernhard Schreglmann; **Redaktion Jobs and Karriere:** Bernhrad Schreglmann; **Redaktion Beilagen / Sonderseiten:** Herwig Steinkellner; **Redaktion Fernsehen / Hörfunk:** Pierre A. Wallnöfer; **Redaktion Finanzen:** Richard Wiens; **Redaktion Finanzen:** Karin Zauner
Editorial Profile: The Salzburger Nachrichten is a regional daily newspaper with news about politics, economics, culture, society and sport, as well as with an advice section on topics such as travel and technology.
Language (s): German
DAILY NEWSPAPER

Tiroler Tageszeitung
Owner: Schlüsselverlag J. S. Moser GmbH
Editorial: Ing.-Etzel-Str. 30, Innsbruck 6021.
T: 43 50403 1600 **E:** redaktion@tt.com
W: http://www.tt.com
Freq: Daily; **Circ:** 102074
Redaktion Film: Peter Angerer; **Redaktion Bildung/Erziehung:** Mr./Ms. Editor; **Unterhaltungsredaktion:** Mr./Ms. Editor; **Redaktion Hobby/Freizeit:** Mr./Ms. Editor; **Redaktion Beilagen / Sonderseiten:** Mr./Ms. Editor; **EDV-Redaktion:** Mr./Ms. Editor; **Umweltredaktion:** Mr./Ms. Editor; **Redaktion TV-Kritik:** Christiane Fasching; **Redaktion Medien:** Ivona Jelcic; **Chef vom Dienst:** Lukas Letzner; **Redaktion Freizeit:** Irene Rapp; **Redaktion Freizeit:** Kathrin Siller; **Redaktion Wohnen:** Frank Tschoner; **Redaktion Freizeit:** Nicole Unger; **Chefredaktion:** Alois Vahrner; **Redaktion Freizeit:** Christian Willim; **Chefredaktion:** Mario Zenhäusern
Editorial Profile: The Tiroler Daily Newspaper is a regional newspaper for Tirol with 8 local editions covering local, regional, national and international news on politics, business, society and sports.
Language (s): German
DAILY NEWSPAPER

Vorarlberger Nachrichten
Owner: Russmedia Verlag GmbH
Editorial: Gutenbergstr. 1, Schwarzach 6858.
T: 43 5572 501 500
E: redaktion@vorarlbergernachrichten.at
W: http://www.vorarlbergernachrichten.at/
Freq: Daily; **Circ:** 69000
Chefredaktion VN: Verena Daum-Kuzmanovic; **Stv. Chefredakteur:** Andreas Dünser; **Redaktion Computer/EDV:** Florian Dünser; **Umweltredaktion:** Mr./Ms. Editor; **Redaktion Finanzen:** Ernest F. Enzelsberger; **Redaktion Wissenschaft:** Klaus Hämmerle; **Chefredaktion:** Kurt Horwitz; **stellv. Chefredaktion:** Johannes Huber; **Redaktion Religion:** Thomas Matt; **Redaktion Bildung/ Erziehung:** Marlies Mohr; **Chefredaktion:** Eugen A. Russ; **Redaktion Technik:** Bettina Swete-Gasser
Editorial Profile: The Vorarlberger Nachrichten is a local newspaper for Arlberg and the surrounding area. It provides local and regional coverage, as well as news from politics, society, economy, culture and sports.
Language (s): German
DAILY NEWSPAPER

WirtschaftsBlatt
Owner: WirtschaftsBlatt Verlag AG
Editorial: Hainburger Str. 33, Wien 1030.
T: 43 1 60117305
E: redaktion@wirtschaftsblatt.at
W: http://www.wirtschaftsblatt.at
Freq: Daily; **Circ:** 30007 ÖAK
Redaktion Finanzen & Börse: Hans-Jörg Bruckberger; **Redakteur / Editor:** Daniela Friedinger; **Editor-in-Chief:** Gerhard Hofer; **Editor-in-Chief:** Eva Komarek; **Redaktion Unternehmen & Märkte:** Robert Lechner; **EDV-Redaktion:** Manfred Mader; **Chefredaktion:** Wolfgang Unterhuber
Editorial Profile: Wirtschaftsblatt is a business newspaper in Austria with news about politics and business. However, topics such as culture, technology and others are also included.
Language (s): German
DAILY NEWSPAPER

NEWS SERVICE/SYNDICATE

Associated Press
Editorial: Laimgrubengasse 10,1960, Vienna 1199. **T:** 43 1 368-4156
Bureau Chief: George Jahn
NEWS SERVICE/SYNDICATE

Bloomberg News
Editorial: Palais Corso, Kaerntenr Ring 9-13, Vienna Win 1010. **T:** 43 1513 2660 50
NEWS SERVICE/SYNDICATE

Reuters

Editorial: Boersegasse 11, A-1010, Vienna.
T: 43 1 5311 20
E: vienna.newsroom@reuters.com
Bureau Chief: Noah Barkin
NEWS SERVICE/SYNDICATE

BROADCASTING

TELEVISION STATIONS

ATV

Owner: ATV Privat TV GmbH & Co KG
Editorial: Aspernbrückengasse 2, Wien 1020.
T: 43 1 213640 **E:** atv@atv.at
W: http://www.atv.at
Editorial Profile: ATV is a private television station in Austria, which offers news and documentaries, infotainment, shows and series.

ORF 2

Owner: Österreichischer Rundfunk ORF
Editorial: Würzburggasse 30, Wien 1136.
T: 43 1 87878 0 **W:** http://tv.orf.at/
Editorial Profile: ORF 2 is the second public TV channel by the ORF, which mainly offers cultural programs with a focus on Austria, as well as news. The program consists primarily of information programs, but also contains entertainment shows.

ORF eins

Owner: Österreichischer Rundfunk ORF
Editorial: Würzburggasse 30, Wien 1136.
T: 43 1 87878 0 **W:** http://tv.orf.at/
Editorial Profile: ORF eins, or ORF 1, is a public service television channel by the ORF, which offers news, information programs, as well as entertainment.

AZERBAIJAN   Tel: 994

Standard Time: GMT +5
Continent: Asia
Capital City: Baku

NEWSPAPERS & PUBLICATIONS

NEWSPAPERS

525 ci qezet

Editorial: S.Mustafayev küç.27/121, Baku AZ1033. **T:** 994 12 566-67-98 **E:** info@525.az
W: http://www.525.az
Freq: Daily; **Circ:** 5000 Pub Statement
Editor-in-Chief: Resad Mecid
Editorial Profile: Newspaper covering national and international news, current affairs, social events, economics and sport.
Language (s): Azeri
DAILY NEWSPAPER

Adalat (Justice)

Owner: Adalat
Editorial: Block 529, Matbuat Avenue, Baku 370146. **T:** 994 12 43 80 550
E: adalatgezeti@rambler.ru
W: http://www.adalet-az.com
Freq: Daily; **Circ:** 4000 Pub Statement
Editor: Etibar Babayev; **Editor-in-Chief:** Irada Tuncay
Editorial Profile: Tabloid newspaper covering legal issues and politics.
Language (s): Azeri
DAILY NEWSPAPER

Ayna

Owner: CBS Publishing House
Editorial: ul. Sharif-zadeh 1, Baku Az 1138.
T: 994 12 49 75 031 **E:** gazeta@zerkalo.az
W: http://www.zerkalo.az **Circ:** 3000 Pub Statement
Editor: Elchin Shikhlintskiy
Editorial Profile: Tabloid newspaper covering national and international news, economics, social events and sport.
Language (s): Azeri
DAILY NEWSPAPER

Azat Artsakh

Editorial: Tumanyan 62, Stepanakert
E: atert@rambler.ru
W: http://www.artsakhtert.com
Freq: Daily; **Circ:** 1000 Pub Statement
Editor-in-Chief: Murad Petrossian
Editorial Profile: Daily newspaper from Nagorno Karabakh region.
Language (s): Armenian
DAILY NEWSPAPER

Azerbaijan

Owner: Azerbaijan Publishing House
Editorial: Matbuat prospekt 529, 4 floor, Baku 3. **T:** 994 12 43 94 920
E: contact@azerbaijan-news.az
W: http://www.azerbaijan-news.az
Freq: Daily; **Circ:** 12000 Pub Statement
Editor-in-Chief: Bakhtiyar Sadigov
Editorial Profile: Official government newspaper featuring social and political reviews.
Language (s): Azeri
DAILY NEWSPAPER

Bakinskiy Rabochiy

Owner: Presidenskiy Aparat
Editorial: Matbuat pr. 529-cu, Baku 370146.
T: 994 12 43 86 198 **E:** bakrab@azerin.com
W: http://www.br.az
Freq: Daily; **Circ:** 3520 Pub Statement
Editor-in-Chief: Agabek Askerov
Editorial Profile: Tabloid newspaper in Russian language providing political, economical and cultural information on all aspects of life in Azerbaijan.
Language (s): Russian
DAILY NEWSPAPER

Baku Sun

Owner: Boston and Baku Television Communications
Editorial: 2 Inshaatchylar Ave, Baku Az 1073.
T: 994 12 497 55 31
E: editor@bakusun.baku.az
W: http://www.bakusun.az **Circ:** 4000 Pub Statement
Editor: Farid Iskenderov
Editorial Profile: English language weekly newspaper which presents latest energy, business and political news of Azerbaijan.
Language (s): English
DAILY NEWSPAPER

Echo

Owner: AYNA
Editorial: 1, Sharifzadeh str., Baku.
T: 994 12 43 23 450 **E:** rauf@echo-az.com
W: http://www.echo-az.com
Freq: Daily; **Circ:** 6000 Pub Statement
Editor In Chief: Rauf Talyshinsky
Editorial Profile: Publishes current political news and articles on economics, cultural life and recent sports events.
Language (s): Russian
DAILY NEWSPAPER

Yeni Musavat

Editorial: Baki Dernegul qes., 3097-ci mehelle, Baku Az 1000. **T:** 994 12 448 23 81
E: yenimusavat@azeronline.com
W: http://www.musavat.com
Freq: Daily
Editorial Profile: Daily newspaper covering general, financial and business news.
Language (s): Azeri
DAILY NEWSPAPER

Zerkalo

Owner: CBS Publishing House
Editorial: ul. Sharif-zadeh 1, Baku 1138.
T: 994 12 497 50 31 **E:** gazeta@zerkalo.az
W: http://www.zerkalo.az
Freq: Daily; **Circ:** 5000 Pub Statement
Editor: Elchin Shikhlintskiy
Editorial Profile: Newspaper covering national and international news, politics, entertainment and sport.
Language (s): Russian
DAILY NEWSPAPER

NEWS SERVICE/SYNDICATE

Azeri-Press Agency

Editorial: Azerbaijan avenue 27, Baku.
T: 994 12 5963358 **E:** apa@azeurotel.com
W: http://en.apa.az
Editor In Chief: Vugar Huseynov; **Editor:** Shahin Jafarli
Editorial Profile: Offers daily news, video footage, bank rankings, weekly and monthly analyses, forecasts and special photo bank in Azerbaijani, Russian, English, French and Arabic.
Language (s): Azeri
NEWS SERVICE/SYNDICATE

AZER-PRESS

Editorial: Baki Iceri Seher, 1-ci Qesr dongesi, 28, Baku Az 1005. **T:** 994 12 447 42 88
E: azerpressmedia@gmail.com
W: http://www.azpress.az
Language (s): Azeri
NEWS SERVICE/SYNDICATE

BROADCASTING

RADIO NETWORKS

Radio Antenn 101 FM

Owner: Independent teleradiocompany Antenn
Editorial: 1 Sharifzade Street, Baku AZ 1138.
T: 994 12 43 37 101 **W:** http://antenn.az
Editorial Profile: Broadcasts news, political programmes and music.

TELEVISION STATIONS

AZ TV

Editorial: 1 M. Huseyn, Baku AZ1011.
T: 994 12 49 23 807 **E:** webmaster@aztv.az
W: http://www.aztv.az
Editorial Profile: Covers current events in Azerbaijan – politics, economics, public life, sport, cultural events and weather.

BAHAMAS   Tel: 1242

Standard Time: GMT -5
Continent: The Americas
Capital City: Nassau (New Province)

NEWSPAPERS & PUBLICATIONS

NEWSPAPERS

The Bahama Journal

Owner: Wendell Jones Communications
T: 1 242 325-3082 **E:** jcnnews@gmail.com
W: http://www.jonesbahamas.com **Circ:** 7000 Not Audited
Publisher: Wendall Jones; **News Editor:** Tameka Lundy; **Editor:** Macushla Pinder
Editorial Profile: Daily newspaper focusing on national and international news, business, religion and sports for the residents of The Bahamas.
Language (s): English
DAILY NEWSPAPER

Freeport News

T: 1242 35 28 321
E: oferguson@nasguard.com
W: http://freeport.nassauguardian.net
Freq: Daily; **Circ:** 6500 Not Audited
Editor: Oswalt Brown; **Publisher:** Anthony Ferguson
Editorial Profile: Freeport News is a daily newspaper focusing on national and local news, business, religion, lifestyle and sports for the residents of Freeport, Grand Bahama.
Language (s): English
DAILY NEWSPAPER

The Nassau Guardian

Editorial: No 4 Carter Street, Oakes Field, Nassau. **T:** 1242 30 22 300
E: editor@nasguard.com
W: http://www.thenassauguardian.com
Freq: Daily; **Circ:** 12000 Not Audited
Publisher: Anthony Ferguson
Editorial Profile: The Nassau Guardian is a daily newspaper focusing on national and international news, business, culture, society and sports.
Language (s): English
DAILY NEWSPAPER

The Punch

Owner: Punch Publications Ltd
Editorial: Warboys House, Farrington Road, Oakes Field, Nassau. **T:** 1242 32 27 112
E: thepunch@coralwave.com
Freq: Mon; **Circ:** 40000 Not Audited
Publisher & Editor: Ivan Johnson
Editorial Profile: The Punch is a twice-weekly newspaper serving residents of Nassau, Bahamas. Focuses on national and international news, business, culture and sports.
Language (s): English
NEWSPAPER

The Tribune (Bahamas)

Owner: The Tribune (Bahamas)
Editorial: PO Box N-3207, Nassau.
T: 1 242 322-1986 **E:** tips@tribunemedia.net
Freq: Daily; **Circ:** 15000 Not Audited
Publisher: Eileen Dupuch Carron; **News Editor:** Paco Nunez
Editorial Profile: Local newspaper focusing on national and international news, business, culture, social life and sport.
Language (s): English
DAILY NEWSPAPER

BROADCASTING

TELEVISION NETWORKS

ZNS TV 13

Editorial: Harcourt Rusty Bethel Dr, Nassau.
T: 242 3224623 **E:** znsnews@gmail.com
W: http://www.znsbahamas.com
Editorial Profile: Television channel presenting information about national news, sports, and entertainment.

BAHRAIN   Tel: 973

Standard Time: GMT +3
Continent: Asia
Capital City: Manama

NEWSPAPERS & PUBLICATIONS

NEWSPAPERS

4PM News

Owner: Strategic Publicity and Advertising Company WLL
Editorial: PO Box 75538, Office 32 & 25, Ebrahim Plaza, Manama. **T:** 973 17 579897
E: 4pmnews@gmail.com
W: http://www.4pmnews.com
Freq: Daily; **Circ:** 10000
Editor: Pradeep Puravankara
Editorial Profile: 4PM News is a tabloid-sized evening newspaper covering news, business and sport. It launched in June 2012, and is aimed at Indian expatriates in Bahrain.
Language (s): Malayalam
DAILY NEWSPAPER

Akhbar Al Khaleej

Owner: Dar Akhbar Al Khaleej Printing & Publishing House WLL
Editorial: PO Box 5300, Manama, Isa Town.
T: 973 17 620111 **E:** local@aaknews.net
W: http://www.akhbar-alkhaleej.com
Freq: Daily; **Circ:** 36000 Rate Card
News Editor: Abdallah Al Ayoobi
Editorial Profile: Akhbar Al Khaleej is a daily Arabic newspaper covering national and international news, current affairs, politics, business, culture and sports. It was first published in 1976.
Language (s): Arabic
DAILY NEWSPAPER

Alwasat

Owner: Dar Alwasat for Publishing & Distribution BSC
Editorial: PO Box 31110, Manama.
T: 973 17 596999 **E:** news@alwasatnews.com
W: http://www.alwasatnews.com
Freq: Daily; **Circ:** 30000 Pub Statement
News Editor: Ali Al Aliwat; **Editor In Chief:** Mansoor Al Jamri
Editorial Profile: Alwasat is a daily Arabic newspaper focusing on national and international news, current affairs, politics, business and sports. It was first published in 2002.
Language (s): Arabic
DAILY NEWSPAPER

Al Ayam

Owner: Al Ayam Publishing Group
Editorial: PO Box 3232, Al Janabia, Manama.
T: 973 17 617777 **E:** localnews@alayam.com
W: http://www.alayam.com
Freq: Daily; **Circ:** 30000 Pub Statement
Editor In Chief: Eisa Al Shaiji
Editorial Profile: Al Ayam (The Days) is a daily Arabic newspaper covering national and international news, current affairs, politics, business, culture and sports. The newspaper launched in 1989, and includes a family magazine supplement, Al Osrah, on Fridays.
Language (s): Arabic
DAILY NEWSPAPER

Al Bilad

Owner: Dar Al Bilad for Journalism, Publishing and Distribution BSC
Editorial: PO Box 385, 4th Floor, 336 Building, Manama. **T:** 973 17 111479
E: info@albiladpress.com
W: http://www.albiladpress.com
Freq: Daily; **Circ:** 25000 Rate Card
News Editor: Omar Al Jaber; **Editor In Chief:** Moanes Almardi
Editorial Profile: Al Bilad is a broadsheet-sized newspaper covering local and international news, politics, business and sport. The Arabic daily was first published in 2008.
Language (s): Arabic

DAILY NEWSPAPER

Daily Tribune
Owner: Al Ayam Publishing Group
Editorial: Flat 31, Ebrahim Plaza, Zinj, Manama. **T:** 973 17 579911 **E:** news@dt.bh
W: http://www.dt.bh
Freq: Daily; **Circ:** 10000 Rate Card
Editorial Profile: Daily Tribune is a tabloid-sized newspaper focusing on national and international news, current affairs, politics, business and sports. The newspaper originally launched as the broadsheet Bahrain Tribune in 1997, but changed its name and size in September 2010.
Language (s): English
DAILY NEWSPAPER

Gulf Daily News
Owner: Al Hilal Publishing and Marketing Group
Editorial: PO Box 5300, Manama.
T: 973 17 620222 **E:** gdnnews@gdn.com.bh
W: http://www.gulf-daily-news.com
Freq: Daily; **Circ:** 12000 Rate Card
News Editor: Geoffrey Bew; **Editor-in-Chief:** George Williams
Editorial Profile: Gulf Daily News is a tabloid-sized newspaper focusing on national and international news, business, politics, culture and sport. The newspaper launched in 1978, and is aimed at English-speaking locals and expatriates in Bahrain.
Language (s): English
DAILY NEWSPAPER

Gulf Madhyamam - Bahrain edition
Owner: Gulf Madhyamam FZ LLC
Editorial: PO Box 21323, Office 17, Jamiyya Building, Muharraq. **T:** 973 17 342825
E: bahrain@gulfmadhyamam.net
W: http://www.gulfmadhyamam.net
Freq: Daily; **Circ:** 21600 Rate Card
Editor-in-Chief: Hamzah Abbas; **Bureau Chief:** Hashim Elamaram
Editorial Profile: Gulf Madhyamam is an international Indian newspaper covering national and international news, current affairs, politics, business and sport. The newspaper is aimed at Malayalam speakers in the Gulf and publishes separate editions for the UAE, Saudi Arabia (Riyadh, Jeddah, Damam & Abha), Qatar, Oman, Bahrain and Kuwait. The newspaper was first published in 1999.
Language (s): Malayalam
DAILY NEWSPAPER

Al Watan
Owner: Al Watan For Publishing & Distribution Co. (B.S.C.)
Editorial: PO Box 38801, Building No 681, Complex 335, Manama. **T:** 973 17 496666
E: local@alwatannews.net
W: http://www.alwatannews.net
Freq: Daily; **Circ:** 27500 Pub Statement
Editor in Chief: Yousef Al Binkhalil
Editorial Profile: Al Watan is a daily Arabic newspaper focusing on local and international news, business, sport and politics. It was first published in 2005.
Language (s): Arabic
DAILY NEWSPAPER

NEWS SERVICE/SYNDICATE

Bahrain News Agency
Owner: Bahrain News Agency
Editorial: PO Box 5421, Ministry of Information, Manama. **T:** 973 17 687007
E: bna.arabicnews@gmail.com
W: http://www.bna.bh
Editor: Khaled Al Zayani; **Editor In Chief:** Ali El Thawadi; **Editor:** Khaled Ismael; **Editor:** Hameed Saleh
Editorial Profile: Official government news agency founded in 1978.
Language (s): Arabic
NEWS SERVICE/SYNDICATE

European Pressphoto Agency - Bahrain Bureau
Owner: European Pressphoto Agency
Editorial: Manama. **T:** 973 39 181515
E: mazennews@gmail.com
W: http://www.epa.eu
Editorial Profile: Photo agency representing 11 European news agencies (DPA, ANSA, EFE, Belga, APA, Athens News Agency, PAP, ANP, MTI, Keystone and LUSA) - covers news, politics, sports, fashion, economy, conflicts, disasters, features and business.
Language (s): Arabic
NEWS SERVICE/SYNDICATE

BROADCASTING

RADIO STATIONS

98.4 Shabab FM
Owner: Bahrain Radio & Television Corporation
Editorial: PO Box 194, Isa Town.
T: 973 17 788353 **E:** malsabbagh@brtc.gov.bh
W: http://www.iaa.bh
Editorial Profile: 98.4 Shabab FM is a youth-orientated radio station broadcasting cultural, social, educational and entertainment programmes. It airs on 98.4 FM and launched in February 2010.

Bahrain 93.3 FM
Owner: Bahrain Radio & Television Corporation
Editorial: PO Box 194, Isa Town.
T: 973 17 682696 **E:** news@brtc.gov.bh
W: http://www.iaa.bh
Editorial Profile: Bahrain 93.3 FM is a national radio station broadcasting music, news, entertainment and cultural programmes. It launched in 2001.

Radio Bahrain 102.3 FM
Owner: Bahrain Radio & Television Corporation
Editorial: PO Box 194, Isa Town.
T: 973 17 871371 **E:** malsabbagh@brtc.gov.bh
W: http://www.iaa.bh
Editorial Profile: Radio Bahrain 102.3 FM broadcasts major local events and news in Bahrain, as well as locally produced drama serials, educational and cultural programmes. It launched in 1955 and airs on 102.3 FM, MW 801, MW 612 and MW 1458.

Radio Bahrain 96.5FM
Owner: Bahrain Radio & Television Corporation
Editorial: PO Box 702, Isa Town.
T: 973 17 871585 **E:** btv@brtc.gov.bh
W: http://www.iaa.bh
Editorial Profile: Radio Bahrain 96.5FM is the English radio station of the Bahrain Radio & Television Corporation, and broadcasts music and entertainment 24-hours a day with local and international news every hour. It launched in 1977 and broadcasts on 96.5 FM and 99.5 FM.

Your FM 104.2
Editorial: PO Box 76024, Office 13, Building 618, Manama. **T:** 973 17 369370
E: pr@yourfm.bh **W:** http://www.yourfm.bh
Editorial Profile: Your FM 104.2 is an independent, commercial radio station broadcasting Asian music and programmes to Bahrain and the Eastern province of Saudi Arabia. The station launched in June 2012, replacing Radio Voice 104.2 which had broadcast on the same frequency since 2007. The station airs 20 hours of Hindi programming and four hours of Malayalam programming daily on 104.2 FM.

TELEVISION STATIONS

Bahrain TV
Owner: Bahrain Radio & Television Corporation
Editorial: PO Box 1075, Al Istiglal Highway, Isa Town. **T:** 973 17 871525
E: news@brtc.gov.bh **W:** http://www.iaa.bh
Editorial Profile: Bahrain TV is a state-owned television channel broadcasting local and international news, current affairs, documentaries, educational programmes, entertainment series and films 24-hours a day. The channel launched in 1971.

Channel 55
Owner: Bahrain Radio & Television Corporation
Editorial: PO Box 1075, Al Istiglal Highway, Isa Town. **T:** 973 17 871309
E: news@brtc.gov.bh **W:** http://www.iaa.bh
Editorial Profile: Channel 55 is a state-owned television station broadcasting news and general entertainment programmes. The channel launched in 1978.

BANGLADESH — Tel: 880

Standard Time: GMT +6
Continent: Asia
Capital City: Dhaka

NEWSPAPERS & PUBLICATIONS

NEWSPAPERS

Daily Bhorer Kagoj
Editorial: Karnaphuli Media Point, 2nd Floor, 70 Shahid Sangbadik Selina Parveen, Dhaka 1000. **T:** 880 29360285 **E:** bkagoj@yahoo.com
W: http://www.bhorerkagoj.net
Freq: Daily; **Circ:** 82001 Not Audited
Editor: Shaymal Dutta
Editorial Profile: Covers of general news.
Language (s): Bengali
DAILY NEWSPAPER

The Daily Inqilab
Editorial: 2/1 R.K. Mission Road, Dhaka 1203.
T: 880 27122771 **E:** inqilab08@dhaka.net
W: http://www.dailyinqilab.com
Freq: Daily; **Circ:** 300003 Not Audited
Editor: A. Bahauddin
Editorial Profile: Covers news and general interests.
Language (s): Bengali
DAILY NEWSPAPER

The Daily Ittefaq
Editorial: 40 Kawran Buzar, Dhaka 1215.
T: 880 2 7122660 **E:** dailyittefaq@yahoo.com
W: http://www.ittefaq.com.bd
Freq: Daily; **Circ:** 300003 Not Audited
Editor: Anwar Hossain
Editorial Profile: Covers news and general interests.
Language (s): Bengali
DAILY NEWSPAPER

Daily Jaijaidin
Editorial: 446/E Love Road, Tejgaon, Dhaka 1208. **T:** 880 28832222 128
W: http://www.jjdin.com
Freq: Weekly; **Circ:** 80003 Not Audited
Editor: Kazi Rukanuddin Ahmed
Editorial Profile: A daily newspaper covering local, national, regional and international news.
Language (s): Bengali
NEWSPAPER

The Daily Jugantor
Editorial: Ka-244, Kuril, Progati, Soroni, Dhaka 1229. **T:** 88 2 84192115
E: jugantor.newspaper@gmail.com
W: http://www.jugantor.com
Freq: Daily
Publisher: Salma Islam
Editorial Profile: Serves as Bangladesh's largest newspaper. Covers national news with a mission of professional journalism, serving as a change catalyst and progressing with innovation and uniqueness.
Language (s): Bangla
DAILY NEWSPAPER

Daily Manab Zamin
Editorial: 21 Kazi Nazrul Islam Avenue, Dhaka 1000. **T:** 880 29661122
E: manabzamin@yahoo.com
W: http://www.manabzamin.com
Freq: Daily; **Circ:** 50003 Not Audited
Publisher: Mahbuba Chowdhury; **Editor in Chief:** Motiur Chowdhury
Editorial Profile: Covers general news.
Language (s): Bangla
DAILY NEWSPAPER

The Daily Nirapekkha
Editorial: 2 R.K Mission Road, Motaled Mansion, Dhaka 1203. **T:** 880 29569751
E: dniro@dhaka.net
Freq: Daily; **Circ:** 50003 Not Audited
Editor: Newaz Shofiqul Rahman
Editorial Profile: Covers news and general interests.
Language (s): Bengali
DAILY NEWSPAPER

Daily Prothom Alo
Editorial: 100 Kazi Nazrul Islam Avenue, Kawran Bazar, Dhaka 1215. **T:** 880 28110081
E: info@prothom-alo.com
W: http://www.prothom-alo.com
Freq: Daily; **Circ:** 200003 Not Audited
Editor: Matiur Rahaman
Editorial Profile: Provides Bangladesh and International news as well as local and regional perspectives.
Language (s): Bengali

DAILY NEWSPAPER

The Daily Rupali
Editorial: 28/A-3 Toyenbi Circular Road, Motijheel C/A, Dhaka 1000. **T:** 880 2 9560080
Freq: Daily; **Circ:** 50003 Not Audited
Editor: S.Q. Quaderi
Editorial Profile: An English daily national newspaper.
Language (s): English
DAILY NEWSPAPER

The Daily Star
Editorial: 19, Karwan Bazar, 1st, 2nd & 3rd Floor, Dhaka 1215. **T:** 880 28124955
E: editor@thedailystar.net
W: http://www.thedailystar.net
Freq: Daily; **Circ:** 80000 Not Audited
Editor: Mahfuz Anam
Editorial Profile: Covers of news and general interests.
Language (s): English
DAILY NEWSPAPER

The Financial Express
Editorial: 45 Topkhana Road, Tropicana Tower, 4th Floor, Dhaka 1000. **T:** 880 29553550
E: tfe@bangla.net
W: http://www.thefinancialexpress-bd.com
Freq: Daily; **Circ:** 13001 Not Audited
Editor: Moazzem Hossain
Editorial Profile: Covering financial and business news.
Language (s): English
DAILY NEWSPAPER

The Independent
Editorial: BEL Tower (5th & 6th Floor), 19 Dhanmondi Road No.1, Dhaka 1205.
T: 880 2 9672091 **E:** editor@bol-online.com
W: http://www.theindependentbd.com
Freq: Daily; **Circ:** 14503 Not Audited
Editor: Shamsur Rahman
Editorial Profile: Covers news and general interests.
Language (s): English
DAILY NEWSPAPER

Janakantha
Editorial: Janakantha Bhaban, 24/A New Eskaton Road, Dhaka 1000. **T:** 880 29347780
E: janakantha@bttb.net.bd
W: http://www.globe-janakantha.com
Freq: Daily; **Circ:** 160003 Not Audited
Editor: Atiqullah Masud
Editorial Profile: Covers news and general interests.
Language (s): Bengali
DAILY NEWSPAPER

New Age
Editorial: Holiday Building, 30 Tejgaon Industrial Area, Dhaka 1208. **T:** 880 2 8153034
E: newagebd@global-bd.net
W: http://www.newagebd.com
Freq: Daily; **Circ:** 35001 Not Audited
Editor: Nurul Kabir; **Publisher:** Shahidullah Khan
Editorial Profile: Covering news and general interests.
Language (s): English
DAILY NEWSPAPER

The New Nation
Editorial: 1 Ramkrishna Mission Road, Dhaka 1203. **T:** 880 2 71 22 660
E: n_editor@bangla.net
Freq: Daily; **Circ:** 45003 Not Audited
Publisher: Mainul Hosein; **Editor:** A.M. Mufazzal
Editorial Profile: Covers news and general interests.
Language (s): English
DAILY NEWSPAPER

Sangram
Editorial: 423 Elephant Road, Bara Magh Bazar, Dhaka 1217. **T:** 880 2 8318128
E: dsangram@gmail.com
W: http://www.dailysangram.com
Freq: Daily; **Circ:** 20003 Not Audited
Editor: Abul Asad
Editorial Profile: A daily general newspaper.
Language (s): Bengali
DAILY NEWSPAPER

Weekly 2000
Editorial: 96/97 New Eskaton Road, Dhaka 1000. **T:** 880 29350953
E: info@shaptahik2000.com
W: http://www.shaptahik2000.com
Freq: Weekly; **Circ:** 35003 Not Audited
Editorial Profile: Covers news and general interests.
Language (s): Bengali
NEWSPAPER

Weekly Holiday
Editorial: Holiday Building, 30 Tejgaon Industrial Area, Dhaka 1208. **T:** 880 29110886
E: holiday@global-bd.net
W: http://www.weeklyholiday.net
Freq: Weekly; **Circ:** 12003 Not Audited
Editor: Syed Kamaluddin
Editorial Profile: Covers general news.
Language (s): English
NEWSPAPER

Young Independent
Editorial: BEL Tower (5th & 6th Floor), 19 Dhanmondi, Road No.1, Dhaka 1205.
T: 880 2 9672091 **E:** editor@bol-online.com
W: http://www.theindependent-bd.com
Freq: Weekly; **Circ:** 25003 Not Audited
Editor: Shamsur Rahman
Editorial Profile: Covers lifestyle and general interests.
Language (s): English
NEWSPAPER

NEWS SERVICE/SYNDICATE

United News of Bangladesh (UNB)
Editorial: Cosmos Center, 69/1 News Circular Road, Malibagh, Dhaka 1217.
T: 880 29345541 **E:** unb_news@yahoo.com
W: http://www.unbnews.org
Freq: Daily
Editor in Chief: Syed Rahman
Editorial Profile: Covers news.
Language (s): Bangla
NEWS SERVICE/SYNDICATE

BROADCASTING

TELEVISION STATIONS

ATN Bangla
Editorial: WASA Bhaban (1st Floor), 98 Kazi Nazrul Islam Avenue, Kawran Bazar, Dhaka 1215. **T:** 880 28111207
E: atn@dhaka.agni.com
W: http://www.atnbangla.tv
Editorial Profile: Covers of news and general interests.

TELEVISION NETWORKS

Ekattor TV
Editorial: 57 Sohrawardi Avenue, Baridhara, Dhaka 1212. **T:** 880 9669-710000
E: news@ekattor.tv **W:** http://www.ekattor.tv
Editorial Profile: Launched in June 2012, serves as the first full high-definition news and current affairs television service available 24/7 in Bangladesh.

BARBADOS **Tel: 1246**
Standard Time: GMT -4
Continent: The Americas
Capital City: Bridgetown

NEWSPAPERS & PUBLICATIONS

NEWSPAPERS

Barbados Advocate
Owner: Advocate Publishers 2000 Inc
T: 1246 46 72 000
E: news@barbadosadvocate.com
W: http://www.barbadosadvocate.com
Freq: Daily; **Circ:** 15000 Not Audited
News Editor: Dorian Bryan
Editorial Profile: Daily newspaper that provides the island with local, national and international news, sports, business and politics.
Language (s): English
DAILY NEWSPAPER

Daily Nation (Barbados)
Owner: Nation Publishing Co. Limited (The)
T: 01 246 4305400
E: epaper@nationnews.com
W: http://www.nationnews.com
Freq: Daily Not Audited
Editor: Barry Alleyne; **News Editor:** Eric Smith
Editorial Profile: Newspaper covering national and international news, sports, business and arts & entertainment. Advertising and subscription rates are quoted in Barbados dollars.
Language (s): English
DAILY NEWSPAPER

BROADCASTING

RADIO NETWORKS

Caribbean Broadcasting Corporation (Radio)
Editorial: PO Box 900, The Pine, St. Michael, Bridgetown BB11000. **T:** 246 4292041
E: nca@cbcbarbados.bb **W:** http://www.cbc.bb
Editorial Profile: Provides news, life music shows. 98.1 FM targets teenagers and provides interviews and top music 94.7FM plays Caribbean music. 100.7 FM provides general government information and provides community service coverage.

Voice of Barbados
Editorial: River Road, Bridgetown.
T: 246 4307300 **E:** info@vob929.com
W: http://www.vob929.com
Editorial Profile: VOB presents interactive programs related to socio-economic issues related to the Barbadians lifestyle. Transmits sports, surveys, regional and business news on the frequency 92.9 FM.

BELARUS **Tel: 375**
Standard Time: GMT +2
Continent: Europe
Capital City: Minsk

NEWSPAPERS & PUBLICATIONS

NEWSPAPERS

BelGazeta
Owner: BelGazeta
Editorial: ul. Kalvariskaya 17 A, office 616A, Minsk 220004. **T:** 375 17 200 40 50
E: bg@bg.org.by **W:** http://www.belgazeta.by
Circ: 21300 Pub Statement
Editorial Profile: National newspaper focusing on news in economics, politics and society in Belarus and in the world.
Language (s): Russian
DAILY NEWSPAPER

Belorusy i Rynok
Owner: Mediarynok ZAO
Editorial: ul. Bogdanovicha 124, office 7, Minsk 220040. **T:** 375 17 28 76 177
E: root@br.minsk.by
W: http://www.br.minsk.by
Freq: Weekly; **Circ:** 10187 Not Audited
Market Editor: Alexander Alesin; **Legal Affairs:** Yury Behterev; **Editor:** Tatiana Kalinovskaya; **Editor-in-Chief:** Vyacheslav Vladimirovich Khodosovskiy; **Editor:** Irina Krilovich; **Editor:** Tatiana Manenok; **News Editor:** Maria Sadovskaya
Editorial Profile: Newspaper providing comprehensive and analytical coverage of business events and economic developments in Belarus.
Language (s): Russian
NEWSPAPER

Ekonomicheskaya Gazeta
Owner: Belbuisnespress
Editorial: ul. Kozyrevskaya 15, Minsk 220028.
T: 375 17 21 31 800 **E:** negrek@neg.by
W: http://www.neg.by
Freq: 2 Times/Week; **Circ:** 13242 Not Audited
Editor-in-Chief: Leonid Fridkin
Editorial Profile: Newspaper containing information about economics, civil law, finance and statistics, business news.
Language (s): Russian
NEWSPAPER

Express Novosti
Owner: KOMSIS
Editorial: pr. Nezavisimosti 77, Minsk 220013.
T: 375 17 29 26 405 **E:** info@expressnews.by
W: http://www.expressnews.by **Circ:** 7000 Pub Statement
Editor In Chief: Stanislav Zhuravlevich
Editorial Profile: Analytical-informative newspaper.
Language (s): Belarusian
DAILY NEWSPAPER

Gomelskaya pravda
Owner: Gomelskaya pravda
Editorial: ul. Lepeshinskogo 1, Gomel 246015.
T: 375 232 57 72 78 **E:** gp@gp.by
W: http://gp.by **Circ:** 21000 Pub Statement
Editor In Chief: Sergey Bespaly

Editorial Profile: Newspaper focused on regional cultural and political issues and changes in Belarus society.
Language (s): Belarusian
DAILY NEWSPAPER

Komputernaya Gazeta
Owner: Nestor Publishers
Editorial: P. O. Box 563, Minsk 220113.
T: 375 17 28 93 713
E: pumpur@nestormedia.com
W: http://www.nestor.minsk.by/kg
Freq: Weekly; **Circ:** 26000 Not Audited
Editor: Svetlana Pumpur
Editorial Profile: Newspaper containing news, reviews, features general hardware and software information. Places emphasis on details about new and forthcoming products.
Language (s): Russian
NEWSPAPER

Komsomolskaya Pravda v Belarusi
Editorial: ul. Platonova 1b, office 401, 4 floor, Minsk 220034. **T:** 375 17 294 27 11
E: kp@belkp.by **W:** http://kp.by
Freq: Daily
Editorial Profile: Byelorussian edition of Russian daily newspaper covering politics, economics, culture and social issues.
Language (s): Russian
DAILY NEWSPAPER

The Minsk Times
Owner: Administration of the President of the Belarus Republic
Editorial: ul. Kiseleva 11, Minsk 220029.
T: 375 17 29 06 113 **E:** times@sb.by
W: http://sb.by/post/64765
Freq: Weekly; **Circ:** 2000 Pub Statement
Editor: Victor Kharkov
Editorial Profile: Socio-political weekly covering political, economic, sports and cultural news of Minsk in English language.
Language (s): English
NEWSPAPER

Music News Weekly
Owner: Nestor Publishers
Editorial: PO Box 563, Minsk 220113.
T: 375 17 28 93 713 **E:** mg@nestormedia.com
W: http://www.nestor.minsk.by/mg
Freq: Weekly; **Circ:** 3500 Not Audited
Editor: Oleg Klimov
Editorial Profile: Newspaper containing information about all styles of pop and rock music with emphasis on alternative and recently discovered artists. Includes interviews, features, news, reviews, chart details and classified ads.
Language (s): Russian
NEWSPAPER

Narodnaya Gazeta
Owner: Narodnaya Gazeta
Editorial: ul. Khmelnitskogo 10A, Etazh 7, Minsk 220013. **T:** 375 17 28 71 870
E: info@ng.by **W:** http://www.ng.by
Freq: Daily; **Circ:** 40000 Pub Statement
Editor-in-Chief: Vladimir Andrievich; **Editor:** Victor Leshchenko
Editorial Profile: Newspaper covering national and international news with features on business and finance, culture, education and lifestyle.
Language (s): Belarusian
DAILY NEWSPAPER

Sovietskaya Belorussia
Owner: Administration of the President of the Belarus Republic
Editorial: vul. Khmelnitskogo 10A, Minsk 220013. **T:** 375 17 29 25 101 **E:** admin@sb.by
W: http://www.sb.by
Freq: Daily; **Circ:** 417966 Pub Statement
Editor In Chief: Pavel Yakubovich
Editorial Profile: Newspaper focusing on financial, economical and social-political issues.
Language (s): Russian
DAILY NEWSPAPER

Vecherny Brest
Owner: Vecherny Brest
Editorial: ul. Pushkinskaya 11, Brest 224005.
T: 375 162 21 54 00 **E:** info@vb.by
W: http://www.vb.by **Circ:** 15000 Pub Statement
Editor: Vladimir Sergeevich Shparlo
Editorial Profile: Regional newspaper containing national and international news, articles on culture, sports and social issues.
Language (s): Belarusian
DAILY NEWSPAPER

Vecherny Minsk
Owner: OOO Izdatelskiy Dom Vecherny Minsk

Editorial: Pr. Fr. Skoriny 44, Minsk 220005.
T: 375 17 28 45 944 **E:** vm@nsys.by
W: http://www.newsvm.com
Freq: Daily; **Circ:** 40000 Pub Statement
Editor: Sergey Sverkunov
Editorial Profile: Newspaper focusing on national and international news, politics and the economy, sport, culture and lifestyle.
Language (s): Russian
DAILY NEWSPAPER

Virtual Joys
Owner: Nestor Publishers
Editorial: PO Box 563, Minsk 220113.
T: 375 17 28 93 713
E: nestorinfo@nestormedia.com
W: http://www.nestor.minsk.by/vr
Freq: Monthly; **Circ:** 25000 Not Audited
Editor: Marina Biryukova
Editorial Profile: Newspaper containing information about computer games and related soft- and hardware.
Language (s): Russian
NEWSPAPER

Znamya Yunosti
Owner: Upravlyenye po Delom Maladyozhy Ministerstva Obrozovanya Respspubliki Belarusi
Editorial: ul. Khmelnitskogo 10 A, Minsk 220013. **T:** 375 17 28 71 684 **E:** zn@zn.by
W: http://zn.by
Freq: Weekly; **Circ:** 32000 Not Audited
Editor-in-Chief: Evgeniy Meleshko
Editorial Profile: Newspaper containing social-political news, articles on history, culture, show business and world-wide youth organisations.
Language (s): Russian
NEWSPAPER

NEWS SERVICE/SYNDICATE

AFN
Editorial: ul. Vostochnaya 129-310, Minsk 220113. **T:** 375 17 21 60 111 **E:** info@afn.by
W: http://www.afn.by
Editor: Mr./Ms. Editor
Editorial Profile: Provides financial and economic news, reviews of investments, funds, banking and currency markets.
Language (s): Belarusian
NEWS SERVICE/SYNDICATE

BelaPAN News Agency
Editorial: ul. Akademicheskaya 17, office 3, Minsk 220012. **T:** 375 17 29 25 501
E: mail@belapan.com
W: http://www.belapan.com
Editor: Alexander Malinovsky; **Editor:** Julia Mitskevich
Language (s): Belarusian
NEWS SERVICE/SYNDICATE

Belarusian News Agency
Editorial: ul. Kirava 26, Minsk 220030.
T: 375 17 22 71 992 **E:** oper@belta.by
W: http://www.belta.by
News Editor: Yuriy Oreshkin
Editorial Profile: BelTA News Agency is the biggest information agency in the Republic of Belarus and has been official national information provider remaining most authoritative source of up-to-date information on activities of supreme government bodies of Belarus. The agency was founded on December 23, 1918.
Language (s): Belarusian
NEWS SERVICE/SYNDICATE

ECOPRESS Information Agency
Editorial: 21-606 Chicherina Street, Minsk 220029. **T:** 375 17 29 34 020
E: market@ecopress.by
W: http://www.ecopress.by
Editor In Chief: Pyotr Borovikov
Editorial Profile: Financial and economic news agency, provision of current financial and economic information (currency exchange rates, deposit rates, securities quotations, etc.) as well as economic and commercial news of the Republic of Belarus.
Language (s): Belarusian
NEWS SERVICE/SYNDICATE

PRIME-TASS Business News Agency
Editorial: 11-2-412 Nezavisimosti Avenue, Minsk. **T:** 375 17 20 99 500
E: market@prime-tass.by
W: http://www.prime-tass.by
Editor: Yelena Lazarchuk; **Editor:** Olga Loiko
Editorial Profile: Business News Agency dealing with distribution of business news from Belarus, live economic newswire, analysis, market surveys and press clippings. Preparation and distribution of press releases

and media monitoring. Coverage of special events, announcements, invitations for media, interviews and accompanying materials.
Language (s): Belarusian
NEWS SERVICE/SYNDICATE

BELGIUM
Tel: 32
Standard Time: GMT +1
Continent: Europe
Capital City: Brussels

NEWSPAPERS & PUBLICATIONS

NEWSPAPERS

La Dernière Heure / Les Sports
Owner: La Dernière Heure / Les Sports
Editorial: Rue des Francs, 79, Bruxelles 1040. **T:** 32 2 744 44 55 **E:** dh.redaction@dhnet.be
W: http://www.dhnet.be
Freq: Daily Pub Statement
Rédacteur: Antoine Clevers
Editorial Profile: Newspaper covering mainly on sports including regional news, media and celebrities Aimed at those with an interest in competitive sport.
Language (s): French
DAILY NEWSPAPER

L' Echo
Owner: mediafin
Editorial: Avenue du port 86C, Boîte 309, Bruxelles 1000. **T:** 32 2 423 16 11
E: redaction@lecho.be **W:** http://www.lecho.be
Freq: Daily
Editor in Chief: Joan Condijts; **Redacteur en Chef Adjoint:** Nicolas Ghislain; **Redacteur en Chef Adjoint:** Marc Lambrechts; **Rédacteur:** Stéphane Wuille
Editorial Profile: Newspaper covering national and international news including politics, economics, business and financial markets.
Language (s): French
DAILY NEWSPAPER

Europolitique
Owner: Europe Information Service s.a
Editorial: Rue d'Arlon, 53, Brussels 1040.
T: 32 2 737 7722
E: redaction@europolitics.info
W: http://www.europolitique.info
Freq: Daily
Editor in Chief: Pierre Lemoine
Editorial Profile: Newspaper providing in-depth, analytical coverage of the European Union, its institutions and policies as well as the key economic, social and international issues high on the agenda today.
Language (s): English
DAILY NEWSPAPER

De Gentenaar - Nieuwsblad
Owner: CORELIO (EX VUM NV)
Editorial: Gosseltaan 30, Gent 1702.
T: 32 9 268 72 70 **E:** nieuws@gentenaar.be
W: http://www.gentenaar.be
Freq: Daily Pub Statement
Chef eindredactie: Nico Vanhee
Editorial Profile: Broadsheet-sized newspaper containing national and international news, business reports and coverage of political events. Read by company directors, managers and senior executives, university students and office personnel, the majority of whom live in Flanders.
Language (s): Flemish
DAILY NEWSPAPER

Het Nieuwsblad
Owner: CORELIO (EX VUM NV)
Editorial: Gossetlaan 30, Groot Bijgaarden 1702. **T:** 32 2 467 22 23
E: nieuws@nieuwsblad.be
W: http://www.nieuwsblad.be
Freq: Daily; **Circ:** 270000 Pub Statement
Editor: Raymond Billen; **Editor:** Els Bloemmen; **Editor:** Werner Bourlez; **Editor:** Philippe de Bruin; **Editor:** Mariena Dewulf; **Editor:** Marcel Kumpen; **News Editor:** Peter Mijlemans; **Editor:** Guido Ostyn; **Editor:** Laurens Raskin; **Editor:** Karen Regelbrugge; **Editor:** Kristof Simoens; **eindredacteur:** Marina Tondeleir; **Editor:** Chris Van Geyte; **Chef Oost-Vlaanderen:** Rudi Van Holderbeke; **Editor:** Kathy Vandeportael; **Editor:** Marianne Vanderauwera; **Editor in Chief:** Peter Vandermeersch; **Editor:** Ludo Vandewalle; **Chef eindredactie:** Nico Vanhee; **Editor:** Johan Vercammen; **Editor:** Christine Verlinde; **Editor:** Kurt Vermeersch; **Editor:** Robert Verniers
Editorial Profile: Newspaper covering national and international news including sports, politics, economics, business, culture and lifestyle.
Language (s): Flemish
DAILY NEWSPAPER

HLN - Het Laatste Nieuws
Owner: DE PERSGROEP
Editorial: Brusselsesteenweg 347, Asse/ kobbegem 1730. **T:** 32 2454 22 11
E: info@hln.be **W:** http://www.hln.be
Freq: Daily Pub Statement
Chef Nieuws: Willy Cardon; **Chef eindredactie:** Edwin Ceulebroeck; **Hoofredacteur:** Paul Daenen; **Eindredacteur:** An Schoemans
Editorial Profile: Broadsheet-sized newspaper providing news and information covering politics, society, sport and regional issues. Aimed at a broad sector of society, 90 percent of whom live in the Flemish part of Belgium.
Language (s): Flemish
DAILY NEWSPAPER

La Libre Belgique - Gazette de Liège
Owner: Groupe Multimedia IPM S.A.
Editorial: Rue des Francs, 79, Bruxelles 1040. **T:** 32 2 744 44 44 **E:** llb.redaction@saipm.com
W: http://www.lalibre.be
Freq: Daily Pub Statement
Editor in Chief: Francis Van de Woestyne
Editorial Profile: Newspaper covering general news and current affairs including politics, economics, culture, sports, entertainment and lifestyle.
Language (s): French
DAILY NEWSPAPER

Metro
Owner: MASS TRANSIT MEDIA
Editorial: S.A. Mass Transit Media, Galerie Ravenstein 4, Brussels 1000.
T: 32 2227 93 43 **E:** metro@metrotime.be
W: http://www.metrotime.be
Freq: Daily; **Circ:** 119398 Pub Statement
Editor In Chief: Arnaud Dujardin
Editorial Profile: Tabloid-sized newspaper containing national and international news, sport and general information. Read by commuters.
Language (s): French
DAILY NEWSPAPER

De Morgen
Owner: De Persgroep
Editorial: Brusselsesteenweg 347, Kobbegem 1730. **T:** 32 2 556 68 11 **E:** info@demorgen.be
W: http://www.demorgen.be
Freq: Daily Pub Statement
Rédacteur: Jan Debackere; **Rédacteur:** Agnes Goyvaerts; **Eindredacteur:** Wilfried Poelmans; **Eindredacteur:** Henricus (Rene) Van Munster
Editorial Profile: Newspaper covering news and current affairs including sports, music, opinion, environment, technology, culture and media.
Language (s): Flemish
DAILY NEWSPAPER

New Europe
Editorial: Avenue de Tervuren 96, Bruxelles 1040. **T:** 32 2 539 00 39 **E:** info@neurope.eu
W: http://www.neurope.eu
Freq: Weekly; **Circ:** 80000
Legal Editor: Ariti Alamanou; **Editor:** Andy Carling; **Editor:** Cillian Donnelly; **Editor:** Kostis Geropoulos
Editorial Profile: Weekly newspaper covering government and politics including current news and analyses on EU institutions and EU-World relations.
Language (s): English
NEWSPAPER

Le Soir
Owner: Rossel & Cie
Editorial: Rue Royale, 100, Bruxelles 1000.
T: 32 2 225 54 32 **W:** http://www.lesoir.be
Freq: Daily; **Circ:** 150000 Pub Statement
Rédacteur en chef adjoint: Christophe Berti; **Rédacteur:** Fabienne Bradfer; **Rédacteur:** Stéphane Druart; **Rédacteur:** Catherine Makereel; **Rédacteur:** Olivier Maloteaux; **Rédacteur:** Gisèle Maréchal; **Rédacteur:** Guy Maron; **chroniqueur:** Leopold Unger
Editorial Profile: Broadsheet-sized evening newspaper covering news and current affairs including business, economics, politics, culture, society, television and sport.
Language (s): French
DAILY NEWSPAPER

De Standaard
Owner: CORELIO (EX VUM NV)
Editorial: Gossetlaan 28, Groot Bijgaarden 1702. **T:** 32 2 467 27 52
E: binnenland@standaard.be
W: http://www.standaard.be
Freq: Daily Pub Statement
Rédacteur: Veerle Beel; **Rédacteur:** Bernard Bulcke; **Rédacteur:** Luc Coppens; **Chef eindredactie:** Peter Cuypers; **Rédacteur:** Steven De Foer; **Rédacteur:** Peter De Lobel; **News Editor:** Karin De Ruyter; **Eindredacteur:** Diebrecht De Smet; **Eindredacteur:** Simon De Vriendt; **Eindredacteur:** Stijn De Wolf; **Rédacteur:** Ilse Degryse; **Rédacteur:** Steven Dekeyser; **Rédacteur:** Yves Delepeleire; **Rédacteur:** Yves Delepeleire; **Rédacteur:** Pascal Dendooven; **Eindredacteur:** Els Depuydt; **Eindredacteur:** Gert Devreese; **Rédacteur:** Mark Eeckhaut; **Grafisch redacteur:** Jan Goossens; **Eindredacteur:** Els Groessens; **Rédacteur:** Kristof Hoefkens; **Eindredacteur:** Astrid Houthuys; **Eindredacteur:** Filip Huysegems; **Rédacteur:** Maryvonne Jacobs; **Eindredacteur:** Frans Kieckens; **Rédacteur:** Dorien Knockaert; **Rédacteur:** Monica Monté; **Rédacteur:** Evita Neefs; **Grafisch Redactrice:** Céline Poppe; **Rédacteur:** Ine Roox; **Rédacteur:** Inge Schelstraete; **Rédacteur:** Pascal Sertyn; **Rédacteur:** Griet Speeckaert; **Coördinator Wetenschap:** Steven Stroeykens; **Hoofdredacteur:** Bart Sturtewagen; **Rédacteur:** Nico Tanghe; **Rédacteur:** Guy Tegenbos; **Rédacteur:** Danny Van Den Eeckhout; **Eindredacteur:** Eva Van Den Eynde; **Rédacteur:** Geert Van Der Speeten; **Redacteur Cultuur & Media:** Jan Van Hove; **Chef Regio:** Diederik Van Vaerenbergh; **Eindredacteur:** Veerle Vanden Bosch; **Eindredacteur:** Frans Vandeputte; **Rédacteur:** Nikolas Vanhecke; **Rédacteur:** Sarah Vankersschaever; **Rédacteur:** Ann Vantournhout; **Grafisch redacteur:** Philip Vercruyssen; **Rédacteur:** Filip Verhoest; **Rédacteur:** Wim Winckelmans; **Redacteur Opinie:** Wouter Woussen; **Rédacteur:** Tom Ysebaert
Editorial Profile: National newspaper covering regional, national and international news and current affairs including business, politics, economics, culture, lifestyle, society and sports.
Language (s): Flemish
DAILY NEWSPAPER

De Tijd
Owner: mediafin
Editorial: Havenlaan 86 C, Bus 309, Brussels 1000. **T:** 32 2 423 16 11
E: persberichten@tijd.be **W:** http://www.tijd.be
Freq: Daily Pub Statement
Hoofdredacteur: Isabel Albers; **Editor:** Bert Broens; **Chef Ondernemingen:** Bas Kurstjens; **Editor:** Michael Sephiha; **Redacteur:** Koen Van Boxem; **Redacteur:** Erik Ziarczyk
Editorial Profile: Newspaper covering business and finance including investment, markets, economics, politics and culture.
Language (s): Dutch
DAILY NEWSPAPER

The Wall Street Journal (Belgium)
Editorial: 87 Boulevard Brand Whitlock, Brussels B-1200. **T:** 32 2 741-1211
DAILY NEWSPAPER

NEWS SERVICE/SYNDICATE

AGENCE ALTER
Editorial: Rue Coenraets, 64, Bruxelles 1060.
T: 32 2541 85 20 **E:** alter@alter.be
W: http://www.alter.be
Language (s): Dutch
NEWS SERVICE/SYNDICATE

Agence Europe
Editorial: Rue de la Gare, 36, Bruxelles 1040.
T: 32 2 737 94 94 **E:** info@agenceurope.com
W: http://www.agenceurope.com
Editor: Lionel Changeur
Editorial Profile: News agency covering European news and current affairs including business, politics, economics, society, culture, agriculture and law.
Language (s): French
NEWS SERVICE/SYNDICATE

Agence France-Presse - Brussels Bureau
Owner: Agence France-Presse
Editorial: Avenue d'Auderghem 22-28, Bruxelles 1040. **T:** 32 22 30 83 94
E: afpbru@afp.com **W:** http://www.afp.com
Bureau Chief: Jean-Luc Bardet
Editorial Profile: Brussels office of the international news agency covering regional, national and international news and current affairs including general interest, politics, business, economics, health, science, education and society.
Language (s): French
NEWS SERVICE/SYNDICATE

Agencia EFE
Editorial: Résidence Palace, Rue de la Loi 155 7th Fl., Brussels 1040. **T:** 32 2 285-4830
Bureau Chief: Elena Moreno Marín
Language (s): Spanish
NEWS SERVICE/SYNDICATE

ANSA - AGENZIA NATIONALE STAMPA ASSOCIATA BELGIQUE
Editorial: Boulevard Charlemagne, 1, Boite 7, Bruxelles 1000. **T:** 32 2 230 81 92
E: ansa.bruxelles@ansa.it
W: http://www.ansa.it
Language (s): Italian
NEWS SERVICE/SYNDICATE

AP DOW JONES NEWS SERVICE - BELGIQUE
Editorial: Boulevard Brand Whithlock 87, Bruxelles 1200. **T:** 32 2 741 12 11
E: djnews.brussels@dowjones.com
W: http://www.dowjones.com
Editor: Laurence Norman
Editorial Profile: Dow Jones is a leading provider of global business news and information services. Its Consumer Media Group publishes The Wall Street Journal, Barron's, MarketWatch and the Far Eastern Economic Review. Its Enterprise Media Group includes Dow Jones Newswires, Factiva, Dow Jones Client Solutions, Dow Jones Indexes and Dow Jones Financial Information Services. Its Local Media Group operates community-based information franchises. Dow Jones owns 50% of SmartMoney and 33% of Stoxx Ltd. and provides news content to radio stations in the U.S. Since 1882, the Dow Jones name has been synonymous with accuracy, integrity and trust.
Language (s): English
NEWS SERVICE/SYNDICATE

Associated Press
Editorial: 1 Bd. Charlemagne, Box 49, Int'l Press Center, Brussels 1041. **T:** 32 2 285-0112
Bureau Chief: Angela Charlton
NEWS SERVICE/SYNDICATE

Belga News Agency
Editorial: Rue Frédéric Pelletier 8B, Bruxelles 1030. **T:** 32 2 743 23 11 **E:** redactie@belga.be
W: http://www.belga.be
Editorial Profile: Belga News Agency, the main provider of news for the Belgian media, delivers reliable and quick information 24/7 in Belgium and abroad. This information can relate to any subject, including politics, economy, social issues, finance, sport and culture.
Language (s): Dutch
NEWS SERVICE/SYNDICATE

Bloomberg News
Editorial: Internation Press Center, Boulevard Charlemagne 1 Box 28, Brussels 1041.
T: 32 22854300 **E:** belgium@bloomberg.net
Legal Editor: Peter Chapman; **Bureau Chief:** Kevin Costelloe
NEWS SERVICE/SYNDICATE

Dow Jones Newswires
Editorial: 87 Boulevard Brand Whitlock, Brussels B-1200. **T:** 32 2 741-1211
NEWS SERVICE/SYNDICATE

DPA - Deutsche Presse-Agentur Belgique
Editorial: Boulevard Charlemagne, 1, Boîte 17, Bruxelles 1041. **T:** 32 2230 36 91
E: dpa@dpa.be **W:** http://www.dpa.com
Editor In Chief: Christian Boehmer
Editorial Profile: The German Press Agency dpa is a trusted, accurate and independent provider of news with the digital and multimedia content to power the media at home and abroad. Our customers benefit from the extensive global network of correspondents and editors maintained by Germany's leading news wire. News gathering is completely free of outside influence which in turn guarantees that coverage lives up to the strict requirements of the dpa charter: This document lays down that reporting must be free of bias and unfettered by political, economic or governmental ideologies.Print media, radio stations, online and mobile communication providers in more than 100 countries rely on this journalistic excellence around-the-clock. Among dpa clients are parliaments, governmental and non-governmental organisations as well as businesses and public relations agencies. They all derive news content from the wide range of products and services provided by the dpa group of companies.
Language (s): Dutch
NEWS SERVICE/SYNDICATE

WORLD NEWS MEDIA

Euronews - Brussels Bureau
Owner: Euronews
Editorial: 223, rue de la Loi, Bruxelles 1000.
T: 32 278 819 19 **W:** http://www.euronews.net
Editorial Profile: Regional office of the TV cable/satellite channel focussing on national and international news and current affairs.
Language (s): English
NEWS SERVICE/SYNDICATE

IDG News Service
Owner: International Data Group
Editorial: Brussels **E:** idgnews@idg.com
Language (s): English
NEWS SERVICE/SYNDICATE

MLex
Owner: MLex Belgium SPRL
Editorial: 67 Rue de la Loi, Box 6, Brussels 1140. **T:** 32 2 300 82 50 **E:** mcleod@mlex.com
W: http://www.mlex.com
Editor In Chief: Robert Mc Leod
Editorial Profile: MLex market intelligence is an independent service that provides in-depth intelligence, commentary and analysis, antitrust probes, state-backed bailouts, intellectual property, trade and regulatory issues. aimed at finance, investment and legal professionals.
Language (s): English
NEWS SERVICE/SYNDICATE

Thomson Reuters - Brussels Bureau
Editorial: Avenue Marnix 17, Bruxelles 1000.
T: 32 2 287 66 11
E: brussels.newsroom@thomsonreuters.com
W: http://www.thomsonreuters.com
Editorial Profile: News agency focussing on news, current affairs and politics.
Language (s): Dutch
NEWS SERVICE/SYNDICATE

ZenithOptimedia Belgium
Owner: ZenithOptimedia
Editorial: Clos Lucien Outers 11-21, Brussels 1160. **T:** 32 2 716 01 20
W: http://www.zenithoptimedia.be
Editorial Profile: Media agency which is part of the global ZenithOptimedia network with 195 offices in 70 countries and which in itself is part of the Publicis Group. ZenithOptimedia positioning is that of 'the ROI Agency'.
Language (s): English
NEWS SERVICE/SYNDICATE

BROADCASTING

RADIO NETWORKS

RTBF
Owner: RTBF
Editorial: Boulevard Auguste Reyers, 52, BBR 100, Bruxelles 1044. **T:** 32 2 737 48 81
E: rtbf.info@rtbf.be **W:** http://www.rtbf.be
Editorial Profile: National network of the Radio Television Belge Francophone.

RTBF - Classic 21
Owner: RTBF
T: 32 6532 7111 **E:** classic21@rtbf.be
W: http://www.classic21.be
Editorial Profile: Belgian classic rock radio, owned by national RTBF media group and based in Mons.

RTBF - International
Owner: RTBF
Editorial: Boulevard Reyers, 52, BRR 016, Bruxelles 1044. **T:** 32 2737 21 11
W: http://www.rtbfi.be
Editorial Profile: Belgian international, shortwave radio station, available in Europe and Central Africa. Owned by RTBF.

RTBF - La Premiere
Owner: RTBF
Editorial: Boulevard Auguste Reyers, 52, BRR 020, Bruxelles 1044. **T:** 32 2737 21 11
E: lpdirection@rtbf.be
W: http://www.rtbf.be/radio/premiere.html

RTBF - Pure FM
Owner: RTBF
T: 32 2737 27 76 **E:** purefm@rtbf.be
W: http://www.rtbf.be/purefm/
Editorial Profile: Young audience orientated radio, owned by national media group RTBF.

RTBF - VivaCité
Owner: RTBF
T: 32 6532 71 01 **E:** vivacite@rtbf.be
W: http://www.rtbf.be/vivacite/

Editorial Profile: Belgian public service radio station, owned by national media company RTBF.

TELEVISION STATIONS

Canal Z
Owner: Roularta Media Group
Editorial: Rue de la Fusée, Bruxelles 1130.
T: 32 2 702 70 91 **E:** info@canalz.be
W: http://www.canalz.be
Editorial Profile: Television channel focusing on economics and finance (French Edition).

Kanaal Z
Owner: RMG - ROULARTA MEDIA GROUP
Editorial: Medialaan 1, Vilvoorde 1800.
T: 32 2 255 37 08 **E:** info@z-nieuws.be
W: http://kanaalz.knack.be/
Editorial Profile: Kanaal Z / Canal Z are managed by NV Belgian Business Television, which was set by Brussels-listed Roularta Media Group. Kanaal Z / Canal Z are broadcasting 24 hours a day news about companies, economy and finances

TV-Brussel
T: 32 2702 87 30 **E:** nieuws@tvbrussel.be
W: http://www.tvbrussel.be
Editorial Profile: tvbrussel is a Dutch-speaking channel which believes in an international approach to a multicultural city. Programmes are subtitled in French and English.

VTM - Vlaamse Televisie Maatschappij
Owner: VLAAMSE MEDIA MAATSCHAPPIJ
Editorial: Medialaan 1, Vilvoorde 1800.
T: 32 2255 3211 **E:** hetnieuws@vtm.be
W: http://www.vtm.be
Editorial Profile: National broadcaster, market leader in information and entertainment, focusing on Flemish productions. "Family" channel.

BELIZE   Tel: 501
Standard Time: GMT -6
Continent: The Americas
Capital City: Belmopan

NEWSPAPERS & PUBLICATIONS

NEWSPAPERS

Amandala
Owner: The Amandala Press
Editorial: 3304 Partridge Street, Belize City.
T: 501 2024477
W: http://www.amandala.com.bz
Freq: 2 Times/Week; **Circ:** 10000 Not Audited
Publisher: Evan Hyde; **Editor:** Russell Vellos
Editorial Profile: Amandala is a newspaper covering national and international news, politics and sport.
Language (s): English
NEWSPAPER

The Belize Times
Owner: The Belize Times Press Ltd
Editorial: 3 Queen Street, Belize City.
T: 501 224 5757 **E:** belizetimesad@yahoo.com
W: http://www.belizetimes.bz
Freq: Weekly; **Circ:** 6000 Not Audited
Editor in Chief: Michael Rudon
Editorial Profile: Newspaper covering general news, finance, economic, politics and sport.
Language (s): English
NEWSPAPER

The Guardian
Owner: The Guardian Newspaper Ltd
Editorial: Corner Ebony St. & BelChina Bridge, Belize City. **T:** 501 207 5347
E: guardian@btl.net
W: http://www.guardian.bz
Freq: Weekly; **Circ:** 4000 Not Audited
Editor: Patrick Henry; **Editor:** Alfonso Noble
Editorial Profile: Newspaper focusing on national and international news, politics, business and sport.
Language (s): English
NEWSPAPER

The Reporter
Owner: The Reporter Press
Editorial: 147 West Allenby Street, PO Box 707, Belize City. **T:** 501 227 2503
W: http://www.reporter.bz
Freq: Weekly; **Circ:** 7000 Not Audited
Editor: Niell Gillett; **Publisher:** Harry Lawrence

Editorial Profile: Newspaper covering national news, business, politics, entertainment and sport.
Language (s): English
NEWSPAPER

BROADCASTING

TELEVISION NETWORKS

Channel 5 Belize
Editorial: 2882 Coney Dr, Belize City.
T: 501 2233745 **E:** gbtv@btl.net
W: http://www.channel5belize.com
Editorial Profile: Local television station broadcasting news and original entertainment shows.

Channel Seven
Editorial: 73 Albert Street, Belize City.
T: 501 2235589 **E:** tvseven@btl.net
W: http://www.7newsbelize.com
Editorial Profile: Provides social, political, and sport news.

BENIN   Tel: 229
Standard Time: GMT +1
Continent: Africa
Capital City: Porto-Novo

NEWSPAPERS & PUBLICATIONS

NEWSPAPERS

La Nation (Benin)
Owner: Onepi
Editorial: BP 1210, Vole De Cadjehoun.
T: 229 21 30 11 52
E: onip@communication.gouv.bj
W: http://www.gouv.bj/presse/lanation
Freq: Daily; **Circ:** 5000 Pub Statement
Rédacteur en Chef: Hubert Akponikpe
Editorial Profile: Newspaper focusing on national and international news, business, politics, entertainment and sport.
Language (s): French
DAILY NEWSPAPER

NEWS SERVICE/SYNDICATE

Agence Bénin Presse
Editorial: 01 BP 72, Cotonou.
T: 229 21 31 26 55 **E:** abpben@bow.intnet.bj
W: http://www.gouv.bj/presse/abp
Editorial Profile: Official News Agency of Benin covering all fields of information.
Language (s): French
NEWS SERVICE/SYNDICATE

BERMUDA   Tel: 1441
Standard Time: GMT -4
Continent: The Americas
Capital City: Hamilton

NEWSPAPERS & PUBLICATIONS

NEWSPAPERS

Bermuda Sun
Owner: Bermuda Sun Ltd
Editorial: 19 Elliott Street, Hamilton HM10.
T: 1 441 295-1944
E: newsroom@bermudasun.bm
W: http://www.bermudasun.bm
Freq: Fri; **Circ:** 12000 Not Audited
Publisher: Randy French; **Editor in Chief:** Tony McWilliam
Editorial Profile: Local newspaper covering business, politics, entertainment and sports.
Language (s): English
NEWSPAPER

The Royal Gazette
Owner: The Royal Gazette Ltd.
Editorial: 2 Par-la-Ville Rd, Hamilton HM-02.
T: 1441 295 5881 **E:** news@royalgazette.bm
W: http://www.royalgazette.com
Freq: Daily; **Circ:** 18500 Not Audited
Editorial Profile: The Royal Gazette is a daily newspaper focusing on national and international news, business and sports for the residents of Bermuda.
Language (s): English
DAILY NEWSPAPER

BROADCASTING

RADIO NETWORKS

1450AM Gold
Editorial: 94 Reid St., Hamilton HM FX.
T: 1 441 292-0050
E: 1450gold@vsbbermuda.com
W: http://www.vsbbermuda.com/1450-am-gold.html
Editorial Profile: Plays music from the 40s, 50s, and 60s. Provides talk shows, daily and weather news from Bermuda.

MIX 106FM
Editorial: 94 Reid St, Hamilton HM FX.
T: 1 441 292-0050
E: mix106@vsbbermuda.com
W: http://www.vsbbermuda.com/mix-106-fm.html
Editorial Profile: Plays today's music including urban, country, hip hop. Provides daily news twice a day.

TELEVISION NETWORKS

VSB TV-11
Editorial: 94 Reid St, Hamilton HM FX.
T: 1 441 276-1111 **E:** news@vsbbermuda.com
W: http://www.vsbbermuda.com
Editorial Profile: Broadcasts local daily news. Presentes different programming including entertainment shows.

BHUTAN   Tel: 975
Standard Time: GMT +5.45 hours
Continent: Asia
Capital City: Thimphu

NEWSPAPERS & PUBLICATIONS

NEWSPAPERS

Kuensel
Owner: Kuensel Corporation
Editorial: PO Box 204, Thimphu.
T: 975 2 32 24 83 **E:** editor@kuensel.com.bt
W: http://www.kuenselonline.com **Circ:** 15000 Pub Statement
Editor In Chief: Dasho Kinley Dorji; **News Editor:** Phuntsho Wangdi
Editorial Profile: Newspaper focusing on national news, politics, business, culture, entertainment and sport.
Language (s): Dzongkha
DAILY NEWSPAPER

BROADCASTING

RADIO NETWORKS

Bhutan Broadcasting Service Radio
Editorial: PO Box 101, Thimphu.
T: 975 2 32 35 80 **E:** bbs@bbs.com.bt
W: http://www.bbs.com.bt

TELEVISION STATIONS

Bhutan Broadcasting Service TV
Editorial: PO Box 101, Thimphu.
T: 975 2 32 35 80 **E:** md@bbs.com.bt
W: http://www.bbs.com.bt

BOLIVIA   Tel: 591
Standard Time: GMT -4
Continent: The Americas
Capital City: La Paz

NEWSPAPERS & PUBLICATIONS

NEWSPAPERS

Correo del Sur
Owner: Editorial Canelas del Sur SRL
Editorial: Calle Kilómetro 7 N° 202, Sucre (chuquisaca). **T:** 591 4 64 61 531
E: correo7@entelnet.bo
W: http://www.correodelsur.net
Freq: Daily; **Circ:** 5000 Not Audited
Editor: Javier Cosulich; **Editor in Chief:** Raykha Flores Cocío; **Editor:** Alberto Guevara;

Editor: Alvaro Sotomayor; **Editor:** Ernesto Torres
Editorial Profile: National newspaper.
Language (s): Spanish
DAILY NEWSPAPER

El Deber
Owner: El Deber SRL
Editorial: Avenida El Trompillo 2 anillo #1144, Santa Cruz. **T:** 591 3 353 8000
E: eldeber@eldeber.com.bo
W: http://www.eldeber.com.bo
Freq: Daily; **Circ:** 50000 Not Audited
News Editor: Roberto Aguirre; **Editor in Chief:** Tuffi Aré Vázquez; **Editor:** Leopoldo Vegas
Editorial Profile: National newspaper containing national and international news, current affairs, business and sport.
Language (s): Spanish
DAILY NEWSPAPER

El Día
Owner: Prisa Internacional
Editorial: Avenida Cristo Redentor 3355, Km 2'5, CP 5344, Santa Cruz. **T:** 591 33434040
E: eldia@eldia.com.bo
W: http://www.eldia.com.bo
Freq: Daily; **Circ:** 15000 Not Audited
Editor in Chief: Róger Cuéllar; **Editor:** Carlos Jordan Paz
Editorial Profile: Newspaper containing national and international news, current affairs, business and sport.
Language (s): Spanish
DAILY NEWSPAPER

El Diario
Owner: El Diario S.A.
Editorial: Calle Loayza 118, La Paz.
T: 591 22150900 **E:** redinfo@eldiario.net
W: http://www.eldiario.net
Freq: Daily; **Circ:** 70000 Not Audited
Editor: Susana Gutiérrez; **Editor in Chief:** Rodrigo Ticona
Editorial Profile: Newspaper covering national and international news, politics, economics, finance, business, culture and sport.
Language (s): Spanish
DAILY NEWSPAPER

Energy Press
Owner: Energy Press.com SRL
Editorial: Equipetrol Norte, Calle F Este 166, CP 3498, Santa Cruz. **T:** 591 3 345 9095
E: prensa1@energypress.com.bo
W: http://www.energypress.com.bo
Freq: Weekly; **Circ:** 7000 Not Audited
Editor: Vesma Marincovic
Editorial Profile: Newspaper focusing on the energetic industry in South America; includes petroleum related news, interviews and statistics.
Language (s): Spanish
NEWSPAPER

La Estrella del Oriente
Owner: Editorial C.S.S.
Editorial: Calle Republiquetas #353, Santa Cruz. **T:** 591 3 332-9011
E: laestrelladeloriente@laestrella.bo
W: http://www.laestrelladeloriente.com
Freq: Daily; **Circ:** 5000 Not Audited
Editor: William Guzman
Editorial Profile: La Estrella del Oriente is a Bolivian daily newspaper providing Local News, Politics, Editorial Page, Sports, Arts & Entertainment, Economy, National and International coverage.
Language (s): Spanish
DAILY NEWSPAPER

Gente
Owner: Editorial Canelas SA
Editorial: Edificio Los Tiempos, Plaza Quintanilla, Planta baja, Cochabamba.
T: 591 4 425 0936 **E:** gente@bo.net
Freq: Daily; **Circ:** 16000 Not Audited
Editor in Chief: Flavios Ramos
Editorial Profile: General news related to criminal justice and policial issues, targeting a low socio-economic status audience.
Language (s): Spanish
DAILY NEWSPAPER

Jornada
Owner: Editorial Aurios SRL
Editorial: Almirante Grau 672, Zona San Pedro, La Paz. **T:** 591 22407789
W: http://www.jornadanet.com
Freq: Daily; **Circ:** 400 Not Audited
Editor: Bernabe López; **Editor in Chief:** Jenny Rodríguez Araníbar
Editorial Profile: Newspaper covering national and international news, politics, economics, finance, business, culture and sport.
Language (s): Spanish
DAILY NEWSPAPER

El Mundo
Owner: El Mundo S.A
Editorial: Parque Industrial Manzano 7, Santa Cruz. **T:** 591 3 346 4646
E: opinionmundo@gmail.com
W: http://www.elmundo.com.bo
Freq: Daily; **Circ:** 13000 Not Audited
Editor: Patricia González
Editorial Profile: Newspaper focusing on national and international news, politics, business and sport.
Language (s): Spanish
DAILY NEWSPAPER

Opinión
Owner: Editorial Opinión SA
Editorial: Calle General Achá N° 0252, Cochabamba. **T:** 591 4 425-4400
E: redaccion@opinion.com.bo
W: http://www.opinion.com.bo
Freq: Daily; **Circ:** 18000 Not Audited
Editor: Ricardo Becerra; **Editor:** Elizabeth Riva Alvarez
Editorial Profile: Newspaper covering national and international news, politics, economics, finance, business, culture and sport.
Language (s): Spanish
DAILY NEWSPAPER

El País
Owner: El País
Editorial: Calle Colón 968, Tarija.
T: 591 4 664 2732 **E:** elpais@entelnet.bo
W: http://www.elpaisonline.com
Freq: Daily; **Circ:** 3000 Not Audited
Editor: Gilberto Villarroel
Editorial Profile: National newspaper.
Language (s): Spanish
DAILY NEWSPAPER

La Palabra del Beni
Owner: Editorial Tiempo del Beni
Editorial: Calle Nicolás Suárez 693, Trinidad (beni). **T:** 591 3 462 0808
E: lpalabra@entelnet.bo
W: http://www.boliviabeni.com/LAPALABRA.htm
Freq: Daily; **Circ:** 1000 Not Audited
Editor: Emar Schrakman
Editorial Profile: National newspaper.
Language (s): Spanish
DAILY NEWSPAPER

La Patria
Owner: Editora SIC Ltda
Editorial: Calle Camacho 1892 Murguia, CP 48, Oruro. **T:** 591 2 525 0780
E: direccion@lapatria.com.bo
W: http://www.lapatriaenlinea.com
Freq: Daily; **Circ:** 8000 Not Audited
Editor: Etzhel Llanquel; **Editor:** Estella Miralles; **Editor in Chief:** Jimena Miralles Iporre
Editorial Profile: National newspaper.
Language (s): Spanish
DAILY NEWSPAPER

El Potosí
Owner: Editorial Canelas del Sur SRL
Editorial: Calle Cochabamba 35, Potosi.
T: 591 2 622 7835 **E:** elpotosi@entelnet.bo
W: http://www.elpotosi.net
Freq: Daily; **Circ:** 4000 Not Audited
Editor in Chief: Guillermo Bullain Iñiguez; **Editor:** Jaime Menduíña; **Editor:** Luis Subieta; **Editor:** Marvin Valda Angulo
Editorial Profile: National newspaper.
Language (s): Spanish
DAILY NEWSPAPER

La Prensa
Owner: Editores Asociados SA
Editorial: Villa Fatima Calle Mayor Lopera 230, La Paz. **T:** 591 2 2 21 88 21
E: laprensa@laprensa.com.bo
W: http://www.laprensa.com.bo
Freq: Daily; **Circ:** 15000 Not Audited
Editor: German Aráuz; **Editor:** Marco Belmonte; **Editor in Chief:** Carlos Morales; **Editor:** Ramiro Siles
Editorial Profile: National newspaper.
Language (s): Spanish
DAILY NEWSPAPER

La Razón
Owner: Prisa Internacional
Editorial: Colinas de Santa Rita, Alto Auquisamaña, Zona Sur, La Paz.
T: 591 2 277-1415 **E:** larazon@la-razon.com
W: http://www.la-razon.com
Freq: Daily; **Circ:** 30000 Not Audited
Editor in Chief: Patricia Cusicanqui
Editorial Profile: Bolivian daily newspaper containing national and international news, current affairs, business and sport.
Language (s): Spanish
DAILY NEWSPAPER

Santa Cruz Económico
Owner: Ilustra
Editorial: Avenida El Trompillo 206, Santa Cruz. **T:** 591 3 353 0944
E: sceconomico@cotas.com.bo
W: http://www.santacruzeconomico.com.bo
Freq: Weekly; **Circ:** 4000 Not Audited
Editor in Chief: Rudy Ortíz
Editorial Profile: National newspaper focusing on financial information.
Language (s): Spanish
NEWSPAPER

Semanario Pulso
Owner: Pulso SA
Editorial: Avenida 6 de Agosto 2530, CP 9056, La Paz. **T:** 591 2 212 0330
E: comunidadboliviana.com.ar@gmail.com
W: http://www.comunidadboliviana.com.ar
Freq: Weekly; **Circ:** 5000 Not Audited
Editor: Daniel Espinoza
Editorial Profile: Covers political and economic news.
Language (s): Spanish
NEWSPAPER

Los Tiempos
Owner: Editorial Canelas SA
Editorial: Edificio Los Tiempos, Plaza Quintanilla Piso 3, Area norte, Casilla 525, Cochabamba. **T:** 591 44254562
W: http://www.lostiempos.com
Freq: Daily; **Circ:** 13000 Not Audited
Editor in Chief: Alcides Flores; **Editor:** Maria Julia Osório
Editorial Profile: Newspaper covering national and international news, politics, economics, finance, business, culture and sport.
Language (s): Spanish
DAILY NEWSPAPER

NEWS SERVICE/SYNDICATE

Agencia de Noticias Fides (ANF)
Editorial: Calle Loayza, Oficina 501, Edificio Ayacucho, La Paz. **T:** 591 2 233 5577
E: noticiasfides@gmail.com
W: http://www.noticiasfides.com
Editor: Jaime Loayza Zegarra
Language (s): Spanish
NEWS SERVICE/SYNDICATE

Agencia EFE
Editorial: Avenida Sánchez Lima 2520, Edificio Aníbal Mz. 01, La Paz. **T:** 591 2 241 9222
E: lapaz@efe.com **W:** http://www.efe.com
Editor: Javier Aliaga
Language (s): Spanish
NEWS SERVICE/SYNDICATE

DPA (Agencia Alemana de Prensa)
Editorial: Ciudad Satélite, Plan 328, calle 5, No. 219, El Alto, La Paz. **T:** 591 22810098
W: http://www.dpa.com
Language (s): Spanish
NEWS SERVICE/SYNDICATE

BROADCASTING

RADIO NETWORKS

Radio Fides
Editorial: Calle Jenaro Sanjines 799 Esquina Sucre, CP 9143, La Paz. **T:** 591 2 240 6363
E: prensa@radiofides.com
W: http://www.radiofides.com
Editorial Profile: Catholic Radio Station covers national news and social programs in which the radio fundraises in benefit of people with low income. Plays Bolivian national music.

Radio Panamericana
Editorial: Edificio 16 de Julio Piso 9, Oficina 902 El Prado, La Paz. **T:** 591 2 231 3980
E: pana@panamericana.bo
W: http://www.panamericana.bo
Editorial Profile: Broadcasts daily news and sports. Plays Surcos Bolivianos and traditional Bolivian music and rhythms.

TELEVISION NETWORKS

P.A.T.
Editorial: Posnansky 1069, Miraflores, La Paz.
T: 591 2 222 4422 **E:** info@red-pat.com
W: http://www.red-pat.com
Editorial Profile: Television network broadcasting a variety of cultural, entertainment programs and the news shows.

BOSNIA-HERZEGOVINA

Tel: 387

Standard Time: GMT +1
Continent: Europe
Capital City: Sarajevo

NEWSPAPERS & PUBLICATIONS

NEWSPAPERS

Dnevni Avaz
Owner: Aroto Press
Editorial: Tešanjska 24a, Sarajevo 71000.
T: 387 33 281360 **E:** redakcija@avaz.ba
W: http://www.avaz.ba
Freq: Daily; **Circ:** 60000 Pub Statement
Editor-in-Chief: Fadil Mandal
Editorial Profile: Newspaper with news on domestic and international politics, finance, culture, social issues, sport and entertainment.
Language (s): Serbo-Croat
DAILY NEWSPAPER

Dnevni List
Owner: NATIONAL HOLDING d.o.o.
Editorial: Kralja Petra Kresimira IV br. 66/2, Mostar 88 000. **T:** 387 36 31 33 70
E: mostar@dnevni-list.ba
W: http://www.dnevni-list.ba
Freq: Daily; **Circ:** 5200 Pub Statement
Editor: Sanja Bjelica Šagovnovic; **Editor-in-Chief:** Dario Lukic; **Editor:** Predrag Zvijerac
Language (s): Serbo-Croat
DAILY NEWSPAPER

Glas Srpske
Owner: AD Glas Srpske Banjaluka
Editorial: Brace Pišteljica 1, Banja Luka 78000. **T:** 387 51 21 28 44
E: dopisnik@glassrpske.com
W: http://www.glassrpske.com
Freq: Daily; **Circ:** 15000 Pub Statement
News Editor: Darko Gavrilovic; **Editor In Chief:** Borjana Radmanovic-Petrovic
Language (s): Serbo-Croat
DAILY NEWSPAPER

Nezavisne Novine
Owner: N.I.G.D. DNEVNE NEZAVISNE NOVINE d.o.o.
Editorial: Brace Pišteljica 1, Banja Luka 78000. **T:** 387 51 33 18 00
E: desk@nezavisne.com
W: http://www.nezavisne.com
Freq: Daily; **Circ:** 20000 Pub Statement
Editor-in-Chief: Gordana Milinkovic
Editorial Profile: Newspaper containing national and international news, current affairs and sport.
Language (s): Serbo-Croat
DAILY NEWSPAPER

Oslobodjenje
Owner: Oslobodjenje d. d.
Editorial: Džemala Bijedica 185, Sarajevo 71000. **T:** 387 33 276900
E: marketing@oslobodjenje.ba
W: http://www.oslobodjenje.ba
Freq: Daily; **Circ:** 25000 Pub Statement
Editor-in-Chief: Vildana Selimbegovic
Editorial Profile: Newspaper focusing on national and international news, business, sport and current affairs.
Language (s): Serbo-Croat
DAILY NEWSPAPER

NEWS SERVICE/SYNDICATE

FEDERALNA NOVINSKA AGENCIJA FENA
Editorial: Cemaluša 1, Sarajevo.
T: 387 33 66 37 72 **E:** fena@fena.ba
W: http://www.fena.ba
Editor: Bisera Džidic; **Editor In Chief:** Zoran Ilic
Editorial Profile: Federal news agency - Fena was founded by the Decree of FBiH Government in November 2000.
Language (s): Serbo-Croat
NEWS SERVICE/SYNDICATE

ONASA News Agency
Editorial: Zmaja od Bosne 4, Hotel Holiday Inn 10th floor, Sarajevo 71000.
T: 387 33 27 65 80 **E:** onasa@onasa.com.ba
W: http://www.onasa.com.ba
Editor: Asim Celebic; **Editor:** Dževad Cesko; **Editor-in-Chief:** Fuad Kovacevic; **Editor:** Belma Tabakovic
Editorial Profile: Provides information, news and comments to domestic and foreign public

related to relevant events in Bosnia and Herzegovina, countries of the former Yugoslavia and in the whole world.
Language (s): Serbo-Croat
NEWS SERVICE/SYNDICATE

Reuters
Editorial: Fra Andjela Zvizdovica 1, Sarajevo 71000. **T:** 387 3366 3864
W: http://www.thomsonreuters.com
Bureau Chief: Daria Sito-Sucic
NEWS SERVICE/SYNDICATE

BROADCASTING

RADIO NETWORKS

BH Radio 1
Editorial: Bulevar Meše Selimovica 12, Sarajevo 71000. **T:** 387 33 46 11 01
E: kontakt@bhrt.ba **W:** http://www.bhrt.ba
Editorial Profile: National radio station broadcasting news, music, religious and social programmes 24 hours a day.

TELEVISION STATIONS

BH TV1
Editorial: Bulevar Meše Selimovica 12, Sarajevo 71000. **T:** 387 33 65 04 52
E: milenko.vockic@bhrt.ba
W: http://www.bhrt.ba
Editorial Profile: Bosnian national TV station broadcasting on the territory of the whole country.

BOTSWANA Tel: 267
Standard Time: GMT +2
Continent: Africa
Capital City: Gaborone

NEWSPAPERS & PUBLICATIONS

NEWSPAPERS

The Botswana Gazette
Owner: News Company Botswana (Pty) Ltd
Editorial: PO Box 1605, Plot 125, Sedimosa House, Gaborone. **T:** 267 391 28 33
E: editor@gazette.bw
W: http://www.gazette.bw **Circ:** 20000 Pub Statement
Editor: Aubrey Lute
Editorial Profile: Newspaper focusing on national and international news, politics, business, entertainment and sport.
Language (s): English
DAILY NEWSPAPER

The Botswana Guardian
Owner: CBET (Pty) Ltd
Editorial: Private Back 153, Gaborone.
T: 267 390 84 32
E: mpho@guardiansun.co.bw
W: http://www.botswanaguardian.co.bw
Freq: Weekly; **Circ:** 20000 Pub Statement
Human Resources: Kgomotso Makgatrhe;
Editor: Mike Mothibi
Editorial Profile: Newspaper focusing on national and international news, business, politics, entertainment and sport.
Language (s): English
NEWSPAPER

The Midweek Sun
Owner: CBET (Pty) Ltd
Editorial: Private Back 153, Gaborone.
T: 267 390 84 32
E: mpho@guardiansun.co.bw
W: http://www.midweeksun.co.bw **Circ:** 22000 Pub Statement
Editor: Mpho Dibeela; **Human Resources:** Kgomotso Makgatrhe
Editorial Profile: Newspaper focusing on national and international news, business, politics, entertainment and sport.
Language (s): English
DAILY NEWSPAPER

Mmegi
Owner: Dikgang Publishing Company (DPC)
Editorial: PO Box BR 50, Private Bag, Gaborone. **T:** 267 397 47 84
E: editor@mmegi.bw
W: http://www.mmegi.bw
Freq: Daily; **Circ:** 9000 Pub Statement
News Editor: Stryker Motlaloso; **Editor:** Guideon Nkala
Editorial Profile: Newspaper focusing on national and international news, business, politics, culture and sport.
Language (s): English
DAILY NEWSPAPER

Mmegi Monitor
Owner: Dikgang Publishing Company (DPC)
Editorial: PO Box BR 50, Private Bag, Gaborone. **T:** 267 397 47 84
E: monitoreditor@mmegi.bw
W: http://www.mmegi.bw
Freq: Weekly; **Circ:** 16000 Pub Statement
Editor: Kagiso Sekokonyane
Language (s): English
NEWSPAPER

The Voice
Owner: Beata Kasale
Editorial: Plot 170, Unit 7, Commerce Park, Gaborone. **T:** 267 316 15 85
E: editorial@thevoicebw.com
W: http://www.thevoicebw.com
Freq: Weekly ABC-Audit Bureau of Circulations
Publisher: Beata Botlhoko Kasale; **Editor:** Pamela Dube; **Marketing:** Lisa Kasale
Editorial Profile: National Newspaper featuring news and current affairs concerning Botswana.
Language (s): English
NEWSPAPER

BROADCASTING

RADIO STATIONS

RB2
Editorial: Department of Broadcasting Services, Private Bag 60, Gaborone.
T: 267 365 8000 **E:** sseisa@btv.gov.bw
W: http://www.btv.gov.bw
Editorial Profile: National Radio broadcasting.

RADIO NETWORKS

RB1
Editorial: Department of Broadcasting Services, Private Bag 60, Gaborone.
T: 267 365 30 00 **E:** sseisa@btv.gov.bw
W: http://www.btv.gov.bw
Editorial Profile: National radio broadcasting.

TELEVISION STATIONS

Botswana Television
Editorial: Department of Broadcasting Services, Private Bag 60, Gaborone.
T: 267 365 30 00 **E:** sseisa@btv.gov.bw
W: http://www.btv.gov.bw
Editorial Profile: National television broadcasting.

BRAZIL Tel: 55
Standard Time: GMT -3
Continent: The Americas
Capital City: Brasilia

NEWSPAPERS & PUBLICATIONS

NEWSPAPERS

Agora São Paulo
Owner: Empresa Folha da Manhã SA
Editorial: Alameda Barão de Limeira, 425 - 5º Andar, Campos Elíseos, Sao Paulo 01202-900.
T: 55 11 3224-3141
W: http://www.uol.com.br/agora
Freq: Daily; **Circ:** 90527 Not Audited
Editor in Chief: Nilson Camargo; **Editor:** Luiz Carlos Duarte; **Editor:** Adriana Mompean
Language (s): Portuguese
DAILY NEWSPAPER

Amazonas Em Tempo
Owner: Norte Editora Ltda.
Editorial: Rua Dr. Dalmir Câmara, 623, Manaus 69033-070. **T:** 55 92 3090-1010
E: opiniao@emtempo.com.br
W: http://www.emtempo.com.br
Freq: Daily; **Circ:** 25000 Not Audited
Editorial Profile: Covers regional, national and international news. Editorial includes politics, sports economy, arts, entertainment, travel and culture.
Language (s): Portuguese
DAILY NEWSPAPER

Amazônia
Editorial: Avenida 25 de Setembro, 2473, Marco, Belèm 66093-000. **T:** 55 91 3216-1017
E: redacao@jornalamazonia.com.br
W: http://www.orm.com.br/amazonia
Freq: Daily; **Circ:** 32000 Not Audited
Editor in Chief: Antônio Carlos Pimentel
Language (s): Portuguese
DAILY NEWSPAPER

Bom Dia Jundiaí
Editorial: Rua Rangel Pestana, 444, Centro, Jundiaí 13201-000. **T:** 55 1145233440
E: redacao@bomdiajundiai.com.br
W: http://www.bomdiajundiai.com.br
Freq: Daily Not Audited
Editor in Chief: Edu Cerioni
Language (s): Portuguese
DAILY NEWSPAPER

Bom Dia Sorocaba
Editorial: Avenida Washington Luiz, 871, Jardim Emília, Sorocaba 18031-000.
T: 55 15 32126001
E: redacao@bomdiasorocaba.com.br
W: http://www.redebomdia.com.br
Freq: Daily; **Circ:** 29990 Not Audited
Editor in Chief: Djalma Benette; **Editor:** Marcelo Macaus
Language (s): Portuguese
DAILY NEWSPAPER

Bragança Jornal Diário
Editorial: Avenida Antônio Pires Pimentel, 957, Centro, Bragança Paulista 12914-000.
T: 55 1140340490 **E:** jornal@bjd.com.br
W: http://www.bjd.com.br
Freq: Daily; **Circ:** 10000 Not Audited
Editor in Chief: José Omair de Oliveira
Editorial Profile: O Bragança Jornal Diário (BJD) passou por sua maior transformação em 10 de Setembro de 1993 com o início da impressão em off-set. A partir dessa data o BJD começou uma nova era e uma grande mudança ocorreu na sua programação visual devido aos recursos fornecidos pela informática. Hoje, o Bragança Jornal Diário entra na era digital com sua Home Page na World Wide Web. Com o grande avanço da Internet em todo o mundo, o BJD abre novas opções para o jornalismo bragantino com a expansão do acesso às notícias provenientes de todo o Brasil e do mundo.
Language (s): Portuguese
DAILY NEWSPAPER

Brasil Econômico
Owner: Empresa Jornalística Econômico S.A.
Editorial: Avenida das Nações Unidas, 11.633, 8° Andar, Sao Paulo 04578-901.
T: 55 11 3320-2000
E: redacao@brasileconomico.com.br
W: http://www.brasileconomico.com.br
Freq: Mon thru Fri
Publisher: Ramiro Alves; **Editor:** Rita Karam;
Editor in Chief: Adriana Teixeira
Editorial Profile: Established on October 8, 2009 and it is the second largest Brazilian newspaper dedicated exclusively to cover all topics related to economy and financial markets in Brazil. Editorial includes articles on national and international economy, finance and financial analysis, investments, trade, stock markets, media industry and companies. Also, offers the latest news on politics and society.
Language (s): Portuguese
DAILY NEWSPAPER

A Cidade
Editorial: Rua São Sebastião, 610, Centro, Ribeirão Preto 14015-040.
T: 55 16 3977-2175
E: jornalismo@jornalacidade.com.br
W: http://www.jornalacidade.com.br
Freq: Daily; **Circ:** 22000 Not Audited
Editor in Chief: Delcy Cruz; **Editor:** Hélio Pelissari
Language (s): Portuguese
DAILY NEWSPAPER

Comércio da Franca
Editorial: Avenida Eliza Verzola Gosuein, 3103, Jardim Ângela Rosa, Franca 14400-630.
T: 55 16 3713-8899
E: jornalismo@comerciodafranca.com.br
W: http://www.comerciodafranca.com.br
Freq: Daily; **Circ:** 16000 Not Audited
Editor in Chief: Joelma Ospedal
Language (s): Portuguese
DAILY NEWSPAPER

Correio
Editorial: Rua Aristides Novis, 123, Federação, Salvador 40210-630. **T:** 55 71 3203-1210
E: redacao@correio24horas.com.br
W: http://www.correiodabahia.com.br
Freq: Daily; **Circ:** 58075 Not Audited
Editora de Produção/Production Editor: Linda Bezerra; **Editor in Chief:** Sergio Costa; **Editor:** Jorge Souza
Language (s): Portuguese
DAILY NEWSPAPER

Correio Braziliense
Owner: Fundação Assis Chateaubriand
Editorial: SIG Qd. 02 Lote 340, Brasilia 70610-901. **T:** 55 61 3214-1180
E: opiniao@correioweb.com.br
W: http://www.correioweb.com.br
Freq: Daily; **Circ:** 43415 Not Audited
Editor: Josemar Dantas; **Editor in Chief:** Ana Dubeux; **Editor:** Luis Carlos Griebeler Tajes; **Editor:** Ana Paula Macedo; **Editor:** Ana Sá; **Editor:** Sandro Silveira; **Editor:** Dad Abi Squarisi; **City Editor:** Marcelo Tokarski
Editorial Profile: Newspaper focusing on national and international news, politics, business and sport.
Language (s): Portuguese
DAILY NEWSPAPER

Correio da Paraíba
Editorial: Avenida Pedro II, 623, Centro, João Pessoa 58013-420. **T:** 55 83 3216-5000
E: redacao@correiodaparaiba.com.br
W: http://www.correiodaparaiba.com.br
Freq: Daily Not Audited
Editor: Carlos Aranha; **City Editor:** Janaína Araújo; **City Editor:** Andréa Batista; **Editor:** Fábio Cardoso; **Editor:** Ana Maria Felippe; **Editor in Chief:** Walter Galvão; **Editor:** José Magalhães; **Editor:** Lílian Moraes; **Editor:** Jãmarrí Nogueira
Language (s): Portuguese
DAILY NEWSPAPER

Correio de Uberlândia
Editorial: Avenida José Andraus Gassani, 4555, Distrito Industrial, Uberlândia 38402-324. **T:** 55 34 3218-7881
E: correiodeuberlandia@correiodeuberlandia.com.br **W:** http://www.jornalcorreio.com.br
Freq: Daily; **Circ:** 12000 Not Audited
Editor in Chief: Roberta Guimarães; **Editor:** Ivan Santos; **Editor:** Selma Silva
Language (s): Portuguese
DAILY NEWSPAPER

Correio do Estado
Owner: Correio do Estado S/A.
Editorial: Avenida Calógeras, 356, Centro, Campo Grande 79004-901.
T: 55 67 3323-6090
W: http://www.correiodoestado.com.br
Freq: Daily Not Audited
City Editor: Milena Crestani; **Editor:** Hordones Echeverria; **Editor in Chief:** Neri Kaspary
Editorial Profile: Covers Local, Regional, National and International News.
Language (s): Portuguese
DAILY NEWSPAPER

Correio do Povo
Owner: Correio do Povo
Editorial: Rua Caldas Júnior 219, Porto Alegre 90019-900. **T:** 55 51 3215-6111
E: pauta@correiodopovo.com.br
W: http://www.cpovo.net
Freq: Daily; **Circ:** 160000 Not Audited
Editor: Eugênio Bortolon; **Editor:** Carlos Brockstedt; **Editor:** Carmem Dóra Chiappetta; **Editor:** Edson Coelho; **Editor:** Letícia Ferreira; **Editor:** Carolina Jardine; **Editor in Chief:** Paulo Mendes; **Editor:** Maria José Vasconcelos
Language (s): Portuguese
DAILY NEWSPAPER

Correio Paranaense
Editorial: Rua Fagundes Varela, 2106, Jardin Social, Curitiba 82520-040. **T:** 55 4132632002
E: geral@jornalcorreioparanaense.com.br
W: http://www.jornalcorreioparanaense.com.br
Freq: Daily; **Circ:** 15000 Not Audited
Editor in Chief: Renato Barroso
Editorial Profile: Note: This outlet has the same telephone and fax number. To send a fax, one must call and request that the telephone line be switched to a fax line.
Language (s): Portuguese
DAILY NEWSPAPER

Correio Popular
Editorial: Rua Sete de Setembro, 189, Vila Industrial, Campinas 13035-350.
T: 55 19 3772-8135 **W:** http://cpopular.com.br
Freq: Daily; **Circ:** 37000 Not Audited
Editor: Ricardo Luis Alécio; **Editor:** Kátia Fonseca; **Editor:** Rui Motta
Language (s): Portuguese
DAILY NEWSPAPER

A Crítica
Editorial: Avenida André Araújo, 1924 A, Bairro Aleixo - Cidade das Comunicações, Manaus 69060-001. **T:** 55 92 3643-1200
E: jornal@acritica.com.br
W: http://acritica.uol.com.br
Freq: Daily Not Audited
Language (s): Portuguese
DAILY NEWSPAPER

Cruzeiro do Sul
Editorial: Avenida Engenheiro Carlos Reinaldo Mendes, 2800, Alto da Boa Vista, Sorocaba 18013-280. **T:** 55 15 2102-5100
E: redacao@jcruzeiro.com.br
W: http://www.cruzeironet.com.br Not Audited
Editor: Estela Casagrande; **Editor in Chief:** Anclar Patric Crippa Mendes; **Editor:** Aldo Fogaça; **Editor:** Admir Machado; **Editor:** Eduardo Santinon; **Editor:** Marcel Stefano; **Editor:** Adalberto Vieira (Pardal)
Language (s): Portuguese
DAILY NEWSPAPER

O Debate - Diário de Macaé
Editorial: Rua Benedito Peixoto, 90, Centro, Macaé 27916-040. **T:** 55 2221066060
E: odebate@odebateon.com.br
W: http://www.odebateon.com.br
Freq: Daily Not Audited
Editor in Chief: Wesley Radaveri
Editorial Profile: Note: This outlet has the same telephone and fax number. To send a fax, one must call and request that the telephone line be switched to a fax line.
Language (s): Portuguese
DAILY NEWSPAPER

Destak
Editorial: Av. Brg. Faria Lima, 2954, 3° Andar, Sao Paulo 01451-000. **T:** 55 11 3077-3600
E: pautadestak@gmail.com
W: http://www.destakjornal.com.br
Freq: Daily; **Circ:** 385000
Editor in Chief: Lúcia Boldrini
Language (s): Portuguese
DAILY NEWSPAPER

O Dia
Owner: Editora O Dia S.A.
Editorial: Rua do Riachuelo 359, 2° andar, Centro, Rio De Janeiro 20230-902.
T: 55 21 2222-8200
W: http://www.odia.com.br
Freq: Daily Not Audited
Editor: Alex Campos; **Editor:** Hélio Cícero; **Editor:** Léo Corrêa; **Editor:** Joana Costa; **City Editor:** João Erthal; **Editor in Chief:** Alexandre Freeland; **Editor:** Marcellus Leitão; **Editor:** Fernanda Portugal
Editorial Profile: O Dia covers local, regional, national and international news, as well as business, entertainment, lifestyle and sports.
Language (s): Portuguese
DAILY NEWSPAPER

O Diário
Editorial: Rua Américo Brasiliense, 140, Centro, Ribeirão Preto 14015-050.
T: 55 1639414414
E: diarioribeirao@netsite.com.br
Freq: Daily; **Circ:** 10000 Not Audited
Editor in Chief: Jubayr Ubyrantan Bispo
Editorial Profile: Note: This outlet has the same telephone and fax number. To send a fax, one must call and request that the telephone line be switched to a fax line.
Language (s): Portuguese
DAILY NEWSPAPER

Diário Catarinense
Owner: RBS Zero Hora Editora Jornalistica S.A.
Editorial: Rua Desembargador Pedro Silva 2958, Itaguaçu, Florianópolis 88080-701.
T: 55 48 3216-3502 **E:** redacao@diario.com.br
W: http://diariocatarinense.clicrbs.com.br/sc/
Freq: Daily; **Circ:** 38713 Not Audited
Editor: Viviane Araújo; **Editor:** Romi de Liz; **Editor:** Mariju Lima
Language (s): Portuguese
DAILY NEWSPAPER

Diário da Franca
Editorial: Rua dos Pracinhas, 345, Residencial Paraíso, Franca 14403-160
E: diario@diariodafranca.com.br
W: http://www.diariodafranca.com.br
Freq: Daily; **Circ:** 20000 Not Audited
Editor: Tania Barreto; **Editor in Chief:** René Moreira
Language (s): Portuguese
DAILY NEWSPAPER

Diário da Manhã
Editorial: Avenida Sete de Setembro, 509, Centro, Passo Fundo 99010-121.
T: 55 54 3316-4800
E: redacao@diariodamanha.net
W: http://www.diariodamanha.com
Freq: Daily; **Circ:** 10000 Not Audited
Editor in Chief: Rosangela Borges Wink
Language (s): Portuguese
DAILY NEWSPAPER

Diário da Manhã
Editorial: Avenida Presidente Vargas, 155, Centro, Erechim 99700-000.
T: 55 54 3522-2711
E: erechim@diariodamanha.net
W: http://www.diariodamanha.com/erechim
Freq: Daily; **Circ:** 33000 Not Audited
Editor in Chief: Ivanor Oliviecki
Language (s): Portuguese
DAILY NEWSPAPER

Diário da Manhã
Editorial: Av. Anhanguera, 2833, Setor Leste Universitário, Goiânia 74610-010.
T: 55 62 3267-1000 **E:** fale@dm.com.br
W: http://www.dm.com.br
Freq: Daily; **Circ:** 25000 Not Audited
Editor in Chief: Batista Custódio; **City Editor:** Jairo Menezes
Language (s): Portuguese
DAILY NEWSPAPER

Diário da Manhã
Editorial: Rua Pedro Vargas 846, Centro, Carazinho 99500-000. **T:** 55 54 3329-9666
E: redacao.carazinho@diariodamanha.net
W: http://www.diariodamanha.com
Freq: Daily; **Circ:** 22000 Not Audited
Editor in Chief: Sérgio Cornélio
Language (s): Portuguese
DAILY NEWSPAPER

Diário da Região
Editorial: Av. Feliciano Sales Cunha, 1515, Distrito Industrial, São José Do Rio Preto 15035. **T:** 55 17 2193-2081
E: redacao@diarioweb.com.br
W: http://www.diarioweb.com.br
Freq: Daily Not Audited
Editor in Chief: Fabricio Carareto
Language (s): Portuguese
DAILY NEWSPAPER

O Diário da Região
Editorial: Rua Ester Rombenso, 349, Centro, Osasco 06090-120. **T:** 55 11 3652-5244
E: webdiario@webdiario.com.br
W: http://www.webdiario.com.br
Freq: Daily; **Circ:** 25000 Not Audited
Editor In Chief: Simone Perez
Language (s): Portuguese
DAILY NEWSPAPER

Diário de Cuiabá
Owner: Diário de Cuiabá Ltda.
Editorial: Av. Beira Rio, 4435, Bairro Dom Aquino, Cuiabá 78025-190. **T:** 55 6536340280
E: redacao@diariodecuiaba.com.br
W: http://www.diariodecuiaba.com.br
Freq: Daily; **Circ:** 12000 Not Audited
Editor: Jonas Jozino; **Editor:** Noelma Oliveira
Language (s): Portuguese
DAILY NEWSPAPER

Diário de Marília
Editorial: Rua Coronel Galdino de Almeida, 55, Centro, Marília 17500-100.
T: 55 14 3402-5122
E: diario@diariodemarilia.com.br
W: http://www.diariodemarilia.com.br
Freq: Daily; **Circ:** 12000 Not Audited
Editor: Wellington Menon; **Editor in Chief:** José Ursílio
Language (s): Portuguese
DAILY NEWSPAPER

O Diário de Mogi
Editorial: Rua Dr. Ricardo Villela, 568, Centro, Mogi Das Cruzes 08710-150.
T: 55 11 3524-2400
E: diario@odiariodemogi.com.br
W: http://www.odiariodemogi.com.br
Freq: Daily; **Circ:** 15000 Not Audited
Editor in Chief: Spártaco Da San Biagio; **City Editor:** Eliane Jose; **Editor:** Gerson Lourenço; **Editor in Chief:** Darwin Valente
Language (s): Portuguese
DAILY NEWSPAPER

Diário de Pernambuco
Owner: Diários Associados
Editorial: Rua do Veiga, 600, Santo Amaro, Recife 50040-110. **T:** 55 81 2122-7666
W: http://www.pernambuco.com
Freq: Daily Not Audited
Editor: Cleide Galdino; **Editor:** Lúcia Guimarães; **Editor:** Ivana Moura; **Editor:** Adriana Reis; **Editor:** Tatiana Sotero
Language (s): Portuguese
DAILY NEWSPAPER

Diário de S. Paulo
Editorial: R. Rua Ricardo Cavatton, 251, Lapa de Baixo, Sao Paulo 05038-110.
T: 55 11 3279-8500
W: http://www.diariosp.com.br
Freq: Daily Not Audited
Editor in Chief: Nelson Nunes
Language (s): Portuguese
DAILY NEWSPAPER

Diário de Santa Bárbara
Editorial: Rua Paulo de Moraes, 190, Centro, Santa Bárbara D'oeste 13450-036.
T: 55 1934551062 **E:** diariosbo@dglnet.com.br
W: http://www.diariosbo.com.br
Freq: Daily; **Circ:** 11000 Not Audited
Editor in Chief: Maria de Camargo; **Editor:** Marcos Antônio de Oliveira
Language (s): Portuguese
DAILY NEWSPAPER

Diário de Santa Maria
Owner: RBS Zero Hora Editora Jornalistica S.A.
Editorial: Av. Maurício Sirotsky Sobrinho, 25, Patronato, Santa Maria 97020-440.
T: 55 55 3220-1700 **E:** leitor@diariosm.com.br
W: http://diariosm.com.br
Freq: Daily; **Circ:** 19000 Not Audited
Editor in Chief: Andreia Fontana
Language (s): Portuguese
DAILY NEWSPAPER

Diário de Sorocaba
Editorial: Rua da Penha, 609, Centro, Sorocaba 18010-900. **T:** 55 1532244123
E: reportagem@diariodesorocaba.com.br
W: http://www.diariodesorocaba.com.br
Freq: Daily; **Circ:** 25000 Not Audited
Editor in Chief: Cláudio Grosso
Language (s): Portuguese
DAILY NEWSPAPER

Diário de Taubaté
Editorial: Rua Engenheiro Fernando de Mattos, 23, Centro, Taubaté 12010-110.
T: 55 1236331527
E: redacao@diariotaubate.com.br
W: http://www.diariotaubate.com.br
Freq: Daily Not Audited
Editor in Chief: Gláucia Moraes
Language (s): Portuguese
DAILY NEWSPAPER

Diário do Aço
Editorial: Av Altina Gonçalves, 95, Iguaçu, Ipatinga 35160-016. **T:** 55 3138228998
E: jornalismo@diariodoaco.com.br
W: http://www.diariodoaco.com.br
Freq: Daily; **Circ:** 10800 Not Audited
Editor in Chief: João dos Reis
Language (s): Portuguese
DAILY NEWSPAPER

Diário do Alto Tietê
Editorial: Rua Carlos Lacerda, 21, Vila Nova Cintra, Sao Paulo. **T:** 55 11 4735-8000
E: redacao@jornaldat.com.br
W: http://www.jornaldat.com.br
Freq: Daily; **Circ:** 15000
Editor: Tiago Pantaleon
Editorial Profile: Offers local, regional, national and international news.
Language (s): Portuguese
DAILY NEWSPAPER

Diário do Amazonas
Editorial: Avenida Djalma Batista, 2010, Bairro Chapada, Manaus 69050-010.
T: 55 9236435060
E: redacao@diarioam.com.br
W: http://www.diarioam.com.br
Freq: Daily; **Circ:** 15000 Not Audited
Language (s): Portuguese
DAILY NEWSPAPER

Diário do Comércio
Owner: Diário do Comércio
Editorial: Rua Boa Vista, 51 - 6º andar, Centro, Sao Paulo 01014-911
E: editoracao@acsp.com.br
W: http://www.dcomercio.com.br
Freq: Daily; **Circ:** 12000 Not Audited
Editor in Chief: José Guilherme Rodrigues Ferreira
Editorial Profile: Covers local, regional, national and international news.
Language (s): Portuguese
DAILY NEWSPAPER

Diário do Comércio
Editorial: Av. Américo Vespúcio, 1660, Nova Esperança, Belo Horizonte 31230-250.
T: 55 31 3469-2011
E: redacao@diariodocomercio.com.br
Freq: Daily; **Circ:** 10000 Not Audited
Editor: Clério da Silva; **Editor:** Amaury de Pinho; **Editor in Chief:** Osires Fecci; **Editor:** Alexandre Horácio; **Editor:** Márcio Panzera
Language (s): Portuguese
DAILY NEWSPAPER

Diário do Comércio
Editorial: Rua Agenor Paes, 122, Centro, Uberlândia 38400-118. **T:** 55 34 3235-4163
E: contato@jornaldiariodocomercio.com.br
W: http://www.jornaldiariodocomercio.com.br
Freq: Daily Not Audited
Editor in Chief: José de Abreu
Language (s): Portuguese
DAILY NEWSPAPER

Diário do Grande ABC
Editorial: Rua Catequese, 562, Centro, Santo André 09090-900. **T:** 55 11 4435-8301
E: online@dgabc.com.br
W: http://www.dgabc.com.br Not Audited
Editor in Chief: Evaldo Novelini
Language (s): Portuguese
DAILY NEWSPAPER

Diário do Litoral
Editorial: Rua General Câmara, 254, Centro, Santos 11010-122. **T:** 55 1332262051
E: editor@diariodolitoral.com.br
W: http://www.diariodolitoral.com.br
Freq: Daily; **Circ:** 32000 Not Audited
Editor in Chief: Tatiane Casemiro
Language (s): Portuguese
DAILY NEWSPAPER

Diário do Litoral Norte
Editorial: Rua Luiz Barreto Barbosa, 359, Centro, Ilha Bela 11630-000.
T: 55 1238961720
E: diariodolitoralnorte@uol.com.br
W: http://www.oancoradouro.com.br
Freq: Daily Not Audited
Editor in Chief: Heloísa Franco
Editorial Profile: Note: This outlet has the same telephone and fax number. To send a fax, one must call and request that the telephone line be switched to a fax line.
Language (s): Portuguese
DAILY NEWSPAPER

Diário do Nordeste
Owner: Editora Verdes Mares Ltda.
Editorial: Praça da Imprensa, s/n, Dionísio Torres, Fortaleza 60135-690.
T: 55 85 3266-9773
W: http://www.diariodonordeste.com.br
Freq: Daily; **Circ:** 36573 Not Audited
Editor: Edgony Bezerra; **Cinema Crictic:** Pedro Martins Freire; **Editor:** Dellano Rios; **Editor in Chief:** Ildefonso Rodrigues
Language (s): Portuguese
DAILY NEWSPAPER

Diário do Noroeste
Editorial: Av. Paraná, 1100, Centro, Paranavaí 87705-190. **T:** 55 4434214050
E: paranavai@diariodonoroeste.com.br
W: http://www.diariodonoroeste.com.br
Freq: Daily; **Circ:** 10600 Not Audited
Editor in Chief: Valdinei Feitosa Dos Santos
Language (s): Portuguese
DAILY NEWSPAPER

O Diário do Norte do Paraná
Editorial: Av. Mauá, 1988, Vila Operária, Maringá 87050-020. **T:** 55 4432216055
E: redacao@odiariomaringa.com.br
W: http://www.odiariomaringa.com.br
Freq: Daily; **Circ:** 18500 Not Audited
Language (s): Portuguese
DAILY NEWSPAPER

Diário do Pará
Editorial: Avenida Almirante Barroso, 2190 - 1º andar, Marco, Belém 66095-000.
T: 55 91 3084-0100
W: http://www.diariodopara.com.br
Freq: Daily; **Circ:** 10000 Not Audited
City Editor: Claudia Aragao; **Editor:** Adaucto Couto; **Editor:** Camila Gaia; **City Editor:** Bernadeth Lameira; **City Editor:** Lazaro Magalhaes
Language (s): Portuguese
DAILY NEWSPAPER

Diário do Povo
Editorial: Rua Sete de Setembro, 189, Vila Industrial, Campinas 13035-350.
T: 55 1937728000
W: http://www.diariodopovo.com.br
Freq: Daily; **Circ:** 15000 Not Audited
Editor: Roselaine Fontana; **Editor in Chief:** Alayr Ruiz
Editorial Profile: <NAIAS> O Diário do Povo faz parte da Rede Anhangüera de

WORLD NEWS MEDIA

Comunicação. Sob administração da RAC, o Diário do Povo cresceu ainda mais, ganhando novo projeto gráfico e uma nova linha editorial que privilegia textos leves, concisos e completos. Seu exemplar tem preço de venda acessível, o que o coloca ao alcance de todas as classes sociais.
Language (s): Portuguese
DAILY NEWSPAPER

Diário do Rio Doce
Editorial: Rua Marechal Deodoro, 715, Centro, Governador Valadares 35010-280.
T: 55 3321012101 **E:** diario@drd.com.br
W: http://www.drd.com.br
Freq: Daily; **Circ:** 14000 Not Audited
Language (s): Portuguese
DAILY NEWSPAPER

Diário do Sudoeste
Editorial: Rua Caramuru, 1267, Centro, Pato Branco 85501-060. **T:** 55 46 32202066
E: redacao@diariodosudoeste.com.br
W: http://www.diariodosudoeste.com.br
Freq: Daily; **Circ:** 15000 Not Audited
Editor in Chief: Rosselani Giordani
Language (s): Portuguese
DAILY NEWSPAPER

Diário do Vale
Editorial: Rue 25A, 23 Vila Santa Cecilia, Volta Redonda 27260. **T:** 55 2433408500
E: redacao@diariodovale.com.br
W: http://www.diariodovale.com.br
Freq: Daily; **Circ:** 15000 Not Audited
Editor: Cláudio Alcântara; **Editor in Chief:** Sônia Paes
Editorial Profile: Note: This outlet has the same telephone and fax number. To send a fax, one must call and request that the telephone line be switched to a fax line.
Language (s): Portuguese
DAILY NEWSPAPER

Diário Gaúcho
Owner: RBS Zero Hora Editora Jornalistica S.A.
Editorial: Avenida Ipiranga 1075, Azenha, Porto Alegre 90160-093. **T:** 55 51 3218-1600
E: atendimento.dg@diariogaucho.com.br
W: http://www.diariogaucho.com.br
Freq: Daily; **Circ:** 162778 Not Audited
Careers Editor: Caren Baldo; **Editor:** Luiz Domingues; **Editor:** Roberto Jardim; **Editor:** Flávia Requião
Language (s): Portuguese
DAILY NEWSPAPER

Diário Popular
Editorial: Rua XV de Novembro, 718, Centro, Pelotas 96015-000. **T:** 55 53 3284-7000
E: diariopopular@diariopopular.com.br
W: http://www.diariopopular.com.br
Freq: Daily; **Circ:** 18000 Not Audited
Editor In Chief: Ivan Rodrigues
Editorial Profile: Covers local, regional, national and international news.
Language (s): Portuguese
DAILY NEWSPAPER

Empresas & Negócios
Owner: Jornal Empresas & Negócios Ltda
Editorial: Rua Boa Vista, 84, 9° andar cj. 909, Sao Paulo 01014-000. **T:** 55 11 3106-4171
W: http://www.jornalempresasenegocios.com.br
Freq: Daily
Editor: Laura Lobato De Baptisti
Language (s): Portuguese
DAILY NEWSPAPER

Estado de Minas
Owner: Diários Associados
Editorial: Avenida Getúlio Vargas, 291, Bairro Funcionários, Belo Horizonte 30112-020.
T: 55 31 3263-5000 **E:** jornalismo@uai.com.br
W: http://www.em.com.br
Freq: Daily; **Circ:** 90000 Not Audited
Editor: Paulo Eduardo de Queiroz; **Editor:** Ângela Márcia de Barros Faria; **Editor:** Boris Feldman; **Editor:** Pedro Lobato; **Editor in Chief:** João Bosco Salles; **Editor:** Ney Soares Filho
Language (s): Portuguese
DAILY NEWSPAPER

O Estado de São Paulo
Owner: Grupo Estado
Editorial: Av. Eng. Caetano Álvares 55, Sao Paulo 02598-900. **T:** 55 11 3856-2340
W: http://www.estadao.com.br
Freq: Daily; **Circ:** 170448 Not Audited
Editor: Roberto Basschera; **Editor:** Ubiratan Brasil; **Editor in Chief:** Cida Damasco; **Editor:** Ricardo Grinbaum; **Editor:** Roberto Lameirinhas; **Editor:** Cátia Luz; **Editor:** Cláudio Marques; **Editor:** Cristina Padiglione; **Editor:** Sônia Racy
Editorial Profile: Founded in 1875 and has the second largest circulation in the City of São Paulo. Provides regional, national and international news covering politics, economy, sports, culture, education and science.
Language (s): Portuguese
DAILY NEWSPAPER

O Estado do Maranhão
Editorial: Avenida Ana Jansen, 200, São Francisco, São Luís 65076-902.
T: 55 98 3215-5162
E: redacao@mirante.com.br
W: http://www.oestadoma.com.br
Freq: Daily; **Circ:** 20000 Not Audited
Editor: Ironara Martins
Language (s): Portuguese
DAILY NEWSPAPER

Expresso
Editorial: Rua Irineu Marinho, 70 - 4º andar, Cidade Nova, Rio De Janeiro 20230-901.
T: 55 21 2534-9751
W: http://www.infoglobo.com.br
Freq: Daily; **Circ:** 40430 Not Audited
Editor in Chief: Marco Antonio Rocha
Language (s): Portuguese
DAILY NEWSPAPER

Expresso Popular
Editorial: Rua João Pessoa, 129 - 10º andar, Centro, Santos 11013-900.
T: 55 13 2102-7000
E: expressopopular@expressopopular.com.br
Freq: Daily; **Circ:** 30000 Not Audited
Language (s): Portuguese
DAILY NEWSPAPER

Extra
Editorial: Rua Irineu Marinho, 70 - 4º andar, Cidade Nova, Rio De Janeiro 20230-901.
T: 55 21 2534-5900 **W:** http://extra.globo.com
Freq: Daily; **Circ:** 180296 Not Audited
Editor: Roberta Ferraz; **Editor:** Gilmar Ferreira; **Editor in Chief:** Octavio Guedes
Language (s): Portuguese
DAILY NEWSPAPER

O Fluminense
Editorial: Rua Visconde de Itaboraí, 184, Centro, Niterói 24035-900.
T: 55 21 2125-3057
E: reportagem@ofluminense.com.br
W: http://www.ofluminense.com.br
Freq: Daily; **Circ:** 35000 Not Audited
Editor in Chief: Sandra Duarte; **Editor:** Fabiana Maia
Language (s): Portuguese
DAILY NEWSPAPER

Folha da Manhã
Editorial: Rua Carlos de Lacerda, 75, Centro, Campos Dos Goytacazes 28013-030.
T: 55 2227268585 **E:** fmanha@fmanha.com.br
W: http://www.fmanha.com.br
Freq: Daily; **Circ:** 20000 Not Audited
Editor in Chief: Aluysio Barbosa; **Editor:** Dora Paula Paes
Editorial Profile: O Jornal Folha da Manhã circula nas seguintes cidades: Campos dos Goytacazes, Aperibé, Bom Jesus do Itabapoana, Cambuci, Cardoso Moreira, Carapebus, Casimiro de Abreu, Conceição de Macabu, Italva, Itaocara, Macaé, Miracema, Natividade, Porciúncula, Quissamã, Rio das Ostras, Santo Antônio de Pádua, São Fidélis, São Francisco do Itabapoana, São João da Barra e Varre-Sai.
Language (s): Portuguese
DAILY NEWSPAPER

Folha da Manhã
Editorial: Rua 2 de Novembro, 206, Centro, Passos 37900-128. **T:** 55 35 35292750
E: folha@folhadamanha.com.br
W: http://www.folhadamanha.com.br
Freq: Daily; **Circ:** 10000 Not Audited
Editor in Chief: Marcelo Renato Silva
Language (s): Portuguese
DAILY NEWSPAPER

Folha da Região
Editorial: Rua Joaquim Fernandes, 445, Jardim Nova Iorque, Araçatuba 16018-280.
T: 55 1836367774
E: redacao@folhadaregiao.com.br
W: http://www.folhadaregiao.com.br
Freq: Daily; **Circ:** 12800 Not Audited
Editor in Chief: Maria Antônio Dario
Editorial Profile: Note: This outlet has the same telephone and fax number. To send a fax, one must call and request that the telephone line be switched to a fax line.
Language (s): Portuguese
DAILY NEWSPAPER

Folha de Boa Vista
Editorial: Rua Lobo D'almada, 21, São Francisco, Boa Vista 69305-050.
T: 55 9536238806 **E:** fale@folhabv.com.br
W: http://www.folhabv.com.br
Freq: Daily Not Audited
Editor in Chief: Loide Gomes; **Editor in Chief:** Jessé Souza
Language (s): Portuguese
DAILY NEWSPAPER

Folha de Londrina
Editorial: Rua Piauí, 241, Centro, Londrina 86010-420. **T:** 55 43 3374-2020
E: editoria@folhadelondrina.com.br
W: http://www.folhadelondrina.com.br
Freq: Daily; **Circ:** 37000 Not Audited
Editor in Chief: Fernanda Mazzini; **City Editor:** Lucília Okamura
Language (s): Portuguese
DAILY NEWSPAPER

Folha de Pernambuco
Editorial: Avenida Marquês de Olinda, 105, Bairro do Recife Antigo, Recife 50030-000.
T: 55 81 3425-5877
E: redacao@folhape.com.br
W: http://www.folhape.com.br
Freq: Daily Not Audited
City Editor: Karina Maux; **Editor:** Cynthia Morato; **Editor in Chief:** Patrícia Raposo; **Editor:** Paulo Salgado
Language (s): Portuguese
DAILY NEWSPAPER

Folha de São Paulo
Owner: Folha da Manhã SA
Editorial: Alameda Barão de Limeiras, 425, 6º Andar, Campos Elíseos, Sao Paulo 01202-900.
T: 55 11 3224-4141
E: direcao.redacao@grupofolha.com.br
W: http://www.folha.uol.com.br
Freq: Daily; **Circ:** 293466 Not Audited
Editor at Large: Silvio Cioffi; **Editor at Large:** Erica Fraga; **Editor at Large:** Fernanda Mena; **Editor:** Letícia Sander
Editorial Profile: Founded in 1921 and covers local, regional, national and international news, as well as business, politics, economy, entertainment, science, technology, lifestyle and sports.
Language (s): Portuguese
DAILY NEWSPAPER

Folha do Estado
Editorial: Rua Professora Tereza Lobo, 319, Consil, Cuiabá 78048-670. **T:** 55 6533177700
E: redacao@folhadoestado.com.br
W: http://www.folhadoestado.com.br
Freq: Daily Not Audited
Editor in Chief: Marisa Batalha; **City Editor:** Patricia Neves; **Editor:** Janaina Pedrotti
Language (s): Portuguese
DAILY NEWSPAPER

Folha do Povo
Editorial: Rua Pedro Coutinho, 97, Jardim dos Estados, Campo Grande 79020-280.
T: 55 67 3213-0309
E: redacao@folhadopovo.com.br
W: http://www.folhadopovo.com.br
Freq: Daily; **Circ:** 12000 Not Audited
Editor in Chief: José Roberto Moura Alves
Language (s): Portuguese
DAILY NEWSPAPER

Folha Metropolitana
Editorial: Rua Ipê, 144, Jardim Guarulhos, Guarulhos 07090-130. **T:** 55 11 2475-7800
E: redacao@folhametro.com.br
Freq: Daily; **Circ:** 60000 Not Audited
Editor: Paulo Manso
Language (s): Portuguese
DAILY NEWSPAPER

A Gazeta
Owner: A Gazeta SA
Editorial: Rua Chafic Murad, 902, Ilha De Monte Belo, Vitoria 29050-901.
T: 55 27 3321-8526
W: http://gazetaonline.globo.com/jornalagazeta
Freq: Daily; **Circ:** 50000 Not Audited
Editor: Cíntia Bento Alves; **Editor:** Lúcia Helena Gonçalves; **Editor:** Zainer Rodrigues Silva; **Editor:** Leonel Ximenes
Editorial Profile: Offers local, regional, national and international news.
Language (s): Portuguese
DAILY NEWSPAPER

A Gazeta
Editorial: Rua Professora Tereza Lobo, 30, Bairro Concil, Cuiabá 78048-700.
T: 55 6536126000
E: red.jornal@gazetadigital.com.br
W: http://www.gazetadigital.com.br
Freq: Daily; **Circ:** 16000 Not Audited
Editor in Chief: Margareth Botelho; **Editor:** Oliveira Júnior
Language (s): Portuguese
DAILY NEWSPAPER

Gazeta de Alagoas
Editorial: Rua Saladanha da Gama, Farol, Maceió 57051-020. **T:** 55 82 4009-7748
E: gazeta@gazetaweb.com
W: http://www.gazetaweb.com
Freq: Daily; **Circ:** 18000 Not Audited
Editor: Fernando Coelho; **Editor in Chief:** Célio Gomes; **Editor:** Enio Lins
Language (s): Portuguese
DAILY NEWSPAPER

Gazeta de Limeira
Editorial: Rua Senador Vergueiro, 319, Centro, Limeira 13480-000. **T:** 55 19 3404-3700
E: gazeta@gazetadelimeira.com.br
W: http://www.gazetadelimeira.com.br
Freq: Daily; **Circ:** 15000 Not Audited
Editor: José Antônio Encinas; **Editor:** Fabiana Lucato; **Editor in Chief:** Roberto Lucato
Editorial Profile: Note: This outlet has the same telephone and fax number. To send a fax, one must call and request that the telephone line be switched to a fax line.
Language (s): Portuguese
DAILY NEWSPAPER

Gazeta de Varginha
Editorial: Av. dos Imigrantes, 445, Santa Maria, Varginha 37022-560.
T: 55 35 3221-4668
E: gazetavga@varginha.com.br
W: http://www.gazetadevarginha.blogspot.com
Freq: Daily; **Circ:** 15000 Not Audited
Editor: Rodrigo Fernandes; **Editor in Chief:** Ana Maria Silva Piva
Language (s): Portuguese
DAILY NEWSPAPER

Gazeta do Paraná
Editorial: Rua Fortunato Bebber, 868, Cascavel 85808-390. **T:** 55 4532182500
E: geral@gazetadoparana.com.br
W: http://www.gazetadoparana.com.br
Freq: Daily; **Circ:** 25000 Not Audited
Editor in Chief: Paulo Alexandre De Oliveira
Language (s): Portuguese
DAILY NEWSPAPER

Gazeta do Povo
Editorial: Rua Pedro Ivo, 459, Centro, Curitiba 80010-020. **T:** 55 41 3321-5000
E: redacao@gazetadopovo.com.br
W: http://www.gazetadopovo.com.br
Freq: Daily; **Circ:** 100000 Not Audited
Editor: Keyse Caldeira; **Editor:** Deise Campos; **Editor:** José Carlos Fernandes; **Editor in Chief:** Sandra Gonçalves; **Editor:** Célio Martins
Language (s): Portuguese
DAILY NEWSPAPER

Gazeta do Sul
Owner: Gazeta Grupo de Comunicações
Editorial: Rua Ramiro Barcelos, 1206, Santa Cruz Do Sul 96901-900. **T:** 55 51 3715-7800
E: redacao@gazetadosul.com.br
W: http://www.gazetadosul.com.br
Freq: Daily; **Circ:** 18000 Not Audited
Editor in Chief: Maria Roselaine Romero
Language (s): Portuguese
DAILY NEWSPAPER

Gazeta Mundial
Editorial: Rua Largo São Vicente de Paulo, 133, Ed. ACIT - Salas 61, 65 e 80, Toledo 85900215. **T:** 55 4530557070
E: editora@gazetamundial.com.br
W: http://www.gazetamundial.com.br
Freq: Daily Not Audited
Editor in Chief: Selma Becker
Language (s): Portuguese
DAILY NEWSPAPER

O Globo
Editorial: Rua Irineu Marinho, 35, Cidade Nova, Rio De Janeiro 20230-901.
T: 55 21 2534-5000 **E:** ccr@oglobo.com.br
W: http://oglobo.globo.com
Freq: Daily; **Circ:** 259347 Not Audited
Editorial Profile: Launched in 1925 and offers local, national and international news in Brazil.
Language (s): Portuguese
DAILY NEWSPAPER

Hoje em Dia
Editorial: Rua Padre Rolim, 652, Santa Efigênia, Belo Horizonte 30130-090.
T: 55 31 3236-8000
W: http://www.hojeemdia.com.br
Freq: Daily Not Audited
Editor: Paulo Leonardo de Carvalho; **Editor in Chief:** Pérsio Fantin; **Editor:** Roberto

Mendonça; **Editor:** Ruy José Pales; **Editor:** Leida Reis
Language (s): Portuguese
DAILY NEWSPAPER

Hora de Santa Catarina
Editorial: Avenida Desembargador Pedro Silva, 2958, Itaguaçú, Florianópolis 88080-701.
T: 55 48 3216-3970
E: redacao@horasc.com.br
W: http://horadesantacatarina.clicrbs.com.br/sc/ **Circ:** 28398 Not Audited
Editor in Chief: Sergio Negrão
Editorial Profile: Daily newspaper of Santa Catarina state, in the southern region of Brazil.
Language (s): Portuguese
DAILY NEWSPAPER

O Imparcial
Owner: Empresa Pacotilha Ltda.
Editorial: Rua Assis Chateaubriand, S/N, Renascença II, #NAME? 65075-670.
T: 55 98 3212 2000
E: redacao@pacotilha.com.br
W: http://www.oimparcial.com.br
Freq: Daily Not Audited
Editor in Chief: Marco Aurélio Oliveira; **Editor:** José Ribamar Praseres
Language (s): Portuguese
DAILY NEWSPAPER

O Imparcial
Editorial: Rua Ernesto Rotta, 83, Jardim Novo Bongiovani, Presidente Prudente 19026-900.
T: 55 18 2104-3737
E: redacao@oimparcial.com.br
W: http://www.oimparcial.com.br
Freq: Daily; **Circ:** 12000 Not Audited
Editor in Chief: Adelmo Santos Rei Vanalli
Language (s): Portuguese
DAILY NEWSPAPER

Imprensa Oficial de Minas Gerais
Owner: Governo de Minas Gerais
Editorial: Avenida Augusto de Lima, 270, Centro, Belo Horizonte 30190-001.
T: 55 3132373453 **E:** libertas@iof.mg.gov.br
W: http://www.iof.mg.gov.br
Freq: Daily; **Circ:** 40000 Not Audited
Editor: Afonso de Oliveira
Editorial Profile: Minas Gerais é um jornal de caráter oficial para divulgação de atos do governo, decretos e regulamentos que devam ter execução no Estado, compreendendo os cadernos: O Noticiário Diário do Executivo Diário do Legislativo Diário do Judiciário Publicação de Terceiros
Language (s): Portuguese
DAILY NEWSPAPER

Indústria & Comércio
Editorial: Rua Imaculada Conceição, 205, Rebouças, Curitiba 80215-030.
T: 55 4133339800 **E:** pauta@induscom.com.br
W: http://induscom.com.br
Freq: Daily; **Circ:** 10000 Not Audited
Editor in Chief: Eliseu Tisato
Language (s): Portuguese
DAILY NEWSPAPER

The International New York Times - Rio De Janeiro
Editorial: Rua Visconde de Pirajá, 550 - sala 2012, Ipanema, Rio De Janeiro 22410-002.
T: 55 2125128686 **Circ:** 1133763 Not Audited
Bureau Chief: Simon Romero
DAILY NEWSPAPER

Jornal Bom Dia
Editorial: Av. Santo dal Bosco, 97, Erechim 99700-000. **T:** 55 54 3520-8500
E: jornalismo@jornalbomdia.com.br
W: http://www.jornalbomdia.com.br
Circ: 16900
Editorial Profile: Traz informações e notícias de interesse aos habitantes de Erechim e regiões próximas. Provides news for the residents of Erechim and surrounding areas.
Language (s): Portuguese
DAILY NEWSPAPER

Jornal Cidade de Rio Claro
Editorial: Av. Cinco, 283, Centro, Rio Claro 13500-380. **T:** 55 1935261000
E: redacaojc@uol.com.br
W: http://www.journalcidade.net
Freq: Daily; **Circ:** 10000 Not Audited
Editor in Chief: Ludimar Gonzalez
Editorial Profile: O Jornal Cidade é expressão viva da imprensa moderna, dinâmica e completa. Pesquisas de mercado revelam a satisfação dos anunciantes pelo retorno garantido a partir de suas veiculações publicitárias. Pioneirismos são as grandes marcas do JC. Sempre presente aos eventos de estímulo ao desenvolvimento empresarial, o JC mantém dinâmica parceria junto a destacadas promoções, como Feira das Noivas, Feira Anual do Comércio e Indústria de Rio Claro (Facirc), ciclo de palestras do grupo empresarial Opção, jogos esportivos do Sesi, serviço de divulgação da Associação dos Corretores de Imóveis de Rio Claro, bem como da rede de supermercados do município.
Language (s): Portuguese
DAILY NEWSPAPER

Jornal Coletivo
Editorial: SIG Quadra 2, Lote 570/590, Brasilia 70610-420. **T:** 55 61 3441-0212
E: redacao@grupocomunidade.com.br
W: http://www.jornalcoletivo.com.br
Freq: Daily; **Circ:** 90000 Not Audited
Editor in Chief: Ricardo Callado
Language (s): Portuguese
DAILY NEWSPAPER

Jornal da Cidade
Editorial: Rua Xingú, 4-44, Higienópolis, Bauru 17013-510. **T:** 55 14 3104-3104
E: jc@jcnet.com.br
W: http://www.jcnet.com.br
Freq: Daily; **Circ:** 28000 Not Audited
Editor: Eliane Barbosa; **Editor:** Giselle Hilário
Language (s): Portuguese
DAILY NEWSPAPER

Jornal da Cidade
Editorial: Avenida Antônio Cabral, 1069, Bairro Industrial, Aracaju 49065-090.
T: 55 79 3226-4800
E: redacao@jornaldacidade.net
W: http://www.jornaldacidade.net
Freq: Daily; **Circ:** 20000 Not Audited
Editor: Dilson Ramos; **Editor In Chief:** Acácia Trindade
Language (s): Portuguese
DAILY NEWSPAPER

Jornal da Manhã
Editorial: Avenida Dr. Fidélis Reis, 820, Bairro Boa Vista, Uberaba 38010-030.
T: 55 34 3331-7900
E: jmonline@jmonline.com.br
W: http://www.jmonline.com.br
Freq: Daily; **Circ:** 15000 Not Audited
Editor in Chief: Marcio Gennari; **Editor:** Marilo Teixeira
Language (s): Portuguese
DAILY NEWSPAPER

Jornal da Manhã
Editorial: Rua 15 de Novembro, 883, Centro, Marília 17500-050. **T:** 55 1433115400
E: jmanha@terra.com.br
W: http://www.jornaldamanhamarizia.com.br
Freq: Daily; **Circ:** 18000 Not Audited
Editor in Chief: Jocelin de Oliveira
Language (s): Portuguese
DAILY NEWSPAPER

Jornal da Mantiqueira
Editorial: Av. João Pinheiro, 177, Centro, Poços De Caldas 37701-387.
T: 55 3537290007
E: redacao@mantiqueira.inf.br
W: http://www.mantiqueira.inf.br
Freq: Daily Not Audited
Editor in Chief: Rui Alves
Editorial Profile: Note: This outlet has the same telephone and fax number. To send a fax, one must call and request that the telephone line be switched to a fax line.
Language (s): Portuguese
DAILY NEWSPAPER

Jornal da Paraíba
Owner: Jornal da Paraíba Ltda.
Editorial: Rua Monsenhor Walfredo Leal 258, Tambia, João Pessoa 58020-540.
T: 55 83 2106 1800
E: jornalismo@jornaldaparaiba.com.br
W: http://www.jornaldaparaiba.com.br
Freq: Daily; **Circ:** 10000 Not Audited
City Editor: Andréa Alves
Language (s): Portuguese
DAILY NEWSPAPER

Jornal de Brasília
Editorial: SIG, Trecho 1, Lotes 585/645, Brasilia 70610-400. **T:** 55 61 3343-8070
E: redacao@jornaldebrasilia.com.br
W: http://www.jornaldebrasilia.com.br
Freq: Daily Not Audited
City Editor: Nelza Cristina; **Editor in Chief:** Paulo Gusmão
Editorial Profile: Offers local, regional, national and international news.
Language (s): Portuguese
DAILY NEWSPAPER

Jornal de Jundiaí
Editorial: Rua Baronesa de Japi, 53, Centro, Jundiaí 13207-000. **T:** 55 1121366070
E: redacao@jj.com.br
W: http://www.portaljj.com.br
Freq: Daily Not Audited
Editor: Luciana Alves; **Editor:** Isabel Bueno; **Editor:** Sandra Marques; **Editor in Chief:** Sidney Mazzoni
Language (s): Portuguese
DAILY NEWSPAPER

Jornal de Limeira
Editorial: Av. Comendador Agostinho Prada, 2651, Jardim Florença, Limeira 13480-220.
T: 55 19 34045050
E: redacao@jornaldelimeira.com.br
W: http://www.jornaldelimeira.com.br
Freq: Daily; **Circ:** 14000 Not Audited
Editor in Chief: Carlos Chinellato
Editorial Profile: Note: This outlet has the same telephone and fax number. To send a fax, one must call and request that the telephone line be switched to a fax line.
Language (s): Portuguese
DAILY NEWSPAPER

Jornal de Piracicaba
Editorial: Avenida Comendador Luciano Guidotti, 2525, Jardim Pacaembu, Piracicaba 13424-589. **T:** 55 19 3428-4170
E: jp@jpjornal.com.br
W: http://www.jornaldepiracicaba.com.br
Freq: Daily; **Circ:** 25000 Not Audited
Editor: Simone Cândido; **Editor:** Eleni Destro; **Editor:** Ude Valetim
Language (s): Portuguese
DAILY NEWSPAPER

Jornal de Santa Catarina
Owner: RBS Zero Hora Editora Jornalistica S.A.
Editorial: Rua Bahia 2291, Salto, Blumenau 89031-002. **T:** 55 47 3221-1555
W: http://www.santa.com.br
Freq: Daily; **Circ:** 14798 Not Audited
Editor in Chief: Edgar Gonçalves
Editorial Profile: Covers local, regional, national and international news.
Language (s): Portuguese
DAILY NEWSPAPER

Jornal de Uberaba
Editorial: Avenida Leopoldino de Oliveira, 2265, Centro, Uberaba 38015-000.
T: 55 3433184433 **E:** jjura@terra.com.br
W: http://www.jornaldeuberaba.com.br
Freq: Daily; **Circ:** 12000 Not Audited
Editor in Chief: Walter Farnezi
Editorial Profile: Note: This outlet has the same telephone and fax number. To send a fax, one must call and request that the telephone line be switched to a fax line. O Jornal de Uberaba oferece aos leitores toda informação sobre os acontecimentos políticos, sociais, econômicos, esportivos, classificados e serviços de utilidade pública da região.
Language (s): Portuguese
DAILY NEWSPAPER

Jornal do Comércio
Editorial: Avenida João Pessoa, 1282, Cidade Baixa, Porto Alegre 90040-001.
T: 55 51 3213-1300
E: redacao@jornaldocomercio.com.br
W: http://jcrs.uol.com.br/site/
Freq: Mon thru Fri Not Audited
Editor in Chief: Pedro Maciel; **Editor:** Paula Sória
Editorial Profile: Jornal do Comércio is a daily newspaper and covers local, regional, national and international news, as well as business, entertainment, lifestyle and sports.
Language (s): Portuguese
DAILY NEWSPAPER

Jornal do Commercio
Owner: Grafica Editora Jornal do Commercio S/A
Editorial: Rua do Livramento, 189, Saúde, Rio De Janeiro 20221-191. **T:** 55 21 2223-8500
E: jornaldocommercio@jcom.com.br
W: http://www.jornaldocommercio.com.br
Freq: Daily; **Circ:** 52480 Not Audited
Editor: Luís Edmundo Araújo; **Editor:** Vinicius Medeiros; **Editor:** Rodrigo Moreira
Editorial Profile: Offers local, national and international news.
Language (s): Portuguese
DAILY NEWSPAPER

Jornal do Commercio
Editorial: Avenida Tefé, 3025, Japiim, Manaus 69078-000. **T:** 55 9221015500
E: redacao@jcam.com.br
W: http://www.jcam.com.br
Freq: Daily; **Circ:** 11500 Not Audited
Editor: Lilian Araújo
Language (s): Portuguese
DAILY NEWSPAPER

Jornal do Commercio
Editorial: Rua da Fundição, 257, Santo Amaro, Recife 50040-100. **T:** 55 81 3413-6178
W: http://www.jc.com.br
Freq: Daily; **Circ:** 39145 Not Audited
Editor: Fabiane Cavalcanti; **Editor:** Ciro Carlos Rocha; **Editor:** Otávio Toscano
Editorial Profile: Offers local, regional, national and international news.
Language (s): Portuguese
DAILY NEWSPAPER

Jornal do Dia
Editorial: Rua Mato Grosso, 296, Tacoval, Macapá 68908-350. **T:** 55 96 3217-1117
E: jornaldodia1@uol.com.br
W: http://www.jdia.com.br
Freq: Daily; **Circ:** 10000 Not Audited
Editor in Chief: Janderson Cantanhede; **Editor:** Marcele Correa
Language (s): Portuguese
DAILY NEWSPAPER

Jornal do Estado
Editorial: Rua Roberto Barrozo, 22, Centro Cívico, Curitiba 80530-120.
T: 55 41 3350-6600
E: je@jornaldoestado.com.br
W: http://www.jornaldoestado.com.br
Freq: Daily; **Circ:** 10000 Not Audited
City Editor: Mario Akira Hisatomi; **Editor in Chief:** Josianne Ritz
Language (s): Portuguese
DAILY NEWSPAPER

Jornal Hora H
Editorial: Rua Alexander Gama Correia, 37, Rancho Novo, Nova Iguaçu 26013-190.
T: 55 2126955360 **E:** editoriahorah@ig.com.br
W: http://www.jornalhorah.com.br
Freq: Daily; **Circ:** 20000 Not Audited
Editor in Chief: Hélio Sampaio
Editorial Profile: Note: This outlet has the same telephone and fax number. To send a fax, one must call and request that the telephone line be switched to a fax line.
Language (s): Portuguese
DAILY NEWSPAPER

Jornal NH
Editorial: Rua Jornal NH, 99, Bairro Ideal, Novo Hamburgo 93334-350.
T: 55 51 3065-4000
E: redacaonh@gruposinos.com.br
W: http://www.jornalnh.com.br
Freq: Daily; **Circ:** 45248 Not Audited
Editor in Chief: Sérgio Pereira
Language (s): Portuguese
DAILY NEWSPAPER

Jornal VS (Vale dos Sinos)
Editorial: Av. João Corrêa, 1017, Centro, São Leopoldo 93020-690. **T:** 55 5135912000
E: redacaovs@gruposinos.com.br
W: http://www.jornalvs.com.br
Freq: Daily; **Circ:** 17405 Not Audited
Editor in Chief: Guilherme Schmidt
Language (s): Portuguese
DAILY NEWSPAPER

Lance!
Editorial: Rua Santa Maria, 47, Cidade Nova, Rio De Janeiro 20211-210.
T: 55 21 3528-5200
E: redacao-rj@lancenet.com.br
W: http://www.lancenet.com.br
Freq: Daily; **Circ:** 47790 Not Audited
Editor in Chief: Luiz Fernando Gomes
Language (s): Portuguese
DAILY NEWSPAPER

O Liberal
Editorial: Avenida 25 de Setembro, 2473, Marco, Belèm 66093-000. **T:** 55 91 3216-1138
E: redacao@orm.com.br
W: http://www.orm.com.br/projetos/oliberal/
Freq: Daily; **Circ:** 40000 Not Audited
Day Editor: Normélia Bastos; **Editor:** Paulo Bemerguy; **Editor:** Orlando Cardoso; **Editor in Chief:** Walmir D' Oliveira; **Editor:** Cary John; **Editor:** Myrian Magalhães; **Editor:** José Menezes; **Editor:** Lázaro Moraes; **Editor:** Raimundo Souza
Editorial Profile: Offers local, national and international news.
Language (s): Portuguese
DAILY NEWSPAPER

O Liberal
Editorial: Rua Tamoio, 875, Vila Santa Catarina, Americana 13466-250.
T: 55 1934710300 **E:** redacao@liberal.com.br

W: http://www.oliberalnet.com.br
Freq: Daily; **Circ:** 15000 Not Audited
Editor: Diógenes Gobbo
Editorial Profile: O Jornal O Liberal é publicado pela Empresa Editora O Liberal Ltda., circula em Americana, Santa Bárbara d'Oeste, Nova Odessa e Sumaré.
Language (s): Portuguese
DAILY NEWSPAPER

Meia Hora
Editorial: Rua do Riachuelo, 359 - 2º andar, Centro, Rio De Janeiro 20235-902.
T: 55 21 2222-8000 **E:** povo@meiahora.com
W: http://www.meiahora.ig.com.br
Freq: Daily; **Circ:** 120000 Not Audited
Editor in Chief: Humberto Tziolas
Language (s): Portuguese
DAILY NEWSPAPER

Meio Norte
Editorial: Rua Professor Alceu Brandão, 2750, Monte Castelo, Teresina 64016-150.
T: 55 86 21073070
E: meionorte@meionorte.com
W: http://www.meionorte.com
Freq: Daily Not Audited
Editor: Tatiara de França
Editorial Profile: Meio Norte is a daily newspaper and covers local, regional, national and international news, as well as business, entertainment, lifestyle and sports. The paper was founded in 1995.
Language (s): Portuguese
DAILY NEWSPAPER

Metro ABC
Owner: Metro Jornal S/A
Editorial: Rua Tabapuã, 81, Itaim, Sao Paulo 04533-010. **T:** 55 11 3528-8500
E: leitor.abc@metrojornal.com.br
W: http://www.readmetro.com/en/brazil/metro-abc
Freq: Mon thru Fri; **Circ:** 30000
Editorial Profile: Regional edition for Metro Jornal focusing on the ABC area in Sao Paulo. Provides news and information on sports, politics, arts, culture and entertainment.
Language (s): Portuguese
DAILY NEWSPAPER

Metrô News
Editorial: Rua Ipê, 144, Centro, Guarulhos 07090-130. **T:** 55 11 2475-7800
E: redacao@folhametro.com.br
W: http://www.metronews.com.br
Freq: Daily; **Circ:** 15000 Not Audited
Editor: Wilson Cardoza de Sa; **Editor:** Roberto Iizuka
Language (s): Portuguese
DAILY NEWSPAPER

Metro Rio de Janeiro
Owner: Metro Jornal S/A
Editorial: Rua Álvaro Ramos, 350, Botafogo, Rio De Janeiro 22280-110.
T: 55 21 2586-9570
E: leitor.rj@metrojornal.com.br
W: http://www.readmetro.com/en/brazil/metro-rio/
Freq: Mon thru Fri; **Circ:** 105530
Editorial Profile: Regional edition for Metro Jornal. Provides news and information on sports, politics, arts, culture and entertainment.
Language (s): Portuguese
DAILY NEWSPAPER

Metro São Paulo
Owner: Metro Jornal S/A
Editorial: Rua Tabapuã, 81, Itaim, Sao Paulo 04533-010. **T:** 55 11 3528-8500
E: leitor.sp@metrojornal.com.br
W: http://www.readmetro.com/en/brazil/metro-sao-paulo
Freq: Mon thru Fri; **Circ:** 151956
Editorial Profile: Regional edition for Metro Jornal for Sao Paulo city. Provides news and information on sports, politics, arts, culture and entertainment.
Language (s): Portuguese
DAILY NEWSPAPER

Mogi News
Editorial: Rua Carlos Lacerda, 21, Vilanova Cintra, Mogi Das Cruzes 08745-200.
T: 55 1147358000
E: moginews@moginews.com.br
W: http://www.moginews.com.br
Freq: Daily; **Circ:** 13000 Not Audited
Editor: Vides Junior; **Editor:** Gisleine Zarbietti
Editorial Profile: Com o Jornal Mogi News você terá diariamente notícias completas sobre a situação ecocômica, política, cultural e esportiva da sua cidade e do resto do mundo. Além de espaço dedicado a lazer informática, educação, saúde e serviços médicos, veículo e transporte, decoração, construção e reforma, imóveis, classificados e muito mais.
Language (s): Portuguese
DAILY NEWSPAPER

Monitor Mercantil
Editorial: Rua Marcílio Dias, 26, Centro, Rio De Janeiro 20221-280. **T:** 55 21 25184343
E: redacao@monitormercantil.com.br
W: http://www.monitormercantil.com.br
Freq: Daily; **Circ:** 26000 Not Audited
Editor in Chief: Marcos de Oliveira; **Editor:** Lauro Freitas
Editorial Profile: O Jornal MONITOR MERCANTIL tem distribuição nacional e presença marcante nos mercados de capitais, de seguros e financeiro. Como reconhecimento, recebeu por três vezes o Prêmio ABAMEC- Rio (Associação Brasileira dos Analistas do Mercado de Capitais), na categoria Imprensa e Comunicação, como melhor veículo especializado na opinião dos analistas de mercado, e melhor Profissional de Imprensa. Recebeu um prêmio da Abamec-Nordeste, também como melhor veículo. Em 2002, recebeu o Prêmio Cobertura de Seguros - Melhor Veículo, feito repetido em 2003. Ainda em 2002, um novo passo: a publicação do MONITOR MERCANTIL SÃO PAULO.
Language (s): Portuguese
DAILY NEWSPAPER

Monitor Mercantil São Paulo
Owner: Grupo Monitor Mercantil S/A
Editorial: Avenida São Gabriel 149 sala 902, Itaim, Sao Paulo 01435-001.
T: 55 11 3165 6192
E: monitor.interpress@hipernetelecom.com.br
W: http://www.monitormercantil.com.br
Freq: Daily Not Audited
Editor in Chief: Ana Borges
Language (s): Portuguese
DAILY NEWSPAPER

O Nacional
Editorial: Rua Silva Jardim, 325 A, Bairro Annes, Passo Fundo 99010-240.
T: 55 5430456266
E: onacional@onacional.com.br
W: http://www.onacional.com.br
Freq: Daily
Editor in Chief: Zumara Colussi
Editorial Profile: O Nacional foi fundado no dia 19 de junho do ano de 1925 pelos Srs. Dr. Herculano A. Annes, Theofilo Guimarães, Americano Araujo Bastos e Hiran Araujo Bastos. Mais tarde foi adquirido por Mucio de Castro, jornalista e ex-Deputado Estadual. Registrar a história, fomentar a intelectualidade de sua gente, abrir espaços para idéias, produzir material literário: assim vem sendo o Jornal O Nacional ao longo destes 77 anos. O Nacional mantém um vínculo permanente com a comunidade de Passo Fundo e região. Não apenas divulgando os fatos, mas também assumindo bandeiras levantadas pelo interesse da própria sociedade. A participação em movimentos de interesse comunitário tiveram nestes anos um engajamento quase compulsório. Foram situações como, por exemplo, a da luta pela formação de uma universidade regional, que é hoje a UPF. Hoje, sob direção de Múcio de Castro Filho, O Nacional permanece ao lado dos interesses maiores da comunidade.
Language (s): Portuguese
DAILY NEWSPAPER

A Notícia
Owner: Grupo RBS
Editorial: Rua Caçador, 112, Atiradores, Joinville 89203-610. **T:** 55 47 3419-2100
E: leitor@an.com.br **W:** http://www.an.com.br
Freq: Daily Not Audited
Editor: Marina Andrade; **Editor in Chief:** Domingos Aquino; **Editor:** Edenilson de Jesus; **News Editor:** Raquel Schiavini
Editorial Profile: Offers local, regional, national and international news.
Language (s): Portuguese
DAILY NEWSPAPER

Notícia Agora
Editorial: Rua Chafic Murad, 902, Ilha de Monte Belo, Vitoria 29050-901.
T: 55 2733218538
E: pautana@redegazeta.com.br
W: http://gazetaonline.com.br **Circ:** 28000 Not Audited
Editor: Ana Carolina Passos; **Editor:** Angela Tejo; **Editor:** Fernanda Zóboli Dalmácio
Language (s): Portuguese
DAILY NEWSPAPER

Oeste Notícias
Editorial: Rua Kametaro Morishita, 95, Cidade Universitária, Presidente Prudente 19050-700.
T: 55 1832290304
E: jornalismo@oestenoticias.com.br
W: http://www.oestenoticias.com.br
Freq: Daily; **Circ:** 12000 Not Audited
Editor in Chief: Cristiano Oliveira
Language (s): Portuguese
DAILY NEWSPAPER

O Paraná
Editorial: Rua Pernambuco, 1600, Centro, Cascavel 85810-021. **T:** 55 4533211000
E: oparana@oparana.com.br
W: http://www.oparana.com.br
Freq: Daily; **Circ:** 18000 Not Audited
Editor in Chief: Antônio Sbadeloto
Language (s): Portuguese
DAILY NEWSPAPER

Pioneiro
Owner: RBS Zero Hora Editora Jornalistica S.A.
Editorial: Rua Jacob Luchesi, 2374, Santa Catarina, Caxias Do Sul 95030-000.
T: 55 54 3218-1200 **E:** redacao@pioneiro.com
W: http://pioneiro.clicrbs.com.br
Freq: Daily Not Audited
Editor: Fábio da Câmara; **Editor in Chief:** Roberto Nielsen
Language (s): Portuguese
DAILY NEWSPAPER

O Popular
Editorial: Rua Thomas Edison - Quadra 7, Setor Serrinha, Goiânia 74835-130.
T: 55 62 3250-1471
W: http://www.opopular.com.br
Freq: Daily; **Circ:** 38000 Not Audited
Editor: Karla Morais
Language (s): Portuguese
DAILY NEWSPAPER

O Povo
Owner: O Povo
Editorial: Av. Aguanambi, 282, Joaquim Távora, Fortaleza 60055-402.
T: 55 85 3255-6101
E: centralderelacionamento@opovo.com.br
W: http://www.opovo.com.br
Freq: Daily Not Audited
Editor in Chief: Erick Guimarães
Language (s): Portuguese
DAILY NEWSPAPER

Povo do Rio
Editorial: Rua Washington Luis, 54, Centro, Rio De Janeiro 20230-025. **T:** 55 21 25092772
E: povodorio@gmail.com
W: http://www.jornalpovo.com
Freq: Daily
Editor in Chief: Renata Onaindia
Editorial Profile: Covers local, regional, national and international news, as well as business, entertainment, lifestyle and sports.
Language (s): Portuguese
DAILY NEWSPAPER

O Progresso
Editorial: Avenida Presidente Vargas, 447, Centro, Dourados 79804-030.
T: 55 6734162600
E: progresso@progresso.com.br
W: http://www.progresso.com.br
Freq: Daily; **Circ:** 15000 Not Audited
Editor in Chief: Vander Verão
Language (s): Portuguese
DAILY NEWSPAPER

A Razão
Editorial: Rua Serafim Valandro, 1284, Centro, Santa Maria 97015-630. **T:** 55 5532202100
E: redacao@arazao.com.br
W: http://www.arazao.com.br
Freq: Daily; **Circ:** 20000 Not Audited
Editor in Chief: José Mauro Batista
Editorial Profile: O jornal A Razão de Santa Maria é um tradicional veículos de comunicação do interior do Rio Grande do Sul. Atinge hoje mais de 40 municípios da região central e fronteira oeste do Rio Grande do Sul, além de cidades importantes como Porto Alegre.
Language (s): Portuguese
DAILY NEWSPAPER

O Rio Branco
Editorial: Avenida Ceará, 2804, Ed. Cristiano M.de Assis - Centro, Rio Branco 69900-460.
T: 55 6833021313
E: redacao@oriobranco.com.br
W: http://www.oriobranco.com.br
Freq: Daily Not Audited
Editor in Chief: Cesar Negreiros
Language (s): Portuguese
DAILY NEWSPAPER

O São Gonçalo
Editorial: Rua Yolanda Saad Abuzaid, 150 - Grupo 917, Alcântara, São Gonçalo 24440-440. **T:** 55 21 26017272
E: redacao@jornalsg.com.br
W: http://www.osaogoncalo.com.br
Freq: Daily; **Circ:** 15000 Not Audited
Editor in Chief: Ari Lopes
Editorial Profile: Covers local, regional, national and international news, as well as business, entertainment, lifestyle and sports.
Language (s): Portuguese
DAILY NEWSPAPER

O Sul
Editorial: Rua Orfanatrófio, 711, Alto Teresópolis, Porto Alegre 90840-440.
T: 55 51 3218-2525 **E:** osul@osul.com.br
W: http://www.redepampa.com.br
Freq: Daily Not Audited
Editor: Cristiane Appen; **Editor:** César Bresolin; **Editor:** Fabíola Brites; **Editor:** Renata da Silva; **Editor:** Jacqueline Guedes; **Editor in Chief:** Elton Primaz; **Editor:** Israel Rahal
Editorial Profile: Offers local, national and international news.
Language (s): Portuguese
DAILY NEWSPAPER

Super Notícia
Owner: Grupo Editorial Sempre Editora
Editorial: Av. B. Camargos, 1645, Contagem 32210-180. **T:** 55 31 2101-3939
E: falesuper@supernoticias.com.br
W: http://www.otempo.com.br/super-noticia
Freq: Daily; **Circ:** 300000
Editor: Rogério Maurício
Editorial Profile: Provides news and information on sports, politics, entertainment and economy.
Language (s): Portuguese
DAILY NEWSPAPER

A Tarde
Editorial: Rua Professor Milton Cayres de Brito, 204, Caminho das Árvores, Salvador 41820-570. **T:** 55 71 3340-8800
E: salvador@grupoatarde.com.br
W: http://www.atarde.com.br
Freq: Daily; **Circ:** 55861 Not Audited
Editor in Chief: Ricardo Mendes; **Editor:** João Mauro Uchôa; **Editor:** Nadja Vladi
Editorial Profile: Covers Local, National and International News.
Language (s): Portuguese
DAILY NEWSPAPER

O Tempo
Editorial: Avenida Babita Camargos, 1645, Cidade Industrial, Contagem 32210-180.
T: 55 31 2101-30001
E: redacao@otempo.com.br
W: http://www.otempo.com.br
Freq: Daily; **Circ:** 72000 Not Audited
City Editor: Carla Alves; **Editor:** João de Castro
Editorial Profile: Covers Local, Regional, National and International News.
Language (s): Portuguese
DAILY NEWSPAPER

TodoDia
Editorial: Avenida São Jerônimo, 2210, Bairro Morada do Sol, Americana 13470-310.
T: 55 1934712700 **E:** redacao@tododia.com.br
W: http://www.tododia.com.br
Freq: Daily; **Circ:** 17300 Not Audited
Editor in Chief: Cláudio Giória
Language (s): Portuguese
DAILY NEWSPAPER

A Tribuna
Editorial: Rua João Pessoa, 129, Centro, Santos 11013-900. **T:** 55 13 2102-7000
E: redacao@atribuna.com.br
W: http://www.atribuna.com.br
Freq: Daily Not Audited
Editor: Giselda Braz; **Editor:** Maria Elizabeth Capelache; **Editor In Chief:** Carlos Conde; **Editor:** Leopoldo Figueiredo; **Editor:** Michella Guijt; **City Editor:** Rafael Motta
Language (s): Portuguese
DAILY NEWSPAPER

A Tribuna
Editorial: Rua Joaquim Plácido da Silva, 225, Ilha de Santa Maria, Vitoria 29051-900.
T: 55 27 3331-9000
E: pauta@redetribuna.com.br
W: http://www.redetribuna.com.br
Freq: Daily Not Audited
Editor: Alevi Carneiro; **City Editor:** Giovana Rangel
Language (s): Portuguese
DAILY NEWSPAPER

A Tribuna
Editorial: Rua Barão do Amazonas, 31, Ponta D'Areia, Niterói 24030-111. **T:** 55 2127191886
E: jornaldelcarai@urbi.com.br
W: http://atribunarj.com.br
Freq: Daily; **Circ:** 10000 Not Audited
Editor in Chief: José Messias Xavier
Language (s): Portuguese
DAILY NEWSPAPER

O Tribuna
Editorial: Rua José Loureiro, 282, Centro, Curitiba 80010-020. **T:** 55 41 3321-5000
E: pauta@parana-online.com.br
W: http://www.parana-online.com.br
Freq: Daily; **Circ:** 23000 Not Audited
Editor: Arlindo Berri
Language (s): Portuguese
DAILY NEWSPAPER

Tribuna
Editorial: Rua São Sebastião, 1380, Centro, Ribeirão Preto 14015-040.
T: 55 16 3632-2200
E: tribuna@tribunaribeirao.com.br
W: http://www.tribunaribeirao.com.br
Freq: Daily; **Circ:** 16000 Not Audited
Editor: Eduardo Ferrari Batista de Santana; **Editor in Chief:** Hilton Hartmann
Language (s): Portuguese
DAILY NEWSPAPER

Tribuna da Bahia
Editorial: Rua Djalma Dutra, 121, Sete Portas, Salvador 40255-000. **T:** 55 71 3321-2161
E: tribunadabahia@tribunadabahia.com.br
W: http://www.tribunadabahia.com.br
Freq: Daily; **Circ:** 30000 Not Audited
Editor in Chief: Paulo Roberto Sampaio
Language (s): Portuguese
DAILY NEWSPAPER

Tribuna de Minas
Editorial: Rua Espírito Santo, 95, Poço Rico, Juiz De Fora 36020-000. **T:** 55 32 2101-4544
E: redacao@tribunademinas.com.br
W: http://www.tribunademinas.com.br
Freq: Daily; **Circ:** 18000 Not Audited
Editor in Chief: Paulo César Magella
Language (s): Portuguese
DAILY NEWSPAPER

Tribuna de Petrópolis
Editorial: Rua Alencar Lima, 26, Centro, Petrópolis 25620-050. **T:** 55 24 2244-2440
E: redacao@e-tribuna.com.br
W: http://www.e-tribuna.com.br
Freq: Daily; **Circ:** 14000 Not Audited
Editor: Alváro Bastos; **Editor in Chief:** Douglas Prado
Language (s): Portuguese
DAILY NEWSPAPER

Tribuna do Norte
Owner: Empresa Jornalistica Tribuna do Norte
Editorial: Avenida Duque de Caxias, 06, Ribeira, Natal 59010-200. **T:** 55 84 4006-6113
E: pauta@tribunadonorte.com.br
W: http://www.tribunadonorte.com.br
Freq: Daily; **Circ:** 23000 Not Audited
Editor: Cinthia Lopes; **Editor in Chief:** Vicente Neto; **Editor in Chief:** Carlos Peixoto; **Editor:** Isaac Ribeiro; **Editor:** Ana Silva
Language (s): Portuguese
DAILY NEWSPAPER

Tribuna do Norte
Editorial: Av. Zilda Seixas Amaral, 4.270, Parque Industrial Norte, Apucarana 86806-380. **T:** 55 43 3420-1177
W: http://www.tribunadonorte.com **Circ:** 15000 Not Audited
Editor: Fernando Klein
Language (s): Portuguese
DAILY NEWSPAPER

Tribuna do Paraná
Editorial: Rua João Tscharnnerl, 800, Cidade da Comunicação - Jardim Mercês, Curitiba 80820-010. **T:** 55 41 3331-5000
E: tribuna@parana-online.com.br
W: http://www.parana-online.com.br
Freq: Daily; **Circ:** 15000 Not Audited
Editor in Chief: Rafael Tavares de Mello
Language (s): Portuguese
DAILY NEWSPAPER

A Tribuna Hoje
Editorial: Av. Presidente Castelo Branco, 3815, Umuarama 87501-170. **T:** 55 44 3056-6050
E: tribunahoje@tribunahoje.jor.br
W: http://www.tribunahoje.jor.br
Freq: Daily; **Circ:** 14000 Not Audited
Editor: Jaqueline Mocellin
Editorial Profile: Focuses on news, politics, regional, society, sports and local news.
Language (s): Portuguese
DAILY NEWSPAPER

Tribuna Impressa
Editorial: Av. Bento de Abreu, 929, Fonte Luminosa, Araraquara 14802-396.
T: 55 16 3303-3339
E: cidades@tribunaimpressa.com.br
W: http://www.tribunaimpressa.com.br
Freq: Daily Not Audited
Editor in Chief: Luis Zakaib
Language (s): Portuguese
DAILY NEWSPAPER

O Vale
Editorial: Avenida Samuel Wainer, 3755, Jardim Augusta, São José Dos Campos 12216-710. **T:** 55 12 3909-3932
E: editoraexecutiva@ovale.com.br
W: http://www.ovale.com.br
Freq: Daily; **Circ:** 14000 Not Audited
Editor in Chief: Hélcio Costa; **Editor:** Felipe Manoukian; **City Editor:** Marcelo Pedrosa
Editorial Profile: Vale Paraibano is a daily newspaper and covers local, regional, national and international news, as well as business, entertainment, lifestyle and sports.
Language (s): Portuguese
DAILY NEWSPAPER

Valor Econômico
Owner: Valor Econômico S/A
Editorial: Av. Francisco Matarazzo, 1500, Torre New York, 1°, 2°, 3° e 8° andares, Sao Paulo 05001-100. **T:** 55 11 3767-1000
E: redacao@valor.com.br
W: http://www.valor.com.br
Freq: Daily Not Audited
Legislation & Tributes Editor: Zinia Baeta; **Editora/Editor:** Alessandra Bellotto; **Careers Editor:** Stela Campos; **Editor:** Camila Dias; **Editor S.A.:** Nelson Niero
Editorial Profile: Established in May 2000, Valor Econômico is considered the most widely-read finance and business newspaper in Brazil. Dedicated to the financial and investment market in the country.
Language (s): Portuguese
DAILY NEWSPAPER

A Voz da Cidade
Editorial: Rua Michel Wardini, 100, Centro, Barra Mansa 27330-100. **T:** 55 2433241879
E: redacao@avozdacidade.com
W: http://www.avozdacidade.com
Freq: Daily Not Audited
Editor: Caroline Macedo; **Editor in Chief:** Antônio Carlos Naves
Editorial Profile: Note: This outlet has the same telephone and fax number. To send a fax, one must call and request that the telephone line be switched to a fax line.
Language (s): Portuguese
DAILY NEWSPAPER

The Wall Street Journal (Brazil)
Editorial: Rua Eng Edgar Egidio de Sousa 485, Sao Paulo 01233-020. **T:** 55 11 3826-2648
Bureau Chief: Marla Dickerson
DAILY NEWSPAPER

Zero Hora
Owner: RBS Zero Hora Editora Jornalistica S.A.
Editorial: Avenida Ipiranga 1075, Azenha, Porto Alegre 90160-093. **T:** 55 51 3218-4300
E: geral@zerohora.com.br
W: http://zerohora.clicrbs.com.br
Freq: Daily; **Circ:** 184566 Not Audited
Editor: Ricardo Chaves; **Editor:** Bete Duarte; **Editor:** Marcelo Ermel; **Editor:** Gilberto Leal; **Editor:** Leandro Maciel; **Editor:** Clóvis Malta; **Editor:** Larissa Roso; **Editor:** Nilson Souza; **Editor in Chief:** Nilson Vargas
Editorial Profile: Covers local, regional, national and international news.
Language (s): Portuguese
DAILY NEWSPAPER

NEWS SERVICE/SYNDICATE

AFP Brazil
Editorial: Av. Almirante Barroso, 52, 10° andar - Sala 1002, Rio De Janeiro 20031-000.
T: 55 21 2215 0222 **W:** http://www.afp.com
Editor in Chief: Gerardo Maronna
Editorial Profile: International news agency.
Language (s): Portuguese
NEWS SERVICE/SYNDICATE

Agência Anhangüera de Notícias
Editorial: Rua Sete de Setembro, 189, Campinas 13035-350. **T:** 55 19 3772-8003
W: http://www.agenciaanhanguera.com.br
Editor in Chief: Guilherme Busch; **City Editor:** Rogério Verzignasse
Language (s): Portuguese
NEWS SERVICE/SYNDICATE

Agência CMA
Owner: Grupo CMA
Editorial: Rua Professor Filadelfo Azevedo, 712, Vila Nova Conceição, Sao Paulo 04508-011. **T:** 55 11 3053-2722
W: http://www.agenciacma.com.br
Editorial Profile: Agência CMA is a Brazilian news service providing international financial and stock market information, focusing on major international stock markets and currency exchange markets.
Language (s): Portuguese
NEWS SERVICE/SYNDICATE

Agência Estado
Owner: Grupo Estado
Editorial: Avenida Professor Celestino Bourroul, 68 - 1º andar, Bairro do Limão, Sao Paulo 02710-000. **T:** 55 11 3856-3500
W: http://institucional.ae.com.br
Editor: Angelo Schincariol
Editorial Profile: Founded in January 1970, Agência Estado, also known as AE, is the largest and one of the most important vehicles of information in the country. In addition to distributing news and pictures to newspapers and Web sites, is recognized by the dissemination of real-time news, quotes and expert analysis for the financial market.
Language (s): Portuguese
NEWS SERVICE/SYNDICATE

Agência RBS
Editorial: Avenida Ipiranga, 1075 - 4º andar, Azenha, Porto Alegre 90169-900.
T: 55 5132184771
E: agenciarbs@zerohora.com.br
W: http://www.agenciarbs.com.br
Bureau Chief: Fabíola Bach
Language (s): Portuguese
NEWS SERVICE/SYNDICATE

Associated Press
Editorial: Av. Paulista, 854, 13 Andar, Conj. 131, Sao Paulo 01310-913.
T: 55 21 3512-8600
Bureau Chief: Bradley Brooks
NEWS SERVICE/SYNDICATE

AutoPress
Owner: Carta Z Notícias Ltda
Editorial: Rua Barão do Flamengo, 32 - 5° andar, Rio De Janeiro 22220-080.
T: 55 21 2286-0020
E: redacao@autopress.com.br
W: http://www.autopress.com.br
Editor in Chief: Eduardo Rocha
Language (s): Portuguese
NEWS SERVICE/SYNDICATE

Bloomberg News
Editorial: Avenue Rio Branco 1, #1802, Rio De Janeiro RJ 2009003. **T:** 55 6133296005
Bureau Chief: Carlos Caminada; **Bureau Chief:** Peter Millard
NEWS SERVICE/SYNDICATE

Bloomberg News
Editorial: Avenida Nações Unidas, 12551 - 21o Andar, World Trade Center, Sao Paulo 04578-903. **T:** 55 1130484530
E: bnbrazil@bloomberg.net
Bureau Chief: Jessica Brice
NEWS SERVICE/SYNDICATE

BR Press
Owner: BR Press
Editorial: Av. Paulista, 2.300 - Andar Pilotis, Sao Paulo 01310-300. **T:** 55 11 2847-4958
E: pauta@brpress.net
W: http://www.brpress.net
Editorial Profile: BR Press Agência Jornalística is a Portuguese-language "boutique" news agency that provides News, International News, Sports, Arts & Entertainment, Culture, Style, Business, Health and Wellness coverage. BR Press also provides customized news reports.
Language (s): Portuguese
NEWS SERVICE/SYNDICATE

Dow Jones Newswires
Editorial: SRTVS Q. 701 Ed, Centro Empresarial Brasilia, Bloco B-Sala 507, Brasilia 70340-907. **T:** 55 61 3335-0832
Bureau Chief: Matthew Cowley
NEWS SERVICE/SYNDICATE

Dow Jones Newswires
Editorial: Av Paulista 854, 5o andar CJ 51, Sao Paulo CEP 01310-910.
T: 55 11 3145-1479 **E:** brazil@dowjones.com
Bureau Chief: Matthew Cowley
NEWS SERVICE/SYNDICATE

Folha Press
Editorial: Alameda Barão de Limeira, 401 - 4º andar, Campos Elíseos, Sao Paulo 01290-900.
T: 55 1132243527
E: folhapress@folhapress.com.br
W: http://www.folhapress.com.br
Editor: Raul Lopes
Language (s): Portuguese
NEWS SERVICE/SYNDICATE

In Press Porter Novelli
Editorial: Rua Lauro Müller, 116-salas, Edifício Rio Sul Center-Botafogo, Rio De Janeiro 22290-906. **T:** 55 2125417414
E: redacao.rj@inpresspni.com.br
W: http://www.inpresspni.com.br
Editor: Renata Jordão
Language (s): Portuguese
NEWS SERVICE/SYNDICATE

KaxiANA
Editorial: Rua 11, Lote 21, Sala 02, Metropolitana, Nucleo Bandeirante, Brasilia 71730-000. **T:** 55 6138796147
E: faleconosco@kaxi.com.br
W: http://www.kaxi.com.br
Editor: Romerito Aquino
Language (s): Portuguese
NEWS SERVICE/SYNDICATE

Kyodo News - Brasil Bureau
Editorial: Avenida Oswaldo Cruz, 149/1206, Flamengo, Rio De Janeiro 22250-060.
T: 55 2125518263 **E:** kyodonews@uol.com.br
W: http://www.kyodonews.com
Language (s): Portuguese
NEWS SERVICE/SYNDICATE

P.I.A. News
Editorial: Rua Guimarães Natal, 23 - Sala 203, Copacabana, Rio De Janeiro 22011-090.
T: 55 2125417757 **E:** pianews@terra.com.br
W: http://www.pianews.net
Editor in Chief: André Queiroz
Language (s): Portuguese
NEWS SERVICE/SYNDICATE

Reuters
Editorial: Av. Das Nacoes Unidas, 17891, 8º andar, Sao Paulo 04795-100.
T: 55 11 56447500
Bureau Chief: Todd Benson; **Editor in Chief:** Cesar Bianconi
NEWS SERVICE/SYNDICATE

BROADCASTING

RADIO STATIONS

Rádio Disney
Owner: Grupo Estado
Editorial: Av Celestino Bourroul, 100-2M, Sao Paulo 02710-000. **T:** 55 11 2108-6742
W: http://radiodisney.disney.com.br

Rádio Eldorado
Owner: Grupo Estado
Editorial: Av Celestino Bourroul, 100-2M, Sao Paulo 02710-000. **T:** 55 11 2108-6472
W: http://www.territorioeldorado.limao.com.br

Rádio Estadão FM
Owner: Grupo Estado
Editorial: Av Celestino Bourroul, 100-2M, Sao Paulo 02710-000. **T:** 55 11 3856-2122
W: http://radio.estadao.com.br

RADIO NETWORKS

Sistema Difusora de Comunicação
Editorial: Av. Camboa, 120, Camboa, São Luís 65020-260. **T:** 55 9832143000
E: jornalismo@sistemadifusora.com.br
W: http://www.sistemadifusora.com.br
Editorial Profile: O Sistema Difusora de Comunicação, é composto por um complexo de emissoras de TVs e Rádios e uma rede de retransmissoras espalhadas em todo o Estado do Maranhão. O Sistema oferece aos telespectadores entretenimento e informação e aos empresários e agências excelentes oportunidades de negócios. Com uma programação local extensa, o Sistema Difusora de Comunicação cumpre sua missão de informar e entreter o público telespectador e ouvinte, sempre levando em consideração, os costumes e tradições culturais da região onde atua, e com isso, estabelecendo uma integração com a comunidade, além, de retransmitir a programação do SBT - Sistema Brasileiro de Televisão a quem está afiliado.

Sistema Globo de Rádio
Editorial: Rua do Russel, 434, Glória, Rio De Janeiro 22210-010. **T:** 55 2125558282
E: cbnrio@cbn.com.br
W: http://globonoar.globo.com

TELEVISION NETWORKS

MTV Brasil
Owner: Editora Abril S.A.
Editorial: Av. Professor Alfonso Bovero, 52, Sumaré, Sao Paulo 01254-000.
T: 55 11 3871-7100
E: mtv.responde@mtvbrasil.com.br
W: http://www.mtv.com.br
Editorial Profile: Launched in 1990, MTV Brasil offers music, entertainment and news targeting teenagers and young adults.

Record News
Editorial: Rua da Várzea, 240, Barra Funda, Sao Paulo 01140-080. **T:** 55 11 33004101
W: http://www.recordnewstv.com.br
Editorial Profile: Launched in 2007, Record News is the first 24-hour free-to-air terrestrial news channel in Brazil.

Rede Bandeirantes
Owner: Grupo Bandeirantes de Comunicação
Editorial: Rua Radiantes 13, Morumbi, Sao Paulo 05699-900. **T:** 55 11 3131-1313
E: cat@band.com.br
W: http://www.band.com.br
Editorial Profile: Offers news, art and entertainment shows. Rede Bandeirantes (Bandeirantes Network), officially nicknamed Band or Band Network, is a television network from Brazil, based in São Paulo. Part of the Grupo Bandeirantes de Comunicação (Bandeirantes Communications Group), it aired for the first time in 1967. Currently, is the fourth TV network in Brazil by the ratings.

Rede Brasil de Televisão
Editorial: Alameda Uapés, 313, Planalto Paulista, Sao Paulo 4067-030.
T: 55 21 5078-5900
W: http://www.rbtv.com.br
Editorial Profile: Launched in 2007, offers news and entertainment.

Rede CNT
Owner: Grupo Empresarial Organizações Martinez
Editorial: Rua Francisco Caron, 29, Pilarzinho, Curitiba 82120-200. **T:** 55 41 2129-7250
W: http://redecnt.com.br
Editorial Profile: Founded on March 15, 1979, the Brazilian television network based in Curitiba/Paraná offers arts & entertainment and news.

Rede Gazeta
Owner: Fundação Cásper Líbero
Editorial: Av. Paulista, 900, Cerqueira César, Sao Paulo 01310-940. **T:** 55 11 3170-5945
W: http://www.tvgazeta.com.br
Editorial Profile: Launched in January 25, 1970. Offers news, arts and entertainment. In 1993 it merged with CNT, and its São Paulo local station became known CNT/Gazeta. In 2000 the partnership ended, and TV Gazeta turned into Rede Gazeta (portuguese for Gazeta Network).

Rede Globo
Owner: Organizações Globo
Editorial: Rua Lopes Quintas, 303, Jardim Botânico, Rio De Janeiro 22460-010.
T: 55 21 2540-2307
W: http://redeglobo.globo.com
Editorial Profile: The Globo Television Network is a national broadcast television network providing a range of general entertainment fare. Launched by media mogul Roberto Marinho on April 26, 1965. It is owned by media conglomerate Organizações Globo, being by far the largest of its holdings. Globo is currently the largest commercial television network of Latin America and the third largest in the world[not in citation given], behind only CBS and NBC, being watched by an estimate of 120 million people daily.

Rede Internacional de Televisão
Owner: Igreja Internacional da Graça de Deus
Editorial: Estrada dos Bandeirantes, 1000, Taguara, Rio De Janeiro 22710-112.
T: 55 21 3344-5959
W: http://www.rittv.com.br
Editorial Profile: Founded in 1999, Rede Internacional de Televisão (The International Network, in English) better known as RIT is a Brazilian television religious channel. Offers children's programs, worship, music and news.

Rede NGT de Televisão
Owner: Rede NGT - Nova Geração de Televisão
Editorial: Av. Magalhães de Castro, 420, Butantã, Sao Paulo 05502-000.
T: 55 11 2827-2600
E: noticias@redengt.com.br
W: http://www.redengt.com.br
Editorial Profile: Launched October 8, 2003 and offers arts and entertainment, sports and news.

Rede Record de Televisão
Owner: Rádio e Televisão Record S/A
Editorial: Rua da Várzea, 240, Barra Funda, Sao Paulo 01140-080. **T:** 55 11 2184-5473
W: http://rederecord.r7.com
Editorial Profile: Offers arts, entertainment and news. Rede Record currently is Brazil's second largest television network. With 57 years of uninterrupted transmission, it is also the oldest TV network in the country.

RedeTV!
Editorial: Av. Presidente Kennedy, 2869, Vila São José, Osasco 06298-190.
T: 55 11 3306-1000
W: http://www.redetv.com.br
Editorial Profile: Offers News and Entertainment. Formed in 1999 using part of Rede Manchete structure. RedeTV! started its transmissions on November 15, 1999. It was the first network worldwide to be broadcast in 3D.

SBT
Owner: Sistema Brasileiro de Televisão
Editorial: Avenida das Comunicações 4, Jaragua, Osasco, Sao Paulo 06278-905.
T: 55 11 3687-3000 **E:** jornalpauta@sbt.com.br
W: http://www.sbt.com.br
Editorial Profile: Offers a variety of news, art & entertainment shows. The network first aired in 1981, and its headquarters are based in Osasco. SBT is owned by Silvio Santos, a popular Brazilian TV host. Its studios are located in São Paulo.

TV Brasil
Owner: Empresa Brasil de Comunicação S.A.
Editorial: SCRN 702/703 Bloco B, Edifício Radiobrás, Brasilia 70323-900.
T: 55 61 3799-5324 **E:** pauta@ebc.com.br
W: http://www.tvbrasil.org.br
Editorial Profile: Offers news, arts and entertainment shows. Brazilian non-profit public broadcasting television network launched on December 2, 2007. It was the first launched by the federal government.

TV Câmara
Owner: Câmara dos Deputados
Editorial: Palácio do Congresso Nacional, Praça dos Três Poderes, Brasilia 70160-900.
T: 55 61 3216-1602
E: jornalismo@camara.gov.br
W: http://www.tv.camara.gov.br
Editorial Profile: Offers broadcasting activities and news from the Brazilian Chamber of Deputies.

TV Cultura
Owner: Fundação Padre Anchieta
Editorial: Rua Cenno Sbrighi, 378, Sao Paulo 05036-900. **T:** 55 11 2182-3546
E: chefiadereportagem@tvcultura.com.br
W: http://www3.tvcultura.com.br
Editorial Profile: TV Cultura (Portuguese: Culture TV) is Brazilian television network headquartered in São Paulo and a part of Fundação Padre Anchieta. It focuses on cultural and education subjects but also has sports as entertainment options.

TV Senado
Owner: Senado Federal
Editorial: Senado Federal, Praça dos Três Poderes, Brasilia 70165-900.
T: 55 61 3303-3198 **E:** tv@senado.gov.br
W: http://www.senado.gov.br/tv
Editorial Profile: Offers broadcasting activity and news from the Brazilian Senate. It was created in 1996 by the Brazilian Senate.The channel broadcasts 24h from the Senate.

BRUNEI Tel: 673
Standard Time: GMT +8
Continent: Asia
Capital City: Bandar Seri Begawan

NEWSPAPERS & PUBLICATIONS

NEWSPAPERS

Pelita Brunei
Owner: Information Department of Brunei
T: 673 2 38 39 41 **E:** pelita@brunet.bn
W: http://www.brunet.bn/news/pelita
Freq: Weekly; **Circ:** 25000 Pub Statement
Editor: Timbang Bakar
Language (s): Bahasa Malaysia
NEWSPAPER

BROADCASTING

TELEVISION STATIONS

Radio Televisyen Brunei
Owner: Radio Televisyen Brunei
T: 673 2243111 127
E: manap_hjadam@rtb.gov.bn
W: http://www.rtb.gov.bn
Editorial Profile: Government run media service projecting the national image at regional and international levels.

BULGARIA Tel: 359
Standard Time: GMT +2
Continent: Europe
Capital City: Sofia

NEWSPAPERS & PUBLICATIONS

NEWSPAPERS

24 Chassa
Owner: Media Holding
Editorial: 47 Tsarigradsko Shose Blvd, Sofia 1504. **T:** 359 2 942 25 14
E: VGocheva@24chasa.bg
W: http://www.24chasa.bg
Freq: Daily; **Circ:** 80000 Pub Statement
Editor-in-Chief: Venelina Gocheva
Editorial Profile: The second most circulated newspaper mainly for the average Bulgarian reader, strong opinion maker with eight regional editions in Varna, Plovdiv, Burgas, Stara Zagora, etc.
Language (s): Bulgarian
DAILY NEWSPAPER

Borba
Owner: Borba Publishing House
Editorial: P.O. Box 71, 2 Bulgaria Boulevard, Veliko Tarnovo 5000. **T:** 359 62 62 38 31
E: borba@vali.bg **W:** http://www.borbabg.com
Freq: Daily; **Circ:** 10000 Pub Statement
Editorial Profile: Borba is an independent newspaper focused on traditions in the region with firm readership. The newspaper provides mainly regional news in the sphere of politics, lifestyle, sports, health and arts.
Language (s): Bulgarian
DAILY NEWSPAPER

Botevgradski Vesti Plus
Editorial: 23 Tzar Osvoboditel Blvd., Botevgrad. **T:** 359 723 2532
E: kabeltv@botevgrad.com
W: http://bvplus.declera.com
Freq: Weekly
Editorial Profile: Informative newspaper with news from the city of Botevgrad and the region.
Language (s): Bulgarian
NEWSPAPER

Cherno more
Owner: Mustang Holding
Editorial: 1 Yane Sandasnski Street, Varna 9004. **T:** 359 52 604505 **E:** more@triada.bg
W: http://www.chernomore.bg
Freq: Daily; **Circ:** 4000 Pub Statement
Editorial Profile: Daily newspaper with news from Varna and the region, the country and the world.
Language (s): Bulgarian
DAILY NEWSPAPER

Class Daily
Owner: MAK Media
Editorial: 2 Nikolay Rakitin, b.5b, floor 2, Sofia 1504. **T:** 359 2 948 48 00
E: klasa@makmedia.bg
W: http://www.class.bg **Circ:** 10000 Pub Statement
Editorial Profile: Daily newspaper mainly for decision-makers and intellectuals, providing national and international coverage on latest business issues.
Language (s): Bulgarian
DAILY NEWSPAPER

Dnevnik
Owner: Economedia
Editorial: 16 Ivan Vazov St., Sofia 1000.
T: 359 2 937 63 00 **E:** dnevnik@dnevnik.bg
W: http://www.dnevnik.bg
Freq: Daily; **Circ:** 11900 Pub Statement
Capital Markets Editor: Vessela Nickolaeva;
Editor-in-Chief: Velislava Popova
Editorial Profile: Daily newspaper published as the only broadsheet in the country. Readership profile: 90% of the readers live in Sofia and big cities and are in their prime. 1/3 of the audience consists of top executives, 1/2 are highly qualified.
Language (s): Bulgarian
DAILY NEWSPAPER

Duma
Owner: PM Press
Editorial: 113A Tsarigradsko Shose Blvd, floor 2, Sofia 1504. **T:** 359 2 970 52 00
E: duma@duma.bg **W:** http://www.duma.bg
Freq: Daily; **Circ:** 9500 Pub Statement
Editorial Profile: Daily newspaper with leftist orientation, with editorial emphasis on social news and comments. Readers' profile: mainly members and supporters of the Bulgarian Socialist Party.
Language (s): Bulgarian
DAILY NEWSPAPER

Eurofootball
Owner: Eurofootballprint
Editorial: 1 Koloman St, Sofia 1618.
T: 359 2 818 91 75 **E:** euro_f@abv.bg
W: http://www.eurofootball.bg **Circ:** 72000 Pub Statement
Editor-in-Chief: Ivailo Stoimenov
Editorial Profile: The newspaper contains information on different sports and matches of world, national and club championships (football, basketball, Formula 1, hockey, tennis, volleyball, etc.).
Language (s): Bulgarian
DAILY NEWSPAPER

Gabrovo Dnes
Editorial: 9 Aprilovska Str., Gabrovo 5300.
T: 359 66 803346
E: gabrovodnes@edasat.com
W: http://gabrovodnes.hit.bg
Freq: Daily
Editorial Profile: The newspaper contains information about the life in Gabrovo Municipality. Gabrovo Dnes offers supplements for culture, healthcare, real estate and business.
Language (s): Bulgarian
DAILY NEWSPAPER

Monitor
Owner: New Bulgarian Media Group
Editorial: 113A Tsarigradsko Shose Blvd, Sofia 1784. **T:** 359 2 960 22 37
E: monitor@monitor.bg
W: http://www.monitor.bg
Freq: Daily; **Circ:** 11500 Pub Statement
Editor-in-Chief: Iva Nikolova
Editorial Profile: Daily newspaper for intellectuals and for the average reader, covering general as well as subject specific news.
Language (s): Bulgarian
DAILY NEWSPAPER

Novinar
Owner: Novinar
Editorial: 44 Oborishte St., Sofia 1505.
T: 359 2 943 45 32 **E:** novinar@novinar.net
W: http://www.novinar.org
Freq: Daily; **Circ:** 12200 Pub Statement
Editorial Profile: Daily newspaper covering news from all spheres of life. It is the cheapest national daily newspaper in the country. Readers' profile: mainly elderly and less educated readers with low income.
Language (s): Bulgarian
DAILY NEWSPAPER

Sega
Owner: Sega
Editorial: 1 Bulgaria Square, Sofia 1463.
T: 359 2 915 23 00 **E:** editors@segabg.com
W: http://www.segabg.com

Freq: Daily; **Circ:** 10700 Pub Statement
Editor-in-Chief: Teodora Peeva
Editorial Profile: Daily newspaper mainly for decision-makers and intellectuals, providing national and international coverage and special news features.
Language (s): Bulgarian
DAILY NEWSPAPER

Standart
Owner: Standart News
Editorial: 49 Bulgaria Blvd, Vitosha Business Center, Sofia 1404. **T:** 359 2 818 23 11
E: office@standartnews.com
W: http://www.standartnews.com
Freq: Daily; **Circ:** 68300 Pub Statement
Editor-in-Chief: Slavka Bozukova
Editorial Profile: National daily newspaper mainly for decision-makers and intellectuals. Edition of Standart News Ltd. Provides objective and fair view of daily issues in Bulgaria and worldwide. It includes 48 pages with interesting articles about politics, economy, sport, culture, humour and society.
Language (s): Bulgarian
DAILY NEWSPAPER

Struma
Owner: Pirin Erkul Company
Editorial: 10 Petko D. Petkov Street, Blagoevgrad. **T:** 359 73 885 703
E: struma@struma.com
W: http://www.struma.com **Circ:** 20000 Pub Statement
Editorial Profile: Struma is a daily newspaper that is prefered by Bulgarians living in southwest part of the country. It has about 150 000 readers. The main topics are news from the region, lifestyle and sports.
Language (s): Bulgarian
DAILY NEWSPAPER

Telegraf
Owner: Press Group Monitor
Editorial: 113A Tsarigradsko Shose Blvd, Sofia 1784. **T:** 359 2 960 22 12
E: telegraph@monitor.bg
W: http://www.telegraph.bg
Freq: Daily; **Circ:** 66000 Pub Statement
Editor-in-Chief: Vladimir Yonchev
Editorial Profile: Daily newspaper for the average reader, covering general as well as subject specific news.
Language (s): Bulgarian
DAILY NEWSPAPER

Trud
Owner: Media Holding
Editorial: 119 Ekzarh Joseph St., Sofia 1000. **T:** 359 2 921 41 40 **E:** reporteri@trud.bg
W: http://www.trud.bg
Freq: Daily; **Circ:** 105000 Pub Statement
Editor-in-Chief: Ivan Mihalev
Editorial Profile: The most circulated newspaper mainly for the average Bulgarian reader with eight regional editions in Varna, Plovdiv, Burgas, Stara Zagora, etc.
Language (s): Bulgarian
DAILY NEWSPAPER

Zemya
Owner: Evromedia
Editorial: 169 Evlogi Georgiev Blvd, Sofia 1504. **T:** 359 2 946 19 02
E: zemia_core@abv.bg
W: http://zemia-news.bg
Freq: Daily; **Circ:** 12000 Pub Statement
Editor-in-Chief: Goran Gotev
Editorial Profile: Daily newspaper with agricultural orientation but also including news from the economic, political and cultural spheres of Bulgarian life.
Language (s): Bulgarian
DAILY NEWSPAPER

NEWS SERVICE/SYNDICATE

ADP Debt News
Owner: All Data Processing Ltd.
Editorial: 16 Ivan Vazov Street, ADP News, Sofia 1000 **W:** http://www.adpnews.info
Freq: Daily
Editorial Profile: Provides financial and loan news.
Language (s): English
NEWS SERVICE/SYNDICATE

ADP Renewable Energy Track
Owner: All Data Processing Ltd.
Editorial: 16 Ivan Vazov Street, ADP News, Sofia 1000 **W:** http://www.adpnews.info
Freq: Daily
Editorial Profile: Provides energy market news.
Language (s): English
NEWS SERVICE/SYNDICATE

Forex News
Editorial: 16 Ivan Vazov Street, Sofia 1000.
T: 359 89994 76 55 **E:** info@forexnews.bg
W: http://forexnews.bg
Editor In Chief: Sasho Slavov
Editorial Profile: Offers a wide range of business and financial news, updated throughout the day.
Language (s): Bulgarian
NEWS SERVICE/SYNDICATE

Reuters
Editorial: 16 Ivan Vazov Street, Suite 1000, Sofia. **T:** 3592 9399 700
W: http://www.thomsonreuters.com
NEWS SERVICE/SYNDICATE

BROADCASTING

RADIO NETWORKS

Bulgarian National Radio
Editorial: 4 Dragan Tsankov Blvd, Sofia 1040.
T: 359 2 933 65 49 **E:** bulgarian@bnr.bg
W: http://www.bnr.bg
Editorial Profile: National state radio of Bulgaria. Main part of it is Radio Bulgaria, which is a main source of information to the million people outside the Bulgarian borders.

Fresh
Owner: Emmis Bulgaria Group
Editorial: 51 Jerusalem Blvd, Business building, Sofia. **T:** 359 2 976 74 99
E: office@radiofresh.bg
W: http://www.radiofresh.bg
Editorial Profile: National radio network Fresh is a musical radio of CHR format (Contemporary Hit Radio). Our radio is for modern hits with audience of young people aged 15-30.

TELEVISION STATIONS

Bulgarian National Television
Editorial: 29 San Stefano St, Sofia 1504.
T: 359 2985591 **E:** programa@bnt.bg
W: http://www.bnt.bg
Editorial Profile: Bulgarian National Television is the first national television. It is a national public broadcasting station.

BURKINA FASO Tel: 226

Standard Time: GMT
Continent: Africa
Capital City: Ouagadougou

NEWSPAPERS & PUBLICATIONS

NEWSPAPERS

L' Indépendant
Editorial: 01 BP 5663, Ouagadougou 1.
T: 226 50 33 37 75 **E:** sebgo@fasonet.bf
W: http://www.independant.bf
Freq: Weekly; **Circ:** 6500 Pub Statement
Rédacteur en Chef: Elie Kaboré
Editorial Profile: Weekly newspaper covering current affairs, politics, social issues and news in brief.
Language (s): French
NEWSPAPER

Journal du Jeudi
Owner: Le Journal du Jeudi
Editorial: 01 BP 3654, Ouagadougou 1.
T: 226 50 31 41 08
E: info@journaldujeudi.com
W: http://www.journaldujeudi.com **Circ:** 8000 Pub Statement
Editeur: Boubakar Diallo; **Rédacteur en Chef:** Amidou Idogo
Editorial Profile: Satirical newspaper focusing on national and international news, business, politics, entertainment and sport.
Language (s): French
DAILY NEWSPAPER

L' Observateur Paalga
Owner: L'Observateur Paalga
Editorial: 01 BP 584, Ouagadougou 1.
T: 226 50 33 27 05 **E:** lobs@fasonet.bf
W: http://www.lobservateur.bf
Freq: Daily; **Circ:** 9000 Pub Statement
Rédacteur en Chef: Ousseni Ilboudo;
Rédacteur adjoint: Bernard Zangré
Editorial Profile: Newspaper covering local and national news, business and economics, sport, entertainment and leisure.

Language (s): French
DAILY NEWSPAPER

Le Pays
Owner: Le Pays
Editorial: Cité 1200 Logements, 01 BP 4577, Ouagadougou 1. **T:** 226 50 36 20 46
E: ed.lepays@cenatrin.bf
W: http://www.lepays.bf
Freq: Daily; **Circ:** 15000 Pub Statement
Editorial Profile: Independent newspaper focusing on general news and current-affairs.
Language (s): French
DAILY NEWSPAPER

Sidwaya Quotidien
Owner: Sidwaya
Editorial: 5 Rue du Marché, 01 BP 507, Ouagadougou 1. **T:** 226 50 30 63 06
E: sidwaya84@yahoo.fr
W: http://www.sidwaya.bf
Freq: Daily; **Circ:** 5000 Pub Statement
Rédacteur en Chef: Jean Philippe Tougouma
Editorial Profile: Newspaper focusing on national and international news, economics, politics, finance, culture, social life and sports.
Language (s): French
DAILY NEWSPAPER

NEWS SERVICE/SYNDICATE

Agence d'Informations du Burkina
Editorial: BP 2507, Ouagadougou 1.
T: 226 50 32 46 40 **E:** infos@aib.bf
W: http://www.aib.bf
Editor In Chief: Jean-Bernard Zongo
Editorial Profile: Official News Agency of the Burkina Faso.
Language (s): French
NEWS SERVICE/SYNDICATE

BROADCASTING

TELEVISION STATIONS

Télévision du Burkina
Editorial: 955 boulevard de la révolution, 01 BP 2530, Ouagadougou 1. **T:** 226 50 31 83 53
E: television@rtb.bf **W:** http://www.tnb.bf
Editorial Profile: Official national television of Burkina Faso covering all areas of information.

BURMA Tel: 95

Standard Time: GMT +6.5
Continent: Asia
Capital City: Pyinmana

NEWSPAPERS & PUBLICATIONS

NEWSPAPERS

The Myanmar Times
Owner: Myanmar Consolidated Media Co Ltd.
Editorial: Myanmar Consolidated Media Co Ltd., No. 379/383 Bo Aung Kyaw Street, Kyauktada Township, Yangon. **T:** 95 1392928
E: newsroom@myanmartimes.com.mm
W: http://www.mmtimes.com
Freq: Weekly; **Circ:** 10001 Not Audited
Editor: Mr. Aung Win; **Editor in Chief:** Ross Dunkley; **Editor:** Mr. Kyaw Thu
Editorial Profile: Covers national and international news, as well as business, entertainment, sports, etc.
Language (s): Burmese
NEWSPAPER

The New Light of Myanmar
Owner: News and Periodicals Enterprise
Editorial: News and Periodicals Enterprise - Ministry of Information, The New Light of Myanmar Press, No 22/30 Strand Road at 43rd Street, Yangon. **T:** 95 1392308
E: nlm@myanmar.com.mm
W: http://www.myanmar.com/newspaper/nlm/
Freq: Daily; **Circ:** 25002 Not Audited
Editor in Chief: Mr. Than Myint Tun
Editorial Profile: Covers local, national, regional and international news, business, etc.
Language (s): English
DAILY NEWSPAPER

BURUNDI Tel: 257

Standard Time: GMT +2
Continent: Africa
Capital City: Bujumbura

NEWSPAPERS & PUBLICATIONS

NEWSPAPERS

Ndongozi y'Uburundi
Owner: Burundi Chatholic Church
Editorial: BP 690, Bujumbara.
T: 257 22 22 27 62 **E:** muyehee@yahoo.fr
Freq: Bi-Weekly; **Circ:** 3000 Pub Statement
Rédacteur en Chef: Philllipe Sindayihebura
Editorial Profile: Newspaper covering current affairs, politics, religion, society and culture.
Language (s): French
NEWSPAPER

Le Renouveau du Burundi
Owner: Ministry of Information
Editorial: BP 2573, Bujumbara.
T: 257 22 22 54 11 **E:** secoppb@yahoo.fr
Freq: Daily; **Circ:** 1000 Pub Statement
Rédactrice en Chef: Stela Buduriganya;
Rédacteur en Chef Adjoint: Salvatore Kadende; **Rédacteur en Chef Adjoint:** Sebastien Ntakarutimana
Editorial Profile: Newspaper covering current affairs and politics.
Language (s): French
DAILY NEWSPAPER

NEWS SERVICE/SYNDICATE

Agence Burundaise de Presse (ABP)
Editorial: Avenue Nicolas Mayugi, BP: 2870, Bujumbara. **T:** 257 22 21 30 83
E: abp@cbinf.com **W:** http://www.abp.info.bi
Language (s): French
NEWS SERVICE/SYNDICATE

BROADCASTING

RADIO NETWORKS

Radio Isanganiro
Owner: Radio Isanganiro
Editorial: 27 Avenue de l'Amitié, BP 810, Bujumbara. **T:** 257 22 24 65 95
E: isanganiro@isanganiro.org
W: http://www.isanganiro.org
Editorial Profile: National radio covering current affairs, politics, cultural, social and freedom of speech issues.

Radio Nationale du Burundi
Editorial: BP 1900, Bujumbara.
T: 257 22 22 32 79 **E:** rtnb@cbinf.com
W: http://www.rtnb.bi/news/index.php
Editorial Profile: National radio of Burundi covering current affairs, sports, politics and general information.

TELEVISION STATIONS

Television Nationale du Burundi
Editorial: BP 1900, Bujumbara.
T: 257 22 22 44 77 **E:** rtnb@cbinf.com
W: http://www.rtnb.bi/news/index.php
Editorial Profile: National television of Burundi covering current affairs, politics, sports and general information.

CAMBODIA Tel: 855

Standard Time: GMT +7
Continent: Asia
Capital City: Phnom Penh

NEWSPAPERS & PUBLICATIONS

NEWSPAPERS

Cambodge Nouveau
Editorial: Cambodge Nouveau, No.58H, Street 302, Phnom Penh. **T:** 855 23 214610
E: cambodge.nouveau@forum.com.kh
W: http://www.cambodgenouveau.com
Freq: Monthly; **Circ:** 501 Not Audited
Editor: Alain Gascuel

Editorial Profile: Cambodge Nouveau is a daily newspaper which covers the national and international news, business, politics, etc.
Language (s): French
NEWSPAPER

Cambodge Soir
Editorial: Cambodge Soir Mekong Co Ltd, 26CD, Street 302, BP 627, Phnom Penh.
T: 855 23 726804
E: cambodgesoirpnh@online.com.kh
W: http://www.cambodgesoir.info
Freq: Weekly; **Circ:** 3001 Not Audited
Editor: Frederic Amat; **Editor in Chief:** Bona Pen
Editorial Profile: Covers local, national, regional and international news, business, etc.
Language (s): French
NEWSPAPER

Cambodia Daily
Editorial: The Cambodia Daily, No. 129, Street 228, Phnom Penh. **T:** 855 23 426602
E: editor@cambodiadaily.com
W: http://www.cambodiadaily.com
Freq: 2 Times/Week; **Circ:** 5001 Not Audited
Editor in Chief: Kevin Doyle; **Publisher:** Bernard Krisher
Editorial Profile: Covers news topics.
Language (s): English
NEWSPAPER

Cambodia News
Editorial: Cambodia News, No.15B, Street 612, Phnom Penh 12152. **T:** 855 17 535-535
E: cambodia_news@yahoo.com
W: http://www.cambodia.org/news
Freq: Weekly; **Circ:** 5001 Not Audited
Editorial Profile: Covers news topics.
Language (s): English
NEWSPAPER

Cambodia Sin Chew Daily
Editorial: Sin Chew Media Corp Bhd., No.107ABC, Street Joseph Broz Tito (Rue214), Sangkat Boeng Prolit, Khan 7 Makara, Phnom Penh. **T:** 855 23 212-628
E: editorial@camsinchew.com
W: http://www.sinchew-i.com/cambodia
Freq: Daily; **Circ:** 6001 Not Audited
Editorial Profile: Covers news topics.
Language (s): Chinese
DAILY NEWSPAPER

Camgodge Soir (Khmer Version)
Editorial: 26cd, Street 302 Bp627, Phnom Penh. **T:** 855 12 815990
E: camgodgesoirpnh@online.com.kh
W: http://www.cambodgesoir.info
Freq: Weekly
Editor in Chief: Pierre Gillette
Editorial Profile: Covers news topics.
Language (s): Khmer
NEWSPAPER

Jian Hua Daily
Editorial: Jian Hua Daily, No.116-118, Street 128, Kampuchea Krom, Phnom Penh.
T: 855 23 883801
E: jianhuadaily@jianhuadaily.com
W: http://www.jianhuadaily.com
Freq: Daily; **Circ:** 5001 Not Audited
Editor in Chief: Xeng Zuang Rong
Editorial Profile: Jian Hua Daily is a daily newspaper which talks about the Local, National, Regional, International news, Business, Politics, etc.
Language (s): Chinese
DAILY NEWSPAPER

Kampuchea Thmey Daily
Editorial: No.805, Kampuchea Krom Blvd (Street 128), San Gkat Tuk Laak 1, Phnom Penh 12156. **T:** 855 23 882535
E: kampucheathmey@gmail.com
Freq: 2 Times/Week; **Circ:** 40001 Not Audited
Editor in Chief: Khieu Navy
Editorial Profile: Discusses the Local, National, Regional and International news.
Language (s): Khmer
NEWSPAPER

Koh Santepheap Daily
Editorial: Koh Santepheap Daily, No.240, Street 271, Beoung Tum Pun, Meancathey, Phnom Penh. **T:** 855 23 9871119
E: kohdaily@gmail.com
W: http://www.kohsantepheapdaily.com.kh
Freq: Daily; **Circ:** 45001 Not Audited
Editor in Chief: Thong Pang; **Editor in Chief:** Saroeun Pol
Editorial Profile: Koh Santepheap Daily is a daily newspaper which covers the latest Local, National, Regional and International news, Entertainment, Sports, etc.
Language (s): Khmer
DAILY NEWSPAPER

The Mirror
Editorial: P.O. Box 177, Phnom Penh, Phnom Penh **E:** mirror@gmx.org
W: http://cambodiamirror.wordpress.com
Freq: Weekly; **Circ:** 141 Not Audited
Editor: Norbert Klein
Editorial Profile: Published since 1997, it covers news, politics and economics.
Language (s): English
NEWSPAPER

Phnom Penh Post
Editorial: Phnom Penh Post, 888 Building F, 8th floor, Phnom Penh Center, Corners of Sothearos and Sihanouk Blvds., Phnom Penh.
T: 855 23 214-311
E: editors@phnompenhpost.com
W: http://www.phnompenhpost.com
Freq: Daily; **Circ:** 5001 Not Audited
Editor in Chief: Alan Parkhouse
Editorial Profile: Covers news topics.
Language (s): English
DAILY NEWSPAPER

Raksmei Angkor
Editorial: No.25Z, Street 372, Sangkat Beng Salang, Khan Toul Kok, Phnom Penh 12160.
T: 855 12 922291
E: raksmeiangkor@yahoo.com
Freq: 2 Times/Week; **Circ:** 5001 Not Audited
Editor in Chief: En Chan Sivutha
Editorial Profile: Cover the latest local and international news.
Language (s): Khmer
NEWSPAPER

Rasmei Kampuchea Daily
Editorial: Rasmei Kampuchea Daily, 476 Monivong Street, Boulevard, Phnom Penh.
T: 855 23 362472
E: rasmei_kampuchea@yahoo.com
Freq: 2 Times/Week; **Circ:** 25001 Not Audited
Editor in Chief: Pen Samitthy
Editorial Profile: Covers news topics.
Language (s): English
NEWSPAPER

Samleng Yuvachun Khmer
Editorial: Khmer Youth News, House 24, Road 374, Tuol Svay Prey 2, Chamkar Mon District, Phnom Penh. **T:** 855 23 997-4701
E: khmeryouthnews@yahoo.com
Freq: Daily; **Circ:** 6001 Not Audited
Editorial Profile: Covers news topics.
Language (s): Khmer
DAILY NEWSPAPER

Somne Themey
Editorial: #6, Street 288, Boeng Kengkang 1, Phonm Penh. **T:** 855 23224303
E: somnethemey@online.com.kh
W: http://www.mcdcambodia.com
Freq: Weekly; **Circ:** 10001 Not Audited
Editor in Chief: Nhet Pheaktra
Editorial Profile: Covers news.
Language (s): Khmer
NEWSPAPER

NEWS SERVICE/SYNDICATE

Agence France Presse
Editorial: Agence France Presse (AFP)-Phnom Penh Bureau, Room A2, No.111, Norodom Boulevard, Phnom Penh 12211.
T: 855 23 426-227 **W:** http://www.afp.com
Freq: Daily
Editorial Profile: Covers news topics as a bureau for the French-based AFP.
Language (s): English
NEWS SERVICE/SYNDICATE

Agence Kampuchea Presse (AKP)
Editorial: Agence Kampuchea Presse (AKP), 62 Monivong, Phnom Penh 12201.
T: 855 23 430564 **E:** akp@camnet.com.kh
W: http://www.camnet.com.kh/akp
Freq: Daily
Editorial Profile: Provides a news service in English, French and Cambodian.
Language (s): English
NEWS SERVICE/SYNDICATE

BROADCASTING

TELEVISION STATIONS

National Television of Cambodia (TVK)
Editorial: National Television Kampuchea (TVK), #62 Preah Monivoing Boulevard, Sangkat Sras Chork, Khan Daun Penh, Phnom Penh 12201. **T:** 855 023 426761
E: tvk@camnet.com.kh
W: http://www.tvk.gov.kh
Editorial Profile: TVK became known in English as the National Television of Cambodia. TVK has broadcast its programmes both regionally and globally by satellite.

CAMEROON Tel: 237

Standard Time: GMT +1
Continent: Africa
Capital City: Yaoundé

NEWSPAPERS & PUBLICATIONS

NEWSPAPERS

Cameroon Tribune
Owner: Cameroon news and Editing Corporation SOPECAM
Editorial: Route de l'Aéroport, BP 1218, Yaoundé. **T:** 237 22 30 41 47
E: cameroon-tribune@cameroon-tribune.cm
W: http://www.cameroon-tribune.net
Freq: Daily; **Circ:** 25000 Pub Statement
Rédacteur en Chef: Martin Badjang Ba Nken
Editorial Profile: National Daily Newspaper covering national and international news, politics, economy, culture and sport.
Language (s): English
DAILY NEWSPAPER

Le Messager
Owner: Free Media Group
Editorial: Rue des Ecoles, BP 5925, Douala.
T: 237 33 42 04 39
E: lemessager@lemessager.net
W: http://www.lemessager.net
Freq: Daily; **Circ:** 7000 Pub Statement
Rédacteur en Chef: Thierry Ndong
Editorial Profile: Newspaper covering national and international news, politics, business and sport.
Language (s): French
DAILY NEWSPAPER

Mutations
Owner: Mutations
Editorial: 183 Rue 1.055, Place Repiquet, Yaoundé. **T:** 237 22 22 51 04
E: jmutations@yahoo.fr
W: http://www.quotidienmutations.info
Freq: Daily; **Circ:** 8000 Pub Statement
Rédacteur en Chef: Junior Binyam
Editorial Profile: National Daily Newspaper covering news, politics and current affairs.
Language (s): French
DAILY NEWSPAPER

La Nouvelle Expression
Owner: La Nouvelle Expression
Editorial: 12, rue Prince de Galles, BP 15333, Douala. **T:** 237 33 43 22 27
E: lanouvelleexpression2005@yahoo.fr
W: http://www.lanouvelleexpression.net
Freq: Daily; **Circ:** 7000 Pub Statement
Rédacteur en Chef: Valentin Siméon Zinga
Editorial Profile: Newspaper focusing on national and international news, politics, economics, culture and sport.
Language (s): French
DAILY NEWSPAPER

The Post Newspaper
Editorial: PO Box 91, Buea.
T: 237 33 32 32 87 **E:** thepostnp@yahoo.com
W: http://www.postnewsline.com
Freq: 2 Times/Week; **Circ:** 5000 Pub Statement
Editor In Chief: Charly Ndi Chia
Editorial Profile: The Post is Cameroon's leading English-language newspaper Slogan: The independent newspaper at the service of the people.
Language (s): English
NEWSPAPER

BROADCASTING

RADIO STATIONS

Radio Equinoxe
Owner: La Nouvelle Expression
Editorial: Rue du Docteur Jamot, BP 5082, Douala. **T:** 237 33 43 94 74
E: t_biamou@yahoo.fr
Editorial Profile: National radio station covering news, current affairs, sports and entertainment.

TELEVISION STATIONS

Cameroon Radio Television
Editorial: BP 16344, Yaoundé.
T: 237 22 21 40 77 **E:** crtvweb@iccnet.cm
W: http://www.crtv.cm
Editorial Profile: National Radio and Television of the Cameroon covering current affairs, sport, politics and broadcasting entertainment.

Equinoxe Télévision
Owner: La Nouvelle Expression
Editorial: Rue du Docteur Jamot, BP 5082, Douala. **T:** 237 33 43 94 74
E: t_biamou@yahoo.fr
Editorial Profile: National television covering news, current affairs, entertainment and sports.

CANADA Tel: 1

Standard Time: GMT -8
Continent: The Americas
Capital City: Ottawa

NEWSPAPERS & PUBLICATIONS

NEWSPAPERS

100 Mile House Newspaper
Owner: Black Press
Editorial: 2-536 Horse Lake Road, 100 Mile House, British Columbia V0K 2E3.
T: 1 250 395-2219
W: http://www.100milefreepress.net
Freq: Weekly; **Circ:** 10657
Editor: Ken Alexander; **Publisher:** Chris Nickless
NEWSPAPER

Les 2 Rives
Owner: Quebecor Communications Inc.
Editorial: 77 rue George, Sorel-Tracy, Quebec J3P 1C2. **T:** 1 450 742-9408
E: info@les2rives.com
W: http://www.les2rives.com **Circ:** 28400
Editorial Profile: Les 2 Rives is a weekly French language newspaper that covers local news and information in Sorel-Tracy, Quebec. Contact the publication by phone, fax or mail.; Full Page Mono: 7.00
Currency: Canada Dollars
NEWSPAPER

24 Heures Montreal
Owner: Quebecor Communications Inc.
Editorial: 800 Rue du Square Victoria, mezzanine, bureau 5, Montreal, Quebec H4Z 1A1. **T:** 1 514 393-1010
E: 24h.redaction@quebecormedia.com
W: http://www.24hmontreal.canoe.ca
Freq: Daily; **Circ:** 145683
Editor: Nicolas Dubois; **Editor in Chief:** Matthieu Payen
Editorial Profile: 24 Heures Montréal is a commuter daily newspaper that is designed for a 20-minute read and targets commuters between the ages of 25 to 49. It features local, national and international headline news. However, the bulk of its content is human interest and lifestyle stories on subjects such as health and fashion.; Full Page Mono: 25.55; Full Page Colour: 29.40
Currency: Canada Dollars
DAILY NEWSPAPER

24 Hours Toronto
Owner: Quebecor Communications Inc.
Editorial: 333 King St E, Toronto, Ontario M5A 3X5 **W:** http://24hourstoronto.sunmedia.ca
Freq: Daily; **Circ:** 265255
Editor in Chief: Wendy Metcalfe; **Publisher:** Mike Power
Editorial Profile: 24 Hours Toronto is a commuter daily newspaper that is distributed free of charge to commuters throughout the Toronto area. It targets mostly women ages 25 to 49. It covers local, national and international news, but also features human interest and lifestyle stories on subjects such as health and fashion. Advertising deadlines for the publication vary. The paper was launched in November 2003. There is no dedicated photo editor, but photo inquiries can be directed to the editor.; Full Page Mono: 43.96; Full Page Colour: 164.85
Currency: Canada Dollars
DAILY NEWSPAPER

24 Hours Vancouver
Owner: Quebecor Communications Inc.
Editorial: 24 2nd Ave W, Vancouver, British Columbia V5Y 1B3. **T:** 1 604 322-2340

E: van24news@sunmedia.ca
W: http://www.vancouver.24hrs.ca
Freq: Daily; **Circ:** 131216
Editorial Profile: 24 hours Vancouver is a free commuter daily newspaper circulating weekdays throughout the Lower Mainland of British Columbia. It contains an upbeat mix of local and world news, entertainment, lifestyle, fashion, business, sports and feature stories.; Full Page Mono: 27.23; Full Page Colour: 102.11
Currency: Canada Dollars
DAILY NEWSPAPER

The Abbotsford News
Owner: Black Press
Editorial: 34375 Gladys Ave, Abbotsford, British Columbia V2S 2H5. **T:** 1 604 853-1144
W: http://www.abbynews.com/ **Circ:** 44395
Publisher: Andrew Franklin; **Editor:** Andrew Holota
Editorial Profile: The Abbotsford News is a community newspaper written for the residents of Abbotsford, British Columbia. It covers local news, sports and opinions from the region. Abbotsford News and Chilliwack Progress produce a publication known as The Fraser Valley Daily, which runs Tuesdays through Fridays and reprints content from the weekly papers.; Full Page Mono: 30.65
Currency: Canada Dollars
NEWSPAPER

ABC Portuguese Canadian Newspaper
Owner: Portuguese Canadian News Network
Editorial: 725 College St, Toronto, Ontario M6G 1C0. **T:** 1 416 995-9904
W: http://www.pcnewsnetwork.com
Editorial Profile: ABC Portuguese Canadian Newspaper is a community newspaper serving the Portuguese-Canadian community of Toronto and the greater Toronto area in Ontario, Canada.
NEWSPAPER

Aboriginal Multi-Media Society
Editorial: 13245-146th St, Edmonton, Alberta T5L 4S8. **T:** 1 780 455-2700
E: market@ammsa.com
W: http://www.ammsa.com **Circ:** 42500
Publisher: Bert Crowfoot; **Editor:** Paul Macedo
NEWSPAPER

L' Acadie Nouvelle
Owner: Éditions de l'Acadie (Les)
Editorial: 476 Boul St-Pierre O, Caraquet, New Brunswick E1W 1A3. **T:** 1 506 727-4444
E: infos@acadienouvelle.com
W: http://www.acadienouvelle.com
Freq: Daily; **Circ:** 20288
News Editor: Gaëtan Chiasson; **Editor in Chief:** Jean Saint-Cyr; **Editor in Chief:** Jean Saint-Cyr
Editorial Profile: L'Acadie Nouvelle is a daily, French-language newspaper written for the residents of Caraquet, New Brunswick. Its editorial mission is to inform the community about local and national news, including politics, sports, education, arts and weather.; Full Page Mono: 1.28; Full Page Colour: 672.63
Currency: Canada Dollars
DAILY NEWSPAPER

ACASA
Owner: Goldmark Productions Inc.
Editorial: 35 Longwood Ave, Richmond Hill, Ontario L4E 4A5. **T:** 1 905 482-1838
E: office@acasamedia.com
W: http://www.acasamedia.com
Freq: Bi-Weekly; **Circ:** 20000
Editor in Chief: Mihai Manolache
Editorial Profile: ACASA is a biweekly Romanian-language newspaper serving the Romanian community in Toronto and surrounding areas.
NEWSPAPER

Accès
Editorial: 727 Principale, Piedmont, Quebec J0R 1K0. **T:** 1 450 227-7999
E: direction@journalacces.ca
W: http://www.journalacces.ca **Circ:** 24770
Editor in Chief: Éric-Olivier Dallard; **Publisher:** Josee Pilotte
Editorial Profile: Accès is a community newspaper that targets the Saint-Sauveur-des-Monts region of Quebec.; Full Page Mono: 6.93
Currency: Canada Dollars
NEWSPAPER

Les Actualites
Owner: Quebecor Communications Inc.
Editorial: 572 1re Av, Asbestos, Quebec J1T 4R4. **T:** 1 819 879-6681
E: redaction.asbestos@hebdosquebecor.com
W: http://www.hebdosquebecor.com/aca/index_aca.asp **Circ:** 15000
Editor in Chief: Nathalie Hurdle; **Publisher:** Carole Pellerin
Editorial Profile: Les Actualités is a weekly French-language newspaper. It covers local and regional information for the residents of Asbestos, Quebec.; Full Page Mono: 5.81; Full Page Colour: 50.00
Currency: Canada Dollars
NEWSPAPER

Actualites Côte-des-Neiges
T: 1 514 342-7638
E: redaction@lesactualites.ca
W: http://www.lesactualites.ca
Freq: Semi-Monthly; **Circ:** 35000
Editor: Emilie Russo
Editorial Profile: Actualités Côte-des-Neiges is a biweekly newspaper covering local news in French.; Full Page Mono: 7.28
Currency: Canada Dollars
NEWSPAPER

The Advertiser
Owner: Advertiser 2008
T: 1 780 354-2592
E: beaverlodge.advertiser@gmail.com
Freq: Monthly; **Circ:** 10000
Publisher & Editor: Clayton Barclay
Editorial Profile: The Advertiser is a free weekly newspaper serving residents of Beaverlodge, Alberta. It contains community news, events and stories of interest to local readers.; Full Page Mono: 6.75; Full Page Colour: 90.00
Currency: Canada Dollars
NEWSPAPER

The Afro News
Owner: Privilege Group Holdings
Editorial: 610-825, Granville Street, Vancouver, British Columbia V6Z 1K9.
T: 1 604 646-0474 **E:** info@theafronews.ca
W: http://www.theafronews.ca
Freq: Monthly; **Circ:** 60000
Editor in Chief: Deidre Heim
Editorial Profile: The Afro News is a weekly newspaper published for the African-American community of Vancouver, British Columbia.; Full Page Mono: 17.27; Full Page Colour: 24.27
Currency: Canada Dollars
NEWSPAPER

Airdrie Echo
Owner: Quebecor Communications Inc.
Editorial: 112 1 Ave NE, Airdrie, Alberta T4B 0R6. **T:** 1 403 948-7280
E: airdrie.echo@shaw.ca
W: http://www.airdrieecho.com **Circ:** 17003
Publisher: Shawn Cornell
Editorial Profile: Airdrie Echo is published weekly for the residents of Airdrie, Alberta. The newspaper covers local news, sports and community events.; Full Page Mono: 8.54; Full Page Colour: 150.00
Currency: Canada Dollars
NEWSPAPER

Ajax-Pickering News Advertiser
Owner: Metroland Media Group Ltd.
Editorial: 865 Farewell St, Oshawa, Ontario L1H 6N8. **T:** 1 905 579-4400
E: newsroom@durhamregion.com
W: http://www.newsdurhamregion.com
Circ: 51400
News Editor: Mike Ruta
NEWSPAPER

Ajit Weekly
Editorial: 7015-2 Tranmere Dr, Mississauga, Ontario L5S 1T7. **T:** 1 905 671-4761
E: info@ajitweekly.com
W: http://www.ajitweekly.com **Circ:** 39500
Editorial Profile: [Punjabi language]; Full Page Mono: 4.00
Currency: Canada Dollars
NEWSPAPER

Akhbaar-e-Pakistan
Owner: Akhbaar-e-Pakistan
Editorial: 3256 Escada Drive, Mississauga, Ontario L5M 7V5. **T:** 1 416 835-1997
E: akhbaar@gmail.com
Freq: Weekly; **Circ:** 41000
Editor in Chief: Badar Munir Chaudhary
Editorial Profile: Akhbaar-e-Pakistan is a weekly Urdu-language newspaper.
NEWSPAPER

Alakhbar (An-Nahar)
Editorial: 2086 Ave Chartier, Dorval, Quebec H9P 1H2. **T:** 1 514 636-4004
E: info@alakhbar.ca
W: http://www.alakhbar.ca **Circ:** 25000
Editorial Profile: Alakhbar (An-Nahar) is weekly paper serving the Arabic community in Dorval, Quebec.
NEWSPAPER

alAmeen Post
Owner: al-Ameen Media Inc.
Editorial: 7184 - 120th Street, Suite 596, Surrey, British Columbia V3W 0M6.
T: 1 604 715-7187 **E:** info@alameenpost.com
W: http://www.alameenpost.com
Freq: Bi-Weekly
Editorial Profile: alAmeen Post is a biweekly newspaper serving the Muslim community in British Columbia, Canada.
NEWSPAPER

Alberni Valley News
Owner: Black Press
Editorial: 4656 Margaret Street, Port Alberni, British Columbia V9Y 6H2. **T:** 1 250 723-6399
E: editor@albernivalleynews.com
W: http://www.albernivalleynews.com
Circ: 11500
Publisher: Teresa Bird; **Editor in Chief:** Susan Quinn; **Editor in Chief:** Susan Quinn
Editorial Profile: Alberni Valley News is a weekly newspaper serving residents of Port Alberni, British Columbia. The paper covers local news, events, schools, sports, businesses and features. Advertising deadlines are at 10am PT. The paper launched in August 2006.; Full Page Mono: 9.17
Currency: Canada Dollars
NEWSPAPER

Alberta Native News
Owner: Alberta LTD.
Editorial: 11460 Jasper Ave, Ste 207, Edmonton, Alberta T5K 0M1.
T: 1 780 421-7966
E: editor@albertanativenews.com
W: http://www.albertanativenews.com
Freq: Monthly; **Circ:** 14000
Editor in Chief: Deborah Shatz
Editorial Profile: Alberta Native News is a monthly, independent tabloid newspaper that features national and regional news and focuses on issues that are important to the Aboriginal communities across Canada.; Full Page Mono: 25.06
Currency: Canada Dollars
NEWSPAPER

Aldergrove Star
Owner: Black Press
Editorial: 27118 Frasey Hwy, Aldergrove, British Columbia V4W 3P5. **T:** 1 604 856-8303
W: http://www.aldergrovestar.com **Circ:** 10000
Editor in Chief: Kurt Langmann; **Publisher:** Dwayne Weidendorf
Editorial Profile: Aldergrove Star is a weekly newspaper covering local news and information for residents of Aldergrove, British Columbia. Deadlines for the publication are Mondays at 4pm PT.; Full Page Mono: 11.42
Currency: Canada Dollars
NEWSPAPER

Alfa
T: 1 514 531-1382 **W:** http://www.journalfa.ca
Freq: Monthly; **Circ:** 14200
Editorial Profile: Alfa is a monthly newspaper that features news and information for the residents of Maghreb and surrounding communities.
NEWSPAPER

Alliston Newspapers
Owner: Metroland Media Group Ltd.
Editorial: 169 Dufferin Street South, Unit 22, Alliston, Ontario L9R 1E6. **T:** 1 705 435-6228
E: herald@simcoe.com
W: http://www.allistonherald.com **Circ:** 24000
Editor: Scott Woodhouse
NEWSPAPER

Al-Mersal
Owner: Malawi (Ziad)
Editorial: 17 Kelfield Street, Toronto, Ontario M9W 5A1. **T:** 1 416 233-9927
E: hm@cdclimo.com
Freq: Monthly; **Circ:** 15000
Editorial Profile: Al-Mersal is a local community newspaper for the residents of Toronto and the surrounding communities.; Full Page Mono: 24.50
Currency: Canada Dollars
NEWSPAPER

Al-Mustakbal Newspapers
Owner: Centre Canadien pour L'Change Culturel et L'Integration
Editorial: 1305 Mazurette, Bureau 200, Montreal, Quebec H4N 1G8.
T: 1 514 334-0909 203
E: info@almustakbal.com
W: http://www.almustakbal.com **Circ:** 60500
Editor in Chief: Ibrahim Ghorayeb; **Publisher:** Joseph Nakhle
NEWSPAPER

Al-Qalam
Editorial: 1010 Richards St., Vancouver, British Columbia V6B 1G?2?.
T: 1 778 237-4546 **E:** info@penlingua.net
W: http://www.penlingua.net
Freq: Weekly
Editor in Chief: B. Abderrazak
Editorial Profile: Al-Qalam is a weekly newspaper that provides International and Community News coverage for the Arabic-speaking community in Vancouver, BC.
NEWSPAPER

La Alternative Latina
Editorial: 7201 Papineau Ave, Montreal, Quebec H2E 2G7. **T:** 1 514 374-2209
E: info@elchasquilatino.com
W: http://www.lalternativalatina.com
Circ: 15000
Editor In Chief: José Ramos
Editorial Profile: La Alternative Latina is a weekly newspaper serving the Hispanic community in Montreal.; Full Page Mono: 7.70
Currency: Canada Dollars
NEWSPAPER

Alto Newspapers
Owner: Alto Inc.
Editorial: 99 Professors Lake Parkway, Brampton, Ontario L6S 4P8.
T: 1 905 790-3229 **Circ:** 21075
Editor in Chief: Christiane Beaupre; **Editor:** Richard Caumartin; **Publisher:** Denis Poirier
Editorial Profile: Alto Newspapers cover local news in three weeklies published for the French speaking communities in Toronto, Niagara-Hamilton, London-Sarnia and surrounding communities in Ontario.
NEWSPAPER

American Life News
Editorial: 3131 Sheppard Ave E, 2nd Floor, Toronto, Ontario M1T 3J7. **T:** 1 416 645-0471
Circ: 17000
Editor in Chief: Thomas Lv; **Publisher:** Zhen Xiang Yi
Editorial Profile: American Life News is a weekly newspaper that carries news related to up-to-date information, job opportunities, local training, career guide, service provision, global trade, life story and classified advertisements. It is available free of charge in approximately 80 locations in the Greater Toronto Area, which include most Chinese supermarkets, Government sponsored employment service locations, HRDC centers, colleges, training schools, libraries, community plazas, and restaurants.
NEWSPAPER

The Anchor Weekly
T: 1 403 774-1352
W: http://www.theanchor.ca/ **Circ:** 10000
Publisher & Editor: Steve Jeffrey
Editorial Profile: The Anchor Weekly is a community newspaper serving the residents of Chestermere and surrounding areas near Calgary in Alberta, Canada. Topics include mostly local coverage of news, politics, and events.
NEWSPAPER

Anishinabek News
Owner: Union of Ontario Indians
Editorial: 1 Miigizi Mikan, North Bay, Ontario P1B 8J8. **T:** 1 705 497-9127
E: info@anishinabek.ca
W: http://www.anishinabek.ca
Freq: Monthly; **Circ:** 11000
Editorial Profile: Anishinabek News is a monthly newspaper published in North Bay, Ontario covering news and events of the Anishinabek aboriginals.; Full Page Mono: 27.30
Currency: Canada Dollars
NEWSPAPER

L' annonceur
Owner: MPA Concept
Editorial: 108, rue Maurault, Pierreville, Quebec J0G 1J0. **T:** 1 450 568-3186
E: lannonceur@lannonceur.ca
W: http://www.soreltracyregion.net/actualite/page/actualite/article/l
Freq: Weekly; **Circ:** 20000
Publisher: Jocelyne Hamel; **Editor:** Sébastien Lacroix
Editorial Profile: L'annonceur offers local news and information to residents of Ras-Richelieu, Bas-St-François and Nicolet-Yamaska, Quebec.
NEWSPAPER

Arab News Int'l-Canada Allam Arabic Publishing
Editorial: 602 Millwood Road, Toronto, Ontario M4S 1K8. **T:** 1 416 362-0307
E: arabnews@yahoo.com
W: http://www.arabnews.ca **Circ:** 43000
Publisher: Salah Allam; **Editor:** Emad Nafeh
NEWSPAPER

Asian Connections
Owner: Asian Connections Newspaper
Editorial: 1180 Midway Blvd, Unit 4, Mississauga, Ontario L5T 2B9.
T: 1 905 564-6200
E: theasianconnectionsnewspaper@gmail.com
W: http://www.acmgc.com/
Freq: Weekly; **Circ:** 32000
Editor: Sukhpreet Giani; **Publisher:** Rakhee Pbhakar
Editorial Profile: Asian Connections is a weekly newspaper providing Community News coverage for the South Asian and Indian Communities in the Greater Toronto area.; Full Page Mono: 12.94
Currency: Canada Dollars
NEWSPAPER

Asian Newsline
Editorial: 1111 Albion Rd Unit 204, Etobicoke, Ontario M9V 1A9. **T:** 1 416 740-7471
E: asiannewsline2004@yahoo.ca
W: http://www.asiannewslineweekly.com
Freq: Weekly
Editor: Pravin Sethi
Editorial Profile: Asian Newsline is a weekly newspaper that provides Community News to the South Asian and Indian communities in the Greater Toronto Area.
NEWSPAPER

Asian Pacific Post
Owner: Asian Post Media Publishing
T: 1 604 821-1954
E: editor@postpeopleinc.com
W: http://www.asianpacificpost.com
Freq: Bi-Weekly; **Circ:** 50000
Editor: Jagdeesh Mann; **Publisher:** Harbinder Sewak
Editorial Profile: Asian Pacific Post, launched in 1993, targets Vancouver, British Columbia Asians and mainstream readers seeking breaking and current news on the island, the Lower Mainland of British Columbia and throughout Asia.; Full Page Mono: 67.82; Full Page Colour: 350.00
Currency: US Dollars
NEWSPAPER

The Asian Star News
Editorial: 7028 120th Street, Surrey, British Columbia V3W 3M8. **T:** 1 604 591-5423
E: editor@theasianstar.com
W: http://www.theasianstar.ca **Circ:** 20000
Publisher: Iftikhar Ahmed; **Editor:** Umendra Singh
Editorial Profile: The Asian Star News is a weekly ethnic newspaper written for the Punjabi-speaking and south Asian communities in British Columbia.
NEWSPAPER

The Atlantic Co-operator
Editorial: 123 Halifax Street, Moncton, New Brunswick E1C 8N5. **T:** 1 506 858-6617
W: http://www.theatlanticco-operator.coop
Freq: Bi-Monthly; **Circ:** 11700
Publisher: Monique Bourque; **Editor in Chief:** Rayanne Brennan
Editorial Profile: Atlantic Co-operator is a Bi-monthly newspaper written for organizations and individuals interested in cooperative business in New Brunswick, Prince Edward Island, Nova Scotia and Newfoundland. It covers cooperative-business events, lifestyles, profiles, news and international cooperative businesses.; Full Page Mono: 34.05
Currency: Canada Dollars
NEWSPAPER

Auroran
Owner: London Publishing Corp.
Editorial: 15213 Younge Street, Ste 8, Aurora, Ontario L4G 1L8. **T:** 1 905 727-3300
W: http://www.auroran.com **Circ:** 18500
Editorial Profile: Auroran is a weekly newspaper serving residents and businesses of Aurora, Ontario. It contains local news, community events and features about local people and places.; Full Page Mono: 8.40
Currency: Canada Dollars
NEWSPAPER

L' Autre Voix
Owner: TC. Transcontinental
Editorial: 10989 boul. Sainte-Anne, Beaupre, Quebec G0A 1E0. **T:** 1 418 827-1511
W: http://www.lautrevoix.com **Circ:** 14800

Editor in Chief: Marc Cochrane; **Publisher:** Yvan Rancourt
Editorial Profile: L'Autre Voix is a French-language weekly newspaper. It features news for the region of Beaupre, Quebec.; Full Page Mono: 7.06
Currency: Canada Dollars
NEWSPAPER

L' Avantage Gaspesien
Owner: TC. Transcontinental
Editorial: 548, avenue du Phare Est, Bureau 102, Matane, Quebec G4W 1A7.
T: 1 418 562-0666
E: gaspesien@lavantage.qc.ca
W: http://www.lavantage.qc.ca **Circ:** 17019
Editor in Chief: Pierre Morel
Editorial Profile: L'Avantage Gaspesien is a weekly French newspaper covering local news and events in Matane and Haute-Gaspesie, Quebec.; Full Page Mono: 6.23
Currency: Canada Dollars
NEWSPAPER

L' Avenir de l'Érable
Owner: TC. Transcontinental
Editorial: 1620 rue Saint-Calixte, Plessisville, Quebec G6L 1P9. **T:** 1 819 362-7049
W: http://www.lanouvelle.net **Circ:** 10811
Publisher: Michel Chalifour; **Editor in Chief:** Ghislain Chauvette
Editorial Profile: L'Avenir de l'Érable is a weekly newspaper covering local news and features for the residents of Victoriaville and Plessisville, Quebec. Topics include municipal news, regional news, sports and arts & entertainment.; Full Page Mono: 13.86
Currency: Canada Dollars
NEWSPAPER

Aylmer Bulletin
Editorial: Unit C-10 181 rue Principale, Gatineau, Quebec J9H 6A6. **T:** 1 819 684-4755
E: abawqp@videotron.ca
W: http://www.bulletinaylmer.com **Circ:** 31280
Publisher & Editor: Fred Ryan
Editorial Profile: Aylmer Bulletin is a weekly community newspaper publisher serving the residents of Gantineau, Quebec.
NEWSPAPER

B.C. Catholic
Owner: Roman Catholic Archdiocese of Vancouver
Editorial: 150 Robson St, Vancouver, British Columbia V6B 2A7. **T:** 1 604 683-0281
E: bccatholic@rcav.org **W:** http://bcc.rcav.org
Circ: 21000
Editor: Paul Schratz
Editorial Profile: B.C. Catholic is written for the Catholic community in British Columbia and is the official newspaper of the Archdiocese of Vancouver. It covers international, national and local news of particular interest to Catholics. It also contains editorials, letters, movie and book reviews, saints, liturgy, questions and answers on faith, morals and Catholic theology, announcements and classifieds. Deadlines are on Tuesdays at noon PT.; Full Page Mono: 16.00
Currency: Canada Dollars
NEWSPAPER

Bancroft This Week
Owner: Quebecor Communications Inc.
Editorial: 254 Hastings St, Bancroft, Ontario K0L 1C0. **T:** 1 613 332-2002
E: btw.newsroom@sunmedia.ca
W: http://www.bancroftthisweek.com
Circ: 12000
Editor: Nate Smelle
Editorial Profile: Bancroft This Week is published weekly for the residents of Bancroft, Ontario and surrounding areas. The newspaper provides information about local news and community events.; Full Page Mono: 8.33; Full Page Colour: 1185.10
Currency: Canada Dollars
NEWSPAPER

Barrhaven Independent
Owner: Morris Newspaper Group
Editorial: 1165 Beaverwood Rd, Manotick, Ontario K4M 1A5. **T:** 1 613 825-9858
E: newscopy@bellnet.ca
W: http://www.barrhavenindependent.on.ca
Circ: 17625
Editorial Profile: Barrhaven Independent is a publication written for the South Nepean community of Barrhaven, Ontario. The publication covers local news, events, and sports. Deadlines for the publication are two weeks before issue date.; Full Page Mono: 9.80
Currency: Canada Dollars
NEWSPAPER

Barrie Advance
Owner: Metroland Media Group Ltd.
Editorial: 21 Patterson Rd, Barrie, Ontario L4N 7W6. **T:** 1 705 726-0573
W: http://www.barrieadvance.com **Circ:** 52800
Editorial Profile: Barrie Advance is a community newspaper written for the residents of Barrie, Ontario. The paper covers local news, sports and feature stories.; Full Page Mono: 86.58; Full Page Colour: 335.00
Currency: Canada Dollars
NEWSPAPER

Battleford Publications
Owner: Glacier Media Inc.
Editorial: 892-104 Street, North Battleford, Saskatchewan S9A 3E6. **T:** 1 306 445-7261
E: battlefords.publishing@sasktel.net
W: http://www.newsoptimist.ca **Circ:** 17259
Editor in Chief: Becky Doig; **Publisher:** Alana Schweitzer
NEWSPAPER

Bay Observer
Editorial: 140 King St E Suite 14, Hamilton, Ontario L8N 1B2. **T:** 1 905 522-6000
W: http://bayobserver.ca
Freq: Monthly; **Circ:** 30000
Editorial Profile: Bay Observer is written for the residents of Hamilton, Ontario.; Full Page Mono: 16.96
Currency: Canada Dollars
NEWSPAPER

Beach Metro Community News
Owner: Ward 9 Community News Inc.
Editorial: 2196 Gerrard St E, Toronto, Ontario M4E 2C7. **T:** 1 416 698-1164
W: http://www.beachmetro.com
Freq: Bi-Weekly; **Circ:** 30000
Publisher: Sheila Blinoff; **Editor:** Jon Muldoon
Editorial Profile: Beach Metro Community News is a non-profit, non-partisan community newspaper covering community news and features in and around Toronto. It was founded in 1972.; Full Page Mono: 20.72; Full Page Colour: 400.00
Currency: Canada Dollars
NEWSPAPER

Beauce Média
Owner: TC. Transcontinental
Editorial: 1147, boul. Vachon Nord, Ste-Marie-de-Beauce, Quebec G6E 1M9.
T: 1 418 387-8000
W: http://www.beaucemedia.canoe.ca
Circ: 19926
Editor: André Boutin; **Publisher:** Lise Doyon
Editorial Profile: Beauce-Média is a weekly French-language newspaper that covers local and regional information for the residents of Saint-Marie-de-Beauce, Quebec.; Full Page Mono: 7.84
Currency: Canada Dollars
NEWSPAPER

Belleville EMC Group
Owner: Metroland Media Group
Editorial: 244 Ashley St, Belleville, Ontario K0K 2B0. **T:** 1 613 966-2034
E: news@shieldmedia.ca
W: http://www.emconline.ca **Circ:** 69003
Editor: Cindy Redding
NEWSPAPER

Beseda/The Conversation
Owner: Kolovarsky (Sophie)
Editorial: 662 Sheppards Ave E, Ste 410, Toronto, Ontario M2K 3E6. **T:** 1 416 226-5026
E: beseda@rogers.com **Circ:** 15000
Publisher & Editor: Sophie Kolovarsky; Full Page Mono: 9.98
Currency: Canada Dollars
NEWSPAPER

Bharat Times
Owner: Bharat Times Inc.
Editorial: 33 Boul Levesque E, Laval, Quebec H7G 1B3. **T:** 1 514 999-8402
E: bharattimes@citpinc.ca
W: http://www.citpinc.biz/bharattimes
Freq: Weekly
Publisher & Editor: Monika Spolia
Editorial Profile: Bharat Times a weekly publication that covers multicultural events and news for the Indian community in Montreal, Canada . It is distributed throughout the Greater Montreal metropolitan area, covering Parc Extension, West Island, Brossard, Longueil, Cote-des-Neiges, Downtown, Montreal West, Ville St. Laurent and Lasalle.
NEWSPAPER

Big and Colourful Print and Publishing
Editorial: 74 Patterson Drive, Stonewall, Manitoba R0C 2Z0. **T:** 1 204 467-5836
Circ: 40617
Editor: Donna Maxwell
NEWSPAPER

Black Press - Castlegar
Owner: Black Press
Editorial: Unit 2, 1810 8th Avenue, Castlegar, British Columbia V1N 2Y2. **T:** 1 250 365-6397
W: http://www.castlegarnews.com **Circ:** 15500
Publisher: Chris Hopkyns; **Editor:** Jim Sinclair
NEWSPAPER

Black Press - Victoria
Owner: Black Press
Editorial: 818 Broughton St, Victoria, British Columbia V8W 1E4. **T:** 1 250 381-3633
W: http://www.blackpress.ca **Circ:** 65094
Publisher: Penny Sakamoto
NEWSPAPER

Black Press Publications
Owner: Black Press
Editorial: 2950 Bremner Ave., Red Deer, Alberta T4R 1M9. **T:** 1 403 343-2400
E: editorial@reddeeradvocate.com
W: http://www.reddeeradvocate.com
Circ: 58530
Publisher: Fred Gorman
NEWSPAPER

Blaue Seiten
Owner: B&Z Vertag Leddin
T: 1 519 576-6225 **E:** bzv@germanyweb.com
W: http://www.redaktion-blaueseiten.de/kanada.htm
Freq: Monthly; **Circ:** 52000
Editor in Chief: Tom Leddin
Editorial Profile: Blaue Seiten is a monthly German-language newspaper.; Full Page Mono: 43.63
Currency: Canada Dollars
NEWSPAPER

Bonus
Owner: Newcon Publishing
Editorial: 1183 Finch Avenue West, Suite 202, Toronto, Ontario M3J 2G2. **T:** 1 416 256-4896
E: bonus@bonus4u.com
W: http://www.newcon-publishing.com
Circ: 12500
Publisher & Editor: Simon Beker; Full Page Mono: 35.00
Currency: Canada Dollars
NEWSPAPER

Booster & Guardian
Owner: Metroland Media Group, Ltd.
Editorial: 7700 Hurontario St., Unit 201, Brampton, Ontario L6Y 4M3.
T: 1 905 454-4344
W: http://www.bramptonguardian.com
Publisher: Dana Robbins
NEWSPAPER

Boundary Publications
Owner: Glacier Media Inc.
Editorial: 68 Souris Ave N, Estevan, Saskatchewan S4A 2M3. **T:** 1 306 634-2654
E: editor@estevanmercury.ca
W: http://www.estevanmercury.ca **Circ:** 12467
NEWSPAPER

Brabant Newspapers
Owner: Metroland Media Group Ltd.
Editorial: 333 Arvin Ave, Stoney Creek, Ontario L8E 2M6. **T:** 1 905 664-8800
W: http://www.brabantnewspapers.com
Circ: 113489
Editor: Abigail Cukier; **Editor:** Debra Downey;
Publisher: Neil Oliver
NEWSPAPER

Bracebridge Publications
Owner: Metroland Media Group Ltd.
Editorial: 34 EP Lee Drive, Bracebridge, Ontario P1L 1V2. **T:** 1 705 645-8771
W: http://www.cottagecountrynow.ca
Circ: 46000
Editor: Kim Good; **News Editor:** Jacqueline Lawrence; **Editor in Chief:** Jack Tynan
Editorial Profile: Bracebridge Publications is a weekly community newspaper publisher serving the residents of Bracebridge and Muskoka, Ontario.
NEWSPAPER

The Bradford Times
Owner: Quebecor Communications Inc.
Editorial: 74 John St W, Bradford, Ontario L3Z 2B8. **T:** 1 905 775-4471
W: http://www.bradfordtimes.ca **Circ:** 11992
Publisher: Sandy Davies; **Editor in Chief:**

Miriam King; Full Page Mono: 7.49; Full Page Colour: 325.00
Currency: Canada Dollars
NEWSPAPER

The Brandon Sun
Owner: FP Canadian Newspapers LP
Editorial: 501 Rosser Ave, Brandon, Manitoba R7A 0K4. **T:** 1 204 727-2451
E: opinion@brandonsun.com
W: http://www.brandonsun.com
Freq: Daily; **Circ:** 13109
Editor: Colin Corneau; **News Night Editor:** Matt Goerzen; **Publisher:** Eric Lawson; **City Editor:** Jim Lewthwaite
Editorial Profile: The Brandon Sun is published daily for the residents of Brandon, Manitoba. The newspaper covers local news, business, sports and entertainment. The paper publishes everyday except Sunday.; Full Page Mono: 34.30; Full Page Colour: 97.27
Currency: Canada Dollars
DAILY NEWSPAPER

Brandon Sun Community News
Owner: FP Canadian Newspapers LP
Editorial: 501 Rosser Ave., Brandon, Manitoba R7A 0K4. **T:** 1 204 727-2451
E: opinion@brandonsun.com
W: http://www.brandonsun.com **Circ:** 40158
News Night Editor: Matt Goerzen; **News Editor:** Jim Lewthwaite; **Publisher:** Ewan Pow
Editorial Profile: The Brandon Sun Community News is a twice-weekly tabloid providing news for the residents of Brandon and Westman in Western Manitoba, Canada. It features sports, lifestyle, entertainment content and national, world and local news. It is published out of the same office as the Brandon Sun daily newspaper.; Full Page Mono: 10.50; Full Page Colour: 138.00
Currency: Canada Dollars
NEWSPAPER

The Brant News
Editorial: 111 Easton Rd, Brantford, Ontario N3P 1J4. **T:** 1 519 758-1157
E: editorial@brantnews.com
W: http://www.brantnews.com **Circ:** 49000
Editor: John Zronik
Editorial Profile: The Brant News is a weekly community newspaper that serves the residents of Brantford and Brant County, Ontario. The paper re-launched October 15, 2009. It had been defunct since the early 1990s.; Full Page Mono: 16.13
Currency: Canada Dollars
NEWSPAPER

Brasil News
Owner: Brasil News Publisher Inc.
Editorial: 390 Burnhamthorpe Rd, Toronto, Ontario M9B 2A8. **T:** 1 416 538-4298
E: brasilnews@brasilnews.ca
W: http://www.brasilnews.ca
Freq: Bi-Weekly; **Circ:** 10000
Editor in Chief: Carolina Ladeira; **Publisher:** Tania Nuttall
Editorial Profile: Since 1997, Brasil News has been the only Brazilian newspaper distributed in Toronto, including neighborhoods in the Greater Toronto Area like Brampton and Mississauga. Covers important local news and events. Also publishes articles from the community members about various subjects.; Full Page Mono: 4.26
Currency: Canada Dollars
NEWSPAPER

Brome County News
Owner: Glacier Media Inc.
Editorial: 5 B Victoria St, Knowlton, Quebec J0E 1V0. **T:** 1 450 242-1188
E: dcolombe@sherbrookerecord.com
W: http://www.sherbrookerecord.com
Circ: 13600
Publisher & Editor: Sharon McCully
Editorial Profile: Brome County News is written for the residents of Brome-Missiquoi and Eastern Townships of Quebec.; Full Page Mono: 16.38
Currency: Canada Dollars
NEWSPAPER

Brooks & County Chronicle
Owner: Rural Roots Marketing Group, Inc.
Editorial: 619 1st St W, Brooks, Alberta T1R 0N3. **T:** 1 403 793-2252
E: thechronicle@telusplanet.net
W: http://brooksinthenews.com **Circ:** 11302
Publisher & Editor: M. Joan Brees
Editorial Profile: Brooks & County Chronicle is a weekly publication that covers local news and events for residents of Brooks, Alberta.; Full Page Mono: 12.32; Full Page Colour: 260.00
Currency: Canada Dollars
NEWSPAPER

Brooks Bulletin Newspapers
Owner: Nesbitt Publishing Ltd.
Editorial: 124 3rd St W, Brooks, Alberta T1R 0S3. **T:** 1 403 362-5571
E: editor@brooksbulletin.com
W: http://www.brooksbulletin.com **Circ:** 15735
NEWSPAPER

Brunswick News Publications - Moncton
Owner: Brunswick News Inc.
Editorial: 939 Main St, Moncton, New Brunswick E1C 8P3. **T:** 1 506 383-2563
E: thisweek@brunswicknews.com
W: http://www.canadaeast.com **Circ:** 98000
Editor: Madeleine Leclerc; **Editor in Chief:** Philippe Ricard
NEWSPAPER

Brunswick Newspapers - Woodstock
Owner: Brunswick News Inc.
Editorial: 110 Carleton St, Woodstock, New Brunswick E7M 1E4. **T:** 1 506 328-8863
E: news@thebugle.ca
W: http://www.telegraphjournal.com
Circ: 34700
NEWSPAPER

Bulgarian Flame
Editorial: 206 – 11 Dervock Cres, Toronto, Ontario M2K 1A6. **T:** 1 416 821-9915
E: info@bulbiz.com
W: http://bulgarianflame.com
Freq: Bi-Weekly
Editor in Chief: Viara Dimitrova
Editorial Profile: Bulgarian Flame is a bi-weekly newspaper covering news and cultural events for the Bulgarian community in Canada and Canadians of Bulgarian ancestry.
NEWSPAPER

Le Bulletin
Owner: TC. Transcontinental
Editorial: 3 Rue Principale, Saint-Andre-Avellin, Quebec J0V 1W0. **T:** 1 819 986-5089
W: http://www.lebulletin.net **Circ:** 14328
Publisher: Eric Lafleur
Editorial Profile: Le Bulletin de la Lièvre is a weekly French-language newspaper published by Transcontinental Publishing. The paper covers local and regional news, entertainment, education, sports, and government for those in and around Buckingham, QC. Contact the publication by phone, fax, or mail.; Full Page Mono: 11.34
Currency: Canada Dollars
NEWSPAPER

The Bulletin
Owner: Community Bulletin Newspaper Group Inc.
Editorial: 121-260 Adelaide St E, Toronto, Ontario M5A 1N1. **T:** 1 416 929-0011
E: info@thebulletin.ca
W: http://www.thebulletin.ca
Freq: Monthly; **Circ:** 77500
Editor in Chief: Frank Touby
Editorial Profile: News & features mailed to downtown Toronto neighborhoods, including St. Lawrence, Harbourfront Toronto Islands, Corktown, Gooderham & Worts, West Don Lands, and South Cabbage Town, King & Queen West, Gardon District.; Full Page Mono: 77.28
Currency: Canada Dollars
NEWSPAPER

The Burlington Post
Owner: Metroland Media Group Ltd.
Editorial: 5040 Mainway, Unit 1, Burlington, Ontario L7L 7G5. **T:** 1 905 632-4444
W: http://www.burlingtonpost.com **Circ:** 45819
Editor in Chief: Jill Davis; **Publisher:** Neil Oliver
Editorial Profile: Burlington Post, published three times a week, is a newspaper serving residents of Burlington, Ontario and surrounding communities. The publication covers local news, sports, arts and entertainment and business.; Full Page Mono: 13.58; Full Page Colour: 1160.00
Currency: Canada Dollars
NEWSPAPER

Burnaby Newspapers
Editorial: 201A - 3430 Brighton Ave., Burnaby, British Columbia V5A 3H4. **T:** 1 604 444-3451
Circ: 120793
Publisher: Brad Alden; **Editor in Chief:** Leneen Robb; **Editor in Chief:** Pat Tracy
NEWSPAPER

Burnaby/New Westminster NewsLeader
Owner: Black Press
Editorial: 7438 Fraser Park Drive, Burnaby, British Columbia V5J 5B9. **T:** 1 604 438-6397
W: http://www.burnabynewsleader.com
Circ: 61500
Editor: Chris Bryan
NEWSPAPER

C.K. News Group
Owner: Charhdi Kala Punjabi Weekly Newspaper International Inc.
Editorial: 7743 128 St Suite 6, Surrey, British Columbia V3W 1L4. **T:** 1 604 590-6397
E: cknewsgroup@telus.net
W: http://www.cknewsgroup.com **Circ:** 37000
Editor: Gurpreet Sahota; **Editor:** Gurpreet Sahota
Editorial Profile: Publishes two weekly Punjabi newspapers covering local, national and international news. They cover articles regarding religious, political and multicultural issues as well as news events from around the world, sports, business, fiction and non fictional articles and entertainment regarding the Punjabi, Sikh and Indo-Canadian community.
NEWSPAPER

Caledon Enterprise
Owner: Metroland Media Group Ltd.
Editorial: 12612 Highway 50, Bolton, Ontario L7E 5T1. **T:** 1 905 857-3433
W: http://www.caledonenterprise.com
Circ: 14685
Editor: Robyn Wilkinson
Editorial Profile: Caledon Enterprise is a newspaper published two times a week for the Caledon, Ontario community. The publication covers local news, sports and entertainment.; Full Page Mono: 21.31
Currency: Canada Dollars
NEWSPAPER

Calgary Herald
Owner: Postmedia Network Inc.
Editorial: 215 16 St SE, Calgary, Alberta T2E 7P5-. **T:** 1 403 235-7100
E: submit@calgaryherald.com
W: http://www.calgaryherald.com
Freq: Daily; **Circ:** 119617
Editorial Profile: Calgary Herald is a broadsheet newspaper established in 1883. The newspaper includes the following sections: Sports, Business, Arts & Style, City and Classifieds. In November 2000, the paper became part of the Southam Publications division of CanWest Global Communications. The Sunday edition ceased publication on July 29, 2012.; Full Page Mono: 101.08; Full Page Colour: 118.68
Currency: Canada Dollars
DAILY NEWSPAPER

The Calgary Sun
Owner: Quebecor Communications Inc.
Editorial: 2615 12 St NE, Calgary, Alberta T2E 7W9-. **T:** 1 403 410-1010
E: cal-news@sunmedia.ca
W: http://www.calgarysun.com
Freq: Daily; **Circ:** 49258
City Editor: Dave Naylor; **Editor in Chief:** Jose Rodriguez; **Editor in Chief:** Jose Rodriguez; **Editor in Chief:** Jose Rodriguez; **Editor in Chief:** Jose Rodriguez
Editorial Profile: The Calgary Sun is written for residents of Calgary, Alberta. The publication covers local, national and international news on politics, business, homes, entertainment and sports. The publication does not offer reader service cards and does not publish an editorial calendar. Editors do not honor non-disclosure agreements. It debuted in August 1980.; Full Page Mono: 26.32; Full Page Colour: 148.83
Currency: Canada Dollars
DAILY NEWSPAPER

The Cambridge Times
Owner: Metroland Media Group Ltd.
Editorial: 475 Thompson Dr Unite 1-4, Cambridge, Ontario N1T 2K7.
T: 1 519 623-7395
W: http://www.cambridgetimes.ca **Circ:** 46525
Editor: Richard Vivian; **Publisher:** Peter Winkler
Editorial Profile: Cambridge Times's editorial mission is, "To deliver the community news the readers have come to expect, issue after issue." The newspaper focuses on local issues, special events, what the kids are doing, who won what, and where to find the goods and services they need. The publication is aimed at residents of Cambridge, aged 25 to 40. It is delivered twice weekly, on Tuesday and Friday, free of charge. The lead time is two days. Deadlines for the publication are Monday and Wednesday at 12:00 p.m. ET before issue date.; Full Page Mono: 31.50; Full Page Colour: 550.00
Currency: Canada Dollars
NEWSPAPER

Campbell River Courier-Islander
Owner: Glacier Media Inc.
Editorial: 1040 Cedar St, Campbell River, British Columbia V9W 7E2. **T:** 1 250 287-7464
E: editor@courierislander.com
W: http://www.courierislander.com **Circ:** 20376
Editorial Profile: Campbell River Courier-Islander provides news and information to the residents of Campbell River.; Full Page Mono: 7.07
Currency: Canada Dollars
NEWSPAPER

Camrose Booster
Owner: Camrose Booster Ltd.
Editorial: 4925-48th St, Camrose, Alberta T4V 1L7. **T:** 1 780 672-3142
E: news@camrosebooster.com
W: http://www.camrosebooster.com
Circ: 13520
Editor in Chief: B.H. Fowler; Full Page Mono: 13.30; Full Page Colour: 465.00
Currency: Canada Dollars
NEWSPAPER

Camrose Canadian
Owner: Quebecor Communications Inc.
Editorial: 4610-49th Avenue, Camrose, Alberta T4V 0M9. **T:** 1 780 672-4421
E: production@camrosecanadian.com
W: http://www.camrosecanadian.com
Circ: 14500
Publisher: Jim Clark; **Editor:** Mark Crown
Editorial Profile: Camrose Canadian is a weekly newspaper serving the residents of Camrose, Alberta.; Full Page Mono: 12.32
Currency: Canada Dollars
NEWSPAPER

Canada China News
Editorial: 1 Cleopatra Dr, Ste 208, Nepean, Ontario K2G 3M9. **T:** 1 613 233-1034
E: info@canadachinanews.com
W: http://www.canadachinanews.com
Circ: 13000
Publisher: Ren Ren Bai; **Editor in Chief:** Ming Yang
Editorial Profile: Canada China News features local and international news concerning Ottawa's Chinese community. Advertising deadline is Friday before publication. Add 30% for color ads.; Full Page Mono: 6.66
Currency: Canada Dollars
NEWSPAPER

The Canadian
Editorial: B.P. 24191, 300 Eagleson Rd., Ottawa, Ontario K2M 2C3. **T:** 1 888 377-2222
E: news@agoracosmopolitan.com
W: http://www.agoracosmopolitan.com
Circ: 500000
Editor in Chief: Peter Tremblay
Editorial Profile: The Canadian is a weekly newpaper featuring national and international news. The paper targets a cross-cultural readership focusing on news, lifestyle, editorial, sexuality, arts & entertainment, travel and health.; Full Page Mono: 86.87
Currency: Canada Dollars
NEWSPAPER

Canadian Asian News
Editorial: 852 Preston Manor Dr, Mississauga, Ontario L5V 2L6. **T:** 1 905 502-5585
E: asiannews1@gmail.com
W: http://www.canadianasiannews.com/can.php **Circ:** 15000
Publisher & Editor: Latafat Ali Siddiqui
Editorial Profile: Canadian Asian News is a community newspaper publisher serving the Asian population of Toronto and Montreal.
NEWSPAPER

Canadian Chinese Times - Calgary
Editorial: 1914A Centre St NE, Calgary, Alberta T2E 2S8. **T:** 1 403 230-8118
E: calcct@gmail.com
W: http://2010cctimes.com/main/index.html
Freq: Weekly
Editorial Profile: Covers national news, world news, entertainment, health, and lifestyle.
NEWSPAPER

Canadian Chinese Times - Edmonton
Owner: CC Times
Editorial: #222 9700-105 AVE, Edmonton, Alberta T5H 4J1. **T:** 1 780 761-3883
E: info@ecctimes.com
W: http://2010cctimes.com/main/index.html

Editorial Profile: Covers national news, world news, entertainment, health and lifestyle.
NEWSPAPER

The Canadian Jewish News
Editorial: 1750 Steeles Ave W Suite 218, Concord, Ontario L4K 2L7. **T:** 1 416 391-1836
E: cjninfo@gmail.com
W: http://www.cjnews.com **Circ:** 35000
Editor: Yoni Goldstein
Editorial Profile: Canadian Jewish News is Canada's largest Jewish newspaper. Published weekly, the CJN has many traditional news sections, including: sports, arts, travel, health, business, food, seniors, and campus life but focuses upon Israeli and Jewish Community issues. In addition, the paper also incorporates important news items about Israel as well as other countries' Jewish news stories. There are two editions: the English-only Toronto edition, and the bilingual French-English Montreal edition. The Toronto edition is a national publication (with international subscribers), while the Montreal edition caters to the Quebec region.; Full Page Mono: 24.00
Currency: Canada Dollars
NEWSPAPER

Canadian Jewish News - Montreal
Editorial: 6900 Decarie Blvd. #3125, Montreal, Quebec H3X 2T8. **T:** 1 514 735-2612
E: montreal@thecjn.ca
W: http://www.cjnews.com **Circ:** 37187
Editor: Yoni Goldstein; Full Page Mono: 27.51
Currency: Canada Dollars
NEWSPAPER

Canadian Mennonite
Owner: Canadian Mennonite Publishing Service
Editorial: 490 Dutton Drive, Unit C 5, Waterloo, Ontario N2L 6H7.
T: 1 519 884-3810
E: submit@canadianmennonite.org
W: http://www.canadianmennonite.org
Freq: Bi-Weekly; **Circ:** 13800
Editorial Profile: Canadian Mennonite aims to promote discussion and build community among Mennonites in Canada.; Full Page Mono: 30.00; Full Page Colour: 175.00
Currency: Canada Dollars
NEWSPAPER

Can-India News
Owner: Marjara (Jaswinder)
Editorial: 2600 Skymark Avenue, Building 11 Unit 103, Mississauga, Ontario L4W 5B2.
T: 1 905 673-6625
W: http://www.canindia.com **Circ:** 30000
Editor: K.B. Kapur; **Publisher & Editor:** Jaswinder Marjara
Editorial Profile: Can-India News is a local newspaper for the Indian residents of Mississauga, Ontario and the surrounding communities.; Full Page Mono: 11.90; Full Page Colour: 14.51
Currency: Canada Dollars
NEWSPAPER

Canstar Community News
Owner: FP Canadian Newspapers LP
Editorial: 1355 Mountain Ave, Winnipeg, Manitoba R2X 3B6-. **T:** 1 204 697-7009
W: http://www.winnipegfreepress.com/our-communities **Circ:** 192357
Publisher: Michelle Pereira
NEWSPAPER

Cape Breton Post
Owner: TC. Transcontinental
Editorial: 255 George St, Sydney, Nova Scotia B1P 6K6. **T:** 1 902 564-5451
W: http://www.capebretonpost.com
Freq: Daily; **Circ:** 24924
Publisher: Anita DeLazzer; **Editor:** Laura Jean Grant
Editorial Profile: Cape Breton Post is written for the residents of Cape Breton, Nova Scotia. It covers sports, business, lifestyles, entertainment and local news with specific coverage of the Sydney, Northside, Victoria, Low Point, Little Pond, Port Hawksesbury, Glace Bay and New Waterford regions. The daily deadline is 11:30pm AT. Lead time varies.; Full Page Mono: 12.04; Full Page Colour: 800.00
Currency: Canada Dollars
DAILY NEWSPAPER

CAPS
Editorial: 201 North Street, Port Perry, Ontario L9L 1B7. **T:** 1 905 985-9755
W: http://www.scugogcg.com/caps.html
Freq: Monthly; **Circ:** 20000
Editor: Deb Bartlett
Editorial Profile: CAPS is a monthly community newspaper for the residents of Port Perry, Ontario and the surrounding communities.; Full Page Mono: 4.98; Full Page Colour: 5.49
Currency: Canada Dollars
NEWSPAPER

Caribbean Xpress
Owner: NB Spring
Editorial: 6765 Invader Crescent, Mississauga, Ontario L5T 2B7. **T:** 1 905 362-0323
E: info@caribbeanxpress.ca
W: http://www.caribbeanxpress.ca
Freq: Bi-Monthly
Publisher: NIrvan Balkissoon
NEWSPAPER

The Cariboo Advisor
Owner: Black Press
Editorial: 68 N Broadway, Williams Lake, British Columbia V2G 1C1. **T:** 1 250 398-5516
E: production@caribooadvisor.com
Circ: 10500
Editor: Laura Kelsey; **Publisher:** Kathy McLean
Editorial Profile: The Cariboo Advisor covers news and events for Williams Lake, British Columbia and the surrounding communities.; Full Page Mono: 6.23
Currency: Canada Dollars
NEWSPAPER

Cariboo Press Publications - Kitimat
Owner: Black Press
Editorial: 626 Enterprise Ave, Kitimat, British Columbia V8C 2E4. **T:** 1 250 632-6144
E: advertising@northernsentinel.com
W: http://www.northernsentinel.com
Circ: 23200
Editor in Chief: Malcolm Baxter; **Publisher:** Louisa Genzale; **Editor:** Cameron Orr
Editorial Profile: The Northern Sentinel has been a part of Kitimat almost from the beginning of the community. Since the first issue hit the muddy, construction-era streets in 1954, it has chronicled the lives and times of this unique town and its people.
NEWSPAPER

Cariboo Press Publications - Salmon Arm
Owner: Black Press
Editorial: 171 Shuswap St. NW, Salmon Arm, British Columbia V1E 4N7. **T:** 1 250 832-2131
W: http://www.saobserver.net **Circ:** 20365
Editor in Chief: Tracy Hughes; **Publisher:** Rick Proznick
NEWSPAPER

Cariboo Press Publications - Williams Lake
Owner: Black Press
Editorial: 188 N 1st Aveve, Williams Lake, British Columbia V2G 1Y8. **T:** 1 250 392-2331
E: editor@wltribune.com
W: http://www.wltribune.com **Circ:** 16070
NEWSPAPER

Central Manitoba Shopper News
Owner: Quebecor Communications Inc.
Editorial: 1943 Saskatchewan Ave W, Portage La Prairie, Manitoba R1N 0R7.
T: 1 204 857-7582
E: cm.shopper@sunmedia.ca
Freq: Bi-Weekly; **Circ:** 12000
Publisher: Elaine Graham
Editorial Profile: Central Manitoba Shopper News is a local paper written for the residents of Portage La Prairie, Manitoba.; Full Page Mono: 10.92
Currency: Canada Dollars
NEWSPAPER

Central Plains Herald-Leader
Owner: Quebecor Communications Inc.
Editorial: 1941 Saskatchewan Ave W, Portage La Prairie, Manitoba R1N 0R7.
T: 1 204 857-3427
E: news.dailygraphic@shawcable.com
W: http://www.thedailygraphic.com
Circ: 11500
Publisher: Barry Clayton; **Editor:** Johnna Ruocco; **Publisher:** Daria Zmiyiwsky
Editorial Profile: Central Plains Herald-Leader is a community newspaper covering local news and information in Portage La Prairie, Manitoba.; Full Page Mono: 14.98
Currency: Canada Dollars
NEWSPAPER

The Centretown Buzz
Editorial: 101-210 Gloucester St., Ottawa, Ontario K2P 2K4. **T:** 1 613 565-6012
E: info@centretown.net
W: http://www.centretownbuzz.com/
Freq: Monthly; **Circ:** 10000
Editorial Profile: The Centretown Buzz is a free community newspaper published monthly for residents of the Sommerset Ward, Ontario community. The paper covers neighborhood issues and notable events of community interest. Short notices for not-for-profit community events may be published at no cost. Larger notices and notices for for-profit events will be accepted as advertising.; Full Page Mono: 10.91
Currency: Canada Dollars
NEWSPAPER

Chambly Express
Owner: TC. Transcontinental
Editorial: 1691 - C, boul. de Périgny, Chambly, Quebec J3L 1X1. **T:** 1 450 658-5559
E: chamblyexpress@tc.tc
W: http://www.chamblyexpress.ca
Freq: Weekly; **Circ:** 27125
Publisher: Claude Deshaies; **Editor:** Lucia Lecours
Editorial Profile: Chambly Express offers local news and information in French to residents in and around Chambly, Quebec.; Full Page Mono: 1.28
Currency: Canada Dollars
NEWSPAPER

Châteauguay Express
Owner: TC. Transcontinental
Editorial: 420, rue Lafleur à Lasalle, Chateauguay, Quebec H8R 3H5.
T: 1 514 363-5656
E: redaction_chateauguayexpress@transcontinental.ca
W: http://www.chateauguayexpress.ca
Freq: Weekly; **Circ:** 40000
News Editor: Josianne Desjardins; **Publisher:** Julie Voyer
Editorial Profile: Châteauguay Express is a bilingual community newspaper offering local news and information in French and English to residents of the Montérégie towns of Châteauguay, Beauharnois, Léry, Mercier, Sainte-Martine, Saint-Rémi, Saint-Isidore, Sainte-Clothilde, Şaint-Chrysostome, Hawick, Saint-Urbain, St-Étienne de Beauharnois, St-Urbain-De-Chateauguay, Melocheville, and Maple-Grove, Quebec.; Full Page Mono: 8.82
Currency: Canada Dollars
NEWSPAPER

The Chatham Daily News
Owner: Quebecor Communications Inc.
Editorial: 138 King St W, Chatham, Ontario N7M 1E3-. **T:** 1 519 354-2000
E: cdn.newsroom@sunmedia.ca
W: http://www.chathamdailynews.ca
Freq: Daily; **Circ:** 12134
Publisher: Dean Muharrem
Editorial Profile: Chatham Daily News serves the Chatham-Kent area in southwestern Ontario. The paper reports on news, travel, sports, business, arts and lifestyle, as well as occasional extra issues devoted to hunting. It publishes Tuesday through Saturday.; Full Page Mono: 13.63; Full Page Colour: 562.74
Currency: Canada Dollars
DAILY NEWSPAPER

Chatham This Week
Owner: Sun Media
Editorial: 138 King St. W, Chatham, Ontario N7M 1E3. **T:** 1 519 351-7331
W: http://www.chathamthisweek.com
Circ: 20000
Editor: Peter Epp; **Publisher:** Dean Muharrem
Editorial Profile: Chatham This Week is a weekly publication written for residents of Chatham, Ontario. It covers local news, weather and sports.; Full Page Mono: 7.49
Currency: Canada Dollars
NEWSPAPER

The Chatham Voice
Owner: C-K Media Inc.
Editorial: 84 Dover St, Chatham, Ontario N7L 1T1. **T:** 1 519 397-2020
W: http://www.chathamvoice.com/
Freq: Weekly; **Circ:** 21000
Editor: Bruce Corcoran
Editorial Profile: The Chatham Voice is written for residents of Chatham centering on the community in its reporting. Sections include News, which has a local angle; Arts; Life; Business; and Sports, covering local sporting events and athletes. This outlet offers a free weekly online E-edition.; Full Page Colour: 1355.00
Currency: Canada Dollars
NEWSPAPER

Chilliwack Progress
Owner: Black Press
Editorial: 45860 Spadina Ave, Chilliwack, British Columbia V2P 6H9. **T:** 1 604 702-5550
E: editor@theprogress.com
W: http://www.theprogress.com **Circ:** 30180
Publisher: Liz Lynch
Editorial Profile: Chilliwack Progress is the oldest weekly newspaper in British Columbia. It covers local news and features for the community of Chilliwack, British Columbia. Abbotsford News and Chilliwack Progress produce a publication known as The Fraser Valley Daily, which runs Tuesdays through Fridays and reprints content from the weekly papers.; Full Page Mono: 25.07; Full Page Colour: 537.00
Currency: Canada Dollars
NEWSPAPER

Chilliwack Times
Owner: Black Press
Editorial: 102-45951 Trethewey Ave 102, Chilliwack, British Columbia V2P 1K4.
T: 1 604 792-9117
E: editorial@chilliwacktimes.com
W: http://www.chilliwacktimes.com
Circ: 30000
Editorial Profile: Chilliwack Times is a local newspaper written for the residents of Chilliwack, British Columbia. The publication covers local news, sports and arts & entertainment.; Full Page Mono: 23.80; Full Page Colour: 400.00
Currency: Canada Dollars
NEWSPAPER

Chinese Canadian Times - Eastern Canada Edition
Editorial: 2528 Bayview Avenue, Toronto, Ontario M2L 1A9. **T:** 1 416 445-7815
E: web@cctimes.ca **W:** http://www.cctimes.ca
Circ: 13000
Publisher: Kathy Lin; **Editor:** Schiller Wang
Editorial Profile: Chinese Canadian Times - Eastern Canada Edition is a local, weekly, Mandarin-language newspaper serving primarily Chinese residents of Toronto.; Full Page Mono: 17.30
Currency: Canada Dollars
NEWSPAPER

Chinese News
Owner: Chinese News Group
Editorial: 50 Weybright Ct, Unit 11, Scarborough, Ontario M1S 5A8.
T: 1 416 504-0761 **E:** cng@096.ca
W: http://www.chinesenewsgroup.com
Circ: 12000
Editor: Nancy Jin
Editorial Profile: Chinese News offers local news and events to the Chinese and Chinese-speaking communities of Toronto.; Full Page Mono: 23.52
Currency: Canada Dollars
NEWSPAPER

The Chinese Press/La Presse Chinoise
Owner: Eastern Chinese Press Inc. La Presse Chinoise de l'Est
Editorial: 1123 Clark St, 2nd Fl, Montreal, Quebec H2Z 1K3. **T:** 1 514 397-9969
E: cpress@chinesepress.com
W: http://www.chinesepress.com **Circ:** 25000
Editorial Profile: The Chinese Press/La Presse Chinoise is a Chinese-language publication for members of the Chinese community in Francophone Canada. The paper includes international, local, Chinese, community, financial and entertainment news.; Full Page Mono: 13.64
Currency: Canada Dollars
NEWSPAPER

Le Chinook
Owner: ViaPlus Communications Inc./Le Chinook
Editorial: 32-805 5th Ave SW, Calgary, Alberta T2P 0N6. **T:** 1 403 457-5250
E: nouvelles@lechinook.com
W: http://www.lechinook.com
Freq: Monthly; **Circ:** 20000
Editorial Profile: Le Chinook is a community newspaper written for the residents of Calgary, Alberta.; Full Page Mono: 7.84; Full Page Colour: 400.00
Currency: Canada Dollars
NEWSPAPER

ChristianWeek Papers
Owner: Fellowship for Print Witness Inc.
Editorial: 204-424 Logan Ave., Winnipeg, Manitoba R3A 0R4. **T:** 1 204 982-2060
E: admin@christianweek.org
W: http://www.christianweek.org **Circ:** 46000
Publisher: Brian Koldyk; **Editor:** Kelly Rempel
NEWSPAPER

The Chronicle Herald
Owner: Halifax Herald Ltd. (The)
Editorial: 2717 Joseph Howe Dr, Halifax, Nova Scotia B3L 4T9-. **T:** 1 902 426-2811
E: newsroom@herald.ca

W: http://thechronicleherald.ca
Freq: Daily; **Circ:** 93351
Editor in Chief: Bob Howse; **News Editor:** Christine Soucie; **News Editor:** Pam Sword
Editorial Profile: The Chronicle Herald is the largest newspaper in Nova Scotia and the highest circulation newspaper in Canada's Atlantic provinces. This broadsheet newspaper targeting Halifax residents was established in 1874 and offers to its readers Nova Scotia, national and international news, business, sports, entertainment and more. The newspaper has won several awards including the National Newspaper Award and Atlantic Journalism Award.; Full Page Mono: 123.51; Full Page Colour: 442.71
Currency: Canada Dollars
DAILY NEWSPAPER

The Chronicle-Journal
Owner: Continental Newspapers Canada Ltd.
Editorial: 75 Cumberland St S, Thunder Bay, Ontario P7B 1A3. **T:** 1 807 343-6200
E: news@chroniclejournal.com
W: http://www.chroniclejournal.com
Freq: Daily; **Circ:** 21558
Day News Editor: Greg Giddens
Editorial Profile: The Chronicle-Journal is written for the Thunder Bay, Ontario vicinity and the Northwestern Ontario general public. The paper covers regional and local news, sports, business, lifestyles and entertainment. All press releases should be sent by fax. Deadlines are daily at 4pm ET.; Full Page Mono: 19.88; Full Page Colour: 75.15
Currency: Canada Dollars
DAILY NEWSPAPER

Le Citoyen de l'Harricana
Owner: TC. Transcontinental
Editorial: 92 Rue Principale S, Amos, Quebec J9T 2J6. **T:** 1 819 732-6531
W: http://www.lecitoyenharricana.canoe.ca
Circ: 11100
Publisher: Caroline Couture; **Editor:** David Prince
Editorial Profile: Le Citoyen de l'Harricana is a weekly newspaper produced by TC Transoncontinental. It is a French-language publication that covers news and events in the Amos region of Quebec.; Full Page Mono: 11.34
Currency: Canada Dollars
NEWSPAPER

Claridge Community Newspapers
Owner: Claridge Community Newspapers
Editorial: 10 1st St, Orangeville, Ontario L9W 2C4. **T:** 1 519 941-2230 **E:** mail@citizen.on.ca
W: http://www.citizen.on.ca **Circ:** 16612
Publisher: Alan Claridge; **Editor in Chief:** Thomas Claridge
NEWSPAPER

Clark's Crossing Gazette
Editorial: 430 D Central St., Warman, Saskatchewan S0K 4S0. **T:** 1 306 668-0575
E: ads@ccgazette.ca
W: http://www.ccgazette.ca **Circ:** 15216
Editorial Profile: Clark's Crossing Gazette is a free, weekly newspaper serving the community of Warman, Saskatchewan. Editorial coverage includes local politics, events and sports. Advertising deadlines fall on Mondays at 5pm and editorial deadlines on Tuesdays at 10am.; Full Page Mono: 16.24
Currency: Canada Dollars
NEWSPAPER

Clarkson's Corners
Owner: RJ Publishing
Editorial: 2673 Burnford Trail, Mississauga, Ontario L5M 5E1. **T:** 1 905 820-5458
E: lettersnlines@rogers.com
W: http://rjentpub.com
Freq: Bi-Monthly; **Circ:** 16000
Editorial Profile: Clarkson's Corners is a bi-monthly newspaper serving the community of Misissauga, Ontario and surrounding areas.; Full Page Mono: 12.57
Currency: Canada Dollars
NEWSPAPER

The Clipper Weekly
Owner: Clipper Publishing Corp.
Editorial: 27A Third Street South, Beausejour, Manitoba R0E 0C0. **T:** 1 204 268-4700
E: mail@clipper.mb.ca
W: http://www.clipper.mb.ca **Circ:** 10576
Editor in Chief: Mark Buss; **Publisher:** Kim MacAulay
Editorial Profile: The Clipper Weekly is a newspaper published for residents of Beausejour, Manitoba. The paper covers local news, weather and events.; Full Page Mono: 14.00
Currency: Canada Dollars

NEWSPAPER

Cloverdale Reporter
Owner: Black Press
Editorial: 17586-56A Ave, Surrey, British Columbia V3S 1G3. **T:** 1 604 575-2405
W: http://www.cloverdalereporter.com
Circ: 21500
Editor: Jennifer Lang
Editorial Profile: Cloverdale Reporter is a monthly newspaper serving the residents of Cloverdale, South Surrey and Sullivan, Hazelmere and Fleetwood in British Columbia. It covers local news, sports, events listings and arts & entertainment.; Full Page Mono: 15.82
Currency: Canada Dollars
NEWSPAPER

Cloverdale Source & The Now Newspapers
Owner: Postmedia Network Inc.
Editorial: 7889 132nd, Suite 201, Surrey, British Columbia V3W 4N2. **T:** 1 604 572-0064
W: http://www.thenownewspaper.com
Circ: 153000
NEWSPAPER

The Coast
Owner: Coast Publishing Ltd.
Editorial: 5567 Cunard St., Halifax, Nova Scotia B3K IC5. **T:** 1 902 422-6278
E: coast@thecoast.ca
W: http://www.thecoast.ca **Circ:** 24000
News Editor: Tim Bousquet; **Publisher:** Christine Oreskovich; **Editor:** Kyle Shaw
Editorial Profile: The Coast is local newspaper published every Thursday by Coast Publishing. The newspaper is published for the residents of Halifax, NS. It covers nightlife, entertainment, music, movies, and social events. The newspapers goal is to be provocative, entertaining, and truthful. The lead time is three days.; Full Page Mono: 35.00; Full Page Colour: 49.80
Currency: Canada Dollars
NEWSPAPER

Coast Reporter
Owner: Glacier Media Inc.
Editorial: 5485 Wharf Rd 5485, PO Box 1388 Wharf Rd, Sechelt, British Columbia V0N 3A0. **T:** 1 604 885-4811
W: http://www.coastreporter.net **Circ:** 13600
Editor: Ian Jacques; **Publisher:** Peter Kvarnstrom
Editorial Profile: Coast Reporter is a weekly newspaper for the Sunshine Coast of British Columbia. Deadlines are Tuesdays at 5pm.; Full Page Mono: 14.14; Full Page Colour: 14.14
Currency: Canada Dollars
NEWSPAPER

Cochrane Eagle
Editorial: 126A River Ave, Cochrane, Alberta T4C 2C2. **T:** 1 403 932-6588
E: letters@cochraneeagle.com
W: http://www.cochraneeagle.com **Circ:** 12360
Editor: Derek Clouthier; **Publisher:** Brenda Tennant; Full Page Mono: 4.13
Currency: Canada Dollars
NEWSPAPER

Cochrane Times
Owner: Quebecor Communications Inc.
Editorial: Bay 8 206 5th Ave. W, Cochrane, Alberta T4C 1X3. **T:** 1 403 932-3500
E: ctimes.editor@sunmedia.ca
W: http://www.cochranetimes.com **Circ:** 11600
Publisher: Shawn Cornell
Editorial Profile: Cochrane Times is a weekly newspaper written for the residents of Cochrane, Alberta. The publication prints articles on local news.; Full Page Mono: 21.00; Full Page Colour: 3207.65
Currency: Canada Dollars
NEWSPAPER

Colchester Weekly News
Owner: TC. Transcontinental
Editorial: 6 Louise Street, Truro, Nova Scotia B2N 563. **T:** 1 902 893-9405
E: news@trurodaily.com
W: http://www.trurodaily.com **Circ:** 21786
Editor: Sherry Martell
Editorial Profile: Colchester Weekly News is a community newspaper for the residents of Truro, Nova Scotia and the surrounding communities.; Full Page Mono: 8.68
Currency: Canada Dollars
NEWSPAPER

Community Digest - Calgary
Owner: Community Digest Multicultural Publications

Editorial: 3545 - 32nd Avenue NE, Suite 660, Calgary, Alberta T1Y 6M6. **T:** 1 604 875-8313
E: digest_news@yahoo.com
W: http://www.communitydigest.ca
Circ: 25000
Editor in Chief: Steve Bowell; **Publisher:** N. Ebrahim
Editorial Profile: Community Digest - Calgary covers multicultural events related to race relations, immigration, diversity and cultural integration in Calgary, Alberta.; Full Page Mono: 51.03
Currency: Canada Dollars
NEWSPAPER

Community Digest - Toronto
Owner: Community Digest Multicultural Publications
Editorial: 4261 Hwy 7, Suite 151, Markham, Ontario L3R 3V7. **T:** 1 416 283-3373
E: digest_news@yahoo.com
W: http://www.communitydigest.ca
Circ: 25000
Editor in Chief: Steve Bowell
Editorial Profile: Community Digest - Toronto is a multicultural newspaper published for English-speaking people of Canadian, European, Middle Eastern, East African and Aboriginal origins.; Full Page Mono: 51.03
Currency: Canada Dollars
NEWSPAPER

Community Digest - Vancouver
Owner: Community Digest Multicultural Publications
Editorial: 1755 Robson St, Ste 216, Vancouver, British Columbia V6G 3B7. **T:** 1 604 875-8313
E: digest_news@yahoo.com
W: http://www.communitydigest.ca
Circ: 25000
Editor in Chief: Steve Bowell
Editorial Profile: Community Digest - Vancouver is a magazine targeted toward the multicultural community, particularly those of the South Asian descent. Distributed free of charge in Vancouver, Montreal, and Toronto libraries, each metropolitan area reaches about 25,000 people. The Vancouver issue is contracted out to a language editor, and is the only bilingual issue. Each area includes approximately half the same stories, with the other half tailored to its geographic locale.; Full Page Mono: 51.03
Currency: Canada Dollars
NEWSPAPER

Community Herald Newspapers
Owner: Halifax Herald Ltd. (The)
Editorial: 2717 Joseph Howe Dr., Halifax, Nova Scotia B3L 4T9. **T:** 1 902 426-2811
E: community@herald.ca
W: http://thechronicleherald.ca/community
Circ: 145009
Publisher: Graham Dennis; **Editor:** Claire McIlveen
Editorial Profile: Community Herald Newspapers share a staff with The Chronicle-Herald in Halifax, Nova Scotia. Although the staff is shared, all editorial content is different. They are distributed to both subscribers, in their papers, and non-subscribers, in their flyer packages, every Thursday.
NEWSPAPER

Community Media Management
Owner: Gleaner Community Press
T: 1 416 504-6987
E: gleanereditor@gmail.com
W: http://gleanernews.ca **Circ:** 50000
Editor in Chief: Emina Gamulin
NEWSPAPER

Community Press
Owner: Sun Media
Editorial: 199 Front St Suite 535, Belleville, Ontario K8N 5H5. **T:** 1 613 962-9171
City Editor: Tim Meeks
NEWSPAPER

Community Press/East Central Times
Owner: Anderson (Kerry)
Editorial: 4925-47 Street, Sedgewick, Alberta T0B 4C0. **T:** 1 780 384-3641
W: http://thecommunitypress.com **Circ:** 37900
Publisher: Eric Anderson; **Editor:** Leslie Cholowsky; **Editor:** Leslie Cholowsky
NEWSPAPER

Community Voice Newspapers
Owner: EJ Lewchuck and Associates Ltd.
Editorial: 15A Albert Avenue, Spruce Grove, Alberta T7X 2Z5. **T:** 1 780 962-9228
E: news@com-voice.com
W: http://www.com-voice.com **Circ:** 16000
Publisher & Editor: Elaine Lewchuck
NEWSPAPER

Comox Valley Echo
Owner: Postmedia Network Inc.
Editorial: 407-D 5th St, Courtenay, British Columbia V9N 1J7. **T:** 1 250 334-4722
W: http://www.canada.com/vancouverisland/comoxvalleyecho **Circ:** 23000
Publisher: Dave MacDonald; **Editor in Chief:** Debra Martin
Editorial Profile: Comox Valley Echo is a local newspaper written for the residents of Courtenay, British Columbia. It covers local and community news, business, arts & entertainment, events and sports.; Full Page Mono: 11.20
Currency: Canada Dollars
NEWSPAPER

Comox Valley Record
Owner: Black Press
Editorial: 765 McPhee Ave, Courtenay, British Columbia V9N 2Z7-. **T:** 1 250 338-5811
W: http://www.comoxvalleyrecord.com
Circ: 22443
Editor: Mark Allan; **Publisher:** Joanna Ross
Editorial Profile: Comox Valley Record is a local newspaper serving the residents of Courtenay, British Columbia. The paper covers breaking news, community events, sports, business and arts & entertainment.; Full Page Mono: 19.60
Currency: Canada Dollars
NEWSPAPER

The Connection
Owner: Metroland Media Group Ltd.
Editorial: #11 Ronell Crescent, Unit B, Collingwood, Ontario L9Y 1E4.
T: 1 705 444-1875 **E:** connection@simcoe.com
W: http://www.collingwoodconnection.com
Circ: 19900
Editor: Scott Woodhouse
Editorial Profile: The Connection is a 20+ page newspaper written for the Collingwood, ON general public. It covers local news, sports, business and entertainment.; Full Page Mono: 20.07
Currency: Canada Dollars
NEWSPAPER

El Contacto Directo
Owner: Colatina International Communications
Editorial: 1259 Kingsway, Vancouver, British Columbia V5V 3E2. **T:** 1 604 729-0622
E: colatina@hotmail.es
W: http://www.elcontactolatino.com
Circ: 10000
Editor: Victor Alvarado
Editorial Profile: A weekly Spanish newspaper in British Columbia that was founded in 1992. It covers National, International and Local news.; Full Page Mono: 6.93; Full Page Colour: 12.13
Currency: Canada Dollars
NEWSPAPER

Corriere Canadese
Editorial: 2700 Dufferin St Suite 90, Toronto, Ontario M6B 4J3. **T:** 1 416 782-9222
W: http://www.corriere.com
Freq: Daily; **Circ:** 10000
Editor in Chief: Francesco Veronesi; **Publisher:** Joe Volpe
Editorial Profile: Corriere Canadese is the oldest daily Italian newspaper outside of Italy. Its mission is to sustain the Italian language and culture throughout Canada. Mainly circulating in Montreal and Toronto, it also reaches Italian communities in Ottawa, the Niagara Peninsula, Windsor, Calgary, Edmonton and Vancouver. Published in Italian, it serves the Canadian Italian community with articles on culture, arts, entertainment, travel, business and local news, national and international news.; Full Page Colour: 22.40
Currency: Canada Dollars
DAILY NEWSPAPER

Corriere Italiano
Owner: TC. Transcontinental
Editorial: 6965, 6ème Avenue, Montreal, Quebec H2A 3E3. **T:** 1 514 279-4536
E: corriereitaliano@transcontinental.ca
W: http://www.corriereitaliano.com
Circ: 24500
Editor: Carole Gagliardi; **News Editor:** Farizio Intravaia
Editorial Profile: Corriere Italiano is a weekly newspaper covering news for the Italian-Canadian communities across Canada. The publication is written in Italian.; Full Page Mono: 8.00
Currency: Canada Dollars
NEWSPAPER

The County Weekly News
Owner: Quebecor Communications Inc.

Editorial: 252 Main Street, Suite 3, Picton, Ontario K0K 2T0. **T:** 1 613 476-4714
W: http://www.countyweeklynews.ca
Freq: Weekly; **Circ:** 13186
Publisher: Maureen Keeler
Editorial Profile: The County Weekly News is written for the residents of Picton County, Ontario.; Full Page Mono: 5.04; Full Page Colour: 341.00
Currency: Canada Dollars
NEWSPAPER

Coup d'œil
Owner: TC. Transcontinental
Editorial: 350 rue Saint-Jacques, Napierville, Quebec J0J 1L0. **T:** 1 450 245-3344
E: coupdoeil@tc.tc
W: http://www.coupdoeil.info **Circ:** 15386
Editor in Chief: Jacques LaRochelle
Editorial Profile: Coup d'œil is a weekly French-language newspaper that covers local news and information, including community news, human-interest stories, sports, and education, for Napierville, Quebec.; Full Page Mono: 15.12
Currency: Canada Dollars
NEWSPAPER

The Courier Press
Owner: Quebecor Communications Inc.
Editorial: 138 King St W, Chatham, Ontario N7M 1E3-. **T:** 1 519 628-5719
W: http://www.wallaceburgcourierpress.com
Circ: 11610
Editor: Peter Epp; **Publisher:** Dean Muharrem
Editorial Profile: The Courier Press is a weekly newspaper written for the residents of Wallaceburg, Ontario. It reports local news, sports and business.; Full Page Mono: 4.83
Currency: Canada Dollars
NEWSPAPER

Le Courrier
Owner: Valeur Média
Editorial: 192A Rue Richelieu, St-Jean-sur-Richelieu, Quebec J3B 6X6. **T:** 1 450 347-6000
E: redaction@valeurmedia.com
W: http://www.journallecourrier.ca
Freq: Semi-Monthly; **Circ:** 180301
Publisher: Khaled Kalille
Editorial Profile: Le Courrier offers local news and information to residents of Montérégie and Île-des-Sœurs, Quebec. All the newspapers are in French, with the exception of the L'Île-des-Sœurs, Candiac and Cowansville editions, which are bilingual English-French.; Full Page Mono: 11.09
Currency: Canada Dollars
NEWSPAPER

Le Courrier De Portneuf
Owner: Cooperative du Courrier de Port Neuf
Editorial: 276 rue Notre-Dame, Donnacona, Quebec G3M 1G7. **T:** 1 418 285-0211
E: journaliste@courrierdeportneuf.com
W: http://www.courrierdeportneuf.com
Circ: 34072
Editor in Chief: Denise Paquin
Editorial Profile: Le Courrier de Portneuf is a local news weekly serving the region of Portneuf, Quebec.; Full Page Mono: 5.95
Currency: Canada Dollars
NEWSPAPER

Le Courrier du Saguenay
Owner: TC. Transcontinental
Editorial: 3635, boul. Harvey, Jonquiere, Quebec G7X 3B2. **T:** 1 418 542-2442
E: redaction.saguenay@transcontinental.ca
W: http://www.courrierdusaguenay.com
Circ: 74200
Publisher: Michel Dupont
Editorial Profile: Le Courrier du Saguenay provides local news and information to residents of Chicoutimi, Jonquière, La Baie, Laterrière, St-Ambroise, Shipshaw, Quebec and the surrounding villages.; Full Page Mono: 12.52
Currency: Canada Dollars
NEWSPAPER

Courrier Frontenac
Owner: TC. Transcontinental
Editorial: 541 boul Frontenac Est, Thetford Mines, Quebec G6G 5V3. **T:** 1 418 338-5181
E: info@courrierfrontenac.com
W: http://www.courrierfrontenac.com
Circ: 22046
News Editor: Alexis Bourque Bouliane; **Editor in Chief:** Pascal Gourdeau; **Publisher:** Lucyl Lachance
Editorial Profile: Courrier Frontenac is a weekly French-language newspaper covering local news in the Thetford Mines, Quebec area. Stories include human-interest features, sports, education, government and news.; Full Page Mono: 6.37

Currency: Canada Dollars
NEWSPAPER

Le Courrier Laval
Editorial: 2700, rue Francis-Hughes, Local 200, Laval, Quebec H7S 2B9.
T: 1 450 667-4360 **E:** redactionlaval@tc.tc
W: http://www.courrierlaval.com **Circ:** 121803
Editor in Chief: Diane Hameury; **Publisher:** Claude Labelle
Editorial Profile: Le Courrier Laval is a newspaper written exclusively in French. It is one of the largest weekly newspapers in francophone Canada and focuses on reporting local news in the Laval, Quebec area. In addition to general news reports, the newspaper also covers sports, weather, cultural events, health and education. Bi-monthly the Édition de Quartier St-Vincent-de-Paul et Duvernay, Édition de Quartier Ste-Dorothée Laval ouest/Auteil Vimont, Édition de Quartier Laval des Rapides/Pont-Viau/Chomedy/Ste-Rose Fabreville are inserted into the paper. Monthly the Mensuel St-François and Mensuel Ste-Dorothée editions are inserted into the paper. Twitter Handle: http://twitter.com/LeCourrierLaval; Full Page Mono: 29.31
Currency: Canada Dollars
NEWSPAPER

Courrier-Sud
Owner: TC. Transcontinental
Editorial: 3255 Marie-Victorin, Nicolet, Quebec J3T 1X5. **T:** 1 819 293-4551
E: redaction_cs@tc.tc
W: http://www.lecourriersud.com **Circ:** 21100
Publisher: Mathieu Allard; **Editor in Chief:** Marie-Eve Veillette
Editorial Profile: Courrier Sud is a weekly French-language newspaper for residents of Nicolet, Quebec and surrounding areas. It covers local news, sports, entertainment, education and government.; Full Page Mono: 14.28
Currency: Canada Dollars
NEWSPAPER

Cowichan News Leader Pictorial
Owner: Black Press
Editorial: #2 5380 Trans Canada Hwy, Duncan, British Columbia V9L 6W4. **T:** 1 250 746-4471
W: http://www.cowichannewsleader.com/ **Circ:** 23380
Publisher: Bill MacAdam
Editorial Profile: Cowichan News Leader Pictorial is newspaper serving the Cowichan Valley, British Columbia area.; Full Page Mono: 17.00; Full Page Colour: 118.00
Currency: Canada Dollars
NEWSPAPER

Cowichan Valley Citizen
Owner: Glacier Media Inc.
Editorial: 469 Whistler St, Duncan, British Columbia V9L 4X5. **T:** 1 250 748-2666
W: http://www.cowichanvalleycitizen.com
Circ: 25700
Editorial Profile: Cowichan Valley Citizen is a community newspaper written for the residents of Duncan, British Columbia.; Full Page Mono: 7.88
Currency: Canada Dollars
NEWSPAPER

Crescent International
Owner: Crescent International Newspaper Inc.
T: 1 905 887-8913 **E:** crescent@ca.inter.net
W: http://www.crescent-online.net
Freq: Monthly; **Circ:** 32000
Editor in Chief: Zafar Bangash
Editorial Profile: Crescent International Specializes in Muslim perspective on the news.; Full Page Mono: 51.13
Currency: Canada Dollars
NEWSPAPER

D.B.C. Communications Publications - Saint Hyacinthe
Owner: D.B.C. Communications Inc.
Editorial: 655 avenue Sainte-Anne, Saint-Hyacinthe, Quebec J2S 5G4.
T: 1 450 773-6028
W: http://www.dbccomm.qc.ca **Circ:** 51107
Editor in Chief: Martin Bourassa; **Publisher & Editor:** Benoît Chartier
Editorial Profile: D.B.C. Communications Publications - Saint Hyacinthe is a community newspaper publisher serving the residents of Quebec.
NEWSPAPER

The Daily Courier
Owner: Continental Newspapers Canada Ltd.
Editorial: 550 Doyle Ave, Kelowna, British Columbia V1Y 7V1-. **T:** 1 250 762-4445
W: http://www.kelownadailycourier.ca

Freq: Daily; **Circ:** 10566
Publisher: Terry Armstrong; **City Editor:** Pat Bulmer
Editorial Profile: The Daily Courier is a broadsheet newspaper written for the Okanagan Valley, British Columbia general public. It is one of the major newspapers in the region covering news, sports, trends and business. It has won several awards, including the Thomson Award for excellent news, graphics and photography.; Full Page Mono: 19.40; Full Page Colour: 487.55
Currency: Canada Dollars
DAILY NEWSPAPER

The Daily Gleaner
Owner: Summit Publishing
Editorial: 984 Prospect St, Fredericton, New Brunswick E3B 5A2. **T:** 1 506 452-6671
E: news@dailygleaner.com
W: http://dailygleaner.canadaeast.com
Freq: Daily; **Circ:** 20048
Publisher: Nancy Cook; **News Editor:** Anne Mooers
Editorial Profile: The Daily Gleaner is written for residents of Fredericton, New Brunswick and greater residential communities. Aside from the coverage of local and national news, the publication also covers money and economy topics in the business section and local sporting news, statistics and events in sports. There is also a daily entertainment news page, a community calendar, humor and advice columns, television listings and a fitness, nutrition and healthy living page. Weekly sections include the books, lifestyles and Real Estate sections.; Full Page Mono: 22.96; Full Page Colour: 26.88
Currency: Canada Dollars
DAILY NEWSPAPER

Das Echo
Owner: Independent
T: 1 514 335-3653 **E:** dasecho@live.ca
W: http://www.dasecho.com
Freq: Monthly; **Circ:** 30000
Editorial Profile: Das Echo is a German-language publication for members of the German community in Canada. It is published on the first of each month. Contact the publication by phone, fax, or mail.; Full Page Mono: 18.76; Full Page Colour: 25.07
Currency: Canada Dollars
NEWSPAPER

The Delta Optimist
Owner: Glacier Media Inc.
Editorial: 207-4840 Delta Street, Delta, British Columbia V4K 2T6. **T:** 1 604 946-4451
E: editor@delta-optimist.com
W: http://www.delta-optimist.com **Circ:** 17250
Publisher: Lori Chalmers; **Editor in Chief:** Ted Murphy
Editorial Profile: The Delta Optimist is a newspaper written for the residents of Delta, British Columbia. The publication covers local news, weather, sports and arts & entertainment.; Full Page Mono: 16.90
Currency: Canada Dollars
NEWSPAPER

Desi News
Owner: Easwar (G.A.)
Editorial: 17600 Yonge St., Newmarket, Ontario L3Y 8J1. **T:** 1 416 695-4357
E: desinews@rogers.com
W: http://www.e-desinews.com
Freq: Monthly; **Circ:** 45000
Editor in Chief: Shagorika Easwar
Editorial Profile: Desi News is a monthly publication serving the South Asian community.; Full Page Mono: 9.47
Currency: Canada Dollars
NEWSPAPER

Desi Times
Editorial: 7655 Rue Cordner, Lasalle, Quebec H8N 2X2. **T:** 1 514 827-2929
E: avtar@avrmedia.com
W: http://www.desitimes.ca
Freq: Weekly
Publisher: Manjeet Singh Atthwal; **Editor in Chief:** Jasvir Singh Sandhu
Editorial Profile: Desi Times provides local coverage to the Punjabi-speaking community in the Montreal metropolitan area. The newspaper is a 32 pages tabloid with 8 pages full color and 24 pages B&W, and is printed weekly and distributed every Friday. Desi Times publishes in English and Punjabi.
NEWSPAPER

Deutsche Presse/German Press
Editorial: 87 Judge Road, Toronto, Ontario M8Z 5B3. **T:** 1 416 595-9714
E: design@austrianpublications.com
Circ: 35000

Publisher & Editor: Rosemarie Meyer; Full Page Mono: 9.31
Currency: Canada Dollars
NEWSPAPER

Le Devoir
Owner: Devoir Inc. (Le)
Editorial: 2050 Rue de Bleury, 9ieme etage, Montreal, Quebec H3A 2J5. **T:** 1 514 985-3333
E: redaction@ledevoir.com
W: http://www.ledevoir.com
Freq: Daily; **Circ:** 32412
Publisher: Bernard Descôteaux
Editorial Profile: Le Devoir is a French-language newspaper favored by Quebec's political and intellectual elites. It includes regional, national and international news. Other topics include politics, economics, business, health, technology, education, sports, theater, film, television and book reviews, restaurant guides, food recipes and wine tasting.; Full Page Mono: 13.62; Full Page Colour: 50.44
Currency: Canada Dollars
DAILY NEWSPAPER

Le Droit
Owner: Power Corporation of Canada
Editorial: 47 Rue Clarence, Ottawa, Ontario K1N 9K1. **T:** 1 613 562-0111
E: nouvelles@lapresse.ca
W: http://www.cyberpresse.ca/le-droit
Freq: Daily; **Circ:** 36049
Editor in Chief: Jean Gagnon; **Editor in Chief:** Jean Gagnon; **Editor in Chief:** Jean Gagnon; **Editor in Chief:** Jean Gagnon; **Publisher:** Jacques Pronovost
Editorial Profile: Established in 1913, Le Droit is a French-language, daily newspaper covering the Outaouais region of Québec and eastern Ontario. It is the only Francophone daily in Ottawa. National, regional and local information are given the most attention while international news is covered mostly by news wires.; Full Page Mono: 25.76; Full Page Colour: 1160.00
Currency: Canada Dollars
DAILY NEWSPAPER

Droit De Parole
Owner: Communications Basse-ville Inc.
Editorial: 266 rue Saint-Vallier Ouest, Quebec, Quebec G1K 1K2. **T:** 1 418 648-8043
E: info@droitdeparole.org
W: http://www.droitdeparole.org
Freq: Bi-Monthly; **Circ:** 17000
Editorial Profile: Established in 1974 and informs people of struggles, concerns and activities in the city of Québec, Québec. Subjects covered include neighborhood living conditions, women, youth, elderly, unemployment, social services and the environment. It is published 8 times a year.; Full Page Mono: 15.82
Currency: Canada Dollars
NEWSPAPER

East Central Alberta Review
Owner: Coronation Review Ltd.
Editorial: 4923 Victoria Ave, Coronation, Alberta T0C 1C0. **T:** 1 403 578-4111
E: publisher@ecareview.com
W: http://www.ecareview.com **Circ:** 24062
Publisher & Editor: Joyce Webster
Editorial Profile: East Central Alberta Review is a local community newspaper serving residents of Coronation, Alberta. Articles cover local news, weather and travel. Advertising deadlines are at noon MT.; Full Page Mono: 10.71; Full Page Colour: 80.00
Currency: Canada Dollars
NEWSPAPER

The Eastern Gazette
Editorial: 141 West Ship Harbour Road, Lake Charlotte, Nova Scotia B0J 1Y0.
T: 1 902 845-2241
W: http://www.easterngazette.ca
Freq: Monthly; **Circ:** 10000
Publisher & Editor: Tracy Foley
Editorial Profile: The Eastern Gazette is a monthly community newspaper serving the Eastern Shore region of Novia Scotia. The paper includes local community news, politics, sports, and arts & entertainment and runs local event listings and business profiles. Only send pitches with a local angle.; Full Page Mono: 5.31
Currency: Canada Dollars
NEWSPAPER

Eastern News
Owner: Urdu Promotion Board, Canada
Editorial: 119 Royal West Drive, Brampton, Ontario L6X 0V4. **T:** 1 905 216-2085
W: http://www.easternnews.ca

Freq: Bi-Monthly; **Circ:** 10000
Editor in Chief: Masood Khan; **Publisher:** Alia Sultana
Editorial Profile: Eastern News is written for the residents of Mississauga, Brampton, Ontario. It is published in English and Pakistani and is written primarily for South Asians.; Full Page Mono: 10.74
Currency: Canada Dollars
NEWSPAPER

L' Écho de Cap-Rouge
Editorial: 940, Boul. du Lac, Quebec, Quebec G2M 0C9. **T:** 1 418 841-3073
W: http://www.lechodecaprouge.ca
Freq: Monthly
Editor: Alain Têtu
Editorial Profile: L'Écho de Cap-Rouge is a monthly newspaper providing Local and Community New coverage to the communities of Cap-Rouge and Pointe-De-Sainte-Foy, QC.
NEWSPAPER

L' Écho De La Baie
Owner: Quebecor Communications Inc.
Editorial: 144 rue Jacques Cartier, Gaspe, Quebec G4X 1M9. **T:** 1 418 392-5083
W: http://www.lechodelabaie.canoe.ca
Circ: 19497
Publisher: Bernard Johnson; **Editor in Chief:** Roxanne Langlois
Editorial Profile: L'Écho de la Baie is a free, weekly, French-language newspaper covering local news and events for residents of New Richmond, Quebec.; Full Page Mono: 14.28
Currency: Canada Dollars
NEWSPAPER

L' Écho de Laval
Owner: Quebecor Communications Inc.
Editorial: 900, Boul. St-Martin Ouest, Laval-Des-Rapides, Quebec. **T:** 1 450 575-2000
E: redaction.écholaval@hebdosquebecor.com
W: http://www.lechodelaval.ca
Freq: Weekly; **Circ:** 150000
Editor in Chief: Marie-Eve Courchesne; **Publisher & Editor:** Éric Mercier
Editorial Profile: L'Écho de Laval is a weekly community newspaper serving Laval, Quebec. The newspaper features local information and exclusive coverage of current events, the economy, arts and entertainment, sports and news in brief of Montreal's north shore.; Full Page Mono: 34.86; Full Page Colour: 34.86
Currency: US Dollars
NEWSPAPER

L' Echo de Maskinonge
Owner: TC. Transcontinental
Editorial: 43, rue Saint-Louis, Louiseville, Quebec J5V 2C7. **T:** 1 819 228-5532
E: redaction_em@transcontinental.ca
W: http://www.lechodemaskinonge.com
Circ: 13000
Editorial Profile: L'Echo de Maskinonge is a weekly, French-language newspaper covering regional and local news for residents of Louiseville, D'Autray and Maskinonge, Quebec.; Full Page Mono: 4.97
Currency: US Dollars
NEWSPAPER

L' Écho de Repentigny
Owner: Quebecor Communications Inc.
Editorial: 544 A Notre-Dame, Repentigny, Quebec J6A 2T8. **T:** 1 450 932-4782
W: http://www.lechoderepentigny.canoe.ca
Circ: 60000
Publisher: Martin Gravel
Editorial Profile: L'Écho de Repentigny is a french-language community newspaper written for residents of Repentigny, Quebec. It covers local news.; Full Page Mono: 7.21
Currency: Canada Dollars
NEWSPAPER

L' Écho de Saint-Jean-sur-Richelieu
Owner: Quebecor Communications Inc.
Editorial: 81 Rue Richelieu Bureau 102B, St-Jean-sur-Richelieu, Quebec J3B 6X2.
T: 1 450 376-4646
W: http://www.lechodesaintjean.ca
Freq: Weekly; **Circ:** 53047
Publisher: Daniel Noiseux; **Editor:** Henri-Paul Raymond; **Editor:** Henri-Paul Raymond; **Editor:** Denis Tetreault
Editorial Profile: L'Écho de Saint-Jean-sur-Richelieu is a weekly newspaper printed for the city and surrounding areas of southeast Monteal near Saint-Jean-sur-Richelieu in Quebec, Canada. The publication began circulation October 18, 2011 and covers a variety of topics, both local and international, from sports and arts & entertainment, to opinion and politics.
NEWSPAPER

L' Écho de Shawinigan
Owner: Quebecor Communications Inc.
Editorial: 795, 5e rue, local 101, Shawinigan, Quebec G9N 1G2. **T:** 1 819 731-0327
W: http://lechodeshawinigan.canoe.ca
Freq: Weekly; **Circ:** 35324
Editor: Philippe Chatillon
Editorial Profile: L'Écho de Shawinigan is a weekly newspaper publication for the city and surrounding areas of Shawinigan, Quebec, Canada. Publication started August 1, 2011, and the paper covers topics ranging from local news, politics, and sports to international news, arts & entertainment, and opinion.
NEWSPAPER

L' Écho de Trois-Rivières
Owner: Quebecor Communications Inc.
Editorial: 3625, boul. du Chanoine-Moreau, Trois-Rivieres, Quebec G8Y 5N6.
T: 1 819 371-4826
W: http://www.lechodetroisrivieres.canoe.ca
Freq: Weekly; **Circ:** 66207
Editor: Philippe Chatillon; **News Editor:** Jocelyn Ouellet
Editorial Profile: L'Écho de Trois-Rivières is a weekly newspaper published through Quebecor Communications Inc. It began publication September 1, 2011, delivering to citizens around the Trois-Rivières area local news mixed with National and International coverage provided by Sun Media, owners of Quebecor Communications Inc. Sections include News, Sports, Arts & Entertainment, as well as Opinion.
NEWSPAPER

L' Écho de Victoriaville
Owner: Quebecor Communications Inc.
Editorial: 106, boul. Bois-Francs Nord, Victoriaville, Quebec. **T:** 1 819 604-6686
W: http://www.lechodevictoriaville.ca
Freq: Weekly; **Circ:** 43872
Publisher: Jean Crépeau
Editorial Profile: L'Écho de Victoriaville is a free weekly newspaper serving the residents of Victoriaville, Plessisville, and Warwick in Quebec, Canada. It was launched in late June 2012 and covers news, sports, opinion, and culture.
NEWSPAPER

Echo Germanica
Owner: Echoworld Communications
Editorial: 118 Tyrrell Ave, Toronto, Ontario M6G 2G5. **T:** 1 416 652-1332
E: info@echoworld.com
W: http://www.echoworld.com
Freq: Monthly; **Circ:** 16000
Editorial Profile: Echo Germanica is a community newspaper written for the German residents of Toronto, Ontario.; Full Page Mono: 21.70
Currency: Canada Dollars
NEWSPAPER

Échos Montréal
Editorial: 387 rue Saint-Paul Ouest bur 3, Montreal, Quebec H2Y 2A7.
T: 1 514 844-2133
E: redaction@journalechos.com
W: http://www.journalechos.com
Freq: Monthly; **Circ:** 19000
Editor in Chief: Carl Bergeron
Editorial Profile: Échos Montréal is a monthly newspaper covering local news in French. Contact the newspaper by e-mail, phone, fax, or mail.; Full Page Mono: 18.41; Full Page Colour: 91.24
Currency: Canada Dollars
NEWSPAPER

Éditions André Paquette - Hawkesbury
Owner: Cie d'Edition A. Paquette Inc.
Editorial: 1100 Rue Aberdeen, Hawkesbury, Ontario K6A 3H1. **T:** 1 613 632-4155
E: nouvelles@eap.on.ca
W: http://www.lecarillon.ca/ **Circ:** 43400
Publisher: Bertrand Castonguay; **Editor in Chief:** Roger Duplantie; **Editor in Chief:** Roger Duplantie
NEWSPAPER

Éditions André Paquette - Lachute
Owner: Cie d'Edition A. Paquette Inc.
Editorial: 52 rue Principale, Lachute, Quebec J8H 3A8. **T:** 1 450 562-8593
E: argenteuil@eap.on.ca
W: http://www.editionap.ca
Freq: Weekly; **Circ:** 31200
Publisher: Bertrand Castonguay
NEWSPAPER

The Edmonton Examiner
Owner: Quebecor Communications Inc.
Editorial: 4990 92 Ave NW Suite 250, Edmonton, Alberta T6B 3A1.
T: 1 780 453-9001
W: http://www.edmontonexaminer.com
Circ: 143157
Publisher: John Caputo; **Editor in Chief:** Steve Serviss
Editorial Profile: The Edmonton Examiner is a weekly newspaper published for the Edmonton, Alberta area. The paper covers local news, sports and arts & entertainment.; Full Page Mono: 27.30
Currency: Canada Dollars
NEWSPAPER

The Edmonton Journal
Owner: Postmedia Network Inc.
Editorial: 10006 101 St NW, Edmonton, Alberta T5J 0S1-. **T:** 1 780 429-5100
E: city@edmontonjournal.com
W: http://www.edmontonjournal.com
Freq: Daily; **Circ:** 101148
Editor in Chief: Margo Goodhand; **News Production Editor:** Therese Kehler; **News Planner:** Kathy Kerr; **Editor:** Janet Vlieg Paquette
Editorial Profile: The Edmonton Journal is a newspaper written for the Edmonton, Alberta general public. It is one of the major newspapers in the area covering news, sports, business and entertainment. The paper has won several honors, including a National Newspaper Award and an international award for outstanding features. The newspaper is known for quality photography and in-depth coverage.; Full Page Mono: 69.09; Full Page Colour: 267.08
Currency: Canada Dollars
DAILY NEWSPAPER

The Edmonton Sun
Owner: Quebecor Communications Inc.
Editorial: 4990 92 Ave NW Suite 250, Edmonton, Alberta T6B 3A1.
T: 1 780 468-0100
E: edm-citydesk@sunmedia.ca
W: http://www.edmontonsun.com
Freq: Daily; **Circ:** 51547
City Editor: Nicole Bergot; **Publisher:** John Caputo; **City Night Editor:** Jeff Cummings; **Editor in Chief:** Steve Serviss
Editorial Profile: The Edmonton Sun covers national and predominantly local news, business, which highlights Alberta or Edmonton specific industries and trends; entertainment and sports. Editors honor non-disclosure agreements. The publication accepts vendor-written articles on a case-by-case basis and does not offer reader-service cards. It was established on April 2, 1978.; Full Page Mono: 27.09; Full Page Colour: 152.14
Currency: Canada Dollars
DAILY NEWSPAPER

El Centro
Editorial: 81626-1057 Steeles Ave W 81626, North York, Ontario M2R 2S9.
T: 1 416 619-4578 **E:** elcentro@rogers.com
W: http://www.elcentronews.ca
Freq: Weekly
Editorial Profile: El Centroamericano is a weekly bilingual Spanish and English newspaper providing news and local coverage to the Latin American community in the Greater Toronto area. It publishes on Fridays.
NEWSPAPER

El-Masri Newspaper
Owner: Egyptian Canadian Friendship Association
Editorial: 879 St-Charles Ave Chomedey, Laval, Quebec H7V 3T5. **T:** 1 450 687-0273
E: masri.93@hotmail.com
W: http://www.el-masrionline.com
Freq: Bi-Monthly; **Circ:** 12000
Editor in Chief: Adel Iskander
Editorial Profile: El-Masri is a Bi-Monthly newspaper written for the Egyptian community in francophone Québec.; Full Page Mono: 15.65; Full Page Colour: 17.39
Currency: Canada Dollars
NEWSPAPER

Elmira Independent Publisher
Owner: Metroland Media Group Ltd.
Editorial: 13A Industrial Drive, Elmira, Ontario N3B 2S1. **T:** 1 519 669-5155
E: editor@elmiraindependent.com
W: http://www.elmiraindependent.com
Circ: 13612
Editor in Chief: Gail Martin
NEWSPAPER

The Enterprise-Bulletin
Owner: Quebecor Communications Inc.
Editorial: 77 Simcoe Street, Collingwood, Ontario L9Y 3J9. **T:** 1 705 445-4611
E: editorial@theenterprisebulletin.com
W: http://www.theenterprisebulletin.com
Circ: 19700
Editorial Profile: The Enterprise-Bulletin is a twice weekly newspaper that covers news and events for residents of Collingwood, Ontario.; Full Page Mono: 8.12
Currency: Canada Dollars
NEWSPAPER

Epoch Times - Ottawa
Editorial: 988 Pinecrest Road, Ottawa, Ontario K2B 6B5. **T:** 1 613 820-2580
E: ottawa@epochtimes.com
W: http://www.theepochtimes.com **Circ:** 15000
Editor & Publisher: Cindy Gu; **Editor:** Pamela McLennan
Editorial Profile: Epoch Times-Ottawa is a free, a week newspaper serving Chinese-speaking residents and businesses in Ottawa. Part of an independent, global media corporation headquartered in New York, its mission is to enrich local communities with news and perspectives on current events which are often overlooked by mainstream media, especially by outlets inside China. It strives to present an alternative and uncensored view to the propaganda generated by the People's Republic of China. It is the most widely-read Chinese newspaper read outside the mainland of China and Taiwan.It is distributed at local newstands, retailers, restaurants, bookstores, apartments and at Chinese community organizations. Contact the editor for lead times.; Full Page Mono: 9.58
Currency: Canada Dollars
NEWSPAPER

Epoch Times - Toronto
Editorial: 418 Consumers Road, Toronto, Ontario M2J 1P8. **T:** 1 416 298-1933
E: newsdesk@epochtimes.com
W: http://www.theepochtimes.com **Circ:** 40000
Editor & Publisher: Cindy Gu
Editorial Profile: Epoch Times-Toronto is a free, weekly newspaper serving English-speaking residents and businesses that are interested in Chinese news globally and in Toronto. Part of an independent, global media corporation headquarterd in New York, its mission is to enrich local communities with news and perspectives on current events which are often overlooked by mainstream media, especially by outlets inside China. It strives to present an alternative and uncensored view to the propaganda generated by the People's Republic of China. It is the most widely-read Chinese newspaper read outside the mainland of China and Taiwan. It is distributed at local newstands, retailers, restaurants, bookstores, apartments and at Chinese community organizations. Contact the editor for lead times.; Full Page Mono: 5.81
Currency: Canada Dollars
NEWSPAPER

Equality News
Owner: Equality Group Inc.
Editorial: 1560 Brimley Rd, #206, Toronto, Ontario M1P 3G9. **T:** 1 416 759-6397
E: equalitygroup@rogers.com
W: http://www.equalitynews.net
Freq: Monthly; **Circ:** 55000
Editorial Profile: Equality News is a 20+ page newspaper written for Caribbean individuals and others interested in local Caribbean news. It covers local Caribbean news, Caribbean sports, and world news. It is published on a monthly basis.; Full Page Mono: 35.00
Currency: Canada Dollars
NEWSPAPER

The Era-Banner
Owner: Metroland Media Group Ltd.
Editorial: 580 B. Steven Court, Newmarket, Ontario L3Y 4X1. **T:** 1 905 773-7627
E: newsroom@erabanner.com
W: http://www.yorkregion.com
Freq: Bi-Weekly; **Circ:** 47879
News Editor: Jay Gutteridge; **Editor in Chief:** Debora Kelly; **Publisher:** Ian Proudfoot
Editorial Profile: The Era-Banner is a newspaper published weekly for the residents of Newmarket, Aurora, Georgina and the Northern York Region in Ontario. It covers regional news and features.; Full Page Mono: 22.89
Currency: Canada Dollars
NEWSPAPER

Erin Newspapers
Owner: Metroland Media Group Ltd.
Editorial: 8 Thompson Cr #5, Erin, Ontario N0B 1T0. **T:** 1 519 833-9603
E: editorial@erinadvocate.com
W: http://www.metroland.com **Circ:** 18070

Editor in Chief: Joan Murray
NEWSPAPER

Essex Free Press
Owner: Essex Free Press Ltd.
Editorial: 16 Centre St, Essex, Ontario N8M 1N9. **T:** 1 519 776-4268
E: essexfreepress@on.aibn.com
W: http://www.sxfreepress.com **Circ:** 11000
News Editor: Andy Comber; **Publisher & Editor:** Richard Parkinson
Editorial Profile: Essex Free Press is a publication written for the members of the Essex, Ontario community. The publication covers local news, weather, sports and entertainment. Deadlines for the publication are one week before issue date.; Full Page Mono: 7.70; Full Page Colour: 200.00
Currency: Canada Dollars
NEWSPAPER

Ethnic Media - Montreal
Editorial: 24 Mont-Royal West, #401, Montreal, Quebec H2T 2S2. **T:** 1 514 737-0151
E: marketing@ethnicmedia.ca
W: http://www.forumbulgare.ca **Circ:** 38000
Publisher & Editor: Borislav Nicolov
NEWSPAPER

L' Etincelle
Owner: Publidiffusion Inc.
Editorial: 193 rue St-Georges, Windsor, Quebec J1S 1J7. **T:** 1 819 845-2705
E: journal@letincelle.qc.ca
W: http://www.letincelle.qc.ca **Circ:** 10529
Editor in Chief: Ralph Côté; **Publisher:** Claude Frenette
Editorial Profile: L'Étincelle is a weekly newspaper covering news and events in the Val St-François region of Québec, from Sherbrooke to Drummondville. It contains local news, including sports, education, and human-interest stories.; Full Page Mono: 10.08
Currency: Canada Dollars
NEWSPAPER

L' Etoile du Lac
Owner: TC. Transcontinental
Editorial: 797, boul. St-Joseph, Ste. 101, Roberval, Quebec G8H 2L4.
T: 1 418 275-2911
E: redaction_roberval@transcontinental.ca
W: http://www.letoiledulac.com **Circ:** 14395
Editor in Chief: Daniel Migneault
Editorial Profile: L'Étoile du Lac is a weekly newspaper covering local news of interest to residents of Roberval, Quebec and the Lac Saint-Jean, Quebec region. The editorial deadlines fall at noon ET on Wednesdays before issue date.; Full Page Mono: 5.88
Currency: Canada Dollars
NEWSPAPER

Exodus
Owner: Jewish Russian Community Centre
Editorial: 5987 Bathurst St, Ste 3, Toronto, Ontario M2R 1Z3. **T:** 1 416 222-7105
E: exodus@jrcc.org
W: http://www.exodusmagazine.org
Freq: Monthly; **Circ:** 18000
Editor: Izzy Greenberg; **Editor in Chief:** Ella Vorovitch; **Publisher:** Yoseph Zaltzman
Editorial Profile: Exodus is a community newspaper written for the Jewish Russian residents of North York, Ontario. The paper is printed in Russian and English.; Full Page Mono: 6.00
Currency: Canada Dollars
NEWSPAPER

The Expositor
Owner: Quebecor Communications Inc.
Editorial: 195 Henry St, Brantford, Ontario N3S 5C9-. **T:** 1 519 756-2020
E: brex.expnews@sunmedia.ca
W: http://www.brantfordexpositor.ca
Freq: Daily; **Circ:** 20801
Publisher: Ken Koyama
Editorial Profile: The Expositor is written for the residents of Brantford, Ontario. It covers news, sports, business and entertainment. Deadlines are 5pm ET.; Full Page Mono: 22.26; Full Page Colour: 15.93
Currency: Canada Dollars
DAILY NEWSPAPER

El Expreso
Editorial: 1233 Nigel Road, Mississauga, Ontario L5J 3S6. **T:** 1 905 823-0602
E: expreso@interlog.com
W: http://www.elexpresocanada.com
Circ: 55000; Full Page Mono: 12.95
Currency: Canada Dollars
NEWSPAPER

L' Express
Owner: TC. Transcontinental
Editorial: 1050 rue Cormier, Drummondville, Quebec J2C 2N6. **T:** 1 819 478-8171
W: http://www.journalexpress.ca **Circ:** 47295
Publisher: Johanne Marceau; **Editor in Chief:** Dominic Villeneuve
Editorial Profile: L'Express is a twice-weekly, French-laguage newspaper covering local news for Drummondville, Quebec and its surroundings. The circulation for the Wednesday edition is 46,375 and the circulation for the Sunday edition is 48,214.; Full Page Mono: 8.82
Currency: Canada Dollars
NEWSPAPER

L' Express Montcalm
Owner: TC. Transcontinental
Editorial: 864, rue St-Isidore, St-Lin-Laurentides, Quebec J5M 2V4.
T: 1 450 439-2525
E: infolanaudiere@transcontinental.ca
W: http://www.lexpressmontcalm.com
Circ: 25000
Editor: Jean Joubert; **Publisher:** Andrew Larivière
Editorial Profile: L'Express Montcalm is a weekly French-language newspaper serving residents of Montcalm region of Lanaudière, Quebec. It covers local news, politics, education, sports and entertainment.; Full Page Mono: 6.09
Currency: Canada Dollars
NEWSPAPER

L' Express Newspapers
Owner: L'Express de Toronto Inc.
Editorial: 888 avenue Eastern, Toronto, Ontario M4L 1A3. **T:** 1 416 465-2107
E: express@lexpress.to
W: http://www.lexpress.to **Circ:** 30000
Editor in Chief: Yann Buxeda; **Editor In Chief:** Normand Champagne; **Publisher:** Jean-Pierre Mazare
NEWSPAPER

The False Creek News
Editorial: 661 A Market Hill, Vancouver, British Columbia V5Z 4B5. **T:** 1 604 876-6770
E: news@thefalsecreeknews.com
W: http://www.thefalsecreeknews.com
Circ: 25000
Editor: Steve Bowell; **Publisher:** M. Juma
Editorial Profile: The False Creek News is a weekly community newspaper serving neighborhood news to Vancouver's fast-growing high-income communities including False Creek, Granville Island and Gairview Slopes. Editorial coverage includes news, local issues and arts & entertainment.; Full Page Mono: 114.94
Currency: Canada Dollars
NEWSPAPER

Familia Portuguesa
Editorial: 949 Dufferin St, Toronto, Ontario M6H 4B2. **T:** 1 416 533-8501
E: minhaf@ica.net **Circ:** 10000
Publisher & Editor: Alberto Cunha
Editorial Profile: Familia Portuguesa is a weekly community newspaper written for the Portuguese speaking resident of Toronto.; Full Page Mono: 5.50
Currency: Canada Dollars
NEWSPAPER

Filipiniana
Editorial: 1531 Queen St W, Toronto, Ontario M6R 1A5. **T:** 1 416 534-7836
E: filipiniananews@rogers.com
Freq: Monthly; **Circ:** 10000
Publisher & Editor: Bin Kon Loo
Editorial Profile: Filipiniana is a local community newspaper for the Filipino residents of Toronto.; Full Page Mono: 7.84
Currency: Canada Dollars
NEWSPAPER

Filipino Journal
Editorial: 46 Pincarrow Rd, Winnipeg, Manitoba R3Y 1E3. **T:** 1 204 489-8894
E: info@filipinojournal.com
W: http://www.filipinojournal.com
Freq: Bi-Weekly; **Circ:** 10000
Editor in Chief: Ronald Cantiveros; Full Page Mono: 5.60; Full Page Colour: 985.00
Currency: Canada Dollars
NEWSPAPER

The Filipino Post
Owner: Asian Post Media Publishing
Editorial: St. 2000 - 1066 West Hastings Street, Vancouver, British Columbia V6E 3X1.
T: 1 604 821-1954
E: editor@postpeopleinc.com
W: http://www.thefilipinopost.com
Freq: Weekly; **Circ:** 25000
Editorial Profile: The Filipino Post is a free weekly newspaper serving the Filipino community in the Vancouver metropolitan area.
NEWSPAPER

First Nations Drum
Owner: Totem Publications
Editorial: 101- 1001 West Broadway, Suite 325, Vancouver, British Columbia V6H 4E4.
T: 1 604 669-5582
E: editor@firstnationsdrum.com
W: http://www.firstnationsdrum.com
Freq: Monthly; **Circ:** 35000
Editor: Rick Littlechild
Editorial Profile: First Nations Drum is a monthly publication that serves the native communities in Saskatchewan, Yukon, Northwest Territories, Alberta and throughout British Columbia with news and information relevant to native culture, tradition and lifestyles. Its editorial mission is to "inform and entertain its readers to strengthen understanding between native and non-native residents of Western Canada." The First Nations Drum features profiles on native artists and covers opportunities for educational advancement of native students in special issues.; Full Page Mono: 30.43
Currency: Canada Dollars
NEWSPAPER

First Nations Voice
Owner: First Nations Voice
T: 1 204 256-0645 **E:** rdeagle@mymts.net
W: http://www.firstnationsvoice.com
Freq: Monthly; **Circ:** 94654
Editor: Patrick Flynn; **Publisher:** Al Isfeld
Editorial Profile: First Nations Voice is a monthly newspaper targeting Manitoba's First Nation/Aboriginal population. Features articles on living, the arts, culture, events, politics and more.
NEWSPAPER

The First Perspective/Drum
Owner: Taiga Communications Inc.
Editorial: 703-44 Princess St 703, Winnipeg, Manitoba R3B 1K2. **T:** 1 204 943-1500
E: staff@taiga-communications.com
W: http://www.firstperspective.ca
Freq: Monthly; **Circ:** 15000
Publisher & Editor: James Wastasecoot
Editorial Profile: The First Perspective/Drum is published 17 times per year. It is a magazine addressing issues related to indigenous peoples of Canada. The paper includes news, commentary, event listings and discussions related to the community.; Full Page Mono: 10.43; Full Page Colour: 1640.00
Currency: Canada Dollars
NEWSPAPER

Flamborough Review
Owner: Metroland Media Group Ltd.
Editorial: 30 Main St N, Waterdown, Ontario L0R 2H0. **T:** 1 905 689-4841
E: editor@flamboroughreview.com
W: http://www.flamboroughreview.com
Circ: 13313
Editor: Brenda Jefferies; **Publisher:** Neil Oliver; Full Page Mono: 6.44
Currency: Canada Dollars
NEWSPAPER

Fort Erie Times Newspapers
Owner: Quebecor Communications Inc.
Editorial: 450 Garrison Rd., Unit 1, Fort Erie, Ontario L2A 1N2. **T:** 1 905 871-3100
W: http://www.forterietimes.ca **Circ:** 23500
Publisher: Michael Cressman; **Publisher:** Tim Dundas; **Editor:** Sarah Ferguson
NEWSPAPER

Fort McMurray Connect
Owner: Brown (Andryia)
Editorial: 22 - 9914 Morrison Street, Fort McMurray, Alberta T9H 4A4.
T: 1 780 790-6627 **E:** info@macmedia.ca
W: http://www.macmedia.ca **Circ:** 25500
Publisher: Andryia Brown; **Editor:** Holly Hashimi
Editorial Profile: Fort McMurray Connect offers community news and events to residents in and around Fort McMurray, Alberta.; Full Page Mono: 13.30
Currency: Canada Dollars
NEWSPAPER

La Gatineau
Owner: Editions Gatineau Ltee. (Les)
Editorial: 135-B, route 105, Maniwaki, Quebec J9E 3A9. **T:** 1 819 449-1725
E: lagatineau@ireseau.com
W: http://www.lagatineau.com **Circ:** 12500
Editor: Jean Lacaille
Editorial Profile: La Gatineau is a weekly newspaper covering local news. It is a French-language publication.; Full Page Mono: 10.08
Currency: Canada Dollars
NEWSPAPER

The Gazette
Owner: Postmedia Network Inc.
Editorial: 1010 Sainte-Catherine St W, Suite 200, Montreal, Quebec H3B 5L1.
T: 1 514 987-2222
W: http://www.montrealgazette.com
Freq: Daily; **Circ:** 94403
Editor in Chief: Lucinda Chodan; **City Editor:** Michelle Richardson
Editorial Profile: The Gazette is an English-language newspaper written for residents in Montréal.; Full Page Mono: 52.99; Full Page Colour: 214.26
Currency: Canada Dollars
DAILY NEWSPAPER

La Gazette de la Mauricie
Editorial: 942 rue Sainte-Genevieve, Trois-Rivieres, Quebec G9A 3X6. **T:** 1 819 375-4012
E: info@lagazette.ca
W: http://www.lagazette.ca
Freq: Monthly; **Circ:** 75000
Editor: Valérie Lupien; **Editor:** Valérie Lupien
Editorial Profile: La Gazette Populaire is a monthly French-language newspaper covering local news and information, especially in the Mauricie region. Its goal is to draw the communities in the region together with news that can help readers form a common regional and political identity.; Full Page Mono: 11.20
Currency: Canada Dollars
NEWSPAPER

The Georgia Straight
Owner: Vancouver Free Press
Editorial: 1701 W Broadway, Vancouver, British Columbia V6J 1Y3. **T:** 1 604 730-7000
E: contact@straight.com
W: http://www.straight.com **Circ:** 120000
Publisher: Dan McLeod; **Editor:** Charlie Smith
Editorial Profile: The Georgia Straight is a local magazine written for the residents of Vancouver, British Columbia. It covers features, articles, news, reviews, arts, music, movies, fashion, travel, business, high tech, food and restaurants, plus a comprehensive listing of entertainment activities and special events. Please send press releases to the main e-mail address.; Full Page Mono: 105.56
Currency: Canada Dollars
NEWSPAPER

Georgina Advocate
Owner: Metroland Media Group Ltd.
Editorial: 184 Simcoe Avenue, Keswick, Ontario L4P 2H7. **T:** 1 905 476-7753
E: admin@georginaadvocate.com
W: http://www.yorkregion.com **Circ:** 16000
Editor in Chief: Tracy Kibble; **Editor in Chief:** Tracy Kibble; **Publisher:** Ian Proudfoot
Editorial Profile: Georgina Advocate covers local news and events for the residents of Georgina, Ontario. Deadlines are on Mondays at 10am ET.; Full Page Mono: 7.35
Currency: Canada Dollars
NEWSPAPER

Glacier Media Inc.
Owner: Glacier Media Inc.
Editorial: 141 Commercial Pl, Thompson, Manitoba R8N 1T1. **T:** 1 204 677-4534
E: editor@thompsoncitizen.net **Circ:** 11500
Editor: John Barker; **Publisher:** Brent Fitzpatrick
NEWSPAPER

The Gleaner Company
Editorial: 1390 Eglinton Ave W, Toronto, Ontario M6C 2E4. **T:** 1 416 784-3002
E: gleanercan@gleanerna.net
W: http://www.jamaica-gleaner.com
Circ: 90000
Publisher: Sheila Alexander; **Editor:** Neil Armstrong
Editorial Profile: Gleaner Company is a weekly community newspaper publisher serving the residents of Toronto.
NEWSPAPER

The Globe and Mail
Owner: Woodbridge Company Limited (The)
Editorial: 444 Front St W, Toronto, Ontario M5V 2S9. **T:** 1 416 585-5000
E: newsroom@globeandmail.com
W: http://www.theglobeandmail.com
Freq: Daily; **Circ:** 347524
Careers Editor: Kathryn Maloney; **Real Estate Editor:** D'Arcy McGovern; **Style Editor:** Danny Sinopoli; **Editor in Chief:** David Walmsley
Editorial Profile: The Globe and Mail is a daily, national, Canadian newspaper.

Throughout the week, there are various special sections, including Globe Travel, Globe Style, Globe Books, Globe T.O., Globe Drive, Focus and Health and Lifestyle. There is also a Weekend Arts section. Lead times for different departments vary. Attachments to electronic communications are not accepted, so place all information in the body of electronic messages. The publication only wishes to correspond through e-mails or phone calls. The paper is a member of the Canadian Press Gallery.; Full Page Mono: 446.32; Full Page Colour: 499.81
Currency: Canada Dollars
DAILY NEWSPAPER

Goderich Newspapers
Owner: Quebecor Communications Inc.
Editorial: 120 Huckins St, Goderich, Ontario N7A 3X8. **T:** 1 519 524-2614
W: http://www.goderichsignalstar.com
Circ: 28122
News Editor: Dave Flaherty
NEWSPAPER

Goldstream News Gazette
Owner: Black Press
Editorial: 117-777 Goldstream Ave, Victoria, British Columbia V9B 2X4. **T:** 1 250 478-9552
W: http://www.goldstreamgazette.com
Circ: 18000
Editor in Chief: Edward Hill; **Publisher:** Penny Sakamoto
Editorial Profile: Goldstream News Gazette is a publication written for the residents of Victoria, British Columbia. The publication covers local news, sports and arts & entertainment targeted at the West Shore of Greater Victoria, including Langford, Colwood, Metchosin, View Royal and the Highlands.; Full Page Mono: 11.97
Currency: Canada Dollars
NEWSPAPER

Graffici
Owner: Cooperative de Solidarite
Editorial: 200B boul. Perron Ouest, New Richmond, Quebec G0C 2B0.
T: 1 418 392-7440 **E:** graffici@graffici.ca
Freq: Monthly; **Circ:** 37100
Editor in Chief: Maite Samuel Leduc
Editorial Profile: Graffici is a French-language community newspaper. It features news, information and cultural events for the New Richmond, Quebec area.
NEWSPAPER

GranbyExpress.com
Owner: TC. Transcontinental
Editorial: 398 rue Principale, Bureau 5, Granby, Quebec J2G 2W6. **T:** 1 450 777-4515
W: http://granby.enregion.ca/ **Circ:** 44929
Editor in Chief: Jean-Philippe Pineault
Editorial Profile: GranbyExpress.com is a weekly French-language newspaper that covers local news and information for Granby, Quebec.; Full Page Mono: 7.07; Full Page Colour: 350.00
Currency: Canada Dollars
NEWSPAPER

Grassroots News
Owner: Aborginal Advertising Inc.
Editorial: Room 107 150 Henry, Winnipeg, Manitoba R3B 0J7. **T:** 1 204 589-7495
E: admin@grassroots.mb.ca
W: http://www.grassroots.mb.com
Freq: Bi-Weekly; **Circ:** 20000
Publisher: Arnold Asham
Editorial Profile: Grassroots News is a bi-weekly newspaper that reaches 63 First Nations and Metis communities throughout Manitoba, including Winnipeg, The Pas, Thompson and Flin Flon. It provides major news and events including, assemblies and conferences, politics, arts and culture. Special sections include news from Southern Chiefs Organization, the Manitoba Metis Federation, Manitoba Keewatinook Ininew Okimowin and the Assembly of Manitoba Chiefs. It also features events on education and training, employment, health, economic development and youth.; Full Page Mono: 16.45; Full Page Colour: 400.00
Currency: Canada Dollars
NEWSPAPER

Great West Publishing
Owner: Great West Newspapers LP
Editorial: 2903 Kingsview Blvd SE Suite 403, Airdrie, Alberta T4A 0C4. **T:** 1 403 948-1885
E: sales@airdrie.greatwest.ca
W: http://www.greatwest.ca **Circ:** 31500
Editor: Stacie Snow
NEWSPAPER

Greek Canadian Tribune
Owner: Manikis (Christos)
Editorial: 7835 B Wiseman Ave, Montreal, Quebec H3N 2N8. **T:** 1 514 272-6873
E: info@bhma.net **W:** http://www.bhma.net
Circ: 13200
Publisher & Editor: Christos Manikis
Editorial Profile: The Greek Canadian Tribune, also known as la Tribune Grecque Canadienne or Ellinokanadiko Vimo, is a French, English and Greek-language newspaper for the Greek community in Francophone, Canada. It covers local news in Quebec, Canadian and Greek politics and events within Hellenic communities and various cultural associations.; Full Page Mono: 7.73
Currency: Canada Dollars
NEWSPAPER

The Greek Press
Owner: Olga Management Limited
Editorial: 1033 Pape Ave, Toronto, Ontario M4K 3W1. **T:** 1 416 465-3243
E: greekpress@greekpress.ca
W: http://www.greekpress.ca
Freq: Weekly; **Circ:** 11000
Publisher & Editor: Costas Kranias; Full Page Mono: 12.25
Currency: Canada Dollars
NEWSPAPER

The Grimsby Lincoln News
Owner: Metroland Media Group Ltd.
Editorial: 32 Main St W, Grimsby, Ontario L3M 1R4. **T:** 1 905 945-8392
E: info@thegrimsbylincolnnews.com
W: http://www.niagarathisweek.com
Circ: 23800
Editor in Chief: Katherine Nadeau; **Publisher:** Neil Oliver
Editorial Profile: The Grimsby Lincoln News is a community newspaper written for the residents of Grimsby, Ontario. The paper covers local news, sports and events.; Full Page Mono: 14.14
Currency: Canada Dollars
NEWSPAPER

Groupe JCL Publications - Sainte-Therese
Owner: Groupe JCL (Le)
Editorial: 50B rue Turgeon, Sainte-Therese, Quebec J7E 3H4. **T:** 1 450 435-6537
W: http://www.groupejcl.com **Circ:** 129424
Editor In Chief: Claude Desjardins; **Publisher:** Jean-Claude Langlois
Editorial Profile: Le Groupe JCL publishes two French weeklies which cover the local news in the communities of Mirabel/Deux-Montagnes and Sainte-Thérèse.
NEWSPAPER

Groupe JCL Publications - St-Eustache
Owner: Groupe JCL (Le)
Editorial: 53 rue Saint-Eustache, St-Eustache, Quebec J7R 2L2. **T:** 1 450 472-3440
E: leveil@groupejcl.com
W: http://www.groupejcl.com **Circ:** 100275
Publisher & Editor: Jean-Claude Langlois
NEWSPAPER

Grove Examiner/Stony Plain Reporter
Owner: Quebecor Communications Inc.
Editorial: 75 South Ave, Spruce Grove, Alberta T7X 3B4. **T:** 1 780 962-4257 **Circ:** 22317
NEWSPAPER

The Guardian
Owner: TC. Transcontinental
Editorial: 165 Prince St, Charlottetown, Prince Edward Island C1A 4R7. **T:** 1 902 629-6000
E: newsroom@theguardian.pe.ca
W: http://www.theguardian.pe.ca
Freq: Daily; **Circ:** 20701
Publisher: Don Brander
Editorial Profile: The Guardian is a 40+ page broadsheet newspaper serving the Prince Edward Island area. It is one of the area's premier newspapers focusing on all types of business, sports and general news coverage.; Full Page Mono: 29.57; Full Page Colour: 105.58
Currency: Canada Dollars
DAILY NEWSPAPER

The Guelph Mercury
Owner: Metroland Media Group Ltd.
Editorial: 8-14 MacDonnell St, Guelph, Ontario N1H 6P7. **T:** 1 519 822-4310
E: editor@guelphmercury.com
W: http://www.guelphmercury.com
Freq: Daily; **Circ:** 13911
Editor In Chief: Lynn Haddrall; **Publisher:** Paul McCuaig; **City Editor:** Brian Williams
Editorial Profile: The Guelph Mercury is a daily newspaper written for the residents of Guelph, Ontario. The publication covers local news and events.; Full Page Mono: 28.70; Full Page Colour: 1000.00
Currency: Canada Dollars
DAILY NEWSPAPER

Guelph Tribune
Owner: Metroland Media Group Ltd.
Editorial: 27 Woodlawn Rd. #1, Guelph, Ontario N1H 1G8. **T:** 1 519 763-3333
W: http://www.guelphtribune.ca **Circ:** 40607
Editor in Chief: Chris Clark; **Publisher:** Peter Winkler
Editorial Profile: Guelph Tribune is a community newspaper serving the residents of Guelph, Ontario. The paper covers news, weather, travel, sports and entertainment.; Full Page Mono: 9.49; Full Page Colour: 550.00
Currency: Canada Dollars
NEWSPAPER

Le/The Guide
Owner: TC. Transcontinental
Editorial: 121 Rue Principale Loc 3, Cowansville, Quebec J2K 1J3.
T: 1 450 263-5288 **E:** leguide@tc.tc
W: http://www.journalleguide.com **Circ:** 18340
Publisher: Cathy Bernard; **Editor in Chief:** Jean-Philippe Pineault
Editorial Profile: Le Guide is a weekly French-language newspaper that covers local news and information in Cowansville, Quebec.; Full Page Mono: 16.94
Currency: Canada Dollars
NEWSPAPER

Gujarat Abroad
Owner: Gujarat Abroad Inc.
Editorial: 72 Cadillac Crescen, Brampton, Ontario L7A 3B6. **T:** 1 905 846-4988
E: editorforga@gmail.com
W: http://www.gujaratabroad.ca
Freq: Weekly; **Circ:** 15000
Editor and Publisher: Vipul Jani
Editorial Profile: Gujarat Abroad is the largest Gujarati weekly newspaper in the Greater Toronto metropolitan area. It publishes every Friday through over 350 outlets throughout Toronto, Mississauga, Brampton, Markham and Oakville.
NEWSPAPER

Gujarat Express
Editorial: 20 Elderwood Place, Brampton, Ontario L6V 3N3. **T:** 1 905 457-7096
E: abgujaratexpress@yahoo.ca
W: http://www.gujaratexpress.ca
Freq: Weekly
Editor and Publisher: Amit Bhatt
Editorial Profile: Gujarat Express is a weekly newspaper written for new immigrants to and South Asian residents of Canada.
NEWSPAPER

Hal-E-Pakistan
Editorial: 2912 Cross Current Drive, Mississauga, Ontario L5W 6K9.
T: 1 905 7850267 **E:** halepakistan@gmail.com
Freq: Bi-Monthly
Publisher: Arshad Khan
Editorial Profile: Hal-E-Pakistan is a community newspaper written for the Pakistani residents of Mississauga and the surrounding communities.; Full Page Mono: 7.84
Currency: Canada Dollars
NEWSPAPER

Hamdard Weekly
Owner: Ontario Ltd.
Editorial: 2-1332 Khalsa Dr, Mississauga, Ontario L5S 0A2. **T:** 1 905 791-9999
E: toronto@hamdardweekly.com
W: http://www.hamdardweekly.com
Circ: 30000
Editor in Chief: Amar Singh Bhullar
Editorial Profile: Hamdard Weekly is written for the residents of Mississauga, ON.; Full Page Mono: 14.64
Currency: Canada Dollars
NEWSPAPER

The Hamilton Spectator
Owner: Metroland Media Group Ltd.
Editorial: 44 Frid St, Hamilton, Ontario L8N 3G3. **T:** 1 905 526-3333
W: http://www.thespec.com
Freq: Daily; **Circ:** 103267
City Editor: Carla Ammerata; **Editor in Chief:** Paul Berton; **Style Editor:** Michele Steeves; **Style Editor:** Michele Steeves
Editorial Profile: The Hamilton Spectator is a broadsheet newspaper written for residents of Hamilton, Ontario. It covers local and national news, sports, entertainment and business. The features section focuses on food, gardening, homes and travel. The newspaper has won several honors, including the National Newspaper Award and a Human Rights Award.; Full Page Mono: 141.10; Full Page Colour: 181.59
Currency: Canada Dollars
DAILY NEWSPAPER

Harbour City Star
Owner: Glacier Media Inc.
Editorial: 2575 McCullough Rd, Nanaimo, British Columbia V9S 4M9. **T:** 1 250 729-4200
E: news@nanaimodailynews.com
W: http://www.canada.com/vancouverisland/star **Circ:** 48800
Publisher: Hugh Nicholson
Editorial Profile: Harbour City Star is a newspaper serving the city of Nanaimo, British Columbia. The paper focuses on local news.; Full Page Mono: 10.57; Full Page Colour: 1820.55
Currency: Canada Dollars
NEWSPAPER

Le Haut Saint-Francois
Owner: Journal Le Haut-Saint-Francois
Editorial: 212 rue Principale Est, Cookshire, Quebec J0B 1M0. **T:** 1 819 875-5501
E: info@journalhsf.com
W: http://www.journalhsf.com
Freq: Bi-Weekly; **Circ:** 11500
Editorial Profile: Since April 1986, Le Haut Saint-François is a French biweekly regional community publication that is delivered, free of charge, by Public-Sac to households in the MRC of Haut-Saint-Francois.; Full Page Mono: 7.00
Currency: Canada Dollars
NEWSPAPER

L' Hebdo Charlevoisien
Owner: L'Hebdo Charlevoisien
Editorial: 45 boulevard Raymond-Mailloux, Baie-Saint-Paul, Quebec G3Z 1W2.
T: 1 418 435-0220 **E:** hebdo@charlevoix.net
W: http://www.charlevoixendirect.com
Circ: 14200
Editor in Chief: Sylvain Desmeules; **Editor:** Charles Warren
Editorial Profile: L'Hebdo Charlevoisien is a weekly publication covering local news for the Charlevoix region of Québec. Contact the News Editor.; Full Page Mono: 9.24
Currency: Canada Dollars
NEWSPAPER

L' Hebdo du St-Maurice
Owner: TC. Transcontinental
Editorial: 2102 avenue Champlain, Shawinigan, Quebec G9N 6T8.
T: 1 819 537-5111
E: redaction_shawinigan@transcontinental.ca
W: http://www.lhebdodustmaurice.com
Circ: 31070
Editor: Léna Sauvageau
Editorial Profile: Hebdo du St-Maurice is a local newspaper for the Saint-Maurice, Quebec. It covers local news, sports and education, focusing on human-interest stories.; Full Page Mono: 8.26
Currency: Canada Dollars
NEWSPAPER

L' Hebdo Journal
Owner: TC. Transcontinental
Editorial: 525 rue Barkoff, Bureau 205, Trois-Rivieres, Quebec G8T 2A5. **T:** 1 819 379-1490
E: redaction.hj@transcontinental.ca
W: http://www.lhebdojournal.com **Circ:** 56000
Publisher: Alain Bernard; **Editor In Chief:** Jocelyn Bourassa; **Editor In Chief:** Jocelyn Bourassa; **Editor In Chief:** Jocelyn Bourassa
Editorial Profile: L'Hebdo Journal is a weekly, French-language newspaper covering local news, including politics, education, sports and entertainment for Cap-de-la-Madeleine, Quebec.; Full Page Mono: 18.76
Currency: Canada Dollars
NEWSPAPER

L' Hebdo Mékinac des Chenaux
Owner: TC. Transcontinental
T: 1 819 537-5111
E: redaction.hmc@transcontinental.ca
W: http://www.lhebdomekinacdeschenaux.com
Circ: 13110
Editor: Bernard Lepage
Editorial Profile: L'Hebdo Mékinac/des Chenaux is a local publication for the Mékinac and des Chenaux regions of Québec. It covers local news, government and education with a focus on human-interest stories. Contact the Editor with PR materials.; Full Page Mono: 4.97
Currency: Canada Dollars
NEWSPAPER

WORLD NEWS MEDIA

L' Hebdo Rive-Nord
Owner: TC. Transcontinental
Editorial: 1004 rue Notre-Dame, Repentigny, Quebec J5Y 1S9. **T:** 1 450 581-5120
W: http://www.hebdorivenord.com **Circ:** 45593
Editorial Profile: L'Hebdo Rive-Nord is a French-language newspaper that is published twice a week. The paper covers local news, including government, education, sports and arts & entertainment for Repentigny, Quebec and surrounding areas.; Full Page Mono: 7.77
Currency: Canada Dollars
NEWSPAPER

Hebdomadaire les Versants du Mont-Bruno
Editorial: 1488 Montarville, Saint-Bruno, Quebec J3V 3T5. **T:** 1 450 441-5300
E: info@versants.com
W: http://www.versants.com **Circ:** 24500
Publisher: Phillipe Clair; **Editor in Chief:** Frank Rodi
NEWSPAPER

Hebdos du Suroit
Editorial: 469 avenue Saint-Charles, Vaudreuil-Dorion, Quebec J7V 2N4. **T:** 1 450 455-6111
E: nouvelles@hebdosdusuroit.com
Circ: 108930
Publisher: Angele M. Prevost; **Editor in Chief:** Evelyne Villers
NEWSPAPER

Hebdos Quebecor-Matane
Owner: Quebecor Communications Inc.
Editorial: 305 rue de la Gare, Ste 107, Matane, Quebec G4W 3J2. **T:** 1 418 562-4040
E: redaction.matane@hebdosquebecor.com
Circ: 15026
Publisher: Jean Gagnon; **Editor in Chief:** Jean-Philippe Thibault
Editorial Profile: Twitter Handle: http://twitter.com/voixgaspematane
NEWSPAPER

Herald Monthly
Owner: Chinese Christian Herald Crusades
Editorial: 300 Steelcase Road West, Unit 28, Markham, Ontario L3R 2W2.
T: 1 905 944-1777 **E:** toronto@cchc.org
W: http://www.heraldmonthly.ca
Freq: Monthly; **Circ:** 76000
Editor in Chief: Helena Lee
Editorial Profile: Herald Monthly is a local newspaper written for the Chinese community in the greater Toronto area and nearby cities.; Full Page Mono: 15.06; Full Page Colour: 22.89
Currency: Canada Dollars
NEWSPAPER

Here's The Scoop
Owner: ADvance Distribution
Editorial: 2903 Kingsview Blvd, Bay 402, Airdrie, Alberta T4A 0C4. **T:** 1 403 948-5529
E: heresthescoop@shaw.ca
W: http://www.heresthescoop.com
Freq: Weekly; **Circ:** 16500
Editor & Publisher: Al Jones
Editorial Profile: Here's The Scoop is a weekly newspaper serving the residents of Airdrie in British Columbia, Canada. It focuses on positive news, including community events, heart warming stories and lots of jokes and humor, highlighting the lighter side of life in a small community.
NEWSPAPER

Heritage Newspaper Group-Kingston
Owner: Metroland Media Group
Editorial: 375 Select Drive, Unit 14, Kingston, Ontario K7M 4Y2. **T:** 1 613 546-8885
E: editorial@theheritageemc.ca
W: http://www.emckingston.ca/home
Circ: 51627
Editor: Kristen Coughlar; **News Editor:** Mark Kerr
NEWSPAPER

Hindi Abroad
Editorial: 7071 Airport Road Unit 204, Mississauga, Ontario L4T 4J3.
T: 1 905 673-9929 **E:** hindiabroad@gmail.com
W: http://www.hindiabroad.com
Freq: Weekly
News Editor: Firoz Khan
Editorial Profile: Hindi Abroad is a weekly newspaper covering local and community news for the Hindi-speaking community in the Greater Toronto area.
NEWSPAPER

Hi-Rise Community Newspaper
Owner: VAL Publications, Ltd.
Editorial: 95 Leeward Glenway, #121, Toronto, Ontario M3C 2Z6. **T:** 1 416 424-1393
E: sec.valdunn@vif.com
W: http://www.hi-risenews.com
Freq: Monthly; **Circ:** 60000
Publisher & Editor: Valerie Dunn
Editorial Profile: Hi-Rise is a monthly newspaper published for the residents in the Toronto area living in high-rise housing complexes. The editorial mission is to help encourage a sense of community and togetherness in the high-rise community, as well as to encourage creative, positive approaches to life. The lead time for Hi-Rise is six weeks. Contact the publication for details on circulation, deadlines, and advertising rates.; Full Page Mono: 34.44
Currency: Canada Dollars
NEWSPAPER

Horizon Armenian Weekly
Owner: Les Publications Armeniennes
Editorial: 3401 Rue Olivar-Asselin, Montreal, Quebec H4J 1L5. **T:** 1 514 332-3757
E: editor@horizonweekly.ca
W: http://www.horizonweekly.ca **Circ:** 15000
Editor: Vahakn Karakashian; **Editor:** Vahakn Karakashian
Editorial Profile: Horizon Armenian Weekly is a weekly newspaper written for the Armenian community in francophone Canada. It is written in Armenian, French, and English and should be contacted by phone, fax, or mail.; Full Page Mono: 7.81; Full Page Colour: 62.61
Currency: Canada Dollars
NEWSPAPER

Hudson Gazette
Owner: Lake of Two Mountains Gazette Inc.
Editorial: 397 Main Road, Hudson, Quebec J0P 1H0. **T:** 1 450 458-5482
E: hudsongazette@videotron.ca
W: http://www.hudsongazette.com **Circ:** 24890
Editor in Chief: Jim Duff; **Publisher:** Greg Jones
Editorial Profile: Hudson Gazette is a weekly English-language newspaper that covers local news and information for Hudson, Quebec. Contact the publication by mail.; Full Page Mono: 18.20; Full Page Colour: 60.00
Currency: Canada Dollars
NEWSPAPER

Il Cittadino Canadese
Owner: Antonina Mormina
Editorial: 5960 Jean Talon E St, Ste 209, Montreal, Quebec H1S 1M2.
T: 1 514 253-2332
E: journal@cittadinocanadese.com
W: http://www.cittadinocanadese.com
Circ: 13000
Publisher: Nina Giordano; **Editor:** Antonina Mormina
Editorial Profile: Il Cittadino Canadese is an Italian-language publication for Italians in Canada.; Full Page Mono: 11.20
Currency: Canada Dollars
NEWSPAPER

Immigrant Newsline
Editorial: 3050 Ellesmere Rd, Toronto, Ontario M1E 5E6. **T:** 1 647 400-6248
E: immigrantnews@gmail.com
W: http://www.immigrantnewsline.ca
Freq: Bi-Weekly; **Circ:** 20000
Publisher & Editor: Anjali Soni
Editorial Profile: Immigrant Newsline covers local and national South Asian news, immigrant news, international news, sports, science and technology, Bollywood entertainment, health, careers and a popular classified section.; Full Page Mono: 13.60
Currency: Canada Dollars
NEWSPAPER

The Independent & Free Press
Owner: Metroland Media Group Ltd.
Editorial: 280 Guelph St Unit 29, Georgetown, Ontario L7G 4B1. **T:** 1 905 873-0301
E: info@theifp.ca
W: http://www.independentfreepress.com
Circ: 22500
Editorial Profile: The Independent & Free Press is a community newspaper written for the residents of Georgetown and Acton, Ontario. The paper is also known as The Georgetown Independent/Acton Free Press.; Full Page Mono: 28.00; Full Page Colour: 1160.00
Currency: Canada Dollars
NEWSPAPER

The Independent Newspaper
Editorial: 1201-125 Village Green Sq 1201, Toronto, Ontario M1S 0G3. **T:** 1 905 460-6351
E: independentnewspaper@aol.com
Freq: Bi-Weekly; **Circ:** 15000
Editorial Profile: Bi-weekly paper serving minority immigrants in Toronto. It also covers topics like sports, health, business and entertainment.; Full Page Mono: 8.88; Full Page Colour: 8.88
Currency: Canada Dollars
NEWSPAPER

The Independent Times
Owner: Foxtrot Communications Ltd.
Editorial: 333 East 1st St., Suite 104, North Vancouver, British Columbia V7L 4W9.
T: 1 604 639-5495
E: info@theindependenttimes.com
W: http://www.theindependenttimes.com
Freq: Monthly; **Circ:** 50000
Publisher: Michael Fox
Editorial Profile: The Independent Times is a monthly newspaper written for active seniors between the ages of 50 and 69. The editorial content features general interest stories, travel, health and housing news. The newspaper has been a leading source for active seniors since 1949.; Full Page Mono: 33.92; Full Page Colour: 2910.00
Currency: Canada Dollars
NEWSPAPER

India Abroad
Editorial: 42 Deanewood Cres, Toronto, Ontario M9B 3B1. **T:** 1 416 622-2600
E: iacanada@rogers.com
W: http://www.indiaabroad.com **Circ:** 10000
Publisher: Ajit Balaarishnan; **Editor in Chief:** Nikhil Lakshman; Full Page Mono: 10.23
Currency: Canada Dollars
NEWSPAPER

India Journal
Editorial: 2355 Derry Road East, Ste 15, Mississauga, Ontario L5S 1V6.
T: 1 905 405-0420 **E:** ads@ijcanada.com
W: http://www.ijcanada.com **Circ:** 40000; Full Page Mono: 24.50
Currency: Canada Dollars
NEWSPAPER

Indo Caribbean World
Editorial: 312 Brownridge Dr, Thornhill, Ontario L4J 5X1. **T:** 1 905 738-5005
E: indocaribbeanworld@gmail.com
W: http://www.indocaribbeanworld.com
Freq: Bi-Weekly; **Circ:** 35000
News Editor: Manshad Mohamed; **News Editor:** Manshad Mohamed; **Publisher & Editor:** Harry Ramkhelawan; **Publisher & Editor:** Harry Ramkhelawan
Editorial Profile: Indo Caribbean World is published bi-weekly for the residents of Thornhill, Ontario and surrounding areas. The newspaper covers local news and community events.; Full Page Mono: 16.80
Currency: Canada Dollars
NEWSPAPER

Indo-Canadian Samay
Editorial: 16 Sled Dog Road, Brampton, Ontario L6R 0H8. **T:** 1 647 707-6100
E: samay.news@gmail.com
W: http://indocanadiansamay.ca
Editorial Profile: Indo-Canadian Samay is a Hindi weekly newspaper covering Local and Community News for the Indian community Greater Toronto area.
NEWSPAPER

Indo-Canadian Times
Editorial: 12414-82nd Ave, Ste 103, Surrey, British Columbia V3W 3E9. **T:** 1 604 599-5408
E: indo@telus.net **Circ:** 35000
Editor in Chief: Rupinder Hayer; **Editor in Chief:** Rupinder Hayer
Editorial Profile: Indo-Canadian Times International Inc. is a weekly Punjabi newspaper that covers news from all over the world of interest to the Canadian Punjabi community. Deadlines for the publication are the day before issue date.; Full Page Mono: 17.89
Currency: Canada Dollars
NEWSPAPER

Info Dimanche
Owner: Editions Info Dimanche Inc (Les)
Editorial: 72 rue Fraser, Riviere-du-Loup, Quebec G5R 1C6. **T:** 1 418 862-1911
E: journal@infodimanche.com
W: http://www.infodimanche.com
Freq: Weekly; **Circ:** 31610
Editor In Chief: Mario Pelletier
Editorial Profile: Info Dimanche is a weekly French-language newspaper that covers local news and information in the Rivière-du-Loup region of Québec.; Full Page Mono: 13.02
Currency: Canada Dollars
NEWSPAPER

Info Week-End
Owner: Editions Info Brunswick (Les)
Editorial: 322 rue Victoria, Edmundston, New Brunswick E3V 2H9. **T:** 1 506 739-5025
E: info@infoweekend.ca
W: http://www.journalinfoweekend.com
Circ: 21600
Editor in Chief: Julie Poulin
Editorial Profile: Info Week-End covers the local news for the French-speaking residents of Edmundston, NB.; Full Page Mono: 11.06
Currency: Canada Dollars
NEWSPAPER

L' Information
Owner: Quebecor Communications Inc.
Editorial: 135 Av Doucet, Mont-Joli, Quebec G5H 1R6. **T:** 1 418 775-4381
E: info.montjoli@hebdosquebecor.com
W: http://www.linformation.ca **Circ:** 10394
Editor In Chief: Sonia Lévesque
Editorial Profile: L'Information is a weekly French-language newspaper that covers local and regional information for Mont-Joli, Quebec.; Full Page Mono: 13.86
Currency: Canada Dollars
NEWSPAPER

L' Information Sainte-Julie
Owner: Quebecor Communications Inc.
Editorial: 566 ave Jules-Choquet, Porte 2, Ste-Julie, Quebec J3E 1W6. **T:** 1 450 649-0719
E: info@infodeste-julie.qc.ca
W: http://www.monsaintejulie.ca **Circ:** 21288
Publisher: Serge Landry; **Editor in Chief:** Charline-Eve Pilon
Editorial Profile: L'Information Sainte-Julie is a weekly French-language newspaper that covers local news and information for Ste-Julie, QC.; Full Page Mono: 10.36
Currency: Canada Dollars
NEWSPAPER

Innisfil Examiner
Owner: Quebecor Communications Inc.
Editorial: 571 Bayfield St N, Innisfil, Ontario L4M 4Z9. **T:** 1 705 726-6537
E: barrie.news@sunmedia.ca
W: http://www.innisfilexaminer.ca **Circ:** 10000
Publisher: Sandy Davies
Editorial Profile: Innisfil Examiner is a weekly newspaper written for the residents of Innisfil, Ontario. Deadlines are Wednesdays at noon ET.; Full Page Mono: 3.92; Full Page Colour: 987.84
Currency: Canada Dollars
NEWSPAPER

Innisfil Journal
Owner: Metroland Media Group Ltd.
Editorial: 21 Patterson Rd, Barrie, Ontario L4N 7W6. **T:** 1 705 726-0573
W: http://www.innisfiljournal.com
Freq: Weekly; **Circ:** 10000
Editorial Profile: Innisfil Journal is a local community newspaper that serves the residents of Innisfil, Ontario.; Full Page Mono: 34.63
Currency: Canada Dollars
NEWSPAPER

InPort News
Owner: Quebecor Communications Inc.
Editorial: 228 E Main St, Welland, Ontario.
T: 1 905 732-2411
W: http://www.inportnews.ca **Circ:** 12300
Publisher: John Tobon
Editorial Profile: InPort News is a free, weekly newspaper serving the residents of Port Colborne, Ontario. It contains stories on community news, events, local politics, schools, sports, businesses and area-specific features. The lead time is one week before publication. Advertising deadlines are on Mondays at noon ET. It is based in the same office as the Tribune in Welland, Ontario.; Full Page Mono: 6.30; Full Page Colour: 1404.00
Currency: Canada Dollars
NEWSPAPER

Inside Drumheller/Drumheller Mail
Editorial: 515 Highway 10 East, Drumheller, Alberta T0J 0Y0. **T:** 1 403 823-2580
E: information@drumhellermail.com
W: http://www.drumhellermail.com
Circ: 10000
Publisher: Ossie Sheddy
NEWSPAPER

Insieme
Owner: Insieme Incorporated
Editorial: 4358 rue Charleroi, Montreal, Quebec H1H 1T3. **T:** 1 514 328-2062
E: info@insiemenews.ca **Circ:** 30000
Editor in Chief: Marco Lucini Ciasdizelira
Editorial Profile: Insieme, which is Italian for together, is a weekly newspaper written in Italian. It covers international, national and local news with a heavy focus on the Italian

community in Montréal and elsewhere in Canada. The paper has specific sections on religion, sports and travel.; Full Page Mono: 28.00
Currency: Canada Dollars
NEWSPAPER

The Intelligencer
Owner: Quebecor Communications Inc.
Editorial: 199 Front St Suite 535, Belleville, Ontario K8N 5H5. **T:** 1 613 962-9171
W: http://www.intelligencer.ca
Freq: Daily; **Circ:** 12503
City Editor: Brice McVicar; **Editor:** Dave Vachon
Editorial Profile: The Intelligencer is a daily broadsheet newspaper written for the residents of the Quinte region of Ontario. The publication usually focuses on the city of Belleville and covers regional news, events, city news, arts & entertainment, and lifestyles involving health, food, homes, travel, gardening and sports. The publication also has a Weekender edition on Saturdays and issues the Sunday Magazine along with the Sunday edition. The newspaper has won several awards, including a National Design Award for layout in 2000.; Full Page Mono: 21.56; Full Page Colour: 1059.00
Currency: Canada Dollars
DAILY NEWSPAPER

Interlake Enterprise
Editorial: 5695 Highway #9, Selkirk, Manitoba R1A 2S5 **E:** info@enterprisenews.ca
W: http://www.enterprisenews.ca **Circ:** 10000
Editorial Profile: Interlake Enterprise is a community newspaper for the residents of the Interlake Region (Manitoba) including Selkirk, Gimli, Arborg, Riverton, Lockport, Petersfield, Clandeboye, St. Andrews, Fisher Branch, etc.; Full Page Mono: 13.12
Currency: Canada Dollars
NEWSPAPER

International Punjabi Tribune Newspaper
Owner: International Punjabi Tribune Inc.
Editorial: 12323 123 st, Surrey, British Columbia. **T:** 1 604 584-5577
E: punjabitribune@shaw.ca
W: http://punjabitribune.ca **Circ:** 22000
Editor: Rashpal Sing Gill
Editorial Profile: Pubjabi paper that has been printed since 1993 serving most parts of BC including the lower mainland, all major cities of BC and some other provinces of Canada including some of the USA as well. It covers Social, Political, Environmental and Financial issues as well as Sports, Technology, Business, Entertainment, Arts.; Full Page Mono: 13.28; Full Page Colour: 16.64
Currency: Canada Dollars
NEWSPAPER

Iran Javan
Editorial: 6075 Yonge St, Ste 301, Toronto, Ontario M2M 3W2. **T:** 1 416 730-0203
E: info@iranjavan.net
W: http://www.iranjavan.net **Circ:** 15000
Publisher & Editor: Babak Reihanypour
Editorial Profile: Iran Javan is a community newspaper written for the residents of North York, Ontario.; Full Page Mono: 5.11
Currency: Canada Dollars
NEWSPAPER

Iran Star
Owner: Iran Star Publishing
Editorial: 169 Steeles Ave. E, Toronto, Ontario M2M 3Y5. **T:** 1 905 763-9770
E: iranstar@iranstar.com
W: http://www.iranstar.com **Circ:** 12500
Editor in Chief: Bijan Binesh; Full Page Mono: 30.68
Currency: Canada Dollars
NEWSPAPER

Island Publishers Limited - Campbell River
Owner: Black Press
Editorial: 104-250 Dogwood St, Campbell River, British Columbia V9W 5Z5.
T: 1 250 287-9227 **Circ:** 52723
Publisher: Zena Williams
NEWSPAPER

Island Tides
Owner: Island Tides Publishing Ltd.
T: 1 250 629-3660
E: islandtides@islandtides.com
W: http://www.islandtides.com
Freq: Bi-Weekly; **Circ:** 18000
Editorial Profile: Island Tides is a weekly newspaper written for the residents of Pender Island, British Columbia.; Full Page Mono: 22.26
Currency: Canada Dollars
NEWSPAPER

Jamac Publications
Owner: Jamac Publishing Ltd.
Editorial: 919 Main St, Kindersley, Saskatchewan S0L 1S0. **T:** 1 306 463-4611
E: editor.jamac@gmail.com **Circ:** 22011
Publisher: Stewart Crump; **Editor in Chief:** Kevin McBain
NEWSPAPER

Jang Canada
Editorial: 2402 Haines Road, Suite 12, Mississauga, Ontario L4Y 4B8.
T: 1 416 835-1693 **E:** jangcanada@gmail.com
W: http://jangcanada.com
Freq: Weekly
Editor: Mirza Baig
NEWSPAPER

The Jewish Tribune
Owner: B'nai Brith Canada
Editorial: 15 Hove St, Toronto, Ontario M3H 4Y8. **T:** 1 416 633-6224
E: info@jewishtribune.ca
W: http://www.jewishtribune.ca
Freq: Weekly; **Circ:** 60410
Publisher: Frank Dimant; **Editor in Chief:** Norm Gordner
Editorial Profile: Jewish Tribune is published by B'Nai Brith of Canada for the nation's Jewish population. It attempts to present a balanced view of the issues facing Jewish Canadians. Deadlines are one week prior to issue date.; Full Page Mono: 25.00
Currency: Canada Dollars
NEWSPAPER

Jornal Do Emigrante/Emigrants' Journal
Owner: Societe Portugaise de Publications, Inc.
Editorial: 4134 St-Laurent Blvd, Montreal, Quebec H2W 1Y8. **T:** 1 514 843-3863
E: jornaldoemigrante@videotron.ca
Freq: Bi-Weekly; **Circ:** 10000
Publisher & Editor: Isaias Lopes
Editorial Profile: Jornal do Emigrante is a bi-weekly newspaper written primarily in Portuguese, with articles in French and English. It contains news and cultural information of interest to Portuguese-Canadians in Québec. Call before sending a fax.; Full Page Mono: 13.08
Currency: Canada Dollars
NEWSPAPER

Le Journal
Owner: Cie d'Edition A. Paquette Inc.
Editorial: 625 Montréal Road, Cornwall, Ontario K6H 1C3. **T:** 1 613 938-1433
E: jcornwall@eap.on.ca
W: http://www.lejournaldecornwall.ca
Circ: 30500
News Editor: Francoise Legault
Editorial Profile: Le Journal de Cornwall covers local news for the French speaking residents of Cornwall, Ontario. The newspaper was previously called Journal de Cornwall.; Full Page Mono: 9.24
Currency: Canada Dollars
NEWSPAPER

Das Journal
Owner: Sol Publishing Group
Editorial: 1278 Dundas Street West, Toronto, Ontario M6J 1X7. **T:** 1 416 534-3177
E: info@dasjournal.com
W: http://dasjournal.ca
Freq: Bi-Weekly; **Circ:** 10000
Publisher: Vasco Evaristo; **Editor:** Mark Liechti
Editorial Profile: Das Journal is a bi-weekly German language publication written for German- Autrian and Swiss-Canadians living in Canada. Published out of Toronto, the paper covers local as well as national and international news.
NEWSPAPER

Le Journal Beauce
Editorial: 117 20 1ére Avenue Bureau 2, Saint-Georges, Quebec G5Y 2C8.
T: 1 418 220-0222
E: info@journaldebeauce.com
W: http://www.journaldebeauce.com
Circ: 32000
Editor: Eric Gagnon Poulin; **Publisher:** Isabelle LeBreton
Editorial Profile: Le Journal Beauce is a local community newspaper for the residents of St-Georges, Ontario and the surrounding communities.; Full Page Mono: 4.75
Currency: US Dollars
NEWSPAPER

Journal de Beauce-Nord
Owner: Publications Beauce-Nord
Editorial: 691, boulevard Vachon Nord, Ste-Marie-de-Beauce, Quebec G6E 1M3.
T: 1 418 387-1205
E: redaction@journaldebeaucenord.com
Freq: Weekly; **Circ:** 23329
Editor: Pierre-Luc LaFrance
Editorial Profile: Journal de Beauce-Nord is a French-language, weekly publication containing local news and information for residents of Ste-Marie-de-Beauce, Quebec and the surrounding area.; Full Page Mono: 5.74
Currency: Canada Dollars
NEWSPAPER

Le Journal de Chambly
Owner: Quebecor Communications Inc.
Editorial: 1685 avenue Bourgogne, Chambly, Quebec J3L 4B3. **T:** 1 450 658-6516
E: info@journaldechambly.com
W: http://www.journaldechambly.com
Circ: 27564
Editor in Chief: Carole Pronovost
Editorial Profile: Le Journal de Chambly is a weekly French-language newspaper that covers local news and information for Chambly, QC. Contact the publication by phone, fax, or mail.; Full Page Mono: 13.02
Currency: Canada Dollars
NEWSPAPER

Le Journal de Joliette
Owner: Quebecor Communications Inc.
Editorial: 1075 Boul Firestone, Joliette, Quebec J6E 6X6. **T:** 1 450 960-2424
E: journaljoliette@hebdosquebecor.com
W: http://www.lejournaldejoliette.ca
Circ: 62379
Editor: Jean Curadeau
Editorial Profile: Le Journal de Joliette, launched in June 2010, is a weekly newspaper written for residents of Joliette, Quebec. It covers local news.; Full Page Mono: 7.21
Currency: Canada Dollars
NEWSPAPER

Le Journal de Levis
Editorial: 5159 boul. de la Rive-Sud, Bureau 204, Levis, Quebec G6V 6R8.
T: 1 418 833-3113 **E:** jdl@journaldelevis.com
W: http://www.icilevis.com
Freq: Weekly; **Circ:** 70407
Editor in Chief: Nathalie St. Pierre
Editorial Profile: Le Journal de Levis is a weekly community newspaper written for the residents of Levis, Quebec.; Full Page Mono: 14.35
Currency: Canada Dollars
NEWSPAPER

Le Journal de Montréal
Owner: Quebecor Communications Inc.
Editorial: 4545 Rue Frontenac, Montreal, Quebec H2H 2R7. **T:** 1 514 521-4545
E: transmission@journalmtl.com
W: http://www.journaldemontreal.com
Freq: Daily; **Circ:** 272000
Editor in Chief: Dany Doucet; **Publisher:** Lyne Robitaille
Editorial Profile: Le Journal de Montréal, established in 1964, is a four color, 80+ page, daily, French-language tabloid newspaper which has one of the largest circulation and readership figures in the province of Quebec. Though national and international stories are regularly featured, the publication's content is predominantly focused on local, Montreal-specific news. Individual daily sections include: local news headlines, usually centered on crime and politics; Society, featuring arts, entertainment, health, and lifestyles information; Politics, including Provincial and Federal government-related issues; Business, which also includes financial news, and Sports, which contains local and national sporting coverage and columns. There are also various weekly sections. Monday through Saturday the newspaper comes with a Business supplement. On Wednesdays and Saturdays the business supplement is intertwined with a Careers, Employment, and Training section. Additionally on Saturday's there are the pullout Homes, TV Listings, and Weekend sections. The Travel supplement is available on Tuesdays. And, Entertainment is present as an individual section Mondays through Fridays, and Sundays. On Saturday it is part on a one page Arts, Entertainment and Lifestyles compilation. The Weekend supplement is a 100 page magazine-style entertainment guide focused on celebrity gossip, arts and entertainment news, and event listings.; Full Page Mono: 79.24; Full Page Colour: 179.40
Currency: Canada Dollars
DAILY NEWSPAPER

Le Journal de Québec
Owner: Québécor Communications Inc.
Editorial: 450 Av Bechard, Quebec, Quebec G1M 2E9-. **T:** 1 418 683-1573
E: commentaires@journaldequebec.com
W: http://www.journaldequebec.com
Freq: Daily; **Circ:** 121261
Publisher: Louise Cordeau; **Editor in Chief:** Sébastien Ménard
Editorial Profile: Le Journal de Québec is a daily newspaper. It was founded in 1967 by Pierre Péladeau (the founder of Québécor Média itself). It is a French-language publication, which covers regional, national, and international news, with a strong focus on the city news of Québec. In Eastern Québec, it holds the distinction of having the largest circulation for a daily, and being the first daily newspaper to print seven days a week.; Full Page Mono: 43.68; Full Page Colour: 213.80
Currency: Canada Dollars
DAILY NEWSPAPER

Le Journal de Saint-Bruno
Owner: Quebecor Communications Inc.
Editorial: 1507 Rue Roberval, Saint-Bruno, Quebec J3V 3P8. **T:** 1 450 653-3685
E: redaction@journaldest-bruno.qc.ca
W: http://www.journaldest-bruno.qc.ca/
Circ: 19601
Publisher: Nathalie Berzosa; **Editor in Chief:** Natalie Gilbert
Editorial Profile: Le Journal de Saint-Bruno is a weekly French-language newspaper that covers local news and information, including local politics, business, sports, education, and entertainment for residents of Saint-Bruno, St-Basile-Le-Grand, and Domaine des Hauts-Bois (Ste-Julie), Quebec.; Full Page Mono: 5.74; Full Page Colour: 305.74
Currency: Canada Dollars
NEWSPAPER

Journal de St-Michel
Owner: TC. Transcontinental
Editorial: C.P. 50, succ. St-Michel, Montreal, Quebec H2A 3L8. **T:** 1 514 721-4911
E: admin@journaldestmichel.com
W: http://www.journaldestmichel.com
Circ: 24155
Publisher: Claude Bricault; **Editor in Chief:** Anouchka Drouin
Editorial Profile: Journal de Saint-Michel is a weekly, French-language newspaper covering local news and information for the residents of Montreal, Quebec.; Full Page Mono: 15.12
Currency: Canada Dollars
NEWSPAPER

Le Journal des Berges
Owner: Journal des Berges
Editorial: 416 Grande Cote O, Lanoraie, Quebec J0K 1E0
E: desberges@personainternet.com
Freq: Monthly; **Circ:** 12879
Editor & Publisher: Jacques De Laplante
Editorial Profile: Le Journal des Berges is a monthly, French-language newspaper covering local news and information. Call the publication before sending a fax.; Full Page Mono: 3.50
Currency: Canada Dollars
NEWSPAPER

Le Journal des Pays d'en Haut / La Vallée
Owner: Quebecor Communications Inc.
Editorial: 94 rue de la Gare, bureau 104, St-Sauveur-des-Monts, Quebec J0R 1R6.
T: 1 450 227-4646
E: redaction.lavallee@hebdosquebecor.com
W: http://www.lejournaldespaysdenhautlavallee.ca **Circ:** 30000
Publisher: Christian Asselin; **Editor:** Éric Nicol
Editorial Profile: Le Journal des Pays d'En Haut / La Vallée is a weekly newspaper serving Ste-Adèle, Saint-Sauveur, Sainte-Agathe-des-Monts, Quebec and the surrounding villages in the Laurentian region.; Full Page Mono: 6.37
Currency: Canada Dollars
NEWSPAPER

Journal La Relève Inc.
Owner: Journal La Relève Inc.
Editorial: 528, rue Saint Charles, Boucherville, Quebec J4B 3M5. **T:** 1 450 641-4844
E: lareleve@lareleve.qc.ca
W: http://www.lareleve.qc.ca **Circ:** 62600
Publisher: Charles Desmarteau; Full Page Mono: 7.70
Currency: Canada Dollars
NEWSPAPER

Journal L'Action Régionale
Owner: Quebecor Communications Inc.

WORLD NEWS MEDIA

Editorial: 155, Sir-Wilfrid-Laurier, Bureau 101, Saint-Basile-le-Grand, Quebec J3N 1A9.
T: 1 450 441-7252
W: http://monteregieweb.com/Action_Regionale
Freq: Weekly; **Circ:** 50000
Editor: Isabelle Verge
Editorial Profile: Le Journal L'Action Régionale publishes local news and information in three editions: Region A: Saint-Bruno-de-Montarville and Saint-Basile-le-Grand, Quebec; Region B: Belœil, Mont-Saint-Hilaire, McMasterville, and Otterburn Park, Quebec; and Region C: Chambly, Carignan and Richelieu, Quebec.; Full Page Mono: 8.19; Full Page Colour: 1735.00
Currency: Canada Dollars
NEWSPAPER

Journal Le Carrefour
Owner: Editions du Joyeux-Drille
Editorial: 405, 3e Avenue, 2e Etage, Quebec, Quebec G1L 2W2. **T:** 1 418 649-0775
E: carrefour@webnet.qc.ca
W: http://www.carrefourdequebec.com
Circ: 40000
Editor in Chief: Marie-Claude Boileau
Editorial Profile: Journal Le Carrefour is a weekly French-language publication covering two regions with two separate distribution schedules: Week A covers the entire city of Québec, while week B covers only the core of the city of Québec.; Full Page Mono: 10.15
Currency: Canada Dollars
NEWSPAPER

Journal Le Courant des Hautes-Laurentides
Editorial: 534, rue de la Madone, Mont-Laurier, Quebec J9L 1S5. **T:** 1 819 623-7374
W: http://www.lecourant.ca
Freq: Weekly; **Circ:** 18500
Editor: Luc Bélisle; **Publisher:** Sylvain Lacasse
Editorial Profile: The Journal Le Courant des Hautes-Laurentides publishes community news and information for residents of Mont-Laurier, Quebec.; Full Page Mono: 4.76; Full Page Colour: 514.76
Currency: Canada Dollars
NEWSPAPER

Journal Le Courrier
Owner: TC. Transcontinental
Editorial: 190 Blvd. Curè-Labelle #204, Local 204, Sainte-Therese, Quebec J7E 2X5.
T: 1 450 434-4144
W: http://www.journallecourrier.com
Circ: 55472
Editor in Chief: Caroline Rioux
Editorial Profile: Journal Le Courrier is a weekly French-language newspaper covering regional information, including news, sports, government and entertainment for residents of Sainte-Thérèse, Quebec.; Full Page Mono: 7.84
Currency: Canada Dollars
NEWSPAPER

Journal Le Nord
Owner: TC. Transcontinental
Editorial: 393 boul. des Laurentides, St-Jerome, Quebec J7Z 4L9. **T:** 1 450 438-8383
E: editeur@tc.tc
W: http://www.journallenord.com **Circ:** 51209
Editor in Chief: Mychel Lapointe
Editorial Profile: Journal le Nord is a weekly French-language newspaper that covers local news and information in Saint-Jérôme, Quebec and its environs.; Full Page Mono: 12.88; Full Page Colour: 275.00
Currency: Canada Dollars
NEWSPAPER

Le Journal Le Nord-Côtier
Owner: Éditions Nordiques (Les)
Editorial: 719, Boul. Laure, Sept-Iles, Quebec G4R 1Y2. **T:** 1 418 960-2090
E: journal@lenord-cotier.com
W: http://www.lenord-cotier.com **Circ:** 20000
Editorial Profile: Journal Le Nord-Cotier is written for the residents of Sept-Iles, Quebec. It covers local news and events.; Full Page Mono: 10.22
Currency: Canada Dollars
NEWSPAPER

Journal Le Voyageur
Owner: Publications Voyageur Inc.
Editorial: 302-336 Pine St., Sudbury, Ontario P3C 1X8. **T:** 1 705 673-3377
E: levoyageur@levoyageur.ca
W: http://www.levoyageur.ca **Circ:** 10000
Publisher: Paul Lefebvre
Editorial Profile: Journal le Voyageur is a weekly French-language journal serving the Francophone community of Sudbury, Ontario and its environs.; Full Page Mono: 8.12
Currency: Canada Dollars

NEWSPAPER

Journal L'Envol
Editorial: 12, rue Potvin, Val-des-Mont, Quebec J8N 7B2. **T:** 1 819 671-1502
E: envol.desmonts@sympatico.ca
Freq: Bi-Weekly; **Circ:** 35500
Publisher & Editor: Nicole-Audrey Thibodeau;
Publisher & Editor: Nicole-Audrey Thibodeau;
Publisher & Editor: Nicole-Audrey Thibodeau
Editorial Profile: Journal L'Envol is a bi-weekly publication covering local news for residents of Val-des-Monts, La Pêche, Chelsea, L'Ange-Gardien and Cantley. It also includes columns on various subjects of interest to the community.; Full Page Mono: 6.02
Currency: Canada Dollars
NEWSPAPER

Journal L'Impact de Drummondville
Owner: Quebecor Communications Inc.
Editorial: 2345, rue St-Pierre, Drummondville, Quebec J2C 5A7. **T:** 1 819 445-7000
E: nouvelle@limpact.ca
W: http://www.limpact.ca
Freq: Weekly; **Circ:** 48800
Publisher: Jean Crépeau; **Editor in Chief:** Guy Levasseur
Editorial Profile: Journal L'Impact de Drummondville offers local news and information to residents of Drummondville, Quebec.
NEWSPAPER

Journal MRG
Editorial: 4705, rue Laval, Lac-Megantic, Quebec G6B 1C4. **T:** 1 819 583-2960
E: mrg@axion.ca
W: http://www.journalmrg.com
Freq: Monthly; **Circ:** 11250
Publisher & Editor: Daniel Poulin
Editorial Profile: Journal MRG is a monthly publication covering local news in Saint-Gédéon-de-Beauce, Scotstown and the MRC of Le-Granit, Québec.; Full Page Mono: 5.42
Currency: Canada Dollars
NEWSPAPER

Le Journal Saint-François
Owner: Quebecor Communications Inc.
Editorial: 55 rue Jacques-Cartier, Salaberry-de-Valleyfield, Quebec J6T 4R4.
T: 1 450 371-6222 **E:** info@st-francois.com
W: http://www.st-francois.com **Circ:** 35300
Editor in Chief: Denis Bourbonnais
Editorial Profile: Le Journal St-François is a weekly French-language newspaper that covers local news and information for the residents of Salaberry-de-Valleyfield, Quebec.; Full Page Mono: 15.96
Currency: Canada Dollars
NEWSPAPER

Journal Vision Prescott/Russell
Owner: Cie d'Édition André Paquette Inc. (La)
Editorial: 1315, rue Laurier, Rockland, Ontario K4K 1C7. **T:** 1 613 446-6456
E: vision@eap.on.ca
W: http://www.visionrockland.ca **Circ:** 23100
Publisher: Bertrand Castonguay
Editorial Profile: Journal Vision Prescott/Russell is a weekly community newspaper.; Full Page Mono: 16.38; Full Page Colour: 500.00
Currency: Canada Dollars
NEWSPAPER

Journ-al.ca Newspapers
Owner: journal.ca inc.
Editorial: 1039 Panneton St, L'Ancienne-Lorette, Quebec G2E 6E7. **T:** 418 780 0999
E: info@journ-al.ca **W:** http://www.journ-al.ca
Freq: Monthly
Editor: Yvon Giroux
NEWSPAPER

Kamloops Review
Owner: Glacier Media Inc.
Editorial: 393 Seymour Street, Kamloops, British Columbia V2C 6P6. **T:** 1 250 372-2331
W: http://www.kamloopsbews.ca **Circ:** 17464
Publisher: Tim Shoults
Editorial Profile: Kamloops Review is written for the residents of Kamloops, British Columbia.; Full Page Mono: 2.38
Currency: US Dollars
NEWSPAPER

Kamloops This Week
Owner: Thompson River Publications Ltd.
Editorial: 1365 B Dalhousie Drive, Kamloops, British Columbia V2C 5P6. **T:** 1 250 374-7467
E: ktw@kamloopsthisweek.com
W: http://www.kamloopsthisweek.com
Circ: 29890
Publisher: Kelly Hall

Editorial Profile: Kamloops This Week covers local news and events of interest to the residents of Kamloops, British Columbia and the surrounding area. Articles include news, weather, events and travel.; Full Page Mono: 27.63
Currency: Canada Dollars
NEWSPAPER

Kawartha Lakes This Week
Owner: Metroland Media Group Ltd.
Editorial: 192 St. David St, Lindsay, Ontario K9V 4Z4-. **T:** 1 705 324-8600
E: lineditor@mykawartha.com
W: http://www.mykawartha.com **Circ:** 29179
Publisher: Bruce Danford; **News Editor:** Mike Lacey
Editorial Profile: Kawartha Lakes This Week is a free, bi-weekly newspaper in Kawartha Lakes, Lindsay, Bobcaygeon and Fenelon Falls, Ontario. It covers local news and community events.; Full Page Mono: 15.40; Full Page Colour: 350.00
Currency: Canada Dollars
NEWSPAPER

Kelowna Capital News
Owner: Black Press
Editorial: 2495 Enterprise Way, Kelowna, British Columbia V1X 7K2. **T:** 1 250 763-3212
E: edit@kelownacapnews.com
W: http://www.kelownacapnews.com
Circ: 48042
Editorial Profile: Kelowna Capital News is a local newspaper delivering news, arts and entertainment, and sports and weather to the residents of the Central Okanagan region of British Columbia.; Full Page Mono: 28.00; Full Page Colour: 500.00
Currency: Canada Dollars
NEWSPAPER

King & Vaughan Weekly Newspapers
Editorial: 34 Main St W, Beeton, Ontario L0G 1A0. **T:** 1 905 729-2287 **Circ:** 30000
News Editor: Angela Gismondi; **News Editor:** Michael McClymont; **Editor:** Mark Pavilons
NEWSPAPER

Kings County Newspapers
Owner: TC. Transcontinental
Editorial: 9185 Commercial St., New Minas, Nova Scotia B4N 3G1. **T:** 1 902 681-2121
W: http://www.novanewsnow.com **Circ:** 10000
Publisher: Fred Fiander; **Editor in Chief:** Sara Keddy
NEWSPAPER

Kings County Weekend
Owner: New Brunswick Publishing Company
Editorial: 593 Main Street, Sussex, New Brunswick E4E 7H5. **T:** 1 506 433-1070
E: news@kingscorecord.com
W: http://www.telegraphjournal.com
Circ: 12000
Editor: David Kelly
Editorial Profile: Kings County Weekend is written for the residents of Sussex, New Brunswick.; Full Page Mono: 8.68
Currency: Canada Dollars
NEWSPAPER

Kingston This Week
Owner: Quebecor Communications Inc.
Editorial: 18 St. Remy Place, Kingston, Ontario K7K 6C4. **T:** 1 613 389-7400
E: news@kingstonthisweek.com
W: http://www.kingstonthisweek.com
Circ: 49087
Editor: Lynn Lambert
Editorial Profile: Kingston This Week is a local newspaper published weekly for the residents of Kingston, Ontario.; Full Page Mono: 17.12
Currency: Canada Dollars
NEWSPAPER

Kitchener Citizen
Editorial: 10 Edinburgh Rd, Kitchener, Ontario N2B 1M5. **T:** 1 519 578-8228
W: http://www.kitchenercitizen.com
Freq: Monthly; **Circ:** 64000
Publisher & Editor: Carrie Debrone; **Publisher & Editor:** Helen Redgwell Hall; **Publisher & Editor:** Helen Redgwell Hall
Editorial Profile: Independent newspaper started in 1996. Covers community items that bigger organizations seem to miss.
NEWSPAPER

Kitchener Post
Owner: Metroland Media
Editorial: 630 Riverbend Dr., Unit 104, Kitchener, Ontario N2K 3S2.
T: 1 519 579-7166
W: http://www.kitchenerpost.ca
Freq: Weekly; **Circ:** 60000
Editor: Charlotte Prong Parkhill; **Publisher:**

Peter Winkler
Editorial Profile: Kitchener Post is a weekly community newspaper serving the residents of Kitchener, Ontario, Canada. The paper is released on Fridays. Topics covered include local news, sports, and arts & events.; Full Page Mono: 59.32
Currency: Canada Dollars
NEWSPAPER

Kitchissippi Times
Owner: Great River Media Inc.
T: 1 613 297-5648 **E:** info@kitchissippi.com
W: http://www.kitchissippi.com
Freq: Bi-Weekly; **Circ:** 17600
Editorial Profile: Kitchissippi Times, published twenty times each year, is a newspaper serving residents of the Ottawa centre-west neighbourhoods of Westboro, Island Park, West Wellington, Hintonburg, Hampton Park, Highland Park, Carlingwood and Civic Hospital.; Full Page Mono: 11.12; Full Page Colour: 360.00
Currency: Canada Dollars
NEWSPAPER

Kootenay News Advertiser
Owner: Black Press
Editorial: 1510 2nd St N, Cranbrook, British Columbia V1C 3L2. **T:** 1 250 489-3455
W: http://www.kootenayadvertiser.com
Circ: 30996
Editorial Profile: The Kootenay News Advertiser is a local newspaper written for the residents of Cranbrook, British Columbia.; Full Page Mono: 19.93
Currency: Canada Dollars
NEWSPAPER

Korea Times Toronto Edition
Editorial: 287 Bridgeland Ave, Toronto, Ontario M6A 1Z6. **T:** 1 416 787-1111
E: news@koreatimes.net
W: http://www.koreatimes.net
Freq: Daily; **Circ:** 16000
Editor in Chief: Anthony Kim; **Publisher:** Lawrence Kim
Editorial Profile: Korea Times Toronto Edition is a daily, Korean-language paper serving the residents of Toronto. It provides local, national and international news.; Full Page Mono: 36.00; Full Page Colour: 142.88
Currency: Canada Dollars
DAILY NEWSPAPER

KV Style
Owner: New Brunswick Publishing Company
Editorial: 122 Hampton Rd, Rothesay, New Brunswick E2E 2N5. **T:** 1 506 847-5900
W: http://kvstyle.canadaeast.com **Circ:** 14000
Editor: Candice Mac Lean
Editorial Profile: KV Style is a free, weekly tabloid-format newspaper that serves residents throughout the Kennebecasis Valley, including Rothesay, New Brunswick. It contains news, events and feature stories. Produced under the umbrella of the Telegraph-Journal in St. Johns, New Brunswick, it is distributed as an insert to the daily paper to area subscribers and as a stand-alone delivered directly to non-subscribers' homes. Advertising deadlines are on Thursdays at noon ET.; Full Page Mono: 5.10
Currency: Canada Dollars
NEWSPAPER

Le Lac St-Jean
Owner: TC. Transcontinental
Editorial: 100 rue St-Joseph Sud local #01, Alma, Quebec G8B 7A6. **T:** 1 418 668-4545
E: redaction_alma@transcontinental.ca
W: http://www.lelacstjean.com **Circ:** 22395
Editorial Profile: Le Lac-Saint-Jean is a weekly publication covering local news and events for the residents of Lac-Saint-Jean Est, Québec.; Full Page Mono: 9.52
Currency: Canada Dollars
NEWSPAPER

Lakeshore News
Owner: Black Press
Editorial: 161 Hudson Ave NE, Salmon Arm, British Columbia V1E 4N8. **T:** 1 250 832-9461
E: lsn@lakeshorenews.bc.ca
W: http://www.lakeshorenews.bc.ca
Circ: 15500
Editor: Wendy Clam; **Editor:** Michelle Weisenger
Editorial Profile: Lakeshore News is a weekly newspaper that serves Salmon Arm, British Columbia and surrounding communities. It covers local news, sports, entertainment and human-interest stories. Deadlines are at noon PT.; Full Page Mono: 17.64
Currency: Canada Dollars
NEWSPAPER

The Langley Advance News
Owner: Glacier Media Inc.
Editorial: 112-6375-202 St, Langley, British Columbia V2Y 1N1. **T:** 1 604 534-8641
W: http://www.langleyadvance.com
Circ: 40100
Editor in Chief: Bob Groeneveld; **Publisher:** Ryan McAdams
Editorial Profile: The Langley Advance News is a community newspaper for residents of Langley, British Columbia and the surrounding area. It provides coverage of local news, editorials, sports and special features.; Full Page Mono: 28.56
Currency: Canada Dollars
NEWSPAPER

Langley Times
Owner: Black Press
Editorial: 20258 Fraser Hwy, Unit 102, Langley, British Columbia V3A 4E6.
T: 1 604 533-4157
E: newsroom@langleytimes.com
W: http://www.langleytimes.com **Circ:** 36371
Editor in Chief: Frank Bucholtz; **Publisher:** Dwayne Weidendorf
Editorial Profile: Langley Times is a local newspaper for residents of Langley, British Columbia and the surrounding areas. The newspaper provides coverage of local news, sports, entertainment, community events, lifestyle topics and feature stories.; Full Page Mono: 28.42
Currency: Canada Dollars
NEWSPAPER

Last Mountain Times Newspapers
Owner: Last Mountain Times Ltd.
Editorial: 103-1st Ave West, Nokomis, Saskatchewan S0G 3R0. **T:** 1 306 528-2020
E: editor@lastmountaintimes.ca
W: http://www.lastmountaintimes.ca
Freq: Weekly; **Circ:** 11882
NEWSPAPER

Laval Newspapers
Editorial: 3860 Notre-Dame Blvd., Suite 304, Laval, Quebec H7V 1S1. **T:** 1 450 978-9999
W: http://newsfirst.ca **Circ:** 89036
NEWSPAPER

L'Avenir & Des Rivieres
Owner: TC. Transcontinental
Editorial: 221 rue Principale Est, Farnham, Quebec J2N 1L5. **T:** 1 450 293-3138
E: lavenir@canadafrancais.com
W: http://farnham.enregion.ca/ **Circ:** 13000
Publisher & Editor: Charles Couture; **Editor in Chief:** Jean-Philippe Pineault
Editorial Profile: L'Avenir et des Rivières is a weekly French-language newspaper that covers local news and information. It contains news, events, business, and feature stories for residents in and around Farmham, Quebec. Contact the publication by phone, fax, or mail.; Full Page Mono: 7.00
Currency: Canada Dollars
NEWSPAPER

The Leader
Owner: Black Press
Editorial: 200-5450 152nd St, Surrey, British Columbia V3S 5J9. **T:** 1 604 575-2744
E: newsroom@surreyleader.com
W: http://www.surreyleader.com **Circ:** 87000
Editor: Paula Carlson
Editorial Profile: The Leader is a twice-weekly newspaper published for residents of the Surrey and North Delta, British Columbia communities. The publication reports local news, events, politics, sports and arts & entertainment.; Full Page Mono: 22.54; Full Page Colour: 805.00
Currency: Canada Dollars
NEWSPAPER

The Leader - Niagara This Week
Owner: Metroland Media Group Ltd.
Editorial: 3300 Merrittville HWY, Unit 1B, Thorold, Ontario L2V 4Y6. **T:** 1 905 641-1984
E: letters@niagarathisweek.com
W: http://www.niagarathisweek.com
Freq: Bi-Weekly; **Circ:** 165300
Publisher: Neil Oliver; **Circulation Mananger:** Tracey Travis-Scott
Editorial Profile: The Leader-Niagara This Week is a publication for the Port Colborne, Ontario community. Articles deal with the news, weather and local events.; Full Page Mono: 89.88; Full Page Colour: 111.98
Currency: Canada Dollars
NEWSPAPER

The Leader Post
Owner: Postmedia Network Inc.
Editorial: 1964 Park St, Regina, Saskatchewan S4N 7M5. **T:** 1 306 781-5211
E: citydesk@leaderpost.com
W: http://www.leaderpost.com
Freq: Daily; **Circ:** 37083
Editor in Chief: Rob McLaughlin
Editorial Profile: The Leader Post, established in 1883, is a daily 30+ page, broadsheet newspaper written for residents of Regina, Saskatchewan and its neighboring communities. Every issue of the publication includes six staple sections: Canada & World, Arts & Life, City & Province, Business & Agriculture, Sports and Classifieds. Additionally, on Mondays the paper includes the Minus 20 section, on Tuesdays the paper includes the Fashion section and Wednesday the paper includes the Food section. On Thursdays one will find What's On, Living Spaces and Body & Health. On Fridays, the publication includes the Travel and Driving sections. Saturdays issues include Weekender, Working, Homes and Children's Corner. On Sundays, one will find the Regina Sun Community News. There are two magazine style publications that arrive monthly with the Regina Leader-Post: Home Lifestyles and Kicks.; Full Page Mono: 30.52
Currency: Canada Dollars
DAILY NEWSPAPER

Leader/Review
Editorial: 67 Park Avenue, Lac du Bonnet, Manitoba R0E 1A0. **T:** 1 204 3458611
Circ: 12235
Publisher: Jenifer Bilsky; **City Editor:** Glen Hallick
NEWSPAPER

Leamington Post and Tri-Town News
Owner: Sun Media
Editorial: 75 Oak St. West, Leamington, Ontario N8H 2B2. **T:** 1 519 326-4434
E: leamington.post@sunmedia.ca
W: http://www.leamingtonpost.ca **Circ:** 17412
Publisher: Shannon Ricker
Editorial Profile: Leamington Post & Tri-Town News is a community newspaper that covers local news and events for the residents of Leamington, Ontario.; Full Page Mono: 14.98
Currency: Canada Dollars
NEWSPAPER

L'Echo de l'Ouest
Editorial: 200 Croissant Joncaire, Montreal, Quebec H9C 2P7. **T:** 1 514 696-3000
E: info@echodelouest.com
W: http://echodelouest.com
Freq: Bi-Weekly; **Circ:** 25000
Publisher: Austin Frances; **Editor:** André Smith
Editorial Profile: L'Echo de l'Ouest is a French-language bi-weekly community newspaper serving the Montréal borough l'Ile-Bizard-Sainte-Geneviève. The paper generally covers community politics, arts, sports and community events, but will occasionally expand its coverage to federal and international affairs. Deadlines are Wednesday one week before publication at noon.; Full Page Mono: 7.00
Currency: Canada Dollars
NEWSPAPER

The Leduc Representative
Owner: Quebecor Communications Inc.
Editorial: 4504-61st Ave, Leduc, Alberta T9E 3Z1. **T:** 1 780 986-2271
W: http://www.leducrep.com **Circ:** 16000
Editor: Michelle Clarke
Editorial Profile: The Leduc Representative is a weekly newspaper written for the residents of Leduc, Alberta. It covers local news and events.; Full Page Mono: 24.36
Currency: Canada Dollars
NEWSPAPER

The Leduc-Westaskiwin Pipestone Flyer
Editorial: 5025 50th St, Millet, Alberta T0C 1Z0. **T:** 1 780 387-5797
E: production@pipestoneflyer.com
W: http://www.pipestoneflyer.com **Circ:** 16588
Editor: Brian Hahn; **Publisher:** Ted Okkerse
Editorial Profile: The Leduc-Westaskiwin Pipestone Flyer is a weekly community newspaper serving the residents of Millet, Alberta.; Full Page Mono: 11.20
Currency: Canada Dollars
NEWSPAPER

Les Les Hebdos Quebecor - Chicoutimi
Owner: Quebecor Communications Inc.
Editorial: 1, Rue du Mont Sainte Claire, Chicoutimi, Quebec G7H 5G3.
T: 1 418 695-2601
W: http://reseauhebdos.canoe.ca **Circ:** 126010
Publisher: Diane Audet; **Editor:** Maurice Locas
NEWSPAPER

The Lethbridge Herald
Owner: Alberta Newspaper Group Inc.
Editorial: 504 Seventh St S, Lethbridge, Alberta T1J 2H1. **T:** 1 403 328-4411
E: circulation@lethbridgeherald.com
W: http://www.lethbridgeherald.com
Freq: Daily; **Circ:** 16901
Editor: Craig Albrecht; **Publisher:** Coleen Campbell; **News Editor:** Randy Jensen
Editorial Profile: The Lethbridge Herald is a broadsheet newspaper written for the Southern Alberta general public. It is one of the major newspapers in Southern Alberta covering business, agriculture, entertainment, sports and world news.; Full Page Mono: 11.41; Full Page Colour: 590.00
Currency: Canada Dollars
DAILY NEWSPAPER

Lethbridge Journal
Owner: Alberta Newspaper Group
Editorial: 504 7 St S, Lethbridge, Alberta T1J 2H1. **T:** 1 403 320-8936
W: http://www.lethbridgejournal.ca
Freq: Bi-Weekly; **Circ:** 28000
Editor: Lisa Doerksen
Editorial Profile: Lethbridge Journal is a weekly community newspaper published every other Thursday. The paper serves Lethbridge, Alberta and surrounding areas.; Full Page Mono: 18.00
Currency: US Dollars
NEWSPAPER

Lethbridge Newspapers
Owner: Alberta Newspaper Group Inc.
Editorial: 504-7 Street South, Lethbridge, Alberta T1J 2H1. **T:** 1 403 328-4411
W: http://www.lethbridgeherald.com
Circ: 49395
NEWSPAPER

The Liberal
Owner: Metroland Media Group Ltd.
Editorial: 50 McIntosh Dr Unit 115, Markham, Ontario L3R 9T3. **T:** 1 905 881-3373
E: newsroom@theliberal.com **Circ:** 74850
Editor in Chief: Debora Kelly; **Publisher:** Ian Proudfoot
Editorial Profile: The Liberal is a community newspaper published two times a week for the residents of Richmond Hill, Vaughan, Thornhill and Markham, Ontario. It covers local news, sports, entertainment and community events.; Full Page Mono: 24.99
Currency: Canada Dollars
NEWSPAPER

Lighthouse Publications
Editorial: 353 York St, Bridgewater, Nova Scotia B4V 3K2. **T:** 1 902 543-2457
E: mail@southshorenow.ca
W: http://www.southshorenow.ca **Circ:** 37169
Publisher: Lynn Hennigar; **Editor:** Vernon Oickle
NEWSPAPER

The Lindsay Post
Owner: Sun Media
Editorial: 17 William St South, Lindsay, Ontario K9V 3Z8. **T:** 1 705 324-2113 238
W: http://www.thepost.ca
Freq: 2 Times/Week; **Circ:** 22000
Publisher: Darren Murphy
Editorial Profile: The Lindsay Post is a local newspaper written for the residents in and around Lindsay, Ontario. The publication covers local news, sports, arts & entertainment and business.; Full Page Mono: 8.45
Currency: Canada Dollars
NEWSPAPER

The Link
Owner: Munish (Kaypel)
Editorial: 13463 78 Ave Suite 101, Surrey, British Columbia V3W 0A8. **T:** 1 604 591-5160
E: editor@thelinkpaper.ca
W: http://www.thelinkpaper.ca **Circ:** 25000
Publisher: Sanjiv Batta; **Editor in Chief:** R. Paul Dhillon
Editorial Profile: The Link is a weekly newspaper written for the Indo-Canadian community in British Columbia. The paper features regional and national news as well as news on South Asia.; Full Page Mono: 12.88
Currency: Canada Dollars
NEWSPAPER

The Lloydminster Source
Owner: The Lloydminster Source
Editorial: 6209A-50th Avenue, Lloydminster, Saskatchewan S9V 1W5. **T:** 1 306 825-5111
W: http://www.lloydminstersource.com
Circ: 17300
Publisher: Reid Keebaugh
Editorial Profile: The Lloydminster Source is a community newspaper that is published twice a week. It covers news and events for the Lloydminster, Saskatchewan area.; Full Page Mono: 15.26
Currency: Canada Dollars
NEWSPAPER

London Community News
Owner: Metroland Media Group Ltd.
Editorial: 1074 Dearness Drive, Unit 80, London, Ontario N6E 1N9. **T:** 1 519 649-2000
W: http://www.londoncommunitynews.com
Circ: 126000
Editorial Profile: London Community News offers local news and information to residents of London, Ontario. Local editions are offered to residents in six different neighbourhoods throughout the city.
NEWSPAPER

The London Free Press
Owner: Quebecor Communications Inc.
Editorial: 369 York St, London, Ontario N6B 3R4-. **T:** 1 519 679-1111
E: lfp.website@sunmedia.ca
W: http://www.lfpress.com
Freq: Daily; **Circ:** 73990
News Editor: Howard Burns; **Publisher:** Susan Muszak; **Editor in Chief:** Joe Ruscitti; **Editor in Chief:** Joe Ruscitti; **News Editor:** Greg Van Moorsel
Editorial Profile: The London Free Press is a daily newspaper written for the London, Ontario general public. It covers local, national and world news as well as arts & entertainment, lifestyle, food, travel, books, television, art, movies, business, features and sports. There is no dedicated photo editor, but photo inquiries can be directed to the news editor.; Full Page Mono: 34.44; Full Page Colour: 132.16
Currency: Canada Dollars
DAILY NEWSPAPER

The Londoner
Owner: Quebecor Communications Inc.
Editorial: 1147 Gainsborough Rd, London, Ontario N6H 5L5. **T:** 1 519 673-5005
W: http://www.thelondoner.ca **Circ:** 108000
Editor: Don Biggs; **Publisher:** Linda Leblanc
Editorial Profile: The Londoner is a local, weekly newspaper written for residents of London, Ontario. It covers local news and events.; Full Page Mono: 14.46
Currency: Canada Dollars
NEWSPAPER

Luby Weekly Chinese Newspaper
Owner: Quebec Chinese Information Inc.
Editorial: 1111 St-Urbain, Suite M-09, Montreal, Quebec H2Z 1Y6. **T:** 1 514 397-0632
E: lubynews@bellnet.ca
W: http://www.lubycanada.com **Circ:** 10000
Publisher: Ya-I Chang
Editorial Profile: Luby Weekly Chinese Newspaper is a weekly publication for the residents of Montreal.; Full Page Mono: 17.50
Currency: Canada Dollars
NEWSPAPER

Main Street
Owner: Éditions Main Street Inc. (Les)
Editorial: 21 Chemin du Mont Oeler, Harrington, Quebec J8G 2S6.
T: 1 819 242-2232 **E:** info@laurentianlife.com
W: http://mainstreetweeknews.com
Freq: Monthly; **Circ:** 12500
Publisher & Editor: Jack Burger
Editorial Profile: Main Street is a free, monthly newspaper for the English-speaking community of the Laurentians, Quebec. Coverage ranges from local community and cultural events to articles on country living to opinion pieces on local, national and international events.; Full Page Mono: 21.00
Currency: Canada Dollars
NEWSPAPER

Le Manic
Owner: Éditions Nordiques (Les)
Editorial: 965, rue de Parfondeval, Baie-Comeau, Quebec G5C 2W8.
T: 1 418 589-2090 **E:** information@lemanic.ca
W: http://www.lemanic.ca
Freq: Weekly; **Circ:** 15963
Editor: Simon Brisson
Editorial Profile: Le Manic is a weekly newspaper covering local news and events from Pessamit to Baie-Trinité, Quebec.; Full Page Mono: 5.18
Currency: Canada Dollars
NEWSPAPER

Manotick Messenger
Owner: Morris Newspaper Group

WORLD NEWS MEDIA

Editorial: 1165 Beaverwood, Manotick, Ontario K431A5. **T:** 1 613 692-6000
W: http://www.manotickmessenger.on.ca
Circ: 15000
Publisher: Jeffrey Morris
Editorial Profile: Manotick Messenger is the weekly local newspaper for the residents of the Manotick, Ontario area. The publication covers news from North Gower, the Rideau Township, and from Osgoode Township. The newspaper covers local news and sports.; Full Page Mono: 6.93
Currency: Canada Dollars
NEWSPAPER

Maple Ridge News
Owner: Black Press
Editorial: 22328-119th Ave, Maple Ridge, British Columbia V2X 2Z3. **T:** 1 604 467-1122
E: newsroom@mapleridgenews.com
W: http://www.mapleridgenews.com
Circ: 30469
Publisher: Jim Coulter; **Editor:** Michael Hall
Editorial Profile: Maple Ridge News is a local newspaper for residents of Meadows, British Columbia, providing readers with local news, business, entertainment, sports and opinion pieces.; Full Page Mono: 11.55
Currency: Canada Dollars
NEWSPAPER

Maple Ridge/Pitt Meadows Times
Owner: Glacier Media Inc.
Editorial: 22345 North Ave, Maple Ridge, British Columbia V2X 8T2. **T:** 1 604 463-2281
E: editorial@mrtimes.com
W: http://www.mrtimes.com **Circ:** 29650
Editor: Bob Groeneveld; **Publisher:** Ryan McAdams
Editorial Profile: Maple Ridge/Pitt Meadows Times is a bi-weekly newspaper written for residents of Maple Ridge and Pitt Meadows, British Columbia. It covers local news, sports and entertainment stories.; Full Page Mono: 11.62
Currency: Canada Dollars
NEWSPAPER

Marketplace
Owner: Quebecor Communications Inc.
Editorial: 16 Packham Road, Stratford, Ontario N5A 6T6. **T:** 1 519 271-2220
W: http://www.stratfordbeaconherald.com/marketplace **Circ:** 16300
Publisher: Dave Carter; **Editor:** Bruce Urquhart
Editorial Profile: Marketplace is a weekly newspaper written for the residents of Stratford, Ontario.; Full Page Mono: 7.77
Currency: Canada Dollars
NEWSPAPER

Markham Economist & Sun
Owner: Metroland Media Group Ltd.
Editorial: 50 McIntosh Dr Unit 115, Markham, Ontario L3R 9T3. **T:** 1 905 294-2200
E: newsroom@econsun.com
W: http://www.yorkregion.com **Circ:** 67000
Editor in Chief: Debora Kelly; **Publisher:** Ian Proudfoot
Editorial Profile: Markham Economist & Sun is a newspaper published two times a week for the residents of Markham, Ontario. The publication contains news aimed at local families and businesses, including news, sports, arts & entetainment, educational and economic news, and weather.; Full Page Mono: 26.25; Full Page Colour: 1160.00
Currency: Canada Dollars
NEWSPAPER

The Masthead News
Owner: Ocean Breeze Distributions
T: 1 902 857-9099
E: themastheadnews@aol.com
W: http://www.themastheadnews.ca
Freq: Bi-Weekly; **Circ:** 15500
Publisher & Editor: Ronald Driskill; Full Page Mono: 32.90
Currency: US Dollars
NEWSPAPER

Medicine Hat News
Owner: Alberta Newspaper Group Inc.
Editorial: 3257 Dunmore Road SE, Medicine Hat, Alberta T1A 7E6. **T:** 1 403 527-1101
E: newsdesk@medicinehatnews.com
W: http://www.medicinehatnews.com
Freq: Daily; **Circ:** 10557
Publisher: Mike Hertz
Editorial Profile: Medicine Hat News is a daily newspaper published for the residents of Medicine Hat, Alberta. The paper focuses on community news and sports, but also includes national news, lifestyle and opinions sections.; Full Page Mono: 17.92; Full Page Colour: 515.00
Currency: Canada Dollars
DAILY NEWSPAPER

The Meridian Booster
Owner: Quebecor Communications Inc.
Editorial: 5714-44th St, Lloydminster, Alberta T9V 0B6. **T:** 1 780 875-3362
W: http://www.meridianbooster.com
Circ: 15020
Publisher: Shaun Jessome
Editorial Profile: The Meridian Booster is a bi-weekly newspaper that covers local news and events for the residents of Lloydminster, Alberta.; Full Page Mono: 13.72
Currency: Canada Dollars
NEWSPAPER

Le Messager Week-End
Owner: TC. Transcontinental Media Inc.
Editorial: 455 Fénelon suite 303, Dorval, Quebec H9S 5T8. **T:** 1 514 636-7314
E: messagerweekend_redaction@tc.tc
W: http://www.lemessagerweekend.ca/
Freq: Monthly
Publisher: Patricia-Ann Beaulieu; **Editor:** Toula Foscolos
Editorial Profile: Le Messager Week-End is a free monthly publication serving residents of south-west Montréal. It covers food, drink, concerts, culture, society, health and community events in and around Dorval and Montréal.
NEWSPAPER

The Metis Voyageur
Owner: Metis Nation
Editorial: 500 Old St. Patrick Street, Ottawa, Ontario K1N 9G4. **T:** 1 613 798-1488
W: http://www.metisnation.org
Freq: Bi-Monthly; **Circ:** 12000
Editor: Linda Lord
Editorial Profile: The Metis Voyageur is a community paper published bi-monthly for the Metis Nation and surrounding communities in Ontario. It covers community news and features and is available free with a suggested donation suscription rate.; Full Page Mono: 24.00
Currency: Canada Dollars
NEWSPAPER

Metro Calgary
Owner: Star Media Group
Editorial: 120-3030 3 Ave NE 120, Calgary, Alberta T2A 6T7. **T:** 1 403 444-0136
E: calgaryletters@metronews.ca
W: http://www.metronews.ca/calgary
Freq: Daily; **Circ:** 77525
Editor in Chief: Charlotte Empey; **Publisher:** Bill McDonald; **Publisher:** Steve Shrout
Editorial Profile: Metro Calgary is a local, commuter daily serving residents of Calgary, Alberta. The paper includes local, national and international news, politics, business, sports, arts & entertainment and pop culture. Sister papers include Metro Vancouver, Metro Edmonton, Metro Toronto, Metro Ottawa, Metro Halifax, Metro Winnipeg, Metro London and Metro Montréal. Combined the newspapers reach around 1.1 million readers.; Full Page Colour: 83.77
Currency: Canada Dollars
DAILY NEWSPAPER

Metro Edmonton
Owner: Star Media Group
Editorial: 2070-10123 99 St NW 2070, Edmonton, Alberta T5J 3H1.
T: 1 780 702-0592
E: edmontonletters@metronews.ca
W: http://www.metronews.ca/edmonton
Freq: Daily; **Circ:** 81815
Editor in Chief: Charlotte Empey; **Publisher:** Bill McDonald; **Publisher:** Steve Shrout
Editorial Profile: Metro Edmonton is a local, commuter daily written for the residents of Edmonton, Alberta. Sister papers include Metro Vancouver, Metro Calgary, Metro Toronto, Metro Ottawa, Metro Halifax, Metro Winnipeg, Metro London and Metro Montréal. Combined, the papers reach around 1.1 million readers.; Full Page Colour: 83.77
Currency: Canada Dollars
DAILY NEWSPAPER

Metro Halifax
Owner: Metro International
Editorial: 3260 Barrington St, Halifax, Nova Scotia B3K 0B5. **T:** 1 902 444-4444
E: halifaxletters@metronews.ca
W: http://www.metronews.ca/halifax
Freq: Daily; **Circ:** 43949
Editor in Chief: Charlotte Empey; **Publisher:** Greg Lutes; **Publisher:** Bill McDonald
Editorial Profile: Metro Halifax is a free newspaper that runs Monday through Friday and serves community, national and international news to the Halifax, Nova Scotia metropolitan population. Sister papers include Metro Vancouver, Metro Edmonton, Metro Toronto, Metro Ottawa, Metro Calgary, Metro Winnipeg, Metro London and Metro Montréal. Combined the newspapers reach around 1.1 million readers.; Full Page Colour: 48.83
Currency: Canada Dollars
DAILY NEWSPAPER

Metro Life News
Editorial: 100 Dynamic Drive, Toronto, Ontario M1V 5C4. **T:** 1 416 299-8229
E: adsmetrolife@gmail.com
Freq: Weekly; **Circ:** 10000
Editor: Richard Liu
Editorial Profile: Metro News Life is a weekly Chinese newspaper that provides Local and Community News coverage to the Chinese community in Toronto, ON.; Full Page Mono: 2.02
Currency: Canada Dollars
NEWSPAPER

Metro London
Owner: Star Media Group
Editorial: 350 Talbot St, London, Ontario N6A 2R6. **T:** 1 519 434-3556
E: londonletters@metronews.ca
W: http://www.metronews.ca/london
Freq: Daily; **Circ:** 34050
Editor in Chief: Charlotte Empey; **Publisher:** Bill McDonald
Editorial Profile: Metro London launched April 4, 2011 as a free, commuter daily newspaper distributed to commuters and residents of the London, Ontario metropolitan area. It targets youthful, active readers between the ages of 18 and 49. The newspaper offers concise articles that focus on local, national and international news, lifestyle, sports and arts & entertainment stories. Sister publications include: Metro Toronto, Metro Montréal, Metro Calgary, Metro Edmonton, Metro Vancouver, Metro Halifax, Metro Ottawa and Metro Winnipeg.; Full Page Colour: 41.65
Currency: Canada Dollars
DAILY NEWSPAPER

Métro Montréal
Owner: TC. Transcontinental
Editorial: 1100 Boul Rene-Levesque O Etage 24E, Montreal, Quebec H3B 4N4.
T: 1 514 286-1066 **E:** info@journalmetro.com
W: http://www.journalmetro.com
Freq: Daily; **Circ:** 163138
Editor in Chief: Éric Aussant; **Publisher:** Nicolas Faucher; **News Editor:** Jennifer Guthrie
Editorial Profile: Métro Montréal is a free commuter daily newspaper published each weekday and serving residents and commuters in the greater Montreal metro area. The French-language paper is designed and packaged for young, urban and well-educated audiences. Local, national and international news reports are combined with the latest entertainment listings and reviews. It also contains articles on topics such as sports, food, health and fitness, education and careers, travel and real estate. Sister papers include Metro Vancouver, Metro Edmonton, Metro Toronto, Metro Ottawa, Metro Halifax and Metro Calgary. Combined the newspapers reach around 1.1 million readers.; Full Page Colour: 138.54
Currency: Canada Dollars
DAILY NEWSPAPER

Metro Ottawa
Owner: Star Media Group
Editorial: 130 Slater St, Ottawa, Ontario K1P 6E2. **T:** 1 613 236-5058
E: ottawaletters@metronews.ca
W: http://www.metronews.ca/ottawa
Freq: Daily; **Circ:** 61541
Editor in Chief: Charlotte Empey; **Publisher:** Bill McDonald
Editorial Profile: Metro Ottawa is a free commuter daily newspaper distributed each weekday to residents and commuters in the greater Ottawa metro area. It is designed and packaged for young, urban and well-educated audiences and it is available at newstands, restaurants and retailers. Local, national and international news reports are combined with the latest entertainment listings and reviews. It also contains articles on topics such as sports, food, health and fitness, education and careers, travel and real estate. Lead times vary depending on editorial department. Advertising rates include full color. Sister papers include Metro Vancouver, Metro Edmonton, Metro Toronto, Metro Calgary, Metro Halifax, Metro Winnipeg, Metro London and Metro Montréal. Combined the newspapers reach around 1.1 million readers.; Full Page Colour: 76.97
Currency: Canada Dollars
DAILY NEWSPAPER

Metro Regina
Owner: Star Media Group
Editorial: Regina, Saskatchewan.
T: 1 306 584-2025 **E:** regina@metronews.ca
W: http://metronews.ca/news/regina/
Freq: Daily; **Circ:** 20000
Editor in Chief: Charlotte Empey
Editorial Profile: Metro Regina is a daily newspaper serving residents of Regina, Saskatchewan, Canada. It began publication on April 2, 2012.; Full Page Colour: 36.78
Currency: Canada Dollars
DAILY NEWSPAPER

Metro Saskatoon
Owner: Star Media Group
Editorial: Saskatoon, Saskatchewan.
T: 1 306 649-2025
E: saskatoon@metronews.ca
W: http://metronews.ca/news/saskatoon/
Freq: Daily; **Circ:** 20000
Editor in Chief: Charlotte Empey
Editorial Profile: Metro Saskatoon is a daily newspaper serving the residents of Saskatoon, Saskatchewan, Canada. It begins publication on April 2, 2012.; Full Page Colour: 36.78
Currency: Canada Dollars
DAILY NEWSPAPER

Metro Toronto
Owner: Star Media Group
Editorial: 625 Church St, Toronto, Ontario M4Y 2G1-. **T:** 1 416 486-4900
E: torontoletters@metronews.ca
W: http://www.metronews.ca/toronto
Freq: Daily; **Circ:** 266476
Editor in Chief: Charlotte Empey; **Publisher:** Bill McDonald
Editorial Profile: Metro Toronto is a free, commuter daily newspaper that is distributed to commuters and residents of the Toronto metropolitan area. It targets young professionals and is intended to be read during a 20-minute morning commute. The newspaper has concise articles that focus on local, national and international news, lifestyle, sports and arts & entertainment stories. Sister papers include Metro Vancouver, Metro Edmonton, Metro Calgary, Metro Ottawa, Metro Halifax, Metro London, Metro Winnipeg and Journal Metro. Combined, the papers reach around 1.1 million readers.; Full Page Colour: 250.17
Currency: Canada Dollars
DAILY NEWSPAPER

Metro Vancouver
Owner: Star Media Group
Editorial: 375 Water St Suite 405, Vancouver, British Columbia V6B 5C6. **T:** 1 604 602-1002
E: vancouverletters@metronews.ca
W: http://www.metronews.ca/vancouver
Freq: Daily; **Circ:** 160982
Editor in Chief: Charlotte Empey; **Publisher:** Bill McDonald
Editorial Profile: Metro Vancouver is a free, commuter daily newspaper distributed throughout the Vancouver, British Columbia metropolitan area. It targets young professionals and is intended to be read during a 20-minute morning commute. The newspaper has concise articles that focus on local, national and international news, lifestyle, sports and arts & entertainment stories. Sister papers include Metro Edmonton, Metro Calgary, Metro Toronto, Metro Ottawa, Metro Halifax, Metro Winnipeg, Metro London and Metro Montréal. Combined, the papers reach around 1.1 million readers.; Full Page Colour: 134.25
Currency: Canada Dollars
DAILY NEWSPAPER

Metro Winnipeg
Owner: Star Media Group
Editorial: 161 Portage Ave E Suite 200, Winnipeg, Manitoba R3B 2L6.
T: 1 204 943-9300
E: winnipegletters@metronews.ca
W: http://www.metronews.ca/winnipeg
Freq: Daily; **Circ:** 51505
Editor in Chief: Charlotte Empey; **Publisher:** Bill McDonald; **Publisher:** Steve Shrout
Editorial Profile: Metro Winnipeg launched April 4, 2011 as a free, commuter daily newspaper distributed to commuters and residents of the Winnipeg, Manitoba metropolitan area. It targets youthful, active readers between the ages of 18 and 49. The newspaper offers concise articles that focus on local, national and international news, lifestyle, sports and arts & entertainment stories. Sister publications include: Metro Toronto, Metro Montréal, Metro Calgary, Metro Edmonton, Metro Vancouver, Metro Halifax, Metro Ottawa and Metro London.; Full Page Colour: 49.78
Currency: Canada Dollars

DAILY NEWSPAPER

Metroland Media Ottawa - Arnprior
Owner: Metroland Media Group Ltd.
Editorial: 8 McGonigal St. W., Arnprior, Ontario K7S 1L8. **T:** 1 613 623-6571
Circ: 14170
News Editor: John Carter
NEWSPAPER

Metroland Media Toronto-East
Owner: Metroland Media Group Ltd.
Editorial: 175 Gordon Baker Rd, Toronto, Ontario M2H 2N7. **T:** 1 416 493-4400
E: contactus@insidetoronto.com
W: http://www.insidetoronto.com **Circ:** 296200
Publisher: Ian Proudfoot
Editorial Profile: When sending faxes, pleases indicate the intended paper in the attention line.
NEWSPAPER

Metroland Media Toronto-West
Owner: Metroland Media Group Ltd.
Editorial: 175 Gordon Baker Rd, Toronto, Ontario M2H 2N7. **T:** 1 416 675-4390
E: contactus@insidetoronto.com
W: http://www.insidetoronto.com **Circ:** 120600
Publisher: Ian Proudfoot
Editorial Profile: When sending faxes, please indicate the intended paper in the subject line.
NEWSPAPER

The Metropolitain
Editorial: 1470 rue Peel, Tour A, Ste. 155, Montreal, Quebec H3A 1T1. **T:** 1 514 759-8541
E: onlineeditor@themetropolitain.ca
W: http://www.themetropolitain.ca
Freq: Bi-Weekly; **Circ:** 40000
Editorial Profile: The Metropolitain is a free, bi-weekly tabloid newspaper featuring ideas and public affairs commentary. The bilingual paper includes articles and columns concerning the Canadian homeland, Canada's place in international affairs, its economy, and art and style reviews. Each article, whether written in English or French, is unique. The articles are not translated and never appear in both languages. The paper's content relies heavily on contributed material, and contributors span the politial spectrum.; Full Page Mono: 34.78
Currency: Canada Dollars
NEWSPAPER

Midland Mirror
Owner: Metroland Media Group Ltd.
Editorial: 488 Dominion Avenue, Midland, Ontario L4R 1P6. **T:** 1 705 527-5500
W: http://www.midlandmirror.com **Circ:** 20994
Editor: Travis Mealing
Editorial Profile: Midland Mirror is a community newspaper published for Midland, Ontario area local residents. It covers local news, sports, entertainment, lifestyle and community events. The lead time is one week. Deadlines for editorial submissions are four days prior to the issue date.; Full Page Mono: 15.54
Currency: Canada Dollars
NEWSPAPER

Midweek
Owner: Asian World Today Inc.
Editorial: 1310 Mid-Way Blvd Unit 31, Mississauga, Ontario L5T 2K5.
T: 1 647 272-8182
W: http://www.southasiandaily.com
Circ: 40000
Editor: Yudhvir Jaswal
Editorial Profile: Covers news weekly as it relates to the South Asian community and includes international, national and community news. It is delivered across Kitchener, Waterloo, Guelph, Hamilton & Stoney Creek.; Full Page Colour: 18.18
Currency: Canada Dollars
NEWSPAPER

O Milenio
Owner: Lola Investments
Editorial: 2379 Central Park Drive, Unit 703, Oakville, Ontario L6H 0E3. **T:** 1 905 257-7740
E: info@mileniostadium.com
W: http://www.mileniostadium.com
Circ: 40000
Publisher & Editor: Alexandre Franco
Editorial Profile: O Milenio is a weekly paper serving the Portuguese speaking communities in Mississauga, Ontario. It is published every Friday.; Full Page Mono: 8.89
Currency: Canada Dollars
NEWSPAPER

Milton Canadian Champion
Owner: Metroland Media Group Ltd.
Editorial: 555 Industrial Dr, Milton, Ontario L9T 5E1. **T:** 1 905 878-2341
W: http://miltoncanadianchampion.com
Circ: 25000
Publisher: Neil Oliver
Editorial Profile: The Milton Canadian Champion serves residents and businesses in Milton, ON. The bi-weekly newspaper contains local news, events, sports, education, business and feature stories. Additionally covered are regional and national wire stories that are of interest to local readers. Deadlines are at noon ET one week prior to publication.; Full Page Mono: 7.00
Currency: Canada Dollars
NEWSPAPER

Ming Pao Daily News
Owner: Ming Pao Holdings (Canada) Ltd
Editorial: 1355 Huntingwood Dr, Scarborough, Ontario M1S 3J1. **T:** 1 416 321-0088
E: information@mingpaotor.com
W: http://www.mingpaotor.com
Freq: Daily; **Circ:** 73390
Editor: Richard Ng; **Publisher:** Maureen Tang; **News Editor:** Tien-Sek Wong
Editorial Profile: Ming Pao Daily News is a daily newspaper written for Chinese Canadian readers. The newspaper covers information about news, business and entertainment for Eastern Canada.; Full Page Mono: 53.00; Full Page Colour: 3856.00
Currency: Canada Dollars
DAILY NEWSPAPER

Ming Pao Daily News
Owner: Ming Pao Holdings (Canada) Ltd
Editorial: 5368 Parkwood Place, Richmond, British Columbia V6V 2N1. **T:** 1 604 231-8998
W: http://www.mingpao.com
Freq: Daily; **Circ:** 54000
Publisher: Ka Ming Lui; **Editor in Chief:** Raymond Yeung
Editorial Profile: Ming Pao Daily News is daily newspaper written for Chinese Canadians. The publications covers information about news, business and entertainment in western Canada.; Full Page Mono: 5.00; Full Page Colour: 125.00
Currency: Canada Dollars
DAILY NEWSPAPER

Miramichi Leader
Owner: Brunswick News Inc.
Editorial: 2428 King George Hwy, Miramichi, New Brunswick E1V 6V9. **T:** 1 506 622-2600
E: news@miramichileader.com
W: http://www.miramichileader.com
Freq: 3 Times/Week; **Circ:** 18641
News Editor: Charlene MacKenzie; **Editor:** Gail Savoy
Editorial Profile: Miramichi Leader is a weekly paper, published three times a week that provides coverage of local news to the residents of Miramichi, NB, and its surrounding areas.; Full Page Mono: 5.25; Full Page Colour: 231.00
Currency: Canada Dollars
NEWSPAPER

Mission City Record
Owner: Black Press
Editorial: 33047 First Ave, Mission, British Columbia V2V 1G2. **T:** 1 604 826-6221
E: news@missioncityrecord.com
W: http://www.missioncityrecord.com
Circ: 10965
Publisher: Andrew Franklin; **Editor in Chief:** Jason Roessle
Editorial Profile: Mission City Record is a weekly newspaper written for the residents of Mission, British Columbia.; Full Page Mono: 11.27
Currency: Canada Dollars
NEWSPAPER

The Mississauga News and Booster Newspapers
Owner: Metroland Media Group Ltd.
Editorial: 3145 Wolfedale Road, Mississauga, Ontario L5C 3A9. **T:** 1 905 273-8111
E: thenews@mississauga.net
W: http://www.mississauga.com **Circ:** 508284
Publisher: Dana Robbins
NEWSPAPER

Modesty Magazine
Owner: Modesty Group Inc
Editorial: 18 Crown Steel Dr Unit 115, Markham, Ontario L3R 9X8.
T: 1 905 513-1232
W: http://www.modestymagazine.com
Freq: Quarterly; **Circ:** 10000
Editor: Glenn Reid; **Editor in Chief:** Tony Wan
Editorial Profile: Modesty Magazine is a quarterly publication for the residents of Markham, Ontario. The newspaper covers local news and community events.; Full Page Mono: 28.51
Currency: Canada Dollars
NEWSPAPER

Moncton Times & Transcript
Owner: Moncton Publishing Company Ltd.
Editorial: 939 Main St, Moncton, New Brunswick E1C 8P3. **T:** 1 506 859-4900
E: news@timestranscript.com
W: http://www.canadaeast.com
Freq: Daily; **Circ:** 35050
City Editor at Large: James Foster; **City Editor at Large:** James Foster
Editorial Profile: Moncton Times & Transcript is a 40+ page broadsheet, daily newspaper written for the New Brunswick general public. The editorial and news content of the publication focuses on Moncton, New Brunswick, but also includes news and events from various parts of northern New Brunswick and eastern Nova Scotia, as well as Albert, Westmoreland and Kent counties. The paper is comprised of four main sections: local and regional news; life and times; sports; and international, national and business news. Special features include national and international commentary, TV Book, What's Up? (a daily list of Moncton events), Saturday Job Market, Leisure Living for weekend reading, Real Estate Tips in the Business section, Homes, and Whatever (a supplement produced by local youths). The publication focuses primarily on issues that have a direct impact on its local readers.; Full Page Mono: 42.00; Full Page Colour: 1654.00
Currency: Canada Dollars
DAILY NEWSPAPER

The Monday News
Owner: TC. Transcontinental
Editorial: 352 E River Rd, New Glasgow, Nova Scotia B2H 5E2. **T:** 1 902 752-3000
E: news@ngnews.ca **Circ:** 19000
Editorial Profile: The Monday News is a local newspaper written for the residents of New Glasgow, Truro and Amherst, Nova Scotia. The paper is a weekly combination of The News- New Glasgow (Nova Scotia), Truro (Nova Scotia) Daily News and Amherst (Nova Scotia) Daily News.; Full Page Mono: 9.80
Currency: Canada Dollars
NEWSPAPER

Monsoon Journal
Editorial: 3107 Sheppard Ave East, Toronto, Ontario M1T 3J7. **T:** 1 416 358-3235
E: toronto@monsoonjournal.com
W: http://www.monsoonjournal.com
Freq: Monthly; **Circ:** 15000
Editorial Profile: Monsoon Journal is a monthly English newspaper that provides Community and International News coverage to the South Asian commnities in the Toronto and the Greater Toronto Area.
NEWSPAPER

The Month Ahead
Editorial: 1271 Gorham St, Unit 14, Newmarket, Ontario L3Y 8Y7.
T: 1 905 967-0473
W: http://www.themonthahead.ca
Freq: Monthly; **Circ:** 44000
Publisher: Hazel Fernandes; **Editor:** Rhonda Solomon
Editorial Profile: The Month Ahead covers community news exclusively and does not welcome outside submissions. They do not want to be contacted.; Full Page Mono: 31.43
Currency: Canada Dollars
NEWSPAPER

Montreal Times
Editorial: 3551 boul. St. Charles, Suite 547, Kirkland, Quebec. **T:** 1 514 457-7656
E: info@westendtimes.ca
W: http://mtltimes.ca
Freq: Weekly; **Circ:** 72000
Publisher & Editor: Tom West
Editorial Profile: Montreal Times is a local community newspaper for the residents of Kirkland, Quebec and the surrounding communities.; Full Page Mono: 6.65
Currency: Canada Dollars
NEWSPAPER

Moose Jaw Times Weekend Edition
Owner: TC. Transcontinental
Editorial: 44 Fairford Street West, Moose Jaw, Saskatchewan S6H 1V1. **T:** 1 306 692-6441
E: editorial@mjtimes.sk.ca
W: http://www.mjtimes.sk.ca **Circ:** 19478
Publisher: Rob Clark
Editorial Profile: Moose Jaw Times Weekend Edition is a free newspaper that serves residents of Moose Jaw, Saskatchewan. It is distributed Saturdays to non-subscribers of the daily Moose Jaw Times Herald. It covers the latest local news, sports, weather, community events, classifieds and entertainment topics. The Times Herald and Weekend Edition share editorial staffs, so please send correspondence to only one of the publications. Deadlines are at noon CT two days prior to issue date.; Full Page Mono: 15.68
Currency: Canada Dollars
NEWSPAPER

The Morning Star
Owner: Black Press
Editorial: 4407-25th Ave, Vernon, British Columbia V1T 1P5. **T:** 1 250 545-3322
E: newsroom@vernonmorningstar.com
W: http://www.vernonmorningstar.com
Circ: 31359
Publisher: Ian Jensen
Editorial Profile: The Morning Star is a local newspaper written for the residents of Vernon, British Columbia. The paper covers news, sports, arts & entertainment and community events.; Full Page Mono: 12.60; Full Page Colour: 371.00
Currency: Canada Dollars
NEWSPAPER

The Morning Star Daily
Owner: Black Press
Editorial: 4407 25th Ave, Vernon, British Columbia V1T 1P5. **T:** 1 250 545-3322
Circ: 33270
Publisher: Ian Jensen; **Editor:** Glenn Mitchell
Editorial Profile: The Morning Star Daily is a free publication written for the residents of Vernon, British Columbia. The paper covers news, sports, arts & entertainment and events.; Full Page Mono: 13.86; Full Page Colour: 371.00
Currency: Canada Dollars
DAILY NEWSPAPER

Mountain View Publishing Inc.
Owner: Great West Newspapers LP
Editorial: 5013-51 Street, Olds, Alberta T4P 1P6. **T:** 1 403 556-7510
E: production@olds.greatwest.ca
W: http://www.oldsalbertan.ca **Circ:** 31300
Publisher: Murray Elliott
NEWSPAPER

Le Mouton NOIR
Owner: Éditions du Berger blanc (Les)
Editorial: 4, rue de l'Évêché Est, CP 113, Rimouski, Quebec G5L 7B7.
T: 1 418 724-6647
E: mouton@moutonnoir.com
W: http://www.moutonnoir.com
Freq: Bi-Monthly; **Circ:** 10000
Editor in Chief: Geneviève Génier Carrier
Editorial Profile: Le Mouton NOIR is an independent bi-monthly newspaper offers news and opinion articles to residents of the Bas-Saint-Laurent and Gaspésie regions of Quebec.; Full Page Mono: 7.63
Currency: Canada Dollars
NEWSPAPER

El Mundo Latino News
Editorial: 352 Vodden Street East, Brampton, Ontario L6V 2N2. **T:** 1 905 306-7929
E: info@elmundolatinonews.ca
W: http://www.elmundolatinonews.ca
Circ: 10000
Editorial Profile: El Mundo Latino News is a weekly newspaper covering local news for Spanish-speaking residents of Mississauga, Ontario.; Full Page Mono: 12.60
Currency: Canada Dollars
NEWSPAPER

Nanaimo Bulletin
Owner: Black Press
Editorial: 777 Popular St, Nanaimo, British Columbia V9S 2H7. **T:** 1 250 753-3707
E: news@nanaimobulletin.com
W: http://www.bclocalnews.com/vancouver_island_central/nanaimonewsbulletin
Circ: 30000
Publisher: Maurice Donn; **Editor:** Melissa Fryer
Editorial Profile: Nanaimo Bulletin serves the residents of Nanaimo, British Columbia. The publication covers local and regional news, entertainment, education, sports and business. It also includes an editorial page, lifestyle articles and a classifieds section.; Full Page Mono: 24.64; Full Page Colour: 670.00
Currency: Canada Dollars
NEWSPAPER

The Napanee Beaver
Owner: Napanee Beaver
Editorial: 72 Dundas St E, Napanee, Ontario K7R 1H9. **T:** 1 613 354-6641

E: beaver@bellnet.ca
W: http://www.napaneebeaver.com **Circ:** 14553
Publisher: Jean Morrison
Editorial Profile: Napanee Beaver is a 12+ page newspaper written for the Napanee, Ontario general public. It covers local news, sports, and business.; Full Page Mono: 5.99
Currency: Canada Dollars
NEWSPAPER

Nasha Canada
Editorial: 40-1110 Finch Ave. W., Suite 1073, Toronto, Ontario M3J 3M2. **T:** 1 647 435-8619
E: nashacanada@yahoo.ca
W: http://www.nashacanada.com
Publisher: Vladimir Turovsky
Editorial Profile: Nasha Canada is a Russian-language newspaper providing Local and Community News coverage to the Russian-speaking communities in Toronto and Greater Toronto Area. It was founded in May 2001. Nasha Canada also offers professional translation services from English to Russian for advertising and marketing materials.
NEWSPAPER

Nasha Gazeta
Owner: Russian Canadian Broadcasting
Editorial: 592 Champagne Drive, Toronto, Ontario M3J 2T9. **T:** 1 416 725-8337
E: wfarsalas@sympatico.ca
W: http://www.mixtv.ca/ **Circ:** 10000
Editor in Chief: T. Toutchinski
Editorial Profile: Nasha Gazeta provides news and information to local residents. The newspaper publishes comprehensive analytical articles and interviews with MPs and MPPs, city councillors, police, government representatives, community and spiritual leaders and artists. Leading specialists in finance, real estate, immigration and law regularly publish serious articles with recommendations of interest as for new immigrants as for long term residents of the country.; Full Page Mono: 13.09
Currency: US Dollars
NEWSPAPER

National Post
Owner: Postmedia Network Inc.
Editorial: 365 Bloor St E Fl 3RD, Toronto, Ontario M4W 3L4. **T:** 1 416 383-2300
W: http://www.nationalpost.com
Freq: Daily; **Circ:** 177782
Driving Editor: Patricia Cancilla; **Front Page Editor:** Joe Hood; **Editor:** Jodi Lai; **Editor in Chief:** Anne Marie Owens
Editorial Profile: National Post incorporates the former Financial Post Newspaper into its four section national newspaper. They prefer to be contacted by their online form. It is published six times a week, and is organized as follows: The first section delivers comprehensive news, political and health reporting from across the country and around the world; the second section contains the Financial Post business news; the third section covers sports with news on golf, auto racing, hockey and football featured daily; the fourth section titled Arts & Life features news on theater, movies, fine arts and other areas of interest. In addition, the Saturday Post includes a magazine style fifth section. In the words of the publishers, "Incorporating The Financial Post, National Post delivers a comprehensive package of news, arts, life, sports and business coverage the way Canadians say they want it - nationally focused with a window on the world." Technology coverage includes business issues, office technology, computers in the home, consumer issues, financial software, and general computer and communications issues. News content emphasizes "the national outlook of Canada, rather than being Toronto-centric." Types of articles include news briefs, company and personality profiles, trend stories, and occasional product announcements and reviews. Special Reports include the following regular feature topics: Travel & Loyalty and Travel Extras, which cover travel across the country, highlighting services available, travel planning, and corporate practices; RRSP and Mutual Funds, which cover Canadian investment trends; Legal Post, which covers topics in business law such as pensions, mergers & acquisitions, class action, clean technology and careers; and Luxury Living, which covers the latest in luxury real estate, fashion and goods.; Full Page Mono: 133.98; Full Page Colour: 608.84
Currency: Canada Dollars
DAILY NEWSPAPER

New Canada
Owner: New Canada Publications
Editorial: 120 Eglinton Ave E, Ste 500, Toronto, Ontario M4P 1E2. **T:** 1 416 481-7793

E: humanrights@sympatico.ca
W: http://www.race-relations.ca
Freq: Weekly; **Circ:** 10000
Editorial Profile: New Canada is a bilingual, weekly publication written for immigrants. Its objective is to support and promote minorities.; Full Page Mono: 21.00; Full Page Colour: 800.00
Currency: Canada Dollars
NEWSPAPER

The News
Owner: Black Press
Editorial: #4-154 Middleton Ave, Parksville, British Columbia. **T:** 1 250 248-4341
E: editor@pqbnews.com
W: http://www.pqbnews.com **Circ:** 15793
Editor in Chief: Steven Heywood
Editorial Profile: The News is a community newspaper that covers the Vancouver Island, British Columbia areas stretching from Deep Bay to the north, Nanoose Bay to the south, and west to Cathedral Grove. This region includes a number of rural communities, including Errington, Coombs, Whiskey Creek, Hilliers, Qualicum Bay, Bowser and Deep Bay, as well as the growing City of Parksville and Town of Qualicum Beach. The paper covers local news, community issues and events.; Full Page Mono: 17.28
Currency: Canada Dollars
NEWSPAPER

Niagara Community Newspapers
Owner: Quebecor Communications
Editorial: 10-1 St. Paul St., St. Catharines, Ontario L2R 7L4. **T:** 1 905 688-4332
Freq: Weekly; **Circ:** 48000
NEWSPAPER

Niagara Falls Review
Owner: Quebecor Communications Inc.
Editorial: 4801 Valley Way, Niagara Falls, Ontario L2E 1W4. **T:** 1 905 358-5711
W: http://www.niagarafallsreview.ca
Freq: Daily; **Circ:** 14384
Publisher: Michael Cressman; **Editor in Chief:** Steven Gallagher
Editorial Profile: Niagara Falls Review is a daily publication that covers local news and events. It serves the municipality of Niagara Falls and Fort Erie, Ontario. Coverage includes local and national news, sports, entertainment, crime and education.; Full Page Mono: 9.94; Full Page Colour: 794.00
Currency: US Dollars
DAILY NEWSPAPER

Niagara Shopping News
Owner: Quebecor Communications Inc.
Editorial: 4949 Victoria Avenue, Niagara Falls, Ontario L2E 4C7. **T:** 1 905 357-2440
Circ: 29000
Publisher: Tim Dundas
Editorial Profile: Niagara Shopping News is a community newspaper that serves the residents of Niagara Falls, Ontario.; Full Page Mono: 4.76
Currency: Canada Dollars
NEWSPAPER

Niagara This Week
Owner: Metroland Media Group Ltd.
Editorial: 3300 Merrittville Hwy Unit 1B, Thorold, Ontario L2V 4Y6. **T:** 1 905 688-2444
E: letters@niagarathisweek.com
W: http://www.niagarathisweek.com
Circ: 206500
Publisher: Neil Oliver
NEWSPAPER

Nipawin Newspapers
Owner: Quebecor Communications Inc.
Editorial: 220 Centre St, Nipawin, Saskatchewan S0E 1E0. **T:** 1 306 862-4618
W: http://www.nipawinjournal.com **Circ:** 27394
Publisher: Ken Sorensen
NEWSPAPER

Le Nord Est
Owner: Quebecor Communications Inc.
Editorial: 781 Boul Laure, Sept-Iles, Quebec G4R 1Y2. **T:** 1 418 962-9441
W: http://www.lenordest.ca **Circ:** 19018
Editor: Catherine Martin
Editorial Profile: Le Nord Est is a weekly French-language newspaper. It covers local and regional information including news, government, sports and arts & entertainment in the Sept-Iles region of Quebec.; Full Page Mono: 6.02
Currency: Canada Dollars
NEWSPAPER

Norfolk News
Owner: Metroland Media Group Ltd.

Editorial: 33 Colborne St S, Simcoe, Ontario N3Y 4H2. **T:** 1 519 428-0058
W: http://www.norfolknews.ca
Freq: Weekly; **Circ:** 24000
Editorial Profile: Launched on October 3, 2013, Norfolk News is a weekly newspaper covering local news, people and events for the residents of Norfolk County.; Full Page Colour: 23.79
Currency: Canada Dollars
NEWSPAPER

North Bay Nipissing News
Owner: Metroland Media Group Ltd.
Editorial: 191 Booth St, Unit 2, North Bay, Ontario P1B 8H8. **T:** 1 705 472-6993
E: northbaynipissing@gmail.com
W: http://www.northbaynipissing.com
Freq: Weekly; **Circ:** 43000
News Editor: Rob Learn
Editorial Profile: North Bay Nipissing News is a community newspaper for residents of North Bay, Ontario and the surrounding Nipissing region.
NEWSPAPER

North Bay Nugget
Owner: Quebecor Communications Inc.
Editorial: 259 Worthington St West, North Bay, Ontario P1B 3B5. **T:** 1 705 472-3200
E: nbay.news@sunmedia.ca
W: http://www.nugget.ca
Freq: Daily; **Circ:** 12000
Publisher: Dan Johnson
Editorial Profile: North Bay Nugget is a 30+ page broadsheet newspaper written for the North Bay, Ontario general public. It is one of the major newspapers in the area covering news, sports and entertainment. Weekly sections include business on Tuesday, technology on Wednesday, entertainment on Thursday, homes on Friday, and lifestyles on Saturday. Lifestyles covers travel, food, gardening and features. The newspaper has won over 20 awards including a Western Ontario Newspaper Award. The newspaper is known for outstanding layout and design. The deadline is 2am ET.; Full Page Mono: 21.70; Full Page Colour: 887.55
Currency: Canada Dollars
DAILY NEWSPAPER

North London Beacon
Editorial: 1673 Richmond Street North, Box 215, London, Ontario N6G 2N3.
T: 1 519 457-1300 **E:** nlbeacon@rogers.com
W: http://www.northlondonbeacon.com
Freq: Bi-Monthly; **Circ:** 17000
Publisher & Editor: Larry Douglas
Editorial Profile: North London Beacon is a local community newspaper for the residents of London, Ontario and the surrounding communities.; Full Page Mono: 6.29
Currency: US Dollars
NEWSPAPER

North Shore News
Owner: Glacier Media Inc.
Editorial: 126 East 15th St., Ste. 100, North Vancouver, British Columbia V7L 2P9.
T: 1 604 985-2131 **E:** editor@nsnews.com
W: http://www.nsnews.com **Circ:** 67000
Publisher: Doug Foot
Editorial Profile: North Shore News is a weekly newspaper that covers arts & entertainment, business, sports and news for North Vancouver, British Columbia. Their editorial mission is to be the best community paper in Canada. The publication is written in English for residents of North and West Vancouver.; Full Page Mono: 49.42
Currency: Canada Dollars
NEWSPAPER

Northeast News
Owner: Northeast News, Ltd.
Editorial: 9909 100th Ave, Fort St. John, British Columbia V1J 1Y4. **T:** 1 250 787-7030
E: editor@northeastnews.ca
W: http://www.northeastnews.ca **Circ:** 20000
Editorial Profile: Northeast News is a weekly newspaper written for the residents of Northeastern British Columbia. It covers local news, sports, features and events.; Full Page Mono: 20.70
Currency: Canada Dollars
NEWSPAPER

Northern Life
Owner: Laurentian Publishing Group Inc.
Editorial: 158 Elgin St, Sudbury, Ontario P3E 3N5. **T:** 1 705 673-5667
E: lifeedit@northernlife.ca
W: http://www.northernlife.ca **Circ:** 50000
Publisher: Abbas Homayed
Editorial Profile: Northern Life is published weekly for the residents of Sudbury, Ontario

and surrounding areas. The newspaper covers local news and community events.; Full Page Mono: 39.46; Full Page Colour: 121.63
Currency: Canada Dollars
NEWSPAPER

Northern News Services Newspapers
Editorial: 5108 50th St, Yellowknife, Northwest Territories X1A 2R1.
T: 1 867 873-4031 **E:** nnsl@nnsl.com
W: http://www.nnsl.com **Circ:** 26786
Publisher: Jack Sigvaldason; **Editor:** Roxanna Thompson
NEWSPAPER

The Northerner
Owner: Glacier Media Inc.
Editorial: 9916-98 Street, Fort St. John, British Columbia V1J 3T8. **T:** 1 250 785-5631
E: compose@ahnfsj.ca
W: http://www.thenortherner.ca **Circ:** 12000
Editorial Profile: The Northerner is a community newspaper serving the residents of Fort St. John, British Columbia.; Full Page Mono: 10.60
Currency: Canada Dollars
NEWSPAPER

Northumberland News
Owner: Metroland Media Group Ltd.
Editorial: 884 Division St Unit 212, Cobourg, Ontario K9A 5V6. **T:** 1 905 373-7355
E: northnews@northumberlandnews.com
W: http://www.northumberlandnews.com
Circ: 22800
Editor in Chief: Joanne Burghardt; **Publisher:** Tim Whittaker
Editorial Profile: Northumberland News is a bi-weekly publication written for the residents of Cobourg and Northumberland, Ontario. The publication includes news, weather, travel and events.; Full Page Mono: 7.28
Currency: Canada Dollars
NEWSPAPER

La Nouvelle de Sherbrooke
Owner: Journaux Trans-Canada
Editorial: 1950, rue Roy, Sherbrooke, Quebec J1K 2X8. **T:** 1 819 564-5450
E: reaction@lanouvelle.ca
W: http://www.lanouvelle.ca **Circ:** 50000
Publisher: Louise Boisvert; **Editor:** Marie-Christine Bouchard
Editorial Profile: La Nouvelle de Sherbrooke is a weekly publication covering local news and events in Sherbrooke, Quebec. It covers news, including government, community events, sports, entertainment and human-interest stories.; Full Page Mono: 9.59
Currency: Canada Dollars
NEWSPAPER

La Nouvelle Union
Owner: TC. Transcontinental
Editorial: 43 rue Notre-Dame est, 2e etage, Victoriaville, Quebec G6P 3Z4.
T: 1 819 758-6211
E: redaction_victo@transcontinental.ca
W: http://www.lanouvelle.net **Circ:** 82021
Editor in Chief: Ghislain Chauvette; **Publisher:** Jean Mercier
Editorial Profile: La Nouvelle Union is a weekly French-language newspaper that covers local and regional information for Victoriaville, Quebec and the surrounding communities.; Full Page Mono: 9.92
Currency: Canada Dollars
NEWSPAPER

Les Nouvelles Chinoises
Owner: Quebec Culture & Commerce Ltee
Editorial: 200 Rene Levesque West, #0004, Montreal, Quebec H2Z 1X4. **T:** 1 514 842-5689
E: chinesenewsad@hotmail.com
W: http://montrealchina.com/portal.php
Circ: 10000
Editor: Larry Thai; **Publisher & Editor:** James Zhang
Editorial Profile: Editorials devoted to the Chinese community for its political, social, cultural and economical developments. News coverage of major events happening in Montreal and Quebec.; Full Page Mono: 14.56
Currency: Canada Dollars
NEWSPAPER

Nouvelles Hebdo
Owner: TC. Transcontinental
Editorial: 1741 Rue des Pins, Dolbeau-Mistassini, Quebec G8L 1M9.
T: 1 418 276-6211
E: redaction.dolbeau@transcontinental.ca
W: http://www.nouvelleshebdo.com/
Circ: 13896
Publisher: Michel Aube; Full Page Mono: 4.34
Currency: Canada Dollars
NEWSPAPER

Le Nouvelliste
Owner: Power Corporation of Canada
Editorial: 1920 Rue Bellefeuille, Trois-Rivieres, Quebec G9A 3Y2. **T:** 1 819 376-2501
E: publicit@lenouvelliste.qc.ca
W: http://www.cyberpresse.ca/le-nouvelliste
Freq: Daily; **Circ:** 44362
Editor in Chief: Stéphan Frappier; **News Editor:** Stéphan Ratelle
Editorial Profile: Le Nouvelliste is four color, daily French-language newspaper, covering local news for the Mauricie and Centre-du-Québec regions of Québec. A particular emphasis is placed on politics and human interest stories. Additional sections are business and sports. The vast majority of stories dealing with technology, lifestyles, arts & entertainment and world news are obtained from news wire services. However, various local editors and journalists also deal with these individual topics.; Full Page Mono: 39.72; Full Page Colour: 51.36
Currency: Canada Dollars
DAILY NEWSPAPER

Nowy Kurier/Polish Canadian Independent Courier
Editorial: 12 Foch Avenue, Toronto, Ontario M8W 3X1. **T:** 1 416 259-4353
E: zkopc549@rogers.com
W: http://www.nowykurier.com
Freq: Bi-Weekly; **Circ:** 20000
Editor: Jolanta Cabaj
Editorial Profile: Nowy Kurier/Polish Canadian Independent Courier is a bi-weekly newspaper serving the Polish community of Toronto, Canada.; Full Page Mono: 10.50
Currency: Canada Dollars
NEWSPAPER

Oakville Beaver
Owner: Metroland Media Group Ltd.
Editorial: 467 Speers Rd, Oakville, Ontario L6K 3S4. **T:** 1 905 845-3824
W: http://www.insidehalton.com/community/oakvillebeaver **Circ:** 47500
Editor in Chief: Jill Davis; **Publisher:** Neil Oliver
Editorial Profile: The Oakville Beaver is a local newspaper published three times a week serving Oakville, ON. Contact the publication by phone, fax, or mail.; Full Page Mono: 27.16
Currency: Canada Dollars
NEWSPAPER

The Observer
Owner: Quebecor Communications Inc.
Editorial: 140 Front St S, Sarnia, Ontario N7T 7M8. **T:** 1 519 344-3641
W: http://www.theobserver.ca
Freq: Daily; **Circ:** 14348
Publisher: Linda Leblanc
Editorial Profile: The Observer is a daily newspaper written for Sarnia and Lambton, Ontario residents. It is one of the major newspapers in the area covering news, sports, business and entertainment. Various news features are included on a weekly basis, and special supplements include product and event flyers, TV times and real estate issues. The daily deadline is 12am ET, although writers prefer to receive press releases in the early evening.; Full Page Mono: 14.00; Full Page Colour: 51.72
Currency: Canada Dollars
DAILY NEWSPAPER

The Observer
Editorial: 106 King Street W., Brockville, Ontario K6V 3P9. **T:** 1 613 342-8777
W: http://www.thebrockvilleobserver.ca
Circ: 14500
Editorial Profile: The Observer is a local community newspaper for the residents of Brockville, Ontario and the surrounding communities.; Full Page Mono: 4.55
Currency: Canada Dollars
NEWSPAPER

Observer Xtra
Owner: Cathedral Communications Inc.
Editorial: 20B Arthur St N, Elmira, Ontario N3B 1Z9. **T:** 1 519 669-5790
E: info@observerxtra.com
W: http://www.observerxtra.com **Circ:** 13741
Editor: Steve Kannon; **Publisher:** Joe Merlihan
Editorial Profile: Woolwich Observer is a weekly newspaper serving the town of Elmira, ON and the surrounding area. The paper covers local news and events. Deadlines for the publication are one week before issue date.; Full Page Mono: 6.20; Full Page Colour: 300.00
Currency: Canada Dollars
NEWSPAPER

The Oceanside Star
Owner: Glacier Media Inc.
Editorial: 166 East Island Highway, Parksville, British Columbia V9P 2G3. **T:** 1 250 954-0600
W: http://www.oceansidestar.com **Circ:** 16800
Editorial Profile: The Oceanside Star covers news and events for the communities of Parksville and Qualicum Beach, British Columbia.; Full Page Mono: 5.81
Currency: Canada Dollars
NEWSPAPER

L' Œil Régional
Owner: Quebecor Communications Inc.
Editorial: 393, boul. Sir-Wilfrid-Laurier, Beloeil, Quebec J3G 4H6. **T:** 1 450 467-1821
E: redaction@oeilregional.com
W: http://www.oeilregional.com **Circ:** 35500
Editor in Chief: Vincent Guilbault
Editorial Profile: L'Œil Régional is a weekly newspaper that covers local news and information, including education, business, crime, and entertainment, for residents of Belœil, Québec.; Full Page Mono: 13.86
Currency: Canada Dollars
NEWSPAPER

L' Oie Blanche
Owner: Cooperative du Journal L'Oie Blanche
Editorial: 70 rue de l'Anse, Montmagny, Quebec G5V 1G8. **T:** 1 418 248-8820
E: oieblanc@globetrotter.net
W: http://www.oieblanc.com **Circ:** 21634
Editorial Profile: L'Oie Blanche is a weekly French-language publication covering local news for Montmagny, L'Islet, and the eastern part of Bellechasse, Quebec.; Full Page Mono: 4.27
Currency: Canada Dollars
NEWSPAPER

The Okanagan
Owner: Postmedia
Editorial: 550 Doyle Ave, Kelowna, British Columbia V1Y 7V1- **Circ:** 20715
Publisher: Terry Armstrong
Editorial Profile: The Okanagan Saturday and Okanagan Sunday are distributed Saturday and Sunday to both the Kelowna (The Daily Courier) and Penticton (The Penticton Herald) markets. The papers cover weekend news and entertainment. The circulation for the Saturday edition is 20,715. The circulation for the Sunday edition is 19,419.; Full Page Mono: 38.54; Full Page Colour: 43.81
Currency: Canada Dollars
NEWSPAPER

Orangeville Banner
Owner: Metroland Media Group Ltd.
Editorial: 37 Mill St, Orangeville, Ontario L9W 2M4. **T:** 1 519 941-1350
E: banner@orangevillebanner.com
W: http://www.orangeville.com **Circ:** 23488
Publisher: Dana Robbins
Editorial Profile: Orangeville Banner is a community newspaper written for the residents of Orangeville, Ontario. It covers news, sports, letters and classifieds.; Full Page Mono: 10.89
Currency: Canada Dollars
NEWSPAPER

Oriental Weekly
Owner: Independent
Editorial: 1215-1110 Center Street NE, Room 215, Calgary, Alberta T2E 2R2.
T: 1 403 230-0872 **E:** info@orientalweekly.com
W: http://www.trendweekly.com **Circ:** 10000
Editor: Paul Wong
Editorial Profile: Oriental News is a weekly newspaper providing Local and Community News coverage for the Chinese community in Calgary and Edmonton, AB.; Full Page Mono: 2.92
Currency: Canada Dollars
NEWSPAPER

Orillia Today
Owner: Metroland Media Group Ltd.
Editorial: 25 Ontario St, Orillia, Ontario L3V 6H1. **T:** 1 705 329-2058
W: http://www.simcoe.com **Circ:** 23829
Editor in Chief: Martin Melbourne; **Publisher:** Sean Silvey
Editorial Profile: Orillia Today is a local newspaper written for the residents of Orillia, Ontario. The paper covers local news and events.; Full Page Mono: 13.37; Full Page Colour: 1160.00
Currency: Canada Dollars
NEWSPAPER

The Oshawa Central
Editorial: 136 Simcoe St N Unit 4, Oshawa, Ontario L1G 4S7. **T:** 1 905 432-2657
E: newspaper@ocentral.com
W: http://www.ocentral.com **Circ:** 75000
Publisher & Editor: Joe Ingino
Editorial Profile: The Oshawa Central is a local newspaper serving the residents of Oshawa, Ontario. The publication covers local and national news, public affairs, current and community events, sports, lifestyle, arts & entertainment, business and politics.; Full Page Mono: 42.80
Currency: Canada Dollars
NEWSPAPER

Oshawa Express
Editorial: 774 Simcoe St S, Oshawa, Ontario L1H 4K6-. **T:** 1 905 571-7334
E: news@oshawaexpress.ca
W: http://www.oshawaexpress.ca **Circ:** 35000
Editor: Greg McDowell; **Publisher:** Sandy McDowell
Editorial Profile: Oshawa Express is a weekly community newspaper written for the residents of Oshawa, Ontario.; Full Page Mono: 10.52
Currency: Canada Dollars
NEWSPAPER

Osprey Media Group-Chatham
Owner: Quebecor Communications Inc.
Editorial: 138 King St W, Chatham, Ontario N7M 1E3. **T:** 1 519 354-2000
W: http://www.chathamdailynews.ca
Circ: 46720
Publisher: Dean Muharrem
NEWSPAPER

Osprey Media Group–Napanee
Owner: Quebecor Communications Inc.
Editorial: 2 Dairy Ave, Napanee, Ontario K7R 3T1. **T:** 1 613 354-6648
W: http://www.napaneeguide.com
Freq: Weekly; **Circ:** 22326
Editor: Meghan Balogh; **Publisher:** Ron Laurin
NEWSPAPER

Ossekeag Publishing
Editorial: 242 Main St., Hampton, New Brunswick E5N 6B8. **T:** 1 506 832-5613
E: info@ossekeag.ca
W: http://www.ossekeag.ca **Circ:** 40201
NEWSPAPER

Ottawa Citizen
Owner: Postmedia Network Inc.
Editorial: 1101 Baxter Rd, Ottawa, Ontario K2C 3Z3. **T:** 1 613 829-9100
E: copydesk@ottawacitizen.com
W: http://www.ottawacitizen.com
Freq: Daily; **Circ:** 112536
Real Deal Editor: Karen Turner
Editorial Profile: Ottawa Citizen is a 60+ page, four-colour, broadsheet, daily newspaper written for residents of central and greater Ottawa, ON. The publication covers primarily municipal news, as well as provincial, regional, national and international topics that would be of interest to its target audience. The newspaper features information on world news, local news, sports, entertainment, stocks, classifieds, career opportunities, technology and other topics of interests to the citizens of Ottawa, ON. High-technology is featured in every issue of the Ottawa Citizen and looks at technology from the corporate stand-point. Specific daily sections are A, which contains the main headlines, as well as health news and columns; B is arts, which also includes entertainment; sports coverage, columns, and results are in C, and D is the city section, containing municipal news. The regular edition comes with various weekly sections, such as: business and high-technology on Tuesdays, food on Wednesdays, technology news, in the form of TechWeekly on Thursdays, and the style section on Saturdays. Saturday's edition also comes with the Citizen's Weekly lifestyles magazine. The Sunday edition will cease publication in Mid-July, 2012.; Full Page Mono: 61.74; Full Page Colour: 105.92
Currency: Canada Dollars
DAILY NEWSPAPER

Ottawa EMC Community Newspapers
Owner: Metroland Media Group Ltd.
Editorial: 80 Colonnade Rd N, Nepean, Ontario K2E 7L2. **T:** 1 613 224-3330
W: http://www.yourottawaregion.com
Circ: 36637
News Editor: John Curry; **News Editor:** Blair Edwards; **News Editor:** Matthew Jay
Editorial Profile: Ottawa EMC Community Newspapers is a weekly community newspaper publisher serving the residents of Nepean and Barrhaven, Ontario.
NEWSPAPER

Ottawa News Publications
Owner: Metroland Media Group
Editorial: 57 Auriga Dr Unit 103, Ottawa, Ontario K2E 8B2. **T:** 1 613 723-5970
E: editor@thenewsemc.ca
W: http://www.ottawacommunitynews.com
Circ: 233799
Publisher: Mike Tracy
NEWSPAPER

Ottawa Sun
Owner: Quebecor Communications Inc.
Editorial: 18A Antares Dr, Ottawa, Ontario K2E 1A9. **T:** 1 613 739-7000
E: ottsun.city@sunmedia.ca
W: http://www.ottawasun.com
Freq: Daily; **Circ:** 49984
Editor in Chief: Mitchell Axelrad; **Publisher:** Rick Gibbons; **Editor:** Pat Hitsman
Editorial Profile: Ottawa Sun is primarily written for residents in the Ottawa-Carleton region and the neighboring communities of Cornwall, Kingston, Pembroke and Smith Falls, Ontario. There is local, national and international news, as well as extensive sports, business, entertainment, features and technology coverage. Editors honor non-disclosure agreements. The publication does not accept vendor-written articles, offer reader service cards or publish an editorial calendar. It was established in 1988.; Full Page Mono: 25.55; Full Page Colour: 143.50
Currency: Canada Dollars
DAILY NEWSPAPER

The Outlook Newspapers
Owner: Black Press
Editorial: #104-908 W. First Street, North Vancouver, British Columbia V7P 3N4.
T: 1 604 903-1000
E: newsroom@northshoreoutlook.com
W: http://www.northshoreoutlook.com
Circ: 56300
Editor: Justin Beddall; **Publisher:** Doug Foot
NEWSPAPER

The Oxford Review Newspapers
Owner: Sun Media Inc.
Editorial: 16 Brock St., Woodstock, Ontario N4S 3B4. **T:** 1 519 537-6657 **Circ:** 63404
Publisher: Andrea DeMeer; **Editor:** Bruce Urquhart
NEWSPAPER

Packet & Times EMC
Owner: Sun Media
Editorial: 425 West Street N., Ste 15, Orillia, Ontario L3V 5E9. **T:** 1 705 325-1355
W: http://www.orilliapacket.com **Circ:** 22000
Publisher: John Hammill; **Editor:** Randy Lucenti
Editorial Profile: Packet & Times EMC is a weekly community newspaper published for the residents of Orillia, Ontario.; Full Page Mono: 21.56
Currency: Canada Dollars
NEWSPAPER

Paivand
T: 1 604 921-4726 **W:** http://paivand.com
Freq: 2 Times/Week; **Circ:** 10000
Publisher & Editor: Ramin Mahjouri
Editorial Profile: An Iranian community newspaper.
NEWSPAPER

Parvasi Weekly
Editorial: 2980 Drew Road, Unit 221, Mississauga, Ontario L4T 0A7.
T: 1 905 673-0600 **E:** office@parvasi.com
W: http://www.parvasi.com
Freq: Weekly; **Circ:** 35000
News Editor: Harinder Jassal
Editorial Profile: Parvasi Weekly provides Community and Local News to the Punjabi-speaking communities in the Greater Toronto Area, Windsor, Montreal, Vancouver and Calgary. The head office is located in Mississauga, ON and there is also a Vancouver office.
NEWSPAPER

Pasquia Publications
Owner: Glacier Media Inc.
Editorial: 1004 - 102nd Ave, Tisdale, Saskatchewan S0E 1T0. **T:** 1 306 873-4515
E: t.recorder@sasktel.net **Circ:** 10601
Publisher: Brent Fitzpatrick; **Editor:** Ivy Wilson
NEWSPAPER

Patrides, A North American Review
Owner: Patrides Publications
Editorial: 100 Queen St. W., Toronto, Ontario M5H 2N2. **T:** 1 416 921-4229
E: saras@patrides.com
W: http://www.patrides.com

Freq: Monthly; **Circ:** 160000
Publisher: Kathy Saras; **Editor In Chief:** Thomas Saras
Editorial Profile: Patrides, A North American Review is a community newspaper written for the Greek community of Toronto, Ontario.; Full Page Mono: 73.93; Full Page Colour: 350.00
Currency: Canada Dollars
NEWSPAPER

The Peace Arch News
Owner: Black Press
Editorial: 200 - 2411 160th St, Surrey, British Columbia V3S 0C8. **T:** 1 604 531-1711
W: http://www.peacearchnews.com
Circ: 37543
Editorial Profile: The Peace Arch News is a community newspaper written for the residents of White Rock, British Columbia. The publication covers stories on local, regional, national and international news.; Full Page Mono: 22.82; Full Page Colour: 887.06
Currency: Canada Dollars
NEWSPAPER

Peace Country Spotlight
Owner: The Bottomline Business Magazine Ltd.
Editorial: 10008 110 Ave, Fort St. John, British Columbia V1J 2T2. **T:** 1 250 663-8747
W: http://www.peacecountryspotlight.ca
Circ: 29000
Publisher & Editor: Dave Thielen
Editorial Profile: Peace Country Spotlight is a free, weekly community newspaper delivered by Canada Post to all local homes, apartments, businesses and farms. Coverage includes local politics, events and sports. Deadlines are on Wednesdays one week before publication.; Full Page Mono: 5.25
Currency: Canada Dollars
NEWSPAPER

Peace Country Sun
Owner: Sun Media Corp.
Editorial: 10604- 100 Street, Grande Prairie, Alberta T8V 6V4. **T:** 1 780 532-1110
W: http://www.peacecountrysun.com
Circ: 14568
Publisher: Amber Ogilvie; **Editor:** Diana Rinne
Editorial Profile: Peace Country Sun is a weekly newspaper published in Grande Prairie, Alberta. It delivers local news and features to rural residents of the Alberta and Northern British Columbia area.; Full Page Mono: 7.63
Currency: Canada Dollars
NEWSPAPER

Pembroke/Petawawa News
Owner: Quebecor Communications Inc.
Editorial: 186 Alexander Street, Pembroke, Ontario K8A-4L9. **T:** 1 613 732-3691
Circ: 37777
Publisher: Jim Kwiatkowski
NEWSPAPER

Peninsula News Review
Owner: Black Press
Editorial: 9843 2nd Street, Unit 6, Sidney, British Columbia V8L 3C7. **T:** 1 250 656-1151
W: http://www.peninsulanewsreview.com
Circ: 15000
Editor in Chief: Erin Cardone
Editorial Profile: Peninsula News Review is a local newspaper serving the Sidney Peninsule in British Columbia, include the local communities of Brentwood Bay, Saanichton and Keating. Coverage includes local news and events. The paper was founded in 1912 and was previously known as the Sidney Review.; Full Page Mono: 11.97; Full Page Colour: 900.50
Currency: Canada Dollars
NEWSPAPER

La Pensée de Bagot
Owner: D.B.C. Communications Inc.
Editorial: 800, rue de Roxton, Acton Vale, Quebec J0H 1A0. **T:** 1 450 546-3271
W: http://www.lapensee.qc.ca **Circ:** 14521
Publisher: Benoît Chartier; **Editor:** Michel Dorais
Editorial Profile: La Pensée de Bagot is a weekly French-language newspaper that covers local news and information published on Sunday. Deadlines are Wednesdays at 5pm ET before issue date. Contact the publication by phone, fax, or mail.; Full Page Mono: 11.00
Currency: Canada Dollars
NEWSPAPER

Penticton Western News
Owner: Black Press
Editorial: 2250 Camrose St, Penticton, British Columbia V2A 8R1. **T:** 1 250 492-3636
W: http://www.pentictonwesternnews.com
Circ: 23629

Editor in Chief: Dan Ebenal; **Publisher:** Mark Walker
Editorial Profile: Penticton Western News is written for the Penticton, British Columbia general public. It covers local news, sports and entertainment.; Full Page Mono: 9.24
Currency: Canada Dollars
NEWSPAPER

Peterborough Examiner
Owner: Quebecor Communications Inc.
Editorial: 60 Hunter Street East, Peterborough, Ontario K9J 8L4.
T: 1 705 745-4641
E: exam.newsroom@sunmedia.ca
W: http://www.thepeterboroughexaminer.com
Freq: Daily; **Circ:** 18483
Publisher: Darren Murphy; **News Night Editor:** Reg Watson
Editorial Profile: Peterborough Examiner is a 30+ page newspaper written for the Peterborough, Ontario general public. It covers national and local news, featuring politics, arts & entertainment, technology, business and sports. It is the largest daily in the Peterborough, Ontario region. The daily deadline is 6pm ET.; Full Page Mono: 18.69; Full Page Colour: 666.00
Currency: Canada Dollars
DAILY NEWSPAPER

Peterborough This Week
Owner: Metroland Media Group Ltd.
Editorial: 884 Ford St, Peterborough, Ontario K9J 5V3. **T:** 1 705 749-3383
W: http://www.mykawartha.com **Circ:** 48484
Publisher: Bruce Danford; **News Editor:** Mike Lacey
Editorial Profile: Peterborough This Week is published for the residents of Peterborough County, Ontario. It covers local news and community events.; Full Page Mono: 21.51; Full Page Colour: 350.00
Currency: Canada Dollars
NEWSPAPER

Le Peuple de la Côte-du-Sud
Owner: Quebecor Communications Inc.
Editorial: 80 boul. Taché Est bureau 200, Montmagny, Quebec G5V 3S7.
T: 1 418 248-0415
E: peuple.cote.sud@hebdosquebecor.com
W: http://lepeuplecotesud.canoe.ca
Circ: 21598
Editor: Diane Gendron; **Publisher:** Claudette Tardif
Editorial Profile: Le Peuple Côte-Sud is a weekly French-language newspaper that covers local and regional information for residents of Montmagny, Quebec.; Full Page Mono: 9.94
Currency: Canada Dollars
NEWSPAPER

Le Peuple Lévis
Owner: Quebecor Communications Inc.
Editorial: 5790, boul. Étienne-Dallaire Local 103B, Levis, Quebec G6V 8V6.
T: 1 418 833-9398
W: http://www.hebdosregionaux.ca/chaudiere-appalaches/le-peuple-levis
Circ: 60320
Editor: Paul Lessard
Editorial Profile: Le Peuple Lévis is a weekly French-language newspaper that covers local and regional news for residents of Levis, Quebec.; Full Page Mono: 11.27
Currency: Canada Dollars
NEWSPAPER

Le Peuple Lotbinière
Owner: Quebecor Communications Inc.
Editorial: 5790, Boul. Étienne-Dalaire, Bureau 103B, Levis, Quebec G6V 8V6.
T: 1 418 728-2131
E: peuple.lotbiniere@hebdosquebecor.com
W: http://lepeuplelotbiniere.canoe.ca
Circ: 13720
Editor: Melanie Labrecque
Editorial Profile: Le Peuple Lotbinière is a weekly French-language newspaper. It covers local and regional information for the Lotbinière region, which includes the communities of Saint-Antoine de Tilly, Saint-Apollinaire, Saint-Agapit, Saint-Gilles, Sainte-Agathe, Dosquet, Saint-Flavien, Laurier-Station, Issoudun, Sainte-Croix, Saint-Édouard, Lotbinière, Deschaillons, Leclercville, Parisville, Fortierville, Sainte-Françoise, Val-Alain, Joly, Saint-Sylvestre, Saint-Patrice and Saint-Narcisse, Quebec.; Full Page Mono: 5.25
Currency: Canada Dollars
NEWSPAPER

Philippine Asian Chronicle
Editorial: 152nd St., Ste: 332-151-10090, Surrey, British Columbia V3W 8X8.

T: 1 778 395-6785
E: philasianchronicle@gmail.com
Freq: Bi-Monthly; **Circ:** 12000
Publisher: Erlinda Juatco; **Publisher & Editor:** Roque Juatco
Editorial Profile: A bi-monthly Filipino newspaper in English distributed all over the Vancouver lower mainland.; Full Page Mono: 24.00; Full Page Colour: 31.00
Currency: Canada Dollars
NEWSPAPER

Philippine Asian News Today
Owner: Reyfort Media Group
Editorial: 9955 149 St, Surrey, British Columbia V3R 7N2. **T:** 1 604 588-6397
E: info@philippinenewstoday.ca
W: http://www.philippineasiannewstoday.com
Freq: Bi-Weekly; **Circ:** 10000
Publisher: Rey Fortaleza
Editorial Profile: A weekly Filipino newspaper distributed all over Vancouver and the Lower Mainland including Delta, Surrey, Langley, New Westminster, Richmond, Burnaby and Coquitlam.; Full Page Mono: 7.22; Full Page Colour: 9.03
Currency: Canada Dollars
NEWSPAPER

The Philippine Courier
Owner: Philippine Courier Publishing and Entertainment
Editorial: 419 Alper Street, Richmond Hill, Ontario L4C 2Z5. **T:** 1 905 780-0114
W: http://philippinecourier.com
Freq: Monthly
Editorial Profile: The Phillipine Courier is a monthly newspaper serving the Filipino community of the greater Toronto area.
NEWSPAPER

The Philippine Journal
Owner: The Philippine Journal Publishing Corporation
Editorial: 201-955 W Broadway Ave, Vancouver, British Columbia V5Z 1K3.
T: 1 604 433-8856
E: philippinejournal@gmail.com
W: http://www.philippinejournal.com
Freq: Bi-Weekly; **Circ:** 10000
Editorial Profile: Philippine Journal is a Filipino-Canadian community newspaper published in Vancouver, British Columbia, Canada. Philippine Journal is a bi-weekly publication featuring RP, Canadian and World News, stimulating editorials, heart tugging human interest stories up-to-date community highlights, light and humorous features and well-written columns that make for interesting, informative and soul lifting reading.; Full Page Mono: 5.95
Currency: Canada Dollars
NEWSPAPER

The Philippine Reporter
Editorial: 2682 Eglinton Ave. East, Scarborough, Ontario M1K 2S3.
T: 1 416 461-8694 **E:** philreporter@gmail.com
W: http://www.philippinereporter.com
Freq: Bi-Weekly; **Circ:** 10000
Publisher & Editor: Hermie Garcia
Editorial Profile: Phillippine Reporter is a community newspaper written for the Filipino residents of Toronto. The paper is issued on the 1st and 16th of each month. Please call prior to submitting a fax.; Full Page Mono: 7.28; Full Page Colour: 11.37
Currency: Canada Dollars
NEWSPAPER

The Picton Gazette
Owner: Picton Gazette
Editorial: 267 Main St, Picton, Ontario K0K 2T0. **T:** 1 613 476-3201 **E:** gazette@bellnet.ca
W: http://www.pictongazette.com **Circ:** 11000
Publisher: Jean Morrison; **News Editor:** Sean Tomlinson
Editorial Profile: The Picton Gazette is a local newspaper serving Prince Edward County, Ontario.; Full Page Mono: 3.85
Currency: Canada Dollars
NEWSPAPER

Pique News Magazine
Owner: Glacier Media Inc.
Editorial: 103-1390 Alpha Lake Rd 103, Whistler, British Columbia V0N 1B1.
T: 1 604 938-0202
E: mail@piquenewsmagazine.com
W: http://www.piquenewsmagazine.com
Circ: 15000
Publisher: Sarah Strother
Editorial Profile: Pique News Magazine is published weekly for residents of Whistler, British Columbia. The newspaper covers local news and community events.; Full Page Mono: 16.80

Currency: Canada Dollars
NEWSPAPER

Le Placoteux
Owner: Placoteux (Le)
Editorial: 491 Av D'Anjou, St-Pascal, Quebec G0L 3Y0. **T:** 1 418 492-2706
E: journaliste@leplacoteux.com
W: http://www.leplacoteux.com
Freq: Weekly
Editor in Chief: Maurice Gagnon; **Publisher:** Bruno Lacroix
NEWSPAPER

Plein Jour de Baie-Comeau
Owner: Quebecor Communications Inc.
Editorial: 625, boul. Laflèche, Bureau 309, Baie-Comeau, Quebec G5C 1C5.
T: 1 418 589-5900
W: http://pleinjourdebaiecomeau.canoe.ca
Circ: 22369
Editor in Chief: Jean-Luc Doumont; **Editor:** Sébastien Rouillard
Editorial Profile: Plein Jour de Baie-Comeau is a weekly French-language newspaper that covers local and regional information for the residents of Sacré-Coeur, Grandes-Bergeronnes, Escoumins, Longue Rive (Sault-au-Mouton and St-Paul-du-Nord), Rivière Portneuf and Forestville, Quebec. The publication features local news and human-interest stories.; Full Page Mono: 6.79; Full Page Colour: 18.70
Currency: Canada Dollars
NEWSPAPER

Point de Vue Laurentides Mont-Tremblant
Owner: TC. Transcontinental
Editorial: 240, rue Léonard, Mont-Tremblant, Quebec J8E 3K1. **T:** 1 819 425-7666
E: infolaurentides@transcontinental.ca
W: http://www.pointdevuemonttremblant.com
Circ: 17785
Editorial Profile: Le Point de Vue Laurentides Mont-Tremblant offers local news and information for residents of Mont-Tremblant, Quebec.; Full Page Mono: 4.34
Currency: Canada Dollars
NEWSPAPER

Point de Vue Laurentides Sainte-Agathe
Owner: TC. Transcontinental
Editorial: 12, rue Ste-Agathe, Ste-Agathe-des-Monts, Quebec J8C 2J4. **T:** 1 819 321-3888
E: infolaurentides@transcontinental.ca
W: http://www.pointdevuesainteagathe.com
Circ: 16131
Editorial Profile: Le Point de Vue Laurentides Sainte-Agathe offers local news and information to residents of Ste-Agathe-des-Monts, Quebec.; Full Page Mono: 4.34
Currency: Canada Dollars
NEWSPAPER

Point Sud
Owner: Journal Communautaire de la Rive-Sud de Montreal Inc. (Le)
Editorial: 24 rue De Gentilly Ouest, Suite 200, Longueuil, Quebec J4H 1Y8.
T: 1 450 677-2626 **E:** info@pointsud.ca
W: http://www.pointsud.ca
Freq: Monthly; **Circ:** 25000
Editor in Chief: Maurice Giroux
Editorial Profile: Point Sud is a monthly French-language newspaper that covers local news and information for people in the Rive-Sud region of Montréal, QC. ; Full Page Mono: 30.24
Currency: Canada Dollars
NEWSPAPER

El Popular Hispanic Daily
Editorial: 2413 Dundas Street West, Toronto, Ontario M6P 1X3. **T:** 1 416 531-2495
E: editor@diarioelpopular.com
W: http://www.diarioelpopular.com
Freq: Daily; **Circ:** 10500
Editor in Chief: Jorge Perez
Editorial Profile: El Popular Hispanic Daily is published for Spanish speaking Canadians. It covers national news, travel, sports, business, arts and lifestyle topics.; Full Page Mono: 6.02; Full Page Colour: 125.00
Currency: Canada Dollars
DAILY NEWSPAPER

Port Perry Star
Owner: Metroland Media Group Ltd.
Editorial: 180 Mary St, Unit 11, Port Perry, Ontario L9L 1C4. **T:** 1 905 985-7383
W: http://www.durhamregion.com **Circ:** 12000
Publisher: Tim Whittaker
Editorial Profile: Port Perry Star is a community newspaper serving the Scugog,

Ontario area. It covers news and events for local residents.; Full Page Mono: 14.00
Currency: Canada Dollars
NEWSPAPER

Port Rowan Good News
Editorial: 8 Church Street, Port Rowan, Ontario N0E 1M0. **T:** 1 519 586-2291
E: prgn@live.ca
W: http://www.longpointbiosphere.com/port-rowan-good-news-articles
Freq: Monthly
Editor: Pat Finney; **Publisher:** Paul Morris
Editorial Profile: Port Rowan Good News is a monthly community newspaper that is published for the residents of Port Rowan, Ontario.
NEWSPAPER

Le Port-Cartois
Owner: TC. Transcontinental
Editorial: 32 Rue Plante, Port-Cartier, Quebec G5B 2E4. **T:** 1 418 766-5321
W: http://www.leportcartois.ca **Circ:** 18570
Publisher: Catherine Martin; **Editor:** Jean St. Pierre
Editorial Profile: Le Port-Cartois is a weekly publication serving several communities in northeast Quebec, including Port-Cartier, Rivière Brochu, Gallix, and Pentecôte. It covers primarily local news, but some regional news as well.; Full Page Mono: 13.58
Currency: Canada Dollars
NEWSPAPER

The Post
Owner: Sun Media
Editorial: 413 18th Ave, Hanover, Ontario N4N 3S5. **T:** 1 519 364-2001
W: http://www.thepost.on.ca **Circ:** 15106
Editorial Profile: The Post is a local newspaper that covers news, sports and entertainment for the residents of Hanover, Ontario and the surrounding areas. Deadlines are Mondays at 10am ET.; Full Page Mono: 12.32
Currency: Canada Dollars
NEWSPAPER

Post City Magazines
Editorial: 30 Lesmill Rd, Toronto, Ontario M3B 2T6. **T:** 1 416 250-7979 **E:** news@postcity.com
W: http://www.postcitymagazines.com
Circ: 175000
Editor in Chief: Ron Johnson; **Publisher:** Lorne London; **News Editor:** Bree Rody-Mantha; Full Page Mono: 2.58
Currency: Canada Dollars
NEWSPAPER

The Post-Gazette
Owner: Brunswick News Inc.
Editorial: 984 Prosepct, Fredericton, New Brunswick E2B 2T8. **T:** 1 506 357-9813
E: oropost@nb.aibn.com **Circ:** 15500
Publisher: Nancy Cook; **Editor:** Heather Grattan; Full Page Mono: 4.62
Currency: Canada Dollars
NEWSPAPER

Prairie Newspaper Group
Owner: Glacier Media Inc.
Editorial: 525 Main St, Humboldt, Saskatchewan S0K 2A0. **T:** 1 306 682-2561
W: http://www.humboldtjournal.ca **Circ:** 13390
Publisher: Al Guthro; **Editor in Chief:** Caitie McRae; **Editor:** Andrea Nicholl
NEWSPAPER

Prairie Post
Owner: Alta Newspaper Group, LP
Editorial: 3257 Dunmore Road SE, Medicine Hat, Alberta T1B 3R2. **T:** 1 403 527-1101
E: ppost@prairiepost.com
W: http://www.prairiepost.com **Circ:** 18071
Publisher: Mike Hertz
Editorial Profile: The Prairie Post is a weekly published newspaper for farmers; Full Page Mono: 16.66
Currency: Canada Dollars
NEWSPAPER

Prairie Post Southwestern Saskatchewan
Owner: Alta Newspaper Group, LP
Editorial: 161 Central Ave N, Ste 7, Swift Current, Saskatchewan S9H 0K9.
T: 1 306 773-8260 **E:** ppost@prairiepost.com
W: http://www.prairiepost.com **Circ:** 18777
Publisher: Mike Hertz
Editorial Profile: Prairie Post Southwestern Saskatchewan is a weekly newspaper that covers news in Southeast Alberta and Southwest Saskatchewan.; Full Page Mono: 21.06
Currency: Canada Dollars
NEWSPAPER

Prescott-Russell Newspapers
Editorial: 1158 Notre Dame, Embrun, Ontario K0A 1W0. **T:** 1 613 443-2753 **Circ:** 26300
Publisher: Roger Duplantie; **Publisher:** Roger Duplantie
Editorial Profile: The Prescott-Russell Newspapers are written for the residents of Embrun, ON.
NEWSPAPER

La Presse
Owner: Power Corporation of Canada
Editorial: 7 rue St Jacques, Montreal, Quebec H2Y 1K9. **T:** 1 514 285-7000
E: nouvelles@lapresse.ca
W: http://www.lapresse.ca
Freq: Daily; **Circ:** 281305
Publisher: Guy Crevier; **Editor in Chief:** Mélanie Thivierge
Editorial Profile: La Presse, established in 1884, is a daily broadsheet French-language newspaper published for residents of Montreal, Quebec and surrounding communities. It covers local, regional, national and international news topics in the areas of socio-cultural, business, economics, lifestyles, automotive, sports, arts and entertainment news.; Full Page Mono: 133.28; Full Page Colour: 4785.00
Currency: Canada Dollars
DAILY NEWSPAPER

Pride News Magazine
Editorial: 158 Hardwood Avenue South, Suite 204, Ajax, Ontario L1S 2H6.
T: 1 905 686-8868 **E:** pridenews@bellnet.ca
W: http://www.pridenewsmagazine.ca
Circ: 25000
Publisher & Editor: Michael Van Cooten
Editorial Profile: Pride News Magazine is a local community newspaper for the residents of Whitby, Ontario and surrounding communities.; Full Page Mono: 20.02
Currency: Canada Dollars
NEWSPAPER

The Prince George Citizen
Owner: Glacier Media Inc.
Editorial: 150 Brunswick St, Prince George, British Columbia V2L 2B3. **T:** 1 250 562-2441
E: news@pgcitizen.com
W: http://www.princegeorgecitizen.com
Freq: Daily; **Circ:** 23634
News Editor: Mick Kearns; **News Editor:** Mick Kearns; **Publisher:** Colleen Sparrow
Editorial Profile: The Prince George Citizen is the daily newspaper founded in 1916 for the town of Prince George, British Columbia. The paper covers local, national, world and business news.; Full Page Mono: 24.36; Full Page Colour: 24.36
Currency: Canada Dollars
DAILY NEWSPAPER

The Prince George Free Press
Owner: Thompson River Publications Ltd.
Editorial: 1773 S Lyon St, Prince George, British Columbia V2N 1T3. **T:** 1 250 564-0005
W: http://www.pgfreepress.com **Circ:** 29018
Editor: Bill Phillips
Editorial Profile: The Prince George Free Press covers local news, entertainment, and events for the residents of Prince George, British Columbia and the surrounding area.; Full Page Mono: 9.17
Currency: Canada Dollars
NEWSPAPER

Le Progrès-Dimanche
Owner: GESCA
Editorial: 1051 Boul Talbot, Chicoutimi, Quebec G7H 5C1. **T:** 1 418 545-4474
E: redaction@lequotidien.com
W: http://www.cyberpresse.ca **Circ:** 39432
Editor in Chief: Denis Bouchard; **Publisher:** Michel Simard
Editorial Profile: Progrès-Dimanche is a weekly French-language newspaper covering news, arts & entertainment, sports and human-interest stories.; Full Page Mono: 13.58; Full Page Colour: 915.00
Currency: Canada Dollars
NEWSPAPER

The Province
Owner: Postmedia Network Inc.
Editorial: 1-200 Granville St 1, Vancouver, British Columbia V6C 3N3-. **T:** 1 604 605-2030
E: tabtips@theprovince.com
W: http://www.theprovince.com
Freq: Daily; **Circ:** 134562
City Editor: David Carrigg; **Publisher:** Gordon Fisher; **City Editor:** Shannon Miller; **Editor in Chief:** Wayne Moriarty; **News Editor:** Lorne Smith
Editorial Profile: The Province is a tabloid sized newspaper written for the general public

of Vancouver, British Columbia and neighboring communities. It is one of the major newspapers in the area covering news specific to Vancouver as well as Canadian national news. It shares offices with the Vancouver Sun but maintains a separate newsroom.; Full Page Mono: 155.96; Full Page Colour: 362.90
Currency: Canada Dollars
DAILY NEWSPAPER

Proxima Publications
Owner: Proxima Publications, Inc.
Editorial: 8180 Devonshire bureau 9 Ville, Mont-Royal, Quebec H4P 2K3.
T: 1 514 736-1133
E: redaction@proxima-p.qc.ca
W: http://www.proxima-p.qc.ca **Circ:** 35000
Publisher: Tristan Roy; **Editor in Chief:** Joachim Tremblay
NEWSPAPER

Przeglad Tygodniowy
Editorial: 6449 Glen Erin, Unit 23, Mississauga, Ontario L5N 2T2.
T: 1 905 286-1774
Freq: Weekly
Publisher: Lidia Ambroziak; **Editor:** Czeslaw Zacharski
Editorial Profile: Przeglad Tygodniowy a weekly publication that covers multicultural events and news for the Polish community in Mississauga, Canada.
NEWSPAPER

The Punjab Star
Editorial: 7370 Bramalea Road, Suite #02, Mississauga, Ontario L5S 1N6.
T: 1 905 673-7666 **W:** http://punjabstar.ca
Freq: Weekly
Editor: Daniel Mattu
Editorial Profile: Punjab Star is a weekly publication that covers multicultural events and news for the Indian community in Ontario, Canada
NEWSPAPER

The Punjabi Daily
Editorial: 1332 Khalsa Drive, Unit #22, Mississauga, Ontario L5S 0A2.
T: 1 416 661-7272 **E:** info@punjabidaily.com
W: http://www.punjabidaily.com/home.php
Freq: Daily
Editor: Sukhminder Hansra
Editorial Profile: The Pujabi Daily is a daily publication that covers multicultural events and news for the Indian community in Mississauga, Canada.
DAILY NEWSPAPER

Punjabi Haak Canada
Editorial: 3671 Corliss Crescent, Mississauga, Ontario L4T 2Z2. **T:** 1 905 612-9639
Freq: Weekly
Editor: Roman Bawa
Editorial Profile: Punjabi Haak Canada is a weekly publication that covers multicultural events and news for the Indian community in Mississauga, Canada.
NEWSPAPER

Punjabi National
Editorial: 501-4656 Westwinds Drive NE, Calgary, Alberta T3J 3Z5. **T:** 1 403 204 0011
E: punjabinational@gmail.com
W: http://www.punjabinational.com
Editor: Aparjit Singh; **Publisher:** Kuldip Singh
Editorial Profile: Punjabi National is a Punjabi-language weekly newspaper providing Local and Community News coverage for the Calgary and Edmonton, AB areas.
NEWSPAPER

Punjabi Post
Editorial: 27 Armthorpe Rd, Unit #3, Brampton, Ontario L4T 1X3.
T: 1 905 793-2202 **E:** news@punjabipost.ca
W: http://www.punjabipost.ca
Freq: Daily
Editor: Jagdish Grewal
Editorial Profile: Punjabi Post is a daily publication that covers multicultural events and news for the Indian community in Brampton, Canada.
DAILY NEWSPAPER

Quebecor Communications - Boucherville
Owner: Quebecor Communications Inc.
Editorial: 391 Boulevard de Mortagne, Boucherville, Quebec J4B 1B7.
T: 1 450 641-3360
W: http://monteregieweb.com **Circ:** 93113
Editor in Chief: Nathalie Gilbert; **Publisher:** Serge Landry
NEWSPAPER

Quebecor Communications - Chibougamau
Owner: Quebecor Communications Inc.
Editorial: 317 3e Rue, CP 250, Chibougamau, Quebec G8P 2K7. **T:** 1 418 748-6406
W: http://reseauhebdos.canoe.ca **Circ:** 10306
Publisher and Editor: Guy Tremblay;
Publisher and Editor: Guy Tremblay
NEWSPAPER

Quebecor Communications - Kapuskasing
Owner: Quebecor Communications Inc.
Editorial: 51 Riverside Drive, Kapuskasing, Ontario P5N 1A7. **T:** 1 705 335-2283
E: kaptimes.news@sunmedia.ca
W: http://www.kapuskasingtimes.com
Circ: 15500
NEWSPAPER

Quebecor Communications - Mont-Laurier
Owner: Quebecor Communications Inc.
Editorial: 369 boul Albiny-Paquette, Mont-Laurier, Quebec J9L 1K5. **T:** 1 819 623-3112
W: http://reseauhebdos.canoe.ca **Circ:** 36400
Editor: Natalie DeBlois
NEWSPAPER

Quebecor Communications - Mont-Tremblant
Owner: Quebecor Communications Inc.
Editorial: 1107 rue de Saint-Jovite, Mont-Tremblant, Quebec J8E 3J9.
T: 1 819 326-1844
E: info.nord@hebdosquebecor.com
W: http://reseauhebdos.canoe.ca **Circ:** 38700
Publisher: Michel Gareau; **News Editor:** Luc Lefebvre; **News Editor:** Luc Lefebvre; **News Editor:** Ronald McGregor
NEWSPAPER

Quebecor Communications - Rimouski
Owner: Quebecor Communications Inc.
Editorial: 217 avenue Leonidas, Rimouski, Quebec G5L 2T5. **T:** 1 418 721-1212
W: http://reseauhebdos.canoe.ca **Circ:** 56049
Publisher: Marc Pitre; **Editor in Chief:** Ernie Wells
NEWSPAPER

Quebecor Communications - Rive Sud
Owner: Quebecor Communications Inc.
Editorial: 267, rue St-Charles Ouest, Longueuil, Quebec J4H 1E3.
T: 1 450 646-3333
E: redactionrs@hebdosquebecor.com
Circ: 227561
Editor in Chief: Serge Labrosse; **Publisher:** Lucie Massé; **News Editor:** Genevieve Michaud
Editorial Profile: Quebecor Publications - Rive Sud publishes four weeklies that cover local news for Montreal's South Shore area, known in French as "Le Rive Sud." Three of the papers publish exclusively in French, while one is bilingual English-French.
NEWSPAPER

Quebecor Communications - Rouyn-Noranda
Owner: Quebecor Communications Inc.
Editorial: 1 rue Du Terminus E., Rouyn-Noranda, Quebec J9X 3B5. **T:** 1 819 762-4361
E: redaction.rouyn@hebdosquebecor.com
W: http://reseauhebdos.canoe.ca **Circ:** 36518
Publisher: Joël Caya; **Editor:** David Prince
NEWSPAPER

Quebecor Communications - Sainte-Thérèse
Owner: Quebecor Communications Inc.
Editorial: 214, boulevard du Curé-Labelle, Bureau 208, Sainte-Therese, Quebec J7E 2X7.
T: 1 450 818-7575 **Circ:** 124000
Publisher: Luc Bélanger
NEWSPAPER

Quebecor Communications - Saint-Georges
Owner: Quebecor Communications Inc.
Editorial: 710, 98è rue, Saint-Georges, Quebec G5Y 8G1. **T:** 1 418 228-8858
E: redaction.saintgeorges@hebdosquebecor.com **W:** http://reseauhebdos.canoe.ca
Circ: 87250
Publisher: Gilbert Bernier; **Editor:** André Boutin; **Editor:** Simon Busque; **Publisher:** Véronique Pouliot
NEWSPAPER

Quebecor Communications - Sherbrooke
Owner: Quebecor Communications Inc.

Editorial: 3330 Rue King O, Sherbrooke, Quebec J1L 1C9-. T: 1 819 565-7777
W: http://reseauhebdos.canoe.ca
Editor in Chief: Claude Croisetière
NEWSPAPER

Quebecor Communications - St-Jérôme
Owner: Quebecor Communications Inc.
Editorial: 179 rue St-Georges, St-Jerome, Quebec J7Z 4Z8. T: 1 450 436-8200
E: atelier.echo@hebdosquebecor.com
W: http://reseauhebdos.canoe.ca Circ: 96433
News Editor: Yolande Brasset; News Editor: Marc Fradellin
NEWSPAPER

Quebecor Communications - Val-d'Or
Owner: Quebecor Communications Inc.
Editorial: 1462 rue de la Québécoise, Val-d'Or, Quebec J9P 5H4. T: 1 819 825-3755
E: atelier.citoyenvaldor@hebdosquebecor.com
W: http://reseauhebdos.canoe.ca Circ: 34300
Publisher: Caroline Couture; Editor: David Prince
NEWSPAPER

Le Quotidien
Owner: Power Corporation of Canada
Editorial: 1051 Boul Talbot, Chicoutimi, Quebec G7H 5C1. T: 1 418 545-4474
W: http://www.cyberpresse.ca/le-quotidien
Freq: Daily; Circ: 27792
News Editor: Catherine Delisle; Publisher: Michel Simard
Editorial Profile: Le Quotidien is a daily, four-color, tabloid-sized, French-language newspaper. Most editorial content concerns local news and information for the Saguenay-Lac-Saint-Jean region of Québec. It also covers national and international news, mostly derived from news wires. It contains additional reporting on sports, business, weather and arts & entertainment.; Full Page Mono: 21.84; Full Page Colour: 880.00
Currency: Canada Dollars
DAILY NEWSPAPER

Record News Publications
Owner: Metroland Media
Editorial: 65 Lorne St, Smiths Falls, Ontario K7A 4T1. T: 1 613 283-3182
E: recordnews@perfprint.ca Circ: 73290
News Editor: Joe Morin; Publisher: Duncan Weir; News Editor: Laurie Weir
NEWSPAPER

Record News Publications - Kanata
Owner: Torstar Corp
Editorial: 57 Auriga Dr., Suite 103, Ottawa, Ontario K2E 8B2. T: 1 613 723-5970
W: http://www.perfprint.ca Circ: 46988
Publisher: Duncan Weir
NEWSPAPER

The Recorder & Times
Owner: Quebecor Communications Inc.
Editorial: 2479A Parkedale Ave, Brockville, Ontario K6V 3H2-. T: 1 613 342-4441
W: http://www.recorder.ca
Freq: Daily; Circ: 11689
Editorial Profile: The Recorder & Times is a daily newspaper serving the residents of Brockville, Ontario. It covers local and national news, features, sports and weather. It also provides editorial opinion and comment. Contact this outlet through the contact form on their site.; Full Page Mono: 20.72; Full Page Colour: 525.00
Currency: Canada Dollars
DAILY NEWSPAPER

Red Deer Advocate
Owner: Black Press
Editorial: 2950 Bremner Ave, Red Deer, Alberta T4R 1M9. T: 1 403 343-2400
E: editorial@reddeeradvocate.com
W: http://www.reddeeradvocate.com
Freq: Daily; Circ: 11313
Publisher: Fred Gorman; City Editor: Carolyn Martindale
Editorial Profile: Red Deer Advocate is a daily newspaper written for the Red Deer, Alberta general public. It covers local and world news, sports, business, travel, classifieds and entertainment.; Full Page Mono: 32.48; Full Page Colour: 615.00
Currency: Canada Dollars
DAILY NEWSPAPER

Red Deer Express
Owner: Black Press
Editorial: #121, 5301-43 St., Red Deer, Alberta T4N 1C8. T: 1 403 346-3356
E: express@reddeerexpress.com
W: http://www.reddeerexpress.com

Circ: 30000
Publisher: Tracey Scheveers; Editor in Chief: Mark Weber
Editorial Profile: Red Deer Express is a community newspaper that covers hometown news and features for Red Deer, Alberta.; Full Page Mono: 23.80; Full Page Colour: 36.85
Currency: Canada Dollars
NEWSPAPER

Le Reflet
Owner: Quebecor Communications Inc.
Editorial: 11 Route 132, Delson, Quebec J5B 1G9. T: 1 450 635-9146 E: info@lereflet.qc.ca
W: http://www.lereflet.qc.ca Circ: 40090
Editor in Chief: Hélène Gingras
Editorial Profile: Le Reflet Régional is a weekly French-language newspaper that covers local news and information in Delson, Quebec. Contact the publication by phone, fax, or mail.; Full Page Mono: 6.79
Currency: Canada Dollars
NEWSPAPER

Le Reflet du Lac
Owner: TC. Transcontinental
Editorial: 101 rue du Moulin, Bureau 104, Magog, Quebec J1X 4A1. T: 1 819 843-3500
W: http://www.lerefletdulac.com Circ: 26271
Publisher: Monique Côté; Editor in Chief: Dany Jacques
Editorial Profile: Le Reflet du Lac is a weekly French-language newspaper published for the residents of Magog, Quebec. The newspaper covers local and regional news.; Full Page Mono: 7.14
Currency: Canada Dollars
NEWSPAPER

Le Regional
Owner: Les Publications du Patrimoine B.C.R. Inc.
Editorial: 124 rue Principale E, Hawkesbury, Ontario K6A 1A3. T: 1 613 632-0112
E: news@le-regional.ca Circ: 34484
Editor in Chief: Jeanette Perrault
Editorial Profile: Le Regional is a community newspaper written for the residents of Hawkesbury, Ontario.; Full Page Mono: 16.80
Currency: Canada Dollars
NEWSPAPER

The Renfrew Mercury EMC
Owner: Metroland Media Group Ltd.
Editorial: 35 Opeongo Road, Renfrew, Ontario K7V 2T2. T: 1 613 432-3655
W: http://www.yourottawaregion.com
Circ: 15600
Editor in Chief: Lucy Hass; Publisher: Mike Mount
Editorial Profile: The Renfrew Mercury EMC is a weekly newspaper serving residents of Renfrew and all areas between McNab/Braeside and Forrester Falls, Ontario. Coverage includes community news, events, schools, sports, business and features.; Full Page Mono: 3.92
Currency: Canada Dollars
NEWSPAPER

Le Réseau des Échos
Owner: Réseau des Échos du Nouveau Brunswick (Le)
Editorial: 8217 rue St-Paul, Bas-Caraquet, New Brunswick E1W 6C4. T: 1 506 727-4749
E: message@canadamunicipal.ca
W: http://www.canadamunicipal.ca
Freq: Monthly; Circ: 12800
Publisher: Brigitte Cladère; Editor in Chief: Gilles Gagné
Editorial Profile: Le Réseau des Échos is a French-language community newspaper publisher in New Brunswick, Canada.; Full Page Mono: 1890.00
Currency: Canada Dollars
NEWSPAPER

La Revue
Owner: TC. Transcontinental
Editorial: 160 Boul de L'Hopital, Gatineau, Quebec J8T 8J1. T: 1 819 568-7736
W: http://www.journallarevue.com Circ: 89752
Publisher: Martin Godcher
Editorial Profile: La Revue is a French-language, weekly newspaper serving residents and businesses in Hull, Aylmer and Gatineau in the region of Outaouasis, QC. Editorial content includes in-depth community news, including local politics, businesses, events, legal news, arts and entertainment, sports and special reports. It also contains a section devoted to a community diary, letters to the editor and photographs submitted by readers. The lead time is one week prior to publication. Deadlines for distribution is on Wednesdays at 5pm ET.; Full Page Mono: 16.52
Currency: Canada Dollars

NEWSPAPER

La Revue De Terrebonne
Owner: Revue de Terrebonne Inc. (La)
Editorial: 231 Rue Sainte-Marie, Terrebonne, Quebec J6W 3E4. T: 1 450 964-4444
E: larevue@larevue.qc.ca
W: http://www.larevue.qc.ca Circ: 57800
Editor in Chief: Veronick Talbot
Editorial Profile: Established in May 1959 and independent to this day, La Revue is a francophone weekly serving the Lanaudière region of Québec and covers local news. Contact the Editor-in-Chief.; Full Page Mono: 7.27; Full Page Colour: 450.00
Currency: Canada Dollars
NEWSPAPER

Richmond News
Owner: Glacier Media Inc.
Editorial: 5731 No 3 Road, Richmond, British Columbia V6X 2C9. T: 1 604 270-8031
E: editor@richmond-news.com
W: http://www.richmond-news.com
Circ: 48000
Publisher: Lori Chalmers
Editorial Profile: Richmond News is a weekly newspaper serving the town of Richmond, British Columbia. The publication provides local news, current events, sports, lifestyle and business.; Full Page Mono: 14.56
Currency: Canada Dollars
NEWSPAPER

Richmond Review
Owner: Black Press
Editorial: 1-3671 Viking Way, Richmond, British Columbia V6V 2J5. T: 1 604 247-3700
W: http://www.richmondreview.com
Circ: 46469
Editor in Chief: Bhreandain Clugston; Publisher: Mary Kemmis
Editorial Profile: Richmond Review is the local newspaper of Richmond, British Columbia. It focuses on news and issues occurring in or directly affecting the Richmond community. The voice of the community since 1932, the paper has a news, sports, business, community, arts & entertainment and classifieds section. The Thursday issue of the newspaper has an emphasis on arts & entertainment, while the Sunday issue has a large business section. Each issue also contains a calendar of events. Contact the editor with story ideas and article submissions.; Full Page Mono: 30.66; Full Page Colour: 2750.00
Currency: Canada Dollars
NEWSPAPER

Rimouski Newspapers
Owner: TC. Transcontinental
Editorial: 183 W. Rue St-Germain Quest, Rimouski, Quebec G5L 4B8.
T: 1 418 722-0205
E: administration@lavantage.qc.ca
W: http://www.lavantage.qc.ca
Freq: Weekly; Circ: 133676
Editor in Chief: René Alary; Publisher: Jean Mercier
NEWSPAPER

Riverside Neighbours
Owner: Brunswick News Inc.
Editorial: 984 Prospect Street, Fredericton, New Brunswick E3B 2T8. T: 1 506 452-6671
E: northside@brunswicknews.com Circ: 16000
Editor: Heather Grattan
Editorial Profile: Riverside Neighbours is a weekly community newspaper written for the residents of New Brunswick.; Full Page Mono: 4.20
Currency: Canada Dollars
NEWSPAPER

Rive-Sud Express
Owner: TC. Transcontinental
Editorial: 1485 rue de Coulomb, Boucherville, Quebec J4B 7L8. T: 1 450 678-6187
E: redactionrivesud@tc.tc
W: http://www.rivesudexpress.ca
Freq: Weekly; Circ: 145000
Editor: Alain Dechoinieve
Editorial Profile: Rive-Sud Express is written for the residents of Montreal's South Shore.; Full Page Mono: 10.99
Currency: Canada Dollars
NEWSPAPER

Road Today Express
Owner: Road Today Publishing Inc.
Editorial: 1295 Shawson Drive, Ste 201, Mississauga, Ontario L4W 1C4.
T: 1 905 487-1320
E: contact@roadtodayexpress.com
W: http://www.roadtodayexpress.com

Freq: Bi-Weekly
Editor: Manan Gupta
Editorial Profile: Road Today is a bi-weekly publication that covers the trucking industry with a special focus on the South Asian community in Ontario, Canada.
NEWSPAPER

Rocky Mountain Outlook
Owner: Black Press
Editorial: 1001 6 Ave, Ste 201, Canmore, Alberta T1W 2V3. T: 1 403 609-0220
E: info@outlook.greatwest.ca
W: http://www.rmoutlook.com Circ: 15000
Publisher: Jason Lyon; Full Page Mono: 4.70
Currency: Canada Dollars
NEWSPAPER

Le Roussillon Express
Owner: TC. Transcontinental
Editorial: 69, boul. St-jean Baptiste, 2e Etage, Chateauguay, Quebec. T: 1 450 692-9111
W: http://www.roussillonexpress.ca
Circ: 49735
Editor: Normand Laberge; Publisher: Julie Voyer
Editorial Profile: A weekly newspaper that covers news, municipal and provincial policy, sports, culture, arts and entertainment, economy and life for residents of Roussillon of the Montérégie region.
NEWSPAPER

Runge Newspapers - Kemptville
Owner: Metroland Media Group Ltd.
Editorial: 113 Prescott St, Kemptville, Ontario K0G 1J0. T: 1 613 258-3451
W: http://www.yourkemptville.com Circ: 44000
Editor: Joe Morin
Editorial Profile: Runge Newspapers - Kemptville is a weekly community newspaper publisher serving the residents of Kemptville and Ottawa, Ontario.
NEWSPAPER

Russian Express
Owner: Russian-Canadian Press Inc.
Editorial: 1881 Steeles Avenue West, Suite 207A, North York, Ontario M3H 5Y4.
T: 1 416 663-3999 E: 4166633999@bellnet.ca
W: http://www.russianexpress.net Circ: 14000
Editorial Profile: The Russian Express is a Russian newspaper written for the residents of Ontario.; Full Page Mono: 7.70
Currency: Canada Dollars
NEWSPAPER

Russian Infotrade Ltd.
Owner: Russian Infotrade Ltd.
Editorial: 5987 Bathurst St, Ste 108, Toronto, Ontario M2R 1Z3. T: 1 416 226-4777
E: info@infogazeta.com
W: http://www.russians.ca Circ: 31300
Publisher & Editor: Boris Nusenbaum
NEWSPAPER

Sach Di Awaaz Newspaper
T: 1 604 503-0840 E: info@sachdiawaaz.ca
W: http://www.sachdiawaa.ca Circ: 50000
Editorial Profile: Sach Di Awaaz Newspaper is a weekly publication that covers multicultural events and news for the Indian community in Surrey, Canada.
NEWSPAPER

Saint-Lambert/Brossard Journal
Editorial: 6 Boul Desaulniers, Saint-Lambert, Quebec J4P 1L3. T: 1 450 671-0014
E: journal.saintlambert@videotron.ca
Freq: Weekly; Circ: 29550
Publisher & Editor: David Leonardo
NEWSPAPER

Le Saint-Laurent-Portage
Owner: Quebecor Communications Inc.
Editorial: 55A rue de l'Hôtel-de-ville, Riviere-du-Loup, Quebec G5R 1L4. T: 1 418 862-1774
W: http://www.lestlaurentportage.canoe.ca
Circ: 40210
Publisher: Francis Desrosiers; Editor In Chief: Gilles Lebel
Editorial Profile: Le Saint-Laurent-Portage is a weekly French-language newspaper that covers local and regional information for people in and around Rivière-du-Loup, Quebec.; Full Page Mono: 13.02
Currency: Canada Dollars
NEWSPAPER

Sarnia & Lambton County This Week
Owner: Quebecor Communications Inc.
Editorial: 140 Front St S, Sarnia, Ontario N7T 7M8. T: 1 519 336-1100
W: http://www.sarniathisweek.com
Circ: 40000
Publisher: Linda Leblanc

Editorial Profile: Sarnia & Lambton County This Week is a local newspaper for the residents of Sarnia, Bright's Grove, Point Edward and Corunna, Ontario. It covers news, sports, features and opinion articles.; Full Page Mono: 16.52
Currency: Canada Dollars
NEWSPAPER

The Sault Star
Owner: Quebecor Communications Inc.
Editorial: 145 Old Garden River Road, Sault Ste. Marie, Ontario P6A 5M5.
T: 1 705 759-3030
W: http://www.saultstar.com
Freq: Daily; **Circ:** 18353
Publisher: Lou Maulucci; **District Editor:** Jeffrey Ougler; **City Editor:** Karen Pomber; **Editor:** Frank Rupnik
Editorial Profile: The Sault Star is a 30+ page, regional newspaper written for the Sault Sainte Marie, Ontario general public. The publication serves as one of the major newspapers in the area covering a mix of news, sports, business and entertainment. Various news features are included on a weekly basis.; Full Page Mono: 11.55; Full Page Colour: 821.00
Currency: Canada Dollars
DAILY NEWSPAPER

Sault Ste. Marie This Week
Owner: Quebecor Communications Inc.
Editorial: 2 Towers St, Sault Ste. Marie, Ontario P6A 2T9. **T:** 1 705 949-6111
W: http://www.saultthisweek.com **Circ:** 32000
Editor in Chief: Sandra Paul
Editorial Profile: Sault Ste. Marie This Week is a weekly newspaper that covers local news, sports and entertainment for the residents of the Sault Ste. Marie, Ontario region.; Full Page Mono: 9.87
Currency: Canada Dollars
NEWSPAPER

Scugog/Uxbridge Standard
Owner: Scugog Standard Company Limited (The)
Editorial: 94A Water St, Port Perry, Ontario L9L 1J2. **T:** 1 905 985-6985
E: office-standard@powergate.ca
W: http://www.thestandardnewspaper.ca/
Circ: 14370
Editor: Darryl Knight
Editorial Profile: The Scugog/Uxbridge Standard covers news for Scugog, Uxbridge, Brock and Manvers, ON area. This independently owned newspaper offers local coverage of the news, politics, and sports. Their offices are located in Port Perry.
NEWSPAPER

Seaway News
Owner: TC. Transcontinental
Editorial: 29 Second St E, Cornwall, Ontario K6H 1Y2. **T:** 1 613 933-0014
E: editorial@cornwallseawaynews.com
W: http://www.cornwallseawaynews.com
Circ: 36541
Editor: Todd Lihou
Editorial Profile: Seaway News is a weekly newspaper written for the citizens of Cornwall, ON. The paper includes a French-language insert, called the Cornwall Express.; Full Page Mono: 11.55
Currency: Canada Dollars
NEWSPAPER

The Senior
T: 1 306 525-8988
E: info@theseniorpaper.com
W: http://www.theseniorpaper.com
Freq: Monthly; **Circ:** 21497
Editor: Clay Stacey
Editorial Profile: The Senior is written for the senior citizen residents of Saskatchewan, Canada.; Full Page Mono: 20.58
Currency: Canada Dollars
NEWSPAPER

Senthamarai
Owner: Thamilar Senthamarai Publication Ltd.
Editorial: Markham East Plaza A, 3351 Markham Road, Unit 130, Scarborough, Ontario M1X 0A6. **T:** 1 416 291-0220
E: thamilars@aol.com
W: http://www.senthamarai.com/ **Circ:** 10300
Editor: Ragee Arasaratnam
Editorial Profile: Senthamarai publishes global news with an emphasis on Sri Lankan, Canadian and South Indian coverage. It also features stories on cinema and sports.; Full Page Mono: 2.80
Currency: Canada Dollars
NEWSPAPER

Shahrvand
Owner: Shahrvand Publications Ltd.

Editorial: 505 Hwy. 7 unit 304, Thornhill, Ontario L3T 7T1. **T:** 1 905 764-7022
E: news@shahrvand.com
W: http://www.shahrvand.com **Circ:** 12000
Editor in Chief: Hassan Zerehi
Editorial Profile: Shahrvand is written for Iranian residents in Downsview, Ontario. It covers news and events.; Full Page Mono: 3.00
Currency: Canada Dollars
NEWSPAPER

Share
Owner: MediaSpawn
Editorial: 658 Vaughan Rd, Toronto, Ontario M6E 2Y5. **T:** 1 416 656-3400
E: share@interlog.com
W: http://www.sharenews.com **Circ:** 40000
Editorial Profile: Share is a weekly community newspaper published for the black and caribbean community of the greater Toronto area of Ontario, Canada.; Full Page Mono: 33.32
Currency: Canada Dollars
NEWSPAPER

Sherbrooke-Valois, Inc.
Owner: Sherbrooke-Valois, Inc.
Editorial: 105-310 Av Victoria 105, Westmount, Quebec H3Z 2M9.
T: 1 514 935-4537
W: http://www.freepresspaper.com **Circ:** 29202
Editor in Chief: Marlene Eisner
NEWSPAPER

Sherwood Park/Strathcona County News
Owner: Quebecor Communications Inc.
Editorial: 168 Kaska Rd, Sherwood Park, Alberta T8A 4G7. **T:** 1 780 464-0033
E: spn.news@sunmedia.ca
W: http://www.sherwoodparknews.com
Circ: 28000
Editor: Michael Di Massa; **Publisher:** Jean Figeat
Editorial Profile: Sherwood Park/Strathcona County News is written for the residents of Strathcona County, Alberta. It covers local news and events.; Full Page Mono: 4.62
Currency: Canada Dollars
NEWSPAPER

The Shoreline News
Owner: Codner Holdings Ltd.
T: 1 709 834-2169 **E:** tsnews@nf.aibn.com
W: http://www.theshorelinenews.com
Circ: 16000
Publisher & Editor: Franklin Petten
Editorial Profile: Shoreline News provides news and information to the residents of Paradise and Conception Bay South, Newfoundland.; Full Page Mono: 13.02; Full Page Colour: 700.00
Currency: Canada Dollars
NEWSPAPER

Simcoe-York Printing & Publishing
Owner: London Publishing Corp.
Editorial: 34 Main St W, Beeton, Ontario L0G 1A0. **T:** 1 905 729-2287
E: admin.syp@rogers.com **Circ:** 22300
News Editor: Breha Bartholet
NEWSPAPER

Sing Tao Daily
Owner: Sing Tao Newspapers Ltd.
Editorial: 8508 Ash St, Vancouver, British Columbia V6P 3M2. **T:** 1 604 321-1111
E: reporter@singtao.ca
W: http://news.singtao.ca/vancouver
Freq: Daily; **Circ:** 31000
Editor: Kat Cheung; **Editor:** Francis Chiang; **Editor in Chief:** Victor Ho; **Publisher:** Calvin Wong
Editorial Profile: Sing Tao Daily is a daily newspaper published for the members of the Chinese speaking community. The newspaper covers local, regional, national and international news as well as entertainment, business and finance and lifestyle issues.; Full Page Mono: 78.40; Full Page Colour: 94.08
Currency: Canada Dollars
DAILY NEWSPAPER

Sing Tao Daily
Owner: Sing Tao Media Group Canada
Editorial: 221 Whitehall Dr, Markham, Ontario L3R 9T1. **T:** 1 905 754-3288
E: newsdesk@singtao.ca
W: http://www.singtao.ca
Freq: Daily; **Circ:** 38000
City Editor: Roger Cheung
Editorial Profile: Sing Tao Daily is a daily newspaper published for the members of the Chinese speaking community. The newspaper covers local, regional, national and international news as well as entertainment,

business and finance and lifestyle issues.; Full Page Mono: 35.95; Full Page Colour: 71.68
Currency: Canada Dollars
DAILY NEWSPAPER

Smart Shopper
Owner: Quebecor Communications Inc.
Editorial: 4525 Rhodes Drive, Unit 400, Windsor, Ontario N8W 5R8.
T: 1 519 966-4500
W: http://www.windsorpennysaver.com
Circ: 120000
Circulation Manger: Carol Grant
Editorial Profile: Windsor Smart Shopper is a weekly publication that only contains advertisements. It is distributed to the residents of Windsor, Ontario.; Full Page Mono: 17.71; Full Page Colour: 1300.00
Currency: Canada Dollars
NEWSPAPER

Sol Portugues/Portuguese Sun
Owner: Sol Portugues Publishing Inc.
Editorial: 977 College St, Toronto, Ontario M6H 1A6. **T:** 1 416 538-1788
E: sol@solnet.com **W:** http://www.solnet.com
Circ: 12000
Editor In Chief: Alice Perinu
Editorial Profile: Sol Portugues is a weekly paper serving the Portugues speaking population in Toronto, Ontario. It is published every Friday.; Full Page Mono: 11.41
Currency: Canada Dollars
NEWSPAPER

Le Soleil
Owner: Power Corporation of Canada
Editorial: 410 Boul Charest E, Quebec, Quebec G1K 8G3-. **T:** 1 418 686-3326
E: webmestre@lesoleil.com
W: http://www.lapresse.ca/le-soleil
Freq: Daily; **Circ:** 77002
Publisher: Claude Gagnon; **Editor:** Mylène Moisan
Editorial Profile: Le Soleil is a 52-page daily newspaper covering local, national and international news. It is a French-language newspaper with a strong focus on the city of Québec. In addition to news features, the paper covers economics, business, finance, stock markets, entertainment, lifestyles, sports and culture.; Full Page Mono: 81.28; Full Page Colour: 281.19
Currency: Canada Dollars
DAILY NEWSPAPER

Le Soleil de Châteauguay
Owner: Quebecor Communications Inc.
Editorial: 82 boulevard Salaberry Sud, Chateauguay, Quebec J6J 4J6.
T: 1 450 692-8552
W: http://monteregieweb.com/Le_Soleil_De_Chateauguay
Freq: 2 Times/Week; **Circ:** 69901
Editor: Carole Gagné; **Editor in Chief:** Michel Thibault
Editorial Profile: Le Soleil de Châteauguay publishes bi-lingual newspapers serving residents in Châteauguay, Mercier, Beauharnois, Léry, Maple-Grove, Sainte-Martine & St-Paul, Saint-Urbain, St-Isidore, Howick and Kahnawake, Quebec.
NEWSPAPER

Le Soleil de Salaberry-de-Valleyfield
Owner: Quebecor Communications Inc.
Editorial: 20 rue Académie, Salaberry-de-Valleyfield, Quebec J6T 6M9.
T: 1 450 373-8555 **E:** info@lesoleil.qc.ca
W: http://www.lesoleil.qc.ca
Freq: Weekly; **Circ:** 36069
Editor in Chief: Mario Pitre
Editorial Profile: Le Soleil de Salaberry-de-Valleyfield is a weekly French-language newspaper that covers local news and information for residents of Salaberry-de-Valleyfield, Quebec.; Full Page Mono: 6.86
Currency: Canada Dollars
NEWSPAPER

Sorel-Tracy Express
Owner: TC. Transcontinental
Editorial: 100, Rue Plante, Sorel-Tracy, Quebec J3P 7P5. **T:** 1 450 746-0886
E: sorel-tracyexpress@transcontinental.ca
W: http://www.sorel-tracyexpress.ca
Freq: Weekly
Editor: Andre Peloquin
Editorial Profile: Sorel-Tracy Express is a weekly newspaper providing Regional, Local and Community News to the citizens of Sorel-Tracy, QC.
NEWSPAPER

Sortir
Owner: Quebecor Communications Inc.

Editorial: 184 Rue de Normandie, Boucherville, Quebec J4B 5S7.
T: 1 450 655-0068 **E:** sortir@hebdos.net
W: http://monteregieweb.com
Freq: Monthly; **Circ:** 150222
Publisher: Andre Cyr; **Editor in Chief:** Nathalie Gilbert
Editorial Profile: Sortir is a free, monthly, French-language publication that offers community news and events to residents in and around Boucherville, Quebec.
NEWSPAPER

South Asian Focus
Owner: Metroland Media Group Ltd.
Editorial: 7700 Hurontario St., Unit 201, Brampton, Ontario L6Y 4M3.
T: 1 905 454-1535
W: http://www.southasianfocus.ca **Circ:** 24000
Editor in Chief: Sunil Rao
Editorial Profile: South Asian Focus is a weekly newspaper written for the residents of Brampton, Ontario. The paper covers news, sports, arts & entertainment, community news and business.; Full Page Mono: 9.29
Currency: Canada Dollars
NEWSPAPER

South Asian Observer
Owner: Global Media Network
Editorial: 29-5160 Explorer Drive, Mississauga, Ontario L4W 4T7.
T: 1 905 612-7281
E: info@southasianobserver.com
W: http://www.southasianobserver.com
Circ: 32000
Editor: Jasbir Shetra; **Publisher:** Jaspal Shetra
Editorial Profile: South Asian Observer is a weekly newspaper printed for South Asian Canadians.; Full Page Mono: 22.40
Currency: Canada Dollars
NEWSPAPER

South Asian Post
Owner: Post Group Multimedia Inc
Editorial: 2953 - 349 West Georgia Street, Vancouver, British Columbia V6B 3X4.
T: 1 604 821-1954
E: editor@postpeopleinc.com
W: http://www.southasianpost.com
Circ: 25000
Publisher: Harbinder Sewak
Editorial Profile: South Asian Post is a weekly newspaper written for the South Asian community in Canada, including Indo-Canadians, East Indians, Punjabis, Pakistanis, Bangladeshis, Fijians and Tamils. It was established in 2005.; Full Page Mono: 26.59; Full Page Colour: 350.00
Currency: Canada Dollars
NEWSPAPER

South Asian Star
Editorial: 1295 Shawson Drive, Ste 201, Mississauga, Ontario L4W 1C4.
T: 1 905 487-1320
E: contact@southasianstar.com
W: http://southasianstar.com
Freq: Bi-Weekly
Publisher & Editor: Manan Gupta
Editorial Profile: South Asian Star is a bi-weekly publication that covers multicultural events and news for the Indian community in Brampton, Canada.
NEWSPAPER

South Asian Vision
Owner: Grewal (Jagdish)
Editorial: 27 Armthorpe Rd., Unit #3, Brampton, Ontario L6T 5M4.
T: 1 905 793-2202 **E:** news@punjabipost.ca
W: http://punjabipost.ca
Freq: Weekly; **Circ:** 25000
Editor: Jagdish Grewal
Editorial Profile: South Asian Vision is a Weekly publication that covers multicultural events and news for the South Asian community in Brampton, Canada.; Full Page Mono: 16.80
Currency: Canada Dollars
NEWSPAPER

South Delta Leader
Owner: Glacier Media Inc.
Editorial: 7-1363 56 St 7, Delta, British Columbia V4L 2P7. **T:** 1 604 948-3640
E: editor@southdeltaleader.com
W: http://www.southdeltaleader.com
Circ: 15903
Publisher: Chrissie Bowker; **Editor:** Robert Mangelsdorf
Editorial Profile: South Delta Leader is a weekly community newspaper written for the resident of Delta, British Columbia.; Full Page Mono: 9.03
Currency: Canada Dollars
NEWSPAPER

South Side Story
Owner: South Side Story Inc.
Editorial: 2140 Regent St South, Unit 10, Sudbury, Ontario P3E 5S8. **T:** 1 705 523-2339
E: southsidestory@eastlink.ca
Freq: Monthly; **Circ:** 36000
Editor in Chief: Monika Berens; **Publisher:** Colin Firth
Editorial Profile: South Side Story is a monthly community newspaper written for the residents of Sudbury, Ontario.; Full Page Mono: 24.43
Currency: Canada Dollars
NEWSPAPER

Southern Exposure
Owner: Continental Newspapers Canada Ltd.
Editorial: 186 Nanaimo Ave. W, Ste. 101, Penticton, British Columbia V2A 1N4.
T: 1 250 492-4002 **Circ:** 46885
Publisher: Andre Martin
Editorial Profile: Southern Exposure is a free, bi-weekly newspaper serving the residents of the Okanagan region, including Penticton, British Columbia. It contains community news, events, sports, local features and editorials.; Full Page Mono: 9.10
Currency: Canada Dollars
NEWSPAPER

Southern Shopper & Review
Editorial: SW 26-3-7W, Darlingford, Manitoba R0G 0L0. **T:** 1 204 246-2492
E: southernshopper@mts.net
W: http://www.theonlinenewspapers.com/thesouthernshopperreview
Freq: Bi-Weekly; **Circ:** 17500
Editorial Profile: Southern Shopper & Review's editorial mission is to provide local editorial coverage of regional events and human interest topics to the residents of Darlingford, MB, and its surrounding areas.; Full Page Mono: 7.87; Full Page Colour: 1200.05
Currency: Canada Dollars
NEWSPAPER

Southwest Booster
Owner: TC. Transcontinental
Editorial: 30-4th AveNW, Swift Current, Saskatchewan S9H 3X4. **T:** 1 306 773-9321
W: http://www.swbooster.com **Circ:** 16729
Publisher: Bob Watson
Editorial Profile: Southwest Booster is a community newspaper publisher for the residents of Swift Current, Saskatchewan and the surrounding areas. It covers local news, sports and events. Deadlines are on Tuesdays.; Full Page Mono: 7.84; Full Page Colour: 385.00
Currency: Canada Dollars
NEWSPAPER

Southwest Newspapers
Owner: Editions Andre Pomerleau Inc. (Les)
Editorial: 52 rue Nicholson, Bureau 201, Salaberry-de-Valleyfield, Quebec J6T 4M8.
T: 1 450 371-8051
E: journal@media-sudouest.com
W: http://www.publications-sudouest.com
Circ: 97000
Publisher & Editor: Andre Pomeleau
NEWSPAPER

Lo Specchio/The Italian Weekly
Editorial: 160 Woodbridge Ave, Ste 101, Woodbridge, Ontario L4L 0B8.
T: 1 905 856-2823 **E:** lospecchio@msn.com
W: http://www.lospecchio.com **Circ:** 20000
Publisher & Editor: Sergio Tagliavini;
Publisher & Editor: Sergio Tagliavini
Editorial Profile: Lo Specchio/The Italian Weekly is written for Canadians of Italian heritage.; Full Page Mono: 35.70
Currency: Canada Dollars
NEWSPAPER

Springwater News
Editorial: 9 Glenview Ave., Elmvale, Ontario L0L 1P0. **T:** 1 705 322-2249
E: springwaternews@rogers.com
Freq: Bi-Weekly; **Circ:** 15400
Publisher & Editor: Michael Jacobs
Editorial Profile: Springwater News is written for the residents of Elmvale, Ontario. It covers local news and events. Deadlines are on Mondays.; Full Page Mono: 9.85
Currency: Canada Dollars
NEWSPAPER

St. Albert Gazette
Owner: Great West Newspapers LP
Editorial: 25 Chisholm Ave, Saint Albert, Alberta T8N 5A5. **T:** 1 780 460-5500
E: gazette@stalbert.greatwest.ca
W: http://www.stalbertgazette.com **Circ:** 27093
Publisher: Brian Bachynski
Editorial Profile: St. Albert Gazette is written for the residents of St. Albert, Morinville, Bon Accord, Legal and the County of Sturgeon in Alberta. It covers local news and information.; Full Page Mono: 14.42; Full Page Colour: 300.00
Currency: Canada Dollars
NEWSPAPER

St. Albert Leader
Owner: RJ Lolly Media Ltd.
Editorial: 13 Mission Ave, Saint Albert, Alberta T8N 1H6. **T:** 1 780 460-1035
E: info@stalbertleader.com
W: http://www.stalbertleader.com/
Freq: Weekly; **Circ:** 20000
Editor: Glenn Cook
Editorial Profile: St. Albert Leader is a free weekly community newspaper serving the residents of Saint Albert, Alberta, Canada. It covers News, Entertainment, Opinions, Community Events, and Lifestyle. E-Editions of the paper can be found through their website.; Full Page Mono: 14.75
Currency: Canada Dollars
NEWSPAPER

The St. Mary's Journal-Argus Newspapers
Owner: Metroland Media Group Ltd.
Editorial: 11 Wellington Street North, Saint Marys, Ontario N4X 1B7. **T:** 1 519 284-2440
E: editor@stmarys.com
W: http://www.stmarys.com **Circ:** 10400
Publisher & Editor: Laura Payton
NEWSPAPER

The St. Thomas/Elgin Weekly News
Owner: Metroland Media Group
Editorial: 15 St. Catharine Street, Saint Thomas, Ontario N5P 2V7. **T:** 1 519 633-1640
W: http://www.theweeklynews.ca **Circ:** 30565
Editor: Dorothy Gebert
Editorial Profile: St. Thomas/Elgin Weekly News is a local community newspaper for the residents of St. Thomas, Ontario and the surrounding communities.
NEWSPAPER

The Standard
Owner: Quebecor Communications Inc.
Editorial: 17 Queen St, St. Catharines, Ontario L2R 5G5. **T:** 1 905 684-7251
E: stcs.standard@sunmedia.ca
W: http://www.stcatharinesstandard.ca
Freq: Daily; **Circ:** 19623
City Editor: Monique Beech; **Editor in Chief:** Peter Conradi; **Publisher:** Mark Cressman
Editorial Profile: The Standard is a 40+ page newspaper written for residents of Niagara, Ontario. It is one of the premier newspapers in the area covering news, business and sports. Spectrum is a daily section including home, film, arts, lifestyles, weather and gardening coverage. The paper has won several honors such as the National Newspaper Award in 2000 for outstanding articles. The daily deadline is 6pm ET.; Full Page Mono: 0.95; Full Page Colour: 2.01
Currency: Canada Dollars
DAILY NEWSPAPER

Standard Freeholder
Owner: Quebecor Communications Inc.
Editorial: 1150 Montreal Rd, Cornwall, Ontario K6H 1E2. **T:** 1 613 933-3160
W: http://www.standard-freeholder.com
Freq: Daily; **Circ:** 13708
Publisher: Milton Ellis; **Publisher:** Pete Padbury
Editorial Profile: Standard Freeholder is a daily community newspaper serving Cornwall, ON and the surrounding area. The paper covers local news and events. Press releases can be sent to the assignment editor who will direct them to the appropriate reporter.; Full Page Mono: 15.68; Full Page Colour: 1.29
Currency: Canada Dollars
DAILY NEWSPAPER

Star News Ltd.
Owner: Star News Inc.
Editorial: 1027 3rd Ave, Wainwright, Alberta T9W 1P6. **T:** 1 780 842-4465
E: info@starnews.ca
W: http://www.starnews.ca **Circ:** 17918
Editor: Kelly Clemmer; **Publisher:** Roger Holmes
NEWSPAPER

The Star Phoenix
Owner: Postmedia Network Inc.
Editorial: 204 Fifth Ave North, Saskatoon, Saskatchewan S7K 2P1. **T:** 1 306 657-6397
E: citydesk@thestarphoenix.com
W: http://www.thestarphoenix.com
Freq: Daily; **Circ:** 44563
City Editor: Dave Hutton; **Publisher:** Marty Klyne
Editorial Profile: The Star Phoenix is written for the Saskatoon, Saskatchewan general public. It covers local, national and international news, including Aboriginal Canadian affairs.; Full Page Mono: 29.12; Full Page Colour: 118.56
Currency: Canada Dollars
DAILY NEWSPAPER

StarBuzz Weekly
Editorial: 1022 Zante Crescent, Mississauga, Ontario L5G 4M8. **T:** 1 647 802-2899
E: starbuzz.ca@gmail.com
W: http://www.starbuzz.ca
Freq: Weekly; **Circ:** 20000
Publisher: Meena Chopra; **Editor:** Tia Virdi
Editorial Profile: StarBuzz is a weekly publication that covers multicultural events, news, entertainment topics and gossip from Bollywood.; Full Page Mono: 22.66
Currency: Canada Dollars
NEWSPAPER

Stonewall Newspapers
Owner: Quebecor Communications Inc.
Editorial: 486 Main St, Stonewall, Manitoba R0C 2Z0. **T:** 1 204 467-2421 **Circ:** 34639
City Editor: Melissa Robbins
NEWSPAPER

Stouffville Free Press
Editorial: 6111 Main St, Stouffville, Ontario L4A 3R4. **T:** 1 905 640-3733
W: http://www.stouffvillefreepress.com/
Freq: Monthly; **Circ:** 11700
Editor in Chief: Kate Gilderdale
Editorial Profile: Stouffville Free Press is a free, monthly newspaper serving residents of Whitchurch-Stouffville, Ontario. It covers local news, human interest stories, sports, features and community events.; Full Page Mono: 9.82; Full Page Colour: 75.00
Currency: Canada Dollars
NEWSPAPER

Stratford Gazette
Owner: Metroland Media Group Ltd.
Editorial: 10 Downie St, Unit 106, Stratford, Ontario N5A 7K4. **T:** 1 519 271-8002
E: news@stratfordgazette.com
W: http://www.southwesternontario.ca/community/stratford-gazette **Circ:** 19000
Editor: Laura Payton
Editorial Profile: Stratford Gazette is a weekly newspaper serving the community of Stratford, Ontario. It covers local news, sports and entertainment.; Full Page Mono: 7.35
Currency: Canada Dollars
NEWSPAPER

Strathmore Times
Editorial: 202 114 Canal Garden, Strathmore, Alberta T1P 1Y4. **T:** 1 403 934-5589
E: info@strathmoretimes.com
W: http://www.strathmoretimes.com
Circ: 12500
Publisher & Editor: Mario Prusina
Editorial Profile: Strathmore Times is a community newspaper for the residents of Strathmore, Alberta and the surrounding areas.; Full Page Mono: 7.95; Full Page Colour: 9.45
Currency: US Dollars
NEWSPAPER

Streeter Publications
Owner: Streeter Publications
Editorial: 46 St. Clair Ave E Suite 204, Toronto, Ontario M4T 1M9. **T:** 1 416 901-8182
E: news@mytowncrier.ca
W: http://www.mytowncrier.ca **Circ:** 327242
City Editor: Dan Hoddinott
Editorial Profile: Streeter Publications is a community newspaper publisher servicing the residents of Toronto.
NEWSPAPER

Suburban Newspapers
Editorial: 7575 Trans-Canada Hwy, Ste 105, Saint Laurent, Quebec H4T 1V6.
T: 1 514 484-1107
E: editor@thesuburban.com
W: http://www.thesuburban.com **Circ:** 140000
Publisher: Michael Sochaczevski; **Editor in Chief:** Beryl Wajsman
NEWSPAPER

The Sudbury Star
Owner: Quebecor Communications Inc.
Editorial: 128 Pine St., Suite 201, Sudbury, Ontario P3C 1X3. **T:** 1 705 674-5271
W: http://www.thesudburystar.com
Freq: Daily; **Circ:** 15643
Editor: Brian MacLeod
Editorial Profile: The Sudbury Star is a daily newspaper written for the residents of Sudbury, Ontario and neighboring localities. The paper covers local-city events, activities, crime, courts, fires, government, politics and business, lifestyles, arts & entertainment and sports. There are also editorial columns, a community section dealing with events and topics of reader interest and a community events page which features an activities calendar. Additionally, non-daily sections are the Saturday issued TV listings, the bi-monthly Parenting supplement and the monthly items Vintage Times and the Real Estate Guide. On the weekend, the newspaper publishes a separate entertainment based publication entitled Weekend Alive. Launched in 1909, the publication, which is Northeastern Ontario's largest newspaper, covers Blind River, Sturgeon Falls, Gogama and Britt.; Full Page Mono: 12.60; Full Page Colour: 695.00
Currency: Canada Dollars
DAILY NEWSPAPER

The Sun Times
Owner: Quebecor Communications Inc.
Editorial: 290 Ninth St E, Owen Sound, Ontario N4K 5P2. **T:** 1 519 376-2250
W: http://www.owensoundsuntimes.com
Freq: Daily; **Circ:** 15049
Publisher: Cheryl McMenemy
Editorial Profile: The Sun Times is a daily newspaper serving residents of Owen Sound, Ontario. It covers national and regional news, sports, business and entertainment. Weekly sections are also devoted to automotive, lifestyles and health coverage. The lead time varies.; Full Page Mono: 9.66; Full Page Colour: 559.00
Currency: Canada Dollars
DAILY NEWSPAPER

Sunday Phoenix
Owner: Postmedia Network Inc.
Editorial: 204 5th Ave N, Saskatoon, Saskatchewan S7K 2P1. **T:** 1 306 657-6231
E: sun@thestarphoenix.com
W: http://www.thestarphoenix.com/index.html
Circ: 95100
Publisher: Marty Klyne
Editorial Profile: The Sunday Phoenix is a weekly community newspaper that is inserted and delivered to subscribers of the daily Star Phoenix.; Full Page Mono: 41.02; Full Page Colour: 49.02
Currency: Canada Dollars
NEWSPAPER

Sunday Post
Owner: Postmedia Network Inc.
Editorial: 1964 Park St, Regina, Saskatchewan S4P 3G4. **T:** 1 306 781-5211
E: citydesk@leaderpost.com
W: http://www.leaderpost.com **Circ:** 87000
Editor in Chief: Rob McLaughlin
Editorial Profile: Sunday Post is a tabloid sized, total market supplement, highlighting local topics and events within a 70 mile radius of Regina including Moose Jaw, Weyburn and Assiniboia. Deadlines are 4:30pm Tuesdays.; Full Page Mono: 35.70
Currency: Canada Dollars
NEWSPAPER

SundayXtra
Owner: FP Canadian Newspapers LP
Editorial: 1355 Mountain Ave, Winnipeg, Manitoba R2X 3B6. **T:** 1 204 697-7000
W: http://www.winnipegfreepress.com/on7
Circ: 25000
Publisher: Bob Cox
Editorial Profile: SundayXtra is a weekly tabloid that covers breaking news, sports and entertainment stories. It is published by the Winnipeg (Manitoba) Free Press and shares the same staff as the paper. It is not available via subscription and can only be found at retail outlets and news stands.; Full Page Mono: 13.59; Full Page Colour: 16.83
Currency: Canada Dollars
NEWSPAPER

Superior Monthly
Editorial: 49 Maple Valley St, Brampton, Ontario L6P 2E8. **T:** 1 905 794-4488
Freq: Bi-Weekly
Editor & Publisher: Saran Ghai
Editorial Profile: Superior Monthly is a bi-weekly publication that covers multicultural events and news for the Indian community in Brampton, Canada.
NEWSPAPER

The Surrey Leader
Owner: Black Press
Editorial: 200-5450 152nd St, Surrey, British Columbia V3S 5J9. **T:** 1 604 575-2744

E: newsroom@surreyleader.com
W: http://www.surreyleader.com Circ: 82573
Editor: Paula Carlson; **Publisher:** Jim Mihaly
Editorial Profile: The Surrey Leader is a weekly community newspaper serving the residents of Surrey, British Columbia.; Full Page Mono: 48.02; Full Page Colour: 32.13
Currency: Canada Dollars
NEWSPAPER

Suthanthiran
Editorial: 780 Ellesmere Rd, Scarborough, Ontario M1P 2W4. **T:** 1 416 840-9752
W: http://www.suthanthiran.com
Freq: Weekly
Editor: Gnanachelvan Chelliah
Editorial Profile: Suthanthiran is a weekly publication that covers multicultural events and news for the Indian community in Scarborough, Canada.
NEWSPAPER

Swadesh
Editorial: 713 Markham Road, Scarborough, Ontario M1H2A8. **T:** 1 416 996-7755
E: swadeshcanada@gmail.com
W: http://www.swadeshnewspaper.com
Freq: Weekly
Editor: Manoj Gandhi
Editorial Profile: Swadesh is a weekly publication that covers multicultural events and news for the Indian community in Canada. Swadesh also has an office in India.
NEWSPAPER

Sylvan Lake Newspapers
Owner: Alberta Newspaper Group Inc.
Editorial: 5020-50A St #103, Sylvan Lake, Alberta T4S 1R2. **T:** 1 403 887-2331
E: admin@sylvanlakenews.com
W: http://www.sylvanlakenews.com
Circ: 75295
Editor in Chief: Steve Dills; **Publisher:** Michele Rosenthal
NEWSPAPER

Take 5 Newsmagazine
Owner: 541806 BC LTD.
Editorial: 622 First Ave, Ladysmith, British Columbia V9G 1A1. **T:** 1 250 245-7015
E: info@take5.ca **W:** http://www.take5.ca
Freq: Monthly; **Circ:** 13500
Editorial Profile: Publication mailed directly to Central Vancouver Island community's homes.; Full Page Mono: 5.09; Full Page Colour: 79.00
Currency: Canada Dollars
NEWSPAPER

TC. Transcontinental - Abitibi
Owner: TC. Transcontinental
Editorial: 1834, 3ème Avenue, Bureau 200, Val-d'Or, Quebec J9P 7A9. **T:** 1 819 874-2151
W: http://www.abitibiexpress.ca
Freq: Weekly; **Circ:** 61152
Publisher: Michel Chalifour; **News Editor:** Louis Lavoie
Editorial Profile: Abitibi Express is published in two local versions, one serving Rouyn-Noranda, Quebec and western Abitibi, and another serving Val d'Or and Amos-Harricana, Quebec. The papers offer local news and information to residents.
NEWSPAPER

TC. Transcontinental - Dollard-des-Ormeaux
Owner: TC. Transcontinental
Editorial: 455 Fenelon Blvd., Ste. 303, Dorval, Quebec H9S 5T8. **T:** 1 514 685-4690
Circ: 91917
NEWSPAPER

TC. Transcontinental - Joliette
Owner: TC. Transcontinental
Editorial: 342 rue Beaudry St. Nord, Joliette, Quebec J6E 6A6. **T:** 1 450 759-3664
E: infolanaudiere@transcontinental.ca
W: http://www.laction.com Circ: 125250
Publisher: Benoît Bazinet; **News Editor:** Francine Rainville
NEWSPAPER

TC. Transcontinental - Lasalle/Lachine
Owner: TC. Transcontinental
Editorial: 418 rue Lafleur, Lasalle, Quebec H8R 3H6. **T:** 1 514 363-5656 Circ: 129317
Publisher: Patricia-Ann Beaulieu; **Editor in Chief:** Pierre Boulanger; **Editor in Chief:** Andre Desrodies; **Editor in Chief:** Robert Leduc; **Publisher:** Tina Lemelin
NEWSPAPER

TC. Transcontinental - Ottawa
Owner: TC. Transcontinental

Editorial: 5300 Canotek Road, Unit 30, Ottawa, Ontario K1J 8R7. **T:** 1 613 744-4800
E: redaction.ontario@transcontinental.ca
W: http://www.eastottawa.ca
Freq: Weekly; **Circ:** 108096
Editor & Publisher: Madeleine Joanisse
NEWSPAPER

TC. Transcontinental - Quebec City
Owner: TC. Transcontinental
Editorial: 1265 boul Charest Ouest, Bureau 900, Quebec, Quebec G1N 4V4.
T: 1 418 686-6400
E: Redaction_quebec@transcontinental.ca
W: http://www.quebechebdo.com
Freq: Weekly; **Circ:** 209232
Editor in Chief: Francois Cattapan; **Publisher:** Lilianne Laprise; **News Editor:** Alain Lepage; **News Editor:** Andrée-Anne Trudel
Editorial Profile: Transcontinental publishes French-language weeklies that cover local news for residents in Quebec City and surrounding communities.
NEWSPAPER

TC. Transcontinental - Saint-Laurent
Owner: TC. Transcontinental
Editorial: 1500, boulevard Jules-Poitras, Bureau 203, Saint-Laurent, Quebec H4N 1X7. **T:** 1 514 855-1292 Circ: 81183
Publisher: Alain De Choinière; **Editor in Chief:** Véronique Leduc; **Editor in Chief:** Sylvain Sarrazin
NEWSPAPER

TC. Transcontinental - St-Jean-sur-Richelieu
Owner: TC. Transcontinental
Editorial: 84 rue Richelieu, St-Jean-sur-Richelieu, Quebec J3B 6X3. **T:** 1 450 347-0323
W: http://canadafrancais.com Circ: 57475
Editor in Chief: Gilles Lévesque
NEWSPAPER

TC. Transcontinental - St-Léonard
Owner: TC. Transcontinental
Editorial: 8770, boul. Langelier, Bureau 210, St-Leonard, Quebec H1P 3C6.
T: 1 514 899-5888
W: http://www.leshebdos.com Circ: 362185
News Editor: Julie Charette; **Editor in Chief:** Marie-Josée Chouinard; **Publisher:** Lucie Lecours
NEWSPAPER

The Telegram
Owner: TC. Transcontinental
Editorial: 430 Topsail Rd., St. John's, Newfoundland A1E 4N1. **T:** 1 709 364-2323
E: telegram@thetelegram.com
W: http://www.thetelegram.com
Freq: Daily; **Circ:** 27412
News Editor: Mark Vaughn Jackson
Editorial Profile: The Telegram is a daily newspaper written for the Saint John's, Newfoundland general public. It covers local and national news, business, sports and lifestyles. Deadlines are daily at 6pm AT.; Full Page Mono: 19.60; Full Page Colour: 877.00
Currency: Canada Dollars
DAILY NEWSPAPER

Telegraph-Journal
Owner: New Brunswick Publishing Company
Editorial: 210 Crown St, Saint John, New Brunswick E2L 2X7. **T:** 1 506 632-8888
E: newsroom@telegraphjournal.com
W: http://promos.telegraphjournal.com/99c
Freq: Daily; **Circ:** 28043
Courts Editor: Mike Mullen; **Editor in Chief:** John Wishart
Editorial Profile: Telegraph-Journal is the highest circulation daily newspaper in New Brunswick. Based in Saint John, New Brunswick's largest city, the paper is distributed throughout the province. The paper places a special emphasis on provincial and national politics, Atlantic Canadian business news and strong analysis, commentary and opinion. It also provides in-depth coverage of the city and its surrounding region, including its burgeoning arts and sports scenes. The Reader, our Saturday supplement, highlights New Brunswickers' stories in feature pieces and personal commentaries.; Full Page Mono: 3.47; Full Page Colour: 1613.00
Currency: Canada Dollars
DAILY NEWSPAPER

Temiskaming Speaker Newspapers
Owner: Temiskaming Printing Company Ltd.
Editorial: 18 Wellington St, New Liskeard, Ontario P0J 1P0. **T:** 1 705 647-6791
W: http://www.speaker.northernontario.ca
Freq: Weekly; **Circ:** 15364
Publisher: David Armstrong; **Editor in Chief:** Gordon Brock

Editorial Profile: Temiskaming Speaker Newspapers is a community newspaper publisher servicing the residents of northern Ontario.
NEWSPAPER

This Week Newspapers
Owner: Metroland Media Group Ltd.
Editorial: 865 Farewell St, Oshawa, Ontario L1H 7L5. **T:** 1 905 579-4400
E: newsroom@durhamregion.com
W: http://www.durhamregion.com
Circ: 107250
Editor In Chief: Joanne Burghardt; **Editor In Chief:** Joanne Burghardt; **News Editor:** Ian McMillan; **News Editor:** Ian McMillan; **News Editor:** Ian McMillan; **Publisher:** Tim Whittaker
NEWSPAPER

Thoi Bao
Owner: Thoi Bao Inc.
Editorial: 1114 College Street, Toronto, Ontario M6H 1B6. **T:** 1 416 925-8607
E: mails@thoibao.com
W: http://www.thoibao.com Circ: 14500
Editorial Profile: Thoi Bao is a community newspaper for the Vietnamese community in Toronto. It features Vietnamese news, stories, poems and entertainment.; Full Page Mono: 8.09
Currency: Canada Dollars
NEWSPAPER

Thunder Bay's Source
Owner: Dougall Media
Editorial: 87 N Hill St, Thunder Bay, Ontario P7A 5V6. **T:** 1 807 346-2600
W: http://www.tbnewswatch.com Circ: 44500
Editorial Profile: Thunder Bay's Source covers local news, sports and entertainment. Materials must be received by 5pm ET on Monday.; Full Page Mono: 20.86
Currency: Canada Dollars
NEWSPAPER

The Tillsonburg Newspapers
Owner: Quebecor Communications Inc.
Editorial: 25 Townline Road, Tillsonburg, Ontario. **T:** 1 519 688-6397
E: tilledit@bowesnet.com
W: http://www.tillsonburgnews.com
Freq: 3 Times/Week; **Circ:** 14655
Publisher: Ken Koyama; **Editor:** Kim Novak; **Editor:** Kim Novak; **Editor:** Kim Novak; **Editor:** Kim Novak
NEWSPAPER

Times Colonist
Owner: Glacier Media Inc.
Editorial: 2621 Douglas St, Victoria, British Columbia V8T 4M2. **T:** 1 250 380-5211
E: localnews@timescolonist.com
W: http://www.timescolonist.com
Freq: Daily; **Circ:** 52017
Editor in Chief: Dave Obee
Editorial Profile: Times Colonist is a daily newspaper written for the Victoria, British Columbia general public. It covers local, regional and national news, as well as business, entertainment, health, travel and sports. It is the oldest newspaper in Western Canada.; Full Page Mono: 3.51; Full Page Colour: 58.13
Currency: Canada Dollars
DAILY NEWSPAPER

The Times Reformer
Owner: Quebecor Communications Inc.
Editorial: 50 Gilbertson Dr., Simcoe, Ontario N3Y 4L2. **T:** 1 519 426-5710
E: refedit@bowesnet.com
W: http://www.simcoereformer.ca Circ: 20000
Editorial Profile: The Times Reformer is a weekly newspaper written for the residents of Simcoe, Ontario.; Full Page Mono: 8.40; Full Page Colour: 612.00
Currency: Canada Dollars
NEWSPAPER

Timmins Times
Owner: Quebecor Communications Inc.
Editorial: 815 Pine St. South, Timmins, Ontario P4N 8S3. **T:** 1 705 268-6252
E: times@timminstimes.com
W: http://www.timminstimes.com
Freq: Weekly; **Circ:** 16478
Editor: Len Gillis; **Publisher:** Wayne Major
Editorial Profile: Timmins Times is an English, weekly newspaper covering local news and information for Timmins, Ontario and its environs.; Full Page Mono: 17.36
Currency: Canada Dollars
NEWSPAPER

Today Commercial News
Editorial: 705 Progress Avenue, Units 41 & 42, Toronto, Ontario M1H 2X1.

T: 1 647 348-8178
E: editorial@todaycommercialnews.com
W: http://www.todaycommercialnews.com
Circ: 20000
Editor: Robert Leung; **Publisher:** Herbert Moon
Editorial Profile: Previously titled Today 701 Magazine. Written for the Chinese residents of Scarborough, Ontario and the surrounding communities. It is published every Saturday.; Full Page Mono: 4.90; Full Page Colour: 7.40
Currency: US Dollars
DAILY NEWSPAPER

tonight
Owner: Annex Business Media
Editorial: 222 Edward St, Aurora, Ontario L4G 1W6. **T:** 1 647 344-1833
E: info@tonightnewspaper.com
W: http://tonightnews.ca Circ: 70000
Editor: Nisean Lorde
Editorial Profile: tonight is a free, commuter weekly with late afternoon distribution throughout Toronto's downtown core on Thursday. It offers local news and events, with content pulled from newswires and local bloggers and columnists. It also offers a branded Financial Post business section as of November 2011 to go with its other news coverage. The paper launched in September 2009.; Full Page Mono: 40.39; Full Page Colour: 40.39
Currency: Canada Dollars
NEWSPAPER

Toronto Star
Owner: Star Media Group
Editorial: 1 Yonge St, Toronto, Ontario M5E 1E5-. **T:** 1 416 367-2000 **E:** city@thestar.ca
W: http://www.thestar.com
Freq: Daily; **Circ:** 361323
Editor In Chief: Michael Cooke; **Publisher:** John Cruickshank; **City Editor:** Irene Gentle; **Editor:** Andrew Phillips
Editorial Profile: The Toronto Star, established in 1892 and distributed mostly in Ontario, is Canada's highest circulation newspaper. Published seven days a week, this broadsheet newspaper offers provincial, national and international news, as well as opinion columns and editorials, entertainment news, municipal news, sports, business and financial news and trends and more. Optional weekend sections include Starweek, a Saturday TV listings supplement, and on Sundays an abridged version of The New York Times' international section, editorials and book reviews. The paper is a member of the Canadian Press Gallery.; Full Page Mono: 461.87; Full Page Colour: 563.78
Currency: Canada Dollars
DAILY NEWSPAPER

The Toronto Sun
Owner: Quebecor Communications Inc.
Editorial: 333 King St E, Toronto, Ontario M5A 3X5. **T:** 1 416 947-2222
W: http://www.torontosun.com
Freq: Daily; **Circ:** 186904
City Editor: Jonathan Kingstone; **Editor in Chief:** Wendy Metcalfe; **Publisher:** Mike Power
Editorial Profile: The Toronto Sun is written for readers in the greater Toronto area. The publication is also available in Kingston, Windsor, Sault St. Marie and Niagara, Ontario. It centers on Toronto in its reporting. Specific daily sections include: News, which has a national, but mainly local angle; Entertainment; Lifestyles, including such topics as relationships, health, restaurants and nightlife; Money, is the business and finance section with columns and articles on products, trends, personal finance and the economy; and Sports, covering local and national sporting events and athletes. Editors honor non-disclosure agreements. The publication is a member of the Canadian Press Gallery.; Full Page Mono: 54.88; Full Page Colour: 339.64
Currency: Canada Dollars
DAILY NEWSPAPER

Torstar Publications
Owner: Metroland Media Group Ltd.
Editorial: 185 Wallace Ave N, Listowel, Ontario N4W 1K8. **T:** 1 519 291-1660
E: editor@northperth.com
W: http://www.northperth.com Circ: 24108
Editor in Chief: Shanna Burrows
NEWSPAPER

Tour of Duty
T: 1 902 468-5141
E: tourofdutynews@gmail.com
Freq: Bi-Monthly; **Circ:** 18000
Editor: William Harris
Editorial Profile: Tour of Duty is local newspaper for active duty military personnel,

veterans and their families.; Full Page Mono: 12.39
Currency: Canada Dollars
NEWSPAPER

Tout Express
Owner: TC. Transcontinental
Editorial: 222 rue St-Ignace, La Prairie, Quebec J5R 1E5. **T:** 1 450 659-6515
E: info@toutmagazine.com
W: http://www.letoutexpress.ca/
Freq: Weekly; **Circ:** 47966
Editor & Publisher: Annie-Julie Ste-Marie
Editorial Profile: Tout Express is a free weekly community newspaper serving the residents of La Prairie, Brossard, Candiac, Saint-Philippe, Saint-Constant, and Saint-Luc. Topics covered include News, Sports, Culture, Economy and Opinion. It is released on Wednesdays.; Full Page Mono: 30.00
Currency: Canada Dollars
NEWSPAPER

Town & Country
Owner: Great West Newspapers LP
Editorial: 9871 - 107 Street, Westlock, Alberta T7P 1R9. **T:** 1 780 349-3033
E: production@westlock.greatwest.ca
Circ: 16800
Editor in Chief: Kevin Berger; **Publisher:** George Blais
Editorial Profile: Town & Country provides news and information to the residents of Westlock, Alberta.; Full Page Mono: 11.90
Currency: Canada Dollars
NEWSPAPER

Le Trait D'Union
Owner: TC. Transcontinental
Editorial: 1300 Grande Allee, Bureau 210, Terrebonne, Quebec J6W 4M4.
T: 1 450 964-4400
W: http://www.letraitdunion.com **Circ:** 55500
Editorial Profile: Le Trait d'Union is a weekly French-language newspaper that covers local and regional information in and around Lachenaie, Quebec.; Full Page Mono: 20.00
Currency: Canada Dollars
NEWSPAPER

Tremblant Express
Editorial: 2046-2 Chemin du Village, Mont-Tremblant, Quebec J8E 1K4.
T: 1 819 425-7875
W: http://www.tremblantexpress.com
Freq: Monthly; **Circ:** 35000
Editor: Denis Primeau
Editorial Profile: Tremblant Express is a monthly newspaper providing Local and Commnunity News coverage for Mont-Tremblant, QC.
NEWSPAPER

The Tribune
Owner: Quebecor Communications Inc.
Editorial: 228 E Main St, Welland, Ontario L3B 5P5. **T:** 1 905 732-2411
W: http://www.wellandtribune.ca
Freq: Daily; **Circ:** 13164
Publisher: John Tobon
Editorial Profile: The Tribune is a daily newspaper published for the Welland and Port Colborne, Ontario communities. The publication reports local news, sports and business.; Full Page Mono: 17.08; Full Page Colour: 657.00
Currency: Canada Dollars
DAILY NEWSPAPER

La Tribune
Owner: Power Corporation of Canada
Editorial: 1950 Rue Roy, Sherbrooke, Quebec J1K 2X8. **T:** 1 819 564-5450
E: redaction@latribune.qc.ca
W: http://www.lapresse.ca/la-tribune
Freq: Daily; **Circ:** 31167
News Editor: Louis-Éric Allard; **News Editor:** Louis-Éric Allard; **News Editor:** Louis-Éric Allard; **Publisher:** Louise Boisvert; **Editor In Chief:** Maurice Cloutier
Editorial Profile: La Tribune is a daily French-language newspaper with strong coverage of local and regional news in Quebec's Eastern Townships. In addition to local information, La Tribune includes national and international news, obtained primarily from news wires.; Full Page Mono: 10.96; Full Page Colour: 931.80
Currency: Canada Dollars
DAILY NEWSPAPER

Tri-City News
Owner: Black Press
Editorial: 1405 Broadway St, Port Coquitlam, British Columbia V3C 6L6. **T:** 1 604 525-6397
W: http://www.tricitynews.com **Circ:** 52324
Editor in Chief: Richard Dal Monte; **Publisher:**

Nigel Lark
Editorial Profile: Tri-City News is written for the tri-city area of Coquitlam Port, Port Moody, Anmore and Belcarra, British Columbia.; Full Page Mono: 17.15; Full Page Colour: 775.00
Currency: Canada Dollars
NEWSPAPER

Trident
Owner: Department of National Defense
Editorial: 2740 Barrington St, Halifax, Nova Scotia B3K 5X5. **T:** 1 902 427-4235
E: accounts@tridentnews.ca
W: http://www.tridentnews.ca
Freq: Bi-Weekly; **Circ:** 10000
Editor: Virginia Beaton
Editorial Profile: Trident is a bi-weekly publication covering news and issues of interest to the Canadian Navy's East Coast fleet based in Halifax, Nova Scotia. It includes articles and columns from both military and civilian members.; Full Page Mono: 16.10
Currency: Canada Dollars
NEWSPAPER

True Buddha News
Owner: True Buddha School
Editorial: 200-357 Hastings St., Vancouver, British Columbia V6A 1P3. **T:** 1 604 685-5548
E: tbnnews@gmail.com
W: http://www.wtbn.org **Circ:** 10000
Editor: Marvin Lu; **Publisher:** M.J. Pai
Editorial Profile: True Buddha News covers current news including local and international. Features Buddhism Dharma teachings.; Full Page Mono: 45.00
Currency: Canada Dollars
NEWSPAPER

Turtle Island News
Owner: Turtle Island News Pub.
Editorial: 2208 Chiefwoods Road, Ohsweken, Ontario N0A 1M0. **T:** 1 519 445-0868
E: news@theturtleislandnews.com
W: http://www.theturtleislandnews.com
Circ: 10000
Publisher & Editor: Lynda Powless
Editorial Profile: Turtle Island News is a community newspaper written for the residents of Ohsweken, Ontario. The paper covers politics, local news, sports, national native news featuring aboriginal headlines from across Canada and a classified section. Deadlines are on Fridays at 5pm ET.; Full Page Mono: 2.12
Currency: Canada Dollars
NEWSPAPER

Two Row Times
Editorial: c/o Garlow Print & Copy, 657 Mohawk Road, Hagersville, Ontario.
T: 519 900 5535 **E:** tworowtimes@gmail.com
W: http://tworowtimes.com
Freq: Weekly; **Circ:** 20000
Publisher: Jonathan Garlow; **Editor in Chief:** Tom Keefer
Editorial Profile: The Two Row Times is a weekly print news publication distributed throughout Ontario, Quebec and New York State.; Full Page Mono: 9.67; Full Page Colour: 12.57
Currency: Canada Dollars
NEWSPAPER

Ulahathamilar
Owner: World Tamil Movement of Ont.
Editorial: 39 Cosentino Drive, Toronto, Ontario M1P 3A3. **T:** 1 416 461-5991
E: editor@worldtamils.com
W: http://www.worldtamils.com **Circ:** 30000
Publisher & Editor: Kamal Nava; **Full Page Mono:** 15.00
Currency: Canada Dollars
NEWSPAPER

Urdu Post
Editorial: 100 Matheson Blvd E, Mississauga, Ontario L4Z 2G7 **E:** canurdu@gmail.com
W: http://www.urdupost.info
Freq: Weekly; **Circ:** 22000
Editor-in-Chief: Fayyaz Walana; **Editor-in-Chief:** Fayyaz Walana
Editorial Profile: Urdu Post is a -weekly publication that covers multicultural events and news for the Indian community in Mississauga, Canada.; Full Page Mono: 44.44
Currency: Canada Dollars
NEWSPAPER

Urdu Times Canada
Editorial: 1310 Mid-way blvd, Unit #28, Mississauga, Ontario L5T 2K5.
T: 1 905 673-7111
E: urdutimes@gondalbrothers.com
W: http://www.urdutimescanada.com

Freq: Weekly; **Circ:** 18000
Editor: Mohammad Azam Gondal
Editorial Profile: Urdu Times Canada is a weekly publication that covers multicultural events and news for the South Asian community in Mississauga, Canada.; Full Page Mono: 8.82
Currency: Canada Dollars
NEWSPAPER

Uxbridge Times-Journal
Owner: Metroland Media Group Ltd.
Editorial: 16 Bascom St, Uxbridge, Ontario L9P 1J3. **T:** 1 905 852-9141
W: http://www.durhamregion.com **Circ:** 10500
Distribution Supervisor: Debbie Amundson;
Editor: Joanne Burghardt; **Publisher:** Tim Whittaker
Editorial Profile: Uxbridge Times-Journal is a community newspaper for the residents of Uxbridge, Ontario. It covers local news, sports, entertainment and community events.; Full Page Mono: 8.40
Currency: Canada Dollars
NEWSPAPER

Vallée-du-Richelieu Express.ca
Owner: TC. Transcontinental
Editorial: 430, boul. Sir-Wilfrid-Laurier, local 200, Mont-Saint-Hilaire, Quebec J3H 3N9.
T: 1 450 467-4666
E: valleedurichelieu@transcontinental.ca
W: http://www.valleedurichelieuexpress.ca
Freq: Weekly; **Circ:** 35707
Publisher & Editor: Lucie Lecours
Editorial Profile: The Vallée-du-Richelieu Express.ca offers local news and information in French to residents of the Quebec towns of Belœil, Mont-Saint-Hilaire, Otterburn Park, Saint-Basile-le-Grand, McMasterville, Sainte-Madeleine, Saint-Charles-sur-Richelieu and Saint-Marc-sur-Richelieu.; Full Page Mono: 8.89
Currency: Canada Dollars
NEWSPAPER

The Valley Gazette
Owner: Lavigne (Michel)
Editorial: 19380 Opeongo Line, Barry's Bay, Ontario K0J 1B0. **T:** 1 613 756-0256
W: http://valleygazette.ca/
Freq: Weekly
Editor: Gregory Zawidzki
Editorial Profile: The Valley Gazette is a weekly community newspaper serving the residents of Whitney, Pembroke, Barry's Bay, and Bancroft in Ontario, Canada. It covers local and regional news, sports, events and opinion. The publication began printing in May 2010.
NEWSPAPER

Valleyfield Express.ca
Owner: TC. Trancontinental
Editorial: 69 boul. St-Jean-Baptiste, 2e étage, Chateauguay, Quebec J6J 3H6.
T: 1 450 692-9111
W: http://www.valleyfieldexpress.ca/
Freq: Weekly; **Circ:** 39062
News Editor: Josianne Desjardins; **Publisher:** Julie Voyer
Editorial Profile: The Valleyfield Express.ca is a free weekly community newspaper serving the residents of Salaberry-de-Valleyfield, Grande-île, Saint-Thimothée, Notre-Dame-du-Sourire, Ormstown, Sainte-Barbe, Saint-Stanislas-de-Kostka, Saint-Louis-de-Gonzague, Cazaville, Saint-Anicet, Sainte-Agnès-de-Dundee, Huntingdon, Athelstan, Dewittville, Godmanchester, Hinchinbrook, Melocheville, Coteau-du-Lac, Saint-Zotique, Saint-Clet, Rivière-Beaudette, Saint-Polycarpe, Les Cèdres and Les Coteaux. Topics covered include News, Sports, Society, Culture, Finance, and Opinon. It is released on Thursday.; Full Page Mono: 9.71
Currency: Canada Dollars
NEWSPAPER

Vancouver Chinese News
Owner: Chinese News Ltd.
Editorial: 1296 Kingsway, Vancouver, British Columbia V5V 3E1. **T:** 1 604 872-6968
E: vancouverchinesenews@yahoo.ca
Freq: Weekly; **Circ:** 50000
Editor & Publisher: Shing Pao; **Editor & Publisher:** Shing Pao
NEWSPAPER

The Vancouver Courier
Owner: Glacier Media Inc.
Editorial: 1574 W 6th Ave, Vancouver, British Columbia V6J 1R2. **T:** 1 604 738-1411
E: releases@vancourier.com
W: http://www.vancourier.com **Circ:** 126000
Publisher: Dee Dhaliwal; **Editor:** Barry Link;
Editor: Barry Link

Editorial Profile: The Vancouver Courier is a twice-weekly, standard sized newspaper for the residents of Vancouver, British Columbia. The publication concentrates specifically on local news and public affairs. The main sections are Local News, Opinions, Entertainment (with a strong focus on theater), Dining - which is mainly local restaurant reviews and Sports. The Vancouver Courier is published in separate editions on Wednesdays and Fridays: one edition is for residents of Eastern Vancouver, and one edition is for residents of Western Vancouver. A downtown edition appears on Friday. The paper's reporters and editors have individually won numerous local and national journalism awards. Cumulatively, the publication has received two awards for best British Columbia Community newspaper.; Full Page Mono: 19.67
Currency: Canada Dollars
NEWSPAPER

Vancouver Express
Owner: Alexander Kulyashov
Editorial: 260 Terminal Ave, Vancouver, British Columbia V6A 2L4. **T:** 1 604 729-3590
E: vancouverexpress@shaw.ca
W: http://www.vancouverexpress.ca
Freq: Bi-Monthly
Publisher & Editor: Alexander Kulyashov
Editorial Profile: A Russian language newspaper.
NEWSPAPER

The Vancouver Sun
Owner: Postmedia Network Inc.
Editorial: 1-200 Granville St 1, Vancouver, British Columbia V6C 3N3-. **T:** 1 604 605-2000
E: sunnewstips@vancouversun.com
W: http://www.vancouversun.com
Freq: Daily; **Circ:** 153202
Publisher: Gordon Fisher; **Editor in Chief:** Harold Munro; **News Editor:** Stephen Snelgrove; **City Editor:** Bev Wake
Editorial Profile: The Vancouver Sun, established in 1886, is a broadsheet newspaper containing news, business, arts & entertainment, dining, events and sports. It shares offices with The Province but maintains a separate newsroom.; Full Page Mono: 75.32; Full Page Colour: 402.63
Currency: Canada Dollars
DAILY NEWSPAPER

Vaughan Citizen
Owner: Metroland Media Group Ltd.
Editorial: 8611 Weston Rd Unit 29, Vaughan, Ontario L4L 9P1. **T:** 1 905 264-8703
W: http://www.vaughancitizen.com **Circ:** 53000
Editor: Kim Champion; **Publisher:** Ian Proudfoot
Editorial Profile: Vaughan Citizen is a community newspaper published once a week for the residents of Vaughan, Ontario. It covers local news, sports, entertainment and community events.; Full Page Mono: 24.26
Currency: Canada Dollars
NEWSPAPER

Vegreville News Advertiser
Owner: Vegreville News Advertiser Ltd.
Editorial: 5110-50 St, Vegreville, Alberta T9C 1R9. **T:** 1 780 632-2861
E: editor@newsadvertiser.com
W: http://www.newsadvertiser.com
Circ: 11717
Publisher & Editor: Dan Beaudette
Editorial Profile: Vegreville News Advertiser is a weekly newspaper for the residents of Vegreville, Alberta.; Full Page Mono: 12.74
Currency: Canada Dollars
NEWSPAPER

Victoria News
Owner: Black Press
Editorial: 818 Broughton St, Victoria, British Columbia V8W 1E4-. **T:** 1 250 381-3484
W: http://www.vicnews.com **Circ:** 23884
Editor: Don Descoteau; **Editor:** Don Descoteau; **Publisher:** Penny Sakamoto
Editorial Profile: Victoria News is a comprehensive source for Victoria, British Columbia local news, community events and issues. The paper covers breaking news, provincial issues and the law, local sports, classified ads, entertainment and obituaries.; Full Page Mono: 23.94
Currency: Canada Dollars
NEWSPAPER

VISTAS
Editorial: 312 Cunningham Avenue, Ottawa, Ontario K1H 6B4. **T:** 1 613 737-3835
E: ctower@sympatico.ca
Freq: Monthly; **Circ:** 12000
Editor in Chief: Celine Tower

Editorial Profile: Vistas is a local newspaper written for the residents of Ottawa.; Full Page Mono: 5.11
Currency: Canada Dollars
NEWSPAPER

The Voice

Owner: The Voice
Editorial: 26 Erindale Ave, Toronto, Ontario M4K 1R9. **T:** 1 647 838-2126
Freq: Monthly; **Circ:** 28000
Publisher & Editor: Colin Grant
Editorial Profile: The Voice is written for the residents of the East Downtown and West Riverdale neighborhoods of Toronto. It covers local news and events. Deadlines for contributions are on the 25th of each month prior to issue date.; Full Page Mono: 21.98
Currency: Canada Dollars
NEWSPAPER

Voice

Owner: Voice Portuguese Canadian Newspaper Publishing Inc.
Editorial: 1278 Dundas Street West, Toronto, Ontario M6J 3X7. **T:** 1 416 538-1788
E: voice@voicenews.ca
W: http://www.voicenews.ca **Circ:** 10000
Editor in Chief: Vasco Evaristo; **Editor in Chief:** Vasco Evaristo
Editorial Profile: Voice is a weekly community newpaper focusing on Canadian Portuguese, Brazilian and community news. The paper also has a Portuguese sports section.; Full Page Mono: 10.52; Full Page Colour: 450.00
Currency: Canada Dollars
NEWSPAPER

Voice Group of Publications

Owner: Indo-Canadian Voice Communications LTD.
Editorial: 102-9360 120 St 102, Surrey, British Columbia V3V 4B9. **T:** 1 604 502-6100
E: newsdesk@voiceonline.com
W: http://www.voiceonline.com
Freq: Weekly
Editor: Rattan Mall
Editorial Profile: Canada's Largest Group of Indo-Canadian publications catering to the South Asian population with an emphasis on those residing in British Columbia.
NEWSPAPER

La Voix

Owner: Quebecor Communications Inc.
Editorial: 58, rue Charlotte, Sorel-Tracy, Quebec J3P 1G3. **T:** 1 450 743-8466
E: redaction@journallavoix.net
W: http://www.journallavoix.net **Circ:** 29217
Publisher: Johanne Berthiaume; **Editor In Chief:** Nycolas Duboys
Editorial Profile: La Voix is a weekly newspaper covering local news for residents of Sorel-Tracy, Quebec and the surrounding area.; Full Page Mono: 166.60
Currency: Canada Dollars
NEWSPAPER

La Voix de l'Est

Owner: Power Corporation of Canada
Editorial: 76 Rue Dufferin, Granby, Quebec J2G 9L4. **T:** 1 450 375-4555
E: redaction@lavoixdelest.ca
W: http://www.cyberpresse.ca/la-voix-de-lest
Freq: Daily; **Circ:** 14660
Editor in Chief: François Beaudoin; **Le Plus Editor:** Isabelle Gaboriault; **News Editor:** Marc Gendron; **Editor in Chief:** Marie-France Létourneau
Editorial Profile: La Voix de l'Est is a daily French-language publication. It covers news and information pertaining to the municipalities of Ange-Gardien, Bromont, Cowansville, East Farnham, Granby, Roxton Pond, Roxton Falls, Saint-Alphonse, Saint-Césaire, Saint-Joachim-de-Shefford, Saint-Paul-d'Abbotsford, Sainte-Anne-de-la-Rochelle, and Sainte-Cécile-de-Milton, Quebec. Contact the publication by phone, fax, e-mail, or mail.; Full Page Mono: 10.67; Full Page Colour: 42.56
Currency: Canada Dollars
DAILY NEWSPAPER

La Voix Du Sud

Owner: TC. Transcontinental
Editorial: 1516 A Route 277, Lac-Etchemin, Quebec G0R 1S0. **T:** 1 418 625-7471
E: redaction_lacetchemin@transcontinental.ca
W: http://www.lavoixdusud.com **Circ:** 28787
Editorial Profile: La Voix du Sud is a weekly French-language paper serving residents in and around Lac-Etchemin, Quebec with regional news.; Full Page Mono: 6.86
Currency: Canada Dollars
NEWSPAPER

La Voz De Montreal

Editorial: 6225 Northcrest Place, Suite 112, Montreal, Quebec H3S 2T5. **T:** 1 514 253-2739
E: lavoz@videotron.ca **W:** http://www.lavoz.ca
Freq: Bi-Weekly; **Circ:** 20000
Editor: Gilberto Miranda
Editorial Profile: La Voz De Montreal is a Spanish-language publication distributed in Montreal, Quebec and in other provinces of Canada. It offers the Hispanic community a wide variety of local, national and international articles, chronicles and reports on current topics of interest. The paper is published the second and fourth Wednesday of the month.; Full Page Mono: 8.93
Currency: Canada Dollars
NEWSPAPER

A Voz de Portugal/Voice of Portugal

Editorial: 4231 St-Laurent Blvd, Montreal, Quebec H2W 1Z4. **T:** 1 514 284-1813
E: jornal@avozdeportugal.com
W: http://www.avozdeportugal.com
Circ: 10000
Publisher & Editor: Eduino Martins; **Editor in Chief:** Sylvio Martins
Editorial Profile: A Voz de Portugal is a weekly newspaper written in Portuguese for the Portuguese community in Francophone Canada.; Full Page Mono: 17.28; Full Page Colour: 328.12
Currency: Canada Dollars
NEWSPAPER

The Wall Street Journal (Canada)

Editorial: 145 King St W Suite 730, Toronto, Ontario M5H 1J8. **T:** 1 416 306-2100
DAILY NEWSPAPER

Waterloo Chronicle

Owner: Metroland Media Group Ltd.
Editorial: 279 Weber St, Unit 20, Waterloo, Ontario N2J 3H8. **T:** 1 519 886-2830
W: http://www.waterloochronicle.ca
Circ: 32000
Publisher: Peter Winkler
Editorial Profile: Waterloo Chronicle's editorial mission is, "To provide community news to the residents of Waterloo." Deadlines for the publication are Monday at 9am ET before the issue date.; Full Page Mono: 7.00
Currency: Canada Dollars
NEWSPAPER

Waterloo Region Record

Owner: Metroland Media Group Ltd.
Editorial: 160 King St E, Kitchener, Ontario N2G 4E5. **T:** 1 519 894-2231
W: http://www.therecord.com
Freq: Daily; **Circ:** 63386
News Editor: Neil Ballantyne; **Editor in Chief:** Lynn Haddrall; **Publisher:** Paul McCuaig
Editorial Profile: Waterloo Region Record is a 40+ page broadsheet newspaper written for the residents of Kitchener, Ontario and surrounding communities. It is one of the major newspapers in the region covering business, sports and entertainment. The weekend edition has an expanded entertainment section including event listings and extra entertainment, food, and health coverage.; Full Page Mono: 98.00; Full Page Colour: 56.11
Currency: Canada Dollars
DAILY NEWSPAPER

Al Wattan

Owner: GQ Multimedia
Editorial: 5004 Timberlea Blvd. Suite 201, Mississauga, Ontario L4W 2C5.
T: 1 905 232-8610 **E:** info@gqmultimedia.com
W: http://gqmultimedia.com
Freq: Bi-Weekly
Editor: Jamal Al-Qaryouti
Editorial Profile: Al Wattan is a bi-weekly newspaper that provides Local and Community News coverage to the Arabic-speaking community in the Greater Toronto area.
NEWSPAPER

The Weekender

Editorial: 211 Watline Ave Unite 210, 211, Mississauga, Ontario L4Z 1P3.
T: 1 905 568-9696
W: http://www.updateweekly.com
Freq: Weekly; **Circ:** 25000
Editor: Usha Pudukkotai
Editorial Profile: The Weekender is a weekly publication that covers multicultural events and news for the South Asian community in Brampton, Canada.; Full Page Mono: 4.05
Currency: Canada Dollars
NEWSPAPER

Weekly Awam

Editorial: 28-1310 Mid-way Blvd., Mississauga, Ontario L5T 2K5.
T: 1 905 673-7115
E: weeklyawam@gondalbrothers.com
W: http://www.awam.ca
Freq: Weekly; **Circ:** 18000
Publisher and Editor: M. Nawaf Gondal; Full Page Mono: 4.05
Currency: Canada Dollars
NEWSPAPER

Weekly Jogajog

Editorial: 2505 11th Ave Suite 106, Regina, Saskatchewan S4P 0K6. **T:** 1 888 884-3777
E: editor@thejogajog.com
W: http://www.thejogajog.com
Freq: Weekly
Editor: Rafique Bhuiyan; **Editor:** Rafique Bhuiyan
Editorial Profile: Weekly Jogajog is a weekly publication that covers multicultural events and news for the South Asian community in Canada.
NEWSPAPER

Weekly Leader Canada

Editorial: 818 Queensbridge Dr., Mississauga, Ontario L5C 3T3. **T:** 1 647 702-9786
E: leadercanada1@gmail.com
W: http://www.leadercanada.com
Freq: Weekly
Editor: Azam Qudrat
Editorial Profile: Weekly Leader Canada is a weekly publication that covers multicultural events and news for the South Asian community in Ontario, Canada.
NEWSPAPER

The Weekly Press and Laker Newspapers

Owner: Advocate Media Inc.
Editorial: 287 Hwy #2, Enfield, Nova Scotia B2T 1C9. **T:** 1 902 883-3181
E: editor@enfieldweeklypress.com
W: http://www.enfieldweeklypress.com
Circ: 10770
Editor: Abby Cameron
NEWSPAPER

Weekly Shomoy

Editorial: 24 Sunderland Crescent, Scarborough, Ontario M1H 2V3.
T: 1 647 955-2802
E: editor@weeklyshomoy.com
W: http://www.weeklyshomoy.com
Freq: Weekly
Editor: Alamgir Hussain; **Editor:** Alamgir Hussain
Editorial Profile: Weekly Shomoy is a weekly publication that covers multicultural events and news for the South Asian community in Scarborough, Canada.
NEWSPAPER

Weekly Sunday Times

Editorial: 7103 Benjamin Ct, Mississauga, Ontario L5W 0E1. **T:** 1 905 276-4048
E: sundaytimes1@aol.com
W: http://www.sundaytimescanada.com
Circ: 30000
Editor in Chief: Adnan Hashmi; **Editor:** Zeba Naureen
Editorial Profile: Weekly Sunday Times is a local, weekly English and Urdu-language newspaper serving Pakistani, Indian and Bangladeshi residents of Mississauga, Ontario. The paper includes news from Pakistan and India, local community news, Canadian and international news. It covers sports, film, religion, literature, politics, fiction and the arts.; Full Page Mono: 20.30
Currency: Canada Dollars
NEWSPAPER

The Weekly Times of India

Editorial: 21 Brisdale Dr., Brampton, Ontario L7A 0H7. **T:** 1 905 256-5630
E: info@weeklytimesofindia.com
W: http://www.weeklytimesofindia.com
Circ: 40000
Editor: Sukirdi Chaudhary; **Publisher:** Shashi Malik
Editorial Profile: The Weekly Times of India is a free, weekly newspaper serving the South Asian community in Toronto, Mississauga, Brampton, Malton, Scarborough, Markham, Etobicoke, Oakville, Hamilton, Kitchener, Ajax and Pickering, Ontario. Published in English, it covers regional and international news, financial news, sports, entertainment, lifestyle and editorial pieces.; Full Page Mono: 8.05
Currency: Canada Dollars
NEWSPAPER

Weekly Voice Newspaper

Owner: Weekly Voice Newspaper

Editorial: 2985 Drew Rd., Unit 206, Mississauga, Ontario L4T 0A4.
T: 1 905 795-8282 **E:** info@weeklyvoice.com
W: http://www.weeklyvoice.com
Freq: 2 Times/Week; **Circ:** 40600
Publisher: Sudhir Anand; **Editor in Chief:** Binoy Thomas
Editorial Profile: Reflects the concerns and interests of the South Asian community in the Greater Toronto Area. Emphasis on local coverage of the community as well as international news and features. Includes regular columns on cars, entertainment, women's issues, youth affairs, real estate, home improvement, recipes and sports.; Full Page Mono: 4.15; Full Page Colour: 350.00
Currency: US Dollars
NEWSPAPER

The Wellington Advertiser

Owner: W.H.A. Publications Ltd.
Editorial: 905 Gartshore St., Fergus, Ontario N1M 2W8. **T:** 1 519 843-5410
W: http://www.wellingtonadvertiser.com
Circ: 39809
Editor: David Adsett; **Publisher:** William Adsett
Editorial Profile: The Wellington Advertiser is written for the community of Fergus, Ontario and contains local news, community concerns and editorials.; Full Page Mono: 8.68
Currency: Canada Dollars
NEWSPAPER

West East

Editorial: Trans-Island 5120, Montreal, Quebec H3W 2Z9. **T:** 1 514 484-9282
E: allmontreal@gmail.com
W: http://1001news.ca
Editor & Publisher: Victoria Sulgina
Editorial Profile: West East is a weekly publication that covers multicultural events and news for the Russian community in Canada.
NEWSPAPER

West Grey Progress

Owner: Metroland Media Group Ltd.
Editorial: 277 Main St., Mount Forest, Ontario N0G 2L0. **T:** 1 519 323-1550
Freq: Monthly
Editor: Lynne Turner
Editorial Profile: West Grey Progress is a monthly community newspaper saluting the businesses, services and citizens of The Municipality of West Grey. Coverage areas include The Municipality of West Grey including the towns of Ayton, Durham, Elmwood, and Neustadt.
NEWSPAPER

Western Catholic Reporter

Owner: Great Western Press Ltd.
Editorial: 8421-101st Ave NW, Edmonton, Alberta T6A 0L1. **T:** 1 780 465-8030
E: wcr@wcr.ab.ca **W:** http://www.wcr.ab.ca
Circ: 35000
Editorial Profile: Western Catholic Reporter is a weekly newspaper published for Canadian Catholics. It provides Catholic inspiration, news and community updates. Its mission is to serve readers by helping them deepen their faith through accurate information and reflective commentary on events and issues of concern to the Catholic church. Deadlines are Fridays before the print day, Wednesday.; Full Page Mono: 29.40; Full Page Colour: 33.74
Currency: Canada Dollars
NEWSPAPER

The Western Sentinel

Owner: Department of National Defence
Editorial: 1 Area Support Group Headquarters, Building 181, Edmonton, Alberta T5J 4J5.
T: 1 780 973-4011
W: http://www.army.forces.gc.ca/ws
Freq: Bi-Weekly; **Circ:** 10000
Editor in Chief: Grant Cree
Editorial Profile: The Western Sentinel is written for all Canadian Army units and bases across the Land Force Western Area from Thunder Bay, Ontario to Vancouver Island.; Full Page Mono: 5.60
Currency: Canada Dollars
NEWSPAPER

Western Wheel Publishing

Owner: Western Wheel Publishing, Ltd.
Editorial: 9 McRae St, Okotoks, Alberta T1S 2A2. **T:** 1 403 938-6397
E: info@westernwheel.com
W: http://www.westernwheel.com **Circ:** 25900
Editor in Chief: Darlene Casten
NEWSPAPER

Westman Journal

Owner: Glacier Media Inc.

Editorial: 315 College Ave., Unit D, Brandon, Manitoba R7A 1E7. **T:** 1 204 725-0209
E: info@wheatcityjournal.ca
W: http://www.wheatcityjournal.ca **Circ:** 35000
Editor: Chris Tataryn
Editorial Profile: Westman Journal is a weekly newspaper that provides community news to the residents of Brandon, Manitoba.; Full Page Mono: 5.74; Full Page Colour: 80.00
Currency: Canada Dollars
NEWSPAPER

Westside Weekly
Owner: Continental Newspapers Canada Ltd.
Editorial: 550 Doyle Ave, Kelowna, British Columbia V1Y 7V1. **T:** 1 250 470-0748
E: westside@ok.bc.ca
W: http://www.kelownadailycourier.ca
Circ: 13150
Publisher: Terry Armstrong; **Editor:** Dave Trifunov
Editorial Profile: Westside Weekly is a community newspaper written for the residents of Kelowna, British Columbia.; Full Page Mono: 0.66
Currency: Canada Dollars
NEWSPAPER

Wetaskiwin Times
Owner: Quebecor Communications Inc.
Editorial: 5013- 51 Street, Wetaskiwin, Alberta T9A 1L4. **T:** 1 780 352-2231
W: http://www.wetaskiwintimes.com
Circ: 11152
Publisher: Jim Clark; **Editor:** Jerold LeBlanc
Editorial Profile: Wetaskiwin Times is a community newspaper written for the residents of Wetaskiwin, Alberta.; Full Page Mono: 6.23
Currency: Canada Dollars
NEWSPAPER

Weyburn Review & Booster Newspapers
Owner: Prairie Newspaper Group L.P.
Editorial: 904 East Ave, Weyburn, Saskatchewan S4H 2Y8. **T:** 1 306 842-7487
E: production@weyburnreview.com
W: http://www.weyburnreview.com
Circ: 11267
Publisher: Darryl Ward; Full Page Mono: 14.32
Currency: Canada Dollars
NEWSPAPER

What's Up Muskoka
Owner: Quebecor Media Inc.
Editorial: Unit 12 - 440 Ecclestone Drive, Bracebridge, Ontario P1L 1Z6.
T: 1 705 646-1314
W: http://www.whatsupmuskoka.com
Freq: Monthly; **Circ:** 24313
Editor: Sandy Lockhart; **Publisher:** Donald Smith
Editorial Profile: What's Up Muskoka is a free, monthly community newspaper serving Bracebridge, Ontario, Muskoka, Ontario and Gravenhurst, Ontario.; Full Page Mono: 37.17
Currency: Canada Dollars
NEWSPAPER

Wheatley/Leamington Southpoint Journal Sun
Editorial: 14 Talbot St. West, Wheatley, Ontario N0P 2P0. **T:** 1 519 825-4541
W: http://www.southpointsun.ca **Circ:** 12000
Publisher: Jim Heyens; **Editor:** Sheila McBrayne
Editorial Profile: Wheatley/Southpoint Journal provides Community News to the Wheatley and Leamington, ON area. It publishes The Wheatley Journal and the Leamington Southpoint Sun.
NEWSPAPER

The Whig-Standard
Owner: Quebecor Communications Inc.
Editorial: 6 Cataraqui St, Kingston, Ontario K7L 4Z7. **T:** 1 613 544-5000
E: local.whig@sunmedia.ca
W: http://www.thewhig.com
Freq: Daily; **Circ:** 21880
News Editor: Jan Murphy
Editorial Profile: The Whig-Standard is written for the Kingston, Ontario general public. It is the oldest continuously published daily newspaper in Canada and covers predominantly local, but also national and provincial news. The daily deadline is 11pm ET. Press releases should be sent to the main e-mail address.; Full Page Mono: 23.10; Full Page Colour: 1173.00
Currency: Canada Dollars
DAILY NEWSPAPER

The Whistler Question
Owner: Glacier Media Inc.
Editorial: 353 - 4370 Lorimer Road, Whistler, British Columbia V0N 1B4. **T:** 1 604 932-5131
E: general@whistlerquestion.com
W: http://www.whistlerquestion.com
Circ: 10480
Publisher: Stephanie Matches; **Editor:** Jennifer Miller
Editorial Profile: The Whistler Question is a newspaper written for the residents of Whistler and Pemberton, British Columbia. The paper covers local news.; Full Page Mono: 11.04
Currency: Canada Dollars
NEWSPAPER

The Windsor Star
Owner: Postmedia Network Inc.
Editorial: 300 Ouellette Ave, Windsor, Ontario N9A 7B4. **T:** 1 519 255-5711
E: news@windsorstar.com
W: http://www.windsorstar.com
Freq: Daily; **Circ:** 55479
Editorial Profile: The Windsor Star, established in 1918, is a 30+ page, four color, broadsheet newspaper. It is the only daily newspaper in Windsor and Essex County, Ontario. The publication covers local, national and international news, business, sports, health, lifestyle, travel, homes and entertainment. The weekend edition comes with a TV Times listing guide. The advertising deadline is 6pm ET two days prior to publication. The lead time varies depending on department.; Full Page Mono: 97.16; Full Page Colour: 2652.00
Currency: Canada Dollars
DAILY NEWSPAPER

Windsor This Week
Owner: Quebecor Communications Inc.
Editorial: 4525 Rhodes Drive, Unit 400, Windsor, Ontario N2W 5R8.
T: 1 519 966-4500
E: windsor.editorial@sunmedia.ca
W: http://www.windsorthisweek.ca
Freq: Weekly; **Circ:** 133000
Publisher: Shannon Ricker
Editorial Profile: Launched in late March 2012, Windsor This Week is a free weekly community newspaper serving residents in and around Windsor in Ontario, Canada.
NEWSPAPER

Windsor-Essex Newspapers
Owner: Postmedia Network Inc.
Editorial: 1116 Lesperance Raod, Tecumseh, Ontario N8N 1X2. **T:** 1 519 735-2080
W: http://www.windsoressexnews.com
Circ: 37700
Publisher: David Calibaba; **Editor In Chief:** Bill England; **Editor In Chief:** Bill England; **Editor:** William Harris
Editorial Profile: Windsor-Essex Newspapers publish the Lakeshore News, LaSalle Post and Shoreline Week.
NEWSPAPER

Winnipeg Free Press
Owner: FP Canadian Newspapers LP
Editorial: 1355 Mountain Ave, Winnipeg, Manitoba R2X 3B6. **T:** 1 204 697-7000
E: city.desk@freepress.mb.ca
W: http://www.winnipegfreepress.com
Freq: Daily; **Circ:** 111338
Publisher: Bob Cox; **Editor:** Paul Samyn; **Editor:** John Sullivan; **Editor:** Jill Wilson
Editorial Profile: Winnipeg Free Press is a broadsheet newspaper written for the general public of Winnipeg, Manitoba. It is one of the major newspapers in the area covering news, business, entertainment and sports, and having the largest readership in the province.; Full Page Mono: 49.49; Full Page Colour: 229.22
Currency: Canada Dollars
DAILY NEWSPAPER

Winnipeg Sun
Owner: Quebecor Communications Inc.
Editorial: 1700 Church Ave, Winnipeg, Manitoba R2X 3A2. **T:** 1 204 694-2022
E: wpgsun.citydesk@sunmedia.ca
W: http://www.winnipegsun.com
Freq: Daily; **Circ:** 43442
Editor in Chief: Mark Hamm; **Editor in Chief:** Mark Hamm; **City Editor:** David Larkins; **City Editor:** Sébastien Perth; **Editor in Chief:** Stephen Ripley; **Editor:** Darryl Sterdan
Editorial Profile: Winnipeg Sun is a daily newspaper written for the Southern Manitoba general public. It covers news, sports, business and entertainment. The newspaper has won several awards. It is known for outstanding news coverage. Deadlines are daily at 6pm CT. Lead time varies.; Full Page Mono: 19.53; Full Page Colour: 1693.00
Currency: Canada Dollars
DAILY NEWSPAPER

World Journal: Toronto Edition
Owner: World Journal Inc.
Editorial: 7755 Warden Ave, Unit 9, Markham, Ontario L3R 0N3. **T:** 1 416 778-0888
E: editorial@worldjournal.net
W: http://www.tor.worldjournal.com
Freq: Daily; **Circ:** 35000
Publisher: Jack Chen; **Editor in Chief:** Sean Mou; **City Editor:** Dan Xin Shen
Editorial Profile: World Journal: Toronto Edition is a daily Chinese-language newspaper serving the residents of Toronto. It covers national and international news, culture, sports, politics, health and education.; Full Page Mono: 75.00; Full Page Colour: 212.00
Currency: Canada Dollars
DAILY NEWSPAPER

World Journal: Vancouver Edition
Owner: World Journal Inc.
Editorial: 2288 Clark Dr, Vancouver, British Columbia V5N 3G8. **T:** 1 604 876-1338
E: edi@worldjournal.bc.ca
W: http://www.van.worldjournal.com
Freq: Daily; **Circ:** 38000
Publisher: Jack Chen; **Editor in Chief:** Shang Ping Han
Editorial Profile: World Journal: Vancouver Edition is a daily Chinese-language newspaper serving the residents of Vancouver. It covers national and international news, culture, sports, politics, health and education. The paper's Web site states that its editorial mission is to "serve all overseas Chinese by helping immigrants bridge the gap to mainstream America, keep in touch with their homeland and local Chinese community news and improve their quality of life."; Full Page Mono: 27.00; Full Page Colour: 39.50
Currency: Canada Dollars
DAILY NEWSPAPER

Yorkton News
Owner: Glacier Media Inc.
Editorial: 18 1st Ave N, Yorkton, Saskatchewan S3N 1J4. **T:** 1 306 783-7355
E: info@yorktonnews.com
W: http://www.yorktonnews.com **Circ:** 26700
Editorial Profile: Yorkton News publishes The News Review and News Review Extra bi-weekly publication to East-Central Saskatchewan and Western Manitoba. The News Review is published on Thursday; The New Review Extra is published on Saturday.
NEWSPAPER

Yorkton Publications
Editorial: 20 Third Avenue North, Yorkton, Saskatchewan S3N 2X3. **T:** 1 306 782-2465
W: http://www.yorktonthisweek.com
Circ: 24617
NEWSPAPER

Your Local Journal
Editorial: 3100 Route Harwood #201, Vaudreuil-Dorion, Quebec J7V 8P2.
T: 1 450 510-4007
E: admin@yourlocaljournal.ca
W: http://www.yourlocaljournal.ca **Circ:** 18543
Publisher: Rodrique Bissonnette; **Editor:** Carmen Marie Fabio
Editorial Profile: Your Local Journal is a weekly community newspaper published every Thursday for the towns of St. Lazare, Hudson and Vaudreuil-Dorion, Quebec.; Full Page Mono: 19.60; Full Page Colour: 46.20
Currency: US Dollars
NEWSPAPER

Ziarul Impact
Editorial: 109 Boulevard Levesque, Laval, Quebec H7G 4P7. **T:** 1 514 667-3920
E: office@impactonline.biz
W: http://www.impactonline.biz
Freq: Bi-Monthly
Editor: Cristian Bucur
Editorial Profile: Ziarul Impact is a bi-monthly newspaper covering International, National and Community news for the Romanian and Moldovan-speaking communities in Quebec.
NEWSPAPER

Zoom NB
Editorial: 191 Robinson Street, Moncton, New Brunswick E1C 5C3. **T:** 1 506 871-3485
Freq: Monthly; **Circ:** 10000
Publisher: Daniel Mlodecki; **Editor:** Cara Stultz
Editorial Profile: Zoom NB is a free monthly community newspaper for the residents of Moncton, New Brunswick and the surrounding communities.; Full Page Mono: 5.11
Currency: US Dollars
NEWSPAPER

NEWS SERVICE/SYNDICATE

Agence France-Presse
Editorial: 165 Sparks Street, Suite 402, Ottawa, Ontario K1P 5B9. **T:** 1 613 232-2943
W: http://www.afp.com
NEWS SERVICE/SYNDICATE

L' Agence QMI
Owner: Quebecor Communications Inc.
Editorial: 800 Square Victoria, Section Mezzanine, Montreal, Quebec H4Z 0A3.
T: 1 514 380-1997 **E:** nouvelles@agenceqmi.ca
W: http://www.agenceqmi.ca
News Editor: Jules Richer; **News Editor:** Patrick White
Editorial Profile: Serves as the news service for Quebecor and Sun Media newspapers.
NEWS SERVICE/SYNDICATE

Agence QMI
Editorial: 207 Queen St, Ste 300, Ottawa, Ontario K1P 6E5. **T:** 1 613 232-6078
E: info@agenceqmi.ca
W: http://www.agenceqmi.ca
NEWS SERVICE/SYNDICATE

L' Agence Science-Presse
Editorial: 1124, rue Marie-Anne Est, Bureau 12, Montreal, Quebec H2J 2B7.
T: 1 514 844-4388
E: editorial@sciencepresse.qc.ca
W: http://www.sciencepresse.qc.ca
Editor in Chief: Pascal Lapointe
Editorial Profile: Agence Science-Presse is the only scientific press agency in Canada, as well as the only one in all of the French-speaking world.
NEWS SERVICE/SYNDICATE

Associated Press
Editorial: 36 King St E, Fl 5, Toronto, Ontario M5C 1E5. **T:** 1 416 368-1388
Bureau Chief: Rob Gillies
NEWS SERVICE/SYNDICATE

Bloomberg News
Editorial: 888 3 St SW Suite 1000, Calgary, Alberta T2P 5C5. **T:** 1 403 232-8188
Bureau Chief: Jeremy van Loon
NEWS SERVICE/SYNDICATE

Bloomberg News
Editorial: 666 Burrard St, Vancouver, British Columbia V6C 2X8. **T:** 1 604 331-1310
E: release@bloomberg.net
W: http://www.bloomberg.com/news/canada
Bureau Chief: Christopher Donville
NEWS SERVICE/SYNDICATE

The Canadian Press
Owner: Canadian Press (The)
Editorial: 36 King St E, Toronto, Ontario M5C 1E5-. **T:** 1 416 507-2159
E: editorial@thecanadianpress.com
W: http://www.thecanadianpress.com
Editor: Lois Abraham; **News Editor:** Patricia Hewitt; **Editor:** Paola Loriggio; **Editor:** Paola Loriggio
Editorial Profile: The Canadian Press, founded in 1917, is a national multimedia Canadian news agency cooperatively owned by more than 100 Canadian newspapers. In addition to enabling news-sharing between these publications, the agency serves more than 500 radio and television broadcasters, as well as a growing number of online publishers, and is a leading supplier of news and information to commercial and government clients. The Canadian Press is also a member of the Canadian Press Gallery.
NEWS SERVICE/SYNDICATE

The Canadian Press
Editorial: 1100 13Th St Nw, Washington, District Of Columbia 20005-4051.
T: 1 202 641-9734
NEWS SERVICE/SYNDICATE

The Canadian Press
Editorial: 215, rue Saint-Jacques, Bureau 100, Montreal, Quebec H2Y 1M6.
T: 1 514 849-3212 **E:** cpmontreal@cp.org
W: http://www.cp.org
French Service Editor: Alain Martineau; **Bureau Chief:** Don McKenzie; **News Editor:** Alexander Panetta
NEWS SERVICE/SYNDICATE

The Canadian Press
Editorial: 100-4th Ave SW, Ste 700, Calgary, Alberta T2P 3N2. **T:** 1 403 233-7004
E: calgary@thecanadianpress.com
W: http://www.thecanadianpress.com
NEWS SERVICE/SYNDICATE

The Canadian Press
Editorial: 1888 Brunswick St, Ste 701, Halifax, Nova Scotia B3J 3J8. **T:** 1 902 422-8496
E: halifax@thecanadianpress.com
W: http://www.thecanadianpress.com
Atlantic News Editor: Tara Brautigan; **Editor:** Michael Tutton; **Bureau Chief:** Kevin Ward
NEWS SERVICE/SYNDICATE

The Canadian Press
Editorial: 139 Water St, The Fortis Bldg, Ste 901, St. John's, Newfoundland A1C 1B2.
T: 1 709 576-0687
E: editorial@thecanadianpress.com
W: http://www.thecanadianpress.com
NEWS SERVICE/SYNDICATE

The Canadian Press
Editorial: 10109-106 St, Ste 504, Edmonton, Alberta T5J 3L7. **T:** 1 780 428-6107
E: edmonton@cp.org
Bureau Chief: Heather Boyd
NEWS SERVICE/SYNDICATE

The Canadian Press
Editorial: 96 St. John St, Fredericton, New Brunswick E3B 5H1. **T:** 1 506 457-0746
W: http://www.thecanadianpress.com
NEWS SERVICE/SYNDICATE

The Canadian Press
Editorial: 165 Sparks St, Ste 800, Ottawa, Ontario K1P 5B9. **T:** 1 613 236-4122
E: ottawa@thecanadianpress.com
W: http://www.thecanadianpress.com
Bureau Chief: Heather Scoffield
Editorial Profile: Please make sure to only send one faxed or e-mailed press release to the bureau, addressed to one contact. They continually receive the same fax addressed to the multiple people at the bureau and find it to be a waste.
NEWS SERVICE/SYNDICATE

The Canadian Press
Editorial: 386 Broadway Ave, Ste 101, Winnipeg, Manitoba R3C 3R6.
T: 1 204 988-1780
NEWS SERVICE/SYNDICATE

The Canadian Press
Editorial: 1050, rue des Parlementaires, Bureau 207, Quebec, Quebec G1R 5A4.
T: 1 418 646-5377
E: quebec@thecanadianpress.com
W: http://www.thecanadianpress.com
NEWS SERVICE/SYNDICATE

The Canadian Press
Editorial: 840 Howe St, Ste 250, Vancouver, British Columbia V6Z 2L2. **T:** 1 604 687-1662
E: vancouver@thecanadianpress.com
W: http://www.thecanadianpress.com
Bureau Chief: Heather Boyd; **News Editor:** Dene Moore
NEWS SERVICE/SYNDICATE

The Canadian Press
Editorial: Room 360 Legislative Building, The Press Gallery, Victoria, British Columbia V8V 1X4. **T:** 1 250 384-4912
W: http://www.thecanadianpress.com
NEWS SERVICE/SYNDICATE

The Canadian Press
Editorial: Saskatchewan Legislative Bldg, Rm 335, Press Gallery, Regina, Saskatchewan S4S 0B3. **T:** 1 306 585-1024
W: http://www.thecanadianpress.com
NEWS SERVICE/SYNDICATE

Dow Jones Newswires
Editorial: 145 King St W Suite 730, Toronto, Ontario M5H 1J8. **T:** 1 416 306-2100
E: djcanada@dowjones.com
NEWS SERVICE/SYNDICATE

Dow Jones Newswires
Editorial: 150 Wellington St Suite 711, Ottawa, Ontario K1A 0A8. **T:** 1 613 237-0668
NEWS SERVICE/SYNDICATE

Média Mosaïque Montréal
Owner: Média Mosaïque Montréal
Editorial: 9071, rue Pie IX, Suites 6A & 5A, Montreal, Quebec H1Z 3V7. **T:** 1 514 991-0263
E: contact@mediamosaique.com
W: http://mediamosaique.com
Editor: Donald Jean
Editorial Profile: Founded in 2006, Média Mosaïque Montréal is a French-language news service that provides general and thematic news to meet the interests of different cultural communities in Quebec.
NEWS SERVICE/SYNDICATE

Parent Previews
Editorial: 83 Midland Crescent SE, Calgary, Alberta T2X 1N8. **T:** 1 800 565-4661
W: http://www.parentpreviews.com
Editor: Donna Gustafson; **Publisher:** Rod Gustafson
Editorial Profile: Since 1993, the columns have appeared in over 50 papers in North America and Canada. It helps take the guess work out of finding appropriate family entertainment. The columns examine popular culture while looking for the good and warning against the dangers. They provide information that will empower individuals to make better choices, enhance their lives and strengthen their families.
NEWS SERVICE/SYNDICATE

Postmedia News
Owner: Postmedia Network Inc.
Editorial: 365 Bloor St E, Toronto, Ontario M4W 3M7. **T:** 1 613 369-4800
E: cns@postmedia.com
W: http://o.canada.com
Editor in Chief: Lou Clancy; **News Editor:** Marc Weisblott
Editorial Profile: Postmedia News has an in-house wire and external field reporters covering national Canadian topics. Stories from Postmedia publications are often picked up by the wire. The news service is a member of the Canadian Press Gallery.
NEWS SERVICE/SYNDICATE

Postmedia News
Editorial: Legislative Building, Queens Park Room 354, Toronto, Ontario M7A 1A2.
T: 1 416 325-7833
NEWS SERVICE/SYNDICATE

Postmedia News
Editorial: 2875 West 29th Ave., Vancouver, British Columbia V6LIY2. **T:** 1 604 605-2000
E: cns@postmedia.com
W: http://www.canada.com/postmedianews
NEWS SERVICE/SYNDICATE

QMI Agency
Owner: Quebecor Communications Inc.
Editorial: 333 King St E, Toronto, Ontario M5A 3X5. **T:** 1 416 947-2258
W: http://www.qmiagency.ca
News Editor: Ted Rath
Editorial Profile: Serves as the news service for Quebecor and Sun Media newspapers.
NEWS SERVICE/SYNDICATE

Reuters
Editorial: 333 Bay St Suite 400, Toronto, Ontario M5H 2R2-. **T:** 1 416 360-8700
E: toronto.newsroom@thomsonreuters.com
W: http://ca.reuters.com
NEWS SERVICE/SYNDICATE

Reuters
Editorial: 407 2 St SW Suite 312, Calgary, Alberta T2P 2Y3. **T:** 1 403 531-1624
W: http://ca.reuters.com/
NEWS SERVICE/SYNDICATE

Torstar Syndication Services
Owner: Metroland Media Group Ltd.
Editorial: 1 Yonge St, Toronto, Ontario M5E 1E6. **T:** 1 416 869-4994
E: syndicationservices@torstar.com
W: http://www.tsscontent.ca
Editorial Profile: Offers columns on personal finance, arts & entertainment, business, home, amusements and international travel.
NEWS SERVICE/SYNDICATE

Young People's Press
Editorial: 374 Fraser St, North Bay, Ontario P1B 3W7. **T:** 1 705 495-8887
E: info@nbdmc.ca **W:** http://nbdmc.ca
Editorial Profile: Young People's Press empowers a large network of youth and young adult writers to have a voice in the mainstream media and a space at the table of public opinion. It showcases the stuff young people care about, including pop culture, politics and social issues.
NEWS SERVICE/SYNDICATE

BROADCASTING

RADIO STATIONS

CBAF-FM
Owner: Société Radio-Canada
Editorial: 250 Av Université, Moncton, New Brunswick E1C 5K3. **T:** 1 506 853-6666
W: http://radio-canada.ca/acadie
Editorial Profile: CBAF-FM is a non-commercial station owned by Société Radio-Canada. The format of the station is variety. CBAF-FM broadcasts to the Moncton, New Brunswick area at 88.5 FM.

CBAF-FM-15
Editorial: Charlottetown, Prince Edward Island.
T: 1 902 629-6400

CBA-FM
Owner: Canadian Broadcasting Corp.
Editorial: 250 University Avenue, Moncton, New Brunswick E1C 8N8. **T:** 1 506 853-6630
W: http://www.cbc.ca/nb
Editorial Profile: CBA-FM is a non-commercial station owned by the Canadian Broadcasting Corp. The station is a part of the Radio 2 network and its format is classical, jazz, world music, and live music of all types. CBA-FM broadcasts to the Moncton, NB area at 95.5 FM.

CBAL-FM
Owner: Société Radio-Canada
Editorial: 250 Universite Ave, Moncton, New Brunswick E1C 5K3. **T:** 1 506 853-6666
W: http://www.radio-canada.ca/Acadie
Editorial Profile: CBAL-FM is a non-commercial station owned by Societe Radio-Canada. The format of the station is classical and jazz. CBAL-FM broadcasts to Moncton, New Brunswick at 98.3 FM.

CBAM-FM
Owner: Canadian Broadcasting Corp.
Editorial: 250 University Ave, Moncton, New Brunswick E1C 5K3. **T:** 1 506 853-6630
W: http://www.cbc.ca/nb
Editorial Profile: CBAM-FM is a commercial station owned by the Canadian Broadcasting Corp. The format of the station is news and talk. CBAM-FM broadcasts to the Moncton, NB area at 106.1 FM.

CBAX-FM
Owner: Canadian Broadcasting Corporation
Editorial: 5600 Sackville St, Halifax, Nova Scotia B3J 1L2. **T:** 1 902 420-8311
W: http://www.cbc.ca/ns
Editorial Profile: CBAX-FM is a non-commercial station owned by the Canadian Broadcasting Corporation. The format for the station is classical, jazz, world, and folk music. CBAX-FM broadcasts to the Halifax, NS area at 91.5 FM.

CBBS-FM
Owner: Canadian Broadcasting Corp.
Editorial: 15 MacKenzie St, Sudbury, Ontario P3C 4Y1. **T:** 1 705 688-3200
E: sudburynews@cbc.ca
W: http://www.cbc.ca/sudbury

CBBX-FM
Owner: Société Radio-Canada
Editorial: 15 MacKenzie St, Sudbury, Ontario P3C 4Y1. **T:** 1 705 688-3200
W: http://radio-canada.ca/ontario
Editorial Profile: CBBX-FM is a non-commercial station owned by the Societe Radio-Canada. The format of the station is variety. CBBX-FM broadcasts to the Sudbury, Ontario area at 90.9 FM.

CBC-AM
Owner: Canadian Broadcasting Corp.
Editorial: 825 Riverside Dr West, Windsor, Ontario N9A 5K9. **T:** 1 519 255-3411
E: windsor@cbc.ca
W: http://www.cbc.ca/windsor

CBCK-FM
Owner: Canadian Broadcasting Corp.
T: 1 613 288-6485 **E:** cbcnewsottawa@cbc.ca
W: http://www.cbc.ca/ottawa
Editorial Profile: CBCK-FM is a non-commercial radio station owned by Canadian Broadcasting Corp. The format of the station is news and talk. CBCK-FM broadcasts to the Kingston, ON at 107.5 FM.

CBCL-FM
Owner: Canadian Broadcasting Corp.
Editorial: 208 Piccadilly, Unit 4, London, Ontario N6A 1S1. **T:** 1 519 667-1990
W: http://www.cbc.ca
Editorial Profile: CBCL-FM is a non-commercial station owned by Canadian Broadcasting Corp. The format of the station is news and talk. CBCL-FM broadcasts to London, Ontario area at 93.5 FM.

CBCS-FM
Owner: Canadian Broadcasting Corp.
Editorial: 15 MacKenzie St, Sudbury, Ontario P3C 4Y1. **T:** 1 705 688-3200
E: sudburynews@cbc.ca
W: http://www.cbc.ca/sudbury
Editorial Profile: CBCS-FM is a non-commercial station owned by the Canadian Broadcasting Corp. The format of the station is news and talk. CBCS-FM broadcasts to the Sudbury, Ontario area on 99.9 FM.

CBCT-FM
Owner: Canadian Broadcasting Corp.
Editorial: 430 University Ave, Charlottetown, Prince Edward Island C1A 4N6.
T: 1 902 629-6400 **W:** http://www.cbc.ca/pei
Editorial Profile: CBCT-FM is a non-commercial station owned by Canadian Broadcasting Corp. The format of the station is news and talk programming. CBCT-FM broadcasts to the Charlottetown, Prince Edward Island area at 96.1 FM.

CBCV-FM
Owner: Canadian Broadcasting Corp.
Editorial: 780 Kings Rd, Victoria, British Columbia V8T 5A2. **T:** 1 250 360-2227
E: victoria@cbc.ca **W:** http://www.cbc.ca/bc
Editorial Profile: CBCV-FM is a non-commercial station owned by the Canadian Broadcasting Corp. The format of the station is news and talk. CBCV-FM broadcasts to the Victoria, British Columbia area at 90.5 FM.

CBCX-FM
Owner: Société Radio-Canada
Editorial: 1724 Westmount Blvd NW, Calgary, Alberta T2P 2M7. **T:** 1 403 521-6000
W: http://www.radio-canada.ca/espace_musique
Editorial Profile: CBCX-FM is a non-commercial station owned by Société Radio-Canada. The format for the station is classical, jazz, world, and folk music. CBCX-FM broadcasts to the Calgary, AB area at 89.7 FM.

CBDB-AM
Owner: Canadian Broadcasting Corp.
Editorial: 3103 3rd Ave, Whitehorse, Yukon Territory Y1A 1E5. **T:** 1 867 668-8400
E: cbcnorth@cbc.ca
W: http://www.cbc.ca/north
Editorial Profile: CBDB-AM is a non-commercial radio station owned by the Canadian Broadcasting Corp. The station serves as the CBC Radio One affiliate for adult listeners throughout Watson Lake, Yukon Territory, and airs locally on 990 AM.

CBDC-AM
Owner: Canadian Broadcasting Corp.
Editorial: 3103 3rd Ave, Whitehorse, Yukon Territory Y1A 1E5. **T:** 1 867 668-8400
E: cbcnorth@cbc.ca
W: http://www.cbc.ca/north
Editorial Profile: CBDC-AM is a non-commercial radio station owned by the Canadian Broadcasting Corp. The station serves as the CBC Radio One affiliate for adult listeners throughout Mayo, Yukon Territory, and airs locally on 1230 AM.

CBDD-AM
Owner: Canadian Broadcasting Corp.
Editorial: 3103 3rd Ave, Whitehorse, Yukon Territory Y1A 1E5. **T:** 1 867 668-8400
E: cbcnorth@cbc.ca
W: http://www.cbc.ca/north
Editorial Profile: CBDD-AM is a non-commercial radio station owned by the Canadian Broadcasting Corp. The station serves as the CBC Radio One affiliate for adult listeners throughout Elsa, Yukon Territory, and airs locally on 560 AM.

CBDF-FM
Owner: Canadian Broadcasting Corp.
Editorial: 3103 3rd Ave, Whitehorse, Yukon Territory Y1A 1E5. **T:** 1 867 668-8400
E: cbcnorth@cbc.ca
W: http://www.cbc.ca/north
Editorial Profile: CBDF-FM is a non-commercial radio station owned by the Canadian Broadcasting Corp. The station serves as the CBC Radio One affiliate for adult listeners throughout Haines Junction, Yukon Territory, and airs locally on 103.5 FM.

CBD-FM
Owner: Canadian Broadcasting Corp.
Editorial: 560 Main St, Saint John, New Brunswick E2K 1J5. **T:** 1 506 632-7745
W: http://www.cbc.ca/nb
Editorial Profile: CBD-FM is a non-commercial station owned by Canadian Broadcasting Corp. The format of the station is news and talk. CBD-FM broadcasts to the Saint John, Canada area at 91.3 FM.

CBDK-AM
Owner: Canadian Broadcasting Corp.
Editorial: 3103 3rd Ave, Whitehorse, Yukon Territory Y1A 1E5. **T:** 1 867 668-8400
E: cbcnorth@cbc.ca
W: http://www.cbc.ca/north
Editorial Profile: CBDK-AM is a non-commercial radio station owned by the Canadian Broadcasting Corp. The station serves as the CBC Radio One affiliate for adult listeners throughout Teslin, Yukon Territory, and airs locally on 940 AM.

CBDL-FM
Owner: Canadian Broadcasting Corp.
Editorial: 3103 3rd Ave, Whitehorse, Yukon Territory Y1A 1E5. **T:** 1 867 668-8400
E: cbcnorth@cbc.ca
W: http://www.cbc.ca/north
Editorial Profile: CBDL-FM is a non-commercial radio station owned by the Canadian Broadcasting Corp. The station serves as the CBC Radio One affiliate for adult listeners throughout Destruction Bay and Burwash Landing, Yukon Territory, and airs locally on 105.1 FM.

CBDM-AM
Owner: Canadian Broadcasting Corp.
Editorial: 3103 3rd Ave, Whitehorse, Yukon Territory Y1A 1E5. **T:** 1 867 668-8400
E: cbcnorth@cbc.ca
W: http://www.cbc.ca/north
Editorial Profile: CBDM-AM is a non-commercial radio station owned by the Canadian Broadcasting Corp. The station serves as the CBC Radio One affiliate for adult listeners throughout Beaver Creek, Yukon Territory, and airs locally on 690 AM.

CBDN-AM
Owner: Canadian Broadcasting Corp.
Editorial: 3103 3rd Ave, Whitehorse, Yukon Territory Y1A 1E5. **T:** 1 867 668-8400
E: cbcnorth@cbc.ca
W: http://www.cbc.ca/north
Editorial Profile: CBDN-AM is a non-commercial radio station owned by the Canadian Broadcasting Corp. The station serves as the CBC Radio One affiliate for adult listeners throughout Dawson City, Yukon Territory, and airs locally on 560 AM.

CBDQ-FM
Owner: Canadian Broadcasting Corp.
Editorial: 500 Vanier, Labrador City, Newfoundland A2V 2W7. **T:** 1 709 944-3616
W: http://www.cbc.ca/nl
Editorial Profile: CBDQ-FM is a non-commercial station owned by Canadian Broadcasting Corp. The target audience of the station is adults, ages 18 to 64. CBDQ-FM broadcasts to the Labrador City, Newfoundland area at 96.3 FM.

CBDX-AM
Owner: Canadian Broadcasting Corp.
Editorial: 3103 3rd Ave, Whitehorse, Yukon Territory Y1A 1E5. **T:** 1 867 668-8400
E: cbcnorth@cbc.ca
W: http://www.cbc.ca/north
Editorial Profile: CBDX-AM is a non-commercial radio station owned by the Canadian Broadcasting Corp. The station serves as the CBC Radio One affiliate for adult listeners throughout Swift River, Yukon Territory, and airs locally on 970 AM.

CBEF-AM
Owner: Société Radio-Canada
Editorial: 825 promenade Riverside West, Windsor, Ontario N9A 5K9. **T:** 1 416 205-2887
E: tjontario@radio-canada.ca
W: http://www.radio-canada.ca/regions/ontario/index.shtml
Editorial Profile: CBEF-AM is a commercial station owned by Societe Radio-Canada. The format of the station is variety. CBEF-FM broadcasts to Windsor, Ontario at 540 AM. CBEF-AM plays 33 hours of Franco-Ontarian programming from CJBC-AM in Toronto; all other programming comes from the Radio-Canada headquarters in Montreal.

CBE-FM
Owner: Canadian Broadcasting Corp.
Editorial: 825 Riverside Drive West, Windsor, Ontario N9A 5K9. **T:** 1 519 255-3411
E: windsor@cbc.ca
W: http://www.cbc.ca/windsor

CBEG-FM
Owner: Canadian Broadcasting Corp.
Editorial: 825 Riverside Drive West, Windsor, Ontario N9A5K9. **T:** 1 519 255-3411
E: windsor@cbc.ca
W: http://www.cbc.ca/windsor

CBEW-FM
Owner: Canadian Broadcasting Corp.
Editorial: 825 Riverside Drive West, Windsor, Ontario N9A 5K9. **T:** 1 519 255-3411
E: windsor@cbc.ca
W: http://www.cbc.ca/windsor
Editorial Profile: CBEW-FM is a non-commercial station owned by the Canadian Broadcasting Corporation. The format of the station is news. CBEW-FM broadcasts to the Windsor, Ontario area at 97.5 FM.

CBF-FM
Owner: Société Radio-Canada
Editorial: 1400 Boul. Rene-Levesque Est, Montreal, Quebec H2L 2M2.
T: 1 514 597-6000
W: http://www.radio-canada.ca/regions/montreal/index.shtml
Editorial Profile: CBF-FM is a non-commercial station owned by Societe Radio-Canada. The format of the station is news and talk. CBF-FM broadcasts to the Montreal area at 95.1 FM. CBF-FM has a transmitter of 5,460 watts broadcasting to the Saint-Donat, Quebec area at 89.7 FM.

CBF-FM-10
Owner: Société Radio-Canada
Editorial: 1335, rue King Ouest, Sherbrooke, Quebec J1J 2B8. **T:** 1 819 620-0000
W: http://www.radio-canada.ca/regions/estrie/index.shtml
Editorial Profile: CBF-FM-10 is a French-language non-commercial station owned by Société Radio-Canada. The format for the station is news and talk. CBF-FM-10 broadcasts to the Sherbrooke area at 101.1 FM.

CBF-FM-8
Owner: Société Radio-Canada
Editorial: 25, rue des Forges, Bureau 101, Trois-Rivieres, Quebec G9A 2G7.
T: 1 819 694-0114
W: http://www.radio-canada.ca/regions/mauricie
Editorial Profile: CBF-FM-8 is a public station owned by Société Radio-Canada. The format for the station is news and talk. CBF-FM-8 broadcasts to the Mauricie - Centre-du-Québec area at 96.5 FM.

CBFX-FM
Owner: Société Radio-Canada
Editorial: 1400 boul Rene-Levesque Est, Montreal, Quebec H2L 2M2.
T: 1 514 597-6000
W: http://radio-canada.ca/espace_musique
Editorial Profile: CBFX-FM is a non-commercial station owned by Societe Radio-Canada. The format of the station is variety. CBFX-FM broadcasts to the Montreal area at 100.7 FM.

CBGA-FM
Owner: Société Radio-Canada
Editorial: 155 rue Saint-Sacrement, Matane, Quebec G4W 1Y9. **T:** 1 418 562-0290
E: nouvellm@radio-canada.ca
W: http://radio-canada.ca/regions/gaspesie-lesiles
Editorial Profile: CBGA-FM is a non-commercial station owned by Societe Radio-Canada. The format of the station is news and talk. CBGA-FM broadcasts to Matane, Quebec at 102.1 FM.

CBG-AM
Owner: Canadian Broadcasting Corp.
Editorial: 98 Sullivan Ave, Gander, Newfoundland A1V 1S2. **T:** 1 709 256-4311
W: http://www.cbc.ca/nl
Editorial Profile: CBG-AM is a non-commercial station owned by Canadian Broadcasting Corp. The format of the station is news and talk. The target audience of the station is adults, ages 18 to 64. CBDQ-FM broadcasts to the Gander, Newfoundland and Labrador area at 1400 AM.

CBHA-FM
Owner: Canadian Broadcasting Corp.
Editorial: 5600 Sackville St, Halifax, Nova Scotia B3J 1L2. **T:** 1 902 420-8311
E: radionews@halifax.cbc.ca
W: http://www.cbc.ca/ns
Editorial Profile: CBHA-FM is a non-commercial radio station owned by the Canadian Broadcasting Corp. The format of the station news and information. The station broadcasts to the Halifax, NS area at 90.5 FM.

CBH-FM
Owner: Canadian Broadcasting Corp.
Editorial: 5600 Sackville St, Halifax, Nova Scotia B3J 3E9. **T:** 1 902 420-8311
W: http://www.cbc.ca/ns
Editorial Profile: CBH-FM is a non-commercial station owned by the Canadian Broadcasting Corp. The format of the station is classical music. CBH-FM broadcasts to the Halifax, Nova Scotia area at 102.7 FM.

CBI-AM
Owner: Canadian Broadcasting Corp.
Editorial: 285 Alexandra St, Sydney, Nova Scotia B1S 2E8. **T:** 1 902 563-4100
E: radionews@sydney.cbc.ca
W: http://www.cbc.ca/ns
Editorial Profile: CBI-AM is a non-commercial station owned by the Canadian Broadcasting Corp. The format of the station is news and talk. CBI-AM broadcasts to the Sydney, Nova Scotia area on 1140 AM.

CBI-FM
Owner: Canadian Broadcasting Corp.
Editorial: 285 Alexandra St, Sydney, Nova Scotia B1S 2E8. **T:** 1 902 563-4100
E: radionews@sydney.cbc.ca
W: http://www.cbc.ca/ns
Editorial Profile: CBI-FM is a non-commercial station owned by the Canadian Broadcasting Corp. The format of the station is variety, a combination of news, talk and regional music programming. CBI-FM broadcasts to the Sydney, Nova Scotia area area at 105.1 FM.

CBJ-FM
Owner: Société Radio-Canada
Editorial: 500 rue des Saguenéens, Chicoutimi, Quebec G7H 6N4.
T: 1 418 696-6600
E: nouvellescbj@radio-canada.ca
W: http://www.radio-canada.ca/regions/saguenay-lac/index.shtml
Editorial Profile: CBJ-FM is a non-commercial station owned by Société Radio-Canada. The format of the station is news and talk. CBJ-FM broadcasts to Chicoutimi, Quebec at 93.7 FM.

CBJX-FM
Owner: Société Radio-Canada
Editorial: 500 rue des Saguenéens, Chicoutimi, Quebec G7H 6N4.
T: 1 418 696-6600
W: http://www.radio-canada.ca/espace_musique
Editorial Profile: CBJX-FM is a non-commercial station owned by Societe Radio-Canada. The format of the station is classical and jazz. CBJX-FM broadcasts to Chicoutimi, Quebec at 100.9 FM.

CBKA-FM
Owner: Canadian Broadcasting Corp.
T: 1 306 347-9540 **W:** http://www.cbc.ca/sask
Editorial Profile: CBKA-FM is a non-commercial radio station owned by the Canadian Broadcasting Corp. The format of the station is news and talk. CBKA-FM broadcasts to the Regina, Saskatchewan area on 105.9 FM.

CBK-AM
Owner: Canadian Broadcasting Corp.
Editorial: 2440 Broad St, Regina, Saskatchewan S4P 0A5. **T:** 1 306 347-9691
E: sasknews@cbc.ca
W: http://www.cbc.ca/sask
Editorial Profile: CBK-AM is a non-commercial station owned by the Canadian Broadcasting Corp. The format of the station is variety. The station broadcasts to the Regina, Saskatchewan area at 540 AM.

CBKF-FM
Owner: Société Radio-Canada
Editorial: 2440 Broad St, Regina, Saskatchewan S4P 0A5. **T:** 1 306 347-9540
W: http://radio-canada.ca/regions/saskatchewan
Editorial Profile: CBKF-FM is a non-commercial station owned by Societe Radio-Canada. The format of the station is variety. CBKF-FM broadcasts to the Regina, Saskatchewan area at 97.7 FM.

CBK-FM
Owner: Canadian Broadcasting Corp.
Editorial: 2440 Broad St, Regina, Saskatchewan S4P 0A5. **T:** 1 306 347-9540
W: http://www.cbc.ca/sask
Editorial Profile: CBK-FM is a non-commercial station owned by the Canadian Broadcasting Corporation. The format of the station is news and talk. CBK-FM broadcasts to the Regina, Saskatchewan area at 102.5 FM.

CBKS-FM
Owner: Canadian Broadcasting Corp.
Editorial: 2440 Broad St, Regina, Saskatchewan S4P 0A5. **T:** 1 306 956-7400
E: sasknews@cbc.ca
W: http://www.cbc.ca/sask
Editorial Profile: CBKS-FM is a non-commercial station owned by the Canadian Broadcasting Corp. The format of the station is variety including classical music. CKBS-FM broadcasts throughout the Saskatoon, Saskatchewan area at 105.5 FM.

CBLA-FM
Owner: Canadian Broadcasting Corp.
Editorial: 205 Wellington St W, Toronto, Ontario M5V 3G7. **T:** 1 416 205-3311
W: http://www.cbc.ca/toronto
Editorial Profile: CBLA-FM is a non-commercial station owned by the Canadian Broadcasting Corp. The format of the station is news and talk. CBLA-FM broadcasts to the Toronto area at 99.1 FM.

CBL-FM
Owner: Canadian Broadcasting Corp.
Editorial: 205 Wellington St W, Toronto, Ontario M5V 3G7. **T:** 1 416 205-3311
W: http://www.cbc.ca/radiotwo

CBLL-FM
Owner: Canadian Broadcasting Corp.
Editorial: 205 Wellington St W, Room 1A-101B, Toronto, Ontario M5V 3G7.
T: 1 416 205-3311
W: http://www.cbc.ca/toronto

CBME-FM
Owner: Canadian Broadcasting Corp.
Editorial: 1400 Boul René-Lévesque E, Montreal, Quebec H2L 2M2.
T: 1 514 597-6000
W: http://www.cbc.ca/montreal
Editorial Profile: CBME-FM is a non-commercial station owned by the Canadian Broadcasting Corp. The format for the station is news and talk. CBME-FM broadcasts to the Montreal area at 88.5 FM.

CBM-FM
Owner: Canadian Broadcasting Corp.
Editorial: 1400 Rene Levesque E, Montreal, Quebec H2L 2M2. **T:** 1 514 597-6665
W: http://www.cbc.ca/radio2

CBMR-FM
Owner: Canadian Broadcasting Corp.
T: 1 416 205-3311
W: http://www.radio-canada.ca/radio

CBN-AM
Owner: Canadian Broadcasting Corp.
Editorial: 342 Duckworth St, St. John's, Newfoundland A1C 1H5. **T:** 1 709 576-5000
W: http://www.cbc.ca/nl
Editorial Profile: CBN-AM is a non-commercial station owned by the Canadian Broadcasting Corp. The format of the station is news and talk. CBN-AM broadcasts to the Saint John's, NL area at 640 AM.

CBN-FM
Owner: Canadian Broadcasting Corp.
Editorial: 342-44 Duckworth St, St. John's, Newfoundland A1C 1H5. **T:** 1 709 576-5225
W: http://www.cbc.ca/nl/
Editorial Profile: CBN-FM is a commercial station owned by Canadian Broadcasting Corp. The format of the station is variety. CBN-FM broadcasts to St. John's, Newfoundland at 106.9 FM.

CBOF-FM
Owner: CBC/ Radio-Canada
Editorial: 181 Queen St, Ottawa, Ontario K1P 1K9. **T:** 1 613 288-6000
E: nouvelles.ottawagatineau@radio-canada.ca
W: http://www.radio-canada.ca/ottawa-gatineau
Editorial Profile: CBOF-FM is a non-commercial station owned by CBC/ Radio-Canada. The format of the station is news and talk. CBOF-FM broadcasts to the Ottawa, Ontario area at 90.7 FM.

CBO-FM
Owner: Canadian Broadcasting Corp.
Editorial: 181 Queen Street, Ottawa, Ontario K1P 1K9. **T:** 1 613 288-6000
E: cbcnewsottawa@cbc.ca
W: http://www.cbc.ca/ottawa
Editorial Profile: CBO-FM is a non-commercial station owned by Canadian Broadcasting Corp. The format of the station is news and talk. CBO-FM broadcasts to the Ottawa, Ontario area at 91.5 FM.

CBON-FM
Owner: Société Radio-Canada

Editorial: 15 MacKenzie St, Sudbury, Ontario P3C 4Y1. **T:** 1 705 688-3200
E: infocbon@radio-canada.ca
W: http://radio-canada.ca/ontario
Editorial Profile: CBON-FM is a non-commercial station owned by Societe Radio-Canada. The format of the station is news and talk. CBON-FM broadcasts to the Sudbury, Ontario area at 98.1 FM. Radio-Canada has over 20 towers that retransmit CBON-FM's signal across northern Ontario.

CBOQ-FM
Owner: Canadian Broadcasting Corp.
Editorial: 181 Queen St, Ottawa, Ontario K1P 1K9. **T:** 1 613 288-6000
E: cbcnewsottawa@cbc.ca
W: http://www.cbc.ca/ottawa
Editorial Profile: CBOQ-FM is a non-commercial station owned by the Canadian Broadcasting Corp. The format of the station is variety. CBOQ-FM broadcasts to the Ottawa, Ontario area at 103.3 FM.

CBOX-FM
Owner: Société Radio-Canada
Editorial: 181 Queen St, Ottawa, Ontario K1P 1K9. **T:** 1 613 288-6000
W: http://www.radio-canada.ca/espace_musique
Editorial Profile: CBOX-FM is a non-commercial station owned by Societe Radio-Canada. The format of the station is classical and jazz. CBOX-FM broadcasts to the Ottawa, Ontario area at 102.5 FM.

CBQF-AM
Owner: Canadian Broadcasting Corp.
Editorial: 3103 3rd Ave, Whitehorse, Yukon Territory Y1A 1E5. **T:** 1 867 668-8400
E: cbcnorth@cbc.ca
W: http://www.cbc.ca/north
Editorial Profile: CBQF-AM is a non-commercial radio station owned by the Canadian Broadcasting Corp. The station serves as the CBC Radio One affiliate for adult listeners throughout Carmacks, Yukon Territory, and airs locally on 990 AM.

CBQJ-AM
Owner: Canadian Broadcasting Corp.
Editorial: 3103 3rd Ave, Whitehorse, Yukon Territory Y1A 1E5. **T:** 1 867 668-8400
E: cbcnorth@cbc.ca
W: http://www.cbc.ca/north
Editorial Profile: CBQJ-AM is a non-commercial radio station owned by the Canadian Broadcasting Corp. The station serves as the CBC Radio One affiliate for adult listeners throughout Ross River, Yukon Territory, and airs locally on 990 AM.

CBQK-FM
Owner: Canadian Broadcasting Corp.
Editorial: 3103 3rd Ave, Whitehorse, Yukon Territory Y1A 1E5. **T:** 1 867 668-8400
E: cbcnorth@cbc.ca
W: http://www.cbc.ca/north
Editorial Profile: CBQK-FM is a non-commercial radio station owned by the Canadian Broadcasting Corp. The station serves as the CBC Radio One affiliate for adult listeners throughout Faro, Yukon Territory, and airs locally on 105.1 FM.

CBQL-FM
Owner: Canadian Broadcasting Corp.
Editorial: 213 East Miles St, Thunder Bay, Ontario P7C 1J5. **T:** 1 807 625-5000
E: thunderbay@cbc.ca
W: http://www.cbc.ca/thunderbay

CBQN-FM
Owner: Canadian Broadcasting Corp.
Editorial: 213 East Miles St, Thunder Bay, Ontario P7C 1J5. **T:** 1 807 625-5000
E: thunderbay@cbc.ca
W: http://www.cbc.ca/thunderbay

CBQP-FM
Owner: Canadian Broadcasting Corp.
Editorial: 213 East Miles St, Thunder Bay, Ontario P7C 1J5. **T:** 1 807 625-5000
E: thunderbay@cbc.ca
W: http://www.cbc.ca/thunderbay

CBQR-FM
Owner: Canadian Broadcasting Corp.
T: 1 867 645-2244 **W:** http://cbc.ca/north
Editorial Profile: CBQR-FM is a non-commercial station owned by Canadian Broadcasting Corp. The format of the station is variety. CBQR-FM broadcasts to the Rankin Inlet, Northwest Territories area at 105.1 FM.

CBQS-FM
Owner: Canadian Broadcasting Corp.
Editorial: 213 Miles St East, Thunder Bay, Ontario P7C 1J5. **T:** 1 807 625-5000
E: thunderbay@cbc.ca
W: http://www.cbc.ca/thunderbay

CBQT-FM
Owner: Canadian Broadcasting Corp.
Editorial: 213 Miles St East, Thunder Bay, Ontario P7C 1J5. **T:** 1 807 625-5001
E: thunderbay@cbc.ca
W: http://www.cbc.ca/thunderbay
Editorial Profile: CBQT-FM is a non-commercial station owned by the Canadian Broadcasting Corp. The format of the station is news and talk. CBQT-FM broadcasts to the Thunder Bay, Ontario region at 88.3 FM.

CBQX-FM
Owner: Canadian Broadcasting Corp.
Editorial: 213 Miles St East, Thunder Bay, Ontario P7C 1J5. **T:** 1 807 625-5000
E: thunderbay@cbc.ca
W: http://www.cbc.ca/thunderbay

CBR-AM
Owner: Canadian Broadcasting Corp.
Editorial: 1724 Westmount Blvd NW, Calgary, Alberta T2N 3G7. **T:** 1 403 521-6000
W: http://www.cbc.ca/calgary
Editorial Profile: CBR-AM is a non-commercial radio station owned by the Canadian Broadcasting Corp. The format of the station is news and talk. CBR-AM broadcasts to the Calgary, AB area on 1010 AM.

CBR-FM
Owner: Canadian Broadcasting Corp.
Editorial: 1724 Westmount Blvd NW, Calgary, Alberta T2N 3G7. **T:** 1 403 521-6222
W: http://www.cbc.ca/calgary

CBRX-FM
Owner: Société Radio-Canada
Editorial: 273 rue St-Jean Baptiste, Rimouski, Quebec G5L 4J8. **T:** 1 418 723-2217
E: cjbr@rimouski.radio-canada.ca
W: http://radio-canada.ca/espace-musique
Editorial Profile: CBRX-FM is a non-commercial station owned by Societe Radio-Canada. The format of the station is classical, jazz and news. CBRX-FM broadcasts to the Rimouski, Quebec area at 101.5 FM.

CBSI-FM
Owner: Société Radio-Canada
Editorial: 350 rue Smith Bureau 30, Sept-Iles, Quebec G4R 3X2. **T:** 1 418 968-0720
E: cbsi@radio-canada.ca
W: http://www.radio-canada.ca/cote-nord
Editorial Profile: CBSI-FM is a non-commercial station owned by Societe Radio-Canada. The format of the station is news and talk. CBSI-FM broadcasts to the Sept-Iles, Quebec area at 98.1 FM.

CBT-AM
Owner: Canadian Broadcasting Corp.
Editorial: 2 Harris Ave, Grand Falls-Windsor, Newfoundland A2A 2Y2. **T:** 1 709 489-2102
E: centralmorning@cbc.ca
W: http://www.cbc.ca/nl
Editorial Profile: CBT-AM is a non-commercial station owned by Canadian Broadcasting Corp. The format of the station is variety. CBT-AM broadcasts to the Grand Falls-Windsor, Newfoundland and Labrador area at 540 AM.

CBTK-FM
Owner: Canadian Broadcasting Corp.
Editorial: 243 Lawrence Ave, Kelowna, British Columbia V1Y 6L2. **T:** 1 250 861-3781
E: daybreakkelowna@cbc.ca
W: http://www.cbc.ca/bc

CBUA-FM
Owner: Canadian Broadcasting Corp.
Editorial: 3103 3rd Ave, Whitehorse, Yukon Territory Y1A 1E5. **T:** 1 867 668-8400
E: cbcnorth@cbc.ca
W: http://www.cbc.ca/north
Editorial Profile: CBUA-FM is a non-commercial radio station owned by the Canadian Broadcasting Corp. The station serves as the CBC Radio One affiliate for adult listeners throughout Atlin, British Columbia, and airs locally on 90.1 FM.

CBU-AM
Owner: Canadian Broadcasting Corp.
Editorial: 775 Cambie St, Vancouver, British Columbia V6B 2R5. **T:** 1 604 662-6000
W: http://www.cbc.ca/bc
Editorial Profile: CBU-AM is a non-commercial radio station owned by the Canadian Broadcasting Corp. The format of the station is news and public affairs programming. CBU-AM broadcasts throughout the Vancouver, British Columbia area at 690 AM.

CBUF-FM
Owner: Société Radio-Canada
Editorial: 775 rue Cambie, Vancouver, British Columbia V6B 2B2. **T:** 1 604 662-6135
W: http://www.radio-canada.ca/regions/colombie-Britannique
Editorial Profile: CBUF-FM is a non-commercial station owned by Societe Radio-Canada. The format of the station is news and talk. CBUF-FM broadcasts to the Vancouver, British Columbia area at 97.7 FM.

CBU-FM
Owner: Canadian Broadcasting Corp.
Editorial: 700 Hamilton St, Vancouver, British Columbia V6B 4A2. **T:** 1 604 662-6000
W: http://www.cbc.ca/bc
Editorial Profile: CBU-FM is a non-commercial station owned by Canadian Broadcasting Corp. The format of the station is a variety of musical genres, news, and public affairs programming. CBU-FM broadcasts to the Vancouver, British Columbia area at 105.7 FM.

CBUX-FM
Owner: Société Radio-Canada
Editorial: 700 Hamilton St, PO Box 4600, Vancouver, British Columbia V6B 4A2.
T: 1 604 662-6000
W: http://www.radio-canada.ca/espace_musique
Editorial Profile: CBUX-FM is a non-commercial station owned by Société Radio-Canada. the format for the station is classical, jazz, world, and folk music. CBUX-FM broadcasts to the Vancouver, BC area at 90.9 FM.

CBVE-FM
Owner: Canadian Broadcasting Corp.
Editorial: 888 St-Jean Street, Quebec, Quebec G1K 9L4. **T:** 1 418 691-3620
W: http://www.cbc.ca/montreal
Editorial Profile: CBVE-FM is a non-commercial station owned by the Canadian Broadcasting Corporation. The format of the station is talk. CBVE-FM broadcasts to the Quebec area at 104.7 FM.

CBV-FM
Owner: Société Radio-Canada
Editorial: 888 rue Saint-Jean, Quebec, Quebec G1R 5H6. **T:** 1 418 654-1341
E: nouvelles.quebec@radio-canada.ca
W: http://radio-canada.ca/quebec
Editorial Profile: CBV-FM is a non-commercial radio station owned by Societe Radio-Canada. The format of the station is news and talk. CBV-FM broadcasts to the Quebec area at 106.3 FM.

CBVX-FM
Owner: Société Radio-Canada
Editorial: 888 rue Saint-Jean, Quebec, Quebec G1R 5H6. **T:** 1 418 654-1341
E: cbv@radio-canada.ca
W: http://www.radio-canada.ca/espace-musique
Editorial Profile: CBVX-FM is a non-commercial station owned by Societe Radio-Canada. The format of the station is classical and jazz. CBVX-FM broadcasts to the Quebec area at 95.3 FM.

CBW-AM
Owner: Canadian Broadcasting Corp.
Editorial: 541 Portage Ave, Winnipeg, Manitoba R3B 2G1. **T:** 1 204 788-3222
E: talkback@cbc.ca
W: http://www.cbc.ca/manitoba
Editorial Profile: CBW-AM is a commercial station owned by the Canadian Broadcasting Corp. The format of the station is news and talk. CBW-AM broadcasts to the Winnipeg, Manitoba area at 990 AM.

CBW-FM
Owner: Canadian Broadcasting Corp.
Editorial: 541 Portage Ave, Winnipeg, Manitoba R3B 2G1. **T:** 1 204 788-3222
E: talkback@cbc.ca
W: http://www.cbc.ca/manitoba
Editorial Profile: CBW-FM is a non-commercial station owned by the Canadian Broadcasting Corp. The format of the station is variety. CBW-FM broadcasts to the Winnipeg, Manitoba area on 98.3 FM

CBWK-FM
Owner: Canadian Broadcasting Corp.
Editorial: 7 Selkirk Ave, Thompson, Manitoba R8N 0M4. **T:** 1 204 677-1682 **E:** north@cbc.ca
W: http://www.cbc.ca/manitoba
Editorial Profile: CBWK-FM is a non-commercial station owned by the Canadian Broadcasting Corp. The format of the station is news and talk. CBWK-FM broadcasts to Thompson, Manitoba at 100.9 FM.

CBX-AM
Owner: Canadian Broadcasting Corp.
Editorial: 123 Edmonton City Centre, (corner 100 Street and 102 Avenue), Edmonton, Alberta T5J 2Y8. **T:** 1 780 468-7401
E: cbx.edmonton@cbc.ca
W: http://www.cbc.ca/edmonton
Editorial Profile: CBX-AM is a non-commercial station owned by the Canadian Broadcasting Corp. The format of the station is talk and news. CBX-AM broadcasts to the Edmonton, Alberta area on 740 AM.

CBX-FM
Owner: Canadian Broadcasting Corp.
Editorial: 123 Edmonton City Centre, Edmonton, Alberta T5J 2Y8.
T: 1 780 468-7500 **E:** cbx.edmonton@cbc.ca
W: http://www.cbc.ca/edmonton
Editorial Profile: CBX-FM is a non-commercial station owned by the Canadian Broadcasting Corp. The station's format is variety. CBX-FM broadcasts to the Edmonton, Alberta area at 90.9 FM.

CBY-AM
Owner: Canadian Broadcasting Corp.
Editorial: 162 Premier Drive, Corner Brook, Newfoundland A2H 6G1. **T:** 1 709 637-1178
E: cbrookradio@cbc.ca
W: http://www.cbc.ca/nl
Editorial Profile: CBY-AM is a non-commercial station owned by Canadian Broadcasting Corp. The format of the station is news and talk. The target audience of the station is adults, ages 18 to 64. CBY-AM broadcasts to the west coast of Newfoundland at 990 AM.

CBYG-FM
Owner: Canadian Broadcasting Corp.
Editorial: 890 Victoria Street, Prince George, British Columbia V2L 5Pl. **T:** 1 250 562-6701
W: http://www.cbc.ca/bc

CBZF-FM
Owner: Canadian Broadcasting Corp.
Editorial: 1160 Regent St, Fredericton, New Brunswick E3B 3Z1. **T:** 1 506 451-4000
W: http://www.cbc.ca/nb

CBZ-FM
Owner: Canadian Broadcasting Corp.
Editorial: 1160 Regent St, Fredericton, New Brunswick E3B 5G4. **T:** 1 506 451-4000
W: http://www.cbc.ca/nb

CFAB-AM
Owner: Maritime Broadcasting System Ltd.
Editorial: 169-A Water St, Windsor, Nova Scotia B0N 2T0. **T:** 1 902 798-2111
E: newsroom@avrnetwork.com
W: http://www.avrnetwork.com
Editorial Profile: CFAB-AM is a commercial station owned by Maritime Broadcasting System Ltd. The format of the station is classic country. CFAB-AM broadcasts to the Windsor, Nova Scotia area at 1450 AM.

CFAC-AM
Owner: Rogers Communications Inc.
Editorial: 2723 37 Ave NE, Calgary, Alberta T1Y 5R8-. **T:** 1 403 246-9696
E: fan960@rci.rogers.com
W: http://www.sportsnet.ca/960
Editorial Profile: CFAC-AM is a commercial station owned by Rogers Communications Inc. The format of the station is sports and talk. CFAC-AM broadcasts to the Calgary, Alberta area at 960 AM.

CFAD-FM
Owner: Salmo Community Radio
Editorial: 6919 Highway 3, Salmo, British Columbia V0G 1Z0. **T:** 1 250 357-2299
E: info@salmofm.ca **W:** http://salmofm.ca
Editorial Profile: CFAD-FM is a non-commercial station owned by Salmo Community Radio. The format of the station is variety. CFAD-FM broadcasats to the Salmo, British Columbia area at 92.1 FM.

CFAI-FM
Owner: Coopérative des Montagnes Ltee
Editorial: 165 boulevard Hebert, 7ieme etage, Edmundston, New Brunswick E3V 2S8.

WORLD NEWS MEDIA

T: 1 506 737-5060 **E:** radio@cfai.fm
W: http://www.cfai.fm
Editorial Profile: CFAI-FM is a non-commercial station owned by La Coopérative des Montagnes Ltee. The format of the station is easy listening. CFAI-FM broadcasts in the Edmunston, New Brunswick area at 101.1 FM.

CFAK-FM
Owner: Université de Sherbrooke(L')
Editorial: 2500, boul de l'Université, Sherbrooke, Quebec J1k 2R1.
T: 1 819 821-8000 62693 **E:** info@cfak.qc.ca
W: http://www.cfak883.usherbrooke.ca
Editorial Profile: CFAK-FM is a non-commercial station owned by the Université de Sherbrooke. The format of the station is variety. CFAK-FM broadcasts to the Sherbrooke, Quebec area at 88.3 FM.

CFAM-AM
Owner: Golden West Broadcasting Ltd.
Editorial: 200-125 Center Ave, Altona, Manitoba R0G 0B0. **T:** 1 204 324-6464
E: info@goldenwestradio.com
W: http://www.cfamradio.com
Editorial Profile: CFAM-AM is a commercial station owned by Golden West Broadcasting Ltd. The format of the station is variety. CFAM-AM broadcasts to the Altona, Manitoba area at 950 AM.

CFAN-FM
Owner: Maritime Broadcasting System Ltd.
Editorial: 396 Pleasant St, Miramichi, New Brunswick E1V 1X3. **T:** 1 506 622-3311
E: cfannews@mbsradio.com
W: http://www.993theriver.com
Editorial Profile: CFAN-FM is a commercial station owned by Maritime Broadcasting System Ltd. The format of the station is hot adult contemporary. CFAN-FM broadcast to Miramichi, New Brunswick at 99.3 FM.

CFAR-AM
Owner: Arctic Radio (1982) Ltd.
Editorial: 316 Green St, Flin Flon, Manitoba R8A 0H2. **T:** 1 204 687-3469
E: cfar@arcticradio.ca
W: http://www.arcticradio.ca
Editorial Profile: CFAR-AM is a commercial station owned by Arctic Radio (1982) Ltd. The format of the station is adult contemporary music. CFAR-AM broadcasts in the Flin Flon, Manitoba area at 590 AM.

CFAX-AM
Owner: Bell Media
Editorial: 1420 Broad St, Victoria, British Columbia V8W 2B1. **T:** 1 250 386-1070
E: cfaxnews@cfax1070.com
W: http://www.cfax1070.com
Editorial Profile: CFAX-AM is a commercial station owned by Bell Media. The format of the station is news and talk. CFAX-AM broadcasts to the Victoria, British Columbia area at 1070 AM.

CFBC-AM
Owner: Maritime Broadcasting System Ltd.
Editorial: 226 Union St, Saint John, New Brunswick E2L 1B1. **T:** 1 506 658-5100
E: mailbag@k100.ca **W:** http://www.cfbc.am/
Editorial Profile: CFBC-AM is a commercial station owned by the Maritime Broadcasting System Ltd. The format of the station is classic country. CFBC-AM broadcasts in the Saint John, New Brunswick area at 930 AM.

CFBG-FM
Owner: Vista Broadcast Group
Editorial: 50-2 Balls Dr, Bracebridge, Ontario P1L 1T1. **T:** 1 705 645-2218
E: moose995.news@moosefm.com
W: http://www.moosefm.com/cfbg
Editorial Profile: CFBG-FM is a commercial station owned by the Vista Broadcast Group. The format of the station is hot adult contemporary. CFBG-FM broadcasts in the Bracebridge, Ontario area at 99.5 FM.

CFBI-FM
Owner: Cambridge Bay Communications Society
T: 1 867 983-3232
Editorial Profile: CFBI-FM is a non-commercial station owned by the Cambridge Bay Communications Society. The format of the station is variety. CFBI-FM broadcasts to the Cambridge Bay, Nunavut area at 97.7 FM.

CFBK-FM
Owner: Vista Broadcast Group
Editorial: 7 John Street, Huntsville, Ontario P1H 1H2. **T:** 1 705 789-4461
E: moose1055.news@moosefm.ca
W: http://moosefm.com/cfbks
Editorial Profile: CFBK-FM is a commercial radio station owned by Vista Broadcast Group. The format of the station is adult contemporary music. CFBK-FM broadcasts to the Huntsville, ON area at 105.5 FM.

CFBL-FM
Owner: Wawatay Native Communications Society
T: 1 807 363-1056
W: http://www.wawataynews.ca/radio
Editorial Profile: CFLB-FM is a commercial station owned by the Wawatay Native Communications Society. The format is talk and its programming is in English and Oji-Cree, a local language. CFLB-FM broacasts to the Bearskin Lake, Ontario area at 89.9 FM.

CFBO-FM
Owner: Radio Beausejour Inc.
Editorial: Cornwall 51, Shediac, New Brunswick E4P 8T8. **T:** 1 506 532-0080
E: cfbo@cfbo.ca **W:** http://www.cfbo.ca
Editorial Profile: CFBO-FM is French-language commercial station owned by Radio Beausejour. The format of the station is adult contemporary. CFBO-FM broadcasts to the Dieppe, New Brunswick area at 90.7 FM.

CFBR-FM
Owner: Astral Media
Editorial: 18520 Stony Plain Road NW, Ste 100, Edmonton, Alberta T5S 2E2.
T: 1 780 486-2800 **E:** news@bear.fm
W: http://www.thebearrocks.com
Editorial Profile: CFBR-FM is a commercial station owned by Astral Media. The format of the station is rock/album-oriented rock music. CFBR-FM broadcasts in the Edmonton, AB area at 100.3 FM.

CFBS-FM
Owner: Radio Blanc-Sablon Inc.
Editorial: 1193 Boul Camille-Marcoux, Lourdes-de-Blanc-Sablon, Quebec G0G 1W0.
T: 1 418 461-2445
E: cfbsradio@globetrotter.net
W: http://cfbsradio.net
Editorial Profile: CFBS-FM is a non-commercial station owned by Radio Blanc-Sablon Inc. The format for the station is variety. CFBS-FM broadcasts to the Lourdes-de-Blanc-Sablon, Quebec area at 89.9 FM.

CFBT-FM
Owner: Bell Media
Editorial: 500-969 Robson St 500, Vancouver, British Columbia V6Z 1X5. **T:** 1 604 871-9000
E: heydj@thebeat.com
W: http://www.thebeat.com
Editorial Profile: CFBT-FM is a commercial station owned by Bell Media. The format of the station is rhythmic Top 40/CHR. CFBT-FM broadcasts to the Vancouver, British Columbia area at 94.5 FM.

CFBU-FM
Owner: Brock University Student Radio
Editorial: 30 Ontario St., St. Catharines, Ontario L2R 7M3. **T:** 1 905 346-2644
E: pd@cfbu.ca **W:** http://www.cfbu.ca
Editorial Profile: CFBU-FM is a non-commercial station owned by the Brock University Student Radio, Inc. The format of the station is variety. CFBU-FM broadcasts to Saint Catharines, Ontario at 103.7 FM

CFBV-AM
Owner: Vista Broadcast Group Inc.
Editorial: 1139 Queen St, Smithers, British Columbia V0J 2N0. **T:** 1 250 847-2521
E: thepeak@thepeak.ca
W: http://www.thepeak.ca
Editorial Profile: CFBV-AM is a commercial station owned by Vista Broadcast Group Inc. The format of the station is hot adult contemporary. CFBV-AM broadcasts to Smithers, British Columbia at 870 AM.

CFBW-FM
Owner: Bluewater Community Radio Inc.
Editorial: 267 10th Street, Hanover, Ontario N4N 1P1. **T:** 1 519 364-0200
E: bluewaterradio@on.aibn.com
W: http://www.bluewaterradio.ca

CFBX-FM
Owner: Kamloops Campus/Community Radio Society
Editorial: 900 McGill Rd, House 8, Kamloops, British Columbia V2C 5N3. **T:** 1 250 377-3988
E: radio@tru.ca **W:** http://www.thex.ca
Editorial Profile: CFBX-FM is a non-commercial station owned by Kamloops Campus/Community Radio Society. The format of the station is variety. CFBX-FM broadcasts to the Kamloops, British Columbia area at 92.5 FM.

CFCA-FM
Owner: Bell Media
Editorial: 255 King St North, Suite 207, Waterloo, Ontario N2J 4V2. **T:** 1 519 884-4470
E: news@koolfm.com
W: http://www.koolfm.com
Editorial Profile: CFCA-FM is a commercial station owned by Bell Media. The format of the station is adult contemporary. CFCA-FM broadcasts to Waterloo, Ontario at 105.3 FM.

CFCB-AM
Owner: Newfoundland Capital Corporation Limited
Editorial: 345 O'Connell Drive, Corner Brook, Newfoundland A2H 7E5. **T:** 1 709 634-4570
E: onair@cfcbradio.com
W: http://www.cfcbradio.com
Editorial Profile: CFCB-AM is a commercial station owned by Newfoundland Capital Corporation Limited. The format of the station is classic country. CFCB-AM broadcasts to the Corner Brook, Newfoundland area at 570 AM.

CFCH-FM
Owner: Chase and District Community Radio Society
Editorial: 320 Shepherd St, Chase, British Columbia V0E 1M0. **T:** 1 250 679-2800
Editorial Profile: CFCH-FM is a non-commercial station owned by Chase and District Community Radio Society. The format is a variety of eclectic music and programming. CFCH-FM broadcasts to the Chase, British Columbia area at 103.5 FM.

CFCO-AM
Owner: Blackburn Radio Inc.
Editorial: 117 Keil Drive South, Chatham, Ontario N7M 3H3. **T:** 1 519 354-2200
E: info@country929.com
W: http://www.country929.com
Editorial Profile: CFCO-AM is a commercial radio station owned by Blackburn Radio Inc. The format of the station is contemporary country. CFCO-AM broadcasts to the Chatham, Ontario area at 630 AM.

CFCO-FM
Owner: Blackburn Radio Inc.
Editorial: 117 Keil Drive South, Chatham, Ontario N7M 3H3. **T:** 1 519 352-3000
E: info@country929.com
W: http://www.630cfco.com
Editorial Profile: CFCO-FM is a commercial station owned by Blackburn Radio Inc. The format of the station is contemporary ountry. CFCO-FM broadcasts to the Chatham, Ontario area at 92.9 FM.

CFCP-FM
Owner: Vista Broadcast Group Inc.
Editorial: 1625-A McPhee Ave, Courtenay, British Columbia V9N 3A6. **T:** 1 250 334-2421
W: http://www.jetfm.ca
Editorial Profile: CFCP-FM is a commercial station owned by Vista Broadcast Group Inc. The format of the station is classic rock. CFCP-FM broadcasts to Courtenay, British Columbia at 98.9 FM.

CFCR-FM
Owner: Community Radio Society of Saskatoon
Editorial: 267 3rd Ave South, Saskatoon, Saskatchewan S7K 2H4. **T:** 1 306 664-6678
E: cfcr@cfcr.ca **W:** http://www.cfcr.ca
Editorial Profile: CFCR-FM is a non-commercial station owned by Community Radio Society of Saskatoon. The format for the station is variety. CFCR-FM broadcasts to the Saskatoon, Saskatchewan area at 90.5 FM.

CFCV-FM
Owner: Newfoundland Capital Corporation Limited
Editorial: 345 O'Connell Dr, Corner Brook, Newfoundland AZH 7E5. **T:** 1 709 634-4570

CFCW-AM
Owner: Newfoundland Capital Corporation Limited
Editorial: 2394 West Edmonton Mall, 8882-170 Street, Edmonton, Alberta T5T 4M2.
T: 1 780 468-3939 **E:** news@cfcw.com
W: http://www.cfcw.com
Editorial Profile: CFCW-AM is a commercial station owned by Newfoundland Capital Corporation Limited. The format of the station is country music. CFCW-AM broadcasts to the Edmonton, Alberta area at 790 AM.

CFCW-FM
Owner: Newfoundland Capital Corporation Limited
Editorial: 5708-48 Ave, Camrose, Alberta T4V 0K1. **T:** 1 780 672-8255
E: feedback@981camfm.com
W: http://www.981camfm.com
Editorial Profile: CFCW-FM is a commercial station owned by Newfoundland Capital Corporation Limited. The format for the station is classic hits. CFCW-FM broadcasts to the Camrose, Alberta area at 98.1 FM.

CFCY-FM
Owner: Maritime Broadcasting System Ltd.
Editorial: 5 Prince St, Charlottetown, Prince Edward Island C1A 4P4. **T:** 1 902 892-1066
E: news@cfcy.pe.ca **W:** http://www.cfcy.fm
Editorial Profile: CFCY-FM is a commercial station owned by Maritime Broadcasting System Ltd. The format of the station is classic country music. CFCY-FM broadcasts to the Charlottetown, Prince Edward Island area at 95.1 FM.

CFDA-FM
Owner: Réseau des Appalaches
Editorial: 55 rue St-Jean Baptiste, Victoriaville, Quebec G6P 4E1. **T:** 1 819 752-5545
E: redaction@passionrock.com
W: http://www.passionrock.com
Editorial Profile: CFDA-FM is a commercial station owned by Réseau des Appalaches. The format of the station is hot adult contemporary. CFDA-FM broadcasts to the Victoriaville, Quebec area at 101.9 FM.

CFDL-FM
Owner: Newfoundland Capital Corporation Limited
Editorial: 345 O'Connell Dr, Corner Brook, Newfoundland A2H 7E5. **T:** 1 709 634-4570
Editorial Profile: CFDL-FM is a commercial station owned by Newfoundland Capital Corporation Limited. The format of the station is classic and contemporary country. CFDL-FM broadcasts to the Corner Brook, Newfoundland area at 97.9 FM.

CFDM-FM
Owner: Flying Dust First Nation
T: 1 306 236-1445 **E:** cfdmradio@hotmail.com
W: http://cfdm.sasktelwebhosting.com
Editorial Profile: CFDM-FM is a non-commercial station owned by Flying Dust First Nation. The format of the station is variety of community radio. CFDM-FM broadcasts to Meadow Lake, Saskatchewan and surrounding areas at 105.7 FM.

CFDV-FM
Owner: Jim Pattison Broadcast Group(The)
Editorial: 2840 Brenner Avenue, 2nd Floor, Red Deer, Alberta T4R 1M9.
T: 1 403 343-7105 **E:** rock@1067thedrive.fm
W: http://www.1067thedrive.fm
Editorial Profile: CFDV-FM is a commercial station owned by The Jim Pattison Broadcast Group. The format is classic rock. CFDV-FM broadcasts to the Red Deer, Alberta area at 106.7 FM.

CFEI-FM
Owner: Astral Media
Editorial: 2596 boulevard Casavant Ouest, Saint-Hyacinthe, Quebec J2S 7R8.
T: 1 450 774-6486
E: receptioncfei@astral.com
W: http://www.boomfm.com
Editorial Profile: CFEI-FM is a commercial station owned by Astral Media. The format of the station is oldies. CFEI-FM broadcasts to the Saint-Hyacinthe, Quebec area at 106.5 FM.

CFEL-FM
Owner: Cogeco
Editorial: 202-5159 de la Rive-Sud Boul 202, Levis, Quebec G6V 4Z5. **T:** 1 418 830-1122
E: nouvelles@1021fm.ca
W: http://www.ckoiquebec.com
Editorial Profile: CFEL-FM is a commercial station owned by Cogeco. The format of the station is hot adult contemporary. CFEL-FM broadcasts to the Levis, Quebec area at 102.1 FM.

CFEP-FM
Owner: Seaside Broadcasting Org.
Editorial: 1540 Shore Rd, Eastern Passage, Nova Scotia b3g 1m5. **T:** 1 902 469-9231
E: wharrett@seasidefm.com
W: http://www.seasidefm.com
Editorial Profile: CFEP-FM is a commercial station owned by Seaside Broadcasting Org. The format is easy listening. CFEP-FM broadcasts to the Eastern Passage, Nova Scotia area at 105.9 FM.

CFEX-FM
Owner: Harvard Broadcasting
Editorial: 400, 255-17th Ave SW, Calgary, Alberta T2S 2T8. **T:** 1 403 670-0210
W: http://www.x929.ca
Editorial Profile: CFEX-FM is a commercial station owned by Harvard Broadcasting. The format of the station is rock alternative. CFEX-FM broadcasts to the Calgary, Alberta area at 92.9 FM.

CFFB-AM
Owner: Canadian Broadcasting Corp.
T: 1 867 979-6100 **E:** nunavut@cbc.ca
W: http://cbc.ca/north
Editorial Profile: CFFB-AM is a non-commercial station owned by the Canadian Broadcasting Corp. The format of the station is news and talk. CFFB-AM broadcasts to Iqalui, Nunavut at 1230 AM.

CFFF-FM
Owner: Trent Radio
Editorial: 715 George St North, Peterborough, Ontario K9H 3T2. **T:** 1 705 741-4011
E: info@trentradio.ca
W: http://www.trentradio.ca
Editorial Profile: CFFF-FM is a non-commercial station owned by Trent Radio. The format of the station is variety. CFFF-FM broadcasts to the Peterborough, Ontario area at 92.7 FM.

CFFM-FM
Owner: Vista Broadcast Group Inc.
Editorial: 83 S First Ave, Williams Lake, British Columbia V2G 1H4. **T:** 1 250 392-6551
E: cariboonews@reachthecariboo.com
W: http://www.therushfm.ca
Editorial Profile: CFFM-FM is a commercial station owned by the Vista Broadcast Group Inc. The format of the station is adult album alternative. CFFM-FM broadcasts to the Williams Lake, British Columbia area at 97.5 FM.

CFFR-AM
Owner: Rogers Communications Inc.
Editorial: 2723 37th Ave NE, Ste 240, Calgary, Alberta T1Y 5R8. **T:** 1 403 291-0000
E: news660@rogers.com
W: http://www.660news.com
Editorial Profile: CFFR-AM is a commercial station owned by Rogers Communications Inc. The format of the station is all news. CFFR-AM broadcasts to the Calgary, Alberta area at 660 AM.

CFGB-FM
Owner: Canadian Broadcasting Corp.
Editorial: 12 Loring Dr, Goose Bay, Newfoundland A0P 1C0. **T:** 1 709 896-2911
E: labradormorning@cbc.ca
W: http://www.cbc.ca/nl
Editorial Profile: CFGB-FM is a non-commercial station owned by Canadian Broadcasting Corp. The format of the station is new and talk. CFGB-FM broadcasts to the Happy Valley - Goose Bay, Newfoundland and Labrador area at 89.5 FM.

CFGE-FM
Owner: Cogeco
Editorial: 4020, boul de Portland, Sherbrooke, Quebec J1L 2V6. **T:** 1 819 822-0937
W: http://www.rythmefm.com/estrie
Editorial Profile: CFGE-FM is a commercial station owned by Cogeco. The format of the station is adult contemporary. CFGE-FM broadcasts to the Sherbrooke, Quebec area at 93.7 FM.

CFGL-FM
Owner: Cogeco
Editorial: 2830, boul. St-Martin Est, Bureau 100, Laval, Quebec H7E 5A1.
T: 1 450 664-4647
W: http://www.rythmefm.com/montreal
Editorial Profile: CFGL-FM is a commercial station owned by Cogeco. The format of the station is adult contemporary. CFGL-FM broadcasts to Greater Montreal at 105.7 FM. As the flagship station of Rythme FM, many of the station's programs are syndicated throughout Quebec.

CFGN-AM
Owner: Newfoundland Capital Corporation Limited
Editorial: 345 O'Connell Dr, Corner Brook, Newfoundland AZH 7E5. **T:** 1 709 634-4570
Editorial Profile: CFGN-AM is a commercial station owned by Newfoundland Capital Corporation Limited. The format of the station is classic country. CFLN-AM broadcasts to the Corner Brook, Newfoundland area at 1230 AM.

CFGO-AM
Owner: Bell Media
Editorial: 87 George St, Ottawa, Ontario K1N 9H7. **T:** 1 613 789-2486
W: http://www.team1200.com
Editorial Profile: CFGO-AM is a commercial station owned by Bell Media. The format of the station is sports. CFGO-AM broadcasts to the Ottawa area at 1200 AM.

CFGP-FM
Owner: Rogers Communications Inc.
Editorial: #200, 9835 101 Ave SUN Bldg, Grande Prairie, Alberta T8V 5V4.
T: 1 780 539-9700 **E:** comments@rock977.ca
W: http://www.rock977.ca
Editorial Profile: CFGP-FM is a commercial station owned by Rogers Communications Inc. The format of the station is rock. CFGP-FM broadcasts to the Grande Prairie, Alberta area at 97.7 FM.

CFGQ-FM
Owner: Corus Entertainment Inc.
Editorial: 170-200 Barclay Parade SW 170, Eau Claire Market, Calgary, Alberta T2P 4R5.
T: 1 403 716-6500 **W:** http://www.q107fm.ca
Editorial Profile: CFGQ-FM is a commercial station owned by Corus Entertainment Inc. The format of the station is classic rock. CFGQ-FM broadcasts in the Calgary, AB area at 107.3 FM.

CFGT-FM
Owner: RNC Media
Editorial: 460 rue Sacre-Coeur Ouest, Bureau 200, Alma, Quebec G8B 1L9.
T: 1 418 662-6888
W: http://www.alma.planeteradio.ca
Editorial Profile: CFGT-FM is a commercial station owned by RNC Media. The format for the station is adult contemporary. CFGT-AM broadcasts to the Alma, Quebec area at 104.5 FM.

CFGW-FM
Owner: Harvard Broadcasting
Editorial: 120 Smith Street East, 4th Floor, Yorkton, Saskatchewan S3N 3V3.
T: 1 306 782-9410
E: ykt-reception@harvardbroadcasting.com
W: http://www.941thefox.com
Editorial Profile: CFGW-FM is a commercial station owned by Harvard Broadcasting. The format of the station is hot adult contemporary. CFGW-FM broadcasts to the Yorkton, Saskatchewan area at 94.1 FM.

CFGX-FM
Owner: Blackburn Radio Inc.
Editorial: 1415 London Road, Sarnia, Ontario N7S 1P6. **T:** 1 519 542-5500
W: http://www.foxfm.com
Editorial Profile: CFGX-FM is a commercial station owned by Blackburn Radio Inc. The format of the station is adult contemporary. CFGX-FM broadcasts to Sarnia, Ontario at 99.9 FM.

CFHK-FM
Owner: Corus Entertainment Inc.
Editorial: 380 Wellington Street, Room 222, London, Ontario N6A-5B5. **T:** 1 519 931-6000
W: http://www.1031freshfm.ca
Editorial Profile: CFHK-FM is a commercial station owned by Corus Entertainment Inc. The format of the station is adult contemporary. CFHK-FM broadcasts to London, Ontario at 103.1 FM.

CFID-FM
Owner: Radio Acton
Editorial: 1185 Rue St. Andre, Acton Vale, Quebec J0H 1A0. **T:** 1 450 546-1037
E: info@radio-acton.com
W: http://www.radio-acton.com
Editorial Profile: CFID-FM is a non-commercial station owned by Radio Acton. The format of the station is variety. CFID-FM broadcasts to Acton Vale, Quebec at 103.7 FM.

CFIF-FM
Owner: Vista Broadcast Group
T: 1 705 272-6467
E: moose981@moosefm.com
W: http://www.moosefm.com
Editorial Profile: CFIF-FM is a commercial station owned by Vista Broadcast Group. The format of the station is lite rock. CFIF-FM broadcasts in the Iroquois Falls, ON area at 101.1 FM.

CFIM-FM
Owner: Diffusion Communautaire des Iles Inc.
Editorial: 1172 Chemin Laverniere, Etang-du-Nord, Iles-de-la-Madeleine, Cap-Aux-Meules, Quebec G0B 1B0. **T:** 1 418 986-5233
E: administration@cfim.ca
W: http://www.cfim.ca
Editorial Profile: CFIM-FM is commercial station owned by Diffusion Communautaire des Iles Inc. The format of the station is adult contemporary. CFIM-FM broadcasts to Cap-aux-Meules, Quebec at 92.7 FM.

CFIN-FM
Owner: Radio Bellechasse
Editorial: 201 rue Claude-Bilodeau, Lac-Etchemin, Quebec G0R 1S0.
T: 1 418 625-3737 **E:** cfinfm@sogetel.net
W: http://www.cfin-fm.com
Editorial Profile: CFIN-FM is a non-commercial station owned by Radio Bellechasse. The format of the station is variety. CFIN-FM broadcasts to the Lac-Etchemin, Quebec area at 100.5 FM.

CFIS-FM
Owner: Prince George Community Radio Society
Editorial: 2880 15th Ave, Prince George, British Columbia V2M 1T1. **T:** 1 250 563-2347
E: mail@cfisfm.com **W:** http://www.cfisfm.com
Editorial Profile: CFIS-FM is a non-commercial station owned by Prince George Community Radio Society. The format of the station is oldies. CFIS-FM broadcasts to the Prince George, BC area at 93.1 FM.

CFIT-FM
Owner: Golden West
Editorial: 105 main st. north, unit 30, Airdrie, Alberta t4b 0r3. **T:** 1 403 217-1061
E: airdrienews@goldenwestradio.com
W: http://discoverairdrie.com
Editorial Profile: CFIT-FM is a commercial station owned by Golden West Broadcasting Ltd. The format is hot adult contemporary. CFIT-FM broadcasts to the Airdrie, Alberta area at 106.1 FM.

CFIX-FM
Owner: Bell Media
Editorial: 267, rue Racine Est, 2è étage, Chicoutimi, Quebec G7H 5K3.
T: 1 418 543-9797
W: http://saguenay.rougefm.ca
Editorial Profile: CFIX-FM is a commercial station owned by Bell Media. The format of the station is adult contemporary. CFIX-FM broadcasts to the Chicoutimi, Quebec area at 96.9 FM.

CFJB-FM
Owner: Central Ontario Broadcasting
Editorial: 431 Huronia Road, Unit 10, Barrie, Ontario L4N 9B3. **T:** 1 705 725-7304
E: newsroom@rock95.com
W: http://www.rock95.com
Editorial Profile: CFJB-FM is a commercial station owned by Central Ontario Broadcasting. The format of the station is classic rock. CFJB-FM broadcasts to the Barrie, Ontario area at 95.7 FM.

CFJL-FM
Owner: Evanov Communications
Editorial: 520 Corydon Avenue, Winnipeg, Manitoba R3L 0P1. **T:** 1 204 477-1221
W: http://www.thebreezefm.ca
Editorial Profile: CFJL-FM is a commercial station owned by Evanov Communications. The format of the station is soft AC. CFJL-FM broadcasts to the Winnipeg, Manitoba area at 100.7 FM.

CFJO-FM
Owner: Réseau des Appalaches
Editorial: 55, rue Saint-Jean-Baptiste, Victoriaville, Quebec G6P 4E1.
T: 1 819 752-2785 **E:** info@o973.com
W: http://www.o973.com
Editorial Profile: CFJO-FM is a commercial radio station owned by Reseau des Appalaches. The format of the station is adult contemporary. CFJO-FM broadcasts to Victoriaville, Quebec at 97.3 FM.

CFJR-FM
Owner: Bell Media
Editorial: 601 Stewart Blvd, Brockville, Ontario K6V 5T4. **T:** 1 613 345-1666
E: comments@1049jrfm.com
W: http://www.1049jrfm.com
Editorial Profile: CFJR-FM is a commercial station owned by Bell Media. The format of the station is adult contemporary. CFJR-FM broadcasts to the Brockville, Ontario area at 104.9 FM.

CFJU-FM
Owner: Radio Communautaire des Hauts-Plateaux Inc.
T: 1 506 235-9000 **E:** cfjufm@rogers.com
W: http://www.cfjufm.com
Editorial Profile: CFJU-FM is a non-commercial station owned by Radio Communautaire des Hauts-Plateaux Inc. The format of the station is variety. CFJU-FM broadcasts to the Kedgwick, New Brunswick area at 90.1 FM.

CFLC-FM
Owner: Newfoundland Capital Corporation Limited
Editorial: 345 O'Connell Drive, Corner Brook, Newfoundland A2H 7E5. **T:** 1 709 634-4570
E: info@bigland.fm **W:** http://www.bigland.fm
Editorial Profile: CFLC-FM is a commercial station owned by Newfoundland Capital Corporation Limited. The format of the station is country. CFLC-FM broadcasts to the Churchill Falls, Labrador area at a frequency of 97.9 FM.

CFLG-FM
Owner: Corus Entertainment Inc.
Editorial: 709 Cotton Mill Street, Cornwall, Ontario K6H 7K7. **T:** 6139325180
E: variety104@seawayvalley.com
W: http://www.thecornwalldaily.com
Editorial Profile: CFLG-FM is a commercial station owned by Corus Entertainment Inc. The format of the station is adult contemporary. CFLG-FM broadcasts to the Cornwall, Ontario area at 104.5 FM.

CFLM-AM
Owner: CFLM Radio Haute Mauricie Inc.
Editorial: 529 rue St Louis, CP850, La Tuque, Quebec G9X 3P6. **T:** 1 819 523-4575
E: radiocflm@lino.com **W:** http://www.cflm.ca
Editorial Profile: CFLM-AM is a commercial station owned by CFLM Radio Haute Mauricie Inc. The format of the station is Adult Contemporary. CFLM-AM broadcasts to the La Tuque, Quebec area at 1240 AM.

CFLN-FM
Owner: Newfoundland Capital Corporation Limited
Editorial: 345 O'Connell Dr, Corner Brook, Newfoundland A2H 7E5. **T:** 1 709 634-4570
W: http://www.bigland.fm
Editorial Profile: CFLN-FM is a commercial station owned by Newfoundland Capital Corporation Limited. The format of the station is adult contemporary. CFLN-FM broadcasts to the Happy Valley Goose Bay, Newfoundland area at 97.9 FM.

CFLO-FM
Owner: Sonème (2007) Inc.
Editorial: 456, rue du Pont, Mont-Laurier, Quebec J9L 2R9. **T:** 1 819 623-6610
E: nouvelles@cflo.ca **W:** http://www.cflo.ca
Editorial Profile: CFLO-FM is a commercial station owned by Sonème (2007) Inc. The format of the station is adult contemporary. CFLO-FM broadcasts to the Mont-Laurier, Quebec area at 104.7 FM.

CFLT-FM
Owner: Rogers Media Inc.
Editorial: 6080 Young Street, Ste 911, Halifax, Nova Scotia B3K 5L2. **T:** 1 902 493-7200
E: news957@rogers.com
W: http://www.lite929.com
Editorial Profile: CFLT-FM is a commercial station owned by Rogers Media Inc. The format of the station is lite rock music. CFLT-FM broadcasts to the Halifax, Nova Scotia area at 92.9 FM.

CFLW-AM
Owner: Newfoundland Capital Corporation Limited
Editorial: 391 Kenmount Rd, St. John's, Newfoundland A1B 3P5. **T:** 1 709 726-5590
E: feedback@vocm.com
W: http://www.vocm.com
Editorial Profile: CFLW-AM is a transmitter located in Wabush, Newfoundland that simulcasts the programming of CFLN-AM. It is owned by Newfoundland Capital Corporation Limited. CFLW-AM broadcasts to the Wabush, Newfoundland area at 1340 AM. The stations are part of NewCap's VOCM brand.

CFLX-FM
Owner: Radio Communautaire de l'Estrie
Editorial: 67 rue Wellington Nord, Sherbrooke, Quebec J1H 5A9. **T:** 1 819 566-2787
E: commentaires@cflx.qc.ca
W: http://www.cflx.qc.ca
Editorial Profile: CFLX-FM is a non-commercial station owned by Radio Communautaire de l'Estrie. The format of the station is adult contemporary. CFLX-FM

WORLD NEWS MEDIA

broadcasts to the Sherbrooke, Quebec area 95.5 FM.

CFLY-FM
Owner: Bell Media
Editorial: 993 Princess St Suite 10, Kingston, Ontario K7L 1H3. **T:** 1 613 544-1380
E: heydeejay@983flyfm.com
W: http://www.983flyfm.com
Editorial Profile: CFLY-FM is a commercial station owned by Bell Media. The format of the station is adult contemporary music. CFLY-FM broadcasts to the Kingston, Ontario area at 98.3 FM.

CFLZ-FM
Owner: Vista Broadcast Group
Editorial: 4673 Ontario Ave, Niagara Falls, Ontario L2E 3R1. **T:** 1 905 356-6710
W: http://www.2dayfm.ca
Editorial Profile: CFLZ-FM is a commercial station owned by Vista Broadcast Group. The format of the station is Top 40/CHR. CKEY-FM broadcasts to the Niagara Falls, Ontario area at 101.1 FM.

CFMB-AM
Owner: CFMB Ltd.
Editorial: 35 York St, Montreal, Quebec H3Z 2Z5. **T:** 1 514 483-2362 **E:** info@cfmb.ca
W: http://www.cfmb.ca
Editorial Profile: CFMB-AM a commercial station owned by CFMB Ltd. The format of the station is a variety. CFMB-AM broadcasts in the Montreal area at 1280 AM.

CFMC-FM
Owner: Rawlco Radio Ltd.
Editorial: 715 Saskatchewan Cres W, Saskatoon, Saskatchewan S7M 5V7.
T: 1 306 934-2222 **E:** c95@c95.com
W: http://www.c95.com
Editorial Profile: CFMC-FM is a commercial station owned by Rawlco Radio Ltd. The format of the station is hot adult contemporary. CFMC-FM broadcasts to Saskatoon, Saskatchewan at 95.1 FM.

CFMF-FM
Owner: Diffusion Fermont
Editorial: 20 Place Daviault, Fermont, Quebec G0G 1J0. **T:** 1 418 287-5147
E: infocfmf@diffusionfermont.ca
W: http://www.cfmf.ca
Editorial Profile: CFMF-FM is a commercial station owned by Diffusion Fermont. The format of the station is Top 40/CHR. CFMF-FM broadcasts to Fermont, Quebec at 103.1 FM.

CFMG-FM
Owner: Bell Media
Editorial: 18520 Stony Plain Rd NW, Edmonton, Alberta T5S 1A8.
T: 1 780 435-1049
W: http://edmonton.virginradio.ca
Editorial Profile: CFMG-FM is a commercial station owned by Bell Media. The format of the station is Top 40/CHR. CFMG-FM broadcasts to Edmonton, Alberta at 104.9 FM.

CFMH-FM
Owner: Campus Radio St. John Inc.
Editorial: T.J. Condon Student Centre, 100 Tucker Park Road, Saint John, New Brunswick E2L 4L5. **T:** 1 506 648-5667
E: cfmh@unbsj.ca **W:** http://www.localfm.ca
Editorial Profile: CFMH-FM is a non-commercial station owned by Campus Radio St. John Inc. The format for the station is college variety. CFMH-FM broadcasts to the Saint John, New Brunswick area at 107.3 FM.

CFMI-FM
Owner: Corus Entertainment Inc.
Editorial: 700 Georgia St W, Vancouver, British Columbia V7Y 1K8. **T:** 1 604 331-2808
E: info@rock101.com
W: http://www.rock101.com
Editorial Profile: CFMI-FM is a commercial station owned by Corus Entertainment Inc. The format of the station is classic rock music. CFMI-FM broadcasts to the Vancouver, BC area at 101.1 FM.

CFMJ-AM
Owner: Corus Entertainment Inc.
Editorial: Corus Quay, 25 Dockside Drive, Toronto, Ontario M5A 0B5. **T:** 1 416 479-7000
E: newstip@640toronto.com
W: http://www.640toronto.com
Editorial Profile: CFMJ-AM is a commercial station owned by Corus Entertainment Inc. The format of the station is news and talk. CFMJ-AM broadcasts in the Toronto, Ontario area at 640 AM.

CFMK-FM
Owner: Corus Entertainment Inc.
Editorial: 170 Queen St, Kingston, Ontario K7K 1B2. **T:** 1 613 544-2340
W: http://www.fm96.ca
Editorial Profile: CFMK-FM is a commercial station owned by Corus Entertainment Inc. The format of the station is classic rock. CFMK-FM broadcasts to Kingston, Ontario at 96.3 FM.

CFML-FM
Owner: BC Institute of Technology
Editorial: 3700 Willingdon Ave, BC Institute of Technology Bldg SE-10, Burnaby, British Columbia V5G 3H2. **T:** 1 604 432-8510
E: sales@evolution1079.com
W: http://www.evolution1079.com
Editorial Profile: CFML-FM is a non-commercial station owned by the BC Institute of Technology. The format of the station is AAA-Adult Album Alternative. CFML-FM broadcasts to the Burnaby, British Columbia area at 107.9 FM. The station is student-run.

CFMM-FM
Owner: Rawlco Radio Ltd.
Editorial: 1316 Central Ave, Prince Albert, Saskatchewan S6V 7R4. **T:** 1 306 763-7421
E: power99fm@rawlco.com
W: http://www.power99fm.com
Editorial Profile: CFMM-FM is a commercial station owned by Rawlco Radio Ltd. The format of the station is adult contemporary. CFMM-FM broadcasts to the Prince Albert, Saskatchewan area at 99.1 FM.

CFMQ-FM
Owner: HB Communications Inc.
Editorial: 635 Prince Street, Hudson Bay, Saskatchewan S0E 0Y0. **T:** 1 306 865-3065
E: cfmq@sasktel.net
Editorial Profile: CFMQ-FM is a commercial station owned by HB Communications Inc. CFMQ-FM's format is variety. CFMQ-FM broadcasts to Hudson Bay, Saskatchewan at 98.1 FM.

CFMU-FM
Owner: McMaster Students' Union
Editorial: McMaster University Rm B119, MUSC Student Centre, Hamilton, Ontario L8S 4S4. **T:** 1 905 525-9140
E: cfmuprod@msu.mcmaster.ca
W: http://cfmu.mcmaster.ca
Editorial Profile: CFMU-FM is a commercial station owned by the McMaster Students' Union. The format for the station is variety. CFMU-FM broadcasts to the Hamilton, Ontario area at 93.3 FM.

CFMV-FM
Owner: Radio du Golfe Inc.
Editorial: 141 rue Commerciale Ouest, Apt 101, Chandler, Quebec G0C 1K0.
T: 1 418 689-4921 **E:** cfmv@fm96-3.com
W: http://www.fm96-3.com
Editorial Profile: CFMV-FM is a commercial station owned by Radio du Golfe Inc. The format of the station is talk. CFMV-FM broadcasts to the Chandler, Quebec area at 96.3 FM.

CFMX-FM
Owner: ZoomerMedia Limited
Editorial: 1 Queen St, Ste 101, Cobourg, Ontario K9A 4W5. **T:** 1 905 372-4366
E: cfmx@primus.ca
W: http://www.classical963fm.com
Editorial Profile: CFMX-FM is a commercial station owned by ZoomerMedia Limited. The format of the station is classical. CFMX-FM broadcasts to the Cobourg, Ontario area at 103.1 FM.

CFMY-FM
Owner: Jim Pattison Broadcast Group(The)
Editorial: 10 Boundary Rd SE, Redcliff, Alberta T0J 2P0-. **T:** 1 403 548-8282
E: my96fm@jpbg.com
W: http://www.my96fm.com
Editorial Profile: CFMY-FM is a commercial station owned by The Jim Pattison Broadcast Group. The format is hot adult contemporary. CFMY-FM broadcasts in the Redcliff, Alberta area at 96.1 FM.

CFMZ-FM
Owner: ZoomerMedia Limited
Editorial: 550 Queen St East, Ste 205, Toronto, Ontario M5A 1V2. **T:** 1 416 367-5353
E: info@classical963fm.com
W: http://www.classical963fm.com
Editorial Profile: CFMZ-FM is a commercial station owned by ZoomerMedia Limited. The format of the station is classical. CFMX-FM broadcasts to the Toronto area at 96.3 FM.

CFNA-FM
Owner: Vista Broadcast Group Inc.
Editorial: 102-5316 54 Ave 102, Bonnyville, Alberta T9N 2C9. **T:** 1 780 812-3997
W: http://99.countryfm.ca
Editorial Profile: CFNA-FM is a commercial station owned by Vista Broadcast Group Inc. The format for the station is country. CFNA-FM broadcasts to the Bonnyville, Alberta area at 99.7 FM.

CFNC-AM
Owner: Cross Lake Radio Committee
T: 1 204 676-2331
Editorial Profile: CFNC-AM is a commercial station owned by Cross Lake Radio Committee. The format of the station is variety. CFNC-AM broadcasts to the Cross Lake, Manitoba area at 1490 AM.

CFND-FM
Owner: Ecole Notre-Dame
Editorial: 581, rue Ouimet, St-Jerome, Quebec J5Z 1R3. **T:** 1 450 432-4472 5763
E: radionotredame@edu.csrdn.qc.ca
W: http://www.csrdn.qc.ca/notre-dame/canvas2.asp?pageid=78
Editorial Profile: CFND-FM is a non-commericial station owned by Ecole Notre-Dame. The format of the station is children. The target audience of the station is children, ages 2 to 12. CFND-FM broadcasts to the Saint-Jerome, Quebec area at 101.9 FM.

CFNI-AM
Owner: Vista Broadcast Group Inc.
Editorial: 5050 Beaver Harbor Road, Port Hardy, British Columbia V0N 2P0.
T: 1 250 949-6500 **E:** onair@theport.ca
W: http://www.theport.ca
Editorial Profile: CFNI-AM is a commercial station owned by Vista Broadcast Group Inc. The format of the station is adult contemporary. CFNI-AM broadcasts to the Port Hardy, British Columbia area at 1240 AM.

CFNJ-FM
Owner: Radio Nord-Joli Inc.
Editorial: 245 rue Beauvilliers, St-Gabriel-de-Brandon, Quebec J0K 2N0. **T:** 1 450 835-3437
E: rnjoli@bellnet.ca **W:** http://www.cfnj.net
Editorial Profile: CFNJ-FM is a commercial station owned by Radio Nord-Joli Inc. The format of the station is a variety of music and talk. CFNJ-FM broadcasts to the St-Gabriel-de-Brandon, Quebec area at 99.1 FM.

CFNN-FM
Owner: Newfoundland Capital Corporation Limited
Editorial: 345 O'Connell Dr, Corner Brook, Newfoundland A2H 7E5. **T:** 1 709 634-4570
E: onair@cfcbradio.com
W: http://www.cfcbradio.com
Editorial Profile: CFNN-FM is a commercial station owned by Newfoundland Capital Corporation Limited. The format of the station is classic country. CFNN-AM broadcasts to the Corner Brook, Newfoundland area at 97.9 FM.

CFNO-FM
Owner: North Superior Broadcasting Ltd.
Editorial: 93 Evergreen Drive, Marathon, Ontario P0T 2E0. **T:** 1 807 229-1010
W: http://www.cfno.fm
Editorial Profile: CFNO-FM is a commercial station owned by North Superior Broadcasting Ltd. The format of the station is adult contemporary music. CFNO-FM broadcasts to the Marathon, Ontario area at 93.1 FM.

CFNR-FM
Owner: Northern Native Broadcasting Terrace
Editorial: 4562B Queensway Drive, Terrace, British Columbia V8G 3X6. **T:** 1 250 638-8137
E: reception@classicrockcfnr.ca
W: http://www.classicrockcfnr.ca

CFNW-AM
Owner: Newfoundland Capital Corporation Limited
Editorial: 345 O'Connell Dr, Corner Brook, Newfoundland AZH 7ES. **T:** 1 709 634-4570
Editorial Profile: CFNW-AM is a commercial station owned by Newfoundland Capital Corporation Limited. The format of the station is classic country. CFNW-AM broadcasts to the Corner Brook, Newfoundland area at 790 AM.

CFNY-FM
Owner: Corus Entertainment Inc.
Editorial: Corus Quay, 25 Dockside Drive, Toronto, Ontario M5A 0B5. **T:** 1 416 408-3343
E: info@edge.ca **W:** http://www.edge.ca
Editorial Profile: CFNY-FM is a commercial station owned by Corus Entertainment Inc. The format of the station is rock alternative. CFNY-FM broadcasts throughout the Toronto metro area at 102.1 FM.

CFOB-FM
Owner: Arcadia Broadcasting
Editorial: 210 Scott Street, Fort Frances, Ontario P9A 1G7. **T:** 1 807 274-5341
E: info@931theborder.ca **W:** http://www.b93.ca
Editorial Profile: CFOB-FM is a commercial station owned by Arcadia Broadcasting. The format of the station is adult contemporary. CFOB-FM broadcasts in the Fort Frances, Ontario area at 93.1 FM.

CFOM-FM
Owner: Cogeco
Editorial: 1305, chemin ste-foy 4th floor, Quebec, Quebec. **T:** 1 418 694-1029
W: http://www.1029quebec.fm
Editorial Profile: CFOM-FM is a commercial station owned by Cogeco. The format for the station is adult contemporary. CFOM-FM broadcasts to the Sainte-Foy, Quebec area at 102.9 FM.

CFOR-FM
Owner: Radio CFOR
Editorial: 139 Principale Sud., Maniwaki, Quebec J9E 1Z8. **T:** 1 819 441-0993
E: cfor993@b2b2c.ca
W: http://www.cforfm.com
Editorial Profile: CFOR-FM is a commercial station owned by Radio CFOR. The format of the station is classic rock. CFOR-FM broadcasts to the Maniwaki, Quebec area at 99.3 FM.

CFOS-AM
Owner: Bayshore Broadcasting Corp.
Editorial: 270 Ninth Street East, Owen Sound, Ontario N4K 1N7. **T:** 1 519 376-2030
E: 560cfos@bayshorebroadcasting.ca
W: http://www.560cfos.ca
Editorial Profile: CFOS-AM is a commercial station owned by Bayshore Broadcasting Corp. The format of the station is oldies music and talk. CFOS-AM broadcasts throughout the Owen Sound, Ontario area at 560 AM.

CFOU-FM
Owner: Université du Québec à Trois-Rivières(L')
Editorial: 3351 Boulevard des Forges, Pavillon Nérée-Beauchemin, Trois-Rivieres, Quebec G9A 5H7. **T:** 1 819 376-5184
E: progcfou@uqtr.ca **W:** http://www.cfou.ca
Editorial Profile: CFOU-FM is a non-commercial station owned by the Université du Québec à Trois-Rivières. The format of the station is variety. CFOU-FM broadcasts to Trois-Rivières, Quebec at 89.1 FM.

CFOX-FM
Owner: Corus Entertainment Inc.
Editorial: 700 West Georgia, Suite 2000, Vancouver, British Columbia V7Y 1K9.
T: 1 604 684-7221 **W:** http://www.cfox.com
Editorial Profile: CFOX-FM is a commercial station owned Corus Entertainment Inc. The format of the station is rock alternative. CFOX-FM broadcasts in the Vancouver, BC area at 99.3 FM.

CFOZ-FM
Owner: Newfoundland Broadcasting Co. Ltd.
Editorial: 446 Logy Bay Rd, St. John's, Newfoundland A1C 5S2. **T:** 1 709 726-2922
E: ozfm@ozfm.com **W:** http://www.ozfm.com

CFPA-FM
Owner: Vista Broadcast Group Inc.
Editorial: 5050 Beaver Harbor Road, Port Hardy, British Columbia V0N 2P0.
T: 1 250 949-6500 **E:** news@jetfm.ca
W: http://www.coastradio.com
Editorial Profile: CFPA-FM is a commercial station owned by Vista Broadcast Group Inc. The format of the station is adult contemporary. CFPA-FM broadcasts in the Port Hardy, British Columbia area at 100.3 FM.

CFPL-AM
Owner: Corus Entertainment Inc.
Editorial: 380 Wellington Street, Room 222, London, Ontario N6A 5B5. **T:** 1 519 931-6000
W: http://www.am980.ca
Editorial Profile: CFPL-AM is a commercial station owned by Corus Entertainment Inc. The format of the station is news, sports and talk. CFPL-AM broadcasts throughout the London, Ontario area at 980 AM. To send a general e-mail to the station please see the comment form on their website.

CFPL-FM
Owner: Corus Entertainment Inc.
Editorial: 380 Wellington Street, Room 222, London, Ontario N6A 5B5. **T:** 1 519 931-6000
W: http://www.fm96.com
Editorial Profile: CFPL-FM is a commercial station owned by Corus Entertainment Inc. The format of the station is album-oriented rock. CFPL-FM broadcasts to London, Ontario at 95.9 FM.

CFPR-AM
Owner: Canadian Broadcasting Corp.
Editorial: 222 3rd Ave W #1, Prince Rupert, British Columbia V8J 1L1. **T:** 1 250 624-2161
E: daybreaknorth@cbc.ca **W:** http://cbc.ca/bc

CFPS-FM
Owner: Bayshore Broadcasting Corp.
Editorial: 382 Goderich Street, Port Elgin, Ontario N0H 2C1. **T:** 1 519 832-9800
E: thebeach@98thebeach.ca
W: http://www.98thebeach.ca
Editorial Profile: CFPS-FM is a commercial station owned by Bayshore Broadcasting Corporation. The format of the station is adult contemporary. The station's tagline is "98 The Beach." CFPS-FM broadcasts to the Port Elgin, Ontario area at 97.9 FM.

CFPV-FM
Owner: McBride Communications & Media Inc.
Editorial: 10760 Fundy Drive, Richmond, British Columbia V7E 5K7. **T:** 1 604 220-8393
E: info@cfpvfm.com
W: http://www.cfpvfm.com
Editorial Profile: CFPV-FM is a commercial station owned by McBride Communications & Media Inc. The format of the station is classic rock. CFPV-FM broadcasts to the Pemberton, British Columbia area at 98.9 FM.

CFPW-FM
Owner: Vista Broadcast Group Inc.
Editorial: #103-4675 Marine Dr, Powell River, British Columbia V8A 2L2. **T:** 1 604 485-4207
E: news@957sunfm.ca
W: http://www.957sunfm.ca
Editorial Profile: CFPW-FM is a commercial station owned by Vista Broadcast Group Inc. The format of the station is Top 40/CHR. CFPW-FM broadcasts to the Powell River, British Columbia area at 95.7 FM.

CFQK-FM
Owner: Dougall Media
Editorial: 87 N Hill St, Thunder Bay, Ontario P7A 5V6. **T:** 1 807 346-2600
E: thunder@thethunder.ca
W: http://www.thethunder.ca
Editorial Profile: CFQK-FM is a commercial station owned by Dougall Media. The format of the station is contemporary country music. CFQK-FM broadcasts to the Thunder Bay, Ontario area at 103.5 FM.

CFQM-FM
Owner: Maritime Broadcasting System Ltd.
Editorial: 1000 St George Blvd, Moncton, New Brunswick E1E 4M7-. **T:** 1 506 858-1220
E: 1039maxfm@mbsradio.com
W: http://www.1039maxfm.com
Editorial Profile: CFQM-FM is a commercial station owned by the Maritime Broadcasting System Ltd. The format of the station is classic hits. CFQM-FM broadcasts throughout the Moncton, New Brunswick area at 103.9 FM.

CFQX-FM
Owner: Astral Media
Editorial: 177 Lombard Avenue, 3rd Floor, Winnipeg, Manitoba R3B 0W5.
T: 1 204 944-1031 **E:** psa@hotqx.com
W: http://www.qx104fm.com
Editorial Profile: CFQX-FM is a commercial station owned by Astral Media. The format of the station is contemporary country. CFQX-FM broadcasts to the Winnipeg, Manitoba area at 104.1 FM.

CFRA-AM
Owner: Bell Media
Editorial: 87 George St, Ottawa, Ontario K1N 9H7. **T:** 1 613 789-2486 **E:** news@cfra.com
W: http://www.cfra.com
Editorial Profile: CFRA-AM is a commercial station owned by Bell Media. The format of the station is news and talk. CFRA-AM broadcasts to the Ottawa, Ontario area at 580 AM.

CFRB-AM
Owner: Bell Media
Editorial: 260 Richmond Street, Toronto, Ontario M5V 1W4. **T:** 1 416 924-5711
E: news@newstalk1010.com
W: http://www.newstalk1010.com
Editorial Profile: CFRB-AM is a commercial station owned by Bell Media. The format of the station is news and talk. CFRB-AM broadcasts to the Toronto area at 1010 AM. CFRB-AM is a member of the Canadian Press Gallery.

CFRC-FM
Owner: Radio Queen's University
Editorial: Queen's University Lower Carruthers Hall, Kingston, Ontario K7L 3N6.
T: 1 613 533-2121 **E:** cfrc@ams.queensu.ca
W: http://www.cfrc.ca
Editorial Profile: CFRC-FM is a non-commercial station owned by Radio Queen's University. The format of the station is variety. CFRC-FM broadcasts to the Kingston, Ontario area at 101.9 FM.

CFRE-FM
Owner: University of Toronto
Editorial: 3359 Mississauga Rd N R#131, University of Toronto at Mississauga, Mississauga, Ontario L5L 1C6.
T: 1 905 369-0504 **E:** staff@cfreradio.com
W: http://www.cfreradio.com
Editorial Profile: CFRE-FM is a college station owned by the University of Toronto. The station airs at 91.9 in the Mississauga, Ontario area.

CFRG-FM
Owner: Association communautaire fransaskoise de Gravelbourg
T: 1 306 648-2374 **E:** info@cfrg.ca
W: http://cfrg.ca

CFRH-FM
Owner: Radio-Huronie FM Communautaire Inc.
Editorial: 63 rue Main, Penetanguishene, Ontario L9M 2G3. **T:** 1 705 549-3116
E: vaguefm@vaguefm.ca **W:** http://vaguefm.ca
Editorial Profile: CFRH-FM is a non-commercial station owned by Radio-Huronie FM Communautaire Inc. The format of the station is adult contemporary. CFRH-FM broadcasts to the Penetanguishene, Ontario area at 88.1 FM

CFRI-FM
Owner: Vista Broadcast Group Inc.
Editorial: 1-11002 104 Ave 1, Grande Prairie, Alberta T8V 7W5-. **T:** 1 780 357-6397
E: news@1047freefm.com
W: http://www.1047freefm.com
Editorial Profile: CFRI-FM is a commercial station owned by Vista Broadcast Group Inc. The format of the station is classic rock. CFRI-FM broadcasts to the Grande Prairie, Alberta area at 104.7 FM.

CFRK-FM
Owner: Newfoundland Capital Corporation Limited
Editorial: 495 Prospect St., Fredericton, New Brunswick E3B 9M4. **T:** 1 506 455-0923
W: http://www.thenewhot923.com
Editorial Profile: CFRK-FM is a commercial station owned by Newfoundland Capital Corporation Limited. The format of the station is Top 40/ CHR. CFRK-FM broadcasts to the Fredericton, New Brunswick area at 92.3 FM.

CFRM-FM
Owner: Timmermans (Craig)
Editorial: 10 Campbell St E, Little Current, Ontario P0P 1K0. **T:** 1 705 368-1419
E: radio@manitoulin.net
W: http://www.theislandfm.com
Editorial Profile: CFRM-FM is a commercial station owned by Craig Timmermans. The format for the station is contemporary country. CFRM-FM broadcasts to the Little Current, Ontario area at 100.7 FM.

CFRN-AM
Owner: Astral Media
Editorial: 18520 Stony Plain Road, Ste 100, Edmonton, Alberta T5S 2E2.
T: 1 780 486-2800 **E:** news@bear.fm
W: http://www.theteam1260.com
Editorial Profile: CFRN-AM is a commercial station owned by Astral Media. The format of the station is sports and talk. CFRN-AM broadcasts to the Edmonton, Alberta area at 1260 AM.

CFRO-FM
Owner: Vancouver Co-Operative Radio
Editorial: 110-360 Columbia St, Vancouver, British Columbia V6A 4J1. **T:** 1 604 684-8494
E: cfro-psa@coopradio.org
W: http://www.coopradio.org
Editorial Profile: CFRO-FM is a non-commercial radio station owned by Vancouver Co-Op Radio. The format of the station is news, talk, and multi-cultural programming. CFRO-FM broadcasts in the Vancouver, British Columbia area at 102.7 FM.

CFRP-FM
Owner: Radio Port-Cartier Inc.
Editorial: 907, rue de Puyjalon, Baie-Comeau, Quebec G5C 1N3. **T:** 1 418 589-3771
E: chlcfm97@globetrotter.net
W: http://www.chlc.com
Editorial Profile: CFRP-FM is a commercial station owned by Radio Port-Cartier Inc. The format of the station is Hot Adult Contemporary. CFRP-FM broadcasts to Forestville, Quebec at 100.5 FM.

CFRQ-FM
Owner: Newfoundland Capital Corporation Limited
Editorial: 3770 Kempt Rd, Halifax, Nova Scotia B3K 4X8-. **T:** 1 902 453-4004
E: halifaxnews@newcap.ca
W: http://www.q104.ca
Editorial Profile: CFRQ-FM is a commercial station owned by Newfoundland Capital Corporation Limited. The format of the station is classic rock. CFRQ-FM broadcasts to Halifax, Nova Scotia at 104.3 FM.

CFRT-FM
Owner: Association des francophones du Nunavut
Editorial: 981 Nunavut Drive, Iqaluit, Nunavut X0A 0H0. **T:** 1 867 979-4606
E: cfrt@nunafranc.ca
W: http://www.franconunavut.ca
Editorial Profile: CFRT-FM is a non-commercial station owned by the Association des francophones du Nunavut. The format of the station is variety. CFRT-FM broadcasts to the Iqaluit, Nunavut area at 107.3 FM.

CFRU-FM
Owner: University of Guelph
Editorial: Level 2 Univ Ctr Univ of Guelph, Guelph, Ontario N1G2W1. **T:** 1 519 824-4120
E: programming@cfru.ca
W: http://www.cfru.ca
Editorial Profile: CFRU-FM is a non-commercial station owned by the University of Guelph. The format is college and community variety. CFRU-FM broadcasts to the Guelph, Ontario area at 93.3 FM.

CFRV-FM
Owner: Rogers Communications Inc.
Editorial: 1015 3rd Avenue South, Lethbridge, Alberta T1J 0J3. **T:** 1 403 328-1077
E: theriver@rci.rogers.com
W: http://www.1077theriver.ca
Editorial Profile: CFRV-FM is a commercial radio station owned by Rogers Communications Inc. The format of the station is adult contemporary. CFRV-FM broadcasts to the Lethbridge, Alberta area at 107.7 FM.

CFRW-AM
Owner: Bell Media
Editorial: 1445 Pembina Hwy, Winnipeg, Manitoba R3T 5C2. **T:** 1 204 477-5120
E: tsngo@bellmedia.ca
W: http://www.tsn.ca/winnipeg
Editorial Profile: CFRW-AM is a commercial station owned by Bell Media. The format of the station is sports. CFRW-AM broadcasts throughout the Winnipeg, Manitoba area at 1290 AM.

CFRY-AM
Owner: Golden West Broadcasting Ltd.
Editorial: 350 River Road, Portage La Prairie, Manitoba R1N 3V6. **T:** 1 204 239-5111
W: http://www.cfryradio.ca

CFRY-FM
Owner: Golden West Broadcasting Ltd.
Editorial: 350 River Road, Portage La Prairie, Manitoba R1N 3V6. **T:** 1 204 239-5111
W: http://www.cfryradio.ca
Editorial Profile: CFRY-FM is a commercial station owned by Golden West Broadcasting Ltd. The format of the station is country music. CFRY-FM broadcasts in Portage la Prairie, Manitoba area at 93.1 FM.

CFSF-FM
Owner: Vista Broadcast Group
Editorial: 130-204 King St, Sturgeon Falls, Ontario P2B 1R7. **T:** 1 705 753-6776
E: sturgeonmoose993@moosefm.com
W: http://www.moosefm.com/cfsf
Editorial Profile: CFSF-FM is a commercial station owned by Vista Broadcast Group. The format for the station is English and French Top 40/CHR. CFSF-FM broadcasts to the Sturgeon Falls, Ontario area at 99.3 FM.

CFSI-FM
Owner: Satnam Media
Editorial: 315 Upper Ganges Rd, #19A, Salt Spring Island, British Columbia V8K 2X4.
T: 1 250 931-1079 **W:** http://www.cfsi-fm.com
Editorial Profile: CFSI-FM, Green FM, is a commercial station owned by Satnam Media. The format of the station is community news and variety of music ranging from punk to classic. CFSI-FM broadcasts to the Salt Spring Island, BC area at 107.9 FM.

CFSL-AM
Owner: Golden West Broadcasting Ltd.
Editorial: 305 Souris Ave, Weyburn, Saskatchewan S4H 2K2. **T:** 1 306 848-1190
E: am1190@goldenwestradio.com
W: http://am1190radio.com/
Editorial Profile: CFSL-AM is a commercial radio station owned by Golden West Broadcasting Ltd. The format of the station is country. CFSL-AM broadcasts to the Weyburn, Saskatchewan area at 1190 AM.

CFSR-FM
Owner: Rogers Communications Inc.
Editorial: 46167 Yale Road, Unit 309, Chilliwack, British Columbia V2P 2P2.
T: 1 604 795-5711
E: starnews@starfm.rogers.com
W: http://www.starfm.com

CFSX-AM
Owner: Newfoundland Capital Corporation Limited
Editorial: 60 West Street, Stephenville, Newfoundland A2N 1C6. **T:** 1 709 643-2191
E: cfsx@vocm.com
W: http://www.cfsxradio.com
Editorial Profile: CFSX-AM is a commercial station owned by Newfoundland Capital Corporation Limited. The format of the station is news, talk and classic country. CFSX-AM broadcasts to the Stephenville, Newfoundland area at 870 AM.

CFTA-FM
Owner: Tantramar Community Radio Society
Editorial: 141-S Victoria St. E., Amherst, Nova Scotia B4H 1X9. **T:** 1 902 660-1079
E: cfta@eastlink.ca
W: http://www.tantramarfm.ca
Editorial Profile: CFTA-FM is an independent commercial station owned by Tantramar Community Radio Society. The format of the station is community news, talk, and local music. CFTA-FM broadcasts to the Amherst, Nova Scotia area at a frequency of 107.9 FM.

CFTE-AM
Owner: Bell Media
Editorial: 500-969 Robson St 500, Vancouver, British Columbia V6Z 1X5. **T:** 1 604 871-9000
E: feedback@teamradio.ca
W: http://www.teamradio.ca
Editorial Profile: CFTE-AM is a commercial station owned by Bell Media. The format of the station is sports. CFTE-AM broadcasts to the Vancouver, British Columbia area at 1410 AM.

CFTH-FM
Owner: Harrington Community Radio
T: 1 418 795-3349 **E:** cfthh1@globetrotter.net
W: http://www.lnscommunityradio.com

CFTK-AM
Owner: Astral Media
Editorial: 4625 Lazelle Ave, Terrace, British Columbia V8G 1S4. **T:** 1 250 635-6316
W: http://www.terrace.themixbc.com
Editorial Profile: CFTK-AM is a commercial station owned by Astral Media. The format of the station is hot adult contemporary. CFTK-AM broadcasts to the Terrace, British Columbia area at 590 AM.

CFTL-FM
Owner: Ayamowin Communications Society
Editorial: Big Trout First Nations Office, Big Trout Lake, Ontario P0V 1G0.
T: 1 807 537-2260

CFTR-AM
Owner: Rogers Communications Inc.
Editorial: 777 Jarvis St, Toronto, Ontario M4Y 3B7. **T:** 1 416 935-8468
E: news680@rogers.com
W: http://www.680news.com
Editorial Profile: CFTR-AM is a commercial station owned by Rogers Communications Inc. The format is news programming. CFTR-AM broadcasts to the Toronto, ON area at 680 AM.

CFTR-AM is a member of the Canadian Press Gallery.

CFTX-FM

Owner: RNC Media
Editorial: 171A, rue Jean-Proulx, Gatineau, Quebec J8Z 1W5. **T:** 1 819 770-1040
W: http://www.capitalerock.ca
Editorial Profile: CFTX-FM is a commercial station owned by RNC Media Inc. The format of the station is rock. CFTX-FM broadcasts to the Gatineau, Quebec area at 96.5 FM.

CFUN-FM

Owner: Rogers Communications Inc.
Editorial: 2440 Ash St, Vancouver, British Columbia V5Z 4J6. **T:** 1 604 877-6357
W: http://www.sonicnation.ca
Editorial Profile: CFUN-FM is a commercial station owned by Rogers Communications Inc. The format of the station is Top 40. CFUN-FM broadcasts to the Vancouver, British Columbia area at 104.9 FM.

CFUR-FM

Owner: Education Alternative Radio Society
Editorial: 3333 University, Prince George, British Columbia V2N 4Z9. **T:** 1 250 960-7664
E: news@cfur.ca **W:** http://www.cfur.ca
Editorial Profile: CFUR-FM is a non-commercial station owned by Education Alternative Radio Society. The format of the station is variety. CFUR-FM broadcasts to the Prince George, British Columbia area at 88.7 FM.

CFUT-FM

Owner: La Radio Campus Communautaire Francophone de Shawinigan Inc.
Editorial: 540, avenue Broadway, Shawinigan, Quebec G9N 1M3. **T:** 1 819 537-0911
E: dg@radioshawinigan.com
W: http://www.radioshawinigan.com
Editorial Profile: CFUT-FM is a non-commercial station owned by La Radio Campus Communautaire Francophone de Shawinigan Inc. The format of the station is variety. CFUT-FM broadcasts to the Shawinigan, Quebec area at 91.1 FM.

CFUV-FM

Owner: University of Victoria Student Radio Society
T: 1 250 721-8702 **E:** cfuvpsa@uvic.ca
W: http://cfuv.uvic.ca
Editorial Profile: CFUV-FM is a commercial station owned by University of Victoria Student Radio Society. The format of the station is variety. CFUV-FM broadcasts to the Victoria, British Columbia area at 101.9 FM.

CFVD-FM

Owner: Radio Dégelis Inc
Editorial: 654 6e rue Est, Degelis, Quebec G5T 1Y1. **T:** 1 418 853-3370 **E:** cfvd@fm95.ca
W: http://www.fm95.ca
Editorial Profile: CFVD-FM is a commercial station owned by Radio Dégelis Inc. The format of the station is Top 40/CHR music. CFVD-FM broadcasts in the Degelis, Quebec area at 95.5 FM.

CFVM-FM

Owner: Astral Media
Editorial: 111, avenue Gaétan-Archambault, Amqui, Quebec G5J 2K1. **T:** 1 418 629-2025
W: http://amqui.rougefm.ca
Editorial Profile: CFVM-FM is a commercial station owned by Astral Media. The format of the station is adult contemporary. CFVM-FM broadcasts to the Amqui, Quebec area at 99.9 FM.

CFVR-FM

Owner: Harvard Broadcasting
Editorial: 9904 Franklin Ave., Fort McMurray, Alberta T9H 2K5. **T:** 1 780 791-0103
E: mixnews@mix1037fm.com
W: http://www.mix1037fm.com
Editorial Profile: CFVR-FM is a commercial station owned by Harvard Broadcasting. The format for the station is hot adult contemporary. CFVR-FM broadcasts to the Fort McMurray, Alberta area at 103.7 FM.

CFWC-FM

Owner: 1486781 Ontario Limited
Editorial: 271 Greenwich Street, Brantford, Ontario N3S 2X9. **T:** 1 519 759-2339
E: info@power93.ca
W: http://www.power93.ca
Editorial Profile: CFWC-FM is a commercial station owned by 1486781 Ontario Limited. The format for the station is Christian. CFWC-FM broadcasts to the Brantford, Ontario area at 93.9 FM.

CFWD-FM

Owner: Harvard Broadcasting
Editorial: 105 21st St E Suite 200, Saskatoon, Saskatchewan S7K 0B3. **T:** 1 306 653-9630
E: heyyou@cruzfm.com
W: http://www.cruzfm.com
Editorial Profile: CFWD-FM is a commercial station owned by Harvard Broadcasting. The format of the station is Classic Hits. CFWD-FM broadcasts to the Saskatoon, Saskatchewan area at 96.3 FM.

CFWE-FM

Owner: Aboriginal Multi-Media Society
Editorial: 13245 146 Street, Edmonton, Alberta T5L 4S8. **T:** 1 780 447-2393
E: info@cfweradio.ca
W: http://www.cfweradio.ca
Editorial Profile: CFWE-FM is a commercial radio station owned by the Aboriginal Multi-Media Society. The format of the station is a mix of Aboriginal and country music, as well as talk. CFWE-FM broadcasts to Edmonton, Alberta at 98.5 FM.

CFWF-FM

Owner: Harvard Broadcasting
Editorial: 1900 Rose Street, Regina, Saskatchewan S4P 0A9. **T:** 1 306 546-6200
W: http://www.thewolfrocks.com
Editorial Profile: CFWF-FM is a commercial station owned by Harvard Broadcasting. The format of the station is rock/album-oriented rock. CFWF-FM broadcasts to the Regina, Saskatchewan area at 104.9 FM.

CFWH-AM

Owner: Canadian Broadcasting Corp.
Editorial: 3103 3rd Ave, Whitehorse, Yukon Territory Y1A 1E5. **T:** 1 867 668-8400
E: cbcnorth@cbc.ca
W: http://www.cbc.ca/north
Editorial Profile: CFWH-AM is a non-commercial radio station owned by the Canadian Broadcasting Corp. The format of the station is a variety of news, talk and information. CFWH-AM broadcasts throughout Whitehorse, Yukon Territory at 560 AM.

CFWM-FM

Owner: Bell Media
Editorial: 1445 Pembina Highway, Winnipeg, Manitoba R3T 5C2. **T:** 1 204 477-5120
E: info@fab943.com
W: http://www.999bobfm.com
Editorial Profile: CFWM-FM is a commercial station owned by Bell Media. The format of the station is adult hits music. CFWM-FM broadcasts in the Winnipeg, Manitoba area at 99.9 FM.

CFXE-FM

Owner: Newfoundland Capital Corporation Limited
Editorial: 422 50th Street, Edson, Alberta T7E 1V8. **T:** 1 780 723-4461 **E:** news@theeagle.ca
W: http://www.theeagle.ca
Editorial Profile: CFXE-FM is a commercial station owned by Newfoundland Capital Corporation Limited. The format of the station is classic hits. CFXE-FM broadcasts to the Edson, Alberta area at 94.3 FM.

CFXG-AM

Owner: Newfoundland Capital Corporation Limited
Editorial: 422 50th Street, Edson, Alberta T7E 1V8. **T:** 1 780 723-4461 **E:** news@theeagle.ca
W: http://www.theeagle.ca
Editorial Profile: CFXG-AM is a commercial station owned by Newfoundland Capital Corporation Limited. The format of the station is classic hits. CFXG-AM broadcasts to the Grande Cache, Alberta area at 1230 AM.

CFXG-FM

Owner: Newcap Radio
Editorial: 422-50th Street 2nd floor, Edson, Alberta T7E 1T1 **E:** news@theeagle.ca
W: http://www.theeagle.ca
Editorial Profile: CFXG-FM is a commercial station owned by Newcap Radio. The format of the station is classic hits. CFXG-FM broadcasts to Grande Cache at 93.3.

CFXH-FM

Owner: Newfoundland Capital Corporation Limited
Editorial: 2nd Floor, 422-50th Street, Edson, Alberta T7E 1T1. **T:** 1 780 723-4461
E: feedback@theeagle.ca
W: http://www.theeagle.ca
Editorial Profile: CFXH-FM is a commercial station owned by Newfoundland Capital Corporation Limited. The format for the station is classic hits. CFXH-FM broadcasts to the Hinton, Alberta area at 97.5 FM.

CFXJ-FM

Owner: Newcap Radio
Editorial: 299 Queen St W, Toronto, Ontario M5V 2Z5-. **T:** 1 416 384-8000
W: http://www.flow935.com
Editorial Profile: CFXJ-FM is a commercial station owned by Newcap Radio. The format for the station is urban contemporary. CFXJ-FM broadcasts to the Toronto area at 93.5 FM.

CFXL-FM

Owner: Newfoundland Capital Corporation Limited
Editorial: 1110 Centre Street NE, Suite 100, Calgary, Alberta T2E 2R2. **T:** 1 403 271-6366
E: news@xl103calgary.com
W: http://www.xl103calgary.com
Editorial Profile: CFXL-FM is a commercial station owned by Newfoundland Capital Corporation Limited. The format of the station is classic hits. CFXL-FM broadcasts to the Calgary, Alberta area at 103.1 FM.

CFXM-FM

Owner: Coopérative de travail de la radio de Granby
Editorial: 135 rue Principale, Bureau 35, Granby, Quebec J2G 2V1. **T:** 1 450 372-5105
E: nouvelles@m105.ca **W:** http://www.m105.ca
Editorial Profile: CFXM-FM is a commercial station owned by the Coopérative de travail de la radio de Granby. The format of the station is adult contemporary. CFXM-FM broadcasts to the Granby, Quebec area at 104.9 FM.

CFXN-FM

Owner: Vista Broadcast Group
Editorial: 118 Main St E, North Bay, Ontario P1B 1A8. **T:** 1 705 475-9991
E: moose1063.news@moosefm.com
W: http://www.moosefm.com/cfxn/
Editorial Profile: CFXN-FM is a commercial station owned by Vista Broadcast Group. The format of the station is adult hits. CFXN-FM broadcasts to the North Bay, ON area at 106.3 FM.

CFXO-FM

Owner: Golden West Broadcasting Ltd.
Editorial: 11-5th Avenue SE, High River, Alberta T1V 1G2. **T:** 1 403 652-2472
W: http://www.sun99radio.com
Editorial Profile: CFXO-FM is a commercial station owned by Golden West Broadcasting Ltd. The format for the station is contemporary country music. CFXO-FM broadcasts to the High River, Alberta area at 99.7 FM.

CFXP-FM

Owner: Newfoundland Capital Corporation Limited
Editorial: 422 50th, 2nd FL, Edson, Alberta T7E 1T1. **T:** 1 780 723-4461
E: feedback@theeagle.ca
W: http://www.theeagle.ca
Editorial Profile: CFXP-FM is a commercial station owned by Newfoundland Capital Corporation Limited. The format of the station is hot adult contemporary. CFXP-FM broadcasts to the Edson, AB area at 95.5 FM.

CFXU-FM

Owner: St. Francis Xavier University
T: 1 902 867-2410 **E:** cfxu@stfx.ca
W: http://www.radiocfxu.ca
Editorial Profile: CFXU-FM is a non-commercial station owned by St. Francis Xavier University. The format is variety. CFXU-FM broadcasts to the Antigonish, Nova Scotia area at 93.3 FM.

CFXW-FM

Owner: Newfoundland Capital Corporation Limited
Editorial: 5118 50th Street, Whitecourt, Alberta T7S 1A1. **T:** 1 780 778-5101
W: http://www.therig.ca
Editorial Profile: CFXW-FM is a commercial station owned by Newfoundland Capital Corporation Limited. The format for the station is classic rock. CFXW-FM broadcasts to the Whitecourt, Alberta area at 96.7 FM.

CFXY-FM

Owner: Bell Media
Editorial: 206 Rookwood Ave, Fredericton, New Brunswick E3B 2M2. **T:** 1 506 454-2444
E: frederictonnewsteam@bellmedia.ca
W: http://www.foxrocks.ca
Editorial Profile: CFXY-FM is a commercial station owned by Bell Media. The format of the station is rock music. CFXY-FM broadcasts to the Fredericton, New Brunswick area at 105.3 FM. Twitter handle: twitter.com/105thefox

CFYK-AM

Owner: Canadian Broadcasting Corp.
Editorial: 5002 Forrest Drive, Yellowknife, Northwest Territories X1A 2N2.
T: 1 867 920-5400 **E:** cbcnorth@cbc.ca
W: http://www.cbc.ca/north
Editorial Profile: CFYK-AM is a non-commercial station owned by the Canadian Broadcasting Corp. The format of the station is news and talk. CFYK-AM broadcasts to the Yellowknife, Northwest Territories area at 1340 AM.

CFYM-AM

Owner: Golden West Broadcasting Ltd.
Editorial: 404 12 Ave E, Bay A, Kindersley, Saskatchewan S0L 1S0. **T:** 1 306 463-2692
E: cjymnews@goldenwestradio.com
W: http://www.cjym.com
Editorial Profile: CFYM-AM is a commercial station owned by Golden West Broadcasting Ltd. The format of the station is classic hits. CFYM-AM broadcasts to the Rosetown, Saskatchewan area at 1210 AM.

CFYT-FM

Owner: Dawson City Community Radio Society
T: 1 867 993-5152 **E:** cfytradio@gmail.com
W: http://www.cfyt.ca
Editorial Profile: CFYT-FM is a community station owned by the Dawson City Community Radio Society. The format of the station is variety. CFYT-FM broadcasts to the Dawson City, Yukon Territory area at 96.7 FM.

CFYX-FM

Owner: Groupe Radio Simard
Editorial: 158 Saint-Germain Ouest, Rimouski, Quebec G5L 4B7. **T:** 1 418 722-2848
W: http://www.cfyx93.com
Editorial Profile: CFYX-FM is a commercial station owned by Groupe Radio Simard. The format of the station is rock/album-oriented rock and talk. CFYX-FM broadcasts to the Rimouski, Quebec area at 93.3 FM.

CFZM-AM

Owner: ZoomerMedia Limited
Editorial: 70 Jefferson Ave, Toronto, Ontario M6K 1Y4. **T:** 1 416 544-0740
W: http://www.zoomerradio.ca
Editorial Profile: CFZM-AM is a commercial station owned by ZoomerMedia Limited. The format of the station is adult standards. CFZM-AM broadcasts to the Toronto area at 740 AM. To send a general e-mail to the station please use the online contact form on their website.

CFZN-FM

Owner: Vista Broadcast Group
Editorial: 152 Highland Street, Box 960, Upper level, Haliburton, Ontario K0M 1S0.
T: 1 705 457-3897
E: moose935.news@moosefm.com
W: http://moosefm.com/cfzn/
Editorial Profile: CFZN-FM is a commercial station owned by the Vista Broadcast Group. The format for the station is classic rock. CFZN-FM broadcasts to the Haliburton, Ontario area at 93.5 FM.

CFZZ-FM

Owner: Astral Media
Editorial: 104 rue Richelieu, St-Jean-sur-Richelieu, Quebec J3B 6X3. **T:** 1 450 346-0104
W: http://www.boomfm.com
Editorial Profile: CFZZ-FM is a French-language commercial station owned by Astral Media. The format of the station is oldies. CFZZ-FM broadcasts to the Saint-Jean-sur-Richelieu, Quebec area at 104.1 FM.

CHAA-FM

Owner: Radio Communautaire de la Rive-Sud Inc.(La)
Editorial: 91 rue St-Jean, Longueuil, Quebec J4H 2W8. **T:** 1 450 646-6800
E: info@fm1033.ca **W:** http://www.fm1033.ca
Editorial Profile: CHAA-FM is a non-commercial station owned by La Radio Communautaire de la Rive-Sud Inc. The format of the station is variety. CHAA-FM broadcasts to the Longueuil, Quebec area at 103.3 FM.

CHAB-AM

Owner: Golden West Broadcasting Ltd.
Editorial: 1704 Main St North, Moose Jaw, Saskatchewan S6J 1L4. **T:** 1 306 694-0800
E: mjnews@goldenwestradio.com
W: http://www.chabradio.com
Editorial Profile: CHAB-AM is a commercial station owned by Golden West Broadcasting Ltd. The format of the station is classic hits music. CHAB-AM broadcasts to the Moose Jaw, Saskatchewan area at 800 AM.

CHAD-FM
Owner: Chetwynd Communications Society
Editorial: 4612 N Access Rd #102, Chetwynd, British Columbia V0C 1J0. **T:** 1 250 788-9452
E: news@peacefm.ca
W: http://www.peacefm.ca
Editorial Profile: CHAD-FM is a non-commercial station owned by Chetwynd Communications Society. The format of the station is full service and variety. CHAD-FM broadcasts to the Chetwynd, British Columbia area at 104.1 FM.

CHAI-FM
Owner: Radio Communautaire Inc.(La)
Editorial: 25 boul St-Francis, Chateauguay, Quebec J6J 1Y2. **T:** 1 450 698-3131
E: chai@videotron.ca
W: http://www.1019fm.net
Editorial Profile: CHAI-FM is a non-commercial station owned by La Radio Communautaire Inc. The format for the station is adult contemporary. WIXO-FM broadcasts to the Chateauguay, Quebec area at 101.9 FM.

CHAK-AM
Owner: Canadian Broadcasting Corp.
Editorial: Bag Service #8, 155 MacKenzie Road, Inuvik, Northwest Territories X0E 0T0.
T: 1 867 777-7615 **E:** cbcnorth@cbc.ca
W: http://cbc.ca/north
Editorial Profile: CHAK-AM is a non-commercial station owned by the Canadian Broadcasting Corp. The format of the station is variety. CHAK-AM broadcasts to the Inuvik, Northwest Territories area at 860 AM.

CHAM-AM
Owner: Astral Media
Editorial: 883 Upper Wentworth Street, Suite 401, Hamilton, Ontario L9A 4Y6.
T: 1 905 574-1150
W: http://www.funny820.com
Editorial Profile: CHAM-AM is a commercial station owned by Astral Media. The format of the station is comedy. CHAM-AM broadcasts in the Hamilton, Ontario area at 820 AM.

CHAS-FM
Owner: Rogers Communications Inc.
Editorial: 642 Great Northern Road, Sault Ste. Marie, Ontario P6B 4Z9. **T:** 1 705 759-9200
W: http://www.ezrocksoo.com
Editorial Profile: CHAS-FM is a commercial station owned by Rogers Communications Inc. The format of the station is adult contemporary. CHAS-FM broadcasts to the Sault Ste. Marie, Ontario area at 100.5 FM.

CHAT-FM
Owner: Jim Pattison Broadcast Group(The)
Editorial: 10 Boundary Rd SE, Redcliff, Alberta T0J 2P0-. **T:** 1 403 548-8282
E: chat945@jpbg.ca
W: http://www.chat945.com
Editorial Profile: CHAT-FM is a commercial station owned by The Jim Pattison Broadcast Group. The format is contemporary country. CHAT-FM broadcasts to the Redcliff, Alberta area at 94.5 FM.

CHAY-FM
Owner: Corus Entertainment Inc.
Editorial: 1125 Bayfield St North, Barrie, Ontario L4N 4S5. **T:** 1 705 737-3511
E: general@b101fm.com
W: http://www.chaytoday.ca
Editorial Profile: CHAY-FM is a commercial radio station owned by Corus Entertainment Inc. The format of the station is adult contemporary. CHAY-FM broadcasts to the Barrie, Ontario area at 93.1 FM.

CHBD-FM
Owner: Astral Media
Editorial: 4303 Albert Street, Suite 100, Regina, Saskatchewan S4S 3R6.
T: 1 306 337-2850
W: http://www.bigdog927.com
Editorial Profile: CHBD-FM is a commercial station owned by Astral Media. The format of the station is contemporary country. CHBD-FM broadcasts to Regina, Saskatchewan at 92.7 FM.

CHBE-FM
Owner: Bell Media
Editorial: 1420 Broad Street, Victoria, British Columbia V8W 2B1. **T:** 1 250 382-1073
W: http://www.1073kool.fm
Editorial Profile: CHBE-FM is a commercial station owned by Bell Media. The format of the station is hot adult contemporary. CHBE-FM broadcasts to the Victoria, British Columbia area at 107.3 FM.

CHBI-FM
Owner: The Burnt Islands Economic Development Board
Editorial: 74 Main St, Burnt Islands, Newfoundland A0M 1B0. **T:** 1 709 698-3110
E: chbi95.7fm@hotmail.com
W: http://www.burntislandsnl.ca
Editorial Profile: CHBI-FM is a non-commercial station owned by The Burnt Islands Economic Development Board. The format of the station is variety. CHBI-FM broadcasts to the Burnt Islands, Newfoundland area at 95.7 FM.

CHBM-FM
Owner: Newcap Radio
Editorial: 2 St Clair Ave W Fl 2ND, Toronto, Ontario M4V 1L5. **T:** 1 416 482-0973
E: info@boom973.com
W: http://www.boom973.com
Editorial Profile: CHBM-FM is a commercial station owned by Newcap Radio. The format of the station is classic hits. CHBM-FM broadcasts to the Toronto area at 97.3 FM.

CHBN-FM
Owner: Rogers Communications Inc.
Editorial: 5915 Gateway Blvd NW, Edmonton, Alberta T6H 2H3. **T:** 1 780 429-0197
W: http://www.thebounce.ca
Editorial Profile: CHBN-FM is a commercial radio station owned by Rogers Communications Inc. The format of the station is Top 40/CHR. CHBN-FM broadcasts to the Edmonton, Alberta area at 91.7 FM.

CHBO-FM
Owner: Golden West Broadcasting Ltd.
Editorial: 640 10th St, Humboldt, Saskatchewan S0K 2A0. **T:** 1 855 476-0155
W: http://www.bolt1075fm.com
Editorial Profile: CHBO-FM is a commercial station owned by Golden West Broadcasting Ltd. The format of the station is adult hits. CHBO-FM broadcasts to the Humboldt, Saskatchewan area at a frequency of 107.5 FM.

CHBV-AM
Owner: Vista Broadcast Group
Editorial: 1940 3rd Avenue, Prince George, British Columbia V2M 1G7. **T:** 1 250 564-2524
W: http://www.thevalleywolf.ca

CHBW-FM
Owner: Jim Pattison Broadcast Group(The)
Editorial: 4814B-49th Street, Rocky Mountain House, Alberta T4T 1S8. **T:** 1 403 844-9450
E: onair@b94.ca **W:** http://b94.ca
Editorial Profile: CHBW-FM is a commercial station owned by The Jim Pattison Broadcast Group. The format is adult hits. CHBW-FM broadcasts to the Rocky Mountain House, Alberta area at 93.9 FM.

CHBZ-FM
Owner: Jim Pattison Broadcast Group(The)
Editorial: 19-9th Ave South, Cranbrook, British Columbia V1C 2L9. **T:** 1 250 426-2224
E: news@thedrivefm.ca **W:** http://www.b104.ca
Editorial Profile: CHBZ-FM is a commercial station owned by The Jim Pattison Broadcast Group. The format of the station is contemporary country music. CHBZ-FM broadcasts in the Cranbrook, British Columbia area at 104.7 FM.

CHCD-FM
Owner: CHCD Inc.
Editorial: 55 Park Rd, Simcoe, Ontario N3Y 4J9. **T:** 1 519 426-7700
E: news989@myfmradio.ca
W: http://www.norfolktoday.ca
Editorial Profile: CHCD-FM is a commercial station owned by CHCD Inc. The format of the station is adult contemporary music. CHCD-FM broadcasts in the Simcoe, Ontario area at 98.9 FM.

CHCM-AM
Owner: Steele Communications
Editorial: Ville Marie Drive, Marystown, Newfoundland A0E 2M0. **T:** 1 709 279-2560
Editorial Profile: CHCM-AM is a commercial radio station owned by the Steele Communications. The format is contemporary country music. CHCM-AM broadcasts in the Marystown, Newfoundland area at 740 AM.

CHCQ-FM
Owner: Starboard Communications Ltd.
Editorial: 497 Dundas St W, Belleville, Ontario K8P 1B6. **T:** 1 613 966-0955
E: news@cool100.ca
W: http://www.cool100.ca
Editorial Profile: CHCQ-FM is a commercial station owned by Starboard Communications Ltd. The format for the station is contemporary country. CHCQ-FM broadcasts to the Belleville, Ontario area at 100.1 FM.

CHCR-FM
Owner: Homegrown Community Radio
Editorial: 14 Lake St., Unit A, Killaloe, Ontario K0J 2A0. **T:** 1 613 757-0657 **E:** radio@chcr.org
W: http://www.chcr.org
Editorial Profile: CHCR-FM is a commercial station owned by Homegrown Community Radio. The format of the station is variety. CHCR-FM broadcasts to the Killaloe, Ontario area at 102.9 FM.

CHDI-FM
Owner: Rogers Communications Inc.
Editorial: 5915 Gateway Boulevard, Edmonton, Alberta T6H 2H3. **T:** 1 780 423-2005
W: http://www.sonic1029.com
Editorial Profile: CHDI-FM is a commercial station owned by Rogers Communications Inc. The format of the station is rock/album-oriented rock. CHDI-FM broadcasts to the Edmonton, Alberta area at 102.9 FM.

CHDR-FM
Owner: Jim Pattison Broadcast Group(The)
Editorial: 19 9th Ave S, Cranbrook, British Columbia V1C 2L9. **T:** 1 250 426-2224
E: news@thedrivefm.ca
W: http://www.thedrivefm.ca
Editorial Profile: CHDR-FM is a commercial station owned by The Jim Pattison Broadcast Group. The format of the station is classic rock music. CHDR-FM broadcasts to Cranbrook, British Columbia at 102.9 FM.

CHED-AM
Owner: Corus Entertainment Inc.
Editorial: 5204 84th Street, Edmonton, Alberta T6E 5N8. **T:** 1 780 440-6300
E: chednews@630ched.com
W: http://www.630ched.com
Editorial Profile: CHED-AM is a commercial station owned by Corus Entertainment Inc. The format of the station is news, talk and sports. CHED-AM broadcasts to the Edmonton, Alberta area at 630 AM.

CHEF-FM
Owner: Radio Matagami
Editorial: 110 Boulevard Matagami, Matagami, Quebec J0Y 2A0. **T:** 1 819 739-9990
E: chef99fm@lino.com
Editorial Profile: CHEF-FM is a commercial station owned by Radio Matagami. The format of the station is adult contemporary. CHEF-FM broadcasts to Matagami, Quebec at 99.9 FM.

CHEQ-FM
Owner: 9174-8004 Quebec Inc.
Editorial: 373, route Cameron, Ste-Marie-de-Beauce, Quebec G6E 3E2. **T:** 1 418 387-1013
E: info@cheqfm.qc.ca
W: http://www.cheqfm.qc.ca
Editorial Profile: CHEQ-FM is a commercial station owned by 9174-8004 Quebec Inc. The format of the station is a mix of adult contemporary and contemporary country. CHEQ-FM broadcasts to the Ste-Marie-de-Beauce, Quebec area at 101.3 FM.

CHER-FM
Owner: Maritime Broadcasting System Ltd.
Editorial: 318 Charlotte St, Sydney, Nova Scotia B1P 1C8. **T:** 1 902 564-5596
E: news@capebretonradio.com
W: http://www.983maxfm.com
Editorial Profile: CHER-FM is a commercial station owned by the Maritime Broadcasting System Ltd. The format of the station is classic hits. CHER-FM broadcasts in the Sydney, Nova Scotia area at 98.3 FM.

CHES-FM
Owner: Erin Radio Membership
Editorial: 8 Thompson Cres, Erin, Ontario N0B 1T0. **T:** 1 519 833-9300 **E:** info@mix881.com
W: http://mix881.com
Editorial Profile: CHES-FM is a non-commercial radio station owned by Erin Radio Membership. The format for the station is community radio. CHES-FM broadcasts to the Erin, Ontario area at 88.1 FM.

CHET-FM
Owner: Chetwynd Communications Society
Editorial: 4612 N Access Rd #102, Chetwynd, British Columbia V0C 1J0. **T:** 1 250 788-9452
E: news@peacefm.ca
W: http://www.peacefm.ca
Editorial Profile: CHET-FM is a non-commercial station owned by Chetwynd Communications Society. The format of the station is variety. CHET-FM broadcasts to the Chetwynd, British Columbia area at 94.5 FM.

CHEY-FM
Owner: Astral Media
Editorial: 1500 rue Royale, Bureau 260, Trois-Rivieres, Quebec G9A 6J4. **T:** 1 819 376-1023
W: http://mauricie.rougefm.ca/
Editorial Profile: CHEY-FM is a commercial station owned by Astral Media. The format of the station is adult contemporary. CHEY-FM broadcasts to the Trois-Rivieres, Quebec area at 94.7 FM.

CHEZ-FM
Owner: Rogers Communications Inc.
Editorial: 2001 Thurston Dr, Ottawa, Ontario K1G 6C9. **T:** 1 613 736-2001
E: ottawanewsroom@ottawaradio.rogers.com
W: http://www.chez106.com
Editorial Profile: CHEZ-FM is a commercial station owned by Rogers Communications Inc. The format of the station is classic rock music. CHEZ-FM's broadcasts to Ottawa, Ontario and surrounding communities at 106.1 FM.

CHFA-AM
Owner: Société Radio-Canada
Editorial: 10062-102 Avenue, Suite 123 Edmonton City Centre, Edmonton, Alberta T5J 2Y8. **T:** 1 780 468-7500
E: nouvelles.alberta@radio-canada.ca
W: http://www.radio-canada.ca/alberta
Editorial Profile: CHFA-AM is a non-commercial station owned by Société Radio-Canada. The format for the station is news and talk. CHFA-AM broadcasts to the Edmonton, Alberta area at 680 AM.

CHFG-FM
Owner: Chisasibi Telecommunications Association
T: 1 819 855-2527 **E:** chisa@ginwat.ca
W: http://www.creeradio.com
Editorial Profile: CHFG-FM is a commercial station owned by the Chisasibi Telecommunications Association. The format of the station is variety. CHFG-FM broadcast to the Chisasibi, Quebec area at 101.1 FM.

CHFI-FM
Owner: Rogers Communications Inc.
Editorial: 1 Ted Rogers Way, Toronto, Ontario M4Y 3B7. **T:** 1 416 935-8298
E: chfi@rci.rogers.com
W: http://www.chfi.com
Editorial Profile: CHFI-FM is a commercial station owned by Rogers Communications Inc. The format is Soft Rock/Soft AC. CHFI-FM broadcasts to the Toronto area at 98.1 FM.

CHFM-FM
Owner: Rogers Communications Inc.
Editorial: 2723 37th Ave NE, Suite 240, Calgary, Alberta T1Y 5R8. **T:** 1 403 246-9696
W: http://www.lite959.com
Editorial Profile: CHFM-FM is a commercial station owned by Rogers Communications Inc. The format for the station is lite rock. CHFM-FM broadcasts to the Calgary, Alberta area at 95.9 FM.

CHFN-FM
Owner: Chippewas of Nawash Unceded First Nation
Editorial: 67 Community Centre Rd, RR#5, Wiarton, Ontario N0H 2T0. **T:** 1 519 534-1003
E: chfn@ymail.com
W: http://www.nawash.ca/index.cfm?page=link_chfn
Editorial Profile: CHFN-FM is a non-commercial station owned by Chippewas of Nawash Unceded First Nation. The format of the station is variety. CHFN-FM broadcasts to Wiarton, ON adt 100.1 FM.

CHFT-FM
Owner: Newfoundland Capital Corporation Limited
Editorial: 9904 Franklin Avenue, Fort McMurray, Alberta T9H 2K5.
T: 1 780 791-0810 **E:** news@krock.fm
W: http://www.krock.fm
Editorial Profile: CHFT-FM is a commercial station owned by Newfoundland Capital Corporation Limited. The format of the station is rock/album-oriented rock. CHFT-FM broadcasts to the Fort McMurray, Alberta area at 100.5 FM.

CHFX-FM
Owner: Maritime Broadcasting System Ltd.
Editorial: 5121 Sackville St, 3rd Floor, Halifax, Nova Scotia B3J 1K1. **T:** 1 902 422-1651
E: chfxnews@chfxradio.com
W: http://www.fx1019.ca
Editorial Profile: CHFX-FM is a commercial station owned by the Maritime Broadcasting System Limited. The format of the station is

contemporary country. CHFX-FM broadcasts to the Halifax, Nova Scotia area at 101.9 FM.

CHGA-FM
Owner: Radio Communautaire de la Haute Gatineau
Editorial: 163 rue Laurier, Maniwaki, Quebec J9E 2K6. **T:** 1 819 449-9730 **E:** chga@chga.fm
W: http://chga.fm
Editorial Profile: CHGA-FM is a commercial station owned by Radio Communautaire de la Haute Gatineau. The format of the station is variety. CHGA-FM broadcasts to Maniwaki, Quebec area at 97.3 FM.

CHGB-FM
Owner: Bayshore Broadcasting Corp.
Editorial: 9937 Hwy 26, Collingwood, Ontario L9Y 3Z3. **T:** 1 705 422-0970
E: news@977thebeach.ca
W: http://www.977thebeach.ca
Editorial Profile: CHGB-FM is a commercial station owned by Bayshore Broadcasting Corp. The format for the station is adult contemporary. CHGB-FM broadcasts to the Wasaga Beach, Ontario area at 97.7 FM.

CHGK-FM
Owner: Vista Broadcast Group Inc.
Editorial: 376 Romeo St S, Stratford, Ontario N5A 4T9-. **T:** 1 519 271-2450
E: news@fm1077stratford.com
W: http://www.fm1077stratford.com
Editorial Profile: CHGK-FM is a commercial station owned by Vista Broadcast Group Inc. The format of the station is adult contemporary. CHGK-FM broadcasts to the Stratford, Ontario area at 107.7 FM.

CHGM-FM
Owner: Radio CHNC Ltee.
Editorial: 153 boul Gerard-D-Levesque, New Carlisle, Quebec G0C 1Z0. **T:** 1 418 752-2215
E: radiochnc@globetrotter.net
W: http://www.radiochnc.com

CHGO-FM
Owner: RNC Media
Editorial: 1729-3e avenue, Val-d'Or, Quebec J9P 1W3. **T:** 1 819 825-0010
E: live@abitibi.capitalerock.ca
W: http://www.goradiox.com
Editorial Profile: CHGO-FM is a commercial station owned by RNC Media. The format of the station is rock. CHGO-FM broadcasts to the Val d'Or, Quebec area at 104.3 FM.

CHHA-AM
Owner: San Lorenzo Latin American Community Center
Editorial: 22 Wenderly Dr, Toronto, Ontario M6B 2N9-. **T:** 1 416 785-8729
W: http://www.sanlorenzo.ca/english/Voces_Latinas_1610_AM.html
Editorial Profile: CHHA-AM is a non-commercial station owned by San Lorenzo Latin American Community Center. The format is Hispanic variety. CHHA-AM broadcasts to the Toronto area at 1610 AM.

CHHO-FM
Owner: La Coopérative de solidarité radio communautaire de la MRC de Maskinongé
Editorial: 50-A rue de la Fabrique, Saint-Leon-le-Grand, Quebec J0K 2W0.
T: 1 819 228-1001 **E:** info@ch2ofm.ca
W: http://www.ch2ofm.com

CHHR-FM
Owner: Newcap Radio
Editorial: 20-11151 Horseshoe Way 20, Richmond, British Columbia V7A 4S5.
T: 1 604 241-2100 **E:** info@shore104.com
W: http://www.shore104.com
Editorial Profile: CHHR-FM is a commercial station owned by Newcap Radio. The format of the station is adult album alternative. CHHR-FM broadcasts to the Vancouver, British Columbia area at 104.3 FM.

CHIC-FM
Owner: Communications CHIC
Editorial: 120, Rue 9è, Rouyn-Noranda, Quebec J9X 2B6. **T:** 1 819 797-4242
E: 887@chicfm.org **W:** http://www.chicfm.org
Editorial Profile: CHIC-FM is a commercial station owned by Communications CHIC. The format for the station is French contemporary Christian. CHIC-FM broadcasts to the Rouyn-Noranda, Quebec area at 88.7 FM.

CHIK-FM
Owner: Astral Media
Editorial: 900 rue d'Youville, 1er etage, Quebec, Quebec G1R 3P7. **T:** 1 418 687-9900
E: receptionchikcitf@astral.com
W: http://www.radionrj.ca/quebec
Editorial Profile: CHIK-FM is a commercial station owned by Astral Media. The format for the station is Top 40/CHR. CHIK-FM broadcasts to the Quebec City area at 98.9 FM.

CHIM-FM
Owner: Celestial Sound
Editorial: Celestial Sound, 226 Delnite Road, Timmins, Ontario P4N 7C2. **T:** 1 705 264-2150
E: chimfm@vianet.ca
W: http://www.chimfm.com
Editorial Profile: CHIM-FM is a non-commercial station owned by Celestial Sound. The format of the station is contemporary Christian. CHIM-FM broadcasts to Timmins, Ontario at 102.3 FM.

CHIN-AM
Owner: Radio 1540 Ltd.
Editorial: 622 College St, Suite 400, Toronto, Ontario M6G 1B6. **T:** 1 416 531-9991
E: info@chinradio.com
W: http://www.chinradio.com
Editorial Profile: CHIN-AM is a commercial station owned by Radio 1540 Ltd. The format of the station is multi-lingual news and talk. CHIN-AM broadcasts to the Toronto area at 1540 AM.

CHIN-FM
Owner: Radio 1540 Ltd.
Editorial: 622 College St, Suite 400, Toronto, Ontario M6G 1B6. **T:** 1 416 531-9991
E: info@chinradio.com
W: http://www.chinradio.com
Editorial Profile: CHIN-FM is a commercial station owned by Radio 1540 Ltd. The format of the station is variety. CHIN-FM broadcasts to Toronto and southern Ontario at 100.7 FM.

CHIP-FM
Owner: Radio Communautaire du Pontiac Inc.
Editorial: 138 Principal Street, Fort-Coulonge, Quebec J0X 1V0. **T:** 1 819 683-3155
E: news@chipfm.com
W: http://www.chipfm.com
Editorial Profile: CHIP-FM is a commercial station owned by Radio Communautaire du Pontiac Inc. The format of the station is variety. CHIP-FM broadcasts to Fort-Coulonge, Quebec at 101.7 FM.

CHIQ-FM
Owner: Bell Media
Editorial: 1445 Pembina Highway, Winnipeg, Manitoba R3T 5C2. **T:** 1 204 477-5120
W: http://www.fab943.com
Editorial Profile: CHIQ-FM is a commercial station owned by Bell Media. The format of the station is classic hits music. CHIQ-FM broadcasts to the Winnipeg, Manitoba area at 94.3 FM.

CHJM-FM
Owner: Groupe Radio Simard
Editorial: 11760- 3e Ave., Saint-Georges, Quebec G5Y 1V4. **T:** 1 418 227-0997
E: nouvelles@radiobeauce.com
W: http://www.mix997.com
Editorial Profile: CHJM-FM is a commercial station owned by Groupe Radio Simard. The format for the station is adult contemporary. WHJM-FM broadcasts to the Saint-Georges, Quebec area at 99.7 FM.

CHJX-FM
Owner: Sound of Faith Broadcasting
Editorial: 254 Adelaide Street, London, Ontario N5Z 3L1. **T:** 1 519 679-9882
E: inspirefm@gmail.com
W: http://www.inspirefm.ca
Editorial Profile: CHJX-FM is a commercial station owned by Sound of Faith Broadcasting. The format of the station is contemporary Christian. CHJX-FM broadcasts to the London, Ontario area at 105.9 FM.

CHKF-FM
Owner: Fairchild Radio Group Ltd.
Editorial: 2723 37th Ave NE, Suite 109, Calgary, Alberta T1Y 5R8. **T:** 1 403 717-1940
E: news@fm947.com
W: http://www.fm947.com
Editorial Profile: CHKF-FM is a commercial station owned by the Fairchild Radio Group Ltd. The format of the station is multi-lingual and multi-ethnic music, news, entertainment, lifestyle, and general interest talk. CHKF-FM broadcasts to Calgary, Alberta at 94.7 FM.

CHKG-FM
Owner: Fairchild Radio Group Ltd.
Editorial: 4151 Hazelbridge Way, Richmond, British Columbia V6X 4J7-. **T:** 1 604 295-1234
E: news@am1470.com
W: http://www.fm961.com
Editorial Profile: CHKG-FM is a commercial station owned by the Fairchild Radio Group Ltd. The format of the station is ethnic music, news, and talk. CHKG-FM broadcasts to Vancouver, British Columbia at 96.1 FM.

CHKS-FM
Owner: Blackburn Radio Inc.
Editorial: 1415 London Road, Sarnia, Ontario N7S 1P6. **T:** 1 519 542-5500
E: rock@k106fm.com
W: http://www.k106fm.com

CHKT-AM
Owner: Fairchild Radio Group Ltd.
Editorial: 151 Esna Park Dr Unit 26-29, Markham, Ontario L3R 3B1.
T: 1 905 415-6265 **E:** news@am1430.com
W: http://www.am1430.com
Editorial Profile: CHKT-AM is a commercial station owned by Fairchild Radio Group Ltd. The format of the station is international variety. CHKT-AM broadcasts to Richmond Hill, Ontario at 1430 AM.

CHKX-FM
Owner: Durham Radio Inc.
Editorial: 589 Upper Wellington Street, Hamilton, Ontario L9A 3P8. **T:** 1 905 388-8911
E: news@kx947.fm **W:** http://www.kx947.fm
Editorial Profile: CHKX-FM is a commercial station owned by Durham Radio Inc. The format of the station is contemporary country. CHKX-FM broadcasts to the Hamilton, Ontario area at 94.7 FM.

CHLB-FM
Owner: Jim Pattison Broadcast Group(The)
Editorial: 401 Mayor Magrath Drive, Lethbridge, Alberta T1J 3L8.
T: 1 403 329-0955 **E:** info@country95.fm
W: http://www.country95.fm
Editorial Profile: CHLB-FM is a commercial station owned by The Jim Pattison Broadcast Group. The format is classic and contemporary country. CHLB-FM broadcasts to Lethbridge, Alberta at 95.5 FM.

CHLC-FM
Owner: Radio Port-Cartier Inc.
Editorial: 907, rue de Puyjalon, Baie-Comeau, Quebec G5C 1N3. **T:** 1 418 589-3771
E: chlcfm97@globetrotter.net
W: http://www.chlc.com
Editorial Profile: CHLC-FM is a commercial station owned by Radio Port-Cartier Inc. The format of the station is Hot Adult Contemporary. CHLC-FM broadcasts to the Baie-Comeau, Quebec area at 97.1 FM.

CHLI-FM
Owner: Rossland Radio Coop
Editorial: 1807 Columbia Ave, Rossland, British Columbia V0G 1Y0. **T:** 1 250 362-0080
E: radio@rosslandradio.com
W: http://www.rosslandradio.com
Editorial Profile: CHLI-FM is non-commercial station owned by Rossland Radio Corp. The format of the station is variety. CHLI-FM broadcasts to the Rossland, British Columbia area at 101.1 FM.

CHLK-FM
Owner: (Perkin) Brian & Norm Wright
Editorial: 43 Wilson St W, Perth, Ontario K7H 2N3. **T:** 1 613 264-8811 **E:** events@lake88.ca
W: http://www.lake88.ca
Editorial Profile: CHLK-FM is a commercial station owned by Norm Wright and Brian Perkin. The format of the station is adult contemporary. CHLK-FM broadcasts to the Perth, Ontario area at 88.1 FM.

CHLM-FM
Owner: Société Radio-Canada
Editorial: 70 avenue Principale, Rouyn-Noranda, Quebec J9X 4P2. **T:** 1 819 762-8155
E: abitibi@radio-canada.ca
W: http://radio-canada.ca/regions/abitibi
Editorial Profile: CHLM-FM is a non-commercial station owned by Societe Radio-Canada. The format of the station is news/talk. CHLM-FM broadcasts to the Rouyn-Noranda, Quebec area at 90.7 FM.

CHLQ-FM
Owner: Maritime Broadcasting System Ltd.
Editorial: 5 Prince Street, Charlottetown, Prince Edward Island C1A 4P4.
T: 1 902 892-1066 **W:** http://q93.fm
Editorial Profile: CHLQ-FM is a commercial station owned by the Maritime Broadcasting System Ltd. The format of the station is classic rock. CHLQ-FM broadcasts to the Charlottetown, Prince Edward Island area at 93.1 FM.

CHLS-FM
Owner: Radio Lillooet Society
Editorial: #415 Main Street, Lillooet, British Columbia V0K 1V0. **T:** 1 250 256-2113
E: station@radiolillooet.ca
W: http://radiolillooet.ca

CHLX-FM
Owner: RNC Media
Editorial: 171-A rue Jean-Proulx, Gatineau, Quebec J8Z 1W5. **T:** 1 819 770-1040
E: infochlx@rncmedia.ca
W: http://gatineau.planeteradio.ca
Editorial Profile: CHLX-FM is a commercial station owned by RNC Media. The format of the station is easy listening and jazz. CHLX-FM broadcasts to the Gatineau, Quebec area at 97.1 FM.

CHLY-FM
Owner: Radio Malaspina Society
Editorial: 34 Victorica Cres. #2, Nanaimo, British Columbia V9R 5B8. **T:** 1 250 716-3410
E: news@chly.ca **W:** http://www.chly.ca
Editorial Profile: CHLY-FM is a non-commercial station owned by Radio Malaspina Society. The format of the station is variety. CHLY-FM broadcasts to the Nanaimo, British Columbia at 101.7 FM.

CHMA-FM
Owner: Attic Broadcasting Co. Ltd.
Editorial: 62 York St, Sackville, New Brunswick E4L 1E2. **T:** 1 506 364-2221
E: chma@mta.ca **W:** http://www.mta.ca/chma
Editorial Profile: CHMA-FM is a non-commercial station owned by Attic Broadcasting Co. Ltd. The format of the station is college variety. CHMA-FM broadcasts to the Sackville, New Brunswick area at 106.9 FM.

CHMB-AM
Owner: Mainstream Broadcasting Corp.
Editorial: 1200 W 73rd Avenue, Suite 100, Vancouver, British Columbia V6P 6G5.
T: 1 604 263-1320 **E:** adm@am1320.com
W: http://www.am1320.com
Editorial Profile: CHMB-AM is a commercial station owned by the Mainstream Broadcasting Corp. The format of the station is ethnic and multicultural music and talk. CHMB-AM broadcasts to the Vancouver, BC area at 1320 AM.

CHMC-FM
Owner: Rawlco Radio Ltd.
Editorial: 9894 42 Ave NW, Edmonton, Alberta T6E 5V5. **T:** 1 780 433-7877
E: contactus@up993.com
W: http://www.up993.com
Editorial Profile: CHMC-FM is a commercial station owned by Rawlco Radio Ltd. The format of the station is soft rock. CHMC-FM broadcasts to the Edmonton, Alberta area at 99.3 FM.

CHME-FM
Owner: Radio Essipit/Haute Cote-Nord Inc.
Editorial: 34 de la Reserve, Les Escoumins, Quebec G0T 1K0. **T:** 1 418 233-2700
E: chme@b2b2c.ca **W:** http://chme949.com
Editorial Profile: CHME-FM is a commercial station owned by Radio Essipit/Haute Cote-Nord Inc. The format of the station is news, talk and rock/album-oriented rock. CHME-FM broadcasts to the Les Escoumins, Quebec area at 94.9 FM.

CHMJ-AM
Owner: Corus Entertainment Inc.
Editorial: 700 West Georgia St, Suite 2000, Vancouver, British Columbia V7Y 1K9.
T: 1 604 331-2844
E: am730traffic@corusent.com
W: http://www.am730.com
Editorial Profile: CHMJ-AM is a commercial station owned by Corus Entertainment Inc. The format of the station is talk. CHMJ-AM broadcasts to the Vancouver, British Columbia area at 730 AM.

CHML-AM
Owner: Corus Entertainment Inc.
Editorial: 875 Main St W, Suite 900 Radio Centre, Hamilton, Ontario L8S 4R1.
T: 1 905 521-9900 **E:** news2@900chml.com
W: http://www.900chml.com
Editorial Profile: CHML-AM is a commercial station owned by Corus Entertainment Inc. The format of the station is news and talk. CHML-AM broadcasts to the Hamilton, Ontario area at 900 AM.

CHMM-FM
Owner: MacKenzie Area Community Radio Society

Editorial: 86 Centennial, MacKenzie, British Columbia V0J 2C0. **T:** 1 250 997-6277
E: chmm1035@chmm.ca
W: http://www.chmm.ca
Editorial Profile: CHMM-FM is a non-commercial station owned by MacKenzie Area Community Radio Society. The format for the station is hot adult contemporary. CHMM-FM broadcasts to the MacKenzie, British Columbia area at 103.5 FM.

CHMN-FM
Owner: Rogers Communications Inc.
Editorial: 749 Railway Ave, Canmore, Alberta T1W 1P2. **T:** 1 403 678-2222
W: http://www.mountainfm.ca
Editorial Profile: CHMN-FM is a commercial station owned by Rogers Communications Inc. The format of the station is hot adult contemporary. CHMN-FM broadcasts to the Canmore, Alberta area at 106.5 FM.

CHMO-AM
Owner: James Bay Broadcasting Corp.
Editorial: 28 First St, Moosonee, Ontario P0L 1Y0. **T:** 1 705 336-2466
E: jbbtcorp@onlink.net
Editorial Profile: CHMO-AM is a non-commercial station owned by James Bay Broadcasting Corp. The format of the station is classic country. CHMO-AM broadcasts to the Moosonee, Ontario at area 1450 AM.

CHMP-FM
Owner: Cogeco
Editorial: 800 Rue de la Gauchetière West, Suite 1100, Montreal, Quebec H5A 1M1.
T: 1 514 789-0985 **W:** http://www.985fm.ca
Editorial Profile: CHMP-FM is a commercial station owned by Cogeco. The format of the station is news and talk. CHMP-FM broadcasts to the Montreal area at 98.5 FM.

CHMR-FM
Owner: Memorial University Students Union
Editorial: University Center, Rm 4C 2009 2nd Fl, St. John's, Newfoundland A1C 5S7.
T: 1 709 737-4777 **E:** chmr@mun.ca
W: http://www.chmr.ca
Editorial Profile: CHMR-FM is a college station owned by Memorial University Students Union. The format of the station is variety. CHMR-FM broadcasts to the St. John's, Newfoundland area at 93.5 FM.

CHMS-FM
Owner: Vista Broadcast Group
Editorial: 30674 Hwy 28 E, Bancroft, Ontario K0L 1C0. **T:** 1 613 332-1423
E: moose977.news@moosefm.com
W: http://www.moosefm.com/chms/index.php
Editorial Profile: CHMS-FM is a commercial station owned by the Vista Broadcast Group. The format of the station is adult contemporary music. CHMS-FM broadcasts to Bancroft, Ontario at 97.7 FM.

CHMT-FM
Owner: Vista Broadcast Group
Editorial: 49 Cedar Street South, Timmins, Ontario P4N 2G5. **T:** 1 705 267-6070
E: moose931.news@moosefm.com
W: http://www.moosefm.com/chmt
Editorial Profile: CHMT-FM is a commercial station owned by Vista Broadcast Group. The format for the station is Top 40/CHR. CHMT-FM broadcasts to the Timmins, Ontario area at 93.1 FM.

CHMX-FM
Owner: Harvard Broadcasting
Editorial: 1900 Rose St., Regina, Saskatchewan S4P 0A9. **T:** 1 306 546-6200
W: http://www.my921.ca
Editorial Profile: CHMX-FM is a commercial station owned by Harvard Broadcasting. The format of the station is hot AC. CHMX-FM broadcasts to the Regina, Saskatchewan area at 92.1 FM.

CHMY-FM
Owner: My Broadcasting Corporation
Editorial: 321B Raglan Street South, Renfrew, Ontario K7V 4H4. **T:** 1 613 432-6936
E: news@myfmradio.ca
W: http://www.myfmradio.ca
Editorial Profile: CHMY-FM is a commercial station owned by My Broadcasting Corporation. The format of the station is adult contemporary. CHMY-FM broadcasts to the Renfrew, Ontario area at 96.1 FM. It is also simulcast to the Arnprior, Ontario area at 107.7 FM.

CHMZ-FM
Owner: McBride Communications & Media Inc.
Editorial: 10760 Fundy Drive, Richmond, British Columbia V7E 5K7. **T:** 1 604 220-8393
E: info@chmzfm.com
W: http://www.chmzfm.com
Editorial Profile: CHMZ-FM is owned and operated by McBride Communications & Media Inc. The format of the station is classic rock. CHMZ-FM broadcasts to the Ucluelet, British Columbia area at 90.1 FM.

CHNC-FM
Owner: Cooperative des travailleurs CHNC
Editorial: 153, boul. Gérard-D-Levesque, New Carlisle, Quebec G0C 1Z0. **T:** 1 418 752-2215
E: radiochnc@globetrotter.net
W: http://www.radiochnc.com
Editorial Profile: CHNC-FM is a commercial station owned by Cooperative des travailleurs CHNC. The format of the station is Adult Contemporary. CHNC-FM broadcasts to the New Carlisle, Quebec area at 610 AM.

CHNI-FM
Owner: Rogers Communications Inc.
Editorial: 55 Waterloo Street, Saint John, New Brunswick E2L 4V9. **T:** 1 506 646-5161
E: news889@rogers.com
W: http://www.news889.com
Editorial Profile: CHNI-FM is a commercial station owned by Rogers Communications Inc. The format of the station is news and talk. CHNI-FM broadcasts to the Saint John, New Brunswick area at 88.9 FM.

CHNL-AM
Owner: NL Broadcasting Ltd.
Editorial: 611 Lansdowne St, Kamloops, British Columbia V2C 1Y6. **T:** 1 250 372-2292
E: nlnews@radionl.com
W: http://www.radionl.com
Editorial Profile: CHNL-AM is a commercial station owned by NL Broadcasting Ltd. The format of the station is news, talk and sports. CHNL-AM broadcasts to Kamloops, British Columbia at 610 AM.

CHNO-FM
Owner: Newfoundland Capital Corporation Limited
Editorial: 493-B Barrydowne Road, Sudbury, Ontario P3A 3T4. **T:** 1 705 560-8323
E: news@rewind1039.ca
W: http://rewind1039.ca
Editorial Profile: CHNO-FM is a commerical station owned by Newfoundland Capital Corporation Limited. The format of the station is classic hits. The station broadcasts to the Sudbury, Ontario area at 103.9.

CHNS-FM
Owner: Maritime Broadcasting System Ltd.
Editorial: 5121 Sackville St 3rd Floor, Halifax, Nova Scotia B3J 1K1. **T:** 1 902 422-1651
E: chfxnews@chfxradio.com
W: http://www.899halfm.com
Editorial Profile: CHNS-FM is a commercial station owned by the Maritime Broadcasting System Ltd. The format of the station is classic rock. CHNS-FM broadcasts to the Halifax, Nova Scotia area at 89.9 FM.

CHNV-FM
Owner: Vista Broadcast Group Inc.
Editorial: 312 Hall Street, Nelson, British Columbia V1L 1Y8. **T:** 1 250 352-1902
W: http://www.1035thebridge.com
Editorial Profile: CHNV-FM is a commercial station owned by Vista Broadcast Group Inc. The format of the station is adult album alternative. CHNV-FM broadcasts to Nelson, British Columbia at 103.5 FM.

CHOA-FM
Owner: RNC Media
Editorial: 380 avenue Murdoch, Rouyn-Noranda, Quebec J9X 1G5. **T:** 1 819 762-0744
E: infocouleurfm@rncmedia.ca
W: http://abitibi.planeteradio.ca
Editorial Profile: CHOA-FM is a commercial station owned by RNC Media. The format of the station is adult contemporary. CHOA-FM broadcasts to Rouyn-Noranda, Quebec and surrounding communities at 96.5 FM.

CHOC-FM
Owner: La Radio Communautaire Intergeneration
Editorial: 93 Rue Lachapelle E, Saint-Remi, Quebec J0L 2L0. **T:** 1 450 454-5500
E: studio@chocfm.com **W:** http://chocfm.com

CHOD-FM
Owner: Radio Communautaire Cornwall-Alexandria Inc.
Editorial: 1111 chemin Montreal, Suite 202, Cornwall, Ontario K6H 1E1. **T:** 1 613 936-2463
E: chodfm@chodfm.ca
W: http://www.chodfm.ca
Editorial Profile: CHOD-FM is a commercial station owned by Radio Communautaire Cornwall-Alexandria Inc. The format of the station is French Lite Rock/Lite AC music. CHOD-FM broadcasts to the Cornwall, Ontario area at 92.1 FM.

CHOE-FM
Owner: Communications Matane Inc.(Les)
Editorial: 800, avenue du Phare Ouest, Matane, Quebec G4W 1V7. **T:** 1 418 562-8181
E: choefm@globetrotter.net
W: http://www.choefm.com
Editorial Profile: CHOE-FM is a commercial station owned by Les Communications Matane Inc. The format of the station is top 40/CHR. CHOE-FM broadcasts to Matane, Quebec at 95.3 FM.

CHOI-FM
Owner: RNC Media
Editorial: 1134, Grande-Allée Ouest, Bureau 300, Quebec, Quebec G1S 1E5.
T: 1 418 687-9810 **W:** http://www.radiox.com
Editorial Profile: CHOI-FM is a commercial station owned by RNC Media. The format of the station is rock alternative and talk. CHOI-FM broadcasts to the Quebec City area at 98.1 FM.

CHOK-AM
Owner: Blackburn Radio Inc.
Editorial: 1415 London Rd, Sarnia, Ontario N7S 1P6. **T:** 1 519 542-5500
E: country@chok.com
W: http://www.chok.com
Editorial Profile: CHOK-AM is a commercial station owned by Blackburn Radio Inc. The format of the station is adult contemporary and classic hits. CHOK-AM broadcasts to the Sarnia, Ontario area at 1070 AM.

CHOK-FM
Owner: Blackburn Radio Inc.
Editorial: 1415 London Road, Sarnia, Ontario N7S 1P6. **T:** 1 519 542-5500
E: country@chok.com
W: http://www.blackburnradio.com
Editorial Profile: CHOK-FM is a commercial station owned by Blackburn Radio Inc. The format of the station is contemporary country. CHOK-FM broadcasts to the Sarnia, ON area at 103.9 FM.

CHOM-FM
Owner: Astral Media
Editorial: 1411 Fort Street, 3rd Floor, Montreal, Quebec H3H 2R1.
T: 1 514 931-2466 **E:** infodesk@chom.com
W: http://www.chom.com
Editorial Profile: CHOM-FM is a commercial station owned by Astral Media. The format of the station is classic rock. CHOM-FM broadcasts to the Montreal area at 97.7 FM.

CHON-FM
Owner: Northern Native Broadcasting Yukon
Editorial: 4230-A 4th Ave, Suite 6, Whitehorse, Yukon Territory Y1A 1K1.
T: 1 867 668-6629 **E:** nnby@nnby.net
W: http://www.nnby.net
Editorial Profile: CHON-FM is a commercial station owned by Northern Native Broadcasting Yukon. The format of the station is variety. CHON-FM broadcasts to the Whitehorse, Yukon Territory area at 98.1 FM.

CHOO-FM
Owner: Golden West Broadcasting Ltd.
Editorial: 105 S. Railway Ave, Drumheller, Alberta T0J 0Y6. **T:** 1 403 823-9936
W: http://995drumfm.com
Editorial Profile: CHOO-FM is a commercial station owned by Golden West Broadcasting Ltd. The format of the station is a variety of news, pop, rock and adult contemporary music. CHOO-FM broadcasts to the Drumheller, Alberta area at 99.5 FM.

CHOQ-FM
Owner: Coopérative Radiophonique de Toronto(La)
Editorial: 425 Rue Adelaide O Bureau 302, Toronto, Ontario M5V 3C1. **T:** 1 416 599-2666
E: info@choqfm.ca **W:** http://www.choqfm.ca
Editorial Profile: CHOQ-FM is a French-language non-commercial station owned by La Coopérative Radiophonique de Toronto. The format of the station is variety. CHOQ-FM broadcasts to the Toronto area at 105.1 FM.

CHOR-FM
Owner: Astral Media
Editorial: 9901 Main St, Suite 200, Summerland, British Columbia V0H 1Z0.
T: 1 250 492-2800
W: http://summerland.myezrock.com/index.aspx
Editorial Profile: CHOR-FM is a commercial station owned by Astral Media. The format of the station is Adult Contemporary. CHOR-FM broadcasts to Summerland, British Columbia and surrounding communities at 98.5 FM.

CHOS-FM
Owner: Newfoundland Broadcasting Co. Ltd.
Editorial: 446 Logy Bay Rd, St. John's, Newfoundland A1C 5S2. **T:** 1 709 726-2922
E: ozfm@ozfm.com **W:** http://www.ozfm.com

CHOU-AM
Owner: Radio Moyen-Orient du Canada
Editorial: 11876, rue Demeulles, Montreal, Quebec H4J 2E6. **T:** 1 514 790-0002
E: pdg@1450am.ca **W:** http://www.1450am.ca
Editorial Profile: CHOU-AM is a commercial station owned by Radio Moyen-Orient du Canada. The format for the station is variety. CHOU-AM broadcasts to the Montreal area at 1450 AM. The target audience of the station is listeners, ages 13 to 100.

CHOW-FM
Owner: Radio Boréale
Editorial: 43, 1ère avenue Est, Amos, Quebec J9T 1H2. **T:** 1 819 732-6991
E: info@radioboreale.com
W: http://www.radioboreale.com
Editorial Profile: CHOW-FM is a commercial radio station owned by Radio Boréale. The format for the station is variety. CHOW-FM broadcasts to the Amos, Quebec area at 105.3 FM.

CHOX-FM
Owner: Groupe Radio Simard
Editorial: 601 1ere rue, Bureau 50, La Pocatiere, Quebec G0R 1Z0.
T: 1 418 856-1310 **E:** chox@chox97.com
W: http://www.chox97.com
Editorial Profile: CHOX-FM is a commercial station owned by Groupe Radio Simard. The format of the station is contemporary pop and rock music. CHOX-FM broadcasts to the La Pocatiere, Quebec area at 97.5 FM.

CHOY-FM
Owner: Maritime Broadcasting System Ltd.
Editorial: 1000 St George Blvd, Moncton, New Brunswick E1E 4M7-. **T:** 1 506 384-2469
W: http://choix999.com
Editorial Profile: CHOY-FM is a commercial station owned by Maritime Broadcasting System Ltd. The format of the station is country. CHOY-FM broadcasts to the Moncton, New Brunswick area at 99.9 FM.

CHOZ-FM
Owner: Newfoundland Broadcasting Co. Ltd.
Editorial: 446 Logy Bay Road, St. John's, Newfoundland A1C 5S2. **T:** 1 709 726-2922
E: ntv@ntv.ca **W:** http://www.ozfm.com
Editorial Profile: CHOZ-FM is a commercial station owned by the Newfoundland Broadcasting Co. Ltd. The format of the station is top 40/CHR. CHOZ-FM broadcasts to Saint John's, Newfoundland and surrounding communities at 94.7 FM.

CHPB-FM
Owner: Vista Broadcast Group
Editorial: 171 6th Ave, Cochrane, Ontario P1L 1C0. **T:** 1 705 272-6467
E: moose981@moosefm.com
W: http://www.moosefm.com/chpb
Editorial Profile: CHPB-FM is a commercial station owned by Vista Broadcast Group. The format of the station is lite rock. The station is broadcast to the Cochrane, ON area at 98.1 FM.

CHPD-FM
Owner: Aylmer & Area Inter-Mennonite Community
Editorial: 16 Talbot Street, Aylmer, Ontario N5H 1H4. **T:** 1 519 773-8555
E: radio@debrigj.org
Editorial Profile: CHPD-FM is a non-commercial station owned by Aylmer & Area Inter-Mennonite Community. The format of the station is ethnic variety including programming in German, Spanish and English. CHPD-FM broadcasts to the Mennonite, Ontario area at 105.9 FM.

CHPK-FM
Editorial: 222 58 Ave SW Suite 600, Calgary, Alberta T2H 2S3. **T:** 1 403 536-3866
W: http://953thepeak.com
Editorial Profile: CHPK-FM is a commercial station owned by The Jim Pattinson Group. The format of the station is AAA. CHPK-FM broadcasts locally at 101.5 FM.

CHPQ-FM

Owner: Jim Pattison Broadcast Group(The)
Editorial: 166 E Island Hwy, Parksville, British Columbia V9P 2H3. **T:** 1 250 248-4211
E: info@thelounge999.com
W: http://www.thelounge999.com
Editorial Profile: CHPQ-FM is a commercial station owned by The Jim Pattison Broadcast Group. The format of the station is adult standards. CHPQ-FM broadcasts to the Parksville, British Columbia at 99.9 FM.

CHPR-FM

Owner: RNC Media
Editorial: 11 rue Argenteuil, Lachute, Quebec J8H 1X8. **T:** 1 450 562-8862
W: http://planetelov.ca
Editorial Profile: CHPR-FM is a commercial station owned by RNC Media. The format of the station is adult contemporary. CHPR-FM broadcasts to Lachute, Quebec at 102.1 FM.

CHQC-FM

Owner: Coopérative radiophonique – La Brise de la Baie
Editorial: 67 chemin Ragged Point, Saint John, New Brunswick E2K 5C3.
T: 1 506 643-6996 **E:** animateurs@chqc.ca
W: http://www.chqc.ca

CHQM-FM

Owner: Bell Media
Editorial: 500-969 Robson St 500, Vancouver, British Columbia V6Z 1X5. **T:** 1 604 871-9000
W: http://www.qmfm.com
Editorial Profile: CHQM-FM is a commercial station owned by Bell Media. The format of the station is Lite Rock/Lite AC music. CHQM-FM broadcasts to the Vancouver, British Columbia area at 103.5 FM.

CHQR-AM

Owner: Corus Entertainment Inc.
Editorial: 170-200 Barclay Parade SW 170, eau claire market 170 170, Calgary, Alberta T2P 4R5. **T:** 1 403 716-6500
W: http://www.newstalk770.com/
Editorial Profile: CHQR-AM is a commercial station owned by Corus Entertainment. The format of the station is news, talk and sports. CHQR-AM broadcasts to the Calgary, Alberta area at 770 AM.

CHQT-AM

Owner: Corus Entertainment Inc.
Editorial: 5204 E 84th St, Edmonton, Alberta T6E 5N8. **T:** 1 780 440-6300
E: news@inews880.com
W: http://www.inews880.com
Editorial Profile: CHQT-AM is a commercial station owned by Corus Entertainment. The format of the station is news. CHQT-AM broadcasts to Edmonton, Alberta and its environs at 880 AM.

CHQX-FM

Owner: Rawlco Radio Ltd.
Editorial: 1316 Central Ave, Box 900, Prince Albert, Saskatchewan S6V 7R4.
T: 1 306 763-7421 **E:** mix101@rawlco.com
W: http://www.mix101fm.com
Editorial Profile: CHQX-FM is a commercial station owned by Rawlco Radio Ltd. The format of the station is album-oriented rock music. CHQX-FM broadcasts to the Prince Albert, Saskatchewan area at 101.5 FM.

CHRB-AM

Owner: Golden West Broadcasting Ltd.
Editorial: 11-5th Ave SE, High River, Alberta T1V 1G2. **T:** 1 403 652-2472
W: http://www.am1140radio.com
Editorial Profile: CHRB-AM is a commercial station owned by Golden West Broadcasting. The format of the station is a variety of Christian, gospel and contemporary country music, inspirational programming and local and agricultural news. CHRB-AM broadcasts to High River, Alberta and its environs at 1140 AM.

CHRD-FM

Owner: Astral Media
Editorial: 2070 rue St-Georges, Drummondville, Quebec J2C 5G6.
T: 1 819 474-1892
W: http://drummondville.rougefm.ca
Editorial Profile: CHRD-FM is a commercial station owned by Astral Media. The format of the station is adult contemporary. CHRD-FM broadcasts to Drummondville, Quebec at 105.3 FM.

CHRE-FM

Owner: Bell Media
Editorial: 12 Yates Street, St. Catharines, Ontario L2R 5R2. **T:** 1 905 688-1057

W: http://www.1057ezrock.com
Editorial Profile: CHRE-FM is a commercial station owned by Bell Media. The format of the station is easy listening. CHRE-FM broadcasts to St. Catharines, Ontario and surrounding communities at 105.7 FM. Twitter handle: twitter.com/1057ezrock

CHRI-FM

Owner: Christian Hit Radio Inc.
Editorial: 1010 Thomas Spratt Place, Suite 3, Ottawa, Ontario K1G 5L5. **T:** 1 613 247-1440
E: chri@chri.ca **W:** http://www.chri.ca
Editorial Profile: CHRI-FM is a commercial station owned by Christian Hit Radio Inc. The format of the station is contemporary Christian music and religious talk. CHRI-FM broadcasts to Ottawa, Ontario and its environs at 99.1 FM.

CHRK-FM

Owner: NewCap Radio
Editorial: 5 Detheridge Drive, Sydney, Nova Scotia B1L 1B8. **T:** 1 902 270-1019
E: reception@giant1019.com
W: http://www.giant1019.com
Editorial Profile: CHRK-FM is a commercial station owned by NewCap Radio. The format of the station is Top 40/CHR. CHRK-FM broadcasts to the Sydney, Nova Scotia area at 101.9 FM.

CHRL-FM

Owner: RNC Media
Editorial: 568 boul St-Joseph, Roberval, Quebec G8H 2K6. **T:** 1 418 275-1831
W: http://roberval.planeteradio.ca
Editorial Profile: CHRL-FM is a commercial station owned by RNC Media. The format of the station is adult contemporary. CHRL-FM broadcasts to the Roberval, Quebec area at 99.5 FM.

CHRM-FM

Owner: Communications Matane Inc.(Les)
Editorial: 800 avenue du Phare Ouest, Matane, Quebec G4W 1V7. **T:** 1 418 562-4141
E: choefm@globetrotter.net
W: http://www.chrmfm.com
Editorial Profile: CHRM-FM is a commercial station owned by Les Communications Matane Inc. The format of the station is adult contemporary. CHRM-FM broadcasts to Matane, Quebec at 105.3 FM.

CHRW-FM

Owner: University of Western Ontario
Editorial: University of Western Ontario, Bldg Rm 250, London, Ontario N6A 3K7.
T: 1 519 661-3601 **E:** news@chrwradio.com
W: http://chrwradio.ca
Editorial Profile: CHRW-FM is a non-commercial station owned by the University of Western Ontario. The format of the station is college variety. CHRW-FM broadcasts to London, Ontario at 94.9 FM.

CHRX-FM

Owner: Bell Media
Editorial: 10532 Alaska Rd, Fort St. John, British Columbia V1J 1B3. **T:** 1 250 785-6634
E: peacenews@astral.com
W: http://www.peacesunfm.com
Editorial Profile: CHRX-FM is a commercial station owned by Bell Media. The format of the station is Top 40/CHR music. CHRX-FM broadcasts to the Fort St. John, British Columbia area at 98.5 FM.

CHRY-FM

Owner: CHRY Community Radio Inc.
Editorial: York University 4700 Keele St, Room #413 Student Centre, Toronto, Ontario M3J 1P3. **T:** 1 416 736-5293
E: chrynews@yorku.ca **W:** http://www.chry.fm
Editorial Profile: CHRY-FM is a non-commercial college station owned by CHRY Community Radio Inc. The format of the station is variety. CHRY-FM broadcasts to the Toronto area at 105.5 FM.

CHSB-FM

Owner: Bedford Baptist Church
Editorial: 158 Rocky Lake Drive, Bedford, Nova Scotia B4A 2T6. **T:** 1 902 835-5966
E: contact@hilltopfm.ca
W: http://www.hilltopfm.ca
Editorial Profile: CHSB-FM is a non-commerical station owned by Bedford Baptist Church. The format of the station is religious and Christian programming. CHSB-FM broadcasts to the Bedford, NS area at 99.3 FM.

CHSJ-FM

Owner: Acadia Broadcasting Ltd.

Editorial: Box 2000 - 58 King Street, Saint John, New Brunswick E2L 3T4.
T: 1 506 633-3323 **E:** mail@country94.ca
W: http://www.country94.ca
Editorial Profile: CHSJ-FM is a commercial station owned by Acadia Broadcasting Ltd. The format of the station is classic country music. CHSJ-FM broadcasts to the Saint John, New Brunswick area at 94.1 FM.

CHSL-FM

Owner: Newfoundland Capital Corporation Limited
Editorial: 221 3rd Ave NW, Slave Lake, Alberta T0G 2A1. **T:** 1 780 849-2569
E: news@lakefm.ca **W:** http://www.lakefm.ca
Editorial Profile: CHSL-FM is a commercial station owned by Newfoundland Capital Corporation Limited. The format of the station is classic hits. CHSL-FM broadcasts to the Slave Lake, Alberta area at 92.7 FM.

CHSM-AM

Owner: Golden West Broadcasting Ltd.
Editorial: 105-32 Brandt Street, Steinbach, Manitoba R5G 2J7. **T:** 1 204 326-3737
E: info@goldenwestradio.com
W: http://www.steinbachonline.com
Editorial Profile: CHSM-AM is a commercial station owned by Golden West Broadcasting Ltd. The format of the station is easy listening music. CHSM-AM broadcasts to Steinbach, Manitoba and its environs at 1250 AM.

CHSN-FM

Owner: Golden West Broadcasting Ltd.
Editorial: 200-1236 5th Street, Estevan, Saskatchewan S4A 0Z6. **T:** 1 306 634-1280
W: http://www.sun102radio.com
Editorial Profile: CHSN-FM is a commercial station owned by Golden West Broadcasting Ltd. The format for the station is adult contemporary. CHSN-FM broadcast to the Estevan, Saskatchewan area at 102.3 FM.

CHSP-FM

Owner: Newfoundland Capital Corporation Limited
Editorial: 201-4341 50th Ave, Saint Paul, Alberta T0A 3A3. **T:** 1 780 645-4425
W: http://www.977thespur.com
Editorial Profile: CHSP-FM is a commercial station owned by Newfoundland Capital Corporation Limited. The format of the station is contemporary country music. CHSP-FM broadcasts to St. Paul, Alberta area at 97.7 FM.

CHSR-FM

Owner: CHSR Broadcasting Inc.
Editorial: 21 Pacey Drive, Room 223, Fredericton, New Brunswick E3B 5A3.
T: 1 506 453-4985 **E:** feedback@chsrfm.ca
W: http://www.chsrfm.ca
Editorial Profile: CHSR-FM is a commercial station owned by CHSR Broadcasting Inc. The format of the station is variety. CHSR-FM broadcasts to the University of New Brunswick in Fredericton, New Brunswick at 97.9 FM.

CHST-FM

Owner: Rogers Communications Inc.
Editorial: 1 Communications Road, London, Ontario N6J 4Z1. **T:** 1 519 690-0102
W: http://www.1023bob.com
Editorial Profile: CHST-FM is a commercial station owned by Rogers Communications Inc. The format of the station is classic hits. CHST-FM broadcasts to the London, Ontario area at 102.3 FM.

CHSU-FM

Owner: Bell Media
Editorial: 435 Bernard Ave, Kelowna, British Columbia V1Y 6N8. **T:** 1 250 860-8600
E: info@thesun.net **W:** http://www.thesun.net
Editorial Profile: CHSU-FM is a commercial station owned by Bell Media. The format of the station is Top 40/CHR. CHSU-FM broadcasts to the Kelowna, British Columbia area at 99.9 FM.

CHTD-FM

Owner: Acadia Broadcasting Ltd.
Editorial: 112 Milltown Boulevard, Saint Stephen, New Brunswick E3L 1G6.
T: 1 506 466-1000 **E:** tidenews@radioabl.ca
W: http://www.thetide.ca
Editorial Profile: CHTD-FM is a commercial station owned by Acadia Broadcasting Ltd. The format of the station is contemporary country. CHTD-FM broadcasts to the Saint Stephen, New Brunswick area at 98.1.

CHTK-FM

Owner: Astral Media

Editorial: 215 Cow Bay Road, Ste 230, Prince Rupert, British Columbia V5J 1A2.
T: 1 250 635-6316
E: webmaster@themixbc.com
W: http://www.princerupert.myezrock.com
Editorial Profile: CHTK-FM is a commercial station owned by Astral Media. The format of the station is adult hits. CHTK-AM broadcasts to Prince Rupert, British Columbia at 560 AM.

CHTM-AM

Owner: Arctic Radio (1982) Ltd.
Editorial: 103 Cree Road, Thompson, Manitoba R8N 0B9. **T:** 1 204 778-7361
E: chtm@arcticradio.ca
W: http://www.thompsononline.ca
Editorial Profile: CHTM-AM is a commercial station owned by Arctic Radio (1982) Ltd. The format of the station is adult contemporary. CHTM-AM broadcasts to the Thompson, Manitoba area at 610 AM.

CHTN-FM

Owner: Newfoundland Capital Corporation Limited
Editorial: 90 University Ave, Ste 320, Charlottetown, Prince Edward Island C1A 4K9.
T: 1 902 569-1003 **E:** news@ocean100.com
W: http://www.ocean100.com
Editorial Profile: CHTN-FM is a commercial station owned by Newfoundland Capital Corporation Limited. The format for the station is classic hits. CHTN-FM broadcasts to Charlottetown, Prince Edward Island and its environs at 100.3 FM.

CHTO-AM

Owner: Canadian Hellenic Toronto Radio Inc.
Editorial: 437 Danforth Ave, Suite 204, Toronto, Ontario M4K 1P1. **T:** 1 416 465-1112
E: info@am1690.ca **W:** http://www.am1690.ca
Editorial Profile: CHTO-AM is a commerical station owned by Canadian Hellenic Toronto Radio Inc. The format of the station is ethnic variety. CHTO-AM broadcasts to the Toronto area at 1690 AM.

CHTT-FM

Owner: Rogers Communications Inc.
Editorial: 817 Fort St, Victoria, British Columbia V8W 1H6. **T:** 1 250 382-0900
W: http://www.1031jackfm.ca
Editorial Profile: CHTT-FM is a commercial station owned by Rogers Communications Inc. The format of the station is adult hits. CHTT-FM broadcasts to Victoria, British Columbia at 103.1 FM.

CHTZ-FM

Owner: Astral Media
Editorial: 12 Yates St, St. Catharines, Ontario L2R 5R2. **T:** 1 905 688-0977
W: http://www.htzfm.com
Editorial Profile: CHTZ-FM is a commercial station owned by Astral Media. The format of the station is classic and contemporary rock music. CHTZ-FM broadcasts to St. Catharines, Ontario and surrounding communities at 97.7 FM.

CHUB-FM

Owner: Jim Pattison Broadcast Group(The)
Editorial: 2840 Bremner Avenue, 2nd Floor, Red Deer, Alberta T4R 1M9.
T: 1 403 343-7105 **E:** heydj@big105.fm
W: http://www.big105.fm
Editorial Profile: CHUB-FM is a commercial station owned by The Jim Pattison Broadcast Group. The format is Top 40/CHR. CHUB-FM broadcasts to Red Deer, Alberta and surrounding communities at 105.5 FM.

CHUC-FM

Owner: Pineridge Broadcasting Inc.
Editorial: 7805 Telephone Road, Cobourg, Ontario K9A 4J7. **T:** 1 905 372-5401
E: news@chuc1450.com
W: http://www.1079thebreeze.com
Editorial Profile: CHUC-FM is a commercial station owned by Pineridge Broadcasting Inc. The format of the station is adult contemporary. CHUC-FM broadcasts to the Cobourg, Ontario area at 107.9 FM.

CHUK-FM

Owner: Corporation Mediatique Teuehikan
Editorial: 1491 Ouiatchouan, Mashteuiatsh, Quebec G0W 2H0. **T:** 1 418 275-4684
E: chuk@chukfm.ca **W:** http://www.chukfm.ca
Editorial Profile: CHUK-FM is a commercial station owned by Corporation Mediatique Teuehikan. The format of the station is variety. CHUK-FM broadcasts to the Mashteuiatsh, Quebec area at 107.3 FM.

CHUM-AM

Owner: Bell Media

Editorial: 299 Queen St W, Toronto, Ontario M5V 2Z5-. **T:** 1 416 870-1050
E: tsngo@bellmedia.ca
W: http://www.tsn.ca/toronto
Editorial Profile: CHUM-AM is a commercial station owned by Bell Media. The format of the station is sports. CHUM-AM broadcasts to the Toronto area at 1050 AM.

CHUM-FM
Owner: Bell Media
Editorial: 299 Queen Street West, Toronto, Ontario M5V 2Z5. **T:** 1 416 925-6666
E: news@chumamfm.com
W: http://www.chumfm.com
Editorial Profile: CHUM-FM is a commercial station owned by Bell Media. The format of the station is hot adult contemporary. CHUM-FM broadcasts to the Toronto area at 104.5 FM.

CHUO-FM
Owner: Radio Ottawa
Editorial: 65 University Pvt., Suite 0038, Ottawa, Ontario K1N 9A5. **T:** 1 613 562-5965
E: info@chuo.fm **W:** http://www.chuo.fm
Editorial Profile: CHUO-FM is a non-commercial station owned by Radio Ottawa. The format of the station is variety. CHUO-FM broadcasts to Ottawa, Ontario at 89.1 FM.

CHUP-FM
Owner: Rawlco Radio Ltd.
Editorial: 6807 Railway Street SE, Suite 110, Calgary, Alberta T2H 2V6. **T:** 1 403 385-4000
E: fun@up977.com **W:** http://www.up977.com
Editorial Profile: CHUP-FM is a commercial station owned by Rawlco Radio Ltd. The format for the station is adult contemporary. CHUP-FM broadcasts to the Calgary, Alberta area at 97.7 FM.

CHUR-FM
Owner: Rogers Communications Inc.
Editorial: 743 Main St E, North Bay, Ontario P1B 1C2. **T:** 1 705 474-2000
W: http://www.kissnorthbay.com
Editorial Profile: CHUR-FM is a commercial station owned by Rogers Communications Inc. The format of the station is Top 40/CHR. CHUR-FM broadcasts to North Bay, Ontario and surrounding communities at 100.5 FM.

CHVD-FM
Owner: RNC Media
Editorial: 1975 boul Wallberg, Dolbeau-Mistassini, Quebec G8L 1J5.
T: 1 418 276-3333 **E:** clemelin@rncmedia.ca
W: http://dolbeau-mistassini.planeteradio.ca
Editorial Profile: CHVD-FM is commercial station owned by RNC Media. The format of the station is adult contemporary. CHVD-FM broadcasts to the Dolbeau-Mistassini, Quebec area at 100.3 FM.

CHVN-FM
Owner: Golden West Broadcasting Ltd.
Editorial: 1-741 St. Mary's Rd 1, Winnipeg, Manitoba R2M 3N5. **T:** 1 204 452-9602
W: http://www.chvnradio.com
Editorial Profile: CHVN-FM is commercial station owned by Golden West Broadcasting Ltd. The format of the station is contemporary Christian music and religious talk. CHVN-FM broadcasts to the Winnipeg, Manitoba area at 95.1 FM.

CHVO-FM
Owner: Newfoundland Capital Corporation Limited
Editorial: 1 CHVO Drive, Carbonear, Newfoundland A1Y 1A2. **T:** 1 709 726-5590
E: info@kixxcountry.ca
W: http://www.kixxcountry.ca
Editorial Profile: CHVO-FM is a commercial station owned by Newfoundland Capital Corporation Limited. The format of the station is country. CHVO-FM broadcasts to the Carbonear, Newfoundland area at 103.9 FM.

CHVR-FM
Owner: Bell Media
Editorial: 595 Pembroke St E, Pembroke, Ontario K8A 3L7. **T:** 1 613 735-9670
E: star96@bellmedia.ca
W: http://www.star96.ca
Editorial Profile: CHVR-FM is a commercial station owned by Bell Media. The format of the station is contemporary country. CHVR-FM broadcasts to the Pembroke, Ontario area at 96.7 FM. Twitter handle: www.twitter.com/Star96FM

CHWC-FM
Owner: Bayshore Broadcasting Corp.
Editorial: 300 Suncoast Drive East, Unit E, Goderich, Ontario N7A 4N7.
T: 1 519 612-1149
E: thebeach@1049thebeach.ca
W: http://www.1049thebeach.ca
Editorial Profile: CHWC-FM is a commercial station owned by Bayshore Broadcasting Corp. The format of the station is adult contemporary. CHWC-FM broadcasts to the Goderich, Ontario area at 104.9 FM.

CHWE-FM
Owner: Evanov Radio Group
Editorial: 520 Corydon Ave, Winnipeg, Manitoba R3L 0P1. **T:** 1 204 477- 1221
E: info@energy106.ca
W: http://www.energy106.ca
Editorial Profile: CHWE-FM is a commercial station owned by Evanov Radio Group. The format of the station is Top 40/CHR. CHWE-FM broadcasts to the Winnipeg, Manitoba area at a frequency of 106.1 FM.

CHWF-FM
Owner: Jim Pattison Broadcast Group(The)
Editorial: 4550 Wellington Road, Nanaimo, British Columbia V9T 2H3. **T:** 1 250 758-1131
E: info@1069thewolf.com
W: http://www.1069thewolf.com
Editorial Profile: CHWF-FM is a commercial station owned by The Jim Pattison Broadcast Group. The format of the station is classic rock/rock alternative. CHWF-FM broadcasts to the Nanaimo, British Columbia area at 106.9 FM.

CHWK-FM
Owner: Fabmar Communications Ltd.
Editorial: 46167 Yale Rd, Chilliwack, British Columbia V2P 2P2-. **T:** 1 604 795-2429
E: info@895thedrive.com
W: http://www.895thedrive.com
Editorial Profile: CHWK-FM is a commercial station owned by Fabmar Communications Ltd. The format of the station is rock music. CHWK-FM broadcasts to the Chilliwack, BC area at 89.5 FM.

CHWV-FM
Owner: Acadia Broadcasting Ltd.
Editorial: Box 2000 - 58 King Street, Saint John, New Brunswick E2L 3T4.
T: 1 506 633-3323 **E:** news@radioabl.com
W: http://www.thewave.ca
Editorial Profile: CHWV-FM is a commercial radio station owned by Acadia Broadcasting Ltd. The format of the station is hot adult contemporary music. CHWV-FM broadcasts to Saint John, New Brunswick at 97.3 FM.

CHXL-FM
Owner: Okanese First Nation
T: 1 306 334-3331 **E:** psa@creekfm.com
W: http://www.creekfm.com
Editorial Profile: CHXL-FM is a non-commercial station owned by O.K. Creek Radio Station Inc. The format of the station is variety. CHXL-FM broadcasts to the Balcarres, Saskatchewan area at 95.3 FM.

CHXX-FM
Owner: RNC Media
Editorial: 1134 Grand Allee Ouest, Suite 300, Quebec, Quebec G1S 1E5. **T:** 1 418 687-9810
W: http://www.radiox2.com
Editorial Profile: CHXX-FM is a commercial station owned by RNC Media. The format of the station is rock. CHXX-FM broadcasts to the Quebec City area at 100.9 FM.

CHYC-FM
Owner: LE5 Communications Inc.
Editorial: 336 Rue Pine, Ste 301, Sudbury, Ontario P3C 1X8. **T:** 1 705 222-8306
W: http://www.leloupfm.com/Sudbury
Editorial Profile: CHYC-FM is a commercial station owned by LE5 Communications Inc. The format of the station is hot adult contemporary. CHYC-FM broadcasts to Sudbury, Ontario at 98.9 FM.

CHYF-FM
Owner: GIMA Radio
Editorial: 53 Corbière Street, M'Chigeeng, Ontario P0P 1G0. **T:** 1 705 282-8955
Editorial Profile: CHYF-FM is a non-profit station owned by GIMA Radio. The format for the station is variety. CHYF-FM broadcasts to the M'Chigeeng, Ontario area at 88.9 FM.

CHYK-FM
Owner: Le5 Communications Inc.
Editorial: 136 Troisième Avenue, Timmins, Ontario P4N 1C6. **T:** 1 705 269-8307
W: http://www.leloupfm.com/Timmins
Editorial Profile: CHYK-FM is a commercial station owned by Le5 Communications Inc. The format of the station is hot adult contemporary. CHYK-FM broadcasts to Timmins, Ontario at 104.1 FM.

CHYM-FM
Owner: Rogers Communications Inc.
Editorial: 305 King St West, Kitchener, Ontario N2G 4E4. **T:** 1 519 743-2611
E: news570@rogers.com
W: http://www.chymfm.com
Editorial Profile: CHYM-FM is a commercial station owned by Rogers Communications Inc. The format of the station is adult contemporary. CHYM-FM broadcasts to the Kitchener, Ontario area at 96.7 FM.

CHYR-FM
Owner: Blackburn Radio Inc.
Editorial: 100 Talbot St East, Leamington, Ontario N8H 1L3. **T:** 1 519 326-6171
W: http://www.mix967.ca
Editorial Profile: CHYR-FM is a commercial station owned by Blackburn Radio Inc. The format of the station is hot adult contemporary. CHYR-FM broadcasts to Leamington, Ontario at 96.7 FM.

CHYZ-FM
Owner: Université Laval(L')
Editorial: Université Laval, 2305 rue de l'Université, Local 0236 Pavillon Maurice Pollack, Quebec, Quebec G1V 0A6.
T: 1 418 656-7007 **E:** information@chyz.ca
W: http://www.chyz.ca
Editorial Profile: CHYZ-FM is a non-commercial station owned by the Université Laval. The format of the station is college variety. CHYZ-FM broadcasts to Quebec City at 94.3 FM.

CIAM-FM
Owner: Care Radio Broadcasting Association
Editorial: 4709 River Road, Fort Vermilion, Alberta T0H 1N0. **T:** 1 780 927-2426
E: news@ciamradio.com
W: http://www.ciam.ciamradio.com
Editorial Profile: CIAM-FM is a non-commercial station owned by Care Radio Broadcasting Association. The station broadcasts to the northern Alberta region. The format of the station is religious.

CIAO-AM
Owner: Evanov Radio Group
Editorial: 5312 Dundas St West, Toronto, Ontario M9B 1B2. **T:** 1 416 213-1035
E: info@evanovradio.com
W: http://www.am530.ca
Editorial Profile: CIAO-AM is a commercial station owned by Evanov Radio Group. The format of the station is news and talk as well as ethnic and multicultural music. CIAO-AM broadcasts to the Toronto area at 530 AM.

CIAU-FM
Owner: CIAU-FM Radio
Editorial: 143 Joliet, Radisson, Quebec J0Y 2X0. **T:** 1 819 638-7033 **E:** ciaufm@lino.com
W: http://www.ciaufm.ca
Editorial Profile: CIAU-FM is a commercial station owned by CIAU-FM Radio. The format of the station is variety. WIXO-FM broadcasts to the Radisson, Quebec area at 103.1 FM.

CIAX-FM
Owner: La Radio Communautaire de Windsor et Region Inc.
Editorial: 49 6e Avenue, Windsor, Quebec J1S 1T2. **T:** 1 819 845-2692
E: unitewindsor@qc.aira.com
W: http://www.ciaxfm.net
Editorial Profile: CIAX-FM is a non-commercial station owned by La Radio Communautaire de Windsor et Region Inc. The format of the station is variety. CIAX-FM broadcasts to the Windsor, Quebec area at 98.3 FM.

CIAY-FM
Owner: Board of Bethany Pentecostal Tabernacle
Editorial: 91806 Alaska Highway, Whitehorse, Yukon Territory Y1A 5B7. **T:** 1 867 393-2429
E: info@lifewhitehorse.com
W: http://lifewhitehorse.com
Editorial Profile: CIAY-FM is a commercial station owned by Board of Bethany Pentecostal Tabernacle. The format of the station is Christian Contemporary. CIAY-FM broadcasts to the Whitehorse, Yukon Territory area at 100.7 FM.

CIBH-FM
Owner: Jim Pattison Broadcast Group(The)
Editorial: 166 E Island Hwy, Parksville, British Columbia V9P 2H3. **T:** 1 250 248-4211
E: info@885thebeach.com
W: http://www.885thebeach.com
Editorial Profile: CIBH-FM is a commercial station owned by The Jim Pattison Broadcast Group. The format of the station is adult contemporary music. CIBH-FM broadcasts to the Parksville, British Columbia area at 88.5 FM.

CIBK-FM
Owner: Astral Media
Editorial: 1110 Centre Street North, Suite 300, Calgary, Alberta T2E 2R2. **T:** 1 403 240-5850
W: http://calgary.virginradio.ca
Editorial Profile: CIBK-FM is a commercial station owned by Astral Media. The format of the station is Top 40/CHR. CIBK-FM broadcasts to the Calgary, Alberta area at 98.5 FM. Beginning June 30, 2010, CIBK-FM will take on Virgin Radio branding.

CIBL-FM
Owner: Radio Communautaire Francophone de Montréal Inc.(La)
Editorial: 2 Ste-Catherine St Est, Suite 201, Montreal, Quebec H2X 1K4.
T: 1 514 526-2581 **E:** direction@cibl1015.com
W: http://www.cibl1015.com
Editorial Profile: CIBL-FM is a non-commercial station owned by La Radio Communautaire Francophone de Montréal Inc. The format of the station is variety. CIBL-FM broadcasts to Montreal at 101.5 FM.

CIBM-FM
Owner: Groupe Radio Simard
Editorial: 64 rue de l'Hotel-de-Ville, Riviere-du-Loup, Quebec G5R 1L5. **T:** 1 418 867-1071
W: http://www.cibm107.com/cibm
Editorial Profile: CIBM-FM is a commercial station owned by Groupe Radio Simard. The format of the station is Lite Rock/Lite AC. CIBM-FM broadcasts to the Rivière-du-Loup, Quebec area at 107.1 FM.

CIBN-FM
Owner: Bufalows Broadcasting Co.
Editorial: 1224 Peterson Box 38, Buffalo Narrows, Saskatchewan S0M 0J0.
T: 1 306 235-4722 **E:** buflo@sasktel.net

CIBO-FM
Owner: Radio Communautaire de Senneterre Inc.(La)
Editorial: 121 1ere rue Est, Senneterre, Quebec J0Y 2M0. **T:** 1 819 737-2222
E: cibo.fm@cableamos.com
Editorial Profile: CIBO-FM is a commercial station owned by La Radio Communautaire de Senneterre Inc. The format of the station is adult contemporary. CIBO-FM broadcasts to the Senneterre, Quebec area at 100.5 FM.

CIBQ-FM
Owner: Newcap Radio
Editorial: 403 2nd Avenue West, Unit 8, Brooks, Alberta T1R 0S3. **T:** 1 403 362-3418
E: cibq@newcap.ca **W:** http://www.q1057.ca
Editorial Profile: CIBQ-FM is a commercial station owned by Newcap Radio. The format of the station is country music. CIBQ-FM broadcasts to Brooks, Alberta and surrounding communities at 105.7 FM.

CIBU-FM
Owner: Blackburn Radio Inc.
Editorial: 215 Carling Terrace, Wingham, Ontario N0G 2W0. **T:** 1 519 357-1310
E: info@945thebull.ca
W: http://www.945thebull.ca
Editorial Profile: CIBU-FM is a commercial station owned by Blackburn Radio Inc. The format of the station is rock alternative music. CIBU-FM broadcasts in the Wingham, Ontario area at 94.5.

CIBW-FM
Owner: Jim Pattison Broadcast Group(The)
Editorial: 5164-52 Avenue, Drayton Valley, Alberta T7A 1V3. **T:** 1 780 542-9290
E: jocks@bigwestcountry.ca
W: http://www.bigwestcountry.ca
Editorial Profile: CIBW-FM is a commercial station owned by The Jim Pattison Broadcast Group. The format is country and easy listening music. CIBW-FM broadcasts to Drayton Valley, Alberta and its environs at 92.9 FM.

CIBX-FM
Owner: Bell Media
Editorial: 206 Rookwood Ave, Fredericton, New Brunswick E3B 2M2. **T:** 1 506 451-9111
E: frederictonnewsteam@bellmedia.ca
W: http://www.capitalfm.ca
Editorial Profile: CIBX-FM is a commercial station owned by Bell Media. The format of the station is adult contemporary. CIBX-FM broadcasts to the Fredericton, New Brunswick

WORLD NEWS MEDIA

area at 106.9 FM. Twitter handle: www.twitter.com/1069_CapitalFM

CICF-FM
Owner: Astral Media
Editorial: 2800 31st St, Vernon, British Columbia V1T 5H4. **T:** 1 250 545-9222
E: reception@thesunonline.ca
W: http://www.thesunonline.ca
Editorial Profile: CICF-FM is a commercial radio station owned by Astral Media. The format of the station is hot adult comtemporary. CICF-FM broadcasts to Vernon, British Columbia at 105.7 FM.

CICR-FM
Owner: Parrsboro Radio Society
Editorial: 396 Upper Main St, Parrsboro, Nova Scotia B0M 1S0. **T:** 1 902 216-0042
E: parrsborocommunityradio@hotmail.com
W: http://www.parrsborocommunityradio.ca
Editorial Profile: CICR-FM is a non-commercial station owned by Parrsboro Radio Society. The format of the station is a mix of classic hits and country music. CICR-FM broadcasts to the Parrsboro, Nova Scotia area at 99.1 FM.

CICS-FM
Owner: Larche Communications Inc.
Editorial: 60 Elm St, Sudbury, Ontario P3C 1R8. **T:** 1 705 671-7330
E: news@kicx917.com
W: http://www.kicx917.com
Editorial Profile: CICS-FM is a commercial station owned by Larche Communications Inc. The format of the station is contemporary country. CICS-FM broadcasts to Sudbury, Ontario at 91.7 FM.

CICV-FM
Owner: Cowichan Valley Community Radio Society
Editorial: 37 Wellington St. West, Trans Canada Trail Blvd., Lake Cowichan, British Columbia V0R 2G0. **T:** 1 250 749-6635
E: admin@cicv.ca **W:** http://www.cvcradio.ca
Editorial Profile: CICV-FM is a non-commercial station owned by Cowichan Valley Community Radio Society. The format of the station is community news. CICV-FM broadcasts to the Lake Cowichan, British Columbia area at 98.7 FM.

CICW-FM
Owner: Centre Wellington Radio
Editorial: 198 St Andrew St W Suite 200, Fergus, Ontario N1M 1N7. **T:** 1 122 63839290
E: info@thegrand929.com
W: http://www.thegrand929.com
Editorial Profile: CICW-FM is a non-commercial station owned by Centre Wellington Radio. The format of the station is adult contemporary. CICW-FM broadcasts to Wellington, ON at 92.9 FM.

CICX-FM
Owner: Larche Communications Inc.
Editorial: 7 Progress Dr RR 1, Orillia, Ontario L3V 6H1. **T:** 1 705 722-5429
E: news@kicxfm.com **W:** http://kicx106.com
Editorial Profile: CICX-FM is a commercial station owned by Larche Communications Inc. The format of the station is contemporary country. CICX-FM broadcasts to Orillia, Ontario at 105.9 FM.

CICY-FM
Owner: Native Communications, Inc.
Editorial: 1507 Inkster Blvd, Winnipeg, Manitoba R2X 1R2. **T:** 1 204 772-8255
E: info@ncifm.com **W:** http://www.ncifm.com
Editorial Profile: CICY-FM is a commercial station owned by Native Communications, Inc. (NCI). The format of the station is aboriginal language news and programming. CICY-FM broadcasts to Selkirk, Manitoba and its environs at 105.5 FM.

CICZ-FM
Owner: Larche Communications Inc.
Editorial: 355 Cranston Crescent, Midland, Ontario L4R 4L3. **T:** 1 705 720-1991
E: events@thedockfm.com
W: http://www.1041thedock.com
Editorial Profile: CICZ-FM is a commercial station owned by Larche Communications Inc. The format of the station is Classic Rock and Classic Hits. CICZ-FM broadcasts in the Midland, Ontario area at 104.1 FM.

CIDC-FM
Owner: Evanov Radio Group
Editorial: 5312 Dundas St West, Toronto, Ontario M9B 1B2. **T:** 1 416 213-1035
E: info@z1035.com **W:** http://www.z1035.com
Editorial Profile: CIDC-FM is a commercial station owned by Evanov Radio Group. The format of the station is Top 40/CHR music. CIDC-FM broadcasts to the Toronto area at 103.5 FM.

CIDG-FM
Owner: Torres Media
Editorial: 380 Hunt Club Road, Ste 203, Ottawa, Ontario K1V 1C1. **T:** 1 613 730-1019
E: info@dawgfm.com
W: http://www.dawgfm.com
Editorial Profile: CIDG-FM is a commercial station owned by Torres Media. The format for the station is blues. CIDG-FM broadcasts to the Ottawa, Ontario and Gatineau, Quebec area at 101.9 FM.

CIDI-FM
Owner: RCM Media
Editorial: 305B Knowlton Road, Knowlton, Quebec J0E 1V0. **T:** 1 450 242-9873
W: http://www.rcmmedia.org
Editorial Profile: CIDI-FM is a non-commercial station owned by RCM Media. The format of the station is variety. CIDI-FM broadcasts to the Knowlton, Quebec area at 99.1 FM.

CIDO-FM
Owner: Creston Community Radio Society
T: 1 250 402-6772 **E:** info@crestonradio.ca
W: http://www.crestonradio.ca
Editorial Profile: CIDO-FM is a non-commercial station owned by Creston Community Radio Society. The format of the station is variety. CIDO-FM broadcasts to the Creston, British Columbia area at 97.7 FM.

CIDR-FM
Owner: Bell Media
Editorial: 1640 Ouellette Ave, Windsor, Ontario N8X 1L1. **T:** 1 519 258-8888
W: http://www.939theriverradio.com
Editorial Profile: CIDR-FM is a commercial station owned by Bell Media.The format of the station is AAA-Adult Album Alternative. CIDR-FM broadcasts to Windsor, Ontario at 93.9 FM.

CIEG-FM
Owner: Rogers Communications Inc.
Editorial: 40147 Glenalder Place, Unit 202, Squamish, British Columbia V8B 0G2.
T: 1 604 892-1021
E: mountainfm@mountainfm.com
W: http://www.mountainfm.com
Editorial Profile: CIEG-FM is a commercial station owned by Rogers Communications Inc. The format of the station is hot adult contemporary. CIEG-FM broadcasts to the Squamish, British Columbia area at 107.5 FM.

CIEL-FM
Owner: Groupe Radio Simard
Editorial: 64 rue de l'Hotel-de-Ville, Riviere-du-Loup, Quebec G5R 1L5. **T:** 1 418 862-8241
W: http://www.ciel103.com/ciel
Editorial Profile: CIEL-FM is a commercial radio station owned by Groupe Radio Simard. The format of the station is adult contemporary. CIEL-FM broadcasts to the Riviere-du-Loup, Quebec area at 103.7 FM.

CIEU-FM
Owner: Diffusion Communautaire Baie-des-Chaleurs
Editorial: 1645 Boul Perron Est, Carleton, Quebec G0C 1J0. **T:** 1 418 364-7094
E: administration@cieufm.com
W: http://www.cieufm.com
Editorial Profile: CIEU-FM is a French-language commercial station owned by Diffusion Communautaire Baie-des-Chaleurs. The format of the station is variety. CIEU-FM broadcasts to the Carleton, Quebec area at 94.9 FM.

CIFA-FM
Owner: Association Radio Clare (L')
T: 1 902 769-2432 **E:** info@cifafm.ca
W: http://www.cifafm.ca
Editorial Profile: CIFA-FM is a non-commercial station owned by L'Association Radio Clare. The format of the station is variety. CIFA-FM broadcasts to the Saulnierville, Nova Scotia area at 104.1 FM.

CIFM-FM
Owner: Jim Pattison Broadcast Group(The)
Editorial: 460 Pemberton Terrace, Kamloops, British Columbia V2C 1T5. **T:** 1 250 372-3322
E: info@98.3cifm.com
W: http://www.98.3cifm.com
Editorial Profile: CIFM-FM is a commercial station owned by The Jim Pattison Broadcast Group. The format of the station is album-oriented rock music. CIFM-FM broadcasts to Kamloops, British Columbia at 98.3 FM.

CIFX-FM
Owner: Mix FM Inc.
Editorial: 37 George Street, Lewisporte, Newfoundland A0G 3A0. **T:** 1 709 535-6000
Editorial Profile: CIFX-FM is a commercial station owned by Mix FM Inc. The format of the station is hot adult contemporary and CHR. CIFX-FM broadcasts to the Lewisporte, Newfoundland area at 93.7 FM.

CIGB-FM
Owner: Astral Media
Editorial: 1500 rue Royale, Bureau 260, Trois-Rivieres, Quebec G9A 6J4. **T:** 1 819 378-1023
W: http://www.radionrj.ca/mauricie
Editorial Profile: CIGB-FM is a commercial station owned by Astral Media. The format of the station is Top 40/CHR. CIGB-FM broadcasts to the Trois-Rivières, Quebec area at 102.3 FM.

CIGL-FM
Owner: Quinte Broadcasting Co. Ltd.
Editorial: 10 South Front St, Belleville, Ontario K8N 2Y3. **T:** 1 613 969-5555
E: info@mix97.com **W:** http://www.mix97.com
Editorial Profile: CIGL-FM is a commercial station owned by Quinte Broadcasting Co. Ltd. The format of the station is hot adult contemporary music. CIGL-FM broadcasts to Belleville, Ontario at 97.1 FM.

CIGM-FM
Owner: Newfoundland Capital Corporation Limited
Editorial: 493B Barrydowne Road, Sudbury, Ontario P3A 3T4. **T:** 1 705 560-8323
E: info@hot935.ca **W:** http://www.hot935.ca
Editorial Profile: CIGM-FM is a commerical station owned by Newfoundland Capital Corporation Limited. The format is Top 40. The station airs at 93.5 FM in the Sudbury, Ontario area.

CIGO-FM
Owner: MacEachern Broadcasting Ltd.
Editorial: 609 Church Street, Suite 201, Port Hawkesbury, Nova Scotia B9A 2X4.
T: 1 902 625-1220
E: news@1015thehawk.com
W: http://www.1015thehawk.com
Editorial Profile: CIGO-FM is a commercial station owned by MacEachern Broadcasting Ltd. The format of the station is adult contemporary. CIGO-FM broadcasts to the Port Hawkesbury, Nova Scotia area at 101.5 FM.

CIGV-FM
Owner: Newfoundland Capital Corporation
Editorial: 125 Nanaimo Ave West, Penticton, British Columbia V2A 1N2. **T:** 1 250 493-6767
E: cigv@img.net
W: http://okanagancountry.com
Editorial Profile: CIGV-FM is a commercial station owned by Newfoundland Capital Corporation. The format of the station is adult contemporary and contemporary country. CIGV-FM broadcasts to Penticton, British Columbia at 100.7 FM.

CIHO-FM
Owner: Radio MF Charlevoix Inc.
Editorial: 315, chemin Cartier Nord, St-Hilarion, Quebec G0A 3V0. **T:** 1 418 457-3333
W: http://www.cihofm.com
Editorial Profile: CIHO-FM is a community radio station owned by Radio MF Charlevoix Inc. The format of the station is variety. CIHO-FM broadcasts to the St-Hilarion, Quebec area at 96.3 FM.

CIHR-FM
Owner: Byrnes Communications Inc.
Editorial: 223 Norwich Avenue, Woodstock, Ontario N4S 3V8. **T:** 1 519 537-8400
W: http://www.1047.ca
Editorial Profile: CIHR-FM is a commercial station owned by Byrnes Communications Inc. The format of the station is adult contemporary. CIHR-FM broadcasts to the Woodstock, Ontario area at 104.7 FM.

CIHS-FM
Owner: Dhillon (David)
Editorial: 5222 - 50 Avenue, Wetaskiwin, Alberta T9A 0S8. **T:** 1 780 361-0245
E: mail@cihsfm.net **W:** http://www.cihsfm.net
Editorial Profile: CIHS-FM is a commercial station owned by David Dhillon. The format of the station is religious, gospel and classic country. CIHS-FM broadcasts to the Wetaskiwin, AB area at 93.5 FM.

CIHT-FM
Owner: Newfoundland Capital Corporation Limited
Editorial: 6 Antares Drive, Phase 1, Unit 100, Ottawa, Ontario K2E 8A9. **T:** 1 613 723-8990
E: news@hot899.com
W: http://www.hot899.com
Editorial Profile: CIHT-FM is a commercial station owned by Newfoundland Capital Corporation Limited. The format of the station is Top 40/CHR music. CIHT-FM broadcasts to Ottawa, Ontario area at 89.9 FM.

CIHW-FM
Owner: Radio Communautaire de Rouyn-Noranda
Editorial: 545 rue Thomas Martin, Wendake, Quebec G0A 4V0. **T:** 1 418 843-3937
E: cihw@megaquebec.net
W: http://www.cihw.org

CIIO-FM
Owner: JMCI
Editorial: #4-700 Glasgow St, Kitchener, Ontario N2M 2N7. **T:** 1 613 489-3299

CIJK-FM
Owner: Newfoundland Capital Corporation Limited
Editorial: 8794 Commercial Street, Suite 3, New Minas, Nova Scotia B4N 3C5.
T: 1 902 365-8930 **E:** info@893krock.com
W: http://893krock.com
Editorial Profile: CIJK-FM is a commercial station owned by Newfoundland Capital Corporation Limited. The format of the station is classic rock. CIJK-FM broadcasts to the New Minas, Nova Scotia area at 89.3 FM.

CIKI-FM
Owner: Astral Media
Editorial: 287 rue Pierre-Saindon, Bureau 502, Rimouski, Quebec G5L 9A7.
T: 1 418 724-2323
E: receptionrimouski@astral.com
W: http://www.radionrj.ca/rimouski
Editorial Profile: CIKI-FM is a commercial station owned by Astral Media. The format of the station is Top 40/CHR. CIKI-FM broadcasts to the Rimouski, Quebec area at 98.7 FM.

CIKR-FM
Owner: Rogers Communications Inc.
Editorial: 863 Princess Street, Suite 301, Kingston, Ontario K7L 5N4. **T:** 1 613 549-1057
W: http://www.krock1057.ca
Editorial Profile: CIKR-FM is a commercial station owned by Rogers Communications Inc. The format of the station is rock/album-oriented rock. CIKR-FM broadcasts to the Kingston, Ontario area at 105.7 FM.

CIKT-FM
Owner: Bear Creek Broadcasting Ltd.
Editorial: 8716-108th St, Ste 104, Grande Prairie, Alberta T8V 4C7. **T:** 1 780 882-6612
E: events@q99live.com
W: http://www.q99live.com
Editorial Profile: CIKT-FM is a commercial station owned by Bear Creek Broadcasting Ltd. The format of the station is adult hits. CIKT-FM broadcasts to the Grande Prairie, Alberta area at 98.9 FM.

CIKX-FM
Owner: Astral Media
Editorial: 399 Broadway Blvd, Grand Falls, New Brunswick E3Z 2K5. **T:** 1 506 473-9393
E: k93@astral.com **W:** http://www.k93.ca
Editorial Profile: CIKX-FM is a commercial station owned by Astral Media. The format of the station is hot adult contemporary music. CIKX-FM broadcasts in the Grand Falls, New Brunswick area at 93.5 FM.

CIKZ-FM
Owner: Rogers Communications Inc.
Editorial: 305 King Street West, 11th Floor, Kitchener, Ontario N2G 4E4.
T: 1 519 743-2611
W: http://www.kix106online.com
Editorial Profile: CIKZ-FM is a commercial station owned by Rogers Communications Inc. The format of the station is New Country music. CIKZ-FM broadcasts to Kitchener, Ontario at 106.7 FM.

CILB-FM
Owner: Newfoundland Capital Corporation Limited
Editorial: 10107 102 Ave., Suite 201, Lac La Biche, Alberta T0A 2C0. **T:** 1 780 623-3744
W: http://www.1035bigdog.com
Editorial Profile: CILB-FM is a commercial station owned by Newfoundland Capital Corporation Limited. The format of the station

is classic hits. CILB-FM broadcasts to the Lac La Biche, Alberta area at 103.5 FM.

CILE-FM
Owner: Radio Télévision Communautaire Havre-Saint-Pierre(La)
Editorial: 992 rue du Bouleau, Havre-St-Pierre, Quebec G0G 1P0. **T:** 1 418 538-2453
E: nouvelles@cilemf.com
W: http://www.cilemf.com
Editorial Profile: CILE-FM is a commercial station owned by La Radio Télévision Communautaire Havre-Saint-Pierre. The format of the station is variety. CILE-FM broadcasts to Havre-St-Pierre, Quebec at 95.1 FM.

CILG-FM
Owner: Golden West Broadcasting Ltd.
Editorial: 1704 Main Street North, Moose Jaw, Saskatchewan S6J 1L4. **T:** 1 306 694-0800
E: country100@goldenwestradio.com
W: http://www.discovermoosejaw.com
Editorial Profile: CILG-FM is a commercial station owned by Golden West Broadcasting Ltd. The format of the station is classic country. CILG-FM broadcasts to the Moose Jaw, Saskatchewan area at 100.7 FM.

CILK-FM
Owner: Bell Media
Editorial: 435 Bernard Ave, Kelowna, British Columbia V1Y 6N8. **T:** 1 250 860-8600
E: kelownainfo@myezrock.com
W: http://kelowna.myezrock.com
Editorial Profile: CILK-FM is a commercial station owned by Bell Media. The format of the station is soft rock/ soft ac. CILK-FM broadcasts to Kelowna, British Columbia at 101.5 FM.

CILQ-FM
Owner: Corus Entertainment Inc.
Editorial: Corus Quay, 25 Dockside Drive, Toronto, Ontario M5A 0B5. **T:** 1 416 221-0107
W: http://www.q107.com
Editorial Profile: CILQ-FM is a commercial station owned by Corus Entertainment Inc. The format of the station is classic rock. CILQ-FM broadcasts to the Toronto, ON area at 107.1 FM.

CILR-FM
Owner: Newfoundland Capital Corporation Limited
Editorial: 5026-50th St., Lloydminster, Alberta T9V 1P3. **T:** 1 780 875-3321
Editorial Profile: CILR-FM is a non-commercial station owned by Newfoundland Capital Corporation Limited. The format of the station is tourist information. CILR-FM broadcasts to the Lloydminster, Alberta area at 98.9 FM.

CILS-FM
Owner: Societe radio communautaire Victoria
Editorial: 200-535 Yates St., Victoria, British Columbia V8W 2Z6. **T:** 1 250 220-4139
E: radio@francocentre.com
W: http://www.cilsfm.ca

CILT-FM
Owner: Golden West Broadcasting Ltd.
Editorial: 105-32 Brandt St, Steinbach, Manitoba R5G 2J7. **T:** 1 204 346-0000
E: info@goldenwestradio.com
W: http://www.mix967radio.com
Editorial Profile: CILT-FM is a commercial station owned by Golden West Broadcasting Ltd. The format of the station is Lite Rock/Lite AC music. CILT-FM broadcasts to the Steinbach, Manitoba area at 96.7 FM.

CILU-FM
Owner: Lakehead University
Editorial: 707 Oliver Road, Thunder Bay, Ontario P7B 5E1. **T:** 1 807 343-8881
E: info@luradio.ca **W:** http://www.luradio.ca
Editorial Profile: CILU-FM is a commerical station owned by Lakehead University. The format of the station is variety. CILU-FM broadcasts to the Thunder Bay, Ontario area at 102.7 FM.

CILV-FM
Owner: Newfoundland Capital Corporation Limited
Editorial: 6 Antares Dr, Ottawa, Ontario K2E 8A9-. **T:** 1 613 688-8888
W: http://www.live885.com
Editorial Profile: CILV-FM is a commercial station owned by Newfoundland Capital Corporation Limited. The format of the station is adult album alternative. CILV-FM broadcasts to the Ottawa, Ontario area at 88.5 FM.

CIMB-FM
Owner: Radio Ntetemuk Inc(La)
Editorial: 8 rue Laletaut, Betsiamites, Quebec G0H 1B0. **T:** 1 418 567-4642
E: betradio@globetrotter.net
W: http://www.cimb.fm
Editorial Profile: CIMB-FM is a non-commercial station owned by La Radio Ntetemuk Inc. The format of the station is talk. CIMB-FM broadcasts to Betsiamites, Quebec at 95.1 FM.

CIME-FM
Owner: Cogeco
Editorial: 120 rue de la Gare, St-Jerome, Quebec J7Z 2C2. **T:** 1 450 431-2463
E: nouvelles@cime.fm **W:** http://www.cime.fm
Editorial Profile: CIME-FM is a commercial station owned by Cogeco. The format of the station is adult contemporary. CIME-FM broadcasts to St-Jerome, Quebec at 103.9 FM.

CIMF-FM
Owner: Astral Media
Editorial: 15, rue Taschereau, Gatineau, Quebec J8Y 2V6. **T:** 1 819 243-5555
E: receptionoutaouais@astral.com
W: http://gatineau.rougefm.ca
Editorial Profile: CIMF-FM is a commercial station owned by Astral Media. The format of the station is adult contemporary. CIMF-FM broadcasts to the Gatineau, Quebec area at 94.9 FM.

CIMG-FM
Owner: Golden West Broadcasting Ltd.
Editorial: 134 Central Avenue North, Swift Current, Saskatchewan S9L 0L1.
T: 1 306 773-4605
E: eaglecontrol@goldenwestradio.com
W: http://www.eagle94.ca
Editorial Profile: CIMG-FM is a commercial radio station owned by Golden West Broadcasting Inc. The format of the station is classic hits. CIMG-FM broadcasts to Swift Current, Saskatchewan and its environs at 94.1 FM.

CIMJ-FM
Owner: Corus Entertainment Inc.
Editorial: 75 Speedvale Ave East, Guelph, Ontario N1E 6M3. **T:** 1 519 824-7000
E: news@cjoy.com
W: http://www.magic106.com
Editorial Profile: CIMJ-FM is a commercial station owned by Corus Entertainment Inc. The format of the station is hot adult contemporary music. CIMJ-FM broadcasts to East Guelph, Ontario at 106.1-FM.

CIML-FM
Owner: Makkovik Radio Society Inc.
Editorial: 59 Anderson St, Makkovik, Newfoundland A0P 1J0. **T:** 1 709 923-2327
Editorial Profile: CIML-FM is a non-commercial station owned by Makkovik Radio Society Inc. The format of the station is variety. CIML-FM broadcasts to the Makkovik, Newfoundland area at 99.5 FM.

CIMM-FM
Owner: McBride Communications & Media Inc.
Editorial: 10760 Fundy Drive, Richmond, British Columbia V7E 5K7. **T:** 1 604 220-8393
W: http://www.cimmfm.com
Editorial Profile: CIMM-FM is owned and operated by McBride Communications & Media Inc. The format of the station is classic hits. CIMM-FM broadcasts to the Richmond, British Columbia area at 99.5 FM.

CIMO-FM
Owner: Astral Media
Editorial: 2185 Rue King O, Sherbrooke, Quebec J1J 2G2. **T:** 1 819 347-1414
W: http://sherbrooke.radionrj.ca
Editorial Profile: CIMO-FM is a commercial station owned by Astral Media. The format of the station is Top 40/CHR. CIMO-FM broadcasts to the Sherbrooke, Quebec area at 106.1 FM.

CIMS-FM
Owner: Cooperative Radio Restigouche Ltee.(La)
Editorial: 1991 Ave des Pionniers, Balmoral, New Brunswick E8E 2W7. **T:** 1 506 826-1040
E: info@cimsfm.ca **W:** http://www.cimsfm.ca
Editorial Profile: CIMS-FM is a non-commercial station owned by La Cooperative Radio Restigouche Ltee. The format of the station is variety. CIMS-FM broadcasts to the Balmoral, New Brunswick area at 103.9 FM.

CIMX-FM
Owner: Bell Media
Editorial: 1640 Ouellette Ave, Windsor, Ontario N8X 1L1-. **T:** 1 519 258-8888
E: programming@89Xradio.com
W: http://www.89xradio.com
Editorial Profile: CIMX-FM is a commercial station owned by Bell Media. The format of the station is rock alternative music. CIMX-FM broadcasts to Windsor, Ontario at 88.7 FM.

CIMY-FM
Owner: My Broadcasting Corporation
Editorial: 84 Isabella St, 2nd Floor, Pembroke, Ontario K8A 5S5. **T:** 1 613 735-6936
E: news@myfmradio.ca
W: http://www.myfmradio.ca
Editorial Profile: CIMY-FM is a commercial station owned by My Broadcasting Corporation. The format of the station is adult contemporary. CIMY-FM broadcasts to the Pembroke, Ontario area at 104.9 FM.

CINA-AM
Owner: Ray, Neeti
Editorial: 1515 Britannia Road East, Suite 315, Mississauga, Ontario L4W 4K1.
T: 1 416 777-1650 **E:** info@cinaradio.com
W: http://www.cinaradio.com
Editorial Profile: CINA-AM is a commercial station owned by Neeti Ray. The format of the station is a variety with a focus on Bollywood hits and Indo-Pakistani programming. CINA-AM broadcasts to the Mississauga, ON area at 1650 AM.

CINB-FM
Owner: New Song Communications Ministries Ltd.
Editorial: 37 Hanover, Saint John, New Brunswick e2l 3xl. **T:** 1 506 657-9600
E: staff@newsongfm.com
W: http://www.newsongfm.com
Editorial Profile: CINB-FM is a non-commercial station owned by New Song Communications Ministries Ltd. The format of the station is contemporary Christian. CINB-FM broadcasts to the Saint John, New Brunswick area at 96.1 FM.

CINC-FM
Owner: Native Communications Inc.
Editorial: 1507 Inkster Boulevard, Winnipeg, Manitoba R2X 1R2. **T:** 1 204 772-8255
E: info@ncifm.com **W:** http://www.ncifm.com
Editorial Profile: CINC-FM is a commercial station owned by Native Communications Inc. The format of the station is aboriginal language news and programming. CINC-FM broadcasts to the Thompson, Manitoba area at 96.3 FM. CICY-FM is a commercial station owned by Native Communications, Inc. (NCI). The format of the station is aboriginal language news and programming.

CIND-FM
Owner: Central Ontario Broadcasting
Editorial: 31R Atlantic Ave, Toronto, Ontario M6K 3E7. **T:** 1 416 588-7595
E: questions@indie88.com
W: http://indie88.com/
Editorial Profile: CIND-FM is a commercial station owned by Central Ontario Broadcasting. The format for the station is indie rock. CIND-FM broadcasts to the Toronto, Ontario area at 88.1 FM.

CING-FM
Owner: Corus Entertainment Inc.
Editorial: 875 Main St W, Hamilton, Ontario L8S 4P9. **T:** 1 905 521-9900
E: info@953freshfm.com
W: http://www.953freshfm.com
Editorial Profile: CING-FM is a commercial station owned by Corus Entertainment Inc. The format of the station is Hot AC. CING-FM broadcasts to Toronto at 95.3 FM.

CINN-FM
Owner: Radio de l'Epinette Noire Inc.
Editorial: 1004 rue Prince, Hearst, Ontario P0L 1N0. **T:** 1 705 372-1011
E: information@cinnfm.com
W: http://www.cinnfm.com
Editorial Profile: CINN-FM is a non-commercial station owned by Radio de l'Épinette Noire Inc. The format of the station is variety. CINN-FM broadcasts to the Hearst, Ontario area at 91.1 FM.

CINQ-FM
Owner: Radio Centre-Ville
Editorial: 5212 boul St-Laurent, 2e etage, Montreal, Quebec H2T 1S1. **T:** 1 514 495-2597
E: cinqfm@radiocentreville.com
W: http://www.radiocentreville.com
Editorial Profile: CINQ-FM is a non-commercial station owned by Radio Centre-Ville. The format of the station is variety. CINQ-FM broadcasts to the Montreal, Quebec area at 102.3 FM.

CINU-FM
Owner: Hope FM Ministries Ltd
Editorial: 217 Harmony Ridge Rd, Truro, Nova Scotia B6L 3P4. **T:** 1 902 843-4673
E: hopefmministries@eastlink.ca
W: http://www.hoperadio.ca

CIOC-FM
Owner: Rogers Communications Inc.
Editorial: 817 Fort St, Victoria, British Columbia V8W 1H6. **T:** 1 250 382-0900
W: http://www.ocean985.com
Editorial Profile: CIOC-FM is a commercial station owned by Rogers Communications Inc. The format of the station is adult contemporary. CIOC-FM broadcasts to Victoria, British Columbia at 98.5 FM.

CIOG-FM
Owner: International Harvesters for Christ Evangelistic Association Inc.
Editorial: 101 Ilsley Ave Unit 3, Dartmouth, Nova Scotia B3B 1S8. **T:** 1 902 468-8854
E: info@cjlufm.com **W:** http://www.ciogfm.com
Editorial Profile: CIOG-FM is a commercial station owned by International Harvesters for Christ Evangelistic Association Inc. The format of the station is Contemporary Christian music. CIOG-FM broadcasts to the Charlottetown, Prince Edward Island, Canada area 93.9 FM.

CIOI-FM
Owner: Mohawk College Radio Co.
Editorial: 135 Fennell Ave W, Room GF11, Hamilton, Ontario L8N 3T2. **T:** 1 905 575-2175
E: info@indifm.ca **W:** http://www.indifm.ca
Editorial Profile: CIOI-FM is a commercial station owned by Mohawk College Radio Co. The format for the station is college variety. CIOI-FM broadcasts to the Hamilton, Ontario area at 101.5 FM.

CIOK-FM
Owner: Maritime Broadcasting System Ltd.
Editorial: 226 Union St, Saint John, New Brunswick E2L 1B1. **T:** 1 506 658-5100
E: mailbag@k100.ca **W:** http://www.k100.ca
Editorial Profile: CIOK-FM is a commercial station owned by Maritime Broadcasting System Ltd. The format of the station is top 40/CHR. CIOK-FM broadcasts to Saint John, New Brunswick and surrounding communities at 100.5 FM.

CION-FM
Owner: Fondation Radio Galilee
Editorial: 3196 Chemin Ste-Foy, Sainte-Foy, Quebec G1X 1R4. **T:** 1 418 659-9090
E: cionfm@radiogalilee.com
W: http://www.radiogalilee.com
Editorial Profile: CION-FM is a non-commercial radio station owned by the Fondation Radio Galilee. The format of the station is religious. CION-FM broadcasts to the Quebec area at 90.9 FM.

CIOO-FM
Owner: Bell Media
Editorial: 2900 Agricola St, Halifax, Nova Scotia B3K 6B2. **T:** 1 902 453-2524
E: c100fm@bellmedia.ca
W: http://www.c100fm.com
Editorial Profile: CIOO-FM commercial station owned by Bell Media. The format of the station is hot adult contemporary. CIOO-FM broadcasts to Halifax, Nova Scotia at 100.1 FM.

CIOR-AM
Owner: Astral Media
Editorial: 5-130 Harold Ave, Princeton, British Columbia V0X 1W0. **T:** 1 250 492-2800
Editorial Profile: CIOR-AM is a commercial station owned by Astral Media. The format of the station is easy listening music. CIOR-AM broadcasts to Penticton, British Columbia at 1400 AM. The station airs CKOR-AM's programming.

CIOT-FM
Owner: Wilderness Ministries, Inc.
T: 1 306 862-2468 **E:** info@lighthousefm.ca
W: http://www.lighthousefm.ca
Editorial Profile: CIOT-FM is a non-commercial station owned by Wilderness Ministries, Inc. The format of the station is gospel and religious music. CIOT-FM broadcasts to the Nipawin, Saskatchewan area at 104.1 FM.

CIOZ-FM
Owner: Newfoundland Broadcasting Co. Ltd.

Editorial: 446 Logy Bay Rd, St. John's, Newfoundland A1C 5S2. **T:** 1 709 726-2922
E: ozfm@ozfm.com **W:** http://www.ozfm.com

CIPC-FM
Owner: Radio Port-Cartier Inc.
Editorial: 52 Rue Élie-Rochefort, Port-Cartier, Quebec G5B 1N2. **T:** 1 418 766-6869
E: cipc991@laradioactive.com
W: http://www.laradioactive.com
Editorial Profile: CIPC-FM is a commercial station owned by Radio Port-Cartier Inc. The format of the station is Top 40/CHR. CIPC-FM broadcasts to Port-Cartier, Quebec at 99.1 FM.

CIPI-FM
Owner: Sipisishk Communications Inc.
Editorial: 49 Lavoie St., Beauval, Saskatchewan S0M 0G0. **T:** 1 306 288-2222
E: cipi@sasktel.net
W: http://www.cipiradio.com

CIPU-FM
Owner: Lnusipuk Communication Information Net
Editorial: 529 Church St, Indian Brook, Micmac, Nova Scotia B0N1W0.
T: 1 902 236-3636 **E:** shubiefm@gmail.com
W: http://shubiefm.com
Editorial Profile: CIPU-FM is a non-commercial station owned by Lnusipuk Communication Information Net. The format of the station is variety. CIPU-FM broadcasts to Mic Mac, NS at 97.1 FM.

CIQB-FM
Owner: Corus Entertainment Inc.
Editorial: 1125 Bayfield Street N, Barrie, Ontario L4M 4S5. **T:** 1 705 726-1011
E: news@b101fm.com
W: http://www.b101fm.com
Editorial Profile: CIQB-FM is a commercial station owned by Corus Entertainment Inc. The format of the station is hot adult contemporary music. CIQB-FM broadcasts to Barrie, Ontario at 101.1 FM.

CIQC-FM
Owner: Vista Broadcast Group Inc.
Editorial: 470 13th Ave, Campbell River, British Columbia V9W 7J4.
T: 1 250 287-7106 **E:** onair@997theriver.ca
W: http://www.997theriver.ca
Editorial Profile: CIQC-FM is a commercial station owned by Vista Broadcast Group Inc. The format of the station is adult contemporary. CFWB-AM broadcasts in the Campbell River, British Columbia area at 99.7 FM.

CIQM-FM
Owner: Bell Media
Editorial: 743 Wellington Rd, London, Ontario N6C 4R5-. **T:** 1 519 686-2525
W: http://london.virginradio.ca/
Editorial Profile: CIQM-FM is a commercial station owned by Bell Media. The format of the station is hot AC music. CIQM-FM broadcasts to the London, Ontario area at 97.5 FM.

CIRA-FM
Owner: Société Radio-Ville-Marie Inc.
Editorial: 4020, rue St-Ambroise, Suite 199, Montreal, Quebec H4C 2C7.
T: 1 514 382-3913 **E:** info@radiovm.com
W: http://www.radiovm.com
Editorial Profile: CIRA-FM is a non-commercial station owned by Société Radio-Ville-Marie Inc. The format of the station is religious. CIRA-FM broadcasts to the Montreal area at 91.3 FM.

CIRH-FM
Owner: JMCI
Editorial: #4-700 Glasgow St, Kitchener, Ontario N2M 2N7. **T:** 1 902 423-5585
W: http://www.informationradio.ca
Editorial Profile: CIRH-FM is a commercial station owned by JMCI. The format of the station is news and talk. CIRH-FM broadcasts to the Halifax, Nova Scotia area at 97.9 FM.

CIRK-FM
Owner: Newfoundland Capital Corporation Limited
Editorial: 2394 West Edmonton Mall, 8882-170 Street, Edmonton, Alberta T5T 4M2.
T: 1 780 437-4996 **E:** news@cfcw.com
W: http://www.k97.ca
Editorial Profile: CIRK-FM is a commercial station owned by Newfoundland Capital Corporation Limited. The format of the station is classic rock music. CIRK-FM broadcasts to Edmonton, Alberta and area at 97.3 FM.

CIRR-FM
Owner: Rainbow Media Group Inc.
Editorial: 5312 Dundas Street West, Toronto, Ontario M9B 1B3. **T:** 1 416 922-1039
E: info@proudfm.com
W: http://www.proudfm.com
Editorial Profile: CIRR-FM is a commercial station owned by Rainbow Media Group Inc. The format of the station is adult contemporary and talk. CIRR-FM broadcasts to the Toronto area at 103.9 FM.

CIRV-FM
Owner: CIRC Radio Inc.
Editorial: 1087 Dundas St West, Toronto, Ontario M6J 1W9. **T:** 1 416 537-1088
E: info@cirvfm.com **W:** http://www.cirvfm.com
Editorial Profile: CIRV-FM is a commercial station owned by CIRC Radio Inc. The format of the station is news and talk. CIRV-FM broadcasts to Toronto, ON at 88.9 FM.

CIRX-FM
Owner: Vista Broadcast Group Inc.
Editorial: 1940 3rd Ave, Prince George, British Columbia V2M 1G7. **T:** 1 250 564-2524
E: onair@94xfm.com
W: http://www.94xfm.com
Editorial Profile: CIRX-FM is a commercial radio station owned by the Vista Broadcast Group Inc. The format of the station is album-oriented rock. CIRX-FM broadcasts to the Prince George, British Columbia area at 94.3 FM.

CISC-FM
Owner: Rogers Media Inc.
Editorial: 40147 Glenalder Place, Unit 202, Squamish, British Columbia V8B 0G2.
T: 1 604 892-1021
E: mountainfm@mountainfm.com
W: http://www.mountainfm.com
Editorial Profile: CISC-FM is a commercial station owned by Rogers Media Inc. The format for the station is hot adult contemporary. CISC-FM broadcasts to the Gibsons, British Columbia at 107.5 FM. CISC FM rebroadcasts the signal from CISQ FM. JL.

CISL-AM
Owner: Newcap Radio
Editorial: 20-11151 Horseshoe Way 20, Richmond, British Columbia V7A 4S5.
T: 1 604 2722100
W: http://www.am650radio.com
Editorial Profile: CISL-AM is a commercial station owned by Newcap Radio. The format of the station is adult standards. CISL-AM broadcasts to Richmond, British Columbia at 650 AM.

CISM-FM
Owner: Communication du Versant Nord Ltd.
Editorial: 2332 Edouard-Montpetit, Bureau C-1509, Montreal, Quebec H3C 3J7.
T: 1 514 343-7511 **W:** http://culturecible.ca
Editorial Profile: CISM-FM is a non-commercial station owned by Communication du Versant Nord Ltd. The format of the station is rock alternative. CISM-FM broadcasts to Montreal at 89.3 FM.

CISN-FM
Owner: Corus Entertainment Inc.
Editorial: 5204 84th St, Edmonton, Alberta T6E 5N8. **T:** 1 780 424-1104
E: info@cisnfm.com
W: http://www.cisnfm.com
Editorial Profile: CISN-FM is a commercial station owned by Corus Entertainment. The format of the station is contemporary country music. CISN-FM broadcasts to the Edmonton, Alberta area at 103.9 FM.

CISO-FM
Owner: Bayshore Broadcasting Corp.
Editorial: 490 W. Street North, suite 2, Orillia, Ontario L3V 5E8. **T:** 1 705 325-9786
E: info@sunshine891.ca
W: http://www.sunshine891.ca
Editorial Profile: CISO-FM is a commercial station owned by Bayshore Broadcasting Corporation. The format of the station is adult contemporary. CISO-FM broadcasts to the Twin Lakes District on 89.1.

CISP-FM
Owner: Rogers Media Inc.
Editorial: 40147 Glenalder Place, Unit 202, Squamish, British Columbia V8B 0G2.
T: 1 604 892-1021 **E:** news@mountainfm.com
W: http://www.mountainfm.com
Editorial Profile: CISP-FM is a commercial station owned by Rogers Media Inc. The format for the station is hot adult contemporary. CISP-FM broadcasts to the Pemberton, British Columbia at 104.5 FM.

CISQ-FM
Owner: Rogers Communications Inc.
Editorial: 40147 Glenalder Place, Unit 202, Squamish, British Columbia V8B 0G2.
T: 1 604 892-1021 **E:** news@mountainfm.com
W: http://www.mountainfm.com
Editorial Profile: CISQ-FM is a commercial station owned by Rogers Communications Inc. The format of the station is hot adult contemporary music. CISQ-FM broadcasts to Squamish, BC area at 107.1 FM. CISQ simulcasts to CISW FM, CISC FM, CISP FM and CIEG FM. JL.

CISS-FM
Owner: Rogers Communications Inc.
Editorial: 2001 Thurston Dr, Ottawa, Ontario K1G 6C9. **T:** 1 613 736-2001
E: ottawanewsroom@ottawaradio.rogers.com
W: http://www.1053kissfm.com
Editorial Profile: CISS-FM is a commercial station owned by Rogers Communications Inc. The format of the station is Top 40/CHR music. CISS-FM broadcasts to the Ottawa, Ontario area at 105.3 FM.

CISW-FM
Owner: Rogers Media Inc.
Editorial: 40147 Glenalder Place, Unit 202, Squamish, British Columbia V8B 0G2.
T: 1 604 892-1021
E: mountainfm@mountainfm.com
W: http://www.mountainfm.com
Editorial Profile: CISW-FM is a commercial station owned by Rogers Media Inc. The format of the station is hot adult contemporary. CISW-FM broadcasts to Whistler, British Columbia at 102.1 FM. CISW-FM rebroadscasts CISQ FM. JL.

CITA-FM
Owner: International Harvesters for Christ Evangelistic Association Inc.
Editorial: 101 Ilsey Avenue, Unit 3, Dartmouth, Nova Scotia B3B 1S8.
T: 1 902 468-8854 **E:** info@cjlufm.com
W: http://www.citafm.com

CITE-FM
Owner: Bell Media
Editorial: 1717 Boul René-Lévesque E, Montreal, Quebec H2L 4T3. **T:** 1 514 529-3229
W: http://montreal.rougefm.ca
Editorial Profile: CITE-FM is a commercial radio station owned by Bell Media. The format of the station is adult contemporary. CITE-FM broadcasts to the Montréal area at 107.3 FM.

CITE-FM-1
Owner: Astral Media
Editorial: 2185 Rue King O Bureau 200, Sherbrooke, Quebec J1J 2G2.
T: 1 819 566-6655
E: nouvelles.estrie@astral.com
W: http://estrie.rougefm.com
Editorial Profile: CITE-FM-1 is a French-language commercial station owned by Astral Media. The format of the station is adult contemporary. CITE-FM-1 broadcasts to the Eastern Townships at 102.7 FM.

CITF-FM
Owner: Astral Media
Editorial: 900 rue D'Youville, 1er etage, Quebec, Quebec G1R 3P7. **T:** 1 418 527-3232
W: http://quebec.rougefm.ca
Editorial Profile: CITF-FM is a commercial station owned by Astral Media. The format of the station is adult contemporary. CITF-FM broadcasts to the Quebec area at 107.5 FM.

CITI-FM
Owner: Rogers Communications Inc.
Editorial: 4-166 Osborne St, Winnipeg, Manitoba R3L 1Y8. **T:** 1 204 788-3400
W: http://www.92citifm.ca
Editorial Profile: CITI-FM is a commercial radio station owned by Rogers Communications Inc. The format of the station is classic rock. CITI-FM broadcasts to Winnipeg, Manitoba at 92.1 FM.

CITR-FM
Owner: Student Radio Society of U.B.C.
Editorial: 6138 Sub Blvd Rm 233, Vancouver, British Columbia V6T 2A5. **T:** 1 604 822-1242
E: news@citr.ca **W:** http://www.citr.ca
Editorial Profile: CITR-FM is a non-commercial station owned by the Student Radio Society of U.B.C. The format of the station is variety. CITR-FM broadcasts to the Vancouver, British Columbia area at 101.9 FM.

CITU-FM
Owner: Co-opérative Radio Richmond Limitée(La)
Editorial: 3435 Route 206, Petit de Grat, Nova Scotia B0E 2L0. **T:** 1 902 226-0981
Editorial Profile: CITU-FM is a commercial station owned by La Co-opérative de Radio Richmond Limitée. The format for the station is country and folk. CITU-FM broadcasts to the Petit-de-Grat, Nova Scotia area at 104.1 FM.

CIUR-FM
Owner: Native Communications Inc.
Editorial: 1507 Inkster Blvd, 2nd Floor, Winnipeg, Manitoba R2X 1R2.
T: 1 204 772-8255 **E:** info@streetzfm.ca
W: http://www.streetzfm.ca
Editorial Profile: CIUR-FM is a commercial station owned by Native Communications Inc. The format of the station is urban contemporary. CIUR-FM broadcasts to the Winnipeg, Manitoba area at 104.7 FM.

CIUT-FM
Owner: University of Toronto Community Radio
Editorial: 89.5 Tower Road, Toronto, Ontario M5S 0A2. **T:** 1 416 978-0909
E: communications@ciut.fm
W: http://www.ciut.fm
Editorial Profile: CIUT-FM is a non-commercial station owned by the University of Toronto Community Radio. The format is a variety of music, news, and talk programming. CIUT-FM broadcasts to the University of Toronto and the broader Toronto community at 89.5 FM.

CIVH-AM
Owner: Vista Broadcast Group Inc.
Editorial: 150 West Columbia, Vanderhoof, British Columbia V0J 3A0. **T:** 1 250 567-4914
E: thewolf@hwy16.com
W: http://thevalleywolf.ca
Editorial Profile: CIVH-AM is a commercial station owned by Vista Broadcast Group Inc. The format for the station is contemporary country. CIVH-AM broadcasts to the Vanderhoof, British Columbia area at 1340 AM.

CIVL-FM
Owner: University of the Fraser Valley
Editorial: 33844 King Road, Abbotsford, British Columbia V2S 7M8. **T:** 1 604 851-6306
E: info@civl.ca **W:** http://www.civl.ca
Editorial Profile: CIVL-FM is a non-commercial station owned by University College of the Fraser Valley. The format of the station is variety. CIVL-FM broadcasts to the Abbotsford, BC area at 88.5 FM.

CIVR-FM
Owner: Association franco-culturelle de Yellowknife
Editorial: 5016 48 Street, Yellowknife, Northwest Territories X1A 1N3.
T: 1 867 766-5172
E: societeradiotaiga@gmail.com
W: http://www.radiotaiga.com
Editorial Profile: CIVR-FM is a non-commercial station owned by Association franco-culturelle de Yellowknife. The format of the station is variety. CIVR-FM broadcasts to the Yellowknife, Northwest Territories area at 103.5 FM.

CIWS-FM
Owner: Whistle Community Radio
Editorial: 6379 Main Street, Stouffville, Ontario L4A 1G7. **T:** 1 905 640-0311
E: admin@whistleradio.com
W: http://www.whistleradio.com
Editorial Profile: CIWS-FM is a non-profit station owned by Whistle Community Radio. The format of the station is variety. CIWS-FM broadcasts to the Stouffville, ON area at 102.7 FM.

CIWW-AM
Owner: Rogers Communications Inc.
Editorial: 2001 Thurston Drive, Ottawa, Ontario K1G 6C9. **T:** 1 613 736-2001
E: ottawanewsroom@ottawaradio.rogers.com
W: http://www.1310news.com
Editorial Profile: CIWW-AM is a commercial station owned by Rogers Communications Inc. The format of the station is news. CIWW-AM broadcasts to the Ottawa, Ontario area at 1310 AM.

CIXF-FM
Owner: Newfoundland Capital Corporation Limited
Editorial: 403 2nd Ave West, Unit 8, Brooks, Alberta T1R 0S3. **T:** 1 403 362-3418
E: theone@newcap.ca
W: http://www.the1brooks.com

Editorial Profile: CIXF-FM is a commercial station owned by Newfoundland Capital Corporation Limited. The format of the station is adult contemporary. CIXF-FM broadcasts to Brooks, Alberta and surrounding communities at 101.1 FM.

CIXK-FM
Owner: Bayshore Broadcasting Corp.
Editorial: 270 Ninth Street East, Owen Sound, Ontario N4K 1N7. **T:** 1 519 376-2030
E: info@bayshorebroadcasting.ca
W: http://www.mix106.ca
Editorial Profile: CIXK-FM is a commercial station owned by Bayshore Broadcasting Corp. The format of the station is adult contemporary. CIXK-FM broadcasts to the Owen Sound, Ontario area at 106.5 FM.

CIXL-FM
Owner: R.B. Communications Ltd.
Editorial: 860 Forks Road W, Welland, Ontario L3B 5R6. **T:** 1 905 732-4433
E: info@giantfm.com
W: http://www.giantfm.com
Editorial Profile: CIXL-FM is a commercial station owned by R.B. Communications Ltd. The format of the station is classic rock. CIXL-FM broadcasts to the St. Catharines-Niagara, Ontario area at 91.7 FM.

CIXM-FM
Owner: Fabmar Communications Ltd.
Editorial: 4912A 50th Avenue, Whitecourt, Alberta T7S 1N9. **T:** 1 780 706-1053
E: info@xm105fm.com
W: http://www.xm105fm.com
Editorial Profile: CIXM-FM is a commercial station owned by Fabmar Investments Ltd. The format of the station is country. CIXM-FM broadcasts to the Whitecourt, Alberta area at 105.3 FM.

CIXN-FM
Owner: Joy FM Network Inc.
Editorial: 1010 Hanwell Road, Suite 10, Fredericton, New Brunswick E3B 6A4.
T: 1 506 454-9600 **E:** welcome@joyfm.ca
W: http://www.joyfm.ca
Editorial Profile: CIXN-FM is a commercial station owned by Joy FM Network Inc. The format of the station is contemporary Christian. CIXN-FM broadcasts to Fredericton, New Brunswick at 96.5 FM.

CIXX-FM
Owner: Radio Fanshawe Inc.
Editorial: 1001 Fanshawe College Blvd., London, Ontario N5V 5R6. **T:** 1 519 453-2810
W: http://www.1069thex.com
Editorial Profile: CIXX-FM is a commercial station owned by Radio Fanshawe Inc. The format of the station is urban contemporary music. CIXX-FM broadcasts to the London, Ontario area at 106.9 FM.

CIYM-FM
Owner: My Broadcasting Corporation
Editorial: 6 Oliphant St, Unit 5, Brighton, Ontario K0K 1H0. **T:** 1 613 475-6936
E: news1009@myfmradio.ca
W: http://www.myfmradio.ca/1009
Editorial Profile: CIYM-FM is a commercial station owned by My Broadcasting Corporation. The format for the station is adult contemporary. CIYM-FM broadcasts to the Brighton, Ontario area at 100.9 FM.

CIYN-FM
Owner: My Broadcasting Corporation
Editorial: 756 Queen St, Kincardine, Ontario N2Z 2Y2. **T:** 1 519 396-7770
W: http://www.myfmradio.ca
Editorial Profile: CIYN-FM is a commercial station owned by My Broadcasting Corporation. The format for the station is classic hits. CIYN-FM broadcasts to the Kincardine, Ontario area at 95.5 FM.

CIZL-FM
Owner: Rawlco Radio Ltd.
Editorial: 210-2401 Saskatchewan Dr, Regina, Saskatchewan S4P 4H8. **T:** 1 306 525-0000
W: http://www.z99.com
Editorial Profile: CIZL-FM is a commercial station owned by Rawlco Radio Ltd. The format for the station is adult contemporary. CIZL-FM broadcasts to the Regina, Saskatchewan area at 98.9 FM.

CIZZ-FM
Owner: Newfoundland Capital Corporation Limited
Editorial: 4920 59th St, Red Deer, Alberta T4N 2N1. **T:** 1 403 343-1303 **E:** news@zedfm.com
W: http://www.zed99.com
Editorial Profile: CIZZ-FM is a commercial station owned by Newfoundland Capital Corporation Limited. The format for the station is rock. CIZZ-FM broadcasts to the Red Deer, Alberta, area at 98.9 FM.

CJAB-FM
Owner: Astral Media
Editorial: 267 rue Racine Est, 2è étage, Chicoutimi, Quebec G7H 1S5.
T: 1 418 545-9450
E: nouvelles.saguenay@astral.com
W: http://www.radionrj.ca/saguenay
Editorial Profile: CJAB-FM is a commercial station owned by Astral Media. The format of the station is Top 40/CHR. CJAB-FM broadcasts to the Chicoutimi, Quebec area at 94.5 FM.

CJAD-AM
Owner: Bell Media
Editorial: 1717 Boul Rene-Levesque E, Montreal, Quebec H2L 4T3-.
T: 1 514 989-2523 **E:** infodesk@cjad.com
W: http://www.cjad.com
Editorial Profile: CJAD-AM is a commercial station owned by Bell Media. The format of the station is news and talk. CJAD-AM broadcasts to the Montreal area at 800 AM.

CJAG-FM
Owner: Athabasca Hotel
T: 1 780 852-7789 **E:** pd@cjagjasper.com
W: http://www.cjagjasper.com
Editorial Profile: CJAG-FM is a commercial station owned by Athabasca Hotel. The format of the station is rock music. CJAG-FM broadcasts to the Jasper, Alberta area at 92.3 FM.

CJAI-FM
Owner: Amherst Island Public Radio
Editorial: 5830 Front Road, Stella, Ontario K0H 2S0. **T:** 1 613 384-8282 **E:** air@cjai.ca
W: http://www.cjai.ca
Editorial Profile: CJAI-FM is a non-commercial station owned Amherst Island Public Radio. The format of the station is a variety of eclectic public radio. CJAI-FM broadcasts to Stella, Ontario at 92.1 FM.

CJAM-FM
Owner: University of Windsor, Student Media Corp.
Editorial: c/o University of Windsor, Univ Centre 401 Sunset Ave, Windsor, Ontario N9B 3P4. **T:** 1 519 971-3606
W: http://www.cjam.ca
Editorial Profile: CJAM-FM is a non-commmercial station owned by the University of Windsor, Student Media Corp. The format is a college variety. CJAM-FM broadcasts to the University of Windsor and the surrounding communities in Windsor, Ontario at 91.5 FM.

CJAN-FM
Owner: Radio Plus BMD Inc
Editorial: 1 rue Hilaire, Asbestos, Quebec J1T 0A3. **T:** 1 819 879-0993 **E:** info@fm993.ca
W: http://www.fm993.ca
Editorial Profile: CJAN-FM is a commercial station owned by Radio Plus BMD Inc. The format of the station is adult contemporary. CJAN-FM broadcasts to the Asbestos, Quebec area at 99.3 FM.

CJAQ-FM
Owner: Rogers Communications Inc.
Editorial: 2723 37th NE, Ste 240, Calgary, Alberta T1Y 5R8. **T:** 1 403 250-9797
W: http://www.jackfm.ca
Editorial Profile: CJAQ-FM is a commercial station owned by Rogers Communications Inc. The format of the station is adult hits. CJAQ-FM broadcasts to Calgary, Alberta at 96.9 FM.

CJAR-AM
Owner: Arctic Radio (1982) Ltd.
Editorial: 133rd St. W, The Pas, Manitoba R9A 1R7. **T:** 1 204 623-5307 **E:** cjar@arcticradio.ca
W: http://www.thepasonline.com
Editorial Profile: CJAR-AM is a commercial station owned by Arctic Radio (1982) Ltd. The format of the station is variety. CJAR-AM broadcasts to The Pas, Manitoba area at 1240 AM.

CJAS-FM
Owner: CJAS Radio Communautaire St. Augustin
T: 1 418 947-2239 **E:** cjasradio@gmail.com
W: http://www.lnscommunityradio.com
Editorial Profile: CJAS-FM is a commercial station owned by CJAS Radio Communautaire St. Augustin. The format of the station is variety. CJAS-FM broadcasts to the St-Augustin, Quebec area at 93.5 FM.

CJAT-FM
Owner: Astral Media
Editorial: 1560 2nd Avenue, Trail, British Columbia V1R 1M4. **T:** 1 250 368-5510
E: webmaster@kbsradio.ca
W: http://kootenays.myezrock.com
Editorial Profile: CJAT-FM is a commercial station owned by Astral Media. The format for the station is hot adult contemporary music. CJAT-FM broadcasts to the Trail, British Columbia area at 95.7 FM.

CJAV-FM
Owner: Jim Pattison Broadcast Group(The)
Editorial: 3296 Third Ave, Port Alberni, British Columbia V9Y 4E1. **T:** 1 250 723-2455
E: info@933thepeak.com
W: http://www.933thepeak.com
Editorial Profile: CJAV-AM is a commercial station owned by The Jim Pattison Broadcast Group. The format of the station is adult contemporary. CJAV-AM broadcasts to the Port Alberni, British Columbia area at 93.3 FM.

CJAW-FM
Owner: Golden West Broadcasting Ltd.
Editorial: 1704 Main Street North, Moose Jaw, Saskatchewan S6J 1L4. **T:** 1 306 694-0800
E: mjnews@goldenwestradio.com
W: http://www.discovermoosejaw.com
Editorial Profile: CJAW-FM is a commercial station owned by Golden West Broadcasting Ltd. The format of the station is adult contemporary. CJAW-FM broadcasts to the Moose Jaw, Saskatchewan area at 103.9 FM.

CJAY-FM
Owner: Bell Media
Editorial: 1110 Centre St NE, Calgary, Alberta T2E 2R2. **T:** 1 403 240-5800
W: http://www.cjay92.com
Editorial Profile: CJAY-FM is a commercial station owned by Bell Media. The format of the station is classic rock. CJAY-FM broadcasts to the Calgary, Alberta area at 92.1 FM.

CJBB-FM
Owner: Woods (Boyd)
Editorial: 50 Third Street, Englehart, Ontario P0J 1H0. **T:** 1 705 544-1121
E: cjbbradio@gmail.com
Editorial Profile: CJBB-FM is a commercial station owned by Boyd Woods. The format is adult contemporary. CJBB-FM broadcasts to the Englehart, Ontario area at 103.2 FM.

CJBC-AM
Owner: Société Radio-Canada
Editorial: 205 Wellington St West, Bureau 5G506, Toronto, Ontario M5V 3G7.
T: 1 416 205-2887
E: tjontario@radio-canada.ca
W: http://radio-canada.ca/regions/ontario
Editorial Profile: CJBC-AM is a non-commercial station owned by Societe Radio-Canada. The format of the station is news/talk. CJBC-AM broadcasts to Toronto at 860 AM. CBJC-AM is a member of the Canadian Press Gallery.

CJBC-FM
Owner: Société Radio-Canada
Editorial: 205 Wellington St West #5G-506, Toronto, Ontario M5V 3G7. **T:** 1 416 205-3311
W: http://www.radio-canada.ca/espace_musique
Editorial Profile: CJBC-FM is a non-commercial station owned by Société Radio-Canada. The format of the station is classical, jazz and adult contemporary. CJBC-FM broadcasts to the Toronto area at 90.3 FM. CBJC-FM is a member of the Canadian Press Gallery.

CJBE-FM
Owner: Radio Communautaire d'Anticosti Inc.
Editorial: 4A Rue Savoy, Port-Menier, Ile d'Anticosti, Quebec G0G 2Y0.
T: 1 418 535-0292
E: radioanticosti@xplornet.com
Editorial Profile: CJBE-FM is a non-commercial station owned by Radio Communautaire d'Anticosti Inc. The format of the station is variety. CJBE-FM broadcasts to the Ile d'Anticosti, Quebec region at 90.5 FM.

CJBK-AM
Owner: Astral Media
Editorial: 743 Wellington Road South, London, Ontario N6C 4R5. **T:** 1 519 686-2525
E: mailbag@cjbk.com **W:** http://www.cjbk.com
Editorial Profile: CJBK-AM is a commercial station owned by Astral Media. The format of the station is news, talk and sports programming. CJBK-AM broadcasts to the London, Ontario area at 1290 AM.

CJBP-FM
Owner: Stillwater Broadcasting Ltd
Editorial: 290 Davidson St., Neepawa, Manitoba R0J 1H0. **T:** 1 204 476-2669
E: news@cj97radio.com
W: http://cj97radio.com
Editorial Profile: CJBP-FM is a commercial station owned by Stillwater Broadcasting Ltd. The format is country. The station airs in the Neepawa, Manitoba area at 97.1FM.

CJBQ-AM
Owner: Quinte Broadcasting Co. Ltd.
Editorial: 10 Front Street South, Belleville, Ontario K8N 2Y3. **T:** 1 613 969-5555
E: news@cjbq.com **W:** http://www.cjbq.com
Editorial Profile: CJBQ-AM is a commercial station owned by Quinte Broadcasting Co. Ltd. The format of the station is classic country and talk. CJBQ-AM broadcasts to the Belleville, Ontario area at 800 AM.

CJBR-FM
Owner: Societe Radio-Canada
Editorial: 273 rue St-Jean Baptiste Ouest, Rimouski, Quebec G5L 4J8.
T: 1 418 723-2217
E: nouvelles.rimouski@radio-canada.ca
W: http://www.radio-canada.ca/regions/bas-st-laurent
Editorial Profile: CJBR-FM is a non-commercial station owned by Societe Radio-Canada. The format of the station is news and talk. CJBR-FM broadcasts to the Rimouski, Quebec area at 89.1 FM.

CJBX-FM
Owner: Astral Media
Editorial: 743 Wellington Rd, London, Ontario N6C 4R5-. **T:** 1 519 686-2525
W: http://www.bx93.com
Editorial Profile: CJBX-FM is a commercial station owned by Astral Media. The format of the station is contemporary country music. CJBX-FM broadcasts to the London, Ontario area at 92.7 FM.

CJBZ-FM
Owner: Jim Pattison Broadcast Group(The)
Editorial: 401 Mayor Magrath Drive, Lethbridge, Alberta T1J 3L8.
T: 1 403 394-9300 **E:** news@country95.fm
W: http://www.b93.fm
Editorial Profile: CJBZ-FM is a commercial station owned by The Jim Pattison Broadcast Group. The format is top 40/CHR. CJBZ-FM broadcasts to the Lethbridge, Alberta area at 93.3 FM.

CJCA-AM
Owner: Touch Canada Broadcasting (2006) Inc.
Editorial: 5316 Calgary Trail, Edmonton, Alberta T6H 4J8. **T:** 1 780 466-4930
E: 105.9@shinefm.com
W: http://www.am930thelight.com
Editorial Profile: CJCA-AM is a commercial station owned by Touch Canada Broadcasting Inc. The format of the station is religious. CJCA-AM broadcasts to the Edmonton, Alberta area at 930 AM.

CJCB-AM
Owner: Maritime Broadcasting System Ltd.
Editorial: 318 Charlotte St, Sydney, Nova Scotia B1P 1C8. **T:** 1 902 564-5596
E: news@capebretonradio.com
W: http://www.cjcbradio.com
Editorial Profile: CJCB-AM is a commercial station owned by the Maritime Broadcasting System Ltd. The format for the station is country music. CJCB-AM broadcasts to the Sydney, Nova Scotia area at 1270 AM.

CJCD-FM
Owner: Vista Broadcast Group Inc.
Editorial: 5114 49th Street, Yellowknife, Northwest Territories X1A 2N2.
T: 1 867 920-2523 **E:** info@cjcd.ca
W: http://www.cjcd.ca
Editorial Profile: CJCD-FM is a commercial station owned by Vista Broadcast Group Inc. The format of the station is adult contemporary. CJCD-FM broadcasts to the Yellowknife, Northwest Territories area at 100.1 FM.

CJCH-FM
Owner: Bell Media
Editorial: 2900 Agricola St, Halifax, Nova Scotia B3K 6A7. **T:** 1 902 453-2524
W: http://www.1013thebounce.com
Editorial Profile: CJCH-FM is a commercial station owned by Bell Media. The format of the station is Top 40/CHR. CJCH-FM broadcasts to the Halifax, Nova Scotia area at 101.3 FM.

CJCI-FM
Owner: Vista Broadcast Group Inc.
Editorial: 1940 3rd Ave, Prince George, British Columbia V2M 1G7. **T:** 1 250 564-2524
E: onair@97fm.ca **W:** http://www.97fm.ca
Editorial Profile: CJCI-FM is a commercial station owned by the Vista Broadcast Group Inc. The format of the station is contemporary country and rock music. CJCI-FM broadcasts to the Prince George, British Columbia area at 97.3 FM.

CJCJ-FM
Owner: Astral Media
Editorial: 131 Queen, Unit 2, Woodstock, New Brunswick E7M 2M8. **T:** 1 506 325-3030
E: cj104@astral.com **W:** http://www.cj104.com
Editorial Profile: CJCJ-FM is a commercial station owned by Astral Media. The format of the station is adult contemporary. CJCJ-FM broadcasts to the Woodstock, New Brunswick area at 104.1 FM.

CJCL-AM
Owner: Rogers Communications Inc.
Editorial: 1 Ted Rogers Way, Toronto, Ontario M4Y 3B7. **T:** 1 416 935-0590
E: contact@fan590.com
W: http://www.sportsnet.ca/590
Editorial Profile: CJCL-AM is a commercial station owned by Rogers Communications Inc. The format is sports. CJCL-AM broadcasts to the Toronto area at 590 AM.

CJCQ-FM
Owner: Rawlco
Editorial: 1711-100 Street, North Battleford, Saskatchewan S9A 0W7. **T:** 1 306 445-2477
E: cjnbnews@rawlco.com

CJCS-AM
Owner: Vista Broadcast Group
Editorial: 376 Romeo St S, Stratford, Ontario N5A 4T9-. **T:** 1 519 271-2450
E: news@cjcsradio.com
W: http://www.cjcsradio.com
Editorial Profile: CJCS-AM is a commercial station owned by Vista Broadcast Group. The format of the station is classic hits and oldies music. CJCS-AM broadcasts to the Stratford, Ontario area at 1240 AM.

CJCV-FM
Owner: Corus Radio
Editorial: 1440 Jack Blick Ave. Unit 200, Winnipeg, Manitoba R3G 0L4.
T: 1 204 786-2471
W: http://www.991freshfm.com
Editorial Profile: CJCV-FM is a commercial station owned by Corus Radio. The format of the station is hot AC. CJCV-FM broadcasts to the Winnipeg, Manitoba area at 99.1 FM.

CJCW-AM
Owner: Maritime Broadcasting System Ltd.
Editorial: 6 Marble Street, Sussex, New Brunswick E4E 5M2. **T:** 1 506 432-2529
E: cjcw@mbsradio.com
W: http://www.590cjcw.com
Editorial Profile: CJCW-AM is commercial station owned by Maritime Broadcasting System Ltd. The format for the station is Jack FM/adult hits. CJCW-AM broadcasts to the Sussex, New Brunswick area at 590 AM.

CJCY-FM
Owner: Clear Sky Radio Inc.
Editorial: 1865 Dunmore Road S.E., Suite 104, Medicine Hat, Alberta T1A 1Z8.
T: 1 403 488-4684 **E:** news@cjcyfm.com
W: http://www.cjcyfm.com
Editorial Profile: CJCY-FM is a commercial station owned by Clear Sky Radio Inc. The format of the station is classic hits. CJCY-FM broadcasts the the Medicine Hat, Alberta area at 102.1 FM.

CJDC-AM
Owner: Bell Media
Editorial: 901 102 Ave, Dawson Creek, British Columbia V1G 2B6. **T:** 1 250 782-3341
W: http://www.cjdccountry.com
Editorial Profile: CJDC-AM is a commercial station owned by Bell Media. The format of the station is classic country. CJDC-AM broadcasts to the Dawson Creek, British Columbia area at 890 AM.

CJDJ-FM
Owner: Rawlco Radio Ltd.
Editorial: 715 Saskatchewan Cres West, Saskatoon, Saskatchewan S7M 5V7.
T: 1 306 934-2222 **E:** rock102@rawlco.com
W: http://www.rock102rocks.com
Editorial Profile: CJDJ-FM is a commercial station owned by Rawlco Radio Ltd. The format of the station is classic rock. CJDJ-FM broadcasts to the Saskatoon, Saskatchewan area at 102.1 FM.

CJDL-FM
Owner: Tillsonburg Broadcasting Ltd.
Editorial: 77 Broadway St, Tillsonburg, Ontario N4G 3P5. **T:** 1 519 842-4281
E: info@easy101.com
W: http://www.country1073.ca
Editorial Profile: CJDL-FM is a commercial station owned by Tillsonburg Broadcasting Ltd. The format of the station is country. CJDL-FM broadcasts to the Tillsonburg, Ontario area at 107.3 FM.

CJDM-FM
Owner: Astral Media
Editorial: 2070 rue St Georges, Drummondville, Quebec J2C 5G6.
T: 1 819 474-1892
E: receptioncjdm@astral.com
W: http://www.radionrj.ca/drummondville
Editorial Profile: CJDM-FM is a commercial station owned by Astral Media. The format of the station is Top 40/CHR. CJDM-FM broadcasts to the Drummondville, Quebec area at 92.1 FM.

CJDR-FM
Owner: Jim Pattison Broadcast Group(The)
Editorial: 19 9th Ave S, Cranbrook, British Columbia V1C 2L9. **T:** 1 250 426-2224
E: news@thedrivefm.ca
W: http://www.thedrivefm.ca
Editorial Profile: CJDR-FM is a commercial station owned by The Jim Pattison Broadcast Group. The format of the station is classic rock. CJDR-FM broadcasts to the Fernie, British Columbia area at 99.1 FM.

CJDV-FM
Owner: Corus Entertainment Inc.
Editorial: 50 Sportsworls Crossing Rd, Unit 210, Kitchener, Ontario N2P 0A4.
T: 1 519 772-1212 **E:** mornings@davefm.com
W: http://www.davefm.com
Editorial Profile: CJDV-FM is a commercial station owned by Corus Entertainment Inc. The format of the station is rock. CJDV-FM broadcasts to the Cambridge, Ontario area at 107.5 FM.

CJEB-FM
Owner: Cogeco
Editorial: 4141, boulevard Saint-Jean, Trois-Rivieres, Quebec G9B 2M8. **T:** 1 819 691-1001
W: http://www.rythmefm.com/mauricie
Editorial Profile: CJEB-FM is a commercial station owned by Cogeco. The format of the station is adult contemporary. CJEB-FM broadcasts to the Trois-Rivières, Quebec area at 100.1 FM.

CJEC-FM
Owner: Cogeco
Editorial: 2136 Chemin Ste-Foy, 3e etage, Quebec, Quebec G1V 1R8. **T:** 1 418 688-0919
W: http://www.rythmefm.com/quebec
Editorial Profile: CJEC-FM is a commercial station owned by Leclerc Comunications, Inc. The format for the station is adult contemporary. CJEC-FM broadcasts to the Quebec City area at 91.9 FM.

CJED-FM
Owner: Vista Radio Limited
Editorial: 4673 Ontario Ave Suite 202, Niagara Falls, Ontario L2E 3R1. **T:** 1 905 356-6710
W: http://www.2dayfm.ca
Editorial Profile: CJED-FM is a commercial station owned by Vista Radio Limited. The format of the station is CHR/Top 40. CJED-FM broadcasts to the Niagara Region in Southern Ontario at 105.1 (CJED-FM).

CJEG-FM
Owner: Newfoundland Capital Corporation Limited
Editorial: 4816 50th Avenue, Bonnyville, Alberta T9N 2G4. **T:** 1 780 812-3058
W: http://www.1013koolfm.com
Editorial Profile: CJEG-FM is a commercial station owned by Newfoundland Capital Corporation Limited. The format of the station is adult contemporary. CJEG-FM broadcasts to the Bonnyville, Alberta area at 101.3 FM.

CJEL-FM
Owner: Golden West Broadcasting Ltd.
Editorial: 277A 1st St, Winkler, Manitoba R6W 4A6. **T:** 1 204 331-9300
E: info@goldenwestradio.com
W: http://www.eagle935fm.com
Editorial Profile: CJEL-FM is a commercial station owned by Golden West Broadcasting. The format for the station is adult contemporary. CJEL-FM broadcasts to the Winkler, Manitoba area at 93.5 FM.

CJEM-FM
Owner: Radio Edmunston Inc.
Editorial: 64, rue Rice, Edmundston, New Brunswick E3V 1T2. **T:** 1 506 735-3351
E: cjem@cjemfm.com
W: http://www.cjemfm.com
Editorial Profile: CJEM-FM is a commercial station owned by Radio Edmunston Inc. The format for the station is adult contemporary. CJEM-FM broadcasts to the Edmunston, New Brunswick area at 92.7 FM.

CJET-FM
Owner: Rogers Communications Inc.
Editorial: 6A Beckwith Street North, Smiths Falls, Ontario K7A 2B1. **T:** 1 613 283-4630
E: ottawanewsroom@rci.rogers.com
W: http://www.923jackfm.com
Editorial Profile: CJET-FM is a commercial station owned by Rogers Communications Inc. The format is adult hits. CJET-FM broadcasts to the Smith Falls, Ontario area at 92.3 FM.

CJEU-AM
Owner: Fondation Radio-Enfant(La)
Editorial: Studio de la Maison de la culture, 855, boul. de la Gappe, pièce 310, Gatineau, Quebec J8T 8H9. **T:** 1 819 243-6226
E: info@radioenfant.ca
W: http://www.radioenfant.ca
Editorial Profile: CJEU-AM is a non-commercial station owned by La Fondation Radio-Enfant. The format of the station is children's programming. CJEU-AM broadcasts to the Gatineau, Quebec area at 1670 AM.

CJEV-AM
Owner: Newfoundland Capital Corporation Limited
Editorial: 13213 20th Ave, Blairmore, Alberta T0K 0E0. **T:** 1 403 562-2806
W: http://www.mountainradiofm.com
Editorial Profile: CJEV-AM is a commercial station owned by Newfoundland Capital Corporation Limited. The format of the station is contemporary country. CJEV-AM broadcasts to the Blairmore, Alberta area at 1340 AM.

CJFM-FM
Owner: Astral Media
Editorial: 1411 Fort Street, 3rd Floor, Montreal, Quebec H3H 2R1.
T: 1 514 989-2536 **E:** infodesk@virginradio.ca
W: http://montreal.virginradio.ca
Editorial Profile: CJFM-FM is a commercial station owned by Astral Media. The format of the station is hot adult contemporary. CJFM-FM broadcasts to the Montreal area at 95.9 FM.

CJFO-FM
Owner: La Radio Communautaire Francophone d'Ottawa
Editorial: 245 Av McArthur, Ottawa, Ontario K1L 6P3. **T:** 1 613 745-5529
E: info@uniquefm.ca **W:** http://uniquefm.ca
Editorial Profile: CJFO-FM is a radio station in Ottawa aimed specifically at the francophone population in the area. The focus of the station will be primarily local featuring local news, arts, and local talent.

CJFW-FM
Owner: Astral Media
Editorial: 4625 Lazelle Ave, Terrace, British Columbia V8G 1S4. **T:** 1 250 635-6316
W: http://www.cjfw.ca
Editorial Profile: CJFW-FM is a commercial station owned by Astral Media. The format of the station is classic country and contemporary country. CJFW-FM broadcasts to the Terrace, British Columbia area at 103.1 FM.

CJFX-FM
Owner: Atlantic Broadcasters Ltd.
Editorial: 85 Kirk St, Antigonish, Nova Scotia B2G 2R9. **T:** 1 902 863-4580
E: 989xfm@989xfm.ca
W: http://www.989xfm.ca
Editorial Profile: CJFX-FM is a commercial station owned by Atlantic Broadcasters Ltd. The format of the station is hot adult contemporary. CJFX-FM broadcasts to the Antigonish, Nova Scotia area at 98.9 FM.

CJFY-FM
Owner: Miramichi Communications
Editorial: 401 Main Street, Blackville, New Brunswick E9B 1T3. **T:** 1 506 843-2208
E: staff@liferadio.ca **W:** http://www.liferadio.ca
Editorial Profile: CJFY-FM is a commercial station owned by Miramichi Communications. The format of the station is contemporary Christian. CJFY-FM broadcasts to the Blackville, New Brunswick area at 107.7 FM.

CJGM-FM
Owner: My Broadcasting Corporation
Editorial: 110 Kate Street, Gananoque, Ontario K7G 2B9. **T:** 1 613 382-6936
W: http://www.myfmradio.ca
Editorial Profile: CJGM-FM is a commercial station owned by My Broadcasting Corporation. The format of the station is soft AC. CJGM-FM broadcasts to the Gananoque/ Kingston, ON area at 99.9 FM.

CJGV-FM
Owner: Corus Entertainment Inc.
Editorial: 1440 Jack Blick Avenue, Suite 200, Winnipeg, Manitoba R3G 0L4.
T: 1 204 786-2471
E: CJKRWebAdmin@corusent.com
W: http://www.991freshfm.com
Editorial Profile: CJGV-FM is a commercial station owned by Corus Entertainment Inc. The format of the station is new and they are hiring new people now. CJGV-FM broadcasts to the Winnipeg, Manitoba area at 99.1 FM.

CJGX-AM
Owner: Harvard Broadcasting
Editorial: 120 Smith St E Fl 4TH, Yorkton, Saskatchewan S3N 3V3-. **T:** 1 306 782-2256
E: ykt-reception@harvardbroadcasting.com
W: http://www.gx94radio.com
Editorial Profile: CJGX-AM is a commercial station owned by Harvard Broadcasting. The format of the station is country music. CJGX-AM broadcasts to the Yorktown, Saskatchewan area at 940 AM.

CJHD-FM
Owner: Rawlco
Editorial: 1711-100 Street, North Battleford, Saskatchewan S9A 0W7. **T:** 1 306 445-2477
W: http://www.rawlco.com
Editorial Profile: CJHD-FM is a commercial station owned by Northwestern Radio Partnership. The format of the station is rock music. CJHD-FM broadcasts to the North Battleford, Saskatchewan area at 93.3 FM.

CJHK-FM
Owner: Acadia Broadcasting Ltd.
Editorial: 135 North St, Bridgewater, Nova Scotia B4V 8Z8. **T:** 1 902 543-2401
W: http://hankfm.ca
Editorial Profile: CJHK-FM is a commercial station owned by Acadia Broadcasting Ltd. The format for the station is contemporary country music. The station broadcasts at 100.7 FM in the Bridgewater, Nova Scotia area.

CJHL-FM
Owner: Hopedale Inuit Community Gov't
Editorial: 1 Sitsik, Hopedale, Newfoundland A0P 1G0. **T:** 1 709 933-3808
Editorial Profile: CJHL-FM is a non-commercial station owned by Hopedale Inuit Community Gov't. The format of the station is variety. CJHL-FM broadcasts to the Hopedale, Newfoundland area at 89.9 FM.

CJHQ-FM
Owner: Columbia Basin Alliance for Literacy
Editorial: Nakusp, British Columbia
E: tunein@thearrow107.com
W: http://thearrow107.com
Editorial Profile: CJHQ-FM is a commercial station owned by Columbia Basin Alliance for Literacy. The format of the station is variety, including a wide range of music and spoken word content. CJHQ-FM broadcasts to the Nakusp, British Columbia area at 107.1 FM.

CJHR-FM
Owner: Valley Heritage Radio
Editorial: 3009 Burnstown, Renfrew, Ontario K7V 4H4. **T:** 1 613 432-9873
E: info@valleyheritageradio.ca
W: http://www.valleyheritageradio.ca
Editorial Profile: CJHR-FM is a commercial station owned by Valley Haritage Radio. The station airs a country and easy listening format at 98.7 FM in the Renfrew, Ontario area.

CJIJ-FM
Owner: Membertou Radio Association Inc.
Editorial: 111 Membertou St, Membertou, Nova Scotia B1S 2M9. **T:** 1 902 562-0009
E: c99@membertou.ca

CJIQ-FM
Owner: Conestoga College
Editorial: 299 Doon Valley Drive, Conestoga College, Kitchener, Ontario N2G 4M4.

T: 1 519 748-5220 E: music@cjiq.fm
W: http://www.cjiqfm.com
Editorial Profile: CJIQ-FM is a non-commercial station owned by Conestoga College. The format for the station is college variety. CJIQ-FM broadcasts to Kitchener, Ontario at 88.3 FM. If mailing materials to the station, be sure to indicate to whose attention you are addressing the package.

CJIT-FM
Owner: Les Productions Du Temps Perdu, Inc.
Editorial: 4766 rue Laval, Lac-Megantic, Quebec G6B 1C7. **T:** 1 819 583-0663
E: radiocjit@bellnet.ca
W: http://www.cjitfm.com
Editorial Profile: CJIT-FM is a commercial station owned by Les Productions Du Temps Perdu, Inc. The format of the station is easy listening. CJIT-FM broadcasts to Lac-Megantic, Quebec at 106.7 FM.

CJIV-FM
Owner: Way of Life Broadcasting
Editorial: 16640 Highway 17 W, Dryden, Ontario P8N 2Y7. **T:** 1 807 216-6811
W: http://www.cjiv973.net
Editorial Profile: CJIV-FM is a non-commercial station owned by Way of Life Broadcasting. The format is religious and airs at 97.3 in the Dryden, Ontario area.

CJJC-FM
Owner: 1010 56012 Saskatchewan Ltd.
Editorial: 395 Riverview Road, Yorkton, Saskatchewan S3N 3V6. **T:** 1 306 786-7625
E: rocktalk@therock985.ca
W: http://www.therock985.ca
Editorial Profile: CJJC-FM is a commercial station owned by 1010 56012 Saskatchewan Ltd. The format for the station is contemporary Christian. CJJC-FM broadcasts to the Yorkton, Saskatchewan area at 98.5 FM.

CJJJ-FM
Owner: Assiniboine Community College
Editorial: 1430 Victoria Ave, Brandon, Manitoba R7A 2A9. **T:** 1 204 725-8700
E: campusradio@assiniboine.net
W: http://cj-106.assiniboine.net
Editorial Profile: CJJJ-FM is a commerical station owned by Assiniboine Community College. The format of the station is variety. CJJJ-FM broadcasts to the Brandon, Manitoba area at 106.5 FM.

CJJM-FM
Owner: Vista Broadcast Group
Editorial: 50 Gray Street, Espanola, Ontario P5E 1G1. **T:** 1 705 869-0578
W: http://www.moosefm.com/cjjm
Editorial Profile: CJJM-FM is a commercial station owned by Vista Broadcast Group. The format for the station is Classic Hits. CJJM-FM broadcasts to the Espanola, Ontario area at 99.3 FM.

CJJR-FM
Owner: Jim Pattison Broadcast Group(The)
Editorial: 1401 W 8th Ave, Suite 300, Vancouver, British Columbia V6H 1C9.
T: 1 604 731-7772 **E:** cjjr@jrfm.com
W: http://www.jrfm.com
Editorial Profile: CJJR-FM is a commercial station owned by The Jim Pattison Broadcast Group. The format for the station is contemporary country. CJJR-FM broadcasts to the Vancouver, British Columbia area at 93.7 FM.

CJKC-FM
Owner: NL Broadcasting Ltd.
Editorial: 611 Lansdowne Street, Kamloops, British Columbia V2C 1Y6. **T:** 1 250 571-1031
E: nlnews@radionl.com
W: http://www.country103.ca
Editorial Profile: CJKC-FM is a commercial station owned by NL Broadcasting Ltd. The format of the station is contemporary country. CJKC-FM broadcasts to the Kamloops, British Columbia area at 103.1 FM.

CJKK-FM
Owner: Newfoundland Broadcasting Co. Ltd.
Editorial: 446 Logy Bay Road, St. John's, Newfoundland A1C 5S2. **T:** 1 709 726-2922
E: ozfm@ozfm.com **W:** http://www.ozfm.com
Editorial Profile: CJKK-FM is a commercial station owned by Newfoundland Broadcasting Co. Ltd. The format of the station is Top 40/CHR. CJKK-FM broadcasts to the St. John's, Newfoundland area at 105.3 FM.

CJKL-FM
Owner: Connelly Communications Corp.
Editorial: 5 Kirkland St, Kirkland Lake, Ontario P2N 3J4. **T:** 1 705 567-3366

E: cjkl@cjklfm.com **W:** http://www.cjklfm.com
Editorial Profile: CJKL-FM is a commercial station owned by Connelly Communications Corp. The format for the station is hot adult contemporary. CJKL-FM broadcasts to the Kirkland Lake, Ontario area at 101.5 FM. .

CJKR-FM
Owner: Corus Entertainment Inc.
Editorial: 20-1440 Jackblick Ave, Winnipeg, Manitoba R3G 0L4. **T:** 1 204 786-2471
W: http://www.power97.com
Editorial Profile: CJKR-FM is a commercial station owned by Corus Entertainment Inc. The format for the station is rock and album-oriented rock. CJKR-FM broadcasts to the Winnipeg, Manitoba area at 97.5 FM.

CJKX-FM
Owner: Durham Radio Inc.
Editorial: 1200 Airport Blvd, Oshawa, Ontario L1J 8P5. **T:** 1 905 571-0949 **E:** kx96@kx96.fm
W: http://www.kx96.fm
Editorial Profile: CJKX-FM is a commercial station owned by Durham Radio Inc. The format for the station is contemporary country music. CJKX-FM broadcasts to the Ajax, Ontario area at 95.9 FM.

CJLA-FM
Owner: RNC Media
Editorial: 11 rue Argenteuil, Lachute, Quebec J8H 1X8. **T:** 1 450 562-8862
W: http://www.planetelov.ca
Editorial Profile: CJLA-FM is a commercial station owned by RNC Media. The format of the station is adult contemporary. CJLA-FM broadcasts to the Lachute, Quebec area at 104.9 FM.

CJLF-FM
Owner: Trust Communications Ministries
Editorial: 115 Bell Farm Road, Suite 111, Barrie, Ontario L4M 5G1. **T:** 1 705 735-3370
W: http://www.lifeonline.fm
Editorial Profile: CJLF-FM is a commercial station owned by Trust Communications Ministries. The format is contemporary Christian. CJLF-FM broadcasts to the Barrie, Ontario area at 100.3 FM.

CJLL-FM
Owner: Radio 1540 Ltd.
Editorial: 30 Murray Street, Suite 100, Ottawa, Ontario K1N 5M4. **T:** 1 613 244-0979
E: chinottawa@chinradio.com
W: http://chinradioottawa.com
Editorial Profile: CJLL-FM is a commercial station owned by Radio 1540 Ltd. The format of the station is variety. CJLL-FM broadcasts to the Ottawa, Ontario area at 97.9 FM.

CJLM-FM
Owner: Coop. Radio-diffusion FM de Lanaudiere
Editorial: 540 rue St-Thomas, Joliette, Quebec J6E 3R4. **T:** 1 450 756-1035
E: radio@m1035fm.com
W: http://www.m1035fm.com
Editorial Profile: CJLM-FM is a commercial station owned by the Coop. Radio-diffusion FM de Lanaudiere. The format for the station is adult contemporary. CJLM-FM broadcasts to Joliette, Quebec at 103.5 FM.

CJLO-AM
Owner: Concordia Students' Broadcasting Corp.
Editorial: 7141 Sherbrooke St W, PO Box 430 Cc #Rm, Montreal, Quebec H4B 1R6.
T: 1 514 848-8663 **E:** feedback@cjlo.com
W: http://www.cjlo.com
Editorial Profile: CJLO-AM is a non-commercial station owned by Concordia Students' Broadcasting Corp. The format for the station is variety. CJLO-AM broadcasts to the Montreal, Quebec area at 1690 AM.

CJLP-FM
Owner: Réseau des Appalaches
Editorial: 327 rue Labbe, Thetford Mines, Quebec G6G 1Z2. **T:** 1 418 335-7533
E: info@passionrock.com
W: http://www.passionrock.com
Editorial Profile: CJLP-FM is a commercial station owned by Réseau des Appalaches. The format of the station is soft/lite adult contemporary. CJLP-FM broadcasts to Thetford Mines, Quebec at 107.1 FM.

CJLR-FM
Owner: Missinipi Broadcasting Corp.
Editorial: 712 Finlayson St, La Ronge, Saskatchewan S0J 1L0. **T:** 1 306 425-4003
E: news@mbcradio.com
W: http://www.mbcradio.com

Editorial Profile: CJLR-FM is a commercial station owned by Missinipi Broadcasting Corp. The format of the station is adult contemporary. CJLR-FM broadcasts to the La Ronge, Saskatchewan area at 89.9 FM.

CJLS-FM
Owner: Radio CJLS Ltd.
Editorial: 328 Main St #201, Yarmouth, Nova Scotia B5A 1E4. **T:** 1 902 742-7175
E: cjls@cjls.com **W:** http://www.cjls.com
Editorial Profile: CJLS-FM is a commercial station owned by Radio CJLS Ltd. The format of the station is adult contemporary. CJLS-FM broadcasts to the Yarmouth, Nova Scotia area at 95.5 FM.

CJLT-FM
Owner: Lighthouse Broadcasting Ltd.
Editorial: 206-1741 Dunmore Rd SE 206, Medicine Hat, Alberta T1A 1Z8.
T: 1 403 529-9599
E: studio@937praisefm.com
W: http://937praisefm.com
Editorial Profile: CJLT-FM is a commercial station owned by Lighthouse Broadcasting Ltd. The format of the station is religious programming and contemporary Christian. CJLT-FM broadcasts to the Medicine Hat, Alberta area at 93.7 FM.

CJLU-FM
Owner: International Harvesters for Christ Evangelistic Association Inc.
Editorial: 101 Ilsley Avenue, Unit 3, Dartmouth, Nova Scotia B3B 1S8.
T: 1 902 468-8854 **E:** info@cjlufm.com
W: http://www.cjlufm.com
Editorial Profile: CJUL-FM is a commercial station owned by International Harvesters for Christ Evangelistic Association Inc. The format of the station is Contemporary Christian music. CJLU-FM broadcasts to the Halifax and Annapolis Valley areas in Nova Scotia Canada at 93.9 FM.

CJLV-AM
Owner: Radio Humsafar Inc.
Editorial: 2040, Autoroute Laval, Laval, Quebec H7S 2M9. **T:** 1 450 680-1570
E: info@1570ampluslaval.com
W: http://www.1570ampluslaval.com
Editorial Profile: CJLV-AM is a commercial station owned by Radio Humsafar Inc. The format of the station is classic hits and oldies. CJLV-AM broadcasts to the Laval, Quebec area at 1570 AM.

CJLX-FM
Owner: Loyalist College Radio Inc.
Editorial: Wallbridge-Loyalist Road, Belleville, Ontario K8N 4Z2. **T:** 1 613 966-0923
E: news@91x.fm **W:** http://www.91x.fm
Editorial Profile: CJLX-FM is a non-commercial station owned by Loyalist College Radio Inc. The format of the station is a rock alternative. CJLX-FM broadcasts to the Belleville, Ontario area at 91.3 FM.

CJLY-FM
Owner: Kootenay Cooperative Radio
Editorial: 308a Hall St, Nelson, British Columbia V1L 1Y8. **T:** 1 250 352-9600
E: admin@kootenaycoopradio.com
W: http://www.cjly.org
Editorial Profile: CJLY is owned by Kootenay Cooperative Radio. The station broadcasts at a frequency of 93.5 FM to Nelson, British Columbia. The station is a community based format and volunteer run.

CJMB-FM
Owner: McNabb Broadcasting
Editorial: 993 Talwood Dr, 2nd floor, Peterborough, Ontario K9J 7R8.
T: 1 705 874-0905 **E:** info@fm905.ca
W: http://www.fm905.ca
Editorial Profile: CJMB-FM is a commercial station owned by McNabb Broadcasting. The format of the station is religious, news and community programming. CJMB-FM broadcasts to the Peterborough, Ontario area at 90.5 FM.

CJMC-FM
Owner: Radio du Golfe Inc.
Editorial: 170 boulevard Ste-Anne Est, Ste-Anne-des-Monts, Quebec G4V 1N1.
T: 1 418 763-5522 **E:** studio@fm100-3.com
W: http://www.fm100-3.com
Editorial Profile: CJMC-FM is a commercial station owned by Radio du Golf Inc. The format of the station is Adult Contemporary. CJMC-FM broadcasts to the Ste-Anne-des-Monts, Quebec area at 100.3 FM.

CJMD-FM
Owner: Radio Communautaire de Lévis(La)
Editorial: 20 Duplessis St., Levis, Quebec G6V 2L1. **T:** 1 418 903-1911
W: http://www.cjmdfm.com
Editorial Profile: CJMD-FM is a non-commercial radio station owned by La Radio Communautaire de Lévis. The format for the station is variety. CJMD-FM broadcasts to the Lévis, Quebec area at 96.9 FM.

CJME-AM
Owner: Rawlco Radio Ltd.
Editorial: 210-2401 Saskatchewan Dr, Regina, Saskatchewan S4P 4H8. **T:** 1 306 525-0000
W: http://www.newstalk980.com
Editorial Profile: CJME-AM is a commercial station owned by Rawlco Radio Ltd. The format of the station is news and talk. CJME-AM broadcasts to the Regina, Saskatchewan area at 980 AM.

CJMF-FM
Owner: Cogeco Diffusion Inc.
Editorial: 1305 chemin Ste-Foy, Suite 402, Quebec, Quebec G1S 4Y5. **T:** 1 418 687-9330
E: studio@fm93.com **W:** http://www.fm93.com
Editorial Profile: CJMF-FM is a commercial station owned by Cogeco. The format of the station is classic rock and talk. CJMF-FM broadcasts to the Quebec City area at 93.3 FM.

CJMG-FM
Owner: Astral Media
Editorial: 33 Carmi Ave, Penticton, British Columbia V2A 3G4. **T:** 1 250 492-2800
E: bcnews@astral.com
W: http://www.sunonline.ca
Editorial Profile: CJMG-FM is a commercial station owned by Astral Media. The format of the station is hot adult contemporary. CJMG-FM broadcasts to the Penticton, Britsh Columbia area at 97.1 FM.

CJMI-FM
Owner: My Broadcasting Corporation
Editorial: 85 Zimmerman Ave Unit 1, Strathroy, Ontario N7G 0A3.
T: 1 519 246-6936 **E:** news@myfmradio.ca
W: http://www.myfmradio.ca
Editorial Profile: CJMI-FM is a commercial station owned by My Broadcasting Corporation. The format of the station is adult contemporary. CJMI-FM broadcasts to the Strathroy, Ontario area at 105.7 FM.

CJMJ-FM
Owner: Bell Media
Editorial: 87 George St, Ottawa, Ontario K1N 9H7-. **T:** 1 613 789-2486
W: http://www.majic100.com
Editorial Profile: CJMJ-FM is a commercial station owned by Bell Media. The format of the station is easy listening music. CJMJ-FM broadcasts to the Ottawa, Ontario area at 100.3 FM.

CJMK-FM
Owner: Saskatoon Media Group
Editorial: 366 3rd Ave S, Saskatoon, Saskatchewan S7K 1M5. **T:** 1 306 244-1975
E: cool@98cool.ca **W:** http://98cool.ca
Editorial Profile: CJMK-FM is a commercial station owned by Saskatoon Media Group. The format of the station is adult contemporary. CJMK-FM broadcasts to the Saskatoon, Saskatchewan area at 98.3 FM.

CJMM-FM
Owner: Astral Media
Editorial: 191 Avenue Murdoch, Rouyn-Noranda, Quebec J9X 1E3. **T:** 1 819 797-2566
W: http://www.radionrj.ca/rouyn
Editorial Profile: CJMM-FM is a commercial station owned by Astral Media. The format of the station is Top 40/CHR. CJMM-FM broadcasts to Rouyn-Noranda, Quebec at 99.1 FM.

CJMO-FM
Owner: Newfoundland Capital Corporation Limited
Editorial: 27 Arsenault Court, Moncton, New Brunswick E1E 4J8. **T:** 1 506 858-5525
E: c103@c103.com **W:** http://www.c103.com
Editorial Profile: CJMO-FM is a commercial station owned by Newfoundland Capital Corporation Limited. The format for the station is classic rock music. CJMO-FM broadcasts to the Moncton, New Brunswick area at 103.1 FM.

CJMP-FM
Owner: Powell River Community Radio Society
Editorial: 4476A Marine Ave, Powell River, British Columbia V8A 2K2. **T:** 1 604 485 0088

E: prcrs09@gmail.com **W:** http://blog.cjmp.ca
Editorial Profile: CJMP-FM is a non-commercial station owned byPowell River Community Radio Society. The format of the station is variety. CJMP-FM broadcasts to the Powell River, BC area at 90.1 FM.

CJMQ-FM
Owner: Radio Bishop's Inc.
Editorial: 184 Queen St, Sherbrooke, Quebec J1M 1J9. **T:** 1 819 822-1838
E: cjmqnews@yahoo.ca
W: http://www.cjmq.fm
Editorial Profile: CJMQ-FM is a non-commercial station owned by Radio Bishop's Inc. The format of the station is variety. CJMQ-FM broadcasts to the Sherbrooke, Quebec area at 88.9 FM.

CJMR-AM
Owner: Whiteoaks Communications Group Limited
Editorial: 284 Church St, Oakville, Ontario L6J 7N2. **T:** 1 905 271-1320
E: contact@cjmr1320.ca
W: http://www.cjmr1320.ca
Editorial Profile: CJMR-AM is a commercial station owned by Whiteoaks Communications Group Limited. The format of the station is variety. CJMR-AM broadcasts to the Oakville, Ontario area at 1320 AM.

CJMS-AM
Owner: Medialex
Editorial: 143 Saint-Pierre, Saint Constant, Quebec J5A 2G9. **T:** 1 450 900-2567
W: http://www.cjms1040.com
Editorial Profile: CJMS-AM is a commercial station owned by Medialex. The format of the station is classic country. CJMS-AM broadcasts to the Saint Constant, Quebec area at 1040 AM.

CJMV-FM
Owner: Astral Media
Editorial: 173 rue Perreault, Val-d'Or, Quebec J9P 2H3. **T:** 1 819 825-2568
W: http://www.radionrj.ca/valdor
Editorial Profile: CJMV-FM is a commercial station owned by Astral Media. The format of the station is Top 40/CHR. CJMV-FM broadcasts to the Val-d'Or, Quebec area at 102.7.

CJMX-FM
Owner: Rogers Communications Inc.
Editorial: 880 LaSalle Blvd, Sudbury, Ontario P3A 1X5. **T:** 1 705 566-4480
W: http://www.ezrocksudbury.com
Editorial Profile: CJMX-FM is a commercial station owned by Rogers Communications Inc. The format of the station is adult contemporary. CJMX-FM broadcasts to the Sudbury, Ontario area at 105.3 FM.

CJNB-AM
Owner: Rawlco
Editorial: 1711- 100 St, North Battleford, Saskatchewan S9A 0W7. **T:** 1 306 445-2477
E: cjnbnews@rawlco.com
W: http://www.cjnb.com/
Editorial Profile: CJNB-AM is a commercial station owned by Rawlco. The format for the station is contemporary country. CJNB-AM broadcasts to the North Battleford, Saskatchewan area at 1050 AM.

CJNC-FM
Owner: Norway House First Nations Communications
Editorial: 250 Kistapinanih, Norway House, Manitoba R0B 1B0. **T:** 1 204 359-6775
Editorial Profile: CJNC-FM is a commercial station owned by Norway House First Nations Communications. The format of the station is variety. CJNC-FM broadcasts to the Norway House, Manitoba area at 97.9 FM.

CJNE-FM
Owner: CJNE-FM Radio Inc.
T: 1 306 862-9478 **E:** pro.cjne@sasktel.net
W: http://www.cjnefm.com
Editorial Profile: CJNE-FM is a commercial station owned by CJNE-FM Radio Inc. The format of the station is classic rock and oldies. CJNE-FM broadcasts to the Nipawin, Saskatchewan area at 94.7 FM.

CJNG-FM
Owner: Radio touristique de Québec inc.(La)
Editorial: 35 Quai Saint-André, Suite 001, Quebec, Quebec G1K 8T3. **T:** 1 418 522-1069
E: info@sortirfm.com
W: http://www.sortirfm.com
Editorial Profile: CJNG-FM is an English-language tourist radio station for the Quebec City, Chaudière-Appalaches and Charlevoix regions of Quebec. CJNG-FM broadcasts at 89.7 FM. Its French-language sister station, CKJF-FM, broadcasts at 106.9 FM.

CJNI-FM
Owner: Rogers Broadcasting Ltd.
Editorial: 6080 Young Street, Suite 911, Halifax, Nova Scotia B3K 5L2.
T: 1 902 493-7200 **E:** news957@rogers.com
W: http://www.news957.com
Editorial Profile: CJNI-FM is a commercial station owned by Rogers Communications Inc. The format of the station is news and talk. CJNI-FM broadcasts to the Halifax, Nova Scotia area at 95.7 FM.

CJNS-FM
Owner: Northwestern Radio Partnership
Editorial: 225 Centre St, Box 1660, Meadow Lake, Saskatchewan S9X 1L5.
T: 1 306 236-6494 **E:** mlprod1@rawlco.com
Editorial Profile: CJNS-FM is a commercial station owned by Northwestern Radio Partnership. The format of the station is contemporary country music. CJNS-FM broadcasts to the Meadow Lake, Saskatchewan area at 102.3 FM.

CJNW-FM
Owner: Harvard Broadcasting
Editorial: 5241 Calgary Trail, Suite 700 center 105, Edmonton, Alberta T6H 5GB.
T: 1 780 435-3023 **W:** http://www.hot107.ca
Editorial Profile: CJNW-FM is a commercial station owned by Harvard Broadcasting. The format of the station is Top 40/CHR. The station broadcasts to the Edmonton, AB area at 107.1 FM.

CJOA-FM
Owner: Thunder Bay Christian Radio
Editorial: 63 Carrie St Rm 42, Thunder Bay, Ontario P7A 4J2. **T:** 1 807 344-9525
E: fm95@cjoa.ca **W:** http://www.cjoa.ca
Editorial Profile: CJOA-FM is a non-commercial station owned by Thunder Bay Christian Radio. The format is religious. The station airs at 95.1 FM in Thunder Bay, Ontario.

CJOB-AM
Owner: Corus Entertainment Inc.
Editorial: 930 Portage Ave, Winnipeg, Manitoba R3G 0P8-. **T:** 1 204 786-2471
E: cjobnews@corusent.com
W: http://www.cjob.com
Editorial Profile: CJOB-AM is a commercial station owned by Corus Entertainment Inc. The format of the station is news, talk and sports. CJOB-AM broadcasts to the Winnipeg, Manitoba area at 680 AM.

CJOC-FM
Owner: Clear Sky Radio Inc.
Editorial: 220 Third Avenue S, Suite 400, Lethbridge, Alberta T1J 0G9.
T: 1 403 388-2910 **E:** info@cjocfm.com
W: http://www.cjocfm.com
Editorial Profile: CJOC-FM is a commercial station owned by Clear Sky Radio Inc. The format of the station is classic hits. CJOC-FM broadcasts to the Lethbridge, Alberta area at 94.1 FM.

CJOI-FM
Owner: Astral Media
Editorial: 287 rue Pierre Saindon, bur 502, Rimouski, Quebec G5L 9A7.
T: 1 418 723-2323
W: http://rimouski.rougefm.ca
Editorial Profile: CJOI-FM is a commercial station owned by Astral Media. The format of the station is adult contemporary. CJOI-FM broadcasts to the Rimouski, Quebec area at 102.9 FM.

CJOJ-FM
Owner: Starboard Communications Ltd.
Editorial: 497 Dundas St W, Belleville, Ontario K8P 1B6. **T:** 1 613 966-0955
E: news@955hitsfm.ca
W: http://www.955hitsfm.ca
Editorial Profile: CJOJ-FM is a commercial station owned by Starboard Communications Ltd. The format for the station is classic hits. CJOJ-FM broadcasts to the Belleville, Ontario area at 95.5 FM.

CJOK-FM
Owner: Rogers Communications Inc.
Editorial: 9912 Franklin Ave, Fort McMurray, Alberta T9H 2K5. **T:** 1 780 743-2246
W: http://www.country933.com
Editorial Profile: CJOK-FM is a commercial station owned by Rogers Communications Inc. The format of the station is contemporary country. CJOK-FM broadcasts to the Fort McMurray, Alberta area at 93.3 FM.

CJOR-AM
Owner: Astral Media
Editorial: 33 Carmi Avenue, Penticton, British Columbia V2A 3G4. **T:** 1 250 492-2800
E: bcnews@astral.com
W: http://www.osoyoos.myezrock.com
Editorial Profile: CJOR-AM is a commercial radio station owned by Astral Media. The format of the station is adult contemporary. CJOR-AM broadcasts to the Penticton, British Columbia area at 1240 AM. CJOR-AM is a transmitter for CKOR-AM.

CJOS-FM
Owner: Larche Communications Inc.
Editorial: 787 9th Ave E, Owen Sound, Ontario N4K 3E6. **T:** 1 519 470-7626
W: http://www.923thedock.com
Editorial Profile: CJOS-FM is a commercial station owned by Larche Communications Inc. The format for the station is classic rock. CJOS-FM broadcasts to the Owen Sound and Grey-Bruce, Ontario area at 92.3 FM.

CJOT-FM
Owner: Corus Entertainment Inc.
Editorial: 1504 Merivale Rd, Ottawa, Ontario K2E 6Z5. **T:** 1 613 225-1069
W: http://www.boom997.com
Editorial Profile: CJOT-FM is a commercial station owned by Corus Entertainment Inc. The format for the station is soft rock/soft AC. CJOT-FM's tagline is "Boom 99.7."

CJOY-AM
Owner: Corus Entertainment Inc.
Editorial: 75 Speedvale Ave East, Guelph, Ontario N1E 6M3. **T:** 1 519 824-7000
E: studio@cjoy.com **W:** http://www.cjoy.com
Editorial Profile: CJOY-AM is a commercial station owned by Corus Entertainment Inc. The format for the station is oldies. CJOY-AM broadcasts to the East Guelph, Ontario area at 1460 AM.

CJOZ-FM
Owner: Newfoundland Broadcasting Co. Ltd.
Editorial: 446 Logy Bay Rd, St. John's, Newfoundland A1C 5S2. **T:** 1 709 726-2922
E: ntv@ntv.ca **W:** http://www.ozfm.com
Editorial Profile: CJOZ-FM is a commercial station owned by Newfoundland Broadcasting Co. Ltd. The format of the station is top 40/CHR. CJOZ-FM broadcasts to St. John's, NF at 92.1 FM.

CJPG-FM
Owner: Golden West Broadcasting Ltd.
Editorial: 350 River Road, Portage La Prairie, Manitoba R1N 3V6. **T:** 1 204 239-5111
E: info@goldenwestradio.com
W: http://www.mix965fm.com

CJPN-FM
Owner: Radio Fredericton Inc.
Editorial: 715 rue Priestman, Fredericton, New Brunswick E3B 5W7. **T:** 1 506 454-2576
E: cjpn@live.ca **W:** http://www.cjpn.ca
Editorial Profile: CJPN-FM is a commercial station owned by Radio Fredericton Inc. The format of the station is variety. CJPN-FM broadcasts in the Fredericton, New Brunswick area at 90.5 FM.

CJPR-FM
Owner: Newfoundland Capital Corporation Limited
Editorial: 13-213 20th Ave, Blairmore, Alberta T0K 0E0. **T:** 1 403 562-2806
W: http://www.mountainradiofm.com
Editorial Profile: CJPR-FM is a commercial station owned by Newfoundland Capital Corporation Limited. The format for the station is contemporary country. CJPR-FM broadcasts to the Blairmore, Alberta at 94.9 FM.

CJPT-FM
Owner: Bell Media
Editorial: 601 Stewart Blvd, Brockville, Ontario K6V 5T4. **T:** 1 613 345-1666
W: http://www.bob.fm
Editorial Profile: CJPT-FM is a commercial station owned by Bell Media. The format of the station is adult hits. CJPT-FM broadcasts to Brockville, Ontario at 103.7 FM.

CJPX-FM
Owner: Radio Classique Montreal, Inc.
Editorial: Ile Notre Dame, 124 Chemin du Chenal Le Moyne Parc Jean-, Montreal, Quebec H3C 1A9. **T:** 1 514 871-0995
E: cjpx@radioclassique.ca
W: http://www.radioclassique.ca
Editorial Profile: CJPX-FM is a commercial station owned by Radio Classique Montreal, Inc. The format of the station is classical. CJPX-FM broadcasts to Montreal, Quebec at 99.5.

CJQM-FM
Owner: Rogers Communications Inc.
Editorial: 642 Great Northern Road, Sault Ste. Marie, Ontario P6B 4Z9. **T:** 1 705 759-9200
W: http://www.qcountry.ca
Editorial Profile: CJQM-FM is a commercial station owned by Rogers Communications Inc. The format for the station is contemporary country. CJQM-FM broadcasts to the Sault Ste. Marie, Ontario area at 104.3 FM.

CJQQ-FM
Owner: Rogers Communications Inc.
Editorial: 260 Second Avenue, Timmins, Ontario P4N 8A4. **T:** 1 705 264-2351
W: http://www.q92timmins.com
Editorial Profile: CJQQ-FM is a commercial station owned by Rogers Communications Inc. The format of the station is classic rock. CJQQ-FM broadcasts to Timmins, Ontario at 92.1 FM.

CJRB-AM
Owner: Golden West Broadcasting Ltd.
T: 1 204 324-6464
E: info@goldenwestradio.com
Editorial Profile: CJRB-AM is a commercial station owned by Golden West Broadcasting Ltd. The format for the station is a mix of adult contemporary and agricultural. CJRB-AM broadcasts to the Boissevain, Manitoba area at 1220 AM.

CJRD-FM
Owner: Radio Drummond
Editorial: 161 rue Marchand, C.P. 801, Drummondville, Quebec J2B 6X1.
T: 1 819 474-2573 **E:** info@cjrd.ca
W: http://www.cjrd.ca
Editorial Profile: CJRD-FM is a non-commercial station owned by Radio Drummond. The format of the station is variety. CJRD-FM broadcasts to the Drummondville, Quebec area at 88.9 FM.

CJRE-FM
Owner: Radio Gaspésie Inc.
Editorial: 162 rue Jacques Cartier, Gaspe, Quebec G4X 1M9. **T:** 1 418 368-3511
E: accueil@radiogaspesie.ca
W: http://www.radiogaspesie.ca
Editorial Profile: CJRE-FM is a commercial station owned by Radio Gaspésie Inc. The format of the station is variety. CJRE-FM broadcasts to Rivière-au-Renard, Quebec at 97.9 FM.

CJRG-FM
Owner: Radio Gaspésie Inc.
Editorial: 162 rue Jacques-Cartier, Gaspe, Quebec G4X 1M9. **T:** 1 418 368-3511
E: accueil@radiogaspesie.ca
W: http://www.radiogaspesie.ca
Editorial Profile: CJRG-FM is a commercial station owned by Radio Gaspésie Inc. The format of the station is adult contemporary. CJRG-FM broadcasts to the Gaspé, Quebec area at 94.5 FM.

CJRI-FM
Owner: Faithway Communications, Inc.
Editorial: 151 Main St, Fredericton, New Brunswick E3A 1C6. **T:** 1 506 472-0947
E: cjrifm@gmail.com
W: http://www.cjrifm.com
Editorial Profile: CJRI-FM is a commercial station owned by Faithway Communications, Inc. The format of the station is Southern Gospel. CJRI-FM broadcasts to the Fredericton, New Brunswick area at a frequency of 104.5 FM.

CJRJ-AM
Owner: i.t. Productions Ltd.
Editorial: 110-3060 Norland Avenue, Burnaby, British Columbia V5B 3A6. **T:** 1 604 299-1727
E: info@rj1200.com **W:** http://www.rj1200.com
Editorial Profile: CJRJ-AM is a commercial station owned by i.t. Productions Ltd. The format of the station is South Asian top 40/CHR. CJRJ-AM broadcasts to the Burnaby, British Columbia area at 1200 AM.

CJRL-FM
Owner: Acadia Broadcasting Ltd.
Editorial: 301 First Ave S, Kenora, Ontario P9N 1W2. **T:** 1 807 468-3181 **W:** http://cjrl.ca
Editorial Profile: CJRL-FM is a commercial station owned by Acadia Broadcasting Ltd. The format of the station is adult

contemporary. CJRL-FM broadcasts to the Kenora, Ontario area at 89.5 FM.

CJRM-FM
Owner: Radio Communautaire Francophone du Labrador
Editorial: 308 Hudson Drive, Labrador City, Newfoundland A2V 1L5. **T:** 1 709 944-7600
E: cjrm@crrstv.net
Editorial Profile: CJRM-FM is a non-commercial station owned by Radio Communautaire Francophone du Labrador. The format of the station is variety. CJRM-FM broadcasts to the Labrador City, Newfoundland area at 97.3 FM.

CJRQ-FM
Owner: Rogers Communications Inc.
Editorial: 880 LaSalle Blvd, Sudbury, Ontario P3A 1X5. **T:** 1 705 566-4480
W: http://www.q92rocks.com
Editorial Profile: CJRQ-FM is a commercial station owned by Rogers Communications Inc. The format for the station is album-oriented rock. CJRQ-FM broadcasts to Sudbury, Ontario at 92.7 FM.

CJRS-AM
Owner: Radio Shalom
Editorial: 4835, Côte Ste-Catherine, Ste 2, Montreal, Quebec H3W 1M4.
T: 1 514 738-8350 **E:** info@radio-shalom.ca
W: http://www.radio-shalom.ca
Editorial Profile: CJRS-AM is a non-commercial station owned by Radio Shalom. The format of the station is talk. CJRS-AM broadcasts to the Montreal area at 1650 AM.

CJRT-FM
Owner: CJRT-FM Inc.
Editorial: 4 Pardee Avenue, Unit 100, Toronto, Ontario M6K 3H5. **T:** 1 416 595-0404
E: info@jazz.fm **W:** http://www.jazz.fm
Editorial Profile: CJRT-FM is a non-commercial station owned by CJRT-FM Inc. The format of the station is jazz. CJRT-FM broadcasts to the Toronto area at 91.1 FM.

CJRV-FM
Owner: Radio Gaspésie Inc.
Editorial: 162 rue Jacques Cartier, Gaspe, Quebec G4X 1M9. **T:** 1 418 368-3511
E: accueil@radiogaspesie.ca
W: http://www.radiogaspesie.ca
Editorial Profile: CJRV-FM is a commercial station owned by Radio Gaspésie Inc. The format of the station is adult contemporary. CJRV-FM broadcasts to L'Anse-à-Valleau, Quebec at 95.3 FM.

CJRW-FM
Owner: Maritime Broadcasting System Ltd.
Editorial: 763 Water St East, Summerside, Prince Edward Island C1N 4J3.
T: 1 902 436-2202 **W:** http://www.spud.fm
Editorial Profile: CJRW-FM is a commercial station owned by the Maritime Broadcasting System Ltd. The format of the station is classic hits. CJRW-FM broadcasts to the Summerside, Prince Edward Island area at 102.1 FM.

CJRX-FM
Owner: Rogers Communications Inc.
Editorial: 1015 3rd Ave South, Lethbridge, Alberta T1J 0J3. **T:** 1 403 320-1220
E: rock106@rci.rogers.com
W: http://www.rock106.ca
Editorial Profile: CJRX-FM is a commercial station owned by Rogers Communications Inc. The format for the station is rock alternative. CJRX-FM broadcasts to the Lethbridge, Alberta area at 106.7 FM.

CJRY-FM
Owner: Touch Canada Broadcasting (2006) Inc.
Editorial: 5316 Calgary Trail, Edmonton, Alberta T6H 4J8. **T:** 1 780 466-4930
W: http://am930thelight.com
Editorial Profile: CJRY-FM is a commerical station owned by Touch Canada Broadcasting (2006) Inc. The format of the station is contemporary Christian. CJRY-FM broadcasts to the Edmonton, Alberta area at 105.9 FM.

CJSA-FM
Owner: Canadian Multicultural Radio
Editorial: 306 Rexdale Blvd, Suite 1, Toronto, Ontario M9W 1R6. **T:** 1 416 593-9300
E: info@cmr.fm **W:** http://www.cmr.fm
Editorial Profile: CJSA-FM is a commerical station owned by Canadian Multicultural Radio. The format of the station is ethnic variety. CJSA-FM broadcasts to the Toronto area at 101.3 FM.

CJSB-FM
Owner: Stillwater Broadcasting Ltd
Editorial: 513 Main Street, Swan River, Manitoba R0L 1Z0. **T:** 1 204 734-6484
E: news@cj104radio.com
W: http://www.cj104radio.com
Editorial Profile: CJSB-FM is a commercial station owned by Stillwater Broadcasting Ltd. The station airs a variety format at 104.5 FM in the Swan River, Manitoba area.

CJSD-FM
Owner: CJSD Inc.
Editorial: 87 N Hill Street, Thunder Bay, Ontario P7A 5V6. **T:** 1 807 346-2600
E: rock@rock94.com
W: http://www.rock94.com
Editorial Profile: CJSD-FM is a commercial station owned by CJSD Inc. The format for the station is classic rock and rock alternative. CJSD-FM broadcasts to the Thunder Bay, Ontario area at 94.3 FM.

CJSE-FM
Owner: Radio Beausejour Inc.
Editorial: Cornwall 51, Shediac, New Brunswick E4P 8T8. **T:** 1 506 532-0080
E: cjse@cjse.ca **W:** http://www.cjse.ca
Editorial Profile: CJSE-FM is a commercial station owned by Radio Beausejour Inc. The format of the station is country music. CJSE-FM broadcasts in the Shediac, New Brunswick area at 89.5 FM.

CJSF-FM
Owner: Simon Fraser Campus Radio Society
Editorial: Simon Fraser University, 8888 University Drive TC 216, Burnaby, British Columbia V5A 1S6. **T:** 1 778 782-3727
E: cjsfmgr@sfu.ca **W:** http://www.cjsf.ca
Editorial Profile: CJSF-FM is a non-commercial station owned by the Simon Fraser Campus Radio Society. The format of the station is college variety. CJSF-FM broadcasts to the Burnaby, British Columbia area at 90.1 FM.

CJSI-FM
Owner: Touch Canada Broadcasting (2006) Inc.
Editorial: 4510 Macleod Trail South, Suite 100, Calgary, Alberta T2G 0A4.
T: 1 403 276-1111 **W:** http://www.cjsi.ca
Editorial Profile: CJSI-FM is a commercial station owned by Touch Canada Broadcasting. The format for the station is contemporary Christian. CJSI-FM broadcasts to the Calgary, Alberta area at 88.9 FM.

CJSL-AM
Owner: Golden West Broadcasting Ltd.
Editorial: 200-1236 5th Street, Estevan, Saskatchewan S4A 0Z6. **T:** 1 306 634-1280
E: cj1280@goldenwestradio.com
W: http://www.cj1280radio.com
Editorial Profile: CJSL-AM is a commercial station owned by Golden West Broadcasting Ltd. The format for the station is contemporary country. CJSL-AM broadcasts to the Estevan, Saskatchewan area at 1280 AM.

CJSN-AM
Owner: Golden West Broadcasting Ltd.
Editorial: 407 Centre St, Shaunavon, Saskatchewan S0N 2M0. **T:** 1 306 297-2671
E: cjsn@goldenwestradio.com
Editorial Profile: CJSN-AM is a commercial station owned by Golden West Broadcasting Ltd. The format for the station is classic country. CJSN-AM broadcast to the Shaunavon, Saskatchewan area at 1490 AM.

CJSO-FM
Owner: Radio Diffusion Sorel-Tracy Inc.
Editorial: 52 rue du Roi, Sorel-Tracy, Quebec J3P 4M7. **T:** 1 450 743-2772
E: info@fm1017.ca **W:** http://www.fm1017.ca
Editorial Profile: CJSO-FM is a commercial station owned by Radio Diffusion Sorel-Tracy Inc. The format of the station is adult contemporary. CJSO-FM broadcasts to Sorel-Tracy, Quebec at 101.7 FM.

CJSP-FM
Owner: Blackburn Radio Inc.
Editorial: 100 Talbot St E, Leamington, Ontario N8H 1L3. **T:** 1 519 326-6171
W: http://country959.com
Editorial Profile: CJSP-FM is a commercial station owned by Blackburn Radio Inc. The format of the station is Country. CJSP-FM broadcasts to the Leamington, Ontario area at 92.7 FM.

CJSQ-FM
Owner: Radio Classique Montreal, Inc.
Editorial: 2525 Boulevard Laurier, Quebec, Quebec G1V 2L2. **T:** 1 418 650-9270
E: cjsq@radioclassique.ca
W: http://www.radioclassique.ca
Editorial Profile: CJSQ-FM is a commercial station owned by Radio Classique Montreal, Inc. The format of the station is classical. CJSQ-FM broadcasts to the Quebec, QC area at 92.7 FM.

CJSR-FM
Owner: First Alberta Campus Radio Association
Editorial: University of Alberta, SUB Lower Level Room 009, Edmonton, Alberta T6G 2J7.
T: 1 780 492-2577 228 **E:** news@cjsr.com
W: http://www.cjsr.com
Editorial Profile: CJSR-FM is a non-commercial station owned by First Alberta Campus Radio Association. The format for the station is variety. CJSR-FM broadcasts to the Edmonton, Alberta area at 88.5 FM.

CJSS-FM
Owner: Corus Entertainment Inc.
Editorial: 709 Cotton Mill St, Cornwall, Ontario K6H 7K7. **T:** 1 613 932 5180
W: http://www.cjssfm.com
Editorial Profile: CJSS-FM is a commercial station owned by Corus Entertainment Inc. The format of the station is classic hits. CJSS-FM broadcasts to the Cornwall, Ontario area at 101.9 FM.

CJSU-FM
Owner: Vista Broadcast Group Inc.
Editorial: 130 Trans-Canada Highway, Duncan, British Columbia V9L 2P7. **T:** 1 250 746-0897
E: news@897sunfm.com
W: http://www.897sunfm.com
Editorial Profile: CJSU-FM is a commercial station owned by Vista Broadcast Group Inc. The format for the station is classic rock music. CJSU-FM broadcasts to the Duncan, British Columbia area at 89.7 FM.

CJSW-FM
Owner: University of Calgary Student Radio Society
Editorial: University of Calgary, Rm 312 MacEwan Hall, Calgary, Alberta T2N 1N4.
T: 1 403 220-3902 **E:** news@cjsw.com
W: http://www.cjsw.com
Editorial Profile: CJSW-FM is a non-commercial station owned by the University of Calgary Student Radio Society. The format of the station is variety. CJSW-FM broadcasts to Calgary, Alberta at 90.9 FM.

CJTB-FM
Owner: Tête-à-la-Baleine
T: 1 418 242-2974 **E:** cjtb@globetrotter.net
Editorial Profile: CJTB-FM is a community radio station owned by Tête-à-la-Baleine. The format of the station is variety. CJTB-FM broadcasts to Tête-à-la-Baleine, Quebec at 93.1 FM.

CJTK-FM
Owner: Eternacom Inc.
Editorial: 2150 La Salle Blvd, Sudbury, Ontario P3C 2A7. **T:** 1 705 674-2585
E: mail@kfmradio.ca
W: http://www.kfmradio.ca
Editorial Profile: CJTK-FM is a commercial station owned by Eternacom Inc. The format of the station is contemporary Christian music. CJTK-FM broadcasts to the Sudbury, Ontario area at 95.5 FM. CJTK-FM has two transmitters. CJTK-FM-1 broadcasts at 103.5 FM in North Bay, Ontario. CJTK-FM-2 broadcasts at 102.1 FM to the Manitoulin/Little Current, Ontario area.

CJTN-FM
Owner: Quinte Broadcasting Co. Ltd.
Editorial: 10 S. Front St., 4th Floor, Belleville, Ontario K8N 2Y3. **T:** 1 613 969-5555
W: http://www.rock107.ca
Editorial Profile: CJTN-FM is a commercial station owned by Quinte Broadcasting Co. Ltd. The format of the station is classic rock. CJTN-FM broadcasts to the Trenton, Ontario area at 107.1 FM.

CJTR-FM
Owner: Radius Communications Inc.
Editorial: 301-1102 8th Ave 301, Regina, Saskatchewan S4R 1C9-. **T:** 1 306 525-7274
E: radius@cjtr.ca **W:** http://www.cjtr.ca
Editorial Profile: CJTR-FM is a commercial station owned by Radius Communications Inc. The format of the station is variety. CJTR-FM broadcasts to the Regina, Saskatchewan area at 480 AM.

CJTT-FM
Owner: Connelly Communications Corp.
Editorial: 55 Whitewood Ave, New Liskeard, Ontario P0J 1P0. **T:** 1 705 647-7334
E: cjtt@cjttfm.com **W:** http://www.cjttfm.com
Editorial Profile: CJTT-FM is a commercial station owned by Connelly Communications Corp. The format of the station is adult contemporary music. CJTT-FM broadcasts to the New Liskeard, Ontario area at 104.5 FM.

CJTW-FM
Owner: Sound of Faith Broadcasting
Editorial: 659 King St East, Ste 207, Kitchener, Ontario N2G 4H6.
T: 1 519 575-9090 **E:** info@faithfm.org
W: http://www.faithfm.org
Editorial Profile: CJTW-FM is a commercial station owned by Sound of Faith Broadcasting. The format is contemporary Christian. CJTW-FM broadcasts to the Kitchener, Ontario area at 94.3 FM.

CJUC-FM
Owner: Utilities Consumers Group
Editorial: Yukon Arts Centre, College Drive, Whitehorse, Yukon Territory Y1A 5X9.
T: 1 867 667-8577 **E:** mail@cjucfm.com
W: http://cjucfm.com
Editorial Profile: CJUC-FM is a non-commercial station owned by Utilities Consumers Group. The format of the station is community radio. CJUC-FM broadcasts to the Whitehorse, Yukon Territory, Canada area at a frequency of 92.5 FM.

CJUI-FM
Owner: Vista Broadcast Group Inc.
Editorial: 1729 Gordon Dr, Kelowna, British Columbia V1Y 3H3. **T:** 1 250 980-9009
W: http://juicefm.ca
Editorial Profile: CJUI-FM is a commercial station owned by Vista Broadcast Group Inc. The format for the station is classic hits. CJUI-FM broadcasts to the Kelowna, BC area at 103.9 FM.

CJUK-FM
Owner: Arcadia Broadcasting
Editorial: 180 Park Avenue, Suite 200, Thunder Bay, Ontario P7B 6J4.
T: 1 807 344-2000 **E:** magic@magic999.ca
W: http://www.magic999.ca
Editorial Profile: CJUK-FM is a commercial station owned by Arcadia Broadcasting. The format of the station is hot adult contemporary. CJUK-FM broadcasts to the Thunder Bay, Ontario area at 99.9 FM.

CJUM-FM
Owner: University of Manitoba Students Union
Editorial: University Centre Room #308, University of Manitoba, Winnipeg, Manitoba R3T 2N2. **T:** 1 204 474-7027
E: cjum@cjum.com **W:** http://www.umfm.com
Editorial Profile: CJUM-FM is a non-commercial station owned by University of Manitoba Students Union. The format is college variety. CJUM-FM broadcasts to the Winnipeg, Manitoba area at 101.5 FM.

CJUV-FM
Owner: L.A. Radio Group Inc.
Editorial: 4725 49B Avenue, Lacombe, Alberta T4L 1K1. **T:** 1 403 786-0194
E: news@sunny94.com
W: http://www.sunny94.com
Editorial Profile: CJUV-FM is a commercial station owned by L.A. Radio Group Inc. The format of the station is classic hits. CJUV-FM broadcasts to the Lacombe, Alberta area at 94.1 FM.

CJVA-AM
Owner: Radio-Acadie Ltd.
Editorial: 195 rue Main, Bathurst, New Brunswick E2A 1A7. **T:** 1 506 546-4600
E: superstation@ckle.fm
W: http://www.ckle.fm
Editorial Profile: CJVA-AM is a commercial station owned by Radio-Acadie Ltd. The format for the station is adult contemporary. CJVA-AM broadcasts to the Bathurst, New Brunswick area at 810 AM.

CJVB-AM
Owner: Fairchild Radio Group Ltd.
Editorial: 4151 Hazelbridge Way, Unit 2090, Richmond, British Columbia V6X 4J7.
T: 1 604 295-1234 **E:** news@am1470.com
W: http://www.am1470.com
Editorial Profile: CJVB-AM is a commercial station owned by the Fairchild Radio Group Ltd. The format of the station is variety. CJVB-FM broadcasts to the Vancouver, British Columbia area at 1470 AM.

CJVD-FM
Owner: Yves Sauvé
Editorial: 2555, rue Dutrisac, Local RC-08 A, Vaudreuil-Dorion, Quebec J7V 7E6.
T: 1 514 790-1001 **E:** info@cjvd.ca
W: http://www.cjvd.ca
Editorial Profile: CJVD-FM is a commercial station owned by Yves Sauvé. The format for the station is adult contemporary. CJVD-FM broadcasts to the Vaudreuil-Dorion, Quebec area.

CJVR-FM
Owner: Fabmar Investments Ltd.
Editorial: 611 Main Street North, Melfort, Saskatchewan S0E 1A0. **T:** 1 306 752-2587
E: news@cjvr.com
W: http://www.yourtownnews.ca/news/97
Editorial Profile: CJVR-FM is a commercial station owned by Fabmar Investments Ltd. The format of the station is contemporary country. CJVR-FM broadcasts to the Melfort, Saskatchewan area at 105.1 FM.

CJWA-FM
Owner: Labbe Media Corp.
Editorial: 96 Broadway Avenue, Wawa, Ontario P0S 1K0. **T:** 1 705 856-4555
E: jjamfmnews@bellnet.ca
Editorial Profile: CJWA-FM is a commercial station owned by Labbe Media Corp. The format of the station is adult contemporary. CJWA-FM broadcasts to Wawa, Ontario at 107.1 FM.

CJWF-FM
Owner: Blackburn Radio Inc.
Editorial: 2090 Wyandotte St E, Windsor, Ontario N8Y 5B2. **T:** 1 519 944-4400
E: news.windsor@blackburnradio.com
W: http://country959.com
Editorial Profile: CJWF-FM is a commercial station owned by Blackburn Radio Inc. The format for the station is contemporary country. CJWF-FM broadcasts to the Windsor, ON area at 95.9 FM.

CJWI-AM
Owner: CPAM Radio Union
Editorial: 3390 blvd. Cremazie est, 2eme Etage, Montreal, Quebec H2A 1A4.
T: 1 514 790-2726
E: nouvelles@cpam1610.com
W: http://www.cpam1610.com
Editorial Profile: CJWI-AM is a commercial station owned by CPAM Radio Union. The format of the station is variety. CJWI-AM broadcasts to the Montreal area at 1610 AM.

CJWL-FM
Owner: Evanov Radio Group
Editorial: 127 York Street, Ottawa, Ontario K1N 5T4. **T:** 1 613 241-9850
E: info@985thejewel.com
W: http://www.985thejewel.com/985/
Editorial Profile: CJWL-FM is a commercial station owned by Evanov Radio Group. The format of the station is easy listening. CJWL-FM broadcasts to the Ottawa, Ontario area at 98.5 FM.

CJWT-FM
Owner: Wawatay Native Communications Society
Editorial: 135 Pine Street, Timmins, Ontario P4N 2K3. **T:** 1 705 360-4556
E: cjwt@wawatay.on.ca
W: http://www.wawataynews.ca
Editorial Profile: CJWT-FM is a commercial station owned by the Wawatay Native Communications Society. The format is a variety of content offered in English, Cree Oji and Ojibway. CJWT-FM broadcast to the Timmins, Ontario area at 106.7 FM.

CJWV-FM
Owner: Pineridge Broadcasting Inc.
Editorial: 360 George St. N, unit 1, Peterborough, Ontario K9H 7E7.
T: 1 705 876-7773
W: http://www.magic967.fm
Editorial Profile: CJWV-FM is a commercial station owned by Pineridge Broadcasting Inc. The format of the station is adult contemporary. CJWV-FM broadcasts to the Peterborough area at 96.7 FM.

CJWW-AM
Owner: Saskatoon Media Group
Editorial: 366 3rd Avenue S, Saskatoon, Saskatchewan S7K 1M5. **T:** 1 306 244-1975
E: cjwwnews@sasktel.net
W: http://www.cjwwradio.com
Editorial Profile: CJWW-AM is a commercial station owned by Saskatoon Media Group. The format of the station is classic country. CJWW-AM broadcasts to the Saskatoon, Saskatchewan area at 600 AM.

CJXK-FM
Owner: Newfoundland Capital Corporation Limited
Editorial: B-5412 55 Street, Cold Lake, Alberta T9M 1R5. **T:** 1 780 594-2459
E: news@k-rock953.com
W: http://www.953krock.com
Editorial Profile: CJXK-FM is a commercial station owned by Newfoundland Capital Corporation Limited. The format for the station is classic rock. CJXK-FM broadcasts to the Cold Lake, Alberta area at 95.3 FM.

CJXL-FM
Owner: Newfoundland Capital Corporation Limited
Editorial: 27 Arsenault Court, Moncton, New Brunswick E1E 4J8. **T:** 1 506 858-5525
E: xl96@xl96.com **W:** http://www.xl96.com
Editorial Profile: CJXL-FM is a commercial station owned by Newfoundland Capital Corporation Limited. The format for the station is contemporary country music. CJXL-FM broadcasts to Moncton, New Brunswick at 96.9 FM.

CJXX-FM
Owner: Jim Pattison Broadcast Group(The)
Editorial: 9817 101st Avenue, Suite 202, Grande Prairie, Alberta T8V 0X6.
T: 1 780 532-0840
E: general@bigcountryxx.com
W: http://www.bigcountryxx.com
Editorial Profile: CJXX-FM is a commercial station owned by The Jim Pattison Broadcast Group. The format is classic country. CJXX-FM broadcasts to the Grande Prairie, Alberta area at 93.1 FM.

CJXY-FM
Owner: Corus Entertainment Inc.
Editorial: 875 Main St W Suite 900, Hamilton, Ontario L8S 4R1. **T:** 1 905 521-9900
E: news@900chml.com **W:** http://www.y108.ca
Editorial Profile: CJXY-FM is a commercial station owned by Corus Entertainment Inc. The format of the station is rock/album-oriented rock. CJXY-FM broadcasts to the Hamilton, Ontario area at 107.9 FM.

CJYC-FM
Owner: Maritime Broadcasting System Ltd.
Editorial: 226 Union St, Saint John, New Brunswick E2L 1B1. **T:** 1 506 658-5100
E: mailbag@k100.ca **W:** http://kool98.fm
Editorial Profile: CJYC-FM is a commercial station owned by Maritime Broadcasting System Ltd. The format of the station is classic hits. CJYC-FM broadcasts to the Saint John, New Brunswick area at 98.9 FM.

CJYE-AM
Owner: Whiteoaks Communications Group Limited
Editorial: 284 Church Street, Broadcast Centre, Oakville, Ontario L6J 7N2.
T: 1 905 845-2821 **E:** contact@joy1250.ca
W: http://www.joy1250.ca
Editorial Profile: CJYE-AM is a non-commercial station owned by Whiteoaks Communications Group Limited. The format is Christian. CJYE-AM broadcasts to the Oakville, Ontario area at 1250 AM.

CJYM-AM
Owner: Golden West Broadcasting Ltd.
Editorial: 208 Highway 4 North, Rosetown, Saskatchewan S0L 2V0. **T:** 1 306 882-2686
E: cjymnews@goldenwestradio.com
W: http://www.cjym.com
Editorial Profile: CJYM-AM is a commercial station owned by Golden West Broadcasting Ltd. The format of the station is classic hits. CFYM-AM broadcasts in the Rosetown, Saskatchewan area at 1330 AM.

CJYQ-AM
Owner: Newfoundland Capital Corporation Limited
Editorial: 391 Kenmount Road, St. John's, Newfoundland A1B 3M7. **T:** 1 709 726-5590
E: radionewfoundland@vocm.com
W: http://www.radionewfoundland.net
Editorial Profile: CJYQ-FM is a commercial station owned by Newfoundland Capital Corporation Limited. The format of the station is variety. CJYQ-FM broadcasts to the St. John's, Newfoundland area at 930 AM.

CJZN-FM
Owner: Jim Pattison Broadcast Group(The)
Editorial: 2750 Quadra St, Top Floor, Victoria, British Columbia V8T 4E8. **T:** 1 250 475-6611
W: http://www.thezone.fm
Editorial Profile: CJZN-FM is a commercial station owned by The Jim Pattison Broadcast Group. The format of the station is rock alternative. CJZN-FM broadcasts to the Victoria, British Columbia area at 91.3 FM.

CKAC-AM
Owner: Cogeco
Editorial: 800, rue de la Gauchetière Ouest, Bureau 1100, Montreal, Quebec H5A 1M1.
T: 1 514 787-0730
W: http://www.radiocirculation.net
Editorial Profile: CKAC-AM is a commercial station owned by Cogeco. The format of the station is traffic and weather. CKAC-AM broadcasts to the Montreal area at 730 AM.

CKAD-AM
Owner: Maritime Broadcasting System Ltd.
Editorial: 29 Oakdene Ave, Kentville, Nova Scotia B4N 1H5. **T:** 1 902 825-3429
E: newsroom@avrnetwork.com
W: http://www.avrnetwork.com
Editorial Profile: CKAD-AM is a commercial station owned by Maritime Broadcasting System Ltd. The format of the station is classic country. CKAD-AM broadcasts to the Middleton, Nova Scotia area at 1350 AM.

CKAG-FM
Owner: Société de communication Ikito Pikogan Ltée(La)
Editorial: 30, rue David Kistabish, Pikogan, Quebec J9T 3A3. **T:** 1 819 727-3237
E: ckagfm@cableamos.com
W: http://www.ckagfm.com
Editorial Profile: CKAG-FM is a community radio station owned by La Société de communication Ikito Pikogan Ltée. The format for the station is variety. CKAG-FM broadcasts to the Pikogan, Quebec area at 100.1 FM. They broadcast Mon - Fri daytime only.

CKAJ-FM
Owner: Cooperative des Artisans Radio-Soleil
Editorial: 3877 Boulevard Harvey, Jonquiere, Quebec G7X 0A6. **T:** 1 418 546-2525
E: ckaj@ckaj.org **W:** http://www.ckaj.org
Editorial Profile: CKAJ-FM is a commercial station owned by Cooperative des Artisans Radio-Soleil. The format of the station is classic country and oldies. CKAJ-FM broadcasts to the Jonquiere, Quebec area at 92.5 FM.

CKAP-FM
Owner: Vista Broadcast Group
Editorial: 22 Queen St Unit 2A, Kapuskasing, Ontario P5N 1G8. **T:** 1 705 335-2379
E: moose1009@moosefm.com
W: http://www.moosefm.com/ckap
Editorial Profile: CKAP-FM is a commercial station owned by Vista Broadcast Group. The format of the station is adult contemporary music. CKAP-FM broadcasts to the Kapuskasing, Ontario area at 100.9 FM.

CKAT-AM
Owner: Rogers Communications Inc.
Editorial: 743 Main St East, North Bay, Ontario P1B 1C2. **T:** 1 705 474-2000
E: nbnews@rci.rogers.com
W: http://www.600ckat.com
Editorial Profile: CKAT-AM is a commercial station owned by Rogers Communications Inc. The format of the station is contemporary country and sports. CKAT-AM broadcasts to North Bay, Ontario at 600 AM.

CKAV-FM
Owner: Aboriginal Voices Radio Inc.
Editorial: 558 Huron St, Toronto, Ontario M6H 4E1. **T:** 1 416 703-1287
E: info@aboriginalvoices.com
W: http://www.aboriginalvoices.com
Editorial Profile: CKAV-FM is a commercial station owned by Aboriginal Voices Radio Inc. The format of the station is variety. CKAV-FM broadcasts to the Toronto area at 106.5 FM.

CKAY-FM
Owner: Westwave Broadcasting
Editorial: 1-1877 Field Road, Sechelt, British Columbia V0N 3A1. **T:** 1 888 741-9170
E: info@ckay.ca **W:** http://www.ckay.ca
Editorial Profile: CKAY-FM is a commercial station owned by Westwave Broadcasting. The format of the station is adult contemporary. CKAY-FM broadcasts to the Sechelt, British Columbia area at 91.7 FM.

CKBA-FM
Owner: New Cap Radio
Editorial: #1 4902-49 Street, Athabasca, Alberta T9S 1C2. **T:** 1 780 675-5301
W: http://www.941theriver.ca
Editorial Profile: CKBA-FM is a commercial station owned by New Cap Radio. The format of the station is adult contemporary music. CKBA-FM broadcasts to the Athabasca, Alberta area at 94.1 FM.

CKBC-FM
Owner: Astral Media
Editorial: 640 St. Peter Ave, Unit 1, Bathurst, New Brunswick E2A 2Y7. **T:** 1 506 547-1360
E: maxfm@radioatl.ca
W: http://www.max1049.ca
Editorial Profile: CKBC-FM is a commercial station owned by Astral Media. The format of the station is adult contemporary music. CKBC-FM broadcasts in Bathurst, New Brunswick at 104.9 FM.

CKBE-FM
Owner: Cogeco
Editorial: 800 de la Gauchetière Ouest, Bureau 1100, Montreal, Quebec H5A 1M1.
T: 1 514 767-9250
W: http://www.925thebeat.ca
Editorial Profile: CKBE-FM is a commercial station owned by Cogeco. The format of the station is adult contemporary. CKBE-FM broadcasts to the Montreal area at 92.5 FM.

CKBI-AM
Owner: Rawlco Radio Ltd.
Editorial: 1316 Central Ave, Box 900, Prince Albert, Saskatchewan S6V 7R4.
T: 1 306 763-7421 **E:** panews@rawlco.com
W: http://www.900ckbi.com
Editorial Profile: CKBI-AM is a commercial station owned by Rawlco Radio Ltd. The format of the station is classic country. CKBI-AM broadcasts to the Prince Albert, Saskatchewan area at 900 AM.

CKBL-FM
Owner: Saskatoon Media Group
Editorial: 366 3rd Avenue S, Saskatoon, Saskatchewan S7K 1M5. **T:** 1 306 244-1975
E: cjwwnews@sasktel.net
W: http://www.929thebullrocks.com
Editorial Profile: CKBL-FM is a commercial station owned by Saskatoon Media Group. The format of the station is contemporary country. CKBL-FM broadcasts to the Saskatoon, Saskatchewan area at 92.9 FM.

CKBN-FM
Owner: Cooperative de solidarite radio communautaire Nicolet-Yamask
Editorial: 10275, rue Leblanc, suite 127, Becancour, Quebec G0X 1B0.
T: 1 819 294-2526 **E:** information@ckbn.ca
W: http://www.ckbn.ca
Editorial Profile: CKBN-FM is a non-commercial station owned by the Cooperative de solidarite radio communautaire Nicolet-Yamaska/Becancour. The format of the station is variety. CKBN-FM broadcasts to the Becancour, Quebec area at 90.5 FM.

CKBT-FM
Owner: Corus Entertainment Inc.
Editorial: 50 Sportsworld Crossing Rd, Unit 210, Kitchener, Ontario N2P 0A4.
T: 1 519 772-1212 **E:** info@915thebeat.com
W: http://www.915thebeat.com
Editorial Profile: CKBT-FM is a commercial station owned by Corus Entertainment Inc. The format for the station is Top 40/CHR. CKBT-FM broadcasts to the Kitchener, Ontario area at 91.5 FM.

CKBW-FM
Owner: Acadia Broadcasting Ltd.
Editorial: 135 North Street, Bridgewater, Nova Scotia B4V 2V7. **T:** 1 902 543-2401
E: ckbwnews@radioabl.ca
W: http://www.ckbw.ca
Editorial Profile: CKBW-FM is a commercial station owned by Acadia Broadcasting Ltd. The format of the station is adult contemporary music. CKBW-FM broadcasts to the Bridgewater, Nova Scotia area at 98.1 FM.

CKBX-AM
Owner: Vista Broadcast Group Inc.
Editorial: 260 3rd Street, 100 Mile House, British Columbia V0K 2E0. **T:** 1 250 395-3848
E: cariboonews@reachthecariboo.com
Editorial Profile: CKBX-AM is a commercial station owned by Vista Broadcast Group Inc. The format of the station is classic country. CKBX-AM broadcasts to 100 Mile House, BC at 840 AM.

CKBY-FM
Owner: Rogers Communications Inc.
Editorial: 2001 Thurston Drive, Ottawa, Ontario K1G 6C9. **T:** 1 613 736-2001
E: ottawanewsroom@ottawaradio.rogers.com

W: http://www.y101.fm
Editorial Profile: CKBY-FM is a commercial station owned by Rogers Communications Inc. The format of the station is contemporary country. CKBY-FM broadcasts to Ottawa, Ontario at 101.1 FM.

CKBZ-FM
Owner: Jim Pattison Broadcast Group(The)
Editorial: 460 Pemberton Terr, Kamloops, British Columbia V2C 1T5. **T:** 1 250 372-3322
W: http://www.b100.ca
Editorial Profile: CKBZ-FM is a commercial station owned by The Jim Pattison Broadcast Group. The format of the station is adult contemporary music. CKBZ-FM broadcasts to the Kamloops, Britsh Columbia area ast 100.1 FM.

CKCB-FM
Owner: Corus Entertainment Inc.
Editorial: 1400 Highway 26 East, Collingwood, Ontario L9Y 4W2. **T:** 1 705 446-9510
E: general@thepeakfm.com
W: http://www.thepeakfm.com
Editorial Profile: CKCB-FM is a commercial station owned by Corus Entertainment Inc. The format of the station is adult contemporary. CKCB-FM broadcasts to the Collingwood, Ontario area at 95.1 FM.

CKCE-FM
Owner: Jim Pattinson Group(The)
Editorial: 222 58 Ave SW Suite 600, Calgary, Alberta T2H 2S3. **T:** 1 403 536-3866
W: http://kool1015.ca
Editorial Profile: CKCE-FM is a commercial station owned by Jim Pattinson Group. The format of the station is hot adult contemporary. CKCE-FM broadcasts to the Calgary, Alberta area at 101.5 FM.

CKCH-FM
Owner: Martin (Barry)
Editorial: 5 Detheridge Drive, Ste 3, Sydney, Nova Scotia B1L 1B8. **T:** 1 902 563-1035
E: onair@eagle1035.com
W: http://www.eagle1035.com
Editorial Profile: CKCH-FM is a commercial station owned by Barry Martin. NewCap Broadcasting Ltd. also has a stake in the station. The format of the station is contemporary country. CKCH-FM broadcasts to the Sydney, Nova Scotia area at 103.1 FM.

CKCI-FM
Owner: Points Eagle Radio
Editorial: 9111 W Ipperwash Rd, Unit 6 RR #2, Kettle & Stony Point First Nation, Forest, Ontario N0N 1J0. **T:** 1 519 786-3883
E: info@eaglecountry.ca
W: http://www.eaglecountry.ca
Editorial Profile: CKCI-FM is a commercial station owned by Points Eagle Radio. The format of the station is contemporary country, classic rock and oldies. CKCI-FM broadcasts to the Sarnia, Ontario area at 103.3 FM.

CKCK-FM
Owner: Rawlco Radio Ltd.
Editorial: 210-2401 Saskatchewan Dr, Regina, Saskatchewan S4P 4H8. **T:** 1 306 525-0000
W: http://www.jackfmregina.com
Editorial Profile: CKCK-FM is a commercial station owned by Rawlco Radio Ltd.The format of the station is adult hits. CKCK-FM broadcasts to the Regina, Saskatchewan area at 94.5 FM.

CKCL-FM
Owner: Golden West Broadcasting Ltd.
Editorial: 2-20 St.Mary's Rd 2, Winnipeg, Manitoba R2H 1H1. **T:** 1 204 256-2525
E: info@classic107.com
W: http://www.classic107.com
Editorial Profile: CFEQ-FM is a commercial station owned by Golden West Broadcasting Ltd. The format of the station is Classical and Jazz. CKCL-FM broadcasts to the Winnipeg, Manitoba area at 107.1 FM.

CKCM-AM
Owner: Steele Communications
Editorial: 35 Grenfell Heights, Grand Falls-Windsor, Newfoundland A2A 2K2.
T: 1 709 489-2192
E: grandfallswindsor@vocm.com
W: http://www.vocm.com
Editorial Profile: CKCM-AM is a commercial station owned by Steele Communications. The format is classic and contemporary country music, news and talk. CKCM-AM broadcasts to the Grand Falls-Windsor, Newfoundland area at 620 AM.

CKCN-FM
Owner: Radio Sept-Iles Inc.
Editorial: 365 Bl. Laure, Sept-Iles, Quebec G4R 1X2. **T:** 1 418 962-3838
E: info@le941.com **W:** http://www.le941.com
Editorial Profile: CKCN-FM is a commercial station owned by Radio Sept-Iles Inc. The format of the station is adult contemporary. CKCN-FM broadcasts to Sept-Iles, Quebec at 94.1 FM.

CKCQ-FM
Owner: Vista Radio Ltd.
Editorial: 502-410 Kinchant St., Quesnel, British Columbia V2J 7J5. **T:** 1 250 992-7046
E: feedback@thewolfonline.ca
W: http://www.thewolfonline.ca
Editorial Profile: CKCQ-FM is a commercial station owned by Vista Radio Ltd. The format of the station is contemporary country and Southern rock. CKCQ-FM broadcasts to Quesnel, British Columbia at 100.3 FM.

CKCR-FM
Owner: Astral Media
T: 1 250 837-2149 **E:** info@myezrock.com
W: http://wwww.revelstoke.myezrock.com
Editorial Profile: CKCR-FM is a commercial station owned by Astral Media. The format of the station is Lite Rock/Lite AC. CKCR-FM broadcasts to the Revelstoke, British Columbia area at 106.1 FM.

CKCU-FM
Owner: CKCU Radio Carleton Inc.
Editorial: Room 517 University Centre, 1125 Colonel By Drive, Ottawa, Ontario K1S 5B6.
T: 1 613 520-2898 **E:** info@ckcufm.com
W: http://www.ckcufm.com
Editorial Profile: CKCU-FM is a non-commercial station owned by CKCU Radio Carleton Inc. The format of the station is variety. CKCU-FM broadcasts to Ottawa, Ontario at 93.1 FM.

CKCV-FM
Owner: Newfoundland Broadcasting Co. Ltd.
Editorial: 446 Logy Bay Rd., St. John's, Newfoundland A1C 5S2. **T:** 1 709 726-2922
E: ntv@ntv.ca **W:** http://www.ozfm.com

CKCW-FM
Owner: Maritime Broadcasting System Ltd.
Editorial: 1000 St George Blvd, Moncton, New Brunswick E1E 4M7. **T:** 1 506 858-1220
W: http://www.k945.ca
Editorial Profile: CKCW-FM is a commercial station owned by Maritime Broadcasting System Ltd. The format for the station is hot adult contemporary. CKCW-FM broadcasts to the Moncton, New Brunswick area at 94.5 FM.

CKDG-FM
Owner: Canadian Hellenic Cable Radio Ltd.
Editorial: 5899 Park Ave, Montreal, Quebec H2V 4H4. **T:** 1 514 273-2481
E: info@mikefm.ca **W:** http://www.mikefm.ca
Editorial Profile: CKDG-FM is a commercial station owned by Canadian Hellenic Cable Radio Ltd. The format for the station is Jack FM-Adult Hits. CKDG-FM broadcasts to the Montreal area at 105.1 FM.

CKDH-FM
Owner: Maritime Broadcasting System Ltd.
Editorial: #38 Highway 6, Amherst, Nova Scotia B4H 3Y4. **T:** 1 902 667-3875
E: ckdh@ckdh.net **W:** http://www.ckdh.net
Editorial Profile: CKDH-FM is a commercial station owned by Maritime Broadcasting System Ltd. The format of the station is easy listening music. CKDH-FM broadcasts to Amherst, Nova Scotia at 101.7 FM.

CKDJ-FM
Owner: Algonquin College
Editorial: Algonquin Col 1385 Woodroffe Avenue, Room N-101, Ottawa, Ontario K2G 1V8. **T:** 1 613 727-4723
E: pihlaid@algonquincollege.com
W: http://www.ckdj.net
Editorial Profile: CKDJ-FM is a commercial station owned by Algonquin College. The format of the station is alternative hip hop. CKDJ-FM broadcasts to the Ottawa, Ontario area at 107.9 FM.

CKDK-FM
Owner: Corus Entertainment Inc.
Editorial: 380 Wellington Street, Room 222, London, Ontario N6A 5B5. **T:** 1 519 931-6000
W: http://www.more1039.ca
Editorial Profile: CKDK-FM is a commercial station owned by Corus Entertainment Inc. The format of the station is classic hits. CKDK-FM broadcasts in the Woodstock, Ontario area at 103.9 FM.

CKDM-AM
Owner: Dauphin Broadcasting Company Ltd.
Editorial: 27 3rd Ave NE, Dauphin, Manitoba R7N 0Y5. **T:** 1 204 638-3230
E: ckdm.news@730ckdm.com
W: http://www.730ckdm.com
Editorial Profile: CKDM-AM is a commercial station owned by Dauphin Broadcasting. The format of the station is news and country music. CKDM-AM broadcasts to Dauphin, Manitoba and surrounding communities at 730 AM.

CKDO-AM
Owner: Durham Radio Inc.
Editorial: 1200 Airport Blvd Suite 207, Oshawa, Ontario L1J 8P5. **T:** 1 905 571-0949
E: newsroom@kx96.fm **W:** http://www.ckdo.ca
Editorial Profile: CKDO-AM is a commercial station owned by Durham Radio Inc. The format of the station is oldies. CKDO-AM broadcasts to the Oshawa, Ontario area at 1580 AM. CKDO-AM airs programming on CKDO-FM.

CKDO-FM
Owner: Durham Radio Inc.
Editorial: 1200 Airport Blvd Suite 207, Oshawa, Ontario L1J 8P5. **T:** 1 905 571-0949
E: newsroom@kx96.fm **W:** http://www.ckdo.ca
Editorial Profile: CKDO-FM is a commercial station owned by Durham Radio Inc. The format of the station is oldies. CKDO-FM broadcasts to Oshawa, Ontario at 107.7 FM. CKDO-FM airs CKDO-AM's programming.

CKDQ-AM
Owner: Newfoundland Capital Corporation Limited
Editorial: 515 Highway 10 East, Drumheller, Alberta T0J 0Y0. **T:** 1 403 823-3384
E: q91@newcap.ca
W: http://www.q91country.com
Editorial Profile: CKDQ-AM is a commercial station owned by Newfoundland Capital Corporation Limited. The format of the station is contemporary country music. CKDQ-AM broadcasts to Drumheller, Alberta and its environs at 910 AM.

CKDR-FM
Owner: Arcadia Broadcasting
Editorial: 122 King St, Dryden, Ontario P8N 2Z4. **T:** 1 807 223-2355 **E:** news@ckdr.net
W: http://www.ckdr.net
Editorial Profile: CKDR-FM is a commercial station owned by Arcadia Broadcasting. The format of the station is adult contemporary. CKDR-FM broadcasts to Dryden, Ontario at 92.7 FM.

CKDU-FM
Owner: CKDU-FM Society
Editorial: Dalhousie University, 6136 University Ave 4th Floor, Halifax, Nova Scotia B3H 4J2. **T:** 1 902 494-6479 **E:** info@ckdu.ca
W: http://www.ckdu.ca
Editorial Profile: CKDU-FM is a non-commercial station owned by CKDU-FM Society. The format of the station is variety. CKDU-FM broadcasts to the Halifax, Nova Scotia area at 88.1 FM.

CKDV-FM
Owner: Jim Pattison Broadcast Group(The)
Editorial: 1810 3rd Ave, 2nd Floor, Prince George, British Columbia V2M 1G4.
T: 1 250 564-8861
W: http://www.993thedrive.com
Editorial Profile: CKDV-FM is a commercial station owned by The Jim Pattison Broadcast Group. The format of the station is classic rock. CKDV-FM broadcasts to the Prince George, British Columbia area at 99.3 FM.

CKDX-FM
Owner: Evanov Radio Group
Editorial: 5312 Dundas St West, Toronto, Ontario M9B 1B3. **T:** 1 416 213-1035
E: info@885thejewel.com
W: http://www.885thejewel.com
Editorial Profile: CKDX-FM is a commercial station owned by Evanov Radio Group. The format of the station is adult standards. CKDX-FM broadcasts to the Toronto area at 88.5 FM.

CKDY-AM
Owner: Maritime Broadcasting System Ltd.
Editorial: 53 Sydney St, Digby, Nova Scotia B0V 1A0. **T:** 1 902 245-2111
E: newsroom@avrnetwork.com
W: http://www.avrnetwork.com
Editorial Profile: CKDY-AM is a commercial station owned by Maritime Broadcasting System Ltd. The format of the station is classic country. CKDY-AM broadcasts to the Digby, Nova Scotia area at 1420 AM.

CKDY-FM
Owner: Maritime Broadcasting System Ltd.
Editorial: 53 Sydney St, Digby, Nova Scotia B0V 1A0. **T:** 1 902 245-2111
E: newsroom@avrnetwork.com
W: http://www.avrnetwork.com

CKEA-FM
Owner: Harvard Broadcasting
Editorial: 104-5241 Calgary Trail NW 104, Edmonton, Alberta T6H 5G8.
T: 1 780 435-3023 **W:** http://www.lite957.ca
Editorial Profile: CKEA-FM is a commercial station owned by Harvard Broadcasting. The format for the station is adult Hits. CKEA-FM broadcasts to the Edmonton, Alberta are at 95.7 FM.

CKEC-FM
Owner: Hector Broadcasting Co. Ltd.
Editorial: 84 Provost St, New Glasgow, Nova Scotia B2H 5E7. **T:** 1 902 752-4200
E: info@ecfm.ca **W:** http://www.ecfm.ca
Editorial Profile: CKEC-FM is a commercial station owned by Hector Broadcasting Co. Ltd. The format of the station is adult contemporary. CKEC-FM broadcasts to the New Glasgow, Nova Scotia area at 94.1 FM.

CKEN-FM
Owner: Maritime Broadcasting System Ltd.
Editorial: 29 Oakdene Ave, Kentville, Nova Scotia B4N 1H5. **T:** 1 902 678-2111
E: newsroom@avrnetwork.com
W: http://www.avrnetwork.com
Editorial Profile: CKEN-FM is a commercial station owned by Maritime Broadcasting System Ltd. The format of the station is classic and contemporary country. CKEN-FM broadcasts to the Kentville, Nova Scotia area at 97.7 FM.

CKER-FM
Owner: Rogers Communications Inc.
Editorial: 10212 Jasper Ave, Edmonton, Alberta T5J 5A3. **T:** 1 780 424-2222
W: http://www.worldfm.ca
Editorial Profile: CKER-FM is a commercial station owned by Rogers Communications Inc. The format of the station is a variety of music, news, public affairs, religion, and general interest talk programs broadcast in multiple languages. CKER-FM broadcasts to Edmonton, AB area at 101.7 FM.

CKFG-FM
Owner: Intercity Broadcasting
Editorial: 34 Kern Road, Toronto, Ontario M3B 1T1 **W:** http://www.g987fm.com/
Editorial Profile: CKFG-FM is a commercial station owned by Intercity Broadcasting. The format for the station is urban adult contemporary. CKFG-FM broadcasts to the Toronto, Ontario area at 98.7 FM.

CKFI-FM
Owner: Golden West Broadcasting Ltd.
Editorial: 134 Central Avenue North, Swift Current, Saskatchewan S9H 0L1.
T: 1 306 773-4605 **W:** http://magic97radio.ca
Editorial Profile: CKFI-FM is a commercial station owned by Golden West Broadcasting Ltd. The format for the station is adult contemporary. CKFI-FM broadcasts to the Swift Current, Saskatchewan area at 97.1 FM.

CKFM-FM
Owner: Bell Media
Editorial: 2 St Clair Ave W Fl 2ND, Toronto, Ontario M4V 1L5. **T:** 1 416 922-9999
E: info@virginradio999.com
W: http://toronto.virginradio.ca
Editorial Profile: CKFM-FM is a commercial station owned by Bell Media. The format of the station is Top 40/CHR. CKFM-FM broadcasts to the Toronto area at 99.9 FM.

CKFR-AM
Owner: Bell Media
Editorial: 435 Bernard Ave, Kelowna, British Columbia V1Y 6N8. **T:** 1 250 860-8600
E: info@am1150.ca **W:** http://www.am1150.ca
Editorial Profile: CKFR-AM is a commercial station owned by Bell Media. The format of the station is news, talk and sports. CKFR-AM broadcasts to the Kelowna, British Columbia area at 1150 AM.

CKFT-FM
Owner: Golden West Broadcasting Ltd.
Editorial: 9940-99th Avenue, Suite 200, Fort Saskatchewan, Alberta. **T:** 780 997 1079
W: http://fortsaskonline.com

CKFU-FM
Owner: Moose Communications

Editorial: 10423 101st Avenue, Fort St. John, British Columbia V1J 2B7. **T:** 1 250 787-7100
E: reception@moosefm.ca
W: http://energeticcity.ca/moosefm
Editorial Profile: CKFU-FM is a commercial station owned by Moose Communications. The format of the station is contemporary country. CKFU-FM broadcasts to the Fort St. John, BC area at 100.1 FM.

CKFX-FM
Owner: Rogers Communications Inc.
Editorial: 743 Main St East, North Bay, Ontario P1B 1C2. **T:** 1 705 474-2000
E: thefox@foxradio.ca
W: http://www.foxradio.ca
Editorial Profile: CKFX-FM is a commercial station owned by Rogers Communications Inc. The format of the station is rock/album-oriented rock. CKFX-FM broadcasts to the North Bay, Ontario area at 101.9 FM.

CKGA-AM
Owner: Newfoundland Capital Corporation Limited
T: 1 709 651-3650 **E:** ckxdnews@vocm.com
W: http://www.vocm.com
Editorial Profile: CKGA-AM is a commercial radio station owned by Newfoundland Capital Corporation Limited. The format of the station is classic country music. CKGA-AM broadcasts to Gander, Newfoundland and surrounding communities at 650 AM.

CKGB-FM
Owner: Rogers Communications Inc.
Editorial: 260 Second Ave, Timmins, Ontario P4N 8A4. **T:** 1 705 264-2351
W: http://www.ezrocktimmins.com
Editorial Profile: CKGB-FM is a commercial station owned by Rogers Communications Inc. The format of the station is adult contemporary. CKGB-FM broadcasts to Timmins, Ontario at 99.3 FM.

CKGC-FM
Owner: Northern Lights Entertainment Inc.
T: 1 877 445-2547
E: 1035capitalfm@gmail.com
W: http://www.1035capitalfm.ca
Editorial Profile: CKGC-FM is a commercial station owned by Northern Lights Entertainment Inc. The format of the station is classic hits with an emphasis on rock music. CKGC-FM broadcasts locally to the Iqaluit, NU, Canada area at a frequency of 103.5 FM.

CKGE-FM
Owner: Durham Radio Inc.
Editorial: 1200 Airport Blvd Suite 207, Oshawa, Ontario L1J 8P5. **T:** 1 905 571-0949
E: newsroom@kx96.fm
W: http://www.therock.fm
Editorial Profile: CKGE-FM is a commercial radio station owned by Durham Radio Inc. The format of the station is album-oriented rock. CKGE-FM broadcasts to Oshawa, Ontario at 94.9 FM.

CKGF-FM
Owner: Vista Broadcast Group Inc.
Editorial: 1101 A 4th Street, Castlegar, British Columbia V1N 2A8. **T:** 1 250 365-7600
E: news@mountainfm.net
W: http://www.mountainfm.net
Editorial Profile: CKGF-FM is a commercial station owned by Vista Broadcast Group Inc. The format of the station is classic rock. CKGF-FM broadcasts to the Castlegar, British Columbia area at 96.7 FM.

CKGL-AM
Owner: Rogers Communications Inc.
Editorial: 305 King St West, 11th Floor, Kitchener, Ontario N2G 4E4.
T: 1 519 743-2611 **E:** news570@rogers.com
W: http://www.570news.com
Editorial Profile: CKGL-AM is a commercial station owned by Rogers Communications Inc. The format of the station is news and talk. CKGL-AM broadcasts to the Kitchener, Ontario area at 570 AM.

CKGM-AM
Owner: Bell Media
Editorial: 1310 Greene Ave, Suite 300, Westmount, Quebec H3Z 2B5.
T: 1 514 931-4487 **E:** writetous@team990.com
W: http://www.tsn.ca/montreal/
Editorial Profile: CKGM-AM is a commercial station owned by Bell Media. The format of the station is sports. CKGM-AM broadcasts to the Montreal area at 990 AM.

CKGN-FM
Owner: Radio Communautaire KapNord Inc.
Editorial: 77 Chemin Brunelle Nord, Kapuskasing, Ontario P5N 2M1.
T: 1 705 335-5915 **E:** ckgn-fm@nt.net
W: http://www.ckgn.ca
Editorial Profile: CKGN-FM is a non-commercial station owned by Radio Communautaire KapNord Inc. The format of the station is variety. CKGN-FM broadcasts to the Kapuskasing, Ontario area at 89.7 FM.

CKGR-FM
Owner: Astral Media
Editorial: 825 10th Ave S, Golden, British Columbia V0A 1H0. **T:** 1 250 344-7177
E: webmaster@myezrock.com
W: http://golden.myezrock.com
Editorial Profile: CKGR-FM is a commercial station owned by Astral Media. The format of the station is soft rock/ soft AC. CKGR-FM broadcasts to Golden, British Columbia at 106.3 FM.

CKGS-FM
Owner: 9202-1617 Quebec Inc
Editorial: 169, 6ème Rue, La Baie, Quebec G7B 0A3. **T:** 1 418 544-2105
E: info@ckgsfm.com
W: http://www.ckgsfm.com
Editorial Profile: CKGS-FM is a commercial station owned by 9202-1617 Quebec Inc. The format of the station is contemporary hits. CKGS-FM broadcasts to the La Baie, Quebec area at 105.5 FM.

CKGW-FM
Owner: UCB
Editorial: 40 Center Square, Chatham, Ontario N7N 5L3. **T:** 1 519 351-1118
W: http://www.ucbchathamkent.com
Editorial Profile: CKGW-FM is a commercial station owned by UCB. The format is adult contemporary music. CKGW-FM broadcasts to the Chatham-Kent, Ontario area at 89.3 FM.

CKGY-FM
Owner: Newfoundland Capital Corporation Limited
Editorial: 4920 59th St, Red Deer, Alberta T4N 2N1. **T:** 1 403 343-1170
E: news@kgcountry.ca
W: http://www.kgcountry.ca
Editorial Profile: CKGY-FM is a commercial station owned by Newfoundland Capital Corporation Limited. The format of the station is contemporary country. CKGY-FM broadcasts to Red Deer, Alberta at 95.5 FM.

CKHA-FM
Owner: Vista Broadcast Group
Editorial: 739 Mountain St., Haliburton, Ontario K0M 1S0. **T:** 1 705 457-9603
E: canoefm@bellnet.ca
W: http://www.canoefm.com
Editorial Profile: CKHA-FM is a non-commercial station owned by Vista Broadcast Group. The format of the station is variety. CKHA-FM broadcasts to the Haliburton, Ontario area at 100.9 FM.

CKHC-FM
Owner: Humber College
Editorial: 205 Humber College Blvd, Humber College, Toronto, Ontario M9W 5L7.
T: 1 416 675-6622
E: radiohumber@humber.ca
W: http://www.radio.humber.ca
Editorial Profile: CKHC-FM is a non-commercial station owned by Humber College. The format of the station is variety. CKHC-FM broadcasts to the Toronto area at 96.9 FM.

CKHJ-AM
Owner: Bell Media
Editorial: 206 Rookwood Ave, Fredericton, New Brunswick E3B 2M2. **T:** 1 506 451-9111
W: http://www.khj.ca
Editorial Profile: CKHJ-AM is a commercial station owned by Bell Media. The format of the station is contemporary country. CKHJ-AM broadcasts to Fredericton, New Brunswick area at 1260 AM.

CKHK-FM
Owner: Evanov Radio Group
Editorial: 1320 Main Street East, Hawkesbury, Ontario K6A 1C5. **T:** 1 613 872-1077
E: info@1077thejewel.com
W: http://www.evanovradio.com
Editorial Profile: CKHK-FM is a commercial station owned by the Evanov Radio Group. The format of the station is easy listening. CKHK-FM broadcasts to the Hawkesbury, Ontario area at 107.7 FM.

CKHL-FM
Owner: Peace River Broadcasting Corp.
T: 1 780 926-4530 **E:** news@ylcountry.com
W: http://www.ylcountry.com
Editorial Profile: CKHL-AM is a commercial station owned by Peace River Broadcasting Corp. The format of the station is classic country music. The station airs locally at 102.1 FM.

CKHT-FM
Owner: Vista Broadcast Group
Editorial: 22 Queen St Unit 2A, Kapuskasing, Ontario P5N 1G8. **T:** 1 705 335-2379
E: moose1009@moosefm.com
W: http://www.moosefm.com/ckap
Editorial Profile: CKHT-FM is a commercial radio station owned by Vista Broadcast Group. The format of the station is adult contemporary music. The target audience of the station is adults, ages 18 to 64 throughout Hearst, Ontario. CKHT-FM is broadcast locally on 94.5 FM.

CKHY-FM
Owner: Evanov Radio Group
Editorial: 5527 Cogswell Street, Halifax, Nova Scotia B3J 1R2. **T:** 1 902 429-1035
E: info@live105.ca **W:** http://www.live105.ca
Editorial Profile: CKHY-FM is a commercial station owned by Evanov Radio Group. The format for the station is modern rock. CKHY-FM broadcasts to the greater Halifax, Nova Scotia area at 105.1 FM.

CKHZ-FM
Owner: Evanov Radio Group
Editorial: 5527 Cogswell Street, Halifax, Nova Scotia B3J 1R2. **T:** 1 902 429-1035
W: http://www.energy1035.ca
Editorial Profile: CKHZ-FM is a commercial station owned by Evanov Radio Group. The format for the station is Top 40/CHR. CKHZ-FM broadcasts to the Halifax, Nova Scotia area at 103.5 FM.

CKIA-FM
Owner: Radio Basse-Ville Inc.
Editorial: 600 Cote d'Abraham, Quebec, Quebec G1R 1A1. **T:** 1 418 529-9026
Editorial Profile: CKIA-FM is a non-commercial station owned by Radio Basse-Ville Inc. The format of the station is French adult contemporary. CKIA-FM broadcasts to the Quebec City, Quebec area at 88.3 FM.

CKII-FM
Owner: Communauté autochtone Muskwa de Mistassini
Editorial: 1708 boul. Wallberg, Dolbeau-Mistassini, Quebec G8L 1H6.
T: 1 418 239-2544

CKIK-FM
Owner: L.A. Radio Group Inc
Editorial: 6751 52nd Ave, #103, Red Deer, Alberta T4N 4K8. **T:** 1 403 358-3100
E: admin@laradiogroup.com
W: http://www.kraze1013.com
Editorial Profile: CKIK-FM is a commercial station owned by L.A. Radio Group Inc. The format of the station is Top 40. CKIK-FM broadcasts to the Red Deer, Alberta area at 101.3 FM.

CKIM-AM
Owner: Steele Communications
Editorial: 35 Grenfell Heights, Grand Falls-Windsor, Newfoundland A2A 2K2.
T: 1 709 489-2192
E: grandfallswindsor@vocm.com
W: http://www.vocm.com

CKIQ-FM
Owner: Northern Lights Entertainment Inc.
T: 1 877 445-2547 **E:** icefmiqaluit@gmail.com
W: http://www.icefm.ca

CKIR-AM
Owner: Astral Media
Editorial: 825 10th Ave South, Golden, British Columbia V0A 1H0. **T:** 1 250 3447177
E: info@myezrock.com
W: http://www.golden.myezrock.com
Editorial Profile: CKIR-AM is a commercial station owned by Astral Media. The format of the station is easy listening. CKIR-AM broadcasts to Golden, British Columbia at 870 AM.

CKIS-FM
Owner: Rogers Communications Inc.
Editorial: 777 Jarvis St, Toronto, Ontario M4Y 3B7. **T:** 1 416 935-8392
W: http://www.kiss925.com
Editorial Profile: CKIS-FM is a commercial station owned by Rogers Communications Inc. The format is Top 40/CHR. CKIS-FM broadcasts to Toronto at 92.5 FM.

CKIX-FM
Owner: Newfoundland Capital Corporation Limited
Editorial: 391 Kenmount Road, St. John's, Newfoundland A1B 3M7. **T:** 1 709 726-5590
E: hitsmail@991hitsfm.com
W: http://www.991hitsfm.com
Editorial Profile: CKIX-FM is a commercial station owned by Newfoundland Capital Corporation Limited. The format of the station is Top 40/CHR. CKIX-FM broadcasts to Saint John's, Newfoundland and surrounding communities at 99.1 FM.

CKIZ-FM
Owner: Jim Pattison Broadcast Group(The)
Editorial: 3313 - 32nd Avenue, Vernon, British Columbia V1T 2M7. **T:** 1 250 545-2141
E: 1075kiss@gmail.com
W: http://www.1075kiss.com
Editorial Profile: CKIZ-FM is a commercial station owned by Jim Pattison Broadcast Group. The format of the station is adult contemporary. CKIZ-FM broadcasts to the Vernon, British Columbia area at 107.5 FM.

CKJF-FM
Owner: Radio touristique de Québec inc.(La)
Editorial: 35 Quai Saint-Andre, Suite 001, Quebec, Quebec G1K 8T3. **T:** 1 418 522-1069
E: info@sortirfm.com **W:** http://sortirfm.com
Editorial Profile: CKJF-FM is a French-language tourist radio station for the Quebec City, Chaudière-Appalaches and Charlevoix regions of Quebec. CKJF-FM broadcasts at 106.9 FM. Its English-language sister station, CJNG-FM, broadcasts at 89.7 FM.

CKJH-AM
Owner: Fabmar Investments Ltd.
Editorial: 611 Main Street North, Melfort, Saskatchewan S0E 1A0. **T:** 1 306 752-2587
E: info@cjvr.com
W: http://www.yourtownnews.ca
Editorial Profile: CKHJ-AM is a commercial station owned by Fabmar Investments Ltd. The format of the station is oldies. CKHJ-AM broadcasts to the Melfort, Saskatchewan area at 750 AM.

CKJJ-FM
Owner: UCB
Editorial: 214 Pinnacle Street, Fl 2, Belleville, Ontario K8N 3A6. **T:** 1 866 388-4488
W: http://www.ucbcanada.com
Editorial Profile: CKJJ-FM is a commercial station owned by UCB. The format is adult contemporary Christian music. CKJJ-FM broadcasts to the Belleville, Ontario area at 102.3 FM.

CKJM-FM
Owner: Cooperative Radio Cheticamp Ltee.
Editorial: 15584 Cabot Trail, Cheticamp, Nova Scotia B0E 1H0. **T:** 1 902 224-1242
E: info@ckjm.ca **W:** http://www.ckjm.ca
Editorial Profile: CKJM-FM is a non-commercial station owned by Cooperative Radio Cheticamp Ltee. The format of the station is variety. CKJM-FM broadcasts to the Cheticamp, Nova Scotia area at 106.1 FM.

CKJN-FM
Owner: Vista Broadcast Group
Editorial: 282 Argyle St S Unit 4, Caledonia, Ontario N3W 1K8. **T:** 1 289 284-1070
E: moose929@moosefm.com
W: http://www.moosefm.com/ckjn
Editorial Profile: CKJN-FM is a commercial station owned by Vista Broadcast Group. The format for the station is easy listening. CKJN-FM broadcasts to the Haldimand, ON area at 92.9 FM.

CKJR-AM
Owner: Newfoundland Capital Corporation Limited
Editorial: 5214A 50th Avenue, Wetaskiwin, Alberta T9A 0S8. **T:** 1 780 352-0144
W: http://www.w1440.com
Editorial Profile: CKJR-AM is a commercial station owned by Newfoundland Capital Corporation Limited. The format of the station is oldies. CKJR-AM broadcasts to Wetaskiwin, Alberta and its environs at 1440 AM.

CKJS-AM
Owner: Evanov Communications
Editorial: 520 Corydon Ave, Winnipeg, Manitoba R3L 0P1. **T:** 1 204 477-1221
E: info@ckjs.com **W:** http://www.ckjs.com
Editorial Profile: CKJS-AM is a commercial station owned by Evanov Communications. The format of the station is multilingual station serving various ethnic groups. CKJS-AM broadcasts to Winnipeg, Manitoba at 810 AM.

CKJX-FM
Owner: CAB-K Broadcasting Ltd.
Editorial: #6-4526 49 Avenue, Olds, Alberta T4H 1A4. **T:** 1 403 586-7625
W: http://www.rock104.ca
Editorial Profile: CKJX-FM is a commercial station owned by CAB-K Broadcasting Ltd. The format of the station is rock/album-oriented rock. CKJX-FM broadcasts to the Olds, Alberta area at 104.5 FM.

CKKC-FM
Owner: Astral Media
Editorial: 513 C Front Street, Nelson, British Columbia V1L 4B4. **T:** 1 250 352-5510
E: webmaster@myezrock.com
W: http://kootenays.myezrock.com
Editorial Profile: CKKC-FM is a commercial station owned by Astral Media. The format of the station is adult contemporary. CKKC-FM broadcasts to the Trail, British Columbia area at 106.9 FM.

CKKL-FM
Owner: Bell Media
Editorial: 87 George St, Ottawa, Ontario K1N 9H7-. **T:** 1 613 789-2486
W: http://www.939bobfm.com
Editorial Profile: CKKL-FM is a commercial station owned by Bell Media. The format of the station is adult hits. CKKL-FM broadcasts to the Ottawa, Ontario area at 93.9 FM.

CKKN-FM
Owner: Jim Pattison Broadcast Group(The)
Editorial: 1810 3rd Ave, 2nd Floor, Prince George, British Columbia V2M 1G4.
T: 1 250 564-8861
W: http://www.1013theriver.com
Editorial Profile: CKKN-FM is a commercial station owned by The Jim Pattison Broadcast Group. The format of the station is hot adult contemporary. CKKN-FM broadcasts to Prince George, British Columbia at 101.3 FM.

CKKO-FM
Owner: Newfoundland Capital Corporation
Editorial: 1601 Bertram St, Kelowna, British Columbia V1Y 2G5. **T:** 1 250 861-5963
E: publicservice@k963.fm
W: http://www.k963.fm
Editorial Profile: CKKO-FM is a commercial station owned by Newfoundland Capital Corporation. The format of the station is classic rock. CKKO-FM broadcasts to the Kelowna, Ontario area at 96.3 FM.

CKKQ-FM
Owner: Jim Pattison Broadcast Group(The)
Editorial: 2750 Quadra St, Top Floor, Victoria, British Columbia V8T 4E8. **T:** 1 250 475-0100
E: news@theq.fm **W:** http://www.theq.fm
Editorial Profile: CKKQ-FM is a commercial station owned by The Jim Pattison Broadcast Group. The format of the station is rock/album-oriented rock. CKKQ-FM broadcasts to Victoria, British Columbia at 100.3 FM.

CKKV-FM
Owner: Vista Broadcast Group
Editorial: 4 Industrial Rd unit#3, Kemptville, Ontario K0G 1J0. **T:** 1 613 258-1786
W: http://www.fm975kemptville.com
Editorial Profile: CKKV-FM is a commercial station owned by Vista Broadcast Group. The format for the station is adult contemporary. CKKV-FM broadcasts to the Kemptville, ON area at 97.5 FM.

CKKW-FM
Owner: Bell Media
Editorial: 255 King St North, Suite 207, Waterloo, Ontario N2J 4V2. **T:** 1 519 884-4470
W: http://www.kfun995.com
Editorial Profile: CKKW-FM is a commercial station owned by Bell Media. The format of the station is adult hits. CKKW-FM broadcasts to Waterloo, Ontario at 99.5 FM.

CKKX-FM
Owner: Peace River Broadcasting Corp.
Editorial: 9807 100th Ave, Peace River, Alberta T8S 1T5. **T:** 1 780 624-2535
E: news@ylcountry.com
W: http://www.kix106.net
Editorial Profile: CKKX-FM is a commercial radio station owned by Peace River Broadcasting Corp. The format of the station is adult contemporary music. CKKX-FM broadcasts to Peace River, Alberta and surrounding communities at 106.1 FM.

CKKY-AM
Owner: Newfoundland Capital Corporation Limited
Editorial: 1037 2 Ave Fl 2ND, Wainwright, Alberta T9W 1K7. **T:** 1 780 842-4311
W: http://www.krock1019.com/
Editorial Profile: CKKY-FM is a commercial station owned by Newfoundland Capital Corporation Limited. The format of the station is rock music. CKKY-FM broadcasts to Wainwright, Lloydminster, Vermillion and its environs at 101.9 FM.

CKLC-FM
Owner: Bell Media
Editorial: 993 Princess St, Ste 10, Kingston, Ontario K7L 1H3. **T:** 1 613 544-1380
E: onair@989thedrive.com
W: http://www.989thedrive.com
Editorial Profile: CKLC-FM is a commercial station owned by Bell Media. The format of the station is AAA-Adult Album Alternative. CKLC-FM broadcasts to the Kingston, Ontario area at 98.9 FM.

CKLD-FM
Owner: Réseau des Appalaches
Editorial: 327 rue Labbe, Thetford Mines, Quebec G6G 1Z2. **T:** 1 418 335-7533
E: redaction@passionrock.com
W: http://www.passionrock.com
Editorial Profile: CKLD-FM is a commercial station owned by Réseau des Appalaches. The format of the station is soft and lite adult contemporary. CKLD-FM broadcasts to Thetford Mines, Quebec at 105.5 FM.

CKLE-FM
Owner: Radio-Acadie Ltd.
Editorial: 195 rue Main, Bathurst, New Brunswick E2A 1A7. **T:** 1 506 546-4600
E: superstation@ckle.fm
W: http://www.ckle.fm
Editorial Profile: CKLE-FM is a commercial station owned by Radio-Acadie Ltd. The format of the station is adult contemporary. CKLE-FM broadcasts in the Bathurst, New Brunswick area at 92.9 FM.

CKLF-FM
Owner: Riding Mountain Broadcasting Ltd.
Editorial: 624 14th Street East, Brandon, Manitoba R7A 7E1. **T:** 1 204 726-8888
E: starfm@starfmradio.com
W: http://www.starfmradio.com
Editorial Profile: CKLF-FM is a commercial station owned by Riding Mountain Broadcasting Ltd. The format of the station is hot adult contemporary. CKLF-FM broadcasts to Brandon, Manitoba at 94.7 FM.

CKLG-FM
Owner: Rogers Communications Inc.
Editorial: 2440 Ash St, Vancouver, British Columbia V5Z 4J6. **T:** 1 604 872-2557
W: http://www.jackfm.com
Editorial Profile: CKLG-FM is a commercial radio station owned by Rogers Communications Inc. The format of the station is adult hits. CKLG-FM broadcasts to Vancouver, British Columbia at 96.9 FM.

CKLH-FM
Owner: Astral Media
Editorial: 883 Upper Wentworth St, Suite 401, Hamilton, Ontario L9A 4Y6. **T:** 1 905 574-1150
W: http://www.k-litefm.com
Editorial Profile: CKLH-FM is a commercial station owned by Astral Media. The format of the station is Lite Rock/Lite AC. CKLH-FM broadcasts to the Hamilton, Ontario area at 102.9 FM.

CKLJ-FM
Owner: CAB-K Broadcasting Ltd.
Editorial: 6-4526 49 Avenue, Olds, Alberta T4H 1A4. **T:** 1 403 556-2628 **E:** cklj@telus.net
W: http://www.ckfm.ca
Editorial Profile: CKLJ-FM is a commercial station owned by CAB-K Broadcasting Ltd. The format of the station is classic country. CKLJ-FM broadcasts to the Olds, Alberta area at 96.5 FM.

CKLM-FM
Owner: Vista Radio Ltd.
Editorial: Site Box 21 Atrium Centre, 5012-49 Street, Lloydminster, Alberta T9V 0K2.
T: 1 780 875-5400 **E:** admin@borderrock.com
W: http://www.borderrock.com
Editorial Profile: CKLM-FM is a commercial station owned by Vista Radio Ltd. The format is classic rock. CKLM-FM broadcasts to Lloydminster, Alberta at 106.1 FM.

CKLO-FM
Owner: Blackburn Radio
Editorial: 700 Richmond St unit 101, London, Ontario N6A 5C7. **T:** 1 519 679-8680
W: http://www.981freefm.ca
Editorial Profile: CKLO-FM is a commercial station owned by Blackburn Radio. The format of the station adult album alternative. CKLO-FM broadcasts to the London, Ontario area at 98.1 FM.

CKLP-FM
Owner: Vista Broadcast Group
Editorial: 60 James St, Parry Sound, Ontario P2A 1T5. **T:** 1 705 746-2163
E: moose1033@moosefm.com
W: http://www.moosefm.com/cklp
Editorial Profile: CKLP-FM is a commercial station owned by the Vista Broadcast Group. The format of the station is easy listening. CKLP-FM broadcasts to Parry Sound, Ontario at 103.3 FM.

CKLQ-AM
Owner: Riding Mountain Broadcasting Ltd.
Editorial: 624 14th St East, Brandon, Manitoba R7A 7E1. **T:** 1 204 726-8888
E: qcountry@cklq.mb.ca
W: http://www.cklq.com
Editorial Profile: CKLQ-AM is a commercial station owned by Riding Mountain Broadcasting Ltd. The format of the station is classic country. CKLQ-AM broadcasts to Brandon, Manitoba at 880 AM.

CKLR-FM
Owner: Jim Pattison Broadcast Group(The)
Editorial: 801 B-29th St, Courtenay, British Columbia V9N 7Z5. **T:** 1 250 703-2200
E: info@973theeagle.com
W: http://www.973theeagle.com
Editorial Profile: CKLR-FM a commercial station owned by The Jim Pattison Broadcast Group. The format of the station is classic hits. CKLR-FM broadcasts to Courtenay, British Columbia and the surrounding area at 97.3 FM.

CKLS-AM
Owner: RNC Media
Editorial: 200 ave Laurier ouest, bureau 250, Montreal, Quebec H2T 2N8.
T: 1 514 871-0919
Editorial Profile: CKLS-FM is a commercial station owned by CKLS Inc. The format of the station is rock. CKLS-FM broadcasts to La Sarre, Quebec at 1240 AM.

CKLU-FM
Owner: Laurentian Student & Community Radio Corp.
Editorial: Laurentian University, 935 Ramsey Lake Road, Sudbury, Ontario P3E 2C6.
T: 1 705 673-6538 **E:** traffic@cklu.ca
W: http://www.cklu.ca
Editorial Profile: CKLU-FM is a non-commercial station owned by Laurentian Student & Community Radio Corp. The format of the station is college variety. CKLU-FM broadcasts to the Laurentian University campus and local community of Sudbury, Ontario at 96.7 FM.

CKLW-AM
Owner: Bell Media
Editorial: 1640 Ouellette Ave, Windsor, Ontario N8X 1L1-. **T:** 1 519 258-8888
E: newscentre@am800cklw.com
W: http://www.am800cklw.com
Editorial Profile: CKLW-AM is a commercial station owned by Bell Media. The format of the station is news and talk. CKLW-AM broadcasts to Windsor, Ontario at 800 AM.

CKLX-FM
Owner: RNC Media
Editorial: 200, avenue Laurier ouest, Suite 250, Montreal, Quebec H2T 2N8.
T: 1 514 871-0919
W: http://www.planetejazz.cahttp://montreal.radiox.com/accueil
Editorial Profile: CKLX-FM is a commercial station owned by RNC Media. The format of the station is jazz. CKLX-FM broadcasts to the Montreal area at 91.9 FM.

CKLY-FM
Owner: Bell Media
Editorial: 249 Kent St West, Lindsay, Ontario K9V 2Z3. **T:** 1 705 324-9103
E: bob@919bobfm.com
W: http://www.919bobfm.com
Editorial Profile: CKLY-FM is a commercial station owned by Bell Media. The format of the station is adult hits. CKLY-FM broadcasts to the Lindsay, Ontario area at 91.9 FM.

CKLZ-FM
Owner: Jim Pattison Broadcast Group(The)
Editorial: 3805 Lakeshore Road, Kelowna, British Columbia V1W 3K6. **T:** 1 250 763-1047
E: newsroom@power104.fm
W: http://www.power104.fm
Editorial Profile: CKLZ-FM is a commercial station owned by The Jim Pattison Broadcast Group. The format of the station is rock alternative music. CKLZ-FM broadcasts to Kelowna, British Columbia and surrounding communities at 104.7 FM.

CKMA-FM
Owner: Radio MirAcadie Inc.
Editorial: 300 chemin Beaverbrook, Miramichi, New Brunswick E1V 1A1. **T:** 1 506 624-9370
E: ckma@ckma.ca **W:** http://www.ckma.ca
Editorial Profile: CKMA-FM is a non-commercial station owned by Radio MirAcadie Inc. The format of the station is variety. CKMA-FM broadcasts to the Miramichi, New Brunswick area at 93.7 FM.

CKMB-FM
Owner: Central Ontario Broadcasting
Editorial: 431 Huronia Rd Unit 10, Barrie, Ontario L4N 9B3. **T:** 1 705 725-7304
E: newsroom@rock95.com
W: http://www.1075koolfm.com
Editorial Profile: CKMB-FM is a commercial station owned by Central Ontario Broadcasting. The format of the station is hot adult contemporary music. CKMB-FM broadcasts to the Barrie, Ontario area at 107.5 FM.

CKMF-FM
Owner: Astral Media
Editorial: 1717 Boul René-Lévesque E, Montreal, Quebec H2L 4T3. **T:** 1 514 529-3229
W: http://www.radionrj.ca/montreal
Editorial Profile: CKMF-FM is a commercial station owned by Astral Media. The format of the station is Top 40/CHR. CKMF-FM broadcasts to Montreal at 94.3 FM.

CKMH-FM
Owner: Rogers Media Inc.
Editorial: 7 Strachan Bay, Suite 107, Medicine Hat, Alberta T1B 4Y2. **T:** 1 403 548-7581
W: http://www.rock1053.ca
Editorial Profile: CKMH-FM is a commercial station owned by Rogers Media Inc. The format is rock/album-oriented rock. CKMH-FM broadcasts to the Medicine Hat, Alberta area at 105.3 FM.

CKMM-FM
Owner: Astral Media
Editorial: 177 Lombard Avenue, 3rd Floor, Winnipeg, Manitoba R3B 0W5.
T: 1 204 944-1031
W: http://winnipeg.virginradio.ca
Editorial Profile: CKMM-FM is a commercial station owned by Astral Media. The format of the station is Top 40/CHR. CKMM-FM broadcasts to Winnipeg, Manitoba at 103.1 FM.

CKMN-FM
Owner: Radio Communautaire du Comte Ltd.(La)
Editorial: 323 Montee Industrielle, Rimouski, Quebec G5M 1A7. **T:** 1 418 722-2566
E: ckmn-fm@cgocable.ca
W: http://www.ckmn.fm
Editorial Profile: CKMN-FM is a commercial station owned by La Radio Communautaire du Comte Ltd. The format of the station is oldies. CKMN-FM broadcasts to Rimouski, Quebec at 96.5 FM.

CKMP-FM
Owner: Newfoundland Capital Corporation Limited
Editorial: 1110 Centre Street NE, Suite 100, Calgary, Alberta T2E 2R2. **T:** 1 403 271-6366
W: http://www.ampradiocalgary.com
Editorial Profile: CKMP-FM is a commercial station owned by Newfoundland Capital Corporation Limited. The format of the station is Top 40/CHR. CKMP-FM broadcasts to the Calgary, Alberta area at 90.3 FM.

CKMQ-FM
Owner: Merritt Broadcasting Ltd.
Editorial: 201-2196 Quilchena Ave, Merritt, British Columbia V1K 1B8. **T:** 1 250 378-4288
E: info@q101.ca **W:** http://q101.ca
Editorial Profile: CKMQ-FM is a commercial station owned by Merritt Broadcasting Ltd. The format for the station is adult contemporary. CKMQ-FM broadcasts to the Merritt, British Columbia area at 101.1 FM.

CKMS-FM
Owner: Corporation of Radio Waterloo Inc.
Editorial: 142 Waterloo St, Waterloo, Ontario N2J 1Y2. **T:** 1 519 886-2567
E: cooperative@soundfm.ca
W: http://soundfm.ca

Editorial Profile: CKMS-FM is a non-commercial campus community radio station. The station is located in Waterloo, Ontario and broadcasts at a frequency of 100.3. The station plays independent and alternative music. CKMS-FM is funded by a co-op of programmers and volunteer run.

CKMW-AM
Owner: Golden West Broadcasting Ltd.
Editorial: 277A 1st St., Winkler, Manitoba R6W 4A6. **T:** 1 204 331-9300
E: info@goldenwestradio.com
W: http://www.ckmwradio.com
Editorial Profile: CKMW-AM is a commercial station owned by Golden West Broadcasting. The format of the station is contemporary country music. CKMW-AM broadcasts to Winkler, Manitoba and surrounding communities at 1570 AM.

CKMX-AM
Owner: Bell Media
Editorial: 1110 Centre St NE, Calgary, Alberta T2E 2R2. **T:** 1 403 240-5800
W: http://www.funny1060.com
Editorial Profile: CKMX-AM is a commercial station owned by Bell Media. The format of the station is comedy. CKMX-AM broadcasts to Calgary, Alberta at 1060 AM.

CKNA-FM
Owner: Radio Communautaire CKNA Inc.(La)
Editorial: 29 Chemin d'en Haut, Edifice Municipale, Natashquan, Quebec G0G 2E0.
T: 1 418 726-3284 **E:** ckna@globetrotter.net
W: http://pages.globetrotter.net/ckna
Editorial Profile: CKNA-FM is a non-commercial station operated by La Radio Communautaire CKNA Inc. The format of the station is variety. CKNA-FM broadcasts to Natashquan, Quebec at 104.1 FM.

CKNB-AM
Owner: Maritime Broadcasting System Ltd.
Editorial: 74 Water Street, Campbellton, New Brunswick E3N 1B1. **T:** 1 506 753-4415
E: cknb@mbsradio.com
W: http://www.95cknb.ca
Editorial Profile: CKNB-AM is a commercial station owned by Maritime Broadcasting System Ltd. The format of the station is variety. CKNB-AM broadcasts to Campbellton, New Brunswick and its environs at 950 AM.

CKNG-FM
Owner: Corus Entertainment Inc.
Editorial: 5204 84 St NW, Edmonton, Alberta T6E 5N8. **T:** 1 780 469-6992
W: http://www.925freshfm.com
Editorial Profile: CKNG-FM is a commercial radio station owned by Corus Entertainment. The format of the station is adult contemporary. CKNG-FM broadcasts to the Edmonton, Alberta area at 92.5 FM.

CKNI-FM
Owner: Rogers Communications Inc.
Editorial: 70 Assomption Boulevard, Moncton, New Brunswick E1C 1A1. **T:** 1 506 872-5678
E: news919@rogers.com
W: http://www.news919.com
Editorial Profile: CKNI-FM is a commercial station owned by Rogers Communications Inc. The format of the station is news. CKNI-FM broadcasts to the Moncton, New Brunswick area at 91.9 FM.

CKNL-FM
Owner: Bell Media
Editorial: 10532 Alaska Rd, Fort St. John, British Columbia V1J 1B3. **T:** 1 250 785-6634
W: http://www.1015thebear.com
Editorial Profile: CKNL-FM is a commercial station owned by Bell Media. The format of the station is classic rock. CKNL-FM broadcasts to the Fort St. John, British Columbia area at 101.5 FM.

CKNO-FM
Owner: Rawlco Radio Ltd.
Editorial: 9894 42 Ave NW, Ste 102, Edmonton, Alberta T6E 5V5.
T: 1 780 433-7877
E: controlroom@1023nowradio.com
W: http://1023nowradio.com
Editorial Profile: CKNO-FM is a commercial station owned by Rawlco Radio Ltd. The format of the station is hot adult contemporary. CKNO-FM broadcasts to the Edmonton, Alberta area at 102.3 FM.

CKNR-FM
Owner: Vista Broadcast Group
Editorial: 144 Ontario Ave, Elliot Lake, Ontario P5A 1Y3. **T:** 1 705 848-3608
E: moose941@moosefm.com

W: http://www.moosefm.com/cknr
Editorial Profile: CKNR-FM is a commercial station owned by Vista Broadcast Group. The format of the station is adult contemporary music. CKNR-FM broadcasts to Elliot Lake, Ontario and its environs at 94.1 FM.

CKNW-AM
Owner: Corus Entertainment Inc.
Editorial: 700 West Georgia, Suite 2000, Vancouver, British Columbia V7Y 1K9.
T: 1 604 331-2711 **E:** nwnews@cknw.com
W: http://www.cknw.com
Editorial Profile: CKNW-AM is a commercial station owned by Corus Entertainment Inc. The format of the station is news, talk and sports. CKNW-AM broadcasts to Vancouver, British Columbia and its environs at 980 AM.

CKNX-AM
Owner: Blackburn Radio Inc.
Editorial: 215 Carling Terrace, Wingham, Ontario N0G 2W0. **T:** 1 519 357-1310
E: news@cknxradio.com
W: http://www.am920.ca
Editorial Profile: CKNX-AM is a commercial station owned by Blackburn Radio Inc. The format of the station is contemporary country music. CKNX-AM broadcasts to Wingham, Ontario and surrounding communities at 920 AM.

CKNX-FM
Owner: Blackburn Radio Inc.
Editorial: 215 Carling Terrace, Wingham, Ontario N0G 2W0. **T:** 1 519 357-1310
E: news@cknxradio.com
W: http://www.1017theone.ca
Editorial Profile: CKNX-FM is a commercial station owned by Blackburn Radio Inc. The format of the station is adult contemporary. CKNX-FM broadcasts to Wingham, Ontario and surrounding communities at 101.7 FM.

CKOA-FM
Owner: Coastal Community Cooperative Ltd.
Editorial: 106 Reserve Street, Glace Bay, Nova Scotia B1A 4W5. **T:** 1 902 849-4301
E: news@coastalradio.ca
W: http://www.coastalradio.ca
Editorial Profile: CKOA-FM is a commercial, non-profit station owned by Coastal Community Cooperative Ltd. The format for the station is a variety of local music programming, news and sports. CKOA-FM broadcasts to the Glace Bay, Nova Scotia area at 89.7 FM.

CKOB-FM
Owner: Cogeco
Editorial: 1350 Rue Royale Bureau 1200, Trois-Rivieres, Quebec G9A 4J4.
T: 1 819 374-3556 **E:** nouvelles@1069fm.net
W: http://www.fm1069.ca
Editorial Profile: CKOB-FM is a commercial station owned by Cogeco. The format of the station is classic hits and oldies music. CKOB-FM broadcasts to the Trois-Rivieres, Quebec area at 106.9 FM.

CKOC-AM
Owner: Bell Media
Editorial: 883 Upper Wentworth St, Hamilton, Ontario L9A 4Y6-. **T:** 1 905 574-1150
W: http://www.oldies1150.com
Editorial Profile: CKOC-AM is a commercial station owned by Bell Media. The format of the station is oldies. CKOC-AM broadcasts to the Hamilton, Ontario area at 1150 AM.

CKOD-FM
Owner: Radio Express Inc.
Editorial: 249 rue Victoria, Suite 103, Salaberry-de-Valleyfield, Quebec J6T 1A9.
T: 1 450 373-0103 **E:** fm103@ckod.qc.ca
W: http://www.ckod.qc.ca
Editorial Profile: CKOD-FM is a commercial station owned by Radio Express Inc. The format of the station is adult contemporary. CKOD-FM broadcasts to Salaberry-de-Valleyfield, Quebec at 103.1 FM.

CKOE-FM
Owner: Houssen Broadcasting
Editorial: 3030 Mountain Road, Moncton, New Brunswick E1G 2W8. **T:** 1 506 384-1009
E: info@ckoefm.com
W: http://www.ckoefm.com
Editorial Profile: CKOE-FM is a commercial station owned by Houssen Broadcasting. The format of the station is contemporary Christian. CKOE-FM broadcasts to the Moncton, New Brunswick area at 107.3 FM.

CKOF-FM
Owner: Cogeco

Editorial: 150 Rue D'Edmonton, Gatineau, Quebec J8Y 3S6. **T:** 1 819 561-8801
W: http://www.fm1047.ca
Editorial Profile: CKOF-FM is a commercial station owned by Cogeco. The format of the station is talk. CKOF-FM broadcasts to the Gatineau, Quebec area at 104.7 FM.

CKOI-FM
Owner: Cogeco
Editorial: 800 rue de la Gauchetière Ouest, bureau 1100, Montreal, Quebec H5A 1M1.
T: 1 514 789-2564 **W:** http://www.ckoi.com
Editorial Profile: CKOI-FM is a commercial station owned by Cogeco. The format of the station is Top 40/CHR. CKOI-FM broadcasts to Montreal at 96.9 FM.

CKOK-AM
Owner: Okalakatiget Society
Editorial: 94 Middlepath Rd, Nain, Newfoundland A0P 1L0. **T:** 1 709 922-2187
E: okradio@oksociety.com
W: http://www.oksociety.com
Editorial Profile: CKOK-AM is a non-commercial station owned by The Okalakatiget Society. The format for the station is variety. CKOK-AM broadcasts to Nain, Newfoundland at 610 AM.

CKOL-FM
Owner: Campbellford Area Radio Association
Editorial: 15 Raglan St South, Campbellford, Ontario K0L 1L0. **T:** 1 705 653-1089
E: ckol-radio@bell.net **W:** http://ckol.webs.com
Editorial Profile: CKOL-FM is a non-commercial station owned by Campbellford Area Radio Association. The format of the station is variety. CKOL-FM broadcasts to the Campbellford, Ontario area at 93.7 FM.

CKOM-AM
Owner: Rawlco Radio Ltd.
Editorial: 715 Saskatchewan Cres W, Saskatoon, Saskatchewan S7M 5V7.
T: 1 306 934-2222 **E:** iwitness@rawlco.com
W: http://newstalk650.com
Editorial Profile: CKOM-AM is a commercial radio station owned by Rawlco Radio Ltd. The format of the station is news and talk. CKOM-AM broadcasts to Saskatoon, Saskatchewan at 650 AM.

CKON-FM
Owner: Community of Akwesasne
T: 1 613 575-2100 **E:** ckonfm@yahoo.com
W: http://www.ckonfm.com
Editorial Profile: CKON-FM is a commercial station owned by the Community of Akwesasne. The format of the station is contemporary country. CKON-FM broadcasts to Cornwall, Ontario at 97.3 FM.

CKOR-AM
Owner: Astral Media
Editorial: 33 Carmi Ave, Penticton, British Columbia V2A 3G4. **T:** 1 250 492-2800
E: bcnews@astral.com
W: http://www.penticton.myezrock.com
Editorial Profile: CKOR-AM is a commercial radio station owned by Astral Media. The format of the station is easy listening music. CKOR-AM broadcasts to Penticton, British Columbia at 800 AM.

CKOT-AM
Owner: Tillsonburg Broadcasting Ltd.
Editorial: 77 Broadway St, Tillsonburg, Ontario N4G 3P5. **T:** 1 519 842-4281
E: info@country1073.ca
W: http://www.country1073.ca
Editorial Profile: CKOT-AM is a commercial station owned by Tillsonburg Broadcasting Ltd. The format is contemporary and classic country. CKOT-AM broadcasts to the Tillsonburg, ON area at 1510 AM.

CKOT-FM
Owner: Tillsonburg Broadcasting Ltd.
Editorial: 77 Broadway St, Tillsonburg, Ontario N4G 3P5. **T:** 1 519 842-4281
E: info@easy101.com
W: http://www.easy101.com/
Editorial Profile: CKOT-FM is a commercial station owned by Tillsonburg Broadcasting Ltd. The format is adult standards music. CKOT-FM broadcasts to Tillsonburg, Ontario and surrounding communities at 101.3 FM.

CKOY-FM
Owner: Cogeco
Editorial: 4020 boulevard de Portland, Sherbrooke, Quebec J1L 2V6.
T: 1 819 563-6363 **W:** http://www.fm1077.ca
Editorial Profile: CKOY-FM is a commercial station owned by Cogeco. The format of the

station is Top 40/CHR. CKOY-FM broadcasts to the Sherbrooke, Quebec area at 107.7 FM.

CKOZ-FM
Owner: Newfoundland Broadcasting Co. Ltd.
Editorial: 446 Logy Bay Rd, St. John's, Newfoundland A1C 5S2. **T:** 1 709 726-2922
E: ozfm@ozfm.com **W:** http://www.ozfm.com

CKPC-AM
Owner: Evanov Radio Group
Editorial: 571 West St, Brantford, Ontario N3R 7C5. **T:** 1 519 759-1000
E: newstips@am1380.ca
W: http://www.am1380.ca
Editorial Profile: CKPC-AM is a commercial station owned by Evanov Radio Group. The format is classic country and news. CKPC-AM broadcasts to the Brantford, Ontario area at 1380 AM.

CKPC-FM
Owner: Evanov Radio Group
Editorial: 571 West St, Brantford, Ontario N3R 7C5. **T:** 1 519 759-1000
W: http://www.jewel92.com
Editorial Profile: CKPC-FM is a commercial station owned by Evanov Communications Inc. The format of the station is soft adult contemporary. CKPC-FM broadcasts to the Brantford, Ontario area at 92.1 FM.

CKPE-FM
Owner: Maritime Broadcasting System Ltd.
Editorial: 318 Charlotte St, Sydney, Nova Scotia B1P 6K2. **T:** 1 902 564-5596
E: news@capebretonradio.com
W: http://www.949thecape.com
Editorial Profile: CKPE-FM is a commercial station owned by the Maritime Broadcasting System Ltd. The format of the station is Adult Contemporary. CKPE-FM broadcasts to Sydney, Nova Scotia and surrounding communities at 94.9 FM.

CKPK-FM
Owner: Jim Pattison Broadcast Group(The)
Editorial: 1401 8th Ave W, Vancouver, British Columbia V6H 1C9-. **T:** 1 604 731-6111
E: thepeak@thepeak.fm
W: http://www.thepeak.fm
Editorial Profile: CKPK-FM is a commercial station owned by The Jim Pattison Broadcast Group. The format of the station is adult album alternative. CKPK-FM broadcasts to the Vancouver, British Columbia area at 102.7 FM.

CKPM-FM
Owner: McBride Communications & Media
Editorial: 2-99 Moray St 2, Port Moody, British Columbia V3H 3M2-.
T: 1 604 917-0197 **E:** info@ckpmfm.com
W: http://ckpmfm.com/
Editorial Profile: CKPM-FM is a commercial station owned by McBride Communications & Media. The format for the station is Adult Album Alternative. CKPM-FM broadcasts to the Port Moody area at 98.7 FM.

CKPR-FM
Owner: H.F. Dougall Company Limited
Editorial: 87 North Hill Street, Thunder Bay, Ontario P7A 5V6. **T:** 1 807 346-2600
E: news@dougallmedia.com
W: http://www.ckpr.com
Editorial Profile: CKPR-FM is a commercial station owned by H.F. Dougall Company Limited. The format of the station is adult contemporary. CKPR-FM broadcasts to Thunder Bay, Ontario at 91.5 FM.

CKPT-FM
Owner: Bell Media
Editorial: 59 George St North, Peterborough, Ontario K9J 3G2. **T:** 1 705 742-8844
E: energy997@bellmedia.ca
W: http://www.energy997.ca
Editorial Profile: CKPT-FM is a commercial station owned by Bell Media. The format of the station is hot adult contemporary. CKPT-FM broadcasts to the Peterborough, Ontario area at 99.7 FM.

CKQB-FM
Owner: Corus Entertainment Inc.
Editorial: 1504 Merivale Rd, Ottawa, Ontario K2E 6Z5. **T:** 1 613 225-1069
W: http://www.jumpradio.ca
Editorial Profile: CKQB-FM is a commercial station owned by Corus Entertainment Inc. The station airs a Top 40/CHR format. CKQB-FM broadcasts to Ottawa, Ontario and surrounding communities at 106.9 FM.

CKQC-FM
Owner: Rogers Communications Inc.

Editorial: 318-31935 S Fraser Way, Abbotsford, British Columbia V2T 5N7.
T: 1 604 853-4756
W: http://www.country1071.com
Editorial Profile: CKQC-FM is a commercial station owned by Rogers Communications Inc. The format of the station is contemporary country. CKQC-FM broadcasts to the Abbotsford, British Columbia area at 107.1 FM.

CKQK-FM
Owner: Newfoundland Capital Corporation Limited
Editorial: 90 University Avenue, Suite 320, Charlottetown, Prince Edward Island C1A 4K9.
T: 1 902 569-1003
W: http://www.hot1055fm.com
Editorial Profile: CKQK-FM is a commercial station owned by Newfoundland Capital Corporation Limited. The format of the station is Top 40/CHR. CKQK-FM broadcasts to the Charlottetown, Prince Edward Island area at 105.5 FM.

CKQM-FM
Owner: Bell Media
Editorial: 59 George St N, Peterborough, Ontario K9J 3G2. **T:** 1 705 742-8844
E: country105@bellmedia.ca
W: http://www.country105.fm
Editorial Profile: CKQM-FM is a commercial station owned by Bell Media. The format of the station is classic country. CKQM-FM broadcasts to the Peterborough, Ontario area at 105.1 FM.

CKQQ-FM
Owner: Jim Pattison Broadcast Group(The)
Editorial: 3805 Lakeshore Rd, Kelowna, British Columbia V1W 3K6. **T:** 1 250 762-3331
E: info@q1031.ca **W:** http://www.q1031.ca
Editorial Profile: CKQQ-FM is a commercial station owned by The Jim Pattison Broadcast Group. The format of the station is hot adult contemporary. CKQQ-FM broadcasts to the Kelowna, British Columbia area at 103.1 FM.

CKQR-FM
Owner: Vista Broadcast Group Inc.
Editorial: 1101 A 4th Street, Castlegar, British Columbia V1N 2A8. **T:** 1 250 365-7600
E: news@mountainfm.net
W: http://www.mountainfm.net
Editorial Profile: CKQR-FM is commercial station owned by Vista Broadcast Group Inc. The format of the station is classic rock. CKQR-FM broadcasts to the Castlegar, British Columbia area at 99.3 FM.

CKQV-FM
Owner: Golden West Broadcasting Ltd.
Editorial: 619 Lakeview Dr, Kenora, Ontario P9N 3P6. **T:** 1 807 468-1045
E: news@kenoraonline.com
W: http://www.kenoraonline.com
Editorial Profile: CKQV-FM is a commercial station owned by Golden West Broadcasting Ltd. The format of the station is hot adult contemporary. CKQV-FM broadcasts to the Kenora, Ontario area at 103.3 FM.

CKRA-FM
Owner: Newfoundland Capital Corporation Limited
Editorial: 2394 West Edmonton Mall, 8882-170 Street, Edmonton, Alberta T5T 4M2.
T: 1 780 437-4996
W: http://www.963capitalfm.com
Editorial Profile: CKRA-FM is a commercial station owned by Newfoundland Capital Corporation Limited. The station's format is classic hits. CKRA-FM broadcasts to the Edmonton, AB area at 96.3 FM.

CKRB-FM
Owner: Groupe Radio Simard
Editorial: 11760-3e Avenue, Saint-Georges, Quebec G5Y 5C4. **T:** 1 418 228-1460
W: http://www.coolfm.biz
Editorial Profile: CKRB-FM is a commercial station owned by Groupe Radio Simard. The format of the station is adult contemporary. CKRB-FM broadcasts to the Saint-Georges, Quebec area at 103.5 FM.

CKRC-FM
Owner: Golden West Broadcasting Ltd.
Editorial: 305 Souris Avenue, Weyburn, Saskatchewan S4H 2K2. **T:** 1 306 848-1190
E: magic103@goldenwestradio.com
W: http://www.discoverweyburn.com
Editorial Profile: CKRC-FM is a commercial station owned by Golden West Broadcasting Ltd. The format of the station is classic hits. CKRC-FM broadcasts to the Weyburn, Saskatchewan area at 103.5 FM.

CKRD-FM
Owner: Touch Canada Broadcasting Inc
Editorial: 37464 Hwy 2, Red Deer, Alberta T4E 1B9. **T:** 1 403 356-9052 **E:** 90.5@shinefm.com
W: http://www.ckrdradio.ca
Editorial Profile: CKRD-FM is a commercial station owned by Touch Canada Broadcasting Inc. The format of the station is contemporary Christian. CKRD-FM broadcasts to the Red Deer area at 90.5.

CKRG-FM
Owner: Glendon College
Editorial: 2275 Bayview Ave, Toronto, Ontario M4N 3M6. **T:** 1 416 487-6739
W: http://www.ckrgfm.com
Editorial Profile: CKRG-FM is a non-commercial station owned by Glendon College. The format of the station is variety. CKRG-FM broadcasts to the Toronto area at 89.9 FM.

CKRH-FM
Owner: Cooperative Radio-Halifax-Metro Limitee
Editorial: 5527 rue Cogswell, Halifax, Nova Scotia B3J 1R2. **T:** 1 902 490-2574
E: info@ckrhfm.ca **W:** http://www.ckrhfm.ca
Editorial Profile: CKRH-FM is a non-commercial station owned by Cooperative Radio-Halifax-Metro Limitee. The format of the station is variety. CHRH-FM broadcasts to the Halifax, Nova Scotia area at 98.5 FM.

CKRI-FM
Owner: Harvard Broadcasting
Editorial: F-3617 50th Avenue, Red Deer, Alberta T4N 3Y5. **T:** 1 403 346-8051
W: http://www.theriverfm.ca
Editorial Profile: CKRI-FM is a commercial radio station owned by Harvard Broadcasting. The format for the station is adult contemporary. CKRI-FM broadcasts to the Red Deer, Alberta area at 100.7 FM.

CKRK-FM
Owner: Kahnawake Broadcasting Service
T: 1 450 638-1313
E: programming@k103radio.com
W: http://www.k103radio.com
Editorial Profile: CKRK-FM is a commercial station owned by the Kahnawake Broadcasting Service. The format of the station is variety. CKRK-FM broadcasts to the Kahnawake, Quebec (south suburban Montreal) area at 103.7 FM.

CKRL-FM
Owner: CKRL MF 89.1 Inc.
Editorial: 405 3è Avenue, Quebec, Quebec G1L 2W2. **T:** 1 418 640-2575
E: ckrl@ckrl.qc.ca **W:** http://www.ckrl.qc.ca
Editorial Profile: CKRL-FM is a non-commercial station owned by CKRL MF 89.1 Inc. The format of the station is variety. CKRL-FM broadcasts to the Quebec City area at 89.1 FM.

CKRM-AM
Owner: Harvard Broadcasting
Editorial: 1900 Rose St., Regina, Saskatchewan S4P 0A9. **T:** 1 306 546-6200
W: http://www.620ckrm.com
Editorial Profile: CKRM-AM is a commercial station owned by Harvard Broadcasting. The format of the station is country music, sports, news and talk. CKRM-AM broadcasts to the Regina, Saskatchewan area at 620 AM.

CKRO-FM
Owner: Radio Peninsule Inc.
Editorial: 142 Route 113, Pokemouche, New Brunswick E8P 1K7. **T:** 1 506 336-9706
E: info@ckro.ca **W:** http://www.ckro.ca
Editorial Profile: CKRO-FM is a commercial station owned by Radio Peninsule Inc. The format of the station is variety. CKRO-FM broadcasts to the Pokemouche, New Brunswick area at 97.1 FM.

CKRP-FM
Owner: ACFA Riviere-La-Paix
Editorial: 308 Rue Principale, Falher, Alberta T0H 1M0. **T:** 1 780 837-2346
E: ckrp_fm@yahoo.ca
W: http://www.acfa-ckrp.ca
Editorial Profile: CKRP-FM is a commercial station owned by ACFA Riviere-La-Paix. The format of the station is adult contemporary. CKRP-FM broadcasts to Falher, Alberta at 95.7 FM.

CKRS-FM
Owner: Radio Saguenay Inc.
Editorial: 121 rue Racine Est, Chicoutimi, Quebec G7H IR6. **T:** 1 418 545-2577
E: infos@lefm98.com
W: http://www.lefm98.com
Editorial Profile: CKRS-FM is a commercial station owned by Radio Saguenay Inc. The format of the station is classic hits and oldies. CKRS-FM broadcasts to the Chicoutimi, Quebec area at 98.3 FM.

CKRU-FM
Owner: Corus Entertainment Inc.
Editorial: 159 King St, Peterborough, Ontario K9J 2R8. **T:** 1 705 748-6101
W: http://www.kruzfm.ca
Editorial Profile: CKRU-FM is a commercial station owned by Corus Entertainment Inc. The format of the station is oldies. CKRU-FM broadcasts to Peterborough, Ontario area at 100.5 FM.

CKRV-FM
Owner: NL Broadcasting Ltd.
Editorial: 611 Lansdowne St, Kamloops, British Columbia V2C 1Y6. **T:** 1 250 372-2197
E: nlnews@radionl.com
W: http://www.ckrv.com
Editorial Profile: CKRV-FM is a commercial station owned by NL Broadcasting Ltd. The format of the station is adult contemporary music. CKRV-FM broadcasts to Kamloops, British Columbia and its environs at 97.5 FM.

CKRW-FM
Owner: Klondike Broadcasting Company Ltd.
Editorial: 203-4103 4th Ave, Whitehorse, Yukon Territory Y1A 1H6. **T:** 1 867 668-6100
E: admin@ckrw.com **W:** http://www.ckrw.com
Editorial Profile: CKRW-FM is a commercial station owned by Klondike Broadcasting Ltd. The format of the station is adult contemporary. CKRW-FM broadcasts to the Whitehorse, Yukon Territory area at 96.1 FM.

CKRX-FM
Owner: Astral Media
Editorial: 5152 Liard St. Box 880, Fort Nelson, British Columbia V0C 1R0. **T:** 1 250 774-2525
W: http://www.1023thebear.com
Editorial Profile: CKRX-FM is a commercial station owned by Astral Media. The format for the station is rock music. CKRX-FM broadcasts to the Ft. Nelson, British Columbia area at 102.3 FM.

CKRY-FM
Owner: Corus Entertainment Inc.
Editorial: 170-200 Barclay Parade SW 170, eau claire market 170, Calgary, Alberta T2P 4R5. **T:** 1 403 716-6500
W: http://www.country105.com
Editorial Profile: CKRY-FM is a commercial station owned by Corus Entertainment Inc. The format of the station is contemporary country. CKRY-FM broadcasts to Calgary, Alberta at 105.1 FM.

CKSA-FM
Owner: Newfoundland Capital Corporation Limited
Editorial: 5026-50th St, Lloydminster, Alberta T9V 1P3. **T:** 1 780 875-3321
E: news@cksa.com
W: http://www.959lloydfm.com
Editorial Profile: CKSA-FM is a commercial station owned by Newfoundland Capital Corporation Limited. The format of the station is classic country. CKSA-FM broadcasts to the Lloydminster, Alberta area at 95.9 FM.

CKSB-AM
Owner: Société Radio-Canada
Editorial: 607 rue Langevin, Saint-Boniface, Manitoba R2H 2W2. **T:** 1 204 788-3235
E: manitoba@radio-canada.ca
W: http://radio-canada.ca/regions/manitoba
Editorial Profile: CKSB-AM is a non-commercial station owned by Société Radio-Canada. The format for the station is variety. CKSB-AM broadcasts to the Winnipeg, Manitoba area at 1050 AM.

CKSB-FM
Owner: Société Radio-Canada
Editorial: 607, rue Langevin, Saint-Boniface, Manitoba R2H 2W2. **T:** 1 204 788-3235
E: manitoba@radio-canada.ca
W: http://www.radio-canada.ca/espace_musique
Editorial Profile: CKSB-FM is a non-commercial station owned by Société Radio-Canada. The format for the station is classical, jazz, world, and folk music. CKSB-FM broadcasts to the Winnipeg, MB area at 89.9 FM.

CKSG-FM
Owner: Pineridge Broadcasting Inc.
Editorial: 7805 Telephone Road Hamilton Township, Cobourg, Ontario K9A 4J7.
T: 1 905 372-5401 **W:** http://www.star933.com
Editorial Profile: CKSG-FM is a commercial station owned by Pineridge Broadcasting Inc. The format for the station is hot adult contemporary. CKSG-FM broadcasts to the Cobourg, Ontario area at 93.3 FM.

CKSJ-FM
Owner: Coast Broadcasting Ltd
Editorial: 95 Bonaventure Ave Suite 201, St. John's, Newfoundland A1B 2X5.
T: 1 709 754-6748 **E:** onair@coast1011.com
W: http://www.coast1011.com
Editorial Profile: CKSJ-FM is a commercial station owned by Coast Broadcasting Ltd. The format for the station is adult contemporary. CKSJ-FM broadcasts to the St. John's, Newfoundland area at 101.1 FM.

CKSL-AM
Owner: Astral Media
Editorial: 743 Wellington Road South, London, Ontario N6C 4R5. **T:** 1 519 686-2525
E: mailbag@am1410.ca
W: http://www.funny1410.ca
Editorial Profile: CKSL-AM is a commercial radio station owned by Astral Media. The format of the station is comedy. CKSL-AM broadcasts to London, Ontario at 1410 AM.

CKSQ-AM
Owner: Newfoundland Capital Corporation Limited
Editorial: 4812A 50th Street, Stettler, Alberta T0C 2L0. **T:** 1 403 742-1400
E: q14news@newcap.ca
W: http://www.q14country.com
Editorial Profile: CKSQ-AM is a commercial station owned by Newfoundland Capital Corporation Limited. The format of the station is contemporary country. CKSQ-AM broadcasts to the Stettler, Alberta area at 1400 AM.

CKSR-FM
Owner: Rogers Communications Inc.
Editorial: 46167 Yale Rd, Unit 309, Chilliwack, British Columbia V2P 2N2. **T:** 1 604 795-5711
E: starnews@starfm.rogers.com
W: http://www.starfm.com
Editorial Profile: CKSR-FM is a commercial station owned by Rogers Communications Inc. The format of the station is adult contemporary. CKSR-FM broadcasts to Chilliwack, British Columbia at 98.3 FM.

CKSS-FM
Owner: Newfoundland Broadcasting Co. Ltd.
Editorial: 446 Logy Bay Road, St. John's, Newfoundland A1C 5S2. **T:** 1 709 726-2922
E: ntv@ntv.ca **W:** http://www.ozfm.com

CKST-AM
Owner: Bell Media
Editorial: 500-969 Robson Street, Vancouver, British Columbia V5Y 1C8. **T:** 1 604 280-8326
E: live@team1040.ca
W: http://www.teamradio.ca
Editorial Profile: CKST-AM is a commercial station owned by Bell Media. The format of the station is sports. CKST-AM broadcasts to the Vancouver, British Columbia area at 1040 AM.

CKSW-AM
Owner: Golden West Broadcasting Ltd.
Editorial: 134 Central Avenue North, Swift Current, Saskatchewan S9H 0L1.
T: 1 306 773-4605
E: scnews@goldenwestradio.com
W: http://www.ckswradio.ca
Editorial Profile: CKSW-AM is a commercial station owned by Golden West Broadcasting Ltd. The format of the station is classic country music. CKSW-AM broadcasts to the Swift Current, Saskatchewan area at 570 AM.

CKSY-FM
Owner: Blackburn Radio Inc.
Editorial: 117 Keil Drive South, Chatham, Ontario N7M 3H3. **T:** 1 519 354-2200
E: info@943cksy.com **W:** http://943cksy.com
Editorial Profile: CKSY-FM is a commercial station owned by Blackburn Radio Inc. The format of the station is adult contemporary. CKSY-FM broadcasts to Chatham, Ontario at 94.3 FM.

CKTB-AM
Owner: Astral Media
Editorial: 12 Yates St, St. Catharines, Ontario L2R 5R2. **T:** 1 905 684-1174
E: newsroom@610cktb.com
W: http://www.610cktb.com
Editorial Profile: CKTB-AM is a commercial station owned by Astral Media. The format of the station is news and talk. CKTB-AM

WORLD NEWS MEDIA

broadcasts to the St. Catharines, Ontario area at 610 AM. Twitter handle: twitter.com/610CKTB

CKTF-FM
Owner: Astral Media
Editorial: 15, rue Taschereau, Gatineau, Quebec J8Y 2V6. **T:** 1 819 243-5555
E: receptionoutaouais@astral.com
W: http://www.radionrj.ca/gatineau
Editorial Profile: CKTF-FM is a commercial station owned by Astral Media. The format of the station is Top 40/CHR. CKTF-FM broadcasts to the Gatineau, Quebec area at 104.1 FM.

CKTG-FM
Owner: Acadia Broadcasting
Editorial: 180 Park Ave Suite 200, Thunder Bay, Ontario P7B 6J4. **T:** 1 807 344-2000
E: country@country1053.ca
W: http://country1053.ca
Editorial Profile: CKTG-FM is a commercial station owned by Acadia Broadcasting. The format of the station is contemporary country. CKTG-FM broadcasts to the Thunder Bay, Ontario area at 105.3 FM.

CKTI-FM
Owner: Points Eagle Radio
Editorial: 9111 W Ipperwash Rd, Unit 6 RR #2, Kettle & Stony Point First Nation, Forest, Ontario N0N 1J0. **T:** 1 519 786-3883
E: info@eaglecountry.ca
W: http://www.eaglecountry.ca
Editorial Profile: CKTI-FM is a commercial station owned by Point's Eagle Radio. The format of the station is contemporary country, classic rock and oldies. CKTI-FM broadcasts to the Kettle Point, Ontario area at 107.7 FM.

CKTK-FM
Owner: Astral Media
Editorial: 4625 Lazelle Ave, Terrace, British Columbia V8G 1S4. **T:** 1 250 635-6316
W: http://kitimat.myezrock.com
Editorial Profile: CKTK-FM is a commercial station owned by Astral Media. The format of the station is hot adult contemporary. CKTK-FM broadcasts to Terrace, British Columbia and surrounding communities at 101.9 FM.

CKTO-FM
Owner: Astral Media
Editorial: 187 Industrial Ave, Truro, Nova Scotia B2N 6V3. **T:** 1 902 893-6060
E: newsroom@astral.com
W: http://www.bigdog1009.ca
Editorial Profile: CKTO-FM is a commercial station owned by Astral Media. The format of the station is adult contemporary. CKTO-FM broadcasts to Truro, Nova Scotia at 100.9 FM.

CKTP-FM
Owner: CKTP Radio Inc.
Editorial: 150 Cliffe Street, Box R13, Fredericton, New Brunswick E3A 0A1.
T: 1 506 474-2795 **E:** info@957thewolf.ca
W: http://cktpradio.com
Editorial Profile: CKTP-FM is a commercial station owned by CKTP Radio Inc. The format of the station is rock and blues. CKTP-FM broadcasts to the Fredericton, New Brunswick area at 95.7 FM.

CKTY-FM
Owner: Astral Media
Editorial: 187 Industrial Ave, Truro, Nova Scotia B2N 6V3. **T:** 1 902 893-6060
E: newsroom@astral.com
W: http://www.catcountry995.ca

CKUA-AM
Owner: CKUA Radio Foundation
Editorial: 9804 Jasper Ave NW Fl 4TH, Edmonton, Alberta T5J 0C5.
T: 1 780 428-7595
E: newsfeed949@yahoo.com
W: http://www.ckua.com
Editorial Profile: CKUA-AM is a commercial station owned by CKUA Radio Foundation. The format for the station is variety. CKUA-AM broadcasts to the Edmonton, Alberta area at 580 AM.

CKUA-FM
Owner: CKUA Radio Foundation
Editorial: 9804 Jasper Ave NW, Edmonton, Alberta T5J 0C5. **T:** 1 780 428-7595
W: http://www.ckua.com
Editorial Profile: CKUA-FM is a non-commercial station owned by CKUA Radio Foundation. The station features an eclectic mix of music including jazz, blues, pop, world music, folk, country and classical. CKUA-FM broadcasts to listeners throughout Edmonton, Alberta at 94.9 FM.

CKUE-FM
Owner: Blackburn Radio Inc.
Editorial: 2090 Wyandotte St. E., Windsor, Ontario N8Y 5B2. **T:** 1 519 944-4400
E: info@canadasrock.ca
W: http://canadasrock.ca
Editorial Profile: CKUE-FM is a commercial station owned by Blackburn Radio Inc. The format of the station is classic rock. CKUE-FM broadcasts to the Windsor, Ontario area at 95.1 FM.

CKUJ-FM
Owner: City Municipal Council Office
T: 1 819 964-2921

CKUL-FM
Owner: Newfoundland Capital Corporation Limited
Editorial: 3770 Kempt Rd, Halifax, Nova Scotia B3K 4X8-. **T:** 1 902 453-4004
W: http://radio965.com/
Editorial Profile: CKUL-FM is a commercial station owned by Newfoundland Capital Corporation Limited. The format of the station is AAA. CKUL-FM broadcasts to Halifax, Nova Scotia at 96.5 FM.

CKUM-FM
Owner: Medias Acadiens Universitaires Inc.(Les)
Editorial: Centre Etudiant 2e etage, Universite de Moncton, Moncton, New Brunswick E1A 3E9. **T:** 1 506 858-4485
W: http://ckum935.com
Editorial Profile: CKUM-FM is a commercial station owned by Les Medias Acadiens Universitaires Inc. The format of the station is Top 40/CHR. CKUM-FM broadcasts to the Moncton, New Brunswick area at 93.5 FM.

CKUT-FM
Owner: McGill Radio Inc.
Editorial: 3647 University Street, 2nd Floor, Montreal, Quebec H3A 2B3.
T: 1 514 448-4041 8992 **E:** news@ckut.ca
W: http://www.ckut.ca
Editorial Profile: CKUT-FM is a non-commercial station owned by McGill Radio Inc. The format for the station is college variety. CKUT-FM broadcasts to the Montreal, Quebec area at 90.3 FM.

CKUV-FM
Owner: Golden West Broadcasting Ltd.
Editorial: 42 McRay St., 2nd Floor, Okotoks, Alberta T1S 1B7. **T:** 1 403 995-9611
E: foothillsnews@goldenwestradio.com
W: http://theeagle1009.com
Editorial Profile: CKUV-FM is a commercial station owned by Golden West Broadcasting Ltd. The format of the station is classic hits music. CKUV-FM broadcasts to the High River, Alberta area at 100.9 FM.

CKUW-FM
Owner: Winnipeg Campus Community Radio Society
Editorial: 515 Portage Rm #4CM11, University of Winnipeg, Winnipeg, Manitoba R3B 2E9.
T: 1 204 786-9782
E: ckuwnews@rocketmail.com
W: http://www.ckuw.ca
Editorial Profile: CKUW-FM is a non-commercial station owned by the Winnipeg Campus Community Radio Society. The format is college variety. CKUW-FM broadcasts to the University of Winnipeg and the surrounding community of Winnipeg, Manitoba at 95.9 FM. Twitter Handle: http://twitter.com/ckuw

CKVH-FM
Owner: Newfoundland Capital Corporation Limited
Editorial: 4833 52 Ave, High Prairie, Alberta T0G 1E0. **T:** 1 780 523-5120
E: news@prairiefm.ca
W: http://www.prairiefm.ca
Editorial Profile: CKVH-FM is a commercial station owned by Newfoundland Capital Corporation Limited. The format of the station is classic hits. CKVH-FM broadcasts to the High Prairie, Alberta area at 93.5 FM.

CKVI-FM
Owner: KCVI Educational Radio Station Inc.
Editorial: 235 Frontenac St., Room 119, Kingston, Ontario K7L 3S7. **T:** 1 613 544-7864
E: ckvi@limestone.on.ca
W: http://www.thecave.ca
Editorial Profile: CKVI-FM is a non-commercial station owned by KCVI Educational Radio Station Inc. The format of the station is variety. CKVI-FM broadcasts to the Kingston, Ontario area at 91.9 FM.

CKVL-FM
Owner: La radio communautaire de LaSalle
Editorial: 55 Ave. Dupras, 3rd Floor, Lasalle, Quebec H8P 4A8. **T:** 1 514 360-2585
E: info@100-1fm.com
W: http://www.100-1fm.com
Editorial Profile: CKVL-FM is a non-commercial station owned by La radio communautaire de LaSalle. The format of the station is variety. CKVL-FM broadcasts to the LaSalle, Quebec area at 100.1 FM.

CKVM-FM
Owner: Radio Temiscamingue Inc.
Editorial: 62 rue Sainte-Anne, Ville-Marie, Quebec J9V 2B7. **T:** 1 819 629-2710
E: ckvm@ckvmfm.com
W: http://http.www.ckvm.qc.ca
Editorial Profile: CKVM-FM is a commercial station owned by Radio Temiscamingue Inc. The format of the station is adult contemporary. CKVM-FM broadcasts to the Ville-Marie, Quebec area at 93.1 FM.

CKVN-FM
Owner: Golden West Broadcasting Ltd.
Editorial: 1277 3rd Avenue S, Lethbridge, Alberta T1J 0K3. **T:** 1 403 327-0981
W: http://www.ckvnradio.com
Editorial Profile: CKVN-FM is a commercial station owned by Golden West Broadcasting. The format of the station is contemporary Christian. CKVN-FM broadcasts to the Lethbridge, Alberta area at 98.1 FM.

CKVO-AM
Owner: Newfoundland Capital Corporation Limited
Editorial: 391 Kenmount Road, St. John's, Newfoundland A1B 3P5. **T:** 1 709 726-5590
W: http://www.vocm.com
Editorial Profile: CKVO-AM is a commercial station owned by Newfoundland Capital Corporation Limited. The format of the station is country music. CKVO-AM broadcasts to the St. John's, NL area at 710 AM.

CKVX-FM
Owner: Golden West Broadcasting Ltd.
Editorial: 404 12 Ave E, Kindersley, Saskatchewan S0L 1S0. **T:** 1 306 463-2692
W: http://www.mix1049fm.ca
Editorial Profile: CKVX-FM is a commercial station owned by Golden West Broadcasting Ltd. The format of the station is adult contemporary. CKVX-FM broadcasts to the Kindersley, Saskatchewan area at 104.9 FM.

CKWB-FM
Owner: Newfoundland Capital Corporation Limited
Editorial: 17-10030 106 Street, Westlock, Alberta T7P 2K4. **T:** 1 780 349-4421
W: http://www.979therange.ca
Editorial Profile: CKWB-FM is a commercial station owned by Newfoundland Capital Corporation Limited. The format of the station is contemporary country. CKWB-FM broadcasts in the Westlock, Alberta area 97.9 FM.

CKWE-FM
Owner: Mohawk Nation Radio
Editorial: 3 chemin Kikinamage Mikan, Maniwaki, Quebec J9E 3C9.
T: 1 819 449-5097 **E:** ckwe.radio@gmail.com
Editorial Profile: CKWE-FM is a commercial station owned by Mohawk Nation Radio. The format of the station is variety. CKWE-FM broadcasts to the Maniwaki, Quebec area at 103.9 FM. The station has programming in English, French and Algonquin.

CKWF-FM
Owner: Corus Entertainment Inc.
Editorial: 159 King St, Peterborough, Ontario K9J 2R8. **T:** 1 705 748-6101
E: info@thewolf.ca **W:** http://www.thewolf.ca
Editorial Profile: CKWF-FM is a commercial station owned by Corus Entertainment Inc. The format of the station is rock/album-oriented rock. CKWF-FM broadcasts to the Peterborough, Ontario area at 101.5 FM.

CKWL-AM
Owner: Vista Broadcast Group Inc.
Editorial: 83 South First Ave, Williams Lake, British Columbia V2G 1H4. **T:** 1 250 392-6551
E: cariboonews@reachthecariboo.com
W: http://www.thewolfonline.ca
Editorial Profile: CKWL-AM is a commercial station owned by Vista Broadcast Group Inc. The format of the station is contemporary country and Southern rock. CKWL-AM broadcasts to the Williams Lake, British Columbia area at 570 AM.

CKWM-FM
Owner: Maritime Broadcasting System Ltd.
Editorial: 29 Oakdene Ave, Kentville, Nova Scotia B4N 1H5. **T:** 1 902 678-2111
E: magic949@magic949.ca
W: http://www.magic949.ca
Editorial Profile: CKWM-FM is commercial station owned by Maritime Broadcasting System Ltd. The format of the station is adult contemporary and classic hits. CKWM-FM broadcasts to Kentville, Nova Scotia and surrounding communities at 94.9 FM.

CKWR-FM
Owner: Wired World Inc.
Editorial: 375 University Avenue East, Waterloo, Ontario N2K 3M7.
T: 1 519 886-9870 **E:** general@ckwr.com
W: http://www.ckwr.com
Editorial Profile: CKWR-FM is a commercial station owned by Wired World Inc. The format of the station is adult contemporary and multicultural programming. CKWR-FM broadcasts to Waterloo, Ontario at 98.5 FM.

CKWS-FM
Owner: Corus Entertainment Inc.
Editorial: 170 Queen Street, Kingston, Ontario K7K 1B2. **T:** 1 613 544-2340
E: newswatch@corusent.com
W: http://www.ckwsfm.com
Editorial Profile: CKWS-FM is a commercial station owned by Corus Entertainment Inc. The format of the station is classic hits. CKWS-FM broadcasts to the Kingston, Ontario area at 104.3 FM.

CKWV-FM
Owner: Jim Pattison Broadcast Group(The)
Editorial: 4550 Wellington Road, Nanaimo, British Columbia V9T 2H3. **T:** 1 250 758-1131
E: info@1023thewave.com
W: http://www.1023thewave.com
Editorial Profile: CKWV-FM is a commercial station owned by The Jim Pattison Broadcast Group. The format of the station is adult contemporary. CKWV-FM broadcasts to the Nanaimo, British Columbia area at 102.3 FM.

CKWW-AM
Owner: Bell Media
Editorial: 1640 Ouellette Ave, Windsor, Ontario N8X 1L1. **T:** 1 519 258-8888
E: info@am580radio.com
W: http://www.am580radio.com
Editorial Profile: CKWW-AM is a commercial station owned by Bell Media. The format of the station is oldies. CKWW-AM broadcasts to Windsor, Ontario and the Detroit area at 580 AM.

CKWX-AM
Owner: Rogers Communications Inc.
Editorial: 2440 Ash St, Vancouver, British Columbia V5Z 4J6. **T:** 1 604 873-2599
E: news1130@news1130.rogers.com
W: http://www.news1130.com
Editorial Profile: CKWX-AM is a commercial radio station owned by Rogers Communications Inc. The format of the station is news, talk and sports programming. CKWX-AM broadcasts to the Vancouver, BC area at 1130 AM.

CKWY-FM
Owner: Newfoundland Capital Corporation Limited
Editorial: 1037 2nd Ave, 2nd Floor, Wainwright, Alberta T9W 1K7.
T: 1 780 842-4311
W: http://www.waynefm.com
Editorial Profile: CKWY-FM is a commercial station owned by Newfoundland Capital Corporation Limited. The format of the station is adult contemporary. CKWY-FM broadcasts to Wainwright, Alberta and its environs at 93.7 FM.

CKXA-FM
Owner: Astral Media
Editorial: 2940 Victoria Ave, Brandon, Manitoba R7B 3Y3. **T:** 1 204 728-1150
E: psabrandon@astral.com
W: http://www.1011thefarm.com
Editorial Profile: CKXA-FM is a commercial station owned by Astral Media. The format of the station is classic country. CKXA-FM broadcasts in the Brandon, Manitoba area at 101.1 FM.

CKXC-FM
Owner: Rogers Communications Inc.
Editorial: 863 Princess St Suite 301, Kingston, Ontario K7L 5N4. **T:** 1 613 549-1057
W: http://www.country935.ca
Editorial Profile: CKXC-FM is a commercial station owned by Rogers Communications Inc.

The format of the station is contemporary country. CKXC-FM broadcasts to the Kingston, Ontario at 93.5 FM.

CKXD-FM

Owner: Newfoundland Capital Corporation Limited
Editorial: 105 Roe Ave, Gander, Newfoundland A1V 1X2. **T:** 1 709 651-3650
E: ckxdnews@vocm.com
W: http://www.987krock.com
Editorial Profile: CKXD-FM is a commercial station owned by Newfoundland Capital Corporation Limited. The format of the station is classic rock. CKXD-FM broadcasts to the Gander, Newfoundland area at 98.7 FM.

CKX-FM

Owner: Bell Media
Editorial: 2940 Victoria Ave, Brandon, Manitoba R7B 3Y3. **T:** 1 204 728-1150
E: brandonnews@astral.com
W: http://www.kx96online.com
Editorial Profile: CKX-FM is a commercial station owned by Astral Media. The format of the station is album-oriented rock. CKX-FM broadcasts to Brandon, Manitoba at 96.1 FM.

CKXG-FM

Owner: Steele Communications
Editorial: 35-A Grenfell Heights, Grand Falls-Windsor, Newfoundland A2A 2K2.
T: 1 709 489-2192
E: grandfallswindsor@vocm.com
Editorial Profile: CKXG-FM is a commercial station owned by Steele Communications. The format is adult contemporary. The station airs at 102.3 FM in the Grand Falls-Windsor, Newfoundland area.

CKXL-FM

Owner: La Radio Communautaire du Manitoba Inc.
Editorial: 340 boul Provencher, Saint-Boniface, Manitoba R2H 0G7.
T: 1 204 233-4243 **E:** info@envol91.mb.ca
W: http://www.envol91.mb.ca
Editorial Profile: CKXL-FM is a non-commercial station owned by La Radio Communautaire du Manitoba Inc. The format of the station is variety. CKXL-FM broadcasts to the Saint-Boniface, Manitoba area at 91.1 FM.

CKXM-FM

Owner: My Broadcasting Corporation
Editorial: 145 Thames Rd W, Unit 6, Exeter, Ontario N0M 1S3. **T:** 1 519 235-3000
W: http://www.myfmradio.ca
Editorial Profile: CKXM-FM is a commercial station owned by My Broadcasting Corporation. The format of the station is adult contemporary. CKXM-FM's tagline is "My FM." CKXM-FM broadcasts to the Exeter, Ontario area at 90.5 FM.

CKXO-FM

Owner: RNC Media
Editorial: 568 boul St Joseph, Roberval, Quebec G8H 2K6. **T:** 1 418 275-1831
W: http://chibougamau.planeteradio.ca

CKXR-FM

Owner: Astral Media
Editorial: 360 Ross St, Salmon Arm, British Columbia V1E 4N2. **T:** 1 250 832-2161
E: jcrouse@astral.com
W: http://www.salmonarm.myezrock.com
Editorial Profile: CKXR-FM is a commercial station owned by Astral Media. The format of the station is adult contemporary music. CKXR-FM broadcasts to the Salmon Arm, British Columbia area at 91.5 FM.

CKXS-FM

Owner: Five Amigos Broadcasting Inc.
Editorial: 520 James St, Wallaceburg, Ontario N8A 2N9. **T:** 1 519 627-0007
E: news@ckxsfm.com
W: http://www.ckxsfm.com
Editorial Profile: CKXS-FM is a commercial station owned by Five Amigos Broadcasting Inc. The format of the station is adult contemporary. CKXS-FM broadcasts to the Wallaceburg, ON area at 99.1 FM.

CKXU-FM

Owner: CKXU Radio Society
Editorial: SU-164 University Drive West, University of Lethbridge, Lethbridge, Alberta T1K 3M4. **T:** 1 403 329-2335
E: manager@ckxu.com
W: http://www.ckxu.com
Editorial Profile: CKXU-FM is a non-commercial college station owned by CKXU Radio Society. The format of the station is

college variety. CKXU-FM broadcast to the Lethbridge, Alberta area at 88.3 FM.

CKXX-FM

Owner: Newfoundland Capital Corporation Limited
Editorial: 345 O'Connell Dr, Corner Brook, Newfoundland A2H 7E5. **T:** 1 709 634-4570
E: ckxxnews@hotmail.com
W: http://www.k-rock1039.com
Editorial Profile: CKXX-FM is a commercial station owned by Newfoundland Capital Corporation Limited. The format of the station is classic rock. CKXX-FM broadcasts to the Corner Brook, Newfoundland area at 103.9 FM.

CKYC-FM

Owner: Bayshore Broadcasting Corp.
Editorial: 270 Ninth Street East, Owen Sound, Ontario N4K 5P5. **T:** 1 519 376-2030
E: country93@bayshorebroadcasting.ca
W: http://www.country93.ca
Editorial Profile: CKYC-FM is a commercial station owned by Bayshore Broadcasting Corp. The format for the station is contemporary country. CKYC-FM broadcasts to the Owen Sound, Ontario area at 93.7 FM.

CKYE-FM

Owner: South Asian Broadcasting
Editorial: #201 8383A 128th St, Surrey, British Columbia V3W 4G1. **T:** 1 604 598-9311
E: info@redfm.ca **W:** http://www.redfm.ca
Editorial Profile: CKYE-FM is a commercial station owned by South Asian Broadcasting. The format of the station is variety, featuring ethnic and multicultural programming. CKYE-FM broadcasts to the Vancouver, British Columbia area at 93.1 FM.

CKY-FM

Owner: Rogers Communications Inc.
Editorial: 166 Osborne Street, Unit 4, Winnipeg, Manitoba R3L 1Y8.
T: 1 204 788-3400
W: http://www.102clearfm.com
Editorial Profile: CKY-FM is a commercial station owned by Rogers Communications Inc. The format of the station is adult contemporary music. CKY-FM broadcasts in the Winnipeg, Manitoba area at 102.3 FM.

CKYK-FM

Owner: RNC Media
Editorial: 345 rue Saguenéens, Local 70, Chicoutimi, Quebec G7H 6K9.
T: 1 418 543-8912
W: http://www.kykradiox.com
Editorial Profile: CKYK-FM is a commercial station owned by RNC Media. The format of the station is rock. CKYK-FM broadcasts to Alma, Quebec at 95.7 FM.

CKYL-AM

Owner: Peace River Broadcasting Corp.
T: 1 780 624-2535 **E:** news@ylcountry.com
W: http://www.ylcountry.com
Editorial Profile: CKYL-AM is a commercial station owned by Peace River Broadcasting Corp. The format of the station is classic country music. CKYL-AM broadcasts throughout Peace River, Alberta at 610 AM.

CKYM-FM

Owner: My Broadcasting Corporation
Editorial: 20 Market Square, Napanee, Ontario K7R 1J3. **T:** 1 613 354-4554
E: news887@myfmradio.ca
W: http://www.myfmradio.ca
Editorial Profile: CKYM-FM is a commercial station owned by My Broadcasting Corporation. The format of the station is adult contemporary. CKYM-FM broadcasts to the Napanee, Ontario area at 88.7 FM.

CKYQ-FM

Owner: 176100 Canada Inc.
Editorial: 1646 avenue St-Laurent, Plessisville, Quebec G6L 2Y6. **T:** 1 819 362-3737
E: studio@kyqfm.com **W:** http://kyqfm.com/
Editorial Profile: CKYQ-FM is a commercial station owned by 176100 Canada Inc. The format of the station is hot adult contemporary. CKYQ-FM broadcasts to Plessisville, Quebec at 95.7 FM.

CKYX-FM

Owner: Rogers Communications Inc.
Editorial: 9912 Franklin Ave, Fort McMurray, Alberta T9H 2K5-. **T:** 1 780 743-2246
W: http://www.rock979.ca
Editorial Profile: CKYX-FM is a commercial station owned by Rogers Communications Inc. The format of the station is classic rock and rock/album oriented. CKYX-FM broadcasts to the Fort McMurray, Alberta area at 97.9 FM.

CKZZ-FM

Owner: Newcap Radio
Editorial: 20-11151 Horseshoe Way 20, Richmond, British Columbia V7A 4S5.
T: 1 604 241-2100 **W:** http://www.z953.ca
Editorial Profile: CKZZ-FM is a commercial station owned by Newcap Radio. The format of the station is hot adult contemporary. CKZZ-FM broadcasts to the Richmond, British Columbia area at 95.3 FM.

CPWA-FM

Owner: CPWA, Inc.
Editorial: 62 Nassau Street, Toronto, Ontario M5T 1M2. **T:** 1 416 596-1566
E: asasdo1@bellnet.ca
W: http://www.asasdoatlantico.com
Editorial Profile: CPWA-FM is a commercial station owned by CPWA, Inc. The format of the station is news, talk, sports and ethnic programming. CPWA-FM broadcasts to the Toronto area at 90.7 FM.

CRFM-FM

Owner: Canadore College
Editorial: 100 College Dr, Canadore College, North Bay, Ontario P1B 8K9.
T: 1 705 474-7601
W: http://www.thepanther.ca
Editorial Profile: CRFM-FM is a non-commercial college station owned by Canadore College. The format of the station is Top 40/CHR. CRFM-FM broadcasts to the North Bay, Ontario area at a frequency of 89.9 FM.

CRNC-FM

Owner: Niagara College
Editorial: 300 Woodlawn Road, Niagara College, Welland, Ontario L3C 7L3.
T: 1 905 735-2211
W: http://www.broadcasting.niagaracollege.ca
Editorial Profile: CRNC-FM is a non-commercial station owned by Niagara College. The format of the station is variety. CRNC-FM broadcasts to the Welland, Ontario area at 90.1 FM.

CSCR-FM

Owner: SCCR Inc.
Editorial: 1265 Military Trail, Rm#CL213, University of Toronto, Toronto, Ontario M1C 1A4. **T:** 1 416 287-7051
E: info@fusionradio.ca
W: http://www.fusionradio.ca
Editorial Profile: CSCR-FM is a non-commercial station owned by SCCR Inc. The format is variety. CSCR-FM broadcasts to the Scarborough, Ontario area at 90.3 FM.

CWRN-FM

Owner: Wawatay Native Communications Society
Editorial: 16-5th Ave, Sioux Lookout, Ontario P0V 2T0. **T:** 1 807 737-2951
E: webmaster@wawatay.on.ca
W: http://www.wawatay.on.ca
Editorial Profile: CWRN-FM is a non-commercial station owned by Wawatay Native Communications Society. The format for the station is news. CWRN-FM broadcasts to the Sioux Lookout, Ontario area at 89.9 FM.

VOAR-AM

Owner: Seventh-Day Adventist Church
Editorial: 1041 Topsail, Mt. Pearl, Newfoundland A1N 5E9. **T:** 1 709 745-8627
E: voar@voar.org **W:** http://www.voar.org
Editorial Profile: VOAR-AM is a non-commercial station owned by the Seventh-Day Adventist Church. The format is contemporary Christian. VOAR-AM broadcasts to the Mt. Pearl, Newfoundland area at 1210 AM.

VOCM-AM

Owner: Newfoundland Capital Corporation Limited
Editorial: 391 Kenmount Road, St. John's, Newfoundland A1B 3P5. **T:** 1 709 726-5590
E: feedback@vocm.com
W: http://www.vocm.com
Editorial Profile: VOCM-AM is a commercial station owned by Newfoundland Capital Corporation Limited. The format of the station is news and talk. VOCM-AM broadcasts to Saint John's, Newfoundland at 590 AM.

VOCM-FM

Owner: Newfoundland Capital Corporation Limited
Editorial: 391 Kenmount Road, St. John's, Newfoundland A1B 3M7. **T:** 1 709 726-5590
E: email@k-rock975.com
W: http://www.k-rock975.com
Editorial Profile: VOCM-FM is a commercial station owned by Newfoundland Capital Corporation Limited. The format of the station

is classic rock. VOCM-FM broadcasts to the Saint John's, Newfoundland area at 97.5 FM.

VOWR-AM

Owner: Wesley United Church Radio Broadcasting
Editorial: 101 Patrick St., St. John's, Newfoundland A1E 5T9. **T:** 1 709 579-9233
E: vowr@vowr.org **W:** http://www.vowr.org
Editorial Profile: VOWR-AM is a non-commercial station owned by Wesley United Church Radio Broadcasting. The format is variety and can be heard at 800 AM in the St. John's, Newfoundland area.

WLYK-FM

Owner: Roger Radio
Editorial: 863 Princess Street, Ste 301, Kingston, Ontario K7L 5N4. **T:** 1 613 549-1057
W: http://www.1027thelake.com
Editorial Profile: WLYK-FM is a commercial station owned by Roger Radio. The format of the station is adult contemporary. WLYK-FM broadcasts to the Watertown, NY area at 102.7 FM.

WTOR-AM

Owner: Birach Broadcasting Corp.
Editorial: 600 The East Mall, Suite 400, Toronto, Ontario M9B4B1. **T:** 1 248 557-3500
W: http://www.birach.com/wtor.html
Editorial Profile: WTOR-AM is a commercial station owned by Birach Broadcasting Corp. The format of the station is variety, featuring ethnic brokered programming. WTOR-AM broadcasts to the Toronto, ON area at 770 AM.

RADIO NETWORKS

CBC Radio One

Owner: Canadian Broadcasting Corp.
Editorial: 205 Wellington St W, Toronto, Ontario M5V 3G7-. **T:** 1 416 205-3311
W: http://www.cbc.ca/radio
Editorial Profile: CBC Radio One airs the CBC network's news and current affairs programming. CBC serves as Canada's largest cultural institution, aiming to touch the lives of the country's citizens on a daily basis. Owned by all Canadians, CBC has a heritage as the nation's supplier of Canadian cultural content. CBC Radio One is a member of the Canadian Press Gallery.

CBC Radio One

Editorial: 181 Queen St, Ottawa, Ontario K1P 1K9. **T:** 1 613 288-6000
E: cbcnewsottawa@cbc.ca
W: http://www.cbc.ca/ottawa

CBC Radio One

Editorial: 123 Edmonton City Centre, 10062-102 Avenue, Edmonton, Alberta T5J 2Y8.
T: 1 780 468-7500 **E:** newsedmonton@cbc.ca
W: http://www.cbc.ca/edmonton
Editorial Profile: The CBC Radio One bureau in Edmonton, Alberta.

CBC Radio One

Editorial: 700 Hamilton St, Vancouver, British Columbia V6B 2R5. **T:** 1 604 662-6000
E: cbcnewsvancouver@cbc.ca
W: http://www.cbc.ca/bc
Editorial Profile: CBC Radio One Vancouver, British Columbia bureau.

CBC Radio One

Editorial: 5600 Sackville St, Halifax, Nova Scotia B3J 1L2. **T:** 1 902 420-8311
W: http://www.cbc.ca/ns
Editorial Profile: Halifax, Nova Scotia bureau of CBC Radio One.

CBC Radio One

Editorial: 1400 Rene-Levesque Blvd Est, Montreal, Quebec H2L 2M2.
T: 1 514 597-6000
W: http://www.cbc.ca/montreal
Editorial Profile: CBC Radio One Montreal, Quebec bureau.

CBC Radio One

Editorial: 2440 Broad St, Regina, Saskatchewan S4P 4A1. **T:** 1 306 347-9540
W: http://www.cbc.ca/sask
Editorial Profile: CBC Radio One Regina, Saskatchewan bureau.

CBC Radio One

Editorial: 747 3rd Ave, Ste 8C, New York, New York 10017. **T:** 1 212 546-0506

CBC Radio One

Editorial: 529 14th St NW, Ste 500, Washington, District Of Columbia 20045.

T: 1 202 383-2900

CBC Radio Two
Owner: Canadian Broadcasting Corp.
Editorial: 700 Hamilton St, Vancouver, British Columbia V6B 2R5. **T:** 1 416 205-3311
E: RadioMusic@cbc.ca
W: http://www.cbc.ca/radio2
Editorial Profile: CBC Radio Two airs the CBC network's music and fine arts programming. CBC serves as Canada's largest cultural institution, aiming to touch the lives of the country's citizens on a daily basis. Owned by all Canadians, CBC has a heritage as the nation's supplier of Canadian cultural content.

CHUM Radio Network
Owner: Bell Media
Editorial: 250 Richmond St W, Toronto, Ontario M5V 1W4. **T:** 1 416 384-4163
E: bellmediacommunications@bellmedia.ca
W: http://www.bellmedia.ca
Editorial Profile: CHUM Radio Network is a music and entertainment syndication service owned by Bell Media. It produces and customizes radio features and infomercials upon request.

Corus Radio Network
Editorial: Corus Quay, 25 Dockside Drive, Toronto, Ontario M5A 0B5. **T:** 1 403 716-6500
W: http://www.corusent.com
Editorial Profile: Network featuring programming and specials revolving around the world of rock music and its personalities. The network specializes in premier properties for radio, nationally sponsored, major market coverage, created, produced and distributed coast to coast.

Fairchild Radio Network
Owner: Fairchild Radio Ltd.
Editorial: 135 E Beaver Creek Road, Unit 8, Richmond Hill, Ontario L4B 1E2.
T: 1 905 763-3350
W: http://www.fairchildradio.com
Editorial Profile: Fairchild Media Group's Chinese language radio operations across the country offer their audiences a varied fare of news and talk radio to serial mini dramas and pop music. Full service radio network programming in more than 18 languages. Offers over 90 hours of Chinese programs every week, featuring a wide array of formats ranging from news, current affairs, everyday information talk show, entertainment, music, and more.

Radio Canada International
Owner: Canadian Broadcasting Corp.
Editorial: 1400 Rene-Levesque Blvd East, Level B, Montreal, Quebec H2L 2M2.
T: 1 514 597-7500 **W:** http://www.rcinet.ca
Editorial Profile: Radio-Canada International is a radio network that broadcasts a full range of daily and weekly programs in English, French, Spanish, Russian, Ukrainian, Portuguese, Mandarin and Arabic. It also broadcasts a selection of CBC/Radio-Canada programs.

Radio-Canada Réseau Espace Musique
Owner: Société Radio-Canada
Editorial: 1400 Boul Rene-Levesque E, Montreal, Quebec H2L 2M2-.
T: 1 514 597-6000 **E:** liaison@radio-canada.ca
W: http://www.radio-canada.ca/espace_musique
Editorial Profile: Radio-Canada Réseau Espace Musique is the French music network of Radio-Canada. It is a publicly-owned corporation established by the Canadian Parliament's Broadcasting Act. Radio-Canada Réseau Espace Musique features a wide variety of musical programming, nearly all Canadian and free of commercial advertising. Radio-Canada Réseau Espace Musique is a member of the Canadian Press Gallery.

Radio-Canada Réseau La Première Chaîne
Owner: Société Radio-Canada
Editorial: 1400 Boul Rene-Levesque E, Montreal, Quebec H2L 2M2-.
T: 1 514 597-6000
E: nouvelles@radio-canada.ca
W: http://www.radio-canada.ca/radio
Editorial Profile: Radio-Canada Réseau La Première Chaîne is the only French language network offering a predominantly Canadian primetime schedule. The French radio network was established as a result of the Canadian Parliament's Broadcasting Act. The network's programming tells stories reflecting the reality and diversity of Canada and provides information about relevant and interesting news and issues.

Radio-Canada Réseau La Première Chaîne
Editorial: 250 avenue Universite, Moncton, New Brunswick E1C 8N8. **T:** 1 506 853-6666
W: http://www.radio-canada.ca/atlantique

Radio-Canada Réseau La Première Chaîne
Editorial: 888 Boul. St-Jean, Quebec, Quebec G1R 5H6. **T:** 1 418 654-1341
W: http://www.radio-canada.ca/regions/quebec
Editorial Profile: Quebec bureau of Radio-Canada's La Première Chaîne.

Radio-Canada Réseau La Première Chaîne
Editorial: 700 Hamilton, Vancouver, British Columbia V6B 4A2. **T:** 1 604 662-6000
E: tjcb@radio-canada.ca
W: http://www.radio-canada.ca/regions/colombie-Britannique
Editorial Profile: Radio-Canada Réseau La Première Chaîne bureau for British Columbia and Yukon.

Radio-Canada Réseau La Première Chaîne
Editorial: 10062-102 Avenue, 125 Edmonton City Centre, Edmonton, Alberta T5J 2Y8.
T: 1 780 468-7500
W: http://www.radio-canada.ca/regions/alberta

Radio-Canada Réseau La Première Chaîne
Editorial: 607, rue Langevin, Saint-Boniface, Manitoba R2H 2W2. **T:** 1 204 788-3235
E: manitoba@radio-canada.ca
W: http://www.radio-canada.ca/regions/manitoba

Radio-Canada Réseau La Première Chaîne
Editorial: 2440 Broad St, Regina, Saskatchewan S4P 4A1. **T:** 1 306 347-9540
W: http://www.radio-canada.ca/regions/saskatchewan

Radio-Canada Réseau La Première Chaîne
Editorial: 430 avenue Universite, Charlottetown, Prince Edward Island C1A 4N6.
T: 1 902 629-6400
W: http://www.radio-canada.ca/regions/atlantique/Radio

Radio-Canada Réseau La Première Chaîne
Editorial: 155 rue Saint-Sacrement, Matane, Quebec G4W 1Y9. **T:** 1 418 562-0290
W: http://www.radio-canada.ca/regions/gaspesie-lesiles/index.shtml

Radio-Canada Réseau La Première Chaîne
Editorial: 181, rue Queen, Ottawa, Ontario K1P 1K9. **T:** 1 613 288-6000
E: nouvelles.ottawagatineau@radio-canada.ca
W: http://www.radio-canada.ca/regions/ottawa/index.shtml
Editorial Profile: Ottawa bureau for Radio-Canada La Première Chaîne.

Radio-Canada Réseau La Première Chaîne
Editorial: 1335, rue King Ouest, Sherbrooke, Quebec J1J 2B8. **T:** 1 819 620-0000
W: http://www.radio-canada.ca/regions/estrie/index.shtml

Radio-Canada Réseau La Première Chaîne
Editorial: 273 rue Saint-Jean-Baptiste Ouest, Rimouski, Quebec G5L 4J8.
T: 1 418 723-2217
E: nouvelles.rimouski@radio-canada.ca
W: http://www.radio-canada.ca/regions/bas-st-laurent/index.shtml

Radio-Canada Réseau La Première Chaîne
Editorial: 70, avenue Principale, Rouyn-Noranda, Quebec J9X 4P2. **T:** 1 819 762-8155
E: abitibi@radio-canada.ca
W: http://www.radio-canada.ca/regions/abitibi/index.shtml

Radio-Canada Réseau La Première Chaîne
Editorial: 500 rue des Saguenéens, Chicoutimi, Quebec G7H 6N4.
T: 1 418 696-6600
W: http://www.radio-canada.ca/regions/saguenay-lac/index.shtml

Radio-Canada Réseau La Première Chaîne
Editorial: 350 rue Smith, Bureau 30, Sept-Iles, Quebec G4R 3X2. **T:** 1 418 968-0720
E: cbsi@radio-canada.ca
W: http://www.radio-canada.ca/regions/cote-nord/index.shtml

Radio-Canada Réseau La Première Chaîne
Editorial: 15 rue MacKenzie, Sudbury, Ontario P3C 4Y1. **T:** 1 705 688-3200
W: http://www.radio-canada.ca/regions/ontario/index.shtml

Radio-Canada Réseau La Première Chaîne
Editorial: 205 rue Wellington Ouest, Toronto, Ontario M5V 3G7. **T:** 1 416 205-3700
E: tjontario@radio-canada.ca
W: http://www.radio-canada.ca/regions/ontario/index.shtml
Editorial Profile: Toronto bureau for Radio-Canada La Première Chaîne.

Radio-Canada Réseau La Première Chaîne
Editorial: 225 rue des Forges, Suite 101, Trois-Rivieres, Quebec G9A 6A7.
T: 1 819 694-0114
W: http://www.radio-canada.ca/regions/mauricie/index.shtml

Radio-Canada Réseau La Première Chaîne
Editorial: 825 Dr Riverside O, Windsor, Ontario N9A 5K9. **T:** 1 519 255-3508
W: http://www.radio-canada.ca/regions/ontario/index.shtml
Editorial Profile: Windsor, Ontario bureau for Radio-Canada Réseau La Première Chaîne.

Le Réseau francophone d'Amérique (RFA)
Owner: Alliance des radios commuautaires du Canada(L')
Editorial: 325, rue Dalhousie, 2è étage, Ottawa, Ontario K1N 7G2. **T:** 1 613 562-0000
W: http://www.radiorfa.com
Editorial Profile: Le Réseau francophone d'Amérique (RFA) is an alliance of member stations that share programming. The RFA itself produces very little programming or news, instead, member stations share shows and content. Inquiries should be directed to the appropriate show producer or hosting station. Member stations include: CJRM-FM in Newfoundland and Labrador; CIFA-FM, CKJM-FM and CKRH-FM in Nova Scotia; CFAI-FM, CFBO-FM, CFJU-FM, CHQC-FM, CIMS-FM, CJPN-FM, CJSE-FM, CKMA-FM, CKRO-FM and CKUM-FM in New Brunswick; CFRH-FM, CHOD-FM, CHOQ-FM, CINN-FM and CKGN-FM in Ontario; CKXL-FM in Manitoba; CFRG-FM in Sakatchewan; CFRT-FM in Nunavut; CKRP-FM in Alberta; CIVR-FM in the Northwest Territories; and CILS-FM in British Columbia.

SiriusXM Canada
Owner: Sirius XM Canada Holdings Inc.
Editorial: 135 Liberty St, 4th fl, Toronto, Ontario M6K 1A7. **T:** 1 416 408-6000
W: http://siriusxm.ca
Editorial Profile: SiriusXM Canada is a Sirius XM Canada is a Canadian radio broadcasting company, which operates as a Canadian affiliate of Sirius XM Radio. SiriusXM Canada is a digital audio platform that offers commercial-free music, sports, news, talk, entertainment and weather.

TELEVISION STATIONS

CBAFT-TV
Owner: Société Radio-Canada
Editorial: 250 Avenue Universite, Moncton, New Brunswick E1C 5K3. **T:** 1 506 853-6666
E: tjacadie@radio-canada.ca
W: http://www.radio-canada.ca/Acadie
Editorial Profile: CBAFT-TV is the Radio-Canada affiliate for the Moncton, New Brunswick market. The station is owned by Societe Radio-Canada. CBAFT-TV broadcasts locally on channel 11.

CBAT-TV
Owner: Canadian Broadcasting Corp.
Editorial: 1160 Regent St, Fredericton, New Brunswick E3B 5G4. **T:** 1 506 451-4000
W: http://www.cbc.ca/nb
Editorial Profile: CBAT-TV is a commercial television station owned by the Canadian Broadcasting Corp. CBAT-TV airs locally on channels 3 and 14.

CBCT-TV
Owner: Canadian Broadcasting Corp.
Editorial: 430 University Ave, Charlottetown, Prince Edward Island C1A 8B9.
T: 1 902 629-6400 **W:** http://www.cbc.ca/pei
Editorial Profile: CBCT-TV is the CBC affiliate for the Charlottetown, Prince Edward Island market. The station is owned by Canadian Broadcasting Corp. CBCT-TV broadcasts locally on channel 13.

CBEFT-TV
Owner: Société Radio-Canada
Editorial: 825 Riverside W, Windsor, Ontario N9A 5K9. **T:** 1 519 255-3411
W: http://www.radio-canada.ca/ontario
Editorial Profile: CBEFT-TV is a transmitter located in Windsor, Ontario, that simulcasts the programming of CBOFT-TV, the Radio-Canada affiliate in Ottawa, Ontario. It is owned by the Societe Radio Canada. CBEFT-TV airs locally on channel 54.

CBET-TV
Owner: Canadian Broadcasting Corp.
Editorial: 825 Riverside Drive West, Windsor, Ontario N9A 5K9. **T:** 1 519 255-3456
W: http://www.cbc.ca/windsor
Editorial Profile: CBET-TV is the CBC affiliate for the Windsor, Ontario market. The station is owned by the Canadian Broadcasting Corp. CBET-TV broadcasts locally on channel 9.

CBFT-TV
Owner: Société Radio-Canada
Editorial: 1400 boul Rene Levesque Est, Montreal, Quebec H2L 2M2.
T: 1 514 597-6000
W: http://www.radio-canada.ca/montreal
Editorial Profile: CBFT-TV is the Radio-Canada affiliate for the Montreal market. The station is owned by Societe Radio-Canada. CBFT-TV airs locally on channel 2.

CBHT-TV
Owner: Canadian Broadcasting Corp.
Editorial: 1840 Bell Road, Halifax, Nova Scotia B3H 2Z5. **T:** 1 902 420-4350 **E:** cbcns@cbc.ca
W: http://www.cbc.ca/ns
Editorial Profile: CBHT-TV is the CBC affiliate for the Halifax, Nova Scotia market. The station is owned by the Canadian Broadcasting Corp. CBHT-TV broadcasts locally on channel 3.

CBIT-TV
Owner: Canadian Broadcasting Corp.
Editorial: 285 Alexandra St, Sydney, Nova Scotia B1S 2E8. **T:** 1 902 539-5050
W: http://www.cbc.ca/ns
Editorial Profile: CBIT-TV is a transmitter located in Sydney, NS that simulcasts the programming of CBHT-TV in Halifax, Nova Scotia. It is owned by the Canadian Broadcasting Corp. CBIT-TV broadcasts locally on channel 5.

CBKFT-TV
Owner: Société Radio-Canada
Editorial: 2440 Broad St, Regina, Saskatchewan S4P 0A5. **T:** 1 306 347-9540
E: tjsask@radio-canada.ca
W: http://www.radio-canada.ca/regions/saskatchewan
Editorial Profile: CBKFT-TV is the Radio-Canada affiliate for the Regina, Saskatchewan market. The station is owned by Societe Radio-Canada. CBKFT-TV broadcasts locally on channel 13.

CBKF-TV
Owner: Canadian Broadcasting Corp.
Editorial: 2440 Broad St, Regina, Saskatchewan S4P 0A5. **T:** 1 306 347-9540
E: sasknews@cbc.ca
W: http://www.cbc.ca/sask
Editorial Profile: CBKF-TV is the CBC affiliate for the Regina, Saskatchewan market. The station is owned by the Canadian Broadcasting Corp. CBKF-TV airs locally on channel 4.

CBKST-TV
Owner: Canadian Broadcasting Corp.
Editorial: 144 2nd Ave S, Saskatoon, Saskatchewan S7K 1K5. **T:** 1 306 347-9540
W: http://www.cbc.ca/sask
Editorial Profile: CBKST-TV is the CBC affiliate for the Saskatoon, Saskatchewan market. The station is owned by Canadian Broadcasting Corp. CBKST-TV broadcasts locally on channel 11.

CBKT-TV
Owner: Canadian Broadcasting Corp.
Editorial: 2440 Broad St, Regina, Saskatchewan S4P 0A5. **T:** 1 306 347-9540
E: sasknews@cbc.ca

W: http://www.cbc.ca/sask
Editorial Profile: CBKT-TV is the CBC affiliate for the Regina, Saskatchewan market. The station is owned by Canadian Broadcasting Corp. CBKT-TV broadcasts locally on channel 9.

CBLFT-TV
Owner: Société Radio-Canada
Editorial: 205 Wellington Ouest, Bureau 5G506, Toronto, Ontario M5V 3G7.
T: 1 416 205-2887
W: http://www.radio-canada.ca/regions/ontario
Editorial Profile: CBLFT-TV is the Television de Radio-Canada affiliate for the Toronto market. The station is owned by Societe Radio-Canada. CBLFT-TV broadcasts locally on channel 12.

CBLN-TV
Owner: Canadian Broadcasting Corp.
Editorial: 250 Front Street, Toronto, Ontario M5V 3G5. **T:** 1 416 205-3311
E: tonews@cbc.ca
W: http://www.cbc.ca/toronto
Editorial Profile: CBLN-TV is the CBC affiliate serving the London, ON area. The station is owned by the Canadian Broadcasting Corp. CBLN-TV broadcasts locally on channel 26 and syndicates CBC Newsworld programming.

CBLT-TV
Owner: Canadian Broadcasting Corp.
Editorial: 250 Front Street, Toronto, Ontario M5V 3G5. **T:** 1 416 205-6309
E: tonews@cbc.ca
W: http://www.cbc.ca/toronto
Editorial Profile: CBLT-TV is the CBC affiliate serving the Toronto market. The station is owned by Canadian Broadcasting Corp. CBLT-TV broadcasts locally on channel 25.

CBMT-TV
Owner: Canadian Broadcasting Corp.
Editorial: 1400 Rene-Levesque Boul Est, Montreal, Quebec H2L 2M2.
T: 1 514 597-6000
W: http://www.cbc.ca/montreal
Editorial Profile: CBMT-TV is the CBC affiliate for the Montreal market. The station is owned by the Canadian Broadcasting Corp. CBMT-TV broadcasts locally on channel 6.

CBNT-TV
Owner: Canadian Broadcasting Corp.
Editorial: 95 University Ave, St. John's, Newfoundland A1B 1Z4. **T:** 1 709 576-5000
W: http://www.cbc.ca/nl/
Editorial Profile: CBNT-TV is the CBC affiliate for the St. John's, Newfoundland market. The station is owned by Canadian Broadcasting Corp. CBNT-TV broadcasts locally on channel 8.

CBOFT-TV
Owner: Société Radio-Canada
Editorial: 181 Queen St, Ottawa, Ontario K1P 1K9. **T:** 1 613 288-6000
E: nouvelles.ottawagatineau@radio-canada.ca
W: http://radio-canada.ca/regions/ottawa/index.shtml
Editorial Profile: CBOFT-TV is the Societe Radio-Canada affiliate serving the Ottawa, Ontario market. The station is owned by Societe Radio-Canada. CBOFT-TV airs locally on channel 9.

CBOT-TV
Owner: Canadian Broadcasting Corp.
Editorial: 181 Queen Street, Ottawa, Ontario K1P 1K9. **T:** 1 613 288-6000
E: cbcnewsottawa@cbc.ca
W: http://www.cbc.ca/ottawa
Editorial Profile: CBOT-TV is the CBC affiliate for the Ottawa, Ontario market. The station is owned by the Canadian Broadcasting Corp. CBOT-TV broadcasts locally on channel 4.

CBRT-TV
Owner: Canadian Broadcasting Corp.
Editorial: 1724 Westmount Blvd NW, Calgary, Alberta T2N 3G7. **T:** 1 403 521-6000
W: http://www.cbc.ca/calgary
Editorial Profile: CBRT-TV is the CBC affiliate for the Calgary, Alberta market. The station is owned by Canadian Broadcasting Corp. CBRT-TV broadcasts locally on channel 9.

CBUFT-TV
Owner: Société Radio-Canada
Editorial: 775 rue Cambie, Vancouver, British Columbia V6B 2R5. **T:** 1 604 662-6135
W: http://www.radio-canada.ca/regions/colombie-britannique
Editorial Profile: CBUFT-TV is the Societe Radio-Canada affiliate serving the Vancouver, British Columbia area. The station is owned by Societe Radio-Canada. CBUFT-TV airs locally on channel 26.

CBUT-TV
Owner: Canadian Broadcasting Corp.
Editorial: 700 Hamilton St, Vancouver, British Columbia V6B 2R5. **T:** 1 604 662-6000
E: cbcnewsvancouver@cbc.ca
W: http://www.cbc.ca/bc
Editorial Profile: CBUT-TV is the CBC affiliate for the Vancouver, British Columbia market. The station is owned by Canadian Broadcasting Corp. CBUT-TV broadcasts locally on channel 2. Press releases and story ideas should be directed to the assignment desk.

CBVT-TV
Owner: Canadian Broadcasting Corp.
Editorial: 2505 Boul Laurier, Quebec, Quebec G1V 2L2. **T:** 1 418 654-1341
W: http://www.radio-canada.ca/quebec

CBVT-TV
Owner: Société Radio-Canada
Editorial: 888 rue Saint-Jean, Quebec, Quebec G1R 5H6. **T:** 1 418 654-1341
E: nouvelles.quebec@radio-canada.ca
W: http://radio-canada.ca/quebec
Editorial Profile: CBVT-TV is the Radio-Canada affiliate serving the Quebec City area. The station is owned by Societe Radio-Canada. CBVT-TV broadcasts locally on channel 11.

CBWFT-TV
Owner: Société Radio-Canada
Editorial: 541 Avenue Portage, Winnipeg, Manitoba R3B 2G1. **T:** 1 204 788-3235
E: manitoba@radio-canada.ca
W: http://radio-canada.ca/regions/manitoba
Editorial Profile: CBWFT-TV is the Radio-Canada-Reseau TV affiliate serving the Winnipeg, Manitoba area. The station is owned by Societe Radio-Canada. CBWFT-TV broadcasts locally on channel 3.

CBWT-TV
Owner: Canadian Broadcasting Corp.
Editorial: 541 Portage Ave, Winnipeg, Manitoba R3B 2G1. **T:** 1 204 788-3222
W: http://www.cbc.ca/manitoba
Editorial Profile: CBWT-TV is the CBC affiliate for the Winnipeg, Manitoba market. The station is owned by the Canadian Broadcasting Corp. CBWT-TV broadcasts locally on channel 6.

CBXA-TV
Owner: Canadian Broadcasting Corp.
T: 1 780 468-7500 **E:** cbx.edmonton@cbc.ca
W: http://www.cbc.ca/edmonton

CBXFT-TV
Owner: Société Radio-Canada
Editorial: 10062-102 Avenue, Suite 123 Edmonton City Centre, Edmonton, Alberta T5J 2Y8. **T:** 1 780 468-7500
W: http://radio-canada.ca/regions/alberta
Editorial Profile: CBXFT-TV is the Radio-Canada affiliate for the Edmonton, Alberta market. The station is owned by Societe Radio-Canada. CBXFT-TV broadcasts locally on channel 11.

CBXT-TV
Owner: Canadian Broadcasting Corp.
Editorial: Ste 123 Edmonton City Centre, 10062 102nd Ave, Edmonton, Alberta T5J 2Y8. **T:** 1 780 468-7500
E: cbx.edmonton@cbc.ca
W: http://www.cbc.ca/edmonton
Editorial Profile: CBXT-TV is the CBC affiliate for the Edmonton, Alberta market. The station is owned by the Canadian Broadcasting Corp. CBXT-TV broadcasts locally on channel 5.

CBYT-TV
Owner: Canadian Broadcasting Corp.
Editorial: 162 Premier Drive, Corner Brook, Newfoundland A2H 6G1. **T:** 1 709 634-3141
E: cbrookradio@stjohns.cbc.ca
W: http://www.cbc.ca/nl
Editorial Profile: CBYT-TV is a transmitter located in Corner Brook, Newfoundland that simulcasts the programming of CBNT-TV in St. John's, Newfoundland. It is owned by Canadian Broadcasting Corp. CBYT-TV broadcasts locally on channel 5.

CFAP-TV
Owner: Remstar Corporation
Editorial: 330 rue Saint-Vallier Est, Bureau 025, Quebec, Quebec G9K 9C5.
T: 1 418 624-2222 **E:** cv@vtele.ca
W: http://vtele.ca
Editorial Profile: CFAP-TV is the V affiliate for the Quebec City market. The station is owned by Remstar Corporation. CFAP-TV broadcasts locally on channel 2.

CFCF-TV
Owner: Bell Media
Editorial: 1205 Papineau Ave, Montreal, Quebec H2K 4R2. **T:** 1 514 273-6311
E: montrealnews@ctv.ca
W: http://montreal.ctvnews.ca
Editorial Profile: CFCF-TV is the CTV affiliate for the Montreal market. The station is owned by Bell Media. CFCF-TV broadcasts locally on channel 12. All press releases and story ideas should be sent to the news department's e-mail address or faxed.

CFCL-TV
Owner: Bell Media
Editorial: 681 Pine St North, Timmins, Ontario P4N 7G3. **T:** 1 705 264-4211
E: tonews@cbc.ca
W: http://www.cbc.ca/toronto
Editorial Profile: CFCL-TV (CBLT7-TV) is the CTV affiliate for the Timmins, Ontario market. The station is owned by Bell Media. CFCL-TV broadcasts locally on channel 6. The station rebroadcasts CBLT-TV programming.

CFCM-TV
Owner: Quebecor Media Inc.
Editorial: 1000 avenue Myrand, Sainte-Foy, Quebec G1V 2W3. **T:** 1 418 688-9330
E: administrationquebec@tva.ca
W: http://tva.canoe.ca/stations/cfcm
Editorial Profile: CFCM-TV is the TVA network affiliate for the Quebec City market. The station is owned by Quebecor Media Inc. CFCM-TV broadcasts locally on channel 4.

CFCNL-TV
Owner: Bell Media
Editorial: 640- 13 Street North, Lethbridge, Alberta AB T1H 2S8. **T:** 1 403 329-3644
E: cfcnlethbridge@ctv.ca
W: http://www.lethbridge.ctv.ca
Editorial Profile: CFCNL-TV is the CTV affiliate for the Lethbridge market. The station is owned by Bell Media. CFCNL-TV broadcasts locally on channel 13. This station is the CFCN-TV transmitter in Lethbridge.

CFCN-TV
Owner: Bell Media
Editorial: 80 Patina Rise SW, Calgary, Alberta T3H 2W4-. **T:** 1 403 240-5600
E: calgarynews@ctv.ca
W: http://calgary.ctvnews.ca
Editorial Profile: CFCN-TV is the CTV affiliate for the Calgary, Alberta; southern Alberta; and southeastern British Columbia market. The station is owned by Bell Media. CFCN-TV broadcasts locally on channel 3.

CFEM-TV
Owner: RNC Media
Editorial: 380 Murdoch Street, Rouyn-Noranda, Quebec J9X 1G5. **T:** 1 819 762-0744
W: http://www.cfem.ca
Editorial Profile: CFEM-TV is the TVA affiliate for the the Rouyn-Noranda, Quebec area. The station is owned by RNC Media. CFEM-TV airs locally on channel 10.

CFER-TV
Owner: Quebecor Media Inc.
Editorial: 465 boul Sainte-Anne, Rimouski, Quebec G5M 1G1. **T:** 1 418 722-6011
E: nouvelles@cfer.tva.ca
W: http://tva.canoe.ca/stations/cfer
Editorial Profile: CFER-TV is the TVA affiliate for the Rimouski, Quebec market. The station is owned by Quebecor Media Inc. CFER-TV broadcasts locally on channel 11.

CFGS-TV
Owner: RNC Media
Editorial: 171A rue Jean-Proulx, Gatineau, Quebec J8Z 1W5. **T:** 1 819 770-1040
W: http://www.tvagatineau.ca
Editorial Profile: CFGS-TV is the TQS affiliate serving the Gatineau, Quebec area. The station is owned by RNC Média. CFGS-TV airs locally on channel 34. CFGS-TV produces its own local newscasts and gets other programming from V.

CFJC-TV
Owner: Jim Pattison Broadcast Group(The)
Editorial: 460 Pemberton Terrace, Kamloops, British Columbia V2C 1T5. **T:** 1 250 372-3322
E: news@cfjctv.com **W:** http://www.cfjctv.com
Editorial Profile: CFJC-TV is an independent station serving the Kamloops, British Columbia market. The station is owned by The Jim Pattison Broadcast Group. CFJC-TV broadcasts locally on channel 7. On September 1, 2012 CFJC-TV will begin airing some content from CITY-TV.

CFJP-TV
Owner: Remstar Corporation
Editorial: 85, rue St-Paul Ouest, Montreal, Quebec H2Y 3V4. **T:** 1 514 390-6100
Editorial Profile: CFJP-TV is the V affiliate serving the Montreal area. The station is owned by Remstar Corporation. CFJP-TV broadcasts locally on channel 35.

CFKM-TV
Owner: Remstar Corporation
Editorial: 926 rue Notre Dame Centre, Trois-Rivieres, Quebec G9A 4W8. **T:** 1 819 377-6053
W: http://www.vtele.ca
Editorial Profile: CFKM-TV is the V affiliate for the Trois-Rivieres, Quebec market. The station is owned by Remstar Corporation. CFKM-TV broadcasts locally on channel 16.

CFKS-TV
Owner: Remstar Corporation
Editorial: 3720 boulevard Industriel, Sherbrooke, Quebec J1L 1Z9.
T: 1 819 565-9232
Editorial Profile: CFKS-TV is the V affiliate for the Sherbrooke, Quebec market. The station is owned by Remstar Corporation. CFKS-TV broadcasts locally on channel 30. CFKS-TV has no news division.

CFMT-TV
Owner: Rogers Media Inc.
Editorial: 33 Dundas St E, Toronto, Ontario M5B 1B8. **T:** 1 416 260-0047
E: info@omni1.ca
W: http://www.omnitv.ca/ontario
Editorial Profile: CFMT-TV, also known as OMNI.1, is an independent station for the Toronto market. The station is owned by Rogers Media Inc. CFMT-TV broadcasts locally on channel 47.

CFPL-TV
Owner: Bell Media
Editorial: 1 Communications Rd, London, Ontario N6J 4Z1. **T:** 1 519 686-8810
E: londonnews@ctv.ca
W: http://london.ctvnews.ca
Editorial Profile: CFPL-TV is the CTV affiliate for the London, Ontario market. The station is owned by Bell Media. CFPL-TV broadcasts locally on channel 10.

CFQC-TV
Owner: Bell Media
Editorial: 216 First Ave North, Saskatoon, Saskatchewan S7K 3W3. **T:** 1 306 665-8600
E: cfqcnews@ctv.ca **W:** http://saskatoon.ctv.ca
Editorial Profile: CFQC-TV is the CTV affiliate for the Saskatoon, Saskatchewan market. The station is owned by Bell Media. CFQC-TV broadcasts locally on channel 8.

CFRE-TV
Owner: Shaw Communications
Editorial: 370 Hoffer Dr, Regina, Saskatchewan S4N 7A4. **T:** 1 306 775-4000
E: regina@globalnews.ca
W: http://www.globalregina.com
Editorial Profile: CFRE-TV is the Global Television affiliate for the Regina, Saskatchewan market. The station is owned by Shaw Communications. CFRE-TV broadcasts locally on channel 11.

CFRN-TV
Owner: Bell Media
Editorial: 18520 Stony Plain Road, Edmonton, Alberta T5S 1A8. **T:** 1 780 483-3311
E: cfrnnewsassignment@ctv.ca
W: http://edmonton.ctv.ca
Editorial Profile: CFRN-TV is the CTV affiliate for the Edmonton, Alberta market. The station is owned by Bell Media. CFRN-TV airs locally on channel 2.

CFRS-TV
Owner: Remstar Corporation
Editorial: 2303 rue Sir-Wilfrid-Laurier, Jonquiere, Quebec G7X 5Z2.
T: 1 418 542-4551 **E:** cv@vtele.ca
Editorial Profile: CFRS-TV is the V affiliate for the Jonquiere, Quebec market. The station is owned by Remstar Corporation. CFRS-TV broadcasts locally on channel 4.

CFSK-TV
Owner: Shaw Communications
Editorial: 218 Robin Crescent, Saskatoon, Saskatchewan S7L 7C3. **T:** 1 306 665-6969
E: globalnews.sas@globaltv.com
W: http://www.globalsaskatoon.com

Editorial Profile: CFSK-TV is the Global Television affiliate for the Saskatoon, Saskatchewan market. The station is owned by Shaw Communications. CFSK-TV broadcasts locally on channel 4.

CFSO-TV
Owner: McCarthy (Corey)
Editorial: 810 2nd Street West, Cardston, Alberta TOK OKO. **T:** 1 403 448-0432
E: news@channel32.ca
W: http://www.channel32.ca
Editorial Profile: CFSO-TV is an independent station for the Cardston, Alberta market. The station is owned by Corey McCarthy. The station airs community-related news and public affairs programming. CFSO-TV broadcasts locally on channel 32.

CFTK-TV
Owner: Astral Media
Editorial: 4625 Lazelle Ave, Terrace, British Columbia V8G 1S4. **T:** 1 250 635-6316
W: http://www.cftktv.com
Editorial Profile: CFTK-TV is the CBC affiliate for the Terrace, British Columbia market. The station is owned by Astral Media. CFTK-TV broadcasts locally on channel 3.

CFTM-TV
Owner: Quebecor Media Inc.
Editorial: 1600 boulevard de Maisonneuve Est, Montreal, Quebec H2L 4P2. **T:** 1 514 526-9251
E: nouvelles@tva.ca **W:** http://tva.canoe.ca
Editorial Profile: CFTM-TV is the TVA affiliate for the Montreal market. The station is owned by Quebecor Media Inc. CFTM-TV broadcasts locally on channel 10.

CFTO-TV
Owner: Bell Media
Editorial: 9 Channel Nine Crt, Toronto, Ontario M1S 4B5-. **T:** 1 416 332-7100
E: feedbacktoronto@ctv.ca
W: http://toronto.ctvnews.ca
Editorial Profile: CFTO-TV is the CTV affiliate for the Toronto market. The station is owned by Bell Media. CFTO-TV broadcasts locally on channel 9.

CFTU-TV
Owner: Corporation pour l'Avancement des Nouvelles Applications des Langages Ltée
Editorial: 2200, rue Sainte-Catherine Est, 1er étage, Montreal, Quebec H2K 2J1.
T: 1 514 509-2222 **E:** info@canalsavoir.tv
W: http://www.canalsavoir.tv
Editorial Profile: CFTU-TV is the Canal Savoir affiliate in the Montreal market. The station is a non-commercial station owned by the Corporation pour l'Avancement des Nouvelles Applications des Langages Ltée (CANAL). CFTU-TV broadcasts locally on channel 29.

CFTV-TV
Owner: Southshore Broadcasting Inc.
Editorial: 164 Oak St, Suite 304, Leamington, Ontario N8H 2B6. **T:** 1 519 326-4000
W: http://www.cftv34.tv
Editorial Profile: CFTV-TV is an independent station for the Leamington, Ontario market. The station is owned by Southshore Broadcasting Inc. CFTV-TV broadcasts locally on channel 34.

CFVS-TV
Owner: RNC Media
Editorial: 1729 3e Avenue, Val-d'Or, Quebec J9P 1W3. **T:** 1 819 825-0010
E: nouvelles@rncmedia.ca
W: http://www.rncmedia.ca
Editorial Profile: CFVS-TV is the V Tele affiliate for the Val-d'Or, Quebec market. The station is owned by RNC Media. CFVS-TV broadcasts locally on channel 25.

CFYK-TV
Owner: Canadian Broadcasting Corp.
Editorial: 5002 Forrest Drive, Yellowknife, Northwest Territories X1A 2N2.
T: 1 867 920-5400 **E:** cbcnorth@cbc.ca
W: http://www.cbc.ca/north
Editorial Profile: CFYK-TV is a CBC affiliate for the Yellowknife, Northwest Territories area. The station is owned by the Canadian Broadcasting Corporation. The station broadcasts locally on channel 10.

CHAN-TV
Owner: Shaw Communications
Editorial: 7850 Enterprise St, Burnaby, British Columbia V5A 1V7. **T:** 1 604 420-2288
E: globalnews.bc@globaltv.com
W: http://www.globaltvbc.com
Editorial Profile: CHAN-TV is the Global Television affiliate for Burnaby, British Columbia. The station is owned by Shaw Communications. CHAN-TV broadcasts locally on channel 8.

CHAT-TV
Owner: Jim Pattison Broadcast Group(The)
Editorial: 10 Boundary Rd SE, Redcliff, Alberta T0J 2P0-. **T:** 1 403 548-8282
E: chatnews@jpbg.ca
W: http://www.chattelevision.ca
Editorial Profile: CHAT-TV is an independent station for the Medicine Hat, Alberta market. The station is owned by The Jim Pattison Broadcast Group. CHAT-TV broadcasts locally on channel 6. On September 1, 2012 CHAT-TV will begin airing some content from CITY-TV.

CHAU-TV
Owner: Tele Inter-Rives Ltee.
Editorial: 349 boulevard Perron, Carleton, Quebec G0C 1J0. **T:** 1 418 364-3344
E: info@chautva.com
W: http://www.chautva.com
Editorial Profile: CHAU-TV is the TVA affiliate for the Carleton, Quebec market. The station is owned by Tele Inter-Rives Ltee. CHAU-TV broadcasts locally on channel 5.

CHBC-TV
Owner: Shaw Communications
Editorial: 342 Leon Ave, Kelowna, British Columbia V1Y 6J2-. **T:** 1 250 762-4535
E: news@chbcnews.ca
W: http://www.chbcnews.ca
Editorial Profile: CHBC-TV is the Global Television affiliate for the Kelowna, British Columbia market. The station is owned by Shaw Communications. CHBC-TV broadcasts locally on channel 13. CHBC-TV is one of five stations in CanWest's CH News division.

CHBX-TV
Owner: Bell Media
Editorial: 119 East St, Sault Ste. Marie, Ontario P6A 3C7. **T:** 1 705 759-8232
E: newsforthenorth@ctv.ca
W: http://northernontario.ctvnews.ca/
Editorial Profile: CHBX-TV is the CTV affiliate for the Sault Ste. Marie, Ontario market. The station is owned by Bell Media. CHBX-TV broadcasts locally on channel 2.

CHCH-TV
Owner: Channel Zero Inc.
Editorial: 163 Jackson St W, Hamilton, Ontario L8P 0A8. **T:** 1 905 522-1101
E: contact@chch.com
W: http://www.chch.com
Editorial Profile: CHCH-TV is an independent superstation for the Ontario market. The station is owned by Channel Zero Inc. CHCH-TV broadcasts in Hamilton on channel 11. CHCH-TV is a member of the Canadian Press Gallery.

CHCT-TV
Owner: Charlotte Community Television
Editorial: 24 Reed Ave, Unit #2, Saint Andrews, New Brunswick E5B 1A1.
T: 1 506 529-8826 **E:** localtv@chct.ca
W: http://www.chct.ca
Editorial Profile: CHCT-TV or Charlotte Community Television is an independent local television station based in St. Andrews, New Brunswick. CHCT-TV broadcasts on channel 26 to local residents.

CHEK-TV
Owner: CHEK Media Group
Editorial: 780 Kings Road, Victoria, British Columbia V8T 5A2. **T:** 1 250 383-2435
E: tips@cheknews.ca
W: http://www.cheknews.ca
Editorial Profile: CHEK-TV an independent station for the Victoria, British Columbia market. The station is owned by CHEK Media Group. CHEK-TV broadcasts to the Victoria, British Columbia area on channel 6.

CHEM-TV
Owner: Quebecor Media Inc.
Editorial: 3625 boul Chanoine-Moreau, Trois-Rivieres, Quebec G8Y 5N6. **T:** 1 819 376-8880
E: nouvelles@chem.tva.ca
W: http://tva.canoe.ca/stations/chem
Editorial Profile: CHEM-TV is the TVA affiliate for the Trois-Rivieres, Quebec market. The station is owned by Quebecor Media Inc. CHEM-TV broadcasts locally on channel 8.

CHEX2-TV
Owner: Corus Entertainment Inc.
Editorial: 743 Monaghan Rd, Peterborough, Ontario K9J 5K2. **T:** 1 905 434-2421
E: studio12news@corusent.com
W: http://www.channel12.ca
Editorial Profile: CHEX-TV2 is the CBC affiliate for the Oshawa, Ontario market. The station is owned by Corus Entertainment Inc. CHEX-TV2 broadcasts locally on channel 12.

CHEX-TV
Owner: Corus Entertainment Inc.
Editorial: 743 Monaghan Road, Peterborough, Ontario K9J 5K2. **T:** 1 705 742-0451
E: newswatch@chextv.com
W: http://www.chextv.com
Editorial Profile: CHEX-TV is the CBC affiliate for the Peterborough, Ontario market. The station is owned by Corus Entertainment Inc. CHEX-TV broadcasts locally on channel 12.

CHFD-TV
Owner: Dougall Media
Editorial: 87 Hill St N, Thunder Bay, Ontario P7A 5V6. **T:** 1 807 346-2600
E: news@dougallmedia.com
Editorial Profile: CHFD-TV is the CTV affiliate for the Thunder Bay, Ontario market. The station is owned by Dougall Media. CHFD-TV broadcasts locally on channel 4.

CHIN-TV
Owner: Lombardi(Lenny)
Editorial: 622 College St, Suite 400, Toronto, Ontario M6G 1B6. **T:** 1 416 531-9991
E: chintv@chinradio.com
W: http://www.chinradio.com
Editorial Profile: CHIN-TV is an independent station for the Toronto market. The station is owned by Lenny Lombardi. CHIN-TV broadcasts locally on channel 7.

CHLF-TV
Owner: Office des télécommunications éducatives de langue francaise de l'Ontario(L')
Editorial: 21 College St Etage 6E, Toronto, Ontario M5G 2B3. **T:** 1 416 968-3536
E: vos_questions@tfo.org
W: http://www.tfo.org
Editorial Profile: CHLF-TV is an independent station for the Toronto market. The station is owned by GroupeMédia TFO with the Office des télécommunications éducatives de langue francaise de l'Ontario (OTÉLFO). CHLF-TV is broadcast locally on channel 19.

CHLT-TV
Owner: Quebecor Media Inc.
Editorial: 3330 rue King Ouest, Sherbrooke, Quebec J1L 1C9. **T:** 1 819 565-7777
E: nouvelles.sherbrooke@tva.ca
W: http://tva.canoe.ca/stations/chlt
Editorial Profile: CHLT-TV is the TVA affiliate for the Sherbrooke, Quebec market. The station is owned by Quebecor Media Inc. CHLT-TV broadcasts locally on channel 7.

CHMG-TV
Owner: TeleMag Quebec
Editorial: 2700 rue Jean-Perrin, Bureau 120, Quebec, Quebec G2C 1S9. **T:** 1 418 670-9078
E: info@tele-mag.tv **W:** http://www.tele-mag.tv
Editorial Profile: CHMG-TV is a commercial station owned by TeleMag Quebec. CHMG-TV broadcasts on channel 10 in the Quebec City region.

CHMI-TV
Owner: Rogers Media Inc.
Editorial: 8 Forks Market Road, Winnipeg, Manitoba R3C 4Y3. **T:** 1 204 947-9613
E: citytvwinnipegfeedback@rci.rogers.com
W: http://www.citytv.com/winnipeg
Editorial Profile: CHMI-TV is branded as part of the CityTV family offering local news programming for the Winnipeg, Manitoba market. The station is owned by Rogers Media Inc. CHMI-TV broadcasts locally on channel 13.

CHNM-TV
Owner: Rogers Media Inc.
Editorial: 180 West 2nd Avenue, Vancouver, British Columbia V5Y 3T9. **T:** 1 604 678-3800
E: news@omnibc.ca **W:** http://www.omnibc.ca
Editorial Profile: CHNM-TV is an independent station for the Vancouver, British Columbia market. The station is owned by Rogers Media Inc.. CHNM-TV broadcasts locally on channel 8.

CHNU-TV
Owner: ZoomerMedia Limited
Editorial: 5668-192 Street, Suite 204, Surrey, British Columbia V3S 2V7. **T:** 1 604 576-6880
E: audience@joytv10.ca
W: http://www.joytv10.ca
Editorial Profile: CHNU-TV is a Christian-based television station for the Surrey, British Columbia market. The station is owned by ZoomerMedia Limited. CHNU-TV broadcasts locally on channel 66.

CHOT-TV
Owner: RNC Media
Editorial: 171A rue Jean-Proulx, Gatineau, Quebec J8Z 1W5. **T:** 1 819 770-1040
E: chot@rncmedia.ca
W: http://www.tvagatineau.ca
Editorial Profile: CHOT-TV is the TVA affiliate serving the Gatineau, Quebec area. The station is owned by RNC Media. CHOT-TV broadcasts locally on channel 40.

CHRO-TV
Owner: Bell Media
Editorial: 87 George Street, Ottawa, Ontario K1N 9H7. **T:** 1 613 789-0606
E: ottawa.producers@ctv.ca
W: http://ctvottawamorning.ca
Editorial Profile: CHRO-TV is the CTV. affiliate for the Ottawa, Ontario market. The station is owned by Bell Media. CHRO-TV broadcasts locally on channel 43.

CHWI-TV
Owner: Bell Media
Editorial: 300 Ouellette Ave, Windsor, Ontario N9A 7B4-. **T:** 1 519 977-7432
E: windsorcontact@ctv.ca
W: http://windsor.ctvnews.ca
Editorial Profile: CHWI-TV is the CTV affiliate for the Windsor, Ontario market. The station is owned by Bell Media. CHWI-TV broadcasts locally on channel 60.

CIBK-TV
Owner: Société de télédiffusion du Québec(La)
Editorial: 436 Boulevard Perron, Carleton, Quebec G0C 1J0. **T:** 1 418 364-7025
E: info@telequebec.tv
W: http://www.telequebec.tv
Editorial Profile: CIBK-TV is the Télé-Québec affiliate for the Gaspésie-Îles-de-la-Madeleine, Quebec market. The station is owned by La Société de télédiffusion du Québec. CIBK-TV broadcasts locally on channel 11.

CICA-TV
Owner: TVOntario
Editorial: 2180 Yonge St, Toronto, Ontario M4S 2B9. **T:** 1 416 484-2600
E: asktvo@tvo.org **W:** http://www.tvo.org
Editorial Profile: CICA-TV is an independent station for the Toronto market. The station is owned by TVOntario. CICA-TV broadcasts locally on channel 19.

CICC-TV
Owner: Bell Media
Editorial: 95 East Broadway, Yorkton, Saskatchewan S3N 0L1. **T:** 1 306 786-8400
E: cicc@ctv.ca **W:** http://regina.ctv.ca
Editorial Profile: CICC-TV is the CTV affiliate for the Yorktown, Saskatchewan market. CICC-TV is owned by Bell Media. CICC-TV broadcasts locally on channel 10.

CICI-TV
Owner: Bell Media
Editorial: 699 Frood Road, Sudbury, Ontario P3C 5A3. **T:** 1 705 674-8301
E: newsforthenorth@ctv.ca
W: http://northernontario.ctv.ca/sudbury/index.html
Editorial Profile: CICI-TV is the CTV affiliate for the Sudbury, Ontario market. The station is owned by Bell Media. CICI-TV broadcasts locally on channel 5.

CICT-TV
Owner: Shaw Communications
Editorial: 222 23rd St NE, Calgary, Alberta T2E 7N2. **T:** 1 403 235-7777
E: globalnews.calg@globaltv.com
W: http://www.globaltvcalgary.com
Editorial Profile: CICT-TV is the Global Television affiliate for the Calgary, Alberta market. The station is owned by Shaw Communications. CICT-TV broadcasts locally on channel 2.

CIHF-TV
Owner: Shaw Communications
Editorial: 2110 Gottingen St, Halifax, Nova Scotia B3K 3B3. **T:** 1 902 481-7400
E: maritimes@globalnews.ca
W: http://globalnews.ca/halifax/
Editorial Profile: CIHF-TV, the Global affiliate for the Dartmouth, Nova Scotia market. The station is owned by Shaw Communications. CIHF-TV broadcasts locally on channel 8.

CIII-TV
Owner: Shaw Communications
Editorial: 81 Barber Greene Rd, Toronto, Ontario M3C 2A2-. **T:** 1 416 446-5460
E: newstips@globaltv.com
W: http://globalnews.ca/toronto

Editorial Profile: CIII-TV, also known as Global Toronto, is a local, commercial television station owned by Shaw Communications. The station serves as the Global Television affiliate, serving viewers throughout the Toronto area. The station airs locally on channels 6 and 41.

CIIT-TV
Owner: ZoomMedia Limited
Editorial: 171 East Liberty Street, Suite 230, Toronto, Ontario M6K 3P6. **T:** 1 416 368-3194
E: audience@joytv11.ca
W: http://www.joytv11.ca
Editorial Profile: CIIT-TV is an independent station for the Winnipeg, Manitoba market. The station is owned by ZoomMedia Limited. CIIT-TV broadcasts locally on channel 35.

CIMC-TV
Owner: Telile
Editorial: Box 87, 17 Conney's Lane, Cape Breton Island, Nova Scotia B0E 1A0.
T: 1 902 226-1928 **E:** telile@telile.tv
W: http://www.telile.tv
Editorial Profile: CIMC-TV is an independent station for the Arichat, Nova Scotia market. The station is owned by Telile. The station airs community-related and public affairs programming. CIMC-TV broadcasts locally on channel 10.

CIMT-TV
Owner: Télé Inter-Rives Ltée
Editorial: 15 rue de la Chute, Riviere-du-Loup, Quebec G5R 5B7. **T:** 1 418 867-1341
E: nouvelles@cimt.ca **W:** http://www.cimt.ca
Editorial Profile: CIMT-TV is the TVA affiliate for the Rivière-du-Loup, Quebec market. The station is owned by Télé Inter-Rives Ltée. CIMT-TV broadcasts locally on channel 9.

CIPA-TV
Owner: Bell Media
Editorial: 22 10th St West, Prince Albert, Saskatchewan S6V 3A5. **T:** 1 306 763-3041
E: cipanews@ctv.ca **W:** http://saskatoon.ctv.ca
Editorial Profile: CIPA-TV is the CTV affiliate for the Prince Albert, Saskatchewan market. The station is owned by Bell Media. CIPA-TV broadcasts locally on channel 6.

CISA-TV
Owner: Shaw Communications
Editorial: 1401 28th St North, Lethbridge, Alberta T1H 6H9. **T:** 1 403 327-1521
E: globalnews.leth@globaltv.com
W: http://www.globallethbridge.com
Editorial Profile: CISA-TV is the Global Television network affiliate for the Lethbridge, Alberta market. The station is owned by Shaw Communications. CISA-TV broadcasts locally on channel 7.

CITL-TV
Owner: Newfoundland Capital Corporation Limited
Editorial: 5026 50th St, Lloydminster, Alberta T9V 1P3. **T:** 1 780 875-3321
E: tvnews@newcap.ca
W: http://www.newcaptv.com
Editorial Profile: CITL-TV is the CTV affliate for the Lloydminster, Alberta market. The station is owned by Newfoundland Capital Corporation Limited. CITL-TV broadcasts locally on channel 4.

CITO-TV
Owner: Bell Media
Editorial: 681 Pine St N, Timmins, Ontario P4N 7L6. **T:** 1 705 264-4211
E: newsforthenorth@ctv.ca
W: http://northernontario.ctvnews.ca/timmins
Editorial Profile: CITO-TV is the CTV affiliate for the Timmins, Ontario market. The station is owned by Bell Media. CITO-TV broadcasts locally on channel 3.

CITS-TV
Owner: Crossroads Television Systems
Editorial: 1295 N Service Road, Burlington, Ontario L7R 4X5. **T:** 1 905 331-7333
E: contactus@ctstv.com
W: http://www.ctstv.com
Editorial Profile: CITS-TV is an independent station serving the Burlington, Ontario market. The station is owned by Crossroads Television Systems. CITS-TV broadcasts locally on channel 36.

CITV-TV
Owner: Shaw Communications
Editorial: 5325 Allard Way, Edmonton, Alberta T6H 5B8. **T:** 1 780 436-1250
W: http://www.globaltvedmonton.com
Editorial Profile: CITV-TV is the Global Television network affiliate for the Edmonton, Alberta market. The station is owned by Shaw Communications. CITV-TV broadcasts locally on channel 13.

CITY-TV
Owner: Rogers Media Inc.
Editorial: 33 Dundas St E, Toronto, Ontario M5B 1B8-. **T:** 1 416 599-2489
E: citytvtorontofeedback@rci.rogers.com
W: http://www.citynews.ca
Editorial Profile: CITY-TV is the City affiliate of the Toronto market. The station is owned by Rogers Media Inc. CITY-TV broadcasts locally on channel 57. CITY-TV reaches about 11.4 million people daily.

CIVA-TV
Owner: Société de télédiffusion du Québec(La)
Editorial: 689 3ème Avenue, Suite 201, Val-d'Or, Quebec J9P 1S7. **T:** 1 819 874-5132
W: http://www.telequebec.tv
Editorial Profile: CIVA-TV is the Tele-Quebec affiliate for the Abitibi-Témiscamingue market. The station is owned by La Société de télédiffusion du Québec. CIVA-TV broadcasts locally on channel 8.

CIVB-TV
Owner: Société de télédiffusion du Québec(La)
Editorial: 79 Rue de l'est Évêché, Rimouski, Quebec G5L 1X7. **T:** 1 418 727-3743
E: bureau.rimouski@telequebec.tv
W: http://www.telequebec.tv
Editorial Profile: CIVB-TV is the Télé-Québec affiliate for the Bas-St-Laurent, QC market. The station is owned by La Société de télédiffusion du Québec. CIVB-TV broadcasts locally on channel 22.

CIVC-TV
Owner: Société de télédiffusion du Québec(La)
Editorial: 1350 Rue Royale, Bureau 201, Trois-Rivieres, Quebec G9A 4J4.
T: 1 819 371-6752 **E:** info@telequebec.tv
W: http://www.telequebec.tv
Editorial Profile: CIVC-TV is the Télé-Québec affiliate for the Mauricie-Centre-du-Québec-Lanaudière-Basses Laurentides region of Quebec. The station is owned by La Société de télédiffusion du Québec. CIVC-TV broadcasts locally on channel 45.

CIVG-TV
Owner: Société de télédiffusion du Québec(La)
Editorial: 410 Rue Evangeline, Sept-Iles, Quebec G4R 2N5. **T:** 1 418 964-8240
E: info@telequebec.tv
W: http://www.telequebec.tv
Editorial Profile: CIVG-TV is the Télé-Québec affiliate for the Côte-Nord, Quebec market. The station is owned by La Société de Télédiffusion, du Québec. CIVG-TV broadcasts locally on channel 22.

CIVI-TV
Owner: Bell Media
Editorial: 1420 Broad St, Victoria, British Columbia V8W 2B1. **T:** 1 250 381-2484
E: islandcontactus@ctv.ca
W: http://ctvvancouverisland.ca
Editorial Profile: CIVI-TV is the CTV affiliate serving the markets of Victoria, Nanaimo and Vancouver in British Columbia. The station is owned by Bell Media. The station airs locally on cable 12.

CIVM-TV
Owner: Société de télédiffusion du Québec(La)
Editorial: 1000 rue Fullum, Montreal, Quebec H2K 3L7. **T:** 1 514 521-2424
E: info@telequebec.tv
W: http://www.telequebec.tv
Editorial Profile: CIVM-TV is the Tele-Quebec affiliate for the Greater Montreal market. The station is owned by La Société de télédiffusion du Québec. CIVM-TV broadcasts locally on channel 17.

CIVO-TV
Owner: Société de télédiffusion du Québec(La)
Editorial: 170, rue de l'Hôtel-de-Ville, 7ème étage, bureau 7.100, Gatineau, Quebec J8X 4C2. **T:** 1 819 772-3471 **E:** info@telequebec.tv
W: http://www.telequebec.tv
Editorial Profile: CIVO-TV is the Télé-Québec affiliate for the Outaouais, Quebec market. The station is owned by La Société de télédiffusion du Québec. CIVO-TV broadcasts locally on channel 11.

CIVQ-TV
Owner: Société de télédiffusion du Québec(La)
Editorial: 270 Chemin Sainte-Foy, Quebec, Quebec G1R 1T3. **T:** 1 418 643-5303
E: bureau.quebec@telequebec.tv
W: http://www.telequebec.tv
Editorial Profile: CIVQ-TV is the Télé-Québec affiliate for the Greater Quebec City and the Chaudière-Appalaches market. The station is owned by La Société de télédiffusion du Québec. CIVQ-TV broadcasts locally on channel 15.

CIVS-TV
Owner: Société de télédiffusion du Québec(La)
Editorial: 3330 Rue King Ouest, Bureau 1000, Sherbrooke, Quebec J1L 1C9.
T: 1 819 820-3436
E: bureau.sherbrooke@telequebec.tv
W: http://www.telequebec.tv
Editorial Profile: CIVS-TV is the Télé-Québec affiliate for the Eastern Townships, Quebec market. The station is owned by La Société de télédiffusion du Québec. CIVS-TV broadcasts locally on channel 24.

CIVT-TV
Owner: Bell Media
Editorial: 969 Robson St, Vancouver, British Columbia V6Z 1X5-. **T:** 1 604 608-2868
E: bcnews@ctv.ca **W:** http://bc.ctvnews.ca
Editorial Profile: CIVT-TV is the CTV affiliate serving the Vancouver, British Columbia area. The station is owned by Bell Media. CIVT-TV broadcasts locally on channel 32.

CIVV-TV
Owner: Société de télédiffusion du Québec(La)
Editorial: 3788, rue de la Fabrique, Pavillon Joseph-Angers, Jonquiere, Quebec G7X 3P4.
T: 1 418 695-8152 **E:** info@telequebec.tv
W: http://www.telequebec.tv
Editorial Profile: CIVV-TV is the Télé-Québec affiliate for the Saguenay-Lac-St-Jean, Quebec market. The station is owned by La Société de télédiffusion du Québec. CIVV-TV broadcasts locally on channel 8.

CJBN-TV
Owner: Shaw Communications Inc.
Editorial: 102 10th St, Keewatin, Ontario P0X 1C0. **T:** 1 807 547-2895
W: http://www.gokenora.com/cjbn/
Editorial Profile: CJBN-TV is the CTV affiliate serving residents of Keewatin, Ontario and its environs. The station is owned by Shaw Communications Inc. CJBN-TV airs locally on channel 13.

CJBR-TV
Owner: Société Radio-Canada
Editorial: 273, rue Saint-Jean-Baptiste Ouest, Rimouski, Quebec G5L 4J8.
T: 1 418 723-2217 **E:** cjbr@radio-canada.ca
W: http://www.radio-canada.ca/est-du-quebec/
Editorial Profile: CJBR-TV is the Radio-Canada affiliate serving the Rimouski, Quebec area. The station is owned by Société Radio-Canada. CBVT-TV broadcasts locally on channel 2.

CJCB-TV
Owner: Bell Media
Editorial: 1283 George St, Sydney, Nova Scotia B1P 1N7. **T:** 1 902 562-5511
E: atlanticnews@bellmedia.ca
W: http://atlantic.ctvnews.ca
Editorial Profile: CJCB-TV is the CTV affiliate for the Sydney, Nova Scotia market. The station is owned by Bell Media. CJCB-TV broadcasts locally on channel 4.

CJCH-TV
Owner: Bell Media
Editorial: 2885 Robie St, Halifax, Nova Scotia B3K 5Z4. **T:** 1 902 453-4000
E: atlanticnews@ctv.ca **W:** http://atlantic.ctv.ca
Editorial Profile: CJCH-TV is the CTV affiliate for the Halifax, Nova Scotia market. The station is owned by Bell Media. CJCH-TV broadcasts locally on channel 9.

CJCH-TV
Owner: ATV New Brunswick Ltd.
T: 1 506 658-1010

CJCN-TV
Owner: Newfoundland Broadcasting Co. Ltd.
Editorial: 446 Logy Bay Rd, St. John's, Newfoundland A1C 5S2. **T:** 1 709 722-5015
E: ntv@ntv.ca **W:** http://www.ntv.ca

CJCO-TV
Owner: Rogers Media Inc.
Editorial: 535-7th Avenue SW, Calgary, Alberta T2P 5A3. **T:** 1 403 508-3542
E: news@omniab.ca **W:** http://www.omniab.ca
Editorial Profile: CJCO-TV is an independent station for the Calgary, Alberta market. The station is owned by Rogers Media Inc. CJCO-TV broadcasts locally on channel 38.

CJDC-TV
Owner: Astral Media
Editorial: 901-102nd Avenue, Dawson Creek, British Columbia V1G 2B6. **T:** 1 250 782-3341
E: peacereception@astral.com
W: http://www.cjdctv.com
Editorial Profile: CJDC-TV is the CBC affiliate in Dawson Creek, British Columbia. The station is owned by Astral Media. CJDC-TV broadcasts locally on channel 5.

CJEO-TV
Owner: Rogers Media Inc.
Editorial: 10212 Jasper Avenue, Edmonton, Alberta T5J 5A3. **T:** 1 780 424-2222
E: news@omniab.ca **W:** http://www.omniab.ca
Editorial Profile: CJEO-TV is an independent station for the Edmonton, Alberta market. The station is owned by Rogers Media Inc. CJEO-TV broadcasts locally on channel 56.

CJIC-TV
Owner: Canadian Broadcasting Corp.
Editorial: 250 Front St, Toronto, Ontario M5V 3G5. **T:** 1 416 205-6309 **E:** tonews@cbc.ca
W: http://www.cbc.ca/toronto
Editorial Profile: CBLT5-TV is a local, commercial television station owned by Canadian Broadcasting Corp. The station serves as the CBC affiliate for Sault-Sainte Marie, and Ontario. CBLT5-TV airs locally on channel 11. There is no physical station or staff located in Sault Ste. Marie, Ontario.

CJIL-TV
Owner: Miracle Channel Association(The)
Editorial: 450 31 St N, Lethbridge, Alberta T1H 3Z3. **T:** 1 403 380-3399
W: http://www.miraclechannel.ca
Editorial Profile: CJIL-TV is a commercial television station for the Lethbridge, Alberta area. The station is owned by The Miracle Channel Association. CJIL-TV broadcasts locally on channel 17.

CJMT-TV
Owner: Rogers Media Inc.
Editorial: 33 Dundas St E, Toronto, Ontario M5B 1B8. **T:** 1 416 260-0047
E: info@omni2.ca
W: http://www.omnitv.ca/ontario
Editorial Profile: CJMT-TV is an independent station for the Toronto, ON market. The station is owned by Rogers Media Inc. CJMT-TV broadcasts locally on channel 69.

CJNT-TV
Owner: Rogers Communications
Editorial: 1751 Richardson St, Suite 2106, Montreal, Quebec H3K 1G6.
T: 1 514 599-2489
W: http://www.citytv.com/montreal
Editorial Profile: CJNT-TV is owned by Rogers Communications. CJNT-TV broadcasts locally on channel 62. On June 4, 2012 CJNT-TV will start airing some content from CITY-TV.

CJOH-TV
Owner: Bell Media
Editorial: 87 George St, Ottawa, Ontario K1N 9H7-. **T:** 1 613 789-0606
E: ottawanews@ctv.ca
W: http://ottawa.ctvnews.ca
Editorial Profile: CJOH-TV is the CTV affiliate for the Ottawa, Ontario market. The station is owned by Bell Media. The station's tagline is CTV Ottawa. CJOH-TV broadcasts locally on channel 13.

CJOM-TV
Owner: Newfoundland Broadcasting Co. Ltd.
Editorial: 446 Logy Bay Rd, St. John's, Newfoundland A1C 5S2. **T:** 1 709 722-5015
E: ntv@ntv.ca **W:** http://www.ntv.ca

CJON-TV
Owner: Newfoundland Broadcasting Co. Ltd.
Editorial: 446 Logy Bay Road, St. John's, Newfoundland A1C 5S2. **T:** 1 709 722-5015
E: ntv@ntv.ca **W:** http://www.ntv.ca
Editorial Profile: CJON-TV is the CTV affiliate for the St. John's, Newfoundland market. The station is owned by Newfoundland Broadcasting Co. Ltd. CJON-TV broadcasts locally on channel 6.

CJPM-TV
Owner: Quebecor Media Inc.
Editorial: 1 rue Mont Ste-Claire, Chicoutimi, Quebec G7H 5G3. **T:** 1 418 549-2576
E: nouvelles@cjpm.tva.ca
W: http://tva.canoe.ca/stations/cjpm
Editorial Profile: CJPM-TV is the TVA affiliate for the Chicoutimi, Quebec market. The station is owned by Quebecor Media Inc. CJPM-TV broadcasts locally on channel 6.

CJWB-TV
Owner: Newfoundland Broadcasting Co. Ltd.
Editorial: 446 Logy Bay Rd, St. John's, Newfoundland A1C 5S2. **T:** 1 709 722-5015
E: ntv@ntv.ca **W:** http://www.ntv.ca

CJWN-TV
Owner: Newfoundland Broadcasting Co. Ltd.
Editorial: 446 Logy Bay Rd, St. John's, Newfoundland A1C 5S2. **T:** 1 709 722-5015
E: ntv@ntv.ca **W:** http://www.ntv.ca

CKAL-TV
Owner: Rogers Media Inc.
Editorial: 535 7 Ave SW, Calgary, Alberta T2P 0Y4. **T:** 1 403 508-2222
W: http://www.citytv.com/calgary
Editorial Profile: CKAL-TV is the CityTV Calgary affiliate for the Calgary, Alberta market. The station is owned by Rogers Media Inc. CKAL-TV broadcasts locally on channel 5.

CKAM-TV
Owner: Bell Media
Editorial: 191 Halifax St, Moncton, New Brunswick E1C 9R7. **T:** 1 506 857-2600
E: news@ctv.ca **W:** http://atlantic.ctv.ca
Editorial Profile: CKAM-TV is the CTV affiliate for the Upsalquitch, New Brunswick market. The station is owned by Bell Media. CKAM-TV broadcasts locally on channel 12.

CKCD-TV
Owner: Bell Media
Editorial: 191 Halifax St, Moncton, New Brunswick E1C 9R7. **T:** 1 506 857-2600
E: news@ctv.ca **W:** http://atlantic.ctv.ca
Editorial Profile: CKCD-TV is the CTV affiliate for the Campbellton, New Brunswick market. The station is owned by Bell Media. CKCD-TV broadcasts locally on channel 7.

CKCK-TV
Owner: Bell Media
Editorial: 1 Highway East, Regina, Saskatchewan S4P 3E5. **T:** 1 306 522-0090
E: ckcknews@ctv.ca
W: http://www.regina.ctv.ca
Editorial Profile: CKCK-TV is the CTV affiliate for the Regina, Saskatchewan market. The station is owned by Bell Media. CKCK-TV broadcasts locally on channel 2.

CKCO-TV
Owner: Bell Media
Editorial: 864 King St W, Kitchener, Ontario N2G 1E8. **T:** 1 519 578-1313
E: news@kitchener.ctv.ca
W: http://kitchener.ctvnews.ca
Editorial Profile: CKCO-TV is the CTV affiliate for the Kitchener, Ontario market. The station is owned by Bell Media. CKCO-TV broadcasts locally on channel 13.

CKCS-TV
Owner: Crossroads Television Systems
Editorial: Atrium 1, 839 5th Ave SW, Ste 100B, Calgary, Alberta T2P 3C8.
T: 1 403 263-3191 **W:** http://www.ctstv.com
Editorial Profile: CKCS-TV is the CTS television affiliate for the Calgary, Alberta market. The station is owned by Crossroads Television Systems. CKCS-TV broadcasts locally on channel 32.

CKCW-TV
Owner: Bell Media
Editorial: 191 Halifax St, Moncton, New Brunswick E1C 9R7. **T:** 1 506 857-2600
E: atlanticnews@bellmedia.ca
W: http://atlantic.ctv.ca
Editorial Profile: CKCW-TV is the CTV affiliate for the Moncton, New Brunswick market. The station is owned by Bell Media. CKCW-TV broadcasts locally on channel 2.

CKEM-TV
Owner: Rogers Media Inc.
Editorial: 10212 Jasper Ave, Edmonton, Alberta T5J 5A3. **T:** 1 780 424-2222
E: newsdesk@citytv.com
W: http://www.citytv.com/edmonton
Editorial Profile: CKEM-TV is the CityTV affiliate for the Edmonton, Alberta market. The station is owned by Rogers Media Inc. CKEM-TV broadcasts locally on channel 51.

CKES-TV
Owner: Crossroads Television Systems
Editorial: 5330 Calgary Trail, Edmonton, Alberta T6H 4J8. **T:** 1 780 433-3118
E: contactus@ctstv.com
W: http://www.ctstv.com
Editorial Profile: CKES-TV is the CTS television affiliate for the Edmonton, Alberta market. The station is owned by Crossroads Television Systems. CKES-TV airs locally on channel 45.

CKLT-TV
Owner: Bell Media
Editorial: 12 Smythe St, Ste 126, Saint John, New Brunswick E2L 5G5. **T:** 1 506 658-1010
E: cklt@ctv.ca **W:** http://atlantic.ctv.ca
Editorial Profile: CKLT-TV is the CTV affiliate for the Saint John, New Brunswick market. The station is owned by Bell Media. CKLT-TV broadcasts locally on channel 9.

CKMI-TV
Owner: Shaw Communications
Editorial: 1010, Rue Ste-Catherine Ouest, Bureau 200, Montreal, Quebec H3B 5L1.
T: 1 514 521-4323
E: globalnews.que@globaltv.ca
W: http://www.globalmontreal.com
Editorial Profile: CKMI-TV is a Global Television Network affiliate for the Montreal market. The station is owned by Shaw Communications. CKMI-TV broadcasts locally on channel 46.

CKND-TV
Owner: Shaw Communications
Editorial: 201 Portage Ave., 30th Fl, Winnipeg, Manitoba R3B 3K6. **T:** 1 204 233-3304
E: globalnews.wpg@globaltv.com
W: http://www.globalwinnipeg.com
Editorial Profile: CKND-TV is the Global Television Network affiliate for the Winnipeg, Manitoba market. The station is owned by Shaw Communications. CKND-TV broadcasts locally on channel 9.

CKNX-TV
Owner: Bell Media
Editorial: 215 Carling Terrace, Wingham, Ontario N0G 2W0. **T:** 1 519 357-4438
E: londonnews@ctv.ca
W: http://www.ctvlondon.ca
Editorial Profile: CKNX-TV is the CTV affiliate for the Wingham, Ontario market. The station is owned by Bell Media. CKNX-TV broadcasts locally on channel 8. The station rebroadcasts CFPL-TV's programming.

CKNY-TV
Owner: Bell Media
Editorial: 245 Oak St E, North Bay, Ontario P1B 8P8-. **T:** 1 705 476-3111
E: newsforthenorth@ctv.ca
W: http://northernontario.ctvnews.ca
Editorial Profile: CKNY-TV is the CTV affiliate for the North Bay, Ontario market. The station is owned by Bell Media. CKNY-TV broadcasts locally on channel 10.

CKPG-TV
Owner: Jim Pattison Broadcast Group(The)
Editorial: 1810 3rd Ave, 2nd Floor, Prince George, British Columbia V2M 1G4.
T: 1 250 564-8861 **E:** ckpgnews@ckpg.com
W: http://www.ckpg.com
Editorial Profile: CKPG-TV is an independent station for the Prince George, British Columbia market. The station is owned by The Jim Pattison Broadcast Group. CKPG-TV broadcasts locally on channel 2. On September 1, 2012 CKPG-TV will begin airing some content from CITY-TV.

CKPR-TV
Owner: Dougall Media
Editorial: 87 Hill St N, Thunder Bay, Ontario P7A 5V6. **T:** 1 807 346-2600
E: news@dougallmedia.com
Editorial Profile: CKPR-TV is the CBC affiliate for the Thunder Bay, Ontario market. The station is owned by Dougall Media. CKPR-TV broadcasts locally on channel 2.

CKRN-TV
Owner: RNC Media
Editorial: 380 Murdoch Street, Rouyn-Noranda, Quebec J9X 1G5. **T:** 1 819 762-0744
W: http://www.rncmedia.ca
Editorial Profile: CKRN-TV is the Radio-Canada Reseaux Television affiliate for the Rouyn-Noranda, Quebec area. The station is owned by RNC Media. CKRN-TV airs locally on channel 4.

CKRT-TV
Owner: Télé Inter-Rives Ltée
Editorial: 15 rue de la Chute, Riviere-du-Loup, Quebec G5R 5B7. **T:** 1 418 867-8080
E: nouvelles@ckrt.ca **W:** http://www.ckrt.ca
Editorial Profile: CKRT-TV is the Radio-Canada affiliate for the Riviere-du-Loup, Quebec market. The station is owned by Télé Inter-Rives Ltée. CKRT-TV broadcasts locally on channel 7.

CKSA-TV
Owner: Newfoundland Capital Corporation Limited
Editorial: 5026 50th St, Lloydminster, Alberta T9V 1P3. **T:** 1 780 875-3321
E: tvnews@newcap.ca
W: http://www.newcaptv.com
Editorial Profile: CKSA-TV is the CBC affiliate for the Lloydminster, Alberta market. The station is owned by Newfoundland Capital Corporation Limited. CKSA-TV airs locally on channel 2.

CKSH-TV
Owner: Société Radio-Canada
Editorial: 1335, rue King Ouest, Sherbrooke, Quebec J1J 2B8. **T:** 1 819 620-0000
E: tjestrie@radio-canada.ca
W: http://www.radio-canada.ca/regions/estrie
Editorial Profile: CKSH-TV is the Radio-Canada affiliate for the Sherbrooke, Quebec market. The station is owned by Société Radio-Canada. CKSH-TV broadcasts locally on channel 9.

CKTM-TV
Owner: Société Radio-Canada
Editorial: 225 des Forges, Suite 101, Trois-Rivieres, Quebec G9A 2G7. **T:** 1 819 694-0114
E: tjmauricie@radio-canada.ca
W: http://www.radio-canada.ca/regions/mauricie
Editorial Profile: CKTM-TV is an affiliate of Radio-Canada for the Trois-Rivieres, Quebec area. The station is owned by Societe Radio-Canada. CKTM-TV broadcasts locally on channel 13.

CKTV-TV
Owner: Société Radio-Canada
Editorial: 500, rue des Saguenéens, Chicoutimi, Quebec G7H 6N4.
T: 1 418 696-6600
E: saguenaylacstjean@radio-canada.ca
W: http://radio-canada.ca/saguenay-lac-saint-jean
Editorial Profile: CKTV-TV is the Radio-Canada affiliate for the Saguenay, Quebec area. The station is owned by Société Radio-Canada. CKTV-TV broadcasts locally on channel 12.

CKVR-TV
Owner: Bell Media
Editorial: 33 Beacon Rd, Barrie, Ontario L4N 9J9. **T:** 1 705 734-3300 **E:** barrienews@ctv.ca
W: http://ctvbarrie.ca
Editorial Profile: CKVR-TV is the CTV affiliate for the Barrie, Ontario market. The station is owned by Bell Media. CKVR-TV broadcasts locally on channel 3.

CKVU-TV
Owner: Rogers Media Inc.
Editorial: 180 W 2nd Ave, Vancouver, British Columbia V5Y 3T9. **T:** 1 604 876-1344
E: news@btvancouver.ca
W: http://www.citytv.com/vancouver
Editorial Profile: CKVU-TV is branded as part of the CityTV family offering local news programming for the Vancouver, British Columbia market. The station is owned by Rogers Media Inc. CKVU-TV broadcasts locally on channel 10.

CKWS-TV
Owner: Corus Entertainment Inc.
Editorial: 170 Queen St, Kingston, Ontario K7K 1B2. **T:** 1 613 544-2340
E: newswatch@corusent.com
W: http://www.ckwstv.com
Editorial Profile: CKWS-TV is the CBC affiliate for the Kingston, Ontario market. The station is owned by Corus Entertainment Inc. CKWS-TV broadcasts locally on channel 11.

CKY-TV
Owner: Bell Media
Editorial: 400-345 Graham Avenue, Winnipeg, Manitoba R3C 5S6. **T:** 1 204 788-3300
E: winnipegnews@ctv.ca
W: http://winnipeg.ctv.ca
Editorial Profile: CKY-TV is the CTV affiliate for the Winnipeg, Manitoba region. The station is owned by Bell Media. CKY-TV broadcasts locally on channel 7.

CRRS-TV
Owner: Community Recreation Rebroad. Service Association
Editorial: 208 Amherst Avenue, Labrador City, Newfoundland A2V 2Y5. **T:** 1 709 944-7676
E: info@crrstv.net **W:** http://www.crrstv.net

TELEVISION NETWORKS

CBC Television Network
Owner: Canadian Broadcasting Corp.
Editorial: 250 Front St W, Toronto, Ontario M5V 3G7. **T:** 1 416 205-3311
E: yournews@cbc.ca
W: http://www.cbc.ca/television
Editorial Profile: The CBC serves as Canada's largest cultural institution, aiming to touch the lives of the country's citizens on a daily basis. Owned by all Canadians, the CBC has a heritage as the nation's supplier of Canadian cultural content and its nationwide presence sets the standard for excellence in Canadian broadcasting.

CBC Television Network
Editorial: 181 Queen Street, Ottawa, Ontario K1P 1K9. **T:** 1 613 288-6000
E: cbcnewsottawa@cbc.ca
W: http://www.cbc.ca/ottawa
Editorial Profile: CBC's Parliamentary Bureau in Ottawa, Ontario.

CBC Television Network
Editorial: 123 Edmonton City Centre, 10062-102 Ave, Edmonton, Alberta T5J 2Y8.
T: 1 780 468-5555 **E:** cbx.edmonton@cbc.ca
W: http://www.cbc.ca/edmonton

CBC Television Network
Editorial: 700 Hamilton Street, Vancouver, British Columbia V6B 2R5. **T:** 1 604 662-6000
E: cbcnewsvancouver@cbc.ca
W: http://www.cbc.ca/bc
Editorial Profile: CBC Television Vancouver, British Columbia bureau.

CBC Television Network
Editorial: 541 Portage Ave, Winnipeg, Manitoba R3B 2G1. **T:** 1 204 788-3222
E: radio893@cbc.ca
W: http://www.cbc.ca/manitoba
Editorial Profile: Manitoba bureau of the CBC Television.

CBC Television Network
Editorial: 1840 Bell Road, Halifax, Nova Scotia B3H 2Z5. **T:** 1 902 420-8311 **E:** cbcns@cbc.ca
W: http://www.cbc.ca/ns
Editorial Profile: Halifax, Nova Scotia bureau of the Canadian Broadcast Corp.

CBC Television Network
T: 1 709 576-5100 **E:** hereandnow.nl@cbc.ca
W: http://www.cbc.ca/nl
Editorial Profile: Newfoundland and Labrador bureau of the CBC Television Network.

CBC Television Network
Editorial: 5002 Forrest Drive, Yellowknife, Northwest Territories X1A 2N2.
T: 1 867 920-5400 **E:** cbcnorth@cbc.ca
W: http://www.cbc.ca/north

CBC Television Network
Editorial: 1400 Rene-Levesque Blvd Est, Ste B96-50, Montreal, Quebec H2L 2M2.
T: 1 514 597-6371
E: cbcnewsmontreal@cbc.ca
W: http://www.cbc.ca/montreal
Editorial Profile: Montreal office for CBC Television Network.

CBC Television Network
Editorial: 745 3rd Ave, Ste 8C, New York, New York 10017. **T:** 1 212 546-0500

CBC Television Network
Editorial: 529 14th St NW, Ste 500529, Washington, District Of Columbia 20045.
T: 1 202 383-2900

CBC Television Network
Editorial: 1724 Westmount Blvd NW, Calgary, Alberta T2N 3G7. **T:** 1 403 521-6000
E: calgary-desk@cbc.ca
W: http://www.cbc.ca/calgary

CBC Television Network
Editorial: 6255 Sunset Blvd, Suite 1500, Los Angeles, California 90028
W: http://www.cbc.ca

CTV Atlantic
Editorial: 90 St John St, Fredericton, New Brunswick E3B 5H1. **T:** 1 506 459-1010

CTV Atlantic
Editorial: 191 Halifax St, Moncton, New Brunswick E1C 9R7. **T:** 1 506 857-2610
E: ckcw@ctv.ca

CTV Atlantic
Editorial: 12 Smythe Street, Suite 126, Saint John, New Brunswick E2L 5G5.
T: 1 506 636-6068

CTV Television Network
Owner: Bell Media
Editorial: 9 Channel Nine Crt, Toronto, Ontario M1S 4B5-. **T:** 1 416 332-5000 **E:** news@ctv.ca
W: http://www.ctv.ca
Editorial Profile: CTV Television Network is owned by Bell Media, Canada's largest private broadcaster and premier multimedia company. The network offers a wide range of quality news, sports, information and entertainment programming that reaches 99% of English-speaking Canadians. It has the number one national newscast, and is the number one choice for primetime viewing.

CTV Television Network
Editorial: 750 Burrard St, Ste 300, Vancouver, British Columbia V6Z 1X5. **T:** 1 604 608-2868
E: bccomments@ctv.ca
Editorial Profile: Vancouver, BC bureau of CTV Television Network.

CTV Television Network
Owner: Bell Media
Editorial: 400345 Graham Street, Winnipeg, Manitoba R3C 5S6. **T:** 1 204 788-3385
E: winnipegnews@ctv.ca
W: http://winnipeg.ctv.ca
Editorial Profile: CTV Winnipeg bureau.

CTV Television Network
Editorial: 2885 Robie St, Halifax, Nova Scotia B3K 2Z4. **T:** 1 902 453-4000
E: atlanticnews@ctv.ca

CTV Television Network
Editorial: 80 Patina Rise SW, Calgary, Alberta T3H 2W4. **T:** 1 403 240-5600
E: calgaryassignmentdesk@bellmedia.ca
W: http://calgary.ctv.ca

CTV Television Network
Editorial: 1205 Papineau Avenue, Montreal, Quebec H2K 4R2. **T:** 1 514 273-6311

CTV Television Network
Owner: Bell Media
Editorial: 100 Queen Street, Ottawa, Ontario K1P 1J9. **T:** 1 613 236-7343
E: ctvottawa@ctv.ca **W:** http://ottawa.ctv.ca

CTV Television Network
Editorial: 9 Channel Nine Court, Toronto, Ontario M1S4B5. **T:** 1 416 384-5000

CTV Television Network
Editorial: 191 Halifax St, Moncton, New Brunswick E1CC 9R7. **T:** 1 506 857-2600

CTV Television Network
Editorial: 1717 Desales St Nw, Suite 354, Washington, District Of Columbia 20036-4401.
T: 1 202 775-0356

E! Entertainment Television (Canada)
Owner: Bell Media
Editorial: 299 Queen St West, Toronto, Ontario M5V 2Z5. **T:** 1 416 591-7400
W: http://www.eonline.com
Editorial Profile: In Canada, the E! network broadcasts into the major markets of Vancouver, British Columbia; Toronto; Calgary, Alberta and Edmonton, Alberta.

Fairchild Television Network
Editorial: 35 E Beaver Creek Road, Unit 8, Richmond Hill, Ontario L4B 1B3.
T: 1 905 889-8090 **E:** newstor@fairchildtv.com
W: http://www.fairchildtv.com
Editorial Profile: Twenty-one hours a day, seven days a week, Fairchild TV provides the Chinese audience with the information they need in their own language. Fairchild is carried on cable in Toronto and throughout Southern Ontario, in Montreal, Vancouver, Calgary and Edmonton and also on the nationwide direct-to-home satellite services. Every day, Fairchild TV produces newscasts covering local and international news from a Chinese-Canadian perspective. It also broadcasts same-day satellite news programs from Hong Kong.

Fairchild Television Network
Editorial: 2723-37 Avenue NE, Suite 130, Calgary, Alberta T1Y 5R8. **T:** 1 403 571-3187
E: info@fairchildtv.com
W: http://www.fairchildtv.com

Fairchild Television Network
Owner: Fairchild Television Ltd.
Editorial: 4151 Hazelbridge Way, Aberdeen Centre, Richmond, British Columbia V6X 4J7.
T: 1 604 295-1313 **E:** info@fairchildtv.com
W: http://www.fairchildtv.com

Global Television Network
Owner: Shaw Communications
Editorial: 81 Barber Greene Rd, Toronto, Ontario M3C 2A2-. **T:** 1 416 446-5460
E: newstips@globaltv.com
W: http://www.globaltv.com
Editorial Profile: Global Television Network, owned by Shaw Communications, is a national television network serving viewers throughout Canada. The network provides a wide variety of programming, ranging from hard news to entertainment. Global Television offers a programming mix aimed at viewers primarily in the 18 to 49 age bracket. The Global Television Network is a member of the Canadian Press Gallery.

Global Television Network
Editorial: 14 Akerley Blvd, Dartmouth, Nova Scotia B3B 1J3. **T:** 1 902 481-7400
E: maritimes@globalnews.ca
W: http://globalnews.ca/halifax

Global Television Network
Editorial: 370 Hoffer Dr, Regina, Saskatchewan S4N 7A4. **T:** 1 306 775-4000
E: globalnews.reg@globaltv.com
W: http://globalnews.ca/regina

Global Television Network
Editorial: 218 Robin Crescent, Saskatoon, Saskatchewan S7L 7C3. **T:** 1 306 978-6397
E: saskatoon@globalnews.ca
W: http://globalnews.ca/saskatoon

Global Television Network
Editorial: 201 Portage Ave, 30th Fl, CanWest Pl, Winnipeg, Manitoba R3B 3K6.
T: 1 204 235-8545
E: globalnews.winnipeg@shawmedia.ca
W: http://globalnews.ca/winnipeg

Global Television Network
Editorial: 1401 28 St N, Lethbridge, Alberta T1H 6H9. **T:** 1 403 327-1507
E: lethbridge@globalnews.ca
W: http://globalnews.ca/lethbridge

Global Television Network
Editorial: 1010, rue Ste-Catherine, Bureau 200, Montreal, Quebec H3B 5L1.
T: 1 514 521-4323
E: globalnews.que@globaltv.ca
W: http://globalnews.ca/montreal

Global Television Network
Editorial: 5325 Allard Way NW, Edmonton, Alberta T6H 5B8. **T:** 1 780 436-1250
W: http://globalnews.ca/edmonton
Editorial Profile: Edmonton, Alberta bureau of the Global Television Network.

Global Television Network
Editorial: 7850 Enterprise St, Burnaby, British Columbia V5A 1V7. **T:** 1 604 420-2288
E: tips@globaltvbc.com
W: http://www.globaltvbc.com

Global Television Network
Editorial: 222 23rd Ave NE, Calgary, Alberta T2E 7N2. **T:** 1 403 235-7777
E: calgary@globalnews.ca

Nickelodeon Canada
Owner: Corus Entertainment Inc.
Editorial: Corus Quay, 25 Dockside Drive, Toronto, Ontario M5A 0B5. **T:** 1 416 479-7000
W: http://www.nickcanada.com
Editorial Profile: This specialty cable network provides programming geared toward children, teens and their parents. It is based off the the programming from Nickelodeon in United States. The network also includes exclusive programs to Canadian kids and features a line-up of award-winning properties, from current live-action comedies and animated favorites to classic hits.

Talentvision
Editorial: 35 E Beaver Creek Road, Unit 8, Richmond Hill, Ontario L4B 1B3.
T: 1 905 889-8090 **E:** prgtor@fairchildtv.com
W: http://www.fairchildtv.com
Editorial Profile: Launched in June 1998, Talentvision is a national network serving the Mandarin community of Canada. The network has regional stations in British Columbia and Ontario, and is distributed via cable and Direct-to-Home satellite services. The network boasts 18 hours of Mandarin programs a day, 7 days a week.

La Télévision de Radio-Canada
Owner: Societe Radio-Canada
Editorial: 1400 Boul Rene-Levesque E, Montreal, Quebec H2L 2M2-.
T: 1 514 597-6000
E: nouvelles@radio-canada.ca
W: http://www.radio-canada.ca/television
Editorial Profile: La Télévision de Radio-Canada is the French equivalent of the CBC Television Network. It is the main French-language television service of the CBC. It broadcasts in all Canadian provinces. La Télévision de Radio-Canada is a member of the Canadian Press Gallery.

TVA
Owner: Quebecor Media Inc.
Editorial: 1600 boulevard Maisonneuve Est, Montreal, Quebec H2L 4P2. **T:** 1 514 526-9251
E: nouvelles@tva.ca **W:** http://tva.canoe.ca
Editorial Profile: TVA creates, produces and airs shows in the areas of entertainment, news and public affairs.

UmeedTV Network
Editorial: 363A-6830 Av du Parc 363A, Montreal, Quebec H3N 1W7.
T: 1 514 495-6699 **E:** info@umeedtv.com
W: http://www.umeedtv.com
Editorial Profile: A multicultural television network presenting news and entertainment that represents the South Asian community.

V
Owner: Remstar Corporation
Editorial: 85, rue St-Paul, Montreal, Quebec H2Y 3V4. **T:** 1 514 390-6100 **W:** http://vtele.ca
Editorial Profile: V is a French-language television network with stations and affiliates throughout Quebec. The name, "V," is a reflection of the new entertainment focus of the network: Vedettes (Stars), Vitesse (Speed), Victoires (Victories), Voyages (Trips) and Vice ou Vérité (Vice or Truth). V does not produce its own news. News is produced by an outside studio, Info 3. All submissions to the newsroom should be directed to the news department's main e-mail address or the news director. V changed its name from TQS (Télévision Quatre Saisons) on August 31, 2009.

CABLE

ABC Spark
Owner: Corus Entertainment Inc.
Editorial: Corus Quay, 25 Dockside, Toronto, Ontario M5A 0B5. **T:** 1 416 479-7000
E: info@abcsparkcanada.com
W: http://www.abcspark.ca
Editorial Profile: ABC Spark offers fun, light-hearted programming with a twist for kids, teens, and adults. The channel features original series and movies, major theatrical releases, and repurposed programming from the ABC Television Network. ABC Spark officially launched on March 26, 2012.

Aboriginal Peoples Television Network
Editorial: 339 Portage Avenue, 2nd Floor, Winnipeg, Manitoba R3B 2C3.
T: 1 204 947-9331 **E:** info@aptn.ca
W: http://www.aptn.ca
Editorial Profile: A network that provides Indigenous people the opportunity to share their stories with the rest of the world on a television outlet dedicated to Aboriginal programming. Through documentaries, news magazines, dramas, entertainment specials, children's series, cooking shows and education programs, APTN offers all Canadians a window into the remarkably diverse worlds of Indigenous peoples in Canada and throughout the world. Headquartered in Winnipeg, Manitoba, APTN offers an unprecedented opportunity for Aboriginal producers, directors, actors, writers and media professionals to create innovative, reflective and relevant programming for Canadian viewers.

Aboriginal Peoples Television Network
Editorial: 100 Queen Street, Suite 600, Ottawa, Ontario K1P 1J9. **T:** 1 613 567-1550
E: info@aptn.ca

Aboriginal Peoples Television Network
Editorial: 1755, boul. René-Lévesque Est, Bureau 102, Montreal, Quebec H2K 4P6.
T: 1 514 495-6424 **E:** info@aptn.ca

Aboriginal Peoples Television Network
Editorial: 210 - 1999 Marine Drive, North Vancouver, British Columbia V7P 3J3.
T: 1 604 986-9843

Action
Owner: Shaw Communications
Editorial: 121 Bloor Street East, 15th Floor Ste B1, Toronto, Ontario M4W 3M5.
T: 1 416 967-0022 **E:** feedback@showcase.ca
W: http://www.action-tv.ca
Editorial Profile: Network which features smash-hit movies with spies and tough guys, adventurers and kung-fu masters. Showcase Action programs include some of the world's greatest heroes like Arnold Schwarzenegger, Sylvester Stallone, Jackie Chan, Bruce Willis and Steve McQueen. Programming includes classic action series and sexy late-night programming.

Addik TV
Owner: Groupe TVA Inc.
Editorial: 1600, boul. de Maisonneuve Est, Montreal, Quebec H2L 4P2. **T:** 1 514 526-9251
E: relations.auditoire@tva.ca
W: http://www.addik.tv
Editorial Profile: Addik TV, formerly Mystère, is a French-language cable network owned by Groupe TVA Inc. It offers movies and series twenty-four hours a day. Its programming includes four different genres: fantasy, crime, action and mystery.

AMI Television
Owner: Accessible Media Inc.
Editorial: 1090 Don Mills Rd, Toronto, Ontario M3C 3R6. **T:** 1 416 422-4222 **E:** info@ami.ca
W: http://www.ami.ca
Editorial Profile: AMI Television broadcasts popular movies and TV shows in open described closed-captioned format for people who are blind, vision-impaired, deaf or hard of hearing.

Animal Planet
Owner: Bell Media
Editorial: 9 Channel Nine Court, Toronto, Ontario M1S 4B5. **T:** 1 416 332-5000
E: comments@animalplanet.ca
W: http://www.animalplanet.ca
Editorial Profile: Animal Planet lets viewers see Earth from a wilder perspective. The world's weirdest, wildest and most wonderful creatures take charge of Animal Planet Canada in the most entertaining and engaging ways. From the most perilous encounters with nature's fiercest predators to the pets we bring into our own family, all creatures big and small are the undeniable stars of Animal Planet.

Argent Télé
Owner: Québécor Média
Editorial: 1600 Boulevard de Maisonneuve Est, Montreal, Quebec H2L 4P2.
T: 1 514 526-9251 **E:** nouvelles@tva.ca
W: http://www.argent.canoe.ca
Editorial Profile: Launched February 21, 2005, Argent Télé is a French-language digital cable television channel. The channel is devoted to financial information and the business world. The channel is owned and operated by Québécor Média. Any news pitches should be sent to the attention of the news director.

ARTV
Owner: Société Radio-Canada/ARTE France
Editorial: 1400 boul René-Lévesque Est, Bureau A-53-1, Montreal, Quebec H2L 2M2.
T: 1 514 597-3636 **E:** auditoire@artv.ca
W: http://www.artv.ca
Editorial Profile: ARTV is a French-language cable television channel featuring non-stop arts programming from Canada and around the world. It offers performances, movies, documentaries, music, dramas and design, twenty four hours a day.

Asian Television Network
Owner: Asian Television Network International Limited
Editorial: 130 Pony Drive, Newmarket, Ontario L3Y 7B6. **T:** 1 905 836-6460
E: atn@asiantelevision.com
W: http://www.asiantelevision.com
Editorial Profile: Programming is geared to people of the South East Asian communities who come from India, Pakistan, Sri Lanka, South Africa, East Africa, Trinidad, Surinam and Guyana. The network reaches Canada, the U.S. and the Caribbean.

AUX TV
Owner: GlassBOX Television Inc.
Editorial: 2196 Dunwin Dr., Mississauga, Ontario L5L 1C7. **T:** 1 905 828-2483
E: info@aux.tv **W:** http://www.aux.tv
Editorial Profile: Offers music videos and music-related programming to a Canadian audience. First launched on an Internet-television model and then as a show on BITE TV, the channel subsequently launched in October 2009.

BBC Canada
Owner: Shaw Communications
Editorial: 121 Bloor Street East, 15th Floor, Suite B-1, Toronto, Ontario M4W 3M5.
T: 1 416 967-1174
W: http://www.bbccanada.com
Editorial Profile: BBC Canada is the home of the best and boldest of British programming from the world-renowned BBC. BBC Canada offers viewers a contemporary feast of edgy comedies, excellent lifestyle programming and dramas.

BBC Kids
Owner: Knowledge Network Corporation
Editorial: 4355 Mathissi Place, Burnaby, British Columbia V5G 4S8. **T:** 1 604 431-3222
E: kids@knowledge.ca
W: http://www.bbckids.ca
Editorial Profile: BBC Kids brings viewers children's programming from across the U.K. and around the world. The network features programs specifically aimed at preschoolers, school-aged children and teenagers. To contact this network please use the online contact form located in the "Contact us" section of the website.

Bio/The Biography Channel
Owner: Rogers Communications Inc.
Editorial: 545 Lakeshore Blvd W, Toronto, Ontario M5V 1A3-. **T:** 1 416 260-3803
E: Viewerrelations@rci.rogers.com
W: http://thebiographychannel.ca
Editorial Profile: The Biography Channel features in-depth, informative biographies of famous individuals from the world of politics, arts, and entertainment. Programming is split into three blocks during the week: Bio-by-Day, Biography Primetime and Biography Late Night. On Saturdays and Sundays, Great Biography Weekends delivers an entire day's worth of attention-grabbing themed programs. The Biography Channel aims to inform, surprise and stimulate its viewers by giving them an insider's look at the lives of exceptional people.

BITE TV
Owner: GlassBOX Television Inc.
Editorial: 2196 Dunwin Dr, Mississauga, Ontario L5L 1C7-. **T:** 1 905 828-2483
E: info@bite.ca **W:** http://www.bite.ca
Editorial Profile: BITE TV is a new kind of lifestyle network for today's wired youth and young adults. BITE TV's interactive Emmy-winning format features the best in short film, animation and guerilla-style reporting, providing an entertaining, fast-paced, first-hand account of the latest events, trends and news affecting today's youth culture.

BNN/Business News Network
Owner: Bell Media
Editorial: 299 Queen Street West, Toronto, Ontario M5V 2Z5. **T:** 1 416 384-8000
E: info@bnn.ca **W:** http://www.bnn.ca
Editorial Profile: Business News Network (BNN) is Canada's only business and financial news network, and is currently available in about 4.5 million Canadian homes. Its editorial team features business journalists, entrepreneurs and financial professionals that deliver up-to-the-minute business news, commentary and interviews with leading business newsmakers.

BNN/Business News Network
Editorial: 80 Patina Rise SW, Calgary, Alberta T3H 2W4. **T:** 1 403 240-5600
E: calgarynews@ctv.ca **W:** http://www.bnn.ca

bold
Owner: Canadian Broadcasting Corp.
Editorial: 205 Wellington St W, Toronto, Ontario M5V 3G7. **T:** 1 416 205-3311
W: http://www.cbc.ca/bold
Editorial Profile: bold is a network of the performing arts, drama, comedy and world championship sports.

bpm:tv
Owner: Stornoway Communications Inc.
Editorial: 105 Gordon Baker Road, 8th Floor, Toronto, Ontario M2H 3P8. **T:** 1 416 756-2404
E: info@bpmtv.com **W:** http://www.bpmtv.com
Editorial Profile: The cable network bpm:tv is Canada's first and only dance channel, specifically programmed to the hip taste-makers who live the active dance lifestyle. The network features high energy music videos rarely seen in Canada. In addition, bpm:tv showcases DJs, club openings, interviews and fashion shows. The network is the connection to the hottest dance culture on television.

The Brand New One
Owner: ZoomerMedia Limited
Editorial: 171 East Liberty Street, Suite 230, Toronto, Ontario M6K 3P6. **T:** 1 416 368-3194
E: audience@onebodymindspirit.com
W: http://www.onebodymindspiritlove.com
Editorial Profile: The Brand New One brings viewers progressive programming from Canada and around the world on natural health, personal growth, new ideas and intriguing possibilities, each of them opening up options for recharging lives and helping viewers reach their maximum potential.

Bravo!
Owner: Bell Media
Editorial: 299 Queen St W, Toronto, Ontario M5V 2Z5-. **T:** 1 416 591-5757
E: bravomail@bravo.ca
W: http://www.bravo.ca
Editorial Profile: Bravo! is dedicated to entertaining, stimulating and enlightening viewers who have a taste for complex television. Bravo! delivers a wide array of fine arts programming, balancing longer-form structured shows and shorter pieces that appear in a more random way as "flow" to create a fluid mix of distinctive music, dance, opera, drama, literature, cinema, visual art, the art of television and the art of talk.

Cable Public Affairs Channel
Owner: CPAC (Cable Public Affairs Channel)
Editorial: 45 O'Connor St, Ste 1750, Ottawa, Ontario K1P 1A4. **T:** 1 613 567-2722
E: comments@cpac.ca **W:** http://www.cpac.ca
Editorial Profile: Launched in 1992. Bilingual English-French, commercial-free coverage of Canadian public affairs issues and live broadcasts of the House of Commons and Standing Committees. Also includes coverage of current events in Canadian politics. CPAC is Canada's top source of parliamentary, political and public affairs programming. CPAC's French title is La Chaîne d'affaires publiques par câble.

Canal Savoir
Owner: Corporation pour l'Avancement des Nouvelles Applications des Langages Ltée (CANAL)
Editorial: 2200, rue Ste-Catherine Est, 1er étage, Montreal, Quebec H2K 2J1.
T: 1 514 509-2222 **E:** info@canalsavoir.tv
W: http://www.canalsavoir.tv
Editorial Profile: Canal Savoir is a nonprofit organization dedicated to spreading knowledge. The station strives to be sure its programming is educational to ensure its viewers are learning. It is trying to promote a desire to gain knowledge.

Cartoon Network (Canada)
Owner: Astral Media and Corus Entertainment
Editorial: Corus Quay, 25 Dockside Drive, Toronto, Ontario M5A 0B5
W: http://www.cartoonnetwork.ca
Editorial Profile: The 24-hour network is devoted to providing cartoon and animation programming. Drawing from the world's largest cartoon library, Cartoon Network showcases unique original cartoon ventures. The network offers cable service in original, acquired and classic entertainment for youth and families. The channel is owned by both Astral Media and Corus Entertainment in Canada.

Casa
Owner: Quebecor Media
Editorial: 1600, boul. de Maisonneuve Est, Montreal, Quebec H2L 4P2. **T:** 1 514 526-9251
E: relations.auditoire@tva.ca
W: http://www.casatv.ca
Editorial Profile: Casa gives Quebecois viewers what's best in the world of "how-to." The network offers Quebecois and foreign programming focusing on the topics of cooking, home decorating, renovation and interior design.

The Cave
Owner: Groupe TVA Inc. & Shaw Media
Editorial: 25 Ontario St, Toronto, Ontario M5A 4L6. **T:** 1 416 601-0010
W: http://www.thecavetv.ca
Editorial Profile: The Cave is a specialty television channel owned by Groupe TVA Inc. & Shaw Media and operated by Sun TV (CKXT-TV). The network caters to men's interest topics for a Canadian audience. Programming spotlights tastes and trends in men's health, lifestyle, hobbies and fashion.

CBC News Express/RDI Express
Editorial: 205 Wellington St. W., Toronto, Ontario M5V 3G7. **T:** 1 416 205-3311
E: yournews@cbc.ca **W:** http://www.cbc.ca
Editorial Profile: Bilingual news and information service available in five large Canadian airports, serving over 62 million travelers annually.

CBC News Network
Owner: Canadian Broadcasting Corp.
Editorial: 205 Wellington St., Toronto, Ontario M5V 3G7. **T:** 1 416 205-3311
W: http://www.cbc.ca/news
Editorial Profile: CBC News Network (CBC NN) is a 24-hour cable news and information service with a special emphasis on round-the-clock national news, live coverage, in-depth specials and award-winning documentaries. CBC News Network is a member of the Canadain Press Gallery.

CMT Canada
Owner: Corus Entertainment Inc.
Editorial: Corus Quay, 25 Dockside Drive, Toronto, Ontario M5A 0B5. **T:** 1 416 479-7000
W: http://www.cmt.ca
Editorial Profile: CMT Canada combines an engaging, entertaining blend of music videos with programs that focus on country artists and their music. CMT provides viewers with the latest news and information as well as videos, artist performances and appearances.

Comedy Gold
Owner: Bell Media
Editorial: 299 Queen Street West, Toronto, Ontario M5V 2Z5. **T:** 1 416 384-8000
E: mail@thecomedynetwork.ca
W: http://www.comedygold.ca
Editorial Profile: Features ground-breaking and iconic comedic series from 1970s, 1980s and 1990s.

The Comedy Network
Owner: Bell Media
Editorial: 9 Channel Nine Court, Toronto, Ontario M1S 4B5. **T:** 1 416 332-5000
E: mail@thecomedynetwork.ca
W: http://www.thecomedynetwork.ca
Editorial Profile: Canada's first-and-only specialty comedy service, The Comedy Network airs comedy of all kinds, 24 hours-a-day, across multiple platforms, including a revolutionary broadband service at thecomedynetwork.ca. Launched in October 1997, The Comedy Network broadcasts, uncut and uncensored, an eclectic mix of scripted, stand-up, sketch, improv, and animated comedy. Also featured are topical comedy talk shows, game shows and classic situation comedies.

Commonwealth Broadcasting Network (CBN)
Owner: Asian Television Network International Limited
Editorial: 130 Pony Dr, Newmarket, Ontario L3Y 7B6. **T:** 1 905 836-6460
E: atn@asiantelevision.com
W: http://asiantelevision.com/atncbnp.htm
Editorial Profile: Commonwealth Broadcasting Network features live cricket coverage, cricket news and highlights, as well as local news and events for the Caribbean and South Asian communities across Canada.

Cosmopolitan TV
Owner: Corus Entertainment Inc.
Editorial: Corus Quay, 25 Dockside, Toronto, Ontario M5A 0B5. **T:** 1 416 479-7000
E: info@cosmotv.ca **W:** http://www.cosmotv.ca
Editorial Profile: Targeting women 18 to 34, CosmoTV programming runs the gamut from comedies and dramas to relationship and reality programming. Like the magazine, the focus for Cosmopolitan TV is men, sex and relationships, packed with the kind of information that best girlfriends share over drinks.

CP24
Owner: Bell Media
Editorial: 299 Queen St W, Toronto, Ontario M5V 2Z5. **T:** 1 416 591-7400
E: breakingnews@cp24.com
W: http://www.cp24.com
Editorial Profile: CP24 is Canada's first and only 24-hour local news channel. CP24's enriched screen provides nine simultaneous and continuous streams of information to meet the demands of today's most sophisticated news consumer.

CTV Atlantic
Owner: Bell Media
Editorial: 2885 Robie St, Halifax, Nova Scotia B3K 5Z4. **T:** 1 902 453-4000 **E:** cjch@ctv.ca
W: http://www.ctv.ca
Editorial Profile: Each week CTV Atlantic produces 27 hours of local programming. With three stations throughout the region, CTV Atlantic reaches viewers across Nova Scotia, New Brunswick and PEI. CTV Atlantic also broadcasts many of Canada's favorite television programs.

CTV News Channel
Owner: Bell Media
Editorial: 9 Channel Nine Crt, Toronto, Ontario M1S 4B5-. **T:** 1 416 384-5000 **E:** news@ctv.ca
W: http://www.ctv.ca/newschannel
Editorial Profile: CTV News Channel is Canada's only national headline news service providing Canadians with up-to-the-minute news. With a perspective that is distinctly Canadian, CTV News Channel offers both quality and immediacy with reports from around the world. A part of the CTV News family, CTV News Channel draws on the resources of CTV's national, international and local news operations, including 21 stations across the country, as well as nine foreign and seven domestic network news bureaus. CTV News Channel is a member of the Canadian Press Gallery.

CTV News Channel
Editorial: 100 Queen St, Ste 1400, Ottawa, Ontario K1P 1J9. **T:** 1 613 236-7343

CTV News Channel
Editorial: 1205, avenue Papineau, Montreal, Quebec H2K 4R2. **T:** 1 514 273-6311

CTV News Channel
Editorial: 1717 Desales St Nw Suite 354, Washington, District Of Columbia 20036-4401.
T: 1 202 775-0356

DejaView
Owner: Shaw Communications
Editorial: 121 Bloor St East, 15th Floor Ste B1, Toronto, Ontario M4W 3M5.
T: 1 416 967-0022 **E:** contactus@globaltv.ca
W: http://www.dejaviewtv.ca
Editorial Profile: A destination for television's ultimate classics from the '70s and '80s. With familiar favorites including The Cosby Show, Who's the Boss, All In the Family, through to Three's Company, Roseanne and other classic sitcoms. Network helps viewers relive the early years of television.

Discovery Channel (Canada)
Owner: Bell Media
Editorial: 9 Channel Nine Court, Scarborough, Ontario M1S 4B5. **T:** 1 416 332-5000
E: comments@discovery.ca
W: http://www.discoverychannel.ca
Editorial Profile: Bold and leading edge, while information and entertaining, Discovery Channel is Canada's leading source for factual programming, as it puts a new spin on exploring adventure, science and technology. This award-winning channel covers the scientific beat, from animals to the animalistic side of humanity, from the sea to space, and the latest in innovation.

Discovery Science
Owner: Bell Media
Editorial: 9 Channel Nine Court, Toronto, Ontario M1S 4B5. **T:** 1 416 332-5000
E: comments@discovery.ca
W: http://www.sciencechannel.ca
Editorial Profile: Discovery Science brings science to an accessible and easy-to-understand level, revealing entertaining facts and relevant applications in daily life. The show delves into the idiosyncrasies of technology and science and introduces the people behind them.

Discovery World HD
Owner: Bell Media
Editorial: 9 Channel Nine Court, Toronto, Ontario M1S 4B5. **T:** 1 416 332-5000
E: comments@discovery.ca
W: http://www.discoveryhd.ca
Editorial Profile: Showcases the world's most dynamic people and places, culture, science and natural history programming.

Disney Junior
Owner: Astral Media
Editorial: 181 Bay St., Ste 100, Toronto, Ontario M5J 2T3. **T:** 1 416 956-2030
E: info@disneyjunior.ca
W: http://www.disneyjunior.ca
Editorial Profile: Disney Junior is the brand name for Disney Channel's preschool programs. The target age for this segment of the channel is children from age 2.

Disney Junior
Owner: Astral
Editorial: 1800 McGill College, Bureau 1600, Montreal, Quebec H3A 3J6. **T:** 1 514 939-3150
E: info@disneyjunior.ca
W: http://www.disneyjunior.ca
Editorial Profile: Disney Junior offers educational and entertainment programming targeting French-speaking preschoolers.

DIY Network Canada
Owner: Shaw Communications
Editorial: 121 Bloor St E, Ste B1, Toronto, Ontario M4W 3M5. **T:** 1 416 967-1174
E: feedback@diy.ca **W:** http://www.diy.ca
Editorial Profile: DIY Network Canada, launched on October 19, 2009, offers Canadians all they need to know about home improvement. Its programs and experts offer creative projects for do-it-yourself enthusiasts, from small-scale fix-it jobs to major home renovations.

documentary
Owner: Canadian Broadcasting Corp.
Editorial: 205 Wellington Street W, Toronto, Ontario M5V 3G7. **T:** 1 416 205-3311
E: documentarychannel@cbc.ca
W: http://www.cbc.ca/documentarychannel
Editorial Profile: documentary is a digital television station devoted to showing the best documentaries from Canada and around the world.

Dusk
Owner: Corus Entertainment Inc.
Editorial: Corus Quay, 25 Dockside Drive, Toronto, Ontario M5A 0B5. **T:** 1 416 479-7000
E: info@dusktv.ca **W:** http://www.dusktv.ca
Editorial Profile: Dusk features non-stop thrills and chills with horror and thriller movies, series and magazine-style shows focusing on the genre. The channel showcases modern-day classics, "teen screamers" and cultish B-movies. Includes new shows, old favorites and obscure programs never before seen on television.

Encore Avenue
Owner: Corus Entertainment Inc.
Editorial: Corus Quay, 25 Dockside, Toronto, Ontario M5A 0B5. **T:** 1 416 479-6784
E: info@moviecentral.ca
W: http://www.encoreavenue.ca
Editorial Profile: Encore Avenue is a 24-hour, commercial-free premium pay TV service available to western Canadians. The two channels of Encore Avenue celebrate the best movies of the 70s, 80s and 90s in a fun and entertaining way.

eqhd
Owner: Blue Ant Media
Editorial: 130 Merton St Suite 200, Toronto, Ontario M4S 1A4. **T:** 1 416 646-4434
E: feedback@blueantmedia.ca
W: http://www.smithsonianchannel.ca
Editorial Profile: Smithsonian Channel is owned and operated by Blue Ant Media.. The channel celebrates ideas, perspectives, and ways of life around the world, by bringing your family smart compelling documentaries and commercial free films that will inspire and engage its audience.

ESPN Classic
Owner: Bell Media
Editorial: 9 Channel Nine Court, Toronto, Ontario M1S 4B5. **T:** 1 416 332-5000
W: http://www.tsn.ca/classic
Editorial Profile: ESPN Classic Canada features great individual performances, controversial victories, huge upsets, momentous comebacks and unforgettable team dynasties. ESPN Classic has encore broadcasts of the most cherished classic games and moments from the world of sports. The network has all the bases covered with baseball, hockey, football, golf, wrestling, boxing, soccer, tennis, skating, Reel Classics sports movies and much more.

EuroWorld Sport
Owner: TLN Telelatino Network Inc.
Editorial: 5125 Steeles Avenue West, Toronto, Ontario M9L 1R5. **T:** 1 416 744-8200
E: info@tlntv.com
W: http://legacy.tlntv.com/soccerspecials/EuroWorldSports
Editorial Profile: Offers around-the-clock coverage of top-league soccer games, including all FIFA tournaments, the UEFA Europa League and Ligue 1 matches.

Évasion
Owner: Groupe Serdy
Editorial: 6, Boul. Desaulniers, bureau 500, Saint-Lambert, Quebec J4P 1L3.
T: 1 450 672-0052 **E:** info@evasion.tv
W: http://www.evasion.tv
Editorial Profile: Évasion is a French-language specialty television channel devoted to travel, tourism and adventure.

Explora
Owner: Radio-Canada
Editorial: 1400, boul. René-Lévesque est, Montreal, Quebec H2L 2M2
E: info.explora@radio-canada.ca
W: http://www.exploratv.ca
Editorial Profile: Explora delivers a larger-than-life viewing experience as it delves into the fascinating worlds of health, science, nature and the environment. The channel is aimed at inquiring minds who like to discover new things, catering especially to young people's passion for adventure.

Family Channel
Owner: Astral Media
Editorial: 181 Bay St, Suite 100, Toronto, Ontario M5J 2T3. **T:** 1 416 956-2030
E: info@family.ca **W:** http://www.family.ca
Editorial Profile: Family Channel is a premium, commercial-free network offering the best in family television entertainment in approximately 5.4 million homes across Canada. Programming includes series, movies and specials aimed at a family audience.

Fashion Television Channel
Owner: Bell Media
Editorial: 299 Queen St West, Toronto, Ontario M5V 2Z5. **T:** 1 416 591-7400
E: fashiontelevision@ctv.ca
W: http://www.fashiontelevision.com
Editorial Profile: Network provides a sexy look at art, architecture, photography and design. It's a fast-paced collage focusing on people's changing lifestyles, sexual attitudes and social conscience, as well as beauty, fitness and health. The Fashion Channel is Canada's first and only 24-hour English language fashion channel dedicated to the world of art, architecture, photography and design, with a celebration of style.

The Fight Network
Owner: Fight Media Inc.
Editorial: 171 East Liberty St Suite 230, Toronto, Ontario M6K 3P6-.
T: 1 416 987-2456
W: http://www.thefightnetwork.com
Editorial Profile: Features several varieties of combat sports: Mixed martial arts, boxing, wrestling, kick boxing and other sports.

Food Network Canada
Owner: Shaw Communications
Editorial: 121 Bloor Street East, Suite B1, Toronto, Ontario M4W 3M5.
T: 1 416 967-1174 **E:** feedback@foodtv.ca
W: http://www.foodnetwork.ca
Editorial Profile: 24-hour cable network dedicated to good food and good times. The network airs a variety of taped and live programs dealing with cooking, health, nutrition and food. Shows emphasize unique recipes, cooking tips and techniques, and feature famous personalities in the cooking world.

FX Canada
Owner: Rogers Broadcasting
Editorial: One Mount Pleasant Road, Toronto, Ontario M4Y 2Y5. **T:** 1 416 935-8294
E: Viewerrelations@rci.rogers.com
W: http://www.fxcanada.ca
Editorial Profile: FX Canada is a digital specialty channel that delivers critically-acclaimed dramas and hit comedies, including FX original series American Horror Story, Wilfred, The League, Lights Out, Terriers and Sons of Anarchy. Delivering compelling entertainment to Canadians, FX Canada's unique content also features movies, and original Canadian programming.

FXX Canada
Owner: Rogers Media
Editorial: 1 Mount Pleasant Rd, Toronto, Ontario M4Y 2Y5-
W: http://www.fxnowcanada.ca
Editorial Profile: FXX is a Canadian English-language digital cable specialty channel devoted primarily to scripted comedies for young adults. It launched in Canada on April 1, 2014.

G4 Canada
Owner: Rogers Communications Inc.
Editorial: 545 Lakeshore Boulevard West, Toronto, Ontario M5V 1A3. **T:** 1 416 260-0060
E: info@g4tv.ca **W:** http://www.g4tv.ca
Editorial Profile: G4 Canada is Canada's only 24-hour television channel dedicated to using technology as a backdrop to entertain, amaze, and engage viewers, by showcasing the latest trends, products and events. G4 Canada is targeted towards young adults. All press releases, pitches and other submissions should be directed to the mailing address.

Game TV
Owner: The GameTV Corporation
Editorial: 184 Pearl St. Suite 302, Toronto, Ontario M5H 1L5. **T:** 1 416 593-0915
W: http://www.igametv.com
Editorial Profile: For Canadians who love to play and watch games, GameTV provides viewers with a wide range of winning programming and online options including classic game shows, reality programming, non-sports gaming and game-related movies and documentaries.

Global News: BC 1
Owner: Shaw Media Inc.
Editorial: 7850 Enterprise St, Burnaby, British Columbia V5A 1V7. **T:** 1 604 420-2288
W: http://www.globaltvbc.com/topics/BC1
Editorial Profile: British Columbia's first 24 hour news channel. A regional, English-language specialty channel Category B service offering a mix of local and regional news, traffic, weather, business, sports and entertainment information devoted to serving residents of British Columbia

Global Reality Channel
Owner: Shaw Communications
Editorial: 121 Bloor Street West, Suite 200, Toronto, Ontario M4W 3M5.
T: 1 416 967-1174
W: http://www.globalreality.ca
Editorial Profile: Offers reality television programs 24/7.

Grace Television Network
Owner: World Impact Ministries
Editorial: 89 St Paul St, St. Catharines, Ontario L2R 3M3. **T:** 1 905 346-4828
E: info@gracetelevision.net
W: http://www.gracetelevision.net
Editorial Profile: Targets Canadian Christians. Features Christian programming from around the world, as well as new content from Canadian and international producers.

HBO Canada
Owner: Corus Entertainment/Astral Media Inc.
Editorial: Corus Quay, 25 Dockside Drive, Toronto, Ontario M5A 0B5. **T:** 1 416 479-7000
W: http://www.hbocanada.com
Editorial Profile: HBO Canada is a multiplex channel offered at no additional charge to customers who subscribe to The Movie Network or Movie Central. The service also offers more than 200 hours of library titles and first-run HBO original films, comedy specials, documentaries, live concerts and sporting events previously unavailable in Canada. HBO Canada rounds out its offering with Canadian films and series. The cable channel does not accept any pitches and is commercial-free.

HGTV Canada
Owner: Shaw Communications
Editorial: 121 Bloor Street East, Ste B1, Toronto, Ontario M4W 3M5.
T: 1 416 967-1174 **E:** feedback@hgtv.ca
W: http://www.hgtv.ca
Editorial Profile: Cable network with national distribution focusing on an array of home, lifestyle, decorating, gardening, hobbies and craft-related topics. Broadcasts a potpourri of original and exclusive programming hosted by experts in these various fields. Programming aired on HGTV Canada is developed by Shaw Communications. and changes quarterly. Viewers are advised to check the channel's Web site for the most updated schedules.

History Television
Owner: Shaw Communications
Editorial: 121 Bloor Street East, Suite 1500, Toronto, Ontario M4W 3M5.
T: 1 416 967-1174 **E:** media@canwest.com
W: http://www.historytelevision.ca
Editorial Profile: History Television chronicles the past with a range of documentaries, historical reenactments, motion pictures and mini-series dealing with significant figures, events and inventions.

HPItv
Owner: Woodbine Entertainment Group
Editorial: 555 Rexdale Boulevard, Toronto, Ontario M9W 5L2
E: hpi@WoodbineEntertainment.com
W: http://www.horseplayerinteractive.com
Editorial Profile: HPItv broadcasts live thoroughbred and standardbred racing, from tracks across North America and the world.

ichannel
Owner: Stornoway Communications Inc.
Editorial: 105 Gordon Baker Rd, Toronto, Ontario M2H 3P8. **T:** 1 416 756-2404
E: comments@ichannel.ca
W: http://www.ichannel.ca
Editorial Profile: The cable network ichannel is a public affairs and social issues channel. The network deals with political and social issues that affect Canadian lives. The network broadcasts documentaries, discussion sessions and feature films. In addition, ichannel strives to present both Canadian and global issues in a way that gives viewers the whole story.

The Independent Film Channel
Owner: Shaw Communications
Editorial: 121 Bloor St East, Ste 1500, Toronto, Ontario M4W 3M5.
T: 1 416 967-1174
E: ifccanada@shawmedia.ca
W: http://www.ifctv.ca
Editorial Profile: The Independent Film Channel(IFC) is Canada's first English-language specialty television service dedicated to the world of filmmakers. IFC presents a rich schedule of cutting-edge and creative films, providing a new avenue of exhibition for Canadian films.

Investigation Discovery
Owner: Bell Media
Editorial: 9 Channel Nine Court, Toronto, Ontario M1S 4B5. **T:** 1 416 332-5000
E: comments@investigationdiscovery.ca
W: http://www.investigationdiscovery.ca
Editorial Profile: Fact-based channel offering insight into the real-life world of investigation, exploration of the latest forensic analysis and true stories that piece together the dramatic puzzles of human nature. Expands on these themes by touching on some less common areas of investigation, including the paranormal and modern mysteries.

Al Jazeera English - Toronto Bureau
Owner: Al Jazeera Network
Editorial: Toronto, Ontario. **T:** 1 416 941-8107
W: http://www.aljazeera.com
Editorial Profile: The Al Jazeera English - Toronto Bureau launched in June 2010.

LCN/Le Canal Nouvelles
Owner: Groupe TVA Inc.
Editorial: 1600 Boul de Maisonneuve E, Montreal, Quebec H2L 4P2. **T:** 1 514 526-9251
E: lcn@tva.ca **W:** http://tvanouvelles.ca
Editorial Profile: Le Canal Nouvelles (LCN) is a 24-hour Canadian French language cable news television channel owned by Groupe TVA Inc. It broadcasts from TVA headquarters in Montreal. It offers viewers continuous, updated news coverage, 24 hours a day, with headlines scrolling at the bottom of the screen. News tips can be directed to the assignment desk.

Leafs TV
Owner: Maple Leaf Sports & Entertainment
Editorial: 50 Bay Street, Suite 500, Toronto, Ontario M5J 2L2. **T:** 1 416 815-5400
E: leafstv@mapleleafsports.com
W: http://mapleleafs.nhl.com/club/page.htm?id=42121
Editorial Profile: Leafs TV is a Canadian specialty cable network owned by Maple Leafs Sports & Entertainment. Features programming revolving around the Toronto Maple Leafs National Hockey League team including broadcasts of games, pre- and post-game shows, and more.

M3
Owner: Bell Media
Editorial: 299 Queen St W, Toronto, Ontario M5V 2Z5-. **T:** 1 416 591-7400
W: http://www.m3tv.ca
Editorial Profile: 24-hour music video and performance showcase. In addition to the day's top videos, this 24-hour service features

the best in concerts, celebrity interviews and profiles, documentaries and movies.

MétéoMédia
Owner: Pelmorex Media, Inc.
Editorial: 1755 boul René-Lévesque Est, Bureau 251, Montreal, Quebec H2K 4P6.
T: 1 514 597-1700
W: http://www.meteomedia.com
Editorial Profile: MétéoMédia is a 24-hour French-language cable television channel owned by Pelmorex Media, Inc. It features continuous, up-to-the-minute reports on weather conditions throughout the world, occasional weather-related feature specials, and regional, local and national forecasts.

Moi & Cie
Owner: Groupe TVA
Editorial: 1600 Boul de Maisonneuve E, Montreal, Quebec H2L 4P2-.
T: 1 514 526-9251 **W:** http://tv.moietcie.ca
Editorial Profile: Moi & Cie is owned by Groupe TVA. This channel is geared towards women with programs on fashion and beauty.

Movie Central
Owner: Corus Entertainment Inc.
Editorial: Corus Quay, 25 Dockside Drive, Toronto, Ontario M5A 0B5. **T:** 1 416 479-6784
E: web.moviecentral@corusent.com
W: http://www.moviecentral.ca
Editorial Profile: Movie Central is a premium subscription TV service available to western Canadians that features first-run hit movies and exclusives. Hollywood blockbusters and independent films are broadcast 24 hours a day, uncut and without commercial interruption.

Movieola-The Short Film Channel
Owner: Channel Zero Inc.
Editorial: 2844 Dundas St West, Toronto, Ontario M6P 1Y7. **T:** 1 416 492-1595
E: info@movieola.ca
W: http://www.movieola.ca
Editorial Profile: This cable network is devoted entirely to short films. From drama to comedy, and animation to documentaries, all films are between 30 seconds and 40 minutes in length. Programming includes film festival winners, cult classics and late night features. Billing itself as "A Feature Film Experience in a Fraction of the Time," Movieola is a one-of-a-kind network.

MovieTime
Owner: Shaw Communications
Editorial: 121 Bloor St East, Ste B1 Suite 1500, Toronto, Ontario M4W 3M5.
T: 1 416 967-1174 **E:** contactus@globaltv.ca
W: http://www.movietimetv.ca
Editorial Profile: MovieTime is the digital channel destination for big-ticket movies seven days a week. With over 250 movie titles each month and back to back movies on the weekend, MovieTime offers movie lovers unparalleled access to an extensive collection of favorite hits. During the week, viewers can enjoy favorite series in the mornings and during prime time, with movies filling the schedule in the afternoons and throughout the night. From adventure-packed blockbusters to definitive movie moments, MovieTime has a star-studded, jam-packed line-up that satisfies viewers' cravings for hit movies.

MTV in Canada
Owner: Bell Media
Editorial: 299 Queen St W, Toronto, Ontario M5V 2Z5. **T:** 1 416 384-3888
E: feedback@mtv.ca **W:** http://www.mtv.ca
Editorial Profile: MTV in Canada is a Canadian programmed and managed business wholly owned by Bell Media. MTV offers a distinctly Canadian interpretation of the MTV brand across multiple platforms, including a revolutionary broadband service, MTV Overdrive, and across an MTV-branded analogue specialty service that delivers innovative lifestyle, talk and documentary programming with a commitment to 71 percent Canadian programming in prime time.

MTV2 in Canada
Owner: Bell Media
Editorial: 299 Queen Street West, Toronto, Ontario M5V 2Z5. **T:** 1 416 591-7400
E: feedback@mtv.ca **W:** http://www.mtv2.ca
Editorial Profile: MTV2 in Canada feeds viewers' needs for the latest in everything from movies and music to video games, fashion, technology, sports and more.

MuchLoud
Owner: Bell Media
Editorial: 299 Queen Street West, Toronto, Ontario M5V 2Z5. **T:** 1 416 591-7400
E: muchloud@muchmusic.com
W: http://www.muchloud.com
Editorial Profile: MuchLoud is a cable channel dedicated to the world of alternative, hard rock, metal, classic metal and punk. It provides artist interviews, specials, classic archival material and up-to-the-minute concert information.

MuchMoreRetro
Owner: Bell Media
Editorial: 299 Queen Street West, Toronto, Ontario M5V 2Z5. **T:** 1 416 591-7400
E: contact@muchmusic.com
W: http://www.muchmoreretro.com
Editorial Profile: MuchMoreRetro is a specialty music cable television station owned by Bell Media. Featuring music of the 1980s and 90s, MuchMoreRetro is uniquely styled for those who grew up watching their music on television.

MuchMusic
Owner: Bell Media
Editorial: 299 Queen Street West, Toronto, Ontario M5V 2Z5. **T:** 1 416 591-7400
E: contact@muchmusic.com
W: http://www.muchmusic.com
Editorial Profile: MuchMusic is live to air approximately eight hours daily from the network's headquarters in downtown Toronto, with programs showcasing exclusive live performances and interviews from today's hottest musical artists and celebrity guests. In addition, the network's specialty programming focuses on the latest music-related news and information.

MuchVibe
Owner: Bell Media
Editorial: 299 Queen Street West, Toronto, Ontario M5V 2Z5. **T:** 1 416 591-7400
E: muchvibe@muchmusic.com
W: http://www.muchvibe.ca
Editorial Profile: MuchVibe is a channel dedicated to fans of the exploding urban music scene. Hip hop, rap, R&B, soul and reggae music videos, as well as urban music-related programming and specials.

MusiMax
Owner: Astral Media
Editorial: 355 rue Sainte-Catherine Ouest, Montreal, Quebec H3B 1A5.
T: 1 514 284-7587 **E:** auditoire@musimax.com
W: http://www.musimax.com
Editorial Profile: MusiMax is a French-language cable television channel owned by Astral Media. MusiMax broadcasts concerts, documentaries, films and other music-based programs.

MusiquePlus
Owner: Astral Media
Editorial: 355, rue Sainte-Catherine Ouest, Montreal, Quebec H3B 1A5.
T: 1 514 284-7587
W: http://www.musiqueplus.com
Editorial Profile: MusiquePlus is a French-language cable music television channel owned by Astral Media. It is the sister network of MusiMax and MuchMusic. The channel airs music videos, numerous special features, documentaries and films about the music industry in addition to celebrity interviews and profiles.

Mystery
Owner: Shaw Communications
Editorial: 121 Bloor St East, Ste B1, Toronto, Ontario M4W 3M5. **T:** 1 416 967-1174
E: contactus@globaltv.ca
W: http://www.mysterytv.ca
Editorial Profile: Mystery is a cable network specializing in mystery-related programming, including dramas, documentaries and series. Its shows include spine-tingling thrillers and horror stories, police dramas, and the best Movies of the Week.

National Geographic Channel
Owner: Shaw Communications
Editorial: 121 Bloor Street East, Ste B1, Toronto, Ontario M4W 3M5.
T: 1 416 967-0022 **E:** media@canwest.com
W: http://natgeotv.com/ca
Editorial Profile: A national cable network providing a range of feature programming derived from the world of the National Geographic Society. The network features "experience" television, with programming in travel, adventure, exploration, natural history, science, culture and news. Aimed at people who are curious and interested in the world around them.

NBA TV Canada
Owner: Maple Leaf Sports & Entertainment
Editorial: 40 Bay St, Ste 400, Toronto, Ontario M5J 2X2. **T:** 1 416 815-5500
W: http://www.nba.com/schedules/national_tv_schedule/canada
Editorial Profile: NBA TV Canada s a cable specialty network owned by Maple Leaf Sports & Entertainment. The network features programming related to the National Basketball Association, with a particular emphasis on the Toronto Raptors.

New Tang Dynasty Television
Owner: New Tang Dynasty Television Canada
Editorial: 420 Consumers Rd, Toronto, Ontario M2J 1P8. **T:** 1 416 787-1577
W: http://www.ntdtv.ca
Editorial Profile: New Tang Dynasty Television is a non-profit general interest Chinese language channel. It airs a unique programming mix of news, cultural shows, educational programs, sports and entertainment. NTD Television Canada officially launched on March 28, 2012.

New Tang Dynasty TV
Editorial: 420 Consumers Rd, Toronto, Ontario M2J 1P8. **T:** 1 416 787-1577
Editorial Profile: Provides news and entertainment in Mandarin and Cantonese to Chinese Canadians.

NHL Network
Owner: National Hockey League
Editorial: 9 Channel Nine Court, Toronto, Ontario M1S 4B5. **T:** 1 416 332-5000
W: http://www.nhl.com
Editorial Profile: NHL Network has round-the-clock hockey programming, offering viewers the most complete and in-depth hockey coverage including news, information and extended highlights from the National Hockey League. To contact the channel use the online contact form located in the contact us section of the website.

Nuevo Mundo TV
Editorial: 4119 Blvd. St. Laurent, Suite 200, Montreal, Quebec H2W 1Y7.
T: 1 514 543-7904
E: info@nuevomundotv.com
W: http://www.nuevomundotv.com
Editorial Profile: Nuevo Mundo TV's mission is to satisfy the communications needs of the Spanish speaking community in Canada and the lovers of the Hispanic culture.

Oasis
Owner: Blue Ant Media
Editorial: 130 Merton St Suite 200, Toronto, Ontario M4S 1A4. **T:** 1 416 646-4434
E: feedback@blueantmedia.ca
W: http://www.oasishd.ca
Editorial Profile: Oasis is owned and operated by Blue Ant Media, Canada's leading HD broadcaster. The channel is the first nature channel committed to continuous programming, showcasing the endless beauty of the natural world. The channel lets viewers explore, reflect and embrace the essence of our exquisite planet, with stories woven together from the finest Canadian and international documentary programming available.

Odyssey Television Network
Owner: Maniatakos(Peter)
Editorial: 437 Danforth Ave, Ste 300, Toronto, Ontario M4K 1P1. **T:** 1 416 462-1200
E: info@odysseytv.ca
W: http://www.odysseytv.ca
Editorial Profile: Odyssey Television Network is a Greek-language broadcaster that airs programming, which targets the Greek-Canadian community. Programming is a mix of local productions and of shows from popular networks in Greece.

OLN/Outdoor Life Network
Owner: Rogers Media Television
Editorial: 545 Lake Shore Blvd W, Toronto, Ontario M5V 1A3. **T:** 1 416 260-0047
E: info@oln.ca **W:** http://oln.ca
Editorial Profile: OLN/Outdoor Life Network fills a unique niche in the specialty television landscape, attracting viewers with an adventurous spirit and a passion for the great outdoors in Canada. From skateboarding to sailing to road trips and shipwrecks, OLN celebrates all aspects of outdoor recreation, conservation, wilderness and adventure programming.

Ontario Parliament Network Broadcasting & Recording Service
Owner: Ontario Legislative Assembly
Editorial: Legislative Assembly, Rm.453, Queen's Park, Toronto, Ontario M7A1A2.
T: 1 416 325-7900 **W:** http://ontla.on.ca
Editorial Profile: The network carries all proceedings of the Ontario Legislative Assembly. Sessions are broadcast live and also rebroadcast twice in the evening.

OUTtv
Owner: 6166954 Canada Inc.
Editorial: 130 Merton st, 2nd floor, Toronto, Ontario M4S 1A4. **T:** 1 416 979-2900
W: http://www.outtv.ca
Editorial Profile: OUTtv is a GLBT (gay, lesbian, bisexual and transgender) television network that provides news, information and entertainment to viewers 24/7. Canadian Gay-owned and operated, OUTtv has the best in GBLT popular movies and comedies from around the world including Canadian and international dramas, arts programming, biographies and variety shows. OUTtv has more original programming than any other digital channel in Canada. OUTtv provides up-to-date in-house GLBT news programming, live call-in shows, current affairs, documentaries, health and fitness, lifestyle, finance, relationships, music, cooking and travel for GLBT and gay-positive viewers.

OWN: The Oprah Winfrey Network
Owner: Corus Entertainment Inc.
Editorial: Corus Quay, 25 Dockside Drive, Toronto, Ontario M5A 0B5. **T:** 1 416 479-7000
E: info@owntv.ca **W:** http://www.owntv.ca
Editorial Profile: OWN: The Oprah Winfrey Show is the network of self-discovery, connecting people to each other and to their greatest potential. The programming includes a mix of nonfiction, short form programming, movies, documentaries and acquisitions. In the United States, OWN is a joint venture between Oprah Winfrey and Discovery Communications and launched on January 1, 2011 in the United States. OWN has a licensing agreement with Corus Entertainment to broadcast in Canada that began March 1, 2011 and replaced VIVA.

The Pet Network
Owner: Stornoway Communications Inc.
Editorial: 105 Gordon Baker Road, Fl 8, Toronto, Ontario M2H 3P8. **T:** 1 416 756-2404
E: comments@thepetnetwork.tv
W: http://www.thepetnetwork.tv
Editorial Profile: The Pet Network is affectionately focused on the wonderful world of pets and the people who love them. From dogs, cats and fish, to the more unique and exotic, we continuously look at animals and their equally-interesting relationship with humans.

PHSN
Owner: The Canadian Health Media network
Editorial: 150 Ferrand Drive, Suite 800, Toronto, Ontario M3C 3E5. **T:** 1 416 486-0110
W: http://www.phsn.ca
Editorial Profile: PHSN is a national television network featuring customized content that is organized into short, themed segments allowing patients to enjoy worthwhile programming and yet engage and disengage in a manner suited to the environment. PHSN can be seen in the waiting rooms of health care professionals across Canada. The company is dedicated to engaging viewers with customized information and entertainment programming. Content is both in-house and advertiser-generated. Content is 95% produced by PHSN and 5% from News Canada. Programs are 30 minutes long consisting of 90 second segments. Each ad is run once every 30 minutes.

Prise 2
Owner: Groupe TVA Inc.
Editorial: 1600 Boulevard de Maisonneuve Est, Montreal, Quebec H2L 4P2.
T: 1 514 526-9251
E: relations.auditoire@tva.ca
W: http://prise2.canoe.ca
Editorial Profile: Presents the classics of Quebecois and American television and film.

PunchMuch
Owner: Bell Media
Editorial: 299 Queen Street West, Toronto, Ontario M5V 2Z5. **T:** 1 416 591-5757
W: http://www.punchmuch.com
Editorial Profile: PunchMuch is Canada's first fully automated, all-request music video service, putting music fans everywhere on the button. Viewers can request videos, participate in on-screen SMS chat, polling and more all via their wireless phones.

radX
Owner: Blue Ant Media
Editorial: 130 Merton St Suite 200, Toronto, Ontario M4S 1A4. **T:** 1 416 646-4434
E: feedback@blueantmedia.ca
W: http://www.radx.ca
Editorial Profile: radX is owned and operated by Blue Ant Media, Canada's leading HD broadcaster. The channel features high risk sports and adrenaline-high shows. The slogan for radX is "risk, adventure, danger." radX airs programming of interest to action sports enthusiasts.

RDI/Le Réseau de l'information
Owner: Societe Radio-Canada
Editorial: 1400, boul. René-Lévesque, Montreal, Quebec H2L 2M2.
T: 1 514 597-7734
E: rdicomm@radio-canada.ca
W: http://www.radio-canada.ca/rdi
Editorial Profile: RDI/Le Réseau de l'Information is a 24-hour Canadian French-language cable news television channel operated by CBC/Radio-Canada. RDI is the French-language equivalent of CBC News Network. RDI provides live coverage of major events, newscasts every 30 minutes, sports and financial news as well as informational programs on a wide range of topics.

RDS - Le Réseau des Sports
Owner: Bell Media
Editorial: 1755 Blv. René-Lévesque Est, Bureau 300, Montreal, Quebec H2K 4P6.
T: 1 514 599-2244 **E:** medias@rds.ca
W: http://www.rds.ca
Editorial Profile: RDS - Le Réseau des Sports is a 24-hour French language, all-sports cable channel owned by Bell Media. It broadcasts games as well as sport-related shows. RDS launched in September 1989.

RDS 2
Owner: Bell Media
Editorial: 1755 Blv René-Lévesque, Bureau 300, Montreal, Quebec H2K 4P6.
T: 1 514 599-2244 **W:** http://www.rds2.ca
Editorial Profile: RDS 2 is a French language all sports cable channel owned by Bell Media.

RDS INFO
Owner: Bell Media
Editorial: 1755 boulevard Rene-Levesque Est, Bureau 300, Montreal, Quebec H2K 4P6.
T: 1 514 599-2244 **E:** medias@rds.ca
W: http://www.rds.ca/ris
Editorial Profile: Features the latest sports headlines as well as hockey, football, baseball and amateur sports. It complements the programming that is featured on RDS/Reseau des Sports.

The Score
Owner: Score Media Inc.
Editorial: 500 King St W Fl 4TH, Toronto, Ontario M5V 1L9. **T:** 1 416 679-8812
E: hello@thescore.com
W: http://www.thescore.com
Editorial Profile: Score Media is a media company committed to delivering interactive and authentic sports entertainment. Created in 1997 in response to the growing desire for increased participation in the consumption of sports, the Company has now established itself as the home for hardcore sports fans. Score Media's primary asset, The Score Television Network ("The Score"), is a national specialty television service providing sports news, information, highlights and live event programming in more than 6.6 million homes across Canada.

Setanta Sports Canada
Owner: Rogers Media Inc.
Editorial: One Mount Pleasant Road, Toronto, Ontario M4Y 3A1. **T:** 1 416 764-6000
E: general@setanta.com
W: http://www.setanta.com/ca
Editorial Profile: International pay-TV sports channel featuring live coverage of the best premium sport including Barclays Premier League, UEFA Champions League, FA Cup, World Cup Qualifiers, Coca-Cola Championship, Le Championnat, Carling Cup, Russian Premier League, Heineken Cup, Tri Nations, RBS 6 Nations, Rugby World Cup, Guinness Premiership, Super 14, Gaelic Sports and much more.

Shopping Channel
Owner: Rogers Media Inc.
Editorial: 59 Ambassador Dr, Mississauga, Ontario L5T 2P9. **T:** 1 905 362-2020
W: http://www.theshoppingchannel.com
Editorial Profile: This network provides a 24/hour Canadian multimedia retailer. It offers thousands of contemporary beauty, fashion, jewelry and home products.

Showcase
Owner: Shaw Communications
Editorial: 121 Bloor Street East, Ste B1, Toronto, Ontario M4W 3M5.
T: 1 416 967-0022 **E:** media@canwest.com
W: http://www.showcase.ca
Editorial Profile: Showcase offers viewers a chance to catch some of the best critically acclaimed TV programming. Showcase gives viewers a chance to catch some of the biggest blockbuster titles in all genres, including dramas, comedies and thrillers.

Showcase Diva
Owner: Shaw Communications
Editorial: 121 Bloor Street East, Ste B1, Toronto, Ontario M4W 3M5.
T: 1 416 967-0022 **E:** media@canwest.com
W: http://www.diva-tv.ca
Editorial Profile: Showcase Diva specializes in star-studded movies with a bold female attitude. The network offers chick flicks for fabulous women of all ages. Viewers enjoy hit movies with favorite stars including Cameron Diaz, Tom Cruise, Julia Roberts, Penelope Cruz, John Cusack and Marilyn Monroe. Programming also includes great series and critically acclaimed premieres.

Silver Screen Classics
Owner: Channel Zero Inc.
Editorial: 2844 Dundas St West, Toronto, Ontario M6P 1Y7. **T:** 1 416 492-1595
E: info@silverscreenclassics.com
W: http://www.silverscreenclassics.com
Editorial Profile: Silver Screen Classics brings viewers motion pictures which have stood the test. From silent classics to twelve-chapter serials; from gritty film noir to splashy musical extravaganzas; from timeless melodramas to madcap screwball comedies, the network inspires, entertains and enthralls viewers.

SKY TG24 Canada
Owner: TLN Telelatino Network Inc.
Editorial: 5125 Steeles Ave W, Toronto, Ontario M9L 1R5. **T:** 1 416 744-8200
E: info@tlntv.com
W: http://www.tlntv.com/tln_SkyTGEnglishAbout.aspx
Editorial Profile: All-news, information and talk channel in Italian, primarily a simulcast of the Italian SKY TG24, with some added Canadian content.

Slice
Owner: Shaw Communications
Editorial: 121 Bloor Street East, Ste B1, Toronto, Ontario M4W 3M5.
T: 1 416 967-0022 **E:** media@canwest.com
W: http://www.slice.ca
Editorial Profile: Geared toward women, this network offers lifestyle entertainment programming about the people, places and experiences that make the journey of life worthwhile and interesting.

Sony Entertainment Television Asia
Owner: Sony Entertainment Television Asia
Editorial: 115 Gordon Baker, Toronto, Ontario M2H 3R6. **T:** 1 416 619-5797
E: viewer_infoCAN@spe.sony.com
W: http://www.setasia.tv
Editorial Profile: Features contemporary programming tailored to South Asian tastes and sensibilities. Reaching the upscale, economically active 18 to 49 year-old age group.

SPACE
Owner: Bell Media
Editorial: 299 Queen St West, Toronto, Ontario M5V 2Z5. **T:** 1 416 591-5757
E: space@spacecast.com
W: http://www.spacecast.com
Editorial Profile: SPACE is a national cable-delivered English-language, science fiction, fact, speculation and fantasy channel owned and operated by Bell Media, available 24 hours.

Sportsnet One
Owner: Rogers Media Inc.
Editorial: 1 Mount Pleasant Rd Fl 7TH, Toronto, Ontario M4Y 2Y5. **T:** 1 416 764-6000
E: assignment@sportsnet.ca
W: http://www.sportsnet.ca
Editorial Profile: National sports channel available across Canada and featuring primarily high-definition content from the Toronto Raptors, the NBA, the Toronto Blue Jays, the Seattle Mariners, Major League Baseball and Barclay's Premier League Soccer.

The Sun News Network
Owner: Quebecor Communications Inc.
Editorial: 25 Ontario St, Toronto, Ontario M5A 4L6. **T:** 1 416 933-5696
W: http://www.sunnewsnetwork.ca
Editorial Profile: Sun News Network is a 24-hour news and information channel. To contact the channel use the contact form located in the "about us" section of the website.

Sun News Network
Owner: Quebecor Communications Inc.
Editorial: 554 East 15th Ave, Vancouver, British Columbia V5T 2R5. **T:** 1 604 322-2340

Sun News Network
Owner: Quebecor Communications Inc.
Editorial: 6 Antares Dr Phase III, Ottawa, Ontario K2E 8A9. **T:** 1 613 739-7000

Sundance Channel (Canada)
Owner: Corus Entertainment Inc.
Editorial: Corus Quay, 25 Dockside Drive, Toronto, Ontario M5A 0B5. **T:** 1 416 479-6785
E: info@sundancechannel.ca
W: http://www.sundancechannel.ca
Editorial Profile: Sundance Channel (Canada) offers movie enthusiasts, movie fans, creative and socially-engaged audiences a lineup of award-winning, diverse and engaging movies. The network presents the best in feature films, festival-selected shorts, documentaries and innovative, original series.

Super Écran
Owner: Astral Media
Editorial: 1800, avenue McGill College, Bureau 1600, Montreal, Quebec H3A 3J6.
T: 1 514 939-5090
E: auditoire@superecran.com
W: http://www.superecran.com
Editorial Profile: Super Écran is a French-language television network owned by Astral Media. It broadcasts the French version of popular movies 24 hours a day, as well as comedy shows and exclusive series. Super Écran's tagline is "La Télé des Cinévores."

TELETOON
Owner: Astral Media Inc./Corus Entertainment
Editorial: Corus Quay, 25 Dockside Drive, Toronto, Ontario M5A 0B5. **T:** 1 416 956-2060
E: info@teletoon.com
W: http://www.teletoon.com
Editorial Profile: The only Canadian 24-hour network devoted to providing cartoon and animation programming. Intended for audiences of all ages, the network broadcasts a variety of classic cartoon series and characters, new cartoons, original productions and animated feature films. Includes English and French-language services.

TELETOON Retro
Owner: Astral Media Inc./Corus Entertainment
Editorial: Corus Quay, 25 Dockside Drive, Toronto, Ontario M5A 0B5. **T:** 1 416 956-2060
E: info@teletoon.com
W: http://www.teletoon.com/retro
Editorial Profile: A nostalgic throwback to timeless cartoons, the network features choice classics like Bugs Bunny, The Flintstones, Scooby-Doo and The Jetsons.

TLN en Español
Owner: TLN Telelatino Network Inc.
Editorial: 5125 Steeles Avenue West, Toronto, Ontario M9L 1R5. **T:** 1 416 744-8200
E: info@tlntv.com
W: http://www.tlntv.com/EspanolAcerca.aspx?video=GenericSpanish09.flv
Editorial Profile: TLN en Español complements TLN Telelatino with 100% Spanish-language programming. TLN includes movies, telenovelas, variety shows, sports, news and more.

TLN Telelatino
Owner: TLN Telelatino Network Inc.
Editorial: 5125 Steeles Avenue West, Toronto, Ontario M9L 1R5. **T:** 1 416 744-8200
E: info@tlntv.com **W:** http://www.tlntv.com
Editorial Profile: TLN means the best coverage of soccer from Italy and Latin America. TLN also is the source for drama, intrigue, and romance portioned out in steamy installments on telenovelas. The network is also known for cryptically bizarre game shows. TLN serves as Canada's window into Hispanic and Italian cultures.

Travel + Escape
Owner: GlassBox Television
Editorial: 2196 Dunwin Dr., Mississauga, Ontario L5L 1C7. **T:** 1 905 828-2483
E: info@glassbox.tv
W: http://www.travelandescape.ca
Editorial Profile: Travel + Escape is the ultimate destination for escapist entertainment. The network seduces viewers with compelling stories that highlight the most exotic and luxurious experiences the world has to offer.

Treasure
Owner: Blue Ant Media
Editorial: 130 Merton St Suite 200, Toronto, Ontario M4S 1A4. **T:** 1 416 646-4434
E: feedback@blueantmedia.ca
W: http://www.hifi.ca
Editorial Profile: HIFI is owned and operated by Blue Ant Media, Canada's leading HD broadcaster. The channel explores and celebrates the cultural treasures that enrich our lives. From quirky pieces of pop culture to priceless vestiges of human civilization in the world's finest museums; from iconic films picked for their originality to classic concerts by the legends who shaped music this channel is where everything that stirs your passion can be found.

Treehouse TV
Owner: Corus Entertainment Inc.
Editorial: Corus Quay, 25 Dockside Drive, Toronto, Ontario M5A 0B5. **T:** 1 416 479-7000
E: info@treehousetv.com
W: http://www.treehousetv.com
Editorial Profile: Treehouse TV is the only national, specialty network in North America dedicated to providing suitable programming to pre-schoolers, age six years and younger. Launched in 1997, Treehouse is now available in over six million Canadian households. Treehouse offers a unique television environment that reflects the interests and developmental levels of this age group. Treehouse is owned by Corus Entertainment, a Canadian based media and entertainment company.

TSN
Owner: Bell Media
Editorial: 9 Channel Nine Court, Toronto, Ontario M1S 4B5. **T:** 1 416 332-5000
E: sdesk@tsn.ca **W:** http://www.tsn.ca
Editorial Profile: TSN (The Sports Network), a division of Bell Media, sets the Canadian sports broadcasting standard. TSN's flagship news program, SportsCentre, was voted the number one source for sports news by sports fans from across the country. TSN's comprehensive broadcast schedule also includes the NHL, international hockey, the Olympic Games, CFL, NFL, golf, curling, NASCAR, iFormula One, IRL auto racing, baseball, basketball, tennis, soccer, boxing and figure skating. The network's slogan is "Canada's Sports Leader."

TSN2
Owner: CTVglobemedia Inc.
Editorial: 9 Channel Nine Court, Toronto, Ontario M1S 4B5. **T:** 1 416 332-5000
E: sdesk@tsn.ca **W:** http://www.tsn.ca/tsn2
Editorial Profile: TSN2 is a 24-hour sports digital network which features more than 800 hours of live events.

TV5 Québec Canada
Owner: TV5 Québec Canada
Editorial: 1755 boulevard René-Lévesque Est, Bureau 101, Montreal, Quebec H2K 4P6.
T: 1 514 522-5322 **E:** info@tv5.ca
W: http://www.tv5.ca
Editorial Profile: TV5 Québec Canada is a cable network that offers French-speaking programs produced in Europe and Africa, as well as in Canada. The programs include news, movies, travel, entertainment, documentaries, reports, debates and interviews. TV5 Québec Canada reaches 6.3 million households in Canada through cable and satellite, 4.1 million of which live out of Québec. TV5 Québec Canada is partnered with TV5, a global television network.

TVA Sports
Owner: Quebecor Media
Editorial: 1600 boulevard Maisonneuve Est, Montreal, Quebec H2L 4P2. **T:** 1 514 526-9251
E: montoposports@tva.ca
W: http://tvasports.ca
Editorial Profile: TVA Sports is a cable channel featuring sports content.

TVTropolis
Owner: Shaw Communications
Editorial: 121 Bloor St East, Toronto, Ontario M4W 3M5. **T:** 1 416 967-1174
E: feedback@tvtropolis.ca
W: http://www.tvtropolis.com
Editorial Profile: Network featuring the best of classic entertainment and informational

programming. TVTropolis' mixture of classic comedies and information ensures that there's something for everyone. The network also airs some of television's most recent iconic hits. Tune in to watch some of the best TV shows ever to hit the airwaves.

Twist TV
Owner: Shaw Communications
Editorial: 121 Bloor Street B1, Ste B1, Toronto, Ontario M4W 3M5.
T: 1 416 967-1174 **E:** feedback@twisttv.ca
W: http://www.twisttv.ca
Editorial Profile: Twist TV is all about real life with a twist; capturing the experiences of everyday people facing extraordinary situations. The channel's diverse cast of characters are always relatable and often outrageous. With programs featuring out of control kids, pageant moms, and life-changing health situations, audiences are guaranteed to be hooked.

Viewer's Choice Canada
Owner: Astral Media
Editorial: Broofield Place, 181 Bay St Ste100, Toronto, Ontario M5J 2T3. **T:** 1 416 956-2010
E: viewerschoice@astral.com
W: http://www.viewerschoice.ca
Editorial Profile: Viewers Choice Pay Per View offers convenient, commercial-free, in home viewing of the latest hit movies, unparalleled live sports and entertainment events on an à la carte basis to cable television affiliates in eastern Canada. Programming on Viewers Choice Pay Per View is offered on multiple channels providing near video-on-demand convenience in both standard and high-definition formats.

VisionTV
Owner: ZoomerMedia Limited
Editorial: 171 East Liberty Street, Suite 230, Toronto, Ontario M6K 3P6. **T:** 1 416 368-3194
E: visiontv@visiontv.ca
W: http://www.visiontv.ca
Editorial Profile: VisionTV presents inspirational, insightful and original programming that celebrates diversity and promotes understanding among people of different faiths and cultures. VisionTV's lineup consists of faith programming presented by groups of various religious denominations, including Catholics, Protestants, Muslims, Sikhs and Hindus.

VoicePrint
Owner: Accessible Media Inc.
Editorial: 1090 Don Mills Rd, Ste 200, Toronto, Ontario M3C 3R6. **T:** 1 416 422-4222
E: info@accessiblemedia.com
W: http://www.voiceprintcanada.com
Editorial Profile: VoicePrint is a free 24-hour news and information audio service. VoicePrint was established in 1990 to bring full-text audio recordings from more than 600 publications to all Canadians, but particularly those who can't access this information due to blindness or vision restrictions, learning or physical disability, low literacy skills or aging. Every day, volunteers record full-length articles, columns and feature reports related to news, sports, health, entertainment, science and more. VoicePrint is delivered via satellite and cable to 8.3 million homes throughout Canada.

W Movies
Owner: Corus Entertainment Inc.
Editorial: Corus Quay, 25 Dockside Drive, Toronto, Ontario M4A 0B5. **T:** 1 416 479-7000
W: http://www.wnetwork.com/Movies/WMovies.aspx
Editorial Profile: W Movies is the go-to destination for women seeking smart, fun and engaging films. The network features Hollywood hits, Canadian films and critically-acclaimed TV movies. W Movies will showcase films for and about women, with genres ranging from romance and comedy to drama and suspense.

W Network
Owner: Corus Entertainment Inc.
Editorial: Corus Quay, 25 Dockside Drive, Toronto, Ontario M5A 0B5. **T:** 1 416 479-7000
E: comments@wnetwork.com
W: http://www.wnetwork.com
Editorial Profile: W Network is a compelling and contemporary television network, committed to bringing Canadian women the best entertainment that television has to offer through distinctive programming. W Network is for women all day, every day and strives to make its 24-hour programming as unique and diverse as the women who watch it. The target demographics are women, ages 25 to 54.

The Weather Network
Owner: Pelmorex Media, Inc.
Editorial: 2655 Bristol Circle, Oakville, Ontario L6H 7W1. **T:** 1 905 829-1159
E: twnweb@pelmorex.com
W: http://www.theweathernetwork.com
Editorial Profile: The Weather Network and its French language counterpart, Meteomedia, are Canada's round-the-clock local, regional, national and international weather service. The network is available on basic cable, direct to home and on the Internet.

World Fishing Network
Owner: Insight Sports Ltd.
Editorial: 184 Pearl St Suite 302, Toronto, Ontario M5H 1L5. **T:** 1 416 593-0915
E: submissions@insightsports.com
W: http://www.insightsports.com
Editorial Profile: World Fishing Network is the only 24/7 television network dedicated to all segments of fishing with programming that covers instruction, tips, tournaments, travel, food, boating, outdoor lifestyle and more.

YOOPA
Owner: Québécor Média
Editorial: 1600 Boul de Maisonneuve E, Montreal, Quebec H2L 4P2. **T:** 1 514 526-9251
E: jeunesse@tva.ca
W: http://www.yoopa.ca/statique/yoopa-tv
Editorial Profile: YOOPA is a fun and educational, specialty television channel, which invites children, ages two to six, to discover a friendly, colorful and contemporary visual universe.

YTV Canada
Owner: Corus Entertainment Inc.
Editorial: Corus Quay, 25 Dockside Drive, Toronto, Ontario M5A 0B5. **T:** 1 416 479-7000
E: info@ytv.com **W:** http://www.ytv.com
Editorial Profile: This specialty cable network provides programming geared toward children, teens, and their parents. The network is seen in over 11 million Canadian households and is aimed at audiences aged 2 to 17 and their families.

CAPE VERDE Tel: 238
Standard Time: GMT -1
Continent: Africa
Capital City: Praia

NEWSPAPERS & PUBLICATIONS

NEWSPAPERS

Expresso das Ilhas
Owner: Media Comunicações SA
Editorial: Avenida OUA, n.° 21, Achada de Santo António, Praia (santiago).
T: 238 261 98 07
E: jornal@expressodasilhas.cv
W: http://www.expressodasilhas.cv **Circ:** 3500 Pub Statement
Editorial Profile: Newspaper focusing on national and international news, politics, business, culture and sport.
Language (s): Portuguese
DAILY NEWSPAPER

Krioulidadi
Editorial: Rotunda do Palmarejo, Avenida Santiago, Praia (santiago)
Freq: Weekly; **Circ:** 5000 Pub Statement
NEWSPAPER

Lance
Editorial: Rotunda do Palmarejo, Avenida Santiago, Praia (santiago)
Freq: Weekly; **Circ:** 5000 Pub Statement
NEWSPAPER

A Semana
Owner: Nova Editora, SARL
Editorial: Rotunda do Palmarejo, Avenida Santiago, Praia (santiago). **T:** 238 262 98 60
E: asemana@cvtelecom.cv
W: http://www.asemana.cv **Circ:** 5000 Pub Statement
Chefe Publicidade: Vivalda Duarte; **Chefe de Redação:** Jose Vicente Lopes
Editorial Profile: Newspaper covering national and international news, politics, economy, culture and sport.
Language (s): Portuguese
DAILY NEWSPAPER

NEWS SERVICE/SYNDICATE

Inforpress
Editorial: C.P. 40a Praia, Santiago.
T: 238 2 62 32 69 **E:** inforpress@cvtelecom.cv
Redactor: Carvalho Santos
Language (s): Portuguese
NEWS SERVICE/SYNDICATE

BROADCASTING

RADIO NETWORKS

Radio Cape Verde
Owner: Radiotelevisão de Cabo Verde
Editorial: Rua 13 de Janeiro, Caixa Postal 1/A, Praia (santiago). **T:** 238 2 60 52 00
E: programas@cvtelecom.cv

TELEVISION STATIONS

RTP África
Editorial: Avenida Cidade de Lisboa, Caixa Postal 482, Praia (santiago). **T:** 238 261 13 15
E: rtpacv2@cvtelecom.cv **W:** http://www.rtp.pt

Televisão Cape Verde
Owner: Radiotelevisão de Cabo Verde
Editorial: Rua 13 de Janeiro, Caixa Postal 1/A, Praia (santiago). **T:** 238 2 60 50 00
E: tvc@tcv.cv

CAYMAN ISLANDS Tel: 1345
Standard Time: GMT -5
Continent: The Americas
Capital City: George Town (Grand Cayman)

NEWSPAPERS & PUBLICATIONS

NEWSPAPERS

The Cayman Islands Journal
Owner: Cayman Free Press Ltd
T: 1345 949 5111
W: http://www.caymanfreepress.com
Freq: Monthly; **Circ:** 30000 Not Audited
Editor: Tammie Chisholm; **Publisher:** Brian Uzenn
Editorial Profile: Focuses on in-depth business news tailored specifically to the Cayman Islands.
Language (s): English
NEWSPAPER

Caymanian Compass
Owner: Cayman Free Press Ltd
Editorial: The Compass Centre, Shedden Road, Grand Cayman KY1-1108.
T: 1345 949 5111 **E:** info@cfp.ky
W: http://www.compasscayman.com
Freq: Daily; **Circ:** 30000 Not Audited
Editor in Chief: Tammie Chisholm
Editorial Profile: Caymanian Compass is a daily newspaper that covers local, national and international news, sports, business and features.
Language (s): English
DAILY NEWSPAPER

NEWS SERVICE/SYNDICATE

Caribbean Net News
Editorial: Miracle Center, 85 North Sound Road., Grand Cayman. **T:** 345 9466060
W: http://caribbeannetnews.com
Editor: Barry Randall
Editorial Profile: Provides news and trade information from around the Caribbean.
Language (s): English
NEWS SERVICE/SYNDICATE

BROADCASTING

RADIO STATIONS

ZFKC-FM
Owner: Government of the Cayman Islands
T: 1 345 949-7799 **E:** rcnews@gov.ky
W: http://www.radiocayman.gov.ky
Editorial Profile: ZFKC-FM is a non-commercial radio station owned by the Government of the Cayman Islands. The format of the station is news and talk. ZFKC-FM broadcasts to the Cayman Islands at 89.9.

ZFKZ-FM
Owner: Government of the Cayman Islands
T: 1 345 949-7799 **E:** rcnews@gov.ky
W: http://www.radiocayman.gov.ky
Editorial Profile: ZFKZ-FM is a non-commercial radio station owned by the Government of the Cayman Islands. The format of the station is a mixture of pop, soca, Latin, reggae, religious and Caribbean music. ZFKZ-FM broadcasts to the Cayman Islands at 105.3 FM.

ZFZZ-FM
Owner: Hurley's Entertainment Corporation Limited
T: +1 345 945-1166 **W:** http://www.z99.ky
Editorial Profile: Z99 (99.9 FM) is a radio station in the Cayman Islands in the British West Indies. The station is owned by Hurley's Entertainment Corporation. Station format is Contemporary Hit Radio. Hurley's Entertainment Corporation Limited was founded in 1992 by Randy L. Merren. Z99FM was the first commercial radio station in the Cayman Islands. It began broadcasting as ZFZZ, issued under the British call sign system, in May 1992. The station's most recent license was issued on 11 December, 2003.

TELEVISION STATIONS

Cayman 27
Owner: Weststar Television
T: 1 345 745-2739
E: news@cayman27.com.ky
W: http://www.cayman27.com.ky
Editorial Profile: Cayman 27 provides the Cayman Islands community with news, sports, and entertainment. The station is owned by Weststar Television. Cayman 27 broadcasts locally on channel 27.

CHAD Tel: 235
Standard Time: GMT +1
Continent: Africa
Capital City: N'Djamena

NEWSPAPERS & PUBLICATIONS

NEWSPAPERS

N'Djamena Bi-Hebdo
Owner: Bi-Hebdo
Editorial: Boulevard des SAO, BP 4498, N'djamena. **T:** 235 22 51 53 14
E: ndjh89@yahoo.fr
W: http://www.ndjamenahebdo.chez.com
Freq: Weekly Pub Statement
Editorial Profile: Newspaper covering regional and national news and current affairs including politics, economics, culture and sport.
Language (s): French
NEWSPAPER

Le Progrès
Owner: Le Progrès
Editorial: Avenue Charles de Gaulle, BP 3055, N'djamena. **T:** 235 22 51 55 86
E: abakar@quotidienleprogres.com
W: http://www.quotidienleprogres.com
Freq: Daily Pub Statement
Editor in Chief: Abderamane Boukar
Editorial Profile: Newspaper covering regional and national news and current affairs including politics, economics and sport.
Language (s): French
DAILY NEWSPAPER

NEWS SERVICE/SYNDICATE

ATP - Agence Tchadienne de Presse
Owner: Agence Tchadienne de Presse
T: 235 22 52 58 67 **E:** atp@infotchad.com
W: http://www.infotchad.com
Editorial Profile: National news agency covering regional, national and international news and current affairs including politics, business, economics, society, health, environment and sport.
Language (s): Arabic
NEWS SERVICE/SYNDICATE

CHILE Tel: 56

Standard Time: GMT -4
Continent: The Americas
Capital City: Santiago

NEWSPAPERS & PUBLICATIONS

NEWSPAPERS

Diario Estrategia
Editorial: Av. Luis Carrera 1289, 16485, Correo 9, Santiago. **T:** 56 26556100
W: http://www.estrategia.cl
Freq: Daily
Redactor: Nicolás Cáceres E.; **Redactor:** Pablo Cañas M.; **Redactor:** Ítalo Cornejo R.; **Editor:** Rodrigo D'amico N.; **Redactora:** Carolina Espinoza; **Editora General:** Alejandra Figueroa García-Huidobro; **Redactor:** Daniel Gómez Y.; **Editora:** Patricia González M.; **Editor:** Brian Gubbins S.; **Editor:** Valentin Magallanes H.; **Editor:** Rodrigo Pacheco C.; **Redactor:** Matías Rodo Y.; **Redactora:** Paulina Rosso V.; **Redactor:** José Pablo Stange C.; **Editora:** Paulina Valenzuela; **Redactor:** César Valenzuela B.
Editorial Profile: A newspaper focusing on business and economy news in Chile. Offers analysis of the business world and financial markets. Covers business trends, management issues, marketing, technology, investments and the people who hold power in Chilean business.
Language (s): Spanish
DAILY NEWSPAPER

Diario La Hora
Editorial: Av. Vicuña Mackenna 1870, 9-D, Santiago. **T:** 56 2 550-7774
E: contacto@lahora.cl **W:** http://www.lahora.cl
Freq: Daily; **Circ:** 250000
Editor: Javier Bobadilla; **Editor:** Ximena Diaz; **Editora:** Ximena Díaz; **Editor Internacional:** Gonzalo López
Language (s): Spanish
DAILY NEWSPAPER

Diario La Tercera
Owner: Grupo Copesa, S.A.
Editorial: Av. Vicuña Mackenna 1962 9-D, Ñuñoa, Santiago 7780133. **T:** 56 22 550-7000
E: correo@latercera.cl
W: http://diario.latercera.com
Freq: Daily
Editora General: Marialí Bofill García; **Editor:** Víctor Cofré Soto; **Editor General:** Felipe Contreras Pedreros; **Editora:** Gabriela De La Maza Palacios; **Editor:** Marcelo Duhalde Casanova; **Editor:** Rodrigo Eyzaguirre Vega; **Editor:** Juan Pablo Iglesias; **Editor:** Mauricio Jürgensen Roldán; **Editor:** Alejandro Maltés Zárate; **Editor Nocturno:** Sergio Maraboli Triviño; **Editor:** Pablo Marín Castro; **Editor:** Noemí Miranda Gómez; **Editor:** Fernando Ojeda Velozo; **Editor:** Marcelo Palomino Montenegro; **Editor:** José Carlos Pérez Hernández; **Editor:** Juan Andrés Quezada Gómez; **Editora:** Sandra Rojas Wirth; **Editor:** Carlos Salvo Callender; **Editor Nacional:** Gabriel Vargas Espinoza
Editorial Profile: Diario La Tercera is a daily newspaper providing Local News, National News, International News, Sports, Arts & Entertainment, Business and Editorial Page coverage in Chile.
Language (s): Spanish
DAILY NEWSPAPER

Diario Publimetro
Owner: Publimetro, S.A.
Editorial: Av. Presidente Kennedy 5735, Of. 701, Torre Poniente, Las Condes, Santiago.
T: 56 2 421-5900 **E:** cronica@publimetro.cl
W: http://www.publimetro.cl
Freq: Daily; **Circ:** 100000
Editor: Mauricio Ávila; **Editor:** Alexis Cares; **Editora:** Alejandra Gallagos; **Editora:** Andrea González
Editorial Profile: Diario Publimetro is a free daily newspaper that provides International News, National News, Sports, Arts & Entertainment, Business coverage for the residents of the Santiago, Chile metropolitan area.
Language (s): Spanish
DAILY NEWSPAPER

El Mercurio
Owner: Empresa El Mercurio S.A.P.
Editorial: Av. Santa María 5542, Vitacura, Santiago. **T:** 56 2 330-1315
E: redaccion@mercurio.cl
W: http://diario.elmercurio.com
Freq: Daily; **Circ:** 136480 Not Audited
Editorial Profile: Newspaper containing national and international news, sports and culture.
Language (s): Spanish
DAILY NEWSPAPER

Pulso
Owner: Grupo Copesa, S.A.
Editorial: El Bosque Sur 90 Piso 4, Las Condes, Santiago 7550248. **T:** 56 2 2230-2810
W: http://www.pulso.cl
Freq: Daily
Editorial Profile: Pulso is a daily financial newspaper providing National and International News coverage on Economy, Finance, Markets, Industry, Technology, Taxes and Politics in Santiago, Chile.
Language (s): Spanish
DAILY NEWSPAPER

Revista Wikén
Editorial: Av. Santa María 5542, 13-D, Correo Central, Santiago. **T:** 56 23301111
W: http://www.emol.com
Freq: Weekly; **Circ:** 159900
Editora: Marcela Aguilar Guzmán; **Editora:** María Isabel Aravena; **Editor:** Gonzalo Argandoña Macmahon; **Editor:** Juan Azócar; **Editor General:** Pedro Azócar; **Editora:** Marialí Bofill García; **Editora:** Bárbara Brain; **Editora:** Estela Cabezas Aguirre; **Editor Internacional:** Iván Cabezas Meléndez; **Editor:** Luis Eugenio Cádiz; **Editor Adjunto:** María Teresa Cárdenas Maturana; **Editora:** Paula Coddou Balmaceda; **Editora:** Pamela Díaz; **Editora:** Claudia Durán; **Editor Nacional:** Andrés Figueroa; **Editora:** Beatriz García-Hidobro; **Editor:** Raúl Gutiérrez Valenzuela; **Editor:** Jaime Huerta; **Editor General:** Luis Inostroza; **Editora:** María Paz Izquierdo; **Editor Adjunto:** Gazi Jalil Figueroa; **Editora:** Marily Lüders Morales; **Editor:** Juan Carlos Maya; **Editor:** Esteban Montero; **Editora:** Paula Olmedo K.; **Editor:** César Olmos Marchant; **Editor General:** Julio Ovalle Schulz; **Editor:** Francisco Poblete; **Editor General:** Roberto Portilla; **Editora General:** Carolina Ramírez O.; **Diseñador:** Felipe Raveau; **Editor:** Cristián Reyes; **Editor:** Luis Rosas; **Editor General:** Gerardo Sánchez; **Editor:** Ana María Sanhueza; **Editor:** Joaquín Santelices; **Editora:** Pilar Segovia Isasi; **Editor General:** Alejandra Sepúlveda; **Editor General:** Patricio Trebilcock K.; **Editor:** Daniel Ulloa; **Editora:** Alejandra Urzúa; **Editor:** Marcelo Valdebenito; **Diseñador:** Cristián Valdés Z.; **Editor:** Carlos Valencia Liendo; **Editor:** Fernando Véliz; **Editora:** Paula Véliz García; **Editor:** Pablo Vergara; **Editor:** Felipe Vidal; **Editora:** Patricia Vildósola; **Editora General:** María Teresa Villafrade; **Editor:** Mauricio Weitzel
Language (s): Spanish
NEWSPAPER

Revista Ya
Editorial: Av. Santa María 5542, 13-D, Correo Central, Santiago. **T:** 56 23301111
W: http://www.elmercurio.cl
Freq: Weekly; **Circ:** 188823
Editora: Marcela Aguilar Guzmán; **Editora:** María Isabel Aravena; **Editor:** Gonzalo Argandoña Macmahon; **Editor:** Juan Azócar; **Editor General:** Pedro Azócar; **Editora:** Marialí Bofill García; **Editora:** Bárbara Brain; **Editora:** Estela Cabezas Aguirre; **Editor Internacional:** Iván Cabezas Meléndez; **Editor:** Luis Eugenio Cádiz; **Editor Adjunto:** María Teresa Cárdenas Maturana; **Editora:** Paula Coddou Balmaceda; **Editora:** Pamela Díaz; **Editora:** Claudia Durán; **Editor Nacional:** Andrés Figueroa; **Editora:** Beatriz García-Hidobro; **Editor:** Raúl Gutiérrez Valenzuela; **Editor:** Jaime Huerta; **Editor General:** Luis Inostroza; **Editora:** María Paz Izquierdo; **Editor Adjunto:** Gazi Jalil Figueroa; **Editora:** Marily Lüders Morales; **Editor:** Juan Carlos Maya; **Editor:** Esteban Montero; **Editora:** Paula Olmedo K.; **Editor:** César Olmos Marchant; **Editor General:** Julio Ovalle Schulz; **Editor:** Francisco Poblete; **Editor General:** Roberto Portilla; **Editora General:** Carolina Ramírez O.; **Diseñador:** Felipe Raveau; **Editor:** Cristián Reyes; **Editor:** Luis Rosas; **Editor General:** Gerardo Sánchez; **Editor:** Ana María Sanhueza; **Editor:** Joaquín Santelices; **Editora:** Pilar Segovia Isasi; **Editor General:** Alejandra Sepúlveda; **Editor General:** Patricio Trebilcock K.; **Editor:** Daniel Ulloa; **Editora:** Alejandra Urzúa; **Editor:** Marcelo Valdebenito; **Diseñador:** Cristián Valdés Z.; **Editor:** Carlos Valencia Liendo; **Editor:** Fernando Véliz; **Editora:** Paula Véliz García; **Editor:** Pablo Vergara; **Editor:** Felipe Vidal; **Editora:** Patricia Vildósola; **Editora General:** María Teresa Villafrade; **Editor:** Mauricio Weitzel
Language (s): Spanish
NEWSPAPER

NEWS SERVICE/SYNDICATE

Agencia Alemana De Prensa Dpa Alemania
Editorial: Ahumada 312, Of.626, Santiago.
T: 56 6733090 **W:** http://www.dpa.com
Language (s): Spanish
NEWS SERVICE/SYNDICATE

Agencia Ansa Italia
Editorial: Moneda 1040, Of.702, Santiago.
T: 56 3601612 **W:** http://www.ansa.it
Language (s): Spanish
NEWS SERVICE/SYNDICATE

Agencia Chile Noticias Acn Chile
Editorial: Av.carlos Antúnez 1884 Of. 104, Santiago. **T:** 56 2230205
W: http://www.chilenoticias.cl
Editor: Norberto Parra H.
Language (s): Spanish
NEWS SERVICE/SYNDICATE

Agencia Dow Jones Newswires Usa
Editorial: Mac Iver 440, Of.1104, 2653, Santiago. **T:** 56 4608546
W: http://www.dowjones.com
Language (s): Spanish
NEWS SERVICE/SYNDICATE

Agencia France Presse Afp Francia
Editorial: Av.alameda Libertador B.o'higgins 1316, Of.92, Santiago. **T:** 56 6960559
W: http://www.afp.com
Language (s): Spanish
NEWS SERVICE/SYNDICATE

Agencia Informativa Latinoamericana - Cuba
Editorial: Bombero Adolfo Ossa 1010, Of.1104, Santiago. **T:** 56 6718222
W: http://www.prensa-latina.cu
Language (s): Spanish
NEWS SERVICE/SYNDICATE

Agencia Informativa Orbe - Chile
Editorial: Av.presidente Errázuriz 2933, Santiago. **T:** 56 2517800 **W:** http://www.orbe.cl
Redactor: Andrés Aguilera; **Redactor:** Gabriel Barrios; **Redactor:** Raúl Beltrán; **Redactora:** Mariela Espinoza; **Redactor:** Cristián Guzmán; **Redactor:** Raúl Jara; **Redactora:** Marisa Latorre; **Editor:** Francisco Javier Leiva; **Editor:** Cristián Quiriván; **Redactor:** José Ignacio Valenzuela; **Redactor:** Andrés Varas; **Editor:** Andrés Venegas
Language (s): Spanish
NEWS SERVICE/SYNDICATE

Agencia Notimex México
Editorial: Catedral 1009, Of.1601, Santiago.
T: 56 6880424 **W:** http://www.notimex.com.mx
Editor: Javier Aguirre; **Editor:** Omar Sepúlveda Pacheco; **Editor:** Julio Wright
Language (s): Spanish
NEWS SERVICE/SYNDICATE

Agencia Reuters Reino Unido
Editorial: Nueva York 33, Piso 11, Santiago.
T: 56 3704200 **W:** http://www.reuters.com
Language (s): Spanish
NEWS SERVICE/SYNDICATE

Asociación Internacional Inter Press Service Agencia Ips Italia
Editorial: José Joaquín Pérez 9940, Santiago.
T: 56 2819835 **W:** http://www.ips.org
Language (s): Spanish
NEWS SERVICE/SYNDICATE

Associated Press
Editorial: Mac Iver 440, Oficina 1104, Santiago. **T:** 56 2 460-8540
Bureau Chief: Michael Warren
NEWS SERVICE/SYNDICATE

Bloomberg News
Editorial: Mira Flores 222 Edificio de las Americas, Piso 13 Rm 1302, Santiago 10022-1240. **T:** 56 26384732
NEWS SERVICE/SYNDICATE

Europa Press Chile
Editorial: Los Conquistadores 1700, Piso 2, Santiago. **T:** 56 4820100
W: http://www.europapress.cl
Language (s): Spanish
NEWS SERVICE/SYNDICATE

Reuters
Editorial: Nueva York 33, Piso 11, Casilla 4248, Correo Central, Santiago.
T: 5411 5554 7306
E: santiago.newsroom@thomsonreuters.com
NEWS SERVICE/SYNDICATE

United Press International Agencia Upi Chile
Editorial: Nataniel Cox 47, Piso 9, Santiago.
T: 56 2 657-0874 **E:** prensa@upi.com
W: http://www.upi.com
Editor: Jaime Zavala Jara
Language (s): Spanish
NEWS SERVICE/SYNDICATE

CHINA Tel: 86

Standard Time: GMT +8 (West Coast), GMT +10 (East Coast)
Continent: Asia
Capital City: Beijing

NEWSPAPERS & PUBLICATIONS

NEWSPAPERS

21st Century Business Herald
Editorial: 5F, PRODUCTION COMPLEX BUILDING OF SOUTHERN DAILY, No.289, GUANGZHOU DADAOZHONG RD, YUEXIU DISTRICT, Guangzhou 510601.
T: 86 20 83000582 **E:** 21cbhad@21cbh.com
W: http://www.21cbh.com
Freq: Weekly Not Audited
Editorial Profile: Provides information about business, market, and investment in China, Asia and worldwide.
Language (s): Chinese
NEWSPAPER

21st Century News
Owner: China Daily Newspaper Group
Editorial: China Daily Press Group, 15 Huixin Dongjie, Chaoyangqu, Beijing 100029.
T: 86 10 64995500 **E:** contact@i21st.cn
W: http://www.i21st.cn
Freq: Weekly Not Audited
Editor in Chief: Lisheng Nie
Editorial Profile: Founded in 1993 as a guide for learning English, covers current affairs, culture, sports and entertainment. Written primarily for Chinese youth.
Language (s): English
NEWSPAPER

21st Century Teens Junior Edition
Owner: China Daily Newspaper Group
Editorial: China Daily Press Group, 15 Huixin Dongjie, Chaoyangqu, Beijing 100029.
T: 86 1064995500
W: http://www.21stcentury.com.cn
Freq: Weekly; **Circ:** 120001 Not Audited
Editor in Chief: Lisheng Nie
Editorial Profile: Founded in 2003, focuses on educational and cultural information and English learning materials for junior high schools students.
Language (s): Chinese
NEWSPAPER

21st Century Teens Senior Edition
Owner: China Daily Newspaper Group
Editorial: China Daily Press Group, 15 Huixin Dongjie, Chaoyangqu, Beijing 100029.
T: 86 10 64918211
E: adsales@21stcentury.com.cn
W: http://www.i21st.cn
Freq: Weekly; **Circ:** 120003 Not Audited
Editor in Chief: Lisheng Nie
Editorial Profile: A newspaper published in English for senior students in high school. Covers current affairs, culture, sports and entertainment.
Language (s): Chinese
NEWSPAPER

Agrigoods Herald
Editorial: Agrigoods Herald, Jia 2, Liupukang Beixiaojie, Beijing 100011. **T:** 86 1082032080
W: http://www.nzdb.com.cn
Freq: 2 Times/Week; **Circ:** 60001 Not Audited
Editor in Chief: Jianqiu Zhang
Editorial Profile: Covers topics for those in the agriculture business.
Language (s): Chinese
NEWSPAPER

Anhui Business News
Editorial: Anhui Daily, 206 Jinzhailu, Hefei 230061. **T:** 86 5515179633
E: ahsb@mail.hf.ah.cn
W: http://www.ahrb.com.cn
Freq: Daily; **Circ:** 480004 Not Audited
Editor in Chief: Yan Zhao
Editorial Profile: It provides latest information on the economy and business in Anhui region.
Language (s): Chinese

DAILY NEWSPAPER

Anhui Economic News
Editorial: Anhui Economic News Press, 200 Tunxilu, Hefei 230001. **T:** 86 5514672920 818
W: http://www.ahjjnews.cn
Freq: 2 Times/Week; **Circ:** 100003 Not Audited
Editor in Chief: Shunsheng Ma
Editorial Profile: Anhui Economic News mainly contains business and finance news in Anhui region and in China.
Language (s): Chinese
NEWSPAPER

Anhui Law News
Editorial: Anhui Daily, 1469 Qianshan Road, Hefei 230071. **T:** 86 5515179831
E: ahfzb@ahfzb.com
W: http://www.ahrb.com.cn/
Freq: 2 Times/Week; **Circ:** 66003 Not Audited
Editor in Chief: Youqun Wang
Editorial Profile: It covers the law-related issues and cases.
Language (s): Chinese
NEWSPAPER

Anhui Market News
Editorial: Anhui Market News Press, 10 Yonghonglu, Hefei 230001. **T:** 86 5512620110
W: http://www.ahscb.com.cn
Freq: Daily; **Circ:** 300003 Not Audited
Editor: Gucheng Ye
Editorial Profile: Covers news about finance, business, and economic developments in Anhui and in China.
Language (s): Chinese
DAILY NEWSPAPER

Antiquarian Books Weekly
Editorial: Antiquarian Books Weekly, 1 Tianyuan Road, Shijiazhuang 50071.
T: 86 31187732149 **E:** cangshubao@126.com
Freq: Weekly; **Circ:** 100002 Not Audited
Editor in Chief: Zhanmin Cheng
Editorial Profile: covers historical, cultural and market information of antiques and books information.
Language (s): Chinese
NEWSPAPER

Asahi Shimbun - Beijing Bureau
Editorial: Asahi Shimbun - Beijing Bureau, Rm 1108 Derun Tower, Beijing 100022.
T: 86 10 58795885 **W:** http://www.asahi.com
Freq: Daily
Editorial Profile: A international newspaper covering global issues and news in China.
Language (s): English
DAILY NEWSPAPER

Asahi Shimbun - Shanghai Bureau
Editorial: 1376 Nanjing Road, Shanghai 200040 **W:** http://www.asahi.com
Freq: Daily
Bureau Chief: Okudera Atsushi
Editorial Profile: Foreign bureau of Asahi Shimbun newspaper in Japan.
Language (s): English
DAILY NEWSPAPER

Auto Today Weekly
Editorial: Auto Today Weekly, Te 8, Youyi Dadao, Wuchang District, Wuhan 430062.
T: 86 2751868506
Freq: Weekly; **Circ:** 100003 Not Audited
Editorial Profile: covers the automotive industry and the development of automotive technology in China. It also provides information and knowledge about the maintenance and repairs of cars.
Language (s): Chinese
NEWSPAPER

Bandao Morning Post
Editorial: Liaoning Daily Press Group, 360 Changchunlu, Xigangqu, Dalian 116013.
T: 86 41182499922
W: http://newspaper.lndaily.com.cn/bdcb
Freq: Daily; **Circ:** 350003 Not Audited
Editor in Chief: Runfu Wang
Editorial Profile: Covers news in Dalian.
Language (s): Chinese
DAILY NEWSPAPER

Basketball News
Editorial: China Sports Publications Group, 8 Tiyuguanlu, Chongwenqu, Beijing 100061.
T: 86 10 67110066
W: http://www.sportsol.com.cn
Freq: Weekly
Editor in Chief: Jie Tan
Editorial Profile: covers national and international news on basketball competitions and basketball players.
Language (s): Chinese
NEWSPAPER

Basketball Pioneers
Editorial: 4-1-501, Tiantan Gongguan, 59 Xinfu Dajie, Chongwenqu, Beijing 100061.
T: 86 2081330007
W: http://www.goalchina.net
Freq: 2 Times/Week; **Circ:** 200003 Not Audited
Bureau Chief: Huifang Cai; **Editor in Chief:** Qun Su
Editorial Profile: Basketball Pioneers is a national newspaper that provides the latest news on basketball.
Language (s): Chinese
NEWSPAPER

Beijing Broadcasting TV News, People Weekly
Editorial: Beijing Television Weekly, 14 Xizhaosijie, Beijing 100061
E: zkzggix@vip.sina.com
W: http://www.bgtv.com.cn
Freq: Weekly; **Circ:** 150004 Not Audited
Editor in Chief: Biao Zhang
Editorial Profile: covers stories and reports of famous people's lifestyles and their interesting stories.
Language (s): Chinese
NEWSPAPER

Beijing Business Today
Editorial: Beijing Business Today Press, 21 Hepingli Xijie, Chaoyangqu, Beijing 100013.
T: 86 10 84276691
W: http://www.bbtnews.com.cn
Freq: 2 Times/Week; **Circ:** 150003 Not Audited
Editor: Chen Jie; **Editor in Chief:** Hai Li;
Bureau Chief: Chengjun Qiu
Editorial Profile: reports on business and financial news. It mainly targets Chinese businessmen.
Language (s): Chinese
NEWSPAPER

Beijing Children News
Editorial: Beijing Children News, Room 1802, Beijing Qingnianbao Dasha, Building A, 23 Dongli, Baijiazhuan, Chaoyagqu, Beijing 100026. **T:** 86 10 65902441
E: bjsnb@ynet.com **W:** http://bjsn.ynet.com
Freq: Weekly; **Circ:** 300003 Not Audited
Editor in Chief: Aixue Zhang
Editorial Profile: covers educational issues and topics about lifestyle and culture of the youth in China.
Language (s): Chinese
NEWSPAPER

Beijing Entertainment Journal
Editorial: Beijing Entertainment Journal, 10F Guorui Dasha, Chongwenmen WaiDajie, Dongchengqu, Beijing 100062.
T: 86 1087555123
W: http://www.stardaily.com.cn/
Freq: Daily; **Circ:** 300000 Not Audited
Bureau Chief: Kun Bi; **Editor:** Bin Chang;
Editor in Chief: Jinghui Si
Editorial Profile: Beijing Entertainment Journal is a metro newspaper which is freely distributed in metro railway stations in Beijing. It mainly covers news and information of entertainment and lifestyle issues.
Language (s): Chinese
DAILY NEWSPAPER

Beijing Evening News
Owner: Beijing Daily Press Group
Editorial: Beijing Daily Press Group, 20 Jianguo Mennei Dajie, Beijing 100734.
T: 86 10 85202144 **E:** wbrxb@vip.sina.com
W: http://www.bjd.com.cn/
Freq: Daily; **Circ:** 1000000 Not Audited
Editor in Chief: Huanying Ren
Editorial Profile: Founded in 1958, covers news, finance, entertainment, sports and social issues.
Language (s): Chinese
DAILY NEWSPAPER

Beijing Job Market News
Editorial: Beijing Job Market News, 3/F, No. 33 DongwangZhuang, Qinghua East Road, Haidian District, Beijing 100083.
T: 86 1062312502 **E:** 2000wujian@163.com
W: http://www.bjrc.com
Freq: 2 Times/Week; **Circ:** 100002 Not Audited
Editor in Chief: Jian Wu
Editorial Profile: It provides comprehensive information on job market and career in Beijing area.
Language (s): Chinese
NEWSPAPER

Beijing Morning Post
Owner: Beijing Daily Group
Editorial: Beijing Daily Group, 3rd Floor, Block A, Donghuan Guangchang, Number 9, Dongzhongjie, Dongchengqu, Beijing 100027.
T: 86 1064183399 **E:** openweek@vip.sina.com
W: http://www.morningpost.com.cn
Freq: Daily Not Audited
Editorial Profile: It covers news, politics, economy, business, sports, entertainment, lifestyle and social issues.
Language (s): Chinese
DAILY NEWSPAPER

The Beijing News
Editorial: The Beijing News, 37 Xingfu Beidajie, Beijing 100061. **T:** 86 10 67106710
E: news@thebeijingnews.com
W: http://www.thebeijingnews.com
Freq: Daily; **Circ:** 500003
Editorial Profile: A daily newspaper.
Language (s): Chinese
DAILY NEWSPAPER

Beijing Today
Editorial: Beijing Youth Press, Beijing Qingnianbao Daxia, Dongli, Baijiazhuang, Chaoyangqu, Beijing 100026.
T: 86 1065902513
E: info@beijingtoday.com.cn
W: http://bjtoday.ynet.com
Freq: Weekly; **Circ:** 50003 Not Audited
Editorial Profile: Launched in 2001, serves Beijing's expat community with news and cultural events.
Language (s): English
NEWSPAPER

Beijing Youth Daily
Editorial: Beijing Youth Press, Building A, 23 Dongli, Baijiazhuang, Chaoyangqu, Beijing 100026. **T:** 86 10 65902200
W: http://bjyouth.ynet.com
Freq: Daily; **Circ:** 600003 Not Audited
Editor: Jingjing Ma; **Editor:** Shanshan Yu;
Editor in Chief: Yabin Zhang
Editorial Profile: Covers politics, economy, finance, lifestyle and culture. Beijing Youth Daily has reported a formation of five subnet issue of the publication pattern, the amount of daily published outside the 48 edition, the daily circulation of about 600,000. The next few years, Beijing Youth Daily will be "Three Represents" as guidance, thoroughly implement the party's congress, emancipate our minds, seek truth from facts, insist firmly grasp the correct guidance of public opinion, insisted close reality, life, and the masses, through the growth of the main industry, the integration of resources, innovation system, to build Beijing Media family of brands and core competencies to achieve in the new situation and new opportunities under the leaps and bounds.
Language (s): Chinese
DAILY NEWSPAPER

Books and Periodicals News
Editorial: Hebei Daily Press Group, 210 Yuhuadonglu, Shijiazhuang 50013.
T: 86 3118631176 **E:** skb186@163.com
W: http://www.hebeidaily.com.cn
Freq: Weekly; **Circ:** 200001 Not Audited
Editor in Chief: Yingchao Zhang
Editorial Profile: Covers information on books and journals, as well as historical books and culture.
Language (s): Chinese
NEWSPAPER

The Bund
Editorial: Shanghai The Bund Media Co. Ltd., 5th Floor, Baoli Dasha, Number 10, Nong 100, Changshulu, Shanghai 200040.
T: 86 2162480708 **W:** http://www.bundpic.com
Freq: Weekly; **Circ:** 150001 Not Audited
Editor in Chief: Lanni Chen
Editorial Profile: Covers cultural and lifestyle information in China and other countries, providing comments and analysis in economic and fashion field. It also includes information on entertainment and business.
Language (s): Chinese
NEWSPAPER

CAAC Journal
Editorial: Civil Aviation Administration of China, Beijing P.O.Box 2264, Shilihe, Chaoyangqu, Beijing 100021.
T: 86 1067301570 **E:** news@caacjournal.com
W: http://www.caacjournal.com
Freq: 2 Times/Week Not Audited
Editor in Chief: Yue Ding
Editorial Profile: covers the latest news and hot issues of Civil Aviation Administration of China, and the latest information of aviation industry.
Language (s): Chinese
NEWSPAPER

CANKAO XIAO XI
Editorial: Xinhua News Agency, 57 Xidajie, Xuanwumen, Beijing 100803.
T: 86 10 63071136 **E:** ckxx@xinhua.org
W: http://www.cankaoa.com
Freq: Daily; **Circ:** 3500000 Not Audited
Editor: Jingli Lu
Editorial Profile: Provides news and social issues of Chinese society. Can kao xiao xi in early November 1931 in Jiangxi founded, as the Xinhua News Agency's issuance of a unique national mainstream media, newspapers published outside the main current affairs news. China's largest circulation daily newspaper, the daily circulation of 4,000,000 copies, distributed nationally, covering multi-level readers, including 25-34 and 35-44 accounted for a larger proportion of the reader, the reader is relatively mature, rational, is backbone of society, they are in the golden age of business development, has got to have the economic base and decision-making capacity; party and government organs, organizations, business unit leaders of the audience is also a faithful reader of the message reference; Reference News News for the layout are, advertising accounted for less than the version provided the rate 1 / 6, is the launch customer reference information to maximize the advertising effect. Reference information is the most representative of China's political news media, is a favorite of newspaper readers.
Language (s): Chinese
DAILY NEWSPAPER

Changchun Daily
Editorial: Changchun Daily Press, 10 Xinmin Dajie, Changchun 130021. **T:** 86 43185611706
Freq: Daily; **Circ:** 180001 Not Audited
Editor in Chief: Fang Lv
Editorial Profile: It covers local and regional news in Jilin province as well as national news.
Language (s): Chinese
DAILY NEWSPAPER

Chengde Daily
Editorial: Chengde Daily, Xinjuzhai, Huochezhanlu, Chengde 67000.
T: 86 31 42152035
W: http://www.cddaily.com.cn
Freq: Daily; **Circ:** 50003 Not Audited
Editor: Jianxin Liu
Editorial Profile: Chengde Daily is a general newspaper with strong local focus covering news, social issues, lifestyle, society, culture, sports and health.
Language (s): Chinese
DAILY NEWSPAPER

Chengdu Business Daily
Editorial: Chengdu Daily Press Group, 159, 2 Duan, Hongxinlu, Chengdu 610017.
T: 86 28 86612222 **W:** http://www.cdsb.com
Freq: Daily Not Audited
Editor in Chief: Shuping Chen
Editorial Profile: Covers business and financial news in Chengdu region.
Language (s): Chinese
DAILY NEWSPAPER

Chengdu Evening News
Editorial: 159 Hongxinglu Erduan, Chengdu 610017. **T:** 86 28 86746906
E: cdwb962111@sina.com
W: http://www.cdwb.com.cn
Freq: Daily Not Audited
Editor: Yuanhang Ren
Editorial Profile: Focuses on news in the Chengdu region of China.
Language (s): Chinese
DAILY NEWSPAPER

China Archives News
Editorial: China Archives News Press, 106 Yong'an Road, Xuanwu District, Beijing 100050. **T:** 86 10 63150625
E: charne@vip.163.com
W: http://www.zgdazxw.com.cn/
Freq: 2 Times/Week; **Circ:** 260003 Not Audited
Editor in Chief: Haiying Guo
Editorial Profile: Covers national archives, as well as government, military service and constitutional records.
Language (s): Chinese
NEWSPAPER

China Art Weekly
Editorial: Zhejiang Daily Press Group, 178 Tiyuchanglu, Hangzhou 310039.
T: 86 57185310158
W: http://www.zjdaily.com.cn
Freq: Weekly
Editor in Chief: Jingfu Cai

Editorial Profile: Covers art trends and art appreciation in China.
Language (s): Chinese
NEWSPAPER

China Automotive News

Editorial: People Daily Group, 115 Fuchenglu, Haidianqu, Beijing 100036. **T:** 86 1088137907
W: http://www.cnautonews.com
Freq: Weekly; **Circ:** 110003 Not Audited
Bureau Chief: Qingwen Li
Editorial Profile: a national newspaper providing information and news about the auto industry in China and overseas.
Language (s): Chinese
NEWSPAPER

China Beauty Fashion Newspaper

Editorial: China Beauty Fashion Newspaper, 46 Jiulongxiang, Shudu Dadao, Chengdu 610017
W: http://www.cbfmg.com/Index.html
Freq: Weekly
Editor in Chief: Xiaomei Zhang
Editorial Profile: China Beauty Fashion Newspaper is a regional publication which covers the latest news and information of beauty, fashion and cosmetics trends in China.
Language (s): Chinese
NEWSPAPER

China Book Business Report

Editorial: China Book Business Report, 3F, Waiyan Dasha, 19 Xisanhuan Beilu, Beijing 100089. **T:** 86 10 88817687
E: zwt9999@cbbr.com.cn
W: http://www.cbbr.com.cn
Freq: 2 Times/Week; **Circ:** 60003 Not Audited
Editor in Chief: Yuemu Sun
Editorial Profile: provides information, comments and critics about the publications in China.
Language (s): Chinese
NEWSPAPER

China Business

Editorial: China Business, Building Number 1, Number 6, Xisihuan Beilu, Beijing 100097.
T: 86 10 88890000 **E:** cbweb@cbnet.com.cn
W: http://www.cb.com.cn
Freq: Weekly Not Audited
Editor in Chief: Peiyu Li
Editorial Profile: Covers corporate management, finance, economics and government regulations. Founded in 1985, the China business newspaper by the Chinese academy of social sciences director, the Chinese academy of social sciences, sponsored by the industrial economy, always adhering to the "lifelong learning and wisdom of good management, social" concept, insight into commercial phenomenon, interpretation of commercial law, thrusting commercial success, to promote the commercial civilization. Is a leading provider of comprehensive financial information provider.Business achievement value, China business newspaper in business management service for readers, to provide comprehensive information product. "The China business news, adhering to the" important and useful, and deeply, can read "news concept, service in the enterprise managers and business people, based on the economic front, capture financial information, mining business value, records and bear witness to China's economic hair. Each issue of 850000, covering the circulation of more than 240 cities. 'The China business news readers more concentrated in 25 to 44 years of age, among them 35 to 44 years old rate of 50%, and the male readers rate of 72.1%. High-end consumer spending is strong, brand loyalty is high, consumer focus on quality of life. Focus on finance, investment, automobile, high-end digital electronic products, high-end wines, watches, clothing and the consumption of the EMBA and know how to enjoy life and constantly improve themselves. Pay attention to the physical and mental health, advocates of lohas way.
Language (s): Chinese
NEWSPAPER

China Business Herald

Owner: China Business News Press Group
Editorial: China Business News Press Group, 1 Baoguosi, Guang'anmennei, Xuanwu District, Beijing 100053. **T:** 86 1063180875
E: zhongguoshangbao@yeah.net
W: http://www.cb-h.com
Freq: Daily; **Circ:** 190002 Not Audited
Editor in Chief: Shiyu Fan
Editorial Profile: This publication covers news from finance, business, trade and investment to automotive trade, retail market and policy related to the industry.
Language (s): Chinese
DAILY NEWSPAPER

China Business News

T: 86 2152132233 **E:** diyicaijing@vip.sina.com
W: http://dycj.ynet.com
Freq: Daily
Editorial Profile: Cost: Paid. Readership/ Audience Profile:Readers are the financial and business professionals, managers and key decision makers in this field, investors and white collars in China. Chinese Publication Number: CN31-0024China Business News is a national financial newspaper co-published by Shanghai Wenguang News Press Group, Beijing Youth News Group and Guangzhou Daily News Group. It focuses on the business and financial news in China and in overseas.
Language (s): Chinese
DAILY NEWSPAPER

China Chemical Industry News

Editorial: China Chemical Industry News, Jia 2, Liupukang Beixiaojie, Beijing 100011.
T: 86 1080032707 **E:** ccinn@ccin.com.cn
W: http://www.ccin.com.cn
Freq: Daily
Editor in Chief: Shuangxin Liu
Editorial Profile: Provides daily news and product updates for professionals in the chemical industry including information on manufacturing, technology, equipment, and supplies.
Language (s): Chinese
DAILY NEWSPAPER

China Coal News

Editorial: China Coal News, Meitan Dasha, Building Number 35, Area 13, Heping Street, Chaoyang District, Beijing 100013.
T: 86 106 4463057 **E:** bs@aqb.cn
W: http://www.ccoalnews.com
Freq: 2 Times/Week; **Circ:** 100001 Not Audited
Editor in Chief: Haijin Bai
Editorial Profile: Covers coal industry and market news, as well as safety of coal mining industry reports.
Language (s): Chinese
NEWSPAPER

China Communications News

Editorial: China Communications News, Block 13, Area 3 Anhuaxili, Andingmenwai, Beijing 100011. **T:** 86 10 64250642
W: http://www.zgjtb.com
Freq: Weekly; **Circ:** 120001 Not Audited
Editor in Chief: Maichi Du
Editorial Profile: Covers news of trucking, shipping, air transport, railroads, traffic control and transportation issues.
Language (s): Chinese
NEWSPAPER

China Computer Education

Editorial: CCID, 16th Floor, Saidi Dasha, 66 Zizhuyuanlu, Haidianqu, Beijing 100044
W: http://www.cce.com.cn
Freq: Weekly; **Circ:** 350003 Not Audited
Editorial Profile: China Computer Education is a national newspaper for IT Industry. It reports news on market trends, policies and regulations related to IT industry; it also introduces the latest software and hardware to the readers.
Language (s): Chinese
NEWSPAPER

China Computer World

Editorial: China Computer World, 3rd Floor, Building 3, 16 Cuiwei Zhongli, Wansinoulu Haidian District, Beijing 100036.
T: 86 1068130909 **W:** http://www.ccw.com.cn
Freq: Weekly; **Circ:** 258001 Not Audited
Editorial Profile: Covers issues about IT products such as computers, phones and softwares.
Language (s): Chinese
NEWSPAPER

China Construction News

Owner: China Construction News Press
Editorial: China Construction News Press, Block 40, Zone 12, 188 Nansihuan Xilu, Fengtai District, Beijing 100070.
T: 86 1063703659 **E:** thong@newsccn.com
W: http://www.newsccn.com
Freq: 2 Times/Week; **Circ:** 100003 Not Audited
Editor in Chief: Qian Deng
Editorial Profile: Covers construction news, projects information and interior decoration issues.
Language (s): Chinese
NEWSPAPER

China Construction News

Editorial: China Construction News, Room 409, Block B, Xinhong Dasha, 5 Building, 8 Yuan, Chedaogou Xilu, Haidian District, Beijing

100089. **T:** 86 1051555511 8669
E: xxtgb@chinajsb.cn
W: http://www.chinajsb.cn
Freq: 2 Times/Week; **Circ:** 79002 Not Audited
Bureau Chief: Shijie Liu
Editorial Profile: covers news in building design, construction materials and construction industry in China.
Language (s): Chinese
NEWSPAPER

China Consumer News

Editorial: China Consumer News Press, 8 Beisanjie, Fuchenglu, Haidian District, Beijing 100037. **T:** 86 1068471315
E: ccn@cen.com.cn
W: http://www.ccn.com.cn
Freq: 2 Times/Week; **Circ:** 150001 Not Audited
Editor in Chief: Xueyin Li
Editorial Profile: a national newspaper covering issues about consumer interest, product quality supervision, and national and international regulations on product quality.
Language (s): Chinese
NEWSPAPER

China Culture Daily

Editorial: China Culture Daily Press, 15 Dongtuchenglu, Chaoyangqu, Beijing 100013.
T: 86 10 85197805 **E:** wenhuanews@ccdy.cn
W: http://www.ccdy.cn
Freq: Daily; **Circ:** 50003 Not Audited
Editor: Biao Jian
Editorial Profile: A national newspaper covering news on Chinese modern and traditional cultures, arts, and history.
Language (s): Chinese
DAILY NEWSPAPER

China Daily

Owner: China Daily Newspaper Group
Editorial: China Daily, 15 Huixindongjie, Chaoyang District, Beijing 100029.
T: 86 10 64995000 **E:** cdw@chinadaily.com.cn
W: http://www.chinadaily.com.cn
Freq: 2 Times/Week Not Audited
Publisher: Yongzhe Huo; **Editor:** Weitao Liu; **Editor:** Han Tianyang; **Editor in Chief:** Ling Zhu
Editorial Profile: Founded in 1981, serves as China's national English-language newspaper that has effectively entered Western mainstream society and is the newspaper most quoted by the foreign press. The paper also has published the largest number of supplements for international meetings in China among all media outlets. Aims to provide an important window for "China to understand the world and be understood by the world".
Language (s): English
NEWSPAPER

China Economic Times

Editorial: China Economic Times, Wangfujie, Pingxifu, Changpingqu, Beijing 102209.
T: 86 1081785100 **E:** info@cet.com.cn
W: http://www.cet.com.cn
Freq: 2 Times/Week; **Circ:** 420001 Not Audited
Editorial Profile: Covers news about economic development in China.
Language (s): Chinese
NEWSPAPER

China Education Daily

Editorial: 10 N WenHuiYuan Road, Haidian District, Beijing. **T:** 86 10 62257722 245
E: wlb@edumail.com.cn
W: http://www.jyb.cn/gb/2004/06/07/zy/home.htm
Editor in Chief: Bo Di
Editorial Profile: Covers education in China. Please note that this outlet is owned by the Chinese government. Often times, these outlets have a set editorial schedule and do not accept press materials or give out staff information. The majority of the staff members speak only Chinese.
Language (s): Chinese
DAILY NEWSPAPER

China Education News

Editorial: China Education Press Agency, 10 Wenhuiyuan Beilu, Haidianqu, Beijing 100082.
T: 86 10 62257722 **W:** http://www.jyb.com.cn
Freq: Daily Not Audited
Editor in Chief: Ning Liu; **Editor:** Wen Yu
Editorial Profile: Focuses on news and information about education policies and related rules.
Language (s): Chinese
DAILY NEWSPAPER

China Electric Power

Editorial: China Power News, 1 Ertiao, Baiguanglu, Xuanwuqu, Beijing 100761.
T: 86 10 63415423 **E:** zgdy@cpnn.com.cn
W: http://www.cpnn.com.cn
Freq: 2 Times/Week; **Circ:** 200000 Not Audited
Editor: Zhao Fei
Editorial Profile: Covers power engineering information, electrical engineering, electrical power industry, as well as electric power delivery, renewable energy sources, automation, control systems and engineering news issues.
Language (s): Chinese
NEWSPAPER

China Electronics News

T: 86 10 88558848 **E:** zbs@cena.com.cn
W: http://www.cena.com.cn
Freq: 2 Times/Week; **Circ:** 87003 Not Audited
Editor: Ying Li; **Editor in Chief:** Dong Liu;
Editor: Bo Ma; **Editor in Chief:** Jianzhong Wang; **Editor in Chief:** Xiaobing Wu; **Editor:** Chenbing Xin
Editorial Profile: Covers information and news in the IT industry. Aimed at local leaders in charge of electronic information, domestic and foreign investors in electronics and information enterprises, operators, managers, and staff in domestic and foreign securities, finance, consulting.
Language (s): Chinese
NEWSPAPER

China Environment News

Editorial: China Environment News, 16 Guangqumennei Dajie, Chongwenqu, Beijing 100062. **T:** 86 1067102729
W: http://www.cenews.com.cn
Freq: 2 Times/Week; **Circ:** 200003 Not Audited
Bureau Chief: Mingsen Yang
Editorial Profile: covers environment protection topics and environment conservation issues.
Language (s): Chinese
NEWSPAPER

China Fashion Weekly

Editorial: China Fashion Weekly, 2 Baizhifang Dongjie, Xuanwu District, Beijing 100054.
T: 86 105 8393998 **E:** zhaolulu@cfw.com.cn
W: http://www.cfw.com.cn
Freq: Weekly Not Audited
Editor in Chief: Zengjun Chen
Editorial Profile: Covers the fashion industry in China.
Language (s): Chinese
NEWSPAPER

China Financial and Economic News

Editorial: China Financial and Economic News, Jia 54, Guang'anlu, Fengtaiqu, Beijing 100161.
T: 86 10 63812638 **W:** http://www.cfen.com.cn
Freq: 2 Times/Week; **Circ:** 220003 Not Audited
Editor in Chief: Guofu Sun
Editorial Profile: covers news on government policies in business, financial sector and accountancy field. Please note that this outlet is owned by the Chinese government. Often times, these outlets have a set editorial schedule and do not accept press materials or give out staff information. The majority of the staff members speak only Chinese.
Language (s): Chinese
NEWSPAPER

China Flowers & Gardening News

Editorial: China Flower and Gardening News, 19 Hengliutiao, Dongtiejiangying, Fengtai District, Beijing 100079. **T:** 86 1087680622
W: http://www.china-flower.com
Freq: 2 Times/Week; **Circ:** 50001 Not Audited
Editor in Chief: Xiangrong Wang
Editorial Profile: Covers the horticulture and gardening industry.
Language (s): Chinese
NEWSPAPER

China Food Quality News

Editorial: China Food Industry Association, 19 Xisihuan Zhonglu, Beijing 100143.
T: 86 1051881559 **E:** cfqn2009@126.com
W: http://www.cfqn.com.cn
Freq: 2 Times/Week
Editor in Chief: Changxue Zhu
Editorial Profile: China Food Quality News is an official publication of China Food Industry Association that mainly provides the latest news and knowledge about food and health.
Language (s): Chinese
NEWSPAPER

China Gold News

Editorial: China Gold News, 15/F, Block B, Luoke Shidai Zhongxin, 103 Huizhongli, Chaoyang District, Beijing 100101.
T: 86 1084871316 **E:** zghjbs@163.com
W: http://www.goldnews.com.cn
Freq: 2 Times/Week; **Circ:** 60003 Not Audited
Editor in Chief: Siyuan Rong
Editorial Profile: China Gold News is a leading national newspaper that mainly focuses on the latest news on gold industry and gold market in China.
Language (s): Chinese
NEWSPAPER

China Green Times

Editorial: China Green Times, 18 Dongjie, Hepingli, Beijing 100714. **T:** 86 1084238640
E: yaowenban@sina.com
W: http://www.greentimes.com
Freq: Daily; **Circ:** 50001 Not Audited
Bureau Chief: Fulin Ding; **Editor in Chief:** Jianzhu Li
Editorial Profile: Focuses on the news of forestry and lumber in China.
Language (s): Chinese
DAILY NEWSPAPER

China High School Students

Editorial: Building 5, Beili, Zuojiazhuang, Chaoyangqu, Beijing 100028.
T: 86 10 84541086
W: http://www.ccppg.com.cn
Freq: 2 Times/Week; **Circ:** 550003 Not Audited
Editor: Wei Si
Editorial Profile: focuses on studies and lives of high school students in China.
Language (s): Chinese
NEWSPAPER

China Human Resources News

Editorial: Human Resources Department, PRC, 5 Yuhuili, Chaoyangqu, Beijing 100010.
T: 86 1084623709 **E:** bin2050@163.com
W: http://www.rensb.com
Freq: Weekly; **Circ:** 100004 Not Audited
Editor: Fengxia Chen; **Editor in Chief:** Baozhong Zhang
Editorial Profile: It reports and promotes government policies on human resource and labor market.
Language (s): Chinese
NEWSPAPER

China Industrial and Commerce News

Owner: China Industrial and Commerce News Press
Editorial: China Industrial and Commerce News Press, 23 Fangyuan Dongli, Jijiamiao, Huaxiang, Fengtaiqu, Beijing 100070.
T: 86 1063784486 **E:** ykf3601@163.com
W: http://www.cicn.com.cn
Freq: 2 Times/Week; **Circ:** 135003 Not Audited
Bureau Chief: Aifu Liang; **Editor in Chief:** Fengwu Zhao
Editorial Profile: provides industrial and commerce news, as well as relevant government policies and regulations issues.
Language (s): Chinese
NEWSPAPER

China Industrial Economy News

Editorial: China Industrial Information News, 3/F, Block 4, 1 Haoyuan Guanzhuang Shuangliu North Street, Chaoyang District, Beijing 100024. **T:** 86 1065439061
E: cjxw1996@vip.163.com
W: http://www.cien.com.cn
Freq: 2 Times/Week; **Circ:** 90003 Not Audited
Bureau Chief: Jun Yao
Editorial Profile: Covers news of current affairs ranging from politics, economy, finance, travel and business news with the focus on industrial development and economic growth.
Language (s): Chinese
NEWSPAPER

China Industry News

Editorial: China Industry News Press, 1 Putaoyuan, Zhanlanlu, Xichengqu, Beijing 100037. **T:** 86 1088378156 **E:** zbs@cinn.cn
W: http://www.cinn.cn
Freq: 2 Times/Week; **Circ:** 120003 Not Audited
Editor in Chief: Shiyong He; **News Editor:** Jiusheng Qu
Editorial Profile: Covers industry news and relevant government regulations issues.
Language (s): Chinese
NEWSPAPER

China Information News

Owner: National Bureau of Statistics of China

Editorial: National Bureau of Statistics of China, 57 Yuetan Nanjie, Sanlihe, Xichengqu, Beijing 100826. **T:** 86 1063376756
E: jrpl@sina.com
W: http://www.zgxxb.com.cn/
Freq: 2 Times/Week; **Circ:** 300002 Not Audited
Editorial Profile: China Information News concerns national news, stastistical information and international news.
Language (s): Chinese
NEWSPAPER

China Inspection and Quarantine Times

Editorial: China Inspection and Quarantine Times, 22 Maizidianjie, Chaoyangqu, Beijing 100026. **T:** 86 10 64194028
Freq: 2 Times/Week; **Circ:** 100003 Not Audited
Editor in Chief: Shunzeng Chen
Editorial Profile: reports on inspection and quarantine news, as well as exports and imports supervision issues.
Language (s): Chinese
NEWSPAPER

China Inspection and Supervision News

Editorial: China Inspection and Supervision News, No. 2, Guang'anmen Nanjiejia, Xuanwu District, Beijing 100053. **T:** 86 1059598025
E: hailong0410@yahoo.cn
W: http://www.mos.gov.cn/csr
Freq: Daily
Editor in Chief: Xiangfeng Meng
Editorial Profile: Covers inspection and supervision news, as well as relevant government regulations and policies.
Language (s): Chinese
DAILY NEWSPAPER

China Insurance News

Editorial: China Insurance News Press, 27 Huayuanlu, Haidian District, Beijing 100088.
T: 86 1063998209 **E:** sinoins@sinoins.com
W: http://www.sinoins.com
Freq: 2 Times/Week; **Circ:** 200003 Not Audited
Editor in Chief: Yongsheng Fan
Editorial Profile: covers insurance and risk professional news, as well as insurance and protection products issues.
Language (s): Chinese
NEWSPAPER

China Intellectual Property News

Editorial: China Intellectual Property News, Block 3, No. 8 Yuan, Huayuan Road, Haidianqu, Beijing 100088. **T:** 86 1082803936
W: http://www.cipnews.com.cn
Freq: 2 Times/Week; **Circ:** 100003 Not Audited
Editor in Chief: Qizhang Li
Editorial Profile: covers issues about intellectual property in China.
Language (s): Chinese
NEWSPAPER

China Land and Resources News

Editorial: China Land and Resources News, Jia 30 Xisi Yangrou Hutong, Xicheng District, Beijing 100011. **T:** 86 1066123059
E: clr-info@126.com **W:** http://www.clr.cn
Freq: Weekly; **Circ:** 75001 Not Audited
Editorial Profile: Reports on Chinese land resources news, relevant government regulations and services issues.
Language (s): Chinese
NEWSPAPER

China Medical Tribune

Editorial: China Medical Tribune, 41 Gulou Xidajie, Xichengqu, Beijing 100009.
T: 86 1064036985 **W:** http://www.cmt.com.cn
Freq: Weekly; **Circ:** 160003 Not Audited
Editorial Profile: Publishes the latest research reports and academic papers in the medical areas, as well as analysis of clinical cases.
Language (s): Chinese
NEWSPAPER

China Medicine News

Owner: China Medicine News Press
Editorial: China Medicine News Press, Jia 2, Wenhuiyuan Nanlu, Haidianqu, Beijing 100088.
T: 86 1062213355 **E:** yyb@cnpharm.com
W: http://www.cnpharm.com
Freq: 2 Times/Week; **Circ:** 300002 Not Audited
Editor in Chief: Xianye Fang
Editorial Profile: China Medicine News reports on medical and health related news and medicinal technology issues. It also covers the medical development in China.
Language (s): Chinese
NEWSPAPER

China Metallurgical News

Editorial: China Metallurgical News Press, Block 26 Sanqu, Anzhenli, Chaoyangqu, Beijing 100029. **T:** 86 10 64453751
W: http://www.csteelnews.com
Freq: 2 Times/Week; **Circ:** 50003 Not Audited
Bureau Chief: Qihua Jiang; **Editor in Chief:** Wenyan Lu
Editorial Profile: provides "useful and meaningful" news reports and economic information to serve China's iron and steel industry and other related field in an all-round manner.
Language (s): Chinese
NEWSPAPER

China Meteorological News

Owner: China Meteorological Administration
Editorial: China Meteorological Administration, 46 Zhongguancun Nandajie, Haidianqu, Beijing 100081. **T:** 86 1068406752
W: http://www.zgqxb.com.cn/
Freq: 2 Times/Week; **Circ:** 50002 Not Audited
Bureau Chief: Xin Hu; **Editor in Chief:** Linghui Zeng
Editorial Profile: covers meteorology news and weather forecast, as well as climate information collecting and analyzing.
Language (s): Chinese
NEWSPAPER

China Mining News

Owner: China Mining News Press
Editorial: China Mining News Press, Room 1701, Block 2, Zhiheng Mingyuan, 23 Nanbinghelu, Guang'anmen, Beijing 100055.
T: 86 13718643421
W: http://www.chinamining.com.cn
Freq: 2 Times/Week; **Circ:** 80003 Not Audited
Editor in Chief: Jiahua Wang
Editorial Profile: provides news and analysis of mining and minerals, it also covers the development of the mining industry, study of environment, geology and management of mining technique.
Language (s): Chinese
NEWSPAPER

China Modern Enterprises

Editorial: Nongmin Daily Press, 15 Huixin Xijie, Chaoyangqu, Beijing 100029.
T: 86 13401197100 **E:** chuan0513@126.com
W: http://www.cmenews.com.cn
Freq: 2 Times/Week; **Circ:** 360003 Not Audited
Editor: Yanling Dong
Editorial Profile: Covers news on related rules and regulations, new achievement and development of township enterprises in China. It also focuses on local and national news.
Language (s): Chinese
NEWSPAPER

China Netizen News

Editorial: People's Posts and Telecommunications News Office, Youdian Xinwen Dasha, 11 Anyuanlu, Chaoyangqu, Beijing 100029. **T:** 86 10 83161101
E: cctvcs8@126.com
W: http://www.chinanetizen.com.cn
Freq: Weekly; **Circ:** 300003 Not Audited
Editor: Chenmei Gu
Editorial Profile: Covers news on ISP/ICP development, internet culture and entertainment and PC, PDA, Set-top and BOX.
Language (s): Chinese
NEWSPAPER

China Network World

Editorial: China Network World, 4th Floor, Block 3, 16 Cuiwei Zhongli, Wanshoulu, Haidianqu, Beijing 100036.
T: 86 10 68130909 8050
W: http://www.cnw.com.cn
Freq: Weekly; **Circ:** 120003 Not Audited
Editor in Chief: Hui Gao
Editorial Profile: covers the management, security amd development of computers systems and networks.
Language (s): Chinese
NEWSPAPER

China Nonferrous Metals News

Editorial: China Nonferrous Metals News, 6th Floor, Yi-12, Fuxinglu, Beijing 100814.
T: 86 1063971476 **E:** ysb@263.net.cn
W: http://www.cnmn.com.cn
Freq: 2 Times/Week; **Circ:** 50003 Not Audited
Editor: Yeping Liu; **Editor in Chief:** Yinping Yuan
Editorial Profile: covers nonferrous metals industry news and the latest products prices, company profiles, industry services and products topics.
Language (s): Chinese
NEWSPAPER

China Ocean News

Editorial: China Ocean News, 1 Fuxingmenwai Dajie, Xicheng District, Beijing 100860.
T: 86 10 68519427 **E:** hyb20091104@163.com
W: http://epaper.oceanol.com
Freq: 2 Times/Week; **Circ:** 100003 Not Audited
Editor in Chief: Guangsheng Gai
Editorial Profile: Covers national ocean news and environment information, as well as oceanography issues.
Language (s): Chinese
NEWSPAPER

China Package News

Editorial: PackChina Corporation, 9 Xinghualu, Dongcheng District, Beijing 100013.
T: 86 10 84271012 **E:** bzbz2012@sohu.com
W: http://www.cpackage.com
Freq: 2 Times/Week; **Circ:** 90003 Not Audited
Editorial Profile: China Package News is a national newspaper for packaging industry in China, covering package development, market trends, policies and regulation related to the industry; it also introduces new products, materials and equipment to the readers.
Language (s): Chinese
NEWSPAPER

China Petrochemical News

Editorial: Sinopec News Press, 58 Anwaidajie, Dongchengqu, Beijing 100011.
T: 86 84277215
W: http://www.sinopecnews.com.cn
Freq: Daily; **Circ:** 110001 Not Audited
Editor in Chief: Dapeng Lv
Editorial Profile: covers market news, tracking the trends and changes in prices that affect the industry, including trade, environmental, and regulatory issues.
Language (s): Chinese
DAILY NEWSPAPER

China Petroleum Daily

Editorial: Jia-3 Anhuali Erqu, Anwai, Chaoyangqu, Beijing 100011.
T: 86 10 64523333 **E:** dzxx@zgsyb.com.cn
W: http://www.zgsyb.com
Freq: 2 Times/Week; **Circ:** 110003 Not Audited
Editor in Chief: Ping Tan
Editorial Profile: Covers oil and gas news for oil exploration, oil sands, oil drilling, drilling rigs, core drilling, as well as relevant oil industry and engineering issues.
Language (s): Chinese
NEWSPAPER

China Philanthropy Times

Editorial: China Philanthropy Times, Jia 6 Baijiazhuanglu, Chaoyang District, Beijing 100020. **T:** 86 10 65953695
W: http://www.china-lottery.net
Freq: Weekly
Editorial Profile: China Philanthropy Times is a national newspaper which mainly covers the information and latest development in social welfare in China and related news of social lottery, social enterprises, social work and social services in China and overseas.
Language (s): Chinese
NEWSPAPER

China Philately News

Editorial: People's Posts and Telecommunications News Office, 3/F, 11 Anyuanlu, Beijing 100029. **T:** 86 1064962938
W: http://www.cnjy.com.cn
Freq: 2 Times/Week
Editorial Profile: covers the latest information of stamps collecting.
Language (s): Chinese
NEWSPAPER

China Police Daily

Editorial: China Police Daily, 9 You'anlu, Fangxingyuan, Fangzhuang, Fengtaiqu, Beijing 100078. **T:** 86 108 3731000
E: wxg@cpd.com.cn
W: http://www.cpd.com.cn
Freq: 2 Times/Week; **Circ:** 300001 Not Audited
Editor in Chief: Huanjing Liu
Editorial Profile: Covers current police news, features, training, and relevant policies as well as police services and responsibilities issues.
Language (s): Chinese
NEWSPAPER

China Population News

Editorial: China Population News, Jia 36 Jiaoda Donglu, Haidian District, Beijing 100044. **T:** 86 1062255622
Freq: 2 Times/Week; **Circ:** 280001 Not Audited
Editor in Chief: Hongwei Yi

Editorial Profile: China Population News is a national newspaper which focuses on national population issues, family planning news, reproductive health, gender, gender equality, women empowerment, adolescent, migrants and international cooperation.
Language (s): Chinese
NEWSPAPER

China Post News
Editorial: China Courier Service Corporation, 173 Yong'anlu, Xuanwuqu, Beijing 100050.
T: 86 1083162921
W: http://www.chinapostnews.com.cn
Freq: 2 Times/Week; **Circ:** 100001 Not Audited
Editor: Jurui Zhang
Editorial Profile: Covers the latest news from China State Post Bureau.
Language (s): Chinese
NEWSPAPER

China Press & Publishing Journal
Editorial: China Press & Publishing Journal, PO Box 2350 Chaoyang District, Beijing 100023. **T:** 86 10 87622075
E: chinaxwcb@126.com
W: http://www.chinaxwcb.com/index/index.htm
Freq: Daily; **Circ:** 80004 Not Audited
Editorial Profile: It covers the latest information on publishing and press industry in China and overseas.It also introduces government policies and regulations.
Language (s): Chinese
DAILY NEWSPAPER

China Quality Daily
Editorial: China Quality Press, 3 Yuhui Nanlu, Chaoyangqu, Beijing 100029.
T: 86 1084639548 **E:** lxwm@cqn.com.cn
W: http://www.cqn.com.cn
Freq: 2 Times/Week; **Circ:** 130001 Not Audited
Editor: Dongling Li; **Editor in Chief:** Wei Meng
Editorial Profile: covers quality assurance, product improvement issues, and market and technical supervision issues.
Language (s): Chinese
NEWSPAPER

China Railway Construction News
Owner: China Railroad Construction News Press
Editorial: China Railroad Construction News Press, 40 Fuxinglu, Beijing 100855
E: zgtdjzb@vip.sina.com
W: http://www.crcn.com.cn/
Freq: 2 Times/Week; **Circ:** 100003 Not Audited
Editor in Chief: Haiyan Zhu
Editorial Profile: Covers information and news of railroad construction industry and business, engineering companies, daily rail news, railroad crossings, construction and track removal, as well as railroad evaluations and inspections issues.
Language (s): Chinese
NEWSPAPER

China Real Estate News
Editorial: China Real Estate News, Jia22 Xiangjun Beili, Chaoyang District, Beijing 100020. **T:** 86 1065079988
W: http://www.china-crb.cn
Freq: Weekly; **Circ:** 120001 Not Audited
Editor in Chief: Guozhen Shi
Editorial Profile: Covers news, market, property management, policies and regulations, investment, planning and development issues in the property field.
Language (s): Chinese
NEWSPAPER

China Reform News
Editorial: China Reform News, 5 Xiaguangli, Sanyuanqiao, Chaoyangqu, Beijing 100027.
T: 86 1064616555 **W:** http://www.crd.net.cn
Freq: 2 Times/Week
Editor in Chief: Yijun Ma
Editorial Profile: covers the achievements of the economic reform and development in China.
Language (s): Chinese
NEWSPAPER

China Safety Production News
Editorial: China Safety Production News Press, 4th Floor, Meitan Daxia, Block 35, Area 13, Hepingjie, Chayang District, Beijing 100013. **T:** 86 1064463042
W: http://www.aqsc.cn
Freq: 2 Times/Week; **Circ:** 140003 Not Audited
Editor in Chief: Haijin Bai
Editorial Profile: covers safety production in coal industry, as well as other related safety issues.
Language (s): Chinese
NEWSPAPER

China Securities Journal
Editorial: China Securities Journal, Jia-97, Xuanwumen Xidajie, Beijing 100031.
T: 86 10 63070233 **E:** csnews@zzb.com.cn
W: http://www.cs.com.cn
Freq: 2 Times/Week; **Circ:** 600003 Not Audited
Editor in Chief: Chen Lin
Editorial Profile: A national business and finance newspaper covering the capital markets and financial markets in China and abroad. "China Securities News" is sponsored by the national Xinhua News Agency Securities Daily, China Securities Regulatory Commission is the designated information disclosure of listed companies the newspaper, the China Insurance Regulatory Commission disclosure of insurance information designated newspapers, the China Banking Regulatory Commission disclosed in a trust company designated Information newspaper."China Securities News," the securities, the financial report for the center, reported that domestic and international economic trends, macro-economic policies; reported that the domestic securities market, listed companies and other professional fields; reported in the United States, Europe, Japan and Hong Kong and Taiwan financial and securities markets; concerned about money, insurance, funds, futures, real estate, foreign exchange, gold and other adjacent markets, and in the broader financial field has a greater influence.
Language (s): Chinese
NEWSPAPER

China Ship News
Editorial: China Ship News, 5 Yuetan Beijie, Beijing 100861. **T:** 86 10 68058257
E: news@chinashipnews.com.cn
W: http://www.chinashipnews.com.cn
Freq: 2 Times/Week; **Circ:** 50007 Not Audited
Editorial Profile: China Ship News engages in business and information service in the shipbuilding industry. It mainly focuses on information service including updated shipbuilding and shipping information, in-depth analysis on the market trend, shipbuilding forum, supply and demand information, marine equipment, etc.
Language (s): Chinese
NEWSPAPER

China Society News
Editorial: China Society News Press Group, Xinlong Dasha, 33 Er'long Lu, Xicheng Qu, Beijing 100032. **T:** 86 1066030951
W: http://zgsh.ceepa.cn
Freq: Daily; **Circ:** 95003 Not Audited
Editor in Chief: Youlu Mi; **Bureau Chief:** Aiping Wang
Editorial Profile: Covers society news and social issues, as well as current government regulations and policies topics.
Language (s): Chinese
DAILY NEWSPAPER

China Space News
Editorial: China Space News, 3.F, Zonghelou, 8 Fuchenglu, Haidian District, Beijing 100830.
T: 86 1068767232
W: http://www.china-spacenews.com
Freq: 2 Times/Week
Editor in Chief: Xu Shi
Editorial Profile: covers information of space science and industry, as well as daily astronomy, star charts, pictures of planets, space missions topics.
Language (s): Chinese
NEWSPAPER

China Special Product
Editorial: China Special Product Press, No. 16, 4 Qu, Anhui Li, Beijing 100723.
T: 86 1084885778
E: techanbao6688@163.com
W: http://www.cntcb.com
Freq: 2 Times/Week; **Circ:** 53003 Not Audited
Editor in Chief: Zhen Liu
Editorial Profile: provides information about special products in different areas in China, as well as news about agricultural industry, agricultural supply and trade issues.
Language (s): Chinese
NEWSPAPER

China Sports Daily
Editorial: China Sports Publications Corporation, 8 Tiyuguanlu, Chongwenqu, Beijing 100061. **T:** 86 10 67110066
W: http://www.sportsol.com.cn
Freq: Daily; **Circ:** 300003
Editorial Profile: Covers both national and international sports news.
Language (s): Chinese
DAILY NEWSPAPER

China Stock News
Owner: Xinhua News Agency
Editorial: No. A97, West Ave, Xuan Wu Men, Xi Cheng District, Beijing 100031
E: csnews@zzb.com.cn
W: http://www.cs.com.cn
Editorial Profile: Covers China Securities News, financial reports, funds, futures, real estate and foreign exchange. It's hosted by Xinhua News Agency.
DAILY NEWSPAPER

China Taxation News
Editorial: China Taxation News, 21 Huaibaishu Houjie, Xuanwu District, Beijing 100053.
T: 86 10 83120012
W: http://www.ctaxnews.com.cn
Freq: 2 Times/Week; **Circ:** 570003 Not Audited
Editor in Chief: Diken Zhang
Editorial Profile: Covers the latest news on the government tax policies and regulations as well as reports related tax issues.
Language (s): Chinese
NEWSPAPER

China Teacher News
Editorial: China Teacher News, 10 Wenhuiyuan Beilu, Haidian District, Beijing 100082. **T:** 86 1082296669
E: zgjsbtougao@21cn.com
W: http://www.chinateacher.com.cn
Freq: Weekly; **Circ:** 200003 Not Audited
Editor in Chief: Tangjiang Liu
Editorial Profile: Covers teaching and education issues in China.
Language (s): Chinese
NEWSPAPER

China Technology Market News
Editorial: China Technology Market News, 11/F, Jinwan Chuanmei Dasha, No. 358 Nanjing Road, Nankai District, Tianjin 300100.
T: 86 2227509515 **E:** zgjsscb@126.com
W: http://www.ctmn.cn
Freq: 2 Times/Week; **Circ:** 160003 Not Audited
Editor in Chief: Qiyuan Miao
Editorial Profile: provides information on the national technology market, including funding, contracting and partnership opportunities issues. It also covers the latest development of the technological issues in China.
Language (s): Chinese
NEWSPAPER

China Television News
Editorial: China Television News, CCTV, Section A, Enfei Keji Dasha, 11 Fuxinglu, Haidian District, Beijing 100859.
T: 86 1068500857 **E:** zgdsb@cctv.com
W: http://www.cntv.cn
Freq: Weekly; **Circ:** 3650000 Not Audited
Editor in Chief: Hong Cheng; **Bureau Chief:** Jiyao Wu
Editorial Profile: It provides the schedules and other information of TV programs broadcast by Chinese Central TV Networks.
Language (s): Chinese
NEWSPAPER

China Textile News
Editorial: China Textile News, Jia 2, 18, Dongsanhuan Zhonglu, Chaoyangqu, Beijing 100022. **T:** 86 10 87751055
W: http://www.zgfzb.net.cn
Freq: Daily; **Circ:** 100003 Not Audited
Bureau Chief: Zhiqi Tong
Editorial Profile: China Textile News started her initial issue in 1986 and has been a publication of both domestic and international delivery ever since. As a weekday publication Monday to Friday, it is the only the comprehensive and giant newspaper in China specialized in textile industry, China Textile News mirrors the economic performance in the textile and apparel industry in a complete and prompt mannner and timely gives out the governmental policies and regulations with regards to the growth production and performance of the textile industry and provides the readers with textile information from domestic and international markets with the news coverage extended to the three important aspects apparel home textile and industrial applications and to the textile machinery raw materials intermediates and finished products and markets and further all the way to management operation science and technology corporate culture.
Language (s): Chinese
DAILY NEWSPAPER

China Three Gorges Project News
Owner: China Three Gorges Project News Press
Editorial: China Three Gorges Project News Press, 80 Dongshanlu, Yichang 443002.
T: 86 7176762587 **E:** ctgpn@163.com
W: http://www.ctgpc.com
Freq: Weekly; **Circ:** 50002 Not Audited
Editor: Chengzhang Jin
Editorial Profile: It focuses on the development of the three gorges projects.
Language (s): Chinese
NEWSPAPER

China Tourism News
Editorial: China Tourism News, Jia-9, Jianguomennei Dajie, Dongchengqu, Beijing 100740. **T:** 86 10 85166219 **E:** jzz@ctnews.com.cn
W: http://www.ctnews.com.cn
Freq: 2 Times/Week; **Circ:** 600003 Not Audited
Editor in Chief: Shunli Gao; **Editor:** Xiuhua Yang
Editorial Profile: provides travel news, guide and information, as well as package holidays, touring holidays and overseas travel issues. In early 1979, China travel tour business travel management bureau decided to publish a professional newspaper, "Tourism Newsletter", April 1, 1979 was officially inaugurated, in January 1981 changed its name to "Travel News", January 1985 and further changed its name to "China Tourism News ", which is China's only national tourism industry newspaper.
Language (s): Chinese
NEWSPAPER

China Trade News
Editorial: China Trade News, 2, Jin'anxijie, Beisanhuandonglu, Chaoyangqu, Beijing 100028. **T:** 86 10 64667333 **E:** lihy@ccpit.org
W: http://www.chinatradenews.com.cn
Freq: 2 Times/Week Not Audited
Editorial Profile: China Trade News is sponsored by China Council for the Promotion of International Trade (CCPIT) and China Chamber of International Commerce (CCOIC). It reports on the latest international trade news and hot issues, and the updates of market trend.
Language (s): Chinese
NEWSPAPER

China Urban-Rural Financial News
Editorial: China Urban-Rural Financial News Press, 32 Babaozhuang, Beijing 100036.
T: 86 1088128486 **W:** http://www.zgcxjrb.com
Freq: 2 Times/Week; **Circ:** 100001 Not Audited
Editorial Profile: Reports on Chinese agribusiness, as well as relevant economics and financial information in urban-rural areas.
Language (s): Chinese
NEWSPAPER

China Water Resources News
Editorial: China Water Resources News Press, 2 Baiguanglu Ertiao, Beijing 100053.
T: 86 10 63205285 **E:** abc@chinawater.com.cn
W: http://www.chinawater.com.cn
Freq: 2 Times/Week; **Circ:** 110003 Not Audited
Editorial Profile: Covers the development of water control, as well as the ecology and tourism issues related to water control.
Language (s): Chinese
NEWSPAPER

China Women's News
Editorial: China Women's News, 103 Xidajie, Di'anmen, Xichengqu, Beijing 100009.
T: 86 1066166311
W: http://www.china-woman.com
Freq: 2 Times/Week; **Circ:** 100001 Not Audited
Editor in Chief: Xiaofei Lu
Editorial Profile: covers politics, social issues, family interest, law, culture, education, healthcare and sports topics centering around women in China.
Language (s): Chinese
NEWSPAPER

China Youth Daily
Editorial: China Youth Daily, 2 Haiyuncang, Dongzhimennei, Beijing 100702.
T: 86 10 64098000 **E:** guojibu@cyd.net.cn
W: http://zqb.cyol.com/html/2011-08/02/nbs.D110000zgqnb_01.htm
Freq: Daily; **Circ:** 600002 Not Audited
Editor in Chief: Xiaochuan Lu
Editorial Profile: China Youth Daily focuses on youth interests including news, technology, society, education, culture, sports and society articles. China Youth Daily, founded in April 27, 1951, is a major influence on a

comprehensive national daily newspaper. China Youth Daily, the national youth-oriented audience, the scale of tens of millions of readers, the issue effectively in major cities across the country.
Language (s): Chinese
DAILY NEWSPAPER

Chinese Business Morning View
Editorial: Chinese Business Morning View, 6th Floor, Guoshi Daxia, 71 Chongshandonglu, Huagnguqu, Shenyang 110032. **T:** 86 2496128
W: http://www.hscb.com.cn
Freq: Daily; **Circ:** 500001 Not Audited
Editor: Yu Yang; **Editor:** Libin Zhang
Editorial Profile: covers local, regional and international news, as well as business and finance issues.
Language (s): Chinese
DAILY NEWSPAPER

Chinese Business View
Editorial: Chinese Business View, 156 Hanguangbeilu, Xi'an 710068.
T: 86 2988429016 **W:** http://www.huash.com
Freq: Daily Not Audited
Bureau Chief: Huaizhong Zhou
Editorial Profile: provides news of business and finance in middle area of China.
Language (s): Chinese
DAILY NEWSPAPER

Chinese Children's News
Owner: China Children's Press & Publication Group
Editorial: China Children's Press & Publication Group, Building 5, Zuojiazhuang Beili, Chaoyangqu, Beijing 100028.
T: 86 1064634863
W: http://paper.ccppg.com.cn/zgetb
Freq: Weekly; **Circ:** 400003 Not Audited
Editor in Chief: Renfang Wang
Editorial Profile: Chinese Children's News is a national newspaper which focuses on news and information of children's education, study, and school life.
Language (s): Chinese
NEWSPAPER

Chinese People's Political Consultative Conference News
Editorial: National Committee of the Chinese People's Political Consultative Conference, 69 Xibalizhuanglu, Haidian District, Beijing 100036. **T:** 86 10 88146900
E: zxb-tlb@vip.163.com
W: http://www.rmzxb.com.cn
Freq: Daily; **Circ:** 120003 Not Audited
Editor: Xiaohui Geng; **Editor:** Youqiang Wang
Editorial Profile: covers government issues, party politics, current affairs, national news and politics.
Language (s): Chinese
DAILY NEWSPAPER

Chinese Photography
Owner: China Photographers Association
Editorial: China Photographers Association, 502, Longjidasha Nanlou, 67 Jinbaojie, Dongdan, Dongchengqu, Beijing 100005.
T: 86 106525189 **E:** cphotoeditor@sina.com
W: http://www.cphoto.com.cn
Freq: 2 Times/Week; **Circ:** 100003 Not Audited
Editorial Profile: Chinese Photography mainly covers news on different kinds of photograph shows and also reports features on photographers both in China and overseas.
Language (s): Chinese
NEWSPAPER

Chinese Teenagers News
Editorial: China Children's Press & Publication Group, Building 5, Zuojiazhuang Beili, Chaoyang District, Beijing 100028.
T: 86 10 64634838
W: http://www.ccppg.com.cn
Freq: Weekly; **Circ:** 990003 Not Audited
Editor in Chief: Zhenglan Wu
Editorial Profile: reports on teenager's interests articles, school and extra-curricular activities issues.
Language (s): Chinese
NEWSPAPER

Chongqing Daily
Editorial: Chongqing Daily Press Group, 85 Jiaochangkou, Yuzhongqu, Chongqing 400010.
T: 86 236 3907042 **E:** cqrb@cqrb.cn
W: http://www.cqnews.net
Freq: Daily; **Circ:** 250003 Not Audited
Editor in Chief: Fengjing Mao
Editorial Profile: Covers news in Chongqing area and national news in China.
Language (s): Chinese
DAILY NEWSPAPER

Chongqing Economic Times
Editorial: Chongqing Economic Times, 39 Changjiang Erlu, Yuzhongqu, Chongqing 400042. **T:** 86 2389099677
W: http://www.chinacqsb.com
Freq: Daily; **Circ:** 240001 Not Audited
Editor: Zhenghua Zhou
Editorial Profile: Chongqing Economic Times is a regional economic and business newspaper centering Chongqing City.
Language (s): Chinese
DAILY NEWSPAPER

Chongqing Evening News
Owner: Chongqing Daily Group
Editorial: Chongqing Daily Group, 85 Jiaochangkou, Yuzhong District, Chongqing 4000010. **T:** 86 2363907399
W: http://www.cqwb.com.cn
Freq: Daily; **Circ:** 300004 Not Audited
Editor: Yunming Liu
Editorial Profile: covers entertainment, business, news, lifestyles, economy, transportation, education, travel, medical care, sports, culture and art.
Language (s): Chinese
DAILY NEWSPAPER

Chongqing Morning Post
Editorial: Chongqing Morning News, 85 Jiaochangkou, Yuzhongqu, Chongqing 400010.
T: 86 23 63907613 **E:** cqcb@cqcb.com
W: http://www.cqcb.com
Freq: Daily; **Circ:** 600001 Not Audited
Editor in Chief: Ainong Fu
Editorial Profile: Focuses on local and national news.
Language (s): Chinese
DAILY NEWSPAPER

Chuncheng Evening News
Editorial: Yunnan Daily Press Group, 337 Xinwenlu, Kunming 650032.
T: 86 8714161886 **W:** http://www.yndaily.com
Freq: Daily; **Circ:** 300003 Not Audited
Editor in Chief: Jianxiang Zhang
Editorial Profile: A daily newspaper mainly focusing on news, lifestyle, social and cultural issues in Kunming.
Language (s): Chinese
DAILY NEWSPAPER

Communication Information News
Editorial: Communication Information News, 13/F, Xinxi Guangchang Xiqu, 7 Dongjie, Fuzhou 350001. **T:** 86 59187529630
W: http://www.txxxb.com
Freq: Weekly; **Circ:** 100003 Not Audited
Editorial Profile: Covers the news and information of telecommunication industry.
Language (s): Chinese
NEWSPAPER

Computer Business Information (East China Edition)
T: 86 2164412101 **E:** sales@cbigroup.com
W: http://www.cbinews.com
Freq: Weekly; **Circ:** 120003 Not Audited
Bureau Chief: Xiaoling Lu
Editorial Profile: Covers the IT industry.
Language (s): Chinese
NEWSPAPER

Computer Business Information (Jiangsu Edition)
Editorial: Computer Business Information (Jiangsu Edition), Room 416, Number 14, Dongda Yingbi, Zhujianglu, Nanjing 210018.
T: 86 2583213831
W: http://www.cbinews.com
Freq: Weekly; **Circ:** 70003 Not Audited
Editorial Profile: Covers the local computer market.
Language (s): Chinese
NEWSPAPER

Computer Business Information (Yunnan Edition)
Editorial: Computer Business Information (Yunnan Edition), 1-1 Block C, Shuidian Shuili, Kunming 650031. **T:** 86 87 15111383
E: xuzw@cbigroup.com
W: http://www.cbinews.com
Freq: Weekly; **Circ:** 50003 Not Audited
Editorial Profile: Computer Business Information (Yunnan Edition) is a regional edition of Computer Business Information focus on the industry news on Yunnan Province. It covers computer news, Network Communication, information about Hardware, Software and Market Trend.
Language (s): Chinese
NEWSPAPER

Computer Business Information (Zhejiang Edition)
T: 86 57189966639 **E:** shuitl@cbigroup.com
W: http://www.cbinews.com
Freq: Weekly; **Circ:** 80003 Not Audited
Editor: Xiuliang Liu; **Editor:** Tianlan Shui
Editorial Profile: Computer Business Information (Zhejiang Edition) is a province focused newspaper covering the computer industry in Zhejiang Province. Its Pages include: Special Features, Hottest Issue, DIY Centre, Second-Hand Trade Market, Technology Gallery, Product Highlight, and Factory Trends.
Language (s): Chinese
NEWSPAPER

Construction Times
Editorial: Construction Times, 3/F No. 110 E Yan'an Road, Shanghai 200002.
T: 86 21 63212166 **E:** jzsbs@jzsbs.com
W: http://www.jzsbs.com
Freq: 2 Times/Week; **Circ:** 80003 Not Audited
Editorial Profile: provides information on architecture design, construction project and construction industry in and outside China.
Language (s): Chinese
NEWSPAPER

Consumption & Quality News
Editorial: Consumption & Quality News, 6/F, Dongfang Shidai Shangcheng, 18 Xiadong Dajie, Chengdu 610017. **T:** 86 28 86671555
W: http://xzb.scol.cn
Freq: Daily; **Circ:** 60003 Not Audited
Editor in Chief: Youxiang Feng
Editorial Profile: mostly covers news and information on consumption and quality control on consumption products in China.
Language (s): Chinese
DAILY NEWSPAPER

Consumption Daily
Editorial: Consumption Daily, Building Number 20, Ding'andongli, Liujiayou, Beijing 100075.
T: 86 10 67609192 **E:** xfw518@163.com
W: http://www.xfrbw.com
Freq: Daily; **Circ:** 170003 Not Audited
Editor in Chief: Songmei Wang; **Bureau Chief:** Bingjing Wu
Editorial Profile: provides in-depth reporting on market trends, business forecasting and related policies and regulations about consumer market in China.
Language (s): Chinese
DAILY NEWSPAPER

Contemporary Health News
Editorial: Jinan Daily Press Group, Number 28-1 Jingqilu, Jinan 250001.
T: 86 53186695668 **W:** http://jkb.e23.cn
Freq: Weekly; **Circ:** 100001 Not Audited
Editor: Lu Chen
Editorial Profile: Covers information and news about health related issues, and provides consult on health and health care for the public.
Language (s): Chinese
NEWSPAPER

Cosmetic Newspaper
Editorial: Cosmetic Newspaper, 10 Lihuangpilu, Wuhan 430014.
T: 86 2782835503 **E:** hzpbbjb@126.com
W: http://www.hzpb.com.cn
Freq: Weekly; **Circ:** 100003 Not Audited
Editor in Chief: Hongjun Du
Editorial Profile: covers issues about beauty, beauty products and brands; perfumes, skincare, cosmetics companies, hair care, cosmetic, professionals, makeup and toiletries market, beauty business news, fragrances and raw materials suppliers topics.
Language (s): Chinese
NEWSPAPER

Culture and Art Weekly
Editorial: Culture and Art Weekly, 6 Beiguanzhengjie, Xi'an 710014.
T: 86 2986225811 **E:** crx1218@vip.sina.com
W: http://www.whysb.net
Freq: Weekly; **Circ:** 80001 Not Audited
Editor in Chief: Ruoxing Chen
Editorial Profile: It provides latest information on culture and art in the world. It also covers the current cultural and art events.
Language (s): Chinese
NEWSPAPER

The Dahe Daily
Editorial: Henan Daily Press Group, 28 Nongye Donglu, Zhengzhou 450008.
T: 86 37165796171 **E:** ygd666@sina.com
W: http://www.dahe.cn
Freq: Daily; **Circ:** 1000003 Not Audited
Editor: Guangdao Yan
Editorial Profile: Covers local, national and international issues.
Language (s): Chinese
DAILY NEWSPAPER

Dalian Daily
Editorial: Liaoning Daily Press Group, 76 Shijijie, Zhongsharqu, Dalian 116001
E: tuwen-email@163.com
W: http://www.daliandaily.com.cn
Freq: Daily
Bureau Chief: Yikui Wang
Editorial Profile: focuses on local, national and international news.
Language (s): Chinese
DAILY NEWSPAPER

Datong Daily
Editorial: Datong Daily, 8 Silingbujie, Datong 37004. **T:** 86 3522050994 **E:** edit@dtnews.cn
W: http://www.dtnews.cn
Freq: Daily
Editor in Chief: Xu Zhang
Editorial Profile: covers news on local, regional, international and financial issues.
Language (s): Chinese
DAILY NEWSPAPER

Datong Evening News
Editorial: Datong Daily, 1 Songzhuang Hanlu, Datong 37006. **T:** 86 3526030991
E: dtwbzl@sohu.com
W: http://www.dtwb.com.cn
Freq: Daily
Editorial Profile: Covers local and regional news.
Language (s): Chinese
DAILY NEWSPAPER

Democracy and Law
Editorial: Democracy and Law, Room 306 Guoji Dasha, 19 Jianguomenwaidajie, Chaoyang District, Beijing 100004.
T: 86 10 85201155 **E:** mzfzsb@163.com
W: http://www.mzyfz.com
Freq: Weekly; **Circ:** 530001 Not Audited
Editor in Chief: Hui Feng
Editorial Profile: It covers legislation, governmental policies, law, work ethics and social issues.
Language (s): Chinese
NEWSPAPER

Development Herald
Owner: Shanxi Daily Press Group
Editorial: Shanxi Daily Press Group, 15/F, Shanxi Ribao Xinwen Dasha, 124 Shuangtasi Dongjie, Taiyuan 30012. **T:** 86 3514282978
W: http://www.fzdb.cn
Freq: 2 Times/Week; **Circ:** 80004 Not Audited
Editorial Profile: It provides news and analysis on economic development, finance and business in Shanxi as well as China.
Language (s): Chinese
NEWSPAPER

Du Shi Kuai Bao
Editorial: Hangzhou Daily Press Group, 218 Tiyuchang Road, Hangzhou 310041.
T: 86 57185151588 **E:** dskb@mail.hz.zj.cn
Freq: Daily; **Circ:** 950000
Editor: Hui Liu; **Editor in Chief:** Xing Yang
Editorial Profile: Provides news in Hangzhou region.
Language (s): Chinese
DAILY NEWSPAPER

Economic Daily
Editorial: Economic Daily Group, 2 Baizhifangdongjie, Xuanwu District, Beijing 100054. **T:** 86 1058392413
E: cesnew@163.com
W: http://paper.ce.cn/jjrb/html/2011-07/28/node_2.htm
Freq: Daily; **Circ:** 800001 Not Audited
Editor: Xiaoguang Liu; **Editor:** Wei Wu; **Editor:** Wenying Xu; **Editor in Chief:** Xiaoguo Zhang
Editorial Profile: a national newspaper reporting issues related to China economic reform and development.
Language (s): Chinese
DAILY NEWSPAPER

Economic Evening News
Editorial: Economic Evening News, 50 Yuzhang Lu, Nanchang 330006.
T: 86 13970071515 **W:** http://www.cnjjwb.com
Freq: Daily; **Circ:** 120001 Not Audited
Editor: Yingying Xiong
Editorial Profile: covers economics and business issues.
Language (s): Chinese
DAILY NEWSPAPER

Economic Herald
Editorial: Economic Herald, 46 Jinshilu, Jinan 500014. **T:** 86 10 84990581 323

W: http://jjdk.periodicals.net.cn
Freq: Weekly; **Circ:** 100001 Not Audited
Editor-in-Chief: Hong Ji
Editorial Profile: Includes business, economics, finance, insurance and management articles.
Language (s): Chinese
NEWSPAPER

Economic Information Daily
Editorial: Xinhua News Agency, Jia101 Xuanwumen Xidajie, Beijing 100803.
T: 86 10 63073790 **E:** jjckbs@xinhuanet.com
W: http://www.jjckb.com
Freq: 2 Times/Week; **Circ:** 160000 Not Audited
Editor in Chief: Yuejin Du
Editorial Profile: Covers China's economic development and national and international economic news and related issues.
Language (s): Chinese
NEWSPAPER

Economic Information Times
Editorial: 100 Xihulu, Guiyang 550002.
T: 86 8515892169 **E:** jjxxsb@vip.163.com
W: http://www.gog.com.cn/jjxxsb
Freq: 2 Times/Week; **Circ:** 50003 Not Audited
Editor in Chief: Ming Yin
Editorial Profile: Mainly focuses on the latest news on financial and economic issues. Readers are mainly the economic and financial professionals in China.
Language (s): Chinese
NEWSPAPER

Elderly News
Owner: Guangzhou Daily Group
Editorial: Guangzhou Daily Group, Room 508, 92 Dadelu, Guangzhou 510120.
T: 86 2081881557 **E:** gzlrb@gzdaily.com
W: http://lrb.dayoo.com
Freq: Weekly; **Circ:** 100003 Not Audited
Editor in Chief: Nancheng Zhao
Editorial Profile: Elderly News is a national newspaper targeting senior citizens. It reports on social news, health, healthcare for the elderly.
Language (s): Chinese
NEWSPAPER

Electronic Newspaper
Owner: Electronic Newspaper Publishing
Editorial: Electronic Newspaper Publishing, 55 Binhe Road, Wanhua, Chengdu 610071.
T: 86 2886142049 **E:** zzdzb@netdzb.com
W: http://www.netdzb.com
Freq: Weekly
Editorial Profile: Covers the electronic industry of China. It mainly provides news and information of electronic products and materials.
Language (s): Chinese
NEWSPAPER

Elite Reference
Editorial: Elite Reference, 2 Dongzhimennei Haiyuncang, Beijing 100702.
T: 86 10 64682086 **W:** http://www.qnck.net.cn
Freq: 2 Times/Week; **Circ:** 300003 Not Audited
Editor in Chief: Ping Liang
Editorial Profile: covers social news, science, sports, communications and military affairs.
Language (s): Chinese
NEWSPAPER

Family Doctor Weekly
Editorial: Family Doctor Weekly, 440 Yangminglu, Nanchang 330006.
T: 86 7916835702 **E:** jthysh@163.com
W: http://www.jtysb.com.cn
Freq: Weekly; **Circ:** 400002 Not Audited
Editor in Chief: Hejing Lin
Editorial Profile: covers clinical trials, medical consultants, health and medicine issues and family and individual health-related issues.
Language (s): Chinese
NEWSPAPER

Famous Brand Times
Editorial: Famous Brand Times, 33 Fuchenglu, Beijing 100037. **T:** 86 1068981140
W: http://www.mpsb.xplus.com
Freq: Weekly; **Circ:** 100003 Not Audited
Editor in Chief: Xiaowei Wang
Editorial Profile: Famous Brand Times is a national newspaper which covers news and issues of famous brands in China.
Language (s): Chinese
NEWSPAPER

Farmer Daily
Owner: Nongmin Daily Press
Editorial: Nongmin Daily Press, 15 Huixinxi Street, Chaoyang District, Beijing 100025.
T: 886 10 84395001
W: http://www.farmer.com.cn
Freq: 2 Times/Week; **Circ:** 300004 Not Audited
Editorial Profile: It covers the latest news and information on agriculture and agribusiness.
Language (s): Chinese
NEWSPAPER

Farmer News
Editorial: Farmer News Press, 181 Donghu Road, Wuchang, Wuhan 430077.
T: 86 27 88567497
W: http://www.cnhubei.com/ncxb/index.htm
Freq: 2 Times/Week
Editorial Profile: provides information about animal feed, breeding and genetics, agribusiness, agricultural contracting and engineering, machinery and equipment, as well as agricultural shows and supply issues.
Language (s): Chinese
NEWSPAPER

Farmer's Daily
Editorial: Nongmin Daily Press, 1 Beili Balizhuang, Chaowai, Beijing 100025.
T: 86 10 85831572
W: http://www.farmer.com.cn
Freq: Weekly; **Circ:** 50001 Not Audited
Publisher: Dexiu Zhang
Editorial Profile: It focuses on the development and current trend of the agriculture and agribusiness in China.
Language (s): Chinese
NEWSPAPER

Fashion News
Editorial: Fashion News Press, 25th Floor, Fangzhi Dasha, 482 Zhongshan donglu, Nanjing 210002. **T:** 86 13851810482
E: njxzw@163.com
Freq: Weekly; **Circ:** 110003 Not Audited
Editor in Chief: Jianmin Zhou
Editorial Profile: Fashion News is a newspaper of fashion industry focusing on East China fashion market. It reports on fashion, fashion accesoories and trendy products.
Language (s): Chinese
NEWSPAPER

Financial News
Editorial: Financial News Press, 18/F, Block D, Jia 18, Zhongguancun Nandajie, Haidian District, Beijing 100081. **T:** 86 1082198111
E: fnweb@126.com
W: http://www.financialnews.com.cn
Freq: 2 Times/Week; **Circ:** 370001 Not Audited
Editor in Chief: Fuliang Song
Editorial Profile: Covers financial news.
Language (s): Chinese
NEWSPAPER

The First
Editorial: No.3 Guangqu Road, Chaoyang District, Beijing 100025. **T:** 86 10 87956000
W: http://www.thefirst.cn
Editor in Chief: Xing wen Xiw
Editorial Profile: Covers information and news of social, cultural and entertainment issues.
Language (s): Chinese
DAILY NEWSPAPER

Fortune Times
Editorial: Fortune Times, 22/F, Block D, Shimao Tianjie, 9 Guanghua Road, Chaoyang District, Beijing 100020. **T:** 86 1065873610
W: http://www.cftmedia.com/
Freq: Daily; **Circ:** 270003 Not Audited
Editor in Chief: Hengdai Zhai
Editorial Profile: Fortune Times is a national newspaper which includes economics, business, finance, accounting, banking, banks and finance companies, as well as e-commerce, international stock markets, securities, investment and insurance.
Language (s): Chinese
DAILY NEWSPAPER

Friday
Editorial: 223 Longpan Zhonglu, Nanjing 210002. **T:** 86 2584686717
W: http://www.njnews.cn
Freq: Weekly
Editor in Chief: Liping Jin
Editorial Profile: Covers news of entertainment, lifestyle, and fashion.
Language (s): Chinese
NEWSPAPER

Friendship News
Editorial: Friendship News, Building 5 Shenfulu, Hangzhou 310007.
T: 86 571 87055285 **E:** lybs@vip.163.com
W: http://www.lybs.com.cn
Freq: 2 Times/Week; **Circ:** 100001 Not Audited
Editor in Chief: Weisheng Yuan
Editorial Profile: It focuses on the governmental policies and social issues.
Language (s): Chinese
NEWSPAPER

Fujian Business Times
Editorial: 7th Floor Shangye Daxia, 23 Zhongshanlu, Fuzhou 350003.
T: 86 59187836149 **E:** fjbt@sina.com
W: http://www.fjbt.net
Freq: 2 Times/Week; **Circ:** 100004 Not Audited
Editorial Profile: Covers China business and financial news with focus on Fujian Province. It also covers marketing, consumer electronics, electrical products and equipment, as well as real estate, travel and health issues.
Language (s): Chinese
NEWSPAPER

Global Knowledge Weekly
Editorial: Changsha Baoye Zhongxin, 267 Wanbao Dadao, Furongqu, Changsha 410016.
T: 86 73182205609 **W:** http://www.zsblb.com
Freq: Weekly
Bureau Chief: Hanqi Zhao
Editorial Profile: Covers current global and regional war affairs and social issues in China.
Language (s): Chinese
NEWSPAPER

Global Times
Owner: People's Daily Press Group
Editorial: People's Daily Press Group, 2 Jintaixilu, Chaoyangqu, Beijing 100733.
T: 86 10 65369565
E: info@globaltimes.com.cn
W: http://www.globaltimes.cn
Freq: Daily; **Circ:** 2000000 Not Audited
Editor in Chief: Xijin Hu
Editorial Profile: Global Times is a national newspaper reporting on international news solely reported and edited by Chinese. It contains political, business, economic and current affairs all over the world.
Language (s): Chinese
DAILY NEWSPAPER

Global Times (English Edition)
Owner: People's Daily Press Group
Editorial: People's Daily Press Group, Global Times (English Edition), 7/F Topnew Tower, 15 Guanghua Road, Chaoyang District, Beijing 100026. **T:** 86 10 52937633
E: info@globaltimes.com.cn
W: http://www.globaltimes.cn
Freq: Daily
Editor in Chief: Xijin Hu
Editorial Profile: Global Times is a national newspaper reporting on international news solely reported and edited by Chinese. It contains political, business, economic and current affairs all over the world.
Language (s): English
DAILY NEWSPAPER

Guangdong Construction News
Editorial: Guangdong Construction News, Yangcheng Wanbao Dayuan, Guangzhou 510085. **T:** 86 2087754527
W: http://www.ycwb.com/gdjsb/gdjsb.htm
Freq: 2 Times/Week; **Circ:** 120003 Not Audited
Editor in Chief: Shigong Wu
Editorial Profile: Covers information and news concerning city construction, environmental protection, building and construction, residential real estates and building material market.
Language (s): Chinese
NEWSPAPER

Guangming Daily
Editorial: Guangming Daily, 5 Dongdajie, Zhushikou, Chongwenqu, Beijing 100062.
T: 86 10 67078755 **E:** net@gmw.cn
W: http://www.gmw.com.cn
Freq: Daily; **Circ:** 330003 Not Audited
Editor in Chief: Zhanfan Hu
Editorial Profile: Covers business, computer technology, current affairs, entertainment, finance, government, home affairs, international news, national news and government information and policies.
Language (s): Chinese
DAILY NEWSPAPER

Guangxi Daily
Editorial: Guangxi Daily Group, 21 Minzhulu, Nanning 530026. **T:** 86 867715690995
E: newgx@gxrb.com.cn
W: http://www.newgx.com.cn
Freq: Daily; **Circ:** 200001 Not Audited
Editor in Chief: Qirui Li; **Editor:** Jie Yao
Editorial Profile: Covers news and information in Guangxi region.
Language (s): Chinese
DAILY NEWSPAPER

Guangzhou Daily
Editorial: Guangzhou Daily Press Group, 10 Tonglelu, Renmin Zhonglu, Guangzhou 510121. **T:** 86 20 81919191
W: http://gzdaily.dayoo.com
Freq: Daily Not Audited
Editor in Chief: Wanfen Li
Editorial Profile: covers local, national and international news on politics, finance, entertainment and culture.
Language (s): Chinese
DAILY NEWSPAPER

Guangzhou Morning Post
Editorial: Guangzhou Daily Press Group, 606 Xuri Daxia, 315 Guangfu Zhonglu, Guangzhou 510140. **T:** 86 2081019227
E: 273346328@qq.com
W: http://www.gzmp.net
Freq: 2 Times/Week; **Circ:** 290001 Not Audited
Editorial Profile: Guangzhou Morning Post is an English newspaper for readers who would like to learn English and broaden their scope. The newspaper covers news, social issues, entertainment and English learning.
Language (s): Chinese
NEWSPAPER

Guiyang Evening News
Editorial: Guiyang Daily Press Group, 25 Zhongshan Donglu, Guiyang 550002.
T: 86 8515870467 **W:** http://www.gywb.cn
Freq: Daily; **Circ:** 280001 Not Audited
Editor in Chief: Xuewu Zhang
Editorial Profile: Covers news on finance, lifestyle, entertainment and sports.
Language (s): Chinese
DAILY NEWSPAPER

Guizhou Business News
Editorial: Guizhou Daily Press, 372 Baoshanbeilu, Guiyang 550001. **T:** 86 6625075
E: gzsbedit@126.com
W: http://gzsb.gog.com.cn
Freq: Daily; **Circ:** 700001 Not Audited
Editor in Chief: Musong Cheng
Editorial Profile: Guizhou Business News is a regional economic newspaper covering economic and market news concerning Guizhou Province.
Language (s): Chinese
DAILY NEWSPAPER

Haikou Evening News
Editorial: 69 Nansha lu, Haikou 570206.
T: 86 89866824257 **W:** http://www.hkwb.net
Freq: Daily
Editor in Chief: Zhili Liu; **Bureau Chief:** Tao Xu
Editorial Profile: Covers city news and financial news.
Language (s): Chinese
DAILY NEWSPAPER

Health Consultation News
Editorial: Capital Medical University, Shoudu Yike Daxue, You'anmenwai, Beijing 100054.
T: 86 1063051195 **W:** http://health.sohu.com
Freq: Weekly; **Circ:** 100003 Not Audited
Editor in Chief: Guozhu Liu
Editorial Profile: Health Consultation News deals with health and healthcare, as well as medical consultants and relevant issues.
Language (s): Chinese
NEWSPAPER

Health News
Editorial: Health News, Jia 6 Xiaojie, Dongzhimenwai, Beijing 100027.
T: 86 1064620055 **E:** master@jkb.com.cn
W: http://www.healthnews.com.cn
Freq: 2 Times/Week; **Circ:** 400001 Not Audited
Editor in Chief: Shuo Wang
Editorial Profile: Covers the latest news and information on health related issues.
Language (s): Chinese
NEWSPAPER

Health News
Editorial: Beijing Dongzhimen Street No. 6A, Beijing 100027. **T:** 86 10 64620055 621
E: fx@jkb.com.cn **W:** http://www.jkb.com.cn
Freq: Daily
Editor: Xue Yan
Editorial Profile: Covers public health issues and topics throughout China.
Language (s): Chinese
DAILY NEWSPAPER

Health Times
Editorial: People's Daily Press Group, 2 Jintaixilu, Chaoyangqu, Beijing 100733.

T: 86 10 65369681 E: jksbtg@jksb.com.cn
W: http://www.jksb.com.cn
Freq: Weekly Not Audited
Editor in Chief: Meng Xianli; **Editor in Chief:** Rui Yang
Editorial Profile: Covers healthcare issues, such as health problems of all walks of life, the application of Chinese medicine and the government policy on healthcare and public hygiene.
Language (s): Chinese
NEWSPAPER

Healthcare Times
Editorial: Healthcare Times, 154 Gulouxi Dajie, Xicheng District, Beijing 100009.
T: 86 10 64028135
W: http://www.baojianshibao.com/
Freq: Weekly
Bureau Chief: Junpu Gao; **Editor in Chief:** Guofa Zhang
Editorial Profile: Covers health related issues.
Language (s): Chinese
NEWSPAPER

Hebei Law News
Editorial: Hebei Law News, 118 Yuhua Xilu, Shijiazhuang 50051. T: 86 31183027456
E: hebfazhi@163.com
W: http://www.hbfzweb.com
Freq: 2 Times/Week; **Circ:** 60003 Not Audited
Editor in Chief: Maokui Liu
Editorial Profile: It covers law news, legislation issues and cases.
Language (s): Chinese
NEWSPAPER

Heilongjiang Labour News
Editorial: Heilongjiang Labour News, 195 Dongdazhijie, Nangangqu, Harbin (ha'erbin) 150001. T: 86 45157826898
E: hljgrb@163.com
Freq: 2 Times/Week; **Circ:** 50000 Not Audited
Editor: Sheng Wang; **Bureau Chief:** Hong Zhang
Editorial Profile: It covers the news on labor market, human resources and labor unions in Heilongjiang region.
Language (s): Chinese
NEWSPAPER

Heilongjiang Morning Post
Editorial: Heilongjiang Morning Post, 101 Changjiianglu, Harbin (ha'erbin) 150090.
T: 86 45188581988 W: http://www.hljcb.com
Freq: Daily; **Circ:** 150003 Not Audited
Editor: Huaxing Lin
Editorial Profile: Heilongjiang Morning Post focuses on regional news and related issues in Heilongjiang region.
Language (s): Chinese
DAILY NEWSPAPER

Henan Business News
Editorial: 6F Zhongqing Dasha, 16-Fu1 Jinshuilu, Zhengzhou 450003.
T: 86 37165866299
W: http://www.shangbw.com
Freq: Daily; **Circ:** 320000 Not Audited
Editor in Chief: Lei Meng
Editorial Profile: Provides news in economic and business in and outside of China, and information of finance situation and investment in Henan.
Language (s): Chinese
DAILY NEWSPAPER

Henan Daily
Editorial: Henan Daily Press Group, 28 Nongyelu, Zhengzhou 450008.
T: 86 37165796302 W: http://www.dahe.cn
Freq: Daily; **Circ:** 400003 Not Audited
Editor: Yining Liu
Editorial Profile: Henan Daily is a publication which focuses on the local, regional and national news in Henan and China.
Language (s): Chinese
DAILY NEWSPAPER

Hohhot Evening News
Editorial: Hohhot Daily Press, 8 Dizhiju Nanjie, Hothot (huhehaote) 10020. T: 86 47 16914000
E: hhwb009@163.com
W: http://news.nmgnews.com.cn
Freq: Daily
Editor in Chief: Li Han; **Bureau Chief:** Guangyi Hang
Editorial Profile: covers news in Hohhot region and China.
Language (s): Chinese
DAILY NEWSPAPER

Hubei Daily
Editorial: Hubei Daily Group, 181 Donghu Road, Wuchang, Wuhan 430077.
T: 86 2786770308 W: http://www.cnhubei.com
Freq: Daily; **Circ:** 210001 Not Audited
Editor in Chief: Yuantao Tang
Editorial Profile: Focuses on political, financial and cultural issues concerning the Hubei province.
Language (s): Chinese
DAILY NEWSPAPER

Huizhou Daily
Editorial: Wenhua Yilu, Jiangbei, Huizhou 516003. T: 86 7522831821
E: hzdaily@hznews.com
W: http://www.hznews.com
Freq: Daily
Editor in Chief: Zhongchu Hu
Editorial Profile: Focuses on political, financial, economic and cultural issues concerning Huizhou.
Language (s): Chinese
DAILY NEWSPAPER

Hunan Daily
Owner: Hunan Daily Press Group
Editorial: Hunan Daily Press Group, 18 Furong Zhonglu, Changsha 410071.
T: 86 73184312999
W: http://hunan.voc.com.cn
Freq: Daily; **Circ:** 300001 Not Audited
Editor in Chief: Yuelin Dong
Editorial Profile: Covers news on political, financial, cultural and entertainment issues.
Language (s): Chinese
DAILY NEWSPAPER

Hunan Economic Daily
Editorial: Research Center of Economics, Hunan Provincial Government, 351 Wuyi Dadao, Shengzhengfu, Jiguan Eryuan Wuzi Zhonglu, Changsha 410011.
T: 86 731 4453570
Freq: 2 Times/Week; **Circ:** 100003 Not Audited
Editor in Chief: Qingsheng Tang
Editorial Profile: Covers news on finance, business and economy in Hunan province.
Language (s): Chinese
NEWSPAPER

Hygiene and Life News
Editorial: Shenyang Daily Press, 67 Beisanjingjie Shenhequ, Shenyang 110014.
T: 86 24 22855122 W: http://www.syd.com.cn
Freq: Weekly; **Circ:** 200001 Not Audited
Editor in Chief: Hongyan He
Editorial Profile: It focuses on hygiene, healthcare and medicine issues.
Language (s): Chinese
NEWSPAPER

Industry and Commercial Guide News
Editorial: Industry and Commercial Guide News, 23F Block C Tianhui Dasha, Hefei 230001. T: 86 551 2652215
E: gsdbs@163.com W: http://www.gsdbs.com
Freq: 2 Times/Week; **Circ:** 170003 Not Audited
Editor: Huaiyu Chu
Editorial Profile: Covers the market information of all kinds of businesses, experience-sharing of successful businesses.
Language (s): Chinese
NEWSPAPER

Information and Market News
Editorial: Information and Market News, 147-2, Hongqi Dajie, Xiangfang District, Harbin (ha'erbin) 150036. T: 86 45188869393
E: xinxiyushichang@126.com
Freq: 2 Times/Week
Editor in Chief: Ling Ma
Editorial Profile: Covers mainly the information of market, consumption and the latest business news.
Language (s): Chinese
NEWSPAPER

Information Daily
Editorial: Jiangxi Daily Press Group, 1326 Hongguzhong Dadao, Nanchang 330006.
T: 86 791 6849117
W: http://jxnews.com.cn/xxrb
Freq: Daily; **Circ:** 350003 Not Audited
Editorial Profile: Covers local and national news in Jiangxi region and China.
Language (s): Chinese
DAILY NEWSPAPER

Inner Mongolia Business Daily
Editorial: Inner Mongolia Business Daily, 64 Xing'an North Road, Hothot (huhehaote) 10050. T: 86 4716515902
E: newhay@126.com
Freq: Daily; **Circ:** 220001 Not Audited
Bureau Chief: Xixiao Li
Editorial Profile: covers social news, business news and finance news.
Language (s): Chinese
DAILY NEWSPAPER

Inner Mongolia Daily
Editorial: Inner Mongolia Daily Group, 61 Xinhua Dajie, Hothot (huhehaote) 10010.
T: 86 47 16635761 E: nmrbybs@163.com
W: http://www.nmgnews.com.cn
Freq: Daily; **Circ:** 100003 Not Audited
Editor in Chief: Xueyi Jia; **Bureau Chief:** Jinghai Liu
Editorial Profile: focuses on politics, finance, culture and society.
Language (s): Chinese
DAILY NEWSPAPER

International Business Daily
Editorial: International Business Daily Group, Building 14, Block 3, Fangxingyuan, Fangzhuang, Beijing 100078.
T: 86 10 58360000 E: gjsbzbs@126.com
W: http://ibdaily.mofcom.gov.cn
Freq: Daily; **Circ:** 380005 Not Audited
Editor: Junsheng Liu
Editorial Profile: Covers information in market, business, stock and government regulations in and around the world.
Language (s): Chinese
DAILY NEWSPAPER

International Finance News
Owner: People Daily Group
Editorial: People Daily Group, 777 Shijidadao, Pudong, Shanghai 200120. T: 86 2158829998
E: ifn@peopledaily.com.cn
Freq: Daily Not Audited
Editor in Chief: Chong Xu
Editorial Profile: Covers the finance news both in China and overseas. It also focuses on business and economic issues.
Language (s): English
DAILY NEWSPAPER

The International New York Times - Beijing
Editorial: Jian Guo Men Wai Bldg #6-2-12, Beijing 100600. T: 86 106 532-3115
Bureau Chief: Philip Pan
DAILY NEWSPAPER

The International New York Times - Shanghai
Editorial: 1376 Nanjing Xilu, Shanghai.
T: 86 2162798585 E: foreign@nytimes.com
Bureau Chief: David Barboza
DAILY NEWSPAPER

Jia jiao zhou bao
Owner: Modern Family Magazine House
Editorial: Modern Family Magazine House, 66 Jianyelu, Nanjing 210004. T: 86 2584221870
E: wzm213@126.com W: http://jjzb.njnews.cn
Freq: Weekly; **Circ:** 800002 Not Audited
Editor in Chief: Mei Fang
Editorial Profile: Covers home schooling and other education issues.
Language (s): Chinese
NEWSPAPER

Jiangmen Daily
Editorial: Jiangmen Daily Press, 25 Huayuanzhong Road, Jiangmen 529000.
T: 86 7503502683 E: info@jmrb.com
W: http://www.jmrb.com.cn
Freq: Daily; **Circ:** 90001 Not Audited
Editor in Chief: Jianguo Zhang
Editorial Profile: Focuses on local and regional news in Jiangmen region.
Language (s): Chinese
DAILY NEWSPAPER

Jiangsu Commercial News
Editorial: Nanjing Daily Press Group, 223 Longpan Zhonglu, Nanjing 210016.
T: 86 25 84686611 W: http://jssb.njnews.cn
Freq: Daily; **Circ:** 120003 Not Audited
Editor in Chief: Lei Jiang
Editorial Profile: covers the news and information of business and finance in Jiangsu.
Language (s): Chinese
DAILY NEWSPAPER

Jiangsu Economic News
Owner: Xinhua Daily Group
Editorial: Xinhua Daily Group, 90 Hujunanlu, Nanjing 210004. T: 86 2552258319
E: sxm90@126.com
Freq: 2 Times/Week; **Circ:** 110003 Not Audited
Editor in Chief: Yi Wu
Editorial Profile: It focuses on the economic events and news in Jiangsu region as well as China.
Language (s): Chinese
NEWSPAPER

Jiangsu Law News
Editorial: Jiangsu Law News, Wenhui Dasha, 101 Caochangmen Dajie, Nanjing 210036.
T: 86 25 86261555 E: zbb@jslegal.com
Freq: Daily; **Circ:** 100003 Not Audited
Editor in Chief: Yan Li
Editorial Profile: It provides news and analysis on law-related issues.
Language (s): Chinese
DAILY NEWSPAPER

Jiangxi Broadcasting & Television News
Editorial: Jiangxi Broadcasting & Television News, 77 Wenjiao Road, Nanchang 330046.
T: 86 7918521749 W: http://jxgdb.jxgdw.com
Freq: Weekly
Editorial Profile: Focuses on entertainment news and television station information in Jiangxi region.
Language (s): Chinese
NEWSPAPER

Jiaozuo Daily
Editorial: Jiaozuo Daily, 56 Shanyang Road, Jiaozuo 454002. T: 86 3913924268
W: http://www.jzrb.com.cn
Freq: Daily
Editor: Jianxin Wang
Editorial Profile: Covers local, regional, national news.
Language (s): Chinese
DAILY NEWSPAPER

Jinan Daily
Owner: Jinan Daily Press Group
Editorial: Jinan Daily Press Group, Number 28-1, Jinqi Road, Shizhongqu, Jinan 250001.
T: 86 53182886163 E: rbzbs@e23.com
W: http://www.e23.cn
Freq: Daily; **Circ:** 300002 Not Audited
Editorial Profile: Covers regional and national news, health, digital produces, travel, education, sports, entertainment, real estate, cars and social issues.
Language (s): Chinese
DAILY NEWSPAPER

Jinling Evening Post
Editorial: Nanjing Daily Press Group, 223 Longpan Zhonglu, Nanjing 210002.
T: 86 2584687113 W: http://www.jlwb.net
Freq: Daily Not Audited
Editor in Chief: Xiaoning Xiang
Editorial Profile: Covers the regional news in Nanjing and national news in China.
Language (s): Chinese
DAILY NEWSPAPER

Jinzhou Evening News
Editorial: Jinzhou Daily Press Group, 2 Nanjinglu Sanduan, Jinzhou 121000.
T: 86 4163705576 W: http://www.lm3d.com
Freq: Daily
Editor in Chief: Hui Jiang; **Editor:** Lin Qi
Editorial Profile: Jinzhou Evening News is a local publication which covers the local and regional news in Jinzhou.
Language (s): Chinese
DAILY NEWSPAPER

Juvenile Encyclopedia Weekly
Editorial: Sichuan Education Publishing House, 49 Nandajie, Chengdu 610041.
T: 86 2886111802 E: sbb@mail.sc.cninfo.net
Freq: Weekly
Editor in Chief: Chilin Tang
Editorial Profile: Covers popular science knowledge including social science and natural science.
Language (s): Chinese
NEWSPAPER

Kunming Daily
Owner: Kunming Daily Press Group
Editorial: Kunming Daily Press Group, 8F-11F, Xinwen Zhongxin, 198 Danxialu, Kunming 650118. T: 86 8715391909
W: http://www.clzg.cn
Freq: Daily; **Circ:** 100002 Not Audited
Editor in Chief: Xueming Sun
Editorial Profile: Covers news on financial, economic, social and cultural issues.
Language (s): Chinese
DAILY NEWSPAPER

Laborers Midday News
Editorial: 53 Taoranting Road, Beijing.
T: 86 10 83548149
W: http://www.ldwb.com.cn
Editor in Chief: Zhaohua Huang
Editorial Profile: Covers national news.
DAILY NEWSPAPER

Labour Daily
Editorial: Labour Daily, 700 Changpinglu, Shanghai 200040. **T:** 86 2162187286
E: ldbsgj@online.sh.cn
W: http://www.shzgh.org
Freq: Daily; **Circ:** 200003 Not Audited
Editor in Chief: Bihua Chen
Editorial Profile: covers the news, information, and employee's benefits of the labour market. It also includes general news on entertainment and culture.
Language (s): Chinese
DAILY NEWSPAPER

Law and Citizens Daily
Editorial: Law and Citizens Daily, 22 Nanpu Road, Guiyang 550002. **T:** 86 8515505030
W: http://www.fzshb.cn
Freq: Weekly; **Circ:** 240003 Not Audited
Editor in Chief: Zhu Li
Editorial Profile: Covers the law news in local community. It also includes the regional government legislation and the effects on the life of local people.
Language (s): Chinese
NEWSPAPER

Law Express
Owner: Law Express Press
Editorial: Law Express Press, 15 Jinzhou Road, Nanning 530022. **T:** 86 7716119221
E: gxzfyw@163.com
Freq: Daily; **Circ:** 160002 Not Audited
Editorial Profile: It covers law and legal issues.
Language (s): Chinese
DAILY NEWSPAPER

Law News
Editorial: Legal Daily Press Group, Jia1 Huajiadi, Chaoyangqu, Beijing 100102.
T: 86 1064361144 2236 **E:** fzwc@sina.com.cn
W: http://www.legaldaily.com.cn
Freq: 2 Times/Week; **Circ:** 500003 Not Audited
Editor in Chief: Guanbin Zhang
Editorial Profile: A national newspaper which mainly focuses on law news and social issues related the laws in China.
Language (s): Chinese
NEWSPAPER

Legal Daily
Editorial: Legal Daily Press Group, Jia 1, Huajiadi, Chaoyangqu, Beijing 100102.
T: 86 1084772288
E: zhengfazongzhi@126.com
W: http://www.legaldaily.com.cn
Freq: Daily; **Circ:** 400001 Not Audited
Editor in Chief: Xiadu Lei
Editorial Profile: Legal Daily is a national newspaper which mainly covers national news and international news on law issues in China.
Language (s): Chinese
DAILY NEWSPAPER

Legal Mirror
Editorial: Legal Mirror, Block A1, Huitong Shidai Guangchang, 71 Jianguolu, Chaoyangqu, Beijing 100025.
T: 86 10 58635959 **E:** fwpl@vip.sohu.com
W: http://www.fawan.com
Freq: Daily; **Circ:** 300001 Not Audited
Editor in Chief: Lin Wang
Editorial Profile: Covers news on political, economic and social issues from the perspective of law, ans also provides legal issue consultant.
Language (s): Chinese
DAILY NEWSPAPER

Lianhe Zaobao - Beijing Bureau
Editorial: Lianhe Zaobao - Beijing Bureau, Unit 805 Raffles City Beijing, No. 1 Dongzhimen Nan Dajie, Dongcheng District, Beijing 100007.
T: 86 1064181587 **E:** lianhe@mail2.a-1.net.cn
W: http://www.zaobao.com
Freq: Daily
Editorial Profile: An internationally distributed Chinese newspaper, with its headquarters in Singapore, covers cultural, political, lifestyle, sports, and entertainment news in China and overseas.
Language (s): Chinese
DAILY NEWSPAPER

Liaoning Law News
Editorial: Liaoning Daily Press Group, 38 Bei Sanjingjie, Hepingqu, Shenyang 110003.
T: 86 2482707000 **E:** lnfzb@126.com
W: http://www.lnfzb.com
Freq: 2 Times/Week; **Circ:** 250003 Not Audited
Editor in Chief: Wei Cui
Editorial Profile: Mainly focuses on the news related to law, government legislation and policies, as well as legal case analysis from different aspects for the general public.
Language (s): Chinese
NEWSPAPER

Life News
Editorial: Life News Press, 2nd Floor, Securities Building, 62 Chunchenglu, Kunming 650011. **T:** 86 8713110110
W: http://www.shxb.net
Freq: Daily; **Circ:** 200001 Not Audited
Editor: MinFei long
Editorial Profile: Focuses on politics, economy and society in Yunnan province.
Language (s): Chinese
DAILY NEWSPAPER

Life Style
Editorial: Life Style, 7th Floor, Haidian Wenhua Yishu Daxia, Jia 28, Zhongguancun Dajie, Beijing 100086. **T:** 86 10 52169000
W: http://www.lifestyle.com.cn
Freq: 2 Times/Week; **Circ:** 300003 Not Audited
Editor: Fei Li; **Editor:** Yanzhu Wang; **Editor in Chief:** Shuxin Zhang
Editorial Profile: covers information for consumers and shopping guide of different areas in China. It mainly covers the high-end products and services.
Language (s): Chinese
NEWSPAPER

Lighting Weekly
Editorial: Lighting Weekly, China Building Decoration Association, Room 1702, Nanguangchang, Beijing 100055.
T: 86 1083993576
W: http://www.lighting-cbda.com
Freq: Weekly; **Circ:** 200001 Not Audited
Editorial Profile: covers the information and news on the lighting industry. It also focuses on the interior design of lights.
Language (s): Chinese
NEWSPAPER

Lingnan Youth News
Editorial: Lingnan Youth News, 602 Xuri Dasha, 315 Guangfu Zhonglu, Guangzhou 510140. **T:** 86 2081019225 **E:** lnxjz@126.com
W: http://www.lnsnb.cn
Freq: Weekly; **Circ:** 250003 Not Audited
Editor: Juxing Tang
Editorial Profile: Covers different aspects of studies and lives of students.
Language (s): Chinese
NEWSPAPER

Lingnan Youth News-Modern Child Raising Weekly
Editorial: Lingnan Youth News, 601 Xuri Dasha, 315 Guangfu Zhonglu, Guangzhou 510140. **T:** 86 2081019271 **E:** lnsnb@163.com
W: http://xdyeb.dayoo.com/gb/node/2004-02/02/node_491.htm
Freq: Weekly; **Circ:** 350002 Not Audited
Editor in Chief: Zengzhi Zhang
Editorial Profile: Covers children's care issues including their lives and studies.
Language (s): Chinese
NEWSPAPER

Los Angeles Times (China)
Editorial: Jianguomenwai 71102, Beijing.
T: 86 1065321982
Bureau Chief: Barbara Demick
DAILY NEWSPAPER

Market Daily Online Version
Editorial: People Daily, No. 1 Block, 2 Jintaixilu, Chaoyangqu, Beijing 100733.
T: 86 1065369460
E: zhaoyinghua@vip.sohu.net
W: http://www.marketdaily.com.cn
Freq: 2 Times/Week; **Circ:** 300002 Not Audited
Editor: Yinghua Zhao
Editorial Profile: Provides latest news and information on markets of different aspects.
Language (s): Chinese
NEWSPAPER

Market Information
Editorial: Market Information, 229 Yingze Dajie, Taiyuan 30001. **T:** 86 3514132553
E: scxxbcn@263.net
W: http://www.scxxb.com.cn
Freq: Daily; **Circ:** 200001 Not Audited
Editor in Chief: Huiming Jiang
Editorial Profile: covers economic news of all main industries in China.
Language (s): Chinese
DAILY NEWSPAPER

Medicine Economic News
Editorial: Institute of Southern Medicine Economic, 6th Floor, West Tower, Tianyu Shangwu Daxia, 753 Dongfeng Donglu, Guangzhou 510405. **T:** 86 20 37886650
E: yyjjb@21cn.com
W: http://www.yyjjb.com.cn
Freq: 2 Times/Week; **Circ:** 200003 Not Audited
Bureau Chief: Jianning Lin; **Editor in Chief:** Jianhong Tao
Editorial Profile: Covers the business and economics of medicine in China. It covers the sales and marketing of medicine, quality assurance, hospital management and other medicine-related issues.
Language (s): Chinese
NEWSPAPER

Metro Express
Editorial: Metro Express, 25F Meiluo Dasha, 30, Tianyaoqiaolu, Shanghai 200031.
T: 86 21 60838383 **E:** shidai@jfdaily.com
W: http://www.metrosh.com
Freq: 2 Times/Week; **Circ:** 600000 Not Audited
Editor in Chief: Yefang Niu
Editorial Profile: Focuses on local and regional news in Shanghai area, and is distributed through metro. "The Age" by Shanghai Jiefang Daily Newspaper Group, published as "white-collar workers on the road commuting to obtain information of the newspaper," as Shanghai Metro Operation Company licensing of free media in the next seven years there will be no new free media into the Shanghai Metro. Newspaper in Shanghai Metro line 9 total more than 200 sites free of charge. Monday to Friday publication, a series of 7:30 am to 9:30 minutes by subway to work the crowd, the current maturity issue amount of 55 to 60 million copies, and with the increase in subway traffic in the year on year increase. The Age of future development with unlimited imagination.
Language (s): Chinese
NEWSPAPER

Middle School Current Affair News
Editorial: Beijing Youth Press, Building A, 23 Dongli, Baijiazhuang, Chaoyangqu, Beijing 100026. **T:** 86 1065902448
E: wunan@ynet.com **W:** http://zxss.ynet.com
Freq: 2 Times/Week
Editor in Chief: Ying Jiang
Editorial Profile: Covering important current affairs.
Language (s): Chinese
NEWSPAPER

Modern Express News
Editorial: Modern Express News, 13th Floor, Dongyu Daxia, 18 Zhenghongjie, Xingjiekou, Nanjing 210005. **T:** 86 84783555
W: http://www.dsqq.cn
Freq: Daily
Editor in Chief: Chen Sha; **Editor:** Yong Xu
Editorial Profile: Covers news, current affairs and consumer's hot issues in Nanjing and the surrounding provinces.
Language (s): Chinese
DAILY NEWSPAPER

Modern Health News
Editorial: Changjiang Daily Gruop, 2 Changjiang Ribaolu, Hankou, Wuhan 430015.
T: 86 2785719416 **W:** http://www.cnhan.com
Freq: Weekly; **Circ:** 100003 Not Audited
Editor: Li Liu
Editorial Profile: Modern Health News is a national newspaper which mainly provides consultant on health problems and medical information to the elderly and the patients.
Language (s): Chinese
NEWSPAPER

Modern Logistics News
Editorial: Modern Logistics News, 25 Yuetan Bejie, Xicheng District, Beijing 100834.
T: 86 1068391412 **E:** yangdaqing@126.com
W: http://www.xd56b.com/
Freq: 2 Times/Week; **Circ:** 120003 Not Audited
Editorial Profile: It covers the latest news in the logistics industry in China.
Language (s): Chinese
NEWSPAPER

Modern Women News
Editorial: Modern Women News, 4 Luxunlu, Zhongshanqu, Dalian 116001.
T: 86 41182650404
Freq: 2 Times/Week
Editor: Yongqian Wu; **Editor in Chief:** Li Zhu
Editorial Profile: Modern Women News is a national newspaper that mainly covers women's interest issues such as fashion, lifestyle, food, entertainment and social hotspots.
Language (s): Chinese
NEWSPAPER

Morning Post
Editorial: 873 Dagu Nanlu, Hexiqu, Tianjin 300211. **T:** 86 22 28201063
W: http://www.tianjinwe.com
Freq: Daily; **Circ:** 700001 Not Audited
Editorial Profile: covers news on financial, business, social and lifestyle issues in Tianjin Region.
Language (s): Chinese
DAILY NEWSPAPER

Music Life News
Editorial: Music Life News Press, 115 Dongzhongjie, Dongcheng District, Beijing 100020. **T:** 86 1065519460
Freq: 2 Times/Week
Editor in Chief: Xinhua Liang
Editorial Profile: Provides information and updated news of music industry in China.
Language (s): Chinese
NEWSPAPER

Nanfang Daily
Editorial: Nanfang Daily Press Group, 289 Guangzhou Dadaozhong, Guangzhou 510601.
T: 86 20 87373998 **E:** nfd@nfdaily.cn
W: http://www.nanfangdaily.com.cn/southnews/
Freq: Daily; **Circ:** 800003 Not Audited
Editor in Chief: Chanfu Wang
Editorial Profile: Provides news in the southern region of China and national news.
Language (s): Chinese
DAILY NEWSPAPER

Nanjing Daily
Editorial: Nanjing Daily Press Group, 223 Longpan Zhonglu, Nanjing 210002.
T: 86 258 449000
W: http://www.njrb.njnews.cn
Freq: Daily; **Circ:** 300001 Not Audited
Editor in Chief: Yu Pu
Editorial Profile: covers the general news in Nanjing region.
Language (s): Chinese
DAILY NEWSPAPER

National Business Daily
Editorial: National Buisness Daily, 8/F, Block A, No. 3 Lou, No. 195 Longtian Road, Xuhui District, Shanghai 200235. **T:** 86 2160900099
W: http://www.nbd.com.cn
Freq: Daily; **Circ:** 100001 Not Audited
Editorial Profile: Focuses on business, economic and financial development in China and overseas.
Language (s): Chinese
DAILY NEWSPAPER

New Countryside Commerce
Editorial: International Business Daily Group, Building 14, Area 3, Fangxingyuan, Fangzhuang, Beijing 100078.
T: 86 1058360188 **E:** xncsb2009@163.com
W: http://xncsb.mofcom.gov.cn
Freq: 2 Times/Week; **Circ:** 190001 Not Audited
Editor in Chief: Jishan Sun
Editorial Profile: covers the news and issues of agriculture business, supply and policy in China.
Language (s): Chinese
NEWSPAPER

New Express Newspaper
Editorial: Yangcheng Evening Press Group, 533 Tianhelu, Guangzhou 510630.
T: 86 20 85180888 **W:** http://www.xkb.com.cn
Freq: Daily
Editor in Chief: Sun Xuan
Editorial Profile: reports news in Guangdong region and national news in China. "Express," the editorial team of high quality, young, modern technical means. "Express" in Guangzhou and the Pearl River Delta-based sales market, the core audience is the most dynamic and social spending power of the white-collar and middle class, but also by ordinary readers love the city, with an increasingly wide range of influence and good advertising.
Language (s): Chinese
DAILY NEWSPAPER

New Legal Report
Owner: Jiangxi Daily Press Group
Editorial: Jiangxi Daily Press Group, 190 Yangming Road, Nanchang 330006.
T: 86 791 6849033
W: http://www.jxnews.com.cn/jxfzb
Freq: 2 Times/Week; **Circ:** 200003 Not Audited
Editor in Chief: Jingping Cheng

Editorial Profile: It covers news and analysis on law and legal issues.
Language (s): Chinese
NEWSPAPER

Nihon Keizai Shimbun - Beijing Bureau
Editorial: Diplomatic Compound Chaoyang, 3-13, Jianguomenwai, Beijing 100600.
T: 86 1065321664 **W:** http://e.nikkei.com
Freq: Daily
Bureau Chief: Suguru Shinada
Language (s): Japanese
DAILY NEWSPAPER

Northern Economic News
Editorial: Inner Mongolia Daily Group, 61 Xinhua Dajie, Hothot (huhehaote) 10016.
T: 86 4716266852
W: http://news.nmgnews.com.cn
Freq: 2 Times/Week; **Circ:** 70001 Not Audited
Editor in Chief: Jan Lan
Editorial Profile: covers regional business and finance news in Inner Mongolia.
Language (s): Chinese
NEWSPAPER

Oriental City and County News
Owner: Oriental City and County News
Editorial: Oriental City and County News, Room 2, Flat 3, 779 Xianxia West Road, Shanghai 200335. **T:** 86 2152161710
W: http://www.dfcxb.com
Freq: Daily; **Circ:** 100002 Not Audited
Editor in Chief: Xiaowen Xi
Editorial Profile: Covers the news of agriculture and other news of the local society in Shanghai region.
Language (s): Chinese
DAILY NEWSPAPER

Oriental Lady
Owner: Jiangxi Women's Association
Editorial: Jiangxi Women's Association, 308 Nanjing Road, Nanchang 330029.
T: 86 7918320090 **E:** fnzhshb@hotmail.com
W: http://www.jxwomen.org.cn/newweb/paper/
Freq: Weekly; **Circ:** 60001 Not Audited
Editor in Chief: Liqun Cai
Editorial Profile: It covers lifestyle, career, family, relationship and other women's interested issues.
Language (s): Chinese
NEWSPAPER

Oriental Morning Post
Editorial: Oriental Morning Post, 839 Yan'zhonglu, Shanghai 200040.
T: 86 2162471234 **E:** dfzb@wxjt.com.cn
W: http://www.dfdaily.com
Freq: Daily Not Audited
Editor: Peng Wang
Editorial Profile: Reports on the news of Shanghai City, Jiangsu and Zhejiang Province.
Language (s): Chinese
DAILY NEWSPAPER

Oriental Sports Daily
Editorial: Oriental Sports Daily, 839 Yan'an Zhonglu, Shanghai 200040. **T:** 86 2162476156
W: http://www.sport1.cn
Freq: Daily
Editor in Chief: Min Du
Editorial Profile: Oriental Sports Daily is a national newspaper which covers national and overseas sporting events and information.
Language (s): Chinese
DAILY NEWSPAPER

Pearl River Times
Editorial: Pearl River Times, 17 Gangkoulu, Guangzhou 528200. **T:** 86 75783000123
E: times@dadao.net
W: http://dadao.net/php/prtime
Freq: Daily
Editor in Chief: Wanjun Li
Editorial Profile: Provides news of Guangzhou region.
Language (s): Chinese
DAILY NEWSPAPER

People's Railway Daily
Editorial: No. 196, Gaoxin Street, Baoji 721013. **T:** 011 86 09172755166
E: admin@bj-baodeli.com
Freq: Daily
Editorial Profile: Focuses on railway development and maintenance in China.
Language (s): Chinese
DAILY NEWSPAPER

People's Court News
Editorial: People's Court News, 22 Beili Xiqu Donghuashi, Chongwenqu, Beijing 100062.
T: 86 1067550723 **E:** xwb@rmfyb.cn
W: http://rmfyb.chinacourt.org/
Freq: Daily
Editor: Yizhong Yang
Editorial Profile: People's Court News is a publication which focuses on the information and news of the courtrooms in China.
Language (s): Chinese
DAILY NEWSPAPER

People's Daily
Editorial: People's Daily, 2 Jintaixilu, Chaoyangqu, Beijing 100733.
T: 86 10 6536 8114
W: http://www.peopledaily.com.cn
Freq: Daily Not Audited
Editor: Rujian Chen; **Editor in Chief:** Hengquan Wu; **Bureau Chief:** Yannong Zhang
Editorial Profile: People's Daily is a national newspaper which covers national news in China and international news worldwide.
Language (s): Chinese
DAILY NEWSPAPER

People's Photography
Owner: People's Photography Press
Editorial: People's Photography Press, 124 Shuangtasijie, Taiyuan 30012.
T: 86 3514297341
W: http://www.peoplephoto.com/
Freq: Weekly
Editor in Chief: Wei Huo
Editorial Profile: covers information about different types of photos and the technique and equipment needed when taking these photos.
Language (s): Chinese
NEWSPAPER

People's Post and Telecommunications
Editorial: People's Posts and Telecommunications News Office, 11 Anyuanlu, Chaoyang District, Beijing 100029.
T: 86 10 64962938
W: http://ermyd.cnii.com.cn
Freq: 2 Times/Week
Editor in Chief: Suoning Wu
Editorial Profile: Covers the latest news and development of postal services and telecommunications industry all around the world.
Language (s): Chinese
NEWSPAPER

People's Railroad News
Editorial: People's Railroad News, 3 Beifengwo, Haidian District, Beijing 100038.
T: 86 1051892022 **E:** tougao@peoplerail.com
W: http://www.rmtd.com.cn/
Freq: Daily; **Circ:** 200002 Not Audited
Editor in Chief: Dan Li
Editorial Profile: People's Railroad News is a national newspaper circulated on trains and in train stations, covering railway related issues and government regulations.
Language (s): Chinese
DAILY NEWSPAPER

PLA Daily
Editorial: PLA Daily Press, 34 Fuwai Dajie, Beijing 100832. **T:** 86 1068586350
E: dzzy@jfjb.com.cn
W: http://www.chinamil.com.cn
Freq: 2 Times/Week
Editor: Qin Song; **Editor:** Zurong Yang; **Editor:** Feng Zhou
Editorial Profile: provides latest news and information of The Chinese People's Liberation Army.
Language (s): Chinese
NEWSPAPER

Popular Life News
Editorial: Popular Life News, 1 Men, Block 4, Youcheng Mingju, 3 Youyi Road, Hexi District, Tianjin 300201. **T:** 86 2258586988
W: http://www.dzshb.com/
Freq: Weekly
Editor in Chief: Gang Li
Editorial Profile: covers social news and entertainment news in China.
Language (s): Chinese
NEWSPAPER

Popular Network News
Editorial: Joyyang, Kexie Daxia, 3 Shuangganglu, Yuzhong District, Chongqing 400013. **T:** 86 2363658818
W: http://www.joyyang.com
Freq: Weekly
Editorial Profile: covers issues on internet games such as online games, classic games and sporting & racing games.
Language (s): Chinese
NEWSPAPER

Popular Science News
Editorial: Popular Science News, 15 Fuxing Road, Beijing 100038. **T:** 86 10 58884048
E: dzkjb@public3.bta.net.cn
W: http://www.stdaily.com/other/dzkj
Freq: 2 Times/Week; **Circ:** 160003 Not Audited
Editor in Chief: Huaying Shu
Editorial Profile: reports on latest science development related to people's life covering social issues, health, leisure and consumer affairs.
Language (s): Chinese
NEWSPAPER

Primary Students Weekly
Editorial: 162 Gupinglu, Fuzhou 350003.
T: 86 59 187872685 **E:** fjedu@fjedu.com.cn
W: http://www.fjedu.com.cn
Freq: 2 Times/Week; **Circ:** 300003 Not Audited
Editorial Profile: covers educational and cultural activities and latest information for primary school students.
Language (s): Chinese
NEWSPAPER

Procuratorial Daily
Editorial: Procuratorial Daily Group, 5 Luguxilu, Shijingshanqu, Beijing 100040.
T: 86 1068630102 **E:** zbs@jcrb.com.cn
W: http://www.jcrb.com/n1
Freq: Daily; **Circ:** 330001 Not Audited
Editor in Chief: Xuehui Li; **Editor in Chief:** Bencai Zhang
Editorial Profile: Covers the general law news and social issues in the society of China.
Language (s): Chinese
DAILY NEWSPAPER

Qilu Evening News
Editorial: Qilu Evening News, 6 Leyuan Dajie, Jinan 250014. **T:** 86 53185193327
E: wl@qlwb.com.cn
W: http://www.qlwb.com.cn
Freq: Daily; **Circ:** 1700000 Not Audited
Editor: Shinan Han; **Editor in Chief:** Hao Keyaun
Editorial Profile: Focuses on both local and regional news.
Language (s): Chinese
DAILY NEWSPAPER

Qingdao Financial Daily
Editorial: Qingdao Daily Press Group, 77 Xuzhu Lu, Qingdao 266071.
T: 86 53280998776
W: http://caijing.qingdaonews.com
Freq: 2 Times/Week; **Circ:** 150001 Not Audited
Editor in Chief: Yachuan Li
Editorial Profile: Covers business, economics, finance and securities, as well as financial technology and services issues.
Language (s): Chinese
NEWSPAPER

Qinghai Law News
Editorial: 18 Nandajie, Xining 810000.
T: 86 9716312623
Freq: Daily
Editorial Profile: It covers law-related news and issues in Qinghai region.
Language (s): Chinese
DAILY NEWSPAPER

Qinzhou Evening News
Editorial: Qinzhou Evening News, Fumin Road, Qinzhou 535000. **T:** 86 7773680037
W: http://www.qzrb.com.cn
Freq: 2 Times/Week
Editorial Profile: Provides news of Qinzhou.
Language (s): Chinese
NEWSPAPER

Reader's Journal
Editorial: 47 Huaishujie, Chengdu 610041.
T: 86 2886272070 812
W: http://www.duzhebao.com.cn
Freq: 2 Times/Week
Editor in Chief: Shihong Wan
Editorial Profile: Reader's Newspaper is a national publication which mainly covers entertainment, lifestyle, news and other related affairs in China.
Language (s): Chinese
NEWSPAPER

Real Estate Times
Editorial: Jiefang Daily Press Group, 25th Floor, 300 Hankou Road, Shanghai 200001.
T: 86 21 63521111 **E:** liji047@jfdaily.com
W: http://www.jfdaily.com/gb/jfxww/xlbk/fangdc/index.html
Freq: Weekly
Editor in Chief: Xinchang Song
Editorial Profile: covers news on new houses, second-hand houses, estate management and interior design.
Language (s): Chinese
NEWSPAPER

Red Scarf News
Editorial: Red Scarf News, 202, 2 Men, 8 Haolou, Xindayuan, Nankaiqu, Tianjin 300192
Freq: Weekly; **Circ:** 300003 Not Audited
Editor in Chief: Shenyong He
Editorial Profile: covers stories of excellent youngsters and reports of youth events, student life and educational issues.
Language (s): Chinese
NEWSPAPER

Reference News
Owner: Xinhua News Agency
Editorial: No. 57 Xi Ave, Xuanwumen, Beijing 100803. **T:** 86 10 63071136
E: ckxx@xinhua.org
W: http://www.cankaoxiaoxi.com
Editor in Chief: Bing Leng; **Editor:** Li Yang
Editorial Profile: Covers news. It's the daily newspaper with largest circulation in China.
DAILY NEWSPAPER

Sangyo Times - Shanghai Bureau
Editorial: Shanghai
E: kuromasa@sangyo-times-sh.com
W: http://www.sangyo-times.co.jp
Freq: Weekly
Language (s): Japanese
NEWSPAPER

Sanya Morning Post
Editorial: Sanya Morning Post, 4/F, Zhuoda Dasha, Yingbinlu, Sanya 572000.
T: 86 89831886999 **E:** zbs@sycb.com.cn
W: http://www.sycb.com.cn
Freq: Daily
Editor in Chief: Shuzhen Huang
Editorial Profile: Covers national and international news, news of lifestyle, culture and entertainment news.
Language (s): Chinese
DAILY NEWSPAPER

Science & Technology Information News
Editorial: Keji Xinxi Baoshe, 19 Dong'erlu, Qianfoshan, Jinan 250014. **T:** 86 53182600789
Freq: 2 Times/Week
Editor in Chief: Jianyi Wang
Editorial Profile: Covers agricultural technology.
Language (s): Chinese
NEWSPAPER

Science and Technology Daily
Editorial: Science and Technology Daily, 15 Fuxinglu, Haidian District, Beijing 100038.
T: 86 1058884048 **E:** gjb@stdaily.com
W: http://www.stdaily.com
Freq: Daily; **Circ:** 300001 Not Audited
Editor: Yunsheng Wu
Editorial Profile: Covers the development and study of science and technology in China and abroad.
Language (s): Chinese
DAILY NEWSPAPER

Science Times
Editorial: Science Times, Yi-3, Zhongguancun Nanyitiao, Haidian District, Beijing 100190.
T: 86 10 82614607 **E:** snnews@stimes.cn
W: http://www.sciencetimes.com.cn
Freq: Daily; **Circ:** 200003 Not Audited
Editor in Chief: Honghai Liu
Editorial Profile: Covers science.
Language (s): Chinese
DAILY NEWSPAPER

Securities Times
Editorial: Securities Times, 3F, Zhongyin Mansion, 5015 Caitian Road Futian District, Shenzhen 518026. **T:** 86 75583501827
E: flyfar@163.com
W: http://www.p5w.net/p5w/home/stime/today/
Freq: 2 Times/Week; **Circ:** 400001 Not Audited
Editor in Chief: Zijian Wen
Editorial Profile: Provides information about securities and stock market, financial services, options and futures, personal savings issues.
Language (s): Chinese
NEWSPAPER

Shandong Electricity News
Editorial: Shandong Electric Power Corporation, 150 Jing'er lu, Jinan 250001.
T: 86 531 80124762 **E:** sddlbs@126.com
W: http://www.sepco.com.cn
Freq: 2 Times/Week
Editor: Mingzhen Xie

Editorial Profile: Shandong Electricity News is an industrial newspaper which covers the development and advancement in the electricity industry of Shandong.
Language (s): Chinese
NEWSPAPER

Shanghai Auto News
Editorial: Shanghai Auto News, Room 1011-1003, Shanghai Qiche Gongye Dasha, 489 Weihai Road, Shanghai 200041.
T: 86 2122011568
W: http://www.shautonews.com
Freq: Weekly; **Circ:** 90003 Not Audited
Editor: Hongwei Du
Editorial Profile: Covers news in the car and automobile industry in China.
Language (s): Chinese
NEWSPAPER

Shanghai Chinese Medicine News
Editorial: Shanghai Chinese Medicine News, 1376 Jiangninglu, Shanghai 200060.
T: 86 21 81874022 **E:** shhzyyb@163.com
Freq: Weekly; **Circ:** 50003 Not Audited
Editor in Chief: Changquan Ling
Editorial Profile: covers the latest news and development of traditional Chinese medicine and its application in daily life.
Language (s): Chinese
NEWSPAPER

Shanghai Daily
Editorial: Shanghai Daily Publishing House, 38th Floor, 755 Weihai Road, Shanghai 200041. **T:** 86 2152920242
E: editor@shanghaidaily.com
W: http://www.shanghaidaily.com
Freq: 2 Times/Week; **Circ:** 110003 Not Audited
Editor in Chief: Ciyun Zhang
Editorial Profile: Provides an English window to the news of China. Business-focused, it also reports on social, cultural and diplomatic developments in Shanghai and the surrounding region.
Language (s): English
NEWSPAPER

Shanghai Evening Post
Owner: Jiefang Daily Press Group
Editorial: Jiefang Daily Press Group, 300 Hankou Road, Shanghai 200001
E: xwwbpl@163.com
W: http://www.jfdaily.com
Freq: Daily Not Audited
Editor: Tang Shan
Editorial Profile: Covers news and related topics. Shanghai Evening Post Launched in January 1, 1999, is a subsidiary of Shanghai Jiefang Daily Group, a part of report. Revised several times through the circulation exceeded 40 million copies, is Shanghai's largest self-distribution networks. Shanghai Evening Post has a network of 27 distribution stations and more than 1,000 members of the young and dynamic issue. Evening News followed the forefront of the times is the Shanghai Evening News in a modern city. Do the most useful information, the best looking newspaper, Evening News has been issued all staff to pursue.
Language (s): Chinese
DAILY NEWSPAPER

Shanghai Family
Editorial: Wenhui - Xinmin United Press Group, 755 Weihailu, Shanghai 200041.
T: 86 215 2921234 **E:** news365@wxjt.com.cn
W: http://shjt.shfamily.com.cn
Freq: Weekly; **Circ:** 80003 Not Audited
Editorial Profile: Covers family and lifestyle issues in Shanghai.
Language (s): Chinese
NEWSPAPER

Shanghai Financial News
Editorial: Shanghai Financial News, 18th Floor, 1090 Pudong Shiji Dadao, Shanghai 200120.
T: 86 2158359626
W: http://www.shfinancialnews.com
Freq: 2 Times/Week; **Circ:** 50001 Not Audited
Editor: Guoquan Gu; **Editor in Chief:** Yujun Zheng
Editorial Profile: Shanghai Financial News is a regional financial newspaper mainly focusing on business and finance news in East China (incl. Shanghai, Zhejiang Province and Fujian Province). It covers investment, insurance, real estates, business and management, securities news. They also have pages for IT, health and leisure news.
Language (s): Chinese
NEWSPAPER

Shanghai Law Journal
Editorial: Shanghai Law News, 4th Floor, Number 1, 268 Nong, Xiaomuqiaolu, Shanghai 200032. **T:** 86 2164179999
W: http://www.jfdaily.com/gb/jfxww/xlbk/shfzb/node47070/
Freq: Daily
Editor in Chief: Lemin Jin
Editorial Profile: Shanghai Law News is a daily newspaper focusing on legal news in Shanghai region.
Language (s): Chinese
DAILY NEWSPAPER

Shanghai Morning Post
Owner: Jiefang Daily Press Group
Editorial: Jiefang Daily Press Group, 300 Hankou Road, Shanghai 200001.
T: 86 216 3521111 **W:** http://www.jfdaily.com
Freq: Daily Not Audited
Editor: Xijing Cao; **Editor in Chief:** Liu Sha
Editorial Profile: A daily newspaper covering mainly news and finance. It has pages for finance news, investment, securities, Shanghai news, national news and international news. It also has pages on sports, culture society and entertainment news. "Shanghai Morning Post" as the Jiefang Daily Group sponsored a new class of comprehensive city daily, open 64 version is 4 now, day circulation of 700,000 copies, the greatest influence in Shanghai, the largest circulation, the highest volume integrated urban Post. Reports related to current affairs, economy, culture, sports and local, international field of more than a dozen, a profound impact on two million Shanghai faithful readers.
Language (s): Chinese
DAILY NEWSPAPER

Shanghai Overseas Chinese News
Editorial: Shanghai Overseas Chinese News, 3/F, 847 Yan'an Zhonglu, Changlelu, Shanghai 200040. **T:** 86 2162891010
W: http://www.yesqiaobao.com
Freq: Weekly; **Circ:** 100003 Not Audited
Editor: Feiyu Huang; **Editor in Chief:** Ronglin Xie
Editorial Profile: Shanghai Overseas Chinese News is a national publication which focuses on the development of Shanghai in business, finance, economics and society and covers the stories and information for oversea Chinese.
Language (s): Chinese
NEWSPAPER

Shanghai Overseas Information
Editorial: Shanghai Far East Publishers, 357 Xianxialu, Shanghai 200336
E: shyb2000@online.sh.cn
Freq: Weekly; **Circ:** 100003 Not Audited
Editor: Yuan Sheng
Editorial Profile: publishes and translates news and articles about politics and current national and international affairs outside Shanghai.
Language (s): Chinese
NEWSPAPER

Shanghai Science and Technology Post
Editorial: Shanghai Science and Technology Post, 57 Nanchang Road, Shanghai 200020.
T: 86 21 63866890 **E:** newskjb@vip.sina.com
W: http://www.shkp.org.cn
Freq: 2 Times/Week; **Circ:** 100003 Not Audited
Editor in Chief: Libo Li
Editorial Profile: focuses on the information and market development of science and technology in Shanghai.
Language (s): Chinese
NEWSPAPER

Shanghai Securities News
Editorial: Shanghai Stock Information Service Corp, 1100 Yanggao Nanlu, Pudong, Shanghai 200127. **T:** 86 4008200277
W: http://www.cnstock.com/
Freq: 2 Times/Week; **Circ:** 400000 Not Audited
Editor in Chief: Wen Gwan; **Editor:** Yi Zhou
Editorial Profile: Focuses on the news and information of the securities market in China.
Language (s): Chinese
NEWSPAPER

Shanghai Times
Editorial: Jiefang Daily Press Group, 300 Hankou Road, Shanghai 200001.
T: 86 2163521111 **E:** shtimes@jfdaily.com
W: http://www.jfdaily.com.cn
Freq: Weekly Not Audited
Editor in Chief: Jinjiang Xu
Editorial Profile: focuses on the issues of culture and lifestyle, life in Shanghai, and other entertainment information.
Language (s): Chinese
NEWSPAPER

Shantou Te Qu Wan Bao
Editorial: Shantou Jingji Teque Baoshe, 99 Jinxin Road, Shantou 515041.
T: 86 754 8826-0688 **E:** sten@stnews.com.cn
W: http://www.stnews.com.cn
Freq: Daily Not Audited
Editor in Chief: Qian Cai
Editorial Profile: Covers news in Shantou region.
Language (s): Chinese
DAILY NEWSPAPER

Shanxi Economic Daily
Editorial: Shanxi Economic Daily, 26 Shuixiguanjie, Taoyuan Beilu, Taiyuan 30002.
T: 86 351 4660816 **E:** sxjjrb@yahoo.com.cn
W: http://www.daynews.com.cn/
Freq: Daily; **Circ:** 100001 Not Audited
Editor in Chief: Jinmin Li
Editorial Profile: Focuses on the economical and business issues in Shanxi and in China. "Shanxi Economic Daily News," founded on July 15, 1985, through 20 years of development and growth, from the original version of the four open four tabloid, become off the eighth edition of the Daily News, newspaper staff of several people from the initial development 120 more than the team. "Shanxi Economic Daily" has been revised twice, hit "a social influence economic events and economic figures, in-depth economic observation, insightful Economic Review, there is concern about the economic issues, valuable economic information" which News Category 6 products, reflected in its value, "the lesson of" embodied in the form of "readability" for "economic decision-makers, business managers, marketing and economic researchers," these four categories of target audience services; form reflected in the layout of its fresh, beautiful, generous style. After these two revision, further enhancing the social influence, 20 years, "Shanxi Economic Daily" to become the province's only economic class newspaper.
Language (s): Chinese
DAILY NEWSPAPER

Shenzhen Overseas Chinese News
Editorial: Shenzhen Overseas Chinese News, 8/F, 8 Hongbao Road, Luohu District, Shenzhen 518001. **T:** 86 755 28949558
E: qbbjb@163.com **W:** http://www.sz-qb.com
Freq: Daily
Editorial Profile: It covers local and national news.
Language (s): Chinese
DAILY NEWSPAPER

Shenzhen Special Zone Daily
Editorial: Shenzhen Special Zone Daily, 6008 Shennan Dadao, Shenzhen 518009.
T: 86 75583510009
W: http://sztqb.sznews.com
Freq: Daily; **Circ:** 440000 Not Audited
Editor in Chief: Liangjun Zhun
Editorial Profile: covers hotspots on political, financial and cultural issues in Shenzhen.
Language (s): Chinese
DAILY NEWSPAPER

Shenzhen Television News
Editorial: Shenzhen Television News, Guangdian Dasha, Yijinglu, Shenzhen 518021.
T: 86 75525160511 **E:** sztvdsb@126.com
W: http://www.sztv.com.cn
Freq: Weekly; **Circ:** 200003 Not Audited
Editor in Chief: Zhijiang Pan; **Editor:** Gui Wang
Editorial Profile: covers the entertainment news and program list of television stations in Shenzhen.
Language (s): Chinese
NEWSPAPER

Shenzhen Youth Daily
Editorial: 6008 Shennan Dadao, Shenzhen 518009. **T:** 86 755 83518395
Freq: Weekly
Editor in Chief: Hongjun Liu
Editorial Profile: covers the general interest of youth in Shenzhen region. It also focuses on family life education, popular science knowledge and other aspects related to youth interest.
Language (s): Chinese
NEWSPAPER

Soccer Fan
Editorial: Tianjin Daily Press Group, 873 Dagu Nanlu, Tianjin 300211. **T:** 86 2228202222
W: http://www.tianjinwe.com
Freq: 2 Times/Week; **Circ:** 50003 Not Audited
Editorial Profile: covers the latest soccer news and information in China and worldwide.
Language (s): Chinese
NEWSPAPER

Soccer News
Editorial: 97 Haizhuzhonglu, Guangzhou 510120. **T:** 86 20 81330003
W: http://www.goalchina.net
Freq: 2 Times/Week
Editor in Chief: Xiaoxin Liu
Editorial Profile: Covers both national and international news in soccer field.
Language (s): Chinese
NEWSPAPER

Soccer Winner
Editorial: 97 Haizhuzhonglu, Guangzhou 510120. **T:** 86 208 1330001
E: soccer-ggb@vip.sina.com
W: http://www.goalchina.net
Freq: 2 Times/Week; **Circ:** 1000003 Not Audited
Editor: Tao Chen; **Editor in Chief:** Xiaoxin Liu; **Editor:** Weihua Yin; **Editor:** Yuan Zhao
Editorial Profile: Soccer Winner is a national newspaper with information about sports lottery.
Language (s): Chinese
NEWSPAPER

South China City News
Editorial: South China City News, Xinwen Daxia, 30 Jinpanlu, Haikou 570216.
T: 86 89866810888
W: http://www.ngdsb.com.cn
Freq: Daily
Editor: Chunshan Feng; **Editor in Chief:** Jieyu Yin
Editorial Profile: South China City News is a regional publication which focuses on the news and entertainment in Hainan region.
Language (s): Chinese
DAILY NEWSPAPER

Southeast Business
Editorial: Ningbo Daily Press Group, 768 Lingqiaolu, Ningbo 315000.
T: 86 57487270000
W: http://dnsb.cnnb.com.cn
Freq: 2 Times/Week Not Audited
Editor: Zhiming Wu
Editorial Profile: covers financial and business news in southeastern part of China.
Language (s): Chinese
NEWSPAPER

South-East Morning News
Editorial: South-East Morning News, Quanzhou Wanbao Dasha, Citong Nanlu, Quanzhou, Fuzhou 350003.
T: 86 59 122505555 **E:** rexian@qzwb.com
W: http://www.dnzb.com.cn
Freq: Daily; **Circ:** 250003 Not Audited
Editorial Profile: South-East Morning News is the most popular newspaper in Fujian that mainly covers news on financial, political, cultural and social issues.
Language (s): Chinese
DAILY NEWSPAPER

Southern County
Editorial: Nanfang Daily Press Group, 289 Guangzhou Dadaozhong, Guangzhou 510601.
T: 86 208 7366121 **E:** nfncb@163.com
W: http://www.nfncb.cn/
Freq: 2 Times/Week
Editor in Chief: Yong Chen
Editorial Profile: It covers agricultural news in the southern area in China.
Language (s): Chinese
NEWSPAPER

Southern Metropolis News
Editorial: Southern Metropolis News, Nanfang Daily Press Group, 6008 Shennan Dadao, Futianqu, Guangzhou 518009.
T: 86 40 08866166
W: http://www.nanfangdaily.com.cn
Freq: Daily
Editor in Chief: Ke Cao
Editorial Profile: Covers political, social and entertainment news.
Language (s): Chinese
DAILY NEWSPAPER

Sports Review
Editorial: Hubei Daily Press Group, 65 Huanglilu, Wuchang, Wuhan 430077.
T: 86 2786794446 **W:** http://tyzb.cnhubei.com
Freq: 2 Times/Week; **Circ:** 100003 Not Audited
Editorial Profile: covers the national sporting events and issues in Hubei province and in China.
Language (s): Chinese
NEWSPAPER

Stage & Television Screen
Editorial: 8th Floor, Xinwen Zhongxin, 43 Guangyulu, Guangzhou 510121.
T: 86 2081883088 3197
W: http://wtyym.dayoo.com
Freq: Weekly
Editor in Chief: Jiangtao Tan
Editorial Profile: covers news and information of the entertainment industry in southern regions of China.
Language (s): Chinese
NEWSPAPER

Strait News
Editorial: Strait News, 1st Floor Fujian Ribao Daxia, 84 Hualinlu, Fuzhou 350003.
T: 86 0591 5911968111
W: http://www.nhaidu.com
Freq: Daily; **Circ:** 750000 Not Audited
Editor in Chief: Dejian Sun
Editorial Profile: focuses on the news from Fujian and Taiwan provinces, covering entertainment, business and finance, lifestyle and society news.
Language (s): Chinese
DAILY NEWSPAPER

Style Weekly
Editorial: Liaoning Daily Press Group, 339 Zhongshan Road, Shenyang 110014.
T: 86 2462254218 **E:** ssshdb@126.com
W: http://newspaper.lndaily.com.cn/styleweekly/
Freq: Weekly
Editor in Chief: Zhengrong Li
Editorial Profile: Provides the latest information and issues on lifestyle, fashions and trends in China and abroad.
Language (s): Chinese
NEWSPAPER

Sunshine Daily
Editorial: Sunshine Daily, 6 Beiguanzhengjie, Xi'an 710014. **T:** 86 2986232639
W: http://www.yangguangbao.com
Freq: 2 Times/Week; **Circ:** 90002 Not Audited
Editorial Profile: Covers news in Xi'an and other neighbouring regions.
Language (s): Chinese
NEWSPAPER

Taiyuan Evening News
Editorial: 15F Xinwen Dasha, 78 Xinjianlu, Taiyuan 30002. **T:** 86 3518222191
W: http://www.tynews.com.cn
Freq: Daily; **Circ:** 150003 Not Audited
Editor in Chief: Qingfu Wang
Editorial Profile: covers news and financial news in Taiyuan region.
Language (s): Chinese
DAILY NEWSPAPER

Tianfu Morning Post
Editorial: Tianfu Morning Post, 70 Erduan, Hongxinglu, Chengdu 610012.
T: 86 28 86969285 **E:** tfzb@scol.com.cn
W: http://morning.scol.com.cn
Freq: Daily; **Circ:** 230003 Not Audited
Editor: Wei Zhang
Editorial Profile: provides news from Sichuan and China.
Language (s): Chinese
DAILY NEWSPAPER

Tianjin Broadcasting and Television News
Editorial: Tianjin Broadcasting and Television News, 143 Weijinlu, Tianjin 300070.
T: 86 2223601012 **E:** tjgbb@sina.com
Freq: Weekly; **Circ:** 350003 Not Audited
Editor: Yan Wang; **Editor in Chief:** Weijing xu; **Editor:** Peng Zhang
Editorial Profile: Tianjin Broadcasting and Television News focus mainly on the program list and news about the TV Stations and broadcasting stations. It also cover national events and interviews with idols and celebrities.
Language (s): Chinese
NEWSPAPER

Tiantian Business News
Owner: Shaoxing Daily Press Group
Editorial: Shaoxing Daily Press Group, 558 Yan'an Donglu, Chengdong Xinqu, Shaoxing 312000. **T:** 86 57588652000 **E:** sbtt@263.net
W: http://www.shaoxing.com.cn
Freq: Daily
Editorial Profile: Tiantian Business News is a local daily newspaper covering business and finance news in Zhejiang province.
Language (s): Chinese
DAILY NEWSPAPER

Tibet Daily
Editorial: Tibet Daily, 36 Duosenge Road, Lasa 850000. **T:** 86 8916323699
E: xzrbyaowen@163.com
W: http://www.chinatibetnews.com
Freq: Daily; **Circ:** 50001 Not Audited
Editor in Chief: Xiaolin Meng
Editorial Profile: covers news in Tibet region and in other areas in China.
Language (s): Chinese
DAILY NEWSPAPER

Time Weekly
Editorial: Time Weekly, 4/F, Yuanyang Mingzhu Dasha Dongta, 19 Huali Road, Zhujiang Xincheng, Guangzhou 510623.
T: 86 2037591420
W: http://www.time-weekly.com
Freq: Weekly
Editor: Xiaolin Wang; **Editor:** Yong Xie
Editorial Profile: provides news and latest issues on current affairs and economy in China.
Language (s): Chinese
NEWSPAPER

Titan Sports
Owner: Titan Media
Editorial: Titan Media, Xiduan, Block 22 Beili Xiqu, Donghuashi, Chongwenqu, Beijing 100062. **T:** 86 51005876 **E:** 24@titan24.com
W: http://www.titansports.cn
Freq: 2 Times/Week; **Circ:** 160000 Not Audited
Editorial Profile: Titan Sports is a national newspaper mainly reports the latest news on different sports and different competitions both in China and overseas.
Language (s): Chinese
NEWSPAPER

Today Fortune
Editorial: Room 336 Jibao Dasha, 6426 Ziyou Dalu, Changchun 130033.
T: 86 431886000058 **E:** jrcfb@126.com
Freq: 2 Times/Week
Editor in Chief: Dongsheng Li
Editorial Profile: covers information and news of finance and money management targeting the general public.
Language (s): Chinese
NEWSPAPER

Today Morning Express
Editorial: Zhejiang Daily Press Group, 178 Tiyuchanglu, Hangzhou 310039.
T: 86 57 188818881 **E:** jrzb@zjnews.com.cn
W: http://jrzb.zjol.com.cn
Freq: Daily; **Circ:** 300003 Not Audited
Editorial Profile: reports news on finance, economy, culture and lifestyle.
Language (s): Chinese
DAILY NEWSPAPER

Today Women's News
Editorial: Today Women's News, 1 Xiaoshan Beilu, Changsha 410011. **T:** 86 7312333618
E: fw@fengone.com
W: http://www.fengone.com
Freq: 2 Times/Week; **Circ:** 300002 Not Audited
Editor: Xian Peng; **Editor in Chief:** Fuhu Wang
Editorial Profile: focuses on the women's interests and lifestyle. It also covers gender and sexuality studies in China.
Language (s): Chinese
NEWSPAPER

Travel Times
Editorial: Travel Times, 101 Puhuitang Road, Xuhuiqu, Shanghai 200030. **T:** 86 2164642513
W: http://www.itraveltimes.com
Freq: Weekly Not Audited
Editor: Zhen Chen
Editorial Profile: releases the latest travel information and news in China. It also covers news on transportation.
Language (s): Chinese
NEWSPAPER

TV & Life Weekly
Editorial: TV & Life Weekly, 4th Floor, Guangzhou Dianshitai Zonghe Dalou, 233 Huanshi Zhonglu, Guangzhou 510010.
T: 86 2086191481 **E:** shengping@gztv.com
W: http://shengping.gztv.com
Freq: Weekly
Editor in Chief: Meijin Niu
Editorial Profile: Covers entertainment news in Southern regions in China. It also includes TV program listings.
Language (s): Chinese
NEWSPAPER

Urumqi Evening News
Editorial: Urumqi Evening News, 20 Qingnianlu, Tianshanqu, Urumqi (wulumuqi) 830002. **T:** 86 99 12628292
E: wlmqzxxw@126.com
W: http://www.wlmqwb.com
Freq: Daily; **Circ:** 140003 Not Audited
Editor in Chief: Weijiang Li
Editorial Profile: provides the regional news of Urumqi.
Language (s): Chinese
DAILY NEWSPAPER

USA Today (China)
Editorial: USA Today - Beijing Bureau, Bldg 10, Apartment 101, Qijiayuan, Diplomatic Apartment, 9 Jianguomenwai Street, Beijing 100060. **T:** 86 1065327729
Bureau Chief: Calum MacLeod
DAILY NEWSPAPER

The Wall Street Journal (China)
Editorial: K. Wah Centre, Ste 2502, 1010 Huaihai Zhong Rd, Shanghai 200071.
T: 86 21 6120-1200
Bureau Chief: Shen Hong
DAILY NEWSPAPER

The Wall Street Journal China
Editorial: 18 Chaoyangmen Wai St, Beijing.
T: 86 10 6588-5848
China Editor: Andrew Browne; **Bureau Chief:** Charles Hutzler; **China News Editor:** Carlos Tejada
DAILY NEWSPAPER

The Washington Post (China)
Editorial: 07/02/2024, Jianwai Diplomatic Compound, Beijing 100600. **T:** 86 1065323464
E: foreign@washpost.com
DAILY NEWSPAPER

The Weekend
Editorial: Nanjing Daily Press Group, 223 Longpan Zhonglu, Nanjing 210002.
T: 86 2584686739 **E:** njzmb@126.com
W: http://www.njrb.com.cn/zm
Freq: Weekly
Editor: Weidong Guan
Editorial Profile: The Weekend is a local publication which covers the news and information of culture and lifestyle in Nanjing region and in China.
Language (s): Chinese
NEWSPAPER

Weekly Guide to Far Eastern Finance and Trade
Editorial: Heilongjiang University, 74 Xuefulu, Nangangqu, Harbin (ha'erbin) 150080.
T: 86 45186608106 **E:** yddb@hlju.edu.cn
Freq: Weekly; **Circ:** 200001 Not Audited
Editor in Chief: Huixin Jin
Editorial Profile: Covering trade news and economic situation of China and Russia, as well as related finance, industry, management, trade and news issues.
Language (s): Chinese
NEWSPAPER

Wenhuibao
Editorial: Wenhui-xinmin United Press Group, 755 Weihailu, Shanghai 200041.
T: 86 2152921234 **E:** whb@wxjt.com.cn
W: http://www.news365.com.cn
Freq: Daily
Editor in Chief: Jiong Xu
Editorial Profile: Wenhuibao is a national newspaper which covers news in China and overseas.
Language (s): Chinese
DAILY NEWSPAPER

Wenzhou Economic Daily
Editorial: Wenzhou Daily Press Group, 202 Liminxilu, Wenzhou 325003.
T: 86 577 88817110 **E:** news@wzsee.com
W: http://www.wzsee.com
Freq: Daily; **Circ:** 300001 Not Audited
Editor in Chief: Kesheng Jin
Editorial Profile: Covers the latest economic news
Language (s): Chinese
DAILY NEWSPAPER

Western Liaoning Business News
Editorial: Jinzhou Daily Press Group, 2 Shifu Donglu, Jinzhou 121003. **T:** 86 4163706592
E: ksb@sina.com **W:** http://www.lm3d.com
Freq: Daily
Editor: Ting Chun Guo
Editorial Profile: covers the business and financial news in the western part of Liaoning province in China.
Language (s): Chinese
DAILY NEWSPAPER

Women's News Today
Editorial: Shaanxi Daily Group, Room 903, Unit 2, Block A, Jinqiao Guoji, 50 Keji Road, Xi'an 710075. **T:** 86 298114600
W: http://www.mladies.com.cn
Freq: Weekly; **Circ:** 100003 Not Audited
Editor: Yongqian Wu
Editorial Profile: Women's News Today is a popular fashion newspaper in Xi'an that mainly covers lifestyle, fashion, female healthcare and society issues.
Language (s): Chinese
NEWSPAPER

Worker's Daily
Editorial: Worker's Daily, 61 Andelujia, Dongcheng District, Beijing 100718.
T: 86 10 84151572 **E:** news@workercn.cn
W: http://txzx.workercn.cn
Freq: Daily; **Circ:** 500003 Not Audited
Editor in Chief: Shi Shusi; **Editor:** Mingjiang Zhang
Editorial Profile: It covers major news, labor market and governmental policies.
Language (s): Chinese
DAILY NEWSPAPER

Wuhan Broadcasting Television Weekly
Editorial: Wuhan Broadcasting Television Weekly, 229 Xiangganglu, Hankou, Wuhan 430015. **T:** 86 27 85711471
E: chanyb@whtv.com.cn
Freq: Weekly
Editor in Chief: Ping
Editorial Profile: covers news and information about TV and radio programmes, with entertainment news inserted.
Language (s): Chinese
NEWSPAPER

Wuhan Morning Post
Editorial: Changjiang Daily Press Group, Teyihao Changjiang Ribaolu, Wuhan 430022.
T: 86 27 85771888 8802
W: http://www.cnhan.com
Freq: Daily; **Circ:** 800003 Not Audited
Editorial Profile: covers the local and regional news in Wuhan region.
Language (s): Chinese
DAILY NEWSPAPER

Wuxi Daily
Editorial: Wuxi Daily, Xinwen Daxia, 1 Xueqian Donglu, Wuxi 214002. **T:** 86 51082757557
E: wxrb@wxrb.com **W:** http://www.wxrb.com
Freq: Daily
Editor in Chief: Chuan Liu
Editorial Profile: Wuxi Daily is a newspaper covers the local and regional news in Wuxi region.
Language (s): Chinese
DAILY NEWSPAPER

Xiamen Business News
Editorial: Xiamen Daily Press, 12th Floor, Number 122, Lvninglu, Xiamen 361009.
T: 86 5928080000 **E:** 8080000@sunnews.com
W: http://www.xmnn.cn
Freq: Daily Not Audited
Editor in Chief: Xingjun Pan
Editorial Profile: Economic newspaper which targets people living in Xiamen.
Language (s): Chinese
DAILY NEWSPAPER

The xiao xue sheng shi jie
Editorial: Jiaoxue Yuekanshe, 140 Wensanlu, Hangzhou 310012. **T:** 86 57188213112
E: xxssjb@xxssj.com
W: http://www.jxyk.com/oldweb/xxssjb.htm
Freq: Weekly; **Circ:** 760003 Not Audited
Editor in Chief: Jingyao Dong
Editorial Profile: The World of Primary Student is a local publication which provides the educational and learning information and knowledge for primary school students.
Language (s): Chinese
NEWSPAPER

Xinhua Daily Telegraph
Editorial: Xinhua Daily Telegraph, 57 Xidajie, Xuanwumen, Xicheng District, Beijing 100803.
T: 86 106 3072070 **E:** xhmrdx@163.com
W: http://www.xinhuanet.com/mrdx
Freq: Daily
Editorial Profile: Reports news from Xinhua News Agency.
Language (s): Chinese
DAILY NEWSPAPER

Xinjiang Economic News
Editorial: Xinjiang Economic News, Tianji Building, No. 90, Jiefangbei Lu, Urumqi (wulumuqi) 830002. **T:** 86 9912332215
E: xwmt119@163.com
W: http://epaper.xjjb.com
Freq: Daily; **Circ:** 150003 Not Audited
Editor in Chief: Jishang Su
Editorial Profile: It focuses on the economic events and financial news in Xinjiang region.
Language (s): Chinese

DAILY NEWSPAPER

Xinjiang Law News
Editorial: Xinjiang Law News, 6 Wenhuaxiang, Jiefang Beilu, Urumqi (wulumuqi) 830002.
T: 86 9912826027 **E:** xjfzb@xjdaily.com
W: http://www.xjfzb.com/xjfzbindex.asp
Freq: 2 Times/Week; **Circ:** 50001 Not Audited
Editor in Chief: Yuzhi Cai
Editorial Profile: Covers law news and law related issues in Xinjiang region.
Language (s): Chinese
NEWSPAPER

Xinmin Evening News
Editorial: Wenhui - Xinmin United Press Group, 755 Weihailu, Shanghai 200041.
T: 86 21 52921234 **E:** xmywn@wxjt.com.cn
W: http://www.xmwb.com.cn
Freq: Daily; **Circ:** 1000000 Not Audited
Editor: Yinghuan Wu
Editorial Profile: Covers the local and national news in Shanghai and China.
Language (s): Chinese
DAILY NEWSPAPER

Y Weekend
Owner: Y Weekend Publishing
Editorial: Y Weekend Publishing, 12/F, Jintai Guoyi Dasha, 103 Chaoyang Beilu, Chaoyang District, Beijing 100123. **T:** 86 1085523009
E: zhangzhuo@yweekend.com
W: http://www.yweekend.com/
Freq: Weekly; **Circ:** 150002 Not Audited
Editor: Zhuo Zhang
Editorial Profile: It covers lifestyle, fashion, entertainment and other youth interested issues.
Language (s): Chinese
NEWSPAPER

Yanbian Morning Post
Editorial: Yanbian Morning Post, 13A Xingrongshangwu, Yanji 133000.
T: 86 4332900108 **E:** ybnews@126.com
W: http://www.ybnews.cn
Freq: Daily
Editor in Chief: Dunliang Lu
Editorial Profile: Covers economic and business developments in Northeast Asia and also focuses on social affairs in the area.
Language (s): Chinese
DAILY NEWSPAPER

Yangtse Evening Post
Editorial: Yangtse Evening Post, 48th Floor, Xinhua Dasha, 55 Zhongshanlu, Nanjing 210005. **T:** 86 25 96096 16096
E: ywb@yangtse.com
W: http://www.yangtse.com
Freq: Daily; **Circ:** 2000000 Not Audited
Editor: Jun Li
Editorial Profile: Covers news in Jiangsu region.
Language (s): Chinese
DAILY NEWSPAPER

Yangtze River
Editorial: People's Changjiang News, 1863 Jiefang Dadao, Hankou, Wuhan 430010.
T: 86 2782926362 **E:** rmcjzz@sina.com
W: http://www.cjw.com.cn
Freq: Weekly
Editor in Chief: Shanzhong Wei
Editorial Profile: mainly covers news and latest research development of Changjiang river.
Language (s): Chinese
NEWSPAPER

Yangzhou Evening News
Editorial: Yangzhou Daily Group, Xinwen Dalou, Xiqu, Wenhui Donglu, Yangzhou 225009. **T:** 86 51485881322
W: http://www.yzwb.com
Freq: Daily; **Circ:** 150001 Not Audited
Editor: Gang Zhao
Editorial Profile: Focuses on the local and regional news in Yangzhou.
Language (s): Chinese
DAILY NEWSPAPER

Yantai Evening News
Editorial: Yantai Daily Media Group, 54 Bei Dajie, Yantai 264001. **T:** 86 53596110
E: shm535@126.com
W: http://www.shm.com.cn
Freq: Daily; **Circ:** 100002 Not Audited
Editorial Profile: Provides local and regional news.
Language (s): Chinese
DAILY NEWSPAPER

Yanzhao Metropolis Daily
Editorial: Hebei Daily News Group, 86 Yuhuadonglu, Shijiazhuang 50013.
T: 86 31188631263
W: http://www.yzdsb.com.cn
Freq: Daily; **Circ:** 1000000
Editor in Chief: Bingxiang Li
Editorial Profile: Covers news in Shijiazhuang.
Language (s): Chinese
DAILY NEWSPAPER

Yiwu Business
Owner: Yiwu Business Press
Editorial: Yiwu Business Press, 369 Jiangdongzhonglu, Yiwu, Jinhua 322000.
T: 86 57985381020 **W:** http://www.ywnews.cn/
Freq: 2 Times/Week; **Circ:** 70003 Not Audited
Editorial Profile: It covers the latest business information and market status in Yiwu region.
Language (s): Chinese
NEWSPAPER

Youth Calligraphy News
Editorial: Qingshaonian Shufa Baoshe, 105 Zhongshan Street, Jiamusi 154002.
T: 86 454 8225419
Freq: Weekly; **Circ:** 100001 Not Audited
Editor in Chief: Changgui He
Editorial Profile: It provides information on Chinese calligraphy as well as features calligraphic works.
Language (s): Chinese
NEWSPAPER

Youth Real Time News
Editorial: China Youth Press, 2 Haiyuncang, Dongzhimennei, Beijing 100702.
T: 86 10 64098920 **W:** http://qnsx.cyol.com
Freq: Weekly; **Circ:** 220003 Not Audited
Editorial Profile: Mainly distributed in the high speed train in China, covering the news about the railway construction and development in China and current social, economic and cultural affairs.
Language (s): Chinese
NEWSPAPER

Youth Times
Editorial: Youth Times, 69 Zhonghe Beilu, Hangzhou 310003. **T:** 86 57185804800
E: qnsb@vip.sina.com
W: http://www.qnsb.com
Freq: Daily; **Circ:** 420001 Not Audited
Editor in Chief: Feng Zhang
Editorial Profile: focuses on the news and information about Youth in China including education, lifestyle and student life.
Language (s): Chinese
DAILY NEWSPAPER

Yulin Daily
Editorial: Yulin Daily, 6 Minzhu Zhonglu, Yulin 537000. **T:** 86 7752820239
W: http://www.gxylnews.com
Freq: Daily
Editor in Chief: Fuguang Li
Editorial Profile: Focuses on news of economic, politics, cultural and social issues.
Language (s): Chinese
DAILY NEWSPAPER

Yunnan Radio & Television Weekly
Editorial: Yunnan Television Station, 182 Renmin Xilu, Kunming 650031.
T: 86 8715385714 **W:** http://paper.yntv.cn
Freq: Weekly; **Circ:** 150003 Not Audited
Editor in Chief: Jianghong Xue
Editorial Profile: Covers the entertainment news and broadcasting information in Yunnan region.
Language (s): Chinese
NEWSPAPER

Yunnan Technology News
T: 86 8713126725 **E:** ynkjb2006@126.com
W: http://ynkjb.yunnan.cn
Freq: 2 Times/Week; **Circ:** 80003 Not Audited
Editor in Chief: Zhiwei Yue
Editorial Profile: Covers news on agricultural business and technological development and application in Yunnan region.
Language (s): Chinese
NEWSPAPER

Zhaotong Daily
Editorial: Zhaotong Daily, 84 Yingfenglu, Zhaoyang District, Zhaotong 657000.
T: 86 8702158272 **W:** http://www.ztnews.net
Freq: Daily
Editor in Chief: Zhenghong Tang
Editorial Profile: Focuses on news in China.
Language (s): Chinese
DAILY NEWSPAPER

Zhejiang Broadcasting Television News
Editorial: Zhejiang Broadcasting Television News, 247 Hushu Nanlu, Hangzhou 310005.
T: 86 57188391055 **E:** xiangdong@zctp.com
Freq: Weekly; **Circ:** 280003 Not Audited
Editorial Profile: Zhejiang Broadcasting Television News is a local publication which reports the program list and entertainment news in China.
Language (s): Chinese
NEWSPAPER

Zhengzhou Daily
Editorial: Zhengzhou Daily, Xinwen Dasha, 80 Longhai Xilu, Zhengzhou 450006.
T: 86 371677655555 **E:** zzrbxzxw@sina.com
W: http://www.zynews.com
Freq: Daily; **Circ:** 273001 Not Audited
Editor: Jinxia Wang
Editorial Profile: Focuses on political, economic, cultural and social issues.
Language (s): Chinese
DAILY NEWSPAPER

Zhuhai Daily
Editorial: Zhuhai Daily, 566 Yinhualu, Zhuhai 519002. **T:** 86 7562639888
E: cf@zhuhaidaily.com.cn
W: http://www.zhuhaidaily.com.cn
Freq: Daily
Editor: Hua Yang
Editorial Profile: Covers the news in Zhuhai.
Language (s): Chinese
DAILY NEWSPAPER

Zhujiang Evening News
Editorial: Zhuhaitequ Press, Jiuzhou Dadao, Zhuhai 519000. **T:** 86 75639333
W: http://www.zhnews.net
Freq: Daily
Editor: Hua Su
Editorial Profile: covers both local and international news and the latest issues related to Zhuhai.
Language (s): Chinese
DAILY NEWSPAPER

Zibo Evening News
Editorial: Zibo Daily Agency, 212 Liuquanlu, Zhangdian Distict, Zibo 255006.
T: 86 53 33182818 **W:** http://www.zbnews.net
Freq: Daily
Bureau Chief: Gongpin Li
Editorial Profile: Zibo Daily has 8 pages in folio, Page 1,2,3,4 are respectively for news in major, local, domestic, international and sports, while page 5,6,7,8 for columns of new life, social science and technology, law, economy and weekend, etc. With intensive information in various fields.
Language (s): Chinese
DAILY NEWSPAPER

NEWS SERVICE/SYNDICATE

Associated Press
Editorial: LG Towers East 2201, B-12 Jianguomenwai Ave., Beijing 100022.
T: 86 10 6568-0330
NEWS SERVICE/SYNDICATE

Biopharm Insight
Editorial: 11A New Shanghai International Tower, 360 Pudong Road S, Shanghai 200120.
T: 86 21 6886 3061
China Bureau Editor: Ying Huang
NEWS SERVICE/SYNDICATE

Bloomberg News
Editorial: 1 Jian Guo Men Wai Avenue, Unit 15, Beijing 100004. **T:** 86 106 5053339
E: chinanews@bloomberg.net
Editor: John Liu; **Editor:** Feifei Shen
NEWS SERVICE/SYNDICATE

Bloomberg News
Editorial: Unit 3404/3405 Bank of China Tower, 200 Ying Cheng Rd, Shanghai 200120.
T: 86 2161047000
Bureau Chief: Matthew Brooker
NEWS SERVICE/SYNDICATE

Dow Jones Newswires
Editorial: K-Wah Center Suite 2502, 1010 Huaihai Zhong Rd, Shanghai 200031.
T: 86 21 6120-1200
Bureau Chief: Shen Hong
NEWS SERVICE/SYNDICATE

Interfax (China) News Agency - Beijing Bureau
Editorial: Interfax News Agency - Beijing Bureau, RM 1206, Saite Dasha, Beijing 100022
W: http://www.interfax.cn
Freq: Continuous
Editor: Gennady Krivosheev
Editorial Profile: Interfax (China) News Agency - Beijing Bureau is a bureau of Interfax China in Shanghai which is mainly responsible for the business news in Beijing and in China.
Language (s): English
NEWS SERVICE/SYNDICATE

Interfax (China) News Agency - Shanghai Bureau
Editorial: Interfax News Agency - Shanghai Bureau, Room 1502, Xincheng Mansion, 167 Jiangning Road, Shanghai 200041.
T: 86 2162153700 **W:** http://www.interfax.cn
Freq: Continuous
Editor: David Lore
Editorial Profile: Covers news includes business news.
Language (s): English
NEWS SERVICE/SYNDICATE

McClatchy Newspapers
Owner: McClatchy Newspapers
Editorial: McClatchy Co., Beijing Bureau, Qijiayuan 8-14-3, Beijing 100600.
T: 86 1065323154
NEWS SERVICE/SYNDICATE

Reuters
Editorial: Chemsunny World Trade Center, Central Tower 2F, No 28 Fuxingmennei St, Xicheng District, Beijing 100031
NEWS SERVICE/SYNDICATE

Reuters
Editorial: 10/F Cityplaza 3, Taikoo Shing, Hong Kong. **T:** 852 29126688
E: hongkong.newsroom@reuters.com
Asia Financial Markets Editor: Eric Burroughs; **Bureau Chief:** Charlie Zhu
NEWS SERVICE/SYNDICATE

Reuters
Editorial: 3004 AZIA Centre, 1233 Lujiazui Huan Rd, Shanghai 200120.
T: 86 21 6104-1688
E: shanghai.newsroom@thomsonreuters.com
Bureau Chief: Jason Subler; **Bureau Chief:** Kazunori Takada
NEWS SERVICE/SYNDICATE

Xinhua Financial Network - Shanghai Bureau
Editorial: Xinhua Financial Network - Shanghai Bureau, 3905-3909 Tower 1 Grand Gateway, 10F ba-shi Century Mansion, 398 Huaihai Road (M), Shanghai 200020.
T: 86 22133315080 **W:** http://www.xfn.com
Freq: Daily
Editorial Profile: Covers financial news.
Language (s): Chinese
NEWS SERVICE/SYNDICATE

Xinhua News Agency
Editorial: Xinhua News Agency, 57 Xidajie, Xuanwumen, Beijing 100803.
T: 86 1063073741 **E:** xinhua381@hotmail.com
W: http://www.xinhuanet.com
Freq: Continuous
Editorial Profile: Serves as the official press agency of China, covering news and related topics in the country and beyond, major breaking news events, laws and regulations, appointments and removals of high-ranking officials.
Language (s): Chinese
NEWS SERVICE/SYNDICATE

BROADCASTING

RADIO STATIONS

China National Radio
Editorial: China National Radio, 2 Fuxingmenwai Dajie, Beijing 100866.
T: 86 1086093114 **E:** cn@cnr.cn
W: http://www.cnr.cn
Editorial Profile: Broadcasts information online.

China Radio International Chinese Channel
Editorial: China Radio International, Jia 16 Shijingshanlu, Beijing 100040.
T: 86 1068892571
W: http://www.chinabroadcast.cn
Editorial Profile: Covers the news and cultural issues.

CABLE

Bloomberg Television
Editorial: Bloomberg Television- Hong Kong, 27/F, Cheung Kong Centre, 2 Queen's Road, Central, Hong Kong SAR. **T:** 852 29 776600
W: http://www.bloomberg.com/tv

China Central Television (CCTV 1)
Editorial: China Central Television, 11 Fuxinglu, Beijing 100859. **T:** 86 10 68509505 **W:** http://www.cctv.com
Editorial Profile: China Central Television is the national television station of the People's Republic of China. CCTV 1 is the Variety Channel which provides news, and entertainment and culture programmes.

China Central Television (CCTV 10)
Editorial: China Central Television, 11 Fuxinglu, Beijing 100859. **T:** 86 10 68509505 **W:** http://www.cctv.com
Editorial Profile: China Central Television is a national television station of People's Republic of China. CCTV-10 (Science and Education Channel) aims to popularize modern science and technology, promote modern education theories and show cultural heritage in China and around the world.

CNN/Cable News Network
Editorial: 12-163 Jianwai Diplomatic Compound, Beijing 100600. **T:** 86 10 65326013 **W:** http://edition.cnn.com/asia

Reuters Television
Editorial: AZIA Center No. 1233 Unit 4, Floor 30, Lujiazui Ring Rd, Shanghai

---

COLOMBIA   Tel: 57
Standard Time: GMT -5
Continent: The Americas
Capital City: Bogotá

NEWSPAPERS & PUBLICATIONS

NEWSPAPERS

El Colombiano
Owner: El Colombiano S.A. & CIA. S.C.A.
Editorial: Carrera 48 #30 sur 119, Av. Las Vegas, Envigado, Medellín. **T:** 57 4 331-5252
E: redaccion@elcolombiano.com.co
W: http://www.elcolombiano.com
Freq: Daily; **Circ:** 85000 Not Audited
Editor: Carlos Mario Gómez; **Editor:** Martha Hoyos Franco; **Editor:** Francisco Alberto Jaramillo; **Editor:** Víctor León Zuluaga; **Editor:** Carlos Olimpo Restrepo; **Editor in Chief:** José Guillermo Palacio Patiño; **Editor:** Monica Quintero; **Editor:** Ramiro Velásquez Gómez
Editorial Profile: Colombian National newspaper published in Medellín covering Medellín and Antioquia.
Language (s): Spanish
DAILY NEWSPAPER

El Espacio
Owner: El Espacio J. Ardila C. S.A.
Editorial: Carrera 69 #44-35 Avenida El Dorado, Bogota. **T:** 57 1 425-1570
E: corresponsales@elespacio.com.co
W: http://www.elespacio.com.co
Freq: Daily
Editor: Enrique Castañeda; **Editor:** Alejandro Monroy; **Editor:** Ricardo Rondón; **Editor in Chief:** Alberto Uribe Gómez
Editorial Profile: National newspaper.
Language (s): Spanish
DAILY NEWSPAPER

El Espectador
Editorial: Avenida El Dorado No. 69-76, Bogota. **T:** 57 1 423-2300
E: servicioalcliente@elespectador.com
W: http://www.elespectador.com
Freq: Daily; **Circ:** 80617
Editor: Olga Lucía Barona; **Editor in Chief:** Jorge Cardona; **Editor:** Hugo Garcia; **Editor in Chief:** Elbert Gutierrez; **Editor:** Luis Fernando Gutierrez; **Editor:** Angelica Lagos
Editorial Profile: News general interest.
Language (s): Spanish
DAILY NEWSPAPER

El Heraldo
Editorial: Calle 53 B #46-25, Barranquilla.
T: 57 5 3715000 **E:** elheraldo@metrotel.net.co
W: http://www.elheraldo.com.co
Freq: Daily; **Circ:** 46000 Not Audited
Editor: Rosario Borrero; **Editor:** José Granados; **Editor:** Martha Guarín; **Editor:** Alix López; **Editor:** Zoraida Noriega; **Editor:** Manuel Ortega
Editorial Profile: National newspaper covering mostly local and regional news, but also covers national and international news, politics, sports, and entertainment.
Language (s): Spanish

DAILY NEWSPAPER

La Libertad
Owner: Esper Editores
Editorial: Carrera 53 No. 55-166, Barranquilla (atlántico). **T:** 57 5 349 1175
E: lalibertad@lalibertad.com.co
W: http://www.lalibertad.com.co
Freq: Daily; **Circ:** 45000 Not Audited
Editor: Monica Bolaños; **Editor in Chief:** Luis Camacho; **Editor:** Javier de la Oz; **Editor:** Eduardo Esper; **Editor:** Wilder Molina
Editorial Profile: National Newspaper.
Language (s): Spanish
DAILY NEWSPAPER

El Mundo
Editorial: Calle 53 #74-50, Los Colores, Medellín. **T:** 57 4 2642800
E: redaccion@elmundo.com
W: http://www.elmundo.com
Freq: Weekly; **Circ:** 25000 Not Audited
Publisher: Irene Gaviria Correa; **Editor:** Patricia Giraldo; **Editor:** Carolina Mejía; **Editor:** José Ignacio Mejía; **Editor:** Elkin Pumarejo Daza; **Editor:** Javier Ramírez Uribe; **Editor:** Carmen Vasquez Gomez
Editorial Profile: Covers national news of Colombia.
Language (s): Spanish
NEWSPAPER

La Opinión
Editorial: Avenida 4 #16-12, Cúcuta.
T: 57 75829999
E: jefederedaccion@laopinion.com.co
W: http://www.laopinion.com.co
Freq: Daily
Editor: Celmira Figueroa; **Editor:** Pedro Jauregui; **Editor in Chief:** Angel Romero; **Editor:** Omar Romero
Editorial Profile: Newspaper General interest.
Language (s): Spanish
DAILY NEWSPAPER

El País
Editorial: Carrera 2da #24-46 Barrio San Nicolás, Cali. **T:** 57 2 898-7000
E: redesociales@elpais.com.co
W: http://www.elpais.com.co/elpais/
Freq: Daily; **Circ:** 95000
Editor: Judith GOmez; **Editor in Chief:** Paola Gomez; **Editor:** Paola Guevara
Editorial Profile: Newspaper general news and interest.
Language (s): Spanish
DAILY NEWSPAPER

El Tiempo
Owner: Casa Editorial El Tiempo
Editorial: Avenida El Dorado #59-70, Bogota.
T: 57 1 294-0100
W: http://www.eltiempo.com
Freq: Daily Not Audited
Editor in Chief: Ernesto Cortés; **Editor:** Adriana Garzón; **Editor:** Julio César Guzman; **Editor:** Liliana Martinez Polo; **Editor:** Gabriel Meluk; **Editor:** Andrés Mompotes; **Graphics Editor:** Beiman Pinilla; **Editor:** Eduard Soto Guerrero
Editorial Profile: National Newspaper.
Language (s): Spanish
DAILY NEWSPAPER

NEWS SERVICE/SYNDICATE

Agencia EFE Colombia
Editorial: Calle 67 No 735 Torre C, Of. 301, Santa Fe De Bogotá. **T:** 57 13214855
E: efecol@efebogota.com.co
W: http://www.efe.es
Editor: Jose Guillermo Herrera; **Editor:** Ana Rosa Mengotti
Editorial Profile: News wire Agency.
Language (s): Spanish
NEWS SERVICE/SYNDICATE

Associated Press
Editorial: Transveral 21 96-17, Bogota 93643.
T: 57 1 602-1414
Bureau Chief: Joshua Goodman; **News Editor:** Camilo Hernandez
NEWS SERVICE/SYNDICATE

Bloomberg News
Editorial: Carrera 7 Numero 71-21, Torre B, Oficina 502, Bogota 801. **T:** 57 13137640
Bureau Chief: Matthew Bristow
NEWS SERVICE/SYNDICATE

Dow Jones Newswires
Editorial: Carrera 14 No 94-44, Torre B, Piso 8, Bogota. **T:** 57 1 610-7044
E: colombia@dowjones.com
NEWS SERVICE/SYNDICATE

Reuters
Editorial: Calle 94-A, No 13-34 Piso 4, Bogota. **T:** 57 16344090
Bureau Chief: Helen Murphy
NEWS SERVICE/SYNDICATE

BROADCASTING

RADIO STATIONS

Radio Guatapurí
Editorial: Calle 17 #15-67, Valledupar.
T: 57 55713872 **E:** radioguatapuri@gmail.com
W: http://www.radioguatapuri.com
Editorial Profile: Tramsmits daily news. The programming includes politic, economy, science and technology, health and cultural topics. Plays Vallenatos, Boleros, and Romantic music through the frequency 740 AM.

TELEVISION STATIONS

Canal RCN
Editorial: Avenida de Las Américas #65-82, Bogota. **T:** 57 1 4269393
E: quienessomos@canalrcn.com
W: http://www.canalrcn.com
Editorial Profile: RCN broadcasts a variety of programming including daily news, sports, and soap operas.

Caracol Televisión
Editorial: Calle 103 #69 B-43, Bogota.
T: 57 16430430 **E:** latino@caracoltv.com.co
W: http://www.canalcaracol.com
Editorial Profile: TV station.

Telecafé
Editorial: Carrera 19 A #43-02, Manizales.
T: 57 68727100 **E:** telecafenoticias@telecafe.tv
W: http://www.telecafe.tv
Editorial Profile: This TV channel airs three news programs that are independently produced. These other programs are UN Noticias, TVA Noticias and Noticias 1A.

TELEVISION NETWORKS

Associated Press Television News
Editorial: Transversal 21 No 96-17, Bogota 571. **T:** 57 16001984 **W:** http://www.aptn.com
Editorial Profile: Associated Press Television News, APTV, is the international division of the American Press, AP. AP delivers breaking global news, sports, entertainment, technology and human video content to broadcasters through the APTV service.

Canal Caracol
Editorial: Calle 103 No. 69B-43, Bogota.
T: 57 1 643 0430 **W:** http://www.caracoltv.com
Editorial Profile: National TV network broadcasting news, sports, cultural and entertainment programs.

COMOROS   Tel: 269
Standard Time: GMT +3
Continent: Africa
Capital City: Moroni

NEWSPAPERS & PUBLICATIONS

NEWSPAPERS

Al Watwan
Editorial: BP 984, Moroni. **T:** 269 773 44 48
E: direction@alwatwan.net
W: http://www.alwatwan.net
Freq: Weekly; **Circ:** 1000 Pub Statement
Rédacteur en Chef: Mohamed Soilihi Ahmed
Editorial Profile: National newspaper focussing on regional, national and international news, current affairs, society, economics, sport and education.
Language (s): Arabic
NEWSPAPER

CONGO   Tel: 242
Standard Time: GMT +1
Continent: Africa
Capital City: Brazzaville

NEWSPAPERS & PUBLICATIONS

NEWSPAPERS

Les Dépêches de Brazzaville
Owner: ADIAC - Agence d'Information d'Afrique Centrale
Editorial: Immeuble les Manguiers, 84, Avenue Paul Doumer, Brazzaville.
T: 242 05 528 59 50
E: redaction@brazzaville-adiac.com
W: http://www.brazzaville-adiac.com
Freq: Daily; **Circ:** 4000 Pub Statement
Editor: Gankama N'siah
Editorial Profile: Daily regional newspaper focusing on news, current affairs, politics, economics, society, arts, culture and sport.
Language (s): French
DAILY NEWSPAPER

COOK ISLANDS   Tel: 682
Standard Time: GMT -10.5
Continent: Oceania
Capital City: Avarua

NEWSPAPERS & PUBLICATIONS

NEWSPAPERS

Cook Islands Herald
Owner: Elijah Communications Ltd
Editorial: PO Box 126, Rarotonga, Cook Islands. **T:** 682 29 460
E: editor@bestread.co.ck
W: http://ciherald.co.ck **Circ:** 1300 Pub Statement
Editorial Profile: Provides current news articles and headlines from the islands.
Language (s): English
DAILY NEWSPAPER

Cook Islands Independent
Owner: Cook Islands Broadcasting & Newspaper Corporation
Editorial: PO Box 126, Rarotonga.
T: 682 29 460 **E:** bestread@ciherald.co.ck
W: http://www.ciherald.co.ck **Circ:** 900 Pub Statement
Editor: Trevor Pitt
Editorial Profile: Newspaper focusing on local political and social news.
Language (s): English
DAILY NEWSPAPER

Cook Islands News
Owner: Cook Islands News Ltd
Editorial: PO Box 15, Rarotonga, Cook Islands. **T:** 682 22999
E: editor@cookislandsnews.com
W: http://cookislandsnews.com **Circ:** 2500 Pub Statement
Editor: John Woods
Editorial Profile: Daily newspaper of the Cook Islands with week's stories, features and sports.
Language (s): English
DAILY NEWSPAPER

BROADCASTING

RADIO NETWORKS

KC FM - Radio Ikurangi
Owner: David Schmidt
Editorial: PO Box 521, Rarotonga, Cook Islands. **T:** 682 23203
E: mariana@oyster.net.ck

Radio Cook Islands
Owner: Elijah Communications Ltd
Editorial: PO Box 126, Rarotonga, Cook Islands. **T:** 682 29 460 **E:** jeanne@oyster.net.ck
W: http://radio.co.ck
Editorial Profile: Immediate, comprehensive and responsive source of news for the whole of the Cook Islands, overseas Cook Islanders and visitors interested in staying in touch with the country.

TELEVISION STATIONS

Cook Islands Television
Owner: Elijah Communications Ltd
Editorial: PO Box 126, Rarotonga, Cook Islands. **T:** 682 29 460 **E:** watchus@citv.co.ck **W:** http://cookislandstelevision.com

COSTA RICA   Tel: 506

Standard Time: GMT -6
Continent: The Americas
Capital City: San José

NEWSPAPERS & PUBLICATIONS

NEWSPAPERS

Al Día
Owner: Grupo Nación GNSA
Editorial: Llorente de Tibás, del cruce 400 metros este y 125 metros norte, Tibás (san José). **T:** 506 22474647
E: redaccion@aldia.co.cr
W: http://www.aldia.cr
Freq: Daily; **Circ:** 82000 Not Audited
Editor in Chief: Mónica Gómez; **Editor:** Alexander Ramírez; **Editor:** Gabriela Solano
Editorial Profile: Regioanl newspaper covering national and international news, politics, economics, finance, business, culture and sport.
Language (s): Spanish
DAILY NEWSPAPER

Diario Extra
Owner: Sociedad Periodistica Extra Ltda.
Editorial: Edificio de la Prensa Libre, Calle 4 Avenida 4, Aptdo 177 - 1009, San Jose.
T: 506 22236666
E: redaccion@diarioextra.com
W: http://www.diarioextra.com
Freq: Daily; **Circ:** 158100 Not Audited
Editor: Paola Hernandez
Editorial Profile: Newspaper focusing on national and international news, politics, business, culture and sport.
Language (s): Spanish
DAILY NEWSPAPER

La Nación
Owner: Grupo Nación GNSA
Editorial: 200 metros al Este del cruce de Llorente de Tibás, Aptdo 10138 - 1000, Llorente De Tibás (san José).
T: 506 22474747 **E:** envela@nacion.com
W: http://www.nacion.com
Freq: Daily; **Circ:** 120000 Not Audited
Editor: Mauricio Martínez; **News Editor:** Ronald Matute; **Editor:** Armando Mayorga; **Editor in Chief:** Larissa Minsky; **Editor:** Victor Hugo Murillo; **Editor:** Maricel Sequeira
Editorial Profile: Local newspaper covering national and international news, politics, economics, finance, business, culture and sport.
Language (s): Spanish
DAILY NEWSPAPER

La Prensa Libre
Owner: Sociedad Periodistica Extra Ltda.
Editorial: Edificio La Prensa Libre - Calle 4 Avenida 4, Aptdo 10121 - 1000, San Jose.
T: 506 2 2236666 **E:** plibre@prensalibre.co.cr
W: http://www.prensalibre.co.cr
Freq: Daily; **Circ:** 55000 Not Audited
Editor in Chief: Sandra Gonzalez; **Editor:** Maria Elena Jimenez; **Editor:** Roberto Portuguez
Editorial Profile: Newspaper covering national and international news, politics, economics, finance, business, culture and sport.
Language (s): Spanish
DAILY NEWSPAPER

La República
Owner: SRB CR Limitada
Editorial: Barrio Tournon, Contiguo al Hotel Radisson, Aptdo 2130 - 1000, San Jose.
T: 506 25223318 **E:** redaccion@larepublica.net
W: http://www.larepublica.net
Freq: Daily; **Circ:** 27300 Not Audited
Editor: Danny Canales; **Editor:** Damaris Ruíz; **Editor in Chief:** Luis Valverde
Editorial Profile: National newspaper covering national and international news, politics, economics, finance, business, culture and sport.
Language (s): Spanish
DAILY NEWSPAPER

COTE D'IVOIRE   Tel: 225

Standard Time: GMT
Continent: Africa
Capital City: Yamoussoukro

NEWSPAPERS & PUBLICATIONS

NEWSPAPERS

Fraternité Matin
Owner: SNPECI - Société Nouvelle de Presses et d'Edition de Côte d'Ivoire
T: 225 20 37 06 66 **E:** info@fratmat.info
W: http://www.fratmat.info
Freq: Daily; **Circ:** 25000 Pub Statement
Editor in Chief: Barthélemy Kouamé
Editorial Profile: Newspaper focusing on national and international news, economy, culture and sports.
Language (s): French
DAILY NEWSPAPER

L' Inter
T: 225 21 21 28 00 **E:** interpoci@yahoo.fr
Freq: Daily; **Circ:** 22000 Pub Statement
Editor in Chief: Jean-Marie Ahoussou
Editorial Profile: National daily newspaper covering news and current affairs including economics, politics, society, culture and sport.
Language (s): French
DAILY NEWSPAPER

Le Patriote
Owner: Mayama Editions et Production
T: 225 20 00 43 42 **E:** lepatriote@afnet.net
W: http://www.lepatriote.net
Freq: Daily; **Circ:** 15000 Pub Statement
Editor in Chief: Koré Emmanuel
Editorial Profile: Newspaper covering national and international news and current affairs including politics, economics, society, culture and sport.
Language (s): French
DAILY NEWSPAPER

Soir Info
T: 225 21 21 28 00
E: quotidiensoirinfo@yahoo.fr
Freq: Daily; **Circ:** 35000 Pub Statement
Editor in Chief: Kikié Nazaire
Editorial Profile: National daily newspaper covering news and current affairs including economics, politics, society, culture and sport.
Language (s): French
DAILY NEWSPAPER

NEWS SERVICE/SYNDICATE

Agence Ivoirienne de Presse
Owner: Agence Ivoirienne de Presse
T: 225 20 22 64 13 **E:** aip@aip.ci
W: http://www.aip.ci
Freq: Daily
Editor in Chief: Pascal Kouao
Editorial Profile: National press agency focussing on news and current affairs including society, economics, sports, politics, culture and media.
Language (s): French
NEWS SERVICE/SYNDICATE

BROADCASTING

TELEVISION STATIONS

Radiodiffusion Télévision Ivoirienne
Owner: Radiodiffusion Télévision Ivoirienne
T: 225 22 44 38 14 **E:** web@rti.ci
W: http://www.rti.ci
Editorial Profile: National broadcasting company regrouping the 2 main national TV stations (La Première & TV2), the 2 main national radio stations (Radio Nationale & Fréquence 2) and 2 cable TV stations (RTI Sport & RTI Music).

CROATIA   Tel: 385

Standard Time: GMT +1
Continent: Europe
Capital City: Zagreb

NEWSPAPERS & PUBLICATIONS

NEWSPAPERS

24 Sata
Owner: Tiskara Zagreb d.o.o.
Editorial: Radnicka cesta 210, Zagreb 10 000.
T: 385 1 60 69 500 **E:** redakcija@24sata.hr
W: http://www.24sata.hr
Freq: Daily; **Circ:** 110000 Not Audited
News Editor: Ivan Buca
Language (s): Serbo-Croat
DAILY NEWSPAPER

Jutarnji list
Owner: Europapress holding d.o.o.
Editorial: Koranska 2, Zagreb 10 000.
T: 385 1 61 03 100 **E:** jutarnji_list@eph.hr
W: http://www.jutarnji.hr
Freq: Daily; **Circ:** 115000 Pub Statement
Editor-in-Chief: Mladen Pleše; **Editor-in-Chief:** Viktor Vresnik
Language (s): Serbo-Croat
DAILY NEWSPAPER

Vecernji list
Owner: Vecernji list d.d.
Editorial: Oreškoviceva 6H/1, Zagreb 10 010.
T: 385 1 6300 605 **E:** vecernji@vecernji.hr
W: http://www.vecernji.hr
Freq: Daily
Editor: Gojko Drljaca; **Editor:** Zdravko Milinovic; **Editor-in-Chief:** Goran Ogurlic
Language (s): Croatian
DAILY NEWSPAPER

Zadarski list
Owner: RTD d.o.o.
Editorial: Grgura Mrganica 6, Zadar 23 000.
T: 385 23 212-988 **E:** redakcija@zadarskilist.hr
W: http://www.zadarskilist.hr
Freq: Daily; **Circ:** 7500 Pub Statement
Editor-in-Chief: Edvard Šprljan
Language (s): Serbo-Croat
DAILY NEWSPAPER

NEWS SERVICE/SYNDICATE

HINA - Croatian News Agency
Editorial: Marulicev trg. 16, Zagreb 10 000.
T: 385 1 48 08 660 **E:** hina@hina.hr
W: http://www.hina.hr
Editor-in-Chief: Serdo Obratov
Language (s): Serbo-Croat
NEWS SERVICE/SYNDICATE

CUBA   Tel: 53

Standard Time: GMT -5
Continent: The Americas
Capital City: Habana

NEWSPAPERS & PUBLICATIONS

NEWSPAPERS

Granma
Owner: Combinado Poligráfico Granma
Editorial: Av. General Suárez y Territorial, Plaza de la Revolución, Habana CP 10699.
T: 53 7 88 13 333 **E:** correo@granma.cip.cu
W: http://www.granma.cubaweb.cu
Freq: Daily; **Circ:** 500000 Not Audited
Editorial Profile: Official newspaper of the Central Committee of the communist party of Cuba.
Language (s): Spanish
DAILY NEWSPAPER

NEWS SERVICE/SYNDICATE

Agencía de Información Nacional
Editorial: Calle 23 no 358 esq.J. Vedado, Plaza de la Revolución, Habana CP 10400.
T: 53 7 83 25 541 **E:** editor@ain.cu
W: http://www.ain.cubaweb.cu
Editor in Chief: Carlos Barrueco
Language (s): Spanish
NEWS SERVICE/SYNDICATE

Associated Press
Editorial: Edificio Lonja del Comercio, Lamparilla 2, Piso 6, Local B, Havana.
T: 53 7 866-0370
Bureau Chief: Michael Weissenstein
NEWS SERVICE/SYNDICATE

Prensa Latina
Editorial: Calle 23 esq N. Vedado, Habana CP 10400. **T:** 53 78383496
E: inter@prensa-latina.cu
W: http://www.prensa-latina.cu
Editorial Profile: Covers national and international news.
Language (s): Spanish
NEWS SERVICE/SYNDICATE

Reuters
Editorial: Calle 21st #104 Apt 3, Vedado, Havana. **T:** 53 78333145
NEWS SERVICE/SYNDICATE

BROADCASTING

RADIO STATIONS

Radio Sancti Spíritus
Editorial: Circunvalación s/n, Olivos 1, Sancti Spíritus. **T:** 53 41328373
E: cip234@cip.enet.cu
W: http://www.radiosanctispiritus.cu
Editorial Profile: Broadcasts daily news, cultural and educational live shows.

RADIO NETWORKS

Radio Habana Cuba
Editorial: Infanta no 105 esq.a 25, Centro Habana, CP 6240, Habana. **T:** 53 7 87 76 533
E: radiohc@enet.cu **W:** http://www.radiohc.cu
Editorial Profile: Provides daily news. Plays current popular music, Salsa, and Ballads.

Radio Rebelde
Editorial: Edificio del ICRT, Calle 23 #258 e/ L y M, Vedado, Habana CP 10600.
T: 53 78313514
W: http://www.radiorebelde.com.cu
Editorial Profile: Provides daily news. Provides different type of music in Spanish and English.

Radio Reloj
Editorial: Calle 23 #258 e/ L y M, Vedado, Habana CP 10400. **T:** 53 78384226
W: http://www.radioreloj.cu/notiweb/
Editorial Profile: National radio providing 24 hours of general news. Covers Cuban and the world news.

CYPRUS   Tel: 357

Standard Time: GMT +2
Continent: Europe
Capital City: Nicosia

NEWSPAPERS & PUBLICATIONS

NEWSPAPERS

Alithia
Owner: Ekdotiki Etaireia Ltd
Editorial: P.O.Box 12669, 26A, Corner Pindaros and Androklis Str., 1512 Nicosia, Nicosia 2251. **T:** 357 22 76 30 40
E: news@alfamedia.press.cy
W: http://alithia.com.cy
Freq: Daily; **Circ:** 7000
Editor In Chief: Pambos Charalambous
Language (s): Greek
DAILY NEWSPAPER

Antilogos
Owner: Drositis Ekdotikes Ltd
Editorial: 24 Elia Papakyriakou, Dafne Building, 1st floor, Acropoli, Nicosia 2081.
T: 357 22 49 14 00
E: antilogos@cytanet.com.cy
Freq: Weekly; **Circ:** 6500 Pub Statement
Editor In Chief: Panikos Petsas
Language (s): Greek
NEWSPAPER

Cyprus Mail
Owner: Cyprus Mail Co Ltd
Editorial: 24 Vassilios Voulgaroktonos Street, Nicosia 1502. **T:** 357 22 81 85 85
E: editor@cyprus-mail.com
W: http://www.cyprus-mail.com

Freq: Daily; **Circ:** 8000 ABC-Audit Bureau of Circulations
Editor in Chief: Jean Kelly-Christou
Language (s): English
DAILY NEWSPAPER

Cyprus Observer
Owner: Akmay Consultancy LTD
Editorial: 45 Naci Talat Street, Kyrenia, Nicosia. **T:** 90 392 815 24 20
E: info@cyprusobserver.net
W: http://www.cyprusobserver.net
Freq: Weekly
Publisher: Can Ercakica; **Editor:** Tanya Tomko
Language (s): English
NEWSPAPER

Cyprus Today
Owner: Diger
Editorial: PO Box 831, Lefkosa, Kibris
E: cyprustoday@yahoo.com
Freq: Weekly; **Circ:** 5000 Pub Statement
Language (s): Turkish
NEWSPAPER

The Cyprus Weekly
Owner: Cyweekly Limited
Editorial: PO Box 24977, Nicosia 1306.
T: 357 22 744400
E: info@cyprusweekly.com.cy
W: http://www.cyprusweekly.com.cy
Freq: Weekly; **Circ:** 15000 Pub Statement
News Editor: Charlie Charalambous;
Publisher: Nicos Chr. Pattichis
Language (s): English
NEWSPAPER

Ergatiki Phoni
Owner: Cyprus Workers' Confederation (SEK)
Editorial: P.O. Box 25 018, Nicosia 1306.
T: 357 22 84 98 49 **E:** sek@sek.org.cy
Freq: Weekly; **Circ:** 12000 Pub Statement
Editor in Chief: Xenis Xenophontos
Language (s): Greek
NEWSPAPER

Haravgi
Owner: Ekdotiki Eteria Tilegrafos
Editorial: Ezekia Papaioannou 6, P.O.Box 21556, Nicosia 1075. **T:** 357 22 76 66 66
E: haravgi@spidernet.com.cy
W: http://www.haravgi.com.cy
Freq: Daily; **Circ:** 5000 Pub Statement
Language (s): Greek
DAILY NEWSPAPER

Kibrisli
Owner: Kibrisli
Editorial: Mecidiye Sok. No: 44, Mersin 10, Lefkosa **E:** kibrisli@kktc.net
W: http://www.kibrisligazetesi.com
Freq: Daily; **Circ:** 2500 Pub Statement
Editor: Sinasi Basaran; **Editor:** Naci Bayramoglu; **Editor:** Suzi Dilara; **Editor:** Ferda Ekinci; **Editor:** Kartal Harman; **Editor:** Candas Özer; **Editor:** Taner Selçuk; **Editor:** Nevruz Taydemir; **Editor:** Ali Tekman
Language (s): Turkish
DAILY NEWSPAPER

Machi
Owner: Atrotos Ltd
Editorial: PO Box 27628, Danais 4a, Nicosia 2408. **T:** 357 22 35 66 76
E: newsmaxi@spidernet.com.cy
Freq: Daily; **Circ:** 5000 Pub Statement
Editor-in-Chief: Babos Mitidis
Language (s): Greek
DAILY NEWSPAPER

O Phileleftheros
Owner: O Phileleftheros Ltd
Editorial: PO Box 21094, 1 Diogenous Str. Engomi, Nicosia 1501. **T:** 357 22 74 40 00
E: mailbox@phileleftheros.com
W: http://www.phileleftheros.com
Freq: Daily; **Circ:** 17720 Pub Statement
Editor-in-Chief: Aristos Michaelides
Language (s): Greek
DAILY NEWSPAPER

Politis
Owner: Arktinos Publications Ltd
Editorial: 8 Vassileiou Voulgaroktonou Str., Nicosia 1524. **T:** 357 22 86 18 61
E: info@politis-news.com
W: http://www.politis-news.com
Freq: Daily; **Circ:** 11000 Pub Statement
Publisher: Yiannis Papadopoulos; **Editor:** Sotiris Paroutis
Language (s): Greek
DAILY NEWSPAPER

I Simerini
Owner: DIAS Publishing House Ltd

Editorial: 31 Archangelos Avenue, Strovolos, Nicosia 2054. **T:** 357 22 58 05 80
E: mail@simerini.com
W: http://www.simerini.com.cy
Freq: Daily; **Circ:** 13000 Pub Statement
Editor In Chief: Christoforos Papastylianou;
Editor In Chief: Georgios Tziortzios
Language (s): Greek
DAILY NEWSPAPER

Vestnik Kipra
Owner: N.G. Cyprus Advertiser Ltd
Editorial: 14b Byron Str., 1 Park Tower, Limassol. **T:** 357 25 58 21 20
E: editor@vestnikkipra.com
W: http://www.cyprusadvertiser.com
Circ: 4000 Pub Statement
Editor: Alena Dolgyh
Language (s): Russian
DAILY NEWSPAPER

YeniDüzen
Owner: YeniDÜZEN Ltd.
Editorial: Yeni Sanayi Bölgesi, Mersin 10, Lefkosa-Kibris. **T:** 392 225 66 58
E: web@yeniduzen.com
W: http://www.yeniduzen.com
Freq: Daily; **Circ:** 3500 Pub Statement
Editor: Çagil Gunalp; **Editor-in-Chief:** Cenk Mutluyakali; **Editor:** Meltem Sonay; **Editor:** Hamide Topcu; **Editor:** Emine Uysal
Language (s): Turkish
DAILY NEWSPAPER

NEWS SERVICE/SYNDICATE

Agence France-Presse - Cyprus Bureau
Editorial: 36 Kypranoros str, 7th and 6th floor, Nicosia 1061. **T:** 357 22 391391
E: myrna.luksitch@afp.com
Language (s): Greek
NEWS SERVICE/SYNDICATE

ANSA Cyprus
Editorial: 28, Irinis str, Strovolos 2018.
T: 357 22 519169
E: ansa-italian@cytanet.co.cy
Language (s): Greek
NEWS SERVICE/SYNDICATE

Associated Press
T: 357 22 492599 **E:** apnicosia@ap.org
Language (s): Greek
NEWS SERVICE/SYNDICATE

Athens News Agency Cyprus
Editorial: 12 RIK Avenue, Aglantzia, Nicosia 2120. **T:** 357 22 663110
E: anacy@cytanet.com.cy
Language (s): Greek
NEWS SERVICE/SYNDICATE

Bloomberg Cyprus
Editorial: 5 Themistokli Dervi str, 3rd floor, Nicosia 1066. **T:** 357 22 503129
E: mchmaytelli@bloomberg.net
Language (s): Greek
NEWS SERVICE/SYNDICATE

Crown News Cyprus
Editorial: P.O. Box 27092, Nicosia 1641.
T: 357 22 357654 **E:** leigh.j@intercollege.ac.cy
Language (s): Greek
NEWS SERVICE/SYNDICATE

Cyprus News Agency
Editorial: 21, Academias Avenue, Aglantzia, Nicosia 2002. **T:** 357 22 556009
E: news@cna.org.cy
W: http://www.cna.org.cy/default.asp?id=24
Editor in Chief: George Penintaex
Language (s): English
NEWS SERVICE/SYNDICATE

DPA Cyprus
Editorial: 4, Valtinou str, Strovolos, Nicosia 2045. **T:** 357 22 320417
E: masis@financialmirror.com
Language (s): Greek
NEWS SERVICE/SYNDICATE

Reuters Cyprus
Editorial: P.O. Box 25725, Nicosia 1386.
T: 357 22 469607
E: michele.kambas@reuters.com
Bureau Chief: Michele Kambas
Language (s): Greek
NEWS SERVICE/SYNDICATE

Xinhua News Agency Cyprus
Editorial: 12, Byzantiou str, office 201, Nicosia 2430. **T:** 357 22 590133
E: xinhuanicosia@gmail.com
Language (s): Greek

NEWS SERVICE/SYNDICATE

BROADCASTING

RADIO NETWORKS

Kiss FM
Editorial: Diogenous 1, Engomi, P.O. Box 21094, Nicosia 1501. **T:** 357 22 74 44 64
E: kissfm@phileleftheros.com
W: http://www.kissfm.com.cy

TELEVISION STATIONS

Lumiere TV
Owner: Lumiere TV Group
Editorial: PO Box 25614, Nicosia 1311.
T: 357 22 35 72 72
E: administration@ltv.com.cy
W: http://www.lumieretv.com

CZECH REPUBLIC
Tel: 420

Standard Time: GMT +1
Continent: Europe
Capital City: Prague

NEWSPAPERS & PUBLICATIONS

NEWSPAPERS

Hospodárské noviny
Owner: Economia
Editorial: Dobrovského 25, Prague 17055.
T: 420 233 073001 **E:** hn@economia.cz
W: http://ihned.cz
Freq: Daily; **Circ:** 60848 ABC-Audit Bureau of Circulations
Editor: Marcela Jurková
Language (s): Czech
DAILY NEWSPAPER

Lidové noviny
Owner: Mafra
Editorial: Karla Engliše 519/11, Prague 15000.
T: 420 225067111 **E:** redakce@lidovky.cz
W: http://www.lidovky.cz
Freq: Daily; **Circ:** 75985 ABC-Audit Bureau of Circulations
Editor-in-Chief: Dalibor Balšínek; **News Editor:** Radek Kedron; **Editor:** Kamila Klausová
Language (s): Czech
DAILY NEWSPAPER

MF Dnes
Owner: Mafra
Editorial: Karla Engliše 519/11, Prague 15000.
T: 420 225062206 **E:** mfdnes@mfdnes.cz
W: http://www.idnes.cz
Freq: Daily; **Circ:** 208000 ABC-Audit Bureau of Circulations
Editor-in-Chief: Robert Cásenský; **Editor:** Martina Riebauerová; **Editor:** Tomáš Vocelka
Language (s): Czech
DAILY NEWSPAPER

Právo
Owner: Borgis
Editorial: Slezská 2127/13, P.O.Box 162, Prague 12150. **T:** 420 221001111
E: redakce@pravo.cz **W:** http://www.pravo.cz
Freq: Daily; **Circ:** 114000 ABC-Audit Bureau of Circulations
Editor-in-Chief: Zdenek Porybný
Language (s): Czech
DAILY NEWSPAPER

NEWS SERVICE/SYNDICATE

Associated Press
T: 4202 21 085-266
NEWS SERVICE/SYNDICATE

Bloomberg News
Editorial: NA Prikope 19-21, Mislbek Building, Prague 11719. **T:** 420 224422100
NEWS SERVICE/SYNDICATE

Dow Jones Newswires
Editorial: Truhlarska 24, Prague 11000.
T: 420 221085273
Bureau Chief: Leos Rousek
NEWS SERVICE/SYNDICATE

BROADCASTING

TELEVISION STATIONS

CT1 - CESKÁ TELEVIZE
Owner: Ceska televize
T: 420 261134632 **E:** info@ceskatelevize.cz
W: http://www.ct24.cz

CT2 - CESKÁ TELEVIZE
Owner: Ceská televize
E: info@ceskatelevize.cz **W:** http://www.ct24.cz

DEMOCRATIC REPUBLIC OF THE CONGO
Tel: 243

Standard Time: GMT +1
Continent: Africa
Capital City: Kinshasa

NEWSPAPERS & PUBLICATIONS

NEWSPAPERS

La Conscience
Editorial: BP 1262, 397 Boulevad du 30 juin, Kinshasa. **T:** 243 998 11 04 06
E: redaction@laconscience.com
W: http://www.laconscience.com
Freq: Weekly; **Circ:** 2000 Pub Statement
Editor: Jean-Marie Mandjeku; **Publisher:** Camille Muissa-Camus
Editorial Profile: Regional weekly newspaper focussing on national and international news, current affairs, politics, economics, society, music, culture, sport, education and regional development.
Language (s): French
NEWSPAPER

L' Observateur
Editorial: 4722 Avenue du Colonel Ebeya, Commune de la Gombe, Kinshasa.
T: 243 815 02 50 79
E: journalobservateur@hotmail.com
W: http://www.lobservateur.cd
Freq: Daily; **Circ:** 3500 Pub Statement
Editor: Luc-Roger Mbala mBemba; **Publisher:** Mankenda Voka
Editorial Profile: National daily newspaper focussing on national and international news, current affairs, economics, politics, society, women's interest, music, sport, culture, tourism and communication.
Language (s): French
DAILY NEWSPAPER

Le Phare
Owner: Journal Le Phare
Editorial: Niveau 2, Building du 29 Juin, 3392, Avenue Colonel Lukusa, Kinshasa.
T: 243 813 33 01 95 **E:** info@lephareonline.net
W: http://www.lephareonline.net
Freq: Daily; **Circ:** 4000 Pub Statement
Editor: Polydor Muboyayi
Editorial Profile: National daily newspaper focussing on news, current affairs, politics, economics, society, arts, culture and sports.
Language (s): French
DAILY NEWSPAPER

Le Potentiel
Editorial: 873 Avenue Bas Congo, BP 11338, Kinshasa / Gombe. **T:** 243 998 13 54 83
E: lepotentiel@yahoo.fr
W: http://www.lepotentiel.com
Freq: Daily; **Circ:** 3000 Pub Statement
Editor in Chief: Freddy Mulumba Kabuayi
Editorial Profile: National daily newspaper focussing on national and international news, current affairs, politics, economics, society, sport, entertainment, culture, science, and media.
Language (s): French
DAILY NEWSPAPER

NEWS SERVICE/SYNDICATE

Agence Congolaise de Presse
Editorial: Kinshasa. **T:** 243 81 350 40 40
E: acprdcongo@yahoo.fr
W: http://www.acpcongo.com
Editor in Chief: Mathieu Yoha
Editorial Profile: National presse agency focussing on national and international news, current affairs, politics, economics, health, science, culture, society, sport and environment.
Language (s): French
NEWS SERVICE/SYNDICATE

Agence France-Presse - Kinshasa Bureau
Owner: Agence France-Presse
Editorial: 10, avenue Batetela, Kinshasa
E: marc.jourdier@afp.com
W: http://www.afp.com
Editorial Profile: Kinshasa bureau of the international news and picture agency Agence France-Presse covering international news and current affairs.
Language (s): English
NEWS SERVICE/SYNDICATE

DENMARK Tel: 45
Standard Time: GMT +1
Continent: Europe
Capital City: Copenhagen

NEWSPAPERS & PUBLICATIONS

NEWSPAPERS

24 TIMER Århus
Owner: JP/Politikens Hus
Editorial: Grøndalsvej 3, Viby 8260.
T: 45 87 38 38 38 **E:** jpaarhus@jp.dk
W: http://www.24timer.dk
Freq: Daily; **Circ:** 60000 Pub Statement
Redaktør: Jens Kaiser
Language (s): Danish; Full Page Colour: 19000.00
Currency: Denmark Kroner
DAILY NEWSPAPER

AABENRAA UGE-AVIS
Owner: Berlingske Lokalaviser A/S
Editorial: Ramsherred 47, Aabenraa 6200.
T: 45 74 62 60 00
E: red.aabenraa@ugeavisen.dk
W: http://www.aabenraaugeavis.dk
Freq: Weekly; **Circ:** 31212 Pub Statement
Chefredaktør: Jan Sternkopf
Language (s): Danish; Full Page Colour: 14274.00
Currency: Denmark Kroner
NEWSPAPER

Aars Avis
Owner: Aars Avis A/S
Editorial: Himmerlandsgade 150, Aars 9600.
T: 45 98 62 17 11 **E:** redaktion@aarsavis.dk
W: http://www.aarsavis.dk
Freq: Weekly; **Circ:** 16825 Pub Statement
Redaktør: Thorkil Christensen
Language (s): Danish; Full Page Colour: 9240.00
Currency: Denmark Kroner
NEWSPAPER

Aarupd og Omegns Folkeblad
Owner: Brødrene Jacobsen
Editorial: Cederfjeldsgade 2, Postboks 90, Aarup 5560. **T:** 45 64 43 11 78
E: info@folkebladet.net
W: http://www.aarupfolkeblad.dk
Freq: Weekly; **Circ:** 25600 Not Audited
Language (s): Danish; Full Page Colour: 9285.00
Currency: Denmark Kroner
NEWSPAPER

Adresseavisen Syddjurs
Owner: Adresseavisen Kalø Vig A/S
Editorial: Grenåvej 10A, Ronde 8410.
T: 45 86 37 10 28 **E:** mail@adresseavisen.dk
W: http://www.adresseavisen.dk
Freq: Weekly; **Circ:** 23427 Not Audited
Editor: Claus Krogh; **Ansvarshavende redaktør:** Lars Norman Thomsen
Language (s): Danish; Full Page Colour: 7161.00
Currency: Denmark Kroner
NEWSPAPER

AKISUASOQ RADIO
E: akisuasoq@greennet.gl
W: http://:www.akisuasoq.gl
Freq: Daily
Redaktionssekretær: Laila Davidsen
Language (s): Danish
DAILY NEWSPAPER

AKTIEUGEBREVET
Owner: AktieUgebrevet ApS
T: 45 40 93 02 20
E: kontakt@aktieugebrevet.dk
W: http://www.aktieugebrevet.dk
Freq: Weekly; **Circ:** 2000 Pub Statement
Redaktør: Bruno Japp
Language (s): Danish; Full Page Colour: 6950.00
Currency: Denmark Kroner
DAILY NEWSPAPER

ALBERTSLUND NÆRRADIO
T: 45 43 64 48 28 **E:** anr@albertslundradio.dk
W: http://www.albertslundradio.dk
Freq: Daily
Ansvarshavende redaktør: Kasper Neergaard
Language (s): Danish
DAILY NEWSPAPER

Albertslund Posten
Owner: Politikens Lokalaviser
Editorial: Stationsporten 9, Albertslund 2620.
T: 45 45 90 82 26 **E:** ap@albertslundposten.dk
W: http://www.albertslundposten.dk
Freq: Weekly; **Circ:** 17520 Pub Statement
Editor in charge: Kim Belmark;
Ansvarshavende redaktør: Jørgen Brieghel
Language (s): Danish; Full Page Colour: 15333.50
Currency: Denmark Kroner
NEWSPAPER

Allerød Nyt
Owner: Hillerød Mediecenter I/S (Politikens Lokalaviser A/S)
Editorial: M.D Madsensvej 13, Allerød 3450.
T: 45 70 13 11 00 **E:** redaktion@allerodnyt.dk
W: http://www.allerodnyt.dk
Freq: Weekly; **Circ:** 15900 Pub Statement
Editor in charge: Kim Belmark
Language (s): Danish; Full Page Colour: 12951.00
Currency: Denmark Kroner
NEWSPAPER

Allerød Nyt Weekend
Owner: Politikens Lokalaviser A/S
Editorial: Madsenvej 13, Allerød 3450.
T: 45 45 908217 **E:** redaktion@allerodnyt.dk
W: http://alleroed.lokalavisen.dk/
Freq: Bi-Weekly; **Circ:** 11000
Language (s): Danish
DAILY NEWSPAPER

Amager Bladet
Owner: AMAGER AVISEN A/S
Editorial: Amagerbrogade 54, 1, Copenhagen 2300. **T:** 45 32 64 41 27
E: red.abl@berlingskemedia.dk
W: http://www.dinby.dk/amager-bladet
Freq: Bi-Weekly; **Circ:** 88375
Ansvarshavende redaktør: Jan Jeppesen
Language (s): Danish; Full Page Colour: 16115.00
Currency: Denmark Kroner
DAILY NEWSPAPER

AMAGER BLADET; 2770
Owner: Berlingske Lokalaviser
T: 45 32 54 21 10
E: redaktionen@amagerbladet.dk
W: http://www.amagerbladet.dk
Freq: Weekly; **Circ:** 25500 Pub Statement
EDITOR: Hanne Bjørton; **Chefredaktør:** Jan Jeppesen
Language (s): Danish
NEWSPAPER

Annonce-Bladet Salling og Fur
Owner: Salling Bogtrykkeri ApS
Editorial: Nørregade 19, Roslev 7870.
T: 45 97 57 14 00
E: sallingavis@sallingavis.dk
W: http://www.annonce-bladet.dk
Freq: Weekly; **Circ:** 10200 Not Audited
Ansvarshavende redaktør: Thorkil Christensen; **Redaktør for daglige nyheder:** Susanne Pedersen
Language (s): Danish; Full Page Colour: 8561.00
Currency: Denmark Kroner
NEWSPAPER

Århus Onsdag
Owner: Århus Stiftstidende
Editorial: Banegårdspladsen 11, Århus 8000.
T: 45 87 40 10 10
E: onsdag-redaktion@stiften.dk
W: http://www.aarhusonsdag.dk
Freq: Weekly; **Circ:** 164930 Pub Statement
Redaktør: Helle Holm
Language (s): Danish; Full Page Colour: 24621.00
Currency: Denmark Kroner
NEWSPAPER

ÅRHUS STIFTSTIDENDE
Owner: Århus Stiftstidende K/S
Editorial: Banegårdspladsen 11, Århus 8000.
T: 45 87 40 10 10 **E:** red@stiften.dk
W: http://www.stiften.dk
Freq: Daily; **Circ:** 48559 Not Audited
Chefredaktør: Dorthe Carlsen; **EDITOR AT LARGE:** Dennis Christensen; **EDITOR AT LARGE:** Lilian Dubgaard; **EDITOR AT LARGE:** Margith Lærke; **EDITOR AT LARGE:** Henrik Lund; **EDITOR AT LARGE:** Uffe Normand; **Chefredaktør:** Jan Schouby; **Redaktionschef:** Jens W. Møller
Language (s): Danish; Full Page Colour: 23711.00
Currency: Denmark Kroner
DAILY NEWSPAPER

ÅRHUS STIFTSTIDENDE BILEN
Owner: Århus Stiftstidende K/S
Editorial: Banegårdspladsen 11, Århus 8000.
T: 45 87 40 10 10 **E:** koergodt@stiften.dk
W: http://www.stiften.dk
Freq: Daily; **Circ:** 48559
EDITOR: Gert C. Nielsen
Language (s): Danish
DAILY NEWSPAPER

ÅRHUS STIFTSTIDENDE Debat
Owner: Århus Stiftstidende K/S
Editorial: Banegårdspladsen 11, Århus 8000.
T: 45 87 40 10 10 **E:** debat@stiften.dk
W: http://www.stiften.dk
Freq: Daily; **Circ:** 48559 Not Audited
Redaktør: Kirsten Thorndahl
Language (s): Danish
DAILY NEWSPAPER

ÅRHUS STIFTSTIDENDE Favrskov
Owner: Århus Stiftstidende K/S
Editorial: Østergade 25, Hadsten 8370.
T: 45 86 98 05 88 **E:** favrskov@stiften.dk
W: http://www.stiften.dk
Freq: Daily; **Circ:** 48559
Language (s): Danish
DAILY NEWSPAPER

ÅRHUS STIFTSTIDENDE Forbrug
Owner: Århus Stiftstidende K/S
Editorial: Banegårdspladsen 11, Århus 8000.
T: 45 87 40 10 10 **E:** redaktion@stiften.dk
W: http://www.stiften.dk
Freq: Daily; **Circ:** 48559
Redaktør: Morten Ravn
Language (s): Danish
DAILY NEWSPAPER

ÅRHUS STIFTSTIDENDE Kultur
Owner: Århus Stiftstidende K/S
Editorial: Banegårdspladsen11, Århus 8000.
T: 45 87 40 10 10 **E:** kultur@stiften.dk
W: http://www.stiften.dk
Freq: Daily; **Circ:** 48559 Not Audited
Language (s): Danish
DAILY NEWSPAPER

ÅRHUS STIFTSTIDENDE Navne
Owner: Århus Stiftstidende K/S
Editorial: Banegaardspladsen 11, Århus 8000.
T: 45 87 40 10 10 **E:** navne@stiften.dk
W: http://www.stiften.dk
Freq: Daily; **Circ:** 48559 Not Audited
Redaktør: Kirsten Thorndahl
Language (s): Danish
DAILY NEWSPAPER

ÅRHUS STIFTSTIDENDE Norddjurs
Owner: ÅRHUS STIFTSTIDENDE K/S
Editorial: Østerbrogade 18, Grenaa 8500.
T: 45 87 58 55 00 **E:** norddjurs@stiften.dk
W: http://www.stiften.dk
Freq: Daily; **Circ:** 48559
Redaktør: Søren Andersen
Language (s): Danish
DAILY NEWSPAPER

ÅRHUS STIFTSTIDENDE Skandeborg
Owner: Århus Stiftstidende K/S
Editorial: Adelgade 106, Skanderborg 8660.
T: 45 86 52 43 00 **E:** skanderborg@stiften.dk
W: http://www.stiften.dk
Freq: Daily; **Circ:** 48559
Language (s): Danish
DAILY NEWSPAPER

ÅRHUS STIFTSTIDENDE Sport
Owner: Århus Stiftstidende K/S
Editorial: Banegårdspladsen 11, Århus 8000.
T: 45 87 40 10 10 **E:** sport@stiften.dk
W: http://www.stiften.dk
Freq: Daily; **Circ:** 48559 Not Audited
Language (s): Danish
DAILY NEWSPAPER

ÅRHUS STIFTSTIDENDE Syddjurs
Owner: ÅRHUS STIFTSTIDENDE K/S
Editorial: Torvet 6, Ebeltoft 8400.
T: 45 86 34 16 77 **E:** syddjurs@stiften.dk
W: http://www.stiften.dk
Freq: Daily; **Circ:** 48559
Redaktionschef: Henrik Ask
Language (s): Danish
DAILY NEWSPAPER

Bagsværd/Søborg Bladet
Owner: Berlingske Lokalaviser, Danske Distriktsblade
Editorial: Centrumgade 7, Ballerup 2750.
T: 45 44 60 03 30
E: red.bsb@berlingskemedia.dk
W: http://www.bagsvaerdbladet.dk
Freq: Weekly; **Circ:** 41297 Not Audited
Redaktør: Lars Schmidt; **Redaktionschef:** Mia Thomsen
Language (s): Danish; Full Page Colour: 22287.00
Currency: Denmark Kroner
NEWSPAPER

Ballerup Bladet
Owner: Berlingske Lokalaviser, Danske Distriktsblade
Editorial: Centrumgade 7, Ballerup 2750.
T: 45 44 60 03 30
E: red.bbl@berlingskemedia.dk
W: http://www.ballerupbladet.dk
Freq: Weekly; **Circ:** 43234 Not Audited
Redaktør: Lars Schmidt; **Ansvarshavende redaktør:** Lars Schmidt; **Redaktionschef:** Mia Thomsen
Language (s): Danish; Full Page Colour: 22518.00
Currency: Denmark Kroner
NEWSPAPER

Berlingske
Owner: Berlingske Media
Editorial: Pilestræde 34, København K 1147.
T: 45 33 75 75 75
E: redaktionen@berlingske.dk
W: http://www.b.dk
Freq: Daily; **Circ:** 102640 Dansk Oplagskontrol
Redaktionschef: Jens Grund; **Chefredaktør:** Tom Jensen; **Nyhetschef:** Benjamin Munk Lund
Language (s): Danish; Full Page Colour: 95312.00
Currency: Denmark Kroner
DAILY NEWSPAPER

Billund Ugeavis
Owner: Billund Bogtrykeri
Editorial: Højmarksvej 5, Billund 7190.
T: 45 75 33 12 18
E: redaktionen@billund-ugeavis.dk
W: http://www.billund-ugeavis.dk
Freq: Weekly; **Circ:** 18600 Pub Statement
Redaktør: Keld Stampe; **Redaktionschef:** Morten Theider
Language (s): Danish; Full Page Colour: 8476.50
Currency: Denmark Kroner
NEWSPAPER

Birkerød & Rudersdal Avis
Owner: Furesøens Mediecenter A/S
Editorial: Gl. Lundtoftevej 1B, 3, Birkerød 2800. **T:** 45 45 94 65 95
E: redaktion@rudersdalavis.dk
W: http://www.birkeroedavis.dk
Freq: Weekly; **Circ:** 12703 Pub Statement
Editor in charge: Kim Belmark
Language (s): Danish; Full Page Colour: 15150.00
Currency: Denmark Kroner
NEWSPAPER

Bjerringbro Avis
Owner: Bjerringbro Avis S.m.b.a.
Editorial: Banegårdspladsen 3, Bjerringbro 8850. **T:** 45 86 68 17 55
E: redaktion@bjerringbro-avis.dk
W: http://www.bjerringbro-avis.dk
Freq: Weekly; **Circ:** 19700 Pub Statement
Language (s): Danish; Full Page Colour: 9041.50
Currency: Denmark Kroner
NEWSPAPER

BOLIGMARKEDET
Owner: Nyhedsavisen
Editorial: Islands Brygge 43, Copenhagen 2300. **T:** 45 23 378 202 **E:** kim@boligm.dk
W: http://www.boligm.dk
Freq: Bi-Weekly; **Circ:** 100000 Pub Statement
Language (s): Danish
DAILY NEWSPAPER

Bornholms Tidende
Owner: A/S Bornholms Tidende
Editorial: Nørregade 11-19, Rønne 3700.
T: 45 56 90 30 00
E: redaktion@bornholmstidende.dk
W: http://www.bornholmstidende.dk
Freq: Daily; **Circ:** 12591 Dansk Oplagskontrol
Nyhedsredaktør/chef: Nanna Krogh; **Redaktør:** Dan Qvitzau; **Nyhedsredaktør/chef:** Richardt Skovgaard
Language (s): Danish; Full Page Colour: 22052.00

Currency: Denmark Kroner
DAILY NEWSPAPER

BORNHOLMS TIDENDE Aakirkeby
Owner: A/S Bornholms Tidende
Editorial: Nørregade 11-19, Aakirkeby 3700.
T: 45 56 90 30 00
E: redaktion@bornholmstidende.dk
W: http://www.bornholmstidende.dk
Freq: Weekly; **Circ:** 13275
Redaktør: Lisbet Holst
Language (s): Danish
DAILY NEWSPAPER

BORNHOLMS TIDENDE Allinge-Gudhjem
Owner: A/S Bornholms Tidende
Editorial: Lindeplads 2, Allinge 3770.
T: 45 56 44 50 71 **E:** tl@bhstid.dk
W: http://www.bornholmstidende.dk
Freq: Daily; **Circ:** 13275
Redaktør: Tove Laursen
Language (s): Danish
DAILY NEWSPAPER

BORNHOLMS TIDENDE Hasle
Owner: A/S Bornholms Tidende
Editorial: Storegade 50, Hasle 3790.
T: 45 56 94 62 01
E: redaktion@bornholmstidende.dk
W: http://www.bornholmstidende.dk
Freq: Daily; **Circ:** 13275
Redaktør: Tove Laursen
Language (s): Danish
DAILY NEWSPAPER

BORNHOLMS TIDENDE Nexø
Owner: A/S Bornholms Tidende
Editorial: Strandgade 15, 1, Nexø 3770.
T: 45 56 44 12 01
E: redaktion@bornholmstidende.dk
W: http://www.bornholmstidende.dk
Freq: Daily; **Circ:** 13275
EDITOR: Elisabeth Krogh
Language (s): Danish
DAILY NEWSPAPER

BORNHOLMS TIDENDE Rønne
Owner: A/S Bornholms Tidende
Editorial: Nørregade 11-19, Rønne 3700.
T: 45 56 90 30 00
E: redaktion@bornholmstidende.dk
W: http://www.bornholmstidende.dk
Freq: Daily; **Circ:** 13275 Not Audited
Redaktør: Henrik Nielsen
Language (s): Danish
DAILY NEWSPAPER

BORNHOLMS TIDENDE Sporten
Owner: A/S Bornholms Tidende
Editorial: Nørregade 11-19, Rønne 3700.
T: 45 56 90 30 00
E: sporten@bornholmstidende.dk
W: http://www.bornholmstidende.dk
Freq: Daily; **Circ:** 13275
Language (s): Danish
DAILY NEWSPAPER

Børsen
Owner: Dagbladet Børsen A/S
Editorial: Møntergade 19, København K 1140.
T: 45 33 32 01 02 **E:** redaktionen@borsen.dk
W: http://www.borsen.dk
Freq: Daily; **Circ:** 72086 Dansk Oplagskontrol
Redaktør: Christopher Arzrouni; **Redaktør:** Thomas Bernt Henriksen; **Redaktør:** Michael Grønnegaard; **Editor in Chief:** Anders Johansen; **Redaktionschef:** Jens Kristian Lai; **Editor:** Niels Lunde; **Redaktør:** Hakon Redder
Language (s): Danish; Full Page Colour: 85080.00
Currency: Denmark Kroner
DAILY NEWSPAPER

Børsen; Christiansborg
Owner: Dagbladet Børsen A/S
Editorial: Møntergade 19, Copenhagen 1140.
T: 45 33 32 01 02 **E:** redaktionen@borsen.dk
W: http://www.borsen.dk **Circ:** 70503
Redaktør: Ulrik Horn
Editorial Profile: Bureau
Language (s): Danish
DAILY NEWSPAPER

Børsen; Fyn/Trekantområdet
Owner: Børsen A/S
Editorial: Nørregade 77, 2, Odense 5100.
T: 45 66 13 15 02
E: jens.bertelsen@borsen.dk
W: http://www.borsen.dk **Circ:** 70503 Not Audited
EDITOR: Jens Bertelsen
Editorial Profile: Bureau
Language (s): Danish
DAILY NEWSPAPER

Børsen; Jylland
Editorial: Algade 44, Postboks 1830, Aalborg 9000 **E:** mach@borsen.dk
W: http://www.borsen.dk
Egnsredaktør: Mads Meisner Christensen
Editorial Profile: Bureau
DAILY NEWSPAPER

Børsen; København/Sjælland
Owner: Dagbladet Børsen A/S
Editorial: Møntergade 19, Copenhagen DK-1140. **T:** 45 33 32 01 02
E: knud.rasmussen@borsen.dk
W: http://www.borsen.dk **Circ:** 70503
Editorial Profile: Bureau
Language (s): Danish
DAILY NEWSPAPER

Børsen; Midt/Vestjylland - Herning
Editorial: Bredgade 55, 1, Postboks 224, Herning 7400. **T:** 45 72 42 32 04
E: helge.andreassen@borsen.dk
W: http://borsen.dk
Egnsredaktør: Bjarne Bang
Editorial Profile: Bureau
Language (s): Danish
DAILY NEWSPAPER

Bov Bladet
Owner: De Berlingske Lokalaviser
Editorial: Nørregade 14, Padborg 6330.
T: 45 74 67 1724
E: red.bob@berlingskemedia.dk
W: http://www.bovbladet.dk
Freq: Weekly; **Circ:** 15888 Not Audited
Editor in Chief: Jan Sternkopf
Language (s): Danish; Full Page Colour: 7237.00
Currency: Denmark Kroner
NEWSPAPER

Brædstrup Avis
Owner: Brædstrup Bogtrykkeri
Editorial: Søndergade 36, Brædstrup 8740.
T: 45 75 75 17 33 **E:** br@braedstrup-avis.dk
W: http://braedstrup-avis.dk
Freq: Weekly; **Circ:** 15960 Not Audited
EDITOR: Anya Wissendorff
Language (s): Danish; Full Page Colour: 6600.00
Currency: Denmark Kroner
NEWSPAPER

Brande Bladet
Owner: Brande Bladet A/S
Editorial: Storegade 25, Posboks 169, Brande 7330. **T:** 45 97 18 28 38
E: post@brandebladet.dk
W: http://www.brandebladet.dk
Freq: Weekly; **Circ:** 16002 Not Audited
Language (s): Danish; Full Page Colour: 8316.00
Currency: Denmark Kroner
NEWSPAPER

Brønshøj-Husum Avis
Owner: Helsingør Dagblad a/s
Editorial: Frederikssundsvej 322 A, Brønshøj 2700. **T:** 45 38 60 30 03 **E:** adm@bha.dk
W: http://www.bha.dk
Freq: Weekly; **Circ:** 28117 Not Audited
Ansvarshavende redaktør: Flemming Antony; **Kommunale emner:** John Pilgaard
Language (s): Danish; Full Page Colour: 16045.00
Currency: Denmark Kroner
NEWSPAPER

BT
Owner: B.T. A/S
Editorial: Pilestræde 34, Copenhagen 1147.
T: 45 33 75 75 33 **E:** bt@bt.dk
W: http://www.bt.dk
Freq: Daily; **Circ:** 98538 Not Audited
Nyhedsredaktør: Simon Andersen; **Ledende redaktionchef:** Henny Christensen;
Nyhedsredaktør: Casper Hjorth;
Nyhedsredaktør og mediechef: Jesper Ludvigsen; **Editor-in-Chief:** Anders Peter Landert; **Chefredaktør:** Olav Skaaning Andersen; **Redaktør:** Jacob Staehelin; **Nyhedsredaktør/chef:** Lars Westh Jacobsen
Language (s): Danish; Full Page Colour: 75161.00
Currency: Denmark Kroner
DAILY NEWSPAPER

BUDSTIKKEN Esbjerg
Owner: Budstikken Vojens A/S
Editorial: Borgergade 38, 2.sal, Esbjerg 6700.
T: 45 75 91 19 11 **E:** red-esb@budstikken.com
W: http://esbjerg.lokalavisen.dk
Freq: Weekly; **Circ:** 44062
EDITOR IN CHIEF: Fred Jacobsen; **EDITOR IN CHIEF:** Fred Jacobsen
Language (s): Danish; Full Page Colour: 17556.00

Currency: Denmark Kroner
NEWSPAPER

BUDSTIKKEN Fredericia
Owner: Budstikken Vojens A/S
Editorial: Riddergade 17, 1. sal, Fredericia 7000. **T:** 45 76 20 04 00
E: red-fre@budstikken.com
W: http://www.budstikken.com/Fredericia.asp
Freq: Weekly; **Circ:** 39854
Ansvarshavende redaktør: Jan Hjortlund Hansen
Language (s): Danish; Full Page Colour: 14437.50
Currency: Denmark Kroner
NEWSPAPER

BUDSTIKKEN Haderslev
Owner: Budstikken Haderslev A/S
Editorial: Gravene 8, Haderslev 6100.
T: 45 74 52 91 08 **E:** red-hv@budstikken.com
W: http://www.budstikken.com
Freq: Weekly; **Circ:** 31031
Ansvarshavende redaktør: Jan Hjortlund Hansen
Language (s): Danish; Full Page Colour: 13860.00
Currency: Denmark Kroner
NEWSPAPER

BUDSTIKKEN Vejen
Owner: Lokalavisen A/S
T: 45 75 39 12 20 **E:** red-vjn@budstikken.com
W: http://www.budstikken.com/vejen_medarbejdere.php **Circ:** 30000
Editor: Claus Krogh
Language (s): Danish; Full Page Colour: 13167.00
Currency: Denmark Kroner
NEWSPAPER

Budstikken; Kolding
Owner: Politikens Lokalaviser A/S
Editorial: Bredgade 33, 1. sal, Kolding 6000.
T: 45 75 50 24 20 **E:** red-kol@lokalavisen.dk
W: http://kolding.lokalavisen.dk/
Freq: Weekly; **Circ:** 43147 Not Audited
Ansvarshavende redaktør: Jan Hjortlund Hansen
Language (s): Danish; Full Page Colour: 15246.00
Currency: Denmark Kroner
NEWSPAPER

Budstikken; Sønderborg
Owner: Budstikken Vojens A/S
Editorial: Perlegade 4, 1. sal, Sønderborg 6400. **T:** 45 74 42 18 01
E: red-sdb@lokalavisen.dk
W: http://soenderborg.lokalavisen.dk/
Freq: Weekly; **Circ:** 38194 Pub Statement
Language (s): Danish; Full Page Colour: 14899.50
Currency: Denmark Kroner
NEWSPAPER

Budstikken; Varde
Owner: Budstikken A/S
Editorial: Vestergade 15 B, Varde 6800.
T: 45 75 44 33 77 **E:** red-var@lokalavisen.dk
W: http://varde.lokalavisen.dk/
Freq: Weekly; **Circ:** 24655 Not Audited
Ansvarshavende redaktør: Jan Hjortlund Hansen
Language (s): Danish; Full Page Colour: 10626.00
Currency: Denmark Kroner
NEWSPAPER

Budstikken; Vejle
Owner: Budstikken A/S
Editorial: Torvegade 17, 1.sal, Vejle 7100.
T: 45 75 735 735 **E:** red-vej@lokalavisen.dk
W: http://vejle.lokalavisen.dk/
Freq: Weekly; **Circ:** 44228 Not Audited
Language (s): Danish; Full Page Colour: 15246.00
Currency: Denmark Kroner
NEWSPAPER

Busdtikken; Aabenraa
Owner: Budstikken Vojens A/S
Editorial: Nørreport 5, Åbenrå 6200.
T: 45 74 62 12 75 **E:** red-aab@lokalavisen.dk
W: http://aabenraa.lokalavisen.dk/
Freq: Weekly; **Circ:** 30110 Not Audited
EDITOR IN CHIEF: Fred Jacobsen; **EDITOR IN CHIEF:** Fred Jacobsen
Language (s): Danish; Full Page Colour: 13167.00
Currency: Denmark Kroner
NEWSPAPER

CHRISTIANSHAVNS KANAL
T: 45 32 57 88 78 **E:** pre-radio@beboerhus.dk
W: http://www.ch-radio.dk
Language (s): Danish

DAILY NEWSPAPER

City Avisen
Owner: Berlingske Lokalaviser A/S
Editorial: Dirch Passers Allé 27, 1. sal, Frederiksberg 2000. **T:** 45 33 88 88 88
E: red.cav@berlingskemedia.dk
W: http://www.cityavisen.dk
Freq: Weekly; **Circ:** 26361 Not Audited
Chefredaktør: Morten Friis Outzen;
Chefredaktør: Christian Olsen
Language (s): Danish; Full Page Colour: 15015.00
Currency: Denmark Kroner
NEWSPAPER

Dagbladet Arbejderen
Owner: Kommunistisk Parti
Editorial: Ryesgade 3F, Copenhagen 2200.
T: 45 35 35 21 93 **E:** redaktion@arbejderen.dk
W: http://www.arbejderen.dk
Freq: Daily; **Circ:** 2000 Not Audited
Ansvarshavende redaktør: Birthe Sørensen
Language (s): Danish; Full Page Colour: 16170.00
Currency: Denmark Kroner
DAILY NEWSPAPER

Dagbladet Arbejderen; Jyllandsredaktionen
Owner: Kommunistisk Parti
Editorial: Mejlgade 49, Postboks 5144, Århus 8000. **T:** 45 46 98 05 94
E: jylland@arbejderen.dk
W: http://www.arbejderen.dk **Circ:** 2500 Pub Statement
Redaktør: Birthe Sørensen
Editorial Profile: Bureau
Language (s): Danish
DAILY NEWSPAPER

DAGBLADET HOLSTEBRO/STRUER
Owner: Midtjyske Medier
Editorial: Lægårdsvej 86, Holstebro 7500.
T: 45 99 12 84 10 **E:** holstebro@bergske.dk
W: http://www.dagbladet-holstebro-struer.dk
Freq: Daily; **Circ:** 11266 Not Audited
Redaktionssekretær: Bianca Johansen;
EDITOR AT LARGE: Hans Krabbe; **EDITOR:** Jesper Markussen; **Redaktionssekretær:** Torben Pedersen; **EDITOR:** Ninna Pirchert;
EDITOR: Lars Thornvig
Language (s): Danish; Full Page Colour: 12969.00
Currency: Denmark Kroner
DAILY NEWSPAPER

DAGBLADET HOLSTEBRO/STRUER Sport
Owner: Bergske Blade K/S
Editorial: Lægårdsvej 86, Holstebro 7500.
T: 45 99 12 84 33 **E:** hede@bergske.dk
W: http://www.dagbladet-holstebro-struer.dk
Freq: Daily; **Circ:** 11266
Language (s): Danish
DAILY NEWSPAPER

DAGBLADET HOLSTEBRO/STRUER Struer
Owner: Bergske Blade K/S
Editorial: Kildegården 3, Struer 7600.
T: 45 96 84 22 01
E: redaktionen.ugeavisenstruer@bergske.dk
W: http://www.dagbladet-holstebro-struer.dk
Freq: Daily; **Circ:** 11266
Redaktør: Ninna Pirchert
Language (s): Danish
DAILY NEWSPAPER

DAGBLADET HOLSTEBRO/STRUER Ulfborg-Vemb
Owner: De Bergske Blade
Editorial: St. Blichers vej 9, Ringkøbing 6950
E: ulfborgvemb@bergske.dk
W: http://www.bergske.dk
Freq: Daily; **Circ:** 11266
Language (s): Danish
DAILY NEWSPAPER

DAGBLADET HOLSTEBRO/STRUER Vinderup
Owner: De Bergske Blade
Editorial: Søndergade 42, 1 sal, Vinderup 7830 **E:** vinderup@bergske.dk
W: http://www.bergske.dk
Freq: Daily; **Circ:** 11266
Redaktør: Jens Work Kristensen
Language (s): Danish
DAILY NEWSPAPER

DAGBLADET KØGE
Owner: Sjællandske Medier A/S
Editorial: Torvet 10, Køge 4600.
T: 45 56 65 07 01 **E:** dagbladet@sj-medier.dk
W: http://www.dagbladetonline.dk

Freq: Daily; Circ: 6600
Ansvarshavende redaktør: Torben Dalby
Larsen; Redaktør: Simon Dinsen Hansen;
Redaktionschef: Charlotte Freiberg
Language (s): Danish; Full Page Colour:
17696.00
Currency: Denmark Kroner
DAILY NEWSPAPER

DAGBLADET KØGE Faxe
Owner: Sjællandske Medier A/S
Editorial: Jernbanegade 14, Haslev 4690
E: faxe.red@sj-medier.dk
W: http://www.dagbladetonline.dk
Freq: Daily; Circ: 7630
Language (s): Danish
DAILY NEWSPAPER

DAGBLADET KØGE Høje-Taastrup
Owner: Sjællandske Medier A/S
Editorial: Taastrup Hovedgade 77, Taastrup
2630. T: 45 43 99 26 08
E: taastrup.red@sj-medier.dk
W: http://www.dagbladetonline.dk
Freq: Daily; Circ: 7630
Language (s): Danish
DAILY NEWSPAPER

DAGBLADET KØGE Køge
Owner: Sjællandske Medier A/S
Editorial: Postbox 70, Torvet 10, Køge 4600
E: koege.red@sj-medier.dk
W: http://www.dagbladetonline.dk
Freq: Daily; Circ: 7630
Redaktør: Simon Dinsen Hansen;
Redaktionssekretær: Helle Schou
Language (s): Danish
DAILY NEWSPAPER

DAGBLADET KØGE Stevns
Owner: Sjællandske Medier A/S
Editorial: Nytorv 6, Store Heddinge 4600
E: stevns.red@sj-medier.dk
W: http://www.dagbladetonline.dk
Freq: Daily; Circ: 7630
Language (s): Danish
DAILY NEWSPAPER

DAGBLADET RINGKJØBING-SKJERN
Owner: Midtjyske Medier
Editorial: St. Blichersvej 5, Ringkøbing 6950.
T: 45 99 75 73 00 E: ringkoebing@bergske.dk
W: http://www.dagbladetringskjern.dk
Freq: Daily; Circ: 6455
Chefredaktør: Søren Christensen;
Redaktionschef: Mikael Sand; Lystfisker:
John Thomsen
Language (s): Danish; Full Page Colour:
12231.00
Currency: Denmark Kroner
DAILY NEWSPAPER

DAGBLADET RINGKJØBING-SKJERN
Ringkøbing-Hvide Sande
Owner: De Bergske Blade
Editorial: St. Blichersvej 5, Ringkøbing 6950.
T: 45 99 75 73 00 E: ulfborgvemb@bergske.dk
W: http://www.bergske.dk
Freq: Daily; Circ: 10779
Chefredaktør: Lars Kryger;
Redaktionssekretær: Leif Nielsen;
Redaktionschef: Mikael Sand
Language (s): Danish
DAILY NEWSPAPER

DAGBLADET RINGKJØBING-SKJERN
Skjern-Tarm
Owner: Bergske Blade K/S
Editorial: Bergs Plads 5, Skjern 6900.
T: 45 96 81 53 00 E: skjern-tarm@bergske.dk
W: http://www.dagbladet-skjern-tarm.dk
Freq: Daily; Circ: 10779 Pub Statement
Language (s): Danish
DAILY NEWSPAPER

DAGBLADET RINGKJØBING-SKJERN
Videbæk
Owner: De Bergske Blade
Editorial: Bredgade 16, Videbæk 6920.
T: 45 97 17 10 61 E: videbaek@bergske.dk
W: http://www.bergske.dk
Freq: Daily; Circ: 10779
Language (s): Danish
DAILY NEWSPAPER

DAGBLADET RINGSTED
Owner: Sjællandske Medier A/S
Editorial: Søgade 4-12, Ringsted 4100.
T: 45 57 61 25 00 E: dagbladet@sn.dk
W: http://www.dagbladetonline.dk
Freq: Daily; Circ: 6796 Not Audited
Chefredaktør: Torben Dalby Larsen;
Ansvarshavende redaktør: Bente
Johannessen; Redaktør: Finn Sinding Yde
Language (s): Danish; Full Page Colour:
17696.00

Currency: Denmark Kroner
DAILY NEWSPAPER

DAGBLADET RINGSTED ~Ringsted
Owner: Sjællandske Medier A/S
Editorial: Søgade 10, Ringsted 4100.
T: 45 57 61 25 00 E: dagbladet@sj-medier.dk
W: http://www.dagbladetonline.dk
Freq: Daily; Circ: 6600
Redaktør: David Arnholm;
Redaktionssekretær: Jakob Fønss
Language (s): Danish
DAILY NEWSPAPER

DAGBLADET RINGSTED
Centralredaktionen
Owner: Sjællandske Medier A/S
Editorial: SØGADE 4-12, Ringsted 4100.
T: 45 57 61 25 00 E: dagbladet@sn.dk
W: http://www.dagbladetonline.dk Circ: 6600
Redaktionssekretær: Karin Ebbesen;
Redaktionschef: Charlotte Freiberg;
Redaktionssekretær: Lene Hüttel;
Redaktionssekretær: Palle Schneider;
Redaktør: Finn Sinding Yde;
Redaktionssekretær: Anders Spanggaard;
Redaktionssekretær: Anja Torp Jørgensen
Language (s): Danish
NEWSPAPER

DAGBLADET RINGSTED Faxe
Owner: Sjællandske Medier A/S
Editorial: JERNBANEGADE 14, Haslev 4690.
T: 45 56 31 20 33 E: faxe.red@sj-medier.dk
W: http://www.dagbladetonline.dk
Freq: Daily; Circ: 6600
Redaktør: Susanne Søhuus
Language (s): Danish
DAILY NEWSPAPER

DAGBLADET RINGSTED Køge
Owner: Sjællandske Medier A/S
Editorial: Postbox 70, Torvet 10, Køge 4600.
T: 45 56 65 07 01 E: koege.red@sn.dk
W: http://www.sn.dk/koege
Freq: Daily; Circ: 6600 Pub Statement
Language (s): Danish
DAILY NEWSPAPER

DAGBLADET RINGSTED
Sjællandsredaktionen
Owner: Sjællandske Medier A/S
Editorial: SØGADE 4-12, Ringsted 4100.
T: 45 57 61 25 00 E: sj@sj-medier.dk
W: http://www.dagbladetonline.dk
Freq: Daily; Circ: 6600
Language (s): Danish
DAILY NEWSPAPER

DAGBLADET RINGSTED Sorø
Owner: Sjællandske Medier A/S
Editorial: ABSALONGADE 1, Sorø 4180.
T: 45 57 83 15 60 E: soroe.red@sj-medier.dk
W: http://www.dagbladetonline.dk
Freq: Daily; Circ: 6600
Language (s): Danish
DAILY NEWSPAPER

DAGBLADET RINGSTED Sport
Owner: Sjællandske Medier A/S
Editorial: SØGADE 4-12, Ringsted 4100.
T: 45 57 67 36 00 E: sporten.db@sj-medier.dk
W: http://www.dagbladetonline.dk
Freq: Daily; Circ: 6600
Language (s): Danish
DAILY NEWSPAPER

DAGBLADET ROSKILDE
Owner: Sjællandske Medier A/S
Editorial: Hersegade 22, Roskilde 4000.
T: 45 46 35 85 00 E: roskilde.red@sn.dk
W: http://www.dagbladetonline.dk
Freq: Daily; Circ: 7391 Not Audited
Redaktør: Lars Ahn Pedersen;
Ansvarshavende redaktør: Torben Dalby
Larsen
Language (s): Danish; Full Page Colour:
17696.00
Currency: Denmark Kroner
DAILY NEWSPAPER

Dagbladet Roskilde ~Køge
Owner: Sjællandske Medier A/S
Editorial: Torvet 10, Postbox 70, Køge 4600
E: koege.red@sj-medier.dk
W: http://www.dagbladetonline.dk
Freq: Daily; Circ: 6660
Redaktør: Simon Dinsen Hansen
Language (s): Danish
DAILY NEWSPAPER

DAGBLADET ROSKILDE Høje-
Taastrup
Owner: Sjællandske Medier A/S
Editorial: Taastrup Hovedgade 77, Taastrup
2630 E: taastrup.red@sj-medier.dk

W: http://www.dagbladetonline.dk
Freq: Daily; Circ: 7300
Language (s): Danish
DAILY NEWSPAPER

DAGBLADET ROSKILDE Lejre-Osted
Owner: Sjællandske Medier A/S
Editorial: Nørretoften 5B. Postbox 1144,
Osted, Roskilde 4000 E: lejre.red@sn.dk
W: http://www.dagbladetonline.dk
Freq: Daily; Circ: 7300
Redaktør: Agnete Vistar
Language (s): Danish
DAILY NEWSPAPER

Dalum-Hjallese Avis
Owner: Ugeavisen Odense
Editorial: Banegårdspladsen, Odense 5100.
T: 45 66 14 14 10 E: red@dh-avis.dk
W: http://dalumhjalleseavis.dk/
Freq: Weekly; Circ: 19145 Pub Statement
Language (s): Danish; Full Page Colour:
11665.50
Currency: Denmark Kroner
NEWSPAPER

DEMOKRATIRADIOEN
Owner: Foreningshuset Højnæsvej
T: 45 36 72 32 00 E: radio@foreninghuset.dk
W: http://www.foreningshuset.dk
Freq: Daily
Language (s): Danish
DAILY NEWSPAPER

DEN BLÅ AVIS Øst
Owner: Den Blå Avis A/S
Editorial: Falkoner Alle 3, 1, Frederiksberg
2000. T: 45 44 85 44 44 E: es@dba.dk
W: http://www.dba.dk Circ: 80000
Language (s): Danish
NEWSPAPER

DEN BLÅ AVIS Vest
Owner: Blå Avis A/S
Editorial: Axel Kiers Vej 11, Århus 8270.
T: 45 87 31 32 33 E: support@dba.dk
W: http://www.dba.dk Circ: 80000
Language (s): Danish; Full Page Colour:
38750.00
Currency: Denmark Kroner
NEWSPAPER

Den Lille Avis
Owner: Isager Bogtryk/offset
Editorial: Industrivej 16, Ringe 5750.
T: 45 62 21 31 60 E: journalist@denlilleavis.dk
W: http://www.denlilleavis.dk
Freq: Weekly; Circ: 6700 Not Audited
Ansvarshavende redaktør: Steen Ahonen
Language (s): Danish; Full Page Colour:
9454.00
Currency: Denmark Kroner
NEWSPAPER

Der Nordschleswiger
Editorial: Skibbroen 4, Aabenraa 6200.
T: 45 74 62 38 80
E: redaktion@nordschleswiger.dk
W: http://www.nordschleswiger.dk/
DAILY NEWSPAPER

DET GRØNNE OMRÅDE
Owner: Det Grønne Områdes Mediecenter A/S
Editorial: Gammel Lundtoftevej 3 C, Kgs.
Lyngby 2800. T: 45 70 13 11 00
E: redaktion@dgo.dk W: http://www.dgo.dk
Freq: 2 Times/Week; Circ: 47606
Language (s): Danish; Full Page Colour:
30954.00
Currency: Denmark Kroner
DAILY NEWSPAPER

DET NY ODSHERRED
Owner: Dragsholm Posten A/S
Editorial: Hørve Stationsvej 9, Hørve 4534.
T: 45 59 64 60 60 E: red.dno@b-l.dk
W: http://www.detnyodsherred.dk
Freq: Weekly; Circ: 22688 Dansk
Oplagskontrol
Language (s): Danish; Full Page Colour:
10347.00
Currency: Denmark Kroner
DAILY NEWSPAPER

Digeposten
Owner: Digeposten
Editorial: Kongevej 5b, Tønder 6270.
T: 45 74 72 33 42 E: redaktion@digeposten.dk
W: http://www.digeposten.dk
Freq: Weekly; Circ: 27744 Not Audited
Language (s): Danish; Full Page Colour:
12236.50
Currency: Denmark Kroner
NEWSPAPER

Din Avis Randers
Owner: Din Avis A/S
Editorial: Brotoften 10, box 174, Randers
8900. T: 45 86 40 12 22
E: redaktion@dinavis.dk
W: http://www.dinavis.dk
Freq: Daily; Circ: 42656 Not Audited
Ansvarshavende redaktør: Ole Søndergaard
Language (s): Danish; Full Page Colour:
9464.00
Currency: Denmark Kroner
NEWSPAPER

Djurslandsposten
Owner: Djurslandsposten A/S
Editorial: Østerbrogade 45, Grenå 8500.
T: 45 87 58 55 00
E: redaktion@djurslandsposten.dk
W: http://dinby.dk/djurslandsposten
Freq: Weekly; Circ: 28100 Pub Statement
Ansvarshavende redaktør: Søren Andersen;
Redaktør: Henrik Dolmer
Language (s): Danish; Full Page Colour:
9471.00
Currency: Denmark Kroner
NEWSPAPER

DNR DRONNINGLUND NÆRRADIO
T: 45 98 28 14 44 E: dnr@dnr.dk
W: http://www.dnr.dk
Freq: Daily
Language (s): Danish
DAILY NEWSPAPER

DR P4 Bornholm Eftermiddag
Owner: DR
Editorial: Åkirkebyvej 52, Rønne 3700.
T: 45 56 94 37 00 E: bornholm@dr.dk
W: http://www.dr.dk/bornholm
Freq: Daily; Circ: 5000 Pub Statement
Language (s): Danish
DAILY NEWSPAPER

DR P4 Bornholm Formiddag
Owner: DR
Editorial: Åkirkebyvej 52, Rønne 3700.
T: 45 56 94 37 00 E: bornholm@dr.dk
W: http://www.dr.dk/bornholm
Freq: Daily
Language (s): Danish
DAILY NEWSPAPER

DR P4 Bornholm Morgen
Owner: DR
Editorial: Åkirkebyvej 52, Rønne 3700.
T: 45 56 94 37 00 E: bornholm@dr.dk
W: http://www.dr.dk/bornholm
Freq: Daily; Circ: 8000 Pub Statement
Language (s): Danish
DAILY NEWSPAPER

DR P4 Fyn Eftermiddag
Owner: DR
Editorial: Lille Tornbjerg Vej 10, Odense 5220.
T: 45 63 15 77 00 E: fyn@dr.dk
W: http://www.dr.dk/fyn
Freq: Daily; Circ: 30000 Pub Statement
Language (s): Danish
DAILY NEWSPAPER

DR P4 Fyn Formiddag
Owner: DR
Editorial: Lille Tornbjerg Vej 10, Odense 5220.
T: 45 63 15 77 00 E: fyn@dr.dk
W: http://www.dr.dk/fyn
Freq: Daily; Circ: 43500 Pub Statement
Language (s): Danish
DAILY NEWSPAPER

DR P4 Fyn Morgen
Owner: DR
Editorial: Lille Tornbjerg Vej 10, Odense 5220.
T: 45 63 15 77 00 E: fyn@dr.dk
W: http://www.dr.dk/fyn
Freq: Daily; Circ: 45000 Pub Statement
Language (s): Danish
DAILY NEWSPAPER

DR P4 København Eftermiddag
Owner: DR
T: 45 35 20 68 00 E: kbh@dr.dk
W: http://www.dr.dk/kbh
Freq: Daily; Circ: 102000 Pub Statement
Language (s): Danish
DAILY NEWSPAPER

DR P4 København Formiddag
Owner: DR
T: 45 35 20 68 00 E: kbh@dr.dk
W: http://www.dr.dk/kbh
Freq: Daily; Circ: 122500 Pub Statement
Language (s): Danish
DAILY NEWSPAPER

DR P4 København Morgen
Owner: DR
T: 45 35 20 68 00 **E:** kbh@dr.dk
W: http://www.dr.dk/kbh
Freq: Daily; **Circ:** 167000 Pub Statement
Language (s): Danish
DAILY NEWSPAPER

DR P4 Midt & Vest Eftermiddag
Owner: DR
Editorial: Postbox 1150, Holstebro 7500.
T: 45 96 10 75 00 **E:** vest@dr.dk
W: http://www.dr.dk/vest
Freq: Daily; **Circ:** 26000 Pub Statement
Language (s): Danish
DAILY NEWSPAPER

DR P4 Midt & Vest Formiddag
Owner: DR
Editorial: Postbox 1150, Holstebro 7500.
T: 45 96 10 75 00 **E:** vest@dr.dk
W: http://www.dr.dk/vest
Freq: Daily; **Circ:** 39000 Pub Statement
Language (s): Danish
DAILY NEWSPAPER

DR P4 Midt & Vest Morgen
Owner: DR
Editorial: Postbox 1150, Holstebro 7500.
T: 45 96 10 75 00 **E:** vest@dr.dk
W: http://www.dr.dk/vest
Freq: Daily; **Circ:** 38000 Pub Statement
Language (s): Danish
DAILY NEWSPAPER

DR P4 Nordjylland Formiddag
Owner: DR
Editorial: Fredrik Bajers Vej 9, Aalborg 9220.
T: 45 96 35 76 00 **E:** nord@dr.dk
W: http://www.dr.dk/nord
Freq: Daily; **Circ:** 45500 Pub Statement
Language (s): Danish
DAILY NEWSPAPER

DR P4 Nordjylland Morgen
Owner: DR
Editorial: Fredrik Bajers Vej 9, Aalborg 9220.
T: 45 96 35 76 00 **E:** nord@dr.dk
W: http://www.dr.dk/nord
Freq: Daily; **Circ:** 52000 Pub Statement
Language (s): Danish
DAILY NEWSPAPER

DR P4 Østjylland Eftermiddag
Owner: DR
Editorial: Olof Palmes Allé 10-12, Århus 8200.
T: 45 87 39 70 00 **E:** p4aarhus@dr.dk
W: http://www.dr.dk/regioner/aarhus
Freq: Daily; **Circ:** 32000 Pub Statement
Language (s): Danish
DAILY NEWSPAPER

DR P4 Østjylland Formiddag
Owner: DR
Editorial: Olof Palmes Allé 10-12, Århus 8200.
T: 45 87 39 70 00 **E:** p4aarhus@dr.dk
W: http://www.dr.dk/regioner/aarhus
Freq: Daily; **Circ:** 42000 Pub Statement
Language (s): Danish
DAILY NEWSPAPER

DR P4 Østjylland Morgen
Owner: DR
Editorial: Olof Palmes Allé 10-12, Århus 8200.
T: 45 87 39 70 00 **E:** p4aarhus@dr.dk
W: http://www.dr.dk/regioner/aarhus
Freq: Daily; **Circ:** 55000 Pub Statement
Language (s): Danish
DAILY NEWSPAPER

DR P4 Sjælland Eftermiddag
Owner: DR
Editorial: Vadestedet 1, Næstved 4700.
T: 45 55 75 34 00 **E:** sjaelland@dr.dk
W: http://www.dr.dk/Regioner/Sjaelland
Freq: Daily; **Circ:** 37000 Pub Statement
Language (s): Danish
DAILY NEWSPAPER

DR P4 Sjælland Formiddag
Owner: DR
Editorial: Vadestedet 1, Næstved 4700.
T: 45 55 75 34 00 **E:** sjaelland@dr.dk
W: http://www.dr.dk/Regioner/Sjaelland
Freq: Daily; **Circ:** 48500 Pub Statement
Language (s): Danish
DAILY NEWSPAPER

DR P4 Sjælland Morgen
Owner: DR
Editorial: Vadestedet 1, Næstved 4700.
T: 45 55 75 34 00 **E:** sjaelland@dr.dk
W: http://www.dr.dk/Regioner/Sjaelland
Freq: Daily; **Circ:** 56000 Pub Statement
Language (s): Danish
DAILY NEWSPAPER

DR P4 Syd Eftermiddag
Owner: DR
Editorial: H.P.Hanssensgade 11, Aabenraa 6200. **T:** 45 73 33 79 99 **E:** syd@dr.dk
W: http://www.dr.dk/syd
Freq: Daily; **Circ:** 23000 Pub Statement
Language (s): Danish
DAILY NEWSPAPER

DR P4 Syd; Formiddag
Owner: DR
Editorial: H.P.Hanssensgade 11, Aabenraa 6200. **T:** 45 73 33 79 99 **E:** syd@dr.dk
W: http://www.dr.dk/syd
Freq: Daily; **Circ:** 31000 Pub Statement
Language (s): Danish
DAILY NEWSPAPER

DR P4 Syd; Morgen
Owner: DR
Editorial: H.P.Hanssensgade 11, Aabenraa 6200. **T:** 45 73 33 79 99 **E:** syd@dr.dk
W: http://www.dr.dk/syd
Freq: Daily; **Circ:** 36000 Pub Statement
Language (s): Danish
DAILY NEWSPAPER

DR P4 Trekanten Eftermiddag
Owner: DR
Editorial: Den hvide Facet 1, 4. sal, Vejle 7100. **T:** 45 76 41 78 00 **E:** trekanten@dr.dk
W: http://www.dr.dk/Regioner/Trekanten
Freq: Daily; **Circ:** 17000 Pub Statement
Language (s): Danish
DAILY NEWSPAPER

DR P4 Trekanten Formiddag
Owner: DR
Editorial: Den hvide Facet 1, 4. sal, Vejle 7100. **T:** 45 76 41 78 00 **E:** trekanten@dr.dk
W: http://www.dr.dk/Regioner/Trekanten
Freq: Daily; **Circ:** 25000 Pub Statement
Language (s): Danish
DAILY NEWSPAPER

DR P4 Trekanten Morgen
Owner: DR
Editorial: Den hvide Facet 1, 4. sal, Vejle 7100. **T:** 45 76 41 78 00 **E:** trekanten@dr.dk
W: http://www.dr.dk/Regioner/Trekanten
Freq: Daily; **Circ:** 26000 Pub Statement
Language (s): Danish
DAILY NEWSPAPER

Dragør Nyt
Owner: Dragør-Nyt A/S
Editorial: Søndre Tangvej 22, Dragør 2791.
T: 45 32 53 08 67
E: redaktion@dragoer-nyt.dk
W: http://www.dragoer-nyt.dk
Freq: Weekly; **Circ:** 7000 Not Audited
Language (s): Danish; Full Page Colour:
4745.00
Currency: Denmark Kroner
NEWSPAPER

E.U. RADIO
T: 45 49 28 26 66 **E:** per-kildahl@adslhome.dk
W: http://www.radiohelsingor.dk
Freq: Daily
Language (s): Danish
DAILY NEWSPAPER

Egtved Posten
Owner: Vejle Amts Folkeblad
Editorial: Aftensang 10, Egtved 6040.
T: 45 75 55 10 99
E: redaktionen@egtved-posten.dk
W: http://www.egtved-post.dk/egtved_posten.php
Freq: Weekly; **Circ:** 9982 Not Audited
EDITOR IN CHIEF: Mogens Madsen
Language (s): Danish; Full Page Colour:
7025.00
Currency: Denmark Kroner
NEWSPAPER

Ekstra Bladet
Owner: JP/Politikens Hus A/S
Editorial: Rådhuspladsen 37, Copenhagen 1785. **T:** 45 33 11 13 13 **E:** redaktionen@eb.dk
W: http://www.ekstrabladet.dk
Freq: Daily; **Circ:** 95107
Editor in Chief: Karen Bro; **Nyhedsredaktør:**
Mogens Madsen
Language (s): Danish; Full Page Colour:
72380.00
Currency: Denmark Kroner
DAILY NEWSPAPER

ELBOBLADET
Owner: Fredericia Lokalblade i/s
Editorial: Nørrebrogade 5, Fredericia 7000.
T: 45 75 92 12 44 **E:** redaktion@elbobladet.dk
W: http://www.elbobladet.dk **Circ:** 39304
Redaktør: Benny Grarup; **Redaktionel**

medarbejder: Lisbeth Larsen
Language (s): Danish; Full Page Colour:
26208.00
Currency: Denmark Kroner
NEWSPAPER

Erhverv/ Fyn
Owner: Mogens Pedersen
Editorial: Ryttermarken 11, Svendborg 5700.
T: 45 62 22 13 14 **E:** post@erhverv-fyn.dk
W: http://www.erhverv-fyn.dk
Freq: Monthly; **Circ:** 21000 Pub Statement
Ansvarshavende redaktør: Mogens Pedersen
Language (s): Danish
NEWSPAPER

Extra Posten
Owner: Extra Posten A/S
Editorial: Nygade 30, Nakskov 4900.
T: 45 54 88 08 20 **E:** post@extraposten.dk
W: http://www.extra-posten.dk
Freq: Weekly; **Circ:** 20543 Not Audited
Language (s): Danish; Full Page Colour:
10979.00
Currency: Denmark Kroner
NEWSPAPER

Fanø Ugeblad
Owner: Fanø Ugeblad A/S
Editorial: Willemoesvej 7, Fanø 6720.
T: 45 75 16 20 53 **E:** post@fanougeblad.dk
W: http://www.fanougeblad.dk
Freq: Weekly; **Circ:** 2400 Not Audited
Ansvarshavende redaktør: Dorte Hembo;
Ansvarshavende redaktør: Gedske Vind
Language (s): Danish; Full Page Colour:
12243.00
Currency: Denmark Kroner
NEWSPAPER

Farsø Avis
Owner: Farsø Avis A/S
Editorial: Søndergården 8, Farsø 9640.
T: 45 98 63 10 11
E: redaktionen@farso-avis.dk
W: http://www.farsoavis.dk
Freq: Weekly; **Circ:** 8023 Not Audited
Ansvarshavende redaktør: Lars Rabøl
Language (s): Danish; Full Page Colour:
8316.00
Currency: Denmark Kroner
NEWSPAPER

FAVRSKOV POSTEN
Owner: Favrskov Gruppen
Editorial: Torvegade 1, Hammel 8450.
T: 45 86 96 17 66
W: http://favrskov-gruppen.dk
Freq: Weekly; **Circ:** 34500 Pub Statement
EDITOR: Claus Krogh
Language (s): Danish; Full Page Colour:
10085.50
Currency: Denmark Kroner
DAILY NEWSPAPER

Favrskovavisen
Owner: Midtjyske Medier
Editorial: Ågade 97, Hadsten 8370.
T: 45 87 61 35 00 **E:** habl@berlingskemedia.dk
W: http://dinby.dk/favrskov-avisen
Freq: Weekly; **Circ:** 30115 Not Audited
Language (s): Danish; Full Page Colour:
10857.00
Currency: Denmark Kroner
NEWSPAPER

Faxe Bugten
Owner: Sjællandske Medier A/S
Editorial: Rønnedevej 62 B, Fakse 4640.
T: 45 56 71 32 31 **E:** kontor@faxebugten.dk
W: http://www.faxebugten.dk
Freq: Weekly; **Circ:** 16500 Not Audited
Redaktør: Torkild Svane Kraft
Language (s): Danish; Full Page Colour:
12012.00
Currency: Denmark Kroner
NEWSPAPER

Fjends Folkeblad
Owner: Fjends Folkeblad A/S
Editorial: Nørregade 15, Stoholm Jylland 7850. **T:** 45 97 54 10 02 **E:** info@fjendsavis.dk
W: http://www.fjendsavis.dk
Freq: Weekly; **Circ:** 8300 Not Audited
EDITOR IN CHIEF: Jesper Sørensen
Language (s): Danish; Full Page Colour:
8662.50
Currency: Denmark Kroner
NEWSPAPER

Fjerritslev Ugeavis
Owner: Nordjyske
Editorial: Østergade 33, Fjerritslev 9690.
T: 45 99 50 58 00
E: jammerbugt.ann@nordjyske.dk
W: http://www.nordjyskeugeaviser.dk

Freq: Weekly; **Circ:** 7571 Not Audited
Chefredaktør: Anne-Marie Dohm;
Chefredaktør: Lars Jespersen; **EDITOR IN CHIEF:** Inger Lise Jønsson; **Redaktionschef:** Jørgen la Cour-Harbo; **Ansvarshavende redaktør:** Per Lyngby; **EDITOR IN CHIEF:** Carl Madsen; **Redaktør:** Hans Peter Kragh; **EDITOR IN CHIEF:** Kirsten Vestergaard
Language (s): Danish; Full Page Colour:
8547.00
Currency: Denmark Kroner
NEWSPAPER

FLENSBORG-AVIS
Owner: Flensborg Avis AG
Editorial: Wittenberger Weg 19, Flensburg.
T: 49 46 15 04 50 **E:** red@fla.de
W: http://www.flensborg-avis.de
Freq: Daily; **Circ:** 6324 Pub Statement
Redakteur / Editor: Jan Christensen;
Redaktionssekretær: Trine Flamming
Language (s): Danish; Full Page Colour:
18826.50
Currency: Denmark Kroner
DAILY NEWSPAPER

FLENSBORG-AVIS Slesvig
Owner: Flensborg Avis AG
E: slesvig@flensborg-avis.de
W: http://www.flensborg-avis.de
Freq: Daily; **Circ:** 7000 Pub Statement
Language (s): Danish
DAILY NEWSPAPER

FLENSBORG-AVIS Sønderjylland
Owner: Flensborg Avis AG
E: sonderjylland@flensborg-avis.de
W: http://www.flensborg-avis.de
Freq: Daily; **Circ:** 7000 Pub Statement
Language (s): Danish
DAILY NEWSPAPER

FLENSBORG-AVIS Sydslesvig
Owner: Flensborg Avis AG
E: sydslesvig@flensborg-avis.de
W: http://www.flensborg-avis.de
Freq: Daily; **Circ:** 7000 Pub Statement
Redaktør: Trine Flamming
Language (s): Danish
DAILY NEWSPAPER

Folkebladet Djursland
Owner: Folkebladet Djursland A/S
Editorial: Mølletorvet 6, Auning 8963.
T: 45 87 58 55 00 **E:** jope@amtsavisen.dk
W: http://www.dinby.dk/folkebladet-djursland/velkommen
Freq: Weekly; **Circ:** 13037 Not Audited
Ansvarshavende redaktør: John Pedersen
Language (s): Danish; Full Page Colour:
7623.00
Currency: Denmark Kroner
NEWSPAPER

Folkebladet for Glostrup, Brøndby og Vallensbæk
Owner: Folkebladet for Glostrup og Vestegnen A/S
Editorial: Glostrup Torv 6, Glostrup 2600.
T: 45 43 96 00 31
E: folkebladet@folkebladet.dk
W: http://www.folkebladet.dk
Freq: Weekly; **Circ:** 36232 Not Audited
Language (s): Danish; Full Page Colour:
29658.00
Currency: Denmark Kroner
NEWSPAPER

FOLKEBLADET LEMVIG
Owner: Lemvig Folkeblad A/S
Editorial: Bredgade 20, Lemvig 7620.
T: 45 96 63 04 00 **E:** lemvig@bergske.dk
W: http://www.lemvig-folkeblad.dk **Circ:** 3300
EDITOR IN CHIEF: Hans Krabbe
Language (s): Danish; Full Page Colour:
12969.00
Currency: Denmark Kroner
NEWSPAPER

Folketidende
Owner: Lollands-Posten A/S
Editorial: Banegårdspladsen 2, Maribo 4930.
T: 45 54 88 08 60
E: redaktion@folketidende.dk
W: http://folketidende.dk
Freq: Weekly; **Circ:** 21913 Not Audited
Redaktør: Jens Bang; **Ansvarshavende redaktør:** Alfred Jensen
Language (s): Danish; Full Page Colour:
20170.00
Currency: Denmark Kroner
NEWSPAPER

FOLKETIDENDE WeekendTid
Owner: Lolland-Falsters Folketidende A/S
Editorial: Tværgade 20, Nykøbing 4800.
T: 45 54 88 02 00

E: weekend@folketidende.dk
W: http://www.folketidende.dk
Freq: Daily; Circ: 7436
Redaktionschef: Pia Winther
Language (s): Danish
DAILY NEWSPAPER

Folketidende; Erhverv
Owner: Lolland-Falster Folketidende A/S
Editorial: Tværgade 20, Nykøbing DK-4800.
T: 45 54 88 02 00 E: hg@folketidende.dk
W: http://www.folketidende.dk
Freq: Daily; Circ: 7436
Language (s): Danish
DAILY NEWSPAPER

FOLKETS RADIO
W: http://www.myspace.com/Folketsradio
Language (s): Danish
DAILY NEWSPAPER

FREDERICIA DAGBLAD
Owner: Vejle Amts Folkeblad A/S
Editorial: Nørrebrogade 5-7, Fredericia 7000.
T: 45 75 92 26 00 E: fd@fredericiadagblad.dk
W: http://www.vejleamtsfolkeblad.dk
Freq: Daily; Circ: 4743 Pub Statement
Chefredaktør: Marianne Husted
Language (s): Danish; Full Page Colour:
35984.00
Currency: Denmark Kroner
DAILY NEWSPAPER

FREDERICIA DAGBLAD Billund
Owner: Vejle Amts Folkeblad A/S
Editorial: Højmarksvej 5, Billund 7190.
T: 45 75 33 80 33
E: billund@vejleamtsfolkeblad.dk
W: http://www.fredericiadagblad.dk
Freq: Daily; Circ: 5084
Language (s): Danish
DAILY NEWSPAPER

FREDERICIA DAGBLAD Bolig
Owner: Vejle Amts Folkeblad A/S
Editorial: Nørrebrogade 5-7, Fredericia 7000.
T: 45 75 92 26 00 E: fd@fredericiadagblad.dk
W: http://www.fredericiadagblad.dk
Circ: 25000
EDITOR AT LARGE: Mette Eriksen; Redaktør:
Marianne Husted
Language (s): Danish
DAILY NEWSPAPER

FREDERICIA DAGBLAD Brande-Ikast
Owner: Vejle Amts Folkeblad A/S
Editorial: Storegade 38, Brande 7330.
T: 45 97 18 06 22
E: brande@vejleamtsfolkeblad.dk
W: http://www.fredericiadagblad.dk
Freq: Daily; Circ: 5084
Redaktør: Søren Rahbek
Language (s): Danish
DAILY NEWSPAPER

FREDERICIA DAGBLAD Debat
Owner: Vejle Amts Folkeblad A/S
Editorial: Bugattivej 8, Vejle 7100
E: debat@vejleamtsfolkeblad.dk
W: http://www.fredericiadagblad.dk
Freq: Daily; Circ: 5084
Redaktionssekretær: Peter Hald; Redaktør:
Marianne Husted
Language (s): Danish
DAILY NEWSPAPER

FREDERICIA DAGBLAD Hedensted
Owner: Vejle Amts Folkeblad A/S
Editorial: Vejlevej 4, Hedensted 8722.
T: 45 75 89 16 44
E: hedensted@vejleamtsfolkeblad.dk
W: http://www.fredericiadagblad.dk
Freq: Daily; Circ: 5084
Language (s): Danish
DAILY NEWSPAPER

FREDERICIA DAGBLAD Motor
Owner: Vejle Amts Folkeblad A/S
Editorial: Bugattivej 8, Vejle 7100.
T: 45 76 41 49 72
E: motor@vejleamtsfolkeblad.dk
W: http://www.vejleamtsfolkeblad.dk
Freq: Weekly; Circ: 5084 Dansk
Oplagskontrol
Language (s): Danish
DAILY NEWSPAPER

FREDERICIA DAGBLAD Navne
Owner: Vejle Amts Folkeblad A/S
Editorial: Bugattivej 8, Vejle 7100.
T: 45 75 92 26 00
E: navne@fredericiadagblad.dk
W: http://www.fredericiadagblad.dk
Freq: Daily; Circ: 5084
Language (s): Danish
DAILY NEWSPAPER

FREDERICIA DAGBLAD Sporten
Owner: Vejle Amts Folkeblad A/S
Editorial: Bugattivej 8, Vejle 7100.
T: 45 75 85 77 88
E: sporten@vejleamtsfolkeblad.dk
W: http://www.vaf-fd.dk
Freq: Daily; Circ: 5084
Language (s): Danish
DAILY NEWSPAPER

Fredericia Dagblad; Vejle-Vejle Vest
Owner: Vejle Amts Folkeblad A/S
Editorial: Bugattivej 8, Vejle 7100.
T: 45 75 85 77 88
E: vaf@vejleamtsfolkeblad.dk
W: http://www.fredericiadagblad.dk
Freq: Daily; Circ: 5084
Redaktionschef: Mogens G. Madsen
Language (s): Danish
DAILY NEWSPAPER

Frederiksberg Bladet
Owner: Berlingske Lokalaviser A/S
Editorial: Dirch Passers Allé 27, 1. sal,
Frederiksberg 2000. T: 45 33 88 88 88
E: red.fbl@berlingskemedia.dk
W: http://www.frederiksbergbladet.dk
Freq: Weekly; Circ: 58225 Not Audited
Language (s): Danish; Full Page Colour:
24304.00
Currency: Denmark Kroner
NEWSPAPER

FREDERIKSBORG AMTS AVIS
Owner: Sjællandske Medier A/S
T: 45 48 24 41 00 E: frederiksborg@sn.dk
W: http://www.frederiksborgamtsavis.dk
Freq: Daily; Circ: 26847 FMK
Redaktionschef: Charlotte Freiberg
Language (s): Danish
DAILY NEWSPAPER

FREDERIKSBORG AMTS AVIS
Frederikssund
Owner: Sjællandske Medier A/S
Editorial: Kockvej 9, Frederikssund 3600.
T: 45 47 31 00 26 E: frederikssund@sn.dk
W: http://www.frederiksborgamtsavis.dk
Freq: Daily; Circ: 26847
Redaktør: Maj-Britt Holm
Language (s): Danish
DAILY NEWSPAPER

FREDERIKSBORG AMTS AVIS
Gribskov
Owner: Sjællandske Medier A/S
T: 45 48 79 69 00 E: gribskov@sn.dk
W: http://www.frederiksborgamtsavis.dk
Redaktør: Karl Erik Frederiksen
Language (s): Danish
DAILY NEWSPAPER

FREDERIKSBORG AMTS AVIS
Halsnæs
Owner: Sjællandske Medier A/S
Editorial: Strandvejen 6 A, Frederiksværk 3300
E: halsnaes@sn.dk
W: http://www.frederiksborgamtsavis.dk
Freq: Daily; Circ: 30000
Redaktør: Malin Westerlund
Language (s): Danish
DAILY NEWSPAPER

FREDERIKSBORG AMTS AVIS
Helsingør
Owner: Dagbladet A/S
Editorial: Torvegade 3, Helsingør 3000.
T: 45 49 21 31 00 E: helsingoer@sn.dk
W: http://www.frederiksborgamtsavis.dk
Freq: Daily; Circ: 26847 Pub Statement
Language (s): Danish
DAILY NEWSPAPER

FREDERIKSBORG AMTS AVIS
Hillerød
Owner: Sjællandske Medier A/S
Editorial: Slotsgade 22 41 00
T: 45 48 22 41 00
E: hilleroed.red@sj-medier.dk
W: http://www.frederiksborgamtsavis.dk
Freq: Daily; Circ: 26847
Chefredaktør: Palle Høj
Language (s): Danish
DAILY NEWSPAPER

FREDERIKSBORG AMTS AVIS
Hørsholm
Owner: Sjællandske Medier A/S
Editorial: Hovedgaden 37B, Box 57, Hørsholm
2970. T: 45 45 86 31 00 E: hoersholm@sn.dk
W: http://www.frederiksborgamtsavis.dk
Freq: Daily; Circ: 26847 Pub Statement
Redaktør: Lars Ramlow
Language (s): Danish
DAILY NEWSPAPER

FREDERIKSBORG AMTS AVIS
Sporten
Owner: Sjællandske Medier A/S
Editorial: Slotsgade 1, Hillerød 3400.
T: 45 48 22 89 20 E: sporten.faa@sn.dk
W: http://www.frederiksborgamtsavis.dk
Freq: Daily; Circ: 26847 Pub Statement
Language (s): Danish
DAILY NEWSPAPER

FREDERIKSHAVN LOKALRADIO
T: 45 98 42 55 42
E: post@frederikshavnlokalradio.dk
W: http://www.frederikshavnlokalradio.dk
Freq: Daily
Language (s): Danish
DAILY NEWSPAPER

Frederiksværk Ugeblad, Halsnæs
Posten
Owner: Berlingske Lokalaviser A/S
Editorial: Valseværksgade 6, Frederiksværk
3300. T: 45 47 77 14 14
E: jeh@berlingskemedia.dk
W: http://www.frederiksvaerkugeblad.dk
Freq: Daily; Circ: 21758 Not Audited
EDITOR IN CHIEF: Julie Mathiesen
Language (s): Danish; Full Page Colour:
13341.50
Currency: Denmark Kroner
NEWSPAPER

FUGLEBJERG POSTEN
Owner: Susålandets Avis Aps
Editorial: Østergade 17B, Glumsø 4171.
T: 45 57 65 04 18 E: ringsted.salg@sn.dk
W: http://www.susaaavisen.dk
Freq: Weekly; Circ: 32600 Pub Statement
EDITOR: Britt Nielsen; EDITOR: Britt Nielsen
Language (s): Danish; Full Page Colour:
10999.50
Currency: Denmark Kroner
DAILY NEWSPAPER

FURESØ AVIS
Owner: Furesøens Mediecenter A/S
Editorial: Frederiksborgvej 15, 1. sal,
Postboks 80, Farum 3520. T: 45 70 13 11 00
E: redaktion@furavis.dk
W: http://www.farumavis.dk
Freq: Weekly; Circ: 11174
EDITOR IN CHIEF: kim Belmark
Language (s): Danish; Full Page Colour:
11680.50
Currency: Denmark Kroner
DAILY NEWSPAPER

FURESØ AVIS
Owner: Furesøens Mediecenter A/S
Editorial: Frederiksborgvej 15, 1. sal, Farum
3520. T: 45 70 13 11 00
E: redaktion@furavis.dk
W: http://www.furesoeavis.dk
Freq: Weekly; Circ: 17306
Editor in Chief: Kim Belmark; Redaktør:
Helene Holm Stolle
Language (s): Danish; Full Page Colour:
22291.50
Currency: Denmark Kroner
DAILY NEWSPAPER

Fyens Stifrstidende; Erhverv
Owner: Fyens Stiftstidende A/S
Editorial: Banegårdspladsen, Odense 5100.
T: 45 65 45 51 35 E: erhverv@fyens.dk
W: http://www.fyens.dk
Freq: Daily; Circ: 59568
Language (s): Danish
DAILY NEWSPAPER

FYENS STIFTSTIDENDE
Owner: Fyens Stiftstidende A/S
Editorial: Banegårdspladsen, Odense C 5100.
T: 45 66 11 11 11 E: redaktion@fyens.dk
W: http://www.fyens.dk
Freq: Daily; Circ: 56379 Dansk Oplagskontrol
Nyhedsredaktør/chef: Torben Christiansen;
Redaktionschef: Jan Kristensen; Editor in
Chief: Erik Stærke Eriksen; Chefredaktør: Per
Westergård
Language (s): Danish; Full Page Colour:
55347.00
Currency: Denmark Kroner
DAILY NEWSPAPER

Fyens Stiftstidende ~Nordøstfyn
Owner: Fyens Stiftstidende A/S
Editorial: Strandgade 1A, Kerteminde 5300.
T: 45 65 32 19 45 E: nordostfyn@fyens.dk
W: http://www.fyens.dk
Freq: Daily; Circ: 59568 FMK
Redaktør: Henrik Mohr
Language (s): Danish
DAILY NEWSPAPER

Fyens Stiftstidende ~Østfyn
Owner: Fyens Stiftstidende A/S
Editorial: Nørretorv, Nørrevoldgade 58,
Nyborg 5800. T: 45 63 31 21 30
E: ostfyn@fyens.dk W: http://www.fyens.dk
Freq: Daily; Circ: 59568 Dansk Oplagskontrol
Redaktør: Niels Andreasen
Language (s): Danish
DAILY NEWSPAPER

Fyens Stiftstidende ~Sydfyn
Owner: Fyens Stiftstidende A/S
Editorial: Gerritsgade 40, Svendborg 5700.
T: 45 62 21 15 55 E: sydfyn@fyens.dk
W: http://www.fyens.dk
Freq: Daily; Circ: 59568 Dansk Oplagskontrol
Language (s): Danish
DAILY NEWSPAPER

Fyens Stiftstidende ~Vestfyn
Owner: Fyens Stiftstidende A/S
Editorial: Østergade 12, Assens 5610.
T: 45 63 71 18 00 E: redaktion@fyens.dk
W: http://www.fyens.dk
Freq: Daily; Circ: 59568 FMK
Language (s): Danish
DAILY NEWSPAPER

FYENS STIFTSTIDENDE Bagsiden
Owner: Fyens Stiftstidende A/S
Editorial: Banegårdspladsen, Odense DK-
5100. T: 45 66 11 11 11
E: bagsiden@fyens.dk
W: http://www.fyens.dk/bagsiden
Freq: Daily; Circ: 59568
Language (s): Danish
DAILY NEWSPAPER

FYENS STIFTSTIDENDE BASE
Owner: Fyens Stiftstidende A/S
Editorial: Banegårdspladsen, Odense 5100.
T: 45 66 11 11 11 E: base@fyens.dk
W: http://www.fyens.dk/bogodt
Freq: Weekly; Circ: 74666
Redaktør: Anette Hyllested
Language (s): Danish
DAILY NEWSPAPER

FYENS STIFTSTIDENDE Debat
Owner: Fyens Stiftstidende A/S
Editorial: Banegårdspladsen, Odense 5100.
T: 45 66 11 11 11 E: debat@fyens.dk
W: http://www.fyens.dk
Freq: Daily; Circ: 59568
Debat / Opinion: Jørgen Aldrich; Debat /
Opinion: Martin Mortensen
Language (s): Danish
DAILY NEWSPAPER

FYENS STIFTSTIDENDE Faaborg
Owner: Fyens Stiftstidende A/S
Editorial: Havnegade 2, Faaborg 5600.
T: 45 63 61 24 00 E: faaborg@fyens.dk
W: http://www.fyens.dk
Freq: Daily; Circ: 59568
Redaktør: Tim Visti
Language (s): Danish
DAILY NEWSPAPER

FYENS STIFTSTIDENDE Fokus
Owner: Fyens Stiftstidende A/S
Editorial: Banegårdspladsen, Odense 5100.
T: 45 66 11 11 11 E: sso@fyens.dk
W: http://www.fyens.dk
Freq: Weekly; Circ: 59568
Language (s): Danish
DAILY NEWSPAPER

FYENS STIFTSTIDENDE Højfyn
Owner: Fyens Stiftstidende A/S
Editorial: Stationsvej 1, Tommerup 5690.
T: 45 64 76 15 55 E: hojfyn@fyens.dk
W: http://www.fyens.dk
Freq: Daily; Circ: 59568
Language (s): Danish
DAILY NEWSPAPER

FYENS STIFTSTIDENDE Kør Godt
Owner: Fyens Stiftstidende A/S
Editorial: Banegårdspladsen, Odense 5100.
T: 45 20 20 92 35 E: cs@fyens.dk
W: http://www.fyens.dk
Freq: Weekly; Circ: 59568
Redaktør: Christian Schacht
Language (s): Danish
DAILY NEWSPAPER

FYENS STIFTSTIDENDE Midtfyn
Owner: Fyens Stiftstidende A/S
Editorial: Østergade 19, Ringe 5750.
T: 45 62 62 13 30 E: midtfyn@fyens.dk
W: http://www.fyens.dk
Freq: Daily; Circ: 59568
Redaktør: Birgit Bakkær
Language (s): Danish
DAILY NEWSPAPER

WORLD NEWS MEDIA

FYENS STIFTSTIDENDE Navne
Owner: Fyens Stiftstidende A/S
Editorial: Postboks 236, Odense 5100.
T: 45 65 45 51 71 **E:** navne@fyens.dk
W: http://www.fyens.dk
Freq: Daily; **Circ:** 59568
Language (s): Danish
DAILY NEWSPAPER

FYENS STIFTSTIDENDE Nordfyn
Owner: Fyens Stiftstidende A/S
Editorial: Østergade 14, Bogense 5400.
T: 45 64 82 19 00 **E:** nordfyn@fyens.dk
W: http://www.fyens.dk
Freq: Daily; **Circ:** 59568
Redaktør: Sander Schmidt Astrup
Language (s): Danish
DAILY NEWSPAPER

FYENS STIFTSTIDENDE Nordvestfyn
Owner: Fyens Stiftstidende A/S
Editorial: Havnegade 41, Middelfart 5500.
T: 45 63 41 13 03 **E:** nordvest@fyens.dk
W: http://www.fyens.dk
Freq: Daily; **Circ:** 59568
Redaktør: Jan Bonde
Language (s): Danish
DAILY NEWSPAPER

FYENS STIFTSTIDENDE Odense
Owner: Fyens Stiftstidende A/S
Editorial: Banegårdspladsen, Odense 5100.
T: 45 66 11 11 11 **E:** odense@fyens.dk
W: http://www.fyens.dk
Freq: Daily; **Circ:** 59568
Redaktør: Poul Kjærgaard
Language (s): Danish
DAILY NEWSPAPER

FYENS STIFTSTIDENDE Sport
Owner: Fyens Stiftstidende A/S
Editorial: Banegårdspladsen, Odense 5100.
T: 45 65 45 52 14 **E:** sporten@fyens.dk
W: http://www.fyens.dk
Freq: Daily; **Circ:** 59568 Not Audited
Language (s): Danish
DAILY NEWSPAPER

FYENS STIFTSTIDENDE Weekend
Owner: Fyens Stiftstidende A/S
Editorial: Banegårdspladsen, Odense 5100.
T: 45 66 11 11 11 **E:** sso@fyens.dk
W: http://www.fyens.dk
Freq: Daily; **Circ:** 59568
Language (s): Danish
DAILY NEWSPAPER

Fyens Stiftstidende; Kultur
Owner: Fyens Stifttidende A/S
Editorial: Banegårdspladsen, Odense 5100.
T: 45 66 11 11 11 **E:** kultur@fyens.dk
W: http://www.fyens.dk/nu
Freq: Weekly; **Circ:** 59568
Language (s): Danish
DAILY NEWSPAPER

FYNS AMTS AVIS
Owner: A/S Svendborg Avis
Editorial: Sankt Nicolai Gade 3, Svendborg 5700. **T:** 45 62 21 46 21 **E:** post@faa.dk
W: http://www.fynsamtsavis.dk
Freq: Daily; **Circ:** 17140 Not Audited
Redaktionssekretær: Gitte Gedde;
Redaktionssekretær: Magnus Gersbo-Møller;
Chefredaktør: Jørgen Krebs; **EDITOR IN CHIEF:** Troels Mylenberg; **Nyhedsredaktør/chef:** Carsten Olsen; **Lystfiskeri:** Bjarne Selvager Hansen; **Redaktionschef:** Søren Stidsholt Nielsen
Language (s): Danish; Full Page Colour: 35360.00
Currency: Denmark Kroner
DAILY NEWSPAPER

FYNS AMTS AVIS ~NYBORG
Owner: A/S Svendborg Avis
Editorial: Kongegade 23, 1. sal, Nyborg 5800.
T: 45 72 28 72 80 **E:** nyborg@faa.dk
W: http://www.fynsamtsavis.dk
Freq: Daily; **Circ:** 17505
Language (s): Danish
DAILY NEWSPAPER

FYNS AMTS AVIS Ærø
Owner: A/S Svendborg Avis
Editorial: Havnepladsen 19, Ærøskøbing 5970.
T: 45 62 52 10 14 **E:** aeroe@faa.dk
W: http://www.fynsamtsavis.dk
Freq: Daily; **Circ:** 17505
EDITOR: Andrea Bisgaard
Language (s): Danish
DAILY NEWSPAPER

FYNS AMTS AVIS Faaborg
Owner: A/S Svendborg Avis
Editorial: Østergade 22, Faaborg 5600.
T: 45 62 61 00 22 **E:** post@fynsamtsavis.dk
W: http://www.fynsamtsavis.dk
Freq: Daily; **Circ:** 17505
Language (s): Danish
DAILY NEWSPAPER

FYNS AMTS AVIS Kultur
Owner: A/S Svendborg Avis
Editorial: Sankt Nicolai Gade 3, Svendborg 5700. **T:** 45 62 21 46 21 **E:** post@faa.dk
W: http://www.fyens.dk
Freq: Daily; **Circ:** 17505
Language (s): Danish
DAILY NEWSPAPER

FYNS AMTS AVIS Langeland
Owner: A/S Svendborg Avis
Editorial: Ørstedsgade 18, Rudkøbing 5900.
T: 45 62 51 10 40 **E:** langeland@faa.dk
W: http://www.fynsamtsavis.dk
Freq: Daily; **Circ:** 17505
Language (s): Danish
DAILY NEWSPAPER

FYNS AMTS AVIS Midtfyn
Owner: A/S Svendborg Avis
Editorial: Algade 59, Ringe 5750.
T: 45 62 62 12 60
E: midtfyn@fynsamtsavis.dk
W: http://www.fynsamtsavis.dk
Freq: Daily; **Circ:** 17505
Language (s): Danish
DAILY NEWSPAPER

FYNS AMTS AVIS Natur
Owner: A/S Svendborg Avis
Editorial: Sankt Nicolai Gade 3, Svendborg 5700. **T:** 45 62 21 46 21 **E:** post@faa.dk
W: http://www.fynsamtsavis.dk
Freq: Weekly; **Circ:** 17505
Language (s): Danish
DAILY NEWSPAPER

FYNS AMTS AVIS Navne
Owner: A/S Svendborg Avis
Editorial: Sankt Nicolai Gade 3, Svendborg 5700. **T:** 45 62 21 46 21
E: post@fynsamtsavis.dk
W: http://www.fynsamtsavis.dk
Freq: Daily; **Circ:** 17505
Language (s): Danish
DAILY NEWSPAPER

FYNS AMTS AVIS Rock & Pop
Owner: A/S Svendborg Avis
Editorial: Sank Nicolai gade 3, Box 40, Svendborg 5700. **T:** 45 62 21 46 21
E: post@fynsamtsavis.dk
W: http://www.fynsamtsavis.dk
Freq: Weekly; **Circ:** 17505
Language (s): Danish
DAILY NEWSPAPER

FYNS AMTS AVIS Sport
Owner: A/S Svendborg Avis
Editorial: Sankt Nicolai Gade 3, Svendborg 5700. **T:** 45 62 21 46 21 **E:** sporten@faa.dk
W: http://www.fynsamtsavis.dk
Freq: Daily; **Circ:** 17505
Language (s): Danish
DAILY NEWSPAPER

FYNS AMTS AVIS Svendborg
Owner: A/S Svendborg Avis
Editorial: Sankt Nicolai Gade 3 - Post Box 40, Svendborg 5700. **T:** 45 62 21 46 21
E: svendborg@faa.dk
W: http://www.fynsamtsavis.dk
Freq: Daily; **Circ:** 17505
Redaktør: Ole Kølster
Language (s): Danish
DAILY NEWSPAPER

FYNS AMTS AVIS Sydfyn til søs
Owner: A/S Svendborg Avis
Editorial: Sankt Nicolai Gade 3, Svendborg 5700. **T:** 45 62 21 46 21
E: post@fynsamtsavis.dk
W: http://www.fynsamtsavis.dk
Freq: Weekly; **Circ:** 17505
Redaktionschef: Søren Stidsholt Nielsen
Language (s): Danish
DAILY NEWSPAPER

FYNS AMTS AVIS Ud med snøren
Owner: A/S Svendborg Avis
Editorial: Sankt Nicolai Gade 3, Svendborg 5700. **T:** 45 62 21 46 21 **E:** post@faa.dk
W: http://www.fynsamtsavis.dk
Freq: Weekly; **Circ:** 17505
Language (s): Danish
DAILY NEWSPAPER

FYNS AMTS AVIS; REPORTAGE
Owner: A/S Svendborg Avis
Editorial: Sankt Nicolai Gade 3, Svendborg DK-5700. **T:** 45 62 21 46 21
E: reportage@faa.dk
W: http://www.fynsamtsavis.dk
Freq: Daily; **Circ:** 17505
Nyhedsredaktør/chef: Carsten Olsen
Language (s): Danish
DAILY NEWSPAPER

Gadsaxe Bladet
Owner: Gladsaxe Bladet Aps
Editorial: Søborg Hovedgade 119, 4 sal, Søborg 2860. **T:** 45 39 56 12 75
E: gb@gladsaxebladet.dk
W: http://www.gladsaxebladet.dk
Freq: Weekly; **Circ:** 38989 Not Audited
Language (s): Danish; Full Page Colour: 18697.50
Currency: Denmark Kroner
NEWSPAPER

Galten og Omegns Folkeblad
Owner: Galten og Omegns Folkeblad A/S
Editorial: Søndergade 25, Galten 8464.
T: 45 86 94 30 88
E: galtenfolkeblad@galtenfolkeblad.dk
W: http://www.galtenfolkeblad.dk
Freq: Weekly; **Circ:** 10150 Not Audited
Language (s): Danish; Full Page Colour: 6436.00
Currency: Denmark Kroner
NEWSPAPER

Give Avis
Owner: Give Bogtrykkeri A/S
Editorial: Østergade 3-5, Give 7323.
T: 45 75 73 22 00 **E:** gb@give-avis.dk
W: http://www.give-avis.dk
Freq: Weekly; **Circ:** 21352 Not Audited
Language (s): Danish; Full Page Colour: 7090.50
Currency: Denmark Kroner
NEWSPAPER

GLOBUS GULD
T: 45 74 84 50 20 **E:** post@radioglobus.dk
W: http://www.globusguld.dk
Freq: Daily
Studievært: Kim Hansen; **Studievært:** Poul Horsbøl; **Debat / Opinion:** Allan Løvkvist; **Studievært:** Niels Sarnov
Language (s): Danish
DAILY NEWSPAPER

GLUMSØ UGEBLAD
Owner: Glumsø Bogtrykkeri A/S
Editorial: Østergade 17B, Glumsø 4171.
T: 45 57 65 04 18 **E:** redaktion@lokalnyt.com
W: http://www.susaaavisen.dk
Freq: Weekly; **Circ:** 32600 Pub Statement
Editor in Chief: Palle Høj; **Editor:** Torben Larsen
Language (s): Danish; Full Page Colour: 10999.50
Currency: Denmark Kroner
DAILY NEWSPAPER

Grenaa Bladet
Owner: Grenaa Bladet A/S
Editorial: Storegade 37, Grenå 8500.
T: 45 86 32 16 77
E: redaktion@grenaabladet.dk
W: http://www.grenaabladet.dk
Freq: Weekly; **Circ:** 23925 Not Audited
Redaktør: Henrik Dolmer
Language (s): Danish; Full Page Colour: 7774.50
Currency: Denmark Kroner
NEWSPAPER

Guldborgsund Avis
Owner: Guldborgsund Mediecenter
Editorial: Karlfeltvej 23, Stubbekøbing 4850.
T: 45 30 86 77 68
E: info@guldborgsundavis.dk
W: http://www.guldborgsundavis.dk
Freq: Weekly; **Circ:** 33170 Pub Statement
Language (s): Danish; Full Page Colour: 6000.00
Currency: Denmark Kroner
NEWSPAPER

HABER
Owner: Kast Media
T: 45 33 22 11 66 **E:** haber@haber.dk
W: http://www.haber.dk
Freq: Monthly; **Circ:** 7000 Pub Statement
Chefredaktør: Cengiz Kahraman
Language (s): Danish
NEWSPAPER

Haderslev Ugeavis
Owner: Berlingske Lokalaviser A/S
Editorial: Nørregade 44, Haderslev 6100.
T: 45 74 52 70 70
E: red.haderslev@ugeavisen.dk
W: http://www.haderslevugeavis.dk
Freq: Weekly; **Circ:** 32912 Not Audited
Ansvarshavende redaktør: Henrik Svensson
Language (s): Danish; Full Page Colour: 17361.50
Currency: Denmark Kroner
NEWSPAPER

HADSUND FOLKEBLAD
Owner: Hadsund Folkeblad
Editorial: Jens-Erik Bechsvej 1, Hadsund 9560. **T:** 45 98 57 23 77
E: tekst@hadsundfolkeblad.dk
W: http://www.hadsundfolkeblad.dk
Freq: Weekly; **Circ:** 20757 Not Audited
Ansvarshavende redaktør: Hans Henrik Rasmussen
Language (s): Danish; Full Page Colour: 8361.00
Currency: Denmark Kroner
NEWSPAPER

Hals Avis
Owner: Nordjyske
Editorial: Aalborgvej 327, Gamdrup 9362.
T: 45 98 25 96 00
E: allan.mortensen@nordjyske.dk
W: http://www.nordjyske.dk
Freq: Weekly; **Circ:** 8433 Not Audited
Ansvarshavende redaktør: Per Lyngby;
EDITOR: Allan Mortensen
Language (s): Danish; Full Page Colour: 6628.50
Currency: Denmark Kroner
NEWSPAPER

Hanbo-Bladet
Owner: Nordjyske Stiftstidende
Editorial: Vestergade 3, Brovst 9460.
T: 45 98 23 17 99
E: hanbo-bladet@nordjyske.dk
W: http://www.nordjyskeugeaviser.dk
Freq: Weekly; **Circ:** 7526 Not Audited
EDITOR: Flemming Dahl; **Chefredaktør:** Anne-Marie Dohm; **Chefredaktør:** Lars Jespersen; **Editor:** Per Lyngby
Language (s): Danish; Full Page Colour: 7206.00
Currency: Denmark Kroner
NEWSPAPER

Hanstholm Posten
Owner: Nordjyske Medier
Editorial: Bødkervej 29, Hanstholm 7730.
T: 45 96 55 07 77
E: hanstholm.posten@nordjyske.dk
W: http://www.nordjyskeugeaviser.dk
Freq: Weekly; **Circ:** 6294 Not Audited
Chefredaktør: Anne-Marie Dohm;
Chefredaktør: Per Lyngby; **Redaktør:** Hans Peter Kragh
Language (s): Danish; Full Page Colour: 7899.00
Currency: Denmark Kroner
NEWSPAPER

Haslev Posten
Owner: Sjællandske Medier A/S
Editorial: Jernbanegade 12, 1. sal, Haslev 4690. **T:** 45 56 31 11 12
E: hp@haslev-posten.dk
W: http://www.haslev-posten.dk
Freq: Weekly; **Circ:** 18379 Not Audited
Ansvarshavende redaktør: Hanne Bisgaard
Language (s): Danish; Full Page Colour: 12936.00
Currency: Denmark Kroner
NEWSPAPER

HEDENSTED AVIS/JUELSMINDE
Owner: Hedensted Avis/Juelsminde Posten A/S
Editorial: Bytorvet 14, Hedensted 8722.
T: 45 75 89 13 66
E: presse@hedensted-avis.dk
W: http://www.hedensted-avis.dk
Freq: Weekly; **Circ:** 22804
Language (s): Danish; Full Page Colour: 19040.00
Currency: Denmark Kroner
DAILY NEWSPAPER

HELSINGØR DAGBLAD
Owner: Dansk Avis Tryk A/S
Editorial: Klostermosevej 101, Helsingør 3000.
T: 45 49 22 21 10 **E:** redaktionen@hdnet.dk
W: http://www.helsingordagblad.dk
Freq: Daily; **Circ:** 6250 Not Audited
Redaktionschef: Mads Birch; **Chefredaktør:** Klaus Dalgas
Language (s): Danish; Full Page Colour: 12231.00
Currency: Denmark Kroner
DAILY NEWSPAPER

HELSINGØR DAGBLAD Sporten
Owner: Dansk Avis Tryk A/S

Editorial: Klostermosevej 101, Helsingør 3000.
T: 45 49 22 21 10 **E:** sport@hdnet.dk
Freq: Daily; **Circ:** 6250 Not Audited
Language (s): Danish
DAILY NEWSPAPER

HELSINGØRKANALEN
T: 45 49 21 18 28 **E:** info@helsingorkanalen.dk
W: http://www.helsingorkanalen.dk
Studievært: Ole Bjørn
Language (s): Danish
DAILY NEWSPAPER

Herlev Bladet
Owner: Mediecentret Herlev Bladet
Editorial: Herlev Bygade 39, Herlev 2730.
T: 45 44 94 10 10
E: herlevbladet@herlevbladet.dk
W: http://www.herlevbladet.dk
Freq: Weekly; **Circ:** 25907 Not Audited
EDITOR: Britt Spangsberg
Language (s): Danish; Full Page Colour: 26669.00
Currency: Denmark Kroner
NEWSPAPER

Herning Bladet
Owner: Herning Bladet A/S
Editorial: Østergade 21, Herning 7400.
T: 45 97 12 15 00
E: redaktion@herningbladet.dk
W: http://www.herningbladet.dk
Freq: Weekly; **Circ:** 50000 Not Audited
Ansvarshavende redaktør: Vagn Buch-Pedersen
Language (s): Danish; Full Page Colour: 11133.00
Currency: Denmark Kroner
NEWSPAPER

Herning Folkeblad
Owner: Herning Folkeblad A/S
Editorial: Østergade 21, Herning 7400.
T: 45 96 26 37 00 **E:** hf@herningfolkeblad.dk
W: http://www.herningfolkeblad.dk
Freq: Daily; **Circ:** 56357 Not Audited
Redaktionssekretær: Jette Bentsen; **Nyhedsredaktør/chef:** Peter Jessen; **Redaktionssekretær:** Karen Klausen; **Redaktionssekretær:** Lillian Krøyer Wind; **Chefredaktør:** Vibeke Larsen; **Ansvarshavende redaktør:** Alex Nielsen; **Redaktionssekretær:** Lars Work Kristensen
Language (s): Danish; Full Page Colour: 22812.00
Currency: Denmark Kroner
DAILY NEWSPAPER

Herning Folkeblad ~Ikast- Brande
Owner: Herning Folkeblad
Editorial: Strøget 5, Ikast 7430
E: ikast@herningfolkeblad.dk
W: http://www.herningfolkeblad.dk
Freq: Daily; **Circ:** 13260
Redaktør: Flemming Thulstrup
Language (s): Danish
DAILY NEWSPAPER

Herning Folkeblad ~Kibæk
Editorial: Nr. Bredgade 10, Kibæk 6933
E: kibaek@herningfolkeblad.dk
Freq: Daily; **Circ:** 13200
Redaktør: Mona Maul
Language (s): Danish
DAILY NEWSPAPER

Herning Folkeblad ~Videbæk
Editorial: Bredgade 26, Videbæk 6920
E: videbaek@herningfolkeblad.dk
Freq: Daily; **Circ:** 13200
Redaktør: Hanne Øxenholt
Language (s): Danish
DAILY NEWSPAPER

HERNING FOLKEBLAD Aulum
Editorial: Kirkegade 1, Aulum 7490
E: aulum@herningfolkeblad.dk
Freq: Daily; **Circ:** 13200
Language (s): Danish
DAILY NEWSPAPER

HERNING FOLKEBLAD Vildbjerg
Owner: Herning Folkeblad
Editorial: Bredgade 10, Vildbjerg 7480
E: trehoeje@herningfolkeblad.dk
Freq: Daily; **Circ:** 13200
Redaktør: Jonas Møller Jensen
Language (s): Danish
DAILY NEWSPAPER

Herning Folkeblad; Erhvervsredaktion
Owner: Herning Folkeblad A/S
Editorial: Østergade 25, Herning 7400.
T: 45 96 26 37 00
E: erhverv@herningfolkeblad.dk
W: http://www.herningfolkeblad.dk
Freq: Daily; **Circ:** 13260
Redaktør: Brian Kjær Andersen
Language (s): Danish
DAILY NEWSPAPER

Herning Folkeblad; Sporten
Editorial: Østergade 25, Herning 7400
E: sporten@herningfolkeblad.dk
Freq: Daily; **Circ:** 13200
Language (s): Danish
DAILY NEWSPAPER

Hillerød Posten
Owner: Politikens Lokalaviser A/S
Editorial: Møllestræde 9, Hillerød 3400.
T: 45 70 13 11 00 **E:** redaktion@hip.dk
W: http://hilleroed.lokalavisen.dk/apps/pbcs.dll/forside
Freq: Weekly; **Circ:** 34924 Not Audited
Redaktør: John Jessen Hansen
Language (s): Danish; Full Page Colour: 16835.00
Currency: Denmark Kroner
NEWSPAPER

HILLERØD POSTEN WEEKEND
Owner: Politikens Lokalaviser A/S
Editorial: Møllestræde 9, Hillerød 3400.
T: 45 70 13 11 00 **E:** redaktion@hip.dk
W: http://www.hip.dk
Freq: Weekly; **Circ:** 28000
Redaktør: John Jessen Hansen
Language (s): Danish; Full Page Colour: 10279.50
Currency: Denmark Kroner
DAILY NEWSPAPER

Hirtshals Bindslev Avis
Owner: Hirtshals-Bindslev Avis A/S
Editorial: Fyensgade 9, Hirtshals 9850.
T: 45 99 245060 **E:** hbavis@nordjyske.dk
W: http://www.hbavis.dk
Freq: Weekly; **Circ:** 11000 Not Audited
EDITOR: Susie Skov
Language (s): Danish; Full Page Colour: 5950.00
Currency: Denmark Kroner
NEWSPAPER

HJERTING POSTEN
Owner: Hjerting Posten
Editorial: Ahornvænget 20, Hjerting, Esbjerg V 6710. **T:** 45 75 47 09 99
E: bgn@hjertingposten.dk
W: http://www.hjerting-posten.dk
Freq: Monthly; **Circ:** 13300 Pub Statement
Ansvarshavende redaktør: Birthe Gaj Nielsen
Language (s): Danish; Full Page Colour: 7491.00
Currency: Denmark Kroner
DAILY NEWSPAPER

HLR HØJDERYGGENS LOKALRADIO
T: 45 75 77 02 00
W: http://www.nsaf.dk/hoejderyggensdadio.htm
Freq: 2 Times/Week
Language (s): Danish
DAILY NEWSPAPER

Hobro Avis
Owner: Hobro Avis A/S
Editorial: Adelgade 56, Hobro 9500.
T: 45 98 52 70 30 **E:** hobroavis@nordjyske.dk
W: http://www.nordjyskeugeaviser.dk
Freq: Weekly; **Circ:** 21142 Not Audited
Chefredaktør: Per Lyngby; **EDITOR IN CHIEF:** Jørgen Tøttrup
Language (s): Danish; Full Page Colour: 10231.50
Currency: Denmark Kroner
NEWSPAPER

HOLBÆK AMTS VENSTREBLAD
Owner: Medieselskabet Nordvestsjælland
Editorial: Bladhuset i Holbæk, Ahlgade 1C, Holbæk 4300. **T:** 45 88 88 43 00
E: red.hav@nordvest.dk
W: http://www.nordvestnyt.dk/
Freq: Daily; **Circ:** 15519 Not Audited
EDITOR: Tove Bonnichsen; **EDITOR:** Jesper Danscher; **Chefredaktør:** Mogens Flyvholm; **Nyhedsredaktør/chef:** Jørgen Rasmussen
Language (s): Danish; Full Page Colour: 11998.00
Currency: Denmark Kroner
DAILY NEWSPAPER

HOLBÆK AMTS VENSTREBLAD Jyderup
Owner: Medieselskabet Nordvestsjælland
Editorial: Industrivej 1B, Postbox 70, Jyderup 4450 **E:** red.jyd@nordvest.dk
Freq: Daily; **Circ:** 15519
Kriminalitet: Jakob Erhardt Pedersen
Language (s): Danish
DAILY NEWSPAPER

Holbæk Amts Venstreblad Nykøbing
Owner: Medieselskabet Nordvestsjælland
Editorial: Grønnehavestræde 1, Postbox 79, Nykjøbing 4500. **T:** 45 88 88 45 30
E: red.ods@nordvest.dk
Freq: Daily; **Circ:** 15519
Redaktør: Povl Arne Petersen; **Redaktør:** Martin Hoffmann König
Language (s): Danish
DAILY NEWSPAPER

HOLBÆK AMTS VENSTREBLAD Sport
Owner: Medieselskabet Nordvestsjælland
Editorial: Ahlgade 1, Holbæk 4300.
T: 45 88 88 43 60 **E:** sport.hav@nordvest.dk
W: http://www.venstrebladet.dk
Freq: Daily; **Circ:** 15519
Language (s): Danish
DAILY NEWSPAPER

HOLBÆK AMTS VENSTREBLAD Tølløse/Jernløse
Owner: Medieselskabet Nordvestsjælland
Editorial: Tølløsevej 4, Tølløse 4340
E: red.tol@nordvest.dk
W: http://www.venstrebladet.dk
Freq: Daily; **Circ:** 15519
Language (s): Danish
DAILY NEWSPAPER

Holstebro Onsdag
Owner: De Bergske Blade K/S
Editorial: Lægårdsvej 86, Holstebro 7500.
T: 45 99 12 83 99 **E:** onsdag@bergske.dk
W: http://www.bergske.dk
Freq: Weekly; **Circ:** 40300 Not Audited
Redaktør: Lars Rask Vendelbjerg
Language (s): Danish; Full Page Colour: 11874.00
Currency: Denmark Kroner
NEWSPAPER

HORSENS FOLKEBLAD
Owner: Horsens Folkeblad A/S
Editorial: Bojsens Gård, Søndergade 47, Horsens 8700. **T:** 45 76 27 20 00
E: redaktionen@horsens-folkeblad.dk
W: http://www.horsens-folkeblad.dk
Freq: Daily; **Circ:** 16363 Not Audited
Redaktør: Sven Grønborg; **Redaktør:** Jørgen Hasseriis; **EDITOR IN CHIEF:** Alex Pedersen
Language (s): Danish; Full Page Colour: 34913.00
Currency: Denmark Kroner
DAILY NEWSPAPER

HORSENS FOLKEBLAD Brædstrup
Owner: Horsens Folkeblad
Editorial: Søndergade 36, Brædstrup 8740.
T: 45 75 75 19 33 **E:** braedstrup@hsfo.dk
W: http://www.horsensfolkeblad.dk
Freq: Daily; **Circ:** 16703
Language (s): Danish
DAILY NEWSPAPER

HORSENS FOLKEBLAD Gedved
Owner: Horsens Folkeblad
Editorial: Søndergade 36, Brædstrup 8740.
T: 45 75 75 19 33 **E:** gedved@hsfo.dk
W: http://www.horsens-folkeblad.dk
Freq: Daily; **Circ:** 16703
Language (s): Danish
DAILY NEWSPAPER

HORSENS FOLKEBLAD Hedensted
Owner: Horsens Folkeblad
Editorial: BYTORVET 12, Hedensted 8722
E: hedensted@horsens-folkeblad.dk
W: http://www.horsens-folkeblad.dk
Freq: Daily; **Circ:** 16703 Dansk Oplagskontrol
Language (s): Danish
DAILY NEWSPAPER

HORSENS FOLKEBLAD Juelsminde
Owner: Horsens Folkeblad A/S
Editorial: Odelsgade 32, Juelsminde 7130.
T: 45 75 69 35 33 **E:** juelsminde@hsfo.dk
W: http://www.horsens-folkeblad.dk
Freq: Daily; **Circ:** 16703
Language (s): Danish
DAILY NEWSPAPER

HORSENS FOLKEBLAD Nørre Snede
Owner: Horsens Folkeblad
Editorial: Storegade 38, Brande 7330
E: nsnede@horsens-folkeblad.dk
W: http://www.horsens-folkeblad.dk
Freq: Daily; **Circ:** 16703
Language (s): Danish
DAILY NEWSPAPER

HORSENS FOLKEBLAD Odder
Owner: Horsens Folkeblad
Editorial: Rosengade 15, Odder 8300
E: odder@horsens-folkeblad.dk
W: http://www.horsens-folkeblad.dk
Freq: Daily; **Circ:** 16703
Language (s): Danish
DAILY NEWSPAPER

HORSENS FOLKEBLAD Skanderborg
Owner: Horsens Folkeblad A/S
Editorial: Rosengade 15, Odder 8300.
T: 45 86 56 18 00
E: skanderborg@horsens-folkeblad.dk
W: http://www.horsens-folkeblad.dk
Freq: Daily; **Circ:** 16703
Language (s): Danish
DAILY NEWSPAPER

HORSENS FOLKEBLAD Sporten
Owner: Horsens Folkeblad A/S
Editorial: Søndergade 47, Horsens 8700
E: sporten@horsens-folkeblad.dk
W: http://www.horsens-folkeblad.dk
Freq: Weekly; **Circ:** 16703
Language (s): Danish
DAILY NEWSPAPER

HORSENS FOLKEBLAD TØRRING
Owner: Hornsens Folkeblad
Editorial: Bytorvet 12, Hedensted 8722.
T: 45 75 89 9966 **E:** hedensted@hsfo.dk
W: http://hsfo.dk/
DAILY NEWSPAPER

Horsens Posten
Owner: Horsens Folkeblad A/S
Editorial: Søndergade 47, Horsens 8700.
T: 45 76 27 2000 **E:** redaktionen@hsfo.dk
W: http://horsens-folkeblad.dk
Freq: Weekly; **Circ:** 62715 Not Audited
Redaktør: Jørgen Hasseriis
Language (s): Danish; Full Page Colour: 21226.50
Currency: Denmark Kroner
NEWSPAPER

Hvidovre Avis
Owner: Hvidovre Avis A/S
Editorial: Hvidovrevej 301, Hvidovre 2650.
T: 45 36 49 55 55
E: redaktion@hvidovreavis.dk
W: http://www.hvidovreavis.dk
Freq: Weekly; **Circ:** 27338 Not Audited
Chefredaktør: Niels Erik Madsen
Language (s): Danish; Full Page Colour: 29976.00
Currency: Denmark Kroner
NEWSPAPER

IKAST AVIS
Owner: Ikast Avis A/S
Editorial: Strøget 40, postboks 70, Ikast 7430.
T: 45 97 15 18 00 **E:** presse@ikastavis.dk
W: http://www.ikastavis.dk
Freq: Weekly; **Circ:** 20975
Ansvarshavende redaktør: Steen Hebsgaard
Language (s): Danish; Full Page Colour: 18323.00
Currency: Denmark Kroner
DAILY NEWSPAPER

INDVARDRERRADIO ÅRHUS
Owner: Foreningen Indvandrerradioen
T: 45 86 18 09 12
E: indvandrerradio@hotmail.com
W: http://www.indvandrerradio.dk
Freq: Daily
Language (s): Danish
DAILY NEWSPAPER

Information
Owner: A/S Dagbladet Information
Editorial: Store Kongensgade 40C, Copenhagen 1264. **T:** 45 33 69 60 00
E: i@information.dk
W: http://www.information.dk
Freq: Daily; **Circ:** 21045 Not Audited
Nyhedsredaktør: Anders Fjordbak-Trier; **Ansvarshavende chefredaktør:** Christian Jensen; **Redaktionssekretær:** Jon Jørgensen; **Redaktør:** Susan Knorrenborg; **Redaktionschef:** Rune Lykkeberg; **Nyhedsredaktør/chef:** Claus O. Knudsen; **Redaktionschef:** Nikolai Thyssen
Language (s): Danish; Full Page Colour: 17193.00
Currency: Denmark Kroner
DAILY NEWSPAPER

JYDERUP POSTEN
Owner: Medieselskabet Nordvestsjælland
Editorial: Industrivej 1 B, Postboks 70, Jyderup 4450. **T:** 45 88 88 44 50
E: red.jp@nordvest.dk
W: http://www.venstrebladet.dk/hav/default.asp?action=ugeaviser&ugeavis=jypost
Freq: Weekly; **Circ:** 18920 Not Audited
EDITOR AT LARGE: May-Brit Bülow; **EDITOR**

WORLD NEWS MEDIA

AT LARGE: May-Brit Bülow; **Ansvarshavende redaktør:** Mogens Flyvholm; **EDITOR IN CHIEF:** Gunner Nielsen; **EDITOR AT LARGE:** Anders Vestergaard; **EDITOR AT LARGE:** Anders Vestergaard
Language (s): Danish; Full Page Colour: 9268.00
Currency: Denmark Kroner
NEWSPAPER

JYDERUP POSTEN SPORTEN
Editorial: Nyvej 14, Holbæk 4450.
T: 45 88 88 44 W: http://www.nordvestnyt.dk
EDITOR: Christian Dahl; EDITOR: Christian Dahl
DAILY NEWSPAPER

Jydske Vestkysten
Owner: Syddanske Medier
Editorial: Banegårdspladsen, Esbjerg 6700.
T: 45 79 12 45 00 E: jydskevestkysten@jv.dk
W: http://www.jv.dk
Freq: Daily; Circ: 76550 Not Audited
Chefredaktør: Peter Gram
Language (s): Danish; Full Page Colour: 57077.00
Currency: Denmark Kroner
DAILY NEWSPAPER

JYDSKE VESTKYSTEN ~ Aabenraa
Owner: A/S JYDSKEVESTKYSTEN
Editorial: Sct. Nicolai Gade 5, Aabenraa 6200.
T: 45 79 12 45 00 E: redaktion.aabenraa@jv.dk
W: http://www.jv.dk
Freq: Daily; Circ: 9457
Redaktør: Mikael Justesen
Language (s): Danish; Full Page Colour: 10900.00
Currency: Denmark Kroner
DAILY NEWSPAPER

JYDSKE VESTKYSTEN ~ Esbjerg
Owner: Jydske Vestkysten A/S
Editorial: Banegårdspladsen, Esbjerg 6700.
T: 45 79 12 45 00 E: redaktion.esbjerg@jv.dk
W: http://www.jv.dk
Freq: Weekly; Circ: 16671
Redaktør for daglige nyheder: Peter Grinderslev; Redaktør: Jesper Nørgaard
Language (s): Danish; Full Page Colour: 10900.00
Currency: Denmark Kroner
DAILY NEWSPAPER

JYDSKE VESTKYSTEN ~ Haderslev
Owner: A/S JYDSKEVESTKYSTEN
Editorial: Gravene 1, Haderslev 6100.
T: 45 79 12 45 00
E: redaktion.haderslev@jv.dk
W: http://www.jv.dk
Freq: Daily; Circ: 8543
Redaktør for daglige nyheder: Bjarne Mortensen
Language (s): Danish; Full Page Colour: 10900.00
Currency: Denmark Kroner
DAILY NEWSPAPER

JYDSKE VESTKYSTEN ~ Ribe
Owner: A/S JYDSKEVESTKYSTEN
Editorial: Saltgade 20, Ribe 6760.
T: 45 75 42 01 00 E: redaktion.ribe@jv.dk
W: http://www.jv.dk
Freq: Daily; Circ: 76550
Language (s): Danish
DAILY NEWSPAPER

JYDSKE VESTKYSTEN ~ Rødding
Owner: A/S JYDSKEVESTKYSTEN
Editorial: Østergade 16, Rødding 6630.
T: 45 74 84 11 14 E: redaktion.roedding@jv.dk
W: http://www.jv.dk
Freq: Daily; Circ: 76550
Language (s): Danish
DAILY NEWSPAPER

JYDSKE VESTKYSTEN ~ Sønderborg
Owner: A/S JYDSKEVESTKYSTEN
Editorial: Store Rådhusgade 5-7, Sønderborg 6400. T: 45 79 12 45 00
E: redaktion.soenderborg@jv.dk
W: http://www.jv.dk
Freq: Daily; Circ: 11529
Redaktør for daglige nyheder: Else Højgaard
Language (s): Danish; Full Page Colour: 10900.00
Currency: Denmark Kroner
DAILY NEWSPAPER

JYDSKE VESTKYSTEN ~ Tarm
Owner: A/S JYDSKEVESTKYSTEN
Editorial: Storegade 19, Tarm 6880.
T: 45 97 37 10 88 E: redaktion.tarm@jv.dk
W: http://www.jv.dk
Freq: Daily; Circ: 76550
Language (s): Danish
DAILY NEWSPAPER

JYDSKE VESTKYSTEN ~ Tønder
Owner: A/S JydskeVestkysten
Editorial: Storegade 2, Tønder 6270.
T: 45 74 72 21 51 E: redaktion.toender@jv.dk
W: http://www.jv.dk
Freq: Daily; Circ: 6886
Language (s): Danish; Full Page Colour: 10900.00
Currency: Denmark Kroner
DAILY NEWSPAPER

JYDSKE VESTKYSTEN ~ Varde
Owner: A/S JydskeVestkysten
Editorial: Torvet 3, Varde 6800.
T: 45 76 95 19 99 E: redaktion.varde@jv.dk
W: http://www.jv.dk
Freq: Daily; Circ: 8443
Language (s): Danish; Full Page Colour: 10900.00
Currency: Denmark Kroner
DAILY NEWSPAPER

JYDSKE VESTKYSTEN ~ Vejen
Owner: A/S JydskeVestkysten
Editorial: Banegårdspladsen 5, 1. sal, Vejen 6600. T: 45 75 36 00 22
E: redaktion.vejen@jv.dk W: http://www.jv.dk
Freq: Daily; Circ: 6800
Language (s): Danish; Full Page Colour: 10900.00
Currency: Denmark Kroner
DAILY NEWSPAPER

JYDSKE VESTKYSTEN Sport
Owner: A/S JYDSKEVESTKYSTEN
Editorial: Banegårdspladsen, Esbjerg DK-6700.
T: 45 79 12 45 00 E: sporten@jv.dk
W: http://www.jv.dk
Freq: Daily; Circ: 76550 Not Audited
Language (s): Danish
DAILY NEWSPAPER

JYDSKE VESTKYSTEN; Bo godt
Owner: A/S JYDSKEVESTKYSTEN
Editorial: Banegårdspladsen, Esbjerg 6700.
T: 45 79 12 45 00 E: sor@jv.dk
W: http://www.jv.dk
Freq: Daily; Circ: 76550
Language (s): Danish
DAILY NEWSPAPER

JYDSKE VESTKYSTEN; Debat
Owner: JYDSKEVESTKYSTEN A/S
Editorial: Banegårdspladsen, Esbjerg 6700.
T: 45 79 12 45 00 E: debat@jv.dk
W: http://www.jv.dk
Freq: Daily; Circ: 76550
Redaktionssekretær: Harry Pedersen
Language (s): Danish
DAILY NEWSPAPER

Jydske Vestkysten; Erhverv
Owner: A/S JYDSKEVESTKYSTEN
Editorial: Banegårdspladsen, Esbjerg 6700.
T: 45 79 12 45 00 E: erhverv@jv.dk
W: http://www.jv.dk
Freq: Daily; Circ: 76550
Language (s): Danish
DAILY NEWSPAPER

JYDSKE VESTKYSTEN; Indland
Owner: A/S JydskeVestkysten
Editorial: Banegårdspladsen, Esbjerg 6700.
T: 45 79 12 45 00 E: jydskevestkysten@jv.dk
W: http://www.jv.dk
Freq: Daily; Circ: 76550
Language (s): Danish
DAILY NEWSPAPER

Jydske Vestkysten; Kolding
Owner: A/S JYDSKEVESTKYSTEN
Editorial: Dalbygade 40 F, Kolding 6000.
T: 45 79 12 45 00 E: redaktion.kolding@jv.dk
W: http://www.jv.dk
Freq: Daily; Circ: 11414
Redaktør: Christian Friis Hansen; Editor: Laust Tuxen Hedegaard
Language (s): Danish; Full Page Colour: 10900.00
Currency: Denmark Kroner
DAILY NEWSPAPER

JYDSKE VESTKYSTEN; KULTURREDAKTIONEN
Owner: A/S JYDSKEVESTKYSTEN
Editorial: BANEGÅRDSPLADSEN, Esbjerg 6700. T: 45 79 12 45 00 E: kultur@jv.dk
W: http://www.jv.dk
Freq: Daily; Circ: 76550
Language (s): Danish
DAILY NEWSPAPER

JYDSKE VESTKYSTEN; Navne
Owner: A/S JydskeVestkysten
Editorial: Banegårdspladsen, Esbjerg 6700.
T: 45 79 12 45 00 E: navne@jv.dk

W: http://www.jv.dk
Freq: Daily; Circ: 76550
Language (s): Danish
DAILY NEWSPAPER

JYDSKE VESTKYSTEN; SAMFUNDSREDAKTIONEN
Owner: A/S JYDSKEVESTKYSTEN
Editorial: Banegårdspladsen, Esbjerg 6700.
T: 45 79 12 45 00 E: redaktion.esbjerg@jv.dk
W: http://www.jv.dk
Freq: Daily; Circ: 76550 Not Audited
Redaktør: Jørn Broch
Language (s): Danish
DAILY NEWSPAPER

Jyllands-Posten
Owner: JP/Politikens Hus A/S
Editorial: Grøndalsvej 3, Viby J 8260.
T: 45 87 38 38 38 E: indland@jp.dk
W: http://jyllands-posten.dk
Freq: Daily; Circ: 125096 Dansk Oplagskontrol
Nyhedsredaktør: Niels Christian Bastholm; Chefredaktør: Pierre Collignon; Chefredaktør: Jørn Mikkelsen; Editor in Chief: Steen Rosenbak; Redaktør: Peter Rosendal; Editor: Kaare Sørensen; Editor: Kaare Sørensen
Language (s): Danish; Full Page Colour: 127050.00
Currency: Denmark Kroner
DAILY NEWSPAPER

Jyllands-Posten; Århus
Owner: JP/Politikens Hus A/S
Editorial: Grøndalsvej 3, Viby 8260.
T: 45 87 38 38 38 E: jpaarhus@jp.dk
W: http://jyllands-posten.dk/aarhus
Freq: Daily; Circ: 34962
Language (s): Danish; Full Page Colour: 32375.00
Currency: Denmark Kroner
DAILY NEWSPAPER

KALUNDBORG NYT
Owner: Kalundborg Nyt A/S
Editorial: Skibbrogade 40-42, Kalundborg 4400. T: 45 88 88 44 10 E: red@nordvest.dk
W: http://www.kalundborg-folkeblad.dk
Freq: Weekly; Circ: 19055 Not Audited
Ansvarshavende redaktør: Rita Sørensen
Language (s): Danish; Full Page Colour: 10465.00
Currency: Denmark Kroner
NEWSPAPER

KANAL KØBENHAVN
T: 45 70 20 00 04 E: info@kanalkobenhavn.dk
W: http://www.kanalkobenhavn.dk
Freq: Daily
Language (s): Danish
DAILY NEWSPAPER

KANAL PLUS FAVORIT
T: 45 36 98 71 35 E: info@kanalplus.fm
W: http://www.kanalplus.fm
Freq: Daily
Language (s): Danish
DAILY NEWSPAPER

KERTEMINDE UGEAVIS
Owner: Kerteminde UgeAvis
Editorial: Strandgade 1B, Kerteminde 5300.
T: 45 65 45 54 40 E: post@faa.dk
W: http://www.kertemindeugeavis.dk
Freq: Weekly; Circ: 20616 Not Audited
Language (s): Danish; Full Page Colour: 13744.50
Currency: Denmark Kroner
NEWSPAPER

KJELLERUP TIDENDE
Owner: Midtjyllands Avis
Editorial: Papirfabrikken 18, Kjellerup 8600.
T: 45 86 82 13 00 E: kjellerup@mja.dk
W: http://www.midtjyllandsavis.dk
Freq: Weekly; Circ: 16498 Not Audited
Ansvarshavende redaktør: Rasmus Viuff
Language (s): Danish; Full Page Colour: 15534.00
Currency: Denmark Kroner
NEWSPAPER

KJERTEMINDE AVIS
Owner: Kjerteminde Avis A/S
Editorial: Ndr. Ringvej 54, Kerteminde 5300.
T: 45 65 32 10 04 E: info@kjavis.dk
W: http://www.kj-avis.dk
Freq: Daily; Circ: 1940
Redaktionssekretær: Jørgen Wind
Language (s): Danish; Full Page Colour: 18998.00
Currency: Denmark Kroner
DAILY NEWSPAPER

W: http://www.jv.dk
Freq: Daily; Circ: 76550
Language (s): Danish
DAILY NEWSPAPER

KNR Radio
E: info@knr.gl
W: http://knr.gl/index.php?id=178
Freq: Daily
Language (s): Danish
DAILY NEWSPAPER

KØGE ONSDAG
Owner: Sjællandske Medier A/S
Editorial: Torvet 10, Køge 4600.
T: 45 56 65 10 05
E: koege.onsdag.red@sj-medier.dk
W: http://www.koege-onsdag.dk
Freq: Weekly; Circ: 42639 Not Audited
Ansvarshavende redaktør: Torben Dalby Larsen; Redaktør: Simon Hansen; EDITOR IN CHIEF: Bente Johannessen
Language (s): Danish; Full Page Colour: 17784.00
Currency: Denmark Kroner
NEWSPAPER

Kolding Ugeavis
Owner: De Berlingske Lokalaviser A/S
Editorial: Dalbygade 40J, Kolding 6000.
T: 45 76 30 80 80
E: red.kolding@ugeavisen.dk
W: http://ugeavisen.dk/kolding
Freq: 2 Times/Week; Circ: 46749
EDITOR IN CHIEF: Louise Lauritsen
Language (s): Danish; Full Page Colour: 17500.00
Currency: Denmark Kroner
DAILY NEWSPAPER

KOMITÉENS RADIO
T: 45 66 14 05 48 E: post@kradio.dk
W: http://www.kradio.dk
Freq: Daily
Language (s): Danish
DAILY NEWSPAPER

KORSØR POSTEN
Owner: Berlingske Lokalaviser A/S
Editorial: Nytorv 10, 1, Slagelse 4200.
T: 45 58 37 00 43
E: red.ks@soendagsavisen.dk
W: http://www.korsorposten.dk
Freq: Weekly; Circ: 10807
EDITOR: Solveig Hansen
Language (s): Danish; Full Page Colour: 10116.00
Currency: Denmark Kroner
DAILY NEWSPAPER

KRAKA.ORG
Editorial: Vester Farimagsgade 1, København V 1606 E: kontakt@kraka.org
W: http://www.kraka.org
Editorial Profile: Bureau
Language (s): Danish
DAILY NEWSPAPER

Kristeligt Dagblad
Owner: A/S Kristeligt Dagblad
Editorial: Vimmelskaftet 47, Copenhagen 1161. T: 45 33 48 05 00
E: kristeligt-dagblad@k.dk
W: http://www.kristeligt-dagblad.dk
Freq: Daily; Circ: 26145 Not Audited
Chefredaktør: Jeppe Duvå; Redaktør: Maria Lyskjær Jørgensen; Redaktør: Kim Schou
Language (s): Danish; Full Page Colour: 21680.00
Currency: Denmark Kroner
DAILY NEWSPAPER

LÆSØ-POSTEN
Owner: Nordjyske Medier
Editorial: Tordenskjoldsgade 2, Frederikshavn 9900. T: 45 99 20 33 33
E: frederikshavn@nordjyske.dk
W: http://www.delokaleugeaviser.dk/dd/default.asp?template=blad&id=4&area=&bladid=7
Freq: Weekly; Circ: 1657 Pub Statement
Ansvarshavende redaktør: Per Lyngby
Language (s): Danish; Full Page Colour: 7165.50
Currency: Denmark Kroner
NEWSPAPER

LICITATIONEN
Owner: Aller Business A/S
Editorial: Marielundvej 46D, Postbox 537, Herlev 2730. T: 45 70 15 02 22
E: licitationen@licitationen.dk
W: http://www.licitationen.dk
Freq: Daily; Circ: 6100 Not Audited
Redaktionschef: Christian Brahe-Pedersen; Redaktør: Peter Kargaard
Language (s): Danish; Full Page Colour: 20550.00
Currency: Denmark Kroner
DAILY NEWSPAPER

LIEBHAVERBOLIGEN
Owner: Avizion

Editorial: Henningsens Alle 68, Hellerup 2900.
T: 45 38 88 66 33
W: http://www.mediehusethellerup.dk/content/liebhaverboligen
Freq: Monthly; **Circ:** 64000 Pub Statement
EDITOR: Steen Blendstrup; **Redaktør:** Dennis Kjærulf; **EDITOR:** Per Kuskner; **EDITOR:** Rasmus Schou; **EDITOR:** Christina Wex
Language (s): Danish; Full Page Colour: 13900.00
Currency: Denmark Kroner
NEWSPAPER

LOKAL NYT
Owner: Grafisk Freelance
Editorial: Nebbelundevej 1, Rødby 4970.
T: 45 54 60 21 08
E: redaktion@lokalnyt-lolland.dk
W: http://www.lokalnyt-lolland.dk
Freq: Monthly; **Circ:** 28200 Pub Statement
Redaktør: Birthe Christensen
Language (s): Danish; Full Page Colour: 5250.00
Currency: Denmark Kroner
DAILY NEWSPAPER

LOKAL NYT LANGÅ AVIS
Owner: Lokal Nyt Langå Avis A/S
Editorial: Bredgade 23, Langå 8870.
T: 45 86 46 14 26 **E:** lokalnyt@wwi.dk
Freq: Weekly; **Circ:** 11000 Not Audited
Language (s): Danish
NEWSPAPER

LOKALAVISEN ASSENS
Owner: Lokalavisen Assens Vestfyn A/S
Editorial: Østergade 78, Assens 5610.
T: 45 65 45 54 54 **E:** laa-redaktion@fyens.dk
W: http://www.lokalavisenassens.dk
Freq: Weekly; **Circ:** 29222
Redaktør: Søren Plovgaard
Language (s): Danish; Full Page Colour: 13167.00
Currency: Denmark Kroner
DAILY NEWSPAPER

LOKALAVISEN FREDERIKSBERG
Owner: Michael Engelbrecht
Editorial: Jacobys Allé 2, Frederiksberg 1806.
T: 45 33 28 88 88
E: michael@lokalavisen-frb.dk
W: http://www.lokalavisen-frb.dk
Freq: Weekly; **Circ:** 59043 Pub Statement
Redaktør: Finn Edvard
Language (s): Danish; Full Page Colour: 19265.50
Currency: Denmark Kroner
DAILY NEWSPAPER

LOKALAVISEN FREDERIKSHAVN
Owner: Nordjyske Medier
Editorial: Tordenskjoldsgade 2, Frederikshavn 9900. **T:** 45 99 20 33 33
E: lokalavisen@nordjyske.dk
W: http://www.nordjyskeugeaviser.dk
Freq: Weekly; **Circ:** 22927 Not Audited
Redaktionschef: Carl Christian Madsen
Language (s): Danish; Full Page Colour: 11375.50
Currency: Denmark Kroner
NEWSPAPER

LOKALAVISEN FREDERIKSSUND
Owner: Lokal-Avisen Fjordbyerne A/S, Søndagsavisen
T: 45 47 35 08 08
E: redaktion.frederikssund@lokalavisen.dk
W: http://frederikssund.lokalavisen.dk/apps/pbcs.dll/forside
Freq: Weekly; **Circ:** 42798 Not Audited
EDITOR IN CHIEF: Kim Belmark; **Redaktør:** Henrik Gregersen
Language (s): Danish; Full Page Colour: 15015.00
Currency: Denmark Kroner
NEWSPAPER

LOKALAVISEN HEDEN/ MIDTSJÆLLANDS AVIS
Owner: Sjællandske Medier A/S
Editorial: Søvej 1, Borup 4140.
T: 45 57 52 22 88
E: info@lokalavisen-heden.dk
W: http://www.lokalavisen-midtsj.dk
Freq: Weekly; **Circ:** 17000
Language (s): Danish; Full Page Colour: 11452.00
Currency: Denmark Kroner
DAILY NEWSPAPER

LOKALAVISEN HELSINGØR
Owner: Helsingør Mediecenter
Editorial: Sankt Olai Gade 47, 1. sal, Helsingør DK-3000. **T:** 45 48 40 50 00 **E:** kb@lokalh.dk
W: http://www.lokalavisenhelsingor.dk
Freq: Daily; **Circ:** 38000
Ansvarshavende redaktør: Kim Belmark
Language (s): Danish
DAILY NEWSPAPER

LOKALAVISEN HORNSHERRED
Owner: Lokalavisen for Hornsherred A/S
Editorial: Hovedgaden 25, Skibby 4050.
T: 45 88 88 43 00 **E:** red.la@nordvest.dk
W: http://hornsherred.lokalavisen.dk/
Freq: Weekly; **Circ:** 12366 Not Audited
EDITOR IN CHIEF: Kim Belmark; **Redaktør:** Henrik Gregersen
Language (s): Danish; Full Page Colour: 9868.60
Currency: Denmark Kroner
NEWSPAPER

LOKALAVISEN KALØ VIG
Owner: Politikens Lokalaviser A/S
T: 45 86 99 45 11 **E:** mail@adresseavisen.dk
W: http://kaloevig.lokalavisen.dk
Freq: Weekly; **Circ:** 25130 Not Audited
EDITOR: Claus Krogh; **Redaktør:** Lars Norman Thomsen
Language (s): Danish; Full Page Colour: 7161.00
Currency: Denmark Kroner
NEWSPAPER

LOKALAVISEN LEMVIG
Owner: De Bergske Blade
Editorial: Bredgade 20, Lemvig 7620.
T: 45 96 63 04 00 **E:** apll@bergske.dk
W: http://www.bergske.dk
Freq: Weekly; **Circ:** 12982 Pub Statement
EDITOR IN CHIEF: Dorthe Carlsen; **Redaktør:** A. P. Christensen
Language (s): Danish; Full Page Colour: 8511.00
Currency: Denmark Kroner
DAILY NEWSPAPER

LOKALAVISEN NORDÅRHUS
Owner: Lokalavisen
Editorial: Tingvej 36, Hornslet 8543.
T: 45 86 99 45 11 **E:** mail@lokalavisen.dk
W: http://www.lokalavisen.dk
Freq: Weekly; **Circ:** 29861
EDITOR IN CHIEF: Kim Belmark
Language (s): Danish; Full Page Colour: 7161.00
Currency: Denmark Kroner
DAILY NEWSPAPER

LOKALAVISEN NORDDJURS
Owner: Lokalavisen Midtdjurs A/S
Editorial: Tingvej 36, Hornslet 8543.
T: 45 86 99 45 11 **E:** mail@lokalavisen.dk
W: http://norddjurs.lokalavisen.dk/section/i/1462
Freq: Weekly; **Circ:** 28440
EDITOR: Claus Krogh; **Redaktør:** Lars Norman Thomsen
Language (s): Danish; Full Page Colour: 6352.50
Currency: Denmark Kroner
DAILY NEWSPAPER

LOKALAVISEN NORDSJÆLLAND
Owner: Nordsjællands Avis A/S
Editorial: Klostermosevej 101, Helsingør 3000.
T: 45 49 22 21 10 **E:** redaktionen@nsnet.dk
W: http://www.nsnet.dk
Freq: Weekly; **Circ:** 37451 Not Audited
Language (s): Danish; Full Page Colour: 16170.00
Currency: Denmark Kroner
NEWSPAPER

LOKALAVISEN NORDVEST
Owner: Fynske Medier
Editorial: Langelinie 1, Otterup 5450.
T: 45 70 22 19 25
E: mail@lokalavisenodense.dk
W: http://lokalavisennordvest.dk
Freq: Weekly; **Circ:** 24177 Not Audited
EDITOR IN CHIEF: Jan Bonde
Language (s): Danish; Full Page Colour: 13398.00
Currency: Denmark Kroner
NEWSPAPER

LOKALAVISEN NYBORG
Owner: Fynske Medier P/S
Editorial: Nørrevoldgade 58, Nyborg 5800.
T: 45 63 31 21 00 **E:** red-lan@fyens.dk
W: http://www.lokalavisennyborg.dk
Freq: Weekly; **Circ:** 20031
EDITOR IN CHIEF: Kasper Riggelsen; **EDITOR IN CHIEF:** Kasper Riggelsen
Language (s): Danish; Full Page Colour: 14091.00
Currency: Denmark Kroner
DAILY NEWSPAPER

LOKALAVISEN ØSTERBRO
T: 45 35 20 16 20
E: red.oav@berlingskemedia.dk
W: http://dinby.dk/oesterbro-avis
Freq: Weekly; **Circ:** 50003 Pub Statement
Redaktør: Thomas Frederiksen
Language (s): Danish
DAILY NEWSPAPER

LOKALAVISEN SKANDERBORG
Owner: Lokalavisen Skanderborg A/S
Editorial: Adelgade 101, Skanderborg 8660.
T: 45 87 94 15 30
E: redaktion@lokalavisenskanderborg.dk
W: http://www.lokalavisenskanderborg.dk
Freq: Weekly; **Circ:** 30000 Pub Statement
EDITOR IN CHIEF: Claus Krogh
Language (s): Danish; Full Page Colour: 8685.50
Currency: Denmark Kroner
DAILY NEWSPAPER

LOKALAVISEN SYDKYSTEN
Owner: Sjællandske Medier A/S
Editorial: Greve Strandvej 24, Greve 2670.
T: 45 43 90 44 22
E: sydkysten.red@sj-medier.dk
W: http://www.sydkysten.dk
Freq: 2 Times/Week; **Circ:** 64000
Redaktør: Jørgen Büchler; **EDITOR:** Jørgen Büchler; **EDITOR:** Jørgen Büchler; **EDITOR IN CHIEF:** Helle Midskov; **EDITOR IN CHIEF:** Helle Midskov
Language (s): Danish; Full Page Colour: 19592.50
Currency: Denmark Kroner
DAILY NEWSPAPER

LOKALAVISEN SYDVESTVENDSYSSEL
Owner: Lokalavisen Sydvestvendsyssel A/S
Editorial: Blokhusvej 1, Pandrup 9490.
T: 45 98 24 77 44 **E:** avis@lokalsyd.dk
W: http://www.nordjyskeugeaviser.dk
Freq: Weekly; **Circ:** 7412 Not Audited
EDITOR AT LARGE: Per Andersen; **EDITOR:** Flemming Hansen; **EDITOR:** Flemming Hansen
Language (s): Danish; Full Page Colour: 6775.00
Currency: Denmark Kroner
NEWSPAPER

LOKALAVISEN TAASTRUP AVIS
Owner: Berlingske Lokalblade
Editorial: Marievej 1D, 1. sal, Taastrup 2630.
T: 45 43 77 26 30
E: mail.lta@berlingskemedia.dk
W: http://dinby.dk/lokalavisen-taastrup
Freq: Weekly; **Circ:** 23446
EDITOR: Peter Erlitz; **Contact:** Pia Walther Jensen
Language (s): Danish; Full Page Colour: 16489.50
Currency: Denmark Kroner
DAILY NEWSPAPER

LOKALAVISEN TREHØJE-AULUM-HADERUP
Owner: Ikast Avis
Editorial: Strøget 40, Ikast 7430.
T: 45 97 15 18 00 **E:** ik@ib-medier.dk
W: http://ugeaviserne.dk/medlem/lokalavisen-trehoeje-aulum-haderup
Freq: Weekly; **Circ:** 12271
EDITOR IN CHIEF: Ivan Kristensen
Language (s): Danish; Full Page Colour: 16844.80
Currency: Denmark Kroner
DAILY NEWSPAPER

LOKALAVISEN UGE NYT
Owner: Politikens Lokalaviser A/S
Editorial: Stenløse Center 69, Stenløse 3660.
T: 45 47 17 00 49 **E:** red@ugenyt.dk
W: http://www.ugenyt.dk
Freq: Weekly; **Circ:** 31084 Not Audited
Language (s): Danish; Full Page Colour: 14296.50
Currency: Denmark Kroner
NEWSPAPER

LOKALAVISEN VALBY
Owner: Michael Engelbrecht
Editorial: VALBY LANGGADE 23, Valby 2500.
T: 45 36 19 25 00
E: karsten@lokalavisenvalby.dk
W: http://www.lokalavisenvalby.dk
Freq: Weekly; **Circ:** 46875 Pub Statement
Redaktør: Finn Edvard; **Ansvarshavende redaktør:** Michael Engelbrecht
Language (s): Danish; Full Page Colour: 17607.60
Currency: Denmark Kroner
DAILY NEWSPAPER

LOKALAVISEN VANLØSE POSTEN
Owner: Berlingske Media
Editorial: Dirch Passers Allé 27, 1. sal, Frederiksberg 2000. **T:** 45 33 88 88 88
E: red.van@berlingskemedia.dk
W: http://dinby.dk/vanloese-bladet
Freq: Weekly; **Circ:** 26442
Ansvarshavende redaktør: Morten Friis Outzen
Language (s): Danish; Full Page Colour: 12400.00
Currency: Denmark Kroner
DAILY NEWSPAPER

LOKALBLADET
Owner: Favrskov Gruppen
Editorial: Torvevej 1, Hammel 8450.
T: 45 86 96 17 66 **E:** eb@favrskov-gruppen.dk
W: http://favrskov-gruppen.dk
Freq: Weekly; **Circ:** 33846 Dansk Oplagskontrol
Chefredaktør: Hans Henrik Laugesen
Language (s): Danish; Full Page Colour: 8685.50
Currency: Denmark Kroner
NEWSPAPER

LOKALBLADET RINGSTED
Owner: Berlingske Lokalaviser A/S
Editorial: Schandorphsvej 10, Ringsted 4100.
T: 45 57 68 22 00 **E:** lokalbladet@sn.dk
W: http://www.lokalbladet-ringsted.dk
Freq: Weekly; **Circ:** 22404 Pub Statement
Redaktør: Bodil Pinholt
Language (s): Danish; Full Page Colour: 9816.00
Currency: Denmark Kroner
DAILY NEWSPAPER

LOKALNYT VESTSJÆLLAND
Owner: Glumsø Avis
Editorial: Østergade 17 B, Glumsø 4171.
T: 45 57 65 04 18 **E:** redaktion@lokalnyt.com
W: http://www.lokalnyt.com
Freq: Weekly; **Circ:** 60000 Pub Statement
Ansvarshavende redaktør: Leif Andersen
Language (s): Danish; Full Page Colour: 13956.00
Currency: Denmark Kroner
DAILY NEWSPAPER

LOKALPOSTEN LEM UGEAVIS
Owner: Videbæk Bogtrykkeri
Editorial: Falkevej 4, Videbæk 6920.
T: 45 97 17 11 22
E: post@videbaek-bogtrykkeri.dk
W: http://www.danske-lokalaviser.dk/blade/LokalpostenLem/LokalpostenLem.htm
Freq: Weekly; **Circ:** 3800 Not Audited
Language (s): Danish; Full Page Colour: 5504.50
Currency: Denmark Kroner
NEWSPAPER

Lokalsavisen Vejle Vest/Jelling
Owner: Lokalavisen Jelling A/S
Editorial: Nordkrogen 19, Jelling 7300.
T: 45 75 87 17 44
E: redaktion@lokalavisenjelling.dk
W: http://www.lokalavisenjelling.dk
Freq: Weekly; **Circ:** 8173 Not Audited
Language (s): Danish; Full Page Colour: 8431.50
Currency: Denmark Kroner
NEWSPAPER

LØKKEN FOLKEBLAD
Owner: Bladgruppen Lokal 7
Editorial: Nørregade 30, Løkken 9480.
T: 45 98 99 11 19 **E:** loekken@nordjyske.dk
W: http://www.nordjyskeugeaviser.dk/Default.aspx?tabid=120
Freq: Weekly; **Circ:** 5650 Not Audited
Editor: Per Lyngby; **EDITOR AT LARGE:** Susie Skov
Language (s): Danish; Full Page Colour: 6313.00
Currency: Denmark Kroner
NEWSPAPER

Lolland-Falsters Folketidende
Owner: Lolland-Falsters Folketidende A/S
Editorial: Tværgade 20, Nykøbing 4800.
T: 45 54 88 02 00
E: redaktion@folketidende.dk
W: http://www.folketidende.dk
Freq: Daily; **Circ:** 21527 Not Audited
NEWS EDITOR: Jesper Bøgh; **Redaktionschef:** Lars Hovgaard
Language (s): Danish; Full Page Colour: 17029.50
Currency: Denmark Kroner
DAILY NEWSPAPER

LOLLAND-FALSTERS FOLKETIDENDE Midt- og Sydlolland
Owner: Lolland-Falsters Folketidende A/S
Editorial: Torvet 7, Rødby 4970.
T: 45 54 88 08 60 **E:** maribo@folketidende.dk
W: http://www.folketidende.dk

WORLD NEWS MEDIA

Freq: Daily; **Circ:** 7436
Redaktør: Jørgen Martinson
Language (s): Danish
DAILY NEWSPAPER

LOLLAND-FALSTERS FOLKETIDENDE Vestlolland
Owner: Lolland-Falsters Folketidende A/S
Editorial: Nygade 30, Nakskov 4900.
T: 45 54 88 08 00 **E:** nakskov@folketidende.dk
W: http://www.folketidende.dk
Freq: Daily; **Circ:** 7436
Redaktør: Torsten Elsvor
Language (s): Danish
DAILY NEWSPAPER

LØRDAGSAVISEN KØGE
Owner: Køge Medie Center A/S
Editorial: Galoche Allé 16, Den Hvide By, Køge 4600. **T:** 45 56 65 82 00
E: redaktion@kmc-as.dk
W: http://koege.lokalavisen.dk
Freq: Weekly; **Circ:** 44700 Pub Statement
Redaktør: Per Møller; **Ansvarshavende redaktør:** Jørgen Petersen
Language (s): Danish; Full Page Colour: 17784.00
Currency: Denmark Kroner
NEWSPAPER

Lunderskov og Omegns Folkeblad
Owner: Lunderskov og Omegns Folkeblad A/S
Editorial: Torvet 3, Lunderskov 6640.
T: 45 75 58 59 90 **E:** avisen@lhhi.dk
W: http://www.lhhi.dk/index.php?/
Lunderskov-og-Omegns-Folkeblad/Ugens-avis/
ugens-avis.html
Freq: Weekly; **Circ:** 7500 Pub Statement
Ansvarshavende redaktør: Niels B. Petersen
Language (s): Danish; Full Page Colour: 6135.50
Currency: Denmark Kroner
NEWSPAPER

LYNGPOSTEN
Owner: Brande Bladet
Editorial: Herningvej 26, Sønder-Omme 7260.
T: 45 29 44 44 44 **E:** post@lyngposten.dk
W: http://www.lyngposten.dk/
Freq: Weekly; **Circ:** 10037 Pub Statement
EDITOR: Henny Eskildsen
Language (s): Danish; Full Page Colour: 7045.50
Currency: Denmark Kroner
DAILY NEWSPAPER

MAGASINET MIDT
Owner: DG Media
Editorial: Regionshuset Viborg, Skottenborg 26, Viborg 8800. **T:** 45 78 41 0620
E: magasinetmidt@rm.dk
W: http://www.rm.dk/om+regionen/aktuelt/
magasinet+midt
Freq: Quarterly; **Circ:** 40000 DG Media
Redaktør: Anne Domino
Language (s): Danish; Full Page Colour: 23500.00
Currency: Denmark Kroner
DAILY NEWSPAPER

MARIAGER AVIS
Owner: Mariager Avis A/S
Editorial: Kirkegade 13, Mariager 9550.
T: 45 98 54 26 22
E: mariageravis@mariageravis.dk
W: http://www.mariageravis.dk
Freq: Weekly; **Circ:** 10700 Not Audited
Redaktør for daglige nyheder: Jytte Andersen;
EDITOR IN CHIEF: Dorthe Carlsen; **EDITOR IN CHIEF:** Dorthe Carlsen
Language (s): Danish; Full Page Colour: 6390.50
Currency: Denmark Kroner
NEWSPAPER

MELFAR POSTEN
Owner: Fyens Stiftstidende
Editorial: Havnegade 41, Middelfart 5500.
T: 45 63 41 13 03 **E:** mfp-red@fyens.dk
W: http://www.melfarposten.dk
Freq: Weekly; **Circ:** 27074 Not Audited
EDITOR: Bjarne Jacobsen; **EDITOR:** Bjarne Jacobsen
Language (s): Danish; Full Page Colour: 14553.00
Currency: Denmark Kroner
NEWSPAPER

MetroXpress MX
Owner: METROXPRESS DANMARK A/S
Editorial: Bygmestervej 61, København Nv 2400. **T:** 45 77 30 57 57 **E:** news@mx.dk
W: http://www.metroxpress.dk
Freq: Daily; **Circ:** 113826 Dansk Oplagskontrol
Redaktør: Nina Ettrup; **Chefsredaktør:** Jonas Rathje; **Redaktionchef:** Lotte Stensgaard;

Redaktør: Niels Thimmer; **News Editor:** Allan Wahlers
Language (s): Danish; Full Page Colour: 97705.00
Currency: Denmark Kroner
DAILY NEWSPAPER

MIDTFYNS POSTEN
Owner: Fyens Stiftstidende
Editorial: Østergade 19, Ringe 5750.
T: 45 62 62 13 30 **E:** mip-red@fyens.dk
W: http://www.midtfynsposten.dk
Freq: Weekly; **Circ:** 18028 Not Audited
EDITOR IN CHIEF: Troels Mylenberg; **EDITOR:** Tim Visti
Language (s): Danish; Full Page Colour: 11088.00
Currency: Denmark Kroner
NEWSPAPER

MIDTHIMMERLANDS FOLKEBLAD
Owner: Midthimmerlands Folkeblad A/S
Editorial: Doktorvænget 6, Postboks 39, Støvring 9530. **T:** 45 98 37 24 00
E: artikler@folkebladetstovring.dk
W: http://www.folkebladetstovring.dk
Freq: Weekly; **Circ:** 14300 Not Audited
Ansvarshavende redaktør: Henrik Møller
Language (s): Danish; Full Page Colour: 8658.00
Currency: Denmark Kroner
NEWSPAPER

MIDTJYLLANDS AVIS Bagsiden
Owner: Silkeborg Avis A/S
Editorial: Papirfabrikken 18, Silkeborg 8600.
T: 45 86 82 13 00 **E:** bagsiden@mja.dk
W: http://www.midtjyllandsavis.dk
Freq: Daily; **Circ:** 16335
Redaktør: Niels R. Hansen
Language (s): Danish
DAILY NEWSPAPER

MIDTJYLLANDS AVIS Bjerringbro
Owner: Silkeborg Avis A/S
Editorial: Nørregade 10, Bjerringbro 8850.
T: 45 86 68 19 00 **E:** bjerringbro@mja.dk
W: http://www.midtjyllandsavis.dk
Freq: Daily; **Circ:** 16335
Redaktør: Kim Simmelsgaard
Language (s): Danish
DAILY NEWSPAPER

MIDTJYLLANDS AVIS Debat
Owner: Silkeborg Avis A/S
Editorial: Papirfabrikken 18, Silkeborg 8600.
T: 45 86 82 13 00 **E:** debat@mja.dk
W: http://www.midtjyllandsavis.dk
Freq: Daily; **Circ:** 16335
Language (s): Danish
DAILY NEWSPAPER

MIDTJYLLANDS AVIS Erhverv
Owner: Silkeborg Avis A/S
Editorial: Papirfabrikken 18, Silkeborg 8600.
T: 45 86 82 13 00 **E:** erhverv@mja.dk
W: http://www.midtjyllandsavis.dk
Freq: Daily; **Circ:** 16335
Language (s): Danish
DAILY NEWSPAPER

MIDTJYLLANDS AVIS Extra
Owner: Silkeborg Avis A/S
Editorial: Papirfabrikken 18, Silkeborg 8600.
T: 45 86 82 13 00
W: http://www.midtjyllandsavis.dk
Freq: Weekly; **Circ:** 16335
Redaktionschef: Helmer Nørregård Jakobsen;
Redaktionssekretær: Niels R. Hansen
Language (s): Danish
DAILY NEWSPAPER

MIDTJYLLANDS AVIS Familie
Owner: Silkeborg Avis A/S
Editorial: Papirfabrikken 18, Silkeborg 8600.
T: 45 86 82 13 00 **E:** familie@mja.dk
W: http://www.midtjyllandsavis.dk
Freq: Weekly; **Circ:** 16335
Language (s): Danish
DAILY NEWSPAPER

MIDTJYLLANDS AVIS Favrskov
Owner: Silkeborg Avis A/S
Editorial: Bane Allé 8, Hammel 8450.
T: 45 87 64 80 00 **E:** favrskov@mja.dk
W: http://www.midtjyllandsavis.dk
Freq: Daily; **Circ:** 16335
Redaktør: Martin Bjerregaard Jensen;
Redaktør: Preben Just
Language (s): Danish
DAILY NEWSPAPER

MIDTJYLLANDS AVIS Kjellerup-Ikast
Owner: Silkeborg Avis A/S
Editorial: Søndergade 23, Kjellerup 8620.
T: 45 86 88 10 00 **E:** kjellerup@mja.dk

W: http://www.midtjyllandsavis.dk
Freq: Daily; **Circ:** 16335
Redaktør: Rasmus Viuff
Language (s): Danish
DAILY NEWSPAPER

MIDTJYLLANDS AVIS Kultur
Owner: Silkeborg Avis A/S
Editorial: Papirfabrikken 18, Silkeborg 8600.
T: 45 86 82 13 00 **E:** kultur@mja.dk
W: http://www.midtjyllandsavis.dk
Freq: Daily; **Circ:** 16335
Chefredaktør: Steffen Lange; **Redaktionschef:** Helmer Nørregård Jakobsen
Language (s): Danish
DAILY NEWSPAPER

MIDTJYLLANDS AVIS Motor
Owner: Silkeborg Avis A/S
Editorial: Papirfabrikken 18, Silkeborg 8600.
T: 45 86 82 13 00 **E:** weekend@mja.dk
W: http://www.midtjyllandsavis.dk
Freq: Weekly; **Circ:** 16335
Language (s): Danish
DAILY NEWSPAPER

MIDTJYLLANDS AVIS Navne
Owner: Silkeborg Avis A/S
Editorial: Papirfabrikken 18, Silkeborg 8600.
T: 45 87 22 84 06 **E:** navne@mja.dk
W: http://www.midtjyllandsavis.dk
Freq: Daily; **Circ:** 16335
Language (s): Danish
DAILY NEWSPAPER

MIDTJYLLANDS AVIS Rejser
Owner: Silkeborg Avis A/S
Editorial: Papirfabrikken 18, Silkeborg 8600.
T: 45 86 82 13 00 **E:** rejser@mja.dk
W: http://www.midtjyllandsavis.dk
Redaktør: Aksel Evin Olesen
Language (s): Danish
DAILY NEWSPAPER

MIDTJYLLANDS AVIS Ry-Skanderborg-Galten
Owner: Silkeborg Avis A/S
T: 45 87 70 20 70 **E:** skanderborg@mja.dk
W: http://www.midtjyllandsavis.dk
Freq: Daily; **Circ:** 16500
Redaktør: Jens Erik Sinnbeck; **Redaktør:** Torben Jakobsen
Language (s): Danish
DAILY NEWSPAPER

MIDTJYLLANDS AVIS Silkeborg
Owner: Silkeborg Avis A/S
Editorial: Papirfabrikken 18, Silkeborg 8600.
T: 45 86 82 13 00 **E:** silkeborg@mja.dk
W: http://www.midtjyllandsavis.dk
Freq: Daily; **Circ:** 14863 Pub Statement
Redaktionssekretær: Knud Jakobsen;
Redaktionssekretær: Jakob Munk Schmidt;
Redaktionssekretær: Bent Nørgaard;
Redaktør: Rasmus Viuff
Language (s): Danish; Full Page Colour: 31172.00
Currency: Denmark Kroner
DAILY NEWSPAPER

MIDTJYLLANDS AVIS Sporten
Owner: Silkeborg Avis A/S
Editorial: Papirfabrikken 18, Silkeborg 8600.
T: 45 86 82 13 00 **E:** sport@mja.dk
W: http://www.midtjyllandsavis.dk
Freq: Daily; **Circ:** 16335
Language (s): Danish
DAILY NEWSPAPER

MIDTJYLLANDS AVIS Them-Gjern
Owner: Silkeborg Avis A/S
Editorial: Papirfabrikken 18, Silkeborg 8600.
T: 45 86 82 13 00 **E:** them@mja.dk
W: http://www.midtjyllandsavis.dk
Freq: Daily; **Circ:** 16335
Language (s): Danish
DAILY NEWSPAPER

MIDTJYSK UGEAVIS
Owner: Midtjysk Ugeblad A/S
Editorial: Jernbanegade 25, Grindsted 7200.
T: 45 75 32 05 00
E: redaktion@midtjyskugeavis.dk
W: http://www.midtjyskugeavis.dk
Freq: Weekly; **Circ:** 20890 Pub Statement
Language (s): Danish; Full Page Colour: 9471.00
Currency: Denmark Kroner
NEWSPAPER

MIDTSJÆLLANDS AVIS
Owner: Sjællandske Medier A/S
Editorial: Søvej 1, Borup 4140.
T: 45 57 52 22 88
E: info@lokalavisen-heden.dk
W: http://www.lokalavisen-midtsj.dk

Freq: Weekly; **Circ:** 17000 Not Audited
Language (s): Danish; Full Page Colour: 11452.00
Currency: Denmark Kroner
NEWSPAPER

MIDTSJÆLLANDS FOLKEBLAD
Owner: Sjællandske Medier A/S
Editorial: Kvarmløsevej 36, Tølløse 4340.
T: 45 59 18 51 57 **E:** folkeblad@midttryk.dk
W: http://www.folkeblad.dk
Freq: Weekly; **Circ:** 27500 Not Audited
Language (s): Danish; Full Page Colour: 10785.60
Currency: Denmark Kroner
NEWSPAPER

MIDTVENDSYSSEL AVIS
Owner: Midtvendsyssel Avis A/S
Editorial: Jernbanegade 3, Hjallerup 9320.
T: 45 98 28 11 99 **E:** mvavis@mvavis.dk
W: http://www.midtvendsysselavis.dk/?id=46
Freq: Weekly; **Circ:** 9100 Not Audited
Language (s): Danish; Full Page Colour: 6466.50
Currency: Denmark Kroner
NEWSPAPER

MIDT-VEST AVIS
Owner: Nordjysk Mediecenter
Editorial: Langagervej 1, Aalborg 9220.
T: 45 99 35 33 00 **E:** redaktion@nordjyske.dk
W: http://www.nordjyske.dk
Freq: Weekly; **Circ:** 42629 Not Audited
Chefredaktør: Anne-Marie Dohm;
Chefredaktør: Anne-Marie Dohm; **Editor:** Per Lyngby; **EDITOR IN CHIEF:** Kirsten Vestergaard
Language (s): Danish; Full Page Colour: 15243.00
Currency: Denmark Kroner
NEWSPAPER

MORSØ FOLKEBLAD
Owner: Morsø Folkeblad A/S
T: 45 97 72 10 00 **E:** redaktion@mf.dk
W: http://www.mf.dk
Freq: Daily; **Circ:** 5728 Not Audited
Redaktør: Anders Holmgaard; **Redaktør:** Leif Kristiansen
Language (s): Danish; Full Page Colour: 9600.00
Currency: Denmark Kroner
DAILY NEWSPAPER

MORSØ FOLKEBLADS UGEAVIS
Owner: Morsø Folkeblad A/S
T: 45 97 72 10 00 **E:** ugeavis@mf.dk
W: http://www.mf.dk
Freq: Weekly; **Circ:** 18690 Not Audited
Redaktør: Anders Holmgaard; **Editor:** Leif Kristiansen; **Editor:** Leif Kristiansen
Language (s): Danish; Full Page Colour: 10866.00
Currency: Denmark Kroner
NEWSPAPER

MX
Owner: Metroxpress A/S
Editorial: Bygmestervej 61, København Nv 2400. **T:** 45 77 30 57 57 **E:** news@mx.dk
W: http://www.mx.dk
Freq: Daily; **Circ:** 150000 Pub Statement
Redaktør: Niels Thimmer
Language (s): Danish; Full Page Colour: 76650.00
Currency: Denmark Kroner
DAILY NEWSPAPER

NÆSTVED-BLADET
Owner: Næstved-Bladet A/S
Editorial: Ringstedgade 11, Næstved 4700.
T: 45 55 73 50 00
E: redaktion@naestved-bladet.dk
W: http://www.naestved-bladet.dk
Freq: Weekly; **Circ:** 42107 Not Audited
Redaktør: Tove Gurresø
Language (s): Danish; Full Page Colour: 13609.00
Currency: Denmark Kroner
NEWSPAPER

NÆSTVED-BLADET; GO' WEEKEND
Owner: De Lokale Ugeaviser
Editorial: Ringstedgade 11, Næstved 4700.
T: 45 55 73 50 00
E: redaktionen@naestved-bladet.dk
W: http://www.go-weekend.dk/
Freq: Weekly; **Circ:** 68900 Not Audited
EDITOR: Jan Jensen
Language (s): Danish
DAILY NEWSPAPER

NIBE AVIS
Owner: NIBE AVIS
Editorial: Jacob Petersens Vej 13, Nibe 9240.
T: 45 98 35 11 45 **E:** nibeavis@nibeavis.dk

W: http://www.nibeavis.dk
Freq: Weekly; **Circ:** 9500 Not Audited
Redaktør: Jacob Søndergaard
Language (s): Danish; Full Page Colour: 7715.40
Currency: Denmark Kroner
NEWSPAPER

NØRAGER AVIS
Owner: Nørager Bogtrykkeri
Editorial: Holmsvej 3, Nørager 9610.
T: 45 98 55 17 44 **E:** post@norager.net
W: http://www.norager.net
Freq: Weekly; **Circ:** 3800 Not Audited
Ansvarshavende redaktør: Preben Lauritzen
Language (s): Danish; Full Page Colour: 5821.00
Currency: Denmark Kroner
NEWSPAPER

NORDFALSTERS AVIS
Owner: Nordfalsters Avis A/S
Editorial: Langgade 24, Nørre Alslev 4840.
T: 45 54 43 41 00 **E:** nf@nordfalstersavis.dk
W: http://www.nordfalstersavis.dk
Freq: Weekly; **Circ:** 9600 Pub Statement
Ansvarshavende redaktør: Claus Olsen
Language (s): Danish; Full Page Colour: 6044.00
Currency: Denmark Kroner
NEWSPAPER

NORDJYSKE
Owner: NORDJYSKE Medier
T: 45 99 35 33 00 **E:** redaktion@nordjyske.dk
W: http://www.nordjyske.dk
Freq: Weekly; **Circ:** 9500 Not Audited
Chefredaktør: Anne-Marie Dohm;
Chefredaktør: Lars Jespersen; **Editor:** Per Lyngby; **Chefredaktør:** Turid Nielsen
Language (s): Danish; Full Page Colour: 7251.00
Currency: Denmark Kroner
NEWSPAPER

NORDJYSKE NYT
Owner: Medieselskabet Nordvest
Editorial: Ahlgade 1 C, Holbæk 4300.
T: 45 88 88 43 00 **E:** red.hol@nordvest.dk
W: http://www.venstrebladet.dk/hav/default.asp?action=ugeaviser&ugeavis=byla
Freq: Weekly; **Circ:** 41679 Not Audited
Language (s): Danish; Full Page Colour: 12964.00
Currency: Denmark Kroner
NEWSPAPER

NORDJYSKE STIFTSTIDENDE
Owner: Nordjyske Medier
T: 45 99 35 35 35 **E:** nordjyske@nordjyske.dk
W: http://www.nordjyske.dk
Freq: Daily; **Circ:** 62075 Not Audited
Redaktionschef: Elsebeth Dissing;
Chefredaktør: Lars Jespersen;
Redaktionssekretær: Flemming Kristensen;
Redaktionschef: Jørgen la Cour-Harbo;
Redaktionschef: Inger Lise Kobber Jønsson;
Ansvarshavende redaktør: Per Lyngby;
Nyhedsredaktør/chef: Karin Pedersen
Language (s): Danish; Full Page Colour: 75936.00
Currency: Denmark Kroner
DAILY NEWSPAPER

NORDJYSKE STIFTSTIDENDE Aalborg
Owner: Nordjyske Medier
Editorial: Langagervej 1, Aalborg 9220.
T: 45 99 35 35 35 **E:** aalborg@nordjyske.dk
W: http://www.nordjyske.dk
Freq: Daily; **Circ:** 12981 Not Audited
Language (s): Danish; Full Page Colour: 31592.00
Currency: Denmark Kroner
DAILY NEWSPAPER

NORDJYSKE STIFTSTIDENDE Aars
Owner: Nordjyske Medier
Editorial: BYMIDTEN 7, Aars 9600.
T: 45 96 98 28 28 **E:** aars@nordjyske.dk
W: http://www.nordjyske.dk
Freq: Daily; **Circ:** 62075
Language (s): Danish
DAILY NEWSPAPER

NORDJYSKE STIFTSTIDENDE Brønderslev
Owner: Nordjyske Medier
Editorial: Bredgade 35, Brønderslev 9700.
T: 45 96 45 55 65
E: broenderslev-dronninglund@nordjyske.dk
W: http://www.nordjyske.dk
Freq: Daily; **Circ:** 13797
Language (s): Danish
DAILY NEWSPAPER

NORDJYSKE STIFTSTIDENDE Christiansborg
Owner: Nordjyske Medier
Editorial: Christiansborg Slotsplads 1, Copenhagen 1218. **T:** 45 33 37 58 19
E: christiansborg@nordjyske.dk
W: http://www.nordjyske.dk
Freq: Daily; **Circ:** 62075
Language (s): Danish
DAILY NEWSPAPER

NORDJYSKE STIFTSTIDENDE Debat
Owner: Nordjyske Medier
Editorial: LANGAGERVEJ 1, Aalborg 9220.
T: 45 99 35 34 06 **E:** debat@nordjyske.dk
W: http://www.nordjyske.dk/debat
Freq: Daily; **Circ:** 62075
Language (s): Danish
DAILY NEWSPAPER

NORDJYSKE STIFTSTIDENDE Frederikshavn
Owner: Nordjyske Medier
Editorial: Tordenskjoldsgade 2, Frederikshavn 9900. **T:** 45 99 20 33 33
E: frederikshavn@nordjyske.dk
W: http://www.nordjyske.dk
Freq: Daily; **Circ:** 6939 Dansk Oplagskontrol
Language (s): Danish; Full Page Colour: 13046.00
Currency: Denmark Kroner
NEWSPAPER

NORDJYSKE STIFTSTIDENDE Himmerland
Owner: Nordjyske Medier
Editorial: Adelgade 56, Hobro 9500.
T: 45 98 52 70 00 **E:** hobro@nordjyske.dk
W: http://www.nordjyske.dk
Freq: Daily; **Circ:** 17579 Not Audited
Language (s): Danish; Full Page Colour: 13046.00
Currency: Denmark Kroner
DAILY NEWSPAPER

NORDJYSKE STIFTSTIDENDE Hjørring
Owner: Nordjyske Medier
Editorial: Frederikshavnsvej 81, Hjørring 9800.
T: 45 99 24 50 60 **E:** hjoerring@nordjyske.dk
W: http://www.nordjyske.dk
Freq: Daily; **Circ:** 8314 Not Audited
Language (s): Danish; Full Page Colour: 13046.00
Currency: Denmark Kroner
DAILY NEWSPAPER

NORDJYSKE STIFTSTIDENDE Jammerbugt
Owner: Nordjyske Medier
Editorial: Østergade 33, Fjerritslev 9690.
T: 45 99 50 58 00
E: jammerbugt@nordjyske.dk
W: http://www.nordjyske.dk
Freq: Daily; **Circ:** 62075
Language (s): Danish; Full Page Colour: 13046.00
Currency: Denmark Kroner
DAILY NEWSPAPER

NORDJYSKE STIFTSTIDENDE Kultur
Owner: Nordjyske Medier
Editorial: Langagervej 1, Aaborg Øst 9220.
T: 45 99 35 35 35 **E:** kultur@nordjyske.dk
W: http://www.nordjyske.dk
Freq: Daily; **Circ:** 62075
Language (s): Danish
DAILY NEWSPAPER

NORDJYSKE STIFTSTIDENDE Navne
Owner: Nordjyske Medier
Editorial: LANGAGERVEJ 1, Aalborg 9220.
T: 45 99 35 35 35 **E:** navne@nordjyske.dk
W: http://www.nordjyske.dk
Freq: Daily; **Circ:** 62075
Language (s): Danish
DAILY NEWSPAPER

NORDJYSKE STIFTSTIDENDE Politi
Owner: Nordjyske Medier
Editorial: Langagervej 1, Aalborg 9220.
T: 45 99 35 35 35 **E:** aalborg@nordjyske.dk
W: http://www.nordjyske.dk
Freq: Daily; **Circ:** 62075
Language (s): Danish
DAILY NEWSPAPER

NORDJYSKE STIFTSTIDENDE Samfund
Owner: NORDJYSKE Medier
Editorial: LANGAGERVEJ 1, Aalborg 9220.
T: 45 99 35 35 35 **E:** redaktion@nordjyske.dk
W: http://www.nordjyske.dk
Freq: Daily; **Circ:** 62075
Language (s): Danish
DAILY NEWSPAPER

NORDJYSKE STIFTSTIDENDE; ERHVERV
Owner: Nordjyske Medier
Editorial: LANGAGERVEJ 1, Aalborg 9220.
T: 45 99 35 35 35 **E:** erhverv@nordjyske.dk
W: http://www.nordjyske.dk/erhverv
Freq: Daily; **Circ:** 62075
Redaktør: Egon Kjøller Nielsen
Language (s): Danish
DAILY NEWSPAPER

NORDJYSKE STIFTSTIDENDE; FAMILIE OG LIVSSTIL
Owner: Nordjyske Medier
Editorial: Langagervej 1, Aalborg 9220.
T: 45 99 35 35 35
E: familielivsstil@nordjyske.dk
W: http://www.nordjyske.dk
Freq: Daily; **Circ:** 62075
Language (s): Danish
DAILY NEWSPAPER

NORDJYSKE STIFTSTIDENDE; SPORTEN
Owner: Nordjyske Medier
Editorial: Langagervej 1, Postboks 8000, Aalborg 9220. **T:** 45 99 35 35 35
E: sport@nordjyske.dk
W: http://www.nordjyske.dk
Freq: Daily; **Circ:** 62075
Language (s): Danish
DAILY NEWSPAPER

NORDKYSTEN TV
T: 45 21 86 58 50 **E:** info@nordkysten.tv
W: http://www.tvnordkysten.dk
Freq: Daily
Redaktør for daglige nyheder: Anouschka Andersen
Language (s): Danish
DAILY NEWSPAPER

NORDSCHLESWIGER
Owner: Bund deutcher Nordschleswiger
Editorial: Skibbroen 4, Aabenraa 6200.
T: 45 74 62 38 80
E: redaktion@nordschleswiger.dk
W: http://www.nordschleswiger.dk
Freq: Daily; **Circ:** 2399 Not Audited
Redaktionssekretær: Claudia Knauer;
Chefredaktør: Siegfried Matlok
Language (s): Danish
DAILY NEWSPAPER

NORDSCHLESWIGER Aabenraa
Owner: Bund deutcher Nordschleswiger
Editorial: Skibbroen 4, Aabenraa 6220.
T: 45 73 32 30 60 **E:** ape@nordschleswiger.dk
W: http://www.nordschleswiger.dk
Freq: Daily; **Circ:** 2399 Not Audited
Language (s): Danish
DAILY NEWSPAPER

NORDSCHLESWIGER Haderslev
Owner: Bund deutcher Nordschleswiger
Editorial: Gammelting 13, Haderslev 6100.
T: 45 74 52 39 15 **E:** had@nordschleswiger.dk
W: http://www.nordschleswiger.dk
Freq: Daily; **Circ:** 2399 Not Audited
Language (s): Danish
DAILY NEWSPAPER

NORDSCHLESWIGER Sønderborg
Owner: Bund deutcher Nordschleswiger
Editorial: Rønhaveplads 11, Sønderborg 6400.
T: 45 74 42 42 41 **E:** son@nordschleswiger.dk
W: http://www.nordschleswiger.dk
Freq: Daily; **Circ:** 2399 Not Audited
Language (s): Danish
DAILY NEWSPAPER

NORDSCHLESWIGER Tinglev
Owner: Bund deutcher Nordschleswiger
Editorial: Hovedgaden 100, Tinglev 6330.
T: 45 74 64 48 03 **E:** tin@nordschleswiger.dk
W: http://www.nordschleswiger.dk
Freq: Daily; **Circ:** 2399 Not Audited
Language (s): Danish
DAILY NEWSPAPER

NORDSCHLESWIGER TØNDER
T: 45 74 721918 **E:** ton@nordschleswiger.dk
EDITOR: Brigitta Lassen
DAILY NEWSPAPER

NØRRE SNEDE AVIS
Owner: Nørre Snede Avis A/S
Editorial: Ørnevej 18, Nørre Snede 8766.
T: 45 75 77 10 40 **E:** mail@nrsnede-avis.dk
W: http://www.nrsnede-avis.dk
Freq: Weekly; **Circ:** 7289 Not Audited
Ansvarshavende redaktør: Ole Weilstrup
Language (s): Danish; Full Page Colour: 5197.50
Currency: Denmark Kroner
NEWSPAPER

NØRRESUNDBY AVIS
Owner: Nordjyske Medier
Editorial: Langagervej 1, Aalborg 9220.
T: 45 99 35 33 80
E: susanne.justsen@nordjyske.dk
W: http://www.nordjyskeugeaviser.dk
Freq: Weekly; **Circ:** 30775 Not Audited
Editor: Per Lyngby; **EDITOR IN CHIEF:** Kirsten Vestergaard; **EDITOR IN CHIEF:** Kirsten Vestergaard
Language (s): Danish; Full Page Colour: 12055.50
Currency: Denmark Kroner
NEWSPAPER

NY TIRSDAG
Owner: Rødding Bogtrykkeri ApS
Editorial: Sdr. Tingvej 8, Rødding 6630.
T: 45 74 84 14 15 **E:** presse@nytirsdag.dk
W: http://www.ugeavisen.dk/roedding
Freq: Weekly; **Circ:** 23000 Pub Statement
Ansvarshavende redaktør: Christian Lund Jepsen; **Redaktør:** Kris Vetter
Language (s): Danish; Full Page Colour: 9240.00
Currency: Denmark Kroner
NEWSPAPER

ODDER AVIS
Owner: Odder Avis A/S
Editorial: Rosengade 15, Odder 8300.
T: 45 86 54 10 11 **E:** redaktion@odderavis.dk
W: http://www.odderavis.dk
Freq: Weekly; **Circ:** 22628 Not Audited
Redaktør: Niels Christensen
Language (s): Danish; Full Page Colour: 18648.00
Currency: Denmark Kroner
NEWSPAPER

ODSHERREDS KYSTEN
Owner: Medieselskabet Nordvestsjælland
Editorial: Grønnehavestræde 1, Nykøbing 4500. **T:** 45 88 88 45 10
E: red.ok@nordvest.dk
W: http://www.odsherreds-kysten.dk
Freq: Weekly; **Circ:** 24696 Not Audited
EDITOR: Jørgen Rasmussen; **EDITOR:** Henrik Uhre-Prahl
Language (s): Danish; Full Page Colour: 10465.00
Currency: Denmark Kroner
NEWSPAPER

Onsdagsavisen Horsens
Owner: Onsdags-Avisen Horsens A/S
Editorial: Nørregade 22, Horsens 8700.
T: 45 75 61 28 77 **E:** info@onsdagsavisen.dk
W: http://www.onsdags-avisen.dk
Freq: Weekly; **Circ:** 43000 Not Audited
Ansvarshavende redaktør: Torben Rasmussen
Language (s): Danish; Full Page Colour: 16450.00
Currency: Denmark Kroner
NEWSPAPER

OPLANDSAVISEN
Owner: Nordjyske Medier
Editorial: Gravensgade 42, Brønderslev 9700.
T: 45 96 45 55 65
E: oplandsavisen@nordjyske.dk
W: http://www.nordjyskeugeaviser.dk/Default.aspx?tabid=74
Freq: Weekly; **Circ:** 30616 Not Audited
Redaktionschef: Inger Lise Kobber Jønsson;
Ansvarshavende redaktør: Per Lyngby
Language (s): Danish; Full Page Colour: 11709.00
Currency: Denmark Kroner
NEWSPAPER

ØSTBIRK AVIS ØSTJYDSK AVIS
Owner: Peter Stougaard
Editorial: Storegade 14, Østbirk 8752.
T: 45 75 78 10 11 **E:** post@oestbirk-avis.dk
W: http://www.oestbirk-avis.dk
Freq: Weekly; **Circ:** 13228 Pub Statement
Ansvarshavende redaktør: Peder Stougaard
Language (s): Danish; Full Page Colour: 7718.00
Currency: Denmark Kroner
NEWSPAPER

ØSTERBRO AVIS
Owner: Berlingske Lokalaviser
Editorial: Østerbrogade 79, 1. sal, København Ø 2100. **T:** 45 35 42 25 15
E: red.oav@berlingskemedia.dk
W: http://dinby.dk/oesterbro-avis
Freq: Weekly; **Circ:** 50531 Dansk Oplagskontrol
Ansvarshavende redaktør: Thomas Frederiksen
Language (s): Danish; Full Page Colour: 21480.00
Currency: Denmark Kroner
NEWSPAPER

ØSTHIMMERLANDS FOLKEBLAD
Owner: Østhimmerlands Folkeblad
Editorial: Refsnæsvej 8, Kongerslev 9293.
T: 45 98 33 10 24 E: avis@oehf.dk
W: http://www.oehf.dk
Freq: Weekly; Circ: 15550 Not Audited
EDITOR: Louise Askou; EDITOR: Louise
Askou; Ansvarshavende redaktør: Peter V.
Franzen
Language (s): Danish; Full Page Colour:
9009.00
Currency: Denmark Kroner
NEWSPAPER

ØSTVENDSYSSEL AVIS
Owner: Østvendsyssel Avis A/S
Editorial: Slotsgade 57, Dronninglund 9330.
T: 45 98 84 17 00 E: avis@oestvend.dk
W: http://www.e-pages.dk/ostvendsysselavis/
91/
Freq: Weekly; Circ: 13600 Not Audited
Editor: Per Lyngby; EDITOR: Susie Skov
Language (s): Danish; Full Page Colour:
6609.50
Currency: Denmark Kroner
NEWSPAPER

ØSTVENDSYSSEL FOLKEBLAD
Owner: Lokal 7+ Nordenfjords
Editorial: Industrivej 12, Østervrå 9750.
T: 45 98 95 18 81 E: avis@oestvend.dk
W: http://www.oestvend.dk
Freq: Weekly; Circ: 9987 Not Audited
Ansvarshavende redaktør: Finn Andersen;
Ansvarshavende redaktør: Søren Ejstrup
Brunse
Language (s): Danish; Full Page Colour:
6444.00
Currency: Denmark Kroner
NEWSPAPER

Politiken
Owner: JP/Politikens Hus A/S
Editorial: Rådhuspladsen 37, Copenhagen
1785. T: 45 33 11 85 11 E: nyheder@pol.dk
W: http://www.politiken.dk
Freq: Daily; Circ: 118718 Pub Statement
Kritikredaktør: Peter Christensen; Editor:
Jacob Fuglsang; Redaktør: Morten Garly
Andersen; Editor: Lars Grarup; Editor: Michael
Jarlner; Ansvarlig Redaktør: Bo Lidegaard;
Chefredaktør: Anne Mette Svane;
Redaktionschef: Per Michael Jespersen;
Redaktør: Annette Nyvang; Chefredaktør: Stig
Ørskov
Language (s): Danish; Full Page Colour:
113006.00
Currency: Denmark Kroner
DAILY NEWSPAPER

RADIO MÆLKEBØTTEN
Owner: Foreningen Radio Mælkebøtten
T: 45 75 91 21 47 E: radiomb@mail.tele.dk
W: http://www.radiomb.dk
Freq: Daily
Language (s): Danish
DAILY NEWSPAPER

RANDERS AMTSAVIS
Owner: Århus Stiftstidende A/S
Editorial: Nørregade 7, Randers 8900.
T: 45 87 12 20 00 E: redaktion@amtsavisen.dk
W: http://www.amtsavisen.dk
Freq: Daily; Circ: 11972 Not Audited
EDITOR: Niels Mandrup; EDITOR: Per
Meldgaard; EDITOR: Per Meldgaard;
Redaktionschef: Axel Præstmark;
Redaktionssekretær: Jytte Træholt
Language (s): Danish; Full Page Colour:
14692.50
Currency: Denmark Kroner
DAILY NEWSPAPER

RANDERS AMTSAVIS Debat
Owner: Århus Stifttidende A/S
Editorial: Nørregade 7, Randers 8900.
T: 45 87 12 20 00 E: debat@amtsavisen.dk
W: http://www.amtsavisen.dk
Freq: Daily; Circ: 11972
Language (s): Danish
DAILY NEWSPAPER

RANDERS AMTSAVIS Favrskov
Owner: Århus Stiftstidende A/S
Editorial: Østergade 25, Hadsten 8370.
T: 45 86 98 05 88 E: favrskov@amtsavisen.dk
W: http://www.amtsavisen.dk
Freq: Daily; Circ: 11972
Language (s): Danish
DAILY NEWSPAPER

RANDERS AMTSAVIS Navne
Owner: Århus Stiftstidende A/S
Editorial: Nørregade 7, Randers 8900.
T: 45 87 12 20 00 E: navne@amtsavisen.dk
W: http://www.amtsavisen.dk
Freq: Daily; Circ: 11972

Language (s): Danish
DAILY NEWSPAPER

RANDERS AMTSAVIS Norddjurs
Owner: Århus Stiftstidende A/S
Editorial: Østerbrogade 18, Grenaa 8500.
T: 45 87 58 55 00
E: norddjurs@amtsavisen.dk
W: http://www.amtsavisen.dk
Freq: Daily; Circ: 11972
Language (s): Danish
DAILY NEWSPAPER

RANDERS AMTSAVIS Sport
Owner: Århus Stiftstidende A/S
Editorial: Nørregade 7, Randers 8900.
T: 45 87 12 20 00 E: sporten@amtsavisen.dk
W: http://www.amtsavisen.dk Circ: 11972 Not
Audited
Language (s): Danish
DAILY NEWSPAPER

Ringsted Posten
Owner: Glumsø Bogtrykkeri A/S
Editorial: Søgade 4-12, Ringsted 4100.
T: 45 57 61 25 00 E: ringsted.red@sn.dk
W: http://www.sn.dk/ringsted
Freq: Weekly; Circ: 30600 Pub Statement
Language (s): Danish; Full Page Colour:
10999.00
Currency: Denmark Kroner
NEWSPAPER

RINGSTED WEEKEND
Owner: Ringsted Avisen Week-end
Editorial: Søgade 10, Ringsted 4100.
T: 45 57 61 25 00 E: dagbladet@sj-medier.dk
W: http://www.ringstedonline.dk
Freq: Weekly; Circ: 22740 Not Audited
Chefredaktør: Torben Dalby Larsen;
Ansvarshavende redaktør: Bente
Johannessen; Redaktør: Finn Sinding Yde
Language (s): Danish; Full Page Colour:
8205.00
Currency: Denmark Kroner
NEWSPAPER

RØDOVRE LOKAL NYT
Owner: Rødovre Lokal Nyt ApS
Editorial: Rødovre Centrum 241, Rødovre
2610. T: 45 36 36 60 00 E: rnn@rnn.dk
W: http://www.rnn.dk
Freq: Weekly; Circ: 22000 Pub Statement
Language (s): Danish; Full Page Colour:
13350.00
Currency: Denmark Kroner
NEWSPAPER

ROLD SKOV BLADET
Owner: De Lokale Ugeaviser
Editorial: Jyllandsgade 3, 1., Skørping 9520.
T: 45 96 82 00 00
E: skoerping@roldskovbladet.dk
W: http://www.roldskovbladet.dk
Freq: Weekly; Circ: 9700 Not Audited
Ansvarshavende redaktør: Jan Andersen
Language (s): Danish; Full Page Colour:
7066.80
Currency: Denmark Kroner
NEWSPAPER

ROSKILDE AVIS
Owner: Roskilde Mediecenter K/S
Editorial: Allehelgensgade 3, Roskilde 4000.
T: 45 46 36 20 11
E: redaktion@roskildeavis.dk
W: http://www.roskildeavis.dk
Freq: 2 Times/Week; Circ: 62076
Ansvarshavende redaktør: Louise Lauritsen
Language (s): Danish
NEWSPAPER

ROSKILDE AVIS Erhvervsavisen
Owner: Roskilde Mediecenter K/S
Editorial: Allehelgensgade 3, Roskilde 4000.
T: 45 46 36 20 11 E: db@roskildeavis.dk
W: http://erhvervsavisen.roskilde-avis.dk/dk
Freq: Bi-Weekly; Circ: 4137 Pub Statement
EDITOR: Torben Kristensen
Language (s): Danish; Full Page Colour:
7989.00
Currency: Denmark Kroner
DAILY NEWSPAPER

RY UGEAVIS
Owner: Annonce-bladet Ry A/S
T: 45 86 8936 10 E: ry@mja.dk
W: http://www.ry-ugeavis.dk
Freq: Weekly; Circ: 6500 Pub Statement
Redaktør: Torben Jakobsen
Language (s): Danish
NEWSPAPER

RYTTERKNÆGTEN
Owner: Bornholms Tidende

Editorial: Nørregade 11-19, Rønne 3700.
T: 45 56 90 30 00
E: redaktion@bornholmstidende.dk
W: http://www.bornholmstidende.dk
Freq: Weekly; Circ: 22908 Not Audited
Redaktør: Dan Qvitzau
Language (s): Danish; Full Page Colour:
12685.00
Currency: Denmark Kroner
NEWSPAPER

SÆBY FOLKEBLAD
Owner: Nordjyske Mediecenter
Editorial: Vestergade 22B, Torvet, Sæby 9300.
T: 45 99 89 14 50 E: folkebladet@nordjyske.dk
W: http://www.e-pages.dk/saebyfolkeblad/92/
Freq: Weekly; Circ: 10949 Not Audited
Ansvarshavende redaktør: Per Lyngby
Language (s): Danish; Full Page Colour:
8814.50
Currency: Denmark Kroner
NEWSPAPER

SAMSØ POSTEN
Owner: Samsø Posten A/S
Editorial: Industrivej 6A, Samsø 8305.
T: 45 86 59 13 45 E: info@samsoposten.dk
W: http://www.samso.dk
Freq: Daily; Circ: 3050 Not Audited
Ansvarshavende redaktør: Morten Christensen
Language (s): Danish; Full Page Colour:
5556.00
Currency: Denmark Kroner
NEWSPAPER

SAXKJØBING AVIS
Owner: Folketidende Gruppen, Saxkjøbing Avis
Editorial: Søndergade 2, Sakskøbing 4990.
T: 45 54 70 47 00 E: kh@saxkjobing-avis.dk
W: http://www.saxkjobing-avis.dk
Freq: Weekly; Circ: 9667 Not Audited
Language (s): Danish; Full Page Colour:
9804.00
Currency: Denmark Kroner
NEWSPAPER

SINDAL AVIS
Owner: Nordjyske Medier
Editorial: Østergade 8, Sindal 9870.
T: 45 98 93 62 00 E: sindalavis@nordjyske.dk
W: http://www.sindalavis.dk
Freq: Weekly; Circ: 7622 Not Audited
Editor: Per Lyngby; Redaktør: Martin Nielsen;
EDITOR: Susie Skov
Language (s): Danish; Full Page Colour:
8730.00
Currency: Denmark Kroner
NEWSPAPER

SJÆLLANDSKE
Owner: Sjællandske Medier A/S
Editorial: Dania 38, Næstved 4700.
T: 45 72 45 11 00 E: red@sj-medier.dk
W: http://www.sj-medier.dk Circ: 23484
EDITOR IN CHIEF: Palle Høj; Editor at Large:
Ellen Iversen; EDITOR IN CHIEF: Bente
Johannessen; Ansvarshavende redaktør:
Torben Larsen
Language (s): Danish
DAILY NEWSPAPER

SJÆLLANDSKE Kalundborg
Owner: Sjællandske Medier A/S
Editorial: Centervej 31, Høng 4270.
T: 45 58 85 23 33 E: kalundborg.red@sn.dk
W: http://www.sj-medier.dk Circ: 987
Redaktør: Bjarne Robdrup
Language (s): Danish
NEWSPAPER

SJÆLLANDSKE Sporten
Owner: Sjællandske Medier A/S
Editorial: Dania 38, Næstved 4700.
T: 45 72 45 11 00 E: sporten@sj-medier.dk
W: http://www.sj-medier.dk
Freq: Daily; Circ: 11384
Language (s): Danish
DAILY NEWSPAPER

SJÆLLANDSKE; NAVNE
Owner: Sjællandske Medier A/S
Editorial: Dania 38, Næstved 4700.
T: 45 72 45 11 00 E: navne@sj-medier.dk
W: http://www.sj-medier.dk
Language (s): Danish
DAILY NEWSPAPER

SJÆLLANDSKE; REPORTAGE
Owner: Sjællandske Medier A/S
Editorial: Dania 38, Næstved 4700.
T: 45 72 45 11 00 E: red@sj-medier.dk
W: http://www.sj-medier.dk
Language (s): Danish
DAILY NEWSPAPER

SJÆLLANDSKE~ FAXE
Owner: Sjællandske Medier A/S
Editorial: Torvet 5A, Haslev 4690.
T: 45 72 45 11 00 E: fakse.red@sj-medier.dk
W: http://www.sj-medier.dk Circ: 1163
Redaktør: Susanne Søhuus
Language (s): Danish
DAILY NEWSPAPER

SJÆLLANDSKE~ NY NÆSTVED
Owner: Sjællandske Medier A/S
Editorial: Dania 38, Næstved 4700.
T: 45 72 45 11 00
E: naestved.red@sj-medier.dk
W: http://www.sj-medier.dk
Freq: Daily; Circ: 8380
Redaktør: Mogens Lorentzen
Language (s): Danish; Full Page Colour:
12500.00
Currency: Denmark Kroner
DAILY NEWSPAPER

SJÆLLANDSKE~ SLAGELSE
Owner: Sjællandske Medier A/S
Editorial: Rosengården 24, Slagelse 4200.
T: 45 58 52 37 00
E: slagelse.red@sj-medier.dk
W: http://www.sj-medier.dk Circ: 8276 Pub
Statement
Redaktør: Kim Brandt
Language (s): Danish; Full Page Colour:
12500.00
Currency: Denmark Kroner
DAILY NEWSPAPER

SJÆLLANDSKE~ SORØ
Owner: Sjællandske Medier A/S
Editorial: Storgade 30 B, 1, Sorø 4180
E: soroe.red@sj-medier.dk
W: http://www.sj-medier.dk
Freq: Daily; Circ: 1807
Redaktør: Lars Andersen
Language (s): Danish
DAILY NEWSPAPER

SJÆLLANDSKE~ VORDINGBORG
Owner: Sjællandske Medier A/S
Editorial: Algade 40, Vordingborg 4760.
T: 45 55 37 00 04
E: vordingborg.red@sj-medier.dk
W: http://www.sj-nyheder.dk Circ: 4367
Redaktør: Henning Gøtz
Language (s): Danish; Full Page Colour:
9450.00
Currency: Denmark Kroner
DAILY NEWSPAPER

SKÆRBÆK AVIS / BY OG LAND
Owner: De Lokale Ugeaviser
Editorial: Ribevej 1, Skærbæk 6780.
T: 45 74 75 22 70 E: post@skaerbaek-avis.dk
W: http://www.skaerbaek-avis.dk
Freq: Weekly; Circ: 12836 Not Audited
Ansvarshavende redaktør: Christian Lund
Jepsen; Ansvarshavende redaktør: Christian
Olesen
Language (s): Danish; Full Page Colour:
10635.00
Currency: Denmark Kroner
NEWSPAPER

SKAGEN ONSDAG
Owner: Skagen Onsdag A/S
Editorial: Skolevej 8, Skagen 9990.
T: 45 96 79 59 00
E: skagen.onsdag@nordjyske.dk
W: http://www.nordjyskeugeaviser.dk/Default.
aspx?tabid=76
Freq: Weekly; Circ: 6962 Not Audited
EDITOR: Hans Jørgen Callesen;
Ansvarshavende redaktør: Per Lyngby
Language (s): Danish; Full Page Colour:
8314.50
Currency: Denmark Kroner
NEWSPAPER

SKIVE FOLKEBLAD
Owner: Garantselskabet Skive Folkeblad
Editorial: Gemsevej 7-9, Skive 7800.
T: 45 97 51 34 11
E: redaktion@skivefolkeblad.dk
W: http://www.skivefolkeblad.dk
Freq: Daily; Circ: 12036 Not Audited
Redaktionschef: Ove Andersen;
Redaktionssekretær: Ove Jacobsen;
Redaktionssekretær: Thomas Johansen;
Redaktør: Merete Just
Language (s): Danish; Full Page Colour:
19366.00
Currency: Denmark Kroner
DAILY NEWSPAPER

SØNDAGSAVISEN Centralredaktionen
Owner: Søndagsavisen /s
Editorial: Gladsaxe Møllevej 28, Søborg 2860.
T: 45 39 57 75 00 E: redak@sondagsavisen.dk
W: http://www.sondagsavisen.dk

Freq: Weekly; **Circ:** 2177571 Not Audited
Redaktionssekretær: Susanne Hjortlund;
EDITOR IN CHIEF: Søren Krogsgaard;
Ansvarshavende redaktør: Arne Ullum
Language (s): Danish; Full Page Colour: 36263.00
Currency: Denmark Kroner
NEWSPAPER

SØNDAGSAVISEN Mad & Sundhed
Editorial: Gladsaxe Møllevej 28, Søborg 2860.
T: 45 39 57 7500 **E:** skr@soendagsavisen.dk
W: http://sondagsavisen.dk/en/mad-og-sundhed.aspx
DAILY NEWSPAPER

Sønderborg Ugeavis
Owner: Berlingske Lokalblade
Editorial: Østergade 3, 1.sal, Sønderborg 6400. **T:** 45 87 54 25 42
E: red.soenderborg@ugeavisen.dk
W: http://ugeavisen.dk/soenderborg
Freq: Weekly; **Circ:** 38923 Pub Statement
Ansvarshavende redaktør: Jens Eilertsen
Language (s): Danish; Full Page Colour: 15431.00
Currency: Denmark Kroner
NEWSPAPER

SORØ POSTEN
Owner: Sjællandske Medier A/S
T: 45 57 62 25 00 **E:** soroe.red@sn.dk
W: http://www.susaaavisen.dk
Freq: Weekly; **Circ:** 32600 Pub Statement
Language (s): Danish; Full Page Colour: 10999.50
Currency: Denmark Kroner
NEWSPAPER

SPØTTRUP UGEAVIS
Owner: Spøttrup Ugevis A/S
Editorial: Søndergade 13b, Spøttrup 7860.
T: 45 97 56 43 30
E: post@spottrup-ugeavis.dk
W: http://www.spottrup-ugeavis.dk/
Freq: Weekly; **Circ:** 4600 Pub Statement
Language (s): Danish; Full Page Colour: 7320.00
Currency: Denmark Kroner
NEWSPAPER

SUNDS-GJELLERUP AVIS
Owner: Ikast Avis
Editorial: Strøget 40, Ikast 7430.
T: 45 97 15 18 00 **E:** pressse@ikastavis.dk
W: http://www.sundsgjellerupavis.dk
Freq: Weekly; **Circ:** 7100 Pub Statement
Language (s): Danish; Full Page Colour: 7738.50
Currency: Denmark Kroner
NEWSPAPER

SYDSJÆLLANDS TIDENDE
Owner: Centraltrykkeriet Vordingborg A/S
Editorial: Torvestræde 4, Vordingborg 4760.
T: 45 55 37 00 09 **E:** redaktion@sydtid.dk
W: http://www.sydtid.dk
Freq: Weekly; **Circ:** 30800 Not Audited
Language (s): Danish; Full Page Colour: 11817.50
Currency: Denmark Kroner
NEWSPAPER

TARM UGEBLAD / SKJERN UGEBLAD
Owner: Tarm Ugeblad / Skjern Ugeblad
Editorial: Trykkerivej 6, Tarm 6880.
T: 45 97 37 14 44 **E:** dtp@tarm-bogtryk.dk
W: http://skjerntarm-ugeblad.dk/
Freq: Weekly; **Circ:** 13700 Not Audited
EDITOR: Ulla Frandsen; **EDITOR:** Ulla Frandsen
Language (s): Danish; Full Page Colour: 7933.50
Currency: Denmark Kroner
NEWSPAPER

THE COPENHAGEN POST In&Out
Owner: CPHPOST.DK ApS
T: 45 33 36 33 00 **E:** inout@cphpost.dk
W: http://www.inout.dk
Freq: Weekly
Redaktionschef: Ben Hamilton
Language (s): Danish
DAILY NEWSPAPER

THISTED DAGBLAD
Owner: Nordjyske Medier
Editorial: Sydhavnsvej 5, Thisted 7700.
T: 45 99 19 93 00 **E:** thisted@nordjyske.dk
W: http://www.nordjyske.dk/thisted/forside.aspx
Freq: Daily; **Circ:** 8593 Not Audited
Chefredaktør: Per Lyngby; **EDITOR IN CHIEF:** Svend Ole Jensen
Language (s): Danish; Full Page Colour: 17932.00
Currency: Denmark Kroner
DAILY NEWSPAPER

THISTED DAGBLAD ~HANSTHOLM
Editorial: Bødkervej 29, Hanstholm 7730.
T: 45 96 55 07 70 **E:** thisted@nordjyske.dk
Freq: Daily; **Circ:** 8739 Not Audited
Editor: Mr./Ms. Editor; **Redaktør:** Jens Fogh Andersen
Language (s): Danish
DAILY NEWSPAPER

THISTED DAGBLAD Sport
Editorial: Sydhavnsvej 5, Thisted 7700.
T: 45 99 19 93 00 **E:** sport@nordjyske.dk
W: http://www.nordjyske.dk/thisted/forside.aspx
Freq: Daily; **Circ:** 8739
Language (s): Danish
DAILY NEWSPAPER

THISTED POSTEN
Owner: Nordjyske Medier
Editorial: Sydhavnsvej 5, Thisted 7700.
T: 45 99 19 93 00
E: thisted.posten@nordjyske.dk
W: http://www.e-pages.dk/thistedposten/90/
Freq: Weekly; **Circ:** 24262 Not Audited
Redaktør: Hans Peter Kragh
Language (s): Danish; Full Page Colour: 10971.00
Currency: Denmark Kroner
NEWSPAPER

THYLANDS AVIS
Owner: Nordjyske Medier
Editorial: Bredgade 139, Hurup, Thy 7760.
T: 45 97 95 21 00
E: thylands.redaktion@nordjyske.dk
W: http://www.e-pages.dk/thylandsavis/90/
Freq: Weekly; **Circ:** 8453 Not Audited
Redaktør: Knud Erichsen; **Ansvarshavende redaktør:** Per Lyngby; **Redaktør:** Hans Peter Kragh
Language (s): Danish; Full Page Colour: 8161.00
Currency: Denmark Kroner
NEWSPAPER

TØRRING FOLKEBLAD
Owner: Tørring Folkeblad A/S
Editorial: Vongevej 17, Tørring 7160.
T: 45 75 80 22 88 **E:** red@folkeblad.net
W: http://www.torring-folkeblad.dk
Freq: Weekly; **Circ:** 14207 Not Audited
EDITOR: Jakob Tornvig
Language (s): Danish; Full Page Colour: 14690.00
Currency: Denmark Kroner
NEWSPAPER

TREKANTENS FOLKEBLAD
Owner: Trekantens Folkeblad A/S
Editorial: Søndergade 2, Børkop 7080.
T: 45 75 86 51 11 **E:** trekantens@mail.dk
W: http://www.trekantens-folkeblad.dk
Freq: Weekly; **Circ:** 8000 Not Audited
Ansvarshavende redaktør: Kasper Kaarøe
Language (s): Danish; Full Page Colour: 8816.87
Currency: Denmark Kroner
NEWSPAPER

TV 2 / DANMARK; SPORTEN
Owner: TV 2 / DANMARK
Editorial: Rugaardsvej 25, Odense 5100.
T: 45 65 91 91 91 **E:** sporten@tv2.dk
W: http://www.sporten.tv2.dk
Language (s): Danish
DAILY NEWSPAPER

TV 2 Go' Morgen Danmark
Owner: TV 2
Editorial: Banegårdspladsen 7, Copenhagen 1570. **T:** 45 36 18 82 00 **E:** gomorgen@tv2.dk
W: http://www.gomorgen.tv2.dk
Freq: Daily; **Circ:** 183000 Pub Statement
Studievært: Morten Resen; **Redaktionschef:** Michael Rydal Ravn; **EDITOR:** Jes Schrøder;
Livsstil generelt: Kamilla Walsøe
Language (s): Danish
DAILY NEWSPAPER

TV 2 GO'AFTEN DANMARK
Owner: TV 2 / DANMARK
Editorial: Banegårdspladsen 7, Copenhagen 1570. **T:** 45 36 18 82 00 **E:** goaften@tv2.dk
W: http://goaften.tv2.dk
Freq: Daily
Debat / Opinion: Mikkel Beha Erichsen;
Studievært: Michèle Bellaiche
Language (s): Danish
DAILY NEWSPAPER

TV FREDERIKSBERG
T: 45 21 69 39 46 **E:** tvf@tvfrederiksberg.dk
W: http://www.tvfrederiksberg.dk
Language (s): Danish
DAILY NEWSPAPER

TV HOLTBJERG
T: 45 96 28 86 71 **E:** line@voresholtbjerg.dk
W: http://voresholtbjerg.dk/index.asp?id=205
Freq: Daily
Ansvarshavende redaktør: Kim Kristensen
Language (s): Danish
DAILY NEWSPAPER

TV MOSAIK
E: m@etnic.dk **W:** http://www.etnic.dk
Language (s): Danish
DAILY NEWSPAPER

TV STRANDPARKEN
T: 45 28 14 90 41 **E:** mhp@tvpc.dk
W: http://www.tv-strandparken.dk
Language (s): Danish
DAILY NEWSPAPER

TYRSTRUP HERREDS TIDENDE/ CHRISTIANSFELD AVIS
Owner: Christiansfeld Avis A/S
Editorial: Lindegade 48, Postboks 76, Christiansfeld 6070. **T:** 45 74 56 14 33
E: info@tht-ugeavis.dk
W: http://www.tht-ugeavis.dk
Freq: Weekly; **Circ:** 5784 Not Audited
Ansvarshavende redaktør: Helle W Ravn
Language (s): Danish; Full Page Colour: 5589.00
Currency: Denmark Kroner
NEWSPAPER

UGE NYT (ÅRHUS SYD)
Owner: Favrskov Gruppen
T: 45 87 32 48 00
W: http://aarhus.lokalavisen.dk/
Freq: Weekly; **Circ:** 32194 Dansk Oplagskontrol
EDITOR IN CHIEF: Claus Krogh
Language (s): Danish; Full Page Colour: 8685.60
Currency: Denmark Kroner
NEWSPAPER

UGE NYT SLAGELSE
Owner: Søndagsavisen a/s
Editorial: Nytorv 10, Slagelse 4200.
T: 45 58 53 32 22
E: ugenyt@sondagsavisen.dk
W: http://www.ugenyt.net
Freq: Weekly; **Circ:** 59960 Pub Statement
Language (s): Danish; Full Page Colour: 13972.50
Currency: Denmark Kroner
NEWSPAPER

UGEAVISEN ANSAGER HELLE
Owner: Bladgruppen Vest
Editorial: Storegade 16-18, Ølgod 6870.
T: 45 75 19 60 90
E: annoncer@ansager-helle.dk
W: http://www.ansager-helle.dk
Freq: Weekly; **Circ:** 8422 Not Audited
Language (s): Danish; Full Page Colour: 8741.88
Currency: Denmark Kroner
NEWSPAPER

UGEAVISEN ESBJERG
Owner: Ugeavisen Esbjerg K/S
Editorial: Kongensgade 110-114, Esbjerg 6700. **T:** 45 76 11 42 00
E: redaktion@ugeavisen-esbjerg.dk
W: http://www.ugeavisen-esbjerg.dk
Freq: Weekly; **Circ:** 69450 Media Scandinavia
Ansvarshavende redaktør: Erik Haldan
Language (s): Danish; Full Page Colour: 14346.75
Currency: Denmark Kroner
DAILY NEWSPAPER

UGEAVISEN FAABORG-MIDTFYN
Owner: Fynske Medier A/S
Editorial: Kanneworffs Gaard 8B, Faaborg 5600. **T:** 45 63 45 22 25
E: redaktion@ugeavisen-faaborg.dk
W: http://ugeavisenfaaborg.dk
Freq: Weekly; **Circ:** 19775 Pub Statement
Redaktør: Torsten Cilleborg
Language (s): Danish; Full Page Colour: 7507.50
Currency: Denmark Kroner
DAILY NEWSPAPER

UGEAVISEN FOR BRAMMING OG OMEGN
Owner: Bladgruppen Vest
Editorial: Sct. Knuds Alle 3, Bramming 6740.
T: 45 75 17 40 00
E: im@ugeavisen-bramming.dk
W: http://www.ugeavisen-bramming.dk
Freq: Weekly; **Circ:** 15767 Not Audited
Language (s): Danish; Full Page Colour: 10635.00
Currency: Denmark Kroner
NEWSPAPER

UGEAVISEN FOR RIBE OG OMEGN
Owner: Bladgruppen Vest
Editorial: Grønnegade 14, Ribe 6760.
T: 45 75 42 23 66
E: redaktion@ugeavisen-ribe.dk
W: http://www.ugeavisen-ribe.dk
Freq: Weekly; **Circ:** 24999 Not Audited
Ansvarshavende redaktør: Christian Lund Jepsen
Language (s): Danish; Full Page Colour: 11105.00
Currency: Denmark Kroner
NEWSPAPER

UGEAVISEN FOR TREKANTEN Vejle-Kolding-Fredericia
Owner: Ugeavisen for Trekanten Vejle-Kolding-Fredericia
Editorial: Bytorvet 14, Hedensted 8722.
T: 45 75 89 13 66
E: presse@hedensted-avis.dk
W: http://www.hedensted-avis.dk
Freq: Weekly; **Circ:** 13260 Not Audited
Language (s): Danish; Full Page Colour: 8757.50
Currency: Denmark Kroner
NEWSPAPER

UGEAVISEN GULDBORGSUND
Owner: Ugeavisen Nykøbing F. A/S
Editorial: Tværgade 20, Nykøbing 4800.
T: 45 54 88 02 34
E: redaktion@ugeavisen-guld.dk
W: http://www.ugeavisen-nyk.dk
Freq: Weekly; **Circ:** 34127
Redaktør: Manfred Sørensen
Language (s): Danish; Full Page Colour: 11379.00
Currency: Denmark Kroner
DAILY NEWSPAPER

UGEAVISEN HOLSTED-BRØRUP-RØDDING-VEJEN
Owner: Bladgruppen Vest
Editorial: Nørregade 24, Brørup 6650.
T: 45 75 38 37 77
W: http://holsted.kivaweb.dk
Freq: Weekly; **Circ:** 21735
Redaktør: Mogens Christensen
Language (s): Danish; Full Page Colour: 9950.63
Currency: Denmark Kroner
DAILY NEWSPAPER

UGEAVISEN KARUP
Owner: I.B. Tryk
Editorial: Bredgade 4 F, Postbox 55, Karup 7470. **T:** 45 97 10 10 22
E: presse@ugeavisen-karup.dk
W: http://www.ugeavisen-karup.dk
Freq: Weekly; **Circ:** 7733 Pub Statement
Redaktør: Knud Gaarn-Larsen;
Ansvarshavende redaktør: Steen Hebsgaard
Language (s): Danish; Full Page Colour: 7854.00
Currency: Denmark Kroner
DAILY NEWSPAPER

UGEAVISEN MIDTSYD
Owner: Bladgruppen Vest
Editorial: Søndergade 18, Toftlund 6520.
T: 45 74 83 22 83 **E:** redaktion@midtsyd.dk
W: http://www.midtsyd.dk
Freq: Weekly; **Circ:** 22455 Not Audited
Language (s): Danish; Full Page Colour: 10197.50
Currency: Denmark Kroner
NEWSPAPER

UGEAVISEN MØLDRUP-AALESTRUP / GEDSTED AVIS
Owner: De Bergske Blade
T: 45 89 276300 **E:** uma@bergske.dk
W: http://www.bergske.dk
Freq: Weekly; **Circ:** 11856 Pub Statement
EDITOR AT LARGE: Dorthe Carlsen; **EDITOR:** Dorte Kristensen; **Chefredaktør:** Lars Norup
Language (s): Danish; Full Page Colour: 7499.00
Currency: Denmark Kroner
DAILY NEWSPAPER

UGEAVISEN NORDFYN
Owner: Område Avisen Nordfyn A/S
Editorial: Østergade 14, Bogense 5400.
T: 45 65 45 57 00
E: uanredaktion@fynskemedier.dk
W: http://www.ugeavisennordfyn.dk
Freq: Weekly; **Circ:** 22447 Not Audited
EDITOR AT LARGE: Thomas Gregersen
Language (s): Danish; Full Page Colour: 13860.00
Currency: Denmark Kroner
NEWSPAPER

UGEAVISEN NYKØBING-RØRVIG
Owner: Holbæk Amts Venstreblad
Editorial: Grønnehavestræde 1, Nykøbing 4500. **T:** 45 88 88 45 10
E: red.ua@nordvest.dk
W: http://www.venstrebladet.dk
Freq: Weekly; **Circ:** 19986 Pub Statement
EDITOR: Martin Hoffmann
Language (s): Danish; Full Page Colour: 10885.00
Currency: Denmark Kroner
DAILY NEWSPAPER

UGEAVISEN ØBOEN
Owner: Fynske Medier P/S
Editorial: Ørstedsgade 18, Rudkøbing 5900.
T: 45 62 51 22 80 **E:** redaktion@oeboen.dk
W: http://ugeavisenoboen.dk
Freq: Weekly; **Circ:** 11300 Pub Statement
Ansvarshavende redaktør: Bjarne Selvager Hansen
Language (s): Danish; Full Page Colour: 11434.50
Currency: Denmark Kroner
NEWSPAPER

Ugeavisen Odense
Owner: Ugeavisen Odense A/S
Editorial: Banegardspladsen, Odense 5100.
T: 45 66 14 14 10 **E:** post@faa.dk
W: http://www.ugeavisen-odense.dk
Freq: Weekly; **Circ:** 117161 Not Audited
EDITOR: Jan Bonde
Language (s): Danish; Full Page Colour: 22888.50
Currency: Denmark Kroner
NEWSPAPER

UGEAVISEN RINGKØBING
Owner: Midtjyske Medier
Editorial: St. Blichersvej 5, Ringkøbing 6950.
T: 45 99 75 73 99
E: ringkoebing.annonce@bergske.dk
W: http://midtjyskemedier.dk
Freq: Weekly; **Circ:** 15072 Pub Statement
Redaktør: Leif Nielsen
Language (s): Danish; Full Page Colour: 10047.00
Currency: Denmark Kroner
NEWSPAPER

UGEAVISEN STRUER-THYHOLM
Owner: Berlingske af 2007 A/S
Editorial: Kildegården 3, Struer 7600.
T: 45 96 84 22 00 **E:** struer@bergske.dk
W: http://www.bergske.dk
Freq: Weekly; **Circ:** 17571 Pub Statement
EDITOR IN CHIEF: Dorthe Carlsen; **EDITOR AT LARGE:** Hans Krabbe; **Redaktør:** Ninna Pirchert; **Redaktør for daglige nyheder:** Jørgen Vestbjerg
Language (s): Danish; Full Page Colour: 11507.50
Currency: Denmark Kroner
DAILY NEWSPAPER

UGEAVISEN SVENDBORG
Owner: Fynske Medier P/S
Editorial: Sankt Nicolai Gade 1A, Svendborg 5700. **T:** 45 62 21 73 21
E: red@ugeavisen-svendborg.dk
W: http://ugeavisensvendborg.dk
Freq: Weekly; **Circ:** 33868 Not Audited
EDITOR IN CHIEF: Troels Mylenberg; **Redaktør:** Michael Thorbjørnsen
Language (s): Danish; Full Page Colour: 13167.00
Currency: Denmark Kroner
NEWSPAPER

UGEAVISEN SVENSTRUP
Owner: Ugeavisen Svenstrup A/S
Editorial: Godthåbsvej 7, Svenstrup 9230.
T: 45 98 38 14 77
E: annonce@uge-avisen.com
W: http://www.delokaleugeaviser.dk/dd/default.asp?template=blad&id=4&area=&bladid=2
Freq: Weekly; **Circ:** 35000 Pub Statement
Language (s): Danish; Full Page Colour: 13167.00
Currency: Denmark Kroner
NEWSPAPER

UGEAVISEN THY
Owner: Thy Medie ApS
Editorial: Chr. Hansens Vej 1, Hanstholm 7730. **T:** 45 96 18 18 22
E: susanne@thymedie.dk
Freq: Weekly; **Circ:** 21857 Not Audited
Redaktør: Torben Tangsig
Language (s): Danish; Full Page Colour: 5859.00
Currency: Denmark Kroner
DAILY NEWSPAPER

UGEAVISEN TISTRUP ØLGOD
Owner: Bladgruppen Vest
Editorial: Storegade 16-18, Ølgod 6870.
T: 45 75 24 45 55 **E:** annoncer@ugeavisen.net
W: http://www.ugeavisen.net
Freq: Weekly; **Circ:** 11489 Not Audited
Language (s): Danish; Full Page Colour: 9626.25
Currency: Denmark Kroner
NEWSPAPER

UGEAVISEN TØNDER
Owner: Bladgruppen Vest
Editorial: Vestergade 76, Tønder 6270.
T: 45 74 72 47 11 **E:** redaktion@uat.dk
W: http://www.uat.dk
Freq: Weekly; **Circ:** 27500 Not Audited
Redaktør: Erik Petersen
Language (s): Danish; Full Page Colour: 12236.63
Currency: Denmark Kroner
NEWSPAPER

UGEAVISEN VARDE
Owner: Bladgruppen Vest
Editorial: Rådhusstræde 5, Varde 6800.
T: 45 75 22 24 44
E: redaktion@ugeavisen-varde.dk
W: http://varde.kivaweb.dk
Freq: Weekly; **Circ:** 26304 Media Scandinavia
Language (s): Danish; Full Page Colour: 10017.00
Currency: Denmark Kroner
DAILY NEWSPAPER

Ugeavisen Vejle
Owner: Vejle Amts Folkeblad A/S
Editorial: Bugattivej 8, Vejle 7100.
T: 45 75 83 10 00
E: redaktion@ugeavisenvejle.dk
W: http://www.ugeavisenvejle.dk
Freq: Weekly; **Circ:** 71843 Not Audited
Ansvarshavende redaktør: Klaus Lindholm
Language (s): Danish; Full Page Colour: 15246.00
Currency: Denmark Kroner
NEWSPAPER

UGEBLADET FOR MØN
Owner: Sjællandske Medier A/S
Editorial: Lille Kirkestræde 2, Stege 4780.
T: 45 55 81 40 34
E: redaktion@ugebladet-for-moen.dk
W: http://www.ugebladet-for-moen.dk
Freq: Weekly; **Circ:** 7630 Not Audited
Ansvarshavende redaktør: Olav Sindalsen
Language (s): Danish; Full Page Colour: 7852.50
Currency: Denmark Kroner
NEWSPAPER

UGEBLADET FOR TINGLEV KOMMUNE
Owner: Tinglev Bogtrykkeri A/S
Editorial: Tværvejen 5, Tinglev 6360.
T: 45 74 64 40 38
E: mail@tinglev-bogtrykkeri.dk
W: http://www.tinglev-bogtrykkeri.dk/ugebladet.php
Freq: Weekly; **Circ:** 6700 Not Audited
Language (s): Danish; Full Page Colour: 6976.20
Currency: Denmark Kroner
NEWSPAPER

UGEBLADET HØRSHOLM
Owner: Hørsholm MedieCenter Aps
Editorial: Hækkevej 2, Hørsholm 2970.
T: 45 45 90 80 00
E: redaktionen@ugebladet.dk
W: http://hoersholm.lokalavisen.dk
Freq: Weekly; **Circ:** 37400
EDITOR IN CHIEF: Kim Belmark; **Redaktør:** Morten Timm
Language (s): Danish; Full Page Colour: 15673.00
Currency: Denmark Kroner
DAILY NEWSPAPER

UGEBLADET NÆSTVED OG OMEGN
Owner: Sjællandske Medier A/S
Editorial: Dania 38, Næstved 4700.
T: 45 72 45 11 00 **E:** ugebladet@sj-medier.dk
W: http://www.sj-medier.dk
Freq: Weekly; **Circ:** 47587 Not Audited
Ansvarshavende redaktør: Helge Wedel
Language (s): Danish; Full Page Colour: 19057.50
Currency: Denmark Kroner
NEWSPAPER

UGEBLADET SKANDERBORG
Owner: Berlingske Media
Editorial: Adelgade 115, Skanderborg 8660.
T: 45 86 52 01 44 **E:** redaktion@uge-bladet.dk
W: http://www.skanderborgnettet.dk/web/uge-bladet/index.htm
Freq: Weekly; **Circ:** 29700 Not Audited
EDITOR IN CHIEF: Dorthe Carlsen; **EDITOR IN CHIEF:** Søren Sohn
Language (s): Danish; Full Page Colour: 9354.00
Currency: Denmark Kroner
NEWSPAPER

UGEBLADET SYDSJÆLLAND
Owner: Sjællandske Medier A/S
Editorial: Adelgade 70, Præstø 4720.
T: 45 55 99 21 21
E: redaktion-ubs@sj-medier.dk
W: http://www.sj-medier.dk
Freq: Weekly; **Circ:** 21859 Pub Statement
Ansvarshavende redaktør: Torben Dalby Larsen; **EDITOR:** Nina Lise; **Chefredaktør:** Helge Wedel
Language (s): Danish; Full Page Colour: 14782.50
Currency: Denmark Kroner
NEWSPAPER

UGEBLADET VESTSJÆLLAND
Owner: Holbæk Amts Venstreblad
Editorial: Ahlgade 1 C, Holbæk 4300.
T: 45 88 88 43 00 **E:** red.hol@nordvest.dk
W: http://www.nordvestnyt.dk/ugebladet
Freq: Weekly; **Circ:** 22045 Not Audited
EDITOR AT LARGE: Agner Ahm; **EDITOR AT LARGE:** Agner Ahm; **EDITOR:** Gunner Nielsen; **Redaktionssekretær:** Flemming Ravnemose; **EDITOR:** Anders Vestergaard; **EDITOR:** Anders Vestergaard
Language (s): Danish; Full Page Colour: 9854.00
Currency: Denmark Kroner
NEWSPAPER

UGEBREV FOR BESTYRELSER
Owner: Forlaget Thomson A/S
Editorial: Slagtehusgade 4-6, Copenhagen 1715. **T:** 45 70 23 40 10
E: kontakt@bestyrelsen.dk
W: http://bestyrelsen.dk/
Freq: Weekly; **Circ:** 436
Chefredaktør: Morten W. Langer
Language (s): Danish
DAILY NEWSPAPER

UGEBREVET A4
Owner: Landsorganisationen i Danmark (LO)
Editorial: Islandsbrygge 32 D, Copenhagen 2300. **T:** 45 35 24 60 00 **E:** ugebreveta4@lo.dk
W: http://www.ugebreveta4.dk
Freq: Weekly; **Circ:** 26000 Pub Statement
Language (s): Danish; Full Page Colour: 20000.00
Currency: Denmark Kroner
DAILY NEWSPAPER

UGE-NYT Fredensborg
Owner: Politikens Lokalaviser
Editorial: Chr. Boecks Vej 3, Fredensborg 3480. **T:** 45 45 90 80 70
W: http://www.uge-nyt.dk
Freq: Weekly; **Circ:** 21400 Pub Statement
Editor in charge: Kim Belmark; **EDITOR:** Peter Klar; **Ansvarshavende redaktør:** Niels Mehnke
Language (s): Danish; Full Page Colour: 15823.50
Currency: Denmark Kroner
NEWSPAPER

UGEPOSTEN Helsinge
Owner: Berlingske Lokalaviser
Editorial: Østergade 33, Helsinge 3200.
T: 45 48 76 09 40
E: red.uhe@berlingskemedia.dk
W: http://www.ugeposten.dk
Freq: Weekly; **Circ:** 21459
EDITOR AT LARGE: Dorthe Carlsen; **Ansvarshavende redaktør:** Jeanette Hougaard
Language (s): Danish; Full Page Colour: 13341.50
Currency: Denmark Kroner
DAILY NEWSPAPER

UGEPOSTEN KIBÆK
Owner: Ugeposten Kibæk A/S
Editorial: Falkevej 4, Kibæk 6920.
T: 45 97 19 10 07
E: ugeposten@videbaek-bogtrykkeri.dk
W: http://www.videbaek-bogtrykkeri.dk
Freq: Weekly; **Circ:** 11212 Not Audited
Language (s): Danish; Full Page Colour: 6659.50
Currency: Denmark Kroner
NEWSPAPER

UGEPOSTEN SKJERN
Owner: De Bergske Blade
Editorial: Bergs plads 5, Skjern 6900.
T: 45 96 81 53 13
E: skjern.annonce@bergske.dk
W: http://dinby.dk/ugeposten-skjern
Freq: Weekly; **Circ:** 25000 Pub Statement
EDITOR IN CHIEF: Dorthe Carlsen; **Redaktør:** Leif Nielsen
Language (s): Danish; Full Page Colour: 10278.00
Currency: Denmark Kroner
NEWSPAPER

VALBY BLADET
Owner: Berlingske Lokalaviser
Editorial: Dirch Passers Allé 27, 1. sal, Frederiksberg 2000. **T:** 45 33 88 88 88
E: red@valbybladet.dk
W: http://dinby.dk/valby-bladet
Freq: Weekly; **Circ:** 41000 Not Audited
Chefredaktør: Peter Erlitz; **Ansvarshavende redaktør:** Morten Outzen
Language (s): Danish; Full Page Colour: 20054.50
Currency: Denmark Kroner
NEWSPAPER

VAMDRUP UGEBLAD
Owner: Vamdrup Ugeblad A/S
Editorial: Østergade 7, Postboks 26, Vamdrup 6580. **T:** 45 75 58 12 00
E: vu@vamdrup-ugeblad.dk
W: http://www.vamdrup-ugeblad.dk
Freq: Weekly; **Circ:** 12848 Not Audited
Language (s): Danish; Full Page Colour: 7006.00
Currency: Denmark Kroner
NEWSPAPER

VANLØSE BLADET
Owner: De Berlingske Lokalaviser
Editorial: Solbjergvej 2A, Erhvervsplan, Frederiksberg 2000. **T:** 45 33 88 88 88
E: red.vf@b-l.dk
W: http://www.vanloesebladet.dk
Freq: Weekly; **Circ:** 23371
Ansvarshavende redaktør: Peter Erlitz; **Ansvarshavende redaktør:** Morten Friis Outzen; **Redaktionschef:** Christian M. Olsen
Language (s): Danish; Full Page Colour: 18699.50
Currency: Denmark Kroner
DAILY NEWSPAPER

VEJEN AVIS
Owner: Jydske Vestkysten A/S
Editorial: Vestergade 2D, Vejen 6600.
T: 45 75 36 00 22 **E:** vejenavis@jv.dk
W: http://www.vejenavis.dk
Freq: Weekly; **Circ:** 36128 Not Audited
EDITOR IN CHIEF: Hanne Højbjerg; **Redaktør:** Jørgen Schultz
Language (s): Danish; Full Page Colour: 10624.50
Currency: Denmark Kroner
NEWSPAPER

VEJGAARD AVIS
Owner: Nordjyske Medier
Editorial: Langagervej 1, Aalborg 9330.
T: 45 99 35 35 35 **E:** vejgaard@nordjyske.dk
W: http://www.vejgaardavis.dk/
Freq: Weekly; **Circ:** 33762 Not Audited
Ansvarshavende redaktør: Per Lyngby; **EDITOR IN CHIEF:** Kirsten Vestergaard; **EDITOR IN CHIEF:** Kirsten Vestergaard
Language (s): Danish; Full Page Colour: 12286.50
Currency: Denmark Kroner
NEWSPAPER

VEJLE AMTS FOLKEBLAD
Owner: Velje Amts Folkeblad A/S
Editorial: Bugattivej 8, Vejle 7100.
T: 45 75 85 77 88
E: vaf@vejleamtsfolkeblad.dk
W: http://www.vejleamtsfolkeblad.dk
Freq: Daily; **Circ:** 17400 Not Audited
Redaktionschef: Mogens G. Madsen; **Redaktør:** Søren Rahbek
Language (s): Danish; Full Page Colour: 36190.00
Currency: Denmark Kroner
DAILY NEWSPAPER

VEJLE AMTS FOLKEBLAD Billund
Owner: Vejle Amts Folkeblad A/S
Editorial: Højmarksvej 5, Billund 7190.
T: 45 75 33 80 33
E: billund@vejleamtsfolkeblad.dk
W: http://www.vaf-fd.dk
Freq: Daily; **Circ:** 18193
Language (s): Danish
DAILY NEWSPAPER

VEJLE AMTS FOLKEBLAD Bolig
Owner: Vejle Amts Folkeblad A/S
Editorial: Bugattivej 8, Vejle 7100.
T: 45 75 85 77 88
E: vaf@vejleamtsfolkeblad.dk
W: http://www.vejleamtsfolkeblad.dk/
Circ: 18193
Language (s): Danish
DAILY NEWSPAPER

VEJLE AMTS FOLKEBLAD Brande-Ikast
Owner: Vejle Amts Folkeblad A/S
Editorial: Storegade 38, Brande 7330.
T: 45 97 18 06 22
E: sora@vejleamtsfolkeblad.dk
W: http://www.vaf-fd.dk
Freq: Daily; **Circ:** 18193
Language (s): Danish
DAILY NEWSPAPER

VEJLE AMTS FOLKEBLAD Debat
Owner: Vejle Amts Folkeblad A/S
Editorial: Bugattivej 8, Vejle 7100.
T: 45 75 85 77 88 **E:** debat@vaf-fd.dk
W: http://www.vaf-fd.dk
Freq: Daily; **Circ:** 18193
Language (s): Danish
DAILY NEWSPAPER

VEJLE AMTS FOLKEBLAD Give-Vest
Owner: Vejle Amts Folkeblad
Editorial: Østergade 16, Give 7323.
T: 45 75 73 56 11
E: vaf@vejleamtsfolkeblad.dk
W: http://www.vaf-fd.dk
Freq: Daily
Language (s): Danish
DAILY NEWSPAPER

VEJLE AMTS FOLKEBLAD Motor
Owner: Vejle Amts Folkeblad A/S
Editorial: Bugattivej 8, Vejle 7100.
T: 45 76 41 49 72
E: motor@vejleamtsfolkeblad.dk
W: http://www.vejleamtsfolkeblad.dk
Freq: Weekly; **Circ:** 18193 Dansk Oplagskontrol
Language (s): Danish
DAILY NEWSPAPER

VEJLE AMTS FOLKEBLAD Navne
Owner: Vejle Amts Folkeblad A/S
Editorial: bugattivej 8, Vejle 7100.
T: 45 75 85 77 88
E: navne@vejleamtsfolkeblad.dk
W: http://www.vejleamtsfolkeblad.dk
Freq: Daily; **Circ:** 18193
Language (s): Danish
DAILY NEWSPAPER

VEJLE AMTS FOLKEBLAD Sporten
Owner: Vejle Amts Folkeblad A/S
Editorial: Bugattivej 8, Vejle 7100.
T: 45 75 85 77 88
E: sporten@vejleamtsfolkeblad.dk
W: http://www.vaf-fd.dk
Freq: Daily; **Circ:** 18193
Language (s): Danish
DAILY NEWSPAPER

Velje Amst Folkeblad; Hedensted
Owner: Vejle Amts Folkeblad A/S
Editorial: Bytorvet 14, Hedensted 8722.
T: 45 75 89 16 44
E: hedensted@vejleamtsfolkeblad.dk
W: http://www.vaf-fd.dk
Freq: Daily; **Circ:** 18193
Language (s): Danish
DAILY NEWSPAPER

VENDELBO POSTEN
Owner: Nordjyske Medier
Editorial: Frederikshavnvej 81, Hjørring 9800.
T: 45 99 24 50 60 **E:** vp@nordjyske.dk
W: http://www.VENDELBOPOSTEN.DK
Freq: Weekly; **Circ:** 35857 Not Audited
EDITOR IN CHIEF: Inger Lise Jønsson;
Ansvarshavende redaktør: Per Lyngby
Language (s): Danish; Full Page Colour: 12217.50
Currency: Denmark Kroner
NEWSPAPER

VESTEGNEN
Owner: Berlingske Lokalaviser A/S
T: 45 70 20 64 01 **E:** redaktion@vestegnen.dk
W: http://www.vestegnen.dk
Freq: Weekly; **Circ:** 153147 Not Audited
EDITOR: Peter Erlitz; **EDITOR:** Peter Erlitz;
Contact: Pia Walther Jensen; **Contact:** Pia Walther Jensen
Language (s): Danish; Full Page Colour: 28373.50
Currency: Denmark Kroner
NEWSPAPER

VESTHIMMERLANDS AVIS
Owner: Himmerlands Tryk A/S
Editorial: Borgergade 17, Aalestrup 9620.
T: 45 98 64 12 55
E: redaktionen@vesthimmerlandsavis.dk
W: http://www.vesthimmerlandsavis.dk
Freq: Weekly; **Circ:** 10432 Not Audited
Ansvarshavende redaktør: Thorkil Christensen

Language (s): Danish; Full Page Colour: 8731.80
Currency: Denmark Kroner
NEWSPAPER

VESTHIMMERLANDS FOLKEBLAD
Owner: Brdr. Eskildsen
Editorial: Blekingevej 13, Løgstør 9670.
T: 45 98 67 37 11 **E:** avis@vf-logstor.dk
W: http://www.vf-logstor.dk
Freq: Weekly; **Circ:** 9600 Not Audited
Ansvarshavende redaktør: Per Eskildsen
Language (s): Danish; Full Page Colour: 8631.90
Currency: Denmark Kroner
NEWSPAPER

VIBORG NYT
Owner: De Bergske Blade
Editorial: Vesterbrogade 8, Viborg 8800.
T: 45 89 27 63 00 **E:** viborgnyt@bergske.dk
W: http://dinby.dk/viborg-nyt
Freq: Weekly; **Circ:** 41630 Not Audited
EDITOR AT LARGE: Dorthe Carlsen; **EDITOR:** Jacob Kaas; **Redaktør:** Dorte Søgaard Kristensen
Language (s): Danish; Full Page Colour: 11352.00
Currency: Denmark Kroner
NEWSPAPER

VIBORG STIFTS FOLKEBLAD
Owner: Midtjyske Medier
Editorial: Vesterbrogade 8, Viborg 8800.
T: 45 89 27 63 00 **E:** viborg@bergske.dk
W: http://www.viborg-folkeblad.dk
Freq: Daily; **Circ:** 11068 Not Audited
Redaktionschef: Ole Bjærge; **Redaktør:** Marianne Brink; **Redaktionssekretær:** Bo Hovgaard Hansen; **Redaktionssekretær:** Torben Mikkelsen; **Chefredaktør:** Lars Norup;
Redaktør: Dorte Søgaard Kristensen
Language (s): Danish; Full Page Colour: 10807.50
Currency: Denmark Kroner
DAILY NEWSPAPER

VIBORG STIFTS FOLKEBLAD Sporten
Owner: Viborg Stifts Folkeblad A/S
Editorial: Vesterbrogade 8, Viborg 8800.
T: 45 89 27 63 00 **E:** viborg@bergske.dk
Freq: Daily; **Circ:** 11242
Language (s): Danish
DAILY NEWSPAPER

VIDEBÆK SPJALD AVIS
Owner: Videbæk Avis A/S
Editorial: Falkevej 4, Videbæk 6920.
T: 45 97 17 11 22
E: post@videbaek-bogtrykkeri.dk
W: http://videbaekspjaldavis.dk/vsavis/paper/index.html
Freq: Weekly; **Circ:** 15500
Language (s): Danish; Full Page Colour: 7668.00
Currency: Denmark Kroner
DAILY NEWSPAPER

VILLABYERNE
Owner: Villabyernes Mediecenter
Editorial: Ordrupvej 101 3. sal, Charlottenlund 2920. **T:** 45 39 63 51 11
E: redaktion@villabyerne.dk
W: http://www.villabyerne.dk
Freq: 2 Times/Week; **Circ:** 37695 Not Audited
Language (s): Danish; Full Page Colour: 44368.00
Currency: Denmark Kroner
NEWSPAPER

VINDERUP AVIS
Owner: De Bergske Blade
Editorial: Søndergade 42, Vinderup 7830.
T: 45 96 95 04 00 **E:** vinderup@bergske.dk
W: http://midtjyskemedier.dk
Freq: Weekly; **Circ:** 8600 Pub Statement
EDITOR: Dorthe Carlsen; **EDITOR IN CHIEF:** Hans Krabbe; **Ansvarshavende redaktør:** Jens Work Kristensen
Language (s): Danish; Full Page Colour: 8995.00
Currency: Denmark Kroner
NEWSPAPER

VOLLSMOSEAVISEN
Owner: Mediehus Vollsmose
Editorial: Vollsmose Alle 14, Odense Nø 5240.
T: 45 40 23 14 40 **E:** avis@vollsmose.dk
W: http://www.vollsmose.dk/Medier/Vollsmose%20avis.aspx
Freq: Bi-Weekly; **Circ:** 17000 Pub Statement
Redaktør: Thomas Juhl Bruun
Language (s): Danish
NEWSPAPER

VORT LANDBOBLAD
Owner: Aars Avis A/S

Editorial: Himmerlandsgade 150, Aars 9600.
T: 45 98 62 17 11 **E:** redaktion@aarsavis.dk
W: http://www.aarsavis.dk
Freq: Weekly; **Circ:** 18902 Not Audited
Redaktør: Torkil Christensen
Language (s): Danish; Full Page Colour: 8902.20
Currency: Denmark Kroner
NEWSPAPER

WEEKENDAVISEN
Owner: Det Berlingske Officin
Editorial: Pilestræde 34, Copenhagen 1147.
T: 45 33 75 25 33
E: weekendavisen@weekendavisen.dk
W: http://www.weekendavisen.dk
Freq: Weekly; **Circ:** 58678 Not Audited
Redaktør: Ole Nyeng; **Redaktionschef:** Lili Ochsner
Language (s): Danish; Full Page Colour: 73645.00
Currency: Denmark Kroner
DAILY NEWSPAPER

WESTEND & OMEGN
Owner: Verdens Mindste Bladhus I/S
Editorial: Verdens Mindste Bladhus, Gammel Kongevej 39d, Copenhagen 1610.
T: 45 46 90 89 60
W: http://www.verdensmindste.dk
Freq: Monthly; **Circ:** 6000
EDITOR IN CHIEF: Rie Holdum
Language (s): Danish
DAILY NEWSPAPER

NEWS SERVICE/SYNDICATE

Agence France-Presse - Copenhagen Bureau
Owner: AFP
Editorial: C/O Ritzau, Store Kongensgade 14, Copenhagen 1264. **T:** 45 33 13 23 31
E: afp@ritzau.dk **W:** http://www.afp.com
Language (s): Danish
NEWS SERVICE/SYNDICATE

Associated Press
Owner: AP
T: 45 33 11 15 04 **E:** copenhagen@ap.org
W: http://www.ap.org
Language (s): Danish
NEWS SERVICE/SYNDICATE

Associated Press
E: copenhagen@ap.org
NEWS SERVICE/SYNDICATE

Berlingske Nyhedsbureau
Owner: Berlingske Media
Editorial: Pilestræde324, Copenhagen 1147.
T: 45 33 75 24 22 **E:** bnb@berlingske.dk
Editor: Anders Hvass; **Nyhedsredaktør:** Jakob Weiss
NEWS SERVICE/SYNDICATE

Bloomberg News
Editorial: Dronningens Tvaergarde 30, Copenhagen 1302. **T:** 45 33322121
E: copenhagen@bloomberg.net
Bureau Chief: Christian Wienberg
NEWS SERVICE/SYNDICATE

Dagbladenes Bureau
Owner: Udgives flere steder
Editorial: Holbergsgade 13, 2 sal, Copenhagen 1057. **T:** 45 33 15 46 01
E: red@dagbladene.dk
W: http://www.dagbladene.dk
Redaktionssekretær: Søren Køhler
Language (s): Danish
NEWS SERVICE/SYNDICATE

Dow Jones Newswires
Editorial: Frederiksborggade 7, Copenhagen 1360. **T:** 45 3312-4488
NEWS SERVICE/SYNDICATE

Newspaq
Owner: Ritzau
Editorial: Store Kongensgade 59B 5. sal, Copenhagen 1264. **T:** 45 38 12 45 00
E: info@newspaq.dk
W: http://www.newspaq.dk
Language (s): Danish
NEWS SERVICE/SYNDICATE

Reuters
Editorial: Meldahlsgade 5, DK-1613, Copenhagen. **T:** 45 33969696 50
E: copenhagen.newsroom@thomsonreuters.com
NEWS SERVICE/SYNDICATE

Ritzau Finans
Editorial: Frederikshoms Kanal 4, 1.tv., Copenhagen 1220. **T:** 45 33 300 600
E: redaktionen@rb-borsen.dk
Nyhedsredaktør: Søren Funch; **Redaktør:** Henning Nielsen
NEWS SERVICE/SYNDICATE

Ritzau; Finans
Owner: Ritzaus Bureau
Editorial: Store Kongensgade 14, Copenhagen 1264. **T:** 45 33 30 03 35 **E:** finans@ritzau.dk
W: http://finans.ritzau.dk
Nyhedsredaktør/chef: Henning Nielsen
Language (s): Danish
NEWS SERVICE/SYNDICATE

RITZAUS BUREAU
Owner: Ritzaus Bureau I/S
Editorial: Store Kongensgade 14, Copenhagen 1264. **T:** 45 33 30 00 00 **E:** ritzau@ritzau.dk
W: http://www.ritzau.dk
EDITOR VIDEO AND RADIO: Rasmus Rosenmeier
Language (s): Danish
NEWS SERVICE/SYNDICATE

RITZAUS BUREAU News Service
Owner: Ritzaus Bureau I/S
Editorial: Store Kongensgade 14, Copenhagen 1264. **T:** 45 33 30 00 00 **E:** ritzau@ritzau.dk
Udlandsnyheder: Ulrik Schack
Language (s): Danish
NEWS SERVICE/SYNDICATE

RITZAUS BUREAU; RITZAUS MEDIASERVICE A/S
Owner: Ritzaus Bureau I/S
Editorial: ÅMARKVEJ 1, Hvidovre 2650.
T: 45 36 34 98 00 **E:** rmas@rmas.dk
W: http://www.rmas.dk
Udlandsnyheder: Bo Ejlerskov
Language (s): Danish
NEWS SERVICE/SYNDICATE

THOMSON REUTERS FINANS
Editorial: Meldahlsgade 5, 4 sal, Copenhagen 1613. **T:** 45 33 96 96 96
E: copenhagen.newsroom@reuters.com
W: http://www.thomsonreuters.com
Redaktør: Ole Mikkelsen
Language (s): Danish
NEWS SERVICE/SYNDICATE

BROADCASTING

RADIO STATIONS

AMAGER LANDS LOKALRADIO
Owner: Amager Lands Lokalradioforening og Øen Amagers Lokal
Editorial: Amager Boulevard 126, Copenhagen 2300. **T:** 45 32 54 35 20
E: post@amagerlandslokalradio.dk
W: http://www.amagerlandslokalradio.dk

ANR
Owner: Nordjuske Medier
Editorial: Langagervej 1, Aalborg 9220.
T: 45 94 34 99 34 **E:** redaktion@anr.dk
W: http://www.radionet.dk

ANR HIT FM ~FREDERIKSHAVN
Owner: Nordjyske Medier
T: 45 99 35 35 35 **E:** redaktion@anr.dk
W: http://www.anr.dk

ANR HIT FM ~HJØRRING
Owner: Nordjyske Medier
Editorial: Frederikshavnsvej 81, Hjørring 9800.
T: 45 99 35 32 96 **W:** http://www.anrhit.dk

BISPEBJERG LOKAL TV OG RADIO
Owner: Bispebjerg Lokal TV
Editorial: Dortheavej 61, 3. sal th., Copenhagen DK-2400 **E:** alexheick@dadlnet.dk
W: http://www.bltv.dk

DR P3 NYHEDERNE
T: 45 35 20 30 40 **E:** dr.dk@dr.dk

DR P4 Bornholm
Owner: DR
Editorial: Åkirkebyvej 52, Rønne 3700.
T: 45 56 94 37 00 **E:** bornholm@dr.dk
W: http://www.dr.dk/bornholm

DR P4 Esbjerg
Owner: DR
Editorial: Torvegade 8,1, Esbjerg 6700.
T: 45 73 33 79 99 **E:** esbjerg@dr.dk
W: http://www.dr.dk/Regioner/Esbjerg

DR P4 Fyn
Owner: DR
Editorial: Lille Tornbjerg Vej 10, Odense 5220.
T: 45 63 15 77 00 E: fyn@dr.dk
W: http://www.dr.dk/fyn

DR P4 København
Owner: DR
Editorial: Emil Holms Kanal 20, Copenhagen
999. T: 45 35 20 68 00 E: kbh@dr.dk
W: http://www.dr.dk/kbh

DR P4 Midt & Vest
Owner: DR
Editorial: Vestergade 1, Holstebro 7500.
T: 45 96 10 75 00 E: vest@dr.dk
W: http://www.dr.dk/vest

DR P4 Nordjylland
Owner: Danmarks Radio
Editorial: Fredrik Bajers Vej 9, Aalborg 9220.
T: 45 96 35 76 00 E: nord@dr.dk
W: http://www.dr.dk/nord

DR P4 Østjylland
Owner: DR
Editorial: Olof Palmes Allé 10-12, Århus 8200.
T: 45 87 39 70 00 E: p4aarhus@dr.dk
W: http://www.dr.dk/regioner/aarhus

DR P4 Sjælland
Owner: DR
Editorial: Vadestedet 1, Næstved 4700.
T: 45 55 75 34 00 E: sjaelland@dr.dk
W: http://www.dr.dk/Regioner/Sjaelland

DR P4 Trekanten
Owner: DR
Editorial: Den hvide Facet 1, 4. sal, Vejle
7100. T: 45 76 41 78 00 E: trekanten@dr.dk
W: http://www.dr.dk/Regioner/Trekanten

DR Syd
Owner: DR
Editorial: H.P.Hanssensgade 11, Aabenraa
6200. T: 45 73 33 79 99 E: syd@dr.dk
W: http://www.dr.dk/syd

GO!FM
T: 45 86 10 01 32 E: gofm@gofm.dk
W: http://www.gofm.dk

LOKALRADIOERNE I BRØNDERSLEV
Owner: Lokalradioerne Brønderslev
Editorial: Algade 32, 1., Brønderslev DK-9700.
T: 45 98 80 15 55 E: bjarne@9700.dk
W: http://www.9700.dk

LØKKEN-VRÅ NÆRRADIO
Owner: Løkken-Vrå Nærradio
Editorial: Stationvej 11, Vrå DK-9760.
T: 45 98 98 19 99 E: lvn@radiolvn.dk
W: http://www.radiolvn.dk

MIDTFJORD RADIO
Owner: Midtfjord Lokalradioforening og
Frederik den VII's K
Editorial: Blindebomsgade 4 B, Løgstør DK-9670. T: 45 98 67 41 00
E: mail@midtfjordradio.dk

NORDSJÆLLANDS LOKALRADIO-RADIO KATTEGAT
Editorial: Stationsvej 6, Vejby DK-3210.
T: 45 48 70 57 87 E: kattegat@post5.tele.dk
W: http://www.radiokattegat.dk

Radio 1
Owner: Radio Silkeborg A/S
Editorial: Papirfabrikken 18, Silkeborg 8600.
T: 45 86 81 65 66 E: redaktion@radio1.nu
W: http://www.radio1.nu

RADIO ABC
Owner: Foreningen Radio ABC
Editorial: Brotoften 10, Randers DK-8900.
T: 45 86 40 12 22 E: abc@radioabc.dk
W: http://www.radioabc.dk

Radio Aktiv
Owner: Svendborg Radio Samvirke AmbA
Editorial: Vestergade 3 B, Postbox 267,
Svendborg 5700. T: 45 62 22 28 28
E: kontor@radioaktiv.dk
W: http://www.radioaktiv.dk

RADIO ALS
Owner: Radio Als SmbA og Øens Nærradio
Editorial: Peblingestien 1, Nordborg DK-6430.
T: 45 74 45 10 10 E: radioals@radioals.dk
W: http://www.radioals.dk

RADIO CHARLIE
Owner: Radio Charlie ApS

Editorial: Sct. Nikolaj Kirke Plads, Varde DK-6800. T: 45 75 22 54 22
E: charlie@radiocharlie.dk
W: http://www.radiocharlie.dk

RADIO CITY ~ÅRHUS
Owner: SBS Radio
Editorial: M. P. Bruuns Gade 25, Århus 8000.
T: 45 87 44 87 87 E: aarhus.red@sbsradio.dk
W: http://www.radio2.dk

RADIO DIABLO
Owner: Radio Diablo ApS
Editorial: Voldgade 9, 1. sal, Svendborg DK-5700. T: 45 62 80 08 41
E: mail@radiodiablo.dk
W: http://www.radiodiablo.dk/

RADIO HALSNÆS
Owner: Radio Halsnæs
Editorial: Nørregade 61, Hundested DK-3390.
T: 45 47 98 10 45 W: http://www.1045fm.dk

RADIO HORSENS
Owner: Radio Horsens ApS
Editorial: Nørregade 42, Horsens DK-8700.
T: 45 76 27 20 70
E: radiohorsens@radiohorsens.dk
W: http://www.radiohorsens.dk

RADIO HUMLEBORG
Owner: Fredensborg-Humlebæk Lokalradio
Editorial: Nørredamsvej 18, Fredensborg DK-3480. T: 45 48 47 59 00
E: radio@humleborg.dk
W: http://www.humleborg.dk/

RADIO KLITHOLM
Owner: Radio Klitholm
Editorial: Nørregade 4, Hvide Sande DK-6960.
T: 45 97 31 23 44 E: post@radioklitholm.dk
W: http://www.radioklitholm.dk

Radio Køge
Owner: Radio Køge ApS
Editorial: Astersvej 23 B, Køge 4600.
T: 45 56 65 52 22 E: radio@radio-koege.dk
W: http://www.radio-koege.dk

RADIO LANGELAND
Owner: Radio Langeland
Editorial: Nørrebro 75 B, Rudkøbing DK-5900.
T: 45 62 51 45 46 E: post@radio-langeland.dk
W: http://www.radio-langeland.dk

RADIO LIMFJORD, NYKØBING MORS
Owner: Foreningen Radio Limfjord
Editorial: Gasværksvej 10, Nykøbing 7900.
T: 45 97 72 37 11
E: nyheder@radiolimfjord.dk
W: http://www.radiolimfjord.dk

RADIO MOJN
Owner: Det Sønderjyske Mediaselskab ApS
Editorial: P.O. Box 44, Aabenraa DK-6200.
T: 45 74 62 63 49 E: nyheder@mojn.dk
W: http://www.mojn.dk

RADIO MOJN
Owner: Mix FM
Editorial: Norgesvej 2, Haderslev DK-6100.
T: 45 74 62 63 49 E: nyheder@mojn.dk
W: http://www.mojn.dk

RADIO ODSHERRED
Owner: LokalRadio Rørvig
Editorial: Vestergade 24, Rørvig DK-4581.
T: 45 59 91 88 01
E: nyheder@radioodsherred.dk
W: http://www.radioodsherred.dk/

Radio Skive
Owner: Foreningen Radio Skive 92
Editorial: Nordbanevej 1, Skive 7800.
T: 45 97 52 77 22 E: radioskive@radioskive.dk
W: http://www.radioskive.dk/

RADIO SLR
Owner: Radio SLR ApS
Editorial: Dania 38, Næstved DK-4700.
T: 45 72 45 11 00
E: radioredaktion@sj-medier.dk
W: http://www.radioslr.dk

RADIO SYDHAVSØERNE
Owner: Radio Sydhavsøerne A/S,
Foreningsradioen
Editorial: Tværgade 16, Nykøbing DK-4800.
T: 45 54 88 03 45
E: redaktion@sydhavsradio.dk
W: http://www.sydhavsradio.dk

RADIO VIBORG HIT FM
Owner: Bergske Radio

Editorial: Vesterbrogade 9, Viborg DK-8800.
T: 45 86 61 02 00 E: kontakt@radioviborg.dk
W: http://radioviborg.dk/

RINGKØBING LOKALRADIO
Owner: Ringkøbing Lokalradio, Service Radio,
Weekend Radio
Editorial: Reberbanen 51, Ringkøbing DK-6950. T: 45 97 32 24 44
E: kontakt@radioringkobing.dk
W: http://www.radioringkobing.dk

SKALA FM
Owner: Radio Skala ApS
Editorial: Dalbygade 40, Kolding DK-6000.
T: 45 79 12 45 00 E: nyheder@skala.fm
W: http://www.skalafm.dk

STEVNS LOKALRADIO
Owner: Foreningen Stevns Lokal Radio
Editorial: Korngården 6. Lejlighed 111, Store
Heddinge DK-4660. T: 45 56 50 42 40
E: slr@stevnslokalradio.dk
W: http://www.stevnslokalradio.dk/

THE VOICE ~ Århus
Owner: SBS Radio
Editorial: M. P. Bruuns Gade 25, Århus 8000.
T: 45 87 44 87 87 E: rikke@voice.dk
W: http://www.thevoice.dk

TV 2 / BORNHOLM
Owner: TV 2 Danmark
Editorial: Brovangen 1, Aakirkeby 3720.
T: 45 56 93 42 00
E: redaktion@tv2bornholm.dk
W: http://www.tv2bornholm.dk/

TV 2 / FYN
Owner: TV 2 / DANMARK
Editorial: Olfert Fischers Vej 31, Odense 5220.
T: 45 63 15 60 00 E: redaktionen@tv2fyn.dk
W: http://www.tv2fyn.dk

TV 2 / MIDT-VEST ~VIBORG-REDAKTIONEN
Owner: TV 2 / MIDTVEST
Editorial: Skottenborg 8, Viborg DK-8800.
T: 45 96 12 13 80
W: http://www.tvmidtvest.dk

TV 2 / ØSTJYLLAND
Owner: TV 2 / DANMARK
Editorial: Skejbyparken 1, Århus 8200.
T: 45 87 42 42 42 E: redaktion@tv2oj.dk
W: http://www.tv2oj.dk

VLR
Owner: VLR Samvirket
Editorial: Nyboesgade 35, Vejle 7100.
T: 45 76 40 04 00 E: nyhed@vlr.dk
W: http://www.vlr.dk/

RADIO NETWORKS

DR P1
Owner: DR (The Danish Broadcasting
Corporation)
Editorial: Emil Holms Kanal 20, Copenhagen
DK-0999. T: 45 35 20 30 40
E: p1online@dr.dk W: http://www.dr.dk/p1

DR P1 Horizont
T: 45 35 20 30 40 E: dr@dr.dk
W: http://www.dr.dk/DR1/horisont

DR P1; Orientering
Owner: DR
Editorial: Emil Holms Kanal 20, Copenhagen
999. T: 45 35 20 59 25 E: orientering@dr.dk
W: http://www.dr.dk/orientering

DR P3
Owner: DR (The Danish Broadcasting
Corporation)
Editorial: Emil Holms Kanal 20, Copenhagen
999. T: 45 35 20 30 40 E: p3@dr.dk
W: http://www.dr.dk/p3

DR P4 Danmarksmester
Owner: DR
E: p4@dr.dk
W: http://www.dr.dk/p4/danmarksmester

Radio24syv
Owner: Berlingske People A/S
Editorial: Vester Farimagsgade 41,
Copenhagen 1606. T: 45 31 247 247
E: nyhedsredaktionen@radio24syv.dk
W: http://www.radio24syv.dk/

TELEVISION STATIONS

DK4
Owner: DK4
Editorial: Rådmandsgade 55, Copenhagen
2200. T: 45 70 25 35 35 E: post@dk4.dk
W: http://www.dk4.dk

DR1
Owner: DR
Editorial: Emil Holms Kanal 20, Copenhagen
999. T: 45 35 20 30 40
W: http://www.dr.dk/dr1

DR2
Owner: DR
Editorial: Emil Holms Kanal 20, Copenhagen
999. T: 45 35 20 30 40 E: dr.dk@dr.dk
W: http://www.dr.dk/dr2

KANAL 4
Owner: SBS TV A/S
Editorial: Mileparken 20A, Skovlunde 2740.
T: 45 70 10 10 10 W: http://www.kanal4.dk

KANAL 4 - FREDERIKSBERG LOKAL TV
Owner: Kanal 23
Editorial: Allégade 12, Frederiksberg 2000.
T: 45 33 26 09 04 E: red@kanal-4.dk
W: http://www.kanal-4.dk

KANAL-1
Owner: Kanal 23
Editorial: Reventlowsgade 14, 3. sal,
Copenhagen DK-1651. T: 45 70 20 00 04
E: kontakt@kanal-1.dk
W: http://www.kanal-1.dk

LORRY
Owner: TV 2 / DANMARK
Editorial: Allégade 7-9, Frederiksberg 2000.
T: 45 38 38 55 55 E: redaktion@lorry.dk
W: http://www.lorry.dk

SBS-NET
Owner: SBS TV A/S
Editorial: Mileparken 20 A, Skovlunde 2740.
T: 45 70 10 10 10 W: http://www.sbstv.dk

SBS-NET ~ØSTJYLLAND
Owner: Sjællandske Medier A/S
Editorial: Gunnar Clausensvej 66, Viby 8260.
T: 45 70 10 00 98 E: info@sbstv.dk
W: http://www.tvdanmark.dk

SBS-NET ~VESTSJÆLLAND
Owner: Sjællandske Medier A/S
Editorial: Dania 38, Næstved 4700.
T: 45 72 45 11 00 E: stst@sj-medier.dk
W: http://www.sj-medier.dk

TV 2 / DANMARK
Owner: TV 2 / DANMARK
Editorial: Rugaardsvej 25, Odense DK-5100.
T: 45 65 91 91 91 E: tv2@tv2.dk
W: http://www.tv2.dk

TV 2 / MIDT-VEST
Owner: TV 2 / DANMARK
Editorial: Søvej 2, Holstebro 7500.
T: 45 96 12 12 12
E: redaktionen@tvmidtvest.dk
W: http://www.tvmidtvest.dk/

TV 2 CHARLIE
Owner: TV 2 Networks
Editorial: Flæsketorvet 23, Copenhagen DK-1711. T: 45 33 31 70 22 E: charlie@tv2.dk
W: http://charlie.tv2.dk

TV 2 ZULU
Owner: TV 2 / DANMARK
Editorial: Flæsketorvet 23, Copenhagen DK-1711. T: 45 39 75 75 75 E: zulu@tv2.dk
W: http://www.zulu.dk

TV3 / TV3+
Owner: Viasat Broadcasting Ltd.
Editorial: Wildersgade 8, Copenhagen 1408.
T: 45 77 30 55 00 E: tv3@viasat.dk
W: http://www.tv3.dk

VESTERBRO LOKAL TV
Owner: Kanal 23
Editorial: Lyrskovgade 4, Copenhagen DK-1758. T: 45 33 88 89 94 E: vltv@hotmail.com
W: http://www.vesterbrolokaltv.dk/

DJIBOUTI
Tel: 253

Standard Time: GMT +3

BROADCASTING

TELEVISION STATIONS

Radiodiffusion Télévision de Djibouti - RTD
Editorial: 1 Avenue Saint Laurent du Var, BP 97, Djibouti. **T:** 253 35 22 94 **E:** rtd@intnet.dj
W: http://www.rtd.dj
Editorial Profile: National television and radio broadcasting office of Djibouti focussing on national and international news, current affairs, politics, economics, culture and entertainment.

DOMINICA
Tel: 1 767

Standard Time: GMT -4
Continent: The Americas
Capital City: Roseau

NEWSPAPERS & PUBLICATIONS

NEWSPAPERS

The Chronicle
Owner: The Chronicle Company
T: 767 4486601 **E:** thechronicle@cwdom.dm
W: http://www.avirtualdominica.com/thechronicle/index.html
Freq: Weekly Not Audited
Editor: Gwen Evelyn
Editorial Profile: The Chronicle is a weekly newspaper covering business, statistics, travel and tourism, arts, culture and lifestyle, photography, outdoor activities, events, geology, history and maps.
Language (s): English
NEWSPAPER

The Sun
Owner: The Sun Inc.
Editorial: 50 Independence Street, Roseau.
T: 767 4484744 **E:** acsun@cwdom.dm
W: http://www.sundominica.com
Freq: Weekly; **Circ:** 35000 Not Audited
Editor: Charles James
Editorial Profile: The Sun is a weekly newspaper featuring national and international news.
Language (s): English
NEWSPAPER

BROADCASTING

RADIO NETWORKS

DBS Radio
T: 767 4483282 **E:** dbsmanager@dbcradio.net
W: http://www.dbcradio.net
Editorial Profile: Provides daily news shows and plays different types of music.

Voice of Life Radio
Editorial: PO Box 205, Madrelle Loubiere.
T: 767 4487017 **E:** volradio@cwdom.dm
W: http://www.voiceoflife.com
Editorial Profile: Christian radio playing gospel music.

DOMINICAN REPUBLIC
Tel: 1 809

Standard Time: GMT -4
Continent: The Americas
Capital City: Santo Domingo

NEWSPAPERS & PUBLICATIONS

NEWSPAPERS

Barrigaverde
Owner: Editora Barrigaverde
Editorial: C/ Thómas F. Reilly No. 45, Villa Alejandra, San Juan De La Maguana.
T: 809 5574434 **E:** editora@barrigaverde.net
W: http://www.barrigaverde.net
Freq: Daily

Editorial Profile: Covers general news of the Dominican Republic. Includes sports, politic, economy and foreign affairs.
Language (s): Spanish
DAILY NEWSPAPER

El Caribe
Owner: EDITORA DEL CARIBE, C. POR A.
Editorial: Calle Defilló No. 4, Los Prados, Santo Domingo. **T:** 809 6838100
E: redaccionweb@elcaribe.com.do
W: http://www.elcaribe.com.do
Freq: Daily; **Circ:** 50000 Not Audited
Editor in Chief: Hector Marte
Editorial Profile: Newspaper covering national and international news, politics, economics, finance, business, culture and sport.
Language (s): Spanish
DAILY NEWSPAPER

El Dia
Owner: Editora Hoy
Editorial: Av. San Martín 236, Distr. Nacional, Santo Domingo. **T:** 809 5655581
E: josemonegro@verizon.net.do
W: http://www.eldia.com.do
Freq: Daily; **Circ:** 100000 Not Audited
Editor in Chief: Franklin Puello
Editorial Profile: Newspaper covering national and international news, includes features on sport, women's interest and entertainment. Distributed Monday through Friday.
Language (s): Spanish
DAILY NEWSPAPER

Diario Libre
Owner: Omnimedia Editorial AA
Editorial: Av. Abraham Lincoln esq, Max Henríquez Ureña, Apartado 20313 Piantini, Santo Domingo. **T:** 809 4767200
W: http://www.diariolibre.com
Freq: Daily; **Circ:** 115000 Not Audited
Editor in Chief: José Maria Reyes; **Editor:** Bienvenido Rojas
Editorial Profile: Newspaper covering national and international news, politics, economics, finance, business, culture and sport.
Language (s): Spanish
DAILY NEWSPAPER

Hoy
Owner: Editora Hoy
Editorial: Av. San Martín 236, Distrito Nacional, Santo Domingo. **T:** 809 5655581
E: periodicohoy@hoy.com.do
W: http://www.hoy.com.do
Freq: Daily; **Circ:** 32500 Not Audited
Editor in Chief: Marien Capitán
Editorial Profile: National newspaper covering news and current-affairs. Includes economy, business, ecology, sports and health.
Language (s): Spanish
DAILY NEWSPAPER

La Información
Owner: Nueva Editora La Información
Editorial: Calle Del Sol No. 3, Santiago.
T: 809 5811915
E: lainformacion@lainformacion.com.do
W: http://lainformacion.com.do
Freq: Daily; **Circ:** 26500 Not Audited
Editor in Chief: Servio Cepeda
Editorial Profile: Daily newspaper in Dominican Republic covering general news and topics related to politics, economics, finance, business, culture and sport.
Language (s): Spanish
DAILY NEWSPAPER

Listín Diario
Owner: Editora Listín Diario
Editorial: Paseo de los Periodistas 52, Ensanche Miraflores, Santo Domingo.
T: 809 6866688
W: http://www.listindiario.com.do
Freq: Daily; **Circ:** 70000 Not Audited
Editor in Chief: Marisabel Sol de Vila
Editorial Profile: Newspaper covering national and international news and current-affairs, includes sport, events and finance.
Language (s): Spanish
DAILY NEWSPAPER

El Nacional
Owner: Publicaciones Ahora
Editorial: Av. San Martín 236, Distr. Nacional, Santo Domingo. **T:** 809 5655581
E: director@elnacional.com.do
W: http://www.elnacional.com.do
Freq: Daily; **Circ:** 70000 Not Audited
Editor in Chief: Hector Minaya
Editorial Profile: National newspaper covering general news and current-affairs in Dominican Republic.
Language (s): Spanish
DAILY NEWSPAPER

El Nuevo Diario
Owner: Editora El Nuevo Diario
Editorial: Av. Francia No. 41, Santo Domingo.
T: 809 6877450 **E:** redaccionnd@gmail.com
W: http://www2.elnuevodiario.com.do
Freq: Daily
Editor in Chief: Ramiro Estrella
Editorial Profile: Newspaper covering general news and current-affairs. Includes politics, the economy, legal issues, sport and fashion.
Language (s): Spanish
DAILY NEWSPAPER

BROADCASTING

RADIO NETWORKS

La Nota Diferente
Editorial: Teleantillas #2 de Fillo, Autopista Duarte, Km 71/2, Santo Domingo.
T: 809 5677751 **W:** http://www.tele-antillas.tv/
Editorial Profile: Broadcasts entertainment and cultural programs. Provides daily news.

TELEVISION NETWORKS

CDN TV
Editorial: Calle Defilló no. 4, Los Prados, Santo Domingo. **T:** 809 6838711
E: redaccion@cdn.com.do
W: http://www.elcaribecdn.com.do
Editorial Profile: Broadcasts daily news, sports, cooking and health programs.

Color Vision
Editorial: Corporación Dominicana de Radio y Televisión, C/A, Emilio A. Morel, esq Luís Perez, ensanche la FE, Santo Domingo.
T: 809 5665875
E: luismundovision@gmail.com
W: http://www.colorvision.com.do
Editorial Profile: Covers the national territory of Dominican Republic. Broadcasts daily news, sports, entertainment programs including live shows related to health and life styles. On Saturdays transmits a children's program.

Teleantillas
Owner: Grupo Corripio
Editorial: Autopista Duarte, km 7 1/2, Santo Domingo. **T:** 809 5677751
E: webmaster@tele-antillas.tv
W: http://www.tele-antillas.tv
Editorial Profile: Broadcasts entertainment, educational, and informative programs. Transmits daily news, sports, international soap-operas and musical shows.

ECUADOR
Tel: 593

Standard Time: GMT -5
Continent: The Americas
Capital City: Quito

NEWSPAPERS & PUBLICATIONS

NEWSPAPERS

El Comercio
Owner: Grupo El Comercio
Editorial: Avenida Pedro Vicente Maldonado 11515, Quito. **T:** 593 2 267-0999
E: redaccion@elcomercio.com
W: http://www.elcomercio.com
Freq: Daily; **Circ:** 70000 Not Audited
Editor: Gonzalo Maldonado; **Editor:** Martin Pallares
Editorial Profile: National newspaper focusing on national and international news, politics, business, entertainment and sports.
Language (s): Spanish
DAILY NEWSPAPER

Diario El Nacional
Owner: Graficos Orenses C.A.
Editorial: Sucre 1222 entre Guayas y Ayacucho, Ciudad Machala, Quito.
T: 593 7 2930375 **E:** elnacional@easynet.ec
Freq: Daily
Editor: Jacinto Castro
Language (s): Spanish
DAILY NEWSPAPER

Diario Expreso
Owner: Graficos Nacionales S.A.
Editorial: Av. Carlos Julio Arosemena, Km 2½, frente al Coliseo Granasa, Guayaquil.
T: 593 4 2201100 **E:** cartas@granasa.com.ec
W: http://www.diario-expreso.com
Editor: Guillermo Lizarzaburo

DAILY NEWSPAPER

Diario Extra
Owner: Graficos Nacionales S.A.
Editorial: Av. Carlos Julio Arosemena Km. 2.5 y Av. Las Monjas, Guayaquil.
T: 593 4 2201100
E: agenciacentenario@granasa.com.ec
W: http://www.diario-extra.com/
Freq: Daily
Editor: Henry Holguin; **Editor in Chief:** Manuel Yepez
Editorial Profile: Diario Extra is a national newspaper that covers national news, politics, sports, and entertainment.
Language (s): Spanish
DAILY NEWSPAPER

Diario Hoy
Owner: Edimpres S.A.
Editorial: Avenida Mariscal Sucre No 6-116 y Catón Cárdenas, El Condado, Aptdo. 17-07-09069, Quito. **T:** 593 2 249 0888
E: hoy@hoy.com.ec
W: http://www.hoy.com.ec
Freq: Daily; **Circ:** 42850 Not Audited
Editor: Raul Chavez; **Editor in Chief:** Juan Tibanlombo; **Editor:** Maria Elena Verdesoto
Editorial Profile: National newspaper covering national and international current affairs, politics, economics, finance and business information.
Language (s): Spanish
DAILY NEWSPAPER

Diario La Prensa
Editorial: Garcia Moreno 2340 y Primera Constituyente, Riobamba (chimborazo).
T: 593 3 2967855
E: direccion@laprensa.com.ec
W: http://www.laprensa.com.ec/
Freq: Daily
Editor: Carlos Chimborazo; **Editor:** Diego Vallejo
Language (s): Spanish
DAILY NEWSPAPER

Diario Meridiano
T: 593 9 9428280
Freq: Daily
Editor: Carlos Logrono; **News Editor:** Antonio Molina
Language (s): Spanish
DAILY NEWSPAPER

Diario Super
Editorial: Av. Domingo Comín, entre calle 11 y Ernesto Albán, Guayaquil. **T:** 593 4 2324460
E: redaccion@super.com.ec
W: http://www.super.com.ec
Freq: Daily
News Editor: Monica Camacho; **Editor:** Victor Vera
Language (s): Spanish
DAILY NEWSPAPER

Ecos de Quevedo
E: diarioecosdequevedo@hotmail.com
Freq: Daily
News Editor: Victor Laborde; **Editor:** Lizzeth Rodriguez
Language (s): Spanish
DAILY NEWSPAPER

La Hora (Edición Nacional)
Owner: Editorial Minotauro SA
Editorial: Panamericana Norte Kilómetro 3 1/2 y Nazarett, Quito. **T:** 593 2 247 5724
E: lahora@uio.satnet.net
W: http://www.lahora.com.ec
Freq: Daily; **Circ:** 120000 Not Audited
Editor: Wilmer Molina; **Editor:** Roque Rivas
Editorial Profile: Newspaper covering national and international news, politics, economics, finance, business, culture and sport.
Language (s): Spanish
DAILY NEWSPAPER

El Norte
Editorial: Av. Juan Jose Flores 1155 y Rafael Rosales, Ibarra (imbabura). **T:** 593 6 2643873
W: http://www.elnorte.ec
Freq: Daily
News Editor: Carla Aguas
Language (s): Spanish
DAILY NEWSPAPER

Opinion
Editorial: Av. 25 de junio Km 1.5 via a pasaje, Machala (el Oro). **T:** 593 7 2982732
E: subdireccion@diariopinion.com
W: http://www.diariopinion.com
Freq: Daily
Editor: Luis Tovar
Language (s): Spanish
DAILY NEWSPAPER

El Telegrafo
Editorial: 10 de Agosto 601 y Boyaca, Guayaquil. **T:** 593 4 2328814
W: http://www.telegrafo.com.ec
Freq: Daily
Editor: Nestor Espinoza
Language (s): Spanish
DAILY NEWSPAPER

Ultimas Noticias
Owner: Grupo el Comercio
Editorial: Av. P. Vicente Maldonado 11515 y el Tablón, Quito. **T:** 593 2 2672870
E: mivoz@ultimasnoticias.ec
W: http://www.ultimasnoticias.ec
Freq: Daily
Editor in Chief: Carlos Mora
Language (s): Spanish
DAILY NEWSPAPER

El Universo
Owner: El Universo
Editorial: Avenida Domingo Comin y Calle 11, Avenida Ernesto Alban, Guayaquil (guayas).
T: 593 4 249 0000
E: redaccion@eluniverso.com
W: http://www.eluniverso.com
Freq: Daily; **Circ:** 133046 Not Audited
Editor: Gustavo Cortez
Editorial Profile: El Universo is a national newspaper covering national and international news, politics, economics, finance, business, culture and sport.
Language (s): Spanish
DAILY NEWSPAPER

NEWS SERVICE/SYNDICATE

Agencia Latinoamericana de Información
Editorial: 12 de Octubre N18-24, Oficina 503, Quito. **T:** 593 2 250 5074 **E:** info@alainet.org
W: http://www.alainet.org
Editor: Sally Burch
Language (s): Spanish
NEWS SERVICE/SYNDICATE

Dow Jones Newswires
Editorial: De los Jazmines y de Los Fresnos, Conjunto Anturios I. Casa No. 6, Quito.
T: 593 2 972-8653
NEWS SERVICE/SYNDICATE

Reuters
Editorial: Avenida Republica, 500 Y La Pradera Edificio Pucara of 402, Quito.
T: 593 2 252-3560
NEWS SERVICE/SYNDICATE

BROADCASTING

RADIO STATIONS

Alfa Radio
Owner: CRTV
Editorial: Km 4 1/2 Av. Juan Tanca Marengo junto a RTS canal 4, Guayaquil.
T: 593 4 3810049 **W:** http://www.alfa.com.ec/
Editorial Profile: Alfa Radio is a commercial station owned by CRTV. The station air Top 40 music. Alfa Radio broadcasts to the Guayaquil, Ecuador area on 104.1 FM.

Antena 1
Editorial: Héroes de Verdeloma 9-15, Cuenca.
T: 593 7 284 9215 **E:** radio@antenaunofm.net
W: http://www.antenaunofm.net

Mix 99.3
Owner: Servidinadica
Editorial: Av J Tanca Marengo Km1 al lado de Almacen Grayman, entrando por India, Guayaquil. **T:** 593 4 2682271
E: gye@servidinamica.com

Radio Activa
Owner: Radio Zaracay
Editorial: Calle George Town y Rio Yamboya, Santo Domingo. **T:** 593 2 2763900
E: radioactiva.maspositiva@gmail.com
W: http://www.zaracayradio.com
Editorial Profile: Radio Activa is a commercial station owned by Radio Zaracay. The station airs a variety of music, news, agriculture news, culture, and education. It broadcasts to the Santo Domingo de los Colores, Ecuador area on 99.7 FM.

Radio Alfa Musical
Editorial: Hermano Miguel 10-68 y Gran Colombia, 2do piso, Cuenca.
T: 593 7 2838451
E: radioalfa1140am@gmail.com

Radio Ambato
Owner: Radio Ambato
Editorial: Sucre 09-42 y Quito, Ambato.
T: 593 3 2822130
E: produccion@radioambato.com
W: http://www.radioambato.com
Editorial Profile: Radio Ambato is a commercial radio station owned by Radio Ambato. The station air sports news and some general news. Radio Ambato broadcasts to the Ambato, Ecuador area on 930 AM.

Radio America
Editorial: Olmedo 974 y Velasco, Ibarra (imbabura). **T:** 593 6 2641742
W: http://www.americaestereo.com/

Radio Amiga
Owner: EDIASA
Editorial: Avenida Metropolitana Eloy Alfaro, 1.1/2 vía a Manta, Aptdo. 13-01-050, Portoviejo (manabí). **T:** 593 5 293 3777
E: cabinaamiga@radioamiga.ec
W: http://www.eldiario.com.ec
Editorial Profile: Alternate news and music from 7:00 AM until 8:00 PM. Every hour the programming includes micronews.

Radio Antena 3
Editorial: Córdova E/ 9 de Octubre y Pedro Carbo Edif. San Francisco 300 Piso 12 Ofic 1201, Guayaquil 593. **T:** 59 34 2560610
E: antena3@radioantena3.com
W: http://www.radioantena3.com
Editorial Profile: Radio Antena 3 is a commercial station in Guayaquil, Ecuador. The format of the station is Hispanic adult contemporary, and broadcasts at 91.7 FM. The target audience of the station is adults, ages 18 to 64.

Radio Canela
Editorial: Via Proano, Cdad Macas, Quito.
T: 593 7 2701387

Radio Caravana Guayaquil
Editorial: Av Juan Tanca Marengo Km 3, Guayaquil 593. **T:** 593 4 2889666
E: info@radiocaravana.com
W: http://www.radiocaravana.com
Editorial Profile: Radio Caravana Guayaquil is a commercial station in Guayaquil, Ecuador. The format of the station is Spanish sports news and talk. The target audience of the station is adults, ages 18 to 64. Radio Caravana broadcasts to the Guayaquil, Ecuador area at 750 AM.

Radio Caravana Quito
Editorial: Pasaje A OE 513 y Vasco de Contreras, Quito. **T:** 593 2 2442951
W: http://www.radiocaravana.com
Editorial Profile: Radio Carvana Quito is a commercial station. The format of the station is sports, news and talk. Radio Caravana Quito broadcasts to the Quito, Ecuador area at 610 AM. The station airs Radio Carvana Guayaquil's programming.

Radio Casa de la Cultura
Owner: Casa de la Cultura
Editorial: 6 de Diciembre N16-224 y Patria, Quito. **T:** 593 2 2223392 **E:** info@cce.org.ec
W: http://www.cce.org.ec

Radio Cenit
Editorial: Av. Quito 806 y 9 de Octubre piso 11 Ofc. #1104, Guayaquil. **T:** 593 4 2282076
E: radio-cenit-guayaquil@hotmail.com
Editorial Profile: Radio Cenit is a commercial station. The station airs a variety of music and news. Radio Cenit broadcasts to the Guayaquil, Ecuador area on 1300 AM.

Radio Centro 97.7
E: noticiero_elobservador@hotmail.com
W: http://www.radiocentro.com.ec
Editorial Profile: Radio Centro is a commercial station. The format of the station is adult contemporary, romantic and pop music. Radio Centro broadcasts in the Guayaquil, Ecuador area at 97.7 FM.

Radio Colón
Owner: ServiDinamica S.A.
Editorial: Juán Tanca Marengo Km.2.5, Guayaquil 593. **T:** 59 34 2682271
E: escucha@radiocolon.ec
Editorial Profile: Radio Colón is a Spanish commercial station owned by ServiDinamica S.A. The format of the station is news and variety. The target audience of the station is adults, ages 18 to 64. It broadcasts to Guayaquil, Ecuador at 92.9 FM.

Radio Cóndor
Editorial: Km 8.5 vía Daule, lotización San Francisco, Av. Primera y calle 4ta, Guayaquil.
T: 593 4 2250528
E: radio.condor@hotmail.com
Editorial Profile: Radio Cóndor is a commercial station in Guayaquil, Ecuador. The format of the station is news, talk, and variety. Radio Cóndor broadcasts to Guayaquil, Ecuador at 1140 AM. The target audience of the station is adults, ages 18 to 64.

Radio Constelación
Editorial: Calle Latacunga y Av. Quito 136, Quito. **T:** 593 2 2751397
E: ventas@radioconstelacionfm.com
W: http://www.radioconstelacionfm.com
Editorial Profile: Radio Constelación is a commercial station in Quito, Ecuador. The format of the station is top 40/CHR, classic hits, and variety. Radio Constelación broadcasts to Quito, Ecuador at 99.3 FM. The target audience for the station is adults, ages 18 to 54.

Radio Cristal
Editorial: 1407-1409 Luque J and Antepara, Guayaquil 593. **T:** 593 4 253160
E: rcristal@ecua.net.ec
Editorial Profile: Radio Cristal is a Spanish commercial station with a format of primarily news and talk, with some variety. The target audience of the station is adults, ages 18 to 64. The station broadcasts to Guayaquil, Ecuador at 870 AM.

Radio Cristal
Editorial: Avs. de la Prensa N60-22 Y Del Maestro, Quito. **T:** 593 2 2595219
E: noticias@amcristal.com
Editorial Profile: Radio Cristal is a commercial station in Quito, Ecuador. The format of the station is news, talk, adult hits, and variety. Radio Cristal broadcasts to Quito, Ecuador at 1380 AM. The target audience of the station is adults, ages 18 to 64.

Radio El Mercurio
Editorial: Av. de las Américas y Francisco Azcazubi, esq, Quito. **T:** 593 7 4095684
E: radio@radioelmercurio.com
W: http://www.radioelmercurio.com.ec
Editorial Profile: Radio El Mercurio is a commercial station in Quito, Ecuador. The format of the station is news, sports, and variety. Radio El Mercurio broadcasts to Quito, Ecuador at 1200 AM.

Radio Eres
Editorial: Av. Amazonas N35-89 y Corea, 4to piso, Edif. Amazonas 4000, Quito.
T: 593 2 2255999 **E:** contacto@radioeres.com
W: http://www.radioeres.com

Radio Estrella
Owner: Radio Estrella Ecuador
Editorial: Cdla. Mirador del Norte, Mz. 21 Solar 12, Guayaquil. **T:** 593 4 2235230
E: radioestrella_921@hotmail.com
W: http://www.radioestrella.com.ec
Editorial Profile: Radio Estrella is a commercial station owned by Radio Estrella Ecuador. The format for the station is classic hits and top 40 CHR. Radio Estrella broadcasts to Guayaquil, Ecuador at 92.1 FM. The target audience is adults, agres 18 to 64.

Radio Forever
Owner: Forever Music Radio
Editorial: Jose Alevedra y Francisco de Orellana, Edificio Ralio Piso 3, Guayaquil 593.
T: 59 34 2690328
E: forever@radioforever925.com
W: http://www.radioforever925.com
Editorial Profile: Radio Forever is a Spanish commercial station owned by Forever Music Radio. The format of the station is news and classic hits. It broadcasts to Guayaquil, Ecuador at 92.5 FM. The target audience of the station is adults, ages 18 to 64.

Radio Francisco Stereo
Owner: Francisco Stereo
Editorial: Cuenca No. 477 y Sucre Bajos, Convento de San Francisco, Quito.
T: 593 2 2289365
E: franciscolaradio@gmail.com
W: http://www.franciscostereo.com
Editorial Profile: Radio Francisco Stereo is a commercial station owned by Francisco Stereo. The format of the station is Religious news and talk. Radio Francisco Stereo broadcasts to Quito, Ecuador at 102.5 FM.

Radio Francisco Stereo
Owner: Francisco Stereo
T: 593 2 2289365
E: franciscolaradio@gmail.com
W: http://www.franciscostereo.com
Editorial Profile: Radio Francisco Stereo is a commercial station owned by Francisco Stereo. The format of the station is Religious news and talk. Radio Francisco Stereo broadcasts to Guayaquil, Ecuador at 106.9 FM.

Radio Fuego
Editorial: Cdla. Kennedy Norte, Mz 1008 villa #21, Guayaquil. **T:** 593 4 2682985
E: noticiero@radiofuego.com
W: http://www.hot106fuego.com
Editorial Profile: Radio Fuego is a commercial station in Guayaquil, Ecuador. The format of the station is top 40 CHR and classic hits. Radio Fuego broadcasts to the Guayaquil, Ecuador area at 106.5 FM. The target audience for the station is adults, ages 18 to 54.

Radio Gitana
Owner: Gitana FM S.A.
Editorial: Av 12 de Octubre N24-402 y Cordero, Casilla 17-01-2105, Quito.
T: 593 2 2529205 **E:** ventas@gitana.com.ec
W: http://www.gitana.com.ec
Editorial Profile: Radio Gitana is a commercial station owned by Gitana FM S.A. The format of the station is classic hits and top 40 CHR. Radio Gitana broadcasts to the Quito, Ecuador area at 94.9 FM.

Radio HCJB-2
Owner: HCJB Global
Editorial: Chambers 301entre 5 de Junio y Domingo Comín, Guayaquil 593.
T: 59 34 244-0759 **E:** miradio@hcjb2.org
W: http://www.hcjb2.org
Editorial Profile: Radio HCJB-2 is a radio station owned by HCJB Global. The format of the station is Christian and religious music and talk, and broadcasts to the Guayaquil, Guayas, Ecuador area at 102.5 FM.

Radio i99
Owner: Radio i99
T: 593 4 2680877 **W:** http://www.i99.com.ec
Editorial Profile: Radio i99 is a commercial station owned by Radio i99. The format of the station is hot AC. Radio i99 broadcasts to the Guayaquil, Ecuador area at 98.9 FM.

Radio Imperio
Editorial: Calle 7 de Octubre y Décima Séptima, Edf.Pedro Pablo, 2do Piso, Guayaquil. **T:** 59 35 2753497
E: radioimperiopog@yahoo.es
W: http://www.radioimperioquevedo.com
Editorial Profile: Radio Imperio is a Spanish commercial station in Quevedo, Ecuador. The format of the station is news, talk, and variety. The target audience of the station is adults, ages 18 to 64. Radio Imperio broadcasts to Quevedo, Ecuador at 101.9 FM.

Radio Iris
Editorial: Portete E10-334 Y Faustino Sarmiento, Quito. **T:** 593 2 2275747
E: marisa6_66@hotmail.com
Editorial Profile: Radio Iris is a commercial station in Quito, Ecuador. The format of the station is news, talk and variety. Radio Iris broadcasts to Quito, Ecuador at 530 AM. The target audience for the station is adults, ages 18-64.

Radio Jesús del Gran Poder
Owner: Francisco Stereo
Editorial: Cuenca No. 477 y Sucre Bajos, Convento de San Francisco, Quito.
T: 593 2 2289365
E: franciscolaradio@gmail.com
W: http://www.franciscostereo.com
Editorial Profile: Radio Jesús del Gran Poder is a commercial station owned by Francisco Stereo. The format of the station is Religious news and talk. Radio Jesús del Gran Poder broadcasts to Quito, Ecuador at 670 AM.

Radio Kiss
Owner: ServiDinamica S.A.
Editorial: Juan Tanca Marengo Km 2 1/2, Guayaquil. **T:** 59 34 2682271
E: admin@kissfm.ec **W:** http://www.kissfm.ec
Editorial Profile: Radio Kiss is a commercial station owned by ServiDinamica S.A. The format of the station is Top 40 CHR. The target audience of the station is adults, ages 18 to 64. Radio Kiss broadcasts to Guayaquil, Ecuador at 90.9 FM.

Radio La Estación
Editorial: Kennedy Norte, Av. Luis Orrantia y calle Victor Hugo Sicouret, Esquina solar 22 y 23, edif. Rafermartz 2do. piso, Guayaquil.
T: 593 4 2682311 **W:** http://www.laestacion.fm

Editorial Profile: Radio La Estación is a commercial station in Guayaquil, Ecuador. The format of the station is top 40 CHR, classic hits, news, and talk. Radio La Estación broadcasts to Guayaquil, Ecuador at 101.3 FM. The target audience for the station is adults, ages 18 to 64.

Radio La Prensa
Owner: Radio La Prensa TV. S.A.
Editorial: Cdla. Adace: Av. Constitución y Av. De las Américas (junto a TC Televisión), Guayaquil. **T:** 593 4 2288094
E: info@radiolaprensatvsa.com
W: http://www.radiolaprensatvsa.com/
Editorial Profile: Radio La Prensa is a commercial station owned by Radio La Prensa TV. S.A. The format of the station is classical music, and some variety music such as jazz and tango, along with news. Radio La Prensa broadcasts to the Guayaquil, Ecuador area at 100.1 FM.

Radio La Rumbera
Owner: Enrique Gallegos Custode
Editorial: Manuel Camacho 143 y Portete, sector Estadio Olímpico Atahualpa, Quito. **T:** 593 2 2442178 **E:** lahoraclave@hotmail.com
W: http://www.radiolarumbera.com
Editorial Profile: Radio La Rumbera is a commercial station owned by Enrique Gallegos. The station airs a variety of music. La Rumbera broadcasts to the Quito, Ecuador area at 99.7 FM.

Radio Majestad 89.7
Editorial: 6 de Diciembre 3981 y Checoslovaquia, Quito. **T:** 593 2 2269918
W: http://www.radiomajestad.com
Editorial Profile: Radio Majestad 89.7 is a commercial station owned by Radio Majestad. The format of the station is top 40 CHR, classic hits, news, and talk. Radio Majestad broadcasts to Quito, Ecuador at 89.7 FM. The target audience for the station is adults, ages 18 to 64.

Radio Mas Candela
Owner: ServiDinamica S.A.
Editorial: Juan Tanca Marengo Km 2.5, Guayaquil. **T:** 59 34 2682271
E: admin@servidinamica.com
Editorial Profile: Radio Mas Candela is a commercial station owned by ServiDinamica S.A. The format of the station is variety and Top 40 CHR. Radio Mas Candela broadcasts to Guayaquil, Ecuador at 96.9 FM.

Radio Morena
Owner: Radio Morena S.A
Editorial: Av. Quito 1200 y Aguirre, esquina Edificio Radio Morena, Guayaquil.
T: 593 4 2519000
E: radiomorena640@hotmail.com
W: http://www.radiomorena640.com/
Editorial Profile: Radio Morena is a commercial station owned by Radio Morena S.A. The format of the station is talk and news. Radio Morena broadcasts to the Guayaquil, Ecuador area at 640 AM.

Radio Nuevo Tiempo
Owner: Unión Ecuatoriana de la Iglesia Adventista del Séptimo Día
Editorial: Tulcán 901 y Hurtado, Guayaquil.
T: 593 4 2371211
E: nuevotiempo@adventistas.ec
W: http://adventistas.ec/
Editorial Profile: Radio Tiempo Nuevo is owned by Unión Ecuatoriana de la Iglesia Adventista del Séptimo Día. The station airs Christian programming, music, and news. Radio Tiempo Nuevo broadcasts to the area on 97.3 FM.

Radio Once Q
Owner: Radio Cadena Musical Uno
Editorial: Velez 905 y 6 de Marzo, Edificio Forum, Piso 25 Suite #8, Guayaquil.
T: 593 4 2323171
W: http://www.radio11q.com.ec
Editorial Profile: Radio Once Q a is a commercial station owned by Radio Cadena Musical Uno. The format of the station is oldies. Radio Once Q broadcasts to the Guayaquil, Ecuador area at 104.9 FM.

Radio Onda Cero
Owner: ServiDinamica S.A.
Editorial: Juan Tanca Marengo Km 2.5, Guayaquil. **T:** 59 34 2682271
E: admin@servidinamica.com
Editorial Profile: Radio Onda Cero is a commercial station owned by ServiDinamica S.A. The format of the station is hip hop. Radio Onda Cero broadcasts to Guayaquil, Ecuador at 96.1 FM.

Radio Onda Positiva
Owner: Radio Onda Positiva
Editorial: Cosme Renella y Av. de las Américas, Edif. La Española P.2, Of. 8, Guayaquil. **T:** 593 4 2396002
W: http://www.radioondapositiva.com
Editorial Profile: Radio Onda Positiva is a commercial station owned by Radio Onda Positiva. The format of the station is top 40 CHR, news, and talk. Radio Onda Positiva broadcasts to Guayaquil, Ecuador at 94.1 FM. The target audience of the station is adults, ages 18 to 64.

Radio Ondas Azuayas
Editorial: Héroes de Verdeloma 9-15, Cuenca (azuay). **T:** 593 7 2831975
E: radioondasazuayas@gmail.com
W: http://www.ondasazuayas.com
Editorial Profile: Radio Ondas Azuayas is a commercial station in Cuenca, Ecuador. The format of the station is news, talk, variety and sports. Radio Ondas Azuayas broadcasts to Cuenca, Ecuador at 1110 AM. The target audience for the station is all ages.

Radio Pasión
Owner: ServiDinamica S.A.
Editorial: Juan Tanca Marengo Km 2.5, Guayaquil. **T:** 59 34 2682271
E: admin@servidinamica.com
Editorial Profile: Radio Pasión is a commercial station owned by ServiDinamica S.A. The format of the station is Smooth AC and Variety. Radio Pasión broadcasts to Guayaquil, Ecuador at 96.5 FM.

Radio Publica de Ecuador
Owner: U.S. Embassy in Ecuador
Editorial: San Salvador E6-49 Y Eloy Alfaro, Quito. **T:** 593 3 970800
W: http://www.radiopublica.info
Editorial Profile: Radio Publica de Ecuador is a commercial station owned by the U.S. Embassy in Ecuador. The format of the station is politics, human rights, news, and talk. Radio Publica de Ecuador broadcasts to the Quito, Ecuador area at 100.9 FM. The target audience of the station is adults, ages 18 to 64.

Radio Punto Rojo
Owner: Extra Radio S.A.
Editorial: Av. 9 de Octubre #1904 y Esmeraldas, Edif. Florida Piso 10, Guayaquil.
T: 59 34 2289922
W: http://www.radiopuntorojo.com
Editorial Profile: Radio Punto Rojo is a commercial station owned by Extra Radio S.A. The format of the station is news, talk, and variety. The target audience of the station is adults, ages 18 to 64. Radio Punta Rojo broadcasts to the Guayaquil, Ecuador area at 89.7 FM.

Radio Quito
Owner: Editores Ecuatorianos S.A.
Editorial: Av. Coruña 2104 and Whimper, Edf. Aragones, P.9. Ecuador, Quito.
T: 593 2 2508301 **E:** info@ecuadoradio.com
W: http://www.radioquito.ec
Editorial Profile: Radio Quito is a commercial station owned by Editores Ecuatorianos S.A. The format of the station is news, talk, sports, and variety. Radio Quito broadcasts to the Quito, Ecuador area at 760 AM.

Radio Romance
Owner: Extra Radio S.A.
Editorial: Av. 9 de Octubre #1904 y Esmeraldas, Edif. Florida Piso 10, Guayaquil.
T: 59 34 2290577
W: http://www.radioromance.com
Editorial Profile: Radio Romance is a Spanish commercial station owned by Extra Radio S.A. The format of the station is news, talk, and Smooth AC. Radio Romance broadcasts to the Guayaquil, Ecuador area at 90.1 FM.

Radio Rumba
Editorial: Chimborazo 115 y Vélez, 1er. Piso, Guayaquil. **T:** 593 4 2328012
E: rumba107@radiorumba.fm
W: http://www.radiorumba.fm
Editorial Profile: Radio Rumba is a Spanish commercial station in Ecuador. The format of the station is variety and Top 40 CHR. The target audience of the station is adults, ages 18 to 64.

Radio Tarqui
Owner: Radio Tarqui
Editorial: García Moreno 1315 y Olmedo, Quito. **T:** 593 2 2582497
E: info@radiotarqui.ec
W: http://www.radiotarqui.com.ec
Editorial Profile: Radio Tarqui is a commercial station in Quito, Ecuador. the format of the station is news, talk, and sports. Radio Tarqui broadcasts to the Quito, Ecuador area at 990 AM.

Radio Tropicana
Owner: Medios Y Proyectos
Editorial: Hurtado 212 y Machala, Edificio FURNAS 4 Piso, Guayaquil 593.
T: 59 34 2511758
E: info@radiotropicana.com.ec
W: http://www.radiotropicana.com.ec
Editorial Profile: Radio Tropicana is a Spanish commercial station owned by Medios Y Proyectos. The format of the station is news, talk and classical. Radio Tropicana broadcasts to Guayaquil, Ecuador at 540 AM.

Radio Universal
T: 593 4 2448410
E: radiouniversalguayaquil@hotmail.com
W: http://es.justin.tv/radiouniversalguayaquil
Editorial Profile: Radio Universal is a commercial station. The format of the station is a variety of music, as well as news and sports. Radio Universal broadcasts in the Guayaquil, Ecuador area at 1270 AM.

Radio Uno
Owner: Radio Cadena Musical Uno
T: 593 4 2323171
W: http://www.radio11q.com.ec
Editorial Profile: Radio Uno is a commercial station owned by Radio Cadena Musical Uno. The format of the station is romantic music. Radio Uno broadcasts in the Guayaquil, Ecuador area at 580 AM.

Radio Vigía
Owner: Policía Nacional del Ecuador
Editorial: Av. Amazonas N53 113 y Japon, Quito. **T:** 593 2 254-4869
E: dnctsv.administracioncaja@policiaecuador.gob.ec
Editorial Profile: Radio Vigía is a non-commercial radio station owned by Policía Nacional del Ecuador. The format of the station is news. Radio Vigía broadcasts to Quito, Ecuador at 840 AM. The target audience of the station is adults, ages 18 to 64.

Radio Visión
Editorial: Francisco Arízaga Luque N34-229 y Federico Páez, Quito. **T:** 593 2 2260315
E: ventas@radiovision.com.ec
W: http://www.radiovision.com.ec
Editorial Profile: Radio Visión is a commercial station in Quito Ecuador. The format of the station is news, talk, and variety. Radio Visión broadcasts to Quito, Ecuador at 91.7 FM.

Radio Zaracay
Owner: Radio Zaracay
Editorial: Av. Quito 1424 y Psaje. Aguavil, Quito. **T:** 593 2 2750140
E: radiozaracay@hotmail.com
W: http://zaracayradio.com/home.html
Editorial Profile: Radio Zaracay is a commercial station owned by Radio Zaracay. The station airs a variety of music. It broadcasts to the Quito, Ecuador area on 100.5 FM.

Teleradio 1350
Owner: Teleradio AM
Editorial: Kennedy Norte Calle Flores Pérez MZ 504 Condominio Colón 1er Piso, Guayaquil. **T:** 593 4 2680696
W: http://www.teleradio.am/
Editorial Profile: Teleradio 1350 is a commercial station owned by Teleradio AM. The format of the station is news and sports talk. Teleradio 1350 broadcasts to the Guayaquil, Ecuador area at 1350 AM.

La Voz de Tomebamba
Owner: Radio La Voz
Editorial: Benigno Malo 15-91, Cuenca.
T: 593 7 2842000
E: info@lavozdeltomebamba.com
W: http://www.lavozdeltomebamba.com
Editorial Profile: La Voz de Tomebamba is a commercial station owned by Radio La Voz. The format is news, talk, sports and variety. La Voz de Tomebamba broadcasts to Cuenca, Ecuador at 102.1 FM. The target audience for the station is adults, ages 18 to 64. The station's tagline is "Nace de todas las voces".

RADIO NETWORKS

CRE Satelital
Owner: Compañia de Radio y Televisión, SA
Editorial: Boyacá 642 y Padre Solano Edificio El Torreón 8 Piso, Guayaquil 593.
T: 59 34 42560900 **E:** cre@cre.com.ec
W: http://www.cre.com.ec
Editorial Profile: CRE Satelital is a Spanish satellite radio service located in Guayquil, Guayas, Ecuador that broadcasts across Ecuador. It broadcasts primarily news and sports news, with 70 percent of its current programming dedicated to sports news.

FM 88.5 Radio Activa
Editorial: Avenida Miguel Cordero y Av. Paucarbamba esquina, Edificio Work Center 5to Piso, Oficina 508, Cuenca (azuay).
T: 593 72814688 **E:** radio@cadenactiva.com
W: http://www.cadenactiva.com
Editorial Profile: Plays Pop, Rock, Ballads, Urban music in Spanish and English. Also broadcasts soccer programs.

JC Radio
Editorial: Av. Isabela Catolica No. 833 y Luis Cordero, Quito. **T:** 593 2 255 4401
E: labruja@jcradio.com.ec
W: http://www.jcradio.com.ec
Editorial Profile: Provides music, sport, tourism news, and call-in programs in which the audience participates and interacts. Targets a youth audience.

Radio Católica Nacional de Ecuador
Editorial: Av. América, 1830, Mercadillo, Quito 17-03-540. **T:** 593 2 255 8916
E: noticias1@radiocatolica.org.ec
W: http://www.radiocatolica.org.ec
Editorial Profile: Broadcasts educational and cultural programs including shows in a Catholic context. Plays different music genres.

Radio Sonorama
Owner: Sonorama S.A.
Editorial: Moscú 378 y República del Salvador, Quito. **T:** 593 2 2442697
E: noticias@sonorama.com.ec
W: http://www.sonorama.com.ec
Editorial Profile: Radio Sonorama features news, sports, talk, and top 40 CHR. Radio Sonorama broadcasts nationally to Ecuador. The target audience is adults, ages 18 to 54. The tagline of the station is "La Gran Señal Nacional".

EGYPT
Tel: 20
Standard Time: GMT +2
Continent: Africa
Capital City: Cairo

NEWSPAPERS & PUBLICATIONS

NEWSPAPERS

Al Ahali
Owner: Al Tajamu Party
Editorial: 1, Karim Al Dawla Street, Talaat Harb Avenue, Cairo. **T:** 20 2 2579 1628
E: cairo680@yahoo.com
W: http://www.al-ahaly.com
Freq: Wed; **Circ:** 55000 Pub Statement
News Editor: Mansour Abdul Ghani; **Editor In Chief:** Farida Al Nakash; **Arab Affairs Editor:** Ahmed Hassan
Editorial Profile: Al Ahali is a weekly Arabic newspaper covering national and international news, business and sport. It launched in 1978 and is published on Wednesdays.
Language (s): Arabic
NEWSPAPER

Ahle Misr
Owner: Al Ahram Establishment
Editorial: 4 El Galaa Street, Abdel Menoeam Reyad Square, Giza. **T:** 20 2 2579 4021
E: ahle_misr@hotmail.com
Freq: Thu; **Circ:** 30000 Pub Statement
Publisher: Maha Elkashef; **News Editor:** Ibrahim Okasha; **Editor In Chief:** Mohammed Shaaban
Editorial Profile: Ahle Misr is a weekly Arabic newspaper covering news, politics, business, sports, society and culture. It was launched in 2011 and published on Thursdays.
Language (s): Arabic
NEWSPAPER

Al Ahram
Owner: Al Ahram Establishment
Editorial: Al Ahram Building, Al Gala' Street, Cairo 11511. **T:** 20 2 2770 3100
E: ahram@ahram.org.eg
W: http://www.ahram.org.eg
Freq: Daily; **Circ:** 1000000 Rate Card
Editor: Mustafa Al Jamal; **Arab News Editor:** Salah Al Nakib; **News Editor:** Hanan Hajaj;

WORLD NEWS MEDIA

Editor in Chief: Abdul Nasser Salameh
Editorial Profile: Al Ahram is a broadsheet-sized Arabic newspaper covering local and international news, current affairs, politics, business and sports. The daily newspaper was launched in 1876 and publishes an Egypt edition for domestic distribution and a Pan Arab edition distributed in the rest of the Arab world. Al Sayarat, a tabloid-sized motoring supplement, is issued with the newspaper on Fridays.
Language (s): Arabic
DAILY NEWSPAPER

Al Ahram - Arab edition
Owner: Al Ahram Establishment
Editorial: Al Ahram Building, Al Gala' Street, Cairo 11511 **E:** ahram@ahram.org.eg
W: http://www.ahram.org.eg
Freq: Daily; **Circ:** 127900 Rate Card
Editorial Profile: The Arab edition of Al Ahram is printed in Jeddah, Riyadh, Bahrain, Kuwait and the UAE and is distributed across the Gulf. The newspaper covers Egyptian and international news, business and sport. An Egypt edition of Al Ahram is also published for domestic distribution.
Language (s): Arabic
DAILY NEWSPAPER

Al Ahram Al-Masaa'i
Owner: Al Ahram Establishment
Editorial: Al Ahram Building, Al Gala'a Street, Cairo 11511. **T:** 20 2 2578 6080
E: press5555514@yahoo.com
W: http://massai.ahram.org.eg
Freq: Daily; **Circ:** 218541
Editor in Chief: Mohamed Kharaja
Editorial Profile: Al Ahram Al-Masaa'i (The Evening Pyramid) is an evening newspaper covering local and international news, current affairs, culture, sport, business and finance. It was first published in January 1991.
Language (s): Arabic
DAILY NEWSPAPER

Al Ahram Hebdo
Owner: Al Ahram Establishment
Editorial: Al Ahram Building, Al Gala'a Street, Cairo 11511. **T:** 20 2 2770 4310
E: hebdo@ahram.org.eg
W: http://hebdo.ahram.org.eg
Freq: Wed; **Circ:** 79781 Rate Card
Cinema Editor: Yasser Moheb; **Editor In Chief:** Hisham Mourad
Editorial Profile: Al Ahram Hebdo is a weekly, tabloid-sized French newspaper covering news and current affairs. The newspaper launched in 1994 and aims to communicate the Egyptian view on regional and international affairs. It is published on Wednesdays.
Language (s): French
NEWSPAPER

Al Ahram Weekly
Owner: Al Ahram Establishment
Editorial: Al Ahram Building, Al Gala'a Street, Cairo 11511. **T:** 20 2 2770 5373
E: weekly@ahram.org.eg
W: http://weekly.ahram.org.eg
Freq: Thu; **Circ:** 86850 Rate Card
Editor in Chief: Galal Nassar
Editorial Profile: Al Ahram Weekly is an English newspaper covering local and international news, business, sport and culture. It launched in 1991 and is published on Thursdays.
Language (s): English
NEWSPAPER

Al Ahrar Daily
Owner: Al Ahrar Party
Editorial: 58 Manshiyat Al Sadr Street, Kobri Al Quba Area, Cairo. **T:** 20 2 2482 3046
E: ahrardaily@gmail.com
Freq: Mon; **Circ:** 80000 Pub Statement
Editor In Chief: Selim Azouz; **News Editor:** Sherif Hamada
Editorial Profile: Al Ahrar Daily is an Arabic newspaper covering news, politics, sports, business and entertainment. The newspaper was launched in 1976 and is published by the Al Ahrar political party.
Language (s): Arabic
NEWSPAPER

Al Akhbar
Owner: Dar Akhbar El Yom
Editorial: 6 & 7 Al Sahafa Street, Cairo.
T: 20 2 2578 2800
E: arabicprint_akhbar@yahoo.com
W: http://www.akhbarelyom.com
Freq: Daily; **Circ:** 1319700 Pub Statement
Editor in Chief: Mohammad Al Banna
Editorial Profile: Al Akhbar (The News) is an Arabic newspaper covering national and international news, current affairs, politics, business and sports. It launched in 1952 and is published daily, except Saturdays.
Language (s): Arabic
DAILY NEWSPAPER

Akhbar Al Riada
Owner: Dar Akhbar El Yom
Editorial: 6 Al Sahafa Street, Cairo.
T: 20 2 2578 2500 **E:** akhbarriada@yahoo.com
W: http://reyada.akhbarelyom.com
Freq: Tue; **Circ:** 316700 Pub Statement
Editor In Chief: Jamal Al Zuhairy; **Editor:** Ayman Badra
Editorial Profile: Akhbar Al Riada (Sports News) is a weekly, tabloid-sized newspaper covering local and international sport. It launched in 1989 and is published on Tuesdays.
Language (s): Arabic
NEWSPAPER

Akhbar El-Yom
Owner: Dar Akhbar El Yom
Editorial: 6 & 7 Al Sahafa Street, Cairo.
T: 20 2 2578 2900 **E:** mohafzat@yahoo.com
W: http://www.akhbarelyom.com
Freq: Sat; **Circ:** 1622850 Pub Statement
Editor in Chief: Suliman Qenawi
Editorial Profile: Akhbar El-Yom is a weekly Arabic newspaper covering national and international news, current affairs, politics, business and sport. It was first published in November 1944 and is issued on Saturdays.
Language (s): Arabic
NEWSPAPER

Alam Al Borsa
Owner: Alam Al Borsa
Editorial: 5th Floor, 39, Ragheb Street, Cairo.
T: 20 100 692 8075
E: ebraheem.3ead@hotmail.com
Freq: Sun; **Circ:** 30000 Pub Statement
Real Estate Editor: Mohammed Azzam; **Real Estate Editor:** Nadia Ibrahim; **Editor In Chief:** Samer Tantawe
Editorial Profile: Alam Al Borsa is a weekly Arabic newspaper covering business, investment, finance, banking and stock markets. It launched in 2007 and is published on Sundays.
Language (s): Arabic
NEWSPAPER

Al Alam Al Youm
Owner: Good News International Corporation
Editorial: 8 Abdul Qawi Shamseddin Street, Dokki, Cairo. **T:** 20 2 3331 0000
E: saadhagras@hotmail.co.uk
W: http://www.gn4me.com/alalamalyoum
Freq: Daily; **Circ:** 164070 Rate Card
Editor in Chief: Saad Hagras; **News Editor:** Adel Selim; **Editor:** Nagwa Taha
Editorial Profile: Al Alam Al Youm (The World Today) is a daily Arabic newspaper covering the business sector in Egypt, the Middle East and internationally. Coverage includes stock market reports, finance and international business trends. It launched in 1991 and is aimed at business executives in Egypt. Regular features in the newspaper include: Industry & Technology (Sat), Bonouk Al Youm (Sun), Etisalat Al Youm (Mon), Business Al Youm (Tues), Alam El Etisalat (Tues), Tourism (Wed), Medical (Wed), Automotive (Thurs), Real Estate (Thurs), Tele-Business (Thurs) and Computer World (daily, except Mondays).
Language (s): Arabic
DAILY NEWSPAPER

Alam Almal
Owner: Alam Almal
Editorial: 3rd Floor, 13, Tobji Street, Giza.
T: 20 2 3337 3855 **E:** info@alamalmal.net
W: http://www.alamalmal.net
Freq: Sun; **Circ:** 20000 Pub Statement
Editor in Chief: Ashraf Al Hamdi; **Editor:** May Saoudi
Editorial Profile: Alam Almal (The World of Money) is a weekly Arabic newspaper covering news, politics, business, industry, agriculture, motoring, tourism, telecommunications and aviation. It launched in 2006 and is published on Sundays.
Language (s): Arabic
NEWSPAPER

Alaqaria
Owner: Al Ghofran Printing & Publishing Company
Editorial: 11, Al Mahrousa Street, Al Mohandiseen, Giza. **T:** 20 2 3302 4151
E: aleqaria@yahoo.com
W: http://www.aleqaria-eg.com
Freq: Sun; **Circ:** 100000 Pub Statement
Editorial Profile: Alaqaria is a 16-page weekly Arabic newspaper focusing on real estate and property in the Arab world, as well as covering business, finance and banking. It launched in 2009 and is published on Sundays.
Language (s): Arabic
NEWSPAPER

Al Anbaa Al Dawlia
Owner: Al Anbaa Al Dawlia
Editorial: Office 6B, 6th Floor, Malakou Building, Hussein Kamal Street, Cairo.
T: 20 2 3762 1119
E: alanbaaaldawliaa@yahoo.com
W: http://www.alanbaa-aldawlia.info
Freq: Tue; **Circ:** 200000 Pub Statement
Editor in Chief: Ahmed Mahfouz
Editorial Profile: Al Anbaa Al Dawlia (International News) is a weekly Arabic newspaper covering national and international news, politics, economics, business, society, sport and culture. It launched in 2006 and is published on Tuesdays.
Language (s): Arabic
NEWSPAPER

Aqidati
Owner: Dar Al Tahrir Publishing & Printing House
Editorial: Al Gomhuriya Building, 111-115 Ramses Street, Cairo. **T:** 20 2 2578 1777
E: ask@aqidati.net.eg
W: http://www.aqidati.net.eg
Freq: Tue; **Circ:** 60000 Pub Statement
Editor In Chief: Megahed Khalaf; **News Editor:** Houssam Wahballah
Editorial Profile: Aqidati (My Faith) is a weekly Islamic newspaper. It launched in 1992 and is published on Tuesdays.
Language (s): Arabic
NEWSPAPER

Al Araby
Owner: Al Nasiry Democratic Arab Party
Editorial: PO Box 38, 30 Yaqoub Street, Cairo.
T: 20 2 2796 1017 **E:** alarabyorg@yahoo.com
Freq: Sun; **Circ:** 40000 Pub Statement
Editor In Chief: Magdy Al Basyouni
Editorial Profile: Al Araby is a weekly Arabic newspaper covering international and national news, politics, sports, business and entertainment. The newspaper is published by the Al Nasiry Democratic Arab Party. It launched in 1993 and is published on Sundays.
Language (s): Arabic
NEWSPAPER

Arrai
Owner: Dar Al Tahrir Publishing & Printing House
Editorial: Al Gomhuriah Building, 111-115 Ramses Street, Cairo. **T:** 20 2 2578 3333
E: arraiorg@gmail.com
W: http://www.arrai.org
Freq: Sun; **Circ:** 20000 Pub Statement
Editor In Chief: Mohamed Al Sharqawi
Editorial Profile: Arrai (Point of View) is a weekly Arabic newspaper covering national news and current affairs, politics, business and culture. It launched in 1990 and is published on Sundays.
Language (s): Arabic
NEWSPAPER

Al Borsa
Owner: Business Media Group
Editorial: 12, Haroun Street, Dokki, Giza.
T: 20 2 3748 6853 **E:** news@alborsanews.com
W: http://www.alborsanews.com
Freq: Daily; **Circ:** 120000 Rate Card
Editorial Profile: Al Borsa is a 16-page daily business newspaper covering economics, real estate, banking, energy, insurance, stock markets, IT, motoring, entertainment and tourism. It launched in 2008, and is aimed at business executives.
Language (s): Arabic
DAILY NEWSPAPER

Al Dostour
Owner: Al Dostor Press & Media
Editorial: 11, Al Sad Al Aali Street, Dokki, Cairo. **T:** 20 2 3748 8249
E: dostor.2011@gmail.com
W: http://www.dostor.org
Freq: Daily; **Circ:** 220000 Pub Statement
News Editor: Ahmed Abdul-Jawad; **Editor in Chief:** Saeed Ahmed
Editorial Profile: Al Dostour is a daily Arabic newspaper covering news, politics, sports and entertainment. It was first published in 1995.
Language (s): Arabic
DAILY NEWSPAPER

The Egyptian Gazette
Owner: Dar Al Tahrir Publishing & Printing House
Editorial: Office 23, 11th Floor, Al Gomhuriya Building, 111-115 Ramses Street, Cairo.
T: 20 2 2578 4646
E: gazette-editor@hotmail.com
W: http://www.egyptiangazette.net
Freq: Daily; **Circ:** 50000 Rate Card
News Editor: Hatem Khedr; **News Editor:** Ashraf Madbouly; **Editor in Chief:** Magdy Qotb
Editorial Profile: The Egyptian Gazette is a daily English newspaper covering news, politics, business, sport, health, IT, culture and arts. The newspaper, called the Egyptian Mail on Tuesdays, is aimed at businessmen, foreign residents, members of the diplomatic corps, students and officials. It was first published from Alexandria on 26 January 1880 as a four-page weekly tabloid, before moving to Cairo in February 1938. Just before the Second World War, ownership of the paper passed to Societe Orientale de Publicite, which had launched the daily Egyptian Mail in 1914.Following the end of the war, and the departure of the bulk of British troops, the Egyptian Mail became a weekly, appearing on Tuesdays when The Egyptian Gazette is not published, which continues today. Following the Egyptian Revolution in 1952, ownership of the paper was ceded to its current owners, Dar Al Tahrir.
Language (s): English
DAILY NEWSPAPER

Egyptian Mail
Owner: Dar Al Tahrir Publishing & Printing House
Editorial: 111-115 Ramses Street, Cairo.
T: 20 2 2579 2072
E: editorofthegazette@hotmail.com
W: http://www.egyptiangazette.net
Freq: Tue; **Circ:** 50000 Pub Statement
Editor in Chief: Magdy Qotb
Editorial Profile: Egyptian Mail is a weekly newspaper covering news, politics, business, sport, health, IT, culture and arts. The newspaper is published on Tuesdays in place of The Egyptian Gazette, and is aimed at businessmen, foreign residents, members of the diplomatic corps, students and officials. The newspaper was launched as a daily in 1914 by Societe Orientale de Publicite, which acquired ownership of The Egyptian Gazette shortly before the Second World War. Following the end of the war, and the departure of the bulk of British troops, the Egyptian Mail became a weekly, appearing on Tuesdays when The Egyptian Gazette is not published, which continues today. Following the Egyptian Revolution in 1952, ownership of the two newspaper was ceded to its current owners, Dar Al Tahrir.
Language (s): English
NEWSPAPER

Ein
Owner: Sout El Omma for Press & Publishing
Editorial: 9 Education Authority Street, off Michel Bakhoum Street, Cairo.
T: 20 2 3761 9856
E: hameednews@yahoo.com
Freq: Thu; **Circ:** 122000 Pub Statement
Editor In Chief: Abdul Hameed Aleesh
Editorial Profile: Ein is a weekly Arabic newspaper covering news, politics and sport. It launched in 2002 and is published on Thursdays. The newspaper was formerly called 3aine.
Language (s): Arabic
NEWSPAPER

Al Ektesadeya
Owner: Alektesadeya Press, Printing and Publishing Company
Editorial: 40, Abdul Khaleq Tharwat Street, Cairo. **T:** 20 2 2396 3228
E: info@ektesadeya.com
W: http://www.ektesadeya.com
Freq: Sun; **Circ:** 50000 Pub Statement
Editor In Chief: Al Sayed Al Najjar; **Stock Market Editor:** Tamer Farooq
Editorial Profile: Al Ektesadeya is a weekly Arabic newspaper covering business, finance, investment, telecommunications, tourism, banking, stock markets and real estate. The newspaper is aimed at business executives in Egypt, and was launched in 2007. It is published on Sundays.
Language (s): Arabic
NEWSPAPER

Elosboa
Owner: Elosboa Press Publishing and Media
Editorial: 45A Champilion Street, Cairo.
T: 20 2 2577 5592 **E:** s.sisy@hotmail.com
W: http://www.elaosboa.com
Freq: Mon; **Circ:** 150000 Pub Statement
News Editor: Omar Abdulali; **Arab Affairs Editor:** Khaled Al-Edaisi
Editorial Profile: Elosboa (The Week) is a weekly Arabic newspaper covering local and international news, politics, business and

sport. It launched in 1997 and is published on Mondays.
Language (s): Arabic
NEWSPAPER

El Fagr
Owner: El Fagr for Press, Printing & Publishing
Editorial: Floor 18 & 19, Building 8, Cairo.
T: 20 2 3336 6164 **E:** elfagr@elfagr.net
W: http://www.elfagr.org
Freq: Thu; **Circ:** 200000 Pub Statement
Editor in Chief: Manal Lasheen
Editorial Profile: El Fagr is a weekly Arabic newspaper covering international and national news, politics, sports, business and entertainment. It launched in 2005 and is published on Thursdays.
Language (s): Arabic
NEWSPAPER

Al Gamaheer
Owner: Sawt Al Gamaheer Press, Printing & Publishing Co.
Editorial: 37 Amman Street, Dokki, Giza.
T: 20 2 3762 5274
E: algamaheer@hotmail.com
Freq: Wed; **Circ:** 30000 Pub Statement
Editor In Chief: Mahmoud Thulathi
Editorial Profile: Al Gamaheer (The Audience) is a weekly Arabic newspaper covering news, politics, business, sports, entertainment, culture and society. It was launched in 2004 and published on Wednesdays.
Language (s): Arabic
NEWSPAPER

Al Gomhuriah
Owner: Dar Al Tahrir Publishing & Printing House
Editorial: 9th Floor, Al Gomhuriah Building, 111-115 Ramses Street, Cairo.
T: 20 2 2578 3333 **E:** eltahrir@eltahrir.net
W: http://www.algomhuria.net.eg
Freq: Daily; **Circ:** 700000 Pub Statement
Editor in Chief: Gamal Abd-El-Reheem; **Stock Markets Editor:** Soliman Fouad
Editorial Profile: Al Gomhuriah (The Republic) is a broadsheet-sized Arabic newspaper covering local and international news, current affairs, business, finance and sport. A 'weekly' edition is published on Thursdays which includes more features, interviews and photos. The newspaper was first published in 1953.
Language (s): Arabic
DAILY NEWSPAPER

Al Horia We Al Adala
Owner: Freedom & Justice Party
Editorial: 20, Al Malik Al Saleh Street, Al Manyal, Cairo. **T:** 20 2 2532 2893
E: f.j.news@hotmail.com
W: http://fj-p.com/view.php?id=20
Freq: Daily; **Circ:** 80000 Pub Statement
Editor In Chief: Adel Al Ansari; **News Editor:** Hani Al Makkawi
Editorial Profile: Al Horia We Al Adala (Freedom & Justice) is a daily Arabic newspaper covering local and international news, current affairs, politics, business and sport. It was launched in 2011 by the Freedom & Justice Party.
Language (s): Arabic
DAILY NEWSPAPER

El Khamis
Owner: Pioneer Press, Printing & Publishing Company
Editorial: 4th Floor, 1, Talaat Harb Square, Cairo. **T:** 20 2 2395 9595
E: elkhamis_2@yahoo.com
W: http://www.elkhamis.com
Freq: Thu; **Circ:** 50000 Pub Statement
Editorial Profile: El Khamis (Thursday) is a weekly Arabic newspaper covering news, politics, sport, society and entertainment. It launched in 1998 and is published on Thursdays.
Language (s): Arabic
NEWSPAPER

Khutt Ahmar
Owner: Dar Khutt Ahmar
Editorial: PO Box 150, Al Bosta Building, 12 Al Manyal Museum Street, Cairo.
T: 20 2 2531 8283
E: ashrafherzawy@yahoo.com
Freq: Wed; **Circ:** 90000 Pub Statement
News Editor: Mustafa Ibrahim; **Editor In Chief:** Mohammad Nawwar; **Editor:** Khaled Zaki
Editorial Profile: Khutt Ahmar (Red Line) is a weekly Arabic newspaper covering international and national news, politics, business and sports. It launched in 2008 and is published on Wednesdays.
Language (s): Arabic
NEWSPAPER

Al Koura Wal Mala'eb
Owner: Dar Al Tahrir Publishing & Printing House
Editorial: Office 23, 12th Floor, Al Gomhuriya Building, Cairo. **T:** 20 2 2578 1919
E: ask@koura.net.eg
W: http://www.koura.net.eg
Freq: Sun; **Circ:** 80000 Pub Statement
Editor in Chief: Khaled Kamel
Editorial Profile: Al Koura Wal Mala'eb is a weekly Arabic newspaper covering local and international sport. It launched in 1976, and is published on Sundays.
Language (s): Arabic
NEWSPAPER

Al Mal
Owner: Egypt Company for Marketing & Distribution
Editorial: 7A Al Sad Al Aali Street, Dokki, Cairo. **T:** 20 2 3748 3104
E: almalnews@yahoo.com
W: http://www.almalnews.com
Freq: Daily; **Circ:** 55000 Pub Statement
Stock Market Editor: Yasmeen Mounir; **Editor In Chief:** Hazem Sherif
Editorial Profile: Al Mal (The Money) is a daily Arabic newspaper covering economics, business, finance, markets, technology, telecommunications, stocks, insurance, banking, tourism, energy, real estate and politics. It launched in 2003 and is aimed at business executives in Egypt.
Language (s): Arabic
DAILY NEWSPAPER

Al Masry Al Youm
Owner: Al-Masry Media Corporation
Editorial: 4th Floor, CIB Bank Building, 49, Mobtadayan Street, Cairo. **T:** 20 2 2798 0100
E: editorial@almasry-alyoum.com
W: http://www.almasry-alyoum.com
Freq: Daily; **Circ:** 250000 Rate Card
Editorial Profile: Al Masry Al Youm is an independent Arabic daily newspaper covering local and international news, politics, business and sport. It launched in 2004.
Language (s): Arabic
DAILY NEWSPAPER

Al Mesryoon
Owner: Al Mesryoon Press, Publishing, Printing and Distribution LLC
Editorial: 6th Floor, 45 Champillion Street, Cairo. **T:** 20 2 2578 3446
E: almesryoon.newspaper@gmail.com
W: http://www.almesryoon.com
Freq: Daily; **Circ:** 80000 Pub Statement
Editorial Profile: Al Mesryoon (The Egyptians) is an Arabic daily newspaper covering national and international news, politics, business, society and sports. It was first published in 2011.
Language (s): Arabic
DAILY NEWSPAPER

Al Messa
Owner: Dar Al Tahrir Publishing & Printing House
Editorial: 10th Floor, Al Gomhuriya Building, 111-115 Ramses Street, Cairo.
T: 20 2 2578 7999 **E:** askmessa@hotmail.com
W: http://www.almessa.net.eg
Freq: Daily; **Circ:** 450000 Pub Statement
Editor in Chief: Momen El Habbaa
Editorial Profile: Al Messa is an evening newspaper covering local and international news, politics, society and sport. It was first published in 1956.
Language (s): Arabic
DAILY NEWSPAPER

The Middle East Observer
Owner: Middle East Observer House
Editorial: 41 Sherif Street, Cairo 11111.
T: 20 2 2393 9732
E: meobserver@hotmail.com
W: http://www.meobserver.org
Freq: Wed; **Circ:** 25000 Pub Statement
Editor In Chief: Hesham Abdel Raouf; **Publisher:** Ahmed Foda
Editorial Profile: The Middle East Observer is an economic journal focusing on Middle East and international news, economic current affairs, politics, business and development. It launched in 1954 and is published on Wednesdays.
Language (s): English
NEWSPAPER

Al Mogaz
Owner: Al Mogaz Press Printing and Publishing
Editorial: 4A, Dareeh Saad Zaghlool Street, off Al Qasr Al Aini Street, Cairo.
T: 20 2 2793 0055 **E:** elmogaz@elmogaz.com
W: http://www.elmogaz.com
Freq: Mon; **Circ:** 150000 Pub Statement
News Editor: Mohamed Salah
Editorial Profile: Al Mogaz is a weekly Arabic newspaper covering local news and current affairs, politics, business, society and sports. It launched in 2002 and is published on Mondays.
Language (s): Arabic
NEWSPAPER

Msaeya
Owner: Dar Akhbar El Yom
Editorial: Sahafa Street, Cairo.
T: 20 2 2794 0266
E: msaeya2011@yahoo.com
W: http://www.almsaeya.com
Freq: Daily; **Circ:** 80000 Pub Statement
Editorial Profile: Msaeya is a daily Arabic newspaper covering current affairs and politics. It was first published in 2006, and was formerly called Al Syasi El-Masry.
Language (s): Arabic
DAILY NEWSPAPER

Al Nabaa Al-Watany
Owner: Dar Al Nabaa Al Watany
Editorial: 9 Musician Ali Ismaeel Street, Al Masaha Square, Cairo. **T:** 20 2 3335 2988
E: alnaba.alwatany@gmail.com
Freq: Sat; **Circ:** 250000 Pub Statement
Editorial Profile: Al Nabaa Al-Watany is a broadsheet-sized Arabic newspaper focusing on local and international news, politics, business and sport. It launched in 1989 and is published on Saturdays.
Language (s): Arabic
NEWSPAPER

Al Nahar
Owner: Al Waqai Al Arabiya for Press & Publishing
Editorial: 1065 Corniche El Nil, Garden City, Cairo. **T:** 20 2 2792 6950
E: alnnhar@yahoo.com
W: http://www.alnaharegypt.com
Freq: Wed; **Circ:** 50000 Pub Statement
News Editor: Hatem Abdul Kader
Editorial Profile: Al Nahar (The Day) is a weekly Arabic newspaper covering news, politics, business, sports, culture and entertainment. It launched in 2007 and is published on Wednesdays.
Language (s): Arabic
NEWSPAPER

Le Progrès Egyptien
Owner: Dar Al Tahrir Publishing & Printing House
Editorial: 10th Floor, Al Gomhuriya Building, 111-115 Ramses Street, Cairo.
T: 20 2 2578 3333
E: leprogresegyptien@yahoo.fr
W: http://www.progres.net.eg
Freq: Daily; **Circ:** 90000 Rate Card
Editor In Chief: Mohammad Al Azzawi; **News Editor:** Marwa Mourad
Editorial Profile: Le Progrès Egyptien is a French daily newspaper covering national and international news, business, politics, culture and sport. It was first published in 1893. On Sundays, the newspaper is called Le Progrès Dimanche.
Language (s): French
DAILY NEWSPAPER

Al Rahma
Owner: Al Rahma Establishment
Editorial: PO Box 4, 6th of October City, Cairo 12573. **T:** 20 2 3838 1663
E: alrahma.press@yahoo.com
Freq: Fri; **Circ:** 100000 Pub Statement
News Editor: Ashraf Al Bahai; **Editor In Chief:** Abdulnasser Al Zouhairy
Editorial Profile: Al Rahma is a weekly Arabic newspaper covering national and international news, politics, society, culture and sport. It launched in 2011 and is published on Fridays.
Language (s): Arabic
NEWSPAPER

Rose Al Youssef
Owner: Rose Al Youssef Group
Editorial: 89A, Al Qasr Al Aini Street, Cairo.
T: 20 2 2795 8503
E: rosaelyoussef@yahoo.com
W: http://www.rosaeveryday.com
Freq: Daily; **Circ:** 55000 Pub Statement
Editor in Chief: Gamal Tayea
Editorial Profile: Rose Al Youssef is a daily Arabic newspaper covering news, politics, sports and business. It was first published in 2005.
Language (s): Arabic
DAILY NEWSPAPER

El Sabah
Owner: El Sabah Establishment For Press
Editorial: 15, Mohammed Hafez Street, off Revolution Street, Giza. **T:** 20 2 3337 4500
E: elsaba7news@gmail.com
W: http://www.elsaba7.com
Freq: Mon; **Circ:** 80000
Editor in Chief: Wael Lotfi
Editorial Profile: El Sabah is weekly Arabic newspaper covering news, politics, business and sport. The newspaper was first published in September 2012 and is issued on Mondays.
Language (s): Arabic
NEWSPAPER

Sawt Al Balad
Owner: Arab Press Agency
Editorial: Building 5, Abed Al Moniem Salem Street, Al Wehda Al Arabia, Giza.
T: 20 2 3586 7576 **E:** balad@apatop.com
W: http://www.baladnews.com
Freq: Thu; **Circ:** 80000 Pub Statement
Editorial Profile: Sawt Al Balad (Voice of the Country) is a weekly Arabic newspaper covering international and national news, politics, business, culture, sports, entertainment, youth and family. It launched in 2007 and is published on Thursdays.
Language (s): Arabic
NEWSPAPER

Shashati
Owner: Dar Al Tahrir Publishing and Printing House
Editorial: PO Box 11511, 111-115 Ramses Street, Cairo. **T:** 20 2 2578 1888
E: allaithyh@yahoo.com
W: http://www.shashati.net.eg
Freq: Thu; **Circ:** 15000
Editor: Mohamed Abdelaziz; **Editor in Chief:** Hussam Al Laithy; **Editor:** Yasser Ezz El Deen
Editorial Profile: Shashati is a weekly Arabic newspaper covering entertainment and arts, including TV programme schedules, entertainment news, cinema, art, culture, literature and technology. It launched in March 2012 and is published on Thursdays.
Language (s): Arabic
NEWSPAPER

Al Shorouk
Owner: Egyptian Company For Publishing
Editorial: 26, Mohamed Kamel Morsy Street, Mohandiseen, Cairo. **T:** 20 2 3762 2221
E: news@shorouknews.com
W: http://www.shorouknews.com
Freq: Daily; **Circ:** 100000 Rate Card
News Editor: Ashraf Al Barbary
Editorial Profile: Al Shorouk (The Dawn) is a daily Arabic newspaper covering local and international news, business, religion, youth, women's issues and sport. It was first published in 2009.
Language (s): Arabic
DAILY NEWSPAPER

Sout El Omma
Owner: Sout El Omma for Press & Publishing
Editorial: 9 Education Authority Street, off Michel Bakhoum Street, Cairo.
T: 20 2 3336 3575
E: soutelomma@yahoo.com
W: http://www.soutalomma.com
Freq: Sat; **Circ:** 100000 Pub Statement
News Editor: Rida Awad; **Editor in Chief:** Abdul Haleem Qandeel
Editorial Profile: Sout El Omma (Voice of the Nation) is a weekly Arabic newspaper covering international and national news, politics, business, sports and entertainment. It launched in 2001 and is published on Saturdays.
Language (s): Arabic
NEWSPAPER

Al Tahrir
Owner: Egyptian Company for Arabic & International Publishing
Editorial: 59, Iran Street, Dokki, Cairo.
T: 20 2 3760 2339 **E:** ta7rir2011@gmail.com
W: http://www.tahrirnews.com
Freq: Daily; **Circ:** 150000 Pub Statement
Editor In Chief: Ibrahim Eissa
Editorial Profile: Al Tahrir (Freedom) is an Arabic daily newspaper covering national and international news, politics, business, sports, art, culture and society. It was first published in 2011.
Language (s): Arabic
DAILY NEWSPAPER

Veto
Owner: Al Ahrar Press, Printing & Publishing
Editorial: 108, Al Neel Street, Al Dokki, Cairo.
T: 20 2 3762 0180 **E:** info@vetogate.com
W: http://www.vetogate.com
Freq: Tue; **Circ:** 80000 Pub Statement
Editor in Chief: Essam Kamel; **News Editor:** Mokhtar Mahmoud

Editorial Profile: Veto is a weekly Arabic newspaper covering politics, business and sport. It launched in 2012 and is published on Tuesdays.
Language (s): Arabic
NEWSPAPER

Al Wafd
Owner: Wafd Opposition Party
Editorial: PO Box 357, 1 Boulis Hanna Street, Giza. **T:** 20 2 3338 3111
E: wafdeg@gmail.com
W: http://www.alwafd.org
Freq: Daily; **Circ:** 150000 Pub Statement
Arab Affairs Editor: Naser Abdul Majeed; **News Editor:** Adel Sabry; **Editor in Chief:** Wagdi Zain Al Deen
Editorial Profile: Al Wafd is a 16-page daily Arabic newspaper covering national and international news, current affairs, politics, business, sports and arts. It was launched in 1984 by the Al Wafd Party and also covers news and activities of the political party.
Language (s): Arabic
DAILY NEWSPAPER

Washwasha
Owner: El Fagr for Press, Printing & Publishing
Editorial: 5 Al Burj Street, Lebanon Square, Cairo. **T:** 20 2 3303 7828
E: info@washwasha.net
W: http://www.washwasha.org
Freq: Mon; **Circ:** 32500 Pub Statement
Editor In Chief: Mohammed Farouk
Editorial Profile: Washwasha (Whispers) is a weekly Arabic newspaper covering entertainment, cinema, celebrities, culture, sports, women's issues and society. It launched in 2006 and is published on Mondays.
Language (s): Arabic
NEWSPAPER

El Watan
Owner: Al Mustaqbal Publishing, Distribution & Press Company
Editorial: 27, Mohiey Al Deen Street, Abu El Aizz, Giza. **T:** 20 2 3761 5197
E: info@elwatannews.com
W: http://www.elwatannews.com
Freq: Daily; **Circ:** 250000 Pub Statement
Editor In Chief: Magdy El Gallad
Editorial Profile: El Watan is a daily Arabic newspaper covering national and international news, business and sport. It launched in 2012.
Language (s): Arabic
DAILY NEWSPAPER

Watani
Owner: Watani Printing & Publishing Corporation
Editorial: 27 Abdel Khalek Tharwat Street, Downtown, Cairo. **T:** 20 2 2393 6051
E: watanipaper@gmail.com
W: http://www.wataninet.com
Freq: Sun; **Circ:** 60000 Pub Statement
News Editor: Noura Najib
Editorial Profile: Watani (My Homeland) is a weekly Arabic newspaper covering national and international news, current affairs, politics, business and sports, as well as Coptic issues, culture, heritage and the Coptic contribution to Egyptian society. It launched in 1958 and is aimed at the Coptic community in Egypt. The newspaper includes English and French supplements and is published on Sundays.
Language (s): Arabic
NEWSPAPER

El Youm
Owner: El Youm For Press, Printing and Publishing LLC
Editorial: 12, Hussein Hegazi Street, Near Health Ministry, Cairo. **T:** 20 2 2793 3700
E: elyoum_cairo@yahoo.com
Freq: Tue; **Circ:** 80000 Pub Statement
News Editor: Emad Taha
Editorial Profile: El Youm (Today) is a weekly Arabic newspaper covering politics, news, business and sports. It launched in 2007 and is published on Tuesdays.
Language (s): Arabic
NEWSPAPER

Youm7
Owner: Egyptian Company for Press, Publishing & Advertising
Editorial: 18th Floor, 54, Al Batal Ahmed Abdul Aziz Street, Cairo. **T:** 20 2 3760 3627
E: info@youm7.com
W: http://www.youm7.com
Freq: Daily; **Circ:** 100000 Pub Statement
Editor In Chief: Khaled Salah
Editorial Profile: Youm7 (The Seventh Day) is a daily Arabic newspaper covering national and international news, politics, business and sport. It was first published in 2008.
Language (s): Arabic
DAILY NEWSPAPER

NEWS SERVICE/SYNDICATE

Agence France-Presse - Cairo Bureau
Owner: Agence France-Presse
Editorial: Tour Al Massryine, 10 Midan El Missaha, Giza. **T:** 20 2 3748 1236
E: afp.lecaire@afp.com
W: http://www.afp.com
Bureau Chief: Emmanuel Giroud
Editorial Profile: Regional office of the Agence France-Presse covering general news and current affairs.
Language (s): Arabic
NEWS SERVICE/SYNDICATE

APTN Egypt
Owner: Associated Press
Editorial: 7th Floor, 1117 Corniche El Nil Street, Cairo 11221. **T:** 20 2 2578 4095
E: aptncairo@gmail.com
W: http://www.aptn.com
Editorial Profile: Associated Press Television News (APTN) is the international television arm of the Associated Press - APTN's operations include a main news service, specialised broadcast services, customised coverage for the Middle East, a productions division, weekly and daily entertainment news and an extensive video archive library.
Language (s): Arabic
NEWS SERVICE/SYNDICATE

Arab Press Agency
Owner: Arab Press Agency
Editorial: 5 Abed Al Mounem Salem, Al Wehda Al Arabia, Giza. **T:** 20 2 3586 7575
E: news@apatop.com
W: http://www.apatop.com
Editorial Profile: Arab Press Agency provides news, features and analysis on events in the Arab world - press reports and photo service.
Language (s): Arabic
NEWS SERVICE/SYNDICATE

Associated Press
Editorial: 1117 Corniche el-Nil St, Cairo 11221. **T:** 20 2 2578-4091 **E:** apcairo@ap.org
NEWS SERVICE/SYNDICATE

Associated Press - Cairo bureau
Owner: Associated Press
Editorial: 4th Floor, 3, Abu Al Fida Street, Cairo 11211. **T:** 20 2 2728 3600
E: mideast@ap.org **W:** http://www.ap.org
Arabic Editor: Zuhair Abdullah; **Bureau Chief:** Hamza Hendawi
Editorial Profile: Cairo bureau of the Associated Press (AP), and also the international wire agency's regional head office for the Middle East.
Language (s): Arabic
NEWS SERVICE/SYNDICATE

Bloomberg - Cairo Bureau
Owner: Bloomberg L.P.
Editorial: 22nd Floor, North Tower, Nile City Towers, Corniche El Nil, Cairo.
T: 20 2 2461 8511
E: egyptnews@bloomberg.net
W: http://www.bloomberg.com
Editorial Profile: Financial news wire service.
Language (s): English
NEWS SERVICE/SYNDICATE

Bloomberg News
Owner: Bloomberg L.P.
Editorial: 22nd Floor, North Tower, Nile City Towers, Corniche El Nil, Cairo 116 24.
T: 20 22 461-8511
E: egyptnews@bloomberg.net
Bureau Chief: Tarek El-Tablawy
NEWS SERVICE/SYNDICATE

Cairo News Company
Owner: Cairo News Company
Editorial: Suite 404, Dohet Maspero Tower, 4 Al-Galaa Street, Cairo 11221.
T: 20 2 2576 2601 **E:** info@caironews.tv
W: http://www.caironews.tv
Bureau Chief: Heba Al Qadi
Editorial Profile: Cairo News Company (CNC) covers breaking news, sport, business news, social trends, environmental news and human-interest stories from Egypt and the Middle East. The company was co-founded in 2004 by brothers Nader and Hisham Gohar and provides news services to news companies, broadcasters and producers from numerous countries, including the USA, UK, France, Germany, Japan, Israel, Qatar, Saudi Arabia and the UAE via satellite transmission on Nilesat and Eutelsat, and SNG services.
Language (s): Arabic
NEWS SERVICE/SYNDICATE

Deutsche Presse-Agentur - Cairo bureau
Owner: Deutsche Presse-Agentur
Editorial: 20 Gamal El Din Abu El Mahasen Street, Garden City, Cairo. **T:** 20 2 2795 6842
E: office.cairo@dpa.com
W: http://www.dpa.com
Editor In Chief: Bahai Eldin Taghian
Editorial Profile: Cairo bureau of German press agency - covers news, politics, sports, fashion, economy, conflicts, disasters, features and business in the Middle East.
Language (s): Arabic
NEWS SERVICE/SYNDICATE

European Pressphoto Agency - Middle East Head Office
Owner: European Pressphoto Agency
Editorial: 1st Floor, 20 Gamal Aldine Abu al Mahasan St., Cairo. **T:** 20 2 2795 6978
E: epacairo@gmail.com **W:** http://www.epa.eu
Editorial Profile: Photo agency representing 11 European news agencies (DPA, ANSA, EFE, Belga, APA, Athens News Agency, PAP, ANP, MTI, Keystone and LUSA) - covers news, politics, sports, fashion, economy, conflicts, disasters, features and business. It is aimed at subscribers around the world, including newspapers, magazines and online news portals.
Language (s): Arabic
NEWS SERVICE/SYNDICATE

Middle East News Agency
Owner: Middle East News Agency
Editorial: PO Box 1165, 17 Hoda Sharawi Street, Cairo 11111. **T:** 20 2 2393 3000
E: ticker-1@mena.org.eg
W: http://www.mena.org.eg
Editorial Profile: Official Egyptian government news agency - founded in 1956.
Language (s): Arabic
NEWS SERVICE/SYNDICATE

Reuters - Cairo Bureau
Owner: Thomson Reuters
Editorial: PO Box 2040, 21st Floor, Bank Misr Building, Cairo 11511. **T:** 20 2 2578 3290
E: cairo.newsroom@reuters.com
W: http://www.reuters.com
Bureau Chief: Michael Georgy
Editorial Profile: Cairo bureau of international news agency supplying news - text, graphics, video and pictures - to subscribers around the world. Covers Egypt and Sudan from Cairo.
Language (s): Arabic
NEWS SERVICE/SYNDICATE

Reuters TV - Cairo Bureau
Owner: Thomson Reuters
Editorial: PO Box 2040, 21st Floor, Bank Misr Tower, Cairo 11511. **T:** 20 2 2577 7150
E: ashraf.fahim@thomsonreuters.com
W: http://www.thomsonreuters.com
Bureau Chief: Michael Georgy
Editorial Profile: Cairo Bureau of Thomson Reuters TV providing television broadcasters and internet providers worldwide with international news video, including breaking news stories, human interest items, sport, business and entertainment news.
Language (s): Arabic
NEWS SERVICE/SYNDICATE

Rossiya Segodnya - Egypt & North Africa bureau
Owner: Rossiya Segodnya
Editorial: 5, Aziz Abaza Street, Zamalek, Cairo.
T: 20 2 2736 9929 **E:** rian@access.com.eg
W: http://ria.ru
Bureau Chief: Rafael Daminov
Editorial Profile: Rossiya Segodnya (Russia Today) is the official Russian government-owned international news agency which has a mandate to 'provide information on Russian state policy and Russian life and society for audiences abroad'. It was founded by presidential decree in December 2013 and incorporates the former RIA Novosti news service and Voice of Russia international radio service. The Egypt & North Africa bureau covers news, political affairs, economics, markets, business and investment.
Language (s): Arabic
NEWS SERVICE/SYNDICATE

Xinhua News Agency - Cairo Bureau
Owner: Xinhua News Agency
Editorial: 27 Corniche El Nile, Maadi, Cairo.
T: 20 2 2358 7950 **E:** terrificln@gmail.com
W: http://www.xinhuanet.com
Bureau Chief: Li Shuting
Editorial Profile: Cairo bureau of the Xinhua News Agency, the official press agency of the People's Republic of China. The Cairo bureau is also the Middle East regional office. Correspondence and press releases should be sent in Arabic or Chinese.
Language (s): Arabic
NEWS SERVICE/SYNDICATE

BROADCASTING

RADIO STATIONS

Al Aghani Radio
Owner: Egypt Radio & Television Union (ERTU)
Editorial: PO Box 1186, Egyptian Radio & TV Building, Cairo. **T:** 20 2 2577 6078
E: ern.news@yahoo.com
W: http://www.ertu.org
Editorial Profile: Al Aghani Radio broadcasts Arabic music and entertainment news on 105.8 FM and 90.9 FM. The station launched in 2000 and is operated by state-owned public broadcaster, the Egypt Radio & Television Union (ERTU).

El Bernameg Al-Aam Egypt
Owner: Egypt Radio & Television Union (ERTU)
Editorial: PO Box 1186, Egyptian Radio & TV Building, Cairo. **T:** 20 2 2578 4124
E: aly_tv@yahoo.com **W:** http://www.ertu.org
Editorial Profile: El Bernameg Al-Aam Egypt, also known as Iza'at Al Gomhuriya Al Masriya Al Arabiya, is a radio station broadcasting music, news and entertainment programmes. The station launched in 1934 and is operated by state-owned public broadcaster, the Egypt Radio & Television Union (ERTU).

Al Quraan Al-Kareem
Owner: Egypt Radio & Television Union (ERTU)
Editorial: PO Box 1186, Egyptian Radio & TV Building, Cairo. **T:** 20 2 2577 5104
E: qurankareem@gmail.com
W: http://www.ertu.org
Editorial Profile: Al Quraan Al-Kareem is a radio station broadcasting Quranic recitals and religious programmes on 98.2 FM. The station launched in 1964 and is operated by state-owned public broadcaster, the Egypt Radio & Television Union (ERTU).

Radio Misr 88.7FM
Owner: Egypt News Center
Editorial: PO Box 1186, Corniche El Nil, Cairo 11511. **T:** 20 2 2578 5893
E: mail@radio-masr.com
W: http://www.radio-masr.com
Editorial Profile: Radio Misr 88.7FM is a radio station broadcasting news, politics and sports programmes on 88.7 FM. The station launched in 2009 and is operated by state-owned public broadcaster, the Egypt Radio & Television Union (ERTU).

Sout Al Arab
Owner: Egypt Radio & Television Union (ERTU)
Editorial: PO Box 1186, 3rd Floor, Egyptian Radio & TV Building, Cairo 11511.
T: 20 2 2578 9421 **E:** lamia_radio@yahoo.com
W: http://www.ertu.org
Editorial Profile: Sout Al Arab is a radio station broadcasting news, society, culture, art, sport and music programmes on 483 AM. The station launched in 1953 and is operated by state-owned public broadcaster, the Egypt Radio & Television Union (ERTU).

TELEVISION STATIONS

Nile News
Owner: Egypt Radio & Television Union (ERTU)
Editorial: Egypt TV & Radio Union, PO Box 1186, Cairo 11511. **T:** 20 2 2578 9355
E: nile_reporter@hotmail.com
W: http://www.nile.eg
Editorial Profile: Nile News is a free-to-air television station broadcasting news, political programmes, current affairs and documentaries. The channel launched in 1998.

Nile TV International
Owner: Egypt Radio & Television Union (ERTU)
Editorial: Egypt Radio & TV Union, PO Box 1186, Cairo 11511. **T:** 20 2 2579 9358
E: osamatv@hotmail.com
W: http://www.nileinternational.net

Editorial Profile: Nile TV International is a television station broadcasting entertainment programmes, films, serials, sports and tourism programmes, news & current affairs, talk shows, French cinema, culture and lifestyle programmes. The channel launched in 1994.

ONTV

Owner: Hawa Ltd.
Editorial: Mezzanine Floor, 35 Abu El Feda Street, Cairo 11211. **T:** 20 2 2737 4202
E: contact@hawaltd.com
W: http://www.ontveg.com
Editorial Profile: ONTV is a free-to-air television station broadcasting news, talk shows, serials and sitcoms 24-hrs a day. Formerly called OTV, the television station launched in 2007.

Al Tahrir TV

Owner: Al Tahrir Satellite Channel
Editorial: Building 7, Misk Studio Complex, Cairo. **T:** 20 122 564 5990
E: info@altahrirtv.com
W: http://www.altahrirtv.com
Editorial Profile: Al Tahrir TV is a television station broadcasting political, social and cultural programmes, as well as drama series. It launched in 2011 and broadcasts free-to-air on satellite.

TELEVISION NETWORKS

CNBC Arabia - Cairo Office

Owner: Middle East Business News
Editorial: 4 Galaa Street, Dohat Maspeero Building, Cairo. **T:** 20 2 2574 8100
E: abdulrahman.albasiouny@cnbcarabia.com
W: http://www.cnbcarabia.com
Editorial Profile: CNBC Arabia is a television station broadcasting regional and international business and financial news 24-hours a day. The Cairo bureau covers business news from Egypt for the Dubai-based channel.

EL SALVADOR Tel: 503

Standard Time: GMT -6
Continent: The Americas
Capital City: San Salvador

NEWSPAPERS & PUBLICATIONS

NEWSPAPERS

El Diario de Hoy

Owner: El Diario de Hoy
Editorial: 11 Calle Oriente y Avenida, Cuscatancingo No. 271, San Salvador.
T: 503 22712271 **E:** redaccion@elsalvador.com
W: http://www.elsalvador.com
Freq: Daily; **Circ:** 105000 Not Audited
Editor in Chief: Ricardo Chacón
Editorial Profile: Newspaper covering national and international news, politics, economics, finance, business, culture and sport.
Language (s): Spanish
DAILY NEWSPAPER

La Prensa Gráfica

Owner: La Prensa Grafica
Editorial: Final Bulevar Santa Elena, frente a la embajada USA, Antiguo Cuscatlán (la Libertad). **T:** 503 22412000
W: http://www.laprensa.com.sv
Freq: Daily; **Circ:** 109177 Not Audited
Editor: Edguar Gutierrez; **Editor in Chief:** Luis Lainez; **Editor in Chief:** Claudia Ramirez
Editorial Profile: Newspaper covering national and international news, politics, economics, finance, business, culture and sport.
Language (s): Spanish
DAILY NEWSPAPER

EQUATORIAL GUINEA Tel: 240

Standard Time: GMT +1
Continent: Africa
Capital City: Malabo (formerly Santa Isabel)

NEWSPAPERS & PUBLICATIONS

NEWSPAPERS

La Gaceta de Guinea Ecuatorial

Owner: La Gaceta de Guinea Ecuatorial
Editorial: Calle Libertad, Malabo.
T: 240 278 649 **E:** gacetadeguinea@yahoo.es
W: http://www.lagacetadeguinea.com
Freq: Monthly; **Circ:** 3000 Pub Statement
Editor: Mr./Ms. Editor; **Redactor Chefe:** Roberto Prieto; **Delegado:** Siméon Sopale
Editorial Profile: Publication focussing on news, current affairs, politics, economics, development and social issues.
Language (s): Spanish
NEWSPAPER

ESTONIA Tel: 372

Standard Time: GMT +2
Continent: Europe
Capital City: Tallinn

NEWSPAPERS & PUBLICATIONS

NEWSPAPERS

Äripäev

Owner: Äripäeva Kirjastuse AS
Editorial: Pärnu mnt. 105, Tallinn 19094.
T: 372 6 6670111 **E:** aripaev@aripaev.ee
W: http://www.ap3.ee
Freq: Daily; **Circ:** 10500 Pub Statement
Editor: Romet Kreek; **News Editor:** Kristi Malmberg; **Editor In Chief:** Meelis Mandel
Language (s): Estonian
DAILY NEWSPAPER

Delovõje Vedomosti

Owner: Äripäeva Kirjastuse AS
Editorial: Pärnu mnt. 105, Tallinn 19094.
T: 372 66 70 111 **E:** aripaev@aripaev.ee
W: http://www.vedomosti.ee **Circ:** 5900 Pub Statement
Editor: Oksana Kabrits
Language (s): Russian
DAILY NEWSPAPER

Den za dnjom

Owner: Zeromark OÜ
Editorial: Pärnu mnt. 130, 3, Tallinn 11313.
T: 372 6 78 82 88 **E:** toimetus@dzd.ee
W: http://www.dzd.ee **Circ:** 14600 Pub Statement
Editor-in-Chief: Jevgenia Garanzha
Language (s): Estonian
DAILY NEWSPAPER

Eesti Ekspress

Owner: Eesti Ekspressi Kirjatuse AS
Editorial: Narva mnt. 11 E, Tallinn 10151.
T: 372 66 98 030 **E:** ekspress@ekspress.ee
W: http://www.ekspress.ee **Circ:** 29600 Pub Statement
Publisher: Hans Luik; **Editor-in-Chief:** Allar Tankler
Language (s): Estonian
DAILY NEWSPAPER

Eesti Päevaleht

Owner: Eesti Päevaleht AS
Editorial: Narva mnt. 13, Tallinn 10151.
T: 372 6 80 44 00 **E:** mail@epl.ee
W: http://epl.delfi.ee
Freq: Daily; **Circ:** 22500 Pub Statement
News Editor: Holger Roonemaa
Language (s): Estonian
DAILY NEWSPAPER

Komsomolskaya Pravda Estonia

Owner: OÜ SKP Media
Editorial: Lembitu 8-2, Tallinn 10114.
T: 372 6688900 **E:** info@kompravda.eu
W: http://www.kompravda.eu
Freq: Weekly; **Circ:** 12900 Pub Statement
Editor-in-Chief: Oleg Samorodni; **Publisher:** Igor Teterin
Language (s): Russian
NEWSPAPER

MK-Estonia

Owner: Baltic Media Alliance
Editorial: Suur-Karja 21, Tallinn.
T: 372 654 1640 **E:** sekretar@1bma.ee
W: http://www.mke.ee
Freq: Weekly; **Circ:** 12500 Pub Statement
Editor: Marek Payu; **Editor:** Stanislav Ryshkevich; **Editor:** Elena Sinkina; **Editor-in-Chief:** Andrei Titov; **Editor:** Liana Turpakova
Language (s): Russian
NEWSPAPER

Õhtuleht

Owner: Eesti Meedia
Editorial: Narva mnt 13 III korrus, Tallinn 10502. **T:** 372 6 14 40 00 **E:** leht@ohtuleht.ee
W: http://www.ohtuleht.ee
Freq: Daily; **Circ:** 49900 Pub Statement
Editor In Chief: Väino Koorberg; **Editor:** Andres Põld
Language (s): Estonian
DAILY NEWSPAPER

Postimees

Owner: Eesti Meedia
Editorial: Maakri 23 A, Tallinn 10145.
T: 372 6 66 22 02 **E:** postimees@postimees.ee
W: http://www.postimees.ee
Freq: Daily; **Circ:** 49700 Pub Statement
Editor: Kadri Inselberg; **News Editor:** Britt Rosen; **Editor:** Eva Tammsaar
Language (s): Estonian
DAILY NEWSPAPER

Postimees (Russian edition)

Owner: Postimees AS
T: 372 6 66 22 02 **E:** vene@postimees.ee
W: http://rus.postimees.ee
Freq: Daily; **Circ:** 15000 Pub Statement
Language (s): Russian
DAILY NEWSPAPER

NEWS SERVICE/SYNDICATE

BNS

Editorial: Toompuiestee 35, Tallinn 15043.
T: 372 6 10 88 00 **E:** bns@bns.ee
W: http://www.bns.ee
Editor-in-Chief: Ainar Ruussaar
Language (s): Estonian
NEWS SERVICE/SYNDICATE

BROADCASTING

TELEVISION STATIONS

etv Eesti Televisioon

Editorial: Gonsiori 27, Tallinn 15029.
T: 372 6 28 41 00 **E:** ak@err.ee
W: http://etv.err.ee

ETHIOPIA Tel: 251

Standard Time: GMT +3
Continent: Africa
Capital City: Addis Ababa

NEWSPAPERS & PUBLICATIONS

NEWSPAPERS

Addis Fortune

Owner: Independent News & Media plc
Editorial: PO Box 259, Code 1110, Addis Ababa. **T:** 251 11 553 81 40
E: tamrat@addisfortune.com
W: http://www.addisfortune.com
Freq: Weekly
Editorial Profile: National weekly newspaper focussing on new and current affairs, business and economic development.
Language (s): English
NEWSPAPER

Capital Ethiopia

Editorial: P.O.Box 95, Code 1110, Addis Ababa. **T:** 251 11 618 32 53
E: info@capitalethiopia.com
W: http:/www.capitalethiopia.com
Freq: Weekly
Editor In Chief: Behailu Desalegn
Editorial Profile: Weekly national newspaper focussing on news and current affairs, business, finance, economical development, art, culture and sport.
Language (s): English
NEWSPAPER

Ethiopian Herald

Owner: Ethiopian Herald

MK-Estonia (right column)

Editorial: PO Box 30232, Addis Ababa.
T: 251 11 66 25 466
E: mesfinzeg@yahoo.com
Freq: Daily; **Circ:** 8000 Pub Statement
Editor In Chief: Dejene Tesseme
Editorial Profile: Newspaper providing national and international news including sport, economy, finance, arts and culture.
Language (s): English
DAILY NEWSPAPER

NEWS SERVICE/SYNDICATE

Ethiopian News Agency - ENA

Editorial: PO Box 530, Addis Ababa.
T: 251 11 155 00 11 **E:** ena@ethionet.et
W: http://www.ena.gov.et
Editorial Profile: National Ethiopian news agency focussing on news and current affairs.
Language (s): English
NEWS SERVICE/SYNDICATE

Ethiopian Press Agency

Editorial: PO Box 30145, Addis Ababa.
T: 251 11 156 98 83 **E:** et.press@ethionet.et
W: http://www.ethpress.gov.et
Editorial Profile: National news agency focussing on news, current affairs, politics, culture and sports. Also publisher of the daily newspapers Addis Zemen (in Amharic) and Ethiopian Herald (in English), and the weekly papers Barrissa (in Oromiffa) and Al-Alem (in Arabic).
Language (s): Amharic
NEWS SERVICE/SYNDICATE

BROADCASTING

RADIO STATIONS

Radio Fana

Editorial: Po Box 30702, Addis Ababa.
T: 251 11 551 67 77 **E:** rfana@radiofanaa.com
W: http://www.radiofana.com
Editorial Profile: National radio station focussing on news, current affairs, politics, economics, sports and entertainment, providing a radio service in Amharic, Afan Oromo, Afar and Somali on medium wave and short wave.

FALKLAND ISLANDS Tel: 500

Standard Time: GMT -4
Continent: The Americas
Capital City: Stanley

NEWSPAPERS & PUBLICATIONS

NEWSPAPERS

The Falkland Islands Gazette

Owner: The Falkland Islands Gazette
Editorial: Government Printing Office, Stanley FIQQ 1ZZ. **T:** 500 01150028460
E: bsteen@sec.gov.fk
W: http://www.falklands.gov.fk
Freq: Monthly; **Circ:** 1000 Not Audited
Editor: Barbara Steen
Editorial Profile: Magazine covering government issues. Includes government notices, appointments and legislation.
Language (s): English
NEWSPAPER

Penguin News

Owner: Penguin News
Editorial: Ross Road, Stanley FIQQ 1ZZ.
T: 500 0050022684
E: editor@penguinnews.co.fk
W: http://www.penguin-news.com
Freq: Fri; **Circ:** 1500 Not Audited
Editorial Profile: Penguin News is a weekly newspaper covering national and international news, business, entertainment, culture and sports.
Language (s): English
NEWSPAPER

FIJI Tel: 679

Standard Time: GMT +12
Continent: Oceania
Capital City: Suva

NEWSPAPERS & PUBLICATIONS

NEWSPAPERS

Fiji Daily Post
Owner: Fiji Daily Post Company Ltd
Editorial: PO Box 2071, Government
Buildings, Fiji Islands. **T:** 679 327 5176
E: iliesatora@gmail.com
W: http://fijidailypost.com
Freq: Daily; **Circ:** 4000 Pub Statement
Editor-in-Chief: Robert Wolfgramm
Editorial Profile: Provides local, business and
sports news.
Language (s): English
DAILY NEWSPAPER

Fiji Sun
Owner: Sun (Fiji) News Ltd
Editorial: 12 Amra Street, Walu Bay, Fiji
Islands. **T:** 679 330 7555
E: leonec@sun.com.fj **W:** http://sun.com.fj
Freq: Daily
Editor: Leone Cabenatabua; **Customer Care
Center Editor:** Wise Nasokia
Editorial Profile: Offers local business
insights, entertainment, business and sports.
Language (s): English
DAILY NEWSPAPER

Fiji Times
Owner: Fiji Times Limited
Editorial: PO Box 1167, Suva, Fiji Islands.
T: 679 3304209/3309044
E: alave@fijitimes.com.fj
W: http://fijitimes.com
Freq: Daily
Publisher: Evan Hannah; **Editor:** Samisoni
Kakaivalu
Editorial Profile: Provides information about
business, news, weather, and sports.
Language (s): English
DAILY NEWSPAPER

Wansolwara Online
Owner: Journalism Division, University of the
South Pacific
Editorial: Journalism Division, University of
the South Pacific, Suva, Fiji Islands.
T: 679 323 2680 **E:** wansolwara@usp.ac.fj
W: http://usp.ac.fj/journ
Freq: Quarterly; **Circ:** 2000 Not Audited
Editorial Profile: South Pacific regional
journalism education site with news,
newspaper and media freedom links and
resources.
Language (s): English
NEWSPAPER

NEWS SERVICE/SYNDICATE

PacNews
Owner: Pacific Islands Broadcasting
Association
Editorial: Private Mail Bag, Suva, Fiji Islands.
T: 679 3303 623 **E:** pacnews@connect.com.fj
W: http://pinanius.com
Freq: Daily
Editor: Makereta Komai
Editorial Profile: Provides full daily coverage
of routine, official, for-the-record news from
across the region.
Language (s): English
NEWS SERVICE/SYNDICATE

BROADCASTING

RADIO NETWORKS

Fiji Broadcasting Corporation Ltd
Owner: Fiji Broadcasting Corporation Ltd
Editorial: PO Box 334, Suva, Fiji Islands.
T: 679 331 4333 **E:** makauola@fbcl.com.fj
W: http://radiofiji.com.fj
Editorial Profile: The Fiji Broadcasting
Corporation Limited is Fiji's national radio
broadcasting service.

TELEVISION STATIONS

Fiji TV
Owner: Fiji Television Ltd

Editorial: PO Box 2442, Govt Buildings, Fiji
Islands. **T:** 679 3305 100 **E:** info@fijitv.com.fj
W: http://fijitv.com.fj
Editorial Profile: Fiji Television is Fiji's premier
television service provider, providing television
services to the Fiji Islands, Papua New Guinea
and other Pacific island countries.

FINLAND Tel: 358

Standard Time: GMT +2
Continent: Europe
Capital City: Helsinki

NEWSPAPERS & PUBLICATIONS

NEWSPAPERS

Aamulehti
Owner: Kustannus Oy Aamulehti
Editorial: Itäinenkatu 11, Tampere 33210.
T: 358 10 66 51 11 **E:** al.kotimaa@aamulehti.fi
W: http://www.aamulehti.fi
Freq: Daily; **Circ:** 121135
Editor in Chief: Jouko Jokinen; **Layout
Designer:** Hannu Kivimäki; **Editor in Chief:**
Jorma Pokkinen
Language (s): Finnish; Full Page Colour:
22764.00
Currency: Euro
DAILY NEWSPAPER

Aamulehti Orivesi
Owner: Kustannus Oy Aamulehti
Editorial: Keskustie 41 B 14, Orivesi 35300.
T: 358 10 66 53 250
E: paula.latva@aamulehti.fi
W: http://www.aamulehti.fi
Editorial Profile: Bureau
Language (s): Finnish
DAILY NEWSPAPER

Aamulehti Parkano
Owner: Kustannus Oy Aamulehti
Editorial: PL 47/ Viinikanrinne 1 A 5, Parkano
39701. **T:** 358 10 66 53 248
E: aulis.alatalo@aamulehti.fi
W: http://www.aamulehti.fi
Editorial Profile: Bureau
Language (s): Finnish
DAILY NEWSPAPER

Aamulehti Valkeakoski
Owner: Kustannus Oy Aamulehti
Editorial: Valtakatu 12, Valkeakoski 37600.
T: 358 10 66 55 745
E: juha.karilainen@aamulehti.fi
W: http://www.aamulehti.fi
Editorial Profile: Bureau
Language (s): Finnish
DAILY NEWSPAPER

Aamulehti Vammala
Owner: Kustannus Oy Aamulehti
Editorial: Puistokatu 28, Vammala 38200.
T: 358 3 51 12 382
E: riitta-liisa.pirttikoski@aamulehti.fi
W: http://www.aamulehti.fi
Editorial Profile: Bureau
Language (s): Finnish
DAILY NEWSPAPER

Aamuposti
Owner: Aamuposti-Mediat Oy
Editorial: PL 14/ Kauppakatu 12, Riihimaki
11101. **T:** 358 20 77 03 462
E: toimitus.aamuposti@lehtiyhtyma.fi
W: http://www.aamuposti.fi
Freq: Daily; **Circ:** 21502
Editor in Chief: Joonas Romppanen
Language (s): Finnish; Full Page Colour:
7828.00
Currency: Euro
NEWSPAPER

Aamuposti Hyvinkää
Owner: Suomen Lehtiyhtymä
Editorial: PL 93/ Kauppalankatu 7-11,
Hyvinkää 5801. **T:** 358 20 77 03 461
E: toimitus.aamuposti@lehtiyhtyma.fi
W: http://www.aamuposti.fi
Freq: Daily; **Circ:** 22212
Editor in Chief: Joonas Romppanen
Language (s): Finnish; Full Page Colour:
7622.00
Currency: Euro
NEWSPAPER

Åbo Underrättelser
Owner: Förlags AB Sydvästkusten
Editorial: PB 211/ Auragatan 1 B, 3 vån, Åbo
20101. **T:** 358 2 27 49 900 **E:** nyheter@fabsy.fi
W: http://www.abounderrattelser.fi **Circ:** 7293

Editor in Chief: Torbjörn Kevin
Language (s): Swedish; Full Page Colour:
2750.00
Currency: Euro
NEWSPAPER

Ähtärinjärven Uutisnuotta
Owner: Suomenselän Sanomat Oy
Editorial: Ostolantie 6, Ähtäri 63700.
T: 358 6 53 31 362
E: uutisnuotta.toimitus@sss.inet.fi
W: http://www.ahtarinjarvenuutisnuotta.net
Freq: Weekly; **Circ:** 3998 Pub Statement
Editor-in-Chief: Tuula Jokiaho; **News:** Kauko
Vainionpää
Language (s): Finnish; Full Page Colour:
2509.00
Currency: Euro
NEWSPAPER

Akaan Seutu
Owner: Akaan Seutu Lehti Oy
Editorial: PL 60 /Alventie 4, Toijala 37801.
T: 358 3 54 09 600 **E:** toimitus@akaanseutu.fi
W: http://www.akaanseutu.fi
Freq: 2 Times/Week; **Circ:** 5927
Editor in Chief: Juha Kosonen
Language (s): Finnish; Full Page Colour:
3049.00
Currency: Euro
NEWSPAPER

Ålands Sjöfart
Owner: Ålands Tidnings-Tryckeri Ab
Editorial: PB 50/ Strandgatan 16, Åland
22101. **T:** 358 18 26 026
E: sjofart@alandstidningen.ax
W: http://www.sjofart.ax/sv/nyheter
Freq: Quarterly; **Circ:** 10000 Pub Statement
Editor: Malin Henriksson
Language (s): Swedish
NEWSPAPER

Ålandstidningen
Owner: Ålands Tidnings Tryckeri AB
Editorial: PB 50/ Strandgatan 16, Mariehamn
22101. **T:** 358 18 26 026
E: 15000@alandstidningen.ax
W: http://www.alandstidningen.ax/ **Circ:** 8829
News: Niklas Lampi
Language (s): Swedish; Full Page Colour:
6329.00
Currency: Euro
NEWSPAPER

Alasatakunta
Owner: Pyhäjärviseudun Paikallislehti Oy
Editorial: PL 19/ Eurantie 6, Eura 27511.
T: 358 2 83 87 92 00
E: toimitus@alasatakunta.fi
W: http://www.alasatakunta.fi
Freq: 2 Times/Week; **Circ:** 10085
Editor in Chief: Erkki Lehtilä
Language (s): Finnish; Full Page Colour:
2628.00
Currency: Euro
NEWSPAPER

Alavieska
Owner: Alavieskan Viri ry
Editorial: PL 20 / Pääskyntie 1, Alavieska
85201. **T:** 358 8 43 01 59
E: alavieskalehti@kotinet.com
W: http://alavieskanviri.sporttisaitti.com/
alavieska-lehti
Freq: Weekly; **Circ:** 1683
Language (s): Finnish
NEWSPAPER

Alma Median Helsingin toimitus
Owner: Alma Media
Editorial: PL 1364/Alvar Aallon katu 3 C, 6.
krs, Helsinki 101. **T:** 358 10 66 56 145
E: kirsi.holtta@almamedia.fi
W: http://www.almamedia.fi/footer/yhteydet/
yhteystiedot-yksikoittain/
Language (s): Finnish
DAILY NEWSPAPER

Aluelehti Saimaa
Owner: Saimaa Oy
Editorial: Mertajärventie 4, Savonlinna 57220.
T: 358 50 54 66 940
E: pasi.pekkonen@saimaalehti.fi
W: http://www.aluelehtisaimaa.fi
Freq: Weekly; **Circ:** 25000 Pub Statement
Editor in Chief: Pasi Pekkonen
Language (s): Finnish; Full Page Colour:
840.00
Currency: Euro
NEWSPAPER

Aluesanomat
Owner: Koivutähti Oy
Editorial: Alinenkatu 12, Uusikaupunki 23500.
T: 358 2 84 13 500
E: toimitus@aluesanomat.fi

W: http://www.aluesanomat.fi
Freq: Weekly; **Circ:** 19000 Pub Statement
Language (s): Finnish; Full Page Colour:
3694.00
Currency: Euro
NEWSPAPER

Alueviesti
Owner: Kustannusliike Aluelehdet Oy
Editorial: PL 101/Hopunkatu 1, Sastamala
38200. **T:** 358 10 22 90 400
E: toimitus@alueviesti.fi
W: http://www.alueviesti.fi
Freq: Weekly; **Circ:** 32000 Pub Statement
Editor in Chief: Maija Latva
Language (s): Finnish
NEWSPAPER

Ankkuri
Owner: Poiju Julkaisut Oy
Editorial: PL 238/ Kymenlaaksonkatu 4, Kotka
48101. **T:** 358 5 21 04 400
E: toimitus@ankkurilehti.fi
W: http://www.kaupunkilehtiankkuri.fi
Freq: 2 Times/Week; **Circ:** 46200 Pub
Statement
Editor in Chief: Petri Piipari
Language (s): Finnish; Full Page Colour:
2997.00
Currency: Euro
NEWSPAPER

**Annonsbladet-Kemiönseudun
Ilmoituslehti**
Owner: Förlags Ab Lindan Kustannus Oy
Editorial: PL 18/ Toimittajanpolku, Kemiö
25701. **T:** 358 2 42 17 25 **E:** abl@abl-kimito.fi
W: http://www.annonsbladet-kimito.fi
Freq: Weekly; **Circ:** 5238 Pub Statement
Editor in Chief: Michael Nurmi
Language (s): Finnish
NEWSPAPER

Auranmaan Viikkolehti
Owner: Priimus Media Oy Auranmaan
Viikkolehti
Editorial: PL 15 / Kehityksentie 3, Kyrö 21801.
T: 358 2 48 64 950 **E:** toimitus@avl.fi
W: http://www.auranmaanviikkolehti.fi
Freq: 2 Times/Week; **Circ:** 8730
Editor in Chief: Asko Virtanen
Language (s): Finnish; Full Page Colour:
3247.00
Currency: Euro
NEWSPAPER

Borgåbladet
Owner: KSF Media
Editorial: PB 200 / Mannerheimgatan 9-11,
Borgå 6101. **T:** 358 20 75 69 622
E: redaktion@bbl.fi
W: http://www.ostnyland.fi/ **Circ:** 7523
Leader Editor: Jan-Erik Andelin; **Editor in
Chief:** Micaela Röman
Language (s): Swedish; Full Page Colour:
4061.00
Currency: Euro
NEWSPAPER

ByaNytt
Owner: Kustmedia Ab Oy
Editorial: Barkamovägen 3, Solf 65450.
T: 358 6 34 41 800 **E:** info@kustmedia.fi
W: http://www.kustmedia.fi
Freq: Monthly; **Circ:** 3400 Pub Statement
Editor-in-Chief: Lisbeth Bäck
Language (s): Swedish
NEWSPAPER

City & Archipelago News
Owner: Förlags Ab Lindan Kustannus Oy
Editorial: PL 18/ Toimittajanpolku, Kemiö
25701. **T:** 358 2 42 17 25 **E:** press@canews.fi
W: http://www.canews.fi
Freq: Quarterly; **Circ:** 40000 Pub Statement
Editor in Chief: Michael Nurmi
Language (s): Finnish; Full Page Colour:
1940.00
Currency: Euro
NEWSPAPER

Dagens Tidning
Owner: Wester Media Group Oy Ab
Editorial: Kanalesplanaden 21, Jakobstad
68600. **T:** 358 6 72 10 245
E: dt@dagenstidning.fi
W: http://www.dagenstidning.fi
Freq: Weekly; **Circ:** 20184 Pub Statement
News: Nicklas Storbjörk
Language (s): Finnish

Demokraatti
Owner: Kustannus Oy Demari
Editorial: Haapaniemenkatu 7-9 B, Helsinki
530. **T:** 358 9 701 041 **E:** toimitus@demari.fi
W: http://www.demari.fi

Freq: Daily; **Circ:** 14347
Editor in Chief: Antti Vuorenrinne
Language (s): Finnish; Full Page Colour: 5694.00
Currency: Euro
DAILY NEWSPAPER

Demokraatti Tampereen aluetoimitus
Owner: Kustannus Oy Demari
Editorial: Hämeenpuisto 28, Tampere 33200.
T: 358 3 21 29 330
E: anna-liisa.blomberg@demari.fi
W: http://www.demari.fi
Editorial Profile: Bureau
Language (s): Finnish
DAILY NEWSPAPER

Demokraatti Turun aluetoimitus
Owner: Kustannus Oy Demari
Editorial: Linnankatu 13 a B 31, Turku 20100.
T: 358 2 27 70 474
E: turku.toimitus@demari.fi
W: http://www.demari.fi
Editorial Profile: Bureau
Language (s): Finnish
DAILY NEWSPAPER

Demokraatti Vaasan aluetoimitus
Owner: Kustannus Oy Demari
Editorial: Pitkäkatu 50 L 1, Vaasa 65100.
T: 358 6 31 74 104
E: sirpa.taskinen@demari.fi
W: http://www.demari.fi
Editorial Profile: Bureau
Language (s): Finnish
DAILY NEWSPAPER

Elimäen Sanomat
Owner: Elimäen Sanomat Oy
Editorial: PL 10/Vanhamaantie 7, Elimäki 47201. **T:** 358 5 74 00 500
E: toimitus@elimaensanomat.fi
W: http://www.elimaensanomat.fi
Freq: Weekly; **Circ:** 2777
Editor in Chief: Raija Anttila
Language (s): Finnish; Full Page Colour: 2090.00
Currency: Euro
NEWSPAPER

Epari
Owner: I-Mediat Oy
Editorial: PL 60/Koulukatu 10, Seinäjoki 60101. **T:** 358 6 24 77 865
E: toimitus@epari.fi **W:** http://www.epari.fi
Freq: Weekly; **Circ:** 46800
Editor in chief: Laura Syväoja
Language (s): Finnish
NEWSPAPER

Espoo Esbo -lehti
T: 358 9 42 42 73 30 **E:** uutiset@espoo-lehti.fi
W: http://www.espoo.fi
Freq: Quarterly; **Circ:** 105000 Pub Statement
Language (s): Finnish
NEWSPAPER

Etelä-Hämeen Lehti
Owner: Victus Oy
Editorial: PL 6/ Keskustie 1, Oitti 12101.
T: 358 50 36 01 170 **E:** toimitus@ehl.fi
W: http://www.ehl.fi
Freq: Weekly; **Circ:** 1531 Pub Statement
Editor in Chief: Juha Reinikainen
Language (s): Finnish; Full Page Colour: 2376.00
Currency: Euro
NEWSPAPER

Etelä-Saimaa
Owner: Sanoma Lehtimedia Oy
Editorial: PL 3/Lauritsalantie 1, Lappeenranta 53501. **T:** 358 5 53 88 13
E: uutinen@esaimaa.fi
W: http://www.esaimaa.fi **Circ:** 25284
Language (s): Finnish; Full Page Colour: 4811.00
Currency: Euro
DAILY NEWSPAPER

Etelä-Saimaa Imatra
Owner: Sanoma Lehtimedia Oy
Editorial: Esterinkatu 10, Imatra 55100.
T: 358 5 538 813
E: toimitus.imatra@lehtimedia.fi
W: http://www.esaimaa.fi
News Editor: Hannu Ojala
Editorial Profile: Bureau
Language (s): Finnish
DAILY NEWSPAPER

Etelä-Suomen Sanomat
Owner: Esan Kirjapaino Oy
Editorial: PL 80/ Ilmarisentie 7, Lahti 15101.
T: 358 3 75 751 **E:** toimitus@ess.fi
W: http://www.ess.fi **Circ:** 53463

Editor in Chief: Heikki Hakala; **Editor:** Esa Rauhanlaakso
Language (s): Finnish; Full Page Colour: 14076.00
Currency: Euro
DAILY NEWSPAPER

Etelä-Uusimaa
Owner: Länsi-Uusimaa Oy
Editorial: PL 16/ Keskuskatu 76, Karjaa 10301. **T:** 358 19 27 88 66
E: toimitus@etela.com
W: http://www.etela.com
Freq: 2 Times/Week; **Circ:** 23000 Pub Statement
Editor in Chief: Ari Hätönen
Language (s): Finnish; Full Page Colour: 2790.00
Currency: Euro
NEWSPAPER

Forssan Lehti
Owner: Forssan Kirjapaino Oy
Editorial: PL 38/ Esko Aaltosen katu 2, Forssa 30101. **T:** 358 3 41 551
E: toimitus@forssanlehti.fi
W: http://www.forssanlehti.fi
Freq: Daily; **Circ:** 13127
Editor in Chief: Kari Grahn
Language (s): Finnish; Full Page Colour: 7654.00
Currency: Euro
NEWSPAPER

Forum 24
Owner: Kaleva Kustannus Oy
Editorial: Lekatie 6, Oulu 90510.
T: 358 20 75 45 700 **E:** toimitus@forum24.fi
W: http://www.forum24.fi
Freq: 2 Times/Week; **Circ:** 93000 Pub Statement
Language (s): Finnish; Full Page Colour: 3148.80
Currency: Euro
NEWSPAPER

Haagalainen
Owner: Haagalaisen Tuki - Stöd ry.
Editorial: PL 4, Helsinki 321.
T: 358 400 15 71 58
E: toimitus@haagalainen.com
W: http://www.haagalainen.com
Freq: Bi-Monthly; **Circ:** 20000 Pub Statement
Editor in Chief: Tuula Salo
Language (s): Finnish; Full Page Colour: 1861.50
Currency: Euro
NEWSPAPER

Haapavesi-lehti
Owner: Jokilaaksojen Kustannus Oy
Editorial: Tähtelänkuja 2, Haapavesi 86600.
T: 358 20 75 04 640
E: toimitus@haapavesi-lehti.fi
W: http://www.haapavesi-lehti.fi
Freq: Weekly; **Circ:** 3230
Editor in Chief: Katariina Anttila
Language (s): Finnish
NEWSPAPER

Hämeen Sanomat
Owner: Hämeen Sanomat Oy
Editorial: PL 530/ Vanajantie 7, Hämeenlinna 13111. **T:** 358 3 61 511
E: toimitus@hameensanomat.fi
W: http://www.hameensanomat.fi
Freq: Daily; **Circ:** 27345
Editor in Chief: Pauli Uusi-Kilponen
Language (s): Finnish; Full Page Colour: 11424.00
Currency: Euro
NEWSPAPER

Hämeenkyrön Sanomat
Owner: Hämeenkyrön Sanomat Oy
Editorial: PL 13 / Nuijamiestentie 1, Hämeenkyrö 39101. **T:** 358 3 31 43 31 00
E: toimitus@hameenkyronsanomat.fi
W: http://www.hameenkyronsanomat.fi
Freq: 2 Times/Week; **Circ:** 5463
Editor in Chief: Katri Linnikko; **Editor:** Annina Ruokoski
Language (s): Finnish; Full Page Colour: 3951.00
Currency: Euro
NEWSPAPER

Hämeenlinnan Kaupunkiuutiset
Owner: Hämeen Sanomat Oy
Editorial: PL 207/ Vanajantie 7, Hämeenlinna 13100. **T:** 358 3 61 511
E: ku.toimitus@hameensanomat.fi
W: http://www.hameensanomat.fi/hameenlinnan-kaupunkiuutiset
Freq: 2 Times/Week; **Circ:** 39570 Pub Statement
Language (s): Finnish

NEWSPAPER

HangöTidningen - HangonLehti
Owner: Förlags Ab Lindan Kustannus Oy
Editorial: PL 2 / Bulevardi 20, Hanko 10901.
T: 358 19 21 24 200
E: newsdesk@hangotidningen.fi
W: http://www.hangotidningen.fi
Freq: Weekly; **Circ:** 2500 Pub Statement
Language (s): Finnish; Full Page Colour: 2250.00
Currency: Euro
NEWSPAPER

Hankasalmen Sanomat
Owner: Maakunnan Sanomat Oy
Editorial: PL 12/Keskustie 32, Hankasalmi 41521. **T:** 358 14 84 11 45
E: toimitus@hankasalmensanomat.fi
W: http://www.hankasalmensanomat.fi
Freq: Weekly; **Circ:** 3324
Editor-in-Chief: Arja Korpela
Language (s): Finnish
NEWSPAPER

Heinäveden Lehti
Owner: Maakunnan Sanomat Oy
Editorial: PL 23 / Kermantie 24 A, Heinävesi 79701. **T:** 358 17 56 25 71
E: uutiset@heinavedenlehti.fi
W: http://www.heinavedenlehti.fi
Freq: Weekly; **Circ:** 3485
Editor-in-Chief: Eija Kosunen
Language (s): Finnish
NEWSPAPER

Helsingin Sanomat
Owner: Sanoma News Oy
Editorial: PL 85/Töölönlahdenkatu 2, Helsinki 89. **T:** 358 9 12 21 **E:** hs.talous@hs.fi
W: http://www.hs.fi
Freq: Daily; **Circ:** 365994
Editor: Pekka Mykkänen; **Editor:** Päivi Niemi;
Editor in Chief: Riikka Venäläinen
Language (s): Finnish; Full Page Colour: 39648.00
Currency: Euro
DAILY NEWSPAPER

Helsingin Sanomat Kuopio
Owner: Sanoma News Oy
Editorial: Haapaniemenkatu 32 b5, Kuopio 70110. **T:** 358 17 21 13 333
E: hs.kuopio@hs.fi **W:** http://www.hs.fi
Editorial Profile: Bureau
Language (s): Finnish
DAILY NEWSPAPER

Helsingin Sanomat Oulu
Owner: Sanoma News Oy
Editorial: Kauppurienkatu 23, Oulu 90100.
T: 358 8 31 20 800 **E:** hs.oulu@hs.fi
W: http://www.hs.fi
Editorial Profile: Bureau
Language (s): Finnish
DAILY NEWSPAPER

Helsingin Sanomat Tampere
Owner: Sanoma News Oy
Editorial: Tuomiokirkonkatu 17 B 31, Tampere 33100. **T:** 358 3 22 31 257
E: hs.tampere@hs.fi
W: http://www.hs.fi/kotimaa/aihe/tampere/
Editorial Profile: Bureau
Language (s): Finnish
DAILY NEWSPAPER

Helsingin Sanomat Turku
Owner: Sanoma News Oy
Editorial: Yliopistonkatu 33, Turku 20100.
T: 358 2 25 16 655 **E:** hs.turku@hs.fi
W: http://www.hs.fi
Editorial Profile: Bureau
Language (s): Finnish
DAILY NEWSPAPER

Helsingin Uutiset
Owner: SLY-Kaupunkilehdet Oy
Editorial: PL 350/ Rälssitie 7a, Vantaa 1511.
T: 358 20 61 00 110
E: helsingin.uutiset@lehtiyhtyma.fi
W: http://www.helsinginuutiset.fi
Freq: 2 Times/Week; **Circ:** 215000 Pub Statement
Editor in Chief: Risto Hietanen
Language (s): Finnish; Full Page Colour: 5631.00
Currency: Euro
NEWSPAPER

Helsinki Times
Owner: Helsinki Times Oy
Editorial: Vilhonvuorenkatu 11 B, Helsinki 500.
T: 358 9 68 96 74 26 **E:** info@helsinkitimes.fi
W: http://www.helsinkitimes.fi

Freq: Weekly; **Circ:** 15000 Pub Statement
Editor in Chief: Alexis Kouros
Language (s): English; Full Page Colour: 1980.00
Currency: Euro
NEWSPAPER

Helsinki-info
Owner: Helsingin kaupunki
Editorial: Helsingin Kaupungintalo, Kaupunginkanslia, Viestintä, Helsinki 170.
T: 358 9 310 1641
E: helsinki-info.palaute@hel.fi
W: http://www.hel.fi/helsinki-info
Freq: Bi-Monthly; **Circ:** 366664 Pub Statement
Editor in Chief: Rita Ekelund
Language (s): Finnish
NEWSPAPER

Hervannan Sanomat
Owner: Kustannus Oy Otsikko
Editorial: PL 99/ Insinöörinkatu 30, 2 krs, Tampere 33721. **T:** 358 10 66 51 15
E: hs@hervannansanomat.fi
W: http://www.hervannansanomat.fi
Freq: Weekly; **Circ:** 22000 Pub Statement
Editor in Chief: Jari Mylläri
Language (s): Finnish; Full Page Colour: 3438.00
Currency: Euro
NEWSPAPER

Hufvudstadsbladet
Owner: KSF Media
Editorial: Mannerheimvägen 18, Helsingfors 100. **T:** 358 9 12 531 **E:** nyheter@hbl.fi
W: http://www.hbl.fi
Freq: Daily; **Circ:** 46395
Language (s): Swedish; Full Page Colour: 5565.00
Currency: Euro
DAILY NEWSPAPER

Hyvinkään Viikkouutiset
Owner: Suomen Lehtiyhtymä
Editorial: PL 93/Kauppalankatu 7-11, 2 krs, Hyvinkää 5801. **T:** 358 20 61 00 120
E: toimitus.rile@lehtiyhtyma.fi
W: http://www.viikkouutiset.fi
Freq: Weekly; **Circ:** 23000 Pub Statement
Editor: Marko Kekki; **Editor in Chief:** Joonas Romppanen
Language (s): Finnish; Full Page Colour: 4039.00
Currency: Euro
NEWSPAPER

Iijokiseutu
Owner: Pohjois-Suomen Paikallisuutiset Oy
Editorial: PL 24 / Puistotie 2, Pudasjärvi 93100. **T:** 358 8 86 00 715
E: toimitus@iijokiseutu.fi
W: http://www.iijokiseutu.fi
Freq: 2 Times/Week; **Circ:** 4413
Editor in Chief: Martta Oinas-Panuma
Language (s): Finnish; Full Page Colour: 3986.00
Currency: Euro
NEWSPAPER

Iisalmen Kaupunkilehti
Owner: YS-Painos Oy
Editorial: Riistakatu 5, Iisalmi 74100.
T: 358 17 81 77 00 **E:** toimitus@ilehti.fi
W: http://www.ilehti.fi
Freq: Weekly; **Circ:** 26000 Pub Statement
Editor in Chief: Toni Hujanen
Language (s): Finnish; Full Page Colour: 950.00
Currency: Euro
NEWSPAPER

Iisalmen Sanomat
Owner: Savon Mediat Oy
Editorial: PL 11/Kilpivirrantie 7, Iisalmi 74101.
T: 358 500 37 19 12
E: toimitus@iisalmensanomat.fi
W: http://www.iisalmensanomat.fi
Freq: Daily; **Circ:** 12560
Editor in Chief: Jarkko Ambrusin; **Editor:** Tarja Tikkanen
Language (s): Finnish; Full Page Colour: 3460.00
Currency: Euro
NEWSPAPER

Iitinseutu
Owner: Iitinlehti Oy
Editorial: PL 37/ Kauppakatu 6, Kausala 47401. **T:** 358 5 32 60 355
E: voitto.ruohonen@iitinseutulehti.fi
W: http://www.iitinseutulehti.fi
Freq: 2 Times/Week; **Circ:** 3436
News: Voitto Ruohonen
Language (s): Finnish
NEWSPAPER

Ilmajoki-lehti
Owner: Ilmajoki-lehti
Editorial: PL 12 / Mikontie 3, Ilmajoki 60801.
T: 358 6 42 44 800
E: toimitus@ilmajoki-lehti.fi
W: http://www.ilmajoki-lehti.fi
Freq: 2 Times/Week; **Circ:** 4957
Editor in Chief: Liisa Äärynen
Language (s): Finnish; Full Page Colour: 1944.00
Currency: Euro
NEWSPAPER

Iltalehti
Owner: Alma Media Suomi Oy
Editorial: Alvar Aallon katu 3 C, Helsinki 100.
T: 358 10 66 51 00 **E:** il.toimitus@iltalehti.fi
W: http://www.iltalehti.fi
Freq: Daily; **Circ:** 102124
Editor: Juho Rissanen; **Editor:** Marko Simonen
Language (s): Finnish; Full Page Colour: 5550.00
Currency: Euro
DAILY NEWSPAPER

Iltalehti Turku
Owner: Kustannus Oy Iltalehti
Editorial: Kuuvuorenkatu 7, Turku 20540.
T: 358 10 66 52 001 **W:** http://www.iltalehti.fi
Editorial Profile: Bureau
Language (s): Finnish
DAILY NEWSPAPER

Iltalohja
Owner: Länsi-Uusimaa Oy
Editorial: PL 60/ Suurlohjankatu 10, Lohja 8101. **T:** 358 20 61 00 130
E: il.toimitus@lehtiyhtyma.fi
W: http://www.iltalohja.fi
Freq: Weekly; **Circ:** 27000 Pub Statement
Language (s): Finnish; Full Page Colour: 1976.00
Currency: Euro
NEWSPAPER

Ilta-Sanomat
Owner: Sanoma News Oy
Editorial: PL 41/ Töölönlahdenkatu 2, Sanoma 89. **T:** 358 9 12 21 **E:** uutiset@iltasanomat.fi
W: http://www.iltasanomat.fi
Freq: Daily; **Circ:** 143321
Editor in Chief: Ulla Appelsin; **News Editor:** Tomi Auremaa; **News Editor:** Simo Holopainen; **News Editor:** Pasi Jaakkonen; **News Editor:** Mika Koskinen; **News Editor:** Timo Myllyniemi; **Editor:** Kari Ylänne
Language (s): Finnish; Full Page Colour: 6200.00
Currency: Euro
DAILY NEWSPAPER

Imatralainen
Owner: Vuoksen Ääni Oy
Editorial: Lappeentie 17, Imatra 55100.
T: 358 20 61 00 113
E: toimitus.imatra@lehtiyhtyma.fi
W: http://www.imatralainen.fi
Freq: Weekly; **Circ:** 24000 Pub Statement
Editor in Chief: Karri Kannala
Language (s): Finnish
NEWSPAPER

Inarilainen
Owner: Ukko-Media Oy
Editorial: PL 145/ Ivalontie 7, Ivalo 99800.
T: 358 20 71 09 050
E: inarilainen@inarilainen.fi
W: http://www.inarilainen.fi
Freq: Weekly; **Circ:** 7500 Pub Statement
Editor in Chief: Jaakko Peltomaa
Language (s): Finnish
NEWSPAPER

Itä-Häme
Owner: Esan Paikallislehdet Oy
Editorial: PL 10/Lampikatu 8, Heinola 18101.
T: 358 3 75 75 05 **E:** iha.toimitus@itahame.fi
W: http://www.itahame.fi
Freq: Daily; **Circ:** 10427
Editor in Chief: Jari Niemi
Language (s): Finnish
NEWSPAPER

Itä-Pirkanmaa
Owner: Promillion Oy
Editorial: Ellintie 2, Kangasala 36201.
T: 358 3 35 88 621 **E:** jyrki.quu@quu.fi
W: http://www.itapirkanmaalehti.fi/
Freq: Bi-Monthly; **Circ:** 39000 Pub Statement
Editor in Chief: Jyrki Jaakkola
Language (s): Finnish
NEWSPAPER

Itä-Savo
Owner: Itä-Savo Oy
Editorial: PL 101/ Olavinkatu 60, Savonlinna 57101. **T:** 358 15 35 03 400

E: toimitus@ita-savo.fi
W: http://www.ita-savo.fi
Freq: Daily; **Circ:** 16279
Editor in Chief: Tiina Ojutkangas
Language (s): Finnish; Full Page Colour: 4778.00
Currency: Euro
NEWSPAPER

Itäväylä
Owner: Itäväylä Viestintä Oy
Editorial: Rihkamatori A, Porvoo 6100.
T: 358 19 521 7500 **E:** toimitus@itavayla.fi
W: http://www.itavayla.fi
Freq: 2 Times/Week; **Circ:** 49080 Pub Statement
Language (s): Finnish; Full Page Colour: 1250.00
Currency: Euro
NEWSPAPER

Jämsän Seutu
Owner: Suomen Paikallissanomat Oy
Editorial: Lindemaninkatu 3, Jämsä 42100.
T: 358 10 66 55 149
E: toimitus.jamsanseutu@almamedia.fi
W: http://www.jamsanseutu.fi
Freq: Daily; **Circ:** 6922
Editor in Chief: Mari Tuohiniemi
Language (s): Finnish; Full Page Colour: 3019.00
Currency: Euro
NEWSPAPER

Jämsän Seutu Vekkari
Owner: Suomen Paikallissanomat Oy
Editorial: Lindemaninkatu 3, Jämsä 42100.
T: 358 10 66 55 149 **E:** vekkari@almamedia.fi
W: http://www.almamedia.fi/yhteystiedot_alma_paikallislehtiryhma
Freq: Weekly; **Circ:** 18000 Pub Statement
Editor in Chief: Mari Tuohiniemi
Language (s): Finnish; Full Page Colour: 2975.00
Currency: Euro
NEWSPAPER

Janakkalan Sanomat
Owner: Suomen Paikallissanomat Oy
Editorial: PL 5/ Harvialantie 7 A, Turenki 14201. **T:** 358 10 66 56 050
E: toimitus.janakkalansanomat@almamedia.fi
W: http://www.janakkalansanomat.fi
Freq: Weekly; **Circ:** 4484
Editor in Chief: Merja Sillasto
Language (s): Finnish; Full Page Colour: 2842.00
Currency: Euro
NEWSPAPER

Järviseudun Sanomat
Owner: Järviseutu-seura ry
T: 358 20 79 40 510
E: toimitus@jarviseudunsanomat.fi
W: http://www.jarviseudunsanomat.fi
Freq: Weekly; **Circ:** 7889
Editor in Chief: Maritta Raudaskoski
Language (s): Finnish
NEWSPAPER

Järviseutu
Owner: Pohjanmaan Lähisanomat Oy
T: 358 6 24 77 890
E: toimitus@jarviseutu-lehti.fi
W: http://www.jarviseutu-lehti.fi
Freq: Weekly; **Circ:** 5314
Editor in Chief: Sari Heinilä
Language (s): Finnish
NEWSPAPER

Jokilaakso
Owner: Suomen Paikallissanomat Oy
Editorial: PL 36/ Kilkunkatu 12, Kokemäki 32801. **T:** 358 10 66 55 700
E: toimitus.jokilaakso@almamedia.fi
W: http://www.jokilaakso.fi
Freq: Weekly; **Circ:** 16000 Pub Statement
Editor in Chief: Timo Simula
Language (s): Finnish; Full Page Colour: 2508.00
Currency: Euro
NEWSPAPER

Joroisten Lehti
Owner: Etelä-Savon Paikallislehdet Oy
Editorial: Joroisniementie 4, Joroinen 79600.
T: 358 15 35 03 154
E: toimitus@joroistenlehti.fi
W: http://www.joroistenlehti.fi
Freq: Weekly; **Circ:** 2389
News: Sirpa Hytönen; **Editor-in-Chief:** Päivi Konttinen
Language (s): Finnish; Full Page Colour: 2719.00
Currency: Euro
NEWSPAPER

Joutsan Seutu
Owner: Joutsan Seutu Oy
Editorial: PL 15/ Jousitie 31, Joutsa 19651.
T: 358 20 18 76 100
E: konttori@joutsanseutu.fi
W: http://www.joutsanseutu.fi
Freq: Weekly; **Circ:** 5040
Editor in Chief: Markku Parkkonen
Language (s): Finnish; Full Page Colour: 2119.00
Currency: Euro
NEWSPAPER

Joutseno
Owner: Sanoma News Oy
Editorial: Keskuskatu 7, Joutseno 54100.
T: 358 5 21 00 25 00
E: toimitus@joutsenolehti.fi
W: http://www.joutsenolehti.fi
Freq: Weekly; **Circ:** 3240
Editor in Chief: Mirja Rantala
Language (s): Finnish; Full Page Colour: 2540.00
Currency: Euro
NEWSPAPER

JP Kunnallissanomat
Owner: Jalasjärvi Oy
Editorial: PL 53 / Torikuja 9, Jalasjärvi 61601.
T: 358 6 45 65 100
E: toimitus@jp-kunnallissanomat.fi
W: http://www.jp-kunnallissanomat.fi
Freq: 2 Times/Week; **Circ:** 6330
Editor in Chief: Terhi Rintala
Language (s): Finnish; Full Page Colour: 1624.00
Currency: Euro
NEWSPAPER

Jurvan Sanomat
Owner: Ilkka Oy
Editorial: Hahdonkuja 2, Jurva 66300.
T: 358 6 24 77 875
E: toimitus@jurvansanomat.fi
W: http://www.jurvansanomat.fi
Freq: Weekly; **Circ:** 2154
Editor in Chief: Jaana Ala-Lahti
Language (s): Finnish; Full Page Colour: 3964.00
Currency: Euro
NEWSPAPER

Juvan Lehti
Owner: Etelä-Savon Paikallislehdet Oy
Editorial: PL 27 / Koulutie 6 A 2, Juva 51901.
T: 358 15 35 03 172 **E:** toimitus@juvanlehti.fi
W: http://www.juvanlehti.fi
Freq: Weekly; **Circ:** 4186
News: Antero Heikkinen
Language (s): Finnish; Full Page Colour: 2686.00
Currency: Euro
NEWSPAPER

Kaakonkulma
Owner: Sanoma News Oy
T: 358 15 35 03 546
E: toimitus@kaakonkulma.fi
W: http://www.kaakonkulma.fi
Freq: Weekly; **Circ:** 4747
Editor in Chief: Jukka Kinnunen
Language (s): Finnish
NEWSPAPER

Kaarina
Owner: Kaarinan Lehti Oy
Editorial: PL 73/Pyhän Katariinantie 7, Kaarina 20781. **T:** 358 2 58 88 600
E: toimitus@kaarina-lehti.fi
W: http://www.kaarina-lehti.fi
Freq: Weekly; **Circ:** 4486
Editor in Chief: Teija Uurinmäki
Language (s): Finnish; Full Page Colour: 4618.00
Currency: Euro
NEWSPAPER

Kainuun Sanomat
Owner: Pohjois-Suomen Media Oy
Editorial: PL 150/ Kauppakatu 11, Kajaani 87101. **T:** 358 10 66 50 33
E: ks.toimitus@kainuunsanomat.fi
W: http://www.kainuunsanomat.fi
Freq: Daily; **Circ:** 16890
Editor in Chief: Markus Pirttijoki
Language (s): Finnish; Full Page Colour: 4710.00
Currency: Euro
NEWSPAPER

Kalajokilaakso
Owner: Jokilaaksojen Kustannus Oy
T: 358 20 75 04 600
E: toimitus@kalajokilaakso.fi
W: http://www.kalajokilaakso-lehti.fi **Circ:** 6989
Editor in Chief: Seppo Kangas

Language (s): Finnish; Full Page Colour: 7072.00
Currency: Euro
NEWSPAPER

Kalajokiseutu
Owner: Keski-Pohjanmaan Kirjapaino Oyj
Editorial: Kalajoentie 4, Kalajoki 85100.
T: 358 20 75 04 730 **E:** anne.mattila@kpk.fi
W: http://www.kalajokilehti.fi
Freq: Weekly; **Circ:** 2147
Editor in Chief: Hanne Haapakoski
Language (s): Finnish
NEWSPAPER

Kaleva
Owner: Kaleva Kustannus Oy
Editorial: PL 170/ Lekatie 1, Oulu 90401.
T: 358 8 53 77 111 **E:** toimitus@kaleva.fi
W: http://www.kaleva.fi **Circ:** 74787
Editor in Chief: Markku Mantila; **Debate Editor:** Anna Mikkonen; **News Producer:** Janne Nyyssönen
Language (s): Finnish; Full Page Colour: 10590.00
Currency: Euro
DAILY NEWSPAPER

Kaleva Kuusamo
Owner: Kaleva Kustannus Oy
Editorial: Kitkantie 19, Kuusamo 93600.
T: 358 44 79 49 785 **W:** http://www.kaleva.fi
Editorial Profile: Bureau
Language (s): Finnish
DAILY NEWSPAPER

Kaleva Raahe
Owner: Kaleva Kustannus Oy
Editorial: Kauppakatu 42, Raahe 92100.
T: 358 44 79 49 787
E: timo.myllykoski@kaleva.fi
W: http://www.kaleva.fi
Editorial Profile: Bureau
Language (s): Finnish
DAILY NEWSPAPER

Kaleva Vaala
Owner: Kaleva Kustannus Oy
Editorial: Asematie 2 A 8, Vaala 91700.
T: 358 400 95 60 45
E: petri.hakkarainen@kaleva.fi
W: http://www.kaleva.fi
Editorial Profile: Bureau
Language (s): Finnish
DAILY NEWSPAPER

Kaleva Ylivieska
Owner: Kaleva Kustannus Oy
Editorial: Kartanontie 1, Ylivieska 84100.
T: 358 44 79 49 790
E: liisa.lehto-peippo@kaleva.fi
W: http://www.kaleva.fi
Editorial Profile: Bureau
Language (s): Finnish
DAILY NEWSPAPER

Kallio-lehti
Owner: Karprint Oy
Editorial: Vanha Turuntie 371, Huhmari 3150.
T: 358 9 413 97 300 **E:** juha.ahola@karprint.fi
W: http://www.kalliolehti.fi
Freq: Bi-Weekly; **Circ:** 40000 Pub Statement
Editor in Chief: Juha Ahola
Language (s): Finnish
NEWSPAPER

Kälviän Seudun Sanomat
Owner: Kälviän seudun sanomat Oy
Editorial: Kälviäntie 36, Kälviä 68300.
T: 358 6 82 43 822
E: toimitus@kalviansanomat.com
W: http://www.kalviansanomat.com
Freq: Weekly; **Circ:** 1699
News: Vesa Rimpeläinen
Language (s): Finnish; Full Page Colour: 2080.00
Currency: Euro
NEWSPAPER

Kamppi-Eira
Owner: Töölöläinen Oy
T: 358 9 44 16 58
E: toimitus@paikallislehdet.com
Freq: Bi-Weekly; **Circ:** 28000 Pub Statement
Editor in Chief: Mikko Keski-Vähälä
Language (s): Finnish; Full Page Colour: 1964.00
Currency: Euro
NEWSPAPER

Kangasalan Sanomat
Owner: Kangasalan Sanomalehti Oy
Editorial: PL 40/Myllystenpohjantie 2, Kangasala 36201. **T:** 358 3 37 76 900
W: http://www.kangasalansanomat.fi

Freq: 2 Times/Week; **Circ:** 8009
News: Matti Kauhanen; **News Producer:** Tuula Ruusumaa
Language (s): Finnish; Full Page Colour: 4284.00
Currency: Euro
NEWSPAPER

Kangasniemen Kunnallislehti
Owner: Etelä-Savon Paikallislehdet Oy
Editorial: PL 115 / Otto Mannisen tie 13, Kangasniemi 51201. **T:** 358 15 35 03 160
E: toimitus@kangasniemen-kunnallislehti.fi
W: http://www.kangasniemen-kunnallislehti.fi
Freq: Weekly; **Circ:** 4362
Language (s): Finnish; Full Page Colour: 1693.00
Currency: Euro
NEWSPAPER

Kankaanpään Seutu
Owner: Suomen Paikallissanomat Oy
Editorial: PL 16 / Linnankatu 1, Kankaanpää 38701. **T:** 358 10 66 55 763
E: toimitus.kankaanpaanseutu@almamedia.fi
W: http://www.kankaanpaanseutu.fi
Freq: 2 Times/Week; **Circ:** 9616
Editor in Chief: Seppo Kummala
Language (s): Finnish
NEWSPAPER

Kansan Tahto
Owner: Kustannus Oy Kansan Tahto
T: 358 8 53 71 724 **E:** toimitus@kansantahto.fi
W: http://www.kansantahto.fi
Freq: Weekly; **Circ:** 6965
Editor in Chief: Tuomas Talvila
Language (s): Finnish; Full Page Colour: 5325.00
Currency: Euro
NEWSPAPER

Käpylä-lehti
Owner: Käpylä-Seura ry
Editorial: Klaneettitie 11, Helsinki 420.
T: 358 9 53 08 19 90 **E:** kapylalehti@eepinen.fi
W: http://www.kaupunginosat.net/kapyla
Freq: Monthly; **Circ:** 18000 Pub Statement
Editor in Chief: Alice Karlsson
Language (s): Finnish; Full Page Mono: 2300.00
Currency: Euro
NEWSPAPER

Karjala
Owner: Karjalan Kirjapaino Oy
T: 358 5 54 14 600 **E:** toimitus@karjala-lehti.fi
W: http://www.karjala-lehti.fi
Freq: Weekly; **Circ:** 10246 Pub Statement
Editor in Chief: Päivi Parjanen
Language (s): Finnish
NEWSPAPER

Karjalainen
Owner: Sanomalehti Karjalainen Oy
Editorial: PL 99/ Kosti Aaltosen tie 9, Joensuu 80141. **T:** 358 10 23 08 080
E: toimitus@karjalainen.fi
W: http://www.karjalainen.fi
Editor in Chief: Pasi Koivumaa
Language (s): Finnish
DAILY NEWSPAPER

Karjalainen Kesälahti
Owner: Sanomalehti Karjalainen Oy
Editorial: Lehmisavuntie 1, Kesälahti 59800.
T: 358 10 23 08 133
E: sirpa.suomalainen@karjalainen.fi
W: http://www.karjalainen.fi
Editorial Profile: Bureau
Language (s): Finnish
DAILY NEWSPAPER

Karjalainen Kitee
Owner: Sanomalehti Karjalainen Oy
Editorial: Pokentie 2 as 4, Kitee 82500.
T: 358 10 23 08 132
W: http://www.karjalainen.fi
Editorial Profile: Bureau
Language (s): Finnish
DAILY NEWSPAPER

Karjalainen Lieksa
Owner: Sanomalehti Karjalainen Oy
Editorial: Siltakatu 1, Lieksa 81700.
T: 358 10 23 08 134
E: jaakko.pikkarainen@karjalainen.fi
W: http://www.karjalainen.fi
Editorial Profile: Bureau
Language (s): Finnish
DAILY NEWSPAPER

Karjalainen Nurmes
Owner: Sanomalehti Karjalainen Oy
Editorial: Pappilansuora 15, Nurmes 75500.
T: 358 10 230 8130 **E:** toimitus@karjalainen.fi

W: http://www.karjalainen.fi
Editorial Profile: Bureau
Language (s): Finnish
DAILY NEWSPAPER

Karjalan Heili
Owner: Karelia Viestintä Oy
Editorial: Torikatu 23 E, Joensuu 80100.
T: 358 10 23 08 500 **E:** toimitus@heili.fi
W: http://www.karjalanheili.fi
Freq: 2 Times/Week; **Circ:** 49478 Pub Statement
Editor in Chief: Arttu Käyhkö
Language (s): Finnish; Full Page Colour: 2320.00
Currency: Euro
NEWSPAPER

Karkkilalainen
Owner: SLY-Paikallislehdet Oy
Editorial: Turuntie 2-4, Karkkila 3600.
T: 358 20 77 03 552
E: toimitus@karkkilalainen.fi
W: http://www.karkkilalainen.fi
Freq: Weekly; **Circ:** 11500 Pub Statement
Editor in Chief: Vesa Valtonen
Language (s): Finnish
NEWSPAPER

Karkkilan Tienoo
Owner: Karprint Oy
Editorial: PL 16/ Huhdintie 10-12, Karkkila 3600. **T:** 358 9 22 56 656
E: kt.toimitus@karprint.fi
W: http://www.karprint.fi/karkkilantienoo
Freq: 2 Times/Week; **Circ:** 15600 Pub Statement
Editor in Chief: Mari Ahola-Aalto
Language (s): Finnish
NEWSPAPER

Kauhajoki-lehti
Owner: Kauhajoen Kunnallislehti Oy
Editorial: PL 5 / Puistotie 25, Kauhajoki 61801. **T:** 358 6 23 57 100
E: toimitus@kauhajoki-lehti.fi
W: http://www.kauhajoki-lehti.fi
Freq: 2 Times/Week; **Circ:** 6960
Editor in Chief: Tuomas Koivuniemi
Language (s): Finnish
NEWSPAPER

Kauppalehti
Owner: Kauppalehti Oy
Editorial: Alvar Aallon katu 3 C, Helsinki 100.
T: 358 10 66 51 01
E: kl.toimitus@kauppalehti.fi
W: http://www.kauppalehti.fi
Freq: Daily; **Circ:** 68252
News Editor: Tiia Kyynäräinen
Language (s): Finnish; Full Page Colour: 13200.00
Currency: Euro
DAILY NEWSPAPER

KaupunkiSanomat
Owner: Kaupunkilehdet
Editorial: KaupunkiSanomat viikkolehti, PL 28, Helsinki 421 **E:** toimitus@kaupunkisanomat.fi
W: http://www.kaupunkisanomat.fi
Freq: Weekly; **Circ:** 20000 Pub Statement
Editor in Chief: Merja Nordbäck-Raunio
Language (s): Finnish; Full Page Colour: 1290.00
Currency: Euro
NEWSPAPER

Keski-Espoon Sanomat
Owner: Keski-Espoo-seura ry
Editorial: Blominkuja 6, Espoo 2780.
T: 358 9 81 65 70 38
E: pirkko.sillanpaa@espoo.fi
W: http://www.keskiespooseura.fi
Freq: Quarterly; **Circ:** 20000 Pub Statement
Editor in Chief: Pirkko Sillanpää
Language (s): Finnish
NEWSPAPER

Keski-Häme
Owner: Hämeen Viestintä Oy
Editorial: Lamminraitti 25, Lammi 16900
E: toimitus@keski-hame.fi
W: http://www.keski-hame.fi
Freq: Weekly; **Circ:** 5326
Editor in Chief: Juha Reinikainen
Language (s): Finnish; Full Page Colour: 2588.00
Currency: Euro
NEWSPAPER

Keşkilaakso
Owner: Sanoma News Oy
Editorial: PL 20 / Valtatie 12, Inkeroinen 46901. **T:** 358 15 35 03 530
E: toimitus@keskilaakso.fi
W: http://www.keskilaakso.fi

Freq: 2 Times/Week; **Circ:** 5119
Editor in Chief: Stiina Kokkonen
Language (s): Finnish
NEWSPAPER

Keskipohjanmaa
Owner: Keski-Pohjanmaan Kustannus Oy
Editorial: PL 45/ Rantakatu 10, Kokkola 67101. **T:** 358 20 75 04 400
E: toimitus@kpk.fi
W: http://www.keskipohjanmaa.net
Circ: 24126
Editor: Jens Oja
Language (s): Finnish
NEWSPAPER

Keski-Savon Uutiset
Owner: Keski-Savon Uutiset Oy
Editorial: Hakakuja 6, Varkaus 78870.
T: 358 45 87 85 779
E: matti.suhonen@spym.fi
Freq: Weekly; **Circ:** 26600 Pub Statement
Language (s): Finnish
NEWSPAPER

Keskisuomalainen
Owner: Keskisuomalainen Oyj
Editorial: PL 159/ Aholaidantie 3, Jyväskylä 40101. **T:** 358 14 62 22 71
E: talous@keskisuomalainen.fi
W: http://www.ksml.fi **Circ:** 68101
News Producer: Anni Kettunen; **Editor in Chief:** Pekka Mervola; **Editor:** Anne Repo
Language (s): Finnish; Full Page Colour: 12444.00
Currency: Euro
DAILY NEWSPAPER

Keskisuomalainen Äänekoski
Owner: Keskisuomalainen Oyj
Editorial: Kauppakatu 1, Äänekoski 44100.
T: 358 14 34 89 563
E: Ira.Blomberg-Kantsila@keskisuomalainen.fi
W: http://www.ksml.fi
Editorial Profile: Bureau
Language (s): Finnish
DAILY NEWSPAPER

Keskisuomalainen Jämsä
Owner: Keskisuomalainen Oyj
Editorial: Keskuskatu 4, Jämsä 42100.
T: 358 14 71 80 71
E: hannu.karjalainen@keskisuomalainen.fi
W: http://www.ksml.fi
Editorial Profile: Bureau
Language (s): Finnish
DAILY NEWSPAPER

Keskisuomalainen Keuruu
Owner: Keskisuomalainen Oyj
Editorial: Kippavuorentie 7, Keuruu 42700.
T: 358 50 54 91 824
E: rainer.liimatainen@keskisuomalainen.fi
W: http://www.ksml.fi
Editorial Profile: Bureau
Language (s): Finnish
DAILY NEWSPAPER

Keskisuomalainen Saarijärvi
Owner: Keskisuomalainen Oyj
Editorial: Kauppakatu 5, PL 68, Saarijärvi 43100. **T:** 358 50 37 61 231
E: maarit.vaaherkumpu@keskisuomalainen.fi
W: http://www.ksml.fi
Editorial Profile: Bureau
Language (s): Finnish
DAILY NEWSPAPER

Keski-Suomen Viikko
Owner: Keski-Suomen Viikkolehti Oy
Editorial: PL 273/ Vasarakatu 1, Jyväskylä 40101. **T:** 358 10 42 34 900
E: toimitus@ksviikko.fi
W: http://www.demari.fi/keski-suomen-viikko/etusivu
Freq: Weekly; **Circ:** 6227
Editor in Chief: Elina Piispanen
Language (s): Finnish
NEWSPAPER

Keski-Uusimaa
Owner: SLY-Paikallislehdet Oy
Editorial: PL 52/ Klaavolantie 5, Tuusula 4301.
T: 358 20 77 03 101
E: toimitus.keskiuusimaa@lehtiyhtyma.fi
W: http://www.keskiuusimaa.fi
Freq: Weekly; **Circ:** 20165
Editor in Chief: Pentti Kiiski
Language (s): Finnish
NEWSPAPER

Kirkkonummen Sanomat
Owner: Kirkkonummen Sanomat Oy
Editorial: PL 28/ Munkinkuja 4, Kirkkonummi 2401. **T:** 358 9 22 19 200
E: toimitus@kirkkonummensanomat.fi

W: http://www.kirkkonummensanomat.fi
Freq: 2 Times/Week; **Circ:** 28000 Pub Statement
Editor in Chief: Jussi Salo
Language (s): Finnish
NEWSPAPER

Kittilälehti
Owner: Kittilämedia Oy
Editorial: Valtatie 42 A, Kittilä 99100.
T: 358 16 64 29 63 **E:** info@kittilalehti.com
W: http://www.kittilalehti.com
Freq: Weekly; **Circ:** 3120 Pub Statement
Editor in Chief: Mari Palomaa; **Student:** Päivi Tohmo
Language (s): Finnish; Full Page Colour: 2109.00
Currency: Euro
NEWSPAPER

Kiuruvesi
Owner: Kiuruvesi Lehti Oy
Editorial: PL 69/ Hovinpelto 3, Kiuruvesi 74701. **T:** 358 17 77 07 700
E: toimitus@kiuruvesilehti.fi
W: http://www.kiuruvesilehti.fi/
Freq: Weekly; **Circ:** 6285
Editor in Chief: Jaana Selander
Language (s): Finnish
NEWSPAPER

KMV-lehti
Owner: Suomen Paikallissanomat Oy
Editorial: PL 33 / Ratakatu 6, Mänttä 35801.
T: 358 10 66 55 630
E: toimitus.kmvlehti@almamedia.fi
W: http://www.kmvlehti.fi
Freq: 2 Times/Week; **Circ:** 6800
Editor in Chief: Teijo Mäki
Language (s): Finnish; Full Page Colour: 2398.00
Currency: Euro
NEWSPAPER

Koillismaan Uutiset
Owner: Koillismaan Uutiset Oy
Editorial: Ouluntaival 1, Torikeskus, Kuusamo 93600. **T:** 358 8 54 53 980
E: toimitus@koillismaanuutiset.fi
W: http://www.koillismaanuutiset.fi
Freq: Weekly; **Circ:** 12726 Pub Statement
Editor in Chief: Pasi Määttälä
Language (s): Finnish
NEWSPAPER

Koillissanomat
Owner: Koillissanomat Oy
Editorial: Kitkantie 31-33, Kuusamo 93600.
T: 358 8 86 00 600
E: toimitus@koillissanomat.fi
W: http://www.koillissanomat.fi
Freq: Daily; **Circ:** 6936
Editor in Chief: Petri Karjalainen
Language (s): Finnish
DAILY NEWSPAPER

Koillis-Savo
Owner: Maakunnan Sanomat Oy
Editorial: PL 31/ Kaavintie 5 A, Kaavi 73601.
T: 358 17 28 87 721 **E:** uutiset@koillis-savo.fi
W: http://www.koillis-savo.fi
Freq: 2 Times/Week; **Circ:** 5873
Editor in Chief: Pirjo Mononen
Language (s): Finnish
NEWSPAPER

Kokkola
Owner: Keski-Pohjanmaan Kustannus Oy
Editorial: PL 45/ Rantakatu 10, Kokkola 67101. **T:** 358 20 75 04 680
E: toimitus@kokkolalehti.fi
W: http://www.kokkola-lehti.fi
Freq: Weekly; **Circ:** 28800 Pub Statement
Language (s): Finnish
NEWSPAPER

Komiat
Owner: Pohjanmaan Lähisanomat Oy
Editorial: Nikolaintie 5 B 12, Kauhava 62200.
T: 358 6 24 77 885 **E:** toimitus@komiatlehti.fi
W: http://www.komiatlehti.fi
Freq: Weekly; **Circ:** 6510 Pub Statement
Editor in Chief: Tarja Kojola
Language (s): Finnish
NEWSPAPER

Kommunbladet-Kunnallisuutiset
Owner: HSS Media Ab
Editorial: PB 52, Vasa 65101.
T: 358 6 78 48 800
W: http://www.vora-maxmo.fi
Freq: Monthly; **Circ:** 4000 Pub Statement
News: Karin Sundström
Language (s): Finnish
NEWSPAPER

Korpilahti
Owner: Korpilahden Paikallislehti Oy
Editorial: Kokkotie 11 C 17, Korpilahti 41800.
T: 358 40 19 77 400
E: toimitus@korpilahtilehti.fi
W: http://www.korpilahtilehti.fi
Freq: Weekly; **Circ:** 3030
News: Maarit Nurminen
Language (s): Finnish; Full Page Colour: 1971.00
Currency: Euro
NEWSPAPER

Koti-Kajaani
Owner: Pohjois-Suomen Media Oy
Editorial: Välikatu 8, Kajaani 87100.
T: 358 10 66 57 202
E: simo.hyttinen@koti-kajaani.fi
W: http://www.koti-kajaani.fi
Freq: 2 Times/Week; **Circ:** 28758 Pub Statement
Editor in Chief: Simo Hyttinen
Language (s): Finnish
NEWSPAPER

Koti-Karjala
Owner: Keski-Karjalan Paikallislehti Oy
Editorial: PL 34 / Pokentie 8, Kitee 82501.
T: 358 13 68 48 411 **E:** toimitus@kotikarjala.fi
W: http://www.kotikarjala.fi
Freq: 2 Times/Week; **Circ:** 6477
Language (s): Finnish; Full Page Colour: 3488.00
Currency: Euro
NEWSPAPER

Koti-Lappi
Owner: Pohjois-Suomen Media Oy
Editorial: PL 19/ Hallituskatu 1, Kemijärvi 98101. **T:** 358 10 66 57 922
E: toimitus.kotilappi@almamedia.fi
W: http://www.koillislappi.fi/a/2012/09/27/
Freq: Weekly; **Circ:** 3279
Editor in Chief: Sami Kasurinen
Language (s): Finnish; Full Page Colour: 3066.00
Currency: Euro
NEWSPAPER

Kotiseudun Sanomat
Owner: Pihtipudas-Seura ry
Editorial: Keskustie 8, Pihtipudas 44800.
T: 358 20 79 31 620
E: toimitus@kotiseudunsanomat.fi
W: http://www.kotiseudunsanomat.fi
Freq: Weekly; **Circ:** 5028
Editor in Chief: Heikki Jämsén
Language (s): Finnish
NEWSPAPER

Kotiseutulehti Lakeuden Joutsen
Owner: Kustannus Kempeleläinen Ky
Editorial: PL 1/ Kauppatie 1, Kempele 90441.
T: 358 8 51 63 27
E: toimitus@lakeudenjoutsen.fi
W: http://www.lakeudenjoutsen.fi
Freq: Weekly; **Circ:** 15000 Pub Statement
Editor in Chief: Susanna Paaso
Language (s): Finnish
NEWSPAPER

KotiseutuPlus
Owner: LMC Media Oy
Editorial: Välikatu 20, Kajaani 87100.
T: 358 10 32 10 770
E: toimitus.kainuu@kotiseutuplus.fi
W: http://www.kotiseutuplus.fi
Freq: Weekly; **Circ:** 25872 Pub Statement
Language (s): Finnish; Full Page Colour: 1980.00
Currency: Euro
NEWSPAPER

Kotiseutu-uutiset
Owner: Liperin Kotiseutu-Uutiset Ky
Editorial: PL 14 / Keskustie 20, Liperi 83101.
T: 358 10 66 66 081
E: toimitus@kotiseutu-uutiset.fi
W: http://www.kotiseutu-uutiset.com
Freq: 2 Times/Week; **Circ:** 3234
News: Tarmo Nenonen
Language (s): Finnish; Full Page Colour: 3441.00
Currency: Euro
NEWSPAPER

Kouvolan Sanomat
Owner: Kymenviestintä Oy
Editorial: PL 40/Lehtikaari 1, Kouvola 45101.
T: 358 5 28 00 14
E: toimitus@kouvolansanomat.fi
W: http://www.kouvolansanomat.fi
Freq: Daily; **Circ:** 24531
News Producer: Katri Mannonen; **News Producer:** Minna Muuronen
Language (s): Finnish; Full Page Colour: 4520.00

Kuhmoisten Sanomat
Owner: Kuhmoisten Sanomat Oy
Editorial: PL 8 / Toritie 52, Kuhmoinen 17801.
T: 358 3 55 51 437
E: toimitus@kuhmoistensanomat.fi
W: http://www.kuhmoistensanomat.fi
Freq: Weekly; **Circ:** 2872
News: Vesa Koivu
Language (s): Finnish; Full Page Colour: 2246.00
Currency: Euro
NEWSPAPER

Kuhmolainen
Owner: Suomen Paikallissanomat Oy
Editorial: Kainuuntie 103, Kuhmo 88900.
T: 358 8 63 25 30
E: toimitus.kuhmolainen@sps.fi
W: http://www.kuhmolainen.fi
Freq: 2 Times/Week; **Circ:** 5777
Editor in Chief: Martti Huusko
Language (s): Finnish
NEWSPAPER

Kulmakunta
Owner: Tmi Kulmis
Editorial: Kousankatu 1, 3 krs, Turku 20610.
T: 358 2 27 44 999
E: lauri.simola@uusikulmis.fi
W: http://www.kulmis.fi
Freq: Weekly; **Circ:** 26000 Pub Statement
Editor in Chief: Pekka Tauriainen
Language (s): Finnish
NEWSPAPER

Kunnallislehti Paimio-Sauvo-Kaarina
Owner: Salon Seudun Sanomat Oy
Editorial: PL 29/Vistantie 38, Paimio 21531.
T: 358 2 58 88 650
E: toimitus@kunnallislehti.fi
W: http://www.kuntsari.fi
Freq: 2 Times/Week; **Circ:** 6458
Editor in Chief: Taina Tukia
Language (s): Finnish
NEWSPAPER

Kuopion Kaupunkilehti
Owner: Kuopion Kaupunkilehti Oy
Editorial: Tulliportinkatu 8, Kuopio 70100.
T: 358 44 28 82 801
E: kuopio.toimitus@kaupunkilehti.fi
W: http://www.kuopionkaupunkilehti.fi
Freq: Weekly; **Circ:** 62670 Pub Statement
Editor in Chief: Aija Pirinen
Language (s): Finnish; Full Page Colour: 1654.00
Currency: Euro
NEWSPAPER

Kuriiri
Owner: Pohjois-Suomen Media Oy
Editorial: PL 25/ Kiertotie 8, Ranua 97701.
T: 358 10 66 56 333
E: kuriiri.toimitus@pohjolansanomat.fi
Freq: Weekly; **Circ:** 6300 Pub Statement
Editor in Chief: Pasi Haarahiltunen
Language (s): Finnish
NEWSPAPER

Kurikka-Lehti
Owner: Kurikka-lehti Oy
Editorial: PL 50 / Laulajantie 4, Kurikka 61301. **T:** 358 6 45 15 500
E: toimitus@kurikka-lehti.fi
W: http://www.kurikka-lehti.fi
Freq: 2 Times/Week; **Circ:** 5058
Editor in Chief: Jaakko Ujainen
Language (s): Finnish
NEWSPAPER

Kurkijokelainen
Owner: Kurkijoki-Säätiö
Editorial: Koulukuja 7, Loimaa 32200.
T: 358 2 76 22 551 **E:** toimitus@kurkijoki.fi
W: http://www.kurkijoki.fi/kurkijokelainen/kj_kjln0.html
Freq: Bi-Weekly; **Circ:** 2000 Pub Statement
Editor in Chief: Raija Hjelm
Language (s): Finnish
NEWSPAPER

Kurun Lehti
Owner: Kuru-Seura
T: 358 44 34 30 031 **E:** toimitus@kurunlehti.fi
W: http://www.kurunlehti.fi
Freq: Bi-Weekly; **Circ:** 2800 Pub Statement
News: Kyösti Aalto; **News:** Juhani Latoniemi
Language (s): Finnish
NEWSPAPER

KustNytt
Owner: Kustmedia Ab Oy

Currency: Euro
NEWSPAPER

Editorial: Barkamovägen 3, Solf 65450.
T: 358 6 34 41 800 **E:** info@kustmedia.fi
W: http://www.kustmedia.fi
Freq: Monthly; **Circ:** 2800 Pub Statement
News: Lisbeth Bäck
Language (s): Swedish; Full Page Colour: 1340.00
Currency: Euro
NEWSPAPER

Kuukkeli
Owner: Santa Claus Medias Oy
Editorial: Lehontie 2 A, Äkäslompolo 95970.
T: 358 16 56 95 67 **E:** toimitus@kuukkeli.com
W: http://www.kuukkeli.fi
Freq: Monthly; **Circ:** 8000 Pub Statement
Editor in Chief: Eero Vapa
Language (s): Finnish
NEWSPAPER

Kymen Sanomat
Owner: Kymen Sanomalehti Oy
Editorial: PL 27/Tornatorintie 3, Kotka 48101.
T: 358 5 21 00 15
E: uutiset@kymensanomat.fi
W: http://www.kymensanomat.fi
Freq: Daily; **Circ:** 22225
News Producer: Marja Luumi-Laasonen
Language (s): Finnish
NEWSPAPER

Kyrönmaa-lehti
Owner: Kyrönmaa-Laihia Oy
Editorial: PL 61/Ruutintie 2 C, Laihia 66401.
T: 358 6 47 76 116
E: toimitus@kyronmaa-lehti.fi
W: http://www.kyronmaa-lehti.fi
Freq: 2 Times/Week; **Circ:** 2975
Editor in Chief: Jaakko Ujainen
Language (s): Finnish; Full Page Colour: 2700.00
Currency: Euro
NEWSPAPER

Lahden Seudun Sanomat
Owner: Green Moon Oy
Editorial: Tarmontie 6 C, Hollola 15860.
T: 358 20 78 09 330
W: http://www.lahdenseudunsanomat.fi
Freq: Weekly; **Circ:** 21000 Pub Statement
Language (s): Finnish
NEWSPAPER

LähiLehti - Sysmä, Hartola
Owner: Sysmän Sanomat Oy
Editorial: Sysmäntie 30, Sysmä 19700.
T: 358 3 87 77 60 **E:** toimitus@lahilehti.com
W: http://www.lahilehti.com
Freq: Weekly; **Circ:** 11000 Pub Statement
Editor in Chief: Timo Korhonen
Language (s): Finnish
NEWSPAPER

Laitilan Sanomat
Owner: Plari Oy
Editorial: PL 8/Keskuskatu 2, Laitila 23801.
T: 358 2 58 88 900
E: toimitus@laitilansanomat.fi
W: http://www.laitilansanomat.fi
Freq: 2 Times/Week; **Circ:** 4900
Editor in Chief: Eija Eskola-Buri
Language (s): Finnish

Längelmävesi-lehti
Owner: Pirkanmaan Viikkokustannus Oy
Editorial: Ellintie 2, Kangasala 36200.
T: 358 3 35 88 640 **E:** lvesi@quu.fi
W: http://www.quu.fi
Freq: Quarterly; **Circ:** 1400 Pub Statement
News: Jyrki Jaakkola
Language (s): Finnish

Länsi-Saimaan Sanomat
Owner: Kustannus Oy Yhteissanomat
Editorial: Peltoinlahdentie 24, Savitaipale 54800. **T:** 358 20 79 28 770
E: toimitus@lansisaimaa.fi
W: http://www.lansisaimaa.fi
Freq: 2 Times/Week; **Circ:** 4684
Language (s): Finnish

Länsi-Savo
Owner: Länsi-Savo Oy
Editorial: PL 6/ Teollisuuskatu 2-6, Mikkeli 50101. **T:** 358 15 35 01
E: toimitus@lansi-savo.fi
W: http://www.lansi-savo.fi
Freq: Daily; **Circ:** 22352
Language (s): Finnish

Länsi-Suomi
Owner: Länsi-Suomi Oy

Editorial: PL 5/ Susivuorentie 2, Rauma
26101. **T:** 358 10 83 361
E: toimitus@marvamedia.fi
W: http://www.lansi-suomi.fi
Freq: Daily; **Circ:** 15313
Editor in Chief: Pasi Katajamäki
Language (s): Finnish; Full Page Colour: 10037.00
Currency: Euro
NEWSPAPER

Länsi-Uusimaa
Owner: Länsi-Uusimaa Oy
Editorial: PL 60/ Seisaketie 15, Lohja 8101.
T: 358 20 61 00 130
E: lu.toimitus@lehtiyhtyma.fi
W: http://www.lansi-uusimaa.fi **Circ:** 13390
Language (s): Finnish; Full Page Colour: 9435.00
Currency: Euro
NEWSPAPER

Länsiväylä
Owner: SLY-Kaupunkilehdet Oy
Editorial: PL 350/ Rälssitie 7 A, Vantaa 1511.
T: 358 20 61 00 110
E: lv.toimitus@lehtiyhtyma.fi
W: http://www.lansivayla.fi
Freq: 2 Times/Week; **Circ:** 114000 Pub Statement
Editor in Chief: Risto Hietanen
Language (s): Finnish; Full Page Colour: 4469.00
Currency: Euro
NEWSPAPER

Lapin Kansa
Owner: Alma Media Oyj
Editorial: Veitikantie 2-8, Rovaniemi 96100.
T: 358 10 665 022 **E:** lktoimitus@lapinkansa.fi
W: http://www.lapinkansa.fi
Freq: Daily; **Circ:** 28735
Editor in Chief: Antti Kokkonen
Language (s): Finnish; Full Page Colour: 6800.00
Currency: Euro
NEWSPAPER

Lappeenrannan Uutiset
Owner: SLY Kaupunkilehdet Oy
Editorial: Kauppakeskus Opri 3. krs, Valtakatu 30, Lappeenranta 53100. **T:** 358 20 610 0112
E: toimitus.lpr@lehtiyhtyma.fi
W: http://www.lappeenrannanuutiset.fi
Freq: Weekly; **Circ:** 67000 Pub Statement
Editor in Chief: Karri Kannala
Language (s): Finnish; Full Page Colour: 1848.00
Currency: Euro
NEWSPAPER

Lappilainen
Owner: Teksti- ja Kuvapalvelu Aakkoset Oy
Editorial: Veitikantie 8, Rovaniemi 96100.
T: 358 40 351 7181 **E:** toimitus@lappilainen.fi
W: http://www.lappilainen.fi
Freq: Weekly; **Circ:** 43700 Pub Statement
Language (s): Finnish; Full Page Colour: 1525.00
Currency: Euro
NEWSPAPER

Lapuan Linkki
Owner: Lapua Säätiö
Editorial: Sanomatie 1, Lapua 62100.
T: 358 6 43 87 352
E: toimitus@lapuansanomat.fi
W: http://www.lapuansanomat.fi
Freq: Weekly; **Circ:** 6950 Pub Statement
Editor in Chief: Hannu Risikko
Language (s): Finnish
NEWSPAPER

Lapuan Sanomat
Owner: Lapua Säätiö
Editorial: Sanomatie 1, Lapua 62100.
T: 358 6 43 87 352
E: toimitus@lapuansanomat.fi
W: http://www.lapuansanomat.fi
Freq: 2 Times/Week; **Circ:** 6495
Editor in Chief: Hannu Risikko
Language (s): Finnish
NEWSPAPER

Laukaa-Konnevesi
Owner: Maakunnan Sanomat Oy
Editorial: PL 1/Laukaantie 26, Laukaa 41341.
T: 358 14 33 97 400
E: toimitus@laukaa-konnevesi.fi
W: http://www.laukaa-konnevesi.fi
Freq: Weekly; **Circ:** 7453
Editor in Chief: Arja Korpela
Language (s): Finnish
NEWSPAPER

Lauttakylä
Owner: Huittisten Sanomalehti Oy

When contacting publications, please mention you found them in Benn's Media

Editorial: PL 36/Karpintie 13, Huittinen 32701.
T: 358 2 55 54 200 **E:** toimitus@lauttakyla.fi
W: http://www.lauttakyla.fi
Freq: 2 Times/Week; **Circ:** 5230
Editor in Chief: Marja-Liisa Hakanen
Language (s): Finnish
NEWSPAPER

Lauttasaari-lehti
Owner: Lauttasaari-Seura
Editorial: Kauppaneuvoksentie 18, Helsinki
200. **T:** 358 10 38 77 080
W: http://www.lauttasaari.fi
Freq: Weekly; **Circ:** 14000 Pub Statement
Editor in Chief: Liisa Stjernberg
Language (s): Finnish; Full Page Colour:
1000.00
Currency: Euro
NEWSPAPER

Lempäälän-Vesilahden Sanomat
Owner: Lempäälän-Vesilahden Sanomat Oy
Editorial: PL 38 / Tampereentie 17, Lempäälä
37501. **T:** 358 3 34 29 000 **E:** toimitus@lvs.fi
W: http://www.lvs.fi
Freq: 2 Times/Week; **Circ:** 7020
Editor in Chief: Satu Lehtonen
Language (s): Finnish
NEWSPAPER

Lepuski
Owner: Viestintätoimisto Luova Ratkaisu Oy
Editorial: PL 120/ Parkvillanpolku, Espoo
2601. **T:** 358 500 67 53 87 **E:** seura@lepuski.fi
W: http://www.lepuski.fi/viestinta/lepuski.html
Freq: Quarterly; **Circ:** 18000 Pub Statement
Editor in Chief: Arja Salmi
Language (s): Finnish; Full Page Colour:
1650.00
Currency: Euro
NEWSPAPER

Lestijoki
Owner: Jokilaaksojen Kustannus Oy
Editorial: PL 1 / Valtakatu 9, Kannus 69101.
T: 358 20 75 04 650
E: toimitus@lestijoki-lehti.fi
W: http://www.lestijoki-lehti.fi
Freq: Weekly; **Circ:** 5107
Editor in Chief: Marja-Leena Mattila-
Numminen
Language (s): Finnish
NEWSPAPER

Lieksan Lehti
Owner: Lieksan Lehti Oy
Editorial: PL 22/ Siltakatu 1, Lieksa 81701.
T: 358 10 23 08 650 **E:** toimitus@lieksanlehti.fi
W: http://www.lieksanlehti.fi
Freq: 2 Times/Week; **Circ:** 6482
Editor in Chief: Marja Mölsä
Language (s): Finnish
NEWSPAPER

Loimaan Lehti
Owner: Priimus Media Oy
Editorial: PL 2/Kartanomäenkatu 4, Loimaa
32201. **T:** 358 2 58 88 000
E: toimitus@loimaanlehti.fi
W: http://www.loimaanlehti.fi
Freq: 2 Times/Week; **Circ:** 8675
Editor in Chief: Kati Uusitalo
Language (s): Finnish
NEWSPAPER

Lopen Lehti
Owner: Karprint Oy
T: 358 19 44 00 59 **E:** lopen.lehti@karprint.fi
W: http://www.karprint.fi/lopenlehti/
Freq: Weekly; **Circ:** 13860 Pub Statement
Editor in Chief: Juha Ahola
Language (s): Finnish
NEWSPAPER

Lounais-Lappi
Owner: Alma Media Oyj
Editorial: Sairaalakatu 2, Kemi 94100.
T: 358 10 665 7760 **E:** toimitus@lounaislappi.fi
W: http://www.lounaislappi.fi
Freq: 2 Times/Week; **Circ:** 37000 Pub
Statement
Editor in Chief: Tiina Nousiainen
Language (s): Finnish
NEWSPAPER

Loviisan Sanomat
Owner: Ksf Media Ab
Editorial: PL 42 / Sibeliuksenkatu 10, Loviisa
7901. **T:** 358 19 53 27 01 **E:** toimitus@lovari.fi
W: http://www.loviisansanomat.net
Freq: 2 Times/Week; **Circ:** 4413
Editor in Chief: Arto Henriksson
Language (s): Finnish; Full Page Colour:
3172.00
Currency: Euro
NEWSPAPER

Luoteis-Lappi
Owner: Heikki Peura Ky
Editorial: Ojapolku 3, Kolari 95900.
T: 358 16 56 11 81 **E:** info@luoteis-lappi.com
W: http://www.luoteis-lappi.com
Freq: Weekly; **Circ:** 5378 Pub Statement
Editor in Chief: Jaakko Kangosjärvi; **Editor in
Chief:** Milla Ollikainen
Language (s): Finnish
NEWSPAPER

Luoteis-Uusimaa
Owner: Karprint Oy
T: 358 9 41 39 73 00 **E:** lu.toimitus@karprint.fi
W: http://www.luoteis-uusimaa.fi
Freq: 2 Times/Week; **Circ:** 16500 Pub
Statement
Editor in Chief: Mari Ahola-Aalto
Language (s): Finnish
NEWSPAPER

Luoteisväylä
Owner: Suomen Paikallissanomat Oy
Editorial: Finpyyntie 9, Noormarkku 29600.
T: 358 10 66 55 640
E: toimitus.luoteisvayla@almamedia.fi
W: http://www.uutismarkku.fi
Freq: Weekly; **Circ:** 3513
Editor in Chief: Kaisla-Kaarina Rostedt
Language (s): Finnish; Full Page Colour:
2321.00
Currency: Euro
NEWSPAPER

Luumäen Lehti
Owner: Sanoma News Oy
Editorial: Linnalantie 53, Taavetti 54500.
T: 358 5 45 72 301
W: http://www.luumaenlehti.fi
Freq: Weekly; **Circ:** 3627
News: Juhani Partanen
Language (s): Finnish; Full Page Colour:
2786.00
Currency: Euro
NEWSPAPER

Maaselkä
Owner: Haapajärvi-Seura ry
Editorial: PL 74/ Puistokatu 37, Haapajärvi
85801. **T:** 358 8 77 27 500
E: toimitus@maaselkalehti.fi
W: http://www.maaselkalehti.fi
Freq: 2 Times/Week; **Circ:** 4206
News: Juha Heikkilä; **News:** Vuokko Nyman
Language (s): Finnish; Full Page Colour:
2208.00
Currency: Euro
NEWSPAPER

Maaseudun Tulevaisuus
Owner: Viestilehdet Oy
Editorial: PL 440/ Simonkatu 6, Helsinki 101.
T: 358 20 41 32 100
E: toimitus@maaseuduntulevaisuus.fi
W: http://www.maaseuduntulevaisuus.fi
Freq: 2 Times/Week; **Circ:** 83259
Editor in Chief: Lauri Kontro
Language (s): Finnish; Full Page Colour:
17645.00
Currency: Euro
DAILY NEWSPAPER

Mäntsälä
Owner: Suomen Lehtiyhtymä Oy
T: 358 20 61 00 152
E: mantsalan.toimitus@lehtiyhtyma.fi
W: http://www.mantsalalehti.fi
Freq: 2 Times/Week; **Circ:** 3390
Editor in Chief: Katri Hämäläinen; **News:** Arto
Jussila; **News:** Pentti Kiiski; **Editor in Chief:**
Laura Liski
Language (s): Finnish; Full Page Colour:
2131.00
Currency: Euro
NEWSPAPER

Mäntsälän Viikkouutiset
Owner: Suomen Lehtiyhtymä
Editorial: Keskustie 4, Mäntsälä 4600.
T: 358 20 61 00 152
E: mantsalan.toimitus@lehtiyhtyma.fi
W: http://www.mvu.fi
Freq: Weekly; **Circ:** 12200 Pub Statement
Editor in Chief: Katri Hämäläinen
Language (s): Finnish
NEWSPAPER

Matkailulehti Ruka
Owner: Pohjoisen Tunturipalvelut Ky
Editorial: Jokimutkantie 5, Kuusamo 93600.
T: 358 40 77 20 606
E: toimitus@matkailulehtiruka.com
W: http://www.matkailulehtiruka.com
Freq: Monthly; **Circ:** 7000 Pub Statement
Editor: Rita Uusitalo
Language (s): Finnish; Full Page Colour:
1200.00

Currency: Euro
NEWSPAPER

Matti ja Liisa
Owner: Maakunnan Sanomat Oy
Editorial: PL 21 / Juhani Ahontie 2, Lapinlahti
73101. **T:** 358 17 73 15 40
E: matti.liisa@mattijaliisa.fi
W: http://www.mattijaliisa.fi
Freq: Weekly; **Circ:** 5119
Editor in Chief: Tero Joutselainen
Language (s): Finnish
NEWSPAPER

Meän Tornionlaakso
Owner: Tornionlaakson Kustannus Oy
Editorial: Alkkulanraitti 48, Ylitornio 95600.
T: 358 40 51 00 213
W: http://www.tornionlaakso.net
Freq: Weekly; **Circ:** 4800 Pub Statement
Editor in Chief: Minna Siilasvuo
Language (s): Finnish; Full Page Colour:
1453.00
Currency: Euro
NEWSPAPER

Merikarvialehti
Owner: Suomen Paikallissanomat Oy
Editorial: PL 3/Kauppatie 36, Merikarvia
29901. **T:** 358 2 55 11 272
E: toimitus.merikarvialehti@almamedia.fi
W: http://www.merikarvialehti.fi
Freq: Weekly; **Circ:** 3379
Editor in Chief: Kaisla-Kaarina Rostedt
Language (s): Finnish; Full Page Colour:
1892.00
Currency: Euro
NEWSPAPER

Metro
Owner: Sanoma News Oy
Editorial: Metro, PL 75, Sanoma 89.
T: 358 9 12 24 362 **E:** metro@sanoma.fi
W: http://metro.fi/
Freq: Daily; **Circ:** 319000 Pub Statement
Language (s): Finnish; Full Page Colour:
6352.00
Currency: Euro
NEWSPAPER

Miilu
Owner: Maakunnan Sanomat Oy
Editorial: PL 5/ Kallentie 1, Sonkajärvi 74301.
T: 358 17 76 13 12 **E:** miilu@miilu.fi
W: http://www.miilu.fi
Freq: Weekly; **Circ:** 3646
News: Heikki Valkonen
Language (s): Finnish
NEWSPAPER

Mikkelin Erikoissanomat
Owner: Mikkelin Erikoissanomat Ky
Editorial: Pulttikatu 2, Mikkeli 50100.
T: 358 440 21 12 91
E: erikoissanomat@haumedia.fi
W: http://www.erikoissanomat.fi
Freq: Monthly; **Circ:** 20000 Pub Statement
Editor in Chief: Jarno Laatikainen
Language (s): Finnish
NEWSPAPER

Mikkelin Kaupunkilehti
Owner: Mikkelin Kaupunkilehti Oy
Editorial: Mikonkatu 8, Mikkeli 50100.
T: 358 15 22 56 01
E: toimitus@mikkelinkaupunkilehti.fi
W: http://www.mikkelinkaupunkilehti.fi/
Freq: Weekly; **Circ:** 35000 Pub Statement
Editor in Chief: Kari Liikanen
Language (s): Finnish
NEWSPAPER

MOBILE
Owner: Mobile Kustannus Oy
Editorial: Brahenkatu 14 D 94, Turku 20100.
T: 358 45 65 67 216
E: toimitus@mobilekustannus.fi
W: http://mobile-lehti.fi/
Freq: Weekly; **Circ:** 5000 Pub Statement
Publisher: Teemu Jaakonkoski
Language (s): Finnish; Full Page Colour:
1350.00
Currency: Euro
NEWSPAPER

Munkinseutu
Owner: Karprint Oy
T: 358 9 41 39 73 00
E: munkinseutu@karprint.fi
W: http://www.karprint.fi/munkinseutu
Freq: Bi-Weekly; **Circ:** 25000 Pub Statement
Editor in Chief: Juha Ahola
Language (s): Finnish
NEWSPAPER

Muuramelainen
Owner: Muuramen kunta
Editorial: PL 1/ Virastotie 8, Muurame 40951.
T: 358 14 65 96 11
E: muuramelainen@muurame.fi
W: http://www.muurame.fi
Freq: Bi-Weekly; **Circ:** 4400 Pub Statement
Language (s): Finnish
NEWSPAPER

Nivala-lehti
Owner: Jokilaaksojen Kustannus Oy
Editorial: PL 2/ Kalliontie 30, Nivala 85501.
T: 358 20 75 04 710 **E:** toimitus@nivala-lehti.fi
W: http://www.nivala-lehti.fi
Freq: 2 Times/Week; **Circ:** 5971
Editor in Chief: Seija Krapu
Language (s): Finnish; Full Page Colour:
2080.00
Currency: Euro
NEWSPAPER

Nokian Uutiset
Owner: Suomen Paikallissanomat Oy
Editorial: PL 13/ Välimäenkatu 23, Nokia
37101. **T:** 358 10 66 51 10
E: toimitus.nokianuutiset@sps.fi
W: http://www.nokianuutiset.fi
Freq: 3 Times/Week; **Circ:** 8479
Editor in Chief: Minna Ala-Heikkilä; **News**
Editor: Henna Sotamaa-Leino
Language (s): Finnish; Full Page Colour:
4314.00
Currency: Euro
NEWSPAPER

Nurmijärven Uutiset
Owner: Medialehdet Oy
Editorial: Kuonomäentie 1 A 9, Klaukkala
1800. **T:** 358 20 61 00 151
E: nurmijarven.uutiset@lehtiyhtyma.fi
W: http://www.nurmijarvenuutiset.fi
Freq: 2 Times/Week; **Circ:** 20444 Pub
Statement
Editor in Chief: Jan Pippingsköld
Language (s): Finnish
NEWSPAPER

Nya Åland
Owner: Nya Ålands Tidning AB
Editorial: PB 21/Uppgårdsvägen 6, Mariehamn
22101. **T:** 358 18 23 444
E: redaktion@nyan.ax **W:** http://www.nyan.ax
Circ: 6683
News: Anna Björkroos; **Editor in chief:** Jonas
Bladh
Language (s): Swedish; Full Page Colour:
5952.00
Currency: Euro
NEWSPAPER

Nyky-Tampere
Owner: Kokoomuksen Tampereen Aluejärjestö
ry
Editorial: Kuninkaankatu 13 B, Tampere
33210. **T:** 358 45 106 33 00
W: http://www.tamperelainenkokoomus.fi/
nykytampere/
Freq: Quarterly; **Circ:** 88000 Pub Statement
Editor in Chief: Harri Airaksinen
Language (s): Finnish
NEWSPAPER

Omalähiö
Owner: Salomaan Kirjapaino Oy
Editorial: Patomäentie 10, Lahti 15610.
T: 358 3 73 52 016 **E:** omalahio@phnet.fi
W: http://www.omalahio.fi
Freq: Weekly; **Circ:** 13000 Pub Statement
News: Petri Salomaa
Language (s): Finnish
NEWSPAPER

Orimattilan Sanomat
Owner: Pitäjäsanomat Oy
Editorial: PL 5 / Erkontie 17, Orimattila 16301.
T: 358 3 87 66 78
E: toimitus@orimattilansanomat.fi
W: http://www.orimattilansanomat.fi
Freq: 2 Times/Week; **Circ:** 4462
News: Vesa Näveri; **News:** Petri Sipiläinen
Language (s): Finnish; Full Page Colour:
6674.00
Currency: Euro
NEWSPAPER

Oriveden Sanomat
Owner: Oriveden Sanomalehti Oy
Editorial: PL 33 / Lehmilaidantie 6, Orivesi
35301. **T:** 358 3 35 89 500
E: toimitus@orivedensanomat.fi
W: http://www.orivedensanomat.fi
Freq: 2 Times/Week; **Circ:** 5325
News: Vesa Kangas
Language (s): Finnish; Full Page Colour:
3951.00
Currency: Euro

NEWSPAPER

Österbottens Tidning
Owner: HSS Media Ab
Editorial: PB 22/Jakobsgatan 13, Jakobstad
68601. **T:** 358 6 78 48 800 **E:** nyheter@ot.fi
W: http://www.ot.fi **Circ:** 14251
Editor in Chief: Henrik Othman
Language (s): Swedish; Full Page Colour:
9996.00
Currency: Euro
NEWSPAPER

Österbottniska posten Öp
Owner: Ab Sidwill OY
Editorial: Kauppapuistikko 10 D, Vaasa 65100.
T: 358 6 32 05 000
W: http://www.webbop.fi/start/
Freq: Monthly; **Circ:** 22300 Pub Statement
Language (s): Swedish; Full Page Colour:
1450.00
Currency: Euro
NEWSPAPER

Östra Nyland
Owner: KSF Media
Editorial: PB 58/ Alexandersgatan 8, Lovisa
7901. **T:** 358 19 55 73 41 **E:** red@on.fi
W: http://www.on.fi **Circ:** 3765
Editor in Chief: Micaela Röman
Language (s): Swedish; Full Page Colour:
3176.00
Currency: Euro
NEWSPAPER

Oulu-lehti
Owner: Joutsen Media Oy
Editorial: PL 52 / Lekatie 4, Oulu 90101.
T: 358 8 53 70 022 **E:** toimitus@oululehti.fi
W: http://www.oululehti.fi
Freq: 2 Times/Week; **Circ:** 100000 Pub
Statement
Editor in Chief: Sauli Pahkasalo
Language (s): Finnish
NEWSPAPER

Oulunkyläinen - Pohjoiset esikaupungit
Owner: Oulunkylä-Seura ry
Editorial: Maanmittarintie 10 B, Helsinki 680.
T: 358 400 93 44 33
E: kaija-leena.sinkko@kolumbus.fi
W: http://www.kaupunginosat.net/oulunkyla/
oulunkylainen/oulunkylainen_lehti.htm
Freq: Bi-Monthly; **Circ:** 21500 Pub Statement
News: Laura Hari; **News:** Kaija-Leena Sinkko
Language (s): Finnish
NEWSPAPER

Outokummun Seutu
Owner: Pohjois-Karjalan Paikallislehdet Oy
Editorial: PL 7 / Koulukatu 2, Outokumpu
83501. **T:** 358 10 23 08 850
E: toimitus@outokummunseutu.fi
W: http://www.outokummunseutu.fi
Freq: 2 Times/Week; **Circ:** 4571
Editor in Chief: Esa Nevalainen
Language (s): Finnish; Full Page Colour:
2738.00
Currency: Euro
NEWSPAPER

Padasjoen Sanomat
Owner: Padasjoen Sanomat Oy
Editorial: PL 3/ Koivutie 8, Padasjoki 17501.
T: 358 3 55 27 500
E: toimitus@padasjoensanomat.fi
W: http://www.padasjoensanomat.fi
Freq: Weekly; **Circ:** 3675
News: Jaana Tanner
Language (s): Finnish; Full Page Colour:
2622.00
Currency: Euro
NEWSPAPER

Paikallisuutiset
Owner: Joutsan Seutu Oy
Editorial: PL 40/ Savonmäentie 1, Vaajakoski
40801. **T:** 358 40 54 75 111
E: toimitus@paikallisuutiset.fi
W: http://www.paikallisuutiset.fi
Freq: Weekly; **Circ:** 1604
News: Markku Parkkonen
Language (s): Finnish; Full Page Colour:
2964.00
Currency: Euro
NEWSPAPER

Pargas Kungörelser - Paraisten Kuulutukset
Owner: Förlags AB Sydvästkusten
Editorial: Strandvägen 24, Pargas 21600.
T: 358 2 45 44 118 **E:** leena.lehtonen@fabsy.fi
W: http://www.pku.fi
Freq: Weekly; **Circ:** 4753
News: Harry Serlo

Language (s): Finnish; Full Page Colour:
1500.00
Currency: Euro
NEWSPAPER

Parikkalan-Rautjärven Sanomat
Owner: Keski-Karjalan Kustannus Oy
Editorial: Parikkalantie 18, Parikkala 59100.
T: 358 10 23 08 900
E: toimitus@parikkalan-rautjarvensanomat.fi
W: http://www.parikkalan-rautjarvensanomat.fi
Freq: 2 Times/Week; **Circ:** 5687
News: Raine Hämäläinen
Language (s): Finnish; Full Page Colour:
3154.00
Currency: Euro
NEWSPAPER

Perhonjokilaakso
Owner: Jokilaaksojen Kustannus Oy
Editorial: Kirkkotanhua 3, Veteli 69700.
T: 358 20 75 04 670
W: http://www.perhonjokilaakso.fi
Freq: Weekly; **Circ:** 6540
News: Mauri Aho
Language (s): Finnish; Full Page Colour:
2518.00
Currency: Euro
NEWSPAPER

Perniönseudun Lehti
Owner: Perniönseudun Lehti Oy
Editorial: PL 35 / Salontie 2, Perniö 25501.
T: 358 2 73 52 301
E: toimitus@pernionseudunlehti.fi
W: http://www.pernionseudunlehti.fi
Freq: Weekly; **Circ:** 4199
News: Pekka Poutanen
Language (s): Finnish; Full Page Colour:
2142.00
Currency: Euro
NEWSPAPER

Petäjävesi
Owner: Petäjäveden Petäjäiset ry
Editorial: Asematie 6, Petäjävesi 41900.
T: 358 14 85 42 40 **E:** toimitus@petajavesi.net
W: http://www.petajavesi.net
Freq: Weekly; **Circ:** 2046
Language (s): Finnish
NEWSPAPER

Pieksämäen Lehti
Owner: Maakunnan Sanomat Oy
Editorial: Hallipussi 2, Pieksämäki 76100.
T: 358 15 34 81 722
E: toimitus@pieksamaenlehti.fi
W: http://www.pieksamaenlehti.fi
Freq: 2 Times/Week; **Circ:** 6597
Editor-In-Chief: Sinikka Hakkarainen; **Editor:**
Eeva McLees
Language (s): Finnish; Full Page Colour:
3574.00
Currency: Euro
NEWSPAPER

Pieksämäen Paikallinen
Editorial: Keskuskatu 14 A, II-krs., Pieksämäki
76100. **T:** 358 40 55 03 035
E: pmaen.paikallinen@co.inet.fi
W: http://www.pmaenpaikallinen.com
Freq: Weekly; **Circ:** 11500 Pub Statement
Editor in Chief: Laila Kimonen-Filppula
Language (s): Finnish
NEWSPAPER

Pielavesi - Keitele
Owner: Maakunnan Sanomat Oy
Editorial: Laaksotie 28, Pielavesi 72400.
T: 358 17 28 87 781
E: pieke@pielavesi-keitele.fi
W: http://www.pielavesi-keitele.fi
Freq: Weekly; **Circ:** 5899
News: Heli Roivainen
Language (s): Finnish
NEWSPAPER

Pielisjokiseutu
Owner: Pohjois-Karjalan Paikallislehdet Oy
Editorial: Liikekeskus, Eno 81200.
T: 358 10 23 08 700
E: toimitus@pielisjokiseutu.fi
W: http://www.pielisjokiseutu.fi
Freq: Weekly; **Circ:** 3600
Editor in Chief: Sami Tolvanen
Language (s): Finnish; Full Page Colour:
2956.00
Currency: Euro
NEWSPAPER

Pietarsaaren Sanomat
Owner: HSS Media Ab
Editorial: PL 105/Jaakonkatu 13, Pietarsaari
68601. **T:** 358 6 78 48 603
E: ps@pietarsaarensanomat.fi
W: http://www.pietarsaarensanomat.fi

Freq: 2 Times/Week; **Circ:** 2612
Editor-In-Chief: Osmo Ojala
Language (s): Finnish; Full Page Colour:
6732.00
Currency: Euro
NEWSPAPER

PikkuKaupunkilainen
Owner: Pikkukaupunkilainen Oy
Editorial: Kauppakatu 19, Äänekoski 44100.
T: 358 44 04 11 268
E: eija.varteva@sisasuomenlehti.fi
W: http://www.pikkukaupunkilainen.net
Freq: Weekly; **Circ:** 11000 Pub Statement
Editor-In-Chief: Eija Varteva
Language (s): Finnish
NEWSPAPER

Pirkkalainen
Owner: Pirkkala-Seura ry
Editorial: Suupantie 2 A 10, Pirkkala 33960.
T: 358 3 3143 1900
E: toimitus@pirkkalainen.com
W: http://www.pirkkalainen.com
Freq: Weekly; **Circ:** 14000 Pub Statement
Editor-In-Chief: Antti Jokinen
Language (s): Finnish; Full Page Colour:
2344.00
Currency: Euro
NEWSPAPER

Pitäjäläinen
Owner: Maakunnan Sanomat Oy
Editorial: Nilsiäntie 71, Nilsiä 73300.
T: 358 17 28 87 790 **E:** uutiset@pitajalainen.fi
W: http://www.pitajalainen.fi
Freq: 2 Times/Week; **Circ:** 4337
Editor-In-Chief: Päivi Laitinen
Language (s): Finnish
NEWSPAPER

Pitäjänuutiset
Owner: Sanoma News Oy
Editorial: Pentinpolku 1, Mäntyharju 52700.
T: 358 15 34 66 00
E: toimitus@pitajanuutiset.fi
W: http://www.pitajanuutiset.fi
Freq: 2 Times/Week; **Circ:** 5540
Editor-In-Chief: Minna Ojamies
Language (s): Finnish; Full Page Colour:
2584.00
Currency: Euro
NEWSPAPER

Pogostan Sanomat
Owner: Pogostan Sanomat Oy
Editorial: Kauppatie 29, Ilomantsi 82900.
T: 358 10 23 08 800
E: toimitus@pogostansanomat.fi
W: http://www.pogostansanomat.fi
Freq: 2 Times/Week; **Circ:** 5623
Editor-In-Chief: Aino Pesu; **Editor in Chief:**
Leila Virnes
Language (s): Finnish
NEWSPAPER

Pohjalainen
Owner: I-Mediat Oy
Editorial: PL 37/ Hietasaarenkatu 19, Vaasa
65101. **T:** 358 6 247 7504
E: toimitus@pohjalainen.fi
W: http://www.pohjalainen.fi
Editor/Producer: Janne Lehtonen; **Editor/
Producer:** Jukka-Pekka Porola; **Editor in Chief:**
Toni Viljanmaa
Language (s): Finnish; Full Page Colour:
13566.00
Currency: Euro
NEWSPAPER

Pohjalainen Härmänmaa
Owner: I-Mediat Oy
Editorial: Nikolaintie 5 B 12, Kauhava 62200.
T: 358 6 24 77 582 **E:** toimitus@pohjalainen.fi
W: http://www.pohjalainen.fi
Editorial Profile: Bureau
Language (s): Finnish
DAILY NEWSPAPER

Pohjalainen Pietarsaari
Owner: Vaasa Oy
Editorial: Jaakonkatu 13, Pietarsaari 68600.
T: 358 6 24 77 581 **E:** toimitus@pohjalainen.fi
W: http://www.pohjalainen.fi
Editorial Profile: Bureau
Language (s): Finnish
DAILY NEWSPAPER

Pohjalainen Seinäjoki
Owner: I-Mediat Oy
Editorial: PL 139/ Koulukatu 10, Seinäjoki
60101. **T:** 358 6 24 77 962
E: toimitus@pohjalainen.fi
W: http://www.pohjalainen.fi
News Editor: Marja-Riitta Vuorela
Editorial Profile: Bureau
Language (s): Finnish

DAILY NEWSPAPER

Pohjalainen Suomenselän-Järviseudun toimitus
Owner: I-Mediat Oy
Editorial: Alavus 63300. **T:** 358 6 24 77 576
E: toimitus@pohjalainen.fi
W: http://www.pohjalainen.fi
Editorial Profile: Bureau
Language (s): Finnish
DAILY NEWSPAPER

Pohjalainen Suupohja
Owner: I-Mediat Oy
Editorial: Topeeka 21, Kauhajoki 61800.
T: 358 6 24 77 930 **E:** toimitus@pohjalainen.fi
W: http://www.pohjalainen.fi
Editorial Profile: Bureau
Language (s): Finnish
DAILY NEWSPAPER

Pohjankyrö-lehti
Owner: Pohjakyrön Media Oy
Editorial: Pohjankyröntie 128, Isokyrö 61501.
T: 358 6 47 15 214
E: toimitus@pohjankyro-lehti.fi
W: http://www.pohjankyro-lehti.fi
Freq: 2 Times/Week; **Circ:** 5556
Editor in Chief: Jaakko Ujainen
Language (s): Finnish; Full Page Colour:
2851.00
Currency: Euro
NEWSPAPER

Pohjois-Kymenlaakso
Owner: Kaupunkilehti Pohjois-Kymenlaakso Oy
Editorial: Kouvolankatu 21, Kouvola 45100.
T: 358 5 75 30 500 **E:** teija.piipari@pklehti.fi
W: http://www.pklehti.fi
Freq: Weekly; **Circ:** 45000 Pub Statement
Editor in Chief: Teija Piipari
Language (s): Finnish
NEWSPAPER

Pohjois-Satakunta
Owner: Präntti Oy
Editorial: Keskisenkatu 1, Ikaalinen 39500.
T: 358 3 31 433 150
E: toimitus@pohjoissatakuntalehti.fi
W: http://www.pohjoissatakuntalehti.fi
Freq: 2 Times/Week; **Circ:** 5276
Editor in Chief: Katri Linnikko
Language (s): Finnish; Full Page Colour:
3788.00
Currency: Euro
NEWSPAPER

Pohjolan Sanomat
Owner: Pohjois-Suomen Media Oy
Editorial: Sairaalakatu 2, Kemi 94100.
T: 358 10 665 6276
E: ps.toimitus@pohjolansanomat.fi
W: http://www.pohjolansanomat.fi
Freq: Daily; **Circ:** 18672
News: Maria Jauho; **Editor in Chief:** Heikki
Lääkkölä; **News:** Tapani Närä; **Editor:** Taina
Nuutinen; **News:** Tapio Rantamartti; **News:**
Jukka Rautiainen
Language (s): Finnish; Full Page Colour:
5146.00
Currency: Euro
NEWSPAPER

Punkalaitumen Sanomat
Owner: Punkalaitumen Sanomat Oy
Editorial: PL 1 / Lauttakyläntie 4, Punkalaidun
31901. **T:** 358 2 76 74 256
E: toimitus@punkalaitumensanomat.fi
W: http://www.punkalaitumensanomat.fi
Freq: Weekly; **Circ:** 3579
News: Juha Aro
Language (s): Finnish; Full Page Colour:
1425.00
Currency: Euro
NEWSPAPER

Puolanka-lehti
Owner: Kustannus Oy Puolangan DTP
Editorial: PL 15 / Kajaanintie 5, Puolanka
89201. **T:** 358 8 65 32 200
E: toimitus@puolanka-lehti.fi
W: http://www.puolanka-lehti.fi
Freq: Weekly; **Circ:** 2302
News: Tuomo Seppänen
Language (s): Finnish
NEWSPAPER

Puoli kaupunkia
Owner: Top Contact Oy
Editorial: Sorvaajankatu 15, Helsinki 880.
T: 358 10 322 1651
E: helsinki.toimitus@avaalehti.fi
W: http://www.puolikaupunkia.fi
Freq: Bi-Weekly; **Circ:** 125200 Pub Statement
Editor in Chief: Kauko Vanajas
Language (s): Finnish; Full Page Colour:
4446.00

Currency: Euro
NEWSPAPER

Puruvesi
Owner: Etelä-Savon Paikallislehdet Oy
Editorial: PL 2 / Kauppatie 16, Punkaharju
58501. T: 358 15 35 03 410
E: uutiset@puruvesi.net
W: http://www.puruvesi.net
Freq: 2 Times/Week; Circ: 6483
Editor in Chief: Esa Hirvonen
Language (s): Finnish; Full Page Colour:
2772.00
Currency: Euro
NEWSPAPER

Putkilahden uutisia
Owner: Putkilahden Kyläseura ry
Editorial: Putkilahden kyläseura ry, Putkilahti
41870. T: 358 14 82 51 10
W: http://www.putkilahti.net
Freq: Monthly; Circ: 320 Pub Statement
News: Aune Turunen
Language (s): Finnish
NEWSPAPER

Puumala
Owner: Puumala-Seura ry
Editorial: PL 12 / Kenttätie 7, Puumala 52201.
T: 358 15 46 81 225
E: toimitus@puumalalehti.fi
W: http://www.puumalalehti.fi
Freq: Weekly; Circ: 3363
News: Elvi Köpman
Language (s): Finnish; Full Page Colour:
2331.00
Currency: Euro
NEWSPAPER

Pyhäjärven Sanomat
Owner: Pyhäjärven Sanomat Oy
Editorial: PL 41/ Asematie 2, Pyhäsalmi
86801. T: 358 8 77 29 000
E: toimitus@pyhajarvensanomat.fi
W: http://www.pyhajarvensanomat.fi
Freq: Weekly; Circ: 4277
Editor in Chief: Jouko Moilanen
Language (s): Finnish; Full Page Colour:
1555.00
Currency: Euro
NEWSPAPER

Pyhäjärven Seutu
Owner: Pyhäjärven Seutu Oy
T: 358 440 30 14 51
E: toimitus@pyhajarvenseutu.fi
W: http://www.pyhajarvenseutu.fi
Freq: Weekly; Circ: 10000 Pub Statement
Editor-in-Chief: Suoma Tirkkonen
Language (s): Finnish
NEWSPAPER

Pyhäjokiseutu
Owner: Suomen Paikallissanomat Oy
Editorial: PL 1/ Asemakatu 1, Oulainen 86301.
T: 358 10 66 55 145
E: toimitus.pyhajokiseutu@almamedia.fi
W: http://www.pyhajokiseutu.fi
Freq: 2 Times/Week; Circ: 6211
Editor in Chief: Sirpa Kortet
Language (s): Finnish; Full Page Colour:
3132.00
Currency: Euro
NEWSPAPER

Pyhäänlehti - Pyttisbladet
Owner: Loviisan Sanomain Oy
Editorial: PL 42/ Sibeliuksenkatu 10, Loviisa
7901. T: 358 19 53 27 01
E: pyhtaanlehti@lovari.fi
W: http://www.helsinki.fi/~pjojala/
Pyhtaan-Lehti.htm
Freq: Bi-Weekly; Circ: 7600 Pub Statement
Editor-in-Chief: Arto Henriksson
Language (s): Finnish
NEWSPAPER

Raahelainen
Owner: Suomen Paikallissanomat Oy
Editorial: Fellmaninpuistokatu 4, Raahe 92100.
T: 358 10 66 55 185 E: rstoimitus@sps.fi
W: http://www.raahelainen.fi
Freq: Weekly; Circ: 17020 Pub Statement
News: Sanna Keskinen; News: Nina
Tuomikoski
Language (s): Finnish; Full Page Colour:
4205.00
Currency: Euro
NEWSPAPER

Raahen Seutu
Owner: Suomen Paikallissanomat Oy
Editorial: PL 61/ Fellmaninpuistokatu 4, Raahe
92101. T: 358 10 66 55 185
E: toimitus.raahenseutu@almamedia.fi
W: http://www.raahenseutu.fi

Freq: Daily; Circ: 8753
News: Vappu Kallio; Editor in Chief: Sanna
Keskinen; News Producer: Nina Tuomikoski
Language (s): Finnish; Full Page Colour:
4205.00
Currency: Euro
NEWSPAPER

Rannikkoseutu
Owner: Suomen Paikallissanomat Oy
Editorial: PL 7/ Tornikatu 2, Raisio 21201.
T: 358 10 66 55 220
E: toimitus.rannikkoseutu@sps.fi
W: http://www.rannikkoseutu.fi
Freq: 2 Times/Week; Circ: 7591
Editor-In-Chief: Raija Leppänen
Language (s): Finnish; Full Page Colour:
2509.00
Currency: Euro
NEWSPAPER

Rantalakeus
Owner: Pohjois-Suomen Paikallisuutiset Oy
Editorial: PL 21/Limingan Säästökeskus,
Liminka 91901. T: 358 8 38 16 85
E: toimitus@rantalakeus.fi
W: http://www.rantalakeus.fi
Freq: Weekly; Circ: 3303
News: Ilkka Ylitalo
Language (s): Finnish
NEWSPAPER

Rantapohja
Owner: Rantapohja Oy
Editorial: PL 15/Huvipolku 6, Haukipudas
90831. T: 358 8 56 37 200
E: toimitus@rantapohja.fi
W: http://www.rantapohja.fi
Freq: 2 Times/Week; Circ: 9578
News: Juha Virranniemi
Language (s): Finnish; Full Page Colour:
1747.00
Currency: Euro
NEWSPAPER

Rantasalmen Lehti
Owner: Rantasalmen Lehti Oy
Editorial: PL 4 / Kylätie 37, Rantasalmi 58901.
T: 358 15 44 07 51
W: http://www.rantasalmenlehti.fi
Freq: Weekly; Circ: 3122
Editor in Chief: Arto Ylhävaara
Language (s): Finnish; Full Page Colour:
1748.00
Currency: Euro
NEWSPAPER

Reimari
Owner: Haminan yrittäjät ry
Editorial: Sibeliuskatu 36, Hamina.
T: 358 10 42 10 200
E: jorma.haapamaki@reimari.fi
W: http://www.reimari.fi
Freq: Weekly; Circ: 15800 Pub Statement
News: Jorma Haapamäki
Language (s): Finnish
NEWSPAPER

Reisjärvi
Owner: Reisjärvi-lehti Oy
Editorial: PL 2/ Kirkkotie 3 H, Reisjärvi 85901.
T: 358 8 77 70 20 E: toimitus@reisjarvilehti.fi
W: http://www.reisjarvilehti.fi
Freq: Weekly; Circ: 2068
Editor in Chief: Leila Lampi; Editor in Chief:
Merja Tytärniemi
Language (s): Finnish
NEWSPAPER

Riihimäen Seudun Viikkouutiset
Owner: Suomen Lehtiyhtymä
Editorial: PL 14/ Hämeenkatu 38, Riihimaki
11101. T: 358 20 61 00 121
E: toimitus.rile@lehtiyhtyma.fi
W: http://www.viikkouutiset.fi
Freq: Weekly; Circ: 23000 Pub Statement
News: Marko Kekki; News: Joonas
Romppanen
Language (s): Finnish; Full Page Colour:
4039.00
Currency: Euro
NEWSPAPER

Ristiinalainen
Owner: Kustannus Janari Oy
Editorial: PL 20/Brahentie 34, Ristiina 52301.
T: 358 15 33 73 560
E: toimitus@ristiinalainen.fi
W: http://www.ristiinalainen.fi
Freq: Weekly; Circ: 2600 Pub Statement
News: Niko Takala
Language (s): Finnish
NEWSPAPER

Rööperin lehti
T: 358 9 41 39 73 00 E: juha.ahola@karprint.fi
W: http://www.rooperinlehti.fi
Freq: Bi-Weekly; Circ: 20000 Pub Statement
Editor in Chief: Juha Ahola
Language (s): Finnish; Full Page Colour:
2348.00
Currency: Euro
NEWSPAPER

Ruokolahtelainen
Owner: Ruokolahden Seudun Kustannus Oy
Editorial: Toritie 6, Ruokolahti 56100.
T: 358 5 26 61 39
E: toimitus@ruokolahtelainen.com
W: http://www.ruokolahtelainen.com
Freq: Weekly; Circ: 1600 Pub Statement
Editor-in-Chief: Helmeri Frondelius; News: Airi
Ruokonen
Language (s): Finnish
NEWSPAPER

Ruovesi
Owner: Ruoveden Sanomalehti Oy
Editorial: PL 2/ Honkalantie 2, 2 krs, Ruovesi
34601. T: 358 3 47 61 400
E: toimitus@ruovesi-lehti.fi
W: http://www.ruovesi-lehti.fi
Freq: Weekly; Circ: 4422
Editor in Chief: Anu Kuivasmäki
Language (s): Finnish; Full Page Colour:
1998.00
Currency: Euro
NEWSPAPER

Saarijärveläinen
Owner: Luoteisen Keski-Suomen Viestintä Ky
Editorial: PL 104, Saarijärvi 43101.
T: 358 14 42 50 67
E: toimitus@saarijarvelainen.fi
W: http://www.saarijarvelainen.fi
Freq: Bi-Weekly; Circ: 12500 Pub Statement
Language (s): Finnish
NEWSPAPER

Saariselän Sanomat
Editorial: PL 33, Saariselkä 99831.
T: 358 400 25 26 52
E: saariselan.sanomat@saariselka.fi
W: http://www.saariselansanomat.fi
Freq: Quarterly; Circ: 17000 Pub Statement
News: Heikki Orava
Language (s): Finnish
NEWSPAPER

Salon Seudun Sanomat
Owner: Salon Seudun Sanomat Oy
Editorial: PL 117/ Örninkatu 14, Salo 24101.
T: 358 2 77 021 E: toimitus@sss.fi
W: http://www.sss.fi Circ: 21459
News Editor: Mari Areva; News Producer:
Johanna Käkönen; Editor in Chief: Ville
Pohjonen
Language (s): Finnish; Full Page Colour:
4600.00
Currency: Euro
NEWSPAPER

Salonjokilaakso
Owner: Salonjokilaakson Sanoma Oy
Editorial: PL 9/ Turuntie 15, Salo 24101.
T: 358 2 72 72 983
E: toimitus@salonjokilaakso.net
W: http://www.salonjokilaakso.net
Freq: Weekly; Circ: 28000 Pub Statement
Language (s): Finnish; Full Page Colour:
2497.00
Currency: Euro
NEWSPAPER

Sampo-lehti
Owner: Maakunnan Sanomat Oy
Editorial: PL 46/ Kauppakatu 5, Saarijärvi
43101. T: 358 14 42 14 60
E: toimitus@sampolehti.fi
W: http://www.sampolehti.fi
Freq: Weekly; Circ: 5930
News: Ilkka Salonen
Language (s): Finnish; Full Page Colour:
2153.00
Currency: Euro
NEWSPAPER

Satakunnan Kansa
Owner: Satakunnan Kirjateollisuus Oy
Editorial: PL 58/ Pohjoisranta 11 E, Pori
28101. T: 358 10 665 132
E: sk.toimitus@satakunnankansa.fi
W: http://www.satakunnankansa.fi
Freq: Daily; Circ: 44674
Editor: Pertti Heikkilä; Editor: Marita Lehtojoki;
Editor: Harri Pullinen; Editor in Chief: Tapio
Vallin
Language (s): Finnish; Full Page Colour:
6500.00
Currency: Euro
NEWSPAPER

Satakunnan Työ
Owner: Kansan Uutiset Oy
Editorial: PL 41/ Eteläpuisto 14, Pori 28101.
T: 358 2 63 03 200
E: toimitus@satakunnantyo.fi
W: http://www.satakunnantyo.fi Circ: 2680
Editor in Chief: Sirpa Koskinen
Language (s): Finnish; Full Page Colour:
4944.00
Currency: Euro
NEWSPAPER

Satakunnan Viikko
Owner: Lalli Oy
Editorial: Gallen-Kallelankatu 8, Pori 28100.
T: 358 2 63 44 500
E: toimitus@satakunnanviikko.fi
W: http://www.satakunnanviikko.fi
Freq: Weekly; Circ: 55000 Pub Statement
Language (s): Finnish; Full Page Colour:
2050.00
Currency: Euro
NEWSPAPER

Savon Sanomat
Owner: Savon Mediat Oy
Editorial: PL 68/Vuorikatu 21, Kuopio 70101.
T: 358 17 30 31 11
E: uutiset@savonsanomat.fi
W: http://www.savonsanomat.fi
Freq: Daily; Circ: 61666
Editor: Tuomo Tynkkynen
Language (s): Finnish; Full Page Colour:
7170.00
Currency: Euro
DAILY NEWSPAPER

Savon Sanomat Keski-Savon aluetoimitus
Owner: Savon Mediat Oy
Editorial: PL 197/ Pirnankatu 4, Varkaus
78201 E: varkaus@savonsanomat.fi
W: http://www.savonsanomat.fi
Editorial Profile: Bureau
Language (s): Finnish
DAILY NEWSPAPER

Savon Sanomat Pieksämäki
Owner: Savon Mediat Oy
Editorial: Keskuskatu 15, Pieksämäki 76100.
T: 358 15 34 16 00
E: pieksamaki@savonsanomat.fi
W: http://www.savonsanomat.fi
Editorial Profile: Bureau
Language (s): Finnish
DAILY NEWSPAPER

Savon Sanomat Ylä-Savon aluetoimitus
Owner: Savon Mediat Oy
Editorial: Kilpivirrantie 7, 2 krs, Iisalmi 74120.
T: 358 17 83 51 480
E: iisalmi@savonsanomat.fi
W: http://www.savonsanomat.fi
Editorial Profile: Bureau
Language (s): Finnish
DAILY NEWSPAPER

Savonmaa
Owner: Savon Mediat Oy
Editorial: PL 14/ Kaartilantie 10, Savonlinna
57101. T: 358 15 57 68 70
E: toimitus@savonmaa.fi
W: http://www.savonmaa.fi
Freq: Weekly; Circ: 25000 Pub Statement
Language (s): Finnish; Full Page Colour:
2268.00
Currency: Euro
NEWSPAPER

Säynätsalon Sanomat
Owner: Monexmedia Oy
Editorial: Kirrintie 11, Palokka 40270.
T: 358 40 51 39 464
E: toimitus@saynatsalonsanomat.fi
W: http://www.saynatsalonsanomat.fi
Freq: Weekly; Circ: 1100 Pub Statement
News: Erkki Keiskoski; News: Kari Ruuska;
Editor-in-Chief: Elina Sukuvaara
Language (s): Finnish
NEWSPAPER

Seinäjoen Sanomat
Owner: SLY Kaupunkimedia Oy
Editorial: Kauppakatu 20, 2.krs (Torikeskus),
Seinäjoki 60100. T: 358 20 6100 165
E: sjk.toimitus@lehtiyhtyma.fi
W: http://www.seinajoensanomat.fi
Freq: Weekly; Circ: 48500 Pub Statement
Editor in Chief: Krista Rintala
Language (s): Finnish; Full Page Colour:
1935.00
Currency: Euro
NEWSPAPER

Seinäjokinen
Owner: Seinäjokinen Lehti Oy
Editorial: Koulukatu 54 A, Seinäjoki 60100.
T: 358 6 42 33 060
W: http://www.seinajokinen.fi
Freq: Weekly; Circ: 24912 Pub Statement
News: Seppo Juvonen
Language (s): Finnish
NEWSPAPER

Seutulainen
Editorial: Seutulainen Oy, Kangasalantie 921,
Kangasala 36200. T: 358 3 364 1362
E: tapio.metsoila@seutulainen.fi
W: http://www.seutulainen.fi
Freq: Monthly; Circ: 94000
Language (s): Finnish; Full Page Colour:
1785.00
Currency: Euro
NEWSPAPER

SeutuMajakka
T: 358 440 47 01 25
E: toimitus@seutumajakka.fi
W: http://www.seutumajakka.fi Circ: 8500
News: Ari Vilminko
Language (s): Finnish
NEWSPAPER

Seutuneloset
Owner: Esan Kaupunkilehdet Oy
Editorial: Hämeenkatu 5 A 4, Lahti 15110.
T: 358 3 88 48 00 E: toimitus@seutuneloset.fi
W: http://www.seutuneloset.fi
Freq: Weekly; Circ: 39370 Pub Statement
Editor in Chief: Stiina Ikonen
Language (s): Finnish
NEWSPAPER

Sieviläinen
Owner: Sievi-Seura r.y.
Editorial: PL 23/Haikolantie 23, Sievi 85411.
T: 358 8 48 02 78
E: sievilainen-lehti@kolumbus.fi
W: http://www.sievilainenlehti.fi
Freq: Weekly; Circ: 2676
Editor-in-Chief: Kati Rahkonen; News: Inka
Saviluoto
Language (s): Finnish
NEWSPAPER

Siikajokilaakso
Owner: Pohjois-Suomen Paikallisuutiset Oy
Editorial: PL 22/Pekkalantie 3, Ruukki 92401.
T: 358 8 27 07 400 E: toimitus@siikkis.fi
W: http://www.siikkis.fi
Freq: 2 Times/Week; Circ: 4535
Editor in Chief: Pekka Keväjärvi
Language (s): Finnish; Full Page Colour:
3000.00
Currency: Euro
NEWSPAPER

Sinun Savo
Editorial: Kauppakatu 20, Varkaus 78200.
T: 358 17 36 69 304 E: toimitus@sinunsavo.fi
W: http://www.sinunsavo.fi
Freq: 2 Times/Week; Circ: 25000 Pub
Statement
Language (s): Finnish
NEWSPAPER

Sipoon Sanomat
Owner: SLY-Paikallislehdet Oy
Editorial: PL 11/Iso Kylätie 20, Sipoo 4131.
T: 358 20 61 00 101
E: sipoon.sanomat@lehtiyhtyma.fi
W: http://www.sipoonsanomat.fi
Freq: Weekly; Circ: 3599
Editor in Chief: Riitta Ketola
Language (s): Finnish; Full Page Colour:
5150.00
Currency: Euro
NEWSPAPER

Sisä-Savo
Owner: Maakunnan Sanomat Oy
Editorial: PL 14/ Iisvedentie 3, Suonenjoki
77601. T: 358 17 28 87 700
E: uutiset@sisa-savolehti.fi
W: http://www.sisa-savonsanomat.fi
Freq: 2 Times/Week; Circ: 7039
News: Tarja Lappalainen
Language (s): Finnish; Full Page Colour:
2686.00
Currency: Euro
NEWSPAPER

Sisä-Suomen Lehti
Owner: Maakunnan Sanomat Oy
Editorial: PL 15/ Kauppakatu 1, Äänekoski
44101. T: 358 14 34 89 500
E: toimitus@sisasuomenlehti.fi
W: http://www.sisasuomenlehti.fi
Freq: 2 Times/Week; Circ: 7222
Editor in Chief: Eija Varteva

Language (s): Finnish; Full Page Colour:
2531.00
Currency: Euro
NEWSPAPER

Soisalon Seutu
Owner: Maakunnan Sanomat Oy
Editorial: PL 32 / Savonkatu 32, Leppävirta
79101. T: 358 17 28 87 741
W: http://www.soisalonseutu.fi
Freq: 2 Times/Week; Circ: 4895
Language (s): Finnish; Full Page Colour:
2997.00
Currency: Euro
NEWSPAPER

Somero
Owner: Salon Seudun Sanomat Oy
Editorial: PL 11/Kiiruuntie 1, Somero 31401.
T: 358 2 58 88 561 E: toimitus@somerolehti.fi
W: http://www.somerolehti.fi
Freq: 2 Times/Week; Circ: 5333
Editor in Chief: Sari Merilä
Language (s): Finnish; Full Page Colour:
2497.00
Currency: Euro
NEWSPAPER

Sompio
Owner: Fourpress Oy
Editorial: PL 69/ Jäämerentie 4 A, Sodankylä
99601. T: 358 10 66 64 140
E: toimitus@sompio.fi
W: http://www.sompio.fi
Freq: 2 Times/Week; Circ: 3482
Language (s): Finnish
NEWSPAPER

Sotkamo-Lehti
Owner: Suomen Paikallissanomat Oy
Editorial: Keskuskatu 10, Sotkamo 88600.
T: 358 10 66 56 000 E: sot.toimitus@sps.fi
W: http://www.sotkamolehti.fi
Freq: 2 Times/Week; Circ: 5602
Editor in Chief: Martti Huusko
Language (s): Finnish; Full Page Colour:
2518.00
Currency: Euro
NEWSPAPER

Sulkava-lehti
Owner: Sulkavan Kotiseutulehti Oy
Editorial: Uitonrinne 18, Sulkava 58700.
T: 358 15 47 15 44 E: sulkava.lehti@co.inet.fi
Freq: Weekly; Circ: 2678
News: Kalle Keränen
Language (s): Finnish; Full Page Colour:
1850.00
Currency: Euro
NEWSPAPER

Suomenmaa Helsinki
Owner: Suomenmaan Kustannus Oy
Editorial: Apollonkatu 11 A, Helsinki 100.
T: 358 44 73 70 262 E: uutiset@suomenmaa.fi
W: http://www.suomenmaa.fi
Freq: 3 Times/Week; Circ: 11197
Language (s): Finnish
NEWSPAPER

Suomenmaa Oulun toimitus
Owner: Suomenmaan Kustannus Oy
Editorial: Lekatie 4, Oulu 90150.
T: 358 8 53 70 334 E: uutiset@suomenmaa.fi
W: http://www.suomenmaa.fi
Freq: 3 Times/Week; Circ: 11197
Language (s): Finnish
DAILY NEWSPAPER

Suomenselän Sanomat
Owner: Suomenselän Sanomat Oy
Editorial: PL 11/ Virtaintie 40, Virrat 34801.
T: 358 3 47 55 320 E: toimitus@sss.inet.fi
W: http://www.suomenselansanomat.net
Freq: Weekly; Circ: 5200 Pub Statement
News: Riikka Alalantela
Language (s): Finnish; Full Page Colour:
2686.00
Currency: Euro
NEWSPAPER

Suupohjan Sanomat
Owner: Pohjanmaan Lähisanomat Oy
Editorial: PL 4/Läntinen Pitkäkatu 15,
Kristiinankaupunki 64101. T: 358 6 24 77 880
E: toimitus@suupohjansanomat.fi
W: http://www.suupohjansanomat.fi
Freq: 2 Times/Week; Circ: 4092
News: Olli Pursiainen
Language (s): Finnish; Full Page Colour:
3197.00
Currency: Euro
NEWSPAPER

Suur-Jyväskylän Lehti
Owner: Keskisuomalainen Oyj

Editorial: PL 115/ Kauppakatu 41 A, Jyväskylä
40101. T: 358 44 406 2337 E: toimitus@sjl.fi
W: http://www.sjl.fi/web/index.php
Freq: 2 Times/Week; Circ: 82000 Pub
Statement
Editor in Chief: Tapani Markkanen
Language (s): Finnish; Full Page Colour:
4884.00
Currency: Euro
NEWSPAPER

Suur-Keuruu
Owner: Suomen Paikallissanomat Oy
Editorial: PL 31 / Niilontie 1, Keuruu 42701.
T: 358 10 66 55 186
E: toimitus.suurkeuruu@almamedia.fi
W: http://www.suurkeuruu.fi
Freq: 2 Times/Week; Circ: 6104
Editor in Chief: Eija Ruoho
Language (s): Finnish; Full Page Colour:
2575.00
Currency: Euro
NEWSPAPER

Suur-Tampere
Owner: Pirkanmaan Sanomat Oy
Editorial: Hämeenkatu 27 B 4 krs, Tampere
33200. T: 358 10 58 44 222
E: salli@suurtampere.fi
W: http://suurtampere.fi
Freq: Weekly; Circ: 139000 Pub Statement
Editor in Chief: Salli Saastamoinen
Language (s): Finnish; Full Page Colour:
1990.00
Currency: Euro
NEWSPAPER

Suvannon Seutu
Owner: Sakkola-Säätiö
Editorial: Rautasemantie 375, Lempäälä
37550. T: 358 3 37 48 448
W: http://www.sakkola.fi/nykypaiva/contacts.
html
Freq: Bi-Monthly; Circ: 1300 Pub Statement
News: Marjo Ristilä-Toikka
Language (s): Finnish
NEWSPAPER

Sydän-Hämeen Lehti
Owner: Sydän-Hämeen Kustannus Oy
Editorial: PL 16 / Onkkaalantie 58, Pälkäne
36601. T: 358 3 53 99 800 E: toimitus@shl.fi
W: http://www.shl.fi
Freq: 2 Times/Week; Circ: 5449
News: Tommi Liljedahl
Language (s): Finnish; Full Page Colour:
2696.00
Currency: Euro
NEWSPAPER

Sydän-Satakunta
Owner: Suomen Paikallissanomat Oy
Editorial: PL 34/ Kilkunkatu 12, Kokemäki
32801. T: 358 10 66 55 700
E: ss.toimitus@sps.fi
W: http://www.sydansatakunta.fi
Freq: 2 Times/Week; Circ: 6897
News: Pirjo Haimila; News: Timo Simula
Language (s): Finnish; Full Page Colour:
2668.00
Currency: Euro
NEWSPAPER

Syd-Österbotten
Owner: Syd-Österbottens Tidnings Ab
Editorial: PB 6/ Närpesvägen 4, Närpes
64201. T: 358 6 78 48 700
E: redaktion@sydin.fi W: http://www.sydin.fi
Circ: 7149
News: Mats Ekman; News: Benita
Kummel-Erikson; News: Lotta Sjöblad
Language (s): Swedish; Full Page Colour:
3816.00
Currency: Euro
NEWSPAPER

Tammerfors Aktuellt
Owner: Svenska Sällskapsklubben i
Tammerfors rf
Editorial: Satamakatu 19, Tammerfors 33200.
T: 358 3 22 31 373
E: tammerfors.aktuellt@elisanet.fi
W: http://www.tammerforsaktuellt.fi
Freq: Bi-Weekly; Circ: 600 Pub Statement
News: Kjell Ahs; News: Kaj Andrésen
Language (s): Swedish
NEWSPAPER

Tammerkoski
Owner: Tampere-Seura
Editorial: Kauppakatu 1, Tampere 33200.
T: 358 3 31 24 14 00
E: tammerkoski-lehti@tampere-seura.fi
W: http://www.tampere-seura.fi
Freq: Bi-Monthly; Circ: 4000 Pub Statement
News: Katriina Avonius

Language (s): Finnish; Full Page Mono:
340.00
Currency: Euro
NEWSPAPER

Tamperelainen
Owner: Kaupunkilehti Tamperelainen Oy
Editorial: Satakunnankatu 13 B, (2. krs.),
Tampere 33100. T: 358 20 61 00 170
E: tre.toimitus@lehtiyhtyma.fi
W: http://www.tamperelainen.fi
Freq: 2 Times/Week; Circ: 132000 Pub
Statement
Editor in Chief: Sakari Nupponen
Language (s): Finnish; Full Page Colour:
4351.00
Currency: Euro
NEWSPAPER

Tanotorvi
Owner: Kaarela-Seura ry
Editorial: Klaneettitie 11, Helsinki 420.
T: 358 9 53 08 19 90 E: tanotorvi@eepinen.fi
W: http://www.kaarela-seura.com/14
Freq: Monthly; Circ: 32000 Pub Statement
Editor in Chief: Kari Varvikko
Language (s): Finnish; Full Page Colour:
2300.00
Currency: Euro
NEWSPAPER

Tapiolan lähiseudun asiakaslehti
Owner: Oy Quality International QI LtdAb
Editorial: Tapiontori 1, 8. krs, Espoo 2100.
T: 358 9 46 41 18
E: tapiolan-lehti@tapiolan.com
W: http://www.tapiolan.com
Freq: Monthly; Circ: 50000 Pub Statement
Editor in Chief: Eva Kivilaakso-Wellmann
Language (s): Finnish; Full Page Colour:
2766.00
Currency: Euro
NEWSPAPER

Teisko-Aitolahti
Owner: Ruoveden Sanomalehti Oy
Editorial: PL 2/ Runoilijankulma, Honkalantie
2, 2 krs, Ruovesi 34601. T: 358 3 47 61 400
E: teisko.aitolahti@ruovesi-lehti.fi
W: http://www.ruovesi-lehti.fi
Freq: Weekly; Circ: 1827
Editor in Chief: Anu Kuivasmäki
Language (s): Finnish; Full Page Colour:
1776.00
Currency: Euro
NEWSPAPER

Tejuka
Owner: Paikallislehti Tejuka Oy
Editorial: PL 16 / Tiilitie 2, Teuva 64701.
T: 358 6 24 74 300 E: toimitus@tejuka-lehti.fi
W: http://www.tejuka-lehti.fi
Freq: Weekly; Circ: 3988
Editor in Chief: Jaakko Ujainen
Language (s): Finnish
NEWSPAPER

Tervareitti
Owner: Tervareitti Oy
Editorial: PL 63/ Aaronkuja 5, Muhos 91501.
T: 358 8 53 13 700 E: toimitus@tervareitti.fi
W: http://www.tervareitti.fi
Freq: 2 Times/Week; Circ: 5965
Editor in Chief: Marianne Ollikainen
Language (s): Finnish; Full Page Colour:
2299.00
Currency: Euro
NEWSPAPER

Töllötin
Owner: Keskisuomalainen Oyj
Editorial: Riistakatu 5, Iisalmi 74100.
T: 358 17 81 77 00 E: ilmoitukset@tollotin.fi
W: http://www.tollotin.fi
Freq: Weekly; Circ: 32000 Pub Statement
Language (s): Finnish; Full Page Colour:
1350.00
Currency: Euro
NEWSPAPER

Töölöläinen
Owner: Töölöläinen Oy
Editorial: Temppelikatu 8, Helsinki 100.
T: 358 9 44 10 51
E: toimitus@paikallislehdet.com
Freq: Bi-Weekly; Circ: 25500 Pub Statement
News: Mikko Keski-Vähälä
Language (s): Finnish; Full Page Colour:
1964.00
Currency: Euro
NEWSPAPER

Torstai -lehti
Owner: Järvi-Pohjanmaan Viestintä Oy
Editorial: PL 85/ Kauppakatu 18, Alajärvi
62901. T: 358 6 55 75 900
E: toimitus@torstai-lehti.fi

W: http://www.torstai-lehti.fi
Freq: Weekly; Circ: 14000 Pub Statement
Editor in Chief: Tuula Jokiaho
Language (s): Finnish
NEWSPAPER

Turkulainen
Owner: Kaupunkilehti Turkulainen Oy
Editorial: PL 396/ Läntinen Pitkäkatu 34, 4.krs, Turku 20101. T: 358 20 6 100 160
E: tku.toimitus@lehtiyhtyma.fi
W: http://www.turkulainen.fi
Freq: 2 Times/Week; Circ: 118100 Pub Statement
Language (s): Finnish; Full Page Colour: 4351.00
Currency: Euro
NEWSPAPER

Turkuposti
Owner: Turun kaupunki
Editorial: PL 355, Turku 20101.
T: 358 2 33 00 00 E: turkuposti@turku.fi
W: http://www.turku.fi/turkuposti
Freq: Bi-Monthly; Circ: 116000 Pub Statement
Editor in Chief: Hannu Waher
Language (s): Finnish
NEWSPAPER

Turun Sanomat
Owner: Turun Sanomat Oy
Editorial: PL 95/ Länsikaari 15, Turku 20101.
T: 358 2 26 93 311 E: ts.uutiset@ts.fi
W: http://www.ts.fi Circ: 103314
Editor in Chief: Riitta Monto; Editor in Chief: Riitta Monto
Language (s): Finnish; Full Page Colour: 11634.84
Currency: Euro
DAILY NEWSPAPER

Turun Sanomat Loimaa
Owner: Turun Sanomat Oy
Editorial: Käsityöläiskatu 10, Loimaa 32200.
T: 358 50 51 20 112 E: anne.savolainen@ts.fi
W: http://www.ts.fi
Editorial Profile: Bureau
Language (s): Finnish
DAILY NEWSPAPER

Turun Sanomat Rauma
Owner: Turun Sanomat Oy
Editorial: Seminaarinkatu 5, Rauma 26100.
T: 358 2 82 11 570 E: jari.rantanen@ts.fi
W: http://www.ts.fi
Editorial Profile: Bureau
Language (s): Finnish
DAILY NEWSPAPER

Turun Sanomat Säkylä
Owner: Turun Sanomat Oy
Editorial: Lehtikallentie 2, Säkylä 27800.
T: 358 2 86 70 940 W: http://www.ts.fi
Editorial Profile: Bureau
Language (s): Finnish
DAILY NEWSPAPER

Turun Sanomat Salo
Owner: Turun Sanomat Oy
Editorial: Katrineholminkatu 7, Salo 24240.
T: 358 2 73 15 255 E: paivi.palm@ts.fi
W: http://www.ts.fi
Editorial Profile: Bureau
Language (s): Finnish
DAILY NEWSPAPER

Turun Sanomat Uusikaupunki
Owner: Turun Sanomat Oy
Editorial: Alinenkatu 29, Uusikaupunki 23500.
T: 358 2 84 51 14 51
E: jaakko.louhivuori@ts.fi W: http://www.ts.fi
Editorial Profile: Bureau
Language (s): Finnish
DAILY NEWSPAPER

Turun Tienoo
Owner: Turun Seutu Oy
Editorial: Elotie 26, Lieto As. 21360.
T: 358 2 48 92 00 E: toimitus@turuntienoo.fi
W: http://www.turuntienoo.fi
Freq: 2 Times/Week; Circ: 5732
News: Rauli Ala-Karvia
Language (s): Finnish; Full Page Colour: 2878.00
Currency: Euro
NEWSPAPER

Tuusulanjärven Viikkouutiset
Owner: Suomen Lehtiyhtymä
Editorial: PL 52/Klaavolantie 5, Tuusula 4300.
T: 358 20 61 00 150
E: vu.toimitus@lehtiyhtyma.fi
W: http://www.viikkouutiset.fi
Freq: 2 Times/Week; Circ: 39000 Pub Statement

Editor in Chief: Pentti Kiiski
Language (s): Finnish; Full Page Colour: 3948.00
Currency: Euro
NEWSPAPER

Tyrvään Sanomat
Owner: Suomen Paikallissanomat Oy
Editorial: PL 21 / Onkiniemenkatu 18, Sastamala 38201. T: 358 10 66 55 781
E: toimitus.tyrvaansanomat@almamedia.fi
W: http://www.tyrvaansanomat.fi
Freq: 2 Times/Week; Circ: 9063 Pub Statement
Language (s): Finnish; Full Page Colour: 2935.00
Currency: Euro
NEWSPAPER

Ulvilan Seutu
Owner: Ulvilan Seutu Oy
Editorial: PL 11/ Friitalantie 13, Ulvila 28401.
T: 358 2 53 11 721 E: toimitus@ulvilanseutu.fi
W: http://www.ulvilanseutu.fi
Freq: Weekly; Circ: 3072
Editor in Chief: Sini Ovaskainen
Language (s): Finnish
NEWSPAPER

Urjalan Sanomat
Owner: Urjalan Sanomat Oy
Editorial: PL 61/ Urjalantie 26, Urjala 31761.
T: 358 40 18 13 020
E: toimitus@urjalansanomat.fi
W: http://www.urjalansanomat.fi
Freq: Weekly; Circ: 5192
Editor in Chief: Minna Mäkelä; Editor in Chief: Olli Ristimäki
Language (s): Finnish; Full Page Colour: 1634.00
Currency: Euro
NEWSPAPER

Uudenkaupungin Sanomat
Owner: Uudenkaupungin Sanomat Oy
Editorial: PL 68/ Alinenkatu 29, Uusikaupunki 23501. T: 358 2 58 88 302
E: toimitus@uudenkaupunginsanomat.fi
W: http://www.uudenkaupunginsanomat.fi
Circ: 7462
Editor in Chief: Matti Jussila
Language (s): Finnish; Full Page Colour: 3635.00
Currency: Euro
NEWSPAPER

Uusi Aika
Owner: Ajan Sana Oy
Editorial: PL 205/Kuninkaanlahdenkatu 7, Pori 28101. T: 358 44 73 00 200
E: ua.toimitus@uusiaika-lehti.fi
W: http://www.uusiaika-lehti.fi Circ: 7121
Editor in Chief: Jukka Vilponiemi
Language (s): Finnish; Full Page Colour: 5191.00
Currency: Euro
NEWSPAPER

Uusi Espoo
Owner: KEA-Invest Oy
Editorial: Itäportti 4 A, Espoo 2210.
T: 358 20 74 88 521
E: taina.vilo@kokoomus.fi
W: http://www.espoonkokoomus.fi/index/etusivu
Freq: Semi-Annual; Circ: 103700 Pub Statement
Editor in Chief: Taina Vilo
Language (s): Finnish
NEWSPAPER

Uusi Lahti
Owner: Esan Paikallislehdet Oy
Editorial: Hämeenkatu 5 A 4, 2 krs., Lahti 15110. T: 358 3 87 68 76
E: toimitus@uusilahti.fi
W: http://www.uusilahti.fi
Freq: 2 Times/Week; Circ: 54700 Pub Statement
Editor in Chief: Tommi Berg
Language (s): Finnish
NEWSPAPER

Uusi Pori
Owner: Kustannusosakeyhtiö Uusi-Tuuli
Editorial: Isolinnankatu 28, Pori 28100.
T: 358 400 788 620 E: toimitus@uusipori.fi
W: http://www.uusipori.fi
Freq: Weekly; Circ: 60000 Pub Statement
Language (s): Finnish
NEWSPAPER

Uusi Rauma
Owner: Länsirannikon Viestintä Oy
Editorial: Susivuorentie 2, Rauma 26100.
T: 358 10 83 36 555 E: toimitus@uusirauma.fi
W: http://www.uusirauma.fi

Freq: 2 Times/Week; Circ: 38600 Pub Statement
Language (s): Finnish; Full Page Colour: 2245.00
Currency: Euro
NEWSPAPER

Uusi Rovaniemi
Owner: Pohjois-Suomen Media Oy
Editorial: Veitikantie 2-8 A, Rovaniemi 96100.
T: 358 10 66 57 806
E: ur.toimitus@uusirovaniemi.fi
W: http://www.uusirovaniemi.fi
Freq: 2 Times/Week; Circ: 31800 Pub Statement
Editor in Chief: Leena Talvensaari
Language (s): Finnish; Full Page Colour: 955.28
Currency: Euro
NEWSPAPER

Uusi Vantaa
Owner: Kokoomuksen Vantaan Kunnallisjärjestö ry
Editorial: Pakkalankuja 5, Vantaa 1510.
T: 358 20 74 88 523
E: kim.zilliacus@kokoomus.fi
W: http://www.vantaankokoomus.fi
Freq: Semi-Annual; Circ: 85500 Pub Statement
Editor in Chief: Kim Zilliacus
Language (s): Finnish
NEWSPAPER

Uusimaa
Owner: Uusimaa Oy
Editorial: PL 15/Teollisuustie 19, Porvoo 6151.
T: 358 20 61 00 140
E: toimitus.uusimaa@lehtiyhtyma.fi
W: http://www.uusimaa.fi Circ: 12603
News: Jari Lammassaari
Language (s): Finnish; Full Page Colour: 7210.00
Currency: Euro
NEWSPAPER

UUTIS alasin
Owner: Tohmajärvi-Värtsilä Lehti Oy
Editorial: PL 6 / Asemantie 2, Tohmajärvi 82601. T: 358 10 42 24 000
E: toimitus@uutisalasin.fi
W: http://www.uutisalasin.fi
Freq: Weekly; Circ: 2373
News: Kari K. Martikainen
Language (s): Finnish
NEWSPAPER

Uutis-Jousi
Owner: Maakunnan Sanomat Oy
Editorial: Asematie 2, Siilinjärvi 71800.
T: 358 17 28 77 800 E: uutiset@uutis-jousi.fi
W: http://www.uutis-jousi.fi
Freq: 2 Times/Week; Circ: 6406
Language (s): Finnish; Full Page Colour: 3796.00
Currency: Euro
NEWSPAPER

Uutisvuoksi
Owner: Sanoma News Oy
Editorial: PL 100/ Esterinkatu 10, Imatra 55101. T: 358 5 2100 2600
E: toimitus@uutisvuoksi.fi
W: http://www.uutisvuoksi.fi
Freq: Daily; Circ: 25000 Pub Statement
Language (s): Finnish; Full Page Colour: 2680.00
Currency: Euro
NEWSPAPER

Vaarojen Sanomat
Owner: Juuka-seura ry
Editorial: Juuantie 9 A, Juuka 83900.
T: 358 10 83 54 004
E: toimitus@vaarojensanomat.fi
W: http://www.juukaseura.fi/fi/Vaarojen+Sanomat.html
Freq: 2 Times/Week; Circ: 3790
Editor in Chief: Pasi Karjalainen
Language (s): Finnish
NEWSPAPER

Vaasan Ikkuna
Owner: I-Mediat Oy
Editorial: Hietasaarenkatu 19, Vaasa 65100.
T: 358 6 24 77 966
E: vaasanikkuna@vaasanikkuna.fi
W: http://www.vaasanikkuna.fi
Freq: Weekly; Circ: 52388 Pub Statement
Editor in Chief: Vesa Koivumäki
Language (s): Finnish; Full Page Colour: 3614.00
Currency: Euro
NEWSPAPER

Vakka-Suomen Sanomat
Owner: Vakka-Suomen Sanomain Kuntayhtymä
Editorial: PL 84/ Rauhankatu 8 A, Uusikaupunki 23501. T: 358 2 84 26 300
E: toimitus@vakka.fi W: http://www.vakkass.fi
Freq: 2 Times/Week; Circ: 8380
Editor in Chief: Jarno Keskinen
Language (s): Finnish; Full Page Colour: 4050.00
Currency: Euro
NEWSPAPER

Valkeakosken Sanomat
Owner: Suomen Paikallissanomat Oy
Editorial: Valtakatu 9-11, 4 krs, Valkeakoski 37600. T: 358 10 66 55 730
E: toimitus.valkeakoskensanomat@almamedia.fi W: http://www.valkeakoskensanomat.fi
Freq: Daily; Circ: 7215
Editor in Chief: Simo Husso; News Producer: Eila Saukkonen
Language (s): Finnish; Full Page Colour: 4314.00
Currency: Euro
NEWSPAPER

Valkealan Sanomat
Owner: Valkealan Sanomat Oy
Editorial: PL 31 / Vanhatie 3, Valkeala 45371.
T: 358 10 66 65 466
E: toimitus@valkealansanomat.fi
W: http://www.valkealansanomat.fi
Freq: Weekly; Circ: 4720 Pub Statement
Editor in Chief: Auli Kousa
Language (s): Finnish; Full Page Colour: 1825.00
Currency: Euro
NEWSPAPER

Vantaalainen
Owner: Vantaan Sosialidemokraattinen Kunnallisjärjestö
Editorial: Lehdokkitie 2 B, Vantaa 1300.
T: 358 9 82 30 595 E: vantaakj@sdp.fi
W: http://www.vantaandemarit.fi
Freq: Quarterly; Circ: 58000 Pub Statement
Language (s): Finnish
NEWSPAPER

Vantaan Sanomat
Owner: SLY-Kaupunkilehdet Oy
Editorial: PL 350/ Rälssitie 7 A, Vantaa 1511.
T: 358 20 61 00 110
E: vantaan.sanomat@lehtiyhtyma.fi
W: http://www.vantaansanomat.fi
Freq: 2 Times/Week; Circ: 89600 Pub Statement
Editor in Chief: Risto Hietanen
Language (s): Finnish; Full Page Colour: 3535.00
Currency: Euro
NEWSPAPER

Vartti Etelä-Karjala
Owner: Sanoma News Oy
Editorial: Lauritsalantie 1, Lappeenranta 53500. T: 358 5 53 88 19
E: toimitus.vartti.ek@sanoma.fi
W: http://www.vartti.fi
Freq: 2 Times/Week; Circ: 65000 Pub Statement
Editor in Chief: Ari Toivonen
Language (s): Finnish; Full Page Colour: 1950.00
Currency: Euro
NEWSPAPER

Vartti Kouvola
Owner: Sanoma News Oy
Editorial: Lehtikaari 1, Kouvola 45130.
T: 358 5 37 52 460
E: varttikouvola@sanoma.fi
W: http://www.varttikouvola.fi
Freq: Weekly; Circ: 48000 Pub Statement
Editor in Chief: Hannu Helineva
Language (s): Finnish; Full Page Colour: 1950.00
Currency: Euro
NEWSPAPER

Vasabladet
Owner: HSS Media Ab
Editorial: PL 52/ Sandögatan 20, Vasa 65101.
T: 358 6 78 48 200 E: nyheter@vasabladet.fi
W: http://www.vasabladet.fi
Freq: Daily; Circ: 20696
Editor: Monica Ahlroth; Editor in Chief: Camilla Berggren
Language (s): Swedish
NEWSPAPER

Västra Nyland
Owner: Ekenäs Tryckeri AB
Editorial: PB 26/ Genvägen 4, Ekenäs 10601.
T: 358 19 22 28 22 E: vnred@vastranyland.fi
W: http://www.vastranyland.fi

Freq: Daily; **Circ:** 10710
Editor: Camilla Lindberg
Language (s): Swedish; Full Page Colour:
3685.00
Currency: Euro
NEWSPAPER

Väylä
Owner: Paltamon Kirjapaino Ky
Editorial: Sairaalatie 8, Paltamo 88300.
T: 358 8 87 19 99
E: aineistot@paltamonkirjapaino.fi
W: http://www.paltamonkirjapaino.fi
Freq: Weekly; **Circ:** 1800 Pub Statement
News: Tuula Keränen
Language (s): Finnish
NEWSPAPER

Vieskalainen
Owner: Jokilaaksojen Kustannus Oy
Editorial: PL 45/ Eteläväylä, Kokkola 67101.
T: 358 20 75 04 400 **E:** toimitus@kpk.fi
W: http://www.vieskalainen.fi
Freq: Weekly; **Circ:** 11300 Pub Statement
Editor in Chief: Seppo Kangas
Language (s): Finnish; Full Page Colour:
1862.00
Currency: Euro
NEWSPAPER

Vihdin Uutiset
Owner: SLY-Paikallislehdet Oy
Editorial: Naaranpajuntie 3, Nummela 3100.
T: 358 20 61 00 133
E: viu.toimitus@lehtiyhtyma.fi
W: http://www.vihdinuutiset.fi
Freq: 2 Times/Week; **Circ:** 16700 Pub
Statement
News: Vesa Valtonen
Language (s): Finnish; Full Page Colour:
6757.00
Currency: Euro
NEWSPAPER

Viikko Pohjois-Karjala
Owner: Sanomalehti Uusi Pohjois-Karjala Oy
Editorial: PL 97/ Niskakatu 7, Joensuu 80101.
T: 358 13 73 75 811 **E:** toimitus@viikkopk.fi
W: http://www.viikkopk.fi
Freq: Weekly; **Circ:** 7193
News: Pekka Kivioja
Language (s): Finnish; Full Page Colour:
5922.00
Currency: Euro
NEWSPAPER

Viikkosavo
Owner: Viikkosavo Oy
Editorial: PL 8/ Snellmaninkatu 35, Kuopio
70100. **T:** 358 17 288 8300
E: toimitus@viikkosavo.fi
W: http://www.viikkosavo.fi
Freq: Weekly; **Circ:** 62500 Pub Statement
Editor in Chief: Tapani Markkanen
Language (s): Finnish
NEWSPAPER

Viikkoset
Owner: ESV-Julkaisut Oy
Editorial: Yrjönkatu 5, Mikkeli 50100.
T: 358 440 35 05 22
E: toimitus.viikkoset@lansi-savo.fi
W: http://www.viikkoset.fi
Freq: Weekly; **Circ:** 26500 Pub Statement
News: Jari Lappalainen
Language (s): Finnish; Full Page Colour:
2244.00
Currency: Euro
NEWSPAPER

Viiskunta
Owner: Pohjanmaan Lähisanomat Oy
Editorial: PL 11/Kirjapainokuja 2, Alavus
63301. **T:** 358 6 24 77 870
E: toimitus@viiskunta.fi
W: http://www.viiskunta.fi
Freq: 2 Times/Week; **Circ:** 5987
Editor in Chief: Ella Nurmi
Language (s): Finnish; Full Page Colour:
3986.00
Currency: Euro
NEWSPAPER

Viispiikkinen
Owner: Maakunnan Sanomat Oy
Editorial: PL 41/ Virastotie 3, Karstula 43501.
T: 358 14 41 77 300
E: toimitus@viispiikkinen.fi
W: http://www.viispiikkinen.fi
Freq: Weekly; **Circ:** 5335
Editor in Chief: Ilkka Salonen
Language (s): Finnish
NEWSPAPER

Viitasaaren Seutu
Owner: Maakunnan Sanomat Oy

Editorial: PL 61 / Keskitie 7, Viitasaari 44501.
T: 358 14 33 97 100
E: seutu.toimitus@keskisuomalainen.fi
W: http://www.viitasaarenseutu.fi
Freq: Weekly; **Circ:** 5297
Editor in Chief: Esa Kilponen
Language (s): Finnish
NEWSPAPER

VPL Pyhäjärvi
Editorial: Rautasemantie 375, Lempäälä
37550. **T:** 358 3 37 48 448
E: marjo.ristila-toikka@kolumbus.fi
W: http://www.vplpyhajarvi.fi
Freq: Monthly; **Circ:** 1900 Pub Statement
Editor-in-Chief: Marjo Ristilä-Toikka
Language (s): Finnish
NEWSPAPER

Vuolijoki -lehti
Owner: Paltamon Kirjapaino Ky
Editorial: Sairaalatie 8, Paltamo 88300.
T: 358 8 87 19 99
E: aineistot@paltamonkirjapaino.fi
W: http://www.paltamonkirjapaino.fi/vuolijoki
Freq: Weekly; **Circ:** 1180
News: Tuula Keränen
Language (s): Finnish
NEWSPAPER

Vuosaari
Owner: Vuopress Ky
Editorial: Merikorttikuja 6 E, Helsinki 960.
T: 358 9 32 12 556
W: http://www.vuosaarilehti.fi
Freq: Weekly; **Circ:** 19000 Pub Statement
Editor in Chief: Eero Honkanen
Language (s): Finnish; Full Page Colour:
2700.00
Currency: Euro
NEWSPAPER

Warkauden Lehti
Owner: Warkauden Lehti Oy
Editorial: Pirnankatu 4, Varkaus 78200.
T: 358 17 77 83 631
E: toimitus@warkaudenlehti.fi
W: http://www.warkaudenlehti.fi **Circ:** 10272
News: Sari Ristamäki
Language (s): Finnish; Full Page Colour:
6963.00
Currency: Euro
NEWSPAPER

Wessmanni
Owner: Joutsan Seutu Oy
Editorial: PL 40/ Savonmäentie 1, Vaajakoski
40801. **T:** 358 40 54 75 111
E: toimitus@paikallisuutiset.fi
W: http://www.paikallisuutiset.fi/wessmanni.
php
Freq: Bi-Weekly; **Circ:** 7200 Pub Statement
Language (s): Finnish
NEWSPAPER

Wiita-Sanomat
Owner: Maakunnan Sanomat Oy
Editorial: PL 61/ Keskitie 7, Viitasaari 44501.
T: 358 14 33 97 100
E: seutu.toimitus@keskisuomalainen.fi
Freq: Bi-Weekly; **Circ:** 10450 Pub Statement
Editor in Chief: Esa Kilponen
Language (s): Finnish; Full Page Colour:
1665.00
Currency: Euro
NEWSPAPER

Ykköset
Owner: Tuurin Lehti Oy
Editorial: Tuurintie 2, Tuuri 63610.
T: 358 6 54 27 200 **E:** toimitus@ykkoset.fi
W: http://www.ykkoset.fi
Freq: Weekly; **Circ:** 311140 Pub Statement
Language (s): Finnish
NEWSPAPER

Ykkös-Lohja
Owner: JK-Vuokralehdet Oy
Editorial: Vihdinkatu 6, 2. krs., Lohja 8100.
T: 358 19 37 51 303 **E:** toimitus@ykkoslohja.fi
W: http://www.ykkoslohja.net
Freq: Weekly; **Circ:** 33000 Pub Statement
Editor in Chief: Jukka Kuparinen
Language (s): Finnish; Full Page Colour:
900.00
Currency: Euro
NEWSPAPER

Ykkössanomat
Owner: Salon Seudun Sanomat Oy
Editorial: Riikantie 2, Nummi 9810.
T: 358 19 37 10 76
E: ykkossanomat@ykkossanomat.fi
W: http://www.ykkossanomat.fi
Freq: Weekly; **Circ:** 3392
News: Paula Rauman

Language (s): Finnish; Full Page Colour:
2109.00
Currency: Euro
NEWSPAPER

Ylä-Kainuu
Owner: Suomen Paikallissanomat Oy
Editorial: PL 63 / Kauppakatu 10 A 1,
Suomussalmi 89601. **T:** 358 8 63 30 00
E: toimitus.ylakainuu@almamedia.fi
W: http://www.ylakainuu.fi
Freq: 2 Times/Week; **Circ:** 7746
Editor in Chief: Martti Huusko
Language (s): Finnish
NEWSPAPER

Ylä-Karjala
Owner: Nurmeksen Kirjapaino Oy
Editorial: PL 5/Pappilansuora 15, Nurmes
75501. **T:** 358 10 23 08 600
E: toimitus@ylakarjala.fi
W: http://www.ylakarjala.fi
Freq: 3 Times/Week; **Circ:** 5448
Editor in Chief: Pertti Meriläinen
Language (s): Finnish
NEWSPAPER

Ylä-Satakunta
Owner: Ylä-Satakunnan Sanomalehti Oy
Editorial: PL 6 / Parkanontie 63, Parkano
39701. **T:** 358 3 44 381
E: toimittajat@ylasatakunta.fi
W: http://www.ylasatakunta.fi
Freq: 2 Times/Week; **Circ:** 7212
Editor in Chief: Veli-Matti Heinisuo
Language (s): Finnish
NEWSPAPER

Ylöjärven Uutiset
Owner: Ylöjärven Sanomat Oy
Editorial: PL 26/ Mikkolantie 7, Ylöjärvi
33471. **T:** 358 3 34 77 200
W: http://www.ylojarvenuutiset.fi
Freq: Weekly; **Circ:** 6296
Editor in Chief: Matti Pulkkinen
Language (s): Finnish; Full Page Colour:
3828.00
Currency: Euro
NEWSPAPER

NEWS SERVICE/SYNDICATE

AFP Agence France-Presse
Editorial: Aleksanterinkatu 17, Helsinki 100.
T: 358 9 68 74 65 46 **E:** helsinki@afp.com
W: http://www.afp.com
Language (s): English
NEWS SERVICE/SYNDICATE

Agencia EFE
Editorial: Korkeavuorenkatu 17 A 7, Helsinki
130. **T:** 358 50 54 19 084
E: efehelsinki@yahoo.es
Language (s): English
NEWS SERVICE/SYNDICATE

All Over Press
Owner: Aller Media
Editorial: PL 170/Pursimiehenkatu 29-31 A, 5.
krs., Helsinki Helsinki 00151 00101.
T: 358 9 77 77 788 **E:** images@alloverpress.fi
W: http://www.alloverpress.fi
Language (s): English
NEWS SERVICE/SYNDICATE

**ANSA Agenzia Nazionale Stampa
Associata**
Editorial: c/o STT, Malminkatu 16 A, Helsinki
100. **T:** 358 9 69 58 13 40
Language (s): English
NEWS SERVICE/SYNDICATE

AP Associated Press
Editorial: Erottajankatu 9 A, Helsinki 130.
T: 358 9 68 02 394 **E:** aphelsinki@ap.org
Language (s): English
NEWS SERVICE/SYNDICATE

Associated Press
Editorial: Erottajankatu 9B, 7th Floor, Helsinki
130. **T:** 358 9 680-2394 **E:** aphelsinki@ap.org
NEWS SERVICE/SYNDICATE

Athens News Agency
Editorial: Ruukinlahdentie 9 A 5, Helsinki 200
E: evangelospatouchas@gmail.com
Language (s): English
NEWS SERVICE/SYNDICATE

Bloomberg
Editorial: Regus Business Ctre, Off 504,
Mannerheimintie 12 B, 5krs, Helsinki 100.
T: 358 9 25 12 37 32
E: helsinkinews@bloomberg.net
W: http://www.bloomberg.com

Editor: Ville Heiskanen; **Bureau Chief:** Kati
Pohjanpalo
Language (s): English
NEWS SERVICE/SYNDICATE

Bloomberg News
Editorial: Mannerheimintie 12, Regus
Business Center Luna House Rm 504, Helsinki
100. **T:** 358 925123732
E: helsinkinews@bloomberg.net
Bureau Chief: Kati Pohjanpalo
NEWS SERVICE/SYNDICATE

IPS Inter Press Service
Editorial: Vilhonvuorenkatu 11 C, Helsinki 500.
T: 358 9 42 59 98 03 **E:** ips@kaapeli.fi
W: http://www.ips.fi
Language (s): English
NEWS SERVICE/SYNDICATE

ITAR-TASS
Editorial: Ratakatu 1 a, B 10, Helsinki 120.
T: 358 9 60 18 77 **E:** itar-tass@kolumbus.fi
Language (s): English
NEWS SERVICE/SYNDICATE

Kirkon tiedotuskeskus
Editorial: PL 185/ Satamakatu 11, Helsinki
161. **T:** 358 9 18 021 **E:** kt@evl.fi
W: http://sakasti.evl.fi/sakasti.nsf/
sp?Open&cid=Content866A6
Editor: Heli Yli-Räisänen
Language (s): Finnish
NEWS SERVICE/SYNDICATE

Nyhetsbyrån FNB
Editorial: PB 550/ Malminkatu 16 A,
Helsingfors 101. **T:** 358 9 69 58 11
E: redaktion@fnb.fi **W:** http://www.stt.fi
Language (s): Swedish
NEWS SERVICE/SYNDICATE

Reuters
Editorial: Urho Kekkosen Katu 5C, 4th Floor,
Helsinki FI-00100. **T:** 358 9680501
Bureau Chief: Ritsuko Ando
NEWS SERVICE/SYNDICATE

STT-Lehtikuva
Editorial: PL 550/ Malminkatu 16 A, Helsinki
101. **T:** 358 9 69 58 11
E: toimitus@stt-lehtikuva.fi
W: http://www.stt.fi
Editor: Kirsi Aarnula; **Editor in Chief:** Minna
Holopainen; **Editor:** Olli Kemppainen; **News
Editor:** Piritta Rautavuori
Language (s): Finnish
NEWS SERVICE/SYNDICATE

Suomen Tietotoimisto Jyväskylä
Editorial: Aholaidantie 3, Jyväskylä 40320.
T: 358 9 69 58 15 40 **W:** http://www.stt.fi
Language (s): Finnish
NEWS SERVICE/SYNDICATE

Suomen Tietotoimisto Kuopio
Editorial: Puistokatu 6 as.5, Kuopio 70110.
T: 358 9 69 58 15 30
E: kuopio@stt-lehtikuva.fi **W:** http://www.stt.fi
Language (s): Finnish
NEWS SERVICE/SYNDICATE

Suomen Tietotoimisto Lappeenranta
Editorial: Liisankatu 5, Lappeenranta 53900.
T: 358 9 69 58 15 70
E: leena.jussila@stt-lehtikuva.fi
W: http://www.stt.fi
Language (s): Finnish
NEWS SERVICE/SYNDICATE

Suomen Tietotoimisto Oulu, Kajaani
Editorial: Kirkkokatu 11 A, Oulu 90100.
T: 358 9 69 58 15 10 **E:** oulu@stt-lehtikuva.fi
W: http://www.stt.fi
Language (s): Finnish
NEWS SERVICE/SYNDICATE

Suomen Tietotoimisto Rovaniemi
Editorial: PL 8200/ Rovakatu 31 A 10,
Rovaniemi 96101. **T:** 358 9 69 58 15 00
E: rovaniemi@stt-lehtikuva.fi
W: http://www.stt.fi
Language (s): Finnish
NEWS SERVICE/SYNDICATE

Suomen Tietotoimisto Tampere
Editorial: Itäinenkatu 11, Tampere 33100.
T: 358 9 69 58 15 50
E: tampere@stt-lehtikuva.fi
W: http://www.stt.fi
Language (s): Finnish
NEWS SERVICE/SYNDICATE

Suomen Tietotoimisto Turku Pori
Editorial: Linnankatu 3 a B, Turku 20100.
T: 358 9 69 58 15 80 **W:** http://www.stt.fi
Language (s): Finnish
NEWS SERVICE/SYNDICATE

Suomen Tietotoimisto Vaasa
Editorial: Alatori 1 B, Vaasa 65100.
T: 358 9 69 58 12 01 **W:** http://www.stt.fi
Language (s): Finnish
NEWS SERVICE/SYNDICATE

Svensk Presstjänst
Editorial: PB 550/ Malmgatan 16, Helsingfors
101. **T:** 358 9 69 58 12 36
E: redaktion@svenskpresstjanst.fi
W: http://www.svenskpresstjanst.fi
Editor: Heidi Hakala
Language (s): Swedish
NEWS SERVICE/SYNDICATE

Thomson Reuters Suomi Oy
Editorial: PL 736/ Urho Kekkosen katu 5 C,
Helsinki 101. **T:** 358 9 68 05 01
E: news@reuters.fi **W:** http://www.reuters.fi
Language (s): Finnish
NEWS SERVICE/SYNDICATE

UP-Uutispalvelu Oy
Editorial: PL 290/ Siltasaarenkatu 6, 7. kerros,
Helsinki 531. **T:** 358 9 47 80 88 00
E: up@up-uutispalvelu.fi
W: http://www.up-uutispalvelu.fi
Editor in Chief: Birgitta Suorsa
Language (s): Finnish
NEWS SERVICE/SYNDICATE

Uutistoimisto Startel
Owner: Sanoma News Oy
Editorial: PL 45/ Töölönlahdenkatu 2, Sanoma
89. **T:** 358 9 12 24 052
E: uutistoimisto.startel@sanoma.fi
W: http://www.startel.fi
Language (s): Finnish
NEWS SERVICE/SYNDICATE

Väli-Suomen Media
Editorial: Aholaidantie 3, Jyväskylä 40101.
T: 358 14 622 000 **W:** http://www.ksml.fi
Language (s): Finnish
NEWS SERVICE/SYNDICATE

Xinhua News Agency
Editorial: Hopeasalmentie 14, Helsinki 570.
T: 358 9 68 47 587
E: xinhuahelsinki@gmail.com
Language (s): English
NEWS SERVICE/SYNDICATE

BROADCASTING

RADIO STATIONS

Helsingin Lähiradio
Editorial: Hämeentie 32, Helsinki 530.
T: 358 9 70 13 300 **E:** lahi.radio@kara.inet.fi
W: http://www.kansanradioliitto.fi

Iskelmä Janne
Editorial: PL 570/ Vanajantie 7, Hämeenlinna
13111. **T:** 358 3 61 51 371
E: radiojanne@hameensanomat.fi
W: http://www.radiojanne.fi

Iskelmä Oikea Asema
Owner: Kevyt Kanava Oy
Editorial: Sammonkatu 16 A, Kuopio 70500.
T: 358 17 28 96 700
E: toimitus@oikeaasema.fi
W: http://www.oikeaasema.fi

Iskelmä Oikea Asema Iisalmi
Owner: Pohjois-Savon Paikallisradio Oy
Editorial: Pohjolankatu 5, Iisalmi 74100.
T: 358 17 28 96 700
E: toimitus@oikeaasema.fi
W: http://www.oikeaasema.fi

Iskelmä Oikea Asema Varkaus
Owner: Kevyt Kanava Oy
Editorial: Pirnankatu 4, Varkaus 78200.
T: 358 17 38 92 701
E: toimitus@oikeaasema.fi
W: http://www.radiomedia.fi/radioasemat/
mediakortit/fi_FI/
iskelma_oikea_asema_varkaus/

Iskelmä Pohjanmaa
Owner: SBS Finland Oy
Editorial: Puistotie 2, Lapua 62100.
T: 358 6 42 32 900
W: http://www.iskelma.fi/paikallissivut/
pohjanmaa

Iskelmä Rex
Editorial: PL 928/ Malmikatu 5 B II krs,
Joensuu 80101. **T:** 358 10 23 11 800
E: toimitus@radiorex.fi
W: http://www.radiorex.fi

Iskelmä Satakunta
Editorial: Kappelikuja 3, Huittinen 32700.
T: 358 2 55 54 291
E: toimitus@iskelmasatakunta.fi
W: http://www.iskelmasatakunta.fi

Järviradio
Owner: Järviseudun Paikallisradio Oy
Editorial: Kiertotie 5, Alajärvi 62900.
T: 358 500 557 234 **E:** jr@jarviradio.fi
W: http://www.jarviradio.fi

Lähiradio KSL
Editorial: Hämeentie 32, Helsinki 530.
T: 358 9 70 13 300 **W:** http://www.lahiradio.fi

Radio Auran Aallot
Editorial: Länsikaari 15, Turku 20240.
T: 358 2 26 93 905 **E:** info@auranaallot.fi
W: http://www.auranaallot.fi

Radio City
Owner: SBS Finland Oy
Editorial: Tallberginkatu 1 C, Helsinki 180.
T: 358 40 56 98 176 **E:** toimitus@radiocity.fi
W: http://www.radiocity.fi/

Radio City Jyväskylä
Owner: SBS Finland Oy
Editorial: PL 480/ Väinönkatu 26 A, Jyväskylä
40101. **T:** 358 20 35 23 52
E: toimitus@radiocity.fi
W: http://www.radiocity.fi/jyvaskyla

Radio City Tampere
Owner: SBS Finland Oy
Editorial: PL 957/ Kehräsaari B porras, 5 krs,
Tampere 33101. **T:** 358 40 56 98 176
E: toimitus@radiocity.fi
W: http://www.radiocity.fi/tampere

Radio City Turku
Owner: SBS Finland Oy
Editorial: Läntinen Rantakatu 53, 2 krs, Turku
20100. **T:** 358 40 56 98 176
E: toimitus@radiocity.fi
W: http://www.radiocity.fi/turku

Radio Dei
Editorial: Ilmalankuja 2 I, Helsinki 240.
T: 358 9 75 14 45 11 **E:** info@radiodei.fi
W: http://www.radiodei.fi

Radio Dei Pohjanmaa
Editorial: Koulukatu 13 C, 2 krs., Seinäjoki
60100. **T:** 358 6 21 40 300
E: toimitus.pohjanmaa@radiodei.fi
W: http://www.radiodei.fi

Radio Dei Turku
Editorial: Kalastajankatu 1 B, Turku 20100.
T: 358 2 46 99 800
E: toimitus.turku@radiodei.fi
W: http://www.radiodei.fi

Radio Folkhälsan
Editorial: Topeliusgatan 20, Helsingfors 250.
T: 358 9 31 50 00 **W:** http://www.folkhalsan.fi

Radio Helsinki
Owner: Sanoma News Oy
Editorial: PL 80/ Töölönlahdenkatu 2, Sanoma
89. **T:** 358 9 41 59 20 32
E: palaute@radiohelsinki.fi
W: http://www.radiohelsinki.fi

Radio Kajaus
Editorial: PL 230/ Kauppakatu 21, 4 krs.,
Kajaani 87101. **T:** 358 8 62 99 57
E: kajaus.toimitus@radiokajaus.fi
W: http://www.radiokajaus.fi

Radio Manta
Owner: Kustannusliike Aluelehdet Oy
Editorial: PL 101/Hopunkatu 1, Sastamala
38201. **T:** 358 10 22 90 400
E: hannu.virtanen@radiomanta.fi
W: http://www.radiomanta.fi/index.php

Radio Melodia
Owner: Turun paikallisradio Oy
Editorial: Länsikaari 15, Turku 20240.
T: 358 2 26 93 890 **E:** info@radiomelodia.fi
W: http://www.radiomelodia.fi

Radio Moreeni
Editorial: Kalevantie 4, Tampereen Yliopisto
33014. **T:** 358 3 35 51 69 46

E: moreeni@uta.fi **W:** http://moreeni.uta.fi

Radio Pooki
Editorial: Niittykatu 5, Raahe 92100.
T: 358 8 21 18 200
E: toimitus.raahe@radiopooki.fi
W: http://www.radiopooki.fi

Radio Pori
Editorial: Itäpuisto 3, Pori 28100.
T: 358 44 59 02 550 **E:** toimitus@radiopori.fi
W: http://www.radiopori.fi

Radio Ramona
Editorial: Itäkatu 5, Rauma 26100.
T: 358 440 933 933
E: ramona@radioramona.fi
W: http://www.radioramona.fi

Radio Robin Hood
Editorial: Itäinen Rantakatu 64, Turku 20810.
T: 358 2 27 73 666 **E:** info@radiorobinhood.fi
W: http://www.radiorobinhood.fi

Radio Sputnik
Owner: Radio Satellite Finland Oy
Editorial: Bulevardi 10 C 26, Helsinki 120.
T: 358 9 34 36 340 **E:** info@radiosputnik.fi
W: http://www.radiosputnik.fi

Radio SUN
Editorial: PL 67/ Pilvilinnankatu 1, Ikaalinen
39501. **T:** 358 43 21 70 645
E: toimitus@radiosun.fi
W: http://www.radiosun.fi

Radio Vaasa
Editorial: PL 371/ Hovioikeudenpuistikko 16,
Vaasa 65101. **T:** 358 6 32 03 910
E: toimitus@radiovaasa.fi
W: http://www.radiovaasa.fi

Radio Voima
Editorial: PL 80/ Aleksanterinkatu 10, Lahti
15101. **T:** 358 3 75 75 986
E: toimitus@radiovoima.fi
W: http://www.radiovoima.fi

Steel FM
Editorial: Strandgränd 2, Mariehamn 22100.
T: 358 18 16 200 **E:** mail@steelfm.net
W: http://www.steelfm.net

The Voice
Owner: SBS Media Group Finland
Editorial: Tallberginkatu 1 C, Helsinki 180.
T: 358 40 56 98 176 **E:** toimitus@voice.fi
W: http://www.voice.fi/

Tuotantoyksikkö Kantti
Editorial: PL 99/ Kotkankallionkatu 12, Kuopio
70101. **T:** 358 17 24 78 900
E: toimitus@kantti.net **W:** http://www.kantti.net

YLE X3M
Editorial: PB 13/ Radiogatan 5, Helsingfors
240. **T:** 358 9 14 801 **E:** hotline@yle.fi
W: http://www.yle.fi/extrem

RADIO NETWORKS

Ålands Radio och TV Ab
Owner: Ålands Radio och TV Ab
Editorial: PB 140/Ålandsvägen 24, Mariehamn
AX-22101. **T:** 358 18 26 060
E: redaktion@radiotv.ax
W: http://www.radiotv.aland.fi

Iskelmäradio
Owner: SBS Finland Oy
Editorial: Kehräsaari B 5, Tampere 33100.
T: 358 20 74 74 100 **E:** ari.ojala@sbs.fi
W: http://www.iskelma.fi

Loop
Editorial: Sanomatalo, Töölönlahdenkatu 2 PL
15, Helsinki 89. **T:** 358 10 800 106
E: studio@loop.fi **W:** http://www.loop.fi/

NRJ (Radio Energy) Helsinki
Owner: NRJ Finland Oy
Editorial: Kiviaidankatu 2 i (4. krs), Helsinki
210. **T:** 358 9 68 19 00 **W:** http://www.nrj.fi

Radio Groove FM & SuomiPOP & Metro FM
Owner: Nelonen Media
Editorial: Töölönlahdenkatu 2, Sanoma 89.
T: 358 20 77 68 360
E: studiogroove@groovefm.fi
W: http://www.metroradio.fi

Radio Nova
Owner: MTV Media
Editorial: PL 123/ Ilmalankatu 2 C, Helsinki
241. **T:** 358 10 30 07 227
E: toimitus@radionova.fi
W: http://www.radionova.fi

Radio Rock & Radio Aalto
Owner: Nelonen Media
Editorial: Töölönlahdenkatu 2, Sanoma 89.
T: 358 9 45 451 **E:** uutiset@radioaalto.fi
W: http://www.radiorock.fi

SR EKOT ; Helsingfors
Editorial: Stora Robertsgatan 43 C 39,
Helsingfors 120. **T:** 358 9 60 42 02
E: jenny.roosqvist@sr.se
W: http://sverigesradio.se/nyheter/

YLE Åboland
Editorial: PB 400/ Auragatan 8, Åbo 20101.
T: 358 2 27 17 859
E: radiovega.aboland@yle.fi
W: http://svenska.yle.fi/aboland

Yle Åboland Kimito
Editorial: Redaktörsstigen 2, Kimito 25700.
T: 358 2 42 17 77 **E:** monica.forssell@yle.fi
W: http://www.yle.fi/vega

Yle Etelä-Karjala Lappeenranta
Editorial: PL 100/ Kristiinankatu 11 A,
Lappeenranta 53101. **T:** 358 5 63 031
E: etelakarjala@yle.fi
W: http://yle.fi/alueet/etela-karjala

Yle Etelä-Savon Radio Mikkeli
Owner: Yleisradio
Editorial: PL 361/ Vilhonkatu 11, Mikkeli
50101. **T:** 358 15 41 57 70 **E:** etelasavo@yle.fi
W: http://www.etelasavonradio.fi

Yle Etelä-Savon Radio Savonlinna
Editorial: Olavinkatu 24, Savonlinna 57130.
T: 358 15 41 57 70 **E:** etelasavo@yle.fi
W: http://www.etelasavonradio.fi

Yle Häme
Editorial: Viipurintie 4 E, Hämeenlinna 13200.
T: 358 3 54 46 969 **E:** hame@yle.fi
W: http://yle.fi/alueet/hame

YLE Häme Forssa
Editorial: Hämeentie 7 II krs, Forssa 30100.
T: 358 3 42 21 521 **E:** hame@yle.fi
W: http://yle.fi/alueet/hame

Yle Helsinki Ylen Aikainen
Editorial: PL 3/ Uutiskatu 5, Yleisradio 24.
T: 358 9 1480 3148 **E:** helsinki@yle.fi
W: http://yle.fi/uutiset/helsinki/

YLE Huvudstadsregionen
Editorial: PB 87/ Radiogatan 5 A, Rundradion
24. **T:** 358 9 14 80 37 02
E: vega.huvudstadsregionen@yle.fi
W: http://www.yle.fi/vega

Yle Kainuun Radio Kajaani
Owner: Yleisradio
Editorial: PL 111/ Lönnrotinkatu 14 B, Kajaani
87101. **T:** 358 8 61 98 80 60 **E:** kainuu@yle.fi
W: http://yle.fi/alueet/kainuu

Yle Kymenlaakson Radio Kotka
Owner: Yleisradio
Editorial: Ruotsinsalmenkatu 12, Kotka 48100.
T: 358 5 81 37 300 **E:** kymenlaakso@yle.fi
W: http://yle.fi/alueet/kymenlaakso

Yle Kymenlaakson Radio Kouvola
Owner: Yleisradio
Editorial: Salpausselänkatu 40, Kouvola
45100. **T:** 358 5 81 37 300
E: kymenlaakso@yle.fi
W: http://yle.fi/alueet/kymenlaakso

Yle Lahti
Owner: Yleisradio
Editorial: PL 120/ Aleksanterinkatu 8, Lahti
15111. **T:** 358 3 46 86 900 **E:** lahti@yle.fi
W: http://yle.fi/alueet/lahti

YLE Lappi
Owner: Yleisradio
Editorial: PL 8113/ Jorma Etontie 8,
Rovaniemi 96101. **T:** 358 16 33 06 000
E: lappi@yle.fi **W:** http://yle.fi/alueet/lappi

Yle Nyheter
Owner: Yleisradio
Editorial: PB 5, Rundradion 24.
T: 358 9 1480 5185 **E:** nyheter@yle.fi
W: http://svenska.yle.fi/

YLE Österbotten Jakobstad
Editorial: Box 1000/ Rådhusgatan 11, Jakobstad 68601. **T:** 358 6 32 00 200
E: radiovega.osterbotten@yle.fi
W: http://svenska.yle.fi/osterbotten

YLE Österbotten Karleby
Editorial: PB 1000/ Strandgatan 16, Karleby 67101. **T:** 358 6 32 00 200
E: radiovega.osterbotten@yle.fi
W: http://svenska.yle.fi/osterbotten

YLE Österbotten Kristinestad
T: 358 6 22 12 830
E: radiovega.osterbotten@yle.fi
W: http://svenska.yle.fi//osterbotten

Yle Österbotten Vasa
Editorial: Box 1000/ Aborrvägen 20, Vasa 65101. **T:** 358 6 22 98 547
E: radiovega.osterbotten@yle.fi
W: http://svenska.yle.fi/osterbotten

YLE Östnyland
Editorial: Krämaregatan 2, Borgå 6100.
T: 358 19 66 18 810
E: radiovega.ostnyland@yle.fi
W: http://www.yle.fi/vega

Yle Oulu
Owner: Yleisradio
Editorial: PL 277/ Sepänkatu 20, Oulu 90101.
T: 358 8 53 73 800 **E:** oulu@yle.fi
W: http://yle.fi/uutiset/oulu/

YLE Pohjanmaan Radio Seinäjoki
Owner: Yleisradio
Editorial: PL 1000/ Marttilantie 24, Seinäjoki 60101. **T:** 358 6 21 18 400
E: pohjanmaa@yle.fi
W: http://yle.fi/alueet/pohjanmaa

YLE Pohjanmaan Radio Vaasa
Owner: Yleisradio
Editorial: PL 1000/ Ahventie 20, Vaasa 65101.
T: 358 6 22 981 **E:** pohjanmaa@yle.fi
W: http://yle.fi/alueet/pohjanmaa

YLE Pohjois-Karjala
Editorial: PL 206/ Kirkkokatu 20, Joensuu 80101. **T:** 358 13 51 07 450
E: pohjoiskarjala@yle.fi
W: http://yle.fi/alueet/pohjois-karjala

Yle Puhe
Owner: Yleisradio
Editorial: PL 78, Yleisradio 24.
T: 358 9 14 801 **E:** yle.puhe@yle.fi
W: http://www.yle.fi/puhe

YLE Radio 1
Owner: Yleisradio
Editorial: PL 6/ Radiokatu 5, Yleisradio 24.
T: 358 9 14 801 **E:** yle.radio1@yle.fi
W: http://www.yleradio1.fi

Yle Radio Itä-Uusimaa
Editorial: PL 903/ Rihkamakatu 2, Porvoo 6101. **T:** 358 9 14 80 88 35 **E:** porvoo@yle.fi
W: http://yle.fi/alueet/helsinki/radio-ita-uusimaa

Yle Radio Keski-Pohjanmaa
Editorial: PL 1000/ Rantakatu 16, Kokkola 67101. **T:** 358 6 21 98 100
E: keskipohjanmaa@yle.fi
W: http://yle.fi/alueet/keski-pohjanmaa

Yle Radio Keski-Suomi
Editorial: PL 3/ Kauppakatu 33, Jyväskylä 40101. **T:** 358 14 44 58 211
E: keskisuomi@yle.fi
W: http://yle.fi/alueet/keski-suomi

YLE Radio Perämeri Kemi
Editorial: Tietokatu 3, toinen kerros, Kemi 94600. **T:** 358 16 33 57 400
E: perameri@yle.fi
W: http://yle.fi/alueet/perameri

Yle Radio Suomi
Owner: Yleisradio
Editorial: PL 8/ Radiokatu 5, Yleisradio 24.
T: 358 9 14 801 **E:** radio.suomi@yle.fi
W: http://www.yle.fi/radiosuomi

YLE Radio Suomi Ajantasa
Owner: Yleisradio
Editorial: PL 8/ Radiokatu 5, Yleisradio 24.
T: 358 9 14 801 **E:** radio.suomi@yle.fi
W: http://yle.fi/radiosuomi

YLE Radio Vega
Editorial: PB 62, Rundradion 24.
T: 358 9 14 801 **E:** nyheter@yle.fi

W: http://www.yle.fi/vega

YLE Radio Ylen läntinen
Editorial: PL 86/ Laurinkatu 57 A, Lohja 8101.
T: 358 19 31 81 00 **E:** lohja@yle.fi
W: http://yle.fi/alueet/helsinki

YLE Saamen radio
Editorial: PL 38/ Menesjärventie 2, Inari 99871. **T:** 358 16 67 57 500
E: sami.radio@yle.fi
W: http://www.yle.fi/samiradio

YLE Saamen Radio Utsjoki
Editorial: Utsjoki 99980. **T:** 358 16 67 57 500
E: sami.radio@yle.fi
W: http://www.yle.fi/samiradio

Yle Satakunta
Editorial: PL 113/ Mikonkatu 4 D, Pori 28101.
T: 358 2 55 57 990 **E:** satakunta@yle.fi
W: http://yle.fi/sataradio

Yle Savo
Editorial: PL 99/ Kotkankallionkatu 12, Kuopio 70101. **T:** 358 17 24 78 900 **E:** savo@yle.fi
W: http://yle.fi/alueet/savo

YLE Tampere
Editorial: PL 110 /Vuolteenkatu 20, 3 krs., Tampere 33101. **T:** 358 3 34 56 111
E: tampere@yle.fi
W: http://yle.fi/alueet/tampere

YLE Turku
Editorial: PL 400/ Aurakatu 8, 7 krs, Turku 20101. **T:** 358 2 27 09 00 **E:** turku@yle.fi
W: http://www.turunradio.fi

YLE Västnyland
Editorial: PB 33/Gustav Wasas gata 8 A, Ekenäs 10601. **T:** 358 19 26 48 846
E: radiovega.vastnyland@yle.fi
W: http://www.yle.fi/vega

YLE Venäjänkielinen toimitus
Owner: Yleisradio
Editorial: PL 3, Yleisradio 24. **T:** 358 9 14 801
E: heidi.zidan@yle.fi
W: http://yle.fi/uutiset/novosti/

Ylen radioiden uutistoiminta
Editorial: PL 3/ Radiokatu 5, Yleisradio 24.
T: 358 9 14 801 **E:** uutiset@yle.fi
W: http://yle.fi/uutiset

Ylen radioiden uutistoimitus Jyväskylä
Editorial: PL3/Kauppakatu 33, Jyväskylä 40101. **T:** 358 14 44 58 243
E: radio.suomi@yle.fi
W: http://yle.fi/alueet/keski-suomi

Ylen radioiden uutistoimitus Kuopio
Editorial: PL 99/ Kotkankallionkatu 12, Kuopio 70101. **T:** 358 17 24 78 900
E: kaija.kervinen@yle.fi
W: http://yle.fi/uutiset/alueelliset_uutiset

Ylen radioiden uutistoimitus Lappeenranta
Editorial: PL 100/ Kristiinankatu 11 A, Lappeenranta 53101. **T:** 358 5 63 031
E: jari.tanskanen@yle.fi
W: http://yle.fi/uutiset/etela-karjala/

Ylen radioiden uutistoimitus Oulu
Editorial: PL 277/ Sepänkatu 20, Oulu 90101.
T: 358 8 53 73 870 **E:** leena.rimpilainen@yle.fi
W: http://yle.fi/uutiset/alueelliset_uutiset

YLEX
Owner: Yleisradio
Editorial: PL 17/ Radiokatu 5 D, Yleisradio 24.
T: 358 9 14 801 **W:** http://www.yle.fi/ylex

TELEVISION STATIONS

Kutonen
Owner: SBS Media Group Finland
Editorial: SBS Discovery Television Oy, Tallberginkatu 1 C, 7. krs, Helsinki 180.
T: 358 20 7 870 850 **E:** info@sbsdiscovery.fi
W: http://www.kutonen.fi/

TSTV
Owner: TS-yhtymä
Editorial: PL 95/ Länsikaari 15, Turku 20101.
T: 358 2 26 93 311 **W:** http://www.ts.fi/tstv

TV5 Finland
Owner: SBS Finland Oy

Editorial: Esterinportti 2, Helsinki 240.
T: 358 20 78 70 850 **E:** info@sbstv.fi
W: http://www.tv5.fi

Wave 100
Owner: Tampereen Kaupunkitelevisio Oy
Editorial: Hämeenkatu 27 B, Tampere 33200
E: kari.pusa@wave100.fi
W: http://www.wave100.fi

TELEVISION NETWORKS

Fox
Owner: Family Channel Oy
Editorial: Mikonkatu 17A, Helsinki 100.
T: 358 20 7644 600 **W:** http://foxtv.fi/

MoonTV.fi
E: palaute@moontv.fi **W:** http://moontv.fi/

MTV Finland (Music TV)
Editorial: Kaisaniemenkatu 3 B 20-21, Helsinki 100. **T:** 358 20 74 24 440
E: info@musictelevision.fi
W: http://www.musictelevision.fi

MTV3 Aluetoimitus Itä-Suomi
Owner: MTV Media
Editorial: Viestintätoimisto Lehtiniemi Oy, Kokontie 10, Joensuu 80230
E: keimo.lehtiniemi@mtv3.fi
W: http://www.mtv3.fi

MTV3 Finland
Owner: MTV Media
Editorial: Ilmalantori 2, Mtv 33.
T: 358 10 300 300 **E:** uutiset@mtv.fi
W: http://www.mtv3.fi

MTV3 Sport
Owner: MTV Media
Editorial: Ilmalantori 2, Mtv 33.
T: 358 10 30 03 00 **E:** sports@mtv3.fi
W: http://www.mtv3.fi/urheilu

MTV3 Uutistoiminta
Owner: MTV Media
Editorial: Ilmalantori 2, Mtv 33.
T: 358 10 30 03 00 **E:** uutiset@mtv3.fi
W: http://www.mtv.fi/uutiset

Nelonen
Owner: Sanoma Television
Editorial: Töölönlahdenkatu 2, Helsinki 89.
T: 358 9 45 451 **E:** uutiset@nelonen.fi
W: http://www.nelonen.fi/

Nelonen Pro
Owner: Nelonen Media
Editorial: Töölönlahdenkatu 2, Helsinki 89.
T: 358 9 45 451 **W:** http://www.nelonenpro.fi

Nelonen uutistoimitus/HSTV
Editorial: Töölönlahdenkatu 2, Helsinki 89.
T: 358 9 1221 **E:** uutiset@nelonenmedia.fi
W: http://www.hs.fi/hstv/

Sub
Owner: MTV Media
Editorial: Ilmalantori 2, Mtv 33.
T: 358 10 30 03 00 **W:** http://www.sub.fi

Swedish Television Helsinki
Editorial: Sjökaptensvägen 9, Helsingfors 890
E: hasse.svens@svt.se
W: http://www.svt.se/nyheter

TV1 Asiaohjelmat
Editorial: PL 97, Yleisradio 24.
T: 358 9 14 801 **E:** airi.vilhunen@yle.fi
W: http://tv1.yle.fi/ohjelmat/asia

TV1 Opetusohjelmat
Editorial: PL 90, Yleisradio 24.
T: 358 9 14 801 **E:** yle.uutiset@yle.fi
W: http://oppiminen.yle.fi

TV2 Asiaohjelmat
Editorial: PL 196/ Tohlopinranta 31, Tampere 33101. **T:** 358 3 34 56 111
W: http://www.yle.fi

TV2 Lastenohjelmat
Editorial: Tohlopinranta 31, Tampere 33270.
T: 358 3 34 56 111 **E:** pikkukakkonen@yle.fi
W: http://yle.fi/lapset/

TV2 Viihdeohjelmat
Editorial: PL 196/ Tohlopinranta 31, Tampere 33101. **T:** 358 3 34 56 111
W: http://tv2.yle.fi/etusivu

Urhotv
Owner: URHOtv Oy
Editorial: Korkeavuorenkatu 34, Helsinki 130.
T: 358 29 00 11 220 **E:** info@urhotv.fi
W: http://www.urhotv.fi/

Yle Asia
Editorial: PL 79, Yleisradio 24.
T: 358 9 14 801 **E:** yle.uutiset@yle.fi
W: http://tv1.yle.fi/ohjelmat/ajankohtaisohjelmat

Yle FEM
Editorial: PB 83, Rundradion 24.
T: 358 9 14 80 33 01 **E:** fst@yle.fi
W: http://svenska.yle.fi/fem/

Yle Fem Nyhetsverksamheten
Editorial: PB 10, Rundradion 24.
T: 358 9 1480 4752 **E:** nyheter@yle.fi
W: http://svenska.yle.fi/nyheter/

Yle Fem Sportredaktionen
Owner: Yleisradio
Editorial: PB 82/ Radiogatan 5, Rundradion 24. **T:** 358 9 14 801 **E:** svenskasporten@yle.fi
W: http://svenska.yle.fi/nyheter/sport.php

Yle Kulttuuri
Owner: Yleisradio
Editorial: PL 92, Yleisradio 24.
T: 358 9 14 801 **E:** yle.kulttuuri@yle.fi
W: http://www.yle.fi/kulttuuri

YLE Lapset ja nuoret
Editorial: PL 95, Yleisradio 24.
T: 358 9 14 801 **W:** http://www.yle.fi/lapset

YLE Teema
Editorial: Radiokatu 5, Yleisradio 24.
T: 358 9 14 801 **W:** http://www.yle.fi/teema

Yle Tv-uutiset
Editorial: PL 10/Radiokatu 5, Yleisradio 24.
T: 358 9 14 801 **E:** yle.uutiset@yle.fi
W: http://www.yle.fi/uutiset

YLE Tv-uutiset Aluetoimitus Kuopio
Editorial: PL 99/ Kotkankallionkatu 12, Kuopio 70101. **T:** 358 17 24 78 900
E: pekka.niiranen@yle.fi **W:** http://yle.fi/uutiset

YLE Tv-uutiset Aluetoimitus Oulu
Editorial: Sepänkatu 20, Oulu 90100.
T: 358 8 537 3800 **E:** oulu@yle.fi
W: http://yle.fi/uutiset

YLE Tv-uutiset Aluetoimitus Tampere
Editorial: PL 110/ Vuolteenkatu 20, Tampere 33101. **T:** 358 3 34 56 111 **E:** tampere@yle.fi
W: http://www.yle.fi/uutiset

YLE Tv-uutiset Aluetoimitus Turku
Editorial: PL 400/ Aurakatu 8, Turku 20101.
T: 358 2 27 09 00 **E:** turku@yle.fi
W: http://www.yle.fi/uutiset

YLE Tv-uutiset Aluetoimitus Vaasa
Editorial: PL 1000/ Ahventie 20, Vaasa 65101.
T: 358 6 21 18 400 **E:** pohjanmaa@yle.fi
W: http://www.yle.fi/tvuutiset

Yleisradio Oy Ab
Editorial: Radiokatu 5, Helsinki 240.
T: 358 9 14 801 **E:** yleinfo@yle.fi
W: http://www.yle.fi

FRANCE   Tel: 33

Standard Time: GMT +1
Continent: Europe
Capital City: Paris

NEWSPAPERS & PUBLICATIONS

NEWSPAPERS

Le 1
Owner: Le 1
Editorial: 8 rue Lamennais, Paris 75008.
T: 33 1 45 61 44 49 **E:** redaction@le1hebdo.fr
W: http://le1hebdo.fr
Freq: Weekly; **Circ:** 250000
Editor in Chief: Laurent Greilsamer
Editorial Profile: Weekly newspaper covering news and current affairs including politics, economics and society.
Language (s): French
NEWSPAPER

20 Minutes Bordeaux
Owner: 20 MINUTES FRANCE SAS
Editorial: 22 cours du Chapeau-Rouge, Bordeaux 33000. **T:** 33 5 56 56 69 59
E: bordeaux@20minutes.fr
W: http://www.20minutes.fr
Freq: Daily; **Circ:** 33000 Pub Statement
Editorial Profile: Daily newspaper of general information on the Bordeaux region. Local Translation:Quotidien d'informations générales de la région de Bordeaux.
Language (s): French; Full Page Colour: 3400.00
Currency: Euro
DAILY NEWSPAPER

20 Minutes Lille
Owner: 20 MINUTES FRANCE SAS
Editorial: 2 rue du Priez, Lille 59800.
T: 33 3 28 38 16 60 **E:** lille@20minutes.fr
W: http://www.20minutes.fr
Freq: Daily; **Circ:** 47800 Pub Statement
Editorial Profile: Daily newspaper of general information on the Lille region. Local Translation:Quotidien d'informations générales de la région de Lille.
Language (s): French; Full Page Colour: 7850.00
Currency: Euro
DAILY NEWSPAPER

20 Minutes Lyon
Owner: 20 MINUTES FRANCE SAS
Editorial: 32 rue Neuve, Lyon 69002.
T: 33 4 72 77 01 74 **E:** lyon@20minutes.fr
W: http://www.20minutes.fr
Freq: Daily; **Circ:** 52080 Pub Statement
Editorial Profile: Daily newspaper of general information on the Lyon agglomeration .
Language (s): French; Full Page Colour: 9000.00
Currency: Euro
DAILY NEWSPAPER

20 Minutes Marseille
Owner: 20 MINUTES FRANCE SAS
Editorial: 38 rue Breteuil, Marseille 13006.
T: 33 4 91 33 59 43
E: marseille@20minutes.fr
W: http://www.20minutes.fr
Freq: Daily; **Circ:** 39940 Pub Statement
Editorial Profile: Daily newspaper of general information on the Marseille region. Local Translation:Quotidien d'informations générales de la région de Marseille.
Language (s): French; Full Page Colour: 9000.00
Currency: Euro
DAILY NEWSPAPER

20 Minutes Paris
Owner: 20 Minutes France S.A.S
Editorial: 50-52, Boulevard Haussmann, Paris 75009. **T:** 33 1 53 26 65 65
E: redaction@20minutes.fr
W: http://www.20minutes.fr
Freq: Daily; **Circ:** 658920 Pub Statement
Editor in Chief: Acacio Pereira
Editorial Profile: Daily newspaper covering general news and current affairs including society, politics, economics, environment, culture, sports, entertainment, celebrity, sports, technology and multimedia.
Language (s): French; Full Page Colour: 55100.00
Currency: Euro
DAILY NEWSPAPER

20 Minutes Strasbourg
Owner: 20 MINUTES FRANCE SAS
Editorial: 2 rue du Saumon, Strasbourg 67000. **T:** 33 3 88 23 96 36
E: strasbourg@20minutes.fr
W: http://www.20minutes.fr
Freq: Daily; **Circ:** 27171 Pub Statement
Editorial Profile: Daily national newspaper of general information including local pages on the Strasbourg region. Local Translation:Quotidien national d'informations générales comportant des pages d'informations locales de la région de Strasbourg.
Language (s): French; Full Page Colour: 3400.00
Currency: Euro
DAILY NEWSPAPER

24 ORE
Editorial: 39 boulevard Paoli, Bastia 20200.
T: 33 04 95 32 34 63 **E:** redaction@24ore.fr
W: http://www.24ore.fr
Freq: Daily; **Circ:** 12000 Pub Statement
Rédacteur en chef: Olivier-Jourdan Roulot
Editorial Profile: Journal d'informations régionales diffusé en Corse.
Language (s): French
DAILY NEWSPAPER

Les Affiches De Grenoble
Editorial: 6 avenue de l'Europe, Grenoble 38029. **T:** 33 04 76 84 32 07
E: redaction@affiches.fr
Freq: Weekly; **Circ:** 11437 OJD
Editorial Profile: Journal isérois d'informations judiciaires, économiques et culturelles. PARUTIONS : vendredi
Language (s): French; Full Page Colour: 1090.00
Currency: Euro
NEWSPAPER

LES AFFICHES DE HAUTE SAONE
Editorial: 29 avenue de la République, BP 157, Lure 70204. **T:** 33 03 84 30 09 08
E: fxd.lesaffiches@wanadoo.fr
Freq: Weekly; **Circ:** 15000 Pub Statement
Rédactrice: Sylviane Boudou; **Gérant:** Jean-François Royer
Editorial Profile: Hebdomadaire régional d'information et de publications légales. PARUTIONS : le vendredi
Language (s): French
NEWSPAPER

L' Aisne Nouvelle
Editorial: 10 Boulevard Henri Martin, BP 149, Saint-Quentin 2103. **T:** 33 03 23 06 36 36
E: redactionstq@aisnenouvelle.fr
W: http://aisnenouvelle.fr
Freq: 2 Times/Week; **Circ:** 19004 OJD
Bureau de Tergnier: Jean-Raoul Boulanger; **Bureau de Tergnier:** Aurélie Bourillon; **Bureau de Guise:** Monique Bourlard; **Bureau de Guise:** Joëlle Braillon; **Bureau de Tergnier:** Pascal Brocheton; **Bureau de Saint Quentin:** Thomas Delavergne; **Bureau de Tergnier:** Marc Delfolie; **Bureau de Guise:** Jérôme Hemard; **Rédaction départementale:** Eric Leskiv; **Bureau de Saint Quentin:** Nassera Lounassi; **Bureau de Saint Quentin:** Jérôme Poinsu; **Bureau de Tergnier:** Ludovic Quillet; **Bureau de Tergnier:** Thibaut Verrier; **Bureau de Saint Quentin:** Aurélien Walti
Editorial Profile: Journal d'information régionale et départementale. PARUTIONS : lundi, mardi, jeudi, samedi.
Language (s): French; Full Page Mono: 2714.00
Currency: Euro
NEWSPAPER

L' Alsace
Owner: SAP L'ALSACE
Editorial: 18 rue de Thann, Mulhouse 68945.
T: 33 03 89 32 70 00 **E:** redaction@lalsace.fr
W: http://www.lalsace.fr
Freq: Daily; **Circ:** 105795 OJD
Editor in Chief: Christian Battesti; **Rédacteur en chef adjoint:** Rémy Bruder; **Cinéma Théâtre:** Pierre-Louis Cereja
Language (s): French; Full Page Mono: 6797.00; Full Page Colour: 8496.00
Currency: Euro
DAILY NEWSPAPER

L' Alsace Bureau Parisien
Owner: SOCIETE ALSACIENNE DE PUBLICATIONS
Editorial: 3 rue des Petites-Ecuries, Paris 75010 **W:** http://www.lalsace.fr
Freq: Daily; **Circ:** 110000 Pub Statement
Editorial Profile: Daily regional and current events newspaper. Local Translation:Quotidien d'actualités régionales et d'informations générales.
Language (s): French
DAILY NEWSPAPER

L' Alsace Edition De Colmar
Owner: SOCIETE ALSACIENNE DE PUBLICATIONS
Editorial: 1 route de Rouffach, BP 40087, Colmar 68002 CEDEX. **T:** 33 3 89 20 50 00
E: redaction-co@lalsace.fr
W: http://www.lalsace.fr
Freq: Daily; **Circ:** 110000 Pub Statement
Editorial Profile: Daily regional and current events newspaper. Local Translation:Quotidien régional d'informations générales.
Language (s): French
DAILY NEWSPAPER

L' ALSACE EDITION DE GUEBWILLER
Owner: SOCIETE ALSACIENNE DE PUBLICATIONS
Editorial: 85-87 rue de la République, BP 84, Guebwiller 68502. **T:** 33 3 89 76 81 05
E: redaction-gu@lalsace.fr
W: http://www.lalsace.fr
Freq: Daily
Editorial Profile: Daily regional newspaper covering general, regional and local current events and sports. 6 to 8 local news pages. Local Translation:Quotidien régional d'informations générales, régionales, locales et sportives. 6 à 8 pages d'informations locales.
Language (s): French
DAILY NEWSPAPER

L' Alsace Edition De Saint-Louis
Owner: SOCIETE ALSACIENNE DE PUBLICATIONS
Editorial: 9 croisée des Lys, Saint-Louis 68300. **T:** +33 3 89 69 13 40
E: redaction-sl@lalsace.fr
W: http://www.lalsace.fr
Freq: Daily; **Circ:** 142000 Pub Statement
Editorial Profile: Daily regional newspaper covering general, regional and local current events and sports. Local Translation:Quotidien régional d'informations générales, régionales, locales et sportives.
Language (s): French
DAILY NEWSPAPER

L' Alsace Edition du Bas-Rhin
Owner: SOCIETE ALSACIENNE DE PUBLICATIONS
Editorial: 6 place de la Victoire, BP 97, Selestat 67600. **T:** +33 3 88 58 88 00
E: redaction-st@lalsace.fr
W: http://www.lalsace.fr
Freq: Daily; **Circ:** 126500 Pub Statement
Editorial Profile: Daily regional newspaper covering general, regional and local current events and sports. Magazine pages, thematic supplements. Local Translation:Presse quotidienne régionale. Informations générales, régionales, locales et sportives. Pages magazine, suppléments à thèmes.
Language (s): French
DAILY NEWSPAPER

L' Alsace Mulhouse - Redaction Locale
Owner: SOCIETE ALSACIENNE DE PUBLICATIONS
Editorial: 2 C rue Schlumberger, BP 52482, Mulhouse CEDEX 9. **T:** +33 3 89 33 40 00
E: redaction-mu@lalsace.fr
W: http://www.lalsace.fr
Freq: Daily; **Circ:** 120000 Pub Statement
Editorial Profile: Daily regional newspaper covering general, regional and local current events and sports. Local Translation:Quotidien régional d'informations générales, régionales, locales et sportives.
Language (s): French
DAILY NEWSPAPER

L' AMI DU PEUPLE
Editorial: 30 rue Thomann, Strasbourg 67082.
T: 33 03 88 22 77 22
E: direction@ami-hebdo.com
Freq: Weekly; **Circ:** 20969 OJD
Rédacteur: Gérard Banholzer; **Rédactrice en chef adjointe:** Christine Nonnenmacher; **Rédacteur:** Albert Odouard
Editorial Profile: Hebdomadaire régional d'information, familial et chrétien. PARUTIONS : le vendredi (daté du dimanche)
Language (s): French; Full Page Mono: 3800.00; Full Page Colour: 4905.00
Currency: Euro
NEWSPAPER

L' Ardennais - Union Des Ardennes
Owner: GROUPE HERSANT MEDIA
Editorial: 38-40 cours Aristide Briand, Charleville-Mezieres 8102.
T: 33 03 24 33 78 73
E: charleville@journal-lunion.fr
W: http://www.lunion.presse.fr
Freq: Daily; **Circ:** 104759 OJD
Editorial Profile: Zone de diffusion : Ardennes et Arrondissements limitrophes. Utilisation de la quadrichromie - Tous les jours - Dans les pages 1 et dernière - Edition du Dimanche. OJD = L'UNION - L'ARDENNAIS. Pour la REDACTION : voir aussi L'UNION
Language (s): French; Full Page Mono: 8480.00
Currency: Euro
DAILY NEWSPAPER

L' Avenir Cote D'Azur
Owner: RICCOBONO
Editorial: 24 boulevard Carnot, Cannes 6400.
T: 33 04 93 39 36 87 **E:** cletil@riccobono.fr
W: http://www.avenir-cotedazur.com
Freq: Weekly; **Circ:** 10000 Pub Statement
Rédacteur en chef NICE: Gérard Cletil
Editorial Profile: Informations économiques départementales - Annonces légales. PARUTIONS : vendredi
Language (s): French; Full Page Colour: 700.00
Currency: Euro
NEWSPAPER

L' Avenir De Artois
Editorial: 17 place Clemenceau, BP 21, Bethune 62401. **T:** 33 03 21 01 66 00
E: redaction@avenir-artois.fr
Freq: Weekly; **Circ:** 14457 OJD
Rédactrice en chef: Anne Despagne
Editorial Profile: PARUTIONS : jeudi - Informations locales
Language (s): French; Full Page Mono: 1043.00; Full Page Colour: 1386.00
Currency: Euro
NEWSPAPER

Le Berry Republicain
Owner: GROUPE CENTRE FRANCE - LA MONTAGNE
Editorial: 1 rue du Général Ferrié, Bourges 18023. **T:** 33 02 48 27 63 63
E: redaction.berry@centrefrance.com
W: http://www.leberry.fr
Freq: Daily; **Circ:** 30168 OJD
Editor in Chief: Philippe Noireaux; **Rédacteur en chef:** Bernard Stephan
Language (s): French; Full Page Colour: 6519.00
Currency: Euro
DAILY NEWSPAPER

Le Bien Public
Owner: EST BOURGOGNE MEDIA
Editorial: 7 boulevard du Chanoine Kir, Dijon 21000. **T:** 33 3 80 42 42 42
E: bienpublic@lebienpublic.fr
W: http://www.bienpublic.com
Freq: Daily; **Circ:** 47788 OJD
Editorial Profile: Daily newspaper covering regional general interest including community news, politics, public issues and leisure activities.
Language (s): French; Full Page Mono: 4312.00; Full Page Colour: 5217.00
Currency: Euro
DAILY NEWSPAPER

LE Bien Public - Les Depeches Edition Beaune
Owner: EBRA
Editorial: 9 rue de Lorraine, Beaune 21200.
T: 33 3 80 26 34 50
E: agc.beaune@lebienpublic.fr
W: http://www.bienpublic.com
Freq: Daily; **Circ:** 46336 OJD
Editorial Profile: Regional daily newspaper focussing on news and current affairs. Local Translation:Journal d'actualités régionales et nationales.
Language (s): French
DAILY NEWSPAPER

LE Bien Public - Les Depeches Edition Haute Cote D'or
Owner: EBRA
Editorial: 6 rue Auguste-Carré, Montbard 21500. **T:** 33 3 80 89 91 11
E: agc.montbard@lebienpublic.fr
W: http://www.bienpublic.com
Freq: Daily; **Circ:** 46336 OJD
Editorial Profile: Regional daily newspaper focussing on news and current affairs. Local Translation:Journal d'actualités régionales et nationales.
Language (s): French
DAILY NEWSPAPER

Le Canard Enchaîné
Editorial: 173 rue Saint Honoré, Paris 75001.
T: 33 1 42 60 31 26
E: redaction@lecanardenchaine.fr
W: http://www.lecanardenchaine.fr
Freq: Weekly; **Circ:** 550000 Pub Statement
Editor in Chief: Érik Emptaz; **Editor in Chief:** Louis-Marie Horeau
Editorial Profile: Satirical newspaper covering general news and current affairs, politics, society and culture with a satirical view. He prefers to be contacted by email.
Language (s): French
NEWSPAPER

CENTRE PRESSE
Editorial: 5 rue Victor Hugo, BP 299, Poitiers 86007. **T:** 33 05 49 55 55 70
E: redaction@centre-presse.fr
W: http://www.centre-presse.fr
Freq: Daily; **Circ:** 22350 OJD
Rédacteur en chef: Richard Lavigne
Editorial Profile: Utilisation de la quadrichromie : tous les jours dans les pages 1, 3, 5 et dernière. Diffusé dans la Vienne.
Language (s): French; Full Page Mono: 7777.00; Full Page Colour: 10110.00
Currency: Euro
DAILY NEWSPAPER

CENTRE PRESSE AVEYRON
Owner: LES JOURNAUX DU MIDI

WORLD NEWS MEDIA

Editorial: Avenue de la Peyrinie - Bel Air, BP 137, Rodez 12021. **T:** 33 05 65 77 78 79
E: redaction@centrepresse.com
Freq: Daily; **Circ:** 20896 OJD
Language (s): French; Full Page Colour: 2277.00
Currency: Euro
DAILY NEWSPAPER

La Charente Libre
Owner: GROUPE SUD OUEST
Editorial: ZI nº 3, Angouleme 16903.
T: 33 05 45 94 16 00
E: charente@charentelibre.fr
W: http://www.charentelibre.fr
Freq: Daily; **Circ:** 38228 OJD
Editor in Chief: Jean-Louis Hervois
Editorial Profile: Utilisation de la quadrichromie - Tous les jours. EVITEZ D'ENVOYER DES DOSSIERS/COMMUNIQUES PAR MAIL. Diffusé en Poitou Charentes.
Language (s): French; Full Page Mono: 4533.00; Full Page Colour: 5220.00
Currency: Euro
DAILY NEWSPAPER

Charlie Hebdo
Owner: Les Éditions Rotative
Editorial: 26 rue Serpollet, Paris 75020.
T: 33 1 76 21 53 00
E: redaction@charliehebdo.fr
W: http://www.charliehebdo.fr
Freq: Weekly; **Circ:** 130000 Pub Statement
Editor in Chief: Gérard Biard
Editorial Profile: Satirical newspaper covering news and current affairs including politics, society, religion, secularity, culture, international, ecology and investigation.
Language (s): French
NEWSPAPER

China Daily (France)
Editorial: 90 rue du Gouverneur Général Eboué, Issy-Les-Moulineaux 92130.
T: 33 1 82159686
DAILY NEWSPAPER

LA CHRONIQUE REPUBLICAINE
Editorial: 39 rue de Nantes, BP 30162, Fougeres 35301. **T:** 33 02 99 99 12 15
Freq: Weekly; **Circ:** 15202 OJD
Editorial Profile: Journal d'informations régionales et locales paraissant le jeudi. NE SOUHAITENT PAS DE COMMUNICATION PAR MAIL
Language (s): French; Full Page Mono: 2808.00; Full Page Colour: 3900.00
Currency: Euro
NEWSPAPER

Le Commingeois
Owner: COMMINGEOIS
Editorial: Zac Porte-de-Muret, 23 rue Pierre-de-Fermat, Muret 31600. **T:** 33 5 61 51 26 52
E: lecommingeois@wanadoo.fr
W: http://www.lecommingeois.fr
Freq: Monthly; **Circ:** 40000 Pub Statement
Editorial Profile: Local current events newspaper.
Language (s): French
NEWSPAPER

CORSE MATIN
Owner: GROUPE HERSANT MEDIA
Editorial: 2 rue Sergent Casalonga, Ajaccio 20000. **T:** 33 04 95 51 74 00
E: redacchef@nicematin.fr
W: http://www.corsematin.com
Freq: Daily; **Circ:** 42312 OJD
Language (s): French; Full Page Mono: 2311.00; Full Page Colour: 2889.00
Currency: Euro
DAILY NEWSPAPER

Le Courrier Cauchois
Editorial: 2 rue Edmond Labbé, BP 129, Yvetot 76194. **T:** 33 02 35 56 29 64
E: redaction@lecourriercauchois.fr
W: http://www.lecourriercauchois.fr
Freq: Weekly; **Circ:** 40972 OJD
Rédacteur en chef adjoint: Ghislain Annetta
Editorial Profile: Hebdomadaire régional d'informations, paraissant le vendredi. 4 Editions Zone de diffusion : de la pointe du Havre à Rouen.
Language (s): French; Full Page Colour: 2028.00
Currency: Euro
NEWSPAPER

Le Courrier De La Mayenne
Owner: EDIT OUEST
Editorial: 108 rue Victor Boissel, BP 529, Laval 53005. **T:** 33 02 43 59 10 40
E: redaction@courrierdelamayenne.com
W: http://www.courriermayenne.com

Freq: Weekly; **Circ:** 27726 OJD
Loisirs: Sophie Santoni
Editorial Profile: Hebdomadaire d'informations locales. PARUTIONS : le jeudi
Language (s): French; Full Page Mono: 3408.00
Currency: Euro
NEWSPAPER

Le Courrier De L'Ouest
Owner: SIPA
Editorial: Boulevard Albert Blanchoin, BP 10728, Angers 49007. **T:** 33 02 41 68 86 88
E: secretariat.redac-chef.angers@courrier-ouest.com
Freq: Daily; **Circ:** 102225 OJD
Rédacteur en chef adjoint - Animateur des équipes rédactionnelles - Respons: Emmanuel Caloyanni; **Rédacteur en chef adjoint Responsable des suppléments et Hors-séries:** Claude Saulais
Language (s): French; Full Page Mono: 12095.00; Full Page Colour: 15893.00
Currency: Euro
DAILY NEWSPAPER

LE Courrier De L'ouest Edition Des Deux-Sevres
Owner: OUEST FRANCE
Editorial: 8 bis rue Paul-Doumer, Bressuire 79300 CEDEX. **T:** +33 5 49 65 00 27
E: bressuire@courrier-ouest.com
W: http://www.courrierdelouest.fr
Freq: Daily; **Circ:** 112000 Pub Statement
Editorial Profile: Deux-Sèvres region news: economy, politics, sport and culture.
Language (s): French
DAILY NEWSPAPER

LE COURRIER DE L'OUEST EDITION DU MAINE-ET-LOIRE
Owner: OUEST FRANCE
Editorial: 16 bis rue Saint-Gilles, BP 38, Beaupreau 49600. **T:** 33 2 41 63 19 79
E: redac.beaupreau@courrier-ouest.com
W: http://www.courrierdelouest.fr
Freq: Daily
Rédacteur en Chef: Pierre-Louis Augereau; **Rédacteur en Chef Adjoint:** Luc Souriau
Editorial Profile: Publication focusing on regional news.
Language (s): French
DAILY NEWSPAPER

Le Courrier Du Pays De Retz
Owner: GROUPE PUBLIHEBDOS
Editorial: 6 rue du Traité de Paris, BP 1529, Pornic 44215. **T:** 33 02 51 74 00 30
E: courrierdupaysderetz@publihebdos.fr
Freq: Weekly; **Circ:** 11276 OJD
Editeur: Eric Lechat; **Rédacteur en chef:** Frédéric Prot
Editorial Profile: Hebdomadaire régional d'informations. PARUTIONS : vendredi
Language (s): French
NEWSPAPER

COURRIER FRANCAIS
Owner: COURRIER FRANCAIS
Editorial: Rue du Docteur Jean Vincent, BP 20238, Bordeaux 33028. **T:** 33 05 56 44 72 24
E: v.david@courrier-francais.fr
W: http://www.courrier-francais.com
Freq: Weekly; **Circ:** 35140 Pub Statement
Bureau de Périgueux: Pascal Audoux; **Bureau de Poitiers:** Daniel Biron; **Bureau d'Agen:** Claire Caillard; **Bureau de Montauban:** Corine Comas; **Bureau de Dax:** Guillaume Pantaignan; **Bureau de La Rochelle:** Olivier Seigneurin; **Bureau d'Angoulême:** Laetitia Thomas
Editorial Profile: Hebdomadaire régional d'information, d'information catholique et d'annonces légales publiant 15 éditions dans 19 départements. PARUTION : vendredi
Language (s): French; Full Page Mono: 1540.00; Full Page Colour: 2030.00
Currency: Euro
NEWSPAPER

Le Courrier Picard
Owner: Courrier Picard
Editorial: 29 rue de la République, BP 1021, Amiens 80010. **T:** 33 3 22 82 60 00
E: redaction@courrier-picard.fr
W: http://www.courrier-picard.fr
Freq: Daily; **Circ:** 62000 OJD
Editor in Chief: David Guévard; **NOYON:** Stéphane Le Barber
Editorial Profile: Regional and local newspaper.
Language (s): French; Full Page Mono: 6535.00; Full Page Colour: 8169.00
Currency: Euro
DAILY NEWSPAPER

LE Courrier Picard Edition De L'oise
Owner: LE COURRIER PICARD

Editorial: 28 rue des Jacobins, Beauvais 60008 CEDEX. **T:** 33 3 44 11 41 80
E: beauvais@courrier-picard.fr
W: http://www.courrier-picard.fr
Freq: Daily; **Circ:** 78000 Pub Statement
Editorial Profile: Daily regional and local newspaper. The Oise editorial offices are located in Clermont, Creil, Beauvais, Compiègne and Noyon. Local Translation:Quotidien d'informations régionales et locales. Pour l'édition de l'Oise, bureaux à Clermont, Creil, Beauvais, Compiègne, Noyon.
Language (s): French; Full Page Mono: 1643.00; Full Page Colour: 2054.00
Currency: Euro
DAILY NEWSPAPER

LE Courrier Picard Edition De Picardie Maritime
Owner: LE COURRIER PICARD
Editorial: 47 place Max-Lejeune, Abbeville 80100 CEDEX. **T:** 33 3 22 20 17 00
E: abbeville@courrier-picard.fr
W: http://www.courrier-picard.fr
Freq: Daily; **Circ:** 86000 Pub Statement
Rédacteur (trice): Karine Galhaut; **Rédacteur (trice):** Fabrice Julien; **Rédacteur (trice):** Hervé Leflond; **Rédacteur (trice):** David Vandevoorde
Editorial Profile: Daily regional and local newspaper covering sports, social life. Life at sea pages every Thursday. Local Translation:Quotidien d'informations régionales et locales, sports, social. Page vie maritime tous les jeudis.
Language (s): French; Full Page Mono: 8054.00; Full Page Colour: 10067.00
Currency: Euro
DAILY NEWSPAPER

LE Courrier Picard Edition Saint-Quentin
Owner: LE COURRIER PICARD
Editorial: 21 place de l'Hôtel-de-Ville, Saint-Quentin 2100. **T:** 33 3 23 60 39 70
E: saint-quentin@courrier-picard.fr
W: http://www.courrier-picard.fr
Freq: Daily; **Circ:** 78000 Pub Statement
Editorial Profile: Daily local current events newspaper. Local Translation: Quotidien d'informations générales et locales.
Language (s): French; Full Page Mono: 1396.00; Full Page Colour: 1745.00
Currency: Euro
DAILY NEWSPAPER

La Croix
Owner: Bayard Presse
Editorial: 18 rue Barbès, Montrouge 92128.
T: 33 1 74 31 60 60
E: lecteurs.lacroix@bayard-presse.com
W: http://www.la-croix.com
Freq: Daily; **Circ:** 104901 OJD
Editor in Chief: Florence Couret; **Editor in Chief:** Guillaume Goubert; **Editor in Chief:** Dominique Greiner; **Publisher:** Georges Sanerot
Editorial Profile: Newspaper covering a broad range of news and current affairs from a Catholic viewpoint including religion, culture, family, ethics and solidarity.
Language (s): French; Full Page Mono: 17000.00; Full Page Colour: 22300.00
Currency: Euro
DAILY NEWSPAPER

La Croix Du Nord
Editorial: 33 rue Négrier, BP 29, Lille 59009.
T: 33 03 20 55 42 60
E: contact@croixdunord.com
Freq: Weekly; **Circ:** 12000 Pub Statement
Rédactrice en chef: Véronique Durand
Editorial Profile: Hebdomadaire régional d'opinion - Diffusion : Nord, Pas-de-Calais PARUTION : Vendredi
Language (s): French; Full Page Mono: 1665.00; Full Page Colour: 2433.00
Currency: Euro
NEWSPAPER

Le Dauphine Libere
Owner: GROUPE DAUPHINE LIBERE
Editorial: Les Iles Cordées, Veurey 38913.
T: 33 04 76 88 71 00
E: jean-pierre.souchon@ledauphine.com
W: http://www.ledauphine.com
Freq: Daily; **Circ:** 241867 OJD
Editorial Profile: Avec une édition du Dimanche : 321 965ex. DIffusé dans la région Rhône Alpes et une partie de PACA.
Language (s): French; Full Page Mono: 10959.00; Full Page Colour: 14247.00
Currency: Euro
DAILY NEWSPAPER

LE Dauphiné Libéré - Edition Annecy
Owner: LE DAUPHINE LIBERE

Editorial: Centre Bonlieu, 1 rue Jean-Jaurès, Annecy 74000. **T:** 33 4 50 51 69 69
E: centre.annecy@ledauphine.com
W: http://www.ledauphine.com
Freq: Daily; **Circ:** 47000 Pub Statement
Editorial Profile: Daily regional newspaper covering national, regional and local current events. Local Translation:Quotidien régional d'informations nationales, régionales et locales.
Language (s): French; Full Page Mono: 5752.00
Currency: Euro
DAILY NEWSPAPER

LE Dauphiné libéré : Edition Léman et Genevois
Owner: LE DAUPHINE LIBERE
Editorial: 36 avenue de la Gare, Annemasse 74100. **T:** 33 4 50 84 24 01
E: redaction.annemasse@ledauphine.com
W: http://www.ledauphine.com
Freq: Daily; **Circ:** 26000 Pub Statement
Editorial Profile: Daily regional newspaper covering national, regional and local current events. Local Translation:Quotidien régional d'informations nationales, régionales et locales.
Language (s): French; Full Page Mono: 4927.00
Currency: Euro
DAILY NEWSPAPER

LE Dauphine Libere Edition Chambery-Aix-Les-Bains
Owner: LE DAUPHINE LIBERE
Editorial: 5 avenue Charles-de-Gaulle, Aix-Les-Bains 73100. **T:** +33 4 79 35 01 16
E: redaction.aixlesbains@ledauphine.com
W: http://www.ledauphine.com
Freq: Daily; **Circ:** 303551 Pub Statement
Editorial Profile: Regional news + 1 to 2 local pages. Local Translation:Actualités départementales + 1 à 2 pages locales.
Language (s): French; Full Page Mono: 4927.00
Currency: Euro
DAILY NEWSPAPER

LE DAUPHINE LIBERE EDITION DE GRAND VALENCE
Owner: LE DAUPHINE LIBERE
Editorial: 13 boulevard Maurice-Clerc, BP 931, Valence 26009. **T:** 33 4 75 79 78 00
E: centre.valence@ledauphine.com
W: http://www.ledauphine.com
Freq: Daily
Editorial Profile: Regional news, 3 pages covering Valence and 5 to 6 pages of local news. Local Translation:Informations départementales, 3 pages sur Valence et 5-6 pages d'actualités locales.
Language (s): French; Full Page Mono: 5752.00
Currency: Euro
DAILY NEWSPAPER

LE Dauphine libere edition Hautes-Alpes - Vallee de L'Ubaye
Owner: LE DAUPHINE LIBERE
Editorial: Place Frédéric-Mistral, Barcelonnette 4400. **T:** 33 4 92 81 30 30
E: centre.gap@ledauphine.com
W: http://www.ledauphine.com
Freq: Daily; **Circ:** 16000 Pub Statement
Editorial Profile: Hautes-Alpes, Ubaye valley and Sisteron region news + common pages of the Dauphiné Libéré edition. Local Translation:Toute l'actualité des Hautes-Alpes, de la vallée de l'Ubaye et de la région de Sisteron + pages communes à toutes les éditions du Dauphiné Libéré.
Language (s): French; Full Page Mono: 3084.00
Currency: Euro
DAILY NEWSPAPER

LE Dauphine Libere Edition Isere Nord Bourgoin - Ville Nouvelle
Owner: LE DAUPHINE LIBERE
Editorial: 19 avenue du Grand-Tissage, Bourgoin-Jallieu 38305. **T:** +33 4 74 28 03 00
E: centre.bourgoin@ledauphine.com
W: http://www.ledauphine.com
Freq: Daily; **Circ:** 330551 Pub Statement
Editorial Profile: Daily regional newspaper covering national, regional and local current events. Local Translation:Quotidien régional d'informations nationales, régionales et locales.
Language (s): French; Full Page Mono: 5453.00
Currency: Euro
DAILY NEWSPAPER

LE DAUPHINE LIBERE EDITION ISERE SUD
Owner: LE DAUPHINE LIBERE
Editorial: 40 avenue Alsace-Lorraine, Grenoble 38040. **T:** 33 4 76 88 73 37
E: centre.grenoble@ledauphine.com
W: http://www.ledauphine.com
Freq: Daily
Editorial Profile: Regional and local news. 5 editions are published in the south Isère region: Grenoble, Romanche & Oisans, Grésivaudan, Chartreuse and south Grésivaudan - Gières. Local Translation:Informations régionales et locales. Dans l'Isère Sud existent 5 éditions :- Grenoble - Romanche & Oisans- Grésivaudan - Chartreuse et sud Grésivaudan- Gières.
Language (s): French; Full Page Mono: 8541.00
Currency: Euro
DAILY NEWSPAPER

LE Dauphine Libere Edition Maurienne-Tarentaise
Owner: LE DAUPHINE LIBERE
Editorial: 51 place de l'Europe, Albertville 73200. **T:** +33 4 79 31 13 70
E: redaction.albertville@ledauphine.com
W: http://www.ledauphine.com
Freq: Daily; **Circ:** 303551 Pub Statement
Editorial Profile: Daily regional newspaper covering national, regional and local current events. Local Translation:Quotidien régional d'informations nationales, régionales et locales.
Language (s): French; Full Page Mono: 4927.00
Currency: Euro
DAILY NEWSPAPER

LE Dauphine Libere Editions Chambery-Aix-Les-Bains/ Maurienne Et Tarentaise
Owner: LE DAUPHINE LIBERE
Editorial: 8 boulevard du Théâtre, BP 387, Chambery CEDEX. **T:** +33 4 79 33 46 18
E: centre.chambery@ledauphine.com
W: http://www.ledauphine.com
Freq: Daily; **Circ:** 303551 Pub Statement
Editorial Profile: The Chambéry regional office is producing 2 Savoy region edition: Chambéry/Aix-Les-Bains and Maurienne/ Tarentaise. Regional news. Local Translation:La direction départementale de Chambéry travaille à deux éditions savoyardes : Chambéry/Aix-Les-Bains et Maurienne/ Tarentaise. Actualités départementales.
Language (s): French; Full Page Mono: 5453.00
Currency: Euro
DAILY NEWSPAPER

LE Dauphiné Libéré: Edition Ardèche Nord
Owner: LE DAUPHINE LIBERE
Editorial: 22 rue Montgolfier, Annonay 7100.
T: 33 4 75 33 31 22
E: redaction.annonay@ledauphine.com
W: http://www.ledauphine.com
Freq: Daily; **Circ:** 33551 Pub Statement
Editorial Profile: Daily regional newspaper covering national, regional and local current events. Local Translation:Quotidien régional d'informations nationales, départementales, locales.
Language (s): French; Full Page Mono: 4927.00
Currency: Euro
DAILY NEWSPAPER

LE Dauphiné Libéré: Edition Isère Nord
Owner: LE DAUPHINE LIBERE
Editorial: 5 rue des Récollets, BP 144, La Tour-Du-Pin 38354 CEDEX.
T: 33 4 74 83 56 30
E: redaction.tourdupin@ledauphine.com
W: http://www.ledauphine.com
Freq: Daily; **Circ:** 33551 Pub Statement
Editorial Profile: Daily regional newspaper covering national, regional and local current events. Local Translation:Quotidien régional d'informations nationales, régionales et locales.
Language (s): French; Full Page Mono: 4927.00
Currency: Euro
DAILY NEWSPAPER

LE Dauphiné Libéré: Edition Isère Nord Vienne et Roussillon
Owner: LE DAUPHINE LIBERE
Editorial: Place de la Halle, Le Peage De Roussillon 38550. **T:** 33 4 74 11 15 70
E: redaction.peage@ledauphine.com
W: http://www.ledauphine.com
Freq: Daily; **Circ:** 34456 Pub Statement
Editorial Profile: Daily regional newspaper covering national, regional and local current events. Local Translation:Quotidien régional d'informations nationales, régionales et locales.
Language (s): French; Full Page Mono: 4927.00
Currency: Euro
DAILY NEWSPAPER

La Dépêche d'Evreux
Owner: GROUPE PUBLIHEBDOS
Editorial: 3 rue Jean Jaurès, BP 143, Evreux 27001. **T:** 33 2 32 39 85 55
E: courrier@ladepeche.com
W: http://www.publihebdos.com
Freq: Weekly; **Circ:** 14447 OJD
Rédacteur en chef: Serge Couasnon;
Publisher: Denis Lejeune
Editorial Profile: Regional newspaper covering news and current affairs.
Language (s): French; Full Page Mono: 2503.00; Full Page Colour: 3004.00
Currency: Euro
NEWSPAPER

La Dépêche du Midi
Owner: Groupe La Dépêche Du Midi
Editorial: Avenue Jean Baylet, Toulouse 31300. **T:** 33 5 62 11 33 00
E: redaction@ladepeche.fr
W: http://www.ladepeche.fr
Freq: Daily; **Circ:** 190875 OJD
Rédacteur en chef: Yann Bouffin;
Madepeche.com: Philippe Rioux
Editorial Profile: Regional newspaper covering news and current affairs including economics, sports, culture and entertainment.
Language (s): French; Full Page Mono: 6100.00; Full Page Colour: 7625.00
Currency: Euro
DAILY NEWSPAPER

La Dépêche du Midi Edition de Haute-Garonne Comminges
Owner: LA DEPECHE DU MIDI
Editorial: 2 place du Maréchal-Juin, Saint-Gaudens 31800. **T:** 33 5 61 94 66 31
E: redaction.saint-gaudens@ladepeche.fr
W: http://www.ladepeche.fr
Freq: Daily; **Circ:** 225114 Pub Statement
Editorial Profile: Regional and local news. Local Translation:Actualité départementale et régionale.
Language (s): French
DAILY NEWSPAPER

LA Depeche Du Midi Edition De Haute-Garonne Sud-Est
Owner: LA DEPECHE DU MIDI
Editorial: Immeuble Le Stratège - Bât. A, BP 14, Labege CEDEX. **T:** 33 5 61 39 22 30
E: contact@ladepeche.com
W: http://www.ladepeche.fr
Freq: Daily; **Circ:** 214445 Pub Statement
Editorial Profile: Regional and local news. Local Translation:Actualité départementale et régionale.
Language (s): French
DAILY NEWSPAPER

LA Depeche Du Midi Edition De L'aude
Owner: LA DEPECHE DU MIDI
Editorial: 20 place Carnot, Carcassonne 11000. **T:** +33 4 68 11 90 11
E: redaction.castelnaudary@ladepeche.fr
W: http://www.ladepeche.fr
Freq: Daily; **Circ:** 250000 Pub Statement
Editorial Profile: General news covering the Aude region. Local Translation:Actualités générales qui concernent tout le département de l'Aude.
Language (s): French
DAILY NEWSPAPER

LA Depeche Du Midi Edition De L'aveyron
Owner: LA DEPECHE DU MIDI
Editorial: 20 rue Lamartine, Capdenac-Gare 12700. **T:** +33 5 65 63 81 30
E: redaction.decazeville@ladepeche.fr
W: http://www.ladepeche.fr
Freq: Daily; **Circ:** 223067 Pub Statement
Editorial Profile: Regional newspaper focussing on news, current affairs, economics, politics, culture and sport. One part general and one regional. Local Translation:Toute l'actualité départementale économique, politique, culturelle, sportive... Une partie générale et une partie départementale.
Language (s): French
DAILY NEWSPAPER

LA Depeche Du Midi Edition Du Lot-Et-Garonne
Owner: LA DEPECHE DU MIDI
Editorial: 109 boulevard Carnot, BP 59, Agen 47003 CEDEX. **T:** +33 5 53 48 05 10
E: redaction.villeneuve@ladepeche.fr
W: http://www.ladepeche.fr
Freq: Daily; **Circ:** 255107 Pub Statement
Editorial Profile: Regional and local news covering the Lot-et-Garonne region. Local Translation:Toute l'actualité régionale et départementale du Lot-et-Garonne.
Language (s): French
DAILY NEWSPAPER

LA Depeche Du Midi Edition Du Tarn Sud
Owner: LA DEPECHE DU MIDI
Editorial: 4 quai Miredames, Castres 81100.
T: +33 5 63 51 42 10
E: redaction.castres@ladepeche.fr
W: http://www.ladepeche.fr
Freq: Daily; **Circ:** 192075 Pub Statement
Editorial Profile: National, regional and local news. Local Translation:Toute l'actualité départementale, régionale et nationale.
Language (s): French
DAILY NEWSPAPER

LA DEPECHE DU MIDI EDITION DU TARN-ET-GARONNE
Owner: LA DEPECHE DU MIDI
Editorial: 3 rue de la république, Moissac 82200. **T:** 33 5 63 04 02 24
E: redaction.moissac@ladepeche.fr
W: http://www.ladepeche.fr
Freq: Daily; **Circ:** 18000 Pub Statement
Editorial Profile: National, regional and local news. Local Translation:Toute l'actualité départementale et régionale.
Language (s): French
DAILY NEWSPAPER

LES Dépêches - Le Progrès édition du Jura
Owner: EBRA
Editorial: 59 rue Jean-Jaurès, BP 30503, Lons-Le-Saunier 39001 CEDEX.
T: 33 3 84 86 07 20
E: accueillons@leprogres.fr
W: http://www.leprogres.fr
Freq: Daily; **Circ:** 30000 Pub Statement
Editorial Profile: News covering the Jura region + national and regional current events. Local Translation:Ensemble de l'actualité concernant la région du Jura + informations nationales et régionales.
Language (s): French; Full Page Mono: 3239.00; Full Page Colour: 3580.00
Currency: Euro
DAILY NEWSPAPER

Les Dernieres Nouvelles d'Alsace - DNA
Owner: DNA
Editorial: 17-21 rue de la Nuée-Bleue, BP 406, Strasbourg 67077 CEDEX.
T: +33 3 88 21 55 00 **E:** a.latham@dna.fr
W: http://www.dna.fr
Freq: Daily; **Circ:** 196301 Pub Statement
Rédacteur en Chef Adjoint: Bernard Delattre; **Rédacteur en Chef Adjoint:** Jean-Claude Frey; **Rédacteur en Chef Adjoint:** Jean-Louis Grussenmeyer; **Rédacteur (trice):** Fabienne Tafani
Editorial Profile: Local, regional, national and international information newspaper.
Language (s): French; Full Page Mono: 12510.00
Currency: Euro
DAILY NEWSPAPER

Dimanche Ouest France
Owner: OUEST FRANCE
Editorial: 10 rue du Breil, ZI Sud Est, Rennes 35051 CEDEX 9. **T:** +33 2 99 32 67 26
E: dimanche@ouest-france.fr
W: http://www.ouest-france.fr
Freq: Weekly; **Circ:** 350055 Pub Statement
Editorial Profile: General, regional and local information newspaper. Divided in 4 parts: News, family, sports and local events guide. Family booklet with 4 pages dedicated to children "Dimoitou" News, comics, games, experiments, DIY, jokes). Local Translation:Journal d'informations générales, régionales et locales. Se divise en quatre cahiers : actualités, famille, sport, guide des événements qui ont lieu dans la région. Dans le cahier Familles, un 4 pages pour les enfants Dimoitou (actu, BD, jeux, expérience, bricolage, blagues).
Language (s): French; Full Page Mono: 1800.00; Full Page Colour: 2340.00
Currency: Euro
NEWSPAPER

DIRECT BORDEAUX7
Owner: GROUPE SUD OUEST
Editorial: 23 quai de Queyries, Bordeaux 33100. **T:** 33 05 35 31 21 75
E: info@bordeaux7.com
W: http://www.bordeaux7.com
Freq: Daily; **Circ:** 27196 OJD
Rédactrice en chef: Stella Dubourg
Editorial Profile: Quotidien d'informations GRATUIT de la métropole bordelaise. PARUTIONS :du lundi au vendredi. Diffusé en Gironde. POUR L'ENVOI DE COMMUNIQUES : N'UTILISER QUE LE MAIL GENERAL.
Language (s): French; Full Page Mono: 1785.00; Full Page Colour: 2040.00
Currency: Euro
DAILY NEWSPAPER

Direct Matin
Owner: Groupe Bolloré
Editorial: 31-32, quai de Dion-Bouton, Puteaux 92800. **T:** 33 1 46 96 31 00
E: presse@directmatin.net
W: http://www.directmatin.fr
Freq: Daily; **Circ:** 350000 Pub Statement
Editor in Chief: Ludovic Pompignoli
Editorial Profile: Daily newspaper covering general news and current affairs including politics, economics, sports, culture, media, celebrities, technology and environment.
Language (s): French; Full Page Colour: 49500.00
Currency: Euro
DAILY NEWSPAPER

Direct Montpellier Plus
Editorial: Arche Jacques Coeur, Montpellier 34923. **T:** 33 4 99 74 34 38
E: redaction@montpellier-plus.com
W: http://www.direct-montpellier-plus.com
Freq: Daily; **Circ:** 30000 Pub Statement
Editor in Chief: Davy Gounel
Editorial Profile: Free regional daily newspaper focussing on general, local, regional, national and international news and current affairs.
Language (s): French
DAILY NEWSPAPER

Direct Strasbourg plus
Owner: GROUPE BOLLORE
T: 33 1 46 96 31 00 **E:** presse@directmatin.net
W: http://www.directstrasbourg.com
Freq: Daily; **Circ:** 30000 Pub Statement
Rédacteur en Chef Adjoint: Ludovic Pompignoli
Editorial Profile: Local Translation: Edition locale de Direct Matin Plus avec un décryptage de l'actualité nationale puis internationale en collaboration avec Le Monde et Courrier International. 4 à 6 pages dédiées à l'actualité nationale, 4 à l'actualité internationale et 4 àl'actualité régionale.
Language (s): French
DAILY NEWSPAPER

Direct Toulouse Plus
Owner: LE MONDE SA
Editorial: 31 - 32 quai de Dion Bouton, Puteaux 92811. **T:** 33 01 46 96 31 00
E: redaction.direct@ladepeche.fr
W: http://www.directtoulouse.com
Freq: Daily; **Circ:** 29230 Pub Statement
Rédacteur en Chef: Ludovic Pompignoli
Editorial Profile: Local Translation: Edition locale de Direct Matin Plus avec un décryptage de l'actualité nationale puis internationale en collaboration avec Le Monde et Courrier International. 4 à 6 pages dédiées à l'actualité nationale, 4 à l'actualité internationale et 4 à l'actualité régionale.
Language (s): French
DAILY NEWSPAPER

DNA - Dernieres Nouvelles D'Alsace Edition De Colmar
Owner: DNA
Editorial: 7 rue de la Gare, Colmar 68000.
T: 33 3 89 20 37 95 **E:** redac.colmar@dna.fr
W: http://www.dna.fr
Freq: Daily
Editorial Profile: Local, regional, national and international information newspaper. Local Translation:Informations nationales, internationales, régionales et locales.
Language (s): French
DAILY NEWSPAPER

DNA - Dernières Nouvelles d'Alsace Edition de Molsheim
Owner: DNA
Editorial: 14, rue de Saverne BP 28, Molsheim 68061. **T:** 33 3 88 49 70 60
E: redac.molsheim@dna.fr
W: http://www.dna.fr
Freq: Daily; **Circ:** 35000 Pub Statement
Editorial Profile: Local, regional, national and international information newspaper. Local

Translation:Informations locales, régionales, nationales et internationales.
Language (s): French
DAILY NEWSPAPER

DNA - Dernieres Nouvelles D'alsace Edition De Selestat Centre Alsace
Owner: DNA
Editorial: 119 rue Ml-de-Lattre-de-Tassigny, Sainte-Marie-Aux-Mines 68160.
T: +33 3 89 58 74 75
E: redac.sainte-marie@dna.fr
W: http://www.dna.fr
Freq: Daily;   **Circ:** 195899 Pub Statement
Editorial Profile: Local, regional, national and international information newspaper. Local Translation:Informations locales, régionales, nationales et internationales.
Language (s): French
DAILY NEWSPAPER

DNA - Dernieres Nouvelles D'alsace Editions Guebwiller-Mulhouse Et Guebwiller-Colmar
Owner: DNA
Editorial: 159 rue de la République, BP 8, Guebwiller CEDEX. **T:** 33 3 89 74 93 45
E: DNAguebwiller@dna.fr
W: http://www.dna.fr
Freq: Daily;   **Circ:** 250000 Pub Statement
Editorial Profile: Local, regional, national and international information newspaper.
Language (s): French
DAILY NEWSPAPER

DNA - Dernières Nouvelles d'Alsace: Edition de Saverne
Owner: DNA
Editorial: 114, Grand'Rue BP 22, BP 22, Saverne 67701 CEDEX. **T:** 33 3 88 01 83 63
E: redac.saverne@dna.fr **W:** http://www.dna.fr
Freq: Daily;   **Circ:** 35000 Pub Statement
Editorial Profile: Local and regional information newspaper. Local Translation:Informations locales, régionales.
Language (s): French
DAILY NEWSPAPER

L' Echo De La Presqu'Ile
Owner: GROUPE PUBLIHEBDOS
Editorial: La Parc Savary, Route de Bréhadour, Guerande 44351. **T:** 33 02 40 15 69 69
E: echodelapresquile@publihebdos.fr
Freq: Weekly;   **Circ:** 16801 OJD
Editeur: Eric Lechat; **Rédacteur en chef:** Christophe Lusseau
Editorial Profile: Hebdomadaire d'informations générales, régionales et locales Loire Atlantique Morbihan, paraissant le vendredi.
Language (s): French
NEWSPAPER

L' ECHO DE L'ARMOR ET DE L'ARGOAT
Owner: GROUPE PUBLIHEBDOS
Editorial: 8 rue Saint Nicolas, BP 20344, Guingamp 22203. **T:** 33 02 96 40 62 40
E: echo@publihebdos.fr
W: http://www.publihebdos.fr
Freq: Weekly;   **Circ:** 11252 OJD
Rédacteur en chef: Jack Malpart
Editorial Profile: Hebdomadaire d'informations locales et d'annonces légales paraissant le jeudi
Language (s): French
NEWSPAPER

L' ECHO DU BERRY
Editorial: 3 rue Ajasson de Grandsagne, BP 318, La Chatre 36400. **T:** 33 02 54 06 11 99
E: echoduberry.dj@orange.fr
Freq: Weekly;   **Circ:** 13509 OJD
Editorial Profile: PARUTION : Jeudi
Language (s): French; Full Page Mono: 1430.00; Full Page Colour: 1715.00
Currency: Euro
NEWSPAPER

L' Echo Republicain
Owner: GROUPE AMAURY
Editorial: 21 rue Vincent Chevard, BP 50189, Chartres 28004. **T:** 33 02 37 88 88 88
E: lucette.dihars@lechorepublicain.presse.fr
W: http://lechorepublicain.fr
Freq: Daily;   **Circ:** 30382 OJD
Rédacteur en chef adjoint: Jacques-Henri Digeon; **Rédacteur en chef:** Hugues De Lestapis
Language (s): French; Full Page Mono: 4552.00; Full Page Colour: 5684.00
Currency: Euro
DAILY NEWSPAPER

L' Echo Républicain Dreux
Owner: AMAURY

Editorial: 17 Grande-Rue, Dreux 28100 CEDEX. **T:** 33 2 37 62 52 70
E: dreux@lechorepublicain.presse.fr
W: http://www.lechorepublicain.fr
Freq: Daily;   **Circ:** 37400 Pub Statement
Editorial Profile: Regional and local news. Local Translation:Actualités régionales et locales.
Language (s): French
DAILY NEWSPAPER

L' Echo Républicain: Edition Châteaudun - Nogent-le-Rotrou
Owner: AMAURY
Editorial: 36 place du 18-Octobre, BP 49, Chateaudun 28200 CEDEX.
T: 33 2 37 45 20 89
E: chateaudun@lechorepublicain.presse.fr
W: http://www.lechorepublicain.presse.fr
Freq: Daily;   **Circ:** 37400 Pub Statement
Editorial Profile: Regional, national and international news covering sports, leisure, economy... Local Translation:Informations régionales, nationales, internationales, sports, loisirs, économie.
Language (s): French
DAILY NEWSPAPER

Les Échos
Owner: Groupe Les Échos
Editorial: 16 rue du Quatre Septembre, Paris 75002. **T:** 33 1 49 53 65 65
E: dvidalrevel@lesechos.fr
W: http://www.lesechos.fr
Freq: Daily;   **Circ:** 125984 OJD
Editor in Chief: David Barroux; **Editor in Chief:** Gilles Denis; **Editor in Chief:** Daniel Fortin; **Editor in Chief:** Etienne Lefebvre; **Editor in Chief:** Guillaume Maujean; **Editor in Chief:** Pascal Pogam
Editorial Profile: National newspaper covering all areas of financial and economic news including national and international news, industry, services, technology, media and financial markets.
Language (s): French; Full Page Mono: 41000.00; Full Page Colour: 64000.00
Currency: Euro
DAILY NEWSPAPER

Les Echos Du Touquet - Journal Montreuil
Editorial: 104 rue de Metz, Le Touquet-Paris-Plage 62520. **T:** 33 03 21 90 06 60 66
E: pierre.leduc@lesechosdutouquet.fr
Freq: Weekly;   **Circ:** 14249 OJD
Rédacteur en chef: Pierre Leduc; **Rédacteur en chef adjoint:** Mathieu Vergoin
Editorial Profile: LES ECHOS DU TOUQUET : 2 540ex, LE JOURNAL DE MONTREUIL : 8 063ex, LE REVEIL DE BERCK : 3 646ex. PARUTIONS : mercredi - Informations locales
Language (s): French; Full Page Mono: 799.00; Full Page Colour: 998.00
Currency: Euro
NEWSPAPER

L' Éclaireur du Gâtinais
Editorial: 48 rue Dorée, BP 237, Montargis 45202. **T:** 33 2 38 07 18 81
E: eclaireur.gatinais@wanadoo.fr
W: http://www.eclaireurdugatinais.fr
Freq: Weekly;   **Circ:** 19009 OJD
Editorial Profile: Regional newspaper covering local news and current affairs.
Language (s): French
NEWSPAPER

L' ÉQUIPE
Owner: SNC L'Equipe
Editorial: 145 rue Jean-Jacques Rousseau, Issy-Les-Moulineaux 92138.
T: 33 1 40 93 20 20
E: courrierdeslecteurs@lequipe.presse.fr
W: http://www.lequipe.fr
Freq: Daily;   **Circ:** 311403 OJD
Editor in Chief: Elie Barth; **Editor in Chief:** Pierre Callewaert; **Editor In Chief:** Dominique Issartel
Editorial Profile: Newspaper covering sports including football, tennis, rugby, motor racing and formula 1, basketball, handball, golf, cycling, athletics, swimming, sailing and horse-racing.
Language (s): French
DAILY NEWSPAPER

L' Essor
Editorial: 37-39 avenue de la Libération, BP 80186, Saint-Etienne 42005.
T: 33 04 77 37 60 60 **E:** redaction@lessor.fr
W: http://www.lessor.fr
Freq: Weekly;   **Circ:** 12566 OJD
Rédacteur en chef: Mathieu Ozanam
Editorial Profile: Hebdomadaire d'informations régionales et locales. PARUTION : Vendredi - 3 éditions : Loire, Rhône, Isère.

Language (s): French; Full Page Mono: 370.00; Full Page Colour: 450.00
Currency: Euro
NEWSPAPER

L' Est Eclair
Owner: GROUPE HERSANT MEDIA
Editorial: BP 532, Troyes 10081.
T: 33 03 25 71 75 75
E: redaction@lest-eclair.fr
W: http://www.lest-eclair.fr
Freq: Daily;   **Circ:** 27821 OJD
Droit - Justice: Valérie Alaniece; **Rédacteur en chef adjoint:** Alain Cadet; **Rédacteur en chef adjoint:** Jean-Pierre Kiehn; **Rédacteur en chef:** Patrick Planchenault
Editorial Profile: Edition du 7ème jour - Utilisation de la quadrichromie - Tous les jours. Diffusé dans l'Aube.
Language (s): French; Full Page Mono: 4166.00; Full Page Colour: 5832.00
Currency: Euro
DAILY NEWSPAPER

L' Est Républicain
Owner: L'Est Républicain
Editorial: 5 bis avenue Foch, Nancy 54000.
T: 33 3 83 59 08 04
E: lerredacncy@estrepublicain.fr
W: http://www.estrepublicain.fr
Freq: Daily;   **Circ:** 60000 Pub Statement
Editorial Profile: Regional, national and international newspaper. The Nancy agency has only one editorial office for 3 editions: Nancy agglomération (City centre), Banlieue Nord (North suburb), Banlieue Sud (South suburb).
Language (s): French; Full Page Mono: 5490.00; Full Page Colour: 6863.00
Currency: Euro
DAILY NEWSPAPER

L' Est Republicain - Edition Bar-Le-Duc
Owner: L'EST REPUBLICAIN
Editorial: 31 place Reggio, Bar-Le-Duc 55001 CEDEX. **T:** 33 3 29 79 40 36
E: lerredacbar@estrepublicain.fr
W: http://www.estrepublicain.fr
Freq: Daily;   **Circ:** 80000 Pub Statement
Editorial Profile: Daily regional and local newspaper. Local Translation:Quotidien d'actualités régionales et locales.
Language (s): French; Full Page Mono: 3443.00; Full Page Colour: 4304.00
Currency: Euro
DAILY NEWSPAPER

L' Est Republicain Edition De Luneville
Owner: L'EST REPUBLICAIN
Editorial: 8 rue Carnot, Luneville 54300.
T: 33 3 83 73 07 56
E: lerredaclune@estrepublicain.fr
W: http://www.estrepublicain.fr
Freq: Daily;   **Circ:** 60000 Pub Statement
Editorial Profile: Regional and local news. Local Translation:Toute l'actualité régionale et locale.
Language (s): French; Full Page Mono: 3184.00; Full Page Colour: 3980.00
Currency: Euro
DAILY NEWSPAPER

L' EST REPUBLICAIN EDITION DE MONTBELIARD
Owner: L'EST REPUBLICAIN
Editorial: 48 rue Cuvier, Montbeliard 25200.
T: 33 3 81 95 53 33
E: lerredacmtb@estrepublicain.fr
W: http://www.estrepublicain.fr
Freq: Daily;   **Circ:** 16300 Pub Statement
Editorial Profile: Regional and local news. Local Translation:Toute l'actualité régionale et locale.
Language (s): French; Full Page Mono: 2648.00; Full Page Colour: 3310.00
Currency: Euro
DAILY NEWSPAPER

L' Est Republicain Edition De Pont-A-Mousson
Owner: L'EST REPUBLICAIN
Editorial: 46 place Duroc, Pont-A-Mousson 54700. **T:** +33 3 83 81 06 58
E: lerredacpam@estrepublicain.fr
W: http://www.estrepublicain.fr
Freq: Daily;   **Circ:** 207000 Pub Statement
Editorial Profile: Daily regional and local newspaper. Local Translation:Quotidien d'actualités régionales et locales.
Language (s): French; Full Page Mono: 2153.00; Full Page Colour: 2691.00
Currency: Euro
DAILY NEWSPAPER

L' Est Republicain edition de Verdun
Owner: L'EST REPUBLICAIN
Editorial: 65 rue Mazel, Verdun 55100.
T: 33 3 29 86 12 49
E: redaction.verdun@estrepublicain.fr
W: http://www.estrepublicain.fr
Freq: Daily;
Editorial Profile: Daily regional and local newspaper. Classified ads supplement every Wednesday: "L'Est Annonces". Local Translation:Quotidien d'actualités régionales et locales. Tous les mercredis, un journal de petites annonces : 'L'Est Annonces'.
Language (s): French; Full Page Mono: 3443.00; Full Page Colour: 4304.00
Currency: Euro
DAILY NEWSPAPER

L' Est Républicain: Edition du Doubs
Owner: L'EST REPUBLICAIN
Editorial: 60 Grande-Rue, BP 149, Besancon 25014 CEDEX. **T:** 33 3 81 21 15 15
E: lerredacbes@estrepublicain.fr
W: http://www.estrepublicain.fr
Freq: Daily;   **Circ:** 42000 Pub Statement
Editorial Profile: Regional and local news. International and national news. Weekday price: 0.90 € - Sunday price: 1.60 € - First Wednesday of the month 1 €. Local Translation:Toute l'actualité locale et régionale. Informations internationales et nationales. Prix semaine : 0,90 € - Prix du dimanche : 1,70 € - 1 € le 1er mercredi du mois.
Language (s): French; Full Page Mono: 3227.00; Full Page Colour: 4034.00
Currency: Euro
DAILY NEWSPAPER

L' Est Républicain: Edition Haute-Doubs
Owner: L'EST REPUBLICAIN
Editorial: 50 rue de la République, BP 67, Pontarlier 25301. **T:** 33 3 81 46 87 88
E: lerredacpon@estrepublicain.fr
W: http://www.estrepublicain.fr
Freq: Daily;   **Circ:** 44000 Pub Statement
Editorial Profile: Regional and local news. International and national news. Weekday price: 0.90 € - Sunday price: 1.60 € - First Wednesday of the month 1 €. Local Translation:Toute l'actualité locale et régionale. Informations internationales et nationales. Prix semaine : 0,90 € - Prix du dimanche : 1,60 € - 1 € le 1er mercredi du mois.
Language (s): French
DAILY NEWSPAPER

L' Eveil De La Haute Loire
Owner: SUD COMMUNICATION
Editorial: 9 place Michelet, BP 24, Le Puy-En-Velay 43001. **T:** 33 04 71 09 32 14
E: redaction@leveil.fr **W:** http://www.leveil.fr
Freq: Daily;   **Circ:** 14422 OJD
Rédacteur en chef: Jean-Luc Broc
Editorial Profile: Diffusion : Haute-Loire et cantons limitrophes de l'Ardèche, de la Lozère.
Language (s): French; Full Page Colour: 2940.00
Currency: Euro
DAILY NEWSPAPER

L' EVEIL DE PONT AUDEMER
Owner: GROUPE PUBLIHEBDOS
Editorial: 9 Place Louis Gillain, BP 415, Pont Audemer 27504. **T:** 33 02 32 41 20 20
E: eveil.pont-audemer@publihebdos.fr
W: http://www.publihebdos.fr
Freq: Weekly;   **Circ:** 10100 OJD
Editeur: Christophe Lemoine; **Rédactrice en chef:** Virginie Veiss
Editorial Profile: Journal d'informations locales et régionales - PARUTIONS : le mardi
Language (s): French; Full Page Mono: 2176.00; Full Page Colour: 2831.00
Currency: Euro
NEWSPAPER

L' EVEIL NORMAND
Owner: GROUPE PUBLIHEBDOS
Editorial: 31 rue Thiers, BP 425, Bernay 27304. **T:** 33 02 32 47 81 00
E: eveil.normand@publihebdos.fr
W: http://www.publihebdos.fr
Freq: Weekly;   **Circ:** 10841 OJD
Rédacteur en chef: Jean-Yves Caruel; **Editeur:** Christophe Lemoine
Editorial Profile: Hebdomadaire d'informations paraissant le mercredi.
Language (s): French; Full Page Mono: 2241.00; Full Page Colour: 2916.00
Currency: Euro
NEWSPAPER

Le Figaro
Owner: Socpresse
Editorial: 14, bd Haussmann, Paris 75009.
T: 33 1 57 08 50 00 **E:** jmsalvator@lefigaro.fr

W: http://www.lefigaro.fr
Freq: Daily; **Circ:** 331022 OJD
Editor in Chief: Bertille Bayart; **Editor in Chief:** Martin Couturie; **Editor in Chief:** Philippe Goulliaud; **Editor in Chief:** Dominique Guiou; **Editor in Chief:** Bruno Jacquot; **Rédactrice en chef le Figaro Réussir:** Christine Lagoutte; **Editor in Chief:** Jean-Pierre Robin; **Editor in Chief:** Catherine Saint Jean; **Editor in Chief:** Jean-Luc Wachthausen
Editorial Profile: Newspaper covering national and international news and current affairs including politics, economic, culture, lifestyle and sport.
Language (s): French; Full Page Mono: 76000.00; Full Page Colour: 102000.00
Currency: Euro
DAILY NEWSPAPER

LE Foot Hebdo
Owner: LAFONT PRESSE
Editorial: 27 bd de Launay, Cedex 9, Nantes 44944. **T:** 33 1 46 10 21 21
W: http://www.lafontpresse.fr
Freq: Weekly
Conseiller: Arnaud Bertrande
Editorial Profile: Weekly journal about sports Local Translation:Journal hebdomadaire dédié au football national et international.
Language (s): French
NEWSPAPER

France Dimanche
Owner: Lagardère Active
Editorial: 149 rue Anatole France, Levallois Perret 92534. **T:** 33 1 41 34 85 30
E: contact.francedimanche@lagardere-active.com **W:** http://www.francedimanche.fr
Freq: Weekly; **Circ:** 424520 OJD
Publisher: Oscar Becerra; **Editor in Chief:** François Charlonnai
Editorial Profile: Sunday newspaper covering gossip news including celebrities and royalty as well as culture and entertainment.
Language (s): French; Full Page Mono: 9200.00; Full Page Colour: 11160.00
Currency: Euro
NEWSPAPER

La Gazette De Manche
Owner: GROUPE PUBLIHEBDOS
Editorial: BP 108, Saint-Hilaire-Du-Harcouet 50600. **T:** 33 02 33 79 30 80
E: info@gazette-manche.fr
Freq: Weekly; **Circ:** 10204 OJD
Editeur: Christian Bouzols; **Rédactrice en chef:** Pascale Brassinne
Editorial Profile: Informations locales. PARUTIONS : mercredi.
Language (s): French
NEWSPAPER

La Gazette De Montpellier
Editorial: 13 Place de la Comédie, CS 39530, Montpellier 34960. **T:** 33 04 67 06 77 77
E: laredaction@gazettedemontpellier.fr
W: http://www.lagazettedemontpellier.fr
Freq: Weekly; **Circ:** 19887 OJD
Chroniqueur: Michel Crespy; **Rédacteur en chef:** Henri-Marc Rossignol
Editorial Profile: City magazine local d'informations sur le Grand Montpellier, accompagné d'un supplément télévision TV GAZETTE. PARUTION : le jeudi.
Language (s): French; Full Page Mono: 1600.00; Full Page Colour: 2600.00
Currency: Euro
NEWSPAPER

La Gazette Nord Pas De Cais
Editorial: 7 rue Jacquemars Giélée, BP 1380, Lille 59015. **T:** 33 03 28 38 45 45
E: redaction@gazettenpdc.fr
W: http://www.gazettenpdc.fr
Freq: 2 Times/Week; **Circ:** 13700 Pub Statement
Editorial Profile: PARUTIONS: mardi (édition Pas-de-Calais) et vendredi (édition Nord). Destiné aux milieux juridiques, industriels, commerciaux et économiques
Language (s): French; Full Page Mono: 1592.00; Full Page Colour: 2229.00
Currency: Euro
NEWSPAPER

LE HAUT ANJOU
Editorial: 44 avenue du Maréchal Joffre, Chateau-Gontier 53200. **T:** 33 02 43 07 20 00
E: hautanjou@hautanjou.fr
Freq: Weekly; **Circ:** 13397 OJD
Rédactrice en chef: Typhaine David; **Rédaction Maine et Loire:** Quentin Lanvierge; **Rédacteur en chef adjoint:** Yannick Mahier
Editorial Profile: Hebdomadaire d'informations générales. PARUTIONS : vendredi. Edite également : LES NOUVELLES D'ANJOU - Mensuel GRATUIT - Renseignements identiques - T.Déclaré : 28 500 ex.
Language (s): French
NEWSPAPER

LA HAUTE SAINTONGE
Editorial: 12 avenue Gambetta, BP 96, Jonzac 17503. **T:** 33 05 46 48 00 48
E: hebdo.haute.saintonge@wanadoo.fr
Freq: Weekly; **Circ:** 10512 OJD
Rédactrice en chef adjointe - Société Histoire: Nicole Bertin
Editorial Profile: Hebdomadaire d'informations régionales. PARUTIONS : le vendredi Zone de diffusion : moitié sud du département de la Charente Maritime.
Language (s): French; Full Page Mono: 1046.00; Full Page Colour: 1298.00
Currency: Euro
NEWSPAPER

Le Havre Presse
Owner: GROUPE HERSANT MEDIA
Editorial: 113 boulevard de Strasbourg, Le Havre 76600. **T:** 33 02 35 19 17 17
Freq: Daily; **Circ:** 13286 OJD
Editorial Profile: Utilisation de la quadrichromie : tous les jours - Pages couleur en fonction de la pagination. REDACTION : SE REPORTER A HAVRE LIBRE. Diffusé en Seine Maritime.
DAILY NEWSPAPER

L' Hebdo du Vendredi
Owner: B2M
Editorial: 195 rue du Barbâtre, Reims 51100. **T:** 33 3 26 36 50 13
E: lhebdoduvendredi.redac@orange.fr
W: http://www.lhebdoduvendredi.com
Freq: Weekly; **Circ:** 40000 Pub Statement
Rédacteur en Chef: Olivier Michaux
Editorial Profile: Local Translation: Journal gratuit d'information locale (de 16 à 32 pages).3 éditions : Reims, Epernay et Châlons-en-Champagne. Bureau de Châlons : 29 rue Jean Jaurès - 51000 Châlons-en-ChampagneRubriques : société, justice, économie, sport, France, monde, Culture, loisirs, sorties, cinéma.
Language (s): French
NEWSPAPER

HEBDO+
Editorial: Pôle Gaston Fébus, Quartier Berlanne, Morlaas 64160.
T: 33 05 59 14 01 45
E: redaction@hebdo-plus.fr
W: http://www.hebdo-plus.fr
Freq: Weekly; **Circ:** 50000 Pub Statement
Editorial Profile: Journal d'information locale GRATUIT.
Language (s): French
NEWSPAPER

L' HERAULT DU JOUR DE LA MARSEILLAISE
Owner: LA MARSEILLAISE
Editorial: 58 allée Paul-Riquet, Beziers 34500. **T:** 33 4 67 49 10 31
E: agbeziers@lamarseillaise.fr
W: http://www.lamarseillaise.fr
Freq: Daily; **Circ:** 12049 Pub Statement
Editorial Profile: Hérault edition of the newspaper "La Marseillaise", the left wing regional community daily newspaper. Current events, 20 local pages (including 3 for Sète and 3 for Béziers). Local Translation:Edition de l'Hérault du journal 'La Marseillaise', quotidien de gauche d'informations régionales de proximité. Informations générales. 20 pages locales (dont 3 pour Sète et 3 pour Béziers).
Language (s): French; Full Page Mono: 5322.00; Full Page Colour: 6919.00
Currency: Euro
DAILY NEWSPAPER

LE HIC
Editorial: 70 rue de Lorraine, BP 1205, Cholet 49312. **T:** 33 02 41 49 02 34
E: redaction@lehic.com
Freq: Weekly; **Circ:** 90000 Pub Statement
Rédactrice (La Flêche/Saumur): Thiphaine David; **Rédactrice (Cholet):** Emmanuelle Echasseriau
Editorial Profile: Hebdomadaire GRATUIT paraissant le mercredi - Arts - Spectacles - Tourisme Sports - Loisirs.4 Editions : Sablé/La Flêche (lundi), Saumur (mardi) Cholet, Bocage (mercredi)
Language (s): French; Full Page Mono: 1755.00; Full Page Colour: 2094.00
Currency: Euro
NEWSPAPER

Le Hic Grand Saumur
Owner: HIC GRAND SAUMUROIS
Editorial: 4 place de la Bilange, BP 111, Saumur 49413 CEDEX. **T:** 33 41 49 02 33
E: redaction.saumur@lehic.com
W: http://www.lehic.com
Freq: Weekly; **Circ:** 49600 Pub Statement
Rédacteur (trice): Typhaine David
Editorial Profile: Regional newspaper focussing on local news and current affairs including associations and culture.
Language (s): French
NEWSPAPER

L' Humanité
Owner: Société nouvelle du journal l'Humanité
Editorial: 164 rue Ambroise Croizat, Saint-Denis 93528. **T:** 33 1 49 22 72 72
E: pam@humanite.fr
W: http://www.humanite.fr
Freq: Daily; **Circ:** 52456 OJD
Editor in Chief: Jean-Emmanuel Ducoin; **Editor in Chief:** Michel Guilloux; **Editor in Chief:** Jean-Paul Pierot
Editorial Profile: Newspaper covering national and international news and current affairs including politics, social issues, economics, society, environment, culture, sports and media.
Language (s): French; Full Page Mono: 12650.00; Full Page Colour: 17650.00
Currency: Euro
DAILY NEWSPAPER

L' Humanite Dimanche
Editorial: 164 rue Ambroise Croizat, Saint-Denis 93528. **T:** 33 01 49 22 72 72
E: plaurent@humanite.fr
W: http://www.humanite.fr
Freq: Weekly; **Circ:** 200000 Pub Statement
Rédacteur en chef: André Ciccodicola
Editorial Profile: Vie sociale - Vie quotidienne. PARUTIONS : le jeudi
Language (s): French
NEWSPAPER

L' Impartial
Owner: GROUPE PUBLIHEBDOS
Editorial: 3/5 rue Sainte Clotilde, BP 507, Les Andelys 27705. **T:** 33 02 32 54 00 84
E: impartial@publihebdos.fr
W: http://www.publihebdos.fr
Freq: Weekly; **Circ:** 12310 OJD
Rédacteur en chef: Jean-Paul Gosselin; **Editeur:** Denis Lejeune
Editorial Profile: Informations générales et régionales - Annonces légales. PARUTIONS : le jeudi
Language (s): French; Full Page Mono: 2169.00; Full Page Colour: 2820.00
Currency: Euro
NEWSPAPER

L' Independant Bureau Parisien
Owner: LES JOURNAUX DU MIDI
Editorial: 80 boulevard Auguste-Blanqui, Paris 75683 CEDEX 14. **T:** 33 1 44 71 80 44
E: redac.paris@midilibre.com
W: http://www.lindependant.com
Freq: Daily; **Circ:** 65523 Pub Statement
Rédacteur (trice): Zoé Cadiot
Editorial Profile: The Paris office is dedicated to the Indépendant issue of the Midi Libre et Centre Presse. Local Translation:Le Bureau de Paris est celui de l'Indépendant, de Midi Libre et de Centre Presse.
Language (s): French
DAILY NEWSPAPER

L' Independant Du Pas De Calais
Editorial: 14 rue des Clouteries, BP 87, Saint-Omer 62502. **T:** 33 03 21 12 22 23
E: vserbourdin@lindependant.net
Freq: Weekly; **Circ:** 17796 OJD
Rédacteur en chef: Benoît Cailliez
Editorial Profile: Information régionale et locale - PARUTIONS : Vendredi.
Language (s): French
NEWSPAPER

L' Independant Rivesaltes
Owner: LES JOURNAUX DU MIDI
Editorial: Mas de la Garrigue, 2 avenue Alfred-Sauvy, Rivesaltes 66605 CEDEX.
T: 33 4 68 64 88 88
E: direction.redaction@lindependant.com
W: http://www.lindependant.com
Freq: Daily; **Circ:** 65523 Pub Statement
Editor: Jean-Luc Bobin; **Rédacteur (trice):** Guillaume Clavaud; **Rédacteur (trice):** Vincent Couture; **Rédacteur (trice):** Estelle Devic; **Rédacteur (trice):** Eric Dubuis; **Rédacteur (trice):** Marine Galonnier; **Rédacteur (trice):** Xavier Hamond; **Rédacteur (trice):** Arnaud Hingray; **Rédacteur (trice):** Valérie Huck; **Rédacteur (trice):** Sylvie Lainé; **Rédacteur (trice):** Martial Mehr; **Rédacteur (trice):** Corinne Sabouraud; **Rédacteur (trice):** Stéphane Sicard; **Rédacteur en Chef Adjoint:** Andrée Sola; **Rédacteur (trice):** Fabrice Voné
Editorial Profile: This daily newspaper was first published in 1846 and covers news.
Language (s): French; Full Page Colour: 8658.00
Currency: Euro
DAILY NEWSPAPER

International New York Times
Owner: The New York Times Company
Editorial: Immeuble le Lavoisier, 4, place des Vosges, Courbevoie 92400.
T: 33 1 41 43 93 00
E: inytletters@nytimes.com
W: http://international.nytimes.com
Freq: Daily; **Circ:** 219188 OJD
Rédactrice en chef: Katherine Knorr; **Bureau Chief:** Alissa Rubin
Editorial Profile: International newspaper covering general news and current affairs including business, politics, sports, culture, society, style, arts and travel.
Language (s): English; Full Page Mono: 59053.00
Currency: Euro
DAILY NEWSPAPER

The International New York Times - Paris
Editorial: Immeuble le Lavoisier, 4, place des Vosges, Courbevoie 92400.
T: 33 1 41 43 93 00
Bureau Chief: Alissa Rubin
DAILY NEWSPAPER

Investir
Owner: Groupe Les Echos
Editorial: 16, rue du 4 Septembre, Paris 75002. **T:** 33 1 44 88 48 00
E: rlebailly@investir.fr
W: http://bourse.lesechos.fr
Freq: Weekly; **Circ:** 77639 OJD
Editor in Chief: Rémy Le Bailly
Editorial Profile: Newspaper covering investment including stock markets and and financial analysis.
Language (s): French; Full Page Mono: 21200.00; Full Page Colour: 27200.00
Currency: Euro
NEWSPAPER

Le Journal De Gien
Editorial: 26 rue du Général Marcel, BP 65, Gien 45502. **T:** 33 02 38 67 19 43
E: journaldegien@wanadoo.fr
Freq: Weekly; **Circ:** 17957 OJD
Rédacteur en chef: Martial Poncet
Editorial Profile: Informations régionales. PARUTIONS : jeudi.
Language (s): French; Full Page Mono: 3460.00; Full Page Colour: 5190.00
Currency: Euro
NEWSPAPER

JOURNAL DE LA CORSE
Editorial: ZI du Vazzio, Ajaccio 20090.
T: 33 04 95 21 50 02
E: redaction@journaldelacorse.net
W: http://www.jdcorse.com
Freq: Weekly; **Circ:** 15000 Pub Statement
Bureau de Bastia: Jean-Noël Colonna; **Rédactrice en chef:** Caroline Siciliano
Editorial Profile: Journal d'informations régionales paraissant le vendredi.
Language (s): French
NEWSPAPER

Le Journal De La Haute Marne
Editorial: 14 rue du Patronage Laïque, BP 2057, Chaumont 52902. **T:** 33 03 25 03 86 40
E: jhmdir@graphycom.com
W: http://www.jhm.fr
Freq: Daily; **Circ:** 25832 OJD
Rédaction départementale: Céline Clement; **Rédacteur en chef adjoint:** Bruno Theveny
Language (s): French; Full Page Mono: 2972.00; Full Page Colour: 3715.00
Currency: Euro
DAILY NEWSPAPER

LE Journal de la Haute-Marne: Edition Nord
Owner: EBRA
Editorial: 45 rue Gambetta, BP 79, Saint-Dizier 52100. **T:** 33 3 25 05 20 04
E: redac@jhmsaint-dizier.com
W: http://www.jhm.fr
Freq: Daily; **Circ:** 31001 OJD
Editorial Profile: General and local news. Sunday price: 1,15 € - Subscription including Sunday: 258 € - Subscription without Sunday issues: 199 €. Local Translation:Informations générales et locales. Prix dimanche 1,15 €. Abonnement avec dimanche 258 € - Abonnement sans dimanche 199 €.
Language (s): French
DAILY NEWSPAPER

Le Journal de Saône-et-Loire
Owner: EST REPUBLICAIN
Editorial: 9-15 rue des Tonneliers, BP 30134, Chalon-Sur-Saone 71104. **T:** 33 3 85 90 68 00
E: infos@lejsl.fr **W:** http://www.lejsl.com
Freq: Daily; **Circ:** 58036 OJD
Rédacteur en chef adjoint: Frédéric Bouvier; **Athlétisme:** Claude Casseville
Language (s): French; Full Page Mono: 4548.00; Full Page Colour: 5504.00
Currency: Euro
DAILY NEWSPAPER

LE Journal De Saone-Et-Loire Edition De Louhans
Owner: EBRA
Editorial: 9 rue d'Alsace, Louhans 71500.
T: 33 3 85 75 22 49
E: accueil-louhans@lejsl.fr
W: http://www.lejsl.com
Freq: Daily; **Circ:** 72000 Pub Statement
Editorial Profile: Regional and local news. Local Translation:Actualités régionales et locales.
Language (s): French
DAILY NEWSPAPER

LE Journal De Saone-Et-Loire Edition De Macon
Owner: EBRA
Editorial: 89 quai Lamartine, Macon 71000.
T: 33 3 85 39 99 00
E: redaction-macon@lejsl.fr
W: http://www.lejsl.com
Freq: Daily; **Circ:** 69889 Pub Statement
Editorial Profile: Regional and local news. Local Translation:Actualités régionales et locales.
Language (s): French
DAILY NEWSPAPER

LE Journal De Saone-Et-Loire Edition Paray-Le-Monial Gueugnon Digoin
Owner: EBRA
Editorial: 49 avenue Charles-de-Gaulle, Digoin 71160. **T:** 33 3 85 53 77 00
E: text-digoin@lejsl.fr **W:** http://www.lejsl.com
Freq: Daily; **Circ:** 65000 Pub Statement
Editorial Profile: Regional and local news. Local Translation:Actualités régionales et locales.
Language (s): French
DAILY NEWSPAPER

Le Journal D'Ici
Editorial: 3 Quai du Carras, BP 309, Castres 81105. **T:** 33 05 63 51 49 49
E: redaction@lejournaldici.com
Freq: Weekly; **Circ:** 13000 Pub Statement
Rédacteur en chef adjoint: Karim Benaouda
Editorial Profile: Informations générales et régionales. PARUTIONS : jeudi
Language (s): French
NEWSPAPER

Le Journal Du Centre
Owner: GROUPE CENTRE FRANCE - LA MONTAGNE
Editorial: 3 rue du Chemin de Fer, BP 106, Nevers 58001. **T:** 33 03 86 71 45 00
E: redaction.jdc@centrefrance.com
W: http://www.lejdc.fr
Freq: Daily; **Circ:** 30050 OJD
Editorial Profile: Utilisation quadri : tous les jours - Dans les pages une, dernière et pages impaires intérieures. Edition du dimanche : JOURNAL DU CENTRE DIMANCHE (12 463 ex). Diffusé en Bourgogne.
Language (s): French; Full Page Mono: 5007.00
Currency: Euro
DAILY NEWSPAPER

Le Journal du Dimanche - JDD
Owner: Hachette Filipacchi Médias
Editorial: 149 rue Anatole France, Levallois Perret 92534. **T:** 33 1 41 34 60 00
E: redaction@lejdd.fr **W:** http://www.lejdd.fr
Freq: Weekly; **Circ:** 267659 OJD
Editor in Chief: Bruno Jeudy; **Editor in Chief:** Laurent Valdiguié
Editorial Profile: Sunday newspaper covering news and current affairs including politics, world news, society, economics, culture, media, sports, leisure and entertainment.
Language (s): French; Full Page Mono: 52800.00; Full Page Colour: 66000.00
Currency: Euro
NEWSPAPER

Le Havre - Paris Normandie
Owner: GHM - GROUPE HERSANT MEDIA
Editorial: 113 boulevard de Strasbourg, Le Havre 76600. **T:** 33 2 35 19 17 17
E: redaction.havre@presse-normande.com
W: http://www.paris-normandie.fr
Freq: Daily; **Circ:** 38300 Pub Statement
Rédacteur en Chef: Sophie Bloch; **Rédacteur (trice):** Patrick Gobbé
Editorial Profile: Daily current events newspapers covering Le Havre and its region. Only the cover page will be different on each title. Circulation: Havre Libre 12.300 copies, Havre Presse 8.200 copies, Paris Normandie Le Havre 6.000 copies. Local Translation:Quotidiens sur Le Havre et sa région. Seule la une diffère d'un titre à l'autre. Tirages : Havre Libre 12.300 ex., Havre Presse 8.200 ex, Paris Normandie Le Havre 6.000 ex.
Language (s): French
DAILY NEWSPAPER

Libération
Owner: SARL Libération
Editorial: 11, rue Béranger, Paris 75003.
T: 33 1 42 76 17 89 **E:** sergent@liberation.fr
W: http://www.liberation.fr
Freq: Daily; **Circ:** 123339 OJD
Editor in Chief: Gérard Lefort; **Editor in Chief:** Marc Semo; **Editor in Chief:** Béatrice Vallaeys
Editorial Profile: Newspaper covering general news and current affairs including politics, society, economics, sports, science, culture, technology, environment and media.
Language (s): French; Full Page Mono: 31600.00; Full Page Colour: 49600.00
Currency: Euro
DAILY NEWSPAPER

LIBERTE - BONHOMME LIBRE
Owner: GROUPE PUBLIHEBDOS
Editorial: 17 rue Commodore Hallet, BP 85341, Caen 14053. **T:** 33 02 31 86 03 32
E: liberte@publihebdos.fr
Freq: Weekly; **Circ:** 17299 OJD
Rédactrice en chef adjointe: Murielle Bouchard
Editorial Profile: Informations générales, régionales et locales, spectacles, enquêtes, sports, annonces légales. PARUTIONS : jeudi.
Language (s): French; Full Page Mono: 2691.00; Full Page Colour: 3510.00
Currency: Euro
NEWSPAPER

LIBERTE DIMANCHE
Owner: GROUPE HERSANT MEDIA
Editorial: 33 rue des Grosses-Pierres, Deville-Les-Rouen 76250. **T:** 33 02 32 08 37 39
E: redaction.liberte@presse-normande.com
Freq: Weekly; **Circ:** 14491 OJD
Rédacteur en chef: Thierry Delacourt
Editorial Profile: PARUTIONS : dimanche - Informations générales, régionales, sportives DIFFUSION : Seine Maritime, Eure.
Language (s): French; Full Page Mono: 8800.00; Full Page Colour: 10560.00
Currency: Euro
NEWSPAPER

LILLEPLUS
Owner: GROUPE LA VOIX DU NORD
Editorial: PGLM, 29 rue Esquermoise, Lille 59000. **T:** 33 03 20 44 80 00
E: contact@directlille.com
W: http://www.directlille.com
Freq: Daily; **Circ:** 50853 OJD
Rédaction régionale: Sabrina Alouache; **Rédactrice en chef:** Adeline Boldoduck; **Rédaction régionale:** Perrine Tiberghien
Editorial Profile: Quotidien GRATUIT d'informations générales et locales pour les urbains actifs de 15/35 ans. (Pages internationales et nationales réalisées par DIRECTMATIN)
Language (s): French; Full Page Colour: 2659.00
Currency: Euro
DAILY NEWSPAPER

LA LOZERE NOUVELLE
Editorial: Boulevard des Capucins, BP 17, Mende 48001. **T:** 33 04 66 49 65 90
E: redaction@lozere-nouvelle.com
W: http://www.lozere-nouvelle.com
Freq: Weekly; **Circ:** 22523 OJD
Rédacteur en chef adjoint: Jean-Marc Gilly
Editorial Profile: Informations locales et générales.
Language (s): French; Full Page Mono: 1470.00
Currency: Euro
NEWSPAPER

LYONPLUS
Owner: GROUPE PROGRES
Editorial: 4 rue Montrochet, Lyon 69002.
T: 33 04 78 14 77 91 **E:** info@lyonplus.com
W: http://www.lyonplus.com
Freq: Daily; **Circ:** 62519 OJD
Rédacteur en chef .: Manuel Da Fonseca
Editorial Profile: Quotidien GRATUIT d'informations locales, nationales, internationales et culturelles distribué dans les gares, le métro etc... NE SOUHAITENT PAS DE COMMUNICATION PAR FAX
Language (s): French; Full Page Colour: 6000.00
Currency: Euro
DAILY NEWSPAPER

Le Maine Libre
Owner: SIPA
Editorial: 28 Place de l'Eperon, Le Mans 72013. **T:** 33 02 43 83 72 30
E: redaction@maine-libre.com
W: http://www.lemainelibre.fr
Freq: Daily; **Circ:** 47205 OJD
Rédacteur en chef adjoint: Serge Danilo; **Rédacteur en chef:** Jérôme Glaize
Editorial Profile: Utilisation de la quadrichromie - Tous les jours - Dans les pages une, trois dernière, antépénultième et 4 pages intérieures. Edition du septième jour : 25 704ex. Diffusé dans la Sarthe.
DAILY NEWSPAPER

LE Maine Libre - Edition le Mans
Owner: OUEST FRANCE
Editorial: 28/30 place de l'Eperon, Le Mans 72013 CEDEX 2. **T:** 33 2-43-83-72-30
E: redaction@maine-libre.com
W: http://www.lemainelibre.fr
Freq: Daily; **Circ:** 46117 OJD
Rédacteur en Chef Adjoint: Serge Danilo; **Rédacteur en Chef:** Jérôme Glaize
Editorial Profile: Daily general, regional and local newspaper: Saturday price: 0,90 € (including TV guide supplement). Sunday price: 0,90 € (including women supplement Version Fémina).Local Translation: Quotidien d'informations générales, régionales, locales et sportives.Le samedi, prix de 0,90 € (avec supplément TV). Le Dimanche, prix 0,90 € (avec le supplément Femmes Version Fémina).
Language (s): French; Full Page Mono: 10072.00; Full Page Colour: 12590.00
Currency: Euro
DAILY NEWSPAPER

LE Maine Libre - Edition Sarthe Loir
Owner: OUEST FRANCE
Editorial: 28-30, place de l'Eperon, Le Mans 72 013 Cedex 2. **T:** 33 2 43 83 72 72
E: agence.chateauduloir@maine-libre.com
W: http://www.lemainelibre.fr
Freq: Daily; **Circ:** 48000 OJD
Editorial Profile: Daily general, regional and local newspaper. Local Translation:Quotidien d'informations générales, régionales, locales.
Language (s): French
DAILY NEWSPAPER

LE Maine Libre Edition Haute Sarthe
Owner: OUEST FRANCE
Editorial: 17 avenue du Général-Leclerc, Alencon 61000. **T:** 33 2 33 82 64 83
E: agence.mamers@maine-libre.com
W: http://www.lemainelibre.fr
Freq: Daily; **Circ:** 47000 OJD
Editorial Profile: Daily general, regional and local newspaper: politics, education, magazine... Local Translation:Quotidien d'informations générales, régionales, locales. Politique, éducation, magazine.
Language (s): French
DAILY NEWSPAPER

La Manche Libre
Editorial: Rue de Coutances, Saint-Lo 50950.
T: 33 02 33 05 10 00
E: direction@lamanchelibre.com
W: http://www.lamanchelibre.fr
Freq: Weekly; **Circ:** 74836 OJD
Editorial Profile: Information générale et départementale. PARUTIONS : Jeudi Edition Calvados : Le Bessin Libre - Le Bocage Libre. Diffusion : 7 éditions couvrant la Manche et l'Ouest du Calvados.
Language (s): French
NEWSPAPER

La Marne
Editorial: 79 avenue de l'Epinette ZI, BP 27, Meaux 77102. **T:** 33 01 64 23 35 00
E: ig@journal-lamarne.fr
Freq: Weekly; **Circ:** 14157 OJD
Rédactrice en chef adjointe - Meaux: Carine Babec; **Editeur:** Olivier Bassine
Editorial Profile: Hebdomadaire d'informations régionales. PARUTIONS : mercredi
Language (s): French; Full Page Mono: 4318.00; Full Page Colour: 7971.00
Currency: Euro
NEWSPAPER

La Marseilise
Editorial: 19 cours d'Estienne d'Orves, BP 91862, Marseille 13222. **T:** 33 04 91 57 75 00
E: lamars@lamarseillaise.fr
W: http://www.journal-lamarseillaise.com
Freq: Daily; **Circ:** 139000 Pub Statement
Rédacteur en chef adjoint: Christian Digne; **Rédacteur en chef:** Rolland Martinez
Editorial Profile: 7 Titres : l'Hérault du Jour, La Marseillaise du Gard, La Marseillaise Vaucluse, La Marseillaise des Alpes, La Marseillaise Bouches du Rhône, La Marseillaise Marseille, La Marseillaise Le Varois. Diffusé en région PACA.
Language (s): French; Full Page Mono: 5670.00; Full Page Colour: 7371.00
Currency: Euro
DAILY NEWSPAPER

MARSEILLE L'HEBDO
Owner: GROUPE HERSANT MEDIA
Editorial: 248 avenue Roger Salengro, BP 100, Marseille 13326. **T:** 33 04 91 84 47 47
E: redaction@marseillelhebdo.com
W: http://www.marseillelhebdo.com
Freq: Weekly; **Circ:** 12503 OJD
Maquettiste: Jean-Marie Ferrara
Editorial Profile: City magazine d'informations sur Marseille. PARUTIONS : le mardi
Language (s): French
NEWSPAPER

MARSEILLEPLUS
Owner: GROUPE HERSANT MEDIA
Editorial: 248 avenue Roger Salengro, Marseille 13015. **T:** 33 04 91 84 80 00
E: redaction@marseilleplus.com
Freq: Daily; **Circ:** 56477 OJD
Rédactrice: Alexanda Cefaï; **Rédactrice:** Audrey Desanto; **Rédacteur:** Jean-Marie Ferrara; **Rédacteur:** Frédérique Jacquemin; **Rédactrice:** Béatrice Jullion; **Rédacteur:** Pierre Psaltis
Editorial Profile: Quotidien régional GRATUIT d'informations générales et locales.
Language (s): French; Full Page Mono: 2900.00; Full Page Colour: 3480.00
Currency: Euro
DAILY NEWSPAPER

Le Mensuel de Rennes
Owner: Le Mensuel
Editorial: 1 Quai Lamennais, Rennes 35000.
T: 33 2 99 79 04 65
E: rennes@lemensuel.com
W: http://www.rennes.lemensuel.com
Freq: Monthly; **Circ:** 10000 Pub Statement
Editor in Chief: Nicolas Legendre
Editorial Profile: Magazine covering regional news and current affairs.
Language (s): French
NEWSPAPER

Le Messager
Owner: GROUPE LA VOIX DU NORD
Editorial: 22 avenue du Général de Gaulle, BP 102, Thonon-Les-Bains 74201.
T: 33 04 50 71 10 14
E: sthomas@lemessager.fr
W: http://www.lemessager.fr
Freq: Weekly; **Circ:** 25415 OJD
Rédacteur en chef: Samuel Thomas
Editorial Profile: Journal régional d'informations. PARUTIONS : jeudi. 3 EDITIONS : Chablais - Genevois - Faucigny.
Language (s): French; Full Page Mono: 2225.00; Full Page Colour: 2670.00
Currency: Euro
NEWSPAPER

Métro - Edition de Lyon
Owner: PUBLICATIONS METRO FRANCE
Editorial: 25 rue Paul-Chenavard, Lyon 69001.
T: 33 4 72 77 01 90
W: http://www.metrofrance.com/info-locale/lyon
Freq: Daily; **Circ:** 46000 Pub Statement
Editorial Profile: Local Translation: Actualités nationales et locales.
Language (s): French
DAILY NEWSPAPER

Métro: Edition de Lille
Owner: PUBLICATIONS METRO FRANCE
Editorial: 11 rue Masurel, Lille 59000.
T: 33 3 20 74 66 67
W: http://www.metrofrance.com/info-locale/lille
Freq: Daily; **Circ:** 33000 Pub Statement
Editorial Profile: Local Translation: Actualités nationales et locales.
Language (s): French
DAILY NEWSPAPER

Métro: Edition de Toulouse
Owner: PUBLICATIONS METRO FRANCE
Editorial: 12 rue Gabriel-Péri, Toulouse 31000.
T: 33 5 34 44 13 00
W: http://www.metrofrance.com/info-locale/toulouse
Freq: Daily; **Circ:** 33500 Pub Statement

Editorial Profile: Local Translation: Actualités nationales et locales.
Language (s): French
DAILY NEWSPAPER

Metronews
Owner: Metro France
Editorial: 35, rue Greneta, Paris 75002.
T: 33 1 55 34 45 00
E: metronewsfr@gmail.com
W: http://www.metronews.fr
Freq: Daily; **Circ:** 632000 Pub Statement
Editor in Chief: Christophe Joly
Editorial Profile: Free regional daily newspaper focussing on general news and current affairs including sports, culture, celebrities, technology, entertainment and video.
Language (s): French; Full Page Mono: 43400.00; Full Page Colour: 62000.00
Currency: Euro
DAILY NEWSPAPER

Midi Libre
Owner: Midi Libre
Editorial: Rue du Mas-de-Grille, Saint-Jean-De-Vedas 34438. **T:** 33 4 67 07 67 07
E: midiloisirs@midilibre.com
W: http://www.midilibre.fr
Freq: Daily; **Circ:** 147392 OJD
Bureau Chief: Frédéric Gautier; **Rédacteur en Chef Adjoint:** Yann Marec; **Rédacteur en Chef:** François Martin; **Bureau Chief:** Monique Raynaud
Editorial Profile: Regional daily newspaper focussing on local, regional and national news and current affairs including entertainment, sports and culture.
Language (s): French; Full Page Colour: 14882.00
Currency: Euro
DAILY NEWSPAPER

MIDI LIBRE EDITION BEZIERS
Owner: MIDI LIBRE
Editorial: 23 rue Jean Roger, Agde 34301.
T: 33 4 67 94 48 85
E: redac.agde@midilibre.com
W: http://www.midilibre.com
Freq: Daily; **Circ:** 22450 Pub Statement
Rédacteur (trice): Laurent Vermorel
Editorial Profile: Regional daily newspaper focussing on news and current affairs. Local Translation:Quotidien régional d'informations. 6 pages locales + 6 pages villages.
Language (s): French
DAILY NEWSPAPER

Midi Libre Edition Nimes Camargue
Owner: Midi Libre
Editorial: 27 ter quai Général-de-Gaulle, Beaucaire 30300. **T:** 33 4 66 58 51 98
E: loisirsgard@midilibre.com
W: http://www.midilibre.com
Freq: Daily
Rédacteur en Chef Adjoint: Yan Barry; **Rédacteur en Chef:** François Charcellay; **Rédacteur (trice):** Thierry Montaner
Editorial Profile: Regional daily newspaper focusing on regional and local news and current affairs.
Language (s): French
DAILY NEWSPAPER

MINIZOU
Editorial: La Petite Presse, 54 montée des Clarines, Jarrie 38560. **T:** 33 04 76 04 98 30
E: minizou38@free.fr
W: http://www.minizou.fr
Freq: Bi-Monthly; **Circ:** 22000 Pub Statement
Editorial Profile: Périodique GRATUIT rassemblant l'actualité jeune public (0-14 ans)en Dauphiné. PARUTIONS : 5 nº/an (23 avril, 1er juillet, 22 septembre, 2 décembre, 13 février).
Language (s): French
NEWSPAPER

Le Monde
Owner: Le Monde
Editorial: 80, boulevard Auguste Blanqui, Paris 75013. **T:** 33 1 57 28 20 00
E: communication2@lemonde.fr
W: http://www.lemonde.fr
Freq: Daily; **Circ:** 319418 OJD
Editor in Chief: Michel Kajman; **Editor in Chief:** Arnaud Leparmentier; **Editor in Chief:** Franck Nouchi; **Editor in Chief:** Cécile Prieur; **Publisher:** Michel Sfeir; **Nicole Vulser:** Nicole Vulser
Editorial Profile: National newspaper covering national and international news and current affairs including politics, society, economy, culture, sports, science, technology and lifestyle.
Language (s): French; Full Page Mono: 89000.00; Full Page Colour: 116800.00
Currency: Euro
DAILY NEWSPAPER

La Montagne
Owner: GROUPE CENTRE FRANCE - LA MONTAGNE
Editorial: 28 rue Morel Ladeuil, Clermont Ferrand 63056. **T:** 33 04 73 17 17 17
E: redaction@centrefrance.com
W: http://www.lamontagne.fr
Freq: Daily; **Circ:** 197424 OJD
GUERET: Hervé Moisan; **BRIVE:** Pascal Ratinaud; **Rédacteur en chef:** Philippe Rousseau
Editorial Profile: Edition du dimanche Groupe : 169 907ex.- Quadrichromie : Tous les jours. 8 pages possibles selon configuration. Diffusé en Auvergne et dans le Limousin.
DAILY NEWSPAPER

LA Montagne Clermont-Ferrand
Owner: CENTRE FRANCE
Editorial: 45 rue du Clos-Four, BP 83, Clermont-Ferrand 63056 CEDEX 2.
T: +33 4 73 17 17 17
E: locale@centrefrance.com
W: http://www.lamontagne.fr
Freq: Daily; **Circ:** 199806
Rédacteur en Chef: Philippe Rousseau; **Rédacteur en Chef Technique:** Philippe Vazeille
Editorial Profile: Regional newspaper - Sports - Current events. Local Translation: Quotidien régional - Sports - Informations générales.
Language (s): French; Full Page Mono: 10990.00
Currency: Euro
DAILY NEWSPAPER

LA Montagne Edition De L'allier Montlucon
Owner: CENTRE FRANCE
Editorial: 13 avenue Marx-Dormoy, Montlucon 3100. **T:** +33 4 70 02 21 00
E: montlucon@centrefrance.com
W: http://www.lamontagne.fr
Freq: Daily; **Circ:** 191639 Pub Statement
Editorial Profile: Regional and local news. 1,60 € on Sunday. Local Translation:Informations régionales et locales. 1,60 € le dimanche.
Language (s): French
DAILY NEWSPAPER

LA Montagne Edition Du Puy-De-Dome Issoire
Owner: CENTRE FRANCE
Editorial: 33 boulevard Jules-Cibrand, Issoire 63500. **T:** +33 4 73 55 25 00
E: issoire@centrefrance.com
W: http://www.lamontagne.fr
Freq: Daily; **Circ:** 191639 Pub Statement
Editorial Profile: Regional and local news. Local Translation:Informations régionales et locales.
Language (s): French
DAILY NEWSPAPER

LA Montagne Edition Du Puy-De-Dome Riom
Owner: CENTRE FRANCE
Editorial: 47 rue du Commerce, Riom 63200.
T: +33 4 73 67 10 00
E: riom@centrefrance.com
W: http://www.lamontagne.fr
Freq: Daily; **Circ:** 191639 Pub Statement
Editorial Profile: Regional and local news.
Language (s): French
DAILY NEWSPAPER

LA Montagne Edition Du Puy-De-Dome Thiers-Ambert
Owner: CENTRE FRANCE
Editorial: 10 rue de la République, Ambert 63600. **T:** +33 4 73 82 44 32
E: ambert@centrefrance.com
W: http://www.lamontagne.fr
Freq: Daily; **Circ:** 191639 Pub Statement
Editorial Profile: National, regional and local news. TV guide and woman supplement on Sunday.
Language (s): French
DAILY NEWSPAPER

NEUILLY - Journal indépendant
Editorial: 80 avenue Charles de Gaulle, Neuilly Sur Seine 92200. **T:** 33 01 46 24 75 06
E: syham@neuillyjournal.com
W: http://www.neuillyjournal.com
Freq: Monthly; **Circ:** 27000 Pub Statement
Rédactrice en chef: Syham Nehab
Editorial Profile: Magazine destiné aux habitants de Neuilly S/Seine. PARUTIONS : 11 nº/an : 1ère semaine du mois.
Language (s): French; Full Page Mono: 2135.00; Full Page Colour: 3354.00
Currency: Euro
NEWSPAPER

NICE MATIN
Owner: GROUPE HERSANT MEDIA
Editorial: 214 route de Grenoble, Nice 6290.
T: 33 04 93 18 28 38
E: redacchef@nicematin.fr
W: http://www.nicematin.fr
Freq: Daily; **Circ:** 114605 OJD
Rédacteur en chef adjoint: Thierry Buchet; **Rédacteur en chef adjoint:** Denis Carreaux; **Rédacteur en chef adjoint:** Patrice Lefevre
Editorial Profile: Edition du dimanche : 109 323ex - Utilisation de la quadrichromie - Tous les jours dans environ 16/20 pages.
DAILY NEWSPAPER

Nice-Matin - Siege Social
Owner: GHM - GROUPE HERSANT MEDIA
Editorial: 214 route de Grenoble, Nice 06290 CEDEX 3. **T:** 33 4 93 18 28 38
E: redacchef@nicematin.fr
W: http://www.nicematin.com
Freq: Daily; **Circ:** 110224
Rédacteur en Chef Adjoint: Thierry Buchet; **Rédacteur en Chef Adjoint:** Denis Carreaux; **Rédacteur (trice):** Nancy Cattan; **Rédacteur en Chef Adjoint:** Patrice Lefebvre
Editorial Profile: Regional newspaper for Nice and surrounding area, containing four pages devoted specifically to Monaco. Local Translation:Quotidien d'actualités régionales. L'édition du dimanche est réalisée par la même équipe de rédaction.Prix du samedi et du dimanche : 1,10 €.
Language (s): French; Full Page Colour: 33096.00
Currency: Euro
DAILY NEWSPAPER

Nice-Matin Edition De Cagnes-Sur-Mer
Owner: GHM - GROUPE HERSANT MEDIA
Editorial: Le Paris, 8 place Général-de-Gaulle, Cagnes-Sur-Mer 6800. **T:** +33 4 92 13 85 10
E: cagnes-sur-mer@nicematin.fr
W: http://www.nicematin.fr
Freq: Daily; **Circ:** 220000 Pub Statement
Editorial Profile: Regional daily newspaper focussing on news and current affairs. Local Translation:Quotidien régional d'informations.
Language (s): French
DAILY NEWSPAPER

NICE-MATIN EDITION DE NICE
Owner: GHM - GROUPE HERSANT MEDIA
Editorial: 15-17 rue de la Liberté, Nice 6000.
T: 33 4 97 03 24 50
E: agencenice@nicematin.fr
W: http://www.nicematin.fr
Freq: Daily; **Circ:** 367000
Editorial Profile: Regional daily newspaper focussing on local and regional news and current affairs. Local Translation:Quotidien d'actualités régionales.
Language (s): French
DAILY NEWSPAPER

Nord Eclair
Owner: La Voix du Nord
Editorial: 8, Place du Général de Gaulle, Lille 59000. **T:** 33 3 20 78 40 40
E: serviceclients@nordeclair.fr
W: http://www.nordeclair.fr
Freq: Daily; **Circ:** 28622 OJD
Bureau de LENS: Gaëlle Caron; **Bureau d'HALLUIN:** Angélique Da Silva; **Bureau de LILLE:** Julia Mereau; **Bureau de TOURCOING:** Jean-François Rebischung
Editorial Profile: Regional daily newspaper covering general news and current affairs.
DAILY NEWSPAPER

NORD LITTORAL
Editorial: 91 boulevard Jacquard, BP 108, Calais 62102. **T:** 33 03 21 19 12 13 12
E: courrier@nord-littoral.fr
W: http://www.nordlittoral.fr
Freq: Daily; **Circ:** 10182 OJD
Language (s): French; Full Page Mono: 1069.00; Full Page Colour: 1437.00
Currency: Euro
DAILY NEWSPAPER

NORMANDIE MAGAZINE
Editorial: 330 rue Valvire, BP 414, Saint-Lo 50004. **T:** 33 02 33 77 32 70
E: redaction@normandie-magazine.fr
W: http://www.normandie-magazine.fr
Freq: Monthly; **Circ:** 20000 Pub Statement
Chroniqueur: Albert Du Roy; **Maquettiste - PAO:** Julie Hec; **Maquettiste - PAO:** Régine Quevillon
Editorial Profile: Mensuel anglo-normand : Manche, Orne, Calvados, Seine-Maritime, Eure, Hampshire Wessex et Sussex, Jersey et Guernesey. Informations sur les activités économiques, politiques et culturelles de cette Euro-Région.
Language (s): French; Full Page Colour: 3810.00
Currency: Euro
NEWSPAPER

Le Nouvel Economiste
Owner: Publications du nouvel Economiste
Editorial: 38 bis, rue du Fer à Moulin, Paris 75005. **T:** 33 1 58 30 64 64
E: patrick.arnoux@nouveleconomiste.fr
W: http://www.nouveleconomiste.fr
Freq: Weekly; **Circ:** 24952 OJD
Editor in Chief: Patrick Arnoux
Editorial Profile: Magazine covering economy and finance.
Language (s): French; Full Page Colour: 4900.00
Currency: Euro
NEWSPAPER

La Nouvelle Republique Des Pyrenees
Owner: GROUPE DEPECHE DU MIDI
Editorial: 48 avenue Bertrand Barère, BP 730, Tarbes 65007. **T:** 33 05 62 44 05 05
E: jean-louis.toulouze@nrpyrenees.com
W: http://www.nrpyrenees.com
Freq: Daily; **Circ:** 12867 OJD
Editorial Profile: Utilisation de la quadrichromie : dans les pages une, trois, avant dernière et & dernière. PARUTIONS : le matin
Language (s): French; Full Page Mono: 2580.00
Currency: Euro
DAILY NEWSPAPER

La Nouvelle République du Centre-Ouest
Editorial: 232 avenue de Grammont, Tours 37048. **T:** 33 2 47 31 70 00
E: nr.redactionenchef@nrco.fr
W: http://www.lanouvellerepublique.fr
Freq: Daily; **Circ:** 205288 OJD
Rédacteur en chef: Bruno Becard; **News Editor:** Denis Daumin
Editorial Profile: Regional daily newspaper covering general news and current affairs including politics, economics, sports and leisure.
Language (s): French; Full Page Mono: 7962.00; Full Page Colour: 10816.00
Currency: Euro
DAILY NEWSPAPER

LA Nouvelle République du Centre-Ouest Dimanche
Owner: LA NOUVELLE REPUBLIQUE DU CENTRE OUEST
Editorial: 232 avenue de Grammont, Tours 37048 CEDEX 1. **T:** 33 2 47 31 70 00
E: nrd@nrco.fr
W: http://www.lanouvellerepublique.fr
Freq: Weekly; **Circ:** 38122 Pub Statement
Editorial Profile: National and regional news, sport and leisure sections. Leisure columns: garden, table, health, fashion, decoration, family relationship, travel, new technologies, Internet, your money, new records, books, DVD, comics, and video games. 1 single issue per region. Women over 40 years old.Local Translation: Actualité régionale et nationale, une partie magazine : jardin, à table, nouvelles technologies, Internet, nouveautés disques, livres, dvd, jeux vidéo, consommation.1 édition par département. Femme à partir de 40 ans
Language (s): French
NEWSPAPER

LA Nouvelle Republique Du Centre-Ouest Edition Sud Deux-Sevres
Owner: LA NOUVELLE REPUBLIQUE DU CENTRE OUEST
Editorial: 10 place de la Comédie, BP 350, Niort 79003 CEDEX. **T:** 33 5 49 77 27 77
E: nr.niort@nrco.fr
W: http://www.lanouvellerepublique.fr
Freq: Daily; **Circ:** 52000 Pub Statement
Editorial Profile: Local, regional and national news: covering politics, finance, art, entertainment, sports, leisure, practical information, and associative life. General news: Sports supplement on Monday – Weekend leisure supplement on Thursday - Weekly TV guide supplement on Saturday - Classified advertisement supplement on Saturday. Local Translation:- Informations locales, régionales, nationales : politique, économie, arts et spectacles, sports, loisirs, informations pratiques, vie associative. - Informations générales.- Cahier des sports le lundi. - 1 supplément loisirs week-end le jeudi.- 1 supplément hebdo TV le samedi. - Cahier petites annonces le samedi.

Language (s): French; Full Page Mono: 5428.00; Full Page Colour: 7726.00
Currency: Euro
DAILY NEWSPAPER

L' Opinion
Owner: Bey Médias Presse & Internet
Editorial: 14 rue de Bassano, Paris 75116.
T: 33 1 47 23 33 33 **E:** contact@lopinion.fr
W: http://www.lopinion.fr
Freq: Daily
Editor in Chief: Rémi Godeau
Editorial Profile: Daily newspaper covering national and international news and current affairs including business and politics.
Language (s): French
DAILY NEWSPAPER

L' Orne Combattante
Owner: GROUPE PUBLIHEBDOS
Editorial: 24 rue Jules Gevelot, BP 018, Flers 61101. **T:** 33 02 33 62 15 15
E: didier.gandon@publihebdos.fr
Freq: Weekly; **Circ:** 14729 OJD
Rédacteur en chef: Frédérick Mace
Editorial Profile: Hebdomadaire régional d'informations. PARUTIONS : jeudi.
Language (s): French; Full Page Mono: 2034.00; Full Page Colour: 3036.00
Currency: Euro
NEWSPAPER

L' Orne Hebdo
Owner: GROUPE PUBLIHEBDOS
Editorial: 9 Place Poulet Malassis, BP 208, Alencon 61006. **T:** 33 02 33 82 15 15
E: orne.hebdo@publihebdos.fr
Freq: Weekly; **Circ:** 10844 OJD
Rédacteur en chef: Jean-Marie Foubert;
Publisher: Laurent Rebours
Editorial Profile: Hebdomadaire d'informations. PARUTIONS : mardi
Language (s): French
NEWSPAPER

Ouest France
Owner: Ouest-France
Editorial: 10 rue du Breil, ZI Sud Est, Rennes 35051 CEDEX 9. **T:** +33 2 99 32 60 00
E: redaction.multimedia@ouest-france.fr
W: http://www.ouest-france.fr
Freq: Daily; **Circ:** 762233 Pub Statement
Editorial Profile: Regional daily newspaper focussing on local and regional news and current affairs.
Language (s): French; Full Page Mono: 14740.00; Full Page Colour: 17688.00
Currency: Euro
DAILY NEWSPAPER

Ouest France Edition Calvados Caen
Owner: OUEST FRANCE
Editorial: 14 place Pierre-Bouchard, BP 174, Caen 14010 CEDEX. **T:** 33 2 31 38 32 32
E: redaction.caen@ouest-france.fr
W: http://www.ouest-france.fr
Freq: Daily
Publisher: Josué Lebigre
Editorial Profile: This regional newspaper prints daily and covers regional news including sports, culture, society, legal issues, economics, social issues and education.
Language (s): French; Full Page Mono: 5647.00; Full Page Colour: 6776.00
Currency: Euro
DAILY NEWSPAPER

Ouest France Edition De Cotes-D'armor Lannion-Paimpol
Owner: OUEST FRANCE
Editorial: 1 rue de Viarmes, Lannion 22300.
T: 33 2 96 46 21 20
E: redaction.lannion@ouest-france.fr
W: http://www.ouest-france.fr
Freq: Daily; **Circ:** 90000 Pub Statement
Editorial Profile: Regional daily newspaper focussing on local, regional, national and international news and current affairs. Local Translation:Informations internationales, nationales, régionales et locales.
Language (s): French; Full Page Mono: 4596.00; Full Page Colour: 5515.00
Currency: Euro
DAILY NEWSPAPER

Ouest France Edition de la Mayenne
Owner: OUEST FRANCE
Editorial: 92 avenue Robert-Buron, Laval 53000. **T:** 33 2 43 59 15 59
E: redaction.chateau-gontier@ouest-france.fr
W: http://www.ouest-france.fr
Freq: Daily; **Circ:** 42000 Pub Statement
Editorial Profile: Regional daily newspaper focussing on general news and current affairs including politics, society, justice, sport, agriculture, education, training, economics, social and culture. Local Translation:Quotidien régional d'informations générales, avec les rubriques : politique, société, justice, sports, agriculture, éducation, formation, économie, social, culture.
Language (s): French; Full Page Mono: 5975.00; Full Page Colour: 7170.00
Currency: Euro
DAILY NEWSPAPER

OUEST FRANCE EDITION DU FINISTERE BREST
Owner: OUEST FRANCE
Editorial: 24 rue Algesiras, Brest 29200.
T: 33 2 98 33 22 00
E: redaction.brest@ouest-france.fr
W: http://www.ouest-france.fr
Freq: Daily
Editorial Profile: Regional daily newspaper focussing on general news and current affairs including culture, society, justice, defence, weapons, sport, health, education, training, economics and social. Local Translation:Quotidien régional d'informations générales, avec les rubriques culture, société, justice, défense, armement, sport, santé, éducation, formation, économie, social.
Language (s): French; Full Page Mono: 4793.00; Full Page Colour: 5752.00
Currency: Euro
DAILY NEWSPAPER

OUEST FRANCE EDITION DU FINISTERE QUIMPER
Owner: OUEST FRANCE
Editorial: 24 boulevard Dupleix, BP 1129, Quimper 29101. **T:** 33 2 98 90 93 93
E: redaction.douarnenez@ouest-france.fr
W: http://www.ouest-france.fr
Freq: Daily
Editorial Profile: Regional daily newspaper focussing on local, regional and national news and current affairs. Local Translation:Informations générales, nationales, régionales et locales. Siège à Rennes.
Language (s): French; Full Page Mono: 6074.00; Full Page Colour: 7288.00
Currency: Euro
DAILY NEWSPAPER

OUEST FRANCE EDITION DU MAINE-ET-LOIRE ANGERS-SEGRE
Owner: OUEST FRANCE
Editorial: 5 bis rue Thiers, BP 65117, Angers 49051. **T:** 33 2 41 25 62 00
E: redaction.angers@ouest-france.fr
W: http://www.ouest-france.fr
Freq: Daily
Editorial Profile: Regional daily newspaper focussing on regional news and current affairs including cultural heritage, culture, environment, tourism, agriculture, education training, economics, social, sport, justice and professional training. Local Translation:Toute l'actualité du Maine et Loire + pages générales. Rubriques : patrimoine culturel, environnement, tourisme, agriculture, culture, éducation, formation, économie, social, sports, justice, formation professionnelle.
Language (s): French; Full Page Mono: 3874.00; Full Page Colour: 4647.00
Currency: Euro
DAILY NEWSPAPER

Ouest France Edition Du Morbihan Lorient
Owner: OUEST FRANCE
Editorial: 55 rue du Port, Lorient 56100.
T: +33 2 97 84 43 00
E: redaction.lorient@ouest-france.fr
W: http://www.ouest-france.fr
Freq: Daily; **Circ:** 112000 Pub Statement
Editorial Profile: Regional daily newspaper focussing on local, regional, national and international news and current affairs. Local Translation:Informations régionales et locales, internationales, nationales, départementales.
Language (s): French; Full Page Mono: 6401.00; Full Page Colour: 7682.00
Currency: Euro
DAILY NEWSPAPER

Ouest France Edition Du Morbihan Vannes
Owner: OUEST FRANCE
Editorial: 15 rue Thomas-de-Closmadeuc, Vannes 56000. **T:** +33 2 97 47 42 05
E: redaction.vannes@ouest-france.fr
W: http://www.ouest-france.fr
Freq: Daily; **Circ:** 112000 Pub Statement
Editorial Profile: Regional daily newspaper focussing on local, regional, national and international news and current affairs including agriculture.
Language (s): French; Full Page Mono: 6861.00; Full Page Colour: 8234.00
Currency: Euro
DAILY NEWSPAPER

Ouest France Edition Loire-Atlantique
Owner: OUEST FRANCE
Editorial: 2 quai François-Mitterrand, BP 80319, Nantes 44203 CEDEX 2.
T: 33 2 40 44 69 69
E: redaction.nantes@ouest-france.fr
W: http://www.ouest-france.fr
Freq: Daily
Editorial Profile: Regional daily newspaper focusing on local and regional news and current affairs.
Language (s): French; Full Page Mono: 5220.00; Full Page Colour: 6264.00
Currency: Euro
DAILY NEWSPAPER

Ouest France Editions Sarthe Nord Et Sarthe Sud
Owner: OUEST FRANCE
Editorial: 9-11 quai Ledru-Rollin, Le Mans 72000. **T:** 33 2 43 21 76 76
E: redaction.lemans@ouest-france.fr
W: http://www.ouest-france.fr
Freq: Daily; **Circ:** 73500 Pub Statement
Rédacteur (trice): Stéphane Bois
Editorial Profile: Regional daily newspaper focussing on general news and current affairs. Local Translation:Toute l'actualité de la Sarthe et des pages générales.
Language (s): French; Full Page Mono: 4432.00; Full Page Colour: 5318.00
Currency: Euro
DAILY NEWSPAPER

Paris Normandie
Owner: GROUPE HERSANT MEDIA
Editorial: 33 rue des Grosses Pierres, BP 40047, Deville-Les-Rouen 76250.
T: 33 2 35 14 56 56
E: redaction.web@paris-normandie.fr
W: http://www.paris-normandie.fr
Freq: Daily; **Circ:** 61425 OJD
Rédacteur en chef adjoint Alimentation Distribution Consommation: Jean-Pierre Boulais; **Rédacteur en chef adjoint Responsable des éditions de l'Eure:** Didier Bureau; **Rédacteur en chef adjoint chargé du développement:** Thierry Rabiller
Editorial Profile: Utilisation de la quadrichromie : tous les jours - Dans toutes les pages. Supplément TV MAGAZINE + VERSION FEMME : samedi - Pages TEMPS LIBRE : tous les jours. Propose également un supplément mensuel consacré à l'automobile, Normandie Auto, parution le 1er samedi de chaque mois ; et un trimestriel consacré au développement durable "Normandie Durable" ; un mensuel consacré à la mode et la consommation baptisé "Moi".
DAILY NEWSPAPER

Le Parisien
Owner: Amaury Médias
Editorial: 25 avenue Michelet, Saint-Ouen 93408 CEDEX. **T:** 33 1 40 10 40 46
E: edition75@leparisien.presse.fr
W: http://www.leparisien.fr
Freq: Daily; **Circ:** 56242 Pub Statement
Editor in Chief: Stéphane Albouy; **Editor in Chief:** Matthieu Croissandeau; **Editor in Chief:** Béatrice Madeline; **Editor in Chief:** François Vey
Editorial Profile: Newspaper covering regional, national and international news and current affairs including society, politics, economics, motoring, celebrities, media, technology, science and health.
Language (s): French; Full Page Mono: 11190.00; Full Page Colour: 18240.00
Currency: Euro
DAILY NEWSPAPER

Patrimoines en région
Editorial: Le Passe Muraille Association, 510A, av.de Barcelone-Le Jupiter, Montpellier 34080.
T: 33 4 67 06 96 04
E: redaction@lepassemuraille.org
W: http://www.carrefour-des-patrimoines.net
Freq: 3 Times/Year; **Circ:** 30000 Pub Statement
Editorial Profile: Local Translation: Revue régionale d'éducation au territoire par les patrimoines.Completée par l'édition (200000 exemplaires) 1 fois par an (en juin) de 'L'Agenda du Patrimoine' qui annonce tous les événements liés aux patrimoines culturel et naturel (balades et visites, concerts et spectacles vivants, gastronomie, vins et terroir, festivités et traditions, expositions...).
Language (s): French
NEWSPAPER

PATRIOTE COTE D'AZUR - PCA HEBDO
Editorial: 3 passage Macari, Nice 6300.
T: 33 04 97 00 09 00
E: redaction@le-patriote.info
W: http://www.le-patriote.info
Freq: Weekly; **Circ:** 12500 Pub Statement
Cinéma (Pigiste): Etienne Ballerini; **Cinéma (Pigiste):** Gérard Camy; **Rédacteur en chef .:** Julien Camy; **Maquettiste:** Guy Viens
Editorial Profile: Hebdomadaire départemental du P.C.F. PARUTIONS : vendredi.
Language (s): French; Full Page Mono: 2350.00; Full Page Colour: 2930.00
Currency: Euro
NEWSPAPER

LE PAYS
Owner: L'ALSACE
Editorial: 10 faubourg de Montbéliard, BP 427, Belfort 90008. **T:** 33 3 84 46 67 69
E: redaction-belfort@lepays.fr
W: http://www.lepays.fr
Freq: Daily; **Circ:** 10000 Pub Statement
Editorial Profile: Daily current events newspaper covering the north of the Franche-Conté region with 3 offices: Belfort, Lure, Montbéliard and 3 editions. Local Translation:Quotidien généraliste couvrant le Nord de la Franche-Comté avec 3 agences : Belfort, Lure, Montbéliard et 3 éditions.
Language (s): French
DAILY NEWSPAPER

Le Pays D'Entre Loire Et Rhone
Editorial: 7 avenue Charles de Gaulle, Tarare 69170. **T:** 33 04 74 63 02 68
E: agence.tarare@le-pays-roannais.com
Freq: Weekly; **Circ:** 10000 Pub Statement
Rédacteur en chef adjoint: Roland Denis; **Rédacteur en chef adjoint:** Jean-François Vaizand
Editorial Profile: Hebdomadaire régional d'informations. Annonces légales - PARUTIONS : jeudi.
Language (s): French; Full Page Mono: 2925.00; Full Page Colour: 4408.00
Currency: Euro
NEWSPAPER

Le Pays Malouin
Owner: GROUPE PUBLIHEBDOS
Editorial: 7 rue Emmanuel Le Guen, BP 183, Saint-Malo 35409. **T:** 33 02 99 40 27 00
E: lepaysmalouin@publihebdos.fr
W: http://www.publihebdos.fr
Freq: Weekly; **Circ:** 11389 OJD
Editeur - Rédacteur en chef: Christian Bouzols; **Rédactrice:** Virginie David; **Rédacteur:** Nicolas Evanno; **Rédactrice:** Adélaïde Hasle; **Rédacteur en chef adjoint:** Samuel Sauneuf
Editorial Profile: Informations locales et annonces légales. PARUTIONS : jeudi
Language (s): French
NEWSPAPER

Le Pays Roannais
Editorial: 10/12 rue de Sully, Roanne 42308.
T: 33 04 77 44 47 47
E: lepays@le-pays-roannais.com
W: http://www.lepaysroannais.fr
Freq: Weekly; **Circ:** 28101 OJD
Rédacteur en chef adjoint: Roland Denis; **Rédacteur en chef adjoint:** Jean-François Vaizand
Editorial Profile: Zone de diffusion : Loire, Rhône, Allier, Saône et Loire. Annonces légales PARUTIONS : jeudi.
Language (s): French
NEWSPAPER

Le Perche
Owner: GROUPE PUBLIHEBDOS
Editorial: 14/16 Place de la République, Mortagne-Au-Perche 61400.
T: 33 02 33 85 20 50
E: le.perche@publihebdos.fr
W: http://www.publihebdos.fr
Freq: Weekly; **Circ:** 11923 OJD
Rédacteur en chef: Luc Moriceau; **Publisher:** Laurent Rebours
Editorial Profile: Hebdomadaire régional d'information pour l'Orne, la Sarthe et l'Eure et Loir PARUTIONS : mercredi.
Language (s): French; Full Page Mono: 1856.00; Full Page Colour: 2410.00
Currency: Euro
NEWSPAPER

Le Petit Journal
Owner: EDITIONS ARC EN CIEL
Editorial: 1300 avenue d'Ardus, BP 386, Montauban 82000. **T:** 33 05 63 20 80 00
E: 82@lepetitjournal.net
Freq: Daily; **Circ:** 10500 Pub Statement
Editorial Profile: Journal d'informations locales.
Language (s): French; Full Page Mono: 457.00; Full Page Colour: 594.00
Currency: Euro

DAILY NEWSPAPER

LE Petit journal Pays Toulousain Lauragais
Editorial: 1300 avenue d'Ardus, BP 386, Montauban 82003 CEDEX.
T: 33 5 63 20 80 00 **E:** 31t@lepetitjournal.net
W: http://www.lepetitjournal.net
Freq: Weekly; **Circ:** 52000 Pub Statement
Editorial Profile: Le Petit Journal affiche déjà plusieurs éditions dans le Grand Sud : Comminges-Sud Garonne, Ariège, Gers, Lot, Aveyron... Il existe aussi une édition Pays toulousain/Lauragais très riche en informations sur la ville rose. C'est un hebdomadaire d'informations générales paraissant le vendredi et habilité à publier les annonces légales et commerciales. Toutes les grandes rubriques de l'actualité sont abordées, de la grande ville au plus petit village de la périphérie toulousaine : politique, culture, sports, faits divers.
Language (s): French
NEWSPAPER

Le Petit Nicois
Owner: EDITION D'AZUR
Editorial: Edition d'Azur, 2 rue Désiré Niel, Nice 6000. **T:** 33 04 93 13 79 89
E: accueil@editiondazur.fr
W: http://www.lepetitnicois.fr
Freq: Weekly; **Circ:** 10000 Pub Statement
Maquettiste: Nicolas Thomas
Editorial Profile: Hebdomadaire généraliste d'informations locales, de Menton à Antibes. PARUTIONS : le jeudi.
Language (s): French
NEWSPAPER

Le Phare De Re
Editorial: 15 Quai Job Foran, BP 104, Saint-Martin-De-Re 17410. **T:** 33 05 46 09 21 09
E: redaction@pharedere.com
Freq: Weekly; **Circ:** 20000 Pub Statement
Rédacteur en chef: Yann Werdefroy
Editorial Profile: Journal d'intérêt local. PARUTIONS : mercredi + 3 suppléments GRATUITS : 'Guide L'Ile de Ré Pratique' (sortie fin juin, 65 000ex.), 'Bonnes adresses du Phare' (sortie à Pâques, 25 000ex.), 'L'Ile de Ré, à chacun sa saison' (Edition Automne : 20 000ex., Edition Hiver : 20 000ex.) + 1 mensuel GRATUIT 'SORTIR' (60 000ex./mois).
Language (s): French; Full Page Colour: 5000.00
Currency: Euro
NEWSPAPER

Le Populaire Du Centre
Owner: GROUPE CENTRE FRANCE - LA MONTAGNE
Editorial: Rue du Général Catroux, BP 541, Limoges 87011. **T:** 33 05 55 58 59 60
E: lepopulaire@centrefrance.com
W: http://www.lepopulaire.fr
Freq: Daily; **Circ:** 43868 OJD
Rédacteur en chef: Jean-Marc Courbarien
Editorial Profile: Utilisation de la quadrichromie - Tous les jours dans une page sur deux.
DAILY NEWSPAPER

Les Potins D'Angele
Editorial: 34 rue Tupin, Lyon 69002.
T: 33 04 78 42 57 97
E: redac@lespotinsdangele.com
Freq: Weekly; **Circ:** 12000 Pub Statement
Editorial Profile: Hebdomadaire satirique de la vie Lyonnaise. PARUTIONS : le jeudi.
Language (s): French
NEWSPAPER

La Presse De Manche
Editorial: 9 rue Gambetta, BP 408, Cherbourg 50104. **T:** 33 02 33 97 16 16
E: redaction.locale@lapressedelamanche.fr
Freq: Daily; **Circ:** 25574 OJD
Cuisine (Recettes): Patricia Lelan-Roussel
Language (s): French; Full Page Mono: 6640.00; Full Page Colour: 10624.00
Currency: Euro
DAILY NEWSPAPER

PRESSE OCEAN
Owner: SIPA
Editorial: 5 rue Santeuil, BP 22418, Nantes 44024. **T:** 33 02 40 44 24 00
E: redac.locale.nantes@presse-ocean.com
W: http://www.presseocean.fr
Freq: Daily; **Circ:** 36443 OJD
Rédacteur en chef adjoint - Pages Féminines: Dominique Bloyet; **Bureau de VALLET:** Rémi Certain; **Bureau de LA BAULE:** Marina Cessa; **Rédacteur en chef:** Marc Dejean; **Rédacteur en chef adjoint - Pages Féminines:** Pierre-Marie Heriand; **Bureau de SAINT NAZAIRE:** Martine Vaillant-Prot
Editorial Profile: Utilisation de la quadrichromie tous les jours. OJD Edition du septième jour : 21 562ex. RENSEIGNEMENTS REDUITS A LA DEMANDE DU JOURNAL. Diffusé en Loire Atlantique.
DAILY NEWSPAPER

PRESSE OCEAN - L'ECLAIR EDITION ST-NAZAIRE LA BAULE
Owner: OUEST FRANCE
Editorial: 41 avenue du Général-de-Gaulle, BP 235, Saint-Nazaire CEDEX.
T: 33 2 51 10 11 50
E: redac.st-nazaire@presse-ocean.com
W: http://www.presseocean.fr
Freq: Daily
Editorial Profile: 2 current affairs regional daily newspapers with the same journalists and columns: covering economy, social, politics, education, training, justice, sports... 1 guide in the summer. Local Translation:2 quotidiens régionaux d'informations générales avec les mêmes journalistes et les mêmes rubriques : économie, social, politique, culture, éducation-formation, justice, sports... 1 guide l'été.
Language (s): French
DAILY NEWSPAPER

Le Progres
Editorial: 4 rue Montrochet, Lyon 69284.
T: 33 04 72 22 23 23
E: redactionenchef@leprogres.fr
W: http://www.leprogres.fr
Freq: Daily; **Circ:** 223522 OJD
Rédacteur en chef: Xavier Antoye; **Rédacteur en chef adjoint (Suppléments):** Lionel Cailles; **Concerts:** Thierry Meissirel; **Rédacteur en chef adjoint:** Philippe Pitaud
Editorial Profile: Utilisation de la quadrichromie : tous les jours. OJD = LE PROGRES + LA TRIBUNE - Editions du Dimanche : 239 725ex www.leprogres.fr : 30 000 visiteurs uniques/jour (source éditeur). Diffusé en Rhône Alpes.
DAILY NEWSPAPER

Le Progrès - Edition Lyon-Villeurbanne-Caluire
Owner: LE PROGRES
Editorial: 4 rue Paul-Montrochet, Lyon 69002.
T: 33 4 72 22 23 23
E: lprquartiers@leprogres.fr
W: http://www.leprogres.fr
Freq: Daily; **Circ:** 222570 OJD
Rédacteur en Chef: Chantal Danon; **Rédacteur en Chef:** Pascal Jalabert; **Rédacteur en Chef:** Philippe Pitaud
Editorial Profile: Daily regional newspaper.
Language (s): French; Full Page Mono: 21812.00; Full Page Colour: 24110.00
Currency: Euro
DAILY NEWSPAPER

LE Progrès -Edition de l'Ain
Owner: LE PROGRES
Editorial: 6 place Joubert, Bourg-En-Bresse 01006 CEDEX. **T:** 33 4 74 21 66 66
E: ain@leprogres.fr
W: http://www.leprogres.fr
Freq: Daily; **Circ:** 45000 Pub Statement
Editorial Profile: Daily regional newspaper including current events pages covering Bourg-en-Bresse, Le Bugey, La Dombes and La Bresse regions. Local Translation:Quotidien régional avec des pages d'actualités Bourg-en-Bresse, Le Bugey, La Dombes, La Bresse... Tirage de 56.000 exemplaires le dimanche.
Language (s): French; Full Page Mono: 3419.00
Currency: Euro
DAILY NEWSPAPER

La Provence
Owner: Groupe Hersant Média
Editorial: 248 avenue Roger Salengro, Marseille 13015. **T:** 33 4 91 84 45 45
E: contact@laprovence.com
W: http://www.laprovence.com
Freq: Daily; **Circ:** 146772 OJD
Rédacteur en chef: Jean-Michel Amiel; **Rédacteur en chef adjoint:** Patrick Fancello; **Rédacteur en chef adjoint Région:** Albert Lugassy; **Rédacteur en chef adjoint - Hors série Suppléments - Opérations spéciales:** Philippe Schmit
Editorial Profile: Newspaper covering regional and local news.
Language (s): French; Full Page Mono: 11000.00; Full Page Colour: 13750.00
Currency: Euro
DAILY NEWSPAPER

LA Provence: Edition de Carpentras
Owner: GHM - GROUPE HERSANT MEDIA
Editorial: 144 place Aristide-Briand, Carpentras 84200. **T:** 33 4 90 67 66 65
E: carpentras@laprovence-presse.fr
W: http://www.laprovence.com
Freq: Daily; **Circ:** 27616 Pub Statement
Editorial Profile: Regional daily current events newspaper.
Language (s): French
DAILY NEWSPAPER

LA Provence: Edition du Haut Vaucluse Orange
Owner: GHM - GROUPE HERSANT MEDIA
Editorial: 21 rue Caristie, Orange 84100.
T: 33 4 90 11 33 00
E: orange@laprovence-presse.fr
W: http://www.laprovence.com
Freq: Daily; **Circ:** 27616 Pub Statement
Editorial Profile: Regional daily current events newspaper.
Language (s): French
DAILY NEWSPAPER

LA Provence: Edition Du Vaucluse
Owner: GHM - GROUPE HERSANT MEDIA
Editorial: 18 rue de la République, Avignon 84000. **T:** 33 4 90 80 70 30
E: avignon@laprovence-presse.fr
W: http://www.laprovence.com
Freq: Daily; **Circ:** 27616 Pub Statement
Editorial Profile: Regional daily current events newspaper.
Language (s): French
DAILY NEWSPAPER

LA Provence: Edition Vaucluse Sud
Owner: GHM - GROUPE HERSANT MEDIA
Editorial: 83 place de la Bouquerie, Apt 84400. **T:** 33 4 90 74 17 53
E: apt@laprovence-presse.fr
W: http://www.laprovence.com
Freq: Daily; **Circ:** 27616 Pub Statement
Editorial Profile: Regional daily current events newspaper. Local Translation:Quotidien régional d'informations générales.
Language (s): French
DAILY NEWSPAPER

La Renaissance
Editorial: 13 rue des Deux Ponts, BP 112, Paray-Le-Monial 71603. **T:** 33 03 85 81 66 00
E: journal@la-renaissance.net
W: http://www.la-renaissance.net
Freq: Weekly; **Circ:** 12198 OJD
Rédactrice en chef: Delphine Mignat
Editorial Profile: PARUTIONS : Vendredi - Informations générales et régionales du Bourbonnais, Charolais, Brionnais, Clusinois, Mâconnais et Allier.
Language (s): French; Full Page Mono: 1193.00; Full Page Colour: 1475.00
Currency: Euro
NEWSPAPER

Le Republicain De L'Essonne
Owner: SEMIF Hebdos
Editorial: Boulevard des Champs Elysées, BP 76, Evry 91002. **T:** 33 01 69 36 57 09 91
E: web@le-republicain.fr
W: http://www.le-republicain.fr
Freq: Weekly; **Circ:** 12426 OJD
Dourdan - Etrechy - Etampes - Méréville: Olivia Bazenet; **Dourdan - Etrechy - Etampes - Méréville:** David Berthelem; **Corbeil-Essonnes - Mennecy - La Ferté-Alais - Evry Milly-la-Fôret - Val-de-:** Pauline Chastenet; **Corbeil-Essonnes - Mennecy - La Ferté-Alais - Evry Milly-la-Fôret - Val-de-:** Marine Guillaume; **Rédacteur en chef technique Actualités départementales Social - Famille:** Fabien Herran
Editorial Profile: Hebdomadaire d'information régionale et d'annonces paraissant le jeudi matin. PANORAMA : magazine hebdomadaire d'informations GRATUIT distribué sur le département à 100 000ex.
Language (s): French
NEWSPAPER

Le Republicain Lorrain
Editorial: 3 avenue des Deux Fontaines, Woippy 57140. **T:** 33 3 87 34 17 89
E: lrlinfo@republicain-lorrain.fr
W: http://www.republicain-lorrain.fr
Freq: Daily; **Circ:** 137042 OJD
Editor in Chief: Jean-Marc Lauer; **Rédacteur en chef adjoint:** Jean-Claude Voelin
Editorial Profile: Regional newspaper covering news and current affairs.
DAILY NEWSPAPER

Le Republicain Lorrain - Metz Bureau
Owner: LE REPUBLICAIN LORRAIN
Editorial: 24 rue Serpenoise, Metz 57000.
T: 33 3 87 38 58 00
E: redaction.metz@republicain-lorrain.fr
W: http://www.republicain-lorrain.fr
Freq: Daily; **Circ:** 145475 OJD
Rédacteur en Chef: Jean-Marc Lauer
Editorial Profile: Regional newspaprer newspaper covering international, national, regional and local news. Local Translation:Informations internationales, nationales, régionales, départementales, locales, magazine.
Language (s): French; Full Page Mono: 6240.00; Full Page Colour: 8112.00
Currency: Euro
DAILY NEWSPAPER

LE Républicain Lorrain Nancy
Owner: LE REPUBLICAIN LORRAIN
Editorial: 33 rue des Carmes, Nancy 54000.
T: 33 3 83 35 50 48
E: redaction.nancy@republicain-lorrain.fr
W: http://www.republicain-lorrain.fr
Freq: Daily; **Circ:** 40000 Pub Statement
Editorial Profile: International, national, regional and local news, magazine. Local Translation:Informations internationales, nationales, régionales, départementales, locale, magazine.
Language (s): French
DAILY NEWSPAPER

La Republique De Seine Et Marne
Owner: GROUPE PUBLIHEBDOS
Editorial: 3 boulevard Victor Hugo, BP 22, Melun 77001. **T:** 33 01 64 87 50 00
E: redaction@larepublique.com
W: http://www.larepublique.com
Freq: Weekly; **Circ:** 22063 OJD
Rédacteur en chef adjoint: Didier Barry; **Editeur:** Thomas Martin
Editorial Profile: Diffusion : arrondissements de Melun, Fontainebleau, Torcy et Provins, sud et centre de la Seine et Marne. 2 éditions : Melun/Val de Seine/Sénart/Melun/Provins/ Plaine de Brie - Fontainebleau/Nemours/ Montereau. Journal d'informations locales et régionales. PARUTIONS : lundi
Language (s): French
NEWSPAPER

La Republique Des Pyrenees
Owner: PYRENEES PRESSE
Editorial: 6/8 rue Despourrins, Pau 64002.
T: 33 05 59 82 20 00
E: jp.cassagne@pyrenees.com
W: http://www.pyrenees.com
Freq: Daily; **Circ:** 32465 OJD
Rédacteur en chef: Jean Marziou
Language (s): French; Full Page Mono: 4347.00; Full Page Colour: 4706.00
Currency: Euro
DAILY NEWSPAPER

La Republique du Centre
Editorial: Rue de la Halte, Fleury-Les-Aubrais 45770. **T:** 33 2 38 78 79 80
E: redac@larep.com **W:** http://www.larep.com
Freq: Daily; **Circ:** 51029 OJD
LOIRET - GIEN: François Basley; **LOIRET - MONTARGIS:** Francis Bonnet; **Rédactrice en chef adjointe:** Christine Broudic; **LOIRET - PITHIVIERS:** Stéphane Lacoume
Editorial Profile: Regional newspaper covering regional news and current affairs.
Language (s): French
DAILY NEWSPAPER

LA République du Centre - Edition de Beaugency
Owner: CENTRE FRANCE LA MONTAGNE
Editorial: 28 place du Martroi, Beaugency 45190. **T:** 33 2 38 46 92 10 **E:** gb@larep.com
W: http://www.larep.com
Freq: Daily; **Circ:** 51029 OJD
Editorial Profile: General, regional and local news. Local Translation:Informations générales, régionales, départementales et locales.
Language (s): French; Full Page Colour: 3838.00
Currency: Euro
DAILY NEWSPAPER

LA République du Centre - Edition de Dreux
Owner: CENTRE FRANCE LA MONTAGNE
Editorial: 7 rue Aux Tanneurs, BP 50126, Dreux 28103 CEDEX. **T:** 33 2 37 63 03 63
E: ag.dreux@larep.com
W: http://www.larep.com
Freq: Daily; **Circ:** 51029 Pub Statement
Editorial Profile: General, regional and local news. Local Translation:Informations générales, régionales, départementales et locales.
Language (s): French
DAILY NEWSPAPER

La République du Centre - Edition de Gien
Owner: CENTRE FRANCE LA MONTAGNE
Editorial: 14 rue Victor-Hugo, Gien 45500. **T:** 33 2 38 29 85 85
E: loiret.larep@centrefrance.com
W: http://www.larep.com
Freq: Daily; **Circ:** 51029 OJD
Editorial Profile: Regional newspaper covering general, regional and local news.
Language (s): French
DAILY NEWSPAPER

LA République du Centre - Edition de Montagris
Owner: CENTRE FRANCE LA MONTAGNE
Editorial: 48 rue Dorée, Montargis 45200. **T:** 33 2 38 07 18 48
E: agence.montargis@larep.com
W: http://www.larep.com
Freq: Daily; **Circ:** 51029 Pub Statement
Editorial Profile: General, regional and local news. Local Translation:Quotidien d'informations générales, régionales et locales.
Language (s): French
DAILY NEWSPAPER

LA République du Centre - Edition de Nogent-Châteaudun
Owner: CENTRE FRANCE LA MONTAGNE
Editorial: 22 place du 18-Octobre, Chateaudun 28200. **T:** 33 2 37 94 00 00
E: ag.chateaudun@larep.com
W: http://www.larep.com
Freq: Daily; **Circ:** 51029 OJD
Editorial Profile: General and local news. Economy, politics, social life... Local Translation:Informations générales et locales, économie, politique, social.
Language (s): French
DAILY NEWSPAPER

LA République du Centre - Edition de Pithiviers
Owner: CENTRE FRANCE LA MONTAGNE
Editorial: 31 rue de la Couronne, Pithiviers 45300. **T:** 33 2 38 30 22 44
E: agence.pithiviers@larep.com
W: http://www.larep.com
Freq: Daily; **Circ:** 51029 Pub Statement
Editorial Profile: General, regional and local news. Local Translation:Informations générales, régionales, départementales et locales.
Language (s): French
DAILY NEWSPAPER

La République du Centre - Edition du Loiret
Owner: CENTRE FRANCE LA MONTAGNE
Editorial: Rue de la Halte, BP 93035, Fleury-Les-Aubrais 45403 CEDEX.
T: 33 2 38 78 79 80
E: loiret.larep@centrefrance.com
W: http://www.larep.com
Freq: Daily; **Circ:** 51029 OJD
Rédacteur en Chef: Christine Broudic
Editorial Profile: Regional newspaper covering general, regional and local news.
Language (s): French
DAILY NEWSPAPER

Le Reveil (neufchatel)
Owner: GROUPE PUBLIHEBDOS
Editorial: 11 rue des Tanneurs, BP 100, Neufchatel-En-Bray 76270.
T: 33 02 32 97 53 80
E: reveil.neufchatel@publihebdos.fr
W: http://www.publihebdos.fr
Freq: Weekly; **Circ:** 12554 OJD
Rédactrice: Sandrine Bossiere; **Rédacteur en chef:** Laurent Hellier; **Rédacteur:** Pierre-Emmanuel Reger; **Rédactrice:** Isabelle Villy; **Editrice:** Catherine Wilmart
Editorial Profile: 2 éditions : Pays de Bray, Bresle et Oise Hebdomadaire régional d'informations paraissant le jeudi
Language (s): French; Full Page Mono: 2482.00; Full Page Colour: 3229.00
Currency: Euro
NEWSPAPER

LE REVEIL DU VIVARAIS
Editorial: 49 avenue de l'Europe, BP 51, Annonay 7102. **T:** 33 04 75 69 25 80
E: contact@reveil-vivarais.fr
W: http://www.reveil-vivarais.fr
Freq: Weekly; **Circ:** 12388 OJD
Rédacteur en chef: Jean-Pierre Bouaffar; **Rédactrice:** Marie-Cécile Chevrier; **Rédacteur:** Jacques Girodet; **Rédacteur:** Gwenaël Pocard; **Rédacteur:** Yves Rivory
Editorial Profile: Hebdomadaire politique et d'information. PARUTIONS : jeudi. Zone de diffusion : Ardèche - Drôme - Loire - Isère
Language (s): French; Full Page Mono: 3165.00
Currency: Euro
NEWSPAPER

LE REVEIL NORMAND
Owner: GROUPE PUBLIHEBDOS
Editorial: 19 bis rue des Emangeards, BP 143, L'aigle 61304. **T:** 33 02 33 24 42 33
E: reveil.normand@publihebdos.fr
W: http://www.publihebdos.fr
Freq: Weekly; **Circ:** 11311 OJD
Rédacteur en chef adjoint: Lionel Lecrivain; **Publisher:** Laurent Rebours
Editorial Profile: Hebdomadaire régional d'informations. Zone de diffusion : 12 cantons de la moitié est de l'Orne, 4 cantons de l'Eure, 2 cantons d'Eure et Loir et périphérie. PARUTIONS : mercredi
Language (s): French; Full Page Mono: 1856.00; Full Page Colour: 2410.00
Currency: Euro
NEWSPAPER

Les Sab-Vendee Journal
Owner: GROUPE PUBLIHEBDOS
Editorial: 16 ter rue de la Caisse d'Epargne, BP 29, Les Sables-D'olonne 85101.
T: 33 02 51 95 42 12
E: redaction.jds@publihebdos.fr
Freq: Weekly; **Circ:** 12598 OJD
Rédacteur en chef: Gérard Heraud; **Editeur:** Ludovic Robet
Editorial Profile: Hebdomadaire d'informations locales. PARUTIONS : jeudi.
Language (s): French; Full Page Mono: 2059.00; Full Page Colour: 2668.00
Currency: Euro
NEWSPAPER

Le Saint Affricain
Editorial: 29 Boulevard Emile Borel, Saint-Affrique 12412. **T:** 33 05 65 49 25 64
E: lesaintaffricain@wanadoo.fr
W: http://www.lesaintaffricain.fr
Freq: Weekly; **Circ:** 10380 Pub Statement
Rédactrice en chef: Delphine Rouquette
Editorial Profile: Journal local GRATUIT du sud Aveyron paraissant le vendredi.
Language (s): French; Full Page Colour: 500.00
Currency: Euro
NEWSPAPER

Le Semeur Hebdo
Editorial: 37 rue Montlosier, Clermont Ferrand 63058. **T:** 33 04 73 98 46 00
E: redaction@semeur.com
Freq: Weekly; **Circ:** 10072 OJD
Humanitaire: Jean-Baptiste Botella
Editorial Profile: PARUTIONS : vendredi.
Language (s): French; Full Page Mono: 800.00
Currency: Euro
NEWSPAPER

Sud Ouest
Owner: Groupe Sud Ouest
Editorial: 23 quai de Queyries, Bordeaux 33094. **T:** 33 5 35 31 31 31
E: s.marraud@sudouest.fr
W: http://www.sudouest.fr
Freq: Daily; **Circ:** 10000 Pub Statement
PYRENEES ATLANTIQUES - Bayonne: Philippe Campa; **LOT ET GARONNE - Agen:** Maryan Charruau; **Oenologie:** César Compadre; **LANDES:** Jean-Pierre Dorian; **PYRENEES ATLANTIQUES - Pau:** Christophe Galichon; **CHARENTE:** Olivier Sarazin; **CHARENTE MARITIME:** Stéphane Vacchiani
Editorial Profile: Regional newspaper covering news and current affairs.
Language (s): French
DAILY NEWSPAPER

Sud Ouest Charente Maritime - Edition la Rochelle-Re
Owner: SUD OUEST
Editorial: Résidence Etoile marine, 29 av. Michel Crépeau, La Rochelle 17025.
T: 33 5 46 28 05 05 **E:** larochelle@sudouest.fr
W: http://www.sudouest.fr
Freq: Daily; **Circ:** 45000 Pub Statement
Editorial Profile: Regional daily newspaper focussing on local, regional, national and international news and current affairs. Local Translation:Informations régionales, locales, nationales et internationales.
Language (s): French; Full Page Mono: 2233.00; Full Page Colour: 2532.00
Currency: Euro
DAILY NEWSPAPER

Sud Ouest Charente Maritime - Edition Royan - Jonzac
Owner: SUD OUEST
Editorial: 27 place du Champ-de-Foire, Jonzac 17500. **T:** 33 5 46 48 56 31
E: jonzac@sudouest.fr
W: http://www.sudouest.fr
Freq: Daily; **Circ:** 50000 Pub Statement
Redacteur: Ronan Chérel
Editorial Profile: Regional daily newspaper focussing on local and regional news and current affairs. Local Translation:Journal d'informations générales et régionales.
Language (s): French; Full Page Mono: 2172.00; Full Page Colour: 2480.00
Currency: Euro
DAILY NEWSPAPER

Sud Ouest Charente-Maritime - Edition Rochefort-Oleron
Owner: SUD OUEST
Editorial: 60 rue de la République, Rochefort 17300. **T:** +33 5 46 99 89 10
E: rochefort@sudouest.fr
W: http://www.sudouest.fr
Freq: Daily; **Circ:** 400000 Pub Statement
Editorial Profile: Regional daily newspaper focussing on local, regional and national news and current affairs. Local Translation:Informations générales, nationales, régionales et locales.
Language (s): French; Full Page Mono: 2010.00; Full Page Colour: 2314.00
Currency: Euro
DAILY NEWSPAPER

Sud Ouest Dimanche
Owner: SUD OUEST
Editorial: 23, quai de Queyries, Bordeaux 33094 CEDEX. **T:** +33 5 35 31 31 31
E: dimanche@sudouest.com
W: http://www.sudouest.com
Freq: Weekly; **Circ:** 286525 OJD
Editorial Profile: Sunday edition of the regional daily newspaper focussing on news and current affairs. Local Translation:Edition du dimanche du quotidien Sud-Ouest.
Language (s): French; Full Page Mono: 12631.00; Full Page Colour: 13890.00
Currency: Euro
NEWSPAPER

Sud Ouest Dordogne - Edition Perigueux
Owner: SUD OUEST
Editorial: 7 bis place Francheville, BP 1054, Perigueux 24001 CEDEX. **T:** 33 5 53 45 24 52
E: perigueux@sudouest.fr
W: http://www.sudouest.fr
Freq: Daily; **Circ:** 38000 Pub Statement
Editorial Profile: Regional daily newspaper focussing on local and regional news and current affairs. Local Translation:Journal d'informations générales et régionales.
Language (s): French; Full Page Mono: 1961.00; Full Page Colour: 2307.00
Currency: Euro
DAILY NEWSPAPER

Sud Ouest Edition Charente
Owner: SUD OUEST
Editorial: 61 bis rue Hergé, BP 1219, Angouleme 16006 CEDEX.
T: +33 5 45 39 95 95
E: angouleme@sudouest.fr
W: http://www.sudouest.fr
Freq: Daily; **Circ:** 406726 Pub Statement
Editorial Profile: Regional daily newspaper focussing on local and regional news and current affairs. Local Translation:Journal d'informations générales et régionales.
Language (s): French; Full Page Mono: 4720.00; Full Page Colour: 5459.00
Currency: Euro
DAILY NEWSPAPER

Sud Ouest Lot-Et-Garonne - Edition Marmandais
Owner: SUD OUEST
Editorial: 69 rue Charles-de-Gaulle, BP 83, Marmande 47200. **T:** +33 5 53 64 96 96
E: marmande@sudouest.fr
W: http://www.sudouest.fr
Freq: Daily; **Circ:** 390000 Pub Statement
Editorial Profile: Regional daily newspaper focussing on local and regional news and current affairs. Local Translation:Journal d'informations générales et régionales.
Language (s): French; Full Page Mono: 795.00; Full Page Colour: 975.00
Currency: Euro
DAILY NEWSPAPER

Sundgau Sans Frontieres
Owner: SUNDGAU SANS FRONTIERES
Editorial: Plume d'Expression, 3C rue du 27-Novembre, Balschwiller 68210.
T: 33 3 89 25 29 72
E: sundgau-sans-frontieres@neuf.fr
W: http://www.sundgau-sans-frontieres.fr
Freq: Monthly; **Circ:** 60000 Pub Statement
Editorial Profile: Regional newspaper focussing on local news and current affairs including cross border information, culture, associations, events, concerts, exhibitions, conferences, sport, history, municipal, society, business, gardening, housing, holidays, motoring, fashion, beauty, well being, shopping and agenda.
Language (s): French
NEWSPAPER

Le Télégramme
Owner: Le Télégramme
Editorial: 7, voie d'accès au Port, BP 67243, Morlaix 29672. **T:** 33 2 98 62 11 33
E: economie@letelegramme.fr
W: http://www.letelegramme.com
Freq: Daily; **Circ:** 201579 Pub Statement
Rédacteur en Chef: Olivier Clech; **Rédacteur en Chef Adjoint:** Christian Direr; **Rédacteur en Chef Adjoint:** Alain Félice; **Rédacteur en Chef Adjoint:** Jacques Guillerm; **Rédacteur en Chef Adjoint:** Catherine Magueur; **Editor:** Samuel Petit
Editorial Profile: Magazine covering regional and national news and current affairs including economics, sports and leisure.
Language (s): French; Full Page Mono: 30930.00; Full Page Colour: 37988.00
Currency: Euro
DAILY NEWSPAPER

LE Telegramme Dimanche
Owner: LE TELEGRAMME DE BREST ET DE L'OUEST
Editorial: 7 voie d'Accès-au-Port, BP 67243, Morlaix 29672. **T:** +33 2 98 62 11 33
E: telegramme@letelegramme.fr
W: http://www.letelegramme.com
Freq: Weekly; **Circ:** 155912
Rédacteur en Chef: Olivier Clech; **Rédacteur en Chef Adjoint:** Christian Direr; **Rédacteur en Chef Adjoint:** Alain Félice; **Rédacteur en Chef Adjoint:** Jacques Guillerm; **Rédacteur en Chef Adjoint:** Catherine Magueur
Editorial Profile: 16 sport report removable pages. International, national and regional news, including several special columns on top of the daily national news: games, celebrities, TV guide... The magazine 'Version Fémina' (published by Hachette Filipacchi Médias) is included as supplément.4 editions: Nord Finistère, Sud Finistère, Côtes d'Armor and Morbihan.
Language (s): French
NEWSPAPER

Temps Libres
Owner: MI TEMPS
T: 33 4 74 50 65 66
E: tempslibre.redaction@wanadoo.fr
Freq: Monthly; **Circ:** 45000 Pub Statement
Editorial Profile: Local Translation: Journal d'actualité sur le département de l'Ain.Annonces loisirs, publireportage, portraits. Habitants de l'Ain
Language (s): French
NEWSPAPER

TOULOUSE MAG
Owner: GROUPE DEPECHE DU MIDI
Editorial: Avenue Jean Baylet, Toulouse 31095. **T:** 33 05 62 11 96 00
E: joelle.porcher@ladepeche.fr
W: http://www.toulousemag.com
Freq: Monthly; **Circ:** 17000 Pub Statement
Rédactrice: Manon Haussy; **Rédactrice en chef:** Joëlle Porcher; **Maquettiste:** Céline Viguier; **Rédactrice:** Julie Vivier
Editorial Profile: Informations régionales Toulouse : culture, voyages, shopping, dossiers, gastronomie.
Language (s): French; Full Page Colour: 3700.00
Currency: Euro
NEWSPAPER

TOUTES LES NOUVELLES
Owner: S.E.H.P.
Editorial: 4 bis avenue de Sceaux, Versailles 78035. **T:** 33 01 30 97 72 00
E: s.gauthier@lesnouvelles.fr
Freq: Weekly; **Circ:** 11476 OJD
Rédacteur en chef: Stéphane Gauthier; **Editeur:** Patrick Wassef
Editorial Profile: Editions : Versailles et Rambouillet / Chevreuse. PARUTIONS : mercredi
Language (s): French
NEWSPAPER

Toutes les nouvelles de Rambouillet
Owner: PUBLIHEBDOS
Editorial: 67 rue du Général-de-Gaulle, Rambouillet 78120. **T:** 33 1 34 83 67 61
E: redac.rbt@lesnouvelles.fr
Freq: Weekly; **Circ:** 40000 Pub Statement
Editeur: Patrick Wassef

Editorial Profile: Regional newspaper focussing on local news and current affairs including celebrities.
Language (s): French
NEWSPAPER

Le Tregor
Owner: GROUPE PUBLIHEBDOS
Editorial: 26 rue Compagnie Roger Barbé, BP 80233, Lannion 22302. **T:** 33 02 96 46 67 67
E: letregor@publihebdos.fr
Freq: Weekly; **Circ:** 21365 OJD
Rédacteur en chef adjoint: Christophe Ganne; **Rédacteur:** Philippe Gestin; **Rédacteur en chef:** Erwann Hirel; **Rédacteur:** Etienne Royer; **Rédactrice:** Marion Valee
Editorial Profile: Informations régionales, locales - Annonces légales pour tout le département. PARUTIONS : jeudi
Language (s): French
NEWSPAPER

La Tribune
Owner: La Tribune
Editorial: 18, rue Pasquier, Paris 75008.
T: 33 1 78 41 40 93
E: latribunelibre@latribune.fr
W: http://www.latribune.fr
Freq: Daily; **Circ:** 78463 OJD
Editor in Chief: Jean-Louis Alcaide; **Editor in Chief:** Michel Cabirol; **Editor in Chief:** Robert Jules; **Editor at Large:** Isabelle Lefort; **Editor in Chief:** Franck Pauly
Editorial Profile: Newspaper covering financial and business news including economics, investment, stock markets, management, related technology and personal finance.
Language (s): French; Full Page Mono: 29800.00; Full Page Colour: 37900.00
Currency: Euro
DAILY NEWSPAPER

La Tribune - Le Progres
Owner: GROUPE PROGRES
Editorial: 24 rue de la Robotique, BP 38, Saint-Etienne 42964. **T:** 33 04 77 91 47 47
E: redactionenchef@leprogres.fr
W: http://www.leprogres.fr
Freq: Daily; **Circ:** 217755 OJD
Rédacteur en chef: Xavier Antoye; **Rédacteur détaché RIVE DE GIER:** Loïc Todesco
Editorial Profile: Utilisation de la quadrichromie : Tous les jours, dans les pages 1, 3, 5, 7 et complémentaires - OJD : LE PROGRES + LA TRIBUNE. Diffusé en Loire et Haute-Loire.
DAILY NEWSPAPER

La Tribune De Montélimar
Editorial: 33 avenue du Gal de Gaulle, Montelimar 26201. **T:** 33 04 75 00 84 00
E: redaction@latribune-montelimar.com
W: http://www.latribune-montelimar.com
Freq: Weekly; **Circ:** 19377 OJD
Edition Ardèche: Hervé Barruhet; **Edition Ardèche:** Pauline Frison; **Edition Montélimar:** Céline Gonin; **Rédacteur en chef Justice:** Marc Loudin; **Rédactrice en chef:** Laure Ostwalt
Editorial Profile: PARUTIONS : le jeudi.
Language (s): French; Full Page Mono: 1011.00; Full Page Colour: 1213.00
Currency: Euro
NEWSPAPER

La Tribune De Tours
Editorial: 19 rue Mirabeau, Tours 37000.
T: 33 02 47 61 24 60
E: tribunetours-redac2@orange.fr
W: http://www.tribune-tours.fr
Freq: Weekly; **Circ:** 28000 Pub Statement
Editorial Profile: Magazine GRATUIT d'informations locales de l'agglomération tourangelle. PARUTIONS : le jeudi
Language (s): French
NEWSPAPER

La Tribune D'Orleans
Editorial: 33 boulevard Rocheplatte, Orleans 45000. **T:** 33 02 38 52 95 54
E: tribuneorleans.redac@orange.fr
W: http://www.tribune-orleans.fr
Freq: Weekly; **Circ:** 26000 Pub Statement
Editorial Profile: Journal d'informations locales : culture, politique, enquêtes.
Language (s): French
NEWSPAPER

La Tribune Le Progres Saint-Etienne
Owner: LE PROGRES
Editorial: 2 place Jean-Jaurès, Saint-Etienne 42000. **T:** 33 4 77 45 10 10
E: chefinfo42@leprogres.fr
W: http://www.leprogres.fr
Freq: Daily
Editorial Profile: National, regional and local news. Sunday price: 1,50 € - Full week subscription including Sunday: 327 €. Local Translation:Actualités départementales et locales, régionales et nationales. Prix du dimanche : 1,50 €.Abonnement semaine + dimanche : 327 €
Language (s): French; Full Page Mono: 3717.00
Currency: Euro
DAILY NEWSPAPER

LA Tribune Le Progrès: Edition Haute-Loire
Owner: LE PROGRES
Editorial: 20 boulevard Saint-Pierre, Yssingeaux 43200. **T:** 33 4 71 56 06 61
E: redaction43@leprogres.fr
W: http://www.leprogres.fr
Freq: Daily; **Circ:** 35000 Pub Statement
Editorial Profile: Regional and local news. Sunday price: 1,05 € and full week subscription including Sunday: 233,60 €. Local Translation:Informations régionales et locales. Prix du dimanche : 1,05 € et abonnement semaine + dimanche : 233,60 €
Language (s): French; Full Page Mono: 1594.00
Currency: Euro
DAILY NEWSPAPER

LA Tribune Valréas
Owner: GROUPE DAUPHINE
Editorial: 18 cours Tivoli, Valreas 84600.
T: 33 4 90 35 19 76
E: sblatribune@hotmail.com
Freq: Weekly; **Circ:** 33000 Pub Statement
Editorial Profile: Vaucluse, Basse-Drôme and Ardèche regions news.
Language (s): French; Full Page Mono: 1011.00; Full Page Colour: 1213.00
Currency: Euro
NEWSPAPER

L' Union – L'Ardennais
Owner: GHM - GROUPE HERSANT MEDIA
Editorial: 5, rue de Talleyrand, Reims 51083.
T: 33 3 26 50 50 50
E: dirgen@journal-lunion.fr
W: http://www.lunion.presse.fr
Freq: Daily; **Circ:** 106384 OJD
Rédacteur en Chef: Hervé Chabaud; **Rédacteur en chef:** Sébastien Lacroix; **Editor in Chief:** Didier Louis
Editorial Profile: Regional daily newspaper covering national, regional and local news and current affairs.
Language (s): French; Full Page Mono: 13059.00
Currency: Euro
DAILY NEWSPAPER

L' Union Edition Chauny - Tergnier - La Fere - St Quentin
Owner: GHM - GROUPE HERSANT MEDIA
Editorial: 4 rue du Général-Leclerc, Chauny 2300. **T:** +33 3 23 52 15 84
E: chauny@journal-lunion.fr
W: http://www.lunion.presse.fr
Freq: Daily; **Circ:** 126325 Pub Statement
Editorial Profile: National, regional and local news. Current events.
Language (s): French
DAILY NEWSPAPER

L' Union Edition De Chalons
Owner: GHM - GROUPE HERSANT MEDIA
Editorial: 23 place de la République, Chalons-En-Champagne 51000. **T:** 33 3 26 68 13 10
E: chalons@journal-lunion.fr
W: http://www.lunion.presse.fr
Freq: Daily; **Circ:** 126325 Pub Statement
Editorial Profile: National, regional and local news. Current events. Local Translation:Actualités locales, départementales, régionales et nationales. Informations générales.
Language (s): French
DAILY NEWSPAPER

L' Union Edition Soissons-Chateau-Thierry
Owner: GHM - GROUPE HERSANT MEDIA
Editorial: 53 rue Carnot, Chateau-Thierry 2400. **T:** +33 3 23 84 11 83
E: chateau@journal-lunion.fr
W: http://www.lunion.presse.fr
Freq: Daily; **Circ:** 126000 Pub Statement
Editorial Profile: National, regional and local news. Current events.
Language (s): French
DAILY NEWSPAPER

L' Union Editions De L'aisne Direction Departementale De Laon
Owner: GHM - GROUPE HERSANT MEDIA
Editorial: 87, rue Léon Nanquette, Laon 2000.
T: +33 3 23 27 78 00
E: dirdep02@journal-lunion.fr
W: http://www.lunion.presse.fr
Freq: Daily; **Circ:** 130000 Pub Statement
Editorial Profile: Local, regional, national and international news. Current events and sport. Saturday price: 1,50 € (including Fémina and TV guide supplements). Local Translation:Actualités locales, départementales, régionales, nationales et internationales. Informations générales et sportives. *Prix : 1,50 € le samedi (avec suppléments TV et Fémina)
Language (s): French; Full Page Mono: 7759.00
Currency: Euro
DAILY NEWSPAPER

VAR MATIN
Owner: GROUPE HERSANT MEDIA
Editorial: 15 boulevard de Strasbourg, Toulon 83000. **T:** 33 04 94 93 31 00
E: rantech@nicematin.fr
W: http://www.varmatin.com
Freq: Daily; **Circ:** 75473 OJD
Editorial Profile: Quadrichromie : tous les jours - Diffusion : 7 éditions sur le Var avec édition du Dimanche - OJD : 74 587ex
DAILY NEWSPAPER

Var-Matin Nice-Matin Edition Brignoles-Le Luc
Owner: GHM - GROUPE HERSANT MEDIA
Editorial: 3 place Saint-Louis, Brignoles 83170. **T:** 33 4 94 69 67 10
E: brignoles@nicematin.fr
W: http://www.varmatin.com
Freq: Daily; **Circ:** 78965 Pub Statement
Editorial Profile: Regional daily newspaper focussing on general news and current affairs. Local Translation:Quotidien régional d'informations générales.
Language (s): French
DAILY NEWSPAPER

Var-Matin Nice-Matin Edition Hyeres-Le Lavandou
Owner: GHM - GROUPE HERSANT MEDIA
Editorial: 15 avenue Joseph-Clotis, Hyeres 83400. **T:** 33 4 94 12 81 90
E: hyeres@nicematin.fr
W: http://www.varmatin.com
Freq: Daily; **Circ:** 70965 Pub Statement
Editorial Profile: Regional daily newspaper focussing on news and current affairs including TV guide and women's interest supplement. Local Translation:Toute l'actualité de la région toulonnaise. Prix : 1,10 € le samedi (avec TV hebdo), 1,10 € le dimanche (avec Version Fémina).
Language (s): French
DAILY NEWSPAPER

VAR-MATIN NICE-MATIN TOULON SIEGE SOCIAL
Owner: GHM - GROUPE HERSANT MEDIA
Editorial: 15 boulevard de Strasbourg, BP 806, Toulon 83051 CEDEX.
T: 33 4 94 93 31 50 **E:** redacchef@nicematin.fr
W: http://www.varmatin.com
Freq: Daily; **Circ:** 75520 OJD
Rédacteur (trice): Catherine Blanchard
Editorial Profile: Regional daily newspaper focussing on news and current affairs. Local Translation:Quotidien régional d'informations. Prix : 1,10 € le samedi, 1,10 € le dimanche.
Language (s): French; Full Page Colour: 19656.00
Currency: Euro
DAILY NEWSPAPER

VAUCLUSE MATIN
Owner: GROUPE DAUPHINE LIBERE
Editorial: 23 rue de la République, Avignon 84000. **T:** 33 04 90 16 78 00
E: centre.avignon@vauclusematin.com
Freq: Daily; **Circ:** 11109 Pub Statement
Language (s): French; Full Page Mono: 4949.00; Full Page Colour: 6434.00
Currency: Euro
DAILY NEWSPAPER

La Vie Correzienne
Owner: COURRIER FRANCAIS
Editorial: 15 rue Fernand Alibert, Brive-La-Gaillarde 19316. **T:** 33 05 55 24 11 44
E: v.david@courrier-francais.fr
W: http://www.lavie-correzienne.com
Freq: Weekly; **Circ:** 11900 Pub Statement
Rédacteur en chef: Gérard Dames
Editorial Profile: Hebdomadaire d'informations générales, départementales et d'information catholique. PARUTIONS : vendredi
Language (s): French; Full Page Mono: 1100.00; Full Page Colour: 1440.00
Currency: Euro
NEWSPAPER

LA VOIX DE L'AIN
Owner: GROUPE HCR
Editorial: 16 rue Lalande, BP 88, Bourg-En-Bresse 1003. **T:** 33 04 74 23 80 50
E: redaction@voixdelain.fr
W: http://www.voixdelain.fr
Freq: Weekly; **Circ:** 22326 OJD
Rédacteur en chef: Nicolas Bernard; **Rédacteur en chef adjoint:** Jean-Yves Flochon; **Rédactrice en chef adjointe:** Corinne Garay
Editorial Profile: Hebdomadaire (catholique) départemental d'information paraissant le vendredi.
Language (s): French; Full Page Mono: 1882.00; Full Page Colour: 2356.00
Currency: Euro
NEWSPAPER

VOIX DU JURA
Editorial: 18 rue de Ronde, BP 173, Lons-Le-Saunier 39005. **T:** 33 03 84 87 16 16
E: redaction@voixdujura.fr
Freq: Weekly; **Circ:** 12187 OJD
Editorial Profile: Journal régional d'informations et d'annonces paraissant le jeudi.
Language (s): French
NEWSPAPER

LA VOIX DU MIDI - GRAND TOULOUSE
Owner: LA VOIX DU MIDI
Editorial: 3 rue Ninau, Toulouse 31000.
T: 33 05 61 99 44 47
E: voixdumidi@wanadoo.fr
Freq: Weekly; **Circ:** 12222 Pub Statement
Editorial Profile: Hebdomadaire régional d'information. PARUTIONS : le jeudi
Language (s): French
NEWSPAPER

La Voix du Nord
Owner: La Voix du Nord
Editorial: 8 Place du Général de Gaulle, BP 549, Lille 59023. **T:** 33 3 20 78 40 40
E: region@lavoixdunord.fr
W: http://www.lavoixdunord.fr
Freq: Daily; **Circ:** 288988 OJD
Livres: Jean-Marie Duhamel; **Rédacteur en chef adjoint toutes éditions:** Patrick Jankielewicz; **Cinéma Radio - Télévision:** Philippe Lagouche; **Rédacteur en chef adjoint toutes éditions:** Bruno Vouters
Editorial Profile: Regional daily newspaper covering general news and current affairs including politics, economics, culture, sports and leisure.
DAILY NEWSPAPER

LA Voix du Nord - Edition Dunkerque
Owner: LA VOIX DU NORD
Editorial: 1-3 place de la République, Dunkerque CEDEX 1. **T:** 33 3 28 59 10 00
E: dunkerque@lavoixdunord.fr
W: http://www.lavoixdunord.fr
Freq: Daily; **Circ:** 26000 Pub Statement
Editorial Profile: Daily regional current events and economy newspaper. Local Translation:Quotidien d'informations générales, économiques, régionales.
Language (s): French
DAILY NEWSPAPER

LA Voix Du Nord Bureau Parisien
Owner: LA VOIX DU NORD
Editorial: 14 rue de Bassano, Paris 75116.
T: +33 1 53 83 15 00 **E:** paris@lavoixdunord.fr
W: http://www.lavoixdunord.fr
Freq: Daily; **Circ:** 300000 Pub Statement
Editorial Profile: Daily regional current events newspaper covering the North, Pas-de-Calais, Somme and Aisne regions. Columns: TV, community news, today.
Language (s): French
DAILY NEWSPAPER

LA Voix Du Nord Edition Du Nord Avesnes Fourmies
Owner: LA VOIX DU NORD
Editorial: 2, rue Gambetta, Fourmies 59610.
T: 33 3 27 61 01 41
E: avesnes@lavoixdunord.fr
W: http://www.lavoixdunord.fr
Freq: Daily; **Circ:** 389867 Pub Statement
Editorial Profile: Daily regional current events and economy newspaper. Local Translation:Quotidien d'informations générales, économiques, régionales.
Language (s): French
DAILY NEWSPAPER

LA Voix Du Nord Edition Du Nord Cambrai
Owner: LA VOIX DU NORD
Editorial: 6/8, rue du Maréchal-de- Lattre-de-Tassigny, Cambrai 59400.

T: +33 3 27 83 68 32
E: cambrai@lavoixdunord.fr
W: http://www.lavoixdunord.fr
Freq: Daily; **Circ:** 389267 Pub Statement
Editorial Profile: Daily regional current events and economy newspaper. The Cambrai edition includes 1 Caudry page and 1 Cateau page produced by the Caudry office. Local Translation:Quotidien d'informations générales, économiques, régionales... L'édition de Cambrai contient une page Caudry et 1 page Le Cateau, réalisées par l'agence de Caudry.
Language (s): French
DAILY NEWSPAPER

LA Voix Du Nord Edition Du Nord Lambersart
Owner: LA VOIX DU NORD
Editorial: 2 rue de la Carnoy, Lambersart 59130. **T:** +33 3 20 17 17 17
E: lambersart@lavoixdunord.fr
W: http://www.lavoixdunord.fr
Freq: Daily; **Circ:** 300000 Pub Statement
Editorial Profile: Daily regional current events and economy newspaper. 2 editions depend on the Lambersart office: 1 edition for Marcq La Madeleine, Lomme, Lambersart, St-André and another edition for Loos, Haubourdin, Les Weppes. Local Translation:Quotidien d'informations générales, économiques, régionales... 2 éditions dépendent du bureau de Lambersart : une édition pour Marcq La Madeleine, Lomme, Lambersart, St-André ; une autre édition pour Loos, Haubourdin, Les Weppes.
Language (s): French
DAILY NEWSPAPER

LA Voix Du Nord Edition Du Nord Le Melantois
Owner: LA VOIX DU NORD
Editorial: 2 rue Jean-Jaurès, Seclin 59113.
T: +33 3 20 90 05 05
E: seclin@lavoixdunord.fr
W: http://www.lavoixdunord.fr
Freq: Daily; **Circ:** 380000 Pub Statement
Editorial Profile: Daily regional current events and economy newspaper. Local Translation:Quotidien d'informations générales, économiques, régionales.
Language (s): French
DAILY NEWSPAPER

LA Voix Du Nord Edition Du Nord Le Pevele - Melantois
Owner: LA VOIX DU NORD
Editorial: 35, boulevard de Valmy, Villeneuve D'ascq 59650. **T:** +33 3 20 91 19 05
E: villeneuvedascq@lavoixdunord.fr
W: http://www.lavoixdunord.fr
Freq: Daily; **Circ:** 340000 Pub Statement
Editorial Profile: Daily regional international and national current events newspaper. Economy, culture, cinema, news in brief... Local Translation:Quotidien d'informations internationales nationales et régionales. Economie, culture, cinéma, faits divers.
Language (s): French
DAILY NEWSPAPER

LA Voix Du Nord Edition Du Nord Le Quesnoy Maubeuge
Owner: LA VOIX DU NORD
Editorial: 6 rue Thiers, Le Quesnoy 59530.
T: +33 3 27 47 54 00
E: lequesnoy@lavoixdunord.fr
W: http://www.lavoixdunord.fr
Freq: Daily; **Circ:** 250000 Pub Statement
Editorial Profile: Daily regional current events and economy newspaper. Local Translation:Quotidien d'informations générales, économiques, régionales.
Language (s): French
DAILY NEWSPAPER

LA Voix Du Nord Edition Pas-De-Calais Bethune Bruay
Owner: LA VOIX DU NORD
Editorial: 23 rue des Treilles, Bethune 62400.
T: +33 3 21 01 14 18
E: bethune@lavoixdunord.fr
W: http://www.lavoixdunord.fr
Freq: Daily; **Circ:** 380000 Pub Statement
Editorial Profile: Daily regional current events and economy newspaper. Local Translation:Quotidien d'informations générales, économiques, régionales.
Language (s): French
DAILY NEWSPAPER

LA Voix Du Nord Edition Pas-De-Calais Lens Henin Carvin
Owner: LA VOIX DU NORD
Editorial: 35 rue Edouard-Plachez, Carvin 62220. **T:** +33 3 21 74 04 00
E: henin@lavoixdunord.fr
W: http://www.lavoixdunord.fr
Freq: Daily; **Circ:** 389267 Pub Statement
Editorial Profile: Daily regional, local, current events, economy, sports, community and leisure newspaper. The Lens pages are common to the Lens Hénin Carvin and the Lens Liévin editions. Local Translation:Quotidien d'informations générales, économiques, régionales, locales. Sports, société, loisirs. Les pages de Lens sont communes aux éditions Lens Hénin Carvin et Lens Liévin.
Language (s): French
DAILY NEWSPAPER

LA Voix Du Nord Edition Pas-De-Calais Lens Lievin
Owner: LA VOIX DU NORD
Editorial: 40 rue de la Gare, Lens 62300.
T: +33 3 21 14 74 74 **E:** lens@lavoixdunord.fr
W: http://www.lavoixdunord.fr
Freq: Daily; **Circ:** 350000 Pub Statement
Editorial Profile: Daily regional, local, current events, economy, sports, community and leisure newspaper. The Lens pages are common to the Lens Hénin Carvin and the Lens Liévin editions. Local Translation:Quotidien d'informations générales, économiques, régionales, locales...Sports, société, loisirs. Les pages de Lens sont communes aux éditions Lens Hénin Carvin et Lens Liévin.
Language (s): French
DAILY NEWSPAPER

LA Voix Du Nord Edition Pas-De-Calais St-Omer
Owner: LA VOIX DU NORD
Editorial: 88 rue de Calais, Saint-Omer 62500.
T: +33 3 21 38 08 33
E: saintomer@lavoixdunord.fr
W: http://www.lavoixdunord.fr
Freq: Daily; **Circ:** 400000 Pub Statement
Editorial Profile: Daily regional current events and economy newspaper. Local Translation:Quotidien d'informations générales, économiques, régionales.
Language (s): French
DAILY NEWSPAPER

VOSGES MATIN
Editorial: 40 quai des Bons Enfants, BP 273, Epinal 88007. **T:** 33 03 29 82 98 00
W: http://www.vosgesmatin.fr
Freq: Daily; **Circ:** 47965 OJD
Cinéma Vidéo: Christophe Gobin; **Maison Décoration:** Sophie Maupetit; **Rédacteur en chef:** Gérard Noel
Editorial Profile: Utilisation de la quadrichromie - Tous les jours - Dans certaines pages. Edition du dimanche : 45 324ex.
DAILY NEWSPAPER

Vosges Matin Agence de Remiremont
Owner: EBRA
Editorial: 16 rue de la Franche-Pierre, Remiremont 88200. **T:** 33 3 29 62 04 03
E: redaction.remiremont@vosgesmatin.fr
W: http://www.vosgesmatin.fr
Freq: Daily; **Circ:** 50000 OJD
Editorial Profile: Regional and local news.
Language (s): French
DAILY NEWSPAPER

Vosges Matin Agence de Saint-Dié
Owner: EBRA
Editorial: 31 rue Thiers, St-Die 88100.
T: 33 3 29 55 78 10
E: redaction.saintdie@vosgesmatin.fr
W: http://www.vosgesmatin.fr
Freq: Daily; **Circ:** 32000 OJD
Editorial Profile: Regional and local news. Local Translation:Actualités départementales et locales.
Language (s): French
DAILY NEWSPAPER

Vosges Matin Agence d'Epinal
Owner: EBRA
Editorial: 40 quai des Bons-Enfants, Epinal 88000. **T:** 33 3 29 82 98 00
E: ojorba@vosgesmatin.fr
W: http://www.vosgesmatin.fr
Freq: Daily; **Circ:** 40000 OJD
Editorial Profile: Local daily news
Language (s): French
DAILY NEWSPAPER

The Wall Street Journal (France)
Editorial: 17 Rue de Surene, Paris 75008.
T: 33 1 4017-1819
Bureau Chief: Grainne McCarthy
DAILY NEWSPAPER

L' Yonne Republicaine
Editorial: 8/12 avenue Jean Moulin, Auxerre 89025. **T:** 33 03 86 49 52 00
E: secretaire.yr@centrefrance.com
W: http://www.lyonne.fr
Freq: Daily; **Circ:** 36472 OJD
Rédacteur en chef adjoint: Daniel Guadarrama; **Rédacteur en chef:** Philippe Noireaux
Editorial Profile: Utilisation de la quadrichromie - Tous les jours - 64 pages.
DAILY NEWSPAPER

L' Yonne Républicaine - Edition Sud
Owner: YONNE REPUBLICAINE
Editorial: 6 rue de Paris, Avallon 89200.
T: 33 3 86 34 99 15
E: secretaire.yr@centrefrance.com
W: http://www.lyonne.fr
Freq: Daily; **Circ:** 36682 Pub Statement
Editorial Profile: National, regional and local news. Including Version Fémina on Wednesday (1 €) and TV Mag on Saturday (1,50 €) . Local Translation:Actualités nationales, régionales et locales. Avec supplément Fémina le mercredi (1 €) et Mag TV le samedi (1,50 €).
Language (s): French
DAILY NEWSPAPER

L' Yonne Républicaine Agence de Joigny
Owner: YONNE REPUBLICAINE
Editorial: 8, avenue Jean Moulin, Auxerre 89000. **T:** 33 3 86 49 52 15
E: secretaire.yr@centrefrance.com
W: http://www.lyonne.fr
Freq: Daily; **Circ:** 50000 OJD
Editorial Profile: Regional news. Local Translation:Actualités régionales.
Language (s): French
DAILY NEWSPAPER

L' Yonne Républicaine Auxerre
Owner: YONNE REPUBLICAINE
Editorial: 8-12 avenue Jean-Moulin, Auxerre 89025 CEDEX. **T:** 33 3 86 49 52 15
E: secretaire.yr@centrefrance.com
W: http://www.lyonne.fr
Freq: Daily; **Circ:** 36682 OJD
Rédacteur en Chef Adjoint: Daniel Guadarrama
Editorial Profile: National, regional and local news. Wednesday price: 1 € (including Version Fémina supplement). Saturday price: 1,50 € (including Yonne Mag and TV Magazine supplements). Local Translation:Actualités nationales, régionales et locales. Prix du mercredi : 1 € (avec supplément Version Fémina). Prix du samedi : 1,50 € (avec suppléments Yonne Mag et TV Magazine).
Language (s): French; Full Page Mono: 3330.00; Full Page Colour: 3996.00
Currency: Euro
DAILY NEWSPAPER

L' Yonne Républicaine: Edition Nord
Owner: YONNE REPUBLICAINE
Editorial: 4 bis rue de la République, Sens 89100 CEDEX. **T:** 33 3 86 83 87 50
E: redaction.sens@centrefrance.com
W: http://www.lyonne-republicaine.fr
Freq: Daily; **Circ:** 36682 OJD
Editorial Profile: National, regional and local news. Local Translation:Actualités nationales, régionales et locales. Vendu le mercredi avec Version Fémina (1,10 €) et le samedi avec TV Mag + Cahier annonces classées + cahier Yonne Mag (1,50).
Language (s): French
DAILY NEWSPAPER

NEWS SERVICE/SYNDICATE

Accroche-press'
Owner: Accroche-press'
Editorial: 8, rue du Delta, Paris 75009.
T: 33 1 48 78 19 96
E: florencepuybareau@accroche-press.fr
W: http://www.accroche-press.fr
Editorial Profile: News service covering economics and finance.
Language (s): French
NEWS SERVICE/SYNDICATE

AFP Relaxnews
Owner: AFP Relaxnews
E: contact@afprelaxnews.com
W: http://www.afprelaxnews.com
Editorial Profile: Press agency covering leisure activities.
Language (s): French
NEWS SERVICE/SYNDICATE

Agence FEP - France Europe Photo
Editorial: 92 rue du Clos de Ville, Sucy-En-Brie 94370. **T:** 33 1 45 90 07 55
E: agence.fep@wanadoo.fr
W: http://www.agencefep.fr
Editorial Profile: Photo agency covering general European news and current affairs.
Language (s): French
NEWS SERVICE/SYNDICATE

Agence France-Presse - Abidjan Bureau
Owner: Agence France-Presse
Editorial: 18 avenue du Docteur Crozet, 01 BP 726, Abidjan. **T:** 225 2 021 9017
E: joris.fioriti@afp.com
W: http://www.afp.com
Bureau Chief: Joris Fioriti
Editorial Profile: Abidjan bureau of international news and picture agency covering general news and current affairs.
Language (s): English
NEWS SERVICE/SYNDICATE

Agence France-Presse - AFP
Owner: Agence France-Presse
Editorial: 11/13, Place de la Bourse, Paris 75002. **T:** 33 1 40 41 46 46
E: contact@afp.com **W:** http://www.afp.com
North America News Editor: David Clark; **Publisher:** Paul Defosseux; **News Editor:** Annie Thomas
Editorial Profile: Main office of the international press agency covering regional, national and international news and current affairs including general interest, politics, business, economics, health, science, education and society.
NEWS SERVICE/SYNDICATE

Agence France-Presse - Bangkok Bureau
Owner: Agence France-Presse
Editorial: 18th Floor, Alma Link Building, 25 Soi Chidlom, Ploenchit, Bangkok 10330.
T: 66 2 650 3230 **E:** bangkok@afp.com
W: http://www.afp.com
Editorial Profile: Bangkok bureau of international news and picture agency covering general news and current affairs.
Language (s): French
NEWS SERVICE/SYNDICATE

Agence France-Presse - Beijing Bureau
Owner: Agence France-Presse
Editorial: 16, Chao Yang Men Wai Street, China Life Tower, Beijing 100020.
T: 86 10 8525 1757
E: sebastien.berger@afp.com
W: http://www.afp.com
Editorial Profile: Beijing bureau of international news and picture agency covering news and current affairs.
NEWS SERVICE/SYNDICATE

Agence France-Presse - Berlin Bureau
Owner: Agence France-Presse
Editorial: Berliner Freiheit 2, Potsdamer Platz, Berlin 10785. **T:** 49 30 308 76 0
E: post@afp.de **W:** http://www.afp.com/de
Editor in Chief: Daniel Jahn
Editorial Profile: Regional office of the Agence France-Presse covering general news and current affairs.
Language (s): German
NEWS SERVICE/SYNDICATE

Agence France-Presse - Dakar Bureau
Owner: Agence France-Presse
Editorial: 2, Place de l'Indépendance, Immeuble SDIH - 2ème étage, Dakar.
T: 221 33 823 08 17 **W:** http://www.afp.com
Editorial Profile: Dakar bureau of the international news and picture agency Agence France-Presse covering international news and current affairs.
Language (s): French
NEWS SERVICE/SYNDICATE

Agence France-Presse - Hong Kong Bureau
Owner: Agence France-Presse
Editorial: 6201 Central Plaza, 18 Harbour Road, Hong Kong. **T:** 852 2829 6200
E: afphkg@afp.com **W:** http://www.afp.com
Editorial Profile: Hong Kong bureau of the international news and picture agency.
Language (s): French
NEWS SERVICE/SYNDICATE

Agence France-Presse - Lilles Bureau
Owner: Agence France-Presse

Editorial: 36 rue de l'Hôpital-Militaire, Lille 59800. **T:** 33 3 20 74 65 00
E: afp.lille@afp.com **W:** http://www.afp.com
Bureau Chief: Pascal Mallet
Editorial Profile: Regional office of the main international press agency in France focussing general interest information.
Language (s): French
NEWS SERVICE/SYNDICATE

Agence France-Presse - Lisbon Bureau
Owner: Agence France-Presse
Editorial: Rua Rosa Araujo, 34, 3º, Lisboa 1250-195. **T:** 351 21 355 6939
E: brigitte.hagemann@afp.com
W: http://www.afp.com
Editorial Profile: Lisbon bureau of international news and picture agency covering general news and current affairs.
NEWS SERVICE/SYNDICATE

Agence France-Presse - Montreal Bureau
Owner: Agence France-Presse
Editorial: 180 Boul Rene-Levesque E, Montreal, Quwbec H2X 1N6.
T: 1 514 288 2777 **E:** marc.braibant@afp.com
W: http://www.afp.com
Bureau Chief: Marc Braibant
Editorial Profile: Montreal bureau of international news and picture agency covering general news and current affairs.
Language (s): French
NEWS SERVICE/SYNDICATE

Agence France-Presse - Rio de Janeiro Bureau
Owner: Agence France-Presse
Editorial: Avenida Almirante Barroso, Nº52, Sala 1002, Rio De Janeiro.
T: 55 21 2217 0025 **W:** http://www.afp.com
Bureau Chief: Laura Bonilla Cal
Editorial Profile: Rio de Janeiro office of the Agence France-Presse covering regional, national and international news and current affairs including general interest, politics, business, economics, health, science, education and society.
Language (s): French
NEWS SERVICE/SYNDICATE

Agencia EFE - Paris Bureau
Owner: EFE
Editorial: 10 rue Saint Marc, 4° bureau 165, Paris 75002. **T:** 33 1 44 82 65 40
E: paris@elfe.com **W:** http://www.efe.es
Editorial Profile: Regional bureau of the Spanish national news agency covering news and current affairs.
NEWS SERVICE/SYNDICATE

AGRA PRESSE
Editorial: 84 boulevard de Sébastopol, Paris 75003. **T:** 33 1 42 74 28 00
W: http://www.agra-online.com
Rédacteur en Chef Adjoint: Sophie Baudin; **Rédacteur en Chef:** Hervé Plagnol; **Rédacteur en Chef:** François-Xavier Simon
Editorial Profile: Press agency focussing on agriculture's economics and politics including business, financial, social, juridical issues. Local Translation:Agence spécialisée dans l'économie et la politique liée à l'agriculture. Les produits :- 'Agra-Presse' : hebdomadaire, rubriques : actualité économique, financière, sociale, politique, agricole, juridique, - 'Agra-Fil' : quotidien transmis par fax at par e-mail : donne l'essentiel de l'actualité agricole du jour,- 'Agra-Europe' : hebdomadaire qui établit un panorama de la vie européenne agricole, politique et juridique, - 'Agra-Valor' : mensuel de la valorisation industrielle des produits agricoles, fait le point sur les dernières évolutions collectées auprès des industriels, des chercheurs et des producteurs.
NEWS SERVICE/SYNDICATE

AITV - AGENCE INTERNATIONALE D'IMAGES DE TELEVISION
Editorial: 35-37 rue Danton, Malakoff 92240.
T: 33 1 55 22 71 04 **W:** http://www.rfo.fr
Rédacteur en Chef: Didier Gaudermen;
Rédacteur en Chef Adjoint: Régis Gourillon
Editorial Profile: International press agency focussing on general interest information. Aimed at the Middle East and Africa.
Language (s): French
NEWS SERVICE/SYNDICATE

ANDIA
Editorial: 10 rue Charles Croizé, ZA de la Teillais, Pace 35740. **T:** 33 2 99 83 50 70
E: photo@andia.fr **W:** http://www.andia.fr
Editorial Profile: Photo agency covering regional news and current affairs including economy, tourism, gastronomy, politics and society.
Language (s): French
NEWS SERVICE/SYNDICATE

APM International
Owner: Wilmington Group plc
Editorial: 33 avenue de la République, Paris 75011. **T:** 33 1 48 06 54 92
E: redaction@apmnews.com
W: http://www.apmnews.com
Gynécologie - Reproduction - Cardiologie: Carole Debray; **Rédactrice en chef adjointe:** Sabine Neulat-Isard; **Diabète:** Adelaïde Robert-Geraudel
Editorial Profile: News agency covering health and medicine.
Language (s): French
NEWS SERVICE/SYNDICATE

Associated Press
Editorial: 162 rue du Faubourg Saint Honoré, Paris 75008. **T:** 33 1 4359-8676
Bureau Chief: Angela Charlton
NEWS SERVICE/SYNDICATE

Bloomberg News
Editorial: 7 Rue Scribe, Paris 75009.
T: 33 153655000 **E:** parisnews@bloomberg.net
Editor: Frank Connelly; **Editor:** Frank Connelly; **Editor:** Frank Connelly; **Editor:** Frank Connelly; **News Editor:** Steve Rhinds; **News Editor:** Steve Rhinds; **News Editor:** Steve Rhinds; **News Editor:** Steve Rhinds; **Bureau Chief:** Vidya Root; **Editor at Large:** Anne Swardson
NEWS SERVICE/SYNDICATE

Bloomberg News Paris Bureau
Editorial: 7, rue Scribe, Paris 75009.
T: 33 1 53.65.50.50
E: parisnews@bloomberg.net
W: http://www.bloomberg.com
Bureau Chief: Vidya Root; **Editor:** Anne Swardson; **Editor:** David Whitehouse
Editorial Profile: International press agency focusing on finance and economics including stock market, politics, sport and leisure.
Language (s): English
NEWS SERVICE/SYNDICATE

COSMOS
Editorial: 56, Boulevard Latour Maubourg, Paris 75007. **T:** 33 1 47 05 44 29
E: info@cosmosphoto.com
W: http://www.cosmosphoto.com
Editorial Profile: Photography news agency.
Language (s): French
NEWS SERVICE/SYNDICATE

CREDO
Owner: Agence de presse CREDO
Editorial: 30 rue des Acacias, Paris 75017.
T: 33 1 44 09 78 80
W: http://info.agencedepresse-credo.fr
Editorial Profile: Press agency covering internal security issues, police, justice and investigation.
Language (s): French
NEWS SERVICE/SYNDICATE

Dow Jones Newswires
Editorial: 6 Bd Haussmann, Paris 75009.
T: 33 140171740
E: paris@priority.emea.dowjones.com
News Editor: Geraldine Amiel; **French Language News Editor:** Eric Chalmet; **News Editor:** Matthew Curtin; **Bureau Chief:** Grainne McCarthy; **French Language Senior Editor:** Thomas Varela
NEWS SERVICE/SYNDICATE

ESDPA – European Security and Defence Press Association
Owner: ESDPA
Editorial: 47, rue Erlanger, Paris 75016.
T: 33 1 40 71 00 62
E: joseph.roukoz@esdpa.org
W: http://www.esdpa.org
Editor: Joseph Roukoz
Editorial Profile: News agency covering the defence and security industry.
Language (s): English
NEWS SERVICE/SYNDICATE

Eureka Presse
Owner: S.A.R.L. Eureka Presse
Editorial: Immeuble Antarès, Téléport 4, Chasseneuil-Du-Poitou 86962.
T: 33 5 49 50 30 65
E: redaction@eurekapresse.com
W: http://www.eurekapresse.com
Editorial Profile: News service covering sports, automotive and new technologies.
NEWS SERVICE/SYNDICATE

Gamma-Rapho
Owner: Gamma-Rapho
Editorial: 104 Boulevard Arago, Paris 75014.
T: 33 1 73 00 70 70
E: presse@gamma-rapho.com
W: http://www.gamma-rapho.com
News - Grands projets: Rafaële Garnot
Editorial Profile: News and photography agency covering news and current affairs including economics, business, arts, culture, sports and celebrities.
Language (s): French
NEWS SERVICE/SYNDICATE

Groupe AEF
Owner: Groupe AEF
Editorial: 137, rue de l'Université, Paris 75007. **T:** 33 1 53 10 39 39
E: habitat@aef.info
W: http://www.groupeaef.info
Editorial Profile: News service covering employment, education, professional training and HR.
Language (s): French
NEWS SERVICE/SYNDICATE

IDG News Service
Owner: International Data Group
Editorial: 40 bd Henri Sellier, Suresnes F-92150. **T:** 33 141970197
W: http://www.idgnews.net
Bureau Chief: Peter Sayer; **Bureau Chief:** Peter Sayer
NEWS SERVICE/SYNDICATE

Infomédia
Owner: Infomédia
Editorial: 58 rue de Châteaudun, Paris 75009.
T: 33 1 48 01 87 35
E: redaction@infomedia-sas.com
W: http://www.infomediamc.fr
Editor in Chief: Olivier Brunet
Editorial Profile: News service covering financial management including asset management, personal finance, retirement, inheritance, life insurance, taxes, investment, property, mortgages, insurance, credits and online banking.
Language (s): French
NEWS SERVICE/SYNDICATE

Market News International
Owner: Market News International Inc.
Editorial: 38, Rue des Blancs Manteaux, Paris 75004. **T:** 1 331 42715540
Bureau Chief: Stephen Sandelius
Language (s): English
NEWS SERVICE/SYNDICATE

Objectif Une
Editorial: 172, rue Duguesclin, Lyon 69003.
T: 33 4 72 32 29 01
E: redaction@objectifune.fr
W: http://www.objectifune.fr
Développement durable: Laure Leter; **Rédactrice en chef adjointe:** Véronique Mauge; **Immobilier Aménagement Placement:** Françoise Sigot
Editorial Profile: General text and photo agency covering news and current affairs.
Language (s): French
NEWS SERVICE/SYNDICATE

PEOPLE TELEVISION
Editorial: Village de la communication, 44-50, avenue du Capitaine Glarner, Saint Ouen 93400. **T:** 33 1 49 48 63 50
E: benjamin.riffle@people-television.com
W: http://www.people-television.com
Editor: Benjamin Riffle
Editorial Profile: Audio visual news agency covering economics.
Language (s): French
NEWS SERVICE/SYNDICATE

RAPSODIA
Editorial: 7 chemin du Vieux Meythet, Meythet 74960. **T:** 33 4 50 24 06 42
E: info@rapsodia.fr **W:** http://www.rapsodia.fr
Editorial Profile: Photo agency covering outdoor sports, travel and nature.
Language (s): French
NEWS SERVICE/SYNDICATE

Relaxnews
Owner: Relaxnews
Editorial: 34 Quai de La Loire, Paris 75019.
T: 33 1 53 19 89 50
E: echarpentier@relaxnews.com
W: http://www.relaxnews.com
Editor in Chief: Emmanuelle Charpentier
Editorial Profile: Press agency covering leisure activities.
Language (s): French
NEWS SERVICE/SYNDICATE

Reuters
Editorial: 6/8 bd Haussmann, 75457 Paris Cedex 09, Paris. **T:** 33 1 4949-5000
Editor: Mark John; **Editor:** Yann Le Guernigou
NEWS SERVICE/SYNDICATE

Sipa Press
Owner: SIPA
Editorial: 101, Boulevard Murat, Paris 75016.
T: 33 1 47 43 47 43 **E:** sipa@sipa.com
W: http://www.sipa.com
Editorial Profile: Photo agency covering news and current affairs, entertainment and sports.
Language (s): French
NEWS SERVICE/SYNDICATE

SUNSET Presse
Owner: SUNSET Presse
Editorial: 23, rue Sébastien Mercier, Paris 75015. **T:** 33 1 45 75 51 79
E: sunsetpresse@sunsetpresse.fr
W: http://www.sunsetpresse.fr
Editorial Profile: Audio-visual press agency covering general new and current affairs including nature, environment, tourism, leisure, sports, celebrities, industry and lifestyle.
Language (s): French
NEWS SERVICE/SYNDICATE

Technoscope
Editorial: 6 Cité de Trévise, Paris 75009.
T: 33 6 70 39 99 31
E: redaction@technoscope.fr
W: http://www.technoscope.fr
Rédactrice en chef - Informatique Biotechnologie: Françoise Breton
Editorial Profile: Press and photo agency covering applied sciences, technology and environment.
Language (s): French
NEWS SERVICE/SYNDICATE

Thomson Reuters - Paris Bureau
Owner: Thomson Reuters
Editorial: 6/8 boulevard Haussmann, Paris 75457. **T:** 33 1 49 49 50 00
E: paris.newsroom@reuters.com
W: http://www.reuters.fr
Rédacteur en chef adjoint Entreprises et marchés: Jean-Michel Belot; **Luxe:** Pascale Denis; **Défense Europe:** Tim Hepher; **Chimie:** Caroline Jacobs; **Rédacteur en chef - Service français:** Marc Joanny; **Distribution:** Noëlle Mennella; **Marché de Taux - Bourse:** Raoul Sachs; **Distribution:** Gustavo Trompiz
Editorial Profile: International press agency focussing on general interest information including economics, politics, science, culture, sports, social, European and global issues.
Language (s): French
NEWS SERVICE/SYNDICATE

BROADCASTING

RADIO NETWORKS

Africa Nº1
Owner: AFRICA Nº1
Editorial: 33 rue du Faubourg-Saint-Antoine, Paris 75011. **T:** +33 1 55 07 58 01
E: africa@africa1.com
W: http://www.africa1.com

Arte Radio
Owner: ARTE
Editorial: 8 rue Marceau, Issy-Les-Moulineaux CEDEX 9. **T:** +33 1 5500 7777
E: contacts@arte-radio.com
W: http://www.arteradio.com

Beur FM Paris 106.7
Editorial: Beur FM, BP 249, Paris 75524.
T: +33 8 9268 1067 **E:** redaction@beurfm.net
W: http://www.beurfm.net

CHERIE FM
Owner: GROUPE NRJ
Editorial: GROUPE NRJ, 22 rue Boileau, Paris 75016. **T:** 33 01 40 71 40 00
W: http://www.cheriefm.fr

Europe 1
Owner: Lagardère Active
Editorial: 26 bis, rue François 1er, Paris 75008. **T:** 33 1 44 31 90 00
E: courrier@europe1.fr
W: http://www.europe1.fr

France Culture
Editorial: 116 avenue du Président-Kennedy, Paris 75220 CEDEX 16. **T:** 33 1 56 40 22 22
W: http://www.radiofrance.fr

FUN RADIO
Editorial: 20 rue Bayard, Paris 75008.
T: 33 01 40 70 48 48
W: http://www.funradio.fr

I>Tele La Radio
Owner: CANAL+
Editorial: 6 allée de la Deuxième D.B., Paris 75015. **T:** +33 1 4114 5353
W: http://www.goomradio.fr/radio/itele-la-radio

Le Mouv'
Owner: RADIO FRANCE
Editorial: 116, avenue du président Kennedy, cedex 16, Paris 75220. **T:** +33 1 56 40 22 22
W: http://www.lemouv.com

Radio France
Owner: Radio France
Editorial: 116 avenue du Président-Kennedy, Paris 75016. **T:** 33 1 56 40 29 07
E: mediateur@radiofrance.com
W: http://www.radiofrance.fr

Radio France Internationale - RFI
Owner: France Médias Monde
Editorial: 116 avenue du Président Kennedy, Paris 75762. **T:** 33 1 56 40 12 12
W: http://www.rfi.fr

RFM
Editorial: 28 rue François 1er, Paris 75008.
T: 33 01 42 32 20 00 **E:** eric.halimi@rfm.fr
W: http://www.rfm.fr

RMC
Owner: RMC INFO
Editorial: 12 rue d'Oradour-sur-Glane, Paris 75740. **T:** 33 1 71 19 11 91 **E:** lsaigre@rmc.fr
W: http://rmc.bfmtv.com

RTL
Owner: RTL
Editorial: 22. rue Bayard, Paris 75008.
T: 33 1 40 70 40 70 **E:** contact.antenne@rtl.fr
W: http://www.rtl.fr

TELEVISION NETWORKS

France Télévisions
Owner: FRANCE TELEVISIONS
Editorial: 7 Esplanade Henri-de-France, Paris 75015. **T:** 33 1 56 22 60 00
W: http://www.francetelevisions.fr

Rai
Editorial: 1 rue du Boccador, Paris 75008.
T: 33 1 56 52 51 50 **E:** raiparis@rai.it
W: http://www.rai.it

CABLE

FOX NewsEdge
Editorial: 10 Rue General Castlenau, Paris 75015. **T:** 33 147349529

FRENCH GUIANA Tel: 594
Standard Time: GMT -3
Continent: The Americas
Capital City: Cayenne

NEWSPAPERS & PUBLICATIONS

NEWSPAPERS

FRANCE-GUYANE
Owner: GHM - GROUPE HERSANT MEDIA
Editorial: 17 rue Lallouette, BP 428, Cayenne 97329. **T:** 594 2 97 00 0
E: france.guyane@media-antilles.fr
W: http://www.franceguyane.fr
Freq: Daily Pub Statement
Rédacteur en Chef: Jérôme Rigolage
Editorial Profile: Daily current events newspapers covering the Guyana region. Circulation: 5000 copies per week days and 8000 copies on Saturdays. Local Translation:Quotidien d'informations de la Guyane. Tirage : 5000 exemplaires la semaine et 8000 exemplaires le samedi.
Language (s): French
DAILY NEWSPAPER

BROADCASTING

TELEVISION STATIONS

RFO GUYANE
Owner: RFO
Editorial: Avenue Le Grand-Boulevard, ZAD Moulin-à-Vent, Remire-Montjoly 97354CEDEX. **T:** 594 5 94 25 6700 **W:** http://www.rfo.fr
Editorial Profile: Local office of the overseas national public TV channel focussing on regional and local news, sport, entertainment, music, ethology, history, faith and traditions.

FRENCH POLYNESIA Tel: 689
Standard Time: GMT -10.5
Continent: Oceania
Capital City: Papeete

NEWSPAPERS & PUBLICATIONS

NEWSPAPERS

Depeche de Tahiti (La)
Owner: Groupe Hersant Media Polynesie
Editorial: BP 50, 98713 Papeete, Tahiti.
T: 689 47 52 83 **E:** journal@ladepeche.pf
W: http://ladepeche.pf
Freq: Daily; **Circ:** 15000 Pub Statement
Editor: Lara Dupuy
Editorial Profile: La Dépêche de Tahiti est le 1er journal d'informations de Polynésie française.
Language (s): French
DAILY NEWSPAPER

Les Nouvel De Tahiti
Owner: GROUPE HERSANT MEDIA
T: 33 00 689 47 52 00
E: redac@lesnouvelles.pf
W: http://www.lesnouvelles.pf
Freq: Daily; **Circ:** 6500 Pub Statement
Rédactrice en chef: Muriel Pontarollo
Editorial Profile: Quotidien (sauf dimanche) d'informations locales, nationales, internationales et sportives - Zone de diffusion : Polynésie Française
Language (s): French
DAILY NEWSPAPER

Nouvelles CalŽdoniennes (Les)
Editorial: BP G5, Noumža Cedex 98848
E: lnc@canl.nc **W:** http://lnc.nc
Freq: Daily; **Circ:** 13000 Pub Statement
Editor-in-Chief: Philippe Minard
Language (s): French
DAILY NEWSPAPER

BROADCASTING

RADIO NETWORKS

NRJ Tahiti
Owner: Groupe Hersant Media Polynesie
W: http://nrj.pf

TELEVISION STATIONS

RFO New Caledonia
Owner: RFO (rŽseau france outre-mer)
Editorial: BP G3, Noumža Cedex 98848
Editorial Profile: National TV station in New Caledonia covering local news.

Tahiti Nui Television
Owner: Tahiti Nui Television
Editorial: BP 348, 98713 Papeete, French Polynesia. **T:** 689 47 36 36
E: redaction@tntv.pf **W:** http://tntv.pf
Editorial Profile: National TV station in Tahiti covering social, cultural and economic issues.

GABON Tel: 241
Standard Time: GMT =1
Continent: Africa
Capital City: Libreville

NEWSPAPERS & PUBLICATIONS

NEWSPAPERS

L' Union (Gabon)
Owner: Sonapresse
Editorial: BP 3849, Libreville. **T:** 241 73 58 60
E: mpg@inet.ga
W: http://www.internetgabon.com/m-actualite. htm
Freq: Daily; **Circ:** 22000 Pub Statement
Editeur: Joël Akouango; **Editor In Chief:** Leonard Mba Assoume
Editorial Profile: Newspaper focusing on national and international news, business, politics, culture and sport.
Language (s): French
DAILY NEWSPAPER

NEWS SERVICE/SYNDICATE

Agence France-Presse - Libreville Bureau
Owner: Agence France-Presse
Editorial: Avenue du Colonel Parent, Immeuble Sogapal Les Filaos, Libreville.
T: 241 7 44 560 **E:** michel.cariou@afp.com
W: http://www.afp.com
Editor in Chief: Michel Cariou
Editorial Profile: Libreville bureau of the international news and picture agency Agence France-Presse covering international news and current affairs.
Language (s): English
NEWS SERVICE/SYNDICATE

Gabonews
Editorial: 9 étages, centre ville, BP 9705, Libreville. **T:** 241 77 87 44
E: gabonews@gabonews.ga
W: http://www.gabonews.ga
Editorial Profile: National news agency focussing on news, current affairs, politics, economics, regional development and sports.
Language (s): French
NEWS SERVICE/SYNDICATE

GAMBIA Tel: 220
Standard Time: GMT
Continent: Africa
Capital City: Banjul

NEWSPAPERS & PUBLICATIONS

NEWSPAPERS

The Point Newspaper
Owner: Point Press
Editorial: 2 Garba Jahumpa Road, PO Box 66 Banjul, Bakau, New Town, Banjul.
T: 220 4 49 74 41 **E:** thepoint13@yahoo.com
W: http://www.thepoint.gm
Freq: Daily; **Circ:** 2500 Pub Statement
Editor: Baboucarr Senghore
Editorial Profile: Newspaper focusing on national and international news, politics, culture and sport.
Language (s): English
DAILY NEWSPAPER

GEORGIA Tel: 995
Standard Time: GMT +4
Continent: Asia
Capital City: Tbilisi

NEWSPAPERS & PUBLICATIONS

NEWSPAPERS

Akhali Taoba
Editorial: 89/24 David Aghmashenebeli Avenue, 11th floor, Tbilisi. **T:** 995 32 95 25 89
E: axtaoba@mail.ru
W: http://www.opentext.org.ge/akhalitaoba
Freq: Daily
Editor: Lali Aslanishvili; **Editor In Chief:** Soso Goginashvili

---

Editorial Profile: Newspaper covering general news, politics, public issues, economy, law, international news.
Language (s): Russian
DAILY NEWSPAPER

Argumenty i Fakty Tbilisi
Owner: Planeta LLC
Editorial: 2/7 Sulkhan Saba Street, Tbilisi.
T: 995 32 2935563
W: http://gazeta.aif.ru/category/external
Freq: Weekly; **Circ:** 16000 Pub Statement
Editor: Ekaterine Eliava
Editorial Profile: Covers politics, economics, culture, education, art, sport and society.
Language (s): Russian
NEWSPAPER

Gazeti Batumelebi
Owner: Gazeti Batumelebi LLC
T: 995 8222 27 45 12 **E:** batumelebi@list.ru
W: http://newspaperbatumelebi.blogspot.com
Freq: Weekly; **Circ:** 2400 Pub Statement
Editorial Profile: Covers politics, education, crime, economy, sport, culture.
Language (s): Russian
NEWSPAPER

Georgia today
Editorial: 41 Irakli Abashidze Str., Apt. 45, Tbilisi 179. **T:** 995 32 91 48 92
E: info@georgiatoday.ge
W: http://www.georgiatoday.ge
Editor: Elene Kvanchilashvili; **US Editor:** David Mapley; **Editor In Chief:** Anthony Shierman
Editorial Profile: Georgia Today aims to create the most comprehensive, objective, and unbiased information about contemporary Georgia and spread it throughout the world.
Language (s): English
DAILY NEWSPAPER

Georgian Business Week
Editorial: 87 Paliashvili Street, Tbilisi.
T: 995 32 22 75 05 **E:** gbw@gbc.ge
Freq: Weekly; **Circ:** 4000 Pub Statement
Editor-in-Chief: Maia Edilashvili
Editorial Profile: Offers a wide range of business news and expert opinions, as well as political stories of specific interest in English language.
Language (s): English
NEWSPAPER

The Georgian Times
Owner: Media holding Georgian times
Editorial: 12 Kikodze Street, Tbilisi 38.
T: 995 32 93 44 05 **E:** editor@goetimes.ge
W: http://www.geotimes.ge **Circ:** 60000 Pub Statement
Publisher: Malkhaz Gulashvili; **Editor-in-Chief:** Georgi Kapanadze
Editorial Profile: Features news on politics, political analysis, business and economics news, religion issues.
Language (s): English
DAILY NEWSPAPER

Komsomolskaya Pravda v Gruzii
Owner: Planeta LLC
Editorial: 2/7 Sulkhan Saba Street, Tbilisi.
T: 995 32 2921859
Freq: Weekly; **Circ:** 3500 Pub Statement
Editor: Nina Argutinskaya
Editorial Profile: Georgian edition of Russian national daily that covers politics, economics, culture, art, education, sport, city life and people.
Language (s): Russian
NEWSPAPER

Kvela Siakhle
Owner: Kviris Palitra
Editorial: Iosebidze str. 49, Tbilisi.
T: 995 32 45 05 47
E: palitra@kvirispalitra.ge
W: http://www.kvirispalitra.ge/jurnalebi/ kvela_siakhle.html
Freq: Weekly
Editor In Chief: Baia Tsanava; **Editor:** Tamaz Tsertsvadze
Editorial Profile: Weekly public-political paper covering general news and entertainment.
Language (s): Russian
NEWSPAPER

Kviris Palitra
Owner: Kviris Palitra
T: 995 32 42 43 40
E: palitra@kvirispalitra.com
W: http://www.kvirispalitra.com/palitra/ frp_palitra.htm
Editorial Profile: Weekly national newspaper covering social and cultural aspects of life.
Language (s): Russian
DAILY NEWSPAPER

The Messenger
Editorial: 43 Belinski Street, Tbilisi.
T: 995 32 93 91 69
E: messenger@messenger.com.ge
W: http://www.messenger.com.ge
Freq: Daily; **Circ:** 4000 Pub Statement
Editor-in-Chief: Zaza Gachechiladze
Editorial Profile: News covered includes market making, banking, investments, marketing surveys, transport, statistics, social issues, currency exchange, tourism, culture, sports and criminal news and provides economic and political analysis of events.
Language (s): English
DAILY NEWSPAPER

Resonance
Editorial: 142 Tsereteli Avenue, 3rd floor, Tbilisi. **T:** 995 32 96 92 60
E: resonancenewspaper@yahoo.com
W: http://www.resonancedaily.com
Freq: Daily; **Circ:** 4500 Pub Statement
Editor In Chief: Lasha Tughushi
Editorial Profile: Covers Georgian news, economy, culture, entertainment, sport.
Language (s): Russian
DAILY NEWSPAPER

Svobodnaya Gruzia
Editorial: 3 Irakli II street, Tbilisi 108
Freq: Weekly; **Circ:** 5000
Editor In Chief: Tato Lakhishvili
Editorial Profile: Newspaper containing general news, digest of Georgian press, news on economy and business, covering political and society aspects.
Language (s): Russian
NEWSPAPER

Version Dossier
Editorial: 7 St. Petersburg St., Tbilisi.
T: 995 32 45 27 13 **E:** dosie@caucasus.net
Freq: 2 Times/Week; **Circ:** 4000 Pub Statement
Publisher: Maia Purtseladze; **Editor:** Tamar Rostaishvili
Editorial Profile: National informative-analytical newspaper.
Language (s): Russian
NEWSPAPER

NEWS SERVICE/SYNDICATE

Prime News Agency
Editorial: 28 Leselidze str., Tbilisi 105.
T: 995 32 92 32 65
E: info@primenewsonline.com
W: http://eng.primenewsonline.com
Editor In Chief: Ia Amazashvili
Editorial Profile: Provides news on politics, economy, culture, social life and sport in Georgia and abroad.
NEWS SERVICE/SYNDICATE

BROADCASTING

RADIO STATIONS

Fortuna
Editorial: 2 Marshal Gelovani Avenue, Tbilisi 179. **T:** 995 22 38 30 30 **E:** tamara@fortuna.ge
W: http://www.fortuna.ge
Editorial Profile: Format of this station is Golden Hits. Fortuna's music library represents the best of the native and world's pop and classical music. The news is broadcasted at the beginning of each hour, after a classical music. The slogan of Radio Fortuna is - "The Best Hits and the Latest Information".

Fortuna+
Editorial: 2 Marshal Gelovani Avenue, Tbilisi 179. **T:** 995 22 38 30 30 **E:** tamara@fortuna.ge
W: http://www.fortunaplus.ge
Editorial Profile: The format of this station is a certain mixture of EHR and Dance formats, that gives it a big popularity.

Hereti FM
T: 995 254 23 766 **E:** office@heretifm.com
W: http://www.heretifm.com
Editorial Profile: Provides best music of all times and modern hits, hourly news on local and international events, special programs and talk-shows. Ratio of news and entertainment programmes is 50-50% .

Hit FM
T: 995 32 55 10 14 **E:** radio@hitfm.ge
W: http://www.hitfm.ge
Editorial Profile: Broadcasts contemporary Russian and Georgian hits combined with entertainment programmes and news.

TELEVISION STATIONS

Adjara TV
T: 995 222 74 370 **E:** info@adjaratv.ge
W: http://www.adjaratv.ge
Editorial Profile: Regional TV channel in Georgia which broadcasts via satellite.

GERMANY   Tel: 49
Standard Time: GMT +1
Continent: Europe
Capital City: Berlin

NEWSPAPERS & PUBLICATIONS

NEWSPAPERS

4 wände
Owner: Schaumburger Nachrichten Verlagsges. mbH & Co. KG
Editorial: Am Markt 12, Stadthagen 31665.
T: 49 5721 809230 **E:** sn@madsack.de
W: http://www.sn-online.de
Freq: Quarterly
Chefredakteur/Editor in Chief: Uwe Graells
Language (s): German
NEWSPAPER

Aachener Nachrichten
Owner: Zeitungsverlag Aachen GmbH
Editorial: Aachener Nachrichten Verlagsgesellschaft GmbH & Co. KG, Postfach 1610, Aachen 52017. **T:** 49 241 51010
E: redaktion@zeitungsverlag-aachen.de
W: http://www.aachener-nachrichten.de/
Freq: Daily; **Circ:** 123648
Chefredakteur / Editor in Chief: Bernd Mathieu; **Redakteur / Editor:** Gerard Peters
Language (s): German
DAILY NEWSPAPER

Aachener Zeitung
Owner: Zeitungsverlag Aachen GmbH
Editorial: Zeitungsverlag Aachen GmbH, Postfach 500110, Aachen 52085
E: redaktion@zeitungsverlag-aachen.de
W: http://www.aachener-zeitung.de/
Freq: Daily; **Circ:** 123648
Redakteur / Editor: Hermann-Josef Delonge; **Chefredakteur / Editor in Chief:** Bernd Mathieu
Language (s): German
DAILY NEWSPAPER

Aalener Nachrichten
Owner: Schwäbische Zeitung GmbH & Co. KG, Drexler, Gessler
Editorial: Aalener Nachrichten & INFO Ostalb, Marktplatz 15, Aalen 73430.
T: 49 7361 570521
E: redaktion@aalener-nachrichten.de
W: http://www.schwaebische.de/region/ostalb/aalen/aalen-sz-team.html **Circ:** 17599
Redakteur / Editor: Jürgen Eschenhorn; **Redaktion / Editor:** Ulrich Geßler; **Redakteurin / Editor:** Claudia Heller; **Redakteur / Editor:** Timo Lämmerhirt; **Redakteur / Editor:** Eckard Scheiderer
Language (s): German
NEWSPAPER

Aar-Bote
Owner: Verlagsgruppe Rhein Main GmbH & Co. KG
Editorial: Verlagsgruppe Rhein Main GmbH & Co. KG, Erich-Dombrowski-Straße 2, Mainz 55127. **T:** 49 611 3550 **E:** impressum@vrm.de
W: http://www.wiesbadener-tagblatt.de
Freq: Daily
Language (s): German
DAILY NEWSPAPER

Abendzeitung München
Owner: Verlag DIE ABENDZEITUNG
Editorial: Verlag DIE ABENDZEITUNG, Rundfunkplatz 4, München 80335.
T: 49 89 23770 **E:** redaktion@abendzeitung.de
W: http://www.abendzeitung-muenchen.de
Freq: Daily; **Circ:** 137689
Redakteur / Editor: Lutz Kuppinger; **Chefredakteur / Editor in chief:** Michael Schilling; **Redakteur / Editor:** Tim Wessling
Language (s): German
DAILY NEWSPAPER

Acher-Rench-Zeitung (Oberkirch)
Owner: Bezirksredaktion ARZ GmbH
Editorial: Lokalredaktion Achern/Oberkirch, Am Marktplatz 4, Oberkirch 77704
W: http://www.bo.de/lokales/achern-oberkirch
Freq: Daily; **Circ:** 12751
'Redakteur / Editor: Andreas Cibis; **Chefredakteur / Editor in Chief:** Rüdiger Keller; **Redakteur / Editor:** Rüdiger Knie; **Redakteur / Editor:** Burkhard Ritter
Language (s): German
DAILY NEWSPAPER

Aichacher Zeitung
Owner: Verlag Mayer & Söhne Druck- und Mediengruppe GmbH & Co KG
Editorial: Oberbernbacher Weg 7, Aichach 86551. **T:** 49 8251 880140
E: redaktion@aichacher-zeitung.de
W: http://www.aichacher-zeitung.de/vorort/
Freq: Daily
Redakteur/ Editor: Berndt Herrmann; **Redakteur / Editor:** Pat Lauer
Language (s): German
DAILY NEWSPAPER

Allgäuer Zeitung
Owner: Allgäuer Zeitungsverlag GmbH
Editorial: Allgäuer Zeitungsverlag GmbH / rta.design GmbH, Heisinger Straße 14, Kempten 87437. **T:** 49 8312 06 5555
E: redaktion.rundschau@azv.de
W: http://www.ihre-az.de/
Freq: Daily; **Circ:** 159473
Redakteurin / Editor: Sonja Krell; **Chefredakteur / Editor in chief:** Markus Niessner
Language (s): German
DAILY NEWSPAPER

Allgemeine Zeitung
Owner: Verlagsgruppe Rhein Main GmbH & Co. KG
Editorial: Erich-Dombrowski-Straße 2, Mainz 55127. **T:** 49 6131 485960
E: az-redaktion@vrm.de
W: http://www.allgemeine-zeitung.de
Freq: Daily; **Circ:** 17990
Redakteur / Editor: Michael Bermeitinger; **Redakteur / Editor:** Thomas Lanfer; **Redakteur / Editor:** Torsten Muders; **Chefredaktion / Editor in Chief:** Friedrich Roeingh; **Redakteur / Editor:** Claus Rosenberg; **Redakteur / Editor:** Claus Wolff
Language (s): German
DAILY NEWSPAPER

Allgemeine Zeitung (Coesfeld)
Owner: Verlag J. Fleißig GmbH & Co.
Editorial: Rosenstraße 2, Coesfeld 48653.
T: 49 2541 921151 **E:** coesfeld@azonline.de
W: http://www.azonline.de
Freq: Daily; **Circ:** 41661
Redakteur / Editor: Hans-Jürgen Barisch; **Redaktion / Editor:** Uwe Goerlich; **Redakteur / Editor:** Ulrich Hörnemann; **Redakteur / Editor:** Thomas Lanfer; **Redakteur / Editor:** Detlef Scherle; **Redakteur / Editor:** Christine Tibroni; **Redakteur / Editor:** Frank Wittenberg
Language (s): German
DAILY NEWSPAPER

Allgemeine Zeitung der Lüneburger Heide
Owner: C. Beckers Buchdruckerei GmbH & Co. KG
Editorial: C. Beckers Buchdruckerei GmbH & Co. KG, Groß Liederner Straße 45, Uelzen 29525. **T:** 49 5818 0891100
E: info@cbeckers.de
W: http://www.az-online.de/
Freq: Daily; **Circ:** 18535
Chefredaktion / Editor in Chief: Ines Bräutigam; **Chefredakteur / Editor in Chief:** Thomas Mitzlaff
Language (s): German
DAILY NEWSPAPER

Allgemeine Zeitung Kirn
Owner: Verlagsgruppe Rhein Main GmbH & Co. KG
Editorial: Langgasse 19, Kirn 55606.
T: 49 6752 94017 **E:** az-kirn@vrm.de
W: http://www.allgemeine-zeitung.de/lokales/kirn/kirn
Freq: Daily; **Circ:** 12054
Chefredaktion / Editor in Chief: Friedrich Roeingh
DAILY NEWSPAPER

Anzeiger für Harlingerland
Owner: Brune-Mettcker Druck- und Verlagsges. mbH
Editorial: Brune-Mettcker Druck- und Verlagsgesellschaft mbH, Postfach 1352, Wittmund 26400. **T:** 49 4462 989180
E: redaktion@harlinger.de
W: http://www.harlinger.de
Freq: Daily; **Circ:** 14620
Redakteur / Editor: Stefanie Heeren; **Chefredakteur / Editor in Chief:** Klaus-Dieter Heimann; **Redakteur / Editor:** Sylke Janßen; **Redakteur / Editor:** Carsten Reimer
Language (s): German
DAILY NEWSPAPER

Anzeiger Lehrte/Sehnde
W: http://www.madsack.de
Language (s): German
NEWSPAPER

Augsburger Allgemeine
Owner: Presse-Druck- und Verlags-GmbH
Editorial: Augsburger Allgemeine Zeitung, Curt-Frenzel-Str. 2, Augsburg 86167.
T: 49 8217 770
E: redaktion@augsburger-allgemeine.de
W: http://www.augsburger-allgemeine.de
Freq: Daily; **Circ:** 99129
Redakteurin / Editor: Anja Christiansen; **Redakteur / Editor:** Detlef Drewes; **Redekteur/ Editor:** Gerrit Hencke; **Herausgeberin / Publisher:** Alexandra Holland; **Redakteurin / Editor:** Eva-Maria Knab; **Redakteurin / Editor:** Barbara Maas; **Redakteurin / Editor:** Mira Nagar; **Redakteur / Editor:** Hauke Normann; **Chefredaktion / Editor in Chief:** Walter Roller; **Redakteur / Editor:** Stefan Stahl; **Redakteur / Editor:** Rudi Wais
Language (s): German
DAILY NEWSPAPER

Augsburger Allgemeine Nordausgabe
Owner: Presse-Druck- und Verlags-GmbH
Editorial: Augsburger Allgemeine Zeitung, Curt-Frenzel-Str. 2, Augsburg 86167.
T: 49 8217 770
E: redaktion@augsburger-allgemeine.de
W: http://www.augsburger-allgemeine.de
Freq: Daily; **Circ:** 225670
Language (s): German
DAILY NEWSPAPER

autoStimme
Owner: Heilbronner Stimme GmbH & Co. KG
Editorial: Heilbronner Stimme GmbH & Co. KG, Allee 2, Heilbronn 74072.
T: 49 7131 615582 **E:** auto@stimme.de
W: http://www.autostimme.de
Freq: Weekly; **Circ:** 88823 Pub Statement
Chefredaktion: Alexander Schnell
Language (s): German; Full Page Mono: 14235.00; Full Page Colour: 19929.00
Currency: Euro
NEWSPAPER

B.Z.
Owner: B.Z. Ullstein GmbH
Editorial: B.Z. Ullstein GmbH, Axel-Springer-Straße 65, Berlin 10888. **T:** 49 3025 9173716
E: redaktion@bz-berlin.de
W: http://www.bz-berlin.de
Freq: Daily; **Circ:** 170235
Chefredakteur / Editor in Chief: Peter Huth
Language (s): German
DAILY NEWSPAPER

Badische Zeitung
Owner: Badischer Verlag GmbH & Co. KG
Editorial: BADISCHER VERLAG GMBH & CO. KG, Basler Straße 88, Freiburg 79115.
T: 49 7614 960
E: redaktion@badische-zeitung.de
W: http://www.badische-zeitung.de
Freq: Daily; **Circ:** 149272
Redakteur / Editor: Michael Brendler; **Redakteur / Editor:** Ronny Gert Bürckholdt; **Chefredaktion / Editor in Chief:** Thomas Hauser; **Redakteur / Editor:** Karlheinz Schiedel
Language (s): German
DAILY NEWSPAPER

Badische Zeitung Waldkirch
Owner: Badischer Verlag GmbH + Co. KG
Editorial: BADISCHER VERLAG GMBH & CO. KG, Basler Straße 88, Freiburg 79115.
T: 49 7681 4779785660
E: redaktion.waldkirch@badische-zeitung.de
W: http://www.badische-zeitung.de
Freq: Daily; **Circ:** 91319
Redakteur / Editor: Bernd Fackler
Language (s): German
DAILY NEWSPAPER

Badische Zeitung, Emmendingen
Owner: Badische Zeitung Emmendingen
T: 49 7641 58095630
Freq: Daily
Redakteur / Editor: Marius Alexander; **Redakteurin / Editor:** Sylvia-Karina Jahn; **Redakteur / Editor:** Patrik Müller
DAILY NEWSPAPER

Badisches Tagblatt
Owner: Badisches Tagblatt GmbH
Editorial: Badisches Tagblatt GmbH, Stephanienstraße 1 - 3, Baden-Baden 76530.
T: 49 7221 2150

E: redaktion@badisches-tagblatt.de
W: http://www.badisches-tagblatt.de
Freq: Daily; **Circ:** 34483
Chefredakteur / Editor in Chief: Markus
Langer; **Redakteur / Editor:** Hartmut Metz
Language (s): German
DAILY NEWSPAPER

Badisches Tagblatt Bühl
Owner: Badisches Tagblatt GmbH
Editorial: Stephanienstraße 1 - 3, Baden-
Baden 76530
Freq: Daily; **Circ:** 13853
Redakteur / Editor: Joachim Eiermann;
Redakteurin / Editor: Edith Fischer;
Redaktktionsleiter / Editor: Gerold Hammes;
Redakteur / Editor: Holger Siebnich
Language (s): German
DAILY NEWSPAPER

Badisches Tagblatt Rastatt/Murgtal
Owner: Badisches Tagblatt Rastatt
Editorial: Stephanienstraße 1 - 3, Baden-
Baden 76530. T: 49 72 21 2 15-0
E: redmurg@badisches-tagblatt.de
W: http://www.badisches-tagblatt.de/
Freq: Daily
DAILY NEWSPAPER

Bayerische Rundschau
Owner: Mediengruppe Oberfranken-
Mantelredaktion GmbH & Co. KG
Editorial: Mediengruppe Oberfranken GmbH &
Co. KG, Gutenbergstraße 1, Bamberg 96050.
T: 49 9221 949211
E: redaktion.kulmbach@infranken.de
W: http://www.infranken.de/regional/kulmbach/
Freq: Daily; **Circ:** 14037
Redakteur / Editor: Stefan Fößel; **Redkteur /
Editor:** Adrian Grodel; **Redakteur / Editor:**
Christian Holhut; **Redakteur / Editor:** Benjamin
Kemmer; **Redaktion / Editor:** Alexander
Müller; **Redakteur / Editor:** Christian Reinisch;
Redakteur / Editor: Falk Zimmermann
Language (s): German
DAILY NEWSPAPER

Bayerwald-Echo
Owner: Mittelbayerischer Verlag KG
W: http://www.mittelbayerische.de
Redakteur / Editor: Claudia Bockholt;
Redakteur / Editor: Claus Gehr; **Redakteur /
Editor:** Heinz Gläser; **Redakteur / Editor:** Maria
Gruber; **Redaktion / Editor:** Markus Heigl;
Redaktion / Editor: Katharina Kellner;
Redakteur / Editor: Birgit Pinzer; **Redakteur /
Editor:** Rainer Plank; **Editor:** Stefan Stark
Language (s): German
NEWSPAPER

Bergedorfer Zeitung
Owner: Bergedorfer Buchdruckerei von Ed.
Wagner (GmbH & Co.)
Editorial: Bergedorfer Buchdruckerei von Ed.
Wagner (GmbH & Co.), Curslacker Neuer
Deich 50, Hamburg 21029. T: 49 4072 566211
E: redaktion@bergedorfer-zeitung.de
W: http://www.bergedorfer-zeitung.de
Freq: Daily; **Circ:** 18291
Redakteur / Editor: Lena Diekmann;
Redakteur / Editor: Volker Gast; **Redakteur /
Editor:** André Herbst; **Redakteur / Editor:** Olaf
Lüttke; **Redakteur / Editor:** Dirk Schulz
Language (s): German
DAILY NEWSPAPER

Bergische Landeszeitung (Wipperfürth)
Owner: Heinen-Verlag GmbH
Editorial: Marktplatz 2, Wipperfürth.
T: 49 2267 657000
W: http://www.rundschau-online.de
Redakteur / Editor: Michael Lenzen;
Redaktion / Editor: Guido Wagner
Language (s): German
NEWSPAPER

Bergische Morgenpost
Owner: Rheinische Post Verlagsges. mbH
Editorial: Weststr. 3, Radevormwald 42477.
T: 49 2195 915922
E: redaktion.radevormwald@
bergische-morgenpost.de
W: http://www.rp-online.de/bergisches-land/
Freq: Daily; **Circ:** 13900 IVW
Redakteur / Editor: Hagen Thiele
Language (s): German
DAILY NEWSPAPER

Berliner Kurier
Owner: Berliner Verlag GmbH & Co.
Editorial: Berliner Kurier, Karl-Liebknecht-
Straße 29, Berlin 10178. T: 49 3023 2327 9
E: post@berliner-kurier.de
W: http://www.berliner-kurier.de
Freq: Daily; **Circ:** 133128
Redakteur / Editor: Klaus Kronsbein;

Redakteur / Editor: Sascha Langenbach;
Redakteur / Editor: Gerhard Lehrke
Language (s): German
DAILY NEWSPAPER

Berliner Kurier am Sonntag
Owner: Berliner Verlag GmbH & Co.
W: http://www.berliner-kurier.de/home/
Chefredaktion / Editor in Chief: Hans-Peter
Buschheuer; **Redakteur / Editor:** Karim
Mahmoud
Language (s): German
NEWSPAPER

Berliner Morgenpost
Owner: Ullstein GmbH
Editorial: Kurfürstendamm 21 - 22, Berlin
10874. T: 49 3025 910
E: redaktion@morgenpost.de
W: http://www.morgenpost.de
Freq: Daily; **Circ:** 122503
Chefredakteur / Editor in Chief: Carsten
Erdmann; **Redakteur / Editor:** Wolfgang
Merkel; **Redakteur / Editor:** Jürgen Stüber;
Redakteurin / Editor: Anna Warnholtz
Language (s): German
DAILY NEWSPAPER

Berliner Zeitung
Owner: Berliner Verlag GmbH
Editorial: Berliner Verlag GmbH, Karl-
Liebknecht-Straße 29, Berlin 10178.
T: 49 3023 279
E: redaktion@berliner-zeitung.de
W: http://www.berliner-zeitung.de
Freq: Daily; **Circ:** 140579
Redakteur / Editor: Harald Biskup;
Redakteurin / Editor: Bettina Cosack;
Chefredakteurin / Editor in Chief: Brigitte
Fehrle; **Redakteur / Editor:** Jörg Hunke;
Redakteur / Editor: Markus Lotter; **Redakteur
/ Editor:** Dagmar Rother
Language (s): German
DAILY NEWSPAPER

Bersenbrücker Kreisblatt
Owner: Neue Osnabrücker Zeitung GmbH &
Co. KG
Editorial: Verlag Neue Osnabrücker Zeitung,
Breiter Gang 10-16, Osnabrück 49032.
T: 49 541 310207 E: chefredaktion@noz.de
W: http://www.noz.de/
bersenbruecker-kreisblatt
Freq: Daily; **Circ:** 13391
Redaktion / Editor: Jürgen Ackmann;
Chefredaktion / Editor in chief: Ralf
Geisenhanslüke; **Redakteur / Editor:** Manuel
Glasfort; **Redakteur / Editor:** Berthold
Hamelmann; **Redakteur / Editor:** Anne
Overesch
Language (s): German
DAILY NEWSPAPER

Bietigheimer Zeitung
Owner: Druck- und Verlagsges. Bietigheim
mbH
Editorial: Druck- und Verlagsgesellschaft
Bietigheim mbH, Kronenbergstraße 10,
Bietigheim-Bissingen 89073. T: 49 7142 4030
E: info@bietigheimerzeitung.de
W: http://www.swp.de/bietigheim
Freq: Daily; **Circ:** 13417
Redakteur / Editor: Michael Krauth; **Redakteur
/ Editor:** Jürgen Kunz; **Chefredaktion / Editor
in Chief:** Andreas Lukesch; **Redakteur /
Editor:** Rüdiger Marggraf; **Redakteur / Editor:**
Inga Stoll
Language (s): German
DAILY NEWSPAPER

Bild
Owner: Axel Springer AG
Editorial: Axel-Springer-Str. 65, Berlin 10969.
T: 49 30 2591 0 E: anfragen@bild.de
W: http://www.axelspringer.de
Freq: Daily; **Circ:** 2435860
Chefredakteur / Editor in Chief: Guido
Brandenburg; **Chefredakteur / Editor in Chief:**
Kai Diekmann; **Redakteurin / Editor:** Wiebke
Eichhorst; **Redakteur / Editor:** Nicolaus Fest;
Redakteur / Editor: Volker Herzig; **Redakteur /
Editor:** Christoph Hülskötter; **Redakteur /
Editor:** Stephanie Jungholt; **Redakteur /
Editor:** Stefan Kost; **Redakteur / Editor:** Kim
Lenar; **Redakteur / Editor:** Sarah Majorczyk;
Redakteur / Editor: Dietrich Menkens;
Redakteur / Editor: Michel Rauch; **Redakteur /
Editor:** Victor Reichhardt; **Redakteurin /
Editor:** Melanie Seidel; **Redakteur / Editor:**
Mathias Sonnenberg; **Redakteur / Editor:** Sven
Stein; **Redakteur / Editor:** Dirk Steinbach;
Redakteur / Editor: Walter M. Straten;
Redakteur / Editor: Willem A. Tell; **Redakteur /
Editor:** Christian Voss; **Redakteur / Editor:**
Lennart Wermke; **Redakteur / Edtior:**
Alexandra Würzbach
Language (s): German

DAILY NEWSPAPER

Bild Aachen
Owner: Axel Springer SE
Editorial: Hohenzollernring 16-18, Koln 50672.
T: 49 221 16044 0 E: INFO@BILD.DE
W: http://www.bild.de/
Freq: Daily; **Circ:** 32333
Language (s): German
DAILY NEWSPAPER

Bild am Sonntag
Owner: Axel Springer AG
Editorial: BILD GMBH & CO. KG, AXEL-
SPRINGER-STRASSE 65, Berlin 10888.
T: 49 3025 910 E: INFO@BILD.DE
W: http://www.bild.de/ **Circ:** 1415546
Chefredakteur / Editor in Chief: Marion Horn;
Redakteur / Editor: Jan Mölleken
Language (s): German
NEWSPAPER

Bild Berlin-Brandenburg
Owner: Axel Springer AG
Editorial: Axel-Springer-Straße 65, Berlin
10888. T: 49 30 2591 0 E: berlin@bild.de
W: http://www.bild.de
Freq: Daily; **Circ:** 108715
Redaktion / Editor: Miriam Krekel
Language (s): German
DAILY NEWSPAPER

Bild Bremen
Owner: Axel Springer AG
Editorial: BILD GMBH & CO. KG, Axel-
Springer-Straße 65, Berlin 10888.
T: 49 421 168920 E: Bremen@bild.de
W: http://www.bremen.bild.de
Freq: Daily; **Circ:** 72869
Redaktion / Editor: Gerhard Buzzi
Language (s): German
DAILY NEWSPAPER

Bild Chemnitz
Owner: Axel Springer SE
Editorial: BILD Chemnitz, Düsseldorfer Platz
1, Chemnitz 9111. T: 49 371 674900
E: chemnitz@bild.de
W: http://www.bild.de/regional/chemnitz/
chemnitz-regional/home-chemnitz-22539154.
bild.html
Freq: Daily; **Circ:** 45295
Language (s): German
DAILY NEWSPAPER

Bild Dresden
Owner: Axel Springer SE
Editorial: BILD Dresden, Devrientstraße 5,
Dresden 1067. T: 49 351 8657300
E: dresden@bild.de
W: http://www.dresden.bild.de
Freq: Daily; **Circ:** 56541
Redaktion / Editor: Robert Kuhne;
Chefredakteur / Editor in Chief: Thomas
Liebenberg
Language (s): German
DAILY NEWSPAPER

Bild Düsseldorf
Owner: Axel Springer AG
Editorial: BILD GMBH & CO. KG, AXEL-
SPRINGER-STRASSE 65, Berlin 10888.
T: 49 211 13010 E: duesseldorf@bild.de
W: http://www.bild.de/regional/duesseldorf/
duesseldorf-regional/home-16337628.bild.html
Freq: Daily; **Circ:** 74836
Language (s): German
DAILY NEWSPAPER

Bild Frankfurt
Owner: Axel Springer SE
Editorial: BILD Frankfurt, Grüneburgweg 2,
Frankfurt Am Main 60322. T: 49 69 8484840
E: bildffm@bild.de
W: http://www.frankfurt.bild.de
Freq: Daily; **Circ:** 120396
Language (s): German
DAILY NEWSPAPER

Bild Halle
Owner: Axel Springer AG
Editorial: BILD Halle, Charlottenstraße 7,
Halle. T: 49 341 2180 500 E: halle@bild.de
W: http://www.bild.de
Freq: Daily; **Circ:** 70697
Language (s): German
DAILY NEWSPAPER

Bild Hamburg
Owner: Axel Springer AG
Editorial: BILD GMBH & CO. KG, AXEL-
SPRINGER-STRASSE 65, Berlin 10888.
T: 49 40 34724929 E: hamburg@bild.de
W: http://hamburg.bild.de
Freq: Daily; **Circ:** 244576
Language (s): German

DAILY NEWSPAPER

Bild Hannover
Owner: Axel Springer AG
Editorial: BILD Hannover, Lister Str. 17,
Hannover 30163. T: 49 511 9604147
E: hannover@bild.de
W: http://www.hannover.bild.de
Freq: Daily; **Circ:** 86911
Redaktion / Editor: Jörg Schaefers
Language (s): German
DAILY NEWSPAPER

Bild Köln
Owner: Axel Springer AG
Editorial: Gereonstr. 18-32, Koln 50670.
T: 49 221 160 440 E: koeln@bild.de
W: http://www.koeln.bild.de
Freq: Daily; **Circ:** 68330
Language (s): German
DAILY NEWSPAPER

Bild Leipzig
Owner: Axel Springer SE
Editorial: BILD Leipzig, Floßplatz 6, Leipzig
4107. T: 49 341 2180500 E: leipzig@bild.de
W: http://www.leipzig.bild.de
Freq: Daily; **Circ:** 67289
Language (s): German
DAILY NEWSPAPER

Bild Magdeburg
Owner: Axel Springer SE
Editorial: BILD Magdeburg, Ernst-Reuter-Allee
5, Magdeburg 39104. T: 49 391 532870
E: magdeburg@bild.de
W: http://www.muenchen.bild.de
Freq: Daily; **Circ:** 44567
Language (s): German
DAILY NEWSPAPER

Bild Mainz-Wiesbaden
Owner: Axel Springer AG
Editorial: Emmeranstraße 27, Mainz 55116.
T: 49 6131 27 75 910
E: bild.mainz-wiesbaden@bild.de
W: http://www.bild.de
Freq: Daily; **Circ:** 39494
Language (s): German
DAILY NEWSPAPER

Bild Mecklenburg-Vorpommern
Owner: Axel Springer AG
Editorial: Axel-Springer-Str. 65, Berlin 10969.
T: 49 30 25910 W: http://www.bild.de
Freq: Daily; **Circ:** 91798 IVW
Language (s): German
DAILY NEWSPAPER

Bild München
Owner: Axel Springer AG
Editorial: BILD München, Isartorplatz 8,
München 80331. T: 49 89 21103200
E: muenchen@bild.de W: http://www.bild.de
Freq: Daily; **Circ:** 118661
Language (s): German
DAILY NEWSPAPER

Bild Münsterland
Owner: Axel Springer SE
Editorial: Dietrich-Oppenberg-Platz 1, Essen
45127. T: 49 201 240534 107
E: mediapilot@axelspringer.de
W: http://www.axelspringer-mediapilot.de/
portrait/
BILD-MueNSTERLAND-BILD-MueNSTERLAN-
D_673014.html
Freq: Daily; **Circ:** 43132
Language (s): German
DAILY NEWSPAPER

Bild Nürnberg
Owner: Axel Springer SE
Editorial: BILD Nürnberg, Schlotfegergasse
26, Nurnberg 90402. T: 49 911 242680
E: nuernberg@bild.de W: http://www.bild.de
Freq: Daily; **Circ:** 69036
Redaktion / Editor: Peter Maskow
Language (s): German
DAILY NEWSPAPER

Bild Ostwestfalen
Owner: Axel Springer SE
Editorial: Dietrich-Oppenberg-Platz 1, Essen
45127
Freq: Daily; **Circ:** 69301
Language (s): German
DAILY NEWSPAPER

Bild Rhein-Main
Owner: Axel Springer SE
Editorial: Grüneburgweg 2, Frankfurt/main
60322. T: 49 69 848484 0 E: info@bild.de
W: http://www.bild.de
Freq: Daily; **Circ:** 624000
Language (s): German

DAILY NEWSPAPER

Bild Rhein-Neckar
Owner: Axel Springer SE
Editorial: BILD Rhein-Neckar, Friedrich König Straße 3, Mannheim 568167.
T: 49 621 438840 **E:** bild.rhein-neckar@bild.de
W: http://www.bild.de
Freq: Daily; **Circ:** 60938
Language (s): German
DAILY NEWSPAPER

Bild Ruhrgebiet
Owner: Axel Springer AG
Editorial: AXEL-SPRINGER-STRASSE 65, Berlin 10888. **T:** 49 201 24 053 40
E: ruhrgebiet@bild.de
W: http://www.ruhrgebiet.bild.de
Freq: Daily; **Circ:** 833000
Language (s): German
DAILY NEWSPAPER

Bild Ruhr-Ost
Owner: Axel Springer AG
Editorial: Axel-Springer-Str. 65, Berlin 10969.
T: 49 231 584439 0 **E:** info@bild.de
W: http://www.ruhrgebiet.bild.de
Freq: Daily; **Circ:** 384000
Language (s): German
DAILY NEWSPAPER

Bild Ruhr-West
Owner: Axel Springer AG
Editorial: Axel-Springer-Straße 65, Berlin 10888. **T:** 49 201 2405 340 **E:** info@bild.de
W: http://www.ruhrgebiet.bild.de
Freq: Daily; **Circ:** 449000
Language (s): German
DAILY NEWSPAPER

Bild Saarland
Owner: Axel Springer AG
Editorial: Bahnhofstraße 31, Saarbrücken 66111. **T:** 49 30 25 91 0 **E:** info@bild.de
W: http://www.bild.de/
Freq: Daily; **Circ:** 57582
Redaktion / Editor: Frank Rolle
Language (s): German
DAILY NEWSPAPER

Bild Stuttgart
Owner: Axel Springer AG
Editorial: BILD Stuttgart, Zeppelinstr. 116, Esslingen 73730. **T:** 49 711 3199321
E: stuttgart@bild.de
W: http://www.stuttgart.bild.de
Freq: Daily; **Circ:** 94297
Redaktion / Editor: Hannes Kohlmaier;
Redakteur / Editor: Jürgen Lück
Language (s): German
DAILY NEWSPAPER

Bild Südwestfalen - Bergisches Land
Owner: Axel Springer SE
Editorial: Dietrich-Oppenberg-Platz 1, Essen 45127. **T:** 49 201 240534 107 **E:** info@bild.de
W: http://www.bild.de
Freq: Daily; **Circ:** 55803
Language (s): German
DAILY NEWSPAPER

Bild Thüringen
Owner: Axel Springer AG
Editorial: BILD Thüringen, Krämpferstr. 2, Erfurt 99084. **T:** 49 361 56556 0
E: erfurt@bild.de **W:** http://www.bild.de
Freq: Daily; **Circ:** 75220 IVW
Language (s): German
DAILY NEWSPAPER

Billerbecker Anzeiger
Owner: Verlag J. Fleißig GmbH & Co.
Editorial: Billerbecker Anzeiger, Lange Str. 8, Billerbeck 48727. **T:** 49 2543 23140
E: coesfeld@azonline.de
W: http://www.azonline.de/Billerbeck
Freq: Daily; **Circ:** 17195
Redaktion / Editor: Stephanie Dircks;
Chefredakteur / editor in chief: Detlef Scherle
Language (s): German
DAILY NEWSPAPER

Böhme-Zeitung
Owner: Mundschenk Nachrichten GmbH & Co. KG
Editorial: Mundschenk Nachrichtengesellschaft mbH & Co. KG, Harburger Str. 63, Soltau 29614. **T:** 49 5191 8080
E: info@mundschenk.de
W: http://www.boehme-zeitung.de/
Freq: Daily; **Circ:** 11409
Redakteur / Editor: Stefan Grönefeld;
Redakteur / Editor: Holger Heitmann;
Redakteur / Editor: Philipp Hoffmann;
Redakteur / Editor: Oliver Hofmann;
Chefredaktion / Editor in Chief: Jörg Jung;
Redakteur / Editor: Andree Küsel; **Redakteur / Editor:** Thomas Lenthe; **Redakteur / Editor:** Marco Ojemann; **Redakteur / Editor:** Iris Schröder; **Redakteur / Editor:** Anja Trappe; **Redakteur / Editor:** Reinhard Vorwerk; **Redakteur / Editor:** Andres Wulfes
Language (s): German
DAILY NEWSPAPER

Bonner Rundschau
Owner: Heinen-Verlag GmbH
Editorial: Bonner Rundschau, Martinsplatz 2a, Bonn 53113. **T:** 49 228 98420
E: Bonner.Rundschau@kr-redaktion.de
W: http://www.rundschau-online.de
Freq: Daily
Redaktion / Editor: Dieter Brockschnieder
Language (s): German
DAILY NEWSPAPER

Bönnigheimer Zeitung
Owner: Druck- und Verlagsges. Bietigheim mbH
Editorial: Druck- und Verlagsgesellschaft Bietigheim mbH, Kronenbergstraße 10, Bietigheim-Bissingen 74321. **T:** 49 7142 4030
E: info@bietigheimerzeitung.de
W: http://www.swp.de/bietigheim/
Freq: Daily; **Circ:** 13462
Redakteur / Editor: Andreas Eberle; **Redakteur / Editor:** Caroline Holowiecki; **Redakteur / Editor:** Michael Krauth; **Redakteur / Editor:** Jürgen Kunz; **Redaktion / Editor:** Andreas Lukesch; **Redakteur / Editor:** Rüdiger Marggraf; **Redakteur / Editor:** Claus Pfitzer; **Redakteur / Editor:** Inga Stoll
Language (s): German
DAILY NEWSPAPER

Börde Volksstimme
Owner: Magdeburger Verlags- und Druckhaus GmbH
Editorial: Magdeburger Verlags- und Druckhaus GmbH, Bahnhofstraße 17, Magdeburg 39104. **T:** 49 3949 946923
E: redaktion.wanzleben@volksstimme.de
W: http://www.volksstimme.de
Freq: Daily; **Circ:** 12153 IVW
Language (s): German
DAILY NEWSPAPER

Borkener Zeitung
Owner: J. Mergelsberg GmbH & Co. KG
Editorial: Verlag J. Mergelsberg GmbH & Co. KG, Bahnhofstraße 6, Borken 46325.
T: 49 2861 9440
E: redaktion@borkenerzeitung.de
W: http://www.borkenerzeitung.de
Freq: Daily; **Circ:** 17358
Redakteur / Editor: Peter Berger; **Redakteur / Editor:** Daniela Göckener; **Redakteur / Editor:** Ulrich Hahn; **Redakteur / Editor:** Birgit Jüttemeier; **Chefredaktion / Editor in Chief:** Sven Kauffelt; **Redakteur / Editor:** Hubert Konert; **Redakteur / Editor:** Ewald Kremer; **Redakteur / editor:** Nina Wickel Nina Wickel; **Redakteur / Editor:** Karin Printing; **Redakteur / Editor:** Marita Rinke; **Redakteur / Editor:** Dirk Rodenbusch; **Redakteur / Editor:** Markus Schönherr
Language (s): German
DAILY NEWSPAPER

Brandenburger Kurier
Editorial: Friedrich-Engels-Straße 24, Potsdam 14473. **T:** 49 331 28 40 0
E: kontakt@MAZ-online.de
W: http://www.maerkischeallgemeine.de
Freq: Daily; **Circ:** 15435
Language (s): German
DAILY NEWSPAPER

Braunschweiger Zeitung
Owner: BZV Medienhaus GmbH
Editorial: BZV Medienhaus GmbH, Hamburger Straße 277, Braunschweig 38114.
T: 49 0531 39000 **E:** redaktion@bzv.de
W: http://www.braunschweiger-zeitung.de/
Freq: Daily; **Circ:** 152086
Redakteur / Editor: Kerstin Löhr;
Chefredaktion / Editor in Chief: Armin Maus
Language (s): German
DAILY NEWSPAPER

Bremer Nachrichten
Editorial: Martinistr. 43, Bremen 28195.
T: 49 421 36710
E: redaktion@bremer-nachrichten.de
W: http://www.bremer-nachrichten.de
Circ: 15228 Not Audited
Chefredakteurin / Editor in Chief: Silke Hellwig
Language (s): German
NEWSPAPER

Brettener Nachrichten
Owner: Badische Neueste Nachrichten Badendruck GmbH
T: 49 7252 9388 3521
E: redaktion.bretten@bnn.de
W: http://www.brettener-nachrichten.de/
Redaktion / Editor: Thilo Kampf; **Redakteur / Editor:** Joachim Schultz; **Redakteur / Editor:** Christina Zäpfel
Language (s): German
NEWSPAPER

Bruchsaler Rundschau
Owner: Badische Neueste Nachrichten Badendruck GmbH
Editorial: Linkenheimer Landstraße 133, Karlsruhe 76149. **T:** 49 721 789-0
E: redaktion@bnn.de
W: http://www.bruchsaler-rundschau.de/
Freq: Daily; **Circ:** 22970
Redakteur / Editor: Peter Huber; **Redakteur / Editor:** Nicole Jannarelli; **Redakteur / Editor:** Klaus-Peter Leipold; **Redaktion / Editor:** Daniel Streib
Language (s): German
DAILY NEWSPAPER

Bünder Zeitung
Owner: Herforder Kreisblatt Busse GmbH & Co. KG
Editorial: Eschstraße 17, Bünde 32257.
T: 49 5223 179 410
E: redaktion@buender-zeitung.de
W: http://www.westfalen-blatt.de/startseite/
Freq: Daily; **Circ:** 19206 IVW
Language (s): German
DAILY NEWSPAPER

Calenberger Zeitung
Owner: Verlagsgesellschaft Madsack GmbH & Co. KG
Editorial: Redaktion Barsinghausen, Marktstraße 10, Barsinghausen 30890.
T: 49 5105 521310
E: barsinghausen@calenberger-zeitung.de
W: http://www.haz.de
Freq: Daily
Chefredakteur/ Editor in Chief: Peter Taubald
Language (s): German
DAILY NEWSPAPER

Chamer Zeitung
Owner: Cl. Attenkofer'sche Buch- und Kunstdruckerei
Editorial: Zeitungsgruppe Straubinger Tagblatt/ Landshuter Zeitung, Ludwigsplatz 32, Straubing 94315. **T:** 49 9421 9400
E: kontakt@idowa.de
W: http://www.idowa.de/zeitung/chamer-zeitung
Freq: Daily; **Circ:** 11947
Language (s): German
DAILY NEWSPAPER

chrismon
Owner: Hansisches Druck- und Verlagshaus GmbH
Editorial: Emil-von-Behring-Straße 3, Frankfurt Am Main 60439. **T:** 49 69 58098 8306
E: redaktion@chrismon.de
W: http://chrismon.evangelisch.de
Freq: Monthly; **Circ:** 1549134
Language (s): German
NEWSPAPER

Coburger Tageblatt
Owner: Coburger Tageblatt Verlag & Medien GmbH & Co. KG
Editorial: Mediengruppe Oberfranken GmbH & Co. KG, Gutenbergstraße 1, Bamberg 96050.
T: 49 9561 888170
E: stadt.coburg@infranken.de
W: http://www.infranken.de/regional/coburg
Freq: Daily; **Circ:** 13417
Redakteur / Editor: Daniel Baczyk; **Redaktuer / Editor:** Birgit Femppel; **Redakteur / Editor:** Wolfgang Görg; **Redakteur / Editor:** Paul-Hermann Gruner; **Redakteur / Editor:** Klaus Honold; **Redakteur / Editor:** Wolfgang Horn; **Redakteur / editor:** Monika Lowak; **Redakteur / editor:** Meike Mittmeyer; **Redakteur / Editor:** Harald Pleines; **Chefredaktion / Editor in Chief:** Oliver Schmidt; **Redakteur / Editor:** Annette Wannemacher-Saal
Language (s): German
DAILY NEWSPAPER

Cuxhavener Nachrichten
Owner: Cuxhaven-Niederelbe Verlagsges. mbH & Co. KG
Editorial: Cuxhaven-Niederelbe Verlagsgesellschaft mbH & Co. KG, Kaemmererplatz 2, Cuxhaven 27472.
T: 49 4721 5850 **W:** http://www.cn-online.de
Freq: Daily; **Circ:** 11952
Redakteur / Editor: Ralf Drossner; **Redaktuer / Editor:** Jörg Fenski; **Redakteurin / Editor:** Bettina Hoffmann; **Redakteur / Editor:** Helmut Huppmann
Language (s): German
DAILY NEWSPAPER

Dachauer Nachrichten
Owner: Zeitungsverlag Oberbayern GmbH & Co. KG
Editorial: Richard-Wagner-Str. 6, Dachau
E: dah-nachrichten@merkur-online.de
W: http://www.merkur-online.de/lokales/dachau/
Freq: Daily; **Circ:** 14161 IVW
Redakteurin / Editor: Manuela Better;
Redakteur / Editor: Christian Deutschländer;
Redakteur / Editor: Florian Weiß
Language (s): German
DAILY NEWSPAPER

Dahme-Kurier
W: http://www.maerkischeallgemeine.de
Language (s): German
NEWSPAPER

Darmstädter Echo
Owner: Echo Zeitungen GmbH
Editorial: Echo Zeitungen GmbH, Holzhofallee 25-31, Darmstadt 64295. **T:** 49 6151 3870
E: echo-zeitungen@darmstaedter-echo.de
W: http://www.echo-online.de
Freq: Daily; **Circ:** 51461
Redakteur / Editor: Norbert Bartnik;
Redakteur / Editor: Johannes Hitz;
Chefredaktion / Editor in Chief: Michael Horn
Language (s): German
DAILY NEWSPAPER

Deggendorfer Zeitung
Owner: Neue Presse Verlags-GmbH
Editorial: Bahnhofstraße 28, Deggendorf 94469. **T:** 49 991 370 0 911 **E:** info@pnp.de
W: http://www.pnp.de/region_und_lokal/landkreis_deggendorf/deggendorf/?
Freq: Daily; **Circ:** 23176
Redaktion / Editor: Stefan Gabriel;
Redakteurin /Editor: Sabine Heinritz;
Redakteurin / Editor: Katrin Schreiber;
Redakteurin / Editor: Sabine Süß; **Redakteur / Editor:** Wendelin Trs; **Redakteur/Editor:** Ben Weinberger
Language (s): German
DAILY NEWSPAPER

Delmenhorster Kreisblatt
Owner: Verlag Rieck GmbH & Co. KG
Editorial: Verlag RIECK GmbH & Co. KG, Lange Straße 122, Delmenhorst 27749.
T: 49 4221 156666 **E:** verlag@dk-online.de
W: http://www.dk-online.de
Freq: Daily; **Circ:** 18124
Redakteur / Editor: Michael Korn;
Chefredaktion / Editor in Chief: Martin Teschke
Language (s): German
DAILY NEWSPAPER

Der Bayerwald-Bote (Zwiesel)
Owner: Neue Presse Verlags-GmbH
Editorial: Medienstraße 5, München 94036.
T: 49 851 8020 **E:** info@pnp.de
W: http://www.pnp.de
Freq: Daily; **Circ:** 18311
Redakteur / editor: Christina Hackl; **Redaktion / Editor:** Michael Lukaschik; **Redakteur / Editor:** Patrick Potstada; **Redakteur / editor:** Rainer Schlenz; **Redakteur / Editor:** Claudia Winter
Language (s): German
DAILY NEWSPAPER

Der Marktspiegel
Owner: Verlag Der Marktspiegel GmbH
Editorial: Verlag Der Marktspiegel GmbH, Burgschmietstr. 2-4, Nurnberg Nürnberg.
T: 49 911 399 080 **E:** media@marktspiegel.de
W: http://www.marktspiegel.de/
Freq: Daily; **Circ:** 462000
Language (s): German
DAILY NEWSPAPER

Der neue Tag
Owner: Der neue Tag Oberpfälzischer Kurier Druck- und Verlagshaus GmbH
Editorial: Medienhaus Der neue Tag, Weigelstraße 16, Weiden 92637.
T: 49 961 85501
E: redaktion@oberpfalznetz.de
W: http://www.oberpfalznetz.de
Freq: Daily; **Circ:** 82175
Editor: Wilhelm Dötsch; **Redakteur / Editor:** Erich Lobenhofer; **Editor:** Josef Maier
Language (s): German
DAILY NEWSPAPER

Der Patriot / Lippstädter Zeitung
Owner: Zeitungsverlag Der Patriot GmbH

WORLD NEWS MEDIA

Editorial: Hansastraße 2, Lippstadt 59557
E: redaktion@derpatriot.de
W: http://www.derpatriot.de
Chefredaktion / Editor in Chief: Georg Boer; **Redakteur / Editor:** Christiane Schulte-Klausfering
Language (s): German
NEWSPAPER

Der Tagesspiegel
Owner: Verlag Der Tagesspiegel GmbH
Editorial: Askanischer Platz 3, Berlin 10963.
T: 49 30 29021 0
E: redaktion@tagesspiegel.de
W: http://www.tagesspiegel.de/
Freq: Daily; **Circ:** 138192
Chefredaktion / Editor in Chief: Stephan-Andreas Casdorff; **Redakteur / Editor:** Cay Dobberke; **Redakteurin / Editor:** Heike Jahberg; **Redakteur / Editor:** Gerd Seidemann
Language (s): German
DAILY NEWSPAPER

Die Glocke
Owner: E. Holterdorf GmbH & Co KG
Editorial: E. Holterdorf GmbH & Co KG, Engelbert-Holterdorf-Straße 4/6, Oelde 59302.
T: 49 2522 730 **E:** postmaster@die-glocke.de
W: http://www.die-glocke.de
Freq: Daily; **Circ:** 56564
Redakteur / Editor: Dirk Baldus; **Redakteur / Editor:** Sven Behler; **Redakteur / Editor:** Mirco Borgmann; **Redakteur / Editor:** Thorsten Bothe; **Redakteurin / Editor:** Nicolette Bredenhöller; **Redakteur / Editor:** Thorsten Duibmann; **Redakteurin / Editor:** Julia Geppert; **Redakteur / Editor:** Martin Gog; **Redakteur / Editor:** Roland Hahn; **Redakteur / Editor:** Christian Havelt; **Redakteurin / Editor:** Stefanie Helmers; **Redakteurin / Editor:** Rita Kleigrewe; **Redakteur / Editor:** Norbert Lohmann; **Redakteur / Editor:** Alfred Mense; **Redakteur / Editor:** Ralf Ostermann; **Redakteurin / Editor:** Andrea Osthaus; **Redakteurin / Editor:** Julia Scharnowski; **Redakteurin / Editor:** Julia Stempfle; **Redakteurin / Editor:** Conny Timmermann; **Redakteur / Editor:** Alexander Volkmann; **Redakteur / Editor:** Peter Wild
Language (s): German
DAILY NEWSPAPER

Die Glocke Beckum-Ahlen
Owner: E. Holterdorf GmbH & Co KG
Editorial: E. Holterdorf GmbH & Co KG, Engelbert-Holterdorf-Straße 4, Oelde 59302.
T: 49 25 22730 **E:** postmaster@die-glocke.de
W: http://www.die-glocke.de/lokalnachrichten/kreiswarendorf/ahlen
Freq: Daily; **Circ:** 22505
Redakteurin / Editor: Anja Husmann; **Redakteur / Editor:** Peter Kirchhoff; **Redakteur / Editor:** Wolfgang Krogmeier; **Redakteur / Editor:** Jürgen Rollié
Language (s): German
DAILY NEWSPAPER

Die Harke
Owner: J. Hoffmann GmbH & Co. KG
Editorial: J. Hoffmann GmbH und Co. KG, An der Stadtgrenze 2, Nienburg 31582.
T: 49 5021 9661 13 **E:** info@dieharke.de
W: http://www.dieharke.de
Freq: Daily; **Circ:** 19520
Redakteur / Editor: Matthias Brosch; **Redakteurin / Editor:** Annika Büsching; **Redakteur / Editor:** Michael Duensing; **Redakteurin / Editor:** Manon Garms; **Redaktion / Editor:** Manon Garms; **Redakteur / Editor:** Rebecca Göllner; **Redakteur / Editor:** Sabine Grulke; **Redakteurin / Editor:** Edda Hagebölling; **Redakteur / Editor:** Helge Nußbaum; **Redakteur / Editor:** Heidi Reckleben-Meyer; **Redakteur / Editor:** Stefan Schwiersch; **Redakteur / Editor:** Sebastian Stüben; **Chefredaktion / Editor in chief:** Martina Thielking-Rumpeltin; **Chefredaktion / Editor in Chief:** Martina Thielking-Rumpeltin; **Chefredakteurin / Editor in Chief:** Martina Thielking-Rumpeltin; **Chefredakteurin / Editor in Chief:** Martina Thielking-Rumpeltin
Language (s): German
DAILY NEWSPAPER

Die Oberbadische
Owner: Oberbadisches Verlagshaus Georg Jaumann GmbH + Co. KG
Editorial: Oberbadisches Verlagshaus Georg Jaumann GmbH & Co.KG, Am Alten Markt 2, Lörrach 79539. **T:** 49 762 1 4033 0
E: info@verlagshaus-jaumann.de
W: http://www.verlagshaus-jaumann.de
Freq: Daily; **Circ:** 17587
Redakteur / Editor: Michael Gerster; **Redakteur / Editor:** Gabriele Hauger; **Redakteur / Editor:** Bernhard Konrad; **Redakteur / Editor:** Ulf Körbs; **Redakteur / Editor:** Kristoff Meller; **Redakteur / Editor:** Tim Nagengast; **Chefredaktion / Editor in Chief:** Guido Neidinger
Language (s): German
DAILY NEWSPAPER

Die Rheinpfalz
Owner: Rheinpfalz Verlag und Druckerei GmbH & Co. KG
Editorial: Amtsstraße 5 - 11, Ludwigshafen 67059. **T:** 49 621 5902 01
E: redaktion@rheinpfalz.de
W: http://www.rheinpfalz.de
Freq: Daily; **Circ:** 246391
Chefredaktion / Editor in Chief: Michael Garthe; **Redakteurin / Editor:** Judith Schäfer
Language (s): German
DAILY NEWSPAPER

Die Rheinpfalz am Sonntag
Owner: Rheinpfalz Verlag und Druckerei GmbH & Co. KG
Editorial: Amtsstraße 5 - 11, Ludwigshafen 67059. **T:** 49 621 3701 6600
E: redaktion@rheinpfalz.de
W: http://www.rheinpfalz.de
Freq: Weekly; **Circ:** 237120
Language (s): German
NEWSPAPER

Die Tagespost
Owner: Johann Wilhelm Naumann Verlag GmbH
Editorial: Dominikanerplatz 8, Würzburg 97070. **T:** 49 931 308 63 0
E: info@die-tagespost.de
W: http://www.die-tagespost.de
Freq: 3 Times/Week; **Circ:** 11563
Chefredaktion / Editor in Chief: Markus Reder
Language (s): German
NEWSPAPER

DIE WELT
Owner: Axel Springer AG
Editorial: Axel-Springer-Str. 65, Berlin 10969.
T: 49 30 2591 0 **E:** redaktion@welt.de
W: http://www.welt.de
Freq: Daily; **Circ:** 214180
Redakteur / Editor: Stefan Beutelsbacher; **Redakteurin / Editor:** Elke Bodderas; **Redakteur / Editor:** Henryk M. Broder; **Redakteur / Editor:** Oliver Creutz; **Redakteur / Editor:** Jan Dams; **Redakteur / Editor:** Michael Dilger; **Redakteur / Editor:** Nikolaus Doll; **Redakteur / Editor:** Robert Dunker; **Redakteur / Editor:** Daniel Eckert; **Redakteur / Editor:** Michael Fabricius; **Redakteur / Editor:** Jörg Forbricht; **Redakteurin / Editor:** Inga Griese; **Redakteur / Editor:** Rainer Haubrich; **Redakteur / Editor:** Richard Herzinger; **Redakteur / Editor:** Jens Hungermann; **Redakteurin / Editor:** Kirsten Johannsen; **Redakteur / Editor:** Jan Küveler; **Redakteurin / Editor:** Claudia Liebram; **Redakteur / Editor:** Claus-Christian Malzahn; **Redakteurin / Editor:** Inga Michler; **Redakteur / Editor:** Uwe Müller; **Redakteur / Editor:** Jürgen Mundt; **Redakteurin / Editor:** Llna Panitz; **Redakteur / Editor:** Mike Paßmann; **Chefredakteur / Editor in Chief:** Jan-Eric Peters; **Redakteur / Editor:** Stefan A. Runne; **Herausgeber / Publisher:** Thomas Schmid; **Redakteur / Editor:** Benjamin von Stuckrad-Barre; **Redakteurin / Editor:** Heike Vowinkel; **Redakteurin / Editor:** Anna Warnholtz; **Redakteur / Editor:** Ulrich Weinzierl
Language (s): German
DAILY NEWSPAPER

Die Welt Berlin
Owner: Axel Springer SE
Editorial: Axel-Springer-Str. 65, Berlin 10888.
T: 49 30 2591 73704 **E:** welt.berlin@welt.de
W: http://www.welt.de
Freq: Weekly; **Circ:** 23291
Language (s): German
NEWSPAPER

Die Welt Hamburg
Owner: Axel Springer SE
Editorial: Axel-Springer-Platz 1, Hamburg 20350. **T:** 49 40 3 472 43 33
E: hamburg@welt.de
W: http://www.welt.de/regionales/hamburg/
Freq: Daily; **Circ:** 66820
Language (s): German
DAILY NEWSPAPER

DIE ZEIT
Owner: Zeitverlag Gerd Bucerius GmbH & Co. KG
Editorial: Zeitverlag Gerd Bucerius GmbH & Co. KG, Buceriusstraße, Eingang Speersort 1, Hamburg 20095. **T:** 49 40 32800
E: diezeit@zeit.de **W:** http://www.zeit.de
Freq: Weekly; **Circ:** 648908
Chefredaktion / Editor in Chief: Giovanni di Lorenzo; **Redakteur / Editor:** Christoph Drösser; **Redakteur Wissen / Science Editor:** Jan Schweitzer; **Redakteur / Editor:** Peer Teuwsen
Language (s): German
NEWSPAPER

Diepholzer Kreisblatt (Stemwede-Wehdem)
Owner: Kreiszeitung Verlagsgesellschaft mbH & Co. KG
Editorial: Am Drieangel 2, Stemwede 32351.
T: 49 5773 91150
E: onlineredaktion@kreiszeitung.de
W: http://www.kreiszeitung.de/lokales/minden-luebbecke/stemwede-Rahden/
Freq: Daily
Redakteur / Editor: Pascal Faltermann; **Redakteur / Editor:** Harald Hinze; **Redakteur / Editor:** Eberhard Jansen; **Redakteurin / Editor:** Lorena Pabelick; **Redaktion / Editor:** Melanie Russ
Language (s): German
DAILY NEWSPAPER

Dill-Post
Owner: Wetzlardruck GmbH
Editorial: Wetzlardruck GmbH, Elsa-Brandström-Straße 18, Wetzlar 35578
E: redaktion.wnz@mittelhessen.de
W: http://www.mittelhessen.de **Circ:** 20460
Redaktion / Editor: Martin Heller; **Redakteur / Editor:** Benjamin Hofmann; **Redakteur / Editor:** Maike Sophie Wessolowski; **Redakteur / Editor:** Dirk Wingender; **Redakteur / Editor:** Arne Wohlfarth
Language (s): German
NEWSPAPER

Dithmarscher Kurier
Owner: Boyens Zeitungen GmbH & Co. KG
Editorial: Koogstr. 9, Brunsbüttel.
T: 49 4852 5464260
E: boyens@boyens-medien.de
W: http://zeitungen.boyens-medien.de/tageszeitung/dithmarschen.html
Chefredaktion / Editor in Chief: Stefan Schmid
Language (s): German
NEWSPAPER

Dithmarscher Landeszeitung
Owner: Boyens Zeitungen GmbH & Co. KG
Editorial: Boyens Zeitungen GmbH & Co. KG, Wulf-Isebrand-Platz 1-3, Heide 25746.
T: 49 4816 8860
E: redaktion@boyens-medien.de
W: http://zeitungen.boyens-medien.de/
Freq: Daily; **Circ:** 28681
Chefredaktion / Editor in Chief: Gerhard Wagner
Language (s): German
DAILY NEWSPAPER

Donau Zeitung
Owner: Presse-Druck- und Verlags-GmbH
Editorial: Donau Zeitung, Große Allee 47, Dillingen 66763. **T:** 49 9071 7949 10
E: redaktion@donau-zeitung.de
W: http://www.donau-zeitung.de
Freq: Daily; **Circ:** 14506
Chefredaktion: Sascha Borowski; **Chefredaktion:** Sascha Borowski; **Redakteurin / Editor:** Daniela Deeg; **Redakteurin / Editor:** Daniela Fischer; **Redakteurin / Editor:** Ina Kresse; **stellv. Chefredaktion:** Norbert Staub
Language (s): German
DAILY NEWSPAPER

Donau-Anzeiger
Owner: Cl. Attenkofer'sche Buch- und Kunstdruckerei
Editorial: Westlicher Stadtgraben 19a, Deggendorf 94469. **T:** 49 991 370 170
E: kontakt@idowa.de **W:** http://www.idowa.de
Freq: Daily; **Circ:** 91319
Language (s): German
DAILY NEWSPAPER

Donaukurier
Owner: Donaukurier Verlagsges. mbH & Co. KG
Editorial: DONAUKURIER Verlagsgesellschaft mbH & Co. KG, Stauffenbergstraße 2a, Ingolstadt 85051. **T:** 49 841 96 66 251
E: redaktion@donaukurier.de
W: http://www.donaukurier.de
Freq: Daily; **Circ:** 89524
Redakteurin / Editor: Sandra Mönius; **Redakteur / Editor:** Carsten Rost; **Chefredaktion / Editor in Chief:** Gerd Schneider; **Redakteurin / Editor:** Angela Wermter
Language (s): German
DAILY NEWSPAPER

Donauwörther Zeitung
Owner: Presse-Druck- und Verlags-GmbH
Editorial: Donauwörther Zeitung, Heilig-Kreuz-Straße 16, Donauwörth 86609. **T:** 49 821 7770
E: redaktion@augsburger-allgemeine.de
W: http://www.augsburger-allgemeine.de/donauwoerth/?
Freq: Daily; **Circ:** 15111
Redakteur / Editor: Anja Christiansen; **Redaktion / Editor:** Barbara Feneberg; **Redakteur/ Editor:** Gerrit Hencke; **Redakteurin / Editor:** Barbara Maas; **Redakteurin / Editor:** Mira Nagar; **Redakteur / Editor:** Hauke Normann
Language (s): German
DAILY NEWSPAPER

doppio
Owner: Publishers Partners GmbH
Editorial: Publishers Partners GmbH, Weinstraße 19, Edenkoben.
T: 49 6323 9884116
E: info@publisherspartners.de
W: http://doppio-magazin.de
Freq: Monthly; **Circ:** 2500000 Pub Statement
Language (s): German; Full Page Mono: 59800.00; Full Page Colour: 59800.00
Currency: Euro
NEWSPAPER

Dorfener Anzeiger
Owner: Zeitungsverlag Oberbayern GmbH & Co. KG
Editorial: Unterer Markt 10, Dorfen
E: dor-anzeiger@merkur-online.de
W: http://www.merkur-online.de/lokales/erding/dorfen/
Freq: Daily; **Circ:** 16112 IVW
Language (s): German
DAILY NEWSPAPER

Dorstener Zeitung
Owner: Verlag Lensing-Wolff GmbH & Co. KG
Editorial: Westenhellweg 86-88, Dorsten 44137. **T:** 49 231 9059 - 0
W: http://www.dorstenerzeitung.de/
Freq: Daily; **Circ:** 13700 IVW
Language (s): German
DAILY NEWSPAPER

Dreieich-Zeitung
Owner: Günther Medien GmbH
Editorial: Günther Medien GmbH, Philipp-Reis-Straße 7, Dreieich 63110.
T: 49 6106 2 83 90 00
W: http://www.dreieich-zeitung.de/
Freq: Daily; **Circ:** 141025
Redakteur / Editor: Kurt Banse; **Redakteur / Editor:** Thomas Mika; **Redakteur / Editor:** Kai Schmidt
Language (s): German
DAILY NEWSPAPER

Dresdner Morgenpost
Owner: Morgenpost Sachsen GmbH
Editorial: Verlag Dresdner Nachrichten GmbH & Co. KG, Dr.-Külz-Ring 12, Dresden 1067.
T: 49 351 80750 **E:** post@dnn-online.de
W: http://www.dnn-online.de/
Freq: Daily; **Circ:** 83249
Chefredaktion / Editor in Chief: Peter Rzepus
Language (s): German
DAILY NEWSPAPER

Dürener Nachrichten
Owner: Zeitungsverlag Aachen GmbH
Editorial: Aachener Nachrichten Verlagsgesellschaft GmbH & Co. KG, Dresdener Straße 3, Aachen 52068.
T: 49 2415 1010
E: redaktion@zeitungsverlag-aachen.de
W: http://www.aachener-nachrichten.de/lokales/dueren
Freq: Daily; **Circ:** 21646
Redakteur / Editor: Sarah Maria Berners; **Redakteur / Editor:** Gudrun Klinkhammer; **Redaktion / Editor:** Ingo Latotzki
Language (s): German
DAILY NEWSPAPER

Dürener Zeitung
Owner: Zeitungsverlag Aachen GmbH
Editorial: Pletzergasse 5, Düren 52349.
T: 49 2421 2259 100
E: az-lokales-dueren@zeitungsverlag-aachen.de
W: http://www.aachener-zeitung.de/lokales/dueren
Freq: Daily; **Circ:** 21646
Language (s): German
DAILY NEWSPAPER

Ebersberger Zeitung
Owner: Zeitungsverlag Oberbayern GmbH & Co. KG
Editorial: Münchener Zeitungs-Verlag GmbH & Co.KG, Eichthalstraße 2, Ebersberg 85560.
T: 49 8092 8282 0
E: ebe-zeitung@merkur-online.de
W: http://www.merkur-online.de/lokales/

ebersberg/
Freq: Daily; **Circ:** 12178
Chefredakteur / Editor in Chief: Michael Acker; **Redaktion / Editor:** Christine Gerneth Gerneth; **Redakteur / Editor:** Eberhard Rienth; **Redakteur / Editor:** Armin Rösl
Language (s): German
DAILY NEWSPAPER

Eichstätter Kurier
Owner: Donaukurier Verlagsges. mbH & Co. KG
Editorial: DONAUKURIER Verlagsgesellschaft mbH & Co. KG, Stauffenbergstraße 2a, Ingolstadt 85051. **T:** 49 841 96660
E: redaktion@donaukurier.de
W: http://www.donaukurier.de/lokales/eichstaett/
Freq: Daily; **Circ:** 11576
Redakteur / Editor: Julia Fröhlich; **Redaktuer / Editor:** Johannes Greiner; **Redaktion / Editor:** Hermann Redl; **Redakteur / Editor:** Horst Richter; **Redakteur / Editor:** Carsten Rost; **Redakteur / Editor:** Timo Schoch; **Redakteur / Editor:** Jesko Schulze-Reimpell; **Redakteur / Editor:** Wolfgang Weber; **Redakteur / Editor:** Angela Wermter
Language (s): German
DAILY NEWSPAPER

Eifeler Nachrichten
Owner: Zeitungsverlag Aachen GmbH
Editorial: Aachener Nachrichten, Dresdener Straße 3, Aachen 52068. **T:** 49 2415 1010
E: redaktion@zeitungsverlag-aachen.de
W: http://www.aachener-nachrichten.de/lokales/eifel
Freq: Daily; **Circ:** 43249
Redakteur / Editor: René Benden; **Redakteur / Editor:** Jutta Geese; **Redaktion / Editor:** Peter Stollenwerk
Language (s): German
DAILY NEWSPAPER

Eifeler Zeitung
Owner: Zeitungsverlag Aachen GmbH
Editorial: Aachener Nachrichten, Dresdener Straße 3, Aachen 52068. **T:** 49 2415 1010
E: redaktion@zeitungsverlag-aachen.de
W: http://www.aachener-zeitung.de/lokales/eifel
Freq: Daily; **Circ:** 43249
Redaktion / Editor: Peter Stollenwerk
Language (s): German
DAILY NEWSPAPER

Elbe-Jeetzel-Zeitung
Owner: Druck- und Verlagsges. Köhring GmbH & Co. KG
Editorial: Druck- und Verlagsgesellschaft Köhring GmbH & Co. KG, Wallstraße 22-24, Lüchow 29439. **T:** 49 5841 1270
E: redaktion@ejz.de **W:** http://www.ejz.de
Freq: Daily; **Circ:** 12425
Redakteur / Editor: Jens Feuerriegel; **Chefredaktion / Editor in Chief:** Hans-Hermann Müller
Language (s): German
DAILY NEWSPAPER

Elmshorner Nachrichten
Owner: sh:z Schleswig-Holsteinischer Zeitungsverlag GmbH & Co. KG
Editorial: Schulstraße 62-66, Elmshorn 25335. **T:** 49 4121 297 1800
E: redaktion.elmshorn@shz.de
W: http://www.shz.de/lokales/elmshorner-nachrichten/
Freq: Daily; **Circ:** 12331
Redakteurin / Editor: Anja Christiansen; **Chefredakteur / Editor in chief:** Joachim Dreykluft; **Redekteur / Editor:** Gerrit Hencke; **Redakteurin / Editor:** Barbara Maas; **Redakteur / Editor:** Hauke Mormann; **Redakteurin / Editor:** Mira Nagar; **Redaktion / Editor:** Jan Schönstedt
Language (s): German
DAILY NEWSPAPER

Emder Zeitung
Owner: Emder Zeitung GmbH & Co. KG
Editorial: Emder Zeitung GmbH & Co. KG, Ringstraße 17 a, Emden 26721.
T: 49 4921 89 00 402
E: redaktion@emderzeitung.de
W: http://www.emderzeitung.de
Freq: Daily; **Circ:** 11125
Chefredakteur / Editor in Chief: Klaus Fackert
Language (s): German
DAILY NEWSPAPER

Erdinger/Dorfener Anzeiger
Owner: Zeitungsverlag Oberbayern GmbH & Co. KG
Editorial: Münchener Zeitungs-Verlag GmbH & Co.KG, Paul-Heyse-Str. 2-4, München 80336.
T: 49 089 5306 0 **E:** info@merkur-online.de
W: http://www.merkur-online.de/lokales/erding/
Freq: Daily; **Circ:** 16506 IVW
Language (s): German
DAILY NEWSPAPER

Erlanger Nachrichten
Owner: Verlag Nürnberger Presse Druckhaus Nürnberg GmbH & Co.
Editorial: Verlag Nürnberger Presse Druckhaus Nürnberg GmbH & Co. KG, Marienstraße 9/11, Nurnberg 90402.
T: 49 911 2160 **E:** info@pressenetz.de
W: http://www.nordbayern.de/region/erlangen
Freq: Daily; **Circ:** 34477 IVW
Language (s): German
DAILY NEWSPAPER

Eschweiler Nachrichten
Owner: Zeitungsverlag Aachen GmbH
Editorial: Aachener Nachrichten, Dresdener Straße 3, Aachen 52068. **T:** 49 2415 1010
E: redaktion@zeitungsverlag-aachen.de
W: http://www.aachener-zeitung.de/lokales/eschweiler
Freq: Daily; **Circ:** 28148
Redakteur / Editor: Friedhelm Ebbecke-Bückendorf; **Redaktion / Editor:** Rudolf Müller; **Redakteur / Editor:** Patrick Nowick; **Redakteur / Editor:** Tobias Röber
Language (s): German
DAILY NEWSPAPER

Eschweiler Zeitung
Owner: Zeitungsverlag Aachen GmbH
Editorial: Postfach 500110, Dresdener Straße 3, Aachen 52085. **T:** 49 241 5101-0
E: redaktion@zeitungsverlag-aachen.de
W: http://www.aachener-zeitung.de/lokales/eschweiler
Freq: Daily
Redaktion / Editor: Rudolf Müller
Language (s): German
DAILY NEWSPAPER

Eßlinger Zeitung
Owner: Bechtle, Graph. Betriebe und Verlagsges. (Bechtle Verlag und Eßlinger Zeitung) GmbH & Co. KG
Editorial: Eßlinger Zeitung, Marktplatz 6, Esslingen 73728. **T:** 49 711 93100
E: redaktion@ez-online.de
W: http://www.esslinger-zeitung.de
Freq: Daily; **Circ:** 43179
Chefredaktion / Editor in Chief: Markus Bleistein; **Redakteur / Editor:** Stephanie Danner; **Redakteur / Editor:** Detlef Holland; **Redakteur / Editor:** Hannes Kern; **Redakteur / Editor:** Katja Köhler; **Redakteur / Editor:** Klaus Laas; **Chefredakteur / Editor in Chief:** Alexander Marinos; **Redakteur / Editor:** Michael Paproth
Language (s): German
DAILY NEWSPAPER

Express
Owner: DuMont Net GmbH & Co. KG
Editorial: Neven DuMont Haus, Amsterdamer Straße 192, Koln 50735. **T:** 49 221 2240
E: post@express.de **W:** http://www.express.de
Freq: Daily; **Circ:** 155171
Redakteur / Editor: Ayhan Demirci; **Redakteur / editor:** Christian Knop; **Redakteur / Editor:** Christian Lorenz; **Redakteur / Editor:** Marcel Schwamborn; **Redakteur / editor:** Jan Wördenweber
Language (s): German
DAILY NEWSPAPER

Express Bonn
Owner: M. DuMont Schauberg Expedition der Kölnischen Zeitung GmbH & Co. KG
Editorial: Berliner Freiheit 36, Bonn 53111.
T: 49 228 729 06-3 **E:** bonn@express.de
W: http://www.express.de
Freq: Daily; **Circ:** 18226
Language (s): German
DAILY NEWSPAPER

EXPRESS Düsseldorf
Owner: DuMont Net GmbH & Co. KG
Editorial: Königsallee 27, Dusseldorf 40212.
T: 49 211 13930 **E:** duesseldorf@express.de
W: http://www.express.de/duesseldorf
Freq: Daily; **Circ:** 46793
Language (s): German
DAILY NEWSPAPER

Fellbach & Rems-Murr-Kreis
Owner: Stuttgarter Nachrichten Verlagsgesellschaft mbH
Editorial: Cannstatter Straße 94, Fellbach.
T: 49 711 9579 670
E: redaktion@fellbacher-zeitung.zgs.de
W: http://www.fellbacher-zeitung.de
Freq: Daily
Language (s): German
DAILY NEWSPAPER

Flensburger Tageblatt
Owner: sh:z Schleswig-Holsteinischer Zeitungsverlag GmbH & Co. KG
Editorial: sh:z Schleswig-Holsteinischer Zeitungsverlag GmbH & Co. KG, Fördestraße 20, Flensburg 24944
E: redaktion.flensburg@shz.de
W: http://www.shz.de/lokales/flensburger-tageblatt/
Freq: Daily; **Circ:** 33479
Redakteur / Editor: Anabela Brandao; **Redakteurin / Editor:** Anja Christiansen; **Chefredakteur / Editor in chief:** Joachim Dreykluft; **Redakteurin / Editor:** Gerrit Hencke; **Redakteurin / Editor:** Barbara Maas; **Chefredaktion / Editor in Chief:** Helge Matthiesen; **Redakteur / Editor:** Hauke Mormann; **Redakteurin / Editor:** Mira Nagar
Language (s): German
DAILY NEWSPAPER

Frankenpost
Owner: Frankenpost Verlag GmbH
Editorial: Frankenpost Verlag GmbH, Poststraße 9/11, Hof 95028. **T:** 49 9281 816 0
E: verlag@frankenpost.de
W: http://www.frankenpost.de
Freq: Daily; **Circ:** 60048
Redakteur / Editor: Sandra Lessner; **Chefredaktion / Editor in Chief:** Johann Pirthauer
Language (s): German
DAILY NEWSPAPER

Frankenpost / Münchberg-Helmbrechtser Tageszeitung
W: http://www.frankenpost.de
Language (s): German
NEWSPAPER

Frankenpost Naila
Owner: Frankenpost Verlag GmbH
Editorial: Frankenpost Verlag GmbH, Poststraße 9/11, Hof 95028. **T:** 49 9282 82280
E: verlag@frankenpost.de
W: http://www.frankenpost.de/lokal/naila/
Freq: Daily
Chefredakteur / Editor in Chief: Johann Pirthauer
DAILY NEWSPAPER

Frankfurter Allgemeine
Owner: Frankfurter Allgemeine Zeitung GmbH
Editorial: Frankfurter Allgemeine Zeitung GmbH, Hellerhofstr. 2, Frankfurt 60327.
T: 49 69 75910 **E:** redaktion@faz.de
W: http://www.faz.net
Freq: Daily; **Circ:** 396159 IVW
Language (s): German
DAILY NEWSPAPER

Frankfurter Allgemeine Sonntagszeitung
Owner: Frankfurter Allgemeine Zeitung GmbH
Editorial: Frankfurter Allgemeine Zeitung, Hellerhofstraße 2-4, Frankfurt 60327.
T: 49 69 7591 0 **E:** sonntagszeitung@faz.de
W: http://www.faz.net
Freq: Weekly; **Circ:** 436959
Language (s): German
NEWSPAPER

Frankfurter Allgemeine Zeitung
Owner: Frankfurter Allgemeine Zeitung GmbH
Editorial: Frankfurter Allgemeine Zeitung, Hellerhofstraße 2-4, Frankfurt 60327.
T: 49 69 7591 0 **E:** redaktion@faz.de
W: http://www.faz.net
Freq: Daily; **Circ:** 373018
Redakteur / Editor: Frank-Holger Appel; **Herausgeber / Publisher:** Werner D'Inka; **Chefredakteurin / Editor in Chief:** Elena Geus; **Redakteurin / Editor:** Heike Göbel; **Redakteur / Editor:** Martin Gropp; **Redakteur / Editor:** Anno Hecker; **Redakteur/Editor:** Georg Paul Hefty; **Redakteur / Editor:** Thomas Heumann; **Redakteurin / Editor:** Anja Holzing; **Redakteurin / Editor:** Christina Hucklenbroich; **Redakteurin / Editor:** Katrin Hummel; **Redakteur / Editor:** Johannes Janssen; **Herausgeber / Publisher:** Berthold Kohler; **Redakteur / Editor:** Philipp Krohn; **Redakteur / Editor:** Freddy Langer; **Redakteurin / Editor:** Verena Lueken; **Redakteur / Editor:** Andreas Mihm; **Chefredakteur / Editor in Chief:** Mathias Müller von Blumencron; **Redakteur / Editor:** Edo Reents; **Redakteurin / Editor:** Anke Schipp; **Redakteurin / Editor:** Monika Schramm; **Redakteur / Editor:** Stefan Schulz; **Herausgeber / Publisher:** Holger Steltzner; **Redakteur / Editor:** Jasper von Altenbockum; **Redakteurin/Editor:** Felicitas von Lovenberg; **Redakteur / Editor:** Winand von Petersdorff; **Redakteur / Editor:** Richard Wagner; **Redakteur / Editor:** Axel Wermelskirchen; **Redakteurin / Editor:** Jennifer Wiebking
Language (s): German
DAILY NEWSPAPER

Frankfurter Neue Presse
Owner: Frankfurter Societäts-Medien GmbH
Editorial: Frankfurter Societäts-Medien GmbH, Frankenallee 71–81, Frankfurt Am Main 60327.
T: 49 6975 010 **E:** redaktion@fnp.de
W: http://www.fnp.de
Freq: Daily; **Circ:** 69732
Redakteur / Editor: Thomas Baumgartner; **Redakteur / Editor:** Matthias Bittner; **Redakteur / Editor:** Michael Forst; **Chefredaktion / Editor in Chief:** Rainer M. Gefeller; **Redakteurin / Editor:** Bianca Leinweber
Language (s): German
DAILY NEWSPAPER

Frankfurter Rundschau
Owner: Frankfurter Rundschau GmbH
Editorial: Frankfurter Rundschau GmbH, Frankenallee 71-81, Frankfurt Am Main 60327.
T: 49 6921 991 **E:** online@fr-online.de
W: http://www.fr-online.de
Freq: Daily; **Circ:** 87136
Redakteur / Editor: Jürgen Ahäuser; **Redakteur / Editor:** Damir Fras; **Redakteurin / Editor:** Frauke Janßen; **Redakteur / Editor:** Miriam Keilbach; **Redakteur / Editor:** Thomas Kilchenstein; **Redakteur / Editor:** Daniel Kortschak; **Redakteur / Editor:** Jan Christian Müller; **Redakteur / Editor:** Jonas Rest; **Chefredaktion / Editor in Chief:** Rouven Schellenberger; **Redakteur / Editor:** Pitt von Bebenburg
Language (s): German
DAILY NEWSPAPER

Fränkische Landeszeitung - Ansbacher Tagblatt
Owner: Fränkische Landeszeitung GmbH
Editorial: Nürnberger Straße 9-17, Ansbach 91522. **T:** 49 9 81 95 00-0
W: http://www.flz.de
Redakteurin / Editor: Nicole Gunkel; **Redakteur / Editor:** Georg Lober; **Redakteur / Editor:** Matthias Metzner; **Chefredaktion / Editor in Chief:** Peter M. Szymanowski
Language (s): German
NEWSPAPER

Fränkische Nachrichten (Wertheim)
W: http://www.fnweb.de
Language (s): German
NEWSPAPER

Fränkische Nachrichten Buchen/ Walldürn
Owner: Fränkische Nachrichten
Editorial: Fränkische Nachrichten Verlags GmbH, Marktstr. 16, Buchen 74722.
T: 49 6281 4090
W: http://www.fnweb.de/region/neckar-odenwald/buchen
Freq: Daily
Redaktuer / Editor: Fabian Greulich; **Redakteur / Editor:** Maximilian Münster; **Redakteur / Editor:** Ralf Scherer; **Chefredaktion / Editor in Chief:** Dieter Schwab
DAILY NEWSPAPER

Fränkische Nachrichten, Bad Mergentheim
Owner: Fränkische Nachrichten
Editorial: Fränkische Nachrichten Verlags-GmbH, Kapuzinerstraße 4, Bad Mergentheim 97980. **T:** 49 7931 5470
E: fn.info@fraenkische-nachrichten.de
W: http://www.fnweb.de/region/main-tauber/bad-mergentheim
Freq: Daily
Language (s): German
DAILY NEWSPAPER

Fränkischer Tag
Owner: Mediengruppe Oberfranken-Mantelredaktion GmbH & Co. KG
Editorial: Mediengruppe Oberfranken GmbH & Co. KG, Gutenbergstraße 1, Bamberg 96050.
T: 49 951 188209 **E:** redaktion@infranken.de
W: http://www.infranken.de
Freq: Daily; **Circ:** 40955
Chefredaktion / Editor in Chief: Frank Förtsch; **Redakteur / Editor:** Benjamin Kemmer
Language (s): German
DAILY NEWSPAPER

Fränkischer Tag Bamberg
Owner: Fränkischer Tag GmbH & Co. KG
Editorial: Mediengruppe Oberfranken GmbH & Co. KG, Gutenbergstraße 1, Bamberg 96050.
T: 49 951 13296 100
E: redaktion.bamberg@infranken.de
W: http://www.infranken.de/regional/bamberg/
Freq: Daily
Language (s): German
DAILY NEWSPAPER

Fränkischer Tag Forchheim
Owner: Fränkischer Tag GmbH & Co. KG
Editorial: Mediengruppe Oberfranken GmbH & Co. KG, Gutenbergstraße 1, Bamberg 96050.
T: 49 9191 708847
E: redaktion.forchheim@infranken.de
W: http://www.infranken.de/regional/forchheim/
Freq: Daily; **Circ:** 11248
Language (s): German
DAILY NEWSPAPER

Freiberger Zeitung
Owner: Chemnitzer Verlag und Druck GmbH & Co. KG
Editorial: Kirchgäßchen 1, Freiberg 9599.
T: 49 3731 3760 **W:** http://www.freiepresse.de
Freq: Daily; **Circ:** 18240
Redakteurin / Editor: Josephine Buchholz; **Redakteurin / Editor:** Gabriele Fleischer; **Redakteurin / Editor:** Ute George; **Redakteur / Editor:** Peter Hertel; **Redakteurin / Editor:** Christine Hirschfelder; **Redakteurin / Editor:** Heike Hubricht; **Redakteur / Editor:** Steffen Jankowski; **Redakteurin / Editor:** Katrin Kablau; **Redakteur / Editor:** Frank Klinger; **Redakteur / Editor:** Uwe Lemke; **Redakteurin / Editor:** Franziska Pester; **Redakteur / Editor:** Johannes Pöhlandt; **Redakteur / Editor:** Thomas Reibetanz; **Redakteur / Editor:** Astrid Ring; **Redakteurin / Editor:** Eveline Rössler; **Redakteurin / Editor:** Rolf Rudolph; **Redakteur / Editor:** Andy Scharf; **Redakteur / Editor:** Jochen Walther
Language (s): German
DAILY NEWSPAPER

Freie Presse
Owner: Chemnitzer Verlag und Druck GmbH & Co. KG
Editorial: Chemnitzer Verlag und Druck GmbH & Co. KG, Brückenstraße 15, Chemnitz 9111.
T: 49 371 6560
E: die.tageszeitung@freiepresse.de
W: http://www.freiepresse.de
Freq: Daily; **Circ:** 268664
Redakteur / Editor: Dietmar Bartel; **Chefredakteur / Editor in Chief:** Torsten Kleditzsch; **Redakteurin / Editor:** Katharina Leuoth; **Redakteurin / Editor:** Martina Martin; **Redakteurin / Editor:** Ramona Nagel; **Redakteur / editor:** Jan Öchsner; **Redakteur / Editor:** Alessandro Peduto; **Redakteur / Editor:** Rudolf Trinks; **Redakteur / Editor:** Christoph Ulrich
Language (s): German
DAILY NEWSPAPER

Freie Presse Annaberg
Owner: Chemnitzer Verlag und Druck
Editorial: Annaberger Zeitung, Markt 8, Annaberg-Buchholz 9456. **T:** 49 3733 1410
E: Red.Annaberg@freiepresse.de
W: http://www.freiepresse.de/LOKALES/ERZGEBIRGE/ANNABERG/
Freq: Daily; **Circ:** 14227
Language (s): German
DAILY NEWSPAPER

Freie Presse Aue
Owner: Freie Presse Aue
Editorial: Auer Zeitung, Schneeberger Str. 17, Aue 8280. **T:** 49 3771 5940
E: Red.Aue@freiepresse.de
W: http://www.freiepresse.de/LOKALES/ERZGEBIRGE/AUE/
Freq: Daily; **Circ:** 16387
Chefredakteur / Editor in Chief: Torsten Kleditzsch
Language (s): German
DAILY NEWSPAPER

Freie Presse Auerbach
Owner: Chemnitzer Verlag und Druck GmbH & Co. KG
Editorial: Auerbacher Zeitung, Nicolaistraße 3, Auerbach 8209. **T:** 49 3744 82760
E: Red.Auerbach@freiepresse.de
W: http://www.freiepresse.de/LOKALES/VOGTLAND/AUERBACH/
Freq: Daily; **Circ:** 11793
Language (s): German
DAILY NEWSPAPER

Freie Presse Freiberg
Owner: Freie Presse Freiberg
Editorial: Freiberger Zeitung, Kirchgäßchen 1, Freiberg 9599. **T:** 49 3732 22960
E: Red.Freiberg@freiepresse.de
W: http://www.freiepresse.de/LOKALES/MITTELSACHSEN/FREIBERG/
Freq: Daily; **Circ:** 18236
Language (s): German
DAILY NEWSPAPER

Freie Presse Oberes Vogtland
Owner: Chemnitzer Verlag und Druck
Editorial: Chemnitzer Verlag und Druck GmbH & Co. KG, Brückenstraße 15, Chemnitz 9111.
T: 49 371 656-0
Freq: Daily; **Circ:** 11695
DAILY NEWSPAPER

Freie Presse Plauen
Owner: Chemnitzer Verlag und Druck GmbH
Editorial: Plauener Zeitung, Postplatz 7, Plauen 8523. **T:** 49 3741 4080
E: Red.Plauen@freiepresse.de
W: http://www.freiepresse.de/LOKALES/VOGTLAND/PLAUEN/
Freq: Daily; **Circ:** 16961
Language (s): German
DAILY NEWSPAPER

Freie Presse Stollberg
Owner: Chemnitzer Verlag und Druck GmbH
Editorial: Stollberger Zeitung, Herrenstraße 19, Stollberg 9366. **T:** 49 3729 669900
E: Red.Stollberg@freiepresse.de
W: http://www.freiepresse.de/LOKALES/ERZGEBIRGE/STOLLBERG/
Freq: Daily; **Circ:** 12780
Language (s): German
DAILY NEWSPAPER

Freie Presse Zwickau
Owner: Freie Presse Zwickau
Editorial: Zwickauer Zeitung, Hauptstraße 13, Zwickau 8056. **T:** 49 375 5490
E: Red.Zwickau@freiepresse.de
W: http://www.freiepresse.de/LOKALES/ZWICKAU/ZWICKAU/
Freq: Daily; **Circ:** 27044
Language (s): German
DAILY NEWSPAPER

Freies Wort
Owner: Suhler Verlagsges. mbH & Co. KG
Editorial: Suhler Verlagsgesellschaft mbH & Co. KG, Schützenstraße 2, Suhl 98527.
T: 49 3681 8510 **E:** redaktion@freies-wort.de
W: http://www.insuedthueringen.de
Freq: Daily; **Circ:** 11975
Redakteur / Editor: Thomas Heigl; **Chefredaktion / Editor in Chief:** Walter Hörmann; **Redakteur / Editor:** Manuel Schwarz
Language (s): German
DAILY NEWSPAPER

Freisinger Tagblatt
Owner: Zeitungsverlag Oberbayern GmbH & Co. KG
Editorial: Münchner Straße 7, Freising 85354.
T: 49 8161 186 0 **E:** info@merkur-online.de
W: http://www.merkur-online.de/lokales/freising/
Freq: Daily; **Circ:** 13870
Redakteur / Editor: Manuela Better; **Redakteur / Editor:** Christian Deutschländer; **Redaktion / Editor:** Helmut Hobmaier; **Redakteur / Editor:** Florian Weiß
Language (s): German
DAILY NEWSPAPER

Friedberger Allgemeine
Owner: Presse-Druck- und Verlags-GmbH
Editorial: Augsburger Allgemeine Zeitung, Curt-Frenzel-Str. 2, Augsburg. **T:** 49 821 7770
E: redaktion@augsburger-allgemeine.de
W: http://www.augsburger-allgemeine.de/friedberg
Freq: Daily; **Circ:** 12973
Chefredaktion: Sascha Borowski; **Redakteur / Editor:** Daniela Deeg; **Redakteur / Editor:** Stefan Drescher; **Redakeur / Editor:** Daniela Fischer; **Redaktion / Editor:** Thomas Goßner; **Reakteur / Editor:** Ina Kreise; **stellv. Chefredaktion:** Norbert Staub
Language (s): German
DAILY NEWSPAPER

Fritzlar-Homberger Allgemeine
Owner: Dierichs GmbH & Co. KG
Editorial: Frankfurter Str. 168, Kassel 34121.
T: 49 561 20300 **E:** info@hna.de
W: http://www.hna.de
Freq: Daily; **Circ:** 14780 IVW
Language (s): German
DAILY NEWSPAPER

Fuldaer Zeitung
Owner: Verlag Parzeller GmbH & Co. KG
Editorial: Verlag Parzeller GmbH & Co. KG, Frankfurter Str. 8, Fulda 36043.
T: 49 661 2800 **E:** redaktion@fuldaerzeitung.de
W: http://www.fuldaerzeitung.de
Freq: Daily; **Circ:** 33364
Redakteur / Editor: Christian Appel; **Redakteurin / Editor:** Anne Baun; **Redakteur / Editor:** Sascha Behnsen; **Redakteur / Editor:** Klaus Nico Bensing; **Redakteurin / Editor:** Helena Brinkmann; **Redakteur / Editor:** Volker Feuerstein; **Redakteur / Editor:** Björn Gauges; **Redakteur / Editor:** Ann-Katrin Göbel; **Redakteurin / Editor:** Viktoria Goldbach; **Redakteur / Editor:** Christian Halling; **Redakteurin / Editor:** Anne Hämel; **Redakteurin / Editor:** Christiane Hartung; **Redakteur / Editor:** Johannes Heller; **Redakteur / Editor:** Laurenz Hiob; **Redakteur / Editor:** Rainer Ickler; **Redakteur / Editor:** Sebastian Kircher; **Redakteurin / Editor:** Angelika Kleemann; **Redakteurin / Editor:** Jacqueline Kleinhans; **Redakteurin / Editor:** Sabine Kohl; **Redakteur / Editor:** Anne Kramer; **Redakteurin / Editor:** Lisa Krause; **Redakteur / Editor:** Walter Kreuzer; **Redakteurin / Editor:** Anna-Katharina Leidheiser; **Redakteur / Editor:** Daniela Petersen; **Redakteurin / Editor:** Lena Quandt; **Redakteurin / Editor:** Leoni Rehert; **Redakteurin / Editor:** Leoni Rehnert; **Redakteurin / Editor:** Helena Sauer; **Redakteurin / Editor:** Helene Sauer; **Redakteur / Editor:** Manfred Schermer; **Redakteur / Editor:** Ulrich Schmid; **Redakteur / Editor:** Stefan Schoder; **Redakteurin / Editor:** Samantha Schwab; **Redakteurin / Editor:** Sophia Steube; **Chefredaktion / Editor in Chief:** Michael Tillmann; **Redakteur / Editor:** Christof Völliger; **Redakteur / Editor:** Christof Völlinger; **Redakteur / Editor:** Harry Wagner; **Redakteur / Editor:** Christian Weber; **Redakteur / Editor:** Patrick Wichmann; **Redakteurin / Editor:** Hanna Wiehe; **Redakteur / Editor:** Norman Zellmer; **Redakteurin / Editor:** Eike Zenner
Language (s): German
DAILY NEWSPAPER

Fürstenfeldbrucker Tagblatt
Owner: Zeitungsverlag Oberbayern GmbH & Co. KG
Editorial: Münchener Zeitungs-Verlag GmbH & Co.KG, Paul-Heyse-Str. 2-4, München 80336.
T: 49 089 53060 **E:** info@merkur-online.de
W: http://www.merkur-online.de/lokales/fuerstenfeldbruck/
Freq: Daily; **Circ:** 17199
Redakteurin / Editor: Manuela Better; **Redakteur / Editor:** Christian Deutschländer; **Redaktion / Editor:** Sabine Kuhn; **Redakteur / Editor:** Florian Weiß
Language (s): German
DAILY NEWSPAPER

Fürther Nachrichten
Owner: Verlag Nürnberger Presse Druckhaus Nürnberg GmbH & Co. KG
Editorial: Moststraße 33, Furth 90762.
T: 49 911 2160 **E:** fn-redaktion@pressenetz.de
W: http://www.nordbayern.de/region/fuerth
Freq: Daily; **Circ:** 31609
Redaktion / Editor: Wolfgang Händel
Language (s): German
DAILY NEWSPAPER

Garmisch-Partenkirchner Tagblatt
Owner: Zeitungsverlag Oberbayern GmbH & Co. KG
Editorial: Münchener Zeitungs-Verlag GmbH & Co.KG, Alpspitzstraße 5a, Garmisch-Partenkirchen 82467. **T:** 49 8821 75717
E: info@merkur-online.de
W: http://www.merkur-online.de/lokales/garmisch-partenkirchen/
Freq: Daily; **Circ:** 15724
Redakteurin / Editor: Manuela Better; **Redakteur / Editor:** Christian Deutschländer; **Redaktion / Editor:** Matthias Holzapfel; **Redakteur / Editor:** Florian Weiß
Language (s): German
DAILY NEWSPAPER

Gäubote
Owner: Verlag Theodor Körner KG
Editorial: Theodor Körner KG, Druckerei und Verlag, Horber Straße 42, Herrenberg 71083.
T: 49 7032 95250 **E:** redaktion@gaeubote.de
W: http://www.gaeubote.de
Freq: Daily; **Circ:** 12228
Redakteur / Editor: Konrad Buck; **Redakteur / Editor:** Dietmar Denner; **Redakteur / Editor:** Simone Denu; **Redakteur / Editor:** Esther Elbers; **Redaktion / Editor:** Harald Marquardt; **Redakteur / editor:** Robert Stadthagen
Language (s): German
DAILY NEWSPAPER

Geislinger Zeitung
Owner: Geislinger Zeitung Verlagsges. mbH & Co. KG
Editorial: GEISLINGER ZEITUNG Verlagsgesellschaft mbH & Co KG, Hauptstraße 38, Geislingen 73312.
T: 49 7331 20242
E: geislinger-zeitung.redaktion@swp.de
W: http://www.swp.de/geislingen/
Freq: Daily; **Circ:** 13123
Redkateur / Editor: Manfred Bomm; **Chefredaktion / Editor in Chief:** Roderich Schmauz
Language (s): German
DAILY NEWSPAPER

Gescherer Zeitung
Owner: Verlag J. Fleißig GmbH & Co.
Editorial: Verlag J. Fleißig GmbH & Co., Rosenstrasse 2, Coesfeld 48653.
T: 49 2541 9210 **E:** gescher@azonline.de
W: http://www.azonline.de/
Freq: Daily
Redakteur / Editor: Jürgen Schroer
Language (s): German
DAILY NEWSPAPER

Geseker Zeitung
Owner: Zeitungsverlag Der Patriot GmbH
Editorial: Bäckstraße 10a, Geseke 59590.
T: 49 2942 973120
W: http://www.derpatriot.de/Lokales/Geseke
Redakteurin / Editor: Ulrike Dietz; **Redaktion / Editor:** Dominik Friedrich
Language (s): German
NEWSPAPER

Gießener Allgemeine
Owner: Mittelhessische Druck- und Verlagsges. mbH
Editorial: Mittelhessische Druck- und Verlagshaus GmbH & Co.KG, Marburger Straße 20, Giessen 35390. **T:** 49 6 41 3003 0
E: redaktion@giessener-allgemeine.de
W: http://www.giessener-allgemeine.de
Freq: Daily; **Circ:** 59971
Chefredaktion / Editor in Chief: Christian Rempel
Language (s): German
DAILY NEWSPAPER

Gießener Anzeiger
Owner: Gießener Anzeiger Verlags GmbH & Co. KG
Editorial: Gießener Anzeiger Verlags GmbH & Co. KG, Am Urnenfeld 12, Giessen 35396.
T: 49 641 95043405
E: online@giessener-anzeiger.de
W: http://www.giessener-anzeiger.de
Freq: Daily; **Circ:** 30578
Chefredakteur / Editor in Chief: Wolfgang Maaß; **Redakteurin / Editor:** Nina Schaub
Language (s): German
DAILY NEWSPAPER

Die Glocke, Beckumer Zeitung
W: http://www.die-glocke.de
Language (s): German
NEWSPAPER

Gmünder Tagespost
Owner: SDZ Druck und Medien GmbH & Co. KG
Editorial: Gmünder Tagespost - Verlagsanstalt und Buchdruckerei Heinrich Haar SDZ Druck und Medien GmbH & CO. KG, Vordere Schmiedgasse 18, Schwäbisch Gmünd 73525.
T: 49 7171 60010
E: redaktion@gmuender-tagespost.de
W: http://www.gmuender-tagespost.de
Freq: Daily; **Circ:** 11282
Redakteur / Editor: Wolfgang Fischer; **Redakteurin / Editor:** Nicole Kiemel; **Redakteur / Editor:** Nicole Kiemel; **Chefredaktion / Editor in Chief:** Michael Länge; **Redakteurin / Editor:** Dagmar Oltersdorf; **Redakteur / Editor:** Dagmar Oltersdorf; **Redakteur / Editor:** Jürgen Steck; **Redakteur / Editor:** Julia Trinkle
Language (s): German
DAILY NEWSPAPER

Goslarsche Zeitung
Owner: Goslarsche Zeitung Karl Krause GmbH & Co. KG
Editorial: Goslarsche Zeitung Karl Krause GmbH & Co. KG Pressehaus, Bäckerstraße 31-35, Goslar 38640. **T:** 49 0532 13330
E: vertrieb@goslarsche-zeitung.de
W: http://www.goslarsche.de
Freq: Daily; **Circ:** 25765
Redakteur / Editor: Jörg Ciszewski; **Chefredakteur / Editor in Chief:** Andreas Rietschel
Language (s): German
DAILY NEWSPAPER

Göttinger Tageblatt
Owner: Göttinger Tageblatt GmbH & Co. KG
Editorial: Göttinger Tageblatt GmbH & Co. KG, Dransfelder Straße 1, Göttingen 37079.
T: 49 551 9011
E: redaktion@goettinger-tageblatt.de
W: http://www.goettinger-tageblatt.de
Freq: Daily; **Circ:** 30870
Chefredakteurin / Editor in Chief: Ilse Stein
Language (s): German
DAILY NEWSPAPER

Grafenauer Anzeiger
Owner: Neue Presse Verlags-GmbH

Editorial: Neue Presse Multimedia GmbH, Medienstraße 5, Passau 94036.
T: 49 851 8020 **E:** info@pnp.de
W: http://www.pnp.de/region_und_lokal/stadt_und_landkreis_passau/
Freq: Daily; **Circ:** 14567
Redakteur / Editor: Ursula Langesee;
Redaktion / Editor: Andreas Nigl
Language (s): German
DAILY NEWSPAPER

Grafschafter Nachrichten
Owner: Grafschafter Nachrichten GmbH & Co. KG
Editorial: Coesfelder Hof 2, Nordhorn 48527.
T: 49 5921 707 0 **E:** gn@gn-online.de
W: http://www.gn-online.de/
Freq: Daily; **Circ:** 25706
Chefredakteur / Editor in Chief: Guntram Dörr
Language (s): German
DAILY NEWSPAPER

Gränzbote
Owner: J. F. Bofinger KG
Editorial: Schwäbisch Media Digital GmbH & Co. KG, Karlstr. 16, Ravensburg 88212.
T: 49 751 29555555
E: redaktion@schwaebische.de
W: http://www.schwaebische.de/Gränzbote?
Freq: Daily; **Circ:** 21744
Redakteurin / Editor: Joerdis Damrath;
Redakteur / Editor: Lothar Häring;
Redakteurin / Editor: Dorothea Hecht;
Redaktion / Editor: Ludger Möllers; **Redakteur / Editor:** David Zapp
Language (s): German
DAILY NEWSPAPER

Griesheimer Anzeiger
Owner: VBG Verlag GmbH + Co. KG
Editorial: Wiesenstr. 8, Griesheim 64347.
T: 49 6155 83830
E: redaktion@griesheimeranzeiger.de
Freq: 2 Times/Week; **Circ:** 203325 Pub Statement
Chefredaktion: Wolfgang Bassenauer
Language (s): German
NEWSPAPER

Groß-Gerauer Echo
Owner: Echo Zeitungen GmbH
Editorial: Echo Zeitungen GmbH, Holzhofallee 25-31, Darmstadt 64295. **T:** 49 6151 3870
E: echo-zeitungen@darmstaedter-echo.de
W: http://www.echo-online.de/region/gross-gerau/gross-gerau/?
Freq: Daily; **Circ:** 16066 IVW
Redakteurin / Editor: Angelica Taubel
Language (s): German
DAILY NEWSPAPER

Günzburger Zeitung
Owner: Presse-Druck- und Verlags-GmbH
Editorial: Augsburger Allgemeine Zeitung, Curt-Frenzel-Str. 2, Augsburg. **T:** 49 821 7770
E: redaktion@augsburger-allgemeine.de
W: http://www.augsburger-allgemeine.de/
Freq: Daily; **Circ:** 15101
Chefredakteur / Editor in chief: Sascha Borowski; **Redakteur / Editor:** Daniela Deeg;
Redakteur / Editor: Stefan Drescher;
Redakeur / Editor: Daniela Fischer; **Reakteur / Editor:** Ina Kresse; **stellv. Chefredaktion:** Norbert Staub; **Redaktion / Editor:** Berthold Veh
Language (s): German
DAILY NEWSPAPER

Güstrower Landkurier
Owner: Verlag + Druck Linus Wittich KG
Editorial: Röbeler Str. 9, Sietow 17209.
T: 49 39931 57914 **E:** info@wittich-sietow.de
W: http://www.wittich.de
Freq: Monthly; **Circ:** 16000 Pub Statement
Chefredaktion: Hans-Joachim Groß
Language (s): German; Full Page Mono: 1100.00; Full Page Colour: 1150.00
Currency: Euro
NEWSPAPER

Haigerer Kurier
Owner: Druck- und Verlagshaus E. Weidenbach GmbH & Co. KG
Editorial: Druck- und Verlagshaus E. Weidenbach GmbH & Co. KG, Rathausstr. 1-3, Dillenburg 35683. **T:** 49 2771 8740
E: info@dill.de **W:** http://www.dill.de
Freq: Daily; **Circ:** 20460
Language (s): German
DAILY NEWSPAPER

Haigerer Zeitung
Owner: Wetzlardruck GmbH
Editorial: Wetzlardruck GmbH, Elsa-Brandström-Straße 18, Wetzlar 35578.
T: 49 6441 959176
E: redaktion.wnz@mittelhessen.de
W: http://www.mittelhessen.de
Freq: Daily; **Circ:** 20460
Redakteurin / Editor: Tanja Eckel; **Redaktion / Editor:** Martin Heller; **Redakteur / Editor:** Klaus Kordesch; **Redakteurin / Editor:** Petra Wagner; **Redakteur / Editor:** Jörg Weirich;
Redakteur / Editor: Maike Sophie Wessolowski; **Redakteur / Editor:** Dirk Wingender
Language (s): German
DAILY NEWSPAPER

Halberstädter Volksstimme
Owner: Magdeburger Verlags- und Druckhaus GmbH
Editorial: Magdeburger Verlags- und Druckhaus GmbH, Bahnhofstraße 17, Magdeburg 39104. **T:** 49 391 59990
E: redaktion@volksstimme.de
W: http://www.volksstimme.de/nachrichten/lokal/halberstadt/?
Freq: Daily; **Circ:** 13629
Redkateur / Editor: Michael Bock; **Redaktion / Editor:** Thomas Juschus; **Redakteur / Editor:** Alois Kösters; **Redaktion / Editor:** Sabine Scholz
Language (s): German
DAILY NEWSPAPER

Haller Kreisblatt
Owner: Haller Kreisblatt Verlags GmbH
Editorial: Haller Kreisblatt Verlags-GmbH, Gutenbergstr. 2, Halle 33790
E: info@haller-kreisblatt.de
W: http://www.haller-kreisblatt.de/?
Freq: Daily; **Circ:** 11933
Redakteurin / Editor: Nicole Donath; **Redaktion / Editor:** Herbert Gontek; **Redakteur / Editor:** Andreas Großpietsch; **Redakteurin / Editor:** Anja Hanneforth; **Redakteur / Editor:** Christian Helmig; **Redakteur / Editor:** Heiko Kaiser;
Redakteur / Editor: Philipp Kreutzer;
Redakteur / Editor: Claus Meyer; **Redakeur / Editor:** Detlef-Hans Serowy; **Redakteur / Editor:** Rolf Uhlemeier
Language (s): German
DAILY NEWSPAPER

Haller Tagblatt
Owner: Zeitungsverlag Schwäbisch Hall GmbH
Editorial: Zeitungsverlag Schwäbisch Hall GmbH, Haalstraße 5 und 7, Schwäbisch Hall 74523. **T:** 49 791 404410
E: redaktion@hallertagblatt.de
W: http://www.swp.de/schwaebisch_hall/
Freq: Daily; **Circ:** 18396
Redakteur / Editor: Karsten Dyba;
Chefredaktion / Editor in Chief: Marcus Haas;
Redakteur / Editor: Jürgen Stegmaier;
Redakteur / Editor: Tobias Würth
Language (s): German
DAILY NEWSPAPER

Hamburg: Das Magazin aus der Metropole
Owner: Magazin Verlagsges. Süddeutsche Zeitung mbH
Editorial: Englische Planke 6, Hamburg 20459.
T: 49 40 468991133
E: magazin@marketing.hamburg.de
W: http://www.hamburg.de/magazin
Freq: Quarterly
Editor: Mr./Ms. Editor; **Chefredaktion:** Mr./Ms. Editor
Language (s): German
NEWSPAPER

Hamburger Abendblatt
Owner: Axel Springer Verlag AG
Editorial: HAMBURGER ABENDBLATT Axel Springer AG, Axel-Springer-Platz 1, Hamburg 20350. **T:** 49 40 34700
E: briefe@abendblatt.de
W: http://www.abendblatt.de
Freq: Daily; **Circ:** 199218
Redakteurin / Editor: Annette Bethune;
Chefredaktion / Editor in Chief: Lars Haider;
Redakteurin / Editor: Beate Kranz;
Chefredakteur / Editor: Jörn Lauterbach;
Redakteur / Editor: Oliver Schade;
Redakteurin / Editor: Cornelia Werner
Language (s): German
DAILY NEWSPAPER

Hamburger Abendblatt Norderstedter Zeitung
Owner: Norderstedter Zeitung
Editorial: Rathausallee 64-66, Norderstedt.
T: 49 40 5289001
Freq: Daily
DAILY NEWSPAPER

Hamburger Abendblatt Pinneberger Zeitung
Owner: Pinneberger Zeitung / Axel Springer Verlag AG
Editorial: Lindenstr. 30, Pinneberg.
T: 49 4101 510100 **E:** pz@abendblatt.de
Freq: Daily
DAILY NEWSPAPER

Hamburger Morgenpost
Owner: Morgenpost Verlag GmbH
Editorial: Morgenpost Verlag GmbH, Griegstraße 75, Hamburg 22763.
T: 49 4080 90570 **E:** verlag@mopo.de
W: http://www.mopo.de
Freq: Daily; **Circ:** 133352
Redakteur / Editor: Christian Burmeister;
Chefredaktion / Editor in Chief: Frank Niggemeier
Language (s): German
DAILY NEWSPAPER

Hanauer Anzeiger
Owner: Hanauer Anzeiger GmbH + Co. Druck- und Verlagshaus
Editorial: Hanauer Anzeiger, Donaustraße 5, Hanau 63452. **T:** 49 6181 2903333
E: redaktion@hanauer.de
W: http://www.hanauer.de
Freq: Daily; **Circ:** 17307
Redakteurin / Editor: Jutta Degen-Peters;
Chefredaktion / Editor in Chief: Dieter Schreier
Language (s): German
DAILY NEWSPAPER

Hanau-Post
Editorial: Metac Medien Verlags GmbH, Waldstraße 226, Offenbach 63071.
T: 49 69 850080 **E:** info@op-online.de
W: http://www.op-online.de/lokales/nachrichten/hanau/
Freq: Daily; **Circ:** 42586
Language (s): German
DAILY NEWSPAPER

Handelsblatt
Owner: Handelsblatt GmbH
Editorial: Kasernenstr. 67, Dusseldorf 40213.
T: 49 211 887 0 **E:** handelsblatt@vhb.de
W: http://www.handelsblatt.com
Freq: Daily; **Circ:** 132560
Redakteurin / Editor: Heike Anger;
Redakteurin / Editor: Catrin Bialek;
Redakteurin / Editor: Heide Braasch;
Redakteur / Editor: Gero Brandenburg;
Redakteurin / Editor: Laura de la Motte;
Redakteur / Editor: Michael Detering;
Redakteur /Editor: Stephan Dörner; **Redakteur / Editor:** Frank Matthias Drost; **Redakteur / Editor:** Matthias Eberle; **Redakteur / Editor:** Hans Eschbach; **Redakteur / Editor:** Jürgen Flauger; **Redakteurin / Editor:** Diana Fröhlich;
Redakteur / Editor: Wolfgang Gillmann;
Redakteur / Editor: Axel Granzow; **Redakteur / Editor:** Jens Hagen; **Redakteur / Editor:** Norbert Häring; **Redakteurin / Editor:** Dana Heide; **Redakteur / Editor:** Frank G. Heide;
Redakteurin / Editor: Stefani Hergert;
Redakteurin / Editor: Dorit Heß; **Redakteur / Editor:** Joachim Hofer; **Redakteur / Editor:** Siegfried Hofmann; **Redakteur / Editor:** Axel Höpner; **Redakteur / Editor:** Till Hoppe;
Redakteur / Editor: Sönke Iwersen; **Redakteur / Editor:** Christoph Kapalschinski; **Redakteur / Editor:** Christof Kerkmann; **Redakteurin / Editor:** Silke Kersting; **Redakteurin / Editor:** Tanja Kewes; **Redakteur / Editor:** Peter Köhler;
Redakteur / Editor: Georgios Kokologiannis;
Redakteurin / Editor: Regina Krieger;
Redakteur / Editor: Robert Landgraf;
Redakteurin / Editor: Elga Lehari-Reichling;
Redakteurin / Editor: Sandra Louven;
Redakteurin / Editor: Kirsten Ludowig;
Redakteur / Editor: Jan Mallien; **Redakteurin / Editor:** Susanne Metzger; **Redakteurin / Editor:** Anja Müller; **Redakteur / Editor:** Martin Murphy; **Redakteur / Editor:** Christian Müßgens; **Redakteur / Editor:** Ingo Narat;
Redakteurin / Editor: Claudia Obmann;
Redakteurin / Editor: Yasmin Osman;
Redakteurin / Editor: Regine Palm;
Redakteurin / Editor: Claudia Panster;
Redakteurin / Editor: Petra Prenzel; **Redakteur / Editor:** Ingo Reich; **Redakteur / Editor:** Reiner Reichel; **Redakteur / Editor:** Udo Rettberg; **Redakteur / Editor:** Wolfgang Reuter; **Redakteurin / Editor:** Anke Rezmer;
Redakteur / Editor: Torsten Riecke; **Redakteur / Editor:** Christoph Schlautmann; **Redakteur / Editor:** Thomas Schmitt; **Redakteurin / Editor:** Katharina Schneider; **Redakteur / Editor:** Stefan Schneider; **Redakteur / Editor:** Christian Schnell; **Redakteurin / Editor:** Susanne Schreiber; **Redakteur / Editor:** Axel Schrinner; **Redakteur / Editor:** Oliver Stock;
Redakteurin / Editor: Maike Telgheder;
Redakteurin / Editor: Katrin Terpitz; **Redakteur / Editor:** Peter Thelen; **Redakteur / Editor:** Thomas Trösch; **Redakteur / Editor:** Georg Weishaupt; **Redakteur / Editor:** Martin Wocher
Language (s): German
DAILY NEWSPAPER

Hannoversche Allgemeine Zeitung
Owner: Verlagsges. Madsack GmbH & Co. KG
Editorial: Verlagsgesellschaft Madsack GmbH & Co. KG, August-Madsack-Straße 1, Hannover 30559. **T:** 49 511 5180
E: redaktion@haz.de **W:** http://www.haz.de
Freq: Daily; **Circ:** 186071
Redakteurin / Editor: Susanna Bauch;
Redakteurin / Editor: Susanne Bauch;
Chefredakteurin / Editor in Chief: Anja Borcherding; **Redakteur / Editor:** Carola Böse-Fischer; **Chefredakteur / Editor in Chief:** Hendrik Brandt; **Redakteur / Editor:** Norbert Fettback; **Redakteur / Editor:** Björn Franz;
Redakteur / Editor: Ewald Frie; **Redakteur / Editor:** Michael Geiss; **Redakteur / Editor:** Jörg Grußendorf; **Redakteur / Editor:** Jens Heitmann; **Redakteurin / Editor:** Bärbel Hilbig;
Redakteur / Editor: Konrad Hugo Jarausch;
Redakteurin / Editor: Margret Jans-Lottmann;
Redaktuer / Editor: Uwe Janssen; **Redakteurin / Editor:** Juliane Kaune; **Redakteur / Editor:** Jörn Kießler; **Chefredaktion / Editor in Chief:** Matthias Koch; **Redakteur / Editor:** Alexander Korb; **Redakteur / Editor:** Uwe Kranz;
Redakteur / Editor: Rüdiger Meise; **Redakteur / Editor:** Gunnar Menkens; **Redakteur / Editor:** Tobias Morchner; **Redakteurin / Editor:** Katja Naumann; **Redakteurin / Editor:** Anna Nolte;
Redakteur / Editor: Jutta Rinas; **Redakteur / Editor:** Andreas Schinkel; **Redakteur / Editor:** Carsten Schmidt; **Redakteur / Editor:** Carsten Schmidt; **Redakteur / Editor:** Joachim Scholz;
Redakteur / Editor: Gabriele Schulte;
Chefredakteur / Editor in Chief: Conrad von Meding; **Redakteur / Editor:** Volker Wiedersheim; **Redakteurin / Editor:** Nicola Zellmer; **Redakteur / Editor:** Michael Zgoll
Language (s): German
DAILY NEWSPAPER

Harzer Volksstimme
Owner: Magdeburger Verlags- und Druckhaus GmbH
Editorial: Magdeburger Verlags- und Druckhaus GmbH, Bahnhofstraße 17, Magdeburg 39104. **T:** 49 391 5999210
E: redaktion@volksstimme.de
W: http://www.volksstimme.de
Redaktion / Editor: Julia Angelov; **Redkateur / Editor:** Michael Bock; **Redaktion / Editor:** Thomas Juschus; **Redakteur / Editor:** Alois Kösters
Language (s): German
NEWSPAPER

Havelberger Volksstimme
Owner: Magdeburger Verlags- und Druckhaus GmbH
Editorial: Magdeburger Verlags- und Druckhaus GmbH, Bahnhofstraße 17, Magdeburg 39104. **T:** 49 391 59990
E: redaktion@volksstimme.de
W: http://www.volksstimme.de/nachrichten/lokal/havelberg/?
Redaktion / Editor: Thomas Juschus;
Redakteur / Editor: Alois Kösters; **Redaktion / Editor:** Andrea Schröder
Language (s): German
NEWSPAPER

HAZ wirtschaft extra
Owner: Madsack Supplement GmbH & Co. KG
Editorial: August-Madsack-Str. 1, Hannover 30559 **E:** haz@madsack.de
W: http://www.haz.de
Language (s): German
NEWSPAPER

Heidenheimer Neue Presse
Owner: Heidenheimer Neue Presse GmbH
Editorial: Heidenheimer Zeitung GmbH & Co KG, Olgastraße 15, Heidenheim 89518.
T: 49 7321 347153 **E:** redaktion@hz-online.de
W: http://www.hz-online.de/
Chefredakteur / Editor in chief: Ulrich Becker;
Redakteur / Editor: Ulf Schlüter
Language (s): German
NEWSPAPER

Heidenheimer Zeitung
Owner: Heidenheimer Zeitung GmbH & Co. KG
Editorial: Heidenheimer Zeitung GmbH & Co KG, Olgastraße 15, Heidenheim 89518.
T: 49 7321 347 153 **E:** redaktion@hz-online.de
W: http://www.hz-online.de
Freq: Daily; **Circ:** 28664
Chefredakteur / Editor in chief: Ulrich Becker;
Chefredaktion / Editor in Chief: Hendrik Rupp;
Redakteur / Editor: Ulf Schlüter
Language (s): German
DAILY NEWSPAPER

Heilbronner Stimme
Owner: Heilbronner Stimme GmbH & Co. KG

Editorial: Heilbronner Stimme GmbH & Co. KG, Allee 2, Heilbronn 74072. **T:** 49 7131 6150
E: redaktion@stimme.de
W: http://www.stimme.de
Freq: Daily; **Circ:** 93764
Redakteur / Editor: Günter Drewnitzky; **Chefredaktion / Editor in Chief:** Uwe Ralf Heer
Language (s): German
DAILY NEWSPAPER

Heilbronner Stimme (Nord Mitte), Neckarsulm
Owner: Heilbronner Stimme GmbH & Co. KG
T: 49 7131 6150 **E:** zeitung@stimme.de
Freq: Daily
Chefredakteur / Editor in Chief: Uwe Ralf Heer
DAILY NEWSPAPER

Heilbronner Stimme Leintal, Schwaigern
Owner: Heilbronner Stimme GmbH & Co. KG
T: 49 7131 6150
Freq: Daily
DAILY NEWSPAPER

Heilbronner Stimme Weinsberger Tal, Weinsberg
Owner: Heilbronner Stimme GmbH & Co. KG
T: 49 7131 6150 **E:** zeitung@stimme.de
Freq: Daily
Chefredakteur / Editor in Chief: Uwe Ralf Heer
DAILY NEWSPAPER

Heiligenhauser Zeitung
Owner: Westdeutsche Allgemeine Zeitungsverlag GmbH
Editorial: Jahnstr. 1, Heiligenhaus 42579.
T: 49 2056 98530 **E:** kontakt@derwesten.de
W: http://www.derwesten.de
Freq: Daily; **Circ:** 12607 IVW
Language (s): German
DAILY NEWSPAPER

Heinsberger Nachrichten
Owner: Zeitungsverlag Aachen GmbH
Editorial: Dresdener Straße 3, Aachen 52068.
T: 49 241 5101 0
E: redaktion@zeitungsverlag-aachen.de
W: http://www.aachener-zeitung.de/lokales/heinsberg
Freq: Daily; **Circ:** 20031
Redaktion / Editor: Rainer Herwartz
Language (s): German
DAILY NEWSPAPER

Hellweger Anzeiger
Owner: Zeitungsverlag Rubens KG
Editorial: Graphische Betriebe F. W. Rubens KG, Wasserstraße 20, Unna 59423.
T: 49 2303 2020
E: verlag@hellwegeranzeiger.de
W: http://www.hellwegeranzeiger.de
Freq: Daily; **Circ:** 36530
Redakteurin / Editor: Bianka Boyke; **Redakteurin / Editor:** Laura Di Betta; **Redakteur / Editor:** Michael Friehs; **Redakteur / Editor:** Kevin Kohues; **Redakteurin / Editor:** Nikola König; **Redakteur / Editor:** Maximilian Löchter; **Redakteurin / Editor:** Barbara Mersmann; **Redakteurin / Editor:** Leonie Prym; **Redakteur / Editor:** Christoph Schmidt; **Chefredaktion / Editor in Chief:** Volker Stennei; **Redakteur / Editor:** Konstantin Tassidis; **Redakteurin / Editor:** Melina Ulbrich
Language (s): German
DAILY NEWSPAPER

Herborner Tageblatt
Owner: Wetzlardruck GmbH
Editorial: Herborner Tageblatt, Rathausstraße 1, Dillenburg 35662. **T:** 49 2771 874400
E: redaktion.dp@mittelhessen.de
W: http://www.mittelhessen.de/lokales/region-dillenburg/herborn.html?
Freq: Daily; **Circ:** 20460
Redaktion / Editor: Martin Heller
Language (s): German
DAILY NEWSPAPER

Herforder Kreisanzeiger
Owner: Zeitungsverlag Neue Westfälische GmbH & Co. KG
Editorial: Niedernstraße 21 - 27, Bielefeld 33602. **T:** 49 521 5550
Freq: Daily; **Circ:** 14483
Chefredakteur / Editor in Chief: André Best; **Chefredakteur / Editor in Chief:** Ulrich Windolph
Language (s): German
DAILY NEWSPAPER

Herforder Kreisblatt
Owner: WESTFALEN-BLATT Vereinigte Zeitungsverlage GmbH
Editorial: Sudbrackstraße 14-18, Bielefeld 33611. **T:** 49 521 179413
E: wb@westfalen-blatt.de
W: http://www.westfalen-blatt.de/
Freq: Daily; **Circ:** 19206 IVW
Language (s): German
DAILY NEWSPAPER

Hessische Allgemeine HNA
Owner: Dierichs GmbH & Co. KG
Editorial: Frankfurter Str. 168, Kassel 34121.
T: 49 561 20300 **E:** info@hna.de
W: http://www.hna.de
Freq: Daily; **Circ:** 226515 IVW
Language (s): German
DAILY NEWSPAPER

Hessische/Niedersächsische Allgemeine
Owner: Verlag Dierichs GmbH & Co KG
Editorial: Frankfurter Str. 168, Kassel 34121.
T: 49 561 20300 **E:** info@hna.de
W: http://www.hna.de
Freq: Daily; **Circ:** 226515 IVW
Redakteur / Editor: Wolfgang Blieffert; **Redakteur / Editor:** Gerd Brehm; **Redakteur / Editor:** Jörg-Stephan Carl; **Redakteurin / Editor:** Tatjana Coerschulte; **Redakteur / Editor:** Daniel Göbel; **Redakteur / Editor:** Florian Hagemann; **Redakteur / Editor:** Peter Klebe; **Redakteur / Editor:** Torsten Kohlhaase; **Redakteur / Editor:** Robin Lipke; **Redakteur / Editor:** Ullrich Riedler; **Redakteur / Editor:** Wolfgang Riek; **Redakteur / Editor:** Gerald Schaumburg; **Redakteur / Editor:** Daniel Schneider; **Redakteur / Editor:** Martin Scholz; **Redakteurin / Editor:** Michaela Streuff; **Redakteurin / Editor:** Barbara Will; **Redakteurin / Editor:** Constanze Wüstefeld
Language (s): German
DAILY NEWSPAPER

Heuberger Bote
Owner: J. F. Bofinger KG
Editorial: Heuberger Bote & INFO - Der Südfinder, Hauptstraße 90, Spaichingen 78549. **T:** 49 7424 949315
E: redaktion.spaichingen@schwaebische.de
W: http://www.schwaebische.de/region/sigmaringen-tuttlingen/spaichingen.html?
Freq: Daily; **Circ:** 21744
Redaktion / Editor: Regina Braungart
Language (s): German
DAILY NEWSPAPER

Hildesheimer Allgemeine Zeitung
Owner: Gebr. Gerstenberg GmbH & Co. KG
Editorial: Gebrüder Gerstenberg GmbH & Co. KG, Rathausstraße 18-20, Hildesheim 31134.
T: 49 5121 106 302
E: redaktion@hildesheimer-allgemeine.de
W: http://www.hildesheimer-allgemeine.de
Freq: Daily; **Circ:** 39987
Redakteur / Editor: Andreas Bode; **Redakteur / Editor:** Rainer Breda; **Redakteurin / Editor:** Saskia Fröhlich; **Herausgeber / Publisher:** Daniel Gerstenberg; **Redakteurin / Editor:** Andrea Hempen; **Chefredakteur / Editor in Chief:** Michael Heun; **Redakteurin / Editor:** Viktoria Hübner; **Redakteurin / Editor:** Renate Klink; **Redakteur / Editor:** Johannes Krupp; **Redakteur / Editor:** Andreas Mayen; **Redakteur / Editor:** Norbert Mierzowsky; **Redakteur / Editor:** Peter Rütters; **Redakteurin / Editor:** Angela Schlegel; **Redakteurin / Editor:** Valea Schweiger; **Redakteur / Editor:** Hans-Joachim Wünsche; **Redakteurin / Editor:** Marita Zimmerhof
Language (s): German
DAILY NEWSPAPER

HNA Fritzlar/Homberg
Owner: Verlag Dierichs GmbH & Co KG
Editorial: Marktplatz 24, Fritzlar 34560.
T: 49 5681 993415 **E:** homberg@hna.de
W: http://www.hna.de/lokales/fritzlar-homberg/
Freq: Daily; **Circ:** 14552
Redakteur / Editor: Olaf Dellit; **Redakteur / Editor:** Jürgen Köcher; **Redakteur / Editor:** Rainer Schmitt; **Redakteurin / Editor:** Christine Thiery; **Redakteurin / Editor:** Maja Yüce
Language (s): German
DAILY NEWSPAPER

Höchster Kreisblatt
Owner: Frankfurter Societäts-Medien GmbH
Editorial: Frankfurter Societäts-Medien GmbH, Frankenallee 71–81, Frankfurt Am Main 60327.
T: 49 6975 010 **E:** redaktion@fnp.de
W: http://www.kreisblatt.de/
Freq: Daily; **Circ:** 44092
Redakteur / Editor: Thomas Ruhmöller; **Redaktion / Editor:** Karl-Josef Schmidt
Language (s): German
DAILY NEWSPAPER

Hockenheimer Tageszeitung
Owner: Schwetzinger Zeitungsverlag GmbH + Co. KG
Editorial: Mannheimer Morgen Großdruckerei und Verlag GmbH, Dudenstraße 12-26, Mannheim 68167. **T:** 49 621 39201
E: info@mamo.de
W: http://www.morgenweb.de/region/schwetzinger-zeitung-hockenheimer-tageszeitung/hockenheim
Freq: Daily; **Circ:** 16695
Redakteur / Editor: Svenja Fischer; **Redakteur / Editor:** Corinna Perner; **Redaktion / Editor:** Hans Schuppel
Language (s): German
DAILY NEWSPAPER

Hofgeismarer Allgemeine
Owner: Dierichs GmbH & Co. KG
Editorial: Bahnhofstraße 6, Hofgeismar 34369.
T: 49 561 20300 **E:** info@hna.de
W: http://www.hna.de
Freq: Daily; **Circ:** 15795 IVW
Language (s): German
DAILY NEWSPAPER

Hohenloher Tagblatt
Owner: Wankmüller GmbH & Co. KG
Editorial: SÜDWEST PRESSE Hohenloher Tagblatt, Ludwigstraße 6-10, Crailsheim 74564. **T:** 49 7951 409321
E: redaktion.ht@swp.de
W: http://www.swp.de/crailsheim/
Freq: Daily; **Circ:** 15428
Redakteur / Editor: Mathias Bartles; **Redakteurin / Editor:** Anna Berger; **Chefredaktion / Editor in Chief:** Andreas Harthan
Language (s): German
DAILY NEWSPAPER

Hohenloher Zeitung
Owner: Heilbronner Stimme GmbH & Co. KG
Editorial: Hohenloher Zeitung, Konsul-Uebele-Straße 6, Künzelsau 74653. **T:** 49 7940 92620
E: redaktion.kuen@stimme.de
W: http://www.hohenloher-zeitung.de
Freq: Daily; **Circ:** 19568 IVW
Language (s): German
DAILY NEWSPAPER

Hohenloher Zeitung (Öhringen)
Owner: Heilbronner Stimme GmbH & Co. KG
Editorial: Bahnhofstraße 11, Öhringen
W: http://www.stimme.de
Language (s): German
NEWSPAPER

Holsteiner Nachrichten
Owner: A. Beig Druckerei und Verlag GmbH & Co
Editorial: Damm 9-19, Pinneberg 25421
E: beig-druckunterlagen@shz.de
Freq: Daily; **Circ:** 29654
Language (s): German
DAILY NEWSPAPER

Holsteinischer Courier
Owner: sh:z Schleswig-Holsteinischer Zeitungsverlag GmbH & Co. KG
Editorial: sh:z Schleswig-Holsteinischer Zeitungsverlag GmbH & Co. KG, Fördestraße 20, Flensburg 24944 **E:** redaktion@shz.de
W: http://www.shz.de/lokales/holsteinischer-courier
Freq: Daily; **Circ:** 14937
Redakteur / Editor: Alexandra Bury; **Redaktion / Editor:** Thorsten Geil; **Redakteur / Editor:** Christian Lipovsek; **Chefredakteur / Editor in Chief:** Helge Matthiesen
Language (s): German
DAILY NEWSPAPER

Holzkirchner Merkur
Owner: Zeitungsverlag Oberbayern GmbH & Co. KG
Editorial: Münchener Zeitungs-Verlag GmbH & Co.KG, Paul-Heyse-Str. 2-4, München 80336.
T: 49 8953 060 **E:** info@merkur-online.de
W: http://www.merkur-online.de/lokales/miesbach/holzkirchen/?
Freq: Daily; **Circ:** 16766
Redakteurin / Editor: Manuela Better; **Redakteur / Editor:** Christian Deutschländer; **Redakteur / Editor:** Florian Weiß
Language (s): German
DAILY NEWSPAPER

Husumer Nachrichten
Owner: sh:z Schleswig-Holsteinischer Zeitungsverlag GmbH & Co. KG
Editorial: sh:z Schleswig-Holsteinischer Zeitungsverlag GmbH & Co. KG, Fördestraße 20, Flensburg 24944 **E:** redaktion@shz.de
W: http://www.shz.de/lokales/husumer-nachrichten
Freq: Daily; **Circ:** 20122
Chefredakteur / Editor in Chief: Helge Matthiesen; **Redakteur / Editor:** Lars Petersen; **Redakteur / Editor:** Stefan Petersen; **Redaktion / Editor:** Jörg von Berg
Language (s): German
DAILY NEWSPAPER

Ibbenbürener Volkszeitung
Owner: ivz.medien GmbH & Co. KG
Editorial: TELAOS GmbH & Co. KG, Wilhelmstraße 240, Ibbenbüren 49475.
T: 49 5451 933 270
E: redaktion@ivz-aktuell.de
W: http://www.ivz-aktuell.de
Freq: Daily; **Circ:** 20363
Redakteur / Editor: Stephan Beermann; **Redakteurin / Editor:** Anke Beiing; **Redakteur / Editor:** Stefan Daviter; **Redakteur / Editor:** Oliver Langemeyer; **Redakteur / Editor:** Daniel Lüns; **Redakteur / Editor:** Henning Meyer-Veer; **Redakteurin / Editor:** Irja Most; **Redakteur / Editor:** Peter Henrichmann-Roock; **Redakteurin / Editor:** Cornelia Ruholl; **Redakteur / Editor:** Jens Thorsten Schmidt; **Redakteur / Editor:** Tobias Vieth
Language (s): German
DAILY NEWSPAPER

Idsteiner Zeitung
W: http://www.wiesbadener-tagblatt.de/
Language (s): German
NEWSPAPER

IKZ - Iserlohner Kreisanzeiger und Zeitung
Owner: Funke Mediengrupe
Editorial: Redaktion Iserlohn, Theodor-Heuss-Ring 4-6, Iserlohn 58636. **T:** 49 2371 822 222
E: red.iserlohn@ikz-online.de
W: http://www.derwesten.de/ikz/ikz-start/
Freq: Daily; **Circ:** 21334
Redakteur / Editor: Andreas Drees; **Redakteur / Editor:** Stefan Drees; **Redakteur / Editor:** Katrin Figge; **Redakteur / Editor:** Tim Gelewski; **Redakteur / Editor:** Sina Heilmann; **Redakteur / Editor:** Stefan Janke; **Redakteurin / Editor:** Jennifer Katz; **Redakteur / Editor:** Jasmin Kleemann; **Redakteur / Editor:** Stefan Kober; **Redaketur / Editor:** Reinhard Köster; **Redakteur /Editor:** Torsten Lehmann; **Redakteurin / Editor:** Cornelia Merkel; **Redakteur / Editor:** Stefan Reinke; **Chefredakteur / Editor in Chief:** Thomas Reunert; **Redakteur / Editor:** Ulrich Steden; **Redakteur / Editor:** Ralf Tiemann
Language (s): German
DAILY NEWSPAPER

The International New York Times - Berlin
Editorial: Grolmanstrasse 52, Berlin 10623.
T: 49 30 3127928 **E:** foreign@nytimes.com
DAILY NEWSPAPER

Ipf- und Jagst-Zeitung
Owner: Schwäbische Zeitung GmbH & Co. KG, Drexler, Gessler
Editorial: Ipf- und Jagst-Zeitung & INFO Ostalb, Aalener Straße 10, Ellwangen 73479.
T: 49 7961 988867
E: redaktion@ipf-und-jagst-zeitung.de
W: http://www.schwaebische.de/region/ostalb/ellwangen
Freq: Daily; **Circ:** 11430
Redakteur / Editor: Norbert Acker; **Redaktion / Editor:** Ulrich Geßler
Language (s): German
DAILY NEWSPAPER

Jülicher Zeitung
Owner: Zeitungsverlag Aachen GmbH
Editorial: Postfach 500110, Dresdener Straße 3, Aachen 52068. **T:** 49 241 5101-0
E: redaktion@zeitungsverlag-aachen.de
W: http://www.aachener-zeitung.de/lokales/juelich
Freq: Daily
Redakteur / Editor: Otto Jonel; **Redakteur / Editor:** Gerard Peters; **Redaktion / Editor:** Volker Uerlings; **Redakteur / Editor:** Antonius Wolters
Language (s): German
DAILY NEWSPAPER

junge Welt
Owner: Verlag 8. Mai GmbH
Editorial: Torstraße 6, Berlin 10119.
T: 49 30 5363 55 0 **E:** redaktion@jungewelt.de
W: http://www.jungewelt.de
Freq: Daily; **Circ:** 18500
Redakteur / Editor: Sebastian Carlens; **Redaktuer / Editor:** Klaus Fischer; **Redakteur / Editor:** Rüdiger Göbel; **Redakteur / Editor:** Andreas Hüllinghorst; **Redakteur/ Editor:** Stefan Huth; **Redakteur / Editor:** Christof Meueler; **Redakteur / Editor:** André Scheer;

Redakteur / Editor: Arnold Schölzel; **Redakteur / Editor:** Peter Wolter
Language (s): German
DAILY NEWSPAPER

Kieler Nachrichten
Owner: Kieler Zeitung Verlags- und Druckerei KG-GmbH & Co.
Editorial: Kieler Nachrichten, Fleethörn 1-7, Kiel 24103. **T:** 49 4319 030
E: ct.red@kieler-nachrichten.de
W: http://www.kn-online.de/
Freq: Daily; **Circ:** 103598
Chefredaktion / Editor in Chief: Christian Longardt; **Redakteur / Editor:** Frank Molter; **Redakteur / Editor:** Günter Schellhase
Language (s): German
DAILY NEWSPAPER

Kölner Stadt Anzeiger Rhein-Erft-Kreis/Bergheim
Owner: M.DuMont Schauberg Expedition der Kölnischen Zeitung GmbH & Co.KG
Editorial: Hauptstr. 55, Bergheim 50126.
T: 49 2271 47 22 20
E: redaktion.erftkreis@ksta.de
W: http://www.ksta.de
Freq: Daily; **Circ:** 18113
Language (s): German
DAILY NEWSPAPER

Kölner Stadt Anzeiger, Leverkusen
Owner: M.DuMont Schauberg Expedition der Kölnischen Zeitung GmbH & Co.KG
Editorial: Friedrich-Ebert-Platz 5, Leverkusen 51373. **T:** 49 214 83 10 11
E: redaktion.leverkusen@ksta.de
W: http://www.ksta.de
Freq: Daily; **Circ:** 21257
Language (s): German
DAILY NEWSPAPER

Kölner Stadtanzeiger
Owner: M.DuMont Schauberg Expedition der Kölnischen Zeitung GmbH & Co.KG
Editorial: Kölner Stadt-Anzeiger, Neven DuMont-Haus, Koln 50735. **T:** 49 221 224 0
E: redaktion-ksta@mds.de
W: http://www.ksta.de
Freq: Daily; **Circ:** 301592
Language (s): German
DAILY NEWSPAPER

Kölner Stadt-Anzeiger
Owner: M. DuMont Schauberg GmbH & Co. KG
Editorial: Neven DuMont-Haus, Amsterdamer Str.192, Koln 50735. **T:** 49 0221 2240
E: redaktion-ksta@mds.de
W: http://www.ksta.de
Freq: Daily; **Circ:** 363068
Redakteurin (online) / Editor (online): Christine Badke; **Redakteur / Editor:** Martin Boldt; **Redakteurin / Editor:** Tanja Brandes; **Redakteur / Editor:** Dirk Breuer; **Redakteur / Editor:** Andreas Damm; **Redakteur / Editor:** Helmut Frangenberg; **Redakteurin / Editor:** Claudia Freytag; **Redakteurin / Editor:** Anne-Kathrin Gerstlauer; **Redakteurin / Editor:** Bettina Janecek; **Redakteur / Editor:** Fabian Klask; **Redakteurin / Editor:** Verena Köplin; **Redakteur / Editor:** Jan Kus; **Redakteurin / Editor:** Tatjana Lajendäcker; **Redakteurin / Editor:** Anna Lampert; **Redakteurin / Editor:** Nike Laurenz; **Redakteur / Editor:** Jürgen Oehler; **Chefredakteur / Editor in Chief:** Peter Pauls; **Redakteur / Editor:** Matthias Pesch; **Redakteur / Editor:** Tobias Peter; **Redakteurin / Editor:** Jutta-Eileen Radix; **Redakteur / Editor:** Philipp Remke; **Redakteur / Editor:** Clemens Schminke; **Redakteur / Editor:** Brian Schneider; **Redakteur / Editor:** Tim Stinauer; **Redakteur / Editor:** Sven Winterschladen
Language (s): German
DAILY NEWSPAPER

Kölner Stadt-Anzeiger - Rhein-Erft Kreis
Owner: DuMont Net GmbH & Co. KG
Editorial: Redaktion Frechen, Hauptstr. 19 - 21, Frechen 50226. **T:** 49 2234 18 37 10
E: redaktion.erftkreis@ksta.de
W: http://www.ksta.de/rhein-erft
Redakteur / Editor: Udo Beißel; **Redakteur / Editor:** Horst Komuth; **Redakteur / Editor:** Frank Kreidler; **Redakteurin / Editor:** Birgit Lehmann; **Redakteurin / Editor:** Anja Musick; **Redakteur / Editor:** Joachim Röhrig; **Redakteur / Editor:** Dennis Vlaminck
Language (s): German
NEWSPAPER

Kölner Stadtanzeiger, Kreis Euskirchen
Owner: M.DuMont Schauberg Expedition der Kölnischen Zeitung GmbH & Co.KG
Editorial: Berliner Str. 48, Euskirchen 53879.
T: 49 22251 70 043029
E: redaktion.euskirchen@ksta.de
W: http://www.ksta.de
Freq: Daily; **Circ:** 26938
Redakteur / Editor: Johannes Bühl; **Redakteur / Editor:** Stephan Everling; **Redakteur / Editor:** Günter Hochgürtel; **Redakteurin / Editor:** Gudrun Klinkhammer; **Redakteurin / Editor:** Heike Nickel; **Redakteur / Editor:** Thomas Schmitz
Language (s): German
DAILY NEWSPAPER

Kölnische Rundschau
Owner: Heinen-Verlag GmbH
Editorial: Kölnische Rundschau, Stolkgasse 25-45, Koln 50667. **T:** 49 221 1632551
E: Koeln@kr-redaktion.de
W: http://www.rundschau-online.de/?
Freq: Daily; **Circ:** 363068
Chefredakteur / Editor in Chief: Engelbert Greis; **Redakteur / Editor:** Berthold Mertes; **Redaktion / Editor:** Julian Stech; **Chefredakteurin / Editor in Chief:** Cordula von Wysocki; **Redakteur / Editor:** Hartmut Wilmes
Language (s): German
DAILY NEWSPAPER

Kölnische Rundschau, Rhein-Erft Kreis / Köln Land
Owner: M.DuMont Schauberg Expedition der Kölnischen Zeitung GmbH & Co.KG
Editorial: Kölnstr. 43, Brühl 50321.
T: 49 2232 50120
E: Rhein-Erft.Rundschau@kr-redaktion.de
W: http://www.ksta.de
Freq: Daily; **Circ:** 37235
Language (s): German
DAILY NEWSPAPER

Kötztinger Umschau
Owner: Mittelbayerischer Verlag KG
Editorial: Kötztinger Umschau, Müllerstraße 7, Bad Kötzting 93444. **T:** 49 994 194077
E: umschau@mittelbayerische.de
W: http://www.mittelbayerische.de/unser-haus/redaktion/lokalredaktionen/bad-koetzting/
Freq: Daily; **Circ:** 14156
Redaktion / Editor: Georg Heeger; **Redaktion / Editor:** Stefan Weber
Language (s): German
DAILY NEWSPAPER

Kreis-Anzeiger
Owner: Rheinpfalz Verlag und Druckerei GmbH & Co.KG
Editorial: Gabelsbergerstraße 1, Dillingen 89407 **W:** http://www.kreisanzeiger.de
Chefredaktion / Editor in Chief: Daniel Heintz
Language (s): German
NEWSPAPER

Kreiszeitung
Owner: Kreiszeitung Verlagsges. mbH & Co. KG
Editorial: Kreiszeitung Verlagsgesellschaft mbH & Co. KG, Am Ristedter Weg 17, Syke 28857. **T:** 49 9071 79360
W: http://www.kreiszeitung.de
Freq: Daily; **Circ:** 80386
Redakteurin Diepholz / Editor Diepholz: Anika Bokelmann; **Redakteurin Diepholz / Editor Diepholz:** Anke Seidel; **Chefredaktion / Editor in Chief:** Hans Willms
Language (s): German
DAILY NEWSPAPER

Kreiszeitung Syke
Owner: Kreiszeitung Verlagsgesellschaft mbH &Co.KG
Editorial: Hauptstraße 6, Syke 28857.
T: 49 4242 934255-0
E: lokales.syke@kreiszeitung.de
W: http://www.kreiszeitung.de/
Freq: Daily; **Circ:** 28230
Redakteur / Editor: Pascal Faltermann; **Redakteurin / Editor:** Lorena Pabelick; **Chefredaktion / Editor in Chief:** Hans Willms
Language (s): German
DAILY NEWSPAPER

Kurier Dachau
Owner: Amper Wochenend Zeitung GmbH
Editorial: Redaktion Kurier Dachau, Von-Herterich-Str. 6a, Dachau 85221.
T: 49 8131 333060 **E:** info@kurier-dachau.de
W: http://www.kurier-dachau.de/
Freq: Weekly; **Circ:** 60225
Chefredakteur/ Editor in Chief: Ernst Kreisl; **Redakteur / Editor:** Sebastian Leiss; **Redakteur / Editor:** Reinhard Alexander Öxler
Language (s): German
NEWSPAPER

Landeszeitung für die Lüneburger Heide
Owner: Landeszeitung für die Lüneburger Heide GmbH
Editorial: Landeszeitung für die Lüneburger Heide GmbH, Am Sande 18-20, Lüneburg 21335 **E:** redaktion@landeszeitung.de
W: http://www.landeszeitung.de/blog/category/lokales/luneburg
Freq: Daily; **Circ:** 32310
Redakteurin / Editor: Fanny Pigliapoco; **Chefredaktion / Editor in Chief:** Christoph Steiner
Language (s): German
DAILY NEWSPAPER

Landsberger Tagblatt
Owner: Presse-Druck- und Verlags-GmbH
Editorial: Curt-Frenzel-Str. 2, Augsburg 86167.
T: 49 821 777 0
E: online-redaktion@augsburger-allgemeine.de
W: http://www.augsburger-allgemeine.de/landsberg/
Freq: Daily; **Circ:** 15699
Chefredaktion: Sascha Borowski; **Redakteur / Editor:** Daniela Deeg; **Redakteur / Editor:** Stefan Drescher; **Reedakeur / Editor:** Daniela Fischer; **Redakteur / Editor:** Ina Kresse; **Redaktion / Editor:** Dieter Mitulla; **stellv. Chefredaktion:** Norbert Staub
Language (s): German
DAILY NEWSPAPER

Landshuter Zeitung
Owner: Josef Thomann'sche Buchdruckerei Verlag
Editorial: Landshuter Zeitung, Altstadt 89, Landshut 84028. **T:** 49 781 850 2184
E: stadtred@landshuter-zeitung.de
W: http://www.idowa.de/zeitung/landshuter-zeitung
Freq: Daily; **Circ:** 50614
Redakteur / Eidtor: Fabian Roßmann
Language (s): German
DAILY NEWSPAPER

Lausitzer Rundschau
Owner: LR Medienverlag und Druckerei GmbH
Editorial: Lausitzer VerlagsService GmbH, Straße der Jugend 54, Cottbus 3050.
T: 49 355 481 555 **E:** red.sachsen@lr-online.de
W: http://www.lr-online.de
Freq: Daily; **Circ:** 89206
Redakteur / Editor: Sven Bock; **Redakteur / Editor:** Sebastian Butt; **Chefredaktion / Editor in Chief:** Johannes M. Fischer; **Redakteur / Editor:** Christin Schaffarzick; **Redakteur / Editor:** Marcus Scheib; **Redakteur / Editor:** Christian Schenk; **Redakteur / Editor:** Susanne Schwarzenau; **Redakteur / Editor:** Bianca Urbicht
Language (s): German
DAILY NEWSPAPER

Lausitzer Rundschau, Finsterwalde
Owner: Lausitzer Rundschau
Editorial: Straße der Jugend 54, Cottbus 3050. **T:** 49 355 481555
E: redaktion@lr-online.de
W: http://www.lr-online.de/regionen/finsterwalde/
Freq: Daily
Chefredaktion / Editor in Chief: Johannes M. Fischer
Language (s): German
DAILY NEWSPAPER

Lausitzer Rundschau, Guben
Owner: Lausitzer Rundschau Medienverlag GmbH
Editorial: Straße der Jugend 54, Cottbus 3050. **T:** 49 355 481555
W: http://www.lr-online.de/regionen/guben
Freq: Daily
Chefredaktion / Editor in Chief: Johannes M. Fischer
Language (s): German
DAILY NEWSPAPER

Lausitzer Rundschau, Hoyerswerda
Owner: LR Medienverlag GmbH
Editorial: Straße der Jugend 54, Cottbus 3050. **T:** 49 355 481555
E: redaktion@lr-online.de
W: http://www.lr-online.de/regionen/hoyerswerda/
Freq: Daily
Chefredaktion / Editor in Chief: Johannes M. Fischer
Language (s): German
DAILY NEWSPAPER

Lausitzer Rundschau, Lübbenau
Owner: LR Medienverlag GmbH
Editorial: Hauptstr. 28, Lübben 15907.
T: 49 3546 22510
W: http://www.lr-online.de/regionen/luebbenau-calau/
Freq: Daily
Chefredaktion / Editor in Chief: Johannes M. Fischer
Language (s): German
DAILY NEWSPAPER

Lausitzer Rundschau, Luckau
Owner: LR Medienverlag GmbH
Editorial: Am Markt 32, Luckau 15926.
T: 49 3544 55500 **E:** redaktion@lr.online.de
W: http://www.lr-online.de/regionen/luckau/
Freq: Daily
Chefredaktion / Editor in Chief: Johannes M. Fischer
Language (s): German
DAILY NEWSPAPER

Lausitzer Rundschau, Senftenberg
Owner: LR Medienverlag GmbH
Editorial: Straße der Jugend 54, Cottbus 3050. **T:** 49 3573 794540
E: red.senftenberg@lr-online.de
W: http://www.lr-online.de/regionen/senftenberg/
Freq: Daily
Chefredaktion / Editor in Chief: Johannes M. Fischer
Language (s): German
DAILY NEWSPAPER

Lausitzer Rundschau, Spremberg
Owner: LR Medienverlag GmbH
Editorial: Badergasse 3, Spremberg 3130.
T: 49 3563 34590
W: http://www.lr-online.de/regionen/spremberg/
Freq: Daily
Chefredaktion / Editor in Chief: Johannes M. Fischer
Language (s): German
DAILY NEWSPAPER

Lausitzer Rundschau, Weißwasser
Owner: LR Medienverlag GmbH
Editorial: Straße der Jugend 54, Cottbus 3050. **T:** 49 355 481555
W: http://www.lr-online.de/regionen/weisswasser/
Freq: Daily
Chefredaktion / Editor in Chief: Johannes M. Fischer
Language (s): German
DAILY NEWSPAPER

LE MONDE diplomatique
Editorial: Rudi-Dutschke-Straße 23, Berlin 10969. **T:** 49 30 25902 0
E: diplo@monde-diplomatique.de
W: http://www.monde-diplomatique.de
Language (s): German
NEWSPAPER

Lebensräume
Owner: Wohnungsbaugenossenschaft Dessau eG
W: http://www.baustoffmarkt-online.de
Language (s): German
NEWSPAPER

Leipziger Volkszeitung
Owner: Leipziger Verlags- und Druckereiges. mbH & Co. KG
Editorial: Leipziger Verlags- und Druckereigesellschaft mbH & Co. KG, Peterssteinweg 19, Leipzig 4107.
T: 49 341 21810 **E:** journal@lvz.de
W: http://www.lvz-online.de
Freq: Daily; **Circ:** 224176
Redakteur / Editor: Andreas Dunte; **Chefredaktion / Editor in Chief:** Jan Emendörfer; **Redakteur / Editor:** Steffen Enigk; **Chefredakteur / Editor in Chief:** Holger Herzberg; **Redakteurin / Editor:** Evelyn Tervehn
Language (s): German
DAILY NEWSPAPER

Leipziger Volkszeitung, Borna/ Geithain
Owner: Leipziger Druck- und Verlagsgesellschaft mbH
Editorial: Peterssteinweg 19, Leipzig 4107.
T: 49 3433 270710 **E:** borna.redaktion@lvz.de
W: http://www.lvz-online.de/region/borna/r-borna.html
Freq: Daily
Chefredaktion / Editor in Chief: Jan Emendörfer; **Chefredakteur / Editor-in-chief:** Frank Prenzel
Language (s): German
DAILY NEWSPAPER

lenz
Owner: Aschendorff Medien GmbH & Co. KG
Editorial: An der Hansalinie 1, Munster 48163.
T: 49 251 690193 **E:** redaktion@lenz-show.de
W: http://www.lenz-show.de

Freq: Bi-Weekly; **Circ:** 120000 Pub Statement
Chefredaktion: Michaela Töns
Language (s): German; Full Page Mono: 2336.00; Full Page Colour: 2336.00
Currency: Euro
NEWSPAPER

Leonberger Kreiszeitung
Owner: Zeitungsverlag Leonberg GmbH
Editorial: Zeitungsverlag Leonberg GmbH, Stuttgarter Straße 7-9, Leonberg 71229.
T: 49 715 2 9 372 811
E: redaktion@leonberger-kreiszeitung.zgs.de
W: http://www.leonberger-kreiszeitung.de
Freq: Daily; **Circ:** 16559
Redakteur / Editor: Rafael Binkowski; **Redakteur / Editor:** Ulrike Otto; **Chefredakteur / Editor in Chief:** Thomas Slotwinsky
Language (s): German
DAILY NEWSPAPER

Leverkusener Anzeiger
Owner: M. DuMont Schauberg GmbH & Co. KG
W: http://www.ksta.de/leverkusen/
Redaktion / Editor: Bert Christoph Gerhards; **Redakteur / Editor:** Bert-Christoph Gerhards; **Redakteur / Editor:** Günter Müller; **Redakteur / Editor:** Jan Sting
Language (s): German
NEWSPAPER

Lingener Tagespost
Owner: Neue Osnabrücker Zeitung GmbH & Co. KG
Editorial: Neue Osnabrücker Zeitung GmbH & Co. KG, Breiter Gang 10-16, Osnabrück 49074.
T: 49 541 310 207 **E:** chefredaktion@noz.de
W: http://www.noz.de/lingener-tagespost?
Freq: Daily; **Circ:** 21393
Redakteur / Editor: Burkhard Müller; **Redakteur / Editor:** Anne Overesch; **Redaktion / Editor:** Thomas Pertz
Language (s): German
DAILY NEWSPAPER

Lippische Landes-Zeitung
Owner: Lippischer Zeitungsverlag Giesdorf GmbH & Co. KG
Editorial: Lippischer Zeitungsverlag Giesdorf GmbH & Co. KG, Ohmstraße 7, Detmold 32758. **T:** 49 523 1911 131
E: detmold@lz-online.de **W:** http://www.lz.de
Freq: Daily; **Circ:** 42816
Redakteurin / Editor: Jana Beckmann; **Chefredaktion / Editor in Chief:** Michael Dahl; **Redakteurin / Editor:** Cordula Gröne; **Redakteurin / Editor:** Barbara Luetgebrune; **Redakteur / Editor:** Dietmar Welle
Language (s): German
DAILY NEWSPAPER

Lübecker Nachrichten
Owner: Lübecker Nachrichten GmbH
Editorial: Ostsee Information & Medien GmbHOstsee Information & Medien GmbH, Herrenholz 10 - 12, Lübeck 23556.
T: 49 451 144 0 **E:** redaktion@ln-luebeck.de
W: http://www.ln-online.de **Circ:** 103772
Redakteur / Editor: Peer Hellerling; **Redakteur / Editor:** Hannes Lintschnig
Language (s): German
NEWSPAPER

Lübecker/Bad Schwartauer N., Bad Schwartau
Owner: Lübecker Nachrichten
Editorial: Lübecker Str. 3, Bad Schwartau 23611. **T:** 49 451 2920813
E: redaktion.bad.schwartau@ln-luebeck.de
W: http://www.ln-online.de/
Freq: Daily
Chefredakteur / Editor in Chief: Gerald Goetsch
Language (s): German
DAILY NEWSPAPER

Lüdenscheider Nachrichten
Owner: Märkischer Zeitungsverlag GmbH & Co. KG
Editorial: Märkischer Zeitungsverlag GmbH & Co. KG, Schillerstraße 20, Lüdenscheid 58511.
T: 49 023 51 1580 **E:** internet@come-on.de
W: http://www.come-on.de
Freq: Daily; **Circ:** 15875
Redakteur / Editor: Bernd Eiber; **Redaktion / Editor:** Wilhelm Finke; **Redakteur / Editor:** Jörg Hellwig; **Redakteur / Editor:** Susanne Kornau; **Redakteur / Editor:** Marc Kusche; **Redakteurin / Editor:** Jutta Rudewig
Language (s): German
DAILY NEWSPAPER

Ludwigsburger Kreiszeitung
Owner: Ungeheuer + Ulmer KG GmbH + Co.
Editorial: "Ungeheuer + Ulmer KG GmbH + Co., Körnerstraße 14–18, Ludwigsburg 71634.
T: 49 714 1 1300 **E:** redaktion@lkz.de
W: http://www.lkz.de
Freq: Daily; **Circ:** 40271
Redakteur / Editor: Thomas Faulhaber; **Chefredaktion / Editor in Chief:** Ulrike Trampus; **Redakteur / Editor:** Christian Walf
Language (s): German
DAILY NEWSPAPER

Ludwigsburger Kreisztg, Freiberg a. Neckar
Owner: Ungeheuer+Ulmer KG GmbH & Co.
T: 49 7141 1300 **E:** redaktion@lkz.de
Freq: Daily
Chefredaktion / Editor in Chief: Ulrike Trampus
Language (s): German
DAILY NEWSPAPER

Ludwigsburger Kreisztg, Remseck/ Kornwesth.
Owner: Ungeheuer+Ulmer KG GmbH & Co.
T: 49 7141 1300 **E:** redaktion@lkz.de
Freq: Daily
Chefredakteurin / Editor in Chief: Ulrike Trampus
Language (s): German
DAILY NEWSPAPER

Ludwigsburger Kreisztg. Strohgäu, Asperg
Owner: Ungeheuer+Ulmer KG GmbH & Co.
T: 49 7141 1300 **E:** redaktion@lkz.de
Freq: Daily
Chefredaktion / Editor in Chief: Ulrike Trampus; **Chefredaktion / Editor in Chief:** Ulrike Trampus
Language (s): German
DAILY NEWSPAPER

Magdeburger Volksstimme
Owner: Magdeburger Verlags- und Druckhaus GmbH
Editorial: Magdeburger Verlags- und Druckhaus GmbH, Bahnhofstraße 17, Magdeburg 39104. **T:** 49 391 59 99210
E: chefredaktion@volksstimme.de
W: http://www.volksstimme.de/nachrichten/magdeburg/
Freq: Daily; **Circ:** 46328 IVW
Redakteur / Editor: Michael Bock; **Redaktion / Editor:** Jan-Thomas Goetze; **Chefredaktion / Editor in Chief:** Alois Kösters; **Redakteur / Editor:** Peter Wendt
Language (s): German
DAILY NEWSPAPER

Main Post
Editorial: Berner Str. 2, Würzburg 97084.
T: 49 931 60010
E: service.center@mainpost.de
W: http://www.mainpost.de **Circ:** 127722
Chefredaktion / Editor in Chief: Michael Reinhard; **Redakteur / Editor:** Torsten Schleicher; **Redakteur / Editor:** Günther Schwärzer
Language (s): German
NEWSPAPER

Main-Echo
Owner: Verlag und Druckerei Main-Echo GmbH & Co. KG
Editorial: Main-Netz Media GmbH, Weichertstr. 20, Aschaffenburg 63741.
T: 49 602 1 3 96 2 29
E: redaktion@main-echo.de
W: http://www.main-netz.de
Freq: Daily; **Circ:** 76990
Chefredaktion / Editor in Chief: Claus Morhart
Language (s): German
DAILY NEWSPAPER

Main-Echo Hessen, Dieburg
Owner: Main-Echo GmbH & Co. KG
Editorial: Weichertstr. 20, Aschaffenburg 63741. **T:** 49 6071 920961
E: info@main-netz.de
Freq: Daily
Chefredakteur / Editor in Chief: Martin Schwarzkopf
Language (s): German
DAILY NEWSPAPER

Main-Echo, Obernburg
Owner: Main-Echo GmbH & Co. KG
T: 49 6022 621086
E: redaktion.obernburg@main-echo.de
W: http://www.main-netz.de/nachrichten/region/obernburg/
Freq: Daily
Chefredakteur / Editor in Chief: Martin Schwarzkopf
Language (s): German
DAILY NEWSPAPER

Main-Post
Owner: Main-Post GmbH & Co. KG
Editorial: Main-Post GmbH & Co. KG, Berner Str. 2, Würzburg 97084. **T:** 49 931 60010
E: red.journal@mainpost.de
W: http://www.mainpost.de
Freq: Daily; **Circ:** 127722
Redakteur / Editor: Wolfgang Ottinger; **Chefredaktion / Editor in Chief:** Roland Schmitt-Raiser
Language (s): German
DAILY NEWSPAPER

Mainzer Rhein-Zeitung
Owner: Mittelrhein Verlag GmbH
Editorial: Mittelrhein-Verlag GmbH, August-Horch-Str. 28, Koblenz 56070.
T: 49 261 892240
E: redaktion@rhein-zeitung.net
W: http://www.rhein-zeitung.de/region/lokales/mainzer-rhein-zeitung.html?
Freq: Daily; **Circ:** 188524
Redaktion / Editor: Axel Ehrlich; **Redakteur / Editor:** Alessandro Fogolin; **Redakteur / Editor:** Andreas Nitsch; **Redakteur / Editor:** Klaus Reimann; **Redakteur / Editor:** Sven Sabock
Language (s): German
DAILY NEWSPAPER

Mangfall-Bote Kolbermoor
W: http://www.ovb-online.de
Language (s): German
NEWSPAPER

Mannheimer Morgen
Owner: Mannheimer Morgen Großdruckerei und Verlag GmbH
Editorial: Mannheimer Morgen Großdruckerei und Verlag GmbH, Dudenstraße 12-26, Mannheim 68167. **T:** 49 261 39201
E: geschaeftsleitung@mamo.de
W: http://www.morgenweb.de/region/mannheimer-morgen
Freq: Daily; **Circ:** 205329
Redakteurin / Editor: Sybille Burmeister; **Redakteur / Editor:** Dennis Christmann; **Redakteur / Editor:** Dirk Mewis
Language (s): German
DAILY NEWSPAPER

Märkische Allgemeine
Owner: Märkische Verlags- und Druck-GmbH Potsdam
Editorial: Märkische Verlags- und Druck-Gesellschaft mbH Potsdam, Friedrich-Engels-Straße 24, Potsdam 14473. **T:** 49 331 28400
E: kontakt@MAZ-online.de
W: http://www.maz-online.de/
Freq: Daily; **Circ:** 138145
Chefredaktion / Editor in Chief: Thoralf Cleven; **Redakteur / Editor:** Torsten Gellner; **Redakteur / Editor:** Igor Göldner; **Redakteur / Editor:** Peter Stein; **Redakteurin / Editor:** Jutta Thieler
Language (s): German
DAILY NEWSPAPER

Märkische Oderzeitung
Owner: Märkisches Verlags- und Druckhaus GmbH & Co. KG
Editorial: Märkisches Verlags- und Druckhaus GmbH & Co. KG, Kellenspring 6, Frankfurt 15230. **T:** 49 335 5530 0
E: chefredaktion@moz.de
W: http://www.moz.de
Freq: Daily; **Circ:** 87713
Redakteur / Editor: Kai Beißer; **Redakteur / Editor:** André Bochow; **Redakteur / Editor:** Ingolf Bunge; **Redakteur / Editor:** Margit Höfer; **Redakteurin / Editor:** Annegret Krüger; **Chefredaktion / Editor in Chief:** Frank Mangelsdorf; **Redakteurin / Editor:** Karin Sandow; **Redakteur / Editor:** Dietrich Schröder; **Redakteur / Editor:** Jens Sell; **Redakteurin / Editor:** Sabine Steinbeiß; **RedaKteur / Editor:** Ullrich Thiessen; **Redakteur / Editor:** Irina Voigt; **Redakteurin / Editor:** Anett Zimmermann
Language (s): German
DAILY NEWSPAPER

Märkische Oderzeitung - Angermünde
Owner: Märkisches Verlags- und Druckhaus GmbH & Co.
Editorial: Kellenspring 6, Frankfurt 15230.
T: 49 3331 260 223
E: angermuende-red@moz.de
Redakteurin / Editor: Daniela Windolff
Editorial Profile: Bureau
Language (s): German
NEWSPAPER

Märkische Oderzeitung - Eberswalde
Owner: Märkisches Verlags- u. Druckhaus GmbH & Co.KG
Editorial: Karl-Marx-Platz 11, Eberswalde.
T: 49 3334 202950 **E:** eberswalde-red@moz.de
Redakteur / Editor: Christian Heinig; **Redaktionsleiter / Managing Editor:** Sven Klamann; **Chefredakteur / Editor in Chief:** Frank Mangelsdorf; **Redakteurin / Editor:** Viola Petersson; **Redakteurin / Editor:** Ellen Werner
Editorial Profile: Bureau
NEWSPAPER

Marler Zeitung
Owner: Verlag J. Bauer KG
Editorial: Verlag J. Bauer KG, Kampstr. 84 b, Marl 45772. **T:** 49 023 651070
E: info@medienhaus-bauer.de
W: http://www.marler-zeitung.de/?
Freq: Daily; **Circ:** 14042
Redaktion / Editor: Gabriele Figge; **Redakteur / Editor:** Gaby Figge; **Redakteur / Editor:** Robert Klose; **Redakteur / Editor:** Dirk Kolakowski; **Redakteur / Editor:** Heinz-Peter Mohr; **Redakteur / Editor:** Martina Möller; **Redakteur / Editor:** Christoph Mrosek; **Redakteur / Editor:** Claus Pawlinka; **Redakteur / Editor:** Klaus Wilker
Language (s): German
DAILY NEWSPAPER

Marner Zeitung
Owner: Boyens Zeitungen GmbH & Co. KG
Editorial: Boyens Medienholding GmbH & Co. KG, Wulf-Isebrand-Platz 1-3, Heide 25746.
T: 49 481 68 86 211
E: redaktion@boyens-medien.de
W: http://zeitungen.boyens-medien.de/tageszeitung/marner-zeitung.html?
Freq: Daily; **Circ:** 28681
Redaktion / Editor: Reinhard Geschke; **Redakteurin / Editor:** Beate Meißner
Language (s): German
DAILY NEWSPAPER

Memminger Zeitung
Owner: Allgäuer Zeitungsverlag GmbH
Editorial: rta.design GmbH, Postfach 3155, Kempten 87440. **T:** 49 831 2060
E: info@all-in.de
W: http://www.all-in.de/nachrichten/rundschau/?
Freq: Daily; **Circ:** 20149
Redaktion / Editor: Helmut Kustermann
Language (s): German
DAILY NEWSPAPER

Meppener Tagespost
Owner: Neue Osnabrücker Zeitung GmbH & Co. KG
Editorial: Verlag Neue Osnabrücker Zeitung, Postfach 4260, Osnabrück 49032.
T: 49 593 1 940 111
E: redaktion@meppener-tagespost.de
W: http://www.noz.de/meppener-tagespost
Freq: Daily; **Circ:** 20356
Redakteur / Editor: Nico Buchholz; **Redaktion / Editor:** Hermann-Josef Hermann-Josef Mammes; **Redakteur / Editor:** Anne Overesch
Language (s): German
DAILY NEWSPAPER

Miesbacher Merkur
Owner: Zeitungsverlag Oberbayern GmbH & Co. KG
Editorial: Münchener Zeitungs-Verlag GmbH & Co.KG, Paul-Heyse-Str. 2-4, München 80336.
T: 49 089 5306 0 **E:** info@merkur-online.de
W: http://www.merkur-online.de/lokales/miesbach/?
Freq: Daily; **Circ:** 17619
Redakteurin / Editor: Manuela Better; **Redakteur / Editor:** Christian Deutschländer; **Redaktion / Editor:** Stephen Hank; **Redakteur / Editor:** Florian Weiß
Language (s): German
DAILY NEWSPAPER

Mindelheimer Zeitung
Owner: Presse-Druck- und Verlags-GmbH
Editorial: Curt-Frenzel-Str. 2, Augsburg 86167
Chefredaktion: Sascha Borowski; **Redakteur / Editor:** Daniela Deeg; **Redakteur / Editor:** Stefan Drescher; **Redakteurin / Editor:** Daniela Fischer; **Reakteur / Editor:** Ina Kresse; **stellv. Chefredaktion:** Norbert Staub
Language (s): German
NEWSPAPER

Mindener Tageblatt
Owner: J. C. C. Bruns Betriebs-GmbH
Editorial: J.C.C.Bruns Betriebs-GmbH, Obermarktstraße 26-30, Minden 32423.
T: 49 571 882240 **E:** mt@mt-online.de
W: http://www.mt-online.de/?
Freq: Daily; **Circ:** 34717
Chefredakteur / Editor in Chief: Christoph Pepper; **Redakteur / Editor:** Marcus Riechmann
Language (s): German

DAILY NEWSPAPER

Mittelbayerische Zeitung
Owner: Mittelbayerische Werbeges. KG
Editorial: Kumpfmühler Straße 15, Regensburg 93047. **T:** 49 9412 0765
E: mz-redaktion@mittelbayerische.de
W: http://www.mittelbayerische.de
Freq: Daily; **Circ:** 117248
Redakteur / Editor: Peter Esser; **Chef vom Dienst:** Kai Gohlke; **Redakteur / Editor:** Thorsten Retta; **Chefredakteur / Editor in chief:** Manfred Sauerer; **Redakteur / Editor:** Holger Schellkopf
Language (s): German
DAILY NEWSPAPER

Mittelbayerische Zeitung für Kelheim, Abensberg und Neustadt
Owner: Mittelbayerischer Verlag KG
Editorial: Kumpfmühler Str. 15, Regensburg 93047. **T:** 49 941 20765
E: mz-redaktion@mittelbayerische.de
W: http://www.mittelbayerische.de
Freq: Daily; **Circ:** 13357 IVW
Language (s): German
DAILY NEWSPAPER

Mitteldeutsche Zeitung
Owner: Mitteldeutsche Druck- und Verlagshaus GmbH & Co. KG
Editorial: Mitteldeutsches Druck- und Verlagshaus GmbH & Co. KG, Delitzscher Straße 65, Halle 6112 **E:** service@mz-web.de
W: http://www.mz-web.de/?
Freq: Daily; **Circ:** 208019
Chefredaktion / Editor in Chief: Hartmut Augustin; **Redakteur / Editor:** Christian Elsaeßer; **Chefredaktion / Editor in Chief:** Hans-Jürgen Greye; **Redakteur / Editor:** Steffen Höhne; **Redakteur / Editor:** Christoph Karpe; **Redakteur / Editor:** Hans-Ulrich Köhler; **Redakteurin / Editor:** Kerstin Metze; **Redakteur / Editor:** Rainer Wozny; **Redakteur / Editor:** Walter Zöller
Language (s): German
DAILY NEWSPAPER

Moosburger Zeitung
Owner: Josef Thomann'sche Buchdruckerei Verlag
Editorial: Zeitungsgruppe Straubinger Tagblatt/ Landshuter Zeitung, Ludwigsplatz 32, Straubing 94315. **T:** 49 942 19400
E: kontakt@idowa.de
W: http://www.idowa.de/zeitung/moosburger-zeitung
Freq: Daily; **Circ:** 35781
Redaktion / Editor: Karin Alt; **Redakteur / Eidtor:** Fabian Roßmann
Language (s): German
DAILY NEWSPAPER

Mühldorfer Anzeiger
Owner: Oberbayerisches Volksblatt GmbH & Co. Medienhaus KG
Editorial: Oberbayerisches Volksblatt GmbH & Co. Medienhaus KG, Hafnerstraße 5-13, Rosenheim 83022. **T:** 49 803 12130
E: info@ovb-heimatzeitungen.de
W: http://www.ovb-online.de/muehldorf/?
Freq: Daily; **Circ:** 14354
Redaktion / Editor: Markus Honervogt
Language (s): German
DAILY NEWSPAPER

Münchner Merkur
Owner: Münchener Zeitungs-Verlag GmbH & Co. KG
Editorial: Münchener Zeitungs-Verlag GmbH & Co.KG, Paul-Heyse-Str. 2-4, München 80336.
T: 49 089 5306 0
E: redaktion@merkur-online.de
W: http://www.merkur-online.de
Freq: Daily; **Circ:** 277306
Redakteur / Editor: Georg Anastasiadis; **Chefredakteurin/ Editor in Chief:** Bettina Bäumlisberger; **Redakteur / Editor:** Matthias Busch; **Redakteur / Editor:** Christian Deutschländer; **Redakteur / Editor:** Armin Gibis; **Redakteur / Editor:** Dominik Müller; **Redakteur / Editor:** Matthias Weinzierl
Language (s): German
DAILY NEWSPAPER

Münchner Merkur Würmtal, Planegg
Owner: Münchener Zeitungs-Verlag GmbH & Co. KG
T: 49 89 8597091
Freq: Daily
Redakteurin / Editor: Manuela Better; **Redakteur / Editor:** Christian Deutschländer; **Redakteur / Editor:** Florian Weiß
DAILY NEWSPAPER

Münsterland Zeitung
Owner: Münstersche Zeitung Medien GmbH & Co. KG
Editorial: Lensing Medien GmbH & Co. KG, Westenhellweg 86-88, Dortmund 44137
E: redaktion@muensterlandzeitung.de
W: http://www.muensterlandzeitung.de/?
Freq: Daily; **Circ:** 20000
Redaktion / Editor: Manfred Elfering
Language (s): German
DAILY NEWSPAPER

Münsterländische Tageszeitung
Owner: Hermann Imsiecke Druck und Verlag GmbH
Editorial: Hermann Imsiecke Druck und Verlag GmbH, Lange Straße 9/11, Cloppenburg 49661. **T:** 49 447 1 1780
E: redaktion@mt-friesoythe.de
W: http://www.mt-news.de/
Freq: Daily; **Circ:** 18518
Chefredakteurin / Editor in Chief: Angelika Hauke; **Redakteur / Editor:** Johannes Klinker; **Redakteur / Editor:** Ludger Langosch; **Redakteur / Editor:** Rolf Wulfers
Language (s): German
DAILY NEWSPAPER

Münsterländische Volkszeitung
Owner: Altmeppen Verlag GmbH & Co. KG
Editorial: Altmeppen Verlag GmbH & Co. KG, Bahnhofstraße 8, Rheine 48431.
T: 49 597 1 4040 **E:** info@mv-online.de
W: http://www.mv-online.de/?
Freq: Daily; **Circ:** 19313
Redaktion / Editor: Reiner Wellmann
Language (s): German
DAILY NEWSPAPER

Münstersche Zeitung
Owner: Münstersche Zeitung Medien GmbH & Co. KG
Editorial: Münstersche Zeitung, Lokalredaktion Münster, Neubrückenstr. 8-11, Munster 48143
E: redaktion.newsdesk@muensterschezeitung.de **W:** http://www.muensterschezeitung.de/?
Freq: Daily; **Circ:** 27104
Chefredakteur / Editor in Chief: Stefan Bergmann; **Redakteur / Editor:** Peter Imkamp
Language (s): German
DAILY NEWSPAPER

Murnauer Tagblatt
Owner: Zeitungsverlag Oberbayern GmbH & Co. KG
W: http://www.merkur-online.de
Language (s): German
NEWSPAPER

Nahe-Zeitung
Owner: Mittelrhein-Verlag GmbH
Editorial: Mittelrhein-Verlag GmbH, August-Horch-Str. 28, Koblenz 56070.
T: 49 261 892240
E: redaktion@rhein-zeitung.net
W: http://www.rhein-zeitung.de/region/lokales/nahe.html?
Freq: Daily; **Circ:** 13752
Redakteur / Editor: Stefan Conradt; **Redakteur / Editor:** Michael Fesntermann; **Redaktion / Editor:** Kurt Knaudt; **Redakteur / Editor:** Klaus Peter Müller; **Redakteur / Editor:** Vera Müller; **Redakteur / Editor:** Andreas Nitsch; **Redakteur / Editor:** Bettina Schäfer; **Redakteur / Editor:** Jörg Staiber
Language (s): German
DAILY NEWSPAPER

Nassauische Neue Presse
Owner: Frankfurter Societäts-Medien GmbH
Editorial: Nassauische Neue Presse, Bahnhofstraße 9, Limburg 65549.
T: 49 643 1 29 43 0 **E:** nnp@fnp.de
W: http://www.nnp.de/?
Freq: Daily; **Circ:** 22283
Redakteur / Editor: Michael Balk; **Redakteur / Editor:** Dieter Sattler; **Redakteur / Editor:** Christiane Warnecke
Language (s): German
DAILY NEWSPAPER

Natürlich
Owner: Medienfabrik Gütersloh GmbH
Editorial: Medienfabrik Gütersloh GmbH, Carl-Bertelsmann-Straße 33, Gütersloh 33311.
T: 49 5241 2348050
E: redaktion@natuerlich-magazin.de
W: http://www.natuerlich-magazin.de/
Freq: Monthly; **Circ:** 500000
Chefredakteur / Editor in Chief: Jan R. Egel
Language (s): German
NEWSPAPER

Naumburger Tageblatt
Owner: Mitteldeutsche Zeitung
Editorial: Zeitungsverlag Naumburg Nebra GmbH & Co. KG, Salzstraße 8, Naumburg 6618. **T:** 49 34 45 230 78 30
E: naumburger.tageblatt@mz-web.de
W: http://www.naumburger-tageblatt.de
Freq: Daily; **Circ:** 13917
Redaktion / Editor: Albrecht Günther; **Redakteur / Editor:** Albrecht Günther
Language (s): German
DAILY NEWSPAPER

Neue Presse
Owner: Druck- und Verlagsanstalt Neue Presse GmbH
Editorial: Druck- und Verlagsanstalt Neue Presse GmbH, Steinweg 51, Coburg 96450.
T: 49 956 1850120 **E:** region@np-coburg.de
W: http://www.np-coburg.de/
Freq: Daily; **Circ:** 25022
Redakteur / Editor: Roland Beck; **Redakteur / Editor:** Stefan Gohlisch; **Redakteur / Editor:** Mathias Mathes; **Redakteur / Editor:** Cornelia Stegner; **Redakteur / Editor:** Steffi Wolf
Language (s): German
DAILY NEWSPAPER

Neue Presse Hannover
Owner: Verlagsgesellschaft Madsack GmbH & Co. KG
Editorial: August-Madsack-Straße 1, Hannover 30559. **T:** 49 511 51 01 0
E: np@neuepresse.de
W: http://www.neuepresse.de
Freq: Daily; **Circ:** 203130
Chefredakteur / Editor in Chief: Bodo Krüger
Language (s): German
DAILY NEWSPAPER

Neue Presse Hassberge Ebern
Owner: Druck- und Verlagsanstalt Neue Presse GmbH
Editorial: Marktplatz 3, Ebern 96106.
T: 49 9531 6067 **E:** ebern@np-coburg.de
W: http://www.np-coburg.de/lokal/hassberge/
Freq: Daily
Language (s): German
DAILY NEWSPAPER

Neue Presse Kronach
Owner: Druck- und Verlagsanstalt Neue Presse GmbH
Editorial: Bahnhofstr. 1, Kronach 96317.
T: 49 9261 601618 **E:** kronach@np-coburg.de
W: http://www.np-coburg.de/lokal/kronach/
Freq: Daily
Language (s): German
DAILY NEWSPAPER

Neue Ruhr / Neue Rhein Zeitung
Owner: Zeitungsverlag Niederrhein GmbH & Co. Essen KG
Editorial: Friedrichstr. 34, Essen 45128.
T: 49 201 8040 **E:** redaktion@nrz.de
W: http://www.derwesten.de
Freq: Daily; **Circ:** 189065 IVW
Redakteur / Editor: Jörg Bartel; **Redaktion / Editor:** Jan Jessen; **Chefredaktion / Editor in Chief:** Manfred Lachniet; **Redaktion / Editor:** Thomas Rünker
Language (s): German
DAILY NEWSPAPER

Neue Westfälische
Owner: Zeitungsverlag Neue Westfälische GmbH & Co. KG
Editorial: Zeitungsverlag Neue Westfälische GmbH & Co. KG, Niedernstraße 21-27, Bielefeld 33602. **T:** 49 521 5550
E: redaktion@nw-news.de
W: http://www.nw-news.de/
Freq: Daily; **Circ:** 25022
Redakteur / Editor: Jörg Fritz; **Redakteurin / Editor:** Heidi Hagen-Pekdemir; **Redakteur / Editor:** Patrick Schlütter; **Chefredaktion / Editor in Chief:** Thomas Seim
Language (s): German
DAILY NEWSPAPER

neues deutschland
Owner: Neues Deutschland Druckerei und Verlag GmbH
Editorial: Verlag Neues Deutschland Druckerei und Verlag GmbH, Franz-Mehring-Platz 1, Berlin 10243. **T:** 49 302 9781111
E: chefredaktion@nd-online.de
W: http://www.neues-deutschland.de/?
Freq: Daily; **Circ:** 37498
Redakteur / Editor: Jürgen Amendt; **Redakteur / Editor:** Uwe Kalbe; **Chefredakteur / Editor in Chief:** Tom Strohschneider
Language (s): German
DAILY NEWSPAPER

Neumarkter Anzeiger
Owner: Oberbayerisches Volksblatt GmbH & Co. Medienhaus KG
Editorial: Oberbayerisches Volksblatt GmbH & Co. Medienhaus KG, Hafnerstraße 5-13, Rosenheim 83022. **T:** 49 803 1 2130
E: redaktion@ovb.net
W: http://www.ovb-online.de/muehldorf/neumarkt-st-veit/
Freq: Daily; **Circ:** 13535
Redakteur / Editor: Willi Börsch; **Redaktion / Editor:** Markus Honervogt
Language (s): German
DAILY NEWSPAPER

Neumarkter Tagblatt
Owner: Mittelbayerischer Verlag KG
Editorial: Ludwigstr. 10, Neu-Ulm 89231.
T: 49 731 7071 11 **E:** redaktion@nuz.de
W: http://www.augsburger-allgemeine.de/neu-ulm
Freq: Daily; **Circ:** 18068
Chefredaktion: Sascha Borowski; **Redakteur / Editor:** Daniela Deeg; **Redakteur / Editor:** Stefan Drescher; **Redakteur / Editor:** Daniela Fischer; **Redaktion / Editor:** Eva Gaupp; **Redakteur / Editor:** Ina Kresse; **stellv. Chefredaktion:** Norbert Staub
Language (s): German
DAILY NEWSPAPER

Neuss-Grevenbroicher Zeitung
Owner: Rheinische Post Verlagsges. mbH
Editorial: Zülpicher Str. 10, Dusseldorf 40549.
T: 49 211 505-2426
W: http://www.ngz-online.de
Freq: Daily; **Circ:** 42888
Redaktion / Editor: Ludger Baten; **Redakteur / Editor:** Jens Krüger
Language (s): German
DAILY NEWSPAPER

Neu-Ulmer Zeitung
Owner: Presse-Druck- und Verlags-GmbH
W: http://www.augsburger-allgemeine.de/?region=b-nu
Chefredaktion: Sascha Borowski; **Redakteur / Editor:** Daniela Deeg; **Redakteur / Editor:** Stefan Drescher; **Redakteur / Editor:** Daniela Fischer; **Redaktion / Editor:** Bernhard Junginger; **Redakteur / Editor:** Ina Kresse; **stellv. Chefredaktion:** Norbert Staub
Language (s): German
NEWSPAPER

Nordbayerische Nachrichten (Pegnitz)
Owner: Verlag Nürnberger Presse Druckhaus Nürnberg GmbH & Co. KG
W: http://www.nordbayern.de/region
Redakteurin / Editor: Christiane Fritz; **Redaktion / Editor:** Rainer Groh; **Redakteur / Editor:** Stefan Jablonka
Language (s): German
NEWSPAPER

Nordbayerische Nachrichten Forchheim
Owner: Nürnberger Presse Druckhaus Nürnb. GmbH & Co
Editorial: Nordbayerische Nachrichten Forchheim, Hornschuchallee 7-9, Forchheim 91301. **T:** 49 9191 722020
E: nn-forchheim-redaktion@pressenetz.de
W: http://www.nordbayern.de/region/forchheim
Freq: Daily
Language (s): German
DAILY NEWSPAPER

Nordbayerische Nachrichten Herzogenaurach
Owner: Verlag Nürnberger Presse Druckhaus Nürnberg GmbH & Co.
Editorial: Nordbayerische Nachrichten Herzogenaurach, An der Schütt 26, Herzogenaurach 91074. **T:** 49 9132 780115
E: nn-herzogenaurach-redaktion@pressenetz.de
W: http://www.nordbayern.de/region/herzogenaurach
Freq: Daily
Language (s): German
DAILY NEWSPAPER

Nordbayerische Nachrichten Pegnitz
Owner: Verlag Nürnberger Presse Druckhaus Nürnberg GmbH & Co.
Editorial: Nordbayerische Nachrichten Pegnitz, Hauptstraße 20, Pegnitz 91257.
T: 49 9241 97120
E: nn-pegnitz-redaktion@pressenetz.de
W: http://www.nordbayern.de/region/pegnitz
Freq: Daily
Language (s): German
DAILY NEWSPAPER

Nordbayerischer Kurier
Owner: Nordbayerischer Kurier GmbH & Co. Zeitungsverlag KG
Editorial: Maximilianstraße 58/60, Bayreuth 95444. **T:** 49 921 294 0
E: redaktion@kurier.tmt.de
W: http://www.nordbayerischer-kurier.de

Freq: Daily; **Circ:** 35842
Redakteurin / Editor: Klaus Altmann-Dangelat; **Redakteur / Editor:** Udo Bartsch; **Redakteurin / Editor:** Martina Bay; **Redakteur / Editor:** Gunter Becker; **Redakteurin / Editor:** Sarah Bernhard; **Redakteur / Editor:** Stefan Brand; **Chefredakteur / Editor in Chief:** Joachim Braun; **Umweltredaktion:** Peter Engelbrecht; **Redakteurin / Editor:** Ute Eschenbacher; **Redakteurin / Editor:** Heike Fauser; **Redakteur / Editor:** Andreas Gewinner; **Redakteur / Editor:** Peter Gisder; **Redakteur / Editor:** Reiner Goeritz; **Redakteur / Editor:** Thorsten Gütling; **Redakteur / Editor:** Thorsten Gütling; **Redakteurin / Editor:** Heike Hampl; **Redakteur / Editor:** Norbert Heimbeck; **Redakteur / Editor:** Moritz Kircher; **Redakteur / Editor:** Roman Kocholl; **Redakteur / Editor:** Tobias Köpplinger; **Redakteur /Editor:** Udo Meixner; **Redakteur / Editor:** Peter Rauscher; **Redakteur / Editor:** Elmar Schatz; **Redakteur / Editor:** Manfred Scherer; **Redakteurin / Editor:** Petra Scholz; **Redakteur / Editor:** Stefan Schreibelmayer; **Redakteur / Editor:** Ulrike Sommerer; **Redakteur / Editor:** Eberhard Spaeth; **Redakteur / Editor:** Herbert Steininger; **Redakteur / Editor:** Michael Weiser
Language (s): German
DAILY NEWSPAPER

Nordbayerischer Kurier Pegnitz
Owner: Nordbayerischer Kurier GmbH & Co. Zeitungsverlag KG
Editorial: Nordbayerischer Kurier Pegnitz, Hauptstraße 20, Pegnitz 91257.
T: 49 9241 98011
E: kurier.pegnitz@kurier.tmt.de
W: http://www.nordbayerischer-kurier.de/region/pegnitz
Freq: Daily
Language (s): German
DAILY NEWSPAPER

Norddeutsche Rundschau
Owner: sh:z Schleswig-Holsteinischer Zeitungsverlag GmbH & Co. KG
Editorial: Fördestraße 20, Flensburg 24944
W: http://www.shz.de
Language (s): German
NEWSPAPER

Nordhannoversche Zeitung (Langenhagen)
Owner: Madsack Heimatzeitungen GmbH & Co. KG
W: http://www.myheimat.de
Chefredaktion / Editor in Chief: Peter Taubald
Language (s): German
NEWSPAPER

Nordsee-Zeitung
Owner: Nordsee-Zeitung GmbH
Editorial: Hafenstraße 140, Bremerhaven 27576. **T:** 49 471 597 0
E: redaktion@nordsee-zeitung.de
W: http://www.nordsee-zeitung.de
Freq: Daily; **Circ:** 61225
Redakteurin / Editor: Christoph Barth; **Redakteur / Editor:** Lars Brockbalz; **Redakteur / Editor:** Thorsten Brockmann; **Redakteur / Editor:** Rainer Donsbach; **Redakteur / Editor:** Wolfgang Ehrecke; **Redakteur / Editor:** Tobia Fischer; **Redakteurin / Editor:** Barbara Fixy; **Redakteurin / Editor:** Inga Hansen; **Redakteurin / Editor:** Ursel Kikker; **Redakteur / Editor:** Ulrich Kroeger; **Redakteurin / Editor:** Heike Leuschner; **Redakteurin / Editor:** Bärbel Litfin; **Chefredakteur / Editor in Chief:** Jost Lübben; **Redakteurin / Editor:** Lili Maffiotte; **Redakteur / Editor:** Jürgen Malekaitis; **Redaktion / Editor:** Gert-Dieter Meier; **Redakteur / Editor:** Torsten Melchers; **Redakteur / Editor:** Klaus Mündelein; **Redakteure / Editor:** Jürgen Rabbel; **Redakteur / Editor:** Oliver Riemann; **Redakteur / Editor:** Dietmar Rose; **Redakteur / Editor:** Andreas Schoener; **Redakteur / Editor:** Ute Schröder; **Redakteur / Editor:** Dörte Schubert; **Redakteurin / Editor:** Susanne Schwan; **Redakteur / Editor:** Tobias Schwerdtfeger; **Redakteurin / Editor:** Anne Stürzer; **Redakteurin / Editor:** Denise von der Ahé; **Redakteur / Editor:** Andy Wackert
Language (s): German
DAILY NEWSPAPER

Nordwest-Zeitung
Owner: Nordwest-Zeitung Verlagsgesellschaft mbH & Co. KG
Editorial: Peterstraße 28-34, Oldenburg 26121. **T:** 49 441 998801
E: red.online@nordwest-zeitung.de
W: http://www.nwzonline.de
Freq: Daily; **Circ:** 122468
Redakteur / Editor: Hauke Richters; **Redakteur / Editor:** Jörg Schürmeyer
Language (s): German
DAILY NEWSPAPER

Northeimer Neueste Nachrichten
Owner: Dierichs GmbH & Co. KG
Editorial: In der Fluth 24, Northeim 37154
W: http://www.hna.de
Redakeurin / Editor: Dorothea Backovic; **Redakteur / Editor:** Andreas Berger; **Redakteurin / Editor:** Jessica Berger; **Redakteurin / Editor:** Gisela Busch; **Redakteur / Editor:** Wilhelm Ditzel; **Redakteurin / Editor:** Martina Eull; **Redakteurin / Editor:** Ina Joop; **Redakteur / Editor:** Sebastian Lammel; **Redakteur / Editor:** Eugen Maier; **Redakteur / Editor:** Philipp David Pries; **Redakteur / Editor:** Moritz Schäfer; **Redaktion / Editor:** Olaf Weiss
Language (s): German
NEWSPAPER

Nürnberger Nachrichten
Owner: Verlag Nürnberger Presse Druckhaus Nürnberg GmbH & Co. KG
Editorial: Marienstraße 9/11, Nurnberg 90402.
T: 49 911 216 2410
E: nn-lokales@pressenetz.de
W: http://www.nuernberger-nachrichten.de
Freq: Daily; **Circ:** 285016
Redakteur / Editor: Hans Böller; **Chefredaktion / Editor in Chief:** Heinz-Joachim Hauck; **Redakteur / Editor:** Lothar Hoja; **Redakteur / Editor:** Gerhard Lauchs; **Redakteurin / Editor:** Verena Litz; **Redakteur / Editor:** Klaus Wonneberger
Language (s): German
DAILY NEWSPAPER

Nürtinger Zeitung
Owner: Senner Verlag GmbH
Editorial: Carl-Benz-Straße 1, Nürtingen 72622. **T:** 49 702 2 9464 0
E: redaktion@ntz.de **W:** http://www.ntz.de
Freq: Daily; **Circ:** 22171 IVW
Redakteurin / Editor: Christa Ansel; **Redakteur / Editor:** Uwe Bauer
Language (s): German
DAILY NEWSPAPER

Oberbayerisches Volksblatt
Owner: Oberbayerisches Volksblatt GmbH & Co. Medienhaus KG
Editorial: Hafnerstraße 5-13, Rosenheim 83022. **T:** 49 803 12130 **E:** redaktion@ovb.net
W: http://www.ovb-online.de
Freq: Daily; **Circ:** 71191
Redakteurin / Editor: Corinna Maier
Language (s): German
DAILY NEWSPAPER

Oberbergische Volkszeitung (Waldbröl)
Owner: Heinen-Verlag GmbH
Editorial: Kaiserstr. 1, Gummersbach 51643.
T: 49 2261 9289-0
E: OVZ.Gummersbach@kr-redaktion.de
W: http://www.rundschau-online.de/
Freq: Daily
Redakteurin / Editor: Uta-Kristina Maul
Language (s): German
DAILY NEWSPAPER

Oberbergischer Anzeiger
Owner: M. DuMont Schauberg GmbH & Co. KG
Editorial: An der Gohrsmühle 10, Bergisch Gladbach 51465. **T:** 49 221 2242744
E: redaktion.oberberg@ksta.de
W: http://www.ksta.de/oberberg/15189242,15189242.html
Redakteur / Editor: Joachim Frank; **Redakteur / Editor:** Peter Pauls; **Chefredakteur / Editor in chief:** Wolfgang Wagner
Language (s): German
NEWSPAPER

Oberfranken Kombi
Owner: Frankenpost Verlag GmbH
Editorial: Frankenpost Verlag GmbH, Poststr. 9 -11, Hof 95028. **T:** 49 9281 8160
E: verlag@frankenpost.de
W: http://www.frankenpost.de/regional/oberfranken/
Freq: Daily
Language (s): German
DAILY NEWSPAPER

Oberhessische Presse
Owner: Hitzeroth Druck + Medien GmbH & Co. KG
Editorial: Franz-Tuczek-Weg 1, Marburg 35039. **T:** 49 642 1 409 0
E: redaktion@op-marburg.de
W: http://www.op-marburg.de
Freq: Daily; **Circ:** 29027
Redakteurin / Editor: Carina Becker; **redakteur / editor:** Till Conrad; **Redakteur / Editor:** Stefan Dietrich; **Redakteur / Editor:** Gianfranco Fain; **Redakteur / Editor:** Tim Gabel; **Redakteur / Editor:** Bodo Ganswindt; **redakteur / editor:** Bodo Ganswindt; **Redakteur / Editor:** Manfred Hitzeroth; **redakteur / editor:** Florian Lerchbacher; **Chefredakteur / Editor in Chief:** Christoph Linne; **Redakteurin / Editor:** Anna Ntemiris; **Redakteur / Editor:** Michael Rinde; **Redakteur / Editor:** Götz Schaub; **Redakteur / Editor:** Holger Schmidt; **Redakteur / Editor:** Michael E. Schmidt; **Redakteurin / Editor:** Maren Schultz; **Redakteur / Editor:** Frank Steinhoff-Wolfart; **Redakteur / Editor:** Thomas Strothjohann
Language (s): German
DAILY NEWSPAPER

Obermain-Tagblatt
Owner: MPO Medien GmbH
Editorial: Bahnhofstraße 14, Lichtenfels 96215. **T:** 49 957 1 788 0
E: redaktion@obermain.de
W: http://www.obermain.de
Freq: Daily; **Circ:** 11737
Redakteur / Editor: Philipp Fischer; **Redakteur / editor:** Stefan Lutter; **Redaktion / Editor:** Roger Martin
Language (s): German
DAILY NEWSPAPER

Odenwälder Echo
Owner: Echo Zeitungen GmbH
Editorial: Hauptstraße 59, Erbach 64711.
T: 49 606 2 9435 27
E: odenwald@darmstaedter-echo.de
W: http://www.echo-online.de
Freq: Daily; **Circ:** 13313
Redaktion / Editor: Gerhard Grünewald; **Redakteur / editor:** Lutz Heider
Language (s): German
DAILY NEWSPAPER

Odenwälder Zeitung
Owner: DiesbachMedien GmbH
Editorial: Friedrichstraße 24, Weinheim 69469.
T: 49 62 01 8 11 00
E: mail@diesbachmedien.de
W: http://www.wnoz.de
Freq: Daily
Redaktion / Editor: Carsten Propp
Language (s): German
DAILY NEWSPAPER

Oeffentlicher Anzeiger (Kirn)
W: http://www.rhein-zeitung.de
Language (s): German
NEWSPAPER

Offenbach-Post
Owner: Pressehaus Bintz-Verlag GmbH & Co. KG
Editorial: Waldstraße 226, Offenbach 63071.
T: 49 895 306 0 **E:** redaktion@op-online.de
W: http://www.op-online.de
Freq: Daily; **Circ:** 42586
Chefredaktion / Editor in Chief: Frank Pröse
Language (s): German
DAILY NEWSPAPER

Offenburger Tageblatt - Schwarzwaldzeitung
Owner: Reiff Verlag KG
Editorial: Reiff Verlag KG - Mittelbadische Presse, Marlener Straße 9, Offenburg 77656.
T: 49 781 5040 **E:** pr-redaktion@reiff.de
W: http://www.bo.de
Freq: Daily; **Circ:** 52641
Redaktion / Editor: Wolfgang Kollmer
Language (s): German
DAILY NEWSPAPER

Oldenburgische Volkszeitung
Owner: Oldenburgische Volkszeitung Druckerei und Verlag KG
Editorial: Neuer Markt 2, Vechta 49377.
T: 49 444 1 9560 0 **E:** info@ov-online.de
W: http://www.ov-online.de
Freq: Daily; **Circ:** 22624
Redakteur / Editor: Normann Berg; **Redakteut / Editor:** Carsten Boning; **Redakteurin / Editor:** Linda Braunschweig; **Redakteur / Editor:** Lars Chowanietz; **Redakteur / Editor:** Dirk Dasenbrock; **Redakteur / Editor:** Andreas Hammer; **Redakteur / Editor:** Andreas Hausfeld; **Redakteurin / Editor:** Ruth Honkomp-Willenbring; **Chefredaktion / Editor in Chief:** Andreas Kathe; **Redakteur / Editor:** Volker Kläne; **Redakteurin / Editor:** Kerstin Köhne; **Redakteur / Editor:** Klaus Peter Lammert; **Redakteur / Editor:** Matthias Niehues; **Redakteur / Editor:** Damian Ryschka; **Redakteur / Editor:** Giorgio Tzimurtas
Language (s): German
DAILY NEWSPAPER

Oranienburger Generalanzeiger
Owner: Märkischer Zeitungsverlag Zweigniederlassung der Westfälischer Anzeiger Verlagsges. mbH & Co. KG
Editorial: Lehnitzstraße 13, Oranienburg 16515. **T:** 49 330 1 59 63 22
E: lokales@oranienburger-generalanzeiger.de
W: http://www.die-mark-online.de/heimat/oranienburg/
Freq: Daily; **Circ:** 12703
Chefredaktion / Editor in Chief: Frank Mangelsdorf; **Redakteur / Editor:** Thomas Pilz; **Redakteur /Editor:** Jürgen Zinke
Language (s): German
DAILY NEWSPAPER

Oschatzer Allgemeine
Owner: Leipziger Verlags- und Druckereiges. mbH & Co. KG
W: http://www.oaz-online.de
Redakteur / Editor: Heinz Großnick; **Redakteur / Editor:** Frank Hörügel; **Redaktion / Editor:** Hagen Rösner
Language (s): German
NEWSPAPER

Osterhofener Zeitung
Owner: Neue Presse Verlags-GmbH
Editorial: Stadtplatz 11, Osterhofen 94486.
T: 49 993 2 953 821
E: red.osterhofen@pnp.de
W: http://www.pnp.de/region_und_lokal/landkreis_deggendorf/osterhofen/
Freq: Daily; **Circ:** 23176
Redakteur / Editor: Josef Schiller; **Redaktion / Editor:** Gabriele Schwarzbözl
Language (s): German
DAILY NEWSPAPER

Osterholzer Kreisblatt
Owner: Bremer Tageszeitungen AG
Editorial: Martinistraße 43, Bremen 28195.
T: 49 4791 3030
Freq: Daily
Redakteur / Editor: Siegfried Deismann; **Redakteurin / Editor:** Gabriela Keller; **Redakteur / Editor:** Sebastian Kelm; **Redakteur / Editor:** Bernhard Komesker; **Redakteurin / Editor:** Brigitte Lange; **Redakteur / Editor:** Fritz Othersen; **Redakteur / Editor:** Peter Otto; **Redakteur / Editor:** Christian Pfeiff; **Redakteur / Editor:** Michael Rabba; **Redakteur / Editor:** Michael Schön; **Redakteurin / Editor:** Charlotte Schuhmacher; **Redakteur / Editor:** Michael Thurm; **Redakteur / Editor:** Peter von Döllen; **Redakteur / Editor:** Michael Wilke
Language (s): German
DAILY NEWSPAPER

Osterländer Volkszeitung
Owner: Leipziger Verlags- und Druckereiges. mbH & Co. KG
Editorial: Kornmarkt 1, Altenburg 4600.
T: 49 344 7 5749 10
E: altenburg.redaktion@lvz.de
W: http://www.ovz-online.de
Freq: Daily; **Circ:** 13615
Redaktion / Editor: Günter Neumann
Language (s): German
DAILY NEWSPAPER

Ostfriesen-Zeitung
Owner: ZGO Zeitungsgruppe Ostfriesland GmbH
Editorial: Maiburger Straße 8, Leer 26789
W: http://www.oz-online.de/-news/ostfriesland
Freq: Daily; **Circ:** 38611
Redakteurin / Editor: Gabriele Boschbach; **Redakteur / Editor:** Norbert Fiks; **Chefredaktion / Editor in Chief:** Uwe Heitmann
Language (s): German
DAILY NEWSPAPER

Ostfriesische Nachrichten
Owner: Ostfriesische Nachrichten GmbH
Editorial: Kirchstraße 8 - 14, Aurich 26603.
T: 49 494 1 1708 0 **E:** redaktion@on-online.de
W: http://www.on-online.de
Freq: Daily; **Circ:** 14368
Chefredaktion / Editor in Chief: Ralf Klöker
Language (s): German
DAILY NEWSPAPER

Ostfriesischer Kurier
Owner: Ostfriesischer Kurier GmbH & Co. KG
Editorial: Stellmacherstr. 14, Norden 26506.
T: 49 493 1 925 230 **E:** ok-redaktion@skn.info
W: http://www.skn.info
Freq: Daily; **Circ:** 14446
Redakteur / Editor: Ingo Janssen; **Chefredakteur / Editor in Chief:** Manfred Menssen; **Redakteur / Editor:** Bernhard Uphoff
Language (s): German
DAILY NEWSPAPER

Ostholsteiner Anzeiger
Owner: sh:z Schleswig-Holsteinischer Zeitungsverlag GmbH & Co. KG

Editorial: Fördestraße 20, Flensburg 24944.
T: 49 452 1 779 0 **E:** redaktion@shz.de
W: http://www.shz.de
Freq: Daily; **Circ:** 24536
Redaktion / Editor: Hartmut Buhmann; **Redakteurin / Editor:** Anja Christiansen; **Redakteurin / Editor:** Gerrit Hencke; **Redakteurin / Editor:** Barbara Maas; **Redakteurin / Editor:** Mira Nagar; **Redakteur / Editor:** Hauke Normann
Language (s): German
DAILY NEWSPAPER

Ostsee-Zeitung
Owner: Ostsee-Zeitung GmbH & Co. KG
Editorial: Richard-Wagner-Straße 1a, Rostock 18055 **E:** redaktion@ostsee-zeitung.de
W: http://www.ostsee-zeitung.de
Freq: Daily; **Circ:** 150119
Chefredaktion / Editor in Chief: Andreas Ebel; **Redakteur / Editor:** Michael Zumpe
Language (s): German
DAILY NEWSPAPER

Ostthüringer Zeitung
Owner: ZGT Verlag GmbH
Editorial: Gottstedter Landstraße 6, Erfurt 99092. **T:** 49 365 77 33 10
E: chefredaktion@otz.de **W:** http://www.otz.de
Freq: Daily; **Circ:** 98559
Redakteurin / Editor: Ilona Berger; **Redakteurin / Editor:** Angelika Bohn; **Redakteur / Editor:** Thomas Fuchs; **Redakteur / editor:** Martin Gerlach; **Redakteur / Editor:** Martin Gerlach; **Redakteurin / Editor:** Margit Kasper; **Redakteurin / Editor:** Petra Lowe; **Redakteur / Editor:** Volkhard Paczulla; **Redakteur / Editor:** Andreas Rabel; **Redakteur /Editor:** Bernd Scheffel; **Redakteurin / Editor:** Sabine Wagner; **Redakteur / Editor:** Tino Zippel
Language (s): German
DAILY NEWSPAPER

Ostthüringer Zeitung OTZ, Jena
Owner: Ostthüringer Zeitung Verlag GmbH & Co. KG
Editorial: Am Holzmarkt 8, Jena 7743.
T: 49 3641 5909123 **E:** jena@otz.de
W: http://www.otz.de
Freq: Daily
Language (s): German
DAILY NEWSPAPER

Paderborner Kreiszeitung
Owner: Zeitungsverlag Neue Westfälische GmbH & Co. KG
Editorial: Gertrud-Gröninger-Str. 12, Paderborn 33102. **T:** 49 5251 29 99 50
E: redaktion@neue-westfaelische.de
W: http://www.nw-news.de
Freq: Daily; **Circ:** 18193
Redakteur / Editor: Karl Finke; **Redakteurin / Editor:** Simone Flörke; **Redakteur / Editor:** Frederik Grabbe; **Redakteur / Editor:** Ralph Meyer; **Redakteurin / Editor:** Julia Renner
Language (s): German
DAILY NEWSPAPER

Passauer Neue Presse
Owner: Neue Presse Verlags-GmbH
Editorial: Medienstraße 5, Passau 94036.
T: 49 851 802 0 **E:** info@pnp.de
W: http://www.pnp.de
Freq: Daily; **Circ:** 171700
Redakteur / Editor: Alexander Brunner; **Redakteur / Editor:** Sebastian Fleischmann; **Chefredaktion / Editor in Chief:** Ernst Fuchs; **Redakteurin / Editor:** Sandra Hiendl; **Redakteurin / Editor:** Karin Polz; **Redakteurin / Editor:** Karin Polz; **Redakteur / Editor:** Reinhard Willhelm
Language (s): German
DAILY NEWSPAPER

Passauer Neue Presse, Freyung Grafenau
Owner: Neue Presse Verlags-GmbH
Editorial: Stadtplatz 8-10, Freyung 94078.
T: 49 8551 57890 **E:** red.freyung@pnp.de
W: http://www.pnp.de/region_und_lokal/landkreis_freyung_grafenau/
Freq: Daily
Redakteurin / Editor: Jennifer Jahns; **Redakteur / Editor:** Karl Lautscham; **Redakteurin / Editor:** Doris Löw; **Chefredakteur / Editor in chief:** Peter Püschel
Language (s): German
DAILY NEWSPAPER

Passauer Neue Presse, Griesbach
Owner: Neue Presse Verlags-GmbH
Editorial: Neue Presse Multimedia GmbH, Medienstraße 5, Passau 94036.
T: 49 8532 920641 **E:** info@pnp.de
Freq: Daily
Redakteurin / Editor: Monika Bormeth; **Redakteurin / Editor:** Bettina Durner; **Redakteurin / Editor:** Carmen Keller; **Redakteurin / Editor:** Tanja Rometta; **Redakteurin /Editor:** Karin Seidl
Language (s): German
DAILY NEWSPAPER

Passauer Neue Presse, Pfarrkirchen
Owner: Neue Presse Verlags-GmbH
Editorial: Medienstraße 5, Passau 94036.
T: 49 8561 234921 **E:** info@pnp.de
Freq: Daily
Language (s): German
DAILY NEWSPAPER

Passauer Neue Presse, Pocking
Owner: Neue Presse Verlags-GmbH
Editorial: Medienstraße 5, Passau 94036.
T: 49 8531 902921 **E:** info@pnp.de
Freq: Daily
Redakteurin / Editor: Monika Bormeth; **Redakteurin / Editor:** Bettina Durner; **Redakteurin / Editor:** Carmen Keller; **Redakteurin / Editor:** Tanja Rometta; **Redakteurin /Editor:** Karin Seidl
Language (s): German
DAILY NEWSPAPER

Pegnitz-Zeitung
Owner: Verlag Hans Fahner GmbH & Co. KG
Editorial: Pegnitz-Zeitung, Nürnberger Str. 19, Lauf 91207. **T:** 49 9123 175155
E: Redaktion@Pegnitz-Zeitung.de
W: http://n-land.de/pegnitz-zeitung/
Freq: Daily; **Circ:** 13319
Redakteur / Editor: Patrick Bär; **Redakteurin / Editor:** Stefanie Buchner-Freiberger; **Redakteurin / Editor:** Tina Chemnitz; **Redakteur/ Editor:** Clemens Fischer; **Redakteur / Editor:** Michael Scholz; **Redakteur / Editor:** Andreas Sichelstiel
Language (s): German
DAILY NEWSPAPER

Peiner Allgemeine Zeitung
Owner: Peiner Allgemeine Zeitung Verlagsges. mbH & Co. KG
Editorial: Werderstraße 49, Peine 31224.
T: 49 517 1 406 131
E: redaktion@paz-online.de
W: http://www.paz-online.de
Freq: Daily; **Circ:** 20600
Chefredakteur / Editor in Chief: Dirk Borth; **Redakteur / Editor:** Carolin Kretzinger; **Redakteur / Editor:** Thomas Kröger; **Redakteur / Editor:** Michael Lieb; **Redakteurin / Editor:** Mirja Polreich
Language (s): German
DAILY NEWSPAPER

Penzberger Merkur
Owner: Zeitungsverlag Oberbayern GmbH & Co. KG
Editorial: Karlstraße 7, Penzberg 82377.
T: 49 885 6 9222 0
E: penz-merkur@merkur-online.de
W: http://www.penzberger-merkur.de
Freq: Daily; **Circ:** 12107
Redaktion / Editor: Wolfgang Schörner
Language (s): German
DAILY NEWSPAPER

pepper
Owner: Service-Redaktion Topas
W: http://www.main-rheiner.de
Chefredaktion / Editor in Chief: Heidrun Braun
Language (s): German
NEWSPAPER

Pfaffenhofener Kurier
Owner: Donaukurier Verlagsges. mbH & Co. KG
Editorial: Hauptplatz 31, Pfaffenhofen 85276.
T: 49 844 1 869 33
E: redaktion@pfaffenhofenerkurier.de
W: http://www.donaukurier.de/lokales/pfaffenhofen/
Freq: Daily; **Circ:** 15697
Redakteur / Editor: Manuel Holscher; **Redaktion / Editor:** Robert Schmidl
Language (s): German
DAILY NEWSPAPER

Pforzheimer Zeitung
Owner: J. Esslinger GmbH + Co. KG
Editorial: Poststraße 5, Pforzheim 75172.
T: 49 723 1933 0 **E:** redaktion@pz-news.de
W: http://www.pz-news.de
Freq: Daily; **Circ:** 39149
Redakteurin / Editor: Nicola Arnet; **Redakteur / Editor:** Sascha Aurich; **Redakteurin / Editor:** Anke Baumgärtel; **Redakteur / Editor:** Cornelius Berends; **Redakteur / Editor:** Sven Bernhagen; **Redakteur / Editor:** Stefan Dworschak; **Redakteur / Editor:** Claudius Erb; **Redakteur / Editor:** Andreas Fiegel; **Redakteur / Editor:** Thomas Frei; **Redakteurin / Editor:** Sylvia Frey; **Redakteur / Editor:** Alexander Heilemann; **Redakteur / Editor:** Alexander Huberth; **Redakteur / Editor:** Dominique Jahn; **Redakteurin / Editor:** Petra Joos; **Redakteur / Editor:** Walter Kindlein; **Redakteur / Editor:** Bruno Knöller; **Redakteur / Editor:** Ralf Kohler; **Redakteur / Editor:** Udo Koller; **Redakteurin / Editor:** Carolin Kraus; **Redakteur / Editor:** Gerd Lache; **Redakteur / Editor:** Olaf Lorch-Gerstenmaier; **Redakteur / Editor:** Maximilian Lutz; **Redakteur / Editor:** Peter Marx; **Redakteur / Editor:** Sabine Mayer-Reichard; **Redakteurin / Editor:** Dorothee Messmer; **Redakteur / Editor:** Martin Mildenberger; **Redakteur / Editor:** Lothar Neff; **Redakteurin / Editor:** Sandra Pfäfflin; **Redakteurin / Editor:** Martina Schaefer; **Redakteur / Editor:** Michael Schenk; **Redakteurin / Editor:** Bärbel Schierling; **Chefredakteur / Editor in Chief:** Magnus Schlecht; **Redakteurin / E ditor:** Nadine Schmid; **Redakteurin / Editor:** Sabine Simon; **Redakteur / Editor:** Ralf Steinert; **Redakteur / Editor:** Simon Walter; **Redakteurin / Editor:** Angelika Wohlfrom
Language (s): German
DAILY NEWSPAPER

Pirmasenser Rundschau
Owner: RHEINPFALZ Verlag und Druckerei GmbH & Co. KG
Editorial: RHEINPFALZ Verlag und Druckerei GmbH & Co. KG, Amtsstraße 5 - 11, Ludwigshafen 67059
E: rheinpfalz@rheinpfalz.de
Freq: Daily; **Circ:** 12182
Redakteur / Editor: Andreas Bahner; **Redakteur / Editor:** Klaus Kadel; **Redakteur / Editor:** Fred G. Schütz; **Redakteurin / Editor:** Gabriele Strauss
Language (s): German
DAILY NEWSPAPER

Plattlinger Zeitung
Owner: Neue Presse Verlags-GmbH
Editorial: Preysingplatz 7, Plattling 94447.
T: 49 993 1 912 40 **E:** Red.Plattling@pnp.de
W: http://www.pnp.de/region_und_lokal/landkreis_deggendorf/plattling/
Freq: Daily; **Circ:** 21981
Redaktion / Editor: Astrid Hahne; **Redakteur / Editor:** Konrad Kellermann
Language (s): German
DAILY NEWSPAPER

Potsdamer Tageszeitung
Owner: Märkische Verlags- und Druck-Gesellschaft mbH Potsdam
Editorial: Märkische Verlags- und Druck-Gesellschaft mbH Potsdam, Friedrich-Engels-Straße 24, Potsdam 14473. **T:** 49 331 28 40 0
E: kontakt@MAZ-online.de
Freq: Daily; **Circ:** 26170
Redakteur / Editor: Jan Bosschaart; **Redakteurin / Editor:** Nadine Fabian; **Redakteurin / Editor:** Regine Greiner; **Redakteurin / Editor:** Carola Hein; **Redakteur / Editor:** Heinz Helwig; **Redakteurin / Editor:** Claudia Krause; **Redakteur / Editor:** Stephan Laude; **Redakteur / Editor:** Volker Oelschläger; **Redakteur / Editor:** Rainer Schüler; **Redakteur / Editor:** Jürgen Stich
Language (s): German
DAILY NEWSPAPER

prisma Gesamt
Owner: Prisma-Verlag GmbH & Co. KG
Editorial: prisma Verlag GmbH & Co. KG, Zülpicher Straße 10, Dusseldorf 40549.
T: 49 2115 07028 **E:** info@prisma-verlag.de
W: http://www.prisma-verlag.de
Redakteur / Editor: Jörg Bärschneider; **Chefredaktion / Editor in Chief:** Detlef Hartlap
Language (s): German
NEWSPAPER

Recklinghäuser Zeitung
Owner: Verlag J. Bauer KG
Editorial: Breite Straße 4, Recklinghausen 45657. **T:** 49 236 1 1805 2414
E: rzredaktion@medienhaus-bauer.de
W: http://www.recklinghaeuser-zeitung.de
Freq: Daily; **Circ:** 62763
Chefredaktion / Editor in Chief: Kurt Bauer; **Redakteur / Editor:** Hermann Böckmann; **Redakateurin / Editor:** Kathrin Grochowski; **Redakteurin / Editor:** Meike Holz; **Redakteur / Editor:** Kevin Korte; **Chefredakteur / Editor in Chief:** Jan Mühldorfer; **Redakteur / Editor:** Alfred Pfeffer; **Redakteur / Editor:** Michael Richter; **Redakteurin / Editor:** Silvia Seimetz; **Redakteurin / Editor:** Alexander Spieß; **Redakteur / Editor:** Ralf Wiethaup
Language (s): German
DAILY NEWSPAPER

Regionale Rundschau
Owner: Bremer Tageszeitungen AG
Editorial: Martinistr. 43, Bremen 28195.
T: 49 421 36710 **E:** redaktion@weser-kurier.de
W: http://www.weser-kurier.de
Freq: Daily; **Circ:** 13323 IVW
Redakteur / Editor: Peter Bauer; **Redakteurin / Editor:** Silke Hellwig
Language (s): German
DAILY NEWSPAPER

Remscheider General-Anzeiger
Owner: Remscheider Medienhaus GmbH & Co. KG
Editorial: Alleestraße 77-81, Remscheid 42853. **T:** 49 219 1 909 0
E: rga@rga-online.de
W: http://www.rga-online.de
Freq: Daily; **Circ:** 18338
Redakteur / Editor: Michael Albrecht; **Redakteur / Editor:** Gunnar Freudenberg; **Chefredaktion / Editor in Chief:** Stefan M. Kob; **Redakteur / Editor:** Andreas Kratz; **Redakteur / Editor:** Peter Kuhlendahl; **Redakteur / Editor:** Mark Saxer; **Redakteur / Editor:** Gerhard Schattat; **Redakteurin / Editor:** Anja Carolina Siebel; **Redakteur / Editor:** Andreas Weber; **Redakteurin / Editor:** Melissa Wienzek
Language (s): German
DAILY NEWSPAPER

Rems-Zeitung
Owner: Remsdruckerei Sigg, Härtel u. Co. KG
Editorial: Paradiesstraße 12, Schwäbisch Gmünd 73527. **T:** 49 717 1 6006 0
W: http://remszeitung.de
Freq: Daily; **Circ:** 15268
Redaktion / Editor: Meinrad Sigg
Language (s): German
DAILY NEWSPAPER

rendezvous
W: http://www.volksfreund.de
Language (s): German
NEWSPAPER

Reutlinger General-Anzeiger
Owner: Reutlinger General-Anzeiger Verlags GmbH & Co. KG
Editorial: Burgstr. 1 - 7, Reutlingen 72706.
T: 49 712 1 302 333 **E:** redaktion@gea.de
W: http://www.gea.de
Freq: Daily; **Circ:** 40089
Redakteur / Editor: Franz Pfluger; **Chefredakteur / Editor in Chief:** Hartmut Troebs
Language (s): German
DAILY NEWSPAPER

Reutlinger Nachrichten
Owner: Georg Hauser GmbH & Co. Zeitungsverlag KG
Editorial: Albstraße 4, Reutlingen 72764.
T: 49 7121 9302 0 **E:** rn.redaktion@swp.de
W: http://www.swp.de/reutlingen/
Freq: Daily; **Circ:** 13416 IVW
Redaktion / Editor: Evelyn Rupprecht
Language (s): German
DAILY NEWSPAPER

Rheiderland Zeitung
Owner: H. Risius KG
Editorial: Risiusstraße 6 – 10, Weener 26826.
T: 49 4951 930 117
W: http://www.rheiderland.de
Freq: Daily
Redakteur / Editor: Tim Boelmann; **Chefredakteur / Editor in Chief:** Kai-Uwe Hanken; **Redakteur / Editor:** Michael Hoegen; **Redakteur / Editor:** Thorin Mentrup; **Redakteurin / Editor:** Martina Nagel; **Redakteur / Editor:** Holger Szyska; **Redakteur / Editor:** Tammo Wübbena
Language (s): German
DAILY NEWSPAPER

Rhein Main Markt
Owner: Zeitungsanzeigenges. RheinMainMedia mbH
Editorial: Frankenallee 71, Frankfurt 60327
E: rmm-text@rhein-main-media.de
W: http://www.rheinmainmedia.de
Freq: Weekly; **Circ:** 500000
Redakteurin / Editor: Jane Gilbert
Language (s): German
NEWSPAPER

Rhein Main Presse
Owner: Verlagsgruppe Rhein Main GmbH & Co. KG
Editorial: Erich-Dombrowski-Straße 2, Mainz 55127. **T:** 49 6131 4830
E: impressum@vrm.de
W: http://www.rhein-main-presse.de
Freq: Daily; **Circ:** 195527
Language (s): German
DAILY NEWSPAPER

Rhein Zeitung, Rhein - Lahn
Owner: Mittelrhein-Verlag GmbH
Editorial: Römerstraße 94, Bad Ems 56130.
T: 49 2603 937450
E: bad-ems@rhein-zeitung.net
W: http://www.rhein-zeitung.de/
Freq: Daily; **Circ:** 16112
Redakteur / Editor: Markus Eschenauer; **Redakteur / Editor:** Andreas Galonska; **Redakteur / Editor:** Alexander Hoffmann; **Redakteur / Editor:** Katrin Kring; **Redakteur / Editor:** Tobias Lui; **Redakteurin / Editor:** Kartin Maue Klaeser; **Redakteur / Editor:** Uli Pohl; **Redaktuer / Editor:** Carlo Rosenkranz
Language (s): German
DAILY NEWSPAPER

Rhein-Hunsrück-Zeitung
Owner: Mittelrhein-Verlag GmbH
Editorial: Aulergasse 10, Am Zentralparkplatz, Simmern 55469. **T:** 49 676 1 96774 40
E: simmern@rhein-zeitung.net
W: http://www.rhein-zeitung.de/region/lokales/hunsrueck.html
Freq: Daily; **Circ:** 13614
Redakteur / Editor: Volker Boch; **Redakteurin / Editor:** Suzanne Breitbach; **Redakteur / Editor:** Werner Dupuis; **Redakteur / Editor:** Maximilian Eckhardt; **Redakteurin / Editor:** Martina Koch; **Redakteur / Editor:** Markus Lorenz; **Redakteur / Editor:** Jochen Magnus; **Redakteur / Editor:** Markus Schwarz; **Redakteur / Editor:** Bettina Tollkamp-Bretz; **Redaktion / Editor:** Thomas Torkler; **Redakteur / Editor:** Lars Wienand
Language (s): German
DAILY NEWSPAPER

Rheinische Post
Owner: Rheinische Post Verlagsges. mbH
Editorial: Zülpicher Straße 10, Dusseldorf 40196. **T:** 49 211 505 0
E: magazin@rheinische-post.de
W: http://www.rp-online.de
Freq: Daily; **Circ:** 348330
Redakteur / Editor: Bertram Müller
Language (s): German
DAILY NEWSPAPER

Rheinische Post (Grenzlandkurier), Viersen
Owner: Rhei-nisch-Ber-gi-sche Ver-lags-ge-sell-schaft mbH
Editorial: Zül-pi-cher Straße 10, Dusseldorf 40196. **T:** 49 211 505 0
E: info@rheinische-post.de
W: http://www.rheinischepostmediengruppe.de
Freq: Daily; **Circ:** 20450
Redakteurin / Editor: Natascha Becker; **Chefredaktion / Editor in Chief:** Oliver Havlat
Language (s): German
DAILY NEWSPAPER

Rheinische Post (MO), Moers
Owner: Rhei-nisch-Ber-gi-sche Ver-lags-ge-sell-schaft mbH
Editorial: Neumarkt 13, Moers 47441.
T: 49 211 505 0 **E:** info@rheinische-post.de
W: http://www.rheinischepostmediengruppe.de
Freq: Daily; **Circ:** 17514
Chefredakteur / Editor in Chief: Oliver Havlat; **Redakteurin / Editor:** Anja Katzke
Language (s): German
DAILY NEWSPAPER

Rheinische Post Ne-GV Neuss-Grevenbroicher
Owner: Rhei-nisch-Ber-gi-sche Ver-lags-ge-sell-schaft mbH
Editorial: Zülpicher Straße 10, Dusseldorf 40196. **T:** 49 211 50 50
E: info@rheinische-post.de
W: http://www.rheinischepostmediengruppe.de
Freq: Daily; **Circ:** 42888
Redakteurin / Editor: Helga Bittner; **Redakteurin / Editor:** Bärbel Broer; **Redakteurin / Editor:** Susanne Genath; **Redakteur / Editor:** Jascha Huschauer; **Redakteur / Editor:** Christoph Kleinau; **Redakteurin / Editor:** Hanna Koch; **Redakteur / Editor:** Klas Libuda; **Redakteurin / Editor:** Julia Rommelfanger; **Redakteurin / Editor:** Susanne Zolke
Language (s): German
DAILY NEWSPAPER

Rheinische Post Rhein-Wupper Ztg., Opladen
Owner: Rhei-nisch-Ber-gi-sche Ver-lags-ge-sell-schaft mbH
Editorial: Zül-pi-cher Straße 10, Dusseldorf 40196. **T:** 49 211 505 0
E: info@rheinische-post.de
W: http://www.rheinischepostmediengruppe.de
Freq: Daily; **Circ:** 14827
Redakteurin / Editor: Ludmilla Hauser; **Chefredakteur / Editor in Chief:** Oliver Havlat
Language (s): German
DAILY NEWSPAPER

Rheinische Post, Geldern
Owner: Rheinische Post Geldern
Editorial: Zül-pi-cher Straße 10, Dusseldorf 40196. **T:** 49 211 505 0
E: info@rheinische-post.de
W: http://www.rheinischepostmediengruppe.de
Freq: Daily; **Circ:** 16714
Redakteur / Editor: Christian Breuer; **Chefredaktion / Editor in Chief:** Oliver Havlat
DAILY NEWSPAPER

Rheinische Post, Kleve
Owner: Rhei-nisch-Ber-gi-sche Ver-lags-ge-sell-schaft mbH
Editorial: Zül-pi-cher Straße 10, Dusseldorf 40196. **T:** 49 211 505 0
E: info@rheinische-post.de
W: http://www.rheinischepostmediengruppe.de
Freq: Daily; **Circ:** 18871
Chefredaktion / Editor in Chief: Oliver Havlat; **Redakteur / Editor:** Philipp Jacobs
Language (s): German
DAILY NEWSPAPER

Rheinische Post, Krefeld
Owner: Rheinische Post Krefeld
Editorial: Zül-pi-cher Straße 10, Dusseldorf 40196. **T:** 49 211 505 0
E: info@rheinische-post.de
W: http://www.rheinischepostmediengruppe.de
Freq: Daily; **Circ:** 20591
Chefredaktion / Editor in Chief: Oliver Havlat
Language (s): German
DAILY NEWSPAPER

Rheinische Post, Mönchengladbach
Owner: Rhei-nisch-Ber-gi-sche Ver-lags-ge-sell-schaft mbH
Editorial: Zül-pi-cher Straße 10, Dusseldorf 40196. **T:** 49 211 505 0
Freq: Daily; **Circ:** 43663
Chefredaktion / Editor in Chief: Oliver Havlat; **Redakteur / Editor:** Christian Lingen
Language (s): German
DAILY NEWSPAPER

Rheinische Post, Wesel - Dinslaken
Owner: Rhei-nisch-Ber-gi-sche Ver-lags-ge-sell-schaft mbH
Editorial: Zül-pi-cher Straße 10, Dusseldorf 40196. **T:** 49 211 505 0
E: info@rheinische-post.de
W: http://www.rheinischepostmediengruppe.de
Freq: Daily; **Circ:** 17535
Chefredaktion / Editor in Chief: Oliver Havlat
Language (s): German
DAILY NEWSPAPER

Rhein-Lahn-Zeitung (Diez)
Owner: Mittelrhein-Verlag GmbH
W: http://www.rhein-zeitung.de
Redakteur / Editor: Hans Georg Egenolf; **Redakteur / Editor:** Andreas Jöckel; **Redakteurin / Editor:** Katrin Maue- Klaeser; **Redakteurin / Editor:** Karin Kring; **Redaktion / Editor:** Michael Stoll
Language (s): German
NEWSPAPER

RheinMainMedia Frankfurt City
Owner: RheinMainMedia GmbH
Editorial: Frankenallee 71-81, Frankfurt Am Main 60327. **T:** 49 69 75 01 40 00
E: service@rheinmainmedia.de
W: http://www.rheinmainmedia.de
Freq: Daily; **Circ:** 74028
Language (s): German
DAILY NEWSPAPER

Rhein-Main-Presse
Owner: Verlagsgruppe Rhein Main Holding GmbH & Co. KG
Editorial: Erich-Dombrowski-Straße 2, Mainz 55127. **T:** 49 6131 48 30
E: impressum@vrm.de **W:** http://www.vrm.de
Freq: Daily; **Circ:** 195527
Redakteurin / Editor: Sarah Burkhard; **Redakteur / Editor:** Knut Ehrhardt; **Redakteurin / Editor:** Alexandra Eisen; **Redakteur / Editor:** Michael Erfurth; **Redakteur / Editor:** Fabian Held; **Redakteur / Editor:** Christian Hoffmann; **Redakteur / Editor:** Gerd Klee; **Redakteur / Editor:** Felix Lieb; **Redakteur / Editor:** Christian Mayer; **Redakteurin / Editor:** Neli Mihaylova; **Redakteurin / Editor:** Monika Nellessen; **Redakteurin / Editor:** Beate Nietzel; **Redakteurin / Editor:** Kerstin Prosch; **Redakteur / Editor:** Andreas Riechert; **Redakteur / Editor:** Torben Schröder; **Redakteurin / Editor:** Carolin Sokele; **Redakteurin / Editor:** Sarah Umla; **Redakteur / Editor:** Manuel Wenda; **Redakteur / Editor:** Wolfgang Ziegler
Language (s): German
DAILY NEWSPAPER

Rhein-Main-Presse Alzey
Owner: Verlagsgruppe Rhein Main Holding GmbH & Co. KG
Editorial: Erich-Dombrowski-Str. 2, Mainz 55127. **T:** 49 6131 4848 30
E: marketing@vrm.de **W:** http://www.vrm.de
Freq: Daily; **Circ:** 11490
Redakteur / Editor: Hans-Hartwig Augustin; **Redakteurin / Editor:** Katharina Bruch; **Redakteur / Editor:** Manfred Janß; **Redakteur / Editor:** Albrecht Langenbach; **Redakteurin / Editor:** Sigrid Scheel; **Redakteurin / Editor:** Carina Schmidt; **Redakteur / Editor:** Karl M. Wirthwein; **Redakteurin / Editor:** Roswitha Wünsche-Heiden
Language (s): German
DAILY NEWSPAPER

Rhein-Main-Presse Bad Kreuznach
Owner: Verlagsgruppe Rhein Main Holding GmbH & Co. KG
Editorial: Erich-Dombrowski-Str. 2, Mainz 55127. **T:** 49 6131 4848 30
E: impressum@vrm.de **W:** http://www.vrm.de/
Freq: Daily; **Circ:** 11186
Redakteurin / Editor: Eva Adrian; **Redakteur / Editor:** Sven Eichstädt; **Redakteurin / Editor:** Daniela Elsässer; **Redakteur / Editor:** Jens Fink; **Redakteur / Editor:** Thomas Haag; **Redakteur / Editor:** Martin Höcker; **Redakteurin / Editor:** Christine Jäckel; **Redakteur / Editor:** Norbert Krupp; **Redakteur / Editor:** Felix Monsees; **Redakteur / Editor:** Robert Neuber; **Redkateur / Editor:** Klaus Pfrengle; **Redakteurin / Editor:** Nadine Poss; **Redakteurin / Editor:** Claudia Römer; **Redakteur / Editor:** Gert Schatto; **Redakteurin / Editor:** Julia Schilling; **Redakteurin / Editor:** Heidi Sturm; **Redakteurin / Editor:** Monika Unger; **Redakteurin / Editor:** Beate Vogt-Gladigau
Language (s): German
DAILY NEWSPAPER

Rhein-Main-Presse Bingen-Ingelheim
Owner: Verlagsgruppe Rhein Main Holding GmbH & Co. KG
Editorial: Erich-Dombrowski-Str. 2, Mainz 55127. **T:** 49 6131 4848 30
E: marketing@vrm.de **W:** http://www.vrm.de
Freq: Daily; **Circ:** 15497
Redakteurin / Editor: Karola Arnold; **Redakteurin / Editor:** Martina Berg; **Redakteur / Editor:** Hans-Willi Blum; **Redakteur / Editor:** Wolfgang Bürkle; **Redakteur / Editor:** Bernd Funke; **Redakteur / Editor:** Egon Goldschmidt; **Redakteur / Editor:** Sören Heim; **Redakteurin / Editor:** Caroline Jerchel; **Redakteurin / Editor:** Sigrid Kaselow; **Redakteurin / Editor:** Denise Kopyciok; **Redakteur / Editor:** Erich Michael Lang; **Redakteur / Editor:** Mario Luge; **Redakteur / Editor:** Siegfried Orzeszko; **Redakteur / Editor:** Klaus Rein; **Redakteurin / Editor:** Nadine Schwarz; **Redakteurin / Editor:** Beate Schwenk; **Redakteurin / Editor:** Beate Schwenk; **Redakteurin / Editor:** Helena Sender-Petry; **Redakteurin / Editor:** Heide Tittel; **Redakteurin / Editor:** Christine Tscherner; **Redakteur / Editor:** Jochen Werner
Language (s): German
DAILY NEWSPAPER

Rhein-Main-Presse Mainz
Owner: Verlagsgruppe Rhein Main Holding GmbH & Co. KG
Editorial: Erich-Dombrowski-Str. 2, Mainz 55127. **T:** 49 6131 4848 30
E: marketing@vrm.de **W:** http://www.vrm.de
Freq: Daily; **Circ:** 57905
Redakteurin / Editor: Alexandra Bidian; **Redakteurin / Editor:** Margit Dörr; **Redakteurin / Editor:** Birgit Emnet; **Redakteur / Editor:** Norbert Fluhr; **Redakteurin / Editor:** Katja Mathes; **Redakteurin / Editor:** Christina Miesch-Schmidt; **Redakteur / Editor:** Steffen Nagel; **Redakteur / Editor:** Dieter Oberhollenzer; **Redakteurin / Editor:** Ruth Rillinger; **Redakteurin / Editor:** Julia Sloboda; **Redakteur / Editor:** Simon Wendling; **Redakteur / Editor:** Wolfgang Wenzel
Language (s): German
DAILY NEWSPAPER

Rhein-Main-Presse Worms
Owner: Verlagsgruppe Rhein Main Holding GmbH & Co. KG
Editorial: Erich-Dombrowski-Str. 2, Mainz 55127. **T:** 49 6131 4848 30
E: impressum@vrm.de **W:** http://www.vrm.de
Freq: Daily; **Circ:** 18013
Redakteur / Editor: Reinhard Breidenbach; **Redakteurin / Editor:** Sandra Dörr; **Redakteurin / Editor:** Nadine Herd; **Redakteur / Editor:** Roland Keth; **Redakteur / Editor:** Gernot Lahr-Mische; **Redakteur / Editor:** Michael Lang; **Redakteur / Editor:** Christian Meinl; **Redakteur / Editor:** Florian Stenner; **Redakteurin / Editor:** Claudia Wößner
Language (s): German
DAILY NEWSPAPER

Rhein-Main-Zeitung
Owner: Frankfurter Allgemeine Zeitung GmbH
Editorial: Frankfurter Allgemeine Zeitung GmbH, Hellerhofstraße 2-4, Frankfurt Am Main 60327. **T:** 49 69 7591 0 **E:** rhein-main@faz.de
W: http://www.faz.net/aktuell/rhein-main/
Freq: Weekly; **Circ:** 105687
Language (s): German
NEWSPAPER

Rhein-Neckar-Zeitung
Owner: Rhein-Neckar-Zeitung GmbH
Editorial: Neugasse 2, Heidelberg 69117.
T: 49 622 1 519 0 **E:** redaktion@rnz.de
W: http://www.rnz.de
Freq: Daily; **Circ:** 94287
Redakteurin / Editor: Susanne Eckl-Gruß; **Chefredaktion / Editor in Chief:** Klaus Welzel
Language (s): German
DAILY NEWSPAPER

Rheinpfalz - Pfälzische Volkszeitung
Editorial: RHEINPFALZ Verlag und Druckerei GmbH & Co. KG, Amtsstraße 5 - 11, Ludwigshafen 67059
Freq: Daily; **Circ:** 33937
Redakteur / Editor: Reiner Henn; **Redakteurin / Editor:** Heidelore Kruse; **Redakteur / Editor:** Hans-Joachim Redzimski; **Redakteur / Editor:** Joachim Schwitalla
Language (s): German
DAILY NEWSPAPER

Rheinpfalz-Die/Westricher Rundschau
Owner: RHEINPFALZ Verlag und Druckerei GmbH & Co. KG
Editorial: Amtsstraße 5, Ludwigshafen 67059.
T: 49 621 590201 **E:** rheinpfalz@rheinpfalz.de
W: http://www.rheinpfalz.de
Freq: Daily; **Circ:** 12381
Language (s): German
DAILY NEWSPAPER

Rhein-Sieg Rundschau
Owner: Heinen-Verlag GmbH
Editorial: Scheerengasse 1, Siegburg 53721.
T: 49 224 1 172 70
E: Rhein-Sieg.Rundschau@kr-redaktion.de
W: http://www.rundschau-online.de/rhein-sieg/15185860,15185860.html
Freq: Daily; **Circ:** 39200
Redaktion / Editor: Reinhard Bernardini; **Redakteur / Editor:** Peter Lorber
Language (s): German
DAILY NEWSPAPER

Rhein-Sieg-Anzeiger
Owner: M. DuMont Schauberg GmbH & Co. KG
Editorial: Markt 16 - 19, Siegburg 53721.
T: 49 2241 17 49 10
E: redaktion.rheinsieg@ksta.de
W: http://www.ksta.de
Redakteur / Editor: Lutz Feierabend; **Chefredakteur / Editor in chief:** Peter Pauls; **Redaktion / Editor:** Jürgen Röhrig
Language (s): German
NEWSPAPER

Rhein-Zeitung
Owner: Mittelrhein-Verlag GmbH
Editorial: August-Horch-Str. 28, Koblenz 56070. **T:** 49 261 892 240
E: redaktion@rhein-zeitung.net
W: http://www.rhein-zeitung.de
Freq: Daily; **Circ:** 195359
Redakteur / Editor: Jörg Hilpert; **Redakteurin / Editor:** Stefanie Höner; **Chefredaktion / Editor in Chief:** Christian Lindner; **Redakteur / Editor:** Hans-Peter Meinhardt
Language (s): German
DAILY NEWSPAPER

Rhein-Zeitung Koblenz
Owner: Mittelrhein-Verlag GmbH
Editorial: August-Horch-Straße 28, Koblenz 56070. **T:** 49 261 892-347
E: redaktion-koblenz@rhein-zeitung.net
W: http://www.rhein-zeitung.de/region/lokales/koblenz.html
Freq: Daily; **Circ:** 31042
Redakteurin / Editor: Anke Mersmann; **Redakteurin / Editor:** Stephanie Mersmann; **Redakteurin / Editor:** Doris Schneider; **Redakteur / Editor:** Hartmut Wagner
Language (s): German
DAILY NEWSPAPER

Rhein-Zeitung Stadt Koblenz
Owner: Mittelrhein-Verlag GmbH
Editorial: August-Horch-Straße 28, Koblenz 56070. **T:** 49 261 892347
E: redaktion-koblenz@rhein-zeitung.net
W: http://www.rhein-zeitung.de
Freq: Daily; **Circ:** 31042
Redakteurin / Editor: Anke Mersmann; **Redakteurin / Editor:** Stephanie Mersmann; **Redakteurin / Editor:** Doris Schneider; **Redakteur / Editor:** Hartmut Wagner
Language (s): German
DAILY NEWSPAPER

Rhein-Zeitung, Mayen-Andernach
Owner: Rhein-Zeitung Mayen
Editorial: August-Horch-Straße 28, Koblenz 56055. **T:** 49 261 2919215
E: redaktion-mayen@rhein-zeitung.net
W: http://www.rhein-zeitung.de/
Freq: Daily; **Circ:** 15526
Redakteurin / Editor: Katrin Franzen; **Chefredaktion / Editor in Chief:** Christian Lindner; **Redakteur / Editor:** Hilko Röttgers
Language (s): German
DAILY NEWSPAPER

Ried Echo
Owner: Echo Zeitungen GmbH
Editorial: Holzhofallee 25-31, Darmstadt 64295. **T:** 49 6151 387 0
E: echo-zeitungen@darmstaedter-echo.de
W: http://www.echo-online.de/region/gross-gerau/riedstadt/
Freq: Daily
Redakteurin / Editor: Angelica Taubel
Language (s): German
DAILY NEWSPAPER

Rieser Nachrichten
Owner: Presse-Druck- und Verlags-GmbH
Editorial: Curt-Frenzel-Str. 2, Augsburg 86167. **T:** 49 821 777 0
E: online-redaktion@augsburger-allgemeine.de
Freq: Daily; **Circ:** 11267
Chefredaktion: Sascha Borowski; **Redakteurin/ Editor:** Daniela Deeg; **Redakteur / Editor:** Stefan Drescher; **Redakteurin / Editor:** Daniela Fischer; **Redakteurin / Editor:** Ina Kresse; **Redakteur / Editor:** Robert Milde; **stellv. Chefredaktion:** Norbert Staub; **Redaktion / Editor:** Carl Völkl
Language (s): German
DAILY NEWSPAPER

Rottaler Anzeiger
Owner: Neue Presse Verlags-GmbH
Editorial: Medienstraße 5, Passau 94036. **T:** 49 851 802 0 **E:** info@pnp.de
W: http://www.pnp.de/
Freq: Daily; **Circ:** 11175
Redaktion / Editor: Wolfgang Gruber
Language (s): German
DAILY NEWSPAPER

Ruhr Nachrichten
Owner: Verlag Lensing-Wolff GmbH & Co. KG
Editorial: Westenhellweg 86-88, Dortmund 44137. **T:** 49 800 66 55 44 3
E: leserinfo@mdhl.de
W: http://www.ruhrnachrichten.de/
Freq: Daily; **Circ:** 73000
Chefredakteur / Editor in Chief: Hermann Beckfeld; **Chefredaktion / Editor in Chief:** Wolfram Kiwit
Language (s): German
DAILY NEWSPAPER

Rüsselsheimer Echo
Owner: Echo Zeitungen GmbH
Editorial: Holzhofallee 25-31, Darmstadt 64295. **T:** 49 615 1 387 0
E: echo-zeitungen@darmstaedter-echo.de
W: http://www.echo-online.de/region/ruesselsheim/
Freq: Daily; **Circ:** 17844
Redaktion / Editor: Elisabeth Schuster
Language (s): German
DAILY NEWSPAPER

Saale-Zeitung
Owner: KVG Kissinger Verlagsgesellschaft mbH & Co. KG
Editorial: Theresienstraße 21, Bad Kissingen 97688. **T:** 49 971 80400
E: redaktion.badkissingen@infranken.de
W: http://www.infranken.de/regional/bad-kissingen/
Freq: Daily; **Circ:** 13821
Redaktion / Editor: Paul Ziegler
Language (s): German
DAILY NEWSPAPER

Saarbrücker Zeitung
Owner: Saarbrücker Zeitung Verlag und Druckerei GmbH
Editorial: Gutenbergstr 11-23, Saarbrücken 66117. **T:** 49 681 502 0 **E:** redaktion@sol.de
W: http://www.saarbruecker-zeitung.de/
Freq: Daily; **Circ:** 146387
Redakteur / Editor: Peter Bylda; **Redakteur / Editor:** Thomas Reinhardt
Language (s): German
DAILY NEWSPAPER

Saarbrücker Zeitung Merzig - Wadern
Owner: Saarbrücker Zeitung Verlag und Druckerei GmbH
Editorial: Gutenbergstr. 11 - 23, Saarbrücken 66111. **T:** 49 681 502-504 **E:** redstv@sz-sb.de
Freq: Daily; **Circ:** 14175
Redakteur / Editor: Wolf Porz
Language (s): German
DAILY NEWSPAPER

Saarbrücker Zeitung Mitte
Owner: Saarbrücker Zeitung Verlag und Druckerei GmbH
Editorial: Gutenbergstr 11-23, Saarbrücken 66117
Freq: Daily; **Circ:** 22554
Language (s): German
DAILY NEWSPAPER

Saarbrücker Zeitung Neunkirchen, Neunkirchen
Owner: Saarbrücker Zeitung Verlag und Druckerei GmbH
Editorial: Gutenbergstr. 11 - 23, Saarbrücken 66111. **T:** 49 681 502504 **E:** redstv@sz-sb.de
Freq: Daily; **Circ:** 17253
Chefredakteur / Editor in Chief: Peter Stefan Herbst; **Redakteurin / Editor:** Heike Jungmann
Language (s): German
DAILY NEWSPAPER

Saarbrücker Zeitung Saarlouis
Owner: Saarbrücker Zeitung Verlag und Druckerei GmbH
Editorial: Gutenbergstr. 11 - 23, Saarbrücken 66111. **T:** 49 681 502504 **E:** redstv@sz-sb.de
Freq: Daily; **Circ:** 16343
Chefredakteur / Editor in Chief: Peter Stefan Herbst; **Redakteur / Editor:** Mathias Winters
Language (s): German
DAILY NEWSPAPER

Saarbrücker Zeitung St. Ingbert
Owner: Saarbrücker Zeitung Verlag und Druckerei GmbH
Editorial: Gutenbergstr. 11 - 23, Saarbrücken 66111. **T:** 49 681 502504 **E:** redstv@sz-sb.de
Freq: Daily; **Circ:** 11928
Redakteur / Editor: Michael Beer
Language (s): German
DAILY NEWSPAPER

Saarbrücker Zeitung St. Wendel
Owner: Saarbrücker Zeitung Verlag und Druckerei GmbH
Editorial: Gutenbergstr. 11 - 23, Saarbrücken 66111. **T:** 49 681 502504 **E:** redstv@sz-sb.de
W: http://www.saarbruecker-zeitung.de
Freq: Daily; **Circ:** 13659
Redakteurin / Editor: Melanie Mai
Language (s): German
DAILY NEWSPAPER

Sachsenheimer Zeitung
Owner: Druck- und Verlagsges. Bietigheim mbH
Editorial: Kronenbergstraße 10, Bietigheim-Bissingen 74321. **T:** 49 7142 403410
E: redaktion@bietigheimerzeitung.de
W: http://www.swp.de/bietigheim/lokales/
Freq: Daily
Chefredakteur / Editor in Chief: Andreas Lukesch
Language (s): German
DAILY NEWSPAPER

Sächsische Zeitung
Owner: Dresdner Druck- und Verlagshaus GmbH & Co. KG
Editorial: Sächsische Zeitung GmbH, Ostra-Allee 20, Dresden 1067. **T:** 49 351 48642273
E: redaktion@dd-v.de
W: http://www.sz-online.de
Freq: Daily; **Circ:** 253274
Redakteur / Editor: Mirko Jakubowsky; **Chefredaktion / Editor in Chief:** Uwe Vetterick
Language (s): German
DAILY NEWSPAPER

Sächsische Zeitung Dresden
Owner: Redaktions- und Verlagsges. Freital-Pirna mbH
Editorial: Ostra-Allee 20, Dresden 1067. **T:** 49 351 48642240 **E:** redaktion@dd-v.de
W: http://www.sz-online.de
Freq: Daily; **Circ:** 367825
Language (s): German
DAILY NEWSPAPER

Sächsische Zeitung Pirna, Pirna
Owner: DD+V Gmbh & Co KG
Editorial: Ostra-Allee 20, Dresden 1067. **T:** 49 351 48640 **E:** redaktion@dd-v.de
W: http://www.sz-online.de
Freq: Daily; **Circ:** 16324
Redakteur / Editor: Christian Eißner; **Redakteurin / Editor:** Heike Sabel
Language (s): German
DAILY NEWSPAPER

Sächsische Zeitung, Bautzen
Owner: DD+V Gmbh & Co KG
Editorial: Ostra-Allee 20, Dresden 1067. **T:** 49 351 48640 **E:** redaktion@dd-v.de
W: http://www.sz-online.de
Freq: Daily; **Circ:** 18560
Redakteurin / Editor: Kerstin Fiedler; **Redakteurin / Editor:** Heike Garten; **Redakteurin / Editor:** Romy Hassert; **Redakteur / Editor:** Sebastian Kositz; **Redakteurin / Editor:** Katja Schäfer; **Redakteur / Editor:** Ulli Schönbach; **Redakteurin / Editor:** Madeleine Siegl-Mickisch
Language (s): German
DAILY NEWSPAPER

Sächsische Zeitung, Freital
Owner: DD+V Gmbh & Co KG
Editorial: Ostra-Allee 20, Dresden 1067. **T:** 49 351 48640 **E:** redaktion@dd-v.de
W: http://www.sz-online.de
Freq: Daily; **Circ:** 11203
Redakteur / Editor: Stephan Klingbeil; **Redakteur / Editor:** Matthias Weigel; **Redakteurin / Editor:** Verena Weiß
Language (s): German
DAILY NEWSPAPER

Sächsische Zeitung, Görlitz
Owner: DD+V Gmbh & Co KG
Editorial: Ostra-Allee 20, Dresden 1067. **T:** 49 351 48640 **E:** redaktion@dd-v.de
W: http://www.sz-online.de
Freq: Daily; **Circ:** 13171
Redakteur / Editor: Sebastian Beutler; **Redakteurin / Editor:** Daniela Pfeiffer
Language (s): German
DAILY NEWSPAPER

Sächsische Zeitung, Kamenz
Owner: Dresdner Druck- und Verlagshaus GmbH + Co. KG
Editorial: Ostra-Allee 20, Dresden 1067. **T:** 49 351 48640 **E:** redaktion@dd-v.de
W: http://www.sz-online.de
Freq: Daily; **Circ:** 12146
Redakteurin / Editor: Manuela Reuß
Language (s): German
DAILY NEWSPAPER

Sächsische Zeitung, Löbau
Owner: Dresdner Druck- und Verlagshaus
Editorial: Ostra-Allee 20, Dresden 1067. **T:** 49 351 48640 **E:** redaktion@dd-v.de
W: http://www.sz-online.de
Freq: Daily; **Circ:** 11984
Redakteurin / Editor: Anja Beutler; **Redakteurin / Editor:** Cornelia Mai
Language (s): German
DAILY NEWSPAPER

Sächsische Zeitung, Meißen
Owner: Sächsische Zeitung
Editorial: Ostra-Allee 20, Dresden 1067. **T:** 49 351 48640 **E:** redaktion@dd-v.de
W: http://www.sz-online.de/verlag/kontakt
Freq: Daily; **Circ:** 13086
Redakteur / Editor: Peter Anderson; **Redakteur / Editor:** Harald Daßler; **Redakteur / Editor:** Erik Gasch; **Redakteur / Editor:** Dieter Hanke; **Redakteur / Editor:** Jürgen Müller; **Redakteurin / Editor:** Kathrin Schade; **Redakteurin / Editor:** Sabine Scharf; **Redakteurin / Editor:** Ines Scholze-Luft
Language (s): German
DAILY NEWSPAPER

Sächsische Zeitung, Riesa
Owner: Sächsische Zeitung
Editorial: Ostra-Allee 20, Dresden 1067. **T:** 49 351 48640 **E:** redaktion@dd-v.de
W: http://www.sz-online.de
Freq: Daily; **Circ:** 12481
Redakteurin / Editor: Antje Steglich; **Redakteurin / Editor:** Britta Veltzke
Language (s): German
DAILY NEWSPAPER

Sächsische Zeitung, Zittau
Owner: DD+V Gmbh & Co KG
Editorial: Ostra-Allee 20, Dresden 1067. **T:** 49 351 48640 **E:** redaktion@dd-v.de
W: http://www.sz-online.de
Freq: Daily; **Circ:** 12653
Redakteurin / Editor: Anja Beutler; **Redakteurin / Editor:** Romy Kühr
Language (s): German
DAILY NEWSPAPER

Salzgitter Zeitung
Owner: BZV Medienhaus GmbH
Editorial: Chemnitzer Straße 33, Salzgitter 38226. **T:** 49 534 1 40 96 34
W: http://www.salzgitter-zeitung.de/
Freq: Daily; **Circ:** 17438
Redaktion / Editor: Alexandra Ritter
Language (s): German
DAILY NEWSPAPER

SauerlandKurier
Owner: Kurier Verlag Lennestadt GmbH
Editorial: Kölner Straße 18, Lennestadt 57368. **T:** 49 2721 1360 **E:** info@sauerlandkurier.de
W: http://www.sauerlandkurier.de
Redakteur / Editor: Gregor Breise; **Redakteurin / Editor:** Miriam Hubmayer; **Redakteur / Editor:** Lars Lenneper; **Redakteur / Editor:** Hartmut Poggel; **Redakteur / Editor:** Sven Prillwitz; **Redakteurin / Editor:** Rebecca Rath; **Redakteurin / Editor:** Stefanie Reinelt; **Redakteurin / Editor:** Anna Sartorius; **Redakteur / Editor:** Michael Sauer; **Chefredaktion:** Torsten-Eric Sendler; **Redakteurin / Editor:** Jana Sudhoff; **Redakteur / Editor:** Marco Twente; **Redakteurin / Editor:** Andrea Vollmert; **Redakteur / Editor:** Christian Weber
Language (s): German
NEWSPAPER

Schaumburger Nachrichten
Owner: Schaumburger Nachrichten Verlagsges. mbH & Co. KG
Editorial: Vornhäger Straße 44, Stadthagen 31655. **T:** 49 572 1 80 92 30
E: sn@madsack.de
W: http://www.sn-online.de/
Freq: Daily; **Circ:** 11681
Chefredaktion / Editor in Chief: Uwe Graells
Language (s): German
DAILY NEWSPAPER

Schenefelder Tageblatt
Owner: A. Beig Druckerei und Verlag GmbH & Co. KG
Editorial: Fördestraße 20, Flensburg 24944. **T:** 49 800 2050 7100 **E:** redaktion@shz.de
W: http://www.shz.de/lokales/schenefelder-tageblatt/
Freq: Daily; **Circ:** 11315
Redakteurin / Editor: Anja Christiansen; **Redekteur/ Editor:** Gerrit Hencke; **Redaktion / Editor:** Katy Krause; **Redakteurin / Editor:** Barbara Maas; **Redakteurin / Editor:** Mira Nagar; **Redakteur / Editor:** Hauke Normann
Language (s): German
DAILY NEWSPAPER

Schlänger Zeitung
Owner: Westfalen-Blatt Vereinigte Zeitungsverlage GmbH
Editorial: Ortsmitte 4, Bielefeld 33189. **T:** 49 521 5850
E: schlangen@westfalen-blatt.de
W: http://www.westfalen-blatt.de
Freq: Daily; **Circ:** 44450 IVW
Language (s): German
DAILY NEWSPAPER

Schleswiger Nachrichten
Owner: sh:z Schleswig-Holsteinischer Zeitungsverlag GmbH & Co. KG
Editorial: Fördestraße 20, Flensburg 24944. **T:** 49 800 2050 7100 **E:** redaktion@shz.de
W: http://www.shz.de/lokales/schleswiger-nachrichten/
Freq: Daily; **Circ:** 14764
Redakteurin / Editor: Anja Christiansen; **Redekteurin / Editor:** Gerrit Hencke; **Redakteurin / Editor:** Barbara Maas; **Redakteurin / Editor:** Mira Nagar; **Redakteur / Editor:** Hauke Normann; **Redaktion / Editor:** Michael Radtke
Language (s): German
DAILY NEWSPAPER

Schleswig-Holsteinische Landeszeitung
Owner: sh:z Schleswig-Holsteinischer Zeitungsverlag GmbH & Co. KG
Editorial: Fördestraße 20, Flensburg 24944. **T:** 49 800 2050 7100 **E:** redaktion@shz.de
W: http://www.shz.de/lokales/landeszeitung/
Freq: Daily; **Circ:** 24101
Chefredakteur / Editor in chief: Joachim Dreykluft; **Redekteur / Editor:** Gerrit Hencke; **Redakteurin / Editor:** Barbara Maas; **Redakteur / Editor:** Hauke Mormann; **Redakteurin / Editor:** Mira Nagar; **Redakteur / Editor:** Wenzel Pleil; **Redakteur / Editor:** Gero

Trittmaack
Language (s): German
DAILY NEWSPAPER

Schönebecker Volksstimme
Owner: Magdeburger Verlags- und Druckhaus GmbH
Editorial: Bahnhofstraße 17, Magdeburg 39104 **E:** redaktion@volksstimme.de
W: http://www.volksstimme.de
Freq: Daily; **Circ:** 12315
Redakteur / Editor: Michael Bock; **Redaktion / Editor:** Jan-Thomas Goetze; **Redakteur / Editor:** Thomas Juschus; **Redakteur / Editor:** Alois Kösters
Language (s): German
DAILY NEWSPAPER

Schöner Monat
Editorial: Buchwaldstr. 1, Hamburg 22143.
T: 49 4067 39780
E: contact@conpart-verlag.de
W: http://www.conpart-verlag-cms.de
Freq: Monthly; **Circ:** 176250
Language (s): German
NEWSPAPER

Schorndorfer Nachrichten
Owner: Zeitungsverlag GmbH & Co. Waiblingen KG
Editorial: Albrecht-Villinger-Straße 10, Waiblingen 71332. **T:** 49 715 1 566 0
E: info@zvw.de **W:** http://www.zvw.de
Freq: Daily; **Circ:** 15574
Redakteurin / Editor: Ramona Adolf; **Redakteurin / Editor:** Pia Eckstein; **Redakteur / Editor:** Frank Nipkau; **Redakteur / Editor:** Jörg Nolle; **Redaktion / Editor:** Hans Pöschko; **Redakteur / Editor:** Peter Schwarz; **Redakteurin / Editor:** Andrea Wüstholz
Language (s): German
DAILY NEWSPAPER

Schwabacher Tagblatt
Owner: Verlag Nürnberger Presse Druckhaus Nürnberg GmbH & Co. KG
Editorial: Spitalberg 3, Schwabach 91126
E: st-redaktion@pressenetz.de
W: http://www.schwabacher-tagblatt.de
Freq: Daily; **Circ:** 15693
Redaktion / Editor: Jürgen Karg
Language (s): German
DAILY NEWSPAPER

Schwäbische Donau Zeitung
W: http://www.swp.de
Language (s): German
NEWSPAPER

Schwäbische Post
Owner: SDZ Druck und Medien GmbH & Co. KG
Editorial: Bahnhofstraße 65, Aalen 73430.
T: 49 7361 5 940
E: redaktion@schwaebische-post.de
W: http://www.schwaebische-post.de/
Freq: Daily; **Circ:** 26930
Redakteur / Editor: Winfried Hofele; **Redakteur / Editor:** Sascha Kurz; **Chefredaktion / Editor in Chief:** Lars Reckermann
Language (s): German
DAILY NEWSPAPER

Schwäbische Zeitung
Owner: Schwäbische Zeitung GmbH & Co. KG, Drexler, Gessler
Editorial: Karlstr. 16, Ravensburg 88212.
T: 49 751 2955 5555
E: info@schwaebische.de
W: http://www.schwaebische.de/
Freq: Daily; **Circ:** 175104
Chefredaktion / Editor in Chief: Hendrik Groth
Language (s): German
DAILY NEWSPAPER

Schwäbische Zeitung Tuttlingen
Owner: Gränzbote & INFO - Der Südfinder
Editorial: Jägerhofstraße 4, Tuttlingen 78532.
T: 49 7461 7015-53
E: redaktion.stadt.tuttlingen@schwaebische.de
W: http://www.schwaebische.de
Freq: Daily; **Circ:** 21744
Redakteurin / Editor: Joerdis Damrath; **Redakteur / Editor:** Lothar Häring; **Redakteurin / Editor:** Dorothea Hecht; **Redaktionsleiter / Maning Editor:** Ludger Möllers; **Redakteur / Editor:** David Zapp; **Redakteur / Editor:** Eric Zerm
Language (s): German
DAILY NEWSPAPER

Schwäbische Zeitung Ulm (Alb-Donau), Laichingen
Owner: Schwäbischer Verlag GmbH & Co. KG
Editorial: Marktplatz 25/1, Laichingen 89150.
T: 49 7333 9657 20
E: redaktion.laichingen@schwaebische.de
W: http://www.schwaebische.de
Freq: Daily; **Circ:** 17599
Redakteur / Editor: Ilja Siegemund; **Redakteur / Editor:** Hansjörg Steidle; **Redakteurin / Editor:** Helen Walter
Language (s): German
DAILY NEWSPAPER

Schwäbische Zeitung, Biberach
Owner: Schwäbische Zeitung Biberach & INFO Biberach/Laupheim
Editorial: Marktplatz 35, Biberach 88400.
T: 49 7351 5002 60
E: redaktion.biberach@schwaebische.de
W: http://www.schwaebische.de
Freq: Daily; **Circ:** 20083
Redakteurin / Editor: Karen Annemaier; **Redakteurin / Editor:** Kathrin Bölstler; **Redakteurin / Editor:** Tanja Bosch; **Redakteur / Editor:** Markus Dreher; **Redakteurin / Editor:** Annette Grüninger; **Redakteur / Editor:** Michael Hänssle; **Redakteur / Editor:** Andreas Wagner; **Redakteur / Editor:** Gregor Westerbarkei
Language (s): German
DAILY NEWSPAPER

Schwäbische Zeitung, Friedrichshafen
Owner: Schwäbische Zeitung Friedrichshafen & INFO Bodensee
Editorial: Schanzstraße 11, Friedrichshafen 88045. **T:** 49 7541 70050
E: redaktion.friedrichshafen@schwaebische.de
W: http://www.schwaebische.de
Freq: Daily; **Circ:** 15232
Redakteur / Editor: Gunnar Flotow; **Redakteur / Editor:** Anton Fuchsloch; **Redakteur / Editor:** Jens Lindenmüller; **Redakteur / Editor:** Alexander Mayer; **Redakteur / Editor:** Ralf Schäfer; **Redakteur / Editor:** Hagen Schönherr
Language (s): German
DAILY NEWSPAPER

Schwäbische Zeitung, Ravensburg
Owner: Schwäbische Zeitung Ravensburg
Editorial: Karlstr.16, Ravensburg 88212.
T: 49 751 29552222
E: redaktion.ravensburg@schwaebische.de
W: http://www.schwaebische.de
Freq: Daily; **Circ:** 23849
Redakteurin / Editor: Ruth Auchter; **Redakteur / Editor:** Daniel Drescher; **Redakteurin / Editor:** Sybille Emmrich; **Redakteurin / Editor:** Karin Kiesel; **Redakteur / Editor:** Philipp Richter; **Redakteur / Editor:** Berthold Rueß; **Redakteurin / Editor:** Adelinde Schwegler; **Redakteurin / Editor:** Annette Vincenz
Language (s): German
DAILY NEWSPAPER

Schwäbisches Tagblatt
Owner: Schwäbisches Tagblatt GmbH
Editorial: Uhlandstraße 2, Tübingen 72072.
T: 49 7071 9340 **E:** redaktion@tagblatt.de
W: http://www.tagblatt.de/Home/nachrichten.html
Freq: Daily; **Circ:** 20383
Redakteur / Editor: Ulrich Janssen; **Chefredaktion / Editor in Chief:** Gernot Stegert
Language (s): German
DAILY NEWSPAPER

Schwabmüncher Allgemeine
W: http://www.augsburger-allgemeine.de/?region=b-sz
Language (s): German
NEWSPAPER

Schwabmünchner Allgemeine
Owner: Presse-Druck- und Verlags-GmbH
W: http://www.presse-druck.de
Chefredaktion: Sascha Borowski; **Redakteur / Editor:** Daniela Deeg; **Redakteur / Editor:** Stefan Drescher; **Redakteur / Editor:** Daniela Fischer; **Redakteurin / Editor:** Ina Kresse; **stellv. Chefredaktion:** Norbert Staub
Language (s): German
NEWSPAPER

Schwarzwälder Bote
Owner: Schwarzwälder Bote Redaktionsges. mbH
Editorial: Kirchtorstr. 14, Oberndorf am Neckar 78727. **T:** 49 742 3 780
E: redaktion@schwarzwaelder-bote.de
W: http://www.schwarzwaelder-bote.de/
Freq: Daily; **Circ:** 126319
Redakteurin / Editor: Imelda Flaig; **Redakteur / Editor:** Michael Gerster; **Redakteurin / Editor:** Stefanie Kübler; **Redakteur / Editor:** Torsten Sadra; **Chefredaktion / Editor in Chief:** Martin Wagner
Language (s): German
DAILY NEWSPAPER

Schwarzwälder Bote Schwarzwald Baar Kreis
Owner: Schwarzwälder Bote Mediengesellschaft mbH
Editorial: Kirchtorstr. 14, Oberndorf am Neckar 78727. **T:** 49 7423 780
E: service@schwarzwaelder-bote.de
Freq: Daily; **Circ:** 11217
Language (s): German
DAILY NEWSPAPER

Schweinfurter Tagblatt
Owner: Mediengruppe Main-Post GmbH & Co. KG
Editorial: Berner Str. 2, Würzburg 97084.
T: 49 931 6001 0
E: service.center@mainpost.de
W: http://www.mainpost.de/regional/schweinfurt/
Freq: Daily; **Circ:** 47450
Redaktion / Editor: Susanne Wiedemann
Language (s): German
DAILY NEWSPAPER

Schweriner Volkszeitung
Owner: Zeitungsverlag Schwerin GmbH & Co. KG
Editorial: Gutenbergstraße 1, Schwerin 19061.
T: 49 385 63 78 0 **E:** redaktion@svz.de
W: http://www.svz.de/
Freq: Daily; **Circ:** 96141
Redakteur / Editor: Roland Güttler; **Redakteur / Editor:** Mario Kuska; **Chefredaktion / Editor in Chief:** Michael Seidel
Language (s): German
DAILY NEWSPAPER

Schweriner Volkszeitung, Schwerin
Owner: Zeitungsverlag Schwerin GmbH & Co. KG
Editorial: Gutenbergstraße 1, Schwerin 19061.
T: 49 385 63 78 8157 **E:** lrswh@svz.de
W: http://www.svz.de
Freq: Daily; **Circ:** 24587
Redakteur / Editor: Bernhard Sprengel; **Redakteur / Editor:** Hans Taken; **Redakteur / Editor:** Timo Weber
Language (s): German
DAILY NEWSPAPER

Schweriner Volksztg. Hagenow
Owner: Hagenower Kreisblatt
Editorial: Lange Straße 35, Hagenow 19230.
T: 49 3883 61 08 8239 **E:** lrhag@svz.de
W: http://www.svz.de
Freq: Daily; **Circ:** 12328
Redakteur / Editor: Dieter Hirschmann
Language (s): German
DAILY NEWSPAPER

Schweriner Volksztg. Sternberg
Owner: Zeitungsverlag Schwerin GmbH & Co. KG
Editorial: Am Markt 2, Sternberg 19406.
T: 49 3847 43028210 **E:** sternberg@svz.de
W: http://www.prignitzer.de
Freq: Daily; **Circ:** 24587
Redakteur / Editor: Roland Güttler; **Redakteurin / Editor:** Roswitha Spöhr
Language (s): German
DAILY NEWSPAPER

Schwetzinger Zeitung
Owner: Schwetzinger Zeitungsverlag GmbH + Co. KG
Editorial: Dudenstraße 12-26, Mannheim 68167. **T:** 49 621 392 01
E: geschaeftsleitung@mamo.de
W: http://www.morgenweb.de/region/schwetzinger-zeitung-hockenheimer-tageszeitung
Freq: Daily; **Circ:** 16695
Chefredaktion / Editor in Chief: Jürgen Gruler
Language (s): German
DAILY NEWSPAPER

Segeberger Zeitung
Owner: C.H. Wäser KG GmbH & Co.
Editorial: Hamburger Straße 26, Bad Segeberg 23795. **T:** 49 455 190430
W: http://www.segeberger-zeitung.de/
Freq: Daily; **Circ:** 12781
Language (s): German
DAILY NEWSPAPER

shp Schleswig-Holstein-Presse Gesamt
Owner: shp Schleswig Holstein Presse
Editorial: Fördestraße 20, Flensburg 24944
E: mediaservice@sh-presse.de
Freq: Daily; **Circ:** 248164
Language (s): German
DAILY NEWSPAPER

Siegener Zeitung
Owner: Siegener Zeitung, Vorländer & Rothmaler GmbH & Co. KG
Editorial: Obergraben 39, Siegen 57072.
T: 49 271 59 400
E: redaktionssekretariat@siegener-zeitung.de
W: http://www.siegener-zeitung.de
Freq: Daily; **Circ:** 58683
Redakteurin / Editor: Irene Hermann-Sobotka; **Chefredaktion / Editor in Chief:** Dieter Sobotka
Language (s): German
DAILY NEWSPAPER

Sindelfinger Zeitung / Böblinger Zeitung
Owner: Röhm Verlag & Medien GmbH & Co. KG
Editorial: Böblinger Str. 76, Sindelfingen 71065. **T:** 49 7031 862210
E: redaktion@szbz.de **W:** http://www.szbz.de
Freq: Daily; **Circ:** 11729 IVW
Chefredaktion: Jürgen Haar; **Chefredaktion:** Hans-Jörg Zürn
Language (s): German
DAILY NEWSPAPER

Soester Anzeiger
Owner: W. Jahn Verlag GmbH & Co. KG
Editorial: Schloitweg 19-21, Soest 59494.
T: 49 292 1 6880
E: internet@soester-anzeiger.de
W: http://www.soester-anzeiger.de/
Freq: Daily; **Circ:** 37007
Redaktion / Editor: Matthias Dietz; **Redakteur / Editor:** Michael Dülberg; **Redakteurin / Editor:** Astrid Gunnemann; **Redakteurin / Editor:** Petra Krause; **Redakteurin / Editor:** Britta Lenze; **Redakteur / Editor:** Nico Rading; **Redakteur / Editor:** Laura Schwabbauer; **Redakteur / Editor:** Holger Strumann; **Redakteur / Editor:** Ludger Tenberge
Language (s): German
DAILY NEWSPAPER

Solinger Tageblatt
Owner: B. Boll Verlag des Solinger Tageblattes GmbH & Co. KG
Editorial: Mummstr. 9, Solingen 42651.
T: 49 212 299100
E: redaktion@solinger-tageblatt.de
W: http://www.solinger-tageblatt.de
Freq: Daily; **Circ:** 23408 IVW
Chefredaktion: Stefan M. Kob; **Redaktion Bildung/Erziehung:** Simone Theyßen-Speich
Language (s): German
DAILY NEWSPAPER

Solms-Braunfelser
Owner: Wetzlardruck GmbH
Editorial: Elsa-Brandström-Str. 18, Wetzlar 35578. **T:** 49 6441 959595
E: redaktion.wnz@mittelhessen.de
W: http://www.mittelhessen.de
Freq: Daily; **Circ:** 24482 IVW
Redakteur / Editor: Martin Heller
Language (s): German
DAILY NEWSPAPER

Speyerer Morgenpost
Owner: VVS Vorderpfälzischer Verlag Speyer
Editorial: Pressehaus, Ludwigstraße 9, Speyer 67346. **T:** 49 6232 60110
E: uvw@mopo-speyer.de
Freq: Daily
Chefredaktion / Editor in Chief: Wolfgang Martin
Language (s): German
DAILY NEWSPAPER

Speyerer Rundschau
Owner: RHEINPFALZ Verlag und Druckerei GmbH & Co. KG
Editorial: Amtsstraße 5 - 11, Ludwigshafen 67059. **T:** 49 621 590201
E: rheinpfalz@rheinpfalz.de
W: http://www.rheinpfalz.de
Freq: Daily; **Circ:** 16517
Redakteur / Editor: Andreas Bahner; **Redakteur / Editor:** Christian Berger; **Chefredaktion / Editor in Chief:** Michael Garthe; **Redakteur / Editor:** Stefan Keller; **Redakteurin / Editor:** Christine Kraus; **Redakteur / Editor:** Patrick Seiler
Language (s): German
DAILY NEWSPAPER

Stader Tageblatt
Owner: Zeitungsverlag Krause GmbH & Co. KG
Editorial: Zeitungsverlag Krause GmbH & Co KG, Glückstädter Straße 10, Stade 21682.
T: 49 414 1 936 333
E: redaktion-std@tageblatt.de
W: http://www.tageblatt.de/
Freq: Daily; **Circ:** 23046
Redakteur / Editor: Jan Bröhan; **Redakteur /**

Editor: Mathias Brückner; **Redakteurin / Editor:** Anja Christiansen; **Redakteurin / Editor:** Claudia Chwialkowski; **Redakteur / Editor:** Miriam Fehlbus; **Redakteurin /Editor:** Susanne Helfferich; **Redekteur / Editor:** Gerrit Hencke; **Redakteur / Editor:** Steffen Kappelt; **Redakteurin / Editor:** Grit Klempow; **Redakteur / Editor:** Hans-Lothar Kordländer; **Redakteurin / Editor:** Sabine Lohmann; **Redakteur / Editor:** Jens Lüneburg; **Redakteur / Editor:** Barbara Maas; **Redakteur / Editor:** Barbara Maas; **Redakteur / Editor:** Mira Nagar; **Chefredaktion / Editor in Chief:** Wolfgang Stephan; **Redakteur / Editor:** Wilfried Stief; **Redakteurin / Editor:** Annika Tiemann; **Redakteur / Editor:** Peter von Allwörden
Language (s): German
DAILY NEWSPAPER

Stendaler Volksstimme
Owner: Magdeburger Verlags- und Druckhaus GmbH
Editorial: Bahnhofstraße 17, Magdeburg 39104. **T:** 49 391 5999 0
E: redaktion@volksstimme.de
W: http://www.volksstimme.de
Freq: Daily; **Circ:** 16327
Redakteur / Editor: Michael Bock; **Redaktion / Editor:** Frank Eckert; **Redaktion / Editor:** Thomas Juschus; **Redakteur / Editor:** Alois Kösters
Language (s): German
DAILY NEWSPAPER

Stolberger Nachrichten
Owner: Zeitungsverlag Aachen GmbH
Editorial: Dresdener Straße 3, Postfach 500110, Aachen 52068. **T:** 49 241 51010
E: redaktion@zeitungsverlag-aachen.de
W: http://www.aachener-nachrichten.de/lokales/stolberg
Freq: Daily; **Circ:** 28531
Redaktion / Editor: Jürgen Lange
Language (s): German
DAILY NEWSPAPER

Stolberger Zeitung
Owner: Zeitungsverlag Aachen GmbH
Editorial: Dresdener Straße 3, Postfach 500110, Aachen 52085. **T:** 49 024 1 51010
E: redaktion@zeitungsverlag-aachen.de
W: https://www.aachener-zeitung.de/lokales/stolberg
Freq: Daily; **Circ:** 20031
Redaktion / Editor: Jürgen Lange
Language (s): German
DAILY NEWSPAPER

Straubinger Tagblatt
Owner: Cl. Attenkofer'sche Buch- und Kunstdruckerei
Editorial: Ludwigsplatz 32, Straubing 94315. **T:** 49 942 1 9400 **E:** kontakt@idowa.de
W: http://www.idowa.de/zeitung/straubinger-tagblatt
Freq: Daily; **Circ:** 81107
Redakteurin / Editor: Ursula Ach; **Redakteurin / Editor:** Elisabeth Ammer
Language (s): German
DAILY NEWSPAPER

Stuttgarter Nachrichten
Owner: Stuttgarter Nachrichten Verlagsges. mbH
Editorial: Plieninger Straße 150, Stuttgart 70567. **T:** 49 711 72050 **E:** cvd@stn.zgs.de
W: http://www.stuttgarter-nachrichten.de/
Freq: Daily; **Circ:** 206645
Chefredakteur / Editor in Chief: Reimund Abel; **Chefredakteur / Editor in Chief:** Gunter Barner; **Redakteur / Editor:** Joe Bauer; **Redakteurin / Editor:** Susanne Benda; **Redakteur / Editor:** Marcus Brauer; **Chefredakteur / Editor in Chief:** Nikolai Forstbauer; **Chefredakteur / Editor in Chief:** Martin Haar; **Redakteur / Editor:** Jürgen Kemmner; **Redakteurin / Editor:** Julia Lutzeyer; **Redakteurin / Editor:** Sandra Markert; **Redakteur / Editor:** Thomas Näher; **Redakteurin / Editor:** Petra Otte; **Chefredaktion / Editor in Chief:** Christoph Reisinger; **Redakteurin / Editor:** Andrea Weller
Language (s): German
DAILY NEWSPAPER

Stuttgarter Zeitung
Owner: Stuttgarter Zeitung Verlagsges. mbH
Editorial: Plieninger Straße 150, Stuttgart 70567. **T:** 49 711 72050 **E:** internet@stz.zgs.de
W: http://www.stuttgarter-zeitung.de/
Freq: Daily; **Circ:** 482483
Redaktion / Editor: Renate Allgöwer; **Chefredaktion / Editor in Chief:** Joachim Dorfs; **Redakteurin / Editor:** Ulrike Frenkel; **Redakteurin / Editor:** Ulla Hanselmann; **Redakteur / Editor:** Helmut Martin-Jung; **Redakteur / Editor:** Jörg Nauke; **Redakteurin / Editor:** Christine Pander; **Redakteurin / Editor:** Tanja Volz; **Redakteur / Editor:** Klaus Zintz
Language (s): German
DAILY NEWSPAPER

Stuttgarter Zeitung Anz.Gem.Ges.ohne NWZ Göppingen
Owner: Stuttgarter Zeitung Werbevermarktung GmbH
Editorial: Plieninger Str. 150, Stuttgart 70567. **T:** 49 711 7205 0 **E:** info@stzw.zgs.de
W: http://www.stzw.de
Freq: Daily; **Circ:** 432565
Language (s): German
DAILY NEWSPAPER

Stuttgarter Zeitung Anzeigengemeinschaft Gesamt
Owner: Stuttgarter Zeitung Werbevermarktung GmbH
Editorial: Plieninger Str. 150, Stuttgart 70567. **T:** 49 711 7205 0 **E:** info@stzw.zgs.de
W: http://www.stzw.de/
Freq: Daily; **Circ:** 465676
Language (s): German
DAILY NEWSPAPER

Süddeutsche Zeitung
Owner: Süddeutsche Zeitung GmbH
Editorial: Hultschiner Str. 8, München 81677. **T:** 49 89 2183 0
E: redaktion@sueddeutsche.de
W: http://www.sueddeutsche.de
Freq: Daily; **Circ:** 486263
Redakteur / Editor: Jochen Arntz; **Redaktion / Editor:** Titus Arnu; **Redakteur / Editor:** Thierry Backes; **Redakteur / Editor:** Michael Bauchmüller; **Redakteur / Editor:** Marc Baumann; **Redakteurin / Editor:** Varinia Bernau; **Redakteurin /Editor:** Christina Berndt; **Redakteur / Editor:** Jan Bielicki; **Redakteur / Editor:** Guido Bohsem; **Chefredakteurin / Editor in Chief:** Alexandra Borchardt; **Redakteurin / Editor:** Roswitha Budeus-Budde; **Redakteur / Editor:** Caspar Busse; **Redakteur / Editor:** Claudio Catuogno; **Redakteur / Editor:** Detlef Esslinger; **Redakteur / Editor:** Alexander Gorkow; **Redakteur / Editor:** Klaus Hoeltzenbein; **Redakteur / Editor:** Rene Hofmann; **Redakteur / Editor:** Patrick Illinger; **Redakteur / Editor:** Joachim Kaiser; **Redakteur / Editor:** Christopher Keil; **Redakteur / Editor:** Josef Kelnberger; **Chefredakteur / Editor in Chief:** Kurt Kister; **Redakteur / Editor:** Hans Leyendecker; **Chefredakteur / Editor in Chief:** Carsten Matthäus; **Redakteur / Editor:** Gerhard Matzig; **Redakteur / Editor:** Frank Müller; **Redakteur / Editor:** Hendrik Munsberg; **Redakteur / Editor:** Johann Osel; **Redakteurin / Editor:** Gudrun Passarge; **Redakteur / Editor:** Nikolaus Piper; **Chefredakteur / Editor in Chief:** Stefan Plöchinger; **Redakteur / Editor:** Jörg Reichle; **Redakteur / Editor:** Nicolas Richter; **Redakteurin / Editor:** Evelyn Roll; **Redakteurin / Editor:** Katja Schnitzler; **Redakteur / Editor:** Markus Schulte von Drach; **Redakteurin / Editor:** Lisa Sonnabend; **Redakteurin / Editor:** Verena Stehle; **Redakteur / Editor:** Jochen Temsch; **Redakteur / Editor:** Dirk von Gehlen; **Redakteur / Editor:** Christian Weber
Language (s): German
DAILY NEWSPAPER

Süddeutsche Zeitung - Ebersberg
Owner: Süddeutsche Zeitung GmbH
Editorial: Ulrichstr. 1, Ebersberg 85560. **T:** 49 8092 8266 0
E: lkr-ebersberg@sueddeutsche.de
W: http://www.sueddeutsche.de/muenchen/ebersberg
Freq: Daily
Redakteurin / Editor: Rita Baedeker; **Redakteur / Editor:** Wieland Bögel; **Redakteur / Editor:** Korbinian Eisenberger; **Redakteurin / Editor:** Carolin Fries; **Redakteurin / Editor:** Karin Kampwerthund; **Redakteurin / Editor:** Barbara Mooser
Language (s): German
DAILY NEWSPAPER

Süddeutsche Zeitung - Erding
Owner: Süddeutsche Zeitung GmbH
Editorial: Lange Zeile 10, Erding 85435. **T:** 49 8122 9730 0
E: lkr-erding@sueddeutsche.de
W: http://www.sueddeutsche.de/muenchen/erding
Redakteur / Editor: Thomas Daller; **Redakteurin / Editor:** Katrin Langhans; **Redakteurin / Editor:** Alexandra Maier; **Redakteurin / Editor:** Isabel Meixner; **Redakteurin / Editor:** Sarah Schiek; **Redakteurin / Editor:** Petra Schneider; **Redakteurin / Editor:** Julia Sgolik; **Redakteurin / Editor:** Antonia Steiger; **Redakteur / Editor:** Florian Tempel; **Redakteur / Editor:** Mathias Weber
Language (s): German
NEWSPAPER

Süddeutsche Zeitung - Freising
Owner: Süddeutsche Zeitung GmbH
Editorial: Johannisstr. 2, Freising 85354. **T:** 49 8161 9687 0
E: lkr-freising@sueddeutsche.de
W: http://www.sueddeutsche.de/muenchen/freising
Redakteurin / Editor: Regina Blume; **Redakteur / Editor:** Maximilian Gerl; **Redakteur / Editor:** Birgit Goormann-Prugger; **Redakteur / Editor:** Birgit Grundner; **Redakteur / Editor:** Thomas Radlmaier; **Redakteurin / Editor:** Kerstin Vogel; **Redakteur / Editor:** Gerhard Wilhelm; **Redakteur / Editor:** Maik Wilke
NEWSPAPER

Süddeutsche Zeitung - Fürstenfeldbruck
Owner: Süddeutsche Zeitung GmbH
Editorial: Schöngeisinger Str. 38 - 40, Fürstenfeldbruck 82256. **T:** 49 8141 6114 0
E: lkr-fuerstenfeldbruck@sueddeutsche.de
W: http://www.sueddeutsche.de/muenchen/fuerstenfeldbruck
Freq: Daily
Redakteur / Editor: Manfred Amann; **Redakteurin / Editor:** Heike A. Batzer; **Redakteurin / Editor:** Julia Bergmann; **Redakteur / Editor:** Peter Bierl; **Redakteur / Editor:** Gerhard Eisenkolb; **Redakteur / Editor:** Karl-Wilhelm Götte; **Redakteurin / Editor:** Viktoria Großmann; **Redakteur / Editor:** Florian J. Haamann; **Redakteur / Editor:** Christian Krügel; **Redakteurin / Editor:** Anna Landefeld-Haamann; **Redakteur / Editor:** Stefan Salger; **Redakteur / Editor:** Kevin Schrein
Language (s): German
DAILY NEWSPAPER

Süddeutsche Zeitung - Starnberg
Owner: Süddeutsche Zeitung GmbH
Editorial: Gautinger Str. 9, Starnberg 82319. **T:** 49 8151 3605 0
E: lkr-starnberg@sueddeutsche.de
W: http://www.sueddeutsche.de/muenchen/starnberg
Redakteurin / Editor: Sabine Bader; **Redakteurin / Editor:** Christiane Bracht; **Redakteurin / Editor:** Christian Deussing; **Redakteur / Editor:** Otto Fritscher; **Redakteur / Editor:** Armin Greune; **Redakteur / Editor:** Peter Haacke; **Redakteur / Editor:** Wolfgang Prochaska; **Redakteurin / Editor:** Christine Setzwein
Language (s): German
NEWSPAPER

Süddeutsche Zeitung - Wolfratshausen
Owner: Süddeutsche Zeitung GmbH
Editorial: Untermarkt 2, Wolfratshausen 82515. **T:** 49 8171 4316 0
E: lkr-wolfratshausen@sueddeutsche.de
W: http://www.sueddeutsche.de/muenchen/wolfratshausen
Redakteurin / Editor: Suse Bucher-Pinell; **Redakteur / Editor:** Benjamin Engel; **Redakteurin / Editor:** Louisa Fanai; **Redakteurin / Editor:** Ingrid Hügenell; **Redakteur / Editor:** Matthias Köpf; **Redakteurin / Editor:** Thekla Kraussenecк; **Redakteur / Editor:** Wolfgang Schäl; **Redakteur / Editor:** Klaus Schieder; **Redakteurin / Editor:** Petra Schneider; **Redakteurin / Editor:** Stephanie Schwaderer; **Redakteurin / Editor:** Alexandra Vecchiato
Language (s): German
NEWSPAPER

Süddeutsche Zeitung Magazin
Owner: Magazin Verlagsges. Süddeutsche Zeitung mbH
Editorial: Hultschiner Straße 8, München 81677. **T:** 49 8321 839540
W: http://sz-magazin.sueddeutsche.de/
Freq: Weekly; **Circ:** 532759
Chefredaktion / Editor in Chief: Michael Ebert; **Redakteur / Editor:** Sebastian Glubrecht; **Redakteur / Editor:** Lars Reichardt
Language (s): German
NEWSPAPER

Südkurier
Owner: Südkurier GmbH
Editorial: SÜDKURIER GmbH Medienhaus, Max-Stromeyer-Str. 178, Konstanz.
T: 49 800 8808000 **E:** kontakt@suedkurier.de
W: http://www.suedkurier.de
Freq: Daily; **Circ:** 130045
Redakteur / Editor: Jörg Braun; **Redakteur / Editor:** Werner Feißt; **Redakteur / Editor:** Hermann Hummler; **Redakteur / Editor:** Nils Köhler; **Redakteurin / Editor:** Hildegard Linßen; **Redakteur / Editor:** Dieter Löffler; **Redakteurin / Editor:** Ramona Löffler; **Redakteur / Editor:** Peter Ludäscher; **Redakteur / Editor:** Michael Lünstroth; **Redakteur / Editor:** Roland Papaenberg; **Redakteurin / Editor:** Nicole Rieß; **Redakteur / Editor:** Matthias Scheibengruber; **Redakteurin / Editor:** Beate Schierle; **Chefredaktion:** Gerd Welte; **Redakteur / Editor:** Wolfgang Wissler
Language (s): German
DAILY NEWSPAPER

Südkurier Bodenseekreis
Editorial: Max-Stromeyer-Str. 178, Konstanz 78467. **T:** 49 800 880 8000
E: info@suedkurier.de
W: http://www.suedkurier.de
Freq: Daily; **Circ:** 20424
Language (s): German
DAILY NEWSPAPER

Südkurier Friedrichshafen
Owner: Südkurier GmbH
Editorial: Max-Stromeyer-Str. 178, Konstanz 78467. **T:** 49 7531 9990
E: redaktion@suedkurier.de
W: http://www.suedkurier.de
Freq: Daily; **Circ:** 20365 IVW
Language (s): German
DAILY NEWSPAPER

Südkurier Konstanz
Owner: SÜDKURIER GmbH, Medienhaus
Editorial: Max-Stromeyer-Str. 178, Konstanz 78467
Freq: Daily; **Circ:** 17334
Redakteur / Editor: Michael Lünstroth
Language (s): German
DAILY NEWSPAPER

Südkurier Radolfzell/Stockach
Editorial: Max-Stromeyer-Str. 178, Konstanz 78467. **T:** 49 800 8808000
E: info@suedkurier.de
W: http://www.suedkurier.de
Freq: Daily; **Circ:** 13276
Redakteurin / Editor: Anja Arning; **Redakteurin / Editor:** Simone Ise
Language (s): German
DAILY NEWSPAPER

Südkurier Region Bodensee
Owner: SÜDKURIER GmbH, Medienhaus
Editorial: Max-Stromeyer-Str. 178, Konstanz 78467. **T:** 49 800 8808000
E: info@suedkurier.de
W: http://www.suedkurier.de
Freq: Daily; **Circ:** 75818
Redakteur / Editor: Manfred Dieterle-Jöchle; **Redakteur / Editor:** Toni Ganter; **Redakteur / Editor:** Stefan Hilser; **Redakteurin / Editor:** Kerstin Mommsen; **Redakteur / Editor:** Winfried Thum
Language (s): German
DAILY NEWSPAPER

Südkurier Region Hochrhein
Owner: SÜDKURIER GmbH, Medienhaus
Editorial: Max-Stromeyer-Str. 178, Konstanz 78467. **T:** 49 800 8808000
E: info@suedkurier.de
W: http://www.suedkurier.de
Freq: Daily; **Circ:** 27950
Redakteur / Editor: Wolfgang Fleig; **Redakteur / Editor:** Roland Gerard; **Redakteur / Editor:** Roland Gerard; **Redakteur / Editor:** Rafael Herrmann; **Redakteurin / Editor:** Uthe Martin
Language (s): German
DAILY NEWSPAPER

Südkurier Region Schwarzwald
Owner: SÜDKURIER GmbH, Medienhaus
Editorial: Max-Stromeyer-Str. 178, Konstanz 78467. **T:** 49 800 8808000
E: info@suedkurier.de
W: http://www.suedkurier.de
Freq: Daily; **Circ:** 26280
Redakteur / Editor: Jürgen Dreher; **Redakteurin / Editor:** Nathalie Göbel; **Redakteur / Editor:** Gerhard Hauser; **Redakteurin / Editor:** Susanna Kurz; **Redakteur / Editor:** Bernhard Lutz; **Redakteur / Editor:** Jens Wursthorn
Language (s): German
DAILY NEWSPAPER

Südkurier, Singen
Owner: SÜDKURIER GmbH, Medienhaus
Editorial: Max-Stromeyer-Str. 178, Konstanz 78467. **T:** 49 880 8000 **E:** info@suedkurier.de
W: http://www.suedkurier.de
Freq: Daily; **Circ:** 17645
Redakteur / Editor: Matthias Biehler; **Redakteurin / Editor:** Susanne Gehrmann-Röhm; **Redakteurin / Editor:** Helene Kerle;

Redakteur / Editor: Roland Sprich; **Redakteurin / Editor:** Gudrun Trautmann; **Redakteurin / Editor:** Karin Zöller
Language (s): German
DAILY NEWSPAPER

Südkurier, Villingen-Schwenningen
Owner: SÜDKURIER GmbH, Medienhaus
Editorial: Max-Stromeyer-Str. 178, Konstanz 78467. **T:** 49 800 8808000
E: info@suedkurier.de
W: http://www.suedkurier.de
Freq: Daily; **Circ:** 11317
Redakteur / Editor: Wolfgang Braun; **Redakteur / Editor:** Rüdiger Fein; **Redakteur / Editor:** Alexander Hämmerling; **Redakteurin / Editor:** Claudia Hoffmann; **Redakteur / Editor:** Eberhard Stadler; **Redakteur / Editor:** Andreas Wilhelm
Language (s): German
DAILY NEWSPAPER

Südkurier, Waldshut-Tiengen
Owner: SÜDKURIER GmbH, Medienhaus
Editorial: Max-Stromeyer-Str. 178, Konstanz 78467 **E:** info@suedkurier.de
W: http://www.suedkurier.de
Freq: Daily; **Circ:** 19797
Redakteur / Editor: Claus Bingold; **Redakteurin / Editor:** Ursula Freudig; **Redakteur / Editor:** Alfred Lins; **Redakteur / Editor:** Rolf Sprenger; **Redakteurin / Editor:** Fabienne Zintl
Language (s): German
DAILY NEWSPAPER

Südostbayerische Rundschau
Owner: Alois Erdl und Walter Pustet Verlags-GmbH & Co. OHG
W: http://www.heimatzeitung.de/
Redaktion / Editor: Jiri Pavelka
Language (s): German
NEWSPAPER

Südthüringer Presse Plus FreiesWort Hildburghausen
Owner: Suhler Verlagsgesellschaft mbH & Co. KG
Editorial: Schützenstraße 2, Suhl 98527.
T: 49 3681 8510 **E:** verlag@freies-wort.de
W: http://www.insuedthueringen.de
Freq: Daily; **Circ:** 11436
Redakteur / Editor: Karl-Wolfgang Fleißig; **Redakteurin / Editor:** Regina Haubold; **Redakteur / Editor:** Cornell Hoppe; **Redakteurin / Editor:** Teresa Schich; **Redakteurin / Editor:** Karin Schlütter; **Redakteur / Editor:** Wolfgang Swietek; **Redakteur / Editor:** Georg Vater; **Redakteurin / Editor:** Katja Wollschläger
Language (s): German
DAILY NEWSPAPER

Südthüringer Presse Plus FW Meininger Tageblatt
Owner: Suhler Verlagsgesellschaft mbH & Co. KG
Editorial: Schützenstraße 2, Suhl 98527.
T: 49 3681 8510 **E:** verlag@freies-wort.de
W: http://www.insuedthueringen.de
Freq: Daily; **Circ:** 11975
Language (s): German
DAILY NEWSPAPER

Südthüringer Presse Plus Gesamt
Owner: Suhler Verlagsgesellschaft mbH & Co. KG
Editorial: Schützenstraße 2, Suhl 98527.
T: 49 3681 8510 **E:** verlag@freies-wort.de
W: http://www.insuedthueringen.de
Freq: Daily; **Circ:** 104381
Language (s): German
DAILY NEWSPAPER

Südthüringer Presse Plus Hauptausgabe
Owner: Suhler Verlagsgesellschaft mbH & Co. KG
Editorial: Schützenstraße 2, Suhl 98527.
T: 49 3681 8510 **E:** verlag@freies-wort.de
W: http://www.insuedthueringen.de
Freq: Daily; **Circ:** 79359
Redakteur / Editor: Jörg Aberger; **Redakteur / Editor:** Heinz Escher; **Redakteur / Editor:** Burkhard Fraune; **Redakteurin / Editor:** Eva Gebhardt; **Redakteurin / Editor:** Bettina Keller; **Redakteur / Editor:** Peter Lauterbach; **Redakteur / Editor:** Dirk Meyer; **Redakteurin / Editor:** Alexandra Paulfranz; **Redakteur / Editor:** Georg-Stefan Russew; **Redakteur / Editor:** Landolf Scherzer; **Redakteurin / Editor:** Jutta Schütz; **Redakteurin / Editor:** Elke Vogel; **Redakteur / Editor:** Jens Wenzel
Language (s): German
DAILY NEWSPAPER

Südthüringer Presse PlusFreiesWort/ STZSchmalkalden
Owner: Suhler Verlagsgesellschaft mbH & Co. KG
Editorial: Schützenstraße 2, Suhl 98527.
T: 49 3681 8510 **E:** verlag@freies-wort.de
W: http://www.insuedthueringen.de
Freq: Daily; **Circ:** 11601
Redakteurin / Editor: Bärbel Bierstädt; **Redakteurin / Editor:** Waltraud Nagel; **Redakteurin / Editor:** Annett Recknagel; **Redakteurin / Editor:** Milina Reichardt-Hahn
Language (s): German
DAILY NEWSPAPER

Südthüringer Zeitung
Owner: Südthüringer Verlag GmbH
Editorial: Andreasstraße 11, Bad Salzungen 36433. **T:** 49 369 5 55 50 50
E: verlag@stz-online.de
W: http://www.insuedthueringen.de/
Freq: Daily; **Circ:** 104381
Redaktion / Editor: Christoph Witzel
Language (s): German
DAILY NEWSPAPER

Südwest Presse
Owner: Neue Presseges. mbH & Co. KG
Editorial: Frauenstraße 77, Ulm 89073.
T: 49 731 156 0 **E:** redaktion@swp.de
W: http://www.swp.de/ulm
Freq: Daily; **Circ:** 316453
Chefredakteur / Editor in Chief: Ulrich Becker; **Redakteur / Editor:** Hubert Kaltenbach
Language (s): German
DAILY NEWSPAPER

SWP/Schwäbische Donauzeitung Neu-Ulm
Owner: Neue Pressegesellschaft mbH & Co. KG
Editorial: Frauenstraße 77, Ulm 89073.
T: 49 731 156234
E: regionalredaktion@swp.de
W: http://www.swp.de
Freq: Daily; **Circ:** 13769
Language (s): German
DAILY NEWSPAPER

TASPO
Owner: Haymarket Media GmbH & Co. KG
T: 49 531 3800411
E: red.taspo@haymarket.de
W: http://www.taspo.de **Circ:** 11742
Chefredaktion / Editor in Chief: Iris Anger; **Redakteurin / Editor:** Gabriele Friedrich; **Redakteur / Editor:** Marion Sippel-Boland; **Chefredaktion:** Renate Veth; **Redakteurin / Editor:** Lorenz Wieland
Language (s): German
NEWSPAPER

Taunus Zeitung
Owner: Frankfurter Societäts-Medien GmbH
Editorial: Frankenallee 71–81, Frankfurt Am Main 60327. **T:** 49 697 5 010
E: redaktion@fnp.de
W: http://www.taunus-zeitung.de/
Freq: Daily; **Circ:** 30820
Redaktion / Editor: Andreas Burger; **Redakteur / Editor:** Thomas Ewald; **Redakteur / Editor:** Michael Forst; **Redakteur / Editor:** Sebastian Holzapfel; **Redakteur / Editor:** Thomas Ruhmöller
Language (s): German
DAILY NEWSPAPER

taz Berlin
Owner: taz Verlags- und Vertriebs GmbH
Editorial: Rudi-Dutschke-Str. 23, Berlin 10969.
T: 49 30 25 902 130 **E:** impressum@taz.de
W: http://www.taz.de
Freq: Daily; **Circ:** 15408
Language (s): German
DAILY NEWSPAPER

taz.die tageszeitung
Owner: taz Verlags- und Vertriebs GmbH
Editorial: taz Verlags u. Vertriebs GmbH, Rudi-Dutschke-Str. 23, Berlin 10969.
T: 49 30 259 02 0 **E:** impressum@taz.de
W: http://www.taz.de
Freq: Daily; **Circ:** 69028
Redakteur / Editor: Wolfgang Löhr; **Chefredaktion / Editor in Chief:** Ines Pohl; **Redakteur / Editor:** Markus Völker
Language (s): German
DAILY NEWSPAPER

Tegernseer Zeitung
Owner: Hofbuchdruckerei Adalbert Boemmel und Sohn
Editorial: Gasse 22, Gmund 83703.
T: 49 664 97 34 356
E: tegernsee@tegernseeaktuell.de
W: http://www.tegernseeaktuell.de
Freq: Daily; **Circ:** 16766
Language (s): German
DAILY NEWSPAPER

Thüringer Allgemeine
Owner: ZGT Verlag GmbH
Editorial: Gottstedter Landstraße 6, Erfurt 99092. **T:** 49 361 2274
E: chefredaktion@thueringer-allgemeine.de
W: http://www.thueringer-allgemeine.de/
Freq: Daily; **Circ:** 165044
Redakteur / Editor: Marco Alles; **Redakteur / Editor:** Sigrid Aschoff; **Redakteur / Editor:** Hans-Peter Blum; **Redakteur / Editor:** Wolf-Dieter Bose; **Redakteur / Editor:** Casjen Carl; **Redakteur / Editor:** Martin Debes; **Redakteur / Editor:** Axel Eger; **Redakteurin / Editor:** Manuela Eiert; **Redakteur / Editor:** Steffen Eß; **Redakteur / Editor:** Henryk Goldberg; **Redakteur / Editor:** Dietmar Grosser; **Redakteurin / Editor:** Britta Henkel; **Redakteur / Editor:** Bernd Jentsch; **Redakteur / Editor:** Marco Kneise; **Layout Redakteurin / Layout Editor:** Doris Mielisch; **Redakteur / Editor:** Kai Mudra; **Redakteur / Editor:** Harald Mühlenbeck; **Redakteur / Editor:** Hanno Müller; **Redakteurin / Editor:** Petra Peuckert; **Redakteurin / Editor:** Elena Rauch; **Chefredaktion / Editor in Chief:** Paul-Josef Raue; **Redakteur / Editor:** Karl-heinz Schmidt; **Redakteur / Editor:** Werner Setz; **Redakteur / Editor:** Jörg Tharan
Language (s): German
DAILY NEWSPAPER

Thüringer Allgemeine TA, Ilmenau
Owner: ZGT Verlag GmbH
Editorial: August-Bebel-Straße 3, Ilmenau 99693. **T:** 49 3677 86 39 11
E: ilmenau@thueringer-allgemeine.de
W: http://www.thueringer-allgemeine.de
Freq: Daily; **Circ:** 13373
Redakteur / Editor: Andre Heß; **Redakteur / Editor:** Arne Martius
Language (s): German
DAILY NEWSPAPER

Thüringer Allgemeine, Nordhausen
Owner: ZGT Verlag GmbH
Editorial: Bahnhofstraße 33, Nordhausen 99734. **T:** 49 3631 605811
E: nordhausen@thueringer-allgemeine.de
W: http://www.thueringer-allgemeine.de
Freq: Daily; **Circ:** 15432
Language (s): German
DAILY NEWSPAPER

Thüringer Allgemeine, Weimar
Owner: Zeitungsgruppe Thüringer Verwaltungsges. mbH
Editorial: Goetheplatz 9a, Weimar 99423.
T: 49 3643 558130
E: weimar@thueringer-allgemeine.de
W: http://www.thueringer-allgemeine.de
Freq: Daily
Language (s): German
DAILY NEWSPAPER

Thüringische Landeszeitung
Owner: ZGT Verlag GmbH
Editorial: Marienstraße 14, Weimar 99423.
T: 49 3643 2063 **E:** chefredaktion@tlz.de
W: http://www.tlz.de/
Freq: Daily; **Circ:** 194956
Redakteur / Editor: Matthias Benkenstein; **Redakteur / Editor:** Elmar Otto; **Redakteur / Editor:** René Röder; **Redakteurin / Editor:** Gerlinde Sommer
Language (s): German
DAILY NEWSPAPER

Thüringische Landeszeitung (Erfurt)
Owner: ZGT Verlag GmbH
Editorial: Thüringische Landeszeitung, Lokalredaktion Erfurt, Erfurt 99084.
T: 49 361 55 50 53 3 **E:** erfurt@tlz.de
W: http://www.tlz.de **Circ:** 296940
Redakteurin / Editor: Anette Elsner; **Redakteur / Editor:** Frank Karmeyer; **Redakteur / Editor:** René Röder; **Redakteurin / Editor:** Lydia Werner
Language (s): German
DAILY NEWSPAPER

Thüringische Landeszeitung (Heiligenstadt)
Owner: ZGT Verlag GmbH
Editorial: TLZ Lokalredaktion Heiligenstadt, Wilhelmstraße 59, Heiligenstadt 37308.
T: 49 3606 66 96 10 **E:** heiligenstadt@tlz.de
W: http://www.tlz.de
Freq: Daily; **Circ:** 296940
Redakteur / Editor: Jürgen Backhaus; **Redakteur / Editor:** Fabian Klaus; **Redakteur / Editor:** Harald Mühlenbeck; **Redakteur / Editor:** Harald Mühlenbeck
Language (s): German
DAILY NEWSPAPER

TLZ Gotha Gothaer Tagespost
Owner: Thüringische Landeszeitung Verlag GmbH u. Co. KG
Editorial: Gartenstraße 28, Gotha 99867.
T: 49 3621 354163 **E:** gotha@tlz.de
W: http://gotha.tlz.de/
Freq: Daily
Chef vom Dienst: Norbert Block; **Redaktuer / Editor:** Florian Girwert; **Redakteurin / Editor:** Sibylle Göbel; **Redakteur / Editor:** Elmar Otto
Language (s): German
DAILY NEWSPAPER

TLZ Weimar Thüringische Landeszeitung
Owner: Thüringische Landeszeitung Verlag GmbH u. Co. KG
Editorial: Marienstr. 14, Weimar 99423.
T: 49 3643 2063 **E:** redaktion@tlz.de
W: http://www.tlz.de
Freq: Daily; **Circ:** 33052 Pub Statement
Redaktion Computer/EDV: Albrecht Brömel; **Leitender Redakteur / Manging Editor:** Nils-Robert Kawig; **Redakteur / Editor:** Peter Michaelis; **Redakteur / Editor:** Frank Quititzsch; **Redakteurin / Editor:** Luise Schendel
Language (s): German
DAILY NEWSPAPER

Traunreuter Anzeiger
Owner: Alois Erdl KG
Editorial: Medienstraße 5, Passau 94036.
T: 49 851 8020 **E:** info@pnp.de
W: http://www.heimatzeitung.de/lokales/landkreis_traunstein/
Freq: Daily; **Circ:** 18000
Redaktion / Editor: Herbert Reichgruber
Language (s): German
DAILY NEWSPAPER

Traunsteiner Tagblatt
Owner: A. Miller, Zeitungsverlag KG
Editorial: Marienstraße 12, Traunstein 83278.
T: 49 861 98770 **E:** kontakt@suedost-news.de
W: http://www.traunsteiner-tagblatt.de/
Redakteur / Editor: Stephanie Brenninger; **Redakteurin / Editor:** Michaela Gnadl; **Redakteur / Editor:** Conny Hohler; **Redakteur / Editor:** Walter Hohler; **Chefredaktion / Editor in Chief:** Martin Miller; **Redakteur / Editor:** Klaus Oberkandler; **Redakteur / Editor:** Andrea Poschinger; **Redakteur / Editor:** Myriam Schmidhammer; **Redakteur / Editor:** Sandra Schwaiger
Language (s): German
NEWSPAPER

Trierischer Volksfreund
Owner: Volksfreund-Druckerei Nikolaus Koch GmbH
Editorial: Volksfreund-Druckerei Nikolaus Koch GmbH, Hanns-Martin-Schleyer-Straße 8, Trier 54294. **T:** 49 651 71990
E: redaktion@volksfreund.de
W: http://www.volksfreund.de/nachrichten/region/trier
Freq: Daily; **Circ:** 92042
Chefredakteurin / Editor in Chief: Isabell Funk; **Redakteurin / Editor:** Birgit Markwitan; **Redakteur / Editor:** Rainer Neubert; **Redakteur / Editor:** Jörg Pistorius
Language (s): German
DAILY NEWSPAPER

Trostberger Tagblatt
Owner: Alois Erdl KG
Editorial: Medienstraße 5, Passau 94036.
T: 49 851 8020 **E:** redaktion@erdl-verlag.de
W: http://www.heimatzeitung.de/
Freq: Daily; **Circ:** 20448
Language (s): German
DAILY NEWSPAPER

Tür-Tor-Fenster-Report
Editorial: VFZ-Verlag für Zielgruppeninformationen GmbH & Co. KG, Hengsener Straße 14, Dortmund 44309.
T: 49 231 92505550 **E:** ttf@vfz-verlag.de
W: http://www.tuer-tor-report.com/
Chefredakteurin / Editor in Chief: Ulrike Götz
Language (s): German
NEWSPAPER

tz
Owner: Zeitungsverlag tz München GmbH & Co. KG
Editorial: Paul-Heyse-Str. 2-4, München 80336. **T:** 49 89 53060
E: sekretariat@tz-online.de
W: http://www.tz.de
Freq: Daily; **Circ:** 176849
Chefredakteur / Editor in Chief: Rudolf Bögel; **Redakteur / Editor:** Jörg Heinrich
Language (s): German
DAILY NEWSPAPER

Uckermark Kurier
Owner: Kurierverlags GmbH & Co. KG
Editorial: Friedrich-Engels-Ring 29, Neubrandenburg 17033. **T:** 49 800 7036030
E: red-templin@uckermarkkurier.de
W: http://www.uckermarkkurier.de/
Freq: Daily; **Circ:** 13639 IVW
Redakteur / Editor: Heiko Schulze
Language (s): German
DAILY NEWSPAPER

Usedom Kurier
Owner: Kurierverlags GmbH & Co. KG
Editorial: Friedrich-Engels-Ring 29, Neubrandenburg 17033. **T:** 49 800 4575 044
E: redaktion@nordkurier.de
W: http://www.nordkurier.de/usedom
Freq: Daily; **Circ:** 22900 IVW
Redakteur / Editor: Jürgen Mladek
Language (s): German
DAILY NEWSPAPER

Verdener Aller-Zeitung
Owner: Kreiszeitung Verlagsges. mbH & Co. KG
Editorial: Am Ristedter Weg 17, Syke 28857. **T:** 49 4242 580
E: onlineredaktion@kreiszeitung.de
W: http://www.kreiszeitung.de/lokales/verden/
Freq: Daily; **Circ:** 22631
Redakteur / Editor: Pascal Faltermann; **Redakteur / Editor:** Harald Hinze; **Redaktion / Editor:** Volkmar Koy; **Redakteurin / Editor:** Lorena Pabelick
Language (s): German
DAILY NEWSPAPER

Viechtacher Bayerwald-Bote
Owner: Neue Presse Verlags-GmbH
Editorial: Medienstraße 5, Passau 94036. **T:** 49 851 8020 **E:** info@pnp.de
W: http://www.pnp.de/region_und_lokal/landkreis_regen/viechtach/
Freq: Daily; **Circ:** 18343
Redakteur / Editor: Helmut Heininger; **Redaktion / Editor:** Jörg Klotzek; **Redakteur / Editor:** Patrick Potstada
Language (s): German
DAILY NEWSPAPER

Volksblatt
Owner: Mediengruppe Main-Post GmbH & Co. KG
Editorial: Berner Str. 2, Würzburg 97084. **T:** 49 931 60010 **W:** http://www.mainpost.de
Freq: Daily; **Circ:** 41267 IVW
Language (s): German
DAILY NEWSPAPER

Volksstimme Halberstadt
Owner: Magdeburger Verlags- und Druckhaus GmbH
Editorial: Westendorf 6, Halberstadt 38820. **T:** 49 3941 69 92 20
E: redaktion.halberstadt@volksstimme.de
W: http://www.volksstimme.de
Freq: Daily; **Circ:** 13629
Language (s): German
DAILY NEWSPAPER

Volksstimme Magdeburg
Owner: Magdeburger Verlags- und Druckhaus GmbH
Editorial: Bahnhofstraße 17, Magdeburg 39104. **T:** 49 391 59 99 232
E: lokalredaktion@volksstimme.de
W: http://www.volksstimme.de
Freq: Daily; **Circ:** 46328
Language (s): German
DAILY NEWSPAPER

Volksstimme Oschersleben/ Wanzleben
Owner: Magdeburger Verlags- und Druckhaus GmbH
Editorial: Hornhäuser Straße 6, Oschersleben 39387. **T:** 49 3949 94 69 20
E: redaktion.oschersleben@volksstimme.de
W: http://www.volksstimme.de
Freq: Daily; **Circ:** 12522
Redkateur / Editor: Michael Bock; **Redaktion / Editor:** Thomas Juschus; **Redakteur / Editor:** Alois Kösters
Language (s): German
DAILY NEWSPAPER

Volksstimme Schönebeck
Owner: Magdeburger Verlags- und Druckhaus GmbH
Editorial: Wilhelm-Hellge-Straße 71, Schönebeck 39218. **T:** 49 3928 48 68 20
E: redaktion.schoenebeck@volksstimme.de
W: http://www.volksstimme.de
Freq: Daily; **Circ:** 12315
Language (s): German
DAILY NEWSPAPER

Volksstimme Stendal
Owner: Magdeburger Verlags- und Druckhaus GmbH
Editorial: Hallstraße 51, Stendal 39576. **T:** 49 3931 6 38 9999
E: redaktion.stendal@volksstimme.de
W: http://www.volksstimme.de
Freq: Daily; **Circ:** 16327
Language (s): German
DAILY NEWSPAPER

Volksstimme Wernigerode
Owner: Magdeburger Verlags- und Druckhaus GmbH
Editorial: Breite Straße 48, Wernigerode 38855. **T:** 49 3943 92 14 20
E: redaktion.wernigerode@volksstimme.de
W: http://www.volksstimme.de
Freq: Daily; **Circ:** 18418
Redkateur / Editor: Michael Bock; **Redakteur / Editor:** Thomas Juschus; **Redakteur / Editor:** Alois Kösters
Language (s): German
DAILY NEWSPAPER

WA Westfälischer Anzeiger WIRA Märkischer Kreis
Owner: WESTFÄLISCHER ANZEIGER Verlagsgesellschaft mbH & Co. KG
T: 49 2381 105227 **E:** anzeigen@wa.de
W: http://www.wa.de
Freq: Daily; **Circ:** 43701
Language (s): German
DAILY NEWSPAPER

WA Westfälischer Anzeiger WIRA Westfalen Mitte
T: 49 2381 105227 **E:** anzeigen@wa.de
W: http://www.wa.de
Freq: Daily; **Circ:** 102739
Language (s): German
DAILY NEWSPAPER

Waiblinger Kreiszeitung
Owner: Zeitungsverlag GmbH & Co. Waiblingen KG
Editorial: Albrecht-Villinger-Straße 10, Waiblingen 71332. **T:** 49 7151 5660
E: kreis@zvw.de **W:** http://www.zvw.de
Freq: Daily; **Circ:** 15810
Redakteurin / Editor: Pia Eckstein; **Redakteur / Editor:** Frank Nipkau; **Redakteur / Editor:** Jörg Nolle; **Redakteur / Editor:** Hans Pöschko; **Redakteurin / Editor:** Andrea Wüstholz
Language (s): German
DAILY NEWSPAPER

Waiblinger Kreiszeitung Gesamt
Owner: Zeitungsverlag GmbH & Co. Waiblingen KG
Editorial: Albrecht-Villinger-Straße 10, Waiblingen 71332. **T:** 49 7151 5660
E: kreis@zvw.de **W:** http://www.zvw.de/
Freq: Daily; **Circ:** 42921
Chefredakteur/ Editor in chief: Frank Nipkau; **Redakteur / Editor:** Jörg Nolle; **Redakteur / Editor:** Hans Pöschko
Language (s): German
DAILY NEWSPAPER

Waldeckische Allgemeine (Korbach/ Waldeck)
Owner: Dierichs GmbH & Co. KG
W: http://www.hna.de
Redaktion / Editor: Ingo Happel-Emrich
Language (s): German
NEWSPAPER

Waldeckische Landeszeitung
Owner: Wilhelm Bing Druckerei und Verlag GmbH
Editorial: Lengefelder Straße 6, Korbach 34497. **T:** 49 5631 56000 **E:** info@wlz-fz.de
W: http://www.wlz-fz.de/
Freq: Daily; **Circ:** 17451
Chefredakteur / Editor in Chief: Jörg Kleine; **Redakteur / Editor:** Achim Rosdorff; **Redakteur / Editor:** Achim Rosdorff
Language (s): German
DAILY NEWSPAPER

Waldkraiburger Nachrichten
Owner: Oberbayerisches Volksblatt GmbH & Co. Medienhaus KG
Editorial: Hafnerstraße 5-13, Rosenheim 83022. **T:** 49 8031 2130
E: info@ovb-heimatzeitungen.de
W: http://www.ovb-online.de/muehldorf/waldkraiburg/
Freq: Daily; **Circ:** 13535
Redakteur / Editor: Willi Börsch; **Redaktion / Editor:** Johann Grundner
Language (s): German
DAILY NEWSPAPER

The Wall Street Journal (Germany)
Editorial: Pressehaus Zi 6200, Schiffbauer damm 40, Berlin 10117. **T:** 49 30 3151700
Bureau Chief: Matthew Karnitschnig
DAILY NEWSPAPER

The Wall Street Journal Germany)
Editorial: Wilhelm Leuschner Strasse 78, Frankfurt 60329. **T:** 49 69 2972-5500
E: djnews.frankfurt@dowjones.com
DAILY NEWSPAPER

Walsroder Zeitung
Owner: J. Gronemann KG, Verlag Walsroder Zeitung
Editorial: Lange Str. 14, Walsrode 29664. **T:** 49 5161 60050
E: WalsroderZeitung@wz-net.de
W: http://www.wz-net.de/
Freq: Daily; **Circ:** 11421
Redakteur / Editor: Manfred Eickhölter; **Redakteurin / Editor:** Silvia Herrmann; **Redakteur / Editor:** Rolf Hillmann; **Redakteur / Editor:** Thomas Künning; **Redakteur / Editor:** Dirk Meyland; **Redaktuer / Editor:** Heiko Oetjen; **Redakteur / Editor:** Jens Reinbold; **Redaktion / Editor:** Eckard Schulz
Language (s): German
DAILY NEWSPAPER

Wasserburger Zeitung
Owner: Oberbayerisches Volksblatt GmbH & Co. Medienhaus KG
Editorial: Hafnerstraße 5-13, Rosenheim 83022. **T:** 49 8031 2130 **E:** redaktion@ovb.net
W: http://www.ovb-online.de/rosenheim/wasserburg/
Freq: Daily; **Circ:** 11118
Chefredakteur / Editor: Willi Börsch; **Redakteurin / Editor:** Sylvia Hampel; **Redakteur / Editor:** Norbert Kotter; **Redakteur / Editor:** Thomas Neumeier; **Redakteur / Editor:** Markus Salzeder; **Redakteurin / Editor:** Ulrike Vonau; **Redakteur / Editor:** Hans-Jürgen Ziegler
Language (s): German
DAILY NEWSPAPER

WAZ Westdeutsche Allgemeine Zeitung
Owner: FUNKE DIGITAL GmbH & Co. KG
Editorial: Friedrichstr. 34-38, Essen 45128. **T:** 49 800 60 60 760
E: zentralredaktion@waz.de
W: http://www.derwesten.de
Freq: Daily; **Circ:** 397145
Redakteur / Editor: Walter Bau; **Redakteurin / Editor:** Petra Koruhn; **Redakteur / Editor:** Christopher Onkelbach; **Redakteur / Editor:** Jürgen Polzin; **Redakteur / Editor:** Frank Preuß; **Chefredaktion / Editor in Chief:** Ulrich Reitz; **Redakteur / Editor:** Friedhelm Schillo
Language (s): German
DAILY NEWSPAPER

WAZ Westdeutsche Allgemeine Zeitung, Bochum
Owner: WAZ Verlags-GmbH & Co. KG E.Brost & J.Funke
Editorial: Huestraße 25, Bochum 44787. **T:** 49 234 966 1433
E: redaktion.bochum@waz.de
Freq: Daily
Language (s): German
DAILY NEWSPAPER

WAZ Westdeutsche Allgemeine Zeitung, Herne
Owner: WAZ Verlags-GmbH & Co. KG E.Brost & J.Funke
Editorial: Markgrafenstraße 1, Herne 44623. **T:** 49 2323 9526 31
E: redaktion.herne@waz.de
Freq: Daily
Language (s): German
DAILY NEWSPAPER

WAZ Westdeutsche Allgemeine Zeitung, Witten
Owner: WAZ Verlags-GmbH & Co. KG E.Brost & J.Funke
Editorial: Bahnhofstraße 62, Witten 58452. **T:** 49 2302 91030 30
E: redaktion.witten@waz.de
Freq: Daily
Language (s): German
DAILY NEWSPAPER

WAZ Westdeutsche Allgemeine, Gladbeck
Owner: WAZ Verlags-GmbH & Co. KG E.Brost & J.Funke
Editorial: Horster Straße 10, Gladbeck 45964. **T:** 49 2043 2998 38
E: redaktion.gladbeck@waz.de
Freq: Daily
Language (s): German
DAILY NEWSPAPER

WB Bielefeld-Halle
Owner: Westfalen-Blatt Vereinigte Zeitungsverlage GmbH
Editorial: Sudbrackstraße 14-18, Bielefeld 33611. **T:** 49 521 585 228
E: nachrichten@westfalen-blatt.de
W: http://www.westfalen-blatt.de
Freq: Daily; **Circ:** 18477
Chefredakteur / Editor in chief: André Best; **Redakteur / Editor:** Ulrich Windolph
Language (s): German
DAILY NEWSPAPER

WB Kreis Herford
Owner: Westfalen-Blatt Vereinigte Zeitungsverlage GmbH
Editorial: Brüderstraße 30, Herford 32052. **T:** 49 5221 590 811
E: herford@westfalen-blatt.de
W: http://www.westfalen-blatt.de
Freq: Daily; **Circ:** 17713
Language (s): German
DAILY NEWSPAPER

WB Kreis Höxter
Owner: Westfalen-Blatt Vereinigte Zeitungsverlage GmbH
Editorial: Westerbachstraße 22, Höxter 37671
Freq: Daily; **Circ:** 23407
Language (s): German
DAILY NEWSPAPER

WB Kreis Paderborn
Owner: Westfalen-Blatt Vereinigte Zeitungsverlage GmbH
Editorial: Senefelderstraße 13, Paderborn 33100. **T:** 49 5251 896 120
E: redaktion@westfaelisches-volksblatt.de
W: http://www.westfalen-blatt.de
Freq: Daily; **Circ:** 45221
Language (s): German
DAILY NEWSPAPER

Weilburger Tageblatt am Sonntag
Owner: Wetzlardruck GmbH
Editorial: Elsa-Brandström-Str. 18, Wetzlar 35578. **T:** 49 6441 959595
E: redaktion.wnz@mittelhessen.de
W: http://www.mittelhessen.de
Freq: Daily
Language (s): German
DAILY NEWSPAPER

Weiler Zeitung
Owner: Oberbadisches Verlagshaus Georg Jaumann GmbH + Co. KG
Editorial: Am Alten Markt 2, Lörrach 79539. **T:** 49 7621 40330
E: info@verlagshaus-jaumann.de
W: http://www.verlagshaus-jaumann.de/lokales/weil_am_rhein
Freq: Daily; **Circ:** 18761
Redakteur / Editor: Claudia Bötsch; **Redakteur / Editor:** Siegfried Feuchter; **Redakteurin / Editor:** Alexandra Günzschel; **Redakteur / Editor:** Clemens Leutz; **Redakteur/ Editor:** Jasmin Soltani
Language (s): German
DAILY NEWSPAPER

Weilheimer Tagblatt
Owner: Zeitungsverlag Oberbayern GmbH & Co. KG
Editorial: Münchener Straße 1, Weilheim 82362. **T:** 49 881 189 0 **E:** info@tz-online.de
W: http://www.merkur-online.de/lokales/weilheim/
Freq: Daily; **Circ:** 12855
Redakteurin / Editor: Manuela Better; **Redakteur / Editor:** Christian Deutschländer; **Redaktion / Editor:** Brigitte Gretschmann; **Redakteur / Editor:** Florian Weiß
Language (s): German
DAILY NEWSPAPER

Weinheimer Nachrichten
Owner: DiesbachMedien GmbH
Editorial: Friedrichstraße 24, Weinheim 69469. **T:** 49 6201 81100 **E:** mail@diesbachmedien.de
W: http://www.wnoz.de/
Freq: Daily; **Circ:** 22081
Redaktion / Editor: Sandro Furlan
Language (s): German
DAILY NEWSPAPER

WELT am SONNTAG
Owner: Axel Springer AG
Editorial: Axel-Springer-Straße 65, Berlin 10969. **T:** 49 30 2591 0 **E:** leser@wams.de
W: http://www.wams.de **Circ:** 575603
Chefredakteur / Editor in Chief: Jan-Eric Peters; **Redakteur / Editor:** Cornelis Rattmann
Language (s): German
NEWSPAPER

WELT KOMPAKT
Owner: Axel Springer AG
W: http://www.welt.de/welt-kompakt
Redakteurin / Editor: Antonia Beckermann; **Redakteur / Editor:** Lars Kreye; **Redakteurin / Editor:** Anna Kröning; **Redakteur / Editor:** Sebastian Lange; **Chefredaktion / Editor in Chief:** Jan-Eric Peters; **Redakteur / Editor:** Grischa Rodust; **Redakteur / Editor:** Falk Schneider
Language (s): German
NEWSPAPER

WELT Kompakt Düsseldorf
Owner: Axel Springer
Editorial: Adersstraße 12, Dusseldorf 40215.
T: 49 211 964 88-251
E: duesseldorf@welt-kompakt.de
W: http://www.welt.de/welt-kompakt
Freq: Daily
Redakteurin / Editor: Katharina Bons; **Redakteurin / Editor:** Hannlore Crolly; **Redakteurin / Editor:** Paulina Czienskowski; **Redakteur / Editor:** Tobias Dupke; **Redakteur / Editor:** Ulrich Exner; **Redakteur / Editor:** Kristian Frigelj; **Redakteur / Editor:** Till-R. Stoldt; **Redakteur / Editor:** Christian Wolf
Language (s): German
DAILY NEWSPAPER

Wendlinger Zeitung
Owner: Senner Verlag GmbH
Editorial: Carl-Benz-Straße 1, Nürtingen 72622. **T:** 49 7022 94640 **E:** support@ntz.de
W: http://www.ntz.de/nachrichten/wendlingen/
Freq: Daily; **Circ:** 22171 IVW
Redakteurin / Editor: Gaby Kiedaisch
Language (s): German
DAILY NEWSPAPER

Werra-Rundschau
Owner: Werra Verlag Kluthe GmbH & Co. KG
Editorial: Vor dem Berge 2, Eschwege 37269.
T: 49 5651 3359 55
E: redaktion@werra-rundschau.de
W: http://www.werra-rundschau.de/
Freq: Daily; **Circ:** 11423
Chefredaktion / Editor in Chief: Dieter Salzmann
Language (s): German
DAILY NEWSPAPER

Weser Kurier
Owner: WESER-KURIER Mediengruppe Bremer Tageszeitungen AG
Editorial: WESER-KURIER Mediengruppe, Bremer Tageszeitungen AG, Bremen 28195.
T: 49 421 3671 0
E: chefredaktion@weser-kurier.de
W: http://www.weser-kurier.de/
Freq: Daily; **Circ:** 165029
Chefredakteurin / Editor in Chief: Silke Hellwig
Language (s): German
DAILY NEWSPAPER

Weser Kurier / Bremer Nachrichten
Owner: Bremer Tageszeitungen AG
Editorial: WESER-KURIER Mediengruppe Bremer Tageszeitungen AG, Martinistraße 43, Bremen 28195. **T:** 49 421 36710
E: lokales@weser-kurier.de
W: http://www.weser-kurier.de/bremen.html
Freq: Daily; **Circ:** 165044
Chefredakteurin / Editor in Chief: Silke Hellwig
Language (s): German
DAILY NEWSPAPER

Weser-Kurier
Owner: Bremer Tageszeitungen AG
Editorial: Martinistraße 43, Bremen 28195.
T: 49 421 36710 **E:** redaktion@weser-kurier.de
W: http://www.weser-kurier.de/
Freq: Daily; **Circ:** 165044
Chefredaktion / Editor in Chief: Silke Hellwig; **Redakteurin / Editor:** Iris Hetscher; **Redakteurin / Editor:** Petra Sigge
Language (s): German
DAILY NEWSPAPER

Westdeutsche Zeitung
Owner: Verlag W. Girardet KG
Editorial: Königsallee 27, Dusseldorf 40212.
T: 49 211 8382 0
E: westdeutsche.zeitung@wz-newsline.de
W: http://www.wz-newsline.de/home
Freq: Daily; **Circ:** 106909
Redakteur / Editor in Chief: Eckhard Fuchs; **Redakteurin / Editor:** Tanja Henkel; **Redakteurin / Editor:** Annette Ludwig; **Redakteur / Editor:** Rolf Nöckel; **Redakteur / Editor:** Stefan Schneider; **Chefredakteurin / Editor in Chief:** Ulli Tückmantel
Language (s): German
DAILY NEWSPAPER

Westerwälder Zeitung (Montabaur)
Owner: Mittelrhein-Verlag GmbH
Editorial: Konrad-Adenauer-Platz 3, Montabaur 56410. **T:** 49 2602 1604-70
E: montabaur@rhein-zeitung.net
W: http://www.rhein-zeitung.de
Freq: Daily
Redakteur / Editor: Thorsten Ferdinand; **Redakteurin / Editor:** nadja hoffmann-heidrich; **Redakteurin / Editor:** Stephanie Kühr-Gilles; **Redaktion / Editor:** Markus Müller; **Redakteurin / Editor:** Silke Müller; **Redakteurin / Editor:** Regine Theunissen; **Redakteur / Editor:** Hartmut Wagner; **Redakteurin / Editor:** Susanne Wilke; **Redakteur / Editor:** Michael Winter
Language (s): German
DAILY NEWSPAPER

Westfalen-Blatt
Owner: Westfalen-Blatt Vereinigte Zeitungsverlage GmbH
Editorial: Sudbrackstraße 14-18, Bielefeld 33611. **T:** 49 521 5850
E: wb@westfalen-blatt.de
W: http://www.westfalen-blatt.de/startseite/
Freq: Daily; **Circ:** 122625
Chefredakteur / Editor in Chief: André Best; **Redakteur / Editor:** Stefan Schütt
Language (s): German
DAILY NEWSPAPER

Westfalenpost
Owner: Westfalenpost GmbH
Editorial: Schürmannstraße 4, Hagen 58097.
T: 49 2331 917 4186
E: westfalenpost@westfalenpost.de
W: http://www.derwesten.de/wp/
Freq: Daily
Chefredaktion / Editor in Chief: Stefan Hans Kläsener; **Redakteur / Editor:** Stefan Pohl
Language (s): German
DAILY NEWSPAPER

Westfälische Nachrichten
Owner: Aschendorff Medien GmbH & Co. KG
Editorial: An der Hansalinie 1, Munster 48163.
T: 49 251 6900
E: kundenservice@aschendorff.de
W: http://www.wn.de/
Freq: Daily; **Circ:** 218675
Redakteurin / Editor: Steffanie Meier; **Redakteurin / Editor:** Kira Presch; **Redaktion / Editor:** Thomas Schubert
Language (s): German
DAILY NEWSPAPER

Westfälische Nachrichten, Steinfurt-Burgsteinfurt
Owner: Aschendorff Medien GmbH & Co. KG
Editorial: Wilhelmsplatz 1, Steinfurt 48565.
T: 49 2551 939470 **E:** redaktion.bur@wn.de
W: http://www.aschendorff.de
Freq: Daily; **Circ:** 12345
Language (s): German
DAILY NEWSPAPER

Westfälischer Anzeiger
Owner: Westfälischer Anzeiger Verlagsges. mbH + Co. KG
Editorial: Westfälischer Anzeiger Verlagsges. mbH + Co. KG, Gutenbergstr. 1, Hamm 59065.
T: 49 2381 1050 **E:** internet@wa.de
W: http://www.wa.de/
Freq: Daily; **Circ:** 102739 IVW
Redakteur / Editor: Johannes Dröge; **Redakteur / Editor:** Thomas Grewe; **Redakteurin / Editor:** Manuela Reinermann; **Redakteur / Editor:** Andreas Wartala
Language (s): German
DAILY NEWSPAPER

Westfälischer Anzeiger, Bönen
Owner: Westfälischer Anzeiger Verlagsges.mbH
Editorial: Westfälischer Anzeiger Verlagsgesellschaft mbH & Co. KG, Gutenbergstr. 1, Hamm 59065.
T: 49 2381 105 0 **E:** internet@wa.de
Freq: Daily
Redakteur / Editor: Sabine Flanse
Language (s): German
DAILY NEWSPAPER

Westfälischer Anzeiger, Werne
Owner: Westfälischer Anzeiger Verlagsgesellschaft mbH & Co. KG
Editorial: Westfälischer Anzeiger Verlagsgesellschaft mbH & Co. KG, Gutenbergstr. 1, Hamm 59065.
T: 49 2381 105 0 **E:** internet@wa.de
Freq: Daily
Redakteur / Editor: Burkhard Halfter; **Redakteurin / Editor:** Susanne Hoffmann; **Redakteur / Editor:** Bernd Kröger; **Redakteurin / Editor:** Luise Lunemann; **Redakteur / Editor:** Jürgen Menke
DAILY NEWSPAPER

Westfälisches Volksblatt
Owner: Zeitungsverlag für das Hochstift Paderborn GmbH
Editorial: WESTFALEN-BLATT Vereinigte Zeitungsverlage GmbH, Postfach 10 31 71, Bielefeld 33611. **T:** 49 521 585 0
E: wb@westfalen-blatt.de
W: http://www.westfalen-blatt.de/startseite/
Freq: Daily; **Circ:** 53000 IVW
Redaktion / Editor: Rüdiger Kache
Language (s): German
DAILY NEWSPAPER

Wetterauer Zeitung
Owner: Mittelhessische Druck- und Verlagsges. mbH
Editorial: Parkstraße 16, Postfach 10 04 62, Bad Nauheim 61217. **T:** 49 6032 9420
E: redaktion@wetterauer-zeitung.de
W: http://www.wetterauer-zeitung.de/Home/Nachrichten/Uebersicht/regid, 3_puid, 1_pageid, 9.html
Freq: Daily; **Circ:** 22127
Redaktion / Editor: Siegfried Klingelhöfer
Language (s): German
DAILY NEWSPAPER

Wetzlarer Neue Zeitung
Owner: Wetzlardruck GmbH
Editorial: Elsa-Brandström-Straße 18, Wetzlar 35578. **T:** 49 6441 959 176
E: redaktion.wnz@mittelhessen.de
W: http://www.mittelhessen.de/lokales/region-wetzlar.html
Freq: Daily; **Circ:** 25118
Redakteurin / Editor: Uta Haase; **Redakteurin / Editor:** Verena Napiontek; **Chefredakteur / Editor in Chief:** Uwe Röndigs
Language (s): German
DAILY NEWSPAPER

Wiesbadener Kurier
Owner: Verlagsgruppe Rhein Main GmbH & Co. KG
Editorial: Erich-Dombrowski-Straße 2, Mainz 552117. **T:** 49 611 3550
E: impressum@vrm.de
W: http://www.wiesbadener-kurier.de/index.htm
Freq: Daily; **Circ:** 66829
Chefredaktion / Editor in Chief: Stefan Schröder
Language (s): German
DAILY NEWSPAPER

Wiesbadener Tagblatt
Owner: Verlagsgruppe Rhein Main GmbH & Co. KG
Editorial: Erich-Dombrowski-Straße 2, Mainz 55127. **T:** 49 611 3550 **E:** impressum@vrm.de
W: http://www.wiesbadener-tagblatt.de/index.htm
Freq: Daily; **Circ:** 66829
Redaktion / Editor: Heinz-Jürgen Hauzel; **Redakteur / Editor:** Birgitte Lamparth
Language (s): German
DAILY NEWSPAPER

Wilhelmshavener Zeitung
Owner: Brune-Mettcker Druck- und Verlags-GmbH
Editorial: Parkstraße 8, Postfach 1265, Wilhelmshaven 26352. **T:** 49 4421 488259
E: redaktion@WZonline.de
W: http://www.wzonline.de/
Freq: Daily; **Circ:** 21501
Chefredaktion / Editor in Chief: Gerd Abeldt; **Redakteur / Editor:** Frank Dresen; **Redakteur / Editor:** Malte Kirchner
Language (s): German
DAILY NEWSPAPER

Wilstersche Zeitung
Owner: sh:z Schleswig-Holsteinischer Zeitungsverlag GmbH & Co. KG
Editorial: Fördestraße 20, Flensburg 24944.
T: 49 800 2050 7100 **E:** redaktion@shz.de
W: http://www.shz.de/lokales/wilstersche-zeitung/
Freq: Daily; **Circ:** 20866
Redakteurin / Editor: Barbara Maas; **Redakteurin / Editor:** Mira Nagar; **Redakteur / Editor:** Hauke Normann; **Redaktion / Editor:** Ilke Rosenburg
Language (s): German
DAILY NEWSPAPER

Wolfsburger Allgemeine
Owner: Adolf Enke GmbH & Co. KG
Editorial: Porschestraße 74, Wolfsburg 38440.
T: 49 5361 20010 **E:** waz@madsack.de
W: http://www.waz-online.de/
Freq: Daily; **Circ:** 38536 IVW
Redakteur / Editor: Christian Buchler; **Redakteur / Editor:** Engelbert Hensel; **stellv. Chefredaktion:** Jörg Lünsmann
Language (s): German
DAILY NEWSPAPER

Wolfsburger Nachrichten
Owner: BZV Medienhaus GmbH
Editorial: Hamburger Straße 277, Braunschweig 38114. **T:** 49 531 39000
E: info@bzv.de
W: http://www.wolfsburger-nachrichten.de/
Freq: Daily; **Circ:** 26583
Language (s): German
DAILY NEWSPAPER

Wolmirstedter Volksstimme
W: http://www.volksstimme.de
Language (s): German
NEWSPAPER

Wolmirstedter Volksstimme
Editorial: Magdeburger Verlags- und Druckhaus GmbH, Bahnhofstraße 17, Magdeburg 39104
E: redaktion.wolmirstedt@volksstimme.de
W: http://www.volksstimme.de/
Redakteur / Editor: Michael Bock; **Redakteur / Editor:** Thomas Juschus; **Redakteur / Editor:** Alois Kösters; **Redakteur / Editor:** Ivar Lüthe
NEWSPAPER

Wormser Zeitung
Owner: Verlagsgruppe Rhein Main GmbH & Co. KG
Editorial: Erich-Dombrowski-Straße 2, Mainz 55127. **T:** 49 611 3550 **E:** impressum@vrm.de
W: http://www.wormser-zeitung.de/index.htm
Freq: Daily; **Circ:** 18266
Redaktion / Editor: Johannes Götzen
Language (s): German
DAILY NEWSPAPER

Wörther Anzeiger
Owner: Mittelbayerischer Verlag KG
Editorial: Kumpfmühler Straße 15, Regensburg 93066. **T:** 49 941 207 65
E: mz-redaktion@mittelbayerische.de
W: http://www.mittelbayerische.de/
Redakteur / Editor: Nina Köstler; **Redakteur / Editor:** Josef Pöllmann; **Redaktion / Editor:** Walter Schießl; **Redakteur / Editor:** Ernst Waller
Language (s): German
NEWSPAPER

WZ Westdeutsche Zeitung Krefeld
Owner: W. Girardet
Editorial: Rheinstraße 76, Krefeld 47799.
T: 49 2151 8552830
E: redaktion.krefeld@wz.de
W: http://www.wz-newsline.de
Freq: Daily; **Circ:** 34286
Redakteur / Editor: Alexander Alber; **Redakteurin / Editor:** Yvonne Brandt; **Redakteur / Editor:** Mirko Braunheim; **Redakteur / Editor:** Karl-Gerhard Deußen; **Redakteur / Editor:** Rolf Eckers; **Redakteur / Editor:** Christoph Elles; **Redakteur / Editor:** Daniel Gonzales; **Redakteurin / Editor:** Dagmar Groß; **Redakteur / Editor:** Ulf Maaßen; **Redakteurin / Editor:** Martina Nickel; **Redakteur / Editor:** Heribert Schmitt
Language (s): German
DAILY NEWSPAPER

WZ Westdeutsche Zeitung Mönchengladbach
Owner: W. Girardet GmbH & Co. KG
Editorial: Rheinstraße 76, Krefeld 47799.
T: 49 2151 855 0
E: redaktion.moenchengladbach@westdeutsche-zeitung.de
W: http://www.wz-newsline.de/lokales/moenchengladbach
Freq: Daily; **Circ:** 38699
Redakteurin / Editor: Anna Busch; **Redakteurin / Editor:** Claudia Kook; **Redakteur / Editor:** Philipp Nieländer
Language (s): German
DAILY NEWSPAPER

WZ Westdeutsche Zeitung Wuppertal
Owner: W. Girardet GmbH & Co. KG
Editorial: Otto-Hausmann-Ring 185, Wuppertal 42115. **T:** 49 202 7170
E: redaktion.wuppertal@wz.de
W: http://www.wz-newsline.de
Freq: Daily; **Circ:** 47906
Redakteur / Editor: Andreas Boller; **Redakteurin / Editor:** Cornelia Breuer-Iff; **Redakteurin / Editor:** Wibke Busch; **Redakteurin / Editor:** Nikola Dünow; **Redakteur / Editor:** Stephan Esser; **Redakteur / Editor:** Eckhard Fuchs; **Redakteurin / Editor:** Anne Grages; **Redakteur / Editor:** Michael Hammes; **Redakteurin / Editor:** Tanja Henkel; **Redakteur / Editor:** Günter Hiege; **Redakteurin / Editor:** Claudia Kasemann; **Redakteur /**

When contacting publications, please mention you found them in Benn's Media

Editor: Klaus Koch; **Redakteur / Editor:** Horst Kuhnes; **Redakteur / Editor:** Peter Kurz; **Redakteur / Editor:** Florian Launus; **Redakteur / Editor:** Lothar Leuschen; **Redakteurin / Editor:** Annette Ludwig; **Redakteur / Editor:** Stefan Melneczuk; **Redakteur / Editor:** Rolf Nöckel; **Redakteur / Editor:** Manuel Praest; **Redakteur / Editor:** Andreas Spiegelhauer; **Redakteur / Editor:** Olaf Steinacker; **Redakteur / Editor:** Martina Thöne; **Redakteurin / Editor:** Vera Zischke
Language (s): German
DAILY NEWSPAPER

WZ Westdeutsche Zeitung, Kreis Mettmann
Owner: W. Girardet
Editorial: Otto-Hausmann-Ring 185, Wuppertal 42115. **T:** 49 202 7172535
E: redaktion.kreis-mettmann@wz.de
W: http://www.wz-newsline.de
Freq: Daily
Redakteurin / Editor: Tanja Albrecht; **Redakteur / Editor:** Joachim Dangelmeyer; **Redakteur / Editor:** Benjamin Dietrich; **Redakteur / Editor:** Norbert Jakobs; **Redakteur / Editor:** Michael Kremer; **Redakteur / Editor:** Thomas Lekies; **Redakteur / Editor:** Arnulf Ramcke; **Redakteur / Editor:** Thomas Reuter; **Redakteurin / Editor:** Andrea Schmitz; **Redakteur / Editor:** Stefan Schneider
Language (s): German
DAILY NEWSPAPER

Zaman Deutschland
Owner: Zukunft Medien GmbH
Editorial: Reinhardtstraße 47a, Berlin 10117.
T: 49 30 24628160 **E:** info@eurozaman.de
W: http://worldmediagroup.eu
Freq: Daily; **Circ:** 30583
Language (s): German
DAILY NEWSPAPER

Zeitung für Ganderkesee
W: http://www.nwzonline.de
Language (s): German
NEWSPAPER

Zollern-Alb-Kurier
Owner: Druck + Verlagshaus Hermann Daniel GmbH + Co. KG
Editorial: Grünewaldstr. 15, Postfach 10 02 64, Balingen 72336. **T:** 49 7433 2660
E: zentrale@zak.de **W:** http://www.zak.de/
Freq: Daily; **Circ:** 22921
Redakteurin / Editor: Jasmin Alber; **Redakteur / Editor:** Andreas Awe; **Redakteur / Editor:** Volker Bitzer; **Redakteur / Editor:** Ralph Conzelmann; **Redakteur / Editor:** Frank D. Engelhardt; **Chefredaktion:** Thomas Godawa; **Redakteur / Editor:** Klaus Irion; **Redakteur / Editor:** Hannes Mohr; **Redakteur / Editor:** Holger Much; **Chefredaktion:** Karl-Otto Müller; **Redaktion / Editor:** Karl-Otto Müller; **Redaktueur / Editor:** Benno Schlagenhauf; **Redakteur / Editor:** Volker schweizer; **Redakteur / Editor:** Daniel Seeburger; **Redakteurin / Editor:** Gudrun Stoll; **Redakteur / Editor:** Michael Würz; **Redakteur / Editor:** Michael Würz
Language (s): German
DAILY NEWSPAPER

NEWS SERVICE/SYNDICATE

Agence France-Presse - Frankfurt Bureau
Owner: Agence France-Presse
Editorial: Gervinusstr. 15, Frankfurt 60322.
T: 49 69 2443 3060
E: wirtschaft.deu@afp.com
W: http://www.afp.com
Language (s): French
NEWS SERVICE/SYNDICATE

Associated Press
Editorial: Moselstrasse 27, Frankfurt Am Main 60329. **T:** 46 69 2722-1730
NEWS SERVICE/SYNDICATE

Associated Press
Editorial: Reinhardtstraße 52, Berlin 10117.
T: 49 30 437-367-0 **E:** apberlin@ap.org
NEWS SERVICE/SYNDICATE

Bloomberg News
Editorial: Neue Mainzer Strasse 75, Frankfurt Main 60311. **T:** 49 69 92041200
E: germany@bloomberg.net
NEWS SERVICE/SYNDICATE

Bloomberg News
Editorial: Pariser Platz 4A, Berlin 10117.
T: 49 30 700106100
Real Estate Team Leader: Andrew Blackman;

Bureau Chief: Angela Cullen; **Editor at Large:** David Rocks
NEWS SERVICE/SYNDICATE

Dow Jones Newswires
Editorial: Wilhelm Leuschner Strasse 78, Frankfurt 60329. **T:** 49 69 2972-5500
E: djnews.frankfurt@dowjones.com
News Editor: Klaus Brune; **Markets Editor:** Eyk Henning
NEWS SERVICE/SYNDICATE

Dow Jones Newswires
Editorial: Pressehaus Zimmer 6200, Schiffbauerdamm 40, Berlin 10117.
T: 49 30 2888410
Bureau Chief: William Boston
NEWS SERVICE/SYNDICATE

dpa Deutsche Presse-Agentur
Owner: dpa Deutsche Presse-Agentur GmbH
Editorial: Markgrafenstr. 20, Berlin 10969.
T: 49 30 2852 0 **E:** info@dpa.com
W: http://www.dpa.com
Chefredakteur / Editor in Chief: Wolfgang Büchner; **Chefredaktion / Editor in Chief:** Sven Gösmann; **Bureau Chief:** Peter Janssen; **Redakteur / Editor:** Friedemann Kohler; **Redakteur / Editor:** Iris Leithold; **Redakteur / Editor:** Alexander Missal; **Redakteur / Editor:** Wolfgang Müller; **Redakteurin / Editor:** Barbara Munker; **Redakteur / Editor:** Aliki Nassoufis
Language (s): German
NEWS SERVICE/SYNDICATE

dpa-AFX Wirtschaftsnachrichten GmbH
Owner: dpa-AFX Wirtschaftsnachrichten GmbH
W: http://www.dpa-afx.de
Chefredaktion / Editor in Chief: Heinz-Rudolf Othmerding
Language (s): German
NEWS SERVICE/SYNDICATE

epd - Evangelischer Pressedienst
Owner: epd Evangelischer Pressedienst
Editorial: Emil-von-Behring-Str. 3, Frankfurt Am Main 60439. **T:** 49 69 58098 0
E: nachrichten@epd.de **W:** http://www.epd.de/
Redakteur / Editor: Marcus Mockler; **Chefredaktion / Editor in Chief:** Thomas Schiller
Language (s): German
NEWS SERVICE/SYNDICATE

European Pressphoto Agency - US Bureau
W: http://www.epa.eu
NEWS SERVICE/SYNDICATE

Reuters
Editorial: Schiffbauerdamm 22, Berlin 102 10117. **T:** 49 30 28885230
E: berlin.newsroom@thomsonreuters.com
Bureau Chief: Noah Barkin
NEWS SERVICE/SYNDICATE

Reuters
Editorial: Friedrich-Ebert Anlage 49, Frankfurt 60327. **T:** 49 69 7565-1245
E: frankfurt.newsroom@reuters.com
Bureau Chief: Noah Barkin
NEWS SERVICE/SYNDICATE

Reuters Deutschland
Owner: Thomson Reuters (Markets) Deutschland GmbH
Editorial: Friedrich-Ebert-Anlage 49, Frankfurt 60327. **T:** 49 69 75651000
W: http://de.reuters.com
Redakteur / Editor: Jens Hack; **Redakteur / Editor:** Christian Krämer; **Redakteurin / Editor:** Irene Preisinger
Language (s): German
NEWS SERVICE/SYNDICATE

teleschau - der mediendienst GmbH
Owner: tele-schau – der medi-en-dienst GmbH
Editorial: Ries-str 17, München 80992.
T: 49 89 1434190 **E:** info@teleschau.de
Redakteur / Editor: Gerd Hilber
Language (s): German
NEWS SERVICE/SYNDICATE

BROADCASTING

RADIO NETWORKS

horads - Hochschulradio Stuttgart
W: http://www.horads.de

CABLE

CNN/Cable News Network
Editorial: Johannisstrasse 20, Berlin 10117.
T: 49 30 726193838

GHANA   Tel: 233
Standard Time: GMT
Continent: Africa
Capital City: Accra

NEWSPAPERS & PUBLICATIONS

NEWSPAPERS

The Accra Mail
Owner: Doodle Publishers Ltd.
Editorial: PO Box CT 4910, Cantonments, Accra. **T:** 233 21 22 00 84
E: accmail@africaonline.com.gh
W: http://www.accra-mail.com
Freq: Daily; **Circ:** 3000 Pub Statement
Editorial Profile: Newspaper focusing on national and international news, business, politics and sport.
Language (s): English
DAILY NEWSPAPER

Daily Graphic
Owner: Graphic Communications Group Ltd
Editorial: 3 Graphic Road, Accra.
T: 233 21 68 40 01
E: graphic@graphic.com.gh
W: http://graphic.com.gh
Freq: Daily; **Circ:** 150000 Pub Statement
Editor: Ransford Tetteh
Editorial Profile: Newspaper covering national and international news including politics, business, sports, lifestyle, entertainment, and features.
Language (s): English
DAILY NEWSPAPER

Ghanaian Chronicle
Owner: General Portfolio Ltd.
Editorial: 37, Bobo Street, Tesano, Accra.
T: 233 302 232713
E: chronicle@africaonline.com.gh
W: http://www.ghanaian-chronicle.com
Freq: Daily; **Circ:** 20000 Pub Statement
Editor: Emmanuel Akli
Editorial Profile: Newspaper covering national and international news including politics, business, sports, lifestyle, entertainment, and features.
Language (s): English
DAILY NEWSPAPER

The Ghanaian Times
Owner: New Times Corporation
Editorial: Ring Road West, PO Box 2638, Accra. **T:** 233 302 228282
E: info@ghanaiantimes.com.gh
W: http://www.ghanaiantimes.com.gh
Freq: Daily; **Circ:** 50000 Pub Statement
Editor: Dave Agbenu
Editorial Profile: Newspaper covering national and international news and current affairs including business, politics, education, culture, entertainment and sports.
Language (s): English
DAILY NEWSPAPER

The Mirror
Owner: Graphic Communications Group Ltd
Editorial: 3 Graphic Road, Accra.
T: 233 30 268 4001 **E:** mirror@graphic.com.gh
W: http://www.graphic.com.gh
Freq: Fri; **Circ:** 100000 Pub Statement
Editor: Ransford Tetteh
Editorial Profile: Newspaper focusing on national and international news, business, politics, culture and sport.
Language (s): English
NEWSPAPER

NEWS SERVICE/SYNDICATE

Ghana News Agency
Editorial: P. O. Box 2118, Accra.
T: 233 302 662381

W: http://www.ghananewsagency.org
Editorial Profile: GNA, acting as a central news collection agent of the state, gathers news from all regional, and some district, capitals. With such national spread, GNA is able to promote a viable, united and cohesive nation by highlighting stories that engender development, integration and peace.
Language (s): English
NEWS SERVICE/SYNDICATE

GIBRALTAR   Tel: 350
Standard Time: GMT +1
Continent: Europe
Capital City: Gibraltar

NEWSPAPERS & PUBLICATIONS

NEWSPAPERS

Gibraltar Chronicle
Owner: Gibraltar Chronicle
Editorial: Watergate House, Casemates, Gibraltar. **T:** 350 200 71627
E: news@chronicle.gi
W: http://www.chronicle.gi
Freq: Daily; **Circ:** 3000 Pub Statement
News Editor: Brian Reyes; **Editor:** Dominique Searle
Editorial Profile: Newspaper focusing on regional general interest as well as local, national and international news, business and sport. Aimed at local population.
Language (s): English
DAILY NEWSPAPER

Panorama
Owner: Panorama Publishing
Editorial: 75 Irish Town, PO Box 225, Gibraltar. **T:** 350 200 79797
E: gibnews@panorama.gi
W: http://www.panorama.gi
Freq: Daily; **Circ:** 4500 Pub Statement
Editor: Joe Garcia
Editorial Profile: Newspaper focusing on national and international news, business, politics and sport.
Language (s): English
DAILY NEWSPAPER

Vox
Owner: Zenith Promotions Ltd
Editorial: PO Box 306, Leon House, Suite 1, Gibraltar. **T:** 350 200 77 414 **E:** info@vox.gi
W: http://www.vox.gi **Circ:** 800 Pub Statement
Editor: Derek McGrail
Editorial Profile: Newspaper focusing on national and international news including regional interest, entertainment, politics, business and sport.
Language (s): English
DAILY NEWSPAPER

BROADCASTING

RADIO NETWORKS

Radio Gibraltar
Editorial: Broadcasting House, 18 South Barrack Road, Gibraltar. **T:** 350 200 79 760
E: radiogibraltar@gbc.gi **W:** http://www.gbc.gi
Editorial Profile: National radio station covering regional news and current affairs.

TELEVISION STATIONS

GBC Television
Owner: Gibraltar Broadcasting Corporation
Editorial: Broadcasting House, 18 South Barrack Road, Gibraltar. **T:** 350 200 79760
E: television@gbc.gi **W:** http://www.gbc.gi
Editorial Profile: National television station covering issues of interest to the people living on The Rock including movies, drama series and international documentaries.

WORLD NEWS MEDIA

GREECE   Tel: 30

Standard Time: GMT +2
Continent: Europe
Capital City: Athens

NEWSPAPERS & PUBLICATIONS

NEWSPAPERS

Adesmeuti
Editorial: Stogiannidou 1, Xanthe 67100.
T: 30 25410 -62222
W: http://adesmeuti-thrakis.blogspot.com
Freq: Daily
Publisher: Ippokratis Galatis
Language (s): Greek
DAILY NEWSPAPER

Agelioforos
Editorial: Tsimiski 45, Thessaloniki 546 23.
T: 30 2310 779111 E: aglfros@otenet.gr
W: http://www.agelioforos.gr
Freq: Daily; Circ: 6500 Pub Statement
Publisher: Alexandros Mpakatsaelos; Editor:
Evris Tsoumis
Editorial Profile: Daily evening political
newspaper published and distributed in
Northern Greece.
Language (s): Greek
DAILY NEWSPAPER

Agelioforos Tis Kyriakis
Editorial: Tsimiski 45, Thessaloniki 546 23.
T: 30 2310 779111 E: aggkyr@otenet.gr
W: http://www.aggelioforos.gr
Freq: Weekly
Editor: Evris Tsoumis
Editorial Profile: Sunday edition of the daily
newspaper including the variety of supplement
magazines.
Language (s): Greek
NEWSPAPER

Aihmi
Editorial: I. Rágkou 6, Mesologgi 302 00.
T: 30 26310 22793 E: aihmi@otenet.gr
W: http://www.aixmi-news.gr
Freq: Daily; Circ: 1500 Pub Statement
Publisher: Démetra Stéliou
Language (s): Greek
DAILY NEWSPAPER

Ebdomi
Editorial: Kanári 18, Pallene 153 51.
T: 30 210-6030655 E: ebdomi7@gmail.com
W: http://ebdomi.com Circ: 5000 Pub
Statement
Publisher: Anna Benetsánou
Language (s): Greek
DAILY NEWSPAPER

Efimerida Ton Artopoion
Editorial: Koumoundourou 1, Athena 104 37.
T: 30 210 5236424 Circ: 9000 Pub Statement
Publisher: Georgila Grika Vilelmini
Language (s): Greek
DAILY NEWSPAPER

Eleftherotypia
Owner: Tegopoulos Editions
Editorial: Minoos 10-16, Neos Kosmos,
Athens 117 43. T: 30 211 1096400
E: eleftherotypia@eleftherotypia.net
W: http://www.enet.gr
Freq: Daily
Editor: Vangelis Delipetros
Editorial Profile: Newspaper covering politics,
economy, culture and social events.
Language (s): Greek
DAILY NEWSPAPER

Epikaira
Editorial: Agias Fotinis 13, Nea Smirni, Athena
17121. T: 30 210 9754888
E: info@e-epikaira.gr W: http://e-epikaira.gr
Freq: Daily; Circ: 2000 Pub Statement
Language (s): Greek
DAILY NEWSPAPER

Espresso
Editorial: Eratosthenous 1, Athina 11635.
T: 30 210 2503000
E: espresso@espressonews.gr
W: http://espressonews.gr
Freq: Daily; Circ: 44000 Pub Statement
Editorial Profile: Tabloid-sized daily with
general interest news, celebs, show biz,
gossip, sports, high life.
Language (s): Greek
DAILY NEWSPAPER

Espresso Tis Kyriakis
Editorial: El. Venizelou 282, Kallithea 17675.
T: 30 210 2503000
E: espresso@espressonews.gr
W: http://espressonews.gr
Freq: Sun; Circ: 64500 Pub Statement
Language (s): Greek
NEWSPAPER

Ethnos
Owner: Pegasus Publishing S.A.
Editorial: ?. Benaki 5, Halandri 152 38.
T: 30 210 60 61 000 E: ethnos@pegasus.gr
W: http://www.ethnos.gr
Freq: Daily; Circ: 100000 Pub Statement
Publisher: Giorgos Mpompolas
Editorial Profile: Newspaper covering national
and international news with features on
business and finance, lifestyle, entertainment
and sport.
Language (s): Greek
DAILY NEWSPAPER

EXPRES
Editorial: Pegasus 14, Maroussi, Athena 151
25. T: 30 213 161 700 E: info@express.gr
W: http://www.express.gr
Freq: Daily
Editor-in-Chief: Giorgos Stouraitis
Editorial Profile: Provides informative articles,
detailed analysis, covering entire spectrum of
the Greek economy, news about listed
companies and major foreign stock markets.
Language (s): Greek
DAILY NEWSPAPER

Imerisia
Owner: Pegasus Publishing S.A.
Editorial: ?. Benaki 5, Chalandri 152 38.
T: 30 210 6061000 E: editor@imerisia.gr
W: http://www.imerisia.gr
Freq: Daily
Editorial Profile: Daily newspaper covering
Greek politics, business and economics.
Language (s): Greek
DAILY NEWSPAPER

Kathimerini
Owner: IHT - Kathimerini S.A.
Editorial: Ethnarhou Makariou & 2 Falireos,
Neo Faliro, Athina 185 47. T: 30 210 4808000
E: info@kathimerini.gr
W: http://www.kathimerini.gr
Freq: Daily; Circ: 26246 Pub Statement
Editorial Profile: Newspaper covering politics,
economy, culture and social events.
Language (s): English
DAILY NEWSPAPER

Kerdos
Owner: Kerdos Ekdotiki A.E.
Editorial: Pisareiou 16, Halandri 152 31.
T: 30 210 67 47 881 E: mail@kerdos.gr
W: http://www.kerdos.gr
Freq: Daily; Circ: 25500 Pub Statement
Editor: Katherina Mpoura
Editorial Profile: Newspaper covering national
and international news, business and
economics, politics and sport.
Language (s): Greek
DAILY NEWSPAPER

Kosmos (Larissa)
Editorial: Deukalionos 16, Larisa 413 35.
T: 30 2410-555540
E: kosmos@kosmoslarissa.gr
W: http://www.kosmoslarissa.gr
Freq: Daily; Circ: 14000 Pub Statement
Editor: Christos Bechlivanos; Publisher:
Konstantinos Tolis
Language (s): Greek
DAILY NEWSPAPER

Metro Greece
Owner: METRORAMA EKDOTIKE E.P.E.
Editorial: Iasonos 2, Pireas, Athena 18537.
T: 30 210 6901420 E: info@metrogreece.gr
W: http://www.metrogreece.gr
Editor: Christina Diamantopoulou
Editorial Profile: Newspaper containing
articles regarding current national and
international affairs, events, science, health,
news on culture and the arts, entertainment
and sport.
Language (s): Greek
DAILY NEWSPAPER

Naftemporiki
Owner: P. Athanassiades & Co S.A
Editorial: Lenorman 205, Kolonos, Athina 104
42. T: 30 210 51 98 000
E: editors@naftemporiki.gr
W: http://www.naftemporiki.gr
Freq: Daily; Circ: 22000 Pub Statement
Publisher: Irene Athanassiadou; Publisher:
Marietta Athanassiadou; Publisher: Angela
Athanassiadou-Kontogouri; Editor: Melina

Kalampoka; Editor-in-Chief: Dimitrios
Plakoutsis
Editorial Profile: Financial newspaper covering
all aspects of the economic and business
environment.
Language (s): Greek
DAILY NEWSPAPER

Proini
Editorial: Kassandrou 15, Kabala 654 03.
T: 30 2510 222288 E: proini3@otenet.gr
W: http://www.proininews.gr
Freq: Daily; Circ: 2500 Pub Statement
Editor: Manóles Genikópoulos; Publisher:
Periklés Genikópoulos
Language (s): Greek
DAILY NEWSPAPER

Proto Thema
Owner: Proto Thema S.A.
Editorial: Apostólou Paúlou 6, Marousi 151
23. T: 30 210 6834444
E: protothema@protothema.gr
W: http://www.protothema.gr
Freq: Weekly; Circ: 280000 Pub Statement
News Editor: Vassilis Anastasopoulos; Editor:
Tassos Karamitsos; Editor: Alexandros
Kasimatis; Editor-in-Chief: Giorgos
Papastafidas
Editorial Profile: Published every Sunday
covering international and domestic political
events.
Language (s): Greek
NEWSPAPER

Real News
Editorial: ??f?s?a? Kifisias 215, Athena
15124. T: 30 211 2008364
E: news@realnews.gr
W: http://www.realnews.gr
Freq: Sun; Circ: 110000 Pub Statement
Editorial Profile: Sunday newspaper with 4
supplements: reallife, realmoney, realplanet
and realsports.
Language (s): Greek
NEWSPAPER

Thessaliki Press
Editorial: Iolou 35, Bolos 38221.
T: 30 24210 33773 E: info@thessalikipress.gr
W: http://www.thessalikipress.gr
Freq: Daily; Circ: 2700 Pub Statement
Language (s): Greek
DAILY NEWSPAPER

To Vima
Owner: Lambrakis Press Group
Editorial: Michalakopoulou 80, Athena 115 28.
T: 30 211 36 57 000 E: tovima@dolnet.gr
W: http://www.tovima.gr
Freq: Daily; Circ: 15100 Pub Statement
Editor: Dimitris Galanis; Editor: Achilles
Hekimoglou
Editorial Profile: Newspaper focusing on
national and international news, business,
politics, culture and sport.
Language (s): Greek
DAILY NEWSPAPER

NEWS SERVICE/SYNDICATE

Agence France-Presse - Athens Bureau
Owner: Agence France-Presse
Editorial: 5 rue Milioni, Athens 10673.
T: 30 210 363 3646 E: odile.duperry@afp.com
W: http://www.afp.com
Editorial Profile: Athens bureau of the
international news and picture agency Agence
France-Presse covering international news and
current affairs.
Language (s): English
NEWS SERVICE/SYNDICATE

Associated Press
Editorial: 34 Filellinon St, Athens 10558.
T: 30 210 331-0802
Bureau Chief: Elena Becatoros; News Editor:
Derek Gatopoulos
NEWS SERVICE/SYNDICATE

Bloomberg News
Editorial: Vasilisis Sofias 60, Athens 11528.
T: 30 2107419090
Bureau Chief: Maria Petrakis
NEWS SERVICE/SYNDICATE

Dow Jones Newswires
Editorial: Filellinon 34, 105 58, Athens 10558.
T: 30 21 0331-2881
E: djnews.athens@dowjones.com
Bureau Chief: Alkman Granitsas
NEWS SERVICE/SYNDICATE

Reuters
Editorial: 8 Othonos Street, 5th Floor, Athens.
T: 30 2103311800
Greek Domestic Service Editor: George
Georgiopoulos
NEWS SERVICE/SYNDICATE

GRENADA   Tel: 1 473

Standard Time: GMT -4
Continent: The Americas
Capital City: St George's

NEWSPAPERS & PUBLICATIONS

NEWSPAPERS

The Grenada Informer
Owner: Moving Target
Editorial: Market Hill, St George's.
T: 473 4405762
E: grenadainformer@yahoo.com
W: http://www.spicegrenada.com
Freq: Weekly Not Audited
Editor: Carla-Rae Briggs
Editorial Profile: The Grenada Informer is a
weekly newspaper featuring national and
international news, politics, entertainment and
sports.
Language (s): English
NEWSPAPER

The Grenadian Voice
Owner: Spice Island Printers Ltd
Editorial: Frequente Industrial Estate, Bldg 1B,
St George's. T: 473 4403983
E: gvoice@spiceisle.com
Freq: Weekly; Circ: 3500 Not Audited
Editorial Profile: The Grenadian Voice is a
weekly newspaper focusing on national and
international news, politics, business and
sports.
Language (s): English
NEWSPAPER

GUADELOUPE   Tel: 590

Standard Time: GMT -4
Continent: The Americas

NEWSPAPERS & PUBLICATIONS

NEWSPAPERS

FRANCE-ANTILLES GUADELOUPE
Editorial: BP 2241, Jarry Cedex 97197.
T: 0590 5 90 25 18 88
W: http://www.guadeloupe.franceantilles.fr
Freq: Daily Pub Statement
Rédacteur en Chef: Pascal Le Moal;
Rédacteur en Chef Adjoint: André-Jean Vidal
Editorial Profile: Daily regional and local
current events newspapers. Local
Translation:Quotidien d'actualités régionales et
locales.
Language (s): French
DAILY NEWSPAPER

BROADCASTING

RADIO STATIONS

**RADIO MEDIA TROPICAL
GUADELOUPE 88.1**
Owner: RADIO MEDIA TROPICAL
GUADELOUPE 88.1
Editorial: 32 résidence Belcourt UB 01, Baie-
Mahault 97122. T: 0590 5 90 25 90 03
E: mediatropicalguadeloupe@hotmail.com
W: http://www.mediatropicalguadeloupe.com

TELEVISION STATIONS

RFO GUADELOUPE
Owner: RFO
Editorial: Morne-Bernard-Destrellan, BP 180,
Baie-Mahault 97122 W: http://www.rfo.fr
Editorial Profile: Regional TV and radio
station focussing on regional interest, news,
sport, magazines, music, ethology, history,
faith and traditions.

GUAM — Tel: 1 671

Standard Time: GMT +10
Continent: Oceania
Capital City: Hagatna (Agana)

NEWSPAPERS & PUBLICATIONS

NEWSPAPERS

Pacific Daily News
Owner: Gannett Co., Inc.
Editorial: 244 Archbishop Flores Street, Hagatna 96910. T: 1 671 472-1736
E: news@guampdn.com
W: http://www.guampdn.com
Freq: Daily Not Audited
Observation Post Editor: Catriona Melyan
Editorial Profile: Pacific Daily News is a newspaper focusing on business, finance, economics, culture, social life, sport and general news for the residents of Guam. The paper won the Robert G. McGruder Award for Diversity Leadership.
Language (s): English
DAILY NEWSPAPER

Pacific Sunday News
Editorial: 244 Archbishop Flores St, Hagatna 96910. T: 671 4790400
E: news@guampdn.com
W: http://www.guampdn.com
Freq: Weekly; **Circ:** 24000 Not Audited
Editorial Profile: Newspaper focusing on business, finance, economics, culture, social life, sport and general news.
Language (s): English
NEWSPAPER

BROADCASTING

RADIO STATIONS

KGUM-AM
Owner: Sorensen Pacific Broadcasting
Editorial: 111 Chalan Santo Papa, Ste 800, Hagatna 96910. T: 671 4775700
W: http://www.k57.com

KGUM-FM
Owner: Sorensen Pacific Broadcasting
Editorial: 111 Chalan Santo Papa, Ste 800, Agana 96910. T: 671 4775700
W: http://www.guamkat.com

KPRG-FM
Owner: Guam Educational Radio Foundation
T: 671 7348930 **W:** http://www.kprgfm.com

KSDA-FM
Owner: Good News Broadcasting Corp.
Editorial: 290 Chalan Palasyo, Agaña Heights 96910. T: 671 4725732 **E:** mail@joy92.net
W: http://www.joy92.net

KUAM-AM
Owner: Pacific Telestations Inc.
Editorial: 600 Harmon Loop, Dededo 96912. T: 1 671 637-5826
E: newsdirector@kuam.com
W: http://www.kuam.com
Editorial Profile: KUAM-AM is a commercial station owned by Pacific Telestations Inc. The format of the station is island music from different pacific islands. KUAM-AM broadcasts to the Dededo, Guam area at 630 AM.

KZGZ-FM
Owner: Sorensen Pacific Broadcasting
T: 671 4775700 **E:** JB@power98.com
W: http://www.power98.com

TELEVISION STATIONS

KUAM-TV
Owner: Pacific Telestations Inc.
Editorial: 600 Harmon Loop, Dededo 96912. T: 671 6375826 **E:** newsdirector@kuam.com
W: http://www.kuam.com

GUATEMALA — Tel: 502

Standard Time: GMT -6
Continent: The Americas
Capital City: Guatemala city

NEWSPAPERS & PUBLICATIONS

NEWSPAPERS

La Hora
Owner: Diario La Hora
Editorial: 9A Calle A 1-56, Zona 1, Guatemala.
T: 502 2 423 1800 **E:** lahora@lahora.com.gt
W: http://www.lahora.com.gt
Freq: Daily; **Circ:** 34000 Not Audited
Editor in Chief: Mario Cordero
Editorial Profile: Local newspaper.
Language (s): Spanish
DAILY NEWSPAPER

El Metropolitano (Xela)
Owner: Publicaciones y Acesorías Metropolitanas
Editorial: 3a Calle 15-29, Zona 8 de Mixco, Ciudad San Cristobal, Guatemala.
T: 502 2 485 4172
E: elmetropolitanoxela@gmail.com
W: http://www.elmetropolitano.net
Freq: Bi-Weekly; **Circ:** 145000 Not Audited
Editor: Jorge García
Language (s): Spanish
NEWSPAPER

Nuestro Diario
Owner: Diarios Modernos S.A.
Editorial: 15 Avenida 24-27, Zona 13, Guatemala. T: 502 2 379 1600
E: opinion@nuestrodiario.com.gt
W: http://www.nuestrodiario.com.gt
Freq: Daily; **Circ:** 275000 Not Audited
Editor: Giovanni Aldana; **Editor in Chief:** Estuardo Pinto
Editorial Profile: Newspaper focusing on economics, culture, social life, sport and general news.
Language (s): Spanish
DAILY NEWSPAPER

El Periódico
Owner: Aldea Global S.A.
Editorial: 15 Avenida 24-51, Zona 13, Guatemala. T: 502 2 427 2300
E: redaccion@elperiodico.com.gt
W: http://www.elperiodico.com.gt
Freq: Daily; **Circ:** 30000 Not Audited
Editor: Ana Carolina Alpirez; **Editor:** Ana Isabel Villela
Editorial Profile: Local newspaper focusing on national and international news, politics, culture, business and sport.
Language (s): Spanish
DAILY NEWSPAPER

Prensa Libre
Owner: Prensa Libre S.A.
Editorial: 13 Calle 9-31, Zona 1, Guatemala.
T: 502 24125600
E: redaccion@prensalibre.com.gt
W: http://www.prensalibre.com.gt
Freq: Daily; **Circ:** 160000 Not Audited
Editorial Profile: National newspaper.
Language (s): Spanish
DAILY NEWSPAPER

El Quetzalteco
Owner: Ediciones Regionales S. A.
Editorial: Avenida Las Américas 9-50 Ofc.4, Zona 3, Centro Comercial Supercom Delco Quetzaltenango, Quetzaltenango.
T: 502 7 767 4331
W: http://www.elquetzalteco.com.gt
Freq: 2 Times/Week; **Circ:** 45000 Not Audited
Editor: Ady Albores
Editorial Profile: Regional newspaper.
Language (s): Spanish
NEWSPAPER

Siglo XXI
Owner: Corporación de Noticias S.A.
Editorial: 14 Avenida 4-33, Zona 1, Guatemala. T: 502 2 423 6350
E: ccastanaza@sigloxxi.com
W: http://www.sigloxxi.com
Freq: Daily; **Circ:** 20000 Not Audited
Editor in Chief: Miguel Cañigral
Editorial Profile: National newspaper covering current affairs, politics, economy, culture and international information.
Language (s): Spanish
DAILY NEWSPAPER

NEWS SERVICE/SYNDICATE

Agencia EFE
Editorial: 8a Avenida 10-24 Zona 1, Edificio 10-24 2°Nivel Oficina 203, Guatemala.
T: 502 2 251 8457
E: guatemala@acan-efe.com
W: http://www.efe.com
Editor: Carlos Arrázola
Language (s): Spanish
NEWS SERVICE/SYNDICATE

Associated Press
T: 502 2332-0618
NEWS SERVICE/SYNDICATE

GUINEA — Tel: 224

Standard Time: GMT
Continent: Africa
Capital City: Conakry

NEWSPAPERS & PUBLICATIONS

NEWSPAPERS

Le Diplomate
Owner: Le Diplomate
Editorial: BP 2222, Conakry.
T: 224 65 5515151
E: sanouciker@hotmail.com
W: http://www.lediplomateguinee.info
Freq: Weekly; **Circ:** 3000 Pub Statement
Rédacteur en Chef: Ibrahima Deing
Editorial Profile: Newspaper covering national and international news and current affairs including politics, economics, diplomacy and regional development.
Language (s): French
NEWSPAPER

NEWS SERVICE/SYNDICATE

Agence Guinéenne de Presse
Editorial: Anciens locaux d'Enelgui, 2ème boulevard, 5ème avenue, Conakry.
T: 224 30 430 549 **E:** agp@sotelgui.net.gn
W: http://agpguinee.com
Editor in Chief: Mohamed Cissé
Editorial Profile: National Press Agency focussing on news and current affairs.
Language (s): French
NEWS SERVICE/SYNDICATE

BROADCASTING

RADIO STATIONS

Radio Kankan
Editorial: Cherifoula kankan, BP 215, Kankan.
T: 224 62 2435635 **E:** info@radio-kankan.com
W: http://www.radio-kankan.com
Editorial Profile: Regional radio station focussing on music, news, current affairs, society, culture, entertainment and sport.

GUYANA — Tel: 592

Standard Time: GMT -4
Continent: The Americas
Capital City: Georgetown

NEWSPAPERS & PUBLICATIONS

NEWSPAPERS

Guyana Chronicle
Owner: Guyana National Newspapers Ltd
Editorial: 1 Lama Avenue, Bel Air Park, Georgetown. T: 592 2 25 31 07
E: editorial@guyanachronicle.com
W: http://www.guyanachronicle.com
Freq: Daily; **Circ:** 8500 Not Audited
Editor in Chief: Mark Rempor
Editorial Profile: Newspaper focusing on national and international news, politics, business, culture and sport. Paper also publishes a Sunday edition of the paper called the Sunday Chronicle.
Language (s): English
DAILY NEWSPAPER

Guyana Times
Owner: Guyana Times, Inc.

Editorial: Atlantic Inudstrial Estate Ruimveldt, Georgetown. T: 592 2258697
E: wnigel10@hotmail.com
W: http://www.guyanatimesgy.com
Freq: Daily
Editor in Chief: Nigel Williams
Editorial Profile: Guyana Times is an English language, daily newspaper serving the residents of Georgetown, Guyana and surrounding areas.
DAILY NEWSPAPER

Kaieteur News
Owner: National Media & Publishing Co.
Editorial: 24 Saffon Street, Charlestown, Georgetown. T: 592 2258465
E: kaieteurnews@yahoo.com
W: http://www.kaieteurnewsonline.com
Freq: Daily; **Circ:** 30000 Not Audited
Editor in Chief: Adam Harris; **Publisher:** Glenn Lall; **Editor:** Nigel McKenzie
Editorial Profile: Kaieteur News is a daily newspaper focusing on crime, corruption, national and international news, politics, business, culture and sports.
Language (s): English
DAILY NEWSPAPER

Mirror (Guyana)
Owner: New Guyana Co. Ltd
Editorial: 8 Industrial Site, Ruimveldt, Georgetown. T: 592 2 26 58 75
E: weekendmirror@gmail.com
W: http://www.mirrornewsonline.com
Freq: Weekly; **Circ:** 40000 Not Audited
Editor: David DeGroot
Editorial Profile: Mirror is a weekly newspaper covering national and international news, politics, economics, finance, business, culture and sports.
Language (s): English
NEWSPAPER

Stabroek News
Owner: Guyana Publications Inc.
Editorial: 46-47 Robb Street, Lacytown, Georgetown. T: 592 2 27 40 80
W: http://www.stabroeknews.com
Freq: Daily; **Circ:** 21107 Not Audited
Publisher: David De Caires; **Editor in Chief:** Anand Persaud; **Editor:** Cheryl Stabroek
Editorial Profile: Stabroek News is a daily newspaper focusing on national and international news, business, culture and sports. The paper also publishes a Sunday edition called the Sunday Stabroek.
Language (s): English
DAILY NEWSPAPER

BROADCASTING

TELEVISION NETWORKS

CNS Television Channel 6
Editorial: 43 Robb and Wellington Streets, Georgetown. T: 592 2261834
E: sharma@cns6.tv **W:** http://www.cns6.tv
Editorial Profile: Television channel providing community news through a variety of shows related to cultural, music, and films.

Guyana Television Broadcasting Company
Editorial: Homestretch Avenue, D'Urban Park, Georgetown. T: 592 2 27 15 66
E: feedback@ncnguyana.com
W: http://www.ncnguyana.com
Editorial Profile: Broadcasts educational, cultural, and entertainment programs for both the urban and the rural areas of the Guyana.

HAITI — Tel: 33

Standard Time: GMT -5
Continent: The Americas
Capital City: Port-au-Prince

NEWSPAPERS & PUBLICATIONS

NEWSPAPERS

Le Matin
Owner: Nouveau Matin S.A. (Le)
Editorial: 3, rue Goulard, Pétionville.
T: 509 3401-8486 **E:** info@lematinhaiti.com
W: http://www.lematinhaiti.com
Freq: Daily
Editor in Chief: Clarens Fortuné
Editorial Profile: Launched April 1, 1907, Le Matin is a daily newspaper distributed in all of Haiti and offering general news.

Language (s): French
DAILY NEWSPAPER

Le Nouvelliste
Owner: Le Nouvelliste
Editorial: 198 Rue du Centre, Port-Au-Prince.
T: 509 22 24-2054
E: redaction@lenouvelliste.com
W: http://www.lenouvelliste.com
Freq: Daily Not Audited
Editor in Chief: Frantz Duval
Editorial Profile: Launched in 1898. Newspaper covering national news, events and sports.
Language (s): French
DAILY NEWSPAPER

NEWS SERVICE/SYNDICATE

L' Agence Haïtienne de Presse (AHP)
Editorial: 6, rue Fernand, Pont Morin, Port-Au-Prince. **T:** 509 22 45-5055
E: ahphaiti@yahoo.com
W: http://www.ahphaiti.org
Editorial Profile: Founded in 1989 L'Agence Haïtienne de Presse is a Haitian news service, which publishes news in English, French and Creole.
Language (s): Creole
NEWS SERVICE/SYNDICATE

BROADCASTING

RADIO STATIONS

Radio Antilles Internationale
Owner: Radio Tele Antilles
Editorial: 175, Rue du Centre, Port-Au-Prince
W: http://www.radioteleantilleshaiti.com
Editorial Profile: Radio Antilles Internationale is a radio station focusing on news.

RADIO NETWORKS

Radio Nationale d'Haiti
Owner: Television Nationale d'Haiţi
Editorial: 174, Rue Magasin de l'État, Port-Au-Prince. **T:** 011 509 22 23 7932
Editorial Profile: Radio Nationale d'Haiti is a government owned and run radio station in Port-au-Prince Haiti.

TELEVISION STATIONS

PVS Antenne
Owner: Raynald Delerme
Editorial: 137 Rue Monseigneur Guilloux, Port-Au-Prince. **T:** 011 509 222-1277
Editorial Profile: PVS Antenne is a private French language television station that primarily covers news events and stories.

Trans-America
Owner: Hébert Pelissier
Editorial: Ruelle Rogers, Gonaives
Editorial Profile: Trans-America is a television station that primarily covers news.

TELEVISION NETWORKS

Television Nationale D'Haiti
Owner: Television Nationale D'Haiti
Editorial: 13400 Delmas., Port-Au-Prince.
T: 011 509 246-0200 **W:** http://haitipaw.kif.fr
Editorial Profile: This station is a government owned television station. Its covers news stories as well as various other cultural topics.

HONDURAS — Tel: 504
Standard Time: GMT -6
Continent: The Americas
Capital City: Tegucigalpa

NEWSPAPERS & PUBLICATIONS

NEWSPAPERS

El Heraldo
Owner: El Heraldo
Editorial: Barrio San Felipe, Av. Los Próceres, Aptdo 1938, Tegucigalpa. **T:** 504 2366000
E: diario@elheraldo.hn
W: http://www.elheraldo.hn
Freq: Daily; **Circ:** 90000 Not Audited
Editor in Chief: Fernando Berrios; **Editor:** Veronica Castro
Editorial Profile: Newspaper covering national and international news, politics, economics, finance, business, culture and sport.
Language (s): Spanish
DAILY NEWSPAPER

La Prensa
Owner: La Prensa
Editorial: 3ª Avenida 6-7 Calle Nor-Oeste No 34, Aptdo Postal 143, Barrio Guamilito, San Pedro Sula. **T:** 504 553-3101
E: redaccion@laprensa.hn
W: http://www.laprensa.hn
Freq: Daily; **Circ:** 65000 Not Audited
Editor in Chief: Nélson García; **Editor in Chief:** Ana Morales; **Editor:** Yesille Ponce
Editorial Profile: National newspaper covering national and international news, politics, economics, finance, business, culture and sport.
Language (s): Spanish
DAILY NEWSPAPER

Tiempo
Owner: Editorial Honduras S.A.
Editorial: Barrio Sta. Anita, 1era calle, 5ta avenida, Noreste, San Pedro Sula.
T: 504 5403388 **E:** tiempo@continental.hn
W: http://www.tiempo.hn
Freq: Daily; **Circ:** 42535 Not Audited
Editor in Chief: Geovanny Dominguez; **Editor in Chief:** Germán Quintanilla
Editorial Profile: Regional newspaper covering national and international news, politics, economics, finance, business, culture and sport.
Language (s): Spanish
DAILY NEWSPAPER

La Tribuna
Owner: La Tribuna
Editorial: Colonia Santa Bárbara Carretera al Primer Batallón de la Infantería, Apdo. 1501, Tegucigalpa. **T:** 504 2343206
E: tribuna@latribuna.hn
W: http://www.latribunahon.com
Freq: Daily; **Circ:** 50000 Not Audited
Editor: Edgardo Dumes Rodríguez; **Editor:** Daniel Vieda
Editorial Profile: Newspaper covering national and international news, politics, economics, finance, business, culture and sport.
Language (s): Spanish
DAILY NEWSPAPER

BROADCASTING

RADIO NETWORKS

Radio HRN La Voz de Honduras
Owner: Emisoras Unidas SA Honduras
Editorial: Blvd. Suyapa, Colonia Florencia Sur, contiguo a la Corporacion Televicentro, Apartado Postal 642, Tegucigalpa.
T: 504 2325178
W: http://www.emisorasunidas.net
Editorial Profile: Broadcasts daily news, sports, and cultural programming.

HONG KONG — Tel: 852
Standard Time: GMT +8
Continent: Asia
Capital City: Victoria

NEWSPAPERS & PUBLICATIONS

NEWSPAPERS

am730
Editorial: 10/F, Overseas Trust Bank Building, 160 Gloucester Rd, Hong Kong.
T: 852 34083730 **E:** info@am730.com.hk
W: http://www.am730.com.hk
Freq: Daily; **Circ:** 272510 Not Audited
Editor: Kusche Cheng; **Editor in Chief:** Kenneth Dai; **Editor:** Ceiling Lee; **Publisher:** Alan Lo
Editorial Profile: Covers local and international news, finance, sport and entertainment news.
Language (s): Cantonese
DAILY NEWSPAPER

Apple Daily
Owner: Next Media Limited
Editorial: Next Media Limited, 8 Chun Ying Street, TKO Industrial West, Tseung Kwan O, N.T., Hong Kong. **T:** 852 29908388
E: adnews@appledaily.com
W: http://appledaily.atnext.com
Freq: Daily
Editor: Siu Bun Ho
Editorial Profile: covers latest news of social issues, politics and entertainment.
Language (s): Chinese
DAILY NEWSPAPER

Asahi Shimbun - Hong Kong Bureau
Editorial: Asahi Shimbun - Hong Kong Bureau., TTG Asia Media Pte Ltd., 11/f, ING Tower, Hong Kong. **T:** 852 22377252
E: asahihongkong@yahoo.com
W: http://www.asahi.com
Freq: Daily
Bureau Chief: Tetsu Kobayashi
Editorial Profile: Covers international and local news in Hong Kong
Language (s): Japanese
DAILY NEWSPAPER

China Daily
Owner: China Daily Newspaper Group
Editorial: Room 1818, Hing Wai Centre, 7 Tin Wan Praya Road, Hong Kong.
T: 852 25185111
W: http://www.chinadaily.com.cn
Freq: 2 Times/Week; **Circ:** 55005
Editor: Albert Au Yeung; **Editor:** Shirley Xiao
Editorial Profile: Launched in 1997, provides a local perspective on national and international news for decision-makers, including HKSAR government official, CEOs, senior executives, scholars and academics.
Language (s): English
NEWSPAPER

Daily 10
Editorial: Step Max Limited., Unit 1F-1H, Casey Building, 38 Tokku Road, Sheung Wan., Hong Kong. **T:** 852 25438262
E: editor@daily7-daily10.com
W: http://www.daily7-daily10.com
Freq: 2 Times/Week
Editor: Melanie Holloway
Editorial Profile: covers children's interests
Language (s): English
NEWSPAPER

Daily 7
Editorial: Step Max Limited., Unit 1F-1H, Casey Building, 38 Tokku Road, Sheung Wan., Hong Kong. **T:** 852 25438262
E: editor@daily7-daily10.com
W: http://www.daily7-daily10.com
Freq: 2 Times/Week
Editor: Melanie Holloway
Editorial Profile: covers news for children and children's interests
Language (s): English
NEWSPAPER

Daily News & Analysis (DNA) - Hong Kong Bureau
Editorial: Daily News & Analysis (DNA) -, Hong Kong Bureau, 2C, Verdant Court, Discovery Bay., Hong Kong. **T:** 852 29879169
W: http://www.dnaindia.com
Freq: 2 Times/Week
Editorial Profile: covers international news
Language (s): English
NEWSPAPER

The Epoch Times
Editorial: Epoch Group Limited., P.O. Box 98992, Tsim Sha Tsui, Hong Kong.
T: 852 25199881 **E:** edt@epochtimes.com.hk
W: http://www.epochtimes.com.hk
Freq: 2 Times/Week; **Circ:** 50009 Not Audited
Editor: Jane Hui
Editorial Profile: covers news on culture, social issues and politics. This newspaper has obvious anti-communist tendency towards Chinese government.
Language (s): Chinese
NEWSPAPER

Headline Daily
Owner: Sing Tao News Corporation Limited
Editorial: Headline Daily Limited, 15th Floor, Sing Tao News Corporation Building, Hong Kong. **T:** 852 3181 3683
E: info@hkheadline.com
W: http://www.hkheadline.com
Freq: Daily Not Audited
Editorial Profile: Covers international, local and social news It is a free daily newspaper.
Language (s): Chinese
DAILY NEWSPAPER

Herald Monthly
Editorial: Chinese Christian Herald Crusades Limited., Room 1602, Hillwood Centre, 17-19 Hillwood Road, Tsimshatsui, Kln, Hong Kong.
T: 852 21483301 **E:** hongkong@cchc.org
W: http://www.cchc.org
Freq: Monthly; **Circ:** 100005 Not Audited
Editorial Profile: It is a monthly newspaper published by Headquarters & Herald Mission Center, covers local and national news; religion events and social issues.
Language (s): Cantonese
NEWSPAPER

Hong Kong Commercial Daily
Editorial: Hong Kong Commercial Daily, 18th Floor, Number 499, King's Road, Hong Kong.
T: 852 25640768 **W:** http://www.hkcd.com.hk
Freq: Daily Not Audited
Editor in Chief: Nam Chan; **Editor:** Shirley Wu
Editorial Profile: Covers local, international and regional economy and financial news. It also provides information and opportunities of investing in mainland China.
Language (s): Cantonese
DAILY NEWSPAPER

Hong Kong Economic Journal
Editorial: Hong Kong Economic Journal, 8th Floor, Tower B, North Point Industrial Building, Hong Kong. **T:** 852 28567549
E: editorial@hkej.com
W: http://www.hkej.com
Freq: Daily Not Audited
Editor in Chief: King Cheung Chan; **Editor:** Franca Lee; **Editor:** Thomas Wong
Editorial Profile: Covers international and local news, business and economics.
Language (s): Cantonese
DAILY NEWSPAPER

Hong Kong Economic Times
Owner: Hong Kong Economic Times Limited
Editorial: Hong Kong Economic Times, 6th Floor, Kodak House II, 321 Java Road, North Point., Hong Kong. **T:** 852 25654288
E: info@hket.com **W:** http://www.hket.com
Freq: Daily Not Audited
Editor: Teddy Au; **Editor in Chief:** Eric Chan; **Editor:** Frankie Ho; **Editor:** Oscar Lee; **Editor:** Joann Wong; **Editor:** Man Ki Yeung
Editorial Profile: Covers local and international news of business, economic, property and technology.
Language (s): Chinese
DAILY NEWSPAPER

The International New York Times - Hong Kong
Editorial: The New York Times - Hong Kong Bureau, 5A Borrett Mansion, 8 Bowen Road, Hong Kong. **T:** 1 852 252-1900
Bureau Chief: Keith Bradsher; **Asia Editor:** Philip McClellan
DAILY NEWSPAPER

Lianhe Zaobao
Editorial: Singapore Press Holding., Room 1308, 13th Floor, Tower II, Lippo Centre, Admiralty, Hong Kong. **T:** 852 25246191
W: http://www.zaobao.com
Freq: Daily
Editorial Profile: Covers international and local news.
Language (s): Chinese
DAILY NEWSPAPER

Metro Daily (Hong Kong)
Owner: Wee (Kenny)
Editorial: Metro Publishing HK Ltd, 25th Floor, 148 Electric Road, North Point, Hong Kong.
T: 852 31961600 **E:** news@metrohk.com.hk
W: http://www.metrohk.com.hk
Freq: 2 Times/Week Not Audited
Editor: Juan Lam; **Editor in Chief:** Jeff Lee; **Editor:** Ivy Sum
Editorial Profile: Launched in 2002, covers international and local news in addition to entertainment news.
Language (s): Chinese
NEWSPAPER

Ming Pao Daily News
Editorial: 15F, A Building, Mingpao Enterprise Corporation Ltd., Block A, 15th Floor, Ming Pao Industrial Centre, 18 Ka Yip Street, Chaiwan, Hong Kong. **T:** 852 25953111
E: mingpao@mingpao.com
W: http://www.mingpao.com
Freq: Daily Not Audited
Editor in Chief: Kin Bor Cheung; **Editor:** Pui Kuen Chung; **Editor:** Bill Ko; **Editor:** Simon Vuo
Editorial Profile: Covers the latest news in politics, entertainment and parenting.
Language (s): Cantonese
DAILY NEWSPAPER

Nihon Keizai Shimbun - Hong Kong Bureau
Editorial: Nihon Keizai Shimbun - Hong Kong Bureau., Suites 1707B-10, Dah Sing, Financial Centre., Hong Kong. **T:** 852 25861863

E: nikkei@nikkei.com.hk
W: http://www.nikkei.com.hk
Freq: Daily
Bureau Chief: Wataru Yoshida
Editorial Profile: covers business news, economic and financial news in both Japan and other different countries.
Language (s): Japanese
DAILY NEWSPAPER

NNA
Editorial: NNA (HK) Limited., Unit 401 4/F Kwai Hung Holdings Centre, 89 King's Road, North Point, Hong Kong. T: 852 28026303
E: nna.sales@nna.hk W: http://nna.asia.ne.jp
Freq: 2 Times/Week
Editor: Shimizu Miyuki
Editorial Profile: Covers financial industry news in of Japan.
Language (s): Japanese
NEWSPAPER

Oriental Daily News
Editorial: Oriental Daily News, Oriental Press Centre, 23 Dai Cheong Street, Tai Po Industrial Estate, Hong Kong. T: 852 36008811
E: news@oriental.com.hk
W: http://orientaldaily.on.cc
Freq: Daily Not Audited
Editorial Profile: Covers all news including entertainment, lifestyle and social issues.
Language (s): Cantonese
DAILY NEWSPAPER

People's Daily Overseas Version
Editorial: People's Daily Overseas Version., 160 Connaught Road West, Hong Kong.
T: 852 23087909
W: http://www.peopledaily.com.cn
Freq: Daily
Bureau Chief: Cao Honglian
Editorial Profile: Covers on local, international news and current affairs.
Language (s): Chinese
DAILY NEWSPAPER

Sing Pao Daily
Editorial: Sing Pao Daily, 3/F CWG Building, 3A Kung Ngam Village Road, Shaukeiwan, Hong Kong. T: 852 25124200
E: webmaster@singpao.com.hk
Freq: Daily; Circ: 75005 Not Audited
Editorial Profile: covers local, regional and international news
Language (s): Chinese
DAILY NEWSPAPER

Sing Tao Daily
Owner: Sing Tao News Corporation Limited
Editorial: 6/F, Sing Tao Building, 1 Wang Kwong Road, Kowloon Bay, Hong Kong.
T: 852 27982323
E: newspaper@singtaonewscorp.com
W: http://www.singtao.com
Freq: Daily Not Audited
Editor: Joey Au; Editor: Joe Mak; News Editor: Vemon Sin; Editor in Chief: Sai Wo Siu; Editor: David Smith
Editorial Profile: Covers business, sports, local and international news
Language (s): Cantonese
DAILY NEWSPAPER

South China Morning Post
Editorial: South China Morning Post Publishers Ltd., Ground Floor, G/F-3/F No.1 Leighton Road, Hong Kong. T: 852 25652222
E: info@scmp.com W: http://www.scmp.com
Freq: Daily
News Editor: Chow Chung Yan; Editor: Peter Kammerer; Editor: Kylie Knott; Editor in Chief: Wang Xiangwei
Editorial Profile: Established in 1903 and written for affluent and influential readers, serves as Hong Kong's premier English language newspaper. Provides analysis on news in Hong Kong, China and the rest of Asia. Aims to foster impartial debates on various issues that speak to making the southeast Asian region a better place in which to live and work.
Language (s): English
DAILY NEWSPAPER

The Standard
Owner: Sing Tao News Corporation Limited
Editorial: 3/F, Sing Tao News Corporation Building, 3 Tung Wong Road, Shau Kei Wan, Hong Kong. T: 852 27982323
E: irene.chan@singtaonewscorp.com
W: http://www.thestandard.com.hk
Freq: Mon thru Fri Not Audited
Editor: Roger Boschman; Editor: Marcal Joanilho; Editor: Zubair Latif; Editor: Roger Ryan; Editor in Chief: Ivan Tong
Editorial Profile: Covers international and local news, social issues, culture and arts and so on. The topics are broad and deep. As a free English newspaper. It has evolved into a powerful, influential medium in Hong Kong with a diverse audience and a broad reach.
Language (s): English
DAILY NEWSPAPER

The Straits Times
Editorial: Room 1308, Tower II, Lippo Centre, 89 Queensway, Hong Kong. T: 852 25269018
W: http://www.asiaone.com
Freq: Daily
Editorial Profile: Covers news
Language (s): English
DAILY NEWSPAPER

Ta Kung Pao
Editorial: Ta Kung Pao, 2nd-3rd Floor, Kodak House II, 39 Healthy Street East, North Point, Hong Kong. T: 852 25757181
E: tkppub@takungpao.com
W: http://www.takungpao.com
Freq: Daily; Circ: 235005 Not Audited
Editor: Suk Fun Choi; News Editor: Kam Fung Kwok; Editor: Man Tung Ma
Editorial Profile: Covers local, national and international news including technology, sports, politics and social issues.
Language (s): Cantonese
DAILY NEWSPAPER

Take Me Home
Editorial: 8/F, Kodak House II, 321 Java Road, North Point, Hong Kong. T: 852 28802874
E: tmh_adv@hket.com
W: http://www.takemehome.com.hk
Freq: Weekly; Circ: 300006 Not Audited
Editorial Profile: covers lifestyle, health, parenting, and food.
Language (s): Chinese
NEWSPAPER

Target Newspaper
Editorial: Target Newspaper Limited., Suite 2901, 29th Floor, Bank of America Tower, Hong Kong. T: 852 25730379
E: info@targetnewspapers.com
W: http://www.targetnewspapers.com
Freq: 2 Times/Week
Editor: Raymonde Sacklyn
Editorial Profile: covers finance and law industry
Language (s): English
NEWSPAPER

todaysliving.com
Editorial: Press Mark Media Limited, Room 2207, 22/F, Westland Centre, Hong Kong.
T: 852 28822230
W: http://www.todaysliving.com
Freq: Monthly; Circ: 35005 Not Audited
Editorial Profile: covers trendy interior design of houses and apartment
Language (s): Chinese
NEWSPAPER

True Buddha News Weekly (Hong Kong Edition)
Editorial: True Buddha Infogroup Hong Kong Limited, Flat H, 26th Floor, Shield Industrial Center, Hong Kong. T: 852 21464989
E: info@tbi.org.hk W: http://www.tbi.org.hk
Freq: Weekly; Circ: 3002 Not Audited
Editor: Ho Shui Lau
Editorial Profile: Covers Buddhism international news.
Language (s): Chinese
NEWSPAPER

United Daily News - Hong Kong Bureau
Editorial: United Daily News - Hong Kong Bureau, 3/F, United Daily Centre, 21 Yuk Yat Street, Tokwawan, Kowloon, Hong Kong.
T: 852 27570228 E: hksit@hkudn.com.hk
W: http://www.udngroup.com.tw
Freq: Daily
Editorial Profile: Covers daily news
Language (s): Chinese
DAILY NEWSPAPER

The Voice
Editorial: St James' Settlement, 85 Stone Nullah Lane, Wanchai, Hong Kong.
T: 852 28313215 E: thevoice@sjs.org.hk
W: http://www.thevoice.org.hk
Freq: Monthly; Circ: 27009 Not Audited
Editor: Ping Lun Chan
Editorial Profile: covers of topics that senior citizens' are interesting
Language (s): Chinese
NEWSPAPER

The Wall Street Journal (Hong Kong)
Editorial: 25th Floor Central Plaza, 18 Harbour Rd, Hong Kong. T: 852 2573-7121
E: wsj.ltrs@wsj.com
W: http://www.wsj-asia.com
Asia Editor: Paul Beckett; Bureau Chief: Ken Brown; Editor of China Wealth and Luxury: Wei Gu; Asia News Editor: Allison Morrow
DAILY NEWSPAPER

The Wall Street Journal Asia
Owner: Dow Jones & Company, Inc.
Editorial: The Wall Street Journal Asia, Dow Jones Publishing Company (Asia), Hong Kong.
T: 852 2573 7121 E: wsj.ltrs@wsj.com
W: http://www.wsj-asia.com
Freq: Mon thru Fri; Circ: 78833
Asia Editor: Paul Beckett; Publisher: Christine Brendel; Asia Technology Editor: Yun-Hee Kim
Editorial Profile: Launched in 1976 and covers global business news for Asia. Focuses on news and analysis of regional and global business developments for a pan-Asian audience of corporate and government decision-makers.
DAILY NEWSPAPER

Wednesday Journal
Editorial: Wednesday Journal Limited., Room 2612-2616, The Metropolis Tower, Hong Kong.
T: 852 28916172
E: sooyo@wednesdayjournal.net
W: http://www.wednesdayjournal.net
Freq: Weekly
Editor in Chief: Brad Lee
Editorial Profile: Covers Korean shops, restaurants and salons, which also focusing on local news, international news, regional news and related Christian community news
Language (s): Korean
NEWSPAPER

Wen Wei Po
Editorial: Wen Wei Po Limited., 2-4rd Floor, Hing Wai Centre, Number 7, Tin Wan Praya Road, Aberdeen, Hong Kong. T: 852 28738288
E: editor@wenweipo.com
W: http://www.wenweipo.com
Freq: Daily; Circ: 200005 Not Audited
Editor: Selina Cheung; Editor: Yuet Kam Leung; Editor in Chief: Xiaohui Li
Editorial Profile: covers local and international news, business, current affair, sports and education.
Language (s): Cantonese
DAILY NEWSPAPER

Women's Wear Daily
Editorial: Women's Wear Daily Publication., 2nd Floor, Kailey Tower, 16 Stanley Street, Central, Hong Kong W: http://www.wwd.com
Freq: Daily
Editorial Profile: covers latest trend of fashion, fashion show and related fashion news
Language (s): English
DAILY NEWSPAPER

NEWS SERVICE/SYNDICATE

Associated Press
Editorial: 4808 Central Plaza, Hong Kong 10020-1605. T: 852 2802-4324
NEWS SERVICE/SYNDICATE

Bloomberg News
Editorial: 2 Queens Road Central, 27th Floor Cheung Kong Centre, Hong Kong.
T: 86 852 2977-6600
E: hknews@bloomberg.net
Developed Markets Stocks Team Leader: Darren Boey; Editor: Young-Sam Cho; Editor: Andrew Davis; Stock Market Editor: Nick Gentle; Bureau Chief: Tan Hwee Ann; Front Page Editor: Adrian Kennedy; Deals Team Leader: Philip Lagerkranser; Editor: Paul Panckhurst; Stock Market Editor: Andreea Papuc; Editor: Nipa Piboontanasawat; Editor at Large: Sheridan Prasso; Editor: James Regan
NEWS SERVICE/SYNDICATE

China News Service
Editorial: China News Service., 22nd Floor, Eastern Center Plaza, Hong Kong.
T: 852 25732253
E: hongkong@chinanews.com.cn
W: http://www.chinanews.com.cn
Freq: Daily
Editorial Profile: covers local and international news
Language (s): Chinese
NEWS SERVICE/SYNDICATE

Dow Jones Newswires
Editorial: 25th Floor Central Plaza, 18 Harbour Road, Hong Kong. T: 852 2802-7002
E: djnews.honkong@dowjones.com
Bureau Chief: Ken Brown
NEWS SERVICE/SYNDICATE

Hong Kong China News Agency
Editorial: Hong Kong China News Agency., 22nd Floor, Easter Center Plaza, 3 Yiu Hing Road, Shau Kei Wan, Hong Kong.
T: 852 2833-2725 E: ngaili0072@hotmail.com
W: http://www.hkcna.hk
Freq: Daily
Bureau Chief: Yu Cheung
Editorial Profile: Covers local and international news.
Language (s): Chinese
NEWS SERVICE/SYNDICATE

WORLD NEWS MEDIA

Interfax China
Editorial: Interfax China., Suite 1601, Wilson House 19-27, Hong Kong. T: 852 25372262
W: http://www.interfax.com
Freq: Daily
Editorial Profile: covers different news like financial and medical issues.
Language (s): English
NEWS SERVICE/SYNDICATE

Kyodo News - Hong Kong Bureau
Editorial: Kyodo News - Hong Kong Bureau., 9 Queen's Road C, Central District, Hong Kong. T: 852 25249750
E: kyodohk@kyodonews.jp
W: http://kyodonews.jp
Freq: Daily
Bureau Chief: Takahashi Shinsuke
Editorial Profile: covers political, financial, business and also Asian Culture
Language (s): English
NEWS SERVICE/SYNDICATE

United Press International
Editorial: Wui Tat Centre 18/F, 55 Connaught Road West, Hong Kong. T: 86 85228582774
E: editor@upiasiaonline.com
W: http://www.upiasiaonline.com
NEWS SERVICE/SYNDICATE

Xinhua News Agency
Editorial: Xinhua News Agency, 4/F, 381 Queen's Road East, Hong Kong.
T: 852 28313558
Freq: Daily
Editorial Profile: Covers local and international news including politics
Language (s): Chinese
NEWS SERVICE/SYNDICATE

Yonhap News Agency - Hong Kong Bureau
Editorial: Yonhap News Agency - Hong Kong Bureau., 11G Tsui Kung Mansion, Taiwan Road, Taikoo Shing, Hong Kong.
T: 852 25138662
W: http://www.yonhapnews.co.kr
Freq: Daily
Editorial Profile: covers news and information to its customers in various part of the world
Language (s): Korean
NEWS SERVICE/SYNDICATE

HUNGARY Tel: 36
Standard Time: GMT +1
Continent: Europe
Capital City: Budapest

NEWSPAPERS & PUBLICATIONS

NEWSPAPERS

168 óra
Owner: Telegráf Kiadó Kft.
Editorial: Bécsi út 3-5., Budapest 1023.
T: 36 1/4385570 E: hirdetes@168ora.hu
W: http://www.168ora.hu Circ: 42294 Pub Statement
Editorial Profile: Newspaper covering national and international news, focusing on politics.
Language (s): Hungarian
DAILY NEWSPAPER

Blikk
Owner: Ringier Kiadó Kft.
Editorial: Futó u. 35-37, Budapest 1082.
T: 36 1 460 2411 W: http://www.blikk.hu
Circ: 305865 Pub Statement
Editor-in-Chief: Marcell Murányi
Editorial Profile: Newspaper focusing on national and international news, politics, business, culture and sport.
Language (s): Hungarian
DAILY NEWSPAPER

The Budapest Times
Owner: BZT Media Kft.

Editorial: Kunigunda útja 18., Budapest 1037.
T: 36 1 4530752 **E:** editor@bzt.hu
W: http://www.budapesttimes.hu **Circ:** 10000 Pub Statement
News Editor: Robert Hodgson
Editorial Profile: The Budapest Times provides Hungarian politics, business, economy, news and culture in English language.
Language (s): Hungarian
DAILY NEWSPAPER

Magyar Hírlap
Owner: Magyar Hírlap Kiadói Kft.
Editorial: Thököly út 105-107., Budapest 1145. **T:** 36 1/2608404
E: hirdetes@magyarhirlap.hu
W: http://www.magyarhirlap.hu
Editorial Profile: Newspaper concerning politics and economics.
Language (s): Hungarian
DAILY NEWSPAPER

Magyar Nemzet
Owner: Nemzet Lap- és Könyvkiadó Kft.
Editorial: Wesselényi u. 8., Budapest 1075.
T: 36 1/3426164 **E:** titkarsag@mahirpress.hu
Circ: 75696 Pub Statement
Editor: Mr./Ms. Editor
Editorial Profile: Broadsheet-sized quality newspaper containing national and international news, current affairs, culture and in-depth stock market news. Provides Internet recommendations, information about Budapest and political issues worldwide.
Language (s): Hungarian
DAILY NEWSPAPER

Metropol
Owner: MTG Metro Gratis Kft.
Editorial: Tüzér u. 39-41., Budapest 1134.
T: 36 1/4316400 **E:** hirdetes@metropol.hu
W: http://www.metropol.hu **Circ:** 320386 Pub Statement
Editor: Mr./Ms. Editor
Editorial Profile: Newspaper covering news and general interest subjects, featuring a job search, entertainment and interior design.
Language (s): Hungarian
DAILY NEWSPAPER

Napi Gazdaság
Owner: Napi Gazdaság Kiadó Kft.
Editorial: Csata u. 32., Budapest 1135.
T: 36 1/4509600 **E:** hirdetes@napi.hu
W: http://www.napi.hu
Editor: Mr./Ms. Editor
Editorial Profile: Newspaper focusing on national and international economics and finance.
Language (s): Hungarian
DAILY NEWSPAPER

Nemzeti Sport
Owner: Ringier Kiadó Kft.
Editorial: Futó u. 35-37, Budapest 1082.
T: 36 1 460 2611
E: szerkesztoseg@nemzetisport.hu
W: http://www.nemzetisport.hu
Freq: Daily; **Circ:** 55000 Pub Statement
Editor: József Buzgó
Editorial Profile: Newspaper covering news from the world of sport. Featuring football, team and individual players nationally and worldwide.
Language (s): Hungarian
DAILY NEWSPAPER

Népszabadság
Owner: Primus Népszabadság Média-képv
Editorial: Bécsi út 122-124., Budapest 1034.
T: 36 1 4364441
E: szerkesztoseg@nepszabadsag.hu
W: http://nol.hu
Freq: Daily; **Circ:** 53000 Pub Statement
Editor: Levente Tóth; **Editor:** Iván Várkonyi
Editorial Profile: National daily newspaper covering home and overseas news, economic and cultural news, sports news and features.
Language (s): Hungarian
DAILY NEWSPAPER

Népszava
Owner: NÉPSZAVA Lapkiadó Kft.
Editorial: Könyvek K. krt. 76., Budapest 1087.
T: 36 1 4779000 **E:** nepszava@nepszava.hu
W: http://www.nepszava.hu **Circ:** 35328 Pub Statement
Editorial Profile: Newspaper providing national and international news with specific focus on politics.
Language (s): Hungarian
DAILY NEWSPAPER

Szabad Föld
Owner: Geomédia Kiadói Zrt.
Editorial: Lajos u. 48-66. B Iph II. em., Budapest 1036. **T:** 36 1/4898846
E: hirdetes@szabadfold.hu **Circ:** 140228 Pub Statement
Editor: Mr./Ms. Editor
Editorial Profile: Newspaper containing articles on national news, general interest subjects and advice sections covering various themes, with a focus on agriculture.
Language (s): Hungarian
DAILY NEWSPAPER

Világgazdaság
Owner: Zöld Újság Zrt.
Editorial: Maros u. 19-21., Budapest 1122.
T: 36 1/4891165 **E:** hirdetes@vg.hu
Circ: 13998 Pub Statement
Editorial Profile: Newspaper covering all aspects of finance and business. Provides in-depth economic, stock market and international share analysis.
Language (s): Hungarian
DAILY NEWSPAPER

NEWS SERVICE/SYNDICATE

Associated Press
T: 36 1 267-0625
NEWS SERVICE/SYNDICATE

Bloomberg News
Editorial: Regus House Budapest, Kalman Imre Utca 1 1054, Budapest. **T:** 36 14751180
E: budapest@bloomberg.net
Bureau Chief: Zoltan Simon
NEWS SERVICE/SYNDICATE

Dow Jones Newswires
Editorial: Bajcsy-Zsilinszky ut12 VI/602, Budapest H-1051. **T:** 36 1 267-0622
E: budapest@dowjones.com
NEWS SERVICE/SYNDICATE

Magyar Tavirati Iroda
Editorial: Naphegy tér 8, Budapest 1016.
T: 36 1 37 56 722 **E:** sales@mti.hu
W: http://hirek.mti.hu
Editor: Ádám Dankó; **Editor:** János Kárpáti
Language (s): Hungarian
NEWS SERVICE/SYNDICATE

ICELAND — Tel: 354
Standard Time: GMT
Continent: Europe
Capital City: Reykjavik

NEWSPAPERS & PUBLICATIONS

NEWSPAPERS

Dagbladid Visir
Owner: Dagbladid-Visir Utgafufelag
Editorial: Editorial dv.is, Tryggvagata 11, Reykjavik 101. **T:** 354 512 70 00
E: ritstjorn@dv.is **W:** http://www.dv.is
Freq: Daily; **Circ:** 20000 Pub Statement
Editor: Jona Trausti Reynisson; **Editor-in-Chief:** Reynir Traustason
Editorial Profile: Newspaper covering news, sports and culture.
Language (s): Icelandic
DAILY NEWSPAPER

Fréttabladid
Editorial: 365 Skaftahlíð, Reykjavik.
T: 354 512 5000 **E:** ritsjorn@frettabladid.is
W: http://www.visir.is
Fréttastjóri: Kristján Hjálmarsson; **Fréttastjóri:** Arndís Þorgeirsdóttir
Editorial Profile: Newspaper covering international and national news, business, sport and culture.
Language (s): Icelandic
DAILY NEWSPAPER

Morgunbladid
Owner: Árvakur nf
Editorial: Hádegismóum 2, Reykjavik 110.
T: 354 569 11 00 **E:** morgunbladid@mbl.is
W: http://www.mbl.is
Freq: Daily; **Circ:** 55000 Pub Statement
News Editor / Fréttir: Sunna Ósk Logadóttir;
News Editor / Fréttir: Sigtryggur Sigtryggsson
Editorial Profile: Newspaper covering news, debate and entertainment, sport.
Language (s): Icelandic
DAILY NEWSPAPER

INDIA — Tel: 91
Standard Time: GMT +4.5 to 5.5
Continent: Asia
Capital City: New Dehli

NEWSPAPERS & PUBLICATIONS

NEWSPAPERS

Aaj - Kanpur Edition
Editorial: AaJ Office, 79/75 Bans Mandi, Deputy Ka Parao, Kanpur 208001.
T: 91 512 2342221
Freq: Daily; **Circ:** 186994 Not Audited
Editor: Shardul Gupta; **Editor:** R. Yadav
Editorial Profile: Articles focus on local and international news.
Language (s): Hindi
DAILY NEWSPAPER

Aaj - Lucknow Edition
Editorial: AaJ Bhawan, Surajdeep Complex, 1 Jopling Road, Lucknow 226001.
T: 91 522 2209315 **E:** aajlucknow@sify.com
Freq: Daily; **Circ:** 66002 Not Audited
Editor in Chief: Shardul Vikram Gupta; **Editor:** R.S. Walia
Editorial Profile: Covers local and world news.
Language (s): Hindi
DAILY NEWSPAPER

Aaj Ka Anand
Editorial: Aaj Ka Anand Building, Opposite Shivaji Statue 365/6 Shivajinagar, Pune 411005. **T:** 91 20 25534888
E: akanand@giaspn01.vsnl.net.in
W: http://www.aajkaanand.com
Freq: Daily; **Circ:** 110002 Not Audited
Editorial Profile: Covers local and national news and current events, astrology, health, spirituality and women's interests.
Language (s): Hindi
DAILY NEWSPAPER

Aajkaal
Editorial: BP 5, Sector 5, Sulplex, Kolkata 700921. **T:** 91 33 30110800
E: aajkaal.net@gmail.com
W: http://www.aajkaal.net
Freq: Daily; **Circ:** 2200002 Not Audited
Editor: Ashok Dasgupta; **Editor:** Rajiv Ghosh;
Editor: J. Khan
Editorial Profile: Covers the latest news in local and international, sports and etc.
Language (s): Bengali
DAILY NEWSPAPER

Aapla Vartahar
Editorial: 220 Narayan Udyog Bhawan, Dr. B A Road, Lal Bagh, Mumbai 400012.
T: 91 22 24715208
Freq: Daily; **Circ:** 100001 Not Audited
Editor: Anil Joshi
Editorial Profile: Aapla Vartahar is a newspaper which covers the news in local and world.
Language (s): Marathi
DAILY NEWSPAPER

Afternoon Despatch & Courier
Editorial: Grace Villa, 125-126, 8th Street, Gandhipuram, Coimbatore 641012.
T: 91 4222496405
E: afternoondaily@rediffmail.com
W: http://www.afternoondc.in
Freq: Daily; **Circ:** 68841 Not Audited
Editor: Carol Andrade; **Editor:** M.N. Appadurai
Editorial Profile: Covers local and regional news, business, sports, education, leisure and etc.
Language (s): English
DAILY NEWSPAPER

Afternoon Despatch and Courier
Editorial: Afternoon Dispatch & Courier, Tanmabhoomi Bhaban, Mumbai 400001.
T: 91 22 40768999
W: http://www.afternoonele.in
Freq: Daily; **Circ:** 85001 Not Audited
Editor: Behram Contractor
Editorial Profile: Afternoon Despatch & Courier is a daily newspaper in Mumbai, India covering local news, sports, business, jobs, and community events.
Language (s): English
DAILY NEWSPAPER

Agrowon
Editorial: 595 Budhwar Peth, Pune 411002.
T: 91 20 24455500 **E:** agrowon@gmail.com
W: http://www.agrowon.com
Freq: Daily; **Circ:** 100002 Not Audited
Editorial Profile: Covers Agriculture & Farming news and issues
Language (s): Marathi
DAILY NEWSPAPER

Ahmedabad Mirror
Editorial: 139 Ashram Rd, Ahmedabad 380009. **T:** 91 79 26583758
W: http://www.ahmedabadmirror.in
Editor: Bharat Desai
DAILY NEWSPAPER

Aj - Gorakhpur Edition
Editorial: Bank Road, Gorakhpur 273001.
T: 91 551 2335350
Freq: Daily; **Circ:** 52002 Not Audited
Editor in Chief: Shardul Vikram Gupta; **Editor:** Ratnakar Singh
Editorial Profile: Covers news.
Language (s): Hindi
DAILY NEWSPAPER

Aj - Patna Edition
Editorial: AJ Bhawan, Mazharul Haque Path, Fraser Road, Patna 800001.
T: 91 612 2235070
Freq: Daily; **Circ:** 900002 Not Audited
Editor: Deepak Pandey
Editorial Profile: Covers the news in local and international.
Language (s): Hindi
DAILY NEWSPAPER

Aj - Ranchi Edition
Editorial: The Aj, Namkum Industrial Area, Namkum Road, Ranchi 834002.
T: 91 651 3207938
Freq: Daily; **Circ:** 60301 Not Audited
Editor in Chief: Shardul Vikram Gupta; **Editor:** Dilip Shrivastav
Editorial Profile: Aj is a Hindi newspaper published in 13 locations which covers the news in local and international.
Language (s): Hindi
DAILY NEWSPAPER

Aj - Varanasi Edition
Editorial: AJ Bhawan, Sant Kabir Road, Varanasi 221001. **T:** 91 542 2393981
E: neerajvahicam@rediffmail.com
Freq: Daily; **Circ:** 220629 Not Audited
Editor in Chief: Shardul Vikram Gupta
Editorial Profile: Covers local and international news.
Language (s): Hindi
DAILY NEWSPAPER

Ajir Asom
Editorial: G S Road, Dispur, Guwahati, Guwahati 781005. **T:** 91 361 2529237
E: thesentinel@satyam.net.in
Freq: Daily; **Circ:** 50002 Not Audited
Editor: Apurva Sharma
Editorial Profile: Focuses on regional, local and international news.
Language (s): Assamese
DAILY NEWSPAPER

Ajit
Editorial: Ajit Bhawan, Nehru Garden Road, Jalandhar 144001. **T:** 91 181 2458588
W: http://www.ajitjalandhar.com
Freq: Daily; **Circ:** 380002 Not Audited
Editorial Profile: publishes in Jalandhar punjab with punjab news and international news.
Language (s): Punjabi
DAILY NEWSPAPER

Ajit Samachar
Editorial: Ajit Bhawan, Nehru Garden Road, Jalandhar 144001. **T:** 91 1812455961
W: http://www.ajitjalandhar.com
Freq: Daily; **Circ:** 120003 Not Audited
Editorial Profile: Covers local and world news.
Language (s): Hindi
DAILY NEWSPAPER

Akali Patrika
Editorial: Patrika House 26, Chahar Bagh, Jalandhar 144001. **T:** 91 181 2456579
Freq: Daily; **Circ:** 85002 Not Audited
Editor in Chief: Ratnesh Sodhi
Editorial Profile: Focuses on local and International news.
Language (s): Punjabi
DAILY NEWSPAPER

Akhbar-E-Mashriq
Editorial: 12 Dargah Road, Kolkata 700017.
T: 91 33 22815157 **E:** mashriq@vsnl.com
Freq: Daily; **Circ:** 60002 Not Audited
Editor: M.W. Haque; **Editor:** Amanullah Mohammed
Editorial Profile: Covers local and international news, as well as sports and etc.

Language (s): Urdu
DAILY NEWSPAPER

Akila
Editorial: Moti Taki Chowk, Rajkot 360001. **T:** 91 2812445111 **E:** akiladaily@yahoo.com
W: http://www.akilanews.com
Freq: Daily; **Circ:** 67001 Not Audited
Editor: Nimish Ganatra
Editorial Profile: Akila is a newspaper which focused on local, regional, and international news.
Language (s): Gujarati
DAILY NEWSPAPER

Akkas
Editorial: 1/A Khetradas Lane 4th Floor, Kolkata 700012. **T:** 91 33 22113298
E: akkasdaily@gmail.com
Freq: Daily; **Circ:** 65001 Not Audited
Editor: Karim Monghyri
Editorial Profile: Focuses on the latest news locally and abroad.
Language (s): Urdu
DAILY NEWSPAPER

All India Appointment Gazette
Editorial: 7 Old Court House Street, Kolkata 700001. **T:** 91 033 22435663
E: uttarmail@sify.com
W: http://www.uttarbangasambad.com
Freq: Weekly; **Circ:** 50003 Not Audited
Editor: S. Talukdar
Editorial Profile: All India Appointment Gazette - an English weekly newspaper which covers the news, business, and etc
Language (s): English
NEWSPAPER

Amar Asom
Owner: G L Publication Ltd.
Editorial: G L Publication Ltd., G S Road, Ulubari, Guwahati 781007. **T:** 91 361 2458395
E: glpghy2009@hotmail.com
W: http://www.amarasom.glpublications.in/#
Freq: Daily; **Circ:** 100002 Not Audited
Editor: Homen Borgohain
Editorial Profile: Covers daily, national, and world news, as well as weather, sports, entertainment, business, travel, health, culture, nature and youth.
Language (s): Assamese
DAILY NEWSPAPER

Amar Ujala - Agra Edition
Editorial: Sikandra Road, Agra 282007.
T: 91 5622601600
W: http://www.amarujala.com
Freq: Daily; **Circ:** 150002 Not Audited
Editor in Chief: Ashok Agarwal; **Editor:** Pushpendra Sharma
Editorial Profile: Covers society and social issues as well as news.
Language (s): Hindi
DAILY NEWSPAPER

Amar Ujala - Bareilly Edition
Editorial: 19 Civil Lines, Shahjahanpur Road, Bareilly 243005. **T:** 91 581 2562843
W: http://www.amarujala.com
Freq: Daily; **Circ:** 140002 Not Audited
Editor in Chief: Ashok Agarwal
Editorial Profile: Covers society and social issues as well as news.
Language (s): Hindi
DAILY NEWSPAPER

Amar Ujala - Chandigarh Edition
Editorial: 49 Industrial Area, Phase II, Panchkula, Chandigarh 134113.
T: 91 1722591459
W: http://www.amarujala.com
Freq: Daily; **Circ:** 80002 Not Audited
Editor in Chief: Ashok Agarwal
Editorial Profile: Covers news, sports, business, banking, society and social issues.
Language (s): Hindi
DAILY NEWSPAPER

Amar Ujala - Dehradun Edition
Editorial: Shed No.2, Patel Nagar Industrial Estate, Dehradun 248001. **T:** 91 1352720378
W: http://www.amarujala.com
Freq: Daily; **Circ:** 125001 Not Audited
Editor: Nisheet Joshi
Editorial Profile: Covers society and social issues. The newspaper is known for some ground breaking journalism and even in today's cut throat competition, Amar Ujala is still selling Authenticity, Honesty and Trust.
Language (s): Hindi
DAILY NEWSPAPER

Amar Ujala - Jalandhar Edition
Editorial: A-5, Sports & Surgical Goods Complex, Kapurthala Road, Jalandhar 1440021. **T:** 91 1812650201
E: editor@jal.amarujala.com
W: http://www.amarujala.com
Freq: Daily Not Audited
Editor: Nisheet Joshi
Editorial Profile: Covers society and social issues. The newspaper is known for some ground breaking journalism and even in today's cut throat competition, Amar Ujala is still selling Authenticity, Honesty and Trust.
Language (s): Hindi
DAILY NEWSPAPER

Amar Ujala - Meerut Edition
Editorial: 164 Mohkampur, Delhi Road, Meerut 250002. **T:** 91 121 2510006
E: bhawanis@mrt.amarujala.com
W: http://www.amarujala.com
Freq: Daily; **Circ:** 1400002 Not Audited
Editor in Chief: Ashok Agarwal
Editorial Profile: Covers society and social issues as well as news.
Language (s): Hindi
DAILY NEWSPAPER

Amar Ujala - Moradabad Edition
Editorial: 588/1 Majhola Delhi Road, Moradabad 24401. **T:** 91 591 2484800
E: editor@amarujala.com
W: http://www.amarujala.com
Freq: Daily; **Circ:** 60003 Not Audited
Editor in Chief: Ashok Agarwal
Editorial Profile: Daily Hindi newspaper from Amar Ujala. Jhansi Edition covers news, sports, society and social issues.
Language (s): Hindi
DAILY NEWSPAPER

Amar Ujala - Varanasi Edition
Editorial: A-6 Big Industrial Estate, Chandpur, Lehartara, Varanasi 221106.
T: 91 542 2373921 **E:** editor@amarujala.com
W: http://www.amarujala.com
Freq: Daily; **Circ:** 100002 Not Audited
Editor in Chief: Ashok Agarwal
Editorial Profile: Covers news, sports, business, banking, society and social issues.
Language (s): Hindi
DAILY NEWSPAPER

Amravati Mandal
Editorial: Behind Irwin Hospital, Khaparde Garden, Amravati 444601. **T:** 91 721 2666600
E: ati_ammandal@sancharnet.in
W: http://www.amravatimandal.com
Freq: Daily; **Circ:** 130002 Not Audited
Editor: Anil Agarwal
Editorial Profile: Covers the latest local, regional, international and national news.
Language (s): Hindi
DAILY NEWSPAPER

Amrit Sandesh
Editorial: Amrit Sandesh Bhawan, P B No. 18, Jawaharlal Nehru Marg, Raipur 492001.
T: 91 771 2535741
E: amritsandesh@yahoo.co.in
Freq: Daily
Editor: Govindlal Vohra
Editorial Profile: Amrit Sandesh is a daily newspaper printed in Hindi covering Local Regional National and International news.
Language (s): Hindi
DAILY NEWSPAPER

Ananda Bazar Patrika
Owner: ABP Pvt. Ltd.
Editorial: 12/4, Ballygunge, Ballygung Park Road, West Bengal, Kolkata 700019.
T: 91 33 22253241
W: http://www.anandabazar.com
Freq: Daily; **Circ:** 692359 Not Audited
Editor in Chief: Aveek Sarkar
Editorial Profile: Articles cover local and international news.
Language (s): Bengali
DAILY NEWSPAPER

Andhra Bhoomi
Editorial: 36 Sarojini Devi Road, Secunderabad 500003. **T:** 91 40 27803930
E: bhoomi@deccanmail.com
W: http://www.andhrabhoomi.net
Freq: Daily; **Circ:** 110489 Not Audited
Editor: M. Shastri
Editorial Profile: Covers the latest news of local, international, national and regional, and etc,
Language (s): Telugu
DAILY NEWSPAPER

Andhra Jyothi
Editorial: Andhra Jyoti Buildings, Plot No:76, HUDA Heights, Ashwani Layout, Road No:70, Journalist Colony, Jubilee Hills, Hyderabad 500033. **T:** 91 40 2355-8233
E: editor@andhrajyothy.com
W: http://www.andhrajyothy.com
Freq: Daily Not Audited
Editor: Vemana Lakshmi; **Editor:** Allam Narayana; **Editor:** K. Srinivas
Editorial Profile: Covers the latest news in local and world, sports, and etc.
Language (s): Telugu
DAILY NEWSPAPER

Andhra Prabha
Editorial: Andhra Prabha Publishing Ltd., 6-3-4 Banjara Hills, Road 1, Prem Nager, Hyderabad 500034. **T:** 91 4023327178
W: http://www.andhraprabha.com
Freq: Daily; **Circ:** 223001 Not Audited
Editor: P. Vijaybabu
Editorial Profile: Andhra Prabha is a newspaper which covers the Hyderabad news, current events, politics and business;
Language (s): Telugu
DAILY NEWSPAPER

Around The Times
Editorial: LG-101, Bharat Chambers, 70 Scindia House, Janpath, Connaught Circus, New Delhi 110001. **T:** 91 11 23350940
Freq: Daily; **Circ:** 75002 Not Audited
Editorial Profile: Around The Times is a newspaper which coves local and world news, sports, business, entertainment and etc.
Language (s): English
DAILY NEWSPAPER

The Asian Age - Kolkata Edition
Editorial: Asian Age Holdings Ltd., 6 Russel Street, Kolkata 700071. **T:** 91 33 22890676
E: kolkatadesk@asianage.com
W: http://www.asianage.com
Freq: Daily; **Circ:** 62002 Not Audited
Bureau Chief: Parwez Hafeez
Editorial Profile: Covers local and international news, business, sports, entertainment, and lifestyle. Also has supplements on movies, fashion and lifestyle, education, information and technology, health, and books.
Language (s): English
DAILY NEWSPAPER

Asian Age - Mumbai Edition
Editorial: The Asian Age, 145, Mathura Das Mill Compound, N.M. Joshi Marg, L, Mumbai 400013. **T:** 91 22 24955825
W: http://www.asianage.com
Freq: Daily; **Circ:** 94657 Not Audited
Editor in Chief: Venkattram Reddy; **Editor:** Olga Tellis
Editorial Profile: Covers local and international news, business, sports, entertainment, and lifestyle. Also has supplements on movies, fashion and lifestyle, education, information and technology, health, and books.
Language (s): Hindi
DAILY NEWSPAPER

Asian Age - New Delhi Edition
Editorial: S - 7, Green Park Main Market, New Delhi 110016. **T:** 91 11 26530001 3
E: delhidesk@asianage.com
W: http://www.asianage.com
Freq: Daily
Editorial Profile: Covers local and international news, business, sports, entertainment, and lifestyle. Also has supplements on movies, fashion and lifestyle, education, information and technology, health, and books.
Language (s): English
DAILY NEWSPAPER

Asomiya Pratidin
Editorial: Maniram Dewan Road, Chandmari, Guwahati 781003. **T:** 91 3612663647
W: http://www.asomiyapratidin.co.in
Freq: Daily; **Circ:** 150002 Not Audited
Editor: Haidar Hussain
Editorial Profile: Covers local, regional, international and national news.
Language (s): Assamese
DAILY NEWSPAPER

Assignments Abroad Times
Owner: Aishwarya Publications Pvt Ltd.
Editorial: 401-404 Centre Point, 18th Road, Chembur, E., Mumbai 400071.
T: 91 22 2529-0102
E: ads@assignmentsabroadtimes.com
W: http://www.assignmentsabroadtimes.com
Freq: 2 Times/Week; **Circ:** 100003 Not Audited
Editor: D. Prasad
Editorial Profile: Provides information on careers.
Language (s): English
NEWSPAPER

Bangalore Mirror
Editorial: SNB Towers, 40/1, Mahatma Gandhi Rd, Shanthala Nagar, Bangalore 560001.
T: 91 80 4220-0000
W: http://www.bangaloremirror.com
Freq: Daily
Editorial Profile: Provides news and analysis on current events, business, finance, economy and sports.
Language (s): English
DAILY NEWSPAPER

Bartaman Patrika
Editorial: 6, J.B.S. Haldane Avenue, Kolkata 700105. **T:** 91 33 23000101
E: bartaman@satyam.net.in
W: http://www.bartamanpatrika.com
Freq: Daily; **Circ:** 470002 Not Audited
Editor: Subha Dutta
Editorial Profile: Covers the latest news in local and world.
Language (s): Bengali
DAILY NEWSPAPER

Bharat Tender News (Weekly)
Editorial: LG-101, Bharat Chambers, 70 Scindia House, Janpath Connaught Circus, New Delhi 110001. **T:** 91 1123326603
E: ashbedi@vsnl.net.in
W: http://www.dalitnews.com
Freq: Weekly; **Circ:** 76003 Not Audited
Editor: Ashok Bedi
Editorial Profile: Weekly newspaper in the capital of India, paper's main focus is probably politics.
Language (s): Hindi
NEWSPAPER

Bhor
Editorial: 4/11, Sukhadia Shopping Centre, P.B. No. 81, Sri Ganga Nagar 335001.
T: 91 154 3093337 **E:** thebhor@yahoo.com
Freq: Daily; **Circ:** 50002 Not Audited
Editorial Profile: Covers the latest news in local and international.
Language (s): Hindi
DAILY NEWSPAPER

Bihar Observer
Editorial: Joraphatak Road, Dhanbad 826001.
T: 91 326 2301104
E: dnb_observer@sancharnet.in
W: http://www.biharobserver.tripod.com
Freq: Daily; **Circ:** 69949 Not Audited
Editor: Sushil Bharti; **Editor:** Ganesh Mishra
Editorial Profile: Covers local, national and international news.
Language (s): English
DAILY NEWSPAPER

Bijnor Times
Editorial: Bijnor Times Road, Bijnore 246701.
T: 91 1342 260002
E: bijnor_times@yahoo.co.in
W: http://www.bijnortimes.com
Freq: Daily; **Circ:** 60002 Not Audited
Editor in Chief: Chanrdramani Raghuvanshi
Editorial Profile: Focuses on the latest news in local and world.
Language (s): Hindi
DAILY NEWSPAPER

Bombay Basanti Ank
Editorial: Red House Opposite Dena Bank, Horniman Circle, Sayed Adbulla Brelvi Road, Fort, Mumbai 400001. **T:** 91 2222045531
E: samachar.bombay@gmail.com
W: http://www.bombaysamachar.com
Freq: Weekly; **Circ:** 150003 Not Audited
Editorial Profile: Local Newspaper.
Language (s): Gujarati
NEWSPAPER

The Bombay Samachar
Editorial: Red House, Abdulla Brelvi Road, Horniman Circle Sayed Fort, Mumbai 400001.
T: 91 22 22045531
E: samachar.bombay@gmail.com
W: http://www.bombaysamachar.com
Freq: 2 Times/Week; **Circ:** 100002 Not Audited
Editorial Profile: Covers the latest in local and national news.
Language (s): Gujarati
NEWSPAPER

Business Deepika
Editorial: Rashtra Deepika Publications, P.O. Box 2252, Cochin 686025. **T:** 91 4813012001
E: editor@deepika.com
W: http://www.deepika.com
Freq: Weekly; **Circ:** 53003 Not Audited
Editorial Profile: Business newspaper.
Language (s): Malayalam
NEWSPAPER

Business Standard - Ahmedabad Edition
Editorial: Room No. 211 & 212 Sakar II, 2nd Fl, Near Ellise Bridge, Ahmedabad.
T: 91 79 26577772

W: http://www.business-standard.com
Freq: Daily
Editorial Profile: Covers banking, finance markets and business.
Language (s): English
DAILY NEWSPAPER

Business Standard- Hyderabad Edition
Editorial: Business Standard Ltd., 3rd Floor, PTA Building, A C Guards, Hyderabad 500004. **T:** 91 4023303158
W: http://www.business-standard.com
Freq: Daily
Bureau Chief: Prashanth Reddy Chintala
Editorial Profile: Business Standard is India's premium business daily newspaper (Mumbai Bangalore Delhi Chennai Kolkata Hyderabad and Ahmedabad) which covers the corporate sector banking and finance markets and business apart from the most influential group of editorial writers and columnists.
Language (s): Hindi
DAILY NEWSPAPER

Central Chronicle
Editorial: Nava Bharat Bhavan, 2, Indira Press Complex, Maharana Pratap Nagar, Zone 1, Bhopal 462011. **T:** 91 755 4282765
W: http://www.centralchronicle.com
Freq: Daily; **Circ:** 50001 Not Audited
Editor in Chief: P.K. Maheshwari; **Editor:** Aneel Pande
Editorial Profile: Coves local news, sports, business, jobs, and community events.
Language (s): English
DAILY NEWSPAPER

Chandigarh Tribune
Editorial: The Tribune House, Sector 29-C, Chandigarh 160030. **T:** 91 172 2655066
E: news@tribuneindia.com
W: http://www.tribuneindia.com
Freq: Daily; **Circ:** 110001 Not Audited
Editor in Chief: H. Dua
Editorial Profile: Chandigarh Tribune is a newspaper which covers the news in local and international, business, and sports.
Language (s): English
DAILY NEWSPAPER

Charhdikala
Editorial: Charhdikala Group of Publications, Private Ltd., 593, SST Nagar Rajpura Road, Punjab 147003. **T:** 91 17 52370301
E: cppl@charhdikala.com
W: http://www.charhdikala.com
Freq: Daily; **Circ:** 52003 Not Audited
Editor in Chief: Jagjit Dardi
Editorial Profile: Punjabi Family newspaper
Language (s): Punjabi
DAILY NEWSPAPER

Daily Excelsior
Editorial: Excelsior House Excelsior Lane, Janipura, Jammu 180007. **T:** 91 191 2537055
E: editor@dailyexcelsior.com
W: http://www.dailyexcelsior.com
Freq: Daily; **Circ:** 190001 Not Audited
Editor in Chief: S.D. Rohmetra
Editorial Profile: Covers local and world news, sports, entertainment, etc.
Language (s): English
DAILY NEWSPAPER

Daily Punjab Kesari
Editorial: Hind Samachar Building, Civil Lines, Jalandhar 144001. **T:** 91 181 2280104
W: http://www.punjabkesari.com
Freq: Daily; **Circ:** 620044 Not Audited
Editorial Profile: Covers local news, sports, business, jobs, and community events.
Language (s): Hindi
DAILY NEWSPAPER

Daily Taskeen
Editorial: Tasken Complex Dalpatian Wazarat Road, Jammu 180001. **T:** 91 191 2543336
Freq: Daily; **Circ:** 60003 Not Audited
Editor in Chief: Maqbool Kazmi
Editorial Profile: Covers local and international news.
Language (s): Urdu
DAILY NEWSPAPER

Daily Thanthi
Editorial: Daily Thanthi, 86 E. V. K. Sampath Road, Chennai 600007. **T:** 91 4426618661
E: editor@dt.co.in
W: http://www.dailythanthi.com
Freq: Daily; **Circ:** 10000003 Not Audited
Editor: M. Dhanasekaran; **Publisher:** V. Sundaresan
Editorial Profile: Covers international and national news.
Language (s): Tamil
DAILY NEWSPAPER

Dainik Agradoot
Editorial: Agradoot Bhavan, Kalipara Road, Dispur, Guwahati 781006. **T:** 91 361 2261923
W: http://www.dainikagradoot.com
Freq: Daily; **Circ:** 92001 Not Audited
Editor: Naresh Kalita
Editorial Profile: Provides city news, city guides, latest news, current event, current news and entertainment guide.
Language (s): Assamese
DAILY NEWSPAPER

Dainik Awantika
Editorial: 2 Rani Laxmi Bai Marg Ujjain, Ujjain 456001. **T:** 91 734 2554455
Freq: Daily; **Circ:** 65002 Not Audited
Editor in Chief: Surendra Mehta
Editorial Profile: Covers local and worldwide news, sports and entertainment.
Language (s): Hindi
DAILY NEWSPAPER

Dainik Bhaskar - Bhopal Edition
Editorial: 6 Dwarka Sadan, Press Complex, M P Nagar, Bhopal 462011. **T:** 91 755 3988884
W: http://www.bhaskar.com
Freq: Daily; **Circ:** 3500002 Not Audited
Editor in Chief: R. Agarwal; **Editor:** Rajesh Upadhyay
Editorial Profile: Dainik Bhaskar is a newspaper which provides the latest local, regional, international and national news, business, lifestyle, sports and etc.
Language (s): Hindi
DAILY NEWSPAPER

Dainik Bhaskar - Gwalior Edition
Editorial: 6 Dwarka Sadan, Press Complex, M.P. Nagar, Bhopal 462011.
T: 91 755 3988884
W: http://www.bhaskar.com
Freq: Daily; **Circ:** 3500002 Not Audited
Editor: Hari Mohan Sharma
Editorial Profile: Provides the latest local, regional, international and national news, business, lifestyle, sports and etc.
Language (s): Hindi
DAILY NEWSPAPER

Dainik Bhaskar - Jabalpur Edition
Editorial: 581 South Civil Lines, Denning Road, Jabalpur 482001. **T:** 91 761 2601352
E: dbjsn@rediffmail.com
W: http://www.bhaskar.com
Freq: Daily; **Circ:** 3500002 Not Audited
Editor in Chief: R. Agarwal; **Editor:** Manish Gupta
Editorial Profile: Covers local, regional, international and national news, business, lifestyle, sports and etc.
Language (s): Hindi
DAILY NEWSPAPER

Dainik Divya Himachal
Editorial: Pathan Court Road, Purana Mataur, Kangra 176001. **T:** 91 1892 264713
E: edit.dshala@divyahimachal.com
W: http://www.divyahimachal.com
Freq: Daily; **Circ:** 91436 Not Audited
Editor in Chief: Anil Soni
Editorial Profile: Covers local and world news, sports, lifestyle and economy
Language (s): Hindi
DAILY NEWSPAPER

Dainik Jagran - Agra Edition
Editorial: Laxmi Hall, Jeevan Mandi, Agra 282004. **T:** 91 5622621662
W: http://www.jagran.com
Freq: Daily; **Circ:** 95002 Not Audited
News Editor: Anand Sharma
Editorial Profile: Covers Local National Regional And International News.
Language (s): Hindi
DAILY NEWSPAPER

Dainik Jagran - Bareilly Edition
Editorial: 130 Civil Lines, Bareilly 243001.
T: 91 5812427556 **E:** bareilly@brl.jagran.com
W: http://in.Jagran.yahoo.com
Freq: Daily; **Circ:** 100001 Not Audited
Editor in Chief: Sanjay Gupta
Editorial Profile: Local reading for anyone in Barielly edition of Dainik Jagran newspaper.
Language (s): Hindi
DAILY NEWSPAPER

Dainik Jagran - Gorakhpur Edition
Editorial: 23 Civil Lines, Gorakhpur 273001.
T: 91 551 2337137 **W:** http://www.jagran.com
Freq: Daily; **Circ:** 100003 Not Audited
Editor in Chief: Sanjay Gupta; **Editor:** Shailendra Mani Tripathi
Editorial Profile: Covers Local National Regional And International News.
Language (s): Hindi
DAILY NEWSPAPER

Dainik Jagran - Kanpur Edition
Editorial: Jagran Building, 2 Sarvodaya Nagar, Kanpur 208005. **T:** 91 5122216161
W: http://www.jagran.com
Freq: Daily; **Circ:** 175727 Not Audited
Editor: Sandeep Gupta
Editorial Profile: Covers Local National Regional And International News.
Language (s): Hindi
DAILY NEWSPAPER

Dainik Jagran - Lucknow Edition
Editorial: 57 A-3 Meera Bai Marg, Lucknow 226001. **T:** 91 5222209484
W: http://www.jagran.com
Freq: Daily; **Circ:** 220002 Not Audited
Editor: Shekhar Tripathi
Editorial Profile: Covers Local National Regional And International News.
Language (s): Hindi
DAILY NEWSPAPER

Dainik Jagran - Meerut Edition
Editorial: Jagran Bhawan, 140-D Saket, Meerut 250006. **T:** 91 1212662245
W: http://www.jagran.com
Freq: Daily; **Circ:** 106298 Not Audited
Editor: Dhirendra Mohan Gupta; **Editor:** Prabhat Gupta
Editorial Profile: Covers Local, National, Regional and International News.
Language (s): Hindi
DAILY NEWSPAPER

Dainik Jagran - New Delhi Edition
Editorial: 501 INS Building, Rafi Marg, New Delhi 110001. **T:** 91 1123359960
W: http://www.jagran.com
Freq: Daily; **Circ:** 132131 Not Audited
Editor: Vikas Dwivedi; **Editor:** Sanjay Gupta
Editorial Profile: Covers Local National Regional And International News.
Language (s): Hindi
DAILY NEWSPAPER

Dainik Jagran - Varanasi Edition
Editorial: Andhra Pul, Varanasi 221002.
T: 91 542 3061000
E: varanasi@vns.jagran.com
W: http://www.jagran.com
Freq: Daily; **Circ:** 114167 Not Audited
Editor: Sanjav Gupta; **Editor:** Virendra Gupta;
Editor: Rajeev Sachan
Editorial Profile: publishes in all languages (including English) and covers local national and international news.
Language (s): Hindi
DAILY NEWSPAPER

Dainik Kashmir Times
Editorial: Kashmir Times Building, Residency Road, Jammu 180001. **T:** 91 1912543676
W: http://www.kashmirtimes.com
Freq: Daily; **Circ:** 160003 Not Audited
Editor in Chief: Prabodh Jamwal
Editorial Profile: Covers the latest local, regional, international and national news, business, sports and etc.
Language (s): Hindi
DAILY NEWSPAPER

Dainik Lokmat - Ahmednagar Edition
Editorial: 2nd Floor Nirlon, A;B Road, Worli, Mumbai 400018. **T:** 91 241 2429902
W: http://www.lokmat.net
Freq: Daily; **Circ:** 1000003 Not Audited
Editor in Chief: Rajendra Darda
Editorial Profile: Covers the latest local and international news.
Language (s): English
DAILY NEWSPAPER

Dainik Mahalaxmi Bhagyodaya
Editorial: 184 Patparganj Industrial Area, Delhi 110092. **T:** 91 11 22140796
E: mahalaxmigroup@hotmail.com
W: http://www.mahalaxmigroup.com
Freq: Daily; **Circ:** 53002 Not Audited
Editor: Praveen Jain
Editorial Profile: Covers the local and world news.
Language (s): Hindi
DAILY NEWSPAPER

Dainik Navajyoti
Editorial: Dainik Navajyoti Complex, P.O. Box 72, Kaisarganj, Lucknow 305001.
T: 91 145 2426636
E: jaipur@dainiknavajyoti.com
W: http://www.dainiknavajyoti.com
Freq: Daily; **Circ:** 591002 Not Audited
Editorial Profile: Covers local and world news and sports.
Language (s): Hindi
DAILY NEWSPAPER

Dainik Rajpath
Editorial: Mitra Nagar, Gular Road, Aligarh 202001. **T:** 91 571 2521104
Freq: Daily; **Circ:** 50002 Not Audited
Editorial Profile: Covers local and world news.
Language (s): Hindi
DAILY NEWSPAPER

Dainik Sambad
Editorial: Jagannath Bari Road, Agartala 799001. **T:** 91 3812326676
E: dainiksambad@yahoo.com
W: http://www.dainiksambad.net
Freq: Daily; **Circ:** 60003 Not Audited
Editor: Pradeep Bhowmick
Editorial Profile: Dainik Sambad is the leading Bengali Daily of Tripura and the largest circulated Bengali newspaper in the North-East India. Dainik Sambad newspaper is also published in Agartala and Tripura.
Language (s): Bengali
DAILY NEWSPAPER

Dainik Udyog Aas-Pass
Editorial: Pujari Bhavan, Tabela Gate, Sikar 332001. **T:** 91 1572-250703
Freq: Daily; **Circ:** 50002 Not Audited
Editorial Profile: Covers Local, National And International News.
Language (s): Hindi
DAILY NEWSPAPER

Deccan Chronicle - Bangalore Edition
Editorial: Deccan Chronicle Holdings Ltd., 58, HM Towers, Brigade Road, Bangalore 560025.
T: 91 80 22226049 **E:** editor@deccanmail.com
W: http://www.deccanchronicle.com/
Freq: Daily
Editor: Goutam Das
Editorial Profile: Covers the news in local, regional, international and national, business, sports, art, and etc.
Language (s): Hindi
DAILY NEWSPAPER

Deccan Chronicle - Hyderabad Edition
Editorial: Deccan Chronicle Holdings Ltd, 36, Sarojini Devi Road, Secunderabad 500003.
T: 91 40 27803930 **E:** editor@deccanmail.com
W: http://www.deccanchronicle.com/
Freq: Daily; **Circ:** 552855 Not Audited
Editor: A. Jayanti
Editorial Profile: Covers the news in local, regional, international and national, business, sports, art, and etc.
Language (s): English
DAILY NEWSPAPER

Deccan Herald
Editorial: The Printers (Mysore) Private Limited, 75 Mahatma Gandhi Road P.O. Box 31, Bangalore 560001. **T:** 91 80 25 88 0000
W: http://www.deccanherald.com
Freq: Daily; **Circ:** 200003 Not Audited
Editor: K.N. Tilak Kumar; **Editor:** K. N. Shanth Kumar
Editorial Profile: A general daily newspaper.
Language (s): English
DAILY NEWSPAPER

Deepika Daily
Owner: Rashtra Deepika Publications
Editorial: Rashtra Deepika Publications, P.O. Box 2252, Cochin 686025.
T: 91 481 301 2001 **E:** editor@deepika.com
W: http://www.deepikaglobal.com
Freq: Daily; **Circ:** 200002 Not Audited
Editor in Chief: Alexander Paikada; **Editor in Chief:** Jose Panthaplamthottiyil
Editorial Profile: Covers local, regional, international and national news, and sports.
Language (s): Malayalam
DAILY NEWSPAPER

Desh Sewak Daily
Editorial: Bhakna Bhawan, Sector 29 D, Opposite Tribune Colony, Chandigarh 160020.
T: 91 172 2657256 **E:** news@deshsewak.com
W: http://www.deshsewak.com
Freq: Daily
Editor: Prem Gorkhi; **Editor:** Jaspal Singh;
Editor: Prem Singh; **Editor:** Tejwant Singh Gill;
Editor: Harbhajan Singh Halwarvi; **Editor:** Joginder Singh Paur; **Editor:** Gulzar Singh Sandhu
Editorial Profile: Focuses on well-known literary and social figures as well as local and international news.
Language (s): Punjabi
DAILY NEWSPAPER

Deshabhimani
Editorial: Deshabhimani, Kaloor, Kochi 682017. **T:** 91 4842530739
W: http://www.deshabhimani.com

Freq: Daily; **Circ:** 500002 Not Audited
Editor in Chief: V. Dakshinamurthy
Editorial Profile: Desabhimani is a Malayalam newspaper which covers the news in local and world, and etc.
Language (s): Malayalam
DAILY NEWSPAPER

Deshbandhu

Editorial: Deshbandhu Ramsagar Para, Raipur 492001. **T:** 91 7714288888
E: deshbandhuraipur@gmail.com
W: http://www.deshbandhu.co.in
Freq: Daily; **Circ:** 60001 Not Audited
Editor: Prabhaker Choubey; **Editor in Chief:** Lalit Surjan
Editorial Profile: Covers news.
Language (s): Hindi
DAILY NEWSPAPER

Deshonnati - Akola Edition

Editorial: Nishant Towers, M.G. Road, Akola 444001. **T:** 91 724 2424404
W: http://www.deshonnati.com
Freq: Daily; **Circ:** 215002 Not Audited
Bureau Chief: Vikrant Patil; **Editor in Chief:** Prakash Pohare
Editorial Profile: Covers local news, sports, business, jobs, and community events.
Language (s): Marathi
DAILY NEWSPAPER

Dharitri

Editorial: B-26 Industrial Estate, Bhubaneshwar 751010. **T:** 91 674 2580101
E: dharitri@sancharnet.in
W: http://www.dharitri.com
Freq: Daily; **Circ:** 200002 Not Audited
Editor: Tathagata Satpathy
Editorial Profile: Covers local and world news, sports, education and science.
Language (s): Oriya
DAILY NEWSPAPER

Dinakaran

Editorial: No. 229, Kutchery Road, Mylapore, Chennai 600004. **T:** 91 44 42209191
E: dotcom@dinakaran.com
W: http://www.dinakaran.com
Freq: Daily; **Circ:** 940002 Not Audited
Editor: Kathir Vel
Editorial Profile: Covers local and world news, business, sports, entertainment, etc.
Language (s): Tamil
DAILY NEWSPAPER

Dinamalar

Editorial: TVR House, Dinamalar Avenue, Madurai 625016. **T:** 91 4522380903
E: dmrmdu@dinamalar.in
W: http://www.dinamalar.com
Freq: Daily; **Circ:** 600001 Not Audited
Editor: R. Krishnamurthy; **Publisher:** R. Lakshmipathy
Editorial Profile: World Number one Tamil daily newspaper.
Language (s): Tamil
DAILY NEWSPAPER

Dinamani

Editorial: Club House Road, Chennai 600002. **T:** 91 44 28461818
W: http://www.dinamani.com
Freq: Daily; **Circ:** 200001 Not Audited
Editor: R.T. Sambandan
Editorial Profile: Covers local and world news, sports, business, economy, entertainment, etc.
Language (s): Tamil
DAILY NEWSPAPER

Divya Bhaskar

Editorial: 280, Sarkhej-Gandhinagar Highway, Near YMCA Club, Ahmedabad 380051.
T: 91 79 39888850 **E:** contact@imcl.co.in
W: http://www.divyabhaskar.co.in
Freq: Daily
Editor: Ajay Umat
Editorial Profile: Covers the local, regional, international and national news, sports, entertainments, lifestyle, religion, and business.
Language (s): Gujarati
DAILY NEWSPAPER

The DQ Week

Editorial: Cyber House, B-35, Sector 32 Institutional, Gurgaon 122001.
T: 91 124 4822222
W: http://www.dqweek.com
Freq: Weekly; **Circ:** 60001 Not Audited
Editorial Profile: Provides information relating to all areas of information technology.
Language (s): English
NEWSPAPER

The Economic Times - Ahmedabad Edition

Owner: Bennett, Coleman & Co. Ltd.
Editorial: 139 Ashram Road, Ahmedabad 380009. **T:** 91 79 6560123
W: http://www.economictimes.com
Freq: Daily; **Circ:** 6000003 Not Audited
Editor: Ashwin Walunjkr
Editorial Profile: Extensively covers the Indian economy, shares prices of commodities and other financial news. Regular topics include personal finance, mutual funds, markets and IPOs.
Language (s): English
DAILY NEWSPAPER

The Economic Times - Chennai Edition

Owner: Bennett, Coleman & Co. Ltd.
Editorial: Times House, 126/127, Chaimers Road, Nandanam, Chennai 600035.
T: 91 44 24342121
E: viswanathan.balasubramanian@timesgroup.com **W:** http://www.economictimes.com
Freq: Daily; **Circ:** 50002 Not Audited
Editor: A. Subramaniam
Editorial Profile: Extensively covers the Indian economy, shares prices of commodities and other financial news. Regular topics include personal finance, mutual funds, markets and IPOs.
Language (s): English
DAILY NEWSPAPER

The Economic Times - Kolkata Edition

Owner: Bennett, Coleman & Co. Ltd.
Editorial: 105/7A, S.N.Banerjee Road, Kolkata 700014. **T:** 91 3322492222
W: http://www.economictimes.com
Freq: Daily; **Circ:** 80003 Not Audited
Editor: Basistha Basu
Editorial Profile: Extensively covers the Indian economy, shares prices of commodities and other financial news. Regular topics include personal finance, mutual funds, markets and IPOs.
Language (s): English
DAILY NEWSPAPER

The Economic Times - Mumbai Edition

Owner: Bennett, Coleman & Co. Ltd.
Editorial: 3rd Floor, The Times of India Building, Dr. D N Road, Mumbai 400001.
T: 91 22 66353535
W: http://www.economictimes.com
Freq: Daily; **Circ:** 170002 Not Audited
Editor: Indrajit Gupta
Editorial Profile: Extensively covers the Indian economy, shares prices of commodities and other financial news. Regular topics include personal finance, mutual funds, markets and IPOs.
Language (s): Hindi
DAILY NEWSPAPER

The Economic Times - New Delhi Edition

Owner: Bennett, Coleman & Co. Ltd.
Editorial: 7 Bahadur Shah Zafar Marg, New Delhi 110002. **T:** 91 11 2331775
W: http://www.economictimes.com
Freq: Daily; **Circ:** 200003 Not Audited
Editor: Bodhisatva Ganguli; **Editor:** Javed Sayed; **Editor:** Amit Tyagi
Editorial Profile: Extensively covers the Indian economy, shares prices of commodities and other financial news. Regular topics include personal finance, mutual funds, markets and IPOs.
Language (s): English
DAILY NEWSPAPER

Eenadu

Editorial: Eenadu Complex, Somajiguda, Hyderabad 500482. **T:** 91 4023318181
E: editor@eenadu.net
W: http://www.eenadu.net
Freq: Daily; **Circ:** 100002 Not Audited
Editor: Rahul Kumar
Editorial Profile: Covers local and world news, sports and etc.
Language (s): Telugu
DAILY NEWSPAPER

Ei Samay

Editorial: 8 Camac St, Shantiniketan Bldg, Fl 15, Kolkata 700017
W: http://eisamay.indiatimes.com
Freq: Daily
Editor: Suman Chattopadhyay
Editorial Profile: Launched in October 2012 and published in the Adda language, covers the Bengali region of India. Aims to enlighten readers with dialogue on social, economic and political life by providing context and

perspective, nuance and texture. Also known as Eyi Shomoy.
Language (s): Bengali
DAILY NEWSPAPER

Employment & NRI Times

Editorial: 704 Gateway Plaza, Hiranandani Gardens, Powai, Mumbai 400076.
T: 91 2267341770 **E:** editorial@enritimes.com
W: http://www.enritimes.com
Freq: Weekly
Editor: E. Vaidyanatyhan
Editorial Profile: A weekly newspaper focusing on career advancement, both in India and abroad.
Language (s): Hindi
NEWSPAPER

Employment News

Editorial: Employment News, East Block IV, Level 5, R K Puram, New Delhi 110066.
T: 91 11 26174975 **E:** editor_rc@yahoo.co.in
W: http://www.employmentnews.gov.in
Freq: Weekly; **Circ:** 700001 Not Audited
Editor in Chief: Rakesh Jha; **Editor:** Nalini Rani
Editorial Profile: Provides information about employment opportunities for young people.
Language (s): English
NEWSPAPER

Financial Chronicle

Owner: Deccan Chronicle Holdings Limited
Editorial: Financial Chronicle, S-7/8 Free Park, Main Market, New Delhi 110016.
T: 91 1126530001
E: mymind@mydigitalfc.com
W: http://www.mydigitalfc.com
Freq: Mon thru Fri Not Audited
Editor in Chief: Shubhrangshu Roy
Editorial Profile: Launched in April 2008 and shares business news.
Language (s): English
DAILY NEWSPAPER

Financial Express - Mumbai Edition

Editorial: Express Tower 2nd Floor, Nariman Point, Mumbai 400021. **T:** 91 22 22022627
E: editor@financialexpress.com
W: http://www.financialexpress.com
Freq: Daily; **Circ:** 150003 Not Audited
Editor in Chief: Shekhar Gupta; **Publisher:** Prashant Raman
Editorial Profile: Mumbai's daily fed on the financial world.
Language (s): English
DAILY NEWSPAPER

Financial Express - New Delhi Edition

Owner: The Indian Express Limited.
Editorial: The Indian Express Limited., 9&10, Bhadur Shah Zafar Marg, Express Building, ITO, New Delhi 110002. **T:** 91 11 23702100
E: editor@expressindia.com
W: http://www.financialexpress.com
Freq: Daily
Editor: Alokananda Chakraborty; **Editor in Chief:** Shekhar Gupta
Editorial Profile: The Financial Express is an Indian business and financial daily newspaper published by the Indian Express group. Articles cover the complete Up-to-date source for business news, finance news, stock market news, world business news, stock market india, market news, and etc
Language (s): English
DAILY NEWSPAPER

Ganashakti

Editorial: 74A Acharya Jagdish Chandra Bose Road, Kolkata 700016. **T:** 91 33 2227-8950
E: mail@ganashakti.co.in
W: http://www.ganashakti.co.in
Freq: Daily; **Circ:** 145002 Not Audited
Editor: Narayan Dutta
Editorial Profile: Covers local and world news, travel, literature, science, and technology.
Language (s): Bengali
DAILY NEWSPAPER

Gavakari

Editorial: M/s. Gavakari Prakashan, 'Gavakari, Bhavan 430 H, Tilak Path, Nashik 422001.
T: 91 25 32305080 **E:** dhlgav@yahoo.com
Freq: Daily; **Circ:** 90002 Not Audited
Editor: Vandan Potnis
Editorial Profile: Covers local and world news.
Language (s): Marathi
DAILY NEWSPAPER

Glimpses Of Future

Editorial: 63 Padha Street, Purani Mandi, Jammu 180001. **T:** 91 191 2546079
Freq: Daily; **Circ:** 85002 Not Audited
Editor in Chief: Prem Nath Sharma
Editorial Profile: Covers local and world news.

Language (s): English
DAILY NEWSPAPER

Grameen Duniya

Editorial: 199 C.M.-1, Jhandewalan Extention, New Delhi 110055. **T:** 91 11 23626465
Freq: Weekly; **Circ:** 1600002 Not Audited
Editor: Sanjay Gupta
Editorial Profile: Focuses on farming and agriculture.
Language (s): Gujarati
NEWSPAPER

Greater Kashmir

Editorial: 6 Pratap Park, Residency Road, Srinagar 190001. **T:** 91 194 2455435
E: editor@greaterkashmir.com
W: http://www.greaterkashmir.com
Freq: Daily; **Circ:** 70824 Not Audited
Editor: Fayaz Ahmed Kaloo
Editorial Profile: Covers the latest local, regional, international and national news, business, sports and etc.
Language (s): English
DAILY NEWSPAPER

Gujarat Samachar

Editorial: Gujarat Samachar Bhavan, Khanpur, Ahmedabad 380001. **T:** 91 79 30410000
W: http://www.gujaratsamachar.com
Freq: Daily; **Circ:** 380002 Not Audited
Editorial Profile: Covers local and world news, sports, business, entertainment, etc.
Language (s): Gujarati
DAILY NEWSPAPER

Gujarat Today Daily

Editorial: Gujarat Today, 33/A, Shah-e-Alam, Ahmedabad 380028. **T:** 91 79 25320330
E: gujarattoday@yahoo.com
W: http://www.gujarattodaydaily.com
Freq: Daily; **Circ:** 61001 Not Audited
Editor: Yunus Patel; **Publisher:** S. Tirmizi
Editorial Profile: Covers the latest news in local, regional, international and national, sports.
Language (s): Gujarati
DAILY NEWSPAPER

Gujarat Vaibhav

Editorial: 6 Mill Officers Colony, Ashram Road, Post Bag No. 9, Ahmedabad 380009.
T: 91 79 2658-9474 **E:** gvd@icenet.net
Freq: Daily; **Circ:** 182617 Not Audited
Editor: V. V. Videh
Editorial Profile: Covers local and world news, sports and etc.
Language (s): Hindi
DAILY NEWSPAPER

Halat-E-Watan

Editorial: B-2/31, 3rd Floor, Taksal Theaters Building, Nadesar, Varanasi 221002.
T: 91 5422500887
Freq: Daily; **Circ:** 62003 Not Audited
Editor: Sandeep Gupta
Editorial Profile: Daily Urdu newspaper.
Language (s): Urdu
DAILY NEWSPAPER

Handelsblatt India

Editorial: 123 Sunder Nagar, 1st Floor, New Delhi 110003. **T:** 91 11 51507270
E: oliver.mueller@airtelbroadband.in
W: http://www.handelsblatt.de
Freq: Daily
Editorial Profile: Indian bureau of German newspaper. Covers finance, economics and current news.
Language (s): German
DAILY NEWSPAPER

Haribhoomi

Editorial: 330 Vinay Nagar, Bypass Road, Rohtak 124001. **T:** 91 1262295801
E: rohtak@haribhoomi.com
W: http://www.haribhoomi.com
Freq: Daily
Editorial Profile: One of the most read Hindi newspapers, covers national news.
Language (s): Hindi
DAILY NEWSPAPER

Herald Young Leader

Editorial: C-101, B.G. Tower, O/S Delhi Gate, Ahmedabad 380004. **T:** 91 7925625000
Freq: Daily; **Circ:** 347002 Not Audited
Editor in Chief: Bharat Bhushan Chhajjer
Editorial Profile: Covers local and world news, analytical articles, film news and views, sports, commercial views.
Language (s): Hindi
DAILY NEWSPAPER

Himachal Times
Editorial: Himachal Times Complex, 21 Rajpur Road, Dehradun 248001. **T:** 91 1352651487
W: http://www.theimachaltimes.com
Freq: Daily; **Circ:** 54002 Not Audited
Editor: Ashok Pandhi; **Editor in Chief:** Vijay Pandhi
Editorial Profile: Covers the local, national and international news.
Language (s): Hindi
DAILY NEWSPAPER

The Hindu
Owner: Hindu Group (The)
Editorial: The Hindu Group, Kasturi Buildings, 859/860, Anna Salai, Chennai 600002.
T: 91 44 2857-6300
E: thehindu@thehindu.com
W: http://www.thehindu.com
Freq: Daily Not Audited
City Editor: Ramya Kannan; **Editor:** Malini Parthasarathy; **Editor in Chief:** N. Ravi
Editorial Profile: Established in 1878, covers the latest local and world news, with features on business, sports and the arts.
Language (s): English
DAILY NEWSPAPER

Hindu Business Line - Bangalore Edition
Editorial: The Hindu Group, 19 & 21 Bhagwan Mahaveer Road (Infantry Road), Bangalore 560001. **T:** 91 8022864240
W: http://www.thehindubusinessline.com
Freq: Daily
Bureau Chief: V.K. Varadarajan
Editorial Profile: Covers the latest in local and world, money, banking, marketing, technology, economics and government.
Language (s): Hindi
DAILY NEWSPAPER

The Hindu Business Line - Chennai Edition
Owner: The Hindu Group
Editorial: Kasturi Buildings, 859/860, Anna Salai, Chennai 600002. **T:** 91 44 28413344
E: bleditor@thehindu.co.in
W: http://www.thehindubusinessline.com
Freq: Daily Not Audited
Editorial Profile: Established in 1994 and covers the latest in local and world, money, banking, marketing, technology, economics, industry, logistic and government.
Language (s): English
DAILY NEWSPAPER

The Hindu Business Line - New Delhi Edition
Editorial: The Hindu Group, 3rd Floor, PTI Building, 4 Parliament Street, New Delhi 110001. **T:** 91 1143579797
W: http://www.thehindubusinessline.com
Freq: Daily
Editorial Profile: Covers the latest in local and world, money, banking, marketing, technology and economics.
Language (s): English
DAILY NEWSPAPER

The Hindu Business Line- Hyderabad Edition
Editorial: 6-3-879b, Begumpet, Hyderabad 500016. **T:** 91 22 22885593
W: http://www.thehindubusinessline.com
Freq: Daily
Editor: K. Venugopal
Editorial Profile: Covers business topics.
Language (s): English
DAILY NEWSPAPER

The Hindu- Hyderabad Edition
Editorial: 6-3-879b, Begumpet, Hyderabad 500016. **T:** 91 44 28576300
Freq: Daily
Editor: S. Sreevatsan
Editorial Profile: Covers the latest local, regional, international, and national news.
Language (s): Hindi
DAILY NEWSPAPER

Hindustan - Lucknow Edition
Editorial: The Hindustan Times House, 25 Ashok Marg, Lucknow 226001.
T: 91 5222205717
E: naveenjoshi@hindustantimes.com
W: http://www.hindustantimes.com
Freq: Daily; **Circ:** 292698 Not Audited
Editor: Naveen Joshi
Editorial Profile: Covers local and world news, sports, business, entertainment, lifestyle, travel, events and etc.
Language (s): English
DAILY NEWSPAPER

Hindustan - Patna Edition
Owner: Hindustan Times Media Ltd.
Editorial: Hindustan Times Media Ltd., Searchlight Building, Budh Marg, Patna 800001. **T:** 91 6122223434
W: http://www.hindustantimes.com
Freq: Daily; **Circ:** 292698 Not Audited
Editor in Chief: Akku Shrivastav
Editorial Profile: Covers local, National, Regional and International news.
Language (s): Hindi
DAILY NEWSPAPER

The Hindustan Times - Bhopal Edition
Owner: HT Media Ltd
Editorial: Park Centra Bldg, 7th Floor, Sector 30, Delhi-Jaipur Highway, Bhopal 122001.
T: 91 124 3954700 **W:** http://www.htmedia.in
Freq: Daily
Editorial Profile: Established in 1924, serves as one of India's most widely read newspapers with news, information, analysis and entertainment.
Language (s): Hindi
DAILY NEWSPAPER

The Hindustan Times - Kolkata Edition
Owner: HT Media Ltd
Editorial: HT Media Ltd., 50 Chowringhee Road, Kolkata 700071. **T:** 91 3322827315
E: feedback@hindustantimes.com
W: http://www.hindustantimes.com
Freq: Daily; **Circ:** 117001 Not Audited
Editor: Rajiv Bagchi
Editorial Profile: Established in 1924, serves as one of India's most widely read newspapers with news, information, analysis and entertainment.
Language (s): English
DAILY NEWSPAPER

Hindustan Times - Mumbai Edition
Owner: HT Media Ltd
Editorial: HT Media Ltd, LJ Cross Rd, No. 1, Mahim, Mumbai 400016. **T:** 91 22 43519500
W: http://www.hindustantimes.com
Freq: Daily
Editor: Soumya Bhattacharya
Editorial Profile: Established in 1924, serves as one of India's most widely read newspapers with news, information, analysis and entertainment.
Language (s): English
DAILY NEWSPAPER

The Hindustan Times - New Delhi Edition
Owner: HT Media Ltd
Editorial: Hindustan Times House, 18-20, K.G. Marg, New Delhi 110001. **T:** 91 11 2336-1234
W: http://www.hindustantimes.com
Freq: Daily; **Circ:** 566585 Not Audited
Editor: Sonal Kalra; **Editor in Chief:** Sanjoy Narayan; **Editor:** Poonam Saxena
Editorial Profile: Established in 1924, serves as one of India's most widely read newspapers with news, information, analysis and entertainment.
Language (s): English
DAILY NEWSPAPER

The Hindustan Times - Patna Edition
Owner: HT Media Ltd
Editorial: Searchlight Building, Budh Marg, Patna 800001. **T:** 91 6122223314
E: ashokmishra@hindustantimes.com
W: http://www.hindustantimes.com
Freq: Daily; **Circ:** 500002 Not Audited
Editor: Sonal Kalra; **Editor:** Poonam Saxena
Editorial Profile: Established in 1924, serves as one of India's most widely read newspapers with news, information, analysis and entertainment.
Language (s): English
DAILY NEWSPAPER

The Hitavada
Editorial: Pandit Jawaharlal Nehru Marg, Wardha Road, Nagpur 440012.
T: 91 7122435737
E: hitavada_ngp@sancharnet.in
W: http://www.ehitavadaonline.com
Freq: Daily; **Circ:** 60001 Not Audited
Editor: Vijay Phanshikar
Editorial Profile: Covers news.
Language (s): English
DAILY NEWSPAPER

HT Mumbai
Owner: HT Media Ltd.
Editorial: HT Media Ltd., 2nd Floor, Mahalaxmi Engineering Estate, Lady Jamshedji First Cross Road, Mahim (W), Mumbai 400016.
T: 91 2266539200
E: samar@hindustantimes.com

W: http://www.hindustantimes.com
Freq: Daily; **Circ:** 200002 Not Audited
Editor: Samar Halarnkar; **Editor:** Akshay Sawai
Editorial Profile: Covers the news in local and international, business, sports, travel, entertainment and etc.
Language (s): English
DAILY NEWSPAPER

Humara Awam
Editorial: Awam, Public Garden Road, Nampally, Hyderabad 500001.
T: 91 4055612734
Freq: Daily; **Circ:** 50001 Not Audited
Editor: K.M. Arifuddin
Editorial Profile: Covers local, regional, international and national news.
Language (s): Urdu
DAILY NEWSPAPER

Indian Express - Chandigarh Edition
Editorial: Plot No. C-5, Institutional Area, Sector-6, Chandigarh 134109.
T: 91 1725024400 **E:** expresschd@gmail.com
W: http://www.expressindia.com
Freq: Daily; **Circ:** 80001 Not Audited
Editor: Vipin Pubby
Editorial Profile: Established in 1932, covers the latest news from India with exclusive current headlines on hot topics, breaking news, business, sports, politics and entertainment.
Language (s): English
DAILY NEWSPAPER

Indian Express - New Delhi Edition
Editorial: The Indian Express Limited, 9&10, Bhadur Shah Zafar Marg, Express Building, ITO, New Delhi 110002. **T:** 91 11 23702100
E: editor@expressindia.com
W: http://www.expressindia.com
Freq: Daily; **Circ:** 100002 Not Audited
Editor: Seema Chishti; **Editor:** Vandana Kalra; **Editor:** Coomi Kapoor; **Editor:** Unni Rajan Shanker; **Bureau Chief:** P. Vaidyanathan
Editorial Profile: Established in 1932, covers the latest news from India with exclusive current headlines on hot topics, breaking news, business, sports, politics and entertainment.
Language (s): English
DAILY NEWSPAPER

Indian Punch
Editorial: Upper Bilasi Town, Jharkhand, Deoghar 814117. **T:** 91 6432 246216
E: indianpunch2000@yahoo.com
Freq: Daily; **Circ:** 65002 Not Audited
Editorial Profile: This Is The Only Newspaper Represents The People Of Santhal Pargana. It Publishes The Current News Related To Political Affairs Sports And Education Crime Culture General Human Interest Stories And Many Others Fields.
Language (s): Hindi
DAILY NEWSPAPER

Indinon
Editorial: I-91, Lubna House, Batla House, Okhla, New Delhi 110025. **T:** 91 11 2379-2121
E: editor@thesedaysindia.com
Freq: Daily
Editor in Chief: S. Asif
Editorial Profile: Indinon is a newspaper which covers the news in local and world.
Language (s): Hindi
DAILY NEWSPAPER

Ingredients South Asia
Editorial: Saffron Media Private Limited, 2nd Floor, Laura Building, 1st Dhobi Talao Lane, Dhobi Talao, Mumbai 400002.
T: 91 22 42202800
E: pnvnair@saffronmedia.in
W: http://www.saffronmedia.in
Freq: Weekly
Editor: P. Nair
Editorial Profile: Ingredients south Asia is a newspaper which focused on Food & Beverage News, the only newspaper for the F&B sector, and Hospital Equipment & Solutions – the indispensable buyer's guide for the time constrained hospital practitioner
Language (s): Hindi
NEWSPAPER

International Business Times
Editorial: 248, 3rd floor, Defence Colony, 80 Ft. Rd, Bangalore 560008. **T:** 91 80 43100900
E: info@ibtimes.co.in
W: http://www.ibtimes.co.in
Freq: Daily
Editorial Profile: Covers the latest headlines pertaining to international and national news.
Language (s): English
DAILY NEWSPAPER

The International New York Times - New Delhi
Editorial: 56 Jan Path, New Delhi 110001.
T: 91 1123321965
Bureau Chief: Ellen Barry
DAILY NEWSPAPER

Iris Business Services
Editorial: T-131, Tower 1, 3rd Floor, International Infotech Park, Vashi, Navi Mumbai, Mumbai 400703. **T:** 91 22 27814436
Editor: Padma Prakash
Editorial Profile: IRIS owns and manages one of India's most comprehensive financial information databases, covering the universe of publicly traded companies, mutual funds, markets reference data to a live news service on Indian business, markets and the economy.
Language (s): English
DAILY NEWSPAPER

Jadeed Indinon
Editorial: I-91, Lubna House, Batla House, Okhla, New Delhi 110001. **T:** 91 1123792121
E: editor@thesedaysindia.com
Freq: Daily
Editor in Chief: S. Asif; **Editor:** R. Singh
Editorial Profile: Covers national and international news.
Language (s): Urdu
DAILY NEWSPAPER

Jag Bani, Jalandhar
Editorial: Hind Samachar Building, Civil Lines, Jalandhar 144001. **T:** 91 1812280104
Freq: Daily; **Circ:** 300001 Not Audited
Editor in Chief: Vijay Kumar Chopra
Editorial Profile: Jag Bani is a daily newspaper in Jalandhar, India covering local news, sports, business, jobs, and community events. The web site is presented in the Punjabi language.
Language (s): Punjabi
DAILY NEWSPAPER

Jai Hind
Editorial: Jai Hind Press Building, Babubhai Shah Marg, Rajkot 360001. **T:** 91 2813048684
E: editor@jaihinddaily.com
W: http://www.jaihinddaily.com
Freq: Daily; **Circ:** 50001 Not Audited
Editor in Chief: Pradeep Shah
Editorial Profile: Daily Gujarati newspaper
Language (s): Gujarati
DAILY NEWSPAPER

Jalte Deep
Editorial: Jalte Deep Building, Jalori Gate, Jodhpur 342003. **T:** 91 291 2435896
E: jaltedeep@sancharnet.in
W: http://www.manak.org
Freq: Daily; **Circ:** 50001 Not Audited
Editor in Chief: Padam Mehta
Editorial Profile: Covers the news, culture lifestyle and etc.
Language (s): Hindi
DAILY NEWSPAPER

Jam-E-Jamshed
Editorial: 2nd Fl, Arya Samaj Bhavan, 232 Perin Nariman St, Maharashtra, Mumbai 400001. **T:** 91 22 2222692572
E: jame1832@rediffmail.com
Freq: Weekly; **Circ:** 50003 Not Audited
Editor: Rusi Dhondy
Editorial Profile: Covers local and world news.
Language (s): English
NEWSPAPER

Janmabhoomi
Editorial: Janmabhoomi Bhavan, Janmabhoomi Marg, Fort, Mumbai 400001.
T: 91 22 22570831 **E:** jbhoomi@yahoo.com
W: http://pravasi.janmabhoominewspapers.com/
Freq: 2 Times/Week; **Circ:** 62001 Not Audited
Editor: Yogesh Pandya; **Editor in Chief:** Kundan Vyas
Editorial Profile: Janma bhoomi Newspaper (epaper) is a Gujarati evening Daily newspaper from Inida which focused on the latest news in local and international.
Language (s): Gujarati
NEWSPAPER

Janmabhoomi Pravasi
Editorial: Janmabhoomi Bhavan, Janmabhoomi Marg, Fort, Mumbai 400001.
T: 91 22 22870831 **E:** jbhoomi@yahoo.com
W: http://pravasi.janmabhoominewspapers.com/
Freq: Weekly; **Circ:** 107001 Not Audited
Editor in Chief: Kundan Vyas
Editorial Profile: Covers local and world news.
Language (s): Gujarati
NEWSPAPER

Janmabhumi
Editorial: 34/114 Perandoor Road, Elamakkara, P.O., Cochin 682026.
T: 91 484 3219925 **E:** janmabhumi@vsnl.in
W: http://www.janmabhumidaily.com
Freq: Daily; **Circ:** 120003 Not Audited
Editor in Chief: Hari Kartha; **Editor:** Leela Menon
Editorial Profile: Covers Cultural topics, Sports, Karshikam (Agriculture), Samakalikam (Recent Events Valuations), Garhikam (House) etc.
Language (s): Malayalam
DAILY NEWSPAPER

Janpath Samachar
Editorial: Janpath House, Seth Srilal Market, Siliguri 734401. **T:** 91 353 22544130
E: janpath_samachar@bsnl.in
W: http://www.janpathsamachar.com
Freq: Daily; **Circ:** 51002 Not Audited
Editor in Chief: Rajendra Baid
Editorial Profile: Covers news and related topics.
Language (s): Hindi
DAILY NEWSPAPER

Jharkhand Classified Weekly
Editorial: 55 Baralal Street, Upper Bazar, Ranchi 834001. **T:** 91 651 2206320
E: news@ranchiexpress.com
W: http://www.ranchiexpress.com
Freq: Weekly; **Circ:** 55002 Not Audited
Editor: Balbir Dutt; **Editor:** Manish Maroo; **Editor:** Chandreshwar Singh
Editorial Profile: Covers the variety of topics such a the latest news in local and international, regional, automobile, business, career, and entertainments
Language (s): English
NEWSPAPER

Kannada Prabha
Editorial: Express Building, 1 Queen's Road, Bangalore 560001. **T:** 91 80 22866893
E: bexpress@bgl.vsnl.net.in
W: http://www.kannadaprabha.com
Freq: Daily; **Circ:** 114808 Not Audited
Editor: Shiva Subramanyam
Editorial Profile: Covers the latest news in local, regional, international and national, and etc.
Language (s): Kannada
DAILY NEWSPAPER

Karmakshetra
Editorial: 29/1-A, Old Ballygunge, 2nd Lane, Kolkata 700019. **T:** 91 33 22835526
E: swarna@cal2.vsnl.net.in
W: http://www.bhraman.com
Freq: Weekly; **Circ:** 115002 Not Audited
Editor in Chief: Amarendra Chakravorty
Editorial Profile: Provides information on business, economics, labor and industrial relations.
Language (s): Bengali
NEWSPAPER

The Kashmir Times
Editorial: Kashmir Times Building, Residency Road, Jammu 180001. **T:** 91 191 5247379
E: vbhasin@sancharnet.in
Freq: Daily; **Circ:** 160003 Not Audited
Editor in Chief: Prabodh Jamwal
Editorial Profile: Covers the latest local, regional, international and national news.
Language (s): English
DAILY NEWSPAPER

Kerala Kaumudi
Editorial: P.O. Box No. 77, Pettah, Thiruvananthapuram 695024.
T: 91 4712461010 **E:** editor@ekaumudi.com
W: http://www.kaumudi.com
Freq: Daily; **Circ:** 141193 Not Audited
Editor in Chief: M. Mani
Editorial Profile: Covers business, the latest news, sports, automobile, entertainment, etc.
Language (s): Malayalam
DAILY NEWSPAPER

Krishak Jagat - Bhopal Edition
Editorial: 14 Indira Press Complex, M.P. Nagar, Bhopal 462011. **T:** 91 755 2768452
E: info@krishakjagat.org
W: http://www.krishakjagat.org
Freq: Weekly; **Circ:** 1500003 Not Audited
Editor in Chief: Vijay Bondriya; **Editor:** Sunil Gangrade
Editorial Profile: Krishak Jagat - Bhopal Edition is a newspaper which covers the news, Agribusiness, Engineering, Agriculture & Farming and Gardening.
Language (s): Hindi
NEWSPAPER

Kutchmitra
Editorial: Chief of News Bureau, Kutchmitra Bhavan, Near Indira Park, Bhuj 370001.
T: 91 2832 252090 **E:** kutchmitra@yahoo.com
W: http://www.kutchmitradaily.com
Freq: Daily; **Circ:** 50002 Not Audited
Editor: Kirti Khatri
Editorial Profile: Covers the latest news in local, regional, national and international and lifestyle.
Language (s): Gujarati
DAILY NEWSPAPER

Lokmat - Aurangabad
Editorial: Lokmat Bhavan, Jalna Road, Aurangabad 431210. **T:** 91 242 2477264
W: http://onlinenews1.lokmat.com
Freq: Daily; **Circ:** 300002 Not Audited
Editor in Chief: Vijay Darda; **Editor:** Dinakar Raikar
Editorial Profile: Discusses news in local, regional, international and national, etc.
Language (s): Hindi
DAILY NEWSPAPER

Lokmat Times - Nagpur Edition
Editorial: Lokmat Bhavan, Pt. J. Nehru Marg, Nagpur 440012. **T:** 91 7122523527
E: lokmat@bom2.vsnl.net.in
Freq: Daily; **Circ:** 166971 Not Audited
Editor in Chief: Vijay Darda
Editorial Profile: Lokmat was conceptualized and started by Loknayak Bapuji Aney as a weapon to fight the British imperialism during the freedom movement of India. The name 'Lokmat' was given by the great freedom fighter and literary person Bal Gangadhar Tilak ("Freedom is my birth right and I shall have it") when the publication was first started as a handwritten newspaper from Yavatmal, then a little known town in Maharashtra. Inspired by the great luminaries of the freedom movement, Late Shri Jawaharlal Darda took over this fortnightly published newspaper in 1953. The former Prime Minister of India, Pt. Jawaharlal Nehru formally inaugurated Lokmat as a daily publication in 1958 at Yavatmal and on December 15th 1971, the first full fledge edition was started from Nagpur, the winter capital of one of India's largest and most affluent states - Maharashtra. From its humble beginning in 1971, the publication eventually emerged as the No.1 circulated and read daily of Maharashtra reaching every corner of the state and catering to the news and entertainment needs of millions of its readers everyday.
Language (s): English
DAILY NEWSPAPER

Lokmat, Jalgaon
Editorial: Lokmat Bhavan, C-19, MIDC Area, Aurangabad Road, Jalgaon 425003.
T: 91 257 2273013 **W:** http://www.lokmat.com
Freq: Daily; **Circ:** 76751 Not Audited
Editor: Vijay Bawiskar; **Editor in Chief:** Vijay Darda; **Editor:** Sudhir Mahajan
Editorial Profile: Covers the latest news in local, regional, International and national, business, and etc.
Language (s): Marathi
DAILY NEWSPAPER

Loksatta
Editorial: Express Towers, Nariman Point, Mumbai 400021. **T:** 91 22 22022627
E: loksatta@expressindia.com
W: http://www.loksatta.com
Freq: Daily; **Circ:** 500002 Not Audited
Editor: Kumar Ketkar
Editorial Profile: Covers the latest local and world news, sports, industry and etc.
Language (s): Marathi
DAILY NEWSPAPER

Maalai Malar
Editorial: Rani Buildings, 1091 Periyar EVR High Road, Chennai 600007.
T: 91 44 25321184
E: malareditor@yahoo.co.in
W: http://www.maalaimalar.com
Freq: Daily; **Circ:** 160002 Not Audited
Editor in Chief: K. Chandragopal
Editorial Profile: Covers local and world news, sports, business and etc.
Language (s): Hindi
DAILY NEWSPAPER

Madhyamam
Editorial: P.O. Box No. 1708, Silver Hills, Calicut/kozhikode 673012. **T:** 91 4952731500
W: http://www.madhyamam.com
Freq: Daily; **Circ:** 1161621 Not Audited
Editor: O. Rahman
Editorial Profile: Covers the latest news in local, regional, international and national, business, sports, and etc
Language (s): Malayalam
DAILY NEWSPAPER

Maharashtra Times
Editorial: Dr D N Road, Fort Mumbai, Dr D N Road, Fort Mumbai, Mumbai 400001.
T: 91 22 66354245 **E:** colourmt@gmail.com
W: http://www.maharashtratimes.com
Freq: Daily; **Circ:** 200001 Not Audited
Editor: Meenal Baghel; **Editor:** Chandrima Pal; **Editor in Chief:** Abhijit Pradhan; **Editor:** Bharat Raut; **Editor:** Mayank Shekhar; **Bureau Chief:** C. Unnikrishnan
Editorial Profile: Provides the latest news in Marathi about the Maharashtra state of India.
Language (s): Marathi
DAILY NEWSPAPER

Mail Today
Editorial: Mediaplex FC-8, Sector - 16A, New Delhi 110001. **T:** 91 11 43530800
W: http://www.mailtoday.in
Freq: Daily; **Circ:** 120002 Not Audited
Editor: Bharat Bhushan
Editorial Profile: Covers the latest local and world news, and a variety of topics through a wide range of sections, including Money Mail, Good Health, Femail and Travel Mail.
Language (s): English
DAILY NEWSPAPER

Malayala Manorama
Editorial: Manorama Buildings, K.K. Road, P.B. No. 26, Kottayam 686001. **T:** 91 4812563646
E: editorial@mm.co.in
W: http://www.manoramaonline.com
Freq: Daily; **Circ:** 1296361 Not Audited
Editor-in-Charge: K. Narayan
Editorial Profile: Covers international and national news.
Language (s): Malayalam
DAILY NEWSPAPER

Mathrubhumi Daily
Editorial: M.J. Krishnamohan Building, K.P. Kesavamenon Road, Calicut/kozhikode 673001. **T:** 91 49 52367744
E: mbiclt@mpp.co.in
W: http://www.mathrubhumi.com
Freq: Daily; **Circ:** 880003 Not Audited
Editor: K. Sreedharan Nair
Editorial Profile: Covers the latest news in local, regional, international and national, business, sports, entertainment, education, health and etc.
Language (s): Malayalam
DAILY NEWSPAPER

Metro Now
Editorial: Metropolitan Media Company Pvt. Ltd., 9-10, Express Building, Ist Floor, Bahadur Shah Zafar Marg, New Delhi 110002.
T: 91 1142512153
W: http://www.metronow.co.in
Freq: Daily
Editor: Kamlesh Singh
Editorial Profile: Focuses on local and international news.
Language (s): English
DAILY NEWSPAPER

Mid Day
Editorial: Mid-day Multimedia Limited, Dr. S.S. Rao Road, Opposite Mahatma Gandhi Hospital, Parel, Mumbai 400012.
T: 91 22 67017171 **E:** cs@mid-day.com
W: http://www.mid-day.com
Freq: Daily; **Circ:** 140003 Not Audited
Editor: Dhiman Chattopadhyay
Editorial Profile: Focuses on general news, entertainments, relationships, lifestyle, sports and health.
Language (s): English
DAILY NEWSPAPER

mint
Owner: HT Media Ltd.
Editorial: HT Media Ltd, 16th Floor, 18-20 Kasturba Gandhi Marg, New Delhi 110001.
T: 91 11 66561234
E: newsroom@livemint.com
W: http://www.livemint.com
Freq: Daily; **Circ:** 85003 Not Audited
Editor: Natasha Badhwar; **Editor:** Leslie D'Monte; **Editor:** Sukumar Ranganathan
Editorial Profile: Launched in February 2007, covers business news in India. Shares news and information by The Wall Street Journal through an exclusive partnership.
Language (s): English
DAILY NEWSPAPER

Mumbai Mirror
Editorial: 4th Floor, The Times of India Building, Dr. D N Road, Mumbai 400001.
T: 91 022 66353535
E: meenal.baghel@timesgroup.com
W: http://www.mumbaimirror.com
Freq: Daily; **Circ:** 558437 Not Audited
Editor: Meenal Baghel; **Editor:** Dinesh Narayanan; **Editor:** Sudharak Olwe; **Editor:** Chandrima Pal; **Editor:** Kunal Pradhan; **Editor:** Bharat Raut; **Editor:** Mayank Shekhar; **Bureau Chief:** C. Unnikrishnan
Editorial Profile: Serves as the largest compact newspaper in Mumbai, featuring local news, sports, entertainment, tech, health and business topics.
Language (s): English
DAILY NEWSPAPER

Munsif Daily
Editorial: 5-9-62, Khan Lateef Khan Estate, FMC Road, Hyderabad 500001.
T: 91 40 66660005 **E:** munsifdaily@eth.net
W: http://www.munsifdaily.com
Freq: Daily; **Circ:** 59002 Not Audited
Editor in Chief: Lateef Khan
Editorial Profile: Covers the latest local, regional, international and national news, sports and etc.
Language (s): Urdu
DAILY NEWSPAPER

My Mobile Infomedia Pvt. Ltd.
Editorial: #25 Shankar Market, Connaught Palace, New Delhi 110001. **T:** 91 11 46206161
W: http://www.mymobile.co.in
Freq: Weekly
Editorial Profile: Offers news, reviews and views on mobile phones, mobile phone prices, value added services, cellular services, tariff plans and reviews of mobile applications and games.
Language (s): English
NEWSPAPER

Mysooru Mithra
Editorial: 15C, Industrial A-Layout, Bannimantap, Mysore 570015.
T: 91 821 2496520
E: voice@starofmysore.com
W: http://www.starofmysore.com
Freq: Daily; **Circ:** 85002 Not Audited
Editor: K. Ganapathy
Editorial Profile: Mysooru Mithra is a newspaper which covers the latest news in local and world, sports and etc.
Language (s): Kannada
DAILY NEWSPAPER

Nai Dunia
Editorial: NaiDuna Media Put Ltd. 60/1, Babu Labhchand Chhajlani Marg, New Delhi 452009.
T: 91 731 2763111 **E:** delhi@naidunia.com
W: http://www.naidunia.com
Freq: Weekly; **Circ:** 59001 Not Audited
Editor: Shravan Garg; **Editor in Chief:** Shahid Siddiqui
Editorial Profile: Discusses news.
Language (s): Urdu
NEWSPAPER

Nava Bharat - Bhopal
Editorial: 3 Indira Press Complex, Maharana Pratap Nagar, Zone 1, Bhopal 462001.
T: 91 755 2551411
E: navabharatbhopal@gmail.com
W: http://www.navabharattimes.indiatimes.com
Freq: Daily; **Circ:** 75614 Not Audited
Editor in Chief: P.K. Maheshwari; **Editor:** Nishant Sharma
Editorial Profile: Brings news in Hindi from India and international news headlines, with top stories on business, politics, sports and entertainment.
Language (s): Hindi
DAILY NEWSPAPER

Nava Bharat - Jabalpur
Editorial: Nava Bharat Bhavan, Opp. Bus Stand, Napier Town, Jabalpur 482001.
T: 91 761 4005111
E: navabharatbhopal@gmail.com
W: http://www.navbharattimes.indiatimes.com
Freq: Daily; **Circ:** 84867 Not Audited
Editor in Chief: P.K. Maheshwari; **Editor:** Abhi Manoj
Editorial Profile: Brings news in Hindi from India and international news headlines, with top stories on business, politics, sports and entertainment.
Language (s): Hindi
DAILY NEWSPAPER

Nava Bharat - Nagpur
Editorial: Nava Bharat, Chhatrapati Chowk, Vardha Road, Nagpur 440025.
T: 91 712 2726677
E: navabharatbhopal@gmail.com
W: http://www.navabharat.net
Freq: Daily; **Circ:** 111083 Not Audited
Publisher: Vinod Maheshwari

Editorial Profile: Brings news in Hindi from India and international news headlines, with top stories on business, politics, sports and entertainment.
Language (s): Hindi
DAILY NEWSPAPER

Nava Bharat - Raipur
Editorial: Nava Bharat Bhavan Press Complex, G E Road, Raipur 492001. **T:** 91 771 2535544
E: navabharatbhopal@gmail.com
W: http://www.navabharat.net
Freq: Daily; **Circ:** 89099 Not Audited
Editor: Anal Shukla
Editorial Profile: Brings news in Hindi from India and international news headlines, with top stories on business, politics, sports and entertainment.
Language (s): Hindi
DAILY NEWSPAPER

Navashakti
Editorial: 215, Free Press House Journal Marg, Nariman Point, Mumbai 400021.
T: 91 22 2287-4566 **E:** fpj@vsnl.com
Freq: Daily; **Circ:** 60004 Not Audited
Editor: Prakash Kulkami; **Editor:** Mahesh Mahatare
Editorial Profile: Discusses the latest local, regional, national and international news.
Language (s): Marathi
DAILY NEWSPAPER

Navbharat Times - New Delhi Edition
Editorial: Navbharat Times, Indian Express Building, IInd Floor, Bahadur Shah Zafar Marg, New Delhi 110003. **T:** 91 1143505340
W: http://www.navbharattimes.com
Freq: Daily; **Circ:** 400001 Not Audited
Editorial Profile: Covers local and international, business, sports, entertainment, technology, lifestyle news and etc.
Language (s): Hindi
DAILY NEWSPAPER

Navbharat Times- Mumbai Edition
Editorial: P.O. Box No. 213, Dr. D.N. Road, Mumbai 400001. **T:** 91 22 66353535
W: http://www.timesofindia.com
Freq: Daily; **Circ:** 166165 Not Audited
Publisher: Sam Dastoor; **Editor:** Sachindra Tripathi
Editorial Profile: Covers news and related topics.
Language (s): Hindi
DAILY NEWSPAPER

Neighbourhood Flash
Owner: TEJ Bandhu Group
Editorial: TEJ Bandhu Group, 8-B Bahadur Shah Zafar Marg, New Delhi 110002.
T: 91 11 52225111
Freq: Daily; **Circ:** 125002 Not Audited
Editor: Poonam Singh
Editorial Profile: Covers news topics.
Language (s): English
DAILY NEWSPAPER

The New Indian Express - Bangalore Edition
Owner: Express Network Private Limited
Editorial: Express Network Private Limited, Express Building, No. 1 Queen's Road, Bangalore 560001. **T:** 91 8022866893
W: http://www.newindpress.com
Freq: Daily; **Circ:** 500002 Not Audited
Editorial Profile: The New Indian Express is a newspaper which covers the news in local and world, business, lifestyle, sports and technology.
Language (s): English
DAILY NEWSPAPER

The New Indian Express - Chennai Edition
Editorial: 29 second Main Road Ampattur Industrial Estate, Chennai 600058.
T: 91 4423457601 **E:** editor@expressindia.com
W: http://www.indian-express.com
Freq: Daily; **Circ:** 310786 Not Audited
Editor: Babu Jayakumar; **Editor:** Shiv Kumar
Editorial Profile: Covers the news in local and world, business, lifestyle, sports and technology with a focus on Chennai
Language (s): English
DAILY NEWSPAPER

Nijukti Khabar
Editorial: TS 3/193, Zone B, Mancheswar Industrial Estate, Bhubaneshwar 700010.
T: 91 674 2582532
E: nijuktikhabar@gmail.com
W: http://www.nijuktikhabar.net
Freq: Weekly; **Circ:** 97102 Not Audited
Editor: Manoranjan Das

Editorial Profile: Covers employment information.
Language (s): English
NEWSPAPER

Nishpaksh Samachar Jyoti - Varanasi
Editorial: 3rd Floor Taksal Theaters Building, Nadesar, Varanasi 221002. **T:** 91 542 2504676
Freq: Daily; **Circ:** 65003 Not Audited
Editor: Suman Gupta
Editorial Profile: Covers general news.
Language (s): Hindi
DAILY NEWSPAPER

Nyaydhish
Editorial: 1A, Patrika Marg, Civil lines, Allahabad 211001. **T:** 91 5322606194
E: nyaydhish@sancharnet.in
Freq: Daily; **Circ:** 140001 Not Audited
Editor: R. Jindal
Editorial Profile: Covers news.
Language (s): Hindi
DAILY NEWSPAPER

Orissa Times
Editorial: Orissa Times, A-114 Unit-III, Kharvelanagar, Bhubaneshwar 751001.
T: 91 674 2380686
E: orissatimes@rediffmail.com
Freq: Daily; **Circ:** 98701 Not Audited
Editor: R. Shastry
Editorial Profile: Covers the latest local and international news.
Language (s): English
DAILY NEWSPAPER

Outlookindia.com
Editorial: The Outlook Group, AB-10 Safdarjung Enclave, New Delhi 110029.
T: 91 011 26191421
W: http://www.outlookindia.com
Editor: Sundeep Dougal; **Editor:** Krishna Prasad
Editorial Profile: Outlookindia.com is a newspaper which cover the news in local and international, business, sports, art, entertainment, society and etc.
Language (s): English
DAILY NEWSPAPER

Panchjanya
Editorial: Sanskriti Bhawan, D B Gupta Marg, Jhandawala, New Delhi 110055.
T: 91 11 23514244
E: editor.panchjanya@gmail.com
W: http://www.panchjanya.com
Freq: Weekly; **Circ:** 70003 Not Audited
Editor in Chief: Baldev Sharma
Editorial Profile: Covers the latest news in local and world, politics and etc.
Language (s): Hindi
NEWSPAPER

Parivartan Bharti
Editorial: LG-101 Bharat Chamber, 70 Scindia House, Connaught Circus, New Delhi 110001.
T: 91 11 23350940
Freq: Daily; **Circ:** 75002 Not Audited
Editorial Profile: Covers local news, international, entertainment and etc.
Language (s): Hindi
DAILY NEWSPAPER

Phulchhab
Editorial: Phulchhab Bhavan, Mahatma Gandhi Road, Near Parsi Agyari, Rajkot 360001.
T: 91 281 2444611
Freq: Daily; **Circ:** 66009 Not Audited
Editor: Kaushik Mehta
Editorial Profile: Covering local news, sports, business, jobs, and community events. The web site is presented in the Gujarati language.
Language (s): Gujarati
DAILY NEWSPAPER

The Pioneer
Editorial: Second Floor, Link House, 3, Bahadur Shah Zafar Marg, New Delhi 110002.
T: 91 11 23 75 52 71
W: http://www.dailypioneer.com
Freq: Daily; **Circ:** 83007 Not Audited
Editor in Chief: Chandan Mitra
Editorial Profile: Founded in 1865, covers the latest news in local and world, business and sports. Notable historic staff include Winston Churchill as a war correspondent during the second Boer War and Rudyard Kipling as an assistant editor.
Language (s): English
DAILY NEWSPAPER

Prabhat Khabar
Editorial: 15-P, Kokar Industrial Area, Ranchi 834001. **T:** 91 651 3053100
E: ranchi@prabhatkhabar.in
W: http://www.prabhatkhabar.com

Freq: Daily; **Circ:** 350002 Not Audited
Editor in Chief: Harivansh Singh
Editorial Profile: Covers local and world news, sports, business, cinema, etc.
Language (s): Hindi
DAILY NEWSPAPER

Prajashakti
Editorial: House No. 1-8-664,21/1 Near RTC, Kalayan Mandapan, Azamabad Industria Area, Hyderabad 500020. **T:** 91 40 27665420
E: editor@prajashakti.com
W: http://www.indiapress.org
Freq: Daily; **Circ:** 100002 Not Audited
Publisher: V. Krishnaiah; **Editor:** S. Vinaykumar
Editorial Profile: Covers the latest news in local and world, business, sprots and etc.
Language (s): Telugu
DAILY NEWSPAPER

The Prajatantra
Editorial: Prajatantra Buildings, Bihari Bag, Cuttack 753002. **T:** 91 6712607183
Freq: Daily; **Circ:** 106233 Not Audited
Editor: Bhartruhari Mahtab
Editorial Profile: Covers the latest local, regional, international and national news.
Language (s): Oriya
DAILY NEWSPAPER

Prajavani
Owner: The Printers (Mysore) Private, Ltd.
Editorial: The Printers (Mysore) Private, Ltd.,75 Mahatma Gandhi Road, Bangalore 560001. **T:** 91 80 25880000
W: http://www.prajavani.net
Freq: Daily; **Circ:** 315583 Not Audited
Editor: Shanth Kumar
Editorial Profile: Covers variety of topics such as the latest news in regional, local, national and international, and etc.
Language (s): Kannada
DAILY NEWSPAPER

Pratah Kamal
Editorial: Sahu Road, Muzaffarpur 242633.
T: 91 621 2246433
E: pratahkamal@rediffmail.com
Freq: Daily; **Circ:** 65001 Not Audited
Editor: Brajesh Kumar; **Editor in Chief:** Radhamohan Thakur
Editorial Profile: Covers local and international news.
Language (s): Hindi
DAILY NEWSPAPER

Pratahkal
Editorial: 108 Inside Surajpole, Udaipur 313001. **T:** 91 294 2417417
E: pratahudr@gmail.com
W: http://www.pratahkal.com
Freq: Daily; **Circ:** 70002 Not Audited
Editor in Chief: Suresh Goyal
Editorial Profile: Discusses the latest local, regional, international and national news, etc.
Language (s): Hindi
DAILY NEWSPAPER

Pratahkal Mumbai
Editorial: Pratahkal, 543 Laxmi Plaza, Laxmi Industrial Estate, SAB TV Lane, New Link Road, Andheri (W), Mumbai 400053.
T: 91 22 23659926 **E:** pratahkal@gmail.com
W: http://www.pratahkal.com
Freq: Daily; **Circ:** 100001 Not Audited
Editor: Mahip Goyal
Editorial Profile: Covers the local news, sports, business, jobs, and community events.
Language (s): Hindi
DAILY NEWSPAPER

Pratidin
Editorial: TS3/193, Zone B, Mancheshwar Industrial Estate, Bhubaneshwar 751010.
T: 91 674 2587533
Freq: Daily; **Circ:** 75003 Not Audited
Editor: Gaurang Samantray
Editorial Profile: Covers local and world news, sports and entertainment.
Language (s): Oriya
DAILY NEWSPAPER

Pratidin Akhbar
Editorial: Devika, Rajapeth, Amravati 444606.
T: 91 7212560155 **E:** pratidin@indiatimes.com
Freq: Daily; **Circ:** 58001 Not Audited
Editor: Nanak Ahuja
Editorial Profile: Daily Hindi newspaper.
Language (s): Hindi
DAILY NEWSPAPER

Punjabi Tribune
Editorial: The Tribune House, Sector 29-C, Chandigarh 160030. **T:** 91 172 2655066
E: editorinchief@tribunemedia.com
W: http://www.tribuneindia.com

Freq: Daily; **Circ:** 70001 Not Audited
Editor in Chief: H.K. Dua; **Editor:** Varinder Walia
Editorial Profile: Covers the latest news in local, regional, international and national, sports, entertainment, business and etc.
Language (s): Punjabi
DAILY NEWSPAPER

Punya Nagri
Editorial: Ground Floor, Gala No. 22, Lalbaug, Industrial Estate, Parel, Mumbai 400012.
T: 91 2224715208
Freq: Daily; **Circ:** 495002 Not Audited
Editor: Subhash Harchekar; **Editor:** Sanjay Malme
Editorial Profile: Marathi Mumbai daily Newspaper
Language (s): Marathi
DAILY NEWSPAPER

Purvanchal Prahari
Editorial: G.S. Road, Ulubari, Guwahati 781007. **T:** 91 361 252-1556
W: http://www.glpublication.com
Freq: Daily; **Circ:** 135002 Not Audited
Editor: G. Agarwalla
Editorial Profile: Covers the latest news in local, regional, international and national news.
Language (s): Hindi
DAILY NEWSPAPER

Rajasthan Patrika - Ahmedabad
Editorial: Sri Krishna Center, 2nd Floor No. 18, Mithakhali, Near Pizza Hut, Navrangpura, Ahmedabad 380009. **T:** 91 79 30611566
W: http://www.rajasthanpatrika.com
Freq: Daily; **Circ:** 130001 Not Audited
Editor: Rajendra Naruka
Editorial Profile: Rajasthan Patrika is a newspaper which covers the local, regional, national and international news, and etc.
Language (s): Hindi
DAILY NEWSPAPER

Rajasthan Patrika - Bikaner
Editorial: 21 Gajner Road, Bikaner 334001.
T: 91 25 23982 **E:** info@rajasthanpatrika.com
W: http://www.rajasthanpatrika.com
Freq: Daily; **Circ:** 63117 Not Audited
Editor: Santosh Jain
Editorial Profile: Covers the local, regional, national and international news, and etc.
Language (s): Hindi
DAILY NEWSPAPER

Rajasthan Patrika - Chennai
Editorial: 2A, Wellington Estate, 24 Commander-in-Chief Road, Egmore, Chennai 600105. **T:** 91 44 28239859
W: http://www.rajasthanpatrika.com
Freq: Daily; **Circ:** 1100002 Not Audited
Editor: Dileep Chari
Editorial Profile: Covers the local, regional, national and international news, sports, business and etc.
Language (s): Hindi
DAILY NEWSPAPER

Rajasthan Patrika - Jaipur
Editorial: Kesargarh, J.L.N. Marg, Jaipur 302004. **T:** 91 141 39404142
W: http://www.rajasthanpatrika.com
Freq: Daily; **Circ:** 157594 Not Audited
Editor: Santosh Jain; **Editor:** Ajit Maindola
Editorial Profile: Covers the local, regional, national and international news, and etc.
Language (s): Hindi
DAILY NEWSPAPER

Rajasthan Patrika - Jodhpur
Editorial: Patrikayan, Manji Ka Hatha, Paota, Jodhpur 342006. **T:** 91 2915109911
W: http://www.rajasthanpatrika.com
Freq: Daily; **Circ:** 92071 Not Audited
Editor: Daulat Chauhan
Editorial Profile: Covers the local, regional, national and international news, and etc.
Language (s): Hindi
DAILY NEWSPAPER

Rajasthan Patrika - Kolkata
Editorial: Near Yogayog Bhawan, 19, Kinderdine Lane, Kolkata 700012.
T: 91 33 3299 8041
W: http://www.rajasthanpatrika.com
Freq: Daily
Editor: Tarkeshwar Mishra
Editorial Profile: Daily newspaper, covering news, sports & business.
Language (s): Hindi
DAILY NEWSPAPER

Rajasthan Patrika - Kota
Editorial: 25 Small Scale Industrial Area, Kota 324007. **T:** 91 74 42363601
E: info@rajasthanpatrika.com

W: http://www.rajasthanpatrika.com
Freq: Daily; **Circ:** 125003 Not Audited
Editor: Siddharth Bhatt
Editorial Profile: Covers News Sports & Business.
Language (s): Hindi
DAILY NEWSPAPER

Ranchi Express
Editorial: 55 Baralal Street, Upper Bazar, Ranchi 834001. **T:** 91 651 2206320
E: news@ranchiexpress.com
W: http://www.ranchiexpress.com
Freq: Daily; **Circ:** 82157 Not Audited
Editor: Balbir Dutt; **Publisher:** Raul Maroo; **Editor:** Chandreshwar Singh
Editorial Profile: Covers the news in local and world, sports, health and education.
Language (s): Hindi
DAILY NEWSPAPER

Rashtradeepika
Owner: Rashtra Deepika Publications
Editorial: Rashtra Deepika Publications, P.O. Box 2252, Cochin 686025. **T:** 91 481 3012001
E: editor@deepika.com
W: http://www.deepika.com
Freq: Daily; **Circ:** 300002 Not Audited
Editorial Profile: Covers local, regional, international and world news.
Language (s): Malayalam
DAILY NEWSPAPER

Rashtriya Sahara Hindi Daily
Editorial: 1216-1220, 12th Floor, Navrang House 21, Kasturba Gandhi Marg, Aliganj, New Delhi 226024. **T:** 91 11 43596017
Freq: Daily; **Circ:** 62003 Not Audited
Editor: Manoj Kumar
Editorial Profile: Covers international, national and local news.
Language (s): Hindi
DAILY NEWSPAPER

Rastradoot
Editorial: Sudharma, M.I. Road, Jaipur 302001. **T:** 91 141 2361613
Freq: Daily; **Circ:** 350001 Not Audited
Editorial Profile: Covers local news and international news.
Language (s): Hindi
DAILY NEWSPAPER

Rastriya Naveen Mail
Editorial: J.J. Road Upper Bazaar, Ranchi 834001. **T:** 91 6512306999
Freq: Daily; **Circ:** 63001 Not Audited
Editor: Jyoti Bajaj; **Editor in Chief:** Suresh Bajaj; **Bureau Chief:** Devendra Sharma
Editorial Profile: Rastriya Naveen Mail is A Daily Newspaper Covering Local National Regional And International News.
Language (s): Hindi
DAILY NEWSPAPER

Rozana Safeer-E-Nau
Editorial: 18 Tulsipor, Rasoolpor, Allahabad 211003. **T:** 91 532 2658114
Freq: Daily; **Circ:** 50002 Not Audited
Editor: Mohammad Hafeezullah Khan
Editorial Profile: Covers the news in local and world, and etc.
Language (s): Urdu
DAILY NEWSPAPER

Saamana (Hindi)
Owner: Prabodhankar Prakashan
Editorial: Sadguru Darshan, Nagu Sayaji Wadi, Dainik Saamana Marg, Prabhadevi, Mumbai 400025. **T:** 91 2224370160
E: saamana89@gmail.com
W: http://www.saamana.com
Freq: Daily; **Circ:** 81002 Not Audited
Publisher: Subhash Desai; **Editor:** Uddhav Thackeray
Editorial Profile: Launched in February 1993 to reach north Indians settled in Maharashtra. Covers local and international news and government and reflects the views of the Shiv Sena political party.
Language (s): Hindi
DAILY NEWSPAPER

Saamana (Marathi)
Owner: Prabodhankar Prakashan
Editorial: Sadguru Darshan, Nagu Sayaji Wadi, Dainik Saamana Marg, Prabhadevi, Mumbai 400025. **T:** 91 22 24370592
W: http://www.saamana.com
Freq: Daily; **Circ:** 80650 Not Audited
Publisher: Subhash Desai; **Editor:** Uddhav Thackeray
Editorial Profile: Launched in January 1988 to convey the views of the Shiv Sena political party to the Marathi masses. Covers local and international news and government.
Language (s): Marathi
DAILY NEWSPAPER

Sadin
Editorial: M.R.D. Road, Chandmari, Guwahati 781003. **T:** 91 361 2660420
E: sadin@pratidinassam.com
W: http://www.pratidinassam.com/sadin
Freq: Weekly; **Circ:** 50003 Not Audited
Editor: Anuradha Pujari
Editorial Profile: Covers the latest news in local and world.
Language (s): Assamese
NEWSPAPER

Sahafat
Editorial: Sahafat Daily, 25 Salempur House, Kaisar Bagh, Lucknow 226018. **T:** 91 522 4155330
E: sahafatdaily@yahoo.co.uk
Freq: Daily; **Circ:** 70002 Not Audited
Editor: Amaan Abbas
Editorial Profile: Covers local, regional, international and national news.
Language (s): Urdu
DAILY NEWSPAPER

Sakaal Kolhapur
Editorial: D-4, MIDC Shiroli, Kolhapur 416422. **T:** 91 2312468383 **E:** webeditor@esakal.com
W: http://www.esakal.com
Freq: Daily; **Circ:** 60003 Not Audited
Editor: Vasant Bhosale
Editorial Profile: Covers general news.
Language (s): Marathi
DAILY NEWSPAPER

Sakaal Pune
Editorial: Sakal Paper Limited, 595 Budhwar Peth, Pune 411002. **T:** 91 20 24405500
E: webeditor@esakal.com
W: http://www.esakal.com
Freq: Daily; **Circ:** 1000001 Not Audited
Editor: Suresh Padhe
Editorial Profile: Sakaal Pune is a newspaper which provides the news in local and international, entertainment, politics, sports, and etc.
Language (s): Marathi
DAILY NEWSPAPER

Sakal Mumbai
Editorial: Sakal Bhavan, Plot No. 42, Sector No. 11, CBD Belapur, Navi Mumbai, Mumbai 400614. **T:** 91 2227572960 **E:** sakal@vsnl.in
W: http://www.esakal.com
Freq: Daily; **Circ:** 80001 Not Audited
Editor in Chief: Uttam Kamble
Editorial Profile: Sukal Mumbai is a newspaper which writes about the news in local and international, sports, entertainment, politics and etc.
Language (s): Marathi
DAILY NEWSPAPER

Sakal Nagpur
Editorial: 5 East High Court Road, Ramdas Estate, Nagpur 44001. **T:** 91 7122531482
E: sakalnagpur@esakal.com
W: http://www.esakal.com **Circ:** 75003 Not Audited
Editor: Shreepad Aprajit
Editorial Profile: Covers news.
Language (s): Marathi
DAILY NEWSPAPER

Samachar Jagat
Editorial: Opp. Prem Prakash Cinema, Jaipur Hotel, Room No. 9 & 10, S.M.S. Highway, Jaipur 302001. **T:** 91 141 2377044
E: samacharjagat@rediffmail.com
W: http://www.samacharjagat.in
Freq: Daily; **Circ:** 230001 Not Audited
Editor in Chief: Rajendra Godha
Editorial Profile: Samachar Jagat is a newspaper which covers the headline, business, sports and entertainment.
Language (s): Hindi
DAILY NEWSPAPER

Samaya
Editorial: Plot No. 44 & 54 Sector A, Zone D, Mancheswar Industrial Estate, Bhubaneshwar 751017. **T:** 91 6742585740
E: thesamaya@yahoo.com
W: http://www.orissasamaya.com
Freq: Daily; **Circ:** 100001 Not Audited
Editor in Chief: Satakadi Hota
Editorial Profile: Covers local, national and international news.
Language (s): Oriya
DAILY NEWSPAPER

Sambhaav Daily
Editorial: Sambhaav House Opposite Chief Justice's Bungalow, Bodakdev, Ahmedabad 380015. **T:** 91 7926873914
E: metro@sambhaav.com
W: http://www.sambhaav.com
Freq: Daily; **Circ:** 69003 Not Audited
Editor: Deepal Trevedi
Editorial Profile: Covers general news.
Language (s): Gujarati
DAILY NEWSPAPER

Sambhaav Metro
Owner: Sambhaav Media Ltd.
Editorial: Sambhaav Media Ltd., Sambhaav House Opposite Judges Bungalow, Premchandnagar, Bodakdev Satellite, Vastrapur, Ahmedabad 380054.
T: 91 7926873914 **E:** metro@sambhaav.com
W: http://www.sambhaav.com
Freq: Daily
Editor: Deepal Trevedi
Editorial Profile: Gujarati daily newspaper
Language (s): Gujarati
DAILY NEWSPAPER

Samyukta Karnataka
Editorial: 2 Residency Road, Bangalore 560025. **T:** 91 80 22214392
E: samkarnataka@rediffmail.com
Freq: Daily; **Circ:** 200003 Not Audited
Editorial Profile: Covers general news.
Language (s): Kannada
DAILY NEWSPAPER

Sandesh
Editorial: Sandesh Ltd. Sandesh Bhavan, Lad Society Road, Badakdev, Ahmedabad 380054. **T:** 91 79 40004000
W: http://www.sandesh.com
Freq: Daily; **Circ:** 800002 Not Audited
Editor: Falgunbhai Patel
Editorial Profile: Covers the latest news in local and world, business, sports and etc.
Language (s): Gujarati
DAILY NEWSPAPER

Sandhya Jyoti Darpan
Editorial: 3-A, Vidhya Aashram Institutional Area, Jawahar Lal Nehru Marg, Jaipur 302017. **T:** 91 141 2709102 **E:** sjdp01@yahoo.co.in
Freq: Daily; **Circ:** 50002 Not Audited
Editor in Chief: Brij Sharma; **Editor in Chief:** Brij Mohan Sharma; **Editor:** Mahendra Yadav
Editorial Profile: Covers the latest news in local and world.
Language (s): Hindi
DAILY NEWSPAPER

Sandhya Mahalaxmi Bhagyodaya
Editorial: 184 Patparganj Industrial Area, New Delhi 110092. **T:** 91 11 22410716
E: mahalaxmigroup@hotmail.com
W: http://www.mahalaxmigroup.com
Freq: Daily; **Circ:** 51001 Not Audited
Editor: Sharad Jain
Editorial Profile: Covers the local, regional, international and national news.
Language (s): Hindi
DAILY NEWSPAPER

Sandhya Times
Editorial: Sandhya Times, 7 Bahadur Shah Zafar Marg, New Delhi 110002.
T: 91 1123302000
E: madhurendra.sinha@timesgroup.com
W: http://www.sandhyatimes.indiatimes.com
Freq: 2 Times/Week; **Circ:** 100001 Not Audited
Editor: Sushma Jagmohan; **Editor in Chief:** Sat Soni
Editorial Profile: One of the largest tabloids in India, serves as a popular information and entertainment source for the commuting reader in Delhi.
Language (s): Hindi
NEWSPAPER

Sandhya Veer Arjun
Editorial: Pratap Bhawan, 5 Bahadur Shah Zafar Marg, New Delhi 110002.
T: 91 11 23312507
Freq: Daily; **Circ:** 52002 Not Audited
Editor: Anil Narendra
Editorial Profile: Covers local and world news, sports, etc.
Language (s): Hindi
DAILY NEWSPAPER

Sandhyanand
Editorial: Aaj Ka Anand Building, 365/6 Shivajinagar, Pune 411005. **T:** 91 20 25534888
W: http://www.sandhyanand.com
Freq: Daily; **Circ:** 350002 Not Audited
Editorial Profile: Covers news topics.
Language (s): Marathi
DAILY NEWSPAPER

Sanjevani
Editorial: Sanjevani, 11/2, Queen's Road, Bangalore 560052. **T:** 91 80 22866260
E: sanjevani@gmail.com
W: http://www.sanjevani.com
Freq: Daily; **Circ:** 300002 Not Audited
Editor: B. Amuthan
Editorial Profile: Covers local and world news.
Language (s): Kannada
DAILY NEWSPAPER

Sanjh Samachar
Editorial: Babubhai Shah Marg, Jai Hind Press Building, Rajkot 360001. **T:** 91 2813048684
E: sanjhsamachar@gmail.com
W: http://www.jaihinddaily.com
Freq: Daily; **Circ:** 50003 Not Audited
Editorial Profile: Covers news.
Language (s): Gujarati
DAILY NEWSPAPER

Sanmarg
Editorial: 160/B, Chittaranjan Avenue, Kolkata 700007. **T:** 91 33 30615020
E: sanmarghindi@gmail.com
W: http://www.sanmarg.in
Freq: Daily; **Circ:** 125003 Not Audited
Editor: Hari Pande
Editorial Profile: Covers the latest local, regional, national and international news.
Language (s): Hindi
DAILY NEWSPAPER

Saurashtra Bhoomi
Editorial: Saurashtra Bhoomi Karyalaya, Jail Road, Junagadh 362001. **T:** 91 285 2621000
E: saurashtrabhoomi@gmail.com
W: http://www.saurashtrabhoomi.com
Freq: Daily; **Circ:** 75002 Not Audited
Editor in Chief: Kartik Upadhyay
Editorial Profile: Covers the latest news in local and world, business, sports and etc.
Language (s): Gujarati
DAILY NEWSPAPER

Seema Sandesh
Editorial: Sandesh Sadan, Chak 7E Chotti, Hanuman Garh Road, Sri Ganga Nagar 335001. **T:** 91 141 4015552
E: editor@seemasandesh.com
Freq: Daily; **Circ:** 50000 Not Audited
Editor: Lalit Sharma
Editorial Profile: Covers the latest news in local and world, business, sports, movie, religion and etc.
Language (s): Hindi
DAILY NEWSPAPER

The Sentinel
Editorial: G.S. Road, Dispur, Guwahati 781005. **T:** 91 361 2529237
E: bikash@sentinelassam.com
W: http://www.sentinelassam.com
Freq: Daily; **Circ:** 50002 Not Audited
Editor: Shankar Rajkhewa
Editorial Profile: Covers of news and general interests.
Language (s): English
DAILY NEWSPAPER

The Siasat Daily
Editorial: Jawaharlal Nehru Road, Opposite Ram Krishna Theatre, Abids, Hyderabad 500001. **T:** 91 40 24744114
E: siasat.daily@yahoo.com
W: http://www.siasat.com
Freq: Daily; **Circ:** 50003 Not Audited
Editor: Aamer Khan; **Editor in Chief:** Zahid Khan
Editorial Profile: A daily newspaper which covers the latest local, regional, international and national news, business, politics, sports and entertainment.
Language (s): English
DAILY NEWSPAPER

Star of Mysore
Editorial: 15-C, Industrial A Layout, Bannimantap, Mysore 570015.
T: 91 821 2496520
E: voice@starofmysore.com
W: http://www.starofmysore.com
Freq: Daily; **Circ:** 75002 Not Audited
Editor: K. Ganapathy
Editorial Profile: Star of Mysore is a newspaper which covers the international and local newspapers and articles.
Language (s): English
DAILY NEWSPAPER

The Statesman
Editorial: The Statesman Ltd, Statesman House, 4 Chowringhee Square, Kolkata 700001. **T:** 91 33 22127070
E: thestatesman@vsnl.com
W: http://www.thestatesman.net
Freq: Daily; **Circ:** 200003 Not Audited
Bureau Chief: Manoj Chaurasia; **Editor in Chief:** Ravindra Kumar
Editorial Profile: Founded in 1875 and a founding member of Asia News Network,

provides objective coverage of national and international news and current events.
Language (s): English
DAILY NEWSPAPER

Sunday Guardian
Editorial: INX News Pvt. Ltd, B-4, 2nd floor, Sector-3, Near Rajnigandha Chowk, New Delhi 20131. **T:** 91 120 4369500
E: mail@sunday-guardian.com
W: http://www.sunday-guardian.com
Freq: Daily
Editor in Chief: M . Akbar
Editorial Profile: Launched in 2010, covers national news and published simultaneously as India on Sunday out of London.
Language (s): English
DAILY NEWSPAPER

Sunday Mid-Day
Editorial: Peninsula Centre; Dr. S.S. Rao Road, Opposite Mahatma Gandhi Hospital; Parel, Mumbai 400011. **T:** 91 22 67017171
E: cs@mid-day.com
W: http://www.mid-day.com
Freq: Weekly; **Circ:** 120003 Not Audited
Editor: Alpana Sawai
Editorial Profile: Covers the latest news in local and international, business, sports, automotive, entertainment, lifestyle and etc.
Language (s): English
NEWSPAPER

Sunday Times
Editorial: S & B Towers, 2nd Floor, 40 Mahatma Road, Bangalore 560001.
T: 91 80 25550000
E: toiblr.reporter@timesgroup.com
W: http://www.indiatimes.com
Freq: Weekly; **Circ:** 302001 Not Audited
Editor: Naheed Ataullah; **Editor:** Shirish Koyal
Editorial Profile: Sunday Times is a newspaper which talks about the latest news in local and international, sports, entertainment, and market.
Language (s): English
NEWSPAPER

Swadesh
Editorial: Swadesh Bhavan, 26-A, Press Complex, Maharana Pratap Nagar, Bhopal 462011. **T:** 91 0755 2556189
E: swadeshbhopal@gmail.com
Freq: Daily; **Circ:** 50001 Not Audited
Editor in Chief: Rajendra Sharma
Editorial Profile: Swadesh is a newspaper which focused on the latest news in local, regional, international, and national.
Language (s): Hindi
DAILY NEWSPAPER

Swatantra Bharat
Editorial: SurajDeep Complex, 2nd Floor, 1 Jopling Road, Lucknow 226001.
T: 91 05222204306 **E:** sbharats@satyam.net.in
W: http://www.swatantrabharat.com
Freq: Daily; **Circ:** 120001 Not Audited
Editorial Profile: Covers news topics.
Language (s): Hindi
DAILY NEWSPAPER

Swatantra Chetna
Owner: D A Chetna Prakashan Pvt Ltd.
Editorial: D A Chetna Prakashan Pvt Ltd., Shahmaroof, Hindi Bazar, Gorakhpur 273001.
T: 91 5512332248
W: http://www.swatantrachetna.com
Freq: Daily; **Circ:** 75002 Not Audited
Editor in Chief: R. Gupta
Editorial Profile: Swatantra Chetnat is a daily newspaper which covers the Local Regional National and International news as well as sports and etc.
Language (s): Hindi
DAILY NEWSPAPER

Syandan Patrika
Editorial: 41 Sakuntala Road, Agartala 799001. **T:** 91 381 2386684
E: syandan@patrikaindia.com
W: http://www.patrikaindia.com
Freq: Daily; **Circ:** 70002 Not Audited
Editor in Chief: Subal Dey; **Editor:** Animesh Dutta
Editorial Profile: Covers the news in local and world.
Language (s): Bengali
DAILY NEWSPAPER

Tehelka, The People's Paper
Editorial: M-76, M-Block Market, First Floor, Greater Kailash II, New Delhi 110048.
T: 91 11 40575757 **E:** editor@tehelka.com
W: http://www.tehelka.com
Freq: Weekly
Editor: Harinder Baweja
Editorial Profile: Covers the latest news locally and internationally, as well as economics, politics, etc.
Language (s): English
NEWSPAPER

The Telegraph
Owner: ABP Ltd.
Editorial: ABP Ltd, 6 Prafulla Sarkar Street, Kolkata 700001. **T:** 91 33 22345374
E: ttedit@abpmail.com
W: http://www.telegraphindia.com
Freq: Daily; **Circ:** 389549 Not Audited
Editor: Rudrankshu Mukherjee; **Editor in Chief:** Aveek Sarkar
Editorial Profile: Launched in July 1982, covers national, international, and business news, sports, entertainment and travel and publishes in English.
Language (s): English
DAILY NEWSPAPER

Tender World
Editorial: Four Square Media Pvt. Ltd., 202 Jaina Extn., Dr. Mukherjee Nagar, Comml.Complex, New Delhi 110009.
T: 91 11 27655127
W: http://www.businessnewspapers.net
Freq: Weekly
Editor in Chief: Dev Joshi
Editorial Profile: Covers more than 3000 industrial products of all trades from all over India & abroad.
Language (s): Hindi
NEWSPAPER

These Days
Editorial: I-91, Lubna House, Batla House, Okhla, New Delhi 110001. **T:** 91 1123792121
E: thesedaysindia@gmail.com
W: http://www.thesedaysindia.com
Freq: Daily
Editor in Chief: S. Asif
Editorial Profile: These Days is a newspaper which covers the latest news in local and world.
Language (s): English
DAILY NEWSPAPER

The Times of India - Ahmedabad Edition
Owner: Bennett, Coleman & Co. Ltd.
Editorial: 139 Ashram Road, Ahmedabad 380009. **T:** 91 79 26553300
W: http://www.timesofindia.com
Freq: Daily; **Circ:** 158002 Not Audited
Editor: Bharat Desai
Editorial Profile: Covers the latest local, regional, international and national news, with regular sections including business, sports, entertainment, lifestyle and women's interest.
Language (s): English
DAILY NEWSPAPER

Times of India - Bangalore Edition
Owner: Bennett, Coleman & Co. Ltd.
Editorial: Times Internet Ltd., #17 Du Park Trinity, Bangalore 560001. **T:** 91 80 40876709
W: http://www.timesofindia.indiatimes.com
Freq: Daily; **Circ:** 4000001 Not Audited
Editorial Profile: Covers the latest local, regional, international and national news, with regular sections including business, sports, entertainment, lifestyle and women's interest.
Language (s): English
DAILY NEWSPAPER

Times of India - Chennai Edition
Editorial: Times House, 126/127, Chamlers Road, Chennai 600035. **T:** 91 44 40401234
W: http://timesofindia.indiatimes.com
Freq: Daily
Editorial Profile: Covers local, national and international news.
Language (s): English
DAILY NEWSPAPER

The Times of India - Lucknow Edition
Owner: Bennett, Coleman & Co. Ltd.
Editorial: 16 Rana Pratap Marg, Lucknow 226001. **T:** 91 522 2209484
W: http://www.timesofindia.com
Freq: Daily; **Circ:** 74003 Not Audited
Editor: Atul Chandra
Editorial Profile: Covers the latest local, regional, international and national news, with regular sections including business, sports, entertainment, lifestyle and women's interest.
Language (s): English
DAILY NEWSPAPER

The Times of India - Mumbai edition
Owner: Bennett, Coleman & Co. Ltd.
Editorial: The Times of India Bldg, 1st Floor, Dr. D. N. Rd, Mumbai 400001.
T: 011 911 22735610
E: info.tbsl@timesgroup.com
Freq: Daily; **Circ:** 776632 Not Audited
Editor: Meena Iyer
Editorial Profile: Covers the latest local, regional, international and national news, with regular sections including business, sports, entertainment, lifestyle and women's interest.
Language (s): English
DAILY NEWSPAPER

The Times of India - New Delhi Edition
Owner: Bennett, Coleman & Co. Ltd.
Editorial: 7 Bahadur Shah Zafar Marg, New Delhi 110002. **T:** 91 11 23302000
W: http://timesofindia.indiatimes.com/Cities/Delhi/articlelist/-2128839596.cms
Freq: Daily Not Audited
Editorial Profile: Covers the latest local, regional, international and national news, with regular sections including business, sports, entertainment, lifestyle and women's interest.
Language (s): English
DAILY NEWSPAPER

Times of Money
Editorial: 4th Floor, Times Tower, Kamala Mills Compound, Senapati Bapat Marg, Lower Parel (W), Mumbai 400013. **T:** 91 2222731263
W: http://www.timesofmoney.com
Editor: Sheena Kapoor
Editorial Profile: Covers money topics.
Language (s): English
DAILY NEWSPAPER

Travel Gazette Of India
Editorial: Level 5 Span Centre, Opposite Central Avenue, Santa Cruise (W), Mumbai 400054. **T:** 91 22 30653258
Editor: Alan Demello
Editorial Profile: Focused on travel and tourism information.
Language (s): English
DAILY NEWSPAPER

The Tribune
Editorial: The Tribune House, Sector 29-C, Chandigarh 160030. **T:** 91 172 26 55 066
E: editorinchief@tribuneindia.com
W: http://www.tribuneindia.com
Freq: Daily; **Circ:** 300003 Not Audited
Editor in Chief: Raj Chengappa
Editorial Profile: A daily newspaper which covers the latest local, regional, international and national news, business, politics, sports and etc.
Language (s): English
DAILY NEWSPAPER

Trinity Mirror
Editorial: No. 1, First Main Road, United India Colony, Kodambakkam, Chennai 600024.
T: 91 44 24734800
Freq: Daily; **Circ:** 72001 Not Audited
Publisher: R Muthukumar
Editorial Profile: Focuses on news in local and international.
Language (s): English
DAILY NEWSPAPER

Udayavani
Editorial: New Udayavani Building, Manipal 576119. **T:** 91 820 2571159
E: udayavani@manipalmedia.com
W: http://www.udayavani.com
Freq: Daily; **Circ:** 189355 Not Audited
Editorial Profile: Covers the latest news in local and world and politics.
Language (s): Kannada
DAILY NEWSPAPER

Utkal Mel
Editorial: C-231 Industrial Estate, Dist Sundargarh, Rourkela 769004.
T: 91 6612401332
E: bbsr_utkalmel@rediffmail.com
W: http://www.utkal
Freq: Daily; **Circ:** 81953 Not Audited
Editor in Chief: Pitabasa Mishra
Editorial Profile: A local newspaper covering local and national news.
Language (s): Hindi
DAILY NEWSPAPER

Uttar Banga Sambad
Editorial: 7 Old Court House Street, Kolkata 700001. **T:** 91 3322435663
W: http://www.uttarbangasambad.com
Freq: Daily; **Circ:** 140002 Not Audited
Editor: S. Talukdar
Editorial Profile: Covering local news, sports, business, jobs, and community events. The web site is presented in the Bengali language.
Language (s): Bengali
DAILY NEWSPAPER

Uttar Ujala
Editorial: Ujala Nagar, Bareilly Road, Haldwani 263139. **T:** 91 5946252129
E: uttarujala@rediffmail.com
Freq: Daily; **Circ:** 55003 Not Audited
Editor: Snehlata Bhandari
Editorial Profile: A daily newspaper in Haldwani India.
Language (s): Hindi
DAILY NEWSPAPER

Vaartha (Hindi)
Editorial: 396 Lower Tank Bund, Hyderabad 500080. **T:** 91 40 66654999
E: editor@vaarttha.com
W: http://www.vaarttha.com
Freq: Daily; **Circ:** 50002 Not Audited
Editor: Radheshyam Shukla
Editorial Profile: Covers news.
Language (s): Hindi
DAILY NEWSPAPER

Vaartha (Telugu)
Editorial: 396 Lower Tank Bund, Hyderabad 500080. **T:** 91 40 66654999
E: editor@vaarttha.com
W: http://www.vaarttha.com
Freq: Daily; **Circ:** 500001 Not Audited
Editor: Ashok Tankshla
Editorial Profile: Covers news.
Language (s): Telugu
DAILY NEWSPAPER

Vacancies For You
Editorial: 401-404 Centre Point Road, 18th Road, Chembur, E., Mumbai 400071.
T: 91 22 2529 0102
W: http://www.vacanciesforyou.com
Freq: Weekly
Editor: D. Prasad
Editorial Profile: Focuses on job hunting.
Language (s): English
NEWSPAPER

Veer Arjun
Editorial: Pratap Bhawan, 5 Bahadurshah Zafar Marg, New Delhi 110002.
T: 91 11 23318276 **E:** dailyvirarjun@gmail.com
W: http://www.virarjun.com
Freq: Daily; **Circ:** 82991 Not Audited
Editor: Seema Kiran; **Editor:** Anil Narendra
Editorial Profile: Veer Arjun is a newspaper which covers the news in local and international, business, education, sports, culture, and etc.
Language (s): Hindi
DAILY NEWSPAPER

Vijay Karnataka
Editorial: No 40 KCCF Compound, Pampa Mahakavi Road, Pampa Mahakavi Road, Bangalore 560018. **T:** 91 8040877666
W: http://vijaykarnataka.indiatimes.com
Freq: Daily; **Circ:** 640003 Not Audited
Editor: Vishveshwar Bhatt; **Editor:** Sugata Srinivasaraju
Editorial Profile: Covers local news, sports, business, jobs, and community events in the Kannada language.
Language (s): Kannada
DAILY NEWSPAPER

Vijay Times
Editorial: #38, A M Road, KPM New Extension, Bangalore 560002.
T: 91 8026992828 **E:** vksbc@bgl.vsnl.net
Freq: Daily; **Circ:** 98002 Not Audited
Editorial Profile: Launched in 2003 and covers news about the latest events, shopping, festivals, music, fashion, movies, eat-outs, real estate and finance, etc.
Language (s): English
DAILY NEWSPAPER

Vishwa Manav
Editorial: Vishwa Manav Bhawan, 103 Civil Lines, Behind Hind Talkies, Bareilly 243001.
T: 91 581 2473967
Freq: Daily; **Circ:** 58641 Not Audited
Editorial Profile: Vishwa Manav is a newspaper which covers the news in local, regional, international and national and etc.
Language (s): Hindi
DAILY NEWSPAPER

Vyapar - Rajkot Edition
Editorial: Phulchhab Bhavan, Mahatma Gandhi Road, Near Parsi Agyari, Rajkot 360001.
T: 91 281 2478317 **W:** http://www.vyapar.com
Freq: 2 Times/Week; **Circ:** 60003 Not Audited
Editor: Madhusudan Barbhaya
Editorial Profile: Covers local and world news within the agriculture industry.
Language (s): Gujarati
NEWSPAPER

Vyapar Bharati
Editorial: K 37, Udyog Nagar, Industrial Area, Rohtak Road, New Delhi 110085.
T: 91 114 2380000 **E:** info@vyaparbharati.net
W: http://www.vyaparbharati.net
Freq: Daily; **Circ:** 60003 Not Audited
Editor: Yyarpar Bharti
Editorial Profile: A daily newspaper about India and international news.
Language (s): Hindi
DAILY NEWSPAPER

The Wall Street Journal (India)
Editorial: Cambatta Bldg, 2nd FL West, 42 J. Tata Road, Mumbai 400020.
T: 91 22 3251-6747
DAILY NEWSPAPER

The Wall Street Journal India
Editorial: 5 Sikandra Rd, Delhi 110001.
T: 91 11 2307-4032 **W:** http://india.wsj.com
Bureau Chief: Gordon Fairclough
DAILY NEWSPAPER

Yashobhumi
Editorial: 220 Narayan Udyog Bhawan, Dr. B A Road, Lal Bagh, Mumbai 400012.
T: 91 22 24715208
Freq: Daily; **Circ:** 130003 Not Audited
Editor: Anand Shukla
Editorial Profile: Covers the latest news in local and world.
Language (s): Hindi
DAILY NEWSPAPER

NEWS SERVICE/SYNDICATE

Agence France-Presse - New Delhi Bureau
Owner: Agence France-Presse
Editorial: 56 Janpath, 3rd floor, New Delhi 110001. **T:** 91 11 2373 8700
E: afpdelhi@afp.com **W:** http://www.afp.com
Bureau Chief: Christian Otton
Editorial Profile: Regional office covering general news and current affairs.
Language (s): Arabic
NEWS SERVICE/SYNDICATE

Associated Press
Editorial: 6b Jor Bagh Lane, New Delhi 110003. **T:** 94 11 230-4940
Bureau Chief: Ravi Nessman
NEWS SERVICE/SYNDICATE

Bloomberg News
Editorial: PTI Building, 4 Parliament Street, New Delhi 110001. **T:** 91 1141792020
E: indianews@bloomberg.net
Bureau Chief: Sam Nagarajan; **News Editor:** Cherian Thomas
NEWS SERVICE/SYNDICATE

Cartographic News Service
Editorial: KBK News Graphic Network, 1st Floor 13 Todarmal Lane, New Delhi 110001.
T: 91 1123315555
E: vijay@kbknewsgraphics.com
W: http://www.kbknewsgraphics.com
Freq: Daily
Editorial Profile: KBK is India's pioneering and leading daily News Graphics agency providing comprehensive coverage of news through graphics. Through an independent reliable and exclusive network the agency has been producing quality infographics for almost half-a-century. With a mix of accredited correspondents creative graphic artists and researchers as its key editorial resource base KBK has carved a niche for itself as a highly professional setup.
Language (s): English
NEWS SERVICE/SYNDICATE

Dow Jones Newswires
Editorial: 518-522 World Trade Centre, Barakhamba Lane, New Delhi 1100 001.
T: 91 11 2620-7315
NEWS SERVICE/SYNDICATE

dpa Deutsche Presse Agentur- New Delhi Bureau
Editorial: 39 Golf Links, New Delhi 110033.
T: 91 1124617792 **E:** dpadelhi@vsnl.com
W: http://www.dpa.com
Freq: Daily
Editorial Profile: Covers national News in India.
Language (s): English
NEWS SERVICE/SYNDICATE

Global Features
Editorial: B-701, Customs Colony, Military Rd, Marol Naka, Mumbai 400059.
T: 011 91 9223419060
Editor: Chandragupta Amritkar
Editorial Profile: Distributes local, national and international news feature stories throughout India.
Language (s): English
NEWS SERVICE/SYNDICATE

IDG News Service
Owner: International Data Group
Editorial: 302 Koramangala Comforts, No. 1, 9th Main, 6th Cross, S.T. Bed, Koramangala 4th Block, Bangalore 560 034.
T: 91 802-553-3341 **E:** idgnews@idg.com
NEWS SERVICE/SYNDICATE

India News and Feature Alliance (INFA)
Editorial: Jeevan Deep, 10 Parliament Street, New Delhi 110001. **T:** 91 1123743330
E: infaservice@infapublications.com
W: http://www.infa.in
Freq: Daily
Editor in Chief: Inder Jit
Editorial Profile: Covers news and general interests.
Language (s): English
NEWS SERVICE/SYNDICATE

India Press Agency (IPA)
T: 91 1123354648
E: indiapressagency@gmail.com
W: http://www.ipanewspack.com
Freq: Daily
Editorial Profile: Provides constant news coverage of politics, defense, oil & gas and business.
Language (s): English
NEWS SERVICE/SYNDICATE

Indo-Asian News Service
Editorial: IANS INDIA PTV.LTD., L-8, Green Park Extension, New Delhi 110016.
T: 91 1139400100 **E:** support@ians.in
W: http://www.ians.in
Freq: Daily
Editor in Chief: Tarun Basu
Editorial Profile: Covers news and general interests.
Language (s): English
NEWS SERVICE/SYNDICATE

Inter Press Service
Editorial: 49 First Floor, Defence Colony Main Market, New Delhi 110024. **T:** 91 1124333489
E: ranjit@ipsnews.net
W: http://www.ipsnews.net
Freq: Daily
Editor: Ranjit Devraj
Editorial Profile: Its main focus is the production of independent news and analysis about events and processes affecting economic, social and political development.
Language (s): English
NEWS SERVICE/SYNDICATE

Kyodo News
Editorial: 201, Silver Arch Apartments, 22 Ferozshah Road, New Delhi 110001.
T: 91 1141503738
E: tanabe.hiroshi@kyodonews.jp
W: http://home.kyodo.co.jp
Freq: Daily
Publisher: Tanabe Hiroshi
Editorial Profile: Kyodo News is a nonprofit cooperative news agency based in Minato, Tokyo. Covers of news and general interests.
Language (s): Chinese
NEWS SERVICE/SYNDICATE

National News Service
Editorial: 25/10 East Punjabi Bagh, New Delhi 110026. **T:** 91 1146867500
E: Support@nnscommoditynews.com
W: http://www.nnscommoditynews.com/commoditynews/
Freq: Daily
Editor: Kesar Gupta; **Editor:** Rajesh Gupta
Editorial Profile: Covers news and general interests.
Language (s): English
NEWS SERVICE/SYNDICATE

News From Non Aligned World
Editorial: A-2/59 Safdarjung Enclave, New Delhi 110029. **T:** 91 1146867500
E: ndt@newsdelhitimes.com
Freq: Weekly
Editor: Vikas Pande
Editorial Profile: Covers news and general interests.
Language (s): English
NEWS SERVICE/SYNDICATE

Press Asia International
Editorial: A-19 Gulmohar Park, New Delhi 110049. **T:** 91 1126567885
Freq: Daily
Editorial Profile: Press Asia International is a Language Feature Service covering topics related to politics and social affairs and with a large number of subscribers across several states.
Language (s): English
NEWS SERVICE/SYNDICATE

Press Trust of India
Editorial: 4 Parliament Street, New Delhi 100001. **T:** 91 112316621 **E:** trans@pti.in
W: http://www.ptinews.com
Freq: Daily
Editorial Profile: Serves as India's premier news agency, with a reach as vast as the Indian Railways. Correspondents are based in leading capitals and important business and administrative centers around the world.
Language (s): Hindi
NEWS SERVICE/SYNDICATE

Reuters
Editorial: East Birla Towers, Fl 10, 25, Barakhamba Road, New Delhi 110001.
T: 91 11 4178-1000
Bureau Chief: Tony Tharakan
NEWS SERVICE/SYNDICATE

Syndicated Journalist
Editorial: C-2-2073, Vasant Kunj, New Delhi 110070. **T:** 91 1126892295
Freq: Daily
Editor in Chief: Narayan Venkat
Editorial Profile: It is a news feature agency which has had its features aired across several countries of the world.
Language (s): English
NEWS SERVICE/SYNDICATE

United News of India (UNI)
Editorial: United News of India (UNI), 9 Rafi Marg, New Delhi 110001. **T:** 91 1123711700
E: vsat@uniindia.com
W: http://www.uniindia.com
Freq: Daily
Bureau Chief: Pradeep Kashyap
Editorial Profile: Covers news about politics, economics, business, sports, entertainment and stock markets.
Language (s): English
NEWS SERVICE/SYNDICATE

Univarta
Editorial: 9 Rafi Marg, New Delhi 110001.
T: 91 1123355838 **E:** varta@uniindia.com
W: http://www.uniindia.com
Freq: Daily
Editor: Mahabir Singh
Editorial Profile: Provides news features on a wide variety of topics, including Art and Culture, Science, Agriculture, Economy, Heritage and India's neighbors.
Language (s): Hindi
NEWS SERVICE/SYNDICATE

Xinhua News Agency
Editorial: D 6/4, Vasant Vihar, New Delhi 110057. **T:** 91 1126142473
E: libaodong@hotmail.com
W: http://www.xinhuanet.com
Freq: Daily
Bureau Chief: Bao Dong Li
Editorial Profile: Foreign news agency based in China.
Language (s): Chinese
NEWS SERVICE/SYNDICATE

BROADCASTING

CABLE

CNN International - South Asia
Editorial: S-2 Level Block F International Trade Tower, Nehru Place, New Delhi 110019.
T: 91 11 41699117
W: http://edition.cnn.com/middleeast

INDONESIA — Tel: 62
Standard Time: GMT +7 to +9
Continent: Asia
Capital City: Jakarta

NEWSPAPERS & PUBLICATIONS

NEWSPAPERS

Bangka Pos
Editorial: PT Bangka Media Grafika, Jl. Abdulrahman Sidik No.1B, Pangkal Pinang 33127. **T:** 62 717437084
E: redaksi@bangkapos.com
W: http://www.bangkapos.com
Freq: Daily; **Circ:** 15002 Not Audited
Editor in Chief: Agus Ismunarno
Editorial Profile: Covers local, national, international news, as well as entertainment, business, politics, etc.
Language (s): Bahasa Indonesia
DAILY NEWSPAPER

Banjarmasin Post
Editorial: Banjasmasin Post, Gedung HJ Djok Mentaya, Jl AS Musyaffa No16, Banjarmasin 70111. **T:** 62 5113354370
E: redaksi@banjarmasinpost.co.id
W: http://www.banjarmasinpost.co.id
Freq: Daily; **Circ:** 40001 Not Audited
Editorial Profile: Newspaper covering regional, national, and international news, as well as entertainment, sports, politics, etc.
Language (s): Bahasa Indonesia
DAILY NEWSPAPER

Batam Pos
Editorial: PT Ripos Bintana Press, Gedung Graha Pena Lt.1-2, Jl. Raya Batam Center, Batam 29461. **T:** 62 778460000
E: redaksi@batampos.co.id
W: http://www.batampos.co.id
Freq: Daily; **Circ:** 50003 Not Audited
Editor in Chief: Hasan Aspahani
Editorial Profile: Newspaper focusing on national, international, and regional news, as well as politics, economy, entertainment, sports, etc.
Language (s): Bahasa Indonesia
DAILY NEWSPAPER

Bisnis Bali
Editorial: Gedung Pers Balik, Jl. Kebo Iwa 63A, Denpasar. **T:** 62 361416676
W: http://www.bisnisbali.com
Freq: Daily; **Circ:** 3501 Not Audited
Editorial Profile: Daily newspaper focusing on business and finance.
Language (s): Bahasa Indonesia
DAILY NEWSPAPER

Bisnis Indonesia
Editorial: Wisma Bisnis Indonesia Lt. 5-8, Jl KH Mas Mansyur Kav 12A Karet Tengsin, Jakarta 10220. **T:** 62 21 5790-1023
W: http://en.bisnis.com
Freq: Daily
Editor in Chief: Arief Budisusilo
Editorial Profile: Launched in December 1985 and covers business and economic news in Indonesia.
Language (s): Indonesian
DAILY NEWSPAPER

Galamedia
Editorial: PT Galamedia Bandung Perkasa, Jln. Blk. Factory No. 2B-2C, Bandung 40111.
T: 62 224210063
E: surga.galamedia@gmail.com
W: http://www.klik-galamedia.com
Freq: Daily; **Circ:** 40001 Not Audited
Editorial Profile: Covers local, national, and international news, as well as business, economy, entertainment, sports, etc.
Language (s): Bahasa Indonesia
DAILY NEWSPAPER

Harian Berita Sore
Editorial: Jl. Letjen Supsapto N.1, Medan 20151. **T:** 62 614150858
E: redaksi@beritasore.com
W: http://www.beritasore.com
Freq: Daily; **Circ:** 8001 Not Audited
Editor in Chief: H. Teruna Said
Editorial Profile: Daily newspaper covering national, regional, and international news, as well as politics, entertainment, business, etc.
Language (s): Bahasa Indonesia
DAILY NEWSPAPER

Harian Bernas
Editorial: Redaksi Hassan Bernas Jogja, Jl. IKIP PGRI - Sonosewu, Yogyakarta 55162.
T: 62 274377559 **E:** editor@bernas.co.id
W: http://www.bernas.co.id
Freq: Daily; **Circ:** 25006 Not Audited
Editor in Chief: Bimo Sukarno
Editorial Profile: Daily newspaper focusing on national, international, and regional news, as well as politics, economy, entertainment, sports, etc.
Language (s): Bahasa Indonesia
DAILY NEWSPAPER

Harian Cenderawasih Pos
Owner: PT. Cenderawasih Arena Intim Press
Editorial: PT. Cenderawasih Arena Intim Press, Jl. Cenderawasih No. 10, Kelapa Dua Entrop, Jayapura 99013 **E:** cepos_jpr@yahoo.com
W: http://www.cenderawasihpos.com

Freq: Daily; **Circ:** 12502 Not Audited
Editor in Chief: Lucky Ireeuw
Editorial Profile: Covers local, national, international news, as well as business, entertainment, politics, sports, etc.
Language (s): Bahasa Indonesia
DAILY NEWSPAPER

Harian Ekonomi Neraca
Editorial: PT Daya Cipta Aksara, Jl.Teuku Cik Di Tiro No.68B, Jakarta Pusat.
T: 62 21 31931991 **E:** neracadaily@yahoo.com
W: http://www.neracaonline.com
Freq: 2 Times/Week; **Circ:** 26004 Not Audited
Editor in Chief: Firdaus Baderi
Editorial Profile: Covers business and financial news.
Language (s): Bahasa Indonesia
NEWSPAPER

Harian Fajar
Editorial: Gedung Graha Pena, Lt. 4, Jl. Urip Sumoharjo No. 21, Jl. Racing Centre 101, Makassar 90231. **T:** 62 411441441
E: redaksi@fajar.co.id
W: http://www.fajar.co.id
Freq: Daily; **Circ:** 65002 Not Audited
Editor in Chief: Sukriansyah Latief
Editorial Profile: Covers local, national, and international news, as well as business, entertainment, politics, sports, etc.
Language (s): Bahasa Indonesia
DAILY NEWSPAPER

Harian Indonesia
Editorial: Jl. Gajah Mada No.96-97, Jakarta Pusat 11140. **T:** 62 2163868348
W: http://www.harian-indonesia.com
Freq: Daily; **Circ:** 50007 Not Audited
Editorial Profile: Daily newspaper focusing on business and financial issues.
Language (s): Chinese
DAILY NEWSPAPER

Harian Komentar
Editorial: PT Azravi, Kompleks Ruko Megamas, Blok IB No. 38, Manado.
T: 62 431879799
E: redaksi@hariankomentar.com
W: http://www.hariankomentar.com
Freq: Daily; **Circ:** 20001 Not Audited
Editor in Chief: Friko S. Poli; **Editor:** Ricky Tulalo
Editorial Profile: Newspaper covering regional, national, and international news, as well as entertainment, sports, politics, etc.
Language (s): Bahasa Indonesia
DAILY NEWSPAPER

Harian Olahraga GOSport
Editorial: Media GO, Jl. Kramat Pela No. 17A, Rt. 08/04 Pulo, Jakarta. **T:** 62 21 98294963
E: redaksi@mediago.or.id
W: http://www.mediago.or.id
Freq: Daily; **Circ:** 250001 Not Audited
Editor in Chief: Rahmi Aries Nova
Editorial Profile: Covers sports news, especially soccer.
Language (s): Bahasa Indonesia
DAILY NEWSPAPER

Indopos
Editorial: Jawa Pos Group, Graha Pena Lantai 10, Jalan Kebayoran Lama No.12, Jakarta Selatan 12210. **T:** 62 2153699556
E: editor@indopos.co.id
W: http://www.indopos.co.id
Freq: Daily; **Circ:** 110002 Not Audited
Editor in Chief: Don Kardono
Editorial Profile: Covers local, national, international news, as well as business, entertainment, politics, sports, etc.
Language (s): Bahasa Indonesia
DAILY NEWSPAPER

Investor Daily Indonesia
Editorial: PT Koran Media Investor Indonesia, Aryaduta Suite, Tower A, Lt. 1, Jl. Gamisun Dalam No.8, Karet Semanggi, Jakarta 12930.
T: 62 2157901350
E: koraninvestor@investor.co.id
W: http://www.investorindonesia.com
Freq: Daily; **Circ:** 40002 Not Audited
Editor: Rizagana -; **Editor:** Muhammad Ali; **Editor:** Abdul Aziz; **Editor in Chief:** Primus Dorimulu; **Editor:** Euis Rita Hartati; **Editor:** Imelda Rahmawati
Editorial Profile: Covers investor issues in Indonesia.
Language (s): Bahasa Indonesia
DAILY NEWSPAPER

The Jakarta Globe
Editorial: PT Jakarta Globe Media, Kawasan Bisnis Granadha, Plaza Semanggi 9th Floor, Jl. Jend. Sudirman Kav. 50, Karet Semanggi, Jakarta 12930. **T:** 62 2125535053
E: contactus@thejakartaglobe.com
W: http://www.thejakartaglobe.com
Freq: Daily
Editor in Chief: Theo L. Sambuaga
Editorial Profile: Daily newspaper focusing on national, international, and regional news, as well as politics, economy, entertainment, sports, etc.
Language (s): English
DAILY NEWSPAPER

The Jakarta Post
Editorial: PT Bina Media Tenggara, Jl. Palmerah Barat 142-143, Jakarta 10270.
T: 62 21 530 04 76
W: http://www.thejakartapost.com
Freq: Daily; **Circ:** 40000 Not Audited
Editor: Bruce Emond; **Editor:** Hendrasyah Tarmizi
Editorial Profile: Covers news and current affairs - national, international, local, sports, etc.
Language (s): English
DAILY NEWSPAPER

Jambi Independent
Owner: PT Jambi Independent Press
Editorial: PT Jambi Independent Press, Jl. Jenderal Sudirman No.100, Thekok, Jambi City. **T:** 62 74135272
E: redaksi@jambi-independent.co.id
W: http://www.jambi-independent.co.id
Freq: Daily; **Circ:** 20002 Not Audited
Editor in Chief: Joni Rizal
Editorial Profile: Covers local, national, international news, as well as business, entertainment, politics, sports, etc.
Language (s): Bahasa Indonesia
DAILY NEWSPAPER

Jawa Pos
Editorial: PT Jawa Pos, Graha Pena Building Lt. 4, Surabaya 60234. **T:** 62 38283333
E: info@jawapos.co.id
W: http://www.jawapos.co.id
Freq: Daily; **Circ:** 380001 Not Audited
Editor in Chief: Leak Koestiya
Editorial Profile: Newspaper covering regional, national, and international news, as well as entertainment, sports, politics, etc.
Language (s): Bahasa Indonesia
DAILY NEWSPAPER

Kedaulatan Rakyat
Editorial: Kedaulatan Rakyat, Jl. P. Mangkubumi No. 40-44, Yogyakarta 55232.
T: 62 274565685 **W:** http://www.kr.co.id
Freq: Daily; **Circ:** 100001 Not Audited
Editorial Profile: Newspaper covering regional, national, and international news, as well as entertainment, sports, politics, etc.
Language (s): Bahasa Indonesia
DAILY NEWSPAPER

Kompas
Owner: PT Kompas Cyber Media
Editorial: PT Kompas Cyber Media, Gedung Kompas Gramedia, Unit 2 Lt. 5, Jl. Palmerah Selatan No. 22-28, Jakarta 10270.
T: 62 215350377 **E:** redaksikcm@kompas.co.id
W: http://www.kompas.com
Freq: Daily Not Audited
Editorial Profile: Covers news, politics, science, travel, entertainment, etc.
Language (s): Bahasa Indonesia
DAILY NEWSPAPER

Kontan
Editorial: PT. Grahanusa Mediatama, Jl. Kebayoran Lama No.3119, Jakarta 12210.
T: 62 21 5357636 **E:** red@kontan.co.id
W: http://www.kontan.co.id
Freq: Daily; **Circ:** 75004 Not Audited
Editor in Chief: Ardian Taufik Gesuri; **Editor:** Gloria Haraito; **Editor:** Hasbi Maulana; **Editor:** Rumanus Cipta Wahyana
Editorial Profile: Covers business and industry news, personal finance, investments, the economy, etc.
Language (s): Bahasa Indonesia
DAILY NEWSPAPER

Kontan Mingguan
Editorial: Gedung Kontan, Jl. Kebayoran Lama No.3119, Jakarta 12210. **T:** 62 215357636
E: red@kontan.co.id
W: http://www.kontan.co.id
Freq: Weekly; **Circ:** 90001 Not Audited
Editor in Chief: Ardian Taufik Gesuri; **Editor:** Harris Hadinata; **Editor:** YN Djumyati Partawidjaja
Editorial Profile: Daily newspaper focusing on business, finance, economy, and investments.
Language (s): Bahasa Indonesia
NEWSPAPER

Koran Tempo
Editorial: Redaksi Tempo Interakrif, Kebayoran Center Blok A 11- A 15, Jalan Kebayoran Baru - Mayestik, Jakarta 12440. **T:** 62 217255625
E: interaktif@tempo.co.in
W: http://www.korantempo.com
Freq: Daily; **Circ:** 200002 Not Audited
Editor in Chief: Malela Mahargesari
Editorial Profile: Newspaper focusing on national, international, and regional news, as well as politics, economy, entertainment, sports, etc.
Language (s): Bahasa Indonesia
DAILY NEWSPAPER

Lampung Post
Editorial: Media Indonesia Group, Jl. Soekarno Hatta No.108, Rajabasa, Bandar Lampung. **T:** 62 721783693
E: redaksil@lampung.co.id
W: http://www.lampungpost.com
Freq: Daily; **Circ:** 30001 Not Audited
Editor in Chief: Djadjat Sudradjat
Editorial Profile: Daily newspaper covering national, international, regional news, as well as entertainment, politics, etc.
Language (s): Bahasa Indonesia
DAILY NEWSPAPER

Malang Post
Editorial: Malang Post, Jl. Sriwijaya 1-9, Malang. **T:** 62 341340081
E: redaksi@malang-post.com
W: http://www.malang-post.com
Freq: Daily; **Circ:** 35007 Not Audited
Editor: Mahmudi -; **Editor in Chief:** Sunavip Ra Indrata
Editorial Profile: Newspaper focusing on national, international, and regional news, as well as politics, economy, entertainment, sports, etc.
Language (s): Bahasa Indonesia
DAILY NEWSPAPER

Manado Post
Owner: Jawa Post Group
Editorial: Jawa Post Group, Manado Post Center, Jl. Babe Palar No.62, Manado.
T: 62 431855558 **E:** infor@jpnn.com
W: http://www.manadopost.com
Freq: Daily; **Circ:** 35002 Not Audited
Editor in Chief: Suhendro Boroma
Editorial Profile: Covers local, national, and international news, as well as sports, entertainment, politics, business, etc.
Language (s): Bahasa Indonesia
DAILY NEWSPAPER

Media Indonesia
Editorial: Komplek Delta Kedoya, Jl. Pilar Raya, Kav. A-D Kedoya Selatan, Kebon Jeruk, Jakarta Barat 11520. **T:** 62 215812088
E: redaksi@mediaindonesia.com
W: http://www.mediaindonesia.com
Freq: Daily; **Circ:** 220001 Not Audited
Editor in Chief: Toeti Adhitama; **Editor:** Sadyo Kristianto; **Editor:** Andy Noya; **Editor:** Rosmery Sihombing
Editorial Profile: Newspaper covering regional, national, and international news, as well as entertainment, sports, politics, etc.
Language (s): Bahasa Indonesia
DAILY NEWSPAPER

Metro Banjar
Editorial: PT Grafika Wangi Kalimantan, Gedung HJ Djok Mentaya, Jl AS Musyaffa No16, Banjarmasin 70111. **T:** 62 5113354370
E: redaksi@banjarmasinpost.co.id
W: http://www.banjarmasinpost.co.id
Freq: Daily; **Circ:** 20001 Not Audited
Editorial Profile: Covers local and international news, as well as entertainment, business, sports, etc.
Language (s): Bahasa Indonesia
DAILY NEWSPAPER

Metro Riau
Editorial: PT Metro Riau, Metro Graha Pena, Jl. Soekarno Hatta No.20-28, Pekanbaru
E: redaksi@metroriau.com
W: http://www.metroriau.com
Freq: Daily
Editor: Saparudin Koto; **Editor:** Adlis Pitrajaya
Editorial Profile: Covers local, national, and international news, as well as entertainment, politics, finance, etc.
Language (s): Bahasa Indonesia
DAILY NEWSPAPER

Padang Ekspres (Daily Morning Express Padang)
Editorial: Jln. By Pass KM., No. 7, Padang.
T: 0751 841254
E: redaksi@padangekspres.co.id
W: http://padangekspres.co.id
Freq: Daily
Editor: Nashrian Bahzein; **Editor:** Heri Sugiarto
Editorial Profile: Daily coverage of Indonesian and international news.
Language (s): Indonesian
DAILY NEWSPAPER

Pekanbaru Pos
Owner: Riau Pos Group
Editorial: Riau Pos Group, Gedung Pekanbaru Pos, Jl. Soekarno Hatta No. 132, Pekanbaru
Freq: Daily; **Circ:** 15002 Not Audited
Editorial Profile: Covers local, national, and international news, as well as business, health, sports. etc.
Language (s): Bahasa Indonesia
DAILY NEWSPAPER

Pikiran Rakyat
Editorial: PT Pikiran Rakyat, Jl. Soekarno Hatta No. 147, Bandung 40223.
T: 62 226037755
E: redaksi@pikiran-rakyat.com
W: http://www.pikiran-rakyat.com
Freq: Daily; **Circ:** 180002 Not Audited
Editor in Chief: Budiana Kartawijaya
Editorial Profile: Covers local, national, and international news, as well as entertainment, business, sports, politics, etc.
Language (s): Bahasa Indonesia
DAILY NEWSPAPER

Pontianak Post
Owner: PT.Akcaya Utama Press Pontianak
Editorial: PT.Akcaya Utama Press Pontianak, Jl. Gajahmada 2-4, Pontianak 78121.
T: 62 561735071
E: redaksi@pontianakpost.com
W: http://www.pontianakpost.com
Freq: Daily; **Circ:** 40002 Not Audited
Editor in Chief: B. Salman
Editorial Profile: Covers local, national, international news, as well as business, entertainment, politics, sports, etc.
Language (s): Bahasa Indonesia
DAILY NEWSPAPER

Pos Kota
Editorial: Yayasan Antar Kota, Jl. Gajah Mada 98-100, Jakarta 11140. **T:** 62 216340874
W: http://www.poskota.co.id
Freq: Daily; **Circ:** 300000 Not Audited
Editor in Chief: Joko Lestasi
Editorial Profile: Daily newspaper focusing on national, international, and regional news, as well as politics, economy, entertainment, sports, etc.
Language (s): Bahasa Indonesia
DAILY NEWSPAPER

Pos Kupang
Editorial: PT Timor Media Grafika, Jl. Kenari No. 1, Naikoten I, Kupang 85115.
T: 62 380 833820 **E:** poskpg@yahoo.com
W: http://www.pos-kupang.com
Freq: Daily; **Circ:** 15003 Not Audited
Editor: Benny Dasman; **Editor:** Damyan Godho; **Editor:** Tony Kleden; **Editor in Chief:** Dion Putra
Editorial Profile: Covers local and international news, as well as entertainment, business, sports, etc.
Language (s): Bahasa Indonesia
DAILY NEWSPAPER

Radar Bogor
Editorial: Pena Graha Bogor, Jl. KH.R. Abdullah Bin. Muhammad Nuh No. 30, Taman Yasmin, Bogor 16310. **T:** 62 2517544001
E: editorial@radar.bogor.com
W: http://www.radar-bogor.co.id
Freq: Daily
Editorial Profile: Daily newspaper focusing on national, international, and regional news, as well as politics, economy, entertainment, sports, etc.
Language (s): Bahasa Indonesia
DAILY NEWSPAPER

Rakyat Merdeka
Editorial: Gedung, Graha Pena, Lt. 8, Jalan Raya Kebayoran Lama No. 12, Jakarta Selatan 12210. **T:** 62 2153699507
W: http://www.rakyatmerdeka.co.id
Freq: Daily; **Circ:** 350001 Not Audited
Editor in Chief: Teguh Santosa
Editorial Profile: Newspaper covering local, national, and international news, as well as politics, entertainment, economy, etc.
Language (s): Bahasa Indonesia
DAILY NEWSPAPER

Republika
Editorial: PT Republika Media Mandiri, Jl. Warung Buncit Raya, No. 37, Jakarta 12510.
T: 62 21 7803747
E: sekretariat@republika.co.id

W: http://www.republika.co.id
Freq: Daily; **Circ:** 150001 Not Audited
Editor in Chief: Ikhwanul Kiram Mashuri
Editorial Profile: Newspaper covering regional, national, and international news, as well as entertainment, sports, politics, etc.
Language (s): Bahasa Indonesia
DAILY NEWSPAPER

Riau Pos
Owner: PT Riau Pos Intermedia
Editorial: PT Riau Pos Intermedia, Gedung Riau Pos Group, Jalan HR Soebrantas KM 10.5, Pekanbaru 28282
E: redaksi@riaupos.co.id
W: http://www.riaupos.com
Freq: Daily; **Circ:** 35002 Not Audited
Editor in Chief: Raja Isyam Azwar
Editorial Profile: Covers local, national, and international news, as well as entertainment, business, sports, politics, etc.
Language (s): Bahasa Indonesia
DAILY NEWSPAPER

Seputar Indonesia
Editorial: MNC Tower Lt.22, Jl. Kebon Sirih Raya No. 17-19, Jakarta 10340.
T: 62 213926955
E: redaksi@seputar-indonesia.com
W: http://www.seputar-indonesia.com
Freq: Daily; **Circ:** 364537 Not Audited
Editor in Chief: Sururi Alfaruq
Editorial Profile: Daily newspaper focusing on national, international, and regional news, as well as politics, economy, entertainment, sports, etc.
Language (s): Bahasa Indonesia
DAILY NEWSPAPER

Serambi Indonesia
Editorial: PT Serambi Prima Grafika, Desa Meunasah, 5 Tanjung Permai, Manyang PA, Ingin Jaya, Aceh Besar, Banda Aceh.
T: 62 651635544
E: redaksi@serambinews.com
W: http://www.serambinews.com **Circ:** 30002 Not Audited
Editor in Chief: Mawardi Ibrahim
Editorial Profile: Covers local, national, and international news, as well as business, economy, entertainment, sports, etc.
Language (s): Bahasa Indonesia
DAILY NEWSPAPER

Solo Pos
Editorial: PT Aksara Solo Pos, Griya Solo Pos, Jl. Adisucipto No.190, Surakarta 57145.
T: 62 27 1724811 **W:** http://www.solopos.co.id
Freq: Daily; **Circ:** 50003 Not Audited
Editor in Chief: Ya Sunyoto
Editorial Profile: Covers local, national, and international news, as well as business, economy, entertainment, sports, etc.
Language (s): Bahasa Indonesia
DAILY NEWSPAPER

Spirit NTT
Editorial: PT Timor Media Grafika, Jl. Kenari No. 1, Kelurahan Naikoten I, Kupang 85118.
T: 62 380828993 **E:** spirit_ntt@yahoo.com
W: http://spiritentete.blogspot.com/
Freq: Weekly; **Circ:** 5001 Not Audited
Editor in Chief: Dion Putra
Editorial Profile: Focuses on news in Kupang and surrounding areas.
Language (s): Bahasa Indonesia
NEWSPAPER

Sriwijaya Post
Editorial: PT Sriwijaya Perdana, Jl. Jend. Basuki Rahmat No.1608 B-D, Palembang 30135. **T:** 62 711310088
W: http://www.palembang.tribunenews.com
Freq: Daily; **Circ:** 42001 Not Audited
Editorial Profile: Covers national, regional, and international news, politics, entertainment, and other current affairs.
Language (s): Bahasa Indonesia
DAILY NEWSPAPER

Suara Karya
Editorial: PT Suara Karya Membangun, Gedung AKA, Jl. Bangka Raya No. 2, Kebayoran Baru, Jakarta 12720.
T: 62 217191352
E: redaksi@suarakarya-online.com
W: http://www.suarakarya-online.com
Freq: Daily; **Circ:** 85001 Not Audited
Editor in Chief: Ricky Rachmadi
Editorial Profile: Newspaper covering regional, national, and international news, as well as entertainment, sports, politics, etc.
Language (s): Bahasa Indonesia
DAILY NEWSPAPER

Suara Merdeka
Editorial: Jl. Pandanasan 30, Semarang.
T: 62 248412600
E: redaksi@suaramerdeka.com
W: http://www.suaramerdeka.com
Freq: Daily; **Circ:** 170006 Not Audited
Editor in chief: Hendra Setiawan Kelana
Editorial Profile: Daily newspaper focusing on national, international, and regional news, as well as politics, economy, entertainment, sports, etc.
Language (s): Bahasa Indonesia
DAILY NEWSPAPER

Suara NTB
Editorial: Global FM Lombok, Jalan Bangau No.15, Cakra Negara, Mataram.
T: 62 370639543
E: hariansuarantb@yahoo.com
W: http://www.suarantb.com
Freq: Daily; **Circ:** 6001 Not Audited
Editorial Profile: Covers local news.
Language (s): Bahasa Indonesia
DAILY NEWSPAPER

Suara Pembaruan
Editorial: The Aryaduta Suites, Tower A, Lt 1, Jl. Garnisun Dalam No. 8 Karet Semanggi, Jakarta 13630. **T:** 62 2157851555
E: koransp@suarapembaruan.com
W: http://www.suarapembaruan.com
Freq: Daily; **Circ:** 200001 Not Audited
Editorial Profile: Daily newspaper covering news, entertainment, politics, etc.
Language (s): Bahasa Indonesia
DAILY NEWSPAPER

Sumatera Ekspres
Editorial: PT Citsa Bumi Sumatera, Jl. kol. Haji Barlian, No.773, KM 6,5 Palembang, Palembang 30152. **T:** 62 711411768
E: redaksi@sumeks.co.id
W: http://www.sumeks.co.id
Freq: Daily; **Circ:** 75006 Not Audited
Editor in Chief: Hj. Mahmud -
Editorial Profile: Daily newspaper focusing on national, international, and regional news, as well as politics, economy, entertainment, sports, etc.
Language (s): Bahasa Indonesia
DAILY NEWSPAPER

Sumut Pos
Editorial: PT Media Medan Pers, Graha Pena Medan Lt.3, Jl. Sisinga Maharaja KM 8,5 No.134, Amplas, Medan 20148.
T: 62 617881661
E: redaksi@hariansumutpos.com
W: http://www.hariansumutpos.com
Freq: Daily
Editor in Chief: Indrawan -; **Editor:** Faliruddin Lubis
Editorial Profile: Covers local, national, and international news, as well as politics, entertainment and economy.
Language (s): Bahasa Indonesia
DAILY NEWSPAPER

Surya
Editorial: Jl. Rungkut Industry III No. 68 & 70 S, SIER, Surabaya 60239. **T:** 62 318419000
E: redaksi@surya.co.id
W: http://www.surya.co.id
Freq: Daily; **Circ:** 140001 Not Audited
Editor: Kistyarini -; **Editor in Chief:** Rusdi Amral; **Editor:** Sigit Sugiharto
Editorial Profile: Newspaper covering regional, national, and international news, as well as entertainment, sports, politics, etc.
Language (s): Bahasa Indonesia
DAILY NEWSPAPER

Tribun Batam
Editorial: PT Tribun Media Grafika, Komplek MCP Jl Kerapu, Batu Ampar, Batam 29433.
T: 62 77 8414326 **E:** redaksi@tribunnews.com
W: http://www.tribunnewsbatam.com
Freq: Daily; **Circ:** 30004 Not Audited
Editor: Febby Mahendra Putra; **Editor:** Dedy Suwadha
Editorial Profile: Covers local, national, regional, and international news, as well as business, entertainment, sports, etc.
Language (s): Bahasa Indonesia
DAILY NEWSPAPER

Tribun Jabar
Editorial: PT Bandung Media Grafika, Jl Sekelimus Utara No. 2-4, Bandung 40266.
T: 62 227530666 **E:** redaksi@tribunjabar.co.id
W: http://tribunjabar.co.id
Freq: Daily; **Circ:** 75001 Not Audited
Editor: Adityas Annas Azhari; **Editor in Chief:** Cecep Bundansyah
Editorial Profile: Newspaper covering regional, national, and international news, as well as entertainment, sports, politics, etc.

Language (s): Bahasa Indonesia
DAILY NEWSPAPER

Tribun Kaltim
Editorial: PT Mahakam Media Grafika, Jl., Rt 52 No. 1 Kampun Timus, Balikpapan 76125.
T: 62 542735015 **E:** redaksi@tribunkaltim.co.id
W: http://www.tribunkaltim.co.id
Freq: Daily; **Circ:** 25002 Not Audited
Editor in Chief: Achmad Subechi
Editorial Profile: Covers local, national, and international news, as well as business, health, sports. etc.
Language (s): Bahasa Indonesia
DAILY NEWSPAPER

Tribun Pekanbaru
Editorial: Kompas Group, Jl. Imam Munandar No.383, RT01/RW04 Bukit Raya, Pekanbaru 28281 **E:** tribunpekanbaru@yahoo.co.id
W: http://www.tribunpekanbaru.com
Freq: Daily
Editor in Chief: RHR Dodi Sarjana
Editorial Profile: Daily newspaper focusing on national, international, and regional news, as well as politics, economy, entertainment, sports, etc.
Language (s): Bahasa Indonesia
DAILY NEWSPAPER

Tribun Timur
Editorial: PT Bosowa Media Grafika, Jl. Cendsawasih No.430, Makassar 90134.
T: 62 4118115555
E: redaksi@tribun-timur.com
W: http://www.tribun-timur.com
Freq: Daily; **Circ:** 40006 Not Audited
Editor in Chief: Dahlan Iskan
Editorial Profile: Newspaper focusing on national, international, and regional news, as well as politics, economy, entertainment, sports, etc.
Language (s): Bahasa Indonesia
DAILY NEWSPAPER

Ujung Pandang Ekspres
Editorial: PT Fajar UjungPandang Intermedia, Fajar Graha Pena Makassar LT1, Jl. Urip Sumoharjo No.20, Makassar. **T:** 62 411457457
E: redaksi@ujungpandangekspres.com
W: http://www.ujungpandangekspres.com
Freq: Daily; **Circ:** 12003 Not Audited
Editorial Profile: Newspaper focusing on national, international, and regional news, as well as politics, economy, entertainment, sports, etc.
Language (s): Bahasa Indonesia
DAILY NEWSPAPER

The Wall Street Journal (Indonesia)
Editorial: Deutsche Bank Building 14th #1402, Jalan Imam Bonjol No 80, Jakarta 10310.
T: 62 21 3983-1336
Bureau Chief: Patrick McDowell
DAILY NEWSPAPER

Waspada
Editorial: Bumi Warta Waspada, Jl Letjen Suprapto/Brigjen Katamso 1, Medan 20151.
T: 62 614150858
E: redaksi.online@waspada.co.id
W: http://www.waspada.co.id
Freq: Daily; **Circ:** 55001 Not Audited
Editor in Chief: Avian E Tumengkol
Editorial Profile: Covers regional, national, and international news, as well as entertainment.
Language (s): Bahasa Indonesia
DAILY NEWSPAPER

NEWS SERVICE/SYNDICATE

Agence France-Presse - Jakarta Bureau
Editorial: 17/F, Deutsche Bank Building, 80 Jalan Imam Bonjol, Jakarta 10310.
T: 62 21 193 6082
E: olivia.rondonuwu@afp.com
W: http://www.afp.com
Editorial Profile: Jakarta bureau of the international news and picture agency.
Language (s): English
NEWS SERVICE/SYNDICATE

Antara
Editorial: Wisma ANTARA, Lt.18-20, Jl. Medan Merdeka Selatan 17, P.O.Box 10012, Jakarta 10112. **T:** 62 21 3802383
E: seksetariatsedaksi@antara.co.id
W: http://www.antara.co.id
Freq: Daily
Editorial Profile: Distributes local, national, and international news.
Language (s): Bahasa Indonesia
NEWS SERVICE/SYNDICATE

Associated Press
Editorial: Deutsche Bank Building, Fl 14, Ste 1403-1404, JL Imam Banjol #80, Jakarta 10310. **T:** 62 21 3983-1269
Southeast Asia News Editor: Chris Brummitt
NEWS SERVICE/SYNDICATE

Bloomberg News
Editorial: Wisma Antara Suite 1604A, JLN Medan Merdeka Selatan 17, Jakarta 10110.
T: 62 2134353020
NEWS SERVICE/SYNDICATE

Dow Jones Newswires
Editorial: Deutsche Bank Building 14th #1402, Jalan Imam Bonjol No 80, Jakarta 10310.
T: 62 21 3983-1336
Bureau Chief: Patrick McDowell
NEWS SERVICE/SYNDICATE

Reuters
Editorial: Kantor Berita Reuter, Jakarta 10001.
T: 62 213846364
NEWS SERVICE/SYNDICATE

BROADCASTING

TELEVISION NETWORKS

BBC Indonesia
Editorial: Deutsche Bank, Lantai 15, Jl. Imam Bonjol No.80, Jakarta 10310.
T: 62 21 39831635 **E:** indonesian@bbc.co.uk
W: http://www.bbc.co.uk/indonesia
Editorial Profile: Covers local, national, and international news, as well as economic and political issues.

IRAN — Tel: 98
Standard Time: GMT +3.5
Continent: Asia
Capital City: Tehran

NEWSPAPERS & PUBLICATIONS

NEWSPAPERS

Abrar
Owner: Abrar Publications Group
Editorial: Block 17, Shaheed Beheshti Street, Qaem Maqam Farahani, Tehran.
T: 98 21 8870 0804 **E:** info@abrarnews.com
W: http://www.abrarnews.com
Freq: Daily
Editorial Profile: Abrar is a daily Persian newspaper covering news, politics, business, cinema, culture and sports. It launched in 1993.
Language (s): Persian
DAILY NEWSPAPER

Abrar Eghtesadi
Owner: Abrar Publications Group
Editorial: Block 17, Shaheed Beheshti Street, Qaem Maqam Farahani, Tehran.
T: 98 21 8870 0804 **E:** abrar1388@yahoo.com
W: http://www.abrarnews.com
Freq: Daily
Editorial Profile: Abrar Eghtesadi (Daily Economic News) is a Persian newspaper covering business, economics, energy, banking, stocks and information technology. The newspaper launched in 2000 and is aimed at business executives in Iran.
Language (s): Persian
DAILY NEWSPAPER

Abrar Varzeshi
Owner: Abrar Publications Group
Editorial: Block 17, Shaheed Beheshti Steet, Qaem Maqam Farahani, Tehran.
T: 98 21 8870 0804
E: varzeshi_abrar@yahoo.com
W: http://www.abrarnews.com
Freq: Daily
Editorial Profile: Abrar Varzeshi is a daily sports newspaper focusing on the latest football news worldwide. The newspaper launched in 1997, and is aimed at Iranian football fans.
Language (s): Persian
DAILY NEWSPAPER

Aftab Yazd
Owner: Chap-e Golriz
Editorial: PO Box 13145-1134, Unit 1, 1st Floor, No 10, 26th Street, Tehran 1513614714.
T: 98 21 8832 1397 **E:** aftab.yz@gmail.com
W: http://www.aftab-yazd.ir
Freq: Daily; **Circ:** 50000 Pub Statement

Editorial Profile: Aftab Yazd is a daily Persian newspaper covering local and international news, business and sport. It launched in 2001.
Language (s): Persian
DAILY NEWSPAPER

Asia
Owner: Asia
Editorial: Seoul Shopping Center, Sheikh Bahayi Square, Tehran. **T:** 98 21 8806 6537
E: info@asianews.ir
W: http://www.asianews.ir
Freq: Daily; **Circ:** 180000 Pub Statement
Editor In Chief: Iraj Jamshidi
Editorial Profile: Asia is a tabloid-sized Persian newspaper covering local and international business news, IT, health and entertainment. It launched in 2002 and is aimed at business executives in Iran.
Language (s): Persian
DAILY NEWSPAPER

Asr-e Eghtesad
Owner: Seifollah Yazdani Publication
Editorial: Unit 2, 1st Floor, Block 11, Dameshq Street, Tehran 14167-83863.
T: 98 21 8894 8104 **E:** eghtesad1@yahoo.com
W: http://www.asre-eqtesad.com
Freq: Daily; **Circ:** 15000 Pub Statement
Editorial Profile: Asr-e Eghtesad is a daily newspaper covering economic, social, cultural and sports news. It launched in 2003 and is mostly written in Persian, with two pages in English.
Language (s): English
DAILY NEWSPAPER

Donya-e-Eqtesad
Owner: Donya Eqtesad Taban
Editorial: PO Box 141-5744-344, No. 370, Between Mirzaye Shirazi and Sana'i Streets, Tehran. **T:** 98 21 8776 2511
E: info@donya-e-eqtesad.com
W: http://www.donya-e-eqtesad.com
Freq: Daily
Editor In Chief: Ali Mirzakhani
Editorial Profile: Donya-e-Eqtesad (Economy World) is a daily Persian newspaper covering national and international economic and business news. It launched in 2002, and is aimed at business executives in Iran.
Language (s): Persian
DAILY NEWSPAPER

Ebtekar
Owner: Kar-e Karghar
Editorial: Ground Floor, Block 56, Zartesht Gharbi, Tehran. **T:** 98 21 8897 5710
E: ebtekarnews@gmail.com
W: http://www.ebtekarnews.com
Freq: Daily; **Circ:** 30000 Pub Statement
Editor In Chief: Farzola Yari
Editorial Profile: Ebtekar is a Persian daily newspaper covering local and international news, politics, business and sport. It launched in 2003.
Language (s): Persian
DAILY NEWSPAPER

Eghtesad Pooya
Owner: Eghtesad Pooya Publication Co.
Editorial: PO Box 14155-8356, Block 44, 21st Street, Kurdestan Street, Tehran.
T: 98 21 8833 1615
E: eghtesadpooya@yahoo.com
W: http://www.eghtesadpooya.com
Freq: Daily; **Circ:** 100000 Pub Statement
Editor In Chief: Afshin Larijani
Editorial Profile: Eghtesad Pooya is a daily Persian newspaper covering business, finance and economics. It launched in 2004 and is aimed at Iranian business executives.
Language (s): Persian
DAILY NEWSPAPER

Esfahan Emrooz
Owner: Esfahan Emrooz Publication
Editorial: No. 5, Naderi Road, Daneshgah Street, Isfahan. **T:** 98 311 662 6566
E: esfahanemrooz@gmail.com
W: http://www.esfahanemrooz.com
Freq: Daily; **Circ:** 17500 Pub Statement
Editor In Chief: Amir Akbary
Editorial Profile: Esfahan Emrooz is a daily Persian newspaper covering news, politics, business and culture. It launched in 2004.
Language (s): Persian
DAILY NEWSPAPER

Etemaad
Owner: Etemaad
Editorial: Block 16, Road No. 8, Khajeh Abdulla Ansari Street, Tehran.
T: 98 21 2286 4761
E: lastpage.etemad@gmail.com
W: http://www.etemaad.ir
Freq: Daily
Editor in Chief: Javad Deliri
Editorial Profile: Etemaad is a Persian daily newspaper covering local and international news, business, politics and sport. It launched in 2001.
Language (s): Persian
DAILY NEWSPAPER

Iran
Owner: Islamic Republic News Agency
Editorial: PO Box 15875-5388, 208 Khoramshahr Street, Tehran.
T: 98 21 8876 1721
E: editorial@iran-newspaper.com
W: http://www.iran-newspaper.com
Freq: Daily; **Circ:** 360000 Pub Statement
Editor In Chief: Mohammad Nouri
Editorial Profile: Iran is a daily Persian newspaper covering national and international news, current affairs, politics, business and sports. It was first published in 1994.
Language (s): Persian
DAILY NEWSPAPER

Iran Daily
Owner: Islamic Republic News Agency
Editorial: PO Box 15875-5388, Block 208, Khorramshahr Avenue, Tehran.
T: 98 21 8875 5762
E: irandailynewspaper@gmail.com
W: http://www.iran-daily.com
Freq: Daily; **Circ:** 12000 Pub Statement
Editor: Mohammad Karimi
Editorial Profile: Iran Daily is a tabloid-sized English newspaper covering national and international news, current affairs, politics, business and sports. It launched in 1997, and is aimed at English speakers in Iran.
Language (s): English
DAILY NEWSPAPER

Iran News
Owner: Sokhan Gostar Institute
Editorial: PO Box 15875-8551, No. 13, Pajouhesh Str., Golestan II Street, Tehran 1463777745. **T:** 98 21 4425 3401
E: info@irannewsdaily.com
W: http://www.irannewsdaily.com
Freq: Daily; **Circ:** 15000 Pub Statement
News Editor: Kianoush Amiri; **Editor in Chief:** Fereydoon Taherpoor
Editorial Profile: Iran News is an English newspaper covering news, politics, economics, society and sports. It is published daily, except Fridays, and launched in 1994.
Language (s): English
DAILY NEWSPAPER

Jahane Sanat
Owner: Iranchap Company
Editorial: No. 60, Arak Street, Ostad Najatalahi Street, Tehran. **T:** 98 21 8893 4806
E: jahan1383@yahoo.com
W: http://www.jahanesanat.ir
Freq: Daily; **Circ:** 40000 Pub Statement
Editorial Profile: Jahane Sanat (World of Industry) is a daily Persian newspaper covering business and economics. It launched in 2004.
Language (s): Persian
DAILY NEWSPAPER

Jam-e-Jam
Owner: Islamic Republic Of Iran Broadcasting (IRIB)
Editorial: No. 129, Mirdamad Street, Tehran.
T: 98 21 2222 2511 **E:** info@jamejamonline.ir
W: http://www.jamejamonline.ir
Freq: Daily; **Circ:** 450000 Pub Statement
Editor In Chief: Mohsen Mandegari
Editorial Profile: Jam-e-Jam is a daily Persian newspaper focusing on national and international news, current affairs, politics, business and sports. The newspaper was launched in 2001.
Language (s): Persian
DAILY NEWSPAPER

Javan Newspaper
Owner: Payam Avaran Publishing
Editorial: No. 384, Shahid Motahari Street, Tehran. **T:** 98 21 8849 8449
E: info@javanonline.ir
W: http://www.javanonline.ir
Freq: Daily; **Circ:** 120000 Pub Statement
Editor In Chief: Seyed Nezamddine Mosavi
Editorial Profile: Javan Newspaper is a Persian daily covering local and international news, politics, business and sport. It was first published in 1999.
Language (s): Persian
DAILY NEWSPAPER

Khorasan
Owner: Khorasan
Editorial: PO Box 91735-511, Shaheed Sadeqi Blvd., Mashhad. **T:** 98 511 763 4000
E: info@khorasannews.com
W: http://www.khorasannews.com
Freq: Daily
Editor In Chief: Mohammad Ahadian
Editorial Profile: Khorasan is a Persian daily newspaper covering national & international news, politics, business, culture and arts. It was first published in 1948.
Language (s): Persian
DAILY NEWSPAPER

Quds
Owner: Astan Quds Radwi Publishing
Editorial: PO Box 91735-577, 14 Khayyam Square, Mashhad. **T:** 98 511 768 5011
E: info@qudsonline.ir
W: http://www.qudsonline.ir
Freq: Daily; **Circ:** 80000 Pub Statement
Editor In Chief: Hamza Vaqaei
Editorial Profile: Quds is a daily Persian newspaper covering national and international news, current affairs, politics, business and sports. It was first published in 1987.
Language (s): Persian
DAILY NEWSPAPER

Resalat
Owner: Resalat Publication
Editorial: No. 1, Shaheed Ismail Mohamadi Street, Tehran 1599976711.
T: 98 21 8891 0806 **E:** tadrisi60@gmail.com
W: http://www.resalat-news.com
Freq: Daily; **Circ:** 900000 Pub Statement
Editor In Chief: Mohammad-Kazem Ambarlaie
Editorial Profile: Resalat is a daily Persian newspaper covering national and international news, current affairs, politics, business and sports. It launched in 1985.
Language (s): Persian
DAILY NEWSPAPER

Sobhe Eghtesad
Owner: Sokhan Gostar Institute
Editorial: PO Box 15875-8551, No. 13, Pazhuhesh Alley, 2nd Golestan Alley, Tehran 1463777746. **T:** 98 21 4425 3335
E: info@sobheco.com
W: http://www.sobh-eqtesad.com
Freq: Daily; **Circ:** 45000 Pub Statement
Editor In Chief: Mariam Behnam-Rad
Editorial Profile: Sobhe Eghtesad (Morning Economy) is a daily Persian newspaper covering social, economic and political issues. It was first published in 1995.
Language (s): Persian
DAILY NEWSPAPER

Tehran Times
Owner: Islamic Ideology Dissemination Organisation
Editorial: PO Box 14155-4843, 18 Bimeh Lane, Tehran 1599814713.
T: 98 21 8889 5450 **E:** info@tehrantimes.com
W: http://www.tehrantimes.com
Freq: Daily; **Circ:** 10000 Pub Statement
Editor In Chief: Abolfazl Amouei
Editorial Profile: Tehran Times is a daily 16-page English newspaper covering national and international news, current affairs, politics, business and sports. It launched in 1979 and is aimed at English speakers in Iran.
Language (s): English
DAILY NEWSPAPER

Vatan-e Emrooz
Owner: Vatan-e Emrooz
Editorial: PO Box 159163-6587, Block 9, Saeed Street, Tehran 1213027200.
T: 98 21 6641 3783
E: vatanemrooz1387@gmail.com
W: http://www.vatanemrooz.ir
Freq: Daily
Editor In Chief: Reza Shakibaei
Editorial Profile: Vatan-e Emrooz is a daily Persian newspaper covering current affairs, politics, business, culture & sports. It launched in 2008.
Language (s): Persian
DAILY NEWSPAPER

Al Vefagh
Owner: Islamic Republic News Agency
Editorial: PO Box 15875-5388, 208 Khoramshahr, Tehran. **T:** 98 21 8847 1207
E: alvefagh@icpi.ir
W: http://www.al-vefagh.com
Freq: Daily; **Circ:** 19000 Pub Statement
Editor in Chief: Mohammad-Amin Bani Namin
Editorial Profile: Al Vefagh is a daily Arabic newspaper covering national and international news, current affairs, politics, business and sports. It launched in 1996.
Language (s): Arabic
DAILY NEWSPAPER

NEWS SERVICE/SYNDICATE

Agence France-Presse - Tehran Bureau
Owner: Agence France-Presse
Editorial: Tehran. **T:** 98 21 8872 3382
E: afp.tehran@afp.com
W: http://www.afp.com
Bureau Chief: Cyril Julien
Editorial Profile: Tehran bureau of international news and picture agency covering general news and current affairs.
Language (s): English
NEWS SERVICE/SYNDICATE

APTN Iran
Owner: Associated Press
Editorial: Unit 1, 6th Floor, Jam-e Jam Building, Tehran 1966843168.
T: 98 21 2202 3788 **E:** tehranaptn@yahoo.com
W: http://www.aptn.com
Editorial Profile: Associated Press Television News (APTN) is the international television arm of the Associated Press - APTN's operations include a main news service, specialised broadcast services, customised coverage for the Middle East, a productions division, weekly and daily entertainment news and an extensive video archive library.
Language (s): English
NEWS SERVICE/SYNDICATE

Fars News Agency
Owner: Fars News Agency
Editorial: PO Box 10815-3614, Block 1, Alley Shahid Saeidi, Tehran. **T:** 98 21 8891 1660
E: abas.info@gmail.com
W: http://www.farsnews.com
Editor In Chief: Abbas Darvish-Tavangar
Editorial Profile: Fars News Agency is an independent news agency covering Iranian news, politics, economics, culture, society, law, sports, and military news in Persian and English.
Language (s): Arabic
NEWS SERVICE/SYNDICATE

Iranian Students' News Agency
Owner: Iranian Students' News Agency
Editorial: Shohadaye Jandarmeri Alley, Fakhrerazi Alley, Tehran 1314744951.
T: 98 21 6641 7324 **E:** info@isna.ir
W: http://www.isna.ir
Editorial Profile: Iranian Students' News Agency is an independent news agency run by university students.
Language (s): Arabic
NEWS SERVICE/SYNDICATE

Islamic Republic News Agency
Owner: Islamic Republic News Agency
Editorial: PO Box 15875-4566, 873 Vali Asr Avenue, Tehran 1595633319.
T: 98 21 8890 5066 **E:** irna@irna.ir
W: http://www.irna.ir
Editorial Profile: Islamic Republic News Agency is an official government news agency founded in 1934.
Language (s): Arabic
NEWS SERVICE/SYNDICATE

Mehr News Agency
Owner: Mehr News Agency
Editorial: 18 Bimeh Lane, Nejatollahi Street, Tehran 1599814713. **T:** 98 21 8880 0789
E: president@mehrnews.com
W: http://www.mehrnews.com
Editorial Profile: Mehr News Agency is a semi-official news agency - transmits news and photos in 7 languages (Persian, English, Russian, German, Arabic, Turkish, and Urdu) - coverage includes culture and art, literature, religion, technology, society, economics, politics, international news, sport, energy and defence.
Language (s): Arabic
NEWS SERVICE/SYNDICATE

BROADCASTING

RADIO STATIONS

IRIB World Service
Owner: Islamic Republic Of Iran Broadcasting (IRIB)
Editorial: PO Box 19395-6767, IRIB English Service, Tehran. **T:** 98 21 2201 3720
E: englishradio@irib.ir **W:** http://english.irib.ir
Editorial Profile: IRIB World Service, also known as English Radio of the Islamic Republic of Iran, is an international radio station broadcasting the recitation of Quranic verses, news, political commentaries, different series and features on special occasions. The

station was established in 1956 with the aim of familiarising world nations with Iran's history and culture, as well as its different regions and historical sites. It is operated by state-owned public broadcaster, Islamic Republic Of Iran Broadcasting (IRIB), and generates around 180 minutes of programming each day in the form of recorded programmes, live news, commentaries and news reports.

TELEVISION STATIONS

Al Alam News Network
Owner: Islamic Republic Of Iran Broadcasting (IRIB)
Editorial: PO Box 19615-885, Vali-Asr Street, Tehran. **T:** 98 21 2216 8720 **E:** info@alalam.ir
W: http://www.alalam.ir
Editorial Profile: Al Alam News Network is a state-owned television station broadcasting news and current affairs programmes in Arabic for 24-hours a day. The channel launched in 2003.

Amouzesh TV
Owner: Islamic Republic Of Iran Broadcasting (IRIB)
Editorial: No. 33, Eastern Shahid Atefi Str., Tehran. **T:** 98 21 2204 4958 **E:** sima7@irib.ir
W: http://www.tv7.ir
Editorial Profile: Amouzesh TV is a state-owned television station broadcasting cultural and educational programmes. The channel launched in 1999.

Azarbaijan-e Sharqi TV
Owner: Islamic Republic Of Iran Broadcasting (IRIB)
Editorial: PO Box 4444, IRIB East Azarbaijan Center, Bahman 29th Boulevard, Tabriz 5166617466. **T:** 98 411 330 3041
E: tabriz@irib.ir **W:** http://tabriz.irib.ir
Editorial Profile: Azarbaijan-e Sharqi TV is a state-owned, regional television station broadcasting youth, family, children's and sports programmes in the East Azarbaijan province of Iran. The chanel launched in 2000.

Channel 1
Owner: Islamic Republic Of Iran Broadcasting (IRIB)
Editorial: PO Box 19395-1351, 10th Floor, Toleed Building, Tehran. **T:** 98 21 2204 0420
E: sima1@irib.ir **W:** http://www.tv1.ir
Editorial Profile: Channel 1 is a state-owned television station broadcasting children's shows, drama series, Iranian movies, talk shows and news. The channel launched in 1966.

Channel 2
Owner: Islamic Republic Of Iran Broadcasting (IRIB)
Editorial: PO Box 15875-6874, Channel 2 Sima, Tehran. **T:** 98 21 8867 8860
E: sima2@irib.ir **W:** http://www.tv2.ir
Editorial Profile: Channel 2 is a state-owned television station broadcasting news and entertainment programmes, including mini-series, comedies, movies, children's shows and talk shows. The channel launched in 1970.

Channel 3
Owner: Islamic Republic Of Iran Broadcasting (IRIB)
Editorial: PO Box 19395-3334, No. 12, Tehran. **T:** 98 21 2204 0092 **E:** sima3@irib.ir
W: http://www.tv3.ir
Editorial Profile: Channel 3 is a state-owned television station broadcasting major Iranian sport events, mini-series, comedies, and movies. The channel launched in 1993.

Channel 4
Owner: Islamic Republic Of Iran Broadcasting (IRIB)
Editorial: PO Box 19395-6767, No.22 Mahnaz Str., Tehran. **T:** 98 21 2621 5600
E: sima4@irib.ir **W:** http://www.tv4.ir
Editorial Profile: Channel 4 is a state-owned television station broadcasting documentaries, academic conferences, interviews with scholars, artistic movies, plays and philosophical discussions. The channel launched in 1996.

Iran News Network
Owner: Islamic Republic Of Iran Broadcasting (IRIB)
Editorial: PO Box 19395-1351, Jam-e-Jam Street, Tehran. **T:** 98 21 2201 3911
E: pr@irinn.ir **W:** http://www.irinn.ir
Editorial Profile: Iran News Network (IRINN) is a free-to-air satellite channel broadcasting news and current affairs, as well as political, sports, science and medical programmes. The station launched in 1999.

Jam-e-Jam 1
Owner: Islamic Republic Of Iran Broadcasting (IRIB)
Editorial: No. 10, 18th Street Garbi, Saadat-Abad, Tehran 1997855533.
T: 98 21 2207 9381 **E:** jjtv@irib.ir
W: http://www.jjtvn.ir
Editorial Profile: Jam-e-Jam 1 is a state-owned television station broadcasting social, religious, cultural, literary, political, news, current affairs, sports and entertainment programmes. Launched in 1997, the free-to-air satellite channel is aimed at Iranian expatriates and Persian speakers in Europe, parts of Asia and the Middle East.

Jam-e-Jam 2
Owner: Islamic Republic Of Iran Broadcasting (IRIB)
Editorial: No. 10, 18th Street Garbi, Saadat-Abad, Tehran 1997855533.
T: 98 21 2207 9381 **E:** jjtv@irib.ir
W: http://www.jjtvn.ir
Editorial Profile: Jam-e-Jam 2 is a state-owned television station broadcasting Iranian movies, TV series, children's programmes, major Iranian sporting events and news. The free-to-air satellite channel is aimed at Iranian expatriates and Persian speakers in Europe, the USA and Canada.

Jam-e-Jam 3
Owner: Islamic Republic Of Iran Broadcasting (IRIB)
Editorial: No. 10, 18th Street Garbi, Saadat-Abad, Tehran 1997855533.
T: 98 21 2207 9381 **E:** jjtv@irib.ir
W: http://www.jjtvn.ir
Editorial Profile: Jam-e-Jam 3 is a state-owned television station broadcasting entertainment, news, sports, Islamic and children's programmes. Launched in 2002, the free-to-air satellite channel is aimed at Iranian expatriates and Persian speakers in the Indian subcontinent, Pakistan, Afghanistan and the Pacific.

Press TV
Owner: Press TV
Editorial: PO Box 19977-66411, 24 East 2nd Street, Block 6, Tehran. **T:** 98 21 2306 6170
E: info@presstv.ir **W:** http://www.presstv.com
Editorial Profile: Press TV is a state-owned television station broadcasting news and current affairs programmes, specifically focusing on the Middle East. The channel launched in 2007.

Sahar Universal Network
Owner: Islamic Republic Of Iran Broadcasting (IRIB)
Editorial: PO Box 19395-6767, Jame-e-Jam Street, Tehran. **T:** 98 21 2216 2887
E: sahartv@irib.ir **W:** http://www.sahartv.ir
Editorial Profile: Sahar Universal Network is a bouquet of television stations broadcasting religious, social and cultural programmes in seven languages. Launched in 1997, the free-to-air satellite network is aimed at viewers around the world.

Tehran TV
Owner: Islamic Republic Of Iran Broadcasting (IRIB)
Editorial: PO Box 19978-54469, Saadat Abad Street, Tehran 7388-19395.
T: 98 21 2351 1000 **E:** sima5@irib.ir
W: http://www.tv5.ir
Editorial Profile: Tehran TV, also known as Channel 5, is a regional television station broadcasting movies, local news, political, cultural, social, Islamic and youth programmes in the province of Tehran. The channel launched in 1995.

IRAQ — Tel: 964
Standard Time: GMT +3
Continent: Asia
Capital City: Baghdad

NEWSPAPERS & PUBLICATIONS

NEWSPAPERS

Al Adala
Owner: Al Adala Est. for Press Printing and Publishing
Editorial: Al Nobal Street, Baghdad.
T: 964 770 316 9999
E: aladalaeditor@yahoo.com
W: http://www.aladalanews.net
Freq: Daily; **Circ:** 6000 Pub Statement
Publisher: Adel Abdel Mahdi; **News Editor:** Morteza Al Jashami; **Editor In Chief:** Ali Khleif
Editorial Profile: Al Adala (Justice) is an Arabic newspaper covering local and international news, politics, business, culture and sport. It launched in 2003 and is published daily, except Fridays.
Language (s): Arabic
DAILY NEWSPAPER

Al Ahali
Owner: Dar Al Ahali Publishing
Editorial: Al Massbah, Baghdad.
T: 964 790 141 6751 **E:** info@ahali-iraq.net
W: http://www.ahali-iraq.net
Freq: Wed; **Circ:** 5000 Pub Statement
Editor In Chief: Heval Zaxoyi
Editorial Profile: Al Ahali is a weekly Arabic newspaper covering local and international news, politics, business and sport. It launched in 2002 and is published on Wednesdays.
Language (s): Arabic
NEWSPAPER

Al Ahali - Babel office
Owner: Dar Al Ahali Publishing
Editorial: Karradah, Babylon.
T: 964 780 171 4030 **E:** info@ahali-iraq.net
W: http://www.ahali-iraq.net
Freq: Wed
News Editor: Mohammad Al Bedayri
Editorial Profile: Babel office of Baghdad-based Al Ahali newspaper. The bureau covers news, politics, business and sport from the Babel region of Iraq.
Language (s): Arabic
NEWSPAPER

Al Ahali - Dohuk Office
Owner: Dar Al Ahali Publishing
Editorial: Bana Area, Dohuk.
T: 964 750 445 5596
E: samannoah@yahoo.com
W: http://www.ahali-iraq.net
Freq: Wed
News Editor: Abdul Karim Al Zebari
Editorial Profile: Dohuk office of Baghdad-based Al Ahali newspaper. The bureau covers news, politics, business and sport from the Dohuk region of Iraq.
Language (s): Arabic
NEWSPAPER

Alhayat
Owner: Al Hayat Art & Media Est.
Editorial: Beside Al Mashreq Club, Al Riyadh Area, Baghdad. **T:** 964 790 136 4515
E: alhayat_iraqi@yahoo.com
W: http://www.alhayatnews.net
Freq: Wed; **Circ:** 2500 Pub Statement
News Editor: Maiyad Al Sudani
Editorial Profile: Alhayat is a weekly broadsheet-sized newspaper covering local and international news, business and sport. It launched in 2005 and is published every Wednesday.
Language (s): Arabic
NEWSPAPER

Al Amal
Owner: Al Amal Publishing
Editorial: 2nd Floor, Roz Building, Salim Street, Sulaimaniyah. **T:** 964 770 156 4353
E: shelalgedo@yahoo.com
Freq: Mon; **Circ:** 2000 Pub Statement
Editor in Chief: Shelal Gedo; **News Editor:** Fethulla Huseyni
Editorial Profile: Al Amal (Hope) is a weekly Arabic newspaper covering local and international news, business and politics. It launched in 2005 and is published on Mondays.
Language (s): Arabic
NEWSPAPER

Attaakhi
Owner: Attaakhi Publishing & Printing House
Editorial: Building 7, Al Wehda Area, Street 52, Al Taharriyat Place 904, Baghdad.
T: 964 770 252 0610 **E:** muraslon@yahoo.com
W: http://www.altaakhipress.com
Freq: Daily; **Circ:** 12000 Pub Statement
Editor in Chief: Badir-Khan Al Sindi
Editorial Profile: Attaakhi is an Arabic newspaper covering local and international news, politics, business and sport. It launched in 1967 and is published daily, except Fridays.
Language (s): Arabic
DAILY NEWSPAPER

Azzaman
Owner: Azzaman International Ltd
Editorial: Building 9, Street no.4, Avenue 905, Baghdad. **T:** 964 1 717 7657
E: info@azzaman.com
W: http://www.azzaman.com
Freq: Daily; **Circ:** 50000 Pub Statement
Editor In Chief: Ahmed Abdulmajeed; **News Editor:** Ali Moussawi
Editorial Profile: Azzaman (The Time) is an Arabic newspaper covering local and international news, current affairs, business, culture and sport. The newspaper was founded in London in 1997 and is printed in Baghdad, London and Beirut. It is published daily, except Fridays.
Language (s): Arabic
DAILY NEWSPAPER

Dar Al-Salam
Owner: Iraqi Islamic Party
Editorial: Al Yarmouk Area, Baghdad.
T: 964 770 251 9999
E: basam_f_80@yahoo.com
Freq: Daily; **Circ:** 10000 Rate Card
News Editor: Bahauddin Naqshabandi
Editorial Profile: Dar Al-Salam is a daily Arabic newspaper covering national and international news, business and sport. It was launched in 2004 by the Iraqi Islamic Party.
Language (s): Arabic
DAILY NEWSPAPER

Al Ghad
Owner: Al Ghad Establishment for Media Production
Editorial: Building 25, Arafat Road, Al Karada Al Sharqiya, Baghdad. **T:** 964 790 172 0000
E: info@alghad-iq.com
W: http://www.alghad-iq.com
Freq: Daily; **Circ:** 7500
Editorial Profile: Al Ghad is a daily newspaper covering news, business, arts and sports. It was first published in January 2012.
Language (s): Arabic
DAILY NEWSPAPER

Al Hoda Newspaper
Owner: Dar Al Hoda for Culture & Media
Editorial: PO Box 155, Al Hussein Street, Karbala. **T:** 964 781 193 9492
E: al-hodaonline@al-hodaonline.com
W: http://www.al-hodaonline.com/np
Freq: Mon; **Circ:** 6000 Pub Statement
News Editor: Muzaffar Abbas; **Editor In Chief:** Nohman Al Tamimi; **News Editor:** Nabeel Mohsen
Editorial Profile: Al Hoda Newspaper is an Arabic weekly covering local and international news. It launched in 2005 and is published on Mondays.
Language (s): Arabic
NEWSPAPER

Al Ittihad
Owner: Patriotic Union of Kurdistan (PUK)
Editorial: PO Box 5436, Al Qadsiyah, Baghdad.
T: 964 770 252 1657
E: ittihadpress@hotmail.com
Freq: Daily; **Circ:** 5000 Pub Statement
News Editor: Satea Raji; **Editor-in-Chief:** Fryad Rwandzy
Editorial Profile: Al Ittihad (The Union) is a national newspaper covering news, business and sport. It was launched in 1992 by the Patriotic Union of Kurdistan (PUK).
Language (s): Arabic
DAILY NEWSPAPER

The Kurdish Globe
Owner: Mukiryani Establishment for Research & Publication
Editorial: Media Center, Maif Road, Erbil.
T: 964 750 774 7784
E: info.kurdishglobe@gmail.com
W: http://www.kurdishglobe.net
Freq: Mon; **Circ:** 3000
Editor in Chief: Gazi Hassan
Editorial Profile: The Kurdish Globe is a 16-page, regional weekly newspaper covering Kurdish and Middle East-related issues, including news, politics, business and culture. The newspaper is aimed at English speakers in Iraqi Kurdistan. It launched in 2005 and is published on Mondays. It was formerly called Hewler Globe.
Language (s): English
NEWSPAPER

Al Mada
Owner: Al Mada Est. For Mass Media, Culture and Arts
Editorial: House no. 141, Abi Nouass Street, Baghdad. **T:** 964 1 717 8859
E: info@almadapaper.net
W: http://www.almadapaper.net
Freq: Daily; **Circ:** 20000 Pub Statement
News Editor: Hamed Al Sayed

Editorial Profile: Al Mada is a regional newspaper covering local and international news, politics, business and sport. It launched in 2003, and is aimed at people living in central Iraq. The newspaper is published daily, except Fridays.
Language (s): Arabic
DAILY NEWSPAPER

Al Mannarah
Owner: South Press & Publishing Est.
Editorial: Okba Ben Nafea Square, Baghdad.
T: 964 40 315758
E: almannarah@almannarah.com
W: http://www.almannarah.com
Freq: 2 Times/Week; **Circ:** 25000 Pub Statement
News Editor: Abdulwadood Al Diwan
Editorial Profile: Al Mannarah is a broadsheet-sized newspaper covering local and international news, politics, business and sport. It launched in 2003 and is published twice a week, on Saturdays and Wednesdays.
Language (s): Arabic
NEWSPAPER

Al Sabah
Owner: Iraqi Media Network
Editorial: Waziriya, Qahira District, Baghdad.
T: 964 790 192 9423
E: al_sabaaah@yahoo.com
W: http://www.alsabaah.iq
Freq: Daily; **Circ:** 55000 Pub Statement
Editor in Chief: Adnan Sherkhan
Editorial Profile: Al Sabah (The Morning) is an Arabic newspaper covering local and international news, politics, business and sport. It launched in 2003 and is published daily, except Fridays.
Language (s): Arabic
DAILY NEWSPAPER

Al Sabah Al Jadeed
Owner: Al Neel Al Akhdar
Editorial: Al Maghreb Street, Al Waziriya, Baghdad. **T:** 964 770 971 9712
E: assabahaljaded@yahoo.com
W: http://www.newsabah.com
Freq: Daily; **Circ:** 15000 Pub Statement
News Editor: Sami Al Obady
Editorial Profile: Al Sabah Al Jadeed (The New Morning) is a daily Arabic newspaper featuring local and international news, current affairs, culture, sport, business and finance. It launched in 2004.
Language (s): Arabic
DAILY NEWSPAPER

Al Seyasa Iraq
Owner: Al-Seyasa Iraq
Editorial: PO Box 75017, Baghdad.
T: 964 790 134 4409
E: alseyasairaq@yahoo.com
W: http://www.alseyasairaq.net
Freq: Daily; **Circ:** 7500 Pub Statement
Editor In Chief: Adel Al Maniee; **News Editor:** Buthaina Kareem
Editorial Profile: Al Seyasa Iraq is an Arabic daily newspaper covering local and international news, culture, art, features and sport. It was first published in 2007.
Language (s): Arabic
DAILY NEWSPAPER

Tareek Alshaab
Owner: Dar Al Rouwad Printing Publishing and Advertising
Editorial: PO Box 55429, Abou Nawass Street, Baghdad. **T:** 964 770 980 7363
E: tareekalshaab@gmail.com
Freq: Daily; **Circ:** 9000 Pub Statement
Editor In Chief: Mofid Al Jazairi; **News Editor:** Yasser Khadir
Editorial Profile: Tareek Alshaab is an Arabic daily newspaper covering local and international news, politics, business and sport. It was launched by the Iraqi Communist Party in 1961.
Language (s): Arabic
DAILY NEWSPAPER

NEWS SERVICE/SYNDICATE

Agence France-Presse - Baghdad Bureau
Owner: Agence France-Presse
Editorial: Gardenia Hotel, Masbah, Baghdad.
T: 964 790 191 3984 **E:** afp.baghdad@afp.com
W: http://www.afp.com
Bureau Chief: Jean-Marc Mojon
Editorial Profile: Baghdad bureau of the international news and picture agency.
Language (s): Arabic
NEWS SERVICE/SYNDICATE

All Iraq News Agency
Owner: All Iraq News Agency
Editorial: 3rd Floor, Al Forat Appartments, Karada, Baghdad. **T:** 964 790 230 8738
E: alliraqnews@yahoo.com
W: http://www.alliraqnews.com
Editor In Chief: Kazim Alatwany; **Editor:** Nisreen Alhasnawi
Editorial Profile: All Iraq News agency covers news, current affairs, business and sport from Iraq.
Language (s): Arabic
NEWS SERVICE/SYNDICATE

National Iraqi News Agency
Owner: National Iraqi News Agency
Editorial: Next to Al-Safeer Hotel, Abunuas Street, Baghdad. **T:** 964 1 717 2251
E: news@ninanews.com
W: http://www.ninanews.com
Editor In Chief: Hafidh Al Rawi
Editorial Profile: National Iraqi News Agency is an independent news agency supplying newspapers, radio and television stations, Internet sites, international media, non-governmental and governmental organisations and diplomatic representatives.
Language (s): Arabic
NEWS SERVICE/SYNDICATE

Reuters - Iraq Bureau
Owner: Thomson Reuters
Editorial: 102 Karada Abu Rawda, House no. 22, Baghdad. **T:** 964 790 191 7052
E: reuters@fastmail.fm
W: http://www.reuters.com
Editorial Profile: Iraq bureau of international news agency supplying news - text, graphics, video and pictures - to subscribers around the world.
Language (s): Arabic
NEWS SERVICE/SYNDICATE

BROADCASTING

RADIO STATIONS

Alrasheed FM
Owner: Al Rasheed Media Services
Editorial: Arafat Street, Arafat Al Hindya, Baghdad. **T:** 964 790 170 4722
E: alrasheedfm@yahoo.com
W: http://www.alrasheedmedia.com
Editorial Profile: Alrasheed FM is a radio station broadcasting entertainment, news, Arabic and foreign pop music, and live programmes. It launched in 2004 and broadcasts on 91.5 FM.

Dar Al-Salam Radio
Owner: Iraqi Islamic Party
Editorial: Al Jamiaa Area, Alrabia Street, Baghdad. **T:** 964 790 194 6621
E: dslr_2003@yahoo.com
W: http://www.darusalam.net
Editorial Profile: Dar Al-Salam Radio is the radio station of the Iraqi Islamic Party and broadcasts news, religious, cultural, social, political and entertainment programmes. It launched in 2003 and broadcasts on 91.0 FM and 1116 MW.

Al Forqan Radio
Owner: Iraqi Media Network
Editorial: Iraqi Media Network Building, King Faisal Roundabout, Baghdad.
T: 964 1 537 2354 **E:** radioforgan@imn.ig
W: http://www.imn.iq
Editorial Profile: Al Forqan Radio is an Islamic radio station broadcasting Holy Quran recitals and religious programmes on 92.5 FM. Originally called Holy Quran Radio, the station launched in 2009 and is operated by state-owned public broadcaster, Iraqi Media Network.

Al Hoda 89.7 FM
Owner: Dar Al Hoda for Culture & Media
Editorial: Baghdad Street, Karbala.
T: 964 780 103 3238
E: al-hodaonline@al-hodaonline.com
W: http://www.al-hodaonline.com
Editorial Profile: Al Hoda 89.7 FM is an Arabic radio station broadcasting Islamic programmes. It launched in 2005 and broadcasts on 89.7 FM.

Al Hurriya Radio
Owner: Patriotic Union of Kurdistan (PUK)
Editorial: Ministry Complex no. 30, 604th Street, Baghdad. **T:** 964 770 005 4255
E: hurriyanet@yahoo.com
W: http://www.hurriya.net
Editorial Profile: Al Hurriya Radio (Freedom Radio) is the radio station of the Patriotic Union of Kurdistan (PUK) political party and broadcasts news, pop music, entertainment and political programmes. It launched in 2003 and airs on 98.7 FM.

Radio Al Iraqia
Owner: Iraqi Media Network
Editorial: Iraqi Media Network Building, King Faisal Roundabout, Baghdad.
T: 964 1 537 2423 **E:** editor@imn.iq
W: http://www.imn.iq
Editorial Profile: Radio Al Iraqia is a national radio station broadcasting news, social, cultural and children's programmes. Originally called Shahrazad Radio, the station launched in 2006 and transmits on 103.3 FM and 105.2 FM. It is owned by Iraqi Media Network, the state-owned public broadcaster.

Radio Al Mustaqbal
Owner: Iraqi National Accord
Editorial: PO Box 1843, Baghdad.
T: 964 790 126 0521
E: aliamustafaz@yahoo.com
W: http://www.wifaq.com
Editorial Profile: Radio Al Mustaqbal, also known as Sawt Al Wifaq Al Watani, is the radio station of the Iraqi National Accord political party and broadcasts music, news, and political talk shows. Launchedi in 1996, it transmits on 95.5 FM and 1305 AM.

Radio Dijla
Owner: Tigris Media Ltd
Editorial: House no. 2, Street 110, Area no. 6 (Kadi Mohammad), Kurdistan
E: post@radiodijla.com
W: http://www.radiodijla.com
Editorial Profile: Radio Dijla is a talk radio station which combines news and entertainment programmes with the opinions of listeners who phone in to air their grievances. The station launched in 2004 and broadcasts on 88.2 FM (Baghdad), 88.4 FM (Basra), 94.0 FM (Mosul) and 93.0 FM (Suleimaniya).

Radio Nawa
Owner: Nawa Establishment
Editorial: Radio Nawa Building, Kursat, Sulaimaniyah. **T:** 964 770 152 0652
E: info@radionawa.com
W: http://www.radionawa.com
Editorial Profile: Radio Nawa is a radio station broadcasting news, music and programmes in Arabic and Kurdish for 24-hrs a day. It launched in 2005 and transmits on 89.7 FM (Kalar, Deyala), 89.9 FM (Baghdad, Babel), 90.6 FM (Sulaimaniyah), 92.6 FM (Erbil), 102.5 FM (Duhok) and 92.0 FM (Basra).

Republic of Iraq Radio
Owner: Iraqi Media Network
Editorial: Iraqi Media Network Building, King Faisal Roundabout, Baghdad.
T: 964 1 537 2360 **E:** editor@imn.iq
W: http://www.imn.iq
Editorial Profile: Republic of Iraq Radio (RIR) is a national radio station broadcasting local news, sports reports and social programmes. It launched in 1936 and is owned by Iraqi Media Network, the state-owned public broadcaster. It transmits on 98.3 FM.

Sumer FM
Owner: Alsumaria Iraqi Satellite TV Network
Editorial: Al Masbah Street, Karada Kharej, Baghdad. **T:** 964 1 719 5910
E: sumerfm@sumerfm.com
W: http://www.sumerfm.com
Editorial Profile: Sumer FM is a national radio station broadcasting music, entertainment, social, cultural and sports programmes. Launched in 2004, it broadcasts on 99.8 FM (Baghdad), 91.8 FM (Basra), 98.2 FM (Erbil), 92.8 FM (Sulaimaniyah), 99.9 FM (Dohuk) and 105.8 FM (Diwaniya).

UR FM
Owner: UR Radio Broadcasting LLC
Editorial: 113 Abu Nuash Street, Baghdad.
T: 964 770 223 7378 **E:** info@radiourfm.com
W: http://www.radiourfm.com
Editorial Profile: UR FM is a radio station broadcasting pop music, entertainment and news 24-hrs a day from studios in Baghdad in Iraq, and Ajman in the United Arab Emirates. Launched in 2005, the station is aimed at Iraqi listeners aged 15-40 years old, and broadcasts on 98.8 FM.

Voice of Iraq
Owner: Voice of Iraq
Editorial: PO Box 74143, Baghdad.
T: 964 1 523 9628 **E:** akhbar@voiraq.com
W: http://www.voiraq.com
Editorial Profile: Voice of Iraq is a national radio station broadcasting discussions and talk shows. Launched in 2003, it transmits on 1179 MW.

TELEVISION STATIONS

Ahlulbayt Satellite Channel
Owner: Ahlulbayt TV
Editorial: Imam Al Hussein Grand Mosque Complex, Qeblat Al Hussien Street, Karbala.
T: 964 770 621 9999
E: ahlulbayt@ahlulbayt.com
W: http://www.ahlulbayt.com
Editorial Profile: Ahlulbayt Satellite Channel is a free-to-air television station broadcasting cultural and Islamic-related programmes, with special emphasis on the Prophet and his household. The channel launched in 2005.

Aldiyar Satellite Channel
Owner: Aldiyar Sat
Editorial: Karadet Mariam, Near Jumhouria Bridge, Baghdad. **T:** 964 1 538 4180
E: diyarsat@hotmail.com
W: http://www.aldiyarsat.net
Editorial Profile: Aldiyar Satellite Channel is a free-to-air television station broadcasting Iraqi news and cultural programmes, as well as dramas, talk shows, music, documentaries, children's programmes, films, series, sports and entertainment programmes for 18-hours a day (9am-3am). The channel launched in 2004.

Almasar Satellite Channel
Owner: Almasar TV
Editorial: Al Fardoss Place, Baghdad.
T: 964 790 168 5660 **E:** info@almasartv.com
Editorial Profile: Almasar Satellite Channel is a free-to-air television station broadcasting local news and current affairs, political talk shows, as well as cultural and social programmes about family and women's issues for 24-hours a day. The channel launched in 2004.

Alrasheed TV
Owner: Al Rasheed Media Services
Editorial: Al Qadsia, Baghdad.
T: 964 780 195 3167
E: t_b_b1956@yahoo.com
W: http://www.alrasheedmedia.com
Editorial Profile: Alrasheed TV is a general entertainment channel broadcasting entertainment and news programmes, as well as Arabic and foreign films. The channel launched in 2004 and broadcasts free-to-air on satellite.

Beladi Satellite Channel
Owner: Beladi Satellite Channel
Editorial: NH 909, Street 52, 412, Karada, Baghdad. **T:** 964 790 111 3022
E: info@beladitv.tv **W:** http://www.beladitv.tv
Editorial Profile: Beladi Satellite Channel is a free-to-air television station broadcasting news reports, talk shows, documentaries and current affairs programmes. It launched in 2004.

Al Forat TV
Owner: Al Forat Information Co.
Editorial: D 903-S 10-B, Karadda, Baghdad.
T: 964 1 718 8394 **E:** info@alforattv.com
W: http://www.alforattv.com
Editorial Profile: Al Forat TV is a free-to-air television station broadcasting news, political, religious and general entertainment programmes for 22-hrs a day. The channel launched in 2004.

Al Forqan TV
Owner: Iraqi Media Network
Editorial: Iraqi Media Network Building, King Faisal Roundabout, Baghdad.
T: 964 1 537 2351 **E:** samerajead@gmail.com
W: http://www.imn.iq
Editorial Profile: Al Forqan TV is a state-owned television station broadcasting Islamic programmes and Quranic recitals, as well as cultural and women's programmes. The channel launched in 2007.

Iraqiya Sports TV
Owner: Iraqi Media Network
Editorial: Iraqi Media Network Building, King Faisal Roundabout, Baghdad.
T: 964 1 537 2423 **E:** info@imn.iq
W: http://www.imn.iq
Editorial Profile: Iraqiya Sports TV is a state-owned television station broadcasting local and international sports programmes for 18-hours a day. The channel launched in 2005.

Iraqiya TV 1
Owner: Iraqi Media Network
Editorial: Iraqi Media Network Building, King Faisal Roundabout, Baghdad.
T: 964 1 537 2351
E: aliraqea_imn2009@yahoo.com
W: http://www.imn.iq
Editorial Profile: Iraqiya TV 1 is a state-owned television station broadcasting news, entertainment and public interest programming. The channel launched in 2003 and broadcasts terrestrially in Iraq and free-to-air on satellite.

Ishtar TV
Owner: Ishtar Broadcasting Cooperation
Editorial: Mahlat 24/414, Hadyab Street, Erbil.
T: 964 66 225 1132 **E:** info@ishtartv.com
W: http://www.ishtartv.com
Editorial Profile: Ishtar TV is a television station broadcasts news, culture and art programmes. The channel launched in 2007 and broadcasts free-to-air on satellite.

MCP Music
Owner: Al Hayat Art & Media Est.
Editorial: Building 13, Street 42, Baghdad.
T: 964 771 322 2220 **E:** hasan_it@ymail.com
Editorial Profile: MCP Music is a free-to-air music channel broadcasting Iraqi and Arabic songs, as well as entertainment programmes. The station launched in 2010.

NRT
Owner: Nalia TV & Radio
Editorial: German Village, Sulaimaniyah.
T: 964 53 239011 **E:** info@nrttv.com
W: http://www.nrttv.com
Editorial Profile: NRT is an independent Kurdish news channel. Launched in 2011, it broadcasts free-to-air on satellite.

Al Salam TV
Owner: Al Salam TV
Editorial: Al Kazemia City, Baghdad.
T: 964 790 396 6848 **E:** mail@tvalsalam.tv
W: http://www.tvalsalam.tv
Editorial Profile: Al Salam TV is a free-to-air satellite channel broadcasting news, politics, entertainment, culture, society and Islamic programmes. The station launched in 2005.

ISRAEL Tel: 972
Standard Time: GMT +2
Continent: Asia
Capital City: Jerusalem

NEWSPAPERS & PUBLICATIONS

NEWSPAPERS

Globes
Owner: Globes Publisher Itonut (1983) Ltd
Editorial: 53 Etzel Street, Po Box: 5126, Rishon Le Zion 75150. **T:** 972 3 953 8611
E: mailbox@globes.co.il
W: http://www.globes.co.il
Freq: Daily; **Circ:** 45000 Pub Statement
Editor in Chief: Haggai Golan; **News Editor:** Eli Tsipori
Editorial Profile: National daily newspaper focussing on business and financial news in Israel including, economics, investment and management.
Language (s): English
DAILY NEWSPAPER

Haaretz
Owner: Haaretz Daily Newspaper Ltd.
Editorial: 21 Schocken Street, PO Box 233, Tel Aviv 61001. **T:** 972 3 512 12 04
E: contact@haaretz.co.il
W: http://www.haaretz.com
Freq: Daily; **Circ:** 75000 Pub Statement
Editor: Dov Alfon; **Publisher:** Amos Schocken
Editorial Profile: National daily newspaper covering news and current affairs including business, economics, politics, travel and culture.
Language (s): English
DAILY NEWSPAPER

The Jerusalem Post
Owner: The Jerusalem Post
Editorial: The Jerusalem Post Building, PO Box 81, Jerusalem 91000. **T:** 972 2 531 5666
E: editors@jpost.com
W: http://www.jpost.com
Freq: Daily; **Circ:** 35000 Pub Statement
Editor in Chief: Steve Linde
Editorial Profile: National daily newspaper focussing on national and international news, current affairs, politics, economics, business, regional interest, Jewish interest, arts, culture, travel, sports, health, science and technology. Aimed at the general public.
Language (s): English, French
DAILY NEWSPAPER

Jerusalem Post - New York Bureau
Owner: The Jerusalem Post
Editorial: 80 Wall St, New York, New York 10005-3601. **T:** 1 212 742-0505
E: editors@jpost.com
W: http://www.jpost.com
Editorial Profile: Local bureau of the national daily newspaper focussing on national and international news, current affairs, politics, economics, business, regional interest, Jewish interest, arts, culture, travel, sports, health, science and technology. Aimed at the general public.
Language (s): English
DAILY NEWSPAPER

Jerusalem Post - Washington Bureau
Owner: The Jerusalem Post
E: editors@jpost.com
W: http://www.jpost.com
Bureau Chief: Hilary Leila Krieger
Editorial Profile: Local bureau of the national daily newspaper focussing on national and international news, current affairs, politics, economics, business, regional interest, Jewish interest, arts, culture, travel, sports, health, science and technology. Aimed at the general public.
DAILY NEWSPAPER

Ma'ariv
Owner: Modin Publishing House
Editorial: 2 Carlebach Street, Tel Aviv 67132.
T: 972 3 563 2111 **E:** chiefeditor@maariv.co.il
W: http://www.maariv.co.il
Freq: Daily; **Circ:** 250000 Pub Statement
Editor In Chief: Doron Galezer; **Editor In Chief:** Ruth Yuval
Editorial Profile: National daily newspaper focusing on national and international news, current affairs, politics, culture, society, regional and general news.
Language (s): Hebrew
DAILY NEWSPAPER

Makor 1
Owner: Hatzofeh
Editorial: 116 Menahen Begin Street, Beth Kalka, Tel Aviv 61570. **T:** 972 3 562 2951
E: limorgrizim@gmail.com
W: http://www.hazofe.co.il **Circ:** 60000 Pub Statement
Editor In Chief: Shlomo Ben-Tzvi; **Editor:** Amnon Lord
Editorial Profile: Newspaper focusing on news, current affairs, politics, culture, local and general news.
Language (s): Hebrew
DAILY NEWSPAPER

Makor Rishon - Hazofe
Editorial: 116 Menahem Begin Street, Beth Kalka, Tel Aviv 61570. **T:** 972 3 627 7770
E: amnonl@makorrishon.co.il
W: http://www.makor1.co.il
Freq: Daily; **Circ:** 100000 Pub Statement
Editor: Amnon Lord
Editorial Profile: National daily newspaper focussing on news, current affairs, politics, economics, culture and general information.
Language (s): Hebrew
DAILY NEWSPAPER

Sawt Al Haq Wal Horriya
Owner: Al Balagh Institution for Communication
Editorial: PO Box: 134, Um Al Fahm 30010.
T: 972 4 631 7890 **E:** sawt@sawt-alhaq.com
W: http://www.sawt-alhaq.com **Circ:** 15000 Pub Statement
Editor: Tawfeeq Jebareen
Editorial Profile: Weekly newspaper focusing on national and international news, current affairs, politics and economics.
Language (s): Arabic
DAILY NEWSPAPER

Yedioth Ahronoth
Owner: Yedioth Tikshoret
Editorial: 127 Yigal Allon Street, Tel Aviv 67433. **T:** 972 3 608 2222
E: news@ynetnews.com
W: http://www.ynetnews.com
Freq: Daily
Editor In Chief: Jon Feder
Editorial Profile: National daily newspaper covering regional, national and international news and current affairs including politics, economics, culture and travel.
Language (s): English
DAILY NEWSPAPER

NEWS SERVICE/SYNDICATE

Agence France-Presse - Jerusalem Bureau
Editorial: Po Box 1507, 206 Jaffa Road, Jerusalem 91014. **T:** 972 2 644 0900
E: sara.hussein@afp.com
W: http://www.afp.com
Editorial Profile: Geographical Focus: Israel
NEWS SERVICE/SYNDICATE

Associated Press
Editorial: 206 Jaffa Rd, JCS Building, Fl 2, Jerusalem 91342
News Editor: Josef Federman; **Bureau Chief:** Dan Perry
NEWS SERVICE/SYNDICATE

Bloomberg - Jerusalem Bureau
Editorial: 23, Hillel Street, 10th Floor, Jerusalem 94582. **T:** 972 2 625 0061
E: israelnews@bloomberg.net
W: http://www.bloomberg.com
Bureau Chief: David Rosenberg
Editorial Profile: Jerusalem bureau of international financial news wire service.
Language (s): Hebrew
NEWS SERVICE/SYNDICATE

Bloomberg News
Editorial: Sderot Rothschild 41, Tel-Aviv 65784. **T:** 11 97 23542-7106
NEWS SERVICE/SYNDICATE

Courier.co.il
E: courier@courier.co.il
W: http://www.courier.co.il
Freq: Daily
Editorial Profile: Online newspaper covering political, economic, cultural and sports news in Israel and CIS countries.
Language (s): Russian
NEWS SERVICE/SYNDICATE

Cursorinfo.co.il
Editorial: P.O. Box 552656, Tel Aviv
E: sales@cursorinfo.co.il
W: http://cursorinfo.co.il
Freq: Daily
Editor: Ilya Kazachkov; **Editor in Chief:** Maks Lurie; **Editor:** Ilya Naimark; **Editor:** Gabriel Wolfson
Editorial Profile: Web news service providing information on life in Israel and former Soviet Union, with political, economic, sports and cultural news.
Language (s): Russian
NEWS SERVICE/SYNDICATE

ISRA.com
W: http://www.isra.com
Freq: Daily
Editorial Profile: Online resource providing political, economic, technologies, cultural, sports news.
Language (s): Russian
NEWS SERVICE/SYNDICATE

IsraLife.com
E: admin@isralife.com
W: http://www.isralife.com
Freq: Daily
Editorial Profile: Online resource covering politics, daily news, culture, sports and entertainment.
Language (s): Russian
NEWS SERVICE/SYNDICATE

Izrus.co.il
E: chief@izrus.co.il **W:** http://www.izrus.co.il
Freq: Daily
Editor: Boris Khotinsky; **Editor:** Alexander Kogan; **Editor:** Galina Malamant
Editorial Profile: Online resource providing news and useful information for Russian-speaking community of Israel.
Language (s): Russian
NEWS SERVICE/SYNDICATE

MIGnews.com
Owner: Media International Group
Editorial: Kaufmann 2, Tel Aviv 61500.
T: 972 54 47 97 074 **E:** editor@mignews.com
W: http://www.mignews.com
Editor in Chief: Michael Grizotsky; **Editor:** Boris Kovalev; **Editor:** Elena Sklyarova
Editorial Profile: Online publication focusing on politics, economics, society, social, science and culture in Russian language.
Language (s): Russian
NEWS SERVICE/SYNDICATE

mnenia.zahav.ru
T: 972 72 2003823 **W:** http://mnenia.zahav.ru
Freq: Weekly
Editor: Alexander Kogan
Editorial Profile: Informative-analytical blog providing forum for exchange of political opinions.
Language (s): Russian
NEWS SERVICE/SYNDICATE

NEWS.IsraelInfo.ru
Owner: InterLink Info Ltd
T: 972 3 9673467 **E:** briker@israelinfo.ru
W: http://news.israelinfo.ru
Freq: Daily
Editorial Profile: Online newswire resource with most updated news on Israel in Russian language.
Language (s): Russian
NEWS SERVICE/SYNDICATE

NEWSru.co.il
Editorial: Menahem Begin 48B, Tel - Aviv 66184. **T:** 972 3 6890202
E: newsru_israel@newsru.co.il
W: http://www.newsru.co.il
Freq: Daily
Editor: Elena Berson; **Editor in Chief:** Evgeniy Finkel; **Editor:** Alexander Pechenkin; **Editor:** Anna Rozina; **Editor:** Mikhail Shafranov; **Editor:** Masha Tamir
Editorial Profile: Popular website for Russians living in Israel which reports latest news from Israel, Middle East and all over the world.
Language (s): Russian
NEWS SERVICE/SYNDICATE

Reuters
Editorial: Jerusalem Technology Center, Tower Bld, 12th Flr, Jerusalem 96951.
T: 972 26322202
Editor in Charge: Jeffrey Heller
NEWS SERVICE/SYNDICATE

Ru.local.co.il
E: info@localru.co.il **W:** http://ru.local.co.il
Freq: Daily
Editorial Profile: Provided information and news on Israeli cities and towns.
Language (s): Russian
NEWS SERVICE/SYNDICATE

Thomson Reuters - Jerusalem Office
Editorial: Technology Park, Tower Building, 12th floor, Jerusalem 96951.
T: 972 2 632 22 22
E: jerusalem.newsroom@thomsonreuters.com
Editorial Profile: News agency focussing on news, current affairs and politics.
Language (s): Hebrew
NEWS SERVICE/SYNDICATE

Thomson Reuters - Tel-Aviv Office
Editorial: 38 Hamasger str, Tel Aviv 67211.
T: 972 3 53 72 211
E: miriam.dembak@thomsonreuters.com
Editorial Profile: News agency focussing on finance and economics.
Language (s): Hebrew
NEWS SERVICE/SYNDICATE

Vestnik Izraela
E: info@vestnik.co.il
W: http://www.vestnik.co.il
Freq: Daily
Editorial Profile: Online resource providing political, economical, science, technologies, health, cultural news and covering recent events.
Language (s): Russian
NEWS SERVICE/SYNDICATE

Zman.com
T: 972 506560108 **E:** info@zman.com
W: http://www.zman.com
Freq: Daily
Editorial Profile: Online resource providing political, economic, tourist, cultural, sports news and entertainment.
Language (s): Russian
NEWS SERVICE/SYNDICATE

BROADCASTING

RADIO NETWORKS

Kol Israel
Owner: Israel Broadcasting Authority
Editorial: 21 Heleni HaMalka, PO 1082, Jerusalem 91010. **T:** 972 1 599 509 510
E: radiodirector@iba.org.il
W: http://www.iba.org.il
Editorial Profile: National radio station covering news and current affairs.

Reshet Bet

Owner: Israel Broadcasting Authority
Editorial: 21 Heleni HaMalka, PO 1082, Jerusalem 91010. **T:** 97 1 599 509 510
E: bet@iba.org.il **W:** http://www.iba.org.il
Editorial Profile: National radio station covering news and current affairs.

TELEVISION STATIONS

Arutz 1 Mabat

Owner: Israel Broadcasting Authority
Editorial: 15 Tora Mizion, P.O.Box 7139, Jerusalem 91071. **T:** 972 2 5301333
E: mabat@iba.org.il **W:** http://www.iba.org.il
Editorial Profile: National television station covering national and international news and current affairs.

Arutz 10

Owner: Arutz 10
Editorial: 53 Derech Hashalom street, Givatayim 53454. **T:** 972 77 6101000
E: rikuz@10.tv **W:** http://10tv.nana10.co.il
Editorial Profile: National television station covering national and international news and current affairs.

Arutz 2

Owner: Israel Broadcasting Authority
Editorial: 12 Raul Vallenberg Street, P.O.Box 58151, Tel-Aviv 61580. **T:** 972 3 7676000
E: info@mako.co.il **W:** http://www.mako.co.il
Editorial Profile: National television station covering national and international news and current affairs.

Israel Plus

Editorial: 6 Meytav Street, Tel Aviv 67898.
T: 972 3 6232999 **W:** http://www.israel-plus.tv
Editorial Profile: National TV station (9 channel) broadcasting news, films, series and entertainment in Russian language.

CABLE

CNN/Cable News Network

Editorial: 208 Jaffa Rd, Jerusalem 91131.
T: 972 25009500

FOX NewsEdge

Editorial: 206 Jaffa Road, Jerusalem 91131

ITALY   Tel: 39

Standard Time: GMT +1
Continent: Europe
Capital City: Rome

NEWSPAPERS & PUBLICATIONS

NEWSPAPERS

L' Arena

Owner: Athesis SpA
Editorial: Corso Porta Nuova, 67, Verona 37122. **T:** 39 045 9600111
E: redazione@larena.it **W:** http://www.larena.it
Freq: Daily; **Circ:** 61191 Pub Statement
Editorial Profile: L'Arena is an Italian local daily newspaper based in Verona, Italy. Founded in 1866, L'Arena is one of the oldest newspapers in Italy and the most popular newspaper in Verona.
Language (s): Italian
DAILY NEWSPAPER

Avvenire

Owner: Avvenire Nuova Ed.It. SpA
Editorial: Piazza Carbonari, 3, Milano 20125.
T: 39 02 67801 **E:** lettere@avvenire.it
W: http://www.avvenire.it
Freq: Daily; **Circ:** 126000 Pub Statement
Editor in Chief: Massimo Calvi; **Editor in Chief:** Piero Chinellato; **Editor in Chief:** Umberto Folena; **Editor in Chief:** Marco Girardo; **Editor in Chief:** Andrea Lavazza; **Editor in Chief:** Riccardo Maccioni; **Editor in Chief:** Luciano Moia; **Editor in Chief:** Giorgio Paolucci; **Editor in Chief:** Francesco Riccardi; **Editor in Chief:** Francesco Riccardi; **Editor in Chief:** Roberto Righetto; **Editor in Chief:** Massimo Rinieri
Editorial Profile: Broadsheet-sized quality newspaper providing national, international, political, financial and religious news from a Catholic viewpoint. Aimed at people with an interest in the Catholic religion.
Language (s): Italian
DAILY NEWSPAPER

Avvenire - Roma bureau

Owner: Avvenire Nuova Ed.It. SpA
Editorial: Piazza Indipendenza, 11/B, Roma 185. **T:** 39 06 688231
E: desk.roma@avvenire.it
W: http://www.avvenire.it
Freq: Daily; **Circ:** 126000 Pub Statement
Editor in Chief: Antonio Maria Mira
Editorial Profile: Rome bureau of Avvenire newspaper.
Language (s): Italian
DAILY NEWSPAPER

BABILONIA

Owner: Ecentodieci Srl
Editorial: Via Tolmino, 21, Sesto San Giovanni Mi 20099. **T:** 39 0236558005
E: redazione@babiloniamagazine.it
W: http://www.babiloniamagazine.it
Language (s): Italian
DAILY NEWSPAPER

CALABRIA ORA

Owner: Paese Sera Editoriale Srl
Editorial: Contrada da Lecco 8, Rende Cs 87036. **T:** 39 0984 837661
E: info@calabriaora.it
W: http://www.calabriaora.it
Freq: Daily
Editorial Profile: Local Translation: Altra mail: regione@calabriaora.it
Language (s): Italian
DAILY NEWSPAPER

Il Cittadino Oggi Corriere Nazionale

Owner: Editrice Grafic Coop Spa di Giornalisti
Editorial: Via Pietro Soriano, 63, Perugia 6132. **T:** 39 075 5280069
E: redazione@corrnaz.it
W: http://www.corrierenazionale.it
Capo Servizio: Manuela Ferretti; **Redattore:** Aldo Fiordelli; **Capo Servizio:** Francesco Giustiniani
Editorial Profile: National newspaper covering national news, international news, sport, culture and current affairs.
Language (s): Italian
DAILY NEWSPAPER

Il Corriere del Sud

Owner: D'Ettoris Editori
Editorial: Via Francesco Antonio Lucifero 38/40, Crotone 88900. **T:** 39 0962 905192
E: redazione@corrieredelsud.it
W: http://www.corrieredelsud.it **Circ:** 50000 Pub Statement
Editorial Profile: Corriere del Sud is a local newspaper of South Italy covering social, political, cultural and economic news. It was first published in 1992.
Language (s): Italian
DAILY NEWSPAPER

Corriere del Veneto

Owner: Editoriale Veneto Srl
Editorial: Via Rismondo 2/E, Padova 35131.
T: 39 049 8238811
E: corriereveneto@corriereveneto.it
W: http://www.corrieredelveneto.it
Freq: Daily
Caporedattore: Alessandro Baschieri; **Redattore:** Marco Bonet; **Redattore:** Michela Nicolussi Moro; **Redattore:** Andrea Priante; **Redattore:** Daniele Rea; **Caporedattore:** Ugo Savoia; **Redattore:** Giovanni Sciancalepore; **Redattore:** Claudio Trabona; **Redattore:** Francesca Visentin; **Redattore:** Alessandro Zuin
Editorial Profile: Corriere del Veneto is a daily regional newspaper covering news from Veneto region. It was first published in November 12, 2002 as the back of the Venetian model of Corriere della Sera Corriere del Mezzogiorno. As part of the reorganization of the local editions launched by RCS Newspapers, since 2006 it is an integral part of the Corriere della Sera.
Language (s): Italian
DAILY NEWSPAPER

Corriere della Sera

Owner: RCS Quotidiani S.p.A.
Editorial: Via Solferino 28, Milano 20121.
T: 39 02 62821 **E:** segretcor@rcs.it
W: http://www.corriere.it
Freq: Daily; **Circ:** 686813 Pub Statement
Capo servizio: Alessandro Balistri; **Capo servizio:** Carlo Baroni; **Inviato:** Adriana Bazzi; **Capo servizio:** Sergio Bocconi; **Capo redattore:** Antonio Bozzo; **Capo redattore:** Fausto Brambilla; **Capo servizio:** Riccardo Bruno; **Capo Servizio:** Stefano Bucci; **Capo redattore:** Alessandro Cannavo'; **Capo redattore:** Claudio Colombo; **Capo redattore:** Daniele Dallera; **Capo redattore:** Vito D'Angelo; **Capo redattore:** Enzo D'Errico; **Capo redattore:** Maurizio Donelli; **Capo Servizio:** Pasquale Elia; **Capo redattore:** Luciano Ferraro; **Capo redattore:** Massimo Fracaro; **Capo servizio:** Mara Gergolet; **Caporedattore:** Luigi Ippolito; **Capo servizio:** Biagio Marsiglia; **Capo servizio:** Luca Mastrantonio; **Capo servizio:** Gianluca Mercuri; **Capo redattore:** Dino Messina; **Capo servizio:** Daniela Monti; **Capo redattore:** Antonio Morra; **Capo Servizio:** Pierluigi Panza; **Capo servizio:** Roberto Perrone; **Capo servizio:** Matteo Persivale; **Capo servizio:** Mario Porqueddu; **Caporedattore Centrale:** Venanzio Postiglione; **Editor:** Paolo Rastelli; **Redattore:** Monica Ricci Sargentini; **Capo servizio:** Stefano Righi; **Capo redattore:** Luigi Ripamonti; **Capo redattore:** Maria Laura Rodota'; **Capo redattore:** Nicola Saldutti; **Capo redattore:** Ugo Savoia; **Capo servizio:** Elisabetta Soglio; **Caporedattore centrale:** Giampaolo Tucci; **Capo servizio:** Flavio Vanetti; **Capo redattore:** Maria Luisa Villa; **Capo servizio:** Maria Volpe
Editorial Profile: Corriere della Sera is an Italian daily newspaper published in Milan, one of Italy's leading newspapers, in terms of both circulation and influence, noted for its foreign coverage and its independence. It is among the oldest and most reputable Italian newspapers.
Language (s): Italian
DAILY NEWSPAPER

Corriere dello Sport - Stadio

Owner: Corriere dello Sport srl
Editorial: Piazza Indipendenza, 11/B, Roma Rm 185. **T:** 39 06 49921
E: redazione@corsport.it
W: http://www.corrieredellosport.it
Freq: Daily; **Circ:** 534000 Pub Statement
Capo servizio: Stefano Chioffi; **Caporedattore:** Alberto Dalla Palma; **Capo servizio:** Mauro De Cesare; **Capo servizio:** Pasquale Di Santillo; **Caporedattore:** Giuliano Riva; **Capo servizio:** Paolo Scalera; **Capo servizio:** Francesco Volpe
Editorial Profile: Broadsheet-sized newspaper focusing on all aspects of competitive sport. Readership includes a broad range of the Italian society with an interest in sport, half of whom live in the regions of Lazio and Campania.
Language (s): Italian
DAILY NEWSPAPER

Corriere di Bologna (Corriere della Sera)

Owner: Editoriale Corriere di Bologna Srl
Editorial: Via Cincinnato Baruzzi 1/2, Bologna 40138. **T:** 39 051 3951201
E: redazione@corrieredibologna.it
W: http://www.corrieredibologna.it
Freq: Daily
Redattore: Marina Amaduzzi; **Capo Redattore:** Gianmaria Canè; **Redattore:** Luciana Cavina; **Redattore:** Amelia Esposito; **Capo Servizio:** Helmut Failoni; **Redattore:** Alessandro Mantovani; **Capo Servizio:** Olivio Romanini
Editorial Profile: Corriere de Bologna is a local edition of Bologna of Corriere della Sera newspaper. It covers news, sports, culture, politics and economy.
Language (s): Italian
DAILY NEWSPAPER

IL CORRIERE DI MONCALIERI

Owner: Publichieri Srl
Editorial: Via Chieri 62, Andezeno To 10020.
T: 39 011 9472101
E: corrieremoncalieri@corrierechieri.it
W: http://www.corrieremoncalieri.it
Freq: Weekly
Editorial Profile: Local Translation: Cronaca Locale
Language (s): Italian
NEWSPAPER

Corriere Fiorentino

Owner: Editoriale Fiorentina Srl
Editorial: Lungarno delle Grazie, 22, Firenze 50122. **T:** 39 05 524825
E: cronaca@corrierefiorentino.it
W: http://www.corrierefiorentino.it
Freq: Daily
Editorial Profile: Local Translation: DORSO del Corriere della Sera per Firenze
Language (s): Italian
DAILY NEWSPAPER

CORRIERE PADANO

Owner: Ed. CPA srl
Editorial: Via XXIV Maggio, 4, Piacenza 29100. **T:** 39 0523 457421
E: redazione@corrierepadano.it
W: http://www.corrierepadano.it
Freq: Weekly
Language (s): Italian
NEWSPAPER

CRONACAQUI Torino

Owner: Editoriale Argo
T: 39 0116669 **E:** redazione.to@cronacaqui.it
W: http://www.cronacaqui.it
Freq: Daily
Language (s): Italian
DAILY NEWSPAPER

DNEWS

Owner: Mag Editoriale Srl
Editorial: Via C. Pesenti 130, Roma 156.
T: 39 0645543900 **W:** http://www.dnews.eu
Freq: Daily
Editorial Profile: Local Translation: Free Press
Language (s): Italian
DAILY NEWSPAPER

Dolomiten

Owner: Athesia Druck Gmbh
Editorial: Via Del Vigneto 7, Bolzano 39100.
T: 39 0471 928888 **E:** dolomiten@athesia.it
W: http://www.athesia.it
Freq: Daily; **Circ:** 55380 Pub Statement
Editorial Profile: Dolomiten is a German speaking local newspaper covering Bolzano area.
Language (s): Italian
DAILY NEWSPAPER

E POLIS Milano

Owner: E Polis Spa
Editorial: Viale Trieste, 40, Cagliari 9123.
T: 39 02 31033196 **E:** milano@epolismilano.it
W: http://www.epolis.sm
Freq: Daily
Language (s): Italian
DAILY NEWSPAPER

E POLIS ROMA

Owner: E Polis Spa
Editorial: Viale Trieste, 40, Cagliari 9100.
T: 39 0642883523 **E:** roma@epolisroma.it
W: http://www.epolis.sm
Freq: Daily
Language (s): Italian
DAILY NEWSPAPER

L' Eco di Bergamo

Owner: Editor S.E.S.A.A.B. SpA
Editorial: V.le P.Giovanni XXIII, 118, Bergamo 24121. **T:** 39 035 386111
E: redazione@eco.bg.it
W: http://www.ecodibergamo.it
Freq: Daily; **Circ:** 70000 Pub Statement
Editorial Profile: Local newspaper covering the town of Bergamo and vicinity. The news include current affairs, economy, culture, sports and current affairs.
Language (s): Italian
DAILY NEWSPAPER

Europa Quotidiano

Owner: Edizioni DLM Europa Srl
Editorial: Via di Ripetta 142, Roma 186.
T: 39 06 684331
E: segr.redazione@europaquotidiano.it
W: http://www.europaquotidiano.it
Freq: Daily
Contact: Stefano Cubeddu
Editorial Profile: Newspaper covering national news, international news, European Union, culture, multimedia and politics.
Language (s): Italian
DAILY NEWSPAPER

FOGGIA SERA

Owner: Area Sud Comunicazione e Immagine Soc. Coop.
Editorial: Via Gramsci 73/A, Foggia (fg) 71100. **T:** 39 0881 686967
E: redazione@quotidianodifoggia.it
Freq: Daily
Language (s): Italian
DAILY NEWSPAPER

Il Foglio Quotidiano

Owner: Il Foglio Quotidiano Società Cooperativa
Editorial: Lungotevere Raffaello Sanzio 8/c, Roma 153. **T:** 39 06 5890901
E: lettere@ilfoglio.it **W:** http://www.ilfoglio.it
Freq: Daily; **Circ:** 51000 Pub Statement
Caporedattore: Claudio Cerasa
Editorial Profile: Il Foglio is an Italian centre-right daily newspaper and founded in 1996 by an Italian journalist Giuliano Ferrara. The main editorial policy of Il Foglio is a summary of the most important news of the day with comment and analysis on them.
Language (s): Italian
DAILY NEWSPAPER

La Gazzetta del Mezzogiorno

Owner: Edisud SpA
Editorial: Viale Scipione L'Africano 264, Bari 70124. **T:** 39 080 5470400
E: segreteria.redazione@gazzettamezzogiorno.it

W: http://www.lagazzettadelmezzogiorno.it
Freq: Daily; **Circ:** 60000 Pub Statement
Capo Redattore Centrale: Michele Partipilo
Editorial Profile: La Gazzetta del Mezzogiorno is an Italian daily newspaper, founded in 1887 in Bari, Italy. It is one of the most important newspaper published in Southern Italy.
Language (s): Italian
DAILY NEWSPAPER

Gazzetta del Sud
Owner: S.E.S. Società Editrice Sud
Editorial: Via Uberto Bonino, 15/C, Messina 98124. **T:** 39 090 2261
W: http://www.gazzettadelsud.it
Freq: Daily; **Circ:** 60000 Pub Statement
Capo Servizio Catania: Domenico Calabrò
Editorial Profile: Gazzetta del Sud is an Italian daily newspaper, founded in 1952 in Messina, Italy. It is one of the most important newspapers published in the Southern Italy: it has the largest readership in Calabria and is the third most read newspaper in Sicily.
Language (s): Italian
DAILY NEWSPAPER

La Gazzetta dello Sport
Owner: RCS Quotidiani S.p.A.
Editorial: Via Solferino, 28, Milano 20121.
T: 39 02 62821 **E:** segretgaz@rcs.it
W: http://www.gazzetta.it
Freq: Daily; **Circ:** 785000 Pub Statement
Capo Servizio: Lorenzo Astori; **Capo redattore Centrale:** Pier Battista Bergonzi; **Capo Servizio:** Antonello Capone; **Capo servizio:** Filippo Di Chiara; **Capo servizio:** Luca Gialanella; **Capo redattore:** Vito Schembari
Editorial Profile: La Gazzetta dello Sport is an Italian newspaper dedicated to coverage of various sports. It was first published on April 3, 1896, allowing it to cover the first modern Olympic Games held in Athens. The newspaper, published on pink paper, sells over 400,000 copies daily, and can claim a readership in excess of three million. A sports magazine, Sportweek, is sold with other newspaper on Saturdays.
Language (s): Italian
DAILY NEWSPAPER

LA GAZZETTA DI LECCO
Owner: Iniziative Editoriali Srl
Editorial: Via Fiume, 8, Lecco Lc 23900.
T: 39 0341 255175
E: redazione@lagazzettadilecco.it
Freq: Weekly
Editorial Profile: Local Translation: In edicola il sabato
Language (s): Italian
NEWSPAPER

Gazzetta di Parma
Owner: SEGEA SpA
Editorial: Via Mantova 68, Parma 43100.
T: 39 05 212251
E: segreteria@gazzettadiparma.net
W: http://www.gazzettadiparma.it
Freq: Daily; **Circ:** 50000 Not Audited
Editorial Profile: Gazzetta di Parma is an Italian daily newspaper covering news in Parma and in the provicnce of Emilia-Romagna.
Language (s): Italian
DAILY NEWSPAPER

Gazzetta di Parma Provincia-Emilia
Editorial: Via Mantova 68, Parma 43100.
T: 39 05 212251 **E:** sito@gazzettadiparma.net
W: http://www.gazzettadiparma.it/primapagina/interna/2/Provincia-Emilia/index.html
Freq: Daily
Editorial Profile: Gazzetta di Parma Provincia-Emilia is a local edition for Province of Emilia of Gazzetta di Parma Newspaper. This edition covers news and issues happening internally in the province of Emilia.
Language (s): Italian
DAILY NEWSPAPER

Il Gazzettino
Owner: Il Gazzettino SPA
Editorial: Via Torino, 110, Venezia 30172.
T: 39 041 665111 **E:** pordenone@gazzettino.it
W: http://www.gazzettino.it
Freq: Daily; **Circ:** 105000 Pub Statement
Editorial Profile: Newspaper covering regional news and current affairs.
Language (s): Italian
DAILY NEWSPAPER

IL Giornale
Owner: Soc. Europea Di Edizioni
Editorial: Via Gaetano Negri, 4, Milano Mi 20123. **T:** 39 02 85661
E: redazione.web@ilgiornale.it
W: http://www.ilgiornale.it
Freq: Daily; **Circ:** 328000 Pub Statement
Caporedattore: Angelo Allegri; **Capo redattore:** Gabriele Barberis; **Caporedattore:** Pierluigi Bonora; **Capo Servizio:** Valeria Braghieri; **Redattore:** Maddalena Camera; **Caporedattore:** Mario Celi; **Caporedattore:** Alessandro Gnocchi; **Caporedattore:** Marco Lombardo; **Redattore:** Stefano Lorenzetto; **Capo Servizio:** Felice Fausto Manti; **Caporedattore:** Giuseppe Marino; **Caporedattore:** Luigi Mascheroni; **Caporedattore:** Elia Pagnoni; **Caporedattore:** Riccardo Pelliccetti; **Capo Servizio:** Laura Rio; **Caporedattore:** Alessandro Rocchi; **Capo Servizio:** Massimo M. Veronese; **Caporedattore:** Marcello Zacche'
Editorial Profile: Broadsheet-sized quality newspaper providing news, financial, economic, political, cultural and sporting information. Also contains events listings. Aimed at leaders in the business community, civil servants, university students and office personnel.
Language (s): Italian
DAILY NEWSPAPER

Il Giornale - Roma Bureau
Owner: Soc. Europea Di Edizioni
Editorial: Via Terenzio 35, Roma Rm 193.
T: 39 06 690031 **E:** interni.rm@ilgiornale.it
W: http://www.ilgiornale.it
Freq: Daily; **Circ:** 300000 Pub Statement
Redattore: Pier Francesco Borgia; **Redattore:** Marcello Di Dio; **Redattore:** Annamaria Greco; **Caporedattore:** Vittorio Macioce; **Caporedattore:** Adalberto Signore; **Redattore:** Patricia Tagliaferri
Editorial Profile: Rome bureau of Il Giornale newspaper.
Language (s): Italian
DAILY NEWSPAPER

IL GIORNALE DEL LAZIO
Owner: Piero Fusaglia
Editorial: Via delle Pietre Piane, 8, Ginestra Sabina Rieti 2033. **T:** 39 392 3329132
E: direttoregdlazio@email.it
W: http://www.ilgiornaledellazio.it
Freq: Daily
Language (s): Italian
DAILY NEWSPAPER

Giornale di Brescia
Owner: Editoriale Bresciana SpA
Editorial: Via Solferino, 22, Brescia 25121.
T: 39 030 37901
E: redazione@giornaledibrescia.it
W: http://www.giornaledibrescia.it
Freq: Daily; **Circ:** 70000 Pub Statement
Editorial Profile: Local newspaper covering the city of Brescia and vicinity.
Language (s): Italian
DAILY NEWSPAPER

GIORNALE DI ERBA
Owner: Editrice Lecchese Srl
Editorial: Corso XXV Aprile, 74/b, Erba Co 22036. **T:** 39 031 646300
E: giornale.erba@giornaledierba.it
W: http://www.giornaledierba.it
Freq: Weekly
Language (s): Italian
NEWSPAPER

Giornale di Sicilia
Owner: Giornali di Sicilia Editoriele Poligrafica
Editorial: Via Lincoln 21, Palermo 90133.
T: 39 091 6627111 **E:** redazioneweb@gds.it
W: http://www.gds.it
Freq: Daily; **Circ:** 89000 Not Audited
Editor: Giacinto Pipitone
Editorial Profile: Giornale di Sicilia is an Italian daily national newspaper based in Palermo, Sicily. It is also the best-selling newspaper in Sicily. It was founded in 1860, immediately following the Expedition of the Thousand headed by Giuseppe Garibaldi; it was first published on June 7 under the name "Giornale Officiale di Sicilia", with Girolamo Ardizzone as its first editor-in-chief. It is currently published in 10 different local versions, one for each province of Sicily plus another one for the city of Palermo.
Language (s): Italian
DAILY NEWSPAPER

Il Giorno
Owner: Poligrafici Ed. SpA
Editorial: Via Stradivari, 4, Milano 20131.
T: 39 02 277991
E: segreteria.redazione.milano@monrif.net
W: http://www.ilgiorno.it
Freq: Daily; **Circ:** 431000 Pub Statement
Capo servizio: Claudia Cangemi; **Capo redattore:** Luisa Ciuni; **Capo redattore:** Barbara Consarino; **Capo redattore:** Ivano Costa; **Capo Servizio:** Silvio Danese; **Caporedattore:** Massimo Degli Esposti; **Caporedattore:** Piero Fachin; **Capo servizio:** Giulio Mola; **Capo redattore:** Cesare Paroli; **Capo servizio:** Simone Stimolo
Editorial Profile: Broadsheet-sized newspaper covering news, current affairs, politics, economics, sport and entertainment. Read by managers, civil servants, office personnel and factory employees, over 80 percent of whom live in Lombardia.Local Translation: Ufficio di Corrispondenza Como tel. 0312769311 - fax 0312769317
Language (s): Italian
DAILY NEWSPAPER

The International New York Times - Rome
Editorial: Corso Vittorio Emanuele, #154, Rome 186. **T:** 39 066833455
DAILY NEWSPAPER

Italia Oggi
Owner: Italia Oggi Ed. Erinne
Editorial: Via Burigozzo, 8, Milano 20122.
T: 39 02 58219522 **E:** italiaoggi@class.it
W: http://www.italiaoggi.it
Freq: Daily; **Circ:** 104000 Pub Statement
Capo Servizio: Giorgio Bertoni; **Redattore:** Marco Capisani; **Redattore:** Luigi Chiarello; **Redattore:** Massimo Galli; **Editor in Chief:** Gianni Macheda; **Redattore:** Silvana Saturno; **Redattore:** Simonetta Scarane
Editorial Profile: Tabloid-sized quality newspaper providing financial, economic, political and legal news. Aimed at leaders in the business and financial sectors, senior managers, office personnel and proprietors of small businesses.
Language (s): Italian
DAILY NEWSPAPER

Leggo
Owner: Caltagirone Editore
Editorial: Via Nazionale, 87, Roma Rm 184.
T: 39 06 4620731 **E:** leggo@leggoposta.it
W: http://www.leggo.it
Freq: Daily; **Circ:** 280000 Pub Statement
Capo Servizio: Mario Fabbroni; **Editor in Chief:** Carlo Fiorini; **Editor:** Franco Pasqualetti
Editorial Profile: Leggo newspaper was first published by Caltagirone Editore in 2001. It publishes 15 local editions for the cities of Rome, Milan, Turin, Naples, Bologna, Florence, Padua, Venice, Verona, Bari, Genoa, Como, Bergamo, Brescia and Varese, with a total circulation of 1.050.000 copies.
Language (s): Italian
DAILY NEWSPAPER

Libero
Owner: Editoriale Libero srl
Editorial: Viale Luigi Majno, 42, Milano 20129.
T: 39 02 999666
E: amministrazione@staff.libero.it
W: http://www.libero-news.it
Freq: Daily; **Circ:** 270000 Pub Statement
Capo Servizio: Claudio Antonelli; **Caporedattore:** Simona Bertuzzi; **Capo Servizio:** Francesco Borgonovo; **Capo Servizio:** Giovanni Longoni; **Capo Servizio:** Daniela Mastromattei; **Capo Servizio:** Antonio Spampinato; **Caporedattore:** Francesco Specchia; **Capo Servizio:** Benedetta Vitetta; **Caporedattore Centrale:** Giuliano Zulin
Editorial Profile: Libero is an Italian Right-wing newspaper founded by journalist Vittorio Feltri and edited by Maurizio Belpietro.
Language (s): Italian
DAILY NEWSPAPER

Libero - Roma bureau
Owner: Editoriale Libero srl
Editorial: Via Barberini 50, Rome 187.
T: 39 06 999333
E: segreteria_roma@liberoquotidiano.eu
W: http://www.liberoquotidiano.it
Freq: Daily; **Circ:** 270000 Pub Statement
Capo Servizio: Brunella Bolloli; **Redattore:** Elisa Calessi; **Capo Servizio:** Antonio Castro; **Capo redattore:** Martino Cervo; **Redattore:** Francesco De Dominicis; **Redattore:** Caterina Maniaci; **Redattore:** Enrico Paoli; **Redattore:** Barbara Romano
Editorial Profile: Rome bureau of Libero newspaper.
Language (s): Italian
DAILY NEWSPAPER

Il Manifesto
Owner: Il Manifesto Coop. Ed.
Editorial: Via A. Bargoni 8, Roma 153.
T: 39 06 687191 **E:** redazione@ilmanifesto.it
W: http://www.ilmanifesto.it
Freq: Daily; **Circ:** 84000 Pub Statement
Caporedattore: Marco Boccitto; **Caporedattore:** Michela Bongi; **Caporedattore:** Giulia Sbarigia; **Caporedattore:** Roberto Zanini
Editorial Profile: Tabloid-sized newspaper covering news, politics, finance, economics, sport and entertainment. Aimed at a broad range of the Italian population.
Language (s): Italian
DAILY NEWSPAPER

IL Mattino
Owner: IL MATTINO spa
Editorial: Via Chiatamone 65, Napoli 80121.
T: 39 081 7947111
E: redazioneinternet@ilmattino.it
W: http://www.ilmattino.it
Freq: Daily
Editorial Profile: Local Translation: Non dispongono di fax e mail di redazione
Language (s): Italian
DAILY NEWSPAPER

IL Messaggero
Owner: Societa' Ed.Il Messaggero
Editorial: Via del Tritone 152, Rome 187.
T: 39 06 47201
E: segreteria.redazione@ilmessaggero.it
W: http://www.ilmessaggero.it
Freq: Daily; **Circ:** 400000 Pub Statement
Capo servizio: Mario Ajello; **Caporedattore:** Raffaele Alliegro; **Capo servizio:** Giorgio Belleggia; **Capo redattore centrale:** Stefano Cappellini; **Capo Servizio:** Nino Cirillo; **Capo Servizio:** Marco Conti; **Caporedattore:** Alessandro Di Lellis; **Capo servizio:** Fabio Ferzetti; **Caporedattore:** Alberto Gentili; **Caporedattore:** Franca Giansoldati; **Capo Servizio:** Massimo Martinelli; **Caporedattore:** Angela Padrone; **Caporedattore:** Massimo Pedretti; **Caporedattore:** Lucia Pozzi; **Capo Servizio:** Paolo Ricci Bitti; **Caporedattore:** Pietro Rocchi; **Capo servizio:** Rita Sala; **Caporedattore:** Gloria Satta; **Caporedattore:** Roberto Stigliano; **Capo redattore:** Giorgio Ursicino
Editorial Profile: Il Messaggero is an Italian newspaper based in Rome, Italy, founded in 1878. It is a broadsheet-sized quality newspaper and provides national and international news and articles on politics, finance, economics, sport and entertainment. It is owned by the Italian publishing company Caltagirone Editore, and its leaders include Azzurra Caltagirone, the partner of the political leader Pierferdinando Casini, on its board. It is read by a wide range of people, predominantly living in the Lazio area. It is the most popular daily newspaper in Rome and central Italy; It provides different local editions for the provinces of Lazio, Umbria, Marche, Abruzzo and Tuscany.
Language (s): Italian
DAILY NEWSPAPER

Messaggero Veneto
Owner: Gruppo Editoriale L'Espresso
Editorial: Viale Palmanova 290, Udine 33100.
T: 39 0432 5271
E: ufficio.centrale@messaggeroveneto.it
W: http://www.messaggeroveneto.it
Freq: Daily; **Circ:** 65000 Pub Statement
Editorial Profile: Messaggero Veneto is an Italian local daily newspaper, based in Udine, Italy. It has the largest readership in Friuli-Venezia Giulia. It was founded in 1946 when Friuli was still part of Veneto and Venezia Giulia was claimed by the Socialist Federal Republic of Yugoslavia. It was acquired by Gruppo Editoriale L'Espresso in 1998.
Language (s): Italian
DAILY NEWSPAPER

Metro
Owner: N.M.E. New Media Enterprise Srl
Editorial: Via Carlo Pesenti, 130, Roma 156.
T: 39 06 49241200 **E:** roma@metroitaly.it
W: http://www.metronews.it
Freq: Daily; **Circ:** 260000 Pub Statement
Editor in chief: Paola Rizzi
Editorial Profile: Metro is a free newspaper distributed in 8 Italian cities: Roma, Milano, Torino, Genova, Bologna, Firenze, Cagliari and Sassari. Metro is the most known and most widespread free press newspaper in Asia, Europa and America and includes a network of more than 400 journalists.
Language (s): Italian
DAILY NEWSPAPER

Metropolis
Owner: Citypress
Editorial: Via Provinciale Schito, 131, Torre Annunziata, Napoli 80058.
T: 39 081 19938089
E: segreteria@metropolisweb.it
W: http://metropolisweb.it
Freq: Daily
Editorial Profile: Newspaper covering local and regional news and current affairs.
DAILY NEWSPAPER

La Nazione
Owner: Poligrafici Ed. SpA
Editorial: Viale Giovine Italia, 17, Firenze 50122. **T:** 39 055 24951
E: redazione.cronaca@lanazione.net
W: http://www.lanazione.it
Freq: Daily; **Circ:** 215000 Pub Statement
Capo Servizio: Luigi Caroppo; **Capo redattore:** Laura Pacciani
Editorial Profile: Newspaper covering regional, national and international news and current affairs including politics, economics, sport and entertainment. Read predominantly by people living in the Tuscany and Umbria regions.
Language (s): Italian
DAILY NEWSPAPER

IL NOSTRO TEMPO
Owner: Prelum Srl
Editorial: Corso Matteotti, 11, Torino To 10121. **T:** 39 011 5621873
E: redazione@ilnostrotempo.it
W: http://www.ilnostrotempo.it
Freq: Weekly
Editorial Profile: Local Translation: Nazionale
Language (s): Italian
NEWSPAPER

LA Nuova Sardegna
Owner: Gruppo Editoriale L'Espresso
Editorial: Predda Niedda, – Strada 31, Sassari 7100. **T:** 39 079 222400
E: redazione@lanuovasardegna.it
W: http://lanuovasardegna.gelocal.it
Freq: Daily; **Circ:** 100000 Pub Statement
Editorial Profile: La Nuova Sardegna is an Italian local daily newspaper, based in Sassari, Italy. The newspaper was founded in 1891 by Enrico Berlinguer, grandfather and namesake of Enrico Berlinguer, national secretary of Italian Communist Party. The newspaper was acquired by Gruppo Editoriale L'Espresso in 1980.
Language (s): Italian
DAILY NEWSPAPER

La Padania - La voce del Nord
Owner: Editoriale Nord Soc. Coop.
Editorial: Via C. Bellerio 41, Milano 20161. **T:** 39 02 662461
E: pubblicita@mediapadania.net
W: http://www.lapadania.com/
Freq: Daily; **Circ:** 80000 Pub Statement
Editorial Profile: La Padania, political newspaper of the Northern League was founded in 1996 by Umberto Bossi in order to spread the ideas and points of view of the party led by him.
Language (s): Italian
DAILY NEWSPAPER

Pagina99
Owner: Finam Media srl
Editorial: Viale Liegi, 41, Roma 198. **T:** 39 06 8880 2801 **E:** redazione@pagina99.it
W: http://www.pagina99.it
Freq: Daily
Editorial Profile: National newspaper covering national land international news and current affairs including economics, politics, society, science and culture.
Language (s): Italian
DAILY NEWSPAPER

POLIS QUOTIDIANO
Owner: Publitime Editore Srl
Editorial: Via Mazzini, 6, Parma 43100. **T:** 39 0521207980
E: redazione@polisquotidiano.it
W: http://www.polisquotidiano.it
Freq: Daily
Editorial Profile: Local Translation: Non esce il lunedì
Language (s): Italian
DAILY NEWSPAPER

La Provincia di Lecco
Owner: La Provincia Ed. SpA
Editorial: Via Raffaello Sanzio, 21, Lecco 23900. **T:** 39 0341 357411
E: redlecco@laprovincia.it
W: http://www.laprovinciadilecco.it
Freq: Daily; **Circ:** 50000 Pub Statement
Editorial Profile: La Provincia di Lecco is a daily local newspaper covering the town of Lecco and vicinity (Lecco, Como, Cantu').
Language (s): Italian
DAILY NEWSPAPER

La Provincia di Sondrio
Owner: La Provincia Ed. SpA
Editorial: Via N. Sauro 13, Sondrio 23100. **T:** 39 0342 535511
E: redsondrio@laprovincia.it
W: http://www.laprovinciadisondrio.it
Freq: Daily; **Circ:** 50000 Pub Statement
Editorial Profile: La Provincia di Sondrio is a local daily newspaper covering Sondrio and vicinity.
Language (s): Italian
DAILY NEWSPAPER

LA PROVINCIA di VARESE
Owner: La Provincia Ed. SpA
Editorial: Via Carrobbio, 1, Varese Va 21100. **T:** 39 0332 836611 **E:** redvarese@laprovincia.it
W: http://www.laprovinciadivarese.it
Freq: Daily
Language (s): Italian
DAILY NEWSPAPER

Pubblico Today
Owner: Flor Media Srl
Editorial: Via Torino 64, Milano 20123. **T:** 39 02 72000035
E: pubblico.today@pubblico-online.it
W: http://www.pubblico-online.it
Freq: Daily
Editor in Chief: Nicola Zonca
Editorial Profile: Pubblico Today is a newspaper covering advertising and integrated communication in Italy and in the world.
Language (s): Italian
DAILY NEWSPAPER

PZ PUSTERTALER ZEITUNG
Owner: Ed. Radio Holiday Pustertaler Medien srl
Editorial: Via Ragen di Sopra, 18, Brunico Bz 39031. **T:** 39 0474 550830
E: sekretariat@pustertaler-zeitung.it
W: http://www.pustertaler-zeitung.it
Freq: Bi-Weekly
Language (s): German
NEWSPAPER

Quatro Ciàcoe
Owner: Editoriale Padova
Editorial: Via Puglie, 3, Padova 35127. **T:** 39 049 8704545 **E:** rivista@quatrociacoe.it
W: http://www.quatrociacoe.it
Language (s): Italian
DAILY NEWSPAPER

Quotidiano della Basilicata
Owner: Luedi Srl
Editorial: Via Nazario Sauro 102, Potenza 85100. **T:** 39 0971 69309
E: ilquotidiano.pz@finedit.com
W: http://www.ilquotidianodellabasilicata.it
Freq: Daily
Redattore: Antonella GIACUMMO; **Redattore:** Alessia GIAMMARIA; **Capo servizio:** Alfonso PECORARO; **Redattore:** Salvatore SANTORO; **Capo redattore:** Lucia SERINO
Editorial Profile: Local Translation: Altra mail: ilquotidiano.pz@finedit.com - potenza@luedi.it
Language (s): Italian
DAILY NEWSPAPER

Quotidiano Nazionale - Roma bureau
Owner: Poligrafici Ed. SpA
Editorial: Piazza S. Silvestro 13, Roma 187
E: roma@quotidiano.net
W: http://www.quotidiano.net
Freq: Daily; **Circ:** 597087 Pub Statement
Redattore: Beatrice Bertuccioli; **Caporedattore:** Andrea Cangini; **Redattore:** Antonella Coppari; **Redattore:** Silvia Mastrantonio; **Redattore:** Olivia Posani
Editorial Profile: Rome bureau of Quotidiano Nazionale newspaper.
Language (s): Italian
DAILY NEWSPAPER

Quotidiano Nazionale (QN)
Owner: Poligrafici Ed. SpA
Editorial: Via E. Mattei 106, Bologna 40138. **T:** 39 051 6006111
E: segreteria.redazione.bologna@monrif.net
W: http://qn.quotidiano.net/
Freq: Daily; **Circ:** 552966 Pub Statement
Caporedattore: Massimo Degli Esposti; **Caporedattore:** Sergio Gioli; **Caporedattore:** Riccardo Iannello; **Capo servizio:** Lorenzo Moroni; **Caporedattore:** Achille Scalabrin; **Caporedattore:** Gianluigi Schiavon
Editorial Profile: Quotidiano Nazionale is an online journal with all the latest news from Italy and the world, real-time news with photos and videos, news, last hour, in-depth news. Quotidiano Nazionale is also a network of newspapers that is owned by Polygraphic Editoriale S.p.A Groups. The network includes 3 newspapers: La Nazione, published in Florence, Il Resto del Carlino, published in Bologna, Il Giorno, published in Milan.
Language (s): Italian
DAILY NEWSPAPER

La Repubblica
Owner: Gruppo Ed. L'Espresso SpA
Editorial: Via Cristoforo Colombo, 90, Roma Rm 147. **T:** 39 06 49821
E: larepubblica@repubblica.it
W: http://www.repubblica.it
Freq: Daily; **Circ:** 597694 Pub Statement
Capo servizio: Stefania Aloia; **Capo redattore:** Ernesto Assante; **Capo redattore:** Aldo Balzanelli; **Capo servizio:** Davide Banfo; **Capo redattore:** Valerio Berruti; **Editor in Chief:** Fabio Bogo; **Editor in Chief:** Giuseppe Casciaro; **Capo redattore:** Giuseppe Cerasa; **Editor:** Arturo Cocchi; **Capo redattore:** Stefania Di Lellis; **Capo servizio:** Francesco Erbani; **Capo servizio:** Roberto Leone; **Capo servizio:** Riccardo Liguori; **Capo servizio:** Angelo Lupoli; **Editor in Chief:** Aurelio Magistà; **Capo redattore:** Giancarlo Mola; **Capo servizio:** Gianluca Moresco; **Editor:** Vincenzo Nigro; **Redattore:** Carlo Picozza; **Editor in Chief:** Aligi Pontani; **Capo servizio:** Lavinia Rivara; **Capo redattore:** Marco Ruffolo; **Capo servizio:** Antonio Scuteri; **Capo servizio:** Fabio Massimo Signoretti; **Editore:** Barbara Spinelli; **Capo redattore:** Claudio Tito; **Redattore Esperto:** Giovanna Vitale
Editorial Profile: La Repubblica is an Italian daily general-interest newspaper. It was founded in 1976 in Rome by Gruppo Editoriale L'Espresso led by Eugenio Scalfari and Carlo Caracciolo and Arnoldo Mondadori Editore. Born as a radical/socialist newspaper, it has since kept a centre-left political stance.
Language (s): Italian
DAILY NEWSPAPER

Il Resto del Carlino
Owner: Poligrafici Ed. SpA
Editorial: Via E. Mattei, 106, Bologna 40138. **T:** 39 051 6006111
E: segreteria.redazione.bologna@monrif.net
W: http://www.ilrestodelcarlino.it
Freq: Daily; **Circ:** 307000 Pub Statement
Caporedattore: Franco Caniato; **Capo Servizio:** Angelo Costa; **Capo Servizio:** Claudio Cumani; **Capo Servizio:** Gianni Gennasi; **Capo Servizio:** Luigi Manfredi; **Caporedattore:** Massimiliano Pandolfi; **Capo Servizio:** Andrea Ropa
Editorial Profile: Il Resto del Carlino is a broadsheet-sized newspaper covering regional, national and international news, politics, economics, sport and entertainment.
Language (s): Italian
DAILY NEWSPAPER

IL Romanista
Owner: Editore I Romanisti S.C.
Editorial: Via Angelo Bargoni, 8, Roma 153. **T:** 39 06 64006501 **E:** posta@ilromanista.it
W: http://www.ilromanista.it
Freq: Daily
Editorial Profile: Il Romanista is a sports daily newspaper, the first in the world dedicated solely to a football team, Roma. The newspaper was first published in the summer of 2004.
Language (s): Italian
DAILY NEWSPAPER

IL Secolo XIX
Owner: Società Editoriale Perrone Spa
Editorial: Piazza Piccapietra, 21, Genova 16121. **T:** 39 010 53881
E: redazione@ilsecoloxix.it
W: http://www.ilsecoloxix.it
Freq: Daily; **Circ:** 127000 Pub Statement
Caporedattore: Eugenio Agosti; **Capo Servizio:** Vittorio De Benedictis; **Capo Servizio:** Francesco Ferrari; **Capo Servizio:** Guido Filippi; **Capo Servizio:** Giuliano Galletta; **Capo Servizio:** Diana Letizia; **Capo Servizio:** Claudio Mangini; **Caporedattore:** Riccardo Massa; **Caporedattore:** Marco Menduni; **Caporedattore:** Roberto Onofrio; **Caporedattore:** Marco Perchiera; **Capo Servizio:** Andrea Plebe; **Capo Redattore Centrale:** Massimo Righi; **Redattore:** Roberto Sangalli; **Capo Servizio:** Roberto Scarcella; **Caporedattore:** Nicola Stella; **Caporedattore:** Giampiero Timossi; **Editor:** Simone Traverso
Editorial Profile: Il Secolo XIX is an Italian newspaper published in the Liguria region and founded in March 1886.
Language (s): Italian
DAILY NEWSPAPER

IL Sole 24 Ore
Owner: Gruppo Il Sole 24 ORE S.p.A.
Editorial: Via Monte Rosa, 91, Milano 20149. **T:** 39 02 30221
E: gruppo24ore@ilsole24ore.com
W: http://www.ilsole24ore.com
Freq: Daily Pub Statement
Capo redattore centrale: Daniele Bellasio; **Capo redattore:** Paola Bottelli; **Capo redattore:** Enrico Brivio; **Redattore:** Enrico Bronzo; **Redattore:** Chiara Bussi; **Redattore:** Micaela Cappellini; **Capo servizio:** Mario Cianflone; **Capo Servizio:** Giorgio Costa; **Redattore:** Monica D'Ascenzo; **Editor:** Luca De Biase; **Capo redattore:** Jean Marie Del Bo; **Capo servizio:** Isabella Della Valle; **Capo redattore:** Massimo Esposti; **Capo servizio:** Carlo Andrea Finotto; **Redattore:** Alberto Grassani; **Capo servizio:** Fabio Grattagliano; **Capo servizio:** Alessandro Graziani; **Redattore:** Lucilla Incorvati; **Caporedattore:** Laura La Posta; **Capo redattore centrale:** Marina Macelloni; **Capo redattore:** Christian Martino; **Capo redattore centrale:** Federico Momoli; **Capo redattore:** Lello Naso; **Capo servizio:** Giovanni Negri; **Capo redattore:** Luca Orlando; **Capo servizio:** Francesca Padula; **Capo redattore centrale:** Salvatore Padula; **Capo redattore centrale:** Guido Palmieri; **Editor:** Fabio Pavesi; **Redattore:** Federica Pezzatti; **Capo servizio:** Guido Plutino; **Editor in Chief:** Christian Rocca; **Editor in Chief:** Fernanda Roggero; **Capo servizio:** Riccardo Sabbatini; **Editor:** Pierangelo Soldavini; **Capo redattore centrale:** Alberto Trevissoi; **Capo servizio:** Marco Valsania; **Capo servizio:** Franco Vergnano
Editorial Profile: Broadsheet-sized quality newspaper providing coverage of national and international news, with particular emphasis on finance and the economy. Read by company directors, senior executives, managers, civil servants, university students and academics.
Language (s): Italian
DAILY NEWSPAPER

La Stampa
Owner: Edizioni La Stampa SpA
Editorial: Via Lugaro, 15, Torino 10126. **T:** 39 011 6568111 **E:** lettere@lastampa.it
W: http://www.lastampa.it
Freq: Daily; **Circ:** 470000 Pub Statement
Capo servizio: Antonella Amapane; **Capo servizio:** Maurizio Assalto; **Capo servizio:** Maurizio Assalto; **Capo servizio:** Gabriele Beccaria; **Capo redattore:** Guido Boffo; **Capo servizio:** Irene Cabiati; **Capo redattore:** Dario Corradino; **Editor in Chief:** Gabriele Ferraris; **Caporedattore:** Luca Ferrua; **Capo redattore:** Anna Masera; **Inviato/New York:** Paolo Mastrolilli; **Capo redattore:** Gianluca Paolucci; **Capo servizio:** Fabio Pozzo; **Capo redattore:** Francesca Sforza; **Capo redattore:** Marco Sodano; **Capo redattore:** Guido Tiberga; **Capo servizio:** Bruno Ventavoli; **Redattore esperto:** Niccolò Zancan; **Redattore:** Raphael Zanotti
Editorial Profile: Tabloid-sized quality newspaper containing national, international and regional news focusing on Piemonte, financial information and articles on society, culture, entertainment and sport. Readership includes directors, senior executives, middle managers and office personnel.
Language (s): Italian
DAILY NEWSPAPER

IL Tempo
Owner: Quotidiano IL TEMPO Srl
Editorial: Piazza Colonna, 366, Roma 187. **T:** 39 06 675881 **E:** segreteria@iltempo.it
W: http://www.iltempo.it
Freq: Daily; **Circ:** 100000 Pub Statement
Capo Servizio: Tiziano Carmellini; **Capo servizio:** Fabrizio Dell'Orefice; **Redattore:** Fabio Di Chio; **Capo Servizio:** Alberto Di Majo; **Capo Servizio:** Lidia Lombardi; **Caporedattore Centrale:** Stefano Mannucci; **Caporedattore Centrale:** Angelo Perfetti; **Capo Servizio:** Matteo Vincenzoni
Editorial Profile: Broadsheet-sized newspaper covering regional, national and international news, finance, politics and sport. Read predominantly by people living in the Lazio and Abruzzi regions.
Language (s): Italian
DAILY NEWSPAPER

Il Tirreno
Owner: Gruppo Editoriale L'Espresso
Editorial: Viale Vittorio Alfieri, 9, Livorno 57124. **T:** 39 0586 220111
E: redazione.li@iltirreno.it
W: http://www.iltirreno.it
Freq: Daily; **Circ:** 121000 Pub Statement
Editor: Elisabetta Arrighi; **Editor:** Luciano Gianfranceschi
Editorial Profile: Il Tirreno is a regional Italian newspaper, which is printed in Livorno and published in Tuscany. Il Tirreno also features sixteen local editions around the whole region. It was founded in 1877 under the name Il Telegrafo, with a moderate centrist political line. Il Tirreno is currently owned by the media company Gruppo Editoriale L'Espresso.
Language (s): Italian
DAILY NEWSPAPER

Il Today
Owner: TVN Media Group Srl
Editorial: Corso Magenta, 85, Milano 20123. **T:** 39 02 4300001

E: comunicati@pubblicitaitalia.it
W: http://www.pubblicitaitalia.it
Freq: Daily
Editorial Profile: Newspaper covering the advertising industry including marketing, media and internet communication.
Language (s): Italian
DAILY NEWSPAPER

Tuttosport
Owner: Nuova Editoriale Sportiva
Editorial: Corso Svizzera, 185, Torino 10149.
T: 39 011 77731 **E:** posta@tuttosport.com
W: http://www.tuttosport.com
Freq: Daily; **Circ:** 205000 Pub Statement
Capo Servizio: Paolo Bramardo; **Capo servizio:** Claudio Casagrande; **Caporedattore Centrale:** Gianni De Pace; **Capo servizio:** Pippo Degrandi; **Capo Servizio:** Alberto Manassero; **Capo Servizio:** Andrea Pavan; **Capo servizio:** Walter Perosino; **Capo Servizio:** Gian Piero Porta; **Capo Servizio:** Giovanni Tosco; **Capo Servizio:** Guido Vaciago; **Capo Servizio:** Walter Vaira
Editorial Profile: Broadsheet-sized newspaper providing coverage of competitive sport in Italy and throughout the world, with particular emphasis on events in the Turin area. Read by a wide range of people interested in sport.
Language (s): Italian
DAILY NEWSPAPER

TuttoSport - Milano bureau
Owner: Nuova Editoriale Sportiva
Editorial: Corso Sempione, 8, Milano 20154.
T: 39 02 316308 **W:** http://www.tuttosport.com
Freq: Daily; **Circ:** 205000 Pub Statement
Redattore: Stefano Pasquino; **Redattore:** Alberto Pastorella
Editorial Profile: Milano Bureau of TuttoSport newspaper.
Language (s): Italian
DAILY NEWSPAPER

TuttoSport - Roma bureau
Owner: Nuova Editoriale Sportiva
Editorial: Via Calderini, 68, Rome 196.
T: 39 06 3236584
W: http://www.tuttosport.com
Freq: Daily; **Circ:** 205000 Pub Statement
Editorial Profile: Rome bureau of TuttoSport newspaper.
Language (s): Italian
DAILY NEWSPAPER

L' Unità
Owner: Nuova Iniziativa Editoriale Spa
Editorial: Via Ostiense 131/L, Roma 154.
T: 39 06 585571 **E:** segreteria@unita.it
W: http://www.unita.it
Freq: Daily
Caporedattore: Daniela Amenta; **Capo Servizio:** Ninni Andriolo; **Caporedattore Centrale:** Paolo Branca; **Capo Servizio:** Marco Bucciantini; **Capo Servizio:** Cesare Buquicchio; **Capo Servizio:** Francesco Cundari; **Caporedattore:** Umberto De Giovannangeli; **Capo Servizio:** Massimo Filipponi; **Capo Servizio:** Claudia Fusani; **Capo Servizio:** Rachele Gonnelli; **Capo Servizio:** Felicia Masocco; **Capo Servizio:** Stefania Scateni; **Capo Servizio:** Cinzia Zambrano
Editorial Profile: Broadsheet newspaper covering trade union news throughout Italy. Official organ of the Partito Democratico di Sinistra, providing a forum for readers to express their opinions on a variety of union issues. Read by union members and supporters.
Language (s): Italian
DAILY NEWSPAPER

L' Unita' - Milano bureau
Owner: Nuova Iniziativa Editoriale Spa
Editorial: Via Antonio da Recanate 2, Milano 20124. **T:** 39 02 8969811
W: http://www.unita.it
Freq: Daily; **Circ:** 125000 Pub Statement
Redattore: Marco Ventimiglia; **Redattore:** Luigina Venturelli; **Redattore:** Giuseppe Vespo
Editorial Profile: Milan bureau of l'Unita' newspaper.
Language (s): Italian
DAILY NEWSPAPER

LA VOCE DI ROMAGNA FO
Owner: Editrice La Voce Srl
Editorial: Corso Garibaldi 40, Forlì 47100.
T: 39 0543 36255
E: forli@lavocediromagna.com
Freq: Daily
Redattore: Roberta INVIDIA; **Capo servizio:** Maria NERI
Language (s): Italian
DAILY NEWSPAPER

The Wall Street Journal (Italy)
Editorial: Via Santa Maria, Via 12, Rome 187.
T: 39 069380691
Bureau Chief: Deborah Ball
DAILY NEWSPAPER

Wall Street Journal (Italy)
Editorial: Via Marco Burigozzo 5, Milano 20122. **T:** 39 02 5821-1901
E: djitaly@dowjones.com
Bureau Chief: Deborah Ball
DAILY NEWSPAPER

NEWS SERVICE/SYNDICATE

ADNKRONOS - GRUPPO
Owner: Adnkronos Spa
Editorial: P.za Mastai, 9, Roma Rm 153.
T: 39 06 58071
E: segreteria.redazione@adnkronos.com
W: http://www.adnkronos.com
Freq: Daily
Capo servizio: Mia GRASSI; **Capo servizio:** Saeed HAYDER; **Capo servizio:** Fabio INSENGA; **Capo servizio:** Marco MAZZU'; **Capo servizio:** Maria Grazia NAPOLITANO; **Capo servizio:** Giuseppe ORLANDO; **Capo servizio:** Patrizia PERILLI; **Redattore:** Alessandro REMIA
Editorial Profile: Media service dedicated to information exchange, research and dialogue between Italy, Europe and the emerging areas of Africa, the Middle East, Asia and Latin America.
Language (s): Arabic
NEWS SERVICE/SYNDICATE

ADNKRONOS SALUTE
Owner: Adnkronos Spa
Editorial: Piazza Mastai 9, Roma 153.
T: 39 06 5807438 **E:** salute@adnkronos.com
W: http://www.adnsalute.it
Freq: Daily
Redattore: Raffaella AMMIRATI; **Capo servizio:** Adelisa MAIO
Editorial Profile: News agency and wire service focussing on health issues.
Language (s): Italian
NEWS SERVICE/SYNDICATE

Agence France-Presse - Milano Bureau
Owner: Agence France Presse
Editorial: Via Vitruvio, 43, Milano Mi 20124.
T: 39 02 67101283 **E:** afp-rome@afp.com
W: http://www.afp.com
Freq: Daily
Editorial Profile: Regional office of the international news agency and wire service focussing on news and current affairs.
Language (s): English
NEWS SERVICE/SYNDICATE

Agence France-Presse - Roma Bureau
Owner: Agence France Presse
Editorial: Piazza Santi Apostoli, 66, Roma Rm 187. **T:** 39 06 6793588 **E:** afp-rome@afp.com
W: http://www.afp.com
Freq: Daily
Bureau Chief: Olivier Baube
Editorial Profile: International news agency and wire service covering news and current affairs.
Language (s): Arabic
NEWS SERVICE/SYNDICATE

AGENPARL - Agenzia Parlamentare
Editorial: Via Uffici del Vicario, 35, Roma 186.
T: 39 06 69797691 **E:** redazione@agenparl.it
W: http://www.agenparl.com
Freq: Daily
Editorial Profile: News agency focussing on parliamentary information including politics and economics. Local Translation:Agenzia stampa telematica parlamentare per l'informazione politica ed economica
Language (s): Italian
NEWS SERVICE/SYNDICATE

AGENZIA RUSSA RIA NOVOSTI
Owner: RIA Novosti
Editorial: Via Elio Vittorini, 78, Roma Rm 144.
T: 39 06 5015840 **W:** http://www.ria.ru
Freq: Daily
Editorial Profile: Regional office of the international Russian news agency and wire service focussing on news and current affairs.
Language (s): English
NEWS SERVICE/SYNDICATE

AGI MI
Editorial: Via Verdi 2, Milano 20121.
T: 39 02722301 **E:** redazione.milano@agi.it
W: http://www.agi.it
Freq: Daily
Redattore: Gianluca ALLIEVI; **Redattore:** Annalisa CRETELLA; **Redattore:** Angelo FERRARI
Editorial Profile: Regional office of the AGI new agency and wire service. Local Translation:Attualita' Cronaca
Language (s): English
NEWS SERVICE/SYNDICATE

ANSA
Owner: Agenzia Nazionale Stampa Associata
Editorial: Via della Dataria, 94, Roma 187.
T: 39 06 6774 1 **E:** redazione.internet@ansa.it
W: http://www.ansa.it
Freq: Daily
Capo redattore: Daniele ALEGIANI SAGNOTTI; **Capo servizio:** Luigi AMBROSINO; **Capo redattore:** Annalisa ANTONUCCI; **Capo servizio:** Michele BACCINELLI; **Capo servizio:** Maria Emilia BONACCORSO; **Capo servizio:** Flaminia BUSSOTTI; **Capo servizio:** Rodolfo CALO'; **Capo Servizio:** Tiziana Caroselli; **Capo servizio:** Gianfranco CARPENTE; **Capo servizio:** Angela CARUSONE; **Capo servizio:** Michele CASSANO; **Editor:** Paola Catani Gagliani; **Capo servizio:** Giuseppe CAVALCANTI; **Capo redattore:** Corrado CHIOMINTO; **Capo servizio:** Giovanna CHIRRI; **Capo redattore:** Angela COARELLI; **Capo servizio:** Massimo COLAIACOMO; **Capo servizio:** Claudia COLETTA; **Capo servizio:** Domitilla CONTE; **Capo servizio:** Paolo CUCCHIARELLI; **Capo redattore centrale:** Candida CURZI; **Capo redattore:** Paolo DALLORSO; **Capo servizio:** Francesco DE FILIPPO; **Capo servizio:** Marco DELL'OMO; **Capo servizio:** Guido DI GIAMMATTEO; **Capo servizio:** Monica DIAMANTI; **Editor:** Carlo Ferraro; **Capo redattore:** Fabrizio FINZI; **Capo servizio:** Luciano FIORAMONTI; **Capo servizio:** Sandra FISCHETTI; **Capo servizio:** Pierluigi FRANCO; **Capo redattore:** Pier Francesco FRERE'; **Capo servizio:** Fausto GASPARRONI; **Capo redattore:** Francesco GERACE; **Capo servizio:** Marzia GIGLIOLI; **Capo servizio:** Carmela GIUDICE; **Capo servizio:** Francesco GRANT; **Capo redattore:** Giancarlo GRAZIOSI; **Capo servizio:** Eugenio GRECO; **Capo servizio:** Elisabetta GUIDOBALDI; **Capo redattore:** Stefania IANTAFFI; **Capo servizio:** Edoardo Roberto LAVIOLA; **Capo servizio:** Gabriele LE MOLI; **Capo servizio:** Andrea LIBERTO; **Capo redattore:** Andrea LINARES; **Capo redattore:** Massimo LOMONACO; **Capo servizio:** Alessandra MAGLIARO; **Capo servizio:** Paola MAIOLI; **Capo redattore:** Angela MAJOLI; **Capo servizio:** Agnese MALATESTA; **Capo redattore:** Giosuè MANIACI; **Capo redattore:** Francesco MARABOTTO; **Capo servizio:** Beatrice MARCHESI; **Capo servizio:** Daniele Maria MARCHETTI; **Capo servizio:** Graziella MARINO; **Capo servizio:** Roberta MARROLLO; **Capo servizio:** Laura MASIELLO; **Capo redattore centrale:** Andrea MORELLI; **Capo servizio:** Patrizio NISSIRIO; **Capo servizio:** Claudio ONORATI; **Capo servizio:** Beatrice OTTAVIANO; **Capo servizio:** Giuliana PALIERI; **Capo servizio:** Cristiano PANDOLFO; **Capo servizio:** Monica PATERNESI; **Capo servizio:** Marina PERNA; **Capo redattore:** Giannantonio PETTINELLI; **Capo servizio:** Elisa PINNA; **Capo servizio:** Nadia PIZZUTI; **Capo redattore:** Stefano POLLI; **Capo redattore:** Piercarlo PRESUTTI; **Capo servizio:** Barbara PRINCIPATO; **Capo servizio:** Aldo PUTHOD; **Capo redattore centrale:** Vincenzo QUARATINO; **Capo servizio:** Flavia RESSMANN; **Capo servizio:** Emanuele RICCARDI; **Capo servizio:** Massimo RICCI; **Capo servizio:** Riccardo ROSSI; **Capo redattore centrale:** Massimo SEBASTIANI; **Capo redattore:** Vincenzo SINAPI; **Capo servizio:** Paola SPADARI; **Capo servizio:** Alberto SPAMPINATO; **Capo redattore centrale:** Alessandra SPITZ; **Capo redattore:** Elisabetta STEFANELLI; **Capo redattore:** Giorgio SVALDUZ; **Capo redattore:** Giuseppe TITO; **Capo servizio:** Maria Novella TOPI; **Capo servizio:** Vittoriano VANCINI; **Capo redattore:** Gianluca VANNUCCHI; **Capo servizio:** Alessandro VERGINELLI
Editorial Profile: National news agency covering regional, national and international news and current affairs including politics, business, economics, society, culture, technology and sports.
Language (s): English
NEWS SERVICE/SYNDICATE

AP - THE ASSOCIATED PRESS
Editorial: P.zza Grazioli, 5, Roma 186.
T: 39 06 69747280 **E:** aprome@ap.org
W: http://www.ap.org
Freq: Daily
Redattore: Colleen BARRY; **Redattore:** Frances D'EMILIO
Language (s): Italian
NEWS SERVICE/SYNDICATE

APA AUSTRIA PRESSE AGENTUR
Editorial: Via dell' Umiltà 83/c, Roma 187.
T: 39 06 675911 **W:** http://www.apa.at
Freq: Daily
Language (s): Italian
NEWS SERVICE/SYNDICATE

APS ALGERIE PRESSE SERVICE
Editorial: Via Asmara, 10/c, Roma 199.
T: 39 0686218505 **W:** http://www.aps.dz
Freq: Daily
Language (s): Italian
NEWS SERVICE/SYNDICATE

ASA PRESS - Agenzia Stampa Motoristica Italiana
Owner: HUB Comunicazione
Editorial: Via Ramazzotti, 20, Monza Mi 20052. **T:** 39 02 22472162
E: redazione@hubcomunicazione.it
Freq: Monthly
Language (s): Italian
NEWS SERVICE/SYNDICATE

Associated Press
Editorial: Piazza Grazioli 5, Rome 186.
T: 39 06 6974-7260
NEWS SERVICE/SYNDICATE

Bloomberg News
Editorial: Piazza Fontana 1, Milan 20122.
T: 39 0280644274
Bureau Chief: Dan Liefgreen
NEWS SERVICE/SYNDICATE

Bloomberg News
Editorial: Piazza del Popolo 18, 4th Floor, Rome 187. **T:** 39 0645206333
E: italynews@bloomberg.net
Bureau Chief: Alessandra Migliaccio
NEWS SERVICE/SYNDICATE

BLOOMBERG NEWS RM
Owner: Bloomberg
Editorial: Piazza del Popolo, 18 4º piano, Roma 187. **T:** 39 06 45206333
E: italynews@bloomberg.net
W: http://www.bloomberg.com
Freq: Daily
Capo redattore: Andrew DAVIS
Language (s): Italian
NEWS SERVICE/SYNDICATE

BULGARIAN NEWS AGENCY
Editorial: Via dell' Umiltà, 83/c, Roma 187.
T: 39 06 675911 **W:** http://www.bta.bg
Freq: Daily
Language (s): Italian
NEWS SERVICE/SYNDICATE

CENTRAL NEWS AGENCY
Editorial: Via dell'Umiltà, 83/C, Roma 187.
T: 39 06 675911 **W:** http://www.cna.com.tw
Freq: Daily
Language (s): Italian
NEWS SERVICE/SYNDICATE

Dow Jones Newswires
Editorial: Via Marco Burigozzo 5, Milano 20122. **T:** 39 02 5821-1901
E: djitaly@dowjones.com
Bureau Chief: Deborah Ball
NEWS SERVICE/SYNDICATE

DPA-DEUTSCHE PRESSE AGENTUR
Owner: Editore DPA
Editorial: via Vespasiano, 12 (int.12), Roma 192. **T:** 39 06 39744348 **E:** roma@dpa.com
W: http://www.dpa.com
Freq: Daily
Language (s): Italian
NEWS SERVICE/SYNDICATE

EASY NEWS PRESS AGENCY
Owner: Easy Rider World Association
Editorial: Casella Postale 5123, Roma 153.
T: 39 178 440 2319 **E:** info@mauriziozini.com
W: http://www.easynewsweb.com
Freq: Monthly
Redattore: Giovan Francesco SERRA DI CASSANO; **Redattore:** Lorenzo VERRI
Language (s): Italian
NEWS SERVICE/SYNDICATE

EUROPA PRESS
Editorial: Via Giuseppe Cerbara, 64, Roma 147. **T:** 39 06 5115799
W: http://www.europapress.es
Language (s): Italian
NEWS SERVICE/SYNDICATE

ITALPRESS
Owner: Italpress
Editorial: Via Dante 69, Palermo 90141.
T: 39 091589674 **E:** info@italpress.com
W: http://www.italpress.com
Freq: Daily
Redattore: Vincenzo BONADONNA; **Redattore:** Paolo COSTA; **Redattore:** Alex DI SCLAFANI; **Redattore:** Maria Grazia GRADANTI; **Redattore:** Dario PASTA; **Redattore:** Salvatore TRAPANI; **Redattore:** Tony VIOLA
Language (s): Italian
NEWS SERVICE/SYNDICATE

MF Dow Jones News
Owner: Class Editori SpA
Editorial: Via Burigozzo, 5, Milano 20122.
T: 39 02 582191
E: redazionemfdj@mfdowjones.it
W: http://www.djnewswires.com/eu
Freq: Daily
Redattore: Marco FUSI; **Capo redattore:** Gabriele LA MONICA; **Redattore:** Alessandro MOCENNI
Language (s): Italian
NEWS SERVICE/SYNDICATE

OMAR PRESS NEWS
Owner: Adriana Barale
Editorial: Via Tolstoj 40, Milano 20146.
T: 39 02 474848 **E:** omarpressnews@libero.it
Freq: Bi-Weekly
Redattore: Sergio CRUGIA
Language (s): Italian
NEWS SERVICE/SYNDICATE

OMNIAPRESS
Owner: Agenzia Omniapress
Editorial: Via Mons. Biraghi 6, Milano 20163.
T: 39 3357184166 **E:** omniapress1@libero.it
Freq: Daily
Capo redattore: Maria Grazia SIRTORI
Language (s): Italian
NEWS SERVICE/SYNDICATE

Reuters
Editorial: Corso D'Italia 39, Rome 198.
T: 39 3487604350
E: rome.newsroom@thomsonreuters.com
Bureau Chief: James Mackenzie
NEWS SERVICE/SYNDICATE

Reuters
Editorial: Via Santa Margherita 1/A, Milan 20121. **T:** 39 02 661-291
E: milan.newsroom@thomsonreuters.com
NEWS SERVICE/SYNDICATE

REUTERS MI - Servizio Internazionale
Owner: Thomson Reuters (Markets) ItaliaSpA
Editorial: Via Santa Margherita, 1/a, Milano Mi 20121. **T:** 39 02 661291
E: reutersitaly@thomsonreuters.com
W: www.reuters.com
Freq: Daily
Capo redattore: Elisabetta JUCCA
Language (s): Italian
NEWS SERVICE/SYNDICATE

REUTERS MI - Servizio Italiano
Owner: Thomson Reuters (Markets) Italia SpA
Editorial: Via Santa Margherita, 1/a, Milano 20121. **T:** 39 02 661291
E: reutersitaly@thomsonreuters.com
W: http://www.reuters.it
Freq: Daily
Redattore: Elisa ANZOLIN; **Capo redattore:** Paola AROSIO; **Redattore:** Stefano REBAUDO; **Redattore:** Sabina SUZZI
Language (s): Italian
NEWS SERVICE/SYNDICATE

REUTERS RM - Servizio Internazionale
Owner: Editoriale Reuters
Editorial: Corso Italia, 39, Roma 198.
T: 39 06 85224350
E: rome.newsroom@news.reuters.com
W: http://www.reuters.com
Freq: Daily
Language (s): Italian
NEWS SERVICE/SYNDICATE

REUTERS RM - Servizio Italiano
Owner: Editoriale Reuters
Editorial: Corso Italia, 39, Rome 198.
T: 39 06 85224352
E: rome.editorial@reuters.com
W: www.reuters.com
Freq: Daily
Language (s): Italian
NEWS SERVICE/SYNDICATE

Il Sole 24 Ore Radiocor
Owner: Gruppo Il Sole 24 ORE S.p.A.
Editorial: Via Monte Rosa 91, Milano 20149.
T: 39 02 30221
E: radiocordesk.mi@ilsole24ore.com
W: http://24pa.ilsole24ore.com/
Freq: Daily
Capo servizio: Manuela BRAMBATI; **Redattore:** Paola CATARSI; **Redattore:** Cheo CONDINA; **Capo redattore:** Lorenzo LANFRANCONE; **Inviato:** Giuliana LICINI; **Capo servizio:** Monica LODI; **Redattore:** Eleonora MICHELI; **Redattore:** Tiziana MONTRASIO; **Capo servizio:** Dario POLLICE; **Capo redattore:** Isabella TASSO
Editorial Profile: Il Sole 24 Ore Radiocor is an Italian business and financial news agency owned by the newspaper Il Sole 24 Ore with offices in Rome, Milan, Turin and Brussels.
Language (s): Italian
NEWS SERVICE/SYNDICATE

TERRA ITALIA NEWS
Owner: Tidpress
Editorial: Via Nomentana, 187, Roma Rm 161.
T: 39 06 44250577 **E:** redazione@tid-press.net
W: http://www.terra-italia.net
Freq: Daily
Language (s): Italian
NEWS SERVICE/SYNDICATE

BROADCASTING

RADIO NETWORKS

CBC - RADIO CANADA
Editorial: Via dell'Umiltà, 83/c, Roma 187.
T: 39 06 675911 **W:** http://www.cbc.ca
Editorial Profile: Local Translation: Marketplace Radio (American Public Media)

CESKI ROZHLAS
Editorial: via dell'Umiltà, 83/C, Roma 187.
T: 39 06 675911 **W:** http://www.rozhlas.cz

CHINA RADIO INTERNATIONAL
Editorial: Via dell'Umiltà, 83/C, Roma 187.
T: 39 06 675911

Ciao Radio
Owner: Dinamica Sas
Editorial: Via dei Fornaciai, 24, Bologna 40129. **T:** 39 051 4187476
E: ciaoradio@ciaoradio.com
W: http://www.ciaoradio.it
Editorial Profile: Regional radio station covering music and news.

CIRCUITO INBLU - NEWS PRESS
Owner: News Press Spa
Editorial: Piazza Carbonari, 3, Milano 20125.
T: 39 02 693121
E: redazione.mi@blusat2000.it
W: http://www.radioinblu.it

DEUTSCHE WELLE SEZIONE EST EUROPEO
Editorial: Via dell'Umiltà, 83/c, Roma 187.
T: 39 06675911 **W:** http://www.dw-world.de

DEUTSCHE WELLE SEZIONE TURCA
Editorial: Via dell' Umiltà 83/c, Roma 18.
T: 39 06675911 **W:** http://www.dw-world.de

DEUTSCHLANDFUNK DLF
Editorial: Via dell'Umiltà, 83/C, Roma 187.
T: 39 06 675911 **W:** http://www.dradio.de/dlf

NATIONAL PUBLIC RADIO
Editorial: Via della Lungara, 27, Roma 165.
T: 39 06 6877270 **W:** http://www.npr.org
Editorial Profile: Local Translation: Altro Fax: 06 68801589

RADIO 100,7
Editorial: via dell'Umiltà, 83/C, Roma 187.
T: 39 06 675911
W: http://www.100komma7.lu

RADIO 105 NETWORK
Owner: Radio 105 Network
Editorial: Via Moscova, 14/A, Milano 20121.
T: 39 02 62537480 **W:** http://www.105.net
Editorial Profile: 110 stations affiliated.

Radio 24 - Il Sole 24 Ore
Owner: Nuova Radio SpA
Editorial: Via Monte Rosa, 91, Milano 20149.
T: 39 02 30221 **E:** info@radio24.it
W: http://www.radio24.it
Editorial Profile: Local Translation: Altro fax: 02 30224514

RADIO 24 - IL SOLE 24 ORE (RM)
Owner: Nuova Radio SpA
Editorial: Piazza Indipendenza 23/b, Roma 185. **T:** 39 06 30226230
E: redazioneroma@radio24.it
W: http://www.radio24.it

RADIO ALEX
Owner: Nuova Factory srl
Editorial: Via Marsala, 20, Alessandria Al 15100. **T:** 39 0131 443593
E: redazione@radioalex.it
W: http://www.radioalex.it
Editorial Profile: Radio station that mostly plays music but also has news and sports programming.

RADIO BREMEN RB
Editorial: via dell'Umiltà, 83/C, Roma 187.
T: 39 06 675911
W: http://www.radiobremen.de

RADIO CAPITAL
Owner: Elemedia SpA
Editorial: Via Cristoforo Colombo, 90, Roma 147. **T:** 39 06 492324117
E: segreteria_capital@capital.it
W: http://www.capital.it
Editorial Profile: Radio station that has news content in addition to playing music.

RADIO CUORE SARDEGNA
Owner: Radio Cuore Sas
Editorial: Via Carpaccio Vittore, 26, Oristano Or 9170. **T:** 39 0783 310221
E: redazione@radiocuore.net
W: http://www.radiocuore.net

RADIO DEEJAY
Owner: Elemedia SpA
Editorial: Via Massena 2, Milano 20145.
T: 39 02 345711 **E:** redazione@deejay.it
W: http://www.deejay.it

RADIO FRANCE
Editorial: via dell'Umiltà, 83/C, Roma 187.
T: 39 06 675911 **W:** http://www.radiofrance.fr

RADIO FRANCE INTERNATIONALE
Editorial: via dell'Umiltà, 83/C, Roma 187.
T: 39 06 675911 **W:** http://www.rfi.fr

RADIO FRANCE INTERNATIONALE SEZ. BRASIL
Editorial: Via dell' Umiltà 83/c, Roma 187.
T: 39 06 675911 **W:** http://www.rfi.fr

RADIO FRANCE INTERNATIONALE SEZ. PORTOGALLO
Editorial: via dell'Umiltà, 83/C, Roma 187.
T: 39 06 675911 **W:** http://www.rfi.fr

RADIO ITALIA SOLO MUSICA IT. - NOTIZIE
Owner: Radio Italia
Editorial: Viale Europa, 49, Cologno Monzese Mi 20093. **T:** 39 02 254441
E: redazione@radioitalia.it
W: http://www.radioitalia.it

Radio Kiss Kiss
Owner: Lucia Niespolo
Editorial: Via Sgambati, 61, Napoli 80131.
T: 39 081 5461212 **E:** segreteria@kisskiss.it
W: http://www.kisskiss.it
Editorial Profile: Radio station covering news and music.

RADIO MONTECARLO - NEWS
Owner: Gruppo Finelco
Editorial: Via Moscova, 14/a, Milano Mi 20121. **T:** 39 02 231521
W: http://www.radiomontecarlo.net
Editorial Profile: 30 stations affiliated. Local Translation: Attualità, Cronaca, Sport

RADIO MORABEZA
Editorial: Via dell'Umiltà, 83/C, Roma 187.
T: 39 06 675911
W: http://www.studiomorabeza.com

RADIO NAZIONALE BULGARA
Editorial: via dell'Umiltà, 83/C, Roma 187.
T: 39 06 675911
W: http://www.bulgaria-italia.com

RADIO POPOLARE
Owner: Radio Popolare Errepi SpA
Editorial: Via priv. Ollearo, 5, Milano 20155.
T: 39 02 392411 **E:** radiopop@radiopopolare.it
W: http://www.radiopopolare.it
Editorial Profile: Local Translation: Attualita' e News

RADIO POPULAR DE ESPANA - CADENA C.O.P.E
Editorial: via dell'Umiltà, 83/C, Roma 187.
T: 39 06 37352177 **W:** http://cope.es

RADIO R101
Owner: Mon Radio
Editorial: Via Ventura, 3, Milano 20134.
T: 39 02 210831 **E:** centralino.r101@r101.it
W: http://www.r101.it

RADIO RADICALE
Owner: Radio Radicale
Editorial: Via Principe Amedeo, 2, Rome 185.
T: 39 06 488781 **E:** redazione@radioradicale.it
W: www.radioradicale.it
Editorial Profile: 70 stations affiliated. Local Translation: Organo di partito politico/Servizio Pubblico di informazione dei lavori parlamentari - Non rilasciano altre mail dirette

RADIO RINASCENCA
Editorial: via dell'Umiltà, 83/C, Roma 187.
T: 39 06 675911 **W:** http://rr.sapo.pt

RADIO SVIZZERA
Owner: RSI
Editorial: Via della Mercede, 33, Roma 187.
T: 39 06 6796476 **W:** http://www.rsi.ch

Radio Vaticana
Owner: Radio Vaticana
Editorial: Palazzo Pio, Piazza Pia, 3, Rome 120. **T:** 39 06 69883551
E: english@vatiradio.va
W: http://www.radiovaticana.va
Editorial Profile: Radio station covering news and current affairs through the eyes of the Christian church.

RAI - GIORNALE RADIO RAI (GR1-GR2-GR3)
Owner: RAI
Editorial: Largo Villy De Luca 5 - Saxa Rubra, Roma 188. **T:** 39 06 33172188 **E:** grr@rai.it
W: http://www.rai.it

RAI - ISORADIO
Owner: RAI
Editorial: L.go Villy de Luca, 4 - Pal. G2 - Saxa Rubra, Roma 188. **T:** 39 06 33176609
E: isoradio@rai.it
W: http://www.radio.rai.it/isoradio
Editorial Profile: Radio station that plays music but also has news programming, weather, sports, and traffic information.

RAI - RADIO GR PARLAMENTO
Owner: RAI
Editorial: Largo Villy De Luca 5 Palazzina G-2, Roma 188. **T:** 39 0633174146
E: grparlamento@rai.it
W: http://www.grparlamento.rai.it
Editorial Profile: Government-owned radio station that covers the Italian government and its institutions.

RAI - RADIODUE - 28 MINUTI
Owner: RAI
Editorial: Via Asiago, 10, Roma 195.
T: 39 06 3612418 **E:** 28minuti@rai.it
W: http://www.radio.rai.it/radio2/28minuti

RAI - RADIODUE - DECANTER
Owner: RAI
Editorial: Via Asiago, 10, Roma Rm 195.
T: 39 199123000 **E:** decanter@rai.it
W: http://www.decanter.rai.it

RAI - RADIODUE - LIBRO OGGETTO
Owner: RAI
Editorial: Via Asiago, 10, Roma Rm 195.
T: 39 199123000 **E:** libro@rai.it
W: http://www.radio.rai.it/radio2/libroggetto
Editorial Profile: Local Translation: Tel. Red. 063226149 - Interviste a Personaggi famosi dello Spettacolo e del Costume: Libri ed Abitudini riguardanti la lettura - In Onda la Domenica alle h 12.57

RAI - RADIOTRE - FAHRENHEIT
Owner: RAI
Editorial: Via Asiago, 10, Roma 195.
T: 39 06 36866535 **E:** fahre@rai.it
W: http://www.fahre.rai.it

RAI - RADIOTRE - HOLLYWOOD PARTY
Owner: RAI
Editorial: Via Asiago, 10, Roma 195.
T: 39 06 3226297 **E:** hollywoodparty@rai.it
W: http://www.radio.rai.it/radio3/hollywood_party
Editorial Profile: Local Translation: Cinema ed Audiovisivi - In Onda dal Lunedì al Venerdì

dalle 19.03 alle 19.40 - " Cinema e la Radio " Domenica dalle 19.00 alle 20.10 - Non rilasciano altre mail dirette

RAI - RADIOTRE - PRIMA PAGINA
Owner: RAI
Editorial: Via Asiago, 10, Roma 195.
T: 39 06 3219932 **E:** primapagina@rai.it
W: http://www.primapagina.rai.it
Editorial Profile: Radio program covering news and current affairs.

RAI - RADIOTRE - SUITE
Owner: RAI
Editorial: Via Asiago, 10, Roma 195.
T: 39 06 3242841 **E:** radio3-suite@rai.it
W: http://www.radio.rai.it/radio3/radio3_suite
Editorial Profile: Radio program covering music, culture, art, and the performing arts.

RAI - RADIOUNO - CON PAROLE MIE
Owner: RAI
Editorial: Saxa Rubra - Largo Villy de Luca 5, Rome 188. **T:** 39 06 33170848
E: conparolemie@rai.it
W: www.radio.rai.it/radio1/conparolemie
Editorial Profile: Local Translation: Attualità - In onda dal Lunedì al Venerdì dalle 14:07 alle 14:41 - Non rilasciano mail dirette

RAI - RADIOUNO - ECONOMIA IN TASCA
Owner: RAI
Editorial: Largo Villy De Luca, 4 - Saxa Rubra - Palazzina G2, Rome 188. **T:** 39 06 33172075
E: grr.economico@rai.it
W: www.radio.rai.it/radio1/economiaintasca
Editorial Profile: Local Translation: Econiomia e Finanze - In Onda dal Lunedì al Venerdì dalle 7,34 alle 7,53

RAI - RADIOUNO - IN EUROPA
Owner: RAI
Editorial: Saxa Rubra L.go Villy de Luca 4, Roma 188. **T:** 39 06 33542834
E: ineuropa@rai.it
W: http://www.radio.rai.it/radio1/ineuropa
Editorial Profile: Radio program covering culture and history in Europe.

RAI - RADIOUNO - Italia istruzioni per l'uso
Owner: RAI
Editorial: Saxa Rubra Largo Villy de Luca 4, Roma 188. **T:** 39 06 33172155
E: istruzioniperluso@rai.it
W: http://www.radio.rai.it/radio1/italiaistruzioniperluso
Editorial Profile: Radio program covering social issues ranging from the rights and duties of citizens to justice, employment, health, and education.

RAI - RADIOUNO - LA MEDICINA
Owner: RAI
Editorial: Largo Villy de Luca 5 - Saxa Rubra, Roma 188. **T:** 39 06 33542140
E: lamedicina@rai.it
W: http://www.radiouno.rai.it
Editorial Profile: Local Translation: In Onda dal Lun. al Ven. alle 19.30 durata 10 min. - Rubr. "Pillole in rosa". in onda sab. durata 10 min. nel Contenitore Pianeta Donna - Non rilasciano altre mail dirette

RAI - RADIOUNO - LA RADIO NE PARLA
Owner: RAI
Editorial: Largo Villy de Luca 4, Roma 188.
T: 39 800 055103 **E:** laradioneparla@rai.it
W: http://www.radio.rai.it/radio1/laradioneparla
Editorial Profile: Radio program covering a variety of public and social issues, featuring discussion with listeners who call in.

RAI - RADIOUNO - QUESTIONE DI BORSA
Owner: RAI
Editorial: Largo Villy de Luca 5 - Saxa Rubra - Palazzina G2, Roma 188. **T:** 39 06 33172075
E: grr.economico@rai.it
W: http://www.radio.rai.it
Editorial Profile: Local Translation: Economia e Borsa - In Onda dal Lunedì al Venerdì dalle 10.06 alle 10.29

RAI - RADIOUNO - RADIO ANCH'IO
Owner: RAI
Editorial: Saxa Rubra Largo Villy de Luca 4, Roma 188. **T:** 39 06 33171541
E: radioanchio@rai.it
W: http://www.radio.rai.it/radio1/radioanchio
Editorial Profile: Radio program covering news, current affairs, and social issues.

RAI - RADIOUNO - TAM TAM LAVORO
Owner: RAI
Editorial: Saxa Rubra - Largo Villy de Luca 4, Roma 188. **T:** 39 06 33542158
E: tamtamlavoro@rai.it
W: http://www.radio.rai.it/radio1/tamtamlavoro
Editorial Profile: Local Translation: In Onda il Sabato dalle 06.20 alle 06.30 e TAM TAM MAGAZINE la Domenica dalle 6.33 alle 6.48 - Non rilasciano mail dirette

RAI - RADIOUNO - ZAPPING
Owner: RAI
Editorial: Saxa Rubra - L.go Villy de Luca, 5, Roma 188. **T:** 39 06 33542301
E: zapping@rai.it
W: http://www.radio.rai.it/radio1/zapping

RAI - RAI INTERNATIONALE
Owner: RAI
Editorial: Largo Villy De Luca 5 - Saxa Rubra, Roma 188. **T:** 39 06 33172264
E: raiinternational@rai.it
W: http://www.international.rai.it
Editorial Profile: Local Translation: Attualita'

RSI RETE 2
Editorial: via dell'Umiltà, 83/C, Roma 187.
T: 39 06 675911 **W:** http://retedue.rsi.ch
Editorial Profile: Radio station that plays music but also features news and cultural programming.

RTL
Editorial: via dell'Umiltà, 83/C, Roma 187.
T: 39 06 675911 **W:** http://www.rtl.fr

RTL 102.5 - NEWS
Owner: RTL 102.5 Hit Radio
Editorial: Via Piemonte, 61/63, Cologno Monzese Mi 20093. **T:** 39 02 250961
W: http://www.rtl.it
Editorial Profile: Local Translation: Attualità, Cronaca, Sport e Spettacoli

RTL 102.5 HIT RADIO RM
Owner: RTL 102.5 Hit Radio
Editorial: Via Virginio Orsini, 8, Roma Rm 192. **T:** 39 06 3641800 **W:** http://www.rtl.it

RTVA - CANAL SUR RADIO, S.A.
Editorial: via dell'Umiltà, 83/C, Roma 187.
T: 39 06 675911 **W:** http://www.canalsur.es

SBS SIDNEY BROADCASTING SYSTEM
Editorial: Via Sarnano, 36, Roma 156.
T: 39 335 395537

TSF - RADIO NOTICIAS
Editorial: via dell'Umiltà, 83/C, Roma 187.
T: 39 06 675911 **W:** http://www.tsf.pt

VIRGIN RADIO
Owner: Gruppo Finelco
Editorial: Largo Donegani, 1, Milano 20121.
T: 39 02 6575661 **E:** info@virginradioitaly.it
W: http://www.virginradio.it
Editorial Profile: Local Translation: EX PLAY RADIO

VOA
Editorial: Via dell'Umiltà, 83/c, Roma 187.
T: 39 06 675911 **W:** http://www.voanews.com
Editorial Profile: Radio network covering international news and current affairs.

THE VOICE OF LOVE AND PEACE
Editorial: via dell'Umiltà, 83/C, Roma 187.
T: 39 06 675911

TELEVISION NETWORKS

RAI Radio Televisione Italiana (UK Office)
Editorial: 29 Bruton Street, London, England W1J 6HG. **T:** 44 20 7409 1683
E: raitvlondon@rai.it **W:** http://www.rai.it
Editorial Profile: National TV station for Italy.

RTL- TELEVISION
Editorial: via dell'Umiltà, 83/C, Roma 187.
T: 39 06 675911 **W:** http://www.rreporter.tv
Editorial Profile: Television station with news content.

JAMAICA — Tel: 1 876

Standard Time: GMT -5
Continent: The Americas
Capital City: Kingston

NEWSPAPERS & PUBLICATIONS

NEWSPAPERS

The Daily Star
Owner: The Gleaner Co Ltd
Editorial: 7 North Street, Kingston W.I..
T: 876 9223400 **E:** editorial@gleanerjm.com
W: http://www.jamaica-star.com
Freq: Daily; **Circ:** 46000 Not Audited
Editor: Sheena Gayle; **Editor:** Dwayne Gordon;
Editor in Chief: Garfield Grandison
Editorial Profile: The Star is a daily newspaper covering national and international news, politics, economics, finance, business, culture and sports. Subscription and advertising rates are quoted in Jamaican dollars.
Language (s): English
DAILY NEWSPAPER

The Gleaner
Owner: The Gleaner Co Ltd
Editorial: 7 North Street, Kingston.
T: 876 9223400
E: feedback@jamaica-gleaner.com
W: http://www.jamaica-gleaner.com
Freq: Daily; **Circ:** 50000 Not Audited
Editor in Chief: Garfield Grandison
Editorial Profile: The Gleaner is a daily newspaper containing news, views, sports and in-depth reports for Kingston, Jamaica.
Language (s): English
DAILY NEWSPAPER

The Jamaica Observer
Owner: Jamaica Observer
Editorial: 40-42 Beechwood Avenue, Kingston 5. **T:** 876 9208136
E: editorial@jamaicaobserver.com
W: http://www.jamaicaobserver.com
Freq: Daily; **Circ:** 35000 Not Audited
Editor: Vernon Davidson; **Editor:** Oliver Hill
Editorial Profile: The Jamaica Observer is a daily newspaper covering national and international news, politics, economics, finance, business, culture and sports.
Language (s): English
DAILY NEWSPAPER

The Sunday Gleaner
Owner: The Gleaner Co Ltd
Editorial: 7 North Street, Kingston W.I..
T: 876 9223400 **E:** editorial@gleanerjm.com
W: http://www.jamaica-gleaner.com
Freq: Sun; **Circ:** 100000 Not Audited
Editor: Lavern Clarke; **Editor in Chief:** Garfield Grandison
Editorial Profile: The Sunday Gleaner covers national and international news, politics, economics, finance, business, culture and sports. Subscription and advertising rates are quoted in Jamaican dollars.
Language (s): English
NEWSPAPER

The Sunday Herald
Owner: New Media Communications Limited
Editorial: 17 Norwood Avenue, Kingston 5.
T: 876 90675724
E: sunherald@cwjamaica.com
W: http://www.sunheraldja.com
Freq: Weekly; **Circ:** 112000 Not Audited
Editorial Profile: The Sunday Herald is a weekly newspaper covering national and international news, politics, economics, finance, business, culture and sports.
Language (s): English
NEWSPAPER

Weekend Star
Owner: The Gleaner Co Ltd
Editorial: 7 North Street, Kingston W.I..
T: 876 9223400 **E:** star@gleanerjm.com
W: http://www.jamaica-star.com
Freq: Weekly; **Circ:** 85000 Not Audited
Editor: Sheena Gayle; **Editor:** Dwayne Gordon;
Editor in Chief: Garfield Grandison
Editorial Profile: Covers national and international news, politics, economics, finance, business, culture and sports.
Language (s): English
NEWSPAPER

JAPAN — Tel: 81

Standard Time: GMT +9
Continent: Asia
Capital City: Tokyo

NEWSPAPERS & PUBLICATIONS

NEWSPAPERS

AdverTimes
Editorial: SENDENKAIGI Co., Ltd., 4F, NBF Alliance Building, 5-2-1 Minami Aoyama, Minato-ku, Tokyo 107-8550. **T:** 81 334 453033
E: adti@sendenkaigi.co.jp
W: http://www.sendenkaigi.com/hanbai/magazine/newspaper/
Freq: Weekly
Editor in Chief: Risa Tanaka
Editorial Profile: AdverTimes is a newspaper which reports weekly news of advertising industry such as new campaigns, personnel relocation of campanies, competitions, legislation changes regarding media.
Language (s): Japanese
NEWSPAPER

Akita Sakigake Shimpo
Editorial: Akita Sakigake Shimpo, 1-1, San-no-rinkai-cho, Akita 010-8601. **T:** 81 18 8881800
W: http://www.sakigake.co.jp
Freq: Daily Not Audited
Bureau Chief: Masanori Waga
Editorial Profile: Akita Sakigake Shimpo is a newspaper which writes about the latest news in Akita district and nation wide.
Language (s): Japanese
DAILY NEWSPAPER

The Apparel Industrial Times
Editorial: The Apparel Industrial Times, 731 Iidabashi Hightown, 2-28, Shimomiyabi-Cho, Shinjuku-ku, Tokyo 162-0822.
T: 81 335 137931
W: http://www.apako-news.com/
Freq: Monthly
Editor in Chief: Toru Honda
Editorial Profile: The Apparel Industrial Times provides all the information about current fashion industry needs, such as textiles, patterning, sewing technique, and Point Of Production.
Language (s): Japanese
NEWSPAPER

Asahi Shimbun
Editorial: 529 14th St NW Ste 1022, Washington, DC 20045-2001.
T: 1 202 783-1000 **E:** asahidc@asahiam.com
Freq: Daily
Bureau Chief: Takeshi Yamawaki
Editorial Profile: Provides domestic and international news.
Language (s): Japanese
DAILY NEWSPAPER

Asahi Shimbun - New York Bureau
Editorial: United Nations, Room S-301, New York, New York 10017. **T:** 1 212 486-5059
Freq: Daily
Editorial Profile: This is the New York bureau for Asahi Shimbun in Tokyo, Japan.
Language (s): English
DAILY NEWSPAPER

Asahi Shimbun (Tokyo)
Editorial: The Asahi Shimbun, 5-3-2, Tsukiji, Chuo-ku, Tokyo 104-8011. **T:** 81 335 450131
E: tokyo@asahi.com **W:** http://www.asahi.com
Freq: Daily; **Circ:** 3357950
Editor: Wataru Sawamura
Editorial Profile: Launching its first edition on January 25, 1879, dedicated to the freedom of speech and democracy in Japan. Provides domestic and international news with up-to-the-minute headlines and updates.
Language (s): Japanese
DAILY NEWSPAPER

Asahi Shimbun (Hokkaido)
Editorial: The Asahi Shimbun Company, 1-1-1, Kita 2-jo-nishi, Chuo-ku, Sapporo 060-8602.
T: 81 112 812131 **E:** hokkaido@asahi.com
W: http://www.mytown.asahi.com/hokkaido
Freq: Daily; **Circ:** 162863 Not Audited
Editorial Profile: Asahi Shimbun (Hokkaido) is a daily newspaper for Sapporo district which mainly reports on regional news.
Language (s): Japanese
DAILY NEWSPAPER

Asahi Shimbun (Osaka)
Editorial: The Asahi Shimbun Company, 3-2-4, Nakanoshima, Kita-ku, Osaka 530-8211.
T: 81 662 310131 **E:** dai-koe@asahi.com
W: http://www.asahi.com/kansai/
Freq: Daily; **Circ:** 3843985 Not Audited
Editorial Profile: Asahi Shimbun (Osaka) is a newspaper for Osaka district which mainly reports on regional news.
Language (s): Japanese
DAILY NEWSPAPER

Cargo News
Editorial: Cargo Japan Co., Ltd., 4-5-10, Roppongi, Minato-ku, Tokyo 106-0032.
T: 81 35 7712101 **E:** info@cargo-news.co.jp
W: http://www.cargo-news.co.jp
Freq: 2 Times/Week; **Circ:** 30722 Not Audited
Editor in Chief: Kouichi Matsuzaki; **Publisher:** Kuninori Nishimura
Editorial Profile: Reports the latest news on logistics, news of shipping companies, legislations, new trucks, information of warehouses, railways, marine transport, air freight, etc.
Language (s): Japanese
NEWSPAPER

Chemical Daily
Editorial: The Chemical Daily Co., Ltd., 3-16-8, Nihonbashi Hamacho, Chuo-ku, Tokyo 103-8485. **T:** 81 33 6637934
E: cd_desk@chemicaldaily.co.jp
W: http://www.chemicaldaily.co.jp
Freq: Daily; **Circ:** 130003 Not Audited
Language (s): Japanese
DAILY NEWSPAPER

Chiba Nippo
Editorial: Chiba Nippo Co., Ltd., 4-14-10 Chuo, Chuo-ku, Chiba 260-0013.
T: 81 43 2229215 **E:** c-nippo@chibanippo.co.jp
W: http://www.chibanippo.co.jp
Freq: Daily; **Circ:** 188285 Not Audited
Editorial Profile: Chiba Nippo is a newspaper which reports regional news in Chiba district.
Language (s): Japanese
DAILY NEWSPAPER

Chubu Keizai Shimbun
Editorial: The Mid-Japan Economist, Aichi-ken Sangyo Roudou Centre 16F, 4-4-38 Meieki, Namamura-ku, Nagoya 450-8561.
T: 81 52 5615212
W: http://www.chukei-news.co.jp
Freq: Daily; **Circ:** 94703 Not Audited
Editorial Profile: Chubu Keizai Shimbun is a newspaper which reports financial information in Nagoya district. Articles also cover general financial news.
Language (s): Japanese
DAILY NEWSPAPER

Chugoku Shimbun
Editorial: The Chugoku Shimbun, 7-1, Dobashi-cho, Naka-ku, Hiroshima 730-8677.
T: 81 822 362111 **E:** denshi@chugoku-np.co.jp
W: http://www.chugoku-np.co.jp
Freq: Daily Not Audited
Editorial Profile: The Chugoku Shimbun is a daily local newspaper which covers local and national news.
Language (s): Japanese
DAILY NEWSPAPER

Chunichi Shimbun - Hokuriku
Editorial: The Chunichi Shimbun, 2-12-30 Nishihonmachi, Kanazawa-city, Ishikawa 920-8573. **T:** 81 762 613111
E: hokuchu@chunichi.co.jp
W: http://www.chunichi.co.jp/hokuriku/
Freq: Daily; **Circ:** 110823 Not Audited
Editorial Profile: Chunichi Shimbun - Hokuriku is a daily regional news paper in Ishikawa district which mainly reports regional news.
Language (s): Japanese
DAILY NEWSPAPER

Daily Automotive News
Editorial: Nikkan Jidosha Shimbun, 2-1-25, Kaigan, Minato-ku, Tokyo 105-0022.
T: 81 33 4555321 **W:** http://www.njd.jp
Freq: Daily; **Circ:** 143004 Not Audited
Publisher: Yoshio Tskuda
Editorial Profile: Daily Automotive News covers the manufacturing engineering, design, production and suppliers with equal emphasis on the retail side of the auto industry.
Language (s): Japanese
DAILY NEWSPAPER

Daily Aviation News
Editorial: Japan Aviation News Co., Ltd., 2-7-7 Kanda-Sukasamachi, Chiyoda-ku, Tokyo 101-0048. **T:** 81 332 927712 **E:** da@da-news.co.jp
W: http://www.da-news.co.jp
Freq: Daily
Editor in Chief: Tsutomu Honda
Editorial Profile: Daily Aviation News is a daily newspaper focused on aviation and engineering.
Language (s): Japanese
DAILY NEWSPAPER

Daily Cargo
Editorial: Kaiji Press, 2-1-15, Iwamoto-cho, Chiyoda-ku, Tokyo 101-0032.
T: 81 35 8354184
W: http://www.kaiji-press.co.jp
Freq: Daily; **Circ:** 25003 Not Audited
Editor in Chief: Takuya Nishi
Editorial Profile: Reports on a wide scope of air-cargo sector including aviation policy and airliners' business performance are reported with details from inside and ouside of the industry. Articles also cover logistic news, industry trend, analysis, and feature articles of Shippers, Logistics Providers and Carriers.
Language (s): Japanese
DAILY NEWSPAPER

Daily Engineering & Construction News
Editorial: The Nikkan Kensetsu Kogyo Shimbun, 2-2-10, Higashi Shinbashi, Minato-ku, Tokyo 105-0021. **T:** 81 33 4337161
W: http://www.decn.co.jp
Freq: Daily
Publisher: Hideki Iizuka
Editorial Profile: Daily Engineering & Construction News is a newspaper which reports logistics, building construction and environmental engineering.
Language (s): Japanese
DAILY NEWSPAPER

Daily News of Logistics
Owner: The Tsu-Un Joho
Editorial: The Tsu-Un Joho, 2-11-11, Sotokanda, Chiyoda-ku, Tokyo 101-0021.
T: 81 332564066 **W:** http://www.tsu-un.co.jp
Freq: Daily
Editor in Chief: Shigeo Kumaki
Editorial Profile: Provides extensive editorial coverage on emerging trends and news to professionals working in the international logistics industry.
Language (s): Japanese
DAILY NEWSPAPER

Daily Sports (Kobe)
Editorial: Daily Sports, 1-5-7, Higashikawasaki-cho, Chuo-ku, Kobe 650-0044. **T:** 81 783 627298
W: http://www.daily.co.jp
Freq: Daily; **Circ:** 576517 Not Audited
Editor: Yuichiro Matsushita
Editorial Profile: Daily Sports reports the latest sports news such as baseball, football, golf as well as entertainment news and horse racing.
Language (s): Japanese
DAILY NEWSPAPER

Daily Sports (Tokyo)
Editorial: 2-14-8 Kiba Koto-Ku, Tokyo 135-8566. **T:** 81 03 36415042
W: http://www.daily.co.jp
Freq: Daily; **Circ:** 414473 Not Audited
Editorial Profile: DAILY SPORTS (TOKYO) is a daily newspaper which covers sports, gossip, and national news.
Language (s): Japanese
DAILY NEWSPAPER

Daily Yomiuri
Editorial: The Yomiuri Shimbun, 1-7-1, Otemachi, Chiyoda-ku, Tokyo 104-0061.
T: 81 332 178231 **E:** dy@yomiuri.com
W: http://www.yomiuri.co.jp/dy
Freq: Daily; **Circ:** 41223 Not Audited
Editorial Profile: Consists of articles from the Yomiuri Shimbun, Japan's largest newspaper, as well as from the world's leading wire services and newspapers.
Language (s): Japanese
DAILY NEWSPAPER

The Daily Yomiuri- United Nations Bureau
Editorial: 747 3rd Ave, 28th Fl, New York, New York 10017-2803. **T:** 1 212 752-2196
E: dy@yomiuri.com
W: http://www.yomiuri.co.jp/dy/
Freq: Daily
Editorial Profile: This is the United Nations bureau for The Daily Yomiuri, the English-language sister publication of Yomirui Shimbun in Tokyo.
Language (s): English
DAILY NEWSPAPER

Dempa Shimbun
Editorial: Dempa Newspaper Co., Ltd., 1-11-15, Higashi Gotanda, Shinagawa-ku, Tokyo 141-8715. **T:** 81 334 456116
W: http://www.dempa.co.jp
Freq: Daily; **Circ:** 300003 Not Audited
Editor: Masaharu Hasegawa; **Editor:** Masashige Nishiyama
Editorial Profile: Focused on engineering and electrical news.
Language (s): Japanese
DAILY NEWSPAPER

Denkei Shimbun
Editorial: DENKEI-SHIMBUN. 7/F Yamaki-Daini Bldg, 3-4-2 Nishi-Shimbashi, Minato-ku, Tokyo 105-0003. **T:** 81 334 376600
E: info@denkeishimbun.co.jp
W: http://www.denkeishimbun.co.jp/
Freq: Weekly
Editor: Naoto Nakayama; **Editor in Chief:** Toshihiko Tanaka
Editorial Profile: Denkei Shimbun is a weekly newspaper which reports news of information and communication industry despite it initially reported news of electronics industry.
Language (s): Japanese
NEWSPAPER

Doshin Sports
Editorial: The Hokkaido Shimbun Press, 3-6, Odori-nishi, Chuo-ku, Sapporo 060-8711.
T: 81 11 2411230 **E:** dou-spo@douspo.com
W: http://www.hokkaido-np.co.jp
Freq: Daily; **Circ:** 132355 Not Audited
Editorial Profile: Doshin Sports is a regional daily sports newspaper in Sapporo district which writes about daily news on sports, leisure and entertainment.
Language (s): Japanese
DAILY NEWSPAPER

Eizo Shimbun
Editorial: Eizo Shimbun Inc., Eizo Building, 1-24-8 Kohinata, Bunkyo-ku, Tokyo 112-0006.
T: 81 339 422161 **E:** press@eizoshimbun.com
W: http://www.eizoshimbun.com
Freq: Weekly; **Circ:** 30003 Not Audited
Editor in Chief: Satoru Fuse; **Editor:** Koji Suginuma
Editorial Profile: The Eizo Shimbun publishes once a week which provides a professional communicative link for educators and industry personnel associated with design, presentation, management, and reproduction of graphic forms of communication.
Language (s): Japanese
NEWSPAPER

Fuji Sankei Business i (Tokyo)
Editorial: Nihon Kogyo Shimbun Sha, 1-7-2, Otemachi, Chiyoda-ku, Tokyo 100-8125.
T: 81 33 2317111 **W:** http://www.sankeibiz.jp
Freq: Daily; **Circ:** 400003 Not Audited
Editor: Yuki Suenaga
Editorial Profile: Covers industry-specific business news in Japan and throughout the world, with additional lifestyle feature stories.
Language (s): Japanese
DAILY NEWSPAPER

Fukui Shimbun
Editorial: Fukui Shimbun, 56, Oowada-cho, Fukui, Fukui 910-8552. **T:** 81 776 575110
W: http://www.fukuishimbun.co.jp
Freq: Daily; **Circ:** 2060336 Not Audited
Editor: Yoichiro Adachi
Editorial Profile: Fukui Shimbun is a daily newspaper in Fukui district which provides the latest regional news, current affairs happening in the region including coverage on economic and regional activities.
Language (s): Japanese
DAILY NEWSPAPER

Fukushima Minpo
Editorial: Fukushima-Minpo Co., Ltd., 13-17, Ota-machi, Fukushima 960-8602.
T: 81 245 314111 **W:** http://www.minpo.jp/
Freq: Daily; **Circ:** 310003 Not Audited
Editorial Profile: Fukushima Mimpo is a daily newspaper in the Fukushima district which reports on local news happening around the neighborhood.
Language (s): Japanese
DAILY NEWSPAPER

Handelsblatt
Editorial: Kasuga 2-23-12, 902 Bunkyo-ku, Tokyo 112-0003. **T:** 81 3 38141220
W: http://www.handelsblatt.com
Freq: Daily
Editorial Profile: Acts as a bureau reporting on Japanese affairs for the Germany-based business and financial newspaper.
Language (s): English
DAILY NEWSPAPER

Health Industry News
Editorial: UBM Media Co., Ltd., Kanda 91 Bldg. 1-8-3 Kaji-cho, Tokyo 101-0044.
T: 81 3 5296-1020 **E:** kenko@cmpjapan.com
W: http://www.kenko-media.com
Freq: Weekly; **Circ:** 65003 Not Audited
Editorial Profile: Covers news for the health products industry, including manufacturing information, trends and legislation.
Language (s): Japanese
NEWSPAPER

Higashi-Aichi Shimbun
Editorial: The Higashi-Aichi Shimbun, 62, Torinawate, Shinsakae-machi, Toyohashi 441-8666. **T:** 81 532 323111
E: hensyu@higashiaichi.co.jp
W: http://www.higashiaichi.co.jp
Freq: Daily Not Audited
Editorial Profile: Higashi-Aichi Shimbun is a newspaper that reports on all aspects of news including economical, political, social and cultural on the Toyohashi district.
Language (s): Japanese
DAILY NEWSPAPER

Hoken Mainichi Shimbun
Editorial: Hokenmainichi.Co. 1-4-7 Iwamoto-cho, Chiyoda-ku, Tokyo 101-0032.
T: 81 338 651401 **W:** http://www.homai.co.jp/
Freq: Daily
Editor: Tokuo Inaba; **Publisher:** Yukimitsu Manabe
Editorial Profile: Hoken Mainichi Shimbun reports life, health, property and casual, reinsurance and multiline insurance companies can use technology to maximize productivity and achieve a clear competitive advantage.
Language (s): Japanese
DAILY NEWSPAPER

Hokkaido Shimbun
Editorial: The Hokkaido Shimbun Press, 3-6, Odori-nishi, Chuo-ku, Sapporo 060-8711.
T: 81 11 2105597
W: http://www.hokkaido-np.co.jp
Freq: Daily; **Circ:** 1232913 Not Audited
Editorial Profile: Hokkaido Shimbun is a daily newspaper in the morning and evening which writes about the news in japan and the world, as well as hokkaido district.
Language (s): Japanese
DAILY NEWSPAPER

Hokkoku Shimbun
Editorial: The Hokkoku Shimbun, 2-1 Minamimachi, Kanazawa 920-8588.
T: 81 76 2603532
W: http://www.hokkoku.co.jp
Freq: Daily; **Circ:** 335826 Not Audited
Editorial Profile: Hokkoku Shimbun is a daily newspaper in Kanazawa district which reports mainly regional news, national and international news.
Language (s): Japanese
DAILY NEWSPAPER

Hokuu Shimpo
Editorial: Hokuu Shimpo Sha. 3-2 Nishidori-machi, Noshiro 016-0891. **T:** 81 18 5543150
E: hokuupost@hokuu.jp
W: http://www.hokuu.co.jp
Freq: Daily; **Circ:** 32423 Not Audited
Publisher: Yasumasa Yamaki
Editorial Profile: Hokuu Shimpo is local newspaper in Northern Akita area which reports mainly local news and useful information in the area.
Language (s): Japanese
DAILY NEWSPAPER

Hoso Times
Editorial: The Hoso Times, 3-1-5, Kanda, Misaki-cho, Chiyoda-ku, Tokyo 101-0061.
T: 81 332 623463
W: http://www.nippo.co.jp/ht
Freq: Weekly; **Circ:** 55003 Not Audited
Editor in Chief: Yasuyoshi Asami
Editorial Profile: Hoso Times is a weekly newspaper which specialized the packaging industry and it centers around issues related to the environment.
Language (s): Japanese
NEWSPAPER

Ibaraki Shimbun
Editorial: The Ibaraki Shimbun Co., Ltd., 2-15, Kitami-cho, Mito 310-8686. **T:** 81 292 485500
E: houdou@mail2.ibaraki-np.co.jp
W: http://www.ibaraki-np.co.jp
Freq: Daily; **Circ:** 118003 Not Audited
Editor: Yasuhiro Numata
Editorial Profile: Ibaraki Shimbun is a newspaper for the Ibaraki-Ken district which mainly reports on local news happening around the neighborhood.
Language (s): Japanese

DAILY NEWSPAPER

Igakukai Shinbun
Editorial: Igaku-Shoin Ltd., 1-282-3 Hongo, Bunkyo-ku, Tokyo 113-8414.
T: 81 246 175694
E: shinbun@igaku-shoin.co.jp
W: http://www.igaku-shoin.co.jp
Freq: Weekly; **Circ:** 55003 Not Audited
Editor in Chief: Yoshiyuki Nakajima
Editorial Profile: Igakukai Shinbun is a weekly news paper which reviews developments of Japan's medical breakthroughs, improvements and technology. Articles also include industrial medicine, managed medical care, vocational rehabilitation, risk management and related businesses.
Language (s): Japanese
NEWSPAPER

The International New York Times - Tokyo
Editorial: Asahi Shimbun Building, 5-3-2 Tsukiji Chuo-Ku, Tokyo 104-8011.
T: 81 335450940
Bureau Chief: Martin Fackler
DAILY NEWSPAPER

International Press - Portuguese Edition
Editorial: IPCWORLD, INC., 2-1-9 Minamiazabu, Minato-ku, Tokyo 106-0047.
T: 81 35 4204581 **E:** redaccion@ipcjapan.com
W: http://www.ipcdigital.com
Freq: Weekly; **Circ:** 60003 Not Audited
Editor in Chief: Luis Álvarez; **Publisher:** Leonardo Takuya Muranaga; **Publisher:** Yuji Muranaga
Editorial Profile: International Press (Portuguese Edition) reports news and information of Japan for Brazilians living in Japan. It is written in Portuguese.
Language (s): Portuguese
NEWSPAPER

Iwaki Minpo
Editorial: Iwaki Minpo Company, 63-7 HirajiTamachi, Fukushima 970-8026.
T: 81 246 231666 **E:** news@iwaki-minpo.co.jp
W: http://www.iwaki-minpo.co.jp
Freq: Daily; **Circ:** 17103 Not Audited
Publisher: Tatsuya Nozawa
Editorial Profile: IWAKI MINPO is a local news paper in Fukushima district, which writes about local news and events.
Language (s): Japanese
DAILY NEWSPAPER

Iwate Nichinichi Shimbun
Editorial: Iwate Nichinichi Shimbun, 60, Minamishin-machi, Ichinoseki 021-8686.
T: 81 191 264204 **E:** henshu@iwanichi.co.jp
W: http://www.iwanichi.co.jp
Freq: Daily Not Audited
Editorial Profile: Iwate Nichinichi Shimbun is a daily regional news paper in the Ichinoseki area of Iwate district which writes about the latest regional news, current affairs happenings in Ichinoseki area, economic and regional activities.
Language (s): Japanese
DAILY NEWSPAPER

Iwate Nippo
Editorial: Iwate Nippo Co., Ltd, 3-7, Uchimaru, Morioka 020-8622. **T:** 81 196 535311
E: houdou@iwate-np.co.jp
W: http://www.iwate-np.co.jp
Freq: Daily; **Circ:** 230003 Not Audited
Editorial Profile: Iwate Nippo is a regional daily newspaper in Iwate prefecture which writes about local news and event, as well as international top news.
Language (s): Japanese
DAILY NEWSPAPER

Japan Agricultural News
Editorial: The Japan Agricultural News, 2-3, Akihabara, Taito-ku, Tokyo 110-8722.
T: 81 352 957411
W: http://www.nougyou-shimbun.ne.jp
Freq: Daily; **Circ:** 420003 Not Audited
Editorial Profile: Japan Agricultural Newspaper is the daily newspaper about agriculture. Articles include agribusiness, general merchandising as well as local autonomous entities.
Language (s): Japanese
DAILY NEWSPAPER

Japan Maritime Daily
Editorial: The Japan Maritime Daily Co., Ltd., 5-19-2, Shimbashi, Minato-ku, Tokyo 105-0004. **T:** 81 33 4363221 **E:** kaiji@jmd.co.jp
W: http://www.jmd.co.jp
Freq: Daily; **Circ:** 55303 Not Audited
Editor in Chief: Itsuro Fujimoto
Editorial Profile: Japan Maritime Daily is a maritime newspaper which reports maritime affairs, marine transportation information and shipbuilding.
Language (s): Japanese
DAILY NEWSPAPER

Japan Medicine
Editorial: Jiho, inc.5th Floor, Hitotsubashi Building, 2-6-3 Hitotsubashi, Chiyoda-ku, Tokyo 101-8421. **T:** 81 332 659351
W: http://www.jiho.co.jp
Freq: 2 Times/Week; **Circ:** 240003 Not Audited
Editor in Chief: Yoshiyuki Numata
Editorial Profile: Japan Medicine is a newspaper which provides the latest medical information.
Language (s): Japanese
NEWSPAPER

The Japan Times (Tokyo)
Editorial: The Japan Times Ltd., Shibaura 4-chome, Tokyo 108-8071. **T:** 81 3 34535312
E: hodobu@japantimes.co.jp
W: http://www.japantimes.co.jp
Freq: Daily; **Circ:** 61929 Not Audited
Editorial Profile: The Japan Times covers wide-ranging topics in an easy-to-read format. Articles covers world events and news in Japan. It has the largest circulation of all Japanese domestic English-language newspapers and reaches by far the largest number of non-Japanese readers living in Japan.
Language (s): English
DAILY NEWSPAPER

The Japan Times Weekly
Editorial: The Japan Times Ltd., 4-5-4 Shibaura, Minato-ku, Tokyo 108-8071.
T: 81 33 4524099
E: jtweekly@japantimes.co.jp
W: http://www.japantimes.co.jp/weekly
Freq: Weekly; **Circ:** 20003 Not Audited
Editorial Profile: The Japan Times Weekly contains editorials and commentary of The Japan Times and leading newspapers in the U.S., Europe and Asia and so much more.
Language (s): English
NEWSPAPER

Joho Sangyo Shimbun
Editorial: Johosangyo Shinbunsha Co., Ltd., 3/F Tokyo Tower, 4-2-8 Shiba Park, Minato-ku, Tokyo 105-0011. **T:** 81 3 34344911
E: info@josan.jp **W:** http://www.josan.jp/
Freq: Weekly; **Circ:** 36003 Not Audited
Editor in Chief: Toshihiro Sato; **Editor:** Satoru Sugita; **Publisher:** Yugo Tabe
Editorial Profile: Focuses on general IT information and the latest news on IT business.
Language (s): Japanese
NEWSPAPER

Joyo Shimbun
Editorial: The Joyo Shimbun, 2-7-6, Manabe, Tsuchiura 300-0051. **T:** 81 29 8211780
W: http://www.joyo-net.com
Freq: Daily; **Circ:** 85003 Not Audited
Editorial Profile: Joyo Shimbun is a daily reigonal newspaper in Tsuchiura district which mainly reports on regional news happening around the neighborhood.
Language (s): Japanese
DAILY NEWSPAPER

Kaiji Press
Editorial: Kaiji Press Co., Ltd., Kaiji Press, 2-1-15, Iwamoto-cho, Chiyoda-ku, Tokyo 101-0032. **T:** 81 35 8354182
E: desk@kaiji-press.co.jp
W: http://www.kaiji-press.co.jp
Freq: Daily; **Circ:** 25003 Not Audited
Editor: Youhei Misaki; **Editor in Chief:** Naoki Nakamura; **Editor:** Kazuhiro Tsushima
Editorial Profile: Reports on shipping, shipbuilding, logistics, ports, marine equipment and administrative issues.
Language (s): Japanese
DAILY NEWSPAPER

Kanagawa Shimbun
Editorial: The Kanagawa Shimbun, 2-23. Ota-cho, Naka-ku, Yokohama 231-8445.
T: 81 45 2270100 **E:** media@kanaloco.jp
W: http://www.kanagawa-shimbun.jp
Freq: Daily Not Audited
Editorial Profile: Kanagawa Shimbun is a daily regional nespaper in Kanagawa district which provides the latest regional news and current affairs happening in Yokohama district. Articles include economic and regional activities and national news and international news.
Language (s): Japanese
DAILY NEWSPAPER

Koureisha-Jutaku Shimbun
Editorial: Koreisha-Jutaku Shimbun Co., Ltd. 8-12-15, Ginza, Chuo-ku, Tokyo 104-0061.
T: 81 335 436852
E: info@koureisha-jutaku.com
W: http://www.koureisha-jutaku.com/
Freq: Daily
Publisher: Toshikazu Amiya; **Editor:** Ritomo Tanabe
Editorial Profile: Koreisha-Jutaku Shimbun is a newspaper which issued three times a month. Articles cover housing for elderly and eldercare facilities as well as elderly's health care and tips for enriching elderly's living.
Language (s): Japanese
DAILY NEWSPAPER

Kumamoto Nichinichi Shimbun
Editorial: Kumamoto Nichinichi Shimbun, 172, Yoyasu-machi, Kumamoto 860-8506.
T: 81 96 3613111
W: http://kumanichi.com/index.cfm
Freq: Daily Not Audited
Editor in Chief: Kensei Tagawa
Editorial Profile: Kumamoto Nichinichi Shimbun is a regional daily newspaper in Kumamoto district in Kyusyu island which reports local news.
Language (s): Japanese
DAILY NEWSPAPER

Kyoto Shimbun
Editorial: The Kyoto Shimbun Co., Ltd., 239, Ebisugawa-agaru, Karasuma-dori, Chukyo-Ku, Kyoto 604-8577. **T:** 81 75 2416119
E: shakaibu@mb.kyoto-np.co.jp
W: http://www.kyoto-np.co.jp
Freq: Daily
Publisher: Michikazu Shiraishi
Editorial Profile: KYOTO SHIMBUN is a local newspaper which reports regional and national news in Kyoto district.
Language (s): Japanese
DAILY NEWSPAPER

Label Shimbun
Editorial: Label Shimbun, Kanda Asakusabashi Building, 3-1-13, Higashi Kanda, Chiyoda-ku, Tokyo 101-0031. **T:** 81 33 8666577
E: info@labelshimbun.com
W: http://www.labelshimbun.com
Freq: Semi-Monthly; **Circ:** 18753 Not Audited
Editor: Yukiko Suzuki
Editorial Profile: Label Shimbun is a newspaper which provides information about Label converters, Label materials, Printing Press, die ink, electronic pre-press systems and so on.
Language (s): Japanese
NEWSPAPER

Logistics Nippon
Editorial: Logistics Nippon News Network Co., Ltd., Hirakawa-cho Building, 1-7-20 Hirakawa-cho, Chiyoda-ku, Tokyo 102-0093.
T: 81 33 2212345 **E:** tokyo@logistics.jp
W: http://www.logistics.jp
Freq: 2 Times/Week; **Circ:** 158003 Not Audited
Editor: Hidenori Kitahara; **Editor in Chief:** Akira Yamada
Editorial Profile: Provides a wealth of information on the latest technology, services and processes needed in the logistics industry.
Language (s): Japanese
NEWSPAPER

Mainichi Shimbun - New York Bureau
Editorial: 757 3rd Ave, Ste 1902, New York, New York 10017. **T:** 1 212 765-1240
W: http://mdn.mainichi.jp
Bureau Chief: Kazuhiko Kusano
Editorial Profile: This is the New York bureau of the Japan-based daily newspaper.
Language (s): Japanese
DAILY NEWSPAPER

Mainichi Shimbun - United Nations Bureau
Editorial: 405 E 42 St, United Nations Rm C-400E, New York, New York 10017.
T: 1 212 319-0146
W: http://www.mdn.mainichi.jp
Freq: Daily
Editorial Profile: This is the United Nations Bureau of the Japanese-based newspaper.
Language (s): English
DAILY NEWSPAPER

Mainichi Shimbun - Washington Bureau
Editorial: 529 14th St NW, Ste 340, Washington, DC 20045. **T:** 1 202 737-2817
Freq: Daily
Editorial Profile: This is the Washington, D.C. bureau of the Mainichi Shimbun in Japan.
Language (s): Japanese
DAILY NEWSPAPER

Mainichi Shimbun (Fukuoka)
Editorial: The Mainichi Newspapers, Mainichi Shimbun Fukuoka, 16-1 Tenjin, Chuo-ku, Fukuoka 810-8551. **T:** 81 927 813100
W: http://www.mainichi.co.jp
Freq: Daily; **Circ:** 660003 Not Audited
Editor: Ryo Iwamatsu
Editorial Profile: Covers Kyushu island, Yamaguchi, Okinawa, and Shimane district in Japan.
Language (s): Japanese
DAILY NEWSPAPER

Mainichi Shimbun (Nagoya)
Editorial: The Mainichi Newspapers, 4-7-1 Meieki, Nakamura-ku, Nagoya 450-8651.
T: 81 525 278010 **W:** http://mainichi.jp/chubu
Freq: Daily; **Circ:** 173893 Not Audited
Editorial Profile: Reports local news on the Chubu region and beyond.
Language (s): Japanese
DAILY NEWSPAPER

Mainichi Shimbun (Osaka)
Editorial: The Mainichi Newspapers, 3-4-5, Umeda, Kita-ku, Osaka 530-8251.
T: 81 663 451551
W: http://www.mainichi.co.jp
Freq: Daily; **Circ:** 1427193 Not Audited
Editorial Profile: Covers news happened in Japan and Osaka region, and national.
Language (s): Japanese
DAILY NEWSPAPER

Mainichi Shimbun (Sapporo)
Editorial: The Mainichi Newspapers, 6-1, Kita 4-jo-nishi, Chuo-ku, Sapporo 060-8643.
T: 81 112 214141
W: http://mainichi.jp/hokkaido
Freq: Daily; **Circ:** 74003 Not Audited
Editorial Profile: Covers regional news in Hokkaido Area and domestic in Japan.
Language (s): Japanese
DAILY NEWSPAPER

Mainichi Shimbun (Tokyo)
Editorial: The Mainichi Newspapers, 1-1-1, Hitotsubashi, Chiyoda-ku, Tokyo 100-8051.
T: 81 332 120321
W: http://www.mainichi.co.jp
Freq: Daily
Editorial Profile: Reports daily news in Japan.
Language (s): Japanese
DAILY NEWSPAPER

Mainichi Weekly
Editorial: The Mainichi Newspapers, 1-1-1, Hitotsubashi, Chiyoda-ku, Tokyo 100-8051.
T: 81 332 123265 **E:** gaishinbu@mainichi.co.jp
W: http://mainichi.jp/life/weekly
Freq: Weekly; **Circ:** 53003 Not Audited
Editor in Chief: Kaori Oowada
Editorial Profile: English publication reports news and events in Japan and throughout the world.
Language (s): English
NEWSPAPER

Material & Industry News
Editorial: Sangyo Shimbun, Chichibu building 5F, 1-8-6, Shinkawa, Chuo-ku, Tokyo 104-0033. **T:** 81 355 668770
W: http://www.japanmetal.com
Freq: Daily
Editor: Toshio Masakiyo; **Publisher:** Toshio Yamamoto
Editorial Profile: Material & Industry News covers the domestic and international trends of metal industry. Articles cover specialised information on iron-steel and non-ferrous metal, scrap yard operators as well as electric furnace steel and integrated steel manufacturers.
Language (s): Japanese
DAILY NEWSPAPER

Minato Shimbun
Editorial: Minato-Yamaguchi Co., Ltd. 1-1-7, Higashi-Yamato-machi, Shimonoseki, Yamaguchi 750-8506. **T:** 81 832 663214
W: http://www.minato-yamaguchi.co.jp/
Freq: Daily; **Circ:** 58003 Not Audited
Editorial Profile: Minato Shimbun is a daily newspaper which features information on fishery industry such as the latest news of the industry, economics, trends logiscitcs etc.
Language (s): Japanese

DAILY NEWSPAPER

Miyazaki Nichinichi Shimbun
Editorial: Miyazaki Nichinichi Shinbun, 1-1-33, Takachiho-dori, Miyazaki 880-8570.
T: 81 985 244201
E: houdou@the-miyanichi.co.jp
W: http://www.the-miyanichi.co.jp
Freq: Daily Not Audited
Editorial Profile: Miyazaki Nichinichi Shimbun is a newspaper for Miyazaki district which reports on regional news happening around the Miyazaki area.
Language (s): Japanese
DAILY NEWSPAPER

Nara Shimbun
Editorial: Nara newspaper, 2-4, Hokkeji-machi, Nara 630-8686. **T:** 81 74 2322113
E: edit@nara-np.co.jp
W: http://www.nara-np.co.jp
Freq: Daily; **Circ:** 126324 Not Audited
Editor in Chief: Tadahiro Kokubo; **Editor:** Eiji Yamashita
Editorial Profile: Reports local and regional news within the Nara District, with a focus on business and the economy.
Language (s): Japanese
DAILY NEWSPAPER

Nihon Keizai Shimbun - Chicago Bureau
Editorial: 1 S Wacker Dr, Ste 1150, Chicago, Illinois 60606-4616. **T:** 1 312 726-9478
Bureau Chief: Yasuko Mouri
Editorial Profile: This is the Chicago bureau of the Japan-based financial paper Nihon Keizai Shimbun.
Language (s): English
DAILY NEWSPAPER

Nihon Keizai Shimbun - New York Bureau
Editorial: 1325 Avenue Of The Americas, New York, New York 10019. **T:** 1 212 261-6323
W: http://e.nikkei.com/e/fr/freetop.aspx
Editorial Profile: This is the New York bureau of the Japan-based financial paper Nihon Keizai Shimbun.
Language (s): English
DAILY NEWSPAPER

Nihon Keizai Shimbun - Palo Alto, CA Bureau
Editorial: 575 High St, Palo Alto, Santa Clara, California 94301. **T:** 1 650 470-7400
W: http://www.nni.nikkei.co.jp
Bureau Chief: Nobuyuki Okada
Editorial Profile: This is the California bureau of the Japan-based financial paper Nihon Keizai Shimbun.
Language (s): English
DAILY NEWSPAPER

Nihon Keizai Shimbun (Tokyo)
Editorial: 1-9-5 Otemachi, Chiyoda-ku, Tokyo 100-8066. **T:** 81 352552196
W: http://e.nikkei.com
Freq: Daily Not Audited
Editorial Profile: Serves as one of the world's largest financial newspapers. Covers market and industry news throughout Asia and the world.
Language (s): Japanese
DAILY NEWSPAPER

Nihon Ryutsu Shinbun
Editorial: Nihon Ryutsu Newspaper, 19, Tsukiji-machi, Shinzuku-ku, Tokyo 162-0818.
T: 81 35 2062615 **E:** ryu-tsu@luck.ocn.ne.jp
W: http://www.ryu-tsu.com
Freq: Weekly; **Circ:** 10003 Not Audited
Editor in Chief: Shinichi Hori; **Editor:** Tadashi Machida
Editorial Profile: Focuses on transportation issues in Japan. Topics include news on road and air transport, logistics, vehicle management and local traffic industry.
Language (s): Japanese
NEWSPAPER

Nihon Securities Journal
Editorial: Nihon Securities Journal Inc, 16-6 Koami-cho, Nihonbashi, Chuo-ku, Tokyo 103-0016. **T:** 81 33 6637279 **E:** news@nsjournal.jp
W: http://www.nsjournal.jp
Freq: Daily
Editor in Chief: Kaoru Suzuki
Editorial Profile: Nihon Securities Journal is the newspaper specialized for Securities.
Language (s): Japanese
DAILY NEWSPAPER

Nihon Shokuryo Shimbun
Editorial: Japan Food Journal Co., Ltd., 1-9-9-5F Yaesu, Tokyo 105-0028. **T:** 81 334 323103
W: http://www.nissyoku.co.jp
Freq: 2 Times/Week; **Circ:** 101303 Not Audited
Publisher: Masayoshi Konno
Editorial Profile: Nihon Shokuryo Shimbun is a news paper every other day. Articles cover the latest news in the food industry such as product development, reducing costs of production process and other related critical issues.
Language (s): Japanese
NEWSPAPER

Niigata Nippo
Editorial: The Niigata Nippo, 772-2 Zen-ku, Niigata-shi, Niigata 950-1189.
T: 81 25 3789400
W: http://www.niigata-nippo.co.jp
Freq: Daily Not Audited
Editorial Profile: Niigata Nippo is a regional daily newspaper which reports the latest regional news in Niigata district.
Language (s): Japanese
DAILY NEWSPAPER

Nikkan Gendai (Tokyo)
Editorial: Nikkan Gendai Co., Ltd., Nakagawa-Tsukiji Bldg., 3-5-4 Tsukiji, Chuo-ku, Tokyo 104-8007. **T:** 81 33 5430531
W: http://www.gendai.net
Freq: Daily; **Circ:** 1600003 Not Audited
Editorial Profile: Nikkan Gendai, a tabloid newspaper which provides readers with information about various local and national events.
Language (s): Japanese
DAILY NEWSPAPER

Nikkan Kenmin Fukui
Editorial: The Chunichi Shimbun, 3-1-8, Ohte, Fukui 910-8567. **T:** 81 776 288611
E: henshu@kenmin-fukui.co.jp
W: http://www.chunichi.co.jp/kenmin-fukui/
Freq: Daily; **Circ:** 40083 Not Audited
Editorial Profile: Nikkan Kenmin Fukui is a general daily newspapers in the Fukui district of Japan which mainly reports on regional news and happenings in the area.
Language (s): Japanese
DAILY NEWSPAPER

Nikkan Ryutsu Journal
Editorial: Ryutsu Journal Co., Ltd., 6F/7F Oizumi Higashiueno Building, 1-8-2 Higashiueno, Taito-ku, Tokyo 110-0015.
T: 81 33 8346771 **E:** rj@ryutsu-j.co.jp
W: http://www.ryutsu-j.co.jp
Freq: Daily
Publisher: Hideo Katou
Editorial Profile: Provides readers with information on distribution networks and channels, rail and ship transport including chain management and automation.
Language (s): Japanese
DAILY NEWSPAPER

Nikkan Sports (Tokyo)
Editorial: Nikkan Sports News, 3-5-10, Tsukiji, Chuo-ku, Tokyo 104-8055. **T:** 81 35 5508888
E: webmast@nikkansports.co.jp
W: http://www.nikkansports.com
Freq: Daily; **Circ:** 1965000 Not Audited
Editor in Chief: Hitoshi Aihara; **Editor:** Fumihiko Sasamori
Editorial Profile: Nikkan Sports is a sports newspaper which writes about daily news on sports and on popular celebrities in Japan.
Language (s): Japanese
DAILY NEWSPAPER

The Nikkei
Editorial: Nikkei Inc., 1-3-7 Otemachi, Chiyoda-ku, Tokyo 100-8066.
T: 81 332 700251 **W:** http://www.nikkei.co.jp
Freq: Daily; **Circ:** 3013563 Not Audited
Editorial Profile: THE NIKKEI is a daily newspaper which provides the latest news and current affairs happening in Japan and World including coverage on economic and politics.
Language (s): Japanese
DAILY NEWSPAPER

Nikkei - New York Bureau
Editorial: 1325 Avenue Of The Americas Suite 2404, New York, New York 10019-6026.
T: 1 212 261-6450
W: http://www.nikkeibp.com
Editorial Profile: This is the New York bureau of Nikkei, which is based in Tokyo, Japan.
Language (s): Japanese
DAILY NEWSPAPER

Nikkei Business Daily (Tokyo)
Editorial: Nikkei Inc., 1-3-7, Otemachi, Chiyoda-ku, Tokyo 100-8065.
T: 81 332 700251
W: http://netplus.nikkei.co.jp/ssbiz/
Freq: Daily; **Circ:** 173763 Not Audited
Editor: Seiji Munakata
Editorial Profile: One of Japan's largest industrial information journals, covers local business news, innovative industries and enterprises.
Language (s): Japanese
DAILY NEWSPAPER

The Nikkei MJ
Editorial: Nikkei Inc. 1-3-7, Otemachi, Chiyoda-ku, Tokyo 100-8066.
T: 81 332 700251
W: http://www.nikkei.co.jp/mj/
Freq: 2 Times/Week Not Audited
Editor in Chief: Shoji Shinohara
Editorial Profile: Provides sources of reliable information on Japanese distribution, retail markets and marketing.
Language (s): Japanese
NEWSPAPER

Nikkei Veritas
Editorial: Nikkei Inc., 1-3-7 Otemachi Chiyoda-ku, Tokyo 100-8065. **T:** 81 3 62562062
W: http://veritas.nikkei.co.jp/
Freq: Weekly
Editor in Chief: Hiroshi Yamasaki
Editorial Profile: NIKKEI VERITAS is a newspaper which focused on finance, banking, and technology.
Language (s): Japanese
NEWSPAPER

Nikkin
Editorial: The Japan Financial News Co., Ltd., 4-3-15, Kudan-Minami, Chiyoda-ku, Tokyo 102-8677. **T:** 81 33 2619971
W: http://www.nikkin.co.jp
Freq: Weekly
Publisher: Sumio Kinoshita; **Editor:** Gen Nishikawa
Editorial Profile: Nikkin is a financial journal which provides banking, financing, and money related news.
Language (s): Japanese
NEWSPAPER

Nishi Nippon Shimbun
Editorial: The Nishinippon Shimbun, 1-4-1, Tenjin, Chuo-ku, Fukuoka 810-8721.
T: 81 92 7115555
W: http://www.nishinippon.co.jp
Freq: Daily
Editor: Akira Kojima; **Editor:** Takeshi Kokubu
Editorial Profile: Nishi Nippon Shimbun is a newspaper which reports local news in Tenjin district in Fukuoka. Articles also cover general news in Japan and national.
Language (s): Japanese
DAILY NEWSPAPER

The Noki Shinbun
Editorial: Shinnorinsha CO., Ltd. 2-7-22, Kanda Nishi-cho, Chiyoda-ku, Tokyo 101-0054.
T: 81 332 913671
W: http://www.shin-norin.co.jp
Freq: Weekly
Editor in Chief: Nobuharu Mori
Editorial Profile: Noki Shinbun is a weekly newspaper which specialized in agriculture and agricultural machinery and agribusiness and research.
Language (s): Japanese
NEWSPAPER

Okayama Nichi-Nichi Shimbun
Owner: The Okayama Nichinichi Shimbun Company
Editorial: The Okayama Nichinichi Shimbun Company, 3-30 Banzan-cho, Okayama 700-8678. **T:** 81 862220601
W: http://www.okanichi.co.jp
Freq: Daily; **Circ:** 45002 Not Audited
Editor in Chief: Yasuhiro Inoue
Editorial Profile: Okayama Nichi-Nichi Shimbun is a daily regional news paper which provides readers with the latest regional news and current affairs happening in Okayama district including coverage on economic and regional activities.
Language (s): Japanese
DAILY NEWSPAPER

Osaka Nichi-Nichi Shimbun
Editorial: Osaka Nichi-Nichi Shimbun, 2-6-8, Bakurouchо, Chuo-ku, Osaka 541-0059.
T: 81 661 201800 **E:** dainichi@nnn.co.jp
W: http://www.nnn.co.jp/dainichi
Freq: Daily; **Circ:** 110003 Not Audited
Editorial Profile: Osaka Nichi-Nichi Shimbun is a daily regional news paper which provides the latest regional news, current affairs happening in Osaka district including coverage on economic and regional activities.
Language (s): Japanese
DAILY NEWSPAPER

Reitou Shokuhin Shimbun
Editorial: Reitou Shokuhin Shimbunsha, 9 Sanei-cho, Shinjyuku-ku, Tokyo 160-0008.
T: 81 333 599191 **E:** edi@reishoku.co.jp
W: http://www.reishoku.co.jp
Freq: Weekly
Editorial Profile: Reitou Shokuhin Shimbun is a weekly newspaper which is specialized in frozen food. Articles include the latest news of the industry such as new products, corporate news etc.
Language (s): Japanese
NEWSPAPER

Ryukyu Shimpo
Editorial: The Ryukyu Shimpo, 905 Ameku, Naha 900-8525. **T:** 81 988655158
E: shakai@ryukyushimpo.co.jp
W: http://www.ryukyushimpo.co.jp
Freq: Daily; **Circ:** 203778 Not Audited
Editor: Osamu Miyagi
Editorial Profile: Ryukyu Shimpo is a newspaper which reports the latest news in Ryukyu district in Okinawa.
Language (s): Japanese
DAILY NEWSPAPER

Ryutsu Journal
Editorial: Ryutsu Journal Co., Ltd., 6F/7F Oizumi Higashiueno Bulding, 1-8-2 Higashiueno, Taito-ku, Tokyo 110-0015.
T: 81 33 8346771 **E:** rj@ryutsu-j.co.jp
W: http://www.ryutsu-j.co.jp
Freq: Weekly; **Circ:** 28003 Not Audited
Publisher: Hideo Katou
Editorial Profile: Discusses chain management and automation industry news.
Language (s): Japanese
NEWSPAPER

Saga Shimbun
Editorial: Saga Shimbun Co., Ltd., 3-2-23, Tenjin, Saga 840-8585. **T:** 81 952 282111
E: houdou@saga-s.co.jp
W: http://www.saga-s.co.jp
Freq: Daily; **Circ:** 135233 Not Audited
Editorial Profile: Saga Shimbun is a daily regional news paper which writes about regional and lifestyle news in Saga district.
Language (s): Japanese
DAILY NEWSPAPER

Saitama Shimbun
Editorial: The Saitama Shimbun, 2-282-3, Yoshino-cho, Kita-ku, Saitama 331-8686.
T: 81 487 959161 **E:** desk@saitama-np.co.jp
W: http://www.saitama-np.co.jp
Freq: Daily; **Circ:** 164003 Not Audited
Editorial Profile: Saitama Shimbun is a regional daily newspaper in Saitama district which reports daily news on business, sports, entertainment and technology.
Language (s): Japanese
DAILY NEWSPAPER

San-In Chuo Shimpo
Editorial: The San-in Chuo Shimpo, Sanin Chuo Building, 383, Tono-machi, Matsue 690-8668. **T:** 81 85 2323320
W: http://www.sanin-chuo.co.jp
Freq: Daily Not Audited
Editor: Yasufumi Fukumaru
Editorial Profile: San-In Chuo Shimpo is a daily newspaper in Shimane and Tottori district which mainly reports on regional news happening around the neighborhood.
Language (s): Japanese
DAILY NEWSPAPER

Sankei Shimbun - New York Bureau
Editorial: United Nations Headquarters, Room S-400, New York, New York 10017.
T: 1 212 702-0454
Freq: Daily
Editorial Profile: This is the New York bureau of Sankei Shimbun, which is based in Tokyo.
Language (s): Japanese
DAILY NEWSPAPER

Sankei Shimbun (Tokyo)
Editorial: The Sankei Shimbun, 1-7-2, Otemachi, Chiyoda-ku, Tokyo 100-8077.
T: 81 33 2758742 **W:** http://sankei.jp.msn.com
Freq: Daily; **Circ:** 2746203 Not Audited
Editorial Profile: Sankei Shimbun is a newspaper which writes about the latest daily news on business, sports, entertainment and technology, etc.
Language (s): Japanese
DAILY NEWSPAPER

Sankei Sports (Tokyo)
Editorial: Sankei Sports, 13rd Floor, Sankei Building, 1-7-2, Otemachi, Chiyoda-Ku, Tokyo 100-8077. **T:** 81 332 758830
E: reader@sanspo.com
W: http://www.sanspo.com

Freq: Daily; **Circ:** 815223 Not Audited
Editorial Profile: Sankei Sports writes about the latest in sports, leisure and entertainment.
Language (s): Japanese
DAILY NEWSPAPER

The Sekai Nippo
Editorial: The Sekainippo Co., Ltd., 2-6-25 Idabashi-ku, Tokyo 174-0041.
T: 81 335 583412 **E:** voice@worldtimes.co.jp
W: http://www.worldtimes.co.jp
Freq: Daily
Editor in Chief: Masahiro Kuroki
Editorial Profile: Sekai Nippo is a daily newspaper which reports mainly international news such as the latest news which is provided by more than 20 overseas correspondents. Articles includes current affairs, economics, social affairs and cultural articles.
Language (s): English
DAILY NEWSPAPER

Shimane Nichi-Nichi Shimbun
Editorial: Shimane NichiNichi Shinbun, 545, Satogata-cho, Izumo 693-0064.
T: 81 853 236766
E: henshu@shimanenichinichi.co.jp
W: http://www.shimanenichinichi.co.jp
Freq: Daily Not Audited
Editor in Chief: Toyomi Hino
Editorial Profile: Shimane Nichi-Nichi Shimbun is a regional daily newspaper in Shimane district which reports local news, national and international news.
Language (s): Japanese
DAILY NEWSPAPER

Shimbun Quint
Editorial: Quintessence Publishing Co., Ltd., Quint House Bldg., 3-2-6 Hongo, Bunkyo-ku, Tokyo 113-0033. **T:** 81 358 422280
E: news-q@quint-j.co.jp
W: http://www.quint-j.co.jp/
Freq: Monthly
Editor in Chief: Yushi Kimiya
Editorial Profile: SHIMBUN QUINT is a monthly newspaper which focused on dental and medical news and knowledges.
Language (s): Japanese
NEWSPAPER

Shinano Mainichi Shimbun
Editorial: The Shinano Mainichi Shimbun, 657, Minami-agata-machi, Nagano 380-8546.
T: 81 262363130 **E:** houdo@shinmai.co.jp
W: http://www.shinmai.co.jp
Freq: Daily Not Audited
Editorial Profile: Covers news amd current affairs in Nagano district including coverage on economic and regional activities.
Language (s): Japanese
DAILY NEWSPAPER

Shipping & Trade News
Editorial: Tokyo News Service, Ltd., 7-16-3 Ginza, Tokyo 104-8415. **T:** 81 335 428521
W: http://www.tokyonews.co.jp
Freq: Daily; **Circ:** 15003 Not Audited
Editor in Chief: Shinrou Tajima
Editorial Profile: The Shipping and Trade News is the English newspaper which reports shipping and trade in Japan, marine transportation and harbors, railways, airlines and the economy, etc.
Language (s): English
DAILY NEWSPAPER

Shonai Nippo
Owner: The Shonai Nippo Press Co., Ltd.
Editorial: The Shonai Nippo Press Co., Ltd., 8-29, Baba-cho, Tsuruoka 997-8691.
T: 81 235221482
W: http://www.shonai-nippo.co.jp
Freq: Daily; **Circ:** 22502 Not Audited
Editorial Profile: Shonai Nippo is a newspaper which writes about the latest news and happenings around Tsuruoka district in Yamagata.
Language (s): Japanese
DAILY NEWSPAPER

Shukan Josei
Owner: SHUFU TO SEIKATSU SHA CO., LTD
Editorial: No. 7, No. five, 3-chome, Kyobashi, Chuo-ku, Tokyo. **T:** 81 3 35635120
E: webmaster@mb.shufu.co.jp
W: http://www.shufu.co.jp/magazine/woman
Editorial Profile: Focuses on women's issues.
Language (s): Japanese
DAILY NEWSPAPER

Sports Hochi (Tokyo)
Editorial: The Hochi Shimbun, 4-6-49, Kohnan, Minato-ku, Tokyo 108-8485.
T: 81 35 4791111 **W:** http://hochi.yomiuri.co.jp
Freq: Daily; **Circ:** 1500003 Not Audited
Editorial Profile: Newspaper covering sports, leisure and entertainment.
Language (s): Japanese
DAILY NEWSPAPER

Sports Nippon (Osaka)
Editorial: Sports Nippon Newspaper, 3-4-5, Umeda, Kita-ku, Osaka 530-8278.
T: 81 66 3468500
W: http://www.sponichi.co.jp
Freq: Daily; **Circ:** 610003 Not Audited
Editor: Haruo Nakagawa
Editorial Profile: Sports Nippon (Osaka) is a sports newspaper which writes about daily news on sports and popular celebrities around Osaka district.
Language (s): Japanese
DAILY NEWSPAPER

Sports Nippon (Tokyo)
Editorial: Sports Nippon Newspapers, 2-1-30, Ecchujima, Koto-ku, Tokyo 135-8517.
T: 81 33 8200700 **E:** customer@sponichi.co.jp
W: http://www.sponichi.co.jp
Freq: Daily; **Circ:** 879742 Not Audited
Editorial Profile: Sports Nippon is a sports newspaper which writes about daily news on sports and on popular celebrities.
Language (s): Japanese
DAILY NEWSPAPER

Suisan Keizai Shimbun
Owner: The Suisan-Keizai
Editorial: The Suisan-Keizai, 6-8-19, Roppongi, Minato-ku, Tokyo 106-0032.
T: 81 334046531 **W:** http://www.suikei.co.jp
Freq: Daily; **Circ:** 610002 Not Audited
Editorial Profile: The Suisan Keizai is a daily newspaper which delivers information on the marine products industry in Japan.
Language (s): Japanese
DAILY NEWSPAPER

Tages-Anzeiger - Tokyo Bureau
Owner: Tamedia AG
Editorial: Tamedia AG, 4-29-13 Kyoto, Setagaya-ku, Tokyo 156-0052.
T: 81 354501162
W: http://www.tagesanzeiger.ch
Freq: Daily
Editorial Profile: The Tages-Anzeiger is a national daily newspaper that focusses on news in politics, economy, culture and sports.
Language (s): German
DAILY NEWSPAPER

Tokachi Mainichi Shimbun
Editorial: Tokachi Mainichi Newspaper Inc., 8-2, Higashi 1-jo-minami, Obihiro 080-8688.
T: 81 155 222121 **E:** info@kachimai.co.jp
W: http://www.tokachi.co.jp
Freq: Daily; **Circ:** 91023 Not Audited
Editorial Profile: Tokachi Mainichi Shimbun is a daily newspaper which delivers the latest regional and lifestyle news on the Obihiro district.
Language (s): Japanese
DAILY NEWSPAPER

Tokushima Shimbun
Editorial: Tokushima Shimbun, 2-5-2, Naka-Tokushima-cho, Tokushima 770-8572.
T: 81 335 557373 **W:** http://www.topics.or.jp
Freq: Daily; **Circ:** 260663 Not Audited
Editor: Satoru Funakoshi
Editorial Profile: TOKUSHIMA SHIMBUN is a daily newspaper which reports regional news in Tokushima district and national news.
Language (s): Japanese
DAILY NEWSPAPER

Tokyo Chunichi Sports
Editorial: The Chunichi Shimbun, 2-1-4 Uchisaiwai-cyo, Chiyoda-ku, Tokyo 100-8505.
T: 81 369 102211 **E:** tochu@tokyo-np.co.jp
W: http://www.chunichi.co.jp/chuspo/
Freq: Daily; **Circ:** 573013 Not Audited
Editorial Profile: Tokyo Chunichi Sports writes about news in sports, leisure, news and entertainment.
Language (s): Japanese
DAILY NEWSPAPER

Tokyo Shimbun (Tokyo)
Editorial: The Chunichi Shimbun, 2-1-4, Uchisaiwai-cho, Chiyoda-ku, Tokyo 100-8505.
T: 81 369 102258 **E:** shakai@tokyo-np.co.jp
W: http://www.chunichi.co.jp/chuspo
Freq: Daily; **Circ:** 620133 Not Audited
Editorial Profile: Ccovers the news in the metropolitan area.
Language (s): Japanese
DAILY NEWSPAPER

Tokyo Shimbun/Chunichi Shumbun - United Nations Bureau
Editorial: 1 Rockefeller Plz, Rm 1714, New York, New York 10020-2044.
T: 1 212 969-1870
Freq: Daily
Bureau Chief: Tomotoshi Aoyagi
Editorial Profile: This is the United Nations Bureau for the Tokyo Shimbun in Tokyo and the Chunichi Shimbun in Nagoya, Japan daily newspapers.
Language (s): Japanese
DAILY NEWSPAPER

Tokyo Sports
Editorial: Tokyo Sports, 4/F 6/F ST Building, 2-1-30, Ecchujima, Koto-ku, Tokyo 135-8721.
T: 81 338 200831
W: http://www.tokyo-sports.co.jp
Freq: Daily; **Circ:** 1173203 Not Audited
Editor: Osamu Sakai
Editorial Profile: Tokyo Sports is a daily sports newspaper which writes about daily news on sports and on popular celebrities.
Language (s): Japanese
DAILY NEWSPAPER

Transportation & Logistics
Owner: Unyu Shimbun
Editorial: Unyu Shimbun, 3/F, Sasaki Building, 3-6-10, Nishinippori, Arakawa-ku, Tokyo 116-0013. **T:** 81 3 56850035
W: http://www.unyu.co.jp
Freq: 2 Times/Week; **Circ:** 45702 Not Audited
Editorial Profile: Reports on all aspects of logistics, such as efficiency and effectiveness, cost evaluation and information systems. Articles also cover stories of ministries which are related to the logistics industry.
Language (s): Japanese
NEWSPAPER

Tsuhan Shimbun
Editorial: Koubun Publishing, 2-14-3 Hongo, Bunkyo-Ku, Tokyo 113-0033.
T: 81 3 38151903 **E:** tsuhan@kbns.co.jp
W: http://www.tsuhanshinbun.com/
Freq: Weekly Not Audited
Editorial Profile: Provides a guide for e-business and electronic commerce.
Language (s): Japanese
NEWSPAPER

The Wall Street Journal (Japan)
Editorial: Prudential Tower 7th Floor, 2-13-10 Nagata-Cho Chiyoda-Ku, Tokyo 100-0014.
T: 81 3 3241-1671
DAILY NEWSPAPER

The Washington Post (Japan)
Editorial: Avex Bldg, 3-1-30 Minami-Aoyama Minato-ku, Tokyo 107. **T:** 81 354116031
DAILY NEWSPAPER

Weekly Logistics News
Editorial: The Weekly Logistics News, 4-15-14, Yamasaka, Higashisumiyoshi-ku, Osaka.
T: 81 666080501 **E:** buturyu@weekly-net.co.jp
W: http://www.weekly-net.co.jp
Freq: Weekly; **Circ:** 165002 Not Audited
Editor in Chief: Hidekazu Nakano; **Publisher:** Naoki Takata
Editorial Profile: Includes coverage on the latest trends of the industry, issues in cost management, maintenance, safety, labor and legislation as well as technical reports on vehicles and component developments.
Language (s): Japanese
NEWSPAPER

Yaeyama Mainichi Shimbun
Editorial: Yaeyama Mainichi Shimbun, 614, Tonoshiro, Ishigaki 907-0004.
T: 81 980822122
W: http://www.y-mainichi.co.jp
Freq: Daily; **Circ:** 14801 Not Audited
Editor: Yoshio Kamichi; **Editor:** Yoshitaka Matsuda
Editorial Profile: Yaeyama Mainichi Shimbun is a newspaper which reports on all aspects of news ranging from economical, political, social and cultural in the Ishigaki district in Okinawa.
Language (s): Japanese
DAILY NEWSPAPER

Yakuji Nippo
Owner: Yakuji Nippo Ltd.
Editorial: Yakuji Nippo Ltd.,1 Izumicho, Kanda, Chiyota-ku, Tokyo 101-8648. **T:** 81 338622141
E: henshu@yakuji.co.jp
W: http://www.yakuji.co.jp
Freq: 2 Times/Week; **Circ:** 53002 Not Audited
Editor in Chief: Norio Koyama
Editorial Profile: Yakuji Nippo is a journal which provides characteristic of newly approved drug, results of clinical studies, post-approval clinical studies now underway or planned; cautions for use and rationale for their establishment, adverse reaction, clinical pharmacology, pharmacokinetics in humans; chemical structure; pharmacology, toxicology, etc
Language (s): Japanese
NEWSPAPER

Yamagata Shimbun
Editorial: Yamagata Shimbun, 2-5-12, Hatagomachi, Yamagata 990-8550.
T: 81 236224546 **E:** info@yamagata-np.jp
W: http://yamagata-np.jp
Freq: Daily; **Circ:** 217767 Not Audited
Editor in Chief: Hiroji Sagae
Editorial Profile: Covers regional and national news.
Language (s): Japanese
DAILY NEWSPAPER

Yamanashi Nichinichi Shimbun
Editorial: The Yamanashi Nichinichi Shimbun, 2-6-10, Kitaguchi, Kofu 400-8515.
T: 81 552313111 **W:** http://www.sannichi.co.jp
Freq: Daily Not Audited
Editorial Profile: Yamanashi Nichinichi Shimbun is a newspaper which reports the reader with the latest news and current affairs happening in Kofu district in Yamanashi.
Language (s): Japanese
DAILY NEWSPAPER

Yomiuri Shimbun - Los Angeles Bureau
Editorial: 601 S Figueroa St Ste 3540, Los Angeles, California 90017-5740.
T: 1 213 623-7699
W: http://www.yomiuri.co.jp
Freq: Daily
Bureau Chief: Tatsuhito Iida
Editorial Profile: Yomiuri Shimbun - Los Angeles Bureau is the Los Angeles bureau of the Tokyo daily newspaper.
Language (s): Japanese
DAILY NEWSPAPER

Yomiuri Shimbun - New York Bureau
Editorial: 747 3rd Ave, 28th Fl, New York, New York 10017. **T:** 1 212 752-2196
W: http://www.yomiuri.co.jp
Freq: Daily; **Circ:** 20400 Not Audited
Bureau Chief: Yoshitoshi Sasaki
Editorial Profile: Yomiuri Shimbun - New York Bureau is the New York bureau of a Toyko daily newspaper.
Language (s): English, Japanese
DAILY NEWSPAPER

Yomiuri Shimbun - Washington, DC Bureau
Editorial: 529 14th St NW, Ste 802, Washington, District Of Columbia 20045.
T: 1 202 783-0186
Bureau Chief: Michiro Okamoto
Editorial Profile: The Yomiuri Shimbun is Japan's largest daily newspaper. It has roughly 60 reporters stationed at general bureaus in Washington, D.C., London, Bangkok and 29 branches around the world. Daily sections offer national and international news, politics, business, city news, sports, lifestyle and television listings. Weekly features include education, economics. science, book reviews and fairy tales. Syndication with the Washington Post provides readers with a broad range of international perspectives.
Language (s): Japanese
DAILY NEWSPAPER

Yomiuri Shimbun (Chubu)
Editorial: The Yomiuri Shimbun, 1-17-6, Sakae, Naka-ku, Nagoya 460-8470.
T: 81 522 111151
W: http://chubu.yomiuri.co.jp
Freq: Daily; **Circ:** 173503 Not Audited
Editor: Shigekatsu Matsunaga; **Editor:** Toru Takahashi
Editorial Profile: Provides the latest regional news and current affairs happening in Aichi, Gihu and Mie district including coverage on economic and regional activities.
Language (s): Japanese
DAILY NEWSPAPER

Yomiuri Shimbun (Hokuriku)
Editorial: The Yomiuri Shimbun, 4-5, Shimonoseki-machi, Takaoka 933-8543.
T: 81 766 266833
W: http://hokuriku.yomiuri.co.jp
Freq: Daily; **Circ:** 119773 Not Audited
Editorial Profile: Yomiuri Shimbun (Hokuriku) is a daily newspaper which provides the latest regional news and current affairs happening in Hokuriku district including coverage on economic and regional activities.
Language (s): Japanese
DAILY NEWSPAPER

Yomiuri Shimbun (Osaka)
Editorial: The Yomiuri Shimbun, 5-9, Nozaki-cho, Kita-ku, Osaka 530-8551.
T: 81 663 611111
W: http://osaka.yomiuri.co.jp
Freq: Daily
Editorial Profile: Yomiuri Shimbun (Osaka) is a daily newspaper which provides the latest regional news and current affairs happening in Osaka district including coverage on economic and regional activities.
Language (s): Japanese
DAILY NEWSPAPER

Yomiuri Shimbun (Seibu)
Editorial: The Yomiuri Shimbun, 1-16-5, Akasaka, Chuo-ku, Fukuoka 810-0042.
T: 81 927 155641 **E:** tousho@yomiuri.com
W: http://kyushu.yomiuri.co.jp
Freq: Daily; **Circ:** 925323 Not Audited
Editor: Ikushi Yoshizuka
Editorial Profile: Yomiuri Shimbun (Seibu) is a dally newspaper which provides the latest regional news and current affairs happening in Kyushu Island and Yamaguchi district including coverage on economic and regional activities.
Language (s): Japanese
DAILY NEWSPAPER

Yomiuri Shimbun (Tokyo)
Editorial: The Yomiuri Shimbun, 1-7-1, Otemachi, Chiyoda-ku, Tokyo 104-0061.
T: 81 332 421111 **E:** shakai@yomiuri.com
W: http://www.yomiuri.co.jp
Freq: Daily; **Circ:** 3850124
Editor: Kazuyuki Kondo; **Editor:** Takeshi Mizoguchi; **Publisher:** Hitoshi Uchiyama
Editorial Profile: Reports all aspects of news ranging from economical, political, social and cultural.
Language (s): Japanese
DAILY NEWSPAPER

Yukan Fuji (Tokyo)
Editorial: The Sankei Shimbun, 1-7-2, Otemachi, Chiyoda-ku, Tokyo 100-004.
T: 81 332 317111 **E:** desk@zakzak.co.jp
W: http://www.zakzak.co.jp
Freq: Daily; **Circ:** 15590003 Not Audited
Editor: Yoshifumi Ejiri; **Editor:** Takeshi Kubo
Editorial Profile: YUKAN FUJI is a newspaper only publishes evening daily. Articles cover news, event, sports and gossip.
Language (s): Japanese
DAILY NEWSPAPER

Yuso Keizai
Editorial: Yuso Keizai Shimbunsha, 2-22-4, Shinkawa, Chuo-ku, Tokyo 104-0033.
T: 81 332 060713 **E:** hanbai@yuso.co.jp
W: http://www.yuso.co.jp
Freq: Weekly; **Circ:** 80003 Not Audited
Publisher: Toru Kodaira; **Editor:** Takuya Matsuzaki
Editorial Profile: Covers industry news for international logistics executives.
Language (s): Japanese
NEWSPAPER

NEWS SERVICE/SYNDICATE

Associated Press
Editorial: Shidome Media Tower 7th Fl, 1-7-1 Higashi-Shimbashi, Minato-ku, Tokyo 105-7207. **T:** 81 3 6215-8931
NEWS SERVICE/SYNDICATE

Biopharm Insight
Editorial: Nishi Shimbashi 1-5-8, Kawate Building, 9th Floor, Tokyo
NEWS SERVICE/SYNDICATE

Bloomberg News
Editorial: Marunouchi Bldg, Fl 22, 2-4-1 Marunouchi, Chiyoda-Ku, Tokyo 100-6321.
T: 81 332018950
E: tokyonews@bloomberg.net
News Editor: Kyung Cho; **Editor at Large:** Peter Langan; **Editor at Large:** Peter Langan; **Editor:** Dave McCombs; **Bureau Chief:** Chian Wei Teo; **Editor:** Beth Thomas
NEWS SERVICE/SYNDICATE

Dow Jones Newswires
Editorial: Nikkei Bldg 4th Floor, 1-9-5 Otemachi Chiyoda-Ku, Tokyo 100-8086.
T: 81 3 6269-2770
E: tokyo.djnews@dowjones.com
Markets Editor: Brad Frischkorn
NEWS SERVICE/SYNDICATE

IDG News Service
Owner: International Data Group
Editorial: 2-18-10 Takanawa, Minato-ku, Tokyo 1048-0074. **T:** 81 80 3000-3000
E: idgnews@idg.com
NEWS SERVICE/SYNDICATE

Jiji Press
Owner: JIJI PRESS LTD.
Editorial: JIJI PRESS LTD., 5-15-8, Ginza, Chuo-ku, Tokyo 104-8178. **T:** 81 3 68001111
E: webmaster@jiji.com **W:** http://www.jiji.com
Freq: Daily
Editor: Kenji Hattori
Editorial Profile: JIJI PRESS is a news service source which reports the latest news in Japan and around the world.
Language (s): Japanese
NEWS SERVICE/SYNDICATE

Kyodo News
Editorial: 1-71-1 Higashi-Shimbashi, Minato-ku, Tokyo 105-7201. **T:** 81 355738000
E: kni@kyodonews.com
W: http://www.kyodo.co.jp
Editor: Tomohide Okuno
Editorial Profile: Founded in 1945, Kyodo is based in Japan and has bureaus all over the world. It is a Japanese news agency independent of government, political and commercial interests. It provides a Japanese-language news service that is distributed to virtually all newspapers and broadcast networks in Japan, as well as English and Chinese language services that reach news agencies, newspapers, and radio and television broadcasters in various parts of the world.
Language (s): English
NEWS SERVICE/SYNDICATE

Kyodo Tsushin
Editorial: Kyodo News, 18th Floor, Shiodome Media Tower, 1-7-1, Higashi-Shimbashi, Minato-ku, Tokyo 105-7201. **T:** 81 362 528101
W: http://www.kyodo.co.jp
Freq: Daily
Editor: Kiyoshi Nakagawa
Editorial Profile: Kyodo News is a portal site which reports the latest news, entertainments, sports, economics, and so on.
Language (s): English
NEWS SERVICE/SYNDICATE

Market News International
Owner: Market News International Inc.
Editorial: 2-7-1 Yurakucho, Chiyoda-ku, 12/F, Yurakucho ITOCiA, Tokyo 100-0006.
T: 81 90 21750040
Asia News Editor: Phillip Day; **Bureau Chief:** Max Sato
Language (s): English
NEWS SERVICE/SYNDICATE

Nihon Denpa News (NDN)
Editorial: Nihon Denpa News, 3/F., Koike Building 1-5-10 Minamiazabu, Minato-ku, Tokyo 106-0032. **T:** 81 357 656810
E: info@ndn-news.co.jp
W: http://www.ndn-news.co.jp
Freq: Daily
Editor: Naoki Shima
Editorial Profile: Nihon Denpa News is a portal site which cover the latest news of Asian countries, Africa, Europe, the Americas, Iraq and Afghanistan and similar turbulent places.
Language (s): Japanese
NEWS SERVICE/SYNDICATE

Platts Global Alert
Owner: McGraw-Hill Companies
Editorial: Marunouchi Kitaguchi Building, 28th Floor, 1-6-5 Marunouchi Chiyoda-ku, Tokyo 100-0005. **T:** 81 3 4550-8842
NEWS SERVICE/SYNDICATE

Reuters
Editorial: 30F Akasaka Biz Tower, 5-3-1 Akasaka, Minato-ku, Tokyo 107-6330.
T: 81 334324141
Bureau Chief: Kevin Krolicki
NEWS SERVICE/SYNDICATE

Sun Telephoto
Editorial: 1-1-1, Hitotsubashi, Chiyoda-ku, Tokyo 100-0003. **T:** 81 332136771
Freq: Daily
Editorial Profile: Sun Telephoto is a photo source which deliver photos from Reuters. It also delivers the latest news photo from China and Hong Kong.
Language (s): Japanese
NEWS SERVICE/SYNDICATE

BROADCASTING

RADIO STATIONS

ARD German Radio - Tokyo Bureau
Editorial: ARD, Denenchofu 39-2, 3-chome, Ota-ku, Tokyo 145-0071. **T:** 81 3 3721-5151
E: ard.radio.tokyo@ndr.de
Editorial Profile: Acts as a bureau for a German public broadcast station.

Nippon Broadcasting System
Editorial: Nippon Broadcasting System, 1-9-3 Yuraku-cho, Tokyo 100-8439.
T: 81 332 871111 **W:** http://www.jolf.co.jp
Editorial Profile: Nippon Broadcasting System is a portal site which writes about the radio program and events information on Nippon Broadcasting System.

Radio Nikkei
Owner: Nikkei Radio Broadcasting Corporation
Editorial: Nikkei Radio Broadcasting Corporation, 1-9-15, Akasaka, Minato-ku, Tokyo 107-8373. **T:** 81 335838151
E: hensei@radionikkei.jp
W: http://www.radionikkei.jp
Editorial Profile: Broadcasts a variety of programs such as music, songs, economics, gamble, and medical.

Tokyo FM Broadcasting (FM Tokyo/TFM)
Owner: TOKYO FM Broadcasting Co., Ltd.
Editorial: TOKYO FM Broadcasting Co., Ltd. 1-7, Kojimachi, Chiyoda-ku, Tokyo 102-8080.
T: 81 332210080 **E:** webmaster@tfm.co.jp
W: http://www.tfm.co.jp
Editorial Profile: FM Tokyo is one of radio stations in Japan which supports the development of events such as digital, Internet, mobile and broadband.

TELEVISION NETWORKS

Asahi Broadcasting Corporation (ABC)
Editorial: Asahi Broadcasting Corporation, 1-1-30 Fukushima, Fukushima-ku, Osaka 553-8503. **T:** 81 664 585321 **W:** http://asahi.co.jp/
Editorial Profile: Asahi Broadcasting Corporation (ABC) is a major broadcaster in Japan, airing entertainment, sports and news programs. Subsidiary TV Asahi Music publishes music as a tie-in to the company's programming.

CBS News
Editorial: CBS Interactive Inc., 3-29-1 KandaJinbo-cho, Tokyo 101-0051.
T: 81 335 871861
W: http://www.cbsnews.com
Editorial Profile: CBS News provides breaking world news and commentary in the U.S. and around the world.

CNBC Asia - Tokyo Bureau
Editorial: 27/F Atago Green Hills, MORI Tower, 2-5-1 Atago, Minato-Ku, Tokyo 105-0002.
T: 81 35 7772501 **E:** tokyo@cnbcasia.com
W: http://www.cnbcasia.com
Editorial Profile: Covers news and related topics in Japan.

Fuji Television Network(CX)
Editorial: Fuji Television Network, 2-4-8, Daiba, Minato-ku, Tokyo 137-8088.
T: 81 355 008888 **W:** http://www.fujitv.co.jp
Editorial Profile: Fuji News Network(FNN) is Japan's most powerful news-gathering organization, with offices at each of the 28 affiliated stations of the Fuji Network System(FNS) throughout Japan.

Nippon Hoso Kyokai/NHK
Owner: Japan Broadcasting Corporation
Editorial: Japan Broadcasting Corporation, 2-2-1, Jinnan, Shibuya-ku, Tokyo 150-8001.
T: 81 334 651111 **W:** http://www.nhk.or.jp
Editorial Profile: Serves as Japan's only public broadcaster, funded by fees received from TV viewers. Delivers a wide range of impartial, high-quality programs, both at home and abroad.

Nippon Television Network Corporation
Editorial: Nippon Television Network Corporation, 1-6-1 Higashishinbashi, Minato-ku, Tokyo 105-7444. **T:** 81 362 151111
W: http://www.ntv.co.jp
Editorial Profile: Nippon Television Network Corporation is one of major television network in Japan. It has a viewer rating of 8.

R-TV Asia
Editorial: Thomson Reuters, 30/F Akasaka Biz Tower, 5-3-1, Akasaka, Minato-ku, Tokyo 107-6330. **T:** 81 364 411200
W: http://www.thomsonreuters.com
Editorial Profile: Thomson Reuters is the world's leading source of intelligent information for businesses and professionals. Thomson Reuters combine industry expertise with innovative technology to deliver critical information to leading decision makers in the financial, legal, tax and accounting, healthcare, science and media markets, powered by the world's most trusted news organization.

Television Asahi
Editorial: Television Asahi, 6-9-1, Roppongi, Minato-ku, Tokyo 106-8001. **T:** 81 364 061111
E: webmaster@tv-asahi.co.jp
W: http://www.tv-asahi.co.jp
Editorial Profile: Television Asahi is a major television network in Japan.

Television Tokyo(TX)
Editorial: TV Tokyo Corporation 4-3-12, Toranomon, Minato-ku, Tokyo 105-8012.
T: 81 334 321212
W: http://www.tv-tokyo.co.jp
Editorial Profile: TV TOKYO is one of major television network in Japan. They plan to continue developing a steady stream of sound, reliable programs and content that will make viewers consciously decide to sit down and watch TV.

Tokyo Hoso
Editorial: Tokyo Broadcasting System, Inc. 5-3-6, Akasaka, Minato-ku, Tokyo 107-8006.
T: 81 337 461111 **E:** houtoku@best.tbs.co.jp
W: http://www.tbs.co.jp
Editorial Profile: (TBS) is one of the major commercial terrestrial networks in Japan and the only one which provides both television and radio broadcasting services.

TV Tokyo- New York Bureau
Editorial: 1325 Avenue Of The Americas, Ste 2402, New York, New York 10019.
T: 1 212 261-6430
W: http://www.tv-tokyo.co.jp/corporation/
Editorial Profile: New York bureau of TV Tokyo.

CABLE

CNBC Cable Network
Editorial: Kandabashi Park Bldg, Fl 4, Tokyo 1010054. **T:** 81 332924315

JORDAN — Tel: 962

Standard Time: GMT +2
Continent: Asia
Capital City: Amman

NEWSPAPERS & PUBLICATIONS

NEWSPAPERS

Ad-Dustour
Owner: Jordan Press & Publishing Company
Editorial: PO Box 591, Addustour Building, Amman 11118. **T:** 962 6 560 8000
E: dustour@addustour.com.jo
W: http://www.addustour.com
Freq: Daily; **Circ:** 80000 Pub Statement
Editor In Chief: Mohammed Al Tall
Editorial Profile: Ad-Dustour is a daily Arabic newspaper covering national and international news, economics, politics, entertainment and sport. It was first published in 1967, and includes youth supplement Shabab on Wednesdays, and cultural supplement Al Thaqafi on Fridays.
Language (s): Arabic
DAILY NEWSPAPER

Ahali
Owner: Jordanian People's Democratic Party (Hashd)
Editorial: PO Box 9966, Near Al Istiqlal Hospital, Amman 11191. **T:** 962 6 562 1827
E: ahali@go.com.jo
W: http://www.hashd-ahali.org.jo
Freq: Thu; **Circ:** 5000 Pub Statement
Editor In Chief: Adnan Abu Khalifa; **News Editor:** Ahmad Abu Shawer

Editorial Profile: Ahali is the official newspaper of the The Jordanian People's Democratic Party (Hashd) and covers national and international news, current affairs, politics and business. The weekly Arabic newspaper launched in 1989 and is published on Thursdays.
Language (s): Arabic
NEWSPAPER

Akhbar Alnas
Owner: Akhbar Al Nas Newspaper
Editorial: PO Box 795, Amman 11910.
T: 962 6 535 0133
E: khayyampress@orange.jo
Freq: Bi-Weekly; **Circ:** 6000 Pub Statement
Editor: Doa'a Al Saleh; **Editor in Chief:** Mamdouh Hawamdah
Editorial Profile: Akhbar Alnas (People's News) is a 16-page, fortnightly Arabic newspaper covering local and international news, sports and society. It launched in 2007 and is published on alternate Sundays.
Language (s): Arabic
NEWSPAPER

Alanbat
Owner: Al Anbat Corporation For Media and Press
Editorial: PO Box 962556, Building 66, Al Jaheth Street, Amman 11196.
T: 962 6 520 0100 **E:** info@alanbat.net
W: http://www.alanbat.net
Freq: Daily; **Circ:** 13000 Pub Statement
Editor In Chief: Fares Shara'an
Editorial Profile: Alanbat is a daily Arabic newspaper covering local and international news, politics, business and sport. It launched in 2005.
Language (s): Arabic
DAILY NEWSPAPER

Al Arab Al Yawm
Owner: Al Watniyah Group for Media Investments.
Editorial: PO Box 962198, Queen Rania Abdulla Street, Amman 11196.
T: 962 6 568 3333 **E:** mail@alarabalyawm.net
W: http://www.alarabalyawm.net
Freq: Daily; **Circ:** 30000 Pub Statement
Editor in Chief: Osama Al Rantisy; **Editor in Chief:** Nabeel Ghishan; **Manufacturing Editor:** Sandra Haddad; **Arab News Editor:** Azzam Jarrar
Editorial Profile: Al Arab Al Yawm (The Arab Today) is a daily Arabic newspaper covering national and international news, politics, business, culture and sport. The newspaper launched in 1997.
Language (s): Arabic
DAILY NEWSPAPER

Asharq Al-Awsat - Amman office
Owner: Saudi Research & Publishing Co.
Editorial: PO Box 616, Office 406, Building 118, Jad Center, Amman 11821.
T: 962 6 551 7102 **E:** srpcjo@orange.jo
W: http://www.aawsat.com
Freq: Daily
News Editor: Mohammad Al Daameh
Editorial Profile: Amman bureau of Asharq Al-Awsat newspaper. The Amman office covers news, business and sport from Jordan for the London-based newspaper which is distributed across the Arab world.
Language (s): Arabic
DAILY NEWSPAPER

Assabeel
Owner: Dar Assabeel for Press & Distribution
Editorial: PO Box 213545, Al Hussein Al Sharqi, Amman 11121. **T:** 962 6 569 2852
E: assabeel@assabeel.net
W: http://www.assabeel.net
Freq: Daily; **Circ:** 20000 Pub Statement
News Editor: Ayman Al-Fdeilat; **Editor-in-Chief:** Atef Jolani
Editorial Profile: Assabeel is a daily Arabic newspaper covering national and international news, current affairs, politics, business and sports. It was first published in 1993.
Language (s): Arabic
DAILY NEWSPAPER

Al Bayda
Owner: Al Bayda Group
Editorial: 2nd Floor, Jabr Complex, Amman.
T: 962 79 686 3461
E: reemash81@yahoo.com
Freq: Sun; **Circ:** 27000 Pub Statement
News Editor: Reema Al Sharbati; **Editor In Chief:** Ziad Al Tahrawi
Editorial Profile: Al Bayda (The Desert) is a weekly Arabic newspaper covering local and international news, business and society. It launched in 2004 and is published on Sundays.
Language (s): Arabic
NEWSPAPER

Al Deyar
Owner: Al Batraa Media Services
Editorial: PO Box 961239, Building 29, Amman 1196. **T:** 962 6 516 6588
E: aldeyar2003@yahoo.com
W: http://www.aldeyarjo.net
Freq: Daily; **Circ:** 15000 Pub Statement
News Editor: Abdulhafiz Abu Gaoud; **Editor In Chief:** Mohammad Salama
Editorial Profile: Al Deyar is an independent daily newspaper covering local and international news, business & economy, art & culture, food, health and sport. The newspaper launched as a weekly in 2003, and went daily in 2004.
Language (s): Arabic
DAILY NEWSPAPER

Al Ekhbarya
Owner: Al Ekhbarya
Editorial: The Islamic Bank Complex, Jabal Al Hussein, Amman. **T:** 962 79 927 4279
E: fayezajrashe@yahoo.com
Freq: Wed; **Circ:** 50000 Pub Statement
Editor in Chief: Fayez Al Ajrashe
Editorial Profile: Al Ekhbarya is a weekly Arabic newspaper covering national news, business and politics. It launched in 2006 and is published on Wednesdays.
Language (s): Arabic
NEWSPAPER

Al Ghad
Owner: United Jordan Press Company
Editorial: PO Box 3535, 59 Zaal Abu Tayeh Street, Amman 11821. **T:** 962 6 554 4000
E: editorial@alghad.jo
W: http://www.alghad.jo
Freq: Daily; **Circ:** 57000 Pub Statement
Editor In Chief: Jumana Ghunaimat
Editorial Profile: Al Ghad (Tomorrow) is a broadsheet-sized Arabic newspaper covering national and international news, current affairs, politics, business and sports. It launched in August 2004 and includes a fortnightly motoring supplement, Sayyarat Al-Ghad, every other Monday.
Language (s): Arabic
DAILY NEWSPAPER

Al Hayat Weekly
Owner: Dar Al Hayat for Printing & Publishing
Editorial: PO Box 961457, Amman 11196.
T: 962 6 539 9955 **E:** info@alhayatnews.com
W: http://www.alhayatnews.com
Freq: Thu; **Circ:** 50000
Editor In Chief: Diya Khureisat
Editorial Profile: Al Hayat Weekly is an Arabic newspaper covering national & international news, business, sports, women's issues and humanitarian issues. It launched in 2006 and is published on Thursdays.
Language (s): Arabic
NEWSPAPER

The Jordan Times
Owner: Jordan Press Foundation
Editorial: PO Box 6710, Queen Rania Al Abdullah Street, Amman 11118.
T: 962 6 560 0800 2392
E: editor@jordantimes.com
W: http://www.jordantimes.com
Freq: Daily; **Circ:** 24000 Pub Statement
Editor In Chief: Samir Barhoum
Editorial Profile: The Jordan Times is an English newspaper covering national and international news, business, politics, culture and sport. The newspaper launched in 1975 and is published daily, except Saturdays.
Language (s): English
DAILY NEWSPAPER

Al Majd
Owner: Al Majd Press
Editorial: PO Box 926856, Makkah Street, Amman 11190. **T:** 962 6 553 0553
E: almajd@almajd.net
W: http://www.almajd.net
Freq: Mon; **Circ:** 5000 Pub Statement
Editor-in-Chief: Fahd Al Rimawi
Editorial Profile: Al Majd (The Glory) is a weekly Arabic newspaper focusing on current affairs and politics. It launched in 1994 and is published on Mondays.
Language (s): Arabic
NEWSPAPER

Al Mannarah - Jordan office
Owner: South Press & Publishing Est.
Editorial: PO Box 963666, Sarh Al Shaheed Street, Amman 11196. **T:** 962 6 515 1306
E: muwaffaq2005@yahoo.com
W: http://www.almannarah.com
Freq: 2 Times/Week
Editorial Profile: Jordan office of Iraq-based Al Mannarah newspaper. The bureau covers news, politics, business and sport from Jordan.
Language (s): Arabic
NEWSPAPER

Al Mashhad
Owner: Al Mashhad for Publishing & Distribution
Editorial: Building 7, Khalda, Amman.
T: 962 6 539 9056 **E:** hanni0789@yahoo.com
Freq: Sun; **Circ:** 35000 Pub Statement
News Editor: Hani Shboul
Editorial Profile: Al Mashhad (The Spectacle) is a weekly Arabic newspaper covering news, politics, culture, health, business and sport. It launched in 2006 and is published on Sundays.
Language (s): Arabic
NEWSPAPER

Al Mira'a
Owner: Gerasa News
Editorial: PO Box 928404, Shaheed Wasf El Tal Street, Amman 11110. **T:** 962 6 567 5725
E: info@gerasanews.com
Freq: Mon; **Circ:** 30000 Pub Statement
Editor In Chief: Jamal Al Muhtasab; **News Editor:** Islam Sawalha
Editorial Profile: Al Mira'a (The Mirror) is a weekly Arabic newspaper covering politics, business, sport and culture. It launched in 1985 and is published on Mondays.
Language (s): Arabic
NEWSPAPER

Al Mowajaha
Owner: Al Mowajaha Press & Publishing
Editorial: PO Box 940337, 4th Floor, Building 33, Sultan Center, Amman 11194.
T: 962 6 586 6279
E: shahenko2001@hotmail.com
Freq: Wed; **Circ:** 32000 Pub Statement
News Editor: Younes Aatiti; **Editor In Chief:** Bassam Al Yassine; **News Editor:** Fadl Sawaeer
Editorial Profile: Al Mowajaha is a weekly Arabic newspaper covering international and national news, society, business, sports and politics. It launched in 2007 and is published on Wednesdays.
Language (s): Arabic
NEWSPAPER

Al Rai
Owner: Jordan Press Foundation
Editorial: PO Box 6710, Queen Rania Al Abdullah Street, Amman 11118.
T: 962 6 560 0800 **E:** alrai@jpf.com.jo
W: http://www.alrai.com
Freq: Daily; **Circ:** 65000 Pub Statement
News Editor: Tayel Al Damin; **Editor In Chief:** Sameer Al Hayari
Editorial Profile: Al Rai (The Opinion) is an Arabic daily newspaper covering local and international news, finance, politics, culture and sport. It was first published in 1971.
Language (s): Arabic
DAILY NEWSPAPER

Al Shahed
Owner: Al Namozajiyah Press
Editorial: PO Box 922859, Next to Comodore Hotel, Amman 11196. **T:** 962 6 565 6433
E: nalsyeed2008@hotmail.com
W: http://www.alshahidonline.net
Freq: Wed; **Circ:** 18000 Pub Statement
News Editor: Abdulla Al Adem; **Editor In Chief:** Nazeera Al Said
Editorial Profile: Al Shahed (The Witness) is a weekly Arabic newspaper covering national and international news, politics, sports and society. It was first published in 2000 and is issued on Wednesdays.
Language (s): Arabic
NEWSPAPER

Al Watan Al Eqtisadi
Owner: Olayan Publishing
Editorial: PO Box 622, Queen Rania Abdulla Street, Amman 11941. **T:** 962 6 535 6616
E: watan.newspaper99@gmail.com
W: http://www.anbaalwatan.com
Freq: Wed; **Circ:** 25000 Pub Statement
Editor: Ahmad Al Qaisy; **Editor In Chief:** Reda Olayan
Editorial Profile: Al Watan Al Eqtisadi is a weekly newspaper covering economics, tourism, investment and business. The newspaper launched in 1997 and is aimed at business executives in Jordan. It is published on Wednesdays.
Language (s): Arabic
NEWSPAPER

NEWS SERVICE/SYNDICATE

Agence France-Presse - Amman Bureau
Owner: Agence France-Presse
Editorial: PO Box 3340, Amman 11181.
T: 962 6 464 4978 **E:** afp.amman@afp.com
W: http://www.afp.com
Bureau Chief: Ahmad Al Khatib
Editorial Profile: Amman bureau of international news agency supplying news - text, graphics, video and pictures - to subscribers around the world.
Language (s): Arabic
NEWS SERVICE/SYNDICATE

APTN Jordan
Owner: Associated Press
Editorial: PO Box 840742, 2nd Floor, Building 46, Amman 11181. **T:** 962 6 569 9396
E: aptn_mes@yahoo.com
W: http://www.aptn.com
News Producer: Mustafa Allan; **Bureau Chief:** Mahmoud Naghawi; **News Producer:** Ahed Rabab'a
Editorial Profile: Associated Press Television News (APTN) is the international television arm of the Associated Press - APTN's operations include a main news service, specialised broadcast services, customised coverage for the Middle East, a productions division, weekly and daily entertainment news and an extensive video archive library.
Language (s): Arabic
NEWS SERVICE/SYNDICATE

Associated Press - Amman Bureau
Owner: Associated Press
Editorial: PO Box 35111, Office 1, Floor 3, Insurance Building, Amman 11180.
T: 962 6 461 4660 **E:** apamman@ap.org
W: http://www.ap.org
Editorial Profile: International wire agency - Amman bureau covers Jordan.
Language (s): English
NEWS SERVICE/SYNDICATE

Bloomberg News
Editorial: Regus Business Center Room 206, Al Husari Street, Shmeisani, Amman 11194.
T: 96 277 720-3737
NEWS SERVICE/SYNDICATE

Dow Jones Newswires - Jordan Bureau
Owner: Dow Jones
Editorial: PO Box 841272, Amman 11181.
T: 962 79 983 1831
E: hassan.hafidh@dowjones.com
W: http://www.dowjones.com
Editorial Profile: Jordan bureau of US-based financial newswire service.
Language (s): Arabic
NEWS SERVICE/SYNDICATE

Jordan News Agency
Owner: Jordan News Agency
Editorial: PO Box 6845, Al-Dakhleyeh Circle, Amman 11118. **T:** 962 6 560 9700
E: petra@petra.gov.jo
W: http://www.petra.gov.jo
Editor: Mohamed Abu Oulba; **Arabic News Editor:** Khalid Alshboul; **Editor:** Sanaa Kurdi; **Editor:** Feras Qutaitan
Editorial Profile: Official government news agency - founded in 1969.
Language (s): Arabic
NEWS SERVICE/SYNDICATE

Reuters
Editorial: Mahmoud Al Abidi Street, PO Box 667, Amman 11118. **T:** 926 6 462-3776
W: http://www.thomsonreuters.com
NEWS SERVICE/SYNDICATE

Reuters - Amman Bureau
Owner: Thomson Reuters
Editorial: PO Box 667, Building 1, Amman 11118. **T:** 962 6 465 7937
E: suleiman.al-khalidi@thomsonreuters.com
W: http://www.reuters.com
Editorial Profile: Amman bureau of international news and picture agency.
Language (s): Arabic
NEWS SERVICE/SYNDICATE

Reuters TV - Amman Bureau
Owner: Thomson Reuters
Editorial: PO Box 667, Building 1, Amman 11118. **T:** 962 6 465 7937
E: suleiman.al-khalidi@thomsonreuters.com
W: http://www.thomsonreuters.com
Editorial Profile: Amman bureau of Thomson Reuters TV providing television broadcasters and internet providers worldwide with international news video, including breaking

news stories, human interest items, sport, business and entertainment news.
Language (s): Arabic
NEWS SERVICE/SYNDICATE

KAZAKHSTAN — Tel: 7

Standard Time: GMT +5 to +6
Continent: Asia
Capital City: Astana

NEWSPAPERS & PUBLICATIONS

NEWSPAPERS

Biznes i vlast
Owner: Mediaholding 31 Kanal
Editorial: Ul. Zharkova 275 A, Almaty 50060.
T: 7 727 24 98 532 **E:** and@and.kz
W: http://www.and.kz
Freq: 2 Times/Week; **Circ:** 8000 Not Audited
Editor In Chief: Oleg Khe
Editorial Profile: A business and financial paper with 4 supplements.
Language (s): Russian
NEWSPAPER

Caravan
Owner: Alma Media
Editorial: Ploshad Respubliki 13, Almaty 50013. **T:** 7 727 258-36-00 **E:** 321@caravan.kz
W: http://www.caravan.kz **Circ:** 220000 Pub Statement
News Editor: Alexandra Myskina
Editorial Profile: Newspaper focusing on national and international news, politics, economics, culture and sport.
Language (s): Russian
DAILY NEWSPAPER

Express K
Owner: TOO Express K
Editorial: Kabantai batyry 30a, Almaty 10000.
T: 7 717 259242 **E:** daily@express-k.kz
W: http://www.express-k.kz
Freq: Daily; **Circ:** 25000 Pub Statement
Editor In Chief: Tlepbergen Bekmaganbetov
Editorial Profile: A daily newspaper covering news on politics, society, social issues and sports.
Language (s): Russian
DAILY NEWSPAPER

Kazakhstanskaya Pravda
Owner: OAO-Respublikanaskaya Gazeta-Kazakhstanskaja Pravda
Editorial: pr. Pobyedy 18, Astana 473000.
T: 7 7172 32 17 29 **E:** astana@kazpravda.kz
W: http://www.kazpravda.kz
Freq: Daily; **Circ:** 107000 Pub Statement
Editor In Chief: Tatyana Kostina
Editorial Profile: Newspaper focusing on politics, economics, culture, society, sport and general news.
Language (s): Russian
DAILY NEWSPAPER

Kursiv
Editorial: pl. Respubliki 15, office 152, Almaty.
T: 7 727 25 01 384 **E:** kursiv@kursiv.kz
W: http://www.kursiv.kz
Freq: Weekly; **Circ:** 28500 Not Audited
Editor: Elena Britskaya; **Editor-in-Chief:** Irina Dorokhova
Editorial Profile: National newspaper on finance and banking, financial markets, politics and economics.
Language (s): Russian
NEWSPAPER

Megapolis
Owner: Mediaholding 31 Kanal
Editorial: Ul. Tazhibayevoy 155, Almaty 50060.
T: 7 727 25 00 987 **E:** info@megapolis.kz
W: http://www.megapolis.kz
Freq: Weekly; **Circ:** 15000
Editor In Chief: Igor Shakhnovich
Editorial Profile: National social and political weekly newspaper.
Language (s): Russian
NEWSPAPER

Novoye Pokolenye
Editorial: Ul. Bogenbai batyra 156a, office 1-2, Almaty 50098. **T:** 7 727 26 13 106
E: np@np.kz **W:** http://www.np.kz **Circ:** 35000
Editor In Chief: Sergey Aparin
Editorial Profile: Covers political, economical, social and cultural aspects of life of modern Kazakhstan.
Language (s): Russian
NEWSPAPER

Panorama
Owner: TOO Gazeta Panorama
Editorial: Pl. Respubliki 15, 6 Floor, office 647, 658, 659, 665, Almaty 50013.
T: 7 727 27 21 632 **E:** panorama@intelsoft.kz
W: http://www.panorama.kz
Freq: Weekly; **Circ:** 12500 Pub Statement
Editor-in-Chief: Lera Tsoy
Editorial Profile: Business weekly specializing in serious analytical information on politics, economics, business and international relations.
Language (s): Russian
NEWSPAPER

Vecherny Almaty
Editorial: pr. Abylai Khana 2, Almaty 50016.
T: 7 727 2792890 **E:** info@vecher.kz
W: http://www.vecher.kz
Freq: 2 Times/Week; **Circ:** 12000 Pub Statement
Editor-in-Chief: Svetlana Mischenko
Editorial Profile: Evening city newspaper covering social, cultural events and entertainment.
Language (s): Russian
NEWSPAPER

Vremya
Editorial: pr. Raiymbeka 117, office 107, Almaty. **T:** 7 727 258-10-04 **E:** info@time.kz
W: http://www.time.kz
Freq: Daily; **Circ:** 30000
Editor-in-Chief: Lev Tarakov
Editorial Profile: Daily political newspaper covering general and economic news and events in Kazakhstan.
Language (s): Russian
DAILY NEWSPAPER

BROADCASTING

RADIO NETWORKS

Kazakhskoye Radio
Owner: RTRK Kazakhstan
Editorial: ul. Zheltoksan 177, Almaty 50013.
T: 7 727 26 11 999 **E:** radio@kazakstan.kz
W: http://kazakstan.kz/rus/radio
Editorial Profile: National radio station with socio-political end entertainment programmes.

TELEVISION STATIONS

Kazakhstan
Owner: RTRK Kazakhstan
Editorial: ul. Zheltoksan 175, Almaty 50013.
T: 7 727 27 21 336 **E:** kaztv@kazakstan.kz
W: http://kazakstan.kz/rus/tv
Editorial Profile: National TV station with informative and entertaining programmes, series and films.

TV 31 Kanal
Owner: Mediaholding 31 Kanal
Editorial: Ulica Tazhibayevoy 155, Almaty 50060. **T:** 7 727 25 05 601 **E:** 31@31.kz
W: http://www.31.kz
Editorial Profile: National informative-analytical and entertaining TV station.

KENYA — Tel: 254

Standard Time: GMT +3
Continent: Africa
Capital City: Nairobi

NEWSPAPERS & PUBLICATIONS

NEWSPAPERS

Coastweek
Owner: Coastweek Newspapers Ltd
Editorial: Nkrumah Road / Mwenye Aboud Rd, Oriental Building, 2nd Floor, Mombasa.
T: 254 41 2230130 **E:** info@coastweek.com
W: http://www.coastweek.com
Freq: Weekly; **Circ:** 14200 Pub Statement
Editor: Gulshan Jivraj
Editorial Profile: Newspaper covering local and national news including politics, economics, entertainment, culture and sports.
Language (s): English
NEWSPAPER

The Daily Nation
Owner: Nation Media Group Limited
Editorial: Nation Centre, Kimathi Street, Nairobi. **T:** 254 20 3288000
E: newsdesk@ke.nationmedia.com
W: http://www.nation.co.ke
Freq: Daily; **Circ:** 220000 Pub Statement
News Editor: Eric Shimoli
Editorial Profile: Newspaper covering national and international news including politics, business, economics, opinion, culture and sport.
Language (s): English
DAILY NEWSPAPER

The East African
Owner: Nation Media Group Limited
Editorial: Nation Centre, Kimithi Street, Nairobi 100. **T:** 254 20 32 88 000
E: newsdesk@ke.nationmedia.com
W: http://www.theeastafrican.co.ke
Freq: Weekly; **Circ:** 35000 Pub Statement
Editorial Profile: Newspaper covering news and current affairs including features, stories and in-depth analysis from each country in the region, in addition to international stories, business news and opinion. Distributed in Kenya and the other countries of the African Great Lakes region, including Tanzania, Uganda and Rwanda.
Language (s): English
NEWSPAPER

Kass Weekly
Owner: Kass Media Group
Editorial: APA Acarde, 2nd flr, room 24, Floor 138, Nairobi. **T:** 254 20 28 75 220
E: info@kassfm.co.ke
W: http://www.kassfm.co.ke
Freq: Weekly
Editorial Profile: Publication covering news, politics, business, economics, education, tourism, sports, politics, history and culture.
Language (s): English
NEWSPAPER

The Standard
Owner: The Standard Group
Editorial: Mombasa Rd, PO Box 30080, Nairobi 00100 GPO. **T:** 254 20 32 22 111
E: ktanui@standardmedia.co.ke
W: http://www.standardmedia.co.ke
Freq: Daily; **Circ:** 60000 Pub Statement
Editorial Profile: Newspaper covering national and international news and current affairs including business, politics, economics, sports and entertainment.
Language (s): English
DAILY NEWSPAPER

The Star
Owner: Radio Africa Group
Editorial: Lion Place, 2nd Floor, Nairobi.
T: 254 20 4244000
E: newsdesk@nairobistar.com
W: http://www.the-star.co.ke
Freq: Daily
Editor: Catherine Gicheru
Editorial Profile: Newspaper covering regional and national news and current affairs including business, economics, opinion, sports, lifestyle and society.
Language (s): English
DAILY NEWSPAPER

The Sunday Nation
Owner: Nation Newspapers Ltd
Editorial: Nation Centre, Kimathi Street, Nairobi. **T:** 254 20 3288000
E: newsdesk@ke.nationmedia.com
W: http://www.nationmedia.com
Freq: Weekly; **Circ:** 250000 Pub Statement
Editorial Profile: Sunday newspaper covering national and international news including politics, business, economics, opinion, culture and sport.
Language (s): English
NEWSPAPER

Taifa Leo
Owner: Nation Media Group
Editorial: P.O. Box 49010-00100 GPO, NBI, Nation Centre, Kimathi Street, Nairobi.
T: 254 20 3288000
W: http://www.nationmedia.com
Freq: Daily
News Editor: Gilbert Mogire
Editorial Profile: Taifa Leo is a daily newspaper in Kenya and it is published in Swahili language.
Language (s): Swahili
DAILY NEWSPAPER

NEWS SERVICE/SYNDICATE

Agence France-Presse - Nairobi Bureau
Owner: Agence France-Presse
Editorial: International Life House, 5th Floor, Mama Ngina Street, Nairobi.
T: 254 203 96 0000 **E:** afpnai@afp.com

W: http://www.afp.com
Bureau Chief: Stefan Smith
Editorial Profile: Nairobi bureau of the international news and picture agency Agence France-Presse covering international news and current affairs.
Language (s): English
NEWS SERVICE/SYNDICATE

Associated Press
Editorial: CVS Plaza, Lenana Rd, Nairobi 100.
T: 254 20 285-9000 **E:** naiburo@ap.org
NEWS SERVICE/SYNDICATE

Bloomberg News
Editorial: 3rd Floor, International House, Mama Ngina St., Nairobi. **T:** 25 42 031-3440
E: pmrichardson@bloomberg.net
NEWS SERVICE/SYNDICATE

IDG News Service
Owner: International Data Group
E: idgnews@idg.com
NEWS SERVICE/SYNDICATE

Reuters
Editorial: Loita St, Finance House, 12th Floor, Nairobi. **T:** 254 20 222-4717
E: nairobi.newsroom@thomsonreuters.com
Editorial Profile: This is the central East Africa bureau and serves as the forwarding office for contacts in the area, including those in Mogadishu, Somalia, Burundi and Uganda.
NEWS SERVICE/SYNDICATE

BROADCASTING

RADIO NETWORKS

BBC East Africa Bureau - BBC World Service
Owner: BBC
Editorial: Longonot Place, 5th Floor, Kijabe St, Nairobi 58621-00200. **T:** 254 202 276000
E: bbcnairobi@gmail.com
W: http://www.bbcswahili.com
Editorial Profile: BBC bureau based in Kenya, making programmes for the BBC World Service and Swahili language service.

Voice of America Radio Network
W: http://www.voanews.com

TELEVISION STATIONS

CNBC Africa
Owner: CNBC Africa
Editorial: 19th Floor, Ambank House, University Way, Nairobi. **T:** 254 20 225 2150
E: info@abndigital.com
W: http://www.abndigital.com

Kenya Broadcasting Corporation
Editorial: Harry Thuku Road, PO Box 30456, Nairobi 100. **T:** 254 20 22 23 75
E: md@kbc.co.ke **W:** http://www.kbc.co.ke
Editorial Profile: Kenya Broadcasting Corporation (KBC) is the state-run media organisation of Kenya. It broadcasts in English and Swahili, as well as in most local languages of Kenya. The corporation started its life in 1928 when Kenya was a British colony. In 1964, when Kenya became an independent country, the corporation's name was changed to Voice of Kenya. In 1989, the Kenyan parliament reverted the corporation's name from Voice of Kenya to Kenya Broadcasting Corporation. Kenya Broadcasting Corporation offers the following radio and television services: Public Service Radios National Kiswahili Service(Radio Taifa) National English Service Regional Eastern Service transmitting in Somali, Borana, Rendile, Burji and Turkana Regional Central Service transmitting in Meru, Embu and Kamba Regional Western Service transmitting in Kuria, Teso, Luhya, Suba and Pokot Commercial Radio Music and Entertainment, Venus FM transmitting to major urban areas of Nairobi, Mombasa, Nakuru, Nyeri, Eldoret and Kisumu. Coro FM transmitting to Nairobi and Mount Kenya Region on 102.3 and 99.5 MGHZ Pwani FM transmitting to coast region on 103.1 MGHZ Nosim FM transmitting to Narok and its environs on 90.5 MGHZ Minto FM transmitting to Kisii and its environs on 101.7 MGHZ Kitwek FM transmitting to Eldoret on 92.9 MGHZ and other areas on 98.0 MGHZ Mayienga FM transmitting to Kisumu and its environs on 93.5 MGHZ Television Services Free to air KBC channel 1

KIRIBATI Tel: 686

Standard Time: GMT +12
Continent: Oceania
Capital City: Tarawa

NEWSPAPERS & PUBLICATIONS

NEWSPAPERS

Kiribati Newstar
Editorial: PO Box 10, Bairiki, Kiribati. T: 686 21652
Freq: Weekly
Editorial Profile: Independent weekly newspaper published every Friday and distributed throughout country to many different islands.
Language (s): English
NEWSPAPER

Te Uekera
Owner: Broadcasting & Publications Authority
Editorial: Te Uekera Printing Services, PO Box 78, Bairiki, Kiribati. **T:** 686 21162
Freq: Weekly; **Circ:** 3000 Pub Statement
Editor: Tearinibeia Eno Teabo
Editorial Profile: State-owned weekly covering national news.
Language (s): English
NEWSPAPER

BROADCASTING

RADIO NETWORKS

Radio Kiribati
Owner: Broadcasting & Publications Authority
Editorial: PO Box 78, Bairiki, Kiribati. T: 686 21187

KOREA (SOUTH) Tel: 82

Standard Time: GMT +9
Continent: Asia
Capital City: Seoul

NEWSPAPERS & PUBLICATIONS

NEWSPAPERS

AM 7
Editorial: Munhwa Ilbo, Munhwa Ilbosa, 68 Chungjeongno 1-ga, Seoul 100-723.
T: 82 2 37015960 **E:** am7@munhwa.co.kr
W: http://www.am7.co.kr
Freq: Daily; **Circ:** 600009 Not Audited
Publisher: Byung-Kyu Lee; **Editor in Chief:** Seung-Hun Oh
Editorial Profile: Provides news on sports, economy, business, lifestyle, celebrities, etc.
Language (s): Korean
DAILY NEWSPAPER

Asahi Shimbun - Seoul Bureau
Editorial: Asahi Shimbun, 9/F Dong-A Media Center, 139 Sejongno, Jongno-gu, Seoul 110-015. **T:** 82 23 139865
W: http://www.asahi.com
Freq: Daily
Bureau Chief: Tetsuya Hakoda
Editorial Profile: Covers information for Japanese news readers, both nationally and internationally,
Language (s): Japanese
DAILY NEWSPAPER

Asia Economy
Editorial: Asia Economy Newspaper Co., Limited., 10-11 Floor, Asia Media Tower, Seoul 150-890. **T:** 82 2 22002114
E: hemes@asiae.co.kr
W: http://www.asiae.co.kr
Freq: Daily; **Circ:** 100008 Not Audited
Editor: Sook-Hye Hwang; **Editor:** Kyung-Tap Lee; **Editor:** Kyu-Sung Lee
Editorial Profile: Provides news on finance, economics, real estate, stock market, investment, etc.
Language (s): Korean
DAILY NEWSPAPER

Busan Ilbo
Editorial: Busan Ilbosa, 1-10, Sujeong-dong, Dong-gu, Busan 601-738. **T:** 82 51 4614114
W: http://www.busan.com
Freq: Daily Not Audited
Editor: Byung-Kil Ahn; **Editor:** Bong-Ijn Choi;
Publisher: Jong-Ryol Kim
Editorial Profile: Provides news on business, sports, entertainment, technology, current issues, etc.
Language (s): Korean
DAILY NEWSPAPER

Chosun Ilbo
Editorial: Chosun Ilbosa, 61 Taepyeongro 1-ga, Jung-gu, Seoul 100-756. **T:** 82 2 7245114
E: webmaster@chosun.com
W: http://www.chosun.com
Freq: Daily; **Circ:** 2400009 Not Audited
Publisher: Sang-Hun Bang; **Editor:** Yong Shik Byeon; **Editor:** Heup Choi; **Editor:** Cheol-Joong Kim; **Editor:** Chul-Min Lee; **Editor:** Yang-Min Song
Editorial Profile: Provides news on current issues of politics, economy, finance, sports, entertainment, etc.
Language (s): Korean
DAILY NEWSPAPER

Chosun Ilbo - United Nations Bureau
Editorial: 405 E 42nd St, United Nations Rm 453-A, New York, New York 10317-3507.
T: 1 212 963-8921 **W:** http://www.chosun.com
Editorial Profile: Chosun Ilbo, established in 1920, first started to promote the freedom of speech in Korea. Standing for justice, building culture, industrial development and impartiality wavering soul, as a paper that "says what needs to be said". The praise given the Chosun Ilbo - accurate, fair and NO.1 - have not changed, either.
Language (s): Korean
DAILY NEWSPAPER

Chungbuk Ilbo
Editorial: Chungbuk Media Co., Limited., 4/F Hyunjeong Building, 2868, Cheongju 361-300.
T: 82 43 2772114 **W:** http://inews365.com
Freq: Daily
Publisher: Sang-Hun Lee
Editorial Profile: Provides news on current issues and local news in Chungbuk province.
Language (s): Korean
DAILY NEWSPAPER

Chungcheong Maeil
Editorial: Chungcheong Daily Newspaper, 962 Uncheon-dong, Heungdeok-gu, Cheongju 361-842. **T:** 82 43 2775555
E: okok916@ccdn.co.kr
W: http://www.ccdn.co.kr
Freq: Daily
Publisher: Ju-Yeon Byun; **Editor:** Woo-Seok Ham; **Editor:** Byung-Gap Jang
Editorial Profile: Provides news on current issues.
Language (s): Korean
DAILY NEWSPAPER

Chungcheong Times
Editorial: Chungcheong Times, 8/F, Inseung Building, Garosu-gil, 80 Heungdeok-gu, Cheongju-si, Cheongju 361-270.
T: 82 43 2795000 **E:** webmaster@ccilbo.com
W: http://www.ccilbo.com
Freq: Daily
Editor: In-Seop Han; **Editor:** Woon-Ki Kim; **Editor:** Sang-Hoon Lee; **Editor in Chief:** Baek-Su Lim
Editorial Profile: Provides news on current issues.
Language (s): Korean
DAILY NEWSPAPER

ChungCheong Today
Editorial: Chungcheong Today, Dunwon 1-gil, 50 Galma 1-dong, Seo-gu, Daejeon 302-172.
T: 82 42 3807101 **E:** cctoday@cctoday.co.kr
W: http://www.cctoday.co.kr
Freq: Daily
Editor: In-Seok Choi; **Publisher:** Nam-Jin Jeong; **Editor:** Won-Seop Lee
Editorial Profile: Provides news on current issues.
Language (s): Korean
DAILY NEWSPAPER

The City
Editorial: City Media, Inc., 3F, Gusegun Building., Seoul 110-061. **T:** 82 2 20132095
E: webmaster@clubcity.kr **W:** http://clubcity.kr
Freq: Daily; **Circ:** 400008 Not Audited
Publisher: Choong-Yeon Cho
Editorial Profile: Provides news on current issues, politics, economy, government, society, entertainment and sports.
Language (s): Korean
DAILY NEWSPAPER

Daegu Ilbo
Editorial: Daegu Ilbo, 177-10, Beome 2-dong, Suseong-gu, Daegu 706-820.
T: 82 53 7575700 **E:** admin@mail.idaegu.com
W: http://www.idaegu.com
Freq: Daily; **Circ:** 87009 Not Audited
Editorial Profile: Provides news on current issues.
Language (s): Korean
DAILY NEWSPAPER

Daegu Shinmun
Editorial: The Daegu Newspaper, 283-8 Sincheon 3-dong, Dong-gu, Daegu 701-823.
T: 82 53 4240004 **E:** webmaster@idaegu.co.kr
W: http://www.idaegu.co.kr
Freq: Daily; **Circ:** 118008 Not Audited
Publisher: Deok-Chi Lim
Editorial Profile: Provides local news and current affairs that are happening in Daegu.
Language (s): Korean
DAILY NEWSPAPER

Daejon Ilbo
Editorial: Daejonilbosa, 1-135, Munhwa-dong, Jung-gu, Daejeon 301-715. **T:** 82 42 2513311
E: ibiz@daejonilbo.com
W: http://www.daejonilbo.com
Freq: Daily; **Circ:** 200008 Not Audited
Editor in Chief: Jae-Sook Gu; **Bureau Chief:** Jae-Keun Kim; **Editor:** Yong-Kyu Ryu;
Publisher: Sue-Yong Shin
Editorial Profile: Provides news on current issues.
Language (s): Korean
DAILY NEWSPAPER

Daily e-Logistics Times
Editorial: Korea Logistics News Co., Limited., 3/F, Sungsan Building, Seoul 121-876.
T: 82 2 7495445 **E:** soungwoo@klnews.co.kr
W: http://www.klnews.co.kr
Freq: Daily; **Circ:** 28008 Not Audited
Publisher: Dae-Yong Jang
Editorial Profile: Provides news on trading on both local and international levels.
Language (s): Korean
DAILY NEWSPAPER

The Daily Focus
Editorial: Focus Shinmoonsa, 3/F, Solbone Building., Seoul 137-070. **T:** 82 2 5802900
E: nib503@focus.co.kr
W: http://focus.fnn.co.kr
Freq: Daily; **Circ:** 662352 Not Audited
Publisher: Hye-Sook Lee
Editorial Profile: Provides news on advertising and printing.
Language (s): Korean
DAILY NEWSPAPER

Digital Times
Editorial: Digital Times, 8/F, Munhwa Ilbo Building, 68, Seoul 100-723.
T: 82 2 37015500 **E:** report@dt.co.kr
W: http://www.dt.co.kr
Freq: Daily; **Circ:** 120008 Not Audited
Editor: Myung-Ho Hong; **Editor:** Wook-Won Kim; **Editor:** Nak-Young Seo; **Editor:** Won-Jun Song
Editorial Profile: Provides news mainly on technology, business, economy, communications, culture, social issues, etc.
Language (s): Korean
DAILY NEWSPAPER

Dong-A Ilbo
Editorial: The Dong-A Ilbo, 139 Sejongno, Jongno-gu, Seoul 110-715. **T:** 82 2 20201310
W: http://www.donga.com
Freq: Daily; **Circ:** 2000007 Not Audited
Editor in Chief: Kyou Chul Choi; **Editor:** Young-Hoon Choi; **Publisher:** Il-Heung Kim;
Editor: Kang-Woon Lee
Editorial Profile: Provides news on current issues.
Language (s): Korean
DAILY NEWSPAPER

Dong-A Ilbo - New York Bureau
Editorial: United Nations, ECOSOC Boot 22, New York, New York 10017.
T: 1 201 689-3145
Editorial Profile: This is the New York bureau of Donga-A Ilbo, a daily newspaper based in Seoul, South Korea.
Language (s): Korean
DAILY NEWSPAPER

Dongyang Ilbo
Editorial: Dongyang Ilbo, Dongyang Daily News Building, Cheongju 360-716.
T: 82 43 2187337
E: webmaster@dynews.co.kr
W: http://www.dynews.co.kr
Freq: Daily; **Circ:** 93009 Not Audited
Publisher: Seong-Hoon Cho; **Editor in Chief:** Dong-Seok Kim
Editorial Profile: Provides news about current issues.
Language (s): Korean
DAILY NEWSPAPER

Eorinyi Dong-A
Editorial: Donga Ilbosa, Dong-A Media Centre, Seoul 110-715. **T:** 82 2 20201390
E: kidsroom@donga.com
W: http://kids.donga.com
Freq: Daily
Editor: Hyuk-Joong Choi; **Editor in Chief:** Ho-Pyo Hong; **Publisher:** Hak-Jun Kim
Editorial Profile: Provides academic information for children.
Language (s): Korean
DAILY NEWSPAPER

Financial News
Editorial: The Financial News, 6, 7/F Financial News Building, Seoul 150-877.
T: 82 2 20037114 **W:** http://www.fnnews.com
Freq: Daily; **Circ:** 100008 Not Audited
Editor: Hoon-Sik Jeong; **Editor in Chief:** Min-Ku Kang; **Editor:** Jang-Gyu Lee; **Editor:** Jong-Taek Lee; **Editor:** Jung-Hyo Lim; **Editor:** Kye-Shin Song; **Editor:** Lee Won-du; **Editor in Chief:** Lee Yong-kyu
Editorial Profile: Provides news on current issues, finance, and real estate.
Language (s): Korean
DAILY NEWSPAPER

Gwangju Dream
Editorial: GJDream.Korea Corp, 4/F Jutaek Hoigwan, 501-15, Gwangju 500-060.
T: 82 62 5208000
E: webmaster@gjdream.com
W: http://www.gjdream.com
Freq: Daily
Editor in Chief: Jeong-Hee Lim
Editorial Profile: Provides the latest news on government, culture, social issues, celebrities, etc.
Language (s): Korean
DAILY NEWSPAPER

Gwangnam Ilbo
Editorial: The Gwangnamilbo Co., Limited., 986-12, Ssangchon-dong, Seo-gu, Gwangju 502-260. **T:** 82 62 3702300
E: webmaster@gwangnam.co.kr
W: http://www.gwangnam.co.kr
Freq: Daily; **Circ:** 67008 Not Audited
Publisher: Haeng-Hwan Park; **Editor in Chief:** Sang-Woo Seo
Editorial Profile: Provides news on current issues including business, sports, entertainment, technology, etc.
Language (s): Korean
DAILY NEWSPAPER

Halla Ilbo
Editorial: The Hallailbo, 568-1, Samdo 1-dong, Jeju 690-711. **T:** 82 64 7502214
E: webmaster@hallailbo.co.kr
W: http://www.hallailbo.co.kr
Freq: Daily
Editor in Chief: Byung-Jun Kim; **Editor:** Chi-Hoon Kim; **Editor:** Tae-Hyun Oh; **Editor:** Bo-Seok Yoon
Editorial Profile: Provides news on current issues.
Language (s): Korean
DAILY NEWSPAPER

Hankook Ilbo
Editorial: Hankook Ilbo Co., Limited, 15/F, Hanjin Building., Seoul 100-770.
T: 82 2 7242114 **E:** webmaster@hankooki.com
W: http://www.hankooki.com
Freq: Daily; **Circ:** 2121543 Not Audited
Editor: Jong-Oh Ha; **Editor:** Kwang-Duck Kim;
Editor: Tae-Sung Ko
Editorial Profile: Provides news on current issues.
Language (s): Korean
DAILY NEWSPAPER

Hankyoreh Shinmun
Editorial: The Hankyoreh, 116-25, Gongdeok 1-dong, Mapo-gu, Seoul 121-750.
T: 82 2 7100114 **W:** http://www.hani.co.kr
Freq: Daily; **Circ:** 1500007 Not Audited
Editor: Seung-Dong Han; **Editor in Chief:** In-Hyun Kim; **Publisher:** Hyung-Su Seo
Editorial Profile: Provides news on current issues including politics, economy, government and social issues.
Language (s): Korean
DAILY NEWSPAPER

Herald Business
Editorial: Herald Media Inc., 3~5/F, 1-17 Jeong-dong, Jung-gu, Seoul 100-120.
T: 82 2 7270114 **E:** webeditor@heraldm.com
W: http://www.heraldbiz.com
Freq: Daily; **Circ:** 700009 Not Audited
Editor: Hae-Chang Hwang; **Editor:** Hwa-Kyun Kim; **Editor in Chief:** Beom-Rok Lee;

WORLD NEWS MEDIA

Publisher: Hang-Hwan Park
Editorial Profile: Provides news on current issues, politics, economy and entertainment.
Language (s): Korean
DAILY NEWSPAPER

Hwankyung Kunsul Ilbo

Editorial: Hwankyung Kunsul Ilbo Co., Limited., 43 Seogye-dong, Yongsan-gu, Seoul 140-827. **T:** 82 2 7355558
E: master@hwankyungdaily.com
W: http://www.hwankyungdaily.com
Freq: Daily; **Circ:** 90008 Not Audited
Publisher: Yong-Hee Cho
Editorial Profile: Provides news on social and economic changes.
Language (s): Korean
DAILY NEWSPAPER

Ilgan Sports

Editorial: Joongang Entertainment and Sports Inc., 16/, Korea Economic Daily News Building., Seoul 100-791. **T:** 82 2 63631334
W: http://isplus.joinsmsn.com
Freq: Daily; **Circ:** 614197 Not Audited
Editor in Chief: Jun-Won Park; **Editor:** Tae-Hoon Park
Editorial Profile: Provides news in sports, leisure, entertainment, etc.
Language (s): Korean
DAILY NEWSPAPER

Incheon Ilbo

Editorial: Incheon Ilbo Co., Limted., 222 Joongbongno, Incheon 400-750.
T: 82 32 4520114 **E:** webmaster@itimes.co.kr
W: http://news.itimes.co.kr
Freq: Daily
Editor: Tae-Hyun Cho; **Publisher:** Sa-In Jang
Editorial Profile: Provides news on the current issues that happens in Incheon, South Korea.
Language (s): Korean
DAILY NEWSPAPER

The International New York Times - Seoul

Editorial: 18/F Korea Press Center, 25 Taepyongno-1-ga, Jung-gu, Seoul 100-101.
T: 1 822 914-8289 **E:** foreign@nytimes.com
Bureau Chief: Choe Sang-Hun
DAILY NEWSPAPER

Jeju Ilbo

Editorial: Jeju Ilbo, 2324-6, Yeon-dong, Jeju 690-713. **T:** 82 64 7406114
E: ksn@jejunews.com
W: http://www.jejunews.com
Freq: Daily; **Circ:** 60008 Not Audited
Publisher: Dae-Seong Kim
Editorial Profile: Provides news on current issues.
Language (s): Korean
DAILY NEWSPAPER

Jeju Times

Editorial: Jeju Times, 1473-1 Ora-dong, Jeju-si, Jeju 690-160. **T:** 82 64 7424502
E: webmaster@jejutimes.co.kr
W: http://www.jejutimes.co.kr
Freq: Daily
Editor in Chief: Heung-Nam Jeong
Editorial Profile: Provides news on business, economy, politics, lifestyle, society, etc.
Language (s): Korean
DAILY NEWSPAPER

Jemin Ilbo

Editorial: Jemin Ilbo, 2627-5 Dodu 1-dong, Jeju 690-241. **T:** 82 64 7413365
E: jemin@jemin.com
W: http://www.jemin.com
Freq: Daily
Publisher: Seong-Beom Jin
Editorial Profile: Provides news on current issues including politics and sports.
Language (s): Korean
DAILY NEWSPAPER

Jeolla Ilbo

Editorial: The Jeollailbo, 140-1, Jeon-dong, Wansan-gu, Jeonju 560-040.
T: 82 63 2323131 **E:** editcont@jeollailbo.com
W: http://www.jeollailbo.com
Freq: Daily
Editor: Byung-Woon Jang; **Editor:** Hee-Sung Kwon; **Editor:** Sang-Deok Lee
Editorial Profile: Provides news on the current issues.
Language (s): Korean
DAILY NEWSPAPER

Jeonbuk Domin Ilbo

Editorial: The Jeonbuk Dominilbo, 417-62, Jinbuk 2-dong, Deokjin-gu, Jeonju 561-706.
T: 82 63 2517111 **E:** domin2@chol.com
W: http://www.domin.co.kr

Freq: Daily
Editor in Chief: Dae-Seong Ha; **Editor:** Sung-Cheon Han; **Editor:** Jae-Keun Jeong; **Editor:** Bang-Hee Lee; **Publisher:** Byung-Chan Lim
Editorial Profile: Provides news on current issues, lifestyle, etc.
Language (s): Korean
DAILY NEWSPAPER

Jeonbuk Ilbo

Editorial: Jeonbuk Ilbo, Wooseok Building, 710-5, Jeonju 561-762. **T:** 82 63 2505500
E: desk@jjan.kr **W:** http://www.jjan.kr
Freq: Daily; **Circ:** 120008 Not Audited
Editor in Chief: Ju-Yeon Hwang; **Editor in Chief:** Soon-Taek Kwon; **Editor:** Seong-Won Lee; **Publisher:** Chang-Hun Seo
Editorial Profile: Provides news on current issues.
Language (s): Korean
DAILY NEWSPAPER

Jeonmin Ilbo

Editorial: Jeonmin Daily Paper, 590 Ua-dong 3-ga, Jeonju 561-823. **T:** 82 63 9013000
E: jmib3000@hanmail.net
W: http://www.jeonminilbo.co.kr
Freq: Daily
Publisher: Yong-Beom Lee
Editorial Profile: Provides news on current issues.
Language (s): Korean
DAILY NEWSPAPER

Jeonnam Ilbo

Editorial: Jeonnam IlboJeonnam Ilbo.com, 700-5, Jungheung-dong, Buk-gu, Gwangju 500-758. **T:** 82 62 5270015
W: http://www.jnilbo.com
Freq: Daily; **Circ:** 36006 Not Audited
Editor: Kwang-Mi Jeon; **News Editor:** Kun-Sang Lee; **Editor in Chief:** Jae-Sung Lim; **Editor:** Il-Jong Oh; **Publisher:** Ki-Jeong Park
Editorial Profile: Provides news on current issues, business, sports, entertainment, technology, etc.
Language (s): Korean
DAILY NEWSPAPER

Jeonnam Maeil

Editorial: Jeonnam Maeil, Samsan Building, 704-9, Gwangju 500-878. **T:** 82 62 7201000
E: jndn@chol.com **W:** http://www.jndn.com
Freq: Daily; **Circ:** 36008 Not Audited
Editor: Rae-Sung Kim; **Editor:** Woo-Kwan Kim; **Editor:** Gyu-Ho Kwak; **Publisher:** Yong-Ho Shin
Editorial Profile: Provides news on current issues.
Language (s): Korean
DAILY NEWSPAPER

JoongAng Daily

Editorial: Joongang Ilbo, 7 Sunhwa-dong, Jung-gu, Seoul 100-759. **T:** 82 2 7519215
E: eopinion@joongang.co.kr
W: http://koreajoongangdaily.joinsmsn.com
Freq: Daily; **Circ:** 150008 Not Audited
Editor: Byung-Gee Hong; **Editor in Chief:** Kilzer Lou; **Editor:** Si-Yoon Sung
Editorial Profile: Provides current news in English.
Language (s): English
DAILY NEWSPAPER

Joongang Ilbo

Owner: JoongAng Media Network
Editorial: Joongang Ilbo, 7 Sunhwa-dong, Jung-gu, Seoul 100-759. **T:** 82 2 7515114
E: comment@joongang.co.kr
W: http://koreajoongangdaily.joinsmsn.com
Freq: Daily
Editor: Sung-Kyu Ahn; **Editor in Chief:** Young-Tae Choi; **Editor:** Byung-Ki Hong; **Editor:** Dong-Sup Kim; **Editor:** Day-Young Oh; **Editor:** Chan-Young Park; **Editor:** Jae-Yong Pyo; **Editor:** Jang-Hwan Son; **Publisher:** Pil-Ho Song
Editorial Profile: Provides news on current issues. Its English edition is titled Korea JoongAng Daily.
Language (s): Korean
DAILY NEWSPAPER

Joongang Ilbo - Ridgeview, NJ Bureau

Editorial: 154 Hope St, Ridgewood, Bergen, New Jersey 7450. **T:** 1 201 444-2931
W: http://joongangdaily.joins.com
Freq: Daily
Editorial Profile: This is the New Jersey bureau of Joongang Ilbo in Seoul, South Korea.
Language (s): English
DAILY NEWSPAPER

Joong-Boo Ilbo

Editorial: The Joongbooilbo, 1010, Gwonseon-dong, Suwon 441-390. **T:** 82 31 2302114
E: webmaster@joongboo.com
W: http://www.joongboo.com
Freq: Daily; **Circ:** 75804 Not Audited
Editor: Deuk-Ho Eom; **Editor:** Kyung-Mook Kang; **Publisher:** Jae-Yul Lim
Editorial Profile: Provides news on the current issues in Joong-Boo district.
Language (s): Korean
DAILY NEWSPAPER

Joongbu Maeil

Editorial: Joongbu Maeil Shinmun, 150-1, Sinbong-dong, Cheongju 361-111.
T: 82 43 2752001 **E:** jb@jbnews.com
W: http://www.jbnews.com
Freq: Daily
Publisher: Seong-Kyu Park; **Editor in Chief:** Chang-Hee Song
Editorial Profile: Provides news on current issues.
Language (s): Korean
DAILY NEWSPAPER

Joongdo Ilbo

Editorial: Joongdo Ilbo, 175-3 Oryu-dong, Jung-gu, Daejeon 301-829. **T:** 82 42 2201114
W: http://www.joongdoilbo.co.kr
Freq: Daily; **Circ:** 102554 Not Audited
Editor: Jae-Heon Choi; **Editor in Chief:** Hyung-Joong Kim; **Publisher:** Won-Sik Kim; **Editor:** Eun-Nam Kwon; **Editor:** Seung-Gyu Lee; **Editor in Chief:** Ki-Sung Park
Editorial Profile: Provides news on current issues.
Language (s): Korean
DAILY NEWSPAPER

Kangwon Domin Ilbo

Editorial: Kangwon Dominilbo, 257-27 Hupyeong 1-dong, Chuncheon 200-707.
T: 82 33 2609000 **E:** namoo@kado.net
W: http://www.kado.net
Freq: Daily; **Circ:** 122807 Not Audited
Publisher: Hyung-Soon Ahn; **Editor in Chief:** Nam-Woo Heo; **Editor:** Chang-Sung Namgung
Editorial Profile: Provides news on current issues.
Language (s): Korean
DAILY NEWSPAPER

Kangwon Ilbo

Editorial: Kwnews Corporation, 53 Jungang-no, 1-ga, Chuncheon 200-705.
T: 82 33 2581114
E: webmaster@kwnews.co.kr
W: http://www.kwnews.co.kr
Freq: Daily; **Circ:** 128008 Not Audited
Publisher: Seung-Ik Choi; **Editor:** Seok-Mahn Kim; **Editor:** Hyun Namgung
Editorial Profile: Provides news on current issues.
Language (s): Korean
DAILY NEWSPAPER

Kids Hankook Ilbo

Editorial: Hankooki.com, 15/F, Hanjin Building., Seoul 100-770. **T:** 82 2 7242402
W: http://kids.hankooki.com
Freq: 2 Times/Week
Editor in Chief: Hoon-Ku Im
Editorial Profile: Provides news on games, sports, entertainment, education, etc for children.
Language (s): Korean
NEWSPAPER

Kiho Ilbo

Editorial: Kiho Ilbo, Jungsan Building, 343-1, Icheon 402-816. **T:** 82 32 7610004
E: webmaster@kihoilbo.co.kr
W: http://www.kihoilbo.co.kr
Freq: Daily
Editor in Chief: Myung-Byung Chae; **Publisher:** Kang-Hun Seo
Editorial Profile: Provides news on current issues.
Language (s): Korean
DAILY NEWSPAPER

Kookje Shinmun

Editorial: Kookje Shinmun, 4~7/F, Kookje Shinmun Building, Busan 611-071.
T: 82 51 5005114 **E:** webmaster@kookje.co.kr
W: http://www.kookje.co.kr
Freq: Daily
Editor in Chief: In-Suk Ahn; **Editor:** Sang-Do Jung; **Publisher:** Suk-Koo Song
Editorial Profile: Provides news on current issues.
Language (s): Korean
DAILY NEWSPAPER

Korea Daily Labor News

Editorial: Labor Today, 607 Byucksan Digital Valley 5-cha, Seoul 153-788. **T:** 82 2 3646900
E: seok@labortoday.co.kr
W: http://www.labortoday.co.kr
Freq: Daily
Publisher: Seong-Guk Bak
Editorial Profile: Provides news on current issues, including politics, economy, government and labor.
Language (s): Korean
DAILY NEWSPAPER

Korea Economic Daily

Editorial: Hankook Kyungje Shinmun, Hankook Kyungje Shinmunsa Building, Seoul 100-791. **T:** 82 2 3604114
E: heeju@hankyung.net
W: http://www.hankyung.com
Freq: Daily; **Circ:** 1000008 Not Audited
Editor: Kim Gi-ung; **Editor in Chief:** Young-Min Jeong; **Editor:** Hong-Jo Kim; **Editor:** Jeong-Ho Kim; **Editor:** Kwang-Cheol Ko; **Editor:** Jeong-Hwan Lee; **Editor:** Hee-Soo Moon; **Editor:** Ki-Seol Yun
Editorial Profile: Provides news on current issues, economy, politics, government and business.
Language (s): Korean
DAILY NEWSPAPER

Korea Financial Times

Editorial: The Korea Financial Times, 6/F, Dadong Building, Seoul 100-180.
T: 82 2 7736300 **E:** webmaster@fntimes.com
W: http://www.fntimes.com
Freq: 2 Times/Week; **Circ:** 50006 Not Audited
Editorial Profile: Provides news on finance.
Language (s): Korean
NEWSPAPER

Korea Herald

Editorial: Herald Media Inc., 3-5Fl, 1-17 Jeong-dong, Jung-gu, Seoul 100-120.
T: 82 2 7270205 **E:** khnews@heraldcorp.com
W: http://www.koreaherald.com
Freq: Daily
Editor in Chief: Sung-Woo Cheon; **Editor:** Min-Hee Kim; **Editor:** Dong-hyun Min
Editorial Profile: Provides news on current issues, politics, economy, business and finance.
Language (s): English
DAILY NEWSPAPER

Korea Medical News

Editorial: Medical Newspaper Co. Limited., 610-1, Jungkok-dong, Kwangjin-gu, Seoul 143-220. **T:** 82 2 4675671
E: webmaster@bosa.co.kr
W: http://www.bosa.co.kr
Freq: 2 Times/Week; **Circ:** 40009 Not Audited
Editor: Jeong-Yoon Lee; **Publisher:** Yeon-Jun Park; **Editor:** Young-Jin Yoon
Editorial Profile: Provides news on medical manufacturing resources, medical technology, and medical equipment.
Language (s): Korean
NEWSPAPER

Korea Metal Journal

Editorial: The Korea Metal Journal Co., Limited., 5~7/F KMJ Building, Seoul 137-870.
T: 82 2 5834161 **E:** webmaster@kmj.co.kr
W: http://www.kmj.co.kr
Freq: 2 Times/Week
Publisher: Jeong-Woon Bae; **Editor in Chief:** Byung-Seon Hwang
Editorial Profile: Provides news on metal industry.
Language (s): Korean
NEWSPAPER

Korea Taxation Times

Editorial: Korea Taxation Times, 201-33, Dongkyo-dong, Mapo-gu, Seoul 100-042.
T: 82 2 3381132 **E:** chg@taxtimes.co.kr
W: http://www.taxtimes.co.kr
Freq: 2 Times/Week; **Circ:** 15008 Not Audited
Editorial Profile: Provides news on taxation.
Language (s): Korean
NEWSPAPER

Korea Textile News

Editorial: 440-15 Seogyo-dong, Mapo-gu, Seoul 121-841. **T:** 82 2 3263600
E: yhlee@ktnews.com
W: http://www.ktnews.co.kr
Freq: 2 Times/Week
Publisher: Si-Joong Kim
Editorial Profile: Provides news about textile industry in Korea.
Language (s): Korean
NEWSPAPER

Korea Times
T: 82 2 7242340 **E:** kt@koreatimes.co.kr
W: http://www.koreatimes.co.kr
Freq: Daily
Editor: Jae-Hyun Cho; **Editor:** Ji-Su Kim; **Editor:** Jong-Chan Kim; **Editor in Chief:** Hee-Soon Lee; **Editor:** Kap-Su Lee; **Editor:** Charles Sherman
Editorial Profile: Provides news on current issues and politics, economy, finance and more.
Language (s): English
DAILY NEWSPAPER

Korea Times - New York Bureau
Editorial: United Nations, Room S-342, New York, New York 10017. **T:** 1 212 869-8484
Editorial Profile: This is the New York bureau of Korea Times, based in Seoul, South Korea.
Language (s): Korean
DAILY NEWSPAPER

Kukmin Ilbo
Editorial: Kukminilbo, 5/F, Kookmin Daily News Building., Seoul 150-968.
T: 82 2 7819341 **W:** http://www.kukinews.com
Freq: Daily
Editorial Profile: Provides news on current issues.
Language (s): Korean
DAILY NEWSPAPER

Kunsul Kyungje
Editorial: The Builders Daily, 12/F, Construction Center, Seoul 135-010.
T: 82 2 5475081 **W:** http://www.cnews.co.kr
Freq: Daily
Editorial Profile: Provides news on current issues focusing on business, technology, social issues, economy and politics.
Language (s): Korean
DAILY NEWSPAPER

Kwangju Daily
Editorial: Kwangju Daily, 1-21 Ku-dong, Nam-gu, Gwangju 503-020. **T:** 82 62 3610100
W: http://www.kjdaily.com
Freq: Daily; **Circ:** 10657 Not Audited
Publisher: Won-Wook Kim; **Editor:** Young-Soon Kim; **Editor:** Kyung-Su Lee; **Editor:** Sung-Soo Oh
Editorial Profile: Provides news on current issues focusing on politics and economy.
Language (s): Korean
DAILY NEWSPAPER

Kwangju Ilbo
Editorial: Kwangju Ilbosa, Mudeung Building., Gwangju 501-711. **T:** 82 62 2228111
E: kwangju@kwangju.co.kr
W: http://www.kwangju.co.kr
Freq: Daily; **Circ:** 200008 Not Audited
Publisher: Jin-Young Kim; **Editor:** Jong-Tae Lee
Editorial Profile: Provides news on current issues.
Language (s): Korean
DAILY NEWSPAPER

Kyeonggi Ilbo
Editorial: Kyeonggiilbo Co., Limited., Gyeonggi Daily News Building., Suwon 440-703.
T: 82 31 2503300 **E:** mylee@kgib.co.kr
W: http://www.kgib.co.kr
Freq: Daily
Editor: Haeng-Yun Heo; **Editor:** Geun-Ho Jeong; **News Editor:** Il-Hyung Jeong; **News Editor:** Jong-Hyun Lee; **Publisher:** Chang-Ki Shin
Editorial Profile: Provides news on current issues.
Language (s): Korean
DAILY NEWSPAPER

Kyeongin Ilbo
Editorial: Kyeongin Ilbo, Gyeongin Daily News Building., Suwon 442-702. **T:** 82 31 2315114
E: ehkim@kyeongin.com
W: http://www.kyeongin.com
Freq: Daily
Editor: Sang-Rok Bae; **Editor:** Woo-Young Choi; **Editor in Chief:** Min-Young Oh; **Editor:** Young-Mi Shim; **Publisher:** Kwang-Seok Song; **Editor:** Jae-Jun Yun
Editorial Profile: Provides news on current issues.
Language (s): Korean
DAILY NEWSPAPER

Kyeongin Maeil
Editorial: Kyeongin Maeil, 201 Shinpoong-dong, Paldal-gu, Suwon 442-040.
T: 82 31 2580114 **E:** webmster@kmaeil.com
W: http://www.kmaeil.com
Freq: Daily
Editor in Chief: Cha-Ju Cho; **Publisher:** Kye-Jung Lee
Editorial Profile: Provides news on current issues.
Language (s): Korean
DAILY NEWSPAPER

Kyongbuk Ilbo
Editorial: The Kyongbuk Ilbo, 579-12 Sangdo-dong, Nam-gu, Pohang 790-828.
T: 82 54 2892262 **E:** kb@kyongbuk.co.kr
W: http://www.kyongbuk.co.kr
Freq: Daily; **Circ:** 135007 Not Audited
Publisher: Jeong-Hwa Jeong
Editorial Profile: Provides news that are happening its region.
Language (s): Korean
DAILY NEWSPAPER

Kyongbuk Maeil
Editorial: Kyongbuk Maeil Co., Limited., 60-14, 1-ga, Dongbin-dong, Pohang 791-060.
T: 82 54 2417112 **E:** jtlee@kbmaeil.com
W: http://www.kbmaeil.com
Freq: Daily; **Circ:** 45007 Not Audited
Publisher: Ki-Ho Kim; **Editor:** Chang-Hyung Lee; **Editor:** Jun-Taek Lee
Editorial Profile: Provides news on business, sports, social issues, etc.
Language (s): Korean
DAILY NEWSPAPER

Kyongnam Domin Ilbo
Editorial: Kyongnam Domin Ilbo Co., Limited., 151-25, Yangdeok 2-dong, Masan 630-811.
T: 82 55 2500141 **W:** http://www.idomin.com
Freq: Daily; **Circ:** 75008 Not Audited
Publisher: Jung-Do Huh
Editorial Profile: Provides news on business, sports, entertainment, technology, social issues, etc.
Language (s): Korean
DAILY NEWSPAPER

Kyongnam Ilbo
Editorial: Kyongnam Ilbo, 237-4 Sangpyeong-dong, Jinju 660-729. **T:** 82 55 7511044
E: gnnews@gnnews.co.kr
W: http://www.gnnews.co.kr
Freq: Daily
Editor: Joong-Ki Han; **Publisher:** In-Tae Hwang; **Editor in Chief:** Mahn-Seok Jeong; **Editor:** Young-Hyo Jung
Editorial Profile: Provides news on current issues on politics, social issues, economiy, etc.
Language (s): Korean
DAILY NEWSPAPER

Kyongnam Shinmun
Editorial: The Kyongnam Shinmun, 100-5, Sinwol-dong, Changwon 641-701.
T: 82 55 2832211 **E:** knnews@knnews.co.kr
W: http://www.knnews.co.kr
Freq: Daily
Editor: Yoon-Je Cho; **Editor:** Choong-Ho Heo; **Editor:** Jae-Ik Kim; **Editor:** Myung-Hyun Kim; **Publisher:** Soon-Bok Lee
Editorial Profile: Provides news on current issues, politics, economy, entertainment, sports, etc.
Language (s): Korean
DAILY NEWSPAPER

Kyunggi Shinmun
Editorial: Kyunggi Shinmun, 255-19 Yeonmu-dong, Jangan-gu, Suwon 440-814.
T: 82 31 2688114 **E:** lkj1@kgnews.co.kr
W: http://www.kgnews.co.kr
Freq: Daily
Editor: Min-Soo Jeong; **Editor in Chief:** Kyung-Jae Lee; **Publisher:** Se-Ho Park; **Editor:** Kye-Tack Yum
Editorial Profile: Provides news on current issues.
Language (s): Korean
DAILY NEWSPAPER

Kyunghyang Shinmun
Editorial: Kyunghyang.com, Kyunghyang Shinmun Building., Seoul 100-702.
T: 82 2 37011114 **E:** webmaster@khan.co.kr
W: http://www.khan.co.kr
Freq: Daily; **Circ:** 1800007 Not Audited
Editor: Ho-Yeon Cho; **Editor in Chief:** Ki-Seong Kang; **Editor:** Bu-Won Kwon; **Editor:** Hak-Soo Moon; **Editor:** Jong-Sung Park
Editorial Profile: Provides news on current issues on politics, economy, business, sports, etc.
Language (s): Korean
DAILY NEWSPAPER

Kyungsang Ilbo
Editorial: Kyungsang Ilbo, 299-10, Mugeo-dong, Nam-gu, Ulsan 680-190.
T: 82 52 2200530 **E:** webmaster@ksilbo.co.kr
W: http://www.ksilbo.co.kr
Freq: Daily
Editor: Chang-Sik Kim; **Editor in Chief:** Sung-Kil Kim; **Editor in Chief:** Ae-Jung Lee; **Editor:** Jae-Myung Lee; **Publisher:** Won-Ho Shin
Editorial Profile: Provides news on current issues.
Language (s): Korean
DAILY NEWSPAPER

Law Times
Editorial: The Lawtimes Co., Limited., 14/F, Gangnam Building, 1321-1, Seoul 137-070.
T: 82 2 34720604
E: webadmin@lawtimes.co.kr
W: http://www.lawtimes.co.kr
Freq: 2 Times/Week
Editor in Chief: Yeon-Su Shin
Editorial Profile: Provides news about laws.
Language (s): Korean
NEWSPAPER

Maeil Business Newspaper
Editorial: Maeil Business Newspaper, 30 Pil-dong 1-ga, Jung-gu, Seoul 100-728.
T: 82 2 20002114 **E:** mkmaster@mk.co.kr
W: http://www.mk.co.kr
Freq: Daily
Publisher: Dae-Hwan Jang; **Editor:** Jong-Young Kim; **Editor:** Gyu-Jun Lim; **Editor:** Jae-Hyun Park; **Editor:** Im-Ho Shin; **Editor:** Hyung-Sik Yoon; **Editor:** Ku-Hyun Yoon
Editorial Profile: Provides news on investing, stocks and savings.
Language (s): Korean
DAILY NEWSPAPER

Maeil Shinmun
Editorial: Maeil Shinmunsa, 26 Seosungro, Jung-gu (71 Kyesan 2 ga), Daegu 700-715.
T: 82 53 2555001 **E:** edit@imaeil.com
W: http://www.imaeil.com
Freq: Daily; **Circ:** 350008 Not Audited
Editor: Hyang-Rae Cho; **Editor:** Byung-Seon Park
Editorial Profile: Provides news on general issues.
Language (s): Korean
DAILY NEWSPAPER

Metro Daily
Editorial: Metro Seoul Holdings Inc., 1-141 Sinmunno 2-ga, Jongno-gu, Seoul 110-062.
T: 82 2 7219822
W: http://www.metroseoul.co.kr
Freq: Daily; **Circ:** 400008 Not Audited
Publisher: Seung-Jong Kim; **Editor in Chief:** Young-Do Seo
Editorial Profile: Provides news on current issues.
Language (s): Korean
DAILY NEWSPAPER

Money Today
Editorial: Money Today, 3/F, Cheongkye 11 Building, Seoul 110-726. **T:** 82 2 7247700
W: http://stock.mt.co.kr
Freq: Daily
Editor: Won-Bae Chae; **Publisher:** Seon-Keun Hong; **Editor:** Ho-Byung Kang; **Editor:** Seung-Je Lee; **Editor:** Hyung-Ki Park
Editorial Profile: Provides news on investing, money and the stock market.
Language (s): Korean
DAILY NEWSPAPER

Moodeung Ilbo
Editorial: The Moodeung Ilbo, 7/F, BYC Building., 1180, Gwangju 502-827.
T: 82 62 6067760 **E:** zmd@chol.com
W: http://www.honam.co.kr
Freq: Daily
Publisher: Young-Jun Jeon; **Editor:** Jong-Seok Kim; **Editor in Chief:** Seung-Yong Kim; **Editor:** Jong-Ju Lee
Editorial Profile: Provides current news on economy, politics, business, sports, etc.
Language (s): Korean
DAILY NEWSPAPER

Munhwa Ilbo
Editorial: Munhwa Ilbo, Munhwa Ilbosa, Seoul 100-723. **T:** 82 2 37015114
E: opinion@munhwa.co.kr
W: http://www.munhwa.com
Freq: Daily; **Circ:** 500008 Not Audited
Editor in Chief: Joong-Hong Choi; **Editor:** Byung-Jik Kim; **Editor:** Seung-Hyun Kim; **Publisher:** Byung-Kyu Lee; **Editor:** Hyun-Jong Lee; **Editor:** Ae-Ri Oh
Editorial Profile: Provides news on current issues.
Language (s): Korean
DAILY NEWSPAPER

Naeil Shinmun
Editorial: Naeil Shinmoon, Naeil Shinmoon Building, Seoul 110-062. **T:** 82 2 22872300
E: tech@naeil.com **W:** http://www.naeil.com
Freq: Daily; **Circ:** 2170009 Not Audited
Editor: Chan-Su Ahn; **Publisher:** Myung-Kook Jang; **Editor:** Jin-Beom Park
Editorial Profile: Provides news on current issues of politics, government, economy, business, finance, etc.
Language (s): Korean
DAILY NEWSPAPER

WORLD NEWS MEDIA

Namdo Ilbo
Editorial: The Namdo Ilbo, Namdo Ilbosa, 541-4, Gwangju 503-774. **T:** 82 62 6701023
E: webmaster@namdonews.com
W: http://www.namdonews.com
Freq: Daily; **Circ:** 100007 Not Audited
Editor: Ik-Hee Kim; **Publisher:** Seong-Ho Park; **Editor:** Kwang-Ho Shin
Editorial Profile: Provides news on current issues.
Language (s): Korean
DAILY NEWSPAPER

Nodong Ilbo
Editorial: Nodong Ilbo, 30-2 Yeouido-dong, Yeongdeungpo-gu, Seoul 150-010.
T: 82 2 7820204 **E:** kim@nodongilbo.com
W: http://www.nodongilbo.com
Freq: Daily; **Circ:** 150007 Not Audited
Editorial Profile: Provides news on domestic and international events, especially in the field of labor.
Language (s): Korean
DAILY NEWSPAPER

Nongmin Shinmun
Editorial: The Farmers Newspaper, National Agricultural Cooperative Federation, Seoul 110-121. **T:** 82 2 37036114
E: master@nongmin.com
W: http://www.nongmin.com
Freq: 2 Times/Week; **Circ:** 330007 Not Audited
Publisher: Won-Byung Choi; **Editor in Chief:** Myung-Han Kim; **Editor:** Jun-Keol Ryu
Editorial Profile: Provides news about agriculture.
Language (s): Korean
NEWSPAPER

Pharmaceutical Industry News
Editorial: Yakup Shinmun Inc., 98-1 Chongpa-dong, 2-ga, Seoul 140-734. **T:** 82 2 32700144
E: webmaster@yakup.co.kr
W: http://www.yakup.com
Freq: 2 Times/Week; **Circ:** 38006 Not Audited
Publisher: Yong-Heon Hahm
Editorial Profile: Provides news on pharmaceutical industry.
Language (s): Korean
NEWSPAPER

Segye Ilbo
Editorial: Saegye Ilbo, Saegye Ilbo, 63-1, Seoul 140-740. **T:** 82 2 20001234
E: webmaster@segye.com
W: http://www.segye.com
Freq: Daily; **Circ:** 600009 Not Audited
Editor: Hyun-Cheol Park
Editorial Profile: Provides news on politics, economy, finance, current issues, etc.
Language (s): Korean
DAILY NEWSPAPER

Seoul Economic Daily
Editorial: Internethankookilbo, 9~11/F, Chungmuro Tower, Seoul 100-013.
T: 82 2 7242114 **E:** webmaster@sedaily.com
W: http://economy.hankooki.com
Freq: Daily
Editor: Hee-Jae Cho; **Editor:** Keum-Hee Kang; **Editor in Chief:** Jong-Seo Kim; **Editor in Chief:** Jeong-Beop Lee; **Publisher:** Jong-Keon Lim
Editorial Profile: Provides news on economic, politics, technology, current issues, sports, entertainment, etc.
Language (s): Korean
DAILY NEWSPAPER

Seoul Shinmun
Editorial: Seoul Shinmunsa, 33 Taepyung-ro, Jung-gu, Seoul 100-745. **T:** 82 2 20009000
E: webmaster@seoul.co.kr
W: http://www.seoul.co.kr
Freq: Daily; **Circ:** 700007 Not Audited
Editor: Byung-Cheol Joo; **Editor:** Tae-Heon Kwak; **Editor:** Chan-Hee Ryu
Editorial Profile: Provides the news on the current issues.
Language (s): Korean
DAILY NEWSPAPER

Sports Chosun
Editorial: Sports Chosun, Sports Chosun, 923-14 Mok 1-dong, Seoul 158-178.
T: 82 2 32198114

W: http://www.sportschosun.com
Freq: Daily; **Circ:** 443008 Not Audited
Publisher: Won Ha; **Editor:** Yong-Pyo Kim;
Editor in Chief: Yeo-Kwang Yoon
Editorial Profile: Provides news on current issues and sports.
Language (s): Korean
DAILY NEWSPAPER

Sports Hankook
Editorial: Hankook Ilbo, 6/F, Hanjin Bldg Bonkwan, Seoul 100-770. **T:** 82 2 7321001
W: http://sports.hankooki.com
Freq: Daily
Editor in Chief: Byung-Chang Choi; **Editor:** Jeong-Sik Kwon; **Publisher:** Jin-Yeol Park
Editorial Profile: Provides news on sports and celebrities.
Language (s): Korean
DAILY NEWSPAPER

Sports Khan
Editorial: Kyunghyang Shinmunsa, Kyunghyang Shinmun Building., Seoul 100-702. **T:** 82 2 37011271
W: http://sports.khan.co.kr
Freq: Daily
Publisher: Young-Jae Ko; **Editor in Chief:** In-Seok Shim
Editorial Profile: Provides news on sports, celebrities, etc.
Language (s): Korean
DAILY NEWSPAPER

Sports Seoul Daily
Editorial: Sports Seoul Daily Co., Limited., 5/F, Block 1, ACE hitech city, 55-20, Seoul 150-972. **T:** 82 2 20010021
E: woosdad@sportsseoul.com
W: http://www.sportsseoul.com
Freq: Daily
Editor: Hee-Young Kim; **Editor in Chief:** Sung-Jin Kim; **Editor:** Jeong-Eun Seong
Editorial Profile: Provides news on sports and celebrities.
Language (s): Korean
DAILY NEWSPAPER

Sports Today
Editorial: 8~9/F Kaya Venture Building, 28~130, Youngdeungpo-dong-2-ga, Seoul 150-900. **T:** 82 2 20020305
W: http://www.stoo.com
Freq: Daily; **Circ:** 500007 Not Audited
Editor: Dong-Hoi Ku; **Publisher:** Jeong-Woo Lee; **Editor:** Yang-Su Park; **Editor in Chief:** Yong-Hwan Yun
Editorial Profile: Provides news on entertainment including celebrities, games and sports.
Language (s): Korean
DAILY NEWSPAPER

Sports World
Editorial: Saegye Ilbo, The Segye Times, 63-1, Seoul 140-740. **T:** 82 2 20001829
W: http://www.sportsworldi.com
Freq: Daily
Editor: Won-Ik Cho; **Editor:** Yong-Mo Kang
Editorial Profile: Provides news on sports and entertainment.
Language (s): Korean
DAILY NEWSPAPER

Standup Korea Times
Editorial: Hankook Ilbo Co, Ltd, 15/F, Hanjin Bldg, Seoul 100-770. **T:** 011 82 27242114
Freq: Daily
Editorial Profile: Covers politics, the economy, society and international news.
Language (s): English
DAILY NEWSPAPER

Transportation News
Editorial: The Transportation News, 6/F, Gyotongshinmunsa Building, Seoul 137-803. **T:** 82 2 5952982 **W:** http://www.gyotongn.com
Freq: 2 Times/Week; **Circ:** 10009 Not Audited
Editor in Chief: Young-Seok Lee; **Publisher:** Young-Rak Yoon
Editorial Profile: Provides news on transportation and traffic industry.
Language (s): Korean
NEWSPAPER

Travel Times
Editorial: The Korea Travel Times Co., Limited., 5/F, Daehan Cheyukhoi Building., Seoul 100-170. **T:** 82 2 7578980
E: tktt@traveltimes.co.kr
W: http://www.traveltimes.co.kr
Freq: 2 Times/Week; **Circ:** 55008 Not Audited
Editor in Chief: Ki-Nam Kim
Editorial Profile: Provides news on traveling.
Language (s): Korean
NEWSPAPER

Ulsan Maeil
Editorial: Ulsan Maeil Shinmunsa, 2/F, Rivertown Building., Ulsan 680-814.
T: 82 52 2431001 **E:** hoon9632@hanmail.net
W: http://www.ulsanmaeil.co.kr
Freq: Daily
Publisher: Kil-Nam Jeong; **Editor:** Young-Soo Kim
Editorial Profile: Provides news on current issues that are happening in both locally and internationally.
Language (s): Korean
DAILY NEWSPAPER

The Wall Street Journal (Korea South)
Editorial: Yonhap News Agency, 85-1 Susong-Dong, Chongno-u, Seoul. **T:** 82 2 1-2416-2000
Bureau Chief: Alastair Gale
DAILY NEWSPAPER

Yeongnam Ilbo
Editorial: Yeongnam Ilbo, 111 Sincheon-dong, Dong-gu, Daegu 701-750. **T:** 82 53 7568001
E: master@yeongnam.com
W: http://www.yeongnam.com
Freq: Daily
Publisher: Seong-Ro Bae; **Editor in Chief:** Jeong-Rae Cho; **Editor:** Jong-Chul Choi; **Editor:** Do-Hyuk Won
Editorial Profile: Provides news on current issues.
Language (s): Korean
DAILY NEWSPAPER

NEWS SERVICE/SYNDICATE

Associated Press
Editorial: 85-1 Fusong, Jongro-ku, Ste 603, Seoul 1110-140. **T:** 82 2 721-0551
E: apseoul@ap.org
NEWS SERVICE/SYNDICATE

Bloomberg News
Editorial: 139 Sjong-Ro Chongro-Ju Dong-A, Ilbo Media Center Building 15-F, Seoul 110-110. **T:** 82 237021600
Bureau Chief: Brett Miller
NEWS SERVICE/SYNDICATE

Dow Jones Newswires
Editorial: Envus Business Plaza #1712, Jongro Tower, Chongno-gu, Seoul. **T:** 82 2 21982230
Bureau Chief: Alastair Gale
NEWS SERVICE/SYNDICATE

Newsis
Editorial: Newsis, 7/F, Seowon Building, Seoul 110-310. **T:** 82 2 7217400
E: news@newsis.com
W: http://www.newsis.com
Editor: Young-Ki Park; **Editor:** Se-Jin Yu
Editorial Profile: covers national and international news.
Language (s): Korean
NEWS SERVICE/SYNDICATE

Reuters
Editorial: Kwanghwamoon Bldg, Fl 14, 64-8 Taepyungro 1 Ka, Chungku, Seoul 100-101.
T: 82 2 37045500
E: seoul.newsroom@thomsonreuters.com
Bureau Chief: David Chance
NEWS SERVICE/SYNDICATE

Yonhap English News
Editorial: Yonhap News, 85-1, Susong-dong, Jongno-gu, Seoul 110-140. **T:** 82 2 3983114
E: english@yonhapnews.co.kr
W: http://english.yonhapnews.co.kr
Freq: Daily
Editor: In-Chol Kim; **Editor:** Seung-Ji Kwok
Editorial Profile: covers international and national news.
Language (s): English
NEWS SERVICE/SYNDICATE

Yonhap News Agency
Editorial: Yonhap News, 85-1, Susong-dong, Jongno-gu, Seoul 110-140. **T:** 82 2 3983114
E: master@yonhapnews.co.kr
W: http://www.yonhapnews.co.kr
Freq: Daily
Editor: Kyung-Sook Hyun; **Editor:** Oh-Yeon Kwon; **Editor:** Byung-Hoon Moon
Editorial Profile: Articles cover international and local news.
Language (s): Korean
NEWS SERVICE/SYNDICATE

KUWAIT	**Tel: 965**
Standard Time: GMT +3	
Continent: Asia	
Capital City: Kuwait City	

NEWSPAPERS & PUBLICATIONS

NEWSPAPERS

Alam Al-Yawm
Owner: National Media Group For Publishing and Distribution
Editorial: B44 Sector, Free Zone, Shuwaikh.
T: 965 2461 3333 **E:** info@alamalyawm.com
W: http://www.alamalyawm.com
Freq: Daily; **Circ:** 90000 Pub Statement
Editorial Profile: Alam Al-Yawm (Today's World) is a daily Arabic national newspaper covering local and international news, politics, business and sport. It launched in 2007.
Language (s): Arabic
DAILY NEWSPAPER

Al Anba
Owner: Bab Al-Kuwait Press Company
Editorial: PO Box 23915, Main Building, Press Street, Safat 13100. **T:** 965 2227 2829
E: editorial@alanba.com.kw
W: http://www.alanba.com.kw
Freq: Daily; **Circ:** 92817 Rate Card
Editor In Chief: Yousef Al-Marzouk
Editorial Profile: Al Anba (The News) is a daily Arabic newspaper covering local and international news, business, finance, sport and features. It launched in 1976.
Language (s): Arabic
DAILY NEWSPAPER

Annahar
Owner: Dar Annahar for Publishing & Distribution
Editorial: PO Box 900, Safat 15251.
T: 965 183 2020 **E:** annahar@annaharkw.com
W: http://www.annaharkw.com
Freq: Daily; **Circ:** 35000 Pub Statement
Editorial Profile: Annahar is a daily Arabic newspaper covering local and international news, politics, business, sport, society and health. It launched in 2007.
Language (s): Arabic
DAILY NEWSPAPER

Arab Times
Owner: Dar Al Seyassah Press Printing & Publishing (WLL)
Editorial: PO Box 2270, Airport Road, Shuwaikh, Safat 13023. **T:** 965 2481 3566
E: arabtimes@arabtimesonline.com
W: http://www.arabtimesonline.com
Freq: Daily; **Circ:** 82659 Pub Statement
Editor-in-Chief: Ahmed Al Jarallah; **News Editor:** Yacoub Zubrim
Editorial Profile: Arab Times is a daily, broadsheet-sized, English newspaper covering local and international news, business, finance, sports, features and classified advertisements. It launched in 1977.
Language (s): English
DAILY NEWSPAPER

Gulf Madhyamam - Kuwait edition
Owner: Gulf Madhyamam FZ LLC
Editorial: PO Box 20867, Safat 13069.
T: 965 97 957790
E: kuwait@gulfmadhyamam.net
W: http://www.gulfmadhyamam.net
Freq: Daily; **Circ:** 21500 Rate Card
Editorial Profile: Gulf Madhyamam is an international Indian newspaper covering national and international news, current affairs, politics, business and sport. The newspaper is aimed at Malayalam speakers in the Gulf and publishes separate editions for the UAE, Saudi Arabia (Riyadh, Jeddah, Damam & Abha), Qatar, Oman, Bahrain and Kuwait. The newspaper was first published in 1999.
Language (s): Malayalam
DAILY NEWSPAPER

Huna Al Kuwait
Owner: SPIN Media
Editorial: First Floor, Mansour Building, Kuwait City. **T:** 965 97 764555 **E:** info@hunakwt.com
W: http://www.hunakwt.com
Freq: Daily; **Circ:** 260000
News Editor: Ahmad Farouq
Editorial Profile: Huna Al Kuwait is a newspaper covering national and international news, business and sport. The newspaper launched in 2012 and is published daily, except Fridays.
Language (s): Arabic

DAILY NEWSPAPER

Al Jarida
Owner: Al Jarida for Printing and Publishing
Editorial: PO Box 29846, Souad Commercial Complex, Safat 13159. **T:** 965 2225 7030
E: mail@aljarida.com
W: http://www.aljarida.com
Freq: Daily; **Circ:** 39100 Pub Statement
Editor In Chief: Khaled Al Mutairi
Editorial Profile: Al Jarida is a daily Arabic newspaper covering local and international news, sport, business and politics. It was first published in 2007.
Language (s): Arabic
DAILY NEWSPAPER

Al Khaleej Newspaper
Owner: Al Jabriya Kuwaiti Group for Journalism & Publishing
Editorial: PO Box 25725, 21 Behbehani Building, Street 65, Safat 13118.
T: 965 2243 3765
E: alkhaleej-newspaper@hotmail.com
W: http://www.alkhaleej-kw.com
Freq: Tue; **Circ:** 45000 Pub Statement
Editorial Profile: Al Khaleej Newspaper (The Gulf Newspaper) is an Arabic weekly covering local and international news, business, sports and culture. It launched in 2009 and is published on Tuesdays.
Language (s): Arabic
NEWSPAPER

Kuwait Times
Owner: Kuwait Times Publishing House
Editorial: PO Box 1301, Safat 13014.
T: 965 2483 3199 **E:** info@kuwaittimes.net
W: http://www.kuwaittimes.net
Freq: Daily; **Circ:** 45000 Pub Statement
Editor In Chief: Abd Al-Rahman Alyan
Editorial Profile: Kuwait Times is a daily, broadsheet-sized English newspaper covering local news, business, finance, sport and features. It was first published in 1961.
Language (s): English
DAILY NEWSPAPER

Al Kuwaityah
Owner: Kuwaiti Awraq Company For Advertising Services
Editorial: PO Box 42444, Sahafa Street, Shuwaikh. **T:** 965 2226 9888
E: info@alkuwaityah.com
W: http://www.alkuwaityah.com
Freq: Daily; **Circ:** 40000
Editor in Chief: Madi Al Khamisi; **News Editor:** Eid El Fadli
Editorial Profile: Al Kuwaityah is a daily Arabic newspaper covering national and international news, business, culture and sport. It was first published in June 2011.
Language (s): Arabic
DAILY NEWSPAPER

Al Qabas
Owner: Dar Al Qabas Press, Printing and Publishing
Editorial: PO Box 21800, Safat 13078.
T: 965 2481 2822 **E:** editor@alqabas.com.kw
W: http://www.alqabas.com.kw
Freq: Daily; **Circ:** 81000 Pub Statement
Editor-in-Chief: Waleed Al Nusuf
Editorial Profile: Al Qabas is a daily Arabic newspaper covering national and international news, business, finance, politics, culture and sport. It was first published in 1972.
Language (s): Arabic
DAILY NEWSPAPER

Al Rai
Owner: AlRai Media Group Company K.S.C.
Editorial: PO Box 761, Safat 13008.
T: 965 2481 7777 **E:** editor@alraimedia.com
W: http://www.alraimedia.com
Freq: Daily; **Circ:** 93000 Pub Statement
Editor In Chief: Majed Al Ali
Editorial Profile: Al Rai is a daily Arabic newspaper covering news, business, finance, sports, features and classified advertisements. The newspaper launched in 1961, and was previously called Al Rai Al Aam.
Language (s): Arabic
DAILY NEWSPAPER

Al Resala
Owner: Dar Al Resala for Press, Printing & Publishing
Editorial: PO Box 2490, Safat 13025.
T: 965 2483 4201 **E:** info@al-resalapress.com
W: http://www.resalah.com.kw
Freq: Mon; **Circ:** 23750 Pub Statement
Editor In Chief: Marzouk Al Jassem
Editorial Profile: Al Resala is a weekly Arabic newspaper covering culture, entertainment, politics and economics. It launched in 1961 and is published on Mondays.

Language (s): Arabic
NEWSPAPER

Al Sabah

Owner: Assabah for Press, Publishing & Distribution
Editorial: PO Box 588, Safat 13006.
T: 965 2455 4950
E: editorial@alsabahpress.com
W: http://www.alsabahpress.com
Freq: Daily; Circ: 28000 Pub Statement
Editor In Chief: Barakat Al-Hedeiban
Editorial Profile: Al Sabah (The Morning) is a daily, broadsheet-sized Arabic newspaper covering national and international news, politics, sports and business. It launched in 2008.
Language (s): Arabic
DAILY NEWSPAPER

Al Seyassah

Owner: Dar Al Seyassah Press Printing & Publishing (WLL)
Editorial: PO Box 2270, Airport Road, Shuwaikh, Safat 13023. T: 965 2481 3566
E: alseyassah@alseyassah.com
W: http://www.alseyassah.com
Freq: Daily; Circ: 112856 Pub Statement
Editor In Chief: Ahmed Al Jarallah; News Editor: Osama Srour
Editorial Profile: Al Seyassah (Politics) is a daily Arabic newspaper covering news, business, finance, sports, features and classified advertisements. It was first published in 1968.
Language (s): Arabic
DAILY NEWSPAPER

Al Shahed

Owner: Dar Al Kuwaitiya for Media
Editorial: PO Box 42122, 11th & 12th Floor, Hussein Makki Jumaa Son's Build, Safat 70652. T: 965 2245 7300
E: info@alshahedkw.com
W: http://www.alshahedkw.com
Freq: Daily; Circ: 45000 Pub Statement
Editor In Chief: Sabah Al-Sabah
Editorial Profile: Al Shahed (The Witness) is a daily Arabic newspaper covering news, politics, business and sport. It launched in 2001.
Language (s): Arabic
DAILY NEWSPAPER

Al Shahed Al-Isbouya

Owner: Dar Al Kuwaitiya for Media
Editorial: PO Box 4856, 11th & 12th Floor, Hussein Makki Jumaa Son's Build, Safat 70652. T: 965 2245 7300
E: info@alshahedkw.com
W: http://www.alshahed.com.kw
Freq: Sat; Circ: 45000
Editor In Chief: Sabah Al-Sabah
Editorial Profile: Al Shahed Al-Isbouya is the Saturday edition of Al Shahed newspaper and covers news, politics, business and sport. It launched in 2001 and is published on Saturdays.
Language (s): Arabic
NEWSPAPER

Al Taleea

Owner: Al Taleea for Printing & Publishing
Editorial: PO Box 1082, Press Street, Airport Road, Safat 13011. T: 965 2484 7207
E: altaleea62@hotmail.com
W: http://altaleea.com
Freq: Wed; Circ: 7000 Pub Statement
Editor In Chief: Abdallah Al Nibari
Editorial Profile: Al Taleea is a weekly Arabic newspaper covering national and international news, current affairs, politics and business. It launched in 1962 and is published on Wednesdays.
Language (s): Arabic
NEWSPAPER

Al Wasat

Owner: Dar Al-Akhbar Printing, Publishing and Distribution
Editorial: PO Box 26541, Building D2, Free Commercial Zone, Safat 13126.
T: 965 2464 5100 E: editorial@alwasat.com.kw
W: http://www.alwasat.com.kw
Freq: Daily; Circ: 40000 Pub Statement
Editor In Chief: Adnan Al Wazan; News Editor: Mazen Kharaba
Editorial Profile: Al Wasat is a daily Arabic newspaper covering local and international news, politics, business and sport. It launched in 2007.
Language (s): Arabic
DAILY NEWSPAPER

Al Watan

Owner: Dar Al Watan Press, Printing and Publishing

Editorial: PO Box 1142, Press Street, Shuwaikh, Safat 13012. T: 965 182 2255
E: locals@alwatan.com.kw
W: http://www.alwatan.com.kw
Freq: Daily; Circ: 70000 Pub Statement
Editor in Chief: Khalifa Al-Sabah
Editorial Profile: Al Watan is a daily Arabic newspaper covering news, business, finance, sports, features and classified advertisements. The newspaper launched in 1974.
Language (s): Arabic
DAILY NEWSPAPER

NEWS SERVICE/SYNDICATE

Kuwait News Agency

Owner: Kuwait News Agency
Editorial: PO Box 24063, Safat 13101.
T: 965 2483 6577 E: sources@kuna.net.kw
W: http://www.kuna.net.kw
Editor in Chief: Saeed Al-Ali
Editorial Profile: Official government news agency founded in 1976.
Language (s): Arabic
NEWS SERVICE/SYNDICATE

Reuters - Kuwait Bureau

Owner: Thomson Reuters
Editorial: PO Box 5616, Safat 13057.
T: 965 2228 3660
E: ahmed.hagagy@thomsonreuters.com
W: http://www.reuters.com
Editorial Profile: Kuwait bureau of International news agency supplying news - text, graphics, video and pictures - to subscribers around the world.
Language (s): Arabic
NEWS SERVICE/SYNDICATE

BROADCASTING

RADIO STATIONS

Kuwait FM

Owner: Ministry of Information, Kuwait
Editorial: PO Box 193, Safat 13002.
T: 965 2241 8730 E: arabicfm@radio.gov.kw
W: http://www.media.gov.kw
Editorial Profile: Kuwait FM is a state-owned radio station broadcasting modern Arabic songs 24-hours a day. It launched in 1995 and transmits on 103.7 FM.

Radio Kuwait - Classical Arabic Music Station

Owner: Ministry of Information, Kuwait
Editorial: PO Box 193, Safat 13002.
T: 965 2232 6268 E: ramilovera@gmail.com
W: http://www.media.gov.kw
Editorial Profile: Radio Kuwait's Classical Arabic Music Station plays local, Gulf and classical Arabic songs for 24-hrs a day, in addition to live broadcast of youth-orientated programmes. This station launched in July 1993 and broadcasts on 87.9 FM.

Radio Kuwait - Main Arabic Programme

Owner: Ministry of Information, Kuwait
Editorial: PO Box 193, Safat 13002.
T: 965 2244 2781 E: s_r_1955@yahoo.com
W: http://www.media.gov.kw
Editorial Profile: Radio Kuwait's Main Arabic Programme is a state-owned radio station broadcasting drama, news, entertainment, literary, scientific, family and children's programmes 24-hrs a day, in addition to programmes developed in cooperation with authorities and ministries in the country. The station launched in 1951 and broadcasts on 89.5 FM.

Radio Kuwait - Second Arabic Programme

Owner: Ministry of Information, Kuwait
Editorial: PO Box 193, Safat 13002.
T: 965 2244 2684 E: a13aa@hotmail.com
W: http://www.media.gov.kw
Editorial Profile: Radio Kuwait's Second Arabic Programme is a state-owned radio station broadcasting programmes of local character, in addition to songs, musical and guidance programmes. The station launched in 1964 and broadcasts for 15 hours per day, from 07:00 to 00:00, on 97.5 FM. Programmes are designed to be relevant to issues of concern to society, and include prominent activities and services undertaken by institutions and authorities, with particular focus on serving local heritage and folklore.

KYRGYZSTAN   Tel: 996

Standard Time: GMT +5
Continent: Asia
Capital City: Bishkek

NEWSPAPERS & PUBLICATIONS

NEWSPAPERS

Delo No

Owner: Delo No
Editorial: Ul. Frunze 282a, Bishkek 720011.
T: 996 312 68 21 36 E: delonom@ktnet.kg
W: http://delo.ktnet.kg Circ: 21000 Pub Statement
Editor: Viktor Michaylovich Zapolskiy
Editorial Profile: Newspaper focusing on national and international news, politics, social events and legal issues, lifestyle issues.
Language (s): Russian
DAILY NEWSPAPER

MK World Weekly

Owner: Inter pressa
Editorial: ul. Usenbayeva 26, Bishkek 720021.
T: 996 312 68 21 72 E: mk@elcat.kg
W: http://www.mk.kg Circ: 7000 Pub Statement
Editor In Chief: Dilbar Borisovets
Editorial Profile: National newspaper with socio-political news.
Language (s): Russian
DAILY NEWSPAPER

MSN

Editorial: Ul. Usenbayeva 2, Bishkek 720021.
T: 996 312 68 25 73 E: city@infotel.kg
W: http://www.msn.kg
Freq: 2 Times/Week; Circ: 3000 Pub Statement
Editor In Chief: Alexander Kim
Editorial Profile: Social-political and informative-entertaining newspaper.
Language (s): Russian
NEWSPAPER

Slovo Kyrgyzstana

Owner: Slovo Kyrgyzstana
Editorial: ul. Abdumomunova 193, Bishkek 720040. T: 996 312 62 20 45
E: slovo@infotel.kg W: http://www.sk.kg
Freq: 2 Times/Week; Circ: 10000 Pub Statement
Editor-in-Chief: Tamara Slasheva
Editorial Profile: National informative - analytical newspaper covering politics, economy, social events, culture, education and sport.
Language (s): Russian
NEWSPAPER

The Times of Central Asia

Owner: Central Asia Media Institut
Editorial: ul. Abdrahmanova 175a, Bishkek 720000. T: 996 312 66 17 37
E: edittimes@timesca.kg
W: http://www.timesca.com Circ: 5000 Pub Statement
Publisher: Giorgio Fiacconi; Editor: Sergey Hvat
Editorial Profile: Newspaper focusing on Central Asian news, politics, economics, society, defence and tourism.
Language (s): English
DAILY NEWSPAPER

Vecherniy Bishkek

Owner: Publishing house "Vecherniy Bishkek"
Editorial: Ul. Usenbaeva 2, Bishkek 720021.
T: 996 312 68 21 21 E: webmaster@vb.kg
W: http://www.vb.kg
Freq: Daily; Circ: 8000 Pub Statement
News Editor: Evgeniy Denisenko; Editor-in-Chief: Kuzmin Gennadiy Alexandrovich
Editorial Profile: Newspaper covering national and international news, politics, economy, culture, social events and sport.
Language (s): Russian
DAILY NEWSPAPER

NEWS SERVICE/SYNDICATE

Kabar

Editorial: ul. Abrakhmanova 175, Bishkek.
T: 996 312 62 05 74 E: s1@kabar.gov.kg
W: http://www.kabar.kg
Editor In Chief: Boris Arabayev
Editorial Profile: Providing daily updated news in Russian, English, Turkish and Kyrgyz languages.
Language (s): Kyrgyz
NEWS SERVICE/SYNDICATE

News Agency AKIPress

Editorial: ul. Moskovskaya 189, Bishkek.
T: 996 312 61 03 96 E: admin@akipress.org
W: http://www.akipress.org
News Editor: Alina Saginbayeva
Language (s): Kyrgyz
NEWS SERVICE/SYNDICATE

BROADCASTING

RADIO NETWORKS

Auto Radio

Editorial: Ul. Ahunbaeva 119 A, Bishkek 720055. T: 996 312 56 50 57
E: autoradio@infotel.kg
Editorial Profile: National radio station with music and news. Broadcasts 60% of music in Russian language and 40% international.

Hit FM

Editorial: Prospekt Chui 36 (13th floor), Bishkek 720065. T: 996 312 68 10 56
E: advert@hitfm.kg W: http://www.hitfm.kg
Editorial Profile: National radio station with news and pop music.

Kyrgyzskoye radio

Editorial: Pr. Molodaya Gvardiya 59, Bishkek 720040. T: 996 312 65 66 39
E: alatoo@netmail.kg W: http://www.ktr.kg
Editorial Profile: National radio station covering daily news, economics and politics.

Radio TRP Piramida

Editorial: ul. Zhantosheva 70, Bishkek 720005.
T: 996 312 51 15 50 E: mar_log@mail.ru
Editorial Profile: National private radio station with news and music.

TELEVISION STATIONS

NTRK

Editorial: Pr. Molodaya Gvardia 59, Bishkek 720040. T: 996 312 65 66 39 E: aatc@ktr.kg
W: http://www.ktr.kg
Editorial Profile: National state TV station with news, documentaries, films and entertainment.

NTS

Editorial: ul. Tokombayeva 46a, Bishkek 720028. T: 996 312 51 23 59 E: info@nts.kg
W: http://www.nts.kg
Editorial Profile: National TV station broadcasting news, films, entertainment programmes and series.

TRP Piramida

Editorial: ul. Zhantosheva 70, Bishkek 720005.
T: 996 312 51 15 50 E: mar_log@mail.ru
Editorial Profile: Private national TV station with informative and entertaining programmes.

LAOS   Tel: 856

Standard Time: GMT +7
Continent: Asia
Capital City: Vientiane

NEWSPAPERS & PUBLICATIONS

NEWSPAPERS

Khao Kila

Owner: Lao National Sports Committee
Editorial: Lao National Sports Committee, National Stadium, Vientiane. T: 856 21 252909
E: khaokila@hotmail.com
W: http://www.laosportnsc.com
Freq: Daily; Circ: 3002 Not Audited
Editor in Chief: Suksakhone Sipraseuth
Editorial Profile: Sports and Entertainment related issues.
Language (s): Lao
DAILY NEWSPAPER

Lao Patthana

Editorial: Lao News Agency, 80 Setthatirath Road, P.O. Box 3770, Vientiane.
T: 856 21 251090 E: kplnews@yahoo.com
W: http://www.kpl.net.la
Freq: Daily
Editor in Chief: Khemthong Sanoubane
Editorial Profile: Focuses on local and national news.
Language (s): Lao
DAILY NEWSPAPER

Pasaxon Newspaper
Editorial: Pasaxon Newspaper, 66 Sethathirath Road, P.O. Box 1110, Vientiane.
T: 856 21212466 **E:** infonews@pasaxou.org.la
W: http://www.pasaxon.org.la
Freq: Daily; **Circ:** 7502 Not Audited
Editorial Profile: Covers news.
Language (s): Lao
DAILY NEWSPAPER

Pasaxon Van Ar-thit
Editorial: Pasaxon Newspaper, 66 Setthathirath Road, P.O. Box 1110, Vientiane.
T: 856 21212466 **E:** infonews@pasaxon.org.la
W: http://www.pasaxon.org.la
Freq: Weekly; **Circ:** 2002 Not Audited
Editorial Profile: Covering news and general interests.
Language (s): Lao
NEWSPAPER

Le Renovateur
Editorial: Vientiane Times, Pangkham Street, P.O. Box 8706, Vientiane. **T:** 856 21217872
E: lerenovateur@hotmail.com
W: http://www.lerenovateur.org.la
Freq: Weekly; **Circ:** 2002 Not Audited
Editor: Khamphout Xayasomroth
Editorial Profile: Covers social issues, culture and related details.
Language (s): French
NEWSPAPER

Vientiane Mai
Editorial: Setthathirath Road, Baan Chungyin, P.O. Box 989, Vientiane. **T:** 856 21212623
E: webmaster@vientianemai.net
W: http://www.vientianemai.net
Freq: Daily; **Circ:** 3502 Not Audited
Editor: Somphet Inthisane
Editorial Profile: Covers government and private companies.
Language (s): Lao
DAILY NEWSPAPER

Vientiane Times
Editorial: Vientiane Times, Pangkham Street, P.O. Box 5723, Vientiane. **T:** 856 21 21 63 64
E: info@vientianetimes.org.la
W: http://www.vientianetimes.org.la
Freq: 2 Times/Week; **Circ:** 3002 Not Audited
Editor in Chief: Savankhone Razmountry;
Editor: Panyasith Thammavongsa
Editorial Profile: Covers news topics.
Language (s): English
NEWSPAPER

NEWS SERVICE/SYNDICATE

Khaosan Pathet Lao (KPL)
Owner: Lao News Agency
Editorial: Lao News Agency, 80 Setthathirath Road, P.O. Box 3770, Vientiane.
T: 856 21215402 **E:** kplcab@laonet.net
W: http://www.kpl.net.la
Freq: Daily
Editor in Chief: Sinhpangna Rattanavong
Editorial Profile: Covers news.
Language (s): Lao
NEWS SERVICE/SYNDICATE

BROADCASTING

RADIO STATIONS

Lao National Radio
Editorial: Lao National Radio, Ban Srisakate Village, Phynam Road, P.O. Box 310, Vientiane. **T:** 856 21 243250
E: laonradio@lnr.org.la **W:** http://www.lnr.org.la
Editorial Profile: Covers news and other topics for Laos.

TELEVISION STATIONS

Lao National Television
Editorial: Lao National Television, P.O. Box 5635, Sivilay Village, Saythany District, Vientiane. **T:** 856 21 710067
E: tnlinfo@tnl.gov.la **W:** http://www.tnl.gov.la
Editorial Profile: Covers of news and general interests.

LATVIA Tel: 371

Standard Time: GMT +2
Continent: Europe
Capital City: Riga

NEWSPAPERS & PUBLICATIONS

NEWSPAPERS

The Baltic Times
Owner: Baltic News Ltd
Editorial: Rupniecibas 1-5, Riga 1050.
T: 371 6 722 99 78
W: http://www.baltictimes.com **Circ:** 12000 Pub Statement
Editor-in-Chief: Dorian Ziedonis
Editorial Profile: Newspaper focusing on current political and social events, business, finance and culture in Estonia, Latvia and Lithuania.
Language (s): English
DAILY NEWSPAPER

Bizness & Baltija
Owner: SIA B&B Redakcija
Editorial: Kr. Valdemara 149, Riga 1013.
T: 371 6 70 33 047 **E:** bb@bb.lv
W: http://www.bb.lv
Freq: Daily; **Circ:** 12000 Pub Statement
Editor In Chief: Alexey Scherbakov
Editorial Profile: Full colour broadsheet-sized newspaper focusing on business and finance in the Baltics.
Language (s): Russian
DAILY NEWSPAPER

Diena
Owner: SIA Laikraksts Diena
Editorial: Mukusalas iela 15, Riga 1004.
T: 371 70 63 100 **E:** diena@diena.lv
W: http://www.diena.lv
Freq: Daily; **Circ:** 31500 Pub Statement
Editor-in-Chief: Gatis Madžinš
Editorial Profile: Broadsheet-sized newspaper focusing on national and international news, politics, business, culture and sport.
Language (s): Latvian
DAILY NEWSPAPER

Dienas Bizness
Owner: SIA Dienas bizness
Editorial: Terbatas 30, Riga 1011.
T: 371 70 84 400 **E:** editor@db.lv
W: http://www.db.lv
Freq: Daily; **Circ:** 12000 Pub Statement
Editor-in-Chief: Gatis Madžinš
Editorial Profile: Tabloid-sized newspaper focusing on business, finance and economics. In addition to daily business news and commentary, it publishes regular supplements on construction and real estate, new technologies, education, employment market and cars.
Language (s): Latvian
DAILY NEWSPAPER

Latvijas Avize
Owner: A/S Lauku Avize
Editorial: AS Lauku Avize, Dzirnavu iela 21, Riga 1010. **T:** 371 67096600 **E:** redakcija@la.lv
W: http://www.la.lv
Freq: Daily Pub Statement
Editor In Chief: Linda Rasa; **News Editor:** Guntis Šcerbinskis
Editorial Profile: National conservative newspaper focusing on national and international news, business and economics, politics, culture and sport.
Language (s): Latvian
DAILY NEWSPAPER

Latvijas Vestnesis
Owner: Latvijas Vestnesis VU
Editorial: Bruninieku 36 - 2, Riga 1011.
T: 371 7 29 88 33 **E:** oskars.gerts@lv.lv
W: http://www.vestnesis.lv
Freq: Daily; **Circ:** 3500 Pub Statement
Editor-in-Chief: Oskars Gerts
Editorial Profile: Broadsheet-sized newspaper produced by the Government, containing legislative information, national and international news, politics and economics.
Language (s): Latvian
DAILY NEWSPAPER

Neatkariga Rita Avize
Owner: SIA Mediju Nams
Editorial: Cesu iela 31 - 2, Riga.
T: 371 78 86 801 **E:** redakcija@nra.lv
W: http://www.nra.lv
Freq: Daily; **Circ:** 35000 Pub Statement
Editor-in-Chief: Anita Daukšte
Editorial Profile: Broadsheet-sized newspaper focusing on national and international news, politics, business and sport.
Language (s): Latvian
DAILY NEWSPAPER

Vesti Segodnya
Owner: SIA Mediasistema
Editorial: Peldu iela 15, Riga LV-1050.
T: 371 6 7088698 **E:** redakcija@vesti.lv
W: http://vesti.lv
Freq: Daily; **Circ:** 74000 Pub Statement
Editor In Chief: Alexsandr Blinov
Editorial Profile: Broadsheet-sized newspaper focusing on national and international news, politics, business and sport.
Language (s): Russian
DAILY NEWSPAPER

NEWS SERVICE/SYNDICATE

LETA News Agency
Editorial: 2 Marijas Street, Riga 1050.
T: 371 67222509 **E:** redaktori@leta.lv
W: http://www.leta.lv
News Editor: Peteris Rugainis; **Editor:** Janis Silakalns
Editorial Profile: LETA is a full service information agency, offering operative, top quality, objective and current information about developments in Latvia, the Baltic States and the world, and furnishes informative services for the mass media, state institutions, business organizations and companies.
Language (s): English
NEWS SERVICE/SYNDICATE

BROADCASTING

TELEVISION STATIONS

TV3 Latvia
Editorial: Maskavas 322, Riga Lv- 1063.
T: 371 76 29 366 **E:** tv3@tv3.lv
W: http://www.tv3.lv
Editorial Profile: National TV station broadcasting form Viaset 3 satellite and received throughout Latvia.

TV5 Riga
Editorial: Elijas iela 17, Riga Lv- 1050.
T: 371 75 03 924 **E:** info@tv5.lv
W: http://www.tv5.lv
Editorial Profile: National TV station focusing on news and reality shows, also broadcasting films and TV serials mostly in Russian language.

LEBANON Tel: 961

Standard Time: GMT +2
Continent: Asia
Capital City: Beirut

NEWSPAPERS & PUBLICATIONS

NEWSPAPERS

Al Akhbar
Owner: Akhbar Beyrouth S.A.L
Editorial: PO Box 113-5963, 6th Floor, Concorde Centre, Beirut. **T:** 961 1 759500
E: mail@al-akhbar.com
W: http://www.al-akhbar.com
Freq: Daily; **Circ:** 16500 Pub Statement
Editor: Omar Nashabe; **News Editor:** Nicolas Nassif
Editorial Profile: Al Akhbar (The News) is a tabloid-sized Arabic newspaper covering local and international news, business, culture and sport. It launched in 2006 and is published daily, except Sundays.
Language (s): Arabic
DAILY NEWSPAPER

Albalad
Owner: Integra Publishing & Marketing Solutions s.a.l.
Editorial: PO Box 116-5360, 2nd Floor, Freeway Centre, Beirut 2058. **T:** 961 1 518500
E: albaladnews@albaladonline.com
W: http://www.albaladonline.com
Freq: Daily; **Circ:** 60000 Rate Card
Editorial Profile: Albalad (The Country) is a tabloid-sized Arabic newspaper covering national and international news, current affairs, politics, business, lifestyle, sport and entertainment. It launched in 2003 and is published daily, except Sundays.
Language (s): Arabic
DAILY NEWSPAPER

An-Nahar
Owner: An Nahar s.a.l
Editorial: PO Box 11226, An Nahar Building, Beirut 2014. **T:** 961 1 994888
E: annahar@annahar.com.lb
W: http://www.annahar.com
Freq: Daily; **Circ:** 45000 Pub Statement
Editor: Ali Hamade
Editorial Profile: An-Nahar is a daily Arabic newspaper covering national and international news, current affairs, politics, business, economy, sport and entertainment. It was first published in 1933.
Language (s): Arabic
DAILY NEWSPAPER

Al Anwar
Owner: Dar Assayad S.A.L
Editorial: PO Box 11-1038, Hazmieh, Beirut.
T: 961 5 456374 **E:** alanwar@alanwar.com
W: http://www.alanwar.com
Freq: Daily; **Circ:** 49043 Rate Card
News Editor: George Berberi; **Editor In Chief:** Michel Raad
Editorial Profile: Al Anwar (The Lights) is a daily Arabic newspaper covering national and international news, current affairs, politics, business, sport and entertainment. It was first published in 1959.
Language (s): Arabic
DAILY NEWSPAPER

Ararad Newspaper
Owner: Massif Society
Editorial: PO Box 175275, Riachi Building, 5th Sector, Beirut. **T:** 961 1 867199
E: aharonshekerdemian@gmail.com
W: http://www.araraddaily.com
Freq: Daily; **Circ:** 3000 Pub Statement
Editor in Chief: Aharon Shekerdemian
Editorial Profile: Ararad Newspaper is a daily newspaper aimed at the Armenian population in Lebanon, and covers news, politics, Armenian issues, economics, education, culture and sport. It is the official journal of the Social Democrat Hunchak Party and launched in 1937.
Language (s): Armenian
DAILY NEWSPAPER

Asharq Al-Awsat - Beirut office
Owner: Saudi Research & Publishing Co.
Editorial: 11th Floor, Bourj El Ghazal Building, Achrafieh, Beirut. **T:** 961 1 218701
E: beirut@asharqalawsat.com
W: http://www.aawsat.com
Freq: Daily
Bureau Chief: Thaer Abbas
Editorial Profile: Beirut bureau of Asharq Al-Awsat newspaper. The Beirut office covers news, business and sport from Lebanon for the London-based newspaper which is distributed across the Arab world.
Language (s): Arabic
DAILY NEWSPAPER

As-Safir
Owner: Dar As Safir
Editorial: PO Box 113-5015, Mneimneh Street, Beirut. **T:** 961 1 350080
E: coordinator@assafir.com
W: http://www.assafir.com
Freq: Daily; **Circ:** 30000 Pub Statement
Editor in Charge: Ghasseb Al Mokhtar; **News Editor:** Hussein Ayoub; **Editor in Chief:** Talal Salman
Editorial Profile: As-Safir (The Ambassador) is an Arabic newspaper covering national and international news, current affairs, politics, business and sport. It launched in 1974 and is published daily, except Sundays.
Language (s): Arabic
DAILY NEWSPAPER

Attamaddon
Owner: Dar Al-Bilad Printing and Media
Editorial: PO Box 90, Al Awkaf Building, Tripoli. **T:** 961 6 441164
E: attamaddon@hotmail.com
W: http://www.attamaddon.com
Freq: Wed; **Circ:** 5000 Pub Statement
Courts Editor: Salim Al Namel; **News Editor:** Khidir Al Sabeen
Editorial Profile: Attamaddon is a weekly Arabic newspaper focusing on local politics, news and current affairs. It launched in 1933 and is published on Wednesdays.
Language (s): Arabic
NEWSPAPER

Aztag Daily
Owner: AZTAG Armenian Daily Company
Editorial: PO Box 80-860, Shaghzoyan Cultural Centre, Beirut. **T:** 961 1 258526
E: info@aztagdaily.com

W: http://www.aztagdaily.com
Freq: Daily; **Circ:** 8000 Pub Statement
News Editor: Arsho Balain; **Editor-in-Chief:** Shahan Kandaharian; **News Editor:** Nora Parseghian
Editorial Profile: Aztag Daily is an Armenian newspaper covering national and international news, current affairs, politics, business, sports and entertainment. It launched in 1927, and is aimed at the Armenian community in Lebanon. The newspaper also includes Aztag Magazine, a monthly magazine supplement covering lifestyle and family issues.
Language (s): Armenian
DAILY NEWSPAPER

Aztag Daily - New York Bureau
Owner: AZTAG Armenian Daily Company
Editorial: 315 E 70th St, 3a 3a, New York, New York 10021-8657. **T:** 1 212 737-7809
Language (s): English
DAILY NEWSPAPER

Al Binaa
Owner: Al Qawmiyah Media Company
Editorial: Al Mizan Building, Al Hamra Street, Beirut. **T:** 961 1 748920 **E:** info@al-binaa.com
W: http://www.al-binaa.com
Freq: Daily; **Circ:** 4000 Pub Statement
Editor in Chief: Kamil Khalil
Editorial Profile: Al Binaa is a daily Arabic newspaper covering national and international news, politics, business, society and sport. It was first published in 1958.
Language (s): Arabic
DAILY NEWSPAPER

The Daily Star
Owner: The Daily Star
Editorial: PO Box 11-987, 3rd Floor, Markaziah Building, Beirut. **T:** 961 1 985311
E: editorial@dailystar.com.lb
W: http://www.dailystar.com.lb
Freq: Daily; **Circ:** 12500 Rate Card
News Editor: Kristin Dailey; **Editor In Chief:** Nadim Ladki
Editorial Profile: The Daily Star is an English newspaper covering national, regional and international news, current affairs, politics, business, arts and culture, sport and entertainment. It launched in 1952 and is published daily, except Sundays.
Language (s): English
DAILY NEWSPAPER

Ad Diyar
Owner: Al Nahdah Publishing
Editorial: PO Box 40-300, Baabda, Beirut. **T:** 961 5 923830 **E:** info@addiyaronline.com
W: http://www.addiyaronline.com
Freq: Daily; **Circ:** 14000 Pub Statement
Editor-in-Chief: Charles Ayoub
Editorial Profile: Ad Diyar is a daily Arabic newspaper covering national and international news, current affairs, politics, business, sport and entertainment. It launched in 1988.
Language (s): Arabic
DAILY NEWSPAPER

Al Hayat - International edition
Owner: Dar Al Hayat
Editorial: PO Box 11-1242, Dar Al Hayat Building, Beirut. **T:** 961 1 987990
E: information@alhayat.com
W: http://www.daralhayat.com
Freq: Daily; **Circ:** 107370 Rate Card
News Editor: Najia Al Hussari; **Editor in Chief:** Ghassan Charbel; **Bureau Chief:** Zouheir Kseibati
Editorial Profile: The International edition of Al Hayat covers national and international news, current affairs, politics, business, sports and entertainment. The newspaper is based in London and Beirut, and also publishes separate editions in Saudi Arabia. It was first published in 1946.
Language (s): Arabic
DAILY NEWSPAPER

Immar Wa Iktissad
Owner: Immar Wa Iktissad
Editorial: PO Box 6517/113, Al Sanobra Building, Beirut. **T:** 961 1 392444
E: info@immarwaiktissad.com
W: http://www.immarwaiktissad.com
Freq: Bi-Weekly; **Circ:** 15000 Pub Statement
Editor in Chief: Hassan Moukalled
Editorial Profile: Immar Wa Iktissad is a fortnightly Arabic business newspaper covering economics and trade. The 16-page tabloid-sized newspaper launched in 1993 and is issued on alternate Fridays.
Language (s): Arabic
NEWSPAPER

Al Joumhouria
Owner: Al Joumhouria News Corp Company S.A.L
Editorial: PO Box 90152-1202, 5th & 6th Floor, Al Amara Building, Metn 2020.
T: 961 1 888051 **E:** info@aljoumhouria.com
W: http://www.aljoumhouria.com
Freq: Daily; **Circ:** 15000 Pub Statement
Editor In Chief: Georges Soulage; **News Editor:** Tarek Tarchichi
Editorial Profile: Al Joumhouria (The Republic) is a tabloid-sized Arabic newspaper covering national and international news, politics, business, sport, entertainment and society. It launched in 2011.
Language (s): Arabic
DAILY NEWSPAPER

El Kalima
Owner: Al Zahliya for Advertising & Publishing Est.
Editorial: 3rd Floor, Al Riyachi and Chouwairi Building, Hay Al Midan, Zahle.
T: 961 8 805750 **E:** info@el-kalima.com
W: http://www.el-kalima.com
Freq: Fri; **Circ:** 2000 Pub Statement
Editor in Chief: Eid Al Ashkar
Editorial Profile: El Kalima (The Word) is a weekly Arabic newspaper covering national and international news, current affairs, politics, business and sport. It launched in 2000 and is published on Fridays.
Language (s): Arabic
NEWSPAPER

Al Liwaa
Owner: Dar Al Liwaa for Press & Publishing s.a.r.l
Editorial: PO Box 11-2402, 2nd Floor, Saredar Building, Beirut. **T:** 961 1 751000
E: aliwaanewspaper@gmail.com
W: http://www.aliwaa.com
Freq: Daily; **Circ:** 20000 Pub Statement
Editorial Profile: Al Liwaa is an Arabic newspaper covering national and international news, current affairs, business, politics, social issues, entertainment and sport. It launched in 1963 and is published daily, except Sundays.
Language (s): Arabic
DAILY NEWSPAPER

Al Mustaqbal
Owner: Arab United Press s.a.l.
Editorial: PO Box 14-5426, Ansoli Building, Al Sanae'a, Beirut. **T:** 961 1 746301
E: almustaqbal@almustaqbal.com.lb
W: http://www.almustaqbal.com
Freq: Daily; **Circ:** 26000 Rate Card
Editor In Chief: Hani Hammoud; **Legal Editor:** Kassem Khalifeh
Editorial Profile: Al Mustaqbal is a daily Arabic newspaper covering national and international news, current affairs, politics, business and sports. It launched in 1999.
Language (s): Arabic
DAILY NEWSPAPER

L' Orient Le Jour
Owner: Société Générale de Presse et d'Edition SAL
Editorial: PO Box 45-254, L'Orient le Jour Building, Beirut. **T:** 961 5 956444
E: redaction@lorientlejour.com
W: http://www.lorientlejour.com
Freq: Daily; **Circ:** 18000 Pub Statement
Editor in Chief: Nagib Aoun; **News Editor:** Elie Fayad
Editorial Profile: L'Orient Le Jour is a French newspaper covering national and international news, current affairs, business and politics. It was founded as L'Orient in 1925 and Le Jour in 1934 before merging in 1971 to become L'Orient-Le Jour. It is published daily, except Sundays. The newspaper includes L'Orient Littéraire, a monthly literary supplement; L'Orient Le Jour Junior, a monthly youth supplement; and bi-monthly health and beauty supplement Santé Beauté.
Language (s): French
DAILY NEWSPAPER

Al Raasmal Al Arabi
Owner: Al Raasmal Al Arabi
Editorial: PO Box 11-124, 4th Floor, Tina Center, Beirut. **T:** 961 1 737271
E: info@raasmalarabi.com
Freq: Bi-Weekly; **Circ:** 20000 Pub Statement
Editorial Profile: Al Raasmal Al Arabi (Arab Capital) is a fortnightly Arabic newspaper covering business, economics, investment, finance, banking and stock markets in the Arab world. The newspaper was first published in 1965 and is aimed at business executives.
Language (s): Arabic
NEWSPAPER

El Shark
Owner: Dar El Shark
Editorial: PO Box 11-838, 1st Floor, Centre Assaf, Beirut. **T:** 961 1 810820
E: info@elshark.com
W: http://www.elsharkonline.com
Freq: Daily; **Circ:** 34000 Rate Card
Publisher: Aouni Al Kaaki; **News Editor:** Tareq Osseibi
Editorial Profile: El Shark (The East) is an Arabic newspaper featuring news, current affairs, cultural and financial news. It launched in 1926 and is published daily, except Sundays.
Language (s): Arabic
DAILY NEWSPAPER

NEWS SERVICE/SYNDICATE

Agence France-Presse - Beirut Bureau
Owner: Agence France-Presse
Editorial: PO Box 11-1461, Building Immobiliere 209, Beirut. **T:** 961 1 730162
E: afp.beyrouth@afp.com
W: http://www.afp.com
Bureau Chief: Sammy Ketz
Editorial Profile: Beirut bureau of international news and picture agency covering general news and current affairs.
Language (s): Arabic
NEWS SERVICE/SYNDICATE

APTN Lebanon
Owner: Associated Press
Editorial: 4th Floor, Shakir Wa Ouani Building, Riyadh Al Solh Square, Beirut.
T: 961 1 988889 **E:** bhatoum@ap.org
W: http://www.aptn.com
Editorial Profile: Associated Press Television News (APTN) is the international television arm of the Associated Press - APTN's operations include a main news service, specialised broadcast services, customised coverage for the Middle East, a productions division, weekly and daily entertainment news and an extensive video archive library.
Language (s): Arabic
NEWS SERVICE/SYNDICATE

Associated Press
Editorial: Oueini & Shaker Bldg, Riad El Solh Square Fl 4, Beirut 2023 6516.
T: 961 1 985-190
Bureau Chief: Zeina Karam
NEWS SERVICE/SYNDICATE

Associated Press - Beirut Bureau
Owner: Associated Press
Editorial: PO Box 11-3780, Riyad Al Solh Square, Beirut. **T:** 961 1 985190
E: zkaram@ap.org **W:** http://www.ap.org
Bureau Chief: Zeina Karam
Editorial Profile: Beirut bureau of international news and photo agency - covers Lebanon and Syria from Beirut. It is aimed at AP subscribers around the world.
Language (s): English
NEWS SERVICE/SYNDICATE

European Pressphoto Agency - Lebanon Bureau
Owner: European Pressphoto Agency
Editorial: 5th floor, Wafa Building, Ahmad Badawi Street, Beirut. **T:** 961 3 651214
E: mounzer@epa.eu **W:** http://www.epa.eu
Bureau Chief: Nabil Mounzer
Editorial Profile: Photo agency representing 11 European news agencies (DPA, ANSA, EFE, Belga, APA, Athens News Agency, PAP, ANP, MTI, Keystone and LUSA) - covers news, politics, sports, fashion, economy, conflicts, disasters, features and business.
Language (s): English
NEWS SERVICE/SYNDICATE

National News Agency
Owner: Ministry of Information, Lebanon
Editorial: Ministry of Information, Hamra, Beirut. **T:** 961 1 754400
E: news@nna-leb.gov.lb
W: http://www.nna-leb.gov.lb
Editor in Chief: Ali Laham
Editorial Profile: Official government news agency.
Language (s): Arabic
NEWS SERVICE/SYNDICATE

Reuters
Editorial: Hibat Al Maarad Bldg, Fl 3, Riad El Solh Sq, Beirut 2011 4810. **T:** 961 1 983-839
NEWS SERVICE/SYNDICATE

Reuters - Beirut Bureau
Owner: Thomson Reuters
Editorial: PO Box 11-1006, 3rd Floor, Hibat Al Maarad Building, Beirut. **T:** 961 1 983885
E: dominic.j.evans@thomsonreuters.com
W: http://www.reuters.com
Bureau Chief: Dominic Evans
Editorial Profile: Beirut bureau of international news and picture agency.
Language (s): English
NEWS SERVICE/SYNDICATE

United Press International - Beirut Bureau
Owner: United Press International
Editorial: 6th Floor, Hyundai Building, Hamra, Beirut. **T:** 961 1 745971
E: arabic_desk@upi.com
W: http://www.upi.com
Editorial Profile: United Press International licences content directly to print outlets, online media and institutions of all types.
Language (s): Arabic
NEWS SERVICE/SYNDICATE

WORLD NEWS MEDIA

LESOTHO — Tel: 266
Standard Time: GMT +2
Continent: Africa
Capital City: Maseru

NEWSPAPERS & PUBLICATIONS

NEWSPAPERS

Public Eye
Editorial: Princess Margarett Road, Old Europa, Maseru 100. **T:** 266 22 32 14 14
E: editor@publiceye.co.ls
W: http://www.publiceye.co.ls/ **Circ:** 22565 Pub Statement
Publishing Editor: Bethuel Thai
Editorial Profile: The Public Eye is an independent forum for sharing of opinions; to understand and express popular feelings; to raise awareness of public issues; to provide information regarding development plans and methods; to aid the growth of literacy; to report development news, successes and failures; to act as watchdog on government and public organizations and to promote and protect the freedom of expression.
Language (s): English
DAILY NEWSPAPER

BROADCASTING

RADIO NETWORKS

Radio Lesotho
Editorial: PO Box 552, Maseru 100, Maseru.
T: 266 22 32 33 71
W: http://www.radiolesotho.co.ls
Editorial Profile: Talk shows based on Current Affairs, Information and educational programmes relating to agriculture, health, women's issues, law, culture and magazine programmes with music, news and sports.

LIBERIA — Tel: 231
Standard Time: GMT
Continent: Africa
Capital City: Monrovia

NEWSPAPERS & PUBLICATIONS

NEWSPAPERS

The Analyst
Owner: The Analyst Newspaper
Editorial: Carey Street - Opp. CBL, Monrovia.
T: 231 65 16 334 **E:** analystliberia@yahoo.com
W: http://www.analystliberia.com
Freq: Daily; **Circ:** 3750 Pub Statement
Publisher: Stanley Seakor; **News Editor:** Ellis Togba
Editorial Profile: National daily newspaper focussing on news, current affairs, politics, education, society and sport.
Language (s): English
DAILY NEWSPAPER

Daily Observer
Owner: Liberian Observer Corporation (LOC)
Editorial: Liberian Observer Corporation (LOC), P.O. Box 1858, Monrovia.
T: 231 7 707 4454
E: editor@liberianobserver.com

W: http://www.liberianobserver.com
Freq: Daily; **Circ:** 5000 Pub Statement
Editorial Profile: Daily newspaper focussing on news, current affairs and politics.
Language (s): English
DAILY NEWSPAPER

The Evidence
Editorial: Carrery Street, Captown Building, Monrovia. **T:** 231 6 532 309
E: evidenceliberia@islandmix.com
Freq: 2 Times/Week; **Circ:** 2500 Pub Statement
Editorial Profile: Twice-weekly newspaper focusing on news, current affairs, politics and sport.
Language (s): English
NEWSPAPER

The New Democrat
Owner: New Democrat Corporation
Editorial: Bushord Island, (Old Peugeot Garage), Monrovia. **T:** 231 7700 7529
E: info@newdemocratnews.com
W: http://newdemocratnews.com
Freq: Daily; **Circ:** 3500 Pub Statement
News Editor: Othello Garblah
Editorial Profile: National daily newspaper providing investigative, Human interest and feature articles as well as analysis.
Language (s): English
DAILY NEWSPAPER

LIBYA   Tel: 218

Standard Time: GMT +1
Continent: Africa
Capital City: Tripoli

NEWSPAPERS & PUBLICATIONS

NEWSPAPERS

Akhbar Al Aan
Owner: Tower Media Middle East FZLLC
Editorial: Al Khiam Hotel, Tripoli.
T: 218 91 387 7988 **E:** libya@alaan.tv
W: http://akhbar.alaan.tv
Freq: Fri; **Circ:** 20000 Pub Statement
Editorial Profile: Akhbar Al Aan is a weekly Arabic newspaper covering news and politics in Libya. It was launched in 2011 by the Dubai-based owners of Al Aan TV, and is published on Fridays.
Language (s): Arabic
NEWSPAPER

Brnieq
Owner: Brnieq Establishment
Editorial: 1st Floor, Military Accounts Complex, Shuab Mekka Road, Benghazi.
T: 218 92 511 8187 **E:** brnieq@yahoo.com
W: http://www.brnieq.com
Freq: 3 Times/Week; **Circ:** 5500 Pub Statement
News Editor: Ibrahim Al-Majdali; **Heritage Editor:** Mohamed Ben Hariz; **Editor In Chief:** Miftah Bouzid
Editorial Profile: Brnieq is an Arabic newspaper covering news, sports and political issues in Libya. It launched as a weekly in 2011 and is now published three times a week (Sundays, Tuesdays and Thursdays).
Language (s): Arabic
NEWSPAPER

Libya Al Jadida
Owner: Libya Al Jadida
Editorial: Aldil Street, Tripoli.
T: 218 21 363 0946 **E:** info@libyaaljadida.com
W: http://www.libyaaljadida.com
Freq: Daily; **Circ:** 10000 Pub Statement
Editor In Chief: Mahmoud El Misrati
Editorial Profile: Libya Al Jadida (New Libya) is a daily Arabic newspaper covering news, business, sport and art. It launched in 2011.
Language (s): Arabic
DAILY NEWSPAPER

Libya Alyoum
Owner: Libya AlYoum Media Establishment
Editorial: Seedi Abdul Jaleel Street, Al Humaida Area, Benghazi. **T:** 218 92 283 2585
E: npla2011@yahoo.co.uk
Freq: Wed; **Circ:** 3000 Pub Statement
Editor in Chief: Salah Al Shamikh
Editorial Profile: Libya Alyoum is a weekly Arabic newspaper covering Libyan news, politics, business and sport. It launched in 2011 and is published on Wednesdays.
Language (s): Arabic
NEWSPAPER

New Libya News
Owner: Alpha Beta Publishers and Media Consultants
Editorial: PO Box 5114, Garden City, Benghazi.
T: 218 91 764 4474
E: newlibyanews@gmail.com
W: http://www.newlibyanews.info
Freq: Mon; **Circ:** 5000 Pub Statement
Editorial Profile: New Libya News is a weekly Arabic newspaper covering news and current affairs in Libya. The editorial team is based in the United Arab Emirates. It was launched in 2011 and is published on Mondays.
Language (s): Arabic
NEWSPAPER

Quryna Al Jadida
Owner: Quryna Al Jadida
Editorial: North Benghazi Investment Club Building, Al Sahli Road, Benghazi.
T: 218 91 663 3286 **E:** info@qurynanew.com
W: http://www.qurynanew.com
Freq: Tue; **Circ:** 6000
News Editor: Rajaa Al Shaikhy; **Editor in Chief:** Fateh Elkhashmi
Editorial Profile: Quryna Al Jadida is a weekly newspaper covering news, business and sport. It launched in 2011 and is published on Tuesdays.
Language (s): Arabic
NEWSPAPER

Souq Al Joumaa
Owner: Al Muntaha Information Technology
Editorial: Al Hassan Street, Souq Al Joumaa Area, Tripoli. **T:** 218 92 706 6376
E: editor@sgnews.ly **W:** http://www.sgnews.ly
Freq: Monthly; **Circ:** 5000
Editor: Mohammad Al Mabrouk; **Editor in Chief:** Khalid Al Mughrabi; **Editor:** Rabee'a Al-Gheryani; **Editor:** Safinaz Emran
Editorial Profile: Souq Al Joumaa (Friday Market) is a monthly newspaper covering news, politics, business, sport and arts in Tripoli. It was first published in 2011 and is distributed in Tripoli.
Language (s): Arabic
NEWSPAPER

Sowt
Owner: Sowt Newspaper
Editorial: Al Mudiriya Street, Beloan Area, Benghazi. **T:** 218 92 547 5005
E: sowtnp@gmail.com
Freq: Thu; **Circ:** 3000 Pub Statement
Editorial Profile: Sowt (Voice) is a weekly Arabic newspaper covering news, politics, business, culture and society. It launched in 2011 and is published on Thursdays.
Language (s): Arabic
NEWSPAPER

The Tripoli Post
Owner: Trade, Publishing & Distribution (TPD) Ltd
Editorial: Office 32, 2nd Floor, Tripoli Tower, Tripoli. **T:** 218 21 336 2069
E: editor@tripolipost.com
W: http://www.tripolipost.com
Freq: Sat; **Circ:** 7000 Pub Statement
News Editor: Al-Adlah Al-Tomi; **Editor In Chief:** Said Laswad
Editorial Profile: The Tripoli Post is a weekly English newspaper covering Libya's politics, news, business, culture, sports and history. It launched in 1999 and is published on Saturdays.
Language (s): English
NEWSPAPER

NEWS SERVICE/SYNDICATE

Libyan News Agency
Owner: Libyan News Agency
Editorial: PO Box 2303, Zaweed Al Dahmany Street, Tripoli. **T:** 218 21 340 2606
E: lananews@yahoo.com
W: http://www.lana-news.ly
Editorial Profile: Libyan national news agency.
Language (s): Arabic
NEWS SERVICE/SYNDICATE

Reuters - Tripoli Bureau
Owner: Thomson Reuters
Editorial: 37 Al Shatt Street, Tripoli.
T: 218 21 340 3820
E: ulf.laessing@reuters.com
W: http://www.reuters.com
Editorial Profile: Tripoli bureau of the Reuters news agency - covers news and politics from Libya for a worldwide audience of subscribers to Reuters news services.
Language (s): English
NEWS SERVICE/SYNDICATE

BROADCASTING

RADIO STATIONS

Al Aan FM
Owner: Tower Media Middle East FZLLC
Editorial: Al Madina Hotel Tower, Shawki Street, Tripoli. **T:** 218 91 387 7988
E: cheikh.saleck@alaan.tv
W: http://www.alaan.fm
Editorial Profile: Al Aan FM is a radio station broadcasting news, music and entertainment programmes. It launched in 2011 and broadcasts on 105.3 FM.

LibyanaHits FM
Editorial: Alnafaq Street, Alhadaeq, Benghazi.
T: 218 91 830 0100 **E:** info@libyanahits.fm
W: http://www.libyanahits.fm
Editorial Profile: LibyanaHits FM is a radio station broadcasting music and entertainment. The station launchedin 2011 and broadcasts to Benghazi and the surrounding area on 100.1 FM.

Tribute FM
Editorial: Benghazi. **T:** 218 21 717 0222
E: info@tributefm.com
W: http://www.tributefm.com
Editorial Profile: Tribute FM is a radio station broadcasting entertainment and music. It launched in 2011 and broadcasts on 98.1 FM.

Tripoli FM 102.5
Owner: Araam Ltd
Editorial: Building 3, French School Street, Tripoli. **T:** 218 21 729 7779
E: info@tripolifm.ly **W:** http://www.tripolifm.ly
Editorial Profile: Tripoli FM 102.5 is an entertainment radio station broadcasting English music, as well as entertainment, culture and society programmes. The station launched in 2011 and broadcasts on 102.5 FM.

LIECHTENSTEIN   Tel: 423

Standard Time: GMT +1
Continent: Europe
Capital City: Vaduz

NEWSPAPERS & PUBLICATIONS

NEWSPAPERS

Liechtensteiner Vaterland
Owner: Vaduzer Medienhaus AG
Editorial: Austrasse 81, Vaduz 9490.
T: 423 236 1616 **E:** redaktion@vaterland.li
W: http://www.vaterland.li
Freq: Daily; **Circ:** 10373 Pub Statement
Redaktion Computer/EDV: Mr./Ms. Editor;
Umweltredaktion: Mr./Ms. Editor; **Chef vom Dienst:** Mr./Ms. Editor; **Redaktion Hobby/Freizeit:** Mr./Ms. Editor; **Redaktion Bildung/Erziehung:** Mr./Ms. Editor;
Unterhaltungsredaktion: Bettina Frick; **Chefredaktion:** Günther Fritz; **stellv. Chefredaktion:** Janine Köpfli; **Redakteur / Editor:** Stefan Lenherr; **Red. Medizin + Gesundheit:** Shusha Meier; **Ratgeber:** Manuela Schädler; **Unterhaltungsredaktion:** Patrick Stahl
Editorial Profile: The Liechtensteiner Vaterland is a national daily newspaper in Liechtenstein with news about politics, business, culture, sports, travel, technology and other consumer topics.
Language (s): German
DAILY NEWSPAPER

Liechtensteiner Volksblatt
Owner: Liechtensteiner Volksblatt AG
Editorial: Im alten Riet 103, Schaan 9494.
T: 42 3 2375161 **E:** redaktion@volksblatt.li
W: http://www.volksblatt.li
Freq: Daily; **Circ:** 9000 Pub Statement
EDV-Redaktion: Fritz Gauer
Editorial Profile: National daily covering politics, economics, sport, travel and the arts.
Language (s): German
DAILY NEWSPAPER

BROADCASTING

RADIO NETWORKS

Radio Liechtenstein
Owner: Radio Liechtenstein

Editorial: Dorfstr. 24, Triesen 9495.
T: 423 399 1313 **E:** redaktion@radio.li
W: http://www.radio.li
Editorial Profile: Radio station for Liechtenstein with news, music and regional information.

LITHUANIA   Tel: 370

Standard Time: GMT +2
Continent: Europe
Capital City: Vilnius

NEWSPAPERS & PUBLICATIONS

NEWSPAPERS

Atgimimas
Owner: Pilietines Minties Institutas
Editorial: T.Vrublevskio g. 6, Vilnius LT-01100. **T:** 370 5 23 13 424
E: indre@atgimimas.lt
W: http://www.atgimimas.lt **Circ:** 3000
Editorial Profile: Newspaper covering national and international politics, news, economics and culture.
Language (s): Lithuanian
DAILY NEWSPAPER

The Baltic Times
Owner: Baltic News Ltd
Editorial: Raugyklos 15, Room 302, Vilnius LT-2001. **T:** 370 5 212 15 45
E: lilija@baltictimes.com
W: http://www.baltictimes.com
Editorial Profile: Newspaper covering national and international news, business, cultural events and sport.
Language (s): English
DAILY NEWSPAPER

Kurier Wilenski
Editorial: Birbyniu g.4A, Vilnius.
T: 370 5 26 08 444 **E:** info@kurierwilenski.lt
W: http://www.kurierwilenski.lt
Freq: Daily; **Circ:** 4000 Pub Statement
Editor: Aleksander Borowik; **Editor:** Helena Gladkowska-Viteniene; **Editor In Chief:** Robert Mickiewicz
Editorial Profile: Covers national and regional news, features cultural events and social issues in Polish language.
Language (s): Polish
DAILY NEWSPAPER

Lietuvos Aidas
Owner: Lietuvos Aidas UAB
Editorial: Gedimino pr. 2, Vilnius LT-2000.
T: 370 5 26 10 544 **E:** Centr@aidas.lt
W: http://www.aidas.lt
Freq: Daily; **Circ:** 16000 Pub Statement
Editorial Profile: Newspaper covering national and international current affairs, also features cultural and sport events.
Language (s): Lithuanian
DAILY NEWSPAPER

Lietuvos Rytas
Owner: Joint Stock Company Lietuvos Rytas
Editorial: Gedimino pr 12 A, Vilnius LT-01103. **T:** 370 5 27 43 600 **E:** daily@lrytas.lt
W: http://www.lrytas.lt
Freq: Daily; **Circ:** 165000 Pub Statement
Style Editor: Giedre Bradauskiene; **Editor:** A. Budrys; **Editor-in-Chief:** Gedvidias Vainauskas
Editorial Profile: Newspaper featuring lifestyle, gardening, sports, medicine, the home, world news, travel, ecology, art and culture.
Language (s): Lithuanian
DAILY NEWSPAPER

Lietuvos Zinios
Owner: UAB Lietuvos Zinios
Editorial: Kestucio g. 4/14, Vilnius LT- 08117.
T: 370 5 249 21 52 **E:** red@lzinios.lt
W: http://www.lzinios.lt
Freq: Daily; **Circ:** 26900 Pub Statement
Editor: Vida Danileviciute; **Editor:** Birute Papartiene; **News Editor:** Raimonda Rameliene; **Editor:** Rima Razmisleviciute
Editorial Profile: Newspaper featuring news, current affairs, finance, sport and cultural events. It has got two supplement magazines: LŽ žurnalas and LŽ gidas.
Language (s): Lithuanian
DAILY NEWSPAPER

Litovskij Kurjer
Owner: Litovskij Kurjer
Editorial: Ul. Sodu 4, Vilnius LT- 03211.
T: 370 5 21 20 320 **E:** info@kurier.lt
W: http://www.kurier.lt **Circ:** 30000 Pub Statement

Editor-in-Chief: V. Tretyakov
Editorial Profile: Newspaper featuring national and regional news, covers current affairs, politics, economics, social issues, culture and sport.
Language (s): Russian
DAILY NEWSPAPER

Respublika
Owner: Respublikos leidiniai
Editorial: A. Smetonos g. 2, Vilnius LT-01115.
T: 370 5 21 21 574 **E:** press@respublika.lt
W: http://www.respublika.lt
Freq: Daily; **Circ:** 37600 Pub Statement
Editorial Profile: National daily newspaper covering politics, economics, business, social issues and entertainment.
Language (s): Lithuanian
DAILY NEWSPAPER

Verslo zinios
Owner: UAB Verslo Žinios
Editorial: Jasinskio 16 a, Vilnius LT-01112.
T: 370 5 25 26 300 **E:** info@vzinios.lt
W: http://www.verslozinios.lt
Freq: Daily; **Circ:** 12600 Pub Statement
Editor-in-Chief: Rolandas Barysas; **Market Editor:** Vytautas Žeimantas
Editorial Profile: A business daily newspaper in Lithuania which reports on major national economic and business processes and publishes foreign business news. Publishes analyses of markets and companies, covers business and political news, introduces and comments on the latest legislation.
Language (s): Lithuanian
DAILY NEWSPAPER

NEWS SERVICE/SYNDICATE

BNS News
Editorial: Jogailos g. 9/1, Vilnius LT- 01116.
T: 370 5 20 58 501 **E:** politika@bns.lt
W: http://www.bns.lt
Editor In Chief: Jurate Damulyte; **Editor:** Ingrida Gumbyte; **Editor:** Aloyzas Knabikas; **Editor:** Džolita Mikulskaite; **Editor:** Donata Motuzaite
Editorial Profile: National and international news agency providing news used by the media, private businesses, banks and the government press office. With its staff of 160 BNS distributes daily around 1,000 news items in five languages (Lithuanian, Latvian, Estonian, Russian and English).
Language (s): Lithuanian
NEWS SERVICE/SYNDICATE

ELTA
Editorial: Gedimino pr 21/2, Vilnius LT- 01103.
T: 370 5 26 28 864 **E:** zinios@elta.lt
W: http://www.elta.lt
Editor In Chief: Gražina Ramanauskaite-Tiumieneviene
Editorial Profile: News agency providing national and international news.
Language (s): Lithuanian
NEWS SERVICE/SYNDICATE

BROADCASTING

RADIO NETWORKS

Lietuvos Radijas
Editorial: S. Konarskio 49, Vilnius LT-03123.
T: 370 5 23 63 000 **E:** lrzinios@lrt.lt
W: http://www.lrt.lt
Editorial Profile: Public, non profit making radio station, broadcasting across the whole of Lithuania. Offers a variety of informative and musical programmes.

Ziniu radijas
Editorial: Laisves pr. 60, Vilnius LT-05120.
T: 370 5 24 31 430 **E:** biuras@ziniuradijas.lt
W: http://www.ziniur.lt
Editorial Profile: National radio station covering political, economical, cultural and sport news.

TELEVISION STATIONS

Baltijos TV
Editorial: Laisves pr. 60, Vilnius LT-05120.
T: 370 5 27 80 805 **E:** biuras@btv.lt
W: http://www.btv.lt
Editorial Profile: National TV station broadcasting form Vilnius and covering 80% of Lithuania.

Lietuvos Televizija
Editorial: S. Konarskio 49, Vilnius LT- 03123.
T: 370 5 23 63 209 **E:** lrt@lrt.lt
W: http://www.lrt.lt
Editorial Profile: State owned national television station, providing a variety of informative and general programmes.

LUXEMBOURG   Tel: 352
Standard Time: GMT +1
Continent: Europe
Capital City: Luxembourg

NEWSPAPERS & PUBLICATIONS

NEWSPAPERS

d'Letzebuerger Land
Owner: EDITIONS D' LETZEBURGER LAND SARL
Editorial: 59 rue Glesener, Luxembourg L-1020. **T:** 352 48 57 57 1 **E:** land@land.lu
W: http://www.land.lu
Freq: Weekly Pub Statement
Editorial Profile: Newspaper covering news and current-affairs, politics, economics and culture for Luxembourg and Europe.
Language (s): English
NEWSPAPER

D'Wort (Luxembourg)
Owner: SAINT-PAUL LUXEMBOURG SA
Editorial: 2, rue Christophe Plantin, Luxembourg L-2988. **T:** 352 49 93 1
E: wort@wort.lu **W:** http://www.wort.lu
Freq: Daily; **Circ:** 82327 Pub Statement
Editor In Chief: Marc Glesner
Editorial Profile: Broadsheet-sized quality newspaper containing national and international news, political, economic and financial information.
Language (s): French
DAILY NEWSPAPER

Lëtzebuerger Journal
Owner: EDITIONS LËTZEBURGER JOURNAL SA
Editorial: BP 2101, Luxembourg L-1021.
T: 352 49 30 331 **E:** journal@journal.lu
W: http://www.journal.lu
Freq: Daily Pub Statement
Editor In Chief: Claude Karger
Editorial Profile: Tabloid-sized quality newspaper providing political, financial and economic coverage.
Language (s): English
DAILY NEWSPAPER

Le Quotidien
Owner: EDITPRESS SA
Editorial: 44, rue du Canal, Esch Sur Alzette L-4050. **T:** 352 54 71 31
E: redaction@lequotidien.lu
W: http://www.lequotidien.lu
Freq: Daily Pub Statement
Editorial Profile: Newspaper providing local, national and international news and current-affairs; includes politics, the economy and sport.
Language (s): French
DAILY NEWSPAPER

Tageblatt - Zeitung fir Letzebuerg
Owner: EDITPRESS SA
Editorial: 44, rue du Canal, Esch Sur Alzette L-4050. **T:** 352 54 08 84 680
E: redaktion@tageblatt.lu
W: http://www.tageblatt.lu
Freq: Daily Pub Statement
Editor in Chief: Danièle Fonck; **Editor in Chief:** Alvin Sold
Editorial Profile: Tabloid-sized quality newspaper providing local, national and international news. Includes articles concerning politics, economics and the stock exchange and coverage of sporting events.
Language (s): French
DAILY NEWSPAPER

ZLV - Zeitung vum Lëtzebuerger Vollek
Owner: ZEITUNG
Editorial: 3 rue Zénon Bernard, Esch-Sur-Alzette L-4030. **T:** 352 44 60 66 1
E: info@zlv.lu **W:** http://www.zlv.lu
Freq: Daily Pub Statement
Editor In Chief: Ali Ruckert
Editorial Profile: Tabloid-sized newspaper providing local, national and international news; includes information on politics and sport. Political outlook: Left wing.
Language (s): French
DAILY NEWSPAPER

MACAU   Tel: 853
Standard Time: GMT +8
Continent: Asia

NEWSPAPERS & PUBLICATIONS

NEWSPAPERS

Macau Daily Times
Editorial: 2nd Floor 62 Av. Infante D., Macau.
T: 853 2871 6081
W: http://www.macaudailytimes.com.mo
Freq: Daily
Editor in Chief: Paulo Coutinho
Editorial Profile: Founded in 2007, covers local, national and regional news. Caters to the constant needs of today's society, keeping in mind new social, economic and political realities that Macau faces on a day-to-day basis.
Language (s): English
DAILY NEWSPAPER

MACEDONIA   Tel: 389
Standard Time: GMT +1
Continent: Europe
Capital City: Skopje

NEWSPAPERS & PUBLICATIONS

NEWSPAPERS

Dnevnik
Owner: Media Print Macedonia
Editorial: Vasil Gjorgov 16, Skopje 1000.
T: 389 2 30 89 201
E: dnevnik@dnevnik.com.mk
W: http://www.dnevnik.com.mk
Freq: Daily; **Circ:** 55000 Publisher's Statement
Editor: Mitko Biljanoski; **Editor:** Liljana Damovska; **Editor-in-Chief:** Darko Janevski
Editorial Profile: Newspaper focusing on national and international news, business, politics, culture and sport.
Language (s): Macedonian
DAILY NEWSPAPER

Makedonski Sport
Owner: Media Print Macedonia
Editorial: Vasil Gjorgov 16, Skopje 1000.
T: 389 2 323 6870
E: makedosnkisport@t-home.mk
W: http://www.sport.com.mk
Freq: Daily; **Circ:** 12000 Publisher's Statement
Editor-in-Chief: Igor Ivanovski; **Editor:** Boban Radulovik
Editorial Profile: Newspaper featuring articles on all types of sport.
Language (s): Macedonian
DAILY NEWSPAPER

Nova Makedonija
Owner: ZONIK DOOEL-Skopje
Editorial: Vasil Gjorgov 16, Skopje 1000.
T: 389 2 551 1711
E: nm@novamakedonija.com.mk
W: http://www.novamakedonija.com.mk
Freq: Daily; **Circ:** 15000 Publisher's Statement
Editor-in-Chief: Aleksandar Dimkovski
Editorial Profile: Newspaper focusing on national and international news, politics, business and sport.
Language (s): Macedonian
DAILY NEWSPAPER

Utrinski Vesnik
Owner: Media Print Macedonia
Editorial: Vasil Gjorgov 16, Skopje 1000.
T: 389 2 3236 900 **E:** vesnik@utrinski.com.mk
W: http://www.utrinski.mk
Freq: Daily; **Circ:** 25000 Publisher's Statement
Editor-in-Chief: Sonja Kramarska
Editorial Profile: Newspaper focusing on national and international news, business, politics, sport and entertainment and supplements.
Language (s): Macedonian
DAILY NEWSPAPER

Vecer
Owner: Vecer Press
Editorial: Ulica Sveti Kliment Ohridski, Skopje 1000. **T:** 389 2 321 9650
E: vecer@vecer.com.mk

W: http://www.vecer.com.mk
Freq: Daily; **Circ:** 10000 Publisher's Statement
Editor-in-Chief: Ivona Talevska
Editorial Profile: Newspaper focusing on national and international news, politics, business and sport.
Language (s): Macedonian
DAILY NEWSPAPER

NEWS SERVICE/SYNDICATE

Macedonian Information Centre
Editorial: Naum Naumovski Borce 73, Skopje 1000. **T:** 389 2 31 17 876
E: contact@micnews.com.mk
W: http://micnews.com.mk
Editorial Profile: Macedonian Information Centre is an independent news agency. MIC's primary task is providing news, information and analyses to the international community, mainly to foreign governments, foreign embassies, governmental organizations, institutes, international businesses, libraries, various research organizations, news agencies and media abroad about Macedonian politics, economy, society, religion, culture, etc.
Language (s): Macedonian
NEWS SERVICE/SYNDICATE

MIA news agency
Editorial: Bojmija K-2, Skopje 1000.
T: 389 2 24 61 600 **E:** mia@mia.com.mk
W: http://www.mia.com.mk
Editor In Chief: Ljupco Jakimoski
Editorial Profile: Macedonian Information Agency. MIA launched the first news on September 30, 1998.
Language (s): Macedonian
NEWS SERVICE/SYNDICATE

BROADCASTING

RADIO NETWORKS

Kanal 77
Editorial: Josif Kovacev 18, Stip 2000.
T: 389 32 39 77 07
E: kanal77@kanal77.com.mk
W: http://www.kanal77.com.mk
Editorial Profile: National radio station focussing on news and current affairs, music and fun.

MADAGASCAR   Tel: 261
Standard Time: GMT +3
Continent: Africa
Capital City: Antananarivo

NEWSPAPERS & PUBLICATIONS

NEWSPAPERS

L' Express de Madagascar
Owner: L'Express de Madagascar S.A
Editorial: Zi nord route des hydrocarbures, Ankorondrano, Antananarivo.
T: 261 20 22 21 934
E: lexpress@malagasy.com
W: http://www.lexpressmada.com
Freq: Daily; **Circ:** 11000 Publisher's Statement
Diffusion: Roger Ithier; **Rédacteur en Chef:** Sylvain Ranjalahy
Editorial Profile: Newspaper covering national and international news, sport and business.
Language (s): French
DAILY NEWSPAPER

La Gazette de la Grande Ile
Owner: Groupe MPE
Editorial: Lot II W 23 L, Ankorahotra, Antananarivo 101. **T:** 261 20 22 61 377
E: redaction@lagazette-dgi.com
W: http://www.lagazette-dgi.com
Freq: Daily; **Circ:** 60000 Publisher's Statement
Editor In Chief: Narilala Andriambelomasina
Editorial Profile: Newspaper focusing on national and international news, current affairs, politics, business, culture, health, sports and entertainment.
Language (s): French, Malagasy
DAILY NEWSPAPER

Inona no Vaovao
Editorial: BP 659, Rue Rainivoninahitriniarivo, Antananarivo 101. **T:** 261 20 22 329 94
E: ranselme@hotmail.com
Freq: Daily; **Circ:** 5000 Publisher's Statement
Editorial Profile: Newspaper focusing on national and international news, politics, finance, culture and sport as well as local issues and concerns.
Language (s): Malagasy
DAILY NEWSPAPER

Madagascar Tribune
Owner: Societe Malgache d'Edition
Editorial: BP 659, Rue Rainivoninahitriniarivo, Antananarivo 101. **T:** 261 20 22 226 35
E: contact@madagascar-tribune.com
W: http://www.madagascar-tribune.com
Freq: Daily; **Circ:** 6500 Publisher's Statement
Rédacteur en Chef: Anselme Randriakoto
Editorial Profile: Newspaper focusing on national and international news, politics, finance, culture and sport.
Language (s): French, Malagasy
DAILY NEWSPAPER

Midi Madagasikara
Owner: Ialana Ravoninahitriniarivo
Editorial: Rue Ravoninahitriniarivo, BP 1414, Antananarivo 101. **T:** 261 33 11 697 79
E: docmidi2000@yahoo.fr
W: http://www.midi-madagasikara.mg
Freq: Daily; **Circ:** 35000 Publisher's Statement
Rédacteur en Chef Adjoint: Clément Rabary; **Rédacteur en Chef:** Zo Rakotoseheno; **Rédacteur en Chef Adjoint:** Olivier Rasamizatovo
Editorial Profile: Newspaper focusing on national and international news, business, politics, entertainment and sport.
Language (s): French, Malagasy
DAILY NEWSPAPER

Weekly
Editorial: BP 659, Rue Rainivoninahitriniarivo, Antananarivo 101. **T:** 261 20 22 329 94
E: ranselme@hotmail.com **Circ:** 5000 Publisher's Statement
Editorial Profile: Newspaper focusing on national and international news, politics, finance, culture and sport as well as local issues and concerns.
Language (s): French
DAILY NEWSPAPER

MALAWI — Tel: 265
Standard Time: GMT +2
Continent: Africa
Capital City: Lilongwe

NEWSPAPERS & PUBLICATIONS

NEWSPAPERS

Nation Sunday
Owner: Nation Publications Ltd
Editorial: PO Box 30408, Chichiri, Blantyre 3. **T:** 265 111 61 18 89
E: nationonline@mwnation.com
W: http://mwnation.com
Freq: Weekly; **Circ:** 15000 Publisher's Statement
Editorial Profile: National Sunday newspaper focussing on news, current affairs, business, politics and sport.
Language (s): English
DAILY NEWSPAPER

MALAYSIA — Tel: 60
Standard Time: GMT +8
Continent: Asia
Capital City: Kuala Lumpur

NEWSPAPERS & PUBLICATIONS

NEWSPAPERS

Asia Times
Editorial: Asia Times Sdn Bhd, No. 555, Likas Bay, Off Jalan Tuaran, P.O.Box 11280, Sabah, Kota Kinabalu 88814. **T:** 60 88 422 821
W: http://www.asiatimes.com.my
Freq: Daily; **Circ:** 20003 Not Audited
Editor: Kim Huat Chua
Editorial Profile: Daily newspaper published in Chinese. Covers general news, current events, lifestyle news for the Chinese community
Language (s): Chinese
DAILY NEWSPAPER

Bacaria
Editorial: Kumpulan Karangkraf Sdn Bhd, Lot 2, Jln. Sepana 15/3, Off Persiaran Selangor, Seksyen 15, Selangor Darul Ehsan, Shah Alam 40200. **T:** 60 3 51 01 38 88
E: editor.bacaria@karangkraf.com.my
W: http://www.karangkraf.com.my
Freq: Weekly; **Circ:** 99001 Not Audited
Editor: Meen Tahrin
Editorial Profile: Covers Entertainment, News, Women, Health, etc.
Language (s): Bahasa Malaysia
DAILY NEWSPAPER

Berita Harian
Editorial: Berita Harian Sdn Bhd, Balai Berita, 31 Jln. Riong, Bangsar, Kuala Lumpur 59100. **T:** 60 322822323 **E:** bhnews@bharian.com.my
W: http://www.bharian.com.my
Freq: Daily; **Circ:** 192917 Not Audited
Editor: Mohammad Khaidir Abd. Majid; **Editor:** Hanizam Abdullah; **Editor:** Azhar Abu Samah; **Editor:** Salbiah Ani; **Editor:** Saidon Idris; **Editor:** Fadzlena Jafar; **Editor:** Badrulhisham Othman
Editorial Profile: Daily newspaper published in Malay. Covers general news, current events and lifestyle
Language (s): Bahasa Malaysia
DAILY NEWSPAPER

Berita Minggu
Editorial: Berita Harian Sdn Bhd, Balai Berita, 31 Jln Riong, Kuala Lumpur 59100.
T: 60 322822323
E: bminggu@bharian.com.my
W: http://www.bharian.com.my
Freq: Daily; **Circ:** 305256 Not Audited
Editor: Norhayati Said
Editorial Profile: Daily newspaper published in Malay. General news, current events, lifestyle
Language (s): Bahasa Malaysia
DAILY NEWSPAPER

The Borneo Post
Editorial: Borneo Post Sdn Bhd, 2nd Floor, Crown Tower, 88 Jln. Pending, Sarawak, Kuching 93450. **T:** 60 82485118
W: http://www.theborneopost.com
Freq: Daily
Editor: Jimmy Adit
Editorial Profile: Daily newspaper published in Malay. Current events, news, lifestyle with a focus on the Sarawak/Borneo region
Language (s): English
DAILY NEWSPAPER

The Borneo Post (Sabah)
Editorial: No.1301 1st Floor Jalan Sri Dgans, Miri Waterfront, Wisma KTS, Jalan Pantai, Sabah, Kota Kinabalu 98000. **T:** 60 854277700
E: borneopostkk@yahoo.com
W: http://www.theborneopost.com
Freq: Daily; **Circ:** 22098 Not Audited
Editor in Chief: Nai Wen Chiu
Editorial Profile: Daily newspaper covering the Sabah area. Current & Local News, International News, Sports, Business, Entertainment, Features, Technology, War, Politics, etc.
Language (s): English
DAILY NEWSPAPER

China Press
Editorial: The China Press Berhad, 80 Jalan Riong, Off Jln Bangsar, Kuala Lumpur 59100.
T: 603 22896363
E: enews@chinapress.com.my
W: http://www.chinapress.com.my
Freq: Daily; **Circ:** 240002 Not Audited
Editor: Soong Yoke Chai; **Editor:** Yee Wei Loh; **Editor in Chief:** Yang Khoon Teoh
Editorial Profile: Covers local and international news, sports, business, entertainment, economy, etc.
Language (s): Chinese
DAILY NEWSPAPER

Daily Express
Editorial: Sabah Publishing House Sdn. Bhd., P.O. Box 10139, Sabah, Kota Kinabalu 88801.
T: 60 88256422 **E:** sph@tm.net.my
W: http://www.dailyexpress.com.my
Freq: Daily; **Circ:** 30002 Not Audited
Editor in Chief: James Sardahthisa
Editorial Profile: Covers a wide range of topics including international, national and local news, financial and business pages, sports, entertainment and leisure.
Language (s): English
DAILY NEWSPAPER

The Edge
Editorial: Leve 3 Monara KLK, No.1, Jalan Pju 7/6, Mutiara Damansara, Petaling Jaya 47810.
T: 60 377218000 **E:** dteoh@bizedge.com
W: http://www.theedgemalaysia.com
Freq: Weekly
Editor in Chief: Kay Tat Ho
Editorial Profile: Daily newspaper covering business, general news, current events, international news, sports, etc.
Language (s): English
DAILY NEWSPAPER

The Edge Financial Daily
Owner: The Edge Communication
Editorial: Level 3, Menara KLK, No. 1 Jalan PJU 7/6, Mutiara Damansara, Selangor, Petaling Jaya 47810. **T:** 603 77218000
E: info@bizedge.com
W: http://www.theedgemalaysia.com
Freq: 2 Times/Week; **Circ:** 15001 Not Audited
Editorial Profile: Covers business and finance.
Language (s): English
DAILY NEWSPAPER

Guang Ming Daily
Editorial: Guang Ming Ribao Sdn Bhd, 19 Jalan Semangat, Selangor, Petaling Jaya 46200. **T:** 60 3 7965 8888
E: gmkl@guangming.com.my
W: http://www.guangming.com.my
Freq: Daily; **Circ:** 99706 Not Audited
Editor in Chief: Chau Huay Poon
Editorial Profile: daily newspaper published in Chinese. Covers general news, current events and lifestyle news for the Chinese community
Language (s): Chinese
DAILY NEWSPAPER

Guang Ming Daily (Penang)
Editorial: No.19 Jalan, Semongat, Petaling Jaya Selangor, Penang 96200.
T: 60 379658888
E: editorial-pg@guangming.com.my
W: http://www.guangming.com.my
Freq: Daily; **Circ:** 70003 Not Audited
Editor in Chief: Chau Huay Poon
Editorial Profile: Malaysian Chinese Community in Penang. Local, National, Regional and International News.
Language (s): Chinese
DAILY NEWSPAPER

Harakah
Editorial: Parti Islam SeMalaysia (PAS), No. 22 Jalan Pahang Barat, Pekiling Business Centre, Kuala Lumpur 53000.
T: 60 340233270
E: editor.harakahdaily@gmail.com
W: http://www.harakahdaily.net
Freq: Daily; **Circ:** 250003 Not Audited
Editor: Roslan Hamid; **Editor:** Tarmizi Mohd Jam; **Editor:** Taufek Yahaya
Editorial Profile: Daily newspaper published in Malay. Covers general news, current events & lifestyle.
Language (s): Bahasa Malaysia
DAILY NEWSPAPER

Harian Metro
Editorial: The News Straits Times Press (M) Bhd, Balai Berita, 31 Jln. Riong, Bangsar, Kuala Lumpur 59100 **E:** am@hmetro.com.my
W: http://www.hmetro.com.my
Freq: Daily; **Circ:** 331003 Not Audited
Editor: Roslan Ibrahim; **Editor:** Othman Mamat; **Editor in Chief:** Sharifuddin Mohamad; **Editor:** Abdul Khalid Mohd Yasin; **Editor:** Adam Salleh
Editorial Profile: Daily newspaper published in Malay. Covers news, current events & lifestyle
Language (s): Bahasa Malaysia
DAILY NEWSPAPER

International Times
Editorial: International Times Sdn Bhd, Lot 2215, Jalan Bengkel, Pending Industrial Estate, Serawak, Kuching 93450. **T:** 60 82487778
E: kuching@intimes.com.my
W: http://www.intimes.com.my
Freq: Daily; **Circ:** 36001 Not Audited
Editor in Chief: Fook Onn Lee
Editorial Profile: Covers local, national, regional and international news, sports, entertainment, economy and politics, etc.
Language (s): Chinese
DAILY NEWSPAPER

Kosmo!
Editorial: Utusan Melayu (Malaysia) Berhad, 46M, Jalan Lima, Off Jalan Chan Sow Lin, Kuala Lumpur 55200. **T:** 60 3 922-14001
W: http://www.kosmo.com.my
Freq: Daily; **Circ:** 108798 Not Audited
Editor: Badrul Azhar Abdul Rahman; **Editor:** Asan Ahmad; **Editor:** Baharom Mahusin
Editorial Profile: Daily newspaper published in Malay targeted at a younger audience
Language (s): Bahasa Malaysia
DAILY NEWSPAPER

Kosmo!Ahad
Editorial: Utusan Melayu (Malaysia) Berhad, 46M, Jalan Lima, Off Jalan Chan Sow Lin, Kuala Lumpur 55200. **T:** 60 392217055
E: berita@kosmo.com.my
W: http://www.kosmo.com.my
Freq: Weekly; **Circ:** 109897 Not Audited
Editor: Zuki Pileh
Editorial Profile: Sunday edition of Kosmo! News lifestyle and entertainment for young adults published in Malay
Language (s): Bahasa Malaysia
DAILY NEWSPAPER

Kwong Wah Yit Poh
Owner: Kwong Wah Yit Poh Press Berhad
Editorial: Kwong Wah Yit Poh Press Berhad, 19, Lebuh Presgrave, Pulau Pinang, Penang 10300. **T:** 60 4 261 2312
E: editor@kwongwah.com.my
W: http://www.kwongwah.com.my
Freq: Daily; **Circ:** 74002 Not Audited
Editor in Chief: Kam Cheong Voo
Editorial Profile: Covers Local, National, Regional and International news.
Language (s): Chinese
DAILY NEWSPAPER

Makkal Osai
Editorial: Makkal Osai Sdn Bhd, 19M, Jalan Murai Dua, Batu Complex, Off Jalan Ipoh, 3 1/4 Mile, Kuala Lumpur 51200.
T: 60 3 6250-4500 **E:** news@makkalosai.com
Freq: Daily; **Circ:** 27002 Not Audited
Editor: B. Rajan
Editorial Profile: Daily newspaper published in Tamil. Provides local news, national news, regional news and international news for the Malaysian community.
Language (s): Tamil
DAILY NEWSPAPER

The Malay Mail
Editorial: Malay Mail Sdn Bhd, B-3A-02, Dataran 3 Dua, No.2, Jalan 19/1, Petaling Jaya 46300. **T:** 60 379472288
E: mmnews@mmail.com.my
W: http://www.mmail.com.my
Freq: Daily; **Circ:** 20816 Not Audited
Editor: Angela Fernandez; **Editor:** Ahmad Najmuddin; **Editor:** Yushaimi Yahaya
Editorial Profile: Daily newspaper covers general news, current events and lifestyle. The Malay Mail is widely read in the Klang Valley conurbation consisting of the nation's capital Kuala Lumpur, Petaling Jaya and heading west towards Klang and Port Klang; Sungai Buluh and Rawang to the north; and the Multimedia Supercorridor extending towards Kajang, Cyberjaya and Putrajaya, the administrative capital of Malaysia.
Language (s): English
DAILY NEWSPAPER

Malaysia Nanban
Editorial: Penerbitan Sahabat (M) Sdn Bhd, 544-3, Batu Complex, Kuala Lumpur 51100.
T: 60 3 6251 5981 **E:** news@nanban.com.my
W: http://nanban2u.com
Freq: Daily; **Circ:** 60007 Not Audited
Editor: Malayandi M.
Editorial Profile: Daily newspaper published in Tamil. Focus on Malaysian Indian Community. General news, Tamil news, Sports and Entertainment. Circulation for Sunday newspaper is 120000 copies.
Language (s): Tamil
DAILY NEWSPAPER

The Malaysian Reserve
Editorial: Syed Hussain Publications Sdn Bhd, Redberry city Lot2 A, Jalan 13/2, Petaling Jaya 46200. **T:** 60 379600027
E: news@themalaysianreserve.com
W: http://www.themalaysianreserve.com
Freq: 2 Times/Week; **Circ:** 20006 Not Audited
Editorial Profile: Newspaper covering business & financial news
Language (s): Bahasa Malaysia
DAILY NEWSPAPER

Melaka Hari Ini
Editorial: Penerbitan IKSEP Sdn Bhd, Bangunan Rumah Media Melaka, Jalan Lingkaran MITC, Ayer Keroh, Melaka 75450.
T: 60 62519315
E: editorial@melakahariini.com.my
W: http://www.melakahariini.com.my
Freq: Daily; **Circ:** 4006 Not Audited
Editor in Chief: Ishak Dalib
Editorial Profile: Daily newspaper published in Malay 90% local & National news :Economy,

Business, Politic, State Development, Entertainment, etc.
Language (s): Bahasa Malaysia
DAILY NEWSPAPER

Merdeka Daily News
Editorial: Merdeka Daily News Sdn Bhd, No. 64 Jalan Utara Batu 3 1/2, Sandakan 90000. **T:** 60 89213704 **E:** merkk@tm.net.my
Freq: Daily; **Circ:** 12003 Not Audited
Editor in Chief: Kon Shing Fung
Editorial Profile: Daily newspaper published in Chinese. Covers general news and current events
Language (s): Chinese
DAILY NEWSPAPER

Metro Ahad
Editorial: The New Straits Times Press (M) Berhad, Balai Berita, Jln. Riong, Bangsar, Kuala Lumpur 59100
W: http://www.hmetro.com.my
Freq: Weekly; **Circ:** 370007 Not Audited
Editor: Sharifuddin Mohamad; **Editor:** Tuan Asri Tuan Hussin
Editorial Profile: Daily paper for Malay readers covers current and Social Affairs, People news, Entertainment, Sports, etc. Published by New Straits Times
Language (s): Bahasa Malaysia
DAILY NEWSPAPER

Mingguan Malaysia
Editorial: Utusan Melayu (M) Bhd, 46M Jalan Lima, Off Jalan Chan Sow Lin, P.O. Box 671, Kuala Lumpur 55200. **T:** 60 392217055
W: http://www.utusan.com.my
Freq: Daily; **Circ:** 459793 Not Audited
Editor: Jamliah Abdullah; **Editor:** Zin Mahmud; **Editor:** Mohd Hassan Mohd Noor
Editorial Profile: Covers regional, national, and international news, as well as entertainment, business, politics, etc.
Language (s): Bahasa Malaysia
DAILY NEWSPAPER

Nanyang Siang Pau
Editorial: Nanyang Siang Pau Sdn Bhd, 1st Floor, No.1, Jalan SS 7/2, Selangor, Petaling Jaya 47301. **T:** 60 3 7872 6888
E: editor@nanyang.com.my
W: http://www.nanyang.com
Freq: Daily; **Circ:** 105847 Not Audited
editor in chief: Chan Aun Kuang Chen; **Editor:** Siok Ching Tong
Editorial Profile: Chinese language daily newspaper covers general news, current events and lifestyle
Language (s): Chinese
DAILY NEWSPAPER

New Sabah Times
Editorial: Inna Kinabalu Sdn Bhd., Jalan Pusat Pembangunan Masyarakat/ Lorong Selungsung D, Off Jalan Mat Salleh, Sembulan, Sabah, Kota Kinabalu 88100.
T: 60 88230055 **E:** nststringers@hotmail.com
W: http://www.newsabahtimes.com.my
Freq: Daily; **Circ:** 23926 Not Audited
Editor in Chief: Boon Heng Ch'ng; **Editor:** Michael De La Harpe; **Editor:** Mohd Amin Muin
Editorial Profile: Covers regional, national, and international news, as well as entertainment, business, politics, etc.
Language (s): English
DAILY NEWSPAPER

New Sarawak Tribune
Editorial: Lot 231, Jalan Nipah, Off Jalan, Abell Utara, Kuching 93050. **T:** 60 82 424411
W: http://www.newsarawaktribune.com
Freq: Daily
Editor: William Chan
Editorial Profile: Covers local and national news.
Language (s): Bahasa Malaysia
DAILY NEWSPAPER

New Straits Times
Editorial: The New Straits Times Press (Malaysia) Berhad, Balai Berita, 31 Jalan Riong, Kuala Lumpur 59100. **T:** 60 322823322
E: news@nstp.com.my
W: http://www.nst.com.my
Freq: Daily; **Circ:** 139767 Not Audited
Editor in Chief: Lionel Morais; **Editor:** Melanie Proctor; **Editor:** Kamarulzaman Salleh
Editorial Profile: Covers general news, current events and lifestyle issues
Language (s): English
DAILY NEWSPAPER

New Sunday Times
Editorial: The New Straits Times Press (M) Berhad, Balai Berita, 31 Jalan Riong, Kuala Lumpur 59100. **T:** 60 322823131
E: news@nstp.com.my
W: http://www.nst.com.my
Freq: Weekly
Editor: Hamidah Atan; **Editior:** Syed Nadzri SyedHarum
Editorial Profile: This is the Sunday edition of New Straits Times. Covers news, analyses of issues, features, informative articles and a variety of leisure reading and entertainment updates.
Language (s): English
DAILY NEWSPAPER

Nichi-Ma Press
Owner: Multi Valiant
Editorial: Multi Valiant Sdn. Bhd, 4D, Jalan Petaling Utama 8 (PJS1/29), Batu 7, Jalan Klang Lama, Petaling Jaya 46000.
T: 60 377842317 **E:** editor@nichimapress.com
W: http://www.nichimapress.com
Freq: Semi-Monthly; **Circ:** 21002 Not Audited
Editor in Chief: A. Watanabe
Editorial Profile: Provides news for the Japanese community living in Malaysia.
Language (s): Japanese
DAILY NEWSPAPER

Oriental Daily News
Editorial: Oriental Daily Sdn Bhd, Wisma Dang Wangi, Jalan Dang Wangi 38, Kuala Lumpur 50100. **T:** 60 326916336
E: news@orientaldaily.com.my
W: http://www2.orientaldaily.com.my
Freq: Daily; **Circ:** 102502 Not Audited
Editor: Chooi Hor Chen; **Editor:** Chai Yoke Ho;
Editor in Chief: Keak Hock Ko
Editorial Profile: Covers general news, current events & lifestyle
Language (s): Chinese
DAILY NEWSPAPER

Overseas Chinese Daily News
Editorial: Sabah Publishing House Sdn Bhd., P.O. Box 10139, Sabah, Kota Kinabalu 88801.
T: 60 88256422 **E:** sph@dailyexpress.com
W: http://www.ocdn.com.my
Freq: Daily; **Circ:** 20006 Not Audited
Editor in Chief: Yuk Seng Hii; **Publisher:** Clement Yeh Chang
Editorial Profile: Covers local, regional, national, and international news.
Language (s): Chinese
DAILY NEWSPAPER

See Hua Daily News
Editorial: See Hua Daily News Bhd, Lot 7705 Jalan Pending, Kuching 93450.
T: 60 843297777
Freq: Daily; **Circ:** 52323 Not Audited
Editor in Chief: Kuok Kiong Ling
Editorial Profile: Daily newspaper published in Chinese. Covers general news, current events and lifestyle
Language (s): Chinese
DAILY NEWSPAPER

See Hua Daily News (Sabah)
Editorial: TB 2097 1st Floor Jin Aps, Hw Dat Lijht Industrial Est, Kota Kinabalu 91000.
T: 60 89912568 **E:** seehuasbh@yahoo.com
W: http://seehua.com
Freq: Daily; **Circ:** 22217 Not Audited
Editor in Chief: Chee Kong Toh
Editorial Profile: Daily newspaper for Malaysian Chinese Community in Sabah area. Current & Local News, International News, Business and Politic, Sports, Entertainment, etc.
Language (s): Chinese
DAILY NEWSPAPER

Sin Chew Daily
Editorial: Pemandangan Sinar Sdn Bhd, 19 Jalan Semangat, Petaling Jaya 46200.
T: 60 3 79658888
E: editorial@sinchew.com.my
W: http://www.mysinchew.com
Freq: Daily
Editor: Yoke Loong Lee; **Editor in Chief:** Ah Lek Pook
Editorial Profile: Covers national and international news, as well as entertainment, business, sports, etc.
Language (s): Chinese
DAILY NEWSPAPER

Sinar Harian
Owner: Akhbar Cabaran
Editorial: Akhbar Cabaran Sdn Bhd, Lot 2 Jalan Sepana 15/3, Off Persiaran Selangor, Seksyen 15, Selangor, Shah Alam 40200.
T: 603 51013888
E: editor.web@sinarharian.com.my
W: http://www.sinarharian.com.my
Freq: Daily; **Circ:** 150002 Not Audited
Editor: Wan Normi Hasan; **Editor:** Muhamad Mat Yakim; **Editor:** Boon Teck Ong; **Editor:** Azmi Tarmizi
Editorial Profile: Covers news, current events and lifestyle.
Language (s): Bahasa Malaysia
DAILY NEWSPAPER

The Star Malaysia
Owner: Star Publications (M) Bhd.
Editorial: Star Publications (M) Bhd, Menara Star, 15 Jalan 16/11, Selangor, Petaling Jaya 46350. **T:** 60 3 79671388
E: editor@thestar.com.my
W: http://www.thestar.com.my
Freq: Daily; **Circ:** 309181 Not Audited
News Editor: Esther Ng; **News Editor:** Foong Pek Yee; **News Editor:** Devid Rajah
Editorial Profile: Covers general news, current events and lifestyle.
Language (s): English
DAILY NEWSPAPER

The Sun
Editorial: Sun Media Corporation Sdn Bhd, 4th Floor, Lot 6, Jln 51/217, Section 51, Selangor Darul Ehsan, Petaling Jaya 46050.
T: 60 3 7784 6688
E: newsdesk@thesundaily.com
W: http://www.sun2surf.com
Freq: Daily; **Circ:** 275003 Not Audited
Editor: Zainon Ahmad; **Editor:** Sebastian Lim; **Editor:** Navjeet Singh; **Editor:** Peter Yap
Editorial Profile: Daily newspaper published in English. Covers general news, current events, lifestyle
Language (s): English
DAILY NEWSPAPER

Sunday Nesan
Editorial: Tamil Nesan (M) Sdn Bhd, No. 23, Jalan SBC 5, Taman Sri Batu Caves, Selangor, Batu Caves 68100. **T:** 60 361841818
E: mytamilnesan@yahoo.com
W: http://www.tamilnewsan.com.my
Freq: Weekly; **Circ:** 95002 Not Audited
Editor: K. Padmanathan
Editorial Profile: Covers general news, sports, politics, economy, entertainment, etc.
Language (s): Tamil
DAILY NEWSPAPER

The Sunday Post
Editorial: The Borneo Post, 2nd Floor, Crown Tower, 88 Jalan Pending, Serawak, Kuching 93450. **T:** 60 82485111
E: bp_editors@yahoo.com
W: http://www.theborneopost.com
Freq: Weekly; **Circ:** 60006 Not Audited
Editor: Aden Nagrace
Editorial Profile: The Sunday Post is the Sunday Edition of The Borneo Post. It covers local and international neews, Entertainment, Sports, and etc. Focus on Sarawak
Language (s): Bahasa Malaysia
DAILY NEWSPAPER

Sunday Star
Owner: Star Publications (Malaysia) Berhad
Editorial: Star Publications (Malaysia) Berhad, Menara Star, 15 Jln. 16/11, Selangor, Petaling Jaya 46350. **T:** 60 3 7967 1388
E: sunday@thestar.com.my
W: http://www.thestar.com.my
Freq: Weekly; **Circ:** 295552 Not Audited
Editor: Asatha Mataayun
Editorial Profile: Covers National and International News, Sports and Entertainment, Economic and Politics, Features, etc.
Language (s): English
DAILY NEWSPAPER

Tamil Nesan
Editorial: Tamil Nesan (M) Sdn Bhd, No. 23, Jalan SBC 5, Taman Sri Batu Caves, Selangor, Batu Caves 68100. **T:** 60 361841818
E: mytamilnesan@yahoo.com
W: http://www.tamilnesan.com.my
Freq: Daily; **Circ:** 45001 Not Audited
Editor in Chief: K. Padmanathan
Editorial Profile: Covers general news, politics, economy, entertainment, sports, etc.
Language (s): Tamil
DAILY NEWSPAPER

Tech & U
Editorial: Tech&U, New Straits Times Sdn.Bhd, 2nd Floor, Balai Berita, Anjung Liku, Kuala Lumpur 59100. **T:** 60 3 2282-3322
W: http://technu.nst.com.my
Freq: Weekly; **Circ:** 139763 Not Audited
Editor: Ahmad Kushairi
Editorial Profile: A pullout from New Strait Times newspaper, publishing twice a week (Mondays and Thursdays). Covers tech news, reviews and information. Formerly Computimes.
Language (s): English
DAILY NEWSPAPER

United Daily News
Editorial: Lot 2597, Block 3, MCLD, Wisma United Borneo Press, Jalan Piasau, Sarawak, Miri 98000. **T:** 60 85 656666
E: miri@uniteddaily.com.my
W: http://www.uniteddaily.com.my
Freq: Daily; **Circ:** 35007 Not Audited
Editorial Profile: Chinese language daily newspaper. Covers news locally and internationally. Also offers information on finance and entertainment and offers readers comics and horoscopes.
Language (s): Mandarin
DAILY NEWSPAPER

Utusan Borneo
Editorial: The Borneo Post Sdn Bhd, No.88, Jalan Pending, Level 2 Crown Tower, Kuching 93450. **T:** 60 82 485 118
W: http://www.theborneopost.com
Freq: Daily; **Circ:** 10003 Not Audited
Editorial Profile: Daily newspaper published in Malay, targeting Sarawak region. General news, current events, lifestyle
Language (s): Bahasa Malaysia
DAILY NEWSPAPER

Utusan Borneo (Sabah)
Editorial: Borneo Post (Sabah) Sdn Bhd, Jln. Tuaran Batu 5 1/2, Kota Kinabalu 88450.
T: 60 88421717
E: utusanborneokk@yahoo.com.my
Freq: Daily
Editor: Samsul Bin Ali Maran
Editorial Profile: Daily newspaper published in Malay. Covers general news current events, lifestyle in the Sabah/Borneo region
Language (s): Bahasa Malaysia
DAILY NEWSPAPER

Utusan Malaysia
Editorial: Utusan Melayu (M) Sdn Bhd, 46M Jalan Lima, Off Jalan Chan Sow Lin, Kuala Lumpur 55200. **T:** 60 392217055
E: pengarang@utusangroup.com.my
W: http://www.utusan.com.my
Freq: Daily; **Circ:** 197033 Not Audited
Editor: Zulkefli Hamzah; **Editor:** Mustapha Kamal; **Editor:** Mowardi Mahmud; **Editor:** Baharom Mahusin; **Editor:** Othman Mohamad; **Editor:** Gamal Nasir Mohd. Ali; **Editor:** Zaharuddin Mustafa
Editorial Profile: Daily newspaper published in Malay. Covers general news, current events, lifestyle
Language (s): Bahasa Malaysia
DAILY NEWSPAPER

The Wall Street Journal (Malaysia)
Editorial: Regus Centres Sdn Bhd, Level 40, Petronas Twin Towers, Tower 2, Kuala Lumpur 50088. **T:** 60 3 2026-1233
E: djn.kl@dowjones.com
Bureau Chief: Abhrajit Gangopadhyay
DAILY NEWSPAPER

NEWS SERVICE/SYNDICATE

Associated Press
Editorial: Suite 21A-8-2 Level 8, Faber Imperial Court, Jalan Sultan Ismail, Kuala Lumpur 50250. **T:** 603 2181-8134
E: apklnews@ap.org
Bureau Chief: Mark Baker; **Southeast Asia News Editor:** Chris Brummitt
NEWS SERVICE/SYNDICATE

Bernama
Editorial: Malaysian National News Agency, Wisma BERNAMA, No 28, Jalan 1/65A, Off Jalan Tun Razak, Kuala Lumpur 50400.
T: 60 326939933 **E:** bgns@bernama.com
W: http://www.bernama.com
Freq: Daily
Editor: Mikhail Raj Abdullah; **Editor:** Muhammad Razee Hassan; **Editor:** Mokhtar Hussain; **Editor:** Mahrus Ibrahim; **Editor:** Amer Hamzah Md Sap; **Editor:** Rohana Mustafa; **Editor in Chief:** Zulkefli Salleh; **Editor:** Thomas Savarimuthu
Editorial Profile: News service providing news and information to news papers, radio and television
Language (s): English
NEWS SERVICE/SYNDICATE

Bloomberg News
Editorial: Petronas Twin Towers, Kuala Lumpur 50088. **T:** 60 323027800
Bureau Chief: Barry Porter
NEWS SERVICE/SYNDICATE

Dow Jones Newswires
Editorial: Regus Centres Sdn Bhd, Level 40, Petronas Twin Towers, Tower 2, Kuala Lumpur 50088. **T:** 60 3 2026-1233

E: djn.kl@dowjones.com
Bureau Chief: Abhrajit Gangopadhyay
NEWS SERVICE/SYNDICATE

Reuters
Owner: Thomson Reuters
Editorial: Reuters Malaysia Sdn Bhd, Level 32,
Petronas Tower 2, Kuala Lumpur 5088.
T: 60 3 23-338000
Bureau Chief: Stuart Grudgings
NEWS SERVICE/SYNDICATE

BROADCASTING

TELEVISION STATIONS

RTM 1
Editorial: RTM, Dept. Of Broadcasting,
Angkasapuri, Kuala Lumpur 50614.
T: 603 2282 5333 **W:** http://www.rtm.gov.my
Editorial Profile: Family programming,
educational programs in Malay and English.

RTM 2
Editorial: RTM, Dept. Of Broadcasting,
Angkasapuri, Kuala Lumpur 50614.
T: 60 322887355 **W:** http://www.rtm.gov.my
Editorial Profile: Government run Malaysian
TV station.

MALDIVES — Tel: 960
Standard Time: GMT +5
Continent: Asia
Capital City: Malé

NEWSPAPERS & PUBLICATIONS

NEWSPAPERS

Haveeru Daily
Owner: Haveeru Daily
Editorial: PO Box 20103, Ameenee Magu,
Male. **T:** 960 332 56 71
E: haveeru@haveeru.com.mv
W: http://www.haveeru.com.mv
Freq: Daily; **Circ:** 4500 Publisher's Statement
Editor: Ali Rafeeq
Editorial Profile: Newspaper focusing on
national and international news, politics,
economics, culture and sport.
Language (s): English
DAILY NEWSPAPER

BROADCASTING

TELEVISION STATIONS

Television Maldives
Editorial: Buruzu magu, Male 20-24.
T: 960 332 31 05 **E:** info@tvm.gov.mv
W: http://www.tvm.gov.mv
Editorial Profile: National TV station focussing
on news, current affairs, entertainment and
sport.

MALI — Tel: 223
Standard Time: GMT
Continent: Africa
Capital City: Bamako

NEWSPAPERS & PUBLICATIONS

NEWSPAPERS

Les Echos
Owner: Jamana
Editorial: Av. Cheick Zayed, Porte 2694,
Bamako. **T:** 223 229 62 89
E: lesechos@jamana.org
W: http://www.jamana.org
Freq: Daily; **Circ:** 5000 Publisher's Statement
Rédacteur en Chef: Alexis Kalambry
Editorial Profile: Daily national newspaper
focussing on news, current affairs, regional
culture, education and humanitarian issues.
Language (s): French
DAILY NEWSPAPER

L' Essor
Owner: Agence Malienne de Presse et de
Publicité (AMAP)
Editorial: Square Patrice Lumumba, BP 141,
Bamako. **T:** 223 222 36 83

E: info@essor.gov.ml
W: http://www.essor.gov.ml
Freq: Daily; **Circ:** 13000 Publisher's
Statement
Rédacteur en Chef: Salim Togola
Editorial Profile: Newspaper focusing on
politics, economics, social life, culture and
general news.
Language (s): French
DAILY NEWSPAPER

L' Indépendant
Editorial: Imm. ABK 5, Hamdallaye ACI,
Bamako. **T:** 223 641 21 04
E: lindependant2004@yahoo.fr
Freq: Daily; **Circ:** 5000 Publisher's Statement
Rédacteur en Chef: Yaya Sidibé
Editorial Profile: National weekly newspaper
focussing on news, current affairs, politics,
economics, culture and sport.
Language (s): French
DAILY NEWSPAPER

Info-Matin
Owner: A2M SARL
Editorial: 350 Rue 56, Bamako-Coura,
Bamako. **T:** 223 223 82 09
E: info-matin@info-matin.net
W: http://www.info-matin.net
Freq: Daily; **Circ:** 1400 Publisher's Statement
Rédacteur en Chef: Sekouba Samaké
Editorial Profile: National daily newspaper
focussing on news, current affairs, politics,
economics, education, art, culture and sport.
Language (s): French
DAILY NEWSPAPER

Le Malien
Editorial: Rue 497 Porte 277, Badialan 3,
Bamako. **T:** 223 221 69 22
E: sangayou@yahoo.fr **Circ:** 3000 Publisher's
Statement
Editorial Profile: National bi-weekly
newspaper focussing on news, current affairs,
politics, economics, culture and sport.
Language (s): French
DAILY NEWSPAPER

Le Nouvel Horizon
Editorial: Rue 608, Porte 21, Banankabougou,
Bamako. **T:** 223 220 06 91
E: zerelani2001@yahoo.fr
Freq: Daily; **Circ:** 1000 Publisher's Statement
Rédacteur en Chef: Daba Balla Keita
Editorial Profile: National daily newspaper
focussing on news, current affairs, politics,
economics, culture and sport.
Language (s): French
DAILY NEWSPAPER

La Nouvelle Tribune
Editorial: 635 rue Djoukamady Sissoko,
Darsalam. **T:** 223 641 71 34
E: lanouvelletribune2005@yahoo.fr **Circ:** 5000
Publisher's Statement
Editorial Profile: National weekly newspaper
focussing on news, current affairs, politics,
economics, culture and sport.
Language (s): French
DAILY NEWSPAPER

Le Soir de Bamako
Editorial: Rue 608, Porte 21, Banankabougou,
Bamako. **T:** 223 220 06 91
E: zerelani2001@yahoo.fr
Freq: Daily; **Circ:** 1000 Publisher's Statement
Editorial Profile: National daily evening
newspaper focussing on news, current affairs,
politics, economics, culture and sport.
Language (s): French
DAILY NEWSPAPER

NEWS SERVICE/SYNDICATE

Agence Malienne de Presse et de Publicité (AMAP)
Editorial: Square Patrice Lumumba, BP 141,
Bamako. **T:** 223 222 23 46
E: amap@essor.gov.ml
Editorial Profile: National and international
news and advertising agency.
Language (s): French
NEWS SERVICE/SYNDICATE

MALTA — Tel: 356
Standard Time: GMT +1
Continent: Europe
Capital City: Valletta

NEWSPAPERS & PUBLICATIONS

NEWSPAPERS

I-orizzont
Owner: Union Press Co. Ltd.
Editorial: A41 Marsa Industrial Estate, Marsa
LQA 06. **T:** 356 21 242 995
E: info@unionrpint.com.mt
W: http://www.orizzont.com.mt
Freq: Daily
Editor: Josef Caruana
Editorial Profile: Newspaper focusing on
national and international news, business,
politics and sport.
Language (s): Maltese
DAILY NEWSPAPER

The Malta Business Weekly
Owner: Standard Publications Ltd
Editorial: Standard House, Birkirkara Hill, St
Julians STJ 11. **T:** 356 21 34 58 88
E: tmbw@independent.com.mt
W: http://www.maltabusinessweekly.com.mt
Circ: 5000 Publisher's Statement
Editor-in-Chief: Fade Noel Grima
Editorial Profile: Magazine covering national
and international business and finance issues.
Language (s): English
DAILY NEWSPAPER

The Malta Independent
Owner: Standard Publications Ltd
Editorial: Standard House, Birkirkara Hill, St
Julians STJ 11. **T:** 356 21 34 58 88
E: mcarabott@independent.com.mt
W: http://www.independent.com.mt
Freq: Daily; **Circ:** 11000 Publisher's
Statement
Editor: Michael Carabott; **Editor-in-Chief:** Fade
Noel Grima
Editorial Profile: Newspaper focusing on
national and international news, politics,
business and sport. Previous title: The Malta
Independent Daily
Language (s): English
DAILY NEWSPAPER

The Malta Independent on Sunday
Owner: Standard Publications Ltd
Editorial: Standard House, Birkirara Hill, St
Julians STJ 11. **T:** 356 21 34 58 88
E: tmis@independent.com.mt
W: http://www.independent.com.mt
Freq: Sun; **Circ:** 20000 Publisher's Statement
Editor: Fade Noel Grima
Editorial Profile: Sunday newspaper focusing
on national and international news, business,
politics and sport.
Language (s): English
DAILY NEWSPAPER

MaltaToday on Sunday
Owner: MediaToday Co. Ltd
Editorial: Vjal ir-Rihan, San Gwann SGN 9016.
T: 356 2138 2741
E: maltatoday@mediatoday.com.mt
W: http://www.maltatoday.com.mt
Freq: Sun; **Circ:** 10000 Publisher's Statement
Editorial Profile: Newspaper focusing on
regional general interest including national and
international news, business, entertainment
and sport.
Language (s): English
DAILY NEWSPAPER

Il Mument
Owner: Media Link
Editorial: Dar Centrali, Herbert Ganado Street,
Pieta HMR 08. **T:** 356 2124 3641
E: mument@media.link.com.mt
Freq: Sun; **Circ:** 20000 Publisher's Statement
Editor: Victor Camilleri
Editorial Profile: Newspaper of the The
Nationalist Party focusing on national and
international news, business, politics, culture
and sport.
Language (s): Maltese
DAILY NEWSPAPER

In Nazzjon
Owner: Media Link
Editorial: Dar Centrali, Herbert Ganado Street,
Pieta HMR 08. **T:** 356 2124 3641
E: news@media.link.com.mt
Freq: Daily; **Circ:** 22000 Publisher's
Statement
Editor: Alex Attard

Editorial Profile: Newspaper focusing on
national and international news, business,
politics, culture and sport.
Language (s): Maltese
DAILY NEWSPAPER

The Sunday Times
Owner: Allied Newspapers Ltd
Editorial: Strickland House, 341 St Paul
Street, Valletta VLT 1211. **T:** 356 25 59 41 00
E: sunday@timesofmalta.com
W: http://www.timesofmalta.com
Freq: Sun; **Circ:** 40000 Publisher's Statement
Editor: Steve Mallia
Editorial Profile: Newspaper focusing on
national and international news, politics,
business and sport.
Language (s): English
DAILY NEWSPAPER

The Times
Owner: Allied Newspapers Ltd
Editorial: Strickland House, 341 St Paul
Street, Valletta VLT 12. **T:** 356 21 24 14 64
E: newsroom@timesofmalta.com
W: http://www.timesofmalta.com
Freq: Daily; **Circ:** 21000 Publisher's
Statement
Editor: Raymond Bugeja
Editorial Profile: Newspaper focusing on
national and international news, politics,
business and sport.
Language (s): English
DAILY NEWSPAPER

It- Torca
Owner: Union Press Co. Ltd.
Editorial: A41 Marsa Industrial Estate, Marsa
LQA 06. **T:** 356 21 24 76 87
E: info@unionprint.com.mt
W: http://www.torca.com.mt
Freq: Sun; **Circ:** 30000 Publisher's Statement
Editor: Aleks Farrugia; **News Editor:** Brian Meli
Editorial Profile: Newspaper focusing on
national and international news, politics,
business and sport.
Language (s): Maltese
DAILY NEWSPAPER

BROADCASTING

RADIO NETWORKS

Radju Malta
Editorial: 75 St. Luke's Road, G'mangia MSD
09. **T:** 356 21 225051 **E:** info@tvm.com.mt
W: http://tvm.com.mt
Editorial Profile: Radju Malta is the radio
station of PBS Ltd, the public service
broadcaster of Malta.

TELEVISION STATIONS

TVM - Television Malta
Owner: Public Broadcasting Services
Editorial: 75 St. Luke's Road, G'mangia PTA
1022. **T:** 356 21 22 50 51 **E:** info@pbs.com.mt
W: http://www.tvm.com.mt
Editorial Profile: National television station of
Malta operated by Public Broadcasting
Services and covering general news and
current affairs including sports, economics,
entertainment, magazines and teleshopping.

MARSHALL ISLANDS — Tel: 692
Standard Time: GMT +8
Continent: Oceania
Capital City: Victoria

NEWSPAPERS & PUBLICATIONS

NEWSPAPERS

Marshall Islands Journal
Owner: Marshall Islands Journal
T: 692 625 8143 **E:** journal@ntamar.net
W: http://majurochamber.net
Freq: Weekly; **Circ:** 15000 Publisher's
Statement
Editor: Giff Johnson
Editorial Profile: Weekly tabloid-size
publication is datelined Friday, but printed on
Wednesday and distributed in Majuro on
Thursday.
Language (s): English
DAILY NEWSPAPER

BROADCASTING

RADIO NETWORKS

V7AB Radio Marshalls
Owner: RMI Government
E: gazette@ntamar.net

MARTINIQUE   Tel: 596

Standard Time: GMT -4
Continent: The Americas
Capital City: Fort-de-France

NEWSPAPERS & PUBLICATIONS

NEWSPAPERS

FRANCE-ANTILLES MARTINIQUE
Editorial: Place François-Mitterrand, BP 577, Fort-De-France Cedex 97207.
T: 0596 5 96 72 88 00
E: redaction.fa@media-antilles.fr
W: http://www.martinique.france-antilles.fr
Freq: Daily
Rédacteur en Chef: Rudi Rabathaly
Editorial Profile: Daily regional and local current events newspapers. Local Translation:Journal d'informations régionales et locales.
Language (s): French
DAILY NEWSPAPER

BROADCASTING

RADIO STATIONS

RADIO APAL 94.9 - 98.1
Editorial: 8 rue Pierre-et-Marie-Curie, Fort-De-France 97200 **E:** radio-apal@orange.fr

RCI (RADIO CARAIBES INTERNATIONAL) MARTINIQUE
Owner: GROUPE RCI
Editorial: 2 boulevard de la Marne, BP 1111, Fort-De-France 97248. **T:** 0596 5 96 63 72 66
E: redaction-martinique@radiocaraibes.com
W: http://www.radiocaraibes.com

TELEVISION STATIONS

RFO MARTINIQUE
Editorial: La Clairière, BP 662, Fort-De-France Cedex 97263 **W:** http://www.rfo.fr
Editorial Profile: Local office of the overseas national public TV channel focussing on regional and local news, sport, entertainment, music, ethology, history, faith and traditions.

MAURITANIA   Tel: 222

Standard Time: GMT
Continent: Africa
Capital City: Nouakchott

NEWSPAPERS & PUBLICATIONS

NEWSPAPERS

Akhbar Nouakchott
Editorial: BP 1905, Nouakchott.
T: 222 525 02 71 **E:** nouakchottinfo@yahoo.fr
W: http://www.mapeci.com
Freq: Daily; **Circ:** 3500 Publisher's Statement
Editorial Profile: National daily newspaper focussing on news, current affairs, politics, economics, culture and sport.
Language (s): Arabic
DAILY NEWSPAPER

Chaab
Editorial: 1540, rue 22-006, BP 467-371, Nouakchott. **T:** 222 525 29 16
E: ami@mauritania.mr **W:** http://www.ami.mr
Freq: Daily; **Circ:** 3000 Publisher's Statement
Editorial Profile: National daily newspaper focussing on news, current affairs, politics, economics, culture and sport.
Language (s): Arabic
DAILY NEWSPAPER

Horizon
Editorial: 1540, rue 22-006, BP 467-371, Nouakchott. **T:** 222 525 29 16

E: ami@mauritania.mr
Freq: Daily; **Circ:** 2000 Publisher's Statement
Editorial Profile: National daily newspaper focussing on news, current affairs, politics, economics, culture and sport.
Language (s): French
DAILY NEWSPAPER

Nouakchott Info
Editorial: Immeuble Abbas, BP 1905, Nouakchott. **T:** 222 525 02 71
E: nouakchottinfo@yahoo.fr
W: http://www.nouakchottinfo.com
Freq: Daily; **Circ:** 2000 Publisher's Statement
Rédacteur en Chef Adjoint: Mohamed Ould Khattatt
Editorial Profile: National news agency focussing on news, current affairs, politics, economics, culture and sport.
Language (s): Arabic
DAILY NEWSPAPER

NEWS SERVICE/SYNDICATE

Agence Mauritanienne d'Information (AMI)
Editorial: 1540, rue 22-006, BP 467-371, Nouakchott. **T:** 222 5 25 29 16
E: ami@mauritania.mr **W:** http://www.ami.mr
Editorial Profile: National news agency of Mauritania focussing on news, current affairs, politics, economics, culture and sport.
Language (s): Arabic
NEWS SERVICE/SYNDICATE

L' Agence Nouakchott d'Information (ANI)
Editorial: BP 1905, Nouakchott.
T: 222 525 02 71 **E:** nouakchottinfo@yahoo.fr
W: http://www.nouakchottinfo.com
Editorial Profile: National news agency focussing on news, current affairs, politics, economics, culture and sport.
Language (s): Arabic
NEWS SERVICE/SYNDICATE

MAURITIUS   Tel: 230

Standard Time: GMT +4
Continent: Africa
Capital City: Port Louis

NEWSPAPERS & PUBLICATIONS

NEWSPAPERS

Chinese Daily News
Owner: Chinese Daily News
Editorial: 32 Remy Ollier Street, PO Box 316, Port Louis. **T:** 230 240 04 72
E: cdn@bow.intnet.mu
Freq: Daily; **Circ:** 1000 Publisher's Statement
Editor In Chief: Wong Yuen Moy
Editorial Profile: Newspaper covering politics, economy, culture and social events.
Language (s): Chinese
DAILY NEWSPAPER

Le Défi Plus
Owner: Le Defi Plus
Editorial: Route Royale, Grande Rivière, Port Louis. **T:** 230 211 77 66
E: l.ramdour@defimedia.info
W: http://www.ledefiplus.info
Freq: Weekly; **Circ:** 65000 Publisher's Statement
Editorial Profile: Newspaper focusing on national and international news, current events, politics, sports, entertainment and leisure.
Language (s): French
DAILY NEWSPAPER

L' Express (Mauritius)
Owner: La Sentinelle Ltd (Mauritius)
Editorial: 3 rue des Oursins, Zone industrielle, Riche-Terre, Baie du Tombeau, Port Louis.
T: 230 206 82 00 **E:** redaction@lexpress.mu
W: http://www.lexpress.mu
Freq: Daily; **Circ:** 34000 Publisher's Statement
Rédacteur en Chef: Raj Meetarbhan
Editorial Profile: National daily newspaper focussing on regional, national and international news, current affairs, politics, economics, society, culture and sport.
Language (s): English, French
DAILY NEWSPAPER

Le Matinal
Owner: AAPCA (Mauritius) Ltd

Editorial: AAPCA House, 6, rue La Poudrière Street, Port-Louis. **T:** 230 207 09 09
E: redaction@lematinal.com
W: http://www.lematinal.com
Freq: Daily; **Circ:** 25000 Publisher's Statement
Rédacteur en Chef: Kiran Ramsahaye
Editorial Profile: Le Matinal, un quotidien majeur en francais et anglais dans le pays.
Language (s): English
DAILY NEWSPAPER

Le Mauricien
Owner: Le Mauricien Ltd
Editorial: 8 St Georges Street, PO Box 7, Port Louis. **T:** 230 207 8200 **E:** marek@intnet.mu
W: http://www.lemauricien.com
Freq: Daily; **Circ:** 25000 Publisher's Statement
Rédacteur en Chef: Gilbert Ahnee
Editorial Profile: National daily newspaper focussing on news, current affairs, politics, economy, society, culture and sport.
Language (s): French
DAILY NEWSPAPER

Mauritius Times
Owner: Prakash Ramlallah Foundation
Editorial: 23 Bourbon Street, Port Louis.
T: 230 292 93 01 **E:** mtimes@intnet.mu
W: http://www.mauritiustimes.com
Circ: 13500 Publisher's Statement
Rédacteur en Chef: Madhukar Ramlallah
Editorial Profile: Newspaper focusing on national and international news and current affairs including, astrology, cookery, fitness, health, education, celebrities, spirituality and women's interest.
Language (s): English, French
DAILY NEWSPAPER

Le Militant
Owner: Mouvement Militant Mauricien
Editorial: 21 Podriere Street, Port Louis.
T: 230 212 65 53 **E:** lemilitant69@yahoo.fr
W: http://www.lemilitant.com **Circ:** 8000 Publisher's Statement
Rédacteur adjoint: Jean Hughes Pierre; **Rédacteur en Chef:** Ananda Rajoo
Editorial Profile: National weekly newspaper focussing on regional and international news, current affairs, politics, economics, society, culture and sport.
Language (s): French
DAILY NEWSPAPER

Le Socialiste
Editorial: 3 Brabant Street, 3rd Floor Manillal Building, Port Louis. **T:** 230 208 80 03
E: lapresseliberesocialiste@yahoo.fr
Freq: Daily; **Circ:** 5000 Publisher's Statement
Rédacteur en Chef: Vedi Balah
Editorial Profile: National daily newspaper focussing on socialist party issues including national and international news, current affairs, politics, economics, society, social issues and sport.
Language (s): French
DAILY NEWSPAPER

Week-End (Mauritius)
Owner: Le Mauricien Ltd
Editorial: 8 rue St Georges, PO Box 7, Port Louis. **T:** 230 207 82 00
E: redaction@lemauricien.com
W: http://www.lemauricien.com/weekend
Freq: Weekly; **Circ:** 75000 Publisher's Statement
Rédacteur en Chef: Gerard Cateaux
Editorial Profile: National Sunday newspaper focussing on regional, national and international news, current affairs, politics, economics, society, entertainment, culture and TV programmes.
Language (s): French
DAILY NEWSPAPER

BROADCASTING

RADIO NETWORKS

Mauritius Radio Station
Owner: Mauritius Broadcasting Corporation
Editorial: Mauritius Broadcasting Corporation, 1 Louis Pasteur Street, Forest Side.
T: 230 602 12 69 **E:** mbcnews@mbc.intnet.mu
W: http://mbc.intnet.mu
Editorial Profile: National radio station focussing on news, current affairs, music, sport and weather.

TELEVISION STATIONS

Mauritius TV
Editorial: Mauritius Broadcasting Corporation, 1 Louis Pasteur Street, Forest Side.
T: 230 602 12 23 **E:** mbcnews@mbc.intnet.mu
W: http://mbc.intnet.mu
Editorial Profile: National TV station focussing on news, current affairs, entertainment, culture, sports and weather forecast.

MAYOTTE   Tel: 262

Standard Time: GMT +3
Continent: Africa
Capital City: Mamoudzou

NEWSPAPERS & PUBLICATIONS

NEWSPAPERS

LES NOUVELLES DE MAYOTTE
Owner: NOUVELLES DE MAYOTTE
Editorial: Kaweni, BP 796, Mamoudzou 97600. **T:** 269 6 39 68 65 65
E: nouvdemay@wanadoo.fr
Freq: Daily
Rédacteur en Chef: Denis Herrmann; **Gérant:** Martine Herrmann
Language (s): French
DAILY NEWSPAPER

BROADCASTING

TELEVISION STATIONS

RFO MAYOTTE
Owner: RFO
T: 269 2 69 60 80 41 **W:** http://www.rfo.fr
Editorial Profile: Local office of the overseas national public TV channel focussing on regional and local news, sport, entertainment, music, ethology, history, faith and traditions.

MEXICO   Tel: 52

Standard Time: GMT -6
Continent: The Americas
Capital City: Mexico City

NEWSPAPERS & PUBLICATIONS

NEWSPAPERS

A.m. De La Piedad
Owner: Reforma
Editorial: Av. México Coyoacán No. 40, Sta. Cruz Atoyac, Michoacán, La Piedad, Michoacan C.P. 03310. **T:** 52 55 56287878
E: guillermo.oropeza@reforma.com
W: http://www.reforma.com.mx
Editor: Sergio Pedroza Gomez
Editorial Profile: The newspaper features national news, entertainment, and sports. It focuses on local news relevant to La Piedad, Michocan, Mexico.
Language (s): Spanish
DAILY NEWSPAPER

A.m. De Querétaro
Owner: Reforma
Editorial: Av. México Coyoacán No. 40, Sta. Cruz Atoyac, Querétaro, Queretaro, Queretaro C.P. 03310. **T:** 52 55 56287878
E: guillermo.oropeza@reforma.com
W: http://www.reforma.com.mx
Editorial Profile: The newspaper features national news, entertainment, and sports. It focuses on local news relevant to Queretaro, Queretaro, Mexico.
Language (s): Spanish
DAILY NEWSPAPER

A.m. De San Francisco
Owner: Reforma
Editorial: Av. México Coyoacán No. 40, Sta. Cruz Atoyac, Guanajuato, San Fco. Del Rincon, Guanajuato C.P. 03310. **T:** 52 55 56287878
E: guillermo.oropeza@reforma.com
W: http://www.reforma.com.mx
Editorial Profile: The newspaper features national news, entertainment, and sports. It focuses on local news relevant to San Francisco del Rincon, Guanajuato, Mexico.
Language (s): Spanish
DAILY NEWSPAPER

a.m. Guanajuato
Owner: Reforma
Editorial: Cantarranas #5, Int #1, Número 16 Interior 3, Guanajuato, Guanajuato C.P. 36000.
T: 52 73 732-7727
W: http://www.periodico.am/guanajuato
Editor: Catalina Reyes
Editorial Profile: a.m. Guanajuato is a daily newspaper features national news, entertainment, and sports. It focuses on local news relevant to Guanajuato, Guanajuato, Mexico.
Language (s): Spanish
DAILY NEWSPAPER

El Agora
Editorial: Calle 9 Av. 3 y 5 #311 Col. Centro, Cordoba, Veracruz 94500. **T:** 52 271 7122750
E: redaccion@elagora.com.mx
W: http://www.elagora.com.mx
Freq: Daily
Editor: Alfredo Rios
Language (s): Spanish
DAILY NEWSPAPER

El Bravo
Owner: Medios Masivos M.
Editorial: Luz Saviñon No. 13, Del Valle, Tamaulipas, Matamoros, Tamaulipas C.P. 03100. **T:** 52 55 53402450
E: alfredo.ramirez@mediosmasivos.com.mx
W: http://www.mediosmasivos.com.mx
Freq: Daily; **Circ:** 60000 Not Audited
Editor: Oscar Aldape; **Publisher:** Jose Carretero Balboa; **Editor:** Alda Guerra; **Editor:** Daniel Lopez; **Editor:** Jose Pedroza
Editorial Profile: El Bravo is a daily newspaper serving residents of Matamoros, Mexico. It covers national, regional and international news, sports, business and entertainment.
Language (s): Spanish
DAILY NEWSPAPER

Contexto De Durango
Owner: Directo
Editorial: Blvd. Luia D. Colosio No. 860, Industrial Korian, Durango, Durango, Durango
W: http://www.contextodedurango.com.mx
Editorial Profile: Cover local, national, and international news, sports, crime, culture and entertainment.
Language (s): Spanish
DAILY NEWSPAPER

La Crítica
Owner: La Crisis
Editorial: Durango No. 233, Roma, Hidalgo, Pachuca, Hidalgo C.P. 06700.
T: 52 311 4560559
E: critica-nay@hotmail.com
W: http://www.diariocritica.com.mx/
Editor: Juan Carlos Guzman
Editorial Profile: La Critica delivers local and national news, sports, entertainment, and crime. It also has a women and family section.
Language (s): Spanish
DAILY NEWSPAPER

La Crónica De Hoy
Owner: La Crónica
Editorial: Londres No. 38, Ciudad Juárez, Mexico City, Distrito Federal C.P. 06600.
T: 52 55 1084-5800
E: publicidad@cronica.com.mx
W: http://www.cronica.com.mx
Freq: Daily
Editor: Adrian Castillo; **Editor:** Nancy Escobar; **Publisher:** Jorge Kahwagi Gastine; **Editor:** Lizbeth Pasillas
Editorial Profile: La Crónica De Hoy delivers local, national and international news, business and economy, opinion, entertainment, sports and academics.
Language (s): Spanish
DAILY NEWSPAPER

La Crónica De Hoy Sintesis
Owner: La Crónica
Editorial: Londres No. 38 P.b., Juárez, Distrito Federal, Mexico City, Distrito Federal C.P. 06600. **T:** 52 55 10845841
E: publicidad@cronica.com.mx
W: http://www.cronica.com.mx
Freq: Daily; **Circ:** 100000 Not Audited
Editorial Profile: La Crónica De Hoy Sintesis delivers local, national and international news, business and economy, opinion, entertainment, sports and academics.
Language (s): Spanish
DAILY NEWSPAPER

De Peso
Owner: Medios Masivos M.
Editorial: Luz Saviñon No. 13, Del Valle, Yucatán, Merida, Yucatan C.P. 03100.
T: 52 55 53402450
E: alfredo.ramirez@mediosmasivos.com.mx
W: http://www.mediosmasivos.com.mx
Editorial Profile: Delivers national and international news, sports and society.
Language (s): Spanish
DAILY NEWSPAPER

De Peso
Owner: Medios Masivos M.
Editorial: Luz Saviñon No. 13, Del Valle, Quintana Roo, Cancun, Quintana Roo C.P. 03100. **T:** 52 55 53402450
E: alfredo.ramirez@mediosmasivos.com.mx
W: http://www.mediosmasivos.com.mx
Circ: 60000 Not Audited
Editorial Profile: Delivers national and international news, sports and society.
Language (s): Spanish
DAILY NEWSPAPER

De Peso
Owner: Medios Masivos M.
Editorial: Luz Saviñon No. 13, Del Valle, Quintana Roo, Chetumal, Quintana Roo C.P. 03100. **T:** 52 55 53402450
E: alfredo.ramirez@mediosmasivos.com.mx
W: http://www.mediosmasivos.com.mx
Editorial Profile: Delivers national and international news, sports and society.
Language (s): Spanish
DAILY NEWSPAPER

Debate
Editorial: Pungarabato Pte No 37, Ciudad Altamirano, Guerrero 40660.
T: 52 76 76722684
W: http://ww.eldebatedeloscalentanos.com
Freq: Daily; **Circ:** 150000 Not Audited
Publisher: Juan Cuevas Roman
Editorial Profile: El Debate mostly local news and has an opinion section.
Language (s): Spanish
DAILY NEWSPAPER

Diario Amanecer De México
Owner: Uno Mas Uno
Editorial: Gabino Barreda No. 86, San Rafael, Mexico State, Toluca, Mexico State C.P. 06351.
T: 52 55 10555500
E: diario_amanecer@yahoo.com.mx
W: http://www.diarioamanecer.com.mx
Freq: Daily; **Circ:** 50000 Not Audited
Editorial Profile: Diario Amanecer De México is a newspaper written for the general public in the Toluca, Mexico area. It offers regional, national, and international news and provides its readers with information on business, politics, and sports.
Language (s): Spanish
DAILY NEWSPAPER

DIARIO BASTA
Owner: Editorial Prosperidad S.A. de C.V.
Editorial: Mexico City, Distrito Federal.
T: 52 55 5254-5244
E: contacto@diariobasta.com
W: http://www.diariobasta.com.mx/index2.php
Freq: Mon thru Fri; **Circ:** 75000
Editor in Chief: David Casco
Editorial Profile: The newspaper focuses on celebrity and entertainment news along with some sport and politics.
Language (s): Spanish
DAILY NEWSPAPER

Diario De México
Owner: Diario De México
Editorial: Chimalpopoca No. 38, Obrera, Distrito Federal, Mexico City, Distrito Federal C.P. 06800. **T:** 52 55 54426500
E: edictos@diariodemexico.com.mx
W: http://www.diariodemexico.com.mx
Freq: Daily
Publisher: Federico Bracamontes Baz; **Editor:** Rosa Colin; **Editor:** Abraham Sheimberg
Editorial Profile: Diario de Juarez is written for the general public in the Mexico City, Mexico area. It offers regional, national, and international news and provides its readers with information on the economy, politics, sports, and entertainment.
Language (s): Spanish
DAILY NEWSPAPER

El Diario de Yucatan
Owner: A.e.e.
Editorial: Calle 60 #521, Merida, Yucatan C.P. 97000. **T:** 52 55 52938240
E: comentarios@yucatan.com.mx
W: http://www.yucatan.com.mx
Freq: Daily; **Circ:** 54600 Not Audited
Editorial Profile: La I is a daily newspaper written for the general public in the Campeche, Campeche, Mexico area. It offers regional, national, and international news and provides its readers with information on the economy, politics, sports, society, family, and entertainment.
Language (s): Spanish
DAILY NEWSPAPER

Diario De Yucatán (&)
Owner: A.e.e.
Editorial: Calle 60 #521, Merida, Yucatan C.P. 97000. **T:** 52 999 942-2222
W: http://www.yucatan.com.mx
Freq: Sun; **Circ:** 58586 Not Audited
Editor: Luis Luna Cetina; **Editor:** Jorge Munoz Menendez; **Editor:** Ruben Menendez Antuniano; **Publisher:** Carlos Menendez Navarrete; **Editor:** Gaspar Povera
Language (s): Spanish
DAILY NEWSPAPER

El Economista
Owner: El Economista
Editorial: Av. Coyoacán No. 515, Del Valle, Distrito Federal, Mexico City, Distrito Federal C.P. 03100. **T:** 52 55 5326-5454
W: http://www.eleconomista.com.mx
Freq: Mon thru Fri
Editor: Alberto Aguirre; **Editor:** Daniel Esparza; **Editor:** Manuel Lino; **Publisher:** Luis Enrique Mercado Sanchez; **Currency Editor:** Ana Prado; **Editor:** Julio Sanchez; **Editor:** Armando Torres
Editorial Profile: El Economista is a daily newspaper specializing in finance, offering regional, national, and international news. It also provides its readers with information on the global economy, technology, finance, business, and politics.
Language (s): Spanish
DAILY NEWSPAPER

Enfoque Diario
Editorial: Calle Guadalupe Victoria #5, Salina Cruz, Oaxaca 70610. **T:** 01 97 1716-3492
E: diarioenfoqued@yahoo.com.mx
W: http://enfoquediario.com
Freq: Daily
Editor: Diana Manzo
Editorial Profile: Enfoque Diario is a daily newspaper written for the general public in the Salina Cruz, Oaxaca, Mexico area. It offers regional, national, and international news and provides its readers with information on the economy, politics, science, technology, culture, sports, and entertainment.
Language (s): Spanish
DAILY NEWSPAPER

Esto
Owner: Organización Editorial Mexicana S.A. de C.V.
Editorial: Guillermo Prieto No. 7, Col. San Rafael, Mexico City, Distrito Federal C.P. 06470. **T:** 52 55 5566-1511
W: http://www.esto.com.mx
Freq: Mon
Editor in Chief: Carlos Gabino Cu Uc; **Publisher:** Mario Vázquez Raña
Editorial Profile: Esto is a daily sports newspaper written for sports fanatics in the Mexico City, Mexico area. It offers regional, national, and international sports news and provides its readers with information on Mexican soccer, boxing, basketball, baseball, wrestling, statistics and more.
Language (s): Spanish
DAILY NEWSPAPER

Excelsior
Owner: Excelsior
Editorial: Bucareli No. 1, Col. Centro, Mexico City, Distrito Federal C.P. 06600.
T: 52 55 5128-3000
E: nacional@nuevoexcelsior.com.mx
W: http://www.excelsior.com.mx
Freq: Daily
Editor: Martha Elena Blanco; **Editor:** Juan Pablo Estrada; **Publisher:** Marco Gonsen; **Editor:** Ernesto Rivera Aguilar; **Editor:** Uriel Trejo
Editorial Profile: First published in 1917, Excelsior is a daily newspaper covering all aspects of Mexican life. The publication provides local, national and international news, politics, economics, finance, information technology, sports and entertainment.
Language (s): Spanish
DAILY NEWSPAPER

El Financiero
Owner: Grupo Multimedia Lauman, SAPI de CV
Editorial: Lago Bolsena No. 176, Anáhuac, Mexico City, Distrito Federal C.P. 11320.
T: 52 55 5449-8600
E: material@elfinanciero.com.mx
W: http://www.elfinanciero.com.mx
Freq: Mon thru Fri
Editor: Antonio Armendarez; **Editor:** Rogelio Barela; **Editor:** Araceli Damian; **Editor:** Lourdes Gonzalez; **Editor:** Olga Ojeda Lajud; **Editor:** Alejandro Ramos; **Editor:** Piro Villamil
Editorial Profile: El Financiero is a newspaper written for the general public in the Mexico City, Distrito Federal, Mexico area. It offers regional, national, and international news and provides its readers with information on finance, the economy, business, politics, society, culture, sports, and entertainment.
Language (s): Spanish
DAILY NEWSPAPER

La I Laguna
Owner: A.e.e.
Editorial: Av. De Las Palmas No. 239, Desp. 203 Y 204, Lomas De Chapultepec, Coahuila, Torreon, Coahuila C.P. 11000.
T: 52 55 52938240 **E:** lai@lailaguna.com.mx
W: http://www.elsiglodetorreon.com.mx/lailaguna/
Freq: Daily; **Circ:** 54600 Not Audited
Editorial Profile: La I Laguna is a daily newspaper written for the general public in the Torreon, Coahuila, Mexico area. It offers regional, national, and international news and provides its readers with information on the economy, finance, politics, sports, society, and entertainment.
Language (s): Spanish
DAILY NEWSPAPER

La I Mérida
Owner: A.e.e.
Editorial: Av. De Las Palmas No. 239, Desp. 203 Y 204, Lomas De Chapultepec, Yucatán, Merida, Yucatan C.P. 11000.
T: 52 55 52938240
E: diario@megamedia.com.mx
W: http://www.laiyucatan.com
Freq: Daily; **Circ:** 54600 Not Audited
Editorial Profile: La I Mérida is a daily newspaper written for the general public in the Merida, Yucatan, Mexico area. It offers regional, national, and international news and provides its readers with information on the economy, politics, sports, society, family, and entertainment.
Language (s): Spanish
DAILY NEWSPAPER

La I Quintana Roo
Owner: A.e.e.
Editorial: Av. De Las Palmas No. 239, Desp. 203 Y 204, Lomas De Chapultepec, Quintana Roo, Cancun, Quintana Roo C.P. 11000.
T: 52 525 5529382 **W:** http://www.aee.com.mx
Freq: Daily; **Circ:** 54600 Not Audited
Editorial Profile: La I is a daily newspaper written for the general public in the Cancun, Quintana Roo, Mexico area. It offers regional, national, and international news and provides its readers with information on the economy, politics, sports, society, family, and entertainment.
Language (s): Spanish
DAILY NEWSPAPER

La I Tijuana
Owner: A.e.e.
Editorial: Av. De Las Palmas No. 239, Desp. 203 Y 204, Lomas De Chapultepec, Baja California, Tijuana, Baja California C.P. 11000.
T: 52 55 52938240 **W:** http://www.aee.com.mx
Freq: Daily; **Circ:** 54600 Not Audited
Editorial Profile: La I Tijuana is a daily newspaper written for the general public in the Tijuana, Baja California, Mexico area. It offers regional, national, and international news and provides its readers with information on the economy, politics, sports, society, family, and entertainment.
Language (s): Spanish
DAILY NEWSPAPER

El Informador (sp)
Owner: Unión Editorialista
Editorial: Av. Paseo De Las Palmas No. 239-203, Lomas De Chapultepec, Jalisco, Guadalajara, Jalisco C.P. 11000.
T: 52 33 36787700
E: atencion@informador.com.mx
W: http://www.informador.com.mx
Freq: Weekly
Editor: Alma Alcaras; **Editor:** Alejandro Cabanillas; **Editor:** Laura Castro; **Publisher:** Carlos Alvarez del Castillo; **Editor:** Carlos Fonseca; **Editor:** Ramon Godinez; **Editor:** Ana Guerrero Santos; **Editor:** Javier Medina Loera; **Editor:** Antonio Flores Pozos; **Editor:** Cecilia Rangel; **Editor:** Ramon Salmeron; **Editor:** Jorge Verea
Editorial Profile: El Informador is a daily newspaper written for the general public in the Guadalajara, Jalisco, Mexico area. It offers regional, national, and international news and provides its readers with information on the economy, politics, technology, society, culture, sports, and entertainment.
Language (s): Spanish

DAILY NEWSPAPER

The International New York Times - Mexico City
Editorial: Anatole France 230, Col. Olanco Reforma, Mexico City, Distrito Federal 11550. **T:** 52 555 211-4160
Bureau Chief: Randal Archibold
DAILY NEWSPAPER

La Jornada
Owner: La Jornada
Editorial: Av. Cuauhtémoc No. 1236, Sta Cruz Atoyac, Distrito Federal, Mexico City, Distrito Federal C.P. 03310. **T:** 52 55 91830300
W: http://www.jornada.unam.mx
Freq: Daily
News Editor: Elena Gallegos; **Editor:** Julie Hernandez; **Editor:** Fabrizio Leon; **Editor:** Emilio Loman Maldonado; **Editor:** Julio Reyna Quiroz Quiroz; **Editor:** Ivan Restrepo; **Publisher:** Carmen Lira Saade; **Editor:** Miguel Velasquez; **Editor:** Jose Zaldua
Editorial Profile: La Jornada is a daily newspaper written for the general public in the Mexico City, Distrito Federal, Mexico area. It offers regional, national, and international news and provides its readers with information on the economy, politics, society & justice, science, technology, culture, sports, and entertainment.
Language (s): Spanish
DAILY NEWSPAPER

El M
Owner: El M
Editorial: Bucareli No. 8, CentroDistrito Federal, Mexico City, Distrito Federal C.P. 06040. **T:** 52 55 57091313
Freq: Mon thru Fri
Editorial Profile: El M cover national and international news, sports and entertainment.
Language (s): Spanish
DAILY NEWSPAPER

El Mañana De Matamoros
Owner: Editora Demar
Editorial: Av. La Rioja No. 119, San Pedro Zacatengo, Tamaulipas, Matamoros, Tamaulipas C.P. 07360. **T:** 52 55 55863008
E: ingantoniovera@prodigy.net.mx
W: http://www.elmananarey.com/diario/seccion/matamoros
Freq: Daily; **Circ:** 70000 Not Audited
Publisher: Heriberto Deandar Martinez; **Editor:** Augustin Lozano Delgado
Editorial Profile: El Mañana de Matamoros offers local news in different sections as well as national and international news, sports, entertainment, opinion and society.
Language (s): Spanish
DAILY NEWSPAPER

El Mañana De Reynosa
Owner: Editora Demar
Editorial: Av. La Rioja No. 119, San Pedro Zacatengo, Tamaulipas, Reynosa, Tamaulipas C.P. 07360. **T:** 52 55 55863008
E: ingantoniovera@prodigy.net.mx
W: http://www.elmananarey.com
Freq: Daily; **Circ:** 65000 Not Audited
Publisher: Heriberto Martinez; **Editor:** Heriberto Robinson; **Editor:** Erasmo Salinas Perez; **Editor:** Arturo Soto
Editorial Profile: El Mañana de Reynosa covers national and international news, sports, opinion, society, entertainment, and culture.
Language (s): Spanish
DAILY NEWSPAPER

El Martinense
Editorial: Blvd Rafael Martínez de la Torre - No. 168 esquina 22 de Noviembre, Col. San Manuel Martínez de la Torre, Veracruz, Veracruz. **T:** 52 232 3248546
E: ilha19@hotmail.com
W: http://www.elmartinense.com.mx
Freq: Mon thru Fri
Language (s): Spanish
DAILY NEWSPAPER

El Mexicano
Editorial: Ave Pioneros #1283, Centro Civico, Mexicali, Baja California 21000.
T: 52 526 557-1078
E: mexmex@el-mexicano.con.mx
Freq: Daily
Bureau Chief: Alfredo García Amaya
Language (s): Spanish
DAILY NEWSPAPER

El Mexicano
Owner: Medios Masivos M.
Editorial: Luz Saviñon No. 13, Piso 6, Colonia del Valle, Mexico City, Distrito Federal C.P. 03100. **T:** 52 55 5340-2450
W: http://www.mediosmasivos.com.mx
Freq: Daily; **Circ:** 57000 Not Audited
Editor: Sergio Anzures
Language (s): Spanish
DAILY NEWSPAPER

El Mexicano
Owner: Editorial Kino, S.A., de C.V.
Editorial: Gral. Lázaro Cárdenas #3743, Fracc. Los Pirules, Tijuana, Baja California 22540.
T: 52 664 104-2400
W: http://www.el-mexicano.com.mx
Freq: Daily; **Circ:** 451556
Publisher & Editor: Enrique Sánchez Díaz
Editorial Profile: Epoch Times is a Chinese-American Daily newspaper.
DAILY NEWSPAPER

Milenio Colima
Owner: Milenio
Editorial: Morelos No. 16, Centro, Colima, Colima, Colima C.P. 06040. **T:** 52 55 51402950
E: publicidad@mileniodiario.com.mx
W: http://www.milenio.com
Freq: Daily
Editorial Profile: Milenio Colima covers national and international news, politics, economy, crime, sports, tendencies, culture and entertainment.
Language (s): Spanish
DAILY NEWSPAPER

Milenio Novedades
Owner: Medios Masivos M.
Editorial: Luz Saviñon No. 13, Del Valle, Yucatán, Merida, Yucatan C.P. 03100.
T: 52 55 53402450
E: alfredo.ramirez@mediosmasivos.com.mx
W: http://www.mediosmasivos.com.mx
Freq: Daily
Editorial Profile: Milenio Novedades covers regional and national news, politics, sports and entertainment.
Language (s): Spanish
DAILY NEWSPAPER

Mundo De Xalapa
Owner: R. Lemus
Editorial: Londres No. 239, Juarez, Veracruz, Xalapa, Veracruz C.P. 06600.
T: 52 55 55252018
W: http://www.mundodexalapa.com/noticias/
Freq: 2 Times/Week
Editorial Profile: El Mundo De Xalapa cover local and national news, sports, economy, politics and entertainment.
Language (s): Spanish
DAILY NEWSPAPER

Mundo Uvm
Owner: S/r
Editorial: Av. De Las Palmas No. 731-1003, Lomas De Barrilaco, Distrito Federal, Mexico City, Distrito Federal C.P. 11010.
T: 52 55 52021166
E: israel.granda@uvmnet.edu
W: http://www.uvmnet.edu/uvm/
Freq: Monthly; **Circ:** 50000 Not Audited
Editorial Profile: This is the official publication for Universidad del Valle de Mexico. It covers university news, and events.
Language (s): Spanish
DAILY NEWSPAPER

Mural
Owner: Grupo Reforma, S.A. de C.V.
Editorial: Av Mariano Otero #4047, Col La Calma, Guadalajara, Jalisco 45070.
T: 52 33 31343800 **W:** http://www.mural.com
Freq: Daily; **Circ:** 51000 Not Audited
Publisher: Alejandro Junco de la Vega; **Editor:** Eliseo Mora
Editorial Profile: Mural covers national and international news, business, sports, style, cars, entertainment, politics, crime, social scene and activities.
Language (s): Spanish
DAILY NEWSPAPER

El Norte
Owner: Grupo Reforma, S.A. de C.V.
Editorial: Washington 629 Oriente, Monterrey, Nuevo Leon 64000. **T:** 52 81 8150-8300
E: portada@elnorte.com
W: http://www.elnorte.com
Freq: Daily; **Circ:** 179729 Not Audited
Editor: Gaspar Bustillos; **Editor:** Juanita Diaza; **Publisher:** Alejandro Junco de la Vega; **Editor:** Luis Alberto Lara; **Editor:** Irenio Morales; **Editor:** Nelly Ramirez; **Editor:** Martha Alicia Trevino
Editorial Profile: El Norte covers mostly regional news, politics, crime, sports, culture, events, society and entertainment.
Language (s): Spanish
DAILY NEWSPAPER

Ovaciones
Owner: Ovaciones
Editorial: Lago Zirahuen No. 279, Anáhuac, Distrito Federal, Mexico City, Distrito Federal C.P. 11320. **T:** 52 55 5328-0700
E: ovaciones@hotmail.com
W: http://www.ovaciones.com
Freq: Daily
Publisher: Miguel Couchonnal; **News Editor:** Rita Magaña; **Editor:** Ignacio Matos; **Editor:** Leopoldo Meraz; **Editor:** Enrique Sanchez Marquez
Editorial Profile: Ovaciones is a Spanish-language daily newspaper that covers national and international soccer news.
Language (s): Spanish
DAILY NEWSPAPER

Periódico ABC de Monterrey
Owner: Grupo Radio Alegria
Editorial: Platón Sánchez Sur 411, Centro, Monterrey, Nuevo Leon C.P. 64000.
T: 52 81 8344-2510
E: contacto@periodicoabc.mx
W: http://www.periodicoabc.com.mx
Freq: Daily; **Circ:** 80000 Not Audited
Editor: Gonzalo Estrada Torres
Editorial Profile: The newspaper features local, national and international news. It also has sections dedicated to sports, women, and celebrities. The company also has radio stations in Mexico.
Language (s): Spanish
DAILY NEWSPAPER

El Periodico de Mexico
Editorial: Insurgentes sur #800 Piso 8, Col. Del Valle, Distrito Federal CP 03100.
T: 52 55 3300-5616
E: contacto@elperiodicodemexico.com
W: http://www.elperiodicodemexico.com
Freq: Daily
Editor: Karen Flores; **Editor:** Edwin Mejia; **Editor:** Iliana Vargas
Editorial Profile: El Periodico de Mexico is a daily newspaper written for the general public in the Mexico City, Distrito Federal, Mexico area. It offers regional, national, and international news and provides its readers with information on the economy, politics, science, technology, culture, sports, and entertainment.
Language (s): Spanish
DAILY NEWSPAPER

El Periodico de Quintana Roo
Editorial: Bonampak 77 Interior 404, SMZ 3, Cancun, Quintana Roo C.P. 77500.
T: 52 998 884-1004
W: http://www.elperiodico.com.mx/
Freq: Daily
Editor in Chief: Gabriela Cruz
Language (s): Spanish
DAILY NEWSPAPER

Periodico Del Centro
Owner: Notmusa
Editorial: Periferico Sur No. 4293, Jardines De La Montaña, Distrito Federal, Mexico City, Distrito Federal C.P. 14210. **T:** 52 55 50896114
E: garredondo@notmusa.com.mx
W: http://www.notmusa.com.mx
Freq: Mon thru Fri; **Circ:** 175000 Not Audited
Editor: Guadalupe Arredondo
Editorial Profile: El Periodico Del Centro cover national and international news, politics, crime and sports.
Language (s): Spanish
DAILY NEWSPAPER

El Porvenir
Owner: Medios Masivos M.
Editorial: Galeana 344 Sur, Monterrey, Nuevo Leon C.P. 64000. **T:** 52 81 8345-4080
E: editorial.elporvenir@prodigy.net.mx
W: http://www.elporvenir.com.mx
Freq: Daily; **Circ:** 75000 Not Audited
Publisher: Jose Gerardo Cantu Escalante; **Editor:** Rogelio Cantu Escalante; **News Editor:** Jose Rodriguez Arroyo
Editorial Profile: El Porvenir is a daily newspaper written for the general public in the Monterrey, Nuevo Leon, Mexico area. It offers regional, national, and international news and provides its readers with information on the economy, politics, society, culture, sports, and entertainment.
Language (s): Spanish
DAILY NEWSPAPER

La Prensa
Owner: La Prensa
Editorial: Basilio Vadillo No. 40, Tabacalera, Distrito Federal, Mexico City, Distrito Federal C.P. 06030. **T:** 52 55 5228-9977
W: http://www.oem.com.mx/laprensa
Freq: Daily
Editor: Mauricio Ortega Camberos; **Editor:** Jesus Sanchez Ramirez; **Publisher:** Mario Vázquez Raña
Editorial Profile: La Prensa is a daily newspaper written for the general public in the Mexico City, Distrito Federal, Mexico area. It offers regional, national, and international news and provides its readers with information on the economy, finance, politics, health, science, technology, culture, sports, and entertainment.
Language (s): Spanish
DAILY NEWSPAPER

Prensa De Reynosa
Owner: Gpo. Lemus R.
Editorial: Durango No. 353, Roma, Tamaulipas, Reynosa, Tamaulipas C.P. 06700.
T: 52 55 52860222
E: ventas@grupo-lemus.com.mx
W: http://www.laprensa.mx
Freq: Daily; **Circ:** 60000 Not Audited
Editor: Enrique Coronado; **Editor:** Felix Garza Elizondo; **Editor:** Luis Triana
Editorial Profile: Prensa De Reynosa is a daily newspaper written for the general public in the Reynosa, Tamaulipas, Mexico area. It offers regional, national, and international news and provides its readers with information on politics, society, culture, sports, and entertainment.
Language (s): Spanish
DAILY NEWSPAPER

Publimetro
Owner: Directo
Editorial: Av. Insurgentes Sur No. 716, Piso 10, Col. Del Valle, Mexico City, Distrito Federal C.P. 03100. **T:** 52 55 5340-0700
W: http://www.publimetro.com.mx
Editor: Juan Pablo
Editorial Profile: Publimetro is a daily newspaper written for the general public in the Mexico City, Distrito Federal, Mexico area. It offers regional, national, and international news and provides its readers with information on the economy, politics, science, technology, culture, sports, and entertainment.
Language (s): Spanish
DAILY NEWSPAPER

Pueblo
Editorial: Calle Ruben Mora #4, Col Guerrero 2000, Chilpancingo, Guerrero 39000.
T: 52 74 74728070
E: puebloguerrero@yahoo.com.mx
W: http://www.puebloguerrero.com.mx
Freq: Daily
Editor: Roberto Carlos Rosa; **Publisher:** Gustavo Salazar Adame
Editorial Profile: Pueblo is a daily newspaper written for the general public in the Chilpancingo, Guerrero, Mexico area. It offers regional, national, and international news and provides its readers with information on the economy, politics, education, culture, and sports.
Language (s): Spanish
DAILY NEWSPAPER

El Pueblo
T: 52 614 4103006
E: reporteros2005@yahoo.com.mx
W: http://www.elpueblo.com
Freq: Daily
Editor: Laura Alba; **News Editor:** Enrique Corte; **Editor in Chief:** Hector Garcia
Language (s): Spanish
DAILY NEWSPAPER

Pulso
Owner: Editora Mival S.A. de C.V.
Editorial: Galeana No 485, Centro, San Luis Potosi, San Luis Potosi 78000.
T: 52 44 48127575 **E:** pulso@pulsoslp.com.mx
W: http://www.pulsoslp.com.mx
Freq: Daily; **Circ:** 60000 Not Audited
Publisher: Pablo Vallardes Garcia
Editorial Profile: Pulso is a daily newspaper written for the general public in the San Luis Potosi, San Luis Potosi, Mexico area. It offers regional, national, and international news and provides its readers with information on the economy, politics, security, sports, and entertainment.
Language (s): Spanish
DAILY NEWSPAPER

Puntual
Owner: Difusa
Editorial: Calle De La Barra No. 57, Casi Esq. Blvd. Temoluco, Fracc. Acueducto De Guadalupe, Mexico State, Toluca, Mexico State C.P. 07279. **T:** 52 55 53919243
E: difusadivprensa@aol.com
Freq: Daily; **Circ:** 60000 Not Audited

Editorial Profile: Puntual is a daily newspaper written for the general public in the Toluca, Mexico, Mexico area. It offers regional, national, and international news and provides its readers with information on the economy, politics, education, science, culture, and entertainment.
Language (s): Spanish
DAILY NEWSPAPER

Puras Ofertas
Owner: Bizcom
Editorial: Av. Paseo De Las Palmas No. 731, Piso 10, Desp. 1003, Lomas De Barrilaco, Guanajuato, Leon, Guanajuato C.P. 11010.
T: 52 55 52021166
E: informes@purasofertas.com.mx
W: http://www.purasofertas.com.mx
Freq: Weekly; **Circ:** 100000 Not Audited
Editorial Profile: A daily newspaper offering promotions and deals written for the general public in the Leon, Guanajuato, Mexico area.
Language (s): Spanish
DAILY NEWSPAPER

El Quiosco
Owner: Editorial Fundadores S.A. de C.V.
Editorial: Simón Bolívar 1730, Col. Zaragoza, Nuevo Laredo, Tamaulipas 88160.
T: 52 867 711-2222 **W:** http://elquiosco.mx
Freq: Daily
News Editor: Ricardo Flores Alvarez; **Editor:** David Dorantes; **Bureau Chief:** Marco Martinez; **News Editor:** Michelle Piedras
Editorial Profile: Covers local, national and international news, as well as sports and entertainment.
Language (s): Spanish
DAILY NEWSPAPER

Récord Guadalajara
Owner: Notmusa
Editorial: Periférico Sur No. 4293, Jardines En La Montaña, Jalisco, Guadalajara, Jalisco C.P. 14210. **T:** 52 55 91409500
E: garredondo@notmusa.com.mx
W: http://www.notmusa.com.mx
Freq: Mon; **Circ:** 146000 Not Audited
Editor: Guadalupe Arredondo
Editorial Profile: A sports newspaper on Guadalajara, Jalisco, Mexico sports, including soccer, basketball, football, and baseball. Editorial includes news, sport and team statistics, player biographies, and major sporting events.
Language (s): Spanish
DAILY NEWSPAPER

Récord Monterrey
Owner: Notmusa
Editorial: Periférico Sur No. 4293, Jardines En La Montaña, Nuevo León, Monterrey, Nuevo Leon C.P. 14210. **T:** 52 55 91409500
E: garredondo@notmusa.com.mx
W: http://www.notmusa.com.mx
Freq: Mon; **Circ:** 146000 Not Audited
Editor: Guadalupe Arredondo
Editorial Profile: Récord Monterrey is a sports newspaper written for the general public in the Monterrey, Nuevo Leon, Mexico area. It provides its readers with information on soccer news, statistics, player biographies, and major events.
Language (s): Spanish
DAILY NEWSPAPER

Reforma
Owner: Reforma
Editorial: Av. México Coyoacán No. 40, Sta Cruz Atoyac, Distrito Federal, Mexico City, Distrito Federal C.P. 03310.
T: 52 55 5628-7100
W: http://www.reforma.com
Freq: Daily
Editor: Roberto Castañeda; **Editor:** Rene Delgado; **Editor:** Adriana Garay; **Editor:** Rodolfo Gerschman; **Editor:** Enrique Guadarrama; **Editor:** Raul Huitron; **Publisher:** Alejandro Junco de la Vega; **Editor:** Raul Munoz; **Editor:** Jaime Rubio; **Editor:** Judith Segura; **Editor:** Martha Trejo; **City Editor:** Hector Zamarron; **Editor:** Juan Zamora
Editorial Profile: Reforma is a daily newspaper written for the general public in the Mexico City, Distrito Federal, Mexico area. It offers regional, national, and international news and provides its readers with information on the economy, politics, society, lifestyle, science, justice, culture, sports, and entertainment.
Language (s): Spanish
DAILY NEWSPAPER

Reforma - Los Angeles Bureau
Owner: Reforma
Editorial: 14014 Nw Passage Apt 224, Marina del Rey, Los Angeles, California 90292-7420.
T: 1 310 403-3562
W: http://www.reforma.com.mx
Freq: Daily
Bureau Chief: Nora Estrada
Editorial Profile: This is the Los Angeles bureau for Reforma, a daily newspaper serving Mexico City.
Language (s): Spanish
DAILY NEWSPAPER

El Regio
Owner: EDITORA REGIO, S.A. DE C.V.
Editorial: Jerónimo Treviño 1702 Poniente, Colonia Centro, Monterrey, Nuevo Leon CP 64000. **T:** 52 81 8372-0597
E: director@elregio.com
W: http://www.elregio.com
Freq: Daily
Editor: Gloria González Solís
Editorial Profile: El Regio is a daily newspaper written for the general public in the Monterrey, Nuevo Leon, Mexico area. It offers regional, national, and international news and provides its readers with information on the economy, politics, science, technology, culture, sports, and entertainment.
Language (s): Spanish
DAILY NEWSPAPER

Rumbo De México
Owner: Grupo Mac
Editorial: Montes Urales No. 425, Lomas De Chapultepec, Distrito Federal, Mexico City, Distrito Federal C.P. 11000.
T: 52 55 3099-3000
W: http://www.rumbodemexico.com.mx
Freq: Daily; **Circ:** 63391 Not Audited
Editorial Profile: Rumbo de Mexico is a daily newspaper written for the general public in the Mexico City, Distrito Federal, Mexico area. It offers regional, national, and international news and provides its readers with information on the economy, politics, society & justice, sports, and entertainment.
Language (s): Spanish
DAILY NEWSPAPER

San Luis Hoy
Owner: Medios Masivos M.
Editorial: Luz Saviñon No. 13, Del Valle, San Luis Potosí, San Luis Potosí, San Luis Potosi C.P. 03100. **T:** 52 55 53402450
E: alfredo.ramirez@mediosmasivos.com.mx
W: http://www.sanluishoy.com.mx
Freq: Daily
Editor: Eduardo Chavez Aguilar; **Publisher:** Pablo Vallardes Garcia
Editorial Profile: San Luis Hoy is a daily newspaper written for the general public in the San Luis Potosi, San Luis Potosi, Mexico area. It offers regional and national news and provides its readers with information on politics, culture, sports, and entertainment.
Language (s): Spanish
DAILY NEWSPAPER

Síntesis
Owner: Síntesis
Editorial: Calle 23 No. 33, San Pedro De Los Pinos, Puebla, Puebla, Puebla C.P. 03800.
T: 52 55 56150088 **E:** sintesisweb@gmail.com
W: http://www.sintesisdigital.com.mx
Freq: Daily
Editor: Luis Benitez Armas; **Editor:** Claudio Cisneros; **Editor:** Adolfo Duran; **Publisher:** Mariano Morales Corona
Editorial Profile: Síntesis is a daily newspaper written for the general public in the Puebla, Puebla, Mexico area. It offers regional, national, and international news and provides its readers with information on the economy, politics, science, society, sports, weather and entertainment.
Language (s): Spanish
DAILY NEWSPAPER

Síntesis De Hidalgo
Owner: Síntesis
Editorial: Calle 23 No. 33, San Pedro De Los Pinos, Hidalgo, Pachuca, Hidalgo C.P. 03800.
T: 52 55 56150088 **E:** sintesisweb@gmail.com
W: http://www.sintesisdigital.com.mx
Freq: Daily
Editorial Profile: Síntesis de Hidalgo is a daily newspaper written for the general public in the Pachuca, Hidalgo, Mexico area. It offers regional, national, and international news and provides its readers with information on the economy, politics, science, society, sports, weather and entertainment.
Language (s): Spanish
DAILY NEWSPAPER

Síntesis De Tlaxcala
Owner: Síntesis
Editorial: Calle 23 No. 33, San Pedro De Los Pinos, Tlaxcala, Tlaxcala, Tlaxcala C.P. 03800.
T: 52 55 56150088 **E:** sintesisweb@gmail.com
W: http://www.sintesisdigital.com.mx
Freq: Daily
Editor: Isabel Gomez Macias; **Editor:** Jose Mendez; **Publisher:** Mariano Morales Corona
Editorial Profile: Síntesis De Tlaxcala is a daily newspaper written for the general public in the Tlaxcala, Tlaxcala, Mexico area. It offers regional, national, and international news and provides its readers with information on the economy, politics, science, society, sports, weather and entertainment.
Language (s): Spanish
DAILY NEWSPAPER

El Sol de Mazatlán
Owner: Organización Editorial Mexicana S.A. de C.V.
Editorial: Av. Miguel Alemán 312, Fracc . Playa sur, Mazatlan, Sinaloa C.P. 82040.
T: 52 669 915-5600 **E:** dirmaz@oem.com.mx
W: http://www.oem.com.mx/elsoldemazatlan
Freq: Daily
Editor: Sergio Ontiveros Salas
Editorial Profile: El Sol de Mazatlán is a daily newspaper written for the general public in the Mazatlan, Sinaloa, Mexico area. It offers regional, national, and international news and provides its readers with information on the economy, finance, politics, health, tourism, science, technology, culture, sports, and entertainment.
Language (s): Spanish
DAILY NEWSPAPER

El Sol de México
Owner: El Sol De México
Editorial: Guillermo Prieto No. 9, San Rafael, Distrito Federal, Mexico City, Distrito Federal C.P. 06470. **T:** 52 55 5566-1511
W: http://www.oem.com.mx/elsoldemexico
Freq: Daily
Editor: Eduardo Correa Platan; **Editor:** Benjamin Cruz; **Editor:** Edgar Gonsalez; **Editor:** Edgar Gonzalez Martinez; **Editor:** Gabriel Jantomila; **Editor:** Mario Leyva; **Editor:** Cristina Roman
Editorial Profile: El Sol De México is a daily newspaper written for the general public in the Mexico City, Distrito Federal, Mexico area. It offers regional, national, and international news and provides its readers with information on the economy, finance, politics, health, tourism, science, technology, culture, sports, and entertainment.
Language (s): Spanish
DAILY NEWSPAPER

El Sol De Puebla
Owner: O.e.m.
Editorial: Guillermo Prieto No. 7, San Rafael, Puebla, Puebla, Puebla C.P. 06351.
T: 52 55 55661511
E: publicidad@elsoldepuebla.com.mx
W: http://www.oem.com.mx/elsoldepuebla
Freq: Daily; **Circ:** 67000 Not Audited
Editor: Candelario Castillo; **Editor:** Jorge Corona; **Editor:** Marco de Leon; **Editor:** Jose Martinez; **Publisher:** Marco Ponce de Leon; **News Editor:** Wendy Sanchez; **Editor:** Maria Sarniza de Meyes; **Editor:** Jorge Zamora
Editorial Profile: El Sol De Puebla is a daily newspaper written for the general public in the Puebla, Morelos, Mexico area. It offers regional, national, and international news and provides its readers with information on the economy, finance, politics, health, tourism, science, technology, culture, sports, and entertainment.
Language (s): Spanish
DAILY NEWSPAPER

Super Ofertas
Owner: Sólo Ofertas
Editorial: Av. López Mateos Sur No. 5142, La Calma Zapopan, Jalisco, Guadalajara, Jalisco C.P. 45071 **W:** http://www.nuevosiglo.com.mx
Freq: Weekly; **Circ:** 180000 Not Audited
Editorial Profile: Super Ofertas is a daily newspaper written for the general public in the Guadalajara, Jalisco, Mexico area. It offers promotions and deals in various grocery and retail stores in Guadalajara.
Language (s): Spanish
DAILY NEWSPAPER

Tabasco Hoy
Owner: Organización Editorial Acuario S.A. de C.V.
Editorial: Luz Saviñon No. 13, Del Valle, Tabasco, Villahermosa, Tabasco C.P. 03100.
T: 52 99 33100229
W: http://www.tabascohoy.com.mx
Freq: Daily; **Circ:** 50000 Not Audited
Editor: Raul Cortes Alamilla; **Editor:** Hector Martinez de Esobar; **Publisher:** Miguel Canton Zetina
Editorial Profile: Tabasco Hoy is a daily newspaper written for the general public in the Villahermosa, Tabasco, Mexico area. It offers regional, national, and international news and provides its readers with information on the economy, finance, politics, culture, sports, and entertainment.
Language (s): Spanish
DAILY NEWSPAPER

La Tarde
Owner: Medios Masivos M.
Editorial: Luz Saviñon No. 13, Del Valle, Tamaulipas, Nvo. Laredo, Tamaulipas C.P. 03100. **T:** 52 55 53402450
E: alfredo.ramirez@mediosmasivos.com.mx
W: http://www.mediosmasivos.com.mx
Freq: Daily
Editorial Profile: La Tarde is a daily newspaper written for the general public in the Nuevo Laredo, Tamaulipas, Mexico area. It offers regional, national, and international news and provides its readers with information on the economy, politics, culture, sports, and entertainment.
Language (s): Spanish
DAILY NEWSPAPER

El Tren De Guadalajara
Owner: Directo
Editorial: Juan Manuel No. 77, Centro, Jalisco, Guadalajara, Jalisco C.P. 44100. **T:** 52 55
E: eltren@informador.com.mx
W: http://www.periodicoeltren.com.mx
Freq: Mon thru Fri; **Circ:** 148802 Not Audited
Editor: Ricardo Barba Rabago
Editorial Profile: El Tren De Guadalajara is a daily newspaper written for the general public in the Guadalajara, Jalisco, Mexico area. It offers regional, national, and international news and provides its readers with information on the economy, politics, health, culture, sports, and entertainment.
Language (s): Spanish
DAILY NEWSPAPER

El Universal
Owner: El Universal
Editorial: Bucareli No. 8, Centro, Distrito Federal, Mexico City, Distrito Federal C.P. 06040. **T:** 52 55 5709-1313
E: guardia@eluniversal.com.mx
W: http://www.eluniversal.com.mx
Freq: Daily
Editor: Walter Alvarado; **Editor:** Jorge Camargo Z.; **Editor:** Joel Hernandez S.; **Editor:** Dulce Lavaniegos; **Editor:** Martha Ortiz; **Editor:** Judith Perez; **Editor:** Roberto Rock L.; **Editor:** Macario Schettino
Editorial Profile: El Universal is a daily newspaper written for the general public in the Mexico City, Distrito Federal, Mexico area. It offers regional, national, and international news and provides its readers with information on the economy, politics, society & justice, science, technology, culture, sports, and entertainment.
Language (s): Spanish
DAILY NEWSPAPER

El Universal Gráfico
Owner: El Universal Gráfico
Editorial: Bucareli No. 8, Centro, Distrito Federal, Mexico City, Distrito Federal C.P. 06040. **T:** 52 55 57091313
W: http://www.eluniversal.com.mx/grafico
Freq: Mon thru Fri
City Editor: Silvia Ojanguren; **Editor:** Rosalinda Palomeque
Editorial Profile: El Universal Gráfico is a daily newspaper written for men in the Mexico City, Distrito Federal, Mexico area. It offers news on celebrities and models.
Language (s): Spanish
DAILY NEWSPAPER

Unomasuno
Owner: Impulsora de Periodismo Mexicano, S.A. de C.V.
Editorial: Gabino Barreda 86 Delegación Cuauhtemoc, Col. San Rafael, Mexico City, Distrito Federal 6470. **T:** 52 55 1055-5500
E: unomasuno@naim.com.mx
W: http://www.unomasuno.com.mx
Freq: Daily
Editor in Chief: Esteban Duran; **Editor:** Sergio Martinez Estrada; **News Editor:** Jose Montana; **Publisher:** Karina Rocha Priego; **Editor:** Raul Ruiz; **Editor:** Luis Carlos Silva Rodriguez; **Editor:** Raul Tavera Arias
Language (s): Spanish
DAILY NEWSPAPER

Valle del Norte
Editorial: Chihuahua No 1245 Sur, Reynosa, Tamaulipas 88630. **T:** 52 89 99238800
E: editorial@valledelnorte.com.mx

W: http://www.valledelnorte.com.mx
Freq: Daily
Publisher: Fernando De Luna Sanchez; **Editor:** Martin Hernandez Martinez
Editorial Profile: La Jornada is a daily newspaper written for the general public in the Reynosa, Tamaulipas, Mexico area. It offers regional, national, and international news and provides its readers with information on the economy, politics, society, security, sports, and entertainment.
Language (s): Spanish
DAILY NEWSPAPER

La Voz de Michoacan
T: 52 434 3422058
W: http://www.vozdemichoacan.com.mx
Freq: Daily
Editor: Alvaro Medina; **Editor in Chief:** Miguel Medina
Language (s): Spanish
DAILY NEWSPAPER

La Voz de Zihuatanejo
Editorial: Calle Pesquera s/n Col Los Reyes, Zihuatanejo, Guerrero 40880.
T: 52 755 5536172
E: vozihuatanejo@hotmail.com
W: http://www.vozihuatanejo.com.mx
Freq: Daily
Editor: Alejandro Alvarado; **Editor in Chief:** Hector Alvarado
Language (s): Spanish
DAILY NEWSPAPER

The Wall Street Journal (Mexico)
Editorial: Tennyson 96, Col. Chapultepec Polanco, Mexico City, Distrito Federal 11560.
T: 52 55 5281-0902
DAILY NEWSPAPER

Zacatecas en Imagen
Owner: Grupo Editorial Zacatecas S.A. de C.V.
Editorial: Calzada Revolucion 24, Col Tierra y Libertad, Zacatecas, Zacatecas 98600.
T: 52 49 29238898
E: capital@imagenzac.com.mx
W: http://www.imagenzac.com.mx
Freq: Daily; **Circ:** 60000 Not Audited
Publisher: Eugenio Mercado Sanchez; **Editor:** Francisco Reynoso
Editorial Profile: Zacatecas en Imagen is a daily newspaper written for the general public in the Zacatecas, Zacatecas, Mexico area. It offers regional, national, and international news and provides its readers with information on the economy, politics, society & justice, science, technology, culture, sports, and entertainment.
Language (s): Spanish
DAILY NEWSPAPER

NEWS SERVICE/SYNDICATE

Agence France-Presse
Editorial: Calle Durango No 183, Colonia Roma Norte, Mexico City, Distrito Federal 6700. T: 52 55 5128-1100
E: redaccion.mexico@afp.com
NEWS SERVICE/SYNDICATE

Agencia de Información Integral Periodística
Editorial: Mexico City, Distrito Federal.
T: 52 55 5440-5284
W: http://www.aiip.com.mx/
Language (s): Spanish
NEWS SERVICE/SYNDICATE

Agencia EFE
Editorial: Lafayette, 69. Colonia Nueva Anzures, Mexico City, Distrito Federal 11590.
T: 52 55 5255-4025 **E:** info@efeamerica.com
W: http://www.efe.com
Bureau Chief: Agustin de Gracia
Language (s): Spanish
NEWS SERVICE/SYNDICATE

Associated Press
Editorial: Reforma 350, Piso 9, Mexico City, Distrito Federal 6600. T: 52 55 5080-3400
E: apmexico@ap.org
Bureau Chief: Katherine Corcoran
NEWS SERVICE/SYNDICATE

AUNAM
T: 52 55 56229438
News Editor: Carmen Solis
Language (s): Spanish
NEWS SERVICE/SYNDICATE

Bloomberg News
Editorial: Paseo de la Reforma 265, Piso 12, Mexico City, Distrito Federal 6500.
T: 52 55 52429200
Bureau Chief: Jose Enrique Arrioja
NEWS SERVICE/SYNDICATE

Dow Jones Newswires
Editorial: Tennyson 96, Col. Chapultepec Polanco, Mexico City, Distrito Federal 11560
E: mexico@dowjones.com
NEWS SERVICE/SYNDICATE

Finsat
T: 52 55 5227-7600
E: material@elfinanciero.com.mx
W: http://www.elfinanciero.com.mx
Editor: Perla Oropeza; **Editor:** Conrado Vasquez
Language (s): Spanish
NEWS SERVICE/SYNDICATE

Notiemp
Owner: Agencia de Noticias Empresariales
Editorial: Ave. de las Américas 1600, 2º Piso, Col. Country Club, Zona Financiera, Guadalajara, Jalisco 44680.
T: 52 33 36789207 **E:** noticias@notiemp.com
W: http://www.notiemp.com/sys/index.php
Editorial Profile: Notiemp is a Mexican News Agency that covers the most recent developments in economy and business news affecting Latin America and the rest of the world. Notiemp offers its subscribers in Mexico and throughout the world, a wide array of services such as text news, digital news, digital audio, TV and audio production, strategic analysis, monitoring, among others, either via satellite or Internet.
Language (s): Spanish
NEWS SERVICE/SYNDICATE

Notimex
Editorial: Morena 110 Col del Valle, Mexico City, Distrito Federal 3100. T: 52 54 201140
W: http://www.notimex.com.mx
Publisher: Aurelio Bueno Hernández
Editorial Profile: Notimex is the Mexican News Agency that covers the most recent developments affecting Latin America and the rest of the world. With over 35 years experience, Notimex offers its subscribers throughout the world, a wide array of services such as text news, digital photography, digital audio, banners, TV and audio production, special coverage of events, among others, either via satellite or Internet.
Language (s): Spanish
NEWS SERVICE/SYNDICATE

Notimex - Los Angeles Bureau
Editorial: 3600 Wilshire Blvd, Ste 2028, Los Angeles, California 90010-2624.
T: 1 213 483-7088 **E:** romerontx9@aol.com
Editor: Jose Romero
Editorial Profile: This is the Los Angeles bureau of Notimex in Mexico City, Mexico.
Language (s): Spanish
NEWS SERVICE/SYNDICATE

Notimex - New York Bureau
Editorial: 405 E 42nd St, New York, New York 10017-3507. T: 1 212 371-1289
Editorial Profile: This is the New York bureau of Notimex in Mexico City.
Language (s): Spanish
NEWS SERVICE/SYNDICATE

Notimex - Washington Bureau
Editorial: 529 14th St NW, Ste 975, Washington, District Of Columbia 20045-1906.
T: 1 202 347-5227
Editorial Profile: This is the Washington, D.C. bureau of Notimex in Mexico City, Mexico.
Language (s): Spanish
NEWS SERVICE/SYNDICATE

Reuters
Editorial: Manuel Avila Camacho Blvd., #36, Torre Esmeralda II, Piso 19, Mexico City, Distrito Federal 11000. T: 52 55 5282-7000
E: mexicocity.newsroom@thomsonreuters.com
Bureau Chief: Simon Gardner; **Latin America Editor:** Kieran Murray
NEWS SERVICE/SYNDICATE

Reuters Mexico
Editorial: 36 Blvd. Manuel Avila Camacho, Fl 19, Mexico City, Distrito Federal 11000.
T: 52 55 5281-7000
E: mexicocity.newsroom@reuters.com
W: http://mx.reuters.com/
Bureau Chief: Krista Hughes
Language (s): Spanish
NEWS SERVICE/SYNDICATE

Xinhua News Agency - Mexico City Bureau
Editorial: Calle Francisco I. Madero No.17, Col.Tlacopac San Ángel, Mexico City, Distrito Federal C.P. 01040. T: 52 55 5661-4209 8081
E: xinhuamx@xinhuanet.com
W: http://spanish.news.cn/
Bureau Chief: Huang Yongxian
NEWS SERVICE/SYNDICATE

BROADCASTING

RADIO STATIONS

XEITE-AM
Owner: Grupo Radio Capital
Editorial: Montes Urales No. 425, 2° Piso, Lomas De Chapultepec, Mexico City, Distrito Federal C.P. 06600. T: 52 55 30993000
W: http://gruporadiocapital.mx/xeite
Editorial Profile: Audience: 2,294,740

RADIO NETWORKS

Radio Educacion
Editorial: Angel Urraza No. 622 Col. del Valle., Mexico City, Distrito Federal 3100.
T: 52 55 41551050
E: contacto@radioeducacion.edu.mx
W: http://www.radioeducacion.edu.mx
Editorial Profile: Radio Educacion is a decentralized body of the Ministry of Education, coordinated by the National Council for Culture and the Arts, whose substantive work is to promote and disseminate expressions educational, cultural and artistic Mexico through the radio.

Radio Fórmula
Editorial: Privada de Horacio 10, Col. Chapultepec, Mexico City, Distrito Federal 11560. T: 52 55 52792200
E: formula_noticias@hotmail.com
W: http://radioformula.com.mx

RTV - Radio
Editorial: Cerro de la Galaxia s/n Col. Unidad del Bosqu, Xalapa, Veracruz.
T: 52 228 8423500 **W:** http://rtv.org.mx

TELEVISION NETWORKS

Azteca Deportes
Editorial: Periférico Sur 4121, Col. Fuentes del Pedregal, Mexico City, Distrito Federal CP 14141. T: 52 55 1720-5749
E: contacto@tvazteca.com
Editorial Profile: Azteca deportes is a division of Azteca America, which broadcasts sports events from the Azteca America television network. Its headquarters are in Mexico City, Distrito Federal.

Enlace
Editorial: Av. San Jeronimo #137 Col. San Angel, Del Alvaro Obregon, Mexico City, Distrito Federal 1000. T: 52 55 55507222
W: http://www.enlacemexicotv.com
Editorial Profile: Broadcasts Christian programming, musical shows, and educational programs. Transmits live and interview shows.

Ritmoson Latino
Editorial: Av. Chapultepec #18, Col. Doctores, Col. Cuauhtemoc, Distrito Federal 6724.
T: 52 55 5224-5657
E: ritmosonlatino@ritmosonlatino.com
W: http://www2.esmas.com/ritmoson-latino
Editorial Profile: The network features Latin music, artists and news in the music industry.

RTV - Television
Editorial: Cerro de la Galaxia s/n Col. Unidad del Bosqu, Xalapa, Veracruz.
T: 52 228 8423500 **W:** http://rtv.org.mx/

Televisa
Editorial: Av. Chapultepec #18, Col. Doctores, Col. Cuauhtemoc, Distrito Federal 6724.
T: 52 55 52245000
E: mesadeinformacion@televisa.com.mx
W: http://noticieros.televisa.com/us
Editorial Profile: Televisa is the largest media company in the Spanish-speaking world and a major participant in the international entertainment business. It has interests in television production and broadcasting, production of pay-television networks, international distribution of television programming, direct-to-home satellite services, cable television and telecommunication services, magazine publishing and distribution, radio production and broadcasting, professional sports and live entertainment, feature-film production and distribution, the operation of an internet portal, and gaming.

TV Azteca
Editorial: Periferico Sur 4121, Col Fuentes del Pedregal, Delegacion Tlalpan, Mexico City, Distrito Federal 14141. T: 52 55 17201313
W: http://www.azteca.com

CABLE

Bloomberg Television
Editorial: Paseo de la Reforma 265, Piso 11, Mexico City, Distrito Federal 6500.
T: 52 55 5242-9200

Cablemas
Editorial: Sevilla No 4, Juárez, Distrito Federal, Mexico City, Distrito Federal 6600.
T: 52 55 52076606
E: phernandezc@cablemas.com.mx
W: http://www.cablemas.com

Cablevisión
Editorial: Av. Chapultepec No. 28-2° Piso, Doctores, Queretaro, Queretaro, Queretaro 6724. T: 52 55 57093333
E: servicio.clientes@cablevision.net.mx
W: http://www.esmas.com/cablevision/

Canal 22
Owner: Television Metropolitana S.A. de C.V.
Editorial: Atletas N.2, Edificio Pedro Infante, Colonia COuntry CLub, Delegacion Coyoacan, Mexico City, Distrito Federal 4220.
T: 52 55 5544-9022
E: internacional@canal22.org.mx
W: http://www.canal22.org.mx

Grupo Megacable
Editorial: Lázaro Cárdenas No. 1694, Del Fresno, Jalisco, Guadalajara, Jalisco 44140.
T: 52 55 013337500020
W: http://www.megacable.com.mx

Milenio TV
Owner: Grupo Multimedios
Editorial: Tennyson No. 80, Col Polanco, Mexico City, Distrito Federal 11570.
T: 52 55 51404900
W: http://www.multimedios.tv

Mvs Tv Networks
Editorial: Blvd.puerto Aéreo No. 486, Moctezuma 2a. Sección, Distrito Federal, Mexico City, Distrito Federal 15530.
T: 52 55 57648262 **E:** orivas@mvs.com
W: http://www.mvs.com.mx

ONCE TV
Owner: Instituto Politecnico Nacional
Editorial: Prolongación Carpio 475 Col. Casco de Sto. Tomás, Mexico City, Distrito Federal 11340. T: 52 55 53561111
E: oncemexico@oncetvmexico.ipn.mx
W: http://www.oncemexico.tv

Pctv
Editorial: Heriberto Frías No. 939, Del Valle, Distrito Federal, Mexico City, Distrito Federal 3100. T: 52 525 5568702
W: http://www.pctv.com.mx

Sony Pictures Televisión
Editorial: Prolg. Pase De La Reforma No. 600 P.h., Santa Fe Peña Blanca, Distrito Federal, Mexico City, Distrito Federal 1210.
T: 52 55 52582799
E: mariana_mendoza@spe.sony.com

Television Mexiquense
Owner: Estado de Mexico
T: 52 722 2754792
E: informes@radioytvmexiquense.mx
W: http://www.radioytvmexiquense.mx

Warner Channel
Editorial: Homero No. 203, 1° Piso, Ofc. 3, Chapultepec Morales, Distrito Federal, Mexico City, Distrito Federal 11560.
T: 52 55 52552080

MICRONESIA Tel: 694

Standard Time: GMT +11

BROADCASTING

RADIO STATIONS

V6AI Radio Yap
Owner: FSM Telecommunications Corporation
T: 691 350 2174 **E:** petergar@mail.fm

V6AJ Radio Kosrae
Owner: FSM Telecommunications Corporation
T: 691 370 3040
E: kosraebroadcast@yahoo.com
W: http://telecom.fm

Voice of Pohnpei V6AH
Owner: FSM Telecommunications Corporation
T: 691 320 2296
Editorial Profile: Provides news, views and interviews of special interest to all Pohnpei residents.

RADIO NETWORKS

V6AK Radio Chuuk
Owner: FSM Telecommunications Corporation
T: 691 330 2596
Editorial Profile: V6AK radio broadcasts daily from 6 am to 12 am.

MOLDOVA Tel: 373

Standard Time: GMT +2
Continent: Europe
Capital City: Chi?inau

NEWSPAPERS & PUBLICATIONS

NEWSPAPERS

Comersant Plus
Owner: Comersant Plus Ltd.
Editorial: str. Puskin 22, Chisinau 2012.
T: 373 22 23 33 18
E: inform@commert.press.md
W: http://www.km.press.md/ **Circ:** 3000 Publisher's Statement
Editor: Artem Varenita
Editorial Profile: Newspaper focusing on politics, economy and finance.
Language (s): Russian
DAILY NEWSPAPER

Jurnal de Chisinau
Owner: SRL "Jurnal de Chichinel"
Editorial: str. Vlaicu Pârcalab 63, etaj 3, Centrul Skytower, Chisinau 2012.
T: 373 22 237645 **E:** cotidian@jurnal.md
W: http://jc.md
Freq: 2 Times/Week; **Circ:** 13489 Publisher's Statement
Editorial Profile: Newspaper containing news and reportages, political, economic, cultural and social commentaries, sports and general interest articles.
Language (s): Romanian
DAILY NEWSPAPER

Kommersant Plus
Editorial: Puskin str., 22, Casa Presei, of. 601, Chisinau. **T:** 373 22 233696
E: inform@commert.press.md
W: http://www.km.press.md
Freq: Weekly; **Circ:** 5000 Publisher's Statement
Editorial Profile: Newspaper focusing on politics, economy and finance.
Language (s): Russian
DAILY NEWSPAPER

Komsomolskaya Pravda v Moldove
Editorial: V.Pircalab str., 45, 5 floor, Chisinau.
T: 373 22 220713 **E:** kp@kp.md
W: http://www.kp.md
Freq: Daily; **Circ:** 9000 Publisher's Statement
Editorial Profile: Komsomolskaya Pravda v Moldove is the Moldova edition of Russian daily national newspaper covering national news, business, economics and society.
Language (s): Russian
DAILY NEWSPAPER

Moldavskie Vedomosti
Owner: Moldavskie Vedomosti

Editorial: Stefan chel mare 182, Chisinau 2012. **T:** 373 22 23 86 18
E: editor@vedomosti.md
W: http://www.vedomosti.md
Freq: 3 Times/Week; **Circ:** 7500 Publisher's Statement
Editorial Profile: Newspaper focusing on politics, business, sport, culture and general news.
Language (s): Russian
DAILY NEWSPAPER

Nezavisimaya Moldova
Owner: Pravidelstvo Respubliki Moldova
Editorial: str. Puskin 22, Chisinau 2012.
T: 373 22 233141
E: nezavisimaia.moldova@gmail.com
W: http://www.nm.md
Freq: Daily; **Circ:** 17000 Publisher's Statement
Editor-in-Chief: Corneliu Mihalache
Editorial Profile: Newspaper focusing on national and international news, politics, business and sport.
Language (s): Russian
DAILY NEWSPAPER

Timpul de dimineata
Owner: Timpul De Diminatea
Editorial: Alexei ?ciusev 98, Chisinau MD-2005. **T:** 373 22 225670
E: secretariat@timpul.md
W: http://www.timpul.md
Freq: Daily; **Circ:** 19227 Publisher's Statement
Editorial Profile: Newspaper focusing on national and international news, culture, society, politics, economics and sport.
Language (s): Romanian
DAILY NEWSPAPER

NEWS SERVICE/SYNDICATE

INTERLIC News Agency
T: 373 22 3 20 67 **E:** info@interlic.md
W: http://www.interlic.md
NEWS SERVICE/SYNDICATE

MS-PUBLICITATE
Editorial: Columna str., 146/1, Chisinau.
T: 373 22 29 47 07 **E:** plescasimion@mail.md
Language (s): Romanian
NEWS SERVICE/SYNDICATE

MONACO Tel: 377

Standard Time: GMT +1
Continent: Europe
Capital City: Monaco

NEWSPAPERS & PUBLICATIONS

NEWSPAPERS

MONACO-MATIN EDITION MONEGASQUE DE NICE-MATIN
Owner: NICE MATIN
Editorial: 41 rue Grimaldi, Monaco 98000.
T: 377 9 31 04 39 0 **E:** monaco@nicematin.fr
W: http://www.nicematin.fr
Freq: Daily
Editorial Profile: Monaco edition of the regional daily newspaper focussing on news and current affairs including TV guide, sport, real estate, economics and women's interest magazine supplement. Local Translation:Edition monégasque de Nice-Matin. Actualités régionales et internationales - Programmes TV. Suppléments : sport le lundi, immobilier le mardi, sortir le mercredi, éco le jeudi, TV le samedi, féminin le dimanche.
Language (s): French
DAILY NEWSPAPER

BROADCASTING

RADIO STATIONS

Riviera Radio
Owner: RIVIERA RADIO MONACO 106.3
Editorial: 10-12 quai Antoine-1er, Monaco 98000. **T:** 377 979 794 75
E: info@rivieraradio.mc
W: http://www.rivieraradio.mc
Editorial Profile: Regional radio station focussing on general interest, international and regional news (BBC) and music. Broadcasted in English.

RADIO NETWORKS

RADIO ETHIC (WEB RADIO)
Editorial: 5 avenue Princesse-Alice, Monaco 98000. **T:** 377 9 33 07 48 2
E: info@radioethic.com
W: http://www.radioethic.com

TELEVISION STATIONS

TMC
Owner: GROUPE AB
Editorial: 6 bis quai Antoine-1er, Monaco 98000. **T:** 377 9 31 51 41 5
W: http://www.tmc.tv
Editorial Profile: TV cable/satellite channel focussing on general interest including movies, entertainment, TV series, sport, magazines, reviews and documentaries.

MONGOLIA Tel: 976

Standard Time: GMT +8
Continent: Asia
Capital City: Ulaanbaatar

NEWSPAPERS & PUBLICATIONS

NEWSPAPERS

The Mongol Messenger
Owner: Montsame News Agency
Editorial: CPO Box 1514, Ulaanbaatar 13.
T: 976 11 325 512
E: monmessenger@magicnet.mn
W: http://www.mongolmessenger.mn/home/index.php **Circ:** 5000 Publisher's Statement
Editor In Chief: Indra Borkhondoin
Editorial Profile: Covering politics, international and domestic news, business, education, health, social issues, arts, culture and sport.
Language (s): English
DAILY NEWSPAPER

The UB Post
Owner: Mongol News Media Group
Editorial: Mongol News Building, Juulchni Street, Ulaanbaatar 211238.
T: 976 70 11 1095
E: ubpost@mongolnews.mn
W: http://ubpost.mongolnews.mn **Circ:** 8000 Publisher's Statement
Editorial Profile: Independent newspaper in English focussing on news, current affairs, politics, economics and sport.
Language (s): English, Spanish
DAILY NEWSPAPER

NEWS SERVICE/SYNDICATE

Montsame News Agency
Editorial: Tiggdgau St 8, Ulaanbaatar.
T: 976 11 263 692
E: editorchief@montsame.mn
W: http://www.montsame.mn
Editor: Ganzorig Gonda; **Editor In Chief:** Purasanbuu Guneatorg
Editorial Profile: National news agency focussing on news, current affairs, politics, business, culture and sport.
Language (s): English
NEWS SERVICE/SYNDICATE

MONTENEGRO Tel: 382

Standard Time: GMT +1
Continent: Europe
Capital City: Podgorica

NEWSPAPERS & PUBLICATIONS

NEWSPAPERS

Pobjeda
Owner: Pobjeda d o o
Editorial: Bulevar Revolucije 11, Poštanski fah 101, Podgorica 81000. **T:** 382 81 24 59 55
E: urednik@cg.yu
W: http://www.pobjeda.cg.yu
Freq: Daily; **Circ:** 30000 Publisher's Statement
Editor In Chief: Andrija Rackovic
Editorial Profile: Newspaper covering international and domestic news, business, economics, sports and culture.
Language (s): Serbo-Croat

DAILY NEWSPAPER

Republika
Owner: Preduzece Millennium
Editorial: Bulevar Revolucije br. 74, Podgorica 81000. **T:** 382 81 21 62 60
E: marketing@republika.cg.yu
W: http://www.republika.cg.yu
Freq: Daily; **Circ:** 5000 Publisher's Statement
Editorial Profile: Daily national newspaper providing political, business and cultural news.
Language (s): Serbo-Croat
DAILY NEWSPAPER

BROADCASTING

RADIO STATIONS

Radio Kotor
Editorial: Stari grad (zgrada SO), Kotor 85330
E: radio.kotor@cg.yu
W: http://radiokotor.info.mn
Editorial Profile: Regional radio station from Kotor town.

RADIO NETWORKS

Antena M
Editorial: 19.decembar 19, Podgorica 81 000.
T: 382 81 66 42 81 **E:** redakcija@antenam.net
W: http://www.antenam.net
Editorial Profile: Broadcasts news, cultural programmes and music.

Radio Corona
Editorial: Jovana Tomasevica Street, G-9, Bar.
T: 382 85 31 77 17 **E:** mcorona@cg.yu
W: http://www.corona-radio.com
Editorial Profile: Radio Station broadcasting music and news throughout Montenegro and in southern parts of Europe.

TELEVISION STATIONS

ntv MONTENA
Editorial: ul. Djoka Miraševica 61, Podgorica 81000. **T:** 382 81 98 97 **E:** ntvm@cg.yu
W: http://www.montena.cg.yu
Editorial Profile: Independent TV station which broadcasts informative-political programmes.

Pink M
Owner: Pink Media Group
Editorial: Bulevar Ivana Crnojevica br.97, Podgorica 81000. **T:** 382 81 40 35 11
E: redakcija@pinkm.cg.yu
W: http://www.pinkm.com
Editorial Profile: Pink M is a part of Pink Media Group based in Beograd and covers the whole territory of Republic of Montenegro, broadcasting news, entertainment programmes and music.

TV Budva
Editorial: Petra I Petrovica 3, Budva 85310.
T: 382 86 45 48 13 **E:** tvbudva@cg.yu
W: http://www.tvbudva.cg.yu
Editorial Profile: Broadcasts regional political and cultural news, documentaries and entertainment programmes.

MONTSERRAT Tel: 1 664

Standard Time: GMT -4
Continent: The Americas
Capital City: Plymouth

NEWSPAPERS & PUBLICATIONS

NEWSPAPERS

The Montserrat Reporter
Owner: Montserrat Printing & Publishing
T: 664 4914715
E: editor@themontserratreporter.com
W: http://www.themontserratreporter.com
Freq: Weekly; **Circ:** 2000 Not Audited
Publisher & Editor: Bennette Roach
Editorial Profile: Focuses on national and international news, politics, business, culture and sports.
Language (s): English
NEWSPAPER

BROADCASTING

RADIO NETWORKS

ZJB Radio Montserrat
T: 664 4912885 **E:** zjb@gov.ms
W: http://www.zjb.gov.ms
Editorial Profile: Transmits news related to Montserrat, the Caribbean, and the world. The ZJB radio also provides entertainment through contest and chat shows.

TELEVISION NETWORKS

PTV
T: 664 4915110 **E:** deedge@candw.ms
Editorial Profile: Local television station providing information about daily news and entertainment.

MOROCCO Tel: 212

Standard Time: GMT
Continent: Africa
Capital City: Rabat

NEWSPAPERS & PUBLICATIONS

NEWSPAPERS

Akhbar Al Youm
Owner: Media 21
Editorial: 8th Floor, Al Habsi Commercial Center, Avenue Des F.A.R., Casablanca.
T: 212 522 545850
E: contact@alyaoum24.com
W: http://www.alyaoum24.com
Freq: Daily; **Circ:** 22828 OJD Maroc
Publisher: Taoufik Bouachrine; **News Editor:** Youness Meskin; **News Editor:** Mbarek Mrabet; **Editor In Chief:** Mokhtar Omari
Editorial Profile: Akhbar Al Youm is a broadsheet-sized, daily Arabic newspaper covering national and international news, business, culture, society, art, politics and sport. It launched in 2009 and was previously called Akhbar Al Youm Maghribiya.
Language (s): Arabic
DAILY NEWSPAPER

Annoukhba
Owner: Selection Presse
Editorial: Appt. 7, 4eme Etage, Al Rizk Building, 73, Avenue de la Resistance, Rabat.
T: 212 537 736164
E: annoukhba365@yahoo.fr
W: http://www.annoukhba.com
Freq: 2 Times/Week; **Circ:** 100000 Publisher's Statement
Editorial Profile: Annoukhba (The Elite) is an Arabic sports newspaper covering football. It launched in 1993 and is published twice a week on Mondays and Thursdays.
Language (s): Arabic
DAILY NEWSPAPER

Assabah
Owner: Groupe Eco-Media
Editorial: 70 Boulevard Al Massira Khadra, Casablanca. **T:** 212 522 953660
E: assabah.info@gmail.com
W: http://www.assabah.press.ma
Freq: Daily; **Circ:** 51111 OJD Maroc
Editor In Chief: Khaled El Horri; **News Editor:** Ihsan Hafizi
Editorial Profile: Assabah (The Morning) is a broadsheet-sized Arabic newspaper covering national and international news, current affairs and politics. It launched in 2000 and is published daily, except Sundays.
Language (s): Arabic
DAILY NEWSPAPER

Assiassah
Owner: Selection Presse
Editorial: Appt.7, eme Etage, Al Rizk Building, 73, Avenue de La Resistance, Rabat.
T: 212 537 736164 **E:** karkori.abdou@yahoo.fr
Freq: Bi-Weekly; **Circ:** 50000 Publisher's Statement
News Editor: Abdelqader AlFarsaoui
Editorial Profile: Assiassah is fortnightly newspaper covering news, business, politics, art & culture and sport. It was first published in 2012.
Language (s): Arabic
DAILY NEWSPAPER

Al Bayane
Owner: Bayane SA
Editorial: PO Box 13152, 2830, rue Benzert, Casablanca 23000. **T:** 212 522 467676
E: albayane@albayane.press.ma
W: http://www.albayane.press.ma
Freq: Daily; **Circ:** 25000 Publisher's Statement
News Editor: Khalid Darfaf
Editorial Profile: Al Bayane is a French newspaper covering national and international news, current affairs and politics. It launched in 1972 and is published daily, except Saturdays.
Language (s): French
DAILY NEWSPAPER

Bayane Al Yaoume
Owner: Bayane SA
Editorial: PO Box 13152, 2830, rue Benzert, Casablanca 23000. **T:** 212 522 467676
E: bayanealyaoume@bayanealyaoume.press.ma **W:** http://www.bayanealyaoume.press.ma
Freq: Daily; **Circ:** 20000 Publisher's Statement
News Editor: Hassan Arabi; **Editor in Chief:** Hussein Chaabi
Editorial Profile: Bayane Al Yaoume is an Arabic newspaper covering national and international news, current affairs and politics. It launched in 1991 and is published daily, except Sundays.
Language (s): Arabic
DAILY NEWSPAPER

Al Massae
Owner: Massae Média Groupe
Editorial: 2eme etage, Centre Commercial Diwane, Angle Place Aknoul, Casablanca.
T: 212 522 200666
E: almassae@almassae.press.ma
W: http://www.almassae.press.ma
Freq: Daily; **Circ:** 81515 OJD Maroc
Editor in Chief: Mohamed Aghbalou
Editorial Profile: Al Massae is a daily Arabic newspaper covering news and current affairs, culture, society, business and sport. It launched in September 2006.
Language (s): Arabic
DAILY NEWSPAPER

Le Matin
Owner: Groupe Maroc Soir
Editorial: 17, Rue Othmane Ben Affane, ex Lafuente, Casablanca. **T:** 212 522 489100
E: lematin@lematin.ma
W: http://www.lematin.ma
Freq: Daily; **Circ:** 21543 OJD Maroc
News Editor: Mohamed Akisra; **Editor in Chief:** Hassan Larch
Editorial Profile: Le Matin, also known as Le Matin du Sahara et du Maghreb, is a French newspaper focusing on national and international news, business, politics and sport. It launched in 1971 and is published daily, except Sundays.
Language (s): French
DAILY NEWSPAPER

L' Observateur Du Maroc
Owner: Medi Edition
Editorial: App 5, Tilila Building, Rue De Berne, Quartier Des Hopitaux, Casablanca.
T: 212 522 465950 **E:** lobsmaroc@gmail.com
W: http://www.lobservateurdumaroc.info
Freq: Fri; **Circ:** 20000 Publisher's Statement
Editor in Chief: Mohammed Zainabi
Editorial Profile: L'Observateur Du Maroc is a weekly French newspaper covering news, economics, society, culture, sport, culture and arts. It launched in 2008 and is published on Fridays.
Language (s): French
DAILY NEWSPAPER

Rissalat Al Oumma
Owner: Union Constitutionnel
Editorial: PO Box 20005, Hay Salam, Casablanca. **T:** 212 522 907180
E: aloumma@yahoo.fr
W: http://www.rissalatalomma.press.ma
Freq: Daily; **Circ:** 30000 Publisher's Statement
Editor in Chief: Abdelaziz Al Maymouni; **News Editor:** Youssef Boukhari
Editorial Profile: Rissalat Al Oumma (The Nation's Message) is a daily Arabic newspaper covering national and international news, politics, business, society and sport. It launched in 1983.
Language (s): Arabic
DAILY NEWSPAPER

Al Watan Al An
Owner: Al Mouahed Establishment LLC
Editorial: 33 Rue Mohamed Bahi, Hay Al Nakheel, Casablanca. **T:** 212 522 251285
E: achefrib@gmail.com
W: http://www.alwatan-press.info
Freq: Thu; **Circ:** 20000 OJD Maroc
Editor in Chief: Boujemaa Achefri; **News Editor:** Mounir Elktaoui
Editorial Profile: Al Watan Al An is a weekly Arabic newspaper covering news, society, politics, business and sport. It launched in 2001 and is published on Thursdays.
Language (s): Arabic
DAILY NEWSPAPER

NEWS SERVICE/SYNDICATE

Agence France-Presse - Rabat Bureau
Owner: Agence France-Presse
Editorial: PO Box 118, 2 Bis, Rue Al Khahira, Rabat. **T:** 212 537 706940
E: afp.rabat@afp.com **W:** http://www.afp.com
Arabic Editor: Jalal Al Makhfi; **French Editor:** Omar Brouksy
Editorial Profile: Rabat bureau of international news agency supplying news - text, graphics, video and pictures - to subscribers around the world.
Language (s): Arabic, English, French
NEWS SERVICE/SYNDICATE

Associated Press
T: 212 661 54-10-50
Bureau Chief: Angela Charlton
NEWS SERVICE/SYNDICATE

Maghreb Arabe Presse
Owner: Maghreb Arabe Presse
Editorial: PO Box 1049, 122 Avenue Allal Ben Abdellah, Rabat 10000. **T:** 212 537 279400
E: com@map.co.ma **W:** http://www.map.ma
Editorial Profile: Maghreb Arabe Presse is a national news agency covering government and royal news, as well as issues of national importance in Morocco.
Language (s): Arabic
NEWS SERVICE/SYNDICATE

Reuters
Editorial: 17 Rue El Ouaraibi Jilali, 20000 Casablanca, Casablanca. **T:** 212 22 486648
E: maghreb.newsroom@thomsonreuters.com
NEWS SERVICE/SYNDICATE

Reuters - Rabat bureau
Owner: Thomson Reuters
Editorial: Bureau 509, 2nd Floor, Immeuble Es-Saada, Rabat 10000. **T:** 212 537 726518
E: maghreb.newsroom@thomsonreuters.com
W: http://www.reuters.com
Editorial Profile: Rabat bureau of international news agency supplying news - text, graphics, video and pictures - to subscribers around the world.
Language (s): Arabic, English
NEWS SERVICE/SYNDICATE

BROADCASTING

RADIO STATIONS

Chaine Inter
Owner: Société Nationale de Radiodiffusion et de Télévision
Editorial: PO Box 1042, 1, rue El Brihi, Rabat 10000. **T:** 212 537 685100
E: lambaraa_5@hotmail.com
W: http://www.chaineinter.ma
Editorial Profile: Chaine Inter is the international radio station of state-owned public broadcaster Société Nationale de Radiodiffusion et de Télévision (SNRT). The station broadcasts music and news, as well as politics, business, family, society and entertainment programmes in French, Spanish and English. It launched in March 2009 and broadcasts on various FM frequencies across the country including 90.0 FM (Casablanca), 87.9 FM (Rabat), 94.2 FM (Agadir) and 91.8 FM (Tanger).

Al Idaa Al Amazighia
Owner: Société Nationale de Radiodiffusion et de Télévision
Editorial: PO Box 1042, 1, rue El Brihi, Rabat 10000. **T:** 212 537 685100
E: tamazight@snrt.ma
W: http://www.alidaa-alamazighia.ma
Editorial Profile: Al Idaa Al Amazighia is a Berber radio station broadcasting news, music, culture and entertainment programmes. It was launched by state-owned public broadcaster Société Nationale de Radiodiffusion et de Télévision in 1938 and broadcasts on 95.3 FM (Casablanca), 104.6 FM (Rabat), 97.5 FM (Agadir), 98.3 FM (Afroud), 94.5 FM (Al Rachidia) and 101.9 FM (Meknes and Fes).

Al Idaa Al Watania
Owner: Société Nationale de Radiodiffusion et de Télévision
Editorial: PO Box 1042, 1 rue El Brihi, Rabat 10000. **T:** 212 537 685100
E: secdirad@yahoo.fr
W: http://www.alidaa-alwatania.ma
Editorial Profile: Al Idaa Al Watania is a state-owned, national radio station broadcasting entertainment programmes and music. Formerly called Al Maghribia Radio, it was launched in 1928 and broadcasts on various FM frequencies across Morocco.

Radio Agadir
Owner: Société Nationale de Radiodiffusion et de Télévision
Editorial: Avenue Hassan II, Agadir 80000.
T: 212 528 840305 **E:** anaghmas@yahoo.fr
W: http://www.snrt.ma
Editorial Profile: Radio Agadir is a state-owned, regional radio station broadcasting music and news bulletins. Launched in 1972, it broadcasts in Arabic and the regional Amazigh language on 87.9 FM in the Agadir area of Morocco.

Radio Casablanca
Owner: Société Nationale de Radiodiffusion et de Télévision
Editorial: Hay al Ousra, Negala Street, Ain Chock, Casablanca. **T:** 212 522 522632
E: radregcas@yahoo.fr **W:** http://www.snrt.ma
Editorial Profile: Radio Casablanca is a state-owned, regional radio station broadcasting music and news bulletins. It launched in 1928 and broadcasts on 98.6 FM in the Casablanca area of Morocco.

Radio Dakhla
Owner: Société Nationale de Radiodiffusion et de Télévision
Editorial: PO Box 37, 21, Avenue Imlili, Dakhla. **T:** 212 528 897341
E: rtmdak2006@yahoo.fr
Editorial Profile: Radio Dakhla is a state-owned, regional radio station broadcasting music and news bulletins in Arabic and the regional Hassani language. It launched in 1980 and broadcasts on 91.8 FM in the Dakhla area of Morocco.

Radio Fes
Owner: Société Nationale de Radiodiffusion et de Télévision
Editorial: Boulevard Moulay Ahmed Loukili, Fes. **T:** 212 535 623050 **E:** essafi2@yahoo.fr
W: http://www.radiofes.ma
Editorial Profile: Radio Fes is a state-owned, regional radio station broadcasting music and news bulletins in Arabic and the regional Amazigh language. It launched in 1961 and transmits on 98.4 FM in the Fes area of Morocco.

Radio Laâyoune
Owner: Société Nationale de Radiodiffusion et de Télévision
Editorial: PO Box 459, Laayoune 70000.
T: 212 528 893363 **E:** zazamed2@yahoo.fr
W: http://www.radiolaayoune.ma
Editorial Profile: Radio Laâyoune is a state-owned, regional radio station broadcasting music and news bulletins. It launched in 1976 and broadcasts on 91.1 FM in the Laâyoune area of Morocco.

Radio Marrakech
Owner: Société Nationale de Radiodiffusion et de Télévision
Editorial: 40 rue de Yougoslavie, Marrakech.
T: 212 524 447945 **E:** snrtmarrakech@yahoo.fr
W: http://www.radio-marrakech.net/
Editorial Profile: Radio Marrakech is a state-owned, regional radio station broadcasting music and news bulletins. Launched in 1968,. it broadcasts on 91.7 FM in the Marrakech area of Morocco.

Radio Meknes
Owner: Société Nationale de Radiodiffusion et de Télévision
Editorial: Rue Okba Ibn Nafie, Place Al Andalouss (Ahouaz Meknes), Meknes.
T: 212 535 527203 **E:** snrtmeknes@gmail.com
W: http://www.snrt.ma
Editorial Profile: Radio Meknes is a state-owned, regional radio station broadcasting music and news bulletins. It launched in 2007 and broadcasts on 92.5 FM in the Meknes area of Morocco.

Radio Mohammed VI du Saint Coran
Owner: Société Nationale de Radiodiffusion et de Télévision
Editorial: PO Box 1042, 1, rue El Brihi, Rabat 10000. **T:** 212 537 685100

E: secdirad@yahoo.fr
W: http://www.idaatmohammedassadiss.ma
Editorial Profile: Radio Mohammed VI du Saint Coran is a radio station broadcasting religious programmes and discussions about Islam and the Holy Quran. It launched in 2004 and broadcasts on 94.2 FM (Rabat and Laayoune), 98.6 FM (Casablanca), 91.7 FM (Marrakech) and 96.1 FM (Oujda).

Radio Oujda
Owner: Société Nationale de Radiodiffusion et de Télévision
Editorial: Avenue Omar Errifi, Oujda.
T: 212 536 682317 **E:** hafid63@hotmail.fr
W: http://www.snrt.ma
Editorial Profile: Radio Oujda is a regional radio station broadcasting music and news bulletins. Launched in 1962, it broadcasts on 96.1 FM in the Oujda region of Morocco.

Radio Tanger
Owner: Société Nationale de Radiodiffusion et de Télévision
Editorial: PO Box 404, 33, Avenue Le Prince Moulay Abdellah, Tangiers. **T:** 212 539 321680
E: radio_tanger@yahoo.fr
W: http://www.radiotanger.ma
Editorial Profile: Radio Tanger is a state-owned, regional radio station broadcasting music and news bulletins. Launched in 1946, it broadcasts on 88.7 FM and 104.0 FM in the Tanger (Tangiers) region of Morocco.

Radio Tetouan
Owner: Société Nationale de Radiodiffusion et de Télévision
Editorial: 30, Avenue Mohamed V, Tetouan.
T: 212 539 963697
E: radiotetouan@gmail.com
W: http://www.snrt.ma
Editorial Profile: Radio Tetouan is a state-owned, regional radio station broadcasting music and news programmes in Arabic and the Amazigh language (Tarifit). Launched in 1984, it broadcasts on 100.2 FM in the Tetouan region of Morocco.

TELEVISION STATIONS

Aflam TV
Owner: Société Nationale de Radiodiffusion et de Télévision
Editorial: PO Box 1042, 1 rue El Brihi, Rabat 10000. **T:** 212 537 685100
E: mfaddou@yahoo.fr
W: http://www.aflamtv.ma
Editorial Profile: Aflam TV (Films TV) is a state-owned television channel broadcasting Moroccan and foreign films, as well as programmes about the Moroccan film industry. It launched in 2008 and brpoadcasts terrestrially within Morocco.

Al Aoula
Owner: Société Nationale de Radiodiffusion et de Télévision
Editorial: 1, rue El Brihi, Rabat 10000.
T: 212 537 685100 **E:** lemediateur@snrt.ma
W: http://www.alaoula.ma
Editorial Profile: Al Aoula, also known as Channel 1, is a state-owned general entertainment channel broadcasting cultural programmes, magazine programmes, films, sport and news for 17-hours a day. The station launched in 1962 and broadcasts free-to-air on satellite.

Arrabia
Owner: Société Nationale de Radiodiffusion et de Télévision
Editorial: 1, rue El Brihi, Rabat 10000.
T: 212 537 685100 **E:** marialatifi@hotmail.com
W: http://www.arrabia.ma
Editorial Profile: Arrabia, also known as Channel 4, is a state-owned educational channel broadcasting teaching programmes, cultural magazine programmes and movies. The station launched in 2005 and broadcasts terrestrially in Morocco and free-to-air on satellite.

Arriyadia
Owner: Société Nationale de Radiodiffusion et de Télévision
Editorial: Rue Michael Nouima, Casablanca.
T: 212 529 025520 **E:** arryadia@arryadia.com
W: http://www.arryadia.ma
Editorial Profile: Arriyadia, also known as Channel 3, is a state-owned sports channel broadcasting local and international sports programmes. Launched in 2006, the station broadcasts terrestrially in Morocco and free-to-air on satellite.

Assadissa
Owner: Société Nationale de Radiodiffusion et de Télévision
Editorial: 1, rue El Brihi, Rabat 10000.
T: 212 537 685100 **E:** assadissa@snrt.ma
W: http://www.assadissatv.ma
Editorial Profile: Assadissa, also known as Channel 6, is a state-owned television station broadcasting religious programmes with the aim of bringing Islam to a wider audience. The channel launched in 2005 and broadcasts terrestrially in Morocco and free-to-air on satellite.

Al Maghribia TV
Owner: Société Nationale de Radiodiffusion et de Télévision
Editorial: PO Box 1042, 1 rue El Brihi, Rabat 10000. **T:** 212 537 685100 **E:** mrinid@yahoo.fr
W: http://www.almaghribia-tv.ma
Editorial Profile: Al Maghribia TV, also known as Channel 5, is a state-owned, general entertainment channel aimed at Moroccans living abroad. The station launched in 2004 and broadcasts free-to-air on satellite.

Tamazight TV
Owner: Société Nationale de Radiodiffusion et de Télévision
Editorial: 1, rue El Brihi, Rabat 10000.
T: 212 537 661735 **E:** tamazight@snrt.ma
W: http://www.tamazight-tv.ma
Editorial Profile: Tamazight TV is a state-owned television station broadcasting political, business, sport, religion and entertainment programmes. The station launched in 2010 and is aimed at the Berber population of Morocco.

TV Laâyoune
Owner: Société Nationale de Radiodiffusion et de Télévision
Editorial: PO Box 550, 1 rue Zerktouni, Laayoune 70000. **T:** 212 528 892767
E: tvregional@gmail.com
W: http://www.snrt.ma
Editorial Profile: TV Laâyoune, also known as Television Regionale De Laâyoune, is a state-owned regional news and entertainment channel. Launched in 2004, the station is aimed at viewers in the Laayoune area of southern Morocco and broadcasts terrestrially and also free-to-air on satellite.

MOZAMBIQUE   Tel: 258

Standard Time: GMT +2
Continent: Africa
Capital City: Maputo

NEWSPAPERS & PUBLICATIONS

NEWSPAPERS

Savana
Editorial: Mediacoop, Caixa Postal 73, Maputo. **T:** 258 82 327 6670
E: editorsav@mediacoop.co.mz
Freq: Weekly
Editor: Fernando Andre; **Editor:** Fernando Gonçalves
Editorial Profile: Cost: Paid. Savana is Mozambique's leading independent weekly newspaper. The Maputo-based Portuguese language publication is published by Mediacoop, the country's principal independent mediahouse. Mediacoop also published the daily mediaFAX. Savana and mediaFAX are the only independent print media being distributed all over Mozambique and Mediacoop operates a network of correspondents throughout the extensive country.
Language (s): Portuguese
DAILY NEWSPAPER

BROADCASTING

TELEVISION STATIONS

Televisao De Mocambique (TVM)
Editorial: Av 25 de Setembro, N° 154, Caixa Postal 2675, Maputo. **T:** 258 21 30 81 17
E: redaccao@tvm.co.mz
W: http://www.tvm.co.mz

NAMIBIA   Tel: 264

Standard Time: GMT +1
Continent: Africa
Capital City: Windhoel

NEWSPAPERS & PUBLICATIONS

NEWSPAPERS

Namibia Economist
T: 264 61 22 19 25
E: daniel@economist.com.na
W: http://www.economist.com.na
Freq: Weekly; **Circ:** 10000 Not Audited
Editor: Chamwe Kaira; **Editor:** Rodrick Mukumbira; **Editor:** Daniel Steinmann
Language (s): English
DAILY NEWSPAPER

The Namibian
Editorial: PO Box 20783, Windhoek.
T: 264 61 27 96 00
E: editor@namibian.com.na
W: http://www.namibian.com.na
Freq: Daily; **Circ:** 40000
Editor-in-Chief: Tangeni Amupadhi
Language (s): English
DAILY NEWSPAPER

Republikein
Editorial: PO Box 3436, Windhoek.
T: 264 612972031
E: republkn@republikein.com.na
W: http://www.republikein.com.na
Freq: Daily
Editor in Chief: Chris Jacobi; **Editor:** Chris Jacobie
Language (s): Afrikaans
DAILY NEWSPAPER

BROADCASTING

TELEVISION NETWORKS

Namibian Broadcasting Corporation (Television)
Editorial: PO Box 321, Windhoek.
T: 264 612913113 **E:** mmuinjo@nbc.com.na
W: http://www.nbc.com.na

NAURU   Tel: 674

Standard Time: GMT +12

BROADCASTING

RADIO NETWORKS

Radio Pasifik Nauru, Triple 9 FM
Owner: University of the South Pacific
Editorial: Private Bag, Post Office, Republic Of Nauru. **T:** 674 444 3744 **E:** lauti_a@usp.ac.fj
W: http://usp.ac.fj/index.php?id=usp_nauru_home
Editorial Profile: Radio Pasifik Nauru, Triple 9 FM, began broadcasting on 2 April. It is a sister station to USP's main student and community radio station.

NEPAL   Tel: 977

Standard Time: GMT +5 3/4
Continent: Asia
Capital City: Kathmandu

NEWSPAPERS & PUBLICATIONS

NEWSPAPERS

Adarsha Samaj
Owner: Adarsh Samaj Bahumukhi Prakashan Pvt Ltd.
Editorial: Adarsh Samaj Bahumukhi Prakashan Pvt Ltd, Bhakti Marg, Newroad, Pokhara.
T: 977 61531200 **E:** adrsamaj@gmail.com
W: http://www.eadarsha.com/
Freq: Daily; **Circ:** 10001 Not Audited
Editor in Chief: Krishna Prasad Bastola
Editorial Profile: Covers of news and general interests.
Language (s): Nepali
DAILY NEWSPAPER

Annapurna Post
Owner: News Media Pvt Ltd.
Editorial: News Media Pvt Ltd., PO Box 23781, Anamnagar-32, Kathmandu.
T: 977 14770629 **E:** editorial@annapost.com
W: http://www.annapurnapost.com
Freq: Daily; **Circ:** 75003 Not Audited
Editor in Chief: Guna Raj Luitel
Editorial Profile: Covering news and general interests.
Language (s): Nepali
DAILY NEWSPAPER

Butwal Today
Editorial: Butwal Media Prakashan Pvt Ltd., Tilottama Path, Butwal-8, Lumbini.
T: 977 71551345 **E:** info@butwaltoday.com
W: http://www.butwaltoday.com
Freq: Daily; **Circ:** 10003 Not Audited
Editor in Chief: Jiblal Sapkota
Editorial Profile: Covers local and national news.
Language (s): Nepali
DAILY NEWSPAPER

City Post
Editorial: CityPost National Daily, Po Box 19155, Dillibazaar, Kathmandu.
T: 977 14416961 **E:** info@citypostdaily.com.np
W: http://www.citypostdaily.com.np
Freq: Daily; **Circ:** 10003 Not Audited
Editor: Lilanath Gautam
Editorial Profile: Covers of news and general interests.
Language (s): Nepali
DAILY NEWSPAPER

Gorkhapatra
Editorial: Gorkhapatra Sansthan, Dharmapath, P.O. Box 23, Kathmandu. **T:** 977 14222921
E: gopa@gorkhapatra.org.np
W: http://www.gorkhapatra.org.np
Freq: Daily; **Circ:** 30003 Not Audited
Editorial Profile: Covers of local, national and international news.
Language (s): Nepali
DAILY NEWSPAPER

The Himalayan Times
Editorial: International Media Network Nepal Pvt. Ltd., PO Box No. 11651, APCA House, Baidya Khana Road, Anam Nagar, Kathmandu.
T: 977 14771489
E: editorial@thehimalayantimes.com
W: http://www.thehimalayantimes.com
Freq: Daily; **Circ:** 45003 Not Audited
Editorial Profile: Covers local, national, regional and international news.
Language (s): Nepali
DAILY NEWSPAPER

Janmabhoomi
Editorial: Janmabhoomi, P.O. Box 3244, Tahachal, Kathmandu. **T:** 977 14271485
E: sbpti@mos.com.np
Freq: Weekly; **Circ:** 10002 Not Audited
Editor in Chief: Ganesh Pradhan
Editorial Profile: Covering local news, sports, business, jobs, and community events.
Language (s): Nepali
DAILY NEWSPAPER

Kantipur
Owner: Kantipur Publications Pvt. Ltd.
Editorial: Kantipur Publications Pvt. Ltd, Kantipur Complex, Subidhanagar, Kathmandu.
T: 977 1 44 80 100 **E:** kanti@kantipur.com.np
W: http://www.ekantipur.com
Freq: Daily; **Circ:** 210002 Not Audited
Editor: Sudheer Sharma; **Editor:** Hari Bahadur Thapa
Editorial Profile: Covers of Local and International News, Sports, Entertainment, Features, etc.
Language (s): Nepali
DAILY NEWSPAPER

The Kathmandu Post
Owner: Kantipur Publications Pvt. Ltd.
Editorial: Kantipur Publications Pvt. Ltd, Kantipur Complex, Subidhanagar, P.O.Box 8559, Kathmandu. **T:** 977 14480100
E: kpost@kantipur.com.np
W: http://www.ekantipur.com
Freq: Daily; **Circ:** 40003 Not Audited
Editor in Chief: Akhilesh Upadhyay
Editorial Profile: Covers of Local and International News, Sports, Entertainment, etc.
Language (s): English
DAILY NEWSPAPER

Madhyanha
Editorial: Madhyanha Daily, PO Box 21934, Bag Bazaar, Kathmandu. **T:** 977 14226366
E: madhyanhadaily@enet.com.np
W: http://www.madhyanhadaily.com.np

Freq: Daily; **Circ:** 5002 Not Audited
Editor: Madan Kumar Shrastha
Editorial Profile: Local news and foreign employment news (news about nepali who works overseas).
Language (s): Nepali
DAILY NEWSPAPER

Majdoor
Editorial: Majdoor Daily, Golmadi, Bhaktapur-7, Bhaktapur. **T:** 977 16610921
E: majdurdaily@gmail.com
W: http://www.majdoor.com.np
Freq: Daily; **Circ:** 10003 Not Audited
Editor: Vishnu Gopal Kushi
Editorial Profile: Local and National News.
Language (s): Nepali
DAILY NEWSPAPER

Nagarik Daily
Editorial: JDA Complex, Kathmandu.
T: 97 71 4265100 **E:** news@nagariknews.com
W: http://www.nagariknews.com
Freq: Daily
Editor in Chief: Prateek Pradhan
Editorial Profile: One of the most comprehensive and up-to-date news portals in Nepal for national and international news.
Language (s): Nepali
DAILY NEWSPAPER

Nepali Times
Editorial: Himalmedia Pvt. Ltd, G.P.O. Box 7251, Kathmandu. **T:** 977 15250333
E: editors@nepalitimes.com
W: http://www.nepalitimes.com
Freq: Weekly; **Circ:** 26003 Not Audited
Publisher & Editor: Kunda Dixit
Editorial Profile: Covers general news.
Language (s): English
DAILY NEWSPAPER

People's Review
Owner: People's Review
Editorial: Pipalbot, Dillibazar, P.O. Box 3052, Kathmandu. **T:** 977 1 4417352
E: preview@ntc.net.up
W: http://www.peoplesreview.com.np
Freq: Weekly; **Circ:** 15001 Not Audited
Editor in Chief: Pushpa Raj Pradhan
Editorial Profile: Covers news and related topics.
Language (s): English
DAILY NEWSPAPER

Rajdhani
Owner: Utsarga Prakashan Pvt Ltd.
Editorial: Utsarga Prakashan Pvt Ltd, PO Box 20503, Chabhil, Kathmandu. **T:** 997 1 4260752
E: rajdhaninews@yahoo.com
W: http://www.rajdhani.com.np
Freq: Daily; **Circ:** 10002 Not Audited
Editor: Jivendra Simkhada
Editorial Profile: Local and World News.
Language (s): Nepali
DAILY NEWSPAPER

The Rising Nepal
Editorial: Gorkhapatra Sanstan, Dharmapath, New Road, Kathmandu. **T:** 977 1 4244435
E: trn@gorkhapatra.org.np
W: http://www.gorkhapatra.org.np
Freq: Daily; **Circ:** 25003 Not Audited
Editorial Profile: Covers local and international news.
Language (s): English
DAILY NEWSPAPER

Sanghu Vernacular Weekly
Editorial: Sanghu Vernacular Weekly, Bagbazar, G.P.O. Box No. 2984, Kathmandu. **T:** 977 14230748 **E:** sanghuweekly@gmail.com
W: http://www.weeklynepal.com/sanghu
Freq: Weekly; **Circ:** 15002 Not Audited
Editor: Gopal Budhathoki
Editorial Profile: Covers of news and general interests.
Language (s): Nepali
DAILY NEWSPAPER

The Telegraph Weekly
Owner: Telegraph Pvt. Ltd.
Editorial: Telegraph Pvt. Ltd., P.O. Box 4063, Laligurans Marg-87, Ghattekulo, Kathmandu 32. **T:** 977 14770370
W: http://www.telegraphnepal.com
Freq: Weekly; **Circ:** 15002 Not Audited
Editorial Profile: Covers of National and International News, Sports, Business, Entertainment, etc.
Language (s): English
DAILY NEWSPAPER

Yugasambad National Weekly
Editorial: Yugasambad Weekly, P.O. Box 5331, New Plaza, Ram Shah Path, Kathmandu.
T: 977 14421454

E: yugasambad@hons.com.np
W: http://www.yugasambad.com.np
Freq: Weekly; **Circ:** 10001 Not Audited
Editorial Profile: Comments on contemporary issues on political, economic, social and environmental as well as gender aspects, interviews, entertainment, etc.
Language (s): Nepali
DAILY NEWSPAPER

NEWS SERVICE/SYNDICATE

Agence France-Presse - Kathmandu Bureau
Editorial: Bhote Bahal South, GPO Box 402, Kathmandu. **T:** 977 1 253 861
E: ammu.kannampilly@afp.com
W: http://www.afp.com
Bureau Chief: Ammu Kannampilly
Editorial Profile: Kathmandu bureau of international news and picture agency covering general news and current affairs.
Language (s): English
NEWS SERVICE/SYNDICATE

Associated Press
Editorial: Kathmandu. **T:** 977 1 4224-705
NEWS SERVICE/SYNDICATE

BROADCASTING

RADIO STATIONS

Image FM 97.9
Owner: Image Group of Companies
Editorial: Image Group of Companies, Image Complex, P.O. Box 5566, Panipokharir, Kathmandu. **T:** 977 14006555
E: imagefm@imagechannels.com
W: http://www.imagechannels.com
Editorial Profile: Provides information, entertainment and news updates.

Radio Nepal
Owner: Radio Broadcasting Service
Editorial: Radio Broadcasting Service (Radio Nepal), G.P.O. Box. No. 634, Singha Durbar, Kathmandu. **T:** 977 14211649
E: news@radionepal.org
W: http://www.radionepal.org
Editorial Profile: Covers news and music.

TELEVISION STATIONS

Nepal Television
Owner: Nepal Television Corporation
Editorial: Nepal Television Corporation, Singha Durbar, P.O. Box 3826, Kathmandu.
T: 977 14220348
E: neptv@vishnu.ccsl.com.np
W: http://www.explorenepal.com
Editorial Profile: Covers of news and general interests.

CABLE

High Himalayan Sky Cable TV
Owner: High Himalayan Sky Cable TV Co. (P) Ltd.
Editorial: High Himalayan Sky Cable TV Co. (P) Ltd., Dhara Tole, Boudha, Kathmandu.
T: 977 14477845
E: highhimalayan@yahoo.com
Editorial Profile: Covering news and general interests.

NETHERLANDS   Tel: 31
Standard Time: GMT +1
Continent: Europe
Capital City: Amsterdam

NEWSPAPERS & PUBLICATIONS

NEWS SERVICE/SYNDICATE

Associated Press
Editorial: Hoogte Kadijk 143/F20, Amsterdam 1018. **T:** 31 20 623-5057
Bureau Chief: Angela Charlton
NEWS SERVICE/SYNDICATE

Bloomberg News
Editorial: Stadhouderskade 14B, Amsterdam 1054. **T:** 31 20 589-8500
Bureau Chief: Fred Pals
NEWS SERVICE/SYNDICATE

Dow Jones Newswires
Editorial: Jozef Israelkade 48H, 1072 SB, Amsterdam. **T:** 31 20 571-5201
E: djnews.amsterdam@dowjones.com
Bureau Chief: Robin van Daalen
NEWS SERVICE/SYNDICATE

Reuters
Editorial: Antonio Vivaldistraat 50, Amsterdam 1083 HK. **T:** 31 20 504-5045
Bureau Chief: Anthony Deutsch
NEWS SERVICE/SYNDICATE

NETHERLANDS ANTILLES   Tel: 599
Standard Time: GMT -4
Continent: The Americas
Capital City: Willemstad

NEWSPAPERS & PUBLICATIONS

NEWSPAPERS

Amigoe
Owner: Uitgeverij Amigoe NV
Editorial: Uitgeverij Amigoe NV, Kaya Fraternan di Skèrpenè z/n, Curacao.
T: 599 97672744
E: management@amigoe.com
W: http://www.amigoe.com
Freq: Daily; **Circ:** 10000 Not Audited
Editor in Chief: Marius Noort; **Editor in Chief:** Linda Van Eekeres
Editorial Profile: Amigoe is a newspaper covering national and international news, politics, culture and sports.
Language (s): Dutch
DAILY NEWSPAPER

The Bonaire Reporter
Owner: Bonaire Reporter
T: 599 7866125 **E:** info@bonairereporter.com
W: http://www.bonairereporter.com
Freq: Bi-Monthly; **Circ:** 3000 Not Audited
Publisher: George De Salvo; **Editor in Chief:** Laura De Salvo
Editorial Profile: The Bonaire Reporter is a bi-monthly newspaper containing information on and analysis of the events on the Bonaire island.
Language (s): English
DAILY NEWSPAPER

The Daily Herald
Owner: The Caribbean Herald NV
Editorial: Bush Road 22, Philipsburg, Sint Maarten. **T:** 599 5 425 253
E: editorial@thedailyherald.com
W: http://www.thedailyherald.com
Freq: Daily
Publisher: Paul Dewindt; **Editor in Chief:** Courtney Gibson
Editorial Profile: Local newspaper distributed in the Caribbean region.
Language (s): English
DAILY NEWSPAPER

La Prensa
Owner: Uitgeverij de Pers NV
Editorial: West Indische Compagniestraat 41, Curacao. **T:** 599 9 462 4086
E: laprensa@laprensacur.com
W: http://www.laprensacur.com
Freq: Daily; **Circ:** 11000 Not Audited
Editor in Chief: Mariano Heyden
Editorial Profile: Local newspaper covering regional, national and international news and current-affairs; includes politics, finance, sport and culture.
Language (s): Dutch
DAILY NEWSPAPER

Ultimo Noticia
Owner: Ultimo Noticia NV
Editorial: Frederikstraat 96, Willemstad, Curacao. **T:** 599 9 462 3466
E: redakshon@ultimo.an
Freq: Daily; **Circ:** 19000 Not Audited
Editor: Angel Kirchner
Editorial Profile: Local newspaper focusing in the native Papiamento language.
Language (s): Dutch
DAILY NEWSPAPER

NEW CALEDONIA   Tel: 687
Standard Time: GMT +11
Continent: Oceania
Capital City: Nouméa

NEWSPAPERS & PUBLICATIONS

NEWSPAPERS

Les Nouvelles Calédoniennes
Owner: GHM - GROUPE HERSANT MEDIA
Editorial: 41, 43 rue de Sébastopol, B.P. G5, Noumea 98848. **T:** 687 2 72 58 4
E: lnc@canl.nc **W:** http://www.lnc.nc
Freq: Daily
Editor in Chief: Patrick Blain; **Rédacteur en Chef:** Xavier Serre
Editorial Profile: Regional daily newspaper covering regional, national and international news and current affairs in New Caledonia including politics, economics, society, sport, classifieds, legal ads, leisure, motoring and TV guide.
Language (s): French
DAILY NEWSPAPER

BROADCASTING

TELEVISION STATIONS

RFO NOUVELLE CALEDONIE
Editorial: 1 rue du Général-Leclerc, BP G3, Noumea Cedex 98848. **T:** 687 2 39 99 9
W: http://www.rfo.fr
Editorial Profile: Local office of the overseas national public TV channel focussing on regional and local news, sport, entertainment, music, ethology, history, faith and traditions.

NEW ZEALAND   Tel: 64
Standard Time: GMT =12
Continent: Oceania
Capital City: Wellington

NEWSPAPERS & PUBLICATIONS

NEWSPAPERS

Bay of Plenty Times
Owner: APN News & Media
Editorial: Private Bag 12002, Tauranga 3143.
T: 64 7 577 7770
E: news@bayofplentytimes.co.nz
W: http://bayofplentytimes.co.nz **Circ:** 20352 ABC-Audit Bureau of Circulations
Editor: Scott Inglis; **News Editor:** Ross Pringle
Editorial Profile: Read by residents of the Western Bay of Plenty. Bay of Plenty Mon-Sat Photo: b+w/col.
Language (s): English
DAILY NEWSPAPER

The Dominion Post
Owner: Fairfax Media
Editorial: PO Box 3740, Wellington 6140.
T: 64 4 474 0196 **E:** news@dompost.co.nz
W: http://stuff.co.nz/dominion-post
Freq: Daily; **Circ:** 84047 ABC-Audit Bureau of Circulations
Editor: Bernadette Courtney
Editorial Profile: The Dominion Post is a metropolitan broadsheet newspaper published in Wellington, New Zealand.
Language (s): English
DAILY NEWSPAPER

Hawke's Bay Today
Owner: APN News
Editorial: PO Box 180, Hastings 4156.
T: 64 6 873 0800 **E:** news@hbtoday.co.nz
W: http://hbtoday.co.nz **Circ:** 24775 ABC-Audit Bureau of Circulations
Editorial Profile: HB province Eve Mon-Fri; morn Sat Photo b+w/col Inc Evening News Dannevirke. Copy ag news to news@hbtoday.co.nz.
Language (s): English
DAILY NEWSPAPER

Manawatu Standard
Owner: Fairfax Media
Editorial: PO Box 3, Palmerston North 4440.
T: 64 6 356 9009 **E:** editor@msl.co.nz
W: http://stuff.co.nz/manawatu-standard
Circ: 17000 ABC-Audit Bureau of Circulations
Editor: Michael Cummings

Editorial Profile: Newspaper focusing on local, national and world news, sport and entertainment. Aimed at general public in Central North Island, New Zealand.Manawatu, Tararua, Rangitikei, Northern Horowhenua Afternoon Mon-Sat Photo col pref PR txt to round by email; pics to ed.
Language (s): English
DAILY NEWSPAPER

Nelson Mail
Owner: Fairfax Media
Editorial: PO Box 244, Nelson 7040.
T: 64 3 548 7079
E: chiefreporter@nelsonmail.co.nz
W: http://nelsonmail.co.nz **Circ:** 15609 ABC-Audit Bureau of Circulations
Editor: Paul McIntyre
Editorial Profile: Nelson and district Mon-Sat Photo b+w/col Text in main body of email (no attachments) JPGs to pic email as attachments.
Language (s): English
DAILY NEWSPAPER

New Zealand Herald
Owner: APN News
Editorial: 46 Albert Street, Auckland 1010.
T: 64 9 379 5050 **E:** newsdesk@nzherald.co.nz
W: http://www.nzherald.co.nz **Circ:** 170677 ABC-Audit Bureau of Circulations
Editor: Michele Crawshaw; **Editor:** Shayne Currie; **Real Estate Editor:** Anne Gibson; **Editor:** Andrew Laxon; **Editor:** Amanda Linnell; **Editor-in-Chief:** Tim Murphy; **Careers Editor:** James Russell
Editorial Profile: The New Zealand Herald provides news and current events from around New Zealand and around the word.
Language (s): English
DAILY NEWSPAPER

Otago Daily Times
Owner: Allied Press Ltd
Editorial: PO Box 181, Dunedin 9054.
T: 64 3 477 4760
E: odt.editorial@alliedpress.co.nz
W: http://odt.co.nz **Circ:** 39097 ABC-Audit Bureau of Circulations
Day Editor: Dave Cannan; **Illustrations Editor:** Stephen Jaquiery; **Editor:** Murray Kirkness; **Racing Editor:** Tayler Strong
Editorial Profile: Area: Timaru - south Mon-Sat + online option Photo b+w/col. A daily regional newspaper withnNews, sport, entertainment, lifestyle and opinion for the Otago region.News Tips: newstips@alliedpress.co.nz, Press Releases: press.releases@alliedpress.co.nz. PR Accepted in: English
Language (s): English
DAILY NEWSPAPER

The Press
Owner: Fairfax Media
Editorial: Private Bag 4722, Christchurch 8140. **T:** 64 3 379 0940
E: reporters@press.co.nz
W: http://stuff.co.nz/the-press **Circ:** 81017 ABC-Audit Bureau of Circulations
Editor - Drive: Dave Moore; **Editor:** Joanna Norris
Editorial Profile: North + central SI Mon-Sat Online option Photo b+w/col Txt by email, pref to reporters@press.co.nz Pix by neg only Wgtn address Parliament Bldgs, Private Bag, Wgtn NB: Due to the Christchurch earthquake of 22 Feb 2011 the Press is operating from temporary premises until further notice DDIs not yet connected (May 2011).
Language (s): English
DAILY NEWSPAPER

The Southland Times
Owner: Fairfax Media
Editorial: PO Box 805, Invercargill 9840.
T: 64 3 211 1130 **E:** news@stl.co.nz
W: http://stuff.co.nz/southland-times
Circ: 28066 ABC-Audit Bureau of Circulations
Design Editor: Chris Chilton; **News Editor:** Jim Dixon; **Editor:** Fred Tulett
Editorial Profile: Southland Central S Otago Mon-Sat. + online option Photo b+w/col PR txt/jpics by email to chief reporter.
Language (s): English
DAILY NEWSPAPER

Sunday News
Owner: Fairfax Media
Editorial: PO Box 1327, Shortland Street, Auckland 1140. **T:** 64 9 925 9700
E: editor@sunday-news.co.nz
W: http://stuff.co.nz/sunday-news
Freq: Weekly; **Circ:** 51740 ABC-Audit Bureau of Circulations
Editor: Jonathan Milne

Editorial Profile: The Sunday News is published by Fairfax Media.
Language (s): English
DAILY NEWSPAPER

Sunday Star-Times
Owner: Fairfax Media
Editorial: PO Box 1327, Shortland Street, Auckland 1140. **T:** 64 9 925 9700
E: news@star-times.co.nz
W: http://stuff.co.nz/sunday-star-times
Freq: Weekly; **Circ:** 160592 ABC-Audit Bureau of Circulations
Editor: David Kemeys; **Racing Editor:** Barry Lichter; **Editor:** Jonathan Milne; **Contact:** Angela Walker
Editorial Profile: National Photo col pref. PR txt to round by email;jpegs to pic ed Alt website: sstlive.co.nz Separate listing for Sunday Magazine.
Language (s): English
DAILY NEWSPAPER

The Taranaki Daily News
Owner: Fairfax Media
Editorial: PO Box 444, Taranaki Mail Centre, New Plymouth 4340. **T:** 64 6 759 0800
E: editor@dailynews.co.nz
W: http://taranakidailynews.co.nz **Circ:** 23005 ABC-Audit Bureau of Circulations
News Editor: Steve Anker; **Editor:** Roy Pilott
Editorial Profile: Taranaki/King Country Mon-Sat Photo col pref.
Language (s): English
DAILY NEWSPAPER

Waikato Times
Owner: Fairfax Media
Editorial: Private Bag 3086, Waikato Mail Centre, Hamilton 3240. **T:** 64 7 849 6180
E: news@waikatotimes.co.nz
W: http://stuff.co.nz/waikato-times **Circ:** 40096 ABC-Audit Bureau of Circulations
News Editor: David Eames; **Editor:** Jonathan MacKenzie
Editorial Profile: Waikato Eve Mon-Fri; morn Sat + online option Photo: b+w/col PR to newsdesk.
Language (s): English
DAILY NEWSPAPER

NEWS SERVICE/SYNDICATE

AAP - Auckland Bureau
Owner: Australian Associated Press
Editorial: PO Box 2941, Auckland 1140.
T: 64 9 378 7157
E: news.auckland@aap.com.au
W: http://aap.com.au
Editorial Profile: Auckland bureau for Australia's national news agency. PR Accepted in: English
Language (s): English
NEWS SERVICE/SYNDICATE

Alert24
Owner: Thomson Reuters
Editorial: PO Box 43, Wellington 6140.
T: 64 4 499 8178
E: warren.wilkie@thomsonreuters.com
W: http://brookers.co.nz
Freq: Daily
News Editor: Warren Wilkie
Editorial Profile: News service consists of 19 news bulletins on developments in key areas of NZ law (see www.brookers.co.nz/whatsNew/about-Alert24.asp) Brookers Legal News Service html/plain text email bulletins.
Language (s): English
NEWS SERVICE/SYNDICATE

Appita
Editorial: PO Box 6042, Whakarewarewa, Rotorua 3043. **T:** 64 7 350 2252
E: appita.nz@xtra.co.nz
W: http://www.appita.com.au
Editorial Profile: Appita is a non-profit technical association serving the New Zealand and Australian pulp and paper industry. Its main purpose is to facilitate the industry's technical network involving all stakeholders to advance the technical capability and expertise. Alternative Co. Name: Australian Pulp and Paper Industry Technical Association
NEWS SERVICE/SYNDICATE

Asia Pacific Economic News Service
Owner: Asia Pacific Economic News Ltd
Editorial: PO Box 3978, Wellington 6140.
T: 64 27 242 2301
E: ahaas@decisionmaker.co.nz
W: http://decisionmaker.co.nz
Bureau Chief: Tony Haas
Language (s): English
NEWS SERVICE/SYNDICATE

Asia Pacific Economic News Service Ltd
Editorial: PO Box 3978, 5 Maurice Terrace, Wellington. **T:** 64 27 24 23 01
E: ahaas@decisionmaker.co.nz
Publisher: Anthony Haas
Language (s): English
NEWS SERVICE/SYNDICATE

Asia Pacific Network
Owner: David Robie Publishing Ltd
Editorial: PO Box 78028, Grey Lynn, Auckland 1245. **T:** 64 99219999 7834
E: delaro@clear.net.nz **W:** http://asiapac.org.fj
Publisher: David Robie
Language (s): English
NEWS SERVICE/SYNDICATE

Associated Press
Owner: Associated Press, Inc.
T: 64 4 471 2990 **E:** nperry@ap.org
W: http://ap.org
Editorial Profile: International news agency PR txt/jpegs to Newsdesk.
Language (s): English
NEWS SERVICE/SYNDICATE

Associated Press
Owner: Associated Press
Editorial: Press Gallery Parliament Buildings, Wellington 6160. **T:** 64 4 471-2990
Bureau Chief: Kristen Gelineau
NEWS SERVICE/SYNDICATE

Bloomberg
Owner: Bloomberg Financial Markets, Commmodities
Editorial: PO Box 122, Wellington 6140.
T: 64 4 498 2201 **E:** nznews@bloomberg.net
W: http://bloomberg.com
Bureau Chief: Chris Bourke
Editorial Profile: Financial wire service.
Language (s): English
NEWS SERVICE/SYNDICATE

Bloomberg News
Editorial: 171 Featherton Street, Level 13 HP Tower, Wellington. **T:** 64 44982201
Bureau Chief: Chris Bourke
NEWS SERVICE/SYNDICATE

businessday.co.nz
Owner: Fairfax Media
Editorial: PO Box 1409, Auckland 1140.
T: 64 9 308 4590
E: business@fairfaxdigital.co.nz
W: http://stuff.co.nz/businessday
Language (s): English
NEWS SERVICE/SYNDICATE

CCTV NEWS
Owner: China Central Television
Editorial: 11 Fuxing Lu, Beijing, China Pc 1008. **T:** 64 8610 6850 6504 **E:** intl@cctv.com
W: http://cctv.com
Editor: Mr./Ms. Editor
Editorial Profile: 24/7 Eng lang news channel available on Sky Channel 93.
Language (s): English
NEWS SERVICE/SYNDICATE

Dow Jones Newswires
Editorial: EMC2, 5-7 Wilestone Street, Wellington. **T:** 64 4 471-5990
NEWS SERVICE/SYNDICATE

Dow Jones Newswires
Owner: News Corporation Ltd
Editorial: PO Box 24136, Manners Street, Wellington 6142. **T:** 64 4 471 5990
E: djnews.wellington@dowjones.com
W: http://dowjonesnews.com
Bureau Chief: Simon Louisson
Editorial Profile: Financial news agency Add to target lists with caution - financial news only All are accredited parliamentary reporters but only cover exceptional events there.
Language (s): English
NEWS SERVICE/SYNDICATE

Fuseworks
Owner: Fuseworks Ltd
Editorial: 1/95 Molesworth Street, Thorndon, Wellington 6011. **T:** 64 4 889 0188
E: news@fuseworks.co.nz
W: http://fuseworks.co.nz
Freq: Daily
Editor: Simon Randall
Editorial Profile: News agency National news, entertainment, technology, sport, business, and politics Alt email diary@fuseworks.co.nz.
Geographical Focus: Sport
Language (s): English
NEWS SERVICE/SYNDICATE

Independent Network News
Owner: Independent Network News
Editorial: 7 Maryport Street, Lawrence, Otago 9532. **T:** 64 3 485 9885
E: newsroom@nzinn.org **W:** http://nzinn.org
Editor: Ian Cunningham
Language (s): English
NEWS SERVICE/SYNDICATE

Indo Asian News Service
Owner: Indo Asian News Service
E: neena@india-voice.com
W: http://www.ians.ian
Editorial Profile: Interested in trade, IT, travel, migration, education, individual profiles of Indian migrants and any other stories that would be of interest to people in the sub-continent and the Indian diaspora.
Language (s): English
NEWS SERVICE/SYNDICATE

infonews.co.nz
Owner: Citizen Media Ltd
Editorial: 27 Littlejohn St, Hillsborough, Auckland 1042. **T:** 64 21 045 5634
E: news@infonews.co.nz
W: http://infonews.co.nz
Editor: Peter Hodge; **Editor:** Fraser Mills
Language (s): English
NEWS SERVICE/SYNDICATE

MSN New Zealand Ltd
Owner: Tasman NineMSN
Editorial: PO Box 8998, Symonds St, Auckland 1150. **T:** 64 9 362 5628
E: liz.fraser@msn.co.nz **W:** http://msn.co.nz
Language (s): English
NEWS SERVICE/SYNDICATE

NZX Newsroom Limited
Owner: NZX (New Zealand Exchange)
Editorial: PO Box 2959, Level 2, Wellington 6011. **T:** 64 44952822
E: editor@newsroom.co.nz
W: http://newsroom.co.nz
Editor in Chief: Peter Fowler
Language (s): English
NEWS SERVICE/SYNDICATE

Pacific Media Centre
Owner: AUT University
Editorial: Public Affairs, AUT University, Private Bag 92006, Auckland 1142.
T: 64 9 921 9999 7834 **E:** pmc@aut.ac.nz
W: http://pmc.aut.ac.nz
Editorial Profile: Media research and community resource centre focusing on Maori, Pasifika and ethnic diversity media and community development Director David Robie.
Geographical Focus: Maori
Language (s): English
NEWS SERVICE/SYNDICATE

Pacific Media Watch
Owner: Pacific Media Centre, AUT University
Editorial: AUT University, PO Box 92006, Auckland 1142. **T:** 64 99219999 7834
E: pmc@aut.ac.nz **W:** http://pmw.c2o.org
Freq: Daily
Editor: Mr./Ms. Editor
Language (s): English
NEWS SERVICE/SYNDICATE

Reuters
Owner: Thomson Reuters
Editorial: PO Box 43, Wellington 6140.
T: 64 4 471 4234
E: wellington.newsroom@thomsonreuters.com
W: http://reuters.com
Editorial Profile: Alt email: wellington.newsroom@reuters.com or news@fin.co.nz.
Language (s): English
NEWS SERVICE/SYNDICATE

Scoop
Owner: Scoop Media Ltd
Editorial: Level 3- 354, Lambton Quay, Wellington 6142. **T:** 64 4 910 1844
E: editor@scoop.co.nz
W: http://scoop.co.nz/about/contact.html
Editorial Profile: Political, business, science, biotechnology, education, health, IT arts/culture, sports, international PR txt/jpegs (up to 200kb) to editor Adv: scoop.co.nz/about/advertising.html.
Language (s): English
NEWS SERVICE/SYNDICATE

Scoop (Ak)
Owner: Scoop Media Ltd
Editorial: Lvl 8, Suite 7, Albert Plaza, Auckland 1001. **T:** 64 9 377 0579 **E:** editor@scoop.co.nz
W: http://scoop.co.nz
Freq: Daily
Language (s): English
NEWS SERVICE/SYNDICATE

Stuff.co.nz
Owner: Fairfax Media
Editorial: PO Box 2595, Wellington 6140.
T: 64 4 474 0090 **E:** newsroom@stuff.co.nz
W: http://stuff.co.nz
Content Editor: Kevin Norquay; **Editor:** Mark Stevens
Editorial Profile: Stuff.co.nz is New Zealand's news and information website. Covers every aspect of news and information, from breaking national and international crises through to in-depth features, sports, business, entertainment and technology articles, weather reports, travel services, movie reviews, rural news.
Language (s): English
NEWS SERVICE/SYNDICATE

TVNZ Interactive
Owner: Television New Zealand
Editorial: PO Box 3819, Auckland 1030.
T: 64 9 916 7000
E: interactivenews@tvnz.co.nz
W: http://tvnz.co.nz
Editor: Sarah Pritchett
Language (s): English
NEWS SERVICE/SYNDICATE

Xinhua News Agency (Wellington)
Owner: People's Republic of China
Editorial: 6 Nether Green Crescent, Johnsonville, Wellington 6037.
T: 64 4 972 8909
E: xinhuawellington@yahoo.com
W: http://xinhuanet.com
Language (s): English
NEWS SERVICE/SYNDICATE

yahoo!xtra
Owner: Xtra Limited/Yahoo
Editorial: PO Box 37381, Parnell, Auckland 1151. **T:** 64 9 368 8100
E: forbes@yahoo-inc.com
W: http://yahooxtra.co.nz
Editor: Marcus Forbes
Language (s): English
NEWS SERVICE/SYNDICATE

NICARAGUA Tel: 505

Standard Time: GMT -6
Continent: The Americas
Capital City: Managua

NEWSPAPERS & PUBLICATIONS

NEWSPAPERS

Bolsa de Noticias
Owner: Grupo Emigdio Suárez Ediciones
Editorial: Colonia Centroamérica de la Iglesia de Fatima 3 cuadras al sur, Casa L#852, Managua. **T:** 505 22700546
E: prensa@bolsadenoticias.com.ni
W: http://www.bolsadenoticias.com.ni
Freq: Daily; **Circ:** 3500 Not Audited
Editor in Chief: María Elena Palacios
Editorial Profile: Regional newspaper focusing on national and international news, politics, business and sport.
Language (s): Spanish
DAILY NEWSPAPER

El Nuevo Diario
Owner: El Nuevo Diario
Editorial: Kilómetro 4.5, Carretera Norte, Managua. **T:** 505 22490499
E: ediciononline@elnuevodiario.com.ni
W: http://www.elnuevodiario.com.ni
Freq: Daily; **Circ:** 46000 Not Audited
Editor: Gustavo Alvarez; **Editor in Chief:** Roberto Fonseca; **Editor:** Juan Ramón Huerta; **Editor:** Edgar Tijerino
Editorial Profile: National newspaper covering national and international news, sport, politics and culture.
Language (s): Spanish
DAILY NEWSPAPER

La Prensa
Owner: Editora La Prensa SA
Editorial: Kilómetro 4 1/2 Carretera Norte, Managua 192. **T:** 505 22556767
E: info@laprensa.com.ni
W: http://www.laprensa.com.ni
Freq: Daily; **Circ:** 42600 Not Audited
Editor in Chief: Eduardo Enríquez; **Editor:** Freddy Potoy; **Editor:** Edgar Rodríguez; **Editor:** Luis Sánchez
Editorial Profile: Newspaper focusing on national and international news, politics and economics.
Language (s): Spanish
DAILY NEWSPAPER

BROADCASTING

TELEVISION NETWORKS

Telenica Canal 8
Editorial: Mansión Teodolinda 1c al sur, 1/2c abajo, Managua. **T:** 505 22665021
W: http://www.telenica.com.ni
Editorial Profile: Provides daily news, soap operas, touristic and cultural programs.

NIGER Tel: 227

Standard Time: GMT +1
Continent: Africa
Capital City: Niamey

NEWSPAPERS & PUBLICATIONS

NEWSPAPERS

Le Démocrate
Owner: Nouvelles Imprimeries du Niger
Editorial: 21 Rue 067 NB Terminus, BP: 11 064, Niamey. **T:** 227 94 85 50 90
E: le_democrate@caramail.com
W: http://www.tamtaminfo.com **Circ:** 1000 Publisher's Statement
Rédacteur en Chef: Assane Saadou
Editorial Profile: Regional weekly newspaper focussing on news & current affairs, politics and culture.
Language (s): French
DAILY NEWSPAPER

L' Enquêteur
Owner: Nouvelles Imprimeries du Niger
Editorial: Quartier Poudrière villa nº 67, (collée au Bar Guiguigna), Niamey.
T: 227 20 34 48 91 **E:** enqueteur@intnet.ne
W: http://www.tamtaminfo.com **Circ:** 2000 Publisher's Statement
Editor In Chief: Salif Dago
Editorial Profile: Fortnightly investigation newspaper focussing on news & current affairs and politics.
Language (s): French
DAILY NEWSPAPER

L' Evènement
Editorial: Zabarkan, Rue de L'Entente, Porte: 654, Niamey. **T:** 227 20 74 15 75
E: levenement@netcourrier.com
W: http://www.tamtaminfo.com **Circ:** 1000 Publisher's Statement
Editor In Chief: Garé Amadou
Editorial Profile: Weekly newspaper focussing on news & current affairs.
Language (s): French
DAILY NEWSPAPER

Le Républicain
Owner: Nouvelles Imprimeries du Niger
Editorial: Quartier terminus, Face pharmacie de l'espoir, Niamey. **T:** 227 20 33 03 03
E: nin@intnet.ne
W: http://www.republicain-niger.com
Circ: 2500 Publisher's Statement
Editorial Profile: Newspaper covering national and international news, politics, business, entertainment and sport.
Language (s): French
DAILY NEWSPAPER

Le Sahel
Owner: Le Sahel Dimanche
Editorial: BP 13182, Niamey.
T: 227 20 73 34 87 **E:** onep@intnet.ne
W: http://www.tamtaminfo.com
Freq: Daily; **Circ:** 3500 Publisher's Statement
Rédacteur en Chef: Fatouma Boubakar; **Rédacteur en Chef:** Assane Soumana
Editorial Profile: Newspaper covering national and international news, politics, business and sport.
Language (s): French
DAILY NEWSPAPER

Le Sahel Dimanche
Owner: Le Sahel Dimanche
Editorial: BP 13182, Niamey.
T: 227 20 73 34 87 **E:** onep@intnet.ne
W: http://www.tamtaminfo.com **Circ:** 4000 Publisher's Statement
Rédacteur en Chef Adjoint: Mamane Bako; **Rédacteur en Chef:** Tchigni Maimouna
Editorial Profile: Newspaper focusing on national and international news, politics, business, entertainment and sport. Classifieds.
Language (s): French
DAILY NEWSPAPER

La Voie Nouvelle
Editorial: BP 10 596, Niamey.
T: 227 20 75 53 11 **E:** issalbia@yahoo.fr
W: http://www.tamtaminfo.com **Circ:** 1000 Publisher's Statement
Editor In Chief: Alio Oumarou Modibo
Editorial Profile: Weekly newspaper focussing on news & current affairs.
Language (s): French
DAILY NEWSPAPER

NIGERIA Tel: 234

Standard Time: GMT +1
Continent: Africa
Capital City: Abuja

NEWSPAPERS & PUBLICATIONS

NEWSPAPERS

Business Day
Owner: Business Day Ltd.
Editorial: 6 Point Road, Apapa, Lagos.
T: 234 1 34 54 501
E: mail@businessdayonline.com
W: http://businessdayonline.com
Freq: Daily
Publisher: Frank Aigbogun; **Editor:** Phillip Isakpa; **News Editor:** John Osadolor
Editorial Profile: Newspaper covering national and international business news including finance, markets, enterprise, banking, economy, business intelligence and personal finance.
Language (s): English
DAILY NEWSPAPER

Daily Champion
Owner: Champion Newspapers Limited
Editorial: PO Box 2276, Oshodi, Lagos
W: http://www.championlinenews.com
Freq: Daily; **Circ:** 80000 Publisher's Statement
Editor in Chief: Nwadiuto Iheakanwa; **Publisher:** Emmanuel Iwuanyanwu
Editorial Profile: Newspaper covering national and international news, business, politics and entertainment.
Language (s): English
DAILY NEWSPAPER

Daily Independent
Owner: Independent Newspapers Limited
Editorial: Block 5, Plot 7D, Wempco Road, Ogba, Lagos. **T:** 234 70 36268493
E: info@dailyindependentnig.com
W: http://www.dailyindependentnig.com
Freq: Daily
News Editor: Rotimi Durojaiye
Editorial Profile: Newspaper covering national and international news including politics, business, economics, lifestyle and sports.
Language (s): English
DAILY NEWSPAPER

Daily Trust
Owner: Media Trust Nigeria Limited
Editorial: No. 20 P.O.W. Mafemi Crescent, Off Soloman Lar way, Abuja. **T:** 234 9 672 62 41
E: dailytrust@yahoo.co.uk
W: http://www.dailytrust.info
Freq: Daily; **Circ:** 20000 Publisher's Statement
Editor in Chief: Mannir Dan Ali
Editorial Profile: Newspaper covering national and international news including politics, business, economics, sport, agriculture, education, environment, religion and health.
Language (s): English
DAILY NEWSPAPER

The Guardian
Owner: Guardian Newspapers Limited
Editorial: Rutam House, Km 4 Apapa-Oshodi Expressway, Lagos. **T:** 234 1 44 89 600
E: letters@ngrguardiannews.com
W: http://www.ngrguardiannews.com
Freq: Daily; **Circ:** 50000 Publisher's Statement
Editor in Chief: Debo Adesina; **News Editor:** Marcel Mbamalu; **Editor (Sunday):** Abraham Ogbodo
Editorial Profile: Newspaper covering national and international news, current affairs, politics, business, sports and arts.
Language (s): English
DAILY NEWSPAPER

Al Mizan
Owner: IM Publications
Editorial: PO Box 686, Babban Dodo, Zariya.
T: 234 80 37023343
E: almizanzariya@yahoo.com
W: http://www.almizan.info **Circ:** 25000 Publisher's Statement
Editor in Chief: Ibrahim Musa
Editorial Profile: Newspaper covering national and international news, politics, religion and sport.
Language (s): Hausa
DAILY NEWSPAPER

The National Mirror
Owner: Global Media Mirror Limited
Editorial: Mirror House, 155/161, Broad Street, Lagos 101001. **T:** 234 70 2710 7407
E: mail@nationalmirroronline.net
W: http://nationalmirroronline.net
Freq: Daily
Editor: Bolaji Tunji
Editorial Profile: Newspaper covering the latest news from Nigeria including politics, business, arts, lifestyle, sports, education and health.
Language (s): English
DAILY NEWSPAPER

Nigerian Tribune
Owner: African Newspapers of Nigeria Ltd
Editorial: Imalefalafia Street, Oke-Ado, Ibadan.
T: 234 80 38064581
E: editornigeriantribune@yahoo.com
W: http://www.tribune.com.ng
Freq: Daily; **Circ:** 45000 Publisher's Statement
Editor: Alhaji Debo Abdulai
Editorial Profile: Newspaper covering the latest news from Nigeria including politics, business, community news, lifestyle, sports, education and health.
Language (s): English
DAILY NEWSPAPER

Peoples Daily
Owner: Peoples Media Ltd
Editorial: 35, Ajose Adeogun Street, 1st Floor, Abuja. **T:** 234 9 873 4478
E: contact@peoplesdailyng.com
W: http://www.peoplesdailyng.com
Freq: Daily
Editor in Chief: Rufai Ibrahim
Editorial Profile: Newspaper covering news and current affairs including business, politics, economics, lifestyle and sports.
Language (s): English
DAILY NEWSPAPER

The Punch
Owner: Punch (Nigeria) Limited
Editorial: Km 14 Lagos-Ibadan expressway, Magboro, Lagos
E: editor@punchontheweb.com
W: http://www.punchng.com
Freq: Daily; **Circ:** 100000 Publisher's Statement
Editor: Steve Ayorinde
Editorial Profile: Newspaper covering news and current affairs including politics, business, sports, opinion and health.
Language (s): English
DAILY NEWSPAPER

The Sun
Owner: The Sun Publishing Limited
Editorial: 2 Coscharis Street, Kirikiri Industrial Layout, Apapa, P.M.B., Lagos 21776.
T: 234 805 633 4351
E: editor@sunnewsonline.com
W: http://www.sunnewsonline.com
Freq: Daily; **Circ:** 80000 Publisher's Statement
Editor in Chief: Femi Adesina
Editorial Profile: Newspaper covering national and international news and current affairs including politics, business, sports and entertainment.
Language (s): English
DAILY NEWSPAPER

This Day
Owner: Leaders & Company Limited
Editorial: 35, Creek Road, Apapa, Lagos.
T: 234 80 22 92 47 21
E: hello@thisdaylive.com
W: http://www.thisdaylive.com
Freq: Daily; **Circ:** 100000 Publisher's Statement
Editor: Ijeoma Nwogwugwu; **Editor in Chief:** Nduka Obaigbena; **Style Editor:** Ruth Osime
Editorial Profile: Newspaper covering national and international news including politics, business, sport, entertainment and lifestyle.
Language (s): English
DAILY NEWSPAPER

Vanguard
Owner: Vanguard Media Limited
Editorial: 2 Vanguard Avenue, Kirikiri Canal, Lagos. **T:** 234 70 61078412
E: citizenreport@vanguardngr.com
W: http://www.vanguardngr.com
Freq: Daily; **Circ:** 120000 Publisher's Statement
Editor: Mideno Bayagbon
Editorial Profile: Newspaper covering national and international news including politics, business, sport, entertainment, technology and lifestyle.
Language (s): English
DAILY NEWSPAPER

Weekly Trust
Owner: Media Trust Nigeria Limited
Editorial: No. 20 P.O.W. Mafemi Crescent, Off Solomon Lar way, Abuja. **T:** 234 9 672 62 41
E: dailytrust@yahoo.co.uk
W: http://www.dailytrust.com
Freq: Weekly; **Circ:** 25000 Publisher's Statement
Editor in Chief: Mannir Dan Ali
Editorial Profile: Newspaper covering national and international news including politics, business, economics, sport, agriculture, education, environment, religion and health.
Language (s): English
DAILY NEWSPAPER

NEWS SERVICE/SYNDICATE

Agence France-Presse - Lagos Bureau
Owner: Agence France-Presse
Editorial: 11 Awolowo Road, Ikoyi, Lagos. **T:** 234 1 461 5982
E: phillip.hazlewood@afp.com
W: http://www.afp.com
Bureau Chief: Phil Hazlewood
Editorial Profile: Lagos bureau of the international news and picture agency Agence France-Presse covering international news and current affairs.
Language (s): French
NEWS SERVICE/SYNDICATE

Associated Press
T: 234 803 403-0364
Stringer: Bashir Adigun
NEWS SERVICE/SYNDICATE

Bloomberg News
Editorial: Africa Head Office, 35 Oladipo Bateye Street, Lagos. **T:** 234 1 775-5486
Bureau Chief: Chris Kay
NEWS SERVICE/SYNDICATE

Reuters
T: 234 1 270-4080
Bureau Chief: Tim Cocks
NEWS SERVICE/SYNDICATE

BROADCASTING

TELEVISION STATIONS

Bloomberg TV Africa
Owner: Optima Media International
Editorial: Africa Head Office, 35 Oladipo Bateye Street, Lagos. **T:** 234 1 775 5486
W: http://bloomafrica2013.mmsite.co.uk
Editorial Profile: Bloomberg TV Africa is a Pan-African TV station broadcasting business and financial news.

CNBC Africa
Owner: CNBC Africa
Editorial: 5th Floor, Left Wing, River State Complex, Plot 83, Ralph Shodeinde Street, Abuja. **T:** 234 9 234 40 76
W: http://www.cnbcafrica.com

NIUE	Tel: 683

Standard Time: GMT -11

BROADCASTING

RADIO NETWORKS

Radio Sunshine
Owner: Broadcasting Corporation of Niue (BCN)
Editorial: PO Box 68, Alofi, Niue. **T:** 683 4026
E: sunshine@mail.gov.nu

TELEVISION STATIONS

Television Niue
Owner: Broadcasting Corporation of Niue (BCN)
Editorial: PO Box 68, Alofi, Niue. **T:** 683 4026
E: gm.bcn@mail.gov.nu

NORFOLK ISLAND	Tel: 672

Standard Time: GMT +11.5
Continent: Oceania
Capital City: Kingston

NEWSPAPERS & PUBLICATIONS

NEWSPAPERS

The Norfolk Islander
Owner: Greenways Press Pty Ltd.
Editorial: PO Box 248, Norfolk Island. **T:** 672 23 22159 **E:** news@islander.nf
W: http://norfolkislander.com **Circ:** 1400 Publisher's Statement
Editor: Tom Lloyd; **Editor:** Jonathan Snell
Editorial Profile: Newspaper focusing on local and regional news, community issues and sport.
Language (s): English
DAILY NEWSPAPER

BROADCASTING

RADIO NETWORKS

Norfolk Island Broadcasting Service
Editorial: PO Box 456, New Cascade Road, Norfolk Island 2899. **T:** 672 32 21 37
E: manager@radio.gov.nf
W: http://www.norfolkisland.gov.nf
Editorial Profile: Norfolk Island Radio (community radio on 1566AM and 89.9) plus rebroadcasts of several Australian stations.

NORTHERN MARIANA ISLANDS	Tel: 1 670

Standard Time: GMT +10
Continent: Oceania
Capital City: Saipan

NEWSPAPERS & PUBLICATIONS

NEWSPAPERS

Marianas Variety News & Views
Owner: Younis Art Studio Inc.
Editorial: Alaihai Avenue, Garapan, Saipan. **T:** 1 6702349797 **E:** younis@pticom.com
W: http://www.mvariety.com
Freq: Daily
Editor: Zaldy Dandan
Editorial Profile: Marianas Variety News & Views is a general-interest daily newspaper covering all of Micronesia. The paper covers local news, sports, business and Pacific Islands news.
Language (s): Chamorro, English
DAILY NEWSPAPER

Saipan Tribune
Owner: Pacific Publications & Printing Inc.
Editorial: 2nd Floor CIC Centre, Beach Road, Garapan, Saipan 96950. **T:** 1 6702356397
E: editor@saipantribune.com
W: http://www.saipantribune.com
Freq: Daily
Editor in Chief: Jayvee Vallejera
Editorial Profile: Saipan Tribune is a daily newspaper serving the Northern Mariana Islands. It was the Commonwealth's first daily newspaper. It provides local news, sports, business, entertainment and features. The national and international news is provided by news services.
Language (s): English
DAILY NEWSPAPER

BROADCASTING

RADIO STATIONS

KRSI-FM
Owner: Sorensen Pacific Broadcasting
T: 1 6702357996
W: http://www.sorensenmediagroup.com
Editorial Profile: Provides local news, entertainment, live music including raggae and other island's rhytms.

NORWAY	Tel: 47

Standard Time: GMT +1
Continent: Europe
Capital City: Oslo

NEWSPAPERS & PUBLICATIONS

NEWSPAPERS

ADRESSEAVISEN
Owner: Adresseavisen ASA
Editorial: Industriveien 13, Trondheim 7003. **T:** 47 0720 0 **E:** redaksjon@adresseavisen.no
W: http://www.adressa.no
Freq: Daily; **Circ:** 75835 MBL
Sjefsredaktør: Arne Blix
Language (s): Norwegian; Full Page Colour: 71294.00
Currency: Norway Kroner
DAILY NEWSPAPER

ADRESSEAVISEN - FOSEN
Owner: Adresseavisen ASA
Editorial: Bjugn 7160. **T:** 47 72 52 72 52
E: redaksjon@adresseavisen.no
W: http://www.adressa.no
Freq: Daily; **Circ:** 77044 MBL
Language (s): Norwegian
DAILY NEWSPAPER

Adresseavisen - Oppdal
Owner: Adresseavisen ASA
Editorial: Inge Krokanns v 11, Oppdal 7340. **T:** 47 072 00
E: camilla.kilnes@adresseavisen.no
W: http://www.adressa.no **Circ:** 79789 MBL
Editorial Profile: Bureau
Language (s): Norwegian
DAILY NEWSPAPER

Adresseavisen - Stjørdal
Editorial: Kjøpmansgate 31, Stjørdal 7500. **T:** 47 07 20 0 **E:** redaksjon@adresseavisen.no
W: http://www.adressa.no **Circ:** 75835 MBL
Editorial Profile: Bureau
Language (s): Norwegian; Full Page Colour: 71294.00
Currency: Norway Kroner
DAILY NEWSPAPER

Aftenposten
Owner: Aftenposten AS
Editorial: Postboks 1, Sentrum, Oslo 51. **T:** 47 22863000 **E:** nyhet@aftenposten.no
W: http://www.aftenposten.no
Freq: Daily; **Circ:** 250179 Not Audited
Nyhetsredaktør: Ola Bernhus; **Sjefsredaktør:** Espen Egil Hansen; **Utviklingsredaktør:** Skjalg Engebø; **Redaksjonssjef:** Ronny Ruud
Language (s): Norwegian; Full Page Colour: 158000.00
Currency: Norway Kroner
DAILY NEWSPAPER

AGDER
Owner: Avisen Agder AS
Editorial: Pb. 40, Flekkefjord 4401. **T:** 47 38 32 03 00
E: administrasjon@avisenagder.no
W: http://www.avisenagder.no
Freq: 2 Times/Week; **Circ:** 8479 Not Audited
Redaktør: Kristen Munksgaard;
Redaksjonssjef: Erik Thime
Language (s): Norwegian; Full Page Colour: 45527.00
Currency: Norway Kroner
NEWSPAPER

AGDERPOSTEN - GRIMSTAD
Owner: AS Agderposten
Editorial: Pb. 144, Grimstad 4891.
T: 47 95 22 47 90
E: redaksjonen@agderposten.no
W: http://www.agderposten.no
Freq: Daily; **Circ:** 23329 MBL
Ansvarlig redaktør: Morten Rød
Language (s): Norwegian
NEWSPAPER

AGDERPOSTEN; NYHETSREDAKSJONEN
Owner: Agderposten AS
Editorial: Pb. 8, Arendal 4801.
T: 47 37 00 37 00
E: tusentips@agderposten.no
W: http://www.agderposten.no
Freq: Daily; **Circ:** 23746 Not Audited
Language (s): Norwegian
NEWSPAPER

AGDERPOSTEN; SPORTSREDAKSJONEN
Editorial: Pb. 8, Arendal 4801.
T: 47 37003700 **E:** sporten@agderposten.no
W: http://www.agderposten.no
Freq: Daily; **Circ:** 23329 MBL
Language (s): Norwegian
NEWSPAPER

AGDERPOSTEN~ AVD. TVEDESTRAND
Owner: Agderposten AS
Editorial: Hovedgata 48, Tvedestrand 4900. **T:** 47 37 16 62 20 **E:** toel@agderposten.no
W: http://www.agderposten.no
Freq: Daily; **Circ:** 23746 Not Audited
Language (s): Norwegian
NEWSPAPER

AKERS AVIS/GRORUDDALEN
Owner: Akers Avis Groruddalen AS
Editorial: Pb. 100 Grorud, Oslo 905.
T: 47 22918820
E: redaksjonen@groruddalen.no
W: http://www.groruddalen.no
Freq: 2 Times/Week; **Circ:** 13945 LLA
Language (s): Norwegian; Full Page Colour: 16688.00
Currency: Norway Kroner
NEWSPAPER

AKERSHUS AMTSTIDENDE
Owner: Akershus Amtstidende AS
Editorial: Pb. 12, Drøbak 1440.
T: 47 64 90 54 00 **E:** redaksjon@amta.no
W: http://www.amta.no
Freq: Daily; **Circ:** 8621 MBL
Language (s): Norwegian; Full Page Colour: 35802.00
Currency: Norway Kroner
DAILY NEWSPAPER

ALTAPOSTEN
Owner: Nordavis AS
Editorial: Labyrinten 5, Alta 9510.
T: 47 78 45 67 00
E: redaksjonen@altaposten.no
W: http://www.altaposten.no
Freq: Daily; **Circ:** 5505 MBL
Language (s): Norwegian; Full Page Colour: 49029.00
Currency: Norway Kroner
DAILY NEWSPAPER

ÅMLIAVISA
Owner: Åmliavisa AS
Editorial: Pb. 41, Åmli 4864.
T: 47 37 08 10 60 **E:** post@amliavisa.no
W: http://www.amliavisa.no
Freq: Weekly; **Circ:** 1281 LLA
Language (s): Norwegian
DAILY NEWSPAPER

ÅNDALSNES AVIS
Owner: Nye Åndalsnes Avis AS
Editorial: Pb. 153, Åndalsnes 6301.
T: 47 71 22 22 22
E: redaksjon@andalsnes-avis.no
W: http://www.andalsnes-avis.no
Freq: 2 Times/Week; **Circ:** 4125 Not Audited
Language (s): Norwegian
NEWSPAPER

ANDØYPOSTEN
Owner: Andøyposten AS
Editorial: Pb. 143, Andenes 8483.
T: 47 76 11 58 70
E: redaksjonen@andoyposten.no
W: http://www.andoyposten.no
Freq: 2 Times/Week; **Circ:** 2010 MBL
Ansvarlig redaktør: Jørn Aune
Language (s): Norwegian; Full Page Colour: 34320.00
Currency: Norway Kroner
NEWSPAPER

ARBEIDETS RETT
Owner: Arbeidets Rett AS
Editorial: Pb. 24, Røros 7361.
T: 47 72 40 64 00 **E:** redaksjonen@retten.no
W: http://www.retten.no
Freq: 2 Times/Week; **Circ:** 8441 Not Audited
Ansvarlig redaktør: Nils Kåre Nesvold
Language (s): Norwegian; Full Page Colour: 43776.00

Currency: Norway Kroner
NEWSPAPER

ARBEIDETS RETT~AVD. TYNSET
Owner: Arbeidets Rett AS
Editorial: Pb. 126, Tynset 2501.
T: 47 62 48 48 62 **E:** redaksjonen@retten.no
W: http://www.retten.no
Freq: 2 Times/Week; **Circ:** 8441 Not Audited
Language (s): Norwegian
DAILY NEWSPAPER

ARENDALS TIDENDE
Owner: Arendals Tidende AS
Editorial: Postboks 383, Arendal 4841.
T: +47 40 69 22 22
E: post@arendalstidende.no
W: http://www.arendals-tidende.no/
Freq: 2 Times/Week; **Circ:** 2136
Ansvarlig redaktør: Morten Kraft
Language (s): Norwegian; Full Page Colour:
7500.00
Currency: Norway Kroner
DAILY NEWSPAPER

ÅS NYTT
Owner: Mediasenteret AS
Editorial: Mediasenteret AS, Postboks 239,
Vestby 1541. **T:** 47 64 98 52 80
E: post@mediasenteret.no
W: http://www.mediasenteret.no/aasnytt
Freq: Monthly; **Circ:** 7050 Synovate MMI
Daglig leder: Ronny Nermo
Language (s): Norwegian
DAILY NEWSPAPER

ÅSANE TIDENDE
Owner: Åsane Tidende AS
Editorial: Postboks 31 Nyborg, Bergen 5879.
T: 47 55 18 50 00 **E:** ove@aasanetidende.no
W: http://www.aasanetidende.no
Freq: 2 Times/Week; **Circ:** 2270 Not Audited
Ansvarlig redaktør: Ove Landro
Language (s): Norwegian
DAILY NEWSPAPER

ASKØYVÆRINGEN
Owner: Askøyværingen AS
Editorial: Pb. 4, Kleppestø 5321.
T: 47 56 15 28 00 **E:** redaksjonen@av-avis.no
W: http://www.askoyv.no
Freq: 2 Times/Week; **Circ:** 5311 MBL
Redaktør: Stig Erik Elliott
Language (s): Norwegian; Full Page Colour:
52531.00
Currency: Norway Kroner
NEWSPAPER

ASKØYVÆRINGEN;
KULTURREDAKSJONEN
Editorial: Pb. 4, Kleppestø 5321.
T: 47 56 15 28 13 **E:** kultur@av-avis.no
W: http://www.askoyv.no
Freq: Daily; **Circ:** 5452 Not Audited
Language (s): Norwegian
NEWSPAPER

ASKØYVÆRINGEN;
NÆRINGSLIVREDAKSJONEN
Owner: Askøyværingen AS
Editorial: Pb 4, Kleppestø 5321.
T: 47 56152800 **E:** naering@av-avis.no
W: http://www.askoyv.no
Freq: 2 Times/Week; **Circ:** 5311 MBL
Language (s): Norwegian
NEWSPAPER

ASKØYVÆRINGEN;
SPORTSREDAKSJONEN
Editorial: Pb. 4, Kleppestø 5321.
T: 47 56152800 **E:** redaksjon@av-avis.no
W: http://www.askoyv.no
Freq: Daily; **Circ:** 5311 MBL
Redaktør: Sveinung Tvedt
Language (s): Norwegian
NEWSPAPER

AURA AVIS
Owner: Mediehus Nordmøre AS
Editorial: Pb. 43, Sunndalsøra 6601.
T: 47 71 58 98 00 **E:** redaksjonen@auraavis.no
W: http://www.auraavis.no
Freq: Daily; **Circ:** 3401 Not Audited
Language (s): Norwegian; Full Page Colour:
31518.00
Currency: Norway Kroner
NEWSPAPER

AUST AGDER BLAD
Owner: Aust Agder Blad AS
Editorial: Pb. 40, Risør 4951.
T: 47 37 14 91 00
E: redaksjon@austagderblad.no
W: http://www.austagderblad.no
Freq: 2 Times/Week; **Circ:** 3857 MBL

Language (s): Norwegian; Full Page Colour:
41324.00
Currency: Norway Kroner
NEWSPAPER

AVISA NORDLAND
Owner: Avisa Nordland AS
Editorial: Avisa Nordland, Storgata 38, Bodø
8002. **T:** 47 75 50 00 00
E: redaksjonen@an.no **W:** http://www.an.no
Freq: Daily; **Circ:** 23716 MBL
Sjefredaktør: Jan-Eirik Hanssen; **Redaktør:**
Reidun Kjelling Nybø; **Redaktør:** Børje Klæboe
Eidissen; **Redaktør:** Vibeke Madsen
Language (s): Norwegian; Full Page Colour:
30675.00
Currency: Norway Kroner
DAILY NEWSPAPER

AVISA NORDLAND - FAUSKE
Editorial: Fauske 8200. **T:** 47 75 60 00 60
E: joi@an.no **W:** http://www.an.no
Freq: Daily; **Circ:** 23716 MBL
Language (s): Norwegian
DAILY NEWSPAPER

AVISA NORDLAND - NORDSALTEN
Owner: Avisa Nordland AS
Editorial: Hamarøy 8298. **T:** 47 97 07 36 11
E: oo@an.no **W:** http://www.an.no
Freq: Daily; **Circ:** 23716 MBL
Language (s): Norwegian
DAILY NEWSPAPER

AVISA NORDLAND - ØRNES
Editorial: Storgata 38, Bodø, Bodø 8002.
T: 47 99 22 67 58 **E:** jv@an.no
W: http://www.an.no
Freq: Daily; **Circ:** 23716 MBL
Language (s): Norwegian
DAILY NEWSPAPER

AVISA NORDLAND; KULTUR-/
REPORTASJEREDAKSJONEN
Owner: Avisa Nordland AS
Editorial: Avisa Nordland, Storgata 38, Bodø
8002. **T:** 47 75500000 **E:** redaksjonen@an.no
W: http://www.an.no
Freq: Daily; **Circ:** 23716 MBL
Language (s): Norwegian
DAILY NEWSPAPER

AVISA NORDLAND;
NYHETSREDAKSJONEN
Owner: Avisa Nordland AS
Editorial: Storgata 38, Bodø 8002.
T: 47 75 50 50 00 **E:** redaksjonen@an.no
W: http://www.an.no
Freq: Daily; **Circ:** 23716 MBL
Language (s): Norwegian
DAILY NEWSPAPER

AVISA NORDLAND;
SPORTSREDAKSJONEN
Owner: Avisa Nordland AS
Editorial: AVISA NORDLAND, Bodø 8002.
T: 47 75500000 **E:** sporten@an.no
W: http://www.an.no
Freq: Daily; **Circ:** 23716 MBL
Gruppeleder: Freddy Toresen
Language (s): Norwegian
DAILY NEWSPAPER

AVISA ROMSDAL
Owner: Avisa Romsdal AS
Editorial: Sandvegen 8, Molde 6413.
T: 47 71 25 53 66 **E:** redaksjon@romsdal.no
W: http://www.romsdal.no
Freq: Monthly; **Circ:** 28500 Pub Statement
Ansvarlig redaktør: Øystein Bjerkeland
Language (s): Norwegian
NEWSPAPER

ÁVVIR
Owner: Sami Aviisa AS
Editorial: Suomageaidnu 14, Karasjok 9730.
T: 47 934 40 700 **E:** redaksjonen@avvir.no
W: http://www.avvir.no
Freq: 2 Times/Week; **Circ:** 1204 MBL
Ansvarlig redaktør: Sara Beate Eira;
Redaksjonsjef: Josef Isak Utsi
Language (s): Norwegian
NEWSPAPER

BÆRINGEN
Owner: Bærum kommune
Editorial: Informasjonsavdelingen, Bærum
Kommune, Sandvika 1304. **T:** 47 67 50 38 56
E: baeringen@baerum.kommune.no
W: https://www.baerum.kommune.no/
baeringen
Freq: Monthly; **Circ:** 47900
Language (s): Norwegian
NEWSPAPER

Bergens Tidende
Owner: Bergens Tidende AS
Editorial: Krinkelkroken 1, Postboks 7240,
Bergen 5020. **T:** 47 05500 **E:** nyhet@bt.no
W: http://www.bt.no
Freq: Daily; **Circ:** 83086 MBL
Language (s): Norwegian; Full Page Colour:
78500.00
Currency: Norway Kroner
DAILY NEWSPAPER

Bergensavisen
Owner: Bergensavisen AS
Editorial: Pb. 824, Sentrum, Bergen 5807.
T: 47 55 23 50 00 **E:** nyhet@ba.no
W: http://www.ba.no
Freq: Daily; **Circ:** 27406 MBL
Sjefredaktør: Anders Nyland
Language (s): Norwegian; Full Page Colour:
44156.00
Currency: Norway Kroner
DAILY NEWSPAPER

BLADET VESTERÅLEN
Owner: Bladet Vesterålen AS
Editorial: Pb. 33, Sortland 8401.
T: 47 76110900 **E:** red@blv.no
W: http://www.blv.no
Freq: Daily; **Circ:** 9692 Not Audited
Language (s): Norwegian; Full Page Colour:
39223.00
Currency: Norway Kroner
DAILY NEWSPAPER

BLADET VESTERÅLEN - ANDØYA
Owner: Bladet Vesterålen AS
Editorial: Postboks 33, Sortland 8401.
T: 47 76 14 14 93 **E:** idar@blv.no
W: http://www.blv.no
Freq: Daily; **Circ:** 9468 MBL
Language (s): Norwegian
DAILY NEWSPAPER

BLADET VESTERÅLEN - HADSEL
Editorial: Postboks 33, Sortland 8401.
T: 47 76 15 12 54 **E:** torjo@blv.no
W: http://www.blv.no
Freq: Daily; **Circ:** 9468 MBL
Language (s): Norwegian
DAILY NEWSPAPER

BLADET VESTERÅLEN - LØDINGEN
Editorial: Postboks 33, Sortland 8401.
T: 47 76 93 02 68 **E:** svein@blv.no
W: http://www.blv.no
Freq: Daily; **Circ:** 9468 MBL
Language (s): Norwegian
DAILY NEWSPAPER

BLADET VESTERÅLEN - ØKSNES
Owner: Bladet Vesterålen AS
Editorial: Postboks 33, Sortland 8401.
T: 47 76 13 34 32 **E:** trond@blv.no
W: http://www.blv.no
Freq: Daily; **Circ:** 9468 MBL
Language (s): Norwegian
DAILY NEWSPAPER

BØ BLAD
Owner: Bø Blad AS
Editorial: Pb. 104, Bø I Telemark 3833.
T: 47 35 95 19 45 **E:** redaksjon@boblad.no
W: http://www.boblad.no
Freq: Weekly; **Circ:** 2355 Not Audited
Language (s): Norwegian; Full Page Colour:
35021.00
Currency: Norway Kroner
NEWSPAPER

BØMLO-NYTT
Owner: A/S Bømlo-nytt
Editorial: Sakseid, Finnås 5437.
T: 47 53 42 10 00
E: redaksjon@bomlo-nytt.no
W: http://www.bomlo-nytt.no
Freq: 2 Times/Week; **Circ:** 3407 MBL
Language (s): Norwegian; Full Page Colour:
40274.00
Currency: Norway Kroner
NEWSPAPER

BRØNNØYSUNDS AVIS
Owner: Brønnøysunds Avis AS
Editorial: Pb. 38, Brønnøysund 8901.
T: 47 75 01 84 00 **E:** desk@ba-avis.no
W: http://www.banett.no
Freq: Daily; **Circ:** 4516 MBL
Nyhetsredaktør: Bård Pedersen
Language (s): Norwegian; Full Page Colour:
20632.00
Currency: Norway Kroner
NEWSPAPER

BUDSTIKKA
Owner: Asker og Bærums Budstikke ASA

Editorial: Pb 133, Billingstad 1376.
T: 47 66 77 00 00 **E:** nett@budstikka.no
W: http://www.budstikka.no
Freq: Daily; **Circ:** 28264 MBL
Ansvarlig redaktør: Andreas Gjølme;
Redaktør: Dag Tufte
Language (s): Norwegian; Full Page Colour:
28855.00
Currency: Norway Kroner
DAILY NEWSPAPER

BUDSTIKKA
Owner: Søgne og Songdalen Budstikke AS
Editorial: Linnegrøvan 24, Søgne 4682.
T: 47 38168000 **E:** post@budstikka.no
W: http://www.budstikka.com
Freq: Weekly; **Circ:** 2793 LLA
Language (s): Norwegian; Full Page Colour:
15185.00
Currency: Norway Kroner
NEWSPAPER

BUDSTIKKA - ASKER
Owner: Asker og Bærum Budstikke AS
Editorial: Meierisvingen 2, Asker 1383.
T: 47 66 77 00 00
E: Torgeir.Strandhagen@budstikka.no
Freq: Daily; **Circ:** 28264 MBL
Language (s): Norwegian
DAILY NEWSPAPER

BUDSTIKKA; KULTUR- OG
REPORTASJEREDAKSJONEN
Owner: Asker og Bærum budstikke AS
T: 47 66 77 00 00 **E:** kultur@budstikka.no
W: http://www.budstikka.no
Freq: Daily; **Circ:** 28264 MBL
Language (s): Norwegian
DAILY NEWSPAPER

BUDSTIKKA;
MAGASINREDAKSJONEN
Owner: Asker og Bærum budstikke AS
Editorial: Pb. 133, Billingstad 1376.
T: 47 66770130 **E:** nett@budstikka.no
W: http://www.budstikka.no
Freq: Weekly; **Circ:** 28264 MBL
Language (s): Norwegian
DAILY NEWSPAPER

BUDSTIKKA; NYHETSREDAKSJONEN
Owner: Asker og Bærum Budstikke AS
Editorial: Pb. 133, Billingstad 1376.
T: 47 66770000 **E:** nett@budstikka.no
W: http://www.budstikka.no **Circ:** 28264 MBL
Nyhetsredaktør: Per Erik Hagen;
Nyhetsredaktør: Hakon Holtan; **Redaktør:** Kaja
Mejlbo; **Redaktør:** Sindre Øen
Language (s): Norwegian
DAILY NEWSPAPER

BUDSTIKKA;
SAMFUNNSREDAKSJONEN
Owner: Asker og Bærum budstikke AS
Editorial: Pb. 133, Billingstad 1376.
T: 47 66 77 00 00 **E:** nett@budstikka.no
W: http://www.budstikka.no
Freq: Daily; **Circ:** 29660
Language (s): Norwegian
DAILY NEWSPAPER

BUDSTIKKA; SPORTSREDAKSJONEN
Owner: Asker og Bærum Budstikke AS
Editorial: Postboks 133, Billingstad 1376.
T: 47 66770000 **E:** sport@budstikka.no
W: http://www.budstikka.no/redaksjonelt/sport
Freq: Daily; **Circ:** 28264 MBL
Language (s): Norwegian
DAILY NEWSPAPER

BYAVISA
Owner: Norsk Avisdrift AS
Editorial: Nardoveien 16 A, Trondheim 7032.
T: 47 73954900 **E:** paul@byavisa.no
W: http://www.byavisa.no
Freq: Weekly; **Circ:** 80000 Not Audited
Konstituert Ansvarlig Redaktør: Karina Lein;
Dagligleder: Espen Tømmervold
Language (s): Norwegian
NEWSPAPER

BYAVISA TØNSBERG
Owner: Lundquist Media AS
Editorial: Nedre Langgate 32, Tønsberg 3126.
T: 47 33 30 88 60 **E:** red@byavisatonsberg.no
W: http://www.byavisatonsberg.no
Freq: Weekly
Language (s): Norwegian
DAILY NEWSPAPER

BYGDANYTT
Owner: Bygdanytt AS
Editorial: Pb. 134 Indre Arna, Bergen 5888.
T: 47 55 53 57 70 **E:** bn@bygdanytt.no
W: http://www.bygdanytt.no

Freq: 2 Times/Week; **Circ:** 4895 Not Audited
Ansvarlig redaktør: Frode Fjellstad;
Markedsansvarlig: Ingunn Mjelde; **Ansvarlig redaktør:** Hallvard Tysse
Language (s): Norwegian
DAILY NEWSPAPER

BYGDEBLADET
Owner: Bygdebladet AS
Editorial: Pb. 120, Ørskog 6249.
T: 47 70 27 08 00 **E:** post@bygdebladet.com
W: http://www.bygdebladet.com
Freq: 2 Times/Week; **Circ:** 3071 Not Audited
Ansvarlig redaktør: Kjell Opsal
Language (s): Norwegian; Full Page Colour:
31518.00
Currency: Norway Kroner
DAILY NEWSPAPER

BYGDEBLADET FOR RANDABERG OG RENNESØY
Owner: Randaberg og Rennesøy Bygdeblad AS
Editorial: Pb. 94, Randaberg 4096.
T: 47 51 41 46 66 **E:** tips@bygdebladet.no
W: http://www.bygdebladet.no
Freq: Weekly; **Circ:** 3231 MBL
Dagligleder: Marianne A. L. Randeberg;
Ansvarlig redaktør: Kirsti K. Sømme
Language (s): Norwegian
DAILY NEWSPAPER

BYGDEPOSTEN
Owner: Bygdeposten AS
Editorial: Pb. 53, Vikersund 3371.
T: 47 32 78 34 40
E: redaksjon@bygdeposten.no
W: http://www.bygdeposten.no
Freq: 2 Times/Week; **Circ:** 6667 MBL
Language (s): Norwegian; Full Page Colour:
40624.00
Currency: Norway Kroner
DAILY NEWSPAPER

Bygdeposten
Owner: Bygdeposten AS
Editorial: Pb. 53, Vikersund 3371.
T: 47 32 78 34 40
E: redaksjon@bygdeposten.no
W: http://www.bygdeposten.no
Freq: 2 Times/Week
Nyhetsleder: Caroline Bartos; **Ansvarlig redaktør:** Knut Bråthen; **Nyhetsleder:** Knut Bråthen
Language (s): Norwegian; Full Page Colour:
40624.00
Currency: Norway Kroner
DAILY NEWSPAPER

Dagbladet
Owner: AS Dagbladet
Editorial: Pb. 1184 Sentrum, Oslo 107.
T: 47 24001000 **E:** nyhet@dagbladet.no
W: http://www.dagbladet.no
Freq: Daily; **Circ:** 105255 MBL
Redaksjonssjef: Bjørn Bore; **Sjefsredaktør:** John Arne Markussen
Language (s): Norwegian; Full Page Colour:
97348.00
Currency: Norway Kroner
DAILY NEWSPAPER

Dagbladet - Skien
Owner: AS Dagbladet
Editorial: Nedre Hjellegate 4, Skien 3724.
T: 47 24 00 10 00 **E:** 2400@db.no
W: http://www.dagbladet.no **Circ:** 123383 MBL
Editorial Profile: Bureau
Language (s): Norwegian
DAILY NEWSPAPER

Dagbladet~ Avd. Bergen
Owner: AS Dagbladet
Editorial: Strandgaten 1, Bergen 5013.
T: 47 24 00 10 00 **E:** lst@dagbladet.no
W: http://www.dagbladet.no **Circ:** 123383 MBL
Editorial Profile: Bureau
Language (s): Norwegian
DAILY NEWSPAPER

DAGEN ~AVD. OSLO
Owner: Dagen Magazinet AS
Editorial: Holbergs gate 1, Oslo 166.
T: 47 22 99 76 90 **E:** redaksjonen@dagen.no
W: http://www.dagen.no
Freq: Daily; **Circ:** 10842 MBL
Sjefredaktør: Vebjørn Selbekk
Language (s): Norwegian
DAILY NEWSPAPER

DAGEN; DAGEN.NO
Owner: Dagbladet Dagen AS
Editorial: Pb. 2394, Solheimsviken, Bergen
5824. **T:** 47 55 55 97 25
E: redaksjonen@dagen.no
W: http://www.dagen.no
Freq: Daily; **Circ:** 10842 MBL
Redaktør: Kari Fure; **Redaktør:** Tarjei Gilje;

Nyhetsredaktør: Fred C. Gjestad; **Sjefredaktør:** Vebjørn Selbekk
Language (s): Norwegian
DAILY NEWSPAPER

DAGENS MEDISIN
Owner: Schibsted ASA
Editorial: Pb 2058, Vika, Oslo 125.
T: 47 93430200
E: redaksjonen@dagensmedisin.no
W: http://www.dagensmedisin.no
Freq: Bi-Weekly; **Circ:** 22500 Pub Statement
Ansvarlig redaktør: Markus Moe
Language (s): Norwegian
NEWSPAPER

Dagens Næringsliv
Owner: Dagens Næringsliv AS
Editorial: Pb. 1182 Sentrum, Oslo 107.
T: 47 22001000 **E:** redaksjonen@dn.no
W: http://www.dn.no
Freq: Daily; **Circ:** 81391 Not Audited
Sjefsredaktør: Amund Djuve; **frontredigerer:** Ivar Folkedal; **Redaksjonssjef:** Jo Martin Fridstrøm; **Nyhetssjef:** Tor Magne Nondal;
Nyhetssjef: Magne Storedal
Language (s): Norwegian; Full Page Colour:
98222.00
Currency: Norway Kroner
DAILY NEWSPAPER

Dagens Næringsliv - Stavanger
Owner: Dagens Næringsliv AS
Editorial: Verksgata 62, Stavanger 4013.
T: +47 51858111 **E:** asgaut.nass@dn.no
W: http://www.dn.no **Circ:** 81391 Not Audited
Editorial Profile: Bureau
Language (s): Norwegian
DAILY NEWSPAPER

Dagens Næringsliv - Tromsø
Editorial: Storgata 124, Tromsø 9008.
T: 47 77665665 **E:** rune.endresen@dn.no
W: http://www.dn.no **Circ:** 81391 Not Audited
Editorial Profile: Bureau
Language (s): Norwegian
DAILY NEWSPAPER

DAGLIGVAREHANDELEN
Owner: Trade Press AS
Editorial: Rosenholmveien 20, Oslo 1252.
T: 47 22629190
E: company@dagligvarehandelen.com
W: http://www.dagligvarehandelen.com
Freq: Weekly; **Circ:** 17625 Fagpressen
Markedsansvarlig: Bjørg Ekelund; **Ansvarlig redaktør:** Arne Giverholt; **Daglig leder og utgiver:** Reidar Molthe; **Ansvarlig redaktør:** Stian Vasvik
Language (s): Norwegian; Full Page Colour:
39800.00
Currency: Norway Kroner
DAILY NEWSPAPER

Dagsavisen
Owner: Stiftelsen Dagsavisen
Editorial: Pb. 1183 Sentrum, Oslo 107.
T: 47 22998000 **E:** samfunn@dagsavisen.no
W: http://www.dagsavisen.no
Freq: Daily; **Circ:** 29041 MBL
Sjefsredaktør: Kaia Storvik; **Sjefsredaktør:** Arne Strand; **Helgeredaktør:** Lars West Johnsen
Language (s): Norwegian; Full Page Colour:
108044.00
Currency: Norway Kroner
DAILY NEWSPAPER

Dagsavisen; Nyhetsredaksjonen
Owner: Stiftelsen Dagsavisen
Editorial: Pb. 1183 Sentrum, Oslo 107.
T: 47 22 99 81 30 **E:** samfunn@dagsavisen.no
W: http://www.dagsavisen.no
Freq: Daily; **Circ:** 31403 Not Audited
Frontredaktør: Else Gro Ommundsen
Language (s): Norwegian
DAILY NEWSPAPER

DAGSAVISEN; SPORTSREDAKSJONEN
Owner: Stiftelsen Dagsavisen
Editorial: Pb. 1183 Sentrum, Oslo 107.
T: 47 81534000 **E:** reidar.sollie@dagsavisen.no
W: http://www.dagsavisen.no
Freq: Daily; **Circ:** 31403
Language (s): Norwegian
DAILY NEWSPAPER

DALANE TIDENDE
Owner: Dalane Tidende og Egersunds Avis AS
Editorial: Pb. 68, Egersund 4379.
T: 47 51 46 11 00
E: redaksjon@dalane-tidende.no
W: http://www.dalane-tidende.no
Freq: 2 Times/Week; **Circ:** 8418 Not Audited
Language (s): Norwegian; Full Page Colour:
39923.00

Currency: Norway Kroner
DAILY NEWSPAPER

DEMOKRATEN
Owner: Demokraten AS
Editorial: Pb. 83, Fredrikstad 1601.
T: 47 69368000
E: demokraten@demokraten.no
W: http://www.demokraten.no
Freq: 2 Times/Week; **Circ:** 8282 MBL
Language (s): Norwegian; Full Page Colour:
20632.00
Currency: Norway Kroner
NEWSPAPER

DEMOKRATEN; SPORTSREDAKSJONEN
Owner: Demokraten AS
Editorial: Pb. 82, Fredrikstad 1601.
T: 47 69368000 **E:** sport@demokraten.no
W: http://www.demokraten.no **Circ:** 8670
Language (s): Norwegian
DAILY NEWSPAPER

DØLEN
Owner: Dølen AS
Editorial: Lomoen, Vinstra 2640.
T: 47 61 29 24 80 **E:** post@dolen.no
W: http://www.dolen.no
Freq: Weekly; **Circ:** 4242 Not Audited
Language (s): Norwegian; Full Page Colour:
48679.00
Currency: Norway Kroner
NEWSPAPER

Drammens Tidende
Owner: Drammens Tidende og Buskeruds Blad AS
Editorial: Pb. 7033, Drammen 3007.
T: 47 32204000 **E:** redaksjonen@dt.no
W: http://www.dt.no
Freq: Daily; **Circ:** 40954 Not Audited
Nyhetsredaktør: Alf Petter Øverli; **Redaktør:** Katrine Strøm
Language (s): Norwegian; Full Page Colour:
49461.00
Currency: Norway Kroner
DAILY NEWSPAPER

Drammens Tidende - Modum
Editorial: Pb 5, Vikersund 3371.
T: 47 32786470 **E:** modumkontoret@dt.no
W: http://www.dt.no **Circ:** 40954 Not Audited
Editorial Profile: Bureau
Language (s): Norwegian
DAILY NEWSPAPER

DRANGEDALSPOSTEN
Owner: Drangedalsposten AS
Editorial: Strandgt. 11, Drangedal 3750.
T: 47 35 99 69 90
E: post@drangedalsposten.no
W: http://www.drangedalsposten.no
Freq: Weekly; **Circ:** 1952 Not Audited
Language (s): Norwegian; Full Page Colour:
37822.00
Currency: Norway Kroner
NEWSPAPER

DRIVA
Owner: Driva-Trykk AS
Editorial: Pb. 143, Sunndalsøra 6601.
T: 47 71 68 97 40 **E:** redaksjon@driva.no
W: http://www.driva.no
Freq: 2 Times/Week; **Circ:** 4217 MBL
Language (s): Norwegian; Full Page Colour:
16991.00
Currency: Norway Kroner
DAILY NEWSPAPER

EIDSVOLL ULLENSAKER BLAD
Owner: Eidsvoll Ullensaker Blad AS
Editorial: Pb. 130, Eidsvoll 2081.
T: 47 63 92 27 00 **E:** redaksjon@eub.no
W: http://www.eub.no
Freq: Daily; **Circ:** 8178 MBL
Language (s): Norwegian; Full Page Colour:
25790.00
Currency: Norway Kroner
NEWSPAPER

EIDSVOLL ULLENSAKER BLAD; SPORTSREDAKSJONEN
Owner: Eidsvoll Ullensaker Blad AS
Editorial: Postboks 130, Eidsvoll 2081.
T: 47 63922700 **E:** sporten@eub.no
W: http://www.eub.no
Freq: Daily; **Circ:** 8256
Language (s): Norwegian
DAILY NEWSPAPER

EIKER BLADET
Owner: Eiker Bladet A/S
Editorial: Pb. 302, Mjøndalen 3051.
T: 47 32 87 20 23
E: redaksjonen@eikerbladet.no

W: http://eiker-ropet.no
Freq: 2 Times/Week; **Circ:** 2676 MBL
Language (s): Norwegian; Full Page Colour:
28931.00
Currency: Norway Kroner
NEWSPAPER

ENEBAKK AVIS
Owner: Enebakk Avis AS
Editorial: Pb. 34, Enebakk 1912.
T: 47 64 92 37 00 **E:** post@enebakkavis.no
W: http://www.enebakkavis.no
Freq: Weekly; **Circ:** 2984 Not Audited
Language (s): Norwegian; Full Page Colour:
13350.00
Currency: Norway Kroner
NEWSPAPER

Fædrelandsvennen
Owner: Fædrelandsvennen AS
Editorial: Pb 369, Kristiansand S 4664.
T: 47 38113000 **E:** 03811@fvn.no
W: http://www.fedrelandsvennen.no
Freq: Daily; **Circ:** 41326 Not Audited
Sjefsredaktør: Eivind Ljøstad; **Redaktør:** Jostein Ravnåsen; **Nyhetsredaktør:** Christian Stavik
Language (s): Norwegian; Full Page Colour:
27893.00
Currency: Norway Kroner
DAILY NEWSPAPER

Fædrelandsvennen - Mandal
Owner: Mediehuset Fædrelandsvennen AS
Editorial: Pb. 93, Mandal 4514.
T: 47 38271740 **E:** jarle.martinsen@fvn.no
W: http://www.fedrelandsvennen.no
Circ: 41326 Not Audited
Editorial Profile: Bureau
Language (s): Norwegian
DAILY NEWSPAPER

FANAPOSTEN
Owner: Fanaposten AS
Editorial: Pb. 374 Nesttun, Bergen 5853.
T: 47 55 11 80 10 **E:** post@fanaposten.no
W: http://www.fanaposten.no
Freq: 2 Times/Week; **Circ:** 4403 Not Audited
Redaktør: Terje Bringsvor Nilsen; **Ansvarlig redaktør:** Ståle Melhus
Language (s): Norwegian; Full Page Colour:
109264.00
Currency: Norway Kroner
NEWSPAPER

FARSUNDS AVIS
Owner: Farsunds Avis
Editorial: Pb. 23, Farsund 4551.
T: 47 38 39 50 00 **E:** redaksjon@favis.no
W: http://www.farsunds-avis.no
Freq: Daily; **Circ:** 6103 MBL
Language (s): Norwegian; Full Page Colour:
21694.00
Currency: Norway Kroner
DAILY NEWSPAPER

FARSUNDS AVIS -LYNGDAL
Owner: Farsunds Avis AS
Editorial: Pb. 80, Lyngdal 4575.
T: 47 38 39 50 40 **E:** lyngdal@favis.no
W: http://www.farsunds-avis.no
Freq: Daily; **Circ:** 6062
Language (s): Norwegian
DAILY NEWSPAPER

Finansavisen
Owner: Hegnar Media AS
Editorial: Pb 724 Skøyen, Oslo 214.
T: 47 2329 63 00 **E:** vaktsjef@finansavisen.no
W: http://www.hegnar.no/finansavisen
Freq: Daily; **Circ:** 24856 MBL
Redaksjonssjef: Are Haram; **Redaksjonssjef IT:** Leif Håvar Kvande; **Ansvarlig redaktør:** Trygve Hegnar
Language (s): Norwegian; Full Page Colour:
45176.00
Currency: Norway Kroner
DAILY NEWSPAPER

FINNMARK DAGBLAD
Owner: Finnmark Dagblad AS
Editorial: Pb. 293, Hammerfest 9615.
T: 47 78 42 86 00 **E:** redaksjonen@fd.no
W: http://www.finnmarkdagblad.no
Freq: Daily; **Circ:** 8813 MBL
Redaktør: Svein G. Jørstad; **Nyhetsredaktør:** Helle Østvik
Language (s): Norwegian; Full Page Colour:
23059.00
Currency: Norway Kroner
DAILY NEWSPAPER

FINNMARK DAGBLAD - ALTA
Owner: A-pressen ASA
Editorial: Pb 293, Hammerfest 9615.
T: 47 78 42 86 00 **E:** redaksjonen@fd.no
W: http://www.fd.no

Freq: Daily; **Circ:** 8813 MBL
Language (s): Norwegian
DAILY NEWSPAPER

FINNMARK DAGBLAD - LAKSELV
Owner: A-pressen ASA
Editorial: Pb 293, Hammerfest 9615.
T: 47 78 42 86 00 **E:** redaksjonen@fd.no
W: http://www.fd.no
Freq: Daily; **Circ:** 8813 MBL
Language (s): Norwegian
DAILY NEWSPAPER

FINNMARK DAGBLAD; DEBATT
Owner: Finnmark Dagblad AS
Editorial: P.b. 293, Hammerfest 9615.
T: 47 78 42 86 00 **E:** debatt@fd.no
W: http://www.fd.no
Freq: Daily; **Circ:** 9188 Not Audited
Redaktør: Svein G. Jørstad
Language (s): Norwegian
DAILY NEWSPAPER

FINNMARK DAGBLAD; KULTUR
Owner: Finnmark Dagblad AS
Editorial: Pb. 293, Hammerfest 9615.
T: 47 78428600 **E:** redaksjonen@fd.no
W: http://www.finnmarkdagblad.no **Circ:** 8813
Nyhetsleder: Helle Østvik
Language (s): Norwegian
DAILY NEWSPAPER

FINNMARK DAGBLAD; SPORTSREDAKSJONEN
Owner: Finnmark Dagblad AS
Editorial: P.b. 293, Hammerfest 9615.
T: 47 78428600 **E:** sporten@fd.no
W: http://www.fd.no/sport
Freq: Daily; **Circ:** 9188
Language (s): Norwegian
DAILY NEWSPAPER

FINNMARKEN
Owner: Dagbladet Finnmarken AS
Editorial: Pb. 616, Vadsø 9811.
T: 47 78 95 55 00 **E:** desk@finnmarken.no
W: http://www.finnmarken.no
Freq: Daily; **Circ:** 7169 Not Audited
Language (s): Norwegian; Full Page Colour:
18811.00
Currency: Norway Kroner
DAILY NEWSPAPER

FINNMARKEN - KIRKENES
Editorial: Pb 97, Vadsø 9811.
T: 47 78 97 02 00 **E:** desk@finnmarken.no
W: http://www.finnmarken.no
Freq: Daily; **Circ:** 7060 MBL
Language (s): Norwegian
DAILY NEWSPAPER

FINNMARKSPOSTEN
Owner: Finnmarksposten AS
Editorial: Pb. 44, Honningsvåg 9751.
T: 47 78 47 19 60
E: redaksjonen@finnmarksposten.no
Freq: Weekly; **Circ:** 1176 MBL
Redaktør: Sverre Joakimsen
Language (s): Norwegian; Full Page Colour:
15000.00
Currency: Norway Kroner
NEWSPAPER

FIRDA
Owner: Avishuset Firda AS
Editorial: Firda Media AS, Pb. 160, Førde
6801. T: 47 57833300 **E:** redaksjon@firda.no
W: http://www.firda.no
Freq: Daily; **Circ:** 13875 MBL
Sjefredaktør: Yngve Årdal; **Nyhetssjef:** Trond
Jan Grimeland
Language (s): Norwegian; Full Page Colour:
23969.00
Currency: Norway Kroner
DAILY NEWSPAPER

FIRDA TIDEND
Owner: Avisdrift Gloppen A/S
Editorial: Pb. 38, Sandane 6821.
T: 47 57 86 87 90 **E:** redaksjon@firdatidend.no
W: http://www.firdatidend.no
Freq: 2 Times/Week; **Circ:** 3056 MBL
Ansvarlig Redaktør: Bjørn Grov;
Markedsansvarlig: Atle Nygård
Language (s): Norwegian; Full Page Colour:
33620.00
Currency: Norway Kroner
DAILY NEWSPAPER

FIRDA; SPORTSREDAKSJONEN
Owner: Mediehuset Firda AS
Editorial: Postboks 38, Sandane 6821.
T: 47 57833366 **E:** sporten@firda.no
W: http://www.firda.no/sport
Freq: Daily; **Circ:** 13875 MBL
Language (s): Norwegian

DAILY NEWSPAPER

FIRDAPOSTEN
Owner: Firdaposten AS
Editorial: Pb. 38, Florø 6901.
T: 47 57 75 73 00
E: redaksjon@firdaposten.no
W: http://www.firdaposten.no
Freq: 2 Times/Week; **Circ:** 5484 MBL
Markedssjef: Sander Ødelien; **Nyhetsredaktør:**
Arve Solbakken
Language (s): Norwegian; Full Page Colour:
16384.00
Currency: Norway Kroner
DAILY NEWSPAPER

FJELL-LJOM
Owner: Avisdrift AS
Editorial: Pb. 204, Røros 7361.
T: 47 72 40 65 90 **E:** redaksjon@fjell-ljom.no
W: http://www.fjell-ljom.no
Freq: Weekly; **Circ:** 2272 LLA
Ansvarlig redaktør: Jon Høsøien
Language (s): Norwegian; Full Page Colour:
29417.00
Currency: Norway Kroner
NEWSPAPER

FJORDABLADET
Owner: Fjordabladet AS
Editorial: Rådhusvegen 6, Nordfjordeid 6770.
T: 47 57 88 53 10
E: redaksjon@fjordabladet.no
W: http://www.fjordabladet.no
Freq: 2 Times/Week; **Circ:** 2800 MBL
Language (s): Norwegian; Full Page Colour:
33270.00
Currency: Norway Kroner
NEWSPAPER

FJORDENES TIDENDE
Owner: Fjordenes Tidende AS
Editorial: Pb. 55, Måløy 6701.
T: 47 57 84 90 00 **E:** fjordenes.tidende@fjt.no
W: http://www.fjt.no
Freq: 2 Times/Week; **Circ:** 5485 MBL
Language (s): Norwegian; Full Page Colour:
32919.00
Currency: Norway Kroner
NEWSPAPER

FJORDINGEN
Owner: Fjordingen AS
Editorial: Pb. 248, Stryn 6781.
T: 47 57 87 45 00 **E:** redaksjon@fjordingen.no
W: http://www.fjordingen.no
Freq: 2 Times/Week; **Circ:** 4285 MBL
Ansvarlig redaktør: Bengt Flaten;
Redaksjonssjef: Hans Holmøyvik
Language (s): Norwegian; Full Page Colour:
32919.00
Currency: Norway Kroner
NEWSPAPER

FJUKEN
Owner: Skjåk Mediautvikling AS
Editorial: Bisvoll, Skjåk 2690.
T: 47 61 21 38 60 **E:** redaksjon@fjuken.no
W: http://www.fjuken.no
Freq: Weekly; **Circ:** 4075 LLA
Ansvarlig redaktør: Asta Brimi
Language (s): Norwegian; Full Page Colour:
22413.00
Currency: Norway Kroner
NEWSPAPER

FOSNA-FOLKET
Owner: Fosna-Folket AS
Editorial: Pb. 205, Brekstad 7129.
T: 47 72 51 57 00
E: firmapost@fosna-folket.no
W: http://www.fosna-folket.no
Freq: 2 Times/Week; **Circ:** 7570 MBL
Language (s): Norwegian; Full Page Colour:
18144.00
Currency: Norway Kroner
DAILY NEWSPAPER

FOSNA-FOLKET - RISSA
Owner: Fosna-Folket AS
Editorial: Rissa 7100. **T:** 47 73 85 60 22
E: sigrun.overland@fosna-folket.no
W: http://www.fosna-folket.no
Freq: 2 Times/Week; **Circ:** 7570 MBL
Language (s): Norwegian
NEWSPAPER

FRAMTID I NORD
Owner: Mediaselskapet Nord-Norge
Samkjøringen AS
Editorial: Sentrum 15, Storslett 9156.
T: 47 77 76 69 00 **E:** desken@finord.no
W: http://www.framtidinord.no
Freq: 2 Times/Week; **Circ:** 5303 Not Audited
Language (s): Norwegian; Full Page Colour:
31518.00
Currency: Norway Kroner

NEWSPAPER

FREDRIKSSTAD BLAD
Owner: Fredrikstad Blad AS
Editorial: Postboks 143, Fredrikstad 1601.
T: 47 46807777 **E:** tips@f-b.no
W: http://www.f-b.no **Circ:** 23442 Not Audited
Redaksjonsjef: Geir Ola Eggen; **Ansvarlig
redaktør:** Erling Omvik
Language (s): Norwegian; Full Page Colour:
32644.00
Currency: Norway Kroner
DAILY NEWSPAPER

FREDRIKSSTAD BLAD; KULTUR
Owner: Fredrikstad Blad AS
Editorial: Pb. 143, Fredrisktad 1601.
T: 47 95896183 **E:** speilet@f-b.no
W: http://www.f-b.no **Circ:** 22883 MBL
Language (s): Norwegian
DAILY NEWSPAPER

FREDRIKSSTAD BLAD; NÆRREDAKSJONEN
Owner: Fredrikstad Blad AS
T: 47 46 80 77 77 **E:** idag@f-b.no
W: http://www.f-b.no
Freq: Daily; **Circ:** 23442 Not Audited
Language (s): Norwegian
DAILY NEWSPAPER

FREDRIKSSTAD BLAD; NYHET, REPORTASJE, FEATURE, SAMFUNN
Owner: Fredrikstad Blad AS
Editorial: Postboks 143, Fredrikstad 1601.
T: 47 46 80 77 77 **E:** tips@f-b.no
W: http://www.f-b.no
Freq: Daily; **Circ:** 23442 Not Audited
Language (s): Norwegian
DAILY NEWSPAPER

FREDRIKSSTAD BLAD; SPORTEN
Owner: Fredrikstad Blad
Editorial: Postboks 143, Fredrikstad 1601.
T: 47 69388000 **E:** sporten@f-b.no
W: http://www.f-b.no
Language (s): Norwegian
DAILY NEWSPAPER

FREMOVER
Owner: Fremover AS
Editorial: Pb. 324, Narvik 8504.
T: 47 76 95 00 00 **E:** redaksjon@fremover.no
W: http://www.fremover.no
Freq: Daily; **Circ:** 8835 MBL
Nyhetssjef: Anders Horne
Language (s): Norwegian; Full Page Colour:
19819.00
Currency: Norway Kroner
DAILY NEWSPAPER

FRIHETEN
Owner: Norges Kommunistiske Parti
Editorial: Postboks 4794 Sofienberg, Oslo
506. **T:** 47 22 71 60 44 **E:** friheten@friheten.no
W: http://www.friheten.no
Freq: Weekly; **Circ:** 2800 Synovate MMI
Redaktør: Harald Øystein Reppesgaard
Language (s): Norwegian
DAILY NEWSPAPER

FROLENDINGEN
Owner: Ca. 100 lokale bedrifter og privar
personer
Editorial: Osedalen, Froland 4820.
T: 47 37 23 65 00 **E:** post@frolendingen.no
W: http://www.frolendingen.no
Freq: Weekly; **Circ:** 1565 Not Audited
Language (s): Norwegian; Full Page Colour:
13457.00
Currency: Norway Kroner
NEWSPAPER

FROSTINGEN
Owner: Frostingen AS
Editorial: Banken, Frosta 7633.
T: 47 74 80 88 35 **E:** frostingen@frostingen.no
W: http://frostingen.no
Freq: Weekly; **Circ:** 1492 Not Audited
Language (s): Norwegian; Full Page Colour:
8495.00
Currency: Norway Kroner
NEWSPAPER

GAULA
Owner: Snøfugl AS
Editorial: Gravråksmoen, Melhus 7224.
T: 47 911 50 123 **E:** bgs@nr123.no
W: http://www.melhusporten.no
Freq: Weekly; **Circ:** 1538 LLA
Language (s): Norwegian; Full Page Colour:
22413.00
Currency: Norway Kroner
DAILY NEWSPAPER

GAULDALSPOSTEN
Owner: Gauldalsposten AS
T: 47 928 08 222 **E:** redaksjon@gposten.no
W: http://www.gposten.no
Freq: Weekly; **Circ:** 1454 LLA
Language (s): Norwegian
DAILY NEWSPAPER

GAUSDØL'N - LOKALAVISA FOR GAUSDAL
Owner: Gausdal Informasjon
Editorial: Vestre Gausdal 2653.
T: 47 61 22 34 23 **E:** firmapost@gausdolen.no
W: http://www.gausdolen.no
Freq: Monthly; **Circ:** 950 Pub Statement
Redaktør: Olav Iverslien; **Frilans:** Tanja Kristin
Staum
Language (s): Norwegian
NEWSPAPER

GJENGANGEREN
Owner: Edda Vestfold AS
Editorial: Pb. 85, Storgt. 38, Horten 3191.
T: 47 33 02 00 00
E: redaksjonen@gjengangeren.no
W: http://www.gjengangeren.no
Freq: Daily; **Circ:** 6015 Not Audited
Markedssjef: Else-Lill Andresen;
Nyhetsredaktør: Audun Bårdseth; **Ansvarlig
redaktør:** Torgeir Lorentzen
Language (s): Norwegian; Full Page Colour:
18174.00
Currency: Norway Kroner
DAILY NEWSPAPER

GJESDALBUEN
Owner: Gjesdalbuen AS
Editorial: Pb. 13, Ålgård 4339.
T: 47 51 61 28 50
E: redaksjon@gjesdalbuen.no
W: http://www.gjesdalbuen.no
Freq: Weekly; **Circ:** 3422 MBL
Ansvarlig redaktør: Bjørn Egil Gilje
Language (s): Norwegian; Full Page Colour:
41324.00
Currency: Norway Kroner
NEWSPAPER

GJØVIKS BLAD
Owner: Gjøviks-Blad AS
T: 47 61 13 03 00 **E:** post@gjoviks-blad.no
W: http://www.gjoviks-blad.no
Freq: Weekly; **Circ:** 14100 Pub Statement
Language (s): Norwegian
DAILY NEWSPAPER

GLÅMDALEN
Owner: Glåmdalen AS
Editorial: PB 757, Kongsvinger 2204.
T: 47 62882500 **E:** redaksjon@glomdalen.no
W: http://www.glomdalen.no
Freq: Daily; **Circ:** 19370 MBL
Sjefsredaktør: Eivind Lid; **Dagvaktsjef:** Per
Håkon Pettersen
Language (s): Norwegian; Full Page Colour:
29729.00
Currency: Norway Kroner
DAILY NEWSPAPER

GLÅMDALEN; SPORTSREDAKSJONEN
Owner: Glåmdalen AS avdelingskontor
Skarnes
Editorial: PB 757, Kongsvinger 2226.
T: 47 62882500 **E:** ms@glomdalen.no
W: http://www.glomdalen.no
Freq: Daily; **Circ:** 19370 MBL
Language (s): Norwegian
DAILY NEWSPAPER

GLÅMDALEN~ AVD. FLISA
Owner: Glåmdalen AS
T: 47 62 95 59 20 **E:** redaksjon@glomdalen.no
W: http://www.glomdalen.no
Freq: Daily; **Circ:** 19370 MBL
Language (s): Norwegian
DAILY NEWSPAPER

GLÅMDALEN~ AVD. SKARNES
Owner: Glåmdalen AS
T: 47 62 88 25 00 **E:** redaksjon@glomdalen.no
W: http://www.glomdalen.no
Freq: Daily; **Circ:** 19370 MBL
Language (s): Norwegian
DAILY NEWSPAPER

GRANNAR
Owner: Grannar AS
Editorial: Pb. 84, Etne 5591.
T: 47 53 77 11 00 **E:** redaksjon@grannar.no
W: http://www.grannar.no
Freq: 2 Times/Week; **Circ:** 3929 Not Audited
Language (s): Norwegian; Full Page Colour:
19267.00
Currency: Norway Kroner
NEWSPAPER

GRENDA
Owner: Grenda AS
Editorial: Pb. 100, Rosendal 5470.
T: 47 53 47 71 00 **E:** post@grenda.no
W: http://www.grenda.no
Freq: 2 Times/Week; **Circ:** 2550 LLA
Language (s): Norwegian; Full Page Colour:
17021.00
Currency: Norway Kroner
NEWSPAPER

GRIMSTAD ADRESSETIDENDE
Owner: Grimstad Adressetidende AS
Editorial: Pb. 70, Grimstad 4891.
T: 47 37 25 80 00 **E:** red@gat.no
W: http://www.gat.no
Freq: 2 Times/Week; **Circ:** 6387 MBL
Language (s): Norwegian; Full Page Colour:
40974.00
Currency: Norway Kroner
NEWSPAPER

GUDBRANDSDØLEN DAGNINGEN
Owner: Gudbrandsdølen Dagningen AS
Editorial: Pb. 954, Lillehammer 2604.
T: 47 61221000 **E:** redaksjonen@gd.no
W: http://www.gd.no
Freq: Daily; **Circ:** 26458 MBL
Redaksjonssekretær: Kjell Haugerud;
Redaksjonssekretær: Jostein Hernæs;
Ansvarlig redaktør: Kristian Skullerud;
Nyhetsredaktør: Anne Stokke; **Redaktør:** Kari
Utgaard
Language (s): Norwegian; Full Page Colour:
30603.00
Currency: Norway Kroner
DAILY NEWSPAPER

GUDBRANDSDØLEN DAGNINGEN - OTTA
Owner: Gudbrandsdølen Dagningen AS
Editorial: Storgata 19, Otta 2670.
T: 47 61 22 10 00 **E:** redaksjonen@gd.no
W: http://www.gd.no
Freq: Daily; **Circ:** 26723 Not Audited
Language (s): Norwegian
DAILY NEWSPAPER

GUDBRANDSDØLEN DAGNINGEN - VINSTRA
Owner: Gudbrandsølen Dagningen AS
Editorial: Byrevn 2, Vinstra 2640.
T: 47 61 22 10 00 **E:** kristin.veskje@gd.no
W: http://www.gd.no
Freq: Daily; **Circ:** 26458 MBL
Language (s): Norwegian
DAILY NEWSPAPER

GUDBRANDSDØLEN DAGNINGEN; DEBATT
Owner: Gudbrandsølen Dagningen AS
Editorial: Pb. 954, Lillehammer 2604.
T: 47 61221000 **E:** debatt@gd.no
W: http://www.gd.no
Freq: Daily; **Circ:** 26723
Language (s): Norwegian
DAILY NEWSPAPER

GUDBRANDSDØLEN DAGNINGEN; SPORTSREDAKSJONEN
Owner: Gudbrandsdølen Dagningen AS
T: 47 61 22 10 00 **E:** sporten@gd.no
W: http://www.gd.no/sport
Freq: Daily; **Circ:** 26723
Language (s): Norwegian
DAILY NEWSPAPER

HADELAND
Owner: Hadeland AS
T: 47 61 31 31 32 **E:** desken@hadeland.net
W: http://www.hadeland.net
Freq: Daily; **Circ:** 7487 MBL
Ansvarlig redaktør: Sissel Skjervum
Bjerkehagen
Language (s): Norwegian
DAILY NEWSPAPER

HADELAND; SPORTSREDAKSJONEN
Editorial: Pb 227, Gran 2711. **T:** 47 91743752
E: sporten@hadeland.net
W: http://www.hadeland.net
Freq: Daily; **Circ:** 7481 Not Audited
Language (s): Norwegian
DAILY NEWSPAPER

HALDEN ARBEIDERBLAD
Owner: Halden Arbeiderblad AS
Editorial: Pb. 113, Halden 1751.
T: 47 69215600 **E:** redaksjonen@ha-halden.no
W: http://www.ha-halden.no
Freq: Daily; **Circ:** 8806 Not Audited
Language (s): Norwegian
DAILY NEWSPAPER

HALDEN ARBEIDERBLAD; SPORTREDAKSJON
Owner: Halden Arbeiderbald AS
Editorial: Pb. 113, Halden 1751.
T: 47 69215600 **E:** sporten@ha-halden.no
W: http://www.ha-halden.no
Freq: Daily; **Circ:** 8806 Not Audited
Language (s): Norwegian
DAILY NEWSPAPER

HALLINGDØLEN
Owner: Hallingdølen AS
Editorial: Pb. 193, Ål 3571. **T:** 47 32086500
E: redaksjonen@hallingdolen.no
W: http://www.hallingdolen.no
Freq: 2 Times/Week; **Circ:** 10038 MBL
Language (s): Norwegian; Full Page Colour:
20632.00
Currency: Norway Kroner
DAILY NEWSPAPER

HALLINGDØLEN~ AVD. NESBYEN
Owner: Hallingdølen AS
Editorial: Pb. 193, Private eiere, Ål 3571.
T: 47 32 07 15 12
E: redaksjonen@hallingdolen.no
W: http://www.hallingdolen.no
Freq: 2 Times/Week; **Circ:** 10215 Not Audited
Language (s): Norwegian
DAILY NEWSPAPER

HAMAR ARBEIDERBLAD
Owner: Hamar Media AS
Editorial: Pb. 264, Hamar 2317 **E:** red@h-a.no
W: http://www.h-a.no
Freq: Daily; **Circ:** 26677 MBL
Nyhetsredaktør: Andre Winje Arntzen;
Sjefredaktør: Carsten Bleness;
Debattredaktør: Anne Ekornholmen;
Hovedvaktsjef: Leif Erik Henriksen;
Hovedvaktsjef: Marianne Thoresen;
Nyhetsredaktør: Andre Winje Arntsen
Language (s): Norwegian; Full Page Colour:
34392.00
Currency: Norway Kroner
DAILY NEWSPAPER

HAMAR ARBEIDERBLAD - ØSTERDALEN
Owner: Hamar Media AS
Editorial: Elverum 2406. **T:** 47 918 28 955
E: hch@h-a.no **W:** http://www.h-a.no
Freq: Daily; **Circ:** 26677 MBL
Language (s): Norwegian
DAILY NEWSPAPER

HAMAR ARBEIDERBLAD - BRUMUNDDAL
Owner: Hamar Media AS
Editorial: Ringsakervn. 4, Brumunddal 2380.
T: 47 62 35 14 20 **E:** ringsaker@h-a.no
W: http://www.ringsaker.no
Freq: Daily; **Circ:** 26677 MBL
Redaktør: John Arne Holmlund
Language (s): Norwegian
DAILY NEWSPAPER

HAMAR ARBEIDERBLAD; HAMAR- / LOKALREDAKSJONEN
Owner: Hamar Media AS
E: red@h-a.no **W:** http://www.h-a.no
Freq: Daily; **Circ:** 27363 Not Audited
Language (s): Norwegian
DAILY NEWSPAPER

HAMAR ARBEIDERBLAD; KULTUR & FEATURE
Owner: Hamar Media AS
Editorial: Pb. 262, Hamar 2302. **T:** 47 02318
E: tips@h-a.no **W:** http://www.h-a.no
Freq: Daily; **Circ:** 26677 MBL
Language (s): Norwegian
DAILY NEWSPAPER

HAMAR ARBEIDERBLAD; SPORTSREDAKSJONEN
Owner: Hamar Arbeiderblad AS
Editorial: Pb. 264, Hamar 2317.
T: 47 92071690 **E:** ha-sporten@h-a.no
W: http://www.h-a.no
Freq: Daily; **Circ:** 26677 MBL
Language (s): Norwegian
DAILY NEWSPAPER

HAMAR DAGBLAD
Owner: Hamar Dagblad AS
Editorial: Pb 325, Hamar 2302.
T: 47 62 54 31 40
E: redaksjonen@hamar-dagblad.no
W: http://www.hamar-dagblad.no
Freq: Daily; **Circ:** 4370 Pub Statement
Redaktør: Tore Svensrud
Language (s): Norwegian; Full Page Colour:
28976.00
Currency: Norway Kroner
DAILY NEWSPAPER

HARDANGER FOLKEBLAD
Owner: Hardanger Folkeblad AS
Editorial: Pb. 374, Odda 5750.
T: 47 53 65 06 00
E: redaksjon@hardanger-folkeblad.no
W: http://www.hardanger-folkeblad.no
Freq: 2 Times/Week; **Circ:** 5499 MBL
Language (s): Norwegian
NEWSPAPER

HARSTAD TIDENDE
Owner: Harstad Tidende AS
Editorial: Pb. 85, Harstad 9481.
T: 47 77018000 **E:** redaksjonen@ht.no
W: http://www.ht.no
Freq: Daily; **Circ:** 13503 Not Audited
Redaktør: Odd Leif Andreassen; **Redaktør:**
Kjell Magne Angelsen; **Sjefredaktør:** Kjell Rune
Henriksen; **Redaktør:** Turid Ingebrigtsen;
Redaktør: Gurid Ivarhus Næss; **Redaktør:**
Ottar Jakobsen; **Redaktør:** Hans Viktor Øye;
Redaktør: Tore Skadal; **Redaktør:** Kjell
Solbakken
Language (s): Norwegian
DAILY NEWSPAPER

HARSTAD TIDENDE - BARDU
Owner: Harstad Tidende AS
Editorial: Pb 171, Bardu 9360.
T: 47 77 18 29 10 **E:** redaksjonen@ht.no
W: http://www.ht.no **Circ:** 13503
Redaktør: Kjell Solbakken
Language (s): Norwegian
DAILY NEWSPAPER

HARSTAD TIDENDE - LØDINGEN
Owner: Harstad Tidende AS
Editorial: Pb. 66, Lødingen 8551.
T: 47 76 93 59 40 **E:** redaksjonen@ht.no
W: http://www.ht.no **Circ:** 13503
Language (s): Norwegian
DAILY NEWSPAPER

HARSTAD TIDENDE; DEBATT
Owner: Harstad Tidende AS
Editorial: Pb. 85, Harstad 9481.
T: 47 77 01 80 00 **E:** debatt@ht.no
W: http://www.ht.no
Freq: Daily; **Circ:** 13503
Language (s): Norwegian
DAILY NEWSPAPER

HARSTAD TIDENDE; SPORTREDAKSJONEN
Owner: Harstad Tidende AS
Editorial: Pb. 85, Harstad 9481.
T: 47 77018001 **E:** sport@ht.no
W: http://www.ht.no **Circ:** 13173
Language (s): Norwegian
DAILY NEWSPAPER

HAUGESUNDS AVIS
Owner: Haugesunds Avis AS
Editorial: Pb. 2024 Postterminalen,
Haugesund 5504. **T:** 47 52720000
E: redaksjonen@haugesunds-avis.no
W: http://www.h-avis.no/
Freq: Daily; **Circ:** 31907 MBL
Ansvarlig redaktør: Elisiv Hauge Nilsen;
Nyhetsleder: Torstein Nymoen
Language (s): Norwegian
DAILY NEWSPAPER

HAUGESUNDS AVIS - BØMLO
Owner: Haugesunds-Avis AS
Editorial: Pb 14, Bremnes 5430.
T: 47 53 42 89 89
E: redaksjonen@haugesunds-avis.no
W: http://www.h-avis.no/2.1342/b%C3%B8mlo
Freq: Daily; **Circ:** 33013 Not Audited
Language (s): Norwegian
DAILY NEWSPAPER

HAUGESUNDS AVIS - KARMØY
Owner: Haugesunds-Avis AS
T: 47 52 72 03 44 **E:** ruth.sveistrup@h-avis.no
W: http://www.haugesunds-avis.no
Freq: Daily; **Circ:** 31907 MBL
Language (s): Norwegian
DAILY NEWSPAPER

HAUGESUNDS AVIS - ODDA
Owner: Haugesunds-Avis AS
Editorial: Pb 183, Odda 5751.
T: 47 52 72 02 85
E: kai.inge.melkeraaen@h-avis.no
W: http://www.h-avis.no
Freq: Daily; **Circ:** 31907 MBL
Language (s): Norwegian
DAILY NEWSPAPER

HAUGESUNDS AVIS - SAUDA
Owner: Haugesunds-Avis AS
Editorial: Pb 88, Sauda 4201.
T: 47 936 83 050 **E:** frank.waal@h-avis.no
W: http://www.h-avis.no/

Freq: Daily; **Circ:** 31907 MBL
Language (s): Norwegian
DAILY NEWSPAPER

HAUGESUNDS AVIS; DEBATT-MENINGER
Owner: Haugesund Avis AS
Editorial: Pb. 2024 Postterminalen,
Haugesund 5504. **T:** 47 52720560
E: ordetfritt@h-avis.no
W: http://www.haugesunds-avis.no
Freq: Daily; **Circ:** 33013
Language (s): Norwegian
DAILY NEWSPAPER

HAUGESUNDS AVIS; KULTURREDAKSJONEN (PULS)
Owner: Haugesunds Avis AS
Editorial: Pb. 2024, Haugesund 5504.
T: 47 52720000 **E:** kultur@h-avis.no
W: http://www.haugesunds-avis.no
Freq: Daily; **Circ:** 33013
Language (s): Norwegian
DAILY NEWSPAPER

HAUGESUNDS AVIS; SPORTSREDAKSJONEN
Editorial: Pb. 2024 Postterminalen,
Haugesund 5501. **T:** 47 52720500
E: sporten@h-avis.no
W: http://www.haugesunds-avis.no
Freq: Daily; **Circ:** 31907 MBL
Language (s): Norwegian
DAILY NEWSPAPER

HELGELAND ARBEIDERBLAD
Owner: AS Helgeland Arbeiderblad
Editorial: Vefsnvegen 7, Mosjøen 8654.
T: 47 75113600
E: vaktsjef@helgeland-arbeiderblad.no
W: http://www.helgeland-arbeiderblad.no
Freq: Daily; **Circ:** 8939 MBL
Sjefredaktør: Geir Arne Glad; **Nyhetsredaktør:**
Asbjørg Sande
Language (s): Norwegian
DAILY NEWSPAPER

HELGELAND ARBEIDERBLAD - BRØNNØYSUND
Editorial: Pb 29, Brønnøysund 8901.
T: 47 75 01 12 20
E: redaksjon@helgeland-arbeiderblad.no
W: http://www.helgeland-arbeiderblad.no
Freq: Daily; **Circ:** 9225 Not Audited
Language (s): Norwegian
DAILY NEWSPAPER

HELGELAND ARBEIDERBLAD - SANDNESSJØEN
Editorial: 8654 Mosjøen, Mosjøen 8654.
T: 47 75 11 36 51
E: jarl.sandholm@helgeland-arbeiderblad.no
W: http://www.helgeland-arbeiderblad.no
Freq: Daily; **Circ:** 8939 MBL
Language (s): Norwegian
DAILY NEWSPAPER

HELGELANDS BLAD
Owner: Helgelands Blad AS
Editorial: Pb. 174, Sandnessjøen 8801.
T: 47 75 07 03 00 **E:** red@hblad.no
W: http://www.hblad.no
Freq: 2 Times/Week; **Circ:** 5758 Not Audited
Language (s): Norwegian
DAILY NEWSPAPER

HITRA-FRØYA
Owner: Hitra-Frøya Lokalavis AS
Editorial: Hitra-Frøya Lokalavis AS,
Mediehuset, Sandstad 7240.
T: 47 72 44 04 00 **E:** post@hitra-froya.no
W: http://www.hitra-froya.no
Freq: 2 Times/Week; **Circ:** 5048 MBL
Ansvarlig redaktør: Svend Sivertsen
Language (s): Norwegian
NEWSPAPER

HORDALAND
Owner: Hordaland bladdrift AS
Editorial: Pb. 38, Voss 5701.
T: 47 56 53 03 00
E: redaksjon@avisa-hordaland.no
W: http://www.avisa-hordaland.no
Freq: 2 Times/Week; **Circ:** 9582 MBL
Language (s): Norwegian
NEWSPAPER

HORDALAND FOLKEBLAD
Owner: Hordaland Folkeblad AS
Editorial: Pb. 94, Norheimsund 5601.
T: 47 56 55 00 20 **E:** redaksjon@hf.no
W: http://www.hf.no
Freq: 2 Times/Week; **Circ:** 5790 Not Audited
Language (s): Norwegian
NEWSPAPER

INDERØYNINGEN
Owner: Inderøyningen AS
Editorial: Pb. 19, Inderøy 7671.
T: 47 40 00 67 45
E: redaksjonen@inderoyningen.no
W: http://www.inderoyningen.no
Freq: Weekly; **Circ:** 1907 Not Audited
Language (s): Norwegian
NEWSPAPER

INDRE AKERSHUS BLAD
Owner: Indre Akershus Blad AS
Editorial: Pb. 68, Bjørkelangen 1941.
T: 47 63 85 48 00 **E:** redaksjon@iablad.no
W: http://www.indre.no
Freq: 2 Times/Week; **Circ:** 7457 Not Audited
Language (s): Norwegian; Full Page Colour:
17598.00
Currency: Norway Kroner
DAILY NEWSPAPER

INNHERREDS FOLKEBLAD/
VERDALINGEN
Owner: Innherreds Folkeblad og Verdalingen
AS
Editorial: Pb. 243, Verdal 7651.
T: 47 74 07 26 60
E: redaksjon@verdalingen.no
W: http://www.verdalingen.no
Freq: 2 Times/Week; **Circ:** 4952 Not Audited
Language (s): Norwegian
NEWSPAPER

ITROMSØ
Owner: Bladet Tromsø AS
Editorial: Pb. 1028, Tromsø 9260.
T: 47 77640600 **E:** nyheter@itromso.no
W: http://www.itromso.no
Freq: Daily; **Circ:** 9858 MBL
Nyhetssjef: Carina Hansen; **Redaktør:** Jonny
Hansen; **Sjefredaktør:** Jørn-Christian Skoglund
Language (s): Norwegian; Full Page Colour:
45527.00
Currency: Norway Kroner
DAILY NEWSPAPER

ITROMSØ; SPORTEN
Editorial: Pb. 1028, Strandveien 144, Tromsø
9620. **T:** 47 77 64 06 00
E: sporten@itromso.no **W:** http://itromso.no
Circ: 9858 MBL
Language (s): Norwegian
DAILY NEWSPAPER

JÆRBLADET
Owner: Jærbladet AS
Editorial: Pb 23, Bryne 4349. **T:** 47 51779900
E: redaksjon@jbl.no **W:** http://www.jbl.no
Freq: 2 Times/Week; **Circ:** 13264 MBL
Language (s): Norwegian
NEWSPAPER

JARLSBERG AVIS
Owner: Jarlsberg Avis AS
Editorial: Pb. 303, Holmestrand 3081.
T: 47 33 09 90 00
E: redaksjonen@jarlsbergavis.no
W: http://www.jarlsbergavis.no
Freq: 2 Times/Week; **Circ:** 3830 MBL
Language (s): Norwegian
NEWSPAPER

KANALEN
Owner: Kanalen A/S
Editorial: Ringsevja 11, Ulefoss 3831.
T: 47 35 94 35 80 **E:** redaktor@kanalen.no
W: http://www.kanalen.no
Freq: Weekly; **Circ:** 2020 Not Audited
Daglig leder: Britt Eriksen; **Markedsansvarlig:**
Rita Næs Sigurdsøn; **Redaktør:** Tor Espen
Simonsen
Language (s): Norwegian; Full Page Mono:
10985.00; Full Page Colour: 11405.00
Currency: Norway Kroner
NEWSPAPER

KARMSUND
Owner: Karmsund AS
Editorial: Strandgata 203, Haugesund 5525.
T: 47 52739800
E: redaksjonen@ka-karmsund.no
W: http://www.karmsundavis.no
Freq: Weekly; **Circ:** 25000 Pub Statement
Language (s): Norwegian
NEWSPAPER

KLAR TALE
Owner: Stiftelsen Klar Tale
Editorial: Pb 1180 Sentrum, Oslo 107.
T: 47 22310260 **E:** tips@klartale.no
W: http://www.klartale.no
Freq: Weekly; **Circ:** 11637 MBL
Redaksjonsjef: Gøril Huse; **Newsdesigner:**
Alexander Schindler; **Redaktør:** Kristin Steien
Bratlie
Language (s): Norwegian

DAILY NEWSPAPER

Klassekampen
Owner: Klassekampen AS
Editorial: Pb. 9257 Grønland, Oslo 134.
T: 47 22059500
E: klassekampen@klassekampen.no
W: http://www.klassekampen.no
Freq: Daily; **Circ:** 12109 MBL
Ansvarlig redaktør: Bjørgulv Braanen;
nyhetssjef: Kjell-Erik Kallset; **Nyhetssjef:**
Katrine Ree Holmøy; **Nyhetssjef:** Mari Skurdal
Language (s): Norwegian
DAILY NEWSPAPER

KRAGERØ BLAD VESTMAR
Owner: Kragerø Blad AS
Editorial: Pb. 55, Kragerø 3791.
T: 47 35 98 67 00 **E:** redaksjonen@kv.no
W: http://kv.no/
Freq: 2 Times/Week; **Circ:** 4584 Not Audited
Language (s): Norwegian
NEWSPAPER

KRISTIANSAND AVIS
Owner: Krut Mosvold og Roy Gundersen
Editorial: Tordenskjoldsgate 9, Kristiansand
4621. **T:** 47 38 69 99 99
E: tips@kristiansandavis.no
W: http://www.kristiansandavis.no
Freq: Weekly; **Circ:** 33000 Pub Statement
Language (s): Norwegian
NEWSPAPER

KULTURAVISA - BREIDABLIKK
Owner: Røros Media AS
T: 47 72 41 27 86 **E:** post@breidablikk.net
W: http://www.breidablikk.net
Freq: Bi-Monthly; **Circ:** 18000 Pub Statement
Redaktør: Bjørn Tore Hindklev
Language (s): Norwegian
NEWSPAPER

KVINNHERINGEN
Owner: Kvinnheringen AS
Editorial: Lonabråtet, Husnes 5460.
T: 47 53 48 21 45
E: redaksjon@kvinnheringen.no
W: http://www.kvinnheringen.no
Freq: 2 Times/Week; **Circ:** 4571 MBL
Language (s): Norwegian
NEWSPAPER

LAAGENDALSPOSTEN
Owner: Laagendalsposten AS
Editorial: Stasjonsbakken 3, Kongsberg 3611.
T: 47 32771000
E: redaksjonen@laagendalsposten.no
W: http://www.laagendalsposten.no
Freq: Daily; **Circ:** 10217 MBL
Nyhetsredaktør: Per Skøien; **Ansvarlig
redaktør:** Jørn Steinmoen
Language (s): Norwegian; Full Page Colour:
19115.00
Currency: Norway Kroner
DAILY NEWSPAPER

LAAGENDALSPOSTEN;
SPORTSREDAKSJONEN
Editorial: Stasjonsbakken 3, Kongsberg 3611
E: sporten@laagendalsposten.no
Freq: Daily; **Circ:** 10293
Language (s): Norwegian
DAILY NEWSPAPER

LEVANGER-AVISA
Owner: Levanger-Avisa AS
Editorial: Pb. 14, Levanger 7601.
T: 47 93 83 44 44
E: redaksjon@levangeravisa.no
W: http://www.levangeravisa.no
Freq: 2 Times/Week; **Circ:** 4287 MBL
Language (s): Norwegian
NEWSPAPER

LEVANGER-AVISA; SPORT
Editorial: Pb. 14, Levanger 7601.
T: 47 93834444 **E:** sport@levangeravisa.no
W: http://www.levangeravisa.no
Language (s): Norwegian
DAILY NEWSPAPER

LIERPOSTEN
Owner: Lierposten AS
Editorial: Vestsideveien 9c, Lier 3400.
T: 47 32 24 07 60
E: redaksjonen@lierposten.no
W: http://www.lierposten.no
Freq: Weekly; **Circ:** 3373 MBL
Language (s): Norwegian; Full Page Colour:
20198.00
Currency: Norway Kroner
NEWSPAPER

LILLEHAMMER BYAVIS
Owner: Lillehammer byavis.no

Editorial: Lillehammer Byavis.no, Storgt. 75,
Lillehammer 2609. **T:** 47 965 02 222
E: redaksjon@byavis.no
W: http://www.byavis.no
Freq: Weekly; **Circ:** 20000 Pub Statement
Redaktør: Tore Feiring
Language (s): Norwegian
DAILY NEWSPAPER

LILLESANDS-POSTEN
Owner: Lillesandspostens driftsselskap AS
Editorial: Pb. 143, Lillesand 4792.
T: 47 37 26 95 00 **E:** redaksjonen@lp.no
W: http://www.lp.no
Freq: 2 Times/Week; **Circ:** 3792 MBL
Language (s): Norwegian; Full Page Colour:
17598.00
Currency: Norway Kroner
NEWSPAPER

LOFOTPOSTEN
Owner: Lofotposten AS
Editorial: Avisgata 15, Svolvær 8305.
T: 47 76 06 78 00 **E:** red@lofotposten.no
W: http://www.lofotposten.no
Freq: Daily; **Circ:** 7133 MBL
Language (s): Norwegian
DAILY NEWSPAPER

LOFOTPOSTEN~ AVD. LEKNES
Owner: Lofotposten ASA
T: 47 760 67800 **E:** red@lofotposten.no
W: http://www.lofotposten.no
Freq: Daily; **Circ:** 7133 MBL
Language (s): Norwegian
DAILY NEWSPAPER

LOFOT-TIDENDE
Owner: Lofoten Kommunikasjon AS
T: 47 76 05 40 00
E: redaksjon@lofot-tidende.no
W: http://www.lofot-tidende.no
Freq: 2 Times/Week; **Circ:** 5182 Not Audited
Language (s): Norwegian
DAILY NEWSPAPER

LOKALAVISA NORDSALTEN
Owner: Lokalavisa Nordsalten AS
Editorial: Pb. 94, Innhavet 8260.
T: 47 75 77 24 50
E: lokalavisa@nord-salten.no
W: http://www.nord-salten.no
Freq: Weekly; **Circ:** 2536 Not Audited
Ansvarlig redaktør: Børge Strandskog
Language (s): Norwegian
DAILY NEWSPAPER

LOKALAVISA SØR-ØSTERDAL;
LOKAL-AVISA.NO
Owner: Sør-Østerdal Media AS
Editorial: Storgata 15, Elverum 2408
W: http://www.lokal-avisa.no/
Freq: 2 Times/Week; **Circ:** 2530 MBL
Ansvarlig redaktør: Halvard Berget
Language (s): Norwegian
NEWSPAPER

LOKALAVISEN FROGNER -
ST.HANSHAUGEN
Owner: Avis Holding AS
Editorial: Postboks 79, Bryn, Oslo 345.
T: 47 23 20 56 00
E: redaksjon.fs@lokalavisen.no
W: http://www.lokalavisenfrogner.no
Freq: Monthly; **Circ:** 30000 Pub Statement
Editor: Fredrik Eckhoff
Language (s): Norwegian
NEWSPAPER

LOKALAVISEN GRORUDDALEN
Owner: Nordstrands Blad AS
Editorial: Postboks 79, BRYN, Oslo 611.
T: 47 22 63 91 00
E: redaksjon@lokalavisen.no
W: http://www.lokalavisen.no
Freq: Weekly; **Circ:** 58500 Synovate MMI
Redaktør: Christian Haksø
Language (s): Norwegian
NEWSPAPER

LOKALAVISEN OPPEGÅRD
Owner: Nordstrands Blad AS
Editorial: co Østlandets Blad, Postboks 3110,
Kolbotn 1402. **T:** 47 66813440
E: tom.ullsgard@oblad.no
W: http://www.oppegard24.no
Freq: Bi-Weekly; **Circ:** 13200 Pub Statement
Language (s): Norwegian
DAILY NEWSPAPER

MALVIK-BLADET
Owner: Malvik Bladet AS
Editorial: Pb. 130, Hommelvik 7551.
T: 47 73 98 00 80 **E:** redaksjonen@mb.no
W: http://www.mb.no
Freq: 2 Times/Week; **Circ:** 3131 Not Audited

Language (s): Norwegian
NEWSPAPER

MARSTEINEN
Owner: Austevoll Forlag AS
Editorial: Storebø 5392. **T:** 47 55 08 21 00
E: redaksjonen@marsteinen.no
W: http://www.marsteinen.no
Freq: Weekly; **Circ:** 2402 Not Audited
Language (s): Norwegian
NEWSPAPER

MELØYAVISA
Owner: Meløyavisa
Editorial: Havneveien 15b, Ørnes 8150.
T: 47 75 71 95 50 **E:** post@meloyavisa.no
W: http://www.meloyavisa.no
Freq: Weekly; **Circ:** 2955 Not Audited
Language (s): Norwegian
NEWSPAPER

MERÅKER-POSTEN
Owner: Meråker-Posten AS
Editorial: Pb. 15, Meråker 7531.
T: 47 74 81 09 80
E: redaksjon@merakerposten.no
Freq: Weekly; **Circ:** 1199 Not Audited
Ansvarlig redaktør: Svein Halvor Moe
Language (s): Norwegian
NEWSPAPER

MØRE
Owner: Aarflots Prenteverk AS
T: 47 70 07 44 21 **E:** red@mre.no
W: http://www.mre.no
Freq: 2 Times/Week; **Circ:** 3752 Not Audited
Redaktør: Tore Aarflot
Language (s): Norwegian
DAILY NEWSPAPER

MØRE-NYTT
Owner: Møre-Nytt AS
Editorial: Pb. 144, Ørsta 6151.
T: 47 70 04 19 00 **E:** avis@morenytt.no
W: http://www.morenytt.no
Freq: 2 Times/Week; **Circ:** 5526 MBL
Ansvarlig redaktør: Rune Sæbønes
Language (s): Norwegian
DAILY NEWSPAPER

Morgenbladet
Owner: Morgenbladet AS
Editorial: Karl Johansgt 25, Oslo 159.
T: 47 21006300
E: redaksjon@morgenbladet.no
W: http://www.morgenbladet.no
Freq: Weekly; **Circ:** 21442 MBL
Ansvarlig redaktør: Anna B Jenssen;
Debattredaktør: Marit K. Slotnæs
Language (s): Norwegian
DAILY NEWSPAPER

MOSS AVIS
Owner: Mediehuset Moss Avis AS
Editorial: Pb. 248/250, Moss 1501.
T: 47 69205000 **E:** desken@moss-avis.no
W: http://www.moss-avis.no
Freq: Daily; **Circ:** 14983 MBL
Ansvarlig redaktør: Pål Enghaug;
Nyhetsredaktør: Magne Henriksen;
Redaksjonssjef: Helge Kjøniksen; **Debatt:** Erik
Sæthre
Language (s): Norwegian
DAILY NEWSPAPER

MOSS AVIS; KULTURREDAKSJONEN
Owner: Mediehuset Moss Avis AS
Editorial: Pb. 250, Moss 1501.
T: 47 46907777 **E:** eva.fretheim@moss-avis.no
W: http://www.moss-avis.no **Circ:** 14983
Language (s): Norwegian
DAILY NEWSPAPER

MOSS AVIS; SPORTSREDAKSJONEN
Owner: Mediehuset Moss Avis AS
Editorial: Pb. 250, Moss 1501.
T: 47 46907777 **E:** sporten@moss-avis.no
W: http://www.moss-avis.no
Freq: Daily; **Circ:** 14983 MBL
Language (s): Norwegian
DAILY NEWSPAPER

NAMDALSAVISA
Owner: Namdalsavisa AS
Editorial: Postboks 100, Namsos 7801.
T: 47 74212100
E: redaksjon@namdalsavisa.no
W: http://www.namdalsavisa.no
Freq: Daily; **Circ:** 12771 MBL
Nyhetsredaktør: Lars Mørkved
Language (s): Norwegian
DAILY NEWSPAPER

Nationen
Owner: Nationen AS

Editorial: Pb. 9390 Grønland, Oslo 135.
T: 47 21310000 **E:** tips@nationen.no
W: http://www.nationen.no
Freq: Daily; **Circ:** 15670 MBL
Nyhetsredaktør: Rino Andersen
Language (s): Norwegian
DAILY NEWSPAPER

Nationen - Trøndelag
Editorial: Kjøpmannsgata 51, Trondheim 7011.
T: 47 73535306 **E:** kato.nykvist@nationen.no
W: http://www.nationen.no **Circ:** 15670 MBL
Editorial Profile: Bureau
Language (s): Norwegian
DAILY NEWSPAPER

NORDDALEN
Editorial: Postboks 954, Lillehammer 2604.
T: 47 977 21 000 **E:** post@norddalen.no
W: http://www.norddalen.no
Freq: Weekly; **Circ:** 2517
Language (s): Norwegian
DAILY NEWSPAPER

NORDHORDLAND
Owner: Avisa Nordhordland AS
Editorial: Kvernhusmyrane 29, Isdalstø 5914.
T: 47 56 35 55 55 **E:** avisa@nordhordland.no
W: http://www.nordhordland.no
Freq: 2 Times/Week; **Circ:** 6294 Not Audited
Ansvarlig redaktør: Randi Bjørlo; **Redaktør:**
Arthur Kleiveland
Language (s): Norwegian
NEWSPAPER

NORDLYS
Owner: Bladet Nordlys AS
Editorial: Pb. 2515, Tromsø 9272
E: nyheter@nordlys.no
W: http://www.nordlys.no
Freq: Daily; **Circ:** 26714 MBL
Redaktør: Nils Harald Hansen;
Nyhetsredaktør: Helge Nitteberg; **Ansvarlig
redaktør:** Anders Opdahl; **Redaktør:** Danny
Pellicer; **Redaktør:** Stian Saur; **Redaktør:** Geir
Taarnesvik
Language (s): Norwegian
DAILY NEWSPAPER

NORDLYS- LØRDAG
Owner: Bladet Nordlys AS
Editorial: Pb. 2515, Tromsø 9272.
T: 47 0776 0 **E:** lordag@nordlys.no
W: http://www.nordlys.no
Freq: Weekly; **Circ:** 26714 MBL
Language (s): Norwegian
DAILY NEWSPAPER

**NORDLYS; DEBATT/
YTRINGREDAKSJONEN**
Owner: Nordlys bladet AS
Editorial: Pb 2515, Tromsø 9272
E: leser@nordlys.no **W:** http://www.nordlys.no
Freq: Daily; **Circ:** 26714 MBL
Language (s): Norwegian
DAILY NEWSPAPER

**NORDLYS;
NÆRINGSLIVSREDAKSJONEN**
Owner: Baldet Nordlys AS
Editorial: Pb. 2515, Tromsø 9272.
T: 47 07760 **E:** naeringsliv@nordlys.no
W: http://www.nordlys.no
Freq: Daily; **Circ:** 27647
Language (s): Norwegian
DAILY NEWSPAPER

**NORDLYS; NORDLYSPULS-
REDAKSJONEN**
Owner: Bladet Nordlys AS
Editorial: Pb. 2515, Tromsø 9272.
T: 47 07760 **E:** kultur@nordlys.no
W: http://www.nordlys.no
Freq: Daily; **Circ:** 26714 MBL
Language (s): Norwegian
DAILY NEWSPAPER

**NORDLYS; NYHETS- OG
REPORTASJEAVDELINGEN**
Owner: Bladet Nordlys AS
Editorial: Pb. 2515, Tromsø 9272.
T: 47 0 77 60 **E:** nyheter@nordlys.no
W: http://www.nordlys.no
Freq: Daily; **Circ:** 26714 MBL
Language (s): Norwegian
DAILY NEWSPAPER

NORDLYS; SPORTSREDAKSJONEN
Owner: Bladet Nordlys AS
Editorial: Pb 2515, Tromsø 9272
E: sporten@nordlys.no
W: http://www.nordlys.no/sport
Freq: Daily; **Circ:** 26714 MBL
Language (s): Norwegian
DAILY NEWSPAPER

NORDLYS~ AVD. BARDUFOSS
Owner: Bladet Nordlys AS
Editorial: Pb. 1194, Bardufoss 9326.
T: 47 77 83 50 30
E: stein.wilhelmsen@nordlys.no
W: http://www.nordlys.no
Freq: Daily; **Circ:** 26714 MBL
Language (s): Norwegian
DAILY NEWSPAPER

NORDLYS~ AVD. FINNSNES
Owner: Bladet Nordlys AS
Editorial: Pb. 14, Finnsnes 9305.
T: 47 77 85 00 53
E: torgeir.braathen@nordlys.no
W: http://www.nordlys.no
Freq: Daily; **Circ:** 26714 MBL
Language (s): Norwegian
DAILY NEWSPAPER

Nordre
Owner: Haramsnytt AS
Editorial: Pb. 53, Brattvåg 6282.
T: 47 70 20 84 82 **E:** robin@nordrenett.no
W: http://nordrenett.no/
Freq: 2 Times/Week; **Circ:** 2800 MBL
Language (s): Norwegian
NEWSPAPER

NORDRE AKER BUDSTIKKE
Owner: Nordre Aker Budstikke AS
Editorial: Postboks 79, Bryn, Oslo 611.
T: 47 23 20 56 60 **E:** redaksjon@dittoslo.no
W: http://dittoslo.no/nordre-aker
Freq: Weekly; **Circ:** 22200 Pub Statement
Redaktør: Fredrik Eckhoff
Language (s): Norwegian
NEWSPAPER

NORDSTRANDS BLAD
Owner: Nordstrands Blad AS
Editorial: Pb. 79, Bryn, Oslo 611.
T: 47 22 63 91 00 **E:** redaksjonen@noblad.no
W: http://www.noblad.no
Freq: 2 Times/Week; **Circ:** 7055 Not Audited
Language (s): Norwegian
NEWSPAPER

NORDVESTNYTT
Owner: Nordvestnytt AS
Editorial: Hopen, Smøla 6571.
T: 47 71 54 44 50
E: redaksjonen@nordvestnytt.no
W: http://www.nordvestnytt.no
Freq: Weekly; **Circ:** 1806 LLA
Language (s): Norwegian
NEWSPAPER

NRK NYHETER, NYHETSDESKEN TV
Owner: Norsk Rikskringkasting AS Avd Oslo
Editorial: Bjørnstjerne Bjørnsonsplass 1, Oslo
340. **T:** 47 23 04 84 10 **E:** 03030@nrk.no
W: http://www.nrk.no/nyheter
Language (s): Norwegian
DAILY NEWSPAPER

NYE TROMS
Owner: Nye Troms AS
Editorial: Pb. 44, Moen 9329.
T: 47 77 83 79 00 **E:** redaksjon@nye-troms.no
W: http://www.nye-troms.no
Freq: 2 Times/Week; **Circ:** 5051 MBL
Markedssjef: Eirik Heim; **Redaksjonssjef:**
Morten Kasbergsen; **Redaktør:** Gjermund
Nilssen
Language (s): Norwegian
NEWSPAPER

NYE TROMS; SPORTSREDAKSJONEN
Owner: Nye Troms AS
Editorial: Boks 44, Moen 9329.
T: 47 77837913 **E:** sporten@nye-troms.no
W: http://www.nye-troms.no
Language (s): Norwegian
DAILY NEWSPAPER

NYE TROMS~AVD. BALSFJORD
Owner: Nye Troms AS
Editorial: Balstun 2, Storsteinnes 9050.
T: 47 77 72 65 05 **E:** balsfjord@nye-troms.no
W: http://www.nye-troms.no
Freq: 2 Times/Week; **Circ:** 5017 Not Audited
Redaktør: Gjermund Nilssen
Language (s): Norwegian
DAILY NEWSPAPER

NYE TROMS~AVD. BARDU
Owner: Nye Troms AS
T: 47 77 18 13 33 **E:** bardu@nye-troms.no
W: http://www.nye-troms.no
Freq: 2 Times/Week; **Circ:** 5017 Not Audited
Language (s): Norwegian
DAILY NEWSPAPER

NYTT I UKA
Owner: Media Vest AS

Editorial: Pb 128, Ålesund 6001.
T: 47 70161919 **E:** redaksjon@nyttiuka.no
W: http://www.nyttiuka.no
Freq: Weekly; **Circ:** 37218 Pub Statement
Language (s): Norwegian
NEWSPAPER

ØKSNESAVISA
Owner: Ingress Media & Reklame AS
Editorial: Pb. 118, Myre 8439.
T: 47 76 11 99 40 **E:** hjalmar@oksnesavisa.no
W: http://www.oksnesavisa.no
Freq: Weekly; **Circ:** 1842 Not Audited
Language (s): Norwegian
NEWSPAPER

OPDALINGEN
Owner: Opdalingen AS
Editorial: Pb. 33, Oppdal 7340.
T: 47 72 40 06 20
E: redaksjon@opdalingen.no
W: http://www.opdalingen.no
Freq: 2 Times/Week; **Circ:** 2655 Not Audited
Language (s): Norwegian
NEWSPAPER

OPPLAND ARBEIDERBLAD
Owner: Oppland arbeiderblad AS
Editorial: Pb 24, Gjøvik 2801. **T:** 47 61189300
E: redaksjonen@oa.no **W:** http://www.oa.no
Freq: Daily; **Circ:** 26578 MBL
Redaktør: Tonje Sagstuen Andersen
Language (s): Norwegian
DAILY NEWSPAPER

**OPPLAND ARBEIDERBLAD;
SPORTSREDAKSJONEN**
Owner: Oppland arbeiderblad AS
Editorial: Pb 24, Gjøvik 2801. **T:** 47 61189316
E: sporten@oa.no **W:** http://www.oa.no
Freq: Daily; **Circ:** 26578 MBL
Language (s): Norwegian
DAILY NEWSPAPER

**OPPLAND ARBEIDERBLAD~ AVD.
HADELAND**
Owner: AS Oppland Arbeiderblad
Editorial: Pb 14, Gran 2711.
T: 47 61 18 93 00 **E:** redaksjonen@oa.no
W: http://www.oa.no
Freq: Daily; **Circ:** 26578 MBL
Language (s): Norwegian
DAILY NEWSPAPER

**OPPLAND ARBEIDERBLAD~ AVD.
LAND**
Owner: Oppland arbeiderblad AS
Editorial: Pb 33, Dokka 2882.
T: 47 61 11 89 00 **E:** redaksjonen@oa.no
W: http://www.oa.no
Freq: Daily; **Circ:** 26578 MBL
Language (s): Norwegian
DAILY NEWSPAPER

**OPPLAND ARBEIDERBLAD~ AVD.
VALDRES**
Owner: Oppland arbeiderblad AS
T: 47 951 85 704 **E:** redaksjonen@oa.no
Freq: Daily; **Circ:** 26578 MBL
Language (s): Norwegian
DAILY NEWSPAPER

OS & FUSAPOSTEN
Owner: Os og Fusaposten AS
Editorial: Pb. 273, Os 5203.
T: 47 56 30 29 50 **E:** post@osogfusa.no
W: http://www.osogfusa.no
Freq: 2 Times/Week; **Circ:** 5793 Not Audited
Language (s): Norwegian
NEWSPAPER

ØSTERDØLEN
Owner: Østerdølen AS
Editorial: Pb. 125, Koppang 2480.
T: 47 62 46 36 50 **E:** nkvaerne@online.no
Freq: Weekly; **Circ:** 1201 Not Audited
Redaksjonssekretær: Mari Kværnes; **Ansvarlig
redaktør** Njaal Kværnes
Language (s): Norwegian; Full Page Colour:
17493.00
Currency: Norway Kroner
NEWSPAPER

ØSTFOLDAVISEN
Owner: Reklameaviser AS
Editorial: Pb 73, Greåker 1720.
T: 47 69127500 **E:** post@ostfoldavisen.no
W: http://www.ostfoldavisen.no
Freq: Monthly; **Circ:** 93000 Not Audited
Ansvarlig redaktør: Thor Gunnar Ryen
Language (s): Norwegian
NEWSPAPER

ØSTHAVET
Owner: Østhavet AS

Editorial: Pb. 103, Vardø 9951.
T: 47 78 98 85 88 **E:** redaksjon@osthavet.as
W: http://www.osthavet.as
Freq: Weekly; **Circ:** 1776 Not Audited
Language (s): Norwegian; Full Page Colour:
30818.00
Currency: Norway Kroner
NEWSPAPER

ØSTKANTAVISA
Owner: Nordstrands Blad AS
Editorial: Postboks 79, Bryn, Oslo 611.
T: 47 23 20 56 30
E: redaksjon@ostkantavisa.no
W: http://www.ostkantavisa.no
Freq: Weekly; **Circ:** 70000 Not Audited
Language (s): Norwegian
NEWSPAPER

ØSTLANDETS BLAD
Owner: AS Østlandets Blad
Editorial: Pb. 3110, Ski 1402. **T:** 47 64855000
E: tips@oblad.no **W:** http://www.oblad.no
Freq: Daily; **Circ:** 15348 MBL
Nyhetsleder: Torbjørn Endal; **Redaksjonssjef:**
Rolf-Otto Eriksen; **Ansvarlig redaktør / daglig
leder:** Martin Gray; **Utviklingsredaktør:** Bengt
Røsth; **Redaktør:** Tom Ullsgård
Language (s): Norwegian; Full Page Colour:
56033.00
Currency: Norway Kroner
DAILY NEWSPAPER

ØSTLANDS-POSTEN
Owner: Mediehuset Østlands-Posten AS
Editorial: Postboks 5, Larvik 3285.
T: 47 33163000 **E:** redaksjonen@op.no
W: http://www.op.no
Freq: Daily; **Circ:** 13932 MBL
Nyhetsredaktør: Gry R. Nordvik; **Ansvarlig
redaktør:** Terje Svendsen; **Redaktør:** Per
Marvin Tennum
Language (s): Norwegian
DAILY NEWSPAPER

**ØSTLANDS-POSTEN;
SPORTSREDAKSJONEN**
Owner: Mediehuset Østalnds-Posten
Editorial: Postboks 5, Larvik 3285.
T: 47 33163000 **E:** sport@op.no
W: http://www.op.no/sport
Freq: Daily; **Circ:** 13932 MBL
Language (s): Norwegian
DAILY NEWSPAPER

ØSTLENDINGEN
Owner: Østlendingen AS
Editorial: Gaarderbakken 3, Elverum 2406.
T: 47 62432500
E: redaksjonen@ostlendingen.no
W: http://www.ostlendingen.no
Freq: Daily; **Circ:** 19142 MBL
Redaktør: Anders Bronken; **Frontredigerer:**
Kjetil B. Dahl; **Nyhetsleder:** Ola Thorset
Language (s): Norwegian; Full Page Colour:
28976.00
Currency: Norway Kroner
DAILY NEWSPAPER

**ØSTLENDINGEN;
SPORTSREDAKSJONEN**
Owner: Østlendingen AS
Editorial: Gaarderbakken 3, Elverum 2406.
T: 47 62432550 **E:** sporten@ostlendingen.no
W: http://www.ostlendingen.no
Freq: Daily; **Circ:** 19142 MBL
Language (s): Norwegian
DAILY NEWSPAPER

ØSTLENDINGEN~AVD. FLISA
Owner: Østlendingen AS
Editorial: Kaffeg. 18, Flisa 2270.
T: 47 62 95 70 70 **E:** flisa@ostlendingen.no
W: http://www.ostlendingen.no
Freq: Daily; **Circ:** 19142 MBL
Language (s): Norwegian
DAILY NEWSPAPER

ØSTLENDINGEN~AVD. KOPPANG
Owner: Østlendingen AS
Editorial: Storg. 107 B, Koppang 2480.
T: 47 62 46 01 55
E: redaksjonen@ostlendingen.no
W: http://www.ostlendingen.no
Freq: Daily; **Circ:** 19142 MBL
Language (s): Norwegian
DAILY NEWSPAPER

ØSTLENDINGEN~AVD. TRYSIL
Owner: Østlendingen AS
Editorial: Storvegen 13, Trysil 2420.
T: 47 62 45 03 15 **E:** trysil@ostlendingen.no
W: http://www.ostlendingen.no
Freq: Daily; **Circ:** 19142 MBL
Frontredigerer: Jan Morten Frengstad
Language (s): Norwegian

DAILY NEWSPAPER

ØSTLENDINGEN~AVD. TYNSET
Owner: Østlendingen AS
Editorial: Brugata 2 A, Tynset 2500.
T: 47 62 40 00 00 **E:** tynset@ostlendingen.no
W: http://www.ostlendingen.no
Freq: Daily; **Circ:** 19142 MBL
Language (s): Norwegian
DAILY NEWSPAPER

ØYAVIS
Owner: Øyavis ANS
Editorial: Midsund 6475. **T:** 47 71 27 90 90
E: post@oyavis.no **W:** http://www.oyavis.no
Freq: Monthly; **Circ:** 1943 Not Audited
Language (s): Norwegian
NEWSPAPER

ØY-BLIKK
Owner: Øy-Blikk AS
Editorial: Øysenteret, Valderøy 6050.
T: 47 70 18 63 80 **E:** redaksjon@oyblikk.no
W: http://www.oyblikk.no
Freq: Weekly; **Circ:** 1864 Not Audited
Redaktør: Jan Erik Andreassen
Language (s): Norwegian
NEWSPAPER

ØYENE
Owner: Mediehuset Østlands-Posten AS
Editorial: Pb. 124 Teie, Nøtterøy 3106.
T: 47 33 34 57 77 **E:** red@oyene.no
W: http://www.oyene.no
Freq: Weekly; **Circ:** 4295 Not Audited
Language (s): Norwegian
NEWSPAPER

ØYPOSTEN
Owner: Øyposten AS
Editorial: Pb. 5, Finnøy 4160.
T: 47 51 71 46 60 **E:** bladstova@oyposten.no
W: http://www.oyposten.no
Freq: Weekly; **Circ:** 1254 Not Audited
Marked- og abonnementansvarlig: Signy
Eike-Kongsvik; **Redaktør:** Per Thime
Language (s): Norwegian
NEWSPAPER

PORSGRUNNS DAGBLAD
Owner: Porsgrunns Dagblad AS
Editorial: Pb. 140, Porsgrunn 3909.
T: 47 35 51 65 00 **E:** erik.enger@pd.no
W: http://www.pd.no
Freq: Daily; **Circ:** 4763 MBL
Redaksjonssjef: Per Arne Rennestraum
Language (s): Norwegian
NEWSPAPER

PUNKTNYTT
Owner: Foreningen norges døvblinde
T: 47 37 02 11 47 **E:** fndbred@online.no
W: http://www.fndb.no
Freq: Daily
Helsevesenet: Bjørn Davidsen
Language (s): Norwegian
DAILY NEWSPAPER

RAKKESTAD AVIS
Owner: Rakkestad Avis AS
Editorial: Storgt. 8, Rakkestad 1890.
T: 47 69 22 25 55 **E:** ra@r-a.no
W: http://www.rakkestad-avis.no
Freq: 2 Times/Week; **Circ:** 2664 MBL
Language (s): Norwegian
DAILY NEWSPAPER

RANA BLAD
Owner: AS Rana Blad
Editorial: boks 55 Vika, Mo I Rana 8601.
T: 47 75125500 **E:** redaksjonen@ranablad.no
W: http://www.ranablad.no
Freq: Daily; **Circ:** 10622 MBL
Nyhetsredaktør: Roger Marthinsen;
Sjefsredaktør: Kirsti Nielsen; **Markedssjef:**
Trine Rimer
Language (s): Norwegian
DAILY NEWSPAPER

RANA BLAD; SPORTSREDAKSJONEN
Owner: Rana Blad AS
Editorial: Pb 55, Mo I Rana 8601.
T: 47 75125500 **E:** sporten@ranablad.no
W: http://www.ranablad.no
Freq: Daily; **Circ:** 10622 MBL
Language (s): Norwegian
DAILY NEWSPAPER

RAUMNES
Owner: Raumnes AS
Editorial: Pb. 44, Årnes 2151.
T: 47 63 91 18 14 **E:** redaksjon@raumnes.no
W: http://www.raumnes.no
Freq: 2 Times/Week; **Circ:** 5441 Not Audited
Language (s): Norwegian; Full Page Colour:
17507.00

Currency: Norway Kroner
NEWSPAPER

REGIONAVISA
Owner: Nye Regionavisa AS
Editorial: Pb 424, Ulsteinvik 6067.
T: 47 70009660 **E:** tips@regionavisa.no
W: http://www.regionavisa.no
Freq: Weekly; **Circ:** 20000 Pub Statement
Ansvarlig redaktør: Hugo Antonsen
Language (s): Norwegian
NEWSPAPER

RINGERIKES BLAD
T: 47 32179500 **E:** redaksjonen@ringblad.no
W: http://www.ringblad.no
Ansvarlig redaktør: Øyvind Lien
Language (s): Norwegian
DAILY NEWSPAPER

RINGSAKER BLAD
Owner: Ringsaker Blad AS
Editorial: Østlendingen, Elverum 2406.
T: 47 62 34 77 00
E: redaksjonen@ringsaker-blad.no
W: http://www.ringsaker-blad.no
Freq: 2 Times/Week; **Circ:** 7172 MBL
Language (s): Norwegian; Full Page Colour:
20328.00
Currency: Norway Kroner
NEWSPAPER

RJUKAN ARBEIDERBLAD
Owner: Rjukan Arbeiderblad AS
Editorial: Storgata 20, Rjukan 3660.
T: 47 35 08 00 50 **E:** ra@rablad.no
W: http://www.rablad.no
Freq: Daily; **Circ:** 2335 Not Audited
Language (s): Norwegian
NEWSPAPER

ROGALANDS AVIS
Owner: Rogalands Avis AS
Editorial: Pb 233, Stavanger 4001.
T: 47 51822000
E: redaksjon@rogalandsavis.no
W: http://www.rogalandsavis.no
Freq: Daily; **Circ:** 12452 Not Audited
Redaktør: Torun Fanuelsen; **Sjefredaktør:**
Bjørn G. Sæbø
Language (s): Norwegian
DAILY NEWSPAPER

ROGALANDS AVIS; SPORTSREDAKSJONEN
Owner: Rogalands Avis AS
Editorial: Pb 233, Stavanger 4001.
T: 47 51822000 **E:** sport@rogalandsavis.no
W: http://www.rogalandsavis.no
Freq: Daily; **Circ:** 11472 MBL
Language (s): Norwegian
NEWSPAPER

ROMERIKES BLAD
Owner: Media Øst Trykk AS
Editorial: Pb 235, Lillestrøm 2001.
T: 47 63 80 50 50 **E:** redaksjonen@rb.no
W: http://www.rb.no
Freq: Daily; **Circ:** 37659 MBL
Redaksjonssjef: Trine Kjus
Language (s): Norwegian; Full Page Colour:
38764.00
Currency: Norway Kroner
DAILY NEWSPAPER

ROMERIKES BLAD - JESSHEIM
Editorial: Pb. 174, Jessheim 2051.
T: 47 63 97 96 00 **E:** jessheimkontoret@rb.no
W: http://www.rb.no
Freq: Daily; **Circ:** 37659 MBL
Language (s): Norwegian
DAILY NEWSPAPER

ROMSDALS BUDSTIKKE
Owner: Romsdals Budstikke AS
Editorial: Pb. 2100, Molde 6402.
T: 47 71250000 **E:** redaksjon@r-b.no
W: http://www.rbnett.no
Freq: Daily; **Circ:** 18167 MBL
Language (s): Norwegian
DAILY NEWSPAPER

ROMSDALS BUDSTIKKE; KULTURREDAKSJONEN
Owner: Romsdals Budstikke AS
Editorial: Pb. 2100, Molde 6402.
T: 47 71250000 **E:** kultur@r-b.no
W: http://www.rbnett.no
Freq: Daily; **Circ:** 18205
Language (s): Norwegian
DAILY NEWSPAPER

ROMSDALS BUDSTIKKE; SPORTSREDAKSJONEN
Owner: Romsdals Budstikke AS

Editorial: Pb 55, Molde 6402. **T:** 47 71250000
E: sport@r-b.no **W:** http://www.rbnett.no
Freq: Daily; **Circ:** 18167 MBL
Language (s): Norwegian
NEWSPAPER

RYFYLKE
Owner: LL Ryfylke
Editorial: Pb. 194, Sauda 4201.
T: 47 52 78 68 00 **E:** ryfylke@ryfylke.net
W: http://www.ryfylke.net
Freq: 2 Times/Week; **Circ:** 2659 LLA
Dagligleder/Redaktør: Linda Merethe Lie
Language (s): Norwegian
DAILY NEWSPAPER

SAGAT
Owner: Ságat-Samisk Avis AS
Editorial: Laatasveien, PB 53, Lakselv 9711.
T: 47 78 46 59 00 **E:** avisa@sagat.no
W: http://www.sagat.no
Freq: Daily; **Circ:** 2722 LLA
Redaksjonssekretær: Oddgeir Johansen;
Nyhetsredaktør: Tor Kjetil Kristoffersen;
Redaksjonssekretær: Lars Birger Persen;
Distriktsleder: Idar Johan Reinås;
Sjefredaktør: Geir Wulff
Language (s): Norwegian; Full Page Colour:
49029.00
Currency: Norway Kroner
DAILY NEWSPAPER

SALTENPOSTEN
Owner: Saltenposten AS
Editorial: Pb. 108, Fauske 8201.
T: 47 75 60 24 60
E: redaksjonen@saltenposten.no
W: http://www.saltenposten.no
Freq: 2 Times/Week; **Circ:** 4972 MBL
Language (s): Norwegian
NEWSPAPER

SAMNINGEN
Owner: Samnanger Bladlag AS
Editorial: Samningen, Årland 5652.
T: 47 56 58 77 05 **E:** post@samningen.no
W: http://www.samningen.no
Freq: Weekly; **Circ:** 1254 Not Audited
Language (s): Norwegian
NEWSPAPER

SANDE AVIS
Owner: Sande Avis AS
Editorial: Revåveien 14, Sande I Vestfold
3070. **T:** 47 33 77 84 45
E: redaksjonen@sandeavis.no
W: http://www.sandeavis.no
Freq: Weekly; **Circ:** 2220 MBL
Language (s): Norwegian
DAILY NEWSPAPER

SANDEFJORDS BLAD
Owner: Sandefjords Blad AS
Editorial: Pb. 143, Sandefjord 3201.
T: 47 33422000 **E:** redaksjonen@sb.no
W: http://www.sb.no
Freq: Daily; **Circ:** 14260 Not Audited
Language (s): Norwegian
DAILY NEWSPAPER

SANDEFJORDS BLAD; DEBATT
Owner: Sandefjords Blad AS
T: 47 33422000 **E:** debatt@sb.no
W: http://www.sb.no
Freq: Daily; **Circ:** 14260
Language (s): Norwegian
DAILY NEWSPAPER

SANDEFJORDS BLAD; SPORTSREDAKSJONEN
Owner: Edda Vestfold AS
Editorial: Pb. 143, Sandefjord 3201.
T: 47 33422000 **E:** sporten@sb.no
W: http://www.sb.no
Freq: Daily; **Circ:** 13995 MBL
Language (s): Norwegian
DAILY NEWSPAPER

SANDNESPOSTEN
Owner: Sandnesposten AS
Editorial: Ole Bulls Gate 14, Sandnes 4306.
T: 47 41 60 70 00
E: redaksjonen@sandnesposten.no
W: http://www.sandnesposten.no
Freq: 2 Times/Week; **Circ:** 4222 MBL
Ansvarlig redaktør: André H. Jamholt;
Redaksjonsleder: Trond Erik Olsen
Language (s): Norwegian
DAILY NEWSPAPER

SARPSBORG ARBEIDERBLAD
Owner: Sarpsborg Arbeiderblad AS
Editorial: Pb. 83, Sarpsborg 1701.
T: 47 69111111 **E:** redaksjonen@sa.no
W: http://www.sa.no
Freq: Daily; **Circ:** 14578 MBL

Language (s): Norwegian
DAILY NEWSPAPER

SARPSBORG ARBEIDERBLAD; SPORTSREDAKSJONEN
Owner: Saprborg Arbeiderblad AS
Editorial: Pb. 83, Sarpsborg 1701.
T: 47 69111111 **E:** sporten@sa.no
W: http://www.sa.no **Circ:** 14578
Language (s): Norwegian
DAILY NEWSPAPER

SELBYGGEN
Owner: Selbyggen AS
Editorial: Pb. 114, Selbu 7581.
T: 47 73 81 08 80 **E:** firmapost@selbyggen.no
W: http://www.selbyggen.no
Freq: Weekly; **Circ:** 3306 LLA
Redaktør: Bodil Uthus
Language (s): Norwegian
NEWSPAPER

SETESDØLEN
Owner: Setesdølen AS
Editorial: Setesdølen AS, Postboks 40,
Bygland 4745. **T:** 47 37 93 45 00
E: avis@setesdolen.no
W: http://www.setesdolen.no
Freq: 2 Times/Week; **Circ:** 4742 MBL
Redaktør: Sigurd Haugsgjerd
Language (s): Norwegian; Full Page Colour:
35021.00
Currency: Norway Kroner
NEWSPAPER

SIRDØLEN
Owner: Sirdølen Avis
Editorial: Sirdølen Media A/S, Pb 6, Tonstad
4441. **T:** 47 900 864 73 **E:** post@sirdolen.no
W: http://www.sirdolen.no
Freq: Monthly; **Circ:** 1800 Pub Statement
Language (s): Norwegian
NEWSPAPER

SMAALENENES AVIS
Owner: Øsfoldpressen AS
Editorial: Pb. B, Askim 1801. **T:** 47 69816100
E: redaksjonen@smaalenene.no
W: http://www.smaalenene.no
Freq: Daily; **Circ:** 13305 MBL
Redaktør: Bjørn Steiner Meyer;
Nyhetsredaktør: Anne Sterri Harestad
Language (s): Norwegian
NEWSPAPER

SMAALENENES AVIS; SPORTSREDAKSJONEN
Owner: Øsfoldpressen AS
Editorial: Pb. B, Askim 1801. **T:** 47 69816156
E: sporten@smaalenene.no
W: http://www.smaalenene.no
Freq: Daily; **Circ:** 13305 MBL
Language (s): Norwegian
DAILY NEWSPAPER

SNÅSNINGEN
Owner: Snåsningen AS
Editorial: Viosen, Snåsa 7761.
T: 47 74 15 15 10 **E:** tips@snasningen.no
W: http://www.snasningen.no
Freq: Weekly; **Circ:** 1647 LLA
Language (s): Norwegian
NEWSPAPER

SOGN AVIS
Owner: Sogningen/Sogns Avis AS
Editorial: Postboks 3, Leikanger 6863.
T: 47 57656000 **E:** redaksjon@sognavis.no
W: http://www.sognavis.no
Freq: Daily; **Circ:** 10085 MBL
Language (s): Norwegian
NEWSPAPER

SOLABLADET
Owner: Solabladet AS
Editorial: Pb. 86, Sola 4097.
T: 47 51 64 64 64 **E:** solabladet@solabladet.no
W: http://www.solabladet.no
Freq: Weekly; **Circ:** 4249 MBL
Language (s): Norwegian
NEWSPAPER

SORTLANDSAVISA
Owner: Sortlandsavisa
T: 47 99155566 **E:** red@sortlandsavisa.no
W: http://www.sortlandsavisa.no
Freq: Weekly; **Circ:** 1189 LLA
Language (s): Norwegian
DAILY NEWSPAPER

SØR-TRØNDELAG
Owner: Sør-Trøndelag AS
Editorial: Orkedalsveien 57, Orkanger 7300.
T: 47 72 48 75 00
E: nyhets.redaksjonen@avisa-st.no
W: http://www.avisa-st.no

Freq: Daily; Circ: 7328 Not Audited
Ansvarlig redaktør: Anders Aa. Morken;
Magasinredaktør: Audhild Øye; **Dagligleder:**
Johan Olav Wiggen
Language (s): Norwegian
DAILY NEWSPAPER

SØR-TRØNDELAG~AVD. HEMNE
Owner: Sør-Trøndelag AS
T: 47 72 45 25 60
E: nyhets.redaksjonen@avisa-st.no
W: http://www.avisa-st.no
Freq: Daily; **Circ:** 7328 Not Audited
Language (s): Norwegian
DAILY NEWSPAPER

SØR-VARANGER AVIS
Owner: Sør-Varanger Avis AS
Editorial: Pb. 63, Kirkenes 9915.
T: 47 78 97 07 00 E: redaksjon@sva.no
W: http://www.sva.no
Freq: 2 Times/Week; **Circ:** 4032 Not Audited
Language (s): Norwegian; Full Page Colour:
42025.00
Currency: Norway Kroner
NEWSPAPER

SØVESTEN
Owner: Søvesten Media AS
Editorial: Hollaveien 2, Kyrksæterøra 7200.
T: 47 72 45 00 50 E: redaksjon@sovesten.no
W: http://www.sovesten.no
Freq: Weekly; **Circ:** 1563 Not Audited
Language (s): Norwegian
NEWSPAPER

STANGEAVISA
Owner: Stangeavisa AS
T: 47 62 58 44 90 E: post@stangeavisa.no
W: http://www.stangeavisa.no
Freq: Weekly; **Circ:** 2007
Language (s): Norwegian; Full Page Colour:
8000.00
Currency: Norway Kroner
DAILY NEWSPAPER

Stavanger Aftenblad
Owner: Stavanger Aftenblad ASA
Editorial: Pb. 229, Stavanger 4001.
T: 47 0515 0 E: tips@aftenbladet.no
W: http://www.aftenbladet.no
Freq: Daily; **Circ:** 68010 Not Audited
Redaktør: Tarald Aano; **Nyhetsredaktør:** Carl
Gunnar Gundersen; **Sjefredaktør:** Lars Helle
Language (s): Norwegian; Full Page Colour:
32177.00
Currency: Norway Kroner
DAILY NEWSPAPER

Stavanger Aftenblad - Bryne
Owner: Stavanger Aftenblad AS
Editorial: Storgata 27A, Bryne 4340.
T: 47 05150 E: jaeren@aftenbladet.no
W: http://www.aftenbladet.no **Circ:** 68010 Not
Audited
Editorial Profile: Bureau
Language (s): Norwegian
DAILY NEWSPAPER

Stavanger Aftenblad - Haugesund
Owner: Stavanger Aftenblad AS
Editorial: Pb 561, Haugesund 5501.
T: 47 52737640
E: thomas.forde@aftenbladet.no
W: http://www.aftenbladet.no **Circ:** 68010 Not
Audited
Editorial Profile: Bureau
Language (s): Norwegian
DAILY NEWSPAPER

Stavanger Aftenblad; Nyhetsredaksjonen
Owner: Stavanger Aftenblad AS
Editorial: Pb. 229, Stavanger 4001.
T: 47 05100 E: tips@aftenbladet.no
W: http://www.aftenbladet.no
Freq: Daily; **Circ:** 68010
Nyhetsredaktør: Carl Gunnar Gundersen;
Nyhetsredaktør: Carl Gunnar Gundersen
Language (s): Norwegian
DAILY NEWSPAPER

STAVANGER AFTENBLAD~ AVD. DALANE
Owner: Stavanger Aftenblad ASA
Editorial: Spinnergt. 2, Egersund 4370.
T: 47 0515 0 E: dalane@aftenbladet.no
W: http://www.aftenbladet.no
Freq: Daily; **Circ:** 68010 Not Audited
Language (s): Norwegian
DAILY NEWSPAPER

STAVANGER AFTENBLAD~ AVD. SANDNES
Editorial: Pb. 645, Sandnes 4305.
T: 47 51604700 E: sandnes@aftenbladet.no

W: http://www.aftenbladet.no **Circ:** 68010 Not
Audited
Editorial Profile: Bureau
Language (s): Norwegian
DAILY NEWSPAPER

STEINKJER-AVISA
Owner: Steinkjer-Avisa AS
Editorial: Pb. 4, Steinkjer 7701.
T: 47 74 10 01 30 E: post@steinkjer-avisa.no
W: http://www.steinkjer-avisa.no
Freq: Weekly; **Circ:** 3917 Not Audited
Language (s): Norwegian
NEWSPAPER

STJØRDALENS BLAD
Owner: Stjørdalens Blad AS
Editorial: Pb. 163, Stjørdal 7501.
T: 47 74 83 95 00 E: redaksjonen@bladet.no
W: http://www.bladet.no
Freq: 2 Times/Week; **Circ:** 7740 MBL
Sjefsredaktør: Kjell-Ivar Myhr;
Redaksjonssjef: Bjørnar Sandvik
Language (s): Norwegian
DAILY NEWSPAPER

STORFJORDNYTT
Owner: Storfjord Bladlag AS
Editorial: Pb. 134, Valldal 6210.
T: 47 70 25 78 50 E: post@storfjordnytt.no
W: http://www.storfjordnytt.no
Freq: Weekly; **Circ:** 1586 Not Audited
Language (s): Norwegian
NEWSPAPER

STRANDBUEN
Owner: Strandbuen AS
Editorial: Pb. 24, Jørpeland 4126.
T: 47 51 74 47 50
E: redaksjon@strandbuen.no
W: http://www.strandbuen.no
Freq: 2 Times/Week; **Circ:** 4354 Not Audited
Language (s): Norwegian
NEWSPAPER

STRILEN
Owner: Forlaget Strilen AS
Editorial: Pb. 3, Isdalstø 5902.
T: 47 56 34 30 30 E: avisa@strilen.no
W: http://www.strilen.no
Freq: 2 Times/Week; **Circ:** 5357 MBL
Markedssjef: Heidi L. Vågenes Villanger;
Ansvarlig redaktør: Hans Egil Storheim;
Redaksjonssekretær: Ketil Tjore
Language (s): Norwegian
NEWSPAPER

SULAPOSTEN
Owner: Sulaposten AS
Editorial: Pb. 85, Langevåg 6039.
T: 47 70 19 86 50 E: redaksjon@sulaposten.no
W: http://www.sulaposten.no
Freq: Weekly; **Circ:** 2465 Not Audited
Language (s): Norwegian
NEWSPAPER

SULDALSPOSTEN
Owner: Suldalsposten AS
Editorial: Pb. 114, Sand 4239.
T: 47 52 79 05 90
E: redaksjon@suldalsposten.no
W: http://www.suldalsposten.no
Freq: 2 Times/Week; **Circ:** 2437 LLA
Language (s): Norwegian
NEWSPAPER

SUNNHORDLAND
Owner: Bladet Sunnhordland AS
Editorial: Pb. 100, Stord 5401.
T: 47 53 45 00 00
E: redaksjonen@sunnhordland.com
W: http://www.sunnhordland.com
Freq: Daily; **Circ:** 7832 MBL
Language (s): Norwegian
DAILY NEWSPAPER

SUNNMØRINGEN
Owner: Sunnmøringen AS
Editorial: Pb. 24, Stranda 6201.
T: 47 70 26 11 22
E: redaksjonen@sunnmoringen.no
W: http://www.sunnmoringen.no
Freq: 2 Times/Week; **Circ:** 1981 LLA
Language (s): Norwegian
DAILY NEWSPAPER

SUNNMØRSPOSTEN
Owner: SUnnmørsposten AS
Editorial: Pb. 123, Ålesund 6001.
T: 47 70120000 E: redaksjonen@smp.no
W: http://www.smp.no
Freq: Daily; **Circ:** 32667 MBL
Ansvarlig redaktør: Hanna Relling Berg;
Markedssjef: Ingrid Sperre
Language (s): Norwegian
DAILY NEWSPAPER

SVALBARDPOSTEN
Owner: Stiftelsen Svalbardposten
Editorial: Pb. 503, Longyearbyen 9171.
T: 47 79 02 47 00 E: post@svalbardposten.no
W: http://www.svalbardposten.no
Freq: Weekly; **Circ:** 3095 LLA
Redaktør: Birger Amundsen
Language (s): Norwegian; Full Page Colour:
29417.00
Currency: Norway Kroner
NEWSPAPER

SVELVIKSPOSTEN
Owner: Svelviksposten AS
Editorial: Storgaten 74, Svelvik 3061.
T: 47 33 77 30 10
E: redaksjon@svelviksposten.no
W: http://www.svelviksposten.no
Freq: Weekly; **Circ:** 2518 MBL
Language (s): Norwegian
NEWSPAPER

SYDVESTEN
Owner: Grieg Lokalaviser AS
Editorial: Spelhaugen 20, Fyllingsdalen 5147.
T: 47 55 16 47 50 E: red@sydvesten.no
W: http://www.sydvesten.no
Freq: Weekly; **Circ:** 2146 Not Audited
Redaktør: Mette L. Skulstad
Language (s): Norwegian
DAILY NEWSPAPER

SYKKYLVSBLADET
Owner: Frank Kjøde og Åge Eikrem
Editorial: Pb. 55, Sykkylven 6239.
T: 47 70 25 48 48
E: redaksjonen@sykkylvsbladet.no
W: http://www.sykkylvsbladet.no
Freq: 2 Times/Week; **Circ:** 2980 LLA
Ansvarlig redaktør: Frank Kjøde
Language (s): Norwegian
NEWSPAPER

SYNSTE MØRE
Owner: Synste Møre AS
Editorial: Boks D, Fiskåbygd 6139.
T: 47 70 02 08 20 E: redaksjonen@synste.no
W: http://www.synste.no
Freq: Weekly; **Circ:** 2385 LLA
Ansvarlig redaktør: Vidar Parr
Language (s): Norwegian
NEWSPAPER

TELEMARKSAVISA
Owner: Telemarksavisa AS
Editorial: Pb. 2833 Kjørbekk, Skien 3702.
T: 47 35585500 E: desken@ta.no
W: http://www.ta.no
Freq: Daily; **Circ:** 22282 MBL
Markedssjef: Glenn Anda Pettersen;
Nyhetsleder: Ørjan Madsen; **Ansvarlig
redaktør:** Ove Mellingen
Language (s): Norwegian
DAILY NEWSPAPER

TELEMARKSAVISA - BAMBLE
Owner: Telemarksavisa AS
Editorial: Krabberødveien 6, Stathelle 3960.
T: 47 35 96 34 10 E: rolf.formo@ta.no
W: http://www.ta.no
Freq: Daily; **Circ:** 22282 MBL
Language (s): Norwegian
DAILY NEWSPAPER

TELEMARKSAVISA - BØ
Editorial: Pb. 88, I Telemark 3800 BØ.
T: 47 35 95 21 88 E: else.borte@ta.no
W: http://www.ta.no
Freq: Daily; **Circ:** 22282 MBL
Language (s): Norwegian
DAILY NEWSPAPER

TELEMARKSAVISA - KRAGERØ
Owner: Telemarksavisa AS
Editorial: Kragerø 3791. T: 47 35 98 06 99
E: espen.nilsen@ta.no W: http://www.ta.no
Freq: Daily; **Circ:** 22282 MBL
Language (s): Norwegian
DAILY NEWSPAPER

TELEMARKSAVISA - NOTODDEN
Owner: Telemarksavisa AS
Editorial: Storgt. 50, Notodden 3631.
T: 47 35011333 E: jarle.pedersen@ta.no
W: http://www.ta.no
Freq: Daily; **Circ:** 22346 Not Audited
Language (s): Norwegian
DAILY NEWSPAPER

TELEMARKSAVISA - PORSGRUNN
Editorial: Porsgrunn 3921. T: 47 90195752
E: lars.lokkebo@ta.no W: http://www.ta.no
Freq: Daily; **Circ:** 22282 MBL
Language (s): Norwegian
DAILY NEWSPAPER

TELEMARKSAVISA; KULTURREDAKSJONEN
Owner: Telemarksavisa AS
Editorial: Pb. 2833 Kjørbekk, Skien 3702.
T: 47 35585500 E: kultur@ta.no
W: http://www.ta.no/pulsen
Freq: Daily; **Circ:** 22346
Language (s): Norwegian
DAILY NEWSPAPER

TELEMARKSAVISA; SPORTSREDAKSJONEN
Owner: Telemarksavisa AS
Editorial: Pb 2833 Kjørbekk, Skien 3702.
T: 47 35585500 E: sport@ta.no
W: http://www.ta.no/lokal_sport
Freq: Daily; **Circ:** 22282 MBL
Language (s): Norwegian
DAILY NEWSPAPER

TELEN
Owner: Telen AS
Editorial: Pb. 83, Notodden 3671.
T: 47 93 23 42 00 E: telen@telen.no
W: http://www.telen.no
Freq: Daily; **Circ:** 5089 MBL
Ansvarlig redaktør: Jens Marius Hammer;
Nyhetsredaktør: Henning Johansson
Language (s): Norwegian
DAILY NEWSPAPER

TIDENS KRAV
Owner: Tidens Krav AS
Editorial: Pb. 8, Kristiansund N 6501.
T: 47 71570000 E: redaksjonen@tidenskrav.no
W: http://www.tk.no
Freq: Daily; **Circ:** 15412 Not Audited
Language (s): Norwegian
DAILY NEWSPAPER

TIDENS KRAV - AVERØY / EIDE
Owner: Tidens Krav AS
Editorial: Sveggesundet, Averøy 6530.
T: 47 71 51 33 86
E: roald.sevaldsen@tidenskrav.no
W: http://www.tk.no
Freq: Daily; **Circ:** 15412 Not Audited
Language (s): Norwegian
DAILY NEWSPAPER

TIDENS KRAV - SURNADAL / RINDE / HALSA
Owner: Tidens Krav AS
Editorial: Surnadal 6650. T: 47 71 66 11 99
E: redaksjonen@tk.no W: http://www.tk.no
Freq: Daily; **Circ:** 15412 Not Audited
Language (s): Norwegian
DAILY NEWSPAPER

TIDENS KRAV; SPORTSREDAKSJONEN
Owner: Tidens Krav AS
Editorial: Pb. 8, Kristiansund N 6501.
T: 47 71570030 E: sporten@tidenskrav.no
W: http://www.tk.no **Circ:** 15412
Sjefredaktør: Tore Dyrnes
Language (s): Norwegian
DAILY NEWSPAPER

TØNSBERGS BLAD
Owner: Edda Vestfold AS
Editorial: Postboks 33, Tønsberg 3103.
T: 47 33373000 E: redaksjonen@tb.no
W: http://www.tb.no
Freq: Daily; **Circ:** 29785 MBL
Ansvarlig redaktør: Håkon Borud;
Redaksjonssjef nyheter: Kristin Monstad
Lund; **Redaktør:** Morten Wang;
Redaksjonssjef: Erik Wold Aunemo
Language (s): Norwegian
DAILY NEWSPAPER

TØNSBERGS BLAD; JOBB- OG NÆRINGSLIVREDAKSJONEN
Owner: Edda Vestfold AS
Editorial: Postboks 33, Tønsberg 3101.
T: 47 33373000 E: jobb@tb.no
W: http://www.tb.no
Freq: Daily; **Circ:** 29785 MBL
Language (s): Norwegian
DAILY NEWSPAPER

TØNSBERGS BLAD; KULTUR/ FEATURE
Owner: Edda Vestfold AS
Editorial: Postboks 33, Tønsberg 3101.
T: 47 33 37 30 00 E: kultur@tb.no
W: http://www.tb.no
Freq: Daily; **Circ:** 29785 MBL
Redaksjonssjef: Marie Olaussen
Language (s): Norwegian
DAILY NEWSPAPER

TØNSBERGS BLAD; SPORTSREDAKSJONEN
Owner: Edda Vestfold AS
Editorial: Postboks 33, Tønsberg 3101.
T: 47 33373000 **E:** sport@tb.no
W: http://www.tb.no
Freq: Daily; **Circ:** 29785 MBL
Language (s): Norwegian
DAILY NEWSPAPER

TØNSBERGS BLAD~ AVD. HOLMESTRAND
T: 47 33 09 94 40 **E:** erik.munsterhjelm@tb.no
W: http://www.tb.no
Freq: Daily; **Circ:** 30354
Language (s): Norwegian
DAILY NEWSPAPER

TOTENS BLAD
Owner: Totens Blad AS
T: 47 61 16 87 50
E: redaksjon@totens-blad.no
W: http://www.totens-blad.no
Freq: Weekly; **Circ:** 12400 Pub Statement
Redaktør: Jon Olav Andersen; **Markedssjef:** Hans Erik Linnerud
Language (s): Norwegian
DAILY NEWSPAPER

TROMS FOLKEBLAD
Owner: Troms Folkeblad AS
Editorial: Pb. 308, Finnsnes 9305.
T: 47 77 85 20 00 **E:** tips@folkebladet.no
W: http://www.folkebladet.no
Freq: Daily; **Circ:** 7779 MBL
Language (s): Norwegian
NEWSPAPER

TROMS FOLKEBLAD; SPORTSREDAKSJONEN
Owner: Troms Folkeblad AS
Editorial: Pb. 308, Finnsnes 9305.
T: 47 77852060 **E:** sporten@folkebladet.no
W: http://www.folkebladet.no/sport **Circ:** 7779
Language (s): Norwegian
DAILY NEWSPAPER

TRØNDER-AVISA - GRONG
Editorial: Grong 7870 **E:** terje.solberg@t-a.no
W: http://www.t-a.no
Freq: Daily; **Circ:** 23142 MBL
Language (s): Norwegian
DAILY NEWSPAPER

TRØNDER-AVISA - LEVANGER
Editorial: Gunnlaug Ormstunges gt. 2, Levanger 7600 **E:** redaksjonen@t-a.no
W: http://www.t-a.no
Freq: Daily; **Circ:** 23142 MBL
Language (s): Norwegian
DAILY NEWSPAPER

TRØNDER-AVISA - NAMSOS
Editorial: Hamnegata 12, Namsos 7800
E: redaksjonen@t-a.no **W:** http://www.t-a.no
Freq: Daily; **Circ:** 23142 MBL
Language (s): Norwegian
DAILY NEWSPAPER

TRØNDER-AVISA - STJØRDAL
Editorial: Stjørdal 7500. **T:** 47 92 06 45 33
E: roar.fordal@t-a.no
Freq: Daily; **Circ:** 23268 MBL
Language (s): Norwegian
DAILY NEWSPAPER

TRØNDER-AVISA - VERDAL
Editorial: Pb 77, Verdal 7651.
T: 47 74 04 43 00 **E:** redaksjonen@t-a.no
W: http://www.t-a.no
Freq: Daily; **Circ:** 23268 Not Audited
Language (s): Norwegian
DAILY NEWSPAPER

TRØNDER-AVISA; SPORTSREDAKSJONEN
Editorial: Hamnegt 20, Steinker 7738
E: sporten@t-a.no **W:** http://www.t-a.no
Freq: Daily; **Circ:** 23142 MBL
Language (s): Norwegian
DAILY NEWSPAPER

TRØNDERBLADET~AVD. STØREN
Owner: Trønderbladet AS
T: 47 982 60 457
E: tronderbladet@tronderbladet.no
W: http://www.tronderbladet.no
Freq: 2 Times/Week; **Circ:** 5754 MBL
Language (s): Norwegian
DAILY NEWSPAPER

TS AVISEN
Owner: TS-Avisen AS
Editorial: PB 383, Arendal 4804.
T: 47 37 06 39 00 **E:** post@ts-avisen.no

W: http://www.ts-avisen.no
Freq: Weekly; **Circ:** 80000 Synovate MMI
Ansvarlig redaktør: Einar Sjøvaag
Language (s): Norwegian
DAILY NEWSPAPER

TV2; TV2 NYHETENE~OSLO
Owner: TV2 AS
Editorial: Pb. 2 Sentrum, Oslo NO-0101.
T: 47 0 22 55 **E:** nyhetstips@tv2.no
W: http://www.tv2.no
Redaksjonssjef: Tor Godal; **Redaksjonssjef:** Niklas Lysvåg
Language (s): Norwegian
DAILY NEWSPAPER

TVEDESTRANDSPOSTEN
Owner: Tvedestrandsposten AS
T: 47 37 16 49 00
E: redaksjonen@tvedestrandsposten.no
W: http://www.tvedestrandsposten.no
Freq: 2 Times/Week; **Circ:** 3605 Not Audited
Language (s): Norwegian; Full Page Colour: 44126.00
Currency: Norway Kroner
DAILY NEWSPAPER

TYSNES
Owner: Bladet Tysnes AS
Editorial: 5685 Uggdal, Uggdal 5685.
T: 47 53 43 22 20
E: redaksjon@tysnesbladet.no
W: http://www.tysnesbladet.no
Freq: Weekly; **Circ:** 2475 Not Audited
Ansvarlig redaktør: Ole M. Skaten
Language (s): Norwegian
NEWSPAPER

TYSVÆR BYGDEBLAD
Owner: Tysvær Bygdeblad AS
Editorial: Pb. 13, Aksdal 5575.
T: 47 52 75 74 00
E: post@tysver-bygdeblad.no
W: http://www.tysver-bygdeblad.no
Freq: Weekly; **Circ:** 1828 LLA
Language (s): Norwegian
NEWSPAPER

UKEAVISEN LEDELSE
Owner: Næringslivets forlag AS
Editorial: Pb. 1180 Sentrum, Oslo 107.
T: 47 22310210
E: ukeavisen@kundesenter.com
W: http://www.ukeavisenledelse.no
Freq: Weekly; **Circ:** 15000 MBL
Redaktør: Magne Lerø
Language (s): Norwegian
NEWSPAPER

ULLERN AVIS / AKERSPOSTEN
Owner: Avis Holding AS
T: 47 23 20 56 60
E: redaksjon@akersposten.no
W: http://www.akersposten.no
Freq: 2 Times/Week; **Circ:** 4026 Synovate MMI
Language (s): Norwegian
DAILY NEWSPAPER

UTROP
Owner: Utrop AS
Editorial: Pb. 8962, Youngstorget, Oslo 28.
T: 47 22041461 **E:** tips@utrop.no
W: http://www.utrop.no **Circ:** 2478
Language (s): Norwegian
NEWSPAPER

VÅGANAVISA
Editorial: Pb 371, Svolvær 8301.
T: 47 90508210 **E:** redaksjon@vaganavisa.no
W: http://www.vaganavisa.no
Freq: Weekly; **Circ:** 1743 Not Audited
Redaktør: Edd Meby
Language (s): Norwegian
NEWSPAPER

VAKSDAL POSTEN
Owner: Vaksdal Posten AS
Editorial: Pb. 1, Vaksdal 5726.
T: 47 56 59 40 00 **E:** post@vaksdalposten.no
W: http://www.vaksdalposten.no
Freq: Weekly; **Circ:** 2405 Not Audited
Language (s): Norwegian
NEWSPAPER

VARDEN
Owner: Varden AS
Editorial: Pb. 2873, Kjørbekk, Skien 3702.
T: 47 35543000 **E:** redaksjonen@varden.no
W: http://www.varden.no
Freq: Daily; **Circ:** 26091 MBL
Redaksjonssjef: Lasse Johannessen;
Ansvarlig redaktør: Lars Kise;
Nyhetsredaktør: Tom Erik Thorsen
Language (s): Norwegian
DAILY NEWSPAPER

VARDEN - BØ
Editorial: Stasjonsveien 5, I Telemark 3800 BØ. **T:** 47 35 95 37 02
E: halvor.ulvenes@varden.no
Freq: Daily; **Circ:** 26091 MBL
Language (s): Norwegian
DAILY NEWSPAPER

VARDEN - NOTODDEN
Owner: Varden AS
Editorial: Heddalsveien 40, Notodden 3674.
T: 47 35 02 67 22 **E:** kjell.aulie@varden.no
W: http://www.varden.no
Freq: Daily; **Circ:** 26091 MBL
Language (s): Norwegian
DAILY NEWSPAPER

VARDEN - PORSGRUNN OG BAMBLE
Owner: Varden AS
Editorial: Varden P.b. 2873, Kjørbekk, Skien 3702. **T:** 47 35 54 30 00
E: karina.hagen@varden.no
W: http://www.varden.no
Freq: Daily; **Circ:** 26091 MBL
Language (s): Norwegian
DAILY NEWSPAPER

VARDEN; KULTURREDAKSJONEN
Owner: Varden AS
Editorial: PB 2873, Kjørbekk, Skien 3702.
T: 47 35543000 **E:** kultur@varden.no
W: http://www.varden.no
Freq: Daily; **Circ:** 27341
Language (s): Norwegian
DAILY NEWSPAPER

VARDEN; SPORTSREDAKSJONEN
Owner: Varden AS
Editorial: Pb. 2873 Kjørbekk, Skien 3702.
T: 47 35543000 **E:** sport@varden.no
W: http://www.varden.no
Freq: Daily; **Circ:** 27341 Not Audited
Language (s): Norwegian
DAILY NEWSPAPER

Vårt Land
Owner: Avisen Vårt Land AS
Editorial: Pb. 1180 Sentrum, Oslo 107.
T: 47 22310310 **E:** tips@vl.no
W: http://www.vl.no
Freq: Daily; **Circ:** 26344 MBL
Utenriksredaktør: Bjarte Botnen;
Redaksjonssjef: Reidar Kristiansen;
Sjefsredaktør: Helge Simonnes
Language (s): Norwegian
DAILY NEWSPAPER

Vårt Land - Bergen
Owner: Avisen Vårt Land AS
Editorial: Bergen. **T:** 47 55369030
W: http://www.vl.no **Circ:** 26344 MBL
Editorial Profile: Bureau
Language (s): Norwegian
DAILY NEWSPAPER

VENNESLA TIDENDE
Owner: Vennesla Tidende AS
Editorial: Pb. 134, Vennesla 4700.
T: 47 38 15 25 90 **E:** red@venneslatidende.no
W: http://www.vt-nett.no
Freq: 2 Times/Week; **Circ:** 3118 Not Audited
Language (s): Norwegian
NEWSPAPER

VESTAVIND
Owner: Vestavind AS
Editorial: Pb 53, Sveio 5559.
T: 47 53 74 01 80
E: redaksjonen@vestavind-sveio.no
W: http://www.vestavind-sveio.no
Freq: Weekly; **Circ:** 1481 Not Audited
Language (s): Norwegian
DAILY NEWSPAPER

VESTBY AVIS
Owner: Vestby Avis As
Editorial: Pb. 17, Vestby 1514.
T: 47 64 98 38 88 **E:** post@vestbyavis.no
W: http://www.vestbyavis.no
Freq: Weekly; **Circ:** 1344 Not Audited
Language (s): Norwegian
DAILY NEWSPAPER

VESTBY NYTT
Owner: Mediasenteret AS
Editorial: Postboks 239, Vestby 1541.
T: 47 64 98 52 80 **E:** post@mediasenteret.no
W: http://www.mediasenteret.no/ Vestby-Nytt-201212
Freq: Monthly; **Circ:** 7050
Daglig leder: Ronny Nermo; **Ansvarlig redaktør:** Roy Nermo
Language (s): Norwegian
DAILY NEWSPAPER

VESTERAALENS AVIS
Owner: Vesterålens Avis AS
Editorial: Pb. 806, Stokmarknes 8455.
T: 47 918 98 885 **E:** red@vesteraalensavis.no
W: http://www.vesteraalensavis.no
Freq: 2 Times/Week; **Circ:** 2388 MBL
Ansvarlig redaktør: Gro Smith
Language (s): Norwegian
NEWSPAPER

VESTFOLDSAMKJØRINGEN
Owner: Mediehuset Østlands-Posten
Editorial: Pb 2000, Larvik 3255.
T: 47 33 16 30 00 **E:** annonse@op.no
W: http://www.vestfoldsamkjoringen.no
Freq: Daily; **Circ:** 22166 Pub Statement
Language (s): Norwegian
DAILY NEWSPAPER

VESTNESAVISA
Owner: Reklamebyrået Vestnesavisa AS
T: 47 71 18 00 00
E: redaksjon@vestnesavisa.no
W: http://www.vestnesavisa.no
Freq: Weekly; **Circ:** 1935 Not Audited
Language (s): Norwegian
DAILY NEWSPAPER

VESTNYTT
Owner: Vestnytt AS
Editorial: VestNytt, Skjenet 2, Straume 5353.
T: 47 56 33 65 00 **E:** redaksjon@vestnytt.no
W: http://www.vestnytt.no
Freq: 2 Times/Week; **Circ:** 6143 Not Audited
Language (s): Norwegian
DAILY NEWSPAPER

VEST-TELEMARK BLAD
Owner: Vest-Telemark Blad AS
Editorial: Postboks 33, Kviteseid 3850.
T: 47 35 06 88 00 **E:** redaksjon@vtb.no
W: http://www.vtb.no
Freq: 2 Times/Week; **Circ:** 5530 MBL
Language (s): Norwegian
DAILY NEWSPAPER

VG
Owner: Verdens Gang AS
Editorial: Pb 1185 Sentrum, Oslo 107.
T: 47 22000000 **E:** pressemeldinger@vg.no
W: http://www.vg.no
Freq: Daily; **Circ:** 284414 MBL
Redaksjonssjef: Svein Arne Haavik;
Redaksjonssjef: Arnstein Johansen; **Ansvarlig redaktør:** Torry Pedersen; **Redaksjonssjef:** Audun Solberg; **Redaktør:** Helje Solberg
Language (s): Norwegian; Full Page Colour: 141358.00
Currency: Norway Kroner
DAILY NEWSPAPER

VG - Kristiansand
Editorial: Pb 491, Kristiansand S 4664
E: pressemeldinger@vg.no **W:** http://vg.no
Circ: 284414 MBL
Editorial Profile: Bureau
Language (s): Norwegian
DAILY NEWSPAPER

VG - Tromsø
Editorial: Grønnegt. 32, Boks 952, Tromsø 9260. **T:** 47 77 60 66 00 **E:** tromso@vg.no
W: http://www.vg.no
Editorial Profile: Bureau
Language (s): Norwegian
DAILY NEWSPAPER

VG - Trondheim
Editorial: Fjordgata 82, Trondheim 7402.
T: 47 73 51 20 00 **E:** trondheim@vg.no
W: http://www.vg.no **Circ:** 284414 MBL
Editorial Profile: Bureau
Language (s): Norwegian
DAILY NEWSPAPER

VG ~ Avd. Bergen
Editorial: Pb 400, Bergen 5001.
T: 47 55 90 04 00 **E:** bergen@vg.no
W: http://www.vg.no **Circ:** 284414 MBL
Editorial Profile: Bureau
Language (s): Norwegian
DAILY NEWSPAPER

VIGGA
Owner: Dombås Informasjonssenter AS
Editorial: Pb. 79, Dombås 2659.
T: 47 61 21 50 10 **E:** post@vigga.no
W: http://www.vigga.no
Freq: Weekly; **Circ:** 2629 Not Audited
Language (s): Norwegian
NEWSPAPER

VIKEBLADET VESTPOSTEN
Owner: Vikebladet Vestposten AS
Editorial: Pb. 128, Ulsteinvik 6067.
T: 47 70 01 85 00 **E:** redaksjon@vikebladet.no

WORLD NEWS MEDIA

W: http://www.vikebladet.no
Freq: 2 Times/Week; **Circ:** 4504 MBL
Language (s): Norwegian
NEWSPAPER

YTRE SOGN AVIS
Owner: Avisforetaket Ytre Sogn AS
Editorial: Pb. 10, Høyanger 6991.
T: 47 57 71 45 90 **E:** redaksjon@ytresogn.no
W: http://www.ytresogn.no
Freq: 2 Times/Week; **Circ:** 1552 Not Audited
Language (s): Norwegian
NEWSPAPER

YTRINGEN
Owner: Ytringen Avis AS
Editorial: Pb. 100, Kolvereid 7970.
T: 47 74 39 60 50 **E:** ytringen@ytringen.no
W: http://www.ytringen.no
Freq: 2 Times/Week; **Circ:** 3344 Not Audited
Dagligleder/Redaktør: Tor Ludvigsen;
Redaksjonssjef: Morten Wengstad
Language (s): Norwegian
NEWSPAPER

NEWS SERVICE/SYNDICATE

AGENCE FRANCE-PRESSE (AFP)
Owner: AFP
Editorial: Haakon VIIs gt 10, Oslo 161.
T: 47 22 83 93 94 **E:** oslo@afp.com
W: http://www.afp.com
Ansvarlig redaktør: Pierre Deshayes
Language (s): Norwegian
NEWS SERVICE/SYNDICATE

ANB AVISENES NYHETSBYRÅ
Owner: Avisenes Nyhetsbyrå (ANB)
Editorial: Pb 8713 Youngstorget, Oslo 28.
T: 47 22 99 84 40 **E:** pm@anb.no
W: http://www.anb.no
Redaktør: Olav Eilifsen; **Redaksjonssekretær:**
Marianne Lae; **Nyhetsredaktør:** Runar Nørstad;
Sjefredaktør: Hallgeir Westrum
Language (s): Norwegian
NEWS SERVICE/SYNDICATE

ANB AVISENES NYHETSBYRÅ; SPORTEN
Editorial: Pb 8713 Youngstorget, Oslo 28.
T: 47 22 99 84 40 **E:** sporten@anb.no
W: http://www.anb.no
Language (s): Norwegian
NEWS SERVICE/SYNDICATE

Associated Press
T: 47 22 20 10 30 **E:** aposl@ap.org
W: http://www.ap.org
Language (s): Norwegian
NEWS SERVICE/SYNDICATE

BLOOMBERG LP
Owner: Bloomberg
Editorial: C J Hambros pl 2 C, Oslo 164.
T: 47 22 99 62 10
E: oslonews@bloomberg.net
W: http://www.bloomberg.com
Language (s): Norwegian
NEWS SERVICE/SYNDICATE

Bloomberg News
Editorial: C.J. Hambros Plass 2C, Fl 2, Oslo
164. **T:** 47 22996210
NEWS SERVICE/SYNDICATE

BROBYGGEREN
Owner: Metodiskirken i Norge
Editorial: PB. 2744 St. Hanshaugen,
Akersbakken 37, Oslo 131. **T:** 47 23 33 27 07
E: brobyggeren@metodistkirken.no
W: http://www.metodistkirken.nohttp://www.
metodistkirken.no/hoved/brobyggeren
Ansvarlig redaktør: Karl Anders Ellingsen
Language (s): Norwegian
NEWS SERVICE/SYNDICATE

Estate Lokaler
Owner: Estate Media
Editorial: Holbergsgate 21, Oslo 166.
T: 47 21951000 **E:** post@estatemedia.no
W: http://www.estatemedia.no
Ansvarlig redaktør: Thor Arne Brun
Language (s): Norwegian; Full Page Colour:
29800.00
Currency: Norway Kroner
NEWS SERVICE/SYNDICATE

KRISTELIG PRESSEKONTOR - KPK
Editorial: Storgt. 10B, Oslo 155.
T: 47 22 42 77 90 **E:** kpk@kpk.no
W: http://www.kpk.no
Language (s): Norwegian
NEWS SERVICE/SYNDICATE

NEWSWIRE
Owner: Newswire AS
Editorial: Postboks 825 Sentrum, Oslo 104.
T: 47 24 15 50 60 **E:** newswire@newswire.no
W: http://www.newswire.no
Dagligleder: Christopher Hoelfeldt–Lund
Language (s): Norwegian
NEWS SERVICE/SYNDICATE

Norges Internasjonale Pressesenter
Owner: NIPS
Editorial: Haakon VII Gt. 10, Oslo 161.
T: 47 22 24 50 60 **E:** fpanorway@gmail.com
Language (s): Norwegian
NEWS SERVICE/SYNDICATE

NTB Norsk Telegram Byrå
Owner: Norsk Telegrambyrå
Editorial: Pb 6817 St. Olavsplass, Oslo 130.
T: 47 22 03 45 45 **E:** vaktsjef@ntb.no
W: http://www.ntb.no
Nyhetssjef: Kristin Aanensen; **Nyhetsredaktør:**
Ole Kristian Bjellaanes; **Sjefredaktør:** Pål
Bjerketvedt; **Organisasjonsjef:** Bård Idås
Language (s): Norwegian
NEWS SERVICE/SYNDICATE

NTB NORSK TELEGRAMBYRÅ; KULTUR
Owner: NTB
Editorial: Pb 6817 St. Olavsplass, Oslo 130.
T: 47 22 03 44 05 **E:** kultur@ntb.no
W: http://www.ntb.no/kultur
Language (s): Norwegian
NEWS SERVICE/SYNDICATE

NTB NORSK TELEGRAMBYRÅ; SPORTEN
Editorial: Pb 6817 St. Olavsplass, Oslo 130.
T: 47 22 03 45 55 **E:** sporten@ntb.no
Language (s): Norwegian
NEWS SERVICE/SYNDICATE

NTB NORSK TELEGRAMBYRÅ; UTENRIKS
Editorial: Pb 6817 St. Olavsplass, Oslo 130.
T: 47 22 03 45 50 **E:** utenriks@ntb.no
Korrspondent: Andreas Bondevik;
Gruppeleder: Ane H. Lunde
Language (s): Norwegian
NEWS SERVICE/SYNDICATE

NTB NORSK TELEGRAMBYRÅ~ AVD. STAVANGER
Owner: NTB
Editorial: Ryfylkegata 13, Stavanger 4014.
T: 47 51 89 50 31
E: mette.bjoberg.estep@ntb.no
W: http://www.ntb.no
Language (s): Norwegian
NEWS SERVICE/SYNDICATE

NTB NORSK TELEGRAMBYRÅ~ AVD. TROMSØ
Editorial: Søndre Tollbodg. 17, Tromsø 9008.
T: 47 77 68 71 00
E: jan-morten.bjornbakk@ntb.no
W: http://www.ntb.no
Language (s): Norwegian
NEWS SERVICE/SYNDICATE

NYNORSK PRESSEKONTOR
Owner: Stiftinga Nynorsk Pressekontor
Editorial: Postboks 6817 St. Olavs Plass, Oslo
130. **T:** 47 22 03 44 00 **E:** npk@npk.no
W: http://www.npk.no
Ansvarlig redaktør: Karoline Riise Kristiansen
Language (s): Norwegian
NEWS SERVICE/SYNDICATE

Opoint AS
Editorial: Akersgata, 28A, Postboks 428
Sentrum, Oslo 103. **T:** +47 21 56 97 50
E: mail@opoint.com
W: http://www.opoint.com/
Nyhetsformidler: Espen Brunvand;
Nyhetsformidler: Lars Flåten;
Nyhetsformidler: Desmond Frimpong;
Nyhetsformidler: Trond Olsgard;
Redaksjonssjef: Finn Picard; **Nyhetsformidler:**
Stig Rogstad; **Nyhetsformidler:** Dag
Steingrimsen
NEWS SERVICE/SYNDICATE

Reuters
Editorial: Karl Johans Gate 37B, 162, Oslo.
T: 47 22936900 **W:** http://www.reuters.com
NEWS SERVICE/SYNDICATE

TDN FINANS
Owner: TDN Dagens Næringsliv Nyhetsbyrå
AS
Editorial: PO Box 1182, Sentrum, Oslo 107.
T: 47 22 00 11 55 **E:** finans@tdn.no
W: http://www.nhst.no/tdn

Ansvarlig redaktør: Thomas Frantsvold
Language (s): Norwegian
NEWS SERVICE/SYNDICATE

THOMSON REUTERS NORGE
Owner: Thomson Reuters Norge AS
Editorial: Karl Johans gate 37B, Oslo 162.
T: 47 22 93 69 00
E: norway.reception@thomsonreuters.no
W: http://www.thomsonreuters.com
Redaksjonssjef: Ole Petter Skonnor;
Redaksjonsjef: Terje Solsvik
Language (s): Norwegian
NEWS SERVICE/SYNDICATE

BROADCASTING

RADIO STATIONS

1 FM
Editorial: Romsdalsgata 15, Molde 6415.
T: 47 71 25 55 55 **E:** ole.welde@r-b.no
W: http://www.1fm.no

1 FM MOLDE
Editorial: Romsdalsgata 15, Molde 6415.
T: 47 71 25 55 55 **E:** redaksjon@1fm.no
W: http://www.1fm.no

ACEM Meditasjon
Owner: Acem Oslo
Editorial: Pb 2559 Solli, Oslo 202.
T: 47 23 11 87 00 **W:** http://www.acem.no

BUDSTIKKA RADIO TRØNDELAG
Owner: Budstikka Radio Trøndelag BA
Editorial: Pb 391, Stjørdal 7501.
T: 47 74 83 95 95 **E:** budstikka.radio@ktv.no
W: http://www.budstikkaradio.no

BYGDERADIO VEST
Owner: Bygderadio Vest AS
Editorial: Pb 216, Volda 6101.
T: 47 70 07 85 00 **E:** gandas@online.no
W: http://bygderadiovest.no

DEN FRIE EVANGELISKE FORSAMLING
Owner: Den Frie Evang Forsamling
Editorial: Fløenbakken 57, Bergen 5009.
T: 47 55 29 85 10
E: menigheten@dfef-bergen.no
W: http://www.dfef-bergen.no

DRANGEDAL NÆRRADIO
Owner: Drangedal Nærradio Ba
Editorial: Kjørkeveien 1, Drangedal 3750.
T: 47 35 99 63 00
E: drangedalsradioen@dean.no

ETS - RADIOEN
Editorial: Pb. 215, Evenskjer 9439.
T: 47 77 08 57 13 **E:** ets@radioen-evenskjer.no
W: http://ets-radioen.no

EXACT MEDIA
Owner: Radio Exact Hamar AS
Editorial: Pb 454, Hamar 2304.
T: 47 62 51 96 30 **E:** red@exact24.no
W: http://www.exact24.no

GIMLEKOLLEN RADIO
Owner: Norea Mediemisjon
Editorial: Serviceboks 410, Kristiansand S
4604. **T:** 47 38 14 50 35 **E:** ksv@gimra.no
W: http://www.gimra.no

GOUVDAGEAINNU LAGASRADIO
Editorial: Postboks 244, Kautokeino 9521.
T: 47 78485300 **E:** glr@glr.no
W: http://www.glr.no

HALLO KRAGERØ
Owner: Hallo Kragerø Stiftelsen
Editorial: Frydenborgveien 4, Kragerø 3770.
T: 47 35 98 00 00
W: http://www.hallokragero.no

HÅPETS RØST
Owner: Håpets Røst
Editorial: Restaurationsveien 1, Hundvåg
4085. **T:** 47 51 86 12 26 **E:** movaag@online.no
W: http://www.haapetsrost.no

HJALARHORNET RADIO
Owner: Hjalarhornet Radio As
Editorial: Pb. 3, Seljord 3840.
T: 47 35 05 20 05 **E:** post@hjalar.no
W: http://www.hjalar.no

JÆREN MISJONSRADIO
Owner: Norsk Lutersk Misjonssamband

Editorial: Tryggheimvegen 13, Nærbø 4365.
T: 47 51 79 80 00 **E:** post@norea.no
W: http://www.norea.no

JÆRRADIOEN (JRG)
Owner: Jærradioen As
Editorial: Pb 10, Sandnes 4301.
T: 47 51 97 92 00 **E:** post@jaerradioen.no
W: http://www.jaerradioen.no

Klem FM
Owner: NRJ Norge AS
Editorial: Trondheimsv. 184, Oslo 570.
T: 47 22 79 75 00 **E:** studio@klemfm.no
W: http://www.klemfm.no

KONTAKT RADIO
Owner: Pinsemenigheten Salem
Editorial: Florsgate 1 B, Sandefjord 3211.
T: 47 33 48 22 22
W: http://salemsandefjord.no

Kystradioen
Owner: Kystradioen AS
Editorial: Skjenet 2, Straume 5353.
T: 47 55 62 62 66 **E:** post@kystradioen.no
W: http://www.kystradioen.no

MJØSRADIOEN (FILADELFIA)
Owner: Filadelfia Hamar
Editorial: Grønnegata 33, Hamar 2317.
T: 47 62 53 45 50 **E:** post@mjosradioen.no
W: http://www.mjosradioen.no

MØTET MED JESUS NÆRRADIO
Owner: Møtet Med Jesus
Editorial: Møtet med Jesus Tro og
Misjonsenter, Farmoveien 9, Sør-Audnedal
4520. **T:** 47 38 25 70 55
E: mmjesus@online.no

NÆRKANALEN
Owner: Radio Meløy BA
Editorial: SPILDERVIKA 10, Ørnes 8150.
T: 47 75 72 05 50 **E:** post@narkanalen.no
W: http://www.narkanalen.no

NARVIK STUDENTRADIO
Owner: Narvik Studentradio
Editorial: Narvik Studentersamfunn, Postboks
385, Narvik 8515. **T:** 47 7696 6000
W: http://nss.samfunnet.no

NB RADIO
Owner: Norges Blindeforbund
Editorial: Vestregate 9, Arendal 4836.
T: 47 37 02 20 66
W: http://www.nbradio.no/Default.aspx

NEA RADIO
Owner: Nea Radio
Editorial: Postboks 60, Selbu 7581.
T: 47 73 81 74 00 **E:** nr-selbu@nearadio.no
W: http://www.nearadio.no

NEA RADIO RØROS
Owner: Nea Radio
Editorial: Pb. 23, Røros 7461.
T: 47 72 41 44 00 **E:** nr-roros@nearadio.no
W: http://www.nearadio.no

NESNA RADIO
Owner: Nesna Radio
Editorial: Moveien 25, Nesna 8700.
T: 47 75 05 65 00
E: postmottak@nesnaradio.no
W: http://nesnaradio.no

Norea Radio Misjon
Editorial: Postboks 410 Lundsiden,
Kristiansand 4604. **T:** 47 38 14 50 00
E: post@norea.no
W: http://www.radiosentrum.org

NORRØNA RADIO, ÅLESUND
Owner: Norsk Luthersk Misjonssamband
Sunnmøre Og Rimsdal
Editorial: Pb. 7503 Spjelkavik, Ålesund 6022.
T: 47 70 17 44 00 **E:** post@norronaradio.no
W: http://www.norronaradio.no

NORRØNA RADIO, MOLDE
Owner: Norsk Lutersk Misjonssamband
Editorial: co/ Hans Bergane, Solemdal, Skåla
6456. **T:** 47 71 25 18 55 **E:** hberga@online.no
W: http://www.nlm.no

NRJ
Owner: NRJ Norge AS
Editorial: Trondheimsveien 184, Oslo 570.
T: 47 22 79 75 00 **E:** info@nrj.no
W: http://www.nrj.no/

NRK ALLTID KLASSISK (KANAL)
Owner: NRK

Editorial: Bj. Bjørnsons Plass 1, Oslo 340

NRK GULL (KANAL)
Owner: NRK
Editorial: Bj. Bjørnsons Plass 1, Oslo 340.
T: 47 23 04 70 00 E: gull@nrk.no
W: http://www.nrk.no/gull

NRK NYHETSDESKEN
Owner: Norsk Rikskringkasting As Avd Oslo
Editorial: Bjørnstjerne Bjørnsonsplass 1, Oslo
340. T: 47 23 04 84 10 E: 03030@nrk.no
W: http://www.nrk.no/nyheter

NRK Østafjells- Buskerud (Distriktskontor)
Owner: NRK
Editorial: PB 733 Strømsø, Drammen 3003
E: 02345@nrk.no
W: http://www.nrk.no/ostafjells

NRK P1 (KANAL)
Editorial: NRK P1, Trondheim 7005.
T: 47 73 88 14 00 E: p1@nrk.no
W: http://www.nrk.no/p1

NRK P1; TRAFIKKRADIO
Editorial: Oslo. T: 47 23048000
E: 03030@nrk.no
W: http://radio.nrk.no/serie/trafikkradio

NRK P1; UKESLUTT
Owner: Norsk Rikskringkasting As Avd Oslo
Editorial: Marienlyst/ Nyhetsavdelingen /
Sp21, Oslo 340. T: 47 23 04 84 10
E: ukeslutt@nrk.no
W: http://radio.nrk.no/serie/ukeslutt

NRK P2 (KANAL)
Owner: Norsk Rikskringkasting As Avd Oslo
Editorial: Bjønstjerne Bjørnsons Plass 1, Oslo
340. T: 47 23 04 84 06 E: p2desken@nrk.no
W: http://www.nrk.no/p2

NRK RADIOSPORTEN
Owner: Norsk Rikskringkasting As Avd Oslo
Editorial: Bjørnstjerne Bjørnsons Plass 1, Oslo
340. T: 47 23 04 95 05 E: nettsport@nrk.no
W: http://www.nrk.no/sport

NRK Rogaland (Distriktskontor)
Owner: Norsk Rikskringkasting As Avd Oslo
Editorial: Pb 614 Madla, Hafrsfjord 4090.
T: 47 51 72 72 72 E: rogaland@nrk.no
W: http://www.nrk.no/rogaland

NRK Sami Radio (Distriktskontor)
Owner: Norsk Rikskringkasting As Avd Oslo
Editorial: Mari Boine geaidnu 12, Karasjok
9730. T: 47 78 46 92 00 E: sapmi@nrk.no
W: http://www.nrk.no/samiradio

NRK SAMI RADIO~ AVD.SKÅNLAND
Owner: Norsk Rikskringkasting As Avd Oslo
Editorial: Pb 183, Evenskjer 9440.
T: 47 77 08 58 00 E: samiradio@nrk.no
W: http://www.nrk.no/samiradio

NRK SAMI RADIO~ AVD.SNÅSA
Owner: Norsk Rikskringkasting As Avd Oslo
Editorial: Pb 70, Snåsa 7760.
T: 47 74 15 11 77 E: risten.persson@nrk.no
W: http://www.samiradio.org

NRK SAMI RADIO~ AVD.TANA
Owner: Norsk Rikskringkasting As Avd Oslo
Editorial: Pb 145, Tana 9845.
T: 47 78 92 77 17 E: samiradio@nrk.no
W: http://nrk.no/sami

NRK SAMI RADIO~ AVD.TROMSØ
Owner: Norsk Rikskringkasting As Avd Oslo
Editorial: Nrk Troms, Tromsø 9291.
T: 47 77 66 12 15 E: kent.valio@nrk.no
W: http://www.samiradio.org

NRK SAMI RADIO~ AVD.TYSFJORD
Owner: Norsk Rikskringkasting As Avd Oslo
Editorial: Arran, Drag 8270. T: 47 75 77 33 35
E: nils.johan.heatta@nrk.no

NRK Troms & Finnmark- Troms (Distriktskontor)
Owner: Norsk Rikskringkasting As Avd Oslo
Editorial: Nrk Troms, Tromsø 9291.
T: 47 77 66 12 00 E: troms@nrk.no
W: http://www.nrk.no/nordnytt

NRK Trønderlag (Distriktskontor)
Owner: Norsk Rikskringkasting As Avd Oslo
Editorial: NRK, Trondheim 7005.
T: 47 73 88 12 00 E: trondelag@nrk.no
W: http://www.nrk.no/trondelag

NYE RADIO LARVIK
Owner: Radiokameratenes Forening, Nye
Radio Larvik
Editorial: Karlsrogate 1, Larvik 3251.
T: 47 33 12 70 60 E: musikk@norgespost.no
W: http://www.freewebs.com/radiokameratene/
index.htm

P4 RADIO
Owner: P4 Radio Hele Norge ASA
Editorial: Postboks P4, Lillehammer 2626.
T: 47 61 24 84 44 E: p4@p4.no
W: http://www.p4.no

P5 FOSEN
Owner: Rissa Radio BA
Editorial: Rådhusveien 21, Rissa 7101.
T: 47 73 85 40 00 E: p5fosen@online.no
W: http://www.p5fosen.no

P5 OSLO
Editorial: Akersgata 73, Oslo 180.
T: 47 23000000 E: p5@p5.no
W: http://oslo.p5.no

P5 Radio Halve Norge AS
Editorial: Akersgata 73, Oslo 180.
T: 47 23000000 E: p5@p5.no
W: http://www.p5.no

P5 TRONDHEIM
Editorial: Søndregate 14, Trondheim 7011.
T: 47 23000000 E: trondheim@p5.no
W: http://trondheim.p5.no

Radio 1 Bergen
Owner: Radio 1, Bergen
Editorial: Christian Michelsensgt. 2a, Bergen
5012. T: 47 55 94 84 00 E: kontakt@radio1.no
W: http://www.radio1.no

Radio 1 Oslo
Owner: Radio 1 AS
Editorial: Pb 1102, Sentrum, Oslo 104.
T: 47 22 02 33 00 E: kontakt@radio1.no
W: http://www.radio1.no

Radio 1 Stavanger
Owner: Radio 1 Stavanger AS
Editorial: Skagen 27, Stavanger 4006.
T: 47 51 53 75 75 E: kontakt@radio1.no
W: http://www.radio1.no

RADIO 102
Owner: Radio 102 AS
Editorial: Pb 102, Haugesund 5506.
T: 47 52 720 102 E: post@radio102.no
W: http://www.radio102.no

Radio 3 Bodø
Owner: Radio Tromsø AS
Editorial: Storgata 38, Bodø 8002.
T: 47 75 52 50 00 E: epost@radio3.no
W: http://www.radio3.no

RADIO 5 INDRE ØSTFOLD NÆRRADIO
Owner: Indre Østfold Nærradio BA
Editorial: Storgt.2, Rakkestad 1890.
T: 47 69 22 31 00 E: post@radio5.no
W: http://radio5.no

Radio Ålesund (JRG)
Owner: Skansen Radio AS
Editorial: Lorkenesgaten 1, Ålesund 6002.
T: 47 70 11 10 50 E: post@radioaalesund.no
W: http://www.radioaalesund.no

Radio Alta
Owner: Nordavis AS, Radio Alta
Editorial: Pb 1193, Alta 9504.
T: 47 78 45 67 00 E: studio@radioalta.no
W: http://www.altaposten.no

RADIO ASKØY
Owner: Askøy Nærradiolag
Editorial: Kleppevegen 75, Kleppestø 5300.
T: 47 56 14 60 02 E: radioaskoy@hotmail.com
W: http://www.radioaskoy.no

Radio Atlantic
Owner: JærRadio Gruppen
Editorial: Radio Atlantic AS, Postboks 10,
Sandnes 4301. T: 47 51 97 92 00
E: post@radioatlantic.no
W: http://www.radioatlantic.no

Radio Beiarn
Owner: Radio Beiarn AL
Editorial: Moldjord, Moldjord 8110.
T: 47 75 56 83 30 E: post@radiobeiarn.no
W: http://www.radiobeiarn.no

RADIO BØ
Owner: Radio Bø Ba
Editorial: Pb. 3, I Vesterålen 8469 BØ.
T: 47 76 11 40 50 E: post@radiobo.no
W: http://www.radiobo.no

RADIO DOMEN
Owner: Radio Domen A/L
Editorial: Vardø 9950. T: 47 78 98 71 01
E: post@radiodomen.no
W: http://www.radiodomen.no

RADIO DSF
Owner: Norges Samemisjon Hovedkontoret
Editorial: Finnlandsveien 14, Karasjok 9730.
T: +47 73 87 62 50
E: radio.dsf@samemisjonen.no
W: http://www.samemisjonen.no/media/
radioarbeidet

RADIO E6
Owner: Medieselskapet OPP AS
Editorial: Inge Krokansvei 11, Oppdal 7340.
T: 47 72 42 20 80 E: perroar@opp.no
W: http://www.opp.no/

RADIO EXACT ELVERUM
Owner: Exact Media AS
Editorial: Postboks 454, Hamar 2304.
T: 47 62 51 96 30 E: red@exact24.no
W: http://www.exact24.no

RADIO FANA
Owner: Nesttun Indremisjon
Editorial: postboks 364 Nesttun, Bergen 5853.
T: 47 55 52 75 30
E: radiofana@nesttunbedehus.no
W: http://nesttunbedehus.no

Radio Filadelfia, Drammen
Owner: Pinsemenigheten Filadelfia
Editorial: Tomtegt. 2, Drammen 3015.
T: 47 32 83 15 50 E: post@radiofiladelfia.no
W: http://www.radiofiladelfia.no

Radio Filadelfia, Kristiansand
Owner: Filadelfiamenigheten Kristiansand
Editorial: Dronningensgate 87-91,
Kristiansand 4610. T: 47 38 02 20 00
E: post@filakrs.no W: http://www.filakrs.no

RADIO FITJAR
Owner: Radio Fitjar
Editorial: Fitjar. T: 47 53 49 79 49
E: elinsoerfonn@yahoo.no
W: http://www.fitjar-bedehus.no/radio.htm

RADIO FOLGEFONN
Owner: Radio Folgefonn
Editorial: Røldalsveien 2, Odda 5750.
T: 47 53 64 44 44 E: post@radiofolgefonn.no
W: http://www.radiofolgefonn.no

RADIO GNISTEN
Owner: Norsk Luthersk Misjonssamband
Bergen Krets
Editorial: Sigurdsgate 6, Bergen 5015.
T: 47 55 90 48 00 E: radiognisten@nlm.no
W: http://www.radiognisten.no

RADIO GODT NYTT BERGEN
Owner: Kilden Frievangelisk Menighet Åsane
Editorial: Heiane 8 Nyborg, Bergen, Åsane.
T: 47 55 19 48 75 E: m-klepp@frisurf.no
W: http://godtnyttradio.wordpress.com

RADIO GRENLAND (JRG)
Owner: Grenlandsradioen AS
Editorial: Storg. 70, Porsgrunn 3921.
T: 47 35 93 03 30 E: post@radiogrenland.no
W: http://www.radiogrenland.no

RADIO GRIMSTAD
Owner: Radio Grimstad AS
Editorial: Pb 300, Grimstad 4892.
T: 47 37 04 30 99 E: post@radiogrimstad.no
W: http://www.radiogrimstad.no

RADIO HALLINGDAL
Owner: Radio Hallingdal BA
Editorial: Pb 54, Hol 3575. T: 47 32 08 91 11
E: post@radiohallingdal.no
W: http://www.radiohallingdal.no

RADIO HARSTAD
Owner: Radio Harstad
Editorial: Pb. 251, Harstad 9483.
T: 47 77 06 14 30 E: post@radioharstad.no
W: http://www.radioharstad.no

Radio Haugaland
Owner: A-Media AS
Editorial: Haraldsgaten 110, Haugesund 5501.
T: 47 52 71 72 73 E: post@radioh.no
W: http://www.radiohaugaland.no

RADIO ISLAM AHMADIYYA
Owner: Islams Ahmadiyya-menighet
Editorial: Pb 3002 Elisenberg, Oslo 207.
T: 47 22 44 71 88 E: kontakt@radioislam.no
W: http://www.radioislamahmadiyya.com

RADIO KONGSVINGER
Editorial: Glåmdalen, postboks 757,
Kongsvinger 2204. T: 47 62 88 24 00
E: studio@radiokongsvinger.no
W: http://www.radiokongsvinger.no

RADIO KVINESDAL
Owner: Radio Kvinesdal AL
Editorial: Elvegaten 1A, Kvinesdal 4480.
T: 47 38 35 81 00 E: post@radiokvinesdal.no
W: http://www.radiokvinesdal.no

RADIO L
Owner: Radio L Lillesand Nærradio AS
Editorial: Svåbekk 5, Lillesand 4790.
T: 47 37 27 26 00 E: post@radio-l.no
W: http://www.radio-l.no

RADIO LATIN-AMERIKA
Owner: Radio America Latina
Editorial: Postboks 50 Torshov, Oslo 412.
T: 47 22 11 04 45
E: post@radiolatinamerika.no
W: http://www.radiolatinamerika.com

RADIO LINDESNES
Owner: Lindesnes Nærradio AL
Editorial: Pb. 162, Sør-Audnedal 4524.
T: 47 918 57 550 E: post@radiosor.no
W: http://www.lnr.no

RADIO LOLAND
Owner: Radio Loland AL
Editorial: Loland, Øvrebø 4715.
T: 47 38 13 96 00 E: post@radiololand.no
W: http://www.radiololand.no

RADIO LUSTER
Owner: Radio Luster AL
Editorial: Pb. 44, Gaupne 6868.
T: 47 57 68 14 10 E: post@radio-luster.org
W: http://www.radio-luster.org

RADIO LYNGDAL
Owner: Radio Lyngdal AL
Editorial: Pb. 318, Lyngdal 4577.
T: 47 38 34 31 90 E: post@radio-lyngdal.no
W: http://www.radio-lyngdal.no

RADIO MEHAMN
Owner: Radio Mehamn Al
Editorial: Pb 353, Mehamn 9770.
T: 47 78 49 65 50 E: radiomehamn@nsn.no

RADIO MELBU
Owner: Radio Melbu
Editorial: Pb 193, Melbu 8459.
T: 47 76 15 80 00 E: radio.melbu@trollfjord.no
W: http://www.radiomelbu.no

RADIO METRO
Owner: Svein Larsen
T: 47 21 555 919
E: redaksjonen@radiometro.no
W: http://www.radiometro.no

RADIO MIDT-ØSTERDAL
Owner: Radio Åmot v/Einar Øfstaas
Editorial: Pb. 49, Rena 2451.
T: +47 62 44 15 51
E: einar.ofstaas@gmail.com
W: http://www.radioamot.no

Radio Midt-Telemark
Owner: Radio Midt-telemark As
Editorial: Pb 163, I Telemark 3833 BØ.
T: 47 35 95 43 43 E: radio@rmt.no
W: http://www.rmt.no

RADIO MODUM
Owner: Radio Modum
Editorial: Folkvangvn. 4, Geithus 3360.
T: 47 32 78 31 10 E: post@radiomodum.no
W: http://www.radiomodum.no

RADIO NEW LIFE
Owner: Radio New Life
Editorial: Pb. 9114 Blindheim, Ålesund 6023.
T: 47 70 14 16 60 E: post@newlifeaalesund.no
W: http://www.newlifeaalesund.no/radio.php

RADIO NORDKAPP
Owner: Radio Nordkapp AL
Editorial: Radio Nordkapp AL, Storgata 9,
Honningsvåg 9750. T: 47 78 47 70 90
E: kontakt@radionordkapp.no
W: http://www.radionordkapp.no

RADIO NORD-SALTEN
Owner: Radio Nord-Salten BA
Editorial: Pb. 50, Leinesfjord 8283.
T: 47 75 77 83 11 E: radio.nordsalten@c2i.net
W: http://www.radionordsalten.no

RADIO NORDSJØ (JRG)
Owner: Radio Nordsjø AS
Editorial: Radio Sandnes AS, Postboks 10,
Sandnes 4301. T: 47 51 97 92 00
E: post@radiosandnes.no
W: http://www.radionordsjo.no

RADIO NORGE
Owner: SBS Radio Norge
Editorial: Jernbanetorget 4 A, 3 etg, PB 1102
Sentrum, Oslo 104. T: 47 07270
E: redaksjon@radionorge.com
W: http://www.radionorge.com

RADIO ØKSNES
Owner: Radio Øksnes
Editorial: Pb. 233, Myre 8439.
T: 47 76 13 39 00 E: studio@radiooksnes.no
W: http://www.radiooksnes.no

RADIO ØST
Owner: Radio Øst Media AS
Editorial: Pb 14, Råde 1641.
T: 47 69 29 42 42
E: redaksjonen@radio-ost.no
W: http://www.radio-ost.no

Radio Østlendingen
Owner: P5 Solungen AS
Editorial: Radio Østlendingen Solør, Postboks
C, Flisa 2271. T: 47 46 900 800
E: studio@radio-ostlendingen.no
W: http://www.radio-ostlendingen.no

RADIO P5
Owner: Radio Agder AS
Editorial: Pb 233, Arendal 4801.
T: 47 37 00 55 70 E: p5@radiop5.no
W: http://radio.agderposten.no

RADIO PRIME FREDRIKSTAD
Owner: Mediehuset Fredrikstad Blad AS
Editorial: Postboks 53, Fredrikstad 1601.
T: 47 69390500
E: fredrikstad@radioprime.com
W: http://www.r-f.no

RADIO PRIME MOSS
Owner: Mediehuset Moss Avis AS
Editorial: Radio Moss, Pb. 235, Moss 1501
E: moss@radioprime.com
W: http://www2.radioprime.com/moss

RADIO PRIME SARPSBORG
Owner: Onair Sarpsborg AS
Editorial: Roald Amundsens gate 36,
Sarpsborg 1702. T: 47 69 14 90 90
E: sarpsborg@radioprime.com
W: http://www.radioprime.com/sarpsborg/

RADIO RANDSFJORD
Owner: Radio Randsfjord AS
Editorial: Pb 55, Jaren 2714.
T: 47 61 33 88 33
E: redaksjon@radiorandsfjord.no
W: http://www.radiorandsfjord.no

Radio Rauma
Owner: Radio Rauma AS
Editorial: Pb 141, Åndalsnes 6301.
T: 47 71 22 60 00
E: radiorauma@hotmail.com
W: http://www.radiorauma.no

RADIO RJUKAN
Owner: Radio Rjukan AS
Editorial: Pb 4, Rjukan 3661.
T: 47 35 08 24 20 E: post@radiorjukan.no
W: http://www.radiorjukan.no

RADIO RØST
Owner: Radio Røst
Editorial: Meland, Røst 8064.
T: 47 76 09 64 25
E: tor.andreassen@rost.kommune.no

RADIO SANDEFJORD (JRG)
Owner: Radio Torshammer Sandefjord
Editorial: Andebuveien 74, Sem 3171.
T: 47 333 19 555 E: post@radiosandefjord.no
W: http://www.radiosandefjord.no

RADIO SANDNES
Owner: Radio Sandnes AS
Editorial: Pb 10, Sandnes 4301.
T: 47 51 97 92 00 E: post@radiosandnes.no
W: http://www.radiosandnes.no

Radio Sentrum, Ålesund
Owner: Sunnmøre Indremisjon
Editorial: Pb 171 Sentrum, Ålesund 6001.
T: 47 70 15 41 00 E: post@radiosentrum.no
W: http://www.radiosentrum.no

Radio Sentrum, Kongsvinger
Owner: Radio Sentrum
Editorial: Pb. 579, Kongsvinger 2208.
T: 47 62 88 86 22
E: gjermund@radiosentrum.net
W: http://www.radiosentrum.net

RADIO SKJEBERG
Owner: Skjeberg Folkehøyskole
Editorial: SKJEBERG FOLKEHØYSKOLE,
Oldtidsveien 35, Skjeberg 1747.
T: 47 69 16 81 04
E: skjeberg.fhs@ostfoldfk.no
W: http://www.skjeberg.fhs.no

RADIO SØR
Owner: Stiftelsen Samsending
Editorial: Pb 721, Kristiansand S 4666.
T: 47 38 00 64 04 E: studio@radiosor.no
W: http://www.radiosor.no

RADIO SOTRA
Owner: Radio Sotra AS
Editorial: Pb 128, Straume 5341.
T: 47 56 31 36 60 E: redaksjon@radiosotra.no
W: http://www.radiosotra.no

RADIO STORFJORD
Owner: Radio Storfjord AS
Editorial: Pb 14, Stranda 6201.
T: 47 70 26 26 26
E: redaksjon@radio-storfjord.no
W: http://www.radiostorfjord.no

RADIO TANGO
Owner: Radio Tango Norge AS
Editorial: Radio Tango, Middelthunsgate 25b,
Postboks 48, Oslo 368. T: 47 21 37 90 89
E: strand@radiotango.no
W: http://www.radiotango.no

RADIO TØNSBERG (JRG)
Owner: Radio Tønsberg AS
Editorial: Andebuveien 74, Sem 3170.
T: 47 33 37 85 55 E: post@radiotonsberg.no
W: http://www.radiotonsberg.no

RADIO TOTEN
Owner: Radio Toten BA
T: 47 61 19 48 00 E: post@radiototen.no
W: http://www.radiototen.no

RADIO TROMSØ
Owner: Radio Tromsø
Editorial: Pb. 1090, Tromsø 9621.
T: 47 77 69 00 00 E: studio@radiotromso.no
W: http://www.radiotromso.no

Radio Trøndelag
Editorial: Pb 391, Stjørdal 7501
E: tips@radiotrondelag.no
W: http://www.radiomt.no

Radio Vest-Telemark
Owner: Radio Vest Telemark AS
Editorial: Rauland 3864. T: 47 35 06 29 20
E: studio@radiovt.no W: http://www.radiovt.no

RADIO VOLDA
Owner: Høgskulen i Volda Avd. for mediefag
Editorial: Høgskulen i Volda, Volda 6100.
T: 47 986 59 517
E: studentradioen@gmail.com
W: http://www.voldastudentradio.no

RADIO YTRINGEN
Owner: Radio Ytringen AS
Editorial: Garstad, Rørvik 7900.
T: 47 74 39 24 70
E: kontakt@radioytringen.com
W: http://radioytringen.com

RADIORAKEL
Owner: Radiorakel
Editorial: Pb. 6826 St.Olavspl., Oslo 130.
T: 47 23 32 69 60 E: redaktor@radiorakel.no
W: http://www.radiorakel.no

RadiOs
Owner: RadiOs BA
Editorial: Pb 234, Holtabrekka 2, Os 5202.
T: 47 56 30 14 30 E: redaksjonen@radios.no
W: http://www.radios.no

RadioTrøndelag
Owner: Budstikka Radio Trøndelag BA
Editorial: Pb 391, Stjørdal 7501.
T: 47 74 83 95 95 E: tips@radiomt.no
W: http://www.radiomt.no

ROCK FM
T: 47 984 20 994 E: post@rockfm.no
W: http://www.rockfm.no

SKJERVØY NÆRRADIO
Owner: Skjervøy Nærradio A/L
Editorial: Strandvegen 40, Skjervøy 9180.
T: 47 77 76 02 11 E: post@snradio.no
W: http://radio.btrb.net/wp

STAVANGER STUDENTRADIO
Owner: Studentmediene i Stavanger
Editorial: Univeristetet i Stavanger, Stavanger
4068. T: 47 99746019 E: hugin@smis.no
W: http://smis.no

STUDENTRADIOEN I TRONDHEIM
Owner: Studentradioen i Trondheim
Editorial: Elgsetergt.1, Trondheim 7030.
T: 47 73 51 88 88 E: red@studentradion.no
W: http://www.studentradion.no

STUDENTRADIOEN, BERGEN
Owner: Stiftelsen Studentradioen i Bergen
Editorial: Parkveien 1, Bergen 5007.
T: 47 55 45 51 58 E: kontakt@srib.no
W: http://www.srib.no

STUDENTRADIOEN, KRISTIANSAND
Owner: Samskipnaden i Kristiansand
Editorial: Serviceboks 422, Kristiansand S
4604. T: 47 38 14 20 98
E: post@studentradioen.no
W: http://www.studentradioen.no

VALDRES RADIO
Owner: Valdres Radio AL
Editorial: Pb 223, Fagernes 2901.
T: 47 61 35 99 70 E: post@valdresradio.no
W: http://www.valdresradio.no/frame2.htm

VÅLER NÆRRADIO
Owner: Stiftelsen Våler Nærradio
Editorial: Våler I Solør 2436.
T: 47 62 42 08 20 E: studio@vaalerradio.net
W: http://vaalerradio.net

RADIO NETWORKS

NRK MP3 (KANAL)
Owner: Norsk Rikskringkasting AS avd Tyholt
Editorial: NRK mPetre, Trondheim 7005.
T: 47 73 88 14 00 E: mp3@nrk.no
W: http://www.nrk.no/mp3/

NRK P1; KVELDSMAT
Editorial: Oslo E: kveldsmat@nrk.no

NRK P1; ØNSKEKONSERTEN
Editorial: Ønskekonserten NRK, Trondheim
7005. T: 47 73 88 14 00
E: onskekonserten@nrk.no
W: http://radio.nrk.no/serie/oenskekonserten

NRK P1; P.I.L.S.
Editorial: Bj. Bjørnsonsplass 1, Oslo 340
E: pils@nrk.no
W: http://radio.nrk.no/serie/p-i-l-s

NRK P1; RUNDT MIDNATT
Editorial: Bj. Bjørnsonsplass 1, Oslo 340.
T: 47 23 04 70 00 E: midnatt@nrk.no
W: http://www.nrk.no/programmer/sider/
rundt_midnatt

NRK P1; RYK OG REIS
Editorial: Ryk og reis, NRK P1, Trondheim
7005 E: rykogreis@nrk.no
W: http://www.nrk.no/rykogreis

NRK P1; SALMER TIL ALLE TIDER
Owner: NRK
Editorial: Salmer til alle tider, NRK P1,
Trondheim 7005. T: 47 73 88 18 15
E: salmer@nrk.no
W: http://radio.nrk.no/serie/salmer-til-alle-tider

NRK P2; BLUESASYLET
Editorial: Bj. Bjørnsonsplass 1, Oslo 340.
T: 47 23 04 72 74 E: bluesasylet@nrk.no
W: http://radio.nrk.no/serie/bluesasylet

NRK P2; JAZZKLUBBEN
Editorial: NRK Jazz, RT 32, NRK, Oslo 340.
T: 47 23 04 85 51 E: jazz@nrk.no
W: http://radio.nrk.no/serie/jazzklubben

NRK P2; MUSEUM
Owner: NRK
Editorial: MUSEUM c/O NRK Østfold Pb. 33,
Gamle Fredrikstad 1629. T: 47 69 38 48 00
E: museum@nrk.no
W: http://radio.nrk.no/serie/museum

NRK P2; MUSIKK I BRENNPUNKTET
E: musikkibrennpunktet@nrk.no
W: http://www.nrk.no/programmer/sider/
musikk_i_brennpunktet

NRK P2; MUSIKKMANESJEN
E: musikkmanesjen@nrk.no
W: http://www.nrk.no/programmer/sider/
musikkmanesjen

NRK P2; PÅ SPORET - NYTT PÅ CD
E: pa.sporet@nrk.no
W: http://www.nrk.no/programmer/sider/
paa_sporet

NRK P2; RADIOFRONT
Editorial: Bj. Bjørnsonsplass 1, Oslo 340.
T: 47 23049309 E: radiofront@nrk.no
W: http://radio.nrk.no/serie/radiofront

NRK P2; RADIOSELSKAPET
T: 47 23 04 94 69 E: radioselskapet@nrk.no
W: http://www.nrk.no/programmer/sider/
radioselskapet

NRK P2; RING INN MUSIKKEN
E: ring.inn.musikken@nrk.no
W: http://www.nrk.no/programmer/sider/
ring_inn_musikken

NRK P2; SPRÅKTEIGEN
Editorial: Språkteigen, NRK P2, Trondheim
7005. T: 47 55 27 52 69 E: teigen@nrk.no

NRK P2; Verden På Lørdag
Owner: Norsk Rikskringkasting As Avd Oslo
Editorial: NRK P2, Oslo 340. T: 47 23048000
E: politikk@nrk.no W: http://www.nrk.no

NRK P2; VERDIBØRSEN
Owner: NRK
T: 47 2304401 E: verdiborsen@nrk.no
W: http://www.nrk.no/programmer/sider/
verdiboersen

NRK P3; PYRO
E: pyro@nrk.no
W: http://www.nrk.no/p3/program/pyro

NRK P3; TOPP 40
Editorial: Bj. Bjørnsonsplass, Oslo 340.
T: 47 23047000 E: topp40@nrk.no
W: http://www.nrk.no/programmer/sider/
topp_40

NRK RADIO SUPER
Owner: Norsk Rikskringkasting As Avd Oslo
Editorial: Bjørnstjerne Bjørnsons Plass 1, Oslo
NO-0340. T: 47 23 04 70 00
W: http://nrksuper.no/super/radio/

P4 RADIO - BERGEN
Editorial: Strandgaten 15, Kløverhuset, Bergen
5013. T: 47 55 90 36 03 E: p4@p4.no

P4 RADIO - KRISTIANSAND
Editorial: Tordenskjolds gate 17, Kristiansand
4612. T: 47 38 02 36 46 E: p4@p4.no

P4 RADIO - OSLO
Editorial: Akersgata 73, Oslo 180.
T: +47 61 24 84 44 E: p4@p4.no

P4 RADIO - TROMSØ
Editorial: Pb. 754, Tromsø 9001.
T: 47 77 64 33 09 E: p4@p4.no

P4 RADIO; MISJONEN MED ANTONSEN OG GOLDEN
Editorial: Pb P4, Lillehammer.
T: 47 61 24 84 44 E: misjonen@p4.no

P4 RADIO; OPP OG HOPP MED NISSA OG ELISABETH
Editorial: Serviceboks, Oslo 2626.
T: 47 61 24 84 44 E: oppoghopp@p4.no

P4 RADIO; VI OG VERDEN - INNENRIKS
Editorial: Serviceboks, Lillehammer 2626.
T: 47 61 24 84 44 E: viogverden@p4.no

Radio Nord-Salten
Owner: Radio Nord-Salten BA
Editorial: Myklebostad, Leinesfjord 8283.
T: 47 75 77 83 11 E: post@radionordsalten.no
W: http://www.radionordsalten.no/

RADIO NORGE; NORGESNYHETENE
Owner: SBS Radio Norge
Editorial: Pb. 144, Fredrikstad 1601.
T: 47 815 110 24 E: nyheter@radionorge.com
W: http://www.radionorge.fm

RADIO PRIME HALDEN
Owner: Radio Prime Halden AS
Editorial: Postboks 233, Halden 1752.
T: 47 69 17 50 00 **E:** halden@radioprime.com
W: http://www2.radioprime.com/halden

TELEVISION STATIONS

CANAL+ FILM 1
Owner: C More Entertainment Norge
Editorial: Pb. 80 Bryn, Oslo 611.
T: 47 22 93 93 33 **E:** dialog@canalplus.no
W: http://www.canalplus.no

CANAL+ FILM 2
Owner: C More Entertainment Norge
Editorial: Pb. 80 Bryn, Oslo 611.
T: 47 22 93 93 33 **E:** dialog@canalplus.no
W: http://www.canalplus.no

CANAL+ FILM 3
Owner: C More Entertainment Norge
Editorial: Pb. 80 Bryn, Oslo 611.
T: 47 22 93 93 33 **E:** dialog@canalplus.no
W: http://www.canalplus.no

CANAL+ MIX FILM
Owner: C More Entertainment Norge
Editorial: Pb. 80 Bryn, Oslo 611.
T: 47 22 93 93 33 **E:** dialog@canalplus.no
W: http://www.canalplus.no

CANAL+ SPORT 1
Owner: C More Entertainment Norge
Editorial: Pb. 80 Bryn, Oslo 611.
T: 47 22 65 72 52 **E:** dialog@canalplus.no
W: http://www.canalplus.no

CANAL+ SPORT 2
Owner: C More Entertainment Norge
Editorial: Pb. 80 Bryn, Oslo 611.
T: 47 22 93 93 33 **E:** dialog@canalplus.no
W: http://www.canalplus.no

CANAL+ SPORT HD
Owner: C More Entertainment Norge
Editorial: Pb. 80 Bryn, Oslo 611.
T: 47 22 93 93 33 **E:** dialog@canalplus.no
W: http://www.canalplus.no

EVANGELIESENTERET TV
Owner: Nordisk Kristen Kringkasting
Editorial: Nordregt. 20, Oslo 51.
T: 47 40 64 73 07 **E:** david.filtvedt@ev-s.no
W: http://www.estv.no

FEM
Owner: Fem TV
Editorial: TVNorge, Pb. 11 Sentrum, Oslo NO-0101. **T:** 47 21 02 20 00
E: tvnorge@tvnorge.no **W:** http://www.fem.no/

HER OG NÅ
Owner: Hjemmet Mortensen AS
Editorial: 0441 Oslo, Oslo 441.
T: 47 22585000 **E:** herogna@hm-media.no
W: http://www.hm-media.no

Kristiansand TV, Gimlekollen Mediesenter
Owner: Mediehøgskolen Gimlekollen
Editorial: Serviceboks 410, Kristiansand S 4604. **T:** 47 38 14 50 00
E: post@mediehogskolen.no
W: http://www.mediehogskolen.no

NÆRSYNET
Owner: Høgskulen i Volda avd for Mediefag
Editorial: Pb 500, Volda 6101.
T: 47 70 07 51 89 **E:** nett@hivolda.no
W: http://www.hivolda.no

NRK 1; AMIGO GRANDE
Editorial: Bj. Bjørnsons Plass 1, Oslo 340.
T: 47 815 65 900 **E:** info@nrk.no
W: http://nrksuper.no/super/amigogrande/familie/

NRK 1; GUDSTJENESTEN
Editorial: NRK, Trondheim 7005.
T: 47 73881815 **E:** gudstjenesten@nrk.no
W: http://www.nrk.no/programmer/sider/gudstjenesten/

NRK 1; KAOSKONTROLL
E: kaoskontroll@nrk.no

NRK 1; NORGE I DAG
Editorial: Marienlyst, Oslo 340.
T: 47 23 04 80 00 **E:** 03030@nrk.no

NRK 1; NYTT PÅ NYTT
Editorial: Bj. Bjørnsonsplass 1, Oslo 340.
T: 47 23047000 **E:** nyttpanytt@nrk.no
W: http://www.nrk.no/nyttpanytt

NRK 2; NATTØNSKET
E: natt@nrk.no

NRK 2; URIX
Editorial: NRK URIX, Oslo 340.
T: 47 23048000 **E:** urix@nrk.no
W: http://tv.nrk.no/serie/urix

NRK DAGSNYTT
Editorial: Marienlyst, Oslo 340.
T: 47 23 04 70 00 **E:** 03030@nrk.no
W: http://www.nrk.no/nyheter

NRK SPORT (AVDELING)
Editorial: NRK Sport, FF13, Oslo 340.
T: 47 23 04 95 05 **E:** nettsporten@nrk.no
W: http://www.nrk.no/sport

NRK SUPER
Owner: NRK
Editorial: Bjørnstjerne Bjørnsons Plass 1, Oslo 340. **T:** 47 23 04 70 00 **E:** 03030@nrk.no
W: http://www.nrksuper.no

SPORTN
Owner: Viasat Sport
Editorial: SportN Pb. Viasat Youngstorget, Oslo 28. **T:** 47 22 99 00 33 **E:** info@sportn.tv
W: http://www.sportn.tv

STUDENT-TV / STV
Editorial: Elgsetergt. 1, Trondheim 7030.
T: 47 73 59 80 94 **E:** tips@dusken.no
W: http://www.stv.no

THE VOICE
Owner: The Voice TV Networks Limited
Editorial: Pb. 1102 Sentrum, Oslo 104.
T: 47 22 02 33 00 **E:** redaksjonen@thevoice.no
W: http://www.thevoicetv.no

TK TV
Owner: TVNordvest AS
Editorial: Postboks 8, Storgata 41, Kristiansund N 6501. **T:** 47 71 57 01 00

TV ADRESSA
Owner: TV Trøndelag AS
Editorial: TV Trøndelag AS, Heimdal 7080
E: tvadressa@adresseavisen.no
W: http://www.adressa.no/tv

TV GRORUDDALEN
Owner: Akers Avis Groruddalen AS
Editorial: Pb 100 Grorud, Oslo NO-0905.
T: 47 22 91 88 20
E: redaksjonen@groruddalen.no
W: http://www.groruddalen.no

TV HÅLOGALAND
Owner: Lokal TV sendinger
Editorial: Pb. 85, Harstad 9481.
T: 47 77 01 87 10 **E:** redaksjonen@ht.no
W: http://www.tvhaalogaland.no

TV Haugaland
Owner: TV Haugaland AS
Editorial: Pb 408, Haugesund 5501.
T: 47 40 40 36 40
E: redaksjon@tvhaugaland.no
W: http://www.tvhaugaland.no

TV Østfold
Owner: TV Østfold AS
Editorial: Pb. 48, Sarpsborg 1706.
T: 47 69 00 00 00 **E:** tvostfold@sa.no
W: http://www.tvostfold.no

TV RØROS
Owner: Infonett Røros
Editorial: Postuttak E, Røros 7374.
T: 47 72 41 48 00 **E:** post@tvroros.no
W: http://www.tvroros.no

TV Telemark
Owner: Tv Telemark AS
Editorial: Pb. 2833, Skien 3702.
T: 47 35 58 55 00 **E:** desken@ta.no
W: http://www.ta.no/tvtelemark

TV VISJON NORGE
Editorial: Pb. 4180, Drammen 3005.
T: 47 32 21 13 00 **E:** mail@visjonnorge.com
W: http://www.visjonnorge.com

TV2
Owner: TV2 Gruppen AS
Editorial: Nøstegaten 72, Pb 7222, Bergen 5020. **T:** 47 02255 **E:** pressemelding@tv2.no

W: http://www.tv2.no

TV2 Bliss
Owner: TV2 Gruppen AS
Editorial: Karl Johansgate 14, Oslo 101.
T: 47 915 02255 **E:** nilsketil.andresen@tv2.no

TV2 FILMKANALEN
Owner: TV2 Gruppen AS
Editorial: Pb. 2, Sentrum, Oslo NO-0101
E: info@tv2filmkanalen.no
W: http://pub.tv2.no/TV2/tv2filmkanalen

TV2 NYHETSKANALEN
Owner: TV2 Gruppen AS
Editorial: Pb. 7222, Bergen NO-5020.
T: 47 02255 **E:** pressemelding@tv2.no
W: http://tv2nyhetene.no

TV2 ZEBRA
Owner: TV 2 AS
Editorial: Pb. 7222, Bergen NO-5020.
T: 47 02 25 5 **E:** info@tv2zebra.no
W: http://www.tv2.no/kanalene/zebra/

TV3
Owner: TV 3 AS
Editorial: Pb TV3 Youngstorget, Oslo 28.
T: 47 22 99 00 33 **E:** info@tv3.no
W: http://www.tv3.no

TV8 Follo
Owner: NTV Produksjon Follo AS
Editorial: Idrettsveien 11, Ski 1400.
T: 47 98 28 90 10 **E:** post@tv8norge.no
W: http://www.tvfollo.no

TVNORGE
Owner: TV Norge AS
Editorial: Postboks 4800 Nydalen, Oslo 422.
T: 47 21 02 20 00 **E:** tvnorge@tvnorge.no
W: http://www.tvnorge.no

TVNORGE - OSLO-TV
Owner: TV Norge
Editorial: Postboks 11, Sentrum, Oslo NO-0101. **T:** 47 23 90 90 70
E: tvnorge@tvnorge.no

VIASAT FILM
Owner: Viasat Norge AS
Editorial: Akersgata 73, Oslo 180.
T: 47 22 99 01 30 **E:** info@viasat.no
W: http://www.viasat.no

VIASAT SPORT
Owner: Viasat Sport
Editorial: Akersgaten 73, Oslo 28.
T: 47 22 99 00 33 **E:** sport@viasatsport.no
W: http://www.viasat.no/sport

VIASAT4 ; NYHETER FRA P4
Editorial: Pb. 8864 Youngstorget, Oslo 28.
T: 47 61 24 84 44 **E:** nyhetene@p4.no
W: http://www.viasat4.no

VOICE OF NORWAY
Owner: Voice Of Norway
Editorial: Pb 860, Moss 1504.
T: 47 69 25 15 55
E: voiceofnorway@hotmail.com

OMAN
Tel: 968

Standard Time: GMT +4
Continent: Asia
Capital City: Muscat

NEWSPAPERS & PUBLICATIONS

NEWSPAPERS

Azzamn
Owner: Azzamn Establishment for Press Publication & Advertising
Editorial: PO Box 2080, Ruwi 112.
T: 968 24 704777
E: omanbestpaper@yahoo.com
W: http://www.azamn.com
Freq: Daily; **Circ:** 5000 Rate Card
News Editor: Zaher Al Aabri
Editorial Profile: Azzamn (Azzamn (The Time) is a tabloid-sized Arabic newspaper covering local and international news, business, education, social events, financial markets and sport. It launched in 2007 and is published daily, except Fridays.
Language (s): Arabic
DAILY NEWSPAPER

Futoon
Owner: Omani Establishment for Press, Printing, Publishing & Distribution LLC
Editorial: PO Box 463, Muscat 100.
T: 968 24 491919 **E:** futoon@alwatan.com.om
Freq: Mon; **Circ:** 55000 Publisher's Statement
Editor In Chief: Abeer Al Amoory
Editorial Profile: Futoon is a tabloid-sized, weekly Arabic newspaper covering family and social affairs, including lifestyle, local events, society, culture, sports, entertainment, fashion, women's interests and parenting. It launched in 2006 and is published on Mondays.
Language (s): Arabic
DAILY NEWSPAPER

Gulf Madhyamam - Oman edition
Owner: Gulf Madhyamam FZ LLC
Editorial: Office 11, 1st Floor, Building no. 1541, Near QNB & Central Bank of Oman, Muscat. **T:** 968 24 703045
E: oman@gulfmadhyamam.net
W: http://www.gulfmadhyamam.net
Freq: Daily; **Circ:** 18850 Rate Card
Bureau Chief: Anwar Haqu
Editorial Profile: Gulf Madhyamam is an international Indian newspaper covering national and international news, current affairs, politics, business and sport. The newspaper is aimed at Malayalam speakers in the Gulf and publishes separate editions for the UAE, Saudi Arabia (Riyadh, Jeddah, Damam & Abha), Qatar, Oman, Bahrain and Kuwait. The newspaper was first published in 1999.
Language (s): Malayalam
DAILY NEWSPAPER

Gulf News - Oman office
Owner: Al Nisr Publishing LLC
Editorial: PO Box 2174, Ruwi 112.
T: 968 24 816777
E: gulfnewsoman@yahoo.co.uk
W: http://www.gulfnews.com
Freq: Daily
Bureau Chief: Sunil Vaidya
Editorial Profile: Oman bureau of Dubai-based Gulf News. The bureau covers news, business and sport from the Sultanate for the UAE daily newspaper.
Language (s): English
DAILY NEWSPAPER

Hi
Owner: Muscat Press & Publishing House (SAOC)
Editorial: PO Box 2998, Ruwi 112.
T: 968 24 726666 **E:** editor@hioman.com
Freq: Fri; **Circ:** 54659 Publisher's Statement
Editor In Chief: Faiq Al Zedjali; **Editor:** Hubert Vaz
Editorial Profile: Hi is a tabloid-sized, weekly English newspaper covering news, views, lifestyle features, information, games and puzzles. It is distributed free to Times of Oman subscribers and available free from various outlets and locations in Oman. It launched in 2007 and is published on Fridays.
Language (s): English
DAILY NEWSPAPER

Al Isbou'a
Owner: Apex Press and Publishing
Editorial: PO Box 2616, Ruwi 112, Muscat.
T: 968 24 799388
E: alisboua@apexmedia.co.om
W: http://www.alisboua.co.om
Freq: Sat; **Circ:** 21000 BPA Worldwide
News Editor: Laila Al Hassani; **Publisher:** Saleh Zakwani
Editorial Profile: Al Isbou'a (The Week) is a free weekly, tabloid-sized Arabic newspaper covering local events and personalities, entertainment, sport, cultural and business news. It launched in 2006 and is published on Saturdays.
Language (s): Arabic
DAILY NEWSPAPER

Koooora Wa Bas
Owner: Sabco Group
Editorial: PO Box 3779, Ruwi 112.
T: 968 2442 6900 **E:** editor@onlykooora.com
W: http://www.koooorawabas.com
Freq: Wed; **Circ:** 61000
Editor in Chief: Said Al Baraami; **Editor:** Maan Naddaf
Editorial Profile: Koooora Wa Bas (Only Football) is a free weekly newspaper covering national and international football. It launched in December 2008 and is published on Wednesdays.
Language (s): Arabic
DAILY NEWSPAPER

Al Malaib
Owner: Omani Establishment for Press, Printing, Publishing & Distribution LLC
Editorial: PO Box 463, Muscat 100.
T: 968 24 491919 **E:** editorial@almalaib.com
W: http://www.almalaib.com
Freq: Sat; **Circ:** 50000 Publisher's Statement
Editor In Chief: Sulaiman Al Taei
Editorial Profile: Al Malaib is a tabloid-sized Arabic newspaper covering local and international sport. It launched in 2006 and is published on Saturdays.
Language (s): Arabic
DAILY NEWSPAPER

Muscat Daily
Owner: Apex Press and Publishing
Editorial: PO Box 2616, Ruwi 112, Muscat.
T: 968 24 799388
E: muscatdaily@apexmedia.co.om
W: http://www.muscatdaily.com
Freq: Daily; **Circ:** 30000 Publisher's Statement
Editorial Profile: Muscat Daily is a 28-page, broadsheet-sized English newspaper covering local and international news, politics, business and sport. It launched in October 2009 and is published daily (Sat-Wed).
Language (s): English
DAILY NEWSPAPER

Oman Arabic Daily
Owner: Oman Establishment for Press, Publication and Advertising
Editorial: PO Box 974, Muscat 100.
T: 968 24 649444 **E:** local@omandaily.om
W: http://www.omandaily.om
Freq: Daily; **Circ:** 41721 Publisher's Statement
Editor In Chief: Saif Al Mahruqi
Editorial Profile: Oman Arabic Daily is a newspaper covering news, business, politics, economics, culture and sport. It launched in 1972.
Language (s): Arabic
DAILY NEWSPAPER

Oman Daily Observer
Owner: Oman Establishment for Press, Publication and Advertising
Editorial: PO Box 974, Muscat 100.
T: 968 24 649444
E: editorobserver@gmail.com
W: http://www.omanobserver.om
Freq: Daily; **Circ:** 55000 Publisher's Statement
Editor in Chief: Abdullah Al Shueili
Editorial Profile: Oman Daily Observer is a broadsheet-sized, English daily newspaper covering local, regional and international news, features, sport and business. It launched in 1981.
Language (s): English
DAILY NEWSPAPER

Oman Tribune
Owner: Omani Establishment for Press, Printing, Publishing & Distribution LLC
Editorial: PO Box 463, Muscat 100.
T: 968 24 491919
E: eomantribune@alwatan.com.om
W: http://www.omantribune.com
Freq: Daily; **Circ:** 36030 Rate Card
Editor In Chief: Abdul Hamied Al Taie; **Editor:** Ajith Das; **News Editor:** Ajay Kumar
Editorial Profile: Oman Tribune is a broadsheet-sized, daily English newspaper focusing on national and international news, current affairs, politics, business and sport. It was first published in 2004.
Language (s): English
DAILY NEWSPAPER

Al Roya Newspaper
Owner: Al Roya Press and Publishing
Editorial: PO Box 343, Qurum, Muscat 118.
T: 968 24 479888 **E:** info@alroya.info
W: http://www.alroya.info
Freq: Daily; **Circ:** 25000 Publisher's Statement
News Editor: Souad Al Orimi
Editorial Profile: Al Roya (The Vision) is a business newspaper covering economics, finance, investment, real estate, culture, sports, politics and arts. It launched in 2009 and is published daily, except Fridays.
Language (s): Arabic
DAILY NEWSPAPER

Sabat Ayam
Owner: Muscat Press & Publishing House (SAOC)
Editorial: PO Box 2998, Ruwi 112.
T: 968 24 726601 **E:** 7ayam@shabiba.com
Freq: Fri; **Circ:** 29861 Publisher's Statement
Editor: Shaima Abdulfatah; **News Editor:** Laila Al Amria; **Editor In Chief:** Mariam Al Zedjali
Editorial Profile: Sabat Ayam (7 Days) is a tabloid-sized, weekly Arabic newspaper covering local and international news, politics, sport, business, travel, cinema, entertainment, competitions, fashion, beauty, culture, health and medicine, art, relationships, food, home, parenting, religion and women's interests. Formerly called Al Youm Al Sabe, the newspaper launched in 2007 and is published on Fridays.
Language (s): Arabic
DAILY NEWSPAPER

Al Shabiba
Owner: Muscat Press & Publishing House (SAOC)
Editorial: PO Box 2998, Ruwi 112.
T: 968 24 726666 **E:** editor@shabiba.com
W: http://www.shabiba.com
Freq: Daily; **Circ:** 45000 Publisher's Statement
News Editor: Khalid Al Shami
Editorial Profile: Al Shabiba is an Arabic newspaper covering local and international news, business, sports, culture and society. It launched in 1993 and is published daily, except Fridays.
Language (s): Arabic
DAILY NEWSPAPER

Times of Oman
Owner: Muscat Press & Publishing House (SAOC)
Editorial: PO Box 2998, Ruwi 112.
T: 968 24 726666 **E:** editor@timesofoman.com
W: http://www.timesofoman.com
Freq: Daily; **Circ:** 40000 Publisher's Statement
News Editor: Mehre Alam; **Editor:** Chinmay Chaudhuri
Editorial Profile: Times of Oman is a broadsheet-sized English newspaper covering local and international news, politics, business and sport, as well as a section of news and features from India. It launched in 1975 and is published daily, except Fridays. The newspaper includes Thursday, a magazine supplement, on Thursdays and a monthly magazine, Faces, in the last week of every month.
Language (s): English
DAILY NEWSPAPER

Al Watan
Owner: Omani Establishment for Press, Printing, Publishing & Distribution LLC
Editorial: PO Box 463, Muscat 100.
T: 968 24 491919 **E:** edit@alwatan.com.om
W: http://www.alwatan.com
Freq: Daily; **Circ:** 62000 Publisher's Statement
News Editor: Abdullah Al Jahouri; **Editor In Chief:** Mohammed Al Taie
Editorial Profile: Al Watan is a daily Arabic newspaper covering news, economy, sports and culture. It was first published in 1971, and includes a weekly health supplement - Sehatuna - on Tuesdays.
Language (s): Arabic
DAILY NEWSPAPER

The Week
Owner: Apex Press and Publishing
Editorial: PO Box 2616, Ruwi 112, Muscat.
T: 968 24 799388
E: theweek@apexmedia.co.om
W: http://www.theweek.co.om
Freq: Thu; **Circ:** 51000 BPA Worldwide
Publisher: Saleh Zakwani; **Editor In Chief:** Sameer Zakwani
Editorial Profile: The Week is a free, tabloid-sized weekly newspaper covering local news, entertainment, motoring, sports, leisure, design and food. It launched in 2003 and is published on Thursdays.
Language (s): English
DAILY NEWSPAPER

NEWS SERVICE/SYNDICATE

Oman News Agency
Owner: Ministry of Information, Oman
Editorial: PO Box 3659, Ministry of Information, Ruwi 112. **T:** 968 24 944700
E: onaarabic@hotmail.com
W: http://www.omannews.gov.om
Arabic Editor: Amer Al-Kalbani
Editorial Profile: Official government news agency founded in 1987.
Language (s): Arabic, English
NEWS SERVICE/SYNDICATE

BROADCASTING

RADIO STATIONS

Radio Oman 90.4 FM
Owner: Public Authority for Radio and Television (PART)
Editorial: PO Box 397, Muscat 113.
T: 968 24 943353
E: feedback@oman-radio.gov.om
W: http://www.part.gov.om/english/
Editorial Profile: Radio Oman 90.4 FM is a state-owned radio station broadcasting English news and entertainment programmes for 17-hours per day (6am to 1am). It launched on 15 December 1975 and broadcasts on 90.4 FM (Muscat and Salalah) and 91.3 FM (Thumrait).

Radio Sultanate of Oman
Owner: Public Authority for Radio and Television (PART)
Editorial: PO Box 397, Muscat 100.
T: 968 24 603888
E: feedback-rd@oman-radio.gov.om
W: http://www.part.gov.om
Editorial Profile: Radio Sultanate of Oman broadcasts Arabic news and entertainment programmes for 24-hrs a day. The station launched in 1970 and broadcasts on 98.8 FM and 100.0 FM.

Al Shabab Radio
Owner: Public Authority for Radio and Television (PART)
Editorial: PO Box 397, Muscat 113.
T: 968 24 603888
E: shabab@oman-radio.gov.om
W: http://www.oman-tv.gov.om/shabab
Editorial Profile: Al Shabab Radio is a youth-orientated radio station broadcasting entertainment programmes, as well as live coverage of festivals, national and cultural events. The state-owned station launched in 2003 and broadcasts on 100.0 FM, 98.5 FM and 94.5 FM.

TELEVISION STATIONS

Majan TV
Owner: Halley Studios
Editorial: PO Box 1825, Al Azeeba 130.
T: 968 24 596464
E: majan-tv@omantel.net.om
W: http://www.majan-tv.com
Editorial Profile: Majan TV is a television station broadcasting entertainment programmes and drama serials. The channel launched in 2009 and broadcasts free-to-air on satellite.

Oman TV
Owner: Public Authority for Radio and Television (PART)
Editorial: PO Box 600, Muscat 113.
T: 968 24 603222 **E:** omantvnews@gmail.com
W: http://www.part.gov.om
Editorial Profile: Oman TV is a state-owned television station broadcasting films, sport, entertainment, local events and news. The channel launched in 1974 and broadcasts terrestrially in Oman and free-to-air on satellite.

Oman TV2
Owner: Public Authority for Radio and Television (PART)
Editorial: PO Box 600, Muscat 113.
T: 968 24 693115 **E:** presstv@oman-tv.gov.om
W: http://www.part.gov.om
Editorial Profile: Oman TV2 is a state-owned television channel primarily focusing on sports programmes, but also broadcasts drama series and movies in English and Arabic. The channel launched in 2006 and broadcasts terrestrially in Oman and free-to-air on satellite.

Qatar TV - Oman bureau
Owner: Qatar Media Corporation
Editorial: PO Box 108, Al-Khuwair 133.
T: 968 24 483962 **E:** zoom-art@hotmail.com
W: http://www.qmc.qa
Editorial Profile: Qatar TV is a state-owned television channel broadcasting entertainment and news programmes. The Oman bureau covers news from the Sultanate for the Doha-based channel.

PAKISTAN — Tel: 92
Standard Time: GMT +5
Continent: Asia
Capital City: Islamabad

NEWSPAPERS & PUBLICATIONS

NEWSPAPERS

Aaj
Editorial: Sikandar Pura, G.T. Road, Peshawar 25000. **T:** 92 912570501
E: dailyaaj@tes.comsath.net.pk
W: http://dailyaaj.com.pk
Freq: Daily; **Circ:** 50001 Not Audited
Editor in Chief: Abdul Wahid Yousafi
Editorial Profile: Daily newspaper published in Urdu. Covers general news and current events
Language (s): Urdu
DAILY NEWSPAPER

Aghaz
Editorial: 11-Japan Mansion, Preedy Street, Saddar, Karachi 74200. **T:** 92 212721688
E: bilal_aghaz@yahoo.com
Freq: Daily; **Circ:** 64001 Not Audited
Editor in Chief: Muhammad Farooqui
Editorial Profile: Daily newspaper published in Urdu. Covers general news and current events
Language (s): Urdu
DAILY NEWSPAPER

Business Recorder
Editorial: Recorder House, 531 Business Recorder Road, Karachi 74550.
T: 92 212250071 **E:** ed.khi@br-mail.com
W: http://www.brecorder.com
Freq: Daily; **Circ:** 115251 Not Audited
Publisher: Asif Zuberi; **Editor:** Wamiq Zuberi
Editorial Profile: Daily newspaper published in English. Covers business and financial news.
Language (s): English
DAILY NEWSPAPER

Daily Awam
Editorial: Al-Rehman Building, I.I. Chundrigar Road, Karachi 74200. **T:** 92 2132635638
E: legharinazir@hotmail.com
Freq: Daily; **Circ:** 257002 Not Audited
Editor: Nazir Leghari
Editorial Profile: Daily newspaper published in Urdu. Covers general news and current events
Language (s): Urdu
DAILY NEWSPAPER

Daily Jang
Editorial: Jang Press Building, I.I. Chundrigar Road, Karachi 74200. **T:** 92 212637111
E: editorjang@jang.com.pk
W: http://www.jang.com.pk
Freq: Daily; **Circ:** 800001 Not Audited
Editorial Profile: Covers news topics.
Language (s): Urdu
DAILY NEWSPAPER

Daily Kawish
Owner: Kawish Group of Publications (The)
Editorial: B/2 Civil Lines, Hyderabad 71000.
T: 92 222780026 **E:** kawish12@gmail.com
W: http://www.dailykawish.com
Freq: Daily; **Circ:** 80001 Not Audited
Editor: Ali Kazi
Editorial Profile: Daily newspaper published in Urdu. Covers general news and current events
Language (s): Sindhi
DAILY NEWSPAPER

Daily Messenger
Editorial: Office No. 1, 2nd Floor, Abdullah Chamber, Dr. Billimoria Street, Off I.I Chundrigar Road, Karachi
E: messengerdaily@yahoo.com
Freq: Daily
Editor: Taqi Alvi
Editorial Profile: Covers national and international news.
Language (s): English
DAILY NEWSPAPER

Daily Nawa-i-Waqt
Owner: Nipco House
Editorial: Nipco House, 4 Shaarey Fatima Jinnah, Lahore 54000. **T:** 92 42 6367580
E: editor@nawaiwaqt.com.pk
W: http://www.nawaiwaqt.com.pk
Freq: Daily; **Circ:** 350002 Not Audited
Editor in Chief: Majeed Nizami
Editorial Profile: Provides national and international news.
Language (s): Urdu
DAILY NEWSPAPER

Daily News
Editorial: I.I. Chundrigar Road, Karachi 74200.
T: 92 212637111 **E:** editorjang@jang.com.pk
W: http://www.jang-group.com
Freq: Daily; **Circ:** 80002 Not Audited
Editor in Chief: Mir Shakil-ur-Rahman
Editorial Profile: It is a daily newspaper printed in English covering Local Regional National and International news.
Language (s): English, Urdu
DAILY NEWSPAPER

Daily Wahdat
T: 92 912214154 **E:** editorwahdat@gmail.com
W: http://dailywahdat.com.pk
Freq: Daily; **Circ:** 60002 Not Audited
Editor: Syed Shah
Editorial Profile: Daily newspaper printed in Pashto and founded in 1976. Appears to cover general news and current events
Language (s): Pashto (Eastern), Pashto (Western)
DAILY NEWSPAPER

Dawn
Owner: Dawn Group of Newspapers
Editorial: Haroon House, Dr. Zia Uddin Ahmed Road, Karachi 74200. **T:** 92 21 111-444-7777
E: editor@dawn.com
W: http://www.dawn.com
Freq: Daily; **Circ:** 140002 Not Audited
Editor: Jahanzaib Haque; **Editor:** Abbas Nasier
Editorial Profile: Daily newspapers published in English. Covers general news and current events
Language (s): English, Urdu
DAILY NEWSPAPER

Express
Editorial: Korangi Creak Road, Century Publication Pvt. Ltd., Plot No. 5, Expressway Off Korangi Road, Karachi 75500.
T: 92 215800051
W: http://www.express.com.pk
Freq: Daily; **Circ:** 145003 Not Audited
Editor: Abbas Ather
Editorial Profile: Daily newspaper published in Urdu. Covers general news and current events
Language (s): Urdu
DAILY NEWSPAPER

The Express Tribune
Editorial: 5 Expressway, Off Korangi Road, Karachi 75500. **T:** 92 21 111397737
W: http://tribune.com.pk
Freq: Daily
Editor: Sadia Ahmed; **Editor:** Vaqas Asghar
Editorial Profile: Partnering with the International Herald Tribune, launched as the first internationally affiliated newspaper of Pakistan. Covers national news, politics, the economy, foreign policy, investment, sports and culture.
Language (s): English
DAILY NEWSPAPER

Ibrat Hyderabad
Editorial: Ibrat Building Gadi Khata, P.O. Box 91, Hyderabad 73000. **T:** 92 22 2781574
E: ibrat@yahoo.com
W: http://www.dailyibrat.com
Freq: Daily; **Circ:** 50003 Not Audited
Editor in Chief: Kazi Asad Abid
Editorial Profile: Covers current events, news and lifestyle
Language (s): Sindhi
DAILY NEWSPAPER

Juraat
Editorial: Juraat House, Aril Jiyeja Street, II Chundrigar Road, Karachi 74000.
T: 92 212637641-44 **E:** juraat@juraat.com
W: http://www.juraat.com
Freq: Daily; **Circ:** 72003 Not Audited
Editor in Chief: Mukhtar Aaqil
Editorial Profile: Daily newspaper published in Urdu. Appears to cover general news and current events
Language (s): Urdu
DAILY NEWSPAPER

Khadim-e-Watan
Editorial: B/2 Civil Lines, Hyderabad 71000.
T: 92 222780026
W: http://www.dailykawish.com
Freq: Daily; **Circ:** 50002 Not Audited
Editorial Profile: Daily newspaper published in Sindhi. Covers general news and current events
Language (s): Sindhi
DAILY NEWSPAPER

The Nation
Owner: Nawa-e-Waqt Group
Editorial: Nipco House, 4 Shaarey Fatima, Jinnah, Lahore 54000. **T:** 92 42 6367580
E: editor@nation.com.pk
W: http://www.nation.com.pk
Freq: Daily; **Circ:** 85002 Not Audited
Editor in Chief: Majeed Nizami
Editorial Profile: Daily newspaper published in English. Covers city, national, sports, foreign and commerce news.
Language (s): English
DAILY NEWSPAPER

The News International
Editorial: Al Rehman Building, I.I Chundrigar Road, Karachi 74200. **T:** 92 212637111
W: http://www.thenews.com.pk
Freq: Daily; **Circ:** 140002 Not Audited
Editor: Talat Aslam; **Editor in Chief:** Mir Shakil-ur-Rahman
Editorial Profile: Daily newspaper published In English Covering All Types Of News.
Language (s): English
DAILY NEWSPAPER

Pakistan Observer
Editorial: Ali Akbar House, Markaz G-8, Islambad 143001. **T:** 92 512852027 8
E: observer@pakobserver.net
W: http://www.pakobserver.net
Freq: Daily; **Circ:** 53002 Not Audited
Editor in Chief: Zahid Malik
Editorial Profile: Daily newspaper published in English. Covers general news and current events
Language (s): English
DAILY NEWSPAPER

Qaumi Akhbar
Editorial: 14 Ramzan Chambers, Dr. Billimoria Street, Off Chundrigar Road, Karachi 74200.
T: 92 21 111778899 **E:** qaumi@hotmail.com
Freq: Daily; **Circ:** 90003 Not Audited
Editor in Chief: Ilyas Shakir
Editorial Profile: Newspaper published in Urdu. Covers general news and current events
Language (s): Urdu
DAILY NEWSPAPER

NEWS SERVICE/SYNDICATE

Agence France-Presse - Islamabad Bureau
Owner: Agence France-Presse
Editorial: H.9A, Street 24, F-7/2, Islamabad.
T: 92 51 111 237 475 **E:** Islamabad@afp.com
W: http://www.afp.com
Bureau Chief: Emmanuel Duparcq
Editorial Profile: Islamabad bureau of international news and picture agency covering general news and current affairs.
Language (s): English
NEWS SERVICE/SYNDICATE

Associated Press
Editorial: House 6A, Street 25 F82, Islamabad.
T: 92 51 2828-397
Stringer: Rasool Dawar; **Stringer:** Riaz Khan;
Bureau Chief: Rebecca Santana
NEWS SERVICE/SYNDICATE

Associated Press of Pakistan (APP)
Editorial: 18, Mauve Area G- 7/1, Islamabad.
T: 92 512203064 **E:** news@app.com.pk
W: http://www.app.com.pk
Freq: Daily
Bureau Chief: Farooq Ahmad
Editorial Profile: Covers the latest international and domestic news.
Language (s): Urdu
NEWS SERVICE/SYNDICATE

Bloomberg News
Editorial: Islamabad
E: nmangi1@bloomberg.net
Bureau Chief: Naween Mangi
Language (s): English
NEWS SERVICE/SYNDICATE

Online International News Network
Editorial: House 69 Bhittai Road, F-714, Islamabad 143001. **T:** 92 51 8435137
E: online@dsl.net.pk
W: http://www.onlinenews.com.pk
Freq: Daily
Editor in Chief: Mohsin Baig; **Editor:** Sohail Iqbal; **Editor:** Zia Islam; **Editor:** Aneela ud Din
Editorial Profile: Online news service covering international, political, financial, political and sports news
Language (s): English
NEWS SERVICE/SYNDICATE

Pak Tribune
Editorial: 30 Kurshid Alam Rood, Westridge 1, Rawalpindi 46000. **T:** 92 515475907
E: editor@paktribune.com
W: http://www.paktribune.com
Editor: Riaz Jafri
Editorial Profile: General news and current events in Pakistan and the surrounding region
Language (s): Urdu
NEWS SERVICE/SYNDICATE

Pakistan Press International (PPI)
Editorial: Press Centre, 1st Floor Shahrah-e-Kamal Attaturk, Karachi 75400.
T: 92 21 2630562
E: pressrelease@ppinewsagency.com
W: http://www.ppinewsagency.com
Editor: Nasir Aijaz; **Editor in Chief:** Farooq Moin
Editorial Profile: Covers general news and current events in Pakistan and the surrounding region
Language (s): Urdu
NEWS SERVICE/SYNDICATE

South Asian News Agency (SANA)
Editorial: 1st Floor Chinar Chamber, Street No. 48, G-6/ 1-1, Islamabad. **T:** 92 51 2870134
E: info@sananews.com.pk
W: http://www.sananews.net
Editor in Chief: Shakeel Ahmed Turabi
Editorial Profile: Covers news topics.
Language (s): English
NEWS SERVICE/SYNDICATE

BROADCASTING

RADIO STATIONS

Radio Pakistan (Pakistan Broadcasting Corporation)
Editorial: National Broadcasting House, G-5 Constitutional Avenue, Islamabad 44000.
T: 92 519208772 **E:** cnoreporting@gmail.com
W: http://www.radio.gov.pk
Editorial Profile: Covers topics for a Pakistan audience.

TELEVISION NETWORKS

ARY OneWorld
Editorial: ARY Communication, 6th Floor Madaina City Mall, Abdullah Haroon Road, Karachi. **T:** 92 215657315
W: http://www.aryoneworld.net
Editorial Profile: Current affair programs with prominent Pakistani journalists are the strength of ARY One World. Its program mix covers all the genres of news & infotainment, and most of its programs are presented by top international anchors such as P.J. Mir, Javed Malik, Ayaz Amir, Faeza Dawood, Kashif Abaasi and Asima Shirazi. ARY One World is one of the first dedicated international news channels in Pakistan. It has exclusive correspondents in almost all major capitals around the globe, a network of over 500 reporters and correspondents in Pakistan, and major international networks as exclusive partners for the exchange of news, information and other technical facilities. The channel also maintains a rich archive library with exclusive footage.

Pakistan Television Corporation (PTV)
Editorial: Federal TV Complex, Constitution Avenue, Islamabad 44000. **T:** 92 519208651
E: ptvgq@hotmail.com
W: http://www.ptv.com.pk
Editorial Profile: National television stations gov't controlled. broadcast news, sports, entertainments, health & lifestyle news

CABLE

JAAG TV
Editorial: CNBC Pakistan Karachi Head Office, Techno City Corporate Towers 13/F, Karachi 74000. **T:** 92 21111262275 **E:** info@jaagtv.com
W: http://jaag.tv
Editorial Profile: Formerly known as CNBC Pakistan, covers frontline news and current affairs in Pakistan with hourly bulletins and various programming features.

PALAU — Tel: 680

Standard Time: GMT +9

BROADCASTING

TELEVISION STATIONS

PNCC Digital TV
Editorial: PO Box 39, Koror 96940.
T: 680 587 35 15 **E:** pncc@palaunet.com
W: http://www.palaunet.com
Editorial Profile: Offers over 46 channels of entertainment, movies, news, music, educational, and children's programming in our Basic Service, including two local channels.

PALESTINE — Tel: 970

Standard Time: GMT +2
Continent: Asia
Capital City: Quds

NEWSPAPERS & PUBLICATIONS

NEWSPAPERS

Al Ayyam
Owner: Al Ayyam Printing & Publishing
Editorial: PO Box 1987, Ramallah.
T: 970 2 298 7341 **E:** news@al-ayyam.com
W: http://www.al-ayyam.ps
Freq: Daily; **Circ:** 18000 Publisher's Statement
News Editor: Abed-Rahman Abu-Shamalah; **Editor In Chief:** Akram Haniah
Editorial Profile: Al Ayyam (The Days) is a daily Arabic newspaper covering national and international news, current affairs, politics and business. It was first published in 1995.
Language (s): Arabic
DAILY NEWSPAPER

Al Hayat Al-Jadedah
Owner: Al Hayat Al-Jadeda Company
Editorial: PO Box 1882, Noor Street, Ramallah. **T:** 970 2 240 7252
E: alhayat@p-ol.com
W: http://www.alhayat-j.com
Freq: Daily; **Circ:** 10623 Publisher's Statement
News Editor: Wael Barghouthi
Editorial Profile: Al Hayat Al-Jadedah (The New Life) is a daily Arabic newspaper covering news, current affairs, politics and sport. It includes weekly business supplement Hayat Wa Souq on Sundays, and was first published in 1995.
Language (s): Arabic
DAILY NEWSPAPER

Kul Al Arab
Owner: Kul Al Arab
Editorial: PO Box 430, Al Namsawi Street, Nazareth. **T:** 970 4 655 8000 **E:** kul@alarab.net
W: http://www.alarab.net
Freq: Fri; **Circ:** 40000 Publisher's Statement
Editor In Chief: Samih Al Kassem; **Editor:** Saeed Hassanein
Editorial Profile: Kul Al Arab is a weekly Arabic newspaper covering national, regional and international news, current affairs, politics, entertainment and events in the Arab world. It launched in 1987 and is published on Fridays.
Language (s): Arabic
DAILY NEWSPAPER

Al Manar
Owner: International Media Company
Editorial: PO Box 20772, Sheikh Jarrah, Jerusalem. **T:** 970 2 532 3749
E: info@manar.com
W: http://www.manar.com
Freq: Mon; **Circ:** 11500 Publisher's Statement
Editor-in-Chief: Ismaiel Ajweh
Editorial Profile: Al Manar is a weekly Arabic newspaper featuring current affairs, culture and finance. It launched in 1991 and is published on Mondays.
Language (s): Arabic
DAILY NEWSPAPER

Al Quds
Owner: Al Quds
Editorial: PO Box 19788, East Jerusalem.
T: 972 2 627 2663 **E:** contact@alquds.com
W: http://www.alquds.com
Freq: Daily; **Circ:** 70000 Publisher's Statement

News Editor: Mohammad Abu Libdeh;
Publisher: Walid Abu Zalaf; **News Editor:** Amjad Omari
Editorial Profile: Al Quds is a daily Arabic newspaper covering news, politics, current affairs, business and sport. It was first published in 1951.
Language (s): Arabic
DAILY NEWSPAPER

NEWS SERVICE/SYNDICATE

Agence France-Presse - Gaza Bureau
Owner: Agence France-Presse
Editorial: PO Box 1133, Gaza.
T: 970 8 282 1533
E: sakher.abueloun@afp.com
W: http://www.afp.com
Bureau Chief: Sakher Abu El Oun
Editorial Profile: Gaza bureau of the AFP news agency - covers the Palestinian territories.
Language (s): Arabic, English, French
NEWS SERVICE/SYNDICATE

APTN Gaza
Owner: Associated Press
Editorial: 11th floor, Al Jalaa Tower, Gaza.
T: 970 8 284 1583 **E:** w.shurafa@yahoo.com
W: http://www.aptn.com
Editorial Profile: Associated Press Television News (APTN) is the international television arm of the Associated Press - APTN's operations include a main news service, specialised broadcast services, customised coverage for the Middle East, a productions division, weekly and daily entertainment news and an extensive video archive library.
Language (s): Arabic, English
NEWS SERVICE/SYNDICATE

Associated Press - Ramallah Bureau
Owner: Associated Press
Editorial: El-Bireh Commercial Tower, Ramallah, West Bank. **T:** 970 2 240 8255
E: jhassan@ap.org **W:** http://www.ap.org
News Producer: Jalal Al-Bwaitel
Editorial Profile: Ramallah Bureau of the Associated Press and APTN.
Language (s): English
NEWS SERVICE/SYNDICATE

Palestine News & Info Agency
Owner: Palestine News & Info Agency
Editorial: Al Masayef, Ramallah.
T: 970 2 298 7767 **E:** edit@wafa.ps
W: http://www.wafa.ps
Editor: Fadel Atwana; **Editor:** Atlal Darwich;
Editor: Bilal Ghaith
Editorial Profile: Official government news agency.
Language (s): Arabic, English, Hebrew
NEWS SERVICE/SYNDICATE

Palestine News Network
Owner: Palestine News Network
Editorial: Al Mahd Street, Bethlehem.
T: 970 2 276 6068 **E:** news@pnn.ps
W: http://www.pnn.ps
Editor: Alaa Hamad; **Editor in Chief:** Monjed Jadou
Editorial Profile: Palestine News Network is a news agency supplying news bulletins to over 13 local Palestinian radio stations in the West Bank and Gaza. Also provides a 24-hour updated news ticker to 10 Palestinian TV stations.
Language (s): Arabic, English, French, German, Spanish
NEWS SERVICE/SYNDICATE

Palestinian Media and Communications Company
Owner: Palestinian Media and Communications Company
Editorial: PO Box 909, Al Shikh Tower, Ramallah. **T:** 970 2 298 4858
E: booking@pmcc.ps **W:** http://alfalstiniah.tv
Editorial Profile: Palestinian Media and Communications Company provides news correspondence and production services to television stations throughout the region using the latest satellite technology and equipment. Located in Ramallah in the West Bank, with studios in East Jerusalem and Gaza City.
Language (s): Arabic, English
NEWS SERVICE/SYNDICATE

Reuters - Ramallah Bureau
Owner: Thomson Reuters
Editorial: PO Box 1079, Ramallah.
T: 970 2 295 0430
E: jerusalem.newsroom@thomsonreuters.com
W: http://www.reuters.com
Bureau Chief: Christian Palmer

Editorial Profile: Ramallah bureau of international news wire service.
Language (s): Arabic, English
NEWS SERVICE/SYNDICATE

PANAMA   Tel: 507

Standard Time: GMT -5
Continent: The Americas
Capital City: Panama City

NEWSPAPERS & PUBLICATIONS

NEWSPAPERS

Crítica (Panamá)
Owner: Editora Panamá América SA
Editorial: Av. Ricardo J. Alfaro, al lado de la USMA, Apdo. 0834-02787, Panama.
T: 507 2307777 7647
E: redaccion.critica@epasa.com
W: http://www.critica.com.pa
Freq: Daily; **Circ:** 65000 Not Audited
Editorial Profile: Newspaper containing national and international news, business, sports and events.
Language (s): Spanish
DAILY NEWSPAPER

Día a Día
Owner: Editora Panamá América SA
Editorial: Av. Ricardo J. Alfaro, Apdo. 0834-02787, Panama. **T:** 507 230 7777
E: editor.diaadia@epasa.com
W: http://www.diaadia.com.pa
Freq: Daily
Editor in Chief: Joyce Baloyes; **Editor:** Diamar Diaz; **Editor:** Didier Gil; **Editor:** Elizabeth Muñoz de Lao; **Editor:** Evidelia Velazquez
Editorial Profile: Newspaper covering national and international news, politics, the economy, society, sport and culture.
Language (s): Spanish
DAILY NEWSPAPER

Diario Panamá América
Owner: Editora Panamá América SA
Editorial: Av. Ricardo J. Alfaro, al lado de la USMA, Apdo. B-4, zona 9-A, Panama.
T: 507 2307777 7612
E: redaccion@epasa.com
W: http://www.epasa.com/
Freq: Daily; **Circ:** 30000 Not Audited
Editor: Julio Aizprua; **Editor:** Flor Cogley;
Editor: Rosa Guizado; **Editor:** Guido Rodríguez
Editorial Profile: Newspaper covering national and international news and current events; includes finance, business, politics, sport and entertainment.
Language (s): Spanish
DAILY NEWSPAPER

La Estrella de Panamá
Owner: La Estrella de Panamá
Editorial: Calle Alejandro A. Duque y Av. Frangipany, Apdo. 0815-00507, zona 4, Panama. **T:** 507 2040964
E: online@laestrella.com.pa
W: http://www.laestrella.com.pa
Freq: Daily; **Circ:** 21080 Not Audited
Editor: Carlos Castillo
Editorial Profile: Newspaper covering national and international news, politics, economics, finance, business, culture and sport.
Language (s): Spanish
DAILY NEWSPAPER

Panamá América
Owner: Grupo Epasa
Editorial: Ave. Ricardo J. Alfaro, Apartado B4, Zona 9A, Panama. **T:** 507 230-7777
E: info@epasa.com
W: http://www.panamaamerica.com.pa
Freq: Daily
Editor: Alberto Pinto
Editorial Profile: Established in 1925 and provides information and news on politics, economics, national and international articles.
Language (s): Spanish
DAILY NEWSPAPER

La Prensa (Panamá)
Owner: Corporación La Prensa
Editorial: Av. 12 de octubre, Apdo. 0819-05620, El Dorado, Hato Pintado Panama.
T: 507 222-1222 **E:** redaccion@prensa.com
W: http://www.prensa.com
Freq: Daily; **Circ:** 44000 Not Audited
Editor in Chief: Juan Luis Batista; **Editor:** Elizabeth Garrido
Editorial Profile: Newspaper covering national and international news, politics, lifestyle, food, cinema and sport.

Language (s): Spanish
DAILY NEWSPAPER

El Siglo
Owner: Geo-Media SA
Editorial: Avenida Frangipany y Calle Alejandro, detras del Hospital Santa Fe, Duque, Edificio de la Antigua Estrella, Panama.
T: 507 2040000 **E:** redaccion@elsiglo.com
W: http://www.elsiglo.com
Freq: Daily; **Circ:** 35000 Not Audited
Editor in Chief: Magaly Montilla
Editorial Profile: Regional newspaper covering national, international and regional news and current affairs; includes politics, the economy, sport and society.
Language (s): Spanish
DAILY NEWSPAPER

NEWS SERVICE/SYNDICATE

Associated Press
T: 1 507 226-4736
Bureau Chief: Joshua Goodman
NEWS SERVICE/SYNDICATE

BROADCASTING

RADIO STATIONS

Omega Stereo
Editorial: Calle G, El Cangrejo, Edificio Don Isaac Planta Baja, Apartado 6-4632, El Dorado.
T: 507 2692237
E: omegaste@omegastereo.com
W: http://www.omegastereo.com
Editorial Profile: Presents daily news, analysis, and music including pop and ballads targeting an audience between 18 and 50 years old.

Radio Hogar
Editorial: Via Cinquentanario No 9 y Av. José Matilde Pérez, Apdo. 0834-00102, Panama.
T: 507 2700142 **E:** radiohogar@cableonda.net
W: http://www.radiohogar.org
Editorial Profile: Provides Catholic news, cultural and educational programs. Includes two daily news broadcasts in the morning and in the afternoon. Plays classic music.

Radio KW Continente
Editorial: Primer Alto, Via Argentina, Edificio Carillón Mezanine, Apdo. 0816-07920, Panama. **T:** 507 2645711
E: noticias@kwcontinente.com
W: http://www.kwcontinente.com
Editorial Profile: Informative radio broadcasts news and opinion shows.

Radio Mia
Editorial: Calle 50 y Vía Brasil, Edificio Plaza 50 Piso 6, Apdo. 5117, Zona 5, Panama.
T: 507 2630946 **E:** radiomia1@cableonda.net
W: http://www.radiomiapanama.com/
Editorial Profile: Provides daily news, sport programs, interviews, radial magazine, and music. Radio Mia 96.7 FM.

Radio Veraguas
Editorial: Calle 9na Norte Santiago Canto del Llano Vía Panamericana, Santiago de Veraguas, Santiago. **T:** 507 9587060
E: rveraguas@pa.inter.net
Editorial Profile: The radio station has two frequencies AM and FM, the AM transmits cultural, religious, and educational programs, the FM transmits news, interviews, and music.

RPC Radio
Owner: MEDCOM Corporation
Editorial: Av. 12 de Octubre, Edificio MEDCOM, 1° piso, Apdo. 082700116, Zona 8, Panama. **T:** 507 3906700
E: rcpradio@medcom.com.pa
W: http://www.rpcradio.com
Editorial Profile: Provides daily news, interviews, sports. Plays national and international music.

TELEVISION NETWORKS

Canal 4 RPC
Editorial: Corporacion Medcom SA, Av. 12 de Octubre, Apdo. 0827-00116, Panama.
T: 507 390 6700
E: kchalmers@medcom.com.pa
W: http://www.rpctv.com/
Editorial Profile: National TV station broadcasting entertainment, sports, and news for Panama.

FETV Canal 5
Editorial: Vía Ricardo J. Alfaro, detrás del Edificio de Postgrado de la USMA, Apdo. 0819-02874, El Dorado Panamá.
T: 507 230 8000 **E:** comentarios@fetv.org
W: http://www.fetv.org
Editorial Profile: Educational and cultural TV channel focusing on the values and traditions of Panama citizens.

Telemetro Canal 13
Editorial: Corporacion Medcom Panamá SA, Av. 12 de Octubre, Apdo. 0827-00116, Panama. **T:** 507 390 6700
W: http://www.telemetro.com
Editorial Profile: National TV broadcasting news, comedies, and movies for Panama. Telemetro targets adults and Tele 7 targets children and youths. Tele 7 is a childrens network that provides children programming from 7am until 8pm. After 8 pm Tele 7 broadcasts programs for mothers.

TVN - Canal 2
Editorial: Vía Simón Bolívar, Transísmica, Panama. **T:** 507 (507)2793711
E: tvn@tvn-2.com **W:** http://www.tvn-2.com
Editorial Profile: Presents daily news and broadcasts cultural and entertainment programs including soap operas.

PAPUA NEW GUINEA
Tel: 675

Standard Time: GMT +10
Continent: Oceania
Capital City: Port Moresby (New Guinea)

NEWSPAPERS & PUBLICATIONS

NEWSPAPERS

The National
Owner: Pacific Star Limited
Editorial: PO Box 6817, Boroko, Papua New Guinea **E:** national@thenational.com.pg
W: http://thenational.com.pg
Freq: Daily
News Editor: Christine Pakakota
Editorial Profile: National English daily, published out of Port Moresby, providing analysis of national and international news.
Language (s): English
DAILY NEWSPAPER

Papua New Guinea Post-Courier
Owner: South Pacific Post Pty Ltdf
Editorial: PO Box 85, Port Moresby, Papua New Guiinea. **T:** 675 30 91 000
E: postcourier@spp.com.pg
W: http://postcourier.com.pg
Freq: Daily; **Circ:** 33500 Publisher's Statement
Editor: Blaise Nangoi; **Editor:** Alexander Rheeney
Editorial Profile: Newspaper in Papua New Guinea covering national news.
Language (s): English
DAILY NEWSPAPER

Wantok Niuspepa
Owner: Word Publishing Co Ltd
Editorial: Head Office, PO Box 1982, Papua New Guinea **E:** nchoi@wantok.com.pg
Freq: Weekly; **Circ:** 12000 Not Audited
Editor: Neville Choi
Editorial Profile: The Wantok Niuspepa is printed by Pacific Star Limited, owners of the National Newspaper.
Language (s): English
NEWSPAPER

BROADCASTING

RADIO NETWORKS

FM100 Rural Radio
Editorial: 2nd Floor, Telikom Technology Haus, Waigani Drive, 4 mile, 121, Port Moresby, Papua New Guinea. **T:** 675 300 4300
E: info@fm100.com.pg
W: http://www.fm100.com.pg
Editorial Profile: FM100 broadcasts 24 hours a day starting from 5am till 1am on manual broadcasting mode which means the on-air announcer is behind the console. From 12am to 6am commercials are played in between songs.

NBC National Radio of Papua New Guinea

Editorial: PO Box 1359, Boroko, Papua New Guinea. **T:** 675 32 55 233 **E:** info@nbc.com.pg
W: http://nbc.com.pg
Editorial Profile: National Broadcasting Corporation (NBC) is established and funded by the Parliament of PNG to provide a national radio service for Papua New Guinea.

PNG FM Ltd

Owner: PNG FM Ltd
Editorial: PO Box 774, Port Moresby, Papua New Guinea. **T:** 675 320 1996
E: pngfmnews@naufm.com.pg
W: http://pngvillage.com.pg
Editorial Profile: PNG government-owned with two AM networks: Karai (national) and Kundu (provincial) and one FM commercial station Kalang.

TELEVISION STATIONS

EMTV

Owner: Fiji Television
Editorial: PO Box 443, Boroko, Papua New Guinea. **T:** 675 325 7322
W: http://emtv.com.pg

PARAGUAY
Tel: 595

Standard Time: GMT -4
Continent: The Americas
Capital City: Asunción

NEWSPAPERS & PUBLICATIONS

NEWSPAPERS

ABC Color

Owner: Editorial AZETA SA
Editorial: Yegros 745, Aptdo. 1421, Asuncion.
T: 595 21 4151000 **E:** azeta@abc.com.py
W: http://www.abc.com.py
Freq: Daily; **Circ:** 46000 Not Audited
Editor in Chief: Juan Luis Gauto
Editorial Profile: Newspaper providing national and international news, includes politics, finance, economics and law.
Language (s): Spanish
DAILY NEWSPAPER

Crónica

Owner: Grafica y Editorial Intersudamericana S.A.
Editorial: Av. Zavala Cué entre 1ª y 2ª, Zona Sur, Fernando De La Mora (central).
T: 595 21 512520 **E:** digital@cronica.com.py
W: http://www.cronica.com.py
Freq: Daily; **Circ:** 30000 Not Audited
Editor: Neri Insfran; **Editor in Chief:** Nestor Izaurralde
Editorial Profile: National newspaper.
Language (s): Spanish
DAILY NEWSPAPER

Diario Popular

Owner: Grupo Multimedia SA
Editorial: Avenida Mariscal López 2948, Aptdo. 1805, Asuncion. **T:** 595 21 603400
E: popular@mm.com.py
W: http://www.diariopopular.com.py
Freq: Daily; **Circ:** 52000 Not Audited
Editor: Adolfo Jiménez; **Editor in Chief:** Carlos Sosa
Editorial Profile: Newspaper covering national and international news, includes politics, sport and culture.
Language (s): Spanish
DAILY NEWSPAPER

Diario Vanguardia

Owner: Editora del Este S.A.
Editorial: Avenida San Blás Km. 8 Acaray, Ciudad Del Este (alto Paraná).
T: 595 61 575530
E: diariovanguardia@diariovanguardia.com.py
W: http://www.diariovanguardia.com.py
Freq: Daily; **Circ:** 110000 Not Audited
Editor in Chief: Thomas Beck
Editorial Profile: Regional newspaper focusing on business, economics, politics, education, tourism and union news from the Departamento de Alto Paraná, Canindeyu, and Itapua. Includes financial statistics and interviews.
Language (s): Spanish
DAILY NEWSPAPER

La Nación

Owner: Grafica y Editorial Intersudamericana S.A.

Editorial: Av Zavala Cué entre 1ª y 2ª, Zona Sur, Fernando De La Mora (central).
T: 595 21 512520
E: redaccion@lanacion.com.py
W: http://www.lanacion.com.py
Freq: Daily; **Circ:** 23580 Not Audited
Editor in Chief: Ricardo Nestor Inzaurralde
Editorial Profile: Newspaper covering national and international news, politics, economics and sport.
Language (s): Spanish
DAILY NEWSPAPER

Ultima Hora

Owner: Editorial El País SA
Editorial: Benjamín Constant 658, Asuncion.
T: 595 21 496261
E: ultimahora@uhora.com.py
W: http://www.ultimahora.com.py
Freq: Daily; **Circ:** 14000 Not Audited
Editor in Chief: Miguel Ortíz; **Editor:** Alejandro Peralta
Editorial Profile: National newspaper.
Language (s): Spanish
DAILY NEWSPAPER

BROADCASTING

RADIO STATIONS

Radio Nacional del Paraguay

Editorial: Cuarta 241 entre Yegros e Iturde, Asuncion. **T:** 595 21 390374
W: http://www.rnpy.com
Editorial Profile: Transmits in two frequencies. The FM plays every 30 minutes traditional Paraguayan music convined with international and latin music. The AM, ZPU Radio Nacional del Paraguay plays traditional Paraguayan music.

RADIO NETWORKS

Radio UNO 650 AM

Owner: Multimedia S.A.
Editorial: Grupo Multimedia SA, Avenida Mariscal López 2948, Asuncion.
T: 595 21 603400 **E:** prensa650@mm.com.py
W: http://www.radiouno.com.py
Editorial Profile: Provides news, sports, interviews, chat, health shows, and life programs. Multimedia S.A. owns also Radio Popular 103.1 FM and Diario Popular that covers news from Paraguay and Argentina.

TELEVISION NETWORKS

SNT - Sistema Nacional de Televisión

Editorial: Television Cerro Cora SA., Avda. Carlos A. López 572, 1135, Asuncion.
T: 595 21 421744 **E:** info@snt.com.py
W: http://www.snt.com.py
Editorial Profile: Broadcasts daily news, entertainment, including films and documentaries.

PERU
Tel: 51

Standard Time: GMT -5
Continent: The Americas
Capital City: Lima

NEWSPAPERS & PUBLICATIONS

NEWSPAPERS

Aja

Owner: Empresa Periodistica Nacional SA
Editorial: Jr Jorge Salazar Aráoz 171, Urb. Santa Catalina, La Victoria, Lima.
T: 51 1 690 8080 **W:** http://www.aja.com.pe
Freq: Daily
Editorial Profile: Newspaper covering news and current-affairs, politics, culture, events and sports.
Language (s): Spanish
DAILY NEWSPAPER

El Comercio (Perú)

Owner: Grupo El Comercio SA
Editorial: Jr. Miró Quesada #300, Lima 1.
T: 51 1 311-6500
E: editorweb@comercio.com.pe
W: http://www.elcomercioperu.com.pe
Freq: Daily; **Circ:** 185000 Not Audited
Editor in Chief: Hugo Guerra
Editorial Profile: Newspaper covering national and international news, politics and business.

Correo

Owner: Empresa Periodistica Nacional SA
Editorial: Jr Jorge Salazar Aráoz 171, Urb. Santa Catalina, La Victoria, Lima.
T: 51 1 690 8080
E: diariocorreo@epensa.com.pe
W: http://www.correoperu.com.pe
Freq: Daily
Editor: Sileña Cisneros; **Editor in Chief:** Marlene Huamanlazo; **Editor:** Luis Ojeda
Editorial Profile: Newspaper containing national and international news and current-affairs, politics, the economy, culture and sports.
Language (s): Spanish
DAILY NEWSPAPER

Diario Correo

Owner: EPENSA
Editorial: Jorge Salazar Araoz 171, Santa Catalina La Victoria, Lima. **T:** 51 1 631-1111
E: diariocorreo@epensa.com.pe
W: http://www.correoperu.com.pe
Freq: Daily; **Circ:** 280000 Not Audited
Editor: Luis Ojeda
Editorial Profile: Newspaper focusing on politics, economics, culture, sport, national and international news.
Language (s): Spanish
DAILY NEWSPAPER

El Expreso

Owner: Editora Sindesa SA
Editorial: Giron Antonio de Elizalde 753, Altura quadra 8, Av. Argentina, Lima.
T: 51 1 612 4000
E: israel.fernandez@expreso.com.pe
W: http://www.expreso.com.pe
Freq: Daily; **Circ:** 60000 Not Audited
Editor: Jose Giles; **Editor in Chief:** Ivan Pisua
Editorial Profile: Newspaper focusing on national and international news, sport, politics and culture.
Language (s): Spanish
DAILY NEWSPAPER

Extra

Owner: Editora Sindesa SA
Editorial: Giron Antonio de Elizalde 753, Altura quadra 8, Av. Argentina, Lima.
T: 51 1 612 4000
Freq: Daily
Editor in Chief: Richard Romero
Editorial Profile: National newspaper covering news and current-affairs.
Language (s): Spanish
DAILY NEWSPAPER

Gestión

Owner: Grupo El Comercio S.A
Editorial: Giron Antonio Miró Quesada 247, piso 8, Lima. **T:** 51 1 311-6500
E: gestion2@diariogestion.com.pe
W: http://www.gestion.pe
Freq: Daily; **Circ:** 25000 Not Audited
Editor: Oscar González Estrada; **Editor:** Julio Lira Segura
Editorial Profile: National newspaper focusing on business, economics and finance.
Language (s): Spanish
DAILY NEWSPAPER

El Men

Owner: Montecristo Editores SAC
Editorial: Jirón Yungay 820-840, Magdalena del Mar, Lima. **T:** 51 13366465
E: elmen@elmen.com.pe
W: http://www.elmen.com.pe
Freq: Daily
Editor in Chief: Pascual Fretel Gutierrez; **Editor:** Danilo Riveros
Editorial Profile: Newspaper covering news and current-affairs.
Language (s): Spanish
DAILY NEWSPAPER

Ojo

Owner: Familia Agois Banchero
Editorial: Jorge Salazar Araoz 171, Urbanización Santa Catalina la Victoria, altura de la cuadra 11 de Nicolas de Ariola, Lima.
T: 51 1 690 8080 **E:** optativos@epensa.com.pe
W: http://www.ojo.com.pe
Freq: Daily; **Circ:** 90000 Not Audited
Editor in Chief: Carlos Basurto; **Editor:** Luis Angeles Laynes
Editorial Profile: Newspaper covering national news, culture, entertainment and sport.
Language (s): Spanish
DAILY NEWSPAPER

El Peruano

Owner: Editora Perú

Editorial: Av. Alfonso Ugarte 873, Lima.
T: 51 1 315 0400
W: http://www.elperuano.com.pe
Freq: Daily; **Circ:** 21000 Not Audited
Editor in Chief: Cesar Chaman
Editorial Profile: Newspaper covering national and international news, politics, sport and culture.
Language (s): Spanish
DAILY NEWSPAPER

El Popular

Owner: Grupo la Republica SA
Editorial: Jirón Camaná 320, Cercado de Lima, Lima. **T:** 51 17116010
W: http://www.elpopular.com.pe
Freq: Daily
Editor: Dennis Alvaro; **News Editor:** Jorge Paucar
Editorial Profile: Newspaper covering news and current-affairs, politics, sports and culture.
Language (s): Spanish
DAILY NEWSPAPER

La Razon

Owner: Montecristo Editores SAC
Editorial: Jirón Yungay 820-840, Magdalena del Mar, Lima. **T:** 51 (511)336-6465
E: diariolarazon@gmail.com
W: http://www.larazon.com.pe
Freq: Daily
Editorial Profile: Newspaper covering news and current-affairs and politics.
Language (s): Spanish
DAILY NEWSPAPER

La República

Owner: Grupo la Republica SA
Editorial: Jirón Camaná 320, Cercado de Lima, Lima. **T:** 51 17116000
E: director@larepublica.com.pe
W: http://www.larepublica.com.pe
Freq: Daily; **Circ:** 125000 Not Audited
Editor: Percy Ruiz
Editorial Profile: Newspaper covering national and international news, politics, economics, finance, business, culture and sport.
Language (s): Spanish
DAILY NEWSPAPER

Todo Sport

Owner: Montecristo Editores SAC
Editorial: Jirón Yungay 820-840, Magdalena del Mar, Lima. **T:** 51 13366465
E: prensats@todosport.com.pe
W: http://www.todosport.com.pe
Freq: Daily; **Circ:** 18000 Not Audited
Editor: Walter Arana
Editorial Profile: Newspaper focusing on sports; includes previews, reports and results.
Language (s): Spanish
DAILY NEWSPAPER

NEWS SERVICE/SYNDICATE

Andina

Editorial: Av. Alfonso Ugarte 873, Lima.
T: 51 1 315 0400
E: andina@editoraperu.com.pe
W: http://www.andina.com.pe
Editor: Guido Canchari; **Editor in Chief:** Rodolfo Espinal
Editorial Profile: Covers news related to politics, economy, culture and entertainment.
Language (s): Arabic
NEWS SERVICE/SYNDICATE

Bloomberg News

Editorial: Avenida Republica de Panama 3545, Piso 11 Oficina 1101, Lima 27.
T: 51 16146806
NEWS SERVICE/SYNDICATE

Dow Jones Newswires

Editorial: Los Rosales 460 3rd Floor, San Isidro, Lima. **T:** 51 1 221-7050
E: peru@dowjones.com
NEWS SERVICE/SYNDICATE

Reuters

Editorial: Calle los Sauces, #374, Oficinas 901-902, Lima. **T:** 51 12212111
E: lima.newsroom@thomsonreuters.com
NEWS SERVICE/SYNDICATE

BROADCASTING

RADIO NETWORKS

Cadena Peruana de Noticias

Editorial: Avenida Aviación 5150, Segundo Piso, Ovalo Higuereta Surco, Lima.

T: 51 14119300 **E:** prensacpn@gestion.com.pe
W: http://www.cpn.com.pe/
Editorial Profile: Radio station focusing on national and international news, politics, finance and economics.

Radio RPP Noticias
Owner: Grupo RPP
Editorial: Grupo RPP SA, Av. Paseo de la República 3866, San Isidro, Lima.
T: 51 1 215 0200 **E:** editor@gruporpp.com.pe
W: http://www.rpp.com.pe
Editorial Profile: Radio Nacional provides 24 hours of news. The programming includes political, cultural, economic, health and entertainment news.

PHILIPPINES   Tel: 63

Standard Time: GMT +8
Continent: Asia
Capital City: Manila

NEWSPAPERS & PUBLICATIONS

NEWSPAPERS

Abante
Owner: Monica Publishing Corporation
Editorial: #167 Liberty Bldg. Roberto S. Oca St, Port Area, Manila 1002. **T:** 63 2 52 73 355
E: abante@abante-tonite.com
W: http://www.abante.com.ph
Freq: Daily
Editorial Profile: VISION AND MISSION "To be the leading and trend setting tabloid in the newspaper industry, ran by highly and technologically creative and innovative Filipino workers, committed and dedicated to serve it's readers by providing credible and accurate news reports and stories that will satisfy the newspaper buying public."
Language (s): English, Filipino
DAILY NEWSPAPER

Abante Tonite
Owner: Monica Publishing Corporation
Editorial: #167 Liberty Building, Roberto S. Oca St, Port Area, Manila. **T:** 63 25276722
E: tonite@abante-tonite.com
W: http://www.abante-tonite.com
Freq: Daily
Editorial Profile: Covers news topics.
Language (s): English, Filipino
DAILY NEWSPAPER

Bulgar
Owner: MVRS Publication Inc
Editorial: 538 Quezon Avenue, Quezon City, Manila 1100. **T:** 63 327490091
W: http://www.bulgar.com.ph
Freq: Daily; **Circ:** 350000 Not Audited
Editorial Profile: Tagalog newspaper published in the Philippines.
Language (s): Tagalog
DAILY NEWSPAPER

BusinessMirror
Owner: Philippine Business Daily Mirror Publishing, Inc.
Editorial: 2113 Chino Roces Avenue corner De La Rosa Street, 2nd Floor, Dominga Building (Annex), Makati City. **T:** 63 28178407
E: news@businessmirror.com.ph
W: http://www.businessmirror.com.ph
Freq: Daily; **Circ:** 62000 Not Audited
Publisher: T. Anthony Cabangon; **Editor:** Lorenzo Lomibao; **Editor in Chief:** Lourdes Molina-Fernandez; **Editor:** Dionisio Pelayo; **Editor:** Gerard Ramos; **Editor:** Lyn Resurreccion
Editorial Profile: Provides readers with a broader look at Filipino business, economy, industries, companies and markets.
Language (s): English
DAILY NEWSPAPER

BusinessWorld
Owner: BusinessWorld Publishing
Editorial: 95 Balete Drive Extension, New Manila, Quezon City 1112. **T:** 63 253599117
E: editor@bworld.com.ph
W: http://www.bworld.com.ph
Freq: Daily; **Circ:** 65000 Not Audited
Editor: Fransisco P. Baltazar; **Editor:** Cris Paraso; **Editor:** Ronnie Romero
Editorial Profile: Covers business and news.
Language (s): English
DAILY NEWSPAPER

BusinessWorld Online
T: 632 535 9901 405
W: http://www.bworldonline.com
Editor: Judy Gulane
Editorial Profile: Philippines' leading business newspaper covering business news. The business paper comes out Monday through Friday, with a Saturday exclusive online edition, with national and foreign circulation totalling 54,000.
DAILY NEWSPAPER

Ilonggo Star
Owner: Sun Star Publishing Inc.
Editorial: 3rd floor, Sun.Star Building, P. del Rosario cor. P. Cui Sts., Cebu City 6000.
T: 63 3322546100 **E:** sunnex@sunstar.com.ph
W: http://www.sunstar.com.ph/iloilo
Freq: Weekly; **Circ:** 60000 Not Audited
Editor in Chief: Nini Cabaero
Editorial Profile: Covers international and national news.
Language (s): English
DAILY NEWSPAPER

Inquirer Libre
Owner: Philippine Daily Inquirer Inc.
Editorial: Chino Roches Avenue, Yague Cor. Mascardo Sts, Makati City 1220.
T: 63 28978808 **E:** libre_pdi@inquirer.com.ph
W: http://www.libre.com.ph
Freq: Daily; **Circ:** 100000 Not Audited
Editor: Armin Adina; **Editor in Chief:** Chito Dela Vega; **Editor:** Dennis Eroa; **Editor:** Romel Lalata
Editorial Profile: Covers international and local news.
Language (s): Tagalog
DAILY NEWSPAPER

Malaya Business Insight
Owner: People's Independent Media Inc.
Editorial: Leyland Bldg, 20th cor. Railroad St, Port Area, Manila. **T:** 63 23393329
E: malayanews@yahoo.com
W: http://www.malaya.com.ph
Freq: Daily; **Circ:** 60000 Not Audited
Editor: Minnie Advincula; **Editor:** Jimmy Cantor; **Publisher:** Amado Macasaep; **Editor in Chief:** Joy Delos Reyes; **Editor:** Gie Triallana; **Editor:** Winnie Valaquez
Editorial Profile: Malaya means "free" in the Filipino language.Founded in 1981 as a Tagalog newspaper by Jose Burgos Jr., Malaya shifted to English when its sister publication, We Forum, was closed down by the Marcos government in 1983 after it came out with a story exposing the fake medals of former strongman. During the politically Marcos troubled years of 1983 to 1986, Malaya was at the forefront of giving the public the truth.The end of the Marcos regime in February 1986 brought changes to the ownership of Malaya. Burgos sold the newspaper to veteran journalist Amado "Jake" P. Macasaet, who was then Malaya's business editor. Throughout all these changes, Malaya has adhered its mission of giving the public the truth fairly and responsibly. The commitment continues.
Language (s): English
DAILY NEWSPAPER

Manila Bulletin
Owner: Manila Bulletin Publishing Corp.
Editorial: Manila Bulletin, Muralla Corner Recoletos Street, Intramuros, Manila 1002.
T: 63 2527812135
E: manila.bulletin@gmail.com
W: http://www.mb.com.ph
Freq: Daily; **Circ:** 260000 Not Audited
Editor: Loreto Cabañes; **Editor:** Pinky Colmenares; **Editor:** Isabel De Leon; **Editor in Chief:** Cris Icban; **Editor:** Cris J. Icban Jr.; **Editor:** Ding Marcelo; **Editor:** Crispina Martinez-Belen; **Publisher:** Hermogenes Pobre; **Publisher:** Napoleon G. Rama
Editorial Profile: Covers news.
Language (s): English
DAILY NEWSPAPER

Manila Shimbun
Owner: Bisuku Company Ltd.
Editorial: Manila Shimbun Building, 1037 Teresa Street, Rizal Village, Makati City.
T: 63 28973731
W: http://www.manila-shimbun.com
Freq: Daily
Editor in Chief: Yoshihiko Sakai
Editorial Profile: Covers international and national news.
Language (s): Japanese
DAILY NEWSPAPER

Manila Standard Today
Owner: Kamahalan Publishing Corporation
Editorial: Leyland Building, Railroad corner 21st Street, Port Area, Manila. **T:** 63 25278351

W: http://www.manilastandardtoday.com
Freq: Daily; **Circ:** 150000 Not Audited
Editor: Ray Enano; **Editor:** Leo Estonito; **Editor:** Riera Mallari; **Editor:** Isah Red
Editorial Profile: Covers national and international news.
Language (s): English
DAILY NEWSPAPER

The Manila Times
Owner: The Manila Times Publishing Corp.
Editorial: 371 A. Bonifacio Drive, Port Area, Manila 1018. **T:** 63 2524566467
E: newsdesk@manilatimes.net
W: http://www.manilatimes.net
Freq: Daily
Editor in Chief: Rene Bas; **Editor:** Conrad M. Carino; **Editor:** Romulo Marinas; **Editor:** Arnold Tenorio
Editorial Profile: Covers local, international news and lifestyle.
Language (s): English, Tagalog
DAILY NEWSPAPER

Mindanao Times
Owner: Mindanao Publishers Inc.
Editorial: UMBN Building - Ponciano Reyes St., Mindanao, Davao City 8000.
T: 63 822250309
E: editorial.mtimes@gmail.com
W: http://www.mindanaotimes.com.ph
Freq: Daily
Editor in Chief: Amalia Cabusao; **Editor:** Jon Develos; **Editor:** Christopher Fabian
Editorial Profile: Covers international and national news.
Language (s): English
DAILY NEWSPAPER

Mount Samat Weekly Forum
Owner: Mount Samat Weekly Forum
Editorial: Capitol Drive, G/F Santiago Building, San Jose, Balanga, Bataan 2100.
T: 63 472375988
Freq: Weekly
Editor: Maricel Galura
Language (s): Tagalog
DAILY NEWSPAPER

The Negros Chronicle
Owner: The Negros Chronicle
Editorial: 106 EJ Blanco Road Piapi, Dumaguete City 6200. **T:** 63 352254760
E: elmarjay@yahoo.com
W: http://www.negroschronicle.com
Freq: Weekly
Editor: Ely P. Dejaresco
Editorial Profile: Covers international and national news.
Language (s): English
DAILY NEWSPAPER

News Express
Owner: Malones Printing Press
Editorial: E. Lopez Street, Jaro, Door 31, Lopez Arcade, Iloilo City 5000.
T: 63 335088725
Freq: 2 Times/Week
Publisher: Teresita Malones; **Editor:** Jun Tillaslor
Language (s): English
DAILY NEWSPAPER

Palawan Sun
Owner: Palawan Sun Publishing Corp.
Editorial: 2/Fl Lustre Building, Malver Street, Puerto Princesa City, Palawan 5300.
T: 63 484334249 **E:** palawan.sun@gmail.com
W: http://palawansun.wordpress.com
Freq: Weekly
Editor in Chief: Redempto Anda
Editorial Profile: Covers international and national news.
Language (s): English
DAILY NEWSPAPER

Panay News
Owner: Panay News Inc.
Editorial: 3rd Floor, La Salette Building, Valeria Street, Iloilo City 5000. **T:** 63 333212749
E: editorial.panaynews@gmail.com
W: http://www.panaynewsphilippines.com
Freq: Daily
Editor in Chief: Danny Fajardo; **Editor:** David Sinay
Editorial Profile: The Valeria address is for the Marketing office, while the Editorial department is located at Mandurriao.
Language (s): English
DAILY NEWSPAPER

People's Taliba
Owner: Journal Group
Editorial: 6th Floor Universal-Re Building, 106 Paseo de Roxas corner Perea & Gallardo Sts, Legaspi Village, Makati City. **T:** 63 2892305258
E: peoples@journal.com.ph

W: http://www.journal.com.ph
Freq: Daily; **Circ:** 230000 Not Audited
Editor in Chief: Jun Abad; **Editor:** Anna Federigan; **Editor:** Marita Pascual Nuque; **Editor in Chief:** Augusto B. Villanueva
Editorial Profile: Covers lifestyle and society.
Language (s): Tagalog
DAILY NEWSPAPER

People's Tonight
Owner: Journal Group
Editorial: 6th Floor Universal-Re Building, 106 Paseo de Roxas Corner Perea & Gallardo Sts, Legaspi Village, Makati City. **T:** 63 2892305258
E: tonight@journal.com.ph
W: http://www.journal.com.ph
Freq: Daily
Editor: Eduardo Andaya; **Editor:** Ian Farrinas; **Editor:** Marita Pascual Nuque; **Editor:** Jun Pisco; **Editor in Chief:** Augusto B. Villanueva
Editorial Profile: Covers lifestyle and entertainment news.
Language (s): English
DAILY NEWSPAPER

Philippine Daily Enquirer
T: 63 2 8978808 **E:** feedback@inquirer.com.ph
W: http://www.inquirer.com.ph
Editorial Profile: The Philippine Daily Inquirer is the country's most widely read and circulated newspaper.
DAILY NEWSPAPER

Philippine Daily Inquirer
Owner: Inquirer Company
Editorial: Yague Cor. Mascardo Sts., Pasong Tamo, Makati City 1220. **T:** 63 28978808
E: daydesk@inquirer.com.ph
W: http://www.inquirer.com.ph
Freq: Daily
Editor: Jorge V. Aruta; **Editor:** Pergentino Bandayrel; **Editor:** Artemio Engracia; **Editor:** Chelo Formoso; **Editor:** Luverne Gueco; **Editor in Chief:** Letty Jimenez-Magsanoc; **Editor:** Raul Marcelo; **Editor:** Teddyvic Melendres; **Editor:** Thelma San Juan; **Editor:** Emmie Velarde
Editorial Profile: Covers International and national news.
Language (s): English
DAILY NEWSPAPER

The Philippine STAR
Owner: Star Group of Publications
Editorial: 13 Corner Railroad St., Port Area, Manila 1016. **T:** 63 2 5277901
E: feedback@philstar.net.ph
W: http://www.philstar.com
Freq: Daily
Editor: Isaac Belmonte
Editorial Profile: Offers news, entertainment and details on related topics.
Language (s): English
DAILY NEWSPAPER

Pilipino Star Ngayon
Owner: Star Group Publications
Editorial: 202 Roberto Oca Street, Port Area, Manila 1018. **T:** 63 2527790115 155
E: psngayon@philstar.net.ph
W: http://www.philstar.com
Freq: Daily
Editor: Jo Abelgas; **Editor:** Salve Asis; **Editor:** Mario Basco; **Editor:** Jojo Cruz; **Editor:** Rowena Del Prado; **Editor:** Ronnie Halos; **Editor in Chief:** Alfonso Pedroche; **Editor:** Dina Villena
Editorial Profile: Covers news.
Language (s): Tagalog
DAILY NEWSPAPER

Quirino Quest
Owner: City Star
Editorial: Malvar Highway, Santiago City, Isabela 3311. **T:** 63 786827449
Freq: Weekly
Editor in Chief: Melvin Gascon
Language (s): English
DAILY NEWSPAPER

Sun.Star Bacolod
Owner: Sun Star Publishing Inc.
Editorial: M13Annex Building, Lopues, Lacson Street, Bacolod City. **T:** 63 347081776
E: sunnex@sunstar.com.ph
W: http://www.sunstar.com.ph/bacolod
Freq: Daily
Editor in Chief: Cheryl Cruz
Editorial Profile: Covers social issues, local and society news.
Language (s): English
DAILY NEWSPAPER

Sun.Star Baguio
Owner: Sun Star Publishing Inc.
Editorial: 110 Wong Buildin, Magsaysay Avenue, Baguio 2600. **T:** 63 744438362

E: sunnex@sunstar.com.ph
W: http://www.sunstar.com.ph/baguio/
Freq: Daily
Editor in Chief: Renato Samuel Bautista
Editorial Profile: Covers local news.
Language (s): English, Tagalog
DAILY NEWSPAPER

Sun.Star Davao
Owner: Sun.Star Publishing Inc.
Editorial: R. Castillo Street, Agdao, Davao City
8000. **T:** 63 822351009
E: sunnex@sunstar.com.ph
W: http://www.sunstar.com.ph/davao/index.
html
Freq: Daily
Editor in Chief: Stella Estremera
Editorial Profile: Covers national and
international news.
Language (s): English
DAILY NEWSPAPER

Sun.Star Gensan
Owner: Sun Star Publishing Inc.
Editorial: Safi 2 Building, Mansanitas Street,
Corner Magsaysay Avenue, General Santos
9500. **T:** 63 822351009
E: sunnex@sunstar.com.ph
W: http://www.sunstar.com.ph/davao/index.
html
Freq: Daily
Editor in Chief: Stella Estremera
Editorial Profile: Covers international and
national news.
Language (s): English
DAILY NEWSPAPER

Sun.Star Pampanga
Owner: Sun Star Publishing Inc.
Editorial: Tire City Compound, McArthur
Highway, Dolores, San Fernando.
T: 63 458600517 **E:** sunnex@sunstar.com.ph
W: http://www.sunstar.com.ph/pampanga
Freq: Daily
Editor in Chief: Jun Malik
Editorial Profile: Covers national and local
news.
Language (s): English
DAILY NEWSPAPER

Sun.Star People's Courier
Owner: Sun Star Publishing Inc.
Editorial: 157 D. Silang Street, Batangas City
4200. **T:** 63 437238416
E: sunnex@sunstar.com.ph
Freq: 2 Times/Week
Editor in Chief: Vicky Florendo
Language (s): English, Tagalog
DAILY NEWSPAPER

Sun.Star People's Courier - Oriental
Mindoro Edition
Owner: Sun Star Publishing Inc.
Editorial: 157 D Silang Street, Batangas City
4200. **T:** 63 437238416
E: sunnex@sunstar.com.ph
Freq: Weekly
Editor in Chief: Vicky Florendo
Language (s): Tagalog
DAILY NEWSPAPER

Sunday Punch
Owner: Sunday Punch, Inc.
Editorial: 2nd Floor, Tuque Tiongson Building,
A.B. Fernandez Avenue, Dagupan City,
Pangasinan. **T:** 63 755155601
E: punch.sunday@gmail.com
W: http://www.dagupan.com/punch
Freq: Weekly
Editor: Ermin Garcia; **Editor in Chief:** Ermin F
Garcia Jr
Editorial Profile: Covers international and local
news.
Language (s): English
DAILY NEWSPAPER

Super Balita
Owner: Sun.Star Publishing Inc.
Editorial: R. Castillo Street, Agdao, Davao City
8000. **T:** 63 822351009
E: sunnex@sunstar.com.ph
W: http://www.sunstar.com.ph/
superbalitadavao
Freq: Daily
Editorial Profile: Covers news of international
and regional.
Language (s): Tagalog
DAILY NEWSPAPER

Il Tempo
Owner: Manila Bulletin Publishing Corp.
Editorial: Manila Bulletin Building, Muralla
corner Recoletos Street, Intramuros, Manila
1002. **T:** 63 2527812135
E: tempo@mb.com.ph
W: http://www.tempo.com.ph

Freq: Daily
Editor in Chief: Cris Icban; **Publisher:**
Hermogenes Pobre; **Editor:** Nestor Quartero;
Editor: Robert Roque
Editorial Profile: Covers sports and
entertainment news.
Language (s): English
DAILY NEWSPAPER

United Daily News
Owner: United Daily News Group
Editorial: 812 - 818 Benavides Street,
Binondo, Metro Manila 1006. **T:** 63 22447171
W: http://www.udn.com
Freq: Daily
Editor: Virginia Cheng; **Editor in Chief:** Thua
Kee
Editorial Profile: Covers international and
national news.
Language (s): Chinese
DAILY NEWSPAPER

Visayan Daily Star
Owner: The Visayan Daily Star Publications
Inc.
Editorial: Araneta Singcang Street, Daily Star
Building, Bacolod City 6100. **T:** 63 344330455
E: visayandailystar@yahoo.com
W: http://www.visayandailystar.com
Freq: 2 Times/Week
Editor: Nida Buenafe; **Editor in Chief:** Ninfa
Leonardia; **Editor:** Patrick Pangilinan
Editorial Profile: Covers nternational and local
news.
Language (s): English
DAILY NEWSPAPER

Vizcaya Vanguard
Owner: City Star Inc.
Editorial: Malvar Highway, Santiago City,
Isabela 3311. **T:** 63 786827449
Freq: Weekly
Editor in Chief: Melvin Gascon; **Publisher:**
Francisco Taguinod
Language (s): Filipino
DAILY NEWSPAPER

The Wall Street Journal
(Philippines)
Editorial: 1209-1210 12Fl Tower 1 Exchange
Plaza, Ayala Triangle, Ayala Avenue, Manila.
T: 63 2 848-5051
Bureau Chief: Cris Larano
DAILY NEWSPAPER

NEWS SERVICE/SYNDICATE

Bloomberg News
Editorial: 1101-1103 Tower One and Exchange
Plaza, Ayala Triangle, Ayala Ave, Makati City
1226. **T:** 63 28497100
NEWS SERVICE/SYNDICATE

Dow Jones Newswires
Editorial: 1209-1210 12Fl Tower 1 Exchange
Plaza, Ayala Triangle, Ayala Avenue, Manila.
T: 63 2 848-5051
Bureau Chief: Cris Larano
NEWS SERVICE/SYNDICATE

The Philippine News Agency
Owner: Republic of the Philippines
Editorial: 2nd Floor, PIA Building, Visayas
Avenue, Quezon City 1104
W: http://www.pna.gov.ph
Freq: Daily
Editorial Profile: Philippines News Agency
also known as PNA is the official new agency
in the Philippines. It was started on March 1,
1973 and it has its headquarters in Manila.
Language (s): English
NEWS SERVICE/SYNDICATE

Reuters
Editorial: 18/F The Enterprise Center, Tower 1,
6766 Ayala Avenue Corner, Paseo de Roxas,
Makati 1200. **T:** 63 916328418900
NEWS SERVICE/SYNDICATE

BROADCASTING

RADIO NETWORKS

Radio Mindanao Network
Owner: Radio Mindanao Network, Inc.
Editorial: 4th Floor, Guadalupe Commercial
Complex Building, Edsa, Makati City
E: webmaster@rmnnews.com
W: http://www.rmn.com.ph
Editorial Profile: Radio Mindanao Network
Inc. or RMN Networks is one of the largest
radio networks in the Philippines. The
network's first radio station is DXCC,

established in Cagayan de Oro on the island of
Mindanao in August 28, 1952. The callsign
meant the radio partnership of Canoy and Cui.
It was changed later to a neutral meaning
Cagayan de Oro Community, as the founder
would soon write it in his memoir. The
Network studios and office in Metro Manila
are located at the 4/F Guadalupe Commercial
Complex Bldg., EDSA Guadalupe, Makati City.

TELEVISION NETWORKS

ABS-CBN Broadcasting Corporation
Owner: ABS-CBN Interactive Inc.
Editorial: 9/F ELJ Communications Center,
Lopez Drive 1103, Quezon City 1100.
T: 632 924-4101 **E:** feedback@abs-cbn.com
W: http://www.abs-cbn.com
Editorial Profile: Provides news and
entertainment television programming to the
community.

PITCAIRN ISLANDS
Tel: 61

Standard Time: GMT -8
Continent: Oceania
Capital City: Adamstown

NEWSPAPERS & PUBLICATIONS

NEWSPAPERS

Pitcairn Miscellany
Editorial: Pitcairn Island, South Pacific Ocean,
Via New Zealand **E:** miscellany@pitcairn.pn
W: http://miscellany.pn
Freq: Monthly
Editorial Profile: Covers island news, stories
of trips to Oeno and Henderson Island,
monthly fish catch, ship arrivals, local gossip,
birthdays, articles written by visitors, local
events and activities.
Language (s): English
NEWSPAPER

POLAND
Tel: 48

Standard Time: GMT +1
Continent: Europe
Capital City: Warsaw

NEWSPAPERS & PUBLICATIONS

NEWSPAPERS

The Wall Street Journal (Poland)
Editorial: Krakowskie Przedmiescie St. 13,
Room 103, Warsaw 00-071.
T: 48 22 447-2432
Bureau Chief: Marcin Sobczyk
DAILY NEWSPAPER

NEWS SERVICE/SYNDICATE

Associated Press
Editorial: Al. Przyjaciol 9/9, Warsaw 00-433.
T: 48 22 628-7231
NEWS SERVICE/SYNDICATE

Bloomberg News
Editorial: Emil Plater 53, 23 Fl Warsaw
Financial Centre, Warsaw 00-113.
T: 48 224334444 **E:** release@bloomberg.net
Editor: Pawel Kozlowski; **Bureau Chief:** David
McQuaid
NEWS SERVICE/SYNDICATE

Dow Jones Newswires
Editorial: Krakowskie Przedmiescie St. 13,
Room 103, Warsaw 00-071.
T: 48 22 447-2432
Bureau Chief: Marcin Sobczyk
NEWS SERVICE/SYNDICATE

Reuters
Editorial: Atrium Business Centre Wola, Aleja
Jana Pawla 2, Warsaw 00-854
NEWS SERVICE/SYNDICATE

PORTUGAL
Tel: 351

Standard Time: GMT
Continent: Europe
Capital City: Lisbon

NEWSPAPERS & PUBLICATIONS

NEWSPAPERS

Acção Socialista
Owner: Partido Socialista Português - PS
Editorial: Largo do Rato, 2, Lisboa 1269-143.
T: 351 213 822 000 **E:** accaosocialista@ps.pt
W: http://www.accaosocialista.net
Freq: Weekly
Editorial Profile: Official periodical of the
national Social Political Party. The events,
opinions and political national news.
National.Local Translation: Jornal nacional do
Partido Socialista. Novidades, opiniões,
eventos e notícias sobre a política nacional.
Language (s): Portuguese
DAILY NEWSPAPER

Açoriano Oriental
Owner: Açormedia - Comunicação Multimédia
e Edição de Publicações, S.A.
Editorial: R. Dr. Bruno Tavares Carreiro, 34/
36, Ponta Delgada 9500-055.
T: 351 296 202 800
E: acorianooriental@acorianooriental.pt
W: www.acorianooriental.pt
Freq: Daily
Editor: Rui Jorge Cabral; **Editor:** Mr./Ms.
Editor: **Editor:** Paulo Amaral Faustino; **Editor:**
Ana Carvalho Melo; **Editor:** Arthur Melo;
Editor: Luís Pedro Silva
Editorial Profile: Daily regional newspaper
containing information about Açores' island.
Current affairs, politics, society, sport,
entertainment and events are some of the
main themes. Read by the population of
Açores.Local Translation: Jornal diário com
informação relativa à ilha dos Açores. Política,
actualidade, sociedade, desporto,
entretenimento e eventos são alguns dos
temas abordados.Phone: +351 296 202 832
Language (s): Portuguese
DAILY NEWSPAPER

Adega de Pegões (DN + JN)
Owner: Global Notícias, Publicações, S.A.
Editorial: Edifício Diário de Notícias, Av. da
Liberdade, 266, Lisboa 1250-149.
T: 351 213 187 500 **E:** dnot@dn.pt
Circ: 168106 Publisher's Statement
Editorial Profile: National. Local
Translation:Suplemento dedicado à Adega de
Pegões, produtora de vinho português.
Language (s): Portuguese
DAILY NEWSPAPER

Agências Funerárias
Owner: Global Notícias, Publicações, S.A.
Editorial: R. de Gonçalo Cristóvão 195-219,
Porto 4049-011. **T:** 351 222 096 100
E: dpe@jn.pt **W:** http://www.jn.pt
Circ: 107777 Publisher's Statement
Editorial Profile: National. Local
Translation:Suplemento sobre o sector
funerário.
Email: secdir@jn.pt; roteiro@jn.pt.Phone:
+351 213 187 300
Language (s): Portuguese
DAILY NEWSPAPER

Ágora
Editorial: Instituto Superior da Maia, Av.
Carlos Oliveira Campos, Avioso S. Pedro
4475-690. **T:** 351 229 825 319
E: info@ismai.pt **W:** www.ismai.pt
Circ: 122218 Publisher's Statement
Editorial Profile: National. Local
Translation:Jornal universitário do Laboratório
do curso de jornalismo do ISMAI, Instituto
Superior da Maia.
Language (s): Portuguese
DAILY NEWSPAPER

Águas
Owner: Global Notícias, Publicações, S.A.
T: 351 222 096 100 **E:** secdir@jn.pt
W: http://www.jn.pt **Circ:** 121713 Publisher's
Statement
Editorial Profile: National. Local
Translation:Suplemento que destaca assuntos
relacionados com a água e sua importância.
Destaque para empresas de distribuição de
água, tratamento e saneamento. Phone: +351
213 187 300
Language (s): Portuguese
DAILY NEWSPAPER

Algarve

Owner: Presselivre - Imprensa Livre, S.A.
Editorial: Arruamento D à R. José Maria Nicolau, 3, Lisboa 1549-023.
T: 351 213 185 200 **E:** direccao@cmjornal.pt
W: www.cmjornal.pt
Freq: Daily; **Circ:** 161374 APCT
Editorial Profile: Algarve edition. Aimed at south Portugal population.Local Translation: Edição local do Correio da Manhã Algarve.Phone: +351 213 540 382; +351 213 540 386
Fax: +351 213 540 386
Language (s): Portuguese
DAILY NEWSPAPER

Ambiente (DN + JN)

Owner: Global Notícias, Publicações, S.A.
Editorial: Edifício Diário de Notícias, Av. da Liberdade, 266, Lisboa 1250-149.
T: 351 213 187 500 **E:** dnot@dn.pt
W: http://www.dn.pt **Circ:** 148762 Publisher's Statement
Editorial Profile: Published with: Jornal de Notícias; Diário de Notícias. National.Local Translation: Edições especiais sobre o ambiente, a eficiência enérgica, a energia eólica e as novidades no sector ambiental.Publicado com: Jornal de Notícias; Diário de Notícias
Language (s): Portuguese
DAILY NEWSPAPER

Angola

Owner: Sojornal - Sociedade Jornalística e Editorial, S.A.
Editorial: Edifício S. Francisco de Sales, R. Calvet de Magalhães, 242, Paço De Arcos 2770-022. **T:** 351 214 544 000
E: ipublishing@impresa.pt
W: http://www.expresso.pt **Circ:** 126575 Publisher's Statement
Editorial Profile: National. Local Translation:A Angola enquanto espaço privilegiado para empreendedores ibéricos e de oportunidades de negócio. Geographical Focus: Africa
Language (s): Portuguese
DAILY NEWSPAPER

Aniversário

Owner: Presselivre - Imprensa Livre, S.A.
Editorial: Av. João Crisóstomo, 72, Lisboa 1069-043. **T:** 351 213 185 200
E: direccao@cmjornal.pt
W: http://www.cmjornal.pt **Circ:** 166701 APCT
Editorial Profile: Special anniversary issue. National.Local Translation: Edição especial de aniversário com entrevistas, informações e curiosidades relativas ao jornal.Phone: +351 213 540 382; +351 213 540 386
Fax: +351 213 540 386
Language (s): Portuguese
DAILY NEWSPAPER

Aqui, Pevidém

Owner: Fábrica da Igreja Paroquial de São Jorge de Selho
Editorial: Paróquia de Selho - R. do Bairro, 2, Pevidém, Guimarães 4810-000.
T: 351 253 532 162
Freq: Weekly
Language (s): Portuguese
DAILY NEWSPAPER

Arte

Owner: Transjornal Edição de Publicações, S.A.
Editorial: Estrada da Outurela, 118, Parque Holanda - Edifício Holanda, Carnaxide 2790-114. **T:** 351 214 169 210
E: metro@metroportugal.com
W: http://www.readmetro.com **Circ:** 130000 Publisher's Statement
Editorial Profile: Special edition about art. Aimed for Aveiro, Braga, Coimbra, Évora, Faro, Leiria, Lisboa and Porto regions.Local Translation: Suplemento especial sobre arte: exposições e eventos.Phone: +351 214 241 430
Fax: +351 214 174 206
Language (s): Portuguese
DAILY NEWSPAPER

Atual

Owner: Sojornal - Sociedade Jornalística e Editorial, S.A.
Editorial: Edifício S. Francisco de Sales, R. Calvet de Magalhães, 242, Paço De Arcos 2770-022. **T:** 351 214 544 000
E: atual@expresso.impresa.pt
W: http://www.expresso.pt
Freq: Weekly; **Circ:** 132175 Publisher's Statement
Editor: Jorge Araújo
Editorial Profile: National. Local Translation:Suplemento dedicado ao mundo das artes e do espectáculo. Cinema, dança,

teatro, música, exposições, livros e entrevistas. Url: http:// aeiou.escape.expresso.pt
Email: ipublishing@impresa.pt.
Language (s): Portuguese
DAILY NEWSPAPER

Auto

Owner: Global Notícias, Publicações, S.A.
Editorial: R. de Gonçalo Cristóvão 195-219, Porto 4049-011. **T:** 351 222 096 100
E: dpe@jn.pt **W:** http://www.jn.pt
Circ: 106688 Publisher's Statement
Editorial Profile: Publication dedicated to the mobile industry and market.
Language (s): Portuguese
DAILY NEWSPAPER

Autódromo do Algarve

Owner: Sociedade Vicra Desportiva, S.A.
Editorial: Travessa da Queimada, 23 - R/C, 1° e 2°, Lisboa 1249-113. **T:** 351 213 463 981
W: http://www.abola.pt **Circ:** 120901 Publisher's Statement
Language (s): Portuguese
DAILY NEWSPAPER

Autódromo do Algarve

Owner: Presselivre - Imprensa Livre, S.A.
Editorial: Av. João Crisóstomo, 72, Lisboa 1069-043. **T:** 351 213 185 462
E: geral@correiomanha.pt
W: http://www.cmjornal.pt **Circ:** 184677 Publisher's Statement
Editorial Profile: National. Local Translation:Suplemento sobre o Autódromo Internacional do Algarve: história, o circuito, calendário, entre outros dados.
Language (s): Portuguese
DAILY NEWSPAPER

Badaladas

Owner: Fábrica da Igreja Paroquial da Freguesia de São Pedro e Santiago de Torres Vedras
Editorial: Praça 25 Abril, 6 - 1° Esq., Torres Vedras 2561-311. **T:** 351 261 335 476
E: geral@badaladas.pt **W:** www.badaladas.pt
Freq: Weekly
Editor: Mr./Ms. Editor
Editorial Profile: Tabloid-sized newspaper featuring the latest news, entertainment and sport from the region. Read in Lisboa region.Local Translation: Jornal de inspiração cristã, em formato tablóide com notícias, actualidade, entretenimento e desporto relativos principalmente à região de Lisboa.Phone: +351 261 335 470
Language (s): Portuguese
DAILY NEWSPAPER

Baixo Mondego

Owner: Pixel - Imagem e Comunicação
Editorial: R. da Cadeia Velha, Montemor-O-Velho 3140-853. **T:** 351 239 687 530
E: baixo.mondego@mail.telepac.pt
Freq: Bi-Weekly
Language (s): Portuguese
DAILY NEWSPAPER

Balada da União

Owner: Convívios Fraternos
Editorial: R. António Maria Pinho, 20, Apartado 12, Avanca 3860-130.
T: 351 234 884 474
E: convivios_fraternos@hotmail.com
Freq: Monthly
Language (s): Portuguese
DAILY NEWSPAPER

Bandeira Azul

Owner: Global Notícias, Publicações, S.A.
T: 351 222 096 100 **E:** secdir@jn.pt
W: http://www.jn.pt **Circ:** 116688 Publisher's Statement
Editorial Profile: National. Local Translation:As praias e marinas classificadas com qualidade e segurança máxima. Phone: +351 213 187 300
Language (s): Portuguese
DAILY NEWSPAPER

Barcelos Popular

Owner: Milho Rei - Cooperativa Popular de Informação e Cultura de Barcelos, C.R.L.
Editorial: Av. João Paulo II, 355, Barcelos 4750-304. **T:** 351 253 813 585
E: geral@barcelos-popular.pt
W: http://www.barcelos-popular.pt
Freq: Weekly
Editorial Profile: Read in Barcelos region. Local Translation:Semanário de informação regional acerca de Barcelos. Política, Concelho, Cultura e Desporto são as secções habituais deste jornal. Phone: +351 917 461 939
Language (s): Portuguese
DAILY NEWSPAPER

A Bola

Owner: Sociedade Vicra Desportiva, S.A.
Editorial: Travessa da Queimada, 23 - R/C, 1° e 2°, Lisboa 1249-113. **T:** 351 213 463 981
E: publicidag@abola.pt
W: http://www.abola.pt
Freq: Daily; **Circ:** 120000 Publisher's Statement
Cartoonist: Luís Afonso; **Editor:** Nélson Marquez Feiteirona; **Cartoonist:** Ricardo Galvão; **Editor:** Nuno Perestrelo; **Editor:** João Pimpim; **Editor:** Hugo Vasconcelos
Editorial Profile: Tabloid-sized newspaper focusing on all aspects of competitive sport in Portugal and throughout the world. Sold in Portugal and in some cities in Brazil, USA and Canada. Read by a broad range of the population, mainly man, with a particular interest in sporting events.Local Translation: Diário em formato tablóide, contendo notícias nacionais e internacionais sobre as mais variadas modalidades de desporto, mas com especial destaque para o futebol.
Language (s): Portuguese
DAILY NEWSPAPER

Boletim Cultural

Owner: Câmara Municipal de Vila Nova de Famalicão
Editorial: R. Augusto Correia, 38 - 2° Dto., Vila Nova De Famalição 4760
E: camaramunicipal@vilanovadefamalicao.org
Language (s): Portuguese
DAILY NEWSPAPER

Boletim da Freguesia de Nogueira

Owner: Junta de Freguesia de Nogueira
Editorial: R. do Agrelo, Braga 4700
Freq: Bi-Monthly
Language (s): Portuguese
DAILY NEWSPAPER

Boletim Informativo (Vale de Cambra)

Owner: Câmara Municipal de Vale de Cambra
Editorial: Edifício da Câmara Municipal, Vale De Cambra 3730
Freq: Monthly
Language (s): Portuguese
DAILY NEWSPAPER

Boletim Informativo Câmara Municipal VN Famalicão

Owner: Câmara Municipal de Vila Nova de Famalicão
Editorial: Edifício da Câmara Municipal, Vila Nova De Famalição 4760-000
Freq: Quarterly
Language (s): Portuguese
DAILY NEWSPAPER

Boletim Informativo de Cavez - B I C

Owner: Grupo Desportivo de Cavez
Editorial: Fojo, 71, Cavez, Cabeceiras De Basto 4860
Freq: Monthly
Language (s): Portuguese
DAILY NEWSPAPER

Boletim Municipal - Braga

Owner: Câmara Municipal de Braga
Editorial: Edifício da Câmara Municipal, Braga 4700
Freq: Quarterly
Language (s): Portuguese
DAILY NEWSPAPER

Boletim Municipal - Castelo de Paiva

Owner: Câmara Municipal de Castelo de Paiva
Editorial: Largo do Conde, Castelo De Paiva 4550-000
Freq: Bi-Monthly
Language (s): Portuguese
DAILY NEWSPAPER

Boletim Municipal - Guimarães

Owner: Câmara Municipal de Guimarães
Editorial: Edifício da Câmara Municipal, Guimarães 4800
Freq: Monthly
Language (s): Portuguese
DAILY NEWSPAPER

Boletim Municipal - Santa Maria da Feira

Owner: Câmara Municipal de Santa Maria da Feira
Editorial: Câmara Municipal de Santa Maria da Feira, Santa Maria Da Feira
Freq: Monthly
Language (s): Portuguese
DAILY NEWSPAPER

Boletim Municipal - Vagos

Owner: Câmara Municipal de Vagos

Editorial: Edifício da Câmara Municipal, Vagos 3840-000. **T:** 351 234 793 754
Freq: Quarterly
Language (s): Portuguese
DAILY NEWSPAPER

O Bom Samaritano

Owner: Centro Social do Distrito de Aveiro
Editorial: Lugar do Paco, Esgueira, Aveiro 3800. **T:** 351 234 311 459
E: csdivinaprovidencia@sapo.pt
Freq: Quarterly
Language (s): Portuguese
DAILY NEWSPAPER

Cabra

Owner: Universidade de Coimbra
Editorial: Secção de Jornalismo da Associação Académica de Coimbra, R. Padre António Vieira, Coimbra 3000-000.
T: 351 239 821 554 **E:** acabra@gmail.com
W: http://www.acabra.net
Freq: Bi-Weekly
Editorial Profile: Local Translation: Jornal universitário de Coimbra de interesse geral. Conta com as secções "Ensino Superior", "Cidade", "Nacional", "Internacional", "Ciência", "Cultura", "Desporto", "Media", "Reportagens" e "Economia". É o mais antigo dos jornais académicos ainda activo. No site está disponível a versão em PDF deste jornal.Phone: +351 239 821 554 +351 239 821 554
Language (s): Portuguese
DAILY NEWSPAPER

Campeão

Owner: Sociedade Vicra Desportiva, S.A.
Editorial: Travessa da Queimada, 23 - R/C, 1° e 2°, Lisboa 1249-113. **T:** 351 213 463 981
E: publicidag@abola.pt
W: http://www.abola.pt **Circ:** 120000 Publisher's Statement
Editorial Profile: Special issue devoted to the winner of the National Football League. Mainland.Local Translation: Edição especial dedicada ao vencedor do campeonato nacional de futebol.
Language (s): Portuguese
DAILY NEWSPAPER

Campeão Nacional

Owner: Global Notícias, Publicações, S.A.
T: 351 222 096 100 **E:** secdir@jn.pt
W: http://www.jn.pt **Circ:** 106871 Publisher's Statement
Editorial Profile: National. Local Translation:Edição especial dedicada ao vencedor do campeonato nacional. Phone: +351 213 187 300
Language (s): Portuguese
DAILY NEWSPAPER

O Campo

Owner: Jota CBS - Comunicação e Imagem, Lda.
Editorial: R. Sanches de Miranda, 12 A, Castro Verde 7780. **T:** 351 286 915 473
Freq: Weekly
Language (s): Portuguese
DAILY NEWSPAPER

Carta do Amigo

Owner: Fraternidade Cristã dos Doentes e Limitados Físicos
Editorial: R. de S. Barnabé, 42, Braga 4710-309 **E:** avila-cha@facfil.ucp.pt
Freq: Bi-Monthly
Language (s): Portuguese
DAILY NEWSPAPER

Cascais Oeiras

Owner: Grupo Lanjet
Editorial: Apartado 165, Carcavelos 2775-321.
T: 351 968 051 982
E: cascaisoeiras@netcabo.pt
Freq: Bi-Weekly
Editorial Profile: Local Translation: Jornal regional com informação geral dos concelhos de Cascais e Oeiras.Phone: +351 309 890 691
Language (s): Portuguese
DAILY NEWSPAPER

Ciclismo

Owner: Edisport - Sociedade de Publicações Desportivas, S.A.
Editorial: Av. Conde de Valbom, 30 - 4°/5°, Lisboa 1050-068. **T:** 351 210 124 900
E: antoniomagalhaes@record.pt
W: http://www.record.xl.pt **Circ:** 109613 Publisher's Statement
Language (s): Portuguese
DAILY NEWSPAPER

Cinco Quinas

Owner: Graficôa - Sociedade de Artes Gráficas e Publicações, Lda.

Editorial: Jornal Cinco Quinas, Lote 36, Zona Industrial, Sabugal 6320-317.
T: 351 271 615 054
E: cincoquinas@gmail.com
W: http://www.cincoquinas.com
Freq: Monthly
Language (s): Portuguese
DAILY NEWSPAPER

Classificados
Owner: Presselivre - Imprensa Livre, S.A.
Editorial: Av. João Crisóstomo, 72, Lisboa 1069-043. **T:** 351 213 185 200
E: direccao@cmjornal.pt
W: http://www.cmjornal.pt
Freq: Daily; **Circ:** 156337 APCT
Editor: Mr./Ms. Editor
Editorial Profile: Newspaper supplement with classified advertisement, arranged according to specific categories or classifications. The three major headings are employment, real estate, and automotive, although there are additional categories (e.g., business opportunities, pets, personal ads and legal notices). National. Read predominantly by public sector employees and those seeking employment of northern Portugal.Local Translation: Caderno de oportunidades com as seguintes categorias: mercado imobiliário, contactos, diversos, automóveis e emprego.Phone: +351 213 540 382; +351 213 540 386
Fax: +351 213 540 386
Language (s): Portuguese
DAILY NEWSPAPER

Classificados
Owner: Edisport - Sociedade de Publicações Desportivas, S.A.
Editorial: Av. Conde de Valbom, 30 - 4°/5°, Lisboa 1050-068. **T:** 351 210 124 900
E: antoniomagalhaes@record.pt
W: http://www.record.xl.pt
Freq: Daily; **Circ:** 115568 APCT
Editorial Profile: Real estate, cars and jobs. Mainland.Local Translation: Caderno de oportunidades nas seguintes categorias: mercado imobiliário, automóveis e emprego.
Language (s): Portuguese
DAILY NEWSPAPER

Classificados Tuti
Owner: Global Notícias, Publicações, S.A.
Editorial: Av. da Liberdade, 266 - 1°, Lisboa 1250-149. **T:** 351 213 187 500
E: master@tuti.pt **W:** www.tuti.pt
Freq: Daily; **Circ:** 106993 Publisher's Statement
Editor: Mr./Ms. Editor
Editorial Profile: Newspaper supplement with classified advertisement. The three major headings are employment, real estate, and automotive, although there are additional categories (e.g., business opportunities, personals, and legal notices). National. General population.Local Translation: Caderno de compra, venda, alguer, arrendamento e troca, com os seguintes sectores: mercado imobiliário, veículos, emprego e diversos.
Language (s): Portuguese
DAILY NEWSPAPER

Classificados Tuti Casas
Owner: Global Notícias, Publicações, S.A.
Editorial: R. de Gonçalo Cristovão, 195, Porto 4049-011. **T:** 351 213 187 500 **E:** secdir@jn.pt
W: http://www.jn.pt **Circ:** 122218 Publisher's Statement
Editorial Profile: National. Local Translation:Caderno de compra, venda, alguer, arrendamento e troca no sector do mercado imobiliário.
Language (s): Portuguese
DAILY NEWSPAPER

Classificados Tuti Emprego
Owner: Global Notícias, Publicações, S.A.
Editorial: R. de Gonçalo Cristovão, 195, Porto 4049-011. **T:** 351 213 187 500 **E:** secdir@jn.pt
W: http://www.jn.pt **Circ:** 112110 Publisher's Statement
Editorial Profile: National. Local Translation:Caderno de divulgação de procura e oferta de emprego.
Language (s): Portuguese
DAILY NEWSPAPER

Classificados Tuti Veículos
Owner: Global Notícias, Publicações, S.A.
Editorial: R. de Gonçalo Cristovão, 195, Porto 4049-011. **T:** 351 213 187 500 **E:** secdir@jn.pt
W: http://www.jn.pt **Circ:** 112110 Publisher's Statement
Editorial Profile: National. Local Translation:Caderno de compra, venda e aluguer de automóveis.
Language (s): Portuguese
DAILY NEWSPAPER

Concelhos
Owner: Edisport - Sociedade de Publicações Desportivas, S.A.
Editorial: Av. Conde de Valbom, 30 - 4°/5°, Lisboa 1050-068. **T:** 351 210 124 900
E: antoniomagalhaes@record.pt
W: http://www.record.xl.pt **Circ:** 110831 APCT
Language (s): Portuguese
DAILY NEWSPAPER

Conferência
Owner: Presselivre - Imprensa Livre, S.A.
Editorial: Av. João Crisóstomo, 72, Lisboa 1069-043. **T:** 351 213 185 462
E: sede@cofina.pt **W:** http://www.cmjornal.pt
Circ: 164141 Publisher's Statement
Editorial Profile: National. Local Translation:Edição especial relativa às Conferências Correio da Manhã, sobre o Estado da Nação.
Language (s): Portuguese
DAILY NEWSPAPER

Congressos
Owner: Global Notícias, Publicações, S.A.
Editorial: R. de Gonçalo Cristovão, 195, Porto 4049-011. **T:** 351 213 187 500 **E:** secdir@jn.pt
W: http://www.jn.pt **Circ:** 107777 APCT
Editorial Profile: National. Local Translation:Suplemento dedicado a variados congressos que têm como mote o património e desenvolvimento do território.
Language (s): Portuguese
DAILY NEWSPAPER

Construção Civil & Obras Públicas
Owner: Global Notícias, Publicações, S.A.
Editorial: R. de Gonçalo Cristóvão 195-219, Porto 4049-011. **T:** 351 222 096 100
E: dpe@jn.pt **W:** http://www.jn.pt
Circ: 107589 APCT
Editorial Profile: National. Local Translation:Suplemento sobre o sector da construção.
Email: secdir@jn.pt; roteiro@jn.pt.Phone: +351 213 187 300
Language (s): Portuguese
DAILY NEWSPAPER

Cooperativas de Habitação
Owner: Presselivre - Imprensa Livre, S.A.
Editorial: Av. João Crisóstomo, N° 72, Lisboa 1069-043. **T:** 351 213 185 462
E: geral@correiomanha.pt
W: http://www.cmjornal.pt **Circ:** 151203 Not Audited
Language (s): Portuguese
DAILY NEWSPAPER

Correio da Manhã
Owner: Presselivre - Imprensa Livre, S.A.
Editorial: Arruamento D à R. José Maria Nicolau, 3, Lisboa 1549-023.
T: 351 213 185 200 **E:** direccao@cmjornal.pt
W: www.cmjornal.pt
Freq: Daily; **Circ:** 161374 APCT
Editor: Márcia Bajouco; **Editor:** Rogério Chambel; **Editor:** Secundino Cunha; **Editor:** Sónia Dias; **Editor:** Carlos Ferreira; **Editor:** Mário Figueiredo; **Editor Chefe:** Paulo Fonte; **Editor Chefe:** Miguel Alexandre Ganhão; **Editor:** João Mira Godinho; **Editor:** Manuela Guerreiro; **Cartoonist:** Carlos Laranjeira; **Editor:** Octávio Lopes; **Editor:** Paulo Marcelino; **Editor:** Maria de Lurdes Mestre; **Editor Chefe:** Ana Luísa Nascimento; **Editor:** Edgar Nascimento; **Editor:** Marco Pereira; **Editor:** Mário Pereira; **Editor:** Leonardo Ralha; **Editor:** Ricardo Ramos; **Editor:** Hugo Real; **Editor:** José Rodrigues; **Editor Chefe:** Paulo João Santos; **Editor:** Fernando Sobral; **Editor Chefe:** Ricardo Tavares; **Editor:** Rui Pedro Vieira; **Editor:** Sérgio A. Vitorino
Editorial Profile: Tabloid-sized newspaper providing coverage of national news, events and current affairs. Contains political, economical and international news, interviews and information concerning the environment and current events. Particular emphasis is placed upon advertising, recruitment, entertainment, motoring and sport. National.Local Translation: Diário generalista em formato tablóide com informação nacional e internacional. Actualidade, sociedade, economia, política, desporto, cultura, media, celebridades, agenda e programação televisiva são alguns dos temas focados. "Vidas" é o suplemento fixo deste jornal.Fax: +351 213 540 386
Language (s): Portuguese
DAILY NEWSPAPER

Correio da Murtosa
Owner: Litoral Texto - Sociedade de Comunicação, Lda.
Editorial: R. 29 de Outubro, 8 - 1° A, Pardelhas - Murtosa 3870-206.
T: 351 234 838 054
E: correio.murtosa@sapo.pt
Freq: Monthly
Editorial Profile: Monthly regional newspaper with information about Murtosa (Aveiro). Politics, current affairs, society, religion, sport, entertainment and events.
Language (s): Portuguese
DAILY NEWSPAPER

Correio do Ribatejo
Owner: João Arruda Sucessores, Lda.
Editorial: R. Serpa Pinto, 98/104, Apartado 323, Santarem 2000-046. **T:** 351 243 333 116
E: geral@correiodoribatejo.com
W: http://www.correiodoribatejo.com
Freq: Weekly
Editorial Profile: Weekly regional newspaper with information about Ribatejo region. Politics, current affairs, society, religion, sport, entertainment and events. Read in Santarém region.Local Translation: Jornal semanal com informação relativa à região do Ribatejo. Política, actualidade, sociedade, religião, desporto, entretenimento e eventos.
Language (s): Portuguese
DAILY NEWSPAPER

Criança
Owner: Global Notícias, Publicações, S.A.
Editorial: Parque Biológico de Gaia, E.M., Estrada Nacional 222, Avintes 4430-757.
T: 351 227 878 120
E: revista@parquebiologico.pt
W: http://www.parquebiologico.pt
Circ: 111762 Publisher's Statement
Editorial Profile: National. Local Translation:Edição especial com informações e dicas de saúde, alimentação, moda e produtos para crianças.
Language (s): Portuguese
DAILY NEWSPAPER

O Crime
Owner: Letra de Forma
Editorial: R. Alexandre Herculano, N° 1 - 2° Dto., Lisboa 1150-005. **T:** 351 210 962 060
E: jornalcrime@gmail.com
Freq: Weekly
Editor: Mr./Ms. Editor
Editorial Profile: Weekly national newspaper covering crime stories. National.Local Translation: Jornal que foca essencialmente a vida das celebridades e casos policiais e judiciais.
Language (s): Portuguese
DAILY NEWSPAPER

Cultura
Owner: Global Notícias, Publicações, S.A.
Editorial: Av. da Liberdade, 266 - 4°, Lisboa 1250-149. **T:** 351 213 187 500 **E:** secdir@jn.pt
W: http://www.jn.pt **Circ:** 107777 APCT
Editorial Profile: National.
Language (s): Portuguese
DAILY NEWSPAPER

Cultura
Owner: Sojornal - Sociedade Jornalística e Editorial, S.A.
T: 351 214 544 000 **E:** expresso@expresso.pt
W: http://www.expresso.pt **Circ:** 134400 Publisher's Statement
Editorial Profile: National. Local Translation:Edição especial ocasional com informações e curiosidades sobre cultura e artes.
Language (s): Portuguese
DAILY NEWSPAPER

D'Angeja - Mensário Informativo e Cultural
Owner: Associação Os Amigos do Jornal D'Angeja
Editorial: R. António Castilho, Angeja 3850-406. **T:** 351 234 911 163 **E:** d.angeja@mail.pt
Freq: Monthly
Language (s): Portuguese
DAILY NEWSPAPER

Datas Festivas
Owner: Transjornal Edição de Publicações, S.A.
T: 351 214 169 210
E: metro@metroportugal.com
W: http://www.readmetro.com **Circ:** 130000 Publisher's Statement
Language (s): Portuguese
DAILY NEWSPAPER

Desporto
Owner: Global Notícias, Publicações, S.A.
Editorial: R. de Gonçalo Cristóvão, 195-219, Porto 4049-011. **T:** 351 222 096 100
E: desporto@jn.pt **W:** http://www.jn.pt
Circ: 112136 APCT
Editorial Profile: Supplement about sports, specially about the national football championship. Sports news, events and interviews. National.Local Translation: Suplemento com especial destaque para o mundo do futebol, com particular incidência no campeonato português de futebol. Composto por notícias do desporto-rei, de eventos a ter lugar e entrevistas com figuras e intervenientes desta modalidade.Phone: +351 213 187 300
Language (s): Portuguese
DAILY NEWSPAPER

Desporto
Owner: R/com
Editorial: R. Ivens, 14, Lisboa 1249-108.
T: 351 213 239 239
E: jornalonline@pagina1.pt
W: http://www.pagina1.pt
Editorial Profile: Sports. National.Local Translation: Edição especial com as principais informações desportivas da actualidade, com especial destaque para o futebol.Phone: +351 213 239 200 Geographical Focus: Sport
Language (s): Portuguese
DAILY NEWSPAPER

Destak
Owner: Cofina Media Internet
Editorial: Arruamento D à R. José Maria Nicolau, 3, Lisboa 1549-023.
T: 351 214 169 210 **E:** destak@destak.pt
W: http://www.destak.pt
Freq: Daily; **Circ:** 135000 Publisher's Statement
Editor: Mr./Ms. Editor
Editorial Profile: Daily free newspaper. Read in Aveiro, Braga, Coimbra, Leiria, Lisboa, Porto and Setúbal districts.Local Translation: O Destak é um jornal diário, de distribuição gratuita. Apresenta notícias curtas e directas, essencialmente sobre actualidade, notícias locais, nacionais e internacionais, desporto, lazer, bem-estar e cultura.
Language (s): Portuguese
DAILY NEWSPAPER

Dia Mundial
Owner: Presselivre - Imprensa Livre, S.A.
Editorial: Av. João Crisóstomo, N° 72, Lisboa 1069-043. **T:** 351 213 185 462
E: geral@correiomanha.pt
W: http://www.cmjornal.pt **Circ:** 163496 APCT
Editorial Profile: National. Local Translation:Suplemento dedicado à comemoração de dias especiais como o Dia Mundial da Alimentação, da Saúde, do Ambiente, entre muitos outros.
Language (s): Portuguese
DAILY NEWSPAPER

Dia Mundial (DN + JN)
Owner: Global Notícias, Publicações, S.A.
T: 351 213 187 500 **E:** dnot@dn.pt
Circ: 165912 Publisher's Statement
Editorial Profile: Published with: Diário de Notícias; Jornal de Notícias. National.Local Translation: Suplemento dedicado à comemoração de dias especiais como o Dia Mundial da Alimentação, da Saúde, do Ambiente, entre muitos outros.Publicado com: Diário de Notícias; Jornal de Notícias
Language (s): Portuguese
DAILY NEWSPAPER

Diário As Beiras
Owner: Sojormedia Beiras, S.A.
Editorial: R. Abel Dias Urbano, 4, 2°, Coimbra 3000-001. **T:** 351 239 980 280
E: beirastexto@asbeiras.pt
W: www.asbeiras.pt
Freq: Daily
Editor: Mr./Ms. Editor; **Editor Chefe:** Dora Loureiro
Editorial Profile: Daily newspaper with information about Aveiro, Coimbra, Leiria, Viseu, Guarda and Castelo Branco regions. Politics, current affairs, society, religion, sport, entertainment and events. Read in Aveiro, Castelo Branco, Coimbra, Guarda, Leiria and Viseu but also in Lisboa and Porto regions.Local Translation: Diário com informação relativa à região centro. Política, actualidade, sociedade, desporto, entretenimento e eventos são alguns dos temas abordados. Apresenta os conteúdos em quatro grandes áreas: Essencial, Pensar, Agir e Viver. Primeiro jornal português com Certificação de Qualidade Serviço.Email: redaccao@asbeiras.pt. Phone: +351 962 107 671
Language (s): Portuguese
DAILY NEWSPAPER

Diário Cidade
Owner: Liberal - Empresa de Artes Gráficas, Lda.
Editorial: PEZO - Parque Industrial Zona Oeste, Lote 7, Socorridos, Câmara De Lobos/ madeira 9304-006. **T:** 351 291 623 499
E: diariocidade@diariocidade.pt
W: http://www.diariocidade.pt
Freq: Daily
Editorial Profile: Free daily newspaper with information regarding Madeira. Local Translation:Diário gratuito de informação regional com informação relativa à Madeira. Actualidade regional, cultura, economia e sociedade são os temas centrais.
Email: edgaraguiar-35m@adv.oa.pt; hvalente@diariocidade.pt.Phone: +351 291 623 696
Language (s): Portuguese
DAILY NEWSPAPER

Diário de Aveiro
Owner: Adriano Lucas - Gestão e Comunicação Social, Lda.
Editorial: Av. Dr. Lourenço Peixinho, 15 - 1° G, Aveiro 3800-801. **T:** 351 234 000 030
E: diarioaveiro@diarioaveiro.pt
W: www.diarioaveiro.pt
Freq: Daily
Editor: Mr./Ms. Editor; **Editor Chefe:** José Manuel Rodrigues Silva
Editorial Profile: Daily magazine with information about Aveiro region. Politics, current affairs, society, sport, entertainment and events. Read by the population of Aveiro.Local Translation: Diário regional com informação relativa a Aveiro. Actualidade, política, sociedade, desporto, eventos e entretenimento.
Language (s): Portuguese
DAILY NEWSPAPER

Diário de Coimbra
Owner: Adriano Lucas - Gestão e Comunicação Social, Lda.
Editorial: R. Adriano Lucas, Apartado 542, Coimbra 3020-264. **T:** 351 239 499 900
E: redac@diariocoimbra.pt
W: www.diariocoimbra.pt
Freq: Daily
Editor Chefe: António Manuel Rodrigues
Editorial Profile: Daily regional newspaper with information about the center region of Portugal. Politics, current affairs, society, religion, sport, entertainment and events. Aimed mainly for Coimbra population, but also distributed in Aveiro, Castelo Branco, Guarda, Lisboa, Porto and Viseu.Local Translation: Jornal regional diário que destaca a informação relativa ao distrito de Coimbra. Política, actualidade, sociedade, desporto, entretenimento e eventos são alguns dos temas abordados.Phone: +351 239 499 930
Language (s): Portuguese
DAILY NEWSPAPER

Diário de Leiria
Owner: Adriano Lucas - Gestão e Comunicação Social, Lda.
Editorial: Edifício Maringá, R. S. Francisco, 7 - 4° Esq., Leiria 2400-000. **T:** 351 244 000 030
E: diarioleiria@diarioleiria.pt
W: www.diarioleiria.pt
Freq: Daily
Editor: Mr./Ms. Editor; **Editor Chefe:** José Carlos Salgueiro
Editorial Profile: Daily regional newspaper with information about Leiria. Politics, current affairs, society, religion, sport, entertainment and events. Read in Leiria region.Local Translation: Jornal reginal com informação sobre Leiria. Política, actualidade, sociedade, religião, desporto, entretenimento e eventos são assuntos habituais.
Language (s): Portuguese
DAILY NEWSPAPER

Diário de Notícias da Madeira
Owner: Empresa Diário de Notícias, Lda.
Editorial: R. Dr. Fernão de Ornelas, 56 - 3°, Funchal 9054-514. **T:** 351 291 202 300
E: secretariado@dnoticias.pt
W: www.dnoticias.pt
Freq: Daily
Cartoonist: Luís Villas-Boas
Editorial Profile: Read by Madeira population. Local Translation:Diário de informação regional relativa à ilha da Madeira. Política, Regional, Desporto, Cultura, Casos do Dia e Dê Notícias são algumas das secções que fazem parte deste jornal. Em 2010 foi considerado o Jornal Europeu do Ano, na edição do European Newspaper Award. O título ganhou na categoria de jornal local. Alternative Title: DN MadeiraEmail: lgouveia@dnoticias.pt.
Language (s): Portuguese
DAILY NEWSPAPER

Diário do Minho
Owner: Empresa Diário do Minho, Lda.
Editorial: R. de Santa Margarida, 4 A, Braga 4710-306. **T:** 351 253 609 460
E: redaccao@diariodominho.pt
W: www.diariodominho.pt
Freq: Daily
Editor: Mr./Ms. Editor; **Editor Chefe:** Damião Pereira
Editorial Profile: Daily regional newspaper with information about the north region of Portugal. Politics, current affairs, society, religion, sport, entertainment and events. Read in Braga and Viana do Castelo regions.Local Translation: Diário regional com informação sobre a região Norte de Portugal, em particular sobre política, actualidade, sociedade, religião, desporto, entretenimento e eventos.
Language (s): Portuguese
DAILY NEWSPAPER

Diário do Sul
Owner: Piçarra & Companhia, Lda.
Editorial: Travessa de Santo André, 6 - 8, Apartado 2037, Evora 7000-951.
T: 351 266 744 444
E: administracao@diariodosul.com.pt
W: http://www.diariodosul.com.pt
Freq: Daily
Editorial Profile: Daily regional newspaper with information about the south region of Portugal. Politics, current affairs, society, religion, sport, entertainment and events. Read in Beja, Évora, Faro, Lisboa, Portalegre and Setúbal.Local Translation: Jornal diário com informação relativa à região do Alentejo. Política, actualidade, sociedade, religião, desporto, entretenimento e eventos são alguns dos temas abordados. Recebeu o Prémio Gazeta Imprensa Regional 2008 atribuído pelo Clube de Jornalistas.Email: redacao@diariodosul.com.pt.
Language (s): Portuguese
DAILY NEWSPAPER

Dica da Semana
Owner: Lidl & Cia - Lojas Alimentares
Editorial: Av. 25 de Abril de 1974, 21A, Linda-A-Velha 2795-197 **W:** http://www.lidl.pt
Freq: Weekly
Editorial Profile: Mainland. Local Translation:Publicação grátis do hipermercado Lidl. Contém os preços de alguns dos produtos do Lidl, sugestões de limpeza e manutenção para a casa.
Language (s): Portuguese
DAILY NEWSPAPER

Dinheiro
Owner: Sojornal - Sociedade Jornalística e Editorial, S.A.
Editorial: Edifício S. Francisco de Sales, R. Calvet de Magalhães, 242, Paço De Arcos 2770-022. **T:** 351 214 544 000
E: ipublishing@impresa.pt
W: http://www.expresso.pt **Circ:** 126575 APCT
Editorial Profile: National. Local Translation:Suplemento sobre poupança: a poupança em Portugal, a educação financeira, os bancos e fundos de investimento.
Language (s): Portuguese
DAILY NEWSPAPER

Dinheiro Vivo (DN + JN)
Owner: Controlinveste SGPS, S.A.
Editorial: Av. da Liberdade, 266 - 5° Piso, Lisboa 1250-149. **T:** 351 213 187 500
E: dinheirovivo@dinheirovivo.pt
W: www.dinheirovivo.pt
Freq: Weekly; **Circ:** 178238 Publisher's Statement
Editor: Gouveia de Albuquerque; **Editor:** Pedro Araújo; **Editor:** Teresa Costa; **Editor:** Armando Fonseca Júnior; **Editor:** Vítor Martins; **Editor Chefe:** Sílvia de Oliveira; **Editor Chefe:** Joana Petiz; **Editor:** Helena Santareno
Editorial Profile: Published with: Diário de Notícias; Jornal de Notícias. National.Local Translation: Suplemento com base no portal Dinheiro Vivo, dedicado a áreas específicas, como Economia, Estado, Empresas e Mercados. Contém ainda um espaço dedicado ao Marketing, Publicidade e Media, o Buzz.Publicado com: Diário de Notícias; Jornal de Notícias Geographical Focus: Wirtschaft
Language (s): Portuguese
DAILY NEWSPAPER

Domingo
Owner: Global Notícias, Publicações, S.A.
Editorial: R. de Gonçalo Cristóvão 195-219, Porto 4049-011. **T:** 351 222 096 100
E: dpe@jn.pt **W:** http://www.jn.pt
Freq: Weekly; **Circ:** 116459 Publisher's Statement
Editorial Profile: National. Local Translation:Suplemento semanal com notícias nacionais e internacionais. Inclui várias temáticas: política, economia, sociedade, desporto, saúde e cultura.
Email: secdir@jn.pt.Phone: +351 213 187 300
Language (s): Portuguese
DAILY NEWSPAPER

O Eco
Owner: Sojormedia - Comunicação Social, S.A.
Editorial: Largo do Carmo, 20 - R/C Esq., Apartado 1, Pombal 3100-464.
T: 351 236 209 930 **E:** ecoregional@sapo.pt
W: http://www.oeco.pt
Freq: Monthly
Editorial Profile: Weekly newspaper. Politics, current affairs, society, religion, sport, entertainment and events. Read by Pombal and northern Leiria district locals.Local Translation: Gratuito de informação regional relativa aos concelhos situados a norte do distrito de Leiria. Actualidade, política, sociedade, negócios e desporto são alguns dos temas habituais neste jornal.Email: adriana.afonso@oeco.pt; info@oeco.pt. Phone: +351 962 108 736
Language (s): Portuguese
DAILY NEWSPAPER

Eco de Vagos
Owner: João dos Santos Ferreira
Editorial: R. Dr. Francisco de Almeida Brito, 65, Soza, Vagos 3840-347.
T: 351 234 791 984
W: http://www.ecodevagos.com
Freq: Monthly
Language (s): Portuguese
DAILY NEWSPAPER

Econews
Owner: Publiregiões - Sociedade Jornalística e Editorial, Lda.
Editorial: Al. António Sérgio, 7 - 1° D, Linda-A-Velha 2799-531. **T:** 351 214 157 200
E: jr-editor@jornaldaregiao.pt
W: http://www.jornaldaregiao.pt **Circ:** 225000 Publisher's Statement
Editorial Profile: Read in Cascais, Oeiras, Amadora e Almada. Local Translation:Suplemento dedicado ao ambiente. Publicado com: Jornal da Região - Cascais; Jornal da Região - Almada; Jornal da Região - Oeiras; Jornal da Região - Amadora; Jornal da Região - Sintra
Language (s): Portuguese
DAILY NEWSPAPER

Economia
Owner: Sojornal - Sociedade Jornalística e Editorial, S.A.
Editorial: Edifício S. Francisco de Sales, R. Calvet de Magalhães, 242, Paço De Arcos 2770-022. **T:** 351 214 544 000
E: economia@expresso.impresa.pt
W: http://www.expresso.pt
Freq: Weekly; **Circ:** 132175 Publisher's Statement
Editor: Mr./Ms. Editor
Editorial Profile: Magazine containing the latest news about national and international economy. Interviews and opinions of famous economists or business people. National.Local Translation: As últimas notícias relativas à economia nacional e internacional. Contém entrevistas e artigos de opinião de economistas e de pessoas ligadas ao mundo dos negócios.Email: ipublishing@impresa.pt.
Language (s): Portuguese
DAILY NEWSPAPER

Ecos da Ria
Owner: Fábrica da Igreja Paroquial de Beduido
Editorial: Residência Paroquial de Beduido, Estarreja 3860-329. **T:** 351 234 843 788
E: ecosdaria@netvisao.pt
Freq: Monthly
Language (s): Portuguese
DAILY NEWSPAPER

Ecos do Sameiro
Owner: Confraria de Nossa Senhora da Conceição do Monte Sameiro
Editorial: Sameiro - Espinho, Braga 4710-023.
T: 351 253 675 521
E: sameiro@diocese-braga.pt
W: http://www.diocese-braga.pt/sameiro
Freq: Monthly
Language (s): Portuguese
DAILY NEWSPAPER

Eleições
Owner: Sociedade Vicra Desportiva, S.A.
Editorial: Travessa da Queimada, 23 - R/C, 1° e 2°, Lisboa 1249-113. **T:** 351 213 463 981
W: http://www.abola.pt **Circ:** 120901 Publisher's Statement
Language (s): Portuguese
DAILY NEWSPAPER

Emprego
Owner: Sojornal - Sociedade Jornalística e Editorial, S.A.
Editorial: Edifício S. Francisco de Sales, R. Calvet de Magalhães, 242, Paço De Arcos 2770-022. **T:** 351 214 544 000
E: ipublishing@impresa.pt
W: http://www.expresso.pt
Freq: Weekly; **Circ:** 132175 Publisher's Statement
Editorial Profile: National. Local Translation:Jornal onde se pode procurar ou divulgar emprego. Informa ainda acerca de formações/especializações que se podem cursar.
Language (s): Portuguese
DAILY NEWSPAPER

Ensino
Owner: Global Notícias, Publicações, S.A.
Editorial: R. de Gonçalo Cristóvão 195-219, Porto 4049-011. **T:** 351 222 096 100
E: dpe@jn.pt **W:** http://www.jn.pt
Circ: 112136 APCT
Editorial Profile: National. Local Translation:Suplemento sobre o ensino, desde o básico ao superior.
Email: secdir@jn.pt.Phone: +351 213 187 300
Language (s): Portuguese
DAILY NEWSPAPER

Ensino Superior
Owner: Sojornal - Sociedade Jornalística e Editorial, S.A.
Editorial: R. Calvet de Magalhães, 242, Laveiras, Paço De Arcos 2770-022.
T: 351 214 544 000
E: guiadoestudante@expresso.pt
W: http://www.expresso.pt **Circ:** 160400 Not Audited
Editorial Profile: National. Local Translation:Suplemento sobre o Instituto Superior Técnico.
Language (s): Portuguese
DAILY NEWSPAPER

Ensino Superior
Owner: Presselivre - Imprensa Livre, S.A.
Editorial: Av. João Crisóstomo, 72, Lisboa 1069-043. **T:** 351 213 185 462
E: geral@correiomanha.pt
W: http://www.cmjornal.pt **Circ:** 184677 APCT
Editorial Profile: National. Local Translation:Suplemento sobre o ensino superior, que contém informação relativa ao concurso nacional de acesso.
Language (s): Portuguese
DAILY NEWSPAPER

Espaços & Casas
Owner: Sojornal - Sociedade Jornalística e Editorial, S.A.
Editorial: Edifício S. Francisco de Sales, R. Calvet de Magalhães, 242, Paço De Arcos 2770-022. **T:** 351 214 544 000
E: ipublishing@impresa.pt
W: http://www.expresso.pt
Freq: Weekly; **Circ:** 132175 Publisher's Statement
Editorial Profile: National. Local Translation:Suplemento onde se podem encontrar anúncios relativos à compra e venda de apartamentos, armazéns, escritórios, lojas, moradias e terrenos. Inclui desde a edição de 1 de Outubro de 2007 duas páginas dedicadas às principais peças do programa Magazine Imobiliário, uma vez que foi estabelecida uma perceria de partilha de conteúdos entre O Magazine Imobiliário, na SIC Notícias, o caderno Espaços & Casas do Expresso e o site Expressoimobiliario.pt.
Language (s): Portuguese
DAILY NEWSPAPER

Exame - Melhores Empresas para Trabalhar em Portugal
Owner: Sojornal - Sociedade Jornalística e Editorial, S.A.
Editorial: Edifício S. Francisco de Sales, R. Calvet de Magalhães, 242, Paço De Arcos 2770-022. **T:** 351 214 544 000
E: expresso@expresso.pt
W: http://www.expresso.pt **Circ:** 133460 Publisher's Statement
Language (s): Portuguese
DAILY NEWSPAPER

Exponor News
Owner: Exponor - Feira Internacional do Porto
Editorial: Exponor - Feira Internacional do Porto, Leça Da Palmeira 4450-617.
T: 351 229 981 400 **E:** info@exponor.pt
W: http://www.exponor.pt **Circ:** 100000 Publisher's Statement
Editorial Profile: Journal focusing on professional exhibitions covering all aspects of trade and industry. Published with:

Público.Aimed at conference organisers, exhibitors, marketing personnel, events organisers and managers. Local Translation:Publicação periódica sobre exposições profissionais, cobrindo todos os aspectos do comércio e da indústria. Publicado com: PúblicoEmail: elsa.fernandes@exponor.pt; olivia.morais@exponor.pt.
Language (s): Portuguese
DAILY NEWSPAPER

Expressinho
Owner: Sojornal - Sociedade Jornalística e Editorial, S.A.
Editorial: Edifício S. Francisco de Sales, R. Calvet de Magalhães, 242, Paço De Arcos 2770-022. **T:** 351 214 544 000
E: ipublishing@impresa.pt
W: http://www.expresso.pt **Circ:** 138380 Publisher's Statement
Editorial Profile: National. Aimed for children. Local Translation:Jornal que conta com uma secção noticiosa e outra lúdica, de modo a incentivar os mais novos a iniciarem o hábito de leitura de um jornal.
Language (s): Portuguese
DAILY NEWSPAPER

Expresso
Owner: Sojornal - Sociedade Jornalística e Editorial, S.A.
Editorial: Edifício S. Francisco de Sales, R. Calvet de Magalhães, 242, Paço De Arcos 2770-022. **T:** 351 214 544 000
E: ipublishing@impresa.pt
W: http://www.expresso.pt
Freq: Weekly; **Circ:** 132175 APCT
Cartoonist: António Moreira Antunes; **Editor:** Rui Cardoso; **Editor:** Pedro Lima; **Editor:** Miguel Martins; **Cartoonist:** Rodrigo de Matos; **Editor:** Martim Silva; **Editor:** Bárbara Simões
Editorial Profile: Berliner-sized national newspaper providing coverage of national and international current affairs and in-depth information concerning finance, economics, business and industry. Also covers society, culture, media, sports, fashion, lifestyle and television. National.Local Translation: Semanário de informação em formato berliner. Composto essencialmente por notícias, artigos de opinião e reportagens. Contém artigos relativos à actualidade, política, sociedade, desporto e cultura. Como suplementos fixos tem: "Única", "Actual", "Economia", "Emprego" e "Espaços & Casas". Em 2010, o seu grafismofoi premiado pela European Newspaper Award recebendo cinco menções honrosas. Em 2011 vai estar disponivel nos tablets.Email: site@expresso.impresa.pt.
Language (s): Portuguese
DAILY NEWSPAPER

Expresso de Felgueiras
Owner: Carvalho & Mendes - Edições Gráficas e Audiovisuais, Lda.
Editorial: Edifício Século XXI, R. Padre Manuel Lopes Dias Rocha, Lixa 4615-656.
T: 351 255 495 751
E: geral@expressofelgueiras.com
W: http://www.expressofelgueiras.com
Freq: Bi-Weekly
Language (s): Portuguese
DAILY NEWSPAPER

Farpas
Owner: Miguel Fonseca Ferreira Alvarenga
E: jornalfarpas@hotmail.com
W: http://farpasblogue.blogspot.com
Freq: Weekly
Language (s): Portuguese
DAILY NEWSPAPER

FC Porto
Owner: Sociedade Vicra Desportiva, S.A.
Editorial: Travessa da Queimada, 23 - R/C, 1° e 2°, Lisboa 1249-113. **T:** 351 213 463 981
W: http://www.abola.pt **Circ:** 126895 Not Audited
Language (s): Portuguese
DAILY NEWSPAPER

Feiras
Owner: Global Notícias, Publicações, S.A.
Editorial: R. de Gonçalo Cristovão, 195, Porto 4049-011. **T:** 351 222 096 100 **E:** secdir@jn.pt
W: http://www.jn.pt **Circ:** 110608 APCT
Editorial Profile: National. Local Translation:Suplemento com informação relativa a diversas feiras e exposições. Phone: +351 213 187 300
Language (s): Portuguese
DAILY NEWSPAPER

Feiras (JN+DN)
Owner: Global Notícias, Publicações, S.A.
Editorial: R. de Gonçalo Cristovão, 195, Porto 4049-011. **T:** 351 222 096 100 **E:** secdir@jn.pt
Circ: 167926 Publisher's Statement
Editorial Profile: National. Local Translation:Suplemento dedicado às feiras realizadas em determinadas regiões do país. Distribuído com: Jornal de Notícias; Diário de NotíciasPhone: +351 213 187 300
Language (s): Portuguese
DAILY NEWSPAPER

Feiras e Festas
Owner: Presselivre - Imprensa Livre, S.A.
Editorial: Av. João Crisóstomo, 72, Lisboa 1069-043. **T:** 351 213 185 200
E: direccao@cmjornal.pt
W: http://www.cmjornal.pt **Circ:** 160521 APCT
Editorial Profile: Fairs and Festivals. National.Local Translation: Suplemento com informação relativa a diversas feiras, festas e exposições.Phone: +351 213 540 382; +351 213 540 386
Fax: +351 213 540 386
Language (s): Portuguese
DAILY NEWSPAPER

Festa das Cruzes
Owner: Global Notícias, Publicações, S.A.
Editorial: R. de Gonçalo Cristóvão 195-219, Porto 4049-011. **T:** 351 222 096 100
E: roteiro@jn.pt **W:** http://www.jn.pt
Circ: 120759 Not Audited
Language (s): Portuguese
DAILY NEWSPAPER

Festas
Owner: Presselivre - Imprensa Livre, S.A.
Editorial: Av. João Crisóstomo, 72, Lisboa 1069-043. **T:** 351 213 185 462
E: geral@correiomanha.pt
W: http://www.cmjornal.pt **Circ:** 171395 APCT
Language (s): Portuguese
DAILY NEWSPAPER

Festas
Owner: Global Notícias, Publicações, S.A.
Editorial: R. de Gonçalo Cristóvão 195-219, Porto 4049-011. **T:** 351 222 096 100
E: dpe@jn.pt **W:** http://www.jn.pt
Circ: 107589 APCT
Editorial Profile: National. Local Translation:Suplemento dedicado a eventos festivos da região e a festividades anuais tais como: Páscoa, Natal, Carnaval, entre outros.
Email: secdir@jn.pt; roteiro@jn.pt.Phone: +351 213 187 300
Language (s): Portuguese
DAILY NEWSPAPER

Festival (DN + JN)
Editorial: Edifício Diário de Notícias, Av. da Liberdade, 266, Lisboa 1250-149.
T: 351 213 187 500 **E:** dnot@dn.pt
Circ: 168106 Publisher's Statement
Editorial Profile: National. Local Translation:Suplemento dedicado ao concelho de Manteigas e ao Festival Serra da Estrela.
Language (s): Portuguese
DAILY NEWSPAPER

Finanças
Owner: Presselivre - Imprensa Livre, S.A.
Editorial: Av. João Crisóstomo, 72, Lisboa 1069-043. **T:** 351 213 185 462
E: geral@correiomanha.pt
W: http://www.cmjornal.pt **Circ:** 164141 Publisher's Statement
Editorial Profile: National. Local Translation:Edição especial dedicada às finanças nacionais.
Language (s): Portuguese
DAILY NEWSPAPER

Flor do Tâmega
Owner: Empresa Gráfica e Jornalística Flor do Tâmega, Lda.
Editorial: Freixo de Cima, Apartado 47, Amarante 4900. **T:** 351 255 496 224
E: flordotamega@sapo.pt
Freq: Monthly
Editor: Mr./Ms. Editor
Language (s): Portuguese
DAILY NEWSPAPER

Florestas
Owner: Global Notícias, Publicações, S.A.
Editorial: R. de Gonçalo Cristovão, 195, Porto 4049-011. **T:** 351 213 187 500 **E:** secdir@jn.pt
W: http://www.jn.pt **Circ:** 106540 Publisher's Statement
Editorial Profile: National. Local Translation:Suplemento dedicado às florestas e sua protecção.
Language (s): Portuguese
DAILY NEWSPAPER

Formação Profissional
Owner: Presselivre - Imprensa Livre, S.A.
Editorial: Av. João Crisóstomo, 72, Lisboa 1069-043. **T:** 351 213 185 200
E: direccao@cmjornal.pt
W: http://www.cmjornal.pt **Circ:** 165562 Publisher's Statement
Editorial Profile: Vocational Training. National.Local Translation: Suplemento com informação relativa a novas oportunidades e formação profissional.Phone: +351 213 540 382; +351 213 540 386
Fax: +351 213 540 386
Language (s): Portuguese
DAILY NEWSPAPER

Formação Profissional (DN + JN)
Owner: Global Notícias, Publicações, S.A.
Editorial: Edifício Diário de Notícias, Av. da Liberdade, 266, Lisboa 1250-149.
T: 351 213 187 500 **E:** dnot@dn.pt
W: http://www.dn.pt **Circ:** 158416 Publisher's Statement
Editorial Profile: Published with: Diário de Notícias; Jornal de Notícias. National.Local Translation: Suplemento sobre Formação Profissional em Portugal.Publicado com: Diário de Notícias; Jornal de Notícias
Email: dn@dn.pt.
Language (s): Portuguese
DAILY NEWSPAPER

Franchising (DN + JN)
Owner: Global Notícias, Publicações, S.A.
Editorial: Edifício Diário de Notícias, Av. da Liberdade, 266, Lisboa 1250-149.
T: 351 213 187 500 **E:** dnot@dn.pt
W: http://www.dn.pt **Circ:** 165912 Publisher's Statement
Editorial Profile: Published with: Diário de Notícias; Jornal de Notícias. National.Local Translation: Edição especial sobre franchising e negócios. Aborda e expõe casos de sucesso, oportunidades de negócio, exemplos práticos e fornece informação sobre como iniciar um negócio.Publicado com: Diário de Notícias; Jornal de Notícias
Language (s): Portuguese
DAILY NEWSPAPER

Fundação Benfica
Owner: Sociedade Vicra Desportiva, S.A.
Editorial: Travessa da Queimada, 23 - R/C, 1° e 2°, Lisboa 1249-113. **T:** 351 213 463 981
W: http://www.abola.pt **Circ:** 120000 Publisher's Statement
Editorial Profile: Mainland. Local Translation:Suplemento sobre as iniciativas e eventos da Fundação Benfica. Geographical Focus: Sport
Language (s): Portuguese
DAILY NEWSPAPER

Futebol
Owner: Edisport - Sociedade de Publicações Desportivas, S.A.
Editorial: Av. Conde de Valbom, 30 - 4°/5°, Lisboa 1050-068. **T:** 351 210 124 900
E: antoniomagalhaes@record.pt
W: http://www.record.xl.pt **Circ:** 102718 APCT
Editorial Profile: Football. Mainland.Local Translation: Caderno dedicado ao futebol em geral.
Language (s): Portuguese
DAILY NEWSPAPER

Futebol
Owner: Presselivre - Imprensa Livre, S.A.
Editorial: Av. João Crisóstomo, 72, Lisboa 1069-043. **T:** 351 213 185 200
E: direccao@cmjornal.pt
W: http://www.cmjornal.pt **Circ:** 165562 APCT
Editorial Profile: Football. National.Local Translation: Suplemento dedicado à modalidade que é o futebol.Phone: +351 213 540 382; +351 213 540 386
Fax: +351 213 540 386
Language (s): Portuguese
DAILY NEWSPAPER

Futuro
Owner: Transjornal Edição de Publicações, S.A.
Editorial: Estrada da Outurela, 118, Parque Holanda - Edifício Holanda, Carnaxide 2790-114. **T:** 351 214 169 210
E: metro@metroportugal.com
W: http://www.readmetro.com **Circ:** 130000 Publisher's Statement
Editorial Profile: Aimed for Aveiro, Braga, Coimbra, Évora, Faro, Leiria, Lisboa and Porto regions. Local Translation:Secção com notícias falsas pois são relativas a anos futuros. Phone: +351 214 241 430
Fax: +351 214 174 206
Language (s): Portuguese
DAILY NEWSPAPER

Futuro - Revista da Associação Industrial do Minho
Owner: Associação Industrial do Minho
Editorial: Av. Dr. Francisco Pires Gonçalves, 45, Braga 4711-954. **T:** 351 253 613 357
E: aiminho@aiminho.pt
Freq: Quarterly
Language (s): Portuguese
DAILY NEWSPAPER

Gadgets
Owner: Transjornal Edição de Publicações, S.A.
Editorial: Estrada da Outurela, 118, Parque Holanda - Edifício Holanda, Carnaxide 2790-114. **T:** 351 214 169 210
E: metro@metroportugal.com
W: http://www.readmetro.com **Circ:** 130000 Publisher's Statement
Editorial Profile: Aimed for Aveiro, Braga, Coimbra, Évora, Faro, Leiria, Lisboa and Porto regions. Local Translation:Edição especial com sugestões de compra de material tecnológico para variadas ocasiões. Phone: +351 214 241 430
Fax: +351 214 174 206
Language (s): Portuguese
DAILY NEWSPAPER

Gazeta de Sátão
Owner: Isabel Maria Rodrigues dos Santos Figueiredo
Editorial: Praça Paulo VI, Lote 6 - 1° Esq., Satão 3560-154. **T:** 351 232 982 689
E: gazetadesatao@sapo.pt
W: http://www.gazetadesatao.pt
Freq: Monthly
Editor: Carlos Andrade
Language (s): Portuguese
DAILY NEWSPAPER

Gazeta Lusófona
Owner: Jornal Gazeta Lusófona Unipessoal, Lda.
T: 41 41 310 06 30
E: a_sa@gazetalusofona.ch
W: http://www.gazetalusofona.ch
Freq: Monthly
Editorial Profile: Newspaper for the Portuguese community in Switzerland. Read by portuguese people living in Switzerland.Local Translation: Jornal mensal dirigido à comunidade portuguesa da Suíça.
Language (s): Portuguese
DAILY NEWSPAPER

Gestão de Condomínios
Owner: Global Notícias, Publicações, S.A.
Editorial: R. de Gonçalo Cristovão, 195, Porto 4049-011. **T:** 351 213 187 500 **E:** secdir@jn.pt
W: http://www.jn.pt **Circ:** 106540 APCT
Editorial Profile: National. Local Translation:Suplemento dedicado à Gestão de Condomínios.
Language (s): Portuguese
DAILY NEWSPAPER

Global Challenge
Owner: Sojornal - Sociedade Jornalística e Editorial, S.A.
Editorial: Edifício S. Francisco de Sales, R. Calvet de Magalhães, 242, Paço De Arcos 2770-022. **T:** 351 214 544 000
E: ipublishing@impresa.pt
W: http://www.expresso.pt **Circ:** 132175 Publisher's Statement
Editorial Profile: National. Local Translation:Competição Internacional do Global Challenge: Management e Investment.
Language (s): Portuguese
DAILY NEWSPAPER

Golfe
Owner: Sojornal - Sociedade Jornalística e Editorial, S.A.
Editorial: Alameda das Linhas de Torres, 179, Lisboa 1750-142. **T:** 351 217 541 450
E: geral@mediagolf.pt
W: http://www.mediagolf.pt **Circ:** 132175 APCT
Editorial Profile: Special supplement about golf. National.Local Translation: Suplemento especial sobre golfe.Url: http://www.expresso.pt
Email: ipublishing@impresa.pt.
Language (s): Portuguese
DAILY NEWSPAPER

Guia do Estudante
Owner: Sojornal - Sociedade Jornalística e Editorial, S.A.
Editorial: Edifício S. Francisco de Sales, R. Calvet de Magalhães, 242, Paço De Arcos 2770-022. **T:** 351 214 544 000
E: guiadoestudante@expresso.pt
W: http://www.guiadoestudante.pt
Circ: 126575 APCT

Editorial Profile: National. Local Translation:Directório de cursos e propostas de formação e pós-graduação.
Language (s): Portuguese
DAILY NEWSPAPER

Inovação & Tecnologia

Owner: Sojornal - Sociedade Jornalística e Editorial, S.A.
Editorial: Eifício S. Francisco de Sales, R. Calvet de Magalhães, 242, Paço De Arcos 2770-022. **T:** 351 214 544 000
E: ipublishing@impresa.pt
W: http://www.expresso.pt **Circ:** 127500 Publisher's Statement
Editorial Profile: National. Local Translation:Edição especial que contém as últimas inovações a nível tecnológico.
Language (s): Portuguese
DAILY NEWSPAPER

O Interior

Owner: Jorinterior - Jornal do Interior, Lda.
Editorial: R. da Corredoura, 80 - R/C Direito C, Guarda 6300-584. **T:** 351 271 212 153
E: ointerior@ointerior.pt **W:** www.ointerior.pt
Freq: Weekly
Editor Chefe: Luís Martins; **Cartoonist:** Luís Veloso
Editorial Profile: Weekly newspaper with information about Guarda and Castelo Branco regions. Politics, current affairs, society, religion, sport, entertainment and events. Aimed for Guarda and Castelo Branco locals.Local Translation: Semanário regional com informação sobre as regiões da Guarda e de Castelo Branco, abrangendo temas como política, actualidade, sociedade, religião, desporto, entretenimento e eventos.
Language (s): Portuguese
DAILY NEWSPAPER

Isolamentos (DN + JN)

Owner: Global Notícias, Publicações, S.A.
T: 351 213 187 500 **E:** dnot@dn.pt
W: http://dn.sapo.pt **Circ:** 167565 Publisher's Statement
Editorial Profile: National.
Language (s): Portuguese
DAILY NEWSPAPER

JN Cidades

Owner: Global Notícias, Publicações, S.A.
Editorial: R. de Gonçalo Cristóvão, 195, Porto 4049-011. **T:** 351 213 187 500 **E:** secdir@jn.pt
W: http://www.jn.pt
Freq: Weekly; **Circ:** 112110 Publisher's Statement
Editorial Profile: Local Translation: Suplemento sobre o desenvolvimento de várias cidades do país: retrato regional de questões relativas a toda a população como transportes, economia ou ambiente; acompanhamento das equipas desportivas locais e respectivos resultados das competições; eventos culturais de cada região e sugestões de momentos lúdicos e culturais perto de casa; os restaurantes e bares que estão na moda, as lojas novas ou remodeladas e descrição da vida académica de cada cidade.Geographical Focus: Sport; Wirtschaft
Language (s): Portuguese
DAILY NEWSPAPER

JN Concelhos

Owner: Global Notícias, Publicações, S.A.
Editorial: R. de Gonçalo Cristóvão, 195, Porto 4049-011. **T:** 351 222 096 100 **E:** dpe@jn.pt
W: http://www.jn.pt **Circ:** 110603 Publisher's Statement
Editorial Profile: National. Local Translation:Suplemento sobre o desenvolvimento de variados concelhos do país.
Email: secdir@jn.pt; roteiro@jn.pt.Phone: +351 213 187 300
Language (s): Portuguese
DAILY NEWSPAPER

JN Gente

Owner: Global Notícias, Publicações, S.A.
Editorial: Av. da Liberdade, 266 - 4°, Lisboa 1250-149. **T:** 351 213 187 500 **E:** secdir@jn.pt
W: http://www.jn.pt **Circ:** 106993 APCT
Editorial Profile: National. Local Translation:Suplemento com artigos e reportagens acerca das celebridades portuguesas e internacionais.
Email: agenda@jn.pt.
Language (s): Portuguese
DAILY NEWSPAPER

JN Negócios

Owner: Global Notícias, Publicações, S.A.
Editorial: R. de Gonçalo Cristóvão, 195-219, Porto 4049-011. **T:** 351 222 096 100

E: dpe@jn.pt **W:** http://www.jn.pt
Freq: Weekly; **Circ:** 112738 Publisher's Statement
Editor: Mr./Ms. Editor
Editorial Profile: Newspaper supplement containing a Portuguese adaptation of the Wall Street Journal. National. Individuals with special interest in the economical and financial business areas.Local Translation: Suplemento semanal sobre economia editado em colaboração com a revista Carteira. Emprego, empresários, salários, produtos e consumidores são alguns dos temas abordados.Email: secdir@jn.pt; economia@jn.pt. Phone: +351 213 187 300
Language (s): Portuguese
DAILY NEWSPAPER

Jornal da Praia

Owner: Grupo de Amigos da Praia da Vitória
Editorial: R. Padre Rocha de Sousa, 28, Apartado 45, Praia Da Vitória 9760-000. **T:** 351 295 543 101
E: jornaldapraia@portugalmail.com
W: http://www.jornaldapraia.com/index.php
Freq: Bi-Weekly
Editorial Profile: Fortnightly regional newspaper with information about Praia da Vitória (Açores). Politics, current affairs, society, religion, sport, entertainment and events.
Language (s): Portuguese
DAILY NEWSPAPER

Jornal da Região

Owner: Publiregiões - Sociedade Jornalística e Editorial, Lda.
Editorial: Al. António Sérgio, 7 - 1° D, Linda-A-Velha 2799-531. **T:** 351 214 157 200
E: jr-editor@jornaldaregiao.pt
W: http://www.jornaldaregiao.pt
Freq: Weekly; **Circ:** 225000 Publisher's Statement
Editor Chefe: João Carlos Sebastião
Editorial Profile: Free weekly regional newspaper with information about Lisboa. Politics, current affairs, society, religion, sport, entertainment and events. Read in Cascais, Sintra, Oeiras, Amadora e Almada.Local Translation: Semanário regional gratuito com informação relativa a seis diferentes concelhos de Lisboa. Política, assuntos actuais, sociedade, desporto, entretenimento e eventos.
Language (s): Portuguese
DAILY NEWSPAPER

Jornal de Alferrarede

Owner: Manuel Martinho da Conceição Francisco Unipessoal, Lda.
Editorial: R. Fonte de S. José, 64 - 1°, Abrantes 2204-906. **T:** 351 241 361 282
E: jornalferrarede@clix.pt
W: http://jornalferrarede.blogspot.com
Freq: Monthly
Editorial Profile: Regional newspaper with information about Abrantes (Santarém). Politics, current affairs, society, religion, sport, entertainment and events. Read in Santerém region.Local Translation: Mensário regional com informação relativa a Abrantes (Santarém). Política, actualidade, sociedade, desporto e cultura são temas habituais.
Language (s): Portuguese
DAILY NEWSPAPER

Jornal de Beja

Owner: Jaime Casimiro Perianes Palma
Editorial: Largo Escritor Manuel Ribeiro, 10 - 2° B, Beja 7802-421. **T:** 351 284 329 866
E: sonia.calvario-1448e@adv.oa.pt
Freq: Weekly
Editorial Profile: Weekly regional newspaper with information about Beja. Politics, current affairs, society, religion, sport, entertainment and events.
Language (s): Portuguese
DAILY NEWSPAPER

Jornal de Ferreira

Owner: Câmara Municipal de Ferreira do Alentejo
Editorial: Edifício da Câmara Municipal, Ferreira Do Alentejo 7900-571.
T: 351 284 738 700
E: geral@cm-ferreira-alentejo.pt
W: http://www.cm-ferreira-alentejo.pt/index.php
Freq: Bi-Monthly
Editorial Profile: Regional newspaper with information about Ferreira do Alentejo (Beja). Politics, current affairs, society, religion, sport, entertainment and events.
Language (s): Portuguese
DAILY NEWSPAPER

Jornal de Notícias

Owner: Global Notícias, Publicações, S.A.
Editorial: R. de Gonçalo Cristóvão, 195-219, Porto 4049-011. **T:** 351 222 096 111
E: secdir@jn.pt **W:** www.jn.pt
Freq: Daily; **Circ:** 106993 Publisher's Statement
Editor in Chief: Rute Araújo; **Editor Chefe:** Rafael Barbosa; **Editor:** Vítor Pinto Basto;
Cartoonist: Zeferino Coelho; **Editor:** Teresa Costa; **Editor:** Miguel Conde Coutinho;
Cartoonist: Aníbal F.; **Editor:** Margarida Fonseca; **Editor:** José Miguel Gaspar; **Editor:** Elmano Madaíl; **Editor:** Manuel Molinos;
Editor: Dora Mota; **Editor:** Jorge Pinto;
Cartoonist: R. Reimão; **Editor:** António Soares
Editorial Profile: National newspaper providing regional, national and international news, political coverage and in-depth information concerning finance, economics and new technologies. Also covers society, culture, the media, sport and television. Contains comic strips, game puzzles and fait-divers. National.Local Translation: Jornal de carácter generalista, caracterizado por notícias e acontecimentos que marcam a actualidade do país de do mundo. Composto por suplementos das mais variadas áreas (política, sociedade, economia, cultura, lazer, desporto, entre outros). Ao fim-de-semana a última página é dedicada a histórias e entrevistas. Distinguido, em 2008 e 2011, com marca de excelência pela Superbrand.Phone: +351 213 187 500
Language (s): Portuguese
DAILY NEWSPAPER

Jornal de Notícias - Norte

Owner: Global Notícias, Publicações, S.A.
Editorial: R. Gonçalo Cristóvão, 195-219, Porto 4049-011. **T:** 351 222 096 100
E: dpe@jn.pt **W:** http://www.jn.pt
Freq: Daily; **Circ:** 109520 Publisher's Statement
Editor Chefe: Rafael Barbosa; **Editor:** Mr./Ms. Editor; **Editor:** Margarida Fonseca; **Editor Chefe:** Paulo Martins; **Editor:** Dora Mota;
Editor: António Soares
Editorial Profile: National newspaper providing regional, national and international news, political coverage and in-depth information concerning finance, economics and new technologies. Also covers society, culture, the media, sport and television. Contains comic strips, game puzzles and fait-divers. Local news regarding the north region of Portugal. Publication that is a part of the newspaper Jornal de Notícias.Aimed at northern Portugal readers. Local Translation:Jornal generalista, especialmente concebido para o segmento em que se insere - zona norte de Portugal (essencialmente Aveiro, Guarda, Viseu, Vila Real, Bragança, Braga e Viana do Castelo). Com notícias de cariz nacional e internacional, comporta ainda a vertente local e regionalista da área a que se destina nas mais variadas temáticas (desporto, economia, novas tecnologias ou o social local). Publicação integrante do Jornal de Notícias.Email: secdir@jn.pt. Phone: +351 213 187 500
Language (s): Portuguese
DAILY NEWSPAPER

Jornal do Centro

Owner: Centro - Produção e Edição de Conteúdos, Lda.
Editorial: Bairro S. João da Carreira, R. D. Maria Gracinda Torres Vasconcelos, Lote 10 - R/C, Viseu 3500-187. **T:** 351 232 437 461
E: redaccao@jornaldocentro.pt
W: http://www.jornaldocentro.pt
Freq: Weekly
Editorial Profile: Weekly regional newspaper with information about Viseu. Politics, current affairs, society, religion, sport, entertainment and events. Read by Viseu locals.Local Translation: Jornal semanal com informação relativa a Viseu. Política, actualidade, sociedade, religião, desporto, entretenimento e eventos. Recebeu em 2003 o Prémio Gazeta Imprensa Regional. Desde Março de 2010 é distribuído gratuitamente com o Expresso na região de Viseu.
Language (s): Portuguese
DAILY NEWSPAPER

Jornal do Centro de Saúde

Owner: Marketing For You, Lda.
Editorial: Beloura Office Park, Edifício 4, Escritório 1.2, Sintra 2710-693.
T: 351 219 247 670
E: redaccao@jornaldocentrodesaude.pt
W: http://www.jornaldocentrodesaude.pt
Freq: Monthly
Editor: Sofia Filipe
Editorial Profile: Elaborated by the Carnaxide health center, Jornal do Centro de Saúde is a

free newspaper foccused on public health and the connection between health center professionals and the patients. National.Local Translation: Elaborado pelo Centro de Saúde de Carnaxide, o Jornal do Centro de Saúde é um mensário gratuito sobre os mais variados campos da saúde pública. Tem como objectivo aumentar a qualidade de vida e criar uma interacção entre o cidadão utente e os profissionais do Centro de Saúde.Email: barbara.tavares@jornaldocentrodesaude.pt.
Language (s): Portuguese
DAILY NEWSPAPER

Jornal do Ténis

Owner: Edisport - Sociedade de Publicações Desportivas, S.A.
Editorial: Av. Conde de Valbom, 30 - 4°/5°, Lisboa 1050-068. **T:** 351 210 124 900
E: antoniomagalhaes@record.pt
W: http://www.record.xl.pt
Freq: Monthly; **Circ:** 102718 APCT
Editor: Mr./Ms. Editor
Editorial Profile: Newspaper containing national and international news regarding tennis. Mainland.Local Translation: Jornal com notícias nacionais e internacionais sobre ténis.Email: jornaldotenis@lagossports.com.
Language (s): Portuguese
DAILY NEWSPAPER

Jornal Raiano

Owner: Jornal Raiano
Editorial: Largo do Adro, 11, Idanha-A-Nova 6060-109. **T:** 351 277 202 169
Freq: Monthly
Editor: Mr./Ms. Editor
Language (s): Portuguese
DAILY NEWSPAPER

Jornal Veris

Owner: Fábrica da Igreja Paroquial da Freguesia de S. Veríssimo de Paranhos
Editorial: Igreja paroquial de S. Veríssimo de Paranhos, Porto 4200-325.
T: 351 225 020 729 **E:** jornal.veris@gmail.com
Freq: Monthly
Editorial Profile: Regional newspaper regarding Paranhos. Aimed at Paranhos' population.Local Translation: Mensário de informação regional relativa a Paranhos e de cariz religioso.
Language (s): Portuguese
DAILY NEWSPAPER

Le Mans Series

Owner: Edisport - Sociedade de Publicações Desportivas, S.A.
T: 351 210 124 900
E: antoniomagalhaes@record.pt
W: http://www.record.xl.pt **Circ:** 115409 APCT
Editorial Profile: Mainland. Local Translation:Suplemento sobre o campeonato Le Mans Series.
Language (s): Portuguese
DAILY NEWSPAPER

Manancial 56 - Pequenos Anúncios, Grandes Negócios

Editorial: Gândara - Cesar, Oliveira De Azeméis 3720-000. **T:** 351 256412648
Freq: Monthly
Editor: Mr./Ms. Editor
Language (s): Portuguese
DAILY NEWSPAPER

Margens do Vouga

Owner: Tavares & Pereira Publicações Periódicas, Lda.
Editorial: Edifício da Torre, Loja 1, Sever Do Vouga 3740-000 **E:** margensdovouga@sapo.pt
Freq: Bi-Weekly
Language (s): Portuguese
DAILY NEWSPAPER

Meios & Publicidade

Owner: Workmedia - Comunicação, S.A.
Editorial: R. General Firmino Miguel, 3 - Torre 2, 3°, Lisboa 1600-100. **T:** 351 210 410 300
E: geral@workmedia.pt
W: http://www.meiosepublicidade.pt
Freq: Weekly
Editor: Maria João Lima
Editorial Profile: Publication providing information on communications, marketing strategies, studies of trends and advertising especially relating to the media. National. Aimed at people working in the advertising and media sectors.Local Translation: Publicação sobre o sector de comunicação e publicidade. As novidades e destaques sobre meios de comunicação sociais, jornalistas, marketeers, estratégias de marketing e publicidade, relações públicas, estudos de marca e todos os assuntos relativos a este sector.Email: igarcez@meiosepublicidade.workmedia.pt.

Language (s): Portuguese
DAILY NEWSPAPER

Mestrados (DN + JN)
Owner: Global Notícias, Publicações, S.A.
T: 351 222 096 100 **E:** secdir@jn.pt
W: http://www.jn.pt **Circ:** 167564 Publisher's Statement
Editorial Profile: Published with: Diário de Notícias; Jornal de Notícias. National.Local Translation: Edição especial com informação relativa aos mestrados da época pós-bolonha e quais as ofertas.Publicado com: Diário de Notícias; Jornal de Notícias Phone: +351 213 187 300
Language (s): Portuguese
DAILY NEWSPAPER

Metro Casa
Owner: Transjornal Edição de Publicações, S.A.
Editorial: Estrada da Outurela, 118, Parque Holanda - Edifício Holanda, Carnaxide 2790-114. **T:** 351 214 169 210
E: metrocasa@metroportugal.com
W: http://www.readmetro.com **Circ:** 130000 Publisher's Statement
Editorial Profile: Tips on home decorating, the latest style on home fashion tendencies, articles and interviews with well-known interior designers, news on the real estate market and the suggested best places where can acquire a property.
Language (s): Portuguese
DAILY NEWSPAPER

Metro do Porto
Owner: Global Notícias, Publicações, S.A.
Editorial: R. de Gonçalo Cristovão, 195, Porto 4049-011. **T:** 351 213 187 500 **E:** secdir@jn.pt
W: http://www.jn.pt **Circ:** 110393 APCT
Editorial Profile: National. Local Translation:Suplemento dedicado ao Metro do Porto.
Language (s): Portuguese
DAILY NEWSPAPER

Metro Portugal
Owner: Transjornal Edição de Publicações, S.A.
Editorial: Arruamento D à R. José Maria Nicolau, 3, Lisboa 1549-023.
T: 351 214 169 210
E: geral@metroportugal.com
W: www.readmetro.com
Freq: Daily; **Circ:** 130000 Publisher's Statement
Cartoonist: Pedro K.
Editorial Profile: Free newspaper concerning national and international news and current affairs. Aimed for Aveiro, Braga, Coimbra, Évora, Faro, Leiria, Lisboa and Porto regions.Local Translation: Diário gratuito com notícias sobre a actualidade. Actualidade local, nacional e internacional, Desporto e Entretenimento são algumas das secções. Regularmente convida personalidades dos mais variados sectores para reunir, seleccionar e editar os conteúdos do jornal. Este projecto é uma parceria entre a Metro Internacional, presente em mais de 23 países, e a Media Capital.Phone: +351 214 241 430
Fax: +351 214 174 206
Language (s): Portuguese
DAILY NEWSPAPER

Metro Verão
Owner: Transjornal Edição de Publicações, S.A.
Editorial: Arruamento D à R. José Maria Nicolau, 3, Lisboa 1549-023.
T: 351 214 169 210
E: metro@metroportugal.com
W: http://www.readmetro.com
Freq: 2 Times/Week; **Circ:** 150000 Publisher's Statement
Editorial Profile: Special summer edition. Aimed for Faro, Lisboa and Porto regions and in the coast region, mainly in the beaches.Local Translation: Edição especial de Verão que aborda temas como saúde, viagens, cuidados com o Sol, entre outros.Phone: +351 214 241 430
Fax: +351 214 174 206
Language (s): Portuguese
DAILY NEWSPAPER

Minha Revista
Owner: Empresa Diário do Minho, Lda.
Editorial: R. Dr. Justino Cruz, 110 - 2° - Sala 13, Braga 4700-314. **T:** 351 253613350
Freq: Monthly
Editorial Profile: Local Translation: Revista regional gratuita, produzida pelos jornalistas do Diário do Minho, que tem como objectivo apresentar a realidade quotidiana do Minho, sobretudo através de histórias de vida (ou institucionais) marcantes.
Language (s): Portuguese
DAILY NEWSPAPER

Modalidades
Owner: Sociedade Vicra Desportiva, S.A.
Editorial: Travessa da Queimada, 23 - R/C, 1° e 2°, Lisboa 1249-113. **T:** 351 213 463 981
E: publicidag@abola.pt
W: http://www.abola.pt **Circ:** 120000 Publisher's Statement
Editorial Profile: Provides special information about sports in general. Mainland.Local Translation: Suplemento dedicado às várias modalidades desportivas existentes nacionais ou internacionais.
Language (s): Portuguese
DAILY NEWSPAPER

Modalidades
Owner: Edisport - Sociedade de Publicações Desportivas, S.A.
Editorial: Av. Conde de Valbom, 30 - 4°/5°, Lisboa 1050-068. **T:** 351 210 124 900
E: antoniomagalhaes@record.pt
W: http://www.record.xl.pt **Circ:** 115296 Publisher's Statement
Language (s): Portuguese
DAILY NEWSPAPER

Mudar de Vida
Editorial: R. João Ortigão Ramos, 19, Lisboa 1500-362 **E:** jornalmudardevida@gmail.com
W: http://www.jornalmudardevida.net
Freq: Monthly
Editorial Profile: Popular political newspaper, which has as main topics the conditions of life, the aspirations and struggles of workers and popular classes.
Language (s): Portuguese
DAILY NEWSPAPER

Mundo Sénior
Owner: Mundo Sénior
T: 351 214 685 361 **E:** geral@mundosenior.pt
W: http://www.mundosenior.pt
Freq: Monthly
Language (s): Portuguese
DAILY NEWSPAPER

Mundo Universitário
Owner: Moving Media, Publicações, Lda.
Editorial: Arruamento D à R. José Maria Nicolau, 3, Lisboa 1549-023.
T: 351 926 726 060
E: info@mundouniversitario.pt
W: http://www.mundouniversitario.pt
Freq: Bi-Weekly
Editor: Luís Magalhães; **Editor:** Nuno Saraiva
Editorial Profile: Free magazine about the university students' lifestyle. Mainland. Distributed in Portuguese universities and Lusomundo cinemas.Local Translation: Quinzenal gratuito com uma secção noticiosa e outra centrada em actividades do interesse dos estudantes fora do recinto universitário. Lifestyle, música (Jukebox), cinema (Sétima Arte), desporto, mundo laboral e a sexualidade dos universitários, numa secção apelidada de Jardim do Éden são algumas das secções habituais.Alternative Title: MU
Language (s): Portuguese
DAILY NEWSPAPER

Museus
Owner: Presselivre - Imprensa Livre, S.A.
T: 351 213 185 462 **E:** geral@correiomanha.pt
W: http://www.cmjornal.pt **Circ:** 158546 APCT
Editorial Profile: National. Local Translation:Suplemento dedicado aos museus, com especial destaque para os museus de Vila Nova de Cerveira.
Language (s): Portuguese
DAILY NEWSPAPER

Norte
Owner: Presselivre - Imprensa Livre, S.A.
Editorial: R. Manuel Pinto de Azevedo, 80 - 1°, Porto 4100-320. **T:** 351 213 185 200
E: direccao@cmjornal.pt
W: http://www.cmjornal.pt
Freq: Daily; **Circ:** 158796 APCT
Editorial Profile: North edition. Local Translation:Diário generalista em formato tablóide com informação nacional e internacional. Actualidade, sociedade, economia, política, desporto, cultura, media, celebridades, agenda e programação televisiva são alguns dos temas focados. "TV", "Vidas" e "Domingo" são alguns dos suplementos fixos deste jornal. Phone: +351 213 540 382; +351 213 540 386
Fax: +351 213 540 386
Language (s): Portuguese
DAILY NEWSPAPER

Notícias CPLP
Editorial: R. de S. Caetano, 32, Lisboa 1200-829. **T:** 351 21 392 85 60 **E:** afpi@afpi.eu.com
W: http://www.cplp.org **Circ:** 195000 Publisher's Statement
Language (s): Portuguese
DAILY NEWSPAPER

Notícias de Avanca
Owner: Fábrica da Igreja Paroquial de Avanca
Editorial: Residência Paroquial de Avanca, Estarreja 3860-000. **T:** 351 234 884 671
Freq: Monthly
Editorial Profile: Regional newspaper of religious tone with information and interest articles about Aveiro.
Language (s): Portuguese
DAILY NEWSPAPER

Notícias de Basto
Owner: Associação Acção Jovem
Editorial: Edifício da Antiga Escola C+S - Sala 15, R. 5 de Outubro, Celorico De Basto 4890-033. **T:** 351 255 323 444
E: noticiasdebasto@gmail.com
W: http://www.noticiasdebasto.com/index.php
Freq: Bi-Weekly
Editorial Profile: Fortnightly regional newspaper with information about Celorico de Basto (Braga). Politics, current affairs, society, religion, sport, entertainment and events.
Language (s): Portuguese
DAILY NEWSPAPER

Notícias de Fafe
Owner: João Paulo Couto Pinto
Editorial: R. dos Combatentes da Grande Guerra, 338, Fafe 4820
Freq: Weekly
Editorial Profile: Weekly regional newspaper with information about Braga. Politics, current affairs, society, religion, sport, entertainment and events.
Language (s): Portuguese
DAILY NEWSPAPER

Notícias de Mirandela
Owner: Tipografia Pinto, Lda.
Editorial: R. Alexandre Herculano, 68, Mirandela 5370-299. **T:** 351 278 265 904
E: noticiasdemirandela@tugamail.com
Freq: Bi-Weekly
Editor: Mr./Ms. Editor
Editorial Profile: Regional newspaper with information about Bragança. Politics, current affairs, society, religion, sport, entertainment and events.
Language (s): Portuguese
DAILY NEWSPAPER

Notícias de Nariz & Fátima
Owner: Fábrica da Igreja Paroquial de Nossa Senhora de Fátima
Editorial: Paróquia de Nossa Senhora de Fátima, Nossa Senhora De Fátima 3810.
T: 351 234 941 241
E: jnnarizefatima@gmail.com
W: http://noticiasdenarizefatima.blogspot.com
Freq: Monthly
Editorial Profile: Regional newspaper of religious tone with information and interest articles about Santarém.
Language (s): Portuguese
DAILY NEWSPAPER

Notícias de Valongo
Owner: Empresa Jornalística Notícias de Valongo, Lda.
Editorial: Praça Manuel Guedes, 242 - 2° Fte., Apartado 78, Gondomar 4420-000
Editor: Mr./Ms. Editor
Editorial Profile: Regional newspaper with information about Porto. Politics, current affairs, society, sport, entertainment and events.
Language (s): Portuguese
DAILY NEWSPAPER

Notícias de Vendas Novas
Owner: Igreja Paroquial de Vendas Novas
Editorial: Igreja Paroquial de Vendas Novas, Apartado 41, Vendas Novas 7080-000.
T: 351 265 892 370
Editor: Mr./Ms. Editor
Editorial Profile: Regional newspaper of religious tone with information and interest articles about Évora.
Language (s): Portuguese
DAILY NEWSPAPER

Notícias de Vila Verde
Owner: Empresa Editorial Vilaverdense, Lda.
Editorial: Praça do Município, 48 - 1°, Vila Verde 4730-000
Freq: Bi-Weekly
Editorial Profile: Fortnightly regional newspaper with information about Braga. Politics, current affairs, society, religion, sport, entertainment and events.
Language (s): Portuguese
DAILY NEWSPAPER

Notícias de Vouzela
Owner: Grupo Media Centro
Editorial: Praça da República, 17, Vouzela 3670-245. **T:** 351 232 772 026
E: jnoticiasdevouzela@sapo.pt
W: http://www.noticiasdevouzela.com
Freq: Weekly
Editor: Mr./Ms. Editor
Editorial Profile: Weekly regional newspaper with information about Viseu. Politics, current affairs, society, religion, sport, entertainment and events. Aimed for Viseu region, mainly for Vouzela population.Local Translation: Semanário de informação regional relativa a Viseu. Política, actualidade, sociedade, religião, desporto, entretenimento e eventos.
Language (s): Portuguese
DAILY NEWSPAPER

Notícias do Comércio
Owner: Active, Lda.
Editorial: R. da Palma, 284 - 2° D, Lisboa 1100-394. **T:** 351 218 860 650
E: maria.joao@ative.pt
Editor: Mr./Ms. Editor
Editorial Profile: Occasional newspaper concerning the nourishing industry.
Language (s): Portuguese
DAILY NEWSPAPER

Notícias do Condomínio
Owner: Franquiger, S.A.
Editorial: Sintra Business Park, 1, 2B, Sintra 2710-089. **T:** 351 219 112 720
E: noticias@ldc.pt
W: http://noticiasdocondominio.wordpress.com
Freq: Quarterly; **Circ:** 250000 Publisher's Statement
Editorial Profile: National. Local Translation:Jornal com notícias relacionadas com o condomínio.
Language (s): Portuguese
DAILY NEWSPAPER

Novas Oportunidades
Owner: Global Notícias, Publicações, S.A.
Editorial: Av. da Liberdade, 266, Lisboa 1250-149. **T:** 351 213 180 000
E: geral@globalnoticias.pt
W: http://www.globalnoticias.pt **Circ:** 166341 Publisher's Statement
Language (s): Portuguese
DAILY NEWSPAPER

Ofereço-me para Trabalhar
Owner: Global Notícias, Publicações, S.A.
Editorial: R. de Gonçalo Cristovão, 195-219, Porto 4049-011. **T:** 351 222 096 111
E: iniciativasolidaria@jn.pt **W:** www.jn.pt
Freq: Weekly; **Circ:** 106993 Publisher's Statement
Editorial Profile: National. Local Translation:Suplemento semanal para divulgação de quem procura trabalho ou tem um serviço específico que fornece como trabalhador por conta própria. Phone: +351 213 187 500
Language (s): Portuguese
DAILY NEWSPAPER

O Olhanense
Owner: Sporting Clube Olhanense
Editorial: Praça da Restauração, 18, Olhão 8700-350. **T:** 351 289 703 168
E: jornalolhanense@iol.pt
Language (s): Portuguese
DAILY NEWSPAPER

Página 1
Owner: R/com
Editorial: R. Ivens, 14, Lisboa 1249-108.
T: 351 213 239 239
E: jornalonline@pagina1.pt
W: www.pagina1.pt
Freq: Daily
Editor: Paulo Ribeiro Pinto
Editorial Profile: National daily newspaper produced by Rádio Renascença. National.Local Translation: Diário nacional produzido pela Rádio Renascença. Publicação exclusivamente online, com notícias do panorama nacional e internacional, entrevistas e temáticas que marcam a actualidade, como política, sociedade, economia, desporto, entre outros. Lançado às 17h00. Disponível na Internet em formato PDF.Phone: +351 213 239 200
Language (s): Portuguese
DAILY NEWSPAPER

Pauta
Owner: Banda de Alcobaça

Editorial: R. Frei António Brandão, 50-52, Alcobaça 2460-047. **T:** 351 262 597 611
E: press@academiamalcobaca.com
W: http://www.academiamalcobaca.com
Editor: David Mariano
Editorial Profile: Local Translation: Publicação electrónica da Academia de Música de Alcobaça com notas, estórias e apontamentos musicais. Edições gratuitamente disponíveis no Issuu.
Language (s): Portuguese
DAILY NEWSPAPER

PEC
Owner: Sojornal - Sociedade Jornalística e Editorial, S.A.
Editorial: Edifício S. Francisco de Sales, R. Calvet de Magalhães, 242, Paço De Arcos 2770-022. **T:** 351 214 544 000
E: ipublishing@impresa.pt
W: http://www.expresso.pt **Circ:** 136650 Publisher's Statement
Editorial Profile: National. Local Translation:Suplemento sobre o PEC: Programa de Estabilidade e Crescimento.
Language (s): Portuguese
DAILY NEWSPAPER

Política
Owner: R/com
Editorial: R. Ivens, 14, Lisboa 1249-108.
T: 351 213 239 239
E: jornalonline@pagina1.pt
W: http://www.pagina1.pt
Editorial Profile: National. Local Translation:Edição especial com artigos sobre a vida política nacional. Phone: +351 213 239 200
Language (s): Portuguese
DAILY NEWSPAPER

Ponto Final
Owner: Títulos & Parágrafos, Lda.
Editorial: Travessa à R. Direita, 5 - Escritório 3, Aveiro 3810-093. **T:** 351 234 181 105
E: redaccao@jornalpontofinal.com
Language (s): Portuguese
DAILY NEWSPAPER

Porto
Owner: Global Notícias, Publicações, S.A.
Editorial: R. de Gonçalo Cristóvão, 195 - 219, Porto 4049-011. **T:** 351 222 096 100
E: dpe@jn.pt **W:** http://www.jn.pt
Freq: Daily; **Circ:** 106688 Publisher's Statement
Editorial Profile: Distributed in Oporto. Local Translation:Jornal generalista, especialmente concebido para o segmento em que se insere - distrito do Porto. Com notícias de cariz nacional e internacional, comporta ainda a vertente local e regionalista da área a que se destina nas mais variadas temáticas (desporto, economia, novas tecnologias ou o social local). Publicação integrante do Jornal de Notícias.Email: secdir@jn.pt; grandeporto@jn.pt. Phone: +351 213 187 300
Language (s): Portuguese
DAILY NEWSPAPER

Portugal - Angola (DN + JN)
Owner: Global Notícias, Publicações, S.A.
T: 351 213 187 500 **E:** dnot@dn.pt
W: http://dn.sapo.pt **Circ:** 165912 Publisher's Statement
Editorial Profile: National. Local Translation:As relações empresariais entre Portugal e Angola - a internacionalização nacional.
Language (s): Portuguese
DAILY NEWSPAPER

Portugal Ano a Ano
Owner: Sojornal - Sociedade Jornalística e Editorial, S.A.
Editorial: Edifício S. Francisco de Sales, R. Calvet de Magalhães, 242, Paço De Arcos 2770-022. **T:** 351 214 544 000
E: ipublishing@impresa.pt
W: http://www.expresso.pt **Circ:** 127500 Publisher's Statement
Editorial Profile: National. Local Translation:Suplemento que indica as medidas políticas e económicas a adoptar no país. **Email:** site@expresso.impresa.pt.
Language (s): Portuguese
DAILY NEWSPAPER

The Portugal News
Owner: Anglopress - Edições e Publicidade, Lda.
Editorial: ANGLOPRESS Edições e Publicidade, Lda., Apartado 13, Lagoa 8400-901. **T:** 351 282 341 100
E: newsdesk@theportugalnews.com
W: http://www.theportugalnews.com
Freq: Weekly
Editor: Brendan de Beer
Editorial Profile: Newspaper containing Portuguese news dedicated to the English population in Portugal. National. Aimed at English imigrants living in Portugal.Local Translation: Semanário de informação geral, dedicado à comunidade inglesa residente em Portugal. Contém notícias da actualidade portuguesa, política internacional, notícias de África, guia semanal de TV e satélite, guia de eventos, arte, viagens, desporto, jardinagem, golfe, motores e anúncios de imóveis.Alternative Title: Portugal News (The) Url: http://www.the-news.net.
Language (s): English
DAILY NEWSPAPER

Poupança
Owner: Presselivre - Imprensa Livre, S.A.
Editorial: Av. João Crisóstomo, N° 72, Lisboa 1069-043. **T:** 351 213 185 462
E: geral@correiomanha.pt
W: http://www.cmjornal.pt **Circ:** 166385 Publisher's Statement
Language (s): Portuguese
DAILY NEWSPAPER

O Povo do Cartaxo
Owner: Artnews - Sociedade de Comunicações e Arte, Lda.
Editorial: Largo do Valverde, 27, Cartaxo 2070-040. **T:** 351 243 702 154
E: opovodocartaxo@gmail.com
Freq: Bi-Weekly
Editor: Mr./Ms. Editor
Editorial Profile: Newspaper with information about Cartaxo. Politics, current affairs, society, sport, entertainment and events. Read by Cartaxo locals.Local Translation: Quinzenário regional com informação relativa ao Cartaxo.
Language (s): Portuguese
DAILY NEWSPAPER

Prazer de Consumir
Owner: Metro News Publicações, S.A.
Editorial: Estrada da Outurela, 118, Parque Holanda - Edifício Holanda, Carnaxide 2790-114. **T:** 351 214 169 210 **E:** destak@destak.pt
W: http://www.destak.pt **Circ:** 120000 Publisher's Statement
Editorial Profile: Local Translation: Suplemento sobre consumo.Email: mjvaz@destak.pt; lfilipe@destak.pt.
Language (s): Portuguese
DAILY NEWSPAPER

Prémio Mulher Activa
Owner: Sojornal - Sociedade Jornalística e Editorial, S.A.
T: 351 214 544 000 **E:** expresso@expresso.pt
W: http://www.expresso.pt **Circ:** 136650 Publisher's Statement
Language (s): Portuguese
DAILY NEWSPAPER

Primeiro Emprego
Owner: Presselivre - Imprensa Livre, S.A.
Editorial: Arruamento D à R. José Maria Nicolau, 3, Lisboa 1549-023.
T: 351 213 185 200 **E:** direccao@cmjornal.pt
W: www.cmjornal.pt
Freq: Weekly; **Circ:** 161374 APCT
Cartoonist: António Maia
Editorial Profile: Employment. National.Local Translation: O Primeiro Emprego divulga as ofertas de emprego disponíveis.Phone: +351 213 540 382; +351 213 540 386
Fax: +351 213 540 386
Language (s): Portuguese
DAILY NEWSPAPER

Produtos Biológicos (DN + JN)
Owner: Global Notícias, Publicações, S.A.
Editorial: Edifício Diário de Notícias, Av. da Liberdade, 266, Lisboa 1250-149.
T: 351 213 187 500 **E:** dnot@dn.pt
Circ: 168106 Publisher's Statement
Editorial Profile: National. Local Translation:Suplemento sobre alimentação saudável: qualidade e segurança alimentar.
Language (s): Portuguese
DAILY NEWSPAPER

Publicidade
Owner: Transjornal Edição de Publicações, S.A.
Editorial: Estrada da Outurela, 118, Parque Holanda - Edifício Holanda, Carnaxide 2790-114. **T:** 351 214 169 210
E: metro@metroportugal.com
W: http://www.readmetro.com **Circ:** 130000 Publisher's Statement
Editorial Profile: Distributed in public transports concerning the most populous areas of Aveiro, Braga, Coimbra, Évora, Faro, Leiria, Lisboa and Porto. Phone: +351 214 241 430
Fax: +351 214 174 206
Language (s): Portuguese
DAILY NEWSPAPER

Rally de Portugal - Reis da Condução
Editorial: Av. Conde Valbom, 30 - 4°/5°, Lisboa 1050-068. **T:** 351 210 124 900
Circ: 276095 Not Audited
Editorial Profile: Published with: Correio da Manhã; Record.
Language (s): Portuguese
DAILY NEWSPAPER

Reciclagem
Owner: Presselivre - Imprensa Livre, S.A.
Editorial: Av. João Crisóstomo, N° 72, Lisboa 1069-043. **T:** 351 213 185 462
E: geral@correiomanha.pt
W: http://www.cmjornal.pt **Circ:** 170737 Publisher's Statement
Language (s): Portuguese
DAILY NEWSPAPER

Revista Portuguesa de Educação
Owner: Universidade do Minho - Ciências da Educação
Editorial: Instituto de Educação e Psicologia, Campus de Gualtar, Braga 4710.
T: 351 253 604 249 **E:** rpe@iep.uminho.pt
W: http://www.scielo.oces.mctes.pt/scielo.php/script_sci_serial/pid_0871-9187/lng_p
Freq: Semi-Annual
Language (s): Portuguese
DAILY NEWSPAPER

O Ribatejo
Owner: Jortejo Jornais, Rádio e Televisão, Lda.
Editorial: Centro Nacional de Exposições - Quinta das Cegonhas, Apartado 355, Santarem 2000-471. **T:** 351 243 309 600
E: info@oribatejo.pt **W:** www.oribatejo.pt
Freq: Weekly
Editor Chefe: João Baptista; **Cartoonist:** António Maia
Editorial Profile: Newspaper featuring economic, business and general news about the Ribatejo region. Read in Santarém region.Local Translation: Jornal regional de informação relativa à região ribatejana.
Language (s): Portuguese
DAILY NEWSPAPER

Rostos
Owner: António de Jesus Sousa Pereira
Editorial: R. Miguel Bombarda, 74, Loja 24 - C. Comercial Bombarda, Barreiro 2830-355.
T: 351 212 066 758 **E:** jornal@rostos.pt
W: http://www.rostos.pt
Freq: Monthly
Editorial Profile: Local Translation: Jornal de cariz local e regional relativo às diversas áreas (empresarial, institucional, política ou ambiental), que caracterizam o distrito de Setúbal.Phone: +351 +351 212 066 779
Language (s): Portuguese
DAILY NEWSPAPER

Santarém
Owner: Presselivre - Imprensa Livre, S.A.
Editorial: Av. João Crisóstomo, N° 72, Lisboa 1069-043. **T:** 351 213 185 462
E: geral@correiomanha.pt
W: http://www.cmjornal.pt **Circ:** 151203 Not Audited
Language (s): Portuguese
DAILY NEWSPAPER

Saúde
Owner: Cofina Media Internet
Editorial: Arruamento D à R. José Maria Nicolau, 3, Lisboa 1549-023.
T: 351 214 169 210 **E:** destak@destak.pt
W: http://www.destak.pt
Freq: Monthly; **Circ:** 135000 Publisher's Statement
Editorial Profile: Health. Read in Lisboa and Setúbal districts.Local Translation: Edição especial dedicada a diferentes assuntos do sector saúde.
Language (s): Portuguese
DAILY NEWSPAPER

Saúde & Bem-estar (CO + CC)
Owner: Lançar Ideias, Lda.
Editorial: Av. dos Bombeiros Voluntários, 19, Loja 1, Martins 2725-592 MEM.
T: 351 219 205 525
E: correiocascais@gmail.com **Circ:** 110000 Publisher's Statement
Editorial Profile: Local Translation: Suplemento sobre sáude e bem-estar e actividades relacionadas.
Language (s): Portuguese
DAILY NEWSPAPER

Saúde Pública
Owner: Sojornal - Sociedade Jornalística e Editorial, S.A.
Editorial: Edifício Lisboa Oriente Office, Av. Infante D. Henrique, 333 H - 5°, Lisboa 1800-282. **T:** 351 218 504 000
E: saudepublica@saudepublica.pt
W: http://www.jasfarma.com
Freq: Monthly; **Circ:** 132175 Publisher's Statement
Editorial Profile: National. Local Translation:Dossier que pretende promover e divulgar informação na área da saúde, com o apoio de especialistas. Phone: +351 964 041 260
Language (s): Portuguese
DAILY NEWSPAPER

Segurança Infantil (DN + JN)
Owner: Global Notícias, Publicações, S.A.
Editorial: Av. da Liberdade, 266 - 4°, Lisboa 1250-149. **T:** 351 213 187 500
E: agenda@jn.pt **W:** http://www.jn.pt
Circ: 156833 Publisher's Statement
Editorial Profile: Special edition about child safety.Published with: Diário de Notícias; Jornal de Notícias.
Language (s): Portuguese
DAILY NEWSPAPER

Soberania do Povo
Owner: Soberania do Povo Editora, S.A.
Editorial: Av. Dr. Eugénio Ribeiro, 89, 3°, Apartado 145, Agueda 3754-909.
T: 351 234 622 626
E: geral@soberaniadopovo.pt
W: http://www.soberaniadopovo.pt
Freq: Weekly
Editorial Profile: Weekly newspaper with information about Águeda region. Politics, current affairs, society, sport, entertainment and events. Aimed for Águeda locals.Local Translation: Semanário de informação regional relativa a Águeda.Phone: +351 234 625 013
Language (s): Portuguese
DAILY NEWSPAPER

Sport
Owner: Presselivre - Imprensa Livre, S.A.
Editorial: Arruamento D à R. José Maria Nicolau, 3, Lisboa 1549-023.
T: 351 213 185 200 **E:** direccao@cmjornal.pt
W: www.cmjornal.pt
Freq: Weekly; **Circ:** 161374 APCT
Editorial Profile: Sport. National.Local Translation: Jornal semanal dedicado ao desporto.Phone: +351 213 540 382; +351 213 540 386
Fax: +351 213 540 386
Language (s): Portuguese
DAILY NEWSPAPER

Sport
Owner: Metro News Publicações, S.A.
T: 351 214 169 210 **E:** destak@destak.pt
W: http://www.destak.pt **Circ:** 135000 Publisher's Statement
Editorial Profile: Local Translation: Edição especial dedicada a diferentes assuntos do sector desportivo.
Language (s): Portuguese
DAILY NEWSPAPER

Superstars Series
Owner: Presselivre - Imprensa Livre, S.A.
T: 351 213 185 462 **E:** geral@correiomanha.pt
W: http://www.cmjornal.pt **Circ:** 158785 Publisher's Statement
Editorial Profile: National. Local Translation:Edição especial da Superstars Series, com lugar no Autódromo do Algarve.
Language (s): Portuguese
DAILY NEWSPAPER

Terras do Homem
Owner: Terraimagem - Edição de Publicações Periódicas, Lda.
Editorial: Av. Professor Machado Vilela, 18 - 3° Dto., Vila Verde 4730-721.
T: 351 253 321 450
E: terrasdohomem@gmail.com
W: www.terrasdohomem.com
Freq: Bi-Weekly
Editorial Profile: Local Translation: Jornal dedicado à actualidade da região de Vila Verde, caracterizando-se por secção noticiosa local/regional, desporto, acontecimentos de ordem nacional e internacional, bem como indíce noticioso de cariz regionalista, (nomeadamente sobre Terras de Bouro, Amares e/ou Vale do Homem).
Language (s): Portuguese
DAILY NEWSPAPER

Timoneiro
Owner: Fábrica da Igreja Paroquial da Gafanha da Nazaré

Editorial: Av. José Estevão, Cartório Paroquial, Gafanha Da Nazaré 3830-908.
T: 351 234 365 803 **E:** j.timoneiro@gmail.com
Freq: Monthly
Editor: Mr./Ms. Editor
Language (s): Portuguese
DAILY NEWSPAPER

Universidades
Owner: Transjornal Edição de Publicações, S.A.
Editorial: Estrada da Outurela, 118, Parque Holanda - Edifício Holanda, Carnaxide 2790-114. **T:** 351 214 169 210
E: metro@metroportugal.com
W: http://www.readmetro.com **Circ:** 130000 Publisher's Statement
Language (s): Portuguese
DAILY NEWSPAPER

Verão
Owner: Cofina Media Internet
Editorial: Arruamento D à R. José Maria Nicolau, 3, Lisboa 1549-023.
T: 351 214 169 210 **E:** destak@destak.pt
W: http://www.destak.pt
Freq: Weekly; **Circ:** 200000 Publisher's Statement
Editorial Profile: Summer. Distributed on the coast region of Portugal.Local Translation: Edição especial de Verão com sugestões de locais para as férias, alimentação, eventos, lazer, cinema e ainda sobre celebridades.
Language (s): Portuguese
DAILY NEWSPAPER

Vida Saudável (DN + JN)
Owner: Global Notícias, Publicações, S.A.
Editorial: Edifício Diário de Notícias, Av. da Liberdade, 266, Lisboa 1250-149.
T: 351 213 187 500 **E:** dnot@dn.pt
W: http://dn.sapo.pt **Circ:** 149901 Publisher's Statement
Editorial Profile: Published with: Jornal de Notícias; Diário de Notícias.
Language (s): Portuguese
DAILY NEWSPAPER

Vila Nova de Gaia
Owner: Global Notícias, Publicações, S.A.
Editorial: Av. da Liberdade, 266 - 4°, Lisboa 1250-149. **T:** 351 213 187 500 **E:** secdir@jn.pt
W: http://www.jn.pt **Circ:** 106854 APCT
Editorial Profile: Aimed for Vila Nova de Gaia locals. Local Translation:Suplemento dedicado ao Concelho de Vila Nova de Gaia.
Email: agenda@jn.pt.
Language (s): Portuguese
DAILY NEWSPAPER

Viver Azeméis
Owner: Câmara Municipal de Oliveira de Azeméis
Editorial: Largo da República, Oliveira De Azeméis 3720-240. **T:** 351 256 674 694
E: geral/cm-oaz.pt **W:** http://www.cm-oaz.pt
Freq: Weekly
Editorial Profile: Local Translation: Boletim de eventos do Município de Oliveira de Azeméis. Disponível no site da Câmara e no Issuu.
Language (s): Portuguese
DAILY NEWSPAPER

Voz da Verdade
Owner: Nova Terra - Empresa Editorial, Lda.
Editorial: Mosteiro de S. Vicente de Fora, Lisboa 1100-473. **T:** 351 218 810 558
E: vozverdade@gmail.com
W: http://www.jornalw.org
Freq: Weekly
Editorial Profile: Local Translation: Jornal diocesano de Lisboa.Alternative Title: Jornal W - Voz da Verdade.
Language (s): Portuguese
DAILY NEWSPAPER

A Voz de Freixianda
Owner: Fábrica da Igreja Paroquial de Freixianda
Editorial: R. Padre Faustino, 1, Freixianda-Ourém 2435-283. **T:** 351 249 551 526
Freq: Monthly
Editor: Mr./Ms. Editor
Language (s): Portuguese
DAILY NEWSPAPER

A Voz de Trás-os-Montes
Owner: Conferências de S. Vicente de Paulo de Vila Real
Editorial: R. D. António Valente da Fonseca, 22, Apartado 212, Vila Real 5001-911.
T: 351 259 340 290
E: geral@avozdetrasosmontes.com
W: www.avozdetrasosmontes.com
Freq: Weekly
Cartoonist: A. Basto

Editorial Profile: Weekly newspaper with information about Trás-os-Montes region. Politics, current affairs, society, sport, entertainment and events. Read in Trás-os-Montes region.Local Translation: Semanário de informação regional relativa à região de Trás-os-Montes.Email: assinaturas@avozdetrasosmontes.com. Phone: +351 914 803 266
Language (s): Portuguese
DAILY NEWSPAPER

Voz do Mar
Owner: Fábrica da Igreja Paroquial da Freguesia de Ajuda da Cidade de Peniche
Editorial: R. D. Luís Ataíde, 19 - 1° D, Peniche 2520-408. **T:** 351 262 783 900
E: avozdomar@sapo.pt
Freq: Bi-Weekly
Editor: Mr./Ms. Editor
Language (s): Portuguese
DAILY NEWSPAPER

Zoom
Owner: Global Notícias, Publicações, S.A.
Editorial: R. de Gonçalo Cristovão, 195-219, Porto 4049-011. **T:** 351 222 096 111
E: secdir@jn.pt **W:** http://www.jn.pt
Circ: 107777 Publisher's Statement
Editorial Profile: National. Local Translation:Publicação com edições temáticas diferentes. Phone: +351 213 187 500
Language (s): Portuguese
DAILY NEWSPAPER

Zoom (DN + JN)
Owner: Global Notícias, Publicações, S.A.
Editorial: Edifício Diário de Notícias, Av. da Liberdade, 266, Lisboa 1250-149.
T: 351 213 187 500 **E:** dnot@dn.pt
W: http://www.dn.pt **Circ:** 157478 Publisher's Statement
Editorial Profile: Different themes. National.Local Translation: Publicação com edições temáticas diferentes.
Language (s): Portuguese
DAILY NEWSPAPER

NEWS SERVICE/SYNDICATE

1/2 Formato - Agência de Fotografia, Lda.
Editorial: R. Paraíso, 184 - 3° D, Porto 4000-375. **T:** 351 222 033 087
W: http://www.meioformato.com
Freq: Daily
Language (s): Portuguese
NEWS SERVICE/SYNDICATE

ADS Press
Owner: Agência de Representações Dias da Silva, Lda.
Editorial: R. Gil Vicente, 26 B, Cotovia, Sesimbra 2970-305. **T:** 351 218 110 270
E: adspress@ads-press.com
Freq: Daily
Language (s): Portuguese
NEWS SERVICE/SYNDICATE

AEI - Agência Europeia de Imprensa
Owner: Agência Europeia de Imprensa, Lda.
Editorial: Largo Rosa, 6, Lisboa 1100-457.
T: 351 210 307 860 **E:** aei@mail.aei.pt
W: http://www.aei.pt
Freq: Daily
Language (s): Portuguese
NEWS SERVICE/SYNDICATE

Agence France-Presse
Owner: Agence France-Presse
Editorial: R. Rosa Araújo, 34 - 3°, Lisboa 1250-195. **T:** 351 213 556 939
E: lisboa@afp.com **W:** http://www.afp.com
Freq: Daily
Language (s): Portuguese
NEWS SERVICE/SYNDICATE

Agência Ecclesia
Editorial: Campo dos Mártires da Pátria, 43, Lisboa 1150-225. **T:** 351 218 855 472
E: agencia@ecclesia.pt
W: http://www.agencia.ecclesia.pt
Freq: Daily
Editor Chefe: Octávio Carmo
Editorial Profile: News agency regarding the catholic world. Local Translation:Agência noticiosa com informação relativa à religião católica e assuntos relacionados.
Language (s): Portuguese
NEWS SERVICE/SYNDICATE

Agência Feriaque
Owner: Fernando Maia Henrique, Herdeiros
Editorial: R. Chagas, 17 CV - D, Lisboa 1249-195. **T:** 351 213 219 310

E: feriaque@agenciaferiaque.pt
Freq: Daily
Language (s): Portuguese
NEWS SERVICE/SYNDICATE

Agência Noticiosa Nova China
Owner: Agência Noticiosa Nova China
Editorial: R. Gonçalo Velho Cabral, 11 A, Lisboa 1400-188. **T:** 351 213 015 783
E: xinhua@mail.telepac.pt
Freq: Daily
Language (s): Portuguese
NEWS SERVICE/SYNDICATE

AIC Banco de Imagens
Owner: AIC Arquivo Internacional de Cor - Comunicação pela Imagem, Lda.
Editorial: R. Brito Capelo, 822 R/C, Matosinhos 4450-068. **T:** 351 229 397 507
E: info@aic.pt **W:** http://www.aic.pt
Editorial Profile: National. Local Translation:Banco de imagens português, especializado em áreas como a Alimentação, Decoração, Arquitectura e Interiores, Viagens e Destinos. Dispõem também de ofertas em imagens de Obras de Arte. Alternative Title: AIC - Arquivo Internacional de CorPhone: +351 229 397 508
Language (s): Portuguese
NEWS SERVICE/SYNDICATE

Algarsat
Editorial: Quinta Estradas Celões, S. Sebastião, Loulé 8100-287.
T: 351 289 399 742 **E:** vista@mail.telepac.pt
Freq: Daily
Language (s): Portuguese
NEWS SERVICE/SYNDICATE

ASF - Agência de Serviços Fotográficos
Owner: Sociedade Vicra Desportiva, S.A.
Editorial: Travessa da Queimada, 23 -3°, Lisboa 1249-113. **T:** 351 213 431 565
E: asf@abola.pt **W:** http://www.abola.pt/asf
Freq: Daily
Editorial Profile: Coverage of national sport events.
Language (s): Portuguese
NEWS SERVICE/SYNDICATE

Associated Press
Editorial: Praca Duque de Saldanha 1, 8-J, 1050, Lisbon. **T:** 351 213 191-860
Bureau Chief: Alan Clendenning
NEWS SERVICE/SYNDICATE

Atlânticopress - Comunicação e Imagem, Lda.
Editorial: Av. Luís Bívar, 73 - 1° D, Lisboa 1050-142. **T:** 351 213 570 786
Freq: Daily
Language (s): Portuguese
NEWS SERVICE/SYNDICATE

Bloomberg News
Editorial: Regis Business Centre, 110, Avenida de Liberdad, Lisbon 1269-046.
T: 351 213404545
E: libsonnews@bloomberg.net
Bureau Chief: Joao Lima
NEWS SERVICE/SYNDICATE

Bloomberg News
Owner: Regus Business Center, Lda.
Editorial: Av. da Liberdade, 110, Lisboa 1250-146. **T:** 351 213 404 545
W: http://www.bloomberg.com
Freq: Daily
Language (s): Portuguese
NEWS SERVICE/SYNDICATE

Brainpix
Owner: Brainpix, Lda.
Editorial: Av. da República, 41 - 6° D, Lisboa 1050-187. **T:** 351 217 931 886
E: info@brainpix.com
W: http://www.brainpix.pt
Language (s): Portuguese
NEWS SERVICE/SYNDICATE

Carlos Afonso Augusto de Sousa Barros
Editorial: Av. Fernão de Magalhães, 858 - 1° E, Porto 4350-152. **T:** 351 225 107 132
Freq: Daily
Language (s): Portuguese
NEWS SERVICE/SYNDICATE

Dow Jones Newswires
Owner: Dow Jones & Company, Inc.
Editorial: Praça Duque de Saldanha, 1 - 10° B, Lisboa 1050-094. **T:** 351 213 191 863
W: http://www.djnewswires.com
Freq: Daily
Language (s): Portuguese

NEWS SERVICE/SYNDICATE

Fórmula Press - Agência Noticiosa Editorial, Lda.
Owner: Fórmula Press - Agência Noticiosa e Editorial, Lda.
Editorial: Praceta Inglaterra 30, 3°-D, Carcavelos, Carcavelos 2775-414.
T: 351 214 574 008
Freq: Daily
Language (s): Portuguese
NEWS SERVICE/SYNDICATE

Image Market Place - Agência Noticiosa, Lda.
Owner: Image Market Place - Agência Noticiosa, Lda.
Editorial: R. Bartolomeu Dias, 71, Caxias 2760-013. **T:** 351 214 412 647
E: info@impagency.com
W: http://www.impagency.com
Freq: Daily
Language (s): Portuguese
NEWS SERVICE/SYNDICATE

João Carreira Bom - Consultores de Comunicação, Lda.
Owner: João Carreira Bom - Consultores de Comunicação, Lda.
Editorial: Praceta Maestro Ivo Cruz, 12 - 5° A, Lisboa 1500-401. **T:** 351 217 111 584
E: jcb@mail.telepac.pt
Freq: Daily
Language (s): Portuguese
NEWS SERVICE/SYNDICATE

Kameraphoto
Editorial: R. da Vinha, 43 A, Lisboa 1200-475.
T: 351 213 431 676
E: editorial@kameraphoto.com
W: http://www.kameraphoto.com
Editorial Profile: National. Local Translation:Agência de fotografia que tem como um dos objectivos divulgar e representar o trabalho de fotógrafos freelancer.
Language (s): Portuguese
NEWS SERVICE/SYNDICATE

Lusa
Owner: Lusa - Agência de Notícias de Portugal, S.A.
Editorial: R. Dr. João Couto, Lote C, Lisboa 1503-809. **T:** 351 217 116 500
E: agencialusa@lusa.pt **W:** http://www.lusa.pt
Freq: Daily
Editor: Henrique Botequilha; **Editor:** Cristina Cardoso; **Editor:** Vítor Costa; **Editor:** Francisco J. Marques
Editorial Profile: National and international. Local Translation:Agência de notícias portuguesa que fornece informação sobre as mais diversas áreas, nomeadamente actualidade nacional e internacional, economia, política, desporto, cultura, artes, etc. Em Portugal, dispõe de delegações ou correspondentes em todas as capitais de distrito e nos concelhos das áreas metropolitanas de Lisboa e Porto. Tem também delegações e correspondentes em Bruxelas, Madrid, Berlim, Londres, Roma, Paris, Luxemburgo, Moscovo e Estónia (Europa); Bissau, Praia, Luanda e Maputo, S. Tomé, Joanesburgo e Argel (África); Díli, Macau e Pequim (Ásia); S. Paulo, Brasília, Porto Alegre, Caracas (América do Sul); Nova Iorque, Newark, Rhode Island, New Bedford, Washington e Quebeque, (América do Norte) e em Sidney (Austrália). É uma das agências de notícias, da Europa e dos EUA, que fundaram a rede internacional de cooperação designada Minds International que tem como objectivo partilhar sistemas, processos e práticas tecnológicas. Tem parceria com a agência noticiosa espanhola EFE. Alternative Title: Lusa - Agência de Notícias de Portugal, S.A.Email: agenda@lusa.pt.
Language (s): Portuguese
NEWS SERVICE/SYNDICATE

Magazine 24
Editorial: R. Victor Cordon, 37 - 6° Dto., Lisboa 1200-482
Freq: Daily
Language (s): Portuguese
NEWS SERVICE/SYNDICATE

Maghreb Arabe Press
Editorial: R. Chagas, 20 - 2° D, Lisboa 1200-107. **T:** 351 213 257 982
W: http://www.map.com.ma
Freq: Daily
Language (s): Portuguese
NEWS SERVICE/SYNDICATE

NFactos
Editorial: Estrada Exterior da Circunvalação, 14618, Matosinhos 4450-097.
T: 351 935 440 440 **E:** jornalistas@nfactos.pt
W: http://www.nfactos.pt
Editorial Profile: National. Local Translation:A nFACTOS é uma empresa noticiosa que se dedica à produção de trabalhos jornalísticos para a imprensa, rádio, televisão e conteúdos informativos para a internet, especialmente na área da imagem.
Language (s): Portuguese
NEWS SERVICE/SYNDICATE

PNN - Portuguese News Network
Editorial: R. Cândido Oliveira, 5 - Sala 1, Braga 4715-012. **T:** 351 253 265 047
E: press@pnn.com.pt
W: http://www.interpnn.com
Freq: Daily
Language (s): Portuguese
NEWS SERVICE/SYNDICATE

Público Online
Owner: Público - Comunicação Social, S.A.
Editorial: R. do Viriato, 17 - 3°, Lisboa 1069-315. **T:** 351 210 111 000
E: publico@publico.pt
W: http://www.publico.clix.pt
Freq: Daily
Editor: Luís Afonso; **Editor:** José Manuel Tavares Almeida Fernandes; **Editor:** Sérgio B. Gomes; **Editor:** António Granado; **Editor:** Alexandre Martins; **Editor:** José Manuel Rocha
Editorial Profile: Web site focused on the latest Portuguese and international breaking news. Headlines on international events, sports, stock markets, Tv and leisure, special editions to collect, blog section, cultural events and art, travelling and auctions galleries are some of the many online services available. General population.Local Translation: Site de cáracter generalista, reflexo da edição impressa, incide e destaca-se pelo indíce noticioso de última hora, bem como por diversas temáticas que caracterizam as sociedades modernas, das quais destacamos política, ciências, desporto, cultura, economia, educação, media e tecnologia ou sociedade, lazer ou entretenimento, bem como informação por vídeo, (resultante da parcerai entre a Reuters, Lusa e France24), com transmissões em directo dos principais temas que caracterizam a actualidade nacional e internacional.Phone: +351 210 111 102
Language (s): Portuguese
NEWS SERVICE/SYNDICATE

Radimprensa, Lda.
Editorial: R. Barros Lima, 761 - 1°, Porto 4300-063. **T:** 351 225 107 137
E: radimprensa@netc.pt
Freq: Daily
Language (s): Portuguese
NEWS SERVICE/SYNDICATE

Reuters
Editorial: Avenida da Liberdade, 190-2 A, 1250-147, Lisbon. **T:** 351 213509200
NEWS SERVICE/SYNDICATE

Reuters
Editorial: Av. da Liberdade, 190 - 2° A, Lisboa 1250-147. **T:** 351 213 509 200
E: reception.lisbon@thomsonreuters.com
W: http://reuters.com
Freq: Daily
Editor: Sérgio Gonçalves
Editorial Profile: Alternative Title: Reuters Europe, S.A. - Sucursal em Portugal
Language (s): Portuguese
NEWS SERVICE/SYNDICATE

RIA - Agência Noticiosa da Rússia
Editorial: Praça Andrade Caminha, 3, Lisboa 1700-039. **T:** 351 217 934 700
E: ria.lisboa@mail.telepac.pt
Freq: Daily
Language (s): Portuguese
NEWS SERVICE/SYNDICATE

SJS - Sociedade Jornalística do Sul, Lda.
Owner: SJS - Sociedade Jornalística do Sul, Lda.
Editorial: Av. 25 de Abril, Lote C 3 - 3° P, Loulé 8100. **T:** 351 289 411 913
E: sjsul@clix.pt
Freq: Daily
Language (s): Portuguese
NEWS SERVICE/SYNDICATE

Teletráfego - Prestação de Serviços de Informação, Lda.
Editorial: Praça da República, 63 - S 5, Montijo 2870-235. **T:** 351 212 306 820
E: teletrafego@netcabo.pt
Freq: Daily
Language (s): Portuguese
NEWS SERVICE/SYNDICATE

Zeta - Fotografia, Media e Comunicação, Lda.
Editorial: R. Damião Góis, 28 - 4° E, Alges 1495. **T:** 351 214 112 210
E: zeta.sil.com@mail.telepac.pt
Freq: Daily
Language (s): Portuguese
NEWS SERVICE/SYNDICATE

BROADCASTING

RADIO NETWORKS

Antena 1
Owner: Rádio Difusão Portuguesa
Editorial: Av. Marechal Gomes da Costa, 37, Lisboa 1849-030. **T:** 351 213 820 000
E: antena1@rtp.pt **W:** tv1.rtp.pt/antena1
Editorial Profile: Generalist radio station. Special emphasis on Portuguese and international news, entertainment, sports latest headlines and Portuguese music promoting. Radio frequency available on 95.7 FM (Monsanto brodcasting station). National. Local Translation: Estação radiofónica destinada à generalidade dos ouvintes. As suas principais componentes são a actualidade nacional e internacional; o entretenimento, com predominância para a música portuguesa; a divulgação de temas de relevância socio-cultural e a actualidade desportiva, com grande destaque para o futebol profissional. Frequência disponível em 95.7 FM (Emissor de Monsanto). Também dispõe de emissão online.

Antena 2
Owner: Rádio Difusão Portuguesa
Editorial: Av. Marechal Gomes da Costa, 37, Lisboa 1849-030. **T:** 351 213 820 000
E: rdp.antena2@rtp.pt **W:** antena2.rtp.pt
Editorial Profile: Radio station whose main purpose is promoting culture, specially the Portuguese cultural scenery. Poetry, music (from jazz to ethnic, but with special emphasis on classical and erudite music), interviews, programs dedicated to the Portuguese language, documentaries, popular traditions, live classical music concerts produced by Antena 2. Radio frequency available on 94.4 FM (Monsanto broadcasting station). National. Local Translation: Estação de rádio da rede RTP - Rádio e Televisão de Portugal, cuja programação é baseada em música clássica e programas culturais. A Antena 2 tem os seus tipos de música organizados por "tons". Assim, são estes os tons que podemos ouvir nesta estação: tons recentes; tons do mundo; tons de voz; tons antigos; tons conhecidos; tons de jazz; tons ao vivo; tons das ideias; tons da noite e outros tons. Transmite música erudita, jazz, fado, notícias e magazines culturais. Frequência disponível em 94.4 FM (Emissor de Monsanto). Também dispõe de emissão online. Phone: +351 213 820 015

Antena 3
Owner: Rádio Difusão Portuguesa
Editorial: Av. Marechal Gomes da Costa, 37, Lisboa 1849-030. **T:** 351 213 820 000
E: antena3@rtp.pt **W:** ww1.rtp.pt/antena3
Editorial Profile: National radio station with a strong identity and a juvenile attitude. Antena 3 represents one third of the Portuguese teenagers radio listening preferences. News and current affairs, humor programmes and music. Radio frequency available on 100.3 FM (Monsanto broadcasting station). National. Mainly youngsters. Local Translation: Rádio de cobertura nacional. A Antena 3 é o canal jovem da RDP, destinado a um universo que representa mais de um terço da escuta de Rádio em Portugal. Com uma forte identidade própria, acompanha a evolução da mentalidade juvenil, proporcionando a melhor música jovem e os acontecimentos marcantes da actualidade. Frequência disponível em 100.3 FM (Emissor de Monsanto). Também dispõe de emissão online.

Renascença
Owner: R/com
Editorial: R. Ivens, 14, Lisboa 1249-108.
T: 351 213 239 200 **E:** mail@rr.pt
W: rr.sapo.pt
Editorial Profile: National generalist radio station, with Catholic orientation. Latest news reports with permanent update, music, listener's participation and opinion, religious programmes, open discussion programmes, interviews and comments by recognized Portuguese personalities on current events and Portuguese cultural promotion characterize this well-known station. Radio frequency available on 105.8 FM. Also available online. General population, but mainly listeners aged between 35 to 55 years old and being part of the A, B and C1 targets. Local Translation: Estação de rádio nacional, de cariz generalista e inspiração católica, pertencente à Igreja católica. É essencialmente composta por programas de informação - notícias, debates, entrevistas, entre outros. Frequência disponível em 105.8 FM no Continente e em 95.2 MHz nos Açores. Dispõe de emissão online. Estabeleceu um protocolo com a ARIC, na área de cedência de conteúdos e formação profissional. Eleita pelo estudo "Marcas de Confiança 2011" (Selecções do Reader's Digest), como uma das estações de rádio em que os portugueses mais confiam.

TSF
Owner: Rádio Notícias, Produções e Publicidade, S.A.
Editorial: Edifício Altejo, R. 3 da Matinha, 3° Piso - Sala 301, Lisboa 1900-823.
T: 351 218 612 500 **E:** tsf@tsf.pt
W: www.tsf.pt
Editorial Profile: National radio station dedicated mainly to national and international news report services, being updated every thirty minutes. Sports and economy/business news, stock market info, weather and traffic reports, chronicles and opinion programmes with special guests and several interactive programmes. National. General population. Local Translation: Estação de carácter informativo e noticioso, composta por notícias nacionais e internacionais referentes à actualidade política, à economia, ao desporto, às artes, entre outros. Contem crónicas e programas de debate e opinião e ainda vários programas interactivos. Eleito em 2010 como uma das marcas de media com melhor reputação em Portugal. A Reportagem TSF ôMissão Haitiô£ foi galardoada com o Prémio Internacional de Jornalismo Rei de Espanha.

PUERTO RICO Tel: 1 787
Standard Time: GMT -4
Continent: The Americas
Capital City: San Juan

NEWSPAPERS & PUBLICATIONS

NEWSPAPERS

Claridad
Editorial: Urb. Santa Rita No. 57, Calle Borinqueña, San Juan 00925-2732.
T: 1 787 777-0534
E: info@claridadpuertorico.com
W: http://www.claridadpuertorico.com
Freq: Weekly
Publisher & Editor: Manuel González
Language (s): Spanish
DAILY NEWSPAPER

El Nuevo Día
Owner: El Día Inc.
Editorial: Carretera 165 Sector Buchanan, Parque Industrial Amalia, Guaynabo 934.
T: 1 787 641-8000 **E:** opinion@elnuevodia.com
W: http://www.elnuevodia.com
Freq: Daily
Publisher: Maria Ferré; **Índice Editor:** Karol Sepúlveda
Editorial Profile: El Nuevo Dia is a daily newspaper which is distributed throughout the San Juan, PR area. The newspaper provides readers with local and national news. Other features include business, education, politics, health, lifestyle, and classifieds. Deadlines are at 4pm ET.
Language (s): Spanish
DAILY NEWSPAPER

Primera Hora
Owner: El Dia Inc.
Editorial: Calle Genova A16, Guaynabo 966.
T: 1 787 641-5454
E: correo@primerahora.com
W: http://www.primerahora.com
Freq: Fri
Editorial Profile: Primera Hora is written for the general public in Puerto Rico. It covers sports, weather, business, local and national news.
Language (s): Spanish
DAILY NEWSPAPER

Puerto Rico Daily Sun
Owner: Cooperativa Prensa Unida
Editorial: 943 Ave. de Diego, San Juan 921.
T: 1 787 675-0113 **E:** editorial@prdailysun.net
W: http://www.prdailysun.com
Freq: Daily
Editor: Rosario Fajardo; **Graphics Editor:** Edgardo Jimenez
Editorial Profile: Puerto Rico Daily Sun is a daily English language newpaper offering news, features, arts & entertainment and sports coverage to residents of Puerto Rico. It is headed and collectively owned by former editors from the the now defunct San Juan Star and is the only English language daily in Puerto Rico.
Language (s): English
DAILY NEWSPAPER

El Visitante Catolico
Owner: Conferencia Episcopal Puertorriquena
Editorial: Pumarada 1704, Santurce 912.
T: 1 787 728-3710 **E:** director@elvisitante.net
W: http://www.elvisitante.net
Freq: Weekly; **Circ:** 65000 Not Audited
Editor: Verónica Cruz; **Editor:** Efrain Zabala
Language (s): Spanish
DAILY NEWSPAPER

El Vocero
Editorial: Ave Ponce de Leon 206, Puerta de Tierra, San Juan 901. **T:** 1 787 721-2300
E: opinion@vocero.com
W: http://www.vocero.com
Freq: Daily
Editorial Profile: El Vocero is written for Puerto Ricans interested in timely news and covers local news, community, business, sports and other relevant topics.
Language (s): Spanish
DAILY NEWSPAPER

NEWS SERVICE/SYNDICATE

Associated Press
T: 52 55 5080-3400 **E:** apsanjuan@ap.org
Bureau Chief: Ben Fox
NEWS SERVICE/SYNDICATE

BROADCASTING

RADIO NETWORKS

Alfa Rock
Editorial: PO Box 9024188, San Juan PR 00902-4188. **T:** 1 787 726-6144
E: alfa@alfarock.com
W: http://www.alfarock.com
Editorial Profile: Ralf Perez Ramirez is the General Manager to whom press releases should be addressed.

QATAR Tel: 974
Standard Time: GMT +3
Continent: Asia
Capital City: Doha

NEWSPAPERS & PUBLICATIONS

NEWSPAPERS

Al Arab
Owner: Dar Al Arab Est.
Editorial: PO Box 22612, Al Arab Newspaper Building, Doha. **T:** 974 4499 7333
E: alarab@alarab.qa **W:** http://www.alarab.qa
Freq: Daily; **Circ:** 22000 Publisher's Statement
Editorial Profile: Al Arab is a daily Arabic newspaper covering news, politics, culture, business and sport. It was first published in 2007 and includes a monthly lifestyle supplement, Lamsa, and a monthly children's supplement, Abnaa Alarab.
Language (s): Arabic
DAILY NEWSPAPER

Doha Stadium Plus
Owner: Aspire Printing, Publishing and Distribution
Editorial: PO Box 24598, Doha.
T: 974 4499 9612
E: editor@dohastadiumplusqatar.com
W: http://www.dohastadiumplusqatar.com
Freq: Wed; **Circ:** 15000 Publisher's Statement
Editor In Chief: Ahmed Al Mohannadi
Editorial Profile: Doha Stadium Plus is a weekly English newspaper covering local and international sport, as well as sports-related

issues. It launched in 2006 and is published on Wednesdays.
Language (s): English
DAILY NEWSPAPER

Estad Aldoha
Owner: Aspire Printing, Publishing and Distribution
Editorial: PO Box 96204, Aspire Building, Doha. **T:** 974 4499 9626
E: estad-aldoha4@hotmail.com
W: http://www.estad-aldoha.com
Freq: 2 Times/Week; **Circ:** 10000 Publisher's Statement
Editor: Abdel-Majeed Al Kazzar; **Editor In Chief:** Majed Al Khulaifi; **Editor:** Fouad Ben Ajmia
Editorial Profile: Estad Aldoha is an Arabic sports newspaper, with particular emphasis on football. It launched in 2005 and is published twice a week on Mondays and Thursdays.
Language (s): Arabic
DAILY NEWSPAPER

Gulf Madhyamam - Qatar edition
Owner: Gulf Madhyamam FZ LLC
Editorial: PO Box 19850, Villa 12, Al Hilal Area, Doha. **T:** 974 4436 2122
E: qatar@gulfmadhyamam.net
W: http://www.gulfmadhyamam.net
Freq: Daily; **Circ:** 21000 Rate Card
Editor-in-Chief: Hamzah Abbas; **Editor in Charge:** Op Shanavas
Editorial Profile: Gulf Madhyamam is an international Indian newspaper covering national and international news, current affairs, politics, business and sport. The newspaper is aimed at Malayalam speakers in the Gulf and publishes separate editions for the UAE, Saudi Arabia (Riyadh, Jeddah, Damam & Abha), Qatar, Oman, Bahrain and Kuwait. The newspaper was first published in 1999.
Language (s): Malayalam
DAILY NEWSPAPER

Gulf Times
Owner: Gulf Publishing and Printing Company
Editorial: PO Box 533, Doha.
T: 974 4435 0478 **E:** editor@gulf-times.com
W: http://www.gulf-times.com
Freq: Daily; **Circ:** 33000 Publisher's Statement
News Editor: K. T. Chacko; **Editor in Chief:** Hamed Darwish
Editorial Profile: Gulf Times is a daily, broadsheet-sized English newspaper covering national and international news, business, politics, entertainment, culture and sport. It was first published in 1978.
Language (s): English
DAILY NEWSPAPER

The Peninsula
Owner: Dar Al Sharq Press, Printing & Distribution
Editorial: PO Box 3488, D-Ring Road, Doha.
T: 974 4455 7741 **E:** editor@pen.com.qa
W: http://www.thepeninsulaqatar.com
Freq: Daily; **Circ:** 18000 Publisher's Statement
Editor In Chief: Khalid Al Sayed; **News Editor:** Mobin Pandit
Editorial Profile: The Peninsula is a daily, broadsheet-sized English newspaper covering national and international news, politics, business, entertainment and sport. It was first published in March 1996.
Language (s): English
DAILY NEWSPAPER

Qatar Tribune
Owner: Qatar Information & Marketing
Editorial: PO Box 23493, Office 11-12, 1st Floor, Building 346, Doha. **T:** 974 4442 2077
E: qatar.editor@gmail.com
W: http://www.qatar-tribune.com
Freq: Daily; **Circ:** 13000 Publisher's Statement
Editor In Chief: Hassan Al Ansari; **News Editor:** Falak Kabir
Editorial Profile: Qatar Tribune is a daily, broadsheet-sized English newspaper covering local and international news, business, entertainment and sport. It was first published in 2006.
Language (s): English
DAILY NEWSPAPER

Al Raya
Owner: Gulf Publishing and Printing Company
Editorial: PO Box 533, Al Daeira Al Thalitha, Doha. **T:** 974 4446 6555 **E:** edit@raya.com
W: http://www.raya.com
Freq: Daily; **Circ:** 45000 Publisher's Statement
Editor In Chief: Saleh Al Kowary

Editorial Profile: Al Raya is a daily Arabic newspaper covering national and international news, politics, business, culture and sport. It was first published in 1979 and includes Al Tebbiya, a monthly health supplement, and Hia Wa Houwa, a monthly lifestyle magazine supplement.
Language (s): Arabic
DAILY NEWSPAPER

Al Sharq
Owner: Dar Al Sharq Press, Printing & Distribution
Editorial: PO Box 3488, D-Ring Road, Doha.
T: 974 4455 7777 **E:** alsharq@al-sharq.com
W: http://www.al-sharq.com
Freq: Daily; **Circ:** 42000 Publisher's Statement
News Editor: Mosaed Abdel Azeem; **Editor In Chief:** Jaber Al Harmi; **News Editor:** Yehia Askar
Editorial Profile: Al Sharq (The East) is a daily Arabic newspaper covering national and international news, politics, business, culture and sport. It was first published in 1987.
Language (s): Arabic
DAILY NEWSPAPER

Varthamanam - Qatar edition
Owner: Dar Al Sharq Press, Printing & Distribution
Editorial: PO Box 246, Office 3, Ground Floor, Al Abdul Ghani Building, Doha.
T: 974 4431 6977
E: qatarvarthamanam@gmail.com
W: http://www.varthamanam.com
Freq: Daily; **Circ:** 24500 Publisher's Statement
Bureau Chief: Mujeeb Rahman
Editorial Profile: Qatar edition of Kerala-based Varthamanam newspaper. The Qatar edition was first published in 2003 and is aimed at Malayalam speakers. It focuses on national and international news, current affairs, politics, business and sport.
Language (s): Malayalam
DAILY NEWSPAPER

Al Watan
Owner: Qatar Information & Marketing
Editorial: PO Box 22345, D-Ring Road, Doha.
T: 974 4465 2244 **E:** news@al-watan.com
W: http://www.al-watan.com
Freq: Daily; **Circ:** 25000 Publisher's Statement
Editor in Chief: Mohammad Al Meri
Editorial Profile: Al Watan is a daily Arabic newspaper covering national and international news, politics, business, entertainment and sport. It was first published in 1995.
Language (s): Arabic
DAILY NEWSPAPER

NEWS SERVICE/SYNDICATE

Bloomberg - Qatar Bureau
Owner: Bloomberg L.P.
Editorial: PO Box 27111, 14th Floor, Commercial Bank Tower, Doha.
T: 974 4452 8148 **E:** rtuttle@bloomberg.net
W: http://www.bloomberg.net
Editorial Profile: Qatar bureau of financial news wire service.
Language (s): English
NEWS SERVICE/SYNDICATE

Dow Jones Newswires - Qatar bureau
Owner: Dow Jones
Editorial: Doha
E: leila.hatoum@dowjones.com
W: http://www.dowjones.com
Editorial Profile: Qatar bureau of US-based financial newswire service.
Language (s): English
NEWS SERVICE/SYNDICATE

Qatar News Agency
Owner: Qatar News Agency
Editorial: PO Box 3299, Doha.
T: 974 4445 0205 **E:** qatarnews@qna.org.qa
W: http://www.qnaol.net
Arabic Editor: Sameh Ahmed; **Arabic Editor:** Mohammed Al Jendi; **Editor:** Samy Al Sayed
Editorial Profile: Official government news agency founded in 1975.
Language (s): Arabic, English
NEWS SERVICE/SYNDICATE

Reuters - Doha Bureau
Owner: Thomson Reuters
Editorial: PO Box 23245, Doha.
T: 974 4496 7619
E: regan.doherty@thomsonreuters.com
W: http://www.reuters.com

Editorial Profile: Doha bureau of International news agency supplying news - text, graphics, video and pictures - to subscribers around the world.
Language (s): English
NEWS SERVICE/SYNDICATE

REUNION   Tel: 262
Standard Time: GMT +4
Continent: Africa
Capital City: Saint-Denis

NEWSPAPERS & PUBLICATIONS

NEWSPAPERS

2512
Owner: 2512
E: redaction@2512.re **W:** http://www.2512.re
Freq: Monthly
Language (s): French
NEWSPAPER

Le Journal De L'I De La Reunion
Owner: GROUPE HERSANT MEDIA
Editorial: Centre d'affaires Cadjee, 62 boulevard du Chaudron, Sainte-Clotilde 97491.
T: 33 02 62 48 66 00 **E:** info@jir.fr
W: http://www.clicanoo.com
Freq: Daily; **Circ:** 34000 Publisher's Statement
Rédacteur en chef: Yves Montrouge
Language (s): French
DAILY NEWSPAPER

Le Quotidien De La Reunion
T: 33 02 62 92 15 15
E: laredaction@lequotidien.re
Freq: Daily; **Circ:** 33020 OJD
Rédacteur en chef adjoint: Idriss Issa
Language (s): French
DAILY NEWSPAPER

BROADCASTING

RADIO STATIONS

RADIO SALAZES 106.6 - 100.2
E: radio@salazes-fm.com
W: http://www.salazes-fm.com

TELEVISION STATIONS

RFO REUNION
Owner: RFO
W: http://www.rfo.fr
Editorial Profile: Local office of the overseas national public TV channel focussing on regional and local news, sport, entertainment, music, ethology, history, faith and traditions.

ROMANIA   Tel: 40
Standard Time: GMT +2
Continent: Europe
Capital City: Bucharest

NEWSPAPERS & PUBLICATIONS

NEWSPAPERS

Adevarul
Owner: SC Adevarul SA
Editorial: Sos. Fabrica de Glucoza, nr 21, Sector 2, Bucuresti. **T:** 40 21 40 77 609
E: contact@adevarul.ro **W:** http://adevarul.ro
Freq: Daily; **Circ:** 100000 Publisher's Statement
Editor-in-Chief: Grigore Cartianu
Editorial Profile: Independent newspaper containing news and background information. Covers national and international politics, economics, finance, society information, culture and sports.
Language (s): Romanian
DAILY NEWSPAPER

Azi
Owner: Cicero SA
Editorial: Calea Victoriei 39 A, O.P. 49, C.P. 45, Bucuresti 70101. **T:** 40 21 31 41 998
E: redactia@azi.ro **W:** http://www.azi.ro
Freq: Daily; **Circ:** 20000 Publisher's Statement
Editor-in-Chief: Ruxandra Negrea

Editorial Profile: Newspaper covering news, economics, politics, sports and culture.
Language (s): Romanian
DAILY NEWSPAPER

Bursa
Owner: SC Ring Press SRL
Editorial: Popa Tatu Str. Nr. 71, Sector 1, Bucuresti 10804. **T:** 40 21 315 4356
E: redactia@bursa.ro **W:** http://www.bursa.ro
Freq: Daily; **Circ:** 23000 Publisher's Statement
Editor-in-Chief: Ancuta Stanciu
Editorial Profile: Newspaper providing extensive financial, economical and business cover.
Language (s): English, Romanian
DAILY NEWSPAPER

Curierul National
Owner: SC. Curierul National SA
Editorial: Str. Cristian Popisteanu 2-4, Sector 1, Bucuresti 10024. **T:** 40 21 59 95 500
E: office@curierulnational.ro
W: http://www.curierulnational.ro
Freq: Daily; **Circ:** 35000 Publisher's Statement
News Editor: Valentin Bolocan; **Editor-in-Chief:** Stefan Radeanu
Editorial Profile: Newspaper covering news and background information on politics, economics, finance, sports and culture.
Language (s): Romanian
DAILY NEWSPAPER

Gandul
Owner: Crucisatorul S.A
Editorial: Strada Aurel Vlaicu, nr. 62-64, Bucuresti. **T:** 40 31 8257125
E: online@gandul.info
W: http://www.gandul.info
Freq: Daily; **Circ:** 16000 Publisher's Statement
Editor: Raluca Ion
Editorial Profile: National newspaper covering current news and politics, business and economics, entertainment and lifestyle, society and social issues.
Language (s): Romanian
DAILY NEWSPAPER

Libertatea
Owner: Ringier Romania
Editorial: Bulevardul Dimitrie Pompeiu nr. 6, Sector 2, Bucuresti 20337. **T:** 40 21 2030804
E: redactie@libertatea.ro
W: http://www.libertatea.ro
Freq: Daily; **Circ:** 320000 Publisher's Statement
Editor: Irinel Antoniu; **Editor:** Rodica Dirzu; **Editor-in-Chief:** Daniel Gorgonaru; **Editor:** Florin Saiu
Editorial Profile: Tabloid newspaper covering news, politics, sports, society and culture.
Language (s): Romanian
DAILY NEWSPAPER

Nine O'Clock
Owner: Casa Editura Nine O'Clock
Editorial: Sfantul Petru Tei 53, 2nd district, Bucuresti. **T:** 40 21 31 77 135
W: http://www.nineoclock.ro
Freq: Daily; **Circ:** 10000 Publisher's Statement
Editor-in-Chief: Gabriela Bogdan
Editorial Profile: Newspaper focusing on business, finance, politics, sport, culture and general news.
Language (s): English
DAILY NEWSPAPER

Romania Libera
Owner: Societatea "R" SA
Editorial: Str. Nerva Traian nr. 3, bl. M 101, etaj 4, Sector 3, Bucuresti 713411.
T: 40 21 202 81 55
E: redactia@romanialibera.ro
W: http://www.romanialibera.ro
Freq: Daily; **Circ:** 47000 Publisher's Statement
Editor In Chief: Dan Cristian Turturica
Editorial Profile: Newspaper covering news, politics, economics, sports and culture.
Language (s): Romanian
DAILY NEWSPAPER

Ziarul Financiar
Owner: Publimedia International SA
Editorial: Str. Aurel Vlaicu, Nr. 62-64, sector 2, Bucuresti. **T:** 40 318 256288 **E:** zf@zf.ro
W: http://www.zf.ro
Freq: Daily; **Circ:** 17000 Publisher's Statement
Publisher: Nicoleta Nedea; **Editor-in-Chief:** Sorin Pislaru

Editorial Profile: Newspaper covering news and background information on economics, finance, business and politics.
Language (s): Romanian
DAILY NEWSPAPER

NEWS SERVICE/SYNDICATE

Agence France-Presse
Editorial: 22B Muzeul Zambaccian street, Bucuresti **E:** bucarest@afp.com
W: http://www.afp.com
Editorial Profile: Romanian bureau for Agence France-Presse. Provides political, business and economics news on the developments in Romania.
Language (s): English
NEWS SERVICE/SYNDICATE

Associated Press
Editorial: Procema SA, Calea Grivitei 136, Bucharest. **T:** 40 21 310-2488
NEWS SERVICE/SYNDICATE

Bloomberg Romania
Editorial: 17 CA Rosetti Street, 5th floor, Bucuresti **W:** http://www.bloomberg.com
Editorial Profile: Romanian office for Bloomberg covering business and financial market news.
NEWS SERVICE/SYNDICATE

IDG News Service
Owner: International Data Group
T: 40 746 825-137 **E:** idgnews@idg.com
NEWS SERVICE/SYNDICATE

Reuters
Editorial: Premium Point Bucharest, 76-80 Buzesti Street, 9th floor, Bucharest 11017.
T: 40 21 315-8772 **W:** http://www.reuters.ro
Bureau Chief: Sam Cage
NEWS SERVICE/SYNDICATE

ROMPRES National News Agency
Editorial: 1 Piata Presei Libere, Bucuresti 13701. **T:** 40 21 22 24 830
E: marketing@rompres.ro
W: http://www.rompres.ro
Editor In Chief: Robert Mihailescu
Editorial Profile: National News Agency.
Language (s): Romanian
NEWS SERVICE/SYNDICATE

Thomson Reuters Romania
T: 40 21 315 8772
E: sam.cage@thomsonreuters.com
W: http://www.reuters.ro
Editorial Profile: Romanian branch of the news agency, providing investing news, world news, business news, technology news, headline news, small business news, news alerts, personal finance, stock market, and mutual funds information.
NEWS SERVICE/SYNDICATE

RUSSIA Tel: 7
Standard Time: GMT +2 (west), GMT +12 (east)
Continent: Europe
Capital City: Moscow

NEWSPAPERS & PUBLICATIONS

NEWSPAPERS

Apteka Pharm-index
Editorial: 12 Liniya 13a, office 511, Sankt Peterburg 199178. **T:** 7 812 327 05 12
E: apt@pharmindex.ru
W: http://www.pharmindex.ru/apteka.asp
Freq: Monthly; **Circ:** 80000 Publisher's Statement
Editor: Anna Egorova; **Editor In Chief:** Vladimir Kirillov; **Editor:** Oleg Pochinyuk
Editorial Profile: Specialized publication on new pharmaceutical products, providing practical advice for professionals and regular readers in St. Petersburg.
Language (s): Russian
DAILY NEWSPAPER

Argumenti nedeli
Editorial: pr. Aeroporta 11, Moskva 125167.
T: 7 495 981 68 36
E: argumenti@argumenti.ru
W: http://www.argumenti.ru
Freq: Weekly; **Circ:** 570000 Publisher's Statement
Editor: Andrey Uglanov
Editorial Profile: Publication focused political analysis and social issues, business and economical developments.
Language (s): Russian
DAILY NEWSPAPER

Belgorodskaya pravda
Editorial: pr. Slavy 100, Belgorod 308800.
T: 7 4722 32 05 62 **E:** Belpravda31@yandex.ru
W: http://www.belpravda.ru
Freq: Daily; **Circ:** 50000 Publisher's Statement
Editor: Leonid Blagasov
Editorial Profile: Covers all aspects of life in Belgorod region.
Language (s): Russian
DAILY NEWSPAPER

The International New York Times - Moscow
Editorial: 12 Sadovaya-Samotechnaya ulitsa, Moscow. **T:** 7 0952000187
Bureau Chief: Neil MacFarquhar
DAILY NEWSPAPER

Izvestia
Editorial: Bumazhniy proyezd 14, str. 2, Moskva 127015. **T:** 7 495 7488704
E: info@izvestia.ru **W:** http://www.izvestia.ru
Freq: Daily; **Circ:** 148000 Not Audited
Editor: Alexander Potapov
Editorial Profile: National newspaper covering all aspects of Russian politics and economy.
Language (s): Russian
DAILY NEWSPAPER

Kommersant
Owner: Izdatelskiy Dom Kommersant
Editorial: ul. Vrubeliya 4/1, Moskva 125080.
T: 7 499 9439750
E: kommersant@kommersant.ru
W: http://www.kommersant.ru
Freq: Daily; **Circ:** 110000 Not Audited
Editorial Profile: Newspaper dedicated to the problems of economics and economic processes of Russian and international markets. Includes analyses of Russian micro- and macroeconomics, monetary and stock exchange markets and investments.
Language (s): Russian
DAILY NEWSPAPER

Komsomolskaya Pravda
Owner: ZAO ID Komsomolskaya Pravda
Editorial: ul. Pravdy, d. 24, 6-y etaz, Moskva 125993. **T:** 7 4952572555 **E:** kp@kp.ru
W: http://www.kp.ru
Freq: Daily; **Circ:** 2470000 Not Audited
Editor in Chief: Vladimir Konstantynovich Mamontov
Editorial Profile: Newspaper covering politics, economics and social news.
Language (s): Russian
DAILY NEWSPAPER

Krasnaya Zvezda
Editorial: Khorosheyevskoye shosse 38, Moskva 123007. **T:** 7 495 941 21 58
E: mail@redstar.ru **W:** http://www.redstar.ru
Freq: Daily; **Circ:** 80000 Publisher's Statement
Editor: Nikolai Efimov
Editorial Profile: Most reliable source of information about military issues and state of Russian Army.
Language (s): Russian
DAILY NEWSPAPER

Los Angeles Times (Russia)
Editorial: 12/24 Sadovaya-Samotechnaya Kv 57, Moscow 127051. **T:** 7 0957558445
DAILY NEWSPAPER

MedPharmVestnik Tatarstana
T: 7 843 267 60 96 **E:** mfvt@mfvt.ru
W: http://www.mfvt.ru
Freq: Bi-Weekly
Editorial Profile: Official professional publication of Ministry of Health of Tatarstan on medical and pharmaceutical issues.
Language (s): Russian
DAILY NEWSPAPER

Metro Moskva
Editorial: ul. Skakovaya 36, Moskva 125040.
T: 7 495 787-1211 **E:** metro@gazetametro.ru
W: http://www.metronews.ru
Freq: Daily; **Circ:** 500000 Publisher's Statement
Editor In Chief: Anna Sirota
Editorial Profile: Entertainment newspaper with city news distributed for free in Moscow.
Language (s): Russian
DAILY NEWSPAPER

Metro Peterburg
Editorial: ul. Avtovskaya 2, Sankt Peterburg 198096. **T:** 7 812 783 27 06
W: http://www.metronews.ru
Freq: Daily; **Circ:** 500000 Publisher's Statement
City News Editor: Anna Lupal; **Editor In Chief:** Anna Sirota
Editorial Profile: City entertainment morning newspaper distributed for free in St. Petersburg.
Language (s): English
DAILY NEWSPAPER

Mir upakovki
Editorial: ul. Suvorovskaya 6, Moskva 107023
W: http://www.magpack.ru
Freq: Quarterly
Editorial Profile: Full colour supplement to magazine 'Tara i upakovka' published for major trade exhibitions, also delivered free to subscribers of the magazine.
Language (s): Russian
DAILY NEWSPAPER

MK Subbota + voskresenye
Owner: Moskovsky Komsomolets
Editorial: ul. 1905 goda 7, Moskva 123995.
T: 7 495 78 14 740 **E:** ok@mk.ru
W: http://www.ok.mk.ru
Freq: Weekly; **Circ:** 600000 Publisher's Statement
Editorial Profile: Weekend entertaining Moscow newspaper with general and show biz news.
Language (s): Russian
DAILY NEWSPAPER

Moskovskaya Pravda
Owner: ZAO Redakcia Gazety Moskovskaya Pravda
Editorial: ul. 1905 goda, d. 7, D-22, GSP-5, Moskva 123995. **T:** 7 4952591404
E: newspaper@mospravda.ru
W: http://www.mospravda.ru
Freq: Daily; **Circ:** 400000 Not Audited
Editor: Natalia Balashova; **Editor:** Lew Moskovkin; **Editor:** Shod Saidovich Muladzhanov; **Editor:** Anna Borysevna Serova
Editorial Profile: Newspaper covering national and international news, politics, economics, culture and social issues.
Language (s): Russian
DAILY NEWSPAPER

Moskovskiy Komsomolets
Owner: ZAO Redakcia Gazety Moskovskiy Komsomolets
Editorial: ul. 1905 goda, d. 7, D-22, Moskva 123995. **T:** 7 495 6094444 **E:** info@mk.ru
W: http://www.mk.ru
Freq: Daily; **Circ:** 1600000 Not Audited
Editor: Pavel Gusev
Editorial Profile: Newspaper focusing on national and international affairs, events, meetings, scientific news, culture and arts.
Language (s): Russian
DAILY NEWSPAPER

Moy raion - Sankt Peterburg
Owner: Schibsted ASA
Editorial: ul. Odoevskogo 27, lit. A, 4 floor, Sankt Peterburg 199155. **T:** 7 812 325 25 15
E: info@mr-spb.ru **W:** http://www.mr-spb.ru
Freq: Weekly; **Circ:** 350000 Publisher's Statement
Editor-in-Chief: Diana Kachalova
Editorial Profile: Entertainment newspaper with information on holidays, shopping, relaxation, local news and practical advice.
Language (s): Russian
DAILY NEWSPAPER

Nezavisimaya Gazeta
Owner: ZAO Redakcia Nezavisimaya Gazeta
Editorial: ul. Myasnitskaya, d. 13, Moskva 101000. **T:** 7 495 981 61 54 **E:** info@ng.ru
W: http://www.ng.ru
Freq: Daily; **Circ:** 56000 Not Audited
Editor: Arkabiy Khancevich; **Editor:** Tatyana Koshkareva; **Editor in Chief:** Ludmila Parfenova
Editorial Profile: Newspaper covering national and international news, politics, business and economy.
Language (s): Russian
DAILY NEWSPAPER

Novaya gazeta
Editorial: Potapovsky per. 3, korp. 1, Moskva 101990. **T:** 7 495 623 68 88
E: 2014@novayagazeta.ru
W: http://www.novayagazeta.ru
Freq: 2 Times/Week; **Circ:** 535000 Publisher's Statement
Editor-in-Chief: Dmitri Muratov
Editorial Profile: National newspaper with regional inserts covering politics, economics, society, culture, sports and investigations.
Alternative Title: ????? ??????
Language (s): Russian
DAILY NEWSPAPER

Novosti Yugry
Editorial: ul. Engelsa 14, Khanty-Mansiisk 628011. **T:** 7 34671 3 21 94
W: http://www.isurgut.ru/~company/newsofyugra
Freq: 2 Times/Week; **Circ:** 52000 Publisher's Statement
Editor: Alexey Dvizov
Editorial Profile: Socio-political newspaper focused on economic, cultural issues of the Siberian region.
Language (s): Russian
DAILY NEWSPAPER

Novye izvestiya
Owner: Novye izvestiya
Editorial: ul. Novoostapovskaya 5, korpus 14, Moskva 107076. **T:** 7 495 783-06-36
E: gorelik@newnews.ru
W: http://www.newizv.ru
Freq: Daily; **Circ:** 108200 Publisher's Statement
Editor: Olga Gorelik
Editorial Profile: Fully colour daily newspaper covering political, social and economical news.
Language (s): Russian
DAILY NEWSPAPER

Podmoskoviye
Owner: Moscovia
Editorial: ul. 1905 goda 7, Moskva 123022.
T: 7 495 707 27 68 **E:** enp@oblnews.ru
W: http://enp.oblnews.ru
Freq: Daily; **Circ:** 65000 Publisher's Statement
Editor: Piyotr Karapetyan
Editorial Profile: Provides informative analytical materials society, economics, social issues, culture and sports in Moscow region.
Language (s): Russian
DAILY NEWSPAPER

Rossiiskaya Gazeta
Owner: Pravitelhstvo Rossiiskoy Federacii
Editorial: Ul. Pravdy 24, Moskva 125993.
T: 7 495 257 52 52 **E:** economic@rg.ru
W: http://www.rg.ru
Freq: Daily; **Circ:** 400000 Not Audited
Editor in Chief: Vladislav Fronin
Editorial Profile: Newspaper covering national and international news, politics, economy, special reports and interview with government officials.
Language (s): Russian
DAILY NEWSPAPER

Russky Kurier
Owner: Russky Kurier
Editorial: Luzhnetskaya nab.2.4, Moskva 119270. **T:** 7 495 981 88 91
E: ruscourier@ruscourier.ru
W: http://www.ruscourier.ru
Freq: Weekly; **Circ:** 102700 Publisher's Statement
Editor: Oleg Vladykin
Editorial Profile: National newspaper bringing up political and economical issues of the country in the light of national interests.
Language (s): Russian
DAILY NEWSPAPER

Slavyanka segodnya
Owner: Nevskaya Storona
Editorial: ul. Karavaevskaya 30, Sankt Peterburg 92177. **T:** 7 812 700 42 57
E: l.az@mail.ru **W:** http://www.nslav.spb.ru
Freq: Weekly; **Circ:** 100000 Publisher's Statement
Editor: Aleksandr Seleznev
Editorial Profile: Provides general and city council news on life in St. Petersburg.
Language (s): Russian
DAILY NEWSPAPER

Sovietskaya Rossiya
Editorial: ul. Pravdy 24, Moskva 125993.
T: 7 499 257 53 00 **E:** sovross@aha.ru
W: http://www.sovross.ru
Freq: Daily; **Circ:** 300000 Publisher's Statement
Editor-in-Chief: Valentin Chikin
Editorial Profile: Independent socialist political newspaper covering Russian issues.
Language (s): Russian
DAILY NEWSPAPER

Torgovaya gazeta
Editorial: Varvarka 14, Moskva 109012.
T: 7 495 698 49 41 **E:** tg@centro.ru
W: http://www.t-gazeta.ru

Freq: 2 Times/Week; **Circ:** 72000 Publisher's Statement
Editor: Valery Burt
Editorial Profile: Professional newspaper on consumer markets and services, goods and prices, sales networks and small business, safety and quality, legal aspects of trade.
Language (s): Russian
DAILY NEWSPAPER

Tribuna
Editorial: Bumazhniy proyezd 14, str.1, Moskva 127015. **T:** 7 499 257 59 13
E: tribuna@tribuna.ru
W: http://www.tribuna.ru
Freq: Daily; **Circ:** 57500 Publisher's Statement
Editor-in-Chief: Oleg Kuzin
Editorial Profile: National daily with analytical articles on politics, economics and social issues.
Language (s): Russian
DAILY NEWSPAPER

Trud
Owner: Trud Publishing
Editorial: Nastasiyensky Per. 4, Moskva 103792. **T:** 7 4952997505 **E:** letter@trud.ru
W: http://www.trud.ru/
Freq: Daily; **Circ:** 612000 Not Audited
Editor: Vladimir Mikheev; **Editor:** Vasiliy Shurov; **Editor:** Yuriy Stroganov
Editorial Profile: National newspaper covering national and international news.
Language (s): Russian
DAILY NEWSPAPER

Vechernaya Moskva
Owner: ZAO Koncern Vechernaya Moskva
Editorial: ul. 1905 goda, d. 7, Moskva 123995. **T:** 7 495 259 81 87 **E:** edit@vm.ru
W: http://www.vm.ru
Freq: Daily; **Circ:** 300000 Not Audited
Editor: Valeriy Petrovich Evceev
Editorial Profile: Newspaper focusing on national and international news, politics, the economy, business and society.
Language (s): Russian
DAILY NEWSPAPER

Vedomosti
Owner: Sanoma Independent Media
Editorial: ul. Polkovaya 3, str.1, Moskva 127018. **T:** 7 495 9563458
W: http://www.vedomosti.ru
Freq: Daily; **Circ:** 65000 Not Audited
Editor in Chief: Tatyana Lysova
Editorial Profile: The business daily Vedomosti was established with the cooperation of business newspapers Financial Times and The Wall Street Journal. Together with the largest Russian publishing house Independent Media, they released Vedomosti since 1999. The main task of the newspaper Vedomosti is to give readers the most prompt, detailed and objective business information. More than 100 journalists in Moscow and Russian regions with the support of the global network of correspondents Financial Times and The Wall Street Journal inform about the most important economic, financial, corporate and political developments, offering analysis and forecasts.
Language (s): Russian
DAILY NEWSPAPER

Voyenno-promyshlenny kurier
Owner: Almaz media Publishing House
Editorial: Leningradsky prospekt 80, Moskva 125190. **T:** 7 495 788 91 90
E: info@vpk-news.ru
W: http://www.vpk-news.ru
Editorial Profile: National newspaper with military and military industry news, new technologies in army and history.
Language (s): Russian
DAILY NEWSPAPER

Vremya novostey
Owner: Publishing house Vremya
Editorial: ul. Pyatnitskaya 25, Moskva 115326. **T:** 7 495 231 18 77 **E:** info@vremya.ru
W: http://www.vremya.ru
Freq: Daily; **Circ:** 51000 Publisher's Statement
Editor In Chief: Vladimir Gurevich
Editorial Profile: Daily business, political and social newspaper.
Language (s): Russian
DAILY NEWSPAPER

The Wall Street Journal (Russian)
Editorial: 5th Floor, 5 Petrouka St., Moscow 107031. **T:** 7 4959378445
DAILY NEWSPAPER

The Washington Post (Russia)
Editorial: 7/4 Kutuzovsky Prospekt #2, Moscow 121248. **T:** 7 0957776661
Bureau Chief: Kathy Lally
DAILY NEWSPAPER

Zavtra
Editorial: Frunzenskaya nab. 18-60, Moskva 119146. **T:** 7 495 726 54 83
E: zavtra@zavtra.ru **W:** http://zavtra.ru
Freq: Weekly; **Circ:** 100000 Publisher's Statement
Editorial Profile: Writes about political, economic and cultural events in Russia.
Language (s): Russian
DAILY NEWSPAPER

Zhizn
Editorial: ul. Vyborgskaya 16, str. 1, 2 floor, Moskva 125212. **T:** 7 495 510 29 84
E: info@zhizn.ru **W:** http://www.zhizn.ru
Freq: Weekly; **Circ:** 2200000 Publisher's Statement
Editor In Chief: Ruslan Sagaev
Editorial Profile: Tabloid-size newspaper covering news, entertainment and gossip.
Language (s): Russian
DAILY NEWSPAPER

NEWS SERVICE/SYNDICATE

Agence France-Presse - Moscow Bureau
Editorial: ul. Dolgorukovskaya 18, korpus 3, Moskva 127006. **T:** 7 495 7265969
E: desk.moscou@afp.com
W: http://www.afp.com
Freq: Daily
Editorial Profile: Regional office of the national French news agency Agence France Presse (AFP) focusing on regional news and current affairs.
Language (s): English
NEWS SERVICE/SYNDICATE

Agencia EFE - Moscow Bureau
Owner: EFE
Editorial: Zubovski blvr 4, Ria Novosti International Press Center, Moskva 119021. **T:** 7 495 637 51 07 **E:** efemos@gmail.com
W: http://www.efe.com
Bureau Chief: Miguel Bas Fernandez
Editorial Profile: EFE Agency bureau based in Moscow. Provides political and current news from Russia and CIS countries.
Language (s): Russian
NEWS SERVICE/SYNDICATE

Associated Press
Editorial: Kutuzovsky Prospekt 7/4, Corpus 5, Office 33, Moscow 121248. **T:** 7 495 974-1654
E: mosed@ap.org
Bureau Chief: Lynn Berry
NEWS SERVICE/SYNDICATE

Associated Press - Moscow bureau
Editorial: Moskva **W:** http://www.ap.org
Language (s): English
NEWS SERVICE/SYNDICATE

Bloomberg News
Editorial: Romanov Dvor II, Romanov Pereulok 4, Moscow 125009. **T:** 7 0957717717
E: moscowbn@bloomberg.net
Editor: Denis Maternovsky
NEWS SERVICE/SYNDICATE

Dow Jones Newswires
Editorial: 5 Petrovka St, Fl 5, Moscow 107031. **T:** 7 495 232-9198
Bureau Chief: Gregory White
NEWS SERVICE/SYNDICATE

DPA - Deutsche Presse-Agentur Moscow Bureau
Editorial: Kutuzovsky pr. 7/4, office 210, Moskva 121170 **E:** moskau@dpa.com
Editorial Profile: dpa editorial bureau based in Moscow. Provides news and political coverage on Russia and CIS countries.
Language (s): English
NEWS SERVICE/SYNDICATE

Interfax
Editorial: ul. 1-ya Tverskaya-Yamskaya, d. 2, Moskva 127006. **T:** 7 495 250 98 40
E: business@interfax.ru
W: http://www.interfax.com
Editorial Profile: News agency providing political, business and financial information from Russia, the CIS, Central and Eastern Europe.
Language (s): Russian
NEWS SERVICE/SYNDICATE

Interfax Information Agency
Editorial: ul. Pervaya Tverskaya-Yamskaya 2, Moskva 127006. **T:** 7 495 250 00 22
E: info@interfax.ru
W: http://www.interfax.com
Freq: Daily
Editor In Chief: Nadezhda Sedova
Editorial Profile: Most comprehensive, up-to-date and reliable real-time news service, covering the economy and financial markets' situation in Russia and the CIS. Over 300 news stories are published daily on the newswire that covers major political, macroeconomic and corporate news and events, and includes market overviews, summary tables and diagrams.
Language (s): English
NEWS SERVICE/SYNDICATE

Interfax Russia
Editorial: Pervaya Tverskaya-Yamskaya 2, str. 1, Moskva 127006. **T:** 7 495 250 98 40
E: info@interfax-russia.ru
W: http://www.interfax-russia.ru
Freq: Daily
Editor In Chief: Alexey Meshkov
Editorial Profile: 24-hour information channel that prioritizes breaking news. Covers political and economic events in Russia as well as sport and culture.
Language (s): Russian
NEWS SERVICE/SYNDICATE

ITAR - TASS
Editorial: Tverskoy Bulvar 10-12, Moskva 103009. **T:** 7 499 791 0018
E: glav@itar-tass.com
W: http://www.itar-tass.com
Editorial Profile: ITAR-TASS is a news agency with more than 130 bureaus and offices in Russia and abroad. ITAR-TASS also cooperates with more than 80 foreign news agencies. ITAR-TASS' editorial and other desks process information from correspondents, check and analyze facts, and translate into five foreign languages.
Language (s): Russian
NEWS SERVICE/SYNDICATE

NIA - Novoye Informatsionnoye Agentstvo
Editorial: ul. Mironovskaya 10 A, Moskva 105318. **T:** 7 495 369 03 59
E: nia@okbprogress.ru
Language (s): Russian
NEWS SERVICE/SYNDICATE

Platts Global Alert
Owner: McGraw-Hill Companies
Editorial: Business Center Mokhovaya, 4/7 Vozdvizhenka Street, Moscow 125009.
T: 7 495 783-4141
Editorial Profile: Platts Global Alert is an energy news and information provider. It aims to help global energy markets enhance their performance through such offerings as independent industry news and price benchmarks. There are 15 offices worldwide that cover the oil, natural gas, electricity, nuclear power, coal, petrochemical and metals markets.
NEWS SERVICE/SYNDICATE

Reuters
Editorial: 5 Petrovka Street, Berlin Haus Business Centre, Moscow 103031.
T: 7 495 961-0100
E: moscow.newsroom@reuters.com
Editor: Dmitry Antonov; **Bureau Chief:** Tim Heritage
NEWS SERVICE/SYNDICATE

Rossiya Segodnya (former RIA Novosti)
Editorial: Zubovskiy Bulvar, d. 4, Moskva 119021. **T:** 7 495 2012424
E: pressclub@rian.ru **W:** http://ria.ru
Editor-in-Chief: Margarita Simonyan
Editorial Profile: News agency providing socio-political, economic, scientific and financial information.
Language (s): Russian
NEWS SERVICE/SYNDICATE

Xinhua News Agency
Editorial: 9A, ST.M.KALITNIKOFSKAYA, Moscow 109029. **T:** 7 495 6701016
Editorial Profile: Covers international news and politics
Language (s): Chinese
NEWS SERVICE/SYNDICATE

BROADCASTING

RADIO NETWORKS

Radio Mayak
Editorial: 5 ul. Yamskogo Polya 19-21, Moskva 125040. **T:** 7 495 950-67-67
E: www@radiomayak.ru
W: http://www.radiomayak.ru

TELEVISION STATIONS

Domashniy
Editorial: ul. Pravdy 15a, Moskva 125124. **T:** 7 495 785 63 33 **E:** info@domashny.ru
W: http:/domashny.ru
Editorial Profile: National TV channel for the whole family with films and programmes on health, home decoration, cooking, children care, etc. Targets women in the age group 35 - 45.

DTV
Editorial: 3 Khorosheevskaya ul. 12, 4 floor, Moskva 123298. **T:** 7 495 287 86 80
E: info@dtv.ru **W:** http://www.dtv.ru
Editorial Profile: National TV informative-entertaining channel covering detective issues and criminal investigations, action films and thrillers, documentary and comedy programmes.

NTV
Editorial: ul. Akademika Koroleva 12, Moskva 127427. **T:** 7 495 725 53 83 **E:** info@ntv.ru
W: http://www.ntv.ru
Editorial Profile: National TV station with news, films, series, sports and entertainment programmes.

Piyaty Kanal
Owner: TRK Peterburg
Editorial: ul. Chapygina 6, str. 2, Sankt Peterburg 197376. **T:** 7 812 335 15 60
E: trk@spbtv.ru **W:** http://www.5-tv.ru
Editorial Profile: National TV station based in St. Petersburg with cultural, political and entertainment programmes.

Rossiya (RTR)
Owner: VGTRK
T: 7 495 232 63 33 **E:** pr@rfn.ru
W: http://www.rutv.ru
Editorial Profile: National TV station covering 98,5% of Russia and broadcasting news, sports, entertainment, films and series.

Rossiya 24
Owner: VGTRK
Editorial: 5 ul. Yamskogo Polya 22, Moskva. **T:** 7 495 221 94 81 **E:** vesti24@vesti.ru
W: http://www.vesti.ru
Editorial Profile: National and international 24/7 Russian-language news channel covering major national and international events with a Russian perspective and a focus on domestic issues with a broad and impartial outline of life in all of Russia's regions from its European enclave of Kaliningrad to Vladivostok in the Far East.

Sport
Owner: VGTRK
T: 7 495 955 83 88 **E:** info@sportbox.ru
W: http://news.sportbox.ru
Editorial Profile: National TV channel entirely dedicated to sports.

Telekanal Kultura
Owner: VGTRK
Editorial: ul. Malaya Nikitinskaya 24, Moskva 123995. **T:** 7 495 780 56 01
E: pr@tv-culture.ru **W:** http://www.tvkultura.ru
Editorial Profile: National TV station with cultural programmes: theatre, music, cinema, literature and history.

CABLE

CNN/Cable News Network
Editorial: Kutuzovsky Prospekt 7/4, Kv 256, Moscow 121248. **T:** 7 0952434056

RWANDA — Tel: 250

Standard Time: GMT +2
Continent: Africa
Capital City: Kigali

NEWSPAPERS & PUBLICATIONS

NEWSPAPERS

Imvaho Nshya
Owner: Orinfor Pecipho
Editorial: ORINFOR PECIPHO, BP 83, Kigali.
T: 250 57 52 18 **E:** ndamafra@yahoo.com
W: http://www.orinfor.gov.rw **Circ:** 12000
Publisher's Statement
Editor In Chief: Frank Ndamage
Editorial Profile: Newspaper focusing on national and international news, current affairs and economics.
Language (s): English, Kinyarwanda
DAILY NEWSPAPER

The New Times
Owner: The New Times
Editorial: BP 4953, Immeuble Aigle Blanc MINIJUST, Kigali. **T:** 250 55 10 69 17
E: editorial@newtimes.co.rw
W: http://www.newtimes.co.rw
Freq: Daily; **Circ:** 3000 Publisher's Statement
Redacteur: David Gusongoirye
Editorial Profile: Newspaper focusing on national and international news, politics, business, culture and sport.
Language (s): English, French, Kinyarwanda, Swahili
DAILY NEWSPAPER

La Nouvelle Relève
Owner: Orinfor Pecipho
Editorial: ORINFOR, 50, Boulevard de la Révolution, Kigali. **T:** 250 08 57 57 35
E: lnr2020@yahoo.fr
W: http://www.orinfor.gov.rw **Circ:** 3000
Publisher's Statement
Rédacteur en Chef: Jean-Claude Rwabulindi
Editorial Profile: Newspaper containing national and international news, current affairs, business and sport.
Language (s): French
DAILY NEWSPAPER

NEWS SERVICE/SYNDICATE

RNA - Rwanda News Agency
Owner: Rwanda News Agency
Editorial: BP 453, Kigali. **T:** 250 587215
E: rwandanewsagency@gmail.com
W: http://www.rnanews.com
Editorial Profile: National news agency of Rwanda focussing on news, current affairs, politics, economics, culture and sport.
Language (s): French, Kinyarwanda
NEWS SERVICE/SYNDICATE

BROADCASTING

RADIO NETWORKS

Radio Rwanda
Owner: Orinfor Pecipho
Editorial: ORINFOR PECIPHO, BP 83, Kigali.
T: 250 08 57 65 40 **E:** radiorwanda@yahoo.fr
W: http://www.orinfor.gov.rw
Editorial Profile: Radio station focussing on news & current affairs, politics and culture.

TELEVISION STATIONS

TV Rwanda
Owner: Orinfor Pecipho
Editorial: ORINFOR PECIPHO, BP 83, Kigali.
T: 250 08 57 75 20 **E:** kmungisha@yahoo.fr
W: http://www.orinfor.gov.rw

SAINT HELENA — Tel: 290

Standard Time: GMT
Continent: Africa
Capital City: Jamestown

NEWSPAPERS & PUBLICATIONS

NEWSPAPERS

St. Helena Independent
Owner: St. Helena Media Productions Ltd.
Editorial: 2nd Floor, Association Hall, Main Street, South Atlantic Ocean STHL 1ZZ.
T: 290 26 60 **E:** fm@cwimail.sh
W: http://www.saint.fm
Publisher: Mike Olsson
Language (s): English
DAILY NEWSPAPER

BROADCASTING

RADIO NETWORKS

Saint FM
Owner: St. Helena Media Productions Ltd.
Editorial: 2nd Floor, Association Hall, Main street, South Atlantic Ocean STHL 1ZZ.
T: 290 26 60 **E:** fm@cwimail.sh
W: http://www.saint.fm

SAINT KITTS AND NEVIS — Tel: 1 869

Standard Time: GMT -4

BROADCASTING

RADIO NETWORKS

VON Voice of Nevis
T: 1 8694691616 **E:** vonradio@sisterisles.kn
W: http://www.vonradio.com
Editorial Profile: Transmits talk shows, news, and provides life coverage of cultural programs, political programs and conferences. Plays hip hop, rock, R&B, reggae.

SAINT LUCIA — Tel: 1 758

Standard Time: GMT -4
Continent: The Americas
Capital City: Castries

NEWSPAPERS & PUBLICATIONS

NEWSPAPERS

The St. Lucia Mirror
Owner: Mirror Publishing Co.
T: 1 7584516186 **E:** mirror@candw.lc
Freq: Weekly; **Circ:** 5000 Not Audited
Publisher & Editor: Guy Ellis
Editorial Profile: The St. Lucia Mirror is a weekly newspaper focusing on politics, business news, community news, sports and entertainment.
Language (s): English
NEWSPAPER

The Voice
Owner: Voice Publishing Co Ltd
Editorial: Odessa Building, Darling Road, Castries. **T:** 1758 45 22 590
E: voice@candw.lc
Freq: 3 Times/Week; **Circ:** 8000 Not Audited
Publisher & Editor: Victor Marquis
Editorial Profile: The Voice is a daily newspaper covering news and sports.
Language (s): English
DAILY NEWSPAPER

BROADCASTING

TELEVISION NETWORKS

Helen Television System
Editorial: PO Box 621, Castries.
T: 1758 45 22 693 **E:** radio@htsstlucia.com
W: http://www.htsstlucia.com

SAINT PIERRE AND MIQUELON — Tel: 508

Standard Time: GMT -3

BROADCASTING

TELEVISION STATIONS

RFO Saint Pierre et Miquelon
Editorial: 14 rue Gloanec, BP 4227, Saint-Pierre-Et-Miquelon 97500 **W:** http://www.rfo.fr
Editorial Profile: Local office of the overseas national public TV channel focussing on regional and local news, sport, entertainment, music, ethology, history, faith and traditions.

SAINT VINCENT AND THE GRENADINES — Tel: 1 784

Standard Time: GMT -4
Continent: The Americas
Capital City: Kingstown

NEWSPAPERS & PUBLICATIONS

NEWSPAPERS

The News
T: 1 784 456-2942 **E:** thenews@vincysurf.com
Freq: Weekly; **Circ:** 14000 Not Audited
Editor: Shelley Clarke
Editorial Profile: The News is a weekly newspaper covering news and current affairs.
Language (s): English
NEWSPAPER

The Vincentian
Owner: The Vincentian Publishing Co Ltd
Editorial: Paul Avenue, Kingstown.
T: 1 7844561123 **E:** vinpub@yahoo.com
W: http://www.thevincentian.com
Freq: Weekly; **Circ:** 9000 Not Audited
Editor in Chief: Cytrian Neehall
Editorial Profile: The Vincentian is daily newspaper covering national and international news, politics, economics, finance, business, culture and sports.
Language (s): English
NEWSPAPER

BROADCASTING

RADIO STATIONS

Hot97 SVG
Owner: RadioActive Ltd
Editorial: RadioActive/Hot 97.1 FM, Moulton Mayers Building, Higginson St, Kingstown.
T: 1 784 452-9797 **E:** hot97ad@gmail.com
W: http://www.hot97svg.com
Editorial Profile: Hot97 SVG is a commercial station owned by RadioActive Ltd, airing in Saint Vincent and the Grenadines. The format of the station is urban contemporary. Hot97 SVG broadcasts to the area at 97.1 FM. The target audience of the station is listeners, ages 18 to 54. The station's tagline is "Hot 97.1".

TELEVISION NETWORKS

SVG TV
Editorial: Dorsetshire Hill, PO Box 617, Kingstown. **T:** 1 7844561078
E: svgbcnews@vincysurf.com
W: http://www.svgbc.com
Editorial Profile: Presents news, sports, and entertainment programming.

SAMOA — Tel: 685

Standard Time: GMT -11
Continent: Oceania
Capital City: Apia (Upolu)

NEWSPAPERS & PUBLICATIONS

NEWSPAPERS

Newsline
Owner: Pio Sioa
Editorial: PO Box 2441, Malifa, Western Samoa **E:** sunline@samoa.ws
W: http://newslinesamoa.com
Editor-in-Chief: Cherelle Jackson
Editorial Profile: Provides latest news on Samoa.
Language (s): English
NEWSPAPER

Samoa Observer
Owner: Samoa Observer Newspapers Ltd
Editorial: PO Box 1572, Apia, Samoa
E: samoaobserver@yahoo.com
W: http://.samoaobserver.ws
Freq: Daily
Publisher: Muliaga Jean Ash Malifa; **Editor-in-Chief:** Savea Sano Malifa
Editorial Profile: Catering to information needs of the whole of Samoa and covering politics, economy, international relations, sports, entertainment, regional news and current affairs.
Language (s): English
DAILY NEWSPAPER

Savali Newspaper
Owner: Ministry of the Prime Minister and Cabinet
Editorial: Government Building, PO Box 1861, Samoa **E:** terrytavita@yahoo.com
Freq: Bi-Weekly
Editor-in-Chief: Tupuola Terry Tavita
Language (s): English
NEWSPAPER

BROADCASTING

RADIO NETWORKS

K-Lite 101.1 FM
Editorial: PO Box 762, Apia
E: info@fmrasdio.ws
W: http://www.fmradio.ws

K-Roq FM96.1
Editorial: PO Box 762, Apia
E: info@fmradio.ws **W:** http://www.fmradio.ws

Magik 98.1 FM
Editorial: PO Box 762, Apia
E: sales@fmradio.ws

Radio Polynesia
Owner: Radio Polynesia Ltd
Editorial: PO Box 762, Apia, Samoa
E: corey@fmradio.ws **W:** http://fmradio.ws
Editorial Profile: Provides news and music broadcasting in English and Samoan.

Talofa 88.5 & 99.9 FM
Editorial: P O Box 762, Apia
E: info@fmradio.ws **W:** http://www.fmradio.ws
Editorial Profile: Talofa FM Samoa's most popular radio station playing latest Samoan music.

TELEVISION STATIONS

SBC TV 1
Owner: Samoa Broadcasting Corporation
Editorial: Mulinuu, Apia, Samoa
E: mhuch69@yahoo.com

SAN MARINO   Tel: 378

Standard Time: GMT +1
Continent: Europe
Capital City: San Marino

NEWSPAPERS & PUBLICATIONS

NEWSPAPERS

La Tribuna Sammarinese
T: 378 0549 990420
E: redazione@latribunasammarinese.net
W: http://www.latribunasammarinese.net
Freq: Daily
Capo redattore: Riccardo Geminiani;
Redattore: Alessia Pieroni
Editorial Profile: National daily newspaper focussing on news, current affairs, politics, economics, culture and sport.
Language (s): Italian
DAILY NEWSPAPER

BROADCASTING

TELEVISION STATIONS

San Marino RTV
T: 378 0549 88 20 17
E: redazione@sanmarinortv.sm
W: http://www.sanmarinortv.sm
Editorial Profile: National radio and television of the republic of San Marino.

SAO TOME & PRINCIPE
Tel: 239

Standard Time: GMT
Continent: Africa

NEWSPAPERS & PUBLICATIONS

NEWSPAPERS

Correio da Semana
Owner: Impressões e Brindas Publicitarias
Editorial: Avenida Amilcar Cabral 382, São Tomé. T: 239 225 299
E: correiodasemana@cstome.net
Freq: Weekly; **Circ:** 3000 Publisher's Statement
Editor: Rafael Branco
Editorial Profile: Newspaper including national and international information: covering economics, politics, society, culture and current affairs.
Language (s): Portuguese
DAILY NEWSPAPER

Vitrina
Owner: PRESCO Lda
Editorial: Rua de Mozambique, Caixa Postal 628, São Tomé. T: 239 227 904
E: diario_vitrina@cstome.net
W: http://www.vitrina.st
Freq: Weekly; **Circ:** 1500 Publisher's Statement
Chefe de Redacção: Herlânder Aguiar
Editorial Profile: National newspaper providing political coverage and articles covering international affairs, finance, economics, society and culture.
Language (s): Portuguese
DAILY NEWSPAPER

BROADCASTING

RADIO NETWORKS

Radio Nacional de São Tomé e Principe
Editorial: Avenida Marginal 12 Julho, Caixa Postal 44, São Tomé. T: 239 223 836
E: rnstp@cstome.net W: http://radionacional.st

TELEVISION STATIONS

RTP África
Editorial: Caixa Postal 855, São Tomé.
T: 239 223 613 E: arquivo@rtp.pt
W: http://www.rtp.pt

Televisão Santomense
Editorial: Caixa Postal 420, São Tomé.
T: 239 221 493 E: tvs@cstome.net

SAUDI ARABIA   Tel: 966

Standard Time: GMT +3
Continent: Asia
Capital City: Riyadh

NEWSPAPERS & PUBLICATIONS

NEWSPAPERS

Alyaum
Owner: Dar Alyaum Press & Publishing
Editorial: PO Box 565, Dammam 31421.
T: 966 13 858 0800 E: edit@alyaum.com
W: http://www.alyaum.com
Freq: Daily; **Circ:** 126000 Publisher's Statement
Editor in Chief: Abdulwahab Al Fayez
Editorial Profile: Alyaum (Today) is a daily Arabic newspaper covering local and international news, society, politics, business and sport. It was first published in 1964.
Language (s): Arabic
DAILY NEWSPAPER

Arab News
Owner: Saudi Research & Publishing Co.
Editorial: PO Box 10452, Omnia Center, Jeddah 21433. T: 966 12 283 6200
E: arabnews@arabnews.com
W: http://www.arabnews.com
Freq: Daily; **Circ:** 72799 Publisher's Statement
Editor In Chief: Mohammed Al-Harthi
Editorial Profile: Arab News is a daily, broadsheet-sized English newspaper covering national and international news, politics, economics, sport and social issues. It was first published in 1975.
Language (s): English
DAILY NEWSPAPER

Arreyadi
Owner: Sab Media FZ LLC
Editorial: PO Box 112193, 2nd Floor, Al Lotus Building, Jeddah. T: 966 12 257 3539
E: email@arreyadi.com
W: http://www.arreyadi.com.sa
Freq: Daily; **Circ:** 116006 Rate Card
Editor in Chief: Saleh Al Khulaif
Editorial Profile: Arreyadi (The Sportsman) is a daily Arabic newspaper covering local and international sport, as well as sections covering youth activities, arts and culture, poetry, gadgets, information technology, cars and motoring. The newspaper was first published in 1994 and is aimed at sports enthusiasts in Saudi Arabia.
Language (s): Arabic
DAILY NEWSPAPER

Arriyadiyah
Owner: Saudi Research & Publishing Co.
Editorial: PO Box 478, Riyadh 11411.
T: 966 11 212 8000
E: editorial4@arriyadiyah.com
W: http://www.arriyadiyah.com
Freq: Daily; **Circ:** 167357 Rate Card
Editor In Chief: Saad Al Mahdi
Editorial Profile: Arriyadiyah is a daily Arabic newspaper covering national and international sport, including cycling, boxing, athletics, tennis, horse racing, basketball, handball and soccer. It was first published in 1987 and is aimed at sports enthusiasts.
Language (s): Arabic
DAILY NEWSPAPER

Asharq Al-Awsat
Owner: Saudi Research & Publishing Co.
Editorial: PO Box 14744, Jeddah 21434.
T: 966 12 283 6200
E: jeddah@alsharqalawsat.com
W: http://www.aawsat.com
Freq: Daily; **Circ:** 263121 Publisher's Statement
Editor in Chief: Adel Al Toraifi; **News Editor:** Ahmad Azouz
Editorial Profile: Asharq Al-Awsat is a daily newspaper covering regional and international news, politics, business and sport. The London-based newspaper was launched in 1978, and is distributed across the Arab world.
Language (s): Arabic
DAILY NEWSPAPER

Al Bilad
Owner: Al Bilad Establishment for Journalism & Publishing
Editorial: PO Box 7095, Assahafa Street, Jeddah 21462. T: 966 12 671 1000
E: b_6711000@hotmail.com
W: http://www.albilddaily.com
Freq: Daily; **Circ:** 74472 Publisher's Statement
Editor In Chief: Ali Hasson
Editorial Profile: Al Bilad is a daily, broadsheet-sized Arabic newspaper covering local and international news, politics, business and sport. It was first published in 1932.
Language (s): Arabic
DAILY NEWSPAPER

Al Eqtisadiah
Owner: Saudi Research & Publishing Co.
Editorial: PO Box 478, Riyadh 11411.
T: 966 11 212 8000 1003 E: edit@aleqt.com
W: http://www.aleqt.com
Freq: Daily; **Circ:** 110713 Publisher's Statement
Real Estate Editor: Sattam Al Thaqil; **Editor in Chief:** Salman Aldossary
Editorial Profile: Al Eqtisadiah is a daily Arabic business newspaper covering finance, business, investment, economics and sport. It was first published in 1992 and is aimed at Arab business executives.
Language (s): Arabic
DAILY NEWSPAPER

Gulf Madhyamam - Saudi edition
Owner: Gulf Madhyamam FZ LLC
Editorial: PO Box 380169, Riyadh 11345.
T: 966 11 414 3132
E: riyadh@gulfmadhyamam.net
W: http://www.gulfmadhyamam.net
Freq: Daily
News Editor: V. M. Ibrahim; **Bureau Chief:** Zameel Illikkal
Editorial Profile: Gulf Madhyamam is an international Indian newspaper covering national and international news, current affairs, politics, business and sport. The newspaper is aimed at Malayalam speakers in the Gulf and publishes separate editions for the UAE, Saudi Arabia (Riyadh, Jeddah, Damam & Abha), Qatar, Oman, Bahrain and Kuwait. The newspaper was first published in 1999.
Language (s): Malayalam
DAILY NEWSPAPER

Al Hayat - Saudi edition
Owner: Dar Al Hayat
Editorial: PO Box 68907, Prince Mohammed Bin Abdulaziz Street, Riyadh 11537.
T: 966 11 461 2626 E: editing@alhayat.com
W: http://ksa.daralhayat.com
Freq: Daily; **Circ:** 160000 Rate Card
Editor In Chief: Jameel Al Theyabi
Editorial Profile: The Saudi Arabia editions (Riyadh, Jeddah and Dammam) of Al Hayat cover national and international news, current affairs, politics, business, sports and entertainment. The newspaper is based in London and Beirut and also publishes an International edition distributed outside Saudi Arabia. The newspaper was first published in 1946.
Language (s): Arabic
DAILY NEWSPAPER

Al Jazirah
Owner: Al Jazirah Corporation Press, Printing & Publishing
Editorial: PO Box 354, Press District, Riyadh 11411. T: 966 11 487 0000
E: ccs@al-jazirah.com.sa
W: http://www.al-jazirah.com
Freq: Daily; **Circ:** 111915 BPA Worldwide
Editor In Chief: Khaled Al Malik
Editorial Profile: Al Jazirah is a daily Arabic newspaper covering national, regional and international news, politics, business, culture and sport. It was first published in 1960. The newspaper includes Al Jaziriah Cultural Magazine, an arts and culture supplement, on Mondays.
Language (s): Arabic
DAILY NEWSPAPER

Al Madina
Owner: Al Madina Press Group
Editorial: PO Box 807, Press Street, Jeddah 21421. T: 966 12 671 2100
E: reporters@al-madina.com
W: http://www.al-madina.com
Freq: Daily; **Circ:** 120000 Publisher's Statement
Editor In Chief: Fahed Al Aqran; **News Editor:** Mohammad Al Muheisen
Editorial Profile: Al Madina (The City) is a daily Arabic newspaper covering news, politics, business and sport. It was first

published in 1936. The newspaper includes a weekly arts supplement, Alarbaa, on Wednesdays, and a weekly religious supplement, Alresalah, on Fridays.
Language (s): Arabic
DAILY NEWSPAPER

Makkah Al Mukarramah
Owner: Makkah for Printing and Media Est.
Editorial: PO Box 5803, Al-Taneem District, Makkah 21995. T: 966 12 520 1733
E: makkah@makkahnp.com
W: http://www.makkahnp.com
Freq: Daily
Editor in Chief: Othman Al Sini; **News Editor:** Yahya Berkassya
Editorial Profile: Makkah Al Mukarramah is a daily newspaper covering national and international news, culture, business, features and sport. The newspaper launched in January 2014.
Language (s): Arabic
DAILY NEWSPAPER

Malayalam News
Owner: Saudi Research & Publishing Co.
Editorial: PO Box 13443, Jeddah 21493.
T: 966 12 283 6200 E: malnews@srpc.com
W: http://www.srpc.com
Freq: Daily; **Circ:** 58303 Publisher's Statement
Editor: Sajith Abdulmajeed; **Editor:** Rafeeq Abdurahman; **Editor:** Mohammed Kananjari; **News Editor:** Hassan Koya; **Editor in Chief:** Tarek Mishkhas; **Editor:** Kunjammed Vanimel
Editorial Profile: Malayalam News is a daily Malayalam newspaper covering national and international news, current affairs, politics, business and sport. It was first published in 1999 and is aimed at Malayalam speakers in the Gulf.
Language (s): Malayalam
DAILY NEWSPAPER

Al Nadi
Owner: Okaz Organization for Press & Publication
Editorial: PO Box 55297, Jeddah 21534.
T: 966 12 676 0000 E: al-nadi@al-nadi.com.sa
W: http://www.al-nadi.com.sa
Freq: Daily; **Circ:** 60000 Publisher's Statement
Editor: Maher Abdulwahab; **Editor:** Saleh Al Eryani; **Editor:** Khaled Al Ghamdi; **Editor in Chief:** Mohammad Al Ghamdi; **Editor:** Abdullah Gayed; **Editor:** Ibrahim Mousa; **Editor:** Helal Salman
Editorial Profile: Al Nadi is a daily, broadsheet-sized Arabic newspaper covering local and international sport. It launched in 1996 and is aimed at sports enthusiasts in Saudi Arabia.
Language (s): Arabic
DAILY NEWSPAPER

Okaz
Owner: Okaz Organization for Press & Publication
Editorial: PO Box 1508, Jeddah 21441.
T: 966 12 676 0000 E: okazjed@okaz.com.sa
W: http://www.okaz.com.sa
Freq: Daily; **Circ:** 170000 Publisher's Statement
Editor: Abdullah Al Harthi; **Editor In Chief:** Hashim Hashim
Editorial Profile: Okaz is a daily Arabic newspaper covering news, politics, business and sport. It was first published in 1958 and includes a monthly motoring supplement, Media Car.
Language (s): Arabic
DAILY NEWSPAPER

Al Riyadh
Owner: Al Yamamah Press Est.
Editorial: PO Box 851, Sahafa Area, Riyadh 11421. T: 966 11 299 6000
E: newsroom@alriyadh.com
W: http://www.alriyadh.com
Freq: Daily; **Circ:** 180000 Publisher's Statement
Editor In Chief: Turki Al-Sediri
Editorial Profile: Al Riyadh is a daily Arabic newspaper covering local and international news, politics, society, business and sport. It was first published in 1965.
Language (s): Arabic
DAILY NEWSPAPER

Saudi Gazette
Owner: Okaz Organization for Press & Publication
Editorial: PO Box 5576, Dallah Street, Jeddah 21432. T: 966 12 676 0000
E: news@saudigazette.com.sa
W: http://www.saudigazette.com.sa

Freq: Daily; **Circ:** 60000 Publisher's Statement
ICT Editor: Molouk Ba-Isa; **Editor in Chief:** Somayya Jabarti; **News Editor:** Sayed Rizvi
Editorial Profile: Saudi Gazette is a broadsheet-sized, daily English newspaper covering local and international news, politics, opinion, business and sport. It was first published in 1976.
Language (s): English
DAILY NEWSPAPER

Al Sharq
Owner: Eastern Press, Printing & Media
Editorial: PO Box 2662, Prince Mohammed Bin Fahd Road, Dammam 31461.
T: 966 13 813 6777 **E:** editorial@alsharq.net.sa
W: http://www.alsharq.net.sa
Freq: Daily; **Circ:** 120000 Publisher's Statement
Editor in Chief: Saeed Al Adwani; **News Editor:** Habib Mahmoud
Editorial Profile: Al Sharq (The East) is a daily Arabic newspaper covering national and international news, politics, business, sport, culture, society and technology. It was first published in 2011.
Language (s): Arabic
DAILY NEWSPAPER

Urdu News
Owner: Saudi Research & Publishing Co.
Editorial: PO Box 13402, Jeddah 21493.
T: 966 12 283 6200
E: editorial3@urdunews.com
W: http://www.srpc.com
Freq: Daily; **Circ:** 67321 Publisher's Statement
News Editor: Syed Absar Ali; **Editor:** Khalid Khursheed; **Editor in Chief:** Tarek Mishkhas
Editorial Profile: Urdu News is a daily newspaper covering news, politics and business. It launched in 1994 and is aimed at Urdu speakers in the Gulf.
Language (s): Urdu
DAILY NEWSPAPER

Al Watan
Owner: Assir Est. for Press & Publishing
Editorial: PO Box 15155, Airport Road, Abha.
T: 966 17 227 3333
E: editorial@alwatan.com.sa
W: http://www.alwatan.com.sa
Freq: Daily; **Circ:** 235000 Publisher's Statement
News Editor: Ibraheem Al Ameer; **Editor In Chief:** Talal Al Shiekh
Editorial Profile: Al Watan is a daily Arabic newspaper covering national and international news, current affairs, politics, economy, culture, society and sports. It was first published in 2000.
Language (s): Arabic
DAILY NEWSPAPER

NEWS SERVICE/SYNDICATE

Bloomberg - Riyadh Bureau
Owner: Bloomberg L.P.
Editorial: c/o Regus Kingdom Center, PO Box 230888, Riyadh 11321. **T:** 966 11 211 8033
E: gcarey8@bloomberg.net
W: http://www.bloomberg.com
Editorial Profile: Riyadh bureau of global financial news wire service.
Language (s): English
NEWS SERVICE/SYNDICATE

Bloomberg News
Editorial: Regus Kingdom Centre, Fl 28, Riyadh. **T:** 966 11 211 8033
NEWS SERVICE/SYNDICATE

Dow Jones Newswires - Saudi bureau
Owner: Dow Jones
Editorial: PO Box 8953, 2nd Floor, Bahrain Tower, Riyadh 12214-2393.
T: 966 11 279 5252
E: ellen.knickmeyer@dowjones.com
W: http://www.dowjones.com
Editorial Profile: Saudi bureau of US-based financial newswire service.
Language (s): English
NEWS SERVICE/SYNDICATE

International Islamic News Agency
Owner: International Islamic News Agency
Editorial: PO Box 5054, Jeddah 21422.
T: 966 12 665 8561 **E:** iina@islamicnews.org
W: http://www.iinanews.com
Editor: Saad Al Herbash; **News Editor:** Zayed Sultan
Editorial Profile: International Islamic News Agency (IINA) covers news about the Muslim world, minorities and communities in various fields, including religion, Islamic education, culture, Islamic organizations, charity and dawa. IINA also welcomes reports, press releases and any other material on the above mentioned subjects in Arabic, English and French.
Language (s): Arabic, English, French
NEWS SERVICE/SYNDICATE

Reuters - Riyadh Bureau
Owner: Thomson Reuters
Editorial: PO Box 62422, Riyadh 11585.
T: 966 11 463 2603
E: angus.mcdowall@thomsonreuters.com
W: http://www.reuters.com
Bureau Chief: Angus McDowall
Editorial Profile: Saudi bureau of international news agency supplying news - text, graphics, video and pictures - to subscribers around the world.
Language (s): Arabic, English
NEWS SERVICE/SYNDICATE

Saudi Press Agency
Owner: Saudi Press Agency
Editorial: PO Box 7186, King Fahd Road, Riyadh 11171. **T:** 966 11 419 3333
E: wass2@spa.gov.sa
W: http://www.spa.gov.sa
News Editor: Mahdi Al Rasheedi
Editorial Profile: Official government news agency - the SPA serves as a central body to collect and distribute local and international news in the kingdom and abroad.
Language (s): Arabic, English
NEWS SERVICE/SYNDICATE

SENEGAL — Tel: 221
Standard Time: GMT
Continent: Africa
Capital City: Dakar

NEWSPAPERS & PUBLICATIONS

NEWSPAPERS

Il est Midi
Editorial: HLM NIMZATT, Villa nº 2699, Dakar.
T: 221 33 864 09 94 **E:** midi@sentoo.sn
W: http://www.ilestmidi.net/pages/accueil.php
Freq: Daily; **Circ:** 15000 Publisher's Statement
Editorial Profile: National daily newspaper focussing on news, current affairs, politics, economics, sports and culture.
Language (s): French
DAILY NEWSPAPER

Le Matin
Owner: Le Matin
Editorial: BP 8076, Route de l'Aéroport Yoff, Dakar. **T:** 221 33 820 92 02
E: canmatin@yahoo.fr
W: http://www.senjournaux.sn/Journal/edito.asp?codeJournal=33
Freq: Daily; **Circ:** 10000 Publisher's Statement
Rédacteur en Chef: Assane Samb
Editorial Profile: Newspaper containing national and international news, business, current affairs and sport.
Language (s): French
DAILY NEWSPAPER

Le Messager
Editorial: Route du Front de Terre, Angle Bourguiba, Dakar. **T:** 221 33 825 50 29
E: lemessager@sentoo.sn
W: http://www.lemessager.sn
Freq: Daily; **Circ:** 10000 Publisher's Statement
Editorial Profile: Daly National Newspaper focussing news, current affairs, politics, economics, sport and culture.
Language (s): French
DAILY NEWSPAPER

Nouvel horizon
Editorial: Sicap liberté 2, villa n 1589, Dakar.
T: 221 33 864 11 52
E: contact@nouvelhorizon-senegal.com
W: http://www.nouvelhorizon-senegal.com
Freq: Daily; **Circ:** 30000 Publisher's Statement
Rédacteur en Chef: Momar Diongue;
Rédacteur en Chef: Mandiaye Thiombane
Editorial Profile: National daily newspaper focussing news, current affairs, politics, economics, culture and sports.
Language (s): French
DAILY NEWSPAPER

Le Quotidien
Owner: Groupe Avenir Communication SA
Editorial: 12, Cité Adama Diop, Yoff, Dakar Fann. **T:** 221 33 869 84 84
E: lequotidien@lequotidien.sn
W: http://www.lequotidien.sn
Freq: Daily; **Circ:** 8000 Publisher's Statement
Editorial Profile: Newspaper containing national and international news, business, current affairs and sport.
Language (s): French
DAILY NEWSPAPER

Le Soleil
Owner: SSPP Le Soleil SA
Editorial: Route du service géographique, Hann, Dakar Rp. **T:** 221 33 859 59 59
E: lesoleil@lesoleil.sn
W: http://www.lesoleil.sn
Freq: Daily; **Circ:** 25000 Publisher's Statement
Rédacteur en Chef: Ibrahima Mbodj
Editorial Profile: Newspaper focusing on national and international news, business, politics, culture and sport.
Language (s): French
DAILY NEWSPAPER

Sud Quotidien
Owner: Groupe Sudcommunication
Editorial: Amitié II, Angle Burguiba, Dakar.
T: 221 33 824 33 06 **E:** sudquotidien@yahoo.fr
W: http://www.sudonline.sn
Freq: Daily; **Circ:** 7000 Publisher's Statement
Rédacteur en Chef: Madior Fall
Editorial Profile: Newspaper covering national and international news, politics, business, culture and sport.
Language (s): French
DAILY NEWSPAPER

Wal Fadjri
Owner: Groupe Wal Fadjri
Editorial: BP 576, Dakar. **T:** 221 33 869 10 71
E: walf@walf.sn **W:** http://www.walf.sn
Freq: Daily; **Circ:** 7000 Publisher's Statement
Editorial Profile: Newspaper focusing on national and international news, business, current affairs, sport and society issues.
Language (s): French
DAILY NEWSPAPER

NEWS SERVICE/SYNDICATE

Agence de Presse Africaine
Editorial: 3, Zone 12 Almadies, BP 29 287, Dakar. **T:** 221 33 869 87 87
E: aap.com@sentoo.sn
W: http://www.apanews.net
Editorial Profile: International News Agency focussing on news and current affairs, politics, sport and culture.
Language (s): English
NEWS SERVICE/SYNDICATE

Associated Press
Editorial: 7 Avenue Carde, Dakar.
T: 221 33 849-2620
NEWS SERVICE/SYNDICATE

PANAPRESS - Pan African News Agency
Editorial: Avenue Bourguiba x Sodida, BP 4056, Dakar. **T:** 221 33 869 12 34
E: redaction@panapress.com
W: http://www.panapress.com
Rédacteur en Chef: Biava Seshie
Editorial Profile: Pan African news agency focussing on news, current affairs, politics, economics, culture and sport.
Language (s): French
NEWS SERVICE/SYNDICATE

Reuters
Editorial: Rue des Ecrivains, angle Rue G, Dakar
NEWS SERVICE/SYNDICATE

BROADCASTING

RADIO NETWORKS

Dakar FM
Editorial: Boulevard de la République, BP 1765, Dakar. **T:** 221 33 821 11 81
E: rts@rts.sn **W:** http://www.rts.sn
Editorial Profile: National radio station focussing on news, current affairs, entertainment and sport.

Radio Senegal International
Editorial: Triangle Sud, Avenue El-Hadj Malick SY, Dakar. **T:** 221 33 849 12 12 **E:** rts@rts.sn
W: http://www.rts.sn
Editorial Profile: National international radio station of Senegal focussing on news, current affairs, entertainment and sport.

RADIODIFFUSION-TELEVISION SENEGALAISE (RTS)
Editorial: Triangle Sud, Avenue El-Hadj Malick Sy, Dakar. **T:** 221 33 849 12 12 **E:** rts@rts.sn
W: http://www.rts.sn
Editorial Profile: National television of Senegal focussing on news, current affairs, sports and entertainment.

TELEVISION STATIONS

RTS 1
Editorial: Triangle Sud, Avenue El-Hadj Malick SY, Dakar BP 1765. **T:** 221 33 849 12 12
E: rts@rts.sn **W:** http://www.rts.sn
Editorial Profile: National TV station of Senegal focussing on news, current affairs, entertainment and sport.

SERBIA — Tel: 381
Standard Time: GMT +1
Continent: Europe
Capital City: Beograd

NEWSPAPERS & PUBLICATIONS

NEWSPAPERS

24 sata
Owner: Ringier Axel Springer d.o.o.
Editorial: Žorža Klemansoa 19, Beograd.
T: 381 11 333 4 555 **E:** redakcija@24sata.rs
W: http://www.24sata.rs
Freq: Daily; **Circ:** 120000 Not Audited
Editor-in-Chief: Veselin Simonovic
Editorial Profile: Full colour daily newspaper distributed free of charge in Beograd and in Serbian second biggest city Novi Sad.
Language (s): Serbo-Croat
DAILY NEWSPAPER

Alo!
Owner: Ringier Axel Springer d.o.o.
Editorial: Žorža Klemansoa 19, Beograd
E: online@alo.rs
Freq: Daily
Editor-in-Chief: Dejan Vukelic
Editorial Profile: Serbian daily tabloid covering national news and gossip.
Language (s): Serbian
DAILY NEWSPAPER

Blic Serbia
Owner: Ringier Axel Springer d.o.o.
Editorial: Žorža Klemansoa 19, Beograd 11 000. **T:** 381 11 333-4-555 **E:** citaoci@ringier.rs
W: http://www.blic.rs
Freq: Daily
Editor-in-Chief: Veselin Simonovic
Editorial Profile: Tabloid Newspaper in Serbia covering national news and gossip.
Language (s): Serbian
DAILY NEWSPAPER

Danas
Owner: DAN GRAF d o o
Editorial: Alekse Nenadovica 19-23, Beograd 11000. **T:** 381 11 344-11 86
E: gl.urednik@danas.rs
W: http://www.danas.rs
Freq: Daily; **Circ:** 30000 Not Audited
Editor in Chief: Zoran Panovic
Editorial Profile: Newspaper featuring domestic and international news, politics, economics, finance, culture and entertainment.
Language (s): Serbo-Croat
DAILY NEWSPAPER

Dnevnik
Owner: Dnevnik d o o
Editorial: Bulevar oslobodenja 81, Novi Sad 21000. **T:** 381 21 66 14 374
E: redakcija@dnevnik.rs
W: http://www.dnevnik.rs
Freq: Daily; **Circ:** 20000 Not Audited
Editor-in-Chief: Miroljub Mijuskovic
Editorial Profile: Newspaper focusing on politics, economics, culture, sport and general news.
Language (s): Serbo-Croat
DAILY NEWSPAPER

Informer Serbia
Editorial: Terazije 5/7, Beograd 11000.
T: 381 11 6555261 **E:** redakcija@informer.rs
W: http://www.informer.rs

Freq: Daily; **Circ:** 115000
Editor-in-Chief: Dragan Vucicevic
Editorial Profile: Tabloid newspaper published in Belgrade and covering politics, national news, gossip and culture, sport.
Language (s): Serbian
DAILY NEWSPAPER

Kurir
Owner: Adria Media Serbia d.o.o.
Editorial: Omladinskih brigada 88a, Beograd 11000. **T:** 381 11 3240 551
E: redakcija@kurir-info.rs
W: http://www.kurir-info.rs
Freq: Daily
Editor in Chief: Saša Milovanovic
Editorial Profile: A high-circulation daily tabloid published in Belgrade.
Language (s): Serbo-Croat
DAILY NEWSPAPER

Politika Serbia
Owner: Politika novine i Magazini d.o.o
Editorial: Makedonska 29, Beograd 11000.
T: 381 11 330-1682 **E:** redakcija@politika.rs
W: http://www.politika.rs
Freq: Daily; **Circ:** 85000 Not Audited
Editor in Chief: Ljiljana Smajlovic
Editorial Profile: Oldest daily on the Balkans covering politics, economics, social and cultural issues.
Language (s): Serbo-Croat
DAILY NEWSPAPER

Vecernje Novosti
Owner: Novosti d o o
Editorial: Trg Nikole Pašica 7, Beograd 11000.
T: 381 11 3028000 **E:** redakcija@novosti.rs
W: http://www.novosti.rs
Freq: Daily; **Circ:** 200000 Not Audited
Editor-in-Chief: Ratko Dmitrovic
Editorial Profile: Newspaper covering general news, politics, economics, culture and sport.
Language (s): Serbo-Croat
DAILY NEWSPAPER

NEWS SERVICE/SYNDICATE

Associated Press
Editorial: Palmoticeva 9, Belgrade 11000.
T: 381 11 3234-166
NEWS SERVICE/SYNDICATE

Kosovapress News Agency
Editorial: Nënë Teresa nr. 20, Prishtinë 10000.
T: 381 38 24 97 21
E: english@kosovapress.com
W: http://www.kosovapress.com
Editor: Nezir Rama
Language (s): Serbo-Croat
NEWS SERVICE/SYNDICATE

Reuters
Editorial: Vladimira Popovica 6, Genex International Building, Apt B 37, 30, Belgrade 11070. **T:** 381 11 311-4305
E: belgrade.newsroom@thomsonreuters.com
NEWS SERVICE/SYNDICATE

Tanjug
Editorial: Beograd. **T:** 381 11 3281608
E: upr@tanjug.rs **W:** http://www.tanjug.rs
Editor-in-Chief: Jadranka Žujovic
Editorial Profile: Tanjug is a news agency which broadcasts around 400 pieces of information and over 100 photographs, video and audio recordings every day. Tanjug is a member of AMAN (the Alliance of Mediterranean News Agencies), ABNA (the Association of the Balkan News Agencies), and BSANNA (the Black Sea Association of National News Agencies).
Language (s): English
NEWS SERVICE/SYNDICATE

Thomson Reuters Srbija
Editorial: Vladimira Popovica 6, Beograd 11070. **T:** 381 11 31 14 011
E: tatjana.sreckovic@thomsonreuters.com
W: http://www.reuters.co.yu
Bureau Chief: Andrew Grey
Language (s): Serbo-Croat
NEWS SERVICE/SYNDICATE

BROADCASTING

RADIO NETWORKS

Radio Srbija
Editorial: Hilandarska 2 /IV, Beograd 11000.
T: 381 11 32 44 455 **E:** radioju@sbb.co.yu
W: http://www.glassrbije.org
Editorial Profile: State-run short-wave radio station broadcasting its programmes to all parts of the world, in thirteen languages - English, French, German, Russian, Spanish, Arabic, Albanian, Greek, Bulgarian, Italian, Hungarian, Chinese and Serbian.

SEYCHELLES Tel: 248

Standard Time: GMT +4
Continent: Africa
Capital City: Victoria

NEWSPAPERS & PUBLICATIONS

NEWSPAPERS

Nation Weekend
Owner: Nation Publishing Services
Editorial: Long Pier Road, PO Box 800, Victoria. **T:** 248 22 57 75
E: nation@seychelles.net
W: http://www.nation.sc
Freq: Weekly; **Circ:** 4000 Publisher's Statement
Editorial Profile: Newspaper focusing on national and international news, current affairs and sport.
Language (s): Creole, English, French
DAILY NEWSPAPER

Seychelles Nation
Owner: Nation Publishing Services
Editorial: Long Pier Road, PO Box 800, Victoria. **T:** 248 22 57 75
E: nation@seychelles.net
W: http://www.nation.sc
Freq: Daily; **Circ:** 2500 Publisher's Statement
Editorial Profile: Newspaper focusing on local and national news, politics, culture and sport.
Language (s): Creole, English, French
DAILY NEWSPAPER

BROADCASTING

RADIO STATIONS

Paradise FM
Editorial: PO Box 321, Victoria, Mahe.
T: 248 28 96 00 **E:** paradise.fm@sbc.sc
W: http://www.sbc.sc
Editorial Profile: Local radio station broadcasting in the Seychelles with news, events and music.

SIERRA LEONE Tel: 232

Standard Time: GMT
Continent: Africa
Capital City: Freetown

NEWSPAPERS & PUBLICATIONS

NEWSPAPERS

Awoko Times
T: 232 76 881 075 **E:** awoko71@hotmail.com
W: http://www.awoko.org
Editor: Kelvin Lewis
DAILY NEWSPAPER

Concord Times
Owner: Concord Times Communications Ltd.
Editorial: 51 Krootown Road, Freetown.
T: 232 22 22 91 99
E: concordtimes100@yahoo.com
W: http://www.concordtimessl.com
Freq: Daily; **Circ:** 1750 Publisher's Statement
Editor: Tanu Jalloh
Editorial Profile: Newspaper focusing on national and international news, business, politics, culture and sport.
Language (s): English
DAILY NEWSPAPER

The Patriotic Vanguard
T: 232 766 84043 **E:** gkgkoroma@gmail.com
W: http://www.thepatrioticvanguard.com
Language (s): English
DAILY NEWSPAPER

Standard Times
Owner: Standard Times
Editorial: 2 A Ascension Town Road, Kingtom Bridge, Freetown. **T:** 232 22 22 96 34
E: standardtimes@justice.com
W: http://standardtimespress.org
Freq: Daily; **Circ:** 2000 Publisher's Statement
Editor: Unisa Bangura; **Editor:** Saidu Kamara; **Editor:** Santigie Kamara; **Editor:** Abubakarr Kargbo; **Editor:** John Koroma
Editorial Profile: Newspaper focusing on national and international news, politics, business, entertainment and sport.
Language (s): English
DAILY NEWSPAPER

SINGAPORE Tel: 65

Standard Time: GMT +8
Continent: Asia
Capital City: Singapore City

NEWSPAPERS & PUBLICATIONS

NEWSPAPERS

Asahi Shimbun- Singapore Bureau
Editorial: Asahi Shimbun- Singapore Bureau, 72 Bendemeer Road #2-20 Luzeme, Singapore 339941. **T:** 65 62203315
E: asahisin@singnet.com.sg
W: http://www.asahi.com
Bureau Chief: Tsuru Etsushi
Editorial Profile: Covers news, entertainment, lifestyle and sports.
Language (s): Japanese
DAILY NEWSPAPER

Berita Harian
Editorial: Singapore Press Holdings (SPH), Level 3, Annexe Block, 1000, Toa Payoh North, Singapore 318994. **T:** 65 63195137
W: http://cyberita.asia1.com.sg/
Freq: Daily; **Circ:** 60007 Not Audited
Editor: Mohd. Saat Abdul Rahman; **Editor:** Mohd. Guntor Sadali
Editorial Profile: Covers international and local news.
Language (s): Bahasa Malaysia
DAILY NEWSPAPER

Berita Minggu
Editorial: Singapore Press Holdings Ltd (SPH), Level 3, Annexe Block, 1000, Toa Payoh North, Singapore 318994.
T: 65 63195665
W: http://cyberita.asia1.com.sg
Freq: Weekly; **Circ:** 72105 Not Audited
Editor: Mohd. Guntor Sadali
Editorial Profile: Covers international and local news.
Language (s): Bahasa Malaysia
DAILY NEWSPAPER

The Business Times
Editorial: Singapore Press Holdings Ltd (SPH), SPH 1000 Toa Payoh North, Podium Level 3, Singapore 318994. **T:** 65 63195318
E: btnews@sph.com.sg
W: http://www.businesstimes.com.sg
Freq: Daily
Editor: Lilian Ang; **Editor:** Amit Choudhury; **Editor:** Jaime Ee; **Editor:** Edmund Loh; **Editor:** Suresh Menon; **Editor in Chief:** Alvin Tay
Editorial Profile: Covers business and economic industry news.
Language (s): English
DAILY NEWSPAPER

Die Welt - Singapore Bureau
Editorial: Die Welt - Singapore Bureau, 33E Barker Road, Lotus at Barker, Singapore 309911. **T:** 65 62530358
Editorial Profile: Covers international and local news.
Language (s): Japanese
DAILY NEWSPAPER

Economic Daily (China) - Singapore Bureau
Editorial: Economic Daily (China) - Singapore Bureau, 121 Meyer Road, #15-09 The Makena, Singapore 437932. **T:** 65 63459056
W: http://www.economicdaily.com.cn
Freq: Daily
Editorial Profile: Covers major news and economic news reports.
Language (s): Chinese
DAILY NEWSPAPER

The Edge Singapore
Editorial: The Edge Publishing Pte Ltd, 150 Cecil Street, 13th Floor, Singapore 69543.
T: 65 62328622
E: theedgespore@bizedge.com
W: http://www.theedgesingapore.com
Freq: Weekly; **Circ:** 26769 Not Audited
Editor: Cecilia Chow; **Editor:** Audrey Simon; **Editor:** Boon Kean Tan; **Editor:** Kelvin Tan
Editorial Profile: Covers general news, as well as business.
Language (s): English
DAILY NEWSPAPER

Frankfurter Allgemeine
Editorial: Frankfurter Allgemeine Zeitung - Singapore Bureau, 42A Taman Nakhoda, Villa delle Rose, Singapore 257764.
T: 65 64755023 **W:** http://www.faz.net
Freq: Daily
Bureau Chief: Christoph Hein
Editorial Profile: Covers major news, international and local news.
Language (s): German
DAILY NEWSPAPER

The Hindu
Editorial: 245 Balestier Road, #06-01 Scenic Heights, Singapore 329929. **T:** 65 62513635
W: http://www.hinduonnet.com
Freq: Daily
Editorial Profile: Covers major news.
Language (s): English
DAILY NEWSPAPER

Hokkaido Shimbun - Singapore Bureau
Editorial: Hokkaido Shimbun - Singapore Bureau, 7 Claymore Road, #09-02, Singapore 229538. **T:** 65 67387786
W: http://www.hokkaido-np.co.jp
Bureau Chief: Masaaki Saito
Editorial Profile: Covers local and international news.
Language (s): Japanese
DAILY NEWSPAPER

Kwong Wah Yit Poh - Singapore Bureau
Editorial: Kwong Wah Yit Poh - Singapore Bureau, Blk 92, Bedok North Ave 4, #09-1481, Singapore 460092. **T:** 65 64443012
W: http://www.kwongwah.com.my
Editorial Profile: Covers major news daily.
Language (s): Japanese
DAILY NEWSPAPER

Lianhe Wanbao
Editorial: Singapore Press Holdings (SPH), Lianhe Wanbao, Podium 4,1000 Toa Payoh North, Singapore 318994. **T:** 65 63196319
E: wanbao@sph.com.sg
Freq: Daily; **Circ:** 124007 Not Audited
Editor: Chim Kang Chua; **Editor:** Gek Tiang Kuek; **Editor:** Wong Yoong Nam; **Editor:** Lam Huat Toh
Editorial Profile: Covers international and local news.
Language (s): Chinese
DAILY NEWSPAPER

Lianhe Zaobao
Editorial: Singapore Press Holdings Ltd (SPH), SPH 1000, Toa Payoh North, Singapore 318994. **T:** 65 6319 6319
E: zblocal@sph.com.sg
W: http://www.zaobao.com
Freq: Daily; **Circ:** 184477 Not Audited
Editor: Sin Hwee Goh; **Editor:** Maureen Shueh Fern Ho; **Editor:** Lim Jim Koon; **Editor:** Jim Koon Lim; **Editor:** Kim Huat Lim; **News Editor:** Han May; **Editor:** Tee Ming San; **Editor:** Say Teck Poh; **Editor:** Ming San Tee; **Editor:** Pow Ang Yong
Editorial Profile: Covers local and international news.
Language (s): Chinese
DAILY NEWSPAPER

My Paper - Wo Bao
Editorial: Singapore Press Holdings Ltd (SPH), 1000 Toa Payoh North, News Centre, Podium, Level 2, Singapore 318994.
T: 65 63196319 **E:** mypaper@sph.com.sg
W: http://www.mypaper.sg
Freq: 2 Times/Week; **Circ:** 300007 Not Audited
Editor: Jill Alphonso; **Editor:** Han Keong Chia; **News Editor:** Hui Chieh Lee; **Editor:** Glenn Low; **Editor:** April Pung; **Editor:** Felix Soh; **Editor:** Wui Teck Woon; **Editor:** Kai Chai Yeow
Editorial Profile: Covers major news, international and local news.
Language (s): Chinese, English
DAILY NEWSPAPER

Nihon Keizai Shimbun - Singapore Bureau
Editorial: 331 North Bridge Road, #13-02/03 Odeon Towers, Singapore 188720.
T: 65 63398200 **E:** news@nikkei.com.sg
W: http://www.nikkei.com.sg
Freq: Daily
Bureau Chief: Kiyoshi Noma
Editorial Profile: Covers Internet Business, economic and major news.

Language (s): Japanese
DAILY NEWSPAPER

NNA - Singapore Bureau

Editorial: NNA - Singapore Bureau, Shenton House #19-01, Singapore 68805.
T: 65 67383333 W: http://nna.asia.ne.jp
Freq: Daily
Editor in Chief: Fujino Hidenori
Editorial Profile: Covers local and international news.
Language (s): English
DAILY NEWSPAPER

Sankei Shimbun - Singapore Bureau

Editorial: Sankei Shimbun - Singapore Bureau, 6 Eu Tong Sen Street #10-02 The central, Singapore 59817. T: 65 62216894
W: http://sankei.jp.msn.com
Freq: Daily
Bureau Chief: Hiroyuki Miyano
Editorial Profile: Covers local, national and international news.
Language (s): Japanese
DAILY NEWSPAPER

Shin Min Daily News

Editorial: Singapore Press Holdings Ltd (SPH), News Centre, SPH 1000, Toa Payoh North, Singapore 318994. T: 65 63192269
E: shinmin@sph.com.sg
Freq: Daily; Circ: 121007 Not Audited
Editor: Kean Huat Chua; Editor: Tan Lye Chwee; Editor: Toh Lam Huat; Editor: Lam Huat Toh; Editor: Ning Yin Chyun
Editorial Profile: Covers international and national news.
Language (s): Chinese
DAILY NEWSPAPER

Singapore American Newspaper

Editorial: American Association of Singapore, 21 Scotts Rd., Singapore 229573.
T: 65 67344811
E: communications@aasingapore.com
W: http://www.aasingapore.com
Freq: Monthly; Circ: 8007 Not Audited
Editor: Brett Gold
Editorial Profile: Covers American community in Singapore.
Language (s): English
DAILY NEWSPAPER

The Straits Times

Editorial: Singapore Press Holding (SPH), SPH 1000, Toa Payoh North, Level 2, Podium Block, Singapore 318994. T: 65 6319 5397
E: stlocal@sph.com.sg
W: http://www.straitstimes.com
Freq: Daily
Editor: Helen Chia; Editor: Lee Hoong Chua; Editor in Chief: Patrick Daniel; Editor: Serene Goh; Editor: Eugene Leow; Editor: Marc Lim; Editor: Keng Fatt Loh; Editor: Ignatius Low; Editor: Dominic Nathan; Editor in Chief: Cheong Yip Seng; Editor: Carl Skadian; Editor: Felix Soh; Editor: Sumiko Tan; Editor: Karen Teng; Editor: Koon Hong Yap; Editor: Ah Seng Yeong
Editorial Profile: Founded July 15, 1845, serves as the flagship publication of the Singapore Press Holdings group. Strives to be an authoritative provider of news and views, with special focus on Singapore and the Asian region.
Language (s): English
DAILY NEWSPAPER

The Sunday Times

Editorial: Singapore Press Holdings (SPH), SPH 1000, Toa Payoh North, Singapore 318994. T: 65 63196319
W: http://www.sph.com.sg
Freq: Weekly; Circ: 399007 Not Audited
Editor in Chief: Patrick Daniel; Editor in Chief: Cheong Yip Seng; Editor: Sumiko Tan
Editorial Profile: Covers major international and local news.
Language (s): English
DAILY NEWSPAPER

Tamil Murasu

Editorial: Singapore Press Holdings Ltd (SPH), 82 Genting Lane, Singapore 349567.
T: 65 6319 6319
W: http://tamilmurasu.com.sg
Freq: Daily; Circ: 10607 Not Audited
Editor: K. Kanagalatha; Editor: G. Krishnan; Editor: Nirmala Murugaian; News Editor: V. Palanisamy; Editor: Chitra Rajaram
Editorial Profile: Covers international and local news.
Language (s): Tamil
DAILY NEWSPAPER

Thanh Nien- Singapore Bureau

Editorial: Thanh Nien- Singapore Bureau, 1 Pearl Bank, #26-09, Singapore 169016.
T: 65 62240810
W: http://www.thanhhiennews.com
Bureau Chief: Thi Thuc Nguyen
Language (s): Japanese
DAILY NEWSPAPER

Thumbs Up

Editorial: Singapore Press Holdings Ltd (SPH), 1000, Toa Payoh Nort, Singapore 318994. T: 65 63191892
E: ThumbsUp@sph.com.sg
W: http://youth.zaobao.com/tu.html
Freq: Weekly; Circ: 38407 Not Audited
Editor: Soon Lan Lim
Editorial Profile: Covers news that interests to young people/ students.
Language (s): Chinese
DAILY NEWSPAPER

Today

Editorial: MediaCorp Press Pte Ltd, Caldecott Broadcast Centre, Annex Building, Level 1, Andrew Road, Singapore 299939.
T: 65 62364888 E: news@newstoday.com.sg
W: http://www.todayonline.com
Freq: Daily; Circ: 300007 Not Audited
Editor: Walter Fernandez; Editor: Agatha Koh Brazil; Editor: Yvonne Lim; Editor at Large: Conrad Raj; Editor: Ariel Tam; Editor: Leonard Thomas; Editor: Richard Valladares; Editor: Phin Wong
Editorial Profile: Covers International, regional, national and local news, lifestyle, features, sports for most of the business people.
Language (s): English
DAILY NEWSPAPER

The Wall Street Journal (Singapore)

Editorial: 10 Anson Road, 32-08 International Plaza, Singapore. T: 65 6415-4240
DAILY NEWSPAPER

Yomiuri Shimbun - Singapore Bureau

Editorial: Yomiuri Shimbun - Singapore Bureau, International plaza #21-04, 10 Anson Road, Singapore 79903. T: 65 62223029
W: http://www.yomiuri.co.jp
Bureau Chief: Akihiro Ito
Editorial Profile: Covers local and international news.
Language (s): Japanese
DAILY NEWSPAPER

NEWS SERVICE/SYNDICATE

Agence France-Presse

Editorial: 28 Maxwell Road, #03-06 Red Dot Traffic Building, Singapore 61920.
T: 65 6590 3788
Bureau Chief: Roberto Coloma
Language (s): English
NEWS SERVICE/SYNDICATE

Associated Press

Editorial: 10 Anson Rd. 32-11, International Plaza, Singapore 79903. T: 65 6220-1849
Bureau Chief: Mark Baker; Southeast Asia News Editor: Chris Brummitt
NEWS SERVICE/SYNDICATE

Bernama

Editorial: 6, Eu Tong Sen Street, The Central #10-04, Singapore 59817. T: 65 62356521
E: bernama_spore@singnet.com.sg
Bureau Chief: Tengku Noor Shamsiah Abdullah
Language (s): English
NEWS SERVICE/SYNDICATE

Bloomberg News

Editorial: 12th Floor Capital Square, 23 Church St, Singapore 49481. T: 65 62121200
E: spnews@bloomberg.net
Asia Trainer: Reinie Booysen; Editor: Rina Chandran; Bureau Chief: Linus Chua; Bureau Chief: Lars Klemming; Editor: Alexander Kwiatkowski; Editor: Adam Majendie; Editor: James Poole; Asia Editor/Team Leader: Amit Prakash
NEWS SERVICE/SYNDICATE

Dow Jones Newswires

Editorial: 10 Anson Road, Singapore 79903.
T: 65 6415-4140
E: djn.singapore.bureau@dowjones.com
News Editor: Reuben Carder; Bureau Chief: Venkat Ramakrishnan; Stock Markets Editor: Leslie Shaffer; Asia Pacific Editor: Sumathi Vaidyanathan
NEWS SERVICE/SYNDICATE

dpa Deutsche Presse-Agentur- Singapore Bureau

Editorial: dpa Deutsche Presse-Agentur-Singapore Bureau, 9 Shelford Road, Shelford Green #04-07, Singapore 288352.
T: 65 64625110 W: http://www.dpa.de
Freq: Daily
Editorial Profile: Covers global news.
Language (s): German
NEWS SERVICE/SYNDICATE

Kyodo News - Singapore Bureau

Editorial: 8 Eu Tong Sen Street #14-88, The Central Singapore, Singapore 59818.
T: 65 6223 3371
Bureau Chief: Toyoda Yukiko
Language (s): English
NEWS SERVICE/SYNDICATE

Market News International

Owner: Market News International Inc.
Editorial: 9 Raffles Place, #56-01, Republic Plaza, Singapore 48619. T: 1 656 632-3411
Asia News Editor: Phillip Day
Language (s): English
NEWS SERVICE/SYNDICATE

Nikkei

Editorial: Nikkei Inc. - Singapore Bureau, 331 North Bridge Road, #13-02/03 Odeon Towers, Singapore 188720. T: 65 63398200
E: news@nikkei.com.sg
W: http://www.nni.nikkei.co.jp
Freq: Weekly
Editorial Profile: Covers financial industry.
Language (s): English
NEWS SERVICE/SYNDICATE

Platts

Editorial: The McGraw-Hill Companies, 30 Cecil Street, #13-00 Prudential Tower, Singapore 49712. T: 65 63322800
W: http://www.platts.com
Editor: Calvin Lee; Editor: Deepa Vijiyasingam
Editorial Profile: Covers energy topics, industry news and prices for oil and natural gas.
Language (s): English
NEWS SERVICE/SYNDICATE

Reuters

Editorial: 18 Science Park Drive, Singapore 118229. T: 65 6775-5088
E: singapore.newsroom@thomsonreuters.com
Asia Pacific News Editor: Muralikumar Anantharaman; Bureau Chief: Rachel Armstrong; Asia Editor: Dayan Candappa; Editor: Matthew Driskill; Editor in Charge: Jonathan Leff; South Asia Specialist Editor: Sanjeev Miglani
NEWS SERVICE/SYNDICATE

Xinhua News Agency

Editorial: Xinhua News Agency - Singapore, 156 Prince Charles Cresent, Tower A, #13-16, Singapore 159015. T: 65 64737153
W: http://www.xinhua.org
Freq: Daily
Editorial Profile: Covers major news, international and local.
Language (s): Chinese
NEWS SERVICE/SYNDICATE

BROADCASTING

TELEVISION NETWORKS

ZDF - Singapore Bureau

Editorial: ZDF - Singapore Bureau, 600 North Bridge Road, #12-08 Parkview Square, Singapore 188778. T: 65 67336065
W: http://www.zdf.de
Editorial Profile: Covers news and public services news.

CABLE

Bloomberg Television

Editorial: 12th Floor Capital Square, 23 Church Street, Singapore 49481.
T: 65 62121200

CNBC Cable Network

Editorial: 10 Anson Rd, #06-01 International Plaza, Singapore 79903. T: 65 116563230488
E: editor@cnbcasia.com
W: http://www.cnbcasia.com

Reuters Television

Editorial: 18 Science Park Drive, Singapore 118229. T: 1 65 67755088
E: rvn.asia@thomsonreuters.com

Editorial Profile: Reuters Television Singapore bureau.

SLOVAKIA Tel: 421

Standard Time: GMT +1
Continent: Europe
Capital City: Bratislava

NEWSPAPERS & PUBLICATIONS

NEWSPAPERS

Hospodárske Noviny

Owner: Ecopress a.s.
Editorial: Seberiniho 1, PO Box 35, Bratislava 820 07. T: 421 2 48 23 81 02
E: redakcia@ecopress.sk W: http://hnonline.sk
Freq: Daily; Circ: 32000 Publisher's Statement
Market Editor: Tomáš Vašuta; Editor-in-Chief: Peter Vavro
Editorial Profile: Broadsheet-sized newspaper featuring economics, politics, finances, national and international news, culture, sport and entertainment. Aimed at business executives, government members and the general public.
Language (s): English, German, Slovak
DAILY NEWSPAPER

Pravda

Owner: Perex a.s.
Editorial: Trnavská cesta 39/A, Bratislava 831 04. T: 421 2 49 59 69 99 E: pravda@pravda.sk
W: http://www.pravda.sk
Freq: Daily; Circ: 90000 Publisher's Statement
Editorial Profile: Newspaper focusing on national and international news, finance, the economy, culture, entertainment and sport.
Language (s): English, Slovak
DAILY NEWSPAPER

The Slovak Spectator

Owner: The Rock spol. s.r.o.
Editorial: Lazaretska 12, Bratislava 811 08.
T: 421 2 59 23 33 00
E: spectator@spectator.sk
W: http://www.slovakspectator.sk Circ: 8500 Publisher's Statement
Editor-in-Chief: Beata Balogova; Publisher: Jan Pallo
Editorial Profile: Newspaper focusing on general news, business issues, culture, opinion and features.
Language (s): English
DAILY NEWSPAPER

SME

Owner: Petit Press a s
Editorial: Lazaretská 12, P.O.Box 77, Bratislava 811 08. T: 421 2 592 335 00
E: redakcia@sme.sk W: http://www.sme.sk
Freq: Daily; Circ: 92369 Publisher's Statement
Editor-in-Chief: Matus Kostolny
Editorial Profile: Newspaper focusing on national and international news, business, politics, culture and sport.
Language (s): English, Slovak
DAILY NEWSPAPER

Új Szó

Owner: Petit Press a s
Editorial: Lazaretská 12, Bratislava 811 08.
T: 421 2 592 334 21 E: redakcia@ujszo.com
W: http://ujszo.com
Freq: Daily; Circ: 35500 Publisher's Statement
Editor In Chief: Norbert Molnár
Editorial Profile: National newspaper for Hungarian speaking residents in Slovakia features: Home Affairs, Regions, International Affairs, Culture, Economics, Sports, Commentaries and Supplements.
Language (s): Hungarian
DAILY NEWSPAPER

NEWS SERVICE/SYNDICATE

Reuters

Editorial: Plynarenska 1, Bratislava 82109.
T: 421 253418402
NEWS SERVICE/SYNDICATE

TASR

Editorial: Lamacská cesta 3, Bratislava 841 04. T: 421 2 59 21 01 66 E: tasr@tasr.sk
W: http://www.tasr.sk
Editor-in-Chief: Richard Kvasnovský

Editorial Profile: The News Agency of the Slovak Republic (TASR) is a public-service agency that provides national and international news. Launched in 2008.
NEWS SERVICE/SYNDICATE

BROADCASTING

RADIO STATIONS

Rádio Slovensko
Editorial: Mýtna 1, P.O.Box 55, Bratislava 817 55. **T:** 421 2 57 27 33 33
W: http://www.slovakradio.sk
Editorial Profile: National radio station.

SLOVENIA   Tel: 386

Standard Time: GMT +1
Continent: Europe
Capital City: Ljubljana

NEWSPAPERS & PUBLICATIONS

NEWSPAPERS

Delo
Owner: Delo d.d.
Editorial: Dunajska 5, Ljubljana 1509.
T: 386 1 4737-400 **E:** tuditi@delo.si
W: http://www.delo.si
Freq: Daily; **Circ:** 93000 Publisher's Statement
Editor-in-Chief: Mateja Babic Stermecki;
Editor: Tanja Jaklic
Editorial Profile: Newspaper focusing on national and international news, economics, finance, culture, entertainment and sport.
Language (s): Slovene
DAILY NEWSPAPER

Dnevnik
Owner: Dnevnik, Casopisna družba d.d.
Editorial: Kopitarjeva 2 in 4, Ljubljana 1510.
T: 386 1 3082-100 **E:** info@dnevnik.si
W: http://www.dnevnik.si
Freq: Daily; **Circ:** 59000 Publisher's Statement
Urednica Zelena Pika: Sonja Hribovšek Vogric; **Urednik Športa:** Boštjan Istenic; **Urednik Strani Svet:** Igor Mekina; **Urednik Posebnih Prilog:** Peter Percic; **Urednik Kronike:** Toni Peric; **Urednica Strani Slovenija:** Jana Petkovšek; **Editor-in-Chief:** Suzana Rankov; **Urednik Elektronskega Dnevnika:** Brane Šalamon
Editorial Profile: Newspaper providing information on national and international politics, news, economics, finance, culture and entertainment.
Language (s): Slovene
DAILY NEWSPAPER

Družina
Owner: Družina d.o.o.
Editorial: Krekov trg 1, p.p. 95, Ljubljana 1000. **T:** 386 1 3602-800
E: druzina@druzina.si
W: http://www.druzina.si **Circ:** 53000 Publisher's Statement
Editor-in-Chief: Franci Petric
Editorial Profile: Newspaper covering all fields of life in the view of catholic social doctrine, features current affairs, cultural and other events.
Language (s): Slovene
DAILY NEWSPAPER

The Slovenia Times
Owner: DOMUS, založba in trgovina d.o.o.
Editorial: Šmartinska 106, Ljubljana 1000.
T: 386 1 5205-084 **E:** info@sloveniatimes.com
W: http://www.sloveniatimes.com
Freq: Bi-Weekly; **Circ:** 10000 Publisher's Statement
Editor-in-Chief: Tilen Majnardi
Editorial Profile: The Slovenia Times is the newspaper in the English language in Slovenia since 2003.
Language (s): English
DAILY NEWSPAPER

Vecer
Owner: CZP Vecer, d.d.
Editorial: Ulica slovenske osamosvojitve 2, Maribor 2504. **T:** 386 2 2353500
E: desk@vecer.com **W:** http://www.vecer.com
Freq: Daily; **Circ:** 65000 Publisher's Statement
News Editor: Srecko Klapš; **Editor-in-Chief:** Katja Šeruga; **Urednik Športa:** Aljoša Stojic

Editorial Profile: Newspaper focusing on national and international news, economics, culture and sport.
Language (s): Slovene
DAILY NEWSPAPER

Žurnal24
Editorial: Bravnicarjeva ulica 13, Ljubljana 1000. **T:** 386 1 620 26 84 **E:** desk@zurnal24.si
W: http://www.zurnal24.si
Freq: Daily; **Circ:** 239000 Publisher's Statement
Editor-in-Chief: Matej Košir
Language (s): Slovene
DAILY NEWSPAPER

SOLOMON ISLANDS   Tel: 677

Standard Time: GMT +11
Continent: Oceania
Capital City: Honiara

NEWSPAPERS & PUBLICATIONS

NEWSPAPERS

Island Sun
Owner: Trade Wind Company
Editorial: PO Box 1170, Honiara, Solomon Islands. **T:** 677 28070
E: islandsun@solomon.com.sb
Editor: Richard Toke
Language (s): English
NEWSPAPER

Solomon Star
Owner: Solomon Star Newspaper
Editorial: PO Box 255, Honiara, Solomon Islands. **T:** 677 22062
E: solstar@solomon.com.sb
W: http://solomonstarnews.com
Freq: Daily
Editor: Robert Iroga
Language (s): English
DAILY NEWSPAPER

BROADCASTING

RADIO STATIONS

Radio Hapi Lagun
Editorial: PO Box 78, Gizo
E: sibcnews@solomon.com.sb
W: http://www.sibconline.com.sb

Radio Temotu
Editorial: PO Box 46, Lata
E: sibcnews@solomon.com.sb
W: http://www.sibconline.com.sb

RADIO NETWORKS

Paua FM
Owner: Communications Fiji Ltd
Editorial: Honiara, Solomon Islands.
T: 677 38 984
E: pacafm@welcam.solomon.com.sb

Radio Happy Isles
Editorial: PO Box 654, Honiara. **T:** 677 20 051
E: sibcnews@solomon.com.sb

Solomon Islands Broadcasting Corporation (SIBC) - HQ
Owner: Solomon Islands Broadcasting Corporation (SIBC)
Editorial: PO Box 654, Honiara, Solomon Islands. **T:** 677 20051
E: sibcnews@solomon.com.sb
W: http://sibconline.com.sb

Wantok FM 96.3
Editorial: PO Box 654, Honiara. **T:** 677 29 600
E: sibcnews@solomon.com.sb
W: http://www.sibconline.com.sb

SOUTH AFRICA   Tel: 27

Standard Time: GMT +2
Continent: Africa
Capital City: Pretoria (Administrative), Cape Town (Legislative)

NEWSPAPERS & PUBLICATIONS

NEWSPAPERS

Beeld
Owner: Media 24: Newspapers
Editorial: PO Box 333, Auckland Park 2006.
T: 27 11 7139000 **E:** briewe@beeld.com
W: http://www.beeld.com
Freq: Daily; **Circ:** 70070 ABC-Audit Bureau of Circulations
Editor: Adriaan Basson; **Editor:** Sonja Carstens; **News Editor:** Sonja Carstens; **News Editor:** Erika de Beer; **Editor:** Tim du Plessis; **Editor In Chief:** Peet Kruger; **Editor:** Andre Le Roux; **Editor:** Liesl Louw; **Editor:** Andriette Stofberg; **Editor:** Marzanne van den Berg; **Editor:** Mariska van Rooyen
Editorial Profile: Major daily newspaper full mix of editorial. See separate listings for regional editions Beeld Johannesburg, Beeld Pretoria, Plus, and business section Sake 24. Afrikaans speaking adults, predominantly in and around the PWV area. See separate listing for Sake Beeld, Beeld Pretoria and Beeld Johannesburg.
Language (s): Afrikaans
DAILY NEWSPAPER

Die Burger, Cape Town
Owner: Media 24: Newspapers
Editorial: PO Box 692, Cape Town 8000.
T: 27 21 406 2815 **E:** dbnred@dieburger.com
W: http://www.dieburger.com
Freq: Daily
Editor: Bun Booyens; **Editor:** Hendrik Coetzee; **News Editor:** Michele O'Connor; **News Editor:** Michelle O'Connor
Editorial Profile: Major daily newspaper with full mix of editorial. The W. Cape editorial edition of Die Burger (combined). Afrikaans speaking adults in the Western Cape.
Language (s): Afrikaans
DAILY NEWSPAPER

Die Burger, Port Elizabeth
Owner: Media 24: Newspapers
Editorial: PO Box 525, Port Elizabeth 6000.
T: 27 41 5036111 **E:** oos@dieburger.com
W: http://www.dieburger.com
Freq: Daily
Editor: Riana de Lange; **Editor:** Jo-Ann Floris; **News Editor:** Reint Grobler
Editorial Profile: Regional daily edition of Die Burger, adapting news of regional interest. Afrikaans speaking adults in the Eastern Cape.Alternative Title: BURGER E. Cape
Language (s): Afrikaans
DAILY NEWSPAPER

Business Day
Owner: BDFM Publishers
Editorial: PO Box 1745, Saxonwold 2132.
T: 27 11 2803000 **W:** http://www.bdlive.co.za
Freq: Daily; **Circ:** 36087 ABC-Audit Bureau of Circulations
Editor-at-Large: Renee Bornochis; **Graphics:** Ruby-Gay Caetano; **Editor:** Elaine Doyle; **Editor-at-Large:** Naomi Larkin; **News Editor:** Charles Leonard; **Editor:** Dave Marrs; **Cartoonist:** Brandon Reynolds; **Graphic Artist:** Shaun Uthum; **Editor:** Ed West; **Companies Editor:** Nick Wilson; **Editor:** Songezo Zibi
Editorial Profile: Business Day is South Africa's daily business newspaper. With daily reports on stock prices, commodities and current affairs as well as in-depth analysis of local and global trends and how they affect your business activity. Previous title: Rand Daily Mail
Language (s): English
DAILY NEWSPAPER

Cape Argus
T: 27 214884911 **E:** argusnews@inl.co.za
W: http://www.capeargus.co.za
Freq: Daily
Editor in Chief: Chris Whitfield
Language (s): English
DAILY NEWSPAPER

The Cape Argus
Owner: Independent Newspapers: Cape
Editorial: PO Box 56, Cape Town 8000.
T: 27 21 4884911 **E:** argusnews@inl.co.za
W: http://www.iol.co.za/capeargus

Freq: Daily; **Circ:** 45924 ABC-Audit Bureau of Circulations
Editor: Jermaine Craig; **Editor:** Chris Whitfield
Editorial Profile: Major afternoon daily with full editorial mix. Includes 3 zoned editions per day. English speaking adults in the Western Cape.Previous title: The Argus
Language (s): English
DAILY NEWSPAPER

Cape Times
Owner: Independent Newspapers: Cape
Editorial: PO Box 11, Cape Town 8000.
T: 27 21 488 4911 **E:** ctletters@inl.co.za
W: http://www.capetimes.co.za
Freq: Daily; **Circ:** 43950 ABC-Audit Bureau of Circulations
Editor: Gasant Abarder; **News Editor:** Janet Heard; **News Editor:** A'Eysha Kassiem; **Editor In Chief:** Chris Whitfield
Editorial Profile: Major morning newspaper with full mix of editorial. English speaking adults in the Western Cape.
Language (s): English
DAILY NEWSPAPER

Citizen
Editorial: 9 Wright Street, Industria West, Johannesburg. **T:** 27 11 2486000
E: editor@citizen.co.za
W: http://www.citizen.co.za
Freq: Daily
Editor: Steven Motale; **Publisher:** Eureka Zandberg
Editorial Profile: The Citizen is a tabloid daily newspaper focused on news, sport, business, politics, entertainment and leisure, motoring, health, analysis, auctions and horse racing.
Language (s): English
DAILY NEWSPAPER

City Press
Owner: RCP Media
Editorial: PO Box 3413, Johannesburg 2000.
T: 27 11 7139001
W: http://www.citypress.co.za
Freq: Weekly
Editor In Chief: Ferial Haffajee; **Bureau Chief:** Wonder Hlongwa; **Editor:** Len Kelane; **Editor:** Simba Makunike; **Editor:** Shalo Mbtha; **Editor:** Lesley Mofokeng; **Editor:** Ruth Motau; **News Editor:** Japhet Ncube; **Editor:** Vukile Pokwana; **Editor:** Jimmy Seepe; **Editor:** Mapula Sibanda; **Editor-in-Chief:** Mathatha Tsedu
Editorial Profile: Major Sunday newspaper with full mix of editorial. Black adults nationally.
Language (s): English
DAILY NEWSPAPER

Daily Dispatch
Owner: Avusa Media Ltd: Eastern Cape
Editorial: PO Box 131, East London 5200.
T: 27 43 7022000 **E:** letters@dispatch.co.za
W: http://www.dispatch.co.za
Editor: Barbara Hollands; **Editor in Chief:** Bongani Siqoko
Editorial Profile: Daily newspaper with full mix of editorial. English speaking adults in East London, Border, Transkei and Ciskei.
Language (s): English
DAILY NEWSPAPER

The Daily News
Owner: Independent Newspapers: KwaZulu-Natal
Editorial: 18 Osborne Street, Durban.
T: 27 31 3082911 **E:** DNnews@inl.co.za
W: http://www.iol.co.za/dailynews
Freq: Daily; **Circ:** 35071 ABC-Audit Bureau of Circulations
News Editor: Kuben Chetty; **Editor:** Alan Dunn; **Bureau Chief:** Sherlissa Peters; **News Editor:** Charmaine Pillay; **Editor:** Sally Scott
Editorial Profile: Major Durban daily newspaper with full mix of editorial. English speaking adults, Durban bias.
Language (s): English
DAILY NEWSPAPER

Daily Sun
Owner: Media 24: Newspapers
Editorial: PO Box 121, Auckland Park 2006.
T: 27 11 8776000 **E:** news@dailysun.co.za
W: http://www.dailysunads.co.za/dailysun
Freq: Daily; **Circ:** 381127 ABC-Audit Bureau of Circulations
Editor-in-Chief: Mazwi Xaba
Editorial Profile: Daily Sun is South Africa's daily paper which is read by over 5.5 million people a day.
Language (s): English
DAILY NEWSPAPER

Mail & Guardian
Owner: M&G Media Limited

Editorial: PO Box 91667, Auckland Park 2006.
T: 27 11 2507300 **E:** newsdesk@mg.co.za
W: http://mg.co.za
Freq: Weekly
Editor: Angela Quintal; **Editor-in-Chief:** Chris Roper
Editorial Profile: Newspaper focusing on analysis and comment on current news, social affairs, economics, the arts and sports. Includes distillation of articles from UK Guardian, Washington Post and Le Monde. Aimed at English speaking adults with an enquiring mind and an active interest in SA current affairs.Previous title: Weekly Mail and Guardian
Language (s): English
DAILY NEWSPAPER

The Mercury SA
Owner: Independent Newspapers: KwaZulu-Natal
Editorial: 18 Osborne Street, Greyville, Durban 4023. **T:** 27 31 3082911
E: mercnews@inl.co.za
W: http://www.iol.co.za/mercury
Freq: Daily
Editor: David Canning; **News Editor:** Philani Makhanya; **Editor-in-Chief:** Philani Mgwaba
Editorial Profile: Major newspaper with full mix of editorial. English speaking adults, Durban bias.Previous title: The Mercury (Natal)
Language (s): English
DAILY NEWSPAPER

The New Age
Editorial: 52 Lechwe Street, Corporate Park, Midrand 1685. **T:** 27 11 5421222
E: info@thenewage.co.za
W: http://www.thenewage.co.za
Editor: Moegsien Williams
Language (s): English
DAILY NEWSPAPER

Post South Africa
Owner: Independent Newspapers: KwaZulu-Natal
Editorial: PO Box 733, Durban 4000.
T: 27 31 308 2413
W: http://www.iol.co.za/thepost
Freq: Weekly
News Editor: Khalil Aniff; **Editor:** Aakash Bramdeo; **Publisher:** Shushi Govender; **Editor:** Brijlall Ramguthee
Editorial Profile: The Post is a newspaper published by News & Media in Durban, South Africa.
Language (s): English
DAILY NEWSPAPER

Rapport
Owner: RCP Media
Editorial: PO Box 8422, Johannesburg 2000.
T: 27 11 7139002 **E:** redakteur@rapport.co.za
W: http://www.rapport.co.za
Freq: Weekly
Editor: Liza Albrecht; **News Editor:** Liesel de Lange; **Editor-in-Chief:** Tim du Plessis; **Bureau Chief:** Chris Karsten; **News Editor:** Inge Kuhne; **Editor:** Buks Pietersen
Editorial Profile: Major newspaper containing full mix of editorial. See separate entries for supplements: Sake Rapport, Rapport Tydskrif, Kaap Rapport and Gauteng Rapport. Afrikaans speaking population nationally.
Language (s): Afrikaans
DAILY NEWSPAPER

Son Cape Town
Owner: Media 24: Newspapers
Editorial: PO Box 692, Cape Town 8000.
T: 27 21 4062121 **W:** http://www.son.co.za
Circ: 92213
Content Editor: Enrico Claassen; **Editor:** Andrew Koopman; **News Editor:** Neil Scott
Editorial Profile: Son is the tabloid to be published in Afrikaans.The newspaper is based on the British tabloids such as The Sun and focuses on news, scandal, gossip, entertainment, sport, and exposés. Son is distributed daily from Monday to Friday in the Western Cape and Eastern Cape.
Language (s): Afrikaans
DAILY NEWSPAPER

Sowetan
Owner: Avusa Media Ltd: Newspapers
Editorial: PO Box 6663, Johannesburg 2000.
T: 27 11 4714000 **E:** newsdesk@sowetan.co.za
W: http://www.sowetanlive.co.za
Freq: Daily
News Editor: Willie Bokala; **Editor-in-Chief:** Thabo Leshilo; **Editor:** Izaak Moledi; **Publisher:** Jason Sequiera
Language (s): English
DAILY NEWSPAPER

The Star
Owner: Independent Newspapers: Gauteng
Editorial: 47 Sauer Street, Johannesburg 2000. **T:** 27 11 633 2410
E: starnews@inl.co.za
W: http://www.iol.co.za/the-star
Freq: Daily
Editor: Justin Brown; **Editor:** Dennis Droppa; **Editor:** Jim Mitchell; **Editor:** Peter Sullivan; **Editor-in-Chief:** Moegsien Williams
Editorial Profile: South Africa's daily newspaper covering the local, national and international news and sport.
Language (s): English
DAILY NEWSPAPER

Sunday Independent
Owner: Independent Newspapers: Gauteng
Editorial: PO Box 1014, Johannesburg 2000.
T: 27 11 6339111
W: http://www.sundayindependent.co.za
Freq: Weekly
Editor: Peter De Ionno; **Editor:** Allan Greenblo; **Editor:** Robert Greig; **Editor:** Rodney Hartman; **Editor:** Elizabeth Kinghorn; **Editor:** Jovial Rantao; **Editor:** Leigh Roberts; **Editor:** Makhudu Sefara
Editorial Profile: Aims to provide top-drawer local & international editorial in two sections. Section one carries news & opinion from SA and overseas. Section two called Sunday Dispatches features politics, review section, international correspondents, the arts, culture, books, sport & business. English speakers aimed at in Gauteng area. Printed also in Cape Town, and distributed in Durban and Port Elizabeth.PR Accepted in: English
Language (s): English
DAILY NEWSPAPER

Sunday Tribune
Owner: Independent Newspapers: KwaZulu-Natal
Editorial: 18 Osborne Street, Greyville, Durban 4023. **T:** 27 31 308 2316
E: tribunenews@inl.co.za
W: http://www.iol.co.za/sunday-tribune
Freq: Weekly
News Editor: Liz Clarke; **Editor:** Philani Mgwaba
Editorial Profile: The Sunday Tribune is a weekend paper that is based in Durban in KwaZulu-Natal, South Africa.
Language (s): English
DAILY NEWSPAPER

Sunday World
Owner: Avusa Media Ltd: Newspapers
Editorial: PO Box 6663, Johannesburg 2000.
T: 27 11 4714000 **E:** tellus@sundayworld.co.za
W: http://www.sundayworld.co.za
Freq: Weekly
News Editor: Amos Mananyetso; **Editor:** Abdul Milazi; **Editor:** Charles Mogale; **News Editor:** Xolile Mtshazo; **News Editor:** Amanda Ngudle; **News Editor:** Zakhele Shiba
Editorial Profile: Major black interest newspaper with full mix of editorial. Gauteng, Mpumalanga, Northern Province, North West Province, Free State, Kimberley.Previous title: Sowetan Sunday World
Language (s): English
DAILY NEWSPAPER

The Times
Owner: Avusa Media Ltd: Newspapers
Editorial: 4 Biermann Avenue, Rosebank 2196.
T: 27 11 2803000
E: newsbreak@timeslive.co.za
W: http://www.timeslive.co.za/thetimes
Freq: Daily
Editor-at-Large: Ray Hartley
Editorial Profile: Times provides breaking SA and international news and leading opinion.
Language (s): English
DAILY NEWSPAPER

Volksblad
Owner: Media 24: Newspapers
Editorial: PO Box 267, Bloemfontein 9300.
T: 27 51 4047600 **E:** nuus@volksblad.com
W: http://www.volksblad.com
Freq: Daily
Editor: Jonathan Crowther; **News Editor:** Cathy Dlodla; **Editor:** Clarissa Grobler; **Editor:** Jannie Hennop; **Editor:** Siska Martin; **Editor:** Braam Muller; **Editor:** Marleen Smith; **Editor:** Johanna van Eeden; **Editor:** Betta van Huyssteen
Editorial Profile: Major daily newspaper with full editorial mix. Afrikaans speaking adults in Free State and Northern Cape.Previous title: Die Volksblad
Language (s): Afrikaans
DAILY NEWSPAPER

The Wall Street Journal (South Africa)
Editorial: 12th Floor, Sandton City Office Tower, 158 5th St., Sandhurst ext. 3, Johannesburg 2196. **T:** 27 11 783-7848
DAILY NEWSPAPER

NEWS SERVICE/SYNDICATE

Agence France-Presse - Johannesburg Bureau
Editorial: 37 Keyes Avenue, Rosebank, Johannesburg 2196. **T:** 27 11 530 9900
E: johannes.myburgh@afp.com
W: http://www.afp.com
Bureau Chief: Christophe Beaudufe
Editorial Profile: Johannesburg office of the international press agency covering regional, national and international news and current affairs including general interest, politics, business, economics, health, science, education and society.
Language (s): English
NEWS SERVICE/SYNDICATE

Associated Press
Editorial: Richmond Sq 15 Napier St, Johannesburg 2092. **T:** 27 11 628-7700
Africa News Editor: Andrew Selsky
NEWS SERVICE/SYNDICATE

Dow Jones Newswires
Editorial: 12th Floor, Sandton City Office Tower, 158 5th St., Sandhurst ext. 3, Johannesburg 2196. **T:** 27 11 783-7848
NEWS SERVICE/SYNDICATE

South African Press Association
Editorial: Cotswold House, Greenacres Office Park, Victory Park, Johannesburg 2000.
T: 27 11 782 1600 **E:** news@sapa.org.za
W: http://www.sapa.org.za
News Editor: Hannes de Wet
Language (s): English
NEWS SERVICE/SYNDICATE

BROADCASTING

TELEVISION STATIONS

Africa News Network 7 (ANN7)
T: 27 11 5421222 **E:** ann7online@ann7.com
W: http://www.ann7.com

BDTV
Editorial: 4 Biermann Ave Rosebank, Johannesburg 2169 **E:** news@summit.co.za
W: http://www.businessdaytv.co.za
Editorial Profile: BusinessDay TV is the South Africa's business & markets channel.

CNBC Africa
Owner: CNBC Africa
Editorial: 5th Floor, The Hudson, No. 30 Hudson Street, De Waterkant, Cape Town 8001. **T:** 27 21 421 74 50
E: feedback@cnbcafrica.com
W: http://www.cnbcafrica.com

eNCA (eNews Channel Africa)
Editorial: 5 Summit Road, Dunkeld West, Johannesburg 2196. **T:** 27 11 537 9300
E: info@enca.com **W:** http://www.enca.com
Editorial Profile: eNews Channel Africa is the South Africa's 24-hour news service with live reports, breaking news, sport, weather, entertainment, financial and business updates all form part of its offering, along with a host of topical current affairs shows.

e-TV
Owner: AZoM.com Pty Ltd
Editorial: PO Box 12124, Mill Street, Gardens 8010. **T:** 27 21 481 45 00 **E:** info@etv.co.za
W: http://www.etv.co.za

SABC 1
Owner: AZoM.com Pty Ltd
Editorial: Private Bag X41, Auckland Park 2006. **T:** 27 11 71 49 111 **E:** info@sabc.co.za
W: http://www.sabc1.co.za
Editorial Profile: National television station covering sport, drama, entertainment and religious programming.

SABC 2
Owner: AZoM.com Pty Ltd
Editorial: Private Bag X41, Auckland Park 2006, Johannesburg. **T:** 27 11 71 49 111
E: info@sabc.co.za **W:** http://www.sabc2.co.za

Editorial Profile: National television station broadcasting kids programmes, entertainment, comedy and drama.

SABC 3
Editorial: Private Bag X41, Auckland Park 2006. **T:** 27 11 71 46 100 **E:** info@sabc.co.za
W: http://www.sabctv.co.za
Editorial Profile: Television station broadcasting news, sport and drama.

TELEVISION NETWORKS

SABC News
T: 27 11 714 9111 **W:** http://www.sabc.co.za

SuperSport
T: 27 11 6866000 **E:** info@supersport.co.za
W: http://www.supersport.com

SPAIN   Tel: 34
Standard Time: GMT +1
Continent: Europe
Capital City: Madrid

NEWSPAPERS & PUBLICATIONS

NEWSPAPERS

El 9 Nou d'Osona i del Ripollès
Owner: Premsa d'Osona SA
Editorial: Plaça de la Catedral, 2, Barcelona E-08500. **T:** 34 93 88 94 949
E: direccio@vic.el9nou.com
W: http://www.el9nou.com
Freq: 2 Times/Week
Editor in Chief: Jaume Espuny
Editorial Profile: Regional daily newspaper focussing on news and current affairs, politics, society, economy, culture, and sports.
Language (s): Catalan
DAILY NEWSPAPER

El 9 Nou-Valles Oriental
Owner: Premsa d'Osona SA
Editorial: Carrer Girona, 34 1er. pis, Granollers E-08400. **T:** 34 938 60 30 20
E: noticies@gra.el9nou.com
W: http://www.el9nou.com
Freq: 2 Times/Week
Editor in Chief: Josep Mas
Editorial Profile: Regional daily newspaper focussing on news and current affairs, politics, society, economy, culture, and sports.
Language (s): Catalan
DAILY NEWSPAPER

ABC
Owner: Diario ABC, S.L.
Editorial: Juan Ignacio Luca de Tena, 7, Madrid 28027. **T:** 34 91 33 99 000
E: abcdiario@abc.es **W:** http://www.abc.es
Freq: Daily; **Circ:** 214639 Not Audited
Editor: Jaime Gonzales; **Editor in Chief:** Sergio Guijarro
Editorial Profile: Newspaper covering regional, national and international news and current affairs including politics, business, economics, culture, lifestyle, society and sports.
Language (s): Spanish
DAILY NEWSPAPER

El Adelantado de Segovia
Owner: El Adelantado de Segovia
Editorial: Calle Morillo, 7 (junto Jardín Botánico), Segovia E-40002.
T: 34 921 43 72 61
E: adelantado@eladelantado.com
W: http://www.eladelantado.com
Freq: Daily
Editor in Chief: Jesús Martínez Calle
Editorial Profile: Daily newspaper covering current regional news and events and international news as well as sports and humor.
Language (s): Spanish
DAILY NEWSPAPER

El Adelanto de Salamanca
Owner: Publicaciones Regionales SA
Editorial: Gran Vía 56, Salamanca E-37001.
T: 34 923 100 599
E: eladelanto@elperiodico.com
W: http://www.eladelanto.com
Freq: Daily
Editorial Profile: Regional daily newspaper focussing news and current affairs, politics, economy and sports.
Language (s): Spanish
DAILY NEWSPAPER

ARA
Owner: Premsa Periòdica Ara
Editorial: Diputació, 119, Barcelona 8015.
T: 34 93 202 95 95 **E:** cartes@ara.cat
W: http://www.ara.cat
Freq: Daily
Editorial Profile: Regional daily newspaper covering news and current affairs including politics, society. culture, economics, sports and media.
Language (s): Catalan
DAILY NEWSPAPER

As
Owner: Diario As SL
Editorial: Calle Valenti Beato 14, 4ª planta, Madrid E-28037. **T:** 34 91 37 52 500
E: diarioas@diarioas.es **W:** http://www.as.com
Freq: Daily
Editor: Carmen Colino; **Editor:** Juan Guiterrez
Editorial Profile: Tabloid-sized newspaper concerning competitive sport, including results and interviews with sporting personalities.
Language (s): Spanish
DAILY NEWSPAPER

Atlántico Diario
Owner: Rías Baixas Comunicación SA
Editorial: Avenida Camelias 104 bajo, Vigo (pontevedra) E-36211. **T:** 34 986 20 86 86
E: atlantico@atlantico.net
W: http://www.atlantico.net
Freq: Daily
Editor in Chief: Ana Fuentes Crego
Editorial Profile: Regional daily newspaper focussing on news and current affairs.
Language (s): Spanish
DAILY NEWSPAPER

Cádiz Información
Owner: Publicaciones del Sur SA
Editorial: Parque Empresarial c/ De la Investigación, Jerez De La Frontera E-11407.
T: 34 956 29 24 58
E: cadiz@publicacionesdelsur.net
W: http://andaluciainformacion.es/cadiz/
Freq: Daily
Editorial Profile: Daily regional newspaper focusing on current news and affairs, sports, politics and economics.
Language (s): Spanish
DAILY NEWSPAPER

Canarias 7
Owner: Informaciones Canarias SA
Editorial: Calle Profesor Lozano 7, Urbanización El Sebadal, Las Palmas De Gran Canaria E-35008. **T:** 34 928 30 13 00
E: webmaster@canarias7.es
Freq: Daily
Editor in Chief: Angeles Arencibia; **Editor in Chief:** Rebeca Chacon
Editorial Profile: Canarias 7 is daily regional newspaper that covers wide range of current news such as business, entertainment, politics and other daily news.
Language (s): Spanish
DAILY NEWSPAPER

El Comercio
Owner: El Comercio SA
Editorial: Calle del Diario El Comerciom 1, Gijón 22307. **T:** 34 98 51 79 800
E: elcomercio@elcomercio.es
W: http://www.elcomercio.es
Freq: Daily
Editorial Profile: Regional daily newspaper covering news and current affairs including general interest, business, sports, economics and entertainment.
Language (s): Spanish
DAILY NEWSPAPER

Córdoba
Owner: Diario Córdoba SA
Editorial: Ingeniero Juan de la Cierva 18 (Pol. Torrecilla), Cordoba E-14013.
T: 34 957 42 03 02
E: redaccion@cordoba.elperiodico.com
W: http://www.diariocordoba.com
Freq: Daily
Editor in Chief: José Luis Blasco; **Editor in Chief:** Manuel Fernández; **Editor in Chief:** José Murillo
Editorial Profile: Regional daily newspaper focussing on news and current affairs.
Language (s): Spanish
DAILY NEWSPAPER

El Correo de Andalucía
Owner: El Correo de Andalucia SL
Editorial: Americo Vespucio 39, Isla De La Cartuca (sevilla) E-41092. **T:** 34 95 448 8500
E: redaccion@correoandalucia.es
W: http://www.correoandalucia.es
Freq: Daily
Editor: Mario Daza; **Editor:** Juan Jose Roldán; **Editor in Chief:** Ana Trujillo
Editorial Profile: Regional daily newspaper focussing on news and current affairs, sports and politics.
Language (s): Spanish
DAILY NEWSPAPER

Deia
Owner: Editorial Iparraguirre SA
Editorial: Camino de Capuchinos 6, 5°-C, Bilbao E-48004. **T:** 34 944 59 91 00
E: Administracion@deia.com
W: http://www.deia.com
Freq: Daily
Editor: Idoia Alonso
Editorial Profile: Regional daily newspaper focusing on news and current affairs as well as politics, society. culture, and sports.
Language (s): Spanish
DAILY NEWSPAPER

El Día
Owner: Editorial Leoncio Rodríguez SA
Editorial: Avenida Buenos Aires 71, Santa Cruz De Tenerife E-38005. **T:** 34 922 23 83 00
E: norte@eldia.es **W:** http://www.eldia.es
Freq: Daily
Editor in Chief: Jorge Espinel; **Editor:** Ventura González
Editorial Profile: Regional daily newspaper focussing on news and current affairs.
Language (s): Spanish
DAILY NEWSPAPER

El Día de Cordoba
Owner: Joly Digital
Editorial: C/Jose Cruz Conde 12, Cordoba E-14008. **T:** 34 95 72 22 050
E: eldia@eldiadecordoba.com
W: http://www.eldiadecordoba.com
Freq: Daily
Editor in Chief: Ramón Villar
Editorial Profile: Regional daily newspaper focussing on news and current affairs.
Language (s): Spanish
DAILY NEWSPAPER

El Día de Valladolid
Owner: PROMECAL, S. L.
Editorial: Edificio PROMECAL, Calle los Astros s/n, Valladolid 47009. **T:** 34 983 32 50 45
E: redaccion@diavalladolid.es
W: http://www.diavalladolid.es
Freq: Daily
Editorial Profile: Regional daily newspaper focussing on news and current affairs, lifestyle and sports.
Language (s): Spanish
DAILY NEWSPAPER

Diari de Terrassa
Owner: Julián Sanz Soria SL
Editorial: Vinyals 61, Terrassa (barcelona) 8221. **T:** 34 937 28 37 00
E: ciudad@diarideterrassa.es
W: http://www.diariterrassa.net
Freq: Daily
Editor in Chief: Josep Arnero Argüello
Editorial Profile: Regional daily newspaper focussing on news and current affairs.
Language (s): Spanish
DAILY NEWSPAPER

Diario de Avisos
Owner: CANAVISA SA
Editorial: Calle Salamanca 5, Santa Cruz De Tenerife E-38006. **T:** 34 92 22 72 350
E: lop@diariodeavisos.com
W: http://www.diariodeavisos.com
Freq: Daily
Editorial Profile: Regional daily newspaper focussing on news and current affairs, politics, economy, society, culture and sports.
Language (s): Spanish
DAILY NEWSPAPER

Diario de Burgos
Owner: Diario de Burgos SA
Editorial: Edificio PROMECAL BurgosAvda., Castilla y León 62-64, Burgos E-09006.
T: 34 947 26 72 80
E: redaccion@diariodeburgos.es
W: http://www.diariodeburgos.es
Freq: Daily
Editor: Ana Isabel Angulo; **Editor:** Antonio Méndez Pozo; **Editor in Chief:** Martin Serrano
Editorial Profile: Regional daily newspaper focussing on news and current affairs and sports.
Language (s): Spanish
DAILY NEWSPAPER

Diario de Cádiz
Owner: Joly Digital
Editorial: Avda de El Puerto, 2, Ed. Fénix, Cádiz 11007. **T:** 34 956 29 79 00
E: nmartinez@diariodecadiz.com
W: http://www.diariodecadiz.es
Freq: Daily
Editor in Chief: Francisco Sanchez Zambrano; **Editor:** PIlar Vera Royo
Editorial Profile: Regional daily newspaper focussing on news and current affairs, sports, technology, culture, television entertainment, and health.
Language (s): Spanish
DAILY NEWSPAPER

Diario de Ibiza
Owner: Diario de Ibiza SA
Editorial: Avda. de la Paz (esquina C/ Aubarca), Ibiza E-07800. **T:** 34 971 19 00 00
E: diariodeibiza@epi.es
W: http://www.diariodeibiza.es
Freq: Daily
Editor in Chief: Sebastián Candela; **Editor in Chief:** Cristina Martin
Editorial Profile: Regional daily newspaper focussing on news and current affairs, sports, economy, and lifestyle.
Language (s): Spanish
DAILY NEWSPAPER

Diario de Jerez
Owner: Joly Digital
Editorial: Patricio Garvey s/n, Jerez De La Frontera, Cádiz 11402. **T:** 34 95 63 21 411
E: redaccion@diariodejerez.com
W: http://www.diariodejerez.com
Freq: Daily
Editor: Pilar Nieto; **Editor:** Manuel Pasqual Fernandez
Editorial Profile: Regional daily newspaper focussing on news and current affairs, sports, technology, culture, and tv entertainment.
Language (s): Spanish
DAILY NEWSPAPER

Diario de León
Owner: Diario de León SA
Editorial: Carretera León-Astorga, Km. 4,5, Trobajo Del Camino (león) 24010.
T: 34 987 84 03 00
E: diariodeleon@diariodeleon.es
W: http://www.diariodeleon.com
Freq: Daily
Editor: Ana Gaitero Alonso
Editorial Profile: Regional daily newspaper focussing on news and current affairs, culture, economy, sports, and international news.
Language (s): Spanish
DAILY NEWSPAPER

Diario de Mallorca
Owner: Editora Balear SA
Editorial: Calle Puerto Rico 15, Polígono de Levante, Palma De Mallorca E-07006.
T: 34 971 17 03 00
E: secretaria.diariodemallorca@epi.es
W: http://www.diariodemallorca.es
Freq: Daily
Editor: Ricardo Cabot; **Editor in Chief:** Pilar Garces
Editorial Profile: Regional daily newspaper focussing on news and current affairs, sports, economy, and lifestyle.
Language (s): Spanish
DAILY NEWSPAPER

Diario de Navarra
Owner: Diario de Navarra SA
Editorial: Ctra. Zaragoza 23, Pamplona E-31191. **T:** 34 948 23 60 50
E: edicion.digital@diariodenavarra.es
W: http://www.diariodenavarra.es
Freq: Daily
Editor: Fernando Hernandez Morondo; **Editor:** Germán Ulzurrun
Editorial Profile: Regional daily newspaper focussing on news and current affairs, sports, international news, economy, culture, society, and television entertainment.
Language (s): Spanish
DAILY NEWSPAPER

Diario de Noticias de Navarra
Owner: Zeroa Multimedia SA
Editorial: Altzutzate 8, Poligono Industrial Areta, Pamplona 31620. **T:** 34 948 33 25 33
E: redaccion@noticiasdenavarra.com
W: http://www.noticiasdenavarra.com
Freq: Daily
Editorial Profile: Regional daily newspaper focussing on news and current affairs, politics, sports and economy.
Language (s): Spanish
DAILY NEWSPAPER

Diario de Pontevedra
Owner: El Progreso de Lugo SL
Editorial: Rua Lepanto 5, Pontevedra E-36001.
T: 34 986 01 11 00
E: pperez@diariodepontevedra.com
W: http://www.diariodepontevedra.com
Freq: Daily
Editorial Profile: Regional daily newspaper focussing on news and current affairs, sports, world news, society, and economy.
Language (s): Spanish
DAILY NEWSPAPER

Diario de Sevilla
Owner: Editorial Andaluza de Periodicos Independientes SA
Editorial: Rioja, 14-16, Sevilla 41001.
T: 34 954 50 62 00
E: secretaria@diariodesevilla.es
W: http://www.diariodesevilla.es
Freq: Daily
Editorial Profile: Regional daily newspaper focussing on news and current affairs, sports, technology, culture, tv entertainment, and health.
Language (s): Spanish
DAILY NEWSPAPER

Diario del Alto Aragón
Owner: Publicaciones y Ediciones del Alto Aragón SA
Editorial: Ronda Estación 4, Huesca E-22005.
T: 34 974 215656
E: admin@diariodelaltoaragon.es
W: http://www.diariodelaltoaragon.es
Freq: Daily
Editor: Miguel Angel Blazco; **Editor in Chief:** Jorge Naya
Editorial Profile: Regional daily newspaper focusing on news and current affairs, world news, economy, culture, sports and tv entertainment.
Language (s): Spanish
DAILY NEWSPAPER

El Diario Montañes
Owner: Editorial Cantábria SA
Editorial: Calle la Prensa s/n, Santander 39012. **T:** 34 942 35 40 00
E: redaccion.dm@eldiariomontanes.es
W: http://www.eldiariomontanes.es
Freq: Daily
Editor in Chief: Miguel Angel Perez Jorrin
Editorial Profile: Regional daily newspaper focussing on news and current affairs including sports, economics, celebrity, media and regional events.
Language (s): Spanish
DAILY NEWSPAPER

El Diario Palentino
Owner: El Diario Palentino SAU
Editorial: c/Calle Mayor 52, Palencia E-34001.
T: 34 979 7 06 308
E: redaccion@diariopalentino.es
W: http://www.diariopalentino.es
Freq: Daily
Editor in Chief: Jorge Cancho González
Editorial Profile: Regional daily newspaper focussing on news and current affairs, and sports.
Language (s): Spanish
DAILY NEWSPAPER

Diario Público
Owner: Mediapubli Sociedad de Publicaciones y Ediciones S. L.
Editorial: CALLE BALMES, 150, 6°, Barcelona 8018. **T:** 34 91 838 7641
E: redaccion@publico.es
W: http://www.publico.es
Freq: Daily; **Circ:** 132441 Publisher's Statement
Editor: Pablo Oliveira y Silva; **Editor:** Jorge Otero Maldonad; **Editor:** Alejandro Torrus; **Editor:** Jorge Yusta
Editorial Profile: Newspaper covering regional, national and international news, politics, finance, culture, society and sport.
Language (s): Spanish
DAILY NEWSPAPER

El Diario Vasco
Owner: Sociedad Vascongada de Publicaciones SA
Editorial: Camino de Portuetxe 2, San Sebastian E-20018. **T:** 34 943 41 07 00
E: redaccion@diariovasco.com
W: http://www.diariovasco.com
Freq: Daily
Editor: Iñigo Beltrán de Heredia; **Editor:** Javier Peña
Editorial Profile: Regional daily newspaper focussing on news and current affairs, sports, economy, and television entertainment.
Language (s): Spanish
DAILY NEWSPAPER

El El Correo
Owner: Diario El Correo SA
Editorial: Pintor Losada, 7, Bilbao E-48004.
T: 34 94 48 70 100
E: redaccion@elcorreo.com

W: http://www.diario-elcorreo.es
Freq: Daily
Editor: Luis Gomez Gonzalez; **Editor:** Octavio Igea; **Editor:** Mikel Iturralde
Editorial Profile: Daily newspaper covering current regional news and affairs, sports, economy, and television entertainment.
Language (s): Spanish
DAILY NEWSPAPER

El Periodico de Huelva
Owner: El Correo de Andalucia SL
Editorial: Calle Jesús de la Pasión, 1, Huelva E-21004. **T:** 34 959 54 08 32
E: redaccion@elperiodicodehuelva.es
W: http://www.elperiodicodehuelva.es/index.php
Freq: Daily
Editor: Javier Barranco
Editorial Profile: Regional daily newspaper focussing on news, current affairs, economics, politics and sport.
Language (s): Spanish
DAILY NEWSPAPER

El Punt Avui +
Owner: Prensa Catalana SA
Editorial: Tapies, 2, Barcelona 8001.
T: 34 93 227 6600
E: info@hermescomunicacion.es
W: http://www.avui.cat
Freq: Daily
Editor: Toni Brosa; **Editor:** Anna Serrano
Editorial Profile: Regional daily newspaper focussing on news and current affairs.
Language (s): Catalan, Spanish
DAILY NEWSPAPER

Europa Sur
Owner: Joly Digital
Editorial: Calle Muro, 3, Algeciras (cádiz) E-11201. **T:** 34 956 58 82 50
E: redaccion@europasur.com
W: http://www.europasur.com
Freq: Daily
Editor in Chief: Federico Joly
Editorial Profile: Regional daily newspaper focussing on news, current affairs, economics, politics and sport.
Language (s): Spanish
DAILY NEWSPAPER

Expansión
Owner: UNIDAD EDITORIAL
Editorial: Avenida de San Luis, 25, Madrid 28033. **T:** 34 91 443 50 00
E: expansion.com@expansion.com
W: http://www.expansion.com
Freq: Daily
Editor in Chief: Tino Fernández Arias; **Editor in Chief:** Clara Ruiz de Gauna
Editorial Profile: Daily Newspaper covering business and finance including economics, society, personal finance, investment, markets and law.
Language (s): Spanish
DAILY NEWSPAPER

Faro de Vigo
Owner: Faro de Vigo SA
Editorial: Factoría de Chapela-Redondela, Vigo (pontevedra) E-36320. **T:** 34 986 81 46 00
E: contenidos@farodevigomedia.es
W: http://www.farodevigo.es
Freq: Daily
Editor: Lara Grana
Editorial Profile: Regional daily newspaper focussing on news, current affairs, economics, politics and sport.
Language (s): Spanish
DAILY NEWSPAPER

La Gaceta
Owner: Grupo Intereconomía
Editorial: Calle Modesto Lafuente, 42, Madrid 28010. **T:** 34 91 432 77 66
E: comunicacion@intereconomia.com
W: http://www.intereconomia.com/la-gaceta
Freq: Daily
Editorial Profile: Newspaper covering business and economics including news, current affairs, politics, society, culture and sports.
Language (s): Spanish
DAILY NEWSPAPER

La Gaceta de los Negocios
Owner: Grupo Negocios de Ediciones y Publicaciones SL
Editorial: Paseo de La Castellana 36-38, Madrid E-28046. **T:** 34 91 43 27 600
E: comunicacion@intereconomia.com
W: http://www.negocios.com/gaceta
Freq: Daily
Editor: Santiago Mata; **Editor:** Joaquín Ortega
Editorial Profile: Tabloid-sized newspaper providing in-depth financial, economic and business news and current regional news.
Language (s): Spanish
DAILY NEWSPAPER

La Gaceta Regional de Salamanca
Owner: Grupo Promotor Salmantino SA
Editorial: Avda. de los Cipreses 81, Salamanca E-37004. **T:** 34 923 12 52 52
E: local@lagacetadesalamanca.com
W: http://www.lagacetadesalamanca.com
Freq: Daily
Editorial Profile: Regional daily newspaper focussing on news, current affairs, economics, politics and sport.
Language (s): Spanish
DAILY NEWSPAPER

Gente en Burgos
Owner: Noticias de burgos SL
Editorial: Calle Victoria, 9, 1°B, Burgos 9004.
T: 34 947 25 76 00
E: directora@genteenburgos.com
W: http://www.genteenburgos.com
Freq: Weekly; **Circ:** 50000 Publisher's Statement
Editor: Lidia Sierra
Editorial Profile: Regional daily newspaper focussing on news, current affairs, economics, politics and sport.
Language (s): Spanish
DAILY NEWSPAPER

Heraldo de Aragón
Owner: Heraldo de Aragón SA
Editorial: Paseo de la Independencia 29, Apdo. 175, Zaragoza E-50001.
T: 34 976 76 50 00 **E:** heraldo@heraldo.es
W: http://www.heraldo.es
Freq: Daily
Editor: Joan F Losilla Eixarch; **Editor:** Silvia Rubio Bueno
Editorial Profile: Regional daily newspaper focussing on news, current affairs, economics, politics and sport.
Language (s): Spanish
DAILY NEWSPAPER

Heraldo de Soria
Owner: Soria Impresión SA
Editorial: El Collado 17, Soria E-42002.
T: 34 975 23 36 07
E: soriaredaccion@heraldo.es
W: http://www.heraldodesoria.es
Freq: Daily
Editor: Luis Casado
Editorial Profile: Daily regional newspaper covering current regional, and international news and affairs as well as economy, society, culture and sports.
Language (s): Spanish
DAILY NEWSPAPER

HOY Diario de Extremadura
Owner: Corporación de Medios de Extremadura SA
Editorial: Carretera Madrid-Lisboa 22, Badajoz 6008. **T:** 34 924 214 300 **E:** redaccion@hoy.es
W: http://www.hoy.es
Freq: Daily
Editor: Alberto García de Frutos; **Editor in Chief:** José Orantos
Editorial Profile: Regional daily newspaper focussing on news, current affairs, economics, politics and sport.
Language (s): Spanish
DAILY NEWSPAPER

Huelva Información
Owner: Huelva Información SA
Editorial: C / Isaac Albéniz, 1, Huelva E-21001. **T:** 34 959 54 11 80
E: redaccion@huelvainformacion.es
W: http://www.huelvainformacion.es
Freq: Daily
Editor in Chief: Victoriano Ruigómez Domínguez
Editorial Profile: Regional daily newspaper focussing on news, current affairs, economics, politics and sport.
Language (s): Spanish
DAILY NEWSPAPER

Ideal
Owner: Corporación de Medios de Andalucía SA
Editorial: C/ Huelva 2, Polígono de ASEGR, Peligros (granada) E-18210.
T: 34 95 88 09 809 **E:** redaccion@ideal.es
W: http://www.ideal.es
Freq: Daily
Editor: Isabel Alcantara Arroyo
Editorial Profile: Regional daily newspaper focussing on news, current affairs, economics, politics and sport.
Language (s): Spanish
DAILY NEWSPAPER

Información
Owner: Editorial Prensa Alicantina SA
Editorial: Avenida del Doctor Rico, 17, Alicante E-03005. **T:** 34 965 98 91 00
E: informacion.alicante@epi.es
W: http://www.diarioinformacion.com
Freq: Daily
Editorial Profile: Regional daily newspaper focussing on news, current affairs, economics, politics and sport, covering the Alicante province.
Language (s): Spanish
DAILY NEWSPAPER

Jaén
Owner: Diario Jaén SA
Editorial: Calle Torredonjimeno 1, Polígono los Olivares, Jaén E-23009. **T:** 34 953 21 11 11
E: diariojaen@diariojaen.es
W: http://www.diariojaen.es
Freq: Daily
Editor in Chief: Juana González Cerezo; **Editor in Chief:** José Manuel Serrano Alba
Editorial Profile: Regional daily newspaper focussing on news, current affairs, economics, politics and sport.
Language (s): Spanish
DAILY NEWSPAPER

La La Mañana
Owner: Diari de Ponent SA
Editorial: Polígono industrial El Segre 118, Apdo. de Correus 11, Lleida E-25080.
T: 34 973 20 46 00
E: lamanyana@lamanyana.cat
W: http://www.lamanyana.es
Freq: Daily
Editor in Chief: Xavier Manau
Editorial Profile: Regional daily newspaper focussing on news, current affairs, economics, politics and sport.
Language (s): Spanish
DAILY NEWSPAPER

La La Tribuna de Albacete
Owner: PUBALSA
Editorial: Paseo de la Cuba 14, Albacete E-02005. **T:** 34 967 19 10 00
E: albacete@latribunadealbacete.es
W: http://www.latribunadealbacete.es
Freq: Daily
Editor: Juan Carrizo; **Editor in Chief:** Adolfo Giménez; **Editor:** Cristóbal Guzmán
Editorial Profile: Daily regional newspaper covering current news and affairs, lifestyle, sports, economy and politics.
Language (s): Spanish
DAILY NEWSPAPER

La La Voz de Almería
Owner: Novotécnica SA
Editorial: Avda. del Mediterraneo 159°, Almeria E-04007. **T:** 34 950 18 18 18
E: local@lavozdealmeria.com
W: http://www.lavozdealmeria.com
Freq: Daily
Editor: Jacinto Castillo; **Editor:** Tony Fernandez; **Editor:** Antonio Fernández; **Editor in Chief:** Leopoldo Nemesio
Editorial Profile: Regional daily newspaper focusing on current news and affairs as well as lifestyle, politics, sports and economy.
Language (s): Spanish
DAILY NEWSPAPER

Levante (El Mercantil Valenciano)
Owner: Editorial Prensa Valenciana SA
Editorial: Traginers 7, Edif. Levante, Valencia E-46014. **T:** 34 963 9 92 200
E: levante-emv@epi.es
W: http://www.levante-emv.es
Freq: Daily
Editor: José Vicente Aleixandre; **Editor:** Miguel Angel Sánchez
Editorial Profile: Regional daily newspaper focussing on news, current affairs, economics, politics and sport.
Language (s): Spanish
DAILY NEWSPAPER

Levante de Castellón
Owner: Editorial Prensa Valenciana SA
Editorial: C/ Zaragoza, 11., Castellón E-12001.
T: 34 964 25 45 12
E: levantedecastello.local@epi.es
W: http://www.levante-emv.com
Freq: Daily
Editor in Chief: Vicente Pérez
Editorial Profile: Regional daily newspaper focussing on news, current affairs, economics, politics and sport.
Language (s): Spanish
DAILY NEWSPAPER

Majorca Daily Bulletin
Owner: Hora Nova SA
Editorial: Passeig de Mallorca 9A, Palma De Mallorca E-07011. **T:** 34 971 78 84 00
E: editorial@majorcadailybulletin.es
W: http://www.majorcadailybulletin.es
Freq: Daily
Editor in Chief: Humphrey Carter
Editorial Profile: Regional daily newspaper focussing on news, current affairs, economics, politics and sport.
Language (s): English
DAILY NEWSPAPER

MARCA
Owner: Unidad Editorial
Editorial: Avenida de San Luis, 25-27, Madrid 28033. **T:** 34 90 299 61 11
E: redaccion@marca.com
W: http://www.marca.com
Freq: Daily; **Circ:** 287393 Not Audited
Editor in Chief: Roberto Palomar; **Editor in Chief:** Germán Pizarro; **Editor in Chief:** José María Rodríguez; **Editor in Chief:** Bruno Sáez
Editorial Profile: Newspaper covering regional, national and international sports news including football, basketball, motor racing, tennis, cycling, golf, athletics and handball.
Language (s): Spanish
DAILY NEWSPAPER

El Matí Independent de Lleida
Owner: El Matí Independent de Lleida
Editorial: Av. Francesc Macià, 27, Lleida 25007. **T:** 34 973 100 835
E: lleida@elmatiindependent.cat
W: http://elmatiindependent.com
Freq: Daily
Editorial Profile: Newspaper covering regional news and current affairs.
Language (s): Catalan
DAILY NEWSPAPER

Menorca Diario Insular
Owner: Editorial Menorca SA
Editorial: Cap de Cavallería 5, Mahón E-07714. **T:** 34 97 13 51 600
E: redaccion@menorca.info
Freq: Daily
Editor in Chief: Pere Melis Nebot
Editorial Profile: Regional daily newspaper focussing on news, current affairs, economics, politics and sport.
Language (s): Spanish
DAILY NEWSPAPER

EL MUNDO
Owner: Unidad Editorial
Editorial: Avenida de San Luis, 25, Madrid 28033. **T:** 34 91 443 50 00
E: elmundo@elmundo.es
W: http://www.elmundo.es
Freq: Daily; **Circ:** 267151 Not Audited
Editorial Profile: Newspaper covering regional, national and international news and current affairs including politics, economics, society, culture, sports, motoring, travel, lifestyle, celebrities, science, health, technology and multimedia.
Language (s): Spanish
DAILY NEWSPAPER

El Mundo de Andalucia
Owner: Unidad Editorial SA
Editorial: Avda. República Argentina 25 - 9ª planta, Sevilla E-41011. **T:** 34 95 49 90 710
E: andalucia@elmundo.es
W: http://www.elmundo.es/elmundo/andalucia.html
Freq: Daily; **Circ:** 286685 Not Audited
Editor: Antonio Salvador
Editorial Profile: Regional daily newspaper focussing on news, current affairs, economics, politics, culture, society and sports.
Language (s): Spanish
DAILY NEWSPAPER

Mundo Deportivo
Owner: El Mundo Deportivo SA
Editorial: Avda. Diagonal 477 - 5° planta, Barcelona E-08036. **T:** 34 93 34 44 100
E: redaccion@mundodeportivo.com
W: http://www.mundodeportivo.com
Freq: Daily
Editor in Chief: Hector Coca
Editorial Profile: Newspaper focusing on all forms of competitive sport in Spain and throughout the world. Read by a wide range of the population with an interest in sport.
Language (s): Spanish
DAILY NEWSPAPER

El Norte de Castilla
Owner: El Norte de Castilla
Editorial: Vázquez de Menchaca, 10, Polígono de Argales, Valladolid 47008.
T: 34 983 412 100

E: redaccion.nc@elnortedecastilla.es
W: http://www.elnortedecastilla.es
Freq: Daily
News Editor: Eloy de la Pisa; **Editor in Chief:** Carmen Diez
Editorial Profile: Regional daily newspaper focussing on news and current affairs including regional general interest, economics, politics and sport.
Language (s): Spanish
DAILY NEWSPAPER

Nueva Alcarria
Owner: Editorial Nueva Alcarria, SA
Editorial: Francisco Aripio 76, Guadalajara E-19004. **T:** 34 949 24 74 72
E: redaccion@nuevaalcarria.com
W: http://www.nuevaalcarria.com
Freq: 2 Times/Week
Editorial Profile: Regional daily newspaper focussing on news, current affairs, economics, politics and sport.
Language (s): Spanish
DAILY NEWSPAPER

La Nueva España
Owner: Editorial Prensa Asturiana SA
Editorial: Calvo Sotelo 7, Oviedo E-33007. **T:** 34 98 52 79 700 **E:** pam@lne.es
W: http://www.lanuevaespana.es
Freq: Daily
Editor: Saul Fernandez
Editorial Profile: Regional daily newspaper focussing on news, current affairs, economics, politics and sport.
Language (s): Spanish
DAILY NEWSPAPER

La Opinión - El Correo de Zamora
Owner: Editorial Prensa Ibérica
Editorial: Rúa de los Francos 20, Zamora E-49001. **T:** 34 980 53 47 59
E: laopinionzamora.rdc@epi.es
W: http://www.laopiniondezamora.es
Freq: Daily
Editor in Chief: Dalmiro Gavilan
Editorial Profile: Regional daily newspaper focussing on news, current affairs, economics, politics and sport.
Language (s): Spanish
DAILY NEWSPAPER

La Opinión de Málaga
Owner: Editorial Prensa Ibérica
Editorial: Granada 42, Málaga E-29015. **T:** 34 95 21 26 200
E: laopiniondemalaga.rd1@epi.es
W: http://www.laopiniondemalaga.es
Freq: Daily
Editor in Chief: Emilio Fernandez
Editorial Profile: Regional daily newspaper focussing on news, current affairs, economics, politics and sport.
Language (s): Spanish
DAILY NEWSPAPER

El País
Owner: Diario El País SL
Editorial: Calle Miguel Yuste, 40, Madrid 28037. **T:** 34 91 337 82 00
E: redacciondigital@elpais.es
W: http://www.elpais.es
Freq: Daily; **Circ:** 377603 Not Audited
Editor in Chief: Ana Alfageme; **Editor in Chief:** Guillermo Altares; **Editor in Chief:** Miguel Jiménez; **Editor in Chief:** José Sámano
Editorial Profile: Newspaper covering national and international news and current affairs including business, politics, economics, culture, society and sports.
Language (s): Spanish
DAILY NEWSPAPER

El Periódico de Catalunya
Owner: Ediciones Primera Plana SA
Editorial: Calle Consell de Cent, 425-427, Barcelona 8009. **T:** 34 93 265 53 53
E: bcn@elperiodico.com
W: http://www.elperiodico.com
Freq: Daily; **Circ:** 134003 Publisher's Statement
Editor in Chief: Joan Cañete Bayle; **Editor in Chief:** Teresa Cendrós; **Editor in Chief:** Olga Grau; **News Editor:** Marta López; **Editor in Chief:** Luis Mauri; **Editor in Chief:** Enric Sala; **Editor in Chief:** Neus Tomás; **Editor in Chief:** David Torras
Editorial Profile: Newspaper covering regional, national and international news and current affairs including politics, business, economics, society, sports, entertainment, culture, lifestyle and television.
Language (s): Spanish
DAILY NEWSPAPER

El Periódico de Extremadura
Owner: Grupo Zeta

Editorial: Calle Doctor Marañón, n° 2, local 7, Caceres 10002. **T:** 34 92 762 06 00
E: epextremadura@elperiodico.es
W: http://www.elperiodicoextremadura.com
Freq: Daily
Editor in Chief: José Luis Guerra
Editorial Profile: Daily newspaper covering regional news and current affairs as well as regional general interest.
Language (s): Spanish
DAILY NEWSPAPER

El Periodico Mediterráneo
Owner: Promociones y Ediciones Culturales SA
Editorial: Carretera Almassora s/n, Castellón E-12005. **T:** 34 964 34 95 00
E: redaccion@epmediterraneo.com
W: http://www.elperiodicomediterraneo.com
Freq: Daily
Editor in Chief: Javier Abad Meliá; **Editor in Chief:** Javier Navarro Cantavella; **Editor in Chief:** Julio Sánchez Isarria
Editorial Profile: This daily newspaper covers current regional news as well as other entertainment media.
Language (s): Spanish
DAILY NEWSPAPER

El Progreso
Owner: El Progreso de Lugo SL
Editorial: Rúa Ribadeo s/n, Lugo E-27002. **T:** 34 982 29 81 00 **E:** redaccion@galiciae.com
W: http://www.elprogreso.es
Freq: Daily
Editor: Santiago Jaureguizar; **Editor:** Ana Rodil
Editorial Profile: Daily regional newspaper covering current news and affairs, culture, sports, and economy.
Language (s): Spanish
DAILY NEWSPAPER

La Provincia
Owner: Editorial Prensa Canaria SA
Editorial: Avda. Alcalde Ramírez Bethencourt, 8, Las Palmas De Gran Canaria 35003. **T:** 34 928 47 94 00 **E:** laprovincia@epi.es
W: http://www.laprovincia.es
Freq: Daily
Editor in Chief: Javier Durán; **Editor in Chief:** Cristobal Rodriguez
Editorial Profile: Daily newspaper that covers current regional news and affairs, sports, finance, society, culture and lifestyle.
Language (s): Spanish
DAILY NEWSPAPER

Las Provincias
Owner: Federico Domenech SA
Editorial: Calle Gremis 4, Valencia 46014. **T:** 34 96 35 02 211
E: redaccion@lasprovinciasdigital.es
W: http://www.lasprovincias.es
Freq: Daily
Editor: Pablo Salazar
Editorial Profile: Newspaper covering national and international news and current affairs, politics, economy, sport and culture.
Language (s): Spanish
DAILY NEWSPAPER

Público (Bureau)
Owner: Mediapubli Sociedad de Publicaciones y Ediciones S. L.
T: 34 902 012031 **E:** cebayo@publico.es
W: http://www.publico.es
Freq: Daily
Editorial Profile: Newspaper covering regional, national and international news, politics, finance, culture, society and sport.
Language (s): Spanish
DAILY NEWSPAPER

El Punt
Owner: Hermes Comunicacions SA
Editorial: Carrer Santa Eugènia, 42, Girona E-17005. **T:** 34 972 18 64 00
E: direccio@elpunt.com
W: http://www.elpunt.com
Freq: Daily
Editor in Chief: Vicent Sanchis
Editorial Profile: Daily newspaper covering current regional and international news and events, including local weather forecast.
Language (s): Spanish
DAILY NEWSPAPER

La Razón
Owner: Audiovisual Española 2000 SA
Editorial: Calle Josefa Valcárcel, 42, Madrid 28027. **T:** 34 91 324 70 00
E: internacional@larazon.es
W: http://www.larazon.es
Freq: Daily; **Circ:** 122070 Not Audited
Editor in Chief: Sergio Alonso Puente; **Editor in Chief:** José Beltrán; **Editor in Chief:** Alejandra Clements; **Editor in Chef:** Carlos de

Miguel; **Editor in Chief:** Julián Redondo
Editorial Profile: National newspaper covering news and current affairs including politics, economics, business, society, opinion, culture, religion, sport, motoring, and lifestyle.
Language (s): Spanish
DAILY NEWSPAPER

Regió 7
Owner: Ediciones Intercomarcales SA
Editorial: Sant Antoni Mª Claret, 32, Manresa, Barcelona 8243. **T:** 34 938 77 22 33
E: regio7@regio7.cat
W: http://www.regio7.com
Freq: Daily
Editorial Profile: Daily regional newspaper that focuses on sports, culture, and economy.
Language (s): Catalan, Spanish
DAILY NEWSPAPER

La Región
Owner: La Región SA
Editorial: Polígono de San Cibrao das Viñas, "David Ferrer", Calle 4, Ourense 32901. **T:** 34 988 511260 **E:** info@laregion.es
W: http://www.laregion.es
Freq: Daily
Editorial Profile: Daily newspaper that covers current regional news and affairs as well as sports, culture, society, and technology.
Language (s): Spanish
DAILY NEWSPAPER

La Rioja
Owner: Nueva Rioja SA
Editorial: Vara del Rey 74, Logroño E-26002. **T:** 34 941 1279169 **E:** director@larioja.com
W: http://www.larioja.com
Freq: Daily
Editor: Jose Maria Martinez Glera; **Editor:** María Jóse Zapata Rico
Editorial Profile: Daily regional newspaper focusing on current news and affairs as well as sports, politics and economy.
Language (s): Spanish
DAILY NEWSPAPER

Segre
Owner: Prensa Leridana SAL
Editorial: Carrer del Ríu 6, Lerida E-25007. **T:** 34 973 24 80 00 **E:** redaccion@segre.com
W: http://www.segre.com
Freq: Daily
Editorial Profile: Daily regional newspaper covering economy, current news and affairs, agriculture, sports, culture and tv entertainment.
Language (s): Catalan, Spanish
DAILY NEWSPAPER

Sport
Owner: Ediciones Deportivas Catalanes SA
Editorial: Consell de Cent, 425-427, Barcelona E-08009. **T:** 34 93 265 53 53
E: redaccion@diariosport.com
W: http://www.diariosport.com
Freq: Daily
Editor: Joaquím Beltran; **Editor:** Javier Rodriguez Marzo
Editorial Profile: Tabloid-sized covering sports show updating the latest scores, news and events.
Language (s): Spanish
DAILY NEWSPAPER

Sur
Owner: Prensa Malagueña SA
Editorial: Avda. Dr Marañón 48, Apdo. 98, Málaga E-29009. **T:** 34 95 26 49 600
E: redaccion@diariosur.es
W: http://www.diariosur.es
Freq: Daily
Editor in Chief: José Vicente Astorga; **Editor:** Ana Barreales
Editorial Profile: Daily newspaper covering current regional news and events, including local weather forecast.
Language (s): Spanish
DAILY NEWSPAPER

La Tribuna de Ciudad Real
Owner: Promecam
Editorial: Polígono industrial Larache, c / Pedro Muñoz, 3, Ciudad Real E-13005. **T:** 34 926 21 53 01
E: redaccioncr@diariolatribuna.com
W: http://www.latribunadeciudadreal.com
Freq: Daily
Editor: Miguel Chavez; **Editor:** Pilar Muñoz
Editorial Profile: Daily regional newspaper focusing on current news and affairs, sports, politics and finance.
Language (s): Spanish
DAILY NEWSPAPER

La Tribuna de Cuenca
Owner: Promecal editorial group

Editorial: Calle Carretería, 32, 1°, Cuenca 16002. **T:** 34 969 23 58 37
E: redaccion.cuenca@diariolatribuna.com
W: http://www.latribunadecuenca.es
Freq: Daily
Editorial Profile: Regional newspaper covering news and current affairs.
Language (s): Spanish
DAILY NEWSPAPER

La Vanguardia
Owner: La Vanguardia Ediciones SL
Editorial: Avenida Diagonal, 477, 3ª planta, Barcelona 8036. **T:** 34 93 270 46 00
E: redaccion@lavanguardia.es
W: http://www.lavanguardia.es
Freq: Daily; **Circ:** 194014 Not Audited
Editor in Chief: Mariángel Alcázar; **Editor in Chief:** Ramon Aymerich; **Editor in Chief:** Jordi Barbeta; **Editor in Chief:** Dagoberto Escorcia; **Editor in Chief:** Celeste López; **Editor in Chief:** Joaquín Luna; **Editor in Chief:** Ignacio Orovio; **Editor in Chief:** Susana Quadrado
Editorial Profile: National newspaper covering national and international news and current affairs including politics, economics, society, opinion, sports, lifestyle, technology, culture, entertainment and leisure activities.
Language (s): Spanish
DAILY NEWSPAPER

La Verdad
Owner: Corporación de Medios de Murcia SA
Editorial: Camino Viejo de Monteagudo, Edificio "La Verdad", Murcia 30160. **T:** 34 968 36 91 00 **E:** lectores@laverdad.es
W: http://www.laverdad.es
Freq: Daily
Editor: Manuel Herrero Carcelen
Editorial Profile: Daily regional newspaper focusing on news and current affairs, sports, economy and politics.
Language (s): Spanish
DAILY NEWSPAPER

La Verdad (Albacete)
Owner: Corporación de Medios de Murcia SA
Editorial: Pza. de la Catedral 6, Albacete E-02005. **T:** 34 967 21 93 11
E: albacete.lv@laverdad.es
W: http://www.laverdad.es/albacete
Freq: Daily
Editor in Chief: José Fidel López; **Editor:** José Luis Royo
Editorial Profile: Daily regional newspaper that focuses on current regional news and affairs, politics, sports, and economy.
Language (s): Spanish
DAILY NEWSPAPER

La Verdad (Alicante)
Owner: Corporación de Medios de Murcia SA
Editorial: Plaza Gabriel Miró, 3, Alicante E-03003. **T:** 34 965 92 19 50
E: alicante.lv@laverdad.es
W: http://www.laverdad.es/alicante
Freq: Daily
Editor: Pepe Antón; **Editor:** Angel García
Editorial Profile: Daily regional newspaper covering current news and affairs, sports, economy and politics.
Language (s): Spanish
DAILY NEWSPAPER

La Voz de Galicia
Owner: La Voz de Galicia SA
Editorial: Avda. de la Prensa 84-85, Polígono de Sabón, Arteixo La Coruña E-15142. **T:** 34 981 18 01 80 **E:** redac@lavoz.es
W: http://www.lavozdegalicia.es
Freq: Daily
Editor: Luis Pousa; **Editor:** Sofía Vázquez
Editorial Profile: Newspaper covers regional and national news as well as daily breaking news including weather forecasts and celebrity gossip.
Language (s): Spanish
DAILY NEWSPAPER

The Wall Street Journal (Spain)
Editorial: Calle de Espronceda 32, Fl 1, Madrid 28003. **T:** 34 91 395-8122
Bureau Chief: Richard Boudreaux
DAILY NEWSPAPER

NEWS SERVICE/SYNDICATE

Agence France-Presse - Madrid Bureau
Owner: Agence France-Presse
Editorial: Calle Prim, 19, 3º piso, Madrid 28004. **T:** 34 91 435 8740
E: david.williams@afp.com
W: http://www.afp.com
Bureau Chief: David Williams

Editorial Profile: Madrid bureau bureau of international news agency covering news and current affairs.
Language (s): English
NEWS SERVICE/SYNDICATE

Agencia EFE
Owner: Agencia EFE
Editorial: Espronceda 32, Madrid 28003. **T:** 34 91 3467100 **E:** efe@efe.com
W: http://www.efe.com
Editor in Chief: Carmen del Portillo; **Editor in Chief:** Carlos Gosch; **Editor in Chief:** Carlos Minguez; **Editor in Chief:** Javier Muñoz;
Editor: Gloria Valenzuela
Editorial Profile: National Spanish news agency covering national and international news and current affairs including politics, economics and culture.
Language (s): Spanish
NEWS SERVICE/SYNDICATE

Agencia EFE - Athens Bureau
Owner: Agencia EFE
Editorial: Agiou Konstantinou, 12, Athens 10431. **T:** 30 210 520 0010 **E:** atenas@efe.es
W: http://www.efe.com.gr
Editorial Profile: Regional bureau of the Spanish news agency covering news and current affairs.
Language (s): English
NEWS SERVICE/SYNDICATE

Agencia Europa Press
Owner: Agencia Europa Press
Editorial: Paseo de la Castellana 210, 2ª Planta, Madrid 28046. **T:** 34 91 359 26 00
E: noticias@europapress.es
W: http://www.europapress.es
Editor in Chief: Loli Muriel
Editorial Profile: Agencia Europa Press is an international news agency with news covering economy, sports, television, culture, and society from several different regions in Spain.
Language (s): Spanish
NEWS SERVICE/SYNDICATE

Associated Press
Editorial: Esproceda 32, 5th Floor, Madrid 28003. **T:** 34 91 395-8101
Bureau Chief: Alan Clendenning
NEWS SERVICE/SYNDICATE

Bloomberg News
Editorial: Paseo de la Castellana 9, Madrid 28046. **T:** 34 917009600
E: madridnews@bloomberg.net
Bureau Chief: Emma Ross-Thomas
NEWS SERVICE/SYNDICATE

Dow Jones Newswires
Editorial: Calle de Espronceda 32, Fl 1, Madrid 28003. **T:** 34 91 395-8122
E: djmadrid@dowjones.com
Bureau Chief: Richard Boudreaux
NEWS SERVICE/SYNDICATE

Reuters
Editorial: Piso de la Casellana 37-41, Madrid 28046. **T:** 34 91 585-2100
W: http://www.reuters.es
NEWS SERVICE/SYNDICATE

Servimedia
Owner: Servimedia S.A.
Editorial: Calle Almansa 66, Madrid 28039.
T: 34 91 391 39 31
E: servimedia@servimedia.es
W: http://www.servimedia.es
Editorial Profile: News service covering national news and current affairs including politics, economics and society.
Language (s): Spanish
NEWS SERVICE/SYNDICATE

SOONimage
Owner: SOONimage
T: 34 93 2691962 **E:** editorial@soonimage.com
W: https://soonimage.com
Editor: Lino De Vallier
Editorial Profile: Press photo agency covering news and current affairs.
Language (s): Spanish
NEWS SERVICE/SYNDICATE

Thomson Reuters - Madrid Bureau
Owner: Thomson Reuters
Editorial: Paseo de Recoletos, 37-41, Madrid 28004. **T:** 34 91 585 21 00
W: http://thomsonreuters.com
Editorial Profile: Regional office of the international press agency focussing on general interest information including economics, politics, science, culture, sports, social, European and global issues.
Language (s): English
NEWS SERVICE/SYNDICATE

Vocento
Owner: Vocento
Editorial: Juan Ignacio Luca de Tena, 7, Madrid 28027. **T:** 34 91 743 81 04
E: prensa@vocento.com
W: http://www.vocento.com
Editor: Luisa Alli Turrillas
Editorial Profile: News service covering general news and current affairs.
Language (s): Spanish
NEWS SERVICE/SYNDICATE

BROADCASTING

RADIO STATIONS

Radio Intereconomía
Owner: Intereconomía
Editorial: Calle Modesto Lafuente, 42, Madrid 28010. **T:** 34 91 432 77 66
E: comunicacion@intereconomia.com
W: http://www.intereconomia.com/oir-intereconomia-radio
Editorial Profile: Radio station broadcasting classical music and economic information.

Radio Santander
Editorial: Pasaje de Peña 2 Int., 7ª planta, Santander E-39008. **T:** 34 942 31 95 95
E: informativos@radiosantander.com
W: http://www.radiosantander.com
Editorial Profile: Radio Santander is a news radio station in Spain.

Talk Radio Europe
Editorial: Centro Comercial La Colonia, San Pedro de Alcántara, Málaga 29670.
T: 34 952 799 953
E: info@talkradioeurope.com
W: http://www.talkradioeurope.com
Editorial Profile: Radio station providing the English speaking communities on the Costas of southern Spain. Geographical Focus: Spain

RADIO NETWORKS

Cadena Dial
Editorial: Gran Vía 32, 7ª planta, Madrid E-28013. **T:** 34 91 34 70 740
E: jmgarciam@unionradio.es
W: http://www.cadenadial.com
Editorial Profile: 78 stations affiliated.

M 80 Radio
Editorial: Gran Vía, 32, 7ª planta, Madrid 28013. **T:** 34 913 47 08 07
E: promoser@cadenaser.com
W: http://www.m80radio.com
Editorial Profile: 32 stations affiliated.

Onda Cero
Editorial: C/ Fuerteventura, 12, San Sebastián de los Reyes, Madrid 28703
E: webmaster@ondacero.es
W: http://www.ondacero.es
Editorial Profile: National radio station covering news and current affairs and entertainment.

radio 3
Owner: RTVE
Editorial: Casa de la Radio, Avda. Radio Televisión, 4, Madrid 28223.
T: 34 91 346 10 00
W: http://www.rtve.es/radio/radio3
Editorial Profile: Radio 3 is a Spanish music and culture radio station and belongs to the Spanish public media group RTVE (Radio Televisión Española).

Radio Cadena Top
Editorial: Calle Manuel Silvela 9, Madrid E-28010. **T:** 34 91 44 75 300
E: info@topradio.es **W:** http://www.topradio.es
Editorial Profile: Pop music station. 30 stations affiliated.

Radio Nacional de España - RNE
Editorial: Casa de la Radio, Avda. Radio Televisión, 4, Madrid 28223.
T: 34 91 346 10 00
E: areaeconomia.rne@rtve.es
W: http://www.rtve.es/radio
Editorial Profile: National radio station covering general news and current affairs including entertainment, politics, economics and culture.

TELEVISION STATIONS

Antena 3 Televisión
Editorial: Avda. Isla Graciosa, 13, San Sebastian De Los Reyes (madrid) 28700.
T: 34 91 62 30 500 **E:** nacional@antena3tv.es
W: http://www.antena3.com
Editorial Profile: National TV station covering news and current affairs, culture and entertainment.

RTV 2
T: 34 91 346 80 00 **E:** rtve.dircom@rtve.es
W: http://www.rtve.es
Editorial Profile: Second channel of the Spain national TV station TVE.

TVE
Editorial: Calle Avenida Radio Televisión, 4, Madrid 28223. **T:** 34 91 34 64 000
E: rtve.dircom@rtve.es
W: http://www.rtve.es/comercial.htmail
Editorial Profile: National television station.

TELEVISION NETWORKS

Radio Televisión Española - RTVE
Owner: Radio Televisión Española - RTVE
Editorial: Casa de la Radio, Avda. Radio Televisión, 4, Madrid 28223.
T: 34 91 346 10 00 **W:** http://www.rtve.es
Editorial Profile: National TV and Radio network.

SRI LANKA — Tel: 94

Standard Time: GMT +5.5
Continent: Asia
Capital City: Colombo

NEWSPAPERS & PUBLICATIONS

NEWSPAPERS

The Bottom Line
Editorial: Rivira Media Corporation Ltd., 742, Maradana Road, Colombo 10.
T: 94 114708888 **E:** thebottomline@rivira.lk
W: http://www.thebottomline.lk
Freq: Weekly; **Circ:** 22003 Not Audited
Editor: Nisthar Cassim
Editorial Profile: The Bottom Line is a newspaper which covers Business, Economics, Finance, National News, Money, Management, etc.
Language (s): Sinhala
DAILY NEWSPAPER

Daily Mirror
Editorial: Wijeya Newspapers Ltd, No.8, Hunupitiya Cross Road, P.O. Box 1136, Colombo 2. **T:** 94 112 436998
E: editorial@dailymirror.wnl.lk
W: http://www.dailymirror.lk
Freq: Daily; **Circ:** 32003 Not Audited
Editor: Channaka de Silva; **Editor:** Sanath Dehmond; **Editor in Chief:** Champika Liyanaarachchi
Editorial Profile: A daily newspaper.
Language (s): English
DAILY NEWSPAPER

Daily News
Owner: The Associated Newspapers of Ceylon Ltd
Editorial: The Associated Newspapers of Ceylon Ltd., 35, D.R. Wijewardana Mawatha, Colombo 10. **T:** 94 112429211
E: editor@dailynews.lk
W: http://www.dailynews.lk
Freq: Daily; **Circ:** 65002 Not Audited
Editor: Ranil Wijayapala
Editorial Profile: Daily News is a daily newspaper which covers the News, Foreign news, Financial news, Business news, Sports news, Features classified.
Language (s): English
DAILY NEWSPAPER

Dinamina
Owner: The Associated Newspapers of Ceylon Ltd
Editorial: The Associated Newspapers of Ceylon Ltd, No. 35, D.R. Wijewardene Mawatha, Colombo 10. **T:** 94 112429241
E: editor@dinamina.lk
W: http://www.lakehouse.lk
Freq: Daily; **Circ:** 60002 Not Audited
Editor in Chief: Mahinda Abeysundara; **Editor:** C. Dodawatta; **Editor:** Vernon Gunasekara;
Editor: Chandrani Marasinghe
Editorial Profile: DINAMINA is a daily newspaper which covers the Political, Cultural, Sports & day to day happen Economics/ Foreign/Religion affairs in Sri Lanka & also other countries.
Language (s): Sinhala
DAILY NEWSPAPER

Lankadeepa
Editorial: Wijeya Newspapers Ltd, No.8, Hunupitiya Cross Road, P.O. Box 1136, Colombo 2. **T:** 94 115 383438
E: epaper@wijeya.lk
W: http://www.lankadeepa.lk
Freq: Daily; **Circ:** 200003 Not Audited
Editor in Chief: Siri Ranasinghe
Editorial Profile: Newspaper covering Local, National, Regional and International News, Sports, Features, Entertainment, Business, etc.
Language (s): Sinhala
DAILY NEWSPAPER

Metro News Daily
Editorial: Express Newspapers (Ceylon) Limited, 185, Grandpass Road, Colombo 14.
T: 94 112320927 **E:** kesari22@virakesari.lk
Freq: Daily; **Circ:** 30003 Not Audited
Editor in Chief: V. Thevaraj
Editorial Profile: Metro News Daily is a radio station targeted for young people. Station covers news and ntertainment.
Language (s): Sinhala
DAILY NEWSPAPER

Metro News Weekly
Editorial: Express Newspapers (Ceylon) Limited, 185, Grandpass Road, Colombo 14.
T: 94 112320927 **E:** Kesarizl@virakesari.lk
W: http://www.virakesari.lk
Freq: Weekly; **Circ:** 45003 Not Audited
Editor in Chief: V. Thevaraj
Editorial Profile: Metro News Weekly is a newspaper for Young people that covers the Local, National, International News and Entertainment.
Language (s): Sinhala
DAILY NEWSPAPER

The Nation
Editorial: Rivira Media Corporation Pvt Ltd, 742, Maradana Road, Colombo 10.
T: 94 114708888 **E:** editor@nation.lk
W: http://www.nation.lk
Freq: Weekly; **Circ:** 97003 Not Audited
Editor in Chief: Gamini Abeywardane
Editorial Profile: The Nation is a newspaper which covers politics, defense, national conflicts, business and sports.
Language (s): Sinhala
DAILY NEWSPAPER

Ravaya
Editorial: 83, Piliyandal Rd, Colombo
E: ravaya@gmail.com **W:** http://www.ravaya.lk
Freq: Weekly
Editor: Viktor Ivan
Editorial Profile: Provides a non-traditional analysis of social, political, cultural and judicial views of Sri Lanka.
Language (s): Sinhala
DAILY NEWSPAPER

Rivira
Editorial: Rivira Media Corporation Pvt Ltd, 742, Maradana Road, Colombo 10.
T: 94 114708888 **W:** http://www.rivira.lk
Freq: Weekly; **Circ:** 195003 Not Audited
Editor: Upali Tennakoon
Editorial Profile: Rivira is a daily newspaper which offers readers news, information, Education, Business, political comments and satire.
Language (s): Sinhala
DAILY NEWSPAPER

Silumina
Owner: The Associated Newspapers of Ceylon Ltd
Editorial: The Associated Newspapers of Ceylon Ltd, No.35, D.R. Wijewardene Mawatha, Colombo 10. **T:** 94 112429261
E: editor@silumina.lk
W: http://www.lakehouse.lk/main
Freq: Weekly; **Circ:** 250003 Not Audited
Editor: Vajira Palpipa; **Editor in Chief:** Karunadasa Sooriaarachchi
Editorial Profile: SILUMINA is a weekly newspaper which covers the Local News, Foreign news, Financial news, Business news, Sports news, Features classified.
Language (s): Sinhala
DAILY NEWSPAPER

Sunday Lankadeepa
Editorial: Wijeya Newspapers Ltd, No 8, Hunupitiya Cross Road, P.O.Box 1136, Colombo 2. **T:** 94 112423919

E: epaper@wijeya.lk
W: http://www.lankadeepa.lk
Freq: Weekly; **Circ:** 325003 Not Audited
Editor: Ariyananda Dombagahawatte; **Editor in Chief:** Siri Ranasinghe; **Editor:** Premakeerthi Ranathunga
Editorial Profile: Sunday Lankadeepa is a news paper which covers News, Sports, Entertainment, Features, etc.
Language (s): Sinhala
DAILY NEWSPAPER

Sunday Observer
Owner: The Associated Newspapers of Ceylon Ltd
Editorial: The Associated Newspapers of Ceylon Ltd, No.35, D.R. Wijewardene Mawatha, Colombo 10. **T:** 94 11 24 29 231
E: editor@sundayobserver.lk
W: http://www.sundayobserver.lk
Freq: Weekly; **Circ:** 200003 Not Audited
Editor in Chief: Dinesh Weerawansa
Editorial Profile: Sunday Observer is a weekly magazine which covers the Local News, Foreign news, Financial news, Business news, Sports news, Features classifide.
Language (s): English
DAILY NEWSPAPER

The Sunday Times
Editorial: Wijeya Newspapers Ltd, No.8, Hunupitiya Cross Road, Colombo 2.
T: 94 112326247
E: editor@sundaytimes.wnl.lk
W: http://www.sundaytimes.lk
Freq: Weekly; **Circ:** 100003 Not Audited
Editor in Chief: Sinha Ratnatunga; **Editor:** Faizal Samath
Editorial Profile: Covers the local, national, regional and international news, sports and entertainment.
Language (s): English
DAILY NEWSPAPER

Thinakaran
Owner: The Associated Newspapers of Ceylon Ltd.
Editorial: The Associated Newspapers of Ceylon Ltd, No. 35, D.R. Wijewardene Mawatha, Colombo 10. **T:** 94 11 24 29 271
E: editor.tkn@lakehouse.lk
W: http://www.lakehouse.lk/main
Freq: Daily; **Circ:** 50002 Not Audited
Editor: K. Kunarasha; **Editor:** K. V. Sivasubramanjam
Editorial Profile: THINAKARAN is a daily newspaper which covers the Political, Cultural, Sports & day to day incidents, Economics/ Religious affairs.
Language (s): Tamil
DAILY NEWSPAPER

Thinakaran Vara Manjari
Owner: The Associated Newspapers of Ceylon Ltd.
Editorial: The Associated Newspapers of Ceylon Ltd, No 35, D.R. Wijewardene Mawatha, Colombo 10. **T:** 94 112429271
E: editor.tkn@lakehouse.lk
W: http://www.lakehouse.lk/main
Freq: Weekly; **Circ:** 70002 Not Audited
Editor: K. Kunarasha; **Editor:** Arul Sathyanathan
Editorial Profile: Thinakaran Vara Manjari is a weekly magazine which covers the Local and International News, Entertainment, Movies, Sports, etc.
Language (s): Tamil
DAILY NEWSPAPER

Thinakkural
Editorial: Thinakkural, No. 68 Ellie House Road, Colombo 15. **T:** 94 11 252-3216
Freq: Daily; **Circ:** 25003 Not Audited
Editor in Chief: V. Thanabalasingham
Editorial Profile: Thinakkural is a Tamil language newspaper published in Sri Lanka which talks about the Local, National, Regional and International News. Also publishes a Sunday edition.
Language (s): Sinhala
DAILY NEWSPAPER

Uthayan
Owner: New Uthayan Publications (Pvt) Ltd.
Editorial: 361, Kasturiyar Road, Jaffna.
T: 94 212229944 **E:** editorial@uthayan.com
W: http://www.uthayan.com
Freq: Daily; **Circ:** 16001 Not Audited
Editor in Chief: MV Kanamylnathan
Editorial Profile: Covers news.
Language (s): Tamil
DAILY NEWSPAPER

Virakesari Weekly
Editorial: Express Newspapers (Ceylon) Limited, 185, Grandpass Road, Colombo 14.

T: 94 112320927 **E:** kesari22@virakesari.lk
W: http://www.virakesari.lk
Freq: Weekly; **Circ:** 150003 Not Audited
Editor: V. Thevaraj
Editorial Profile: A radio station which covers the latest News, Politics, Current Affairs, etc.
Language (s): Tamil
DAILY NEWSPAPER

NEWS SERVICE/SYNDICATE

Associated Press
T: 94 11 230-4940
NEWS SERVICE/SYNDICATE

Bloomberg News
Editorial: World Trade Center, Level 26, East Tower, Colombo. **T:** 94 112351303
NEWS SERVICE/SYNDICATE

Reuters
Editorial: Level 8 - East Tower, World Trade Center, Echelon Sq, Colombo.
T: 94 11 232-5540
NEWS SERVICE/SYNDICATE

SURINAME   Tel: 597

Standard Time: GMT -3
Continent: The Americas
Capital City: Paramaribo

NEWSPAPERS & PUBLICATIONS

NEWSPAPERS

Dagblad Suriname
Owner: FaFam Publishing NV
Editorial: Zwartenhovenbrugstraat 154, Paramaribo. **T:** 597 011597426336
E: general@dbsuriname.com
W: http://www.dbsuriname.com
Freq: Daily
Editor: James Lal'Mohammad
Editorial Profile: Daily newspaper written for the residents of Suriname. It covers national and international news, current-affairs, sport, entertainment and culture.
Language (s): Dutch
DAILY NEWSPAPER

De Ware Tijd
Owner: Erven C.J. Jong Tjien Fa
Editorial: Malebatrumstraat No 9, Paramaribo.
T: 597 011597472823 **E:** dwt@dwt.net
W: http://dwtdatabase-com.web5.tempwebsite.net
Freq: Daily; **Circ:** 26500 Not Audited
Editor in Chief: Meredith Helstone; **Editor:** Julian Paneux; **Editor in Chief:** Indra Toelsie
Editorial Profile: De Ware Tijd is a daily newspaper covering national news, including politics, economy, culture and sports.
Language (s): Dutch
DAILY NEWSPAPER

De West
Owner: De West
Editorial: Mr. Dr. J.C. de Mirandastr 2-6, Paramaribo. **T:** 597 011597473327
E: dewest@sr.net
W: http://www.dewestonline.cq-link.sr
Freq: Daily; **Circ:** 7000 Not Audited
Editor in Chief: George Findlay
Editorial Profile: Newspaper covering news and current-affairs; includes politics, economy, sport and culture.
Language (s): Dutch
DAILY NEWSPAPER

BROADCASTING

RADIO NETWORKS

ABC Radio
Editorial: Maystraat 52, Paramaribo.
T: 597 011597464555 **E:** ampies@sr.net
W: http://www.abcsuriname.com
Editorial Profile: Plays different type of music and provides news and entertainment shows.

TELEVISION NETWORKS

ABC TV
Editorial: Maystraat 57, Paramaribo.
T: 597 011597434247 **E:** ampies@sr.net
W: http://www.abcsuriname.com

Editorial Profile: Provides daily news, cultural and special entertainment programs targeting youth.

ATV
Editorial: Van 't Hogerhuysstraat 58-60, Paramaribo. **T:** 597 011597404611
E: atvnews@sr.net W: http://www.atv.sr
Editorial Profile: Provides educational and recreative programming.

STVS
Editorial: Letitia Vriesdelaan 5, Paramaribo.
T: 597 011597473032 **E:** info@stvs.sr
W: http://www.parbo.com/stvs
Editorial Profile: Television station presenting local and international news. The programming includes children and sport shows.

SWAZILAND   Tel: 268

Standard Time: GMT +2
Continent: Africa
Capital City: Mbabane

NEWSPAPERS & PUBLICATIONS

NEWSPAPERS

The Swazi Observer
Owner: Swazj Observer (Pty) Ltd
Editorial: Observer House, 3 West Street, Mbabane. **T:** 268 40 49 600
E: info@observer.org.sz
W: http://www.observer.org.sz
Freq: Daily; **Circ:** 25000 Publisher's Statement
Editor: Alec Lushaba; **Editor In Chief:** Mufa Ndlangamandla; **News Editor:** Ackelo Zwane
Editorial Profile: Newspaper focusing on national and international news, business, politics, culture and sport.
Language (s): English
DAILY NEWSPAPER

Times of Swaziland
Owner: African Echo (Pty) Ltd.
Editorial: PO Box 156, Mbabane.
T: 268 40 42 211 **E:** editor@times.co.sz
W: http://www.times.co.sz
Freq: Daily; **Circ:** 25000 Publisher's Statement
Editor: Martin Dlamini
Editorial Profile: Newspaper focusing on national and international news, politics, business, entertainment and sport.
Language (s): English
DAILY NEWSPAPER

SWEDEN   Tel: 46

Standard Time: GMT +1
Continent: Europe
Capital City: Stockholm

NEWSPAPERS & PUBLICATIONS

NEWSPAPERS

100 Procent Östersund
Editorial: Karlslundsvägen 1, Östersund 831 42. **T:** 46 63 13 42 42
W: http://www.100procentostersund.se
Circ: 43000 Pub Statement
Ansvarig utgivare: Gunnel Edvardsson
Language (s): Swedish
NEWSPAPER

8 Sidor
Owner: Centrum för Lättläst
Editorial: Box 9145, Unavailable 102 72.
T: 46 8 640 70 90 **E:** 8sidor@8sidor.se
W: http://www.8sidor.se **Circ:** 14000
Chefredaktör & Ansvarig utgivare: Malin Crona
Language (s): Swedish; Full Page Colour: 16000.00
Currency: Sweden Kronor
NEWSPAPER

Aftonbladet
Owner: Aftonbladet Hierta AB
Editorial: Västra Järnvägsgatan 21, Stockholm 111 64. **T:** 46 8 725 20 00
E: 71000@aftonbladet.se
W: http://www.aftonbladet.se
Freq: Daily; **Circ:** 896000 TS
Redaktionell Projektledare: Liisa Aus;

Redaktionschef: Marica Finnsiö; **Chefredaktör, Ansvarig utgivare & VD:** Jan Helin
Language (s): Swedish; Full Page Colour: 206927.00
Currency: Sweden Kronor
DAILY NEWSPAPER

Alekuriren
Owner: Alekuriren
Editorial: Göteborgsvägen 94, Älvängen 446 33. **T:** 46 303 74 99 40 **E:** info@alekuriren.se
W: http://www.alekuriren.se
Freq: Weekly; **Circ:** 15100 Pub Statement
Redaktör: Jonas Andersson; **Chefredaktör & Ansvarig utgivare:** Per-Anders Klöversjö; **Redaktör:** Johanna Roos
Language (s): Swedish; Full Page Colour: 13800.00
Currency: Sweden Kronor
NEWSPAPER

Alingsås Kuriren
Owner: AlingsåsKurirens Förvaltnings AB
Editorial: Box 627, Alingsås 441 17.
T: 46 322 66 83 00 **E:** red@alingsaskuriren.se
W: http://www.alingsaskuriren.se
Freq: Weekly; **Circ:** 25300
Redigerare: Tore Carlson; **Chefredaktör & Ansvarig utgivare:** Anna-Karin Jansson
Language (s): Swedish; Full Page Mono: 22500.00
Currency: Sweden Kronor
NEWSPAPER

Alingsås Tidning
Owner: AB William Michelsens Boktryckeri
Editorial: Södra Ringgatan 14, Alingsås 441 85. **T:** 46 322 67 00 00 **E:** red@alingtid.se
W: http://www.alingsastidning.se **Circ:** 13000
Redigerare: Kerstin Brandqvist;
Redaktionschef: Urban Kärvling; **Ansvarig utgivare:** Bengt Michelsen; **Redigerare:** Ida Wikell
Language (s): Swedish; Full Page Colour: 31700.00
Currency: Sweden Kronor
NEWSPAPER

Alingsås Tidning ~ Herrljunga
Editorial: Storgatan 42, Herrljunga 524 30.
T: 46 513 107 75
W: http://www.alingsastidning.se **Circ:** 13500
Language (s): Swedish
NEWSPAPER

Alingsås Tidning ~ Lerum
Editorial: Göteborgsvägen 3, Lerum 443 30.
T: 46 302 510 50
E: redaktion@lerumstidning.com
W: http://www.lerumstidning.se **Circ:** 17400
Redaktionschef: Christina Lundin; **Redaktör:** Carina Svensson
Language (s): Swedish
NEWSPAPER

Alingsås Tidning ~ Vårgårda
Editorial: Box 60, Vårgårda 447 30.
T: 46 322 62 18 00 **E:** vgared@alingtid.se
Circ: 13500
Language (s): Swedish
NEWSPAPER

Annonsbladet i Sandviken
Owner: Hedemora Grafiska AB
Editorial: Box 176, Sandviken 811 23.
T: 46 26 24 84 84 **E:** annons@annonsbladet.se
W: http://www.annonsbladet.se
Freq: Weekly; **Circ:** 25000 Pub Statement
Language (s): Swedish; Full Page Colour: 24500.00
Currency: Sweden Kronor
NEWSPAPER

Annons-Markna'n
Owner: AnnonsMarknan
Editorial: Kulla 11, Bollebygd 517 91.
T: 46 33 28 41 20
E: annons@annonsmarknan.se
W: http://www.annonsmarknan.se
Freq: Bi-Weekly; **Circ:** 13200 Pub Statement
Language (s): Swedish
NEWSPAPER

Arbetarbladet
Owner: Arbetarbladet AB
Editorial: Box 287, Gävle 801 04.
T: 46 26 15 93 00
E: redaktionen@arbetarbladet.se
W: http://www.arbetarbladet.se **Circ:** 23900
Redigerare: Leif Carlsson; **Ansvarig utgivare:** Sven Johansson; **Nyhetschef & Stf Ansvarig utgivare:** Helena Nyman; **Redaktör:** Anne Sjödin
Language (s): Swedish; Full Page Colour: 30000.00
Currency: Sweden Kronor
NEWSPAPER

Arbetarbladet ~ Älvkarleby
Editorial: Centralgatan 4, Skutskär 814 30.
T: 46 26 767 17
E: redaktionen@arbetarbladet.se
W: http://www.arbetarbladet.se Circ: 25400
Language (s): Swedish
NEWSPAPER

Arbetarbladet ~ Hofors
Editorial: Skolgatan 12, Hofors 813 30.
T: 46 290 220 75
E: lynda.lundin@arbetarbladet.se
W: http://www.arbetarbladet.se Circ: 25400
Language (s): Swedish
NEWSPAPER

Arbetarbladet ~ Ockelbo
Editorial: Södra Åsgatan 42, Ockelbo 816 30.
T: 46 297 406 19
E: redaktionen@arbetarbladet.se
W: http://www.arbetarbladet.se Circ: 25400
Redaktör: Sofia Wike
Language (s): Swedish
NEWSPAPER

Arbetarbladet ~ Sandviken
Editorial: Box 105, Sandviken 811 22.
T: 46 26 27 88 00
E: redaktionen@arbetarbladet.se
W: http://www.arbetarbladet.se Circ: 27000
Language (s): Swedish
NEWSPAPER

Arbetarbladet ~ Tierp
Owner: Arbetarbladet AB
Editorial: Järnvägsesplanaden 12, Tierp 815
38. T: 46 293 126 65 E: tierp@arbetarbladet.se
W: http://www.arbetarbladet.se Circ: 25400
Language (s): Swedish
NEWSPAPER

Arvika Nyheter
Owner: Nya Wermlands-Tidningen AB
Editorial: Box 925, Arvika 671 29.
T: 46 570 71 44 00
E: redaktion@arvikanyheter.se
W: http://www.arvikanyheter.se Circ: 12500
Ansvarig utgivare: Jan Nordenberg
Language (s): Swedish; Full Page Colour:
19872.00
Currency: Sweden Kronor
NEWSPAPER

Backa/Kärra
Editorial: Burggrevegatan 15, Goteborg 411
03 E: ulf@litelokalt.se
W: http://www.litelokalt.se/
Freq: Monthly; Circ: 20000
Redaktionschef: Ulf Jörnvik
Language (s): Swedish
NEWSPAPER

Bålsta-Upplands-Bro-Järfälla-BLADET
Owner: Enabygdens Reklam AB
Editorial: Stockholmsvägen 13, Bålsta 746 21.
T: 46 171 15 31 50 E: manus@balstabladet.se
W: http://www.direktpress.se/balstabladet/
Freq: Weekly; Circ: 24000 RS
Ansvarig Utgivare/ VD: Ove Rickardsson
Language (s): Swedish
NEWSPAPER

Barometern - OT
Owner: Sydostpress AB
Editorial: Kalmar 391 88. T: 46 480 591 00
E: nyhetschefen@barometern.se
W: http://www.barometern.se Circ: 43000
Redaktionschef: Pär Argus; Chefredaktör &
Ansvarig utgivare: Anders Enström; Chef:
Mikael Larsson Ek; Nyhetschef: Peter
Sigfridsson
Language (s): Swedish; Full Page Colour:
40513.00
Currency: Sweden Kronor
NEWSPAPER

Barometern - OT ~ Borgholm
Editorial: Västra Kyrkogatan 26, Borgholm
387 32. T: 46 485 433 85
E: oland@barometern.se
W: http://www.barometern.se Circ: 44000
Redaktör: Annelie Frank; Redaktör: Sofia
Hedman
Language (s): Swedish
NEWSPAPER

Barometern - OT ~ Emmaboda
Editorial: Järnvägsgatan 30, Emmaboda 361
30. T: 46 471 313 90
E: emmaboda@barometern.se
W: http://www.barometern.se Circ: 44000
Redaktör: Jan Andersson
Language (s): Swedish
NEWSPAPER

Barometern - OT ~ Färjestaden
Editorial: Storgatan 9, Färjestaden 386 31.
T: 46 485 433 86 E: oland@barometern.se
W: http://www.barometern.se Circ: 44000
Redaktör: Annelie Frank; Redaktör: Sofia
Hedman
Language (s): Swedish
NEWSPAPER

Barometern - OT ~ Högsby
Editorial: Storgatan 48, Högsby 579 30.
T: 46 491 273 50 E: hogsby@ot.se
W: http://www.barometern.se Circ: 44000
Redaktör: Åsa Borefur
Language (s): Swedish
NEWSPAPER

Barometern - OT ~ Hultsfred
Editorial: Västra Långgatan 46, Hultsfred 577
30. T: 46 495 153 40 E: hultsfred@ot.se
W: http://www.barometern.se Circ: 44000
Redaktör: Tommy Nilsson
Language (s): Swedish
NEWSPAPER

Barometern - OT ~ Mönsterås
Editorial: Storgatan 53, Mönsterås 383 30.
T: 46 499 483 20 E: monsteras@ot.se
W: http://www.barometern.se Circ: 44000
Redaktör: Eva Bergquist Andersson; Redaktör:
Åsa Borefur
Language (s): Swedish
NEWSPAPER

Barometern - OT ~ Nybro
Editorial: Hornsgatan 8, Nybro 382 40.
T: 46 481 427 40 E: nybro@barometern.se
W: http://www.barometern.se Circ: 44000
Redaktör: Björn Boode; Redaktör: Jan
Stenqvist
Language (s): Swedish
NEWSPAPER

Barometern - OT ~ Oskarshamns-Tidningen
Editorial: Box 922, Oskarshamn 572 29.
T: 46 491 575 00 E: redaktion@ot.se
W: http://www.oskarshamnstidningen.se
Circ: 11300
Nyhetschef: Karin Ahlgren
Language (s): Swedish; Full Page Colour:
14200.00
Currency: Sweden Kronor
NEWSPAPER

Barometern - OT ~ Torsås
Editorial: Badhusgatan 13, Torsås 385 30.
T: 46 486 233 70 E: torsas@barometern.se
W: http://www.barometern.se Circ: 44000
Redaktör: Bo Lundquist
Language (s): Swedish
NEWSPAPER

Barometern - OT ~ Virserum
Editorial: Storgatan 23, Virserum 570 80.
T: 46 495 153 40
E: virserum@oskarshamnstidningen.se
W: http://www.barometern.se Circ: 44000
Redaktör: Camilla Ärleskog; Redaktör: Tommy
Nilsson
Language (s): Swedish
NEWSPAPER

Blekinge Läns Tidning
Owner: Blekinge Läns Tidning AB
Editorial: Ronnebygatan 28, Karlskrona 371
89. T: 46 455 770 00 E: nyhetschef@blt.se
W: http://www.blt.se
Freq: Daily; Circ: 32800
Language (s): Swedish; Full Page Colour:
49824.00
Currency: Sweden Kronor
NEWSPAPER

Blekinge Läns Tidning ~ Karlshamns Allehanda
Owner: Blekinge Läns Tidning AB
Editorial: Drottninggatan 56, Karlshamn 374
35. T: 46 454 30 60 00
E: karlshamnsredaktionen@blt.se
W: http://www.blt.se
Freq: Daily; Circ: 32800
Language (s): Swedish; Full Page Colour:
49824.00
Currency: Sweden Kronor
NEWSPAPER

Blekinge Läns Tidning ~ Olofström
Owner: Blekinge Läns Tidning AB
Editorial: Ådalsvägen 2 B, Olofström 293 34.
T: 46 454 342 30
E: olofstromsredaktionen@blt.se
W: http://www.blt.se Circ: 32800
Language (s): Swedish
NEWSPAPER

Blekinge Läns Tidning ~ Ronneby
Owner: Blekinge Läns Tidning AB
Editorial: Övre Brunnsvägen 2, Ronneby 372
36. T: 46 457 789 80
E: ronnebyredaktionen@blt.se
W: http://www.bltsydostran.se/nyheter/
ronneby/
Freq: Daily; Circ: 32800
Language (s): Swedish
NEWSPAPER

Blekinge Läns Tidning ~ Sölvesborgs-Tidningen
Owner: Blekinge Läns Tidning AB
Editorial: Köpmansgatan 6 C, Sölvesborg 294
33. T: 46 456 788 40
E: solvesborgsredaktionen@blt.se
W: http://www.blt.se/nyheter/solvesborg/?
Circ: 32800
Language (s): Swedish; Full Page Colour:
49824.00
Currency: Sweden Kronor
NEWSPAPER

Bohusläningen
Owner: Bohusläningens AB
Editorial: Uddevalla 451 83. T: 46 522 990 00
E: redaktionen@bohuslaningen.se
W: http://www.bohuslaningen.se Circ: 31600
Nyhetschef: Karl af Geijerstam; Nyhetschef:
Ingela Hydén
Language (s): Swedish; Full Page Colour:
45600.00
Currency: Sweden Kronor
NEWSPAPER

Bohusläningen ~ Dalsland
Owner: Bohusläningens AB
Editorial: Håvestensvägen 2, Färgelanda 458
32. T: 46 522 99 000
E: dalsland@bohuslaningen.se
W: http://www.bohuslaningen.se Circ: 32600
Language (s): Swedish
NEWSPAPER

Bohusläningen ~ Lysekil
Editorial: Landsvägsgatan 7, Lysekil 453 35.
T: 46 523 146 91 E: lysekil@bohuslaningen.se
W: http://www.bohuslaningen.se Circ: 32600
Language (s): Swedish
NEWSPAPER

Bohusläningen ~ Munkedal
Editorial: Stationsvägen 24, Munkedal 455 31.
T: 46 524 718 89
E: munkedal@bohuslaningen.se
W: http://www.bohuslaningen.se Circ: 32600
Redaktör: Stefan Karlsson
Language (s): Swedish
NEWSPAPER

Bohusläningen ~ Orust
Editorial: N. Strandvägen 1, Henån 473 34.
T: 46 304 309 95 E: orust@bohuslaningen.se
W: http://www.bohuslaningen.se Circ: 32600
Language (s): Swedish
NEWSPAPER

Bohusläningen ~ Sotenäs
T: 46 523 321 14
E: sotenas@bohuslaningen.se
W: http://www.bohuslaningen.se
Freq: Daily; Circ: 32600 TS
Language (s): Swedish
NEWSPAPER

Bohusläningen ~ Tanumshede
Editorial: Affärsvägen 1, Tanumshede 457 30.
T: 46 525 292 40 E: tanum@bohuslaningen.se
W: http://www.bohuslaningen.se Circ: 32600
Language (s): Swedish
NEWSPAPER

BollnäsNytt
Owner: Magnus Söderlund
Editorial: Box 1059, Stationsgatan 8, Bollnäs
821 12. T: 46 27 82 75 50
E: redaktion@helahalsingland.se
W: http://www.helahalsingland.se
Freq: Weekly; Circ: 14200 Pub Statement
Ansvarig utgivare: Mats Omwall; Redaktör:
Kristian Westin
Language (s): Swedish; Full Page Colour:
22320.00
Currency: Sweden Kronor
NEWSPAPER

Borås Tidning
Owner: Gota Media AB
Editorial: Allégatan 67, Borås 501 85.
T: 46 33 700 07 00 E: redaktionen@bt.se
W: http://www.bt.se Circ: 49200
Chefredaktör & Ansvarig utgivare: Stefan
Eklund; Nyhetschef: Hanna Grahn Strömbom;
Redaktionschef / stf ansvarig utgivare::
Anneli Johannisson

Language (s): Swedish; Full Page Colour:
50880.00
Currency: Sweden Kronor
NEWSPAPER

Borås Tidning ~ Bollebygd
Owner: Gota Media AB
Editorial: Kungsbackavägen 1, Bollebygd 517
34. T: 46 33 20 60 51 E: bollebygd@bt.se
W: http://www.bt.se Circ: 49200
Redaktör: Anne Engström
Language (s): Swedish
NEWSPAPER

Borås Tidning ~ Mark
Owner: Gota Media AB
Editorial: Stationsgatan 4, Kinna 511 51.
T: 46 3 202 055 40 E: mark@bt.se
W: http://www.bt.se Circ: 49100
Redaktör: Magnus Larsson
Language (s): Swedish
NEWSPAPER

Borås Tidning ~ Svenljunga/Tranemo
Owner: Gota Media AB
Editorial: Box 148, Svenljunga 512 23.
T: 46 325 61 68 90 E: kind@bt.se
W: http://www.bt.se Circ: 49100
Redaktör: Magnus Josefsson
Language (s): Swedish
NEWSPAPER

City Lund
Editorial: Sydsvenskan/City, Skomakaregatan
1, Lund 223 50. T: 46 40 28 24 30
E: redaktionen@citylund.se
W: http://cityskane.se/lund
Freq: Daily; Circ: 14700
Language (s): Swedish; Full Page Colour:
37392.00
Currency: Sweden Kronor
NEWSPAPER

City Malmö
Editorial: Sydsvenskan/City, Stortorget 9,
Malmo 205 05. T: 46 40 28 24 30
E: redaktionen@citymalmo.se
W: http://cityskane.se/malmo/
Freq: Daily; Circ: 41800
Language (s): Swedish; Full Page Colour:
37392.00
Currency: Sweden Kronor
NEWSPAPER

Commersen
Owner: Carlshamns Commersen AB
Editorial: Carlshamns Commersen AB,
Lotsgatan 5, Karlshamn 374 35.
T: 46 454 341 30 E: info@commersen.se
W: http://www.commersen.se
Freq: Weekly; Circ: 16900 Pub Statement
Language (s): Swedish; Full Page Colour:
20710.00
Currency: Sweden Kronor
NEWSPAPER

Dagbladet, Nya Samhället
Owner: Dagbladet Sundsvall AB
Editorial: Box 466, Sundsvall 851 06.
T: 46 60 66 35 00 E: nyhetschef@dagbladet.se
W: http://www.dagbladet.se Circ: 12000
Nyhetschef: Arne Åkerlund; Nyhetschef: Leif
Johansson; Chefredaktör & Ansvarig
utgivare: Patricia Svensson; Ledarskribent:
Linnea Swedenmark
Language (s): Swedish; Full Page Colour:
19440.00
Currency: Sweden Kronor
NEWSPAPER

Dagen
Owner: Dagen
Editorial: Kungsholmstorg 5, Stockholm 105
36. T: 46 8 619 24 00
E: redaktionen@dagen.se
W: http://www.dagen.se
Freq: 3 Times/Week; Circ: 16800 Pub
Statement
Redaktör: Thérése Alhult; Redaktör: Marlene
Antonson; Marknadschef: Åke Lindh;
Redaktionschef: Thomas Österberg; Redaktör:
Therese Peterson; Chefredaktör, Ansvarig
utgivare & VD: Felicia Svaeren Ferreira;
Nyhetschef: David Wingren
Language (s): Swedish; Full Page Colour:
28500.00
Currency: Sweden Kronor
DAILY NEWSPAPER

Dagens ETC
Owner: ETC förlag AB
Editorial: Box 4403, Björngårdsgatan 15,
Stockholm 102 68. T: 46 8 410 357 00
E: dagens@etc.se W: http://www.etc.se
Freq: Daily; Circ: 3900 TS
Chefredaktör: Andreas Gustavsson; Stf

redaktör: Karin Holmberg; **Nyhetschef:** Eigil Söderin; **Redaktionssekreterare:** Klara Strandberg
Language (s): Swedish; Full Page Colour: 50000.00
Currency: Sweden Kronor
DAILY NEWSPAPER

Dagens Industri
Owner: Dagens Industri AB
Editorial: Torsgatan 21, Stockholm 113 90.
T: 46 8 573 650 00 **E:** red@di.se
W: http://www.di.se
Freq: Daily; **Circ:** 103100 TS
Krönikör: Maria Borelius; **Redigeringschef:** Mats Brohagen; **Redaktionschef:** Lotta Edling; **Chefredaktör & Ansvarig Utgivare:** Peter Fellman
Language (s): Swedish; Full Page Colour: 142200.00
Currency: Sweden Kronor
DAILY NEWSPAPER

Dagens Nyheter
Owner: Dagens Nyheter AB
Editorial: Gjörwellsgatan 30, Stockholm 105 15. **T:** 46 8 738 10 00 **E:** centralred@dn.se
W: http://www.dn.se
Freq: Daily; **Circ:** 292100 TS
Redigeringschef: Lotta Härdelin; **Chefredaktör & Ansvarig utgivare:** Peter Wolodarski
Language (s): Swedish; Full Page Colour: 302075.00
Currency: Sweden Kronor
DAILY NEWSPAPER

Dala-Demokraten
Owner: Dala Demokraten
Editorial: Postadress: Box 825, Besöksadress: Stigaregatan 17, Falun 791 29.
T: 46 23 475 00
W: http://www.dalademokraten.com
Circ: 14800
Redaktionschef & Ansvarig utgivare: Bosse Andersson; **Chefredaktör:** Göran Greider
Language (s): Swedish; Full Page Colour: 40176.00
Currency: Sweden Kronor
NEWSPAPER

Dala-Demokraten ~ Borlänge
Owner: Dala-Demokraten
Editorial: Box 302, Wasabryggeriet, Borlänge 781 24. **T:** 46 243 920 00 **E:** red@daladem.se
W: http://www.dalademokraten.se **Circ:** 21600
Nyhetschef: Kerstin Eriksson
Language (s): Swedish
NEWSPAPER

Dala-Demokraten ~ Leksand
Editorial: Sparbanksgatan 4F, Leksand 793 91.
T: 46 247 611 50 **E:** red@daladem.se
W: http://www.dalademokraten.com
Circ: 21600
Language (s): Swedish
NEWSPAPER

Dala-Demokraten ~ Mora
Owner: Dala Demokraten
Editorial: Vasagatan 32, Mora 792 32.
T: 46 23 476 82 **E:** red@daladem.se
W: http://www.dalademokraten.com
Circ: 21600
Language (s): Swedish
NEWSPAPER

Det händer-Med köpenhamnsdelen
Owner: ShutterBug Sweden AB
Editorial: Enegatan 3, Lomma 234 37.
T: 46 40 41 10 92 **W:** http://www.dethander.se
Circ: 35000
Redaktionschef: Ditte Tengvall
Language (s): Swedish
NEWSPAPER

DT Borlänge Tidning
Owner: Dalarnas Tidningar
Editorial: Box 29, Borlänge 781 21.
T: 46 243 644 08 **E:** bt.red@dt.se
W: http://www.dt.se **Circ:** 15000
Redaktör: Sven-Erik Olsson; **Nyhetschef:** Jan Svensson; **Redaktionschef/ Ansvarig Utgivare:** Ewa Wirén
Language (s): Swedish; Full Page Colour: 23300.00
Currency: Sweden Kronor
NEWSPAPER

DT Falu Kuriren
Owner: Dalarnas Tidningar
Editorial: Zettergrens väg 7, Box 265, Falun 79177. **T:** 46 23 936 00 **E:** fk.red@dt.se
W: http://www.dt.se
Freq: Daily; **Circ:** 54400
Nyhetschef: Jenny Andreasson;
Redaktionschef: Carl-Johan Bergman;
Nyhetschef: Inger Wallin; **Redaktionschef & Ansvarig utgivare:** Ewa Wirén
Language (s): Swedish; Full Page Colour: 39744.00
Currency: Sweden Kronor
NEWSPAPER

DT Falu Kuriren ~ Gagnef
Owner: Dalarnas Tidningar
Editorial: Skogsvägen 2, Gagnef 780 41.
T: 46 241 105 80 **E:** gagnef@dt.se
W: http://www.dt.se
Freq: 3 Times/Week; **Circ:** 28000
Language (s): Swedish
NEWSPAPER

DT Falu Kuriren ~ Leksand
Editorial: Norsgatan 27, Leksand 793 30.
T: 46 247 79 20 31 **E:** leksand@dt.se
W: http://www.dt.se **Circ:** 28000
Language (s): Swedish
NEWSPAPER

DT Falu Kuriren ~ Malung
Editorial: Box 31, Postgatan 1, Malung 782 21. **T:** 46 280 125 15 **E:** malung@dt.se
W: http://www.dt.se **Circ:** 28000
Language (s): Swedish
NEWSPAPER

DT Falu Kuriren ~ Rättvik
Editorial: Storgatan 4, Rättvik 795 30.
T: 46 248 130 07 **E:** rattvik@dt.se
W: http://www.falukuriren.se **Circ:** 28000
Redaktör: Katarina Cham
Language (s): Swedish
NEWSPAPER

DT Falu Kuriren ~ Vansbro
Editorial: Allégatan 23, Vansbro 780 50.
T: 46 281 718 30 **E:** vansbro@dt.se
W: http://www.dt.se **Circ:** 28000
Language (s): Swedish
NEWSPAPER

Emmaboda Tidning
Owner: Emmaboda Tidning AB
Editorial: Kalmar 392 33. **T:** 46 471 339 84
W: http://www.emmabodatidning.se
Freq: Monthly; **Circ:** 10100 Not Audited
Ansvarig utgivare: Per-Olof Persson
Language (s): Swedish; Full Page Colour: 15330.00
Currency: Sweden Kronor
NEWSPAPER

Ena-Håbo Tidningen
Editorial: Vårfrugatan 2A, Enköping 745 34.
T: 46 171 338 35 **E:** redaktionen@enahabo.se
W: http://www.direktpress.se/enahabotidningen
Circ: 28000
Redaktionschef: Robert Österlind; **Ansvarig Utgivare/ VD:** Ove Rickardsson
Language (s): Swedish; Full Page Colour: 10185.00
Currency: Sweden Kronor
NEWSPAPER

Eskilstuna-Kuriren / Strengnäs Tidning
Owner: Eskilstuna-Kuriren AB
Editorial: Box 120, Eskilstuna 631 02.
T: 46 16 15 60 00 **E:** redaktion@ekuriren.se
W: http://www.ekuriren.se **Circ:** 30700
Redaktör: Matthias Johansson; **Redaktör:** Therése Norén; **Nyhetschef:** Lars Skärlund; **Ansvarig utgivare:** Peo Wärring
Language (s): Swedish; Full Page Colour: 45500.00
Currency: Sweden Kronor
NEWSPAPER

Eskilstuna-Kuriren / Strengnäs Tidning ~ Flen
Editorial: Götgatan 2 A, Flen 642 37.
T: 46 157 133 50 **E:** flen@ekuriren.se
W: http://www.ekuriren.se **Circ:** 33200
Nyhetschef: Lars Skärlund
Language (s): Swedish
NEWSPAPER

Eskilstuna-Kuriren / Strengnäs Tidning ~ Strängnäs
Editorial: Box 3, Strängnäs 645 21.
T: 46 152 474 00 **E:** strangnas@ekuriren.se
W: http://www.strengnastidning.se **Circ:** 33200
Ansvarig utgivare: Peo Warring
Language (s): Swedish
NEWSPAPER

Expressen
Owner: AB Kvällstidningen Expressen
Editorial: Gjörwellsgatan 30, Stockholm 105 16. **T:** 46 8 738 30 00 **E:** 71717@expressen.se
W: http://www.expressen.se
Freq: Daily; **Circ:** 228000 Pub Statement
Redaktionschef för nyheter och samhälle: Magnus Alselind; **Editionschef- Riks:** Christofer Brask; **Editionschef:** Leif Kasvi; **Redaktör:** Christina Lundell; **Chefredaktör & Ansvarig utgivare:** Thomas Mattsson
Language (s): Swedish; Full Page Colour: 180000.00
Currency: Sweden Kronor
DAILY NEWSPAPER

Extra Östergötland
Owner: AB Östgöta Correspondenten, Norrköpings Tidningars AB
Editorial: Extra Östergötland, Stohagsgatan 6a, Norrköping, Norrköping 601 83.
T: 46 11 495 88 80
E: extra@extraostergotland.se
W: http://www.extraostergotland.se
Circ: 42000
Redaktionschef och ansvarig utgivare: Mikael Sönne
Language (s): Swedish; Full Page Colour: 24240.00
Currency: Sweden Kronor
NEWSPAPER

Finnveden Nu
Owner: Finnveden Nu Tidnings AB
Editorial: Box 111, Värnamo 331 32.
T: 46 370 69 16 40 **E:** redaktion@finnveden.nu
W: http://www.finnveden.nu **Circ:** 41600
Ansvarig utgivare: Stefan Fels; **Nyhetschef:** Lena Gärdemalm; **Platschef:** Krister Kühlwein; **Platschef:** Hans Thomson; **Redaktionschef, Ansvarig utgivare, VD:** Mats Tidstrand
Language (s): Swedish; Full Page Colour: 20440.00
Currency: Sweden Kronor
NEWSPAPER

Gefle Dagblad
Owner: Gävle Tidningar
Editorial: Box 367, Hattmakargatan 14, Gävle 801 05. **T:** 46 26 15 96 00
E: gefle.dagblad@gd.se **W:** http://www.gd.se
Circ: 26500
Redigerare: Magnus Bragman; **Chefredaktör & Ansvarig utgivare:** Maria Brander; **Nyhetschef:** Marika Kvarnström; **Nyhetschef:** Magnus Lundquist
Language (s): Swedish; Full Page Colour: 33360.00
Currency: Sweden Kronor
NEWSPAPER

Gefle Dagblad ~ Sandviken
Owner: MittMedia AB
Editorial: Box 308, Hyttgatan 14, Sandviken 811 30. **T:** 46 26 15 96 00
E: sandviken@gd.se **W:** http://www.gd.se
Circ: 27700
Language (s): Swedish
NEWSPAPER

Göteborgs Manhattan
Editorial: Burggrevegatan 15, Goteborg 411 03 **E:** ulf@litelokalt.se
W: http://www.litelokalt.se/
Freq: Monthly; **Circ:** 20000
Redaktionschef: Ulf Jörnvik
Language (s): Swedish
NEWSPAPER

Göteborgs-Posten
Owner: Stampen
Editorial: Polhemsplatsen 5, Goteborg 405 02.
T: 46 31 62 40 00 **E:** nyheter@gp.se
W: http://www.gp.se
Freq: Daily; **Circ:** 216300 TS
Redaktionschef och ansvarig utgivare: Anders Goliger; **Redaktionschef:** Ninni Jonzon; **Chefredaktör & Ansvarig utgivare:** Cecilia Krönlein
Language (s): Swedish; Full Page Colour: 163270.00
Currency: Sweden Kronor
DAILY NEWSPAPER

Göteborgs-Posten ~ Lerum/Alingsås
Editorial: Göteborgsvägen 14, Alingsås 441 43. **T:** 46 31 62 57 92
E: lerum.alingsas@gp.se
W: http://www.gp.se/nyheter/lerumalingsas
Freq: Daily; **Circ:** 216300
Language (s): Swedish
NEWSPAPER

Gotlands Allehanda
Owner: Gotlands Media AB
Editorial: Broväg 21, Box 1284, Visby 621 23.
T: 46 498 20 25 50
E: redaktion@gotlandsallehanda.se
W: http://www.helagotland.se **Circ:** 10100
Nyhetschef & tf Ansvarig utgivare: Eva Buskas; **Redaktionschef & Ansvarig utgivare:** Ulrica Fransson Ingelmark
Language (s): Swedish; Full Page Colour: 31136.00
Currency: Sweden Kronor
NEWSPAPER

Gotlands Tidningar
Owner: Gotlandspress AB
Editorial: Box 1223, Visby 621 23.
T: 46 498 20 24 00
E: redaktion.gt@gotlandstidningar.se
W: http://www.helagotland.se **Circ:** 21800
Redaktionschef & Ansvarig utgivare: Ulf Hammarlund; **Redigerare:** Elisabet Kicki Norén
Language (s): Swedish; Full Page Colour: 31136.00
Currency: Sweden Kronor
NEWSPAPER

GT
Owner: AB Kvällstidningen Expressen
Editorial: Postadress: Box 417, Besöksadress: Kungstorget 2, Goteborg 401 26.
T: 46 31 725 90 00 **E:** redaktionen@gt.se
W: http://www.gt.se **Circ:** 57700
Chefredaktör: Frida Boisen; **Nyhetschef:** Markus Hankins; **Chefredaktör/ Ansvarig utgivare:** Thomas Mattsson
Language (s): Swedish; Full Page Colour: 36900.00
Currency: Sweden Kronor
DAILY NEWSPAPER

Hallå! Helsingborg
Owner: Helsingborgs Dagblad
Editorial: Vasatorpsvägen 1, Helsingborg 251 83. **T:** 46 42 489 93 17
E: redaktion@tidningenhalla.se
W: http://hd.se/halla/helsingborg/
Freq: Weekly; **Circ:** 62008
Language (s): Swedish
NEWSPAPER

Hallands Nyheter
Owner: Stampen
Editorial: Falkenberg 311 81.
T: 46 346 290 00 **E:** redaktionen@hn.se
W: http://www.hn.se **Circ:** 31200
Chef: Hans-Olof Elled; **Chefredaktör & Ansvarig utgivare:** Malin Henrikson; **Redaktör:** Camilla Magnusson; **Nyhetschef:** Lena Strömberg
Language (s): Swedish; Full Page Colour: 38880.00
Currency: Sweden Kronor
NEWSPAPER

Hallands Nyheter ~ Varberg
Editorial: Box 162, Varberg 432 24.
T: 46 340 62 90 00 **E:** redaktionen@hn.se
W: http://www.hn.se **Circ:** 31600
Language (s): Swedish
NEWSPAPER

Hallandsposten
Owner: Hallandsposten
Editorial: Halmstad 301 81.
T: 46 10471 51 00
E: redaktionen@hallandsposten.se
W: http://www.hallandsposten.se **Circ:** 32900
Redaktör: Ulrika Ahlberg; **Redaktör:** Annelie Bodin; **Ansvarig utgivare:** Viveka Hedbjörk; **Redaktör:** Marko Korkeasalo; **Redaktionssekreterare:** Cecilia Kristensson; **Nyhetschef:** Hanna Sjöberg
Language (s): Swedish; Full Page Colour: 50500.00
Currency: Sweden Kronor
NEWSPAPER

Hallandsposten ~ Hyltebruk
Editorial: Box 23, Hyltebruk 314 21.
T: 46 345 480 90 **E:** hylte@hallandsposten.se
W: http://www.hallandsposten.se **Circ:** 33000
Redaktionssekreterare: Åsa Montan
Language (s): Swedish
NEWSPAPER

Hallandsposten ~ Laholm
Editorial: Laholm 312 21. **T:** 46 430 792 10
E: laholm@hallandsposten.se
W: http://www.hallandsposten.se **Circ:** 33000
Redaktör: Jonatan Gernes
Language (s): Swedish
NEWSPAPER

Halmstad 7 dagar
Owner: Gratistidningar i Väst AB
Editorial: Nässjögatan 6, Halmstad.
T: 46 35 219990 **E:** redaktion@hstd7dagar.se
W: http://hstd7dagar.se/
Freq: Weekly; **Circ:** 46000
Redaktör: Fanny Ekström
Language (s): Swedish
NEWSPAPER

Handelsstaden Örebro
Owner: HKM Publishing AB

Editorial: Näbbtorgsgatan 2, Orebro 701 47
E: info@hkm.se
Freq: Monthly; **Circ:** 101362 Pub Statement
Redaktör: Peter Steen-Christensen
Language (s): Swedish
NEWSPAPER

Helsingborgs Dagblad
Owner: Helsingborgs Dagblad
Editorial: Vasatorpsvägen 1, Helsingborg 251
83. **T:** 46 42 489 91 00 **E:** redaktionen@hd.se
W: http://www.hd.se **Circ:** 72600
Redigeringschef: Göran Andersson;
Redaktionschef: Anna Bergenström;
Redigerare/teknik: Cay-Ove Högberg;
Redaktör- grävnavet: Emma Johansson;
Chefredaktör & Ansvarig utgivare: Lars
Johansson; **Redigerare:** Agneta Jonsson;
Redigerare: Ingvor Jonsson; **Redigerare:**
Hedvig Juhasz-Toth; **Helgtidningschef:** Brith
Lindahl; **Redigerare:** Lars Ljunggren;
Redigerare: Cilla Nilsson; **Nyhetschef-**
Helsingborg: Kristian Nilsson; **Nyhetschef:**
Sofia Nilsson; **Redaktör- Familjeliv:** Marika
Rasmusson; **Redigerare:** Helena Schoug
Language (s): Swedish; Full Page Colour:
119616.00
Currency: Sweden Kronor
NEWSPAPER

Helsingborgs Dagblad ~ Ängelholm
Owner: Helsingborgs Dagblad
Editorial: Laxgatan 1b, Ängelholm 262 32.
T: 46 431 842 50 **E:** angelholm@hd.se
W: http://www.hd.se **Circ:** 20000
Language (s): Swedish; Full Page Colour:
26000.00
Currency: Sweden Kronor
NEWSPAPER

Hemmets Vän
Owner: Evangeliipress Förlags AB
Editorial: Box 220 10, Orebro 702 02.
T: 46 19 16 54 20
E: redaktion@hemmetsvan.se
W: http://www.hemmetsvan.se
Freq: Weekly; **Circ:** 13700 Not Audited
Editor: Agneta Andersson; **Editor:** Per
Danielsson; **Chefredaktör/ Ansvarig Utgivare:**
Berndt-Åke Hällzon; **Editor:** Bo Lenells
Language (s): Swedish; Full Page Colour:
25200.00
Currency: Sweden Kronor
DAILY NEWSPAPER

Höglandet Nu
Owner: Höglandet Nu Tidnings AB
Editorial: Box 344, Nässjö 571 24.
T: 46 380 55 44 70 **E:** redaktion@hogland.nu
W: http://www.nutidningen.nu **Circ:** 39900
Platschef: Roger Odeén
Language (s): Swedish; Full Page Colour:
25513.00
Currency: Sweden Kronor
NEWSPAPER

Hudiksvalls Tidning
Owner: Hälsingetidningar AB
Editorial: Box 1201, Hudiksvall 824 15.
T: 46 650 355 00 **E:** redaktion@ht.se
W: http://www.helahalsingland.se **Circ:** 15700
Redaktör: Per Åkerblom; **Chef:** Ulf Eriksson;
Ansvarig utgivare & Chefredaktör: Gunilla
Kindstrand; **Nyhetschef:** Lars Larsson;
Redaktör: Håkan Persson; **Redigerare:** Marie
Pousard; **Redigerare:** Pia Trybom
Language (s): Swedish; Full Page Colour:
18720.00
Currency: Sweden Kronor
NEWSPAPER

Hudiksvalls Tidning ~ Nordanstig
Editorial: Storgatan 3, Bergsjö 820 70.
T: 46 652 102 47 **E:** alexandra.sievers@ht.se
W: http://www.ht.se **Circ:** 15700
Nyhetschef: Lisa Hall
Language (s): Swedish
NEWSPAPER

iHyllie
Editorial: DinPublik AB, Skeppsgatan 19,
Malmo 211 19. **T:** 0046 40 627 85 80
E: info@ihyllie.se
Freq: Quarterly; **Circ:** 20000
Chefredaktör / Ansvarig utgivare: Emilia
Olofsson
Language (s): Swedish; Full Page Colour:
13900.00
Currency: Sweden Kronor
NEWSPAPER

Jönköping Nu
Owner: Jönköping Nu Tidnings AB
Editorial: Box 264, Jönköping 551 14.
T: 46 36 30 94 90 **E:** redaktion@jonkoping.nu
W: http://www.nutidningen.nu
Freq: Weekly; **Circ:** 69500

Language (s): Swedish; Full Page Colour:
34400.00
Currency: Sweden Kronor
NEWSPAPER

Jönköpings-Posten
Owner: Herenco AB
Editorial: Jönköping 551 80.
T: 46 36 30 40 50
E: red@jonkopingsposten.se
W: http://www.jonkopingsposten.se
Circ: 37100
Nyhetschef: Anna Alexandersson; **Redaktör:**
Janne Johansson; **Chef:** Marie Johansson
Flyckt; **Ansvarig utgivare:** Mats Ottosson
Language (s): Swedish; Full Page Colour:
66350.00
Currency: Sweden Kronor
NEWSPAPER

Jönköpings-Posten ~ Bankeryd-Habo
Editorial: Jönköpingsvägen 13, Habo 566 31.
T: 46 36 460 31
E: habo.red@jonkopingsposten.se
W: http://www.jonkopingsposten.se
Circ: 41700
Redaktör: Göran Bard
Language (s): Swedish
NEWSPAPER

Jönköpings-Posten ~ Gränna
Editorial: Sjögatan 29, Gränna 563 31.
T: 46 390 121 95
E: granna.red@jonkopingsposten.se
W: http://www.jonkopingsposten.se
Circ: 41700
Language (s): Swedish
NEWSPAPER

Jönköpings-Posten ~ Huskvarna
Editorial: Erik Dalbergsgatan 26, Huskvarna
561 32. **T:** 46 36 14 05 12
E: huskvarna.red@jonkopingsposten.se
W: http://www.jonkopingsposten.se
Circ: 41700
Redaktör: Ola Pilhem; **Redaktör:** Anette
Svensson
Language (s): Swedish
NEWSPAPER

Jönköpings-Posten ~ Mullsjö
Editorial: Kyrkvägen 10 A, Unavailable 535 31.
T: 46 392 100 55
E: mullsjo.red@jonkopingsposten.se
W: http://www.jonkopingsposten.se
Circ: 41700
Language (s): Swedish
NEWSPAPER

Jönköpings-Posten ~ Norrahammar
Editorial: Hammarvägen 46, Norrahammar
562 32. **T:** 46 36 602 40
E: norrahammar.red@jonkopingsposten.se
W: http://www.jonkopingsposten.se
Circ: 41700
Redaktör: Sandra Lindén
Language (s): Swedish
NEWSPAPER

Jönköpings-Posten ~ Skillingaryd
Editorial: Box 16, Skillingaryd 568 30.
T: 46 370 702 09
E: skillingaryd.red@jonkopingsposten.se
W: http://www.jonkopingsposten.se
Circ: 41700
Redaktör: Daniel Henriksson; **Redaktör:**
Jeanette Johnsson
Language (s): Swedish
NEWSPAPER

Jönköpings-Posten ~ Vaggeryd
Editorial: Vaggeryd 567 30. **T:** 46 393 106 90
E: vaggeryd.red@jonkopingsposten.se
W: http://www.jonkopingsposten.se
Circ: 41700
Redaktör: Jenny Folkesson; **Redaktör:** Hans
Nilsson
Language (s): Swedish
NEWSPAPER

KalmarPosten
Owner: V-TAB, Norrtälje 2006
Editorial: Jenny Nyströms gränd 2, Kalmar
392 33. **T:** 46 480 72 02 00
E: tidningen@kalmarposten.se
W: http://www.kalmarposten.se
Freq: Weekly; **Circ:** 78800 Pub Statement
Language (s): Swedish; Full Page Colour:
36792.00
Currency: Sweden Kronor
NEWSPAPER

Katrineholms-Kuriren
Owner: Katrineholms-Kuriren AB
Editorial: Box 111, Katrineholm 641 22.
T: 46 150 728 00 **E:** redaktion@kkuriren.se

W: http://www.kkuriren.se **Circ:** 12400
Chefredaktör: Elisabeth Bäck; **Redigerare:**
Ingela Gustafsson; **Mänskligtredaktör:** Kristina
Rönnqvist; **Redaktör:** Sören Soldan;
Nyhetschef: Henrik Wising
Language (s): Swedish; Full Page Colour:
31000.00
Currency: Sweden Kronor
NEWSPAPER

Katrineholms-Kuriren ~ Flen
Owner: Katrineholms-Kuriren AB
Editorial: Götgatan 2 A, Flen 642 37.
T: 46 157 133 51 **E:** flen@kkuriren.se
W: http://www.kkuriren.se **Circ:** 12900
Language (s): Swedish
NEWSPAPER

Katrineholms-Kuriren ~ Vingåker
Editorial: Box 54, Vingåker 643 30.
T: 46 151 120 52 **E:** vingaker@kkuriren.se
W: http://www.kkuriren.se **Circ:** 12900
Language (s): Swedish
NEWSPAPER

KH aktuellt
Owner: Svensk Mediakonsult AB
Editorial: Svensk mediakonsult AB, Ilanda
Gård 120, Karlstad 653 50. **T:** 46 54 18 77 18
E: redaktionen@svenskmediakonsult.se
W: http://www.svenskmediakonsult.se/
khaktuellt.html
Freq: Monthly; **Circ:** 53100 Pub Statement
Redaktör: Helena Bengtsson; **Redaktör:**
Mathias Eriksson
Language (s): Swedish
NEWSPAPER

Kristianstadsbladet
Owner: Kristianstadsbladet
Editorial: Nya Boulevarden 4, Kristianstad 291
84. **T:** 46 44 18 55 00
E: nyheter@kristianstadsbladet.se
W: http://www.kristianstadsbladet.se
Circ: 29500
Redaktör- Bilagor: Maria Nilson; **Nyhetschef:**
Bengt-Inge Schölin; **Chefredaktör & Ansvarig**
Utgivare: Jörgen Svensson; **Redaktör:** Lotta
Tholin
Language (s): Swedish; Full Page Colour:
54480.00
Currency: Sweden Kronor
NEWSPAPER

Kristianstadsbladet ~ Bromölla
Editorial: Bromölla 295 31. **T:** 46 456 290 00
E: nyheter@kristianstadsbladet.se
W: http://www.kristianstadsbladet.se
Circ: 31900
Language (s): Swedish
NEWSPAPER

Kristianstadsbladet ~ Hässleholm
Editorial: Box 77, Hässleholm 281 01.
T: 46 451 830 50
E: nyheter@kristianstadsbladet.se
W: http://www.kristianstadsbladet.se
Circ: 31900
Redaktör: Johannes Linden
Language (s): Swedish
NEWSPAPER

Kristianstadsbladet ~Östra Göinge/
Broby
Editorial: Torggatan 1, Broby 280 60.
T: 46 44 470 00
E: nyheter@kristianstadsbladet.se
W: http://www.kristianstadsbladet.se
Circ: 31900
Language (s): Swedish
NEWSPAPER

Kristinehamns-Aktuellt
Owner: Information & Design Reklambyrå
Editorial: Box 158, Kristinehamn 681 23.
T: 46 550 199 00
E: redaktion@kristinehamnsaktuellt.se
W: http://www.kristinehamnsaktuellt.se
Freq: Monthly; **Circ:** 18000 RS
Chefredaktör & Ansvarig utgivare: Roland
Thomas
Language (s): Swedish
NEWSPAPER

Kungälvs-Posten
Owner: Ortstidningar i Väst AB
Editorial: Box 523, Kungälv 442 15.
T: 46 303 20 68 00
E: redaktion@kungalvsposten.se
W: http://www.kungalvsposten.se **Circ:** 10800
Ansvarig utgivare: Roger Boström;
Chefredaktör: Ingrid Fredriksson; **Redigerare:**
Stefan Nodesjö
Language (s): Swedish; Full Page Colour:
17400.00
Currency: Sweden Kronor
NEWSPAPER

Kvällsposten
Owner: AB Kvällstidningen Expressen
Editorial: AB kvällstidningen Expressen
Kvällsposten, Södergatan 24, Malmo 205 26.
T: 46 40 602 01 00 **E:** redaktionen@kvp.se
W: http://www.expressen.se/kvp
Freq: Daily; **Circ:** 55800
Redaktionschef: Susanne Lindén
Language (s): Swedish; Full Page Colour:
39650.00
Currency: Sweden Kronor
DAILY NEWSPAPER

Kvällsposten ~ Helsingborg
Owner: AB Kvällstidningen Expressen
Editorial: Kullagatan 8, Helsingborg 252 20.
T: 46 42 12 79 15 **E:** redaktionen@kvp.se
W: http://www.kvp.se
Freq: Daily; **Circ:** 55800
Language (s): Swedish
NEWSPAPER

Kvibergs-Staden
Editorial: Burggrevegatan 15, Goteborg 411
03
Freq: Monthly; **Circ:** 20000
Redaktionschef: Ulf Jörnvik
Language (s): Swedish
NEWSPAPER

Länstidningen Norr/Vimmerby
Tidning ~ Hultsfred
Editorial: Bryggerigatan 1 C, Hultsfred 577 30.
T: 46 495 140 00
E: hfredred@vimmerbytidning.se
W: http://www.vimmerbytidning.com
Circ: 11900
Language (s): Swedish
NEWSPAPER

Länstidningen Norr/Vimmerby
Tidning ~ Kinda
Owner: Vimmerby Tidning och Tryckeri
Ekonomisk Fören
Editorial: Storgatan 3, Kisa 590 40.
T: 46 494 101 00 **E:** redaktion@kindaposten.se
W: http://www.vimmerbytidning.se **Circ:** 11900
Language (s): Swedish
NEWSPAPER

Länstidningen Norr/Vimmerby
Tidning ~ Mariannelund
Editorial: Centralgatan 2, Mariannelund 570
33. **T:** 46 496 105 00
E: mlundred@vimmerbytidning.se
W: http://www.vimmerbytidning.com
Circ: 11900
Language (s): Swedish
NEWSPAPER

Länstidningen Östersund
Owner: AB Länstidningen
Editorial: Biblioteksgatan 15, Besöksadress:
Kyrkgatan 52, Östersund 831 89.
T: 46 63 15 55 30 **E:** redaktionen@ltz.se
W: http://www.ltz.se **Circ:** 14300
Nyhetschef: Ulrica Dahlqvist; **Redaktör:**
Solbrith Eidenby; **Nyhetschef:** Lasse
Ljungmark; **Nyhetschef:** Alexandra Westerlund
Karlsson; **Chefredaktör & Ansvarig utgivare:**
Viktoria Winberg
Language (s): Swedish; Full Page Colour:
25056.00
Currency: Sweden Kronor
NEWSPAPER

Länstidningen Östersund ~ Berg
Editorial: Kyrkgatan 52, Östersund 831 89.
T: 46 687 515 20 **E:** jonas.solberger@ltz.se
W: http://www.ltz.se **Circ:** 19100
Redaktör: Sandra Högman
Language (s): Swedish
NEWSPAPER

Länstidningen Östersund ~ Krokom
Editorial: Biblioteksgatan 15, Östersund 831
89. **T:** 46 63 15 55 29 **E:** jan.andersson@ltz.se
W: http://www.ltz.se **Circ:** 19100
Language (s): Swedish
NEWSPAPER

Länstidningen Östersund ~
Strömsund
Editorial: Box 56, Besöksadress: Sventegatan
5, Strömsund 833 21. **T:** 46 670 61 45 50
W: http://www.ltz.se **Circ:** 19100
Language (s): Swedish
NEWSPAPER

Länstidningen Södertälje
Owner: Länstidningen, Södertälje AB
Editorial: Södertälje 151 82.
T: 46 8 550 921 00 **E:** redaktion@lt.se
W: http://www.lt.se **Circ:** 14700
Redigerare: Gert Fundin; **Redigerare:** Jessica
Jeppson; **Ansvarig utgivare:** Thelma Kimsjö;

Nyhetschef: Thomas Leitner; **Redaktör:** Anna Levin; **Nyhetschef:** Monika Nilsson Lysell
Language (s): Swedish; Full Page Colour: 32640.00
Currency: Sweden Kronor
NEWSPAPER

Länstidningen Södertälje ~ Järna
Editorial: Storgatan 1, Järna 153 30.
T: 46 8 551 708 40 **E:** redaktion@lt.se
W: http://www.lt.se **Circ:** 16300
Language (s): Swedish
NEWSPAPER

Länstidningen Södertälje ~ Nykvarn
Editorial: Box 20, Nykvarn 155 21.
T: 46 8 552 409 50 **E:** redaktion@lt.se
W: http://www.lt.se **Circ:** 16300
Redaktör: Mathias Jonsson
Language (s): Swedish
NEWSPAPER

Lerums Tidning
Editorial: Göteborgsvägen 3, Lerum 443 30.
T: 46 302 510 50
E: redaktion@lerumstidning.com
W: http://www.lerumstidning.com
Freq: Weekly; **Circ:** 18600 Pub Statement
Redaktionschef: Christina Lundin; **Ansvarig utgivare:** Bengt Michelsen
Language (s): Swedish; Full Page Colour: 17300.00
Currency: Sweden Kronor
NEWSPAPER

Limhamns-Tidningen
Owner: Karl-Heinz Forsberg
Editorial: Järnvägsgatan 74, Limhamn 216 16.
T: 46 40 15 74 77
E: malmotidningen@telia.com
Freq: Quarterly; **Circ:** 15000 Pub Statement
Ansvarig utgivare: Karl-Heinz Forsberg
Language (s): Swedish
NEWSPAPER

Linköpings Tidning
Owner: Swepress
Editorial: Badhusgatan 8, Linköping 582 22.
T: 46 13 25 32 02
E: tommy.pettersson@linkopingstidning.se
W: http://www.linkopingstidning.se
Circ: 12000
Ansvarig utgivare & VD: Bengt Ingemarsson; **Redaktör:** Tommy Pettersson
Language (s): Swedish; Full Page Colour: 52080.00
Currency: Sweden Kronor
NEWSPAPER

Linköpings-Posten
Owner: Kipson AB
Editorial: Badhusgatan 8, Linköping 582 22.
T: 46 13 25 32 00
E: redaktion@linkopingsposten.se
W: http://www.linkopingsposten.se
Freq: Weekly; **Circ:** 79100
Layoutansvarig: Emelie Nilsson; **Redaktionschef:** Alf Wesik
Language (s): Swedish; Full Page Colour: 34560.00
Currency: Sweden Kronor
NEWSPAPER

Ljusnan
Owner: Hälsingetidningar AB
Editorial: Box 1059, Bollnäs 821 12.
T: 46 278 275 00 **E:** nyhetschefen@ljusnan.se
W: http://www.helahalsingland.se **Circ:** 13000
Redaktör: Siv Hedebrink; **Nyhetschef:** Malena Hilding; **Ansvarig utgivare & Chefredaktör:** Gunilla Kindstrand
Language (s): Swedish; Full Page Colour: 20160.00
Currency: Sweden Kronor
NEWSPAPER

Ljusnan ~ Edsbyn
Editorial: Edsbyn 828 32. **T:** 46 271 771 511
E: redaktion@ljusnan.se
W: http://www.ljusnan.se **Circ:** 15200
Redaktionschef: Klas-Göran Sannerman
Language (s): Swedish
NEWSPAPER

Lokaltidningen Alvesta
Editorial: Fabriksgatan 21, Alvesta 342 32.
T: 46 472 440 30
E: redaktion.alvesta@lokaltidningen.se
W: http://www.lokaltidningen.se **Circ:** 12285
Redaktör: Thomas Edgren
Language (s): Swedish; Full Page Colour: 17827.00
Currency: Sweden Kronor
NEWSPAPER

Lokaltidningen Ängelholm
Owner: Politikens Lokalaviser
Editorial: Storgatan 40, Ängelholm 262 43.
T: 46 431 881 22
E: redaktion.angelholm@lokaltidningen.se
W: http://www.lokaltidningen.se **Circ:** 20200
Chef: Alex Nielsen; **Redigerare:** Mattias Svantesson
Language (s): Swedish; Full Page Colour: 21500.00
Currency: Sweden Kronor
NEWSPAPER

Lokaltidningen Backa/Kärra; Tidningenbk.se
Owner: Martinsson Säljmedia
Editorial: Martinsson Säljmedia, Box 87, Hisings Kärra 425 02. **T:** 46 31 57 50 39
E: redaktion@tidningenbk.se
W: http://www.tidningenbk.se **Circ:** 30000
Ansvarig utgivare: Kurt Martinsson; **Ansvarig utgivare:** Leif Martinsson
Language (s): Swedish
NEWSPAPER

Lokaltidningen Halmstad
Owner: Politikens Lokalaviser
Editorial: Syskonhamnsgatan 4, Halmstad 302 45. **T:** 46 35 17 16 91
E: nicole.blomstrand@lokaltidningen.se
W: http://halmstad.lokaltidningen.se
Circ: 35095
Redaktör: Martin Bergström; **Redigerare:** Mattias Svantesson; **Redaktionschef:** Lotta Wahlqvist
Language (s): Swedish
NEWSPAPER

Lokaltidningen Hässleholm
Owner: Politikens Lokalaviser
Editorial: Frykholmsgatan 17, Hässleholm 281 31. **T:** 46 451 38 61 51
E: redaktion.hassleholm@lokaltidningen.se
W: http://www.lokaltidningen.se **Circ:** 25600
Language (s): Swedish; Full Page Colour: 21500.00
Currency: Sweden Kronor
NEWSPAPER

Lokaltidningen Helsingborg
Owner: Politikens Lokalaviser
Editorial: Möllegränden 8, Helsingborg 252 23. **T:** 46 42 19 47 00
E: redaktion.hbg@lokaltidningen.se
W: http://helsingborg.lokaltidningen.se
Freq: Weekly; **Circ:** 62500
Nyhetschef: Anders Sjölin
Language (s): Swedish; Full Page Colour: 40158.00
Currency: Sweden Kronor
NEWSPAPER

Lokaltidningen Höganäs
Owner: Politikens Lokalaviser
Editorial: Bruksgatan 18, Helsingborg 252 23.
T: 46 42 19 47 00
E: redaktion.hoganas@lokaltidningen.se
W: http://www.lokaltidningen.se **Circ:** 13100
Nyhetschef: Anders Sjölin; **Redigerare:** Mattias Svantesson
Language (s): Swedish; Full Page Colour: 16490.00
Currency: Sweden Kronor
NEWSPAPER

Lokaltidningen Kävlinge Nya
Owner: Politikens Lokalaviser
Editorial: Mårtensgatan 2, Kävlinge 244 30.
T: 46 46 73 66 60
E: redaktion.kavlingenya@lokaltidningen.se
W: http://www.lokaltidningen.se
Freq: Bi-Weekly; **Circ:** 30000 Pub Statement
Nyhetschef: Sarah Bernshed
Language (s): Swedish; Full Page Colour: 20700.00
Currency: Sweden Kronor
NEWSPAPER

Lokaltidningen Klippan/Perstorp/Bjuv/Åstorp/Örkelljunga
Owner: Politikens Lokalaviser
Editorial: Storgatan 40, Ängelholm 262 43.
T: 46 431 881 22
E: alex.nielsen@lokaltidningen.se
W: http://www.lokaltidningen.se **Circ:** 24800
Redaktör: Linda Lundell; **Chef:** Alex Nielsen
Language (s): Swedish; Full Page Colour: 22160.00
Currency: Sweden Kronor
NEWSPAPER

Lokaltidningen Kristianstad
Owner: Politikens Lokalaviser
Editorial: Tredalagatan 3, Kristianstad 291 34.
T: 46 44 12 74 90
E: redaktion.kristianstad@lokaltidningen.se
W: http://www.lokaltidningen.se **Circ:** 43300
Redaktör: Paola Nordgren; **Redigerare:** Mattias Svantesson
Language (s): Swedish; Full Page Colour: 31800.00
Currency: Sweden Kronor
NEWSPAPER

Lokaltidningen Laholm
Owner: Politikens Lokalaviser
Editorial: Storgatan 40, Ängelholm 262 43.
T: 46 431 881 22
E: martin.bergstrom@lokaltidningen.se
W: http://www.lokaltidningen.se **Circ:** 16500
Redaktör: Martin Bergström; **Chef:** Alex Nielsen; **Chef:** Titti Olsson
Language (s): Swedish; Full Page Colour: 16490.00
Currency: Sweden Kronor
NEWSPAPER

Lokaltidningen Landskrona
Owner: Politikens Lokalaviser
Editorial: Lilla Strandgatan 5 B, Landskrona 261 31. **T:** 46 418 223 50
E: trolle@lokaltidningen.se
W: http://www.lokaltidningen.se **Circ:** 27000
Redigerare: Nina Ganeteg; **Redaktör:** Evelina Olsson; **Chef:** Carl-Gustaf Trolle
Language (s): Swedish; Full Page Colour: 20700.00
Currency: Sweden Kronor
NEWSPAPER

Lokaltidningen Limhamn/Bunkeflo
Owner: Politikens Lokalaviser AS
Editorial: Celsiusgatan 31, Malmo 212 14.
T: 46 40 25 44 50
E: lotta.wahlqvist@lokaltidningen.se
W: http://www.lokaltidningen.se
Freq: Weekly; **Circ:** 13642 Pub Statement
Redaktör: Fredrik Magnusson
Language (s): Swedish; Full Page Colour: 28500.00
Currency: Sweden Kronor
NEWSPAPER

Lokaltidningen Ljungby
Owner: Politikens Lokalaviser A/S
Editorial: Fabriksgatan 21, Alvesta 342 32.
T: 46 472 440 30 **E:** ljungby@lokaltidningen.se
W: http://www.lokaltidningen.se **Circ:** 13900
Language (s): Swedish; Full Page Colour: 17827.00
Currency: Sweden Kronor
NEWSPAPER

Lokaltidningen LommaBladet
Owner: Politikens Lokalaviser
Editorial: Kävlinge 234 30. **T:** 46 46 73 66 60
E: lommabladet@lokaltidningen.se
W: http://lommabladet.lokaltidningen.se
Freq: Bi-Weekly; **Circ:** 28100 Not Audited
Ansvarig utgivare: Lotta Wahlqvist
Language (s): Swedish; Full Page Colour: 20104.00
Currency: Sweden Kronor
NEWSPAPER

Lokaltidningen Lund
Owner: Politikens Lokalaviser
Editorial: Paradisgatan 1, Lund 223 50.
T: 46 46 32 76 54
E: redaktion.lund@lokaltidningen.se
W: http://lund.lokaltidningen.se
Freq: Weekly; **Circ:** 51700
Language (s): Swedish; Full Page Colour: 39485.00
Currency: Sweden Kronor
NEWSPAPER

Lokaltidningen Malmö
Owner: Politikens Lokalaviser AS
Editorial: Celsiusgatan 31, Malmo 212 14.
T: 46 40 25 44 60
E: redaktion.malmo@lokaltidningen.se
W: http://malmo.lokaltidningen.se
Freq: Weekly; **Circ:** 70900
Language (s): Swedish; Full Page Colour: 56144.00
Currency: Sweden Kronor
NEWSPAPER

Lokaltidningen Mellanskåne
Owner: Politikens Lokalaviser
Editorial: Stora torg 2, Eslöv 241 30.
T: 46 413 663 31
E: redaktion.mellanskane@lokaltidningen.se
W: http://www.lokaltidningen.se **Circ:** 29100
Ansvarig utgivare: Lotta Wahlqvist
Language (s): Swedish; Full Page Colour: 21000.00
Currency: Sweden Kronor
NEWSPAPER

Lokaltidningen Östra Malmö
Owner: Politikens Lokalaviser AS
Editorial: Celsiusgatan 31, Malmo 212 14.
T: 46 40 25 44 60
E: redaktion.malmo@lokaltidningen.se
W: http://www.lokaltidningen.se
Freq: Weekly; **Circ:** 19589
Redaktör: Markus celander; **Redaktör:** Fredrik Magnusson; **Ansvarig utgivare:** Lotta Wahlqvist
Language (s): Swedish; Full Page Colour: 20963.00
Currency: Sweden Kronor
NEWSPAPER

Lokaltidningen Simrishamn
Editorial: Västerleden 43, Ystad 271 44.
T: 46 411 779 40
E: anna.naxelius@lokaltidningen.se
W: http://www.simrishamn.lokaltidningen.se
Circ: 10000
Redaktör: Caroline Stenbäck
Language (s): Swedish
NEWSPAPER

Lokaltidningen Trelleborg
Owner: Politikens Lokalaviser
Editorial: Malmo 212 14. **T:** 46 4 025 44 60
E: redaktion.trelleborg@lokaltidningen.se
W: http://trelleborg.lokaltidningen.se
Circ: 34600
Language (s): Swedish; Full Page Colour: 16600.00
Currency: Sweden Kronor
NEWSPAPER

Lokaltidningen Västbo Andan
Owner: Västbo Andan AB
Editorial: Torggatan 10, Gislaved 332 25.
T: 46 371 58 91 50
E: redaktion.gislaved@lokaltidningen.se
W: http://www.vastboandan.se
Freq: Weekly; **Circ:** 24400 RS
Language (s): Swedish; Full Page Colour: 18720.00
Currency: Sweden Kronor
NEWSPAPER

Lokaltidningen Vellinge - Näset
Editorial: Box 100, Trelleborg 231 22.
T: 46 410 35 15 10
E: redaktion.vellinge@lokaltidningen.se
W: http://www.lokaltidningen.se **Circ:** 13200
Nyhetschef: Fredrik Magnusson; **Ansvarig utgivare:** Lotta Wahlqvist
Language (s): Swedish; Full Page Colour: 14235.00
Currency: Sweden Kronor
NEWSPAPER

Lokaltidningen Ystad
Owner: Politikens Lokalaviser
Editorial: Västerleden 43, Ystad 271 44.
T: 46 411 779 40
E: lotta.wahlqvist@lokaltidningen.se
W: http://www.lokaltidningen.se **Circ:** 13813
Nyhetschef: Lotta Dahlsjö
Language (s): Swedish
NEWSPAPER

Magazinet
Owner: Bengt Ingmarsson
Editorial: Storgatan 1, Växjo 352 33.
T: 46 470 71 99 50
E: lena.olofsson@magazinet.nu
W: http://www.magazinet.nu
Freq: Weekly; **Circ:** 50000
Redkationschef: Lena Olofsson
Language (s): Swedish; Full Page Colour: 29760.00
Currency: Sweden Kronor
NEWSPAPER

Mälaröarnas Nyheter
Owner: Mälarö Media AB
Editorial: Box 100, Ekerö 178 22.
T: 46 8560 358 00
E: red@malaroarnasnyheter.se
W: http://www.malaro.com
Freq: Bi-Weekly; **Circ:** 11700 Pub Statement
Redaktör: Lo Bäcklinder; **Redaktör:** Ewa Linnros; **Ansvarig utgivare:** Laila Westerberg
Language (s): Swedish; Full Page Colour: 22800.00
Currency: Sweden Kronor
NEWSPAPER

Malmötidningen
Owner: Karl-Heinz Forsberg
Editorial: Järnvägsgatan 74, Limhamn 216 16.
T: 46 40 15 74 77
E: malmotidningen@telia.com
Freq: Bi-Monthly; **Circ:** 40000 Pub Statement
Redaktör: Ingrid Andersson; **Ansvarig utgivare:** Karl-Heinz Forsberg
Language (s): Swedish
NEWSPAPER

Mariestads-Tidningen
Owner: Nya Wermlands-Tidningen AB
Editorial: Box 242, Mariestad 542 23.
T: 46 501 687 00
E: redaktion@mariestadstidningen.se
W: http://www.mariestadstidningen.se
Circ: 13300
Ansvarig utgivare, Chefredaktör: Karin Eriksson
Language (s): Swedish; Full Page Colour: 26100.00
Currency: Sweden Kronor
DAILY NEWSPAPER

Mariestads-Tidningen ~ Hova
Editorial: Hova 548 32. **T:** 46 506 74 79 65
E: hova@mariestadstidningen.se
W: http://www.tsl-mt.se **Circ:** 13300
Language (s): Swedish
NEWSPAPER

Mariestads-Tidningen ~ Töreboda
Editorial: Box 87, Töreboda 545 22.
T: 46 506 711 40
E: toreboda@mariestadstidningen.se
W: http://www.mariestadstidningen.se
Circ: 13300
Language (s): Swedish
NEWSPAPER

Markbladet
Owner: Markbladet AB
Editorial: Box 113, Kinna 511 21.
T: 46 320 20 91 40
E: redaktion@markbladet.se
W: http://www.markbladet.se
Freq: Weekly; **Circ:** 23000 Pub Statement
Redaktör: Per Niklasson
Language (s): Swedish; Full Page Colour: 21700.00
Currency: Sweden Kronor
NEWSPAPER

Masen
Editorial: Box 220, Mora 792 24.
T: 46 250 713 85 W: http://www.masen.se
Freq: Weekly; **Circ:** 16500 Pub Statement
Ansvarig utgivare: Hans Nyström
Language (s): Swedish
NEWSPAPER

Maskinkontakt
Owner: Maskinkontakt
Editorial: Gustaf V:s väg 11, Särö 429 43.
T: 46 31 68 00 05 **E:** info@maskinkontakt.se
W: http://maskinkontakt.se
Ansvarig utgivare: Björn Johansson
Language (s): Swedish
NEWSPAPER

Mera Linköping
Editorial: Stohagsgatan 6 A, Norrköping 601 83 **E:** redaktion@meralinkoping.se
W: http://www.meralinkoping.se/
Freq: Weekly; **Circ:** 73000
Redaktionschef & Ansvarig utgivare: Mikael Sundgren
Language (s): Swedish
NEWSPAPER

Metro
Owner: Tidnings AB Metro
Editorial: Besöksadress: Ringvägen 52, Postadress: Box 45075, Stockholm 104 30.
T: 46 8 402 20 30 **E:** redaktionen@metro.se
W: http://www.metro.se **Circ:** 305200
Nyhetschef: Josefin Berglund;
Utbildningsredaktör - AllaStudier.se: Johanna Boussard; **Krogrecensent:** Karin Ericson;
Nyhetschef: Kristoffer Rengfors
Language (s): Swedish; Full Page Colour: 208679.00
Currency: Sweden Kronor
NEWSPAPER

Metro Värmland
Owner: Tidnings AB Metro / Värmlands Folkblad
Editorial: Värmlands Folkblad, Säterivägen 7, Karlstad 653 41. **T:** 46 54 17 55 00
E: redaktion@metrovarmland.se
W: http://www.metro.se **Circ:** 15000
Language (s): Swedish
NEWSPAPER

Metro Värmland; Weekend
Owner: Tidnings AB Metro / Värmlands Folkblad
Editorial: Värmlands Folkblad, Säterivägen 7, Karlstad 653 41. **T:** 46 54 17 55 00
E: redaktionen@metro.se
W: http://www.metro.se
Freq: Monthly; **Circ:** 70000
Chefredaktör- Värmlands Folkblad: Peter Franke
Language (s): Swedish
NEWSPAPER

Mitt i Botkyrka Salem
Owner: Lokaltidningen Mitt i Stockholm AB
Editorial: Box 47309, Stockholm 100 74.
T: 46 8 550 551 23 **E:** botkyrka@mitti.se
W: http://www.mitti.se
Freq: Weekly; **Circ:** 39700 Not Audited
Ansvarig utgivare: Niclas Breimar;
Nyhetschef: Camilla Moestedt
Language (s): Swedish; Full Page Colour: 26168.00
Currency: Sweden Kronor
NEWSPAPER

Mitt i Bromma
Owner: Lokaltidningen Mitt i Stockholm AB
Editorial: Box 47309, Stockholm 100 74.
T: 46 8 550 551 72 **E:** bromma@mitti.se
W: http://www.mitti.se
Freq: Weekly; **Circ:** 33300 Not Audited
Ansvarig utgivare: Niclas Breimar;
Nyhetschef: Jakob Larsson
Language (s): Swedish; Full Page Colour: 23184.00
Currency: Sweden Kronor
NEWSPAPER

Mitt i Danderyd
Owner: Lokaltidningen Mitt i Stockholm AB
Editorial: Box 47309, Stockholm 100 74.
T: 46 8 550 550 44 **E:** danderyd@mitti.se
W: http://www.mitti.se
Freq: Weekly; **Circ:** 13300 Not Audited
Ansvarig utgivare: Niclas Breimar
Language (s): Swedish; Full Page Colour: 17781.00
Currency: Sweden Kronor
NEWSPAPER

Mitt i Haninge
Owner: Lokaltidningen Mitt i Stockholm AB
Editorial: Årstaängsvägen 11, 6 tr. Marievik, Stockholm 100 74. **T:** 46 8 550 551 05
E: haninge@mitti.se **W:** http://www.mitti.se
Freq: Weekly; **Circ:** 33900 Not Audited
Chefredaktör & Ansvarig utgivare: Niclas Breimar
Language (s): Swedish; Full Page Colour: 28519.00
Currency: Sweden Kronor
NEWSPAPER

Mitt i Huddinge
Owner: Lokaltidningen Mitt i Stockholm AB
Editorial: Box 47309, Stockholm 100 74.
T: 46 8 550 551 25 **E:** huddinge@mitti.se
W: http://www.mitti.se
Freq: Weekly; **Circ:** 41700 Not Audited
Ansvarig utgivare: Niclas Breimar
Language (s): Swedish; Full Page Colour: 26853.00
Currency: Sweden Kronor
NEWSPAPER

Mitt i Järfälla
Owner: Lokaltidningen Mitt i Stockholm AB
Editorial: Box 47309, Stockholm 100 74.
T: 46 8 550 551 87 **E:** jarfalla@mitti.se
W: http://www.mitti.se
Freq: Weekly; **Circ:** 29100 Not Audited
Ansvarig utgivare: Niclas Breimar
Language (s): Swedish; Full Page Colour: 22418.00
Currency: Sweden Kronor
NEWSPAPER

Mitt i Kista
Owner: Lokaltidningen Mitt i Stockholm AB
Editorial: Box 47309, Stockholm 100 74.
T: 46 8 550 550 44 **E:** kista@mitti.se
W: http://www.mitti.se
Freq: Weekly; **Circ:** 15000 Not Audited
Ansvarig utgivare: Niclas Breimar;
Nyhetschef: Maria Stomrud
Language (s): Swedish; Full Page Colour: 18386.00
Currency: Sweden Kronor
NEWSPAPER

Mitt i Kungsholmen
Owner: Lokaltidningen Mitt i Stockholm AB
Editorial: Box 47309, Stockholm 100 74.
T: 46 8 550 550 78 **E:** kungsholmen@mitti.se
W: http://www.mitti.se **Circ:** 39400
Nyhetschef: Jakob Larsson
Language (s): Swedish; Full Page Colour: 19999.00
Currency: Sweden Kronor
NEWSPAPER

Mitt i Lidingö
Owner: Lokaltidningen Mitt i Stockholm AB
Editorial: Box 47309, Stockholm 100 74.
T: 46 8 550 550 72 **E:** lidingo@mitti.se
W: http://www.mitti.se **Circ:** 23800
Ansvarig utgivare: Niclas Breimar;
Nyhetschef: Jakob Larsson; **Nyhetschef:** Maria Stomrud
Language (s): Swedish; Full Page Colour: 20120.00
Currency: Sweden Kronor
NEWSPAPER

Mitt i Nacka
Owner: Lokaltidningen Mitt i Stockholm AB
Editorial: Box 47309, Stockholm 100 74.
T: 46 8 550 550 28 **E:** nacka@mitti.se
W: http://www.mitti.se
Freq: Weekly; **Circ:** 37900 Not Audited
Ansvarig utgivare: Niclas Breimar
Language (s): Swedish; Full Page Colour: 25402.00
Currency: Sweden Kronor
NEWSPAPER

Mitt i Östermalm
Owner: Lokaltidningen Mitt i Stockholm AB
Editorial: Box 47309, Stockholm 100 74.
T: 46 8 550 550 76 **E:** ostermalm@mitti.se
W: http://www.mitti.se
Freq: Weekly; **Circ:** 44400 RS
Ansvarig utgivare: Niclas Breimar;
Nyhetschef: Jakob Larsson; **Nyhetschef:** Fredrik Söderberg Bruce
Language (s): Swedish; Full Page Colour: 19918.00
Currency: Sweden Kronor
NEWSPAPER

Mitt i Södermalm
Owner: Lokaltidningen Mitt i Stockholm AB
Editorial: Årstaängsvägen 11, 6 tr, Marlevik, Box 47309, Stockholm 100 74.
T: 46 8 550 550 00 **E:** sodermalm@mitti.se
W: http://www.mitti.se
Freq: Weekly; **Circ:** 67300
Nyhetschef: Jakob Larsson
Language (s): Swedish; Full Page Colour: 29662.00
Currency: Sweden Kronor
NEWSPAPER

Mitt i Söderort A
Owner: Lokaltidningen Mitt i Stockholm AB
Editorial: Box 47309, Stockholm 100 74.
T: 46 8 550 551 29 **E:** soderort@mitti.se
W: http://www.mitti.se
Freq: Weekly; **Circ:** 45900
Ansvarig utgivare: Niclas Breimar; **Redaktör:** Carl Godani
Language (s): Swedish; Full Page Colour: 26351.00
Currency: Sweden Kronor
NEWSPAPER

Mitt i Söderort B
Owner: Lokaltidningen Mitt i Stockholm AB
Editorial: Box 47309, Stockholm 100 74.
T: 46 8 550 551 29 **E:** soderort@mitti.se
W: http://www.mitti.se
Freq: Weekly; **Circ:** 47500 Not Audited
Ansvarig utgivare: Niclas Breimar; **Redaktör:** Carl Godani
Language (s): Swedish; Full Page Colour: 26934.00
Currency: Sweden Kronor
NEWSPAPER

Mitt i Söderort C
Owner: Lokaltidningen Mitt i Stockholm AB
Editorial: Box 47309, Stockholm 100 74.
T: 46 8 550 551 30 **E:** soderort@mitti.se
W: http://www.mitti.se
Freq: Weekly; **Circ:** 14800 Not Audited
Ansvarig utgivare: Niclas Breimar; **Redaktör:** Eva Cloarec
Language (s): Swedish; Full Page Colour: 19112.00
Currency: Sweden Kronor
NEWSPAPER

Mitt i söderort D
Owner: Lokaltidningen Mitt i Stockholm AB
Editorial: Box 47309, Stockholm 100 74.
T: 46 8 550 551 30 **E:** soderort@mitti.se
W: http://www.mitti.se
Freq: Weekly; **Circ:** 26100 Not Audited
Ansvarig utgivare: Niclas Breimar; **Redaktör:** Eva Cloarec; **Nyhetschef:** Katarina Linde
Language (s): Swedish; Full Page Colour: 21612.00
Currency: Sweden Kronor
NEWSPAPER

Mitt i söderort E
Owner: Lokaltidningen Mitt i Stockholm AB
Editorial: Box 47309, Stockholm 100 74.
T: 46 8 550 551 71 **E:** soderort@mitti.se
W: http://www.mitti.se **Circ:** 22000
Ansvarig utgivare: Niclas Breimar; **Redaktör:** Eva Cloarec
Language (s): Swedish; Full Page Colour: 20362.00
Currency: Sweden Kronor

Mitt i Södra Roslagen
Owner: Lokaltidningen Mitt i Stockholm AB
Editorial: Box 47309, Stockholm 100 74.
T: 46 8 550 550 00 **E:** sodraroslagen@mitti.se
W: http://www.mitti.se
Freq: Weekly; **Circ:** 22900 Not Audited
Ansvarig utgivare: Niclas Breimar;
Nyhetschef: Niclas Carron
Language (s): Swedish; Full Page Colour: 20604.00
Currency: Sweden Kronor
NEWSPAPER

Mitt i Sollentuna
Owner: Lokaltidningen Mitt i Stockholm AB
Editorial: Box 47309, Stockholm 100 74.
T: 46 8 550 550 89 **E:** sollentuna@mitti.se
W: http://www.mitti.se
Freq: Weekly; **Circ:** 27700 Not Audited
Ansvarig utgivare: Niclas Breimar;
Nyhetschef: Niclas Carron
Language (s): Swedish; Full Page Colour: 21692.00
Currency: Sweden Kronor
NEWSPAPER

Mitt i Solna
Owner: Lokaltidningen Mitt i Stockholm AB
Editorial: Box 47309, Stockholm 100 74.
T: 46 8 550 550 92 **E:** solna@mitti.se
W: http://www.mitti.se
Freq: Weekly; **Circ:** 38200 Not Audited
Ansvarig utgivare: Niclas Breimar
Language (s): Swedish; Full Page Colour: 25684.00
Currency: Sweden Kronor
NEWSPAPER

Mitt i Sundbyberg
Owner: Lokaltidningen Mitt i Stockholm AB
Editorial: Box 47309, Stockholm 100 74.
T: 46 8 550 550 91 **E:** sundbyberg@mitti.se
W: http://www.mitti.se
Freq: Weekly; **Circ:** 20000 Not Audited
Ansvarig utgivare: Niclas Breimar;
Nyhetschef: Jakob Larsson
Language (s): Swedish; Full Page Colour: 19636.00
Currency: Sweden Kronor
NEWSPAPER

Mitt i Täby
Owner: Lokaltidningen Mitt i Stockholm AB
Editorial: Box 47309, Stockholm 100 74.
T: 46 8 550 550 93 **E:** taby@mitti.se
W: http://www.mitti.se
Freq: Weekly; **Circ:** 27900 Not Audited
Ansvarig utgivare: Niclas Breimar;
Nyhetschef: Niclas Carron
Language (s): Swedish; Full Page Colour: 23144.00
Currency: Sweden Kronor
NEWSPAPER

Mitt i Tensta Rinkeby
Owner: Lokaltidningen Mitt i Stockholm AB
Editorial: Box 47309, Stockholm 100 74.
T: 46 8 550 550 73 **E:** tensta@mitti.se
W: http://www.mitti.se **Circ:** 12800
Ansvarig utgivare: Niclas Breimar;
Nyhetschef: Jakob Larsson
Language (s): Swedish; Full Page Colour: 17459.00
Currency: Sweden Kronor
NEWSPAPER

Mitt i Tyresö
Owner: Lokaltidningen Mitt i Stockholm AB
Editorial: Box 47309, Stockholm 100 74.
T: 46 8 550 550 35 **E:** tyreso@mitti.se
W: http://www.mitti.se
Freq: Weekly; **Circ:** 19200 Not Audited
Ansvarig utgivare: Niclas Breimar
Language (s): Swedish; Full Page Colour: 20120.00
Currency: Sweden Kronor
NEWSPAPER

Mitt i Upplands Väsby
Owner: Lokaltidningen Mitt i Stockholm AB
Editorial: Box 47309, Stockholm 100 74.
T: 46 8 550 550 90 **E:** upplandsvasby@mitti.se
W: http://www.mitti.se
Freq: Weekly; **Circ:** 18300 Not Audited
Ansvarig utgivare: Niclas Breimar;
Nyhetschef: Niclas Carron
Language (s): Swedish; Full Page Colour: 19797.00
Currency: Sweden Kronor
NEWSPAPER

Mitt i Upplands-Bro
Owner: Lokaltidningen Mitt i Stockholm AB
Editorial: Box 47309, Stockholm 100 74.
T: 46 8 550 550 00 **E:** upplandsbro@mitti.se

(Stomrud)
Language (s): Swedish; Full Page Colour: 20120.00
Currency: Sweden Kronor
NEWSPAPER

W: http://www.mitti.se
Freq: Weekly; **Circ:** 10300 Not Audited
Ansvarig utgivare: Niclas Breimar
Language (s): Swedish; Full Page Colour: 16934.00
Currency: Sweden Kronor
NEWSPAPER

Mitt i Vallentuna
Owner: Lokaltidningen Mitt i Stockholm AB
Editorial: Box 47309, Stockholm 100 74.
T: 46 8 550 550 81 **E:** vallentuna@mitti.se
W: http://www.mitti.se
Freq: Weekly; **Circ:** 12100 RS
Ansvarig utgivare: Niclas Breimar
Language (s): Swedish; Full Page Colour: 17338.00
Currency: Sweden Kronor
NEWSPAPER

Mitt i Värmdö
Owner: Lokaltidningen Mitt i Stockholm AB
Editorial: Box 47309, Stockholm 100 74.
T: 46 8 550 550 26 **E:** varmdo@mitti.se
W: http://www.mitti.se
Freq: Weekly; **Circ:** 17800 Not Audited
Ansvarig utgivare: Niclas Breimar
Language (s): Swedish; Full Page Colour: 19958.00
Currency: Sweden Kronor
NEWSPAPER

Mitt i Vasastan
Owner: Lokaltidningen Mitt i Stockholm AB
Editorial: Box 47309, Stockholm 100 74.
T: 46 8 550 550 79 **E:** vasastan@mitti.se
W: http://www.mitti.se **Circ:** 39600
Ansvarig utgivare: Niclas Breimar;
Nyhetschef: Fredrik Söderberg Bruce
Language (s): Swedish; Full Page Colour: 18749.00
Currency: Sweden Kronor
NEWSPAPER

Mitt i Västerort
Owner: Lokaltidningen Mitt i Stockholm AB
Editorial: Box 47309, Stockholm 100 74.
T: 46 8 550 550 71 **E:** vasterort@mitti.se
W: http://www.mitti.se
Freq: Weekly; **Circ:** 37300 Not Audited
Ansvarig utgivare: Niclas Breimar;
Nyhetschef: Jakob Larsson
Language (s): Swedish; Full Page Colour: 24837.00
Currency: Sweden Kronor
NEWSPAPER

Mora Tidning
Owner: Dalarnas Tidningar AB
Editorial: Strandgatan 28, Mora 792 30.
T: 46 250 59 24 20 **E:** mt.red@dt.se
W: http://www.dt.se **Circ:** 11100
Nyhetschef: Berit Olars; **Redaktionschef:** Ewa Wirén
Language (s): Swedish; Full Page Colour: 36288.00
Currency: Sweden Kronor
NEWSPAPER

Mora Tidning ~ Älvdalen
Editorial: Box 14, Älvdalen 796 21.
T: 46 251 103 01 **E:** mt.red@dt.se
W: http://www.dt.se **Circ:** 12300
Language (s): Swedish
NEWSPAPER

Mora Tidning ~ Orsa
Editorial: Box 113, Orsa 794 21.
T: 46 250 401 67 **E:** mt.red@dt.se
W: http://www.dt.se **Circ:** 12300
Language (s): Swedish
NEWSPAPER

Nacka Värmdö Posten
Owner: Nackaposten AB
Editorial: Värmdövägen 205, Box 735, Nacka 131 24. **T:** 46 8 555 266 20 **E:** red@nvp.se
W: http://www.nvp.se
Freq: Weekly; **Circ:** 71800 RS
Chefredaktör & Ansvarig utgivare: Anders Milde
Language (s): Swedish; Full Page Colour: 30190.00
Currency: Sweden Kronor
NEWSPAPER

Nerikes Allehanda
Owner: Tidningsbolaget Promedia i Mellansverige AB
Editorial: Norra Strandgatan 5, Orebro 701 92.
T: 46 19 15 50 00 **E:** nyhet@na.se
W: http://www.na.se **Circ:** 60700
Nyhetschef och stf ansvarig utgivare: Angela Hanagarth; **Nyhetschef:** Ida Johansson;
Redaktör: Helena Sträng
Language (s): Swedish; Full Page Colour: 74880.00
Currency: Sweden Kronor
NEWSPAPER

Nerikes Allehanda ~ Askersund
Owner: Tidningsbolaget Promedia i Mellansverige AB
Editorial: Sundsbrogatan 24, Askersund 696 39. **T:** 46 19 15 54 14 **E:** askersund@na.se
W: http://na.se/nyheter/askersund
Freq: Daily; **Circ:** 60700
Language (s): Swedish; Full Page Colour: 29232.00
Currency: Sweden Kronor
NEWSPAPER

Nerikes Allehanda ~ Hallsberg
Owner: Tidningsbolaget Promedia i Mellansverige AB
Editorial: Västra Storgatan 16, Hallsberg 694 30. **T:** 46 19 15 54 12 **E:** hallsberg@na.se
W: http://na.se/nyheter/hallsberg
Freq: Daily; **Circ:** 60700
Language (s): Swedish; Full Page Colour: 74880.00
Currency: Sweden Kronor
NEWSPAPER

Nerikes Allehanda ~ Kumla
Owner: Tidningsbolaget Promedia iMellansverige AB
Editorial: Trädgårdsgatan 9, Kumla 692 31.
T: 46 19 15 54 42 **E:** kumla@na.se
W: http://na.se/nyheter/kumla **Circ:** 61300
Language (s): Swedish
NEWSPAPER

Nerikes Allehanda ~ Laxå
Owner: Tidningsbolaget Promedia i Mellansverige AB
Editorial: Järnvägsgatan 7, Laxå 695 30.
T: 46 19 15 54 21 **E:** laxa@na.se
W: http://na.se/nyheter/laxa
Freq: Daily; **Circ:** 60700
Language (s): Swedish; Full Page Colour: 29232.00
Currency: Sweden Kronor
NEWSPAPER

Nerikes Allehanda ~ Lekeberg
Owner: Tidningsbolaget Promedia i Mellansverige AB
Editorial: Storgatan 20, Fjugesta 716 30.
T: 46 19 15 54 27 **E:** fjugesta@na.se
W: http://na.se/nyheter/lekeberg
Freq: Daily; **Circ:** 60700
Language (s): Swedish; Full Page Colour: 29232.00
Currency: Sweden Kronor
NEWSPAPER

Nerikes Allehanda ~ Nora
Owner: Tidningsbolaget Promedia i Mellansverige AB
Editorial: Prästgatan 7, Nora 713 31.
T: 46 19 15 54 52 **E:** nora@na.se
W: http://na.se/nyheter/nora
Freq: Daily; **Circ:** 60700
Language (s): Swedish; Full Page Colour: 25872.00
Currency: Sweden Kronor
NEWSPAPER

Norra Halland
Owner: Ortstidningen Norra Halland
Editorial: Box 10244, Kungsbacka 434 24.
T: 46 300 107 95
E: redaktionen@norrahalland.se
W: http://www.norrahalland.se **Circ:** 12000
Nyhetschef: Kristian Alm; **Nyhetschef:** Christina Forlin
Language (s): Swedish; Full Page Colour: 25000.00
Currency: Sweden Kronor
NEWSPAPER

Norra Skåne
Owner: Skånska Dagbladet, AB
Editorial: Väpnaregatan 6, Hässleholm 281 50.
T: 46 451 74 50 00 **E:** nyhetschefen@nsk.se
W: http://www.nsk.se **Circ:** 20700
Redaktör: Hans Bryngelson; **Chefredaktör & Ansvarig utgivare:** Mimmi Karlsson-Bernfalk;
Redaktör: Carina Koskinen; **Redaktör:** Kristina Larsson; **Redaktör:** Marie Strömberg-Andersson
Language (s): Swedish; Full Page Colour: 32160.00
Currency: Sweden Kronor
NEWSPAPER

Norran
Owner: Stiftelsen Skellefteåpress
Editorial: Kanalgatan 59, Skellefteå 931 32.
T: 46 910 577 00 **E:** nv@norran.se
W: http://www.norran.se **Circ:** 27500
Chefredaktör & Ansvarig utgivare: Lars Andersson; **Ledarskribent:** Mikael Bengtsson;
Nyhetschef: Karin Israelsson
Language (s): Swedish; Full Page Colour: 39718.00
Currency: Sweden Kronor
NEWSPAPER

Norrbottens-Kuriren
Owner: Norrbottens-Kuriren AB
Editorial: Robertsviksgatan 5, Luleå 971 81.
T: 46 920 26 29 03
E: redaktionen@kuriren.com
W: http://www.kuriren.nu **Circ:** 25200
Redaktör: Jackie Bortz; **Chefredaktör & Ansvarig utgivare:** Mats Ehnbom; **Nyhetschef:** Jimmy Landström; **Nyhetschef:** Lotta Sandhammar
Language (s): Swedish; Full Page Colour: 39672.00
Currency: Sweden Kronor
NEWSPAPER

Norrköpings Tidningar
Owner: Erik och Asta Sundins stiftelse
Editorial: Norrköping 601 83.
T: 46 11 20 00 00 **E:** redaktionen@nt.se
W: http://www.nt.se
Freq: Daily; **Circ:** 39500
Redigerare: Lena Jonsson; **Nyhetschef:** Fredrik Lagerqvist; **Ansvarig utgivare:** Anders Nilsson; **Nyhetschef:** Marianne Odelius;
Nyhetschef: Mikael Pihlblad; **Redaktör:** Jan Rådegård; **Konsumentfrågor:** Gun Stenehall;
Redaktionschef: Petra Wetterström
Language (s): Swedish; Full Page Colour: 64998.00
Currency: Sweden Kronor
NEWSPAPER

Norrköpings Tidningar ~ Finspång
Owner: Karl-Ake Bredenberg
Editorial: Bergslagsvägen 6, Finspång 612 21.
T: 46 122 150 02 **E:** finspong@nt.se
W: http://www.nt.se **Circ:** 48900
Language (s): Swedish
NEWSPAPER

Norrköpings Tidningar ~ Söderköping
Editorial: Storgatan 4, Söderköping 614 30.
T: 46 121 100 88 **E:** soderkoping@nt.se
W: http://www.nt.se **Circ:** 48900
Platschef: Henrik Johansson
Language (s): Swedish
NEWSPAPER

Norrköpings Tidningar ~ Valdemarsvik
Editorial: Box 59, Storgatan 9, Valdemarsvik 615 22. **T:** 46 123 514 00
E: valdemarsvik@nt.se **W:** http://www.nt.se
Circ: 48900
Language (s): Swedish
NEWSPAPER

Norrländska Socialdemokraten
Editorial: Luleå 971 83. **T:** 46 920 263 000
E: redaktion@nsd.se **W:** http://www.nsd.se
Freq: Daily; **Circ:** 31000
Redaktör: Ulf Bengtsson; **Nyhetschef:** Ida Folkesson; **Redigerare:** Bodil Resare;
Chefredaktör & Ansvarig utgivare: Kalle Sandhammar; **Redaktionschef:** Tommy Ström;
Redaktör: Jonny Vikström
Language (s): Swedish; Full Page Colour: 35136.00
Currency: Sweden Kronor
NEWSPAPER

Norrländska Socialdemokraten ~ Boden
Editorial: Drottninggatan 21C, Boden 961 35.
T: 46 921 136 20 **E:** redaktion@nsd.se
W: http://www.nsd.se
Freq: Daily; **Circ:** 40000
Language (s): Swedish
NEWSPAPER

Norrländska Socialdemokraten ~ Gällivare
Editorial: Malmbergsvägen 2, Gällivare 982 31. **T:** 46 970 120 90 **E:** redaktion@nsd.se
W: http://www.nsd.se
Freq: Daily; **Circ:** 40000
Language (s): Swedish
NEWSPAPER

Norrländska Socialdemokraten ~ Kalix
Editorial: Box 53, Kalix 952 33.
T: 46 923 659 70 **E:** redaktion@nsd.se
W: http://www.nsd.se **Circ:** 40000
Language (s): Swedish
NEWSPAPER

Norrländska Socialdemokraten ~ Kiruna
Owner: Lennart Håkansson
Editorial: Mangigatan 24 A, Kiruna 981 33.
T: 46 980 121 50 **E:** redaktion@nsd.se
W: http://www.nsd.se
Freq: Daily; **Circ:** 40000
Language (s): Swedish
NEWSPAPER

Norrländska Socialdemokraten ~ Tornedalen
Editorial: Solbacken 26, Hedenäset 957 95.
T: 46 927 303 45 **E:** redaktion@nsd.se
W: http://www.nsd.se **Circ:** 40000
Language (s): Swedish
NEWSPAPER

Norrtelje Tidning
Owner: Norrtelje Tidning AB
Editorial: Norrtälje 761 84. **T:** 46 176 795 00
E: redaktionen@norrteljetidning.se
W: http://www.norrteljetidning.se **Circ:** 14500
Redigerare: Grethel Hjuberger; **Chef:** Monica Linder; **Redaktör:** Sofi Piehl; **Redaktör:** Ann Sjöblom
Language (s): Swedish; Full Page Colour: 36400.00
Currency: Sweden Kronor
NEWSPAPER

Norrtelje Tidning ~ Hallstavik
Editorial: Carl Wahrens väg 26, Hallstavik 763 35. **T:** 46 175 686 75
E: redaktionen@norrteljetidning.se
W: http://www.norrteljetidning.se **Circ:** 14600
Redaktör: Gunilla Flink-Lindström
Language (s): Swedish
NEWSPAPER

Nya Lidköpings-Tidningen
Owner: Nya Lidköpings-Tidningen AB
Editorial: Lidköping 531 81. **T:** 46 510 897 00
E: redaktionen@nlt.se **W:** http://www.nlt.se
Circ: 26400
Redaktör: Urban Arenblad; **Redigerare:** Christoffer Dunälv; **Ansvarig utgivare:** Anders Hörling; **Redigerare:** Anders Järnebrand;
Nyhetschef: Håkan Johansson; **Nyhetschef:** Mats Österman; **Redigerare:** Monica Weihard
Language (s): Swedish; Full Page Colour: 30000.00
Currency: Sweden Kronor
NEWSPAPER

Nya Lidköpings-Tidningen ~ Götene
Editorial: Box 23, Götene 533 21.
T: 46 511 504 78 **E:** gotene.red@nlt.se
W: http://www.nlt.se **Circ:** 26600
Redaktör: Göran Gustafsson
Language (s): Swedish
NEWSPAPER

Nya Lidköpings-Tidningen ~ Grästorp
Editorial: Box 123, Grästorp 467 22.
T: 46 514 105 73 **E:** grastorp.red@nlt.se
Circ: 26600
Language (s): Swedish
NEWSPAPER

Nya Lidköpings-Tidningen ~ Vara
Editorial: Box 53, Vara 534 21.
T: 46 512 109 40 **E:** vara.red@nlt.se
W: http://www.nlt.se **Circ:** 26600
Redaktör: Lillemor Karlin-Flink
Language (s): Swedish
NEWSPAPER

Nya Lidköpings-Tidningen~ Essunga
Editorial: Nossebro. **T:** 46 512 503 30
E: essunga.red@nlt.se
W: http://nlt.se/startsidan/essunga **Circ:** 26600
Redaktör: Börje Andersson
Language (s): Swedish
NEWSPAPER

Nya Wermlands-Tidningen
Owner: Nya Wermlands-Tidningen AB
Editorial: Våxnäsgatan 20, Karlstad 651 02.
T: 46 54 19 90 00 **E:** redaktion@nwt.se
W: http://www.nwt.se **Circ:** 51900
Chefredaktör: Staffan Ander; **Redigerare:** Kent Andersson; **Redigerare:** Claes Bonde;
Nyhetschef / Stf ansvarig utgivare: Kasper Norling; **Nyhetschef:** Olov Öström; **Ansvarig Utgivare:** Mikael Rothsten
Language (s): Swedish; Full Page Colour: 51170.00
Currency: Sweden Kronor
NEWSPAPER

Nya Wermlands-Tidningen ~ Årjäng
Owner: Nya Wermlands-Tidningen AB
Editorial: Storgatan 39, Årjäng 672 30.
T: 46 573 76 10 70 **E:** arjang@nwt.se

W: http://www.nwt.se
Freq: Daily; Circ: 51900
Language (s): Swedish
NEWSPAPER

Nya Wermlands-Tidningen ~ Arvika
Owner: Nya Wermlands-Tidningen AB
Editorial: Magasinsgatan 5, Arvika 671 29.
T: 46 570 71 44 00 E: arvika@nwt.se
W: http://www.nwt.se
Freq: Daily; Circ: 51900
Language (s): Swedish
NEWSPAPER

Nya Wermlands-Tidningen ~ Hagfors
Editorial: Dalavägen 15, Hagfors 683 30.
T: 46 563 79 10 60 W: http://www.nwt.se
Freq: Daily; Circ: 51900
Language (s): Swedish
NEWSPAPER

Nya Wermlands-Tidningen ~ Kristinehamn
Owner: Nya Wermlands-Tidningen AB
Editorial: Kungsgatan 40, Kristinehamn 681
31. T: 46 550 41 25 51
E: kristinehamn@nwt.se W: http://www.nwt.se
Freq: Daily; Circ: 51900
Language (s): Swedish
NEWSPAPER

Nya Wermlands-Tidningen ~ Malung
Owner: Nya Wermlands-Tidningen Ab
Editorial: Lisagatan 32 C, Malung 782 31.
T: 46 280 79 19 90 E: malung@nwt.se
W: http://www.nwt.se
Freq: Daily; Circ: 51900
Language (s): Swedish
NEWSPAPER

Nya Wermlands-Tidningen ~ Sunne
Owner: Nya Wermlands-Tidningen Ab
Editorial: Storgatan 22, Sunne 686 30.
T: 46 565 68 82 15 E: sunne@nwt.se
W: http://www.nwt.se
Freq: Daily; Circ: 51900
Language (s): Swedish
NEWSPAPER

Nya Wermlands-Tidningen ~ Torsby
Owner: Nya Wermlands-Tidningen Ab
Editorial: Järnvägsgatan 10, Torsby 685 30.
T: 46 560 79 10 80 E: torsby@nwt.se
W: http://www.nwt.se
Freq: Daily; Circ: 51900
Language (s): Swedish
NEWSPAPER

Nybro-Extra
Editorial: Box 119, Nybro 382 22.
T: 46 481 161 11 E: info@nybroextra.se
W: http://www.nybroextra.se Circ: 12000
Language (s): Swedish
NEWSPAPER

Offensiv
Owner: Tidskriftsföreningen Offensiv
Editorial: Box 73, Farsta 123 22.
T: 46 8 605 94 00
E: offensiv@socialisterna.org
W: http://www.socialisterna.org
Freq: Weekly; Circ: 2400 Not Audited
Chefredaktör & Ansvarig utgivare: Arne
Johansson
Language (s): Swedish; Full Page Colour:
5000.00
Currency: Sweden Kronor
DAILY NEWSPAPER

Örebroar'n
Owner: GISAB (Gratis tidningar i Sverige AB)
Editorial: Östra Bangatan 26, Orebro 703 61.
T: 46 19 15 53 77 E: redaktion@orebroarn.se
W: http://www.orebroarn.se Circ: 65300
Language (s): Swedish
NEWSPAPER

Örgryte & Härlanda Posten
Owner: Direktpress
Editorial: (c/o Vibergs Foto), Olskrokstorget 6,
Goteborg 416 65 E: redaktionen@ohposten.se
W: http://www.ohposten.se
Freq: Monthly; Circ: 20000 Pub Statement
Ansvarig utgivare: Helene Fasth; Redaktör:
Attila Hein
Language (s): Swedish
NEWSPAPER

Örnsköldsviks Allehanda
Owner: Örnsköldsviks Allehanda
Editorial: Box 110, Örnsköldsvik 891 23.
T: 46 660 29 55 00
E: oaredaktion@allehanda.se
W: http://www.allehanda.se Circ: 17400
Redigerare: Peter Forssell;
Redaktionssekreterare: Anette Jonsson;

Nyhetschef: Marcus Melinder; Ansvarig
utgivare: Jimmie Näslund
Language (s): Swedish; Full Page Colour:
32160.00
Currency: Sweden Kronor
NEWSPAPER

ÖsterlenMagasinet
Owner: Skånemedia AB
Editorial: Storgatan 36A, Simrishamn 272 31.
T: 46 414 179 80
W: http://www.osterlenmagasinet.se
Freq: Weekly; Circ: 20000 Pub Statement
Ansvarig utgivare: Dan Andersson; Platschef:
Anna Bjurnemark
Language (s): Swedish; Full Page Colour:
40000.00
Currency: Sweden Kronor
NEWSPAPER

Östermalmsnytt
Owner: Innerstadspress AB
Editorial: Box 5290, Stockholm 102 46.
T: 46 8 545 870 70 E: info@direktpress.se
W: http://www.ostermalmsnytt.se
Freq: Weekly; Circ: 41700 RS
Redigerare: Joakim Eriksson;
Redigeringsansvarig: Lotta Waller
Language (s): Swedish; Full Page Colour:
17850.00
Currency: Sweden Kronor
NEWSPAPER

Östersunds-Posten
Owner: Östersunds-Postens Tryckeri AB
Editorial: Kyrkgatan 52, Box 720, Östersund
831 28. T: 46 63 16 16 51 E: redaktion@op.se
W: http://www.op.se Circ: 25000
Nyhetschef: Gabrielle Bäckström; Nyhetschef:
Olof Ekerlid; Chefredaktör & Ansvarig
utgivare: Hans Lindeberg; Redaktör- ÖP TV:
Per Lindh
Language (s): Swedish; Full Page Colour:
46992.00
Currency: Sweden Kronor
NEWSPAPER

Östersunds-Posten ~ Härjedalen
Editorial: Tidningen Härjedalen, Dalagatan 1,
Sveg 842 32. T: 46 680 553 90
E: redaktion@op.se
W: http://www.op.se/harjedalen
Freq: Daily; Circ: 25100
Language (s): Swedish
NEWSPAPER

Östgöta Correspondenten
Owner: AB Östgöta Correspondenten
Editorial: Badhusgatan 5, Linköping 581 89.
T: 46 13 280 000 E: nyhet@corren.se
W: http://www.corren.se/ Circ: 46900
Chefredaktör & Ansvarig utgivare: Charlotta
Friborg; Planeringsredaktör: Fredrik Kylberg;
Nyhetsgruppchef: Ewa Nyrinder; Nyhetschef:
Nils Olauson; Editionsredaktör: Therese
Trogen; Redigerare: Mikael Wiik
Language (s): Swedish; Full Page Colour:
68680.00
Currency: Sweden Kronor
NEWSPAPER

Östgötatidningen 3:an
Owner: Lokaltidningen
Editorial: Box 357, Mjölby 595 24.
T: 46 141 472 800
E: redaktion@ostgotatidningen.se
W: http://www.ostgotatidningen.se Circ: 51000
Redaktör: Pernilla Alsén; Chef: Lars-Åke
Pettersson
Language (s): Swedish; Full Page Colour:
23664.00
Currency: Sweden Kronor
NEWSPAPER

Östran / Nyheterna
Owner: Östra Småland AB
Editorial: Box 612, Kalmar 391 26.
T: 46 480 613 00 E: nyhetschefen@ostran.se
W: http://www.ostran.se Circ: 14200
Nyhetschef: Erik Arenius; Redaktionschef &
ansvarig utgivare: Gunilla Persson
Language (s): Swedish; Full Page Colour:
31000.00
Currency: Sweden Kronor
NEWSPAPER

Östran / Nyheterna ~ Borgholm
Owner: Östra Småland AB
Editorial: Storgatan 18, Borgholm 387 31.
T: 46 485 103 40 E: oland@ostran.se
W: http://www.ostrasmaland.se Circ: 11800
Language (s): Swedish
NEWSPAPER

Östran / Nyheterna ~ Emmaboda
Owner: Östra Småland AB

Editorial: Järnvägsgatan 32, Emmaboda 361
30. T: 46 471 104 56 E: emmaboda@ostran.se
W: http://www.ostrasmaland.se Circ: 11800
Language (s): Swedish
NEWSPAPER

Östran / Nyheterna ~ Färjestaden
Owner: Östra Småland AB
Editorial: Storgatan 41, Färjestaden 386 31.
T: 46 485 305 50 E: oland@ostran.se
W: http://www.ostrasmaland.se Circ: 11800
Language (s): Swedish
NEWSPAPER

Östran / Nyheterna ~ Högsby
Owner: Östra Småland AB
Editorial: Storgatan 24, Högsby 579 30.
T: 46 491 202 46 E: hogsby@ostran.se
W: http://www.nyheterna.net Circ: 11800
Language (s): Swedish
NEWSPAPER

Östran / Nyheterna ~ Mönsterås
Owner: Östra Småland AB
Editorial: Storgatan 49, Mönsterås 383 37.
T: 46 499 102 02 E: monsteras@ostran.se
W: http://www.ostrasmaland.se Circ: 11800
Language (s): Swedish
NEWSPAPER

Östran / Nyheterna ~ Nybro
Owner: Östra Småland AB
Editorial: G:a Stationsgatan 4, Nybro 382 23.
T: 46 481 155 52 E: nybro@ostran.se
W: http://www.ostran.se Circ: 17800
Language (s): Swedish
NEWSPAPER

Östran / Nyheterna ~ Torsås
Owner: Östra Småland AB
Editorial: Box 82, Torsås 385 21.
T: 46 481 104 41 E: torsas@ostran.se
W: http://www.ostrasmaland.se Circ: 11800
Language (s): Swedish
NEWSPAPER

Östran / Nyheterna; Insändare
Owner: Östra Småland AB
Editorial: Box 612, Kalmar 391 26.
T: 46 480 613 61 E: insandare@ostran.se
W: http://www.ostrasmaland.se Circ: 11800
Chefredaktör: Ulf Carlsson
Language (s): Swedish
NEWSPAPER

Östran / Nyheterna; Kulturredaktionen
Owner: Östra Småland AB
Editorial: Box 612, Kalmar 391 26.
T: 46 480 613 31
W: http://www.ostrasmaland.se Circ: 17900
Language (s): Swedish
NEWSPAPER

Östran / Nyheterna; Sportredaktionen
Owner: Östra Småland AB
Editorial: Box 612, Kalmar 391 26.
T: 46 480 613 13 E: sporten@ostran.se
W: http://www.ostrasmaland.se Circ: 17900
Language (s): Swedish
NEWSPAPER

Partille Tidning
Owner: W Michelsens Boktryckeri
Editorial: Box 100, Partille 433 33.
T: 46 31 340 24 30
E: redaktion@partilletidning.se
W: http://www.partilletidning.se Circ: 17700
Language (s): Swedish; Full Page Colour:
16845.00
Currency: Sweden Kronor
NEWSPAPER

Piteå-Tidningen
Owner: Piteå-Tidningens AB
Editorial: Box 193, Piteå 941 24.
T: 46 911 645 00
E: redaktionen@pitea-tidningen.se
W: http://www.pitea-tidningen.se Circ: 15900
Nyhetschef: Annika Lahti; Redaktionschef /
Stf ansvarig utgivare: Bengt Larsson;
Ansvarig utgivare: Matti Lilja;
Redaktionssekreterare & Familjeredaktör:
Jan Lundquist
Language (s): Swedish; Full Page Colour:
38592.00
Currency: Sweden Kronor
NEWSPAPER

Sigtunabygden Märsta Tidning
Owner: Upsala Nya Tidning
Editorial: Nymärstagatan 2, Märsta 195 30.
T: 46 8 594 405 70
E: redaktion@sigtunabygden.se
W: http://www.sigtunabygden.se

Freq: Weekly; Circ: 27400 RS
Redaktör: Anna Orring
Language (s): Swedish; Full Page Colour:
20640.00
Currency: Sweden Kronor
NEWSPAPER

Skånska Dagbladet
Owner: Skånska Dagbladet, AB
Editorial: Östergatan 17, Malmo 201 21.
T: 46 40 660 55 00 E: redaktion@skd.se
W: http://www.skanskan.se Circ: 26600
Chefredaktör & Ansvarig utgivare: Lars
Eriksson; Redaktionschef: Pia Lobell;
Frilansande Krönikör: Alice Teodorescu
Language (s): Swedish; Full Page Colour:
62592.00
Currency: Sweden Kronor
NEWSPAPER

Skaraborgs Allehanda
Owner: Skaraborg Allehanda
Editorial: Box 407, Skövde 541 28.
T: 46 500 46 75 00 E: redaktion@sla.se
W: http://www.sla.se Circ: 24300
Marknadschef: Erling Ekelund; Nyhetschef:
Peter Henriksson; Redigerare: Yvonne
Keymer; Redigerare: Carina Krusell;
Redigerare: Monica Sjöstrand; Redigerare:
Linus Wennblom
Language (s): Swedish; Full Page Colour:
29900.00
Currency: Sweden Kronor
NEWSPAPER

Skaraborgs Allehanda ~ Hjo
Editorial: Sjögatan 5, Hjo 544 30.
T: 46 503 74 79 90
E: glenn.svensson@hjotidning.se
W: http://www.sla.se Circ: 24200
Redaktör: Glenn Svensson
Language (s): Swedish
NEWSPAPER

Skaraborgs Allehanda ~ Karlsborg
Editorial: Storgatan 11, Karlsborg 546 30.
T: 46 505 64 79 70 E: redaktion@sla.se
W: http://www.sla.se Circ: 24200
Language (s): Swedish
NEWSPAPER

Skaraborgs Allehanda ~ Stenstorp
Editorial: Storgatan 29, Stenstorp 520 20.
T: 46 5 004 675 71 E: rikard.jansson@sla.se
W: http://www.sla.se Circ: 24200
Redaktör: Rikard Jansson
Language (s): Swedish
NEWSPAPER

Skaraborgs Allehanda ~ Tibro
Editorial: Box 199, Tibro 543 22.
T: 46 504 767984 E: tibro@sla.se
W: http://www.sla.se Circ: 24200
Redaktör: Lars-Ola Carlén
Language (s): Swedish
NEWSPAPER

Skaraborgsbygden
Owner: Skaraborgsbygdens Tidningsförening
upa
Editorial: Box 204, Skara 532 23.
T: 46 511 302 50
E: redaktion@skaraborgsbygden.se
W: http://www.skaraborgsbygden.se
Freq: Weekly; Circ: 11600 Not Audited
Ansvarig utgivare: Sven Gärdekrans;
Chefredaktör: Thomaz Magnusson
Language (s): Swedish; Full Page Colour:
15695.00
Currency: Sweden Kronor
NEWSPAPER

Skövde Nyheter
Owner: Västgöta-Tidningar AB
Editorial: Storgatan 17, Unavailable SE-541
30. T: 46 500 78 48 50 E: red.sn@vgt.se
Freq: Daily; Circ: 2600 Not Audited
Nyhetssamordnare: Börje Andersson;
Nyhetschef: Leif Claesson; Chefredaktör/
Ansvarig Utgivare: Ronny Karlsson; Redaktör:
Anna Kuylenstierna
Language (s): Swedish
DAILY NEWSPAPER

Smålandsposten
Owner: Smålandsposten AB
Editorial: Växjo 351 70. T: 46 470 77 05 00
E: nyhet.red@smp.se W: http://www.smp.se
Circ: 38600
Krönikör: Kent Axelsson; Redaktionschef: Åsa
Carlsson; Redigeringschef: Gun-Britt
Iderheim; Ansvarig utgivare: Magnus
Karlsson; Redaktör: Stefan Nilsson;
Nyhetschef: Bitte Paulander; Redaktör: Berne
Persson; Nyhetschef: Johan Persson
Language (s): Swedish; Full Page Colour:
45744.00

Currency: Sweden Kronor
NEWSPAPER

Smålandsposten ~ Älmhult
Editorial: N Esplanaden 10, Älmhult 343 30.
T: 46 476 487 50 **E:** almhult.red@smp.se
W: http://www.smp.se **Circ:** 38600
Language (s): Swedish
NEWSPAPER

Smålandsposten ~ Alvesta
Editorial: Storgatan 16, Alvesta 342 22.
T: 46 472 473 40 **E:** alvesta.red@smp.se
W: http://www.smp.se **Circ:** 38600
Language (s): Swedish
NEWSPAPER

Smålandsposten ~ Lessebo
Editorial: Bruksgatan 4, Lessebo 360 50.
T: 46 478 481 40 **E:** lessebo.red@smp.se
W: http://www.smp.se **Circ:** 40200
Language (s): Swedish
NEWSPAPER

Smålandsposten ~ Tingsryd
Editorial: Storgatan 55A, Tingsryd 362 22.
T: 46 477 105 30 **E:** tingsryd.red@smp.se
W: http://www.smp.se **Circ:** 40200
Language (s): Swedish
NEWSPAPER

Smålandsposten ~ Uppvidinge/Åseda
Editorial: Storgatan 2, Åseda 360 70.
T: 46 474 717 50 **E:** uppvidinge.red@smp.se
W: http://www.smp.se **Circ:** 40200
Language (s): Swedish
NEWSPAPER

Smålands-Tidningen
Owner: Smålandstidningens Tryckeri AB
Editorial: Box 261, Stora torget 4, Eksjö 575
23. **T:** 46 381 63 85 00 **E:** centralred@smt.se
W: http://www.smalandstidningen.se
Circ: 29000
Redaktionschef & Ansvarig utgivare: Johan
Hedberg
Language (s): Swedish; Full Page Colour:
33800.00
Currency: Sweden Kronor
NEWSPAPER

Smålands-Tidningen ~ Ydre
Editorial: Torget 1, Österbymo 570 60.
T: 46 381 606 08 **E:** ydrered@smt.se
W: http://www.smalandstidningen.se
Circ: 33100
Language (s): Swedish
NEWSPAPER

Smålands-Tidningen ~ Aneby
Editorial: Köpmansgatan 10, Aneby 578 32.
T: 46 380 419 10 **E:** anebyred@smt.se
W: http://www.smalandstidningen.se
Circ: 33100
Language (s): Swedish
NEWSPAPER

Smålands-Tidningen ~ Åseda
Editorial: Olovsgatan 17, Åseda 360 70.
T: 46 474 712 68 **E:** asedared@smt.se
Circ: 33100
Language (s): Swedish
NEWSPAPER

Smålands-Tidningen ~ Eksjö
Editorial: Box 261, Eksjö 575 23.
T: 46 381 132 07 **E:** eksjored@smt.se
Circ: 32600
Redaktionschef & Ansvarig utgivare: Johan
Hedberg
Language (s): Swedish
NEWSPAPER

Smålands-Tidningen ~ Mariannelund
Editorial: Torget, Mariannelund 570 30.
T: 46 496 103 50 **Circ:** 32600
Language (s): Swedish
NEWSPAPER

Smålands-Tidningen ~ Nässjö
Editorial: Box 906, Unavailable 571 29.
T: 46 380 138 00 **E:** nassjored@smt.se
Circ: 33100
Redaktionschef: Christer Undfors
Language (s): Swedish
NEWSPAPER

Smålands-Tidningen ~ Sävsjö
Editorial: Lundbergsplan 1, Sävsjö 576 36.
T: 46 382 102 63 **E:** savsjored@smt.se
Circ: 33100
Language (s): Swedish
NEWSPAPER

Smålands-Tidningen ~ Tranås
Editorial: Missionsgatan 2, Tranas 573 28.
T: 46 140 674 50 **E:** tranasred@smt.se
Circ: 32600
Language (s): Swedish
NEWSPAPER

Smålands-Tidningen ~ Vetlanda
Editorial: Box 63, Vetlanda 574 21.
T: 46 383 76 32 10 **E:** vetlandared@smt.se
Circ: 32600
Language (s): Swedish
NEWSPAPER

Smålänningen
Owner: Herenco AB
Editorial: Box 304, Ljungby 341 26.
T: 46 372 692 00 **E:** redax@smalanningen.se
W: http://www.smalanningen.se **Circ:** 12900
Redigerare: Eva-Stina Andersson; **Nyhetschef:**
Lars Davidsson; **Redaktionssekreterare:**
Sven-Inge Idofsson; **Redaktionschef:** Anita
Johansson
Language (s): Swedish; Full Page Colour:
25995.00
Currency: Sweden Kronor
NEWSPAPER

Smålänningen ~ Älmhult
Editorial: Stora Torggatan 8, Älmhult 343 22.
T: 46 476 100 60
W: http://www.smalanningen.se **Circ:** 12900
Nyhetschef: Anna H Liljeqvist
Language (s): Swedish
NEWSPAPER

Smålänningen ~ Markaryd
Editorial: Drottninggatan 18, Markaryd 285
22. **T:** 46 433 120 90
E: markaryd@smalanningen.se
W: http://www.smalanningen.se **Circ:** 12900
Language (s): Swedish
NEWSPAPER

Sméjournalen
Owner: GISAB
Editorial: Tunprint AB, Box 457, Eskilstuna
633 42. **T:** 46 16 200 30 20
E: redaktion@smejournalen.se
W: http://www.smejournalen.se
Freq: Weekly; **Circ:** 46120 Pub Statement
Ansvarig utgivare: Staffan Lönner
Language (s): Swedish; Full Page Colour:
19000.00
Currency: Sweden Kronor
NEWSPAPER

SöderhamnsNytt
Owner: Hälsingetidningar AB
Editorial: Box 514, Brädgårdsgatan 6,
Söderhamn 826 27. **T:** 46 270 26 53 50
E: redaktion@helahalsingland.se
W: http://helahalsingland.se/kontakt/
soderhamnsnytt
Freq: Weekly; **Circ:** 14200 Pub Statement
Redaktör: Sara Oscarsson
Language (s): Swedish
NEWSPAPER

Södermalmsnytt
Owner: Direktpress
Editorial: Box 5290, Vallhallavägen 184,
Stockholm 102 46. **T:** 46 8 545 870 70
E: sn@direktpress.se
W: http://www.sodermalmsnytt.se
Freq: Weekly; **Circ:** 71500
Chefredaktör: Helene Claesson; **Redigerare:**
Lotta Waller
Language (s): Swedish; Full Page Colour:
26596.00
Currency: Sweden Kronor
NEWSPAPER

Södermanlands Nyheter
Owner: Södermanlands Nyheter AB
Editorial: Nyköping 611 79. **T:** 46 155 767 00
E: redaktionen@sn.se **W:** http://www.sn.se
Circ: 25500
Ansvarig utgivare: Göran Carstorp; **Redaktör:**
Thomas Harne; **Chef:** Åsa Lundqvist; **Kyrka /
Religion:** Gunnel Magnusson; **Redaktör:** Lena
Nestor; **Nyhetschef:** Johan Pfriem; **Redaktör:**
Pernilla Yderbo
Language (s): Swedish; Full Page Colour:
41450.00
Currency: Sweden Kronor
NEWSPAPER

Södermanlands Nyheter ~ Gnesta
Editorial: V Storgatan 9, Gnesta 646 31.
T: 46 158 102 06 **E:** gnesta@sn.se
W: http://www.sn.se **Circ:** 25200
Language (s): Swedish
NEWSPAPER

Södermanlands Nyheter ~ Oxelösund
Editorial: Prisman, Torggatan 11, Oxelösund
613 30. **T:** 46 155 767 30
E: redaktionen@sn.se **W:** http://www.sn.se
Circ: 25200
Language (s): Swedish
NEWSPAPER

Södermanlands Nyheter ~ Trosa
Editorial: Ö Långgatan 33, Trosa 619 30.
T: 46 156 137 10 **W:** http://www.sn.se
Circ: 25200
Language (s): Swedish
NEWSPAPER

Södertälje Posten
Owner: Tidningsbolaget Promedia i
Mellansverige AB
Editorial: Storgatan 3-5, Södertälje 151 82.
T: 46 8 550 921 61
E: redaktion@sodertaljeposten.se
W: http://www.sodertaljeposten.se
Freq: Weekly; **Circ:** 50200 Pub Statement
Language (s): Swedish; Full Page Colour:
30000.00
Currency: Sweden Kronor
NEWSPAPER

Södra Dalarnes Tidning ~ Säter
Editorial: Torggatan 8, Säter 783 30.
T: 46 225 511 50 **E:** sdt.red@dt.se
W: http://www.dt.se **Circ:** 16100
Language (s): Swedish
NEWSPAPER

Södra Sidan
Owner: Medborgarpress Stockholm AB
Editorial: Skärholmen 127 48.
T: 46 8 740 07 82 **E:** redaktion@sodrasidan.se
W: http://www.sodrasidan.se **Circ:** 50000
Ansvarig utgivare: Petter Beckman; **Redaktör:**
Rouzbeh Djalaie; **Redaktör &**
Redaktionssekreterare: Stella Papapanagiotou
Language (s): Swedish
NEWSPAPER

Spegeln Staffanstorp
Owner: Stefan & Co Tidningsproduktion
Editorial: Box 830, Staffanstorp 245 18.
T: 46 46 25 02 02 **E:** info@spegeln.se
W: http://www.spegeln.se **Circ:** 17000
Redigerare: Peder Svensson; **Ansvarig
utgivare:** Stefan Svensson
Language (s): Swedish
NEWSPAPER

Spegeln Svedalabladet
Owner: Stefan & Co Tidningsproduktion
Editorial: Box 830, Staffanstorp 245 18.
T: 46 46 25 02 02 **E:** info@spegeln.se
W: http://www.spegeln.se
Freq: Monthly; **Circ:** 17000 Pub Statement
Ansvarig utgivare: Stefan Svensson
Language (s): Swedish
NEWSPAPER

ST Tidningen
Owner: Nordanvindsgatans Tidning AB
Editorial: Östra Köpmansgatan 18,
Stenungsund 444 30. **T:** 46 303 72 82 30
E: redaktionen@sttidningen.se
W: http://www.sttidningen.se
Freq: Weekly; **Circ:** 28500
Chefredaktör: Thomas Clausson; **Redaktör:**
Kurt Nilsson
Language (s): Swedish; Full Page Mono:
20895.00
Currency: Sweden Kronor
NEWSPAPER

Stan i dag
Owner: Östersundsposten
T: 46 63 161 600 **E:** stanidag@op.se
W: http://www.op.se **Circ:** 35000
Ansvarig utgivare: Per Åhlin; **Redaktör:**
Fredrik Alverland; **Redaktör:** Sussane Kvarnlöf
Language (s): Swedish
NEWSPAPER

Sundsvalls Nyheter
Owner: Sundsvalls Nyheter
Editorial: Badhusparken 1, Sundsvall 851 72.
T: 46 10 709 84 80 **E:** redaktion@sn24.se
W: http://www.sn24.se
Freq: Weekly; **Circ:** 69700
Redaktionsansvarig: Sanna Berglund
Language (s): Swedish; Full Page Colour:
45216.00
Currency: Sweden Kronor
NEWSPAPER

Sundsvalls Tidning
Owner: Sundsvall Tidning AB
Editorial: Badhusparken 1, Sundsvall 851 72.
T: 46 60 19 70 00 **W:** http://www.st.nu

Freq: Daily; **Circ:** 27300
Chefredaktör & Ansvarig utgivare: Anders
Ingvarsson; **Nyhetschef:** Karin Näslund;
Nyhetschef: Jan Olby
Language (s): Swedish; Full Page Colour:
55238.00
Currency: Sweden Kronor
NEWSPAPER

Sundsvalls Tidning ~ Ånge
Editorial: Box 40, Ånge 841 00.
T: 46 690 125 00 **W:** http://www.st.nu
Circ: 35900
Language (s): Swedish
NEWSPAPER

Sundsvalls Tidning ~ Nordanstig
Editorial: Gingstavägen 21, Gnarp 820 77.
T: 46 652 241 00 **W:** http://www.st.nu
Circ: 35900
Language (s): Swedish
NEWSPAPER

Sundsvalls Tidning ~ Timrå
Editorial: Box 148, Timrå 861 24.
T: 46 60 57 10 95 **W:** http://www.st.nu
Circ: 35900
Redaktör: Lars Windh
Language (s): Swedish
NEWSPAPER

Svenljunga & Tranemo Tidning
Owner: Svenljunga & Tranemo Tidning AB
Editorial: Box 33, Tranemo 514 23.
T: 46 325 400 00 **E:** info@stthuset.com
W: http://www.stthuset.com
Freq: Weekly; **Circ:** 25050 Pub Statement
Redaktionschef: Tina Hjorth Svensson
Language (s): Swedish; Full Page Colour:
15860.00
Currency: Sweden Kronor
NEWSPAPER

Svenska Dagbladet
Owner: Svenska Dagbladet AB
Editorial: Västra järnvägsgatan 21, Stockholm
105 17. **T:** 46 8 13 50 00 **E:** nyheter@svd.se
W: http://www.svd.se
Freq: Daily; **Circ:** 186000 TS
Stf ansvarig utgivare och redaktionschef: Ann
Axelsson; **Nyhetsredaktör:** Kristofer
Gustafsson; **Redigerare:** Pernilla Rosenlind;
Redaktionschef: Olle Zachrison
Language (s): Swedish; Full Page Colour:
165800.00
Currency: Sweden Kronor
DAILY NEWSPAPER

Sydöstran
Owner: Sydöstran AB
Editorial: Landbrogatan 17, Karlskrona 371
88. **T:** 46 455 33 46 00
E: redaktion@sydostran.se
W: http://www.sydostran.se **Circ:** 13800
Nyhetschef: Anders Nilsson; **Chefredaktör/
Ansvarig utgivare:** Gunnar Svensson
Language (s): Swedish; Full Page Colour:
31776.00
Currency: Sweden Kronor
NEWSPAPER

Sydöstran ~ Karlshamn
Editorial: Rådhusgatan 14, Karlshamn 374 36.
T: 46 454 32 59 00
E: karlshamn@sydostran.se
W: http://www.sydostran.se **Circ:** 16000
Language (s): Swedish
NEWSPAPER

Sydöstran ~ Olofström
Editorial: Ådalsvägen 1, Olofström 293 34.
T: 46 454 489 80 **E:** olofstrom@sydostran.se
W: http://www.sydostran.se **Circ:** 16000
Language (s): Swedish
NEWSPAPER

Sydöstran ~ Ronneby
Editorial: Box 6, Ronneby 372 21.
T: 46 457 289 30 **E:** ronneby@sydostran.se
W: http://www.sydostran.se **Circ:** 16000
Platschef: Göran Sundén
Language (s): Swedish
NEWSPAPER

Sydöstran ~ Sölvesborg
Editorial: Södergatan 19, Sölvesborg 294 31.
T: 46 456 789 60 **E:** solvesborg@sydostran.se
W: http://www.sydostran.se **Circ:** 16000
Language (s): Swedish
NEWSPAPER

Sydsvenskan
Owner: Sydsvenska Dagbladet AB
Editorial: Krusegatan 19, Malmo 205 05.
T: 46 40 28 12 00
E: nyhetsred@sydsvenskan.se

WORLD NEWS MEDIA

W: http://www.sydsvenskan.se **Circ:** 120000
Chefredaktör & VD: Lars Dahmén; **Redaktör - bostadsbilaga:** Anders Fähltman; **Redaktör:** Malena Henriksson; **Nyhetschef och bitr redaktionschef:** Jonas Nyrén; **Nyhetschef och bitr redaktionschef:** Pia Rehnquist; **Utvecklingsredaktör:** Martin Skogsberg
Language (s): Swedish; Full Page Colour: 249136.00
Currency: Sweden Kronor
DAILY NEWSPAPER

Tidningen Ångermanland
Owner: MittMedia Förvaltnings AB
Editorial: Härnösand 871 81.
T: 46 611 55 48 00
E: taredaktion@allehanda.se
W: http://www.allehanda.se **Circ:** 20400
Nyhetschef: Tomas Hamrin; **Nyhetschef:** Marcus Melinder; **Ansvarig utgivare:** Jimmie Näslund; **Nyhetschef:** Ulf Westman
Language (s): Swedish; Full Page Colour: 40320.00
Currency: Sweden Kronor
NEWSPAPER

Tidningen Ångermanland ~ Kramfors
Editorial: Box 83, Kramfors 872 22.
T: 46 612 77 17 50
E: taredaktion@allehanda.se
W: http://www.allehanda.se **Circ:** 25300
Platschef: Anders Lidén; **Redaktionssekreterare:** Katarina Lind
Language (s): Swedish
NEWSPAPER

Tidningen Ångermanland ~ Sollefteå
Editorial: Järnvägsgatan 43, Sollefteå 881 25.
T: 46 620 257 80 **E:** taredaktion@allehanda.se
W: http://www.allehanda.se **Circ:** 25300
Language (s): Swedish
NEWSPAPER

Tidningen Ångermanland; Släkt & Vänner
Editorial: Härnösand 871 81.
T: 46 611 55 48 00 **E:** sov@allehanda.se
W: http://www.allehanda.se/slaktvanner
Circ: 25300
Redaktör: Christina Almgren; **Redaktör:** Anki Eriksson
Language (s): Swedish
NEWSPAPER

Tidningen Extra
Owner: Norbottens Media AB
Editorial: Robertsviksgatan 5, Luleå 972 41.
T: 46 920 26 28 20
E: redaktionen@tidningenextra.se
W: http://www.tidningenextra.se **Circ:** 56000
Chef & Ansvarig utgivare: Anneli Hanno
Language (s): Swedish
NEWSPAPER

Tidningen Hisingen
Owner: DirektPress Tidningsförlag AB
Editorial: Direktpress, Britta Sahlgrens gata 8 c, Västra Frölunda 421 31. **T:** 46 31 7205591
E: hisingen@gbg.direktpress.se
W: http://www.tidningenhisingen.se/
Freq: Bi-Weekly; **Circ:** 52200
Chefredaktör & Ansvarig utgivare: Magnus Johansson; **Nyhetschef:** Joanna Klasén
Language (s): Swedish; Full Page Colour: 19104.00
Currency: Sweden Kronor
NEWSPAPER

Tidningen Nordost
Owner: DirektPress Tidningsförlag AB
Editorial: Direktpress, Britta Sahlgrens gata 8 c, Västra Frölunda 421 31
E: nordost@gbg.direktpress.se
W: http://www.tidningennordost.se/
Circ: 42000
Chefredaktör & Ansvarig utgivare: Magnus Johansson; **Nyhetschef:** Joanna Klasén
Language (s): Swedish
NEWSPAPER

Tidningen Sydväst
Owner: DirektPress Tidningsförlag AB
Editorial: Direktpress, Britta Sahlgrens gata 8 c, Västra Frölunda 421 31. **T:** 46 31 720 55 95
E: sydvast@gbg.direktpress.se
W: http://www.tidningensydvast.se
Freq: Weekly; **Circ:** 17000
Language (s): Swedish
NEWSPAPER

Torslanda Tidningen
Owner: Torslanda Tidningen
Editorial: Flygmotorvägen 3, Torslanda 423 37. **T:** 46 31 92 45 80 **E:** info@tidningen.se
W: http://www.tidningen.se
Freq: Weekly; **Circ:** 18000 Pub Statement
Redigerare: Therese Sjöqvist; **Ansvarig utgivare:** Bengt Wester
Language (s): Swedish
NEWSPAPER

Totalt Umeå
Owner: VK-koncernen
Editorial: Förrådsvägen 9, Umeå 901 70.
T: 46 90 70 28 30 **E:** redaktion@totaltumea.se
W: http://totaltumea.se
Freq: Weekly; **Circ:** 62500
Chefredaktör & Ansvarig utgivare: Hampus Råde
Language (s): Swedish; Full Page Colour: 24000.00
Currency: Sweden Kronor
NEWSPAPER

TTELA
Owner: Tvåstads Tidnings AB
Editorial: Box 111, Vänersborg 462 22.
T: 46 521 26 46 00 **E:** redaktionen@ttela.se
W: http://www.ttela.se **Circ:** 28500
Kyrka / Religion: Jan Björk; **Redaktör:** Karin Engqvist; **Nyhetschef:** Marita Engqvist; **Redaktör:** Suzanne Werner
Language (s): Swedish; Full Page Colour: 45600.00
Currency: Sweden Kronor
NEWSPAPER

TTELA ~ Lilla Edet
Editorial: Göteborgsvägen 53B, Lilla Edet 463 21. **T:** 46 520 65 71 85
E: redaktionen@ttela.se **W:** http://www.ttela.se
Circ: 17800
Language (s): Swedish
NEWSPAPER

TTELA ~ Mellerud
Editorial: Box 2, Mellerud 464 21.
T: 46 530 123 25 **E:** redaktionen@ttela.se
W: http://www.ttela.se **Circ:** 13800
Language (s): Swedish
NEWSPAPER

Tyresö Nyheter
Owner: Tyresö Nyheter Ekonomisk Förening
Editorial: Björkbacksvägen 37, Tyresö 135 40.
T: 46 8 798 91 01
W: http://www.tyresonyheter.nu
Freq: Bi-Monthly; **Circ:** 16000 Pub Statement
Redaktör: Ingela Carlsson; **Ansvarig utgivare:** Anders Linder
Language (s): Swedish
NEWSPAPER

Uppsalatidningen
Owner: DirektPress
Editorial: Fyrisborgsgatan 3, 1 tr, Uppsala 751 45. **T:** 46 18 418 11 11
E: redaktion@uppsalatidningen.se
W: http://www.direktpress.se/uppsalatidningen
Freq: Weekly; **Circ:** 94800
Redigerare: Tone Gellerstedt; **Redaktionsansvarig:** Inger Nilsson
Language (s): Swedish; Full Page Colour: 36000.00
Currency: Sweden Kronor
NEWSPAPER

Upsala Nya Tidning
Owner: Upsala Nya Tidning
Editorial: Dragarbrunns torg 2, Uppsala 751 03. **T:** 46 18 478 00 00 **E:** 72018@unt.se
W: http://www.unt.se **Circ:** 45600
Redaktionschef: Åsa Pallarp Beckman
Language (s): Swedish; Full Page Colour: 65400.00
Currency: Sweden Kronor
NEWSPAPER

Vallentuna Nya
Owner: WB Media
Editorial: Cedersdalsvägen 5 D, Vallentuna 186 40. **T:** 46 8 732 40 42
E: info@vallentunanya.se
W: http://www.vallentunanya.se **Circ:** 14700
Chefredaktör: Peter Palmqvist; **Ansvarig utgivare:** Peter Pettersson
Language (s): Swedish
NEWSPAPER

Varbergs Posten
Owner: Västsvenska Lokaltidningar AB, Roger Ivarsson 9 %
Editorial: Box 93, Varberg 432 22.
T: 46 340 177 71
E: redaktion@varbergsposten.se
W: http://www.varbergsposten.se
Freq: Weekly; **Circ:** 28800 Pub Statement
Ansvarig utgivare: Roger Thilander
Language (s): Swedish; Full Page Colour: 28470.00
Currency: Sweden Kronor
NEWSPAPER

Värmlands Folkblad
Owner: Värmlands Folkblad AB
Editorial: Box 67, Karlstad 651 03.
T: 46 54 17 55 00 **E:** redaktion@vf.se
W: http://www.vf.se **Circ:** 19500
Chefredaktör & Ansvarig utgivare: Peter Franke; **Nyhetschef:** Björn Stefanson; **Redaktör:** Annika Ström
Language (s): Swedish; Full Page Colour: 21000.00
Currency: Sweden Kronor
NEWSPAPER

Värmlands Folkblad ~ Arvika
Editorial: Box 55, Arvika 671 31.
T: 46 570 199 25 **E:** redaktion@vf.se
W: http://www.vf.se **Circ:** 24700
Redaktör: Lars Swanö
Language (s): Swedish
NEWSPAPER

Värmlands Folkblad ~ Kristinehamn
Editorial: Box 181, Kristinehamn 681 24.
T: 46 550 123 16 **E:** redaktion@vf.se
W: http://www.vf.se **Circ:** 24700
Redaktör: Lars Myr; **Redaktör:** Britta Staake
Language (s): Swedish
NEWSPAPER

Värmlands Folkblad ~ Nordvärmland
Editorial: Köpmangatan 9, Hagfors 683 30.
T: 46 563 610 90 **E:** redaktion@vf.se
W: http://www.vf.se **Circ:** 24700
Redaktör: Thony Liljemark
Language (s): Swedish
NEWSPAPER

Värmlands Folkblad ~ Sunne
Editorial: Byggaregatan 5, Sunne 686 26.
T: 46 565 106 20 **E:** redaktion@vf.se
W: http://www.vf.se **Circ:** 24700
Language (s): Swedish
NEWSPAPER

Värnamo Nyheter
Owner: Hallpressen AB
Editorial: Värnamo 331 84.
T: 46 370 30 06 00
E: redaktion@varnamonyheter.se
W: http://www.varnamonyheter.se **Circ:** 20600
Redaktionschef & Ansvarig utgivare: Inger Abram Ohlsson; **Nyhetsredaktör:** Madeleine Hammarström; **Chef:** Dan Karlsson; **Nyhetsredaktör:** Per-Ola Nilsson; **Nyhetschef:** Christer Nordmark
Language (s): Swedish; Full Page Colour: 57966.00
Currency: Sweden Kronor
NEWSPAPER

Värnamo Nyheter ~ Gislaved
Editorial: Box 73, Gislaved 332 22.
T: 46 371 58 69 90
E: gisred@varnamonyheter.se
W: http://www.varnamonyheter.se **Circ:** 22200
Language (s): Swedish
NEWSPAPER

Värnamo Nyheter ~ Gnosjö
Editorial: Box 24, Gnosjö 335 30.
T: 46 370 917 86
E: redaktion@varnamonyheter.se
W: http://www.varnamonyheter.se **Circ:** 22200
Language (s): Swedish
NEWSPAPER

Värnamo Nyheter ~ Rydaholm
Editorial: Box 23, Rydaholm 330 17.
T: 46 472 203 44
E: redaktion@varnamonyheter.se
W: http://www.varnamonyheter.se **Circ:** 22200
Editor: Mr./Ms. Editor
Language (s): Swedish
NEWSPAPER

Värnamo Nyheter ~ Skillingaryd/ Vaggeryd
Editorial: Box 163, Skillingaryd 568 30.
T: 46 370 707 77
E: redaktion@varnamonyheter.se
W: http://www.varnamonyheter.se **Circ:** 22200
Language (s): Swedish
NEWSPAPER

Vårt Kungsholmen
Owner: Innerstadspress AB
Editorial: Box 5290, Stockholm 102 46.
T: 46 8 545 870 70 **E:** vk@direktpress.se
W: http://www.vartkungsholmen.se
Freq: Weekly; **Circ:** 39400
Ansvarig utgivare: Helene Claesson; **Platschef:** Carina Rydberg
Language (s): Swedish
NEWSPAPER

Vårt Malmö
Owner: Malmö Stad
Editorial: Malmö stad, Stadskontoret, Malmo 205 80. **T:** 46 40 34 10 00
E: info.malmo@givakt.se
W: http://www.malmo.se/vartmalmo
Freq: Bi-Monthly; **Circ:** 157000 Pub Statement
Ansvarig utgivare: Gunilla Konradsson; **Redaktör:** Åsa Lempert
Language (s): Swedish; Full Page Colour: 16900.00
Currency: Sweden Kronor
NEWSPAPER

Västerås Tidning
Owner: DirektPress
Editorial: Norra Källgatan 17, Västerås 722 11.
T: 46 21 30 46 00
E: redaktion@vasterastidning.se
W: http://www.vasterastidning.se
Freq: 2 Times/Week; **Circ:** 89700 RS
Ansvarig utgivare: Lasse Blom; **Redaktionschef:** Jonas Edberg
Language (s): Swedish; Full Page Colour: 52560.00
Currency: Sweden Kronor
NEWSPAPER

Västerbottens Folkblad
Owner: Nya Västerbottens Folkblad AB
Editorial: Box 3164, Umeå 903 04.
T: 46 90 17 00 00
E: redaktionen@folkbladet.nu
W: http://www.folkbladet.nu **Circ:** 13000
Chefredaktör: Anna Lith; **Krönikör:** Mats Rosin
Language (s): Swedish; Full Page Colour: 13600.00
Currency: Sweden Kronor
NEWSPAPER

Västerbottens Folkblad ~ Lycksele
Editorial: Box 233, Lycksele 921 24.
T: 46 950 234 65 **E:** inland@folkbladet.nu
W: http://www.folkbladet.nu **Circ:** 15500
Redaktör: Donald Paulsson
Language (s): Swedish
NEWSPAPER

Västerbottens Folkblad ~ Skellefteå
Editorial: Box 60, Skellefteå 931 21.
T: 46 910 142 70 **E:** skelleftea@folkbladet.nu
W: http://www.folkbladet.nu **Circ:** 15500
Language (s): Swedish
NEWSPAPER

Västerbottens Folkblad ~ Vilhelmina
Editorial: Box 48, Vilhelmina 912 21.
T: 46 940 132 20 **E:** inland@folkbladet.nu
W: http://www.folkbladet.nu **Circ:** 15500
Language (s): Swedish
NEWSPAPER

Västerbottens-Kuriren
Owner: Västerbottens Kuriren AB
Editorial: Förrådsvägen 9, Umeå 901 70.
T: 46 90 17 60 10 **E:** redaktion@vk.se
W: http://www.vk.se **Circ:** 35800
Redaktör: Emma Ågrahn; **Nyhetschef:** Carina Ask; **Ansvarig utgivare:** Sture Bergman; **Nyhetschef:** Karin Bernspång; **Redaktör:** Roland Edlund; **Nyhetschef:** Gunnar Falck; **Nyhetschef:** Ulf Henriksson; **Redaktör:** Bibi Karbin; **Chefredaktör/ Ansvarig Utgivare:** Ingvar Näslund; **Redaktör:** Erica Sjöström
Language (s): Swedish; Full Page Colour: 37000.00
Currency: Sweden Kronor
NEWSPAPER

Västerviks-Tidningen
Owner: Västerviks-Tidningen
Editorial: Stora Torget 2, Västervik 593 82.
T: 46 490 666 00 **E:** vt.red@vt.se
W: http://www.vt.se **Circ:** 11800
Redigerare: Kay Ekström; **Redigerare:** Margareta Karlsson; **Nyhetschef:** Christoffer Nielsen; **Redaktör:** Illka Ranta
Language (s): Swedish; Full Page Colour: 25000.00
Currency: Sweden Kronor
NEWSPAPER

Västerviks-Tidningen ~ Ankarsrum
Owner: Västerviks-Tidning
Editorial: Kungsvägen 21, Ankarsrum 590 90.
T: 46 490 500 11 **E:** anders.jacobsson@vt.se
W: http://www.vt.se **Circ:** 13100
Redaktör: Anders Jacobsson
Language (s): Swedish
NEWSPAPER

Västerviks-Tidningen ~ Gamleby
Owner: Västerviks-Tidningen
Editorial: Centrum, Gamleby 594 00.
T: 46 493 512 40 **E:** gby.red@vt.se
W: http://www.vt.se **Circ:** 13100

Language (s): Swedish
NEWSPAPER

Vestmanlands Läns Tidning
Owner: Vestmanlands Läns Tidning AB
Editorial: Box 3, Västerås 721 03.
T: 46 21 19 90 00 **E:** nyheter@vlt.se
W: http://www.vlt.se **Circ:** 42200
Redigerare: Marit Blomquist; **Nyhetschef:** Alisa Bosnic; **Redaktionschef:** Mårten Enberg; **Redaktionssekreterare:** Helena Eriksson; **Ansvarig utgivare:** Thelma Kimsjö; **Redigerare:** Jan Pargell; **Redigerare:** Mikael Teglund; **Nyhetschef:** Karin Thornberg
Language (s): Swedish; Full Page Colour: 60165.00
Currency: Sweden Kronor
NEWSPAPER

Vestmanlands Läns Tidning ~ Hallsta/Sura
Editorial: Parkgatan 2, Hallstahammar 734 35.
T: 46 220 530 00 **W:** http://www.vlt.se
Circ: 47200
Language (s): Swedish
NEWSPAPER

Vestmanlands Läns Tidning; Idag
Editorial: Box 3, Västerås 721 03
E: direkt@vlt.se **W:** http://www.vlt.se
Circ: 47200
Language (s): Swedish
NEWSPAPER

Vi i Vasastan
Owner: Innerstadspress AB
Editorial: Box 5290, Stockholm 102 46.
T: 46 8 545 870 70 **E:** info@direktpress.se
W: http://www.viivasastan.se **Circ:** 38500 RS
Chefredaktör: Helene Claesson; **Nyhetschef:** Jacob Hellgren
Language (s): Swedish; Full Page Colour: 17850.00
Currency: Sweden Kronor
NEWSPAPER

Vi i Väsby
Owner: Direktpress
Editorial: Kanalvägen 1 A 2 tr, Upplands Väsby 194 61 **E:** redaktion@viivasby.se
W: http://www.viivasby.se
Freq: Weekly; **Circ:** 40000
Nyhetschef: Mats Hedström; Full Page Colour: 16400.00
Currency: Sweden Kronor
NEWSPAPER

Vi på Näset
Editorial: Järnvägsgatan 74, Malmo 216 16.
T: 46 40 15 74 77
E: malmotidningen@telia.com
Freq: Bi-Monthly; **Circ:** 18000 Pub Statement
Redaktör: Ingrid Andersson; **Ansvarig utgivare:** Karl-Heinz Forsberg
Language (s): Swedish
NEWSPAPER

Wall Street Journal (Sweden)
Editorial: Kungsgatan 12-14, 7th Floor, Stockholm 11135. **T:** 46 854513090
Freq: Daily
News Editor: Anna Molin
DAILY NEWSPAPER

Ystads Allehanda
Owner: Skånemedia AB
Editorial: Lilla Norregatan 9, Ystad 271 81.
T: 46 411 55 78 00
E: red.ys@ystadsallehanda.se
W: http://www.ystadsallehanda.se **Circ:** 24000
Redaktionschef: Helena Blendberg; **Ansvarig utgivare:** Margaretha Engström; **Nyhetschef:** Peter Hellemarck; **Chefredaktör:** Lars Mohlin; **Redaktionschef:** Pia Röding; **Nyhetschef:** Martin Runol; **Redigerare:** Niklas Steuernagel; **Chefredaktör & Ansvarig Utgivare:** Jörgen Svensson; **Redigerare:** Annika Thunell
Language (s): Swedish; Full Page Colour: 17520.00
Currency: Sweden Kronor
NEWSPAPER

Ystads Allehanda ~ Simrishamn
Editorial: Storgatan 12, Simrishamn 272 31.
T: 46 414 289 90 **E:** red.si@ystadsallehanda.se
W: http://www.ystadsallehanda.se **Circ:** 26100
Language (s): Swedish
NEWSPAPER

Ystads Allehanda ~ Sjöbo
Editorial: Norregatan 1C, Sjöbo 275 30.
T: 46 416 192 10 **E:** red.sj@ystadsallehanda.se
W: http://www.ystadsallehanda.se **Circ:** 26100
Nyhetschef: Britt Risberg
Language (s): Swedish
NEWSPAPER

Ystads Allehanda ~ Skurup
Editorial: Svantorget, Skurup 274 01.
T: 46 411 55 79 00
E: red.sk@ystadsallehanda.se
W: http://www.ystadsallehanda.se **Circ:** 26100
Nyhetschef: Britt Risberg
Language (s): Swedish
NEWSPAPER

Ystads Allehanda ~ Tomelilla
Editorial: Centralgatan 7, Tomelilla 273 30.
T: 46 417125 85 **E:** red.to@ystadsallehanda.se
W: http://www.ystadsallehanda.se **Circ:** 26100
Language (s): Swedish
NEWSPAPER

NEWS SERVICE/SYNDICATE

Associated Press
Editorial: Norrlandsgatan 7, Stockholm 111 43. **T:** 46 8 545-13-080
Bureau Chief: Karl Ritter
NEWS SERVICE/SYNDICATE

Bloomberg News
Editorial: Sturegatan 4 Plan 2, Stockholm 11483. **T:** 46 86100700
E: stockholmnew@bloomberg.net
Stock Market Editor: Toby Alder; **Bureau Chief:** Kim McLaughlin; **Bureau Chief:** Kim McLaughlin
NEWS SERVICE/SYNDICATE

Dow Jones Newswires
Editorial: Kungsgatan 12-14, 7th Floor, Stockholm 11135. **T:** 46 8 5451-3090
E: djnews.stockholm@dowjones.com
News Editor: Anna Molin
NEWS SERVICE/SYNDICATE

Liberala nyhetsbyrån
Owner: Liberala Landsortstidningar
Editorial: Pressvåningen, RV 7, Riksdagen, Stockholm 100 12. **T:** 46 8 786 41 25
E: redaktionen@lnb.se **W:** http://www.lnb.se
Chef: Svend Dahl; **Ledarskribent & Debattredaktör:** Lars Kriss; **Ledarskribent:** Susanne Nyström
Language (s): Swedish
NEWS SERVICE/SYNDICATE

LTF Feature
Owner: Ylva Berlin
Editorial: Box 2033, Stockholm 103 11.
T: 46 8 20 70 38 **E:** info@ltffeature.com
W: http://www.ltffeature.com
Redaktör: Ylva Åkesson; **Redaktionschef & Ansvarig utgivare:** Ylva Berlin; **Redaktör:** Hanseman Calås; **Redaktör:** Birdie Dahlberg
Language (s): Swedish
NEWS SERVICE/SYNDICATE

Montel Powernews
Owner: Montal A/S
Editorial: Hornsgatan 116, Stockholm 117 26.
T: 46 730 290 255
E: se@montelpowernews.com
W: http://www.montelpowernews.com
Language (s): Swedish
NEWS SERVICE/SYNDICATE

Nattbyrån
W: http://www.xn--nattbyrn-g0a.se/
Language (s): Swedish
NEWS SERVICE/SYNDICATE

News Øresund
Owner: Øresundsinstituttet
Editorial: Øresund Media Platform, Øresundsinstituttet, Malmo 211 25
E: johan.wessman@oresundsinstituttet.org
W: http://www.oresundmediaplatform.org
Chefredaktör: Johan Wessman
Language (s): Danish
NEWS SERVICE/SYNDICATE

Nyheter i Norr ~ Arjeplog
Editorial: Storgatan 6, Arjeplog 930 90.
T: 46 961 106 30 **E:** info@nyheterinorr.se
W: http://www.nyheterinorr.se
Language (s): Swedish
NEWS SERVICE/SYNDICATE

Nyheter i Norr ~ Arvidsjaur
Editorial: Storgatan 23, Arvidsjaur 933 32.
T: 46 960 472 70 **E:** info@nyheterinorr.se
W: http://www.nyheterinorr.se
Language (s): Swedish
NEWS SERVICE/SYNDICATE

Nyhetsbyrån Direkt
Editorial: Jakobsbergsgatan 13 plan 6, Stockholm 111 44. **T:** 46 8 519 179 00
E: br@direkt.se **W:** http://www.direkt.se
Chefredaktör: Lars Östlund; **Redaktionssekreterare:** Viveka Romander-Bergman; **Nyhetschef:** Mikael Sandbladh; **Nyhetschef- Börs:** Mats Torgander; **Nyhetsredaktör:** Kristine Trapp
Language (s): Swedish
NEWS SERVICE/SYNDICATE

Nyhetsbyrån Direkt; SME Direkt
Editorial: Stockholm 111 43.
T: 46 8 519 179 00 **E:** sme@direkt.se
W: http://www.direkt.se
Redakör: Kristian Lang; **Redaktör:** Marcus Larsson
Language (s): Swedish
NEWS SERVICE/SYNDICATE

Nyhetsbyrån Siren
Editorial: Björns Trädgårdsgränd 1, Stockholm 116 21. **T:** 46 8 720 31 17 **E:** red@siren.se
W: http://www.siren.se
Nyhetschef: Emma Boëthius
Language (s): Swedish
NEWS SERVICE/SYNDICATE

Nytt från Öresund, NFÖ
Owner: Kristian Svensson
Editorial: Box 4140, Malmo 203 12.
T: 46 40 30 17 90 **E:** red@nfo.nu
W: http://www.nfo.nu
Chefredaktör / Ansvarig utgivare: Kristian Svensson
Language (s): Swedish
NEWS SERVICE/SYNDICATE

Presstext
Owner: Bonnier Affärsinformation AB
Editorial: Ynglingagatan 2, Stockholm 105 99.
T: 46 8 517 577 80
E: information.se@bisnode.com
W: http://www.presstext.se
Editor: Mr./Ms. Editor
Language (s): Swedish
NEWS SERVICE/SYNDICATE

Rapidus Nyhetstjänst
Owner: Kristian Svensson
Editorial: Box 4140, Malmo 203 12.
T: 46 40 30 17 90 **E:** rapidus@rapidus.se
W: http://www.rapidus.se
Köpenhamnsredaktör: Keld Broksø; **Nyhetschef:** Erik Olausson; **Nyhetschef:** Joel Persson; **Chefredaktör & Ansvarig utgivare:** Kristian Svensson
Language (s): Swedish
NEWS SERVICE/SYNDICATE

Reuters
Editorial: Kungsgatan 36, 1tr, Stockholm 11135. **T:** 46 8 700-1000
E: stockholm.newsroom@thomsonreuters.com
Bureau Chief: Alistair Scrutton
NEWS SERVICE/SYNDICATE

Scanpix
Owner: Bonnier AB och Scanpix Scandinavia AB (Schibsted)
Editorial: Scanpix Sweden AB, Stockholm 112 88. **T:** 46 8 738 38 00
E: picturedesk@scanpix.se
W: http://www.scanpix.se
Language (s): Swedish
NEWS SERVICE/SYNDICATE

Scanpix; Nyhetsredaktionen
Owner: Bonnier AB och Scanpix Scandinavia AB (Schibsted)
Editorial: Scanpix Sweden AB, Box 90249, Stockholm 112 88. **T:** 46 8 738 38 60
E: picturedesk@scanpix.se
W: http://www.scanpix.se
Language (s): Swedish
NEWS SERVICE/SYNDICATE

SIX News
Owner: SIX Financial Information AB
Editorial: SIX Financial Information Sweden AB, Olof Palmes Gata 11, Stockholm 103 62.
T: 46 8 58 61 63 00 **E:** red@six.se
W: http://www.six.se
Redaktionschef: Andreas Johansson; **Chefredaktör:** Lars Johansson; **Nyhetschef Makro:** Erik Palmung
Language (s): Swedish
NEWS SERVICE/SYNDICATE

Svenska Nyhetsbyrån
Owner: Svenska Nyhetsbyrån
Editorial: Box 3553, Stockholm 103 69.
T: 46 8 14 07 50 **E:** red@snb.se
W: http://www.snb.se
Ledarskribent & Debattredaktör: Marika Formgren; **Frilansande skribent:** Adam Nelvin; **Chefredaktör:** Per Selstam
Language (s): Swedish
NEWS SERVICE/SYNDICATE

TT Nyhetsbyrån
Owner: Tidningarnas Telegrambyrå AB
Editorial: Tidningarnas Telegrambyrå, Katarinavägen 15, Stockholm 105 12.
T: 46 8 692 26 00 **E:** redaktionen@tt.se
W: http://www.tt.se
Nyhetschef: Margareta Gustafsson Kubista; **Redaktionschef:** Mats Johansson; **Nyhetschef:** Britt Ledberg; **Redaktionschef:** Agneta Magnusson; **Nyhetschef- Output:** Karl Vicktor Olsson; **Chef:** Mats Olsson; **Nyhetschef-Intake:** Magnus Persson
Language (s): Swedish
NEWS SERVICE/SYNDICATE

TT Nyhetsbyrån ~ Göteborg
Editorial: Box 11901, Östra Hamngatan 30, Goteborg 404 39. **T:** 46 31 755 16 00
E: goteborg@tt.se **W:** http://www.tt.se
Redaktionschef Göteborg: Margareta Gustafsson Kubista
Language (s): Swedish
NEWS SERVICE/SYNDICATE

TT Nyhetsbyrån ~ Malmö
Editorial: Storgatan 22 A, Malmo 211 42.
T: 46 40 10 05 00 **E:** malmo@tt.se
W: http://www.tt.se
Redaktionschef Malmö: Cecilia Klintö
Language (s): Swedish
NEWS SERVICE/SYNDICATE

TT Nyhetsbyrån; Bildredaktionen
Owner: Svenska Grafikbyrån
Editorial: TT Nyhetsbyrån, Katarinavägen 15, Stockholm 105 12. **T:** 46 8 738 38 60
E: picturedesk@tt.se **W:** http://bild.tt.se/
Redaktör: Anders Kjellström
Language (s): Swedish
NEWS SERVICE/SYNDICATE

TT Nyhetsbyrån; Centralredaktionen
Editorial: Tidningarnas Telegrambyrå, Katarinavägen 15, Stockholm 105 12.
T: 46 8 692 27 00 **E:** redaktionen@tt.se
W: http://www.tt.se
Nyhetschef: Lisa Abrahamsson; **Redigerare:** Kenneth Ahlborn; **Kvällsredaktör:** Daniel Berg; **Redaktör:** Helena Björkvall; **Redigerare:** Johan Brännström; **Redaktör:** Rebecka Fogelmarck; **Redaktör:** Daniel Kjellberg; **Redigerare:** Daniel Martinsson; **Redaktör:** Elisabeth Modig-Blåder; **Chef:** Mats Olsson; **Redigerare:** Olle Svanberg
Language (s): Swedish
NEWS SERVICE/SYNDICATE

TT Nyhetsbyrån; Feature
Owner: Tidningarnas Telegrambyrå AB
Editorial: Katarinavägen 15, Stockholm 105 12. **T:** 46 8 692 26 00 **E:** feature@tt.se
W: http://tt.se/
Redaktör: Linda Gustavsson; **Redaktör:** Lisa Wallström
Language (s): Swedish
NEWS SERVICE/SYNDICATE

TT Nyhetsbyrån; Inrikesredaktionen
Editorial: Tidningarnas Telegrambyrå, Katarinavägen 15, Stockholm 105 12.
T: 46 8 692 26 00 **E:** redaktionen@tt.se
W: http://www.tt.se
Language (s): Swedish
NEWS SERVICE/SYNDICATE

TT Nyhetsbyrån; Nöjes- och kulturredaktion
Editorial: Katarinavägen 15, Stockholm 105 12. **T:** 46 8 692 26 00 **E:** noje@tt.se
W: http://www.tt.se
Language (s): Swedish
NEWS SERVICE/SYNDICATE

TT Nyhetsbyrån; Politik/ Ekonomiredaktionen
Editorial: Katarinavägen 15, Stockholm 105 12. **T:** 46 8 692 26 00 **E:** ekonomi@tt.se
W: http://www.tt.se
Language (s): Swedish
NEWS SERVICE/SYNDICATE

TT Nyhetsbyrån; Sportredaktionen
Editorial: Katarinavägen 15, Stockholm 105 12. **T:** 46 8 692 28 40 **E:** sport@tt.se
W: http://www.tt.se
Language (s): Swedish
NEWS SERVICE/SYNDICATE

TT Nyhetsbyrån; TV-redaktionen
Editorial: Katarinavägen 15, Stockholm 105 12. **T:** 46 8 692 26 00 **E:** tvred@tt.se
W: http://www.tt.se
Redaktör: Cajsa Alriksson; **Redigerare:** Kristina Erkenborn; **Redigerare:** Henrik Gurås; **Redigerare:** Ann Jonsson; **Redigerare:** Jin Mavesson; **Redigerare:** James Mollan; **Redaktör:** Mikael Nilsson; **Redigerare:** Jenny

Östman; **Redigerare:** Agneta Pettersson;
Redigerare: Gun Porling; **Redigerare:** Emilie
Sterckx; **Redigerare:** Elisabeth Ström;
Redigerare: Linda Welin-Berger; **Redigerare:**
Åsa Yngve
Language (s): Swedish
NEWS SERVICE/SYNDICATE

TT Nyhetsbyrån; Utrikesredaktionen
Editorial: Tidningarnas Telegrambyrå,
Katarinavägen 15, Stockholm 105 12.
T: 46 8 692 26 80 **W:** http://www.tt.se
Language (s): Swedish
NEWS SERVICE/SYNDICATE

TT Nyhetsbyrån; Videoredaktionen
Editorial: Tidningarnas Telegrambyrå,
Katarinavägen 15, Stockholm 105 12.
T: 46 8 738 39 90 **E:** video@tt.se
W: http://www.tt.se
Redaktionschef: Birgitta Nilsson
Language (s): Swedish
NEWS SERVICE/SYNDICATE

Wighsnews
Owner: Wigh:s Nyhetscentral AB
Editorial: Hollsta Udde, Norrköping 605 95.
T: 46 11 34 33 22
W: http://www.wighsnews.se
Ansvarig utgivare: Ulf Wigh
Language (s): Swedish
NEWS SERVICE/SYNDICATE

Wighsnews; Bildredaktionen
Owner: Wigh:s Nyhetscentral AB
Editorial: Hollsta Udde, Norrköping 605 95.
T: 46 11 34 33 22
W: http://www.wighsnews.se
Redaktionschef: Ulf Wigh
Language (s): Swedish
NEWS SERVICE/SYNDICATE

Wighsnews; Internet/
Webbredaktionen
Owner: Ulf Wigh
Editorial: Hollsta Udde, Norrköping 605 95.
T: 46 11 34 35 22
W: http://www.wighsnews.se
Language (s): Swedish
NEWS SERVICE/SYNDICATE

Wighsnews; Nyhetsredaktionen
Editorial: Hollsta Udde, Norrköping 605 95.
T: 46 11 34 35 22
W: http://www.wighsnews.se
Ansvarig utgivare: Ulf Wigh
Language (s): Swedish
NEWS SERVICE/SYNDICATE

BROADCASTING

RADIO STATIONS

Bandit Rock 106-3
Owner: MTG Radio
Editorial: MTG Radio, Box 17115, Stockholm
104 62. **T:** 46 8 562 720 00
E: mattias.arwidson@mtgradio.com
W: http://www.bandit.se

Guld 106,6 Sundsvall
Editorial: Torggatan 9, Sundsvall 851 72.
T: 46 60 17 85 00 **E:** guld@st.nu
W: http://www.guld.nu

Guldkanalen 102,6
Owner: DB Media AB
Editorial: Staffanstorp. **T:** 46 46 252 752
E: info@dbmedia.se
W: http://www.guldkanalen.se

Lugna Favoriter 104,7
Owner: MTG Radio
Editorial: MTG Radio, Södermälarstrand 43,
Stockholm 118 25. **T:** 46 8 562 720 00
W: http://www.lugnafavoriter.com

Mix Megapol
Owner: SBS Radio AB
Editorial: Gjörwellsgatan 30, Stockholm 100
26. **T:** 46 8 450 33 00
E: info@mixmegapol.com
W: http://www.radioplay.se/mixmegapol

Mix Megapol ~ 104,2 Bohuslän
Owner: SBS Radio AB
Editorial: Kungsgatan 17, Lysekil 453 33.
T: 46 5 231 21 60 **E:** info@mixmegapol.se
W: http://www.mixmegapol.se/?loc=bohuslan

Mix Megapol ~ 104,3 & 92,0
Stockholm/Södertälje
Owner: SBS Radio AB

Editorial: Gjörwellsgatan 30, BOX 34108,
Stockholm 100 26. **T:** 46 8 450 33 00
E: info@mixmegapol.com
W: http://www.mixmegapol.se/?loc=sodertalje

Mix Megapol ~ 104,7 Örebro
Owner: SBS Radio AB
Editorial: Box 245, Orebro 702 22.
T: 46 19 17 01 04 **E:** info@mixmegapol.com
W: http://www.mixmegapol.se/?loc=orebro

Mix Megapol ~ 104.2 Umeå & 105,2
Norra Norrland
Owner: SBS Radio AB
Editorial: Umestan Företagspark, hus 7, Umeå
903 47. **T:** 46 911 21 10 70
E: info@mixmegapol.se
W: http://www.mixmegapol.se/?loc=kiruna

Mix Megapol ~ 105,5 Falun/
Borlänge
Owner: SBS Radio AB
Editorial: Box 265, Falun 791 26.
T: 46 239 35 78 **E:** info@mixmegapol.com
W: http://www.mixmegapol.se/?loc=falun

Mix Megapol ~ 106,1 Västmanland
Owner: SBS Radio AB
Editorial: c/o Radiobokningen, Västerås 722
12. **T:** 46 21 19 90 10
E: info@mixmegapol.com
W: http://www.mixmegapol.com

Mix Megapol ~ 106,7 Gävle/
Sandviken
Owner: SBS Radio AB
Editorial: Box 1028, Gävle 801 34.
T: 46 26 14 17 30 **E:** gavle@mixmegapol.com
W: http://www.mixmegapol.com

Mix Megapol ~ 106,8 Mora/Sälen
Owner: SBS Radio AB
Editorial: Box 265, Falun 791 26.
T: 46 243 22 81 05 **E:** info@mixmegapol.com
W: http://www.mixmegapol.se/?loc=mora

Mix Megapol ~ 106,9 & 99,2
Östergötland/Motala
Owner: SBS Radio AB
Editorial: Box 655, Linköping 582 23.
T: 46 13 14 14 53
E: linkoping@mixmegapol.com
W: http://www.mixmegapol.se/
?loc=ostergotland

Mix Megapol ~ 107,3 & 93,1
Sörmland
Owner: SBS Radio AB
Editorial: Rinmansgatan 18, Eskilstuna 633
46. **T:** 46 16 12 10 73
E: eskilstuna@mixmegapol.com
W: http://www.mixmegapol.se/?loc=sormland

Mix Megapol ~ 107,3 Göteborg
Owner: SBS Radio AB
Editorial: Kajskjul 107, Frihamnen 16A,
Goteborg 417 07. **T:** 46 31 726 10 00
E: info.gbg@radiocity.se
W: http://www.mixmegapol.se

Mix Megapol ~ 107,3 Skaraborg
Owner: SBS Radio AB
Editorial: Mariestadsvägen 86, Skövde 541
45. **T:** 46 500 42 75 00
E: skovde@mixmegapol.com
W: http://www.mixmegapol.se/?loc=skovde

Mix Megapol Gotland - Radio Four
Owner: SBS Radio AB
Editorial: Box 1444, Brovägen 10, Visby 621
58. **T:** 46 498 20 24 40
E: info@mixmegapol.com
W: http://www.mixmegapol.se/?loc=gotland

NRJ
Owner: MTG Radio
Editorial: Box 17115, Gjörwellsgatan 30,
Stockholm 112 60. **T:** 46 8 562 720 00
E: rickard.keilor@nrj.se
W: http://www.radioplay.se/nrj

NRJ ~ 105,1 Stockholm
Owner: MTG Radio
Editorial: Box 17115, Stockholm 104 62.
T: 46 8 562 720 00 **E:** rickard.keilor@nrj.se
W: http://www.nrj.se

Premier
Editorial: Premier Radio Sweden,
Lägerhyddsvägen 2, Hus 38, Uppsala 752 37
E: info@premierradio.se
W: http://www.premierradio.se

Radio Siljan
Owner: Radio Siljan Mora
Editorial: Box 131, Mora 792 22.
T: 46 250 105 00 **E:** info@radiosiljan.com
W: http://www.radiosiljan.com

Radio Umeå 102,3 Mhz
Owner: Radio Umeå (Robert Jacobsson)
Editorial: Bölevägen 38, Umeå 904 31.
T: 46 90 19 74 70
E: redaktion@radioumea.com
W: http://www.radioumea.com

Radio1 101,9 ~ Stockholm
Owner: MTG Radio
Editorial: Radio1, Ringvägen 52, Stockholm
118 67. **T:** 46 8 562 720 00
E: stefan.halvardsson@mtgradio.com
W: http://www.radio1.se

RIX FM
Owner: MTG Radio AB
Editorial: Box 171 15, Ringvägen 52,
Stockholm 118 67. **T:** 46 8 562 720 00
E: rix@zradio.se **W:** http://www.rixfm.com

Rockklassiker
Owner: SBS Radio AB
Editorial: Box 34108, SBS Radio AB,
Stockholm 110 26. **T:** 46 8 450 33 00
E: cloffe@rockklassiker.se
W: http://www.rockklassiker.se

Sveriges Radio Göteborg
Owner: Sveriges Radio AB
Editorial: P4 Sveriges Radio Göteborg,
Pumpgatan 2, Goteborg 405 13.
T: 46 31 83 76 00
E: P4goteborg@sverigesradio.se
W: http://sverigesradio.se/goteborg

Sveriges Radio P4 Blekinge
Owner: Sveriges Radio AB
Editorial: Besöksadress: Högabersgatan 3,
Karlskrona 371 25. **T:** 46 455 36 68 00
E: nyheter.blekinge@sverigesradio.se
W: http://www.sverigesradio.se/blekinge

Sveriges Radio P4 Blekinge;
Nyhetsredaktionen
Owner: Sveriges Radio AB
Editorial: Box 305, Besöksadress:
Högabergsgatan 3, Karlskrona 371 25.
T: 46 455 36 68 00 **E:** nyheter.blekinge@sr.se
W: http://sverigesradio.se/sida/default.
aspx?programid=105

Sveriges Radio P4 Dalarna
Owner: Sveriges Radio AB
Editorial: Box 123, Engelbrektsgatan 27 B,
Falun 791 23. **T:** 46 23 77 77 00
E: dalarna@sverigesradio.se
W: http://www.sverigesradio.se/dalarna

Sveriges Radio P4 Dalarna; Klartext
Owner: Sveriges Radio AB
Editorial: Box 123, Engelbrektsgatan 27B,
Falun 791 23. **T:** 46 23 77 77 50
E: klartext@sr.se
W: http://sverigesradio.se/sida/default.
aspx?programid=493

Sveriges Radio P4 Dalarna;
Nyhetsredaktionen
Owner: Sveriges Radio AB
Editorial: Box 123, Engelbrektsgatan 27 B,
Falun 791 23. **T:** 46 23 77 77 70
E: dalanytt@sverigesradio.se
W: http://sverigesradio.se/sida/default.
aspx?programid=2069

Sveriges Radio P4 Dalarna;
Sportredaktionen
Owner: Sveriges Radio
Editorial: Box 123, Engelbrektsgatan 27 B,
Falun 791 23. **T:** 46 23 77 77 30
E: sporten.dalarna@sr.se
W: http://sverigesradio.se/sida/gruppsida.
aspx?programid=22&grupp=3825

Sveriges Radio P4 Gävleborg
Owner: Sveriges Radio AB
Editorial: Nygatan 29, Gävle 801 04.
T: 46 26 66 65 00
E: nyheterna.gavleborg@sverigesradio.se
W: http://www.sverigesradio.se/gavleborg

Sveriges Radio P4 Gävleborg ~
Bollnäs
Owner: Sveriges Radio
Editorial: Vågvägen 13, Bollnäs 821 42.
T: 46 26 66 65 51 **E:** info.gavleborg@sr.se
W: http://www.sverigesradio.se/gavleborg

Sveriges Radio P4 Gävleborg ~
Hudiksvall
Owner: Sveriges radio
Editorial: Storgatan 47, Hudiksvall 824 52
W: http://www.sverigesradio.se/gavleborg

Sveriges Radio P4 Gävleborg;
Nyhetsredaktionen
Owner: Sveriges Radio
Editorial: Box 311, Nygatan 29 3tr, Gävle 801
04. **T:** 46 26 66 65 31
E: nyheterna.gavleborg@sverigesradio.se
W: http://sverigesradio.se/sida/default.
aspx?programid=99

Sveriges Radio P4 Gävleborg;
Sportredaktionen
Owner: Sveriges Radio AB
Editorial: Box 311, Nygatan 29 3tr, Gävle 801
04. **T:** 46 26 66 65 00
E: sporten.gavleborg@sr.se
W: http://sverigesradio.se/sida/gruppsida.
aspx?programid=24&grupp=3827

Sveriges Radio P4 Göteborg;
Göteborg Direkt
Owner: Sveriges Radio
Editorial: Sveriges Radio P4, Göteborg Direkt,
Pumpgatan 2, Goteborg 405 13
E: p4goteborg@sverigesradio.se
W: http://sverigesradio.se/sida/
avsnitt?programid=2240

Sveriges Radio P4 Göteborg;
Nyhetsredaktionen
Owner: Sveriges Radio
Editorial: Sveriges Radio P4 Göteborg,
Pumpgatan 2, Goteborg 405 13.
T: 46 31 83 76 00
E: P4goteborg@sverigesradio.se
W: http://sverigesradio.se/sida/default.
aspx?programid=104

Sveriges Radio P4 Göteborg;
Sportredaktionen
Owner: Sveriges Radio
Editorial: Sveriges Radio P4 Göteborg,
Pumpgatan 2, Goteborg 405 13.
T: 46 31 83 70 00 **E:** sporten.gbg@sr.se
W: http://sverigesradio.se/sida/gruppsida.
aspx?programid=25&grupp=3828

Sveriges Radio P4 Gotland; Nyhets-
& programredaktion
Owner: Sveriges Radio AB
Editorial: Sveriges Radio Gotland, Box 1324,
Visby 621 24. **T:** 46 498 75 00 00
E: gotlandsnytt@sverigesradio.se
W: http://sverigesradio.se/gotland

Sveriges Radio P4 Gotland;
Sportredaktionen
Owner: Sveriges Radio AB
Editorial: Box 1324, Östra Hansegatan 28,
Visby 621 24. **T:** 46 498 75 00 00
E: gotlandssporten@sr.se
W: http://sverigesradio.se/sida/gruppsida.
aspx?programid=23&grupp=3826

Sveriges Radio P4 Halland
Owner: Sveriges Radio AB
Editorial: Box 133, Köpmansgatan 41,
Halmstad 301 04. **T:** 46 35 17 27 00
E: radio.halland@sr.se
W: http://www.sr.se/halland

Sveriges Radio P4 Halland ~
Varberg
Owner: Sveriges Radio
Editorial: Otto Torells gata 14, Varberg 432 44
E: nyheter.halland@sr.se
W: http://www.sverigesradio.se/halland

Sveriges Radio P4 Halland;
Nyhetsredaktionen
Owner: Sveriges Radio AB
Editorial: Box 133, Köpmansgatan 41 (vid Lilla
torg), Halmstad 301 04. **T:** 46 35 17 27 00
E: nyheter.halland@sverigesradio.se
W: http://www.sverigesradio.se/halland

Sveriges Radio P4 Halland;
Sportredaktionen
Owner: Sveriges Radio AB
Editorial: Box 133, Besöksadress:
Köpmansgatan 41, Halmstad 301 04.
T: 46 35 17 27 00 **E:** sporten.halland@sr.se
W: http://sverigesradio.se/sida/gruppsida.
aspx?programid=26&grupp=3829

Sveriges Radio P4 Jämtland
Owner: Sveriges Radio AB
Editorial: Lingonvägen 7B, Box 476,
Östersund 831 26. **T:** 46 63 16 06 00

E: p4jamtland@sverigesradio.se
W: http://sverigesradio.se/jamtland

**Sveriges Radio P4 Jämtland;
Nyhetsredaktionen**
Owner: Sveriges Radio AB
Editorial: Lingonvägen 7B, Box 476,
Östersund 831 26. T: 46 63 16 06 32
E: nyheter.jamtland@sverigesradio.se
W: http://www.sverigesradio.se/jamtland

**Sveriges Radio P4 Jämtland;
Sportredaktionen**
Owner: Sveriges Radio AB
Editorial: Lingonvägen 7B, Box 476,
Östersund 831 26. T: 46 63 16 06 86
E: sport.jamtland@sverigesradio.se
W: http://sverigesradio.se/sida/gruppsida.
aspx?programid=27&grupp=3830

Sveriges Radio P4 Jönköping
Owner: Sveriges Radio AB
Editorial: Barnarpsgatan 35 D, Jönköping 551
92. T: 46 36 215 66 00
E: news.jkp@sverigesradio.se
W: http://www.sverigesradio.se/jonkoping

**Sveriges Radio P4 Jönköping ~
Värnamo**
Owner: Sveriges Radio
Editorial: Jönköpingsvägen 43 B, Värnamo
331 34. T: 46 36 215 66 60
E: news.jkp@sverigesradio.se
W: http://www.sverigesradio.se/jonkoping

**Sveriges Radio P4 Jönköping;
Nyhetsredaktionen**
Owner: Sveriges Radio AB
Editorial: Sveriges Radio Jönköping,
Barnarpsgatan 35 D, Jönköping 551 92.
T: 46 36 215 66 00
E: news.jkp@sverigesradio.se
W: http://www.sverigesradio.se/jonkoping

**Sveriges Radio P4 Jönköping;
Sportredaktionen**
Owner: Sveriges Radio AB
Editorial: Sveriges Radio Jönköping,
Besöksadress: Barnarpsgatan 35 D, Jönköping
551 92. T: 46 36 215 66 00
W: http://sverigesradio.se/sida/gruppsida.
aspx?programid=28&grupp=3831

Sveriges Radio P4 Kalmar
Owner: Sveriges Radio AB
Editorial: Norra Vägen 22, Kalmar 391 83.
T: 46 480 45 80 00
E: nyheter.kalmar@sverigesradio.se
W: http://sverigesradio.se/kalmar/

**Sveriges Radio P4 Kalmar;
Nyhetsredaktionen**
Owner: Sveriges Radio AB
Editorial: Norra vägen 22, Kalmar 391 83.
T: 46 480 45 80 00
E: nyheter.kalmar@sverigesradio.se
W: http://www.sverigesradio.se/kalmar

**Sveriges Radio P4 Kalmar;
Sportredaktionen**
Owner: Sveriges Radio
Editorial: Norra vägen 22, Kalmar 391 83.
T: 46 480 45 80 00
E: sport.kalmar@sverigesradio.se
W: http://sverigesradio.se/sida/gruppsida.
aspx?programid=30&grupp=3832

Sveriges Radio P4 Kristianstad
Owner: Sveriges Radio AB
Editorial: Box 505, Besöksadress:
Gasverksgatan 2, Kristianstad 291 25.
T: 46 44 775 12 00
E: nyheterna.kristianstad@sverigesradio.se
W: http://sverigesradio.se/kristianstad/

**Sveriges Radio P4 Kristianstad ~
Simrishamn**
Owner: Sveriges Radio
Editorial: Box 6, Järnvägsgatan 5, Simrishamn
272 21. T: 46 414 146 55
E: nyheterna.kristianstad@sverigesradio.se
W: http://www.sverigesradio.se/kristianstad

**Sveriges Radio P4 Kristianstad;
Nyhetsredaktionen**
Owner: Sveriges Radio AB
Editorial: Box 505, Besöksadress:
Gasverksgatan 2, Kristianstad 291 25.
T: 46 44 775 12 00
E: nyheterna.kristianstad@sverigesradio.se
W: http://sverigesradio.se/kristianstad

**Sveriges Radio P4 Kristianstad;
Sportredaktionen**
Owner: Sveriges Radio AB
Editorial: Box 505, Gasversksgatan 2,
Kristianstad 291 25. T: 46 44 775 12 00
E: sporten.kristianstad@sverigesradio.se
W: http://sverigesradio.se/sida/gruppsida.
aspx?programid=29&grupp=3833

Sveriges Radio P4 Kronoberg
Owner: Sveriges Radio AB
Editorial: Västergatan 1, Box 62, 351 03
Växjö, Växjo 352 30. T: 46 470 72 60 00
E: nyheter.kronoberg@sverigesradio.se
W: http://www.sverigesradio.se/kronoberg

**Sveriges Radio P4 Kronoberg;
Nyhetsredaktionen**
Owner: Sveriges Radio AB
Editorial: Västergatan 1, Box 62, 351 03
Växjö, Växjo 352 30. T: 46 470 72 60 50
E: nyheter.kronoberg@sverigesradio.se
W: http://www.sverigesradio.se/kronoberg

**Sveriges Radio P4 Kronoberg;
Sportredaktionen**
Owner: Sveriges Radio AB
Editorial: Västergatan 1, Box 62, 351 03
Växjö, Växjo 352 30. T: 46 470 72 60 00
E: sporten.kronoberg@sverigesradio.se
W: http://sverigesradio.se/sida/gruppsida.
aspx?programid=31&grupp=3834

Sveriges Radio P4 Malmö
Owner: Sveriges Radio AB
Editorial: Balzarsgatan 16, Malmo 211 01.
T: 46 40 666 55 00
E: p4malmohus@sverigesradio.se
W: http://www.sverigesradio.se/malmo

**Sveriges Radio P4 Malmö/SR P4
Kristianstad ~ Helsingborg**
Owner: Sveriges Radio AB
Editorial: Drottninggatan 72 A, Helsingborg
252 21. T: 46 42 13 33 00
E: nordvast@sverigesradio.se
W: http://sverigesradio.se/malmo/

**Sveriges Radio P4 Malmö;
Nyhetsredaktionen**
Owner: Sveriges Radio AB
Editorial: Baltzarsgatan 16, Malmo 211 01.
T: 46 40 666 55 00
E: news.malm@sverigesradio.se
W: http://sverigesradio.se/malmo/

**Sveriges Radio P4 Malmö; Skåne
Direkt**
Owner: Sveriges Radio AB
Editorial: Balzarsgatan 16, Malmo 211 01.
T: 46 40 666 55 00
E: p4malmohus@sverigesradio.se
W: http://sverigesradio.se/sida/artikel.
aspx?programid=96&artikel=5479093

**Sveriges Radio P4 Malmö;
Sportredaktionen**
Owner: Sveriges Radio AB
Editorial: Balzarsgatan 16, Malmo 211 01.
T: 46 40 666 55 00
E: sporten.malm@sverigesradio.se
W: http://sverigesradio.se/sida/gruppsida.
aspx?programid=32&grupp=3835

Sveriges Radio P4 Norrbotten
Owner: Sveriges Radio AB
Editorial: Nygatan 3, Luleå 971 71.
T: 46 920 27 53 00
E: p4norrbotten@sverigesradio.se
W: http://sverigesradio.se/norrbotten/

**Sveriges Radio P4 Norrbotten
(Sisuradio) ~ Pajala**
Editorial: Pajala 984 21. T: 46 978 757 00
W: http://www.sverigesradio.se/norrbotten

**Sveriges Radio P4 Norrbotten ~
Gällivare**
Owner: Sveriges Radio AB
Editorial: Box 264, Industrigatan 4, Gällivare
982 31. T: 46 970 789 70
E: nyheter.norrbotten@sverigesradio.se
W: http://sverigesradio.se/sida/gruppsida.
aspx?programid=98&grupp=3592

**Sveriges Radio P4 Norrbotten;
Nyhetsredaktionen**
Owner: Sveriges Radio AB
Editorial: Nygatan 3, Luleå 971 71.
T: 46 920 27 53 00
E: nyheter.norrbotten@sverigesradio.se
W: http://sverigesradio.se/norrbotten

**Sveriges Radio P4 Norrbotten;
Sportredaktionen**
Owner: Sveriges Radio AB
Editorial: Nygatan 3, Luleå 971 71.
T: 46 920 27 53 70
E: sporten.norrbotten@sverigesradio.se
W: http://sverigesradio.se/sida/gruppsida.
aspx?programid=33&grupp=3836

Sveriges Radio P4 Örebro
Owner: Sveriges Radio AB
Editorial: Västra Bangatan 15, Orebro 701 80.
T: 46 19 19 20 00
E: p4orebro@sverigesradio.se
W: http://www.sverigesradio.se/orebro

**Sveriges Radio P4 Örebro;
Nyhetsredaktionen**
Owner: Sveriges Radio AB
Editorial: Västra Bangatan 15, Orebro 701 80.
T: 46 19 19 20 00
E: nyheter.orebro@sverigesradio.se
W: http://sverigesradio.se/orebro

**Sveriges Radio P4 Örebro;
Sportredaktionen**
Owner: Sveriges Radio AB
Editorial: Västra Bangatan 15, Orebro 701 80.
T: 46 19 19 20 00
E: sporten.orebro@sverigesradio.se
W: http://sverigesradio.se/sida/gruppsida.
aspx?programid=44&grupp=3847

Sveriges Radio P4 Östergötland
Owner: Sveriges Radio AB
Editorial: Box 500, Västgötegatan 13 A,
Norrköping 601 07. T: 46 11 495 41 00
E: nyheter.ostg@sverigesradio.se
W: http://sverigesradio.se/ostergotland

**Sveriges Radio P4 Östergötland ~
Linköping**
Owner: Sveriges Radio AB
Editorial: Apotekaregatan 13 D, Linköping 582
24. T: 46 11 495 41 00 E: nyheter.ostg@sr.se
W: http://sverigesradio.se/ostergotland

**Sveriges Radio P4 Östergötland;
Nyhetsredaktionen**
Owner: Sveriges Radio AB
Editorial: Box 500, Västgötegatan 13 A,
Norrköping 601 07. T: 46 11 495 41 00
E: nyheter.ostg@sverigesradio.se
W: http://sverigesradio.se/ostergotland

**Sveriges Radio P4 Östergötland;
Sportredaktionen**
Owner: Sveriges Radio AB
Editorial: Box 500, Västgötegatan 13 A,
Norrköping 601 07. T: 46 11 495 41 00
E: sport.ostg@sverigesradio.se
W: http://sverigesradio.se/sida/gruppsida.
aspx?programid=45&grupp=3848

Sveriges Radio P4 Sjuhärad
Owner: Sveriges Radio AB
Editorial: Box 27, Katrinedalsgatan 22, Borås
503 05. T: 46 33 17 75 00
E: p4sjuharad@sverigesradio.se
W: http://www.sverigesradio.se/sjuharad

**Sveriges Radio P4 Sjuhärad;
Nyhetsredaktionen**
Owner: Sveriges Radio AB
Editorial: Box 27, Katrinedalsgatan 22, Borås
503 05. T: 46 33 17 75 00
E: news.sjuharad@sverigesradio.se
W: http://www.sverigesradio.se/sjuharad

**Sveriges Radio P4 Sjuhärad;
Sportredaktionen**
Owner: Sveriges Radio AB
Editorial: Box 27, Katrinedalsgatan 22, Borås
503 05. T: 46 33 17 75 00
E: sporten.sjuharad@sr.se
W: http://sverigesradio.se/sida/gruppsida.
aspx?programid=34&grupp=3839

Sveriges Radio P4 Skaraborg
Owner: Sveriges Radio AB
Editorial: Norra Bergvägen 4, Skövde 541 24.
T: 46 500 77 30 00
E: p4.skaraborg@sverigesradio.se
W: http://www.sverigesradio.se/skaraborg

**Sveriges Radio P4 Skaraborg;
Nyhetsredaktionen**
Owner: Sveriges Radio AB
Editorial: Norra Bergvägen 4, Skövde 541 24.
T: 46 500 77 30 10
E: nyheter.skaraborg@sverigesradio.se
W: http://www.sverigesradio.se/skaraborg

**Sveriges Radio P4 Skaraborg;
Sportredaktionen**
Owner: Sveriges Radio AB
Editorial: Norra Bergvägen 4, Skövde 541 24.
T: 46 500 77 30 00
E: sporten.skaraborg@sverigesradio.se
W: http://sverigesradio.se/sida/gruppsida.
aspx?programid=35&grupp=3840

Sveriges Radio P4 Sörmland
Owner: Sveriges Radio AB
Editorial: Box 641, 631 08, Rademachergatan
1, Eskilstuna 632 21. T: 46 16 16 16 00
E: sormland@sverigesradio.se
W: http://sverigesradio.se/sormland/

**Sveriges Radio P4 Sörmland ~
Nyköping**
Owner: Sveriges Radio AB
Editorial: S:t Annegatan 4, Nyköping 611 34.
T: 46 16 16 16 00
E: sormland@sverigesradio.se
W: http://www.sverigesradio.se/sormland

**Sveriges Radio P4 Sörmland;
Nyhetsredaktionen**
Owner: Sveriges Radio AB
Editorial: Sveriges Radio Sörmland, Box 641,
Eskilstuna 631 08. T: 46 16 16 16 00
E: sormland@sverigesradio.se
W: http://sverigesradio.se/sormland/

**Sveriges Radio P4 Sörmland;
Sportredaktionen**
Owner: Sveriges Radio AB
Editorial: Box 641, Rademachergatan 1,
Eskilstuna 631 08. T: 46 16 16 16 00
E: sport.sormland@sverigesradio.se
W: http://sverigesradio.se/sida/gruppsida.
aspx?programid=37&grupp=3841

Sveriges Radio P4 Stockholm
Owner: Sveriges Radio AB
Editorial: Oxenstiernsgatan 20, Stockholm 105
10. T: 46 8 784 95 00
E: p4stockholm@sverigesradio.se
W: http://sverigesradio.se/stockholm

**Sveriges Radio P4 Stockholm;
Nyhetsredaktionen**
Owner: Sveriges Radio AB
Editorial: Sveriges Radio P4 Radio Stockholm,
Oxenstiernsgatan 20, Stockholm 105 10.
T: 46 8 784 95 00
E: news.sth@sverigesradio.se
W: http://sverigesradio.se/stockholm

**Sveriges Radio P4 Stockholm;
Sportredaktionen**
Owner: Sveriges Radio AB
Editorial: Sveriges Radio P4 Radio Stockholm,
Oxenstiernsgatan 20, Stockholm 105 10.
T: 46 8 784 95 00
E: sportstockholm@sverigesradio.se
W: http://sverigesradio.se/sida/gruppsida.
aspx?programid=36&grupp=3837

Sveriges Radio P4 Uppland
Owner: Sveriges Radio AB
Editorial: Box 1552, Bredgränd 7, Uppsala
751 45. T: 46 18 17 40 00
E: p4uppland@sverigesradio.se
W: http://www.sverigesradio.se/uppland

**Sveriges Radio P4 Uppland;
Nyhetsredaktionen**
Owner: Sveriges Radio AB
Editorial: Box 1552, Bredgränd 7, Uppsala
751 45. T: 46 18 17 40 00
E: upplandsnytt@sverigesradio.se
W: http://www.sverigesradio.se/uppland

**Sveriges Radio P4 Uppland;
Sportredaktionen**
Owner: Sveriges Radio AB
Editorial: Box 1552, Bredgränd 7, Uppsala
751 45. T: 46 18 17 40 00
E: sporten.uppland@sverigesradio.se
W: http://sverigesradio.se/sida/gruppsida.
aspx?programid=38&grupp=3842

Sveriges Radio P4 Värmland
Owner: Sveriges Radio AB
Editorial: Box 98, 651 03 Karlstad,
Verkstadsgatan 20, Karlstad 652 19.
T: 46 54 777 26 00
E: p4varmland@sverigesradio.se
W: http://www.sverigesradio.se/varmland

**Sveriges Radio P4 Värmland ~
Torsby**
Owner: Sveriges Radio AB
Editorial: Box 73, 685 22 Torsby, Alstigen 8C,
Torsby 685 22. T: 46 54 777 26 00
E: p4varmland@sverigesradio.se

W: http://www.sverigesradio.se/varmland

Sveriges Radio P4 Värmland; Nyhetsredaktionen
Owner: Sveriges Radio AB
Editorial: Box 98, 651 03 Karlstad, Verkstadsgatan 20, Karlstad 652 19.
T: 46 54 777 26 34
E: nyheter.varmland@sverigesradio.se
W: http://www.sverigesradio.se/varmland

Sveriges Radio P4 Värmland; Sportredaktionen
Owner: Sveriges Radio AB
Editorial: Box 98, 651 03 Karlstad, Verkstadsgatan 20, Karlstad 652 19.
T: 46 54 777 26 00
E: sporten.varmland@sverigesradio.se
W: http://sverigesradio.se/sida/gruppsida.aspx?programid=39&grupp=3843

Sveriges Radio P4 Väst
Owner: Sveriges Radio AB
Editorial: Box 654, Södergatan 11, Uddevalla 451 24. T: 46 522 67 00 00
E: p4vast@sverigesradio.se
W: http://www.sverigesradio.se/vast

Sveriges Radio P4 Väst ~ Åmål
Owner: Sveriges Radio AB
Editorial: Norra Långgatan 26, Åmål 662 30.
T: 46 532 158 80
E: nyheter.vast@sverigesradio.se
W: http://www.sverigesradio.se/vast

Sveriges Radio P4 Väst; Nyhetsredaktionen
Owner: Sveriges Radio AB
Editorial: Box 654, Södergatan 11, Uddevalla 451 24. T: 46 522 67 00 25
E: nyheter.vast@sverigesradio.se
W: http://www.sverigesradio.se/vast

Sveriges Radio P4 Väst; Sportredaktionen
Owner: Sveriges Radio AB
Editorial: Box 654, Södergatan 11, Uddevalla 451 24. T: 46 522 67 00 00
E: sporten.vast@sverigesradio.se
W: http://sverigesradio.se/sida/gruppsida.aspx?programid=41&grupp=3838

Sveriges Radio P4 Västerbotten
Owner: Sveriges Radio AB
Editorial: Mariehemsvägen 4, Umeå 906 15.
T: 46 90 17 17 00
E: p4vasterbotten@sverigesradio.se
W: http://www.sverigesradio.se/vasterbotten

Sveriges Radio P4 Västerbotten ~ Lycksele
Owner: Sveriges Radio AB
Editorial: Box 103, Storgatan 29, Lycksele 921 31. T: 46 950 123 20
E: lycksele@sverigesradio.se
W: http://www.sverigesradio.se/vasterbotten

Sveriges Radio P4 Västerbotten ~ Skellefteå
Owner: Sveriges Radio AB
Editorial: Box 299, Stationsgatan 9, Skellefteå 931 23. T: 46 910 887 55
E: skelleftea@sverigesradio.se
W: http://www.sverigesradio.se/vasterbotten

Sveriges Radio P4 Västerbotten; Nyhetsredaktionen
Owner: Sveriges Radio AB
Editorial: Mariehemsvägen 4, Umeå 906 15.
T: 46 90 17 17 00
E: news.vbtn@sverigesradio.se
W: http://www.sverigesradio.se/vasterbotten

Sveriges Radio P4 Västerbotten; Sportredaktionen
Owner: Sveriges Radio AB
Editorial: Mariehemsvägen 4, Umeå 906 15.
T: 46 90 17 17 00
E: sporten.vbtn@sverigesradio.se
W: http://sverigesradio.se/sida/gruppsida.aspx?programid=42&grupp=3844

Sveriges Radio P4 Västernorrland
Owner: Sveriges Radio AB
Editorial: Krönvägen 18, Sundsvall 851 79.
T: 46 60 19 03 00
E: p4vasternorrland@sverigesradio.se
W: http://www.sverigesradio.se/vasternorrland

Sveriges Radio P4 Västernorrland ~ Örnsköldsvik
Owner: Sveriges Radio AB
Editorial: Strandgatan 15, Örnsköldsvik 891 33. T: 46 660 139 45
E: p4vasternorrland@sverigesradio.se
W: http://www.sverigesradio.se/vasternorrland

Sveriges Radio P4 Västernorrland; Nyhetsredaktionen
Owner: Sveriges Radio AB
Editorial: Krönvägen 18, Sundsvall 851 79.
T: 46 60 19 03 00
E: news.vasternorrland@sverigesradio.se
W: http://www.sverigesradio.se/vasternorrland

Sveriges Radio P4 Västernorrland; Sportredaktionen
Owner: Sveriges Radio AB
Editorial: Krönvägen 18, Sundsvall 851 79
E: sport.vasternorrland@sverigesradio.se
W: http://sverigesradio.se/sida/gruppsida.aspx?programid=40&grupp=3845

Sveriges Radio P4 Västmanland
Owner: Sveriges Radio AB
Editorial: Box 850, Mäster Ahls Gata 6, Västerås 721 22. T: 46 21 495 25 00
E: p4vastmanland@sverigesradio.se
W: http://www.sverigesradio.se/vastmanland

Sveriges Radio P4 Västmanland; Nyhetsredaktionen
Owner: Sveriges Radio AB
Editorial: Box 850, Mäster Ahls Gata 6, Västerås 721 22. T: 46 21 495 25 00
E: nyheterna.vstm@sverigesradio.se
W: http://www.sverigesradio.se/vastmanland

Sveriges Radio P4 Västmanland; Sportredaktionen
Owner: Sveriges Radio AB
Editorial: Box 850, Mäster Ahls Gata 6, Västerås 721 22. T: 46 21 495 25 00
E: sporten.vstm@sverigesradio.se
W: http://sverigesradio.se/sida/gruppsida.aspx?programid=43&grupp=3846

Sveriges Radio; Sporten P4 Blekinge
Editorial: Box 305, Karlskrona 371 25.
T: 46 455 36 68 00 E: sporten.blekinge@sr.se
W: http://sverigesradio.se/sida/gruppsida.aspx?programid=21&grupp=3824

The Voice
Owner: SBS Radio AB
Editorial: Box 341 08, Stockholm 100 26.
T: 46 8 450 33 00
E: hakan.morland@sbsradio.se
W: http://www.thevoice.se

Vinyl 107
Owner: SBS Radio AB
Editorial: Box 34108, Stockholm 100 26.
T: 46 8 450 33 00 E: info@vinyl107.se
W: http://www.vinyl107.se

RADIO NETWORKS

Metropol 93,8
Owner: Sveriges Radio
Editorial: Sveriges Radio, Oxenstiernsgatan 20, Stockholm 105 10. T: 46 8 784 95 00
E: metropol@sverigesradio.se
W: http://www.sverigesradio.se/metropol

Sveriges Radio Analys & Kommunikation
Owner: Sveriges Radio AB
Editorial: Oxenstiernsgatan 20, Stockholm 105 10. T: 46 8 784 50 00
E: eva.sahlin@sverigesradio.se
W: http://www.sr.se

Sveriges Radio Ekot
Owner: Sveriges Radio AB
Editorial: Radiohuset, Oxenstiernsgatan 20, Stockholm 105 10. T: 46 8 784 70 00
E: ekot@sr.se
W: http://www.sverigesradio.se/nyheter

Sveriges Radio Ekot; Nyheter/ Inrikes
Owner: Sveriges Radio AB
Editorial: Radiohuset, Oxenstiernsgatan 20, Stockholm 105 10. T: 46 8 784 70 00
E: ekot@sr.se
W: http://www.sverigesradio.se/nyheter

Sveriges Radio Ekot; Nyheter/ Nyhetsgruppen
Owner: Sveriges Radio AB
Editorial: Radiohuset, Oxenstiernsgatan 20, Stockholm 105 10. T: 46 8 784 50 00
E: ekot@sr.se
W: http://www.sverigesradio.se/ekot

Sveriges Radio Ekot; Nyheter/ Studioreportrar
Owner: Sveriges Radio AB
Editorial: Radiohuset, Oxenstiernsgatan 20, Stockholm 105 10. T: 46 8 784 70 00
E: ekot@sr.se
W: http://www.sverigesradio.se/ekot

Sveriges Radio Ekot; Utrikesredaktionen
Editorial: Radiohuset, Oxenstiernsgatan 20, Stockholm 105 10. T: 46 8 784 70 00
E: utrikesdesk.eko@sr.se
W: http://www.sverigesradio.se

Sveriges Radio P1
Editorial: Sveriges Radio P1, Oxenstiernsgatan 20, Stockholm 105 10. T: 46 8 784 50 00
E: press.p1@sr.se
W: http://sverigesradio.se/P1

Sveriges Radio P1 Kultur; Kulturradion
Owner: Sveriges Radio
Editorial: Sveriges Radio, Oxenstiernsgatan 20, Stockholm 105 10
E: kulturradion@sverigesradio.se
W: http://sverigesradio.se/sida/default.aspx?programid=767

Sveriges Radio P2 Musikradion
Owner: Sveriges Radio AB
Editorial: Radiohuset, Oxenstiernsgatan 20, Stockholm 105 10. T: 46 8 784 50 00
W: http://sverigesradio.se/sida/tabla.aspx?programid=2562

Sveriges Radio P3
Owner: Sveriges Radio AB
Editorial: Sveriges Radio P3, Radiohuset, Oxenstiernsgatan 20, Stockholm 105 10.
T: 46 8 784 50 00 E: webmaster.p3@sr.se
W: http://www.sverigesradio.se/p3

Sveriges Radio P4
Owner: Sveriges Radio AB
Editorial: Sveriges Radio P4, Oxenstiernsgatan 20, Stockholm 105 10. T: 46 8 784 95 00
E: p4stockholm@sverigesradio.se
W: http://sverigesradio.se/p4

Sveriges Radio P4 Gotland
Owner: Sveriges Radio AB
Editorial: Sveriges Radio Gotland, Box 1324, Visby 621 24. T: 46 498 75 00 00
E: gotlandsnytt@sverigesradio.se
W: http://sverigesradio.se/sida/default.aspx?programid=94

Sveriges Radio Radiosporten
Owner: Sveriges Radio AB
Editorial: Radiohuset, Oxenstiernsgatan 20, Stockholm 105 10. T: 46 8 784 28 00
E: radiosporten@sverigesradio.se
W: http://www.sverigesradio.se/radiosporten

Sveriges Radio Sameradion / Sápmi
Owner: Sveriges Radio AB
Editorial: Sveriges Radio Sameradion, Österleden 21, Kiruna 981 24.
T: 46 980 750 20
E: sameradion@sverigesradio.se
W: http://sverigesradio.se/sameradion/

Sveriges Radio Sisuradio
Owner: Sveriges Radio AB
Editorial: Oxenstiernsgatan 20, Stockholm 105 10. T: 46 8 784 24 00
E: sisuradio@sverigesradio.se
W: http://www.sverigesradio.se/sisuradio

Sveriges Radio Vetenskap & Miljö
Owner: Sveriges Radio AB
Editorial: Vetenskapsredaktionen, Box 1552, Uppsala 751 45. T: 46 18 17 40 00
E: vet@sverigesradio.se
W: http://sverigesradio.se/sida/default.aspx?programid=406

TELEVISION STATIONS

SVT Allmän-tv-divisionen; Vetenskapsredaktionen
Owner: Sveriges Television AB
Editorial: Sveriges Television, Oxenstiernsgatan 26-34, Stockholm 105 10.
T: 46 8 784 00 00
E: vetenskapsnyheter@svt.se
W: http://www.svt.se/nyheter/vetenskap

SVT Falun
Owner: Sveriges Television AB
Editorial: Box 212, Myntgatan 45, Falun 791 25. T: 46 23 765 000 E: gavledala@svt.se
W: http://www.svt.se/nyheter/regionalt/gavledala

SVT Göteborg
Owner: Sveriges Television AB
Editorial: SVT Göteborg, Pumpgatan 2, Goteborg 417 55. T: 46 31 83 70 00
W: http://www.svt.se/

SVT Karlstad
Owner: Sveriges Television AB
Editorial: Kungsgatan 10, Karlstad 651 83.
T: 46 5 423 02 50 E: varmlandsnytt@svt.se
W: http://www.svt.se

SVT Luleå
Owner: Sveriges Television AB
Editorial: Kungsgatan 23 A, Luleå.
T: 46 92 023 98 00 E: nordnytt@svt.se
W: http://www.svt.se

SVT Malmö
Owner: Sveriges Television AB
Editorial: Stora Varvsgatan 2, Malmo 212 01.
T: 46 40 22 70 00 E: sydnytt@svt.se
W: http://www.svt.se

SVT Malmö; Antikrundan
Owner: Sveriges Television AB
Editorial: Malmo 212 01. T: 46 40 22 70 00
E: antikrundan@svt.se
W: http://svt.se/antikrundan

SVT Norrköping
Owner: Sveriges Television AB
Editorial: Box 288, Norrköping 601 04.
T: 46 11 21 01 00
E: norrkoping.receptionen@svt.se
W: http://www.svt.se/nyheter/regionalt/ostnytt/

SVT Örebro
Owner: Sveriges Television AB
Editorial: Orebro 701 84. T: 46 19 35 35 35
E: tvarsnytt@svt.se W: http://www.svt.se

SVT Örebro; Tvärsnytt/ Västmanlandsnytt
Owner: Sveriges Television AB
Editorial: Fabriksgatan 18, Orebro 701 84
E: tvarsnytt@svt.se
W: http://www.svt.se/tvarsnytt

SVT Örebro; Tvärsnytt/ Västmanlandsnytt ~ Västerås
Owner: Sveriges Television AB
Editorial: Fabriksgatan 18, Orebro 701 84.
T: 46 19 35 35 00 E: tvarsnytt@svt.se
W: http://www.svt.se/tvarsnytt

SVT Sundsvall
Owner: Sveriges Television AB
Editorial: Sundsvall 851 80. T: 46 60 19 01 90
E: mittnytt@svt.se W: http://www.svt.se

SVT Umeå
Owner: Sveriges Television AB
Editorial: Box 6094, Formvägen 14, Umeå 906 03. T: 46 90 17 50 00 E: vbnytt@svt.se
W: http://svt.se/vasterbottensnytt

SVT Umeå; Plus
Owner: Sveriges Television AB
Editorial: Box 6094, Formvägen 14, Umeå 906 03. T: 46 90 17 50 00 E: plus@svt.se
W: http://www.svt.se/plus

SVT Växjö
Owner: Sveriges Television AB
Editorial: Box 3050, Växjo 350 33.
T: 46 470 77 87 00 E: smalandsnytt@svt.se
W: http://www.svt.se

TV4 Sverige AB ~ TV4 Kalmar
Owner: TV4 Sverige AB
Editorial: Dagövägen 1, Kalmar.
T: 46 480 42 04 01
E: nyheterna.kalmar@tv4.se
W: http://nyhetskanalen.se/lokalt/kalmar

TV4 Sverige AB ~ TV4 Väst
Owner: TV4 Sverige AB
Editorial: Österlånggatan 52B, Trollhättan 461 30. T: 46 52040 37 01
E: nyheterna.vast@tv4.se
W: http://www.tv4play.se/nyheter_och_debatt/nyheterna_vast

TV4 Sverige AB ~ TV4 Växjö
Owner: TV4 Sverige AB
Editorial: Oxtorget 4, Växjo 352 32.
T: 46 470 73 20 20 E: nyheterna.vaxjo@tv4.se
W: http://nyhetskanalen.se/lokalt/vaxjo

TV4 Sverige AB~ TV4 Göteborg
Owner: TV4 Sverige AB
Editorial: Goteborg 411 17.
T: 46 31 726 80 00
E: nyheterna.goteborg@tv4.se
W: http://nyhetskanalen.se/lokalt/goteborg

TV4 Sverige AB~ TV4 Halland
Owner: TV4 Sverige AB
Editorial: Köpmansgatan 41, Halmstad 202 42. **T:** 46 3 518 17 20
E: nyheterna.halland@tv4.se
W: http://nyhetskanalen.se/lokalt/halland

TV4 Sverige AB~ TV4 Helsingborg
Owner: TV4 Sverige AB
Editorial: Helsingborg 252 67.
T: 46 40 698 94 00
E: nyheterna.helsingborg@tv4.se
W: http://nyhetskanalen.se/lokalt/helsingborg

TV4 Sverige AB~ TV4 Jönköping
Owner: TV4 Sverige AB
Editorial: Box 414, Jönköping 551 16.
T: 46 36 34 14 00
E: nyheterna.jonkoping@tv4.se
W: http://nyhetskanalen.se/lokalt/jonkoping

TV4 Sverige AB~ TV4 Karlstad
Owner: TV4 Sverige AB
Editorial: Kungsgatan 6, Karlstad 652 24.
T: 46 54 775 30 00
E: nyheterna.karlstad@tv4.se
W: http://nyhetskanalen.se/lokalt/karlstad

TV4 Sverige AB~ TV4 Luleå
Owner: TV4 Sverige AB
Editorial: Luleå 972 32. **T:** 46 920 55 90 00
E: nyheterna.lulea@tv4.se
W: http://nyhetskanalen.se/lokalt/lulea

TV4 Sverige AB~ TV4 Malmö
Owner: TV4 Sverige AB
Editorial: Box 4063, Malmo 203 11
E: nyheterna.malmo@tv4.se
W: http://nyhetskanalen.se/lokalt/malmo

TV4 Sverige AB~ TV4 Norrköping
Owner: TV4 Sverige AB
Editorial: Box 644, Norrköping 601 14.
T: 46 11 440 51 60
E: nyheterna.norrkoping@tv4.se
W: http://nyhetskanalen.se/lokalt/norrkoping

TV4 Sverige AB~ TV4 Skaraborg
Owner: TV4 Sverige AB
Editorial: Lögegatan 11, Skövde 541 30.
T: 46 500 44 65 00
E: nyheterna.skaraborg@tv4.se
W: http://www.nyhetskanalen.se/lokalt/skaraborg

TV4 Sverige AB~ TV4 Skellefteå
Owner: TV4 Sverige AB
Editorial: Storgatan 40, Skellefteå 931 31.
T: 46 90203 23 30
E: nyheterna.skelleftea@tv4.se
W: http://nyhetskanalen.se/lokalt/skelleftea

TV4 Sverige AB~ TV4 Sundsvall
Owner: TV4 Sverige AB
Editorial: Metropol, Sundsvall 851 71.
T: 46 60 16 97 02
E: nyheterna.sundsvall@tv4.se
W: http://nyhetskanalen.se/lokalt/sundsvall

TV4 Sverige AB~ TV4 Umeå
Owner: TV4 Sverige AB
Editorial: Box 22, Umeå 901 02.
T: 46 90 18 44 00 **E:** nyheterna.umea@tv4.se
W: http://nyhetskanalen.se/lokalt/umea

TV4 Sverige AB~ TV4 Uppsala
Owner: TV4 Sverige AB
Editorial: Box 946, Uppsala 751 09.
T: 46 18 480 10 50
E: nyheterna.uppsala@tv4.se
W: http://nyhetskanalen.se/lokalt/uppsala

TV4 Sverige AB~ TV4 Västerås
Owner: TV4 Sverige AB
Editorial: Box 1160, Västerås 721 29.
T: 46 21 360 74 10
E: nyheterna.vasteras@tv4.se
W: http://nyhetskanalen.se/lokalt/vasteras

TELEVISION NETWORKS

Axess Television
Owner: Nordstjernan
Editorial: Jakobsbergsgatan 2, 6 tr, Stockholm 111 44. **T:** 46 8 788 50 50 **E:** info@axess.se
W: http://www.axess.se/tv

C More
Owner: C More Entertainment AB
Editorial: Tegeluddsvägen 3-5, Stockholm 115 84. **T:** 46 20 24 00 24 **E:** info@cmore.se
W: http://www.cmore.se

C more; Sportredaktionen
Owner: C More Entertainment AB
Editorial: Tegeluddsvägen 3-5, Stockholm 115 84. **T:** 46 20 24 00 24 **E:** info@cmore.se
W: http://www.cmore.se

Eurosport Television AB
Owner: Stampen Sport Media
Editorial: Box 1177, Sundbyberg 172 24.
T: 46 8 506 610 00
W: http://www.eurosport.se

Horse1
E: press@horse1.se **W:** http://www.horse1.se/

Kanal 11
Owner: SBS TV
Editorial: SBS TV, Rådmansgatan 42, Stockholm 113 57. **T:** 46 8 520 55 555
E: calle.jansson@sbstv.se
W: http://www.kanal11play.se/

Kanal 5
Owner: SBS Media Group Sweden
Editorial: Rådmansgatan 42, Stockholm 114 99. **T:** 46 8 520 555 55 **E:** info@kanal5.se
W: http://www.kanal5play.se

Kanal 5; Text-TV
Owner: SBS Media Group Sweden
Editorial: Rådmansgatan 42, Stockholm 114 99. **T:** 46 8 520 555 55 **E:** info@kanal5.se
W: http://www.kanal5play.se

Kanal 9
Owner: SBS Broadcasting Network Ltd
Editorial: Kanal 9, Rådmansgatan 42, Stockholm 114 99. **T:** 46 8 520 55 555
E: info@kanalnio.se **W:** http://www.kanalnio.se

Öppna Kanalen i Göteborg
Owner: Öppna Kanalen i Göteborg
Editorial: Goteborg 413 04. **T:** 46 31 24 30 80
E: goteborg@oppnakanalen.se
W: http://www.oppnakanalen.se/goteborg

Öppna kanalen i Lund - STEVE
Owner: Kabelsändarföreningen Öppna Kanalen Lund
Editorial: Sandgatan 2, Lund 223 50.
T: 46 46 13 78 25 **E:** stationschef@s-teve.se
W: http://www.s-teve.se

Öppna Kanalen i Skövde
Owner: Nils-Åke Pehrsson
Editorial: Box 249, Skövde 541 25.
T: 46 500 41 04 20
E: redaktionen@oppnakanalenskovde.se
W: http://lokaltv.webbplay.se

Öppna Kanalen i Stockholm
Owner: Föreningen Öppna Kanalen i Stockholm
Editorial: Box 4332, Stockholm 102 67.
T: 46 8 714 51 00
E: stockholm@oppnakanalen.se
W: http://www.oppnakanalenstockholm.se

SVT AB
Owner: Sveriges Television AB
Editorial: Oxenstiernsgatan 26-34, Stockholm 105 10. **T:** 46 8 784 00 00
W: http://www.svt.se

SVT Allmän-tv-divisionen
Owner: Sveriges Television AB
Editorial: Oxenstiernsgatan 26-34, Stockholm 105 10. **T:** 46 8 784 00 00
W: http://www.svt.se

SVT Barnkanalen
Editorial: Oxenstiernsgatan 26-34, Stockholm 105 10. **T:** 46 8 784 00 00
E: barnkanalen@svt.se
W: http://www.svt.se/barn

SVT Kunskapskanalen
Owner: SVT & UR
Editorial: Oxenstiernsgatan 26-34, Stockholm 105 10. **T:** 46 8 784 00 00
E: info@kunskapskanalen.se
W: http://www.kunskapskanalen.se

SVT Nyhetsdivisionen
Owner: Sveriges Television AB
Editorial: Sveriges Television AB Nyhetsdivisionen, Oxenstiernsgatan 26-34, Stockholm 105 10. **T:** 46 8 784 00 00
E: svtnyheter@svt.se
W: http://www.svt.se/nyheter

SVT Nyhetsdivisionen; Ekonomi/ Näringsliv/Arbetsmarknad
Owner: Sveriges Television AB
Editorial: Oxenstiernsgatan 26-34, Stockholm 105 10. **T:** 46 8 784 00 00 **E:** rapport@svt.se
W: http://www.svt.se

SVT Nyhetsdivisionen; Utrikesredaktionen
Owner: Sveriges Television AB
Editorial: Oxenstiernsgatan 26-34, Stockholm 105 10. **T:** 46 8 784 00 00
E: svtnyheter@svt.se
W: http://www.svt.se/nyheter/varlden

SVT Nyhetsdivisionen; Uutiset / Finska redaktionen
Owner: Sveriges Television AB
Editorial: SVT / Uutiset, TH-E22, Stockholm 105 10. **T:** 46 8 784 74 35 **E:** uutiset@svt.se
W: http://www.svt.se/nyheter/uutiset/

SVT Sápmi
Owner: Sveriges Television AB
Editorial: Sveriges Radio Sameradion & SVT Sápm, Box 225 981 24, Kiruna, Kiruna 981 38. **T:** 46 980 750 00 **E:** oddasat@svt.se
W: http://www.svtplay.se/oddasat

SVT Sport
Owner: Sveriges Television AB
Editorial: Oxenstiernsgatan 26-34, Stockholm 105 10. **T:** 46 8 784 76 10 **E:** svtsport@svt.se
W: http://www.svt.se/sport

SVT Teckenspråk
Owner: Sveriges Television AB
Editorial: Myntgatan 45, Falun 791 25.
T: 46 23 76 51 13 **E:** nyhetstecken@svt.se
W: http://www.svt.se/nyheter/nyhetstecken/

SVT Teckenspråk / Nyheter & Samh. (Sthlm)
Owner: Sveriges Television AB
Editorial: Oxenstiernsgatan 26, Stockholm 105 10. **T:** 46 8 784 00 00 **W:** http://www.svt.se

TV Malmö - Öppna Kanalen
Owner: Malmö Allemans-TV (Ideell förening)
Editorial: Jespersgatan 2, Malmo 214 45.
T: 46 40 23 01 00 **W:** http://www.tvmalmo.se

TV3 Sverige AB
Owner: MTG
Editorial: MTG TV, Ringvägen 52, Stockholm 104 62. **T:** 46 8 562 023 00 **E:** press@tv3.se
W: http://www.tv3.se

TV4 AB
Owner: TV4-Gruppen
Editorial: Tegeluddsvägen 3-5, Stockholm 115 79. **T:** 46 8 459 40 00 **E:** tips@tv4.se
W: http://www.tv4.se

TV4 AB; Sjuan
Owner: TV4 Gruppen
Editorial: Tegeluddsvägen 3-5, Stockholm 115 79. **T:** 46 8 459 40 00 **E:** tittarservice@tv4.se
W: http://www.sjuan.se

TV4 AB; TV12
Owner: TV4-Gruppen
Editorial: Tegeluddsvägen 3-5, Stockholm 115 79. **T:** 46 8 459 40 00
W: http://www.tv4play.se/kanaler/tv12

TV4 AB; TV4 Fakta
Editorial: Tegeluddsvägen 3-5, Stockholm 115 79. **T:** 46 8 459 40 00 **E:** press@tv4.se
W: http://www.tv4fakta.se

TV4 AB; TV4 Fakta XL
Owner: TV4-Grupppen
Editorial: Tegeluddsvägen 3-5, Stockholm 115 79. **T:** 46 8 459 40 00 **E:** nic.edwards@tv4.se
W: http://www.tv4faktaxl.se

TV4 AB; TV4 Film
Owner: TV4-Gruppen
Editorial: Tegeluddsvägen 3-5, Stockholm 115 79. **T:** 46 8 459 40 00 **E:** bo.thornwall@tv4.se
W: http://www.tv4film.se

TV4 AB; TV4 Guld
Owner: TV4-Gruppen
Editorial: Tegeluddsvägen 3-5, Stockholm 115 79. **T:** 46 8 459 40 00 **E:** bo.thornwall@tv4.se
W: http://www.tv4guld.se

TV4 AB; TV4 Komedi
Owner: TV4-Gruppen
Editorial: Tegeluddsvägen 3-5, Stockholm 115 79. **T:** 46 8 459 40 00 **E:** bo.thornwall@tv4.se
W: http://www.tv4komedi.se

TV4 AB; TV4 Sport
Owner: TV4-Gruppen
Editorial: Tegeluddsvägen 3-5, Stockholm 115 79. **T:** 46 8 459 40 00 **E:** tv4sport@tv4.se
W: http://www.tv4sport.se

TV6
Owner: Viasat Broadcasting UK Ltd
Editorial: BOX 17115, Ringvägen 52, Stockholm 104 62. **T:** 46 8 562 023 00
E: redaktionen@tv6.se **W:** http://www.tv6.se

TV8
Owner: Modern Times Group Sverige
Editorial: Box 17054, Ringvägen 52, Stockholm 104 62. **T:** 46 8 562 023 00
E: tittarombud@tv8.se **W:** http://www.tv8.se

UR
Owner: Förvaltningsstiftelsen för SVT AB, SR AB och UR AB
Editorial: Sveriges Utbildningsradio AB, Oxenstiernsgatan 34, Stockholm 105 10.
T: 46 8 784 40 00 **E:** kundtjanst@ur.se
W: http://www.ur.se

UR; Barn- och Ungdomsredaktionen
Owner: Förvaltningsstiftelsen för SVT AB, SR AB och UR AB
Editorial: Sveriges Utbildningsradio AB, Oxenstiernsgatan 34, Stockholm 105 10.
T: 46 8 784 40 00 **E:** kundtjanst@ur.se
W: http://www.ur.se

UR; Samtiden
Owner: Förvaltningsstiftelsen för SVT AB, SR AB och UR AB
Editorial: Sveriges Utbildningsradio AB, Oxenstiernsgatan 34, Stockholm 105 10.
T: 46 8 784 00 00 **E:** samtiden@ur.se
W: http://www.ur.se/Webbar/UR-Samtiden

UR; Vuxenredaktionen / Högskoleredaktionen
Owner: Förvaltningsstiftelsen för SVT AB, SR AB och UR AB
Editorial: Sveriges Utbildningsradio AB, Oxenstiernsgatan 34, Stockholm 105 10.
T: 46 8 784 40 00 **E:** kundtjanst@ur.se
W: http://www.ur.se

Viasat Sport
Editorial: Erik Dahlbergsgatan 46, Box 2094, Stockholm 115 57. **T:** 46 8 562 023 00
E: fredrik.johansson@viasat.se
W: http://www.viasatsport.se

SWITZERLAND Tel: 41
Standard Time: GMT +1
Continent: Europe
Capital City: Berne

NEWSPAPERS & PUBLICATIONS

NEWSPAPERS

20 Minuten
Owner: 20 Minuten AG
Editorial: Werdstrasse 21, Zurich 8004.
T: 41 44 248 68 20
E: redaktion@20minuten.ch
W: http://www.20min.ch
Freq: Daily; **Circ:** 493236 Pub Statement
Chefredakteur / Editor in Chief: Marc Boselliu
Editorial Profile: 20 Minutes is a regional daily newspaper for the German part of Switzerland with nationwide and worldwide news.
Language (s): German
DAILY NEWSPAPER

24 heures
Owner: Tamedia Publications romandes SA
Editorial: 33 Avenue de la Gare, Lausanne 1001. **T:** 41 21 349 44 44
E: 24heures@24heures.ch
W: http://www.24heures.ch
Freq: Daily; **Circ:** 71957 Pub Statement
Editor in Chief: Thierry Meyer
Editorial Profile: 24 heures is a daily newspaper for the french part of Switzerland, covering news and current affairs including regional, national and international news, politics, economics, markets, sport, culture, celebrities, lifestyle, cars, technology, science, travel and the arts.
Language (s): French

DAILY NEWSPAPER

az norwestschweiz
Owner: verlag@azmedien.ch
Editorial: Neumattstrasse 1, Aarau 5001.
T: 41 58 200 58 58 **E:** verlag@azmedien.ch
W: http://www.azwerbung.ch/zeitungen/print/az-nordwestschweiz
Freq: Daily (Mon-Fri); **Circ:** 281088
Editorial Profile: The az nordwestschweiz is a national newspaper, which forms the mantle part of the national daily newspapers az Aargauer Zeitung, bz Basellandschaftliche Zeitung, bz Basel, az Limmattaler Zeitung, az Solothurner Zeitung, az Grenchner Tagblatt, Oltner Tagblatt and Zofinger Tagblatt. The headquarters are located in Aargau. The mantle part provides national news from politics, economy, society and culture, while each regional edition manages its own regional sections.
Language (s): German
DAILY NEWSPAPER

Blick
Owner: Ringier AG
Editorial: Dufourstr. 23, Zurich 8008.
T: 41 44 2596262 **E:** redaktion@blick.ch
W: http://www.blick.ch
Freq: Daily; **Circ:** 179181 Pub Statement
Unterhaltungsredaktion: Martina Abächerli; **Ratgeber:** Roland Grüter; **Redaktion GesundBlick:** Roland Grüter; **Editor-at-Large:** Peter Hossli; **Unterhaltungsredaktion:** Dominik Hug; **Chef vom Dienst:** Daniel Kistler; **Editor-in-Chief:** René Lüchinger; **Redakteurin / Editor:** Franca Siegfried; **Chefredaktion:** Marc Walder
Editorial Profile: Blick is a daily newspaper for the German-speaking Swiss, with covering regional, national and international news on politics, economy, culture, society and sports. Additionally, it offers consumer information on topics such as travel and technology, as well as entertainment.
Language (s): German
DAILY NEWSPAPER

BZ Berner Zeitung
Owner: Berner Zeitung AG
Editorial: Dammweg 9, Bern 3013.
T: 41 31 330 33 33
E: redaktion@bernerzeitung.ch
W: http://www.bernerzeitung.ch
Freq: Daily; **Circ:** 162855
Redaktion Beilagen / Sonderseiten: Sonja Agho-Hodel; **Chef vom Dienst:** Emil Bohnenblust; **Redaktion Beilagen / Sonderseiten:** Jean-Luc Brülhart; **Redakteur:** Anfrea Freiermuth; **EDV-Redaktion:** Martin Haslebacher; **Editor:** Michael Hug; **Editor in Chief:** Peter Jost; **News Editor:** Wolf Röcken; **Ratgeber:** Giuseppe Wuest; **Unterhaltungsredaktion:** Giuseppe Wuest
Editorial Profile: The Berner Newspaper is a regional daily newspaper covering politics, economics, sport, travel, technology and the arts.
Language (s): German
DAILY NEWSPAPER

Die Südostschweiz
Owner: Südostschweiz Presse AG
Editorial: Comercialstr. 22, Chur 7007.
T: 41 81 2555050
E: zentralredaktion@suedostschweiz.ch
W: http://www.suedostschweiz.ch
Freq: Daily; **Circ:** 125323 Pub Statement
EDV-Redaktion: Hans Bärtsch; **stellv. Chefredaktion:** Pieder Carminada; **Redaktion Frauen / Mode:** Gisela Femppel; **stellv. Chefredaktion:** René Mehrmann; **Chefredaktion:** David Sieber
Editorial Profile: The Südostschweiz is a regional daily newspaper with news about politics, economy, culture, society and sports for the south-east of Switzerland. It offers the main portion of the regional papers Südostschweiz Graubünden, Bündner Tagblatt, La Quotidiana, Südostschweiz Glarus, Südostschweiz Gaster & See, March-Anzeiger, Höfner Volksblatt and Sarganserländer.
Language (s): German
DAILY NEWSPAPER

Le Matin Dimanche
Owner: Tamedia Publications romandes SA
Editorial: Avenue de la Gare 33, Lausanne 1001. **T:** 41 21 349 49 49 **E:** info@lematin.ch
W: http://www.lematin.ch
Freq: Weekly; **Circ:** 203838 Pub Statement
Editor in Chief: Ariane Dayer
Editorial Profile: Le Matin Dimanche is the sunday edition of the newspaper Le Matin, covering regional general interest including politics, business, culture, sports, travel and technology.
Language (s): French
NEWSPAPER

Neue Luzerner Zeitung
Owner: Neue Luzerner Zeitung AG
Editorial: Maihofstr. 76, Luzern 6002.
T: 41 41 4295151 **E:** info@luzernerzeitung.ch
W: http://www.luzernerzeitung.ch
Freq: Daily; **Circ:** 132900 Pub Statement
Chefredaktion: Thomas Bornhauser; **Redakteur / Editor:** Arthur Bucher; **Redakteur / Editor:** Michael Graber; **Redakteurin / Editor:** René Leupi
Editorial Profile: Regional daily newspaper covering politics, economics, sport, travel, technology and the arts.
Language (s): German
DAILY NEWSPAPER

NZZ Neue Zürcher Zeitung
Owner: Neue Zürcher Zeitung AG
Editorial: Falkenstr. 11, Zurich 8021.
T: 41 44 2581111 **E:** redaktion@nzz.ch
W: http://www.nzz.ch
Freq: Daily; **Circ:** 139732 Pub Statement
Redaktion Beilagen / Sonderseiten: Friedemann Bartu; **Redakteur:** Francesco Benini; **Redaktion Beilagen / Sonderseiten:** Stefan Betschon; **Editor:** Katharina Fontana; **Redaktion Bundeshaus:** Daniel Gerny; **Redaktion Bundeshaus:** Markus Häfliger; **Redaktion Beilagen / Sonderseiten:** Walter Hagenbüchle; **Redakteurin / Editor:** Anja Knabenhans; **Redaktion Beilagen / Sonderseiten:** Susanna Müller; **Redaktor Inland:** Davide Scruzzi; **Editor-in-Chief:** Markus Spillmann; **Redaktion Bundeshaus:** Beat Waber; **stellv. Chefredaktion:** René Zeller
Editorial Profile: The Neue Zürcher Zeitung is a tabloid-sized quality newspaper covering regional, national and international news, as well as politics, finance, economics, sport, culture and leisure.
Language (s): German
DAILY NEWSPAPER

SonntagsBlick
Owner: Ringier AG
Editorial: Dufourstr. 23, Zurich 8008.
T: 41 44 259 62 62
E: redaktion@sonntagsblick.ch
W: http://www.blick.ch/sonntagsblick
Freq: Weekly (Sunday); **Circ:** 203351
Unterhaltungsredaktion: Martina Abächerli; **Redakteurin / Editor:** Gabriele Haschke; **Unterhaltungsredaktion:** Dominik Hug; **Redakteur / Editor:** Max Kern; **stellv. Chefredaktion:** Philippe Pfister; **Chef vom Dienst:** Daniel Römer; **Redaktion Bundeshaus:** Joël Widmer; **Chefredaktion:** Karsten Witzmann
Editorial Profile: SonntagsBlick is a national weekly paper covering news from politics, economics, culture, society and sports. It also offers a consumer section covering topics such as travel and technology. The publication is the sunday edition of the newspaper Blick.
Language (s): German
NEWSPAPER

SonntagsZeitung
Owner: Tamedia AG
Editorial: Werdstr. 21, Zurich 8021.
T: 41 44 242 4783
E: redaktion@sonntagszeitung.ch
W: http://www.sonntagszeitung.ch
Freq: Weekly; **Circ:** 194764 WEMF
Redakteurin / Editor: Silvia Aeschbach; **Redaktion Hobby / Freizeit:** Christoph Ammann; **Editor:** Simon Bärtschi; **Redakteur / Editor:** Daniel Glaus; **Redakteur / Editor:** Andreas Kunz; **Unterhaltungsredaktion:** Matthias Lerf; **Redakteurin / Editor:** Simone Luchetta; **Chefredaktion:** Arthur Rutishauser; **Redakteur:** Roger Schawinski; **News Editor:** Benno Tuchschmid; **Umweltredaktion:** Nik Walter; **EDV-Redaktion:** Nik Walter; **Editor:** Bettina Weber
Editorial Profile: The SonntagsZeitung is a weekly newspaper for the German-speaking part of Switzerland. It is divided into nine different subject areas, which include news, sports, culture, business, travel, trends and science. Thus, the Sunday newspaper offers a mix of news and entertainment.
Language (s): German
NEWSPAPER

Tages Anzeiger
Owner: Tamedia AG
Editorial: Werdstr. 21, Zurich 8021.
T: 41 44 2484411
E: redaktion@tages-anzeiger.ch
W: http://www.tagesanzeiger.ch
Freq: Daily (Mon-Fri); **Circ:** 188602 WEMF
Chef vom Dienst: Hanspeter Bürgin; **Redaktion Bildung/Erziehung:** Antonio Cortesi; **stellv. Chefredaktion:** Daniela Decurtins; **Chef vom Dienst:** Rita Flubacher; **Inlandressort Leiter:** Daniel Foppa; **Redaktion Beilagen / Sonderseiten:** Ulrike Hark; **Unterhaltungsredaktion:** Ulrike Hark; **Redaktion Frau und Mode:** Ulrike Hark; **Redaktion Medien:** Hannes Nussbaumer; **stellv. Chefredaktion:** Arthur Rutishauser; **Redakteur:** Alexander Saheb; **Redaktion Bildung / Erziehung:** Daniel Schneebeli; **Chefredaktion:** Andreas Strehle; **Redaktion Computer/EDV:** Roger Zedi
Editorial Profile: The Tages Anzeiger is a daily newspaper, which offers national and international news on politics, economy and society.
Language (s): German
DAILY NEWSPAPER

The Wall Street Journal (Switzerland)
Editorial: 59 Loewenstrasse, Zurich CH-8001.
T: 41 434438040
Bureau Chief: Andrew Morse
DAILY NEWSPAPER

NEWS SERVICE/SYNDICATE

Associated Press
Editorial: Palais des Nation, Room C12 CH-1211, Geneva. **T:** 41 22 919-4222
NEWS SERVICE/SYNDICATE

Bloomberg News
Editorial: Seidengasse 20, CH-8001, Zurich.
T: 41 442244130
E: switzerland@bloomberg.net
NEWS SERVICE/SYNDICATE

Bloomberg News
Editorial: 40 Rue du Marche, Geneva 1204.
T: 41 223179200
Editor: Thomas Mulier; **Bureau Chief:** Matthias Wabl
NEWS SERVICE/SYNDICATE

Bloomberg News
Editorial: Medienzentrum Bundeshaus, Bundesgasse 8-12, Bern 3003.
T: 41 313114035
NEWS SERVICE/SYNDICATE

Dow Jones Newswires
Editorial: 59 Loewenstrasse, Zurich CH-8032.
T: 41 43 443-8040
E: zurichdjnews@dowjones.com
Bureau Chief: Andrew Morse
NEWS SERVICE/SYNDICATE

Reuters
Editorial: Palais des Nation, 8-14 Av de la Paix, Geneva 1211. **T:** 41 22 733-3831
E: geneva.newsroom@thomsonreuters.com
NEWS SERVICE/SYNDICATE

Reuters
Editorial: Hufgasse 10, Zurich 8022.
T: 41 44 631-7311
E: zurich.newsroom@reuters.com
Bureau Chief: Emma Thomasson
NEWS SERVICE/SYNDICATE

BROADCASTING

TELEVISION STATIONS

SRF 1
Owner: Schweizer Radio und Fernsehen
Editorial: Fernsehstr. 1-4, Zurich 8052.
T: 41 44 3056611 **E:** srf@srf.ch
W: http://www.srf.ch
Editorial Profile: 1 SRF is the national public television station of the SRF in German. In addition to news of the station offers information programs, as well as entertainment.

SRF 2
Owner: Schweizer Rundfunk und Fernsehen
Editorial: Fernsehstr. 1, Zurich 8052.
T: 41 44 3056611 **E:** srf@srf.ch
W: http://www.srf.ch
Editorial Profile: SRF 2 is the second television channel of the SRF, which is primarily aimed at a younger audience. The program includes mainly movies, series and sports, but also a share of information and news formats.

TeleZüri
Owner: AZ Medien AG
Editorial: Redaktion TeleZüri, Heinrichstr. 267, Zurich 8005. **T:** 41 44 447 24 24
E: redaktion@telezueri.ch
W: http://www.telezueri.ch
Editorial Profile: TeleZüri is a private, Swiss TV station for the area Zürich with news, information programs and entertainment.

SYRIA — Tel: 963
Standard Time: GMT +2
Continent: Asia
Capital City: Damascus

NEWSPAPERS & PUBLICATIONS

NEWSPAPERS

An-nour
Owner: Syrian Communist Party
Editorial: PO Box 7394, The White Bridge, Omar Ben Mokhtar Street, Damascus.
T: 963 11 332 4914 **E:** annourscs@gmail.com
W: http://www.an-nour.com
Freq: Wed; **Circ:** 9500 Publisher's Statement
Editor in Chief: Bassem Abdo; **News & Society Editor:** Mahmoud Hilal
Editorial Profile: An-nour is the weekly newspaper of the Syrian Communist Party and covers news, politics, current affairs, social issues and cultural activities. It launched in 1955 and is published on Wednesdays.
Language (s): Arabic
DAILY NEWSPAPER

Al Baath
Owner: Dar Al Baath for Press, Printing, Publishing and Distribution
Editorial: PO Box 9389, Al Mazzeh Highway, Damascus. **T:** 963 11 662 2141
E: baath-n@net.sy
W: http://www.albaath.news.sy
Freq: Daily; **Circ:** 56000 Publisher's Statement
Editor In Chief: Mohammad Kanaissi
Editorial Profile: Al Baath is a daily Arabic newspaper covering news, politics, business and sport. It was first published in 1946.
Language (s): Arabic
DAILY NEWSPAPER

Baladna
Owner: United Group for Publishing, Advertising & Marketing
Editorial: PO Box 1999, Huda Building, 5 Iskandaria Street, Damascus. **T:** 963 11 2025
E: info@ug.com.sy
W: http://baladnaonline.net
Freq: Daily; **Circ:** 90000 Publisher's Statement
Editor in Chief: Ali Hassoun
Editorial Profile: Baladna (Our Country) is a daily Arabic newspaper covering local and international news, politics, business and sport. It was first published in 2006.
Language (s): Arabic
DAILY NEWSPAPER

Bourses and Markets
Owner: Al Marsad Syrian Company for Media and Business
Editorial: PO Box 16545, Damascus.
T: 963 11 662 5315 **E:** info@syriandays.com
W: http://www.syriandays.com
Freq: Sun; **Circ:** 10000 Publisher's Statement
Editorial Profile: Bourses and Markets is a weekly Arabic business newspaper covering local and international business news, stocks and stock markets. It launched in 2004 and is published on Sundays.
Language (s): Arabic
DAILY NEWSPAPER

Al Fedaa
Owner: Al Wahda Foundation For Press, Printing and Publishing
Editorial: PO Box 395, Al Andalus Street, Hamah. **T:** 963 33 360503 **E:** al-fida@mail.sy
W: http://fedaa.alwehda.gov.sy
Freq: Daily; **Circ:** 16000 Publisher's Statement
Rédacteur en Chef: Hussein Abbas; **Editor:** Ali Adelah
Editorial Profile: Al Fedaa is a regional newspaper distributed in the Hamah area of Syria. It launched in 1963 and focuses on local news, politics, culture and sport. It is published daily, except Fridays and Saturdays.
Language (s): Arabic
DAILY NEWSPAPER

Al Jamahir
Owner: Al Wahda Foundation For Press, Printing and Publishing
Editorial: Beside Jamea Al Abara, Al Abara Area, Aleppo. **T:** 963 21 212 9321
E: aljamaheerdailynews@hotmail.com

W: http://jamahir.alwehda.gov.sy
Freq: Daily; Circ: 18000 Publisher's Statement
Editor in Chief: Jihad Steif
Editorial Profile: Al Jamahir (Audiences) is a regional newspaper distributed in the Aleppo area of Syria focusing on local news and current affairs. It launchedin 1963 and is published daily, except Fridays and Saturdays.
Language (s): Arabic
DAILY NEWSPAPER

Al Mawkef Al-Riadi
Owner: Al Wahda Foundation For Press, Printing and Publishing
Editorial: PO Box 2448, Kafar Souseh, Damascus. T: 963 11 219 3291
E: gh_shamma@yahoo.com
W: http://riadi.alwehda.gov.sy
Freq: Sat; Circ: 30000 Publisher's Statement
Editorial Profile: Al Mawkef Al-Riadi is a weekly Arabic newspaper covering local, regional and international sport. It was launched in 1963 and is published on Saturdays.
Language (s): Arabic
DAILY NEWSPAPER

Al Qandel
Owner: Al Qandel
Editorial: 1st Floor, Al Rifai Building, Ibn Sina Street, Damascus. T: 963 11 222 8069
E: info@shamlife.com
W: http://www.shamlife.com
Freq: Sun; Circ: 15000 Publisher's Statement
Editorial Profile: Al Qandel is a weekly Arabic newspaper covering business, culture, society and technology. It launched in 2007 and is published on Sundays.
Language (s): Arabic
DAILY NEWSPAPER

Teshreen Daily
Owner: Al Wahda Foundation For Press, Printing and Publishing
Editorial: PO Box 5452, Corniche Al Medan, Damascus. T: 963 11 213 1100
E: info@tishreen.news.sy
W: http://tishreen.news.sy
Freq: Daily; Circ: 60000 Publisher's Statement
Editor in Chief: Raghda Mardini
Editorial Profile: Teshreen Daily is an Arabic newspaper covering national and international news, current affairs, politics, business and sport. It was first published in 1975.
Language (s): Arabic
DAILY NEWSPAPER

Al Thawra
Owner: Al Wahda Foundation For Press, Printing and Publishing
Editorial: PO Box 2448, Kafar Sosah, Damascus. T: 963 11 222 2399
E: mail@thawraonline.sy
W: http://thawra.alwehda.gov.sy
Freq: Daily; Circ: 80000 Publisher's Statement
News Editor: Ahmed Al Wadi; Editor in Chief: Ali Kasem
Editorial Profile: Al Thawra (The Revolution) is an Arabic newspaper covering local and international news, politics, current affairs, business and sport. The newspaper launched in 1963 and is published daily, except Fridays.
Language (s): Arabic
DAILY NEWSPAPER

Al Watan
Owner: Al A'amal Al Iqtisady Group
Editorial: Al Watan Building, Damascus Free Zone, Damascus. T: 963 11 213 7400
E: news@alwatan.sy
W: http://www.alwatan.sy
Freq: Daily; Circ: 28000 Publisher's Statement
Editor in Chief: Waddah Abd Rabbo; News Editor: Jambulat Shtay
Editorial Profile: Al Watan is an Arabic newspaper covering local, regional and international news, politics, business and sport. It launched in 2006 and is published daily, except Fridays and Saturdays.
Language (s): Arabic
DAILY NEWSPAPER

Al Wehda
Owner: Al Wahda Foundation For Press, Printing and Publishing
Editorial: PO Box 1174, Al Thawra Street, Lattakia. T: 963 41 439974
E: moneer49@gmail.com
W: http://wehda.alwehda.gov.sy
Freq: Daily; Circ: 24000 Publisher's Statement
Editor in Chief: Malek Al Rifaei
Editorial Profile: Al Wehda (Union) is a regional, daily newspaper distributed in the Lattakia area of Syria. The newspaper covers local news and current affairs, and was first published in 1984.
Language (s): Arabic
DAILY NEWSPAPER

NEWS SERVICE/SYNDICATE

Agence France-Presse - Damascus Bureau
Owner: Agence France-Presse
Editorial: PO Box 2400, Damascus.
T: 963 11 231 8200
E: roueida.mabardi@afp.com
W: http://www.afp.com
Bureau Chief: Roueida Mabardi
Editorial Profile: Damascus bureau of the French international news agency.
Language (s): Arabic, Dutch, English, French, Portuguese, Spanish
NEWS SERVICE/SYNDICATE

APTN Syria
Owner: Associated Press
Editorial: 7th floor, Tabaae Building, Damascus. T: 963 11 213 9768
E: g-saliba7@hotmail.com
W: http://www.aptn.com
Bureau Chief: George Saliba
Editorial Profile: Associated Press Television News (APTN) is the international television arm of the Associated Press - APTN's operations include a main news service, specialised broadcast services, customised coverage for the Middle East, a productions division, weekly and daily entertainment news and an extensive video archive library.
Language (s): Arabic, English
NEWS SERVICE/SYNDICATE

Syrian Arab News Agency
Owner: Ministry of Information, Syria
Editorial: PO Box 2661, Baramka, Damascus.
T: 963 11 212 9702 E: sana@sana.sy
W: http://sana.sy
Editor: Nezha Al Kouzi; Editor: Yara Ismaeel
Editorial Profile: The Syrian Arab News Agency (SANA) is the official government news agency of Syria. It was founded in 1965.
Language (s): Arabic, Chinese, English, French, Russian, Spanish, Turkish
NEWS SERVICE/SYNDICATE

BROADCASTING

TELEVISION STATIONS

Syria Drama Channel
Owner: General Organisation of Radio and TV
Editorial: Sahat Al Omaween, Damascus.
T: 963 11 225 0963 E: drama@rtv.gov.sy
W: http://www.rtv.gov.sy
Editorial Profile: Syria Drama Channel is a state-owned television channel broadcasting films and drama serials. The station launched in 2009 and broadcasts free-to-air on satellite.

Syria TV - Channel 1
Owner: General Organisation of Radio and TV
Editorial: General Organisation of Radio & TV Building, Omawyeen Square, Damascus.
T: 963 11 373 7414 E: srtv@rtv.gov.sy
W: http://www.rtv.gov.sy
Editorial Profile: Channel 1 of Syria TV is a state-owned television station broadcasting entertainment, news and drama programmes. The channel launched in 1960 and broadcasts terrestrially in Syria and free-to-air on satellite.

Syria TV - Channel 2
Owner: General Organisation of Radio and TV
Editorial: General Organisation of Radio & TV Building, Omayad Square, Damascus.
T: 963 11 222 3763 E: e-naser@scs-net.org
W: http://www.rtv.gov.sy
Editorial Profile: Channel 2 of Syria TV is a state-owned television station broadcasting documentaries and sports programmes. The channel launched in 1985 and broadcasts terrestrially in Syria.

TAIWAN Tel: 886
Standard Time: GMT +8
Continent: Asia
Capital City: Taipei

NEWSPAPERS & PUBLICATIONS

NEWSPAPERS

Apple Daily
Editorial: Next Media Limited, Number 38, Lane 141, Xing-Ai Road, Neihu District, Taipei 114. T: 886 266013456
E: news@appledaily.com.tw
W: http://www.appledaily.com.tw
Freq: Daily; Circ: 750003 Not Audited
Editor in Chief: Wei-Ming Ma
Editorial Profile: It covers local news and social issues.
Language (s): Chinese
DAILY NEWSPAPER

China Daily News
Editorial: China Daily News., Number 57, Xinhua Street, Tainan 704. T: 886 62296381
E: cdn@ms1.hinet.net
W: http://www.cdns.com.tw
Freq: Daily; Circ: 250003 Not Audited
Editor in Chief: Xiong Huang
Editorial Profile: It covers local news, politics and social issues.
Language (s): Chinese
DAILY NEWSPAPER

The China Post
Editorial: The China Post., Number 8, Fu Shun Street, Taipei 104. T: 886 2 25969971
E: editor@mail.chinapost.com.tw
W: http://www.chinapost.com.tw
Freq: Daily; Circ: 300003 Not Audited
Editor in Chief: Jack Huang
Editorial Profile: It covers local and international news.
Language (s): English
DAILY NEWSPAPER

China Times
Editorial: China Times., B3, Number 303, Meng Jia Da Dao, Taipei 10801.
T: 886 223087111 5550
E: editorplan@mail.chinatimes.com.tw
W: http://news.chinatimes.com
Freq: Daily; Circ: 1000003 Not Audited
Editor: Chi-Chin Chang; Editor in Chief: Yu-Lin Tang; Publisher: Albert Yu
Editorial Profile: It covers politics, economy, society, business, culture, local news and international news.
Language (s): Chinese
DAILY NEWSPAPER

Commercial Times
Editorial: Commercial Times., 5th Floor, Number 303, Mengjia Da Dao, Taipei 108.
T: 886 223087111 5727
E: commercialtimes@mail.chinatimes.com.tw
W: http://news.chinatimes.com
Freq: Daily; Circ: 350003 Not Audited
Editorial Profile: It covers economy, financial news, business and investment information.
Language (s): Chinese
DAILY NEWSPAPER

The Commons Daily
Editorial: The Commons Daily., 31st Floor -3, Number 38, Xing Guang Road, Linya District, Kaohsiung. T: 886 72692121
E: commons911@gmail.com
Freq: Daily
Editor in Chief: Fu-Lai Chou
Editorial Profile: It covers politics, economy and social issues.
Language (s): Chinese
DAILY NEWSPAPER

Dempa Shimbun
Editorial: Dempa Publications, Inc - Taiwan Branch., 7f-1, No. 36 Nanking West Road, Taipei. T: 886 225581817
W: http://www.dempa.net
Freq: Daily
Editor: Tricia Huang
Editorial Profile: Covers the electrical industry, electrical equipment and products as well as electronic materials.
Language (s): Japanese
DAILY NEWSPAPER

DigiTimes
Editorial: DIGITIMES Inc., 12th Floor, Number 133, Section 4, Min Sheng East Road, Songshan District, Taipei 105.
T: 886 287128866
E: newsroom@digitimes.com
W: http://www.digitimes.com.tw
Freq: 2 Times/Week; Circ: 60003 Not Audited
Editor in Chief: Vincent Mao
Editorial Profile: It covers the latest news on IT, telecommunications and other digital technology.
Language (s): Chinese, English
DAILY NEWSPAPER

Economic Daily News
Editorial: United Daily News Group, Number 369, Section 1, Da Tong Road, Shijr 22161.
T: 886 286925588 W: http://www.udn.com
Freq: Daily; Circ: 400003 Not Audited
Editor: Tian-Liang Lin; Editor in Chief: Hank Weng
Editorial Profile: It covers economy, finance, business, investment and stock markets.
Language (s): Chinese
DAILY NEWSPAPER

The Epoch Times
Editorial: The Epoch Times., 5th Floor-1, Number 9, Aiguo West Road, Taipei 100.
T: 886 222697097
E: editor_tw@epochtimes.com
W: http://www.epochtimes.com.tw
Freq: 2 Times/Week; Circ: 50003 Not Audited
Editor in Chief: Yi-Ching Lui; Bureau Chief: Hui-Ling Zhao
Editorial Profile: It covers news, politics, economy and social issues in Taiwan.
Language (s): Chinese
DAILY NEWSPAPER

Investor Weekly
Editorial: Invest Ment Media Ltd., 7th Floor, Number 52, Section 1, Nanjing East Road, Taipei 104. T: 886 22544548
E: wstock@invest.com.tw
W: http://www.investor.com.tw
Freq: Weekly
Editor in Chief: Rong-Chuan Guo
Editorial Profile: It focuses on investment news.
Language (s): Chinese
DAILY NEWSPAPER

Keng Sheng Daily News
Editorial: Keng Sheng Daily News., Number 36, Wuchuan Street, Hualien 970.
T: 886 38340131 E: kengshen@ms6.hinet.net
W: http://www.ksnews.com.tw
Freq: Daily; Circ: 100003 Not Audited
Editorial Profile: It focuses on the local news and events in Taidong and Hualian.
Language (s): Chinese
DAILY NEWSPAPER

Lianhe Zaobao
Editorial: Lian He Zao Bao - Singapore Press Holding., 2nd Floor, Number 130, Bo-Ai Road, Taipei 100. T: 886 223832732
W: http://www.zaobao.com
Freq: 2 Times/Week
Editorial Profile: It covers local and international news.
Language (s): Chinese
DAILY NEWSPAPER

Liberty Times
Editorial: Liberty Square Plaza No. 399 Ruiguang Road, Neihu District, Taipei 114.
T: 886 2 2656-2828
W: http://www.libertytimes.com.tw
Freq: Daily; Circ: 1200003 Not Audited
Editor in Chief: Chin-Rung Chen
Editorial Profile: Covers local and international news, entertainment, technology and travel.
Language (s): Taiwanese
DAILY NEWSPAPER

Mandarin Daily News
Editorial: Mandarin Daily News., 3rd Floor, Number 2, Fuzhou Street, Taipei 100.
T: 886 223921133
E: mdnnews@email.mdnkids.com
W: http://www.mdnkids.com.tw
Freq: Daily; Circ: 180003 Not Audited
Editor in Chief: Zhi-Mei Feng
Editorial Profile: It focuses on the education in Taiwan.
Language (s): Chinese
DAILY NEWSPAPER

Merit Times
Editorial: Merit Times Daily News, 2nd Floor, Section 1, No. 369, Da-Tong Road., Taipei Xian, Shijr 221. T: 886 226919448
E: newsmaster@merit-times.com.tw
W: http://www.merit-times.com.tw
Freq: Daily; Circ: 20003 Not Audited
Editorial Profile: It focuses on the latest news of the Buddhism religion.
Language (s): Chinese

DAILY NEWSPAPER

Metro Times

Editorial: Metro Times., 10th Floor-4., Number 23, Section 1, Heng Zhou Nan Road, Taipei 100. **T:** 886 223217759
E: metro.times@msa.hinet.net
W: http://www.metrotimes.com.tw
Freq: 2 Times/Week
Publisher: Zhong-Yi Chow
Editorial Profile: It covers local, regional and international news in Taiwan.
Language (s): Chinese
DAILY NEWSPAPER

Pots Weekly

Editorial: Lihpao Daily., 1st Floor, Number 43, Fu-Xing Road, Xin-Dian City, Taipei Hsien, Taipei 231. **T:** 886 286676655 243
E: pots@pots.tw **W:** http://www.pots.tw
Freq: Weekly; **Circ:** 80003 Not Audited
Editor in Chief: Sun-Quan Huang
Editorial Profile: It covers culture, society, entertainment, movies, literatures, lifestyle, and arts.
Language (s): Chinese
DAILY NEWSPAPER

The Straits Times - Taipei Bureau

Editorial: The Straits Times - Taipei Bureau., 2nd Floor, Number 130 Bo Ai Road, Taipei 100. **T:** 886 223703727
Freq: Daily
Editorial Profile: It focuses on the international news.
Language (s): English
DAILY NEWSPAPER

Taipei Times

Editorial: Taipei Times, 14th Floor, Number 399, Ruiguang Road, Neihu District, Taipei 114. **T:** 886 226561000
E: newsdesk@taipeitimes.com
W: http://www.taipeitimes.com
Freq: Daily; **Circ:** 300003 Not Audited
Editor: Kevin Chen
Editorial Profile: Launched in June 1999 with the mission of presenting an English-language journal of record for national and international readers, presented from a Taiwanese perspective. Showcases three main sections of local and international news, features and sports.
Language (s): English
DAILY NEWSPAPER

Taiwan Lih Pao

Editorial: Lih Pao., 1st Floor, Number 43, Fu-Xing Road, Xin-Dian City, Taipei Hsien, Taipei 231. **T:** 886 286676655 **E:** johann@lihpao.com
W: http://www.lihpao.com
Freq: 2 Times/Week; **Circ:** 30001 Not Audited
Editorial Profile: It focuses on the education issues in Taiwan.
Language (s): Chinese
DAILY NEWSPAPER

Taiwan News

Editorial: Taiwan News, 7th Floor, Number 88, Section 2, Xinyi Road, Taipei 106.
T: 886 223517666
E: editor@etaiwannews.com
W: http://www.etaiwannews.com
Freq: Daily; **Circ:** 250003 Not Audited
Bureau Chief: Jack Ong
Editorial Profile: Established in 1949 as the first English newspaper in Taiwan. Written for stakeholders in trade, foreign affairs, tourism and other areas of government. Also covers local and national news.
Language (s): English
DAILY NEWSPAPER

Taiwan Pacific Daily News

Editorial: Pacific Daily News., 6th Floor, Number 8, Ruiguang Road, Neihu District, Taipei 114. **T:** 886 287911588
E: tpdn@ms23.hinet.net
W: http://www.pacificnews.com.tw
Freq: 2 Times/Week; **Circ:** 60003 Not Audited
Editor: Jia-Min Lin
Editorial Profile: It covers politics, economy, finance, and social issues.
Language (s): Chinese
DAILY NEWSPAPER

Taiwan Shin Sheng Daily News

Editorial: Taiwan Shin Sheng Daily News., 9th Floor, Number 40, FuHsin North Road, Taipei 104. **T:** 886 287723058
E: tss.ad@msa.hinet.net
W: http://www.tssdnews.com.tw
Freq: Daily; **Circ:** 150003 Not Audited
Editorial Profile: It covers politics, economy, social issues, and healthcare.
Language (s): Chinese
DAILY NEWSPAPER

Taiwan Times

Editorial: Taiwan Times., Number 32, Gau-Nan-Guang Road, Ren-Wu Xiang, Kaohsiung 814. **T:** 886 73428666
E: smart@twtimes.com.tw
W: http://www.twtimes.com.tw
Freq: Daily; **Circ:** 200003 Not Audited
Bureau Chief: Shih-Ying Lin
Editorial Profile: It covers local news, politics, economy, culture and social issues.
Language (s): Chinese
DAILY NEWSPAPER

T-ynews Online Newspaper

Editorial: Tian Yan News International Corporation, Limited., 1st Floor, Number 60, Alley 30, Lane 53, Gongye South Road, Taoyuan 32460. **T:** 886 323885335
E: ty.news@msa.hinet.net
W: http://www.t-ynews.com.tw
Freq: Daily
Editorial Profile: It covers politics, legal news and social issues.
Language (s): Chinese
DAILY NEWSPAPER

U Paper

Editorial: U Paper., Number 369, Section 1, Da Tong Road, Shijr 22161. **T:** 886 286925588
E: upaper@udngroup.com
Freq: 2 Times/Week
Editorial Profile: Readership/Audience Profile:Targets: General Public. U Paper is a local newspaper which covers on society, social issues, current affairs, politics and national news.
Language (s): Chinese
DAILY NEWSPAPER

United Daily News

Editorial: United Daily News Group, Number 369, Section 1, Da Tong Road, Shijr 22161. **T:** 886 28 6925588 **E:** u9036@udngroup.com
W: http://udn.com
Freq: Daily; **Circ:** 1000003 Not Audited
Editor in Chief: Guo-Jun Luo
Editorial Profile: Covers local and international news and entertainment.
Language (s): Mandarin
DAILY NEWSPAPER

United Evening News

Editorial: United Evening News, No.369, Section 1, Da Tong Road, Shijr 22161.
T: 886 286925588 **E:** abc002@udngroup.com
W: http://udnnews.com
Freq: Daily; **Circ:** 500003 Not Audited
Bureau Chief: Kuo-Ning Hsiang; **Editor in Chief:** Mei-Yue You; **Editor:** Shun-Xiong Zhuang
Editorial Profile: It covers local news, international news, economy, entertainment, sports and lifestyle.
Language (s): Chinese
DAILY NEWSPAPER

The Wall Street Journal (Taiwan)

Owner: News Corporation, Ltd.
Editorial: Boss Tower, 11F-3, No. 111, Sung Kiang Road, Taipei 104. **T:** 886 2 225-0512
Bureau Chief: Aries Poon
DAILY NEWSPAPER

Wealth News

Editorial: 7th Floor, Number 52, Section 1, Nanjing East Road, Taipei 104.
T: 886 225512561 210
E: news@wealthgrp.com.tw
W: http://www.wealth.com.tw
Freq: Daily; **Circ:** 150003 Not Audited
Editor in Chief: Hui-Min, Sarah Guo
Editorial Profile: It focuses on finance, business and investment.
Language (s): Chinese
DAILY NEWSPAPER

Wonder Daily

Editorial: China Times Inc., B3, Number 303, Meng Jia Da Dao, Taipei 108.
T: 886 223087111
W: http://news.chinatimes.com
Freq: Daily
Editor in Chief: Qing-Long Huang
Editorial Profile: It covers politics, economy, travel and social issues.
Language (s): Chinese
DAILY NEWSPAPER

World Journal - Taipei Bureau

Editorial: World Journal - Taipei Bureau., Number 369, Section 1, Da Tong Road, Shijr 22161. **T:** 886 286925588 2343
E: wjtpe1@udngroup.com
W: http://www.worldjournal.com
Freq: Daily

Editorial Profile: It covers international, national and local news on politics, economy and social issues.
Language (s): Chinese
DAILY NEWSPAPER

NEWS SERVICE/SYNDICATE

Bloomberg News

Editorial: 10-C Hung Tai Century Building, 156 Ming Cheng Rd East Section 3, Taipei.
T: 886 0277191500
NEWS SERVICE/SYNDICATE

The Central News Agency

Editorial: The Central News Agency., Number 209, Songjiang Road, Taipei 104.
T: 886 225051180
E: services@mail.cna.com.tw
W: http://www.cna.com.tw
Freq: Daily
Bureau Chief: Sheng-Qing Chen
Editorial Profile: It is a Taiwan-wide news agency focusing on local news and international news.
Language (s): Chinese
NEWS SERVICE/SYNDICATE

Chiao Kwang News Agency

Owner: Federation Of Overseas Chinese Associations
Editorial: Federation Of Overseas Chinese Associations -, Chiao Kwang News Agency., 7th Floor-16, Number 121, Section 1, Chongqing South Road, Taipei 100.
T: 886 223759675 **E:** focat@ms51.hinet.net
W: http://www.focat.org.tw
Freq: Daily
Editorial Profile: It is a local news agency providing major news in Taiwan and overseas.
Language (s): Chinese
NEWS SERVICE/SYNDICATE

China Economic News Service (CENS)

Editorial: China Economic News Service (CENS)., No. 369, section 1, Da Tong Road, Shijr 22161. **T:** 886 2 86925588
E: webmaster@cens.com
W: http://news.cens.com
Freq: Daily
Editorial Profile: China Economic News Service provides a variety of economic-related publications.
Language (s): English
NEWS SERVICE/SYNDICATE

Deutsche Presse-Agentur

W: http://www.dpa.de
Freq: Daily
Editorial Profile: A German agency offering local and international news.
Language (s): English
NEWS SERVICE/SYNDICATE

Dow Jones Newswires

Editorial: 11F-2, 111 Sung Kiang Rd, Taipei 104. **T:** 886 2 2502-2557
E: djnews.taipei@dowjones.com
Bureau Chief: Aries Poon
NEWS SERVICE/SYNDICATE

Reuters

Editorial: 10 Fl 196 Chien Kuo North Road, Setion 2, Taipei. **T:** 886 225080815
Bureau Chief: Jonathan Standing
NEWS SERVICE/SYNDICATE

TAJIKISTAN Tel: 992

Standard Time: GMT +5
Continent: Asia
Capital City: Dushanbe

NEWSPAPERS & PUBLICATIONS

NEWSPAPERS

Asia-Plus

Owner: Asia-Plus Information Agency
Editorial: Prospekt Saadi Sherozi 16, 2 floor, Dushanbe. **T:** 992 372 38 73 35
E: info@asiaplus.tj
W: http://news.tj/ru/newspaper
Freq: Weekly; **Circ:** 10000 Not Audited
Editor: Nargis Hamrabaeva; **News Editor:** Roza Shaposhnik
Editorial Profile: Weekly publication focusing on current affairs and related issues.
Language (s): Russian
DAILY NEWSPAPER

Charkhi Gardun

Owner: Charkhi Gardun
Editorial: pr. S. Sherozi 16, Dushanbe 734018.
T: 992 372 23 85 384 **E:** chg@gazeta.tj
W: http://www.gazeta.tj/chg
Freq: Weekly; **Circ:** 15000 Publisher's Statement
Editorial Profile: The newspaper providing business and political news, culture and arts, medicine and sports, education, celebrities, live stories of readers and letters to editors.
Language (s): Tajik
DAILY NEWSPAPER

Digest press

Owner: Charkhi Gardun
Editorial: pr. S. Sherozi 16, Dushanbe.
T: 992 372 23 85 346 **E:** dp@gazeta.tj
W: http://www.gazeta.tj
Freq: Weekly; **Circ:** 9750 Publisher's Statement
Editor In Chief: Ravshan Melikshoev
Editorial Profile: Covers political news, business, education, sports, celebrities, and provides practical advice in health issues.
Language (s): Russian
DAILY NEWSPAPER

Jumhuriyat

Owner: Jumkhuriat
Editorial: Saadi Sherozi 16, 5 etazh, Dushanbe. **T:** 992 372 21 73 66
W: http://www.jumhuriyat.tj
Freq: Daily; **Circ:** 22000 Publisher's Statement
Editorial Profile: Government newspaper containing news on politics, economics and current affairs.
Language (s): Tajik
DAILY NEWSPAPER

Sadoi mardum

Editorial: pr. S. Sherozi 16, Dushanbe.
T: 992 372 385371 **E:** info@sadoimardum.tj
W: http://sadoimardum.tj
Freq: Daily; **Circ:** 8256 Publisher's Statement
Editor: Khairulloi Abdulavakhob
Editorial Profile: Presents political and governmental news.
Language (s): Tajik
DAILY NEWSPAPER

Vecherniy Dushanbe

Owner: Charkhi Gardun
Editorial: pr. S. Sherozi 16, Dushanbe 734018.
T: 992 372 23 85 364 **E:** vd@tojikiston.com
W: http://www.gazeta.tj
Freq: Daily; **Circ:** 2230 Publisher's Statement
Editor-in-Chief: Ravshan Makhsumov
Editorial Profile: Daily evening newspaper covering city news, analytic political and economical materials, health, society, etc.
Language (s): Russian
DAILY NEWSPAPER

NEWS SERVICE/SYNDICATE

Asia-Plus

Owner: Asia-Plus Information Agency
Editorial: prospekt Saadi Sherozi 16, Dushanbe. **T:** 992 372 21 78 63
E: agency@asiaplus.tj **W:** http://news.tj
Editorial Profile: Provides information and analytic news in English and Russian languages aiming foreign embassies accredited in Tajikistan and majority of international organizations.
Language (s): English, Russian, Tajik
NEWS SERVICE/SYNDICATE

Avesta news agency

Editorial: Sherozi Ave.16, 1 floor, Dushanbe.
T: 992 372 27 14 44 **E:** info@avesta.tj
W: http://www.avesta.tj
Editorial Profile: Agency providing current news in Russian and English languages.
Language (s): Tajik
NEWS SERVICE/SYNDICATE

Khovar news agency

Editorial: prospekt Rudaki 40, Dushanbe 734025. **T:** 992 372 22 32 383
E: niat.khovar@gmail.com
W: http://www.khovar.tj
Editorial Profile: National official news agency at the Government of Tajikistan. Provides news in Russian, Tajik, English, Farsi, Arabic and Uzbek languages.
Language (s): Tajik
NEWS SERVICE/SYNDICATE

BROADCASTING

TELEVISION STATIONS

Perviy kanal Tadjikskogo televideniya
Editorial: Bekhzod 25, Dushanbe
E: shabakaiaval@1tv.tj **W:** http://www.1tv.tj
Editorial Profile: National TV station with political and analytical programmes, entertainment, films and sports.

TV Safina
Editorial: ul. Bukhoro 43, Dushanbe.
T: 992 372 27 80 29 **E:** info@safina.tj
W: http://www.safina.tj
Editorial Profile: National TV station providing informative, cultural-entertaining and sports programmes.

TANZANIA Tel: 255
Standard Time: GMT +3
Continent: Africa
Capital City: Dar es Salaam

NEWSPAPERS & PUBLICATIONS

NEWSPAPERS

Amani
Owner: Global Publishers and General Enterprises Ltd
Editorial: Ali Hassan Mwinyi/Shekilango Roads, Sinza Bamaga, Dar Es Salaam
E: globalpublishers@bol.co.tz
W: http://www.globalpublisherstz.com
Circ: 40000 Publisher's Statement
Editor: Amran Kaima
Editorial Profile: Newspaper covering national and international news, current affairs, politics and entertainment.
Language (s): Swahili
DAILY NEWSPAPER

The Arusha Times
Owner: FM Arusha Ltd.
Editorial: New Safari Hotel Business Centre, Suite 108, Arusha. **T:** 255 27 250 6438
E: arushatimes@habari.co.tz
W: http://www.arushatimes.co.tz
Editor: William Lobulu
Editorial Profile: Regional newspaper focussing on news, current affairs, politics and economics.
Language (s): English
DAILY NEWSPAPER

Championi
Owner: Global Publishers and General Enterprises Ltd
Editorial: Ali Hassan Mwinyi/Shekilango Roads, Sinza Bamaga, Dar Es Salaam, United Republic of Tanzania. **T:** 255 22 277 33 57
E: globalpublishers@bol.co.tz
W: http://www.globalpublisherstz.com
Freq: 2 Times/Week; **Circ:** 60000 Not Audited
Editor: Charles Mganga
Editorial Profile: Tabloid-sized newspaper focusing on sport, entertainment and music.
Language (s): Swahili
DAILY NEWSPAPER

Daily News (Tanzania)
Owner: Tanzania Standard (Newspapers) Ltd
Editorial: PO Box 9033, Dar Es Salaam.
T: 255 22 21 10 595
E: newsdesk@dailynews-tsn.com
W: http://www.dailynews-tsn.com
Freq: Daily; **Circ:** 15000 Publisher's Statement
News Editor: Japhet Sanga
Editorial Profile: Newspaper focusing on politics, finance, business, culture, sport and general news.
Language (s): English
DAILY NEWSPAPER

The Guardian
Owner: The Guardian Limited
T: 255 22 2700735 **E:** info@guardian.co.tz
W: http://www.guardian.co.tz
Freq: Daily; **Circ:** 25000 Publisher's Statement
Editorial Profile: Newspaper covering national and international news and current affairs including economics, politics, business, culture and sport.
Language (s): English
DAILY NEWSPAPER

Ijumaa
Owner: Global Publishers and General Enterprises Ltd
Editorial: Ali Hassan Mwinyi/Shekilango Roads, Sinza Bamaga, Dar Es Salaam.
T: 255 22 277 33 57
E: globalpublishers@bol.co.tz
W: http://www.globalpublisherstz.com
Circ: 55000 Publisher's Statement
Editor: Luqman Maloto
Editorial Profile: Newspaper covering national and international news, current affairs, politics and entertainment.
Language (s): Swahili
DAILY NEWSPAPER

Ijumaa Wiki'nda
Owner: Global Publishers and General Enterprises Ltd
Editorial: PO Box 7534, Dar Es Salaam.
T: 255 22 277 33 57
E: globalpublishers@bol.co.tz
W: http://www.globalpublisherstz.com
Circ: 90000 Publisher's Statement
Editor: Abraham Ojuku
Editorial Profile: Newspaper covering entertainment and leisure.
Language (s): Swahili
DAILY NEWSPAPER

Nipashe (Daily)
Owner: IPP Media Ltd.
Editorial: PO Box 31042, Dar Es Salam.
T: 255 22 27 00 735
E: jmaganga@gauardian.co.tz
Freq: Daily; **Circ:** 7000 Publisher's Statement
Editor: Wilson Kaigarula
Editorial Profile: Newspaper covering national and international news, current affairs, politics, business, sports and leisure.
Language (s): Swahili
DAILY NEWSPAPER

Nipashe Jumapili
Owner: IPP Media Ltd.
Editorial: The Guardian Limited, Mikocheni Industrial Area, Opposite ITV Station, Dar Es Salam. **T:** 255 22 27 00 735
E: info@guardian.co.tz
W: http://ippmedia.com
Freq: Sun; **Circ:** 10000 Publisher's Statement
Editor: Wilson Kaigarula
Editorial Profile: Newspaper covering national and international news, current affairs, politics, business, sports and entertainment.
Language (s): Swahili
DAILY NEWSPAPER

Risasi Jumamosi
Owner: Global Publishers and General Enterprises Ltd
Editorial: Global Publishers & General Enterprises Ltd, Ali Hassan Mwinyi/Shekilango Roads, Dar Es Salaam. **T:** 255 22 277 33 57
E: globalpublishers@bol.co.tz
W: http://www.globalpublisherstz.com
Circ: 60000 Publisher's Statement
Editor: Saloum Mette
Editorial Profile: Newspaper covering national and international news, current affairs, politics and entertainment.
Language (s): Swahili
DAILY NEWSPAPER

Risasi Mchanganyiko
Owner: Global Publishers and General Enterprises Ltd
Editorial: Global Publishers & General Enterprises Ltd, Ali Hassan Mwinyi/Shekilango Roads, Dar Es Salaam. **T:** 255 22 277 33 57
E: globalpublishers@bol.co.tz
W: http://www.globalpublisherstz.com
Circ: 100000 Publisher's Statement
Editor: Saloum Mette
Editorial Profile: Newspaper covering national and international news and current affairs.
Language (s): Swahili
DAILY NEWSPAPER

Sunday News (Tanzania)
Owner: Tanzania Standard (Newspapers) Ltd
Editorial: PO Box 9033, Dar Es Salam.
T: 255 22 21 10 595
E: newsdesk@dailynews-tsn.com
W: http://www.dailynews-tsn.com
Freq: Sun; **Circ:** 12000 Publisher's Statement
Editor: James Mpinga; **News Editor:** Japhet Sanga
Editorial Profile: Newspaper covering national and international news, current affairs, politics, business, sports and entertainment.
Language (s): English
DAILY NEWSPAPER

Sunday Observer
Owner: IPP Media Ltd.
Editorial: The Guardian Limited, Mikocheni Industrial Area, Opposite ITV Station, Dar Es Salam. **T:** 255 22 27 00 735
E: info@guardian.co.tz
W: http://www.guardian.co.tz/sundayobserver.html
Freq: Sun; **Circ:** 15000 Publisher's Statement
Editor: Wilson Kaigarula
Editorial Profile: Newspaper covering national and international news, current affairs, politics, business, economics, sports and culture.
Language (s): English
DAILY NEWSPAPER

Uwazi Na Ukweli
Owner: Global Publishers and General Enterprises Ltd
Editorial: Global Publishers & General Enterprises Ltd, Ali Hassan Mwinyi/Shekilango Roads, Dar Es Salaam. **T:** 255 22 277 33 57
E: globalpublishers@bol.co.tz
W: http://www.globalpublisherstz.com
Circ: 45000 Publisher's Statement
Editor: Alvan Stambuli
Editorial Profile: Newspaper covering national and international news, current affairs and politics.
Language (s): Swahili
DAILY NEWSPAPER

THAILAND Tel: 66
Standard Time: GMT +7
Continent: Asia
Capital City: Bangkok (Krung Thep Maha Nakhon)

NEWSPAPERS & PUBLICATIONS

NEWSPAPERS

A Day Bulletin
Editorial: Day Poets, 3 Ekamai 10, Sukhumvit 63, North Klongtan, Wattana, Bangkok 10110.
T: 66 220 31040 815
E: adaybulletin@daypoets.com
W: http://www.daypoets.com
Freq: Weekly
Editor: Wilairat Ame-lam
Editorial Profile: Covers of lifestyle, social issue, and business.
Language (s): English
DAILY NEWSPAPER

The Andaman
Editorial: Mittraphap Media, 314, Moo 1, Thepkrasatri Rd., Thalang, Phuket 83110.
T: 66 7622 5873
Freq: Monthly; **Circ:** 5003 Not Audited
Editor: Nualnoi Hitopakorn
Editorial Profile: Covers local news, visitor's guide.
Language (s): English
DAILY NEWSPAPER

Andaman Times
Editorial: Andaman Times, 28/4 Moo 4, Thaphaya, Palian, Trang 92140.
T: 66 75268124 **E:** andamantimes@thai.com
Freq: Semi-Monthly; **Circ:** 1503 Not Audited
Editor: Phonchai Nakponl
Editorial Profile: Covers news and general interest.
Language (s): Thai
DAILY NEWSPAPER

Awol
Editorial: Awol, 136/229 Emerald Hill, Soi 6, Borfai, Hua Hin 77110. **T:** 66 816 498361
E: info@awolonline.net
W: http://www.awolonline.net
Freq: Weekly
Editor: Steve James
Editorial Profile: Covers the latest news on travel
Language (s): English
DAILY NEWSPAPER

Bangkok Post
Editorial: The Post Publishing, 136 Na Ranong Road, off Sunthorn Kosa Road, Klong Toey, Bangkok 10110. **T:** 662 6164000
W: http://www.bangkokpost.com
Freq: Daily; **Circ:** 37473 ABC-Audit Bureau of Circulations
News Editor: Soonruth Bunyamanee; **Editor:** Pattnapong Chantraonontwong; **Editor in Chief:** Pichai Chuensuksawadi; **Editor:** Pitsinee Jitpleecheep; **Editor:** Kajornsak Leu; **Editor:** Saritdet Marukatat; **Editor:** Pongpet Mekloy; **Editor:** Sayant Pornnantharat; **Editor:** Wanchai Rujawongsanti; **Editor:** Borisuthiboun Tasaneeyavej
Editorial Profile: Provides breaking local, national and international news as the leading English-language daily newspaper in Thailand and has the longest history of any newspaper in existence in the country. Targets well-educated decision makers, including top executives and high-ranking government officials.
Language (s): English
DAILY NEWSPAPER

Bangkok Shuho
Editorial: Bangkok Shuho, R.S. Tower Bldg. 19/F, 121/64-65 Rajadapisek Rd., Dindaeng, Bangkok 10400. **T:** 66 2247 8991
E: bkkshuho@loxinfo.co.th
W: http://www.bangkokshuho.com
Freq: Weekly; **Circ:** 12603 Not Audited
Editor: Kazuko Otsuka
Editorial Profile: Japanese newspaper.
Language (s): English, Japanese
DAILY NEWSPAPER

Bangkok Times
Editorial: Sachino, 138/157 Moo 4, Kannayao, Kannayao, Bangkok 10230. **T:** 66 2919 7308
E: bangkoktimes@hotmail.com
W: http://www.bangkok.co.jp
Freq: Monthly; **Circ:** 8003 Not Audited
Editor: Wichart Hampisalpipat
Editorial Profile: Newspaper which targets Thai people living in Japan Promotion of Relations between Thailand and Japan by providing information to the Thai people in Japan. And dissemination of knowledge about the culture to the public.
Language (s): Thai
DAILY NEWSPAPER

Banmuang
Editorial: Nawakit Banmuang, 1 Soi Pleummanee, Vibhavadee-Rangsit Road, Lardyao, Chatuchak, Bangkok 10900.
T: 66 2513 0230 3
E: presscenter@banmuang.co.th
W: http://www.banmuang.co.th
Freq: Daily; **Circ:** 380003 Not Audited
Editor in Chief: Polathit Phookphiboon; **Editor:** Chutimol Srikham
Editorial Profile: Covers the economy, politics, environment, culture, and business news.
Language (s): Thai
DAILY NEWSPAPER

Builder News
Editorial: TTF International, 200/12-14 6/F., A.E. House, Ramkamhaeng 4, Ramkamhaeng, Suanluang, Bangkok 10250. **T:** 66 27172477
E: editor@buildernews.in.tn
W: http://www.buildernews.in.tn
Freq: Semi-Monthly; **Circ:** 50001 Not Audited
Editor in Chief: Tommy Jensen; **Editor:** Wimolwal Piboonvech
Editorial Profile: Focuses on the business information industry, construction, materials, construction equipment, technology, design, and real estate.
Language (s): Thai
DAILY NEWSPAPER

Bus & Truck
Editorial: TTF International, 200/12-14 7/F., A.E. House, Ramkamhaeng 4, Ramkamhaeng, Suanluang, Bangkok 10250.
T: 66 27172477 171 **E:** info@ttfintl.com
W: http://www.busandtrucks.com
Freq: Semi-Monthly; **Circ:** 30001 Not Audited
Editor: Seksan Chaiyaphuak
Editorial Profile: Focuses on commercial vehicles.
Language (s): Thai
DAILY NEWSPAPER

Business News Centre (Soon Ruam Khao Thurakij)
Editorial: Business News Centre, 124, 126 Jaransanitwong 36, Janransanitwong Rd., Arun-ammarin, Bangkok 10700.
T: 66 28860800 **E:** pooky@ksc.th.com
W: http://www.bnc.co.th
Freq: Daily; **Circ:** 10001 Not Audited
Editor: Jaran Inthakallaya
Editorial Profile: Covers the latest in business news.
Language (s): Thai
DAILY NEWSPAPER

Champ
Editorial: Central Express, 28/39 Soi Kehabangbua 4, Viphawadee 60 Rd., Taladbangken, Laksi, Bangkok 10210.
T: 66 25 6148635
E: centralexpress@hotmail.com
Freq: Weekly; **Circ:** 150003 Not Audited
Editor: Suwanna Srisongkram
Editorial Profile: Publishes twice a week Covers of sports, boxing.

Language (s): Thai
DAILY NEWSPAPER

Chiangmai Business
Editorial: Chiang Mai Raiwan, 164, Rachchiangsaen Rd., Haiya, Muang, Chiangmai 50100. **T:** 66 532796867 201
E: cmnews@chiangmainews.co.th
W: http://www.chiangmainews.co.th
Freq: Weekly
Editor in Chief: Krailas Jatuwattanakul
Editorial Profile: Covers business.
Language (s): Thai
DAILY NEWSPAPER

Chiangmai Mail
Editorial: Chiengmai Mail Publishing, 209/5 Moo 6, Faham, Muang, Chiangmai 50000. **T:** 66 53 852557
E: editor@chiangmai-mail.com
W: http://www.chiangmai-mail.com
Freq: Weekly; **Circ:** 5001 Not Audited
Editorial Profile: Covers of local news in Chiangmai area.
Language (s): English
DAILY NEWSPAPER

ChiangmaiNews
Editorial: Chiang Mai Rai Wan, 164 Rachchiangsaen Rd., Haiya, Muang, Chiangmai 50100. **T:** 66 5327 9686 201
E: cmnews@chiangmainews.co.th
W: http://www.chiangmainews.co.th
Freq: Daily; **Circ:** 30003 Not Audited
Editor: Sunthad Suksoong
Editorial Profile: Covers local news.
Language (s): Thai
DAILY NEWSPAPER

Co-op News
Editorial: The Coorperative League of Thailand, 4 Phichai Rd., Dusit, Bangkok 10310. **T:** 662 669 3254 **E:** clt@clt.or.th
W: http://www.clt.or.th **Circ:** 10003 Not Audited
Editor: Sitthidej Attakrit
Editorial Profile: Publishes on the 10th & 22nd of every month providing business news for members of cooperation.
Language (s): Thai
DAILY NEWSPAPER

CTV News
Editorial: Cable TV Chantaburi, 49/1, Thachalab Rd., Muang, Chantaburi 22000. **T:** 66 393 11749 3 **E:** ctv@ctv.co.th
W: http://www.ctv.co.th
Freq: Semi-Monthly
Editor: Ponvit Swatdekant
Editorial Profile: The 1st and 16th of every month Covers of business, politics, and local news., etc.
Language (s): Thai
DAILY NEWSPAPER

Dailynews
Editorial: Siphraya Karnphim, 1/4 Moo 2, Viphawadee-Rangsit Rd., Talad Bangkhen, Laksi, Bangkok 10210. **T:** 66 25611456 9
E: editor@dailynews.co.th
W: http://www.dailynews.co.th
Freq: Daily; **Circ:** 600001 Not Audited
Editor: Suphorn Numnoi
Editorial Profile: Covers of local, sports, social issues, politics, and international news.
Language (s): Thai
DAILY NEWSPAPER

Dara Daily
Editorial: Idea Power, 48/18, Soi Ladphrao 15, Ladphrao Rd., Jomphol, Jatujak, Bangkok 10900. **T:** 66 293856478 34
E: daradaily@gmail.com
Freq: Daily; **Circ:** 300000 Not Audited
Editor in Chief: Chalermkiat Somwang
Editorial Profile: Covers of celebrities, gossip.
Language (s): Thai
DAILY NEWSPAPER

Dokbia Turakij (The Interest Business)
Editorial: Dokbia, 61/33-34 Park Ploenchit Building, 8th Floor, Sukhumvit 1, Wattana, Bangkok 10110. **T:** 66 26552401
E: dokbia@hotmail.com
Freq: Weekly; **Circ:** 135001 Not Audited
Editorial Profile: Publishes Every Monday Copy Deadline: One week Before the publish date
Language (s): Thai
DAILY NEWSPAPER

Econ News
Editorial: Econnews, 44/30-31 Ngamwongwan Rd., Lardyao, Chatuchak, Bangkok 10900.
T: 66 29 5345026 **E:** econnews@econnews.org
W: http://www.econnews.org

Freq: Monthly; **Circ:** 25003 Not Audited
Editorial Profile: Target: Executive and over (A / B Class) in both public and private sectors. Cover events like the economy / society and politics.
Language (s): Thai
DAILY NEWSPAPER

Focus Pakati (Rai Sapda)
Editorial: Focus Multimedia Group, 3, Soi 24, Niphatsongkhrao 1 Rd., Hadyai, Songkhla 90110. **T:** 66 74 3685223 20
E: focuspaktai@yahoo.com
W: http://www.focuspaktai.com
Freq: Weekly; **Circ:** 10003 Not Audited
Editor: Prasan Suksai
Editorial Profile: Covers of local news in south area.
Language (s): Thai
DAILY NEWSPAPER

Global Business
Editorial: Global Business (Sri Benjachot Group), 1511/52, Phaholyothin Rd., Samsen Nai, Phayathai, Bangkok 10400.
T: 66 26157003 **E:** gb.newspaper@gmail.com
W: http://www.globalbusiness.co.th
Freq: Weekly
Editor in Chief: Thitichai Atthawatchara
Editorial Profile: Covers business.
Language (s): Thai
DAILY NEWSPAPER

HotGolf
Editorial: TTF International, 200/12-14 7th F., A.E. House, Ramkamhaeng 4, Ramkamhaeng, Suanluang, Bangkok 10250.
T: 66 27172477 180
E: hotgolfeditor@yahoo.com
W: http://www.hotgolfclub.com
Freq: Semi-Monthly; **Circ:** 3001 Not Audited
Editorial Profile: Covers of golf industry.
Language (s): Thai
DAILY NEWSPAPER

Hua Hin Today
Editorial: Hua Hin Today, 58 Naresdamri Rd., Hua Hin, Hua Hin 77110. **T:** 66 32 511535
E: info@huahintoday.net
W: http://www.huahintoday.net
Freq: Monthly; **Circ:** 7003 Not Audited
Editor: Julaporn Wannapruk
Editorial Profile: Providing information of Hua Hin.
Language (s): English
DAILY NEWSPAPER

Intertransport Logistics
Editorial: ITL Trade Media, 230 Ladpraowanghin, Ladprao, Bangkok, Bangkok 10230. **T:** 66 251 42839
E: itl@logisticthailand.com
W: http://www.logisticsthailand.com
Freq: Semi-Monthly
Editor: Arun Borirak
Editorial Profile: Covers latest news on logistics
Language (s): Thai
DAILY NEWSPAPER

Isaan Bizweek
Editorial: Isaan Bizweek, 498, Moo 12, Baannonmuang, Sila, Muang, Khon Kaen 40000. **T:** 66 432 03683
E: kunluk@yahoo.com
Freq: Semi-Monthly
Editor in Chief: Charoenrak Phetpradab
Editorial Profile: Covers of local news.
Language (s): Thai
DAILY NEWSPAPER

Jakkawan Muai
Editorial: Central Express, 28/39 Soi Kehabangbua 4, Viphawadee 60 Rd., Taladbangken, Laksi, Bangkok 10210.
T: 66 25 6148635
E: centralexpress@hotmail.com
Freq: Weekly; **Circ:** 80003 Not Audited
Editor: Suwanna Srisongkram
Editorial Profile: Publishes twice a week.Focus: boxing
Language (s): Thai
DAILY NEWSPAPER

Job Express
Editorial: Wattasarn Media, 105/7, Mooban Sasiwan, Moo 11, Soi Suanphak 32, Suanphak Rd., Talingchan, Talingchan, Bangkok 10170.
T: 66 28842929 **E:** webmaster@jobbyyou.com
W: http://www.wm.co.th
Freq: Weekly
Editorial Profile: Covers information for college graduates.
Language (s): Thai
DAILY NEWSPAPER

Job Request
Editorial: Sappasan, 71/17 Borommarachachonnanee Rd., Arun Amarin, Bangkok Noi, Bangkok 10700.
T: 66 2435 2345 126
W: http://www.mrthaijob.com
Freq: Weekly; **Circ:** 80001 Not Audited
Editorial Profile: Covers the latest information on employment.
Language (s): Thai
DAILY NEWSPAPER

Joh Game
Editorial: Siam Sport Syndicate, 66/26-29 Moo12, Soi Ramindra 40, Ramindra Rd., Nualjan, Buengkum, Bangkok 10310.
T: 66 2508808586
W: http://www.siamsport.co.th
Freq: Daily; **Circ:** 100001 Not Audited
Editorial Profile: Covers of sport news.
Language (s): Thai
DAILY NEWSPAPER

Kanchon
Editorial: Kanchon Newspaper, 34, Khuankhanun Rd., Tabtiang, Muang, Trang 92000. **T:** 66 89 7302889
W: http://www.trangtodaynews.com
Freq: Daily; **Circ:** 1203 Not Audited
Editor: Peerapol Janphak
Editorial Profile: Focus: local news
Language (s): Thai
DAILY NEWSPAPER

Kaohoon Thurakij Raiwan
Editorial: BURAPA TASNA (1999) Co., Ltd, 48/5-6 2/F Preecha complex, Rajadapisek Rd., Samsennok, Huaykwang, Bangkok 10320. **T:** 66 2 6934555 108110
E: kao_hoon@yahoo.com
W: http://www.kaohoon.com
Freq: Daily; **Circ:** 70001 Not Audited
Publisher: Kaset Siwakua
Editorial Profile: Covers of stock news.
Language (s): Thai
DAILY NEWSPAPER

Khao Seree
Editorial: Khao Seree, 324 Kantang Rd., Tabtiang, Muang, Trang 92000.
T: 66 75213019
E: kaosayre2535@hotmail.com
Freq: Weekly; **Circ:** 3003 Not Audited
Editor: Jessada Rakkhong
Editorial Profile: Covers business, politics, and local news.
Language (s): Thai
DAILY NEWSPAPER

Khaosod
Editorial: Matichon Group, 12 Mooban Prachaniwes 1, Thedsaban Narumarn Rd., Lardyao, Chatuchak, Bangkok 10900.
T: 66 29544999 **E:** khaosod.eng@gmail.com
W: http://www.khaosod.co.th
Freq: Daily; **Circ:** 500001 Not Audited
Editor: Thakoon Boonparn
Editorial Profile: Covers the latest in international and local news.
Language (s): Thai
DAILY NEWSPAPER

Khon Ha Ngan
Editorial: Krasae Khao, 337/50 Umpher Road, Makhamtia, Maung, Suratthani 84000.
T: 66 77282559
E: krasaenewsofsouth@yahoo.com
W: http://www.southnewsonline.com
Freq: Monthly; **Circ:** 2001 Not Audited
Editor: Santat Jedsamianmai
Editorial Profile: Focus on career.
Language (s): Thai
DAILY NEWSPAPER

Komchadluek
Editorial: The Nation, 1854 Bangna-Trad Road (KM 4.5), Bangkok 10260.
T: 66 23383333 3325
E: komchad@nationgroup.com
W: http://www.komchadluek.com
Freq: Daily; **Circ:** 800001 Not Audited
Editor: Saranya Hai
Editorial Profile: Quality daily newspaper with strengths in the " different creative " by focusing on social responsibility. It is suitable for everyone in the family.
Language (s): Thai
DAILY NEWSPAPER

Krabi News
Editorial: Krabi News, 17/6, Watchara Rd., Paknam, MuangKrabi Yai, Muang, Krabi 81000. **T:** 66 75620572
E: krabinews17@yahoo.com
Freq: Semi-Monthly; **Circ:** 1001 Not Audited
Editor: Prasong Praditsap
Editorial Profile: Covers of local news

Language (s): Thai
DAILY NEWSPAPER

Krasae Khao Taksin
Editorial: Krasae Khao, 331/50 Umpher Road, Makhamtia, Maung, Suratthani 84000.
T: 66 77282559
E: krasaenewsofsouth@yahoo.com
W: http://www.southnewsonline.com
Freq: Monthly; **Circ:** 2001 Not Audited
Editor: Santat Jedsamianmai
Editorial Profile: Covers of local news.
Language (s): Thai
DAILY NEWSPAPER

Krungthep Turakij
Editorial: The Nation, 1854 Bangna-Trad Road (KM 4.5), Bangna, Bangkok 10260.
T: 66 2338 3333 3386
E: ktfor@nationgroup.com
W: http://www.bangkokbiznews.com
Freq: Daily; **Circ:** 145503 Not Audited
Editor: Orawan Hoichan; **Editor in Chief:** Chalao Kanjana
Editorial Profile: Covers business.
Language (s): Thai
DAILY NEWSPAPER

Lanna Thurakij
Editorial: Lanna Thurakij, 309/7, Patan Rd. Patan, Muang, Chiangmai 50300.
T: 66 53872386 **E:** lannanews@gmail.com
W: http://hjttp://www.lannanews.com
Freq: Monthly
Editor: Pathiyuth Jaturat
Editorial Profile: A local newspaper that intended audience in the northern province.
Language (s): Thai
DAILY NEWSPAPER

Lannathai News
Editorial: Great Sun & Stars Media (GSSM), 29/9-12, Thepharak Rd., Changphuek, Muang, Chiangmai 50300. **T:** 66 53 357977 14
E: lannathainews@yahoo.com
W: http://www.lannathai-news.com
Freq: Semi-Monthly
Editor: Nopniwat Krairoek
Editorial Profile: Covers local news.
Language (s): Thai
DAILY NEWSPAPER

Leader Time Newspaper
Editorial: Leader Time, 1111/112 Baan Klangkrung (Ratchada-Ladprao), Ladyao, Jatujak, Bangkok 10900. **T:** 66 25139191 79
E: ying99leadertime@gmail.com
W: http://www.leadertimeonline.com
Freq: Semi-Monthly; **Circ:** 10003 Not Audited
Editorial Profile: Covers business.
Language (s): Thai
DAILY NEWSPAPER

Lok Wannee Raiwan
Editorial: Watta Classifieds, 71/30 Boromrajchonnee Road, Arun-amarin, Bangkoknoi, Bangkok 10700.
T: 66 2 422-8101 9 **E:** worldtoday@watta.co.th
W: http://www.dailyworldtoday.com
Freq: 2 Times/Week; **Circ:** 100000 Not Audited
Editor: Suntorn Kullawattanaworaphong
Editorial Profile: Covers of social issue, national news, sports, and business news.
Language (s): Thai
DAILY NEWSPAPER

Lok Wannee Wansuk
Editorial: Watta Classifieds, 71/30 Boromrajchonnee Road, Arun-amarin, Bangkoknoi, Bangkok 10700. **T:** 66 24228101
E: worldtoday@watta.co.th
W: http://www.dailyworldtoday.com
Freq: Weekly; **Circ:** 100001 Not Audited
Editor: Suntorn Kullawattanaworaphong
Editorial Profile: Covers news topics.
Language (s): Thai
DAILY NEWSPAPER

Matichon
Editorial: Matichon Group, 12 Thedsaban Narumarn Rd., Ladyao, Jatujak, Bangkok 10900. **T:** 66 258 00021
E: weekly@matichon.co.th
W: http://www.matichon.co.th
Freq: Daily; **Circ:** 600001 Not Audited
Editor: Pairat Pongpanit
Editorial Profile: Covers of business, politics, economy, and international news.
Language (s): Thai
DAILY NEWSPAPER

Matitrang
Editorial: Matitrang Newspaper, 35 Phattalung Rd., Muang, Trang 92000. **T:** 66 752 20931
E: thong820@hotmail.com
Freq: Semi-Monthly; **Circ:** 1001 Not Audited

Editorial Profile: Covers of local news.
Language (s): Thai
DAILY NEWSPAPER

Maya Channel

Editorial: Maya Channel, 90/106 Viphawadi 20, Viphawadi Rod, Bangkok 10900.
T: 66 2691 5252 221
Freq: 2 Times/Week; **Circ:** 250003 Not Audited
Editor in Chief: Pakorn Thongboriboon
Editorial Profile: Covers celebrities, movies, and fashion.
Language (s): Thai
DAILY NEWSPAPER

Muay Siam Today

Editorial: Siam Sport Syndicate, 66/26-29 Moo12, Soi Ramindra 40, Ramindra Rd., Nualchan, Buengkum, Bangkok 10230.
T: 66 2 5088000
E: webmaster@siamsport.co.th
W: http://www.siamsport.co.th
Freq: Daily; **Circ:** 100003 Not Audited
Editorial Profile: Covers of boxing.
Language (s): Thai
DAILY NEWSPAPER

Naewna

Editorial: Naewna Newspaper Co. Ltd., 96 Moo 3 Vibhavadee-Rangsit Road, Talard Bangken, Bangkok 10210. **T:** 66 29734250
E: naewna@naewna.com
W: http://www.naewna.com
Freq: Daily; **Circ:** 200001 Not Audited
Editorial Profile: covers of news
Language (s): Thai
DAILY NEWSPAPER

The Nation

Editorial: The Nation, 1854 Bangna-Trad Road (KM 4.5), Bangna, Bangkok 10260.
T: 66 2 3383333
W: http://www.nationmultimedia.com
Freq: Daily
Editor: Achara Deboonme
Editorial Profile: Covers business, politics, international and local news.
Language (s): English
DAILY NEWSPAPER

Ngan Duan

Editorial: Wattasarn Media, 105/7, Mooban Sasiwan, Moo 11, Soi Suanphak 32, Suanphak Rd, Talingchan, Talingchan, Bangkok 10170.
T: 66 28842929 **E:** webmaster@jobbyyou.com
W: http://www.wm.co.th
Freq: Weekly
Editorial Profile: Covers employment and careers.
Language (s): Thai
DAILY NEWSPAPER

Ngan Tua Thai

Editorial: Watta Classifieds, 71/30 Boromrajchonnee Road, Bangkoknoi, Bangkok 10700. **T:** 66 24228000 9
E: ejobeasy@watta.co.th
W: http://www.ejobeasy.com
Freq: Semi-Monthly; **Circ:** 80001 Not Audited
Editorial Profile: Covers of jobs, careers.
Language (s): Thai
DAILY NEWSPAPER

Northern Business Newspaper

Editorial: Sveb Group, 36/2, Moo 4, Outer Ring Rd., San Pheesue, Muang, Chiangmai 50300. **T:** 66 5311 0677
E: sveb_group@hotmail.com
W: http://www.svebgroup.com
Freq: Monthly
Editorial Profile: Covers business in the northern area.
Language (s): Thai
DAILY NEWSPAPER

Palang Chon

Editorial: Palang Chon, 110/1 Baan Pagrad Rd., Banpong, Rachaburi 70110.
T: 66 818412992
E: phalangchon@hotmail.com
Freq: Semi-Monthly; **Circ:** 5001 Not Audited
Editor: Surin Phiphakphakorn
Editorial Profile: Covers of local news
Language (s): Thai
DAILY NEWSPAPER

Patiroop

Editorial: Patiroop, 28/1 Pokarong Rd., Tarab, Muang, Petchaburi 76000. **T:** 66 3240 01748
E: reformnews@hotmail.com
Freq: Semi-Monthly; **Circ:** 5003 Not Audited
Editor: Sirikul Sitarom
Editorial Profile: Publishes on the 1st and 16th of every month Covers of local news.
Language (s): Thai
DAILY NEWSPAPER

Pattaya Blatt

Editorial: Pattaya Mail Publishing, 370/7-8 Pattaya Second Road, Chonburi, Pattaya 20260. **T:** 66 384 112401
E: redaktion@pattayablatt.com
W: http://www.pattayablatt.com
Freq: Weekly; **Circ:** 7001 Not Audited
Editorial Profile: Covers all the local news in Pattaya.
Language (s): German
DAILY NEWSPAPER

Pattaya Mail

Editorial: Pattaya Mail Publishing, 370/7-8 Pattaya Second Road, Pattaya City, Chonburi 20150. **T:** 66 384112401
E: ptymail@pattayamial.com
W: http://www.pattayamail.com
Freq: Weekly; **Circ:** 10501 Not Audited
Editorial Profile: Covers local news.
Language (s): English
DAILY NEWSPAPER

Pattaya People Weekly

Editorial: Dragon Enterprises, 20/15-16 M. 10 Soi Day-Night Hotel, South Pattaya Road, Pattaya City, Chonburi 20150. **T:** 66 38420707
E: info@pattayapeople.com
W: http://www.pattayapeople.com
Freq: Weekly; **Circ:** 5001 Not Audited
Editorial Profile: Covers of local news, international news., etc.
Language (s): Thai
DAILY NEWSPAPER

Pattaya Today

Editorial: Siamese Mission Media, 42/91, M.9, Sukhumvit Rd., Nongprue, Banglamung, Chonburi 20150. **T:** 66 384 10077
E: info@pattayatoday.net
W: http://www.pattayatoday.net
Freq: Semi-Monthly; **Circ:** 8001 Not Audited
Editor: Lucksika Natham
Editorial Profile: Covers of real estate, business and local news.
Language (s): English
DAILY NEWSPAPER

Phalang Ras

Editorial: Krasae Khao, 331/50, Makhamtia. Maung, Suratthani 84000. **T:** 66 772 82559
E: krasaenewsofsouth@yahoo.com
W: http://www.southnewsonline.co
Freq: Monthly; **Circ:** 2001 Not Audited
Editorial Profile: Focus: local news
Language (s): Thai
DAILY NEWSPAPER

Phitsanulok Today

Editorial: Phitsanulok Today, 86/1 Moo 7, Watjan, Muang, Phitsanulok 65000.
T: 66 55 216541 **E:** plk_today@yahoo.com
Freq: Semi-Monthly; **Circ:** 2003 Not Audited
Editor: Yossakrai Kledjeen
Editorial Profile: Covers local news.
Language (s): Thai
DAILY NEWSPAPER

Phoo Chad Karn Rai Sapada

Editorial: ASTV Manager, 102/1 Phra-Arthit Road, Chanasongkarm, Phranakhorn, Bangkok 10200. **T:** 66 26 294488
W: http://www.manager.co.th
Freq: Weekly; **Circ:** 180003 Not Audited
Editorial Profile: Covers news.
Language (s): Thai
DAILY NEWSPAPER

Phoo Chad Karn Rai Wan

Editorial: ASTV Manager, 102/1 Phra-Arthit Road, Chanasongkarm, Phranakhorn, Bangkok 10200. **T:** 66 26 294488
E: wm@manager.co.th
W: http://www.gotomanager.com
Freq: Daily; **Circ:** 280003 Not Audited
Editor: Kriengsak Yiengsuphanon
Editorial Profile: Covers news.
Language (s): Thai
DAILY NEWSPAPER

Phuket Gazette

Editorial: The Phuket Gazette, 79/94, Moo 4, Thepkasattree Rd., Koh Kaew, Muang, Phuket 83000. **T:** 66 762 73555
E: nid@phuketgazette.net
W: http://www.phuketgazette.net
Freq: Weekly; **Circ:** 12001 Not Audited
Editorial Profile: Provides local news, in-depth analysis, lifestyle features and sports coverage for all with an interest in Phuket and the Andaman.
Language (s): English
DAILY NEWSPAPER

Post Today

Editorial: The Post Publishing, 136 Na Ranong Road, Klong Toey, Bangkok 10110.

T: 66 22403700 **W:** http://www.posttoday.com
Freq: Daily; **Circ:** 83001 Not Audited
Editor: Na Kan Loahawichai
Editorial Profile: Reports business news in a simple, comprehensive way for general readers and also covers politics, general, foreign and sports news and articles.
Language (s): Thai
DAILY NEWSPAPER

Prachachat Turakij

Editorial: Matichon Group, 12 Mooban Prachaniwes 1, Thedsaban Narumarn Rd., Ladyao, Jatujak, Bangkok 10900.
T: 66 25890020 1505
E: pcconline@matichon.co.th
W: http://www.prachachat.net
Freq: 2 Times/Week; **Circ:** 150001 Not Audited
Editor: Somprathana Khlaiwichian; **Editor:** Phattanaphan Wongphan
Editorial Profile: Covers of news.
Language (s): Thai
DAILY NEWSPAPER

Property Report Singapore-Malaysia-Indonesia

Editorial: Ensign Media, 23/4 Moo 3, Kwang Rd., Wichit, Muang, Phuket 83150.
T: 66 762 64756 **E:** info@property-report.com
W: http://www.ensign-media.com
Freq: Monthly
Editorial Profile: Focus on one of the three country's real estate sectors, a key interview with an important industry figure and regular sections on finance, legal issues, interiors and architecture.
Language (s): Thai
DAILY NEWSPAPER

Property Report Thailand

Owner: Ensign Media
Editorial: Ensign Media, 23/4 Moo 3, Kwang Rd., Wichit, Muang, Phuket 83000.
T: 66 76264756 **E:** info@property-report.com
W: http://www.property-report.com
Freq: Monthly; **Circ:** 20002 Not Audited
Editorial Profile: Property Report Thailand presents up-to-date information and coverage of industry trends and innovations. Each issue incorporates an in-depth special focus on one of the country's real estate hot spots, a key interview with an important industry figure and regular sections on construction, finance, legal issues, interiors and architecture. The remainder of the publication is devoted to pertinent reportage and in-depth analysis of property news.
Language (s): Thai
DAILY NEWSPAPER

Rak Trang

Editorial: Rak Trang Group, 26/21 Soi 6, Wienkaphang Rd., Tabtieng, Muang, Trang 92000. **T:** 66 75 211480
Freq: Semi-Monthly; **Circ:** 1003 Not Audited
Editor: Methee Muangkaew
Editorial Profile: Coves local news.
Language (s): Thai
DAILY NEWSPAPER

Ruam Lang Ngan

Editorial: Wattasarn Media, Sin-Satorn Tower, 28/F, Bangkok 10600. **T:** 66 2862 3333 1600
E: wm@wm.co.th **W:** http://www.wm.co.th
Freq: Weekly
Editorial Profile: Focus: employment, career, recruitment.
Language (s): Thai
DAILY NEWSPAPER

Samak Duen

Editorial: Sappasan, 71/17 Borommarachachonnanee Rd., Arun-Amarin, Bangkok-Noi, Bangkok 10700.
T: 66 2435 2345 126
W: http://www.mrthaijob.com
Freq: 2 Times/Week; **Circ:** 140001 Not Audited
Editorial Profile: Shares information on government jobs.
Language (s): Thai
DAILY NEWSPAPER

Samila Times

Editorial: Samila Times, 41 Khlongrian 2 Rd, Hatyai, Songkhla 90110. **T:** 66 74356804
E: info@samilatimes.co.th
W: http://www.samilatimes.co.th
Freq: Weekly; **Circ:** 5001 Not Audited
Editor: Sumrit Boonrat
Editorial Profile: Covers of local news.
Language (s): Thai
DAILY NEWSPAPER

Sarn Pheun Sem

Editorial: Semsikkha 29/15 Ramkhamhang 21, Ramkhamhang Road, Plubpla, Bangkok 10310.
T: 66 231 473856
E: semsikkhasam@yahoo.com
W: http://www.semsikkha.org
Freq: Quarterly; **Circ:** 4001 Not Audited
Editor: Jenjira Rocha
Editorial Profile: Covers of lifestyle, religion, Buddhism.
Language (s): Thai
DAILY NEWSPAPER

Seangsawan

Editorial: 49/1 Tachalab Road, Watmai, Muang, Chantaburi 22000. **T:** 66 39 311749
E: sakda@chantaburi.com
Freq: Semi-Monthly; **Circ:** 3001 Not Audited
Editor in Chief: Sakda Yookasem
Editorial Profile: Covers information for people in Chantaburi and Trat Provinces.
Language (s): Thai
DAILY NEWSPAPER

Sentangnakkai

Editorial: Sumret Dot Com, 1148/203-204 Pichai Condominium, Nakornchaisri Rd., Dusit, Bangkok 10300. **T:** 66 2 667401
E: photosumret@hotmail.com
W: http://www.sumret.com
Freq: Semi-Monthly; **Circ:** 75003 Not Audited
Editorial Profile: Covers of business strategies.
Language (s): Thai
DAILY NEWSPAPER

Siam Banterng

Editorial: Inspire Entertainment, 115/66 Moo12, Soi Ramindra 40, Klongkum, Buengkum, Bangkok 10230. **T:** 66 25088100
E: contact@inspire.co.th
W: http://www.inspire.co.th
Freq: 2 Times/Week; **Circ:** 140001 Not Audited
Editorial Profile: Covers of news-entertainment.
Language (s): Thai
DAILY NEWSPAPER

Siam Dara

Editorial: Siam Sport Syndicate, 66/26-29 Moo12, Soi Ramindra 40, Ramindra Rd., Nualjan, Buengkum, Bangkok 10230.
T: 66 2508 8000
E: webmaster@siamsport.co.th
W: http://www.siamsport.co.th
Freq: Daily
Editorial Profile: Covers of celebrities, gossip star.
Language (s): Thai
DAILY NEWSPAPER

Siam Keela Raiwan

Editorial: Siam Sport Syndicate, 66/26-29 Moo12, Soi Ramindra 40, Ramindra Rd., Nualjian, Buengkum, Bangkok 10310.
T: 66 2508808586
E: webmaster@siamsport.co.th
W: http://www.siamsport.co.th
Freq: Daily; **Circ:** 200001 Not Audited
Editorial Profile: Covers of sports.
Language (s): Thai
DAILY NEWSPAPER

Siam Rath Raiwan

Editorial: Siam Rath, 12 Building 6, Rajdamnoen Road, Bangkok 10200.
T: 66 2662 1810 322
E: siamrath@siamrath.co.th
W: http://www.siamrath.co.th
Freq: Daily; **Circ:** 300003 Not Audited
Editor in Chief: Viroj Wattanathadakul
Editorial Profile: Covers news.
Language (s): Thai
DAILY NEWSPAPER

Siam Rath Sapda Wijan

Editorial: Siam Rath, 12 Building 6, Rajdamnoen Road, Phranakorn, Bangkok 10200. **T:** 66 2662 1810 322
E: siamweekly@hotmail.com
W: http://www.siamrath.co.th
Freq: Weekly; **Circ:** 80003 Not Audited
Editor in Chief: Viroj Wattanathadakul
Editorial Profile: Weekly newspaper focusing on politics.
Language (s): Thai
DAILY NEWSPAPER

Siam Settakij

Editorial: Siam Settakij, 12/3 Arun-amarin Rd., Bangkok Noi, Bangkok 10700.
T: 66 24348080 19
E: siam_settakij@hotmail.com
Freq: Monthly; **Circ:** 50003 Not Audited
Editor: Tongphoon Phensophee
Editorial Profile: Covers business news.

Language (s): Thai
DAILY NEWSPAPER

Siam Turakij

Editorial: Siam Turakij Media, 6/88 Soi Ladphrao 25, Ladphrao Rd., Jankasem, Jatujak, Bangkok 10900. **T:** 66 29 381555
E: news@siamturakij.com
W: http://www.siamturakij.com
Freq: 2 Times/Week; **Circ:** 120003 Not Audited
Editor: Chaiporn Janthanaroj; **Editor:** Jaturong Kobkaew
Editorial Profile: Covers business.
Language (s): Thai
DAILY NEWSPAPER

Siangtai Daily

Editorial: Siangtai Raiwan, 1/25, Tepkasattree Rd., Tatsada, Muang, Phuket 83000.
T: 66 76212751 **E:** siangtai@e-mail.in.th
W: http://www.siangtai.com
Freq: Daily; **Circ:** 35001 Not Audited
Editor: Chaowaphong Mekharakkul
Editorial Profile: Covers of local news.
Language (s): Thai
DAILY NEWSPAPER

Sing Sian Yit Pao

Editorial: Sing Jong Eian, 267 New Road, Baan Bart, Pomprab, Bangkok 10100.
T: 66 2 225-0070 **E:** admin@singsian.net
W: http://www.singsian.net
Freq: Daily; **Circ:** 70001 Not Audited
Editorial Profile: Covers topics for Chinese people living in Thailand.
Language (s): Chinese
DAILY NEWSPAPER

Sportman

Editorial: Siam Sport Syndicate, 66/26-29 Moo12, Soi Ramindra 40, Ramindra Rd., Khlongkum, Buengkum, Bangkok 10230.
T: 66 250 88000
E: webmaster@siamsport.co.th
W: http://www.sia, msport.co.th
Freq: Daily; **Circ:** 140001 Not Audited
Editorial Profile: A supplementary to Sport Pool in nature plus wider coverage in North American Sports.
Language (s): Thai
DAILY NEWSPAPER

Sportpool Rai Wan

Editorial: Siam Sport Syndicate, 66/26-29 Moo12, Soi Ramindra 40, Ramindra Rd., Khlongkum, Buengkum, Bangkok 10310.
T: 66 250 88000
E: webmaster@siamsport.co.th
W: http://www.siamsport.co.th
Freq: Daily; **Circ:** 300001 Not Audited
Editorial Profile: Covers of Sports (soccer)
Language (s): Thai
DAILY NEWSPAPER

Star Soccer Rai Wan

Editorial: Siam Sport Syndicate, 66/26-29 Moo12, Soi Ramindra 40, Ramindra Rd., Khlongkum, Buengkum, Bangkok 10230.
T: 66 250 88000
E: webmaster@siamsport.co.th
W: http://www.siamsport.co.th
Freq: Daily; **Circ:** 320001 Not Audited
Editorial Profile: Covers of soccer.
Language (s): Thai
DAILY NEWSPAPER

Sue Klang

Editorial: Sueklang Advertising, 420/5 Chiengmai Land Village, Changkhlan Rd., Changkhlan, Muang, Chiangmai 50100.
T: 66 532836345 **E:** sueklang@hotmail.com
Freq: Weekly; **Circ:** 10001 Not Audited
Editor: Wariphan Thammawilaibutr
Editorial Profile: Covers of local news.
Language (s): Thai
DAILY NEWSPAPER

T -News inside

Editorial: Multimedia Group, 50/33, Moo 5, Pracharat 1 Rd., Talad Kwan, Muang, Nontaburi 11000. **T:** 66 252 54242 103
E: nantita@tnews.co.th
W: http://www.tnews.co.th
Freq: Semi-Monthly
Editorial Profile: Covers of politics and business news.
Language (s): Thai
DAILY NEWSPAPER

Telecom Journal

Editorial: Telecom Journal, 327/17-19 Soi Sri Amporn (Phaholyothin 32), Senanikom 1 Road, Lardyao, Chatuchak, Bangkok 10900.
T: 66 2561 4993
E: telecomjournal@yahoo.com
W: http://www.telecomjournal.net

Freq: Weekly; **Circ:** 120003 Not Audited
Editorial Profile: Focuses on telecommunication, IT and technology.
Language (s): Thai
DAILY NEWSPAPER

Thai Post

Editorial: Thai Journal Group, 1850-1862 Kasemrath Road, Klongtoey, Bangkok 10110.
T: 66 22402612 **E:** reporter@thaipost.net
W: http://www.thaipost.net
Freq: Daily; **Circ:** 200001 Not Audited
Editor in Chief: Chatchai Namtapee
Editorial Profile: Covers of politics, economics, sports, local and international business news.
Language (s): Thai
DAILY NEWSPAPER

Thai Rath

Editorial: Vacharaphol, 1 Vibhavadee-Rangsit Road, Lardyao, Chatuchak, Bangkok 10900.
T: 66 2 2721030 1342
W: http://www.thairath.co.th
Freq: Daily; **Circ:** 1000001 Not Audited
Editorial Profile: Covers of political, international, business, sports, and local news.
Language (s): Thai
DAILY NEWSPAPER

Thainews

Editorial: Banjob-Praphin Limjaroon, 56 Samlan Rd., Phrasingha, Muang, Chiangmai 50200. **T:** 66 532772524
W: http://www.thainews70.com
Freq: Daily; **Circ:** 50001 Not Audited
Editorial Profile: Covers of local news.
Language (s): Thai
DAILY NEWSPAPER

Thansettakij

Editorial: Jutamas Building 7/F, 89/169-770 Vipavadee-Rangsit Road, Bangkok 10900.
T: 66 2 973-5254
E: editoronline@thannews.th.com
W: http://www.thannews.th.com
Freq: 2 Times/Week; **Circ:** 120001 Not Audited
Editor: Suvipa Budsayabantoon
Editorial Profile: Covers the latest in business news.
Language (s): Thai
DAILY NEWSPAPER

Thunhoon

Editorial: Traffic Corner Publishing, 21/59-60, Block C, 3/F, RCA, Soi Soonvijai, Phetchburi Rd., Bangkapi, Huaykhwang, Bangkok 10320.
T: 66 22 031040 636 **E:** tunhoon@yahoo.com
W: http://www.thunhoon.com
Freq: Daily
Editorial Profile: Focus: stock
Language (s): Thai
DAILY NEWSPAPER

Tong Hua News

Editorial: Tong Hua Communications Public Co., Ltd., 877-881 Chareon Krung Road, Talardnoi, Sompantawong, Bangkok 10100.
T: 66 223601434
E: tonghua_dailynews@tonghuagroup.com
Freq: Daily; **Circ:** 80003 Not Audited
Editor: Pavit Tokakuna
Editorial Profile: Chinese newspaper.
Language (s): Chinese
DAILY NEWSPAPER

Transport Journal

Editorial: Sri Benjachot, 1/3 Moo 24, Soi Mooban Khetkhayaimai, Terddamri Rd., Bnagsue, Bangkok 10800. **T:** 66 25561624
E: transport_j2004@yahoo.com
W: http://www.transportnews.co.th
Freq: Weekly; **Circ:** 120003 Not Audited
Editorial Profile: Covers logistics, shipping and transportation.
Language (s): Thai
DAILY NEWSPAPER

Udomsarn Weekly

Editorial: Catholic Social Communications of Thailand, 122/11 Soi Naksuwan, Nonsee Rd., Chongnonsee, Yannawa, Bangkok 10120.
T: 66 26813900 180
E: thcatcom@loxinfo.co.th
W: http://www.udomsarn.com
Freq: Weekly
Editorial Profile: Covers of religion, society and culture.
Language (s): Thai
DAILY NEWSPAPER

Viang Chiangmai with Bangkok

Editorial: Oriental Noise, 55/1, Soi 3, Rachawong Rd., Changmoi, Muang, Chiangmai 50300. **T:** 66 53 232383
E: info@oriental-noise.com

W: http://www.oriental-noise.com
Freq: Monthly; **Circ:** 5003 Not Audited
Publisher: Noritoshi Urano
Editorial Profile: Providing information about living in Chiangmai.
Language (s): Japanese
DAILY NEWSPAPER

The Wall Street Journal (Thailand)

Editorial: CEO Suite Bangkok, Athenee Tower, 23rd Floor, 63 Wireless Rd, Bangkok 10330.
T: 66 2 238-2661
DAILY NEWSPAPER

Weekly News

Editorial: Weekly News, 35/83 Mooban Yingruey Niwes, Prachachuen Road., Pakkred, Nontaburi 11120. **T:** 66 25734265
E: weekly-news@hotmail.com
Freq: Weekly
Editor: Kasem Osathanukror
Editorial Profile: Focus on celebrities.
Language (s): Thai
DAILY NEWSPAPER

Yuadyan Newspaper (Automotive Newspaper)

Editorial: Grand Prix International, 4/299, 2/F, Moo 5 Soi Lardplaklow 66, Lardplaklow Road, Autsawaree, Bangken, Bangkok 10220.
T: 66 25 2217318
E: yuadyan@grandprixgroup.com
W: http://www.grandprixgroup.com
Freq: Semi-Monthly; **Circ:** 50003 Not Audited
Editor in Chief: Veerachot Duangruethai
Editorial Profile: Covers automotive industry news.
Language (s): Thai
DAILY NEWSPAPER

NEWS SERVICE/SYNDICATE

Associated Press

Editorial: 942/149 Charm Isssara Building, Rama 4, Bangkok 10500. **T:** 66 2 266-0740
News Editor: Scott McDonald; **Bureau Chief:** Todd Pitman
NEWS SERVICE/SYNDICATE

Bloomberg News

Editorial: 87 Wireless Road, Bangkok 10330.
T: 66 26540255 **E:** thainews@bloomberg.net
Bureau Chief: Tony Jordan; **Editor at Large:** Lee Miller
NEWS SERVICE/SYNDICATE

Dow Jones Newswires

Editorial: CEO Suite Bangkok, Athenee Tower, 23rd Floor, 63 Wireless Rd, Bangkok 10330.
T: 66 2 690-4200
E: djnews.bangkok@dowjones.com
NEWS SERVICE/SYNDICATE

National News Bureau

Editorial: National News Bureau, Government Public Relations Departmnet, 90/91 New Petchaburi Road, Bangkapi, Huay Kwang, BKK, Bangkok 10320. **T:** 66 2 369-2587
E: thainews.nnt@gmail.com
W: http://www.thainews.prd.go.th
Freq: Daily
Editorial Profile: Covers news and general interest throughout Thailand.
Language (s): Bahasa Indonesia, Burmese, Chinese, English, French, German, Japanese, Khmer, Lao, Malayalam, Thai, Vietnamese
NEWS SERVICE/SYNDICATE

Reuters

Editorial: 34-35th Floor U Chu Liang Building, 968 Rama IV Road, Silom, Bangrak, Bangkok 10500. **T:** 66 2 648-9600
Bureau Chief: Jason Szep
NEWS SERVICE/SYNDICATE

BROADCASTING

RADIO STATIONS

Nation Radio

Editorial: Nation Group, 1854 Bangna-Trad Road (KM 4.5), Bangna, Bangkok 10260.
T: 66 23383333 2704
E: lekkungs@hotmail.com
W: http://www.nationradioonline.com
Editorial Profile: News and general interest programming

RADIO NETWORKS

GGNews Network

Editorial: GG News Network Group, 459 Soi Ladprao 48, Ladprao Road, Samsennok, Huaykwang, Bangkok 10310.
T: 66 26934777 600
W: http://www.ggnews.co.th
Editorial Profile: Covers business news.

T-News Radio

Owner: Multimedia Group
Editorial: Multimedia Group, 50/33, Moo 5, Pracharat 1 Rd., Talad Kwan, Muang, Nontaburi 11000. **T:** 66 25254242 108
E: nantita@tnews.co.th
W: http://www.tnews.co.th
Editorial Profile: Covers of news and general interests.

TELEVISION NETWORKS

Nagoya Television - Bangkok Bureau

Owner: TV Asahi Corporation
Editorial: TV Asahi Corporation, 93/1 Dietham Tower, Wireless Rd., Lumpini, Patumwan, Bangkok 10330. **T:** 66 22543134
Editorial Profile: Covers of news and general interests.

Thai PBS

Owner: Thai Public Broadcasting Service
Editorial: Thai Public Broadcasting Service, 1010 Chinnawatra Tower 3, 13/F, Viphawadee-Rangsit Rd., Jatujak, Bangkok 10900.
T: 66 27911000 1622
E: program@thaipbs.or.th
W: http://www.thaipbs.or.th/
Editorial Profile: Focuses on news and general interests.

TV Asahi - Bangkok Bureau

Editorial: 93/1 Dietham Tower, Wireless Road, Lumpini, Patumwan, Bangkok 10330.
T: 66 22543134 **E:** tv-asahi@inet.co.th
W: http://www.tv-asahi.co.jp
Editorial Profile: Covers of news and general interests.

TOGO   Tel: 228

Standard Time: GMT +1
Continent: Africa
Capital City: Lomé

NEWSPAPERS & PUBLICATIONS

NEWSPAPERS

Le Canard Indépendant

Owner: Le Canard Independant
Editorial: BP 8168, Lome. **T:** 228 1 904 60 94
E: lecanardin@yahoo.fr
Freq: Weekly; **Circ:** 3000 Publisher's Statement
Editor in Chief: Koffi Amega
Editorial Profile: National weekly newspaper focusing on regional, national and international news, current affairs, politics, economics, society, entertainment and sport.
Language (s): French
DAILY NEWSPAPER

Le Regard

Editorial: BP 81213, Lome. **T:** 228 336 45 82
E: leregard13@yahoo.fr
Freq: Weekly; **Circ:** 4000 Publisher's Statement
Editor in Chief: Kenneth Lawson
Editorial Profile: National weekly newspaper focussing on news, current affairs, politics, economics, culture and sport.
Language (s): French
DAILY NEWSPAPER

BROADCASTING

RADIO STATIONS

Kanal FM

Editorial: Immeuble DECAMPOS, Avenue de la Nouvelle Marche, Lome. **T:** 228 2 220 01 89
E: kanalfm@cafe.tg **W:** http://www.kanalfm.tg
Editorial Profile: Regional radio station focussing on music, news, current affairs, politics, economics and sport.

Nana FM
Editorial: Bld du 13 janvier, Angle rue Biblos Night Club, Lome. **T:** 228 220 12 02
E: nanafm@yahoo.fr
Editorial Profile: Regional radio station focussing on music, news, current affairs, entertainment and sport.

RADIO NETWORKS

La Legende
Editorial: 14 Avenue de la Victoire, BP 13836, Lome. **T:** 228 2 222 25 41
E: lalegende@yahoo.fr
W: http://www.nostalgie.tg
Editorial Profile: National radio station focussing on music, news, current affairs, entertainment, culture and sport.

TELEVISION STATIONS

TV2
Editorial: BP 13100, Lome.
T: 228 2 251 49 93 **E:** tg_tv2@yahoo.fr
Editorial Profile: Regional TV station covering from Lomé to Palimero and focussing on regional, national and international news, current affairs, entertainment, culture and sport.

TVT - Télévision Togolaise
Editorial: BP 3286, Lome. **T:** 228 2 221 53 57
E: televisiontogolaise@yahoo.fr
W: http://www.tvt.tg
Editorial Profile: National TV station focussing on entertainment, news, politics, economics, society, health, culture and sport.

TONGA   Tel: 676
Standard Time: GMT +13
Continent: Oceania
Capital City: Nuku'alofa (Tongatapu)

NEWSPAPERS & PUBLICATIONS

NEWSPAPERS

Ko e Kele'a
Owner: 'Akilisi Pohiva
Editorial: Tonga, PO Box 1567, Kingdom Of Tonga. **T:** 676 25 480
Freq: Bi-Weekly
Editor: Tavake Fusimalohi
Language (s): English
NEWSPAPER

Tonga Chronicle (Kalonikali Tonga)
Owner: Government of Tonga
Editorial: PO Box 197, Old Vaiola (off Taufa'ahau Rd), Kingdom Of Tonga.
T: 676 23 302 **E:** chroni@candw.to
Freq: Weekly
Editorial Profile: Published in English and Tongan covers current topics and news.
Language (s): English
NEWSPAPER

BROADCASTING

RADIO NETWORKS

Millennium Radio 2000 (A3V)
Editorial: A3V Radio 2000, PO Box 838, Kingdom Of Tonga. **T:** 676 25 891
Editorial Profile: A3V The Millenium Radio 2000 broadcasts popular music format in the Kingdom of Tonga on FM89.1.

Radio Tonga 1 (A3Z)
Owner: Tonga Broadcasting Commission
Editorial: Fasi, Nuku'alofa, Kingdom Of Tonga.
T: 676 23 556 **E:** nanisefifita@yahoo.com
W: http://radiotonga.com
Editorial Profile: Provides best Tongan and English languages' music.

TELEVISION STATIONS

TV Tonga
Owner: Tonga Broadcasting Corporation
Editorial: Nuku'alofa, Tonga. **T:** 676 23 555
E: eamanaki@tonga-broadcasting.com
W: http://tonga-broadcasting.com
Editorial Profile: Tonga Broadcasting Commission (TBC) is the first Broadcasting which began operations in 1961.

TRINIDAD & TOBAGO
Tel: 1 868
Standard Time: GMT -4
Continent: The Americas
Capital City: Port of Spain

NEWSPAPERS & PUBLICATIONS

NEWSPAPERS

Friday Mirror
Owner: TNT News Centre Ltd
Editorial: 35 Rapsey St, Curepe, Barataria.
T: 1 868 645-3391 **E:** ttnews@tstt.net.tt
W: http://www.tntmirror.com/friday/fridayindex.html
Freq: Weekly; **Circ:** 40000 Not Audited
Editorial Profile: Friday Mirror is a daily newspaper covering national and international news, current affairs, business and sports.
Language (s): English
DAILY NEWSPAPER

Newsday
Owner: Daily News Limited
Editorial: 23A Chacon Street, Port Of Spain.
T: 1 868 623-4929 **E:** newsday@newsday.co.tt
W: http://www.newsday.co.tt
Freq: Daily; **Circ:** 67000 Not Audited
Editor: Suzanne Mills; **News Editor:** Stephon Nicholas
Editorial Profile: Newsday is a daily newspaper featuring national and international news, current affairs, business, lifestyle and sports.
Language (s): English
DAILY NEWSPAPER

Trinidad Express
Owner: Trinidad Express Newspapers Ltd
Editorial: 35 Independence Square, Port Of Spain. **T:** 1 868 623-1711
E: express@trinidadexpress.com
W: http://www.trinidadexpress.com
Freq: Daily
Editor in Chief: Omatie Lyder
Editorial Profile: Trinidad Express is a daily newspaper covering national and international news, politics, sports and current affairs. The Sunday edition is called Sunday Express.
Language (s): English
DAILY NEWSPAPER

The Trinidad Guardian
Owner: Trinidad Publishing Co Ltd
Editorial: 22-24 St. Vincent Street, Port Of Spain. **T:** 1 868 623-8871 **E:** letters@ttol.co.tt
W: http://www.guardian.co.tt
Freq: Daily
News Editor: Robert Alonzo; **News Editor:** Debra Wanser
Editorial Profile: The Trinidad Guardian is a daily newspaper containing national and international news, business, current affairs and sports. The Saturday and Sunday editions of the paper are called the Sunday Guardian.
Language (s): English
DAILY NEWSPAPER

BROADCASTING

RADIO STATIONS

91.1 Talk City
Owner: Caribbean New Media Group
T: 1 868 622-4141 **E:** talkcity91fm@gmail.com
W: http://www.talkcity91fm.com
Editorial Profile: The station's format is talk. They also feature local music and culture and acts from Trinidad & Tobago and the Caribbean.

i95.5
Owner: One Caribbean Media
Editorial: 47 Tragerete Road, Newtown, Port Of Spain. **T:** 1 868 628-4955
W: http://i955fm.com
Editorial Profile: i95.5 FM is a commercial station owned by One Caribbean Media. The format of the station is gospel and urban music. Their target audience is gospel music listeners, ages 18 to 64, in the Newtown, Trinidad & Tobago area. The station airs locally at 95.5 FM.

TELEVISION STATIONS

CNC3 Television
Owner: Guardian Media Limited

Editorial: 22-24 St Vincent Street, Port Of Spain. **T:** 1 868 623-8870
W: http://www.cnc3.co.tt
Editorial Profile: CNC3 Television features news and entertainment programming.

Gayelle Television
Owner: Fabien (Errol)
Editorial: 43 Eastern Main Road, Port Of Spain. **T:** 1 868 221-8832
E: gayelletv@gmail.com
W: http://www.gayelletv.com
Editorial Profile: Gayelle Television offers local and Caribbean programming.

TUNISIA   Tel: 216
Standard Time: GMT +1
Continent: Africa
Capital City: Tunis

NEWSPAPERS & PUBLICATIONS

NEWSPAPERS

Al Akhbar
Owner: Dar Tunis Hebdo
Editorial: Rue Ali Bach Hamba, Tunis 1000.
T: 216 71 344100 **E:** alakhbar@planet.tn
Freq: Thu; **Circ:** 70000 Publisher's Statement
News Editor: Kamel Ben Amor; **Editor in Chief:** Imed Jnane
Editorial Profile: Al Akhbar (The News) is a weekly Arabic newspaper covering local and international news, politics and arts. It launched in 1984 and is published on Thursdays.
Language (s): Arabic
DAILY NEWSPAPER

Akhbar Al-Joumhouria
Owner: Akhbar Media
Editorial: 14, rue Ibn Al-Jazzar, Tunis 1002.
T: 216 71 797055
E: akhbar.joumhouria@gnet.tn
W: http://jomhouria.com
Freq: Thu; **Circ:** 80000 Publisher's Statement
News Editor: Chiraz Ben Mrad; **Editor in Chief:** Najib Khouildi
Editorial Profile: Akhbar Al-Joumhouria (The Republic News) is a weekly Arabic newspaper covering society, politics, the arts and sport. It launched in 1990 and is published on Thursdays.
Language (s): Arabic
DAILY NEWSPAPER

Les Annonces de Tunisie
Owner: TEC
Editorial: PO Box 2014, Megrine St Gobain, Route Z4, Ben Arous. **T:** 216 71 432860
E: lesannonces1978@hotmail.com
Freq: 2 Times/Week; **Circ:** 70000 Publisher's Statement
Editor in Chief: Khalid Al Nouri
Editorial Profile: Les Annonces de Tunisie is a bi-lingual (Arabic & French) newspaper covering news and current affairs, politics, sports, society and the arts. It launched in 1978 and is published twice a week on Tuesdays and Fridays.
Language (s): Arabic
DAILY NEWSPAPER

Al Anwar
Owner: Dar Anwar Press, Publishing & Distribution
Editorial: 25 Avenue Jean Jaurès, Tunis 1000.
T: 216 71 331000 **E:** manbar@alanouar.com
W: http://www.alanouar.com
Freq: Sat; **Circ:** 90000 Publisher's Statement
Editor in Chief: Najmeddine Akkari; **News Editor:** Kamal Eddayekh
Editorial Profile: Al Anwar is a weekly Arabic newspaper covering local news, culture, social activities and sport. It launched in 1981 and is published on Saturdays.
Language (s): Arabic
DAILY NEWSPAPER

Assabah
Owner: Dar Assabah
Editorial: PO Box 441, Boulevard Mohamed Bouazizi, El Menzah 1004. **T:** 216 71 238222
E: rafik75.kram@yahoo.fr
Freq: Daily; **Circ:** 45000 Publisher's Statement
Editor in Chief: Ali Al Telili; **News Editor:** Rafik Benabdallah
Editorial Profile: Assabah (The Morning) is an Arabic newspaper covering national and international news, current affairs, politics,

---

sport and entertainment. It launched in 1951 and is published daily, except Mondays.
Language (s): Arabic
DAILY NEWSPAPER

Assabah Al Ousboui
Owner: Dar Assabah
Editorial: PO Box 441, Boulevard Mohamed Bouazizi, El Menzah 1004. **T:** 216 71 238222
E: redaction@alousboui.com.tn
Freq: Mon; **Circ:** 70000 Publisher's Statement
News Editor: Jamal Al Farchichi; **Editor in Chief:** Noureddine Ashour
Editorial Profile: Assabah Al Ousboui is a weekly Arabic newspaper covering national and international news, current affairs, politics, sports and entertainment. It launched in 1975 and is published on Mondays.
Language (s): Arabic
DAILY NEWSPAPER

Assarih
Owner: Assarih
Editorial: PO Box 2058, Route de Bizerte, Ariana. **T:** 216 71 821721
E: essarih1@gmail.com
Freq: Daily; **Circ:** 40000 Publisher's Statement
News Editor: Mohamed Abdelmoumen
Editorial Profile: Assarih (The Virtuous) is a daily Arabic newspaper covering local and international news, business and sport. It was first published in 1995.
Language (s): Arabic
DAILY NEWSPAPER

Attounissia
Owner: Dar Attounissia
Editorial: 7 Bis, rue Docteur Alfons Levarant, Belvedere, Tunis 1002. **T:** 216 71 890888
E: attounissiajournal@yahoo.fr
W: http://www.attounissia.com.tn
Freq: Daily; **Circ:** 50000 Publisher's Statement
Editor in Chief: Habib El Guizani
Editorial Profile: Attounissia is a daily Arabic newspaper covering national and international news, business and sport. It was first published in 2011.
Language (s): Arabic
DAILY NEWSPAPER

El Bayane
Owner: Union Tunisienne de l'Industrie du Commerce et de l'Artisanat
Editorial: 61, rue Abdel Razzak Al Charaibi, Tunis 1001. **T:** 216 71 339633
E: albayane@gmail.com
W: http://www.elbayane.tn
Freq: Mon; **Circ:** 90000 Publisher's Statement
News Editor: Lotfi El Mekni
Editorial Profile: El Bayane is the weekly newspaper of the Union Tunisienne de l'Industrie du Commerce et de l'Artisanat and covers news, politics, business, arts and sport. It launched in 1977 and is published on Mondays.
Language (s): Arabic
DAILY NEWSPAPER

Chams El-Janoub
Owner: La Gazette Communication Group
Editorial: PO Box 609, Route de Teniour Km 3, Sfax 3018. **T:** 216 74 435500
E: redaction@chamseljanoub.tn
W: http://www.chamseljanoub.tn
Freq: Thu; **Circ:** 8000 Publisher's Statement
Editor in Chief: Ali Baklouti
Editorial Profile: Chams El-Janoub is a regional, weekly newspaper distributed in the Sfax area in the south of Tunisia. It covers local news, current affairs, economics, sport, society and world news. The newspaper launched in 1980 and is published on Thursdays.
Language (s): Arabic
DAILY NEWSPAPER

Al Chourouk
Owner: Dar Anwar Press, Publishing & Distribution
Editorial: 25 Avenue Jean Jaurès, Tunis 1000.
T: 216 71 331000
E: montage@alchourouk.com
W: http://www.alchourouk.com
Freq: Daily; **Circ:** 110000 Publisher's Statement
Editor in Chief: Abdelraouf Al Mkadmi; **News Editor:** Sofiane El Aswad
Editorial Profile: Al Chourouk (The Sunrise) is a daily, tabloid-sized newspaper covering national and international news, current affairs and politics. It was first published in 1982.
Language (s): Arabic
DAILY NEWSPAPER

Echaâb
Owner: Union Générale Tunisienne du Travail (UGTT)
Editorial: 41, Avenue Ali Darghouth, Tunis 1001. **T:** 216 71 255020
E: echaab_technique@yahoo.com
W: http://www.echaab.info.tn
Freq: Fri; **Circ:** 40000 Publisher's Statement
News Editor: Habib Chabi
Editorial Profile: Echaâb is the weekly newspaper of the Tunisian General Labour Union and covers local and international news, trade union affairs, culture and business. It launched in 1959 and is published on Fridays.
Language (s): Arabic
DAILY NEWSPAPER

Elhadath Journal
Owner: Dar Jridi Press & Publishing
Editorial: 122, rue Radhia Haddad, Tunis 1000. **T:** 216 20 264426
E: r.benali@rocketmail.com
Freq: Wed; **Circ:** 45000 Publisher's Statement
Editor in Chief: Sleh Jridi; **News Editor:** Adel Talbi
Editorial Profile: Elhadath Journal is a weekly Arabic newspaper covering local news, current affairs and politics. It launched in 1993 and is published on Wednesdays.
Language (s): Arabic
DAILY NEWSPAPER

Es-Sahafa
Owner: La SNIPE
Editorial: 17 Rue Ghari Baldi, Tunis 1000. **T:** 216 71 335025 **E:** contact@essahafa.info.tn
W: http://www.essahafa.info.tn
Freq: Daily; **Circ:** 15000 Publisher's Statement
News Editor: Ibrahim Al Khlefi; **Editor in Chief:** Lotfi El Arbi Snoussi
Editorial Profile: Es-Sahafa (The Press) is an Arabic newspaper covering national and international news, current affairs, politics, sports and entertainment. It launched in 1989 and is published daily, except Mondays.
Language (s): Arabic
DAILY NEWSPAPER

Al Mijhar
Owner: Societe Ramzi et Elissa
Editorial: 5th Floor, Al Saadi Building, Block CD 7, Place de 10 Decembre, Ariana. **T:** 216 71 234909 **E:** info@al-mijhar.tn
Freq: Fri; **Circ:** 50000
Editorial Profile: Al Mijhar (The Microscope) is a weekly tabloid-sized newspaper covering national and international news, business, sports and culture. The newspaper launched in January 2013 and is issued on Fridays.
Language (s): Arabic
DAILY NEWSPAPER

Al Moussawar
Owner: Dar Al Moussawar for Publishing & Distribution
Editorial: 41, Immeuble Les Jardins de Bacha, Block 5, Avenue Khaireddine Bacha, Tunis 1073. **T:** 216 71 902904
E: almoussawar_tunisie@yahoo.fr
Freq: Mon; **Circ:** 55000 Publisher's Statement
Editor in Chief: Radia Abbou; **News Editor:** Walid Ferchichi
Editorial Profile: Al Moussawar is a weekly Arabic newspaper covering news, business and sport. It launched in 1985 and is published on Mondays. The newspaper was formerly called El Ousbou Moussawar.
Language (s): Arabic
DAILY NEWSPAPER

La Presse de Tunisie
Owner: La SNIPE
Editorial: 17 Rue Ghari Baldi, Tunis 1000. **T:** 216 71 341066 **E:** contact@lapresse.tn
W: http://www.lapresse.tn
Freq: Daily; **Circ:** 50000 Publisher's Statement
Editor in Chief: Salah-Eddine Grichi
Editorial Profile: La Presse de Tunisie is a daily French newspaper covering national and international news, economy, culture and sport. It was first published in 1936.
Language (s): French
DAILY NEWSPAPER

Le Quotidien
Owner: Dar Anwar Press, Publishing & Distribution
Editorial: 25 Avenue Jean Jaurès, Tunis 1000. **T:** 216 71 331000
E: redac-en-chef@lequotidien-tn.com
W: http://www.lequotidien-tn.com
Freq: Daily; **Circ:** 30000 Publisher's Statement
News Editor: Hassan Ghdiri
Editorial Profile: Le Quotidien is a French newspaper covering national and international news, current affairs and politics. It launched in 2001 and is published daily, except Mondays.
Language (s): French
DAILY NEWSPAPER

Le Temps
Owner: Dar Assabah
Editorial: PO Box 441, Boulevard Mohamed Al Bouazizi, El Menzah 1004. **T:** 216 71 238222
E: khalsiroufa@yahoo.fr
Freq: Daily; **Circ:** 35000 Publisher's Statement
Editor In Chief: Raouf Khalsi
Editorial Profile: Le Temps (The Time) is a French newspaper covering national and international news, current affairs, politics, business, sport and entertainment. It launched in 1954 and is published daily, except Mondays.
Language (s): French
DAILY NEWSPAPER

Tunis Hebdo
Owner: Dar Tunis Hebdo
Editorial: 11 Rue Ali Bach Hamba, Tunis 1000. **T:** 216 71 344100
E: tunishebdo@tunishebdo.com.tn
W: http://www.tunishebdo.com.tn
Freq: Mon; **Circ:** 35000 Publisher's Statement
Editor in Chief: Mohamed Ben Youssef; **News Editor:** Taher Selmi
Editorial Profile: Tunis Hebdo is a weekly French newspaper covering national and international news, current affairs, politics, business, sport, culture and entertainment. It launched in 1973 and is published on Mondays.
Language (s): French
DAILY NEWSPAPER

NEWS SERVICE/SYNDICATE

Agence France-Presse - Tunis bureau
Owner: Agence France-Presse
Editorial: Le Colisee 45, Avenue Habib Bourguiba, Tunis 1000. **T:** 216 71 330124
E: afp.tunis@afp.com **W:** http://www.afp.com
Bureau Chief: Antoine Lambroschini
Editorial Profile: Tunis bureau of international French news agency.
Language (s): Arabic, French
NEWS SERVICE/SYNDICATE

Agence Tunis Afrique Presse
Owner: Agence Tunis Afrique Presse
Editorial: 7, Avenue Slimane Ben Slimane, Manar II, Tunis 2092. **T:** 216 71 889000
E: desk.national@email.ati.tn
W: http://www.tap.info.tn
Editor in Chief: Lotfi Arfaoui
Editorial Profile: Agence Tunis Afrique Presse is a Tunisian national news agency - covers government news and matters of national importance.
Language (s): Arabic
NEWS SERVICE/SYNDICATE

Reuters - Tunis bureau
Owner: Thomson Reuters
Editorial: PO Box 369, 3 rue Ibn Rachiq, Tunis 1002. **T:** 216 71 786655
E: tarek.amara@reuters.com
W: http://www.reuters.com
Editorial Profile: Tunis bureau of international news agency covering news, business and sport for a worldwide audience.
Language (s): Arabic, English, French
NEWS SERVICE/SYNDICATE

TURKEY — Tel: 90
Standard Time: GMT +2
Continent: Europe
Capital City: Ankara

NEWSPAPERS & PUBLICATIONS

NEWSPAPERS

Aksam
Owner: Çukurova Grubu
Editorial: Davutpasa C. No.34 34020, Zeytinburnu, Istanbul. **T:** 90 212 4493000
E: haber@aksam.com.tr
W: http://www.aksam.com.tr
Freq: Daily; **Circ:** 142277 Publisher's Statement
Editor: Melis Apaydin; **Editor:** Osman Can; **Editor:** Murat Kelkitlioglu; **News Editor:** Özkan Tamirak
Editorial Profile: Newspaper focusing on national and international news and current affairs.
Language (s): Turkish
DAILY NEWSPAPER

Birgün
Editorial: Kemeralti Cad. No:1-3 Kat 4, Karaköy, Istanbul. **T:** 90 212 2440980
E: info@birgun.net **W:** http://www.birgun.net
Freq: Daily; **Circ:** 22734 Publisher's Statement
Editor: Gülsen Candemir; **Editor:** Deniz Sari
Editorial Profile: Daily newspaper with current news.
Language (s): Turkish
DAILY NEWSPAPER

Bugün
Owner: Koza Ipek Basin ve Basim San. Tic. A.S.
Editorial: Meliha Avni Sözen Cad. No:17 B Blok Mecidiyeköy, Sisli, Istanbul.
T: 90 212 355 85 00 **E:** bkoc@bugun.com.tr
W: http://www.bugun.com.tr
Freq: Daily; **Circ:** 159629 Publisher's Statement
Editor: Volkan Becar
Editorial Profile: Daily newspaper in Turkey covering world political and business news from today and all major news.
Language (s): Turkish
DAILY NEWSPAPER

Cumhuriyet
Owner: Cumhuriyet Grubu
Editorial: Prof. Nurettin Mazhar Öktel Sok. No: 2 34381, Sisli, Istanbul. **T:** 90 212 343 72 74
E: editor@cumhuriyet.com.tr
W: http://www.cumhuriyet.com.tr
Freq: Daily; **Circ:** 51149 Publisher's Statement
News Editor: Oguz Güven; **Editor:** Güray Öz
Editorial Profile: Newspaper containing national and international news, business, current affairs and sport.
Language (s): Turkish
DAILY NEWSPAPER

Dünya
Owner: Dünya Grubu
Editorial: Globus Dünya Bas. 100.Yil Mh. Matbaacilar Sitesi Yani 34440, Bagcilar, Istanbul. **T:** 90 212 6811913
E: dunyaonline@dunyagazetesi.com.tr
W: http://www.dunya.com
Freq: Daily; **Circ:** 54719 Publisher's Statement
News Editor: Ibrahim Ilktug Gokman; **Editor:** Seda Tuzlu
Editorial Profile: Daily newspaper covering national news, business and economics.
Language (s): Turkish
DAILY NEWSPAPER

Fanatik
Owner: Dogan Gazetecilik A.S.
Editorial: Kustepe Mah. Mecidiyeköy Yolu Cad. Trump Towers Kule 2 Kat:7-8-9 No:12, 34387 Sisli, Istanbul. **T:** 90 212 5056542
E: bilgi@fanatik.com.tr
W: http://www.fanatik.com.tr/default.aspx
Freq: Daily; **Circ:** 190595 Publisher's Statement
Editor: Seçil Sengelir
Editorial Profile: Tabloid-sized newspaper focusing on sport with a special emphasize on football; includes previews, results, reports and interviews.
Language (s): Turkish
DAILY NEWSPAPER

Fanatik Basket
Owner: Dogan Grubu
Editorial: Dogan Medya Center 34204, Bagcilar, Istanbul. **T:** 90 212 5056524
Freq: Weekly; **Circ:** 9000 Not Audited
Editorial Profile: Newspaper featuring in-depth coverage of national and international professional and amateur basketball leagues.
Language (s): Turkish
DAILY NEWSPAPER

Günes
Owner: Türkmedya Yayin Grubu
Editorial: Merkez Mahallesi, 29 Ekim Caddesi, Türkmedya Binasi, No: 11, 34197, Bahçelievler, Istanbul. **T:** 90 212 449 30 00
E: editor@turkmedya.com.tr
W: http://www.gunes.com
Freq: Daily; **Circ:** 102927 Publisher's Statement
Editor: Nurettin Soydan
Editorial Profile: Newspaper featuring national and international news, economy, sport and features.
Language (s): Turkish
DAILY NEWSPAPER

Hürriyet
Owner: Hürriyet Gazetecilik ve Matbaacilik A.S
Editorial: Hürriyet Medya Towers 34212, Günesli, Istanbul. **T:** 90 212 6770000
E: editor@hurriyet.com.tr
W: http://www.hurriyet.com.tr
Freq: Daily; **Circ:** 388116 Publisher's Statement
Editor: Taha Akyol; **Editor:** Yalçin Bayer; **Editor:** Ugur Cebeci; **Editor:** Gökhan Kimsesizcan; **Editor:** Savas Özbey; **Editor:** Cengiz Semercioglu; **Editor:** Sahrap Soysal; **Editor:** Altan Tanrikulu
Editorial Profile: Newspaper focusing on national and international news, politics, business and sport.
Language (s): Turkish
DAILY NEWSPAPER

Hürriyet Daily News
Owner: Hürriyet Gazetecilik ve Matbaacilik A.S
Editorial: Hürriyet Dünyasi, 100.Yil Mahallesi, Matbaacilar Caddesi, No : 78, Bagcilar, Istanbul 34204. **T:** 90 212 677 00 00
E: english@hurriyet.com.tr
W: http://www.hurriyet.com.tr/english/home
Freq: Daily; **Circ:** 5428 Publisher's Statement
Editor-in-Chief: Murat Yetkin
Editorial Profile: Daily newspaper in English covering domestic and world news, finance, lifestyle and sports.
Language (s): English
DAILY NEWSPAPER

Milli Gazete
Editorial: Millî Gazete Tesisleri Inönü Mah. Muammer Aksoy Cad. Dere Sk. No: 70, Sefaköy-Küçükçekmece, Istanbul 34620.
T: 90 212 697 10 00
E: milli@milligazete.com.tr
W: http://www.milligazete.com.tr
Freq: Daily; **Circ:** 22538 Publisher's Statement
Editor-in-Chief: Ercan Özcan
Editorial Profile: Provides political, economic news and developments in Turkey and the world's last-minute news, developments and information services.
Language (s): Turkish
DAILY NEWSPAPER

Milliyet
Owner: Milliyet Gazetecilik ve Yayincilik A.S.
Editorial: Izzet Pasa Mah. Abide-i Hürriyet Cad. No:162, Çaglayan-Sisli, Istanbul 34387.
T: 90 212 337 99 99
W: http://www.milliyet.com.tr
Freq: Daily; **Circ:** 194037 Publisher's Statement
Editor: Sami Kohen
Editorial Profile: Newspaper focusing on national and international news, politics, business and sport.
Language (s): Turkish
DAILY NEWSPAPER

Ortadogu
Owner: Diger
Editorial: Fabrikalar Cd. No:1 K.2 Besyol, Sefaköy, Istanbul. **T:** 90 212 425 36 50
E: haber@ortadogugazetesi.net
W: http://www.ortadogugazetesi.net
Freq: Daily; **Circ:** 5898 Publisher's Statement
Editor-in-Chief: Mehmet Müftüoglu
Editorial Profile: Daily newspaper covering political news and issues.
Language (s): Turkish
DAILY NEWSPAPER

Posta
Owner: Dogan Gazetecilik A.S.
Editorial: Kustepe Mah. Mecidiyeköy Yolu Cad., Trump Towers Kule 2, Istanbul 34387.
T: 90 212 5056111 **E:** internet@posta.com.tr
W: http://www.posta.com.tr
Freq: Daily; **Circ:** 397299 Publisher's Statement
Editor: Mehmet Ali Birand; **Editor-in-Chief:** Mehmet Coskundeniz; **Editor:** Candas Tolga Isik
Editorial Profile: Newspaper focusing on national and international news, society, entertainment and sport.
Language (s): Turkish
DAILY NEWSPAPER

Radikal
Owner: Hürriyet Gazetecilik ve Matbaacilik A.S
Editorial: Dogan Medya Center 34204, Bagcilar, Istanbul. **T:** 90 212 5056111
E: iletisim@radikal.com.tr

W: http://www.radikal.com.tr
Freq: Daily; **Circ:** 22024 Publisher's Statement
News Editor: Ömer Erbil; **Editor-in-Chief:** Eyup Can Saglik
Editorial Profile: Newspaper focusing on national and international news, economics, business and politics as well as culture and the arts.
Language (s): Turkish
DAILY NEWSPAPER

Referans
Owner: Dogan Grubu
Editorial: Hürriyet Medya Towers Günesli 34212, Günesli, Istanbul. **T:** 90 212 677 00 00
E: info@referansgazetesi.com
W: http://www.referansgazetesi.com
Freq: Daily; **Circ:** 11174 Publisher's Statement
Editorial Profile: Daily newspaper covering economics, stock markets and currencies, financial and agricultural issues.
Language (s): Turkish
DAILY NEWSPAPER

Sabah
Owner: Sabah Grubu
Editorial: Barbaros Bulvari Cam Han No:125 K:5, Besiktas, Istanbul. **T:** 90 212 3543000
E: editor@sabah.com.tr
W: http://www.sabah.com.tr
Freq: Daily; **Circ:** 323885 Publisher's Statement
News Editor: Burak Artuner
Editorial Profile: Newspaper focusing on national and international news, politics, business and sport.
Language (s): Turkish
DAILY NEWSPAPER

Sok
Owner: Diger
Editorial: Hocapasa Mah. Hüdavendigar Cad No:23 pk:34112, Sirkeci, Istanbul.
T: 90 212 5127494
W: http://www.gazetesok.com
Freq: Daily; **Circ:** 51773 Publisher's Statement
News Editor: Serkan BAYAR
Editorial Profile: Tabloid daily newspaper with news, last-minute events, posts and comments.
Language (s): Turkish
DAILY NEWSPAPER

Sözcü
Owner: Estetik Yayincilik A.S
Editorial: Halkali Merkez Mah. Abay Cad. Atlas Sokak, Atlas Is Merkezi, A Blok, No: 6-8/4, Istanbul. **T:** 90 212 698 3535
E: net@sozcu.com.tr
W: http://www.sozcu.com.tr
Freq: Daily; **Circ:** 342540 Publisher's Statement
Editor: Mediha Olgun
Editorial Profile: Sözcü is a Turkish daily newspaper launched in 2007 and distributed nationwide.
Language (s): Turkish
DAILY NEWSPAPER

Star
Owner: Diger
Editorial: Mehmet Akif Mh. Inönü Cd. Basin Ekspres Yolu Star Sk. No:2 34679, Ikitelli, Istanbul. **T:** 90 212 4488000
E: editor@stargazete.com
W: http://www.stargazete.com
Freq: Daily; **Circ:** 113214 Publisher's Statement
News Editor: Mehmet Yücel
Editorial Profile: Newspaper focusing on national and international news, economy, current affairs and sport.
Language (s): Turkish
DAILY NEWSPAPER

Takvim Gazetesi
Owner: Turkuvaz Gazete Dergi Basim A.S.
Editorial: Barbaros Bulvari, No:153, Cam Han, Kat:5 Besiktas, Istanbul. **T:** 90 212 354 30 00
E: takvim@takvim.com.tr
W: http://www.takvim.com.tr
Freq: Daily; **Circ:** 106953 Publisher's Statement
News Editor: Mevlüt Yüksel
Editorial Profile: Daily national newspaper with current political, economic and social news.
Language (s): Turkish
DAILY NEWSPAPER

Taraf
Owner: Taraf Gazetecilik Sanayi ve Ticaret A.S
Editorial: Misbah Muhayyes Damga ve Neset Ömer Sok. No:23-25, Kadiköy, Istanbul 34710.
T: 210 216 348 99 22 **E:** haber@taraf.com.tr
W: http://www.taraf.com.tr
Freq: Daily; **Circ:** 69141
Editor-in-Chief: Nese Düzel
Editorial Profile: Taraf is a Turkish national newspaper in Turkey. It covers news, social and political affairs.
Language (s): Turkish
DAILY NEWSPAPER

Today's Zaman
Owner: Feza Gazetecilik A.S
Editorial: Ahmet Taner Kislali Cad. No: 6, Yenibosna, Istanbul. **T:** 90 212 4541444
E: editor@todayszaman.com
W: http://www.todayszaman.com
Freq: Daily; **Circ:** 11063 Publisher's Statement
Editor In Chief: Bülent Kenes
Editorial Profile: Today's Zaman is filled with national and international news in the fields of business, diplomacy, politics, culture, arts, sports and economics, in addition to commentaries, specials and features.
Language (s): English
DAILY NEWSPAPER

Turkish Daily News
Owner: Dogan Grubu
Editorial: Hurriyet Medya Towers, Gunesli, Istanbul. **T:** 90 212 2516580
E: tdn@tdn.com.tr
W: http://www.turkishdailynews.com.tr
Freq: Daily; **Circ:** 2535 Publisher's Statement
News Editor: Nejat Basar; **Editor-in-Chief:** David Judson
Editorial Profile: Newspaper focusing on national and international news, politics, economics, society and culture.
Language (s): English
DAILY NEWSPAPER

Türkiye Gazetesi
Owner: Ihlas Grubu
Editorial: Merkez Mahallesi 29 Ekim Caddesi, Ihlas Plaza No:11 A/41 34197, Istanbul.
T: 90 212 641 8484 **E:** info@tg.com.tr
W: http://www.turkiyegazetesi.com
Freq: Daily; **Circ:** 167089 Publisher's Statement
Editorial Profile: Newspaper focusing on national and international news, politics, business, culture and sport.
Language (s): Turkish
DAILY NEWSPAPER

Vatan
Owner: Vatan Gazetecilik A.S
Editorial: Büyükdere Cad. No:123, Gayrettepe, Istanbul 34349. **T:** 90 212 337 9037
E: bizeulasin@gazetevatan.com
W: http://www.gazetevatan.com
Freq: Daily; **Circ:** 101871 Publisher's Statement
Editorial Profile: National daily covering politics, economics, business, culture, social issues and entertainment.
Language (s): Turkish
DAILY NEWSPAPER

Yeni Asir
Owner: Sabah Grubu
Editorial: Gaziosmanpasa Bulvari No:5 35210, Çankaya, Izmir. **T:** 90 232 4415000
E: yasir@yeniasir.com.tr
W: http://www.yeniasir.com.tr
Freq: Daily; **Circ:** 37106 Publisher's Statement
Editor-in-Chief: Sebnem Bursali
Editorial Profile: Newspaper containing national and international news, business and current affairs.
Language (s): Turkish
DAILY NEWSPAPER

Yeni Asya
Owner: Diger
Editorial: Gülbahar Cad. Günay Sk. No:434212, Günesli, Istanbul.
T: 90 212 655 88 59
E: iletisim@yeniasya.com.tr
W: http://www.yeniasya.com.tr
Freq: Daily; **Circ:** 9300 Publisher's Statement
Editorial Profile: Daily newspaper covering politics, economics, culture and sports.
Language (s): Turkish
DAILY NEWSPAPER

Yeni Çag
Owner: Diger
Editorial: A Yayincilik Gazetecilik ve Matbaacilik As. Baski Tesisleri Çobançesme Mah. Kalender Sok., Yenibosna, Istanbul.
T: 90 212 4524040
E: yenicag@yenicaggazetesi.com.tr
W: http://www.yenicaggazetesi.com.tr
Freq: Daily; **Circ:** 56923 Not Audited
Editorial Profile: Daily newspaper providing political news, current news, entertainment and sports.
Language (s): Turkish
DAILY NEWSPAPER

Yeni Mesaj
Editorial: Senlikköy Mahallesi, Sehitözcan Canik Sokak, No: 4 / A Kat: 2, Inönü Caddesi No: 96 Florya, Istanbul. **T:** 90 212 4251066
E: editor@yenimesaj.com.tr
W: http://www.yenimesaj.com.tr
Freq: Daily; **Circ:** 47282 Publisher's Statement
Editor: Mehmet Emin Koç
Editorial Profile: 'New Message' published in Turkey is a daily national newspaper.
Language (s): Turkish
DAILY NEWSPAPER

Yeni Safak
Owner: Yeni Safak Gazetecilik A.S.
Editorial: Yenidogan Mah. Senay Sok. No:2 Kat:1, Bayrampasa, Istanbul.
T: 90 212 612 29 30 **E:** sm@yenisafak.com.tr
W: http://yenisafak.com.tr
Freq: Daily; **Circ:** 126630 Publisher's Statement
Editor: Fuat Atik; **News Editor:** Fatma Demircioglu; **Editor:** Idris Saruhan
Editorial Profile: Newspaper focusing on national and international news, economics, politics, culture, society and sport.
Language (s): Turkish
DAILY NEWSPAPER

Zaman
Owner: Feza Gazetecilik A.S
Editorial: Zaman Gazetesi, Yenibosna, Istanbul. **T:** 90 212 454 14 54
E: zaman@zaman.com.tr
W: http://www.zaman.com.tr
Freq: Daily; **Circ:** 958051 Publisher's Statement
Readers' Editor: Selim Budak; **Domestic Affairs Editor:** Aziz Istegün; **News Editor:** Fatih Ugur
Editorial Profile: Daily newspaper covering political, business, financial, economic, cultural, social and sports news.
Language (s): Turkish
DAILY NEWSPAPER

NEWS SERVICE/SYNDICATE

Agence France-Presse - Ankara Bureau
Owner: Agence France-Presse
Editorial: And Sokak 8/13, Cankaya, Ankara 6680. **T:** 90 312 468 9680
E: afp.ankara@afp.com
W: http://www.afp.com
Bureau Chief: Michel Sailhan
Editorial Profile: Ankara office of the international press agency covering regional, national and international news and current affairs including general interest, politics, business, economics, health, science, education and society.
Language (s): English
NEWS SERVICE/SYNDICATE

Associated Press
Editorial: Iran Caddesi, Hayat Apt 17B, Daire 404, Ankara 6700. **T:** 90 312 428-2709
NEWS SERVICE/SYNDICATE

Associated Press
Editorial: Abdi Ipekci Caddesi, No. 61/4 Kat 4 Macka, Istanbul 34367. **T:** 90 212 231-1616
NEWS SERVICE/SYNDICATE

Bloomberg News
Editorial: Piyabe Sokak, Portakal Bldg Cicegi, Apt 18, C Block #7, Ankara 6540.
T: 90 3124388990
NEWS SERVICE/SYNDICATE

Bloomberg News
Editorial: Kanyon Office Block, Buyukdere Cd.; Kat 4, Istanbul. **T:** 90 212-317-3950
E: turkeynews@bloomberg.net
NEWS SERVICE/SYNDICATE

BloombergHT
Owner: C Görsel Yayinlar A.S.
Editorial: Abdülhakhamit Cad., No:25 Beyoglu/ Taksim, Istanbul 34437. **T:** 90 212 1316000
E: editor@bloomberght.com
W: http://www.bloomberght.com
Editor: Tugçe Özsoy; **Editor:** Süheyla Yilmaz
Editorial Profile: BloombergHT is a 24-hour network providing business and financial news. Launched in 2010.
Language (s): Turkish
NEWS SERVICE/SYNDICATE

Reuters
Editorial: Is Kuleleri Kule 2 Kat 1-2, Istanbul 806204 LEVENT. **T:** 90 212 350-7000
NEWS SERVICE/SYNDICATE

BROADCASTING

TELEVISION STATIONS

ATV
Owner: Çalik Holding
Editorial: Barbaros Bulvari. No: 153, Cam Han, Istanbul. **T:** 90 216 474 20 20
E: iletisim@atv.com.tr
W: http://www.atv.com.tr
Editorial Profile: atv (Actual Television) is a nationwide TV channel in Turkey, founded in 1993.

NTV
Owner: Dogus Yayin Grubu Anonim Sirketi
Editorial: Eski Büyükdere Caddesi USO Center No. 61, Maslak, Istanbul 80660.
T: 90 212 335 00 00 **E:** ntv@ntv.com.tr
W: http://www.ntvmsnbc.com/ntv
Editorial Profile: Satellite TV channel with political, business and sport news and informative-analytical programmes.

TURKMENISTAN Tel: 993
Standard Time: GMT +5
Continent: Asia
Capital City: Ashgabad

NEWSPAPERS & PUBLICATIONS

NEWSPAPERS

Ashgabat
Owner: Ashgabat
Editorial: Ulica Atabaeva 20 (Galkanysh), Ashgabat 744004. **T:** 993 12 22 33 04
Freq: 2 Times/Week; **Circ:** 17891 Publisher's Statement
Editor In Chief: Saperverdy Harahauvich
Editorial Profile: Newspaper focusing on national and regional news, business, politics, culture and sport.
Language (s): Turkmen
DAILY NEWSPAPER

Neytralniy Turkmenistan
Owner: Neytralniy Turkmenistan
Editorial: Garazhshyzlak shaily, Centr svobodnogo tvorchestva, Ashgabat.
T: 993 12 38 61 18 **E:** nt@online.tm
W: http://www.tmpress.gov.tm
Freq: Daily; **Circ:** 39000 Publisher's Statement
Editor In Chief: Geren Taimova
Editorial Profile: Newspaper focusing on business, politics, economics, sport, culture and national and international news.
Language (s): Russian
DAILY NEWSPAPER

Turkmen Gundogary
Owner: Turkmen Gundogary
Editorial: ul. Niyazova 44, Turkmenabat 746100. **T:** 993 422 61 435
Freq: 2 Times/Week; **Circ:** 45050 Publisher's Statement
Editor: Abdyreshit Tashov
Editorial Profile: Covers regional news.
Language (s): Turkmen
DAILY NEWSPAPER

Turkmenistan
Owner: Turkmenistan
Editorial: Garashsyzlyk, Ashgabat.
T: 993 12 38 60 88
Freq: Daily; **Circ:** 28090 Publisher's Statement
Editor: Kakabay Iliyasov
Editorial Profile: A daily newspaper focusing on Turkmenistan news, business, politics, economics, culture and sport.
Language (s): Turkmen
DAILY NEWSPAPER

WORLD NEWS MEDIA

BROADCASTING

RADIO NETWORKS

Turkmen Radio Vatan
Editorial: 5 Navoi Street, Ashgabat 744000.
T: 993 12 51 12 37

TELEVISION STATIONS

Turkmen National TV
Editorial: Ulica Navoi 5, Ashgabat 744000.
T: 993 12 39 25 20 E: tvkm@online.tm

TURKS AND CAICOS ISLANDS
Tel: 1 649

Standard Time: GMT -5
Continent: The Americas
Capital City: Cockburn Town (Grand Turk)

NEWSPAPERS & PUBLICATIONS

NEWSPAPERS

The Turks & Caicos Free Press
Owner: Turks & Caicos Free Press Ltd
Editorial: The Marketplace, Leeward Highway, Providenciales. T: 649 9415615
E: news@tcifreepress.com
W: http://www.tcifreepress.com
Freq: Thu
Editorial Profile: The Turks & Caicos Free Press is a daily newspaper focusing on national news, business, politics and sports.
Language (s): English
NEWSPAPER

BROADCASTING

RADIO NETWORKS

Radio Turks & Caicos
Editorial: PO Box 69, Grand Turk.
T: 649 9462007 E: rtc@tciway.tc
W: http://www.rtc.tc
Editorial Profile: Local radio station broadcasting news, sports, health and music shows.

TUVALU
Tel: 688

Standard Time: GMT +12

BROADCASTING

RADIO NETWORKS

Radio Tuvalu
Owner: Tuvalu Media Corporation
Editorial: Private Mail Bag, Vaiaku, Tuvalu.
T: 688 20 138 E: meltaape@yahoo.co.ck
Editorial Profile: Radio Tuvalu broadcasts on Funafuti, the capital of Tuvalu in the Central Pacific.

TELEVISION NETWORKS

Tuvalu-news.tv
Editorial: Tuvalu Media Corporation, Private Mail Bag, Funafuti E: media@tuvalu.tv
Editorial Profile: Tuvalu ISP is the first ISP here in Tuvalu. This ISP is under the Tuvalu Government and is operated under the department of ICT (Information Communication and Transportation), off the Ministry of Communication Transportation and Tourism.

UGANDA
Tel: 256

Standard Time: GMT +3
Continent: Africa
Capital City: Kampala

NEWSPAPERS & PUBLICATIONS

NEWSPAPERS

Bukedde
Owner: Vision Group
Editorial: 19/21 First Street, Industrial Area, Kampala. T: 256 414 337 000
E: bukedde@newvision.co.ug
W: http://bukedde.co.ug
Freq: Daily
Editor in Chief: Barbara Kaija
Editorial Profile: Newspaper covering national news and current affairs including business, politics, entertainment and sports.
Language (s): English
DAILY NEWSPAPER

Daily Monitor
Owner: Monitor Publications Ltd
Editorial: 29-35, 8th Street, PO Box 12141, Kampala. T: 256 41 77 44 100
E: editorial@ug.nationmedia.com
W: http://www.monitor.co.ug
Freq: Daily; Circ: 27000 Publisher's Statement
News Editor: Alex Atuhaire
Editorial Profile: Newspaper covering national and international news including business, politics, economics, sports, entertainment and culture.
Language (s): English
DAILY NEWSPAPER

ETOP
Owner: Vision Group
Editorial: 19/21 First Street, Industrial Area, Kampala. T: 256 414 337 000
E: editorial@newvision.co.ug
W: http://www.etop.co.ug
Freq: Thu
Editor in Chief: Barbara Kaija
Editorial Profile: Newspaper covering regional news and current affairs including relationship advice, sports, community news and gossip, business, pictorial and readers' letters and opinions. Published in Ateso weekly every Thursday, the main circulation area covers North Eastern Uganda, Soroti, Katakwa and Kumi.
NEWSPAPER

The New Vision
Owner: Vision Group
Editorial: 19/21 First Street, Industrial Area, Kampala. T: 256 414 337 000
E: editorial@newvision.co.ug
W: http://www.newvision.co.ug
Freq: Daily
Editor in Chief: Barbara Kaija; News Editor: Hellen Mukiibi
Editorial Profile: Newspaper covering national and international news and current affairs including sport, business, entertainment, health, multimedia and lifestyle.
Language (s): English
DAILY NEWSPAPER

The Observer
Owner: Observer Media Ltd.
Editorial: 1, Tagore Crescent, Kamwokya, Kampala. T: 256 414 230433
E: editor@observer.ug
W: http://www.observer.ug
Freq: Daily
Editorial Profile: Newspaper covering national and international news and current affairs including business, politics, education, features and sports.
Language (s): English
DAILY NEWSPAPER

Orumuri
Owner: Vision Group
Editorial: 19/21 First Street, Industrial Area, Kampala. T: 256 414 337 000
E: amakuru@newvision.co.ug
W: http://www.orumuri.co.ug
Editor in Chief: Barbara Kaija
Editorial Profile: Newspaper covering regional news and current affairs including gossip, relationship education, politics, community news and gossip, wedding pictorial, business, herbal remedies, farming, weekly news round up and sports. Published in Runyakore/Rukiga weekly every Monday, the main circulation area is the western part of Uganda, from Masaka to Kabale, including Toro, Kasese, Bunyoro.
NEWSPAPER

Rupiny
Owner: Vision Group
Editorial: 19/21 First Street, Industrial Area, Kampala. T: 256 414 337 000
E: editorial@newvision.co.ug
W: http://rupiny.co.ug
Editor in Chief: Barbara Kaija
Editorial Profile: Newspaper covering regional news and current affairs including politics, relationship advice, sports, community news & gossip, business, leisure, crazy crazy country, pictorials and readers' letters and opinions. Published in Luo weekly every Wednesday, main circulation area is the northern part of Uganda including Gulu and Lira.
Language (s): English
NEWSPAPER

UKRAINE
Tel: 380

Standard Time: GMT +2
Continent: Europe
Capital City: Kiev

NEWSPAPERS & PUBLICATIONS

NEWSPAPERS

Den
Owner: The Ukrainian Press Group
Editorial: Blvd. Marshala Tymoshenka 2L, Kyiv 4212. T: 380 44 41 44 331
E: chedit@day.kiev.ua
W: http://www.day.kiev.ua
Freq: Daily; Circ: 62500 Publisher's Statement
Editor-in-Chief: Larysa Ivshina
Editorial Profile: Newspaper in Ukrainian, Russian and English versions covering politics, current-affairs, economics and culture.
Language (s): English, Russian, Ukrainian
DAILY NEWSPAPER

Donbass
Owner: Donbass
Editorial: Kievsky Avenue 48, Donetsk 83118. T: 380 62 3116 610 E: che@donbass.dn.ua
W: http://www.donbass.dn.ua
Freq: Daily
Editor-in-Chief: Alexander Brizh
Editorial Profile: Tabloid-sized newspaper featuring national news, politics, business, culture and sport.
Language (s): Russian
DAILY NEWSPAPER

Fakty i kommentarii
Owner: Fakty i kommentarii
Editorial: ul. Vandy Vasilevskoy 27/29, Kyiv 4116. T: 380 44 24 45 781
E: info@facts.kiev.ua
W: http://www.facts.kiev.ua
Freq: Daily; Circ: 784275 Publisher's Statement
Editor In Chief: Aleksander Shvets
Editorial Profile: Newspaper covering news, politics, the economy, culture, foreign affairs and sport.
Language (s): Russian
DAILY NEWSPAPER

Krymskaya Pravda
Owner: Krymskaya Pravda Co., Ltd.
Editorial: 44 Generala Vasileva, office 142, Simferopol 95000. T: 380 652 44 69 40
E: postm@kp.crimea.com
W: http://www.kp.crimea.com
Freq: Daily; Circ: 51000 Publisher's Statement
Editorial Profile: Newspaper covering major events in Crimea and Ukraine, also features international news and articles on politics, economics, science and culture.
Language (s): Russian
DAILY NEWSPAPER

Kyiv Post
Owner: Public Media
Editorial: ul. Pushkinska 31a, office 600, Kyiv 1004. T: 380 44 5913344
E: news@kyivpost.com
W: http://www.kyivpost.com Circ: 25000 Publisher's Statement
Editor: Brian Bonner; Editor: Katya Gorchinskaya; Guides Editor: Alexandra Matoshko; Editor: Roman Olearchyk; Editor: Mark Rachkevych; Publisher: Jed Sunden

Editorial Profile: Newspaper containing national and international news, business and current affairs.
Language (s): English
DAILY NEWSPAPER

Segodnya
Owner: Segodnya Multimedia
Editorial: Ul. Borshagovskaya 152-B, Kyiv 305656. T: 380 44 45 72 399
E: info@segodnya.ua
W: http://www.segodnya.ua
Freq: Daily; Circ: 135000 Publisher's Statement
Editor-in-Chief: Igor Guzhva
Editorial Profile: Newspaper covering national and international news, politics, sport and entertainment.
Language (s): Russian
DAILY NEWSPAPER

Sport Arena
Owner: Donbass
Editorial: pr. Kievsky 48, 9 floor, Donetsk 83118. T: 380 62 38 56 289
E: sport@donbass.dn.ua
W: http://www.sport-arena.com.ua
Freq: 2 Times/Week; Circ: 15000 Not Audited
Editor-in-Chief: Eduard Kiselev
Editorial Profile: National newspaper on sports, sport events in Ukraine and abroad, interviews with sport celebrities and coaches.
Language (s): Russian
DAILY NEWSPAPER

Ukraina Moloda
Owner: PP Ukraina Moloda
Editorial: pr. Peremogi 50, 5 floor, Kyiv 3047. T: 380 44 45 48 392 E: post@umoloda.kiev.ua
W: http://uamedia.visti.net/um
Freq: Daily; Circ: 130884 Publisher's Statement
Publisher: Mihailo Doroshenko
Editorial Profile: Informative -analytical newspaper covering news, politics and economic issues.
Language (s): Ukrainian
DAILY NEWSPAPER

Vechirniy Kyiv 100
Owner: Comunalne Predpriyemstvo Redaktsya Gazety Vechirny Kyiv
Editorial: ul. Marshala Grechka 13, Kyiv 4136. T: 380 44 43 46 109 E: office@vk-100.ua
W: http://www.vechirnij.kiev.ua Circ: 20000 Publisher's Statement
Editor In Chief: Olga Stoyan
Editorial Profile: National newspaper, covering politics, business and current affairs.
Language (s): Ukrainian
DAILY NEWSPAPER

Yuridicheskaya Practika
Owner: Yuridicheskaya Practika Publishing
Editorial: 22 Zakrevskogo Str., 4 Floor, Kyiv 2660. T: 380 44 49 52 727
E: info@yurpractika.com
W: http://www.yurpractika.com
Freq: Weekly; Circ: 10000 Not Audited
Editor In Chief: Yuriy Zabara
Editorial Profile: Newspaper focusing on law issues and legal practice includes advice on optimisation taxation, stock share issues, notary issues and family law.
Language (s): Russian
DAILY NEWSPAPER

Zerkalo Nedeli
Owner: IZDATELSKIY DOM ORMOS
Editorial: ul. Tverskaya 6, Kyiv 3150.
T: 380 44 52 97 822 E: info@mirror.kiev.ua
W: http://www.zerkalo-nedeli.com Circ: 57515 Publisher's Statement
Editor-in-Chief: Vladimir Mostovyy
Editorial Profile: Newspaper covering national and international news with features on business and finance, politics, lifestyle, entertainment and sport.
Language (s): Russian, Ukrainian
DAILY NEWSPAPER

NEWS SERVICE/SYNDICATE

Associated Press
Editorial: Krutiy Uzviz 6/2 of. 59, Kiev 1004.
T: 380 44 234-0512
NEWS SERVICE/SYNDICATE

Interfax-Ukraina
Editorial: ul. Reitarskaya 8/5a, Kiev 1034.
T: 380 44 270 74 65 E: office@interfax.kiev.ua
W: http://www.interfax.com.ua
Editorial Profile: News agency with coverage of news in three languages: Russian, Ukrainian and English.
Language (s): Ukrainian

NEWS SERVICE/SYNDICATE

Reuters
Editorial: Room 112 - 115, ulitsa Bogdana Khmelnitskovo 8-16, Kiev 252006.
T: 380 44 244-91-50
NEWS SERVICE/SYNDICATE

Ukrinform
Editorial: ul. Bogdana Khmelnytskogo 8/16, GSP, Kyiv 1001. **T:** 380 44 22 98 152
E: office@ukrinform.ua
W: http://www.ukrinform.ua
Editor: Marina Tarnovska
Editorial Profile: Offers online free access to updated political, economic, financial, medicinal, cultural news in Russian, Ukrainian and English languages.
Language (s): Ukrainian
NEWS SERVICE/SYNDICATE

UNIAN
Editorial: ul. Khreshatik 4, Kyiv 1001.
T: 380 44 27 93 131 **E:** info@unian.net
W: http://www.unian.net
Editor-in-Chief: Mykhailo Gannytskyi
Editorial Profile: Provides political and economic news about most important events in Ukraine's capital and regions, official decisions of highest legislative and executive bodies, as well as unbiased comments of experts and politicians.
Language (s): Ukrainian
NEWS SERVICE/SYNDICATE

BROADCASTING

RADIO NETWORKS

Gala Radio Network
Editorial: ul. Saksaganskogo 91, 4 floor, office 1, Kyiv 1032. **T:** 380 44 49 07 100
E: fm100@galaradio.com
W: http://www.galaradio.com
Editorial Profile: National radio network broadcasting news and pop music.

Radio Svoboda
Editorial: Ukrainskaya Redaksya Radio Svoboda, Hreshatik 19a, Kyiv 10011.
T: 380 44 49 02 900 **E:** Chalupal@rferl.org
W: http://www.radiosvoboda.org
Editorial Profile: Radio Svoboda is a part of Radio Free Europe with the head office in Washington, USA.

TELEVISION STATIONS

ICTV
Editorial: ul. Pankovskaya 11, Kiev 1033.
T: 380 44 288 1919 **E:** site@ictv.ua
W: http://ictv.ua
Editorial Profile: ICTV has got a priority in the information broadcast with information programs Facts, Business Facts, the final analytical news project Facts of the week with Oksana Sokolova. Recently, a cohort of IT projects become Facts. Outcome of the day - informative-analytical program, which summarizes and analyzes most of the day resonant events and their impact on the further development of the country.

Inter
Editorial: ul. Dmytrivska 30, Kiev 1054.
T: 380 44 490 67 65 **E:** pr@inter.ua
W: http://inter.ua
Editorial Profile: Inter TV Channel is the Ukrainian national broadcaster since 20th of October 1996. During all that time it has managed to hold the leading position in the domestic television market. Its position Inter holds due to the wisely chosen conception of family channel, which considers needs of all social and age groups in Ukraine.

Inter+
Editorial: ul. Dmytrivska 30, Kiev 1054.
T: 380 44 490 67 65 **E:** interplus@interplus.tv
W: http://interplus.ua
Editorial Profile: The international television channel Inter+ started broadcasting on January 13th, 2003. It represents an international license-cleared version of Inter, the leading Ukrainian TV channel seasoned with the best projects of other Ukrainian TV production companies.

NTN TV
Editorial: ul. Degtyarevskaya 48, Kiev 4112.
T: 380 44 206 03 03 **E:** ntn@ntn.tv
W: http://ntn.ua

Editorial Profile: NTN - a general format broadcasting station. NTN technical coverage is 88.3% of the country. It's 88 cities with populations over 50 thousand people. In 83 cities and towns of Ukraine television programs are included in packages of cable operators.

Pershiy Diloviy Kanal
Editorial: ul. Yakira 13b, Kiev 4119.
T: 380 44 207 47 17 **E:** office@tv1.com.ua
W: http://fbc.net.ua
Editorial Profile: First Business TV is a specialized business television, which provides business news and analytical information round the clock, 7 days a week.

Strana Sovietov kanal
Editorial: ul. Kanatnaya 83, office 419/1, Odessa 65107. **T:** 380 48 714 85 61
E: personal@glas.odessa.ua
W: http://www.glasweb.com
Editorial Profile: The Land of the Soviets TV seeks to convey as much useful information to each viewer and create a good mood among the audience. Programs reflect all aspects of our lives: spiritual, intellectual, social, cultural, political and economic-financial. This multiplicity is due to diverse interests of the audience of the channel.

UNITED ARAB EMIRATES **Tel: 971**

Standard Time: GMT +4
Continent: Asia
Capital City: Abu Dhabi

NEWSPAPERS & PUBLICATIONS

NEWSPAPERS

7Days
Owner: Al Sidra Media
Editorial: PO Box 35207, Belhoul Group Building, Dubai. **T:** 971 4 283 1317
E: news@7days.ae **W:** http://www.7days.ae
Freq: Daily; **Circ:** 61097 BPA Worldwide
Editor in Chief: Mahmood Al Awadhy; **News Editor:** David Dunn; **Editor:** Barry King
Editorial Profile: 7Days is a tabloid-sized English newspaper covering local and international news, current affairs, politics, business and sport. The newspaper is published daily (Sun-Thurs) and distributed free to homes in Dubai, Abu Dhabi and Sharjah. It includes Wellbeing, a quarterly lifestyle magazine supplement published in January, April, June and September. The newspaper launched in April 2003 as a weekly, before increasing its frequency a year later. It publishes weekly on Thursdays during the month of Ramadan. It is owned by the UK-based Daily Mail & General Trust Plc which bought a 60% stake in 2006 and increased its ownership to 100% in March 2011.
Language (s): English
DAILY NEWSPAPER

Alroeya
Owner: I-Media
Editorial: PO Box 502850, Mezzanine Floor, Shatha Tower, Dubai. **T:** 971 4 439 2000
E: press@alrroya.com
W: http://www.alroeya.com
Freq: Daily; **Circ:** 80000 Rate Card
News Editor: Firas Al Ali; **Editor In Chief:** Mohammed Al Tunisi
Editorial Profile: Alroeya is a daily Arabic newspaper covering news, business and sport. It launched in 2009 as business newspaper Alrroya Aleqtissadiya, before re-launching as Alroeya in December 2012.
Language (s): Arabic
DAILY NEWSPAPER

Al Bayan
Owner: Dubai Media Incorporated
Editorial: PO Box 2710, Sheikh Zayed Road, Dubai. **T:** 971 4 344 4400
E: bayan@albayan.ae
W: http://www.albayan.ae
Freq: Daily; **Circ:** 88800 Rate Card
Editorial Profile: Al Bayan is a daily, broadsheet-sized Arabic newspaper covering news, current affairs, politics, business and sport. It also includes a weekly arts supplement, Massarat, on Sundays. The newspaper launched in 1980 and is owned by the Government of Dubai through Dubai Media Incorporated.
Language (s): Arabic
DAILY NEWSPAPER

Emarat Al Youm
Owner: Dubai Media Incorporated
Editorial: PO Box 191919, Emarat Al Youm Building, Near Safa Park, Dubai.
T: 971 4 306 2222
E: local@emaratalyoum.com
W: http://www.emaratalyoum.com
Freq: Daily; **Circ:** 80000 Rate Card
Editor In Chief: Sami Al Reyami
Editorial Profile: Emarat Al Youm is a tabloid-sized, daily Arabic newspaper covering local and international news, politics, business, entertainment, culture and sport. It was first published in 2005, and is owned by the Government of Dubai through Dubai Media Incorporated.
Language (s): Arabic
DAILY NEWSPAPER

Al Gharbia Fee Ousbou
Owner: Al Jewa Group for Culture and Arts
Editorial: PO Box 57887, Zayed City, Abu Dhabi. **T:** 971 2 887 0005 **E:** aljewa@aljewa.ae
W: http://www.algharbianews.ae
Freq: Sun; **Circ:** 100000
Editorial Profile: Al Gharbia Fee Ousbou is a tabloid-sized weekly newspaper covering news, business, sports, culture and society in the Western region of Abu Dhabi. The 32-page newspaper was launched in January 2013 and is issued on Sundays.
Language (s): Arabic
DAILY NEWSPAPER

Gulf Madhyamam - UAE edition
Owner: Gulf Madhyamam FZ LLC
Editorial: PO Box 4243, Office 232, Building 10, Dubai. **T:** 971 4 390 2628
E: dubai@gulfmadhyamam.net
W: http://www.gulfmadhyamam.net
Freq: Daily; **Circ:** 63850 Rate Card
Editor-in-Chief: Hamzah Abbas
Editorial Profile: Gulf Madhyamam is an international Indian newspaper covering national and international news, current affairs, politics, business and sport. The newspaper is aimed at Malayalam speakers in the Gulf and publishes separate editions for the UAE, Saudi Arabia (Riyadh, Jeddah, Dammam & Abha), Qatar, Oman, Bahrain and Kuwait. The UAE edition was first published in 1999.
Language (s): Malayalam
DAILY NEWSPAPER

Gulf News
Owner: Al Nisr Publishing LLC
Editorial: PO Box 6519, Gulf News Building, Dubai. **T:** 971 4 344 7100
E: editor@gulfnews.com
W: http://www.gulfnews.com
Freq: Daily; **Circ:** 103594 BPA Worldwide
Editor In Chief: Abdul Hamid Ahmad;
Readers' Editor: Anupa Kurian; **Editor-at-Large:** Francis Matthew; **GCC & Middle East Editor:** Layelle Saad
Editorial Profile: Gulf News is a berliner-sized, daily English newspaper covering local and international news, politics, business and sport. It includes tabloid!, an entertainment and lifestyle supplement from Sunday to Thursday, and the expanded tabloid! on Saturday on Saturdays. On Fridays, the newspaper includes lifestyle magazine supplement Friday and Weekend Review, which takes an in-depth look at the issues behind the news. The newspaper was first published as a tabloid in September 1978, and re-launched as a broadsheet in December 1985.
Language (s): English
DAILY NEWSPAPER

The Gulf Time
Owner: Al Wathba For Media
Editorial: PO Box 54040, Abu Dhabi.
T: 971 2 448 6000 **E:** editor@gulftimes.ae
W: http://www.gulftimes.ae
Freq: Daily; **Circ:** 60000
Editorial Profile: The Gulf Time is a daily, broadsheet newspaper covering local and international news, opinion, business and sport. It was first published in July 2013.
Language (s): English
DAILY NEWSPAPER

Al Ittihad
Owner: Abu Dhabi Media
Editorial: PO Box 791, Abu Dhabi.
T: 971 2 445 5555 **E:** local@alittihad.ae
W: http://www.alittihad.ae
Freq: Daily; **Circ:** 109640 Rate Card
Editorial Profile: Al Ittihad (Union) is a broadsheet-sized, daily Arabic newspaper covering local and international news, current affairs, politics, business and sport. It includes a daily lifestyle section, Dunia. The newspaper launched in 1969 and is owned by the

Government of Abu Dhabi through its Abu Dhabi Media division.
Language (s): Arabic
DAILY NEWSPAPER

Al Khaleej
Owner: Dar Al Khaleej for Press, Printing & Publishing
Editorial: PO Box 30, Al Khan Street, Sharjah.
T: 971 6 577 7777 **E:** alkhaleej@alkhaleej.ae
W: http://www.alkhaleej.ae
Freq: Daily; **Circ:** 147400 Rate Card
Editor in Chief: Khalid Omran; **News Editor:** Hisham Safi
Editorial Profile: Al Khaleej (The Gulf) is a broadsheet-sized, daily Arabic newspaper covering local and international news, politics, business, economics, culture and sport. It was first published in 1970.
Language (s): Arabic
DAILY NEWSPAPER

Khaleej Times
Owner: Galadari Printing & Publishing LLC
Editorial: PO Box 11243, Khaleej Times Offices, Dubai. **T:** 971 4 338 3535
E: news@khaleejtimes.com
W: http://www.khaleejtimes.com
Freq: Daily; **Circ:** 96150 Publisher's Statement
City Editor: Mustafa Al Zarooni; **News Editor:** Zahid Mukhtar
Editorial Profile: Khaleej Times is a broadsheet-sized, daily English newspaper covering local and international news, sport, business and finance. The newspaper was first published in 1978 and includes City Times, a daily tabloid supplement covering entertainment and celebrity news; wknd. magazine on Fridays; and a health supplement, Better Health, which is published twice a year in March and November.
Language (s): English
DAILY NEWSPAPER

Malayala Manorama - Gulf edition
Owner: M M Publications Ltd
Editorial: PO Box 502638, Office 1505, Al Thuraya Tower 2, Dubai. **T:** 971 4 374 8920
E: manoramagulf@gmail.com
W: http://www.manoramaonline.com
Freq: Daily; **Circ:** 96000 Publisher's Statement
Bureau Chief: Jaimon George
Editorial Profile: Gulf edition of Indian newspaper Malayala Manorama. It covers international and local news, politics, sport, business, entertainment and technology, and is aimed at Malayalam speakers in the Gulf.
Language (s): Malayalam
DAILY NEWSPAPER

Middle East Chandrika
Owner: Kerala Muslim Printing and Publishing Co Ltd
Editorial: PO Box 50066, 1st Floor, DKMCC Building, Dubai. **T:** 971 4 238 6888
E: editor@mechandrika.ae
W: http://gulf.chandrikadaily.com
Freq: Daily; **Circ:** 55000 Publisher's Statement
Editor in Charge: Abdul Jaleel Pattambi
Editorial Profile: Middle East Chandrika is the UAE edition of Indian newspaper Chandrika, and covers local and international news, sport, business, religion and politics. It was first published in 2005 and is aimed at Malayalam speakers in the UAE.
Language (s): Malayalam
DAILY NEWSPAPER

The National
Owner: Abu Dhabi Media
Editorial: PO Box 111434, 15th Street, Abu Dhabi. **T:** 971 2 414 5328
E: newsdesk@thenational.ae
W: http://www.thenational.ae
Freq: Daily; **Circ:** 65000 Rate Card
Editor in Chief: Mohammed Al Otaiba; **News Editor:** Michael Jabri-Pickett
Editorial Profile: The National is a broadsheet-sized newspaper covering local and international news, business and sport. The newspaper includes Arts & Life, a tabloid-sized arts and lifestyle supplement from Sunday to Thursday; the Weekend lifestyle section on Fridays, cultural supplement The Review on Saturdays, and a monthly lifestyle magazine, Luxury. The newspaper launched in 2008 and is owned by the Government of Abu Dhabi through its Abu Dhabi Media division.
Language (s): English
DAILY NEWSPAPER

The Wall Street Journal (UAE)
Editorial: Building 5, Office 314, Dubai.
T: 971 43314260

DAILY NEWSPAPER

Al Watan
Owner: Al Wathba For Media
Editorial: PO Box 54040, Abu Dhabi.
T: 971 2 448 6000 **E:** info@al-watan.ae
W: http://www.alwatannewspaper.ae
Freq: Daily; **Circ:** 109000 Publisher's Statement
News Editor: Hisham Yehia
Editorial Profile: Al Watan is a daily Arabic newspaper covering news, business, politics and sport. It was first published in 1999 as Akhbar Al-Arab, later re-launching as Al Watan.
Language (s): Arabic
DAILY NEWSPAPER

XPRESS - Dubai edition
Owner: Al Nisr Media FZ LLC
Editorial: PO Box 6519, Al Nisr Media Offices, Dubai. **T:** 971 4 344 7100
E: news@xpress4me.com
W: http://www.xpress4me.com
Freq: Thu; **Circ:** 53931 BPA Worldwide
Editor In Chief: Abdul Hamid Ahmad; **Editor:** Bobby Naqvi
Editorial Profile: XPRESS is a tabloid-sized English newspaper distributed free to homes in Dubai. The newspaper covers local news, features, sport, entertainment, human interest stories and leisure. It launched in March 2007 and is published on Thursdays. An Abu Dhabi edition was introduced in March 2013.
Language (s): English
DAILY NEWSPAPER

NEWS SERVICE/SYNDICATE

Agence France-Presse - Dubai Bureau
Owner: Agence France-Presse
Editorial: PO Box 502108, Villa 12, Boutique Offices, Dubai. **T:** 971 4 366 4567
E: afp.dubai@afp.com **W:** http://www.afp.com
Editorial Profile: Dubai bureau of international news agency supplying news - text, graphics, video and pictures - to subscribers around the world.
Language (s): Arabic, English, French
NEWS SERVICE/SYNDICATE

Argus Media - Dubai bureau
Owner: Argus Media
Editorial: PO Box 502821, Office 2607, Al Shatha Tower, Dubai. **T:** 971 4 365 8667
E: dubai@argusmedia.com
W: http://www.argusmedia.com
Editorial Profile: Dubai office of UK-based independent energy news agency.
Language (s): English
NEWS SERVICE/SYNDICATE

Associated Press
Editorial: Dubai Media City, Building 4 Office 304, Dubai. **T:** 971 4 390-8120
Bureau Chief: Brian Murphy
NEWS SERVICE/SYNDICATE

Associated Press - Dubai Bureau
Owner: Associated Press
Editorial: PO Box 53872, Office 304, Building 4, Dubai. **T:** 971 4 390 8120
E: apdubai@ap.org **W:** http://www.ap.org
Editorial Profile: Dubai bureau of international wire agency - covers the UAE, Saudi Arabia, Bahrain, Kuwait, Qatar, Oman and Iran from Dubai.
Language (s): English
NEWS SERVICE/SYNDICATE

Bloomberg - Dubai Bureau
Owner: Bloomberg L.P.
Editorial: PO Box 506707, 10th Floor, Al Fattan Currency House, Dubai.
T: 971 4 364 1020
E: mideastnews@bloomberg.net
W: http://www.bloomberg.com
Bureau Chief: Claudia Maedler
Editorial Profile: Dubai bureau of financial news wire service.
Language (s): English
NEWS SERVICE/SYNDICATE

Bloomberg News
Editorial: The Gate, 84 West, Dubai.
T: 971 4 364 1000
NEWS SERVICE/SYNDICATE

Deutsche Presse-Agentur - Dubai bureau
Owner: Deutsche Presse-Agentur
Editorial: Dubai **E:** dpa.dubai@yahoo.com
W: http://www.dpa.com
Editorial Profile: Dubai bureau of German press agency - covers news, politics, sports, fashion, economy, conflicts, disasters, features and business in the Middle East.
Language (s): German
NEWS SERVICE/SYNDICATE

Dow Jones Newswires - Dubai bureau
Owner: Dow Jones
Editorial: PO Box 502585, Office 314, Building 5, Dubai. **T:** 971 4 446 1695
E: djnews.dubai@dowjones.com
W: http://www.dowjones.com
Editorial Profile: Financial newswire service - covers the UAE, Kuwait, Iran, Iraq, Oman, Qatar, Sudan and Saudi Arabia from Dubai.
Language (s): English
NEWS SERVICE/SYNDICATE

Emirates News Agency
Owner: Emirates News Agency
Editorial: PO Box 3790, Abu Dhabi.
T: 971 2 404 4333 **E:** edit@wam.ae
W: http://www.wam.ae
Editorial Profile: Official government news agency founded in 1976.
Language (s): Arabic, English
NEWS SERVICE/SYNDICATE

Emirates News Agency - Dubai office
Owner: Emirates News Agency
Editorial: PO Box 5010, Dubai.
T: 971 4 261 5500
E: dubainews@wamdubai.ae
W: http://www.wam.ae
Editor: Halima Al Shamsi; **Editor:** Salma Al Shamsi; **Editor:** Munira Al Sumaiti; **Editor:** Aysha Al Suwaidy
Editorial Profile: Dubai office of official UAE government news agency.
Language (s): Arabic
NEWS SERVICE/SYNDICATE

European Pressphoto Agency - UAE Bureau
Owner: European Pressphoto Agency
Editorial: PO Box 454580, Dubai.
T: 971 4 395 0089 **E:** haider@epa.eu
W: http://www.epa.eu
Editorial Profile: Photo agency representing 11 European news agencies (DPA, ANSA, EFE, Belga, APA, Athens News Agency, PAP, ANP, MTI, Keystone and LUSA) - covers news, politics, sports, fashion, economy, conflicts, disasters, features and business.
Language (s): English
NEWS SERVICE/SYNDICATE

Integrated Regional Information Networks
Owner: IRIN
Editorial: PO Box 506011, International Humanitarian City, Dubai. **T:** 971 4 368 0272
E: dubaieditorial@irinnews.org
W: http://www.irinnews.org
Bureau Chief: Amina Zubairi
Editorial Profile: Humanitarian news and analysis agency - a service of the UN Office for the Coordination of Humanitarian Affairs. Alternative Co. Name: IRIN
Language (s): Arabic, English, French
NEWS SERVICE/SYNDICATE

Platts - Dubai bureau
Owner: McGraw-Hill Companies
Editorial: PO Box 73360, Office 211/212, Building 1, Dubai. **T:** 971 4 391 3170
E: tamsin_carlisle@platts.com
W: http://www.platts.com
Editorial Profile: Platts is a worldwide energy information and price assessment agency. Coverage includes energy, oil and gas (upstream and downstream), OPEC affairs, analysis of energy trends and energy pricing - services include real time electronic news, daily newsletters and market reports.
Language (s): English
NEWS SERVICE/SYNDICATE

Reuters
Editorial: Dubai Media City, Reuters Building, 5th Floor, Office 501, Sheikh Zayed Road, Dubai. **T:** 971 4391-8301
E: dubai.newsroom@thomsonreuters.com
Editor: Sami Aboudi; **Bureau Chief:** William Maclean
NEWS SERVICE/SYNDICATE

Reuters - Dubai Bureau
Owner: Thomson Reuters
Editorial: PO Box 1426, 5th Floor, Thomson Reuters Building, Dubai. **T:** 971 4 391 8301
E: dubai.newsroom@thomsonreuters.com
W: http://www.reuters.com
Editorial Profile: Dubai bureau of international news agency supplying news - text, graphics, video and pictures - to subscribers around the world.
Language (s): English
NEWS SERVICE/SYNDICATE

Reuters TV - Gulf Bureau
Owner: Thomson Reuters
Editorial: PO Box 1426, Office 501, Thomson Reuters Building, Dubai. **T:** 971 4 391 8300
E: ahmed.seif@thomsonreuters.com
W: http://www.reuters.com
Bureau Chief: William Maclean
Editorial Profile: Gulf bureau of Thomson Reuters TV providing television broadcasters and internet providers worldwide with international news video, including breaking news stories, human interest items, sport, business and entertainment news.
Language (s): English
NEWS SERVICE/SYNDICATE

Xinhua News Agency - Abu Dhabi Bureau
Owner: Xinhua News Agency
Editorial: PO Box 44696, Abu Dhabi.
T: 971 2 643 1397 **E:** anjiang56@hotmail.com
W: http://www.xinhuanet.com
Bureau Chief: An Jiang
Editorial Profile: Abu Dhabi bureau of the Xinhua News Agency, the official press agency of the People's Republic of China. Correspondence and press releases should be sent in Arabic or Chinese.
Language (s): Arabic
NEWS SERVICE/SYNDICATE

Xinhua News Agency - Dubai Bureau
Owner: Xinhua News Agency
Editorial: PO Box 454385, Dubai.
T: 971 4 451 6739 **E:** lizhen2013@xinhua.org
W: http://www.xinhuanet.com
Editorial Profile: Dubai bureau of the Xinhua News Agency, the official press agency of the People's Republic of China. Correspondence and press releases should be sent in Arabic or Chinese.
Language (s): Arabic
NEWS SERVICE/SYNDICATE

BROADCASTING

RADIO STATIONS

104.8 Channel 4 FM
Owner: Ajman Independent Studios LLC
Editorial: PO Box 442, Ajman.
T: 971 6 746 1444 **E:** info@channel4fm.com
W: http://www.channel4fm.com
Editorial Profile: 104.8 Channel 4 FM is a commercial radio station broadcasting contemporary English music 24-hours a day with news on the top of the hour. Launched in 1997, the station broadcasts on 104.8 FM and forms part of the Channel 4 Radio Network, a wholly owned subsidiary of Ajman Independent Studios LLC.

105.4 FM Radio Spice
Owner: V3 Media Solutions FZ LLC
Editorial: PO Box 8372, Dubai.
T: 971 4 339 1110 **E:** mail@radiospicefm.com
W: http://www.radiospicefm.com
Editorial Profile: 105.4 FM Radio Spice is a radio station broadcasting entertainment programmes, hit music, news, business, sport and competitions. Launched in 2006, the station is aimed at Hindi-speaking expatriates in the UAE and broadcasts on 105.4 FM.

106.2 Hum FM
Owner: Shamal Media Services
Editorial: PO Box 20212, Sharjah.
T: 971 6 565 1919 **E:** zeeshan@humfm.com
W: http://www.humfm.com
Editorial Profile: 106.2 Hum FM is a radio station broadcasting music, news, sports programmes. Launched in 1998, the station is aimed at Indian expatriates in the UAE and broadcasts on 106.2 FM.

107.8 Al Rabea FM
Owner: Ajman Independent Studios LLC
Editorial: PO Box 442, Ajman.
T: 971 6 746 4222 **W:** http://www.1078fm.com
Editorial Profile: 107.8 Al Rabea FM is a radio station broadcasting contemporary Arabic music along with news on the top of the hour and financial, sports news and traffic updates every half hour. Launched in 2001, the station is aimed at Arabic-speaking listeners aged 22-34 years. It broadcasts on 107.8 FM and forms part of the Channel 4 Radio Network, a wholly owned subsidiary of Ajman Independent Studios LLC.

89.1 Radio 4FM
Owner: Ajman Independent Studios LLC
Editorial: PO Box 442, Ajman.
T: 971 6 746 0000 **E:** info@radio4fm.com
W: http://www.radio4fm.com
Editorial Profile: 89.1 Radio 4FM is a radio station broadcasting contemporary hit music 24-hours a day with news on the hour. Launched in 1999, the station is aimed at Hindi-speaking listeners aged 22-34 years. It broadcasts on 89.1 FM and forms part of the Channel 4 Radio Network, a wholly owned subsidiary of Ajman Independent Studios LLC.

Abu Dhabi Classic FM
Owner: Abu Dhabi Media
Editorial: PO Box 3966, Abu Dhabi.
T: 971 2 445 9999
E: matthew.sansom@admedia.ae
W: http://www.abudhabiclassicfm.ae
Editorial Profile: Abu Dhabi Classic FM is a radio station broadcasting classical, jazz & world music. The station plays well-known, mainstream, popular and accessible classical music during the day, special programming dedicated to Jazz fans during the evenings, and then chill out music into the early hours. The station launched on 23 October 2009 and broadcasts on 91.6 FM in Abu Dhabi, 87.9 FM in Dubai and 105.2 FM in Al Ain. It is owned by Abu Dhabi Media, the media division of the Abu Dhabi government, and forms part of the company's Abu Dhabi Radio Network.

Abu Dhabi Qur'an Kareem
Owner: Abu Dhabi Media
Editorial: PO Box 3966, Abu Dhabi.
T: 971 2 414 5535 **E:** quran@admedia.ae
W: http://www.qurankareem.ae
Editorial Profile: Abu Dhabi Qur'an Kareem is a religious radio station broadcasting Quranic recitals and religious programmes. Launched in 1979, the station broadcasts on 98.1 FM. It is owned by Abu Dhabi Media, the media division of the Abu Dhabi government, and forms part of the company's Abu Dhabi Radio Network.

Abu Dhabi Radio
Owner: Abu Dhabi Media
Editorial: PO Box 3966, Abu Dhabi.
T: 971 2 445 9999
E: abdulla.alzaabi@admedia.ae
W: http://www.adradio.ae/abudhabiradio
Editorial Profile: Abu Dhabi Radio is a radio station broadcasting classic Arabic music and news programmes. The station launched in 1969 and airs on 90.0 FM. It is owned by Abu Dhabi Media, the media division of the Abu Dhabi government, and forms part of the company's Abu Dhabi Radio Network.

Al Arabiya 99 FM
Owner: Arabian Radio Network
Editorial: PO Box 502012, Office 103,407, Building 2, Dubai. **T:** 971 4 391 2000
E: nmajid@arn.ae
W: http://www.alarabiya99.com
Editorial Profile: Al Arabiya 99 FM is a radio station broadcasting hit music, chat and competitions. The station launched in 2001 and broadcasts on 99.0 FM.

Asianet Radio 657 AM
Owner: Asianet Global FZ LLC
Editorial: PO Box 62787, Villa 10, Boutique Offices, Dubai. **T:** 971 4 391 4151
E: radio657@asianetworld.tv
W: http://www.asianetradio.me
Editorial Profile: Asianet Radio 657 AM is a radio station broadcasting infotainment, news and music 24-hours a day. The station launched in 2000 and broadcasts on 657 AM.

City 101.6 FM
Owner: Arabian Radio Network
Editorial: PO Box 502012, Office 103, Building 2, Dubai. **T:** 971 4 391 2000
E: fmunro@arnonline.com
W: http://www.city1016.ae
Editorial Profile: City 101.6 FM is a radio station broadcasting hit music, news, talk shows and entertainment programmes. It launched in 2002 and airs on 101.6 FM.

Dubai 92
Owner: Arabian Radio Network
Editorial: PO Box 502012, Building BS-16, Dubai. **T:** 971 4 435 4700
E: englishnews@arnonline.com
W: http://www.dubai92.com
Editorial Profile: Dubai 92 is a radio station broadcasting hit music from the 80s, 90s and current day, as well as event coverage, news, weather and traffic updates. The station launched in 2004 and is aimed at the 18-35

year-old expat community. It broadcasts on 92.0 FM.

Dubai Eye 103.8 FM
Owner: Arabian Radio Network
Editorial: PO Box 502012, Building BS-16, Dubai. **T:** 971 4 435 4700
E: dubaieye@arnonline.com
W: http://www.dubaieye1038.com
Editorial Profile: Dubai Eye 103.8 FM is a talk radio station broadcasting news, current affairs, business, sports and lifestyle programmes for 24-hours a day. Launched in 2004, the station airs on 103.8 FM.

Dubai FM
Owner: Dubai Media Incorporated
Editorial: PO Box 835, Dubai.
T: 971 4 307 7939 **E:** dubaifm@dmi.ae
W: http://www.dmi.ae/dubairadio
Editorial Profile: Dubai FM is a radio station broadcasting music, entertainment and chat shows. It launched in 2011 and airs on 93.0 FM. The station is owned by the government of Dubai through its Dubai Media Incorporated division.

Emarat FM
Owner: Abu Dhabi Media
Editorial: PO Box 3966, Abu Dhabi.
T: 971 2 445 9999 **E:** alrousi2007@gmail.com
W: http://www.adradio.ae/emaratfm
Editorial Profile: Emarat FM is a national radio station broadcasting entertainment, live programmes and music. It launched in 1995 and is owned by the Government of Abu Dhabi through its Abu Dhabi Media division. The station broadcasts on 95.8 FM (Abu Dhabi), 94.9 FM (Al Ain), 97.1 FM (Dubai & Sharjah), 88.5 FM (Ras Al Khaimah) and 103.9 FM (Fujairah).

Fujairah 92.6
Owner: Fujairah Media FZ LLC
Editorial: PO Box 4422, 16th-20th Floor Creative Tower, Fujairah. **T:** 971 9 207 1477
E: info@926.fm **W:** http://www.926.fm
Editorial Profile: Fujairah 92.6 is a news-orientated radio station re-broadcasting programmes from Radio Monte Carlo, as well as producing its own local news programmes. The station launched in 2006 and broadcasts on 92.6 FM.

Gold 101.3 FM
Owner: Ajman Independent Studios LLC
Editorial: PO Box 442, Ajman.
T: 971 6 746 5000 **E:** info@gold1013fm.com
W: http://www.gold1013fm.com
Editorial Profile: Gold 101.3 FM is a radio station broadcasting contemporary Malayalam hit music and entertainment. Launched in 2010, the station is aimed at Malayalam speakers in the UAE. It broadcasts on 101.3 FM and forms part of the Channel 4 Radio Network, a wholly owned subsidiary of Ajman Independent Studios LLC.

Hayat FM 95.6
Owner: Gulf News Broadcasting
Editorial: PO Box 6519, Gate 3, Gulf News Building, Dubai. **T:** 971 4 344 6366
W: http://www.hayatfm.ae
Editorial Profile: Hayat FM 95.6 is a commercial radio station broadcasting Arabic music and entertainment, along with local and international news. It launched on 10 June 2012 and broadcasts on 95.6 FM.

Hit 96.7 FM
Owner: Arabian Radio Network
Editorial: PO Box 502012, Office 103-104, Building 2, Dubai. **T:** 971 4 391 2018
E: hit967@arnonline.com
W: http://www.hit967.ae
Editorial Profile: Hit 96.7 FM is a radio station broadcasts hit music from South India, news, talk shows and other entertainment programmes. Launched in 2004, the station is aimed at South Indian expatriates in the UAE and broadcasts on 96.7 FM.

Josh 97.8
Owner: Gulf News Broadcasting
Editorial: PO Box 6519, Gulf News Building, Dubai. **T:** 971 4 344 6366
W: http://www.joshfm.ae
Editorial Profile: Josh 97.8 is a commercial radio station broadcasting Hindi music and international hits, along with news, sport and entertainment programmes. Launched in 2012, the station is targeted at 18-35 year-old South Asian expats and broadcasts on 97.8 FM.

Al Khaleejiya 100.9 FM
Owner: Arabian Radio Network
Editorial: PO Box 502012, Office 103-104, CNN Building, Dubai. **T:** 971 4 391 2366
E: mohd@arn.ae
W: http://www.alkhaleejiya1009.ae
Editorial Profile: Al Khaleejiya 100.9 FM is a radio station broadcasting Khaleeji (Gulf) music, news, talk shows and entertainment programmes. Launched in 2003, the station is aimed at UAE and GCC nationals and broadcasts on 100.9 FM.

MBC FM
Owner: MBC Group
Editorial: PO Box 72627, MBC Building, Dubai. **T:** 971 4 391 9999 **E:** fm@mbc.net
W: http://www.mbc.net/mbcfm
Editorial Profile: MBC FM is a Pan Arab radio station broadcasting Khaleeji (Gulf) music, entertainment, competitions and news 24-hours a day. Launched in 1994, the station broadcasts on various FM frequencies in Saudi Arabia, 92.0 FM in Qatar and 101.9 FM in Bahrain.

Noor Dubai 93.9 FM
Owner: Dubai Media Incorporated
Editorial: PO Box 835, Dubai.
T: 971 4 336 9999
E: badriya.mohammed@dmi.ae
W: http://www.dmi.ae/noordubai
Editorial Profile: Noor Dubai 93.9 FM is an Islamic-oriented station broadcasting news, talk and social issues relating to youths in the Emirates. The station launched on 9 May 2006 and broadcasts on 93.9 FM. It is owned by the government of Dubai through its Dubai Media Incorporated division.

Panorama FM
Owner: MBC Group
Editorial: PO Box 72627, MBC Building, Dubai. **T:** 971 4 391 9999 **E:** panofm@mbc.net
W: http://www.mbc.net/panoramafm
Editorial Profile: Panorama FM is a radio station broadcasting contemporary Arabic music, entertainment programming, competitions and on-the-hour news 24-hours a day. Launched in 2003, the station broadcasts on various FM frequencies in Saudi Arabia, 88.6 FM in Baghdad and 103.0 FM in Bahrain.

Radio 1
Owner: Gulf News Broadcasting
Editorial: PO Box 6519, Gulf News Broadcasting, Dubai. **T:** 971 4 344 6366
E: studio@myradio1.ae
W: http://www.myradio1.ae
Editorial Profile: Radio 1 is a national radio station broadcasting contemporary hit music. Launched in 1999, the station is aimed at 15-30 year-olds in the UAE and broadcasts on 104.1 FM (Dubai) and 100.5 FM (Abu Dhabi). It is managed by Gulf News Broadcasting on behalf of Abu Dhabi Media, which owns the station's licence and frequency.

Radio 2
Owner: Gulf News Broadcasting
Editorial: PO Box 6519, Gulf News Building, Dubai. **T:** 971 4 344 6366
E: studio@myradio2.ae
W: http://www.myradio2.ae
Editorial Profile: Radio 2 is a national radio station playing music from the 80s, 90s and now, along with news, sport and entertainment programmes. Launched in 1999, the station is aimed at English-speaking listeners over 30 years-old and broadcasts on 99.3 FM (Dubai) and 106.0 FM (Abu Dhabi). It is managed by Gulf News Broadcasting on behalf of Abu Dhabi Media, which owns the station's licence and frequency.

Radio Asia
Owner: Radio Asia Network
Editorial: PO Box 4300, Ras Al Khaimah.
T: 971 4 453 4950 **E:** admin@radioasia.ae
W: http://www.radioasiauae.com
Editorial Profile: Radio Asia is a radio station broadcasting news, current affairs and entertainment programmes. Launched in 1994, the station is aimed at South Asian expatriates in the GCC and broadcasts on 1269 AM.

Radio Hello 89.5 FM
Owner: Malar Global Media
Editorial: PO Box 94029, Port Saeed, Dubai.
T: 971 4 602 8900 **E:** connect@hello.fm
W: http://www.radio895.com/
Editorial Profile: Radio Hello 89.5 FM is a radio station broadcasting music and entertainment 24-hours a day. The station launched in 2010 and is aimed at the Tamil and South Indian communities in the UAE.

Radio Mirchi UAE
Owner: Abu Dhabi Media
Editorial: PO Box 63, Abu Dhabi.
T: 971 2 414 5516
E: feedback@radiomirchiuae.ae
W: http://www.radiomirchiuae.ae
Editorial Profile: Radio Mirchi UAE is a radio station broadcasting Indian music, news from Bollywood and entertainment programmes. It launched in February 2012 as a joint venture between Radio Mirchi in India and Abu Dhabi Media. The station targets Hindi-speakers in the UAE and broadcasts on 88.8 FM (Dubai), 97.3 FM (Abu Dhabi) & 95.6 FM (Al Ain). Radio Mirchi was launched in India in 2001 by Entertainment Network (India) Limited and operates in 32 cities across the country.

Radio Shoma 93.4
Owner: Arabian Radio Network
Editorial: PO Box 502012, Office 103-104, Building 2, Dubai. **T:** 971 4 391 2000
E: shaun.valentine@arnonline.com
W: http://radioshoma934.ae
Editorial Profile: Radio Shoma 93.4 is a radio station broadcasting Persian music, entertainment, culture, business and sports programmes. Launched in 2011, the station is aimed at Iranian expatriates in the UAE and broadcasts on 93.4 FM.

Russian Radio 96.3 FM
Owner: Russian Radio Network
Editorial: Office 811, Gold Crest Executive Building, Dubai. **T:** 971 4 450 9895
E: info@russianradioworld.com
W: http://www.russianradioworld.com
Editorial Profile: Russian Radio 96.3 FM is a radio station broadcasting Russian music and entertainment programmes. Launched in 2009, it is aimed at Russian expatriates in the UAE and broadcasts on 96.3 FM.

Sharjah FM
Owner: Sharjah Media Corporation
Editorial: PO Box 111, Sharjah.
T: 971 6 501 1111 **E:** info@smc.ae
W: http://www.smc.ae
Editorial Profile: Sharjah FM is a regional radio station broadcasting religious, cultural and educational programmes 24-hours a day in the emirate of Sharjah. Launched on 31 August 1972, it is owned by the government of Sharjah's media division, Sharjah Media Corporation, and broadcasts on 94.4 FM (Sharjah), 107.6 FM (Khor Fakkan and Dibba) and 107.7 FM (Kalba).

Star FM
Owner: Abu Dhabi Media
Editorial: PO Box 3966, Abu Dhabi.
T: 971 2 445 9999 **E:** info@starfm.ae
W: http://www.starfm.ae
Editorial Profile: Star FM is a youth-orientated radio station broadcasting a mixture of English and Arabic songs, interspersed with light entertainment, news updates and listener-generated content. The station launched in 2009 and broadcasts on 92.4 FM (Abu Dhabi), 99.9 FM (Dubai) and 100.1 FM (Al Ain). It is owned by Abu Dhabi Media, the media division of the Abu Dhabi government, and forms part of the company's Abu Dhabi Radio Network.

Suno 1024
Owner: Radio Asia Network
Editorial: PO Box 31876, Office 1602, Al Shafar Tower, Dubai. **T:** 971 4 453 4950
E: admin@radioasia.ae
W: http://www.suno1024.com
Editorial Profile: Suno 1024 is a radio station broadcasting hit music from South Asia. It launched in 2011 and broadcasts on 102.4 FM.

Super 94.7 FM
Owner: Radio Asia Network
Editorial: PO Box 31876, Office 211, Al Maya Super Market Building, Dubai.
T: 971 4 453 4950 **E:** admin@radioasia.ae
W: http://www.super947.fm
Editorial Profile: Super 94.7 FM is a Malayalam and Tamil radio station broadcasting news, music and entertainment programmes. Launched in 2011, the station is aimed at the South Asian community in the UAE and broadcasts on 94.7 FM.

Tag 91.1
Owner: Arabian Radio Network
Editorial: PO Box 502012, Building BS-16, Dubai. **T:** 971 4 435 4700 **E:** roy@arn.ae
W: http://www.tag911.ae
Editorial Profile: Tag 91.1 is a radio station broadcasting Filipino music, news and entertainment. Launched in March 2013, the station is aimed at the Filipino community in the UAE and broadcasts on 91.1 FM.

Virgin Radio Dubai
Owner: Arabian Radio Network
Editorial: PO Box 502012, Building BS-16, Dubai. **T:** 971 4 435 4700 **E:** virgin@arn.ae
W: http://www.virginradiodubai.com
Editorial Profile: Virgin Radio Dubai is a radio station broadcasting hit music, chat and competitions. The station launched in 2008 and broadcasts on 104.4 FM.

Zayed Radio for Qura'an
Owner: Fujairah Culture & Media Authority
Editorial: PO Box 7444, Fujairah Tower, Fujairah. **T:** 971 9 222 6645
E: zuriaqat@zayedquran.gov.ae
W: http://www.zayedquran.gov.ae
Editorial Profile: Zayed Radio for Qura'an is a radio station broadcasting Quranic recitals and religious programmes. It launched in 2009 and broadcasts on 97.6 FM. The station is owned by the government of Fujairah through its Fujairah Culture & Media Authority division.

RADIO NETWORKS

All India Radio (Prasar Bharati) - Middle East bureau
Owner: All India Radio
Editorial: PO Box 6999, Dubai.
T: 971 4 227 2767
E: dubainewsairdd@gmail.com
W: http://www.newsonair.com
Editorial Profile: Middle East bureau of All India Radio (AIR), India's National Public Service Broadcaster, which was established in 1936 to inform, educate and entertain the masses. The Middle East bureau is located in Dubai and provides news content from the region to All India Radio's home service, which comprises 277 radio stations located across India and reaches nearly 92% of the country's area and 99.19 % of its total population, with programming in 23 languages and 146 dialects.

UNITED STATES OF AMERICA Tel: 1

Standard Time: GMT -5 (East Coast), GMT -8 (West Coast), GMT -9 (Alaska), GMT -10 (Hawaii)
Continent: The Americas
Capital City: Washington DC

NEWSPAPERS & PUBLICATIONS

NEWSPAPERS

22nd Century Media, North Suburbs
Owner: 22nd Century Media
Editorial: 60 Revere Dr Ste 888, Northbrook, Illinois 60062-1580. **T:** 1 847 272-4565
W: http://www.22ndcenturymedia.com
Editor: Jamie Bradley; **Editor:** April Dahlquist; **Editor:** Dayna Fields; **Editor:** Alex Mayster; **Publisher:** Jack Ryan
Editorial Profile: 22nd Century Media North Suburbs is a multiple publisher that produces weekly community newspapers serving the residents of the North Shore suburbs of Chicago, including the Wilmette Beacon, the Winnetka Current, the Glenview Lantern and the Northbrook Tower.
NEWSPAPER

22nd Century Media, SW Suburbs
Owner: 22nd Century Media
Editorial: 11516 W 183rd St, Unit SW, Office Condo #3, Orland Park, Illinois 60467.
T: 1 708 326-9170
W: http://22ndcenturymedia.com **Circ:** 73200 Not Audited
Editor: Dennis Jacobs; **Editor:** Will O'Brien; **Publisher:** Jack Ryan
Editorial Profile: 22nd Century Media Southwest Suburbs is a multiple publisher that produces weekly community newspapers serving the residents of the Southwest suburbs of Chicago, including the Homer Horizon, the Mokena Messenger, the New Lenox Patriot, the Orland Park Prairie, the Tinley Junction, the Lockport Legend and the Frankfort Station.
NEWSPAPER

280 Living
Owner: Starnes Publshing

Editorial: 3 Office Park Circle, Suite 316, Birmingham, Alabama 35223.
T: 1 205 370-0732
W: http://280living.wordpress.com
Freq: Monthly; **Circ:** 13500
Publisher: Dan Starnes
Editorial Profile: 280 Living is a monthly newspaper providing Local and Community News coverage to the residents living in the 280 Corridor along Highway 280, encompassing the communities of Birmingham, Cahaba Heights, Inverness, Mountain Brook, Chelsea and Oak Park, AL
NEWSPAPER

6000 Bees LLC

Owner: 6000 Bees LLC
Editorial: 4104 E. Jefferson Ave., Wellington, Colorado 80549. **T:** 1 970 221-0213
E: info@northfortynews.com **Circ:** 26700 Not Audited
Editorial Profile: 6000 Bees LLC in Wellington, CO publishes The Wellington, a weekly newspaper, and North Forty News, a monthly publication.
NEWSPAPER

77 Square

Owner: Capital Newspapers
Editorial: 1901 Fish Hatchery Rd, Madison, Wisconsin 53713-1248. **T:** 1 608 252-6400
E: 77cal@madison.com
W: http://host.madison.com/entertainment
Freq: Thu; **Circ:** 87000 Not Audited
Editor: Paul Fanlund
Editorial Profile: 77 Square is a weekly newspaper that highlights arts, entertainment and culture. It also features the local music scene, film, radio, television and the sports fan's experience. The arts are covered, focusing on classical music, the visual arts, theater and dance. The paper also explores current trends, including the local retail scene, relationships, homes, fashion, books, travel, gardening and more.; Full Page Mono: 75.35
Currency: US Dollars
NEWSPAPER

A.J.'s Printing

Editorial: 215 S 8th St, Conway Springs, Kansas 67031. **T:** 1 620 456-2232
E: ajprinting@havilandtelco.com **Circ:** 925 Not Audited
NEWSPAPER

Abbeville Meridional

Owner: Louisiana State Newspapers
Editorial: 318 N Main St, Abbeville, Louisiana 70510. **T:** 1 337 893-4223
W: http://vermiliontoday.com/
Freq: Daily; **Circ:** 4804 Not Audited
Editor: Chris Rosa
Editorial Profile: Abbeville Meridional's editorial mission is to provide the most up-to-date news and information about the Abbeville, LA region. The publication is written for citizens in the Abbeville area as well as people all over the country who are interested with this part of the country. The Abbeville Meridional is a daily publication.; Full Page Mono: 10.00; Full Page Colour: 58.71
Currency: US Dollars
DAILY NEWSPAPER

ABC Newspapers

Owner: ECM Publishers, Inc.
Editorial: 4101 Coon Rapids Blvd NW, Coon Rapids, Minnesota 55433-2585.
T: 1 763 421-4444
W: http://www.abcnewspapers.com
Circ: 11300 Not Audited
Publisher: Julian Andersen
NEWSPAPER

The Aberdeen American News

Owner: Schurz Communications Inc.
Editorial: 124 S 2nd St, Aberdeen, South Dakota 57401-4010. **T:** 1 605 225-4100
E: americannews@aberdeennews.com
W: http://www.aberdeennews.com
Freq: Daily; **Circ:** 14958 Not Audited
Publisher: Cory Bollinger
Editorial Profile: The Aberdeen American News is a local daily newspaper serving 18 counties in South and North Dakota. It provides the local community with information on news, events, sports and weather.; Full Page Mono: 23.25; Full Page Colour: 225.00
Currency: US Dollars
DAILY NEWSPAPER

Abilene Reflector Chronicle

Owner: Walls Newspapers
Editorial: 303 N Broadway St, Abilene, Kansas 67410-2616. **T:** 1 785 263-1000
W: http://www.abilene-rc.com

Freq: Daily; **Circ:** 3387 Not Audited
Editor & Publisher: Dave Bergmeier; **City Editor:** Carla Strand
Editorial Profile: Abilene Reflector Chronicle offers coverage of local news, sports, classifieds, deaths, community calendar, business, youth, a photo gallery and senior sections. The publication is geared toward residents of Abilene, KS and surrounding areas.; Full Page Mono: 7.50; Full Page Colour: 57.87
Currency: US Dollars
DAILY NEWSPAPER

Abilene Reporter-News

Owner: E.W. Scripps Co.
Editorial: 101 Cypress St, Abilene, Texas 79601-5888. **T:** 1 325 673-4271
E: publishme@reporternews.com
W: http://www.reporternews.com
Freq: Daily; **Circ:** 24380 Not Audited
Newsroom Content Editor: Greg Jaklewicz; **Editor:** Doug Williamson; **Editor:** Doug Williamson; **Editor:** Doug Williamson
Editorial Profile: Abilene Reporter-News is a local daily newspaper written for residents of Abilene, TX. The newspaper provides information on news and events of interest to the local community. The lead time varies depending on the editorial material.; Full Page Mono: 50.00; Full Page Colour: 316.85
Currency: US Dollars
DAILY NEWSPAPER

About Our Town Newspapers

Editorial: 2 Lakeview Ave, Ste 312, Piscataway, New Jersey 8854.
T: 1 732 968-1615 **E:** aot@aboutourtown.com
W: http://www.aboutourtown.com **Circ:** 40408
Publisher: Ronald Chilson; **Editor:** Claire Pyecroft
Editorial Profile: About Our Town Newspapers is a publication that provides the community of Piscataway, NJ with local newspapers.; Full Page Mono: 225.00
Currency: US Dollars
NEWSPAPER

The AC Phoenix

Editorial: 1959 Peace Haven Rd #151, Winston Salem, North Carolina 27106-4850.
T: 1 336 635-4096 **E:** acphoenix@bellsouth.net
Freq: Monthly; **Circ:** 25000 Not Audited
Publisher: Rodney Sumler
Editorial Profile: The AC Phoenix is a community newspaper for and about residents of the Piedmont Triad, including Greensboro, Winston-Salem and High Point. Its primary focus is on the issues that affect the quality of life in our neighborhoods, including religion, education, politics, economic and development issues and neighborhood and business profiles. It is distributed the first weekend of each month via home delivery or for purchase at churches, libraries, schools and selected retailers throughout the area. Deadlines are on the last Thursdays of the month prior to publication.; Full Page Mono: 14.57
Currency: US Dollars
NEWSPAPER

Academy Spirit

Owner: Dolan Media
Editorial: 2304 Cadet Drive, Suite 3100, Colorado Springs, Colorado 80840.
T: 1 719 333-7731 **E:** usafa.pai@usafa.af.mil
W: http://csmng.com
Freq: Wed; **Circ:** 12600 Not Audited
Editor: Ray Bowden
Editorial Profile: Academy Spirit is the official newspaper of the U.S. Air Force Academy. The publication provides coverage of campus news and events pertinent to cadets, military personnel, faculty and staff.; Full Page Mono: 12.77
Currency: US Dollars
NEWSPAPER

ACE Weekly

Owner: Realitytruck LLC
Editorial: 185 Jefferson St, Lexington, Kentucky 40508. **T:** 1 859 225-4889
E: publisher@aceweekly.com
W: http://www.aceweekly.com
Freq: Thu; **Circ:** 10000 Not Audited
Editorial Profile: ACE Weekly is a free newspaper that features arts, commentary, entertainment and current events in the Lexington, KY area. The mailing address is only used for billing and accounting; send press releases to the street address. The fax number is used only by the advertising department.; Full Page Mono: 27.79
Currency: US Dollars
NEWSPAPER

Acento Latino

Owner: Fayetteville Publishing Co.
Editorial: 458 Whitfield St, Fayetteville, North Carolina 28306. **T:** 1 910 323-4848 223
E: editor@acentolatino.com
W: http://www.acentolatino.com
Freq: Bi-Weekly; **Circ:** 10000 Not Audited
Publisher: Charles Broadwell; **Editor:** Ed Panas
Editorial Profile: Acento Latino is a bi-weekly newspaper focusing on the Hispanic communities of Central and Southeastern North Carolina. The magazine, written in Spanish, covers topics such as health, English as a second language and local news. The publication is distributed throughout the counties of Lee, Moore, Harnett, Hoke, Cumberland, Sampson, Robeson and Bladen, NC.; Full Page Mono: 10.01; Full Page Colour: 590.00
Currency: US Dollars
NEWSPAPER

AcheiUSA

Owner: Jose Nunes
Editorial: 816 SE 9th St, Deerfield Beach, Florida 33441-5637. **T:** 1 954 570-7568
E: info@acheiusa.com
W: http://www.acheiusa.com
Freq: Weekly; **Circ:** 12000
Publisher: Jorge Nunes; **Editor:** Antonio Tozzi
Editorial Profile: Launched on November 2000, the newspaper covers news of interest to the Brazilian Community in Florida (in Portuguese).; Full Page Mono: 41.90
Currency: US Dollars
NEWSPAPER

The Acorn Newspapers

Owner: J.Bee Publications
Editorial: 30423 Canwood St Ste 108, Agoura Hills, California 91301-4313.
T: 1 818 706-0266 **E:** newstip@theacorn.com
W: http://www.theacornonline.com
Circ: 135761 Not Audited
Editor: Kyle Jorrey; **Publisher:** James Rule; **Editor:** Scott Tittrington; **Editor:** Dan Wolowicz
NEWSPAPER

Action Unlimited

Editorial: 100 Domino Dr, 1, Concord, Massachusetts 01742-2817.
T: 1 978 371-2442
E: articles@actionunlimited.com
W: http://www.actionunlimited.com
Circ: 113450 Not Audited
Editorial Profile: Action Unlimited is the local newspaper providing news to the community of Concord, MA.
NEWSPAPER

Actualidad

Owner: Actualidad Corp.
Editorial: 5801 E Washington Blvd, Commerce, California 90040-2323.
T: 1 562 505-8187
W: http://www.actualidadnewspaper.com
Freq: Monthly; **Circ:** 25000 Not Audited
Publisher: Anita Valdivieso; **Editor:** Pedro Valdivieso
Editorial Profile: Actualidad is a monthly Spanish-language newspaper serving the Peruvian community of Los Angeles, CA.; Full Page Mono: 4.29
Currency: US Dollars
NEWSPAPER

Ada News

Owner: Community Newspaper Holdings, Inc.
Editorial: 116 N Broadway Ave, Ada, Oklahoma 74820-5004. **T:** 1 580 332-4433
E: news@theadanews.com
W: http://www.theadanews.com
Freq: Daily; **Circ:** 7879 Not Audited
Publisher: Loné Beasley; **City Editor:** Randy Mitchell
Editorial Profile: Ada News is a daily newspaper for the residents of Ada, OK, and the surrounding areas. It provides information on news and events of interest to the local community.; Full Page Mono: 17.10; Full Page Colour: 64.35
Currency: US Dollars
DAILY NEWSPAPER

Addison Eagle

Owner: Newmarket Press
Editorial: 16 Creek Rd, Ste 5A, Middlebury, Vermont 5753. **T:** 1 802 388-6397
E: newmarketpress@denpubs.com
W: http://www.denpubs.com
Freq: Sat; **Circ:** 12266 Not Audited
Publisher: Edward Coats
Editorial Profile: Addison Eagle is a weekly newspaper serving residents of Addison County, VT including the communities of Bristol, Huntington, Ferrisburg, Hinesburg,

Monkton, New Haven, Starkboro, Middlebury, Orwell, Bridport and Shoreham, VT. It covers local news, sports, schools, businesses, arts & entertainment and features of interest. National and state news stories are also covered if they have a direct impact on the paper's audience. Advertising deadlines are at 4pm ET.; Full Page Mono: 19.00
Currency: US Dollars
NEWSPAPER

Adirondack Daily Enterprise

Owner: Ogden Newspapers
Editorial: 54 Broadway, Saranac Lake, New York 12983-1704. **T:** 1 518 891-2600
E: adenews@adirondackdailyenterprise.com
W: http://www.adirondackdailyenterprise.com
Freq: Daily; **Circ:** 5300 Not Audited
Publisher: Catherine Moore; **News Editor:** Brittany Proulx
Editorial Profile: Adirondack Daily Enterprise is published for the residents of the Adirondack, NY region. Coverage includes local news, sports, community events and arts & entertainment.; Full Page Mono: 20.41; Full Page Colour: 235.70
Currency: US Dollars
DAILY NEWSPAPER

The Adirondack Express

Owner: William J. Kline & Sons, Inc.
Editorial: 2955 St. Rt. 28, Old Forge, New York 13420. **T:** 1 315 369-2237
W: http://www.adirondackexpress.com
Freq: Tue; **Circ:** 39000
Editor: Leslie Bailey; **Publisher:** Kevin McClary
Editorial Profile: The Adirondack Express is a community newspaper serving residents of Old Forge, NY and the surrounding areas.; Full Page Mono: 6.35
Currency: US Dollars
NEWSPAPER

Advance Newspapers

Owner: Newhouse Newspapers
Editorial: 2141 Port Sheldon St, Jenison, Michigan 49428-9315. **T:** 1 616 669-2700
E: advancenewssubmissions@mlive.com
W: http://www.mlive.com/advancenewspapers
Freq: Weekly; **Circ:** 185309 Not Audited
Editorial Profile: Advance Newspapers publishes weekly community newspapers serving the Grand Rapids, MI area.
NEWSPAPER

Advance Publications of Perry and Juniata Counties Inc.

Editorial: 51 Church St, New Bloomfield, Pennsylvania 17068-9683. **T:** 1 717 582-4305
W: http://www.perrycountytimes.com
Circ: 10487 Not Audited
Editor: Wade Fowler; **Editor:** Wade Fowler; **Publisher:** Rick White
Editorial Profile: Advance Publications of Perry and Juniata Counties Inc. is a weekly community newspaper publisher serving the residents of New Bloomfield, Perry County and Duncannon, PA.
NEWSPAPER

The Advertiser

Owner: Hearst Newspapers
Editorial: 29 Sheer Rd, Averill Park, New York 12018. **T:** 1 518 674-2841
E: articles@theadvertiser.us
Freq: Thu; **Circ:** 34000 Not Audited
Publisher: Patrick Smith
Editorial Profile: The Advertiser is a weekly newspaper written for residents of Rensselaer County, NY. There are two editions of the newspaper, one for South Rensselaer County and one for North Rensselaer County. It covers local news, sports, government and lifestyles. The majority of the editorial copy is written by freelancers. Send all press materials to the main e-mail address.; Full Page Mono: 27.49; Full Page Colour: 1921.00
Currency: US Dollars
NEWSPAPER

The Advertiser News of Spring Hill

Owner: Stephens Media
Editorial: 3011 Harrah Dr., Ste J, Spring Hill, Tennessee 37174. **T:** 1 615 302-0647
W: http://cdh.columbiadailyherald.com/affiliate/advertisernews
Freq: Wed; **Circ:** 14400 Not Audited
Editorial Profile: The Advertiser News of Spring Hill is a community newspaper written for the residents of Spring Hill, TN and the surrounding areas.; Full Page Mono: 10.02
Currency: US Dollars
NEWSPAPER

The Advertiser-Tribune

Owner: Ogden Newspapers

Editorial: 320 Nelson St, Tiffin, Ohio 44883-8956. **T:** 1 419 448-3200
E: newsroom@advertiser-tribune.com
W: http://www.advertiser-tribune.com
Freq: Daily; **Circ:** 7219 Not Audited
Publisher: Chris Dixon; **Editor:** Nick Dutro; **News Editor:** MJ McVay; **News Editor:** MJ McVay; **Editor:** Rob Weaver
Editorial Profile: The Advertiser-Tribune is a local newspaper serving the Seneca County, OH area. It provides residents with information on local news, events, weather and sports. The lead time for editorial submissions is one week. Deadlines for the publication are one week before issue date.; Full Page Mono: 21.15; Full Page Colour: 151.92
Currency: US Dollars
DAILY NEWSPAPER

The Advertizer Herald Publishing Co.
Editorial: 369 McGee St, Bamberg, South Carolina 29003. **T:** 1 803 245-5204
E: ahpublisher@bellsouth.net
W: http://www.advertizerherald.com **Circ:** 5550 Not Audited
NEWSPAPER

The Advisor
Editorial: 83 State St, North Haven, Connecticut 6473. **T:** 1 203 239-5404
W: http://www.advisor-newspaper.com
Freq: Tue; **Circ:** 30000 Not Audited
Publisher: Patricia Flagg
Editorial Profile: The Advisor is a community newspaper written for the residents of North Haven, CT and the surrounding areas.; Full Page Mono: 9.50
Currency: US Dollars
NEWSPAPER

Advisor & Source Newspapers
Owner: Journal Register Company
Editorial: 19176 Hall Rd Ste 200, Clinton Township, Michigan 48038-6914.
T: 1 586 731-1000
W: http://www.sourcenewspapers.com
Circ: 125536
Editor: Jody McVeigh; **Publisher:** Jim O'Rourke
NEWSPAPER

The Advocate
Owner: Hearst Corporation
Editorial: 9A Riverbend Dr S, Stamford, Connecticut 06907-2524. **T:** 1 203 964-2200
E: letters.advocate@scni.com
W: http://www.stamfordadvocate.com
Freq: Daily; **Circ:** 9450 Not Audited
Publisher: Henry B. Haitz
Editorial Profile: The Advocate is a regional daily newspaper that covers Fairfield County, CT. The editorial mission of the paper is to provide the best news and information with the highest journalistic integrity. The paper features local news, sports and business.; Full Page Mono: 80.80; Full Page Colour: 458.26
Currency: US Dollars
DAILY NEWSPAPER

The Advocate
Owner: Gannett Co., Inc.
Editorial: 22 N 1st St, Newark, Ohio 43055.
T: 1 740 345-4053
E: advocate@newarkadvocate.com
W: http://www.newarkadvocate.com
Freq: Daily; **Circ:** 11293 Not Audited
Editorial Profile: The Advocate is a daily local newspaper serving residents of the Newark, OH area. It covers local, national and international news as well as lifestyle, sports and entertainment information that pertains to the community.; Full Page Mono: 35.50; Full Page Colour: 206.79
Currency: US Dollars
DAILY NEWSPAPER

The Advocate
Owner: Capital City Press
Editorial: 7290 Bluebonnet Blvd, Baton Rouge, Louisiana 70810-1611. **T:** 1 225 383-1111
W: http://www.theadvocate.com
Freq: Daily; **Circ:** 118125 Not Audited
News Editor: Kenneth Duhe; **News Editor:** Kenneth Duhe; **Publisher:** John Georges; **Editor:** Peter Kovacs
Editorial Profile: The Advocate is a daily broadsheet newspaper distributed in the Baton Rouge, LA area. The newspaper covers local news, politics, government, education, entertainment, and sports, as well as travel, food and dining, religion, books, and community events. The publication also features national and international news coverage, but the content is taken almost exclusively from wire services. Deadlines vary, but final news deadlines fall at 11pm. The lead time is one day for breaking news and up to several months for features.; Full Page Mono: 73.33; Full Page Colour: 920.00
Currency: US Dollars
DAILY NEWSPAPER

The Advocate
Owner: Capital City Press
Editorial: 815 Johnston St, Lafayette, Louisiana 70501-7901. **T:** 1 337 234-0174
Bureau Chief: Richard Burgess
DAILY NEWSPAPER

The Advocate
Editorial: 2626 S Range Ave, Denham Springs, Louisiana 70726-5553.
T: 1 225 664-9058
Bureau Chief: Heidi Kinchen
DAILY NEWSPAPER

The Advocate
Editorial: 911 7th St, Port Allen, Louisiana 70767-2113. **T:** 1 225 326-6627
DAILY NEWSPAPER

The Advocate
Editorial: 13057 Highway 44, Gonzales, Louisiana 70737-6863. **T:** 1 225 647-8447
Bureau Chief: Darlene Denstorff
DAILY NEWSPAPER

The Advocate
Editorial: 14317 Plank Rd, Baker, Louisiana 70714-5427. **T:** 1 225 775-7005
Bureau Chief: Steven Ward
DAILY NEWSPAPER

The Advocate
Editorial: 900 N 3rd St, Baton Rouge, Louisiana 70802-5236. **T:** 1 225 342-7279
Capitol Editor: Mark Ballard; **Capitol Editor:** Mark Ballard
DAILY NEWSPAPER

The Advocate
Owner: Newspapers of New England
Editorial: 124 American Legion Dr, North Adams, Massachusetts 1247.
T: 1 413 664-6900
E: news@advocateweekly.com
W: http://www.advocateweekly.com
Freq: Thu; **Circ:** 15000 Not Audited
Publisher: Robert Chapman
Editorial Profile: The Advocate is a weekly newspaper serving the residents of Berkshire County, MA, and Southern Vermont. It contains local news, arts & entertainment, community events and features. Advertising deadlines are at 4pm ET.; Full Page Mono: 11.85; Full Page Colour: 50.00
Currency: US Dollars
NEWSPAPER

The Advocate and Democrat
Owner: Jones Media, Inc.
Editorial: 609 E North St, Sweetwater, Tennessee 37874-3137. **T:** 1 423 337-7101
W: http://www.advocateanddemocrat.com
Freq: Sun; **Circ:** 14500 Not Audited
Editor: Tommy Millsaps; **Publisher:** Tommy Wilson
Editorial Profile: The Advocate and Democrat provides local news and sports coverage for the Monroe County, TN area.; Full Page Mono: 13.50
Currency: US Dollars
NEWSPAPER

The Advocate-Messenger
Owner: Schurz Communications Inc.
Editorial: 330 S 4Th St, Danville, Kentucky 40422-2033. **T:** 1 859 236-2551
W: http://www.amnews.com
Freq: Mon thru Fri; **Circ:** 11995 Not Audited
Editor: Clay Jackson; **Editor & Publisher:** Scott Schurz
Editorial Profile: The Advocate-Messenger is a local daily paper for residents in and around Danville, KY. The publication covers local news, sports and events.; Full Page Mono: 18.10; Full Page Colour: 125.47
Currency: US Dollars
DAILY NEWSPAPER

African-American News & Issues
Editorial: 6130 Wheatley St, Houston, Texas 77091-3947. **T:** 1 713 692-1892
E: sales@aframnews.com
W: http://www.aframnews.com
Freq: Mon; **Circ:** 425000 Not Audited
Editorial Profile: African-American News & Issues is a weekly African American newspaper serving Austin, San Antonio, Dallas, Galveston, Harris, Tarrant, Bexar, Jefferson, Travis, Fort Bend, Bell, Smith, McLennan, El Paso, Gregg, Bowie, Brazoria, Denton, Lubbock, Coryell, Harrison, Collin and Brazos, TX.; Full Page Mono: 69.00
Currency: US Dollars
NEWSPAPER

African-American Observer
Editorial: 483 10Th Ave Rm 325, New York, New York 10018-1177. **T:** 1 212 586-4141
Freq: Tue; **Circ:** 55000 Not Audited
Editorial Profile: The African-American Observer is a weekly newspaper written for the African-American, Caribbean and African communities in New York, NY. The advertising deadline is 5pm ET on Thursdays. Editorial submissions are due at 1pm ET on Fridays.; Full Page Mono: 59.00; Full Page Colour: 64.90
Currency: US Dollars
NEWSPAPER

Agawam Advertiser-News
Owner: Turley Publications, Inc.
Editorial: 23 Southwick St, Feeding Hills, Massachusetts 1030. **T:** 1 413 786-7747
E: aan@turley.com **W:** http://www.turley.com
Freq: Weekly; **Circ:** 12000 Not Audited
Publisher: Patrick Turley; **Editor:** Jennifer Wroblewski
NEWSPAPER

Agua Viva
Owner: Diocese of Las Cruces
Editorial: 1280 Med Park Dr, Las Cruces, New Mexico 88005-3239. **T:** 1 575 523-7577
E: aguaviva@dioceseoflascruces.org
W: http://www.dioceseoflascruces.org/agua-viva.html
Freq: Monthly; **Circ:** 13800
Editor: Christina Anchondo; **Publisher:** Óscar Cantu
Editorial Profile: Agua Viva is a monthly newspaper for the Diocese of Las Cruces, NM.; Full Page Mono: 16.00
Currency: US Dollars
NEWSPAPER

El Aguila del Hudson Valley
Owner: Maximo Publications
Editorial: 2 William St Ste 205, White Plains, New York 10601-1908. **T:** 1 914 686-2598
E: editor@elaguilanews.com
W: http://www.elaguilanews.com
Freq: Monthly; **Circ:** 30000 Not Audited
Editorial Profile: Aguila del Hudson Valley is a free montly Spanish Publication out of White Plains, NY.; Full Page Mono: 63.63
Currency: US Dollars
NEWSPAPER

Ahora
Owner: Puerto Rican Congress of New Jersey, Inc.
Editorial: 571 Saint Pauls Ave, Cliffside Park, New Jersey 07010-1712. **T:** 1 201 478-3997
E: redaccion@ahoranews.net
W: http://www.ahoranews.net
Freq: Weekly
Editor in Chief: Estella Barreto Roque
Editorial Profile: Ahora is a Spanish-language community newspaper providing International and Local News coverage to the Residents of Bergen County, NJ and New York, NY. The newspaper also covers Arts & Entertainment, Health, Sports, Business, People and Travels.
NEWSPAPER

Ahora Now Newspaper
Editorial: 601 E San Ysidro Blvd, Ste 180, San Ysidro, California 92173-3132.
T: 1 619 428-2277
E: ahoranow2008@hotmail.com
W: http://www.ahoranow.com
Freq: Thu; **Circ:** 10000 Not Audited
Editorial Profile: Ahora Now is a weekly Spanish language newspaper serving residents in San Diego. It covers local news, arts & entertainment, health and general topics of interest to the Hispanic community.; Full Page Mono: 18.00
Currency: US Dollars
NEWSPAPER

Ahora si!
Owner: Cox Media Group, Inc.
Editorial: 305 S Congress Ave, Austin, Texas 78704-1200. **T:** 1 512 912-2500
W: http://www.ahorasi.com
Freq: Thu; **Circ:** 25000 Not Audited
Publisher: George Gutierrez; **Publisher:** George Gutierrez; **Publisher:** George Gutierrez; **Editor:** Josefina Villicana Casati; **Editor:** Josefina Villicana Casati
Editorial Profile: Ahora si! is a Spanish newspaper written for the Spanish-speaking community and residents in central Texas.; Full Page Mono: 21.30
Currency: US Dollars
NEWSPAPER

Ahwatukee Foothills News
Owner: 10/13 Communications
Editorial: 10631 S 51st St, Phoenix, Arizona 85044-5225. **T:** 1 480 898-7900
E: afnnews@aztrib.com
W: http://www.ahwatukee.com
Freq: 3 Times/Week; **Circ:** 28000 Not Audited
Editorial Profile: Ahwatukee Foothills News twice weekly community newspaper geared toward the residents of the Ahwatukee Foothills in Arizona. Coverage includes community politics, crime, education, sports, travel, arts & entertainment and special interest stories.; Full Page Mono: 19.00
Currency: US Dollars
NEWSPAPER

Aiken Standard
Owner: Evening Post Publishing Co.
Editorial: 326 Rutland Dr, Aiken, South Carolina 29801-4010. **T:** 1 803 648-2311
E: editorial@aikenstandard.com
W: http://www.aikenstandard.com
Freq: Daily; **Circ:** 15759 Not Audited
News Editor: Haley Hughes; **Publisher:** Ellen Priest
Editorial Profile: Aiken Standard is a daily community newspaper published for the residents of Aiken, SC and its surrounding areas. The newspaper cover all aspects of local news, and offers national news relevant to the community.; Full Page Mono: 32.82; Full Page Colour: 46.51
Currency: US Dollars
DAILY NEWSPAPER

Akron Beacon Journal
Owner: Black Press
Editorial: 44 E Exchange St, Akron, Ohio 44328-0001. **T:** 1 330 996-3000
W: http://www.ohio.com
Freq: Daily; **Circ:** 77471 Not Audited
Publisher: Mark Cohen
Editorial Profile: Akron Beacon Journal is a morning edition newspaper written for the general public in the Akron, OH area. The Business section is featured daily, covering local and national business stories, daily stock market rates, and real estate. Articles include features, breaking news, trends, analyses, profiles and investigative stories. The publication has won the Best in Business award by the Society of American Business Editors and Writers, along with four Pulitzer Prizes. The paper does not publish a Holiday Gift Guide.; Full Page Mono: 135.04; Full Page Colour: 151.08
Currency: US Dollars
DAILY NEWSPAPER

Al Dia
Owner: A.H. Belo Corp.
Editorial: 508 Young St Fl 2, Dallas, Texas 75202-4808. **T:** 1 469 977-3600
W: http://www.aldiatx.com
Freq: Sat; **Circ:** 120000
Editor in Chief: Alfredo Carbajal; **Publisher:** Alejandro Sanchez
Editorial Profile: Al Dia is a Spanish language newspaper serving the residents of Dallas.; Full Page Mono: 42.00; Full Page Colour: 500.00
Currency: US Dollars
NEWSPAPER

Al Día
Owner: Al Dia Newspaper Inc.
Editorial: 1835 Market St Fl 4, Philadelphia, Pennsylvania 19103-2968. **T:** 1 215 569-4666
E: editor@aldianews.com
W: http://www.pontealdia.com
Freq: Sun; **Circ:** 62000 Not Audited
Editorial Profile: Al Dia is a weekly newspaper written for Spanish-speaking residents of Philadelphia and surrounding areas.; Full Page Mono: 56.00; Full Page Colour: 3820.00
Currency: US Dollars
NEWSPAPER

Al Dia en America
Owner: Donis (Jose Neil)
Editorial: 2210 Goldsmith Ln, Louisville, Kentucky 40218-1038. **T:** 1 502 451-8489
E: news@aldiaenamerica.com
W: http://www.aldiaenamerica.com
Freq: Bi-Weekly; **Circ:** 65000 Not Audited
Editorial Profile: Al Dia en America is a bi-weekly newspaper written for Latin Americans in Louisville, KY, and the surrounding areas. Contact them via e-mail.; Full Page Mono: 5.50
Currency: US Dollars
NEWSPAPER

Al-Akhbar - New York Bureau

Editorial: United Nations, Room 301, New York, New York 10017. **T:** 1 212 688-8910
Editorial Profile: This is the New York bureau of Al-Akhbar, which is based in Cairo, Egypt.
DAILY NEWSPAPER

Alameda Sun

Owner: Steller Media Group
Editorial: 3215 Encinal Ave Ste J, Alameda, California 94501-4882. **T:** 1 510 263-1471
W: http://www.alamedasun.com
Freq: Thu; **Circ:** 23000 Not Audited
Editorial Profile: Alameda Sun is a community newspaper written for the residents of Alameda, CA. It covers local news, sports, events, features, business, politics and education.; Full Page Mono: 22.00
Currency: US Dollars
NEWSPAPER

Alamogordo Daily News

Owner: Gannett Co., Inc.
Editorial: 518 24th St, Alamogordo, New Mexico 88310-6198. **T:** 1 575 437-7120
E: communitynews@alamogordonews.com
W: http://www.alamogordonews.com
Freq: Daily; **Circ:** 5611
Editorial Profile: Alamogordo Daily News is published daily for the residents of Alamogordo, NM. The newspaper covers international, national and local news, sports, business, lifestyles and entertainment Deadlines are the day before issue at 5:30pm MT.; Full Page Mono: 19.61; Full Page Colour: 129.56
Currency: US Dollars
DAILY NEWSPAPER

Albany Democrat-Herald

Owner: Lee Enterprises, Inc.
Editorial: 600 Lyon St S, Albany, Oregon 97321-2919. **T:** 1 541 926-2211
E: news@dhonline.com
W: http://www.democratherald.com
Freq: Daily; **Circ:** 12376
City Editor: Kim Jackson
Editorial Profile: Albany Democrat-Herald is published daily for the residents of Albany, OR. The newspaper covers local news, business, sports and arts & entertainment. It also covers national and statewide stories that have a direct impact on the local area. The paper switched to morning delivery seven days a week in October 2010.; Full Page Mono: 64.79; Full Page Colour: 211.50
Currency: US Dollars
DAILY NEWSPAPER

The Albany Herald

Owner: Southern Community Newspapers Inc.
Editorial: 126 N Washington St, Albany, Georgia 31701. **T:** 1 229 888-9300
E: news@albanyherald.com
W: http://www.albanyherald.com
Freq: Daily; **Circ:** 13971 Not Audited
Publisher: Michael J. Gebhart
Editorial Profile: The Albany Herald is a daily newspaper written for the residents of Albany, GA. The newspaper covers local news, event calendars, sports, religion, business, arts & entertainment and lifestyles. Deadlines are on Wednesdays at 5pm ET.; Full Page Mono: 61.81; Full Page Colour: 200.08
Currency: US Dollars
DAILY NEWSPAPER

Albany Southwest Georgian

Editorial: 311 S Jackson St, Ste A, Albany, Georgia 31701-2874. **T:** 1 229 436-2156
E: aswgeorgian@gmail.com
Freq: Wed; **Circ:** 19000 Not Audited
Editorial Profile: Albany Southwest Georgian is a weekly community newspaper written for the residents of Albany, GA.; Full Page Mono: 17.05
Currency: US Dollars
NEWSPAPER

Albert Lea Tribune

Owner: Boone Newspapers Inc.
Editorial: 808 W Front St, Albert Lea, Minnesota 56007-1947. **T:** 1 507 373-1411
E: news@albertleatribune.com
W: http://www.albertleatribune.com
Freq: Daily; **Circ:** 6630 Not Audited
Editor: Tim Engstrom; **Publisher:** Scott Schmeltzer
Editorial Profile: Albert Lea Tribune is a community newspaper that is published six days a week for residents of southern Minnesota and northern Iowa. The publication is owned by Albert Lea Tribune Inc. According to the publisher, "one of our most important goals at The Albert Lea Tribune is to put our readers in touch with their neighbors. We offer much more than just what you see online.

There are local parents' organizations trying to get their word to you about bake sales and car washes, clubs and community organizations with special programs, churches with special services, and businesses with prices and products to share."; Full Page Mono: 17.85; Full Page Colour: 110.35
Currency: US Dollars
DAILY NEWSPAPER

Albia Newspapers

Editorial: 109 Benton Ave E, Albia, Iowa 52531-2094. **T:** 1 641 932-7121
W: http://www.albianews.com **Circ:** 12400 Not Audited
NEWSPAPER

Albuquerque Journal

Owner: Journal Publishing Co.
Editorial: 7777 Jefferson St NE, Albuquerque, New Mexico 87109-4343. **T:** 1 505 823-3800
E: journal@abqjournal.com
W: http://www.abqjournal.com
Freq: Daily; **Circ:** 92868 Not Audited
Publisher & Owner: Tom Lang; **City Editor:** Charlie Moore; **City Editor:** Charlie Moore
Editorial Profile: Albuquerque Journal is New Mexico's most widely circulated daily newspaper. Coverage includes business, arts, science and technology, travel, sports, health and regional New Mexico news, as well as national news. Articles include feature and trend stories, company profiles, product announcements and reviews. The newspaper has special sections periodically throughout the year, including Mature Living, Summer Guide Journal, Indian Market Journal, Balloon Fiesta and High Country Holidays. It also has regional sections. Journal North and West Side Journal are daily sections, and the Mountain View Journal is a weekly section.; Full Page Mono: 133.70; Full Page Colour: 438.78
Currency: US Dollars
DAILY NEWSPAPER

Albuquerque Journal

Editorial: 328 Galisteo St, Santa Fe, New Mexico 87501-2606. **T:** 1 505 988-8881
E: jnorth@abqjournal.com
DAILY NEWSPAPER

Albuquerque Journal

Editorial: 345 N Water St, Las Cruces, New Mexico 88001-1220
Editorial Profile: Southern Bureau.
DAILY NEWSPAPER

Alexander City Outlook

Owner: Boone Newspapers Inc.
Editorial: 548 Cherokee Rd, Alexander City, Alabama 35010-2503. **T:** 1 256 234-4281
E: editor@alexcityoutlook.com
W: http://www.alexcityoutlook.com
Freq: Daily; **Circ:** 3445 Not Audited
News Editor: Austin Nelson
Editorial Profile: Alexander City Outlook is a local newspaper that is published six days a week; Tuesday through Sunday. The publication is written for residents of Alexander City and Tallapoosa County, AL. The publication covers local news, sports, and community events.; Full Page Mono: 13.90; Full Page Colour: 84.14
Currency: US Dollars
DAILY NEWSPAPER

Alexandria News Weekly

Editorial: 1746 Mason St, Alexandria, Louisiana 71301-6242. **T:** 1 318 443-7664
E: anwnews@bellsouth.net
Freq: Thu; **Circ:** 10000
Publisher: Leon Coleman
Editorial Profile: Alexandria News Weekly is a local community newspaper targeting African-American residents of Alexandria, LA.; Full Page Mono: 15.00
Currency: US Dollars
NEWSPAPER

Alexandria Times

Owner: Alexandria Times Publishing Co.
Editorial: 110 S Pitt St, Ste 200, Alexandria, Virginia 22314-3126. **T:** 1 703 739-0001
W: http://www.alextimes.com
Freq: Thu; **Circ:** 19311 Not Audited
Publisher: Patrice Culligan
Editorial Profile: Alexandria Times is a free, weekly newspaper serving residents of Alexandria, VA. It strives to be an alternative voice of news and information, which focuses on local government, politics, business, sports, culture, arts, lifestyle, entertainment and social issues of particular interest to the local community.; Full Page Mono: 23.44
Currency: US Dollars
NEWSPAPER

Algemeiner Journal

Editorial: 508 Montgomery St, Brooklyn, New York 11225. **T:** 1 718 771-0400
E: algemeiner@aol.com
W: http://www.algemeiner.com
Freq: Wed; **Circ:** 25000 Not Audited
Publisher: Simon Jacobson; **Editor in Chief:** Yosef Jacobson
Editorial Profile: Algemeiner Journal is a weekly newspaper intended to inform and enlighten the Jewish community. The publication was founded in 1972 and is written in Yiddish. It also includes a four-page English section.; Full Page Mono: 15.71
Currency: US Dollars
NEWSPAPER

Alianza Metropolitan News

Editorial: 1090 Lincoln Ave, Ste 8, San Jose, California 95125-3156. **T:** 1 408 272-9394
W: http://www.alianzanews.com
Freq: Bi-Weekly; **Circ:** 40000 Not Audited
Publisher: Rossana Drumond; **Editor:** Gerardo Fernández
Editorial Profile: Alianza Metropolitan News is a weekly newspaper published for the Hispanic community in San Francisco and San Jose, CA. The editorial content covers business-related information, classifieds, entertainment news, events, food, Hispanic issues, travel, local issues, politics, sports, and information for women and youth.; Full Page Mono: 24.50
Currency: US Dollars
NEWSPAPER

Alice Newspapers, Inc.

Owner: American Consolidated Media
Editorial: 405 E Main St, Alice, Texas 78332-4968. **T:** 1 361 664-6588
E: newsclerk@aliceechonews.com
W: http://www.alicetx.com
Freq: Fri
News Clerk: Marisol Marquez; **Publisher:** Michael Murray; Full Page Mono: 13.00; Full Page Colour: 71.23
Currency: US Dollars
NEWSPAPER

Allen Publishing

Owner: Allen Publishing Company LLC
Editorial: 2570 FM 407, Suite 204, Highland Village, Texas 75077-3094. **T:** 1 972 966-0631
E: allenpublishing@gmail.com
W: http://allenpub.com
Editorial Profile: Allen Publishing is a community newspaper publisher based in Highland Village, TX, and produces four monthly community newspapers serving the Denton County, TX area: The Flower Mound (TX) Connection, The Highland Village (TX) Connection, Lantana (TX) Living, and The Copper Canyon/Double Oak (TX) Connection.
NEWSPAPER

Alliance Publishing Company

Owner: Alliance Publishing Company
Editorial: 177 Curry St, Minerva, Ohio 44657. **T:** 1 330 868-5222 **Circ:** 6600 Not Audited
Publisher: G. Charles Dix; **Editor:** Kimberly Lewis; **Editor:** Kimberly Lewis; **Editor:** Kimberly Lewis; **Editor:** Kimberly Lewis; **Editor:** Karen Mundy
NEWSPAPER

Alliance Regional Newspapers

Owner: McClatchy Newspapers
Editorial: 1103 Keller Pkwy, Ste 101, Keller, Texas .76248. **T:** 1 817 431-2231 **Circ:** 60300 Not Audited
Editor: Alice Murray; **Publisher:** Gary Wortel
Editorial Profile: Alliance Regional Newspapers in Keller, TX is a publisher of community newspapers, including the Colleyville (TX) Courier, Keller Citizen, Grapevine (TX) Courier, Southlake (TX) Journal and The Times Register in Keller, TX.
NEWSPAPER

The Alliance Review

Owner: Alliance Publishing Company
Editorial: 40 S Linden Ave, Alliance, Ohio 44601-2447. **T:** 1 330 821-1200
E: reviewedit@the-review.com
W: http://www.the-review.com
Freq: Daily; **Circ:** 13200 Not Audited
Publisher: G. Charles Dix
Editorial Profile: This paper covers local news from Alliance, OH and surrounding counties.; Full Page Mono: 16.95; Full Page Colour: 370.00
Currency: US Dollars
DAILY NEWSPAPER

Alliance Times-Herald

Owner: Alliance Publishing Company
Editorial: 114 E 4th St, Alliance, Nebraska 69301. **T:** 1 308 762-3060

E: athnews@alliancetimes.com
W: http://www.alliancetimes.com
Freq: Daily; **Circ:** 3125 Not Audited
City Editor: Mark Dykes; **Publisher:** Fred Kuhlman
Editorial Profile: Alliance Times-Herald is published daily for the residents of Alliance, NE and surrounding communities. Coverage includes local news, sports, arts & entertainment, farm news, lifestyles and community events.; Full Page Mono: 9.25; Full Page Colour: 30.75
Currency: US Dollars
DAILY NEWSPAPER

Allied News

Owner: Community Newspaper Holdings, Inc.
Editorial: 201 Erie St, Ste A, Grove City, Pennsylvania 16127. **T:** 1 724 458-5010
E: news@alliednews.com
W: http://alliednews.com
Freq: Sat; **Circ:** 15000 Not Audited
Editor: Kim Curry; **Editor:** Stephanie Hartle; **Publisher:** Sharon Sorg
Editorial Profile: Allied News is written for residents in the Grove City, PA area. It focuses on news that affects county residents, including business and educational news, sports, entertainment and life-event news.; Full Page Mono: 16.91; Full Page Colour: 1854.00
Currency: US Dollars
NEWSPAPER

The Almanac

Owner: Embarcadero Publishing Co.
Editorial: 3525 Alameda De Las Pulgas, Menlo Park, California 94025. **T:** 1 650 854-2626
E: editor@almanacnews.com
W: http://www.almanacnews.com
Freq: Wed; **Circ:** 18000 Not Audited
News Editor: Renee Batti; **Editor:** Richard Hine
Editorial Profile: The Almanac is published weekly for the San Francisco peninsula communities of Menlo Park, Atherton, Portola Valley, Woodside, Ladera, Los Trancos Woods, Sharon Heights, Stanford Hills and southern San Mateo County, CA. The newspaper covers local news, sports, lifestyle, business, arts & entertainment and community events. The news deadline falls on Thursday, the week prior to publication.; Full Page Mono: 21.00; Full Page Colour: 400.00
Currency: US Dollars
NEWSPAPER

The Almanac

Owner: Observer Publishing Company
Editorial: 395 Valleybrook Rd, Ste 2, McMurray, Pennsylvania 15317-3345.
T: 1 724 941-7725 **E:** aanews@thealmanac.net
W: http://www.thealmanac.net
Freq: Wed; **Circ:** 50000 Not Audited
Editorial Profile: The Almanac is published weekly for the residents of Washington County, PA. The newspaper covers local news, sports, education, crime and community events. News deadlines are on Fridays at 5pm ET.; Full Page Mono: 33.06
Currency: US Dollars
NEWSPAPER

The Alpena News

Owner: Ogden Newspapers
Editorial: 130 Park Pl, Alpena, Michigan 49707-2889. **T:** 1 989 354-3111
E: newsroom@thealpenanews.com
W: http://www.thealpenanews.com
Freq: Mon thru Fri; **Circ:** 7616 Not Audited
Editor: Steve Murch; **Editor:** Steve Murch; **Publisher:** Bill Speer
Editorial Profile: The Alpena News is written for the residents of Northeastern Michigan. Since 1899, the paper has played a significant role in reporting on the history and growth of the Northeastern Michigan region. It contains in-depth stories and telling photographs of both the tragedies and the triumphs of the area's people and industries. The majority of the content focuses on local and national news, local sports, lifestyle and entertainment. The Alpena News also contains classified and obituary sections. There are also special sections on certain days. Each Monday there is a special grocery section. On Thursdays there are special entertainment and real estate/business sections. A special entertainment section is run on Fridays as well. Finally, Saturday is the weekend edition filled with special outdoor, health and religion sections.; Full Page Mono: 22.40; Full Page Colour: 148.96
Currency: US Dollars
DAILY NEWSPAPER

Altamont News/Banner, Inc.

Owner: Better Newspapers Inc.
Editorial: 111 N Main St, Altamont, Illinois 62411-1447. **T:** 1 618 483-6176

E: news@altnewsban.com
Freq: Wed; **Circ:** 2000 Not Audited
Editor: Clyde Barr; **Publisher:** Greg Hoskins; Full Page Mono: 8.00
Currency: US Dollars
NEWSPAPER

Altoona Mirror
Owner: Ogden Newspapers
Editorial: 301 Cayuga Ave, Altoona, Pennsylvania 16602. **T:** 1 814 946-7411
E: news@altoonamirror.com
W: http://www.altoonamirror.com
Freq: Daily; **Circ:** 23159 Not Audited
Editor: John Cavrich; **Publisher:** Ed Kruger; **City Editor:** Margaret Moses
Editorial Profile: Altoona Mirror is a daily newspaper published for the residents of Altoona, PA and surrounding areas. It provides local news and information.; Full Page Mono: 55.49; Full Page Colour: 71.07
Currency: US Dollars
DAILY NEWSPAPER

The Altus Times
Owner: Heartland Publications
Editorial: 218 W Commerce St, Altus, Oklahoma 73521-3895. **T:** 1 580 482-1221
W: http://www.altustimes.com
Freq: Daily; **Circ:** 4400 Not Audited
Publisher: Dan Taylor
Editorial Profile: The Altus Times is a daily, local newspaper serving residents of the Altus, OK area. It covers local and national news, lifestyle, features, entertainment and sports information.; Full Page Mono: 9.70; Full Page Colour: 252.00
Currency: US Dollars
DAILY NEWSPAPER

Alva Review-Courier
Owner: Martin Broadcasting Corporation
Editorial: 620 Choctaw St, Alva, Oklahoma 73717-1626. **T:** 1 580 327-2200
E: news@alvareviewcourier.net
W: http://www.alvareviewcourier.com
Freq: Daily; **Circ:** 2300 Not Audited
News Editor: Helen Barrett; **Publisher:** Lynn Martin; **Editor:** Marione Martin
Editorial Profile: Alva Review-Courier is a local daily newspaper serving residents in the Woods County, OK area. The paper is published everyday except Wednesday and Saturday. On Wednesday a free newspaper called the NewsGram is distributed in a three-county area. Advertising deadlines are at noon the day before publication.; Full Page Mono: 5.20; Full Page Colour: 150.00
Currency: US Dollars
DAILY NEWSPAPER

Alvin Sun & Advertiser Newspapers
Owner: Hartman Newspapers, Inc.
Editorial: 570 Dula St, Alvin, Texas 77511. **T:** 1 281 331-4422 **E:** alvinsun@swbell.net
W: http://www.alvinsun.net **Circ:** 30000
Editor: Steve Collins
Editorial Profile: Alvin Sun & Advertiser Newspapers is a community newspaper publisher serving the residents of Houston, as well as Baytown and Sugar Land, TX.
NEWSPAPER

Al-Watan
Editorial: 800 S Brookhurst St, Ste 3G, Anaheim, California 92804-4301.
T: 1 714 502-9908 **E:** editor@watan.com
W: http://www.watan.com
Freq: Fri; **Circ:** 35000 Not Audited; Full Page Mono: 35.00
Currency: US Dollars
NEWSPAPER

am New York
Owner: Cablevision Systems Corp.
Editorial: 240 W 35th St Fl 9, New York, New York 10001-2506. **T:** 1 646 293-9499
W: http://www.amny.com
Freq: Mon thru Fri; **Circ:** 325469 Not Audited
Publisher: Valerie Green; **News Editor:** Robert Levin
Editorial Profile: Touted as "boiled down, high energy and to the point", am New York is a free commuter daily newspaper aimed at readers aged 18 to 35. The paper's regular features include an opinion page, a daily column and political cartoon. It also has weekend, entertainment and sports sections, classifieds and TV listings. It is designed to be read in 20 minutes, and gives those who normally don't read newspapers a quick update on New York City and their world.; Full Page Mono: 327.50; Full Page Colour: 360.25
Currency: US Dollars
DAILY NEWSPAPER

Amarillo Globe-News
Owner: Morris Communications
Editorial: 900 S Harrison St, Amarillo, Texas 79101. **T:** 1 806 376-4488
E: citydesk@amarillo.com
W: http://amarillo.com
Freq: Daily; **Circ:** 29948 Not Audited
News Night Editor: Matthew Hutchison; **Publisher:** Lester Simpson
Editorial Profile: Amarillo Globe-News is a local daily newspaper published for the residents of Amarillo, TX and surrounding communities. The newspaper covers local, national, and international news, including politics, lifestyle, sports, entertainment, business and economics. The Amarillo Daily News and the Amarillo News & Globe-Times were both combined to create the Amarillo Globe-News.; Full Page Mono: 56.49; Full Page Colour: 629.00
Currency: US Dollars
DAILY NEWSPAPER

The Amelia Bulletin Monitor
Owner: ABM Enterprises, Inc.
Editorial: 16311 Goodes Bridge Rd, Amelia Court House, Virginia 23002.
T: 1 804 561-3655
E: contactus@ameliamonitor.com
W: http://www.ameliamonitor.com
Freq: Thu; **Circ:** 10500 Not Audited
Editor: Wayne Russell; **Publisher:** Ann Salster
Editorial Profile: The Amelia Bulletin Monitor is a weekly newspaper which covers local news and events occurring in the Amelia County area. The newspaper has been serving the citizens of Amelia County and surrounding areas since 1973 with news, commentary and advertising.; Full Page Mono: 8.25
Currency: US Dollars
NEWSPAPER

America Oggi
Owner: Gruppo Editoriale Oggi, Inc.
Editorial: 475 Walnut St, Norwood, New Jersey 07648-1318. **T:** 1 212 268-0250
E: americoggi@aol.com
W: http://www.americaoggi.info
Freq: Daily; **Circ:** 40000 Not Audited
Publisher & Editor: Andrea Mantineo
Editorial Profile: America Oggi is a weekly newspaper published for Italian communities in the tri-state area around New York City. The publication covers state and national news, entertainment, features and sports. It does not cover local news.; Full Page Mono: 25.00
Currency: US Dollars
DAILY NEWSPAPER

American Free Press
Editorial: 645 Pennsylvania Ave SE Ste 100, Washington, District Of Columbia 20003-4379.
T: 1 202 544-5977
E: editor@americanfreepress.net
W: http://www.americanfreepress.net
Freq: Mon; **Circ:** 39000 Not Audited
Editorial Profile: American Free Press is a weekly community newspaper written for residents of Washington, D.C. It covers local and national news. Contact the newspaper via online form.; Full Page Mono: 17.84
Currency: US Dollars
NEWSPAPER

The American News
Owner: Don Roberto Group, Inc.
Editorial: 14240 Saint Andrews Dr, Ste 201, Victorville, California 92395-4308.
T: 1 909 889-7677
E: samerisam1@earthlink.net
W: http://www.sbamerican.com
Freq: Thu; **Circ:** 10000 Not Audited
Editorial Profile: The American News is written for the residents of San Bernardino, CA. The newspaper covers minority issues and local news.; Full Page Mono: 17.85
Currency: US Dollars
NEWSPAPER

American Press
Owner: Shearman Newspapers
Editorial: 4900 Highway 90 E, Lake Charles, Louisiana 70615-4037. **T:** 1 337 433-3000
E: news@americanpress.com
W: http://www.americanpress.com
Freq: Daily; **Circ:** 25686 Not Audited
Publisher: Thomas Shearman
Editorial Profile: American Press is a daily newspaper written for residents of the Lake Charles, LA area. The newspaper covers local news, weather, sports, and community events. Feature articles cover entertainment, lifestyle, business, finance, travel and leisure, and health.; Full Page Mono: 35.00; Full Page Colour: 47.91
Currency: US Dollars
DAILY NEWSPAPER

Las Americas Newspaper
Editorial: 5811 Arnet St, Falls Church, Virginia 22041. **T:** 1 703 256-4200
E: lasamericasnewspaper@yahoo.com
W: http://www.lasamericasnews.com
Freq: Fri; **Circ:** 25000 Not Audited
Publisher: Fernando Alvarez; **Editor:** Abraham Ustariz
Editorial Profile: Las Americas Newspaper is a weekly Spanish-language newspaper covering local, national and Latino news and serving readers in Virginia, Maryland and Washington, D.C. Deadlines fall on Mondays at 5pm ET.; Full Page Mono: 20.00
Currency: US Dollars
NEWSPAPER

The Americus Sumter Observer
Editorial: 217 Forrest St, Americus, Georgia 31709-3943. **T:** 1 229 924-0880
E: obsvrj@bellsouth.net
W: http://www.americusumterobserver.com
Freq: Monthly; **Circ:** 20000
Publisher: John Marshall
Editorial Profile: The Americus Sumter Observer is an African American monthly community newspaper written for the residents of Americus, GA. Covers general community news, national and world events, features, entertainment, sports and business.
NEWSPAPER

Amherst Bulletin
Owner: Newspapers of New England
Editorial: 9 E Pleasant St, Amherst, Massachusetts 1002. **T:** 1 413 549-2000
E: amherst@gazettenet.com
W: http://www.gazettenet.com
Freq: Fri; **Circ:** 14000 Not Audited
Publisher: Jim Foudy; **Editor:** Debra Scherban
Editorial Profile: Amherst Bulletin is a weekly newspaper which brings readers in the Amherst, MA area local and national news. Other features include editorials, letters to the editor, classifieds, real estate, employment opportunities and community events. Do not send ANY information via fax. Deadlines are Monday morning.; Full Page Mono: 16.61
Currency: US Dollars
NEWSPAPER

Amherst-Nelson Publishing Company
Owner: BH Media Group
Editorial: 134 2Nd St, Amherst, Virginia 24521-2710. **T:** 1 434 946-7195 **Circ:** 7986 Not Audited
Publisher: Dean Smith
NEWSPAPER

Amigo Publications
Editorial: 1502 Avenue M, Lubbock, Texas 79401. **T:** 1 806 763-3841
E: eleditor@sbcglobal.net
W: http://www.eleditor.com **Circ:** 29800
Editorial Profile: Amigo Publications is a local publication providing news to the community of Lubbock, TX.
NEWSPAPER

Anadarko Daily News
Owner: Anadarko Publishing Company (The)
Editorial: 117 E Broadway St, Anadarko, Oklahoma 73005. **T:** 1 405 247-3331
E: news@anadarko-news.com
Freq: Daily; **Circ:** 4207 Not Audited
Editorial Profile: Anadarko Daily News provides readers in the community with local, state and nationwide news coverage. Other features include sports, entertainment, classifieds, community events, politics, education, and health-related news. The advertising deadline is 10am CT.; Full Page Mono: 7.50; Full Page Colour: 58.50
Currency: US Dollars
DAILY NEWSPAPER

The Anchor
Editorial: 887 Highland Ave, Fall River, Massachusetts 2720. **T:** 1 508 675-7151
E: theanchor@anchornews.org
W: http://www.anchornews.org
Freq: Fri; **Circ:** 28000 Not Audited
Publisher: George Coleman; **Editor:** Dave Jolivet
Editorial Profile: The Anchor is a weekly community newspaper serving the Catholic residents of Fall River, MA and surrounding areas.; Full Page Mono: 17.50
Currency: US Dollars
NEWSPAPER

Anchorage Daily News
Owner: Alaska Dispatch Publishing LLC
Editorial: 1001 Northway Dr, Anchorage, Alaska 99508-2025. **T:** 1 907 257-4200
E: newstips@adn.com
W: http://www.adn.com
Freq: Daily; **Circ:** 51266 Not Audited
Publisher: Patrick Doyle
Editorial Profile: Alaska Dispatch News provides local, national, and international news to readers in and around Anchorage, AK. It was first published as a weekly newspaper in 1946. It became a daily publication in 1948 and provided Alaska's first Sunday paper on June 13, 1965. Since then, the newspaper has expanded its services by becoming a member of the Associated Press and the Los Angeles Times/Washington Post News Service.; Full Page Mono: 121.60; Full Page Colour: 399.20
Currency: US Dollars
DAILY NEWSPAPER

The Anchorage Press
Owner: Wick Communications Inc.
Editorial: 540 E 5th Ave, Anchorage, Alaska 99501. **T:** 1 907 561-7737
E: contact@anchoragepress.com
W: http://www.anchoragepress.com
Freq: Thu; **Circ:** 20000 Not Audited
Publisher: Steve Abeln; **Editor:** Victoria Barber
Editorial Profile: The Anchorage Press is a weekly newspaper written for residents of Anchorage, AK.; Full Page Mono: 22.00
Currency: US Dollars
NEWSPAPER

Andalusia Star News
Owner: Boone Newspapers Inc.
Editorial: 207 Dunson St, Andalusia, Alabama 36420-3705. **T:** 1 334 222-2402
E: editor@andalusiastarnews.com
W: http://www.andalusiastarnews.com
Freq: Daily; **Circ:** 3400 Not Audited
News Editor: Stephanie Nelson
Editorial Profile: The Andalusia Star-News is published daily with the exception of Sunday, Monday and Christmas and New Year's Day by Andalusia Newspapers Inc. The newspaper focuses on local city and statewide news coverage, while sometimes even covering national news. Other features include sports, entertainment, lifestyle, health and classifieds.; Full Page Mono: 9.80; Full Page Colour: 72.21
Currency: US Dollars
DAILY NEWSPAPER

Anderson Independent-Mail
Owner: E.W. Scripps Co.
Editorial: 1000 Williamston Rd, Anderson, South Carolina 29621-6500.
T: 1 864 224-4321
E: newsroom@independentmail.com
W: http://www.independentmail.com
Freq: Daily; **Circ:** 24169 Not Audited
Editor: John Huff; **Publisher:** Susan Kelly-Gilbert; **City Editor:** David Williams; **Content Editor:** Kylie Yerka
Editorial Profile: Anderson Independent-Mail reaches readers in the Anderson County, Oconee County, Pickens County, SC, and the Northeastern Georgia. Coverage includes local, national and international news, sports, lifestyle, business, editorials, weather, community events and obituaries. The paper does not publish a Holiday Gift Guide.; Full Page Mono: 59.85; Full Page Colour: 289.59
Currency: US Dollars
DAILY NEWSPAPER

Anderson Publications
Editorial: 210 W Main St, Canistota, South Dakota 57012. **T:** 1 605 296-3181
E: news@andersonpublications.com
Circ: 2385 Not Audited
NEWSPAPER

Andrews Gazette
Owner: Comprint Military Publications
Editorial: 9030 Comprint Ct, Gaithersburg, Maryland 20877-1307. **T:** 1 202 433-9714
W: http://www.dcmilitary.com/section/news09
Freq: Fri; **Circ:** 15000
Editor: Andrea Blackstone; **Publisher:** John Rives
Editorial Profile: Andrews Gazette is a weekly community newspaper serving Andrews Air Force Base, including local news and entertainment, with features on military life.; Full Page Mono: 19.93; Full Page Colour: 24.18
Currency: US Dollars
NEWSPAPER

Andy Anderson Corporation
Editorial: 314 S Main St, Hartford, Kentucky 42347-1129. **T:** 1 270 298-7100 **Circ:** 15200 Not Audited
Publisher: Andy Anderson; **Editor:** Rita Dukes
NEWSPAPER

Anishinaabeg Today
Owner: White Earth Reservation Tribal Council

Editorial: 3550 Eagle View Rd, Ogema, Minnesota 56569. **T:** 1 218 983-4640 5903
E: today@whiteearth.com
W: http://www.whiteearth.com
Freq: Monthly; **Circ:** 12750 Not Audited
Editorial Profile: Anishinaabeg Today is a monthly newspaper serving the community of White Earth Indian Reservation Tribal Council in Omega, MN.; Full Page Mono: 6.00
Currency: US Dollars
NEWSPAPER

Ankeny Press-Citizen
Owner: Shopper-News Network
Editorial: 121 SW 3rd St, Ankeny, Iowa 50023-3112. **T:** 1 515 964-0639
E: news@presscitizen-shopper.com
W: http://www.desmoinesregister.com/section/COMM01
Freq: Tue; **Circ:** 22000 Not Audited
Publisher: Amy Duncan
Editorial Profile: Ankeny Press-Citizen is a free, weekly newspaper serving the residents of Ankeny, IA. Coverage includes local news, sports, community events and arts & entertainment. The news and advertising deadlines fall on Thursdays at noon CT.; Full Page Mono: 11.20; Full Page Colour: 16.25
Currency: US Dollars
NEWSPAPER

The Ann Arbor News
Owner: AnnArbor.com LLC
Editorial: 301 E Liberty St Ste 700, Ann Arbor, Michigan 48104-2283. **T:** 1 734 623-2500
E: news@annarbor.com
W: http://www.annarbor.com
Freq: 2 Times/Week; **Circ:** 25396
Publisher: Laurel Champion; **Editor:** Paula Gardner
Editorial Profile: Ann Arbor News was established in July 2009 for residents and visitors of Ann Arbor, Mich., and features news and information from the area. Editorial content focuses on government, education, crime, business, health care, the environment and more. Part of MLive Media Group.
NEWSPAPER

Anna Maria Island Sun
Editorial: 9801 Gulf Dr, Suite 6, Anna Maria, Florida 34216. **T:** 1 941 778-3986
E: amisun@tampabay.rr.com
W: http://www.amisun.com
Freq: Wed; **Circ:** 15000 Not Audited
Editorial Profile: Anna Maria Island Sun is published weekly for the residents of Anna Maria, FL. Coverage includes local news, business news, sports and community events. The news deadline falls on Wednesdays.; Full Page Mono: 10.90
Currency: US Dollars
NEWSPAPER

An-Nahar - New York Bureau
Editorial: 405 E 42nd St, Rm L250A, New York, New York 10017-3507.
T: 1 917 365-0942
Bureau Chief: Ali Barada
Editorial Profile: This is the New York bureau of An-Nehar in Beirut, Lebanon.
DAILY NEWSPAPER

Anniston Star
Owner: Consolidated Publishing
Editorial: 4305 Mcclellan Blvd, Anniston, Alabama 36206-2812. **T:** 1 256 236-1551
E: news@annistonstar.com
W: http://www.annistonstar.com
Freq: Daily; **Circ:** 16043 Not Audited
Publisher: H. Brandt Ayers; **Editor:** Bob Davis
Editorial Profile: Anniston Star is a daily newspaper serving Anniston, AL and surrounding Calhoun County. The publication covers local and statewide news, business, entertainment, lifestyle and sports. The papers Monday edition is call jumpStart.; Full Page Mono: 42.00; Full Page Colour: 475.00
Currency: US Dollars
DAILY NEWSPAPER

Antelope Valley Press
Owner: Markham (William)
Editorial: 37404 Sierra Hwy, Palmdale, California 93550-9343. **T:** 1 661 273-2700
E: editor@avpress.com
W: http://www.avpress.com
Freq: Daily; **Circ:** 19000 Not Audited
Editor in Chief: Dennis Anderson; **Editor in Chief:** Dennis Anderson; **Publisher:** William Markham; **City Editor:** John Wise; **City Editor:** John Wise; **News Editor:** William Wu
Editorial Profile: Antelope Valley Press is a local daily newspaper written for residents of North Los Angeles County and Southeastern Kern County, in Southern California. The paper covers local and national news, sports and religion.; Full Page Mono: 68.84; Full Page Colour: 219.89
Currency: US Dollars
DAILY NEWSPAPER

Antigo Daily Journal
Owner: Berner Bros. Publishing Co., Inc.
Editorial: 612 Superior St, Antigo, Wisconsin 54409. **T:** 1 715 623-4191 **E:** adj@dwave.net
W: http://www.antigodailyjournal.com
Freq: Daily; **Circ:** 6382 Not Audited
Editor: Fred Berner; **News Editor:** Lisa Haefs
Editorial Profile: Antigo Daily Journal is a the local newspaper for the Antigo, WI area. This daily newspaper covers local news and sports stories as well as important statewide and national stories that have an impact of their community.; Full Page Mono: 5.48; Full Page Colour: 210.00
Currency: US Dollars
DAILY NEWSPAPER

Anton Community Newspapers
Owner: Anton Community Newspapers
Editorial: 132 E 2nd St, Mineola, New York 11501-3522. **T:** 1 516 747-8282
E: editorial@antonnews.com
W: http://www.antonnews.com **Circ:** 52029 Not Audited
Publisher: Angela Anton; **Editor:** Dave De Rubio; **Editor:** Rich Forestano; **Editor:** Karen Gellender; **Editor:** Pat Grace; **Editor:** Christy Hinko; **Editor:** Wendy Kreitzman; **Editor:** Jill Nossa; **Editor in Chief:** John Owens; **Editor:** Katie Piacentini; **Editor:** Ron Scaglia; **Editor:** Joseph Scotchie; **Publisher:** Joseph Scotchie; **Editor:** Joseph Scotchie
Editorial Profile: Anton Community Newspapers in Mineola, NY is a publisher of community newspapers.
NEWSPAPER

Apache Junction News
Owner: Foothills Publishing
Editorial: 115 N Apache Trl, Apache Junction, Arizona 85220. **T:** 1 480 982-6397
E: ajnews@ajnews.com
W: http://www.ajnews.com
Freq: Mon; **Circ:** 24500 Not Audited
Editorial Profile: Apache Junction News is published weekly for the residents of Apache Junction, AZ. Coverage includes local news, sports, arts & entertainment and community events. Deadlines are on Thursdays at 5pm MT.; Full Page Mono: 20.60
Currency: US Dollars
NEWSPAPER

Appalachian News-Express
Editorial: 129 Caroline Ave, Pikeville, Kentucky 41501-1101. **T:** 1 606 437-4054
E: news@news-expressky.com
W: http://www.news-expressky.com
Freq: Fri; **Circ:** 10500
Publisher: Jeff Vanderbeck
Editorial Profile: Appalachian News-Express is a local newspaper serving residents of eastern Kentucky. It covers news, sports, editorials, businesses, events and features of interest to residents of eastern Kentucky.; Full Page Mono: 9.95
Currency: US Dollars
NEWSPAPER

Appeal-Democrat
Owner: Freedom Communications Inc.
Editorial: 1530 Ellis Lake Dr, Marysville, California 95901-4269. **T:** 1 530 741-2345
E: adnewsroom@appealdemocrat.com
W: http://www.appeal-democrat.com
Freq: Daily; **Circ:** 20428 Not Audited
News Editor: Andrew Cummins; **Editor:** Steve Miller; **Publisher:** Glenn Stifflemire
Editorial Profile: Appeal-Democrat is a local daily newspaper covering news, weather, sports, events, arts & entertainment and education for the residents of Yuba City and Northern California.; Full Page Mono: 27.00; Full Page Colour: 179.57
Currency: US Dollars
DAILY NEWSPAPER

Appen Newspapers
Owner: Appen Newspapers, Inc.
Editorial: 319 N Main St, Alpharetta, Georgia 30004. **T:** 1 770 442-3278
E: news@northfulton.com
W: http://www.appeninc.com **Circ:** 84000 Not Audited
Publisher: Ray Appen
Editorial Profile: Appen Media Group is a community newspaper publisher serving North Fulton and Forsyth, GA counties. Its weekly publications include: Johns Creek Herald; Forsyth Herald; the Revue & News; and the Milton Herald.
NEWSPAPER

The Arab American News
Editorial: 5706 Chase Rd, Dearborn, Michigan 48126. **T:** 1 313 582-4888
E: info@arabamericannews.com
W: http://www.arabamericannews.com
Freq: Sat; **Circ:** 35000 Not Audited
Editorial Profile: Bilingual Arab and English newspaper offering an Arab perspective on American, Arab and international news.; Full Page Mono: 24.38
Currency: US Dollars
NEWSPAPER

Arab Voice
Owner: Arab Voice Inc.
Editorial: 85-99 Hazel St, Paterson, New Jersey 07503-2462. **T:** 1 973 523-7815
W: http://www.arabvoice.com
Freq: Sat; **Circ:** 35000 Not Audited
Editorial Profile: Arab Voice in Paterson, NJ, is a weekly newspaper that serves Arab-Americans in five states.; Full Page Mono: 9.00
Currency: US Dollars
NEWSPAPER

The Arab World
Editorial: 512 S Brookhurst St Ste 4, Anaheim, California 92804-2448.
T: 1 714 758-3507 **E:** lanamanale@aol.com
W: http://www.awnews.net
Freq: Fri; **Circ:** 45000 Not Audited
Publisher: Ahmed Alam; **Editor:** Riad Saeid
Editorial Profile: The Arab World in Anaheim, CA is a weekly newspaper written for Arabic-speaking residents and covers local news and events.; Full Page Mono: 10.00
Currency: US Dollars
NEWSPAPER

Aramica
Editorial: 4222 Hylan Blvd, Staten Island, New York 10308-3360. **T:** 1 718 921-4788
E: info@aramica.com
W: http://www.aramica.com
Freq: Bi-Weekly; **Circ:** 30000 Not Audited
Editor: Dagney Taggart
Editorial Profile: Aramica is the leading bilingual, non-partisan and non-denominational Arab American newspaper on the East Coast.; Full Page Mono: 11.00
Currency: US Dollars
NEWSPAPER

Arcadia News
Owner: Shark Publications LLC
Editorial: 3850 E Indian School Rd, Ste 1, Phoenix, Arizona 85018-5242.
T: 1 602 840-6379
W: http://www.arcadiadaily.com
Freq: Monthly; **Circ:** 20000 Not Audited
Publisher: Greg Bruns
Editorial Profile: Arcadia News is published monthly for residents of the Arcadia, AZ. It is available free of charge at authorized distributors.; Full Page Mono: 72.50
Currency: US Dollars
NEWSPAPER

The Arcadian
Editorial: 108 S Polk Ave, Arcadia, Florida 34266-3952. **T:** 1 863 494-7600
E: arcadian.editor@gmail.com
W: http://www.yoursun.net
Freq: Daily; **Circ:** 3000 Not Audited
Publisher: David Dunn-Rankin; **Editor:** Susan Hoffman
Editorial Profile: The Arcadian Sun is a local daily newspaper written for the residents of Arcadia, FL.; Full Page Mono: 11.00
Currency: US Dollars
DAILY NEWSPAPER

Arctic Warrior
Editorial: 10480 22nd St., Elmendorf AFB, Alaska 99506. **T:** 1 907 552-8918
W: http://www.jber.af.mil/
Freq: Weekly; **Circ:** 14000
Editor: David Bedard
Editorial Profile: Weekly paper printed in the interest of families within Joint Base Elmendorf-Richardson (JBER) community near Anchorage, Alaska.
NEWSPAPER

Area News Group Papers
Owner: Area News Group Papers
Editorial: 17 Executive Dr Ste 1, Hudson, New Hampshire 03051-4903. **T:** 1 603 880-1516
E: news@areanewsgroup.com
W: http://areanewsgroup.com **Circ:** 37500 Not Audited
Publisher: Leonard Lathrop; **Publisher:** Leonard Lathrop; **Publisher:** Leonard Lathrop
Editorial Profile: Area News Group Papers publishes the Hudson-Litchfield News, the Pelham-Winham News and the Salem Community Patriot for Hudson, NH and the surrounding communities.
NEWSPAPER

Areawide Media
Owner: Rust Communications
Editorial: 388 Highway 62 W, Salem, Arkansas 72576. **T:** 1 870 895-3207
E: news@areawidenews.com
W: http://www.areawidenews.com **Circ:** 24900
Publisher: Janie Flynn; **Editor:** Erma Harris
Editorial Profile: Areawide Media is a community newspaper publisher servicing the residents of Springfield, MO.
NEWSPAPER

The Argonaut
Owner: Southland Publishing, Inc.
Editorial: 5355 McConnell Ave, Los Angeles, California 90066-7025. **T:** 1 310 822-1629
W: http://www.argonautnews.com
Freq: Thu; **Circ:** 30000 Not Audited
Publisher: David Comden; **Editor:** Joe Piasecki
Editorial Profile: The Argonaut is published weekly for residents of Marina del Rey, Playa del Rey, Westchester, Venice and Santa Monica, CA. The newspaper covers local news, weather, sports and community events. Feature articles cover business, education, arts & entertainment and lifestyle.; Full Page Mono: 26.25
Currency: US Dollars
NEWSPAPER

The Argus
Owner: MediaNews Group
Editorial: 37468 Fremont Blvd, Fremont, California 94536-3705. **T:** 1 510 353-7027
W: http://www.insidebayarea.com/argus
Freq: Daily; **Circ:** 26749 Not Audited
Editorial Profile: The Argus is written for the residents of Fremont, Union City and Newark, CA. It covers local news, events, weather and sports. It also offers features reports on education, living, entertainment and business. The paper is a part of the Bay Area News Group subsidiary of MediaNews Group.; Full Page Mono: 125.00; Full Page Colour: 727.79
Currency: US Dollars
DAILY NEWSPAPER

Argus Leader
Owner: Gannett Co., Inc.
Editorial: 200 S Minnesota Ave, Sioux Falls, South Dakota 57104-6314. **T:** 1 605 331-2200
E: editor@argusleader.com
W: http://www.argusleader.com
Freq: Daily; **Circ:** 35191 Not Audited
Publisher: Randell Beck; **City Editor:** Jim Helland
Editorial Profile: Argus Leader in Sioux Falls, SD aims to "provide reliable, fair and accurate news coverage in response to the changing interests and needs of our readers." The newspaper's readers are residents of Sioux Falls, SD and the surrounding area. They do not publish a holiday gift guide.; Full Page Mono: 73.55; Full Page Colour: 544.40
Currency: US Dollars
DAILY NEWSPAPER

Argus Observer
Owner: Wick Communications Inc.
Editorial: 1160 SW 4th St, Ontario, Oregon 97914-4365. **T:** 1 541 889-5387
E: editor@argusobserver.com
W: http://www.argusobserver.com
Freq: Daily; **Circ:** 5582 Not Audited
Publisher: John Dillon
Editorial Profile: Argus Observer is a daily news publication written for local residents of Ontario, OR. The newspaper covers local news, events, sports, and politics. As of April 1998, the Acreage Magazine was implemented into the Argus Observer as the Farming section, printed every other Monday. Deadline for the Farming section is one week before issue date. There are four editorial editions for the Argus Observer: Travel, Car Care, and Home and Garden publish in the spring and winter; and a Farm Edition publishes in the summer.; Full Page Mono: 13.00; Full Page Colour: 79.37
Currency: US Dollars
DAILY NEWSPAPER

The Argus-Press
Owner: Argus-Press Company (The)
Editorial: 201 E Exchange St, Owosso, Michigan 48867-3094. **T:** 1 989 725-5136
E: news@argus-press.com
W: http://www.argus-press.com
Freq: Daily; **Circ:** 10736 Not Audited
Publisher: Tom Campbell
Editorial Profile: The Argus-Press is a local newspaper that serves the Owosso, MI area and targets residents and businesses of

Shiawassee County. It provides community residents with information on local news, events, weather and sports.; Full Page Mono: 17.00; Full Page Colour: 59.21
Currency: US Dollars
DAILY NEWSPAPER

Arizona Daily Star
Owner: Lee Enterprises, Inc.
Editorial: 4850 S Park Ave, Tucson, Arizona 85714-1637. **T:** 1 520 573-4142
E: advocate@azstarnet.com
W: http://www.azstarnet.com
Freq: Daily; **Circ:** 84826 Not Audited
Editorial Profile: Arizona Daily Star provides news and information for the residents of Tucson, AZ. The paper features local, regional and state news, business and sports. The ad rate is a combination rate with the Tucson Citizen.; Full Page Mono: 213.90; Full Page Colour: 215.70
Currency: US Dollars
DAILY NEWSPAPER

Arizona Daily Sun
Owner: Lee Enterprises, Inc.
Editorial: 1751 S Thompson St, Flagstaff, Arizona 86001-8716. **T:** 1 928 774-4545
E: azdsnews@azdailysun.com
W: http://www.azdailysun.com
Freq: Daily; **Circ:** 9136 Not Audited
Editor: Jake Bacon; **News Team Leader:** Larry Hendricks; **Publisher:** Don Rowley; **Editor:** Randy Wilson
Editorial Profile: Arizona Daily Sun is a daily newspaper serving Flagstaff and Northern Arizona. The newspaper provides residents with information on local news, weather, sports and events.; Full Page Mono: 35.20; Full Page Colour: 358.50
Currency: US Dollars
DAILY NEWSPAPER

Arizona Hispana
Editorial: 2334 S 4th Ave, Tucson, Arizona 85713-3515. **T:** 1 520 770-9261
E: contacto@arizonahispana.com
W: http://www.arizonahispana.com
Freq: Bi-Weekly
Editorial Profile: Arizona Hispana is a bi-weekly newspaper providing Local and Community News coverage for the Hispanic community in Tucson, AZ.
NEWSPAPER

Arizona Informant
Editorial: 1301 E Washington St, Phoenix, Arizona 85034-1103. **T:** 1 602 257-9300
W: http://www.azinformant.com
Freq: Wed; **Circ:** 15000 Not Audited
Editorial Profile: Arizona Informant is a weekly African American newspaper for Arizona residents. Deadlines are on Fridays.; Full Page Mono: 45.83; Full Page Colour: 2784.00
Currency: US Dollars
NEWSPAPER

The Arizona Republic
Owner: Gannett Co., Inc.
Editorial: 200 E Van Buren St, Phoenix, Arizona 85004-2238. **T:** 1 602 444-8000
E: newstips@arizonarepublic.com
W: http://www.azcentral.com
Freq: Daily; **Circ:** 261174 Not Audited
Publisher: John Zidich
Editorial Profile: The Arizona Republic is the state's largest newspaper. It offers readers a strong focus on local news, along with national and international news. There is also sports, business, features and lifestyle coverage. It debuted on May 19, 1890.; Full Page Mono: 495.00; Full Page Colour: 538.33
Currency: US Dollars
DAILY NEWSPAPER

The Arizona Republic
Editorial: 1575 I St NW, Washington, District Of Columbia 20005-1105. **T:** 1 703 854-8932
DAILY NEWSPAPER

The Arizona Republic
Editorial: 8800 E Raintree Dr Ste 250, Scottsdale, Arizona 85260-3965.
T: 1 602 444-6810
DAILY NEWSPAPER

The Arizona Republic
Editorial: 106 E Baseline Rd, Mesa, Arizona 85210-6204. **T:** 1 602 444-7931
DAILY NEWSPAPER

The Arizona Republic
Editorial: 17235 N 75th Ave Ste A100, Glendale, Arizona 85308-0884.
T: 1 602 444-6935
Editorial Profile: Known as the Arrowhead branch of the Arizona Republic, this office also publishes the Southwest Valley Republic, Glendale Republic, Northwest Valley Republic and the Peoria Republic newspapers.
DAILY NEWSPAPER

Arizona Republic
Editorial: 15635 W Illini St, Goodyear, Arizona 85338-3619. **T:** 1 602 444-8000
DAILY NEWSPAPER

Arkadelphia Daily Siftings Herald
Owner: GateHouse Media Inc.
Editorial: 205 S 26th St, Arkadelphia, Arkansas 71923-5455. **T:** 1 870 246-5525
E: siftingsherald@yahoo.com
W: http://www.siftingsherald.com
Freq: Daily; **Circ:** 2800 Not Audited
Editor: Wendy Ledbetter
Editorial Profile: Arkadelphia Daily Siftings Herald is a local newspaper serving the Arkadelphia, AR area. It provides residents with information on local news, sports, weather and events.; Full Page Mono: 12.80; Full Page Colour: 262.80
Currency: US Dollars
DAILY NEWSPAPER

Arkansas City Traveler
Owner: Seaton Newspapers
Editorial: 200 E 5th Ave, Arkansas City, Kansas 67005-2606. **T:** 1 620 442-4200
E: arkcity@arkcity.net
W: http://www.arkcity.net
Freq: Daily; **Circ:** 5000 Not Audited
Publisher: David Seaton
Editorial Profile: Arkansas City Traveler is a daily newspaper serving Arkansas City, KS. It provides residents with information on local news, events, weather, and sports. The lead time for Arkansas City Traveler is one day. Contact the managing editor with any further inquiries.; Full Page Mono: 9.15; Full Page Colour: 165.00
Currency: US Dollars
DAILY NEWSPAPER

Arkansas Democrat-Gazette
Owner: Wehco Media Inc.
Editorial: 121 E Capitol Ave, Little Rock, Arkansas 72201-3819. **T:** 1 501 378-3400
E: news@arkansasonline.com
W: http://www.arkansasonline.com
Freq: Daily; **Circ:** 147467 Not Audited
City & Projects Editor: Lawrence Albarado; **City & Projects Editor:** Lawrence Albarado; **High Profile Editor:** Bobby Ampezzan; **Publisher:** Walter Hussman; **City Editor:** Danny Shameer
Editorial Profile: Arkansas Democrat-Gazette is a daily, general interest newspaper written for the general public in the Little Rock, AR area. The paper was founded in 1819.; Full Page Mono: 248.00; Full Page Colour: 788.20
Currency: US Dollars
DAILY NEWSPAPER

Arkansas Democrat-Gazette
Editorial: 529 14th St NW Ste 1190, Washington, District Of Columbia 20045-2101.
T: 1 202 662-7690
DAILY NEWSPAPER

Arkansas Democrat-Gazette
Editorial: State Capitol Press Room, Little Rock, Arkansas 72201. **T:** 1 501 378-3438
DAILY NEWSPAPER

Arkansas Democrat-Gazette
Editorial: 121 Pine St., Pine Bluff, Arkansas 71611. **T:** 1 870 536-2285
Bureau Chief: John Worthen
DAILY NEWSPAPER

Arkansas Democrat-Gazette
Editorial: 201 W Washington Ave, Jonesboro, Arkansas 72401-2840. **T:** 1 870 932-3612
Bureau Chief: Kenneth Heard; **Bureau Chief:** Kenneth Heard
DAILY NEWSPAPER

Arkansas Democrat-Gazette
Editorial: 2560 N Lowell Rd, Springdale, Arkansas 72764-1818. **T:** 1 479 751-6200
Northwest City Editor: Jennifer Cook; **Northwest Editor:** Susan Scantlin
DAILY NEWSPAPER

Arkansas Democrat-Gazette
Editorial: 1020 Main St, Conway, Arkansas 72032-5426. **T:** 1 501 327-6751
Bureau Chief: Debra Hale-Shelton
DAILY NEWSPAPER

Arkansas Democrat-Gazette
Editorial: 101 N 10th St Ste G6, Fort Smith, Arkansas 72901-2716. **T:** 1 479 785-9966
Bureau Chief: Dave Hughes
DAILY NEWSPAPER

Arkansas Democrat-Gazette - Zoned Editions
Owner: Wehco Media Inc.
Editorial: 121 E Capitol Ave, Little Rock, Arkansas 72201-3819. **T:** 1 501 918-4527
Freq: Sat
NEWSPAPER

Arkansas Weekly
Owner: W. R. D. Entertainment, Inc.
Editorial: 920 Harrison St, Ste C, Batesville, Arkansas 72501. **T:** 1 870 793-4196
W: http://www.arkansasweekly.com
Freq: Wed; **Circ:** 21500 Not Audited
Editorial Profile: Arkansas Weekly is a community newspaper written for the residents of Batesville, AR.; Full Page Mono: 8.95
Currency: US Dollars
NEWSPAPER

Arlington Catholic Herald
Owner: Catholic Diocese of Arlington
Editorial: 200 N Glebe Rd, Ste 600, Arlington, Virginia 22203. **T:** 1 703 841-2590
E: editorial@catholicherald.com
W: http://www.catholicherald.com
Freq: Thu; **Circ:** 63000 Not Audited
Publisher: Paul Loverde
Editorial Profile: Arlington Catholic Herald is written for Catholics in Arlington, VA.; Full Page Mono: 31.50
Currency: US Dollars
NEWSPAPER

Army Flier
Owner: Fort Rucker Army Aviation Center
Editorial: Fort Rucker Public Affairs Office, Building 131, Fort Rucker, Alabama 36362.
T: 1 334 255-1239
W: http://www.dothaneagle.com/army_flier
Freq: Thu; **Circ:** 10000 Not Audited
Editorial Profile: Army Flier is a free, weekly newspaper serving the miltary personnel and residents of the U.S. Army's Aviation Training and Command Center in Fort Rucker, AL. It has an emphasis on local news, family activities, command news, Department of Defense news and social events. All editorial content is supplied by military personnel, while advertising is handled by the Dothan (AL) Eagle . Deadlines are at 5pm ET.; Full Page Mono: 11.50
Currency: US Dollars
NEWSPAPER

Around Town
Owner: Around Town Publications Inc.
Editorial: 1280 S Powerline Rd, Ste 28, Pompano Beach, Florida 33069.
T: 1 954 971-8008
E: aroundtown@earthlink.net
W: http://www.aroundtownnews.com
Freq: Bi-Weekly; **Circ:** 22000 Not Audited
Editorial Profile: Around Town is a bi-weekly publication for residents of South Florida. The newspaper covers hospitality and social events.; Full Page Mono: 23.50
Currency: US Dollars
NEWSPAPER

Artesia Daily Press
Owner: Valley Newspapers Inc.
Editorial: 503 W Main St, Artesia, New Mexico 88210. **T:** 1 575 746-3524
E: news@artesianews.com
W: http://www.artesianews.com
Freq: Daily; **Circ:** 3400
Editor: Tim Menicutch
Editorial Profile: Artesia Daily Press is a local newspaper serving the area of Artesia, NM. It provides residents with information on local news, events, weather and sports. Deadines for editorial submissions are the previous noon MT during weekdays and Thursday for the Sunday edition. Do not send anything via e-mail.; Full Page Mono: 6.85; Full Page Colour: 231.85
Currency: US Dollars
DAILY NEWSPAPER

Arvin Tiller & Lamont Reporter Newspapers
Owner: Reed, (Frank and Donald)
Editorial: 5409 Aldrin Ct, Bakersfield, California 93313-2104. **T:** 1 661 845-3704
E: lamontreporter@earthlink.net **Circ:** 8100 Not Audited
Editor: Toni DeRosa; **Publisher:** Donald Reed
Editorial Profile: Arvin Tiller & Lamont Reporter Newspapers provides news to the community of Shafter, CA.
NEWSPAPER

Asahi Shimbun International Satellite Edition
Editorial: 620 8th Ave, New York, New York 10018-1618. **T:** 1 212 398-0257
E: m.glennon@asahiam.com
W: http://www.asahi.com
Freq: Daily; **Circ:** 7500 Not Audited
Bureau Chief: Diana Yung
Editorial Profile: Asahi Shimbun International Satellite Edition was established in 1986 in the United States and is widely read among Japanese Americans. It covers political and economic news, regional news, metro news, international news, sports news, science news and arts and culture. It also cites information that is useful both to newly transferred Japanese businessmen and their families and to readers already well established in the United States. The lead time is 12 hours. Deadlines for the publication are the day prior to the issue date at 11:30am and 10:30pm ET.; Full Page Mono: 24.37
Currency: US Dollars
DAILY NEWSPAPER

Asbarez Armenian Daily
Owner: Armenian Media Network
Editorial: 1203 N Vermont Ave, Los Angeles, California 90029-1703. **T:** 1 323 284-9222
E: editor@asbarez.com **W:** http://asbarez.com
Freq: Fri; **Circ:** 8000 Not Audited
Editor: Apo Borghigian
Editorial Profile: Asbarez Armenian Daily is a local newspaper serving the Armenian community of Fresno, CA and the surrounding area. It provides information on news and events of Armenian interest.; Full Page Mono: 3.50
Currency: US Dollars
NEWSPAPER

Asbury Park Press
Owner: Gannett Co., Inc.
Editorial: 3601 State Route 66, Neptune, New Jersey 07753-2604. **T:** 1 732 922-6000
E: editors@app.com **W:** http://www.app.com
Freq: Daily; **Circ:** 83594 Not Audited
Publisher: Tom Donovan
Editorial Profile: Asbury Park Press, a Gannett newspaper, reaches the New Jersey counties of Ocean, Monmouth, and Middlesex. According to the media kit, the publication considers itself the main newspaper reaching the edge of the New York DMA. Coverage includes world, national, regional, and local news, sports, weather, business, arts and entertainment, and health. The following sections run on Sunday: Turning Point, Well Being, On the Scene, Entertainment, Etc., Destinations, Business, Food, The Local Front, Impact, Real Estate & Home, Sports Weekend, and TV Week. The following sections run on Monday: Money Monday, Sports Weekend Wrap-up, Critters, Learning Curve, and Blitz (September - January). The Health and Whatever (teen) sections run on Tuesday. On Wednesday, the following sections appear: Food & Spirits, Community, TechWorld, Kid Stuff, and Brainstorm (12 times a year). The Home & Family and Day in the Life (monthly) sections run on Thursday. Jersey Alive, Wheels, and Real Estate run on Friday. On Saturday, readers can find Rally (school sports), Sports Weekend, Saturday People, Out and About, and Community Weekend. The Asbury Park Press shares some of its staff and stories with its sister newspapers, also published by Gannett, Inc.; Full Page Mono: 225.86; Full Page Colour: 2060.27
Currency: US Dollars
DAILY NEWSPAPER

Asbury Park Press
Editorial: 235 Willow Brook Rd, Freehold, New Jersey 07728-2882. **T:** 1 732 863-1500
DAILY NEWSPAPER

Asbury Park Press
Editorial: 1451 Route 37 W, Toms River, New Jersey 08755-4969. **T:** 1 732 349-3000
Bureau Chief: Joe Cacchioli
DAILY NEWSPAPER

Asheville Citizen-Times
Owner: Gannett Co., Inc.
Editorial: 14 Ohenry Ave, Asheville, North Carolina 28801-2604. **T:** 1 828 252-5611
W: http://www.citizen-times.com
Freq: Daily; **Circ:** 28813 Not Audited
News Editor: Katie Wadington; **News Editor:** Katie Wadington; **News Editor:** Katie Wadington; **News Editor:** Katie Wadington

Editorial Profile: Asheville Citizen-Times is a daily broad sheet serving the greater Asheville, NC community. Sections include local news, business, arts & entertainment, features, city and county government, courts and law enforcement, education, politics, medicine and health. Regional news encompasses all of Western North Carolina outside the Buncombe-Madison area. Please mail all materials to the PO Box address. Advertising rates vary.; Full Page Mono: 107.25; Full Page Colour: 366.75
Currency: US Dollars
DAILY NEWSPAPER

Ashland Daily Tidings
Owner: GateHouse Media Inc.
Editorial: 111 N Fir St, Medford, Oregon 97501-2772. **T:** 1 541 776-4411
E: news@dailytidings.com
W: http://www.dailytidings.com
Freq: Daily; **Circ:** 3800 Not Audited
Editor: Bert Etling; **Editor in Chief:** Bob Hunter; **Publisher:** James Grady Singletary
Editorial Profile: Ashland Daily Tidings is a local newspaper serving the Ashland, OR area. It provides information on news and events in the area. The newspaper focuses on Rogue Valley people and institutions. It offers a balanced selection on information, entertainment, opinion, and advertising. Please only send press releases with a local emphasis.; Full Page Mono: 7.85; Full Page Colour: 11.42
Currency: US Dollars
DAILY NEWSPAPER

Ashland Times-Gazette
Owner: Dix Communications
Editorial: 40 E 2nd St, Ashland, Ohio 44805-2304. **T:** 1 419 281-0581
E: newsroom@times-gazette.com
W: http://www.times-gazette.com
Freq: Daily; **Circ:** 11374 Not Audited
Editor: Ted Daniels; **Publisher:** Troy Dix
Editorial Profile: Ashland Times-Gazette is a local daily newspaper serving the Ashland County, OH area. It provides residents with information on local news, events, sports and weather. Deadlines for the publication are one week before issue date.; Full Page Mono: 14.00
Currency: US Dollars
DAILY NEWSPAPER

Asia
Editorial: 2920 1St Ave Apt G, San Diego, California 92103-5921. **T:** 1 619 521-8008
E: editorial@asiamediainc.com
W: http://www.asiamediainc.com
Freq: Bi-Monthly; **Circ:** 192000 Not Audited
Editorial Profile: Asia is an English bi-monthly newspaper for the Asia and Pacific Islander communities in Southern California.; Full Page Mono: 70.00
Currency: US Dollars
NEWSPAPER

Asian American Press
Editorial: 417 University Ave W, Saint Paul, Minnesota 55103-1934. **T:** 1 651 224-6570
E: aanews@aapress.com
W: http://aapress.com
Freq: Fri; **Circ:** 15000
Editorial Profile: Asian American Press is a weekly newspaper serving the Asian community of Minneapolis and St. Paul, MN.; Full Page Mono: 32.00
Currency: US Dollars
NEWSPAPER

Asian Gazette
Editorial: 12809 Audelia Rd, Dallas, Texas 75243-2275. **T:** 1 972 907-1919
E: chinese9071919@yahoo.com
Freq: Fri; **Circ:** 10000 Not Audited
Publisher: Wei Lee; Full Page Mono: 20.00
Currency: US Dollars
NEWSPAPER

Asian Journal Publications
Owner: Asian Journal Publications, Inc.
Editorial: 1150 Wilshire Blvd, Los Angeles, California 90017. **T:** 1 213 250-9797
E: editor@asianjournalinc.com
W: http://www.asianjournal.com **Circ:** 93000 Not Audited
Publisher: Roger Oriel; **News Editor:** Joseph Peralta; **Editor in Chief:** Momar Visaya
NEWSPAPER

Asian Journal/Philippines Today
Editorial: 550 E 8th St, Ste 6, National City, California 91950. **T:** 1 619 474-0588
E: asianjournal@aol.com
W: http://www.asianjournalusa.com
Circ: 70000 Not Audited
NEWSPAPER

The Asian Reporter
Owner: Asian Reporter Publications, Inc.
Editorial: 922 N Killingsworth St Ste 1A, Portland, Oregon 97217-2261.
T: 1 503 283-4440
E: news@asianreporter.com
W: http://www.asianreporter.com
Freq: Mon; **Circ:** 25000 Not Audited
Publisher: Jamie Lim; **Editor:** Jeff Wenger
Editorial Profile: The Asian Reporter is written for Asian-Americans living in Oregon. It covers international, national and local news and events with an Asian focus.; Full Page Mono: 23.00; Full Page Colour: 1788.00
Currency: US Dollars
NEWSPAPER

Asian Weekly and Chinese Post Newspapers
Editorial: 412 Maynard Ave S, Seattle, Washington 98104. **T:** 1 206 223-5559
E: info@nwasianweekly.com
W: http://www.nwasianweekly.com
Circ: 26000 Not Audited
Editor: Rebecca Ip; **Editor:** Charles Lam;
Publisher: Assunta Ng
NEWSPAPER

Aspen Daily News
Owner: Dave Danforth
Editorial: 517 E Hopkins Ave, Aspen, Colorado 81611-1964. **T:** 1 970 925-2220
W: http://www.aspendailynews.com
Freq: Daily; **Circ:** 14500 Not Audited
Publisher: Dave Danforth; **Editor:** Carolyn Sackariason
Editorial Profile: Aspen Daily News is a daily newspaper written for the residents of Aspen, Snowmass Village, Woody Creek, Basalt, El Jebel, Carbondale and Glenwood Springs, CO. It reports national and local news and community events.; Full Page Mono: 10.50
Currency: US Dollars
DAILY NEWSPAPER

Aspen Times
Owner: Swift Newspapers
Editorial: 310 E Main St, Aspen, Colorado 81611-1930. **T:** 1 970 925-3414
E: mail@aspentimes.com
W: http://www.aspentimes.com
Freq: Mon thru Fri; **Circ:** 11000
Editor: Rick Carroll
Editorial Profile: Aspen Times is a daily newspaper written for the residents of Aspen, CO. It reports news and events in the local community.; Full Page Mono: 29.27; Full Page Colour: 95.54
Currency: US Dollars
DAILY NEWSPAPER

Athens Banner-Herald
Owner: Morris Communications Corp.
Editorial: 1 Press Pl, Athens, Georgia 30601-2605. **T:** 1 706 549-0123
E: news@onlineathens.com
W: http://www.onlineathens.com
Freq: Daily; **Circ:** 18575 Not Audited
Editor: Allison Floyd; **News Editor:** Ed Morales; **Publisher:** Scot Morrissey
Editorial Profile: Athens Banner-Herald is published daily for residents of Athens, GA and surrounding communities. The publication covers local news, weather, sports and community events.; Full Page Mono: 35.27; Full Page Colour: 380.00
Currency: US Dollars
DAILY NEWSPAPER

The Athens Messenger
Owner: American Consolidated Media
Editorial: 9300 Johnson Rd, Athens, Ohio 45701-9028. **T:** 1 740 592-6612
E: info@athensmessenger.com
W: http://www.athensmessenger.com
Freq: Daily; **Circ:** 12101 Not Audited
Editor: John Halley; **Editor:** Ann Kamody;
Publisher: Monica Nieporte; **News Editor:** Steve Robb
Editorial Profile: Athens Messenger is written for the residents of Athens County, OH. It includes local news, classifieds and obituaries.; Full Page Mono: 23.94; Full Page Colour: 145.73
Currency: US Dollars
DAILY NEWSPAPER

Athens News
Editorial: 14 N Court St, Athens, Ohio 45701-2429. **T:** 1 740 594-8219
E: news@athensnews.com
W: http://www.athensnews.com
Freq: Mon; **Circ:** 17500 Not Audited
Publisher: Bruce Mitchell; **Editor:** Terry Smith
Editorial Profile: Athens News is a twice-weekly newspaper serving residents of Athens, OH. It covers news and events occurring in Athens, OH and at Ohio University. It is Athens County's only locally owned newspaper.; Full Page Mono: 9.65
Currency: US Dollars
NEWSPAPER

Athens Review
Owner: Community Newspaper Holdings, Inc.
Editorial: 201 S Prairieville St, Athens, Texas 75751-2541. **T:** 1 903 675-5626
W: http://www.athensreview.com
Freq: Fri; **Circ:** 5000 Not Audited
Editor: Jeff Riggs; **Publisher:** Lange Svehlak
Editorial Profile: Athens Review is a daily newspaper published for the residents of Athens, TX area. The editorial content covers local sports, lifestyle and general news and to promote the goodwill of the community.; Full Page Mono: 12.46; Full Page Colour: 89.23
Currency: US Dollars
NEWSPAPER

Athol Daily News
Owner: Athol Press Inc.
Editorial: 225 Exchange St, Athol, Massachusetts 1331. **T:** 1 978 249-3535
E: newsroom@atholdailynews.com
W: http://www.atholdailynews.com
Freq: Daily; **Circ:** 5000 Not Audited
Publisher: Richard Chase; **Editor:** Deborah Porter
Editorial Profile: Athol Daily News serves the residents of Athol, MA.; Full Page Mono: 7.60; Full Page Colour: 49.88
Currency: US Dollars
DAILY NEWSPAPER

Atlanta Daily World
Owner: Real Times Media
Editorial: 100 Hartsfield Centre Parkway Suite 522, Atlanta, Georgia 30354.
T: 1 678 515-2053
W: http://www.atlantadailyworld.com
Freq: Thu; **Circ:** 27000 Not Audited
Editorial Profile: Atlanta Daily World is a weekly newspaper for the African American residents of Atlanta.; Full Page Mono: 47.00
Currency: US Dollars
NEWSPAPER

The Atlanta Inquirer
Owner: Smith Sr. (John)
Editorial: 947 Martin Luther King Jr Dr NW, Atlanta, Georgia 30314. **T:** 1 404 523-6086
E: news@atlinq.com
W: http://www.atlinq.com
Freq: Thu; **Circ:** 40000 Not Audited
Editorial Profile: The Atlanta Inquirer is a local newspaper written for the African-American community in Atlanta.; Full Page Mono: 32.34; Full Page Colour: 3713.34
Currency: US Dollars
NEWSPAPER

Atlanta Intown
Owner: Springs Publishing LLC
Editorial: 6065 Roswell Rd Ste 225, Sandy Springs, Georgia 30328-4012.
T: 1 404 917-2200
W: http://www.atlantaintownpaper.com
Freq: Monthly; **Circ:** 42000 Not Audited
Editor: Collin Kelley; **Editor:** Collin Kelley;
Editor: Collin Kelley; **Editor:** Collin Kelley;
Publisher: Steve Levene
Editorial Profile: Atlanta Intown is a monthly newspaper written for the residents of Virginia-Highland, Morningside, Druid Hills, Ansley Park, Midtown, Downtown, Little Five Points, Grant Park and East Atlanta, GA. It covers news and events in the local, in-town community.; Full Page Mono: 46.36
Currency: US Dollars
NEWSPAPER

Atlanta Jewish Times
Owner: Zadok Publishing, LLC
Editorial: 270 Carpenter Dr Ste 320, Atlanta, Georgia 30328-4933. **T:** 1 404 883-2130
W: http://www.atlantajewishtimes.com
Freq: Fri; **Circ:** 15000
Publisher: Clifford Weiss
Editorial Profile: Atlanta Jewish Times is a local newspaper written for the Jewish community of Atlanta, GA. The paper covers a calendar of events, arts and entertainment and lifestyle features.; Full Page Mono: 27.95
Currency: US Dollars
NEWSPAPER

Atlanta Journal-Constitution
Owner: Cox Media Group, Inc.
Editorial: 223 Perimeter Center Pkwy NE, Atlanta, Georgia 30346-1301.
T: 1 404 526-5151 **E:** listen@ajc.com
W: http://www.ajc.com
Freq: Daily; **Circ:** 168693 Not Audited
Publisher: Amy Glennon; **Editor:** Kevin Riley
Editorial Profile: Atlanta Journal-Constitution (AJC) is the leading general interest daily paper in Atlanta. The Atlanta Constitution was founded in 1868 and the Atlanta Journal was founded in 1883. The two papers combined weekend sections in 1950, but did not fully combine until 2001. The paper covers world and local news as well as sports, entertainment, weather, business and travel. In August 2009, the paper joined a national sports content-sharing alliance with several other papers across the country. The paper also offers multiple special sections, including a weekend arts section.; Full Page Mono: 566.00; Full Page Colour: 4320.00
Currency: US Dollars
DAILY NEWSPAPER

The Atlanta Voice
Editorial: 633 Pryor St SW, Atlanta, Georgia 30312. **T:** 1 404 524-6426
W: http://www.theatlantavoice.com
Freq: Fri; **Circ:** 30000 Not Audited
Publisher: Janis Ware
Editorial Profile: Atlanta Voice, established in 1966, is a weekly newspaper designed to serve and salute the African American community throughout metro Atlanta. It covers local and national news, sports and entertainment.; Full Page Mono: 65.17; Full Page Colour: 72.11
Currency: US Dollars
NEWSPAPER

Atlantic County Weeklies
Owner: Gannett Co., Inc.
Editorial: 115 12th St, Hammonton, New Jersey 08037-1521. **T:** 1 609 561-2300
W: http://www.thehammontonnews.com
Circ: 35723 Not Audited
Editorial Profile: Placing an ad in just one paper is not an option. The advertising rate provided is based on an estimated group rate.
NEWSPAPER

Atlantic News-Telegraph
Owner: Community Media Group
Editorial: 410 Walnut St, Atlantic, Iowa 50022-1378. **T:** 1 712 243-2624
W: http://www.atlanticnewstelegraph.com
Freq: Daily; **Circ:** 3241 Not Audited
Publisher: Connie Collins
Editorial Profile: Atlantic News-Telegraph is a daily newspaper for the residents of Atlantic, IA. It covers news and events in the local community.; Full Page Mono: 13.10; Full Page Colour: 78.91
Currency: US Dollars
DAILY NEWSPAPER

Atwater Signal
Editorial: 3033 G St, Merced, California 95340-2108. **T:** 1 209 722-1511
Freq: Fri; **Circ:** 10000
Publisher: Gene Lieb; **Editor:** Kim Yancey
Editorial Profile: The Atwater Signal is a free weekly newspaper published for the residents of Atwater, CA. It is published from the offices of the Merced Sun Star.; Full Page Mono: 10.25
Currency: US Dollars
NEWSPAPER

Auburn Journal
Owner: Brehm Communications, Inc.
Editorial: 1030 High St, Auburn, California 95603-4707. **T:** 1 530 885-5656
E: ajournal@goldcountrymedia.com
W: http://www.auburnjournal.com
Freq: Mon thru Fri; **Circ:** 9670 Not Audited
Publisher: Todd Frantz; **News Editor:** Jenifer Gee; **Editor:** Dennis Noone; **Editor:** Gloria Young
Editorial Profile: Auburn Journal is a daily newspaper for the residents of Auburn, CA. It covers news and events in the local community.; Full Page Mono: 21.25; Full Page Colour: 26.25
Currency: US Dollars
DAILY NEWSPAPER

Auburn Reporter
Owner: Sound Publishing Inc.
Editorial: 19426 68th Ave. S., Kent, Washington 98032. **T:** 1 253 833-0218
E: letters@auburn-reporter.com
W: http://www.auburn-reporter.com
Freq: Bi-Weekly; **Circ:** 33000 Not Audited
Editor: Mark Klaas; **Publisher:** Polly Shepherd
Editorial Profile: Auburn Reporter in Kent, WA is a weekly newspaper that covers local news and events.; Full Page Mono: 28.00
Currency: US Dollars
NEWSPAPER

Audubon County Newspapers
Owner: Community Media Group
Editorial: 517 Leroy St, Audubon, Iowa 50025-1206. **T:** 1 712 563-2741
E: news@auduboncountynews.com
W: http://www.auduboncountynews.com
Circ: 9428 Not Audited
Editorial Profile: Audobon County Newspapers is a weekly community newspaper publisher serving the residents of Cass County and Audobon County, IA.
NEWSPAPER

The Auglaize Merchandiser
Owner: Horizon Publications
Editorial: 520 Industrial Dr, Wapakoneta, Ohio 45895-9200. **T:** 1 419 738-2128
W: http://www.wapakdaily.com
Freq: Tue; **Circ:** 11200 Not Audited
Publisher: Dianna Epperly; **Editor:** William Laney
Editorial Profile: The Auglaize Merchandiser is a weekly newspaper written for the residents of Wapakoneta, OH. The paper covers news, social issues, business, sports and events in the local community.; Full Page Mono: 6.15
Currency: US Dollars
NEWSPAPER

The Augusta Chronicle
Owner: Morris Communications
Editorial: 725 Broad St, Augusta, Georgia 30901-1336. **T:** 1 706 724-0851
E: newsroom@augustachronicle.com
W: http://chronicle.augusta.com
Freq: Daily; **Circ:** 45265 Not Audited
Day News Editor: Glynn Moore; **Publisher:** William Morris
Editorial Profile: The Augusta (GA) Chronicle is a daily newspaper that covers local news and events.; Full Page Mono: 54.41; Full Page Colour: 1004.00
Currency: US Dollars
DAILY NEWSPAPER

The Augusta Chronicle
Editorial: 4272 Washington Rd Ste 3B, Evans, Georgia 30809-3073. **T:** 1 706 868-1222
E: cnt@newstimesonline.com
DAILY NEWSPAPER

Augusta Daily Gazette
Owner: GateHouse Media Inc.
Editorial: 204 E 5Th Ave, Augusta, Kansas 67010-1012. **T:** 1 316 775-2218
W: http://www.augustagazette.com
Freq: Daily; **Circ:** 2089 Not Audited
Publisher: Kent Bush; **Editor:** Belinda Larsen
Editorial Profile: Augusta Daily Gazette is the local daily newspaper of Butler County and the cities of Augusta, Douglass and Rose Hill, KS. The publication covers local and world news, sports, food, weather, lifestyles, obituaries, business, community news and health.; Full Page Mono: 8.75; Full Page Colour: 58.51
Currency: US Dollars
DAILY NEWSPAPER

Aurora Media Group
Owner: Aurora Media Group, LLC
Editorial: 12100 E Iliff Ave Ste 102, Aurora, Colorado 80014-1277. **T:** 1 303 750-7555
E: news@aurorasentinel.com
W: http://www.aurorasentinel.com
Freq: Thu; **Circ:** 6200
Publisher: James Gold; **Editor:** Dave Perry
NEWSPAPER

Aurora Sentinel Free Daily
Owner: Aurora Media Group, LLC
Editorial: 12100 E Iliff Ave Ste 102, Aurora, Colorado 80014-1277. **T:** 1 303 750-7555
E: news@aurorasentinel.com
Freq: Mon thru Fri; **Circ:** 10000 Not Audited
Publisher: James Gold; **Editor:** Dave Perry
Editorial Profile: Aurora Sentinel Free Daily is issued Monday through Thursday and Aurora Sentinel Weekend on Friday. It is written for the residents of Aurora, CO.; Full Page Mono: 28.00; Full Page Colour: 31.96
Currency: US Dollars
DAILY NEWSPAPER

Austin American-Statesman
Owner: Cox Media Group, Inc.
Editorial: 305 S Congress Ave, Austin, Texas 78704-1200. **T:** 1 512 445-3500
E: news@statesman.com
W: http://www.statesman.com
Freq: Daily; **Circ:** 132873 Not Audited
Publisher: Susie Ellwood; **Editor:** Debbie Hiott; **Editor:** Debbie Hiott; **Editor:** Debbie Hiott; **Editor:** Debbie Hiott; **Content Marketing Strategist:** Lisa Ogle
Editorial Profile: Austin American-Statesman, "the paper of Central Texas," is a daily broadsheet covering regional, national and international news. The paper's daily sections include a Metro/state section, focusing on local and regional news, business, a Sports section, life/entertainment, as well as editorial articles and classified ads. In addition, the paper's weekly sections offer a more specific focus on a number of topics. Austin360 includes news and features on music, dance, dining and other topics related to arts and entertainment. The publication offers in-depth technology coverage in its Tech Monday section. Coverage includes consumer electronics, area technology firms, as well as computer and technology-related news. Other offerings include Weekly Business Review on Saturdays, a complete package of the entire week's stock market and mutual fund activity; Travel, featuring travel advice, and features related to travel and vacation destinations.; Full Page Mono: 222.96; Full Page Colour: 4380.57
Currency: US Dollars
DAILY NEWSPAPER

Austin American-Statesman
Editorial: 203 E Main St, Round Rock, Texas 78664-5207. **T:** 1 512 246-7400
E: news@statesman.com
DAILY NEWSPAPER

Austin American-Statesman
Editorial: 109 E Hopkins St, San Marcos, Texas 78666-5746. **T:** 1 512 392-8751
E: news@statesman.com
Editorial Profile: This is the Hays County bureau for the Austin American-Statesman.
DAILY NEWSPAPER

Austin Chronicle
Owner: Austin Chronicle Corp.
Editorial: 4000 N Interstate 35, Austin, Texas 78751-4801. **T:** 1 512 454-5766
E: mail@austinchronicle.com
W: http://www.austinchronicle.com
Freq: Thu; **Circ:** 90000 Not Audited
Publisher: Nick Barbaro; **Editor:** Louis Black; **News Editor:** Michael King; **Editor:** Kate Messer
Editorial Profile: Austin Chronicle is written for residents of Austin, TX. It covers political and environmental concerns, the local cultural scene and in-depth information on arts & entertainment, which includes venues, restaurants, recreational activities and outdoor excursions. Do NOT send pitches for alcohol & spirits, beer and wine to the food editor; direct those pitches to the appropriate writer.; Full Page Mono: 5.00
Currency: US Dollars
NEWSPAPER

Austin Daily Herald
Owner: Boone Newspapers Inc.
Editorial: 310 2nd St NE, Austin, Minnesota 55912-3487. **T:** 1 507 433-8851
E: newsroom@austindailyherald.com
W: http://www.austindailyherald.com
Freq: Daily; **Circ:** 4996 Not Audited
Publisher: Dave Churchill; **Editor:** Adam Harringa
Editorial Profile: Austin Daily Herald is published daily for the residents of Austin, MN and surrounding areas. The newspaper provides information about local and state news, business, education, sports, lifestyles and entertainment.; Full Page Mono: 18.50; Full Page Colour: 117.50
Currency: US Dollars
DAILY NEWSPAPER

The Australian - Washington, D.C. Bureau
Owner: News Limited
Editorial: 529 14th St NW, Ste 446, Washington, District Of Columbia 20045. **T:** 1 202 628-6269
Editorial Profile: This is the Washington, D.C. bureau of The Australian in Surry Hills, Australia.
DAILY NEWSPAPER

The Avenue News
Owner: Chesapeake Publishing and Printing
Editorial: 617 Stemmers Run Rd Ste D, Essex, Maryland 21221-3361. **T:** 1 410 687-7775 **E:** editor@avenuenews.com
W: http://www.avenuenews.com
Freq: Thu; **Circ:** 47000 Not Audited
Editor: Ted Barnhardt; **Publisher:** David Fike
Editorial Profile: The Avenue News is a weekly newspaper written for the local residents of Baltimore, MD. The newspaper covers local news, sports, business, special events, lifestyles and general information. Deadlines for editorial submissions are on Tuesdays at noon ET prior to the issue date.; Full Page Mono: 25.00
Currency: US Dollars
NEWSPAPER

El Aviso
Owner: El Aviso De Ocasion Inc.
Editorial: 6728 Seville Ave, Huntington Park, California 90255. **T:** 1 323 586-9199
E: elaviso@aol.com
W: http://www.elaviso.com
Freq: Mon; **Circ:** 275000 Not Audited
Editor in Chief: Jose Ruiz; **Publisher:** Jose Zepeda
Editorial Profile: El Aviso is a weekly Spanish language magazine for the Hispanic community of Los Angeles. It acts primarily as a television guide, but it also provides useful advice on personal health and relationships, as well as sports coverage. Deadlines are on Thursdays at noon PT.; Full Page Mono: 48.08
Currency: US Dollars
NEWSPAPER

Avoyelles Journal
Editorial: 105 N Main St, Marksville, Louisiana 71351. **T:** 1 318 253-5413
E: newsonline@avoyelles.com
W: http://www.avoyellestoday.com
Freq: Sun; **Circ:** 16500 Not Audited
Editorial Profile: The Avoyelles Journal is a news source for Marksville, LA and the surrounding towns.; Full Page Mono: 10.90
Currency: US Dollars
NEWSPAPER

Azle Tri-County Advertiser Inc.
Owner: The Azle News and HCN Online Services
Editorial: 321 W Main St, Azle, Texas 76020-2903. **T:** 1 817 270-3340 **E:** tips@azlenews.net
W: http://www.azlenews.net **Circ:** 6000 Not Audited
News Editor: Mark Campbell; **Publisher:** Kim Ware
Editorial Profile: The Azle News is a weekly newspaper providing Local and Community News coverage to the residents of Tarrant, Parker and Wise counties near Azle, Texas.
NEWSPAPER

Azteca News
Editorial: 810 N Broadway, Santa Ana, California 92701. **T:** 1 714 972-9912
E: aztecanews@aol.com
W: http://www.aztecanews.com
Freq: Wed; **Circ:** 42000 Not Audited
Editor: Fernando Velo
Editorial Profile: Azteca News in Santa Ana, CA is a weekly newspaper that covers local news and community events for the Spanish-speaking community.; Full Page Mono: 19.50
Currency: US Dollars
NEWSPAPER

b the Newspaper
Owner: Tribune Company
Editorial: 501 N Calvert St, Baltimore, Maryland 21202. **T:** 1 410 332-6891
W: http://www.baltimoresun.com/entertainment/bthesite
Freq: Wed; **Circ:** 50000
Editorial Profile: b the Newspaper, launched on April 14, 2008 is a commuter newspaper targeting young adults in the Baltimore market. It features news, sports and opinion pages along with entertainment and nightlife coverage.; Full Page Mono: 38.26; Full Page Colour: 63.12
Currency: US Dollars
NEWSPAPER

Back Fork Publishing
Owner: Back Fork Publishing
Editorial: 219 Back Fork St, Webster Springs, West Virginia 26288. **T:** 1 304 847-5828
E: websterecho@citlink.net **Circ:** 6400 Not Audited
Editor: Thomas Clark
NEWSPAPER

Baier Publishing Company
Editorial: 119 W Garfield, Cissna Park, Illinois 60924. **T:** 1 815 457-2245
E: rickbaier@yahoo.com
Freq: Thu; **Circ:** 2000
Editorial Profile: Baier Publishing Company is a community newspaper publisher located in Cissna Park, IL, and prints the Cissna Park (IL) News and Rankin (IL) Independent.; Full Page Mono: 5.25
Currency: US Dollars
NEWSPAPER

Bajo El Sol
Owner: Freedom Communications Inc.
Editorial: 2055 S Arizona Ave, Yuma, Arizona 85364-6549. **T:** 1 928 539-6850
W: http://www.bajoelsol.com
Freq: Fri; **Circ:** 15000 Not Audited
Editor: John Vaughn
Editorial Profile: Bajo El Sol is a local newspaper for the Hispanic community of Yuma, AZ. The newspaper covers national, local and community news.; Full Page Mono: 21.69; Full Page Colour: 3192.40
Currency: US Dollars
NEWSPAPER

Baker City Herald
Owner: Western Communications Inc.
Editorial: 1915 1st St, Baker City, Oregon 97814. **T:** 1 541 523-3673
E: news@bakercityherald.com
W: http://www.bakercityherald.com
Freq: Daily; **Circ:** 3396 Not Audited
Publisher: Kari Borgen; **Editor:** John Collins; **Editor:** Jayson Jacoby
Editorial Profile: Baker City Herald is published daily for the residents of Baker County, OR. The newspaper covers local and state news, business, sports, lifestyles and entertainment.; Full Page Mono: 10.00; Full Page Colour: 65.63
Currency: US Dollars
DAILY NEWSPAPER

Bakersfield Californian
Editorial: 1707 Eye St, Bakersfield, California 93301. **T:** 1 661 395-7500
E: local@bakersfield.com
W: http://www.bakersfield.com
Freq: Daily; **Circ:** 35070 Not Audited
Publisher: Ginger Moorhouse
Editorial Profile: Bakersfield Californian is a daily newspaper written for the residents of Bakersfield, CA. The newspaper covers local news and events, sports, education and arts & entertainment.; Full Page Mono: 45.79; Full Page Colour: 147.85
Currency: US Dollars
DAILY NEWSPAPER

Balita Media
Editorial: 520 E Wilson Ave, Ste 210, Glendale, California 91206. **T:** 1 818 552-4503
E: editor@balita.com
W: http://www.balita.com **Circ:** 140000 Not Audited
Editor: Rhony Laigo; **Publisher:** Luchie Mendoza-Allen
NEWSPAPER

Ballantine Communications, Inc.
Owner: Ballantine Communications, Inc.
Editorial: 123 E Roger Smith Ave, Cortez, Colorado 81321-2827. **T:** 1 970 565-8527
Circ: 9400 Not Audited
Editor: Don Lindley; **Publisher:** Suzy Meyer; **Editor:** Jeanne Richardson
Editorial Profile: Ballantine Communications, Inc. is a weekly community newspaper publisher offering the Mancos Times, Pine River Journal, Dolores Star and Cortez Journal, and also publishes the daily Durango Herald.
NEWSPAPER

The Baltic Times - New York Bureau
Editorial: 40 Central Park South, New York, New York 10019. **T:** 1 212 591-1940
Editorial Profile: This is the New York Bureau for The Baltic Times which is based in Vilnius, Lithuania.
DAILY NEWSPAPER

The Baltimore Guide Publications
Editorial: 526 S Conkling St, Baltimore, Maryland 21224. **T:** 1 410 732-6600
E: newsroom@baltimoreguide.com
W: http://www.baltimoreguide.com
Circ: 67000 Not Audited
Editor: Jacqueline Watts
NEWSPAPER

Baltimore Jewish Times
Owner: Clipper City Media
Editorial: 11459 Cronhill Dr Ste A, Owings Mills, Maryland 21117-6280.
T: 1 410 902-2300
E: contact@jewishtimes.com
W: http://www.jewishtimes.com
Freq: Fri; **Circ:** 20000 Not Audited
Publisher: Andrew Buerger; **Editor in Chief:** Maayan Jaffe; **Editor:** Joshua Runyan
Editorial Profile: Baltimore Jewish Times is the oldest and largest weekly Jewish newspaper in Baltimore. The newspaper is published weekly and aims to promote the highest and best traditions of Baltimore's Jewish community.; Full Page Mono: 21.35; Full Page Colour: 1970.00
Currency: US Dollars
NEWSPAPER

The Baltimore Sun
Owner: Tribune Company
Editorial: 501 N Calvert St, Baltimore, Maryland 21278-1000. **T:** 1 410 332-6000
W: http://www.baltimoresun.com
Freq: Daily; **Circ:** 174010 Not Audited
Editorial Profile: The Baltimore Sun is a general interest daily newspaper written for the general public, business readers and consumers. It touts itself as "Maryland's leading provider of news for more than 150 years." Services used include Associated Press, Bloomberg News, The New York Times News Service, and Reuters. Coverage areas include news, business, consumer, health, and technology. The Business section, which is located inside the Maryland Section Tuesday through Friday, contains: Business Digest, a group of newsbriefs; Business Calendar, a listing of business events; and People on the Move, which lists personnel moves. On Sundays a Money & Life section runs as a stand-alone. The paper does not publish an editorial calendar. This is a morning newspaper. The outlet offers RRS (Real Simple Syndication). The paper is available for home delivery on Thursday and Sunday only. It is available at retail locations the rest of the week.; Full Page Mono: 328.90; Full Page Colour: 685.03
Currency: US Dollars
DAILY NEWSPAPER

Baltimore Sun Media Group
Owner: Tribune Company
Editorial: 501 N Calvert St, Baltimore, Maryland 21278-1000. **T:** 1 410 332-6347
W: http://baltimoresunmediagroup.com
Circ: 67252 Not Audited
Editor: Angela Bornemann; **Editor:** Keith Meisel; **Editor:** Larry Perl; **Editor:** Pete Pichaske; **Publisher:** Timothy Ryan
NEWSPAPER

The Baltimore Times Inc. Newspapers
Owner: The Baltimore Times, Inc.
Editorial: 2513 N Charles St, Baltimore, Maryland 21218-4602. **T:** 1 410 366-3900
E: editorial@btimes.com
W: http://www.baltimoretimes-online.com
Circ: 25000 Not Audited
Publisher: Joy Bramble
Editorial Profile: The Baltimore Times Inc. Newspapers is a publication that delivers several local newspapers for the community of Baltimore, MD.
NEWSPAPER

Banda Oriental Latino America
Owner: Banda Oriental Inc.
Editorial: 781 W Grand Ave, Rahway, New Jersey 07065-3420. **T:** 1 732 388-8383
E: bandao@aol.com
W: http://www.bandaoriental.net
Freq: Monthly; **Circ:** 30000 Not Audited
Publisher: Julia Moreira
Editorial Profile: Banda Oriental Latino America is a monthly newspaper written for Hispanics in New York and New Jersey. The newspaper is written in Spanish. Coverage includes local and national news and other topics of interest to the Hispanic community.; Full Page Mono: 35.00
Currency: US Dollars
NEWSPAPER

Bangla Patrika
Editorial: 3806 31st St, 2nd Fl, Long Island City, New York 11101. **T:** 1 718 753-0086
E: banglapatrikausa@gmail.com
W: http://www.banglapatrika.com
Freq: Mon; **Circ:** 15000 Not Audited
Editorial Profile: Bangla Patrika is a weekly newspaper written for the residents of Jackson Heights, NY.; Full Page Mono: 15.00
Currency: US Dollars
NEWSPAPER

Bangor Daily News
Owner: Bangor Publishing Co.
Editorial: 491 Main St, Bangor, Maine 04401-6296. **T:** 1 207 990-8000
E: bdnmail@bangordailynews.com
W: http://www.bangordailynews.com
Freq: Daily; **Circ:** 35348 Not Audited
Editor at Large: Julie Murchison Harris; **Publisher:** Richard Warren
Editorial Profile: Bangor Daily News is a daily newspaper published for residents in all the Eastern and Northern region in Maine. The paper has four editions throughout the day and has three sections. The publication covers all local, national, and international news.; Full Page Mono: 76.53; Full Page Colour: 250.60
Currency: US Dollars
DAILY NEWSPAPER

Bangor Daily News
Editorial: 37 Bangor St, Houlton, Maine 04730-1739. **T:** 1 207 532-9257
DAILY NEWSPAPER

Bangor Daily News
Editorial: 119 Main St, Pittsfield, Maine 04967-4364. **T:** 1 207 932-3315
DAILY NEWSPAPER

Bangor Daily News
Editorial: 93 Main St, #2, Belfast, Maine 04915-6536. **T:** 1 207 338-9546
Bureau Chief: Tom Groening
DAILY NEWSPAPER

Bangor Daily News
Editorial: 84 Main Rd, Sangerville, Maine 04479-3025. **T:** 1 207 876-4579
Bureau Chief: Diana Bowley
DAILY NEWSPAPER

Bangor Daily News
Editorial: Statehouse Station 50, Augusta, Maine 04333-0001
DAILY NEWSPAPER

Bangor Daily News
Owner: Bangor Publishing Co.
Editorial: 6 Myers Ln, Machias, Maine 04654-1095. **T:** 1 207 255-0618
DAILY NEWSPAPER

The Banner
Owner: E.W. Scripps Co.
Editorial: 26381 S Tamiami Trl, Ste 116, Bonita Springs, Florida 34134.
T: 1 239 213-6000
E: bannereditor@bonitanews.com
W: http://www.naplesnews.com
Freq: Sat; **Circ:** 30000 Not Audited
Editor: Elysa Delcorto
Editorial Profile: The Banner is a bi-weekly local newspaper, geared toward the residents of Bonita, FL. The newspaper covers all aspects of local news, including sports, weather, entertainment and community news.; Full Page Mono: 10.00; Full Page Colour: 925.00
Currency: US Dollars
NEWSPAPER

The Banner
Owner: Saylor Broadcasting
Editorial: 35 Lovell Ln, Mount Vernon, Kentucky 40456-2914. **T:** 1 606 256-9144
E: bannernewspaper@aol.com
W: http://www.thebanner.us
Freq: Semi-Monthly; **Circ:** 16000 Not Audited
Publisher & Owner: Charles Saylor
Editorial Profile: The Banner is a local newspaper written for residents of Mount Vernon, KY.; Full Page Mono: 5.00; Full Page Colour: 9.00
Currency: US Dollars
NEWSPAPER

Banner-Graphic
Owner: Concord Publications, Inc.
Editorial: 100 N Jackson St, Greencastle, Indiana 46135-1240. **T:** 1 765 653-5151
E: news@bannergraphic.com
W: http://www.bannergraphic.com
Freq: Fri; **Circ:** 5800 Not Audited
Publisher: Randy List
Editorial Profile: Banner-Graphic is a local newspaper published daily except Sunday. It is targeted for the people of Putnam County, IN and the surrounding area. The paper includes articles about local news events, sports, weather and people.; Full Page Mono: 14.25; Full Page Colour: 89.68
Currency: US Dollars
NEWSPAPER

The Baptist Courier
Editorial: 100 Manly St, Greenville, South Carolina 29601-3025. **T:** 1 864 232-8736
E: news@baptistcourier.com
W: http://www.baptistcourier.com
Freq: Bi-Weekly; **Circ:** 69000 Not Audited
Editor: Don Kirkland
Editorial Profile: The Baptist Courier is a bi-weekly newspaper serving Southern Baptist churches and individuals in South Carolina.; Full Page Mono: 75.00
Currency: US Dollars
NEWSPAPER

Baptist Messenger
Owner: Baptist General Convention of Oklahoma
Editorial: 3800 N May Ave, Oklahoma City, Oklahoma 73112-6639. **T:** 1 405 942-3800
E: baptistmessenger@okbaptist.net
W: http://baptistmessenger.com
Freq: Thu; **Circ:** 59665 Not Audited
Editorial Profile: The Baptist Messenger is a local newspaper written for churches in Oklahoma. Editorial mission is to do the work of Jesus Christ by assisting churches in accomplishing their Biblical mission and providing channels for cooperative ministry in Oklahoma and the world.; Full Page Mono: 63.00
Currency: US Dollars
NEWSPAPER

Baptist Standard
Editorial: 7161 Bishop Rd Suite G200, Plano, Texas 75024-3634. **T:** 1 214 630-4571
W: http://www.baptiststandard.com
Freq: Bi-Weekly; **Circ:** 40000 Not Audited
Editorial Profile: Baptist Standard in Plano, TX is a weekly newspaper written for Southern Baptists in Texas. Regular features include Around the State, On the Move, a religious cartoon, and Bible study. Deadlines for the publication fall one week before issue date.; Full Page Mono: 65.00
Currency: US Dollars
NEWSPAPER

Baptist Trumpet
Owner: Baptist Missionary of Arkansas (The)
Editorial: 10712 Interstate 30, Little Rock, Arkansas 72209. **T:** 1 501 565-4601
W: http://www.baptisttrumpet.com
Freq: Wed; **Circ:** 11600 Not Audited
Editor: Diane Spriggs
Editorial Profile: Baptist Trumpet is the official publication of the Baptist Missionary Association of Arkansas.; Full Page Mono: 10.00
Currency: US Dollars
NEWSPAPER

Baraboo News-Republic
Owner: Capital Newspapers
Editorial: 714 Matt's Ferry Rd, Baraboo, Wisconsin 53913-2526. **T:** 1 608 356-4808
E: bnr-news@capitalnewspapers.com
W: http://www.baraboonewsrepublic.com
Freq: Daily; **Circ:** 3895 Not Audited
Editor: Ben Bromley; **Editor:** Ben Bromley; **Editor:** Ben Bromley; **Editor:** Todd Krysiak
Editorial Profile: Baraboo News-Republic provides local news, sports and community events for residents of Baraboo and Sauk County, WI. Deadlines are at 10:30pm CT.; Full Page Mono: 31.19; Full Page Colour: 97.83
Currency: US Dollars
DAILY NEWSPAPER

The Barksdale Warrior
Owner: Gannett Co., Inc.
Editorial: 222 Lake St, Shreveport, Louisiana 71101-3738. **T:** 1 318 456-3241
E: warrior@gannett.com
W: http://www.shreveporttimes.com/apps/pbcs.dll/section?category=barkdsdalewarrior
Freq: Fri; **Circ:** 10000 Not Audited
Publisher: Donald Bailey; **Editor:** Sarah Stegman
Editorial Profile: The Barksdale Warrior is a weekly newspaper serving the Barksdale Air Force Base, LA 2nd Bomb Wing. It provides local news, military news, events and stories of interest to military personnel, civilian residents and employees of the Air Force base. All editorial content is provided by the 2nd Bomb Wing Public Affairs office. Advertising is handled by The Times in Shreveport, LA. Editorial submissions should be e-mailed or mailed to the Public Affairs office by 4:30pm CT. Advertising should be sent to The Times by 4:30pm CT.; Full Page Mono: 15.00
Currency: US Dollars
NEWSPAPER

Barrington Times & Warren Times-Gazette
Owner: East Bay Newspapers
Editorial: 1 Bradford St, Bristol, Rhode Island 02809-1906. **T:** 1 401 245-6000
W: http://www.eastbayri.com **Circ:** 8241 Not Audited
Editor: Josh Bickford; **Publisher:** Matthew Hayes
NEWSPAPER

Barry County Advertiser
Editorial: 904 West St, Cassville, Missouri 65625-1356. **T:** 1 417 847-4475
E: events@4bca.com
Freq: Wed; **Circ:** 12500 Not Audited
Editor: Mary Beth Winder
Editorial Profile: Barry County Advertiser is published weekly for residents in Barry County, MO. The newspaper covers local news and community events. Deadlines are on Tuesdays at noon CT.; Full Page Mono: 4.65
Currency: US Dollars
NEWSPAPER

Bartlesville Examiner-Enterprise
Owner: Stephens Media Group
Editorial: 4125 Nowata Rd, Bartlesville, Oklahoma 74006-5120. **T:** 1 918 335-8200
W: http://www.examiner-enterprise.com
Freq: Daily; **Circ:** 10287 Not Audited
Editor: Susan Albert; **City Editor:** Jessica Miller
Editorial Profile: Bartlesville Examiner-Enterprise is published daily for the residents of Bartlesville, OK. The newspaper covers local news, sports, entertainment, lifestyle, health and community events.; Full Page Mono: 22.66; Full Page Colour: 30.09
Currency: US Dollars
DAILY NEWSPAPER

The Barton Publications
Owner: Barton Publications, Inc.
Editorial: 113 W. Center St., Kyle, Texas 78640. **T:** 1 512 268-7862
E: news@haysfreepress.com
W: http://haysfreepress.com
Freq: Wed; **Circ:** 9000
NEWSPAPER

The Base 68113
Owner: Omaha World-Herald Co.
Editorial: 109 Washington Sq, Ste 221, Offutt AFB, Nebraska 68113. **T:** 1 402 294-3663
E: airpulse@offutt.af.mil
W: http://www.offutt.af.mil
Freq: Fri; **Circ:** 13200 Not Audited
Publisher: Shon Barenklau
Editorial Profile: The Base 68113 provides news and information for and about the Offutt Air Base in Nebraska. The publication is written for active duty members of the Air Force at the Offutt Air Base. The publication does not accept press releases or editorial submissions.; Full Page Mono: 24.70; Full Page Colour: 29.70
Currency: US Dollars
NEWSPAPER

Bastrop Daily Enterprise
Owner: Fortress Investment Group, LLC
Editorial: 119 E Hickory, Bastrop, Louisiana 71220-4549. **T:** 1 318 281-4421
E: news@bastropenterprise.com
W: http://www.bastropenterprise.com
Freq: Daily; **Circ:** 4697
Editorial Profile: Bastrop Daily Enterprise is a local daily newspaper published for the residents of the Morehouse Parish community. The publication covers local news, events and sports.; Full Page Mono: 11.00; Full Page Colour: 72.56
Currency: US Dollars
DAILY NEWSPAPER

Batavia Daily News
Owner: Johnson Newspaper Corp.
Editorial: 2 Apollo Dr, Batavia, New York 14020. **T:** 1 585 343-8000
E: news@batavianews.com
W: http://www.batavianews.com
Freq: Daily; **Circ:** 12499 Not Audited
Editor: Ray Coniglio; **News Editor:** Dirk Hoffman; **Publisher:** Thomas Turnbull
Editorial Profile: Batavia Daily News is published daily for the residents of Genesee, Wyoming and Orleans Counties, NY. The newspaper covers local news, events, weather, sports and other related topics.; Full Page Mono: 22.94; Full Page Colour: 297.94
Currency: US Dollars
DAILY NEWSPAPER

Batesville Daily Guard
Owner: Batesville Guard-Record Co., Inc.
Editorial: 258 W Main St, Batesville, Arkansas 72501-6711. **T:** 1 870 793-2383
E: news@guardonline.com
W: http://www.guardonline.com
Freq: Mon thru Fri; **Circ:** 8928 Not Audited
Publisher: Pat Jones
Editorial Profile: Batesville Guard is a daily evening newspaper published for the residents of Batesville, AR and surrounding areas. It covers local news, features, sports, opinions, births and obituaries.; Full Page Mono: 10.78; Full Page Colour: 41.34
Currency: US Dollars
DAILY NEWSPAPER

The Bath County News-Outlook
Editorial: 18 Water St, Owingsville, Kentucky 40360. **T:** 1 859 289-6425
Freq: Wed; **Circ:** 11000 Not Audited
News Editor: Brad Ballinger; **News Editor:** Brad Ballinger; **News Editor:** Brad Ballinger
Editorial Profile: The Bath County News-Outlook is a weekly newspaper published for the residents of Bath County, KY. The

publication features local news, sports, and community events. The news deadline falls on Tuesday at noon ET.; Full Page Mono: 4.50; Full Page Colour: 587.80
Currency: US Dollars
NEWSPAPER

Battle Creek Enquirer
Owner: Gannett Co., Inc.
Editorial: 77 Michigan Ave E, Battle Creek, Michigan 49017-7029. **T:** 1 269 964-7161
W: http://www.battlecreekenquirer.com
Freq: Daily; **Circ:** 12049 Not Audited
Editorial Profile: Battle Creek Enquirer is a daily newspaper published for the residents of Battle Creek, MI. The publication features news and information about local events, sports, business, crime, politics, and health.; Full Page Mono: 53.28; Full Page Colour: 368.80
Currency: US Dollars
DAILY NEWSPAPER

The Baxter Bulletin
Owner: Gannett Co., Inc.
Editorial: 16 W 6th St, Mountain Home, Arkansas 72653. **T:** 1 870 508-8000
E: newsroom@baxterbulletin.com
W: http://www.baxterbulletin.com
Freq: Daily; **Circ:** 8496 Not Audited
Publisher: Tom Tate
Editorial Profile: The Baxter Bulletin is published daily for the residents of Mountain Home and surrounding communities within Baxter County, AR. The newspaper covers local news, sports, schools, health, government and community events.; Full Page Mono: 12.60; Full Page Colour: 15.60
Currency: US Dollars
DAILY NEWSPAPER

Bay Area News Group - Alameda
Owner: MediaNews Group
Editorial: 1516 Oak St, Alameda, California 94501-2947. **T:** 1 510 748-1683
E: ccnvoice@bayareanewsgroup.com
W: http://www.insidebayarea.com **Circ:** 58500 Not Audited
Editor: Jon Kawamoto; **Editor:** Jon Kawamoto; **Editor:** Jon Kawamoto; **Editor:** Jon Kawamoto
Editorial Profile: The newspapers are a part of the Bay Area News Group subsidiary of MediaNews Group.
NEWSPAPER

Bay Area News Group - Oakland
Owner: MediaNews Group
Editorial: 1970 Broadway Ste 100, Oakland, California 94612-2249. **T:** 1 510 208-6450
W: http://insidebayarea.com **Circ:** 99952 Not Audited
Editorial Profile: The newspapers are a part of the Bay Area News Group subsidiary of MediaNews Group.
DAILY NEWSPAPER

Bay Area News Group - Pleasanton
Owner: MediaNews Group
Editorial: 127 Spring St, Pleasanton, California 94566-6623. **T:** 1 925 935-2525 **Circ:** 114958 Not Audited
Publisher: Steve Rossi
Editorial Profile: The newspapers are a part of the Bay Area News Group subsidiary of MediaNews Group.
DAILY NEWSPAPER

Bay Area News Group - Richmond
Owner: MediaNews Group
Editorial: 4301 Lakeside Dr, Richmond, California 94806-5281. **T:** 1 510 262-2724
W: http://www.insidebayarea.com **Circ:** 31800 Not Audited
Editorial Profile: Bay Area News Group - Richmond is a part of the Bay Area News Group subsidiary of MediaNews Group.
NEWSPAPER

Bay Area News Group - Walnut Creek
Owner: MediaNews Group
Editorial: 175 Lennon Ln Ste 100, Walnut Creek, California 94598-2466.
T: 1 925 943-8300
E: ccnnewsrelease@bayareanewsgroup.com
W: http://www.contracostatimes.com
Circ: 36377 Not Audited
Editor: Catherine Jacobson
Editorial Profile: Bay Area News Group - Walnut Creek, CA is a part of the Bay Area News Group subsidiary of MediaNews Group.
NEWSPAPER

The Bay Area Observer
Owner: Bay Area Observer
Editorial: 527 N Shady Ln, La Porte, Texas 77571-7243. **T:** 1 281 907-3140

E: editor@bayareaobserver.com
W: http://www.bayareaobserver.com
Freq: Thu
Editorial Profile: The Bay Area Observer is a weekly newspaper providing Local and Community News coverage for the residents of Seabrook, La Porte, Kemah, TX, as well as the Galveston Bay Area, TX.
NEWSPAPER

The Bay Beacon
Owner: Beacon Newspapers
Editorial: 1181 John Sims Pkwy E, Niceville, Florida 32578. **T:** 1 850 678-1080
E: info@baybeacon.com
W: http://baybeacon.com
Freq: Wed; **Circ:** 15500 Not Audited
Editorial Profile: The Bay Beacon is a weekly newspaper published for the residents of Niceville, Valparaiso, Blue Water Bay and Freeport, FL.; Full Page Mono: 14.95
Currency: US Dollars
NEWSPAPER

Bay City Times
Owner: MLive Media Group
Editorial: 311 5th St, Bay City, Michigan 48708-5806. **T:** 1 989 895-8551
E: bcnews@mlive.com
W: http://www.mlive.com/bctimes **Circ:** 16548
Editorial Profile: Bay City Times is a daily newspaper published for the residents of Bay City, MI. The publication covers local news, business, sports, education, city and county government, police agencies, health, science, human services and community events. Deadlines are daily between 7:30am and 10am ET. Circulation figures for Thursday are 20,721, for Friday 21,235 and for Sunday 31,721.; Full Page Mono: 38.27; Full Page Colour: 229.88
Currency: US Dollars
DAILY NEWSPAPER

The Bay State Banner
Editorial: 23 Drydock Ave, Boston, Massachusetts 2210. **T:** 1 617 261-4600
E: news@bannerpub.com
W: http://www.baystatebanner.com
Freq: Thu; **Circ:** 32351 Not Audited
Editorial Profile: The Bay State Banner covers news stories for the African-American community of Greater Boston.; Full Page Mono: 42.00; Full Page Colour: 1925.76
Currency: US Dollars
NEWSPAPER

Bay Weekly
Owner: New Bay Enterprises, Inc.
Editorial: 1629 Forest Dr, Annapolis, Maryland 21403. **T:** 1 410 626-9888
E: editor@bayweekly.com
W: http://bayweekly.com
Freq: Thu; **Circ:** 19000 Not Audited
Editorial Profile: Bay Weekly is written for the residents of Severna Park, greater Annapolis, southern Anne Arundel County and Calvert County, MD. The news deadlines fall on Fridays at noon ET.; Full Page Mono: 30.00
Currency: US Dollars
NEWSPAPER

The Bayonet
Owner: Landmark Military Newspapers
Editorial: 35 Ridgeway Looop, Ste 381, Fort Benning, Georgia 31905. **T:** 1 706 545-4622
W: http://www.ledger-enquirer.com/bayonet
Freq: Fri; **Circ:** 22000 Not Audited
Editorial Profile: The Bayonet is a weekly newspaper published for Fort Benning Base, GA. The publication covers local news and community events. Deadlines are on Fridays at noon, ET.; Full Page Mono: 22.00
Currency: US Dollars
NEWSPAPER

Bayonne Community News
Owner: Hudson Reporter Newspapers
Editorial: 170 Broadway, Bayonne, New Jersey 7002. **T:** 1 201 437-2460
E: bcneditorial@hudsonreporter.com
W: http://hudsonreporter.com
Freq: Wed; **Circ:** 28000 Not Audited
Editor: Kate Rounds
Editorial Profile: Bayonne (NJ) Community News is a weekly newspaper that covers local news and events in a region that includes Country Village, Society Hill, Franklin Park and Port Liberte in Jersey City, NJ.; Full Page Mono: 19.25
Currency: US Dollars
NEWSPAPER

The Bayou Journal
Owner: Bayou Co. LLC
Editorial: 3415 Highway 70 S, Pierre Part, Louisiana 70339-4524. **T:** 1 985 252-0501

E: bayoujournal@teche.net
W: http://www.bayoujournal.com
Freq: Tue
Editorial Profile: The Bayou Journal is a weekly community newspaper serving the Assumption Parish communities of Pierre Part and Belle River, LA, and also surrounding communities in Ascension and Saint Mary Parishes. The publications includes community news, events and sports.
NEWSPAPER

Bayside Gazette
Owner: Flag Publications
Editorial: 11 S Main St, Berlin, Maryland 21811-1426. **T:** 1 410 641-0039
E: Info@baysidegazette.com
W: http://www.baysideoc.com
Freq: Thu; **Circ:** 10000 Not Audited
Editor: Nathan Brunet
Editorial Profile: Bayside Gazette is a weekly community newspaper written for the residents of Berlin, MD and the surrounding areas.; Full Page Mono: 15.00
Currency: US Dollars
NEWSPAPER

Baytown Sun
Owner: Southern Newspapers, Inc.
Editorial: 1301 Memorial Dr, Baytown, Texas 77520-2401. **T:** 1 281 422-8302
E: sunnews@baytownsun.com
W: http://baytownsun.com
Freq: Daily; **Circ:** 9363 Not Audited
Editor & Publisher: Janie Halter
Editorial Profile: Baytown Sun is a daily newspaper published for the residents of Baytown, TX. The newspaper covers local news, sports and lifestyle. The weekend edition of the paper is a combination of Saturday, Sunday and Monday.; Full Page Mono: 14.50; Full Page Colour: 89.85
Currency: US Dollars
DAILY NEWSPAPER

BDN weekend
Owner: Fortress Investment Group, LLC
Editorial: 412 High St, Boonville, Missouri 65233-1242. **T:** 1 660 882-5335
E: news@boonvilledailynews.com
W: http://www.boonvilledailynews.com
Freq: Wed; **Circ:** 10000 Not Audited
Editor: Ben Bennett; **Publisher:** Deborah Marshall
Editorial Profile: BDN Weekend is a free weekly newspaper that is available on newsstands and is also delivered to subscribers of Boonville Daily News as an insert in the paper. It previews and lists local weekend happenings.; Full Page Mono: 12.30
Currency: US Dollars
NEWSPAPER

The Beach Reporter
Owner: MediaNews Group
Editorial: 2615 Pacific Coast Hwy Ste 329, Hermosa Beach, California 90254-2229.
T: 1 310 372-0388
E: beachreporter@gmail.com
W: http://www.tbrnews.com
Freq: Thu; **Circ:** 50000 Not Audited
Editor: Eric Stitt
Editorial Profile: The Beach Reporter in Hermosa Beach, CA covers local news, business, sports, health, entertainment and community events for residents of Manhattan Beach, Hermosa Beach, Redondo Beach and El Segundo, CA.; Full Page Mono: 9.90; Full Page Colour: 276.00
Currency: US Dollars
NEWSPAPER

Beachcomber
Owner: Beeler & Associates
Editorial: 5199 E Pacific Coast Hwy, Ste 608, Long Beach, California 90804.
T: 1 562 597-8000
E: editor@longbeachcomber.com
W: http://www.longbeachcomber.com
Freq: Bi-Weekly; **Circ:** 42000 Not Audited
Publisher: Jay Beeler
Editorial Profile: Beachcomber in Long Beach, CA is a community newspaper that covers local news and events.; Full Page Mono: 36.00
Currency: US Dollars
NEWSPAPER

The Beacon
Editorial: 205 SE Catawba Rd, Ste G, Port Clinton, Ohio 43452. **T:** 1 419 732-2154
W: http://www.thebeacon.net
Freq: Thu; **Circ:** 14239 Not Audited
Editorial Profile: The Beacon is a weekly newspaper serving Ottawa County, OH. It covers news related to arts & entertainment, sports, business and health. Deadlines for news releases, classifieds and advertisements

are at 4pm on Mondays.; Full Page Mono: 13.75
Currency: US Dollars
NEWSPAPER

The Beacon
Owner: West Publishing and Advertising, Inc.
Editorial: N2759 State Road 67, Williams Bay, Wisconsin 53191-3704. **T:** 1 262 245-1877
E: beaconnews@charter.net
W: http://www.readthebeacon.com
Freq: Bi-Weekly; **Circ:** 20000 Not Audited
Editorial Profile: The Beacon is published weekly for the residents of Williams Bay, WI and surrounding areas. The newspaper covers local news, features and community events.; Full Page Mono: 13.00
Currency: US Dollars
NEWSPAPER

The Beacon
Owner: Diocese of Patterson
Editorial: 775 Valley Rd, Clifton, New Jersey 07013-2205. **T:** 1 973 279-8845
E: catholicbeacon@patersondiocese.org
W: http://www.patersondiocese.org/index.cfm
Freq: Weekly; **Circ:** 30000
News Editor: Michael Wojcik
Editorial Profile: The Beacon is written for the Diocese of Paterson, NJ.; Full Page Mono: 25.50
Currency: US Dollars
NEWSPAPER

Beacon Communications
Editorial: 1944 Warwick Ave, Warwick, Rhode Island 2889. **T:** 1 401 732-3100
W: http://www.rhodybeat.com **Circ:** 19525
Editor: Daniel Kittredge
NEWSPAPER

Beacon Newspapers
Owner: National County Publications
Editorial: 5 Centre St, Hempstead, New York 11550. **T:** 1 516 481-5400
E: thebeaconnews5@aol.com
Freq: Weekly; **Circ:** 23100 Not Audited
Publisher: Kathleen Hoegl; **Editor:** John McGill
NEWSPAPER

Beacon Senior Newspaper
Owner: VanGundy (Kevin)
Editorial: 524 30 Rd Ste 1, Grand Junction, Colorado 81502-4437. **T:** 1 970 243-8829
E: beacon@pendantpublishing.com
W: http://www.beaconseniornews.com
Freq: Monthly; **Circ:** 14000 Not Audited
Publisher: Kevin VanGundy
Editorial Profile: Beacon Senior Newspaper is a monthly paper that focuses on adults 40+ in Delta, Montrose and Mesa Counties, CO.; Full Page Mono: 28.45
Currency: US Dollars
NEWSPAPER

Beardstown Newspapers, Inc.
Editorial: 1210 Wall St, Beardstown, Illinois 62618. **T:** 1 217 323-1010
E: stargazette@casscomm.com
W: http://www.beardstownnewspapers.com
Circ: 4350 Not Audited
Editor: Marla Blair
NEWSPAPER

Beatrice Daily Sun
Owner: Lee Enterprises, Inc.
Editorial: 200 N 7th St, Beatrice, Nebraska 68310. **T:** 1 402 223-5233
E: news@beatricedailysun.com
W: http://www.beatricedailysun.com
Freq: Daily; **Circ:** 4524 Not Audited
Publisher and Editor: Patrick Ethridge
Editorial Profile: Beatrice Daily Sun is a daily newspaper published everyday except Sunday for the residents of Gage County, NE. It reports the local news and events in the community. The lead time is the day prior to publication by 5pm CT. Deadline is one day prior to publication issue date.; Full Page Mono: 16.46; Full Page Colour: 280.00
Currency: US Dollars
DAILY NEWSPAPER

The Beaufort Gazette
Owner: McClatchy Newspapers
Editorial: 1556 Salem Rd, Beaufort, South Carolina 29902-5236. **T:** 1 843 524-3183
E: gazette@beaufortgazette.com
W: http://www.islandpacket.com/beaufortgazette
Freq: Daily; **Circ:** 10439 Not Audited
Publisher: Sara Johnson Borton; **Editor:** Jeff Kidd
Editorial Profile: The Beaufort Gazette is a daily newspaper for the residents of Beaufort, SC. The newspaper began printing in the early 1900s. It covers local news, sports, lifestyles

and community events.; Full Page Mono: 40.00; Full Page Colour: 234.48
Currency: US Dollars
DAILY NEWSPAPER

Beaumont Enterprise
Owner: Beaumont Enterprise-Hearst Newspapers
Editorial: 380 Main St, Beaumont, Texas 77701-2331. **T:** 1 409 833-3311
E: localnews@beaumontenterprise.com
W: http://www.beaumontenterprise.com
Freq: Daily; **Circ:** 21717 Not Audited
Editor: Tim Kelly; **Editor:** Tim Kelly; **Editor:** Tim Kelly
Editorial Profile: Beaumont Enterprise provides news coverage for residents of Beaumont and southeast Texas. The paper covers local and regional news, arts & entertainment, sports and business. Do not fax in press releases.; Full Page Mono: 56.51; Full Page Colour: 183.36
Currency: US Dollars
DAILY NEWSPAPER

Beauregard Daily News
Owner: GateHouse Media Inc.
Editorial: 903 W 1st St, Deridder, Louisiana 70634-3701. **T:** 1 337 462-0616
E: newsdeskbdn@gmail.com
W: http://www.beauregarddailynews.net
Freq: Daily; **Circ:** 6700 Not Audited
Editor: Linda Barron
Editorial Profile: Beauregard Daily News offers in-depth coverage of local news and sporting events for the residents of Deridder, LA.; Full Page Mono: 13.70; Full Page Colour: 17.70
Currency: US Dollars
DAILY NEWSPAPER

Beaver County Times
Owner: Calkins Media
Editorial: 400 Fair Ave, Beaver, Pennsylvania 15009-1998. **T:** 1 724 775-3200
E: timesnews@timesonline.com
W: http://www.timesonline.com
Freq: Mon thru Fri; **Circ:** 25580 Not Audited
Editor: Larry Howsare; **Publisher:** Lisa Reese
Editorial Profile: Beaver County Times' editorial mission is to provide local news coverage to the residents of Beaver County, PA. The publication is geared toward local residents. Deadlines for the publication are same day before issue date.; Full Page Mono: 41.25; Full Page Colour: 54.66
Currency: US Dollars
DAILY NEWSPAPER

Beaverton Leader
Owner: Oregon Live LLC
Editorial: 4800 SW Griffith Dr Ste 230, Beaverton, Oregon 97005-8709.
T: 1 503 294-5950
E: newsclerk@beavertonleader.com
W: http://www.oregonlive.com/beaverton-leader/
Freq: Wed
Editor: Amy Wang
Editorial Profile: Beaverton Leader is a weekly newspaper providing Local News, Sports, Business and Features coverage for the residents of Beaverton, OR.
NEWSPAPER

Bedford Gazette
Owner: Bedford Gazette
Editorial: 424 W Penn St, Bedford, Pennsylvania 15522-1230. **T:** 1 814 623-1151
E: bedfordgazette@embarqmail.com
W: http://www.bedfordgazette.com
Freq: Daily; **Circ:** 9837 Not Audited
Publisher: Joseph Beegle
Editorial Profile: Bedford Gazette is a daily newspaper for the residents of Bedford, PA. It covers news and events in the local community.; Full Page Mono: 15.73; Full Page Colour: 53.00
Currency: US Dollars
DAILY NEWSPAPER

Bedford Now
Owner: Monroe Publishing Company
Editorial: 8336 Monroe Rd, Lambertville, Michigan 48144-9753. **T:** 1 734 847-0505
E: info@bedfordnow.com
W: http://www.bedfordnow.com
Freq: Sat; **Circ:** 12000 Not Audited
Publisher: Lonnie Cappler-Moyer; Full Page Mono: 12.50
Currency: US Dollars
NEWSPAPER

Bedford Press
Editorial: 3363 Hemmingway Ln, Lambertville, Michigan 48144-9653. **T:** 1 737 8566680
E: bedfordpress@aol.com
Freq: Bi-Weekly; **Circ:** 14000 Not Audited
Editorial Profile: The Bedford Press is a local weekly newspaper serving the residents of Southern Monroe County, MI. It provides local news and information for Southern Monroe County, MI. Currently, the paper does not have a Website.; Full Page Mono: 8.75
Currency: US Dollars
NEWSPAPER

The Bee
Owner: Community Newspapers Inc.
Editorial: 1837 SE Harold St, Portland, Oregon 97202. **T:** 1 503 232-2326
E: readthebee@myexcel.com
W: http://vvvvvv.portlandtribune.com/the-bee-news
Freq: Monthly; **Circ:** 19500 Not Audited
Publisher: Brian Monihan; **Editor:** Eric Norberg
Editorial Profile: The Bee is a free, monthly newspaper serving southeast Portland, including the communities of Sellwood, Eastmoreland, Westmoreland, Garthwick, Brooklyn, Woodstock, Ardenwald and Reed, OR. It covers local news, events, schools, businesses, sports and features.; Full Page Mono: 23.00
Currency: US Dollars
NEWSPAPER

Bee & Herald Publishing Company
Editorial: 214 N Wilson Ave, Jefferson, Iowa 50129. **T:** 1 515 386-4161
E: news@beeherald.com **Circ:** 10700 Not Audited
Editor: Frederick Morain; **Editor:** Doug Rieder
NEWSPAPER

Bee Publications
Owner: Bee Publications, Inc.
Editorial: 5564 Main St, Williamsville, New York 14221-5410. **T:** 1 716 632-4700
W: http://www.beenews.com **Circ:** 60220
Editor: Tim Chipp; **Editor:** Keaton DePriest; **Editor:** Christopher Gordon; **Editor:** Julie Halm; **Editor:** Andrea Kimbriel; **Editor:** Kimberly McDowell; **Editor:** Paul Olczak
Editorial Profile: Bee Publications is a weekly community newspaper publisher serving the residents of Buffalo, NY and the surrounding area.
NEWSPAPER

The Bee Publishing Co.
Owner: Bee Publishing Company, Inc.
Editorial: 5 Church Hill Rd, Newtown, Connecticut 6470. **T:** 1 203 426-3141
E: editor@thebee.com
W: http://www.thebee.com **Circ:** 15475 Not Audited
Editor: Curtiss Clark; **Editor:** Shannon Hicks
NEWSPAPER

The Belle Plaine News
Editorial: 431 N Merchant St, Belle Plaine, Kansas 67013. **T:** 1 620 488-2234
E: bpnews@sktc.net
Freq: Weekly; **Circ:** 1300 Not Audited
Publisher: Shayleen Casteel; **Editor:** Joshua Delaughder
Editorial Profile: The Belle Plaine News is a weekly community newspaper publisher serving the residents of Belle Plaine and Oxford, KS.
NEWSPAPER

Bellefontaine Examiner
Owner: Hubbard Publishing Company
Editorial: 127 E Chillicothe Ave, Bellefontaine, Ohio 43311. **T:** 1 937 592-3060
E: news@examiner.org
W: http://www.examiner.org
Freq: Daily; **Circ:** 9130 Not Audited
Editor: Miriam Baier; **Publisher:** Janet Hubbard; **Editor:** Joel Mast; **Editor:** Sue Pitts
Editorial Profile: Bellefontaine Examiner is a daily newspaper for the residents of Bellefontaine, OH. For the past 110 years the Bellefontaine Examiner has been reporting the local news and events of Logan County.; Full Page Mono: 11.75; Full Page Colour: 40.01
Currency: US Dollars
DAILY NEWSPAPER

Belleville News-Democrat
Owner: McClatchy Newspapers
Editorial: 120 S Illinois St, Belleville, Illinois 62220. **T:** 1 618 234-1000
E: newsroom@bnd.com
W: http://www.bnd.com
Freq: Daily; **Circ:** 37626 Not Audited
Editor: Suzanne Boyle; **Editor:** Suzanne Boyle; **Editor:** Suzanne Boyle; **Editor:** Suzanne Boyle; **City Editor:** Gary Dotson; **City Editor:** Gary Dotson; **News Editor:** Mike Koziatek; **News Editor:** Mike Koziatek; **Publisher:** Jay Tebbe
Editorial Profile: Belleville News-Democrat is a daily newspaper serving residents in Southern Illinois. It focuses on local, breaking news and features about lifestyle, arts & entertainment and sports. On Fridays, the Pinckneyville (IL) Democrat is inserted in the paper to provide in-depth, local news about Pinckneyville and its residents.; Full Page Mono: 53.77; Full Page Colour: 143.40
Currency: US Dollars
DAILY NEWSPAPER

Belleville News-Democrat
Editorial: 142A N Main St, Ste 4, Edwardsville, Illinois 62025-1902. **T:** 1 618 692-9481
DAILY NEWSPAPER

Bellevue Gazette
Owner: Ohio Community Media LLC.
Editorial: 107 N Sandusky St, Bellevue, Ohio 44811. **T:** 1 419 483-4190
W: http://www.thebellevuegazette.com
Freq: Daily; **Circ:** 2580 Not Audited
Publisher: Rick Miller
Editorial Profile: Bellevue Gazette is a daily newspaper for the residents of Bellevue, OH. It covers news and events in the local community.; Full Page Mono: 12.45; Full Page Colour: 215.00
Currency: US Dollars
DAILY NEWSPAPER

Bellevue Reporter
Owner: Black Press
Editorial: 2700 Richards Rd Ste 201, Bellevue, Washington 98005-4200. **T:** 1 425 453-4270
E: news@bellevuereporter.com
W: http://www.bellevuereporter.com
Freq: Fri; **Circ:** 43000
Editor: Craig Groshart; **Publisher:** Janet Taylor
Editorial Profile: Bellevue Reporter is a local, weekly newspaper serving residents of Bellevue, WA. The paper includes local news, entertainment, business, sports and community events.; Full Page Mono: 34.15
Currency: US Dollars
NEWSPAPER

Bellingham Herald
Owner: McClatchy Newspapers
Editorial: 1155 N State St, Bellingham, Washington 98225-5037. **T:** 1 360 676-2600
E: newsroom@bellinghamherald.com
W: http://www.bellinghamherald.com
Freq: Daily; **Circ:** 16562 Not Audited
Publisher: Mark Owings
Editorial Profile: Bellingham Herald is a daily newspaper for the residents of Bellingham, WA. It covers the news and events of the local community.; Full Page Mono: 44.88; Full Page Colour: 145.85
Currency: US Dollars
DAILY NEWSPAPER

Beloit Daily News
Owner: Hagadone Corp.
Editorial: 149 State St, Beloit, Wisconsin 53511-6299. **T:** 1 608 365-8811
E: news@beloitdailynews.com
W: http://www.beloitdailynews.com
Freq: Daily; **Circ:** 13975 Not Audited
Editor: William Barth; **Publisher:** Kent Eymann; **City Editor:** Clint Wolf; **City Editor:** Clint Wolf
Editorial Profile: Beloit Daily News is a daily newspaper for Rock County, WI and Winnebago, IL. It covers news and events in the local community.; Full Page Mono: 32.14; Full Page Colour: 87.34
Currency: US Dollars
DAILY NEWSPAPER

Beltsville News
Editorial: 11007 Emack Rd, Beltsville, Maryland 20705-2803. **T:** 1 301 937-6796
W: http://www.beltsville.com/beltsvillenews
Freq: Monthly; **Circ:** 14000
Editorial Profile: Beltsville News is a monthly newspaper for the residents of Beltsville, MD.; Full Page Mono: 6.50
Currency: US Dollars
NEWSPAPER

Belvidere Daily Republican
Owner: Rock Valley Publishing LLC
Editorial: 130 S State St Ste 101, Belvidere, Illinois 61008-3697. **T:** 1 815 547-0084
E: bdrnews@rvpublishing.com
W: http://www.belvideredailyrepublican.net
Freq: Daily; **Circ:** 4317 Not Audited
Publisher: Pete Cruger; **Editor:** Tony Dalpra
Editorial Profile: Belvidere Daily Republican is published for the residents of Boone County, IL. The newspaper covers news, business, sports, education and entertainment.; Full Page Mono: 16.80; Full Page Colour: 19.90
Currency: US Dollars
DAILY NEWSPAPER

Belvoir Eagle
Owner: BH Media Group
Editorial: 9820 Flagler Rd, Fort Belvoir, Virginia 22060-5610. **T:** 1 703 805-2019
E: editor@belvoireagle.com
W: http://www.belvoireagle.com
Freq: Thu; **Circ:** 20000 Not Audited
Editor: Kyle Ford
Editorial Profile: Belvoir Eagle is a weekly newspaper written for active duty military personnel in Fort Belvoir, VA. It covers news and events.; Full Page Mono: 19.67
Currency: US Dollars
NEWSPAPER

The Bemidji Pioneer
Owner: Forum Communications Co.
Editorial: 1320 Neilson Ave Se, Bemidji, Minnesota 56601-5406. **T:** 1 218 333-9200
E: news@bemidjipioneer.com
W: http://www.bemidjipioneer.com
Freq: Daily; **Circ:** 8229 Not Audited
Editor: Matt Cory; **Publisher:** Dennis Doeden
Editorial Profile: The mission of The Bemidji Pioneer is to be the source for news, sports, events and community coverage in North Central, MN. Readers of the paper are residents of North Central, MN. Topics covered include news, sports, government, education and others.; Full Page Mono: 19.75; Full Page Colour: 64.60
Currency: US Dollars
DAILY NEWSPAPER

Benicia Herald
Owner: Gibson Group
Editorial: 820 1st St, Benicia, California 94510. **T:** 1 707 745-0733
E: beniciaherald@gmail.com
W: http://beniciaheraldonline.com
Freq: Daily; **Circ:** 9000 Not Audited
Editor: Marc Ethier; **Publisher:** David Payne
Editorial Profile: Benicia Herald is a local newspaper written for residents of Benicia, CA. The newspaper, published daily except for Monday and Saturday, covers local news, business, sports, social issues and community events.; Full Page Mono: 12.60; Full Page Colour: 46.86
Currency: US Dollars
DAILY NEWSPAPER

Bennington Banner
Owner: MediaNews Group
Editorial: 425 Main St, Bennington, Vermont 05201-2149. **T:** 1 802 447-7567
E: news@benningtonbanner.com
W: http://www.benningtonbanner.com
Freq: Daily; **Circ:** 5761 Not Audited
County News Editor: Mark Rondeau; **News Editor:** Stephanie Ryan; **News Editor:** Stephanie Ryan; **News Editor:** Stephanie Ryan
Editorial Profile: Bennington Banner is a daily newspaper for the residents of Bennington, VT. It covers news and events of the local community as well as nationwide news.; Full Page Mono: 22.60; Full Page Colour: 248.00
Currency: US Dollars
DAILY NEWSPAPER

The Benton County Daily Record
Owner: Wehco Media Inc.
Editorial: 104 SW A St, Bentonville, Arkansas 72712-5867. **T:** 1 479 271-3700
E: newsroom@nwaonline.com
W: http://www.nwaonline.com
Freq: Daily; **Circ:** 11264 Not Audited
Publisher: Jeff Jeffus; **Editor:** Mike Jones
Editorial Profile: The Benton County Daily Record is written for the residents of Benton County, AR. The outlet offers RSS (Really Simple Syndication).; Full Page Mono: 13.98; Full Page Colour: 51.82
Currency: US Dollars
DAILY NEWSPAPER

The Benton Evening News
Owner: GateHouse Media Inc.
Editorial: 111 E Church St, Benton, Illinois 62812-2238. **T:** 1 618 438-5611
E: benton@clearwave.com
W: http://www.bentoneveningnews.com
Freq: Mon thru Fri; **Circ:** 3000 Not Audited
Editorial Profile: The Benton Evening News is a daily newspaper for the residents of Benton and Franklin County, IL. The publication covers news and events in the local and national community.; Full Page Mono: 10.75; Full Page Colour: 35.04
Currency: US Dollars
DAILY NEWSPAPER

The Berkshire Eagle
Owner: MediaNews Group

Editorial: 75 S Church St, Pittsfield, Massachusetts 01201-6157.
T: 1 413 447-7311
E: news@berkshireeagle.com
W: http://www.berkshireeagle.com
Freq: Daily; **Circ:** 28608 Not Audited
Editor: William Everhart; **Editor:** Ben Garver; **Publisher:** Andrew Mick
Editorial Profile: The Berkshire Eagle is a daily, morning newspaper serving Berkshire County, MA and the surrounding area. It covers local and regional news, sports, health, lifestyle, business and obituaries.; Full Page Mono: 38.35; Full Page Colour: 450.00
Currency: US Dollars
DAILY NEWSPAPER

Berks-Mont News
Owner: Journal Register Company
Editorial: 29 N Hanover St, Pottstown, Pennsylvania 19464-5449. **T:** 1 610 367-6041
E: adstaff@berksmontnews.com
W: http://www.berksmontnews.com
Circ: 10831 Not Audited
Editor: Rebecca Blanchard; **Editor:** Matthew D'Ippolito; **Editor:** Lisa Mitchell; **Editor:** Matt Reichl; **Editor:** Emily Thiel
Editorial Profile: Berks-Mont News in Pottstown, PA is a publisher of community newspapers, including The Hamburg Area Item, Tri County Record, The Southern Berks News, Boyertown Area Times, Kutztown Area Patriot and The Phoenix Reporter & Item.
NEWSPAPER

The Berlin Citizen
Owner: Record-Journal Publishing Company
Editorial: 979 Farmington Ave, Kensington, Connecticut 6037. **T:** 1 860 829-5720
E: news@theberlincitizen.com
W: http://www.theberlincitizen.com
Freq: Thu; **Circ:** 10000 Not Audited
Publisher: Eliot White
Editorial Profile: The Berlin Citizen is a weekly newspaper for residents and businesses in Berlin, East Berlin and Kensington, CT. The publication covers news and events. Deadlines are Thursdays at 5pm ET.; Full Page Mono: 16.45
Currency: US Dollars
NEWSPAPER

Berlin Daily Sun
Owner: Country News Club, Inc.
Editorial: 164 Main St, Berlin, New Hampshire 03570-2477. **T:** 1 603 752-5858
E: bds@berlindailysun.com
W: http://www.berlindailysun.com
Freq: Daily; **Circ:** 8925 Not Audited
Publisher: Mark Guerringue; **Editor:** Adam Hirshan
Editorial Profile: Berlin Daily Sun is a daily newspaper for the Northern New Hampshire Lakes Region. It covers news and events in the local communities.; Full Page Mono: 6.50; Full Page Colour: 175.00
Currency: US Dollars
DAILY NEWSPAPER

The Berlin Journal Company
Editorial: 301 June St, Berlin, Wisconsin 54923. **T:** 1 920 361-1515
E: news@theberlinjournal.com **Circ:** 8540 Not Audited
Editor: Jason Fox; **Publisher:** Ty Gonyo
NEWSPAPER

Bernice Banner-News
Owner: Boyett (Jessie)
Editorial: 227 Boyette Rd, Bernice, Louisiana 71222. **T:** 1 318 285-7424
E: bernicebanner@oeccwildblue.com
Freq: Thu; **Circ:** 12000 Not Audited
Editorial Profile: Bernice (LA) Banner-News is a weekly publication written for residents of the Bernice, Junction City, Spearsville and Lillie, LA. The newspaper focuses on local and national news, politics, sports, education and arts & entertainment. Deadlines are Mondays at noon CT.; Full Page Mono: 5.00
Currency: US Dollars
NEWSPAPER

Bettendorf News
Owner: Lee Enterprises, Inc.
Editorial: 500 E 3rd St, Davenport, Iowa 52801. **T:** 1 563 383-2396
E: bettnews@qctimes.com
W: http://www.thebettendorfnews.com
Freq: Thu; **Circ:** 10000 Not Audited
Publisher: Julie Bechtel; **Editor:** Janet Hill; **Editor:** Janet Hill; **Editor:** Janet Hill; **Editor:** Janet Hill
Editorial Profile: Bettendorf News is written for those who live and/or are interested in Bettendorf, LeClaire, Pleasant Valley and Riverdale, IA. The newspaper covers local news, national news that has an impact on their readership, local sports, local politics, local arts & entertainment and local education issues. Deadlines are on Mondays.; Full Page Mono: 18.75; Full Page Colour: 905.41
Currency: US Dollars
NEWSPAPER

Beverly Hills Courier
Owner: Kent Meehan (Paula)
Editorial: 9100 Wilshire Blvd Ste 360, Beverly Hills, California 90212-3415.
T: 1 310 278-1322 **E:** editorial@bhcourier.com
W: http://bhcourier.com
Freq: Fri; **Circ:** 39975 Not Audited
Publisher: Marcia Wilson Hobbs
Editorial Profile: Beverly Hills Courier is a local newspaper published for the residents of Beverly Hills, CA area. The newspaper covers local and national news, sports, politics, arts & entertainment and education issues.; Full Page Mono: 65.30; Full Page Colour: 75.38
Currency: US Dollars
NEWSPAPER

Beverly Hills Weekly
Editorial: 140 S Beverly Dr Ste 201, Beverly Hills, California 90212-3050.
T: 1 310 887-0788 **E:** editor@bhweekly.com
W: http://www.bhweekly.com
Freq: Thu; **Circ:** 15000 Not Audited
Editor: Andrea Aldana; **Publisher:** Josh Gross
Editorial Profile: Beverly Hills Weekly is the weekly local newspaper written for those who live and/or are interested in Beverly Hills, CA. The newspaper covers local news, sports, politics, arts & entertainment and education issues. It also covers national news that has an impact on their readership. All releases should be addressed to the editor. Deadlines for the publication are three days before publication before issue date.; Full Page Mono: 13.13
Currency: US Dollars
NEWSPAPER

Beverly Press/Park Labrea News
Editorial: 5150 Wilshire Blvd, Suite 330, Los Angeles, California 90036-4303.
T: 1 323 933-5518
W: http://www.beverlypress.com
Freq: Thu; **Circ:** 13000 Not Audited
Editorial Profile: Beverly Press/Park Labrea News is a weekly, local newspaper written for residents of Los Angeles and Beverly Hills, CA. It publishes the same content under two different banners, Park Labrea News or Beverly Press, depending on its area of distribution.; Full Page Mono: 16.00; Full Page Colour: 20.38
Currency: US Dollars
NEWSPAPER

BHG, Inc.
Owner: BHG Inc.
Editorial: 91 N Main St, Garrison, North Dakota 58540-7166. **T:** 1 701 463-2201
W: http://www.bhgnews.com **Circ:** 15888 Not Audited
Publisher: Mike Gackle; **Editor:** Stu Merry
NEWSPAPER

Biblical Recorder
Owner: Biblical Recorder, Inc.
Editorial: 205 Convention Drive, Cary, North Carolina 27511. **T:** 1 919 847-2127
E: editor@brnow.org
W: http://www.brnow.org/
Freq: Sat; **Circ:** 20000 Not Audited
Editorial Profile: Biblical Recorder is a weekly newspaper in Raleigh, NC, serving North Carolina's Baptist community, with news articles, feature stories, editorials, and an events calendar.; Full Page Mono: 52.00; Full Page Colour: 1750.00
Currency: US Dollars
NEWSPAPER

Big Island Weekly
Owner: Stephens Media, LLC
Editorial: 65-1279 Kawaihae Rd Ste 217, Kamuela, Hawaii 96743-8444.
T: 1 808 930-8668
E: editor@bigislandweekly.com
W: http://www.bigislandweekly.com
Freq: Wed; **Circ:** 15000
Editorial Profile: Big Island Weekly is a free, weekly community newspaper serving Hilo, HI. Editorial features include community news, sports and features.; Full Page Mono: 23.00
Currency: US Dollars
NEWSPAPER

Big Spring Herald
Owner: Horizon Publications Inc
Editorial: 710 Scurry St, Big Spring, Texas 79720-2723. **T:** 1 432 263-7331
E: citydesk@bigspringherald.com
W: http://www.bigspringherald.com
Freq: Daily; **Circ:** 4700 Not Audited
City Editor: Thomas Jenkins; **Editor/News Editor:** Bill McClellan; **Publisher:** Ron Midkiff
Editorial Profile: Big Spring Herald is a local newspaper written for the residents of Big Spring, TX. It covers local and national news, sports, politics, education and arts & entertainment. All releases should be addressed to the editor.; Full Page Mono: 20.14; Full Page Colour: 50.55
Currency: US Dollars
DAILY NEWSPAPER

The Bilingual News
Editorial: 5th Ave., Bay Shore, New York 11706. **T:** 1 800 256-8161
E: bilingualnews@gmail.com
W: http://www.thebilingualnews.com
Freq: Mon; **Circ:** 115000 Not Audited
Editorial Profile: The Bilingual News is a free, weekly newspaper published in English and Spanish that serves the residents of Long Island, Nassau, West Suffolk, East Suffolk, Queens, Brooklyn, the Bronx and Manhattan, NY. It covers general interest news, education, technology, business, science, advice, culture, sports, entertainment and health. Send press releases via e-mail, not fax. Deadlines are at noon ET.; Full Page Mono: 8.64
Currency: US Dollars
NEWSPAPER

Billings Gazette
Owner: Lee Enterprises, Inc.
Editorial: 401 N 28th St, Billings, Montana 59101. **T:** 1 406 657-1200
E: citynews@billingsgazette.com
W: http://www.billingsgazette.com
Freq: Daily; **Circ:** 36300 Not Audited
Publisher: Michael Gulledge; **Editor in Chief:** Steve Prosinski; **City Editor:** Tom Tollefson; **City Editor:** Tom Tollefson; **City Editor:** Tom Tollefson; **City Editor:** Tom Tollefson
Editorial Profile: Billings Gazette is written daily for the residents of Billings, MT. The newspaper provides local news, community news, national news and world news.; Full Page Mono: 76.50; Full Page Colour: 247.52
Currency: US Dollars
DAILY NEWSPAPER

Billings Outpost
Owner: Wild Raspberry Inc.
Editorial: 2501 Montana Ave. Suite 9, Billings, Montana 59101. **T:** 1 406 248-1616
E: outpost@billingsnews.com
W: http://www.billingsnews.com
Freq: Thu; **Circ:** 10000 Not Audited
Editorial Profile: Billings Outpost is a local newspaper serving residents of Billings, Hardin, Laurel and Red Lodge, MT.; Full Page Mono: 11.32; Full Page Colour: 12.11
Currency: US Dollars
NEWSPAPER

The Birmingham News
Owner: Advance Publications, Inc.
Editorial: 2201 4th Ave N, Birmingham, Alabama 35203-3863 **E:** bhamnews@al.com
W: http://www.al.com/birmingham
Freq: Daily; **Circ:** 88023 Not Audited
Editorial Profile: The Birmingham News features include the main News section, Metro-State news section, Sports, Money and LifeStyle sections. The LifeStyle section includes features covering a range of topics, including family life, fashion, fitness, food, consumer issues, fads and trends.; Full Page Mono: 193.21; Full Page Colour: 643.74
Currency: US Dollars
DAILY NEWSPAPER

The Birmingham News
Editorial: 3075 John Hawkins Pkwy Ste R, Hoover, Alabama 35244-3060.
T: 1 205 325-3255
DAILY NEWSPAPER

The Birmingham Times
Owner: Birmingham Times Publishing Co.
Editorial: 115 3rd Ave W, Birmingham, Alabama 35204-4114. **T:** 1 205 251-5158
W: http://www.birminghamtimes.com
Freq: Thu; **Circ:** 16500 Not Audited
Editor: Cheryl Eldridge; **Publisher:** James Lewis
Editorial Profile: The Birmingham Times is a weekly newspaper that covers the news and events of the local African American community of Birmingham, AL. The publication covers local news, sports, entertainment and religious issues.; Full Page Mono: 15.20
Currency: US Dollars
NEWSPAPER

Birmingham Weekly
Owner: Magnolia Media LLC
Editorial: 2257 Highland Ave. South, Birmingham, Alabama 35205.
T: 1 205 991-4440 **E:** editor@bhamweekly.com
W: http://www.bhamweekly.com
Freq: Thu; **Circ:** 20000 Not Audited
Editorial Profile: Birmingham Weekly is written for residents of Birmingham, AL.; Full Page Mono: 26.75
Currency: US Dollars
NEWSPAPER

Bishop's Bulletin
Owner: Diocese of Sioux Falls
Editorial: 523 N Duluth Ave, Sioux Falls, South Dakota 57104-2714
Freq: Monthly; **Circ:** 37500
Publisher: Paul Swain
Editorial Profile: The Bishop's Bulletin is a community newspaper written for the Diocese of Sioux Falls, SD.; Full Page Mono: 20.00
Currency: US Dollars
NEWSPAPER

The Bismarck Tribune
Owner: Lee Enterprises, Inc.
Editorial: 707 E Front Ave, Bismarck, North Dakota 58504-5646. **T:** 1 701 223-2500
E: news@bismarcktribune.com
W: http://www.bismarcktribune.com
Freq: Daily; **Circ:** 22788 Not Audited
Publisher: Brian Kroshus; **City Editor:** Steve Wallick
Editorial Profile: The Bismarck Tribune is published daily for the residents of Bismarck, ND and surrounding areas. The newspaper covers local and national news, sports, politics, arts & entertainment & education.; Full Page Mono: 44.23; Full Page Colour: 133.20
Currency: US Dollars
DAILY NEWSPAPER

The Black Chronicle
Owner: Perry Publishing And Broadcasting
Editorial: 1528 NE 23rd St, Oklahoma City, Oklahoma 73111-3260. **T:** 1 405 424-4695
W: http://www.blackchronicle.com
Freq: Thu; **Circ:** 31000 Not Audited
Publisher: Russell Perry
Editorial Profile: The Black Chronicle is a weekly newspaper that is written for the African-American community in Oklahoma City, OK. The newspaper aims to bring its readers information on local and national news, sports and events. Deadlines are on Tuesdays at 1pm CT.; Full Page Mono: 16.44
Currency: US Dollars
NEWSPAPER

Black Hills Pioneer
Owner: Seaton Newspapers
Editorial: 315 Seaton Cir, Spearfish, South Dakota 57783-3212. **T:** 1 605 642-2761
W: http://www.bhpioneer.com
Freq: Mon thru Fri; **Circ:** 3951 Not Audited
Publisher: Letitia Lister
Editorial Profile: Black Hills Pioneer is a daily newspaper serving Spearfish, SD and the surrounding area. Newspaper coverage includes local news, sports, business, lifestyle and political items. Deadlines for the publication fall on the same day as the issue date.; Full Page Mono: 11.95; Full Page Colour: 225.00
Currency: US Dollars
DAILY NEWSPAPER

Black News
Owner: Diversity City Media
Editorial: 1310 Harden St, Columbia, South Carolina 29204. **T:** 1 803 799-5252
E: scbnews@aol.com
W: http://www.scblacknews.com
Freq: Thu; **Circ:** 75000 Not Audited
Editorial Profile: Black News is a local paper written for the African American community of Columbia, SC. The paper covers state and local news, sports, arts & entertainment, lifestyle and health. Deadlines are on Fridays.; Full Page Mono: 36.91
Currency: US Dollars
NEWSPAPER

The Black River News
Editorial: 5 Vista Dr, Flanders, New Jersey 07836-4026. **T:** 1 973 768-1815
W: http://www.blackrivernews.com
Freq: Monthly; **Circ:** 62000 Not Audited
Editorial Profile: The Black River News is a free, monthly newspaper serving communities along the Black River, including Chester and Long Valley, NJ. It covers local news, events, businesses, schools and feature stories. It is mailed to homes in the area on the 15th of each month. News and advertising deadlines

are on the first of the month. It was launched in September 2006.; Full Page Mono: 14.95
Currency: US Dollars
NEWSPAPER

Black Star News
Editorial: 32 Broadway, Ste 511, New York, New York 10004. **T:** 1 212 481-7745
E: editor@blackstarnews.com
W: http://www.blackstarnews.com
Freq: Thu; **Circ:** 50000 Not Audited
Publisher: Milton Allimadi
Editorial Profile: Black Star News is a weekly newspaper written for the African American population of New York.; Full Page Mono: 56.00
Currency: US Dollars
NEWSPAPER

The Black Voice News
Owner: Ohio Community Media LLC.
Editorial: 4290 Brockton Ave, Riverside, California 92501-3447. **T:** 1 951 682-6070
E: pressrelease@blackvoicenews.com
W: http://www.blackvoicenews.com
Freq: Thu; **Circ:** 10000 Not Audited
Editor: Lee Ragin
Editorial Profile: The Black Voice News is a weekly newspaper concentrating on news, events, and issues effecting the African American community. In addition to news and weather, the publication covers topics such as health, travel, and money.; Full Page Mono: 35.06
Currency: US Dollars
NEWSPAPER

Blackstone Valley Tribune
Owner: Stonebridge Press
Editorial: 25 Elm St, Southbridge, Massachusetts 1550. **T:** 1 508 909-4130
W: http://www.blackstonevalleytribune.com
Freq: Fri; **Circ:** 10000 Not Audited
Publisher: Frank Chilinski; **Editor:** Adam Minor
Editorial Profile: Blackstone Valley Tribune is a free weekly newspaper that covers local news and events. The newspaper is written for residents of Oxbridge, Northbridge, and Uxbridge, MA.; Full Page Mono: 10.00
Currency: US Dollars
NEWSPAPER

The Blade
Owner: Block Communications Inc.
Editorial: 541 N Superior St, Toledo, Ohio 43660-1000. **T:** 1 419 724-6000
E: citydesk@theblade.com
W: http://www.toledoblade.com
Freq: Daily; **Circ:** 103443 Not Audited
City Editor: Kim Bates; **News Editor:** Tony Durham
Editorial Profile: The Blade, published since 1835, is a broadsheet, general interest, daily newspaper that covers regional, national and international news. It is Toledo's only morning newspaper and the primary newspaper of Northwest Ohio and Southeast Michigan. The paper prefers faxes be sent to the newsroom.; Full Page Mono: 141.62; Full Page Colour: 160.45
Currency: US Dollars
DAILY NEWSPAPER

The Blade
Editorial: 1 Capitol Sq Rm 107, Columbus, Ohio 43215. **T:** 1 614 221-0496
DAILY NEWSPAPER

Blaine Banner
Editorial: 13602 Jefferson St Ne, Ham Lake, Minnesota 55304-6926. **T:** 1 763 755-3832
E: littlepaper@comcast.net
Freq: Monthly; **Circ:** 10000 Not Audited
Editor: Marilyn Hamm
Editorial Profile: Blaine Banner is a community newspaper written for the residents of Blaine, MN. It covers local news. It publishes the first Wednesday of the month.; Full Page Mono: 15.00
Currency: US Dollars
NEWSPAPER

Blank Slate Media
Owner: Blank Slate Media
Editorial: 105 Hillside Ave, Williston Park, New York 11596. **T:** 1 516 307-1043
E: news@theislandnow.com
Publisher: Steven Blank; **Editor:** Karen Rubin
Editorial Profile: Blank Slate Media was found in March 2010 by Steven Blank. They publish the community newspapers Great Neck News, New Hyde Park Herald Courier and The Williston Times.
NEWSPAPER

Blue Mountain Town & Country Gazette
Owner: Innovative Designs & Publishing, Inc.
Editorial: 4685 Lehigh Dr, Walnutport, Pennsylvania 18088-9574. **T:** 1 610 767-9600
E: askus@townandcountrygazette.com
W: http://www.townandcountrygazette.com
Freq: Bi-Weekly; **Circ:** 11000
Editor: Joe Korba; **Publisher:** Paul Prass
Editorial Profile: Blue Mountain Town & Country Gazette is written for the residents of Walnutport, PA.
NEWSPAPER

The Blue Ridge Leader
Editorial: 128 S 20th St, Purcellville, Virginia 20132. **T:** 1 703 943-8806
E: editor@brleader.com
W: http://brleader.com
Freq: Monthly; **Circ:** 15000 Not Audited
Editorial Profile: The Blue Ridge Leader is a free local paper covering Loudoun County.; Full Page Mono: 14.00
Currency: US Dollars
NEWSPAPER

Bluebonnet Publishing-Brownsboro
Owner: Bluebonnet Publishing, LLC
Editorial: 205 State Highway 31 E, Chandler, Texas 75758-2378. **T:** 1 903 849-3333
E: news@c-bstatesman.com
W: http://www.c-bstatesman.com **Circ:** 6300 Not Audited
News Editor: Chad Wilson; **Publisher:** Bill Woodall
Editorial Profile: Bluebonnet Publishing - Brownsboro in Chandler, TX is a community newspaper publisher that produces Lake View News and the Chandler & Brownboro Statesman.
NEWSPAPER

Bluefield Daily Telegraph
Owner: Community Newspaper Holdings, Inc.
Editorial: 928 Bluefield Ave, Bluefield, West Virginia 24701. **T:** 1 304 327-2800
E: news@bdtonline.com
W: http://bdtonline.com
Freq: Daily; **Circ:** 15546 Not Audited
Publisher: Darryl Hudson; **Editor:** Charles Owens; **News Editor:** Andy Patton
Editorial Profile: Bluefield Daily Telegraph is a daily local newspaper that is written for those who live and/or are interested in the Bluefield, WV area. The newspaper covers local news, national news that has an impact on their readership, local sports, local politics, local arts & entertainment and local education issues. The publication welcomes submissions of community news, events or letters to the editor.; Full Page Mono: 39.25; Full Page Colour: 125.57
Currency: US Dollars
DAILY NEWSPAPER

Bluejacket & Star Newspapers
Owner: West 10 Newspapers, Inc.
Editorial: 7834 Church St, Millington, Tennessee 38053-2403. **T:** 1 901 872-2286
E: bmillingtonstar@yahoo.com
W: http://millingtonstar.com **Circ:** 8600 Not Audited
Editor: Thomas Sellars
Editorial Profile: Bluejacket & Star Newspapers is a weekly community newspaper publisher serving the residents of Memphis, TN.
NEWSPAPER

Bluff Country Newspaper Group
Owner: Phillips Publishing Inc.
Editorial: 112 N Broadway St, Spring Valley, Minnesota 55975-1224. **T:** 1 507 346-7365
E: news@bluffcountrynews.com
W: http://www.bluffcountrynews.com
Circ: 18800 Not Audited
NEWSPAPER

Bluffton Today
Owner: Morris Communications Corp.
Editorial: 52 Persimmons St, Bluffton, South Carolina 29910-7682. **T:** 1 843 815-0800
W: http://www.blufftontoday.com
Freq: Daily; **Circ:** 17571 Not Audited
Editor: Lawrence Conneff
Editorial Profile: Bluffton Today is written for residents of Bluffton, SC. The outlet offers RSS (Really Simple Syndication).; Full Page Mono: 23.04; Full Page Colour: 90.73
Currency: US Dollars
DAILY NEWSPAPER

Blytheville Courier News
Owner: Rust Communications
Editorial: 900 N Broadway St, Blytheville, Arkansas 72315-1714. **T:** 1 870 763-4461
W: http://www.couriernews.net
Freq: Daily; **Circ:** 3259 Not Audited
Publisher: David Tennyson; **Editor:** Andy Weld
Editorial Profile: Blytheville Courier News is a daily local newspaper that is written for those who live and/or are interested in the Blytheville, AR area. The newspaper covers local news, national news that has an impact on their readership, sports, politics, arts & entertainment and education issues.; Full Page Mono: 10.00; Full Page Colour: 36.21
Currency: US Dollars
DAILY NEWSPAPER

Blythewood Country Chronicle
Owner: Camden Media Co.
Editorial: 509 Main St, Blythewood, South Carolina 29016-8303. **T:** 1 803 786-5681
Freq: Thu; **Circ:** 12300
Publisher: Mike Mischner; **Editor:** Martin Mobley
Editorial Profile: Blythewood Country Chronicle is a weekly community newspaper written for the residents of Blythewood and Columbia, SC.; Full Page Mono: 13.15
Currency: US Dollars
NEWSPAPER

Boca Raton Tribune
Editorial: 399 NW Boca Raton Blvd Ste 212, Boca Raton, Florida 33432-3794. **T:** 1 561 807-6300
E: news@bocaratontribune.com
W: http://bocaratontribune.com
Freq: Thu; **Circ:** 21800
Editor in Chief: C. Ron Allen
Editorial Profile: Boca Raton (FL) Tribune was founded in January 15, 2010 and provides news for the communities of Boca Raton, Highland Beach, and Delray Beach, FL. It is published every Thursday. Do NOT call the publication. Send all press releases via email.; Full Page Mono: 16.75; Full Page Colour: 43.85
Currency: US Dollars
NEWSPAPER

Boise Weekly
Owner: Bar Bar Inc.
Editorial: 523 W Broad St, Boise, Idaho 83702-7642. **T:** 1 208 344-2055
E: info@boiseweekly.com
W: http://www.boiseweekly.com
Freq: Wed; **Circ:** 35000 Not Audited
Publisher: Sally Freeman; **Editor in Chief:** Zach Hagadone; **News Editor:** George Prentice
Editorial Profile: Boise Weekly is a community newspaper serving Boise, ID, and its surrounding communities. The newspaper is an alternative, independent publication covering hard local news as well as other feature stories pertinent to the area.; Full Page Mono: 51.80
Currency: US Dollars
NEWSPAPER

The Bolivar Commercial
Owner: Walls Newspapers
Editorial: 821 N Chrisman Ave, Cleveland, Mississippi 38732-2110. **T:** 1 662 843-4241
E: news@bolivarcommercial.com
W: http://www.bolivarcom.com
Freq: Daily; **Circ:** 6205 Not Audited
Publisher & Editor: Mark Williams
Editorial Profile: The Bolivar Commercial is a local daily newspaper geared toward the community of Cleveland, MS. The newspaper covers international, national and local news. Content consists of hard news, sports, lifestyle features, business news and What's Going On, a community-based news section.; Full Page Mono: 10.50; Full Page Colour: 37.19
Currency: US Dollars
DAILY NEWSPAPER

Boney Publishing
Owner: Boney Publishers, Inc.
Editorial: 114 W Elm St, Graham, North Carolina 27253-2802. **T:** 1 336 228-7851
E: news@thealamancenews.com **Circ:** 12500 Not Audited
NEWSPAPER

Bonner County Daily Bee
Owner: Hagadone Corp.
Editorial: 310 Church St, Sandpoint, Idaho 83864-1345. **T:** 1 208 263-9534
E: bcdailybee@bonnercountydailybee.com
W: http://www.bonnercountydailybee.com
Freq: Daily; **Circ:** 5850 Not Audited
Publisher: David Keyes; **News Editor:** Keith Kinnaird; **Editor:** Caroline Lobsinger
Editorial Profile: Bonner County Daily Bee is a local newspaper serving the residents of Bonner County, ID.; Full Page Mono: 12.95; Full Page Colour: 54.82
Currency: US Dollars
DAILY NEWSPAPER

Boone Newspapers - Ahoskie
Owner: Boone Newspapers Inc.
Editorial: 801 Parker Ave E, Ahoskie, North Carolina 27910-3641. **T:** 1 252 332-2123
W: http://www.roanoke-chowannewsherald.com **Circ:** 9130
Editor: Calvin Bryant; **Editor:** Calvin Bryant; **Editor:** Calvin Bryant; **Editor:** Calvin Bryant
NEWSPAPER

Boone Newspapers, Inc.
Editorial: 103 Hickory St, Greenville, Alabama 36037. **T:** 1 334 382-3111
W: http://www.greenvilleadvocate.com
Circ: 17100 Not Audited
Publisher: Tracy Salter
NEWSPAPER

Boonville Daily News
Owner: GateHouse Media Inc.
Editorial: 412 High St, Boonville, Missouri 65233-1284. **T:** 1 660 882-5335
W: http://www.boonvilledailynews.com
Freq: Daily; **Circ:** 2574 Not Audited
Editor: Ben Bennett; **Publisher:** Deborah Marshall
Editorial Profile: Boonville Daily News is a daily, local newspaper serving the residents of Boonville, MO and its surrounding communities. The newspaper covers all aspects of local, regional, national, and international news. Coverage of local news is extensive, including sports, entertainment, health, politics, and business news.; Full Page Mono: 10.44; Full Page Colour: 36.67
Currency: US Dollars
DAILY NEWSPAPER

The Booster
Editorial: 2435 S Miracle Mile, Bullhead City, Arizona 86442-7311. **T:** 1 928 763-2505
W: http://www.mohavedailynews.com
Freq: Sun; **Circ:** 12663 Not Audited
Editor: Bill McMillen; **Publisher:** Chuck Rathbon
Editorial Profile: The Booster is a twice-weekly newspaper reporting local news and events of Bullhead City and the Mohave Valley, AZ.; Full Page Mono: 15.11; Full Page Colour: 120.00
Currency: US Dollars
NEWSPAPER

Bopp Publishing
Owner: Bopp (David)
Editorial: 140 S Cedar St, Spalding, Nebraska 68665. **T:** 1 308 497-2153
E: spalding2002@hotmail.com **Circ:** 940 Not Audited
News Editor: Phyllis Waymire
Editorial Profile: Bopp Publishing is a local newspaper providing the community of Spalding, NE with news.
NEWSPAPER

Borger News-Herald
Owner: Horizon Publications
Editorial: 207 N Main St, Borger, Texas 79007. **T:** 1 806 273-5611
W: http://www.borgernewsherald.com
Freq: Daily; **Circ:** 4255 Not Audited
Editor: Michelle Berry; **Publisher:** Debra Wells
Editorial Profile: Borger News-Herald is a local, daily newspaper that serves the residents of Borger, TX and its surrounding areas. The editorial content covers sports, technology, weather, business, and community news and events. The deadline is one day before the issue date. Advertising deadlines are one week prior to insertion.; Full Page Mono: 11.38; Full Page Colour: 38.18
Currency: US Dollars
DAILY NEWSPAPER

Boscobel Dial
Owner: Morris Multimedia, Inc.
Editorial: 901 Wisconsin Ave, Boscobel, Wisconsin 53805-1531. **T:** 1 608 375-4458
E: dialeditor@boscobeldial.net **Circ:** 7950 Not Audited
Publisher: John Ingebritsen; **Editor:** David Krier
NEWSPAPER

Bossier Press-Tribune
Owner: Specht Newspapers Inc.
Editorial: 4250 Viking Dr, Bossier City, Louisiana 71111. **T:** 1 318 747-7900
E: newsroom@bossierpress.com
W: http://www.bossierpress.com
Freq: 3 Times/Week; **Circ:** 20000
Publisher: Jim Knudsen; **Editor:** Jeffrey Loftin
Editorial Profile: Bossier Press-Tribune is a local newspaper serving the residents of Bossier City, LA and is distributed Monday through Friday. The newspaper offers extensive coverage of local and regional news,

including weather, sports, business and community news. National and world headlines are also often covered.; Full Page Mono: 18.00; Full Page Colour: 62.00
Currency: US Dollars
NEWSPAPER

Bossier Voices & Southeast Voices
Owner: Gannett Co., Inc.
Editorial: 222 Lake St, Shreveport, Louisiana 71101. **T:** 1 318 459-3200
W: http://www.shreveporttimes.com
Circ: 30000
Publisher: Donald Bailey; **Editor:** Barbara Widner
NEWSPAPER

Boston Chinese News
Editorial: 29 Baker St, Belmont, Massachusetts 02478-4024.
T: 1 617 338-1170
E: info@bostonchinesenews.com
W: http://www.bostonchinesenews.com
Freq: Fri; **Circ:** 10000 Not Audited
Editor: Emerald Wu
Editorial Profile: Boston Chinese News is a weekly newspaper for Chinese-Americans in the Boston region. The newspaper offers local news and event listings, as well as news from China. Deadlines are Tuesdays prior to the issue date.; Full Page Mono: 7.14
Currency: US Dollars
NEWSPAPER

Boston Courant
Owner: Courant Publications, Inc.
Editorial: 129 Newbury St, Ste 204, Boston, Massachusetts 02116-2961.
T: 1 617 267-2700
Freq: Fri; **Circ:** 35000 Not Audited
Editorial Profile: Boston Courant is a weekly newspaper published for the residents of the Back Bay, Beacon Hill, Fenway and South End sections of Boston. The newspaper covers local news, activities and information.; Full Page Mono: 25.00
Currency: US Dollars
NEWSPAPER

The Boston Globe
Owner: Henry (John)
Editorial: 135 William T Morrissey Blvd, Boston, Massachusetts 02125-3310.
T: 1 617 929-2000 **E:** newstip@globe.com
W: http://www.bostonglobe.com
Freq: Daily; **Circ:** 274538 Not Audited
Ideas Editor: Stephen Heuser; **Style & Celebrities Editor:** Hayley Kaufman; **Editor:** Brian McGrory; **Editor:** Brian McGrory; **Content Producer:** Lara Salahi; **City Editor:** Stephen Smith
Editorial Profile: The Boston Globe focuses on news for the general public in the New England area as well as state, national and international news. Other coverage areas include business, healthcare, technology, features, lifestyle, arts and sports. There is also an emphasis on regional and suburban coverage. Lead times vary depending on the department. The staff won a 2003 Pulitzer prize for public service. The paper does not publish a Holiday Gift Guide.; Full Page Mono: 655.00; Full Page Colour: 764.00
Currency: US Dollars
DAILY NEWSPAPER

The Boston Globe
Owner: Henry (John)
Editorial: 1130 Connecticut Ave NW Ste 520, Washington, District Of Columbia 20036-3947.
T: 1 202 857-5050
Bureau Chief: Christopher Rowland
DAILY NEWSPAPER

The Boston Globe
Owner: Henry (John)
Editorial: Massachusetts State House #490, Boston, Massachusetts 2133.
T: 1 617 367-4030
Bureau Chief: Frank Phillips
DAILY NEWSPAPER

The Boston Globe
Owner: Henry (John)
Editorial: 1 City Hall Plz, Boston, Massachusetts 02108-2102.
T: 1 617 367-4020 **E:** newstip@globe.com
Bureau Chief: Andrew Ryan
DAILY NEWSPAPER

Boston Herald
Owner: GateHouse Media Inc.
Editorial: 70 Fargo St Ste 600, Boston, Massachusetts 02210-2131.
T: 1 617 426-3000
E: citydesk@bostonherald.com
W: http://www.bostonherald.com
Freq: Daily; **Circ:** 101380 Not Audited
Publisher: Patrick Purcell
Editorial Profile: Boston Herald is a 70+ page general-interest tabloid with an emphasis on local area coverage. The morning paper aims to be the primary news and information source for Boston-area residents. Business coverage is company-oriented with the focus on more general news, not specific products. Significant breaking news that affects the high-tech industry and earnings reports is also covered. Consumer features run on Wednesday. Special sections include Business Extra (Monday), an expanded business section with all current local, national and international news, including personnel news; and Small Business (Tuesday) which focuses on small businesses and features advice columns and small business profiles. The Edge is the publication's Arts & Entertainment section.; Full Page Mono: 71.84; Full Page Colour: 262.65
Currency: US Dollars
DAILY NEWSPAPER

Boston Herald
Editorial: 24 Beacon St Ste 115, Boston, Massachusetts 02133-1099.
T: 1 617 619-6418
DAILY NEWSPAPER

Boston Neighborhood News
Owner: Boston Neighborhood News
Editorial: 150 Mount Vernon St, Ste 120, Dorchester, Massachusetts 2125.
T: 1 617 436-1222
E: newseditor@dotnews.com **Circ:** 27200 Not Audited
News Editor: Gintautas Dumcius; **Publisher:** Edward Forry
NEWSPAPER

Bothell/Kenmore Reporter
Owner: Black Press
Editorial: 11630 Slater Ave NE Ste 9, Kirkland, Washington 98034-4100. **T:** 1 425 483-3732
W: http://www.bothell-reporter.com
Circ: 59471
Editorial Profile: Bothell/Kenmore Reporter in Kirkland, WA is a publisher of community newspapers.
NEWSPAPER

Boulder Weekly
Owner: Sallo (Stewart)
Editorial: 690 S Lashley Ln, Boulder, Colorado 80305-5920. **T:** 1 303 494-5511 6
E: editorial@boulderweekly.com
W: http://www.boulderweekly.com
Freq: Thu; **Circ:** 25000 Not Audited
Editor: Joel Dyer; **Publisher:** Stewart Sallo
Editorial Profile: Boulder (CO) Weekly is a weekly newspaper that covers local and national news relevant to the Boulder County area.; Full Page Mono: 22.50
Currency: US Dollars
NEWSPAPER

Bowie County Citizens Tribune
Owner: Westward Communications, LLC
Editorial: 129 E North Front St., New Boston, Texas 75570-2924. **T:** 1 903 628-5801
W: http://www.bowiecountynow.com
Freq: 2 Times/Week; **Circ:** 12500 Not Audited
Publisher: Woody Morgan
Editorial Profile: Bowie County Citizens Tribune is a weekly community newspaper serving the Bowie County, TX area, including news, sports, lifestyle, opinion and community event listings.; Full Page Mono: 9.05
Currency: US Dollars
NEWSPAPER

Bozeman Daily Chronicle
Owner: Pioneer Newspapers
Editorial: 2820 W College St, Bozeman, Montana 59718-3925. **T:** 1 406 587-4491
E: citydesk@dailychronicle.com
W: http://www.bozemandailychronicle.com
Freq: Daily; **Circ:** 14668 Not Audited
City Editor: Michael Becker
Editorial Profile: Bozeman Daily Chronicle is a daily, local newspaper serving the residents of Bozeman, MT and its surrounding areas. It covers the outdoors, religion, health, travel, business and local news.; Full Page Mono: 17.88; Full Page Colour: 53.09
Currency: US Dollars
DAILY NEWSPAPER

Bradenton Herald
Owner: McClatchy Newspapers
Editorial: 102 Manatee Ave W, Bradenton, Florida 34205-8810. **T:** 1 941 748-0411
W: http://www.bradenton.com
Freq: Daily; **Circ:** 32120 Not Audited
Publisher: Bob Turner
Editorial Profile: Bradenton Herald is a daily newspaper serving residents of Bradenton, Manatee and Sarasota, FL. It contains regional, national and international news. Coverage also extends to sports, business, education, entertainment, features, weather and community news. The paper is also printed for the residents of Lakewood Ranch, FL under the title Lakewood Ranch Herald.; Full Page Mono: 59.99; Full Page Colour: 625.00
Currency: US Dollars
DAILY NEWSPAPER

Bradford County Telegraph, Inc.
Editorial: 131 W Call St, Starke, Florida 32091-3210. **T:** 1 904 964-6305
E: editor@bctelegraph.com **Circ:** 10050 Not Audited
Editor: Mark Crawford; **Publisher:** John Miller
Editorial Profile: Bradford County Telegraph, Inc. is a weekly community newspaper publisher serving the residents of Bradford County, Union County and Keystone Flights, FL.
NEWSPAPER

The Bradford Era
Owner: Bradford Publishing Co.
Editorial: 43 Main St, Bradford, Pennsylvania 16701-2019. **T:** 1 814 362-6531
E: info@bradfordera.com
W: http://www.bradfordera.com
Freq: Daily; **Circ:** 11200 Not Audited
Editor/Publisher: John Satterwhite; **City Editor:** Mike Schreiber
Editorial Profile: The Bradford Era is a daily publication for residents of the Bradford, PA area. It reports news and events of the local area. Deadlines for the editorial submissions is one day prior to the issue date.; Full Page Mono: 16.18; Full Page Colour: 375.00
Currency: US Dollars
DAILY NEWSPAPER

The Brainerd Dispatch
Owner: Morris Multimedia, Inc.
Editorial: 506 James St, Brainerd, Minnesota 56401-2942. **T:** 1 218 829-4705
E: newstips@brainerddispatch.com
W: http://www.brainerddispatch.com
Freq: Daily; **Circ:** 10327 Not Audited
Editor: Matt Erickson; **Editor:** Steve Kohls; **Publisher:** Terry McCollough
Editorial Profile: Brainerd Daily Dispatch is regional newspaper serving Central Minnesota communities. It is issued six days per week, Sunday through Friday. The newspaper offers in depth coverage of international, national and local news. Content includes news, weather, politics, arts & entertainment, business, education, sports and community news, events and listings.; Full Page Mono: 13.40; Full Page Colour: 49.73
Currency: US Dollars
DAILY NEWSPAPER

Brasileiras & Brasileiros
Editorial: 5534 Hansel Ave, Orlando, Florida 32809. **T:** 1 407 855-9541
E: archersb@bellsouth.net
W: http://jornalbb.com
Freq: Monthly; **Circ:** 10000 Not Audited
News Editor: Fabio Lobo; **Publisher:** Eraldo Manes; **Editor:** Maida Manes
Editorial Profile: Brasileiras & Brasileiros is published monthly for the Brazilian residents of Orlando, FL. The newspaper provides information about cultural news and events, Brazilian businesses, music and tourism.; Full Page Mono: 10.75
Currency: US Dollars
NEWSPAPER

The Brasilians
Owner: Brasilians Press
Editorial: 16 W 46th St, Ste 302, New York, New York 10036-4503. **T:** 1 212 382-1630
E: tthebrasil@aol.com
W: http://www.thebrasilians.com
Freq: Monthly; **Circ:** 60000 Not Audited
Publisher: Joao de Matos; **Editor:** Edilberto Mendes
Editorial Profile: The Brasilians is a monthly newspaper published for Brazilian-Americans. It focuses on the relationship between the United States and Brazil.; Full Page Mono: 17.39
Currency: US Dollars
NEWSPAPER

Brattleboro Reformer
Owner: MediaNews Group
Editorial: 62 Black Mountain Rd, Brattleboro, Vermont 05301-9241. **T:** 1 802 254-2311
E: news@reformer.com
W: http://www.reformer.com
Freq: Mon thru Fri; **Circ:** 7550 Not Audited
Publisher: Edward Woods
Editorial Profile: Brattleboro Reformer is a daily, local newspaper serving the residents of Brattleboro, VT, and its surrounding areas. It provides in-depth local, regional, national and world news. Content also includes entertainment, business, sports, weather, education, health, religion and community events. Advertising deadlines are at 5pm ET. It shares offices with The Vermont Observer Brattleboro and the Town Crier.; Full Page Mono: 25.30; Full Page Colour: 82.51
Currency: US Dollars
DAILY NEWSPAPER

El Bravo - Brownsville Edition
Owner: Comania Periodistica El Bravo
Editorial: 1114 Lincoln St Ste C, Brownsville, Texas 78521. **T:** 1 956 542-5800
E: adpro@elbravo.com.mx
W: http://www.elbravomatamoros.com
Freq: Daily; **Circ:** 5000 Not Audited
Publisher: Nancy Carretero; **Editor:** Agustin Lozano
Editorial Profile: El Bravo is a Spanish-language newspaper for the residents of Brownsville, TX.; Full Page Mono: 52.13; Full Page Colour: 84.49
Currency: US Dollars
DAILY NEWSPAPER

Brazil Times
Owner: Rust Communications
Editorial: 100 N Meridian St, Brazil, Indiana 47834-2172. **T:** 1 812 446-2216
W: http://www.thebraziltimes.com
Freq: Daily; **Circ:** 5000 Not Audited
Publisher: Randy List
Editorial Profile: Brazil Times serves the residents of Clay County, IN. The paper covers local and regional news and occasionally reports on national news that directly affects the local area. Local coverage is extensive and covers sports, weather, business, education, crime, politics and community news and events.; Full Page Mono: 12.21; Full Page Colour: 41.16
Currency: US Dollars
DAILY NEWSPAPER

Brazilian Pacific Times
Owner: Pribyl (Jaroslav)
Editorial: 3045 Rosecrans St Ste 113, San Diego, California 92110-4828.
T: 1 619 223-2790
E: editor@brazilianpacifictimes.com
W: http://www.bptonline.com
Freq: Monthly; **Circ:** 10000 Not Audited
Editorial Profile: Brazilian Pacific Times is a weekly newspaper for the Brazilian and Portuguese-speaking communities in and around San Diego.; Full Page Mono: 70.00
Currency: US Dollars
NEWSPAPER

Brazilian Times
Editorial: 311 Broadway Ste 102, Somerville, Massachusetts 02145-1933.
T: 1 877 625-0079
E: news@braziliantimes.com
W: http://www.braziliantimes.com
Freq: Fri; **Circ:** 16000 Not Audited
Editorial Profile: Brazilian Times is a weekly newspaper targeted toward the Brazilian community of New England. The newspaper aims to bring together the public and the private sectors to support, strengthen and benefit from the integration of Brazil and the world. This includes providing timely information on Brazil and access to Brazilian resources, as well as promoting Brazilian perspectives on issues of global interest. Deadlines are on Thursdays at noon ET.; Full Page Mono: 9.04; Full Page Colour: 9.34
Currency: US Dollars
NEWSPAPER

Brazilian Voice
Editorial: 412 Chestnut St, Newark, New Jersey 07105-2433. **T:** 1 973 491-6200
E: info@brazilianvoice.com
W: http://www.brazilianvoice.com
Freq: Sat; **Circ:** 55000 Not Audited
Editorial Profile: Brazilian Voice is a newspaper serving the Brazilian-American community.; Full Page Mono: 50.00
Currency: US Dollars
NEWSPAPER

Brazoria County News
Editorial: 113 E Bernard St, West Columbia, Texas 77486. **T:** 1 979 345-3127
E: bcneditor@embarqmail.com
W: http://www.brazoriacountynews.org
Freq: Thu; **Circ:** 11000 Not Audited
Editor: Teena Maenza

Editorial Profile: Brazoria County News is a weekly newspaper written for residents of Brazoria County, TX. The newspaper covers local news, government, sports and lifestyle.; Full Page Mono: 7.00; Full Page Colour: 1080.00
Currency: US Dollars
NEWSPAPER

Breeze Courier

Owner: Breeze Printing Company
Editorial: 212 S Main St, Taylorville, Illinois 62568-2219. **T:** 1 217 824-2233
E: breezecourier@breezecourier.com
W: http://www.breeze-courier.com
Freq: Mon thru Fri; **Circ:** 5541
Publisher & Editor: Marylee Lasswell
Editorial Profile: Breeze Courier is written for the residents of Taylorville, IL and their surrounding areas. It covers local news, weather, sports, business and announcements. It also includes an opinion column, classified ads and features stories. National news is covered when directly affecting the area. Deadlines are on the days prior to the issue date at 5pm CT.; Full Page Mono: 8.50; Full Page Colour: 200.00
Currency: US Dollars
DAILY NEWSPAPER

Breeze Newspapers–Fort Myers

Owner: Breeze Newspapers
Editorial: 19260 San Carlos Blvd, Fort Myers Beach, Florida 33931. **T:** 1 239 765-0400
W: http://www.breezenewspapers.com
Freq: Weekly; **Circ:** 26500 Not Audited
Publisher: Scott Blonde; **Editor:** Robert Petcher; **Editor:** Melissa Schneider
Editorial Profile: Breeze Newspapers–Fort Myers is a regional office for Breeze Newspapers in Cape Coral, FL.; Full Page Mono: 8.48; Full Page Colour: 90.00
Currency: US Dollars
NEWSPAPER

Breeze Newspapers–Sanibel

Owner: Breeze Newspapers
Editorial: 2340 Periwinkle Way, Sanibel, Florida 33957-3221. **T:** 1 239 472-1587
W: http://www.breezenewspapers.com
Freq: Weekly; **Circ:** 8000 Not Audited
Publisher: Scott Blonde
Editorial Profile: Breeze Newspapers–Sanibel is a regional office for Breeze Newspapers in Cape Coral, FL.; Full Page Mono: 8.48; Full Page Colour: 90.00
Currency: US Dollars
NEWSPAPER

Brehm Communications - Democrat Division

Owner: Brehm Communications, Inc.
Editorial: 1226 Avenue H, Fort Madison, Iowa 52627. **T:** 1 319 372-6421 **Circ:** 1277
Editor: Robin Delaney
NEWSPAPER

Brehm Communications, Inc.

Owner: Brehm Communications, Inc.
Editorial: 28200 Highway 189, Lake Arrowhead, California 92352-9700.
T: 1 909 336-3555
W: http://www.brehmcommunications.com/
Circ: 11000 Not Audited
Publisher: Harry Bradley; **Editor:** Mary-Justine Lanyon
NEWSPAPER

Brenham Banner-Press

Owner: Hartman Newspapers, Inc.
Editorial: 2430 Stringer St, Brenham, Texas 77833-5724. **T:** 1 979 836-7956
E: edit@brenhambanner.com
W: http://www.brenhambanner.com
Freq: Daily; **Circ:** 6500 Not Audited
Editor: Rich Bray; **News Editor:** Derek Hall; **Publisher & Editor:** Mike Mueck
Editorial Profile: Brenham Banner-Press is written for the residents of Brenham, Burton, Bellville and College Station, TX. It covers local news, lifestyles, sports, education, arts & entertainment, politics, business, real estate and community events.; Full Page Mono: 8.16; Full Page Colour: 270.00
Currency: US Dollars
DAILY NEWSPAPER

Brentwood News

Owner: MediaNews Group
Editorial: 1700 Cavallo Rd, Antioch, California 94509. **T:** 1 925 634-2125
E: bnews@bayareanewsgroup.com
W: http://www.contracostatimes.com/ brentwood
Freq: Fri; **Circ:** 41000 Not Audited
Editor: Judy Prieve

Editorial Profile: Brentwood News is a weekly insert newspaper included in the East County Times serving residents of Brentwood, CA. It operates out of the office of the East County Times in Antioch, CA.; Full Page Mono: 18.00
Currency: US Dollars
NEWSPAPER

Brentwood Press Newspapers

Editorial: 248 Oak St, Brentwood, California 94513. **T:** 1 925 634-1441
E: ads@brentwoodpress.com
W: http://www.brentwoodpress.com
Circ: 43500 Not Audited
Editor: Rick Lemyre; **Publisher:** Greg Robinson
Editorial Profile: Brentwood (CA) Press Newspapers is a local newspaper group serving Contra Costa County.
NEWSPAPER

Bridgeport News

Editorial: 3506 S Halsted St, Chicago, Illinois 60609-1605. **T:** 1 773 927-0025
W: http://www.bridgeportnews.net
Freq: Wed; **Circ:** 25300 Not Audited
Publisher: Joseph Feldman; **Editor:** Janice Racinowski; **Editor:** Janice Racinowski
Editorial Profile: Bridgeport News in Chicago, IL is published weekly and focuses on local news and community events, including high school sports, local entertainment, business, breaking news and classifieds.; Full Page Mono: 33.00
Currency: US Dollars
NEWSPAPER

Bridwell Publishing

Editorial: 916 Halsell St, Bridgeport, Texas 76426. **T:** 1 940 683-4021
W: http://www.bridgeportindex.com **Circ:** 3700 Not Audited
Editorial Profile: Bridwell Publishing is a weekly community newspaper serving the residents of Bridgeport, TX. The Editorial and Advertising deadlines are noon on the Mondays prior to issue date.
NEWSPAPER

Briefing

Owner: A.H. Belo Corp.
Editorial: 508 Young St, Dallas, Texas 75202-4808. **T:** 1 214 977-8222
E: briefing@dallasnews.com
W: http://www.dallasnews.com/briefing
Freq: Daily; **Circ:** 118738 Not Audited
Publisher: Rich Alfano; **Editor:** Erin Booke
Editorial Profile: Briefing, launched on August 27, 2008, is aimed at time-crunched families who want a quick-read newspaper. It is distributed Wednesdays through Saturdays to households that don't currently subscribe to The Dallas Morning News, it's sister newspaper.; Full Page Mono: 133.65; Full Page Colour: 149.52
Currency: US Dollars
DAILY NEWSPAPER

The Brigantine Times

Editorial: 902 W Brigantine Ave, Brigantine, New Jersey 08203-2341. **T:** 1 609 266-2486
E: etinbrig@comcast.net
W: http://www.brigantinetimes.com
Freq: Fri
Editor: Emmett Turner
Editorial Profile: The Brigantine Times is a weekly newspaper providing Local and Community News coverage for the residents of Brigantine, NJ.
NEWSPAPER

The Bright Beacon

Owner: Beacon Publishing Co.
Editorial: 24486 State Line Rd Ste F, Lawrenceburg, Indiana 47025-9802.
T: 1 812 637-0660
W: http://www.thebrightbeaconindiana.com/
Freq: Monthly; **Circ:** 15000
Editorial Profile: The Bright Beacon is a free monthly news publication delivered to the residents of Bright, Hidden Valley Lake, Valley Woods, St. Leon, Aurora, Lawrenceburg, Greendale, West Harrison, Logan, Guilford, Dover, New Alsace, Yorkville, Dillsboro, Moores Hill, Manchester, and Sunman, Indiana. It covers community news, sports, business news, politics, and community events.
NEWSPAPER

Bright Side Community Newspapers

Owner: Thompson (Carol)
Editorial: 3492 Nowlin Rd NW, Kennesaw, Georgia 30144-1031. **T:** 1 770 423-9555
E: brightnews@aol.com
W: http://www.brightsidenews.com
Freq: Monthly; **Circ:** 49000

NEWSPAPER

The Bright Side Newspaper

Owner: Bright Side Publications
Editorial: 1560 Route 83, Cape May Court House, New Jersey 08210-1245.
T: 1 609 861-2034
E: news@brightsidenewspaper.com
W: http://www.brightsidenewspaper.com
Freq: Bi-Weekly; **Circ:** 10000
Editorial Profile: The Bright Side Newspaper is a bi-weekly community newspaper published for residents in and around Cape May Court House, NJ. It focuses solely on positive news and family values. Send materials via mail.; Full Page Mono: 11.00
Currency: US Dollars
NEWSPAPER

The Bright Side Newspapers

Owner: Lipsett & Associates, Inc.
Editorial: 3330 Cumberland Blvd., Suite 500, Atlanta, Georgia. **T:** 1 770 426-9388
E: news@brightsidecobb.com
W: http://www.brightsidecobb.com
Circ: 41000 Not Audited
NEWSPAPER

Brighton Park/McKinley Park Life

Editorial: 2949 W Pope John Paul II Dr, Chicago, Illinois 60632-2589.
T: 1 773 523-3663
E: brightonparklife@aol.com
Freq: Thu; **Circ:** 20000 Not Audited
Editorial Profile: Brighton Park-Mckinley Life's editorial mission is to provide Chicago residnets with local news and information. The publication is written for Chicago, IL residents.; Full Page Mono: 10.00
Currency: US Dollars
NEWSPAPER

Bristol Herald Courier

Owner: BH Media Group
Editorial: 320 Bob Morrison Blvd, Bristol, Virginia 24201-3812. **T:** 1 276 669-2181
W: http://www.tricities.com
Freq: Daily; **Circ:** 27110 Not Audited
Editorial Profile: Bristol Herald Courier is a daily newspaper written for residents in the Mountain Empire Region (southwestern Virginia and northeastern Tennessee.) The newspaper covers both local and national news. Topics covered include news, sports, arts & entertainment, lifestyle, classifieds, business and community events. Deadlines are at 10pm ET the day before issue date.; Full Page Mono: 56.95; Full Page Colour: 205.02
Currency: US Dollars
DAILY NEWSPAPER

The Bristol Press

Owner: Central Connecticut Communications
Editorial: 188 Main St, Bristol, Connecticut 06010-6308. **T:** 1 860 584-0501
W: http://www.bristolpress.com
Freq: Mon thru Fri; **Circ:** 4388 Not Audited
Editorial Profile: The Bristol Press is a local newspaper that covers Bristol, Plymouth, Plainville, Terryville, Thomaston and Burlington, CT. The paper provides readers with local news, business, education, lifestyle, sports, entertainment and classifieds. It combines with The Herald in New Britian, CT on Sundays.; Full Page Mono: 29.48; Full Page Colour: 45.60
Currency: US Dollars
DAILY NEWSPAPER

Bristow News & Record-Citizen

Owner: Central Oklahoma Publications LLC
Editorial: 112 W 6th Ave, Bristow, Oklahoma 74010-2810. **T:** 1 918 367-2282
E: bristownews@sbcglobal.net **Circ:** 5600 Not Audited
NEWSPAPER

British Weekly

Editorial: 171 Pier Ave, #121, Santa Monica, California 90405-5311. **T:** 1 310 452-2621
E: editor@british-weekly.com
W: http://www.british-weekly.com
Freq: Sat; **Circ:** 25000 Not Audited
Editorial Profile: British Weekly in Santa Monica, CA is the only newspaper in the USA serving the British expat market. It is published every Saturday and offers readers a 20-page digest of news, entertainment and sport from the United Kingdom, plus news from Southern California's British expat community.; Full Page Mono: 14.78
Currency: US Dollars
NEWSPAPER

Broad Street Media

Owner: Broad Street Media

Editorial: 2512 Metropolitan Dr, Trevose, Pennsylvania 19053-6738. **T:** 1 215 355-9009
W: http://www.bsmphilly.com **Circ:** 1367678 Not Audited
Publisher: Perry Corsetti; **Editor:** Tom Waring
Editorial Profile: Broad Street Media is a weekly community newspaper publisher serving the residents of Philadelphia, Camden, Wilmington, Bucks County, Chester County, Girard, Port Richmond, Fishtown, Bridesburg, Gloucester County, Burlington County, Camden County, Delaware County and Montgomery County, PA.
NEWSPAPER

The Broadcaster

Owner: MediaNews Group
Editorial: 491 Dutton St, Lowell, Massachusetts 01854-4289.
T: 1 978 458-7100 **E:** jcbroadcaster@aol.com
W: http://www.freebroadcaster.com
Freq: Fri; **Circ:** 37841 Not Audited
Editor: David McArdle
Editorial Profile: The Dracut Dispatch is a free weekly publication for the residents of Nashua, NH area.; Full Page Mono: 18.00; Full Page Colour: 4500.00
Currency: US Dollars
NEWSPAPER

The Bronx Free Press

Editorial: 2030 Broadway, Suite 801, New York, New York 10023-5060
E: editor@thebronxfreepress.com
W: http://bronxfreepress.com
Freq: Wed
Editor: Debralee Santos
Editorial Profile: The Bronx Free Press is a weekly bilingual newspaper serving the Latin American community in The Bronx, NY, focusing on local news. The paper includes articles in English and Spanish.
NEWSPAPER

Bronx Times Reporter Newspapers

Owner: Community Media, LLC
Editorial: 900 E 132nd St, Bronx, New York 10454-3628. **T:** 1 718 742-3398
E: bronxtimes@aol.com
W: http://www.bxtimes.com **Circ:** 57000
NEWSPAPER

Brookhaven Daily Leader

Owner: Brookhaven Newsmedia, LLC
Editorial: 128 N Railroad Ave, Brookhaven, Mississippi 39601-3043. **T:** 1 601 833-6961
E: news@dailyleader.com
W: http://www.dailyleader.com
Freq: Mon thru Fri; **Circ:** 5826 Not Audited
Publisher: Rick Reynolds
Editorial Profile: Brookhaven Daily Leader is a local newspaper distributed throughout Lincoln County, MS everyday except Saturday. The newspaper provides readers with local, regional and national news, as well as sports, business, entertainment and lifestyle coverage.; Full Page Mono: 12.89; Full Page Colour: 49.19
Currency: US Dollars
DAILY NEWSPAPER

Brookings Register

Owner: News Media Corp.
Editorial: 312 5th St, Brookings, South Dakota 57006. **T:** 1 605 692-6271
E: registernews@brookingsregister.com
W: http://www.brookingsregister.com
Freq: Daily; **Circ:** 3954 Not Audited
Editor: Doug Kott; **Publisher:** Billy McMacken; **Publisher:** Billy McMacken
Editorial Profile: Brookings Register is written for the residents of Brookings County, SD. The newspaper provides local community news and some national news to its readers. The focus is on the events occurring in the community and the people who live in the community. Some local features include sports, education, business, politics, entertainment, and classifieds.; Full Page Mono: 16.00; Full Page Colour: 53.09
Currency: US Dollars
DAILY NEWSPAPER

The Brooklyn Daily Eagle & Daily Bulletin

Owner: Brooklyn Eagle Publications
Editorial: 16 Court St, Brooklyn, New York 11241-0102. **T:** 1 718 422-7400
E: edit@brooklyneagle.net
W: http://www.brooklyneagle.com
Freq: Daily; **Circ:** 10000 Not Audited
Publisher: Dozier Hasty; **Legal/Legislation Editor:** Ryan Thompson; **Editor:** John Torenli
Editorial Profile: The Brooklyn Daily Eagle & Daily Bulletin is a daily newspaper serving readers in Brooklyn, NY with local and national news. Coverage also includes sports,

business, education, politics, entertainment, lifestyle and classifieds.; Full Page Mono: 21.00
Currency: US Dollars
DAILY NEWSPAPER

Brooklyn Eagle Publications
Owner: Eagle Publishing Partners
Editorial: 30 Henry St, Brooklyn, New York 11201-1338. **T:** 1 718 422-7400
E: news@brooklyneagle.com
W: http://www.brooklyneagle.com
Freq: Weekly; **Circ:** 198500 Not Audited
Publisher: Dozier Hasty
NEWSPAPER

The Brooklyn Paper Publications
Owner: Community Media, LLC
Editorial: 1 Metrotech Ctr N Ste 1001, Brooklyn, New York 11201-3832.
T: 1 718 260-2500
E: newsroom@cnglocal.com
W: http://www.brooklynpaper.com **Circ:** 47500 Not Audited
Editor-in-Chief: Vince DiMiceli
NEWSPAPER

Brooks Community Newspapers - Bridgeport
Owner: Hearst Corporation
Editorial: 410 State St., Bridgeport, Connecticut 06840-4827. **T:** 1 203 333-0161
Circ: 9154
Publisher: Michelle McAbee; **Editor:** Ashley Varese
NEWSPAPER

Brooks Community Newspapers- Fairfield
Owner: Hearst Corporation
Editorial: 220 Carter Henry Dr, Fairfield, Connecticut 06824-5701. **T:** 1 203 255-4561
W: http://www.fairfieldcitizenonline.com
Circ: 9929
Editor: James Doody; **Publisher:** Michelle McAbee
NEWSPAPER

Broomfield Enterprise
Owner: MediaNews Group
Editorial: 3400 Industrial Ln, Suite 2, Broomfield, Colorado 80020-1650.
T: 1 303 448-9898
W: http://www.broomfieldenterprise.com
Freq: Fri; **Circ:** 20000 Not Audited
Editor: Julie Baxter; **Publisher:** Albert Manzi
Editorial Profile: Broomfield Enterprise is distributed throughout Boulder County, CO on Wednesday afternoons and Saturday mornings. The newspaper is owned by Boulder Publishing and provides local news to readers in the community. Local features include high school sports, business, education, government and politics, and lifestyle. The best time to reach the editorial department is in the early afternoon MT. Deadlines for the publication are Tuesdays for the Wednesdays issue and Thursdays for the Saturdays issue.; Full Page Mono: 15.34
Currency: US Dollars
NEWSPAPER

The Brown County Press
Owner: Clermont Sun Publishing Company
Editorial: 219 S High St, Mount Orab, Ohio 45154-9039. **T:** 1 937 444-3441
E: bcpress@frontier.com
W: http://www.browncountypress.com
Freq: Sun; **Circ:** 18000 Not Audited
Editor: Wayne Gates; **Publisher:** William Latham
Editorial Profile: Brown County Press is a local, weekly newspaper serving the residents of Brown County, OH. The publication focuses on local news and community events. Deadlines are Thursdays at 4pm ET.; Full Page Mono: 9.05
Currency: US Dollars
NEWSPAPER

Brown Publishing Company
Owner: Ohio Community Media LLC.
Editorial: 30 S Oak St, London, Ohio 43140.
T: 1 740 852-1616
E: editor@madison-press.com
W: http://www.madison-press.com **Circ:** 9850 Not Audited
Editor: Fran Odyniec
NEWSPAPER

The Brownsville Herald
Owner: Freedom Communications Inc.
Editorial: 1135 E Van Buren St, Brownsville, Texas 78520-7055. **T:** 1 956 542-4301
W: http://www.brownsvilleherald.com
Freq: Daily; **Circ:** 12935 Not Audited
Publisher: Daniel Cavazos; **Editor:** Ryan Henry

Editorial Profile: The Brownsville Herald is published daily and distributed throughout Brownsville, TX and surrounding areas in Southern Texas. The newspaper provides readers with both local and national news coverage. It also features business, education, politics, lifestyle, entertainment, sports, classifieds and weather. It has a Spanish version called El Heraldo de Brownsville. The contacts are the same for both newspapers and should only be contacted once since both newspapers print the same content.; Full Page Mono: 23.79; Full Page Colour: 85.64
Currency: US Dollars
DAILY NEWSPAPER

Brownwood Bulletin
Owner: American Consolidated Media
Editorial: 700 Carnegie St, Brownwood, Texas 76801-7040. **T:** 1 325 646-2541
E: news@brownwoodbulletin.com
W: http://www.brownwoodbulletin.com
Freq: Daily; **Circ:** 7120 Not Audited
Publisher: Jerry Pye; **Editor:** Derrick Stuckley;
Editor: Derrick Stuckly
Editorial Profile: Founded in 1900, Brownwood Bulletin is a daily newspaper which provides local and national news coverage to readers throughout Brown County, TX. It features sports, education, politics, lifestyle, entertainment, opinions, obituaries, weather, classifieds and letters to the editor.; Full Page Mono: 14.78; Full Page Colour: 47.82
Currency: US Dollars
DAILY NEWSPAPER

The Brunswick Beacon
Owner: Landmark Community Newspapers, Inc.
Editorial: 208 Smith Ave, Shallotte, North Carolina 28470-4458. **T:** 1 910 754-6890
E: editor@brunswickbeacon.com
W: http://www.brunswickbeacon.com
Freq: Thu; **Circ:** 17000 Not Audited
Publisher: Scott Harrell; **Editor:** Stacey Manning
Editorial Profile: The Brunswick Beacon is a weekly newspaper which provides readers throughout Brunswick County, NC with local community news. The newspaper covers local issues such as: politics, education, entertainment, business, lifestyle, classifieds, and weather. Their mission is to keep the community connected by focusing on local events and people. Deadlines are on Mondays at noon ET.; Full Page Mono: 15.59
Currency: US Dollars
NEWSPAPER

The Brunswick Citizen
Owner: Citizen Communications Inc.
Editorial: 101 W Potomac St, Brunswick, Maryland 21716-1114. **T:** 1 301 834-7722
E: citizen@mip.net
W: http://www.citizennewspapers.com
Circ: 6500 Not Audited
Publisher: J. Peter Maynard; **Editor:** Julie Maynard
Editorial Profile: The Brunswick Citizen provides local coverage for Brunswick, Knoxville, Rosemont, Jefferson, Burkittsville, Point of Rocks, Lovettsville, and Pleasant Valley, MD. It also publishes The Valley Citizen, which covers Middletown, Myersville, Wolfsville and Braddock Heights, as well as South Washington County (the Boonsboro, Keedysville, and Rohrersville area) in Western Maryland.
NEWSPAPER

The Brunswick News
Owner: Brunswick News Publishing Company
Editorial: 3011 Altama Ave, Brunswick, Georgia 31520-4059. **T:** 1 912 265-8320
E: newsroom@thebrunswicknews.com
W: http://www.thebrunswicknews.com
Freq: Daily; **Circ:** 17800
Publisher & Editor: Buff Leavy
Editorial Profile: The Brunswick News is distributed throughout Brunswick and Golden Isles, GA. It provides local coverage of Brunswick, Jekyll Island, St. Simons Island and Brantley, Camden and McIntosh counties, GA. Local features include business, entertainment, sports and education. Deadlines are the day before publication at 1pm ET.; Full Page Mono: 19.95; Full Page Colour: 319.95
Currency: US Dollars
DAILY NEWSPAPER

Bryan County Now
Owner: Morris Communications Corp.
Editorial: 10610 Ford Ave., Richmond Hill, Georgia 31324. **T:** 1 912 756-5566
W: http://savannahnow.com/bryancountynow
Freq: Thu; **Circ:** 10000 Not Audited
Editor: Jamie Parker; **Publisher:** Michael

Traynor
Editorial Profile: Bryan County Now is a local, weekly newspaper serving residents of Richmond Hill and Bryan County, GA. The paper includes local news, business, politics, arts & entertainment, sports and community information. The paper shares a few of the same staff members at the Savannah (GA) Morning News. Advertising rates are based on a minimum one-week run.; Full Page Mono: 12.48; Full Page Colour: 180.00
Currency: US Dollars
NEWSPAPER

The Bryan Times
Owner: Bryan Publishing Company
Editorial: 127 S Walnut St, Bryan, Ohio 43506-1718. **T:** 1 419 636-1111
E: news@bryantimes.com
W: http://www.bryantimes.com
Freq: Daily; **Circ:** 7640 Not Audited
Editor: Tami Brigle; **Publisher:** Christopher Cullis
Editorial Profile: The Bryan Times provides local news to readers throughout Williams County, OH. The newspaper is published Monday through Saturday and focuses on local community news including business, lifestyle, entertainment, religion, farm, sports, school and service and classifieds.; Full Page Mono: 11.80; Full Page Colour: 300.00
Currency: US Dollars
DAILY NEWSPAPER

Buckeye Lake Beacon
Owner: Impact Publications
Editorial: 4675 Walnut Road, Buckeye Lake, Ohio 43008. **T:** 1 740 928-5541
E: thebeaconnews@hotmail.com
W: http://www.buckeyelakebeacon.net
Freq: Sat; **Circ:** 14500 Not Audited
Editorial Profile: Buckeye Lake Beacon is a local weekly newspaper that is distributed to readers throughout Perry, Fairfield, and Licking County, OH. The paper provides readers with local news and community events. Some local features include politics, business, education, lifestyle, sports and classifieds. Deadlines are Fridays at 4pm ET.; Full Page Mono: 8.30
Currency: US Dollars
NEWSPAPER

Bucks County Courier Times
Owner: Calkins Media
Editorial: 8400 N. Bristol Pike, Levittown, Pennsylvania 19057. **T:** 1 215 949-4000
E: newstips@calkins.com
W: http://www.buckscountycouriertimes.com
Freq: Mon thru Fri; **Circ:** 33769 Not Audited
News Content Editor: Jackie Massott
Editorial Profile: Bucks County Courier Times is a daily newspaper published by Calkins Newspapers for the residents of Bucks County, PA and surrounding communities. The newspaper provides readers with local and national news coverage. Other features include business, entertainment, sports, education, lifestyle, real estate, community and classifieds. The lead time for submissions varies. Deadlines are one day prior to the issue date.; Full Page Mono: 239.00; Full Page Colour: 695.00
Currency: US Dollars
DAILY NEWSPAPER

Bucks County Herald
Owner: Bucks County Herald Corp.
Editorial: 5761 Rte 202, Lahaska, Pennsylvania 18938. **T:** 1 215 794-1096
E: herald@buckscountyherald.com
W: http://www.buckscountyherald.com
Freq: Thu; **Circ:** 25000 Not Audited
Editor: Bridget Wingert; **Publisher:** Joseph Wingert
Editorial Profile: Bucks County Herald in Lahaska, PA is a community newspaper that covers local news, events, school districts, sports and features. Deadlines are on Tuesdays at 5pm ET.; Full Page Mono: 22.00
Currency: US Dollars
NEWSPAPER

Bucks InterCounty Newspaper Group
Owner: Digital First Media PA
Editorial: 209 Commerce Dr., Fort Washington, Pennsylvania 19034.
T: 1 215 542-0200 **E:** calendar@ingnews.com
W: http://www.buckslocalnews.com
Freq: Weekly; **Circ:** 20500
Editor: Tim Chicirda; **Publisher:** William Murray; **Editor:** R. Kurt Osenlund; **Editor:** Jeff Werner
NEWSPAPER

Bucyrus Telegraph-Forum
Owner: Gannett Co., Inc.

Editorial: 113 W Rensselaer St, Bucyrus, Ohio 44820-2215. **T:** 1 419 562-3333
E: tfnews@nncogannett.com
W: http://www.bucyrustelegraphforum.com
Freq: Daily; **Circ:** 3403 Not Audited
Publisher & Editor: Tom Brennan
Editorial Profile: Bucyrus Telegraph-Forum is a local daily newspaper serving Crawford County, OH. The newspaper focuses on local news and community events, also featuring national and international news. Local features include politics, business, lifestyle, education and sports.; Full Page Mono: 15.50; Full Page Colour: 51.61
Currency: US Dollars
DAILY NEWSPAPER

The Budget
Owner: Sugarcreek Budget Publishers, Inc.
Editorial: 134 N Factory St, Sugarcreek, Ohio 44681. **T:** 1 330 852-4634
E: localnews@thebudgetnewspaper.com
W: http://thebudgetnewspaper.com
Freq: Wed; **Circ:** 18000 Not Audited
Editor: Fannie Erb-Miller; **Publisher:** Keith Rathbun
Editorial Profile: The Budget is written for members of Amish and Mennonite communities. Deadlines are on Fridays at 5pm ET.; Full Page Mono: 10.95
Currency: US Dollars
NEWSPAPER

The Buffalo Criterion
Owner: Buffalo Criterion
Editorial: 623 William St, Buffalo, New York 14206. **T:** 1 716 853-2973
E: criterion@apollo3.com
W: http://www.buffalocriterion.com
Freq: Sat; **Circ:** 10000 Not Audited
Publisher: Evelyn Merriweather; **Editor:** Frances Merriweather
Editorial Profile: The Buffalo Criterion is a weekly newspaper written for residents of the inner city community in Buffalo, NY. The editorial mission is to try to keep the community appraised of important events and news that would be vital to the survival of the community. The newspaper includes news and editorials on local and national events, education, fitness, health, arts, and other information of interest to the community. It is written for the African American community in Buffalo, NY and surrounding areas. Deadlines are Mondays by 5pm prior to the issue dates.; Full Page Mono: 13.00; Full Page Colour: 1479.50
Currency: US Dollars
NEWSPAPER

The Buffalo News
Owner: Berkshire Hathaway
Editorial: 1 News Plz, Buffalo, New York 14203-2930. **T:** 1 716 849-3434
E: citydesk@buffnews.com
W: http://www.buffalonews.com
Freq: Daily; **Circ:** 137797 Not Audited
Editor: Mike Connelly; **City Editor:** William Flynn; **NeXt Editor:** Sharon Gleason; **Editor:** Susan Martin; **Editor:** Susan Martin; **Gusto Editor:** Toni Ruberto; **Gusto Editor:** Toni Ruberto; **Niagara Editor:** Scott Scanlon; **Niagara Editor:** Scott Scanlon; **Niagara Editor:** Scott Scanlon; **Urban Affairs Editor:** Rod Watson; **Urban Affairs Editor:** Rod Watson
Editorial Profile: The Buffalo News is a daily newspaper written for the general public in the greater Buffalo, NY area. The business section appears daily, covering local and national business stories, daily stock market rates and real estate. Articles include features, breaking news, trends, analysis, profiles and investigative stories. Consumer-related topics include: entertainment, lifestyles, TV topics, travel, viewpoints, health, money, a kid section, a computer page and a real estate section. Advertising rates are unavailable to media industry services and must be obtained by individual buyers through their sales department.; Full Page Mono: 588.44; Full Page Colour: 8495.13
Currency: US Dollars
DAILY NEWSPAPER

The Buffalo News
Editorial: 1715 15th St NW Apt 24, Washington, District Of Columbia 20009-3876.
T: 1 202 234-3188
Bureau Chief: Jerry Zremski
DAILY NEWSPAPER

The Buffalo News
Editorial: State Capitol LCA Pressroom 3rd Fl, Albany, New York 12224. **T:** 1 518 434-6365
Bureau Chief: Tom Precious
DAILY NEWSPAPER

Buffalo Rocket
Owner: Rocket Communications, Inc.
Editorial: 1249 Hertel Ave., Buffalo, New York 14216. **T:** 1 716 873-2594
E: editor.buffalorocket@gmail.com
W: http://www.buffalorocket.com
Freq: Thu; **Circ:** 10000 Not Audited
Publisher: David Gallagher
Editorial Profile: Buffalo Rocket is a local, weekly newspaper serving residents of North Buffalo, West Side and Riverside, NY. The paper includes local news, business, sports, arts & entertainment and community information.; Full Page Mono: 10.00
Currency: US Dollars
NEWSPAPER

Bukharian Times
Editorial: 106-16 70th Ave, 5th Fl, Forest Hills, New York 11375-4253. **T:** 1 718 261-1595
E: bukhariantimes@aol.com
Freq: Fri; **Circ:** 10000 Not Audited; Full Page Mono: 50.00
Currency: US Dollars
NEWSPAPER

The Bulletin
Owner: GateHouse Media Inc.
Editorial: 66 Franklin St, Norwich, Connecticut 06360-5806. **T:** 1 860 887-9211
E: news@norwichbulletin.com
W: http://www.norwichbulletin.com
Freq: Daily; **Circ:** 13287 Not Audited
Publisher: Chris Voccio
Editorial Profile: The Bulletin is a daily newspaper written for residents in Eastern Connecticut. It covers local news, sports, lifestyle and technology.; Full Page Mono: 35.35
Currency: US Dollars
DAILY NEWSPAPER

The Bulletin
Owner: Western Communications Inc.
Editorial: 1777 Sw Chandler Ave, Bend, Oregon 97702-3200. **T:** 1 541 382-1811
E: bulletin@bendbulletin.com
W: http://www.bendbulletin.com
Freq: Daily; **Circ:** 26406 Not Audited
Publisher: Gordon Black; **Editor In Chief:** John Costa; **Editor:** Dean Guernsey; **News Editor:** Jan Jordan
Editorial Profile: The Bulletin is published daily for the residents of Bend, OR, including Deschutes, Crook and Jefferson counties. The newspaper covers local and state news, business, sports, education, lifestyles and entertainment. Deadlines are one day prior to publications at 4pm PT.; Full Page Mono: 45.60; Full Page Colour: 166.31
Currency: US Dollars
DAILY NEWSPAPER

Bulletin Newspapers
Owner: Bulletin Newspapers, Inc.
Editorial: 1 Westinghouse Plz, Hyde Park, Massachusetts 2136. **T:** 1 617 361-8400
E: news@bulletinnewspapers.com
W: http://www.bulletinnewspapers.com
Circ: 24000 Not Audited
NEWSPAPER

Bullseye
Owner: Aerotech News and Review Inc.
Editorial: 3355 Spring Mountain Rd Ste 44, Las Vegas, Nevada 89102-8637.
T: 1 702 876-4589
E: bullseye@aerotechnews.com
W: http://www.nellisafbnews.com
Freq: Fri; **Circ:** 15000 Not Audited
Editor: Lila Dee Edwards; **Publisher:** Paul Kinison
Editorial Profile: Bullseye is a weekly newspaper for active members of the United States Air Force stationed at Nellis Air Force Base in Nevada. Deadlines are on Thursdays prior to issue date.; Full Page Mono: 15.70
Currency: US Dollars
NEWSPAPER

Bunker Hill Publications
Owner: Galer (John)
Editorial: 150 N Washington, Bunker Hill, Illinois 62014-1316. **T:** 1 618 585-4411
E: gazette7@frontiernet.net
Freq: Thu; **Circ:** 5850
Editor: Laura Dabbs; **Publisher:** John Galer
Editorial Profile: Bunker Hill Publications is a community newspaper publisher servicing the residents of St. Louis, MO.
NEWSPAPER

Burbank Leader
Owner: Tribune Company
Editorial: 202 W 1st St, Los Angeles, California 90012-4299. **T:** 1 818 637-3200
E: burbankleader@latimes.com
W: http://www.burbankleader.com
Freq: Sat; **Circ:** 10223 Not Audited
Editor: Dan Evans
Editorial Profile: Burbank Leader is a bi-weekly newspaper published by the Tribune Company for the residents of Burbank. It covers local news, business, sports, arts and entertainment. The paper is inserted within the Los Angeles Times and it is also available for free at area news racks. Deadlines fall on Fridays at 5pm PT for the Wednesday issue and on Thursdays at 5pm PT for the Saturday issue. On Sundays, the paper combines with the Glendale News-Press to put out a Sunday issue, the Sunday News-Press & Leader.; Full Page Mono: 22.95
Currency: US Dollars
NEWSPAPER

The Burbank Times
Editorial: 3917 W Riverside Dr, 2nd Fl, Burbank, California 91505. **T:** 1 818 841-6397
E: burbanktimes@gmail.com
Freq: Fri; **Circ:** 25000 Not Audited
Editorial Profile: The Burbank Times is published weekly for the residents of Burbank, Glendale and North Hollywood, CA. The newspaper covers local news, business, sports, entertainment and community events.; Full Page Mono: 24.50
Currency: US Dollars
NEWSPAPER

Burleson-Crowley Connection
Owner: Community Newspaper Holdings, Inc.
Editorial: 108 S Anglin St, Cleburne, Texas 76031. **T:** 1 817 645-2441
W: http://burlesoncrowley.com
Freq: Tue; **Circ:** 20000 Not Audited
News Editor: Monica Faram
Editorial Profile: Burleson-Crowley Connection is a community newspaper written for the residents of Cleburne, Burleson and Crowley, TX. It covers local news and sports.; Full Page Mono: 10.50
Currency: US Dollars
NEWSPAPER

Burlington County Times
Owner: Calkins Media
Editorial: 4284 Route 130, Willingboro, New Jersey 08046-2027. **T:** 1 609 871-8000
E: mesposito@phillyburbs.com
W: http://www.phillyburbs.com/news/local/burlington_county_times_news/
Freq: Mon thru Fri; **Circ:** 20147 Not Audited
Editorial Profile: Burlington County Times is a daily newspaper published for the residents of Burlington County, NJ. The newspaper focuses on local news and community events. Features include business, education, lifestyle, entertainment, sports, and politics. Deadlines are daily at noon ET.; Full Page Mono: 239.00; Full Page Colour: 274.90
Currency: US Dollars
DAILY NEWSPAPER

The Burlington Free Press
Owner: Gannett Co., Inc.
Editorial: 100 Bank St Ste 700, Burlington, Vermont 05401-4946. **T:** 1 802 863-3441
E: metro@burlingtonfreepress.com
W: http://www.burlingtonfreepress.com
Freq: Daily; **Circ:** 32089 Not Audited
Editorial Profile: The Burlington Free Press is a daily newspaper serving the residents of Burlington, VT and surrounding communities. The publication covers local and national news, sports, business and community information.; Full Page Mono: 81.10; Full Page Colour: 265.74
Currency: US Dollars
DAILY NEWSPAPER

But Viet News
Editorial: 9780 Walnut St, Ste 180, Dallas, Texas 75243-2396. **T:** 1 972 808-9700
E: butviet@aol.com
Freq: Fri; **Circ:** 62500
Editor: Phung Pham; **Publisher:** Duke Van Mai
Editorial Profile: But Viet News is a twice-weekly newspaper written for Vietnamese-Americans and Vietnamese residents in Dallas.; Full Page Mono: 5.50
Currency: US Dollars
NEWSPAPER

Butler Eagle
Owner: Eagle Printing Company
Editorial: 114 W Diamond St, Butler, Pennsylvania 16001-5747. **T:** 1 724 282-8000
E: news@butlereagle.com
W: http://www.butlereagle.com
Freq: Daily; **Circ:** 23859 Not Audited
City Editor: David Heastings; **Publisher:** Vernon Wise
Editorial Profile: Butler Eagle is a daily newspaper published for the residents of Butler County, PA. The paper covers local news, business, education and sports. Deadlines are daily at 9:30am ET.; Full Page Mono: 30.00; Full Page Colour: 97.87
Currency: US Dollars
DAILY NEWSPAPER

C & G Newspapers
Owner: C & G Publishing
Editorial: 13650 E 11 Mile Rd, Warren, Michigan 48089-1422. **T:** 1 586 498-8000
W: http://www.candgnews.com **Circ:** 601585 Not Audited
Editor: Annie Bates; **Editor:** Jon Malavoti; **Editor:** David Wallace
NEWSPAPER

C & S Media Inc. - Farmersville
Owner: C & S Media Inc.
Editorial: 101 S Main St, Farmersville, Texas 75442. **T:** 1 972 784-6397 **Circ:** 3909 Not Audited
NEWSPAPER

C & S Media Inc. - Wylie News
Owner: C & S Media Inc.
Editorial: 110 N Ballard Ave, Wylie, Texas 75098. **T:** 1 972 442-5515
E: publisher@wylienews.com **Circ:** 11021 Not Audited
NEWSPAPER

The Cabinet Press, Inc.
Owner: McLean Communications, Inc.
Editorial: 54 School St, Milford, New Hampshire 03055-4543. **T:** 1 603 673-3100
E: cabnews@cabinet.com
W: http://www.cabinet.com **Circ:** 33250 Not Audited
Editor: Kathy Cleveland; **Editor:** Kathy Cleveland; **Editor:** Michael Cleveland
NEWSPAPER

Cadillac News
Owner: Huckle (Chris)
Editorial: 130 N Mitchell St, Cadillac, Michigan 49601-1856. **T:** 1 231 775-6565
E: news@cadillacnews.com
W: http://www.cadillacnews.com
Freq: Daily; **Circ:** 9603 Not Audited
Publisher: T. Christopher Huckle; **Editor:** Matthew Seward
Editorial Profile: Cadillac News is written for the residents of Wexford, Missaukee, Osceola and Eastern Lake Counties, MI. It covers area news, events, sports, business and community information. Deadlines are daily at 8pm ET the day prior to the issue date.; Full Page Mono: 17.40; Full Page Colour: 60.47
Currency: US Dollars
DAILY NEWSPAPER

Cairo Messenger
Editorial: 31 1st Ave NE, Cairo, Georgia 39828. **T:** 1 229 377-2032
E: news@cairomessenger.com
W: http://www.cairomessenger.com
Freq: Wed; **Circ:** 13195 Not Audited
Editorial Profile: Cairo Messenger covers local news in and around Cairo, GA. Deadlines for editorial submissions are on Mondays at noon ET.; Full Page Mono: 6.60; Full Page Colour: 893.80
Currency: US Dollars
NEWSPAPER

Calaveras Newspapers
Editorial: 15 Main St, San Andreas, California 95249. **T:** 1 209 754-3861 **Circ:** 29357 Not Audited
Publisher: Ralph Alldredge; **Editor:** Mike Taylor
NEWSPAPER

Caldwell County Newspapers
Owner: H & H Publishing, LLC
Editorial: 101 S Davis St, Hamilton, Missouri 64644. **T:** 1 816 583-2116
E: news@mycaldwellcounty.com
W: http://www.mycaldwellcounty.com
Freq: Wed; **Circ:** 2300 Not Audited
Editor: Debbie Rankin; Full Page Mono: 4.25
Currency: US Dollars
NEWSPAPER

The Caledonian-Record
Owner: Todd Smith
Editorial: 190 Federal St, Saint Johnsbury, Vermont 05819-2621. **T:** 1 802 748-8121
E: news@caledonian-record.com
W: http://caledonianrecord.com
Freq: Daily; **Circ:** 9993 Not Audited
Publisher: Mark Smith
Editorial Profile: The Caledonian-Record is a daily newspaper written for the residents of the Northeast Kingdom of Vermont and the North Country of New Hampshire. The publication covers local news, business, sports, entertainment, health, education, religion, food and fashion. They are only interested in releases directly germane to their five county area of distribution and coverage. Press releases should be submitted one week before an event is held. Deadlines fall two days prior to the issue date at 5pm ET. Please send all press releases to the PO Box.; Full Page Mono: 8.25; Full Page Colour: 41.70
Currency: US Dollars
DAILY NEWSPAPER

California Advocate
Editorial: 1555 E St, Fresno, California 93706. **T:** 1 559 268-0941 **E:** ads@caladvocate.com
W: http://www.caladvocate.com
Freq: Fri; **Circ:** 33013 Not Audited
Editorial Profile: California Advocate is a newspaper serving the Fresno, CA area. It provides the African-American community with information on important issues and events. Deadlines are on Mondays before the issue date.; Full Page Mono: 39.50
Currency: US Dollars
NEWSPAPER

California Community Newspapers
Owner: California Community Newspapers
Editorial: 4346 Sepulveda Blvd, Culver City, California 90230-4722. **T:** 1 310 398-6397
Circ: 23000 Not Audited
Editor: Mitch Chortkoff; **Publisher:** Stephen Hadland
NEWSPAPER

California Crusader News
Editorial: 11633 Hawthorne Blvd, Ste 211, Hawthorne, California 90250-2322.
T: 1 310 673-5555 **E:** ccneditorial@pacbell.net
W: http://www.calcrusnews.com
Freq: Thu; **Circ:** 25000 Not Audited
Editorial Profile: California Crusader News in Hawthorne, CA covers local news, sports, entertainment, health, food, religion and events for residents of Inglewood, CA, Los Angeles and surrounding communities.; Full Page Mono: 30.00
Currency: US Dollars
NEWSPAPER

California Newspapers Partnership
Owner: MediaNews Group
Editorial: 450 N Franklin St, Fort Bragg, California 95437-3210. **T:** 1 707 964-5642
Circ: 7800 Not Audited
Publisher: Sharon Dimauro
NEWSPAPER

California Sun Times
Editorial: 3010 Wilshire Blvd, Ste 553, Los Angeles, California 90010.
T: 1 213 614-0534 115
E: calsuntimes2@yahoo.com
Freq: Fri
Publisher: Dave Shumann
Editorial Profile: California Sun Times is published weekly for the residents of Los Angeles and surrounding areas. The newspaper provides information about local news and community events.; Full Page Mono: 15.00
Currency: US Dollars
NEWSPAPER

The Call
Owner: R.I.S.N. Operations Inc.
Editorial: 75 Main St, Woonsocket, Rhode Island 02895-4312. **T:** 1 401 762-3000
E: news@woonsocketcall.com
W: http://www.woonsocketcall.com
Freq: Daily; **Circ:** 6703 Not Audited
Publisher: Mary Lynn Bosiak
Editorial Profile: The Call is a daily newspaper written for the community of Woonsocket, RI. The paper includes local, state and some national and world news, politics, business, sports and entertainment.; Full Page Mono: 26.53; Full Page Colour: 85.65
Currency: US Dollars
DAILY NEWSPAPER

The Call
Editorial: 1715 E 18th St, Kansas City, Missouri 64108. **T:** 1 816 842-3804
E: kccallnews@hotmail.com
W: http://www.kccall.com
Freq: Fri; **Circ:** 19000 Not Audited
Editorial Profile: The Call is one of the six largest African American weeklies in the country and serves the communities surrounding Kansas City, MO. The newspaper covers local news, social issues, religion, education and community events.; Full Page Mono: 15.00

Currency: US Dollars
NEWSPAPER

Call and Post
Owner: King Media Enterprises Inc.
Editorial: 11800 Shaker Blvd, Cleveland, Ohio 44120-1919. **T:** 1 216 588-6700
E: into@call-post.com
W: http://www.callandpost.com
Freq: Wed; **Circ:** 45600 Not Audited
Publisher: Don King; **Editor:** James Wade
Editorial Profile: Call and Post is dedicated to providing news to the African-American communities in Cincinnati and Cleveland. It covers local news, business, arts & entertainment and sports.; Full Page Mono: 65.49
Currency: US Dollars
NEWSPAPER

Call Publishing, Inc.
Owner: Concord Publications, Inc.
Editorial: 9977 Lin Ferry Dr, Saint Louis, Missouri 63123-6913. **T:** 1 314 843-0102
E: news1@callnewspapers.com
W: http://www.callnewspapers.com
Freq: Thu; **Circ:** 101471 Not Audited
Publisher: Deborah Baker
Editorial Profile: Call Publishing, Inc. is a weekly community newspaper publisher serving the residents of St. Louis, Concord, Oakville and Green Park, MO.; Full Page Mono: 23.81; Full Page Colour: 27.42
Currency: US Dollars
NEWSPAPER

Callahan County Newspapers
Editorial: 117 S 1st St, Clyde, Texas 79510. **T:** 1 325 893-4244
E: clydejournal@earthlink.net
W: http://clydenewspaper.com **Circ:** 4325 Not Audited
Editor: Sheri Allen; **Editor:** Danny Tabor; **Publisher:** Donald Tabor
NEWSPAPER

The Call-Leader
Owner: Elwood Publishing Co.
Editorial: 317 S Anderson St, Elwood, Indiana 46036-2018. **T:** 1 765 552-3355
E: elpub@elwoodpublishing.com
W: http://www.elwoodpublishing.com
Freq: Daily; **Circ:** 2800 Not Audited
Editor: Sandy Burton; **Editor:** Ed Hamilton; **Publisher:** Robert Nash
Editorial Profile: The Call-Leader is written for the residents of Elwood, IN. It covers local news, sports, lifestyle, education, business and entertainment.; Full Page Mono: 9.95; Full Page Colour: 159.95
Currency: US Dollars
DAILY NEWSPAPER

The Calvert Recorder
Owner: Gazette Newspapers Inc.
Editorial: 134 Main St, Prince Frederick, Maryland 20678. **T:** 1 410 535-1214
W: http://www.somdnews.com/recorder
Freq: Fri; **Circ:** 12000 Not Audited
Publisher: Karen Acton; **Editor:** Rob Perry
Editorial Profile: The Calvert Recorder is a local newspaper covering all of Calvert County, MD. Coverage includes local news, events, sports, arts & entertainment, travel, food and lifestyle topics.; Full Page Mono: 12.85
Currency: US Dollars
NEWSPAPER

Camas-Washougal Post Record
Owner: Columbian Publishing Co.
Editorial: 425 NE 4th Ave, Camas, Washington 98607. **T:** 1 360 834-2141
W: http://www.camaspostrecord.com
Freq: Tue; **Circ:** 10000 Not Audited
Editor: Heather Acheson; **Publisher:** Mike Gallagher
Editorial Profile: Camas-Washougal Post Record is a local weekly newspaper serving Camas and Washougal, WA. It provides residents with information on news, events, sports and weather.; Full Page Mono: 10.60; Full Page Colour: 1206.30
Currency: US Dollars
NEWSPAPER

Camden Community News
Owner: Camden Community News, Inc.
Editorial: 3526 Humboldt Ave N, Minneapolis, Minnesota 55412. **T:** 1 612 521-3060
E: info@camdenews.org
W: http://www.camdenews.org
Freq: Monthly; **Circ:** 12700 Not Audited
Editorial Profile: Camden Community News is a monthly newspaper that serves Northwestern Minneapolis.; Full Page Mono: 23.00
Currency: US Dollars
NEWSPAPER

Camden Media Company
Owner: Camden Media Co.
Editorial: 909 W Dekalb St, Camden, South Carolina 29020-4259. **T:** 1 803 432-6157
Freq: Fri; **Circ:** 24716 Not Audited
Editor: Martha Bruce; **Publisher:** Mike Mischner; **Editor:** Tarsha Storey; **Editor:** Keri Todd
Editorial Profile: Camden Media Company is a weekly community newspaper publisher serving the residents of Kershaw County, SC.
NEWSPAPER

Camden News
Owner: Wehco Media Inc.
Editorial: 113 Madison Ave, Camden, Arkansas 71701-3549. **T:** 1 870 836-8192
E: camdennews@camdenarknews.com
W: http://www.camdenarknews.com
Freq: Daily; **Circ:** 4368 Not Audited
Editor: Kelly Blair; **Publisher:** Walter Hussman
Editorial Profile: Camden News is a local daily newspaper serving Camden, AR. The newspaper covers local news, community events, weather and sports. It combines with the El Dorado (AR) News-Times and the Magnolia (AR) Banner-News on Sundays.; Full Page Mono: 13.49; Full Page Colour: 45.93
Currency: US Dollars
DAILY NEWSPAPER

Cameron Herald/Thorndale Champion
Owner: Granite Publications
Editorial: 108 E 1st St, Cameron, Texas 76520-3341. **T:** 1 254 697-6671
E: herald@cameronherald.com **Circ:** 5411 Not Audited
NEWSPAPER

Caminos de Southern Colorado
Owner: Star Journal Publishing Corporation
Editorial: 825 W 6th St, Pueblo, Colorado 81003. **T:** 1 719 404-2763
W: http://www.caminos.us
Freq: Bi-Monthly; **Circ:** 10000 Not Audited
Editor: Pablo Mora; **Publisher:** Robert Rawlings
Editorial Profile: Caminos de Southern Colorado is a free, bi-monthly, bilingual newspaper distributed throughout northern New Mexico and Southern Colorado. It explores Hispanic people, issues, events and the cultural landscape of the region. It is published by the editorial staff of the Pueblo (CO) Chieftan.; Full Page Mono: 7.62
Currency: US Dollars
NEWSPAPER

Cam-News
Editorial: 1305 Raymond Ave, Ste A, Long Beach, California 90804. **T:** 1 562 987-4532
E: cam-news@hotmail.com
W: http://www.camnews.org
Freq: Bi-Weekly; **Circ:** 10000 Not Audited; Full Page Mono: 27.00
Currency: US Dollars
NEWSPAPER

Campbell Publishing Co.
Owner: Campbell Publications
Editorial: 115 W Jefferson St, Pittsfield, Illinois 62363. **T:** 1 217 285-2345
E: ppnews@campbellpublications.net
W: http://www.pikepress.com **Circ:** 8400 Not Audited
NEWSPAPER

Campus News
Owner: Johnson (Darren)
Editorial: 39 County Route 70, Greenwich, New York 12834-6300. **T:** 1 518 507-6359
E: editor@campus-news.org
W: http://campus-news.org
Freq: Bi-Weekly; **Circ:** 10000
Editorial Profile: Founded in February 2010, Campus News is a community newspaper serving college students at New York, New England and New Jersey two-year colleges. The paper prints monthly/bi-weekly during the school year and is distributed to 27 campus in the region. Writers are all college students and faculty, with occasional pieces from Scripps interns and student freelancers.; Full Page Mono: 18.71; Full Page Colour: 21.29
Currency: US Dollars
NEWSPAPER

The Cannoneer
Editorial: USA FACFS, Attn: ATZR-A Public Affairs, Fort Sill, Oklahoma 73503-5100. **T:** 1 580 442-5150
Freq: Thu; **Circ:** 15000
Editor: Keith Pannell
Editorial Profile: The Cannoneer is written for the military base in Fort Sill, OK. It covers news, features, training events, sports and recreational activites within the base. Send all materials to the street address.; Full Page Mono: 8.88
Currency: US Dollars
NEWSPAPER

The Cañon City Daily Record
Owner: Lehman Communications Corp.
Editorial: 701 S 9th St, Canon City, Colorado 81212-4911. **T:** 1 719 275-7565
W: http://www.canoncitydailyrecord.com
Freq: Daily; **Circ:** 5142 Not Audited
Editor: Charlotte Burrous; **Publisher:** Ed Lehman
Editorial Profile: Cañon City Daily Record publishes news for the residents of Fremont and Custard counties, CO. The newspaper covers local news, business, sports and arts & entertainment stories.; Full Page Mono: 13.63
Currency: US Dollars
DAILY NEWSPAPER

Canyon News
Editorial: 264 S La Cienega Blvd, Ste 439, Beverly Hills, California 90211.
T: 1 310 277-6017
W: http://www.canyon-news.com
Freq: Sun; **Circ:** 40000 Not Audited
Publisher: Glenn Kelly; **Editor:** Rachel Knuese
Editorial Profile: Canyon News in Beverly Hills, CA is a weekly newspaper covering all of the Canyon, including Bel Air, Beachwood Canyon, Benedict Canyon, Brentwood, Laurel Canyon, Los Feliz, Malibu, Melrose, Pacific Palisades, Santa Monica, Sherman Oaks, Studio City, Topanga Canyon, Westwood, Woodland Hills and all of the Hollywood Hills, CA. Publication requests that users register on website; it does not take calls from publicists.; Full Page Mono: 7.24
Currency: US Dollars
NEWSPAPER

Cape Cod Times
Owner: GateHouse Media Inc.
Editorial: 319 Main St, Hyannis, Massachusetts 2601. **T:** 1 508 775-1200
E: news@capecodonline.com
W: http://www.capecodonline.com
Freq: Daily; **Circ:** 32527 Not Audited
Editor: Wendy Lopata; **Publisher:** Peter Meyer; **News Editor:** Susan Moeller; **Editor:** Paul Pronovost
Editorial Profile: Cape Cod Times is written for residents of Cape Cod, MA. The paper covers arts & entertainment, travel, technology, health and local news.; Full Page Mono: 65.21; Full Page Colour: 206.22
Currency: US Dollars
DAILY NEWSPAPER

Cape Cod Times
Editorial: 12 Main St, Orleans, Massachusetts 2653. **T:** 1 508 255-0408
DAILY NEWSPAPER

Cape Cod Times
Editorial: 668 Main St, Falmouth, Massachusetts 02540-5201.
T: 1 508 548-9300
Bureau Chief: George Brennan; **Bureau Chief:** George Brennan
DAILY NEWSPAPER

Cape Gazette
Owner: Cape Gazette Ltd.
Editorial: 17585 Nassau Commons Blvd, Lewes, Delaware 19958-6286.
T: 1 302 645-7700
E: newsroom@capegazette.com
W: http://www.capegazette.com
Freq: Fri; **Circ:** 15000 Not Audited
Publisher: Dennis Forney; **News Editor:** Laura Ritter
Editorial Profile: Cape Gazette is a local weekly newspaper serving Delaware's Cape region. It provides residents with information on local news, events, sports and weather. Deadlines are on Wednesdays at noon ET.; Full Page Mono: 11.75
Currency: US Dollars
NEWSPAPER

Cape Publications, Inc.
Owner: Gannett Co., Inc.
Editorial: One Gannett Plaza, Melbourne, Florida 32940. **T:** 1 321 242-3500
W: http://www.floridatoday.com **Circ:** 185300 Not Audited
Publisher: Jeff Kiel
NEWSPAPER

The Capital
Owner: Capital Gazette Communications Inc.
Editorial: 2000 Capital Dr, Annapolis, Maryland 21401-3155. **T:** 1 410 268-5000
E: capstaff@capitalgazette.com
W: http://www.capitalgazette.com
Freq: Daily; **Circ:** 29254 Not Audited
Editor: Steve Gunn; **Publisher:** Pat Richardson
Editorial Profile: The Capital is a daily newspaper serving the Annapolis, MD area. The publication dates back to the 18th century. The paper covers local news, sports, art & entertainment and business issues.; Full Page Mono: 39.15; Full Page Colour: 129.99
Currency: US Dollars
DAILY NEWSPAPER

Capital City Weekly
Owner: Morris Communications
Editorial: 134 N Franklin St, Juneau, Alaska 99801-1223. **T:** 1 907 789-4144
E: editor@capweek.com
W: http://www.capitalcityweekly.com
Freq: Wed; **Circ:** 15550 Not Audited
Editorial Profile: Capital City Weekly is a local weekly newspaper serving residents of Juneau, AK. It provides residents of Southeastern Alaska with information on news, events, sports and weather.; Full Page Mono: 17.82
Currency: US Dollars
NEWSPAPER

Capital Community News
Owner: Fagon Publishing Group
Editorial: 224 7th St SE, Washington, District Of Columbia 20003. **T:** 1 202 543-8300
E: bulletinboard@hillrag.com
W: http://www.capitalcommunitynews.com
Circ: 60000 Not Audited
Publisher: Jean-Keith Fagon
NEWSPAPER

Capital Flyer
Owner: Comprint Military Publications
Editorial: 1535 Command Dr, Andrews Air Force Base, Maryland 20762.
T: 1 301 981-9465
E: 316wg.pa.capflyer@andrews.af.mil
W: http://www.dcmilitary.com/section/news09
Freq: Fri; **Circ:** 15000 Not Audited
Editor: Andrew Polvino; **Publisher:** John Rives
Editorial Profile: Capital Flyer is a newspaper for Andrews Air Force Base, MD. The publication accepts press releases only by the military and for the military. Do not call the main phone number for advertising inquiries. Call 240-473-7538 to place an ad.; Full Page Mono: 19.16
Currency: US Dollars
NEWSPAPER

Capital Gazette Newspapers
Owner: Capital Gazette Communications Inc.
Editorial: 2000 Capital Dr, Annapolis, Maryland 21401-3155. **T:** 1 410 268-5000
E: breakingnews@capitalgazette.com
W: http://www.capitalgazette.com **Circ:** 83550 Not Audited
Editor: David Emanuel; **Editor:** Steve Gunn; **Editor:** Rick Hutzell; **Publisher:** Pat Richardson
Editorial Profile: Capital Gazette Newspapers in Annapolis, MD publishes the Bowie Blade-News, the Maryland Gazette and the Crofton-West County News Gazette. It shares offices with the Capital daily newspaper.
NEWSPAPER

Capital Journal
Owner: Wick Communications Inc.
Editorial: 333 W Dakota Ave, Pierre, South Dakota 57501-4512. **T:** 1 605 224-7301
E: news@capjournal.com
W: http://www.capjournal.com
Freq: Mon thru Fri; **Circ:** 3903 Not Audited
Publisher: Steve Baker
Editorial Profile: Capital Journal is published daily for the residents of Pierre, SD and surrounding areas. The newspaper covers local news, sports, business and lifestyles. The paper is published 48 weeks out of the year.; Full Page Mono: 9.63; Full Page Colour: 38.31
Currency: US Dollars
DAILY NEWSPAPER

Caribbean New Yorker - New York bureau
Editorial: 362 5Th Ave Ste 803, New York, New York 10001-2210. **T:** 1 718 275-0459
Editorial Profile: This is the New York bureau of The Caribbean New Yorker, based in Jamaica, New York.
DAILY NEWSPAPER

Caribbean Today
Owner: Webley (Peter A.)
Editorial: 9020 SW 152nd St, Miami, Florida 33157-1928. **T:** 1 305 238-2868

E: editor@caribbeantoday.com
W: http://www.caribbeantoday.com
Freq: Monthly; **Circ:** 39000 Not Audited
Editorial Profile: Caribbean Today is a local newspaper written for the Caribbean and American residents of Miami.; Full Page Mono: 55.92
Currency: US Dollars
NEWSPAPER

Caribbean Voice
Owner: Caribbean Voice Inc. (The)
Editorial: 1936 Daly Ave, Bronx, New York 10460-4312. **T:** 1 718 542-4454
E: caribvoice@aol.com
Freq: Monthly; **Circ:** 25000 Not Audited
Editorial Profile: Caribbean Voice is written for people interested in the Caribbean. The newspaper covers news, information and political views about events in the Caribbean.; Full Page Mono: 8.70; Full Page Colour: 67.83
Currency: US Dollars
NEWSPAPER

The Carmel Pine Cone
Owner: Miller (Paul)
Editorial: 734 Lighthouse Ave, Pacific Grove, California 93950-2522. **T:** 1 831 624-0162
E: mail@carmelpinecone.com
W: http://www.carmelpinecone.com
Freq: Fri; **Circ:** 20000 Not Audited
Editorial Profile: The Carmel Pine Cone is a weekly newspaper covering the town of Carmel-by-the-Sea, CA. The paper provides local news and events for residents of the town.; Full Page Mono: 17.20
Currency: US Dollars
NEWSPAPER

The Carmi Times
Owner: GateHouse Media Inc.
Editorial: 323 E Main St, Carmi, Illinois 62821-1810. **T:** 1 618 382-4176
E: carmitimes@clearwave.com
W: http://www.carmitimes.com
Freq: Daily; **Circ:** 2735 Not Audited
Editorial Profile: The Carmi Times is a daily newspaper serving residents of Carmi, IL. The newspaper covers news, business, sports, entertainment and lifestyles.; Full Page Mono: 12.99; Full Page Colour: 34.41
Currency: US Dollars
DAILY NEWSPAPER

The Carolina Forest Chronicle
Editorial: 2510 Main St, Conway, South Carolina 29526. **T:** 1 843 236-4810
Freq: Thu; **Circ:** 13500 Not Audited
Publisher: Steve Robertson; **Editor:** Michael Smith
Editorial Profile: The Carolina Forest Chronicle is written for the residents of Forestbrook, SC and surrounding areas. The publication was incepted in November 2007. The newspaper covers local news and community events.; Full Page Mono: 14.00
Currency: US Dollars
NEWSPAPER

Carolina Journal
Owner: John Locke Foundation
Editorial: 200 W Morgan St, Ste 200, Raleigh, North Carolina 27601. **T:** 1 919 828-3876
W: http://www.carolinajournal.com
Freq: Monthly; **Circ:** 20000 Not Audited
Publisher: John Ham
Editorial Profile: Carolina Journal is published monthy for the residents of Raleigh, NC. It covers state news, education, local government news, books and arts. The newspaper does not accept any advertising.
NEWSPAPER

Carolina Panorama
Owner: MDB Media
Editorial: 2346 Two Notch Rd, Columbia, South Carolina 29204. **T:** 1 803 256-4015
E: cpanorama@aol.com
W: http://carolinapanorama.net
Freq: Thu; **Circ:** 16000 Not Audited
Publisher: Nat Abraham; **Editor:** Nat Abraham
Editorial Profile: Carolina Panorama is a weekly newspaper that provides local news coverage for residents of Columbia, South Carolina.; Full Page Mono: 15.00
Currency: US Dollars
NEWSPAPER

Carolina Weekly Newspaper Group
Owner: Charlotte Weekly Newspaper Group, LLC
Editorial: 10100 Park Cedar Dr Ste 154, Charlotte, North Carolina 28210-8906.
T: 1 704 849-2261
W: http://www.carolinaweeklynewspapers.com
Circ: 59000 Not Audited
Publisher: Alain Lillie
Editorial Profile: Carolina Weekly Newspaper Group in Charlotte, NC is the publisher of community newspapers.
NEWSPAPER

The Carolinian
Editorial: 501 E Davie St, Raleigh, North Carolina 27601. **T:** 1 919 834-5558
E: thecarolinian@bellsouth.net
W: http://www.raleighcarolinian.com
Freq: Mon; **Circ:** 14202 Not Audited
Editor: Cash Michaels
Editorial Profile: The Carolinian is written for African American residents in Raliegh, NC. It covers local news, business, sports and arts & entertainment stories. It also covers national and statewide stories if they have a direct impact on the readership.; Full Page Mono: 24.00
Currency: US Dollars
NEWSPAPER

Carriage Towne News
Owner: Community Newspaper Holdings, Inc.
Editorial: 14 Church St, Kingston, New Hampshire 3848. **T:** 1 603 642-4499
E: info@carriagetownenews.com
W: http://www.carriagetownenews.com
Freq: Tue; **Circ:** 30614 Not Audited
Editorial Profile: Carriage Towne News is a local newspaper covering news in Atkinson, Brentwood, Danville, East Hampstead, East Kingston, Epping, Exeter, Fremont, Hampstead, Kensington, Kingston, Newton, Newton Junction, Plaistow, Raymond, Sandown, South Hampton and Stratham, NH.; Full Page Mono: 20.25
Currency: US Dollars
NEWSPAPER

Carroll County Times
Owner: Landmark Community Newspapers, Inc.
Editorial: 201 Railroad Ave, Westminster, Maryland 21157-4854. **T:** 1 410 848-4400
E: cctnews@carrollcountytimes.com
W: http://www.carrollcountytimes.com
Freq: Daily; **Circ:** 20939 Not Audited
City Editor: Wayne Carter; **Editor:** Jim Lee; **News Night Editor:** Brian Patterson;
Publisher: Pat Richardson
Editorial Profile: Carroll County Times is a daily newspaper serving the community of Carroll County, MD. The county has undergone a recent shift from an agricultural town to an affluent suburb of Baltimore and Washington, D.C. The paper focuses on local news and events but also covers some regional, national, and international news.; Full Page Mono: 27.01; Full Page Colour: 635.00
Currency: US Dollars
DAILY NEWSPAPER

The Carroll News
Owner: Heartland Publications
Editorial: 707 N Main St, Hillsville, Virginia 24343. **T:** 1 276 728-7311
W: http://www.thecarrollnews.com
Freq: Wed; **Circ:** 13500 Not Audited
Editorial Profile: The Carroll News is a local newspaper written for the residents of Hillsville, VA. The paper provides local news and events.; Full Page Mono: 10.95
Currency: US Dollars
NEWSPAPER

Carroll Publishing
Editorial: 145 Taylor St NE, Washington, District Of Columbia 20017.
T: 1 202 281-2410 **Circ:** 84421 Not Audited
Editor: Rafael Roncal; **Publisher:** Thomas Schmidt; **Editor:** Mark Zimmermann
Editorial Profile: Carroll Publishing is a media organization for the Archdiocese of Washington D.C. and publisher of the Catholic Standard and El Pregonero. The Catholic Standard targets nearly 600,000 Catholics in region including the counties of St. Mary's, Charles, Calvert, Prince George in Maryland. El Pregonero is the region's oldest Spanish-language weekly.
NEWSPAPER

Carroll Star News
Owner: Georgia Rail & Press Co.
Editorial: 961 Maple St, Carrollton, Georgia 30117-3657. **T:** 1 770 214-9900
Freq: Monthly; **Circ:** 10500 Not Audited
Editorial Profile: Carroll Star News is published monthly for the residents of Carroll County, GA. The newspaper covers local news and community events. The online edition is updated daily. Deadlines are on Wednesdays at noon ET.; Full Page Mono: 11.30
Currency: US Dollars
NEWSPAPER

The Carroll Weekly
Editorial: 901 Hays Mill Rd, Carrollton, Georgia 30117-9576. **T:** 1 770 834-6631
W: http://www.times-georgian.com
Freq: Wed; **Circ:** 32000 Not Audited
Editor: Amy Lavender; **News Editor:** Adam Smith; **Publisher:** Leonard Woolsey
Editorial Profile: The Carroll Weekly is a weekly newspaper dedicated to the residents of Carrollton, GA. The paper covers news, sports, business and features.; Full Page Mono: 8.00
Currency: US Dollars
NEWSPAPER

The Carteret County News-Times
Owner: Carteret Publishing Company
Editorial: 4206 Bridges St, Morehead City, North Carolina 28557. **T:** 1 252 726-7081
E: production@thenewstimes.com
W: http://www.carteretnewstimes.com
Freq: Fri; **Circ:** 10924 Not Audited
Publisher: Lockwood Phillips
Editorial Profile: The Carteret County News-Times is a local newspaper written for the residents of Morehead City, NC. The circulation rate is 9,515 on on Wednesday and Friday and 10,924 on Sunday.; Full Page Mono: 13.10
Currency: US Dollars
NEWSPAPER

Cartersville Newspapers
Owner: Cleveland Newspapers Inc.
Editorial: 251 S Tennessee St, Cartersville, Georgia 30120-3699. **T:** 1 770 382-4545
E: news@daily-tribune.com
W: http://www.daily-tribune.com **Circ:** 30722 Not Audited
Editorial Profile: All materials must be sent to PO Box address.
NEWSPAPER

Carthage Press
Owner: GateHouse Media Inc.
Editorial: 800 W Central Ave, Carthage, Missouri 64836-1023. **T:** 1 417 358-2191
W: http://www.carthagepress.com
Freq: Daily; **Circ:** 4000 Not Audited
Publisher: Steve Boggs
Editorial Profile: Carthage Press is a daily newspaper distributed to the residents of Jasper County, MO. The paper focuses on local news and events but also includes some international news.; Full Page Mono: 10.20; Full Page Colour: 68.70
Currency: US Dollars
DAILY NEWSPAPER

Cary News/Southwest Wake News
Owner: McClatchy Newspapers
Editorial: 1100 Situs Ct Ste 100, Raleigh, North Carolina 27606-4295.
T: 1 919 460-2600
E: carynews@newsobserver.com
W: http://www.carynews.com
Publisher: Felicia Gressette; **Editor:** Sarah Nagem
NEWSPAPER

Casa Grande Dispatch
Owner: Kramer Publications
Editorial: 200 W 2Nd St, Casa Grande, Arizona 85122-4409. **T:** 1 520 836-7461
E: ads@trivalleycentral.com
W: http://www.trivalleycentral.com
Freq: Daily; **Circ:** 8568
Editorial Profile: Casa Grande Dispatch is a daily newspaper covering local news and events for residents of Casa Grande, AZ.; Full Page Mono: 14.17; Full Page Colour: 52.27
Currency: US Dollars
DAILY NEWSPAPER

Cascadia Weekly
Editorial: 1155 N State St Ste 600, Bellingham, Washington 98225-5024.
T: 1 360 647-8200
E: info@cascadiaweekly.com
W: http://www.cascadiaweekly.com
Freq: Wed; **Circ:** 20000 Not Audited
Editorial Profile: Cascadia Weekly is published weekly for the residents of Bellingham, WA and surrounding areas. The newspaper covers local news, arts and entertainment. Deadlines are at noon PT prior to issue date.; Full Page Mono: 11.47
Currency: US Dollars
NEWSPAPER

Casper Journal
Owner: Lee Enterprises, Inc.
Editorial: 170 Star Ln, Casper, Wyoming 82604-2883. **T:** 1 307 265-3870
W: http://www.casperjournal.com
Freq: Wed; **Circ:** 26000 Not Audited
Editorial Profile: Casper Journal is a weekly newspaper written for the residents of Casper, WY. The newspaper covers local news, entertainment, sports, politics and community events. The deadlines for the publication are on Wednesdays at 5pm MT.; Full Page Mono: 23.00; Full Page Colour: 38.00
Currency: US Dollars
NEWSPAPER

Casper Star-Tribune
Owner: Lee Enterprises, Inc.
Editorial: 170 Star Ln, Casper, Wyoming 82604-2883. **T:** 1 307 266-0520
E: editors@trib.com **W:** http://www.trib.com
Freq: Daily; **Circ:** 22821 Not Audited
Editor: Jason Adrians; **Publisher:** Nathan Bekke
Editorial Profile: Casper Star-Tribune is a daily newspaper written for residents in Wyoming. The newspaper covers statewide news and events. The deadline is 7:30pm MT the day before publication.; Full Page Mono: 41.96; Full Page Colour: 137.11
Currency: US Dollars
DAILY NEWSPAPER

Castro Valley Forum
Editorial: 3742 Castro Valley Blvd, Castro Valley, California 94546-4406.
T: 1 510 537-1792
Freq: Wed; **Circ:** 22500 Not Audited
Editorial Profile: Castro Valley Forum is a community newspaper for residents of Castro Valley, CA.; Full Page Mono: 16.50
Currency: US Dollars
NEWSPAPER

Catamaran Media
Editorial: 507 Route US 9 S, Marmora, New Jersey 08223-1258. **T:** 1 609 624-8900
W: http://www.catamaranmedia.com
Circ: 46000 Not Audited
Editor: Bill Barlow; **Publisher:** Rick Travers
NEWSPAPER

Catholic Accent
Owner: Roman Catholic Diocese of Greensburg
Editorial: 725 E Pittsburgh St, Greensburg, Pennsylvania 15601-2660. **T:** 1 724 834-4010
E: news@dioceseofgreensburg.org
W: http://www.dioceseofgreensburg.org
Freq: Bi-Weekly; **Circ:** 46370 Not Audited
Publisher: Lawrence Brandt; **Editor:** Jerry Zufelt
Editorial Profile: Catholic Accent is a bi-weekly newsletter that provides news, event calendars and scripture for members of the Diocese of Greensburg, PA. The articles also provide interviews with priests who answer questions relating to faith.; Full Page Mono: 16.50
Currency: US Dollars
NEWSPAPER

Catholic Advance
Owner: Diocese of Wichita
Editorial: 424 N Broadway St, Wichita, Kansas 67202. **T:** 1 316 269-3965
E: advancenews@cdowk.org
W: http://www.catholicdioceseofwichita.org/advance
Freq: Fri; **Circ:** 37800 Not Audited
Editor: Christopher Riggs
Editorial Profile: The Catholic Advance in Wichita, KS targets residents in the Diocese of Wichita and covers news and commentary of interest to Catholics.; Full Page Mono: 12.25
Currency: US Dollars
NEWSPAPER

Catholic Anchor
Owner: Archdiocese of Anchorage
Editorial: 225 Cordova St, Anchorage, Alaska 99501-2409. **T:** 1 907 297-7730
E: catholicanchor@gci.net
W: http://www.catholicanchor.org/wordpress
Freq: Fri; **Circ:** 11500
Editor: Joel Davidson; **Publisher:** Roger Schweitz
Editorial Profile: Catholic Anchor is a monthly newspaper for the Archdiocese of Anchorage, AK.; Full Page Mono: 17.00
Currency: US Dollars
NEWSPAPER

The Catholic Chronicle
Owner: Catholic Diocese of Toledo
Editorial: 1933 Spielbusch Ave, Toledo, Ohio 43604-5360. **T:** 1 419 244-6711
E: ccnews@toledodiocese.org
W: http://www.catholicchronicle.org
Freq: Fri; **Circ:** 31000 Not Audited
Publisher: Leonard Blair; **Editor:** Angela Kessler

Editorial Profile: The Catholic Chronicle in Toledo, OH is a monthly newspaper published by the Catholic diocese that covers local, national and international Catholic news. Press releases should be sent by fax to the attention of the editor.; Full Page Mono: 43.00; Full Page Colour: 1495.00
Currency: US Dollars
NEWSPAPER

Catholic East Texas
Owner: Diocese of Tyler
Editorial: 1015 E Southeast Loop 323, Tyler, Texas 75701-9656. **T:** 1 903 534-1077
E: editorcet3@excite.com
W: http://cet.dioceseoftyler.org/catholiceasttexas
Freq: Monthly; **Circ:** 14203
Publisher: Álvaro Corrada; **Editor:** Jim D'Avignon
Editorial Profile: Catholic East Texas is a monthly newspaper written for the Diocese of Tyler, TX.; Full Page Mono: 10.00
Currency: US Dollars
NEWSPAPER

The Catholic Free Press
Owner: Roman Catholic Bishop of Worcester
Editorial: 51 Elm St, Worcester, Massachusetts 1609. **T:** 1 508 757-6387
E: editor@catholicfreepress.org
W: http://www.catholicfreepress.org
Freq: Fri; **Circ:** 15500 Not Audited
Publisher: Robert McManus
Editorial Profile: The Catholic Free Press is a weekly publication written for the catholics in the Diocese of Worcester, MA.; Full Page Mono: 16.30
Currency: US Dollars
NEWSPAPER

Catholic Herald
Owner: Diocese of Sacramento
Editorial: 2110 Broadway, Sacramento, California 95818-2518. **T:** 1 916 733-0173
W: http://www.catholicheraldsacramento.org
Freq: Bi-Weekly; **Circ:** 42000 Not Audited
Editor: Julie Sly
Editorial Profile: Catholic Herald is a biweekly newspaper published in Sacramento, California. The paper aims to reach members of the diocese and provide them with local, national, and international news of the Catholic church. The publication comes bi-weekly with the exception of coming out monthly in July, August and December.; Full Page Mono: 35.00
Currency: US Dollars
NEWSPAPER

The Catholic Herald
Owner: Diocese of Madison
Editorial: 702 S High Point Rd, Madison, Wisconsin 53719-3522. **T:** 1 608 821-3070
E: info@madisoncatholicherald.org
W: http://www.madisoncatholicherald.com
Freq: Thu; **Circ:** 26000
Publisher: Robert Morlino; **Editor:** Mary Uhler
Editorial Profile: The Catholic Herald is a weekly newspaper written for the Diocese of Madison, WI.; Full Page Mono: 20.85
Currency: US Dollars
NEWSPAPER

Catholic Herald
Owner: Milwaukee Catholic Press Apostolate
Editorial: 3501 S Lake Dr, Saint Francis, Wisconsin 53235-0900. **T:** 1 414 769-3500
E: chnonline@archmil.org
W: http://www.chnonline.org
Freq: Thu; **Circ:** 36000
Publisher: Jerome Listecki
Editorial Profile: The Catholic Herald is the official newspaper for the Archdiocese of Milwaukee. It provides weekly Community News content for the members of the Catholic faith community in Milwaukee, WI and southeastern Wisconsin.; Full Page Mono: 32.71; Full Page Colour: 52.46
Currency: US Dollars
NEWSPAPER

The Catholic Key
Owner: Catholic Diocese of Kansas City
Editorial: 300 E 36th St, Kansas City, Missouri 64111-1410. **T:** 1 816 756-1850
E: catholickey@diocesekcsj.org
W: http://www.catholickey.org
Freq: Fri; **Circ:** 22000 Not Audited
Publisher: Robert Finn; **Editor:** Jack Smith
Editorial Profile: The Catholic Key is a weekly newspaper published by the Diocese of Kansas City-St. Joseph. The publication covers local and world Catholic news for members of the diocese. Display advertising deadlines are on Thursdays. Classified advertising deadlines are on Mondays at 3pm CT.; Full Page Mono: 19.55; Full Page Colour: 960.00
Currency: US Dollars
NEWSPAPER

The Catholic Light
Owner: Roman Catholic Diocese of Scranton
Editorial: 300 Wyoming Ave, Ste 10, Scranton, Pennsylvania 18503-1287.
T: 1 570 207-2229
W: http://www.dioceseofscranton.org/media/catholic-light
Freq: Monthly; **Circ:** 45000
Publisher: Joseph Bambera; **Editor In Chief:** William Genello
Editorial Profile: The Catholic Light is a monthly newspaper for the Diocese of Scranton, PA.; Full Page Mono: 20.00
Currency: US Dollars
NEWSPAPER

The Catholic Messenger
Editorial: 780 W Central Park Ave, Davenport, Iowa 52804-1901. **T:** 1 563 323-9959
E: messenger@davenportdiocese.org
W: http://www.catholicmessenger.org
Freq: Thu; **Circ:** 18934 Not Audited
Publisher: Martin Amos; **Editor:** Barbara Arland-Fye
Editorial Profile: The Catholic Messenger is a weekly newspaper published in Davenport, IA. The paper covers local, national and international news regarding the Catholic church.; Full Page Mono: 8.76
Currency: US Dollars
NEWSPAPER

Catholic Mirror
Editorial: 601 Grand Ave, Des Moines, Iowa 50309. **T:** 1 515 243-7653
E: mirror@dmdiocese.org
W: http://www.dmdiocese.org
Freq: Monthly; **Circ:** 35000 Not Audited
Editor: Anne Marie Cox
Editorial Profile: Catholic Mirror in Des Moines, IA serves the members of the local diocese and focuses on local news, events and political issues that affect the Catholic community. It also provides advice to its readers on how to include religion in everyday life.; Full Page Mono: 13.50
Currency: US Dollars
NEWSPAPER

Catholic Miscellany
Editorial: 119 Broad St, Charleston, South Carolina 29401-2400. **T:** 1 843 724-8375
W: http://www.themiscellany.org
Freq: Thu; **Circ:** 29100 Not Audited
Publisher: Robert Guglielmone; **Editor:** Deidre Mayes
Editorial Profile: Catholic Miscellany is published weekly except for the second and last weeks of June, July, August and the last week in December.; Full Page Mono: 10.00
Currency: US Dollars
NEWSPAPER

Catholic Missourian
Editorial: 2207 W Main St, Jefferson City, Missouri 65109. **T:** 1 573 635-9127
E: cathmo@diojeffcity.org
W: http://www.diojeffcity.org
Freq: Fri; **Circ:** 22000 Not Audited
Publisher: John Gaydos; **Editor:** Jay Nies
Editorial Profile: Catholic Missourian is a weekly newspaper written for the Catholic community of Jefferson City, MO and surrounding areas.; Full Page Mono: 10.00
Currency: US Dollars
NEWSPAPER

The Catholic Moment
Owner: Roman Catholic Diocese of Lafayette
Editorial: 610 Lingle Ave, Lafayette, Indiana 47901-1740. **T:** 1 765 742-2050
E: moment@dol-in.org
W: http://www.thecatholicmoment.org
Freq: Sun; **Circ:** 28000 Not Audited
Editor: Kevin Cullen; **Publisher:** Timothy Doherty
Editorial Profile: The Catholic Moment in Lafayette, IN is published weekly and focuses on local news, events and political issues that affect the Roman Catholic community of North Central Indiana.; Full Page Mono: 13.00
Currency: US Dollars
NEWSPAPER

Catholic New York
Owner: Ecclesiastical Communications Corp.
Editorial: 1011 1st Ave Ste 1721, New York, New York 10022-4112. **T:** 1 212 688-2399
E: cny@cny.org **W:** http://www.cny.org
Freq: Bi-Weekly; **Circ:** 132931 Not Audited
News Editor: Christie Chicoine; **Publisher:** Timothy Dolan; **Editor In Chief:** John Woods
Editorial Profile: Catholic New York is a bi-weekly newspaper published by the Archdiocese of New York. It covers news and events of the Archdiocese for members of the church, focusing on positive and practical information. It also provides human interest stories about priests, lay people, and international religious works, such as disaster relief efforts. It began publication in August 1981.; Full Page Mono: 60.00
Currency: US Dollars
NEWSPAPER

The Catholic Post
Owner: Diocese of Peoria
Editorial: 419 Ne Madison Ave, Peoria, Illinois 61603-3719. **T:** 1 800 340-5630
E: cathpost@mcleodusa.net
W: http://www.thecatholicpost.com/post
Freq: Bi-Weekly; **Circ:** 14000
Editor in Chief: Tom Dermody; **Publisher:** Richard Jenky
Editorial Profile: The Catholic Post is a bi-weekly newspaper for the Diocese of Peoria.; Full Page Mono: 15.50
Currency: US Dollars
NEWSPAPER

The Catholic Register
Owner: Diocese of Altoona-Johnstown
Editorial: 925 S Logan Blvd, Hollidaysburg, Pennsylvania 16648-3035. **T:** 1 814 695-7563
W: http://www.ajdiocese.org/catholic-register
Freq: Bi-Weekly; **Circ:** 34000
Publisher: Mark Bartchak; **Editor:** Timothy Stein
Editorial Profile: The Catholic Register is a bi-weekly newspaper for the Diocese of Altoona-Johnstown, PA covering news, events and issues.; Full Page Mono: 15.00
Currency: US Dollars
NEWSPAPER

Catholic Review
Owner: Cathedral Foundation
Editorial: 880 Park Ave, Baltimore, Maryland 21201. **T:** 1 443 524-3150
E: mail@catholicreview.org
W: http://www.catholicreview.org
Freq: Bi-Weekly; **Circ:** 47000 Not Audited
Publisher: William Lori
Editorial Profile: Catholic Review in Baltimore, MD is a weekly newspaper of record for the Archdiocese of Baltimore, covering most of the state. It provides news about events and issues of interest to people who are in involved in parishes, schools and other Catholic activities.; Full Page Mono: 45.00
Currency: US Dollars
NEWSPAPER

Catholic San Francisco
Owner: Archdiocese of San Francisco
Editorial: 1 Peter Yorke Way, San Francisco, California 94109-6602. **T:** 1 415 614-5632
E: info@sfarchdiocese.org
W: http://www.catholic-sf.org
Freq: Fri; **Circ:** 77000 Not Audited
Editor: Rick DelVecchio; **Publisher:** George Niederhauer
Editorial Profile: Catholic San Francisco is a weekly newspaper for the Catholic community of San Francisco, CA and the surrounding area. It provides information on developments within the Archdiocese of San Francisco as well as other topics of interest to the Catholic community.; Full Page Mono: 48.00; Full Page Colour: 3800.00
Currency: US Dollars
NEWSPAPER

Catholic Sentinel Publications
Owner: Oregon Catholic Press
Editorial: 5536 NE Hassalo St, Portland, Oregon 97213. **T:** 1 503 281-1191
E: sentinel@catholicsentinel.org
W: http://www.catholicsentinel.org **Circ:** 34000 Not Audited
News Editor: Jon DeBellis; **Publisher:** John Limb; **Editor:** Robert Pfohman; **Editor:** Robert Pfohman; **Editor:** Robert Pfohman; **Editor:** Robert Pfohman; **Editor:** Rocio Rios
Editorial Profile: Catholic Sentinel Publications produced the Catholic Sentinel, the official newspaper of the Archdiocese of Portland, and reported to be the oldest Catholic newspaper on the West Coast.
NEWSPAPER

The Catholic Spirit
Owner: Diocese of Metuchen (The)
Editorial: 146 Metlars Ln, Piscataway, New Jersey 08854-4303. **T:** 1 732 562-2424
E: news@catholicspirit.com
W: http://www.catholicspirit.com
Freq: Thu; **Circ:** 20000 Not Audited
Publisher: Paul Bootkoski
Editorial Profile: The Catholic Spirit is a weekly publication for the Catholic communities within the Diocese of Metuchen, New Jersey, which encompasses Middlesex, Somerset, Hunterdon and Warren counties.; Full Page Mono: 24.00
Currency: US Dollars
NEWSPAPER

The Catholic Spirit
Editorial: 1300 Byron St, Wheeling, West Virginia 26003-3315
Freq: Bi-Weekly; **Circ:** 35000
Publisher: Michael Bransfield; **Editor:** Colleen Rowan
Editorial Profile: The Catholic Spirit is a bi-weekly newspaper that is written for the Diocese of Wheeling/Charleston.; Full Page Mono: 13.38
Currency: US Dollars
NEWSPAPER

Catholic Star Herald
Owner: Catholic Diocese of Camden, NJ
Editorial: Pastoral Center, 15 N 7th St, Camden, New Jersey 8102. **T:** 1 856 756-7900
W: http://www.catholicstarherald.org
Freq: Fri; **Circ:** 65000 Not Audited
Publisher: Joseph Galante
Editorial Profile: Catholic Star Herald provides news and information to the members of the Catholic community in the Diocese of Camden, NJ.; Full Page Mono: 40.00
Currency: US Dollars
NEWSPAPER

The Catholic Sun
Owner: Roman Catholic Diocese of Phoenix
Editorial: 400 E Monroe St, Phoenix, Arizona 85004. **T:** 1 602 354-2139
E: info@catholicsun.org
W: http://www.catholicsun.org
Freq: Bi-Weekly; **Circ:** 120812 Not Audited
Editor: Rob DeFrancesco; **Editor:** Rob DeFrancesco; **Publisher:** Thomas Olmsted
Editorial Profile: The Catholic Sun is a local community newspaper for the Catholic residents of Phoenix and the surrounding communities.; Full Page Mono: 37.00
Currency: US Dollars
NEWSPAPER

Catholic Sun
Owner: Diocese of Syracuse
Editorial: 420 Montgomery St, Syracuse, New York 13202. **T:** 1 315 422-8153
E: catholicsun@yahoo.com
W: http://www.catholicsun.com
Freq: Thu; **Circ:** 21327 Not Audited
Editor: Connie Berry; **Publisher:** Robert Cunningham
Editorial Profile: Catholic Sun is the weekly newspaper of the Diocese of Syracuse, NY.; Full Page Mono: 24.00
Currency: US Dollars
NEWSPAPER

The Catholic Telegraph
Owner: Archdiocese of Cincinnati
Editorial: 100 E 8th St, Cincinnati, Ohio 45202-2129. **T:** 1 513 421-3131
E: cteditorial@catholiccincinnati.org
W: http://www.thecatholictelegraph.com
Freq: Monthly; **Circ:** 59000 Not Audited
News Editor: Eileen Connelly
Editorial Profile: Catholic Telegraph is the official newspaper of the Archdiocese of Cincinnati and is written for members of the Catholic church in Cincinnati. Deadlines are on Tuesdays by noon ET.; Full Page Mono: 32.71
Currency: US Dollars
NEWSPAPER

Catholic Times
Owner: Diocese of Columbus
Editorial: 197 E Gay St, Columbus, Ohio 43215. **T:** 1 614 224-5195
E: commailbox@colsdioc.org
W: http://www.ctonline.org
Freq: Sun; **Circ:** 15000
Publisher: Frederick Campbell; **Editor:** David Garick
Editorial Profile: Catholic Times is the official newspaper of the Catholic Diocese of Columbus, which includes 23 counties across Central and Southern Ohio. It is written for Catholics of Columbus, OH.; Full Page Mono: 18.55
Currency: US Dollars
NEWSPAPER

Catholic Times
Owner: Diocese of Springfield in Illinois
Editorial: 1615 W Washington St, Springfield, Illinois 62702-4757. **T:** 1 217 698-8500
E: catholictimes@dio.org
W: http://www.dio.org
Freq: Bi-Weekly; **Circ:** 45000 Not Audited

Editorial Profile: Catholic Times is a local newspaper for the Catholic community in Springfield, IL.; Full Page Mono: 16.25
Currency: US Dollars
NEWSPAPER

The Catholic Times
Owner: Diocese of LaCrosse
Editorial: 3710 East Ave S, La Crosse, Wisconsin 54601-7215. **T:** 1 608 788-1524
E: catholictimes@dioceseoflacrosse.com
W: http://www.thecatholictimes.com
Freq: Thu; **Circ:** 31500 Not Audited
Editor: Stanton Gould
Editorial Profile: The Catholic Times in La Crosse, WI is a bi-weekly newspaper that features news, events and other issues of importance to members of the local Catholic community.; Full Page Mono: 32.00
Currency: US Dollars
NEWSPAPER

Catholic Transcript
Owner: Archdiocese of Hartford
Editorial: 467 Bloomfield Ave, Bloomfield, Connecticut 6002. **T:** 1 860 286-2828
E: info@catholictranscript.org
W: http://www.catholictranscript.org
Freq: Monthly; **Circ:** 85000 Not Audited
Publisher: Henry Mansell; **News Editor:** Jack Sheedy
Editorial Profile: Catholic Transcript is a monthly newspaper written for the Roman Catholic Archdiocese of Hartford, CT.; Full Page Mono: 28.00; Full Page Colour: 525.00
Currency: US Dollars
NEWSPAPER

Catholic Universe Bulletin
Owner: Catholic Diocese of Cleveland
Editorial: 1404 E 9Th St, Cleveland, Ohio 44114-1740. **T:** 1 216 696-6525
W: http://www.catholicuniversebulletin.org
Freq: Bi-Weekly; **Circ:** 32005 Not Audited
Editor: Nancy Erikson
Editorial Profile: Catholic Universe Bulletin is written for the Catholic Diocese of Cleveland.; Full Page Mono: 44.65
Currency: US Dollars
NEWSPAPER

The Catholic Voice
Owner: Roman Catholic Diocese of Oakland
Editorial: 2121 Harrison St, Ste 100, Oakland, California 94612-3788. **T:** 1 510 893-5339
E: voice@oakdiocese.org
W: http://www.catholicvoiceoakland.org
Freq: Bi-Monthly; **Circ:** 90000 Not Audited
Editorial Profile: The Catholic Voice is a community newspaper serving the Catholic community of Oakland, CA.; Full Page Mono: 29.00
Currency: US Dollars
NEWSPAPER

Catholic Voice
Editorial: 6060 Nw Radial Hwy, Omaha, Nebraska 68104-3426. **T:** 1 402 558-6611
E: tcvomaha@archomaha.org
W: http://www.catholicvoiceomaha.com
Freq: Semi-Monthly; **Circ:** 47500 Not Audited
Publisher: George Lucas; **News Editor:** Joe Ruff
Editorial Profile: Catholic Voice in Omaha, NE is the publication of the Archdiocese of Omaha, NE. The newspaper focuses on local news, events, and political issues that affect the Catholic community. The paper also provides advice to its readers on how to include religion in everyday life. All inquiries should be addressed to the editor.; Full Page Mono: 31.00
Currency: US Dollars
NEWSPAPER

Catholic Weekly and Times
Owner: G.L.S. Diocesan Reports, Inc.
Editorial: 1520 Court St, Saginaw, Michigan 48602. **T:** 1 989 793-7661
E: catholicweekly@sbcglobal.net
W: http://www.catholicweekly.org
Freq: Fri; **Circ:** 10300 Not Audited
Publisher: Mark Myczkowiak
Editorial Profile: Catholic Weekly and Times is a weekly newspaper published in Saginaw, MI. The publication covers news of interest to the local Catholic community. The paper is published in two different editions every Friday; Saginaw and Gaylord. For these editions, the national and world news is the same, but the local news section is focused on the region of each edition's distribution. In addition to the two Catholic Weekly editions, the company publishes a paper covering the Lansing Diocese called the Catholic Times.; Full Page Mono: 7.75
Currency: US Dollars
NEWSPAPER

The Catholic Witness
Owner: Diocese of Harrisburg
Editorial: 4800 Union Deposit Rd, Harrisburg, Pennsylvania 17111-3710.
T: 1 717 657-4804 201
E: witness@hbgdiocese.org
W: http://www.hbgdiocese.org
Freq: Bi-Weekly; **Circ:** 80000
Publisher: Joseph McFadden; **Editor:** Jen Reed
Editorial Profile: The Catholic Witness is a bi-weekly newspaper published for the Diocese of Harrisburg, PA. The paper does not accept outside advertising.
NEWSPAPER

Cecil Whig
Owner: Adams Publishing Group LLC
Editorial: 601 N Bridge St, Elkton, Maryland 21921-5307. **T:** 1 410 398-3311
E: whigletters@chespub.com
W: http://www.cecildaily.com
Freq: Daily; **Circ:** 12756 Not Audited
Publisher: David Fike
Editorial Profile: Cecil Whig is a daily newspaper written for residents of Cecil County, MD. The publication covers local news, sports, features and community events.; Full Page Mono: 22.95; Full Page Colour: 76.20
Currency: US Dollars
DAILY NEWSPAPER

Cedar Park Citizen/Leander Ledger
Owner: Cox Media Group, Inc.
Editorial: 19621 Fm 1431, Jonestown, Texas 78645-4784. **T:** 1 512 267-4449
E: news@cedarparkcitizen.com **Circ:** 23800
Editor: Mike Parker
NEWSPAPER

Cedar Street Times
Owner: Jameson (Marge Ann)
Editorial: 306 Grand Ave, Pacific Grove, California 93950-3422. **T:** 1 831 324-4742
E: editor@cedarstreettimes.com
W: http://cedarstreettimes.com
Freq: Fri
Editorial Profile: Cedar Street Times is a weekly community newspaper serving residents of Pacific Grove, CA with local news, sports, opinion, and features. Deadlines are Wednesdays at noon PT.; Full Page Mono: 18.00; Full Page Colour: 22.50
Currency: US Dollars
NEWSPAPER

Cedar Valley Times
Owner: Mid-America Publishing Corporation
Editorial: 108 E 5th St, Vinton, Iowa 52349.
T: 1 319 472-2311
E: editor@cedarvalleydailytimes.com
W: http://communitynewspapergroup.com/cedar_valley_daily_times/front
Freq: Daily; **Circ:** 2000 Not Audited
Editor: Anelia Dimitrova; **Publisher:** Deb Weigel
Editorial Profile: Cedar Valley Times is a daily community newspaper written for the residents of Vinton, IA and surrounding communities. The publication covers local news, events, sports and weather.; Full Page Mono: 10.10; Full Page Colour: 35.90
Currency: US Dollars
DAILY NEWSPAPER

Centerville Daily Iowegian
Owner: CNHI
Editorial: 201 N 13Th St, Centerville, Iowa 52544-1748. **T:** 1 641 856-6336
W: http://dailyiowegian.com
Freq: Daily; **Circ:** 2500 Not Audited
Editor: Krystal Fowler; **Publisher:** Becky Maxwell
Editorial Profile: Centerville Daily Iowegian is a daily newspaper serving Appanoose County since 1864. The paper covers local news and community events for all or part of Appanoose, Wayne, Putnam, Sullivan counties including Centerville and surrounding communities.; Full Page Mono: 8.00; Full Page Colour: 36.39
Currency: US Dollars
DAILY NEWSPAPER

Central City News & Capital City News
Owner: Community Press, LLC
Editorial: 910 N Foster Dr, Baton Rouge, Louisiana 70806-1807. **T:** 1 225 261-5055
Editorial Profile: Central City News and Capital City News are weekly community newspapers serving the East Baton Rouge Parish, LA, including the City of Central and the capital city of Baton Rouge. Content is tailored to the coverage city, and the papers publish on alternating Thursdays weekly.
NEWSPAPER

Central Connecticut Weeklies
Owner: Central Connecticut Communications
Editorial: 1 Court St., 4th Floor, New Britain, Connecticut 6051. **T:** 1 860 225-4601
E: info@newingtontowncrier.com **Circ:** 5246 Not Audited
Editorial Profile: Central Connecticut Weeklies publishes three community weeklies and shares offices with the daily newspaper the Herald in New Britain, CT.
NEWSPAPER

El Central Hispanic News
Owner: Sanchez Communications
Editorial: 4124 W Vernor Hwy, Detroit, Michigan 48209-2145. **T:** 1 313 841-0100
E: elcentral1@aol.com
Freq: Thu; **Circ:** 14000 Not Audited
Editorial Profile: El Central Hispanic News provides news and information to Michigan's Hispanic population. The publication covers local, national and international news.; Full Page Mono: 16.00; Full Page Colour: 1705.00
Currency: US Dollars
NEWSPAPER

Central Illinois Business
Owner: News Media Corp.
Editorial: 5005 N Glen Park Place Rd, Peoria, Illinois 61614-4677. **T:** 1 217 351-5276
W: http://www.centralillinoisbusiness.com
Freq: Weekly; **Circ:** 40000 Not Audited
Editor: Jodi Heckel
Editorial Profile: Central Illinois Business is a weekly section within the Champaign News-Gazette, a local newspaper in Champaign, IL. The publication covers business within Clinton and the surrounding Champaign County area.; Full Page Colour: 750.00
Currency: US Dollars
NEWSPAPER

Central Louisiana Publishing Co.
Editorial: 145 Court St, Ville Platte, Louisiana 70586. **T:** 1 337 363-3939
W: http://www.villeplattetoday.com **Circ:** 6500 Not Audited
Editor: Michael Bordelon; **Editor:** Carissa Hebert; **Publisher:** David Ortego
NEWSPAPER

Central Record & Intercounty News Group
Owner: 21st Century Media
Editorial: 176 Route 70, Medford, New Jersey 08055-8704. **T:** 1 609 654-5000
W: http://www.southjerseylocalnews.com
News Editor: Jenn Lucas; **Publisher:** William Murray
NEWSPAPER

The Central Ridge Visitor
Owner: Landmark Community Newspapers, Inc.
Editorial: 1624 N Meadowcrest Blvd, Crystal River, Florida 34429. **T:** 1 352 563-6363
E: visitor@chronicleonline.com
Freq: Sat; **Circ:** 12676 Not Audited
Editor: Ken Melton; **Publisher:** Gerald Mulligan
Editorial Profile: The Central Ridge Vistor is a weekly community newspaper for the residents of Crystal River, FL.; Full Page Mono: 12.47
Currency: US Dollars
NEWSPAPER

The Central Virginian
Owner: Lakeway Publishers, Inc.
Editorial: 89 Rescue Ln, Louisa, Virginia 23093. **T:** 1 540 967-0368
W: http://www.thecentralvirginian.com
Freq: Thu; **Circ:** 10000 Not Audited
Editor: Greg Dorazio; **Publisher:** Steve Weddle
Editorial Profile: The Central Virginian is a weekly local newspaper serving the counties of Louisa and Fluvanna, VA. The publication covers local news, events, sports and arts & entertainment. It also includes the regional section named the Goochland Courier.; Full Page Mono: 12.85
Currency: US Dollars
NEWSPAPER

Central Wisconsin Sunday
Editorial: 800 Scott St, Wausau, Wisconsin 54403. **T:** 1 715 842-2101
W: http://www.wausaudailyherald.com
Freq: Sun; **Circ:** 21000 Not Audited
Editorial Profile: Central Wisconsin Sunday is published on Sundays by the four local Gannett dailies: The Daily Tribune in Wisconsin Rapids, WI, Marshfield (WI) News-Herald, Stevens Point (WI) Journal and Wausau (WI) Daily Herald. It is included in the Sunday edition of these four papers, but readers can also purchase a seperate subscription. The contact information is for The Wausau Daily Herald.; Full Page Mono: 29.60
Currency: US Dollars
NEWSPAPER

Centre Daily Times
Owner: McClatchy Newspapers
Editorial: 3400 E College Ave, State College, Pennsylvania 16801. **T:** 1 814 238-5000
E: cdtnewstips@centredaily.com
W: http://www.centredaily.com
Freq: Daily; **Circ:** 16921 Not Audited
Editor: Fran Jacobs; **Publisher:** Susan Leath; **City Editor:** Christopher Passante
Editorial Profile: Centre Daily Times is a daily local newspaper written for residents of Centre County, PA. The newspaper covers local news, sports and events.; Full Page Mono: 51.63; Full Page Colour: 221.00
Currency: US Dollars
DAILY NEWSPAPER

Centro Tampa
Owner: Media General Inc.
Editorial: 202 S Parker St Ste 202, Tampa, Florida 33606-2308. **T:** 1 813 259-8183
E: info@centrotampa.com
W: http://www.centrotampa.com
Freq: Fri; **Circ:** 51584 Not Audited
Publisher: Brian Burns; **Editor in Chief:** Javier Maymí
Editorial Profile: Centro Tampa is a Spanish-language community newspaper serving the Latino population of Tampa Bay, FL. The paper covers news, events and features stories in conjunction with Media General's other Spanish-language products, centrotampa.com, its Web site and Centro Capsulas, which provides radio and television broadcasting. Deadlines are on Tuesdays at 5pm ET.; Full Page Mono: 16.80
Currency: US Dollars
NEWSPAPER

Ceres Courier
Owner: Morris Multimedia, Inc.
Editorial: 138 S. Center St., Turlock, California 95380. **T:** 1 209 537-5032
W: http://www.cerescourier.com
Freq: Wed; **Circ:** 19500 Not Audited
Editor: Jeff Benziger; **Publisher:** Hank Vanderveen
Editorial Profile: Ceres Courier is a community newspaper located in Ceres, CA. It is published weekly and covers local news, events, sports, and government issues.; Full Page Mono: 12.95
Currency: US Dollars
NEWSPAPER

Chagrin Valley Publishing Co.
Editorial: 525 E Washington St, Chagrin Falls, Ohio 44022-4455. **T:** 1 440 247-5335
E: editor@chagrinvalleytimes.com
W: http://www.chagrinvalleytimes.com
Circ: 19850 Not Audited
Publisher: Harold Douthit; **Editor:** David Lange
NEWSPAPER

The Challenge Group
Editorial: 1195 Atlantic Ave, Brooklyn, New York 11216-2709. **T:** 1 718 636-9500
Circ: 117141 Not Audited
Editor: Janel Gross; **Editor:** Tatianna Singleton; **Publisher:** Tom Watkins
NEWSPAPER

Challenger Community News
Editorial: 1337 Jefferson Ave, Buffalo, New York 14208. **T:** 1 716 897-0442
Freq: Wed; **Circ:** 11000 Not Audited
Editorial Profile: Challenger Community News is a weekly newspaper published for the African American communities of Buffalo, NY. The publication covers local news and community events. News deadlines are on Fridays at 5pm ET.; Full Page Mono: 16.00
Currency: US Dollars
NEWSPAPER

The Champion
Owner: ACE III Communications, Inc.
Editorial: 114 New St, Ste E, Decatur, Georgia 30030. **T:** 1 404 373-7779
W: http://www.championnewspaper.com
Freq: Thu; **Circ:** 25000 Not Audited
Editorial Profile: The Champion is published weekly for the residents of DeKalb County, GA. The newspaper covers local news, business, lifestyle, sports and community events. Press releases should be sent directly to the editor.; Full Page Mono: 10.00; Full Page Colour: 1550.00
Currency: US Dollars

NEWSPAPER

Champion Newspapers
Owner: Champion Publications of Chino, Inc.
Editorial: 13179 9th St, Chino, California 91710-4216. **T:** 1 909 628-5501
E: news@championnewspapers.com
W: http://www.championnewspapers.com
Freq: Sat; **Circ:** 42432 Not Audited
Publisher: Bruce Wood
Editorial Profile: Champion Newspapers provides the community of Chino, CA with news.; Full Page Mono: 36.50
Currency: US Dollars
NEWSPAPER

Chanute Tribune
Owner: Family Media, Inc.
Editorial: 15 N Evergreen Ave, Chanute, Kansas 66720-1831. **T:** 1 620 431-4100
E: tribune@chanute.com
W: http://www.chanute.com
Freq: Daily; **Circ:** 4100 Not Audited
Publisher: Shanna Guiot
Editorial Profile: Chanute Tribune is a daily newspaper published for the residents of Chanute, KS. The newspaper covers news, events and sports.; Full Page Mono: 8.54; Full Page Colour: 28.59
Currency: US Dollars
DAILY NEWSPAPER

Chariton Publishing Company
Editorial: 815 Braden Ave, Chariton, Iowa 50049. **T:** 1 641 774-2137
E: charnews@charitonleader.com
W: http://www.charitonleader.com **Circ:** 6000 Not Audited
Publisher: David Paxton
NEWSPAPER

Charles City Press
Owner: Fortress Investment Group, LLC
Editorial: 801 Riverside Dr, Charles City, Iowa 50616-2248. **T:** 1 641 228-3211
E: editor@charlescitypress.com
W: http://www.charlescitypress.com
Freq: Daily; **Circ:** 3200 Not Audited
Publisher: Gene Hall; **Editor:** Mark Wicks
Editorial Profile: Charles City Press covers local news, sports and business in Charles City, IA.; Full Page Mono: 13.42; Full Page Colour: 345.00
Currency: US Dollars
DAILY NEWSPAPER

Charleston City Paper
Owner: Jones Street Publishers, LLC
Editorial: 1049 Morrison Dr, Charleston, South Carolina 29403-3819. **T:** 1 843 577-5304
E: editor@charlestoncitypaper.com
W: http://www.charlestoncitypaper.com
Freq: Wed; **Circ:** 40000 Not Audited
Publisher: Noel Mermer
Editorial Profile: Charleston (SC) City Paper is a community newspaper that covers local news, opinion articles, music and restaurant reviews.; Full Page Mono: 21.14
Currency: US Dollars
NEWSPAPER

Charleston Daily Mail
Owner: MediaNews Group
Editorial: 1001 Virginia St E, Charleston, West Virginia 25301-2816. **T:** 1 304 348-5140
E: dmnews@dailymailwv.com
W: http://www.charlestondailymail.com
Freq: Daily; **Circ:** 18600
Publisher & Editor: Brad McElhinny; **City Editor:** Lauren McGill
Editorial Profile: Charleston Daily Mail is a daily newspaper written for the residents of Charleston, WV. It covers local news, sports, politics, business, health, education, lifestyle and religion. Pairs up with the Charleston Gazette on Saturdays and Sundays.; Full Page Mono: 89.70; Full Page Colour: 675.00
Currency: US Dollars
DAILY NEWSPAPER

The Charleston Gazette
Owner: Daily Gazette Co.
Editorial: 1001 Virginia St E, Charleston, West Virginia 25301-2816. **T:** 1 304 348-5140
E: gazette@wvgazette.com
W: http://www.wvgazette.com
Freq: Daily; **Circ:** 38238 Not Audited
News Editor: Vic Burkhammer; **Publisher:** Elizabeth Chilton; **Editor In Chief:** James Haught; **City Editor:** Greg Moore
Editorial Profile: The Charleston Gazette, established in 1873, is the leading newspaper in West Virginia. It covers local news, sports, government, food and local industry news. It combines with the Charleston Daily Mail on Saturdays and Sundays to form the Sunday Gazette Mai.; Full Page Mono: 89.70; Full Page Colour: 285.72
Currency: US Dollars
DAILY NEWSPAPER

Charleston Mercury
Owner: Evening Post Publishing Co.
Editorial: 134 Columbus St, Charleston, South Carolina 29403-4809. **T:** 1 843 937-5547
E: editor@charlestonmercury.com
W: http://www.charlestonmercury.com
Freq: Bi-Weekly; **Circ:** 15100
Editorial Profile: Charleston Mercury is a biweekly community newspaper that covers news, community events and features to residents of Charleston, SC and the surrounding, largely affluent Lowland, SC region, including East Cooper and West Ashley, SC and James, Kiawah, Seabrook and Edisto.; Full Page Mono: 24.00; Full Page Colour: 250.00
Currency: US Dollars
NEWSPAPER

Charlotte County Florida Weekly
Owner: Florida Media Group LLC
Editorial: 1205 Elizabeth St Ste G, Punta Gorda, Florida 33950-6054. **T:** 1 239 333-2135
E: pgnews@floridaweekly.com
W: http://www.floridaweekly.com
Freq: Thu; **Circ:** 12800
Editor: Kathy Grey; **Publisher:** Mike Hearn
Editorial Profile: Charlotte County Florida Weekly is a community newspaper written for residents of Punta Gorda and Southwest Florida. It covers local governments, politics, arts, nightlife, social scene, events, features and investigative reports.; Full Page Mono: 15.68
Currency: US Dollars
NEWSPAPER

The Charlotte Observer
Owner: McClatchy Newspapers
Editorial: 600 S Tryon St, Charlotte, North Carolina 28202-1842. **T:** 1 704 358-5000
E: localnews@charlotteobserver.com
W: http://www.charlotteobserver.com
Freq: Daily; **Circ:** 131254 Not Audited
Reading Life Editor: Pam Kelley
Editorial Profile: The Charlotte Observer is written for the general public in the greater Charlotte, NC area. The Business section is featured daily, covering local and national business stories, daily stock market rates, and real estate. Articles include features, breaking news, trends, analysis, profiles, and investigative stories. The paper asserts itself as being the only daily newspaper in America to win two Pulitzer Prizes for public service in the 1980s. It received a Pulitzer Prize in 1981 for reporting on brown-lung disease and the textile industry, and in 1988 for its coverage of Jim Bakker and the PTL.; Full Page Mono: 353.00; Full Page Colour: 390.98
Currency: US Dollars
DAILY NEWSPAPER

The Charlotte Observer
Editorial: 371 Concord Pkwy N, Concord, North Carolina 28027-9681.
T: 1 704 786-2185
E: northneighbors@charlotteobserver.com
DAILY NEWSPAPER

The Charlotte Post
Owner: Charlotte Post Publishing Co.
Editorial: 1531 Camden Rd, Charlotte, North Carolina 28203-4753. **T:** 1 704 376-0496
W: http://www.thecharlottepost.com
Freq: Thu; **Circ:** 12000 Not Audited
Publisher: Gerald Johnson; **Editor in Chief:** Herbert White; **Editor in Chief:** Herbert White; **Editor in Chief:** Herbert White
Editorial Profile: The Charlotte Post covers local news, events, sports, health, travel, business, life and religious topics for the African American community in Charlotte, NC. Send press releases to the editor in chief.; Full Page Mono: 30.00
Currency: US Dollars
NEWSPAPER

Charlotte Sun
Owner: Sun Coast Media Group Inc.
Editorial: 23170 Harborview Rd, Port Charlotte, Florida 33980-2100.
T: 1 941 206-1000
W: http://www.charlotte-sun.com
Freq: Daily; **Circ:** 42014 Not Audited
Publisher: David Dunn-Rankin; **Editor:** Rusty Pray
Editorial Profile: Charlotte Sun is a daily newspaper serving the residents of Charlotte County, FL. It covers local and national news, business, sports, lifestyles and entertainment.; Full Page Mono: 38.25; Full Page Colour: 49.25
Currency: US Dollars
DAILY NEWSPAPER

The Chatham News Publishing Co.
Editorial: 303 W Raleigh St, Siler City, North Carolina 27344-3725. **T:** 1 919 663-3232
W: http://www.thechathamnews.com
Freq: Thu; **Circ:** 9200 Not Audited
Editorial Profile: The Chatham News Publishing Co. is a community newapaper publisher servicing the residents of Chatham County in NC.; Full Page Mono: 7.25
Currency: US Dollars
NEWSPAPER

Chattanooga Courier/Nashville Pride
Owner: Pride Publishing Group, Inc.
Editorial: 625 Main St, Nashville, Tennessee 37206-3624. **T:** 1 615 292-9150
E: pridepublishers@comcast.net
W: http://pridepublishinggroup.com
Circ: 64000
NEWSPAPER

Chattanooga Pulse
Owner: Brewer Media Group
Editorial: 1305 Carter St, Chattanooga, Tennessee 37402-4412. **T:** 1 423 648-7857
E: info@chattanoogapulse.com
W: http://www.chattanoogapulse.com
Freq: Wed; **Circ:** 12500 Not Audited
Editor: Mike McJunkin
Editorial Profile: Chattanooga Pulse is a local newspaper serving the residents of Chattanooga, TN. The alternative paper provides articles on news, columns, art, music, dining guides and calendar of events for the area.; Full Page Mono: 12.60
Currency: US Dollars
NEWSPAPER

Chattanooga Times Free Press
Owner: Wehco Media Inc.
Editorial: 400 E 11th St, Chattanooga, Tennessee 37403-4200. **T:** 1 423 756-6900
E: news@timesfreepress.com
W: http://www.timesfreepress.com
Freq: Daily; **Circ:** 65759 Not Audited
Editorial Profile: Chattanooga Times Free Press is a local daily newspaper serving the city of Chattanooga, TN and the surrounding area. The publication covers local news, sports, business and community information.; Full Page Mono: 63.91; Full Page Colour: 77.91
Currency: US Dollars
DAILY NEWSPAPER

Chattanooga Times Free Press
Editorial: 28 Legislative Plaza, Nashville, Tennessee 37201. **T:** 1 615 255-0550
DAILY NEWSPAPER

Cheboygan Tribune
Owner: Fortress Investment Group, LLC
Editorial: 308 N Main St, Cheboygan, Michigan 49721-1545. **T:** 1 231 627-7144
W: http://www.cheboygannews.com
Freq: Daily; **Circ:** 4665 Not Audited
Editor: Richard Crofton; **Publisher:** Gary Lamberg
Editorial Profile: Cheboygan Tribune is a daily newspaper published for the residents of Cheboygan County, MI. The publication covers local news, sports, social issues, arts & entertainment, health, obituaries, community events and features.; Full Page Mono: 11.50; Full Page Colour: 300.00
Currency: US Dollars
DAILY NEWSPAPER

The Cherokee Chronicle Inc.
Owner: Cherokee Chronicle, Inc. (The)
Editorial: 423 N Limestone St, Gaffney, South Carolina 29340. **T:** 1 864 488-1016
E: cherokeechronicle@yahoo.com
W: http://www.thecherokeechronicle.com
Circ: 7800 Not Audited
News Editor: James Holland
NEWSPAPER

Cherokee Ledger-News
Owner: Lakeside Publishing, Inc.
Editorial: 103 E Main St, Woodstock, Georgia 30188-5008. **T:** 1 770 928-0706
W: http://www.ledgernews.com
Freq: Wed; **Circ:** 41000 Not Audited
Publisher: David Caughman
Editorial Profile: Cherokee Ledger-News is a community newspaper published for residents of Cherokee County, GA. It covers news, local events and entertainment.; Full Page Mono: 18.95
Currency: US Dollars
NEWSPAPER

Cherokee Phoenix and Indian Advocate
Owner: Cherokee Nation
Editorial: 17675 S Muskogee Ave, Tahlequah, Oklahoma 74464-5492. **T:** 1 918 456-0671
E: communications@cherokee.org
W: http://www.cherokee.org
Freq: Monthly; **Circ:** 35000 Not Audited
Editor: Bryan Pollard
Editorial Profile: Cherokee Phoenix and Indian Advocate is a quarterly newspaper of the Cherokee Nation. The publication is written for members of the Native American tribe, the Cherokee. The publication reports on tribal news and members. Deadlines are the first week of every quarter.; Full Page Mono: 21.33
Currency: US Dollars
NEWSPAPER

Cherokee Post
Editorial: 100 E Main St, Centre, Alabama 35960. **T:** 1 256 927-4476
E: info@postpaper.com
W: http://www.postpaper.com
Freq: Mon; **Circ:** 17000 Not Audited
Publisher: David Crawford; **Editor:** Scott Wright
Editorial Profile: Cherokee Post is published weekly for the residents of Centre, AL and surrounding areas. The newspaper covers local news and community events.; Full Page Mono: 6.00
Currency: US Dollars
NEWSPAPER

Cherokee Scout
Owner: Community Newspapers Inc.
Editorial: 89 Sycamore St, Murphy, North Carolina 28906-2954. **T:** 1 828 837-5122
E: news@cherokeescout.com
W: http://www.cherokeescout.com
Freq: Wed; **Circ:** 10000 Not Audited
Publisher: David Brown; **Editor:** Matthew Osborne
Editorial Profile: Cherokee Scout is a local weekly newspaper written for residents of Cherokee County, NC. The publication covers local news, events, politics, opinions and sports. Deadlines are 5pm ET on the Fridays.; Full Page Mono: 13.50
Currency: US Dollars
NEWSPAPER

Cherokee Tribune
Owner: Times Journal Inc.
Editorial: 521 E Main St, Canton, Georgia 30114-2805. **T:** 1 770 479-1441
E: tribune@cherokeetribune.com
W: http://www.cherokeetribune.com
Freq: Daily; **Circ:** 4253 Not Audited
Publisher: Otis Brumby
Editorial Profile: Cherokee Tribune is a local newspaper paper, published Wednesday through Sunday for the residents of Cherokee County, GA. It has four sections every day with four, full-color front pages. It provides readers with comprehensive local news and sports, as well as a new lifestyle section that focuses on food, religion, community events and neighbors. The Wednesday edition, called the Cherokee Tribune Plus, is sent to all nonsubscribers for free. Press releases can be sent by e-mail to the appropriate editors. Only press releases containing information about Cherokee County are accepted. Advertising deadlines are at noon ET.; Full Page Mono: 22.80; Full Page Colour: 450.00
Currency: US Dollars
DAILY NEWSPAPER

Cherokee Tribune Plus
Owner: Times Journal Inc.
Editorial: 521 E Main St, Canton, Georgia 30114. **T:** 1 770 479-1441
W: http://www.cherokeetribune.com
Freq: Wed; **Circ:** 16577 Not Audited
Publisher: Otis Brumby
Editorial Profile: Cherokee Tribune Plus is a free, weekly newspaper distributed for free to nonsubscribers of the daily newspaper, the Cherokee Tribune, in Cherokee County, GA. The paper shares its editorial staff and content with the daily. Press releases can be sent by fax to the appropriate editors. Only press releases containing information about Cherokee County are accepted. Advertising deadlines are at noon ET.; Full Page Mono: 22.80; Full Page Colour: 200.00
Currency: US Dollars
NEWSPAPER

Cherry Creek Newspapers
Editorial: 3236 Newton St, Denver, Colorado 80211-3139. **T:** 1 303 458-7541 **Circ:** 26000 Not Audited
Publisher: Guerin Green
NEWSPAPER

Chesapeake Publishing Co.
Editorial: 601 N Bridge St, Elkton, Maryland 21921-5307. **T:** 1 302 737-0724
E: news@newarkpostonline.com
W: http://www.newarkpostonline.com
Circ: 30700 Not Audited
Publisher: David Fike; **Editor:** Josh Shannon
NEWSPAPER

Chester County Press
Owner: Ad Pro, Inc.
Editorial: 144 S Jennersville Rd, West Grove, Pennsylvania 19390-9430. **T:** 1 610 869-5553
E: info@chestercounty.com
W: http://www.chestercounty.com
Freq: Wed; **Circ:** 14900 Not Audited
Editor: Steve Hoffman; **Publisher:** Randall Lieberman
Editorial Profile: Chester County Press is a weekly newspaper serving the residents of Southern Chester County, including the communities of Oxford, West Grove, Avondale, New London, Kemblesville, Landenberg and Kennett Square, PA. It provides local news, events, lifestyle stories and sports. Advertising deadlines are at noon ET.; Full Page Mono: 14.70
Currency: US Dollars
NEWSPAPER

Chesterfield Observer
Owner: The Observer, Inc.
Editorial: 4600 Market Square Ln, Midlothian, Virginia 23112-4875. **T:** 1 804 545-7500
W: http://www.chesterfieldobserver.com
Freq: Mon; **Circ:** 69244 Not Audited
News Editor: Michael Buettner; **Editor:** Nancy Nusser; **Publisher:** Greg Pearson
Editorial Profile: Chesterfield Observer is a local, weekly newspaper serving residents of Chesterfield and Midlothian, VA and surrounding areas. The paper includes local and national news, business, politics, sports and entertainment.; Full Page Mono: 95.00
Currency: US Dollars
NEWSPAPER

Chesterton Tribune
Owner: Chesterton Tribune, Inc.
Editorial: 193 S Calumet Rd, Chesterton, Indiana 46304-2433. **T:** 1 219 926-1131
E: news@chestertontribune.com
W: http://www.chestertontribune.com
Freq: Daily; **Circ:** 5000 Not Audited
Publisher: Warren Canright
Editorial Profile: Chesterton Tribune is published Monday through Friday for the residents of Chesterton, IN and surrounding areas. The newspaper covers local news, business, sports and community events. Deadlines for the editorial submissions are 5pm CT two days prior to the issue date.; Full Page Mono: 7.00
Currency: US Dollars
DAILY NEWSPAPER

Chicago China News Digest
Editorial: 122 Enclave Cir, Unit E, Bolingbrook, Illinois 60440-3568. **T:** 1 630 739-2838
E: ccnd@sbcglobal.net
W: http://www.ccndchicago.com
Freq: Bi-Weekly; **Circ:** 15000
Editor in Chief: David Xu; **Editor in Chief:** David Xu; **Editor in Chief:** David Xu; **Publisher:** David Zhang
Editorial Profile: Chicago China News Digest is a bi-weekly community newspaper written for Chinese-speaking residents in and around Chicago. It covers all American news and commentaries, especially related to China and Taiwan. The major goal of the paper is to build an information bridge between mainstream American businesses and the Asian community. Though the paper is mostly written in Chinese, it does include occasional English pages.; Full Page Mono: 40.00; Full Page Colour: 500.00
Currency: US Dollars
NEWSPAPER

The Chicago Crusader
Owner: Chicago Crusader Newspaper
Editorial: 6429 S King Dr, Chicago, Illinois 60637-3116. **T:** 1 773 752-2500
E: achicagocrusader@aol.com
W: http://www.chicagocrusader.com
Freq: Thu; **Circ:** 90071 Not Audited
Editor: Raymond Ward
Editorial Profile: The Chicago Crusader is a local newspaper published every Saturday for African Americans in Chicago. The newspaper covers topics on employment, equal rights, social justice, sports and entertainment. The paper prefers not to be contacted on Wednesday.; Full Page Mono: 136.24
Currency: US Dollars
NEWSPAPER

Chicago Defender
Owner: Real Times Media, Inc.
Editorial: 4445 S Dr Martin Luther King Jr Dr, Chicago, Illinois 60653-3310.
T: 1 312 225-2400
E: editorial@chicagodefender.com
W: http://www.chicagodefender.com
Freq: Wed; **Circ:** 30000 Not Audited
Editorial Profile: The Chicago Defender is a weekly newspaper, website and multi-platform news organization providing relevant content to Chicago's influential African-American community. Topics covered include news, business, politics, arts & culture, technology, commentary, African and African-American issues, neighborhood news, religion, entertainment, lifestyle, society news and sports.; Full Page Mono: 131.22
Currency: US Dollars
NEWSPAPER

Chicago Deportivo
Editorial: 3748 Cleveland Ave, Brookfield, Illinois 60513-1510. **T:** 1 708 387-7724
Freq: Fri; **Circ:** 10000
Editorial Profile: Offers news and sports to Chicago's Hispanic communities.; Full Page Mono: 8.50
Currency: US Dollars
NEWSPAPER

Chicago Jewish News
Editorial: 5301 Dempster St Ste 100, Skokie, Illinois 60077-1800. **T:** 1 847 966-0606
W: http://www.chicagojewishnews.com
Freq: Fri; **Circ:** 40000 Not Audited
Editorial Profile: Chicago Jewish News reports news, events and features that are relevant to the Jewish communities in and around Chicago.; Full Page Mono: 37.50; Full Page Colour: 2840.00
Currency: US Dollars
NEWSPAPER

Chicago Pollster
Editorial: 771 E. 134 Place, Chicago, Illinois 60827. **T:** 1 312 671-0240
W: http://www.chicagopollster.com
Freq: Monthly; **Circ:** 50000 Not Audited
Editorial Profile: Chicago Pollster is an independent newspaper specializing in investigative reporting. With a focus on Chicago politics, the paper's mission is to promote policies leading to clean and safe environmental conditions, an end to health and economic crises and a pursuit of fairness in government for all people.; Full Page Mono: 40.00
Currency: US Dollars
NEWSPAPER

Chicago Reader
Owner: Wrapports LLC
Editorial: 350 N Orleans St, Chicago, Illinois 60654-1975. **T:** 1 312 222-6920
E: mail@chicagoreader.com
W: http://www.chicagoreader.com
Freq: Wed; **Circ:** 117663 Not Audited
Editor: Mara Shalhoup
Editorial Profile: Chicago Reader serves residents and commuters of Chicago. It focuses on specialized features over news and covers urban issues and politics, arts & culture and literary work. It also publishes a separate guide to arts & entertainment happenings in Chicago and the surrounding area. Press releases that are faxed to the editorial office will be forwarded to the appropriate staff member. Advertising and editorial deadlines are the Fridays prior to publication.; Full Page Mono: 30.00
Currency: US Dollars
NEWSPAPER

Chicago Sun-Times
Owner: Wrapports LLC
Editorial: 350 N Orleans St, Chicago, Illinois 60654-1975. **T:** 1 312 321-3000
W: http://www.suntimes.com
Freq: Daily; **Circ:** 337164 Not Audited
Pulse Editor: Meg Moore
Editorial Profile: Chicago Sun-Times is a daily newspaper offering news from international to local community news, sports, features, editorials, arts & entertainment, business and weather for the Chicago metro area.; Full Page Mono: 632.00; Full Page Colour: 2475.80
Currency: US Dollars
DAILY NEWSPAPER

Chicago Sun-Times
Editorial: 529 14th St NW Ste 1206, Washington, District Of Columbia 20045-2200. **T:** 1 202 662-8808
Bureau Chief: Lynn Sweet
DAILY NEWSPAPER

Chicago Sun-Times
Editorial: State House Bldg Press Rm, Springfield, Illinois 62706-0001.
T: 1 217 753-2986
DAILY NEWSPAPER

Chicago Tribune
Owner: Tribune Company
Editorial: 435 N Michigan Ave, Chicago, Illinois 60611-4066. **T:** 1 312 222-3232
E: tips@tribune.com
W: http://www.chicagotribune.com
Freq: Daily; **Circ:** 439731 Not Audited
Dining & TV Editor: Carmel Carrillo;
Publisher: Tony Hunter; **Editor:** Gerould Kern;
Content Editor: Pete Reinwald; **Real Estate Editor:** Brenda Richardson; **Real Estate Editor:** Brenda Richardson
Editorial Profile: Chicago Tribune covers local, regional, national and international news, as well as business, entertainment, lifestyle and sports. The paper was founded in 1847. Its editorial staff has won more than 24 Pulitzer Prizes. News is gathered at dozens of suburban, regional, national and foreign bureaus. In August 2009, Tribune Company formed a national sports content-sharing alliance between its properties, most notably between the Chicago Tribune and the Los Angeles Times. In October 2002, the paper launched its RedEye edition. This weekday tabloid is aimed at growing readership among young, urban professionals. In addition to reaching readers in print, the paper also operates related Web sites, including metromix.com, Chicago's complete entertainment guide; ChicagoSports.com, a comprehensive local sports site; and dogood.chicagotribune.com, a site linking Chicagoans with volunteer work.; Full Page Mono: 667.00; Full Page Colour: 733.70
Currency: US Dollars
DAILY NEWSPAPER

Chicago Tribune
Editorial: State House Press Rm, Springfield, Illinois 62706-0001. **T:** 1 217 782-4523
DAILY NEWSPAPER

Chicago Tribune
Editorial: 3 Westbrook Corporate Ctr, Westchester, Illinois 60154-5703.
T: 1 708 498-4217 **E:** ctc-west@tribune.com
Bureau Chief: Peter Hernon
DAILY NEWSPAPER

Chicago Tribune
Editorial: 1717 N Penny Ln, Schaumburg, Illinois 60173-5602. **T:** 1 847 755-8911
E: ctc-northwest@tribune.com
Bureau Chief: Diana Wallace
DAILY NEWSPAPER

Chicago Tribune
Editorial: 616 Atrium Dr Ste 200, Vernon Hills, Illinois 60061-1713. **T:** 1 847 918-2800
E: ctc-northshore@tribune.com
DAILY NEWSPAPER

Chicago Tribune
Editorial: 18450 Crossing Dr, Tinley Park, Illinois 60487-9279. **T:** 1 708 342-5600
E: ctc-southwest@tribune.com
Bureau Chief: Patrick Regan
DAILY NEWSPAPER

Chico Enterprise-Record
Owner: MediaNews Group
Editorial: 400 E Park Ave, Chico, California 95928-7127. **T:** 1 530 891-1234
E: localnews@chicoer.com
W: http://www.chicoer.com
Freq: Daily; **Circ:** 28695 Not Audited
Buzz Editor: Lauren Brooks; **News Editor:** Michelle King; **Editor:** David Little; **City Editor:** Steve Schoonover
Editorial Profile: Chico Enterprise-Record is a daily local newspaper serving residents in Butte County, CA and surrounding counties. The newspaper covers local and national news, lifestyle, sports, and arts and entertainment.; Full Page Mono: 67.03; Full Page Colour: 600.00
Currency: US Dollars
DAILY NEWSPAPER

Chico News & Review
Owner: Chico Community Publishing, Inc.
Editorial: 353 E 2nd St, Chico, California 95928. **T:** 1 530 894-2300
E: chiconewstips@newsreview.com
W: http://www.newsreview.com/chico
Freq: Thu; **Circ:** 38000 Not Audited
Editor: Melissa Daugherty; **Publisher:** Jeff von Kaenel
Editorial Profile: Chico News & Review is a local newspaper published for residents of Chico and surrounding Butte County, CA. It covers local and national news, calendar & events information, sustainability, arts & entertainment, the environment, politics, diversity and women's issues.; Full Page Mono: 32.00
Currency: US Dollars
NEWSPAPER

The Chicopee Register
Owner: Turley Publications, Inc.
Editorial: 333 Front St, Chicopee, Massachusetts 1013. **T:** 1 413 592-3599
W: http://www.turley.com/chicopee
Freq: Thu; **Circ:** 13000 Not Audited
Editor: Kathleen Mitchell; **Publisher:** Patrick Turley
Editorial Profile: The Chicopee Register is a weekly local paper serving the readers of Chicopee, MA. It covers all aspects of local news from politics to sports. The newspaper was founded in 1998. Advertising and editorial deadlines are Tuesdays at noon ET.; Full Page Mono: 11.50
Currency: US Dollars
NEWSPAPER

Chicot County Publishing, Inc.
Editorial: 105 N Court St, Lake Village, Arkansas 71653. **T:** 1 870 265-2071
E: news@chicotnewspapers.com **Circ:** 2850 Not Audited
Publisher: Barney White; **Editor:** Whitney White
NEWSPAPER

The Chief
Owner: NY Civil Service Employees Publishing Co., Inc.
Editorial: 277 Broadway, Ste 1506, New York, New York 10007. **T:** 1 212 962-2690
E: thechief.leader@rcn.com
W: http://www.thechief-leader.com
Freq: Fri; **Circ:** 26228 Not Audited
Publisher: Edward Prial; **Editor:** Richard Steier
Editorial Profile: The Chief is a weekly newspaper for civil service employees in New York, NY. The newspaper focuses on job opportunities, the civil service examination, and other relevant issues for employees of governmental organizations. Deadlines for the publication are on the Monday before issue date. This paper will not accept unsolicited information sent via e-mail. Send press releases by fax.; Full Page Mono: 35.00
Currency: US Dollars
NEWSPAPER

Chillicothe Constitution-Tribune
Owner: GateHouse Media Inc.
Editorial: 818 Washington St, Chillicothe, Missouri 64601-2232. **T:** 1 660 646-2411
E: ctnews@chillicothenews.com
W: http://www.chillicothenews.com
Freq: Daily; **Circ:** 3525 Not Audited
Publisher: Rod Dixon; **Editor:** Laura Schuler
Editorial Profile: Chillicothe Constitution-Tribune is a local newspaper serving the residents of Livingston County, MO. The publication covers local news, sports and community events.; Full Page Mono: 7.90; Full Page Colour: 160.00
Currency: US Dollars
DAILY NEWSPAPER

Chillicothe Gazette
Owner: Gannett Co., Inc.
Editorial: 50 W Main St, Chillicothe, Ohio 45601. **T:** 1 740 773-2111
E: gaznews@nncogannett.com
W: http://www.chillicothegazette.com
Freq: Daily; **Circ:** 7714 Not Audited
Editorial Profile: Chillicothe Gazette is a daily local newspaper serving the residents in Pike, Chillicothe, and Ross Counties, OH. The publication covers local news and community events. The editorial mission is to supply their readers with current news.; Full Page Mono: 4.55; Full Page Colour: 20.43
Currency: US Dollars
DAILY NEWSPAPER

China Daily (U.S. Edition)
Owner: China Daily Distribution Corporation
Editorial: 1500 Broadway Ste 2800, New York, New York 10036-4015. **T:** 1 212 537-8888
E: editor@chinadailyusa.com
W: http://usa.chinadaily.com.cn
Freq: Mon thru Fri; **Circ:** 180000
Editorial Profile: The U.S. Edition of China Daily is a tailor-made version of China Daily, China's national English-language newspaper, for North American readers. The paper launched in 2009 and is published Monday through Friday, providing a window into China with the Chinese perspective on major financial, political and social issues affecting

China and the United States today. The U.S. Edition features reporting on Chinese business, politics, society, and culture from both sides of the Pacific.
DAILY NEWSPAPER

China Press
Editorial: 2121 W Mission Rd, Alhambra, California 91803-1420. **T:** 1 626 281-8500
E: reporter@cpwc.com
W: http://la.uschinapress.com
Freq: Daily; **Circ:** 30000 Not Audited
Publisher & Editor: Xiaodong Liu; **Editor:** Di Shen Wang
Editorial Profile: China Press is a newspaper serving the Chinese and Chinese American community.; Full Page Mono: 40.00
Currency: US Dollars
DAILY NEWSPAPER

China Press
Editorial: 15 E 40th St, New York, New York 10016. **T:** 1 212 683-8282
E: news@chinapress.net
W: http://www.chinapressusa.com
Freq: Daily; **Circ:** 40000 Not Audited
Editor In Chief: Id Jeng; **Editor:** David Li
Editorial Profile: China Press was founded on Jan. 5, 1990. The number one goal of the paper has always been to best serve the interests of Chinese Americans living in the United States.; Full Page Mono: 240.00
Currency: US Dollars
DAILY NEWSPAPER

Chinese American News
Editorial: 733 W 26th St, Chicago, Illinois 60616-1854. **T:** 1 312 225-5600
E: canews@canews.com
W: http://www.canews.com
Freq: Fri; **Circ:** 12000 Not Audited
Editorial Profile: Chinese American News is a weekly newspaper written for Chinese-speaking residents in Chicago.; Full Page Mono: 22.00
Currency: US Dollars
NEWSPAPER

Chinese News
Editorial: 4463 University Ave, San Diego, California 92105-1731
E: chinesenews@cox.net
Freq: Fri; **Circ:** 12000 Not Audited
Editorial Profile: Chinese News is a weekly newspaper focused to the Chinese residents in the San Diego area.; Full Page Mono: 5.10
Currency: US Dollars
NEWSPAPER

The Chippewa Herald
Owner: Lee Enterprises, Inc.
Editorial: 321 Frenette Dr, Chippewa Falls, Wisconsin 54729-3372. **T:** 1 715 723-5515
W: http://www.chippewa.com
Freq: Daily; **Circ:** 5481 Not Audited
Editor: Ross Evavold
Editorial Profile: The Chippewa Herald is a daily local newspaper serving residents of Chippewa County, WI. The publication covers local news and community events.; Full Page Mono: 14.91; Full Page Colour: 225.00
Currency: US Dollars
DAILY NEWSPAPER

The Christian Courier
Owner: ProBuCalls Association
Editorial: 9733 W. Greenfield Ave., West Allis, Wisconsin 53214. **T:** 1 414 344-7300
E: christiancourier@juno.com
W: http://www.christiancouriernewspaper.com
Freq: Bi-Monthly; **Circ:** 10000 Not Audited
Editorial Profile: The Christian Courier is a community newspaper serving the Milwaukee metropolitan area, covering news and events of importance to the Christian community.
NEWSPAPER

The Christian Index
Editorial: 6405 Sugarloaf Pkwy, Duluth, Georgia 30097-4092. **T:** 1 770 936-5590
E: editor@christianindex.org
W: http://www.christianindex.org
Freq: Thu; **Circ:** 35000 Not Audited
Editor: J. Harris
Editorial Profile: Christian Index was founded in 1822 and is the oldest religious newspaper in the nation. The publication is written for Baptists living in Georgia. It covers news and issues facing the Baptist religion. An online-only subscription is available for $6 per year.; Full Page Mono: 30.00
Currency: US Dollars
NEWSPAPER

Christian News Northwest
Owner: Christian News Northwest Ministries Inc.

Editorial: 3100 Ivy Dr, Newberg, Oregon 97132. **T:** 1 503 537-9220
E: cnnw@cnnw.com **W:** http://www.cnnw.com
Freq: Monthly; **Circ:** 29000 Not Audited
Editorial Profile: Christian News Northwest is a monthly newspaper serving the evangelical Christian community in Portland and Salem, OR, Vancouver, WA, and surrounding communities throughout Western and Central Oregon and Southwest Washington. It provides news that is oriented to the ministry. It is available for pick-up at churches, bookstores, libraries, schools, businesses and public locations throughout the area.; Full Page Mono: 12.00; Full Page Colour: 50.00
Currency: US Dollars
NEWSPAPER

The Christian Science Monitor
Owner: First Church of Christ Scientist
Editorial: 210 Massachusetts Ave, Boston, Massachusetts 02115-3012.
T: 1 617 450-2000
W: http://www.csmonitor.com
Freq: Sun; **Circ:** 77185
Editor: Clayton Collins; **Editor:** Clayton Collins; **Editor:** Marshall Ingwerson; **Publisher:** Jonathan Wells
Editorial Profile: Founded in 1908, The Christian Science Monitor is recognized as one of the leading U.S. newspapers specializing in international reporting. With a reputation for balanced coverage of complex issues and in-depth analysis of events, the award-winning paper offers both news and features from its 16 bureaus in the U.S. and abroad and from freelance reporters across the globe. Please send press materials via e-mail.; Full Page Mono: 97.39; Full Page Colour: 104.35
Currency: US Dollars
NEWSPAPER

The Chronicle
Owner: Crosbie (Kevin)
Editorial: 1 Chronicle Rd, Willimantic, Connecticut 6226. **T:** 1 860 423-8466
E: news@thechronicle.com
W: http://www.thechronicle.com
Freq: Daily; **Circ:** 8940 Not Audited
City Editor: Mike Lemanski; **Editor:** Charles Ryan; **Editor:** Charles Ryan
Editorial Profile: The Chronicle is a daily newspaper published for residents of Willimantic, CT. It covers local events, sports and community news.; Full Page Mono: 30.15; Full Page Colour: 350.00
Currency: US Dollars
DAILY NEWSPAPER

The Chronicle
Owner: Lafromboise Newspapers, Inc.
Editorial: 321 N Pearl St, Centralia, Washington 98531. **T:** 1 360 736-3311
W: http://www.chronline.com
Freq: Daily; **Circ:** 13912 Not Audited
Publisher: Dennis Waller
Editorial Profile: The Chronicle is a daily local newspaper written for residents of Lewis County, WA. The newspaper covers local news, sports, lifestyle, police and courts, education and business.; Full Page Mono: 16.25; Full Page Colour: 82.14
Currency: US Dollars
DAILY NEWSPAPER

The Chronicle
Owner: Lone Oak Publishing Co., Inc.
Editorial: 15 Ridge St, Glens Falls, New York 12801. **T:** 1 518 792-1126
E: contact@readthechronicle.com
W: http://www.readthechronicle.com
Freq: Thu; **Circ:** 30000 Not Audited
Editor: Mark Frost; **Editor:** Mark Frost; **Editor:** Mark Frost; **News Editor:** Gordon Woodworth
Editorial Profile: The Chronicle is an arts weekly in the greater Glens Falls/Lake George region, covering Warren, Washington and northern Saratoga Counties.; Full Page Mono: 21.00
Currency: US Dollars
NEWSPAPER

The Chronicle
Editorial: 208 Elm St, Valparaiso, Indiana 46383-3615. **T:** 1 219 531-4639
E: chronicle@greatlakesmarketing.net
W: http://www.thechroniclenwi.com
Freq: Wed; **Circ:** 30000
Editorial Profile: The Chronicle is a community newspaper written for the residents of Valparaiso, IN.; Full Page Mono: 18.00
Currency: US Dollars
NEWSPAPER

Chronicle & Sun Newspapers
Owner: Community Newspaper Holdings, Inc.

Editorial: 125 West Ave, Crossville, Tennessee 38555. **T:** 1 931 484-5145
W: http://crossville-chronicle.com **Circ:** 41000 Not Audited
Editor: Mike Moser; **Editor:** Mike Moser; **Editor:** Clayta Richards; **Publisher:** Pauline Sherrer
Editorial Profile: Moreover.
NEWSPAPER

The Chronicle News
Editorial: 200 Church St, Trinidad, Colorado 81082-2603. **T:** 1 719 846-3311
W: http://www.trinidadchroniclenews.com
Freq: Daily; **Circ:** 3275 Not Audited
Editor: Michael Hiesiger; **Publisher:** Tom Shearman
Editorial Profile: The Chronicle News serves the residents of Trinidad, CO, The paper aims to provide up-to-date information and reports on local news, national news and community events.; Full Page Mono: 11.13; Full Page Colour: 100.00
Currency: US Dollars
DAILY NEWSPAPER

The Chronicle of Mount Juliet
Editorial: 11509 Lebanon Rd, Mount Juliet, Tennessee 37122-5500. **T:** 1 615 754-6111
E: thechronicle@thechronicleofmtjuliet.com
W: http://www.thechronicleofmtjuliet.com
Freq: Wed; **Circ:** 12000 Not Audited
Editorial Profile: The Chronicle of Mount Juliet is a community newspaper serving residents of Mount Juliet, TN. The paper covers wedding and birth announcements, community news, events and local business news.; Full Page Mono: 10.99; Full Page Colour: 13.70
Currency: US Dollars
NEWSPAPER

The Chronicle Shopper
Owner: Chronicle Printing Co. Inc.
Editorial: 1 Chronicle Rd, Willimantic, Connecticut 06226-1932. **T:** 1 860 423-8466
E: news@thechronicle.com
W: http://www.thechronicle.com
Freq: Thu; **Circ:** 27470 Not Audited
Editor: Charles Ryan; **Editor:** Charles Ryan
Editorial Profile: The Chronicle Shopper is a free, weekly newspaper published by The Chronicle. It is sent to non-subscribers of The Chronicle and provides local news, community events and feature stories of interest to residents in northeastern Connecticut. Advertising must be purchased as a combination buy with the daily paper.; Full Page Mono: 28.75
Currency: US Dollars
NEWSPAPER

Chronicle Times
Owner: Rust Communications
Editorial: 111 S 2nd St, Cherokee, Iowa 51012-1839. **T:** 1 712 225-5111
W: http://www.chronicletimes.com
Freq: Daily; **Circ:** 6000 Not Audited
Publisher: Randy List
Editorial Profile: Chronicle Times, formerly Cherokee Daily Times, offers coverage of local news, sports and entertainment to the residents of Cherokee County, IA.; Full Page Mono: 11.00; Full Page Colour: 35.09
Currency: US Dollars
DAILY NEWSPAPER

The Chronicle-Telegram
Owner: Lorain County Printing & Publishing
Editorial: 225 East Ave, Elyria, Ohio 44035-5639. **T:** 1 440 329-7000
E: ctnews@chroniclet.com
W: http://www.chroniclet.com
Freq: Daily; **Circ:** 23754 Not Audited
Publisher: A. Cooper Hudnutt; **News Editor:** Ben Nagy; **Editor:** Andy Young
Editorial Profile: The Chronicle-Telegram brings local news to the tri-county area of Elyria, OH.; Full Page Mono: 33.65; Full Page Colour: 300.00
Currency: US Dollars
DAILY NEWSPAPER

Chronicle-Tribune
Owner: Paxton Media Group
Editorial: 610 S Adams St, Marion, Indiana 46953. **T:** 1 765 664-5111 **E:** ctreport@att.net
W: http://www.chronicle-tribune.com
Freq: Daily; **Circ:** 12536 Not Audited
Editor: David Penticuff
Editorial Profile: Chronicle Tribune is published daily for the residents of Grant County, IN. The newspaper provides information about local news, sports, entertainment and community events. Editorial deadlines are one day prior to issue date at noon ET.; Full Page Mono: 18.00

Currency: US Dollars
DAILY NEWSPAPER

The Cincinnati Enquirer
Owner: Gannett Co., Inc.
Editorial: 312 Elm St, Cincinnati, Ohio 45202-2739. **T:** 1 513 721-2700
E: localnews@enquirer.com
W: http://news.cincinnati.com
Freq: Daily; **Circ:** 118721 Not Audited
Editorial Profile: The Cincinnati Enquirer is a broadsheet newspaper that covers local, national and world news. It is distributed to the eight counties in the greater Cincinnati area.; Full Page Mono: 371.57; Full Page Colour: 434.02
Currency: US Dollars
DAILY NEWSPAPER

The Cincinnati Enquirer
Editorial: 50 W Broad St Ste 1130, Columbus, Ohio 43215-5948. **T:** 1 614 224-4640
DAILY NEWSPAPER

The Cincinnati Enquirer
Editorial: 7700 Service Center Dr, West Chester, Ohio 45069-2442. **T:** 1 513 755-4140
DAILY NEWSPAPER

Cinco Dias - New York Bureau
Editorial: 200 Schermerhorn St, Apt 723, Brooklyn, New York 11201-5897.
T: 1 718 237-6050
W: http://www.cincodias.com
Editorial Profile: This is the New York bureau of Cinco Dias in Madrid, Spain.
DAILY NEWSPAPER

The Circleville Herald
Owner: American Consolidated Media
Editorial: 120 Watt St, Circleville, Ohio 43113-1747. **T:** 1 740 474-3131
E: news@circlevilleherald.com
W: http://www.circlevilletoday.com/
Freq: Daily; **Circ:** 7048 Not Audited
Editorial Profile: The Circleville Herald is a daily newspaper published for the residents of Circleville County, OH. The newspaper covers local news, sports, entertainment and business.; Full Page Mono: 9.80
Currency: US Dollars
DAILY NEWSPAPER

The Citizen
Owner: Lee Publications, Inc.
Editorial: 25 Dill St, Auburn, New York 13021-3605. **T:** 1 315 253-5311
E: citizennews@lee.net
W: http://www.auburnpub.com
Freq: Daily; **Circ:** 6903
Publisher: Rob Forcey
Editorial Profile: The Citizen is a daily newspaper serving the residents of Auburn, NY and the surrounding areas. It covers national, regional and local news, sports, weather, community events, public announcements and features.; Full Page Mono: 23.33; Full Page Colour: 26.78
Currency: US Dollars
DAILY NEWSPAPER

The Citizen Courier
Owner: TexRay Media LLC
Editorial: 2816 N 19th St Apt C, Waco, Texas 76708-2872. **T:** 1 254 754-3511
E: editor@texraymedia.com
W: http://www.thecitizencourier.com
Freq: Thu
Editorial Profile: Citizen Courier is a weekly community newspaper serving residents of McLennan County, TX with local news, sports, business, lifestyle and opinion. Prior to purchase by TexRay Media, the paper was known separately as the Waco Citizen and Suburban Courier.; Full Page Mono: 10.00
Currency: US Dollars
NEWSPAPER

Citizen Newspaper Corp.
Owner: Citizen Newspaper Corp.
Editorial: 806 E 78th St, Chicago, Illinois 60619-2937. **T:** 1 773 783-1251
E: editorial@thechicagocitizen.com
W: http://www.thechicagocitizen.com
Circ: 121000 Not Audited
Editorial Profile: Citizen Newspaper Corp. produces weekly newspapers serving Chicagoland's African-American communities, with a focus on Chatham, the West Side, South Side, South End, Hyde Park, West Side and South Suburbs. Five editions are published and serve different regions: Chicago Weekend, Hyde Park Citizen, South End Citizen, South Suburban Citizen and Chatham-Southeast Citizen.
NEWSPAPER

The Citizen Newspapers
Owner: Fayette Publishing, Inc.
Editorial: 310 Glynn St N, Ste B, Fayetteville, Georgia 30214. **T:** 1 770 719-1880
W: http://www.thecitizennews.com **Circ:** 58785 Not Audited
NEWSPAPER

The Citizen of Laconia
Owner: Citizen Publishing Co.
Editorial: 171 Fair St, Laconia, New Hampshire 03246-3323. **T:** 1 603 524-3800
E: news@citizen.com
W: http://www.citizen.com
Freq: Daily; **Circ:** 7242 Not Audited
Editor: Krista Marrs
Editorial Profile: The Citizen of Laconia is a daily newspaper serving the residents of Laconia, NH. Editorial content includes local and state news, sports, community announcements and a calendar of events. The paper has a combined Saturday and Sunday weekend edition that is called Weekend Citizen.; Full Page Mono: 11.60; Full Page Colour: 435.00
Currency: US Dollars
DAILY NEWSPAPER

Citizen Tribune
Owner: Lakeway Publishers, Inc.
Editorial: 1609 W 1st North St, Morristown, Tennessee 37814-3724. **T:** 1 423 581-5630
E: ctmaned@lcs.net
W: http://www.citizentribune.com
Freq: Daily; **Circ:** 18727 Not Audited
Publisher: Mike Fishman
Editorial Profile: Citizen Tribune is a local daily newspaper written for residents in the seven county area of Tennessee. The editorial mission is to deliver local and national news.; Full Page Mono: 18.55; Full Page Colour: 450.00
Currency: US Dollars
DAILY NEWSPAPER

Citizen's News
Owner: Maitland Publishing, LLC.
Editorial: 71 Weid Dr, Naugatuck, Connecticut 6770. **T:** 1 203 729-2228
E: editor@mycitizensnews.com
W: http://mycitizensnews.com
Freq: Thu; **Circ:** 15000 Not Audited; Full Page Mono: 7.70
Currency: US Dollars
NEWSPAPER

The Citizens Voice
Owner: Times-Shamrock Communications
Editorial: 75 N Washington St, Wilkes-Barre, Pennsylvania 18711-0501. **T:** 1 570 821-2000
E: citydesk@citizensvoice.com
W: http://www.citizensvoice.com
Freq: Daily; **Circ:** 45608 Not Audited
Editor: Jonathan Bombulie; **Publisher:** Scott Lynett
Editorial Profile: The Citizens Voice is a local daily newspaper written for residents of Luzerne County, PA. The newspaper covers local news, sports, travel and events. The deadline for the newspaper falls at 7pm ET.; Full Page Mono: 39.20; Full Page Colour: 335.20
Currency: US Dollars
DAILY NEWSPAPER

Citrus County Chronicle
Owner: Landmark Community Newspapers, Inc.
Editorial: 1624 N Meadowcrest Blvd, Crystal River, Florida 34429-8751. **T:** 1 352 563-6363
E: newsdesk@chronicleonline.com
W: http://www.chronicleonline.com
Freq: Daily; **Circ:** 21692 Not Audited
Editor: Michael Arnold; **Editor:** Matt Beck; **Publisher:** Gerald Mulligan
Editorial Profile: Citrus County Chronicle is a daily newspaper serving the residents of Crystal River, FL.; Full Page Mono: 38.73; Full Page Colour: 470.00
Currency: US Dollars
DAILY NEWSPAPER

City & State
Owner: Manhattan Media
Editorial: 61 Broadway Rm 2825, New York, New York 10006-2817. **T:** 1 212 284-9712
E: editor@cityandstateny.com
W: http://www.cityandstateny.com
Freq: Bi-Monthly; **Circ:** 13000
Publisher: Tom Allon; **Editor in Chief:** Morgan Pehme
Editorial Profile: City & State is a bi-monthly newspaper targeting the politicians, lobbyists, unions, staffers and issues which shape New York City and State. It concentrates on the analysis of policy and politics; but it also covers the lighter side of political life, with articles about restaurants, fashion and celebrities of interest to those involved in the New York political world. City & State is a publication combined from City Hall and The Capitol.
NEWSPAPER

City Beat
Owner: Lightborne Publishing Inc.
Editorial: 811 Race St, Cincinnati, Ohio 45202-2041. **T:** 1 513 665-4700
E: letters@citybeat.com
W: http://www.citybeat.com/cincinnati
Freq: Wed; **Circ:** 50000 Not Audited
Publisher: Dan Bockrath
Editorial Profile: City Beat in Cincinnati, OH aims to provide an alternative source of information for progressive, open-minded readers, and to explore, explain and discuss issues involving the community in a way that encourages readers to participate as better citizens. The newspaper is written for the people of Greater Cincinnati and Northern Kentucky. The newspaper covers local news, social issues and arts & entertainment, including: film, live and recorded music, theater and dance, art and literature.; Full Page Mono: 56.72
Currency: US Dollars
NEWSPAPER

City News
Owner: City News Newspaper, LLC
Editorial: 16781 Chagrin Blvd, Ste 283, Shaker Heights, Ohio 44120.
T: 1 216 591-1900
W: http://www.citynewsohio.com
Freq: Thu; **Circ:** 70000 Not Audited
Editor: Sandra Clark; **Publisher:** James Crosby
Editorial Profile: City News is published weekly for African American and Hispanic residents in Cleveland and surrounding areas. It covers local news and community events.; Full Page Mono: 52.00
Currency: US Dollars
NEWSPAPER

City NewsHound
Owner: Neighborhood Newspaper Group
Editorial: 6219 W 63Rd St, Chicago, Illinois 60638-5134. **T:** 1 773 229-1900
E: media@citynewshound.com
Freq: Thu; **Circ:** 25000 Not Audited
Editorial Profile: City NewsHound is a free, weekly newspaper serving residents of Garfield Ridge and Clearing in southwest Chicago. It covers community news, events, sports, local businesses, schools and features of interest to readers. It is home-delivered to residents and available at area senior centers and libraries. It only accepts press releases for local news or events.; Full Page Mono: 9.80
Currency: US Dollars
NEWSPAPER

City Newspaper
Owner: WMT Publications Inc.
Editorial: 250 Goodman St N, Rochester, New York 14607-1100. **T:** 1 585 244-3329
E: themail@rochester-citynews.com
W: http://www.rochestercitynewspaper.com
Freq: Wed; **Circ:** 39000 Not Audited
News Editor: Christine Fien
Editorial Profile: City Newspaper is written for Rochester, NY residents. The editorial mission is to provide coverage of arts and alternative lifestyles.; Full Page Colour: 1937.00
Currency: US Dollars
NEWSPAPER

City Pages
Owner: Voice Media Group
Editorial: 401 N 3rd St Ste 550, Minneapolis, Minnesota 55401-1387. **T:** 1 612 375-1015
E: news@citypages.com
W: http://www.citypages.com
Freq: Wed; **Circ:** 79600 Not Audited
Editor in Chief: Kevin Hoffman
Editorial Profile: City Pages is a weekly newspaper published for the residents of Minneapolis, MN. The newspaper covers news, sports and entertainment.; Full Page Mono: 59.00; Full Page Colour: 4474.00
Currency: US Dollars
NEWSPAPER

City Pages
Owner: City Pages, Inc.
Editorial: 300 3rd St, Wausau, Wisconsin 54403. **T:** 1 715 845-5171
W: http://www.thecitypages.com
Freq: Thu; **Circ:** 14574 Not Audited
Editorial Profile: City Pages' editorial mission is to provide news to residents of Central Wisconsin. The paper only wants to receive news of local, regional or state interest. National press information is generally ignored. Deadlines are Mondays at 5pm CT.; Full Page Mono: 21.00
Currency: US Dollars
NEWSPAPER

City Paper
Owner: Times-Shamrock Communications
Editorial: 812 Park Ave, Baltimore, Maryland 21201. **T:** 1 410 523-2300
E: letters@citypaper.com
W: http://citypaper.com
Freq: Wed; **Circ:** 91000 Not Audited
Editor: Evan Serpick
Editorial Profile: City Paper is a weekly newspaper written for the residents of Baltimore, MD. The editorial mission of the newspaper is to serve as a resource of arts & entertainment. The newspaper provides coverage of local news, politics, communities, culture and arts & entertainment.; Full Page Mono: 18.25
Currency: US Dollars
NEWSPAPER

City Paper
Owner: Tribune Company
Editorial: 123 Chestnut St, Philadelphia, Pennsylvania 19106-3060. **T:** 1 215 735-8444
E: editorial@citypaper.net
W: http://www.citypaper.net
Freq: Thu; **Circ:** 86000 Not Audited
Editor in Chief: Lillian Swanson
Editorial Profile: City Paper is published weekly for the residents of Philadelphia, New Jersey and Delaware. The newspaper covers local and national news, arts & entertainment and opinions.; Full Page Colour: 4404.00
Currency: US Dollars
NEWSPAPER

City Pulse
Owner: To The Max LLC
Editorial: 1905 E Michigan Ave, Lansing, Michigan 48912-2828. **T:** 1 517 371-5600
W: http://www.lansingcitypulse.com/lansing
Freq: Wed; **Circ:** 20000 Not Audited
News Editor: Andy Balaskovitz; **News Editor:** Sam Inglot
Editorial Profile: City Pulse is a weekly newspaper written for the residents of Lansing, MI. The editorial content includes news, entertainment, events, arts and other topics of general interest.; Full Page Mono: 37.00
Currency: US Dollars
NEWSPAPER

City Sun Times - Northeast Valley
Owner: Tatum Sun Times LLC (The)
Editorial: 10645 N Tatum Blvd, Ste 200, Phoenix, Arizona 85028. **T:** 1 480 922-8732
E: news@citysuntimes.com
W: http://news.citysuntimes.com
Freq: Monthly; **Circ:** 41000 Not Audited
Publisher: Hope Ozer
Editorial Profile: Arizona's City Sun Times - Northeast Valley is a complimentary community newspaper serving the expanding Northeast Valley, including the Tatum Corridor, Kierland, Desert Ridge and Tatum Ranch, AZ. Coverage includes local businesses, services, arts & entertainment, community news, travel, health & wellness, homes, food, religion and youth & education stories.; Full Page Mono: 20.26
Currency: US Dollars
NEWSPAPER

Cityview
Owner: Big Green Umbrella
Editorial: 5619 NW St. Suite 600, Johnston, Iowa 50131. **T:** 1 515 953-4822
E: editor@dmcityview.com
W: http://www.dmcityview.com
Freq: Thu; **Circ:** 30000 Not Audited
Editorial Profile: Cityview in Johnston, IA aims to provide an alternative news source for residents of Des Moines and central Iowa, and covers local events, music, arts & entertainment, food and trends.; Full Page Mono: 77.00; Full Page Colour: 2223.00
Currency: US Dollars
NEWSPAPER

Clanton Advertiser
Owner: Boone Newspapers Inc.
Editorial: 1109 7th St N, Clanton, Alabama 35045-2113. **T:** 1 205 755-5747
E: newsroom@clantonadvertiser.com
W: http://www.clantonadvertiser.com
Freq: Daily; **Circ:** 12100 Not Audited
Publisher: Tim Prince
Editorial Profile: Clanton Advertiser is a daily newspaper published for the residents of Clanton, AL. The newspaper covers local news and information. Please send all correspondence to the PO Box.; Full Page Mono: 12.70
Currency: US Dollars
DAILY NEWSPAPER

The Clare County Review
Editorial: 2141 E Ludington Dr, Clare, Michigan 48617-8801. **T:** 1 989 386-4414
E: news@clarecountyreview.com
W: http://www.clarecountyreview.com
Freq: Fri; **Circ:** 10000 Not Audited
Editorial Profile: The Clare County Review is a weekly community newspaper. Its editorial mission is to provide residents of Clare County, MI with local news, sports and entertainment. Deadlines are on Wednesdays at 5pm ET.; Full Page Mono: 10.25
Currency: US Dollars
NEWSPAPER

Claremore Daily Progress
Owner: Community Newspaper Holdings, Inc.
Editorial: 315 W Will Rogers Blvd, Claremore, Oklahoma 74017-7021. **T:** 1 918 341-1101
E: editor@claremoreprogress.com
W: http://claremoreprogress.com
Freq: Daily; **Circ:** 6158 Not Audited
Publisher: Bailey Dabney; **Editor:** Tom Fink
Editorial Profile: Claremore Daily Progress is published daily for the residents of Claremore, OK and surrounding areas. The newspaper covers local and state news, sports, business, lifestyles and entertainment.; Full Page Mono: 9.74; Full Page Colour: 1221.69
Currency: US Dollars
DAILY NEWSPAPER

Clarendon Citizen
Owner: Citizen Media, LLC
Editorial: 8 N Brooks St, Manning, South Carolina 29102-3206. **T:** 1 803 433-6397
E: citizen@clarendoncitizen.com
W: http://www.clarendoncitizen.com
Freq: Wed; **Circ:** 12000
Editorial Profile: Clarendon Citizen is a weekly community newspaper serving residents of Clarendon County, SC with local news, sports, business, politics, editorials and community event listings. Deadlines are at noon on Fridays the week preceding publication.
NEWSPAPER

El Clarin Newspapers
Editorial: 40 Broadway, Haverstraw, New York 10927-1140. **T:** 1 845 429-2949
E: elclarinusa@aol.com **Circ:** 65000 Not Audited
NEWSPAPER

The Clarion
Editorial: 2819 Veterans Dr, Scottsboro, Alabama 35769-4225. **T:** 1 256 259-2455
W: http://www.theclarion.org **Circ:** 15000
Editorial Profile: The Clarion is a weekly community newspaper in Scottsboro, AL.; Full Page Mono: 8.20
Currency: US Dollars
NEWSPAPER

Clarion Dispatch
Owner: Morris Communications
Editorial: 150 Trading Bay Dr, Ste 1, Kenai, Alaska 99611-7716. **T:** 1 907 283-7551
E: news@peninsulaclarion.com
W: http://www.peninsulaclarion.com
Freq: Wed; **Circ:** 10000 Not Audited
Publisher: Vitto Kleinschmidt
Editorial Profile: Clarion Dispatch is a weekly community newspaper servicing the residents of Kenai, AK.; Full Page Mono: 11.47
Currency: US Dollars
NEWSPAPER

Clarion Herald
Owner: Clarion Herald Publishing Company
Editorial: 1000 Howard Ave, Ste 400, New Orleans, Louisiana 70113. **T:** 1 504 596-3035
E: clarionherald@clarionherald.org
W: http://www.clarionherald.org
Freq: Sat; **Circ:** 56000 Not Audited
Publisher: Gregory Aymand
Editorial Profile: Clarion Herald is the official Catholic newspaper of the Archdiocese of New Orleans. The paper's editorial mission is to enable readers to grow and develop into mature, well-informed Catholics and to deepen their commitment to the Lord, their Catholic faith and their church.; Full Page Mono: 36.00
Currency: US Dollars
NEWSPAPER

Clarion News and Corydon Democrat Newspapers
Editorial: 301 N Capitol Ave, Corydon, Indiana 47112-1140. **T:** 1 812 738-2211
W: http://www.corydondemocrat.com
Circ: 24400 Not Audited

Editor: Chris Adams; **Publisher:** Jon O'Bannon; **Editor:** Jo Ann Spieth-Saylor
NEWSPAPER

The Clarion-Ledger
Owner: Gannett Co., Inc.
Editorial: 201 S Congress St, Jackson, Mississippi 39201-4202. **T:** 1 601 961-7000
W: http://www.clarionledger.com
Freq: Daily; **Circ:** 49285 Not Audited
Editorial Profile: The Clarion-Ledger is a daily newspaper covering news in Jackson, MS, and the surrounding areas with an emphasis on breaking events, local and state government, health, education, environment, business, finance, consumer issues and sports.; Full Page Mono: 175.29; Full Page Colour: 547.45
Currency: US Dollars
DAILY NEWSPAPER

Clark County Community Newspapers
Editorial: 705 Main St., Ashland, Kansas 67831. **T:** 1 620 635-2312
E: minneola_record@hotmail.com **Circ:** 1300 Not Audited
NEWSPAPER

El Clasificado
Owner: de la Torre (Martha)
Editorial: 11205 Imperial Hwy, Norwalk, California 90650-2229. **T:** 1 323 278-5310
E: elclasificado@elclasificado.com
W: http://www.elclasificado.com
Freq: Tue; **Circ:** 500000 Not Audited
Editor: Hilda Hernandez
Editorial Profile: El Clasificado offers goods and services to the Latino community of greater Los Angeles. Classified sections include automotive sales, automotive services, rentals, employment opportunites, free community events, general services, home services, miscellaneous services, professional services, real estate and business opportunites.; Full Page Mono: 110.91
Currency: US Dollars
NEWSPAPER

Clay Center Dispatch
Owner: Clay Center Publishing Co.
Editorial: 805 5th St, Clay Center, Kansas 67432-2530. **T:** 1 785 632-2127
E: dispatch@claycenter.com
W: http://www.claycenter.com
Freq: Mon thru Fri; **Circ:** 3900 Not Audited
Editor: Dave Berggren; **Editor:** Kay Ouellette; **Editor:** Ned Valentine; **Editor:** Ned Valentine; **Editor:** Ryan Wilson
Editorial Profile: Clay Center Dispatch is a daily local newspaper published for residents of Clay County, KS. The paper covers local news, weather and sports.; Full Page Mono: 6.90; Full Page Colour: 80.00
Currency: US Dollars
DAILY NEWSPAPER

Clayton News Daily
Owner: Southern Community Newspapers Inc.
Editorial: 138 Church St, Jonesboro, Georgia 30236-3514. **T:** 1 770 478-5753
E: editor@news-daily.com
W: http://www.news-daily.com
Freq: Daily; **Circ:** 6625 Not Audited
Publisher: Bonnie Pratt
Editorial Profile: Clayton News Daily is a daily newspaper that covers local news, business, sports and community news in Clayton County, GA. It combines with the Daily Herald in McDonough, GA on Saturdays.; Full Page Mono: 17.50; Full Page Colour: 320.00
Currency: US Dollars
DAILY NEWSPAPER

Clearwater Gazette
Owner: Tampa Media Group, Inc.
Editorial: 2401 W Bay Drive Bldg 100, Suite 124, Largo, Florida 33770-4900.
T: 1 727 446-6723
E: newsdesk@clearwatergazette.com
W: http://www.clearwatergazette.com
Freq: Thu; **Circ:** 17000 Not Audited
Editor: Jane Bongo; **Publisher:** E. Fields Puckett
Editorial Profile: Clearwater Gazette and Beach Views is a weekly newspaper serving the residents of Clearwater, FL. Founded in 1950, the paper covers mainly local news but also includes selected national news items.; Full Page Mono: 14.00
Currency: US Dollars
NEWSPAPER

Cleburne Times-Review
Owner: Community Newspaper Holdings, Inc.
Editorial: 108 S Anglin St, Cleburne, Texas 76031-5602. **T:** 1 817 645-2441
E: editor@trcle.com

W: http://www.cleburnetimesreview.com
Freq: Mon thru Fri; **Circ:** 6443 Not Audited
News Editor: Monica Faram
Editorial Profile: Cleburne Times-Review is a local daily newspaper written for the residents of Cleburne and Johnson County, TX. Topics that do not directly pertain to the local residents are very rarely published. Deadlines are at noon CT, the day before issue date.; Full Page Mono: 13.15; Full Page Colour: 380.00
Currency: US Dollars
DAILY NEWSPAPER

Cleveland Daily Banner
Owner: Cleveland Newspapers Inc.
Editorial: 1505 25th St NW, Cleveland, Tennessee 37311-3610. **T:** 1 423 472-5041
E: news@clevelandbanner.com
W: http://www.clevelandbanner.com
Freq: Daily; **Circ:** 11427 Not Audited
Publisher & Editor: Stephen Crass
Editorial Profile: Cleveland Daily Banner is a local daily newspaper written for the residents of Cleveland, TN. The newspaper covers the local news of the Cleveland, TN area. The lead time is two to three days.; Full Page Mono: 11.00; Full Page Colour: 300.00
Currency: US Dollars
DAILY NEWSPAPER

The Cleveland Jewish News
Editorial: 23880 Commerce Park, Beachwood, Ohio 44122-5830. **T:** 1 216 454-8300
E: editorial@cjn.org
W: http://www.clevelandjewishnews.com
Freq: Fri; **Circ:** 10000 Not Audited
Editorial Profile: The Cleveland Jewish News is written for northeast Ohio's Jewish Community with local, national and international news, features and commentary.; Full Page Mono: 31.97
Currency: US Dollars
NEWSPAPER

Cleveland Scene
Owner: Times Shamrock
Editorial: 1468 W 9th St, Ste 805, Cleveland, Ohio 44113-1299. **T:** 1 216 241-7550
E: scene@clevescene.com
W: http://www.clevescene.com
Freq: Wed; **Circ:** 45000 Not Audited
Editor: Vince Grzegorek; **Publisher:** Chris Keating
Editorial Profile: Cleveland Scene is written for residents of Cleveland. It features magazine-style news and features, award-winning music coverage with film and theater sections, restaurant reviews and listings, and a comprehensive regional calendar of events. The publication targets young urban professionals hungry for smart, uncompromising civic journalism. The paper merged with the Cleveland Free Times on July 30, 2008.; Full Page Mono: 28.66
Currency: US Dollars
NEWSPAPER

Clifton Journal
Owner: North Jersey Media Group Inc.
Editorial: 935 Allwood Rd Ste 200, Clifton, New Jersey 07012-1988. **T:** 1 973 778-2500
E: cliftonjournal@northjersey.com
W: http://www.northjersey.com/clifton
Freq: Fri; **Circ:** 30000 Not Audited
Publisher: Mike Lawson; **Editor:** Albina Sportelli
Editorial Profile: Clifton Journal is a community newspaper serving Clifton, NJ and the surrounding areas.; Full Page Mono: 17.50
Currency: US Dollars
NEWSPAPER

Clinton Daily Democrat
Owner: Democrat Publishing Co., Inc.
Editorial: 212 S Washington St, Clinton, Missouri 64735-2073. **T:** 1 660 885-2281
E: ddem.news@embarqmail.com
Freq: Daily; **Circ:** 4000 Not Audited
Editorial Profile: Clinton Daily Democrat is a daily local newspaper written for the residents of Henry County, MO. Coverage includes local news and events, sports, business and social issues. The deadline is noon CT the day prior to issue date.; Full Page Mono: 5.75; Full Page Colour: 70.00
Currency: US Dollars
DAILY NEWSPAPER

Clinton Daily News
Owner: Clinton Daily News Co.
Editorial: 522 Avant Ave, Clinton, Oklahoma 73601-3436. **T:** 1 580 323-5151
E: cdnews@swbell.net
W: http://www.clintondailynews.com
Freq: Daily; **Circ:** 5218 Not Audited
Editor: Gerald Green; **Publisher & Editor:** Rod Serfoss; **Editor:** Sean Stephens

Editorial Profile: Clinton Daily News is published daily for the residents of Clinton, OK and surrounding areas. The newspaper covers local and state news, sports, lifestyles and entertainment. Deadlines are at 1pm CT one day prior to issue date.; Full Page Mono: 9.26; Full Page Colour: 100.00
Currency: US Dollars
DAILY NEWSPAPER

Clinton Herald
Owner: Community Newspaper Holdings, Inc.
Editorial: 221 6th Ave S, Clinton, Iowa 52732-4305. **T:** 1 563 242-7101
E: news@clintonherald.com
W: http://www.clintonherald.com
Freq: Mon thru Fri; **Circ:** 7790
Editor: Charlene Bielema
Editorial Profile: Clinton Herald is a daily newspaper written for the community of Clinton, IA. The newspaper covers local news, business, sports and arts & entertainment.; Full Page Mono: 17.90
Currency: US Dollars
DAILY NEWSPAPER

Clipper Press Newspapers-Duxbury
Owner: Clipper Press Inc.
Editorial: 11 S Station St, Duxbury, Massachusetts 02332-4534.
T: 1 781 934-2811 **Circ:** 7500 Not Audited
NEWSPAPER

Clipper Press Newspapers-Hanson
Owner: Clipper Press Inc.
Editorial: 1375 Main St, Hanson, Massachusetts 02341-1551.
T: 1 781 293-0420 **Circ:** 3710 Not Audited
NEWSPAPER

Clipper-Herald & People Plus Newspapers
Owner: Omaha World-Herald Co.
Editorial: 114 W 5th St, Lexington, Nebraska 68850. **T:** 1 308 324-5511 **E:** news@lexch.com
W: http://www.lexch.com **Circ:** 13900 Not Audited
Publisher: Terrie Baker; **Editor:** Ben Schwartz
NEWSPAPER

Clovis News Journal
Owner: Freedom Communications Inc.
Editorial: 521 Pile St, Clovis, New Mexico 88101-6637. **T:** 1 575 763-3431
W: http://cnjonline.com
Freq: Daily; **Circ:** 7050 Not Audited
News Editor: Robin Fornoff; **Editor:** David Stevens; **Publisher:** Ray Sullivan
Editorial Profile: Clovis News Journal is a local daily newspaper written for residents of Clovis, NM. The main topics covered are local news, sports and area features.; Full Page Mono: 12.85; Full Page Colour: 1533.55
Currency: US Dollars
DAILY NEWSPAPER

CMT Publishing
Owner: CMT Phoenix Inc.
Editorial: 160 Cleveland Dr, Croton On Hudson, New York 10520. **T:** 1 914 271-2088
Circ: 4000 Not Audited
Publisher: Gary Cahill; **Editor:** May Tierney
NEWSPAPER

CNI Newspapers
Owner: Journal Communications
Editorial: 1741 Dolphin Ct, Ste A, Waukesha, Wisconsin 53186-1429. **T:** 1 414 224-2100
E: news@cninow.com
W: http://www.mycommunitynow.com
Circ: 36864 Not Audited
Editor: Marilyn Jozwik; **Editor:** Jon Olson; **Editor in Chief:** Scott Peterson; **Editor in Chief:** Scott Peterson; **Editor:** Jim Riccioli
NEWSPAPER

CNY Latino
Editorial: 201 E Jefferson St, Ste 224, Syracuse, New York 13202-2644.
T: 1 315 415-8593
W: http://www.cnylatino.com
Freq: Monthly; **Circ:** 10000 Not Audited
Publisher: Hugo Acosta; **Editor:** Marisol Hernandez
Editorial Profile: CNY Latino is a monthly, Spanish and English language newspaper serving bilingual and Spanish-speaking Latinos in Onondaga County, NY. The entire content is intended to be in a bilingual format and targeted to a diverse consumer. It contains periodic columns and each month bears a theme that either is related to the month or to a current issue, usually of direct interest to the Latino population.; Full Page Mono: 22.60
Currency: US Dollars
NEWSPAPER

The Coalfield Progress
Owner: American Hometown Publishing
Editorial: 725 Park Ave, Norton, Virginia 24273. **T:** 1 276 679-1101
W: http://www.thecoalfieldprogress.com
Circ: 13900
News Editor: Jeff Lester; **Editor:** Paula Tate
NEWSPAPER

The Coast News Group
Owner: The Coast News Group
Editorial: 828 N Coast Highway 101 Ste C, Encinitas, California 92024-2055.
T: 1 760 436-9737
E: community@coastnewsgroup.com
W: http://www.thecoastnews.com **Circ:** 65300 Not Audited
Publisher: Jim Kydd; **Publisher:** Jim Kydd; **Publisher:** Jim Kydd; **Publisher:** Jim Kydd
NEWSPAPER

The Coast Star
Owner: Star News Group, Inc.
Editorial: 13 Broad St, Manasquan, New Jersey 08736-2906. **T:** 1 732 223-0076
E: info@thecoaststar.com
W: http://www.starnewsgroup.com
Freq: Thu; **Circ:** 12852 Not Audited
Publisher: James Manser; **Editor:** Doug Paviluk; **Editor:** Doug Paviluk
Editorial Profile: The Coast Star is a local newspaper written for residents of Southern Monmouth County, NJ and the communities of Avon, Brielle, Belmar, Manasquan, Sea Girt, South Belmar, Spring Lake, Spring Lake Heights and Wall, NJ.; Full Page Mono: 8.50; Full Page Colour: 10.48
Currency: US Dollars
NEWSPAPER

Coastal Community Newspapers
Owner: Community Media Corp
Editorial: 4351 Sepulveda Blvd, Culver City, California 90230-4715. **T:** 1 310 437-4401
E: editor@culvercitynews.org
W: http://www.culvercitynews.org **Circ:** 2700 Not Audited
Editor: Lori Fusaro; **Publisher:** Alan Moskal
NEWSPAPER

The Coastal Journal
Owner: Maine Today Media Inc.
Editorial: 832 Washington St, Bath, Maine 04530-2662. **T:** 1 207 443-6241
W: http://www.coastaljournal.com
Freq: Thu; **Circ:** 20000 Not Audited
Editorial Profile: Coastal Journal is published weekly for the residents of Freeport and Rockland, ME. The newspaper covers local news, sports and community events.; Full Page Mono: 16.00
Currency: US Dollars
NEWSPAPER

Coastal Point
Owner: Coastal Point Inc.
Editorial: 111 Atlantic Ave, Suite 2, Ocean View, Delaware 19970-9166.
T: 1 302 539-1788
W: http://www.coastalpoint.com
Freq: Fri; **Circ:** 17000 Not Audited
Publisher: Susan Lyons; **Editor:** Darin McCann; **News Editor:** M. Patricia Titus
Editorial Profile: Costal Point is a community newspaper written for the Ocean View, DE area.; Full Page Mono: 9.73
Currency: US Dollars
NEWSPAPER

The Coastal Star Newspapers
Owner: Lower (Jerry) & Leming (Mary Kate)
Editorial: 5011 N Ocean Blvd, Ocean Ridge, Florida 33435-7355. **T:** 1 561 337-1553
E: news@thecoastalstar.com
W: http://www.thecoastalstar.com
Freq: Monthly; **Circ:** 16000
Publisher: Jerry Lower
Editorial Profile: The Coastal Star is a monthly community newspaper for the residents of Ocean Ridge, Hypoluxo Island, South Palm Beach, Manalapan, Briny Breezes, Gulf Stream and Delray Beach, FL.
NEWSPAPER

Coastline Pilot
Owner: Tribune Company
Editorial: 1375 Sunflower Ave, Costa Mesa, California 92626-1665. **T:** 1 714 966-4696
E: coastlinepilot@latimes.com
W: http://www.coastlinepilot.com
Freq: Fri; **Circ:** 15000 Not Audited
Editor: John Canalis
Editorial Profile: Coastline Pilot is a weekly newspaper for the residents of Laguna Beach, CA. The paper features news, sports, business, education, opinion, politics, government, entertainment, events, features,

public safety and religion content. Advertising deadlines are Mondays before publication.; Full Page Mono: 9.50
Currency: US Dollars
NEWSPAPER

Coeur d'Alene Press
Owner: Hagadone Corp.
Editorial: 201 N 2nd St, Coeur D Alene, Idaho 83814-2803. **T:** 1 208 664-8176
E: news@cdapress.com
W: http://www.cdapress.com
Freq: Daily; **Circ:** 24012 Not Audited
City Editor: Maureen Dolan; **Publisher:** Jim Thompson
Editorial Profile: Coeur d'Alene Press is a daily newspaper published for the residents of Coeur d'Alene, ID. The publication features articles about local news, business, sports, and arts & entertainment.; Full Page Mono: 32.67; Full Page Colour: 209.00
Currency: US Dollars
DAILY NEWSPAPER

Coffeyville Journal
Owner: Sumner Newspapers Inc.
Editorial: 302 W 8th St, Coffeyville, Kansas 67337-5829. **T:** 1 620 251-3300
Freq: Mon thru Fri; **Circ:** 3500 Not Audited
Publisher & Editor: Bethany Bunch
Editorial Profile: Coffeyville Journal provides community news for residents of Coffeyville, KS. The paper covers local and national news.; Full Page Mono: 9.67; Full Page Colour: 62.20
Currency: US Dollars
DAILY NEWSPAPER

Colby Free Press
Owner: Haynes Publishing Company
Editorial: 155 W 5th St, Colby, Kansas 67701-2312. **T:** 1 785 462-3963
E: colby.editor@nwkansas.com
W: http://www.nwkansas.com/cfpwebpages/cfpmain.html
Freq: Daily; **Circ:** 2046 Not Audited
Publisher: Sharon Friedlander
Editorial Profile: Colby Free Press is a local daily newspaper written for the residents of Thomas County, KS which covers Colby, Brewster and Rexford, KS. The focus of the newspaper is on local news and events in Thomas County, KS. The Colby Free Press is published daily Monday through Friday.; Full Page Mono: 7.95; Full Page Colour: 99.00
Currency: US Dollars
DAILY NEWSPAPER

Colfax County Press
Editorial: 242 Pine St, Clarkson, Nebraska 68629. **T:** 1 402 892-3547
E: ccpress@qwestoffice.net **Circ:** 2812 Not Audited
Publisher: Helen Evans; **Editor:** T.A. Evans
NEWSPAPER

Collier County Publishing Company
Owner: E.W. Scripps Co.
Editorial: 1100 Immokalee Rd, Naples, Florida 34110-4810. **T:** 1 239 213-6077
E: news@colliercitizen.com
W: http://www.naplesnews.com/news/citizen
Circ: 78000 Not Audited
Editor: Albert Sabina; **Editor:** Leigh Tahirovic; **Editor:** Kaydee Tuff; **Publisher:** Russell Tuff; Full Page Mono: 15.00
Currency: US Dollars
NEWSPAPER

El Colombiano
Owner: Latinwork Publishing Co.
Editorial: 3408 W 84Th St Ste 206, Hialeah, Florida 33018-4942. **T:** 1 954 430-1090
E: editor@elcolombiano.net
W: http://www.elcolombiano.net
Freq: Fri; **Circ:** 35000 Not Audited
Editorial Profile: El Colombiano is a free, weekly newspaper serving the Hispanic population and Colombian Americans in Miami-Dade, Broward and Palm Beach counties, FL. It relays current events occurring in Colombia, everything from news to entertainment. It also provides analysis of international news.; Full Page Mono: 20.00
Currency: US Dollars
NEWSPAPER

Colorado Episcopalian
Owner: Episcopal Diocese of Colorado
Editorial: 1300 Washington Street, Denver, Colorado 80203-2008. **T:** 1 303 837-1173
E: cenews@coloradodiocese.org
W: http://www.coloradodiocese.org
Freq: Quarterly; **Circ:** 19500 Not Audited
Editor: Beckett Stokes
Editorial Profile: Colorado Episcopalian is a publication of the Episcopal Diocese of Colorado. Colorado Episcopalian is read by members of the Episcopal Diocese of Colorado. The paper provides news regarding events, programs, and churches within the Diocese.
NEWSPAPER

Colorado Hometown Weekly
Editorial: 350 Terry St, Longmont, Colorado 80501-5440. **T:** 1 303 776-2244
E: news@coloradohometown.com
W: http://www.coloradohometownweekly.com
Freq: Wed; **Circ:** 18400 Not Audited
Publisher: Ed Lehman
Editorial Profile: Colorado Hometown Weekly is a local weekly newspaper serving the residents of Louisville, Erie, Lafayette and Superior, CO. The newspaper covers local news, sports, schools, opinion, and community events.; Full Page Mono: 14.50; Full Page Colour: 249.00
Currency: US Dollars
NEWSPAPER

Colorado Springs Independent
Editorial: 235 S Nevada Ave, Colorado Springs, Colorado 80903-1906.
T: 1 719 577-4545 **E:** newsroom@csindy.com
W: http://www.csindy.com
Freq: Wed; **Circ:** 37500 Not Audited
Publisher: John Weiss; **Editor in Chief:** Kirk Woundy
Editorial Profile: Colorado Springs (CO) Independent is a weekly alternative newspaper featuring arts & entertainment, dining, music, film, opinion, events and news.; Full Page Mono: 25.25; Full Page Colour: 2267.00
Currency: US Dollars
NEWSPAPER

Columbia Basin Herald
Owner: Hagadone Corp.
Editorial: 813 W 3rd Ave, Moses Lake, Washington 98837-2008. **T:** 1 509 765-4561
E: editor@columbiabasinherald.com
W: http://www.columbiabasinherald.com
Freq: Mon thru Fri; **Circ:** 8200 Not Audited
Publisher: Harlan Beagley; **City Editor:** Candice Boutilier
Editorial Profile: Columbia Basin Herald is a daily paper that provides the community with local news and information affecting the Columbia Basin area of Washington. Coverage includes sports, business, education and entertainment.; Full Page Mono: 17.80; Full Page Colour: 60.60
Currency: US Dollars
DAILY NEWSPAPER

The Columbia County News-Times
Owner: Morris Communications
Editorial: 4272 Washington Rd, Ste 3B, Evans, Georgia 30809-3073. **T:** 1 706 863-6165
E: cnt@newstimesonline.com
W: http://www.newstimesonline.com
Freq: Sun; **Circ:** 48000 Not Audited
Publisher: Barry Paschal
Editorial Profile: The Columbia County News-Times provides local and national news coverage for the Columbia County, GA area.; Full Page Mono: 21.50
Currency: US Dollars
NEWSPAPER

Columbia Daily Tribune
Owner: Tribune Publishing Company
Editorial: 101 N 4th St, Columbia, Missouri 65201-4416. **T:** 1 573 815-1500 5
E: editor@tribmail.com
W: http://www.columbiatribune.com
Freq: Daily; **Circ:** 16429
Publisher: Vicki Russell; **City Editor:** Lora Wegman
Editorial Profile: Columbia Daily Tribune is published daily for the residents of Columbia, MO and the surrounding areas. The newspaper provides local and national news coverage, sports and features. Deadlines are at 11am CT one day prior to issue date.; Full Page Mono: 15.00; Full Page Colour: 410.00
Currency: US Dollars
DAILY NEWSPAPER

Columbia Missourian
Owner: Missourian Publishing Association
Editorial: 221 S 8th St, Columbia, Missouri 65201. **T:** 1 573 882-5700
E: editor@columbiamissourian.com
W: http://www.columbiamissourian.com
Freq: Daily; **Circ:** 6202 Not Audited
Editor: Phill Brooks; **Publisher:** Dean Mills; **City Editor:** John Schneller; **Editor:** Scott Swafford
Editorial Profile: Columbia Missourian is a daily newspaper published by the Missourian Publishing Association, which is affiliated with the University of Missouri. It provides state and local news, sports and campus news and events for readers in Columbia, MO and the surrounding area.; Full Page Mono: 7.90; Full Page Colour: 150.00
Currency: US Dollars
DAILY NEWSPAPER

The Columbia Star
Owner: Star Reporter Corp. (The)
Editorial: 723 Queen St, Columbia, South Carolina 29205. **T:** 1 803 771-0219
W: http://www.thecolumbiastar.com
Freq: Fri; **Circ:** 15000 Not Audited
Publisher: Mimi Maddock
Editorial Profile: The Columbia Star is written for the residents of Columbia, SC. It covers local news, society, education and legal sections. Deadlines for publication are Fridays at 5pm ET.; Full Page Mono: 15.00
Currency: US Dollars
NEWSPAPER

The Columbian
Owner: Columbian Publishing Co.
Editorial: 701 W 8th St, Vancouver, Washington 98660-3008. **T:** 1 360 694-3391
E: metrodesk@columbian.com
W: http://columbian.com
Freq: Daily; **Circ:** 45816 Not Audited
Editor: Lou Brancaccio; **Publisher:** Scott Campbell; **Editor:** Greg Jayne; **Editor:** Greg Jayne
Editorial Profile: The Columbian is a daily newspaper published for residents of Clark County, WA. Coverage includes local news, sports and general lifestyle stories.; Full Page Mono: 63.50; Full Page Colour: 222.24
Currency: US Dollars
DAILY NEWSPAPER

Columbus Alive
Owner: Dispatch Printing Company (The)
Editorial: 34 S 3rd St, Columbus, Ohio 43215-4201. **T:** 1 614 221-2449
W: http://www.columbusalive.com
Freq: Thu; **Circ:** 55000 Not Audited
Editor: Justin McIntosh; **Publisher:** Katie Wolfe Lloyd
Editorial Profile: Columbus Alive is written for residents of Columbus, OH. It covers news, arts and culture as well as commentary on national issues that are of concern to the readership.; Full Page Mono: 19.96
Currency: US Dollars
NEWSPAPER

The Columbus Dispatch
Owner: Dispatch Printing Company (The)
Editorial: 34 S 3rd St, Columbus, Ohio 43215-4201. **T:** 1 614 461-5000
E: storyideas@dispatch.com
W: http://www.dispatch.com
Freq: Daily; **Circ:** 138386 Not Audited
Editor: Ben Marrison
Editorial Profile: Columbus Dispatch is a daily newspaper serving Columbus, OH that covers regional as well as national and international news. Regular sections include features, business, international and national news and metropolitan Columbus news. Business coverage focuses on local business, personal finance, construction, manufacturing, banking and finance, insurance, retailers, automakers. Business coverage is featured daily and Sunday in the business pages.; Full Page Mono: 319.31; Full Page Colour: 991.14
Currency: US Dollars
DAILY NEWSPAPER

The Columbus Dispatch
Editorial: 400 N Capitol St Nw Ste 750, Washington, District Of Columbia 20001-1536
DAILY NEWSPAPER

The Columbus Dispatch
Editorial: 23 1/2 S Park Pl Ste 205, Newark, Ohio 43055-5500. **T:** 1 740 345-3688
DAILY NEWSPAPER

The Columbus Dispatch
Editorial: 2 W Winter St Ste 305, Delaware, Ohio 43015-1965. **T:** 1 740 363-0861
DAILY NEWSPAPER

The Columbus Dispatch
Editorial: 117 E Main St, Suite 105, Lancaster, Ohio 43130-3761. **T:** 1 740 653-3520
DAILY NEWSPAPER

Columbus Ledger-Enquirer
Owner: McClatchy Newspapers
Editorial: 17 W 12th St, Columbus, Georgia 31901-5254. **T:** 1 706 324-5526
E: newsroom@ledger-enquirer.com
W: http://www.ledger-enquirer.com
Freq: Daily; **Circ:** 28283 Not Audited
Northland Neighbors Editor: Mark Rice
Editorial Profile: Columbus Ledger-Enquirer is a daily newspaper serving Columbus, GA and surrounding communities. The paper covers local news, national news, sports, family, health, home, garden, business and entertainment.; Full Page Mono: 69.25; Full Page Colour: 225.95
Currency: US Dollars
DAILY NEWSPAPER

Columbus Messenger Company
Owner: Messenger Newspapers, Inc.
Editorial: 3500 Sullivant Ave, Columbus, Ohio 43204-1105. **T:** 1 614 272-5422
W: http://www.columbusmessenger.com
Freq: Weekly; **Circ:** 118344 Not Audited
News Editor: Andrea Cordle; **News Editor:** Kristy Zurbrick
Editorial Profile: Columbus (OH) Messenger Company produces five biweekly newspapers serving different neighborhoods of Greater Columbus, OH.; Full Page Colour: 1625.00
Currency: US Dollars
NEWSPAPER

Columbus Telegram
Owner: Lee Enterprises, Inc.
Editorial: 1254 27th Ave, Columbus, Nebraska 68601-5656. **T:** 1 402 564-2741
E: col.editor@lee.net
W: http://columbustelegram.com
Freq: Mon thru Fri; **Circ:** 7156 Not Audited
Editorial Profile: Columbus Telegram is dedicated to providing the latest news, sports and advertising to its readers. Since 1879, the paper has delivered news and shopping information to the homes and businesses of East-central Nebraska. Do not send them anything via e-mail.; Full Page Mono: 14.23; Full Page Colour: 292.00
Currency: US Dollars
DAILY NEWSPAPER

The Columbus Times
Owner: Columbus Times
Editorial: 2230 Buena Vista Rd, Columbus, Georgia 31906-3111. **T:** 1 706 324-2404
E: news@columbustimes.com
W: http://www.columbustimes.com
Freq: Wed; **Circ:** 10000 Not Audited
Editor: Ophelia Mitchell
Editorial Profile: The Columbus Times is a weekly publication covering regional, national and international news of minority and race issues for the residents of Columbus, GA and Ft. Benning and Phoenix City, AL. Deadlines are on Mondays at 5pm ET.; Full Page Mono: 21.25; Full Page Colour: 1839.00
Currency: US Dollars
NEWSPAPER

El Colusa News
Editorial: 2550 NW 72nd Ave, Ste 308, Miami, Florida 33122. **T:** 1 786 845-6868
E: info@elcolusa.com
W: http://www.elcolusa.com
Freq: Thu; **Circ:** 27000 Not Audited
Editor: Johanna Amorocho; **Publisher:** Silvana Martinez
Editorial Profile: El Colusa News is a free weekly community newspaper distributed in the Miami area.; Full Page Mono: 10.15
Currency: US Dollars
NEWSPAPER

El Comercio
Owner: Impre Media
Editorial: 10432 Balls Ford Rd Ste 370, Manassas, Virginia 20109-2514.
T: 1 703 393-6388
E: info@elcomercionewspaper.com
W: http://www.elcomercionewspaper.com
Freq: Fri; **Circ:** 50000 Not Audited
Editor: Carlos Aylas; **Publisher:** Ronald Virto
Editorial Profile: El Comercio is a free Spanish-language newspaper written for the Hispanic residents of Manassas, VA and the surrounding areas. It covers local, state, national and international news as well as real estate, entertainment, fashion, design, sports, politics, auto shows and Mamacita de la Semana.; Full Page Mono: 10.00; Full Page Colour: 35.00
Currency: US Dollars
NEWSPAPER

El Comercio de Colorado
Owner: Image Impressions
Editorial: 6805 Broadway, Denver, Colorado 80221-2878. **T:** 1 303 308-9486
E: elcomercio@imageimpressions.com
W: http://www.elcomerciocolorado.com
Freq: Thu; **Circ:** 30000
Editor: Eva Tejada
Editorial Profile: El Comercio de Colorado is a weekly Spanish-language newspaper providing Local and Community News coverage to the

Arvada, Aurora, Boulder, Brighton, Commerce City, Dacono, Denver, Federal Heights, Fort Lupton, Golden, Greeley, Lafayette, Lakewood, Littleton, Longmont, Loveland, Northglenn, Parker, Thornton, Westminster and Wheat Ridge.
NEWSPAPER

The Commercial Appeal
Owner: E.W. Scripps Co.
Editorial: 495 Union Ave, Memphis, Tennessee 38103-3217. **T:** 1 901 529-2345
W: http://www.commercialappeal.com
Freq: Daily; **Circ:** 103957 Not Audited
Editor: Louis Graham
Editorial Profile: The Commercial Appeal is published daily for the residents of Memphis, TN and surrounding areas. The newspaper covers local, national and international news, business, sports, arts & entertainment, technology and stock market listings. The Memphis Commercial (founded in 1889), The Appeal (founded in 1841) and The Avalanche (founded in 1867) consolidated into The Commercial Appeal in 1894.; Full Page Mono: 175.00; Full Page Colour: 202.50
Currency: US Dollars
DAILY NEWSPAPER

The Commercial Appeal
Editorial: 1090 Vermont Ave NW, Washington, District Of Columbia 20005-4905.
T: 1 202 408-2726
DAILY NEWSPAPER

The Commercial Appeal
Editorial: 5959 Pepper Chase Dr, Southaven, Mississippi 38671-7416. **T:** 1 901 333-2020
DAILY NEWSPAPER

Commercial Dispatch
Owner: Imes Jr. (Birney)
Editorial: 516 Main St, Columbus, Mississippi 39701. **T:** 1 662 328-2424
E: news@cdispatch.com
W: http://www.cdispatch.com
Freq: Daily; **Circ:** 12184 Not Audited
Editor: Adam Minichino; **News Editor:** Carmen Sisson
Editorial Profile: Commercial Dispatch provides local news coverage for the Columbus, MS area. It is an afternoon paper which is published daily with the exception of Saturday.; Full Page Mono: 12.90; Full Page Colour: 200.00
Currency: US Dollars
DAILY NEWSPAPER

Commercial Recorder
Owner: Ratcliff Publications, Inc.
Editorial: 3032 S Jones St, Fort Worth, Texas 76104-6747. **T:** 1 817 926-5351
E: recorder@flash.net
W: http://www.comlrec1.site.aplus.net
Freq: Mon thru Fri
Publisher: Genevieve Ratcliff
Editorial Profile: The Commercial Recorder is a daily newspaper providing current court and commercial information. It provides up-to-date court records, public notices, legal transactions, and business leads and business news each weekday.; Full Page Mono: 8.20
Currency: US Dollars
DAILY NEWSPAPER

The Commercial Review
Owner: Graphic Printing Company Inc.
Editorial: 309 W Main St, Portland, Indiana 47371-1803. **T:** 1 260 726-8141
E: cr.news@comcast.net
W: http://www.thecr.com
Freq: Daily; **Circ:** 5000
Publisher & Editor: Jack Ronald
Editorial Profile: The Commercial Review is published for the residents of Portland, IN and surrounding areas. The newspaper covers local and state news, business, sports, education, lifestyles and entertainment.; Full Page Mono: 9.25; Full Page Colour: 255.00
Currency: US Dollars
DAILY NEWSPAPER

Commercial-News
Owner: Community Newspaper Holdings, Inc.
Editorial: 17 W North St, Danville, Illinois 61832-5796. **T:** 1 217 446-1000
E: info@dancomnews.com
W: http://commercial-news.com
Freq: Daily; **Circ:** 10182
Editor: Larry Smith
Editorial Profile: Commercial-News is published daily for the residents of Danville, IL and surrounding areas. The newspaper covers local and regional news, business, sports, lifestyles and entertainment.; Full Page Mono: 20.75; Full Page Colour: 46.75
Currency: US Dollars
DAILY NEWSPAPER

Commonwealth Journal
Owner: Community Newspaper Holdings, Inc.
Editorial: 110-112 E Mount Vernon St, Somerset, Kentucky 42501-1411.
T: 1 606 678-8191
E: news@somerset-kentucky.com
W: http://www.somerset-kentucky.com
Freq: Mon thru Fri; **Circ:** 9700 Not Audited
Publisher: Jack McNeely; **News Editor:** Jeff Neal; **Editor:** Ken Shmidheiser
Editorial Profile: Commonwealth Journal is a daily newspaper published for the residents of Pulaski County, KY. It covers local news and information.; Full Page Mono: 12.75; Full Page Colour: 1797.00
Currency: US Dollars
DAILY NEWSPAPER

Community Advertiser
Editorial: 20 Peter Path, Farmingdale, Maine 4344. **T:** 1 207 582-8486
E: ads@comadvertiser.com
W: http://www.comadvertiser.com
Freq: Mon; **Circ:** 13000 Not Audited
Editorial Profile: The Community Advertiser is a weekly publication, mailed free of charge to every address in several central Maine communities. The publication provides local news coverage. The lead time for Community Advertiser is three days.; Full Page Mono: 7.50; Full Page Colour: 400.00
Currency: US Dollars
NEWSPAPER

Community Advocate
Owner: Community Advocate, Inc.
Editorial: 32 South St, Westborough, Massachusetts 1581. **T:** 1 508 366-5500
E: news@communityadvocate.com
W: http://www.communityadvocate.com
Freq: Fri; **Circ:** 19000 Not Audited
Editor: Kathy Behan
Editorial Profile: Community Advocate is a weekly community newspaper serving Westborough, MA.; Full Page Mono: 12.95
Currency: US Dollars
NEWSPAPER

Community Common
Owner: Heartland Publications
Editorial: 637 6th St., Portsmouth, Ohio 45662. **T:** 1 740 353-1151
E: ccnews@communitycommon.com
W: http://www.communitycommon.com
Freq: Sun; **Circ:** 36700 Not Audited
Editorial Profile: Community Common provides local news for the Ohio and Kentucky areas. Coverage includes local news and events, business, politics and social issues.; Full Page Mono: 15.50; Full Page Colour: 1768.50
Currency: US Dollars
NEWSPAPER

Community Courier
Editorial: 92 E Main St Ste 202, Somerville, New Jersey 08876-2319. **T:** 1 908 243-6630
Freq: Thu; **Circ:** 49000
Editor: Paul Grzella
Editorial Profile: Community Courier is written for the residents of Somerville County, NJ.; Full Page Mono: 16.00
Currency: US Dollars
NEWSPAPER

Community Impact Newspaper - Austin
Owner: John Garrett and Jennifer Garrett
Editorial: 821 Grand Avenue Pkwy Bldg 4, Pflugerville, Texas 78660-2196.
T: 1 512 989-6808 **E:** press@impactnews.com
W: http://www.impactnews.com **Circ:** 702773
Editor: Brett Thorne
NEWSPAPER

Community Impact Newspaper - Dallas-Fort Worth
Owner: John Garrett and Jennifer Garrett
Editorial: 1452 Hughes Rd Ste 323, Grapevine, Texas 76051-7369.
T: 1 682 223-1418
W: http://www.impactnews.com/dfw-metro
Editorial Profile: Community Impact Newspapers, of Grapevine, TX, publishes 13 community newspapers around Houston, Dallas and Austin, providing localized news to the surrounding communities.
NEWSPAPER

Community Impact Newspaper - Houston
Owner: John Garrett and Jennifer Garrett
Editorial: 8400 N Sam Houston Pkwy W Ste 220, Houston, Texas 77064-3462.
T: 1 218 469-6181
E: pressdesk@impactnews.com
W: http://www.impactnews.com/houston-metro
Publisher: Jason Culpepper; **Editor:** Marie Leonard
NEWSPAPER

Community Journals
Editorial: 148 River St, Ste 120, Greenville, South Carolina 29601. **T:** 1 864 467-9070
E: news@communityjournals.com
W: http://www.communityjournals.com
Circ: 65551 Not Audited
Editor: Susan Clary Simmons; **Publisher:** Mark Johnston
Editorial Profile: Community Journals in Greenville, SC publishes the Spartanburg (SC) Journal and the Greenville Journal.
NEWSPAPER

Community Media Group- Kentland
Owner: Community Media Group
Editorial: 305 E Graham St, Kentland, Indiana 47951. **T:** 1 219 474-5532
W: http://www.newtoncountyenterprise.com
Circ: 3176 Not Audited
Publisher: John Perrotto
NEWSPAPER

Community Media NYC
Owner: Community Media, LLC
Editorial: 515 Canal St Unit 1C, New York, New York 10013-1330. **T:** 1 212 229-1890
W: http://www.communitymediallc.com
Circ: 121000 Not Audited
Editor: Lincoln Anderson; **Editor:** Lincoln Anderson; **Publisher:** Jennifer Goodstein; **Editor:** Josh Rogers
NEWSPAPER

Community Media of Colorado-Englewood
Owner: ASP Westward LP
Editorial: 9137 Ridgeline Blvd Ste 210, Highlands Ranch, Colorado 80129-2394.
T: 1 303 566-4100
E: pressreleases@ourcoloradonews.com
W: http://www.ourcoloradonews.com
Circ: 46500 Not Audited
Publisher: Jim Diaz
NEWSPAPER

Community Media of Colorado-Woodland
Owner: ASP Westward LP
Editorial: 1200 E US Highway 24, Woodland Park, Colorado 80863-9213.
T: 1 719 687-3006
W: http://coloradocommunitynewspapers.com
Circ: 18000 Not Audited
NEWSPAPER

Community Media Publishing Co.
Editorial: 403 Warren Ave, Caruthersville, Missouri 63830-1417. **T:** 1 573 333-4336
E: news@democratargus.com **Circ:** 15300 Not Audited
Editor: Herb Smith; **Publisher:** David Tenyson
NEWSPAPER

The Community Merchant
Owner: Ohio Community Media LLC.
Editorial: 1451 N Vandemark Rd, Sidney, Ohio 45365-3547. **T:** 1 937 498-8088
W: http://www.sidneydailynews.com
Freq: Mon; **Circ:** 12000 Not Audited
News Editor: Melanie Speicher; **News Editor:** Melanie Speicher; **News Editor:** Melanie Speicher; **News Editor:** Melanie Speicher
Editorial Profile: The Community Merchant is a free, weekly newspaper published by the Sidney Daily News. It is mailed directly to households in and around Sidney and Wapakoneta, OH, including portions of Shelby, Auglaize, Champaign and Logan counties. In addition to offering expanded market opportunities for advertisers, the paper also provided news and entertainment features if interest to local readers. Each issue includes human-interest articles, a review of local news highlights and previews of stories slated to appear in upcoming issues of the Sidney Daily News. Deadlines are Thursdays at 5pm ET prior to distribution.; Full Page Mono: 8.00
Currency: US Dollars
NEWSPAPER

Community News
Owner: Journal Register Company
Editorial: 20 Lake Ave, Saratoga Springs, New York 12866-2314. **T:** 1 518 583-8729
E: cnews@saratogian.com
W: http://www.cnweekly.com
Freq: Fri; **Circ:** 28501 Not Audited
Editor: Charlie Kraebel; **Publisher:** Michael O'Sullivan
Editorial Profile: Community News in Saratoga Springs, NY is written for residents of Southern Saratoga County, NY.; Full Page Mono: 25.58
Currency: US Dollars
NEWSPAPER

Community News
Editorial: 352 W Foothill Blvd, Glendora, California 91741. **T:** 1 626 914-7945
E: glencomnews@yahoo.com
W: http://www.glendoracommunitynews.com
Circ: 35500 Not Audited
NEWSPAPER

Community News Network
Owner: Community News Network, Inc.
Editorial: 6 S Haddon Ave, Haddonfield, New Jersey 8033. **T:** 1 856 428-3399
W: http://news.mywebpal.com/index.cfm?pnpid=292 **Circ:** 22000
Publisher: David Hunter
NEWSPAPER

Community News Newspapers
Owner: Huneke Publications Inc.
Editorial: 2139 Bryan Valley Commercial Dr, O'Fallon, Missouri 63366. **T:** 1 636 379-1775
E: info@mycnews.com
W: http://www.mycnews.com
Freq: Wed; **Circ:** 57000 Not Audited
Publisher: Robert Huneke; **Editor:** Andrew Tessmer; Full Page Mono: 65.00
Currency: US Dollars
NEWSPAPER

Community News Publications
Owner: Manatee Media Inc.
Editorial: 1930 Land O Lakes Blvd Ste 14, Lutz, Florida 33549-2924. **T:** 1 813 909-2800
E: news@cnewspubs.com
W: http://www.cnewspubs.com **Circ:** 100000 Not Audited
Editorial Profile: Community News Publications in Land O'Lakes, FL is a community newspaper publisher.
NEWSPAPER

Community News Service
Owner: Community News Service LLC
Editorial: 2 Princess Rd, Lawrenceville, New Jersey 08648-2320. **T:** 1 609 396-1511
E: info@mercerspace.com
W: http://www.communitynewsnj.com
Circ: 72000 Not Audited
NEWSPAPER

Community Newspaper Holdings Inc. - Oak Hill
Editorial: 417 Main St W, Oak Hill, West Virginia 25901. **T:** 1 304 469-3373 **Circ:** 5500 Not Audited
Editor: Cheryl Keenan; **Publisher:** Frank Wood
NEWSPAPER

Community Newspapers
Editorial: 6 Central St, Moravia, New York 13118. **T:** 1 315 497-1551
E: comnewsmoravia@yahoo.com
Freq: Wed; **Circ:** 14406 Not Audited
Editorial Profile: Please send all press releases via the P.O. Box.; Full Page Mono: 9.95
Currency: US Dollars
NEWSPAPER

Community Newspapers - Lavonia
Owner: Community Newspapers, Inc.
Editorial: 12150 Augusta Rd, Lavonia, Georgia 30553-1208. **T:** 1 706 356-8557
W: http://www.franklincountycitizen.com
Circ: 6100
NEWSPAPER

Community Newspapers-Lake Oswego
Owner: Community Newspapers Inc.
Editorial: 400 2nd St, Lake Oswego, Oregon 97034. **T:** 1 503 635-8811
E: email@lakeoswegoreview.com
W: http://www.lakeoswegoreview.com
Circ: 10400
Editor: Martin Forbes; **Publisher:** Brian Monihan
NEWSPAPER

Community Press & Recorder - East/Northeast Group
Owner: Gannett Co., Inc.
Editorial: 394 Wards Corner Rd Suite 170, Loveland, Ohio 45140-8339.
T: 1 513 248-8600
W: http://www.communitypress.com
Circ: 113568 Not Audited
Editor: Dick Maloney; **Editor:** Eric Spangler
NEWSPAPER

The Community Press & Recorder - Northern Kentucky
Owner: Gannett Co., Inc.
Editorial: 228 Grandview Dr #B, Fort Mitchell, Kentucky 41017-2702. **T:** 1 859 283-0404
E: kynews@communitypress.com
W: http://www.communitypress.com
Circ: 67027 Not Audited
Editorial Profile: The Community Press & Recorder - Northern Kentucky publishes the following weekly community newspapers: Campbell Community Recorder; Campbell County Recorder; Boone County Recorder, the Alexandria Recorder; the Boone Community Recorder; the Fort Thomas Recorder; South Kenton Recorder; the Florence Recorder; the Union Recorder and Community Now.
NEWSPAPER

Community Press & Recorder - West/Northwest Group
Owner: Gannett Co., Inc.
Editorial: 5556 Cheviot Rd, Cincinnati, Ohio 45247-5202. **T:** 1 513 923-3111
W: http://communitypress.cincinnati.com
Freq: Weekly; **Circ:** 63868 Not Audited
NEWSPAPER

Community Times
Owner: Landmark Community Newspapers, Inc.
Editorial: 201 Railroad Ave, Westminster, Maryland 21157. **T:** 1 410 875-5449
E: ctimes@lcniofmd.com
W: http://www.carrollcountytimes.com/community_times
Freq: Wed; **Circ:** 13000 Not Audited
Publisher: Pat Richardson
Editorial Profile: Community Times is published weekly for the residents of Westminster, MD and surrounding areas. The newspaper covers local news, government, education, business and community events.; Full Page Mono: 13.25; Full Page Colour: 2047.00
Currency: US Dollars
NEWSPAPER

The Community Times
Owner: BBS Communications
Editorial: 430 W Cheves St, Florence, South Carolina 29501. **T:** 1 843 667-1818
W: http://www.scvillagevoices.com
Freq: Thu; **Circ:** 36000 Not Audited
Publisher: Diana Smith
Editorial Profile: The Community Times is a local newspaper written for the African American community of Florence, SC. The paper covers local news.; Full Page Mono: 16.00; Full Page Colour: 1648.00
Currency: US Dollars
NEWSPAPER

The Compass
Owner: QOL Publications
Editorial: 24 Opera House Sq, Claremont, New Hampshire 03743-5408. **T:** 1 603 287-4016
E: news@compasspaper.com
W: http://www.compasspaper.com
Freq: Thu; **Circ:** 10000
Publisher: Lee Gohndrow
Editorial Profile: The Compass is a weekly community newspaper that serves Claremont, Springfield, Newport, Windsor and Charlestown, NH as well as surrounding towns.; Full Page Mono: 4.23
Currency: US Dollars
NEWSPAPER

The Compton Bulletin/Carson Bulletin/Wilmington Beacon/The Californian
Owner: American Print Media
Editorial: 800 E Compton Blvd, Compton, California 90221. **T:** 1 310 635-6776
W: http://www.thecomptonbulletin.com
Freq: Wed; **Circ:** 75000 Not Audited
Editor: Chris Frost
Editorial Profile: The Compton Bulletin/Carson Bulletin/Wilmington Beacon/The Californian is a weekly newspaper that provides local news coverage for residents in the Compton, Carson and Wilmington, CA area. It covers news relating to politics, business, social issues and community events. Advertising deadlines are at 3pm PT.; Full Page Mono: 35.00; Full Page Colour: 250.00
Currency: US Dollars
NEWSPAPER

Comunidade News
Editorial: 155 Main St, Ste 212, Danbury, Connecticut 06810-7844. **T:** 1 203 748-0123
E: info@comunidadenews.com
W: http://www.comunidadenews.com
Freq: Tue; **Circ:** 80000

Editorial Profile: Offers news and events to the Brazilian and Portuguese language communities of Connecticut, New Jersey and New York.; Full Page Mono: 10.20
Currency: US Dollars
NEWSPAPER

Concord Monitor
Owner: Newspapers of New England
Editorial: 1 Monitor Dr, Concord, New Hampshire 03301-1834. **T:** 1 603 224-5301
E: news@cmonitor.com
W: http://www.concordmonitor.com
Freq: Daily; **Circ:** 19885 Not Audited
Ideas & Opinion Editor: Felice Belman; **City Editor:** Annmarie Timmins; **Publisher:** Mark Travis; **Editor:** Jen VanPelt
Editorial Profile: Concord Monitor is a local daily newspaper serving Concord, NH and the surrounding areas. It covers local, state, New England, national and world news. The paper also covers politics, opinion, sports, business news, arts & entertainment and community news, including wedding, birth and engagement announcements.; Full Page Mono: 16.75; Full Page Colour: 330.00
Currency: US Dollars
DAILY NEWSPAPER

Concordia Blade-Empire
Owner: Blade-Empire Publishing Co. Inc.
Editorial: 510 Washington St, Concordia, Kansas 66901-2117. **T:** 1 785 243-2424
E: bladeempire@nckcn.com
W: http://www.bladeempire.com
Freq: Daily; **Circ:** 3000 Not Audited
Editor: Sharon Coy; **Publisher & Editor:** Brad Lowell
Editorial Profile: Concordia Blade-Empire is a daily publication that provides local news and sports coverage for the Concordia, KS area. Deadlines are at 2pm CT.; Full Page Mono: 5.35; Full Page Colour: 70.00
Currency: US Dollars
DAILY NEWSPAPER

Condo News
Editorial: 2827 Exchange Ct Ste C, West Palm Beach, Florida 33409-4000. **T:** 1 561 471-0329
E: info@condonewsonline.com
W: http://www.condonewsonline.com
Freq: Bi-Weekly; **Circ:** 13000 Not Audited
Editor: Betty Thomas; **Publisher:** C.E. Tzoumas
Editorial Profile: Condo News is distributed to condominium complex clubhouses in Palm Beach County, FL. It provides local news coverage. Regular features include Food Fun & Entertainment, Out & About, and Fit after Fifty. It is a socially oriented newspaper featuring news supplied by correspondents from the various communities. The lead time for editorial submissions falls on Friday prior to publication date.; Full Page Mono: 13.25
Currency: US Dollars
NEWSPAPER

Conexion
Owner: Hearst Newspapers
Editorial: Ave E & 3rd St, San Antonio, Texas 78205. **T:** 1 210 250-2535
W: http://www.conexionsa.com
Freq: Thu; **Circ:** 50000 Not Audited
Editorial Profile: Conexion in San Antonio, TX is a weekly bicultural publication that targets Hispanic and bicultural households in south Texas. It is published by the San Antonio Express-News. Advertising and news submissions must be received by 5pm CT.; Full Page Mono: 34.36
Currency: US Dollars
NEWSPAPER

Connect Savannah
Editorial: 1800 E Victory Dr Ste 7, Savannah, Georgia 31404-4195. **T:** 1 912 238-2040
W: http://www.connectsavannah.com
Editor in Chief: Jim Morekis
Editorial Profile: Connect Savannah is a weekly community newspaper serving the residents of Savannah, GA. It covers a range of topics including News, Entertainment, Music, Film and Culture.
NEWSPAPER

Connecticut Post
Owner: Hearst Corporation
Editorial: 410 State St, Bridgeport, Connecticut 06604-4501. **T:** 1 203 333-0161
E: edit@ctpost.com **W:** http://www.ctpost.com
Freq: Daily; **Circ:** 37778 Not Audited
Publisher: Henry B. Haitz; **News Editor:** Linda Levinson
Editorial Profile: Connecticut Post is a daily paper written for southwestern Connecticut. It covers local and national news, sports and

entertainment.; Full Page Mono: 118.50; Full Page Colour: 2238.19
Currency: US Dollars
DAILY NEWSPAPER

The Connection Newspapers
Editorial: 1606 King St, Alexandria, Virginia 22314-2719. **T:** 1 703 821-5050
E: info@connectionnewspapers.com
W: http://www.connectionnewspapers.com
Circ: 155439 Not Audited
Publisher: Mary Kimm; **Editor in Chief:** Steve Mauren; **Editor in Chief:** Steve Mauren; **Editor in Chief:** Steve Mauren; **Editor in Chief:** Steve Mauren; **Editor:** Michael O'Connell
NEWSPAPER

Connersville News-Examiner
Owner: Paxton Media Group
Editorial: 406 N Central Ave, Connersville, Indiana 47331-1926. **T:** 1 765 825-0581
E: newsexaminer@newsexaminer.com
W: http://www.newsexaminer.com
Freq: Daily; **Circ:** 6500 Not Audited
Publisher: Rachael Raney
Editorial Profile: Connersville News-Examiner is a daily newspaper based in Connersville, IN. The publication covers local, state and national news.; Full Page Mono: 17.96; Full Page Colour: 225.00
Currency: US Dollars
DAILY NEWSPAPER

El Conquistador
Editorial: 4531 W Forest Home Ave, Milwaukee, Wisconsin 53219-4837.
T: 1 414 383-1000
E: conquistador@bizwi.rr.com
W: http://spanishelconquistador.com/
Freq: Fri; **Circ:** 15000 Not Audited
Editorial Profile: El Conquistador is a weekly Hispanic newspaper writting for the residents of Milwaukee, WI. It covers local news, health, home politics, sports culture and arts & entertainment.; Full Page Mono: 12.00; Full Page Colour: 13.72
Currency: US Dollars
NEWSPAPER

Conroe Courier
Owner: Houston Community Newspapers
Editorial: 100 Avenue A, Conroe, Texas 77301-2946. **T:** 1 936 521-3300
E: couriernews@hcnonline.com
W: http://www.yourhoustonnews.com/courier/
Freq: Daily; **Circ:** 9562 Not Audited
Editorial Profile: Conroe Courier provides local news, community news, sports and events information for the residents of Conroe, TX.; Full Page Mono: 18.00; Full Page Colour: 250.00
Currency: US Dollars
DAILY NEWSPAPER

Conservative Publishing, Co.
Owner: Conservative Publishing Co.
Editorial: 124 W 5th St, Tipton, Iowa 52772.
T: 1 563 886-2131
W: http://www.tiptonconservative.com
Circ: 5200 Not Audited
Editorial Profile: Conservative Publishing, Co. is a local newspaper for the community of Tipton, IA.
NEWSPAPER

Continental
Editorial: 200 49Th St, Union City, New Jersey 07087-7727. **T:** 1 201 864-9505
E: continews@aol.com
Freq: Mon; **Circ:** 38000 Not Audited
Publisher: Ofelia Dones
Editorial Profile: Continental is a weekly Spanish newspaper serving the Hispanic community of Union City, NJ. The newspaper covers local news, arts & entertainment, health and general interest topics.; Full Page Mono: 35.00
Currency: US Dollars
NEWSPAPER

Contra Costa Times
Owner: MediaNews Group
Editorial: 175 Lennon Ln Ste 100, Walnut Creek, California 94598-2466.
T: 1 925 935-2525
E: ccnnewsrelease@bayareanewsgroup.com
W: http://www.contracostatimes.com
Freq: Daily; **Circ:** 146999 Not Audited
Editorial Profile: Contra Costa Times is a daily newspaper for residents in Northern California. It covers breaking news, features, profiles, trends, news analyses and investigative stories. The paper is a part of the Bay Area News Group subsidiary of MediaNews Group.; Full Page Mono: 57.00; Full Page Colour: 1134.60
Currency: US Dollars

DAILY NEWSPAPER

The Conway Daily Sun
Owner: Country News Club, Inc.
Editorial: 64 Seavey St, North Conway, New Hampshire 03860-5355. **T:** 1 603 356-3456
E: dailysun@conwaydailysun.com
W: http://www.mountwashingtonvalley.com
Freq: Daily; **Circ:** 14400 Not Audited
Publisher: Mark Guerringue; **Editor:** Adam Hirshan
Editorial Profile: The Conway Daily Sun is a daily newspaper serving the community of Mount Washington Valley, NH. The publication covers news, with a special focus on the North Conway, NH region. Deadlines are one day prior to the issue date at noon ET.; Full Page Mono: 7.00; Full Page Colour: 25.25
Currency: US Dollars
DAILY NEWSPAPER

Co-op City Times
Owner: Riverbay Corporation
Editorial: 2049 Bartow Ave, Rm 21, Bronx, New York 10475-4613. **T:** 1 718 320-3375
Freq: Sat; **Circ:** 18000 Not Audited
Editorial Profile: Co-op City Times is a weekly newspaper written for the residents of Co-op City, NY.; Full Page Mono: 5.45
Currency: US Dollars
NEWSPAPER

Copper Area News Publishers
Owner: Copper Area News Publishers
Editorial: 366 Alden Rd, Kearny, Arizona 85137-9900. **T:** 1 520 363-5554
E: editor@minersunbasin.com
W: http://www.copperarea.com **Circ:** 13800 Not Audited
Publisher: James Carnes
Editorial Profile: Copper Area News Publishers is a local newspaper providing the community of Kearny, AZ with news.
NEWSPAPER

Copper Country News
Owner: Calico Ent. LLC
Editorial: 1776 E Ash St, Globe, Arizona 85501. **T:** 1 928 425-0355
E: globeccn@yahoo.com
W: http://www.coppercountrynews.com
Freq: Wed; **Circ:** 20000 Not Audited
Editorial Profile: The Copper Country News is a local newspaper serving Globe, AZ.; Full Page Mono: 12.95
Currency: US Dollars
NEWSPAPER

Cordele Dispatch
Owner: Community Newspaper Holdings, Inc.
Editorial: 306 W 13th Ave, Cordele, Georgia 31015. **T:** 1 229 273-2277
W: http://cordeledispatch.com
Freq: Daily; **Circ:** 5000 Not Audited
Publisher & Editor: Peggy King
Editorial Profile: Cordele Dispatch is a local newspaper written for residents of Cordele, GA. It covers local news, sports and events in the area.; Full Page Mono: 16.50; Full Page Colour: 56.70
Currency: US Dollars
DAILY NEWSPAPER

Core Media Group, Inc.
Owner: Core Media Group Inc.
Editorial: 125 E Chestnut Ave, Monrovia, California 91016-3411. **T:** 1 626 301-1010
E: editorial@coremg.net
W: http://www.coremg.net **Circ:** 28000 Not Audited
Editor: Terry Miller; **Publisher:** Von Raees
NEWSPAPER

CornerStone Media
Owner: CornerStone Media
Editorial: 120 W. North St., Peotone, Illinois 60468. **T:** 1 708 258-3473
E: newsdesk@cornerstone-media.net
W: http://russell-publications.com
Freq: Thu; **Circ:** 16850; Full Page Mono: 7.25
Currency: US Dollars
NEWSPAPER

Corpus Christi Caller-Times
Owner: E.W. Scripps Co.
Editorial: 820 N Lower Broadway St, Corpus Christi, Texas 78401-2025. **T:** 1 361 884-2011
E: metrodesk@caller.com
W: http://www.caller.com
Freq: Daily; **Circ:** 41195 Not Audited
Publisher: Darrell Coleman
Editorial Profile: Corpus Christi Caller-Times was founded in 1883. It is a daily publication. It was taken over by the Scripps-Howard group in 1997. It provides Corpus Christi, TX and its surrounding communities with local, regional, national and international news. It

also covers sports, arts & entertainment, business and special reports.; Full Page Mono: 188.67; Full Page Colour: 280.32
Currency: US Dollars
DAILY NEWSPAPER

El Correo - New York Bureau
Editorial: 405 E 42nd St, United Nations, New York, New York 10017-3507.
T: 1 212 935-1964
Editorial Profile: This is the New York bureau of El Correo in Spain.
DAILY NEWSPAPER

Corriere Della Sera - New York Bureau
Editorial: 31 W 57th St, 4th Floor, New York, New York 10019. **T:** 1 212 308-2000
W: http://www.corriere.it
Freq: Daily
Editorial Profile: New York bureau of the national newspaper Corriere della Sera covering regional, national and international news and current affairs including business, politics, economics, society, sports, culture, entertainment, health, education, science, technology, motoring, travel, home and lifestyle.
DAILY NEWSPAPER

Corry Journal
Owner: Sample News Group
Editorial: 28 W South St, Corry, Pennsylvania 16407-1810. **T:** 1 814 665-8291
E: corryjournal@tbscc.com
W: http://www.thecorryjournal.com
Freq: Daily; **Circ:** 4100 Not Audited
City Editor: Maryann Mook
Editorial Profile: Corry Journal is published daily for the residents of Corry, PA and surrounding areas. The newspaper covers local and state news, business, sports, lifestyles and entertainment.; Full Page Mono: 8.00; Full Page Colour: 9.50
Currency: US Dollars
DAILY NEWSPAPER

Corsicana Daily Sun
Owner: Community Newspapers Holdings, Inc.
Editorial: 405 E Collin St, Corsicana, Texas 75110-5325. **T:** 1 903 872-3931
E: dailysun@corsicanadailysun.com
W: http://corsicanadailysun.com
Freq: Daily; **Circ:** 3962 Not Audited
City Editor: Janet Jacobs; **Publisher:** Raymond Linex
Editorial Profile: Corsicana Daily Sun is the daily newspaper for Corsicana, TX. Sections include local news, world news, sports, lifestyle, business and arts & entertainment.; Full Page Mono: 13.50; Full Page Colour: 300.00
Currency: US Dollars
DAILY NEWSPAPER

Cortland Standard
Owner: Cortland Standard Printing Company, Inc.
Editorial: 110 Main St, Cortland, New York 13045-6607. **T:** 1 607 756-5665
E: news@cortlandstandard.net
W: http://www.cortlandstandard.net
Freq: Daily; **Circ:** 10120 Not Audited
Editor: Skip Chapman; **Publisher:** Kevin Howe
Editorial Profile: Cortland Standard is a local newspaper for residents of Cortland County, NY. The publication offers coverage of local news, weather and sports. Deadlines are at 12:30pm ET the day before issue date.; Full Page Mono: 10.70; Full Page Colour: 270.00
Currency: US Dollars
DAILY NEWSPAPER

Corvallis Gazette-Times
Owner: Lee Enterprises, Inc.
Editorial: 600 SW Jefferson Ave, Corvallis, Oregon 97333-4510. **T:** 1 541 753-2641
E: news@gazettetimes.com
W: http://www.gazettetimes.com
Freq: Daily; **Circ:** 11075 Not Audited
News Editor: Paul Davies; **City Editor:** Theresa Novak
Editorial Profile: Corvallis Gazette-Times is a daily newspaper for the residents of Mid-Willamette Valley in Oregon. The publication is a general newspaper that contains the sections news, sports, business, leisure, opinion, calendar, and classified ads. National and international news is provided by the Associated Press. Contact the publication for the advertising rates and editorial submission guidelines.; Full Page Mono: 34.85; Full Page Colour: 375.00
Currency: US Dollars
DAILY NEWSPAPER

Coshocton Tribune
Owner: Gannett Co., Inc.
Editorial: 550 Main St, Coshocton, Ohio 43812. **T:** 1 740 622-1122
E: coshocton@nncogannett.com
W: http://www.coshoctontribune.com
Freq: Daily; **Circ:** 3688 Not Audited
Editorial Profile: Coshocton Tribune is a daily newspaper written for the residents of Coshocton, OH and the surrounding area. The publication covers local and regional news.; Full Page Mono: 15.52; Full Page Colour: 175.00
Currency: US Dollars
DAILY NEWSPAPER

The Coulter Press
Owner: Henry (John)
Editorial: 156 Church St, Clinton, Massachusetts 01510-2506.
T: 1 978 368-0176
W: http://www.telegram.com/section/coulter
Freq: Fri; **Circ:** 6200 Not Audited
Publisher: Gary Hutner; Full Page Mono: 18.00
Currency: US Dollars
NEWSPAPER

Council Grove Republican
Editorial: 208 W Main St, Council Grove, Kansas 66846. **T:** 1 620 767-5123
E: cgnews@cgtelco.net
Freq: Daily; **Circ:** 2100 Not Audited
Editor: Craig McNeal
Editorial Profile: Council Grove Republican is a local newspaper serving the Morris County, KS community. It covers local news and area events.; Full Page Mono: 5.55; Full Page Colour: 55.00
Currency: US Dollars
DAILY NEWSPAPER

Country Gazette
Owner: GateHouse Media Inc.
Editorial: 159 S Main St, Milford, Massachusetts 1757. **T:** 1 508 634-7500
E: gazette@wickedlocal.com
W: http://www.wickedlocal.com/bellingham
Freq: Fri; **Circ:** 31030 Not Audited
Editor: Heather McCarron
Editorial Profile: Country Gazette is a free, weekly newspaper serving residents of Millford, Bellingham, Franklin, Foxboro, Wrentham, Medway, Millis and Norfolk, MA and surrounding areas. It covers local news and events. Advertising deadlines are on Tuesdays at 3pm ET.; Full Page Mono: 41.25; Full Page Colour: 100.00
Currency: US Dollars
NEWSPAPER

The Country Today
Owner: Eau Claire Press Company
Editorial: 701 S Farwell St, Eau Claire, Wisconsin 54701. **T:** 1 715 833-9270
E: thecountrytoday@ecpc.com
W: http://www.thecountrytoday.com
Freq: Wed; **Circ:** 22602 Not Audited
Publisher: Pieter Graaskamp; **Editor:** Jim Massey
Editorial Profile: The Country Today is an agricultural newspaper focusing on farming industry news and trends. It also covers general agricultural business and the rural lifestyle.; Full Page Mono: 19.71
Currency: US Dollars
NEWSPAPER

The County News
Editorial: 211 S Center St, Ste 307, Statesville, North Carolina 28677-5873.
T: 1 704 873-1054
Freq: Wed; **Circ:** 12000
Editorial Profile: The County News is a newspaper published on Wednesdays. It caters to the African American population in Iredell County, NC. It provides county news, government, sports and features of interest to readers in the area.; Full Page Mono: 20.00; Full Page Colour: 75.00
Currency: US Dollars
NEWSPAPER

The County Press & County Line Reminder
Owner: JAMS Media
Editorial: 1521 Imlay City Rd, Lapeer, Michigan 48446-3175. **T:** 1 810 664-0811
E: editor@mihomepaper.com **Circ:** 23452
News Editor: Jeff Hogan
NEWSPAPER

County Press Enterprises
Owner: County Press Enterprises LLC
Editorial: 208 S Central St, Ferris, Texas 75125-2622. **T:** 1 972 544-2369

Editorial Profile: County Press Enterprises is a community newspaper publisher producing the weekly papers Ellis County Press and Red Oak Record.
NEWSPAPER

County Press Newspapers
Owner: JAMS Media
Editorial: 529 N. Port Crescent Rd., Bad Axe, Michigan 48413. **T:** 1 989 269-9918
E: hcpeditor@mihomepaper.com
W: http://huroncountyview.mihomepaper.com
Circ: 27736 Not Audited
Editor: Kelly Jerome; **Publisher:** Jane Vanderpoel
NEWSPAPER

The County Seat
Editorial: 77 Hudson St, Hackensack, New Jersey 07601-6947. **T:** 1 201 488-5795
E: info@cntyseat.com
W: http://www.cntyseat.com
Freq: Monthly; **Circ:** 35000 Not Audited
Publisher: Gail Zisa; **Editor in Chief:** Lauren Zisa
Editorial Profile: The County Seat is a community newspaper serving Hackensack, South Hackensack, Maywood, Rochelle Park, Paramus, Little Ferry, Teaneck and Teterboro, NJ and the surrounding areas with local news and community events.; Full Page Mono: 26.75
Currency: US Dollars
NEWSPAPER

County Times
Owner: Southern Maryland Publishing
Editorial: 43251 Rescue Lane, Hollywood, Maryland 20636. **T:** 1 301 373-4125
E: news@countytimes.net
W: http://countytimes.somd.com
Freq: Thu; **Circ:** 10000 Not Audited
Publisher: Thomas McKay; **Editor:** Sean Rice
Editorial Profile: County Times is a locally owned and operated newspaper that serves the St. Mary's County, MD area. Published weekly, the paper reports the news as it happens while focusing strongly on the local community.; Full Page Mono: 7.26
Currency: US Dollars
NEWSPAPER

The Courier
Owner: Paxton Media Group
Editorial: 201 E 2nd St, Russellville, Arkansas 72801-5102. **T:** 1 479 968-5252
E: newsclerk@couriernews.com
W: http://www.couriernews.com
Freq: Daily; **Circ:** 9358 Not Audited
News Editor: Adam Franks; **News Editor:** Adam Franks; **Publisher:** David Meadows
Editorial Profile: The Courier is a daily newspaper published for the residents of Russellville, AR and surrounding communities. The publication covers local news, sports, lifestyles and community events.; Full Page Mono: 15.15; Full Page Colour: 325.00
Currency: US Dollars
DAILY NEWSPAPER

The Courier
Owner: GateHouse Media Inc.
Editorial: 2201 Woodlawn Rd, Ste 350, Lincoln, Illinois 62656-9645.
T: 1 217 732-2101
E: courier@lincolncourier.com
W: http://www.lincolncourier.com
Freq: Daily; **Circ:** 5623 Not Audited
Publisher: Greg Baumer
Editorial Profile: The Courier is published daily for the residents of Lincoln, IL and surrounding areas. The newspaper covers local news, sports, business, education and community events.; Full Page Mono: 14.88; Full Page Colour: 256.00
Currency: US Dollars
DAILY NEWSPAPER

The Courier
Owner: Halifax Media Holdings LLC
Editorial: 3030 Barrow St, Houma, Louisiana 70360-7641. **T:** 1 985 857-2222
E: news@houmatoday.com
W: http://www.houmatoday.com
Freq: Daily; **Circ:** 11598
Publisher: Miles Forrest
Editorial Profile: The Courier is published daily for the residents of Houma, LA and surrounding areas. The newspaper provides information on local and national news, business, sports and lifestyles. All advertising appeas in both The Courier and The Daily Comet.; Full Page Mono: 43.91; Full Page Colour: 468.00
Currency: US Dollars
DAILY NEWSPAPER

The Courier
Owner: Findlay Publishing Company (The)
Editorial: 701 W Sandusky St, Findlay, Ohio 45840-2325. **T:** 1 419 422-5151
E: news@thecourier.com
W: http://www.thecourier.com
Freq: Daily; **Circ:** 20878 Not Audited
Publisher: Karl Heminger; **City Editor:** Kurt Leonard; **Editor:** Peter Mattiace; **Editor:** Randy Roberts
Editorial Profile: The Courier is writen for residents of northwest Ohio. It covers local news, sports, editorial and community events. Deadlines are 11pm ET the day before publication.; Full Page Mono: 16.45; Full Page Colour: 240.00
Currency: US Dollars
DAILY NEWSPAPER

The Courier
Owner: Diocese of Winona
Editorial: 55 W Sanborn St, Winona, Minnesota 55987-3655. **T:** 1 507 454-4643
E: keich@dow.org **W:** http://www.dow.org
Freq: Monthly; **Circ:** 42000 Not Audited
Editor: Joel Hennessy; **Publisher:** John Quinn
Editorial Profile: The Courier is a monthly newspaper of the Diocese of Winona written for the residents of Winona, MN and surrounding communities.; Full Page Mono: 21.40
Currency: US Dollars
NEWSPAPER

Courier Journal
Owner: Colbert Courier, Inc.
Editorial: 1828 Darby Dr, Florence, Alabama 35630. **T:** 1 256 764-4268
E: editor@courierjournal.net
W: http://www.courierjournal.net
Freq: Wed; **Circ:** 68162 Not Audited
Editorial Profile: Courier Journal is a weekly advertising newspaper serving the consumers of Northwestern Alabama. The publication only runs advertising, and does not regularly publish articles. The lead time is one week and deadlines are one week prior to publication.; Full Page Mono: 12.25; Full Page Colour: 1245.00
Currency: US Dollars
NEWSPAPER

The Courier MAX!
Owner: Community Newspaper Holdings, Inc.
Editorial: 213 E 2Nd St, Ottumwa, Iowa 52501-2902. **T:** 1 641 684-4611
E: news@ottumwacourier.com
W: http://www.ottumwacourier.com
Freq: Mon thru Fri; **Circ:** 22500 Not Audited
Publisher: Martin Cody
Editorial Profile: The Courier MAX! is a free weekly newspaper created and distributed by the Ottumwa (IA) Courier. The MAX, which stands for Maximum Audience eXposure, provides news and advertising to residents and businesses in the Ottumwa, IA area. It attempts to reach non-subscribers of the daily newspaper. Advertising rates are based on the Courier's rates plus an additional charge for the greater readership. Advertising within the MAX! must also run in the Courier.; Full Page Mono: 20.25
Currency: US Dollars
NEWSPAPER

The Courier News
Owner: Gannett Co., Inc.
Editorial: 92 E Main St, Ste 202, Somerville, New Jersey 08876-2319. **T:** 1 908 243-6600
E: cnmetro@mycentraljersey.com
W: http://www.mycentraljersey.com
Freq: Daily; **Circ:** 14072 Not Audited
Editor: Paul Grzella; **Real Estate Editor:** Pam MacKenzie
Editorial Profile: The Courier News is a local newspaper serving the residents of Somerset, Hunterdon, Middlesex and Union counties, NJ. The newspaper covers local news, sports, arts & entertainment and business.; Full Page Mono: 61.09; Full Page Colour: 600.00
Currency: US Dollars
DAILY NEWSPAPER

Courier News Weekly
Owner: Buxmont Media LLC
Editorial: 70 Souderton Hatfield Pike Ste 250, Souderton, Pennsylvania 18964-1939.
T: 1 267 663-6300
W: http://www.buxmontmedia.com
Freq: Wed; **Circ:** 65000 Not Audited
Editorial Profile: Courier News Weekly is a community newspaper serving the residents of Indian Valley, Perkiomen Valley and Harleysville, PA. The publication covers local news and community events.; Full Page Mono: 43.88
Currency: US Dollars
NEWSPAPER

Courier Publications
Owner: Hagel Publication, Inc
Editorial: 100 Ford Ln, Washington, Illinois 61571. **T:** 1 309 444-3139
E: haglnews@mtco.com
W: http://www.courierpapers.com **Circ:** 18200 Not Audited
Editor: Joi DeArmmond; **Publisher:** Roger Hagel
NEWSPAPER

Courier Publishing Company, Inc.
Editorial: 142 Prestonsburg St, West Liberty, Kentucky 41472-1028. **T:** 1 606 743-3551
E: courier@mrtc.com **Circ:** 7900 Not Audited
Publisher: Earl Kinner; **Editor:** J.B. Stamper
NEWSPAPER

The Courier-Express
Owner: McLean Publishing Co.
Editorial: 500 Jeffers St, Du Bois, Pennsylvania 15801. **T:** 1 814 371-4200
E: newsroom@thecourierexpress.com
W: http://www.thecourierexpress.com
Freq: Daily; **Circ:** 9414 Not Audited
News Editor: Alisha Bish Sylvis; **Publisher & Editor:** Denny Bonavita; **Editor:** Tom Bukousky
Editorial Profile: The Courier-Express provides news and information to residents of DuBois, PA. It covers world, national and local news, features, lifestyles and entertainment.; Full Page Mono: 22.18; Full Page Colour: 52.50
Currency: US Dollars
DAILY NEWSPAPER

The Courier-Herald
Owner: Courier Herald Publishing Company
Editorial: 115 S Jefferson St, Dublin, Georgia 31021-5176. **T:** 1 478 272-5522
E: news@courier-herald.com
W: http://www.courier-herald.com
Freq: Mon thru Fri; **Circ:** 8768
Publisher: Griffin Lovett; **Editor:** DuBose Porter; **Editor:** Joey Wilson
Editorial Profile: The Courier-Herald is published daily for the residents of Dublin, GA and surrounding areas. The newspaper covers local and regional news, business, sports, lifestyle and entertainment.; Full Page Mono: 14.25; Full Page Colour: 240.00
Currency: US Dollars
DAILY NEWSPAPER

Courier-Herald Newspapers
Owner: Black Press
Editorial: 1627 Cole St, Enumclaw, Washington 98022-3509. **T:** 1 360 825-2555
E: news@courierherald.com
W: http://www.pnwlocalnews.com **Circ:** 30140 Not Audited
Editor: Kevin Hanson; **Editor:** Kevin Hanson
NEWSPAPER

The Courier-Journal
Owner: Gannett Co., Inc.
Editorial: 525 W Broadway, Louisville, Kentucky 40202-2206. **T:** 1 502 582-4011
W: http://www.courier-journal.com
Freq: Daily; **Circ:** 120739 Not Audited
Indiana Editor: Nick Hollkamp; **Publisher:** Wes Jackson
Editorial Profile: The Courier-Journal is a 70+ page, broadsheet newspaper aimed at the general public in the Lousiville, KY area and southern Indiana. It covers local and regional news, business, sports, entertainment, and lifestyle. The Business section appears daily. A weekly, consumer-focused Health & Fitness section runs on Thursday.; Full Page Mono: 318.12; Full Page Colour: 995.95
Currency: US Dollars
DAILY NEWSPAPER

The Courier-Journal
Editorial: 1575 I St NW Ste 350, Washington, District Of Columbia 20005-1114.
T: 1 202 906-8141
DAILY NEWSPAPER

The Courier-Journal
Editorial: 2500 Lincoln Dr, Clarksville, Indiana 47129-1652. **T:** 1 812 948-1315
DAILY NEWSPAPER

The Courier-Journal
Editorial: 332 Capitol Ave, Frankfort, Kentucky 40601-2835. **T:** 1 502 875-5136
Bureau Chief: Tom Loftus
DAILY NEWSPAPER

Courier-Life Inc.
Owner: News Corporation Ltd.
Editorial: 1 Metrotech Ctr, 10th Fl, Brooklyn, New York 11201-3831. **T:** 1 718 260-2500
E: editorial@cnglocal.com
W: http://www.yournabe.com
Freq: Weekly; **Circ:** 282500 Not Audited
Editor: Vince DiMiceli; **Editor:** Kenton Kirby; **Publisher:** Clifford Luster
NEWSPAPER

Courier-Post
Owner: Gannett Co., Inc.
Editorial: 301 Cuthbert Blvd, Cherry Hill, New Jersey 08002-2905. **T:** 1 856 663-6000
E: cpsjonline@gannett.com
W: http://www.courierpostonline.com
Freq: Daily; **Circ:** 39091 Not Audited
Publisher: Ellen Leifeld; **Content Editor:** Phaedra Trethan; **Content Editor:** Phaedra Trethan
Editorial Profile: Courier-Post is a daily newspaper serving New Jersey. The publication covers local and regional news, business, lifestyle, arts & entertainment and sports. The newspaper's forerunner was founded in 1875 as a weekly newspaper. Gannett bought the publication in 1959. By the end of the 1970s, the paper became a daily, morning paper. In 1979, the first Sunday edition was published.; Full Page Mono: 102.33; Full Page Colour: 538.26
Currency: US Dollars
DAILY NEWSPAPER

The Courier-Times
Owner: Paxton Media Group
Editorial: 201 S 14th St, New Castle, Indiana 47362. **T:** 1 765 529-1111
W: http://www.thecouriertimes.com
Freq: Daily; **Circ:** 9153 Not Audited
Editorial Profile: The Courier-Times is a daily newspaper serving residents of New Castle, IN and the surrounding area. The paper focuses on local news and sports.; Full Page Mono: 17.00; Full Page Colour: 250.00
Currency: US Dollars
DAILY NEWSPAPER

The Courier-Tribune
Owner: Stephens Media Group
Editorial: 500 Sunset Ave, Asheboro, North Carolina 27203-5330. **T:** 1 336 625-2101
W: http://www.courier-tribune.com
Freq: Daily; **Circ:** 13829 Not Audited
Editor: Ray Criscoe; **Editor:** Dennis Garcia; **News Editor:** Annette Jordan; **Publisher:** Diane Winnemuller
Editorial Profile: The Courier-Tribune offers coverage of events and issues in Randolph, Montgomery, Moore, and Chatham counties, as well as for the town of Denton in Davidson County in North Carolina. The newspaper is published daily and provides local information for the general public.; Full Page Mono: 13.50; Full Page Colour: 118.50
Currency: US Dollars
DAILY NEWSPAPER

Cox North Carolina Publications, Inc.
Owner: Cox North Carolina Publications, Inc.
Editorial: 102 Front, Kenansville, North Carolina 28349. **T:** 1 910 296-0239
E: duplintimes@ncweeklies.com
W: http://theduplintimes.com **Circ:** 17800
NEWSPAPER

Craig Daily Press
Owner: WorldWest Limited Liability Co.
Editorial: 466 Yampa Ave, Craig, Colorado 81625-2610. **T:** 1 970 824-7031
E: news@craigdailypress.com
W: http://www.craigdailypress.com
Freq: Daily; **Circ:** 3200
Editorial Profile: Craig Daily Press is published daily for residents of Moffat County, CO. As a community publication, its mission is to present the most unbiased information available to its readers.; Full Page Mono: 10.00; Full Page Colour: 165.00
Currency: US Dollars
DAILY NEWSPAPER

Cranberry Eagle
Owner: Eagle Printing Company
Editorial: 20701 Route 19, Cranberry Twp, Pennsylvania 16066-6009. **T:** 1 724 776-4270
E: cranberryads@gmail.com
W: http://www.thecranberryeagle.com
Freq: Sun; **Circ:** 22585 Not Audited
Editor: Kris Smith; **Publisher:** John Wise
Editorial Profile: The Cranberry Eagle provides local news, weather, and sports information to the residents of Cranberry Township, PA.; Full Page Mono: 12.50
Currency: US Dollars
NEWSPAPER

Cranberry Journal
Owner: Tribune-Review Publishing Co.
Editorial: 503 Martindale St, Pittsburgh, Pennsylvania 15212-5746.
T: 1 412 856-7400 8607
W: http://www.yourcranberry.com
Freq: Thu; **Circ:** 15530
Editor: Dave McElhinny
Editorial Profile: The Cranberry Journal is a local weekly newspaper providing Local News coverage for the residents of Cranberry Township, Seven Fields, Evans City and Zelie, PA.
NEWSPAPER

Creative Loafing
Owner: Atalaya Capital Management
Editorial: 1911 N 13th St Ste W200, Tampa, Florida 33605-3652. **T:** 1 813 739-4800
W: http://cltampa.com
Freq: Wed; **Circ:** 82000 Not Audited
Editor: Mitch Perry; **Editor:** David Warner
Editorial Profile: Creative Loafing is a weekly newspaper covering arts & entertainment and public issues in Tampa, FL. Features include classifieds, entertainment and dining as well as social and political views. The newspaper shares some stories with the Sarasota edition.; Full Page Mono: 26.25; Full Page Colour: 150.00
Currency: US Dollars
NEWSPAPER

Creative Loafing
Owner: SouthComm, Inc.
Editorial: 115 Martin Luther King Jr Dr Ste 301, Atlanta, Georgia 30303-3536.
T: 1 404 688-5623
W: http://www.creativeloafing.com
Freq: Wed; **Circ:** 113000 Not Audited
Editor in Chief: Debbie Michaud; **Publisher:** Sharry Smith; **News Editor:** Thomas Wheatley
Editorial Profile: Creative Loafing is written for socially conscious and aware readers who want to experience what Atlanta has to offer in its growing arts & entertainment scene.; Full Page Mono: 148.24
Currency: US Dollars
NEWSPAPER

Creative Loafing
Owner: SouthComm, Inc.
Editorial: 1000 NC Music Factory Blvd Apt C2, Charlotte, North Carolina 28206-6010.
T: 1 704 522-8334 **W:** http://www.clclt.com/
Freq: Thu; **Circ:** 47000 Not Audited
Editor: Kimberly Lawson
Editorial Profile: Creative Loafing is a weekly newspaper covering arts & entertainment and public issues generally geared toward readers ages 22 to 45 in the metro Charlotte, NC area. Features include classifieds, entertainment and dining as well as social and political views. Deadlines fall on Wednesdays.; Full Page Mono: 11.88
Currency: US Dollars
NEWSPAPER

Creative Printers
Owner: French (Audrey)
Editorial: 238 Main St, Stapleton, Nebraska 69163. **T:** 1 308 636-2444
E: creativeprinters@gpcom.net **Circ:** 2247 Not Audited
Publisher: Audrey French; **Editor:** Marcia Hora; **Editor:** Janet Larreau
NEWSPAPER

The Crescent-News
Owner: Dix Communications
Editorial: 624 W 2nd St, Defiance, Ohio 43512-2161. **T:** 1 419 784-5441
E: crescent@crescent-news.com
W: http://www.crescent-news.com
Freq: Daily; **Circ:** 14876 Not Audited
City Editor: Todd Helberg; **Editor:** Darlene Prince; **News Editor:** Al Smith
Editorial Profile: The Crescent-News is published daily for residents of Defiance, OH and surrounding areas. The publication is a general interest newspaper, including articles on local and national news, weather, sports, business, arts & entertainment and other information of interest to the Defiance community.; Full Page Mono: 18.45; Full Page Colour: 335.00
Currency: US Dollars
DAILY NEWSPAPER

Cresco Times-Plain Dealer
Owner: Evans Publishing LLC.
Editorial: 214 N Elm St, Cresco, Iowa 52136.
T: 1 563 547-3601
W: http://www.crescotimes.com
Freq: Wed; **Circ:** 12300 Not Audited
News Editor: Patti Bryant; **Publisher:** Daniel Evans
Editorial Profile: Cresco Times-Plain Dealer is the official newspaper of Howard County, IA and the city of Cresco. Published weekly, it is both a source of information about the people and events of Howard and surrounding counties and an historical record of the times. Each newspaper published since the 1860s is on file at the Times Plain Dealer offices and is a constant source of information for historians, genealogists, students and people interested in researching their family history.; Full Page Mono: 9.18
Currency: US Dollars
NEWSPAPER

Creston News Advertiser
Owner: Shaw Media
Editorial: 503 W Adams St, Creston, Iowa 50801-3192. **T:** 1 641 782-2141
E: news@crestonnews.com
W: http://www.crestonnews.com
Freq: Daily; **Circ:** 5317 Not Audited
Publisher: Rich Paulsen
Editorial Profile: Creston News Advertiser is a daily newspaper written for residents of Union County, IA and surrounding communities. The publication is a general interest newspaper, covering local and national news, sports, business, arts and entertainment, and feature articles.; Full Page Mono: 10.20; Full Page Colour: 85.00
Currency: US Dollars
DAILY NEWSPAPER

Crete News
Editorial: 1201 Linden Ave, Crete, Nebraska 68333. **T:** 1 402 826-2147
E: newsdesk@cretenews.net
W: http://www.cretenews.net
Freq: Weekly; **Circ:** 8000 Not Audited
NEWSPAPER

The Criterion
Owner: Roman Catholic Archdiocese of Indianapolis
Editorial: 1400 N Meridian St, Indianapolis, Indiana 46202-2305. **T:** 1 317 236-1570
E: criterion@archindy.org
W: http://www.CriterionOnline.com
Freq: Fri; **Circ:** 73000 Not Audited
Publisher: Daniel Buechlein; **Editor:** Mike Krokos
Editorial Profile: The Criterion is the official weekly newspaper for the Roman Catholic Archdiocese of Indianapolis. The newspaper's focus is on religion.; Full Page Mono: 8.76
Currency: US Dollars
NEWSPAPER

Crofton Newspapers
Editorial: 108 W Main St, Crofton, Nebraska 68730. **T:** 1 402 388-4355
E: journal@gpcom.net **Circ:** 1500 Not Audited
Editor: Valerie Zach
NEWSPAPER

Crookston Daily Times
Owner: GateHouse Media Inc.
Editorial: 124 S Broadway, Crookston, Minnesota 56716-1955. **T:** 1 218 281-2730
E: news@crookstontimes.com
W: http://www.crookstontimes.com
Freq: Daily; **Circ:** 1900 Not Audited
Editorial Profile: Crookston Daily Times is published Monday through Friday for residents of Crookston, MN and surrounding areas. The publication is a general interest newspaper covering local news, sports, weather, business and arts & entertainment.; Full Page Mono: 13.85
Currency: US Dollars
DAILY NEWSPAPER

The Cross Roads
Owner: Diocese of Lexington
Editorial: 1310 W Main St, Lexington, Kentucky 40508-2048. **T:** 1 859 253-1993
W: http://www.crossroads.cdlex.org/index.cfm
Freq: Weekly
Editorial Profile: The Cross Roads is a weekly newspaper for the Diocese of Lexington, KY.
NEWSPAPER

The Cross Timbers Gazette
Owner: Miller Media Holdings, LLC
Editorial: 6101 Long Prairie Rd Suite 744-186, Flower Mound, Texas 75028-6201.
T: 1 940 728-8284
E: editor@crosstimbersgazette.com
W: http://www.crosstimbersgazette.com
Freq: Monthly; **Circ:** 30000
Editorial Profile: Cross Timbers Gazette covers community news and people in Southern Denton County, TX, including the communities of Argyle, Bartonville, Copper Canyon, Double Oak, Flower Mound, Highland Village, Lantana and Robson Ranch, TX. It is direct mailed to households in its coverage area and is also available at newsstands and online. The paper only runs full color advertisements.; Full Page Colour: 17.39

Currency: US Dollars
NEWSPAPER

Crowley Post-Signal
Owner: Louisiana State Newspapers
Editorial: 602 N Parkerson Ave, Crowley, Louisiana 70526-4354. **T:** 1 337 783-3450
W: http://www.acadiaparishtoday.com
Freq: Daily; **Circ:** 4350 Not Audited
News Editor: Howell Dennis
Editorial Profile: Crowley Post-Signal is published daily for residents of Crowley and Arcadia Parish, LA. The publication is a general interest newspaper, providing local news, sports, business, entertainment and other information of interest to the Crowley community. The deadline for the publication is at noon CT.; Full Page Mono: 10.18; Full Page Colour: 325.00
Currency: US Dollars
DAILY NEWSPAPER

The Cryer
Editorial: 96 Maine St Ste 253, Brunswick, Maine 04011-2013. **T:** 1 207 504-3733
W: http://www.thecryeronline.com
Freq: Monthly; **Circ:** 20000
Editorial Profile: The Cryer is a local community newspaper written for the residents of Bailey Island, Bowdoin, Bowdoinham, Cundy's Harbor, Freeport, Harpswell, Orr's Island, Pownal and Tosham, ME. It is mailed out monthly and is also available at Mid Coast Maine newsstands.; Full Page Mono: 15.00; Full Page Colour: 42.00
Currency: US Dollars
NEWSPAPER

CSI Publications
Owner: CSI Media, LLC
Editorial: 120 Wright St, Delavan, Wisconsin 53115. **T:** 1 262 728-3424
E: newsdesk@communityshoppers.com
W: http://www.communityshoppers.com
Freq: Sun; **Circ:** 102927; Full Page Mono: 19.80; Full Page Colour: 21.74
Currency: US Dollars
NEWSPAPER

CTNow
Owner: Tribune Broadcasting
Editorial: 285 Broad St, Hartford, Connecticut 06105-3785. **T:** 1 860 548-9300
E: info@ct.com **W:** http://www.ct.com/
Freq: Thu; **Circ:** 150000
Editorial Profile: CTNow is a weekly publication focusing on Music and Arts and Entertainment in the state of Connecticut. It is distributed on newstands in addition to being included in the Thursday edition of the Hartford Courant.
NEWSPAPER

The Cullman Times
Owner: Community Newspaper Holdings, Inc.
Editorial: 300 4th Ave SE, Cullman, Alabama 35055-3699. **T:** 1 256 734-2131
E: sallee@cullmantimes.com
W: http://www.cullmantimes.com
Freq: Daily; **Circ:** 11086 Not Audited
Publisher: Bill Morgan; **Editor:** David Palmer; **News Editor:** Amanda Shavers-Davis
Editorial Profile: The Cullman Times is published daily for residents of Cullman, AL and surrounding areas. It covers local news, weather, sports, business, arts & entertainment and other information of interest to local residents.; Full Page Mono: 12.10; Full Page Colour: 220.00
Currency: US Dollars
DAILY NEWSPAPER

The Cullman Tribune
Owner: Blalock Publishing, L.L.C.
Editorial: 219 2nd Ave SE, Cullman, Alabama 35055-3513. **T:** 1 256 739-1351
Freq: Thu; **Circ:** 15000 Not Audited
Editorial Profile: The Cullman Tribune is a local weekly newspaper serving the residents of Cullman, AL. Coverage includes local news and events, business, politics and social issues. Deadline for submission of press releases is Monday at noon CT.; Full Page Mono: 12.00; Full Page Colour: 874.00
Currency: US Dollars
NEWSPAPER

Culpeper Star-Exponent
Owner: BH Media Group
Editorial: 471 James Madison Hwy Ste 201, Culpeper, Virginia 22701-2364.
T: 1 540 825-0771
W: http://www.starexponent.com
Freq: Daily; **Circ:** 6041 Not Audited
Publisher: Mitch Sneed
Editorial Profile: Culpeper Star-Exponent is published daily for residents of Culpeper, VA and surrounding areas. It is a general interest newspaper covering local news, sports, business, entertainment, education and other information of interest to the area.; Full Page Mono: 18.30; Full Page Colour: 351.00
Currency: US Dollars
DAILY NEWSPAPER

The Culvert Chronicles
Editorial: 13545 227Th St, Laurelton, New York 11413-2447. **T:** 1 718 276-0405
E: culvertchronicles@nyc.rr.com
W: http://theculvertchronicles.com
Freq: Thu; **Circ:** 60000
Editorial Profile: The Culvert Chronicles is a weekly community newspaper serving the African-American community of Laurelton, NY.; Full Page Mono: 25.00
Currency: US Dollars
NEWSPAPER

Cumberland County Reminder
Owner: Cohansey Cove Publishing, Inc.
Editorial: 2 W Vine St, Millville, New Jersey 08332-3823. **T:** 1 856 825-8811
E: editor@remindernewspaper.net
W: http://www.reminderusa.net
Freq: Wed; **Circ:** 24352 Not Audited
Editor: Dan Podehl
Editorial Profile: Cumberland County Reminder is a weekly newspaper for residents of Millville, NJ and surrounding areas. The paper provides community news, education information, entertainment, sports and more. Deadlines are Fridays before the issue date.; Full Page Mono: 14.36
Currency: US Dollars
NEWSPAPER

Cumberland Times-News
Owner: Community Newspaper Holdings, Inc.
Editorial: 19 Baltimore St, Cumberland, Maryland 21502-3023. **T:** 1 301 722-4600
E: ctn@times-news.com
W: http://www.times-news.com
Freq: Daily; **Circ:** 20164 Not Audited
Editor: Jim Goldsworthy; **City Editor:** Debra Meyer; **Publisher:** Ron Monahan; **News Editor:** John Smith
Editorial Profile: Cumberland Times-News is published daily for the residents of Cumberland, Garrett, Allegany, Mineral and Hampshire, MD. It is a general interest newspaper that covers events, opportunities and community issues.; Full Page Mono: 44.52; Full Page Colour: 299.00
Currency: US Dollars
DAILY NEWSPAPER

Current News Magazine
Owner: The Current News Magazine, LLC
Editorial: 540 E Osage St, Pacific, Missouri 63069-1706. **T:** 1 636 271-0990
W: http://www.currentnewsmagazine.com
Circ: 70019
Publisher: Mike Kircher
NEWSPAPER

The Current Newspapers
Editorial: 5185 MacArthur Blvd NW Ste 102, Washington, District Of Columbia 20016-3349. **T:** 1 202 244-7223
E: newsdesk@currentnewspapers.com
W: http://www.currentnewspapers.com
Freq: Wed; **Circ:** 54375 Not Audited; Full Page Mono: 46.25
Currency: US Dollars
NEWSPAPER

The Current Newspapers
Owner: Catamaran Media
Editorial: 3120 Fire Rd Ste 102B, Egg Harbor Township, New Jersey 08234-5886.
T: 1 609 383-8994
E: current@catamaranmedia.com
W: http://www.catamaranmedia.com
Circ: 58300 Not Audited
Editor: James Fitzpatrick; **Publisher:** Rick Travers
Editorial Profile: Current Newspapers provides weekly Community and Local News coverage for the Atlantic County communities of Northfield, Linwood, Somers Point, Egg Harbor Township, Downbeach, Galloway, Port Republic, Mays Landing, Hamilton Township, Absecon and Pleasantville, NJ.
NEWSPAPER

Current Publishing LLC
Owner: Current Publishing LLC
Editorial: 30 S Range Line Rd, Carmel, Indiana 46032-2131. **T:** 1 317 489-4444
E: info@youarecurrent.com
W: http://youarecurrent.com **Circ:** 104339
Editorial Profile: Current Publishing LLC publishes weekly newspapers serving residents of Indianapolis, IN, specifically Carmel, Noblesville, Westfield and Fishers. The paper includes sections on finance, arts and entertainment, aging, government, religion, editorials and community news. Deadlines are Tuesdays at 5pm. Advertising rates are based on a mandatory four-time consecutive insertion rate. Contact for advertising rates.
NEWSPAPER

Current Publishing Newspapers
Owner: Current Publishing LLC
Editorial: 840 Main St, Westbrook, Maine 4092. **T:** 1 207 854-2577
E: news@keepmecurrent.com
W: http://www.keepmecurrent.com
Circ: 25500 Not Audited
Publisher: Lee Hews
Editorial Profile: Current Publishing Newspapers in Westbrook, ME publishes American Journal, The Current, Lakes Region Suburban Weekly and Tritown Weekly.
NEWSPAPER

Current Publishing Newspapers - Saco
Owner: Current Publishing LLC
Editorial: 840 Main St, Westbrook, Maine 4092. **T:** 1 207 854-2577
E: news@keepmecurrent.com
W: http://www.keepmecurrent.com
Circ: 36000 Not Audited
Publisher: Lee Hews
NEWSPAPER

Current-Argus
Owner: MediaNews Group
Editorial: 620 S Main St, Carlsbad, New Mexico 88220-6243. **T:** 1 575 887-5501
W: http://www.currentargus.com
Freq: Daily; **Circ:** 5943 Not Audited
Editorial Profile: Current-Argus is published daily for residents of Carlsbad, NM and surrounding areas. The publication is a general interest newspaper, including local, state, national and international news and features, comics and puzzles, syndicated columnists, classified and display advertising, weather, business and financial reports, obituaries, and local, state and national sports. The newspaper also includes editorials, letters and opinions, astrological forecasts, and other features as space permits. Deadlines are two weeks prior to the issue date.; Full Page Mono: 17.15; Full Page Colour: 225.00
Currency: US Dollars
DAILY NEWSPAPER

C-Ville Weekly
Owner: C-Ville Holdings, LLC.
Editorial: 308 E Main St, Charlottesville, Virginia 22902-5234. **T:** 1 434 817-2749
E: editor@c-ville.com
W: http://www.c-ville.com
Freq: Tue; **Circ:** 24000 Not Audited
Publisher: Frank Dubec; **News Editor:** Brendan Fitzgerald
Editorial Profile: C-Ville Weekly is the weekly news and arts paper of Charlottesville, VA. It is the largest locally owned paper in Charlottesville. The paper is published every Tuesday. It is distributed to residents of Charlottesville and Albemarle Country. The publication covers music, film, and photography. Special issues cover notable artists from the area such as Dave Matthews Band and Dispatch.; Full Page Mono: 19.84
Currency: US Dollars
NEWSPAPER

Daily & Sunday Review
Owner: Scranton Times
Editorial: 116 Main St, Towanda, Pennsylvania 18848-1843. **T:** 1 570 265-2151
E: reviewnews@thedailyreview.com
W: http://www.thedailyreview.com
Freq: Daily; **Circ:** 8228 Not Audited
Editor: Kelly Andrus; **Publisher:** Greg Zyla
Editorial Profile: Daily & Sunday Review serves the residents of Towanda, PA and the surrounding areas. The newspaper provides local and national news, sports and entertainment. Send press releases by fax or mail to the city editor.; Full Page Mono: 18.44; Full Page Colour: 75.00
Currency: US Dollars
DAILY NEWSPAPER

The Daily Advance
Owner: Cooke Communications, LLC
Editorial: 215 S Water St, Elizabeth City, North Carolina 27909-4844. **T:** 1 252 335-0841
E: elizabethcity@dailyadvance.com
W: http://www.dailyadvance.com
Freq: Daily; **Circ:** 9416 Not Audited
News Editor: Julian Eure; **Editor:** Michael Goodman; **Publisher:** Ann Hoffman
Editorial Profile: The Daily Advance is a local, daily newspaper for residents of Northeast Elizabeth City, NC. It covers community news and daily events.; Full Page Mono: 19.93; Full Page Colour: 275.00
Currency: US Dollars
DAILY NEWSPAPER

The Daily Advertiser
Owner: Gannett Co., Inc.
Editorial: 1100 Bertrand Dr, Lafayette, Louisiana 70506-4110. **T:** 1 337 289-6300
E: news@theadvertiser.com
W: http://www.theadvertiser.com
Freq: Daily; **Circ:** 23164 Not Audited
Editorial Profile: The Daily Advertiser is a local newspaper written for residents in Acadiana, LA. The newspaper, published seven days a week, covers local news, sports, entertainment and community events.; Full Page Mono: 45.50; Full Page Colour: 221.00
Currency: US Dollars
DAILY NEWSPAPER

The Daily American
Owner: GateHouse Media Inc.
Editorial: 111 S Emma St, West Frankfort, Illinois 62896-2729. **T:** 1 618 932-2146
E: newsroom@dailyamericannews.com
W: http://www.dailyamericannews.com
Freq: Mon thru Fri; **Circ:** 2000 Not Audited
Publisher: Kevin Haezebroeck
Editorial Profile: The Daily American's editorial mission is to provide local news coverage for the West Frankfort, IL region. It covers local news, sports, politics and entertainment.; Full Page Mono: 8.05; Full Page Colour: 37.09
Currency: US Dollars
DAILY NEWSPAPER

Daily American
Owner: Schurz Communications Inc.
Editorial: 334 W Main St, Somerset, Pennsylvania 15501-1502. **T:** 1 814 444-5900
E: news@dailyamerican.com
W: http://www.dailyamerican.com
Freq: Daily; **Circ:** 11504 Not Audited
Publisher: Andrew Bruns; **City Editor:** Rick Kazmer; **News Editor:** Brian Schrock; **Editor:** Brian Whipkey
Editorial Profile: Daily American is a daily newspaper written for the residents of Somerset County, PA. The publication provides news, weather, sports and community events.; Full Page Mono: 22.00; Full Page Colour: 380.00
Currency: US Dollars
DAILY NEWSPAPER

Daily American Republic
Owner: Rust Communications
Editorial: 208 Poplar St, Poplar Bluff, Missouri 63901. **T:** 1 573 785-1414
E: news@darnews.com
W: http://www.darnews.com
Freq: Daily; **Circ:** 8862 Not Audited
Editor: Stan Berry; **Editor:** Paul Davis; **Editor:** Brian Rosener; **Publisher:** Don Schrieber
Editorial Profile: Daily American Republic is written for residents in and around Poplar Bluff, MO. The paper covers local news, sports and weather.; Full Page Mono: 12.37; Full Page Colour: 400.00
Currency: US Dollars
DAILY NEWSPAPER

The Daily Ardmoreite
Owner: GateHouse Media Inc.
Editorial: 117 W Broadway St, Ardmore, Oklahoma 73401. **T:** 1 580 223-2200
W: http://www.ardmoreite.com
Freq: Daily; **Circ:** 8642 Not Audited
News Editor: Marsha Miller
Editorial Profile: The Daily Ardmoreite is published daily for the residents of Ardmoreite, OK and surrounding areas. The newspaper covers local and state news, business, sports, lifestyles and entertainment.; Full Page Mono: 11.25; Full Page Colour: 130.00
Currency: US Dollars
DAILY NEWSPAPER

The Daily Astorian
Owner: East Oregonian Publishing Co.
Editorial: 949 Exchange St, Astoria, Oregon 97103-4605. **T:** 1 503 325-3211
E: news@dailyastorian.com
W: http://www.dailyastorian.com
Freq: Daily; **Circ:** 8082 Not Audited
Editor: Steve Forrester; **Editor:** Kathleen Strecker
Editorial Profile: The Daily Astorian is a daily newspaper for the residents of Astoria, OR. It covers news and events in the local community. Deadlines are one day prior to

issue date.; Full Page Mono: 17.05; Full Page Colour: 316.00
Currency: US Dollars
DAILY NEWSPAPER

Daily Breeze
Owner: MediaNews Group
Editorial: 21250 Hawthorne Blvd Ste 170, Torrance, California 90503-5514.
T: 1 310 540-5511
E: newsroom@dailybreeze.com
W: http://www.dailybreeze.com
Freq: Daily; **Circ:** 79327 Not Audited
Editorial Profile: Daily Breeze is published for residents of Torrance, CA. This paper is a part of the Los Angeles Newspaper Group, a subsidiary of Media News Group. The newspaper covers local news, sports and weather.; Full Page Mono: 1426.54; Full Page Colour: 2121.48
Currency: US Dollars
DAILY NEWSPAPER

Daily Challenge
Owner: Challenge Group
Editorial: 1195 Atlantic Ave, Brooklyn, New York 11216-2709. **T:** 1 718 636-9500
E: challengegroup@yahoo.com
Freq: Daily; **Circ:** 81000 Not Audited
Editor: Dawad Philip; **Editor:** Dawad Philip;
Publisher: Tom Watkins
Editorial Profile: Daily Challenge is a daily newspaper serving the African-American community in the New York metropolitan area. The paper features local, national and international news from the Caribbean, Latin America and Africa and from wherever issues confronting Africans throughout the Diaspora are unfolding. Topics include entertainment, health, sports, books and a forum page.; Full Page Mono: 67.98; Full Page Colour: 600.00
Currency: US Dollars
DAILY NEWSPAPER

Daily Chief-Union
Owner: Barnes Newspapers (Ray)
Editorial: 111 W Wyandot Ave, Upper Sandusky, Ohio 43351-1348.
T: 1 419 294-2332
E: dcueditor@dailychiefunion.com
W: http://www.dailychiefunion.com
Freq: Daily; **Circ:** 3946 Not Audited
Publisher & Editor: Jeff Barnes
Editorial Profile: Daily Chief-Union is written for the Upper Sandusky, OH community. The newspaper covers world news, local news, community news, sports news, obituaries, weather and job vacancies.; Full Page Mono: 6.75; Full Page Colour: 75.00
Currency: US Dollars
DAILY NEWSPAPER

Daily Chronicle
Owner: Shaw Media
Editorial: 1586 Barber Greene Rd, Dekalb, Illinois 60115-7900. **T:** 1 815 756-4841
E: news@daily-chronicle.com
W: http://www.daily-chronicle.com
Freq: Mon thru Fri; **Circ:** 8419
Publisher: Don Bricker; **City Editor:** Jillian Duchnowski; **Editor:** Eric Olson; **Editor:** Eric Olson
Editorial Profile: Daily Chronicle is published for the residents of Dekalb County, IL and surrounding areas. It covers local, national and international news, sports, weather, religion, legal and lifestyle.; Full Page Mono: 29.15; Full Page Colour: 2669.10
Currency: US Dollars
DAILY NEWSPAPER

The Daily Citizen
Owner: Paxton Media Group
Editorial: 3000 E Race Ave, Searcy, Arkansas 72143-4808. **T:** 1 501 268-8621
E: editor@thedailycitizen.com
W: http://www.thedailycitizen.com
Freq: Daily; **Circ:** 6131 Not Audited
News Editor: Wendy Jones; **Publisher:** Mike Murphy
Editorial Profile: The Daily Citizen is a local newspaper serving Searcy, AR and the surrounding community. It provides readers with local news, sports, government and arts & entertainment coverage.; Full Page Mono: 11.25; Full Page Colour: 125.00
Currency: US Dollars
DAILY NEWSPAPER

The Daily Citizen
Owner: Community Newspaper Holdings, Inc.
Editorial: 308 S Thornton Ave, Dalton, Georgia 30720-8268. **T:** 1 706 217-6397
W: http://daltondailycitizen.com
Freq: Daily; **Circ:** 11162 Not Audited
Publisher: William Bronson; **Editor:** Wes Chance; **Editor:** Jamie Jones; **Editor:** Victor

Miller
Editorial Profile: The Daily Citizen is written for the Dalton, GA community. The newspaper covers local and state news, sports, business, lifestyles and entertainment.; Full Page Mono: 19.50; Full Page Colour: 240.00
Currency: US Dollars
DAILY NEWSPAPER

Daily Citizen
Owner: Capital Newspapers
Editorial: 805 Park Ave, Beaver Dam, Wisconsin 53916-2205. **T:** 1 920 887-0321
E: dc-news@capitalnewspapers.com
W: http://www.wiscnews.com/bdc
Freq: Daily; **Circ:** 8676 Not Audited
Publisher & Editor: James Kelsh
Editorial Profile: Daily Citizen is a local newspaper written for residents of Dodge County, WI. The newspaper covers local news, sports and events.; Full Page Mono: 11.60; Full Page Colour: 72.04
Currency: US Dollars
DAILY NEWSPAPER

Daily Clintonian
Owner: Clinton Color Crafters Inc.
Editorial: 422 S Main St, Clinton, Indiana 47842. **T:** 1 765 832-2443 **E:** cccc@mikes.net
W: http://www.ccc-clintonian.com
Freq: Daily; **Circ:** 5200 Not Audited
Editor: Jinanne Carey; **Editor:** Pat Farrington
Editorial Profile: Daily Clintonian is written for local residents of Clinton, IN as well as those in surrounding counties. The publication covers the latest news, sports, legal issues and events for the community.; Full Page Mono: 8.00; Full Page Colour: 25.42
Currency: US Dollars
DAILY NEWSPAPER

Daily Comet
Owner: Halifax Media Holdings LLC
Editorial: 104 Hickory St, Thibodaux, Louisiana 70301-2008. **T:** 1 985 448-7600
E: editor@dailycomet.com
W: http://www.dailycomet.com
Freq: Mon thru Fri; **Circ:** 7695 Not Audited
Publisher: Miles Forrest
Editorial Profile: Daily Comet serves the local community of Thibodaux, LA. The publication reports daily on local news, events and community programs, as well as regional and national highlights.; Full Page Mono: 43.91
Currency: US Dollars
DAILY NEWSPAPER

The Daily Commercial
Owner: Harbor Point Media LLC
Editorial: 212 E Main St, Leesburg, Florida 34748. **T:** 1 352 365-8200
E: news@dailycommercial.com
W: http://www.dailycommercial.com
Freq: Daily; **Circ:** 21093 Not Audited
Editor: Todd McNiff; **Publisher:** Rich Pinder
Editorial Profile: The Daily Commercial is a local daily newspaper written for the residents of Lake and Sumter counties, FL. The newspaper covers local news, sports and community events.; Full Page Mono: 28.91; Full Page Colour: 98.35
Currency: US Dollars
DAILY NEWSPAPER

Daily Commercial Record
Owner: Independent
Editorial: 706 Main St Bsmt 2, Dallas, Texas 75202-3699. **T:** 1 214 741-6366
E: dcr@dailycommercialrecord.com
W: http://www.dailycommercialrecord.com
Freq: Daily; **Circ:** 3200 Not Audited
Editor: Emily Cates; **Publisher:** Nuel Cates
Editorial Profile: The Daily Commercial Record is a daily newspaper providing current court and commercial information. It provides up-to-date court records, public notices, legal transactions, and business leads and business news each weekday.; Full Page Colour: 306.00
Currency: US Dollars
DAILY NEWSPAPER

Daily Corinthian
Owner: Paxton Media Group
Editorial: 1607 S Harper Rd, Corinth, Mississippi 38834-6653. **T:** 1 662 287-6111
E: news@dailycorinthian.com
W: http://www.dailycorinthian.com
Freq: Daily; **Circ:** 6153 Not Audited
Editor: Logan Mosby; **Editor:** Lee Smith;
Publisher: Reece Terry
Editorial Profile: Daily Corinthian provides local community news, weather and sports. The publication is written for residents of Corinth, MS.; Full Page Mono: 16.95; Full Page Colour: 215.00
Currency: US Dollars
DAILY NEWSPAPER

The Daily Courier
Owner: Western Newspapers, Inc.
Editorial: 1958 Commerce Center Cir, Prescott, Arizona 86301-4454.
T: 1 928 445-3333
E: editorial@prescottaz.com
W: http://www.dcourier.com
Freq: Daily; **Circ:** 14483 Not Audited
Publisher: Kelly Soldwedel; **Editor:** Les Stukenberg
Editorial Profile: The Daily Courier is a daily newspaper published by Western Newspapers Inc., for residents of Prescott, AZ. The newspaper covers local news, events and sports.; Full Page Mono: 15.68; Full Page Colour: 690.00
Currency: US Dollars
DAILY NEWSPAPER

The Daily Courier
Owner: Paxton Media Group
Editorial: 601 Oak St, Forest City, North Carolina 28043-3471. **T:** 1 828 245-6431
W: http://www.thedigitalcourier.com
Freq: Daily; **Circ:** 12401 Not Audited
Editor: Matthew Clark; **Publisher:** Wanda Moeller
Editorial Profile: The Daily Courier provides the community with local news and information. The newspaper is written for residents of Forest City, NC and the surrounding area. Topics covered include local schools, government and the environment.; Full Page Mono: 11.45
Currency: US Dollars
DAILY NEWSPAPER

The Daily Courier
Owner: Tribune-Review Publishing Co.
Editorial: 127 W Apple St, Connellsville, Pennsylvania 15425. **T:** 1 724 628-2000
E: dailycourier@tribweb.com
W: http://www.pittsburghlive.com/x/dailycourier
Freq: Daily; **Circ:** 7544 Not Audited
Publisher: Richard Scaife; **Editor:** Rose Snyder
Editorial Profile: The Daily Courier is published daily for the residents of Connellsville, PA and surrounding areas. The newspaper cover local and regional news, business, sports, lifestyles and entertainment.; Full Page Mono: 14.76; Full Page Colour: 64.76
Currency: US Dollars
DAILY NEWSPAPER

Daily Courier-Observer
Owner: St. Lawrence County Newspapers, Inc.
Editorial: 1 Harrowgate Commons, Massena, New York 13662-2201. **T:** 1 315 769-2451
E: courier@ogd.com
W: http://www.mpcourier.com
Freq: Fri; **Circ:** 7800 Not Audited
Editorial Profile: Daily Courier-Observer is written for residents of Massena and Potsdam, NY. It covers international, national, state and local news, sports, editorials, social events and features of interest to local readers.; Full Page Mono: 11.90; Full Page Colour: 70.00
Currency: US Dollars
NEWSPAPER

The Daily Democrat
Owner: MediaNews Group
Editorial: 711 Main St, Woodland, California 95695-3406. **T:** 1 530 662-5421
E: news@dailydemocrat.com
W: http://www.dailydemocrat.com
Freq: Daily; **Circ:** 8520 Not Audited
Publisher: Jim Gleim
Editorial Profile: The Daily Democrat is published for the residents of Woodland, CA and surrounding areas. The paper covers local and national news and finance with a democratic edge.; Full Page Mono: 15.00; Full Page Colour: 2320.00
Currency: US Dollars
DAILY NEWSPAPER

The Daily Democrat
Owner: Brehm Communications, Inc.
Editorial: 1226 Avenue H, Fort Madison, Iowa 52627-4544. **T:** 1 319 372-6421
W: http://www.dailydem.com
Freq: Daily; **Circ:** 5800 Not Audited
Editor: Robin Delaney; **Publisher:** Gary Milks
Editorial Profile: The Daily Democrat is published for the residents of Fort Madison, IA and surrounding areas. The newspaper covers local and state news, business, sports, lifestyles and entertainment.; Full Page Mono: 14.40; Full Page Colour: 49.63
Currency: US Dollars
DAILY NEWSPAPER

The Daily Dunklin Democrat
Owner: Rust Communications
Editorial: 203 1st St, Kennett, Missouri 63857-2052. **T:** 1 573 888-4505
W: http://www.dddnews.com
Freq: Daily; **Circ:** 3068 Not Audited
Publisher: Bud Hunt; **News Editor:** Dustin Ward
Editorial Profile: The Daily Dunklin Democrat serves the residents of Kennett, MO and the surrounding area. The publication covers local and national news.; Full Page Mono: 12.10; Full Page Colour: 280.00
Currency: US Dollars
DAILY NEWSPAPER

Daily Freeman
Owner: Journal Register Company
Editorial: 79 Hurley Ave, Kingston, New York 12401. **T:** 1 845 331-5000
E: news@freemanonline.com
W: http://www.dailyfreeman.com
Freq: Daily; **Circ:** 13675 Not Audited
Publisher: Ira Fusfeld; **City Editor:** Jeremy Schiffres
Editorial Profile: Daily Freeman is a daily newspaper published for the local community of Kingston, NY. The publication covers local news, events, people and sports in the area.; Full Page Mono: 33.55; Full Page Colour: 312.00
Currency: US Dollars
DAILY NEWSPAPER

Daily Freeman-Journal
Owner: Marshalltown Newspaper Inc.
Editorial: 720 2nd St, Webster City, Iowa 50595-1463. **T:** 1 515 832-4350
W: http://www.freemanjournal.net
Freq: Daily; **Circ:** 2036 Not Audited
Publisher: Terry Christensen
Editorial Profile: Daily Freeman-Journal is a daily newspaper which covers the news of Hamilton County, IA. The publication is written for residents of Hamilton County, IA and the surrounding areas.; Full Page Mono: 10.30; Full Page Colour: 63.54
Currency: US Dollars
DAILY NEWSPAPER

Daily Gate City
Owner: Brehm Communications, Inc.
Editorial: 1016 Main St, Keokuk, Iowa 52632-4656. **T:** 1 319 524-8300
E: gatecity@dailygate.com
W: http://www.dailygate.com
Freq: Daily; **Circ:** 5079 Not Audited
Editor: Brad Cameron; **Publisher:** Mark Smidt
Editorial Profile: The Daily Gate City serves Keokuk, IA and surrounding communities. The publication provides local, regional and national news, business, sports, editorials and features of interest to readers in the area. Its delivery area extends from Farmington, IA in the north to Warsaw, IL in the south, Kahoka, MO to the west and Carthage, IL to the east.; Full Page Mono: 15.90; Full Page Colour: 19.26
Currency: US Dollars
DAILY NEWSPAPER

The Daily Gazette
Owner: Daily Gazette Co.
Editorial: 2345 Maxon Rd Ext, Schenectady, New York 12308-1105. **T:** 1 518 374-4141
E: gazette@dailygazette.net
W: http://www.dailygazette.com
Freq: Daily; **Circ:** 56296 Not Audited
Publisher: John DeAugustine; **News Editor:** Bill Finelli; **City Editor:** Miles Reed
Editorial Profile: The Daily Gazette is published daily for residents of Schenectady, NY and surrounding communities. The newspaper covers local and national news, weather and sports. Feature articles cover business, arts & entertainment, lifestyle and community events.; Full Page Mono: 102.41; Full Page Colour: 149.28
Currency: US Dollars
DAILY NEWSPAPER

The Daily Globe
Owner: Stevenson Newspapers
Editorial: 118 E McLeod Ave, Ironwood, Michigan 49938-2120. **T:** 1 906 932-2211
E: news@yourdailyglobe.com
W: http://www.yourdailyglobe.com
Freq: Daily; **Circ:** 5773 Not Audited
Editorial Profile: The Daily Globe is written for the citizens of Gogebic and Ononagon County, MI as well as Iron County, WI. The publication covers local news and sports. Deadlines are at noon CT two days prior to publication.; Full Page Mono: 11.46; Full Page Colour: 60.00
Currency: US Dollars
DAILY NEWSPAPER

Daily Globe

Owner: Forum Communications Co.
Editorial: 300 11th St, Worthington, Minnesota 56187-2451. **T:** 1 507 376-9711
E: dgnews@dglobe.com
W: http://www.dglobe.com
Freq: Daily; **Circ:** 8699 Not Audited
Publisher: Joni Harms
Editorial Profile: Worthington Daily Globe is a local daily newspaper for residents of Nobles County, MN. The publication's editorial mission is to provide local news, sports, and events coverage for the area.; Full Page Mono: 23.95; Full Page Colour: 510.00
Currency: US Dollars
DAILY NEWSPAPER

Daily Guide

Owner: GateHouse Media Inc.
Editorial: 108 Holly Dr, Saint Robert, Missouri 65584-4641. **T:** 1 573 336-3711
W: http://www.waynesvilledailyguide.com
Freq: Daily; **Circ:** 1550 Not Audited
Publisher: Floyd Jernigan; **Editor:** Mandy Matney
Editorial Profile: Daily Guide is a daily newspaper serving the residents of Crocker, Dixon, Laquey, Fort Leonard Wood, Richland, St. Robert and Waynesville, MO.; Full Page Mono: 7.60; Full Page Colour: 50.00
Currency: US Dollars
DAILY NEWSPAPER

Daily Hampshire Gazette

Owner: Newspapers of New England
Editorial: 115 Conz St, Northampton, Massachusetts 01060-4426.
T: 1 413 584-5000
E: newsroom@gazettenet.com
W: http://www.gazettenet.com
Freq: Mon thru Fri; **Circ:** 14475 Not Audited
Publisher: James Foudy; **City Editor:** Laurie Loisel; **Editor in Chief:** Larry Parnass
Editorial Profile: Daily Hampshire Gazette is a daily broadsheet newspaper serving Northampton and Hampshire County, MA. The publication covers local news, entertainment, sports, and lifestyle. Local business coverage is contained primarily in the biweekly Business section in the Monday and Thursday editions. Other regular sections include Tuesday's Health, Wednesday's lifestyle and books page, Thursday's entertainment and home and garden sections, Friday's Hampshire Life Magazine and Real Estate EXTRA. The Saturday edition is the paper's expanded weekend edition, covering topics such as religion, senior issues, travel, society news, food, automotive, and television. The paper has no Sunday edition.; Full Page Mono: 20.43; Full Page Colour: 465.00
Currency: US Dollars
DAILY NEWSPAPER

Daily Herald

Owner: Wick Communications Inc.
Editorial: 916 Roanoke Ave, Roanoke Rapids, North Carolina 27870-2720.
T: 1 252 537-2505
E: heraldnews@rrdailyherald.com
W: http://www.rrdailyherald.com
Freq: Daily; **Circ:** 11153 Not Audited
Editor: Kris Smith; **Publisher:** Titus Workman
Editorial Profile: Daily Herald is published weekly for the residents of Roanoke Rapids, NC and surrounding areas. It covers local news, sports, lifestyle, business, agriculture and entertainment.; Full Page Mono: 17.45; Full Page Colour: 109.50
Currency: US Dollars
DAILY NEWSPAPER

The Daily Herald

Owner: Sample News Group
Editorial: 1067 Pennsylvania Ave, Tyrone, Pennsylvania 16686-1513. **T:** 1 814 684-4000
Freq: Daily; **Circ:** 1500 Not Audited
Editor: Christina Pryor
Editorial Profile: The Daily Herald covers local news and community events for residents of Blair County, PA. Deadlines fall on the issue day at 9:30am ET.; Full Page Mono: 7.10; Full Page Colour: 172.10
Currency: US Dollars
DAILY NEWSPAPER

The Daily Herald

Owner: Stephens Media
Editorial: 1115 S Main St, Columbia, Tennessee 38401. **T:** 1 931 388-6464
E: newsroomc@c-dh.net
W: http://www.columbiadailyherald.com
Freq: Daily; **Circ:** 9612 Not Audited
Editor: Chris Fletcher; **Editor:** Chris Fletcher; **Publisher:** Mark Palmer; **Editor:** Susan Thurman
Editorial Profile: The Daily Herald is a local newspaper written for residents of Columbia,

Maury County, and Southern Middle Tennessee. The newspaper covers local news, sports, government, business, schools, police and events.; Full Page Mono: 13.45; Full Page Colour: 293.45
Currency: US Dollars
DAILY NEWSPAPER

Daily Herald

Owner: Lee Enterprises, Inc.
Editorial: 1555 N Freedom Blvd, Provo, Utah 84604-2519. **T:** 1 801 373-5050
E: dhnews@heraldextra.com
W: http://www.heraldextra.com
Freq: Daily; **Circ:** 25033 Not Audited
Publisher: Rona Rahlf
Editorial Profile: The Daily Herald is a daily newspaper that covers national, international and local news, sports, lifestyles, culture, and entertainment in Utah. Contact the publication for advertising and circulation information.; Full Page Mono: 37.35; Full Page Colour: 225.00
Currency: US Dollars
DAILY NEWSPAPER

Daily Herald - Cook County

Owner: Paddock Publications
Editorial: 155 E Algonquin Rd, Arlington Heights, Illinois 60005-4617.
T: 1 847 427-4300
W: http://www.dailyherald.com
Freq: Daily; **Circ:** 89982 Not Audited
Editor: John Lampinen; **Publisher:** Doug Ray
Editorial Profile: Daily Herald - Cook County is a daily newspaper circulated primarily in the suburban area Northwest of Chicago. The paper features major local, regional, national and world news. Local stories come from around the city and surrounding suburbs. Business coverage includes national and world economic news, stock listings, and coverage of start-ups and local entrepreneurs. The newspaper also covers national and international news and features, arts & entertainment, travel, books, health and fitness, relationships, money, family and sports. The total circulation for the Daily Herald group of publications for the Cook, Dupage, McHenry and Lake markets is approximately 130,000.; Full Page Mono: 133.95; Full Page Colour: 144.70
Currency: US Dollars
DAILY NEWSPAPER

Daily Herald - DuPage County

Owner: Paddock Publications
Editorial: 4300 Commerce Ct, Lisle, Illinois 60532-3698. **T:** 1 630 955-3500
E: news@dailyherald.com
W: http://www.dailyherald.com **Circ:** 31046 Not Audited
Editor: Gerry Alger; **Bureau Chief:** Jim Davis; **Publisher:** Doug Ray; **City Editor:** Bob Smith; **City Editor:** Bob Smith
Editorial Profile: The Daily Herald is a daily newspaper circulated primarily in the suburban areas of Chicago. The paper features major local, regional, national, and world news. Local stories come from around the city and surrounding suburbs. Business coverage includes national and world economic news, stock listings, and coverage of start-ups and local entrepreneurs. The newspaper also covers national and international news and features, arts and entertainment, travel, books, health and fitness, relationships, money, family, and sports. The total circulation for the Daily Herald group of publications for the Cook, Dupage, McHenry and Lake markets is approximately 130,000. See Daily Herald - Cook County for a list of special sections. Deadlines are two days before distribution.
DAILY NEWSPAPER

Daily Herald - Lake County

Owner: Paddock Publications
Editorial: 1795 N Butterfield Rd, Ste 100, Libertyville, Illinois 60048-1212.
T: 1 847 680-5800 **E:** news@dailyherald.com
W: http://www.dailyherald.com **Circ:** 20100 Not Audited
Editor: Gerry Alger; **Editor:** John Lampinen; **Bureau Chief:** Pete Nenni; **Bureau Chief:** Pete Nenni; **Bureau Chief:** Pete Nenni; **Bureau Chief:** Pete Nenni
Editorial Profile: The Daily Herald is a daily newspaper circulated primarily in the suburban areas of Chicago. The paper features major local, regional, national, and world news. Local stories come from around the city and surrounding suburbs. Business coverage includes national and world economic news, stock listings, and coverage of start-ups and local entrepreneurs. The newspaper also covers national and international news and features, arts and entertainment, travel, books, health and fitness, relationships, money,

family, and sports. The total circulation for the Daily Herald group of publications for the Cook, Dupage, McHenry and Lake markets is approximately 130,000. See Daily Herald, IL-D30 for a list of special sections. Deadlines are two days before distribution.
DAILY NEWSPAPER

Daily Herald - McHenry

Owner: Paddock Publications
Editorial: 385 Airport Rd, Ste A, Elgin, Illinois 60123-9341. **T:** 1 847 608-2700
E: news@dailyherald.com
W: http://www.dailyherald.com **Circ:** 25173 Not Audited
Editor: Gerry Alger; **Publisher:** Doug Ray
Editorial Profile: The Daily Herald is a series of daily newspapers circulated primarily in the suburban areas of Chicago. The papers feature major local, regional, national, and world news. Local stories come from around the city and surrounding suburbs. Business coverage includes national and world economic news, stock listings, and coverage of start-ups and local entrepreneurs. The newspapers also cover national and international news and features, arts and entertainment, travel, books, health and fitness, relationships, money, family, and sports. Deadlines are two days before distribution.
DAILY NEWSPAPER

The Daily Home

Owner: Consolidated Publishing
Editorial: 4 Sylacauga Highway, Talladega, Alabama 35161. **T:** 1 256 362-1000
E: news@dailyhome.com
W: http://www.dailyhome.com
Freq: Daily; **Circ:** 9321 Not Audited
Editor: Jimmy Creed; **Editor:** Laura Nation
Editorial Profile: The Daily Home is published for the residents of Talladega, Sylacauga and Pell City, AL. It covers local news and events.; Full Page Mono: 9.75
Currency: US Dollars
DAILY NEWSPAPER

The Daily Iberian

Owner: Wick Communications Inc.
Editorial: 926 E Main St, New Iberia, Louisiana 70560-3866. **T:** 1 337 365-6773
E: news@daily-iberian.com
W: http://www.iberianet.com
Freq: Daily; **Circ:** 13193 Not Audited
Publisher: Will Chapman
Editorial Profile: The Daily Iberian is the official legal journal for the Iberia Parish.; Full Page Mono: 16.76; Full Page Colour: 129.00
Currency: US Dollars
DAILY NEWSPAPER

The Daily Independent

Owner: GateHouse Media Inc.
Editorial: 224 E Ridgecrest Blvd, Ridgecrest, California 93555-3975. **T:** 1 760 375-4481
W: http://www.ridgecrestca.com
Freq: Daily; **Circ:** 7493 Not Audited
City Editor: Jack Barnwell; **Publisher:** John Watkins
Editorial Profile: The Daily Independent is published for the residents of Ridgecrest, CA and the surrounding areas. All mail must be sent to the P.O. box address.; Full Page Mono: 12.27; Full Page Colour: 18.57
Currency: US Dollars
DAILY NEWSPAPER

The Daily Inter Lake

Owner: Hagadone Corp.
Editorial: 727 E Idaho St, Kalispell, Montana 59901-3202. **T:** 1 406 755-7000
E: edit@dailyinterlake.com
W: http://www.dailyinterlake.com
Freq: Daily; **Circ:** 15112 Not Audited
Publisher: Rick Weaver
Editorial Profile: The Daily Inter Lake is a daily newspaper published for the residents of Kalispell, MT. It provides information on local news and events.; Full Page Mono: 24.91; Full Page Colour: 161.27
Currency: US Dollars
DAILY NEWSPAPER

The Daily Item

Owner: Hastings and Sons Publishing Co.
Editorial: 38 Exchange St, Lynn, Massachusetts 01901-1425.
T: 1 781 593-7700 **E:** contactus@itemlive.com
W: http://www.itemlive.com
Freq: Daily; **Circ:** 13109 Not Audited
Publisher: Peter Gamage; **City Editor:** Ryan York
Editorial Profile: The Daily Item is a family-owned, independent newspaper serving the Lynn, Lynnfield, Marblehead, Nahant, Peabody, Revere, Saugus and Swampscott, MA areas. The newspaper is published Monday through

Saturday.; Full Page Mono: 37.26; Full Page Colour: 122.10
Currency: US Dollars
DAILY NEWSPAPER

The Daily Item

Owner: Community Newspaper Holdings, Inc.
Editorial: 200 Market St, Sunbury, Pennsylvania 17801. **T:** 1 570 286-5671
E: news@dailyitem.com
W: http://dailyitem.com
Freq: Daily; **Circ:** 19652 Not Audited
City Editor: Bill Bowman; **News Editor:** William Foley; **Publisher:** Gary Grossman
Editorial Profile: The Daily Item is a local newspaper for residents of Northumberland, Columbia, Snyder, Perry, Montour, Union and Juniata counties, PA. The newspaper covers local news, sports, entertainment, politics and community events.; Full Page Mono: 53.91; Full Page Colour: 300.00
Currency: US Dollars
DAILY NEWSPAPER

Daily Jefferson County Union

Owner: Hoard & Sons Co. (W.D.)
Editorial: 28 Milwaukee Ave W, Fort Atkinson, Wisconsin 53538-2018. **T:** 1 920 563-5553
E: dailyunion@dailyunion.com
W: http://www.dailyunion.com
Freq: Mon thru Fri; **Circ:** 8600 Not Audited
Publisher: Brian Knox; **Editor:** Ryan Whisner
Editorial Profile: Daily Jefferson County Union provides local and national news for residents of the Jefferson County, WI.; Full Page Mono: 12.15; Full Page Colour: 76.47
Currency: US Dollars
DAILY NEWSPAPER

The Daily Jeffersonian

Owner: Dix Communications
Editorial: 831 Wheeling Ave, Cambridge, Ohio 43725-2316. **T:** 1 740 439-3531
E: newsroom@daily-jeff.com
W: http://www.daily-jeff.com
Freq: Daily; **Circ:** 12625 Not Audited
Publisher: Andrew Dix
Editorial Profile: The Daily Jeffersonian is published for the residents of Guernsey, Noble, Muskingum, Belmont and Tuscarawas counties in Southeastern Ohio. It covers local news, government, business, sports and lifestyle. The newspaper also features national stories if they have a direct impact on the readership.; Full Page Mono: 16.00; Full Page Colour: 265.00
Currency: US Dollars
DAILY NEWSPAPER

The Daily Journal

Owner: Small Newspaper Group
Editorial: 8 Dearborn Sq, Kankakee, Illinois 60901-3945. **T:** 1 815 937-3300
E: editorial@daily-journal.com
W: http://www.daily-journal.com
Freq: Mon thru Fri; **Circ:** 30000 Not Audited
Publisher: Robert Small
Editorial Profile: The Daily Journal is published daily for the residents of Kankakee, IL and surrounding areas. The newspaper covers local news, business, sports and entertainment.; Full Page Mono: 30.71; Full Page Colour: 101.43
Currency: US Dollars
DAILY NEWSPAPER

Daily Journal

Owner: Home News Enterprises
Editorial: 2575 N Morton St, Franklin, Indiana 46131-8886. **T:** 1 317 736-7101
E: newstips@dailyjournal.net
W: http://www.dailyjournal.net
Freq: Mon thru Fri; **Circ:** 18455 Not Audited
Editor: Michele Holtkamp; **Publisher:** Charles Wells
Editorial Profile: Daily Journal is a local newspaper written for residents of Johnson County, IN. The newspaper covers local news, sports and events.; Full Page Mono: 21.91; Full Page Colour: 318.00
Currency: US Dollars
DAILY NEWSPAPER

The Daily Journal

Owner: Boone Newspapers Inc.
Editorial: 914 E Channing Ave, Fergus Falls, Minnesota 56537-3700. **T:** 1 218 736-7511
E: newsroom@fergusfallsjournal.com
W: http://www.fergusfallsjournal.com
Freq: Daily; **Circ:** 7162 Not Audited
Editorial Profile: The Daily Journal is written for residents in and around Furgus Falls, MN. The paper covers local news, sports, lifestyle and weather. The lead time varies.; Full Page Mono: 14.00; Full Page Colour: 75.00
Currency: US Dollars
DAILY NEWSPAPER

The Daily Journal
Owner: Lee Enterprises, Inc.
Editorial: 1513 S Saint Joe Dr, Park Hills, Missouri 63601. **T:** 1 573 431-2010
E: editorial@dailyjournalonline.com
W: http://www.dailyjournalonline.com
Freq: Daily; **Circ:** 4933 Not Audited
Publisher: Gary Berblinger
Editorial Profile: The Daily Journal is a local daily newspaper published for the residents of Parks Hill, MO. Covers local news, sports, entertainment, business and community events.; Full Page Mono: 17.75; Full Page Colour: 230.00
Currency: US Dollars
DAILY NEWSPAPER

The Daily Journal
Owner: Gannett Co., Inc.
Editorial: 891 E Oak Rd, Vineland, New Jersey 08360-2396. **T:** 1 856 691-5000
W: http://www.thedailyjournal.com
Freq: Daily; **Circ:** 11337 Not Audited
Editorial Profile: The Daily Journal is published for the residents of Vineland, NJ and surrounding areas. The newspaper covers local and state news, sports, education, lifestyles and entertainment.; Full Page Mono: 54.74; Full Page Colour: 468.00
Currency: US Dollars
DAILY NEWSPAPER

Daily Journal
Owner: SMDJ, LLC
Editorial: 800 S Claremont St, Ste 210, San Mateo, California 94402. **T:** 1 650 344-5200
E: news@smdailyjournal.com
W: http://www.smdailyjournal.com
Freq: Daily; **Circ:** 15000 Not Audited
Publisher: Jerry Lee; **Editor In Chief:** Jon Mays
Editorial Profile: Daily Journal is a local newspaper published six days a week for residents of San Mateo, CA, and surrounding communities. The newspaper covers local and national news, weather, sports and community events.; Full Page Mono: 25.00; Full Page Colour: 299.00
Currency: US Dollars
DAILY NEWSPAPER

Daily Leader
Owner: GateHouse Media Inc.
Editorial: 318 N Main St, Pontiac, Illinois 61764. **T:** 1 815 842-1153
E: ldrnews@mchsi.com
W: http://www.pontiacdailyleader.com
Freq: Mon; **Circ:** 4170 Not Audited
Publisher: Pam McDowell
Editorial Profile: Daily Leader is a local daily newspaper written for residents in and around Pontiac, IL and Livingston County, IL. The paper covers local news, sports, entertainment, business and weather.; Full Page Mono: 11.87; Full Page Colour: 190.00
Currency: US Dollars
NEWSPAPER

Daily Ledger
Owner: GateHouse Media Inc.
Editorial: 53 W Elm St, Canton, Illinois 61520. **T:** 1 309 647-5100
E: editor@cantondailyledger.com
W: http://www.cantondailyledger.com
Freq: Daily; **Circ:** 4932 Not Audited
Editor: John Froehling
Editorial Profile: Daily Ledger is a local daily published newspaper written for the residents of Canton and Fulton County, IL. The publication covers local and national news, entertainment, health, sports and business issues.; Full Page Mono: 12.30; Full Page Colour: 240.00
Currency: US Dollars
DAILY NEWSPAPER

Daily Local News
Owner: Journal Register Company
Editorial: 250 N Bradford Ave, West Chester, Pennsylvania 19382-1912. **T:** 1 610 696-1775
E: news@dailylocal.com
W: http://www.dailylocal.com
Freq: Daily; **Circ:** 26772 Not Audited
Publisher: Ed Condra; **Editor:** Andrew Hachadorian; **News Editor:** Mike Rellahan
Editorial Profile: Daily Local News in West Chester, PA covers local news, sports, events, business and politics affecting residents of Chester County, PA. It also covers national news if it has direct impact on the readership.; Full Page Mono: 52.87; Full Page Colour: 865.00
Currency: US Dollars
DAILY NEWSPAPER

The Daily Mail
Owner: Johnson Newspaper Corp.

Editorial: 414 Main St, Catskill, New York 12414-1303. **T:** 1 518 943-2100
E: editorial@thedailymail.net
W: http://www.thedailymail.net
Freq: Daily; **Circ:** 2713 Not Audited
Editor: Raymond Pignone
Editorial Profile: The Daily Mail is a daily newspaper serving the residents of Green County, NY. The editorial content covers sports, technology, weather, business, and community news and events.; Full Page Mono: 10.50
Currency: US Dollars
DAILY NEWSPAPER

The Daily Messenger
Owner: GateHouse Media Inc.
Editorial: 73 Buffalo St, Canandaigua, New York 14424-1001. **T:** 1 585 394-0770
E: messengerpost@messengerpostmedia.com
W: http://www.mpnnow.com
Freq: Daily; **Circ:** 11255 Not Audited
Publisher: Chris Miller; **Publisher:** Richard Procida; **Editor:** Dave Wheeler
Editorial Profile: The Daily Messenger is a local daily newspaper for residents of Ontario County, NY. The paper is dedicated to linking its readers and advertisers to the greater Rochester and Western Finger Lakes, NY region by focusing on local and neighborhood news. The paper also provides national news coverage provided by news services.; Full Page Mono: 17.80
Currency: US Dollars
DAILY NEWSPAPER

The Daily Mining Gazette
Owner: Ogden Newspapers
Editorial: 206 Shelden Ave, Houghton, Michigan 49931-2134. **T:** 1 906 482-1500
E: clerk@mininggazette.com
W: http://www.mininggazette.com
Freq: Mon thru Fri; **Circ:** 6142 Not Audited
Publisher: Michael Scott
Editorial Profile: The Daily Mining Gazette is published for residents of Houghton, MI and surrounding areas. The publication covers local news, business, sports, lifestyles and entertainment.; Full Page Mono: 17.29; Full Page Colour: 2070.50
Currency: US Dollars
DAILY NEWSPAPER

Daily Mountain Eagle
Owner: Cleveland Newspapers Inc.
Editorial: 1301 Viking Dr, Jasper, Alabama 35501-4983. **T:** 1 205 221-2840
E: jasper@mountaineagle.com
W: http://www.mountaineagle.com
Freq: Daily; **Circ:** 7745 Not Audited
Editor: Ron Harris; **Publisher & Editor:** Jerome Wassmann
Editorial Profile: Daily Mountain Eagle is written for the residents of Jasper, AL. It covers local news, high school sports and lifestyle.; Full Page Mono: 18.06; Full Page Colour: 231.00
Currency: US Dollars
DAILY NEWSPAPER

Daily News
Owner: MediaNews Group
Editorial: 545 Diamond Ave, Red Bluff, California 96080-4302. **T:** 1 530 527-2151
W: http://www.redbluffdailynews.com
Freq: Mon thru Fri; **Circ:** 6727
Publisher: Greg Stevens; **Editor:** Chip Thompson
Editorial Profile: The Daily News was founded in 1885. It is a daily newspaper serving the residents of Tehama County, CA.; Full Page Mono: 16.98; Full Page Colour: 201.60
Currency: US Dollars
DAILY NEWSPAPER

Daily News
Owner: News Publishing Company
Editorial: 813 College St, Bowling Green, Kentucky 42101-2100. **T:** 1 270 781-1700
E: editor@bgdailynews.com
W: http://www.bgdailynews.com
Freq: Daily; **Circ:** 20279
Publisher: Pipes Gaines; **Editor:** Steve Gaines; **City Editor:** Robyn Minor; **City Editor:** Robyn Minor; **City Editor:** Daniel Pike
Editorial Profile: Daily News is a local, weekly newspaper serving Bowling Green, KY and surrounding communities. The newspaper offers extensive local news, sports, weather, entertainment, community news and events and relevant national news. Deadlines for the publication are 3:30 p.m.CT day prior to, and 9:30 p.m. CT, date of issue.; Full Page Mono: 22.42; Full Page Colour: 575.00
Currency: US Dollars
DAILY NEWSPAPER

The Daily News
Owner: Heartland Publications
Editorial: 120 N 11th St, Middlesboro, Kentucky 40965-1024. **T:** 1 606 248-1010
W: http://www.middlesborodailynews.com
Freq: Fri; **Circ:** 6143 Not Audited
Editorial Profile: The Daily News is a local newspaper serving the Kentucky area. The publication's editorial mission is to keep its readers aware of all news and events going on in the tri-state area.; Full Page Mono: 15.02; Full Page Colour: 117.00
Currency: US Dollars
NEWSPAPER

Daily News
Owner: Wick Communications
Editorial: 525 Avenue V, Bogalusa, Louisiana 70427. **T:** 1 985 732-2565
E: edit@edailynews.info
W: http://www.gobogalusa.com
Freq: Daily; **Circ:** 6500 Not Audited
Editor: Jan Gibson; **Publisher & Editor:** J. Kennon
Editorial Profile: Bogalusa Daily News is a local newspaper covering the community of Bogalusa, LA and its surrounding area. The newspaper is put out daily, except Saturdays, and covers all aspects of local news; including sports, weather, entertainment and community news.; Full Page Mono: 8.75; Full Page Colour: 11.50
Currency: US Dollars
DAILY NEWSPAPER

The Daily News
Owner: Community Newspaper Holdings, Inc.
Editorial: 23 Liberty St, Newburyport, Massachusetts 01950-2750.
T: 1 978 462-6666
E: ndn@newburyportnews.com
W: http://www.newburyportnews.com
Freq: Daily; **Circ:** 8456 Not Audited
Editor: Bryan Eaton; **City Editor:** Katie Lovett; **Editor:** John Macone; **Publisher:** Sheila Smith
Editorial Profile: The Daily News provides local news and sports coverage and information about community events to the residents of Newburyport, MA.; Full Page Mono: 22.50; Full Page Colour: 500.00
Currency: US Dollars
DAILY NEWSPAPER

The Daily News
Owner: Stafford Communications Group
Editorial: 109 N Lafayette St, Greenville, Michigan 48838-1853. **T:** 1 616 754-9301
E: news@staffordgroup.com
W: http://www.thedailynews.cc
Freq: Daily; **Circ:** 7754 Not Audited
Publisher: Rob Stafford
Editorial Profile: The Daily News is a local newspaper covering news, sports and entertainment for residents of Montcalm, Kent and Ionia County, MI. Deadlines are at 8am CT the day before issue date.; Full Page Mono: 15.75; Full Page Colour: 18.75
Currency: US Dollars
DAILY NEWSPAPER

The Daily News
Owner: Ogden Newspapers
Editorial: 215 E Ludington St, Iron Mountain, Michigan 49801-2994. **T:** 1 906 774-2772
E: news@ironmountaindailynews.com
W: http://www.ironmountaindailynews.com
Freq: Mon thru Fri; **Circ:** 6958 Not Audited
News Editor: Jim Anderson; **Publisher:** Bob Johnson
Editorial Profile: The Daily News is serves the communities of Iron Mountain and Kingsford on Michigan's upper peninsula. The publication covers local news, recreation, business and high school sports. Regional, national and international news is taken exclusively from news wires.; Full Page Mono: 26.70; Full Page Colour: 370.00
Currency: US Dollars
DAILY NEWSPAPER

The Daily News
Owner: Halifax Media Holdings LLC
Editorial: 724 Bell Fork Rd, Jacksonville, North Carolina 28540-6311.
T: 1 910 353-1171
E: jdnhappenings@jdnews.com
W: http://www.jdnews.com
Freq: Daily; **Circ:** 14526 Not Audited
City Editor: Timmi Toler; **City Editor:** Timmi Toler
Editorial Profile: The Daily News is the local newspaper for Jacksonville, NC and its surrounding community. It covers local business, news, lifestyle and sports stories. During the week, one page of the local news section is devoted to news about the military bases located in Eastern North Carolina. The

page is called Liberty.; Full Page Mono: 28.93; Full Page Colour: 615.00
Currency: US Dollars
DAILY NEWSPAPER

The Daily News
Owner: Wick Communications Inc.
Editorial: 601 Dakota Ave, Wahpeton, North Dakota 58075-4325. **T:** 1 701 642-8585
E: editor@wahpetondailynews.com
W: http://www.wahpetondailynews.com
Freq: Daily; **Circ:** 2584 Not Audited
Publisher: Ken Harty
Editorial Profile: The Daily News serves the Wahpeton, ND and Breckenridge, MN areas. The publication covers local news, sports and events.; Full Page Mono: 10.50; Full Page Colour: 12.50
Currency: US Dollars
DAILY NEWSPAPER

The Daily News
Owner: Philadelphia Media Network Inc
Editorial: 325 Penn St, Huntingdon, Pennsylvania 16652-1455. **T:** 1 814 643-4040
E: dnews@huntingdondailynews.com
Freq: Daily; **Circ:** 9258 Not Audited
News Editor: Polly McMullin
Editorial Profile: The Daily News is written for residents of Huntington, PA and surrounding areas.; Full Page Mono: 14.85; Full Page Colour: 240.00
Currency: US Dollars
DAILY NEWSPAPER

The Daily News
Owner: The Tribune-Review Publishing Co.
Editorial: 401-409 Walnut St, McKeesport, Pennsylvania 15132-2613. **T:** 1 412 664-9161
E: mcknews@dailynewsemail.com
W: http://www.pittsburghlive.com/x/dailynewsmckeesport
Freq: Daily; **Circ:** 12338 Not Audited
City Editor: Bonnijean Coony Adams
Editorial Profile: The Daily News covers local news, sports, local events and obituaries. The publication is written for residents of McKeesport, PA and the surrounding community. Deadlines for the publication are 10am ET the day before issue date.; Full Page Mono: 37.38
Currency: US Dollars
DAILY NEWSPAPER

The Daily News
Owner: Lee Enterprises, Inc.
Editorial: 770 11th Ave, Longview, Washington 98632-2412. **T:** 1 360 577-2500
E: frontdoor@tdn.com **W:** http://www.tdn.com
Freq: Daily; **Circ:** 23129 Not Audited
Publisher: Rick Parrish; **City Editor:** Andre Stepankowsky; **Editor:** Roger Werth
Editorial Profile: The Daily News is written for the residents of the Longview, WA and the surrounding area. It covers local news, sports, outdoor recreation and arts & entertainment.; Full Page Mono: 29.35; Full Page Colour: 33.40
Currency: US Dollars
DAILY NEWSPAPER

Daily News
Owner: Daily News L.P.
Editorial: 4 New York Plz, New York, New York 10004-2413. **T:** 1 212 210-2100
E: news@nydailynews.com
W: http://www.nydailynews.com
Freq: Daily; **Circ:** 456360 Not Audited
Editor in Chief: Colin Myler; **New York Vue Editor:** Dan Wasserman
Editorial Profile: Daily News is a general-interest daily newspaper serving the New York City and Long Island metropolitan area. Business coverage gives readers both a national and local perspective on news and carries the top stories from Wall Street, as well as the top performing stocks and mutual funds. Consumer topics include lifestyle issues, arts and entertainment, as well as health and medicine. Deadlines fall every afternoon at 5pm ET.; Full Page Mono: 936.67; Full Page Colour: 1170.84
Currency: US Dollars
DAILY NEWSPAPER

Daily News
Owner: MediaNews Group
Editorial: 21860 Burbank Blvd, Suite 200, Woodland Hills, California 91367-6477.
T: 1 818 713-3000
E: dnmetro@dailynews.com
W: http://www.dailynews.com
Freq: Daily; **Circ:** 385602 Not Audited
City Editor: Harrison Sheppard
Editorial Profile: The Los Angeles Daily News is a general interest broadsheet daily newspaper serving the residents of Los

Angeles and San Fernando Valley, CA. This paper is a part of the Los Angeles Newspaper Group, a subsidiary of Media News Group.; Full Page Mono: 88.06; Full Page Colour: 99.26
Currency: US Dollars
DAILY NEWSPAPER

Daily News
Editorial: 200 N Spring St, Ste 345, Los Angeles, California 90012. **T:** 1 213 978-0390
DAILY NEWSPAPER

The Daily News
Editorial: 369 N 100 W, Ste 1, Cedar City, Utah 84720-2590. **T:** 1 435 865-4520
Freq: Daily; **Circ:** 5692 Not Audited
Publisher: Donny Welch
Editorial Profile: The Daily News is a daily, local newspaper serving the residents of Cedar City and Iron County, UT. The newspaper covers local news, sports and other topics of interest to the readers.; Full Page Mono: 12.80
Currency: US Dollars
DAILY NEWSPAPER

Daily News - Bronx Bureau
Editorial: 1892 Eastchester Rd, Bronx, New York 10461-2331. **T:** 1 718 822-1174
E: bronxboronews@nydailynews.com
DAILY NEWSPAPER

Daily News - Brooklyn Bureau
Editorial: 16 Court St Ste 503, Brooklyn, New York 11241-1035. **T:** 1 718 875-4455
E: brooklynnews@nydailynews.com
DAILY NEWSPAPER

Daily News - City Hall Bureau
Editorial: Rm 9 City Hall, New York, New York 10007-1203. **T:** 1 212 210-2214
DAILY NEWSPAPER

Daily News - Courts Bureau
Editorial: 225 Cadman Plz E, Brooklyn, New York 11201-1832. **T:** 1 718 834-1517
DAILY NEWSPAPER

Daily News - Police Bureau
Editorial: 1 Police Plz, New York, New York 10038-1403. **T:** 1 212 210-2234
Bureau Chief: Rocco Parascandola
DAILY NEWSPAPER

Daily News - Queens Bureau
Editorial: 11835 Queens Blvd, Forest Hills, New York 11375-7200. **T:** 1 718 793-3328
E: queensnews@nydailynews.com
DAILY NEWSPAPER

Daily News - State House Bureau
Editorial: State Capitol LCA 3rd Floor, Albany, New York 12224. **T:** 1 518 463-4287
Bureau Chief: Kenneth Lovett
DAILY NEWSPAPER

Daily News - Washington D.C. Bureau
Editorial: 1050 Thomas Jefferson St NW, Washington, District Of Columbia 20007-3837. **T:** 1 202 467-6670
DAILY NEWSPAPER

Daily News Community Newspapers
Owner: Daily News L.P.
Editorial: 4 New York Plz, New York, New York 10004-2413. **T:** 1 212 210-2100
E: news@nydailynews.com
W: http://www.nydailynews.com **Circ:** 230000 Not Audited
Editor: Jim Harney
NEWSPAPER

The Daily News Journal
Owner: Gannett Co., Inc.
Editorial: 224 N Walnut St, Murfreesboro, Tennessee 37130-3622. **T:** 1 615 893-5860
W: http://www.dnj.com
Freq: Daily; **Circ:** 10325 Not Audited
Editorial Profile: The Daily News Journal is a daily publication serving residents of Murfreesboro, TN and the surrounding counties. The paper focuses on local news, sports and politics with some national coverage.; Full Page Mono: 21.06; Full Page Colour: 147.00
Currency: US Dollars
DAILY NEWSPAPER

Daily News Publications - Palo Alto
Owner: MediaNews Group
Editorial: 255 Constitution Dr, Menlo Park, California 94025-1108. **T:** 1 650 391-1000
E: eventsandnews@dailynewsgroup.com
W: http://www.mercurynews.com/peninsula
Freq: Daily; **Circ:** 21100 Not Audited
City Night Editor: Victor Gonzales
DAILY NEWSPAPER

Daily News-Record
Owner: Byrd Newspapers
Editorial: 231 S Liberty St, Harrisonburg, Virginia 22801-3621. **T:** 1 540 574-6200
W: http://www.dnronline.com
Freq: Daily; **Circ:** 28161 Not Audited
Publisher: Thomas Byrd; **City Editor:** Rob Longley; **Editor:** Peter Yates
Editorial Profile: Daily News-Record covers local and world news for residents of Harrisonburg and the Shenandoah Valley, VA as well as counties in neighboring West Virginia. The publication also features business news, local politics, education, arts & entertainment and lifestyle.; Full Page Mono: 26.00; Full Page Colour: 495.00
Currency: US Dollars
DAILY NEWSPAPER

Daily News-Sun
Owner: 10/13 Communications
Editorial: 10102 W Santa Fe Dr, Sun City, Arizona 85351. **T:** 1 623 977-8351
W: http://www.yourwestvalley.com
Freq: Mon thru Fri; **Circ:** 7171 Not Audited
Publisher: Jason Joseph
Editorial Profile: Daily News-Sun is published for the residents of Sun City, Youngtown, El Mirage, Glendale, Peoria and Surprise, AZ and surrounding areas. It covers local news, sports and events.; Full Page Mono: 16.00; Full Page Colour: 300.00
Currency: US Dollars
DAILY NEWSPAPER

Daily News-Sun Publishing
Owner: 10/13 Communications
Editorial: 10102 W Santa Fe Dr, Sun City, Arizona 85351-3106. **T:** 1 623 977-8351
W: http://yourwestvalley.com **Circ:** 74000 Not Audited
Publisher: Jason Joseph
NEWSPAPER

The Daily Nonpareil
Owner: Southwest Iowa Newspaper Association
Editorial: 535 W Broadway, Ste 300, Council Bluffs, Iowa 51503-0831. **T:** 1 712 328-1811
E: editorial@nonpareilonline.com
W: http://www.nonpareilonline.com
Freq: Daily; **Circ:** 12788
News Editor: Chad Nation; **Publisher:** Thomas Schmitt
Editorial Profile: The Daily Nonpareil is written for residents in and around Council Bluffs, IA. The paper covers local news, sports and weather.; Full Page Mono: 25.00; Full Page Colour: 82.42
Currency: US Dollars
DAILY NEWSPAPER

Daily Pilot
Owner: Tribune Company
Editorial: 1375 Sunflower Ave, Costa Mesa, California 92626-1665. **T:** 1 714 966-4600
E: dailypilot@latimes.com
W: http://www.dailypilot.com
Freq: Fri; **Circ:** 17031 Not Audited
Editor: John Canalis
Editorial Profile: Daily Pilot is a free, local newspaper written for residents of Costa Mesa, CA. It is distributed as an insert with the Los Angeles Times Orange County edition. The newspaper covers local news, sports and community events.; Full Page Mono: 29.90; Full Page Colour: 325.00
Currency: US Dollars
NEWSPAPER

Daily Post
Owner: San Francisco Daily LLC
Editorial: 324 High St, Palo Alto, California 94301-1042. **T:** 1 650 328-7700
E: news@padailypost.com
W: http://www.padailypost.com
Freq: Mon thru Fri; **Circ:** 7500 Not Audited
Editorial Profile: Daily Post is a free newspaper that is published each weekday. Its focus is on the Marina, Cow Hollow, Fillmore, Noe Valley and Castro districts of San Francisco. Although neighborhood issues and local news dominate the paper, it also contains regional, national and international news stories. The paper is distributed in stores, coffee shops, restaurants and workplaces and circulates from Mountain View and Los Altos to the Golden Gate Bridge. Advertising deadlines are daily at 3pm PT.; Full Page Mono: 15.00; Full Page Colour: 18.00
Currency: US Dollars
DAILY NEWSPAPER

The Daily Post-Athenian
Owner: Jones Media, Inc.
Editorial: 320 S Jackson St, Athens, Tennessee 37303. **T:** 1 423 745-5664
E: news@dailypostathenian.com
W: http://www.dpa.xtn.net
Freq: Daily; **Circ:** 10334 Not Audited
News Editor: Jennifer Cathey; **Editor:** Douglas Headrick; **Editor:** Autumn Hughes; **Publisher:** Tommy Wilson
Editorial Profile: The Daily Post-Athenian is a local newspaper written for residents of McMinn and Meigs counties in TN. The newspaper covers local news, sports, business and lifestyles.; Full Page Mono: 15.50; Full Page Colour: 260.00
Currency: US Dollars
DAILY NEWSPAPER

Daily Press
Owner: New Media Investment Group, Inc.
Editorial: 13891 Park Ave, Victorville, California 92392. **T:** 1 760 241-7744
E: vvnews@vvdailypress.com
W: http://www.vvdailypress.com
Freq: Daily; **Circ:** 25059 Not Audited
City Editor: Kris Reilly; **Publisher:** Stephan Wingert
Editorial Profile: Daily Press is a newspaper serving Victorville, CA and the surrounding Victor Valley in San Bernardino County. The publication covers local news, sports, and entertainment.; Full Page Mono: 38.12; Full Page Colour: 400.00
Currency: US Dollars
DAILY NEWSPAPER

Daily Press
Owner: Ogden Newspapers
Editorial: 600 Ludington St, Escanaba, Michigan 49829-3830. **T:** 1 906 786-2021
E: news@dailypress.net
W: http://www.dailypress.net
Freq: Mon thru Fri; **Circ:** 6316 Not Audited
News Editor: Mary Ann Heath; **Publisher:** Dan McDonald; **Editor:** Brian Rowell
Editorial Profile: Daily Press is published weekly for residents of Escanaba, MI. The newspaper covers local news and community events.; Full Page Mono: 26.40; Full Page Colour: 205.00
Currency: US Dollars
DAILY NEWSPAPER

The Daily Press
Owner: Horizon Publications
Editorial: 245 Brusselles St, Saint Marys, Pennsylvania 15857-1594. **T:** 1 814 781-1596
E: smnews@smdailypress.com
W: http://www.smdailypress.com
Freq: Mon thru Fri; **Circ:** 5550 Not Audited
Publisher: Darlene Coder
Editorial Profile: The Daily Press serves the residents of Saint Marys, PA. It provides local, regional and national news coverage.; Full Page Mono: 9.05; Full Page Colour: 200.00
Currency: US Dollars
DAILY NEWSPAPER

The Daily Press
Owner: Macquarie Media Group
Editorial: 122 3rd St W, Ashland, Wisconsin 54806. **T:** 1 715 682-2313
E: pressnews@ashlanddailypress.net
W: http://www.ashlandwi.com
Freq: Daily; **Circ:** 6153 Not Audited
Editor: Larry Servinsky
Editorial Profile: The Daily Press is a daily newspaper published for the residents of Ashland, WI and surrounding areas. It provides information on local news and events. On Tuesdays, the paper is published online-only.; Full Page Mono: 12.50; Full Page Colour: 14.05
Currency: US Dollars
DAILY NEWSPAPER

Daily Press
Owner: Tribune Company
Editorial: 7505 Warwick Blvd, Newport News, Virginia 23607-1517. **T:** 1 757 247-4600
W: http://www.dailypress.com
Freq: Daily; **Circ:** 52078 Not Audited
Editorial Profile: Daily Press is written for the residents of Newport, Hampton, York, Williamsburg, Gloucester, Matthews, Middlesex, Isle of Wight and Surrey, VA. The newspaper covers local, national and international news, along with sports, arts & entertainment and features.; Full Page Mono: 79.55; Full Page Colour: 255.46
Currency: US Dollars
DAILY NEWSPAPER

Daily Press
Editorial: 216 Ironbound Rd, Williamsburg, Virginia 23188-2618. **T:** 1 757 247-4600
DAILY NEWSPAPER

The Daily Progress
Owner: BH Media Group
Editorial: 685 Rio Rd W, Charlottesville, Virginia 22901-1413. **T:** 1 434 978-7200
W: http://www.dailyprogress.com
Freq: Daily; **Circ:** 23080 Not Audited
Editorial Profile: The Daily Progress covers news for residents of Charlottesville, VA and Albemarle, Buckingham, Fluvanna, Greene, Louisa, Madison, Orange and Nelson Counties. Coverage includes local, national and international news, as well as business, local courts, arts & entertainment, politics and weather.; Full Page Mono: 44.56; Full Page Colour: 1630.00
Currency: US Dollars
DAILY NEWSPAPER

Daily Record
Owner: Lewis Newspapers
Editorial: 1209 State St, Lawrenceville, Illinois 62439. **T:** 1 618 943-2331
E: lawnews@lawdailyrecord.com
W: http://www.lawdailyrecord.com
Freq: Mon thru Fri; **Circ:** 4012 Not Audited
Publisher: Kathleen Lewis
Editorial Profile: Daily Record is published for the residents of Lawrence County, IL. It provides information on local news and events.; Full Page Mono: 7.50; Full Page Colour: 195.00
Currency: US Dollars
DAILY NEWSPAPER

The Daily Record
Owner: Record Publishing Co.
Editorial: 99 W Broad St, Dunn, North Carolina 28334. **T:** 1 910 891-1234
E: news@mydailyrecord.com
W: http://www.mydailyrecord.com
Freq: Daily; **Circ:** 8517 Not Audited
Editorial Profile: The Daily Record is a daily newspaper serving Dunn, NC and the surrounding communities. It covers local and national news, business, government and lifestyle. Deadlines are daily at 9:30am ET.; Full Page Mono: 13.40
Currency: US Dollars
DAILY NEWSPAPER

The Daily Record
Owner: Dix Communications
Editorial: 212 E Liberty St, Wooster, Ohio 44691-4394. **T:** 1 330 264-1125
W: http://www.the-daily-record.com
Freq: Daily; **Circ:** 19076 Not Audited
News Editor: Jeanine Kendle; **Publisher:** Bill McKinney
Editorial Profile: The Daily Record is a daily, local newspaper serving the Wooster, OH area. Local, national and international news are covered, as well as local entertainment, sports, and lifestyle information.; Full Page Mono: 29.52; Full Page Colour: 485.00
Currency: US Dollars
DAILY NEWSPAPER

Daily Record
Owner: Pioneer Newspapers
Editorial: 401 N Main St, Ellensburg, Washington 98926-3107. **T:** 1 509 925-1414
W: http://dailyrecordnews.com
Freq: Daily; **Circ:** 5700 Not Audited
Editorial Profile: Daily Record provides coverage of local news, sports, events and commentary to the residents of Kittitas County, WA.; Full Page Mono: 13.15; Full Page Colour: 29.50
Currency: US Dollars
DAILY NEWSPAPER

Daily Record
Owner: Gannett Co., Inc.
Editorial: 6 Century Dr, Parsippany, New Jersey 07054-4608. **T:** 1 973 428-6200
E: newsroom@dailyrecord.com
W: http://www.dailyrecord.com
Freq: Daily; **Circ:** 14609 Not Audited
Editorial Profile: Daily Record is a local daily newspaper for Morris County, NJ. The paper covers local and national news, sports, government, entertainment, crime and business.; Full Page Mono: 55.59
Currency: US Dollars
DAILY NEWSPAPER

Daily Reflector
Owner: Cooke Communications, LLC
Editorial: 1150 Sugg Pkwy, Greenville, North Carolina 27834. **T:** 1 252 752-6166
W: http://www.reflector.com
Freq: Daily; **Circ:** 20465 Not Audited
Publisher: John Cooke, Jr.
Editorial Profile: Daily Reflector provides local news, sports and weather to the residents of

Pitt County, NC.; Full Page Mono: 12.55; Full Page Colour: 1985.80
Currency: US Dollars
DAILY NEWSPAPER

Daily Reporter
Owner: Home News Enterprises
Editorial: 22 W New Rd, Greenfield, Indiana 46140. **T:** 1 317 462-5528
W: http://www.greenfieldreporter.com
Freq: Daily; **Circ:** 7800 Not Audited
Editor: David Hill; **Editor:** David Hill; **Editor:** David Hill; **Editor:** David Hill; **Publisher:** Charles Wells
Editorial Profile: Daily Reporter is a newspaper written for residents of Freenfield, IN and surrounding areas. The newspaper covers local news, arts & entertainment, sports and community events.; Full Page Mono: 12.75; Full Page Colour: 18.75
Currency: US Dollars
DAILY NEWSPAPER

The Daily Reporter
Owner: Fortress Investment Group, LLC
Editorial: 15 W Pearl St, Coldwater, Michigan 49036-1097. **T:** 1 517 278-2318
W: http://www.thedailyreporter.com
Freq: Daily; **Circ:** 5562 Not Audited
Publisher: David Ferro
Editorial Profile: The Daily Reporter is published for the residents of Coldwater, MI. It covers local news and sports.; Full Page Mono: 14.69; Full Page Colour: 53.96
Currency: US Dollars
DAILY NEWSPAPER

Daily Reporter-Herald
Owner: Lehman Communications Corp.
Editorial: 201 E 5th St, Loveland, Colorado 80537-5605. **T:** 1 970 669-5050
E: news@reporter-herald.com
W: http://www.reporterherald.com
Freq: Daily; **Circ:** 18848 Not Audited
Publisher: Ed Lehman
Editorial Profile: Daily Reporter-Herald is a daily newspaper written for the residents of Loveland, CO. The paper covers news and events on a local, state and national level.; Full Page Mono: 26.01; Full Page Colour: 101.50
Currency: US Dollars
DAILY NEWSPAPER

Daily Republic
Owner: McNaughton Newspapers
Editorial: 1250 Texas St, Fairfield, California 94533. **T:** 1 707 425-4646
W: http://www.dailyrepublic.com
Freq: Daily; **Circ:** 17710 Not Audited
Publisher: Bill James
Editorial Profile: Daily Republic is published for the residents of Fairfield, CA and surrounding areas. The newspaper covers local and state news, business, sports, lifestyles and arts & entertainment.; Full Page Mono: 23.80; Full Page Colour: 96.95
Currency: US Dollars
DAILY NEWSPAPER

The Daily Republic
Owner: Forum Communications Co.
Editorial: 120 S Lawler St, Mitchell, South Dakota 57301-3443. **T:** 1 605 996-5514
E: webmaster@mitchellrepublic.com
W: http://www.mitchellrepublic.com
Freq: Daily; **Circ:** 12400 Not Audited
Editor: Seth Tupper; **Publisher:** Korrie Wenzel
Editorial Profile: The Daily Republic is published daily for the residents of Mitchell, SD and surrounding areas. The newspaper covers local news, business, sports, education and lifestyles.; Full Page Mono: 21.30; Full Page Colour: 30.45
Currency: US Dollars
DAILY NEWSPAPER

Daily Republican-Register
Owner: Brehm Communications, Inc.
Editorial: 115 E 4th St, Mount Carmel, Illinois 62863. **T:** 1 618 262-5144
E: news@mtcarmelregister.com
W: http://www.mtcarmelregister.com
Freq: Daily; **Circ:** 3973 Not Audited
Editor: Andrea Howe; **Editor:** Andrea Howe; **Editor:** Andrea Howe; **Editor:** Andrea Howe; **Publisher:** Phil Summers; **News Editor:** Amanda Thombleson
Editorial Profile: Mount Carmel Republican-Register is published daily for the residents of Wabash County, IL. The newspaper covers local news and community events.; Full Page Mono: 12.15; Full Page Colour: 160.00
Currency: US Dollars
DAILY NEWSPAPER

The Daily Review
Owner: MediaNews Group
Editorial: 22533 Foothill Blvd, Hayward, California 94541. **T:** 1 510 783-6111
W: http://www.insidebayarea.com/dailyreview
Freq: Daily; **Circ:** 31183 Not Audited
City Editor: Alice Crane
Editorial Profile: The Daily Review in Hayward, CA is published for residents of Hayward, Fairview, San Leandro, San Lorenzo, Ashland, Cherryland and Castro Valley, CA. Coverage includes community news, sports, entertainment, weather, education, health and politics. The paper is a part of the Bay Area News Group subsidiary of MediaNews Group.; Full Page Mono: 149.00; Full Page Colour: 1262.00
Currency: US Dollars
DAILY NEWSPAPER

The Daily Review
Owner: LSN Publishing Co. LLC
Editorial: 1014 Front St, Morgan City, Louisiana 70380-3226. **T:** 1 985 384-8370
E: news@daily-review.com
W: http://www.daily-review.com
Freq: Daily; **Circ:** 5621 Not Audited
Publisher & Editor: Allan Von Werder
Editorial Profile: The Daily Review is published for the residents of Morgan City, LA. The newspaper covers local and world news and information.; Full Page Mono: 8.40; Full Page Colour: 300.00
Currency: US Dollars
DAILY NEWSPAPER

Daily Review Atlas
Owner: GateHouse Media Inc.
Editorial: 400 S Main St, Monmouth, Illinois 61462. **T:** 1 309 734-3176
E: communitynews@reviewatlas.com
W: http://www.reviewatlas.com
Freq: Daily; **Circ:** 2800 Not Audited
Publisher: Tony Scott; **Editor:** Marty Touchette
Editorial Profile: Daily Review Atlas is published daily for the residents of Monmouth, IL and surrounding areas. The newspaper offers local, national and international news.; Full Page Mono: 11.25; Full Page Colour: 180.00
Currency: US Dollars
DAILY NEWSPAPER

Daily Rocket-Miner
Owner: Rock Springs Newspapers, Inc.
Editorial: 215 D St, Rock Springs, Wyoming 82901. **T:** 1 307 362-3736
W: http://www.rocketminer.com
Freq: Daily; **Circ:** 7140 Not Audited
Publisher: Holly Dabb; **Editor:** Michele DePue
Editorial Profile: Daily Rocket-Miner is a local news publication for Rock Springs, WY. The publication runs daily, with the exception of Sunday and Monday. The paper covers mainly local and national news.; Full Page Mono: 12.56; Full Page Colour: 100.00
Currency: US Dollars
DAILY NEWSPAPER

The Daily Sentinel
Owner: Seaton Publishing
Editorial: 734 S 7th St, Grand Junction, Colorado 81501. **T:** 1 970 242-5050
E: letters@gjsentinel.com
W: http://www.gjsentinel.com
Freq: Daily; **Circ:** 24129 Not Audited
City Editor: Tim Harty; **Publisher:** Jay Seaton
Editorial Profile: The Daily Sentinel is a local newspaper published for the residents of Grand Junction, CO. The newspaper covers national and local news, sports, business, education and events.; Full Page Mono: 43.21; Full Page Colour: 750.00
Currency: US Dollars
DAILY NEWSPAPER

Daily Sentinel
Owner: Rome Sentinel Company
Editorial: 333 W Dominick St, Rome, New York 13440-5701. **T:** 1 315 337-4000
E: sentinel@rny.com
W: http://www.romesentinel.com
Freq: Daily; **Circ:** 9203 Not Audited
Publisher: Stephen Waters
Editorial Profile: Daily Sentinel is published for the residents of Rome, NY. It covers local news, community events, sports and arts & entertainment. Deadlines are daily at 11am ET.; Full Page Mono: 15.19; Full Page Colour: 265.00
Currency: US Dollars
DAILY NEWSPAPER

Daily Sentinel
Owner: Southern Newspapers, Inc.
Editorial: 4920 Colonial Dr, Nacogdoches, Texas 75965-3021. **T:** 1 936 564-8361
W: http://dailysentinel.com
Freq: Daily; **Circ:** 8724 Not Audited
Publisher and Editor: Robin Land
Editorial Profile: Daily Sentinel provides readers with information about current news and events taking place in the area of Nacogdoches County, TX. Deadlines are at 4pm CT.; Full Page Mono: 14.42; Full Page Colour: 315.00
Currency: US Dollars
DAILY NEWSPAPER

Daily Sitka Sentinel
Owner: Verstovia Corporation
Editorial: 112 Barracks St, Sitka, Alaska 99835. **T:** 1 907 747-3219
E: news@sitkasentinel.com
W: http://www.sitkasentinel.com
Freq: Daily; **Circ:** 3010 Not Audited
Editorial Profile: Daily Sitka Sentinel is written for residents of Sitka, AK. The publication covers local, international and national news.; Full Page Mono: 13.85; Full Page Colour: 57.09
Currency: US Dollars
DAILY NEWSPAPER

The Daily Southerner
Owner: Community Newspaper Holdings, Inc.
Editorial: 504 W Wilson St, Tarboro, North Carolina 27886-4239. **T:** 1 252 823-3106
W: http://dailysoutherner.com
Freq: Daily; **Circ:** 4168 Not Audited
Publisher & Editor: John Walker
Editorial Profile: The Daily Southerner is published daily for residents of Tarboro, NC and surrounding areas. The newspaper covers local and national news, business, sports and arts & entertainment.; Full Page Mono: 9.25; Full Page Colour: 32.98
Currency: US Dollars
DAILY NEWSPAPER

The Daily Sparks Tribune
Owner: Tribune Publishing Company
Editorial: 1002 C St, Sparks, Nevada 89431. **T:** 1 775 358-8061
W: http://www.dailysparkstribune.com
Freq: Daily; **Circ:** 6374 Not Audited
Publisher: Cindy Mikkelson
Editorial Profile: The Daily Sparks Tribune is a local, daily newspaper. Its editorial mission is to present the best news to the residents of Sparks, NV. It covers national and local news.; Full Page Mono: 17.00; Full Page Colour: 60.32
Currency: US Dollars
DAILY NEWSPAPER

The Daily Standard
Owner: Standard Printing Company (The)
Editorial: 123 E Market St, Celina, Ohio 45822-1798. **T:** 1 419 586-2371
E: newsroom@dailystandard.com
W: http://www.dailystandard.com
Freq: Daily; **Circ:** 10914 Not Audited
Publisher: Frank Snyder
Editorial Profile: The Daily Standard's editorial mission is to provide local coverage for the Grand Lake Saint Mary's area. It is written for residents in the in the county and community and also covers world and national news.; Full Page Mono: 11.00; Full Page Colour: 230.00
Currency: US Dollars
DAILY NEWSPAPER

The Daily Star
Owner: Paxton Media Group
Editorial: 725 S Morrison Blvd, Hammond, Louisiana 70403-5401. **T:** 1 985 254-7827
W: http://www.hammondstar.com
Freq: Daily; **Circ:** 9595
Publisher: Keenan Gingles; **City Editor:** Anthony James
Editorial Profile: The Daily Star is published for the residents of Hammond, LA and surrounding areas. The newspaper covers local news, business, sports and arts & entertainment stories. It also features national and statewide stories if they have a direct impact on the community.; Full Page Mono: 20.00; Full Page Colour: 365.00
Currency: US Dollars
DAILY NEWSPAPER

The Daily Star
Owner: Community Newspaper Holdings, Inc.
Editorial: 102 Chestnut St, Oneonta, New York 13820-2492. **T:** 1 607 432-1000
E: news@thedailystar.com
W: http://www.thedailystar.com
Freq: Daily; **Circ:** 10126 Not Audited
Publisher: Mitchell Lynch; **Editor:** Sam Pollak
Editorial Profile: The Daily Star is a daily newspaper that offers coverage of local and national news, weather, sports, local arts & entertainment and opinion. The newspaper is written for residents of Oneonta, NY.; Full Page Mono: 30.55; Full Page Colour: 350.00
Currency: US Dollars
DAILY NEWSPAPER

The Daily Star-Journal
Owner: The News-Press & Gazette Co.
Editorial: 135 E Market St, Warrensburg, Missouri 64093. **T:** 1 660 747-8123
E: dsjnews@npgco.com
W: http://www.dailystarjournal.com
Freq: Daily; **Circ:** 4796 Not Audited
Publisher: William James; **Editor:** Jack Ventimiglia
Editorial Profile: The Daily Star-Journal is written for residents of Johnson County, MO. The publication covers local, international and national news, along with local sports, entertainment, agricultural news and milestones. Deadlines for the publication are two days before issue date.; Full Page Mono: 10.50; Full Page Colour: 137.00
Currency: US Dollars
DAILY NEWSPAPER

The Daily Statesman
Owner: Rust Communications
Editorial: 133 S Walnut St, Dexter, Missouri 63841-2141. **T:** 1 573 624-4545
W: http://www.dailystatesman.com
Freq: Daily; **Circ:** 2519 Not Audited
Publisher: Bud Hunt; **Editor:** Noreen Hyslop
Editorial Profile: The Daily Statesman is written for the citizens of Stoddard County, MO. The publication covers local, sports, national and international news.; Full Page Mono: 12.00; Full Page Colour: 370.00
Currency: US Dollars
DAILY NEWSPAPER

Daily Sun News
Owner: Eagle Newspapers
Editorial: 600 S 6th St, Sunnyside, Washington 98944-2111. **T:** 1 509 837-4500
E: dailysunnews@dailysunnews.com
W: http://www.dailysunnews.com
Freq: Daily; **Circ:** 3800 Not Audited
Publisher: Tim Graff
Editorial Profile: Daily Sun News is published daily for residents of Sunnyside, WA and surrounding areas. It covers local news and events.; Full Page Mono: 9.00; Full Page Colour: 180.00
Currency: US Dollars
DAILY NEWSPAPER

The Daily Telegram
Owner: GateHouse Media Inc.
Editorial: 133 N Winter St, Adrian, Michigan 49221. **T:** 1 517 265-5111
E: editor@lenconnect.com
W: http://www.lenconnect.com
Freq: Daily; **Circ:** 12647 Not Audited
Editor: Marge Ferguson; **Publisher:** Paul Heidbreder; **Editor:** Mark Lenz; **News Editor:** David Panian
Editorial Profile: The Daily Telegram is a daily, evening newspaper serving Adrian, MI. It covers news, sports, and entertainment. The lead time varies. Contact the publication for advertising rates and circulation figures.; Full Page Mono: 26.25; Full Page Colour: 785.00
Currency: US Dollars
DAILY NEWSPAPER

The Daily Telegraph (New York)
Editorial: 584 Broadway, New York, New York 10012-3229. **T:** 1 212 219-8131
US Editor: Philip Sherwell
Editorial Profile: New York Bureau for the Daily Telegraph, covering the latest news & current affairs, politics, finance and business in New York for the newspaper.
DAILY NEWSPAPER

The Daily Telegraph (Washington DC)
Editorial: 1310 G St NW, Washington, District Of Columbia 20220-0007. **T:** 1 202 393-5195
US Editor: Peter Foster
Editorial Profile: Washington Bureau for the Daily Telegraph, covering the latest news & current affairs, politics, finance and business in Washington for the newspaper.
DAILY NEWSPAPER

The Daily Times
Owner: Gannett Co., Inc.
Editorial: 618 Beam St, Salisbury, Maryland 21801-7803. **T:** 1 410 749-7171
E: newshub@delmarvanow.com
W: http://www.delmarvanow.com
Freq: Daily; **Circ:** 14582 Not Audited
Editor: Cindy Robinson
Editorial Profile: The Daily Times is a daily newspaper serving Salisbury, MD and the surrounding areas. It covers local and national

news, sports and opinion.; Full Page Mono: 30.32; Full Page Colour: 400.00
Currency: US Dollars
DAILY NEWSPAPER

The Daily Times
Owner: MediaNews Group
Editorial: 201 N Allen Ave, Farmington, New Mexico 87401-6212. **T:** 1 505 325-4545
W: http://www.daily-times.com
Freq: Daily; **Circ:** 20140 Not Audited
Publisher: John Elchert
Editorial Profile: The Daily News is a local daily newspaper written for the residents of Farmington, NM. The paper covers local news, sports and features.; Full Page Mono: 23.10; Full Page Colour: 77.43
Currency: US Dollars
DAILY NEWSPAPER

Daily Times
Owner: Community Newspaper Holdings, Inc.
Editorial: 105 S Adair St, Pryor, Oklahoma 74361-3625. **T:** 1 918 825-3292
E: prynews@swbell.net
W: http://www.pryordailytimes.com
Freq: Daily; **Circ:** 3787 Not Audited
Publisher: Ken Jones
Editorial Profile: Daily Times is published daily for the residents of Pryor, OK and surrounding areas. The newspaper covers local news, business, sports, lifestyles and entertainment.; Full Page Mono: 12.41; Full Page Colour: 16.41
Currency: US Dollars
DAILY NEWSPAPER

The Daily Times
Owner: Blount County Publishers LLC
Editorial: 307 E Harper Ave, Maryville, Tennessee 37804. **T:** 1 865 981-1100
E: editor@thedailytimes.com
W: http://www.thedailytimes.com
Freq: Daily; **Circ:** 18425 Not Audited
News Editor: Richard Dodson; **Editor:** Bob Norris; **Editor:** Melanie Tucker; **Editor:** Steve Wildsmith
Editorial Profile: The Daily Times is a daily newspaper published for residents of Maryville, TN. The editorial content includes local news, sports, opinion, events, education, business, lifestyle and health. Advertising deadlines are at 2pm CT.; Full Page Mono: 28.80; Full Page Colour: 450.00
Currency: US Dollars
DAILY NEWSPAPER

Daily Times Chronicle
Owner: Woburn Daily Times, Inc.
Editorial: 1 Arrow Dr, Woburn, Massachusetts 1801. **T:** 1 781 933-3700
W: http://www.woburnonline.com
Freq: Mon thru Fri; **Circ:** 10795 Not Audited
Editor in Chief: James Haggerty; **Publisher:** Peter Haggerty; **Editor:** Gordon Vincent
Editorial Profile: Daily Times Chronicle is a local newspaper written for the residents of Woburn, Reading, Burlington, Winchester and Wakefield, MA. It provides local and national news, community events, schools, businesses, politics, sports and features.; Full Page Mono: 21.50; Full Page Colour: 150.00
Currency: US Dollars
DAILY NEWSPAPER

Daily Times Leader
Owner: Horizon Publications
Editorial: 227 Court St, West Point, Mississippi 39773-2926. **T:** 1 662 494-1422
E: dtleditor@bellsouth.net
W: http://www.dailytimesleader.com
Freq: Daily; **Circ:** 3410 Not Audited
Publisher: Donald Norman
Editorial Profile: Daily Times Leader is written for residents of West Point, MS. Deadlines are daily at 10:30am CT.; Full Page Mono: 8.70; Full Page Colour: 130.00
Currency: US Dollars
DAILY NEWSPAPER

Daily Times-Call
Owner: Prairie Mountain Publishing, Co.
Editorial: 350 Terry St, Longmont, Colorado 80501-5440. **T:** 1 303 776-2244
E: news@times-call.com
W: http://www.timescall.com
Freq: Daily; **Circ:** 20953 Not Audited
Publisher: Dean Lehman; **Day News Editor:** Travis Pryor; **News Editor:** K.J. Ritter; **Editor:** Rob Spencer
Editorial Profile: Daily Times-Call's editorial mission is to provide the most comprehensive news coverage about public and private news issues. The publication is written for the general public in Boulder, Weld and Larimer counties, CO.; Full Page Mono: 21.78; Full Page Colour: 536.00

Currency: US Dollars
DAILY NEWSPAPER

The Daily Tribune
Owner: Journal Register Company
Editorial: 100 Macomb Daily Dr, Mount Clemens, Michigan 48043-5802.
T: 1 888 622-6629 **E:** editor@dailytribune.com
W: http://www.dailytribune.com
Freq: Daily; **Circ:** 6386 Not Audited
Publisher: Jeff Parra
Editorial Profile: The Daily Tribune is a daily newspaper serving Southern Oakland County, MI. It targets the communities of Hazel Park, Royal Oak, Troy, Clawson, Madison Heights, Berkley, Oak Park and Ferndale. Its sister paper is the Macomb Daily in Mount Clemens, MI. The Daily Tribune covers sports, news, city government, features, arts & entertainment, schools and police for the Southern Oakland County area.; Full Page Mono: 14.15; Full Page Colour: 19.15
Currency: US Dollars
DAILY NEWSPAPER

The Daily Tribune
Owner: Gannett Co., Inc.
Editorial: 220 1st Ave S, Wisconsin Rapids, Wisconsin 54495-4154. **T:** 1 715 423-7200
E: news@wisconsinrapidstribune.com
W: http://www.wisconsinrapidstribune.com
Freq: Daily; **Circ:** 8275 Not Audited
Editorial Profile: The Daily Tribune is a local newspaper serving the cities of Wisconsin Rapids and Nekoosa, WI, as well as the villages of Biron and Port Edwards, WI. It provides coverage of local news, events, politics, sports, lifestyle and more. It combines with the Marshfield News-Herald and the Stevens Point Journal on Sundays. Deadlines are one day prior to issue date.; Full Page Mono: 25.50; Full Page Colour: 357.00
Currency: US Dollars
DAILY NEWSPAPER

The Daily Tribune-News
Owner: Walls Group
Editorial: 251 S Tennessee St, Cartersville, Georgia 30120-3605. **T:** 1 770 382-4545
E: news@daily-tribune.com
W: http://www.daily-tribune.com
Freq: Daily; **Circ:** 5798 Not Audited
Publisher & Editor: Johnette Dawson
Editorial Profile: The Daily Tribune-News is published for the residents of Cartersville, GA and surrounding areas. The newspaper covers local and regional news.; Full Page Mono: 11.10; Full Page Colour: 200.00
Currency: US Dollars
DAILY NEWSPAPER

The Daily Triplicate
Owner: Western Communications Inc.
Editorial: 312 H St, Crescent City, California 95531-4018. **T:** 1 707 464-2141
E: webmaster@triplicate.com
W: http://www.triplicate.com
Freq: Daily; **Circ:** 4738 Not Audited
Editor: Matthew Durkee; **Publisher:** Cindy Vosburg
Editorial Profile: The Daily Triplicate is a local newspaper that is published Tuesday to Saturday. The editorial mission is to provide the residents of Del Norte County, CA with information on community news and events.; Full Page Mono: 17.65; Full Page Colour: 62.71
Currency: US Dollars
DAILY NEWSPAPER

Daily World
Owner: Gannett Co., Inc.
Editorial: 1206 Heather Dr, Opelousas, Louisiana 70570-7712. **T:** 1 337 942-4971
W: http://www.dailyworld.com
Freq: Daily; **Circ:** 4673 Not Audited
City Editor: Evan Moore
Editorial Profile: Daily World serves the residents of Opelousas, LA and surrounding areas. It covers news, sports, community events, editorials and entertainment.; Full Page Mono: 30.11; Full Page Colour: 35.36
Currency: US Dollars
DAILY NEWSPAPER

The Daily World
Owner: Stephens Media Group
Editorial: 315 S Michigan St, Aberdeen, Washington 98520-6037. **T:** 1 360 532-4000
E: press_releases@thedailyworld.com
W: http://www.thedailyworld.com
Freq: Daily; **Circ:** 12662
Publisher: Bill Crawford; **City Editor:** Dan Jackson
Editorial Profile: The Daily World is a local newspaper that serves the Grays Harbor and northern Pacific counties in Southwest

Washington. It prides itself on being "the only daily newspaper on the coast of Washington state." The newspaper provides residents with important information on local news, politics, sports, lifestyles, recreation, entertainment, and more. The editorial deadline is one day prior to the issue date.; Full Page Mono: 27.85; Full Page Colour: 490.00
Currency: US Dollars
DAILY NEWSPAPER

Dakota Catholic Action
Owner: Roman Catholic Diocese of Bismarck
Editorial: 520 N Washington St, Bismarck, North Dakota 58501-3482. **T:** 1 877 405-7435
W: http://www.bismarckdiocese.com/news
Freq: Monthly; **Circ:** 24000
Publisher: David Kagan; **Editor:** Jane Longtin
Editorial Profile: Dakota Catholic Action is a monthly newspaper for the Diocese of Bismarck, ND. The paper does not accept outside advertising.
NEWSPAPER

Dallas County News, Inc.
Owner: Stephens Media
Editorial: 705 Main St, Adel, Iowa 50003.
T: 1 515 993-4233 **E:** news@adelnews.com
W: http://www.adelnews.com Circ: 9700 Not Audited
Editor: Bill Haglund; **Editor:** Bill Haglund; **Editor:** Bill Haglund; **Editor:** Bill Haglund;
Publisher: Geoff Schumacher
NEWSPAPER

The Dallas Morning News
Owner: A.H. Belo Corp.
Editorial: 508 Young St, Dallas, Texas 75202-4808. **T:** 1 214 977-8222
E: metro@dallasnews.com
W: http://www.dallasnews.com
Freq: Daily; **Circ:** 413480 Not Audited
Editor in Chief: Bob Mong
Editorial Profile: The Dallas Morning News is a daily newspaper covering regional, national and international news. Technology coverage runs daily in the business section. Business and technology-related editorial content consists mostly of news and trend articles analyzing the impact of technology on the economy and industry. Consumer-related topics include health and fitness, food, arts & entertainment, and book, movie and theater reviews. Deadlines for business news are daily at 5:30pm CT. The lead times for daily news is two hours. For features, the lead time is one to two weeks.; Full Page Mono: 650.00; Full Page Colour: 747.50
Currency: US Dollars
DAILY NEWSPAPER

The Dallas Morning News
Editorial: 529 14th St NW Ste 1252, Washington, District Of Columbia 20045-2202.
T: 1 202 661-8410
DAILY NEWSPAPER

The Dallas Morning News
Editorial: 1005 Congress Ave, Ste 930, Austin, Texas 78701-2415. **T:** 1 512 499-0581
Bureau Chief: Christy Hoppe; **Bureau Chief:** Christy Hoppe; **Bureau Chief:** Christy Hoppe
DAILY NEWSPAPER

The Dallas Morning News
Editorial: 1410 E Renner Rd, Ste 260, Richardson, Texas 75082-2228.
T: 1 469 330-5600
Editorial Profile: This is the Collin County Bureau.
DAILY NEWSPAPER

Dallas Newspapers
Owner: Wilkes-Barre Publishing Co.
Editorial: 15 N Main St, Wilkes-Barre, Pennsylvania 18711. **T:** 1 570 675-5211
E: news@mydallaspost.com
W: http://www.mydallaspost.com Circ: 54215
Editor: Dotty Martin
Editorial Profile: Dallas Newspapers is a community newspaper publisher serving Wilkes-Barre and Scranton, PA. It shares offices with the daily newspaper the Times Leader.
NEWSPAPER

Dallas Observer
Owner: Voice Media Group
Editorial: 2501 Oak Lawn Ave Ste 700, Dallas, Texas 75219-4058. **T:** 1 214 757-9000
E: retail@dallasobserver.com
W: http://www.dallasobserver.com
Freq: Thu; **Circ:** 83300 Not Audited
Editor: Joe Tone
Editorial Profile: Dallas Observer is a community newspaper written for the residents of Dallas. It includes investigative

stories about government, politics, business, sports, music and the arts.; Full Page Mono: 36.00
Currency: US Dollars
NEWSPAPER

Dallas Post Tribune
Owner: Tribune Publishing Inc.
Editorial: 2726 S Beckley Ave, Dallas, Texas 75224. **T:** 1 214 946-7678
E: posttrib@airmail.net
W: http://www.dallaspost.com
Freq: Thu; **Circ:** 10000 Not Audited
Editorial Profile: Dallas Post Tribune is weekly newspaper that promotes equality in the Dallas area. Deadlines are on Mondays at noon CT.; Full Page Mono: 35.00
Currency: US Dollars
NEWSPAPER

The Dallas Weekly
Editorial: 3101 Martin Luther King Jr Blvd, Dallas, Texas 75215. **T:** 1 214 428-8958
E: editorial@dallasweekly.com
W: http://www.dallasweekly.com
Freq: Thu; **Circ:** 17500 Not Audited
Publisher: Jim Washington
Editorial Profile: The Dallas Weekly covers local news and events of interest to the African American community in Dallas.; Full Page Mono: 41.00; Full Page Colour: 3186.00
Currency: US Dollars
NEWSPAPER

The Dalles Chronicle
Owner: Eagle Newspapers
Editorial: 315 Federal St, The Dalles, Oregon 97058-2115. **T:** 1 541 296-2141
E: tdchron@thedalleschronicle.com
W: http://www.thedalleschronicle.com
Freq: Fri; **Circ:** 5067 Not Audited
News Editor: Matthew Neal; **Publisher:** Marilyn Roth; **Editor:** Kathy Ursprung
Editorial Profile: The Dalles Chronicle is the largest newspaper in the Columbia River Gorge serving Wasco, Sherman, Hood River and Klickitat counties. This newspaper is the news source for metroplex technology leaders.; Full Page Mono: 11.00; Full Page Colour: 300.00
Currency: US Dollars
NEWSPAPER

Dan's Papers
Owner: Manhattan Media LLC
Editorial: 158 Country Road 39, Southampton, New York 11968. **T:** 1 631 537-0500
E: editor@danspapers.com
W: http://www.danshamptons.com
Freq: Fri; **Circ:** 45000
Editor in Chief: Dan Rattiner
Editorial Profile: Dan's Papers' editorial mission is to provide entertainment and take stances on current events. The publications are written for people interested in elegant lifestyles in Long Island, NY.; Full Page Mono: 44.47
Currency: US Dollars
NEWSPAPER

Danville News
Owner: Community Newspaper Holdings, Inc.
Editorial: 345 Mill St, Danville, Pennsylvania 17821-2063. **T:** 1 570 275-3235
E: news@thedanvillenews.com
W: http://www.thedanvillenews.com
Freq: Daily; **Circ:** 4200 Not Audited
News Editor: Bill Foley; **Publisher:** Gary Grossman
Editorial Profile: Danville News is a daily newspaper written for the residents of Danville, Sunbury and Susquehanna Valley, PA. It covers local news, sports, events, business and classifieds.; Full Page Mono: 8.42; Full Page Colour: 100.00
Currency: US Dollars
DAILY NEWSPAPER

Danville Register and Bee
Owner: BH Media Group
Editorial: 700 Monument St, Danville, Virginia 24541-1512. **T:** 1 434 793-2311
E: news@registerbee.com
W: http://www.godanriver.com
Freq: Daily; **Circ:** 17058 Not Audited
Editor: Robert Benson; **Publisher:** Steve Kaylor
Editorial Profile: Danville Register and Bee is written for residents of Danville, VA. It covers local news, business, sports, arts & entertainment, national and statewide stories.; Full Page Mono: 27.48; Full Page Colour: 404.25
Currency: US Dollars
DAILY NEWSPAPER

Davis County Clipper

Owner: Clipper Publishing Co., Inc.
Editorial: 1370 S 500 W, Woods Cross, Utah 84010. **T:** 1 801 295-2251
E: news@davisclipper.com
W: http://www.davisclipper.com
Freq: Thu; **Circ:** 11350 Not Audited
Editor: Tom Busselberg; **Publisher:** R. Gale Stahle
Editorial Profile: Davis County Clipper provides residents of Davis County, UT with local news.; Full Page Mono: 14.00
Currency: US Dollars
NEWSPAPER

The Davis Enterprise

Owner: McNaughton Newspapers
Editorial: 315 G St, Davis, California 95616.
T: 1 530 756-0800
E: newsroom@davisenterprise.net
W: http://www.davisenterprise.com
Freq: Daily; **Circ:** 9468 Not Audited
Publisher: R. Burt McNaughton
Editorial Profile: The Davis Enterprise is a local daily newspaper written for residents of Davis, Woodland, El Macero, Winters and Dixon, CA. The newspaper covers local news, world news, sports and arts & entertainment.; Full Page Mono: 18.00; Full Page Colour: 450.00
Currency: US Dollars
DAILY NEWSPAPER

Davis Publications, Inc.

Owner: Davis Publications Inc.
Editorial: 416 Broadway St, Valley Falls, Kansas 66088. **T:** 1 785 945-3257
W: http://www.jeffcountynews.com **Circ:** 4716 Not Audited
Publisher: Clarke Davis; **News Editor:** Marveta Davis; **Editor:** Dennis Sharkey
NEWSPAPER

The Davison Index

Owner: JAMS Media
Editorial: 220 N Main St, Davison, Michigan 48423. **T:** 1 810 653-3511
E: daveditor@mihomepaper.com
W: http://www.thedavisonindex.com
Freq: Thu; **Circ:** 14139 Not Audited
Publisher: Rick Burrough
Editorial Profile: The Davison Index is published weekly for the residents of Davison and Richfield, MI. The newspaper provides information on local news and community events.; Full Page Mono: 12.82
Currency: US Dollars
NEWSPAPER

Dawn - New York Bureau

Editorial: United Nations, Room S-344A, New York, New York 10017. **T:** 1 917 367-4139
Editorial Profile: This is the New York bureau of Dawn, based in Karachi, Pakistan.
DAILY NEWSPAPER

The Day

Owner: Day Publishing Co.
Editorial: 47 Eugene Oneill Dr, New London, Connecticut 06320-6306. **T:** 1 860 442-2200
E: editor@theday.com
W: http://www.theday.com
Freq: Daily; **Circ:** 23698 Not Audited
News Editor: Jenna Cho; **Publisher:** Gary Farrugia
Editorial Profile: The Day's editorial mission is to be the leading source of news and information for Eastern Connecticut. The publication is written for a general audience from teens to senior citizens.; Full Page Mono: 36.22
Currency: US Dollars
DAILY NEWSPAPER

Dayton City Paper

Owner: Dayton City Paper New, LLC
Editorial: 126 N. Main St, Suite 240, Dayton, Ohio 45402. **T:** 1 937 222-8855
E: contactus@daytoncitypaper.com
W: http://www.daytoncitypaper.com
Freq: Tue; **Circ:** 17000 Not Audited
Publisher: Paul Noah; **Editor:** Nicole Wroten
Editorial Profile: Dayton City Paper is a local newspaper serving the Miami Valley, including Dayton, OH and its suburbs.; Full Page Mono: 22.83
Currency: US Dollars
NEWSPAPER

Dayton Daily News

Owner: Cox Media Group, Inc.
Editorial: 1611 S Main St, Dayton, Ohio 45409-2547. **T:** 1 937 225-2000
E: csdayton@coxohio.com
W: http://www.daytondailynews.com
Freq: Daily; **Circ:** 97800 Not Audited
Content Team Leader: Sharon Wilmore Buggs

Editorial Profile: Dayton Daily News is a daily newspaper serving the Dayton, OH area. Coverage includes local, regional, and national news, sports, entertainment and recreation. The Life sections covers entertainment and lifestyle topics, as well as health and food. Advertising rates are combined with Springfield News-Sun.; Full Page Mono: 102.77; Full Page Colour: 253.56
Currency: US Dollars
DAILY NEWSPAPER

Dayton Daily News

Editorial: 34 S 3rd St, Columbus, Ohio 43215-4201. **T:** 1 614 224-1608
DAILY NEWSPAPER

Dayton Weekly News

Editorial: 118 Salem Ave, Dayton, Ohio 45406-5803. **T:** 1 937 223-8060
E: daytonweek@aol.com
Freq: Thu; **Circ:** 25000 Not Audited
Editorial Profile: Dayton Weekly News is written for the African American residents in Dayton, OH. It covers news and trends.; Full Page Mono: 22.00
Currency: US Dollars
NEWSPAPER

The Daytona Beach News-Journal

Owner: Halifax Media Holdings LLC
Editorial: 901 6th St, Daytona Beach, Florida 32117-3352. **T:** 1 386 252-1511
E: metro@news-jrnl.com
W: http://www.news-journalonline.com
Freq: Daily; **Circ:** 68250 Not Audited
Editor: Pat Rice; **Publisher:** Ron Wallace
Editorial Profile: The Daytona Beach News-Journal covers local, state and national news, as well as business, sports, special reports and politics. There is also features and entertainment news, including lifestyles, movies, television and events. In 1986, The Morning Journal and The Evening News combined to create the current News-Journal. The paper was founded in 1928. Deadlines vary by department. The outlet offers RSS (Really Simple Syndication).; Full Page Mono: 146.70; Full Page Colour: 491.17
Currency: US Dollars
DAILY NEWSPAPER

De Norte A Sur

Owner: De Norte Sur Inc.
Editorial: 61 Willow St, Elmwood Park, New Jersey 07407-1837. **T:** 1 201 300-2914
E: denorteasur@denorteasur.com
W: http://www.denorteasur.com
Freq: Monthly; **Circ:** 35000 Not Audited
Editorial Profile: De Norte A Sur is a free, monthly Spanish-language newspaper. It covers local and national news from Argentina, Uruguay, the United States and Canada. The paper is distributed in the New York/New Jersey area, Philadelphia, Miami, Los Angeles, Puerto Rico, Chicago, Alaska, Canada and Spain during the first week of each month.; Full Page Mono: 21.50
Currency: US Dollars
NEWSPAPER

Dearborn Times Herald

Owner: Bewick Publications
Editorial: 13730 Michigan Ave, Dearborn, Michigan 48126-3520. **T:** 1 313 584-4000
E: times.herald@timesheraldnewspapers.com
W: http://downriversundaytimes.com
Freq: Sun; **Circ:** 27000 Not Audited
Publisher: Michael Bewick; **Editor:** Scott Bewick
Editorial Profile: Dearborn (MI) Times Herald is published twice per week and covers local news, weather, sports, business, features and community events. Deadlines fall on Friday.; Full Page Mono: 23.50; Full Page Colour: 2135.00
Currency: US Dollars
NEWSPAPER

The Decatur Daily

Owner: Tennessee Valley Printing Co. Inc.
Editorial: 201 1st Ave SE, Decatur, Alabama 35601-2333. **T:** 1 256 353-4612
E: news@decaturdaily.com
W: http://www.decaturdaily.com
Freq: Daily; **Circ:** 16256
Publisher & Editor: Clint Shelton
Editorial Profile: The Decatur Daily is a daily newspaper written for residents of Decatur, AL and surrounding areas. The publication covers local and state news, events, people, sports, business and arts & entertainment stories. On August 30, 2004 it became a morning newspaper.; Full Page Mono: 34.27; Full Page Colour: 386.00
Currency: US Dollars
DAILY NEWSPAPER

Decatur Daily Democrat

Owner: Horizon Publications
Editorial: 141 S 2nd St, Decatur, Indiana 46733. **T:** 1 260 724-2121
E: comp@decaturdailydemocrat.com
W: http://www.decaturdailydemocrat.com
Freq: Daily; **Circ:** 6000 Not Audited
Publisher: Ron Storey
Editorial Profile: Decatur Daily Democrat is a local daily published newspaper. Its editorial mission is to cover news and events for the town of Decatur, IN and the surrounding communities.; Full Page Mono: 12.35; Full Page Colour: 41.04
Currency: US Dollars
DAILY NEWSPAPER

Decatur Tribune

Owner: Osborne Publications, Inc.
Editorial: 240 N Park St, Decatur, Illinois 62523. **T:** 1 217 422-9702
E: decaturtribune@aol.com
W: http://news.mywebpal.com/index.cfm?pnpid=469
Freq: Wed; **Circ:** 25000 Not Audited
Editorial Profile: The publication is written to serve their customers with the news of Decatur, IL and surrounding areas. The lead time for Decatur Tribune is one week. Deadlines for the publication are one week before issue date.; Full Page Mono: 7.00
Currency: US Dollars
NEWSPAPER

Decorah News Company

Owner: Anundsen Publishing
Editorial: 107 E Water St, Decorah, Iowa 52101-1801. **T:** 1 563 382-4221
E: news@decorahnewspapers.com
W: http://www.decorahnewspapers.com
Circ: 10300 Not Audited
News Editor: Sarah Strandberg
Editorial Profile: Decorah News Company produces award-winning weekly newspapers, features up-to-date and accurate news, sports and community information for Winneshiek County, IA.
NEWSPAPER

Deer Valley Times

Owner: DeerValleyTimes.com
Editorial: 23460 N 19th Ave Ste 150, Phoenix, Arizona 85027-2166. **T:** 1 623 806-1212
E: news@deervalleytimes.com
W: http://www.deervalleytimes.com
Freq: Monthly
Publisher: Stacy Deprey-Purper; **Editor:** Jen Wolfe
Editorial Profile: Deer Valley Times is a monthly newspaper providing Local and Community News for the residents of Deer Valley News, North Valley News, Anthem, Black Canyon City, Cave Creek and Norterra in the Phoenix North Valley, AZ.
NEWSPAPER

Defender Newspaper

Owner: Defender Media Group
Editorial: 12401 S. Post Oak Rd., Ste.223, Houston, Texas 77045. **T:** 1 713 663-6996
E: news@defendermediagroup.com
W: http://defendernetwork.com
Freq: Thu; **Circ:** 23000 Not Audited
Publisher: Sonceria Messiah Jiles
Editorial Profile: Defender Newspaper is written for African American residents in the Houston area. The publication covers national and global news, sports, business, food, health and arts & entertainment news. Deadlines are on Mondays at 5pm CT.; Full Page Mono: 36.00; Full Page Colour: 4432.00
Currency: US Dollars
NEWSPAPER

Del Rio News-Herald

Owner: Southern Newspapers, Inc.
Editorial: 2205 N Bedell Ave, Del Rio, Texas 78840-8007. **T:** 1 830 775-1551
E: newsroom@delrionewsherald.com
W: http://www.delrionewsherald.com
Freq: Daily; **Circ:** 4852 Not Audited
Editorial Profile: Del Rio News-Herald is a local daily newspaper written for residents of Del Rio, TX. The newspaper covers local news, sports and events.; Full Page Mono: 14.10; Full Page Colour: 448.00
Currency: US Dollars
DAILY NEWSPAPER

Delaware County Daily Times

Owner: Journal Register Company
Editorial: 500 Mildred Ave, Secane, Pennsylvania 19018-2914. **T:** 1 610 622-8800
E: newsroom@delcotimes.com
W: http://www.delcotimes.com
Freq: Daily; **Circ:** 28837 Not Audited
Publisher: Ed Condra; **Editor in Chief:** Philip

Heron; **Editor in Chief:** Philip Heron
Editorial Profile: Delaware County Daily Times serves residents of Delaware County, PA. The newspaper includes local community news and national news headlines. The national news is provided by the Associated Press. Local features cover entertainment, education, business, lifestyle, high school sports and classifieds. The paper does not publish a holiday gift guide.; Full Page Mono: 72.40; Full Page Colour: 123.67
Currency: US Dollars
DAILY NEWSPAPER

Delaware Gazette

Owner: Ohio Community Media LLC.
Editorial: 18 E William St, Delaware, Ohio 43015-4313. **T:** 1 740 363-1161
W: http://www.delgazette.com
Freq: Daily; **Circ:** 6384 Not Audited
Publisher: Scott Koon
Editorial Profile: Delaware Gazette is a local daily newspaper serving the Delaware, OH area. It provides the local community with information on news, events, sports and weather. The lead time varies depending on the editorial material. Deadlines are at 9am ET before publication.; Full Page Mono: 12.25; Full Page Colour: 180.00
Currency: US Dollars
DAILY NEWSPAPER

Delaware State News

Owner: Independent Newspapers Inc.
Editorial: 110 Galaxy Dr, Dover, Delaware 19901. **T:** 1 302 674-3600
E: newsroom@newszap.com
W: http://www.newszap.com/DelawareStateNews
Freq: Daily; **Circ:** 17250 Not Audited
Publisher: Ed Dulin; **Editor:** Andrew West
Editorial Profile: Delaware State News is a daily newspaper serving the residents of Dover, DE and surrounding areas. It is a state-read publication that covers local, regional and national news and information.; Full Page Mono: 34.11; Full Page Colour: 200.00
Currency: US Dollars
DAILY NEWSPAPER

Delaware Wave

Owner: Gannett Co., Inc.
Editorial: Len Hickman Plaza, Route 1S, Bethany Beach, Delaware 19930-9801.
T: 1 302 537-1881 **E:** wave@dmg.gannett.com
W: http://www.delmarvanow.com
Freq: Tue; **Circ:** 22500 Not Audited
Editor: Laren Hughes-Hall
Editorial Profile: Delaware Wave is a local weekly newspaper serving the Bethany Beach, DE area. It provides the local community with information on news, events, sports and weather.; Full Page Mono: 16.38
Currency: US Dollars
NEWSPAPER

Delphos Daily Herald

Owner: Delphos Herald Inc.
Editorial: 405 N Main St, Delphos, Ohio 45833-1598. **T:** 1 419 695-0015
W: http://www.delphosherald.com
Freq: Daily; **Circ:** 3682 Not Audited
Publisher: Murray Cohen; **Editor:** Nancy Spencer
Editorial Profile: Delphos Daily Herald is a local newspaper serving Delphos, OH and the surrounding area. It provides information on news and events.; Full Page Mono: 10.00; Full Page Colour: 41.81
Currency: US Dollars
DAILY NEWSPAPER

Delta Democrat Times

Owner: Emmerich Newspapers Inc.
Editorial: 988 N Broadway St, Greenville, Mississippi 38701-2349. **T:** 1 662 335-1155
E: ddtnews@ddtonline.com
W: http://www.ddtonline.com
Freq: Mon thru Fri; **Circ:** 5707 Not Audited
Publisher & Editor: Jon Alverson; **News Editor:** Demetrius Thompson
Editorial Profile: Delta Democrat Times is the local daily newspaper for the residents of Greenville, MS. The paper covers local news, sports, entertainment, business and events.; Full Page Mono: 17.65; Full Page Colour: 300.00
Currency: US Dollars
DAILY NEWSPAPER

Delta News-Citizen

Editorial: 127 W Main St, Malden, Missouri 63863-2162. **T:** 1 573 276-5148
E: deltanews@dailystatesman.com
Freq: Wed; **Circ:** 11000 Not Audited
Publisher: Bud Hunt

Editorial Profile: Delta News-Citizen is a local weekly newspaper serving Malden, MO and the surrounding area. It provides the local community with information on news, events, sports and weather. Deadlines are Mondays at noon CT.; Full Page Mono: 11.95
Currency: US Dollars
NEWSPAPER

Deming Headlight
Owner: MediaNews Group
Editorial: 219 E Maple St, Deming, New Mexico 88030-4267. **T:** 1 575 546-2611
W: http://www.deminghheadlight.com
Freq: Daily; **Circ:** 3668 Not Audited
Editor: Billy Armendariz
Editorial Profile: Deming Headlight is a local daily newspaper serving Deming, NM. It provides the local community with information on news, events, sports and weather.; Full Page Mono: 11.85; Full Page Colour: 110.00
Currency: US Dollars
DAILY NEWSPAPER

Democrat Publishing Company
Editorial: 212 S Washington St, Clinton, Missouri 64735. **T:** 1 660 885-2281
Circ: 14400 Not Audited
Editorial Profile: Send press releases by fax.
NEWSPAPER

Demopolis Times
Owner: Boone Newspapers Inc.
Editorial: 315 E Jefferson St, Demopolis, Alabama 36732-2255. **T:** 1 334 289-4017
E: news@demopolistimes.com
W: http://www.demopolistimes.com
Freq: Daily; **Circ:** 3300 Not Audited
Publisher & Editor: Justin Averette
Editorial Profile: Demopolis Times is a local newspaper serving Demopolis, AL and the surrounding area. It provides information on news and events of importance to the local community.; Full Page Mono: 25.00
Currency: US Dollars
DAILY NEWSPAPER

Denham Springs Publishing Company
Editorial: 688 Hatchell Ln, Denham Springs, Louisiana 70726-3099. **T:** 1 225 665-5176
E: editor@livingstonparishnews.com
W: http://www.livingstonparishnews.com
Circ: 22644 Not Audited
Publisher: Jeff David; **Editor:** Mike Dowty
NEWSPAPER

Denison Newspapers, Inc.
Owner: Western Iowa Newspapers, Inc.
Editorial: 1410 Broadway, Denison, Iowa 51442. **T:** 1 712 263-2123
E: dbr-editor@bulletinreview.com
W: http://southwestiowanews.com/denison/front **Circ:** 8200 Not Audited
Publisher: Greg Wehle; **Editor:** Gordon Wolf
NEWSPAPER

Denson Publishing
Editorial: 323 E Renfrow, Arnett, Oklahoma 73832. **T:** 1 580 885-7788 **Circ:** 1575 Not Audited
NEWSPAPER

Denton Publications
Editorial: One High St, Elizabethtown, New York 12932. **T:** 1 518 873-6368
E: denpubs@denpubs.com
W: http://www.denpubs.com **Circ:** 70915 Not Audited
Publisher: Dan Alexander; **Editor:** Fred Herbst; **Editor:** Thom Randall
Editorial Profile: Denton Publications in Elizabethtown, NY is a publisher of community newspapers.
NEWSPAPER

Denton Record-Chronicle
Owner: A.H. Belo Corp.
Editorial: 314 E Hickory St, Denton, Texas 76201-4272. **T:** 1 940 387-3811
E: drconline@dentonrc.com
W: http://www.dentonrc.com
Freq: Daily; **Circ:** 13336 Not Audited
Publisher: Bill Patterson; **City Editor:** Matt Zabel; **City Editor:** Matt Zabel
Editorial Profile: Denton Record-Chronicle is a local daily newspaper published for the residents of Denton, TX. It provides information on news, events, sports, arts & entertainment and weather.; Full Page Mono: 36.50; Full Page Colour: 220.00
Currency: US Dollars
DAILY NEWSPAPER

Denver Catholic Register
Editorial: 1300 S Steele St, Denver, Colorado 80210. **T:** 1 303 715-3215
E: editor@archden.org
W: http://www.archden.org
Freq: Wed; **Circ:** 89000 Not Audited
Publisher: Charles Chaput; **Editor:** Roxanne King
Editorial Profile: Denver Catholic Register is a weekly publication published by the Archdiocese of Denver. It provides local and regional news about Catholic parishes, as well as local Denver news. Denver Catholic Register also reports on news in the archdiocese of Denver and news and updates from the Vatican. Deadlines are at 3pm CT. Special sections submissions must be received 10 days prior to publication date.; Full Page Mono: 38.90
Currency: US Dollars
NEWSPAPER

The Denver Post
Owner: MediaNews Group
Editorial: 101 W Colfax Ave Ste 600, Denver, Colorado 80202-5315. **T:** 1 303 954-1010
E: newsroom@denverpost.com
W: http://www.denverpost.com
Freq: Daily; **Circ:** 391096 Not Audited
Editor: Greg Moore
Editorial Profile: Denver Post is a general-interest broadsheet that reaches both a local and regional audience. The daily newspaper includes six sections, which are main news, local news, living, sports, business and classifieds.; Full Page Mono: 854.65; Full Page Colour: 915.11
Currency: US Dollars
DAILY NEWSPAPER

Denver Post
Editorial: 2693 Caribbean Dr, Grand Junction, Colorado 81506-1759. **T:** 1 970 256-1957
DAILY NEWSPAPER

Denver Post
Editorial: 13949 W Colfax Ave Ste 195, Lakewood, Colorado 80401-3250.
T: 1 303 278-3217
W: http://www.denverpost.com
DAILY NEWSPAPER

Denver Post
Editorial: 1333 W 120th Ave Ste 122, Westminster, Colorado 80234-2710.
T: 1 720 929-0907
DAILY NEWSPAPER

Denver Weekly News
Editorial: 2937 Welton St, Denver, Colorado 80205. **T:** 1 303 292-5158
E: dwnews2@yahoo.com
W: http://www.denverweeklynews.net
Freq: Thu; **Circ:** 10000 Not Audited
Editor: Lynn Durant; **Editor:** Lynn Durant
Editorial Profile: Denver Weekly News is a newspaper for the African American community of Denver, CO. It provides information on news and events of importance to the city's African American community. The lead time for Denver Weekly News is two weeks. Deadlines for the publication are two weeks before issue date on Monday at 5pm CT. Contact the editor with any further inquiries.; Full Page Mono: 30.00
Currency: US Dollars
NEWSPAPER

Der Blatt
Editorial: 76 Rutledge St, Brooklyn, New York 11211-7814. **T:** 1 718 625-3400
E: news@derblatt.com
Freq: Thu; **Circ:** 10000 Not Audited; Full Page Mono: 12.00
Currency: US Dollars
NEWSPAPER

Der Yid
Editorial: 84 Broadway, Brooklyn, New York 11211-8665. **T:** 1 718 797-3900
E: adv@deryid.org
Freq: Thu; **Circ:** 51000 Not Audited
Editorial Profile: Der Yid weekly newspaper carrying world news widely read within the "black hat" community. It uses a Yiddish dialect more common to Satmar Chasidim.; Full Page Mono: 14.00
Currency: US Dollars
NEWSPAPER

Des Moines Register
Owner: Gannett Co., Inc.
Editorial: 400 Locust St Ste 500, Des Moines, Iowa 50309-2355. **T:** 1 515 284-8000
E: metroiowa@dmreg.com
W: http://www.desmoinesregister.com
Freq: Daily; **Circ:** 86982 Not Audited
Iowa Life Editor: Sarah Dose
Editorial Profile: Des Moines Register is the largest newspaper in Iowa. It was founded in 1849 as the Iowa Star and got its current name in 1915.; Full Page Mono: 275.95; Full Page Colour: 3673.90
Currency: US Dollars
DAILY NEWSPAPER

Deseret News
Owner: Church of Jesus Christ of LDS (The)
Editorial: 55 N 300 W, Salt Lake City, Utah 84101-3502. **T:** 1 801 237-2100
W: http://www.deseretnews.com
Freq: Daily; **Circ:** 139101 Not Audited
Church News Editor: Gerry Avant
Editorial Profile: Deseret News, established in 1850, is a daily broadsheet newspaper distributed in the Salt Lake City area. The publication covers local news, sports and entertainment, as well as regional, national and international news. The newspaper maintains joint advertising, printing, circulation and business functions with The Salt Lake Tribune, but the two papers operate independent editorial departments.; Full Page Mono: 202.77; Full Page Colour: 695.18
Currency: US Dollars
DAILY NEWSPAPER

Desert Dispatch
Owner: New Media Investment Group, Inc.
Editorial: 130 Coolwater Ln, Barstow, California 92311. **T:** 1 760 256-2257
W: http://www.desertdispatch.com
Freq: Daily; **Circ:** 3259 Not Audited
Publisher: Stephan Wingert
Editorial Profile: Desert Dispatch is a daily newspaper covering local news from Barstow, Daggett, Fort Irwin, Hinkley, Lenwood, Newberry Springs and Yemo, CA. The publication includes local news, sports and entertainment topics.; Full Page Mono: 22.21; Full Page Colour: 330.00
Currency: US Dollars
DAILY NEWSPAPER

The Desert Leaf
Owner: Desert Leaf Publications, Inc.
Editorial: 3978 E Fort Lowell Rd, Tucson, Arizona 85712. **T:** 1 520 881-5188
E: info@desertleaf.com
W: http://www.desertleaf.com
Freq: Monthly; **Circ:** 56000 Not Audited
Editor: Karen Nystedt; **Publisher:** Mary Swiergol
Editorial Profile: The Desert Leaf is a monthly newspaper serving the Catalina Foothills communities of Tucson, AZ. It provides general interest articles as well as a community forum for information on news and events. Deadlines for the publication are two months before issue date.; Full Page Mono: 50.00; Full Page Colour: 2095.00
Currency: US Dollars
NEWSPAPER

Desert Mobile Home News
Owner: Brehm Communications, Inc.
Editorial: 41995 Boardwalk, Ste L2, Palm Desert, California 92211. **T:** 1 760 568-6633
E: news@desertmobilehomenews.com
Freq: Thu; **Circ:** 18000 Not Audited
Publisher: Ken Larson; **Editor:** Claudia McVeigh
Editorial Profile: Desert Mobile Home is a community paper that covers general and local news. The publication is written for mobile home seniors in Coachella Valley, CA.; Full Page Mono: 11.00
Currency: US Dollars
NEWSPAPER

Desert Shamrock
Owner: The Irish Group Ltd.
Editorial: 5025 N Central Ave, #600, Phoenix, Arizona 85012. **T:** 1 602 449-1966
E: shamrockaz@cox.net
W: http://www.desertshamrock.com
Freq: Bi-Monthly; **Circ:** 20000 Not Audited
Publisher: Julie O'Mahar
Editorial Profile: Desert Shamrock provides news from Ireland as well as news and events in the Irish communities of Arizona. It is published every other month and is written for Irish American communities.; Full Page Mono: 16.70
Currency: US Dollars
NEWSPAPER

Desert Star Weekly
Owner: Praxis Communications, Inc.
Editorial: 66538 8th St, Desert Hot Springs, California 92240-3217. **T:** 1 760 671-6604
E: editor@desertstarweekly.com
W: http://desertstarweekly.com
Freq: Thu; **Circ:** 10000
Publisher: Richard Perry
Editorial Profile: Desert Star Weekly is a community newspaper serving the Coachella Valley and High Desert region of Southern California.
NEWSPAPER

The Desert Sun
Owner: Gannett Co., Inc.
Editorial: 750 N Gene Autry Trl, Palm Springs, California 92262-5463. **T:** 1 760 322-8889
E: localnews@thedesertsun.com
W: http://www.desertsun.com
Freq: Daily; **Circ:** 38518 Not Audited
Publisher: Mark Winkler
Editorial Profile: The Desert Sun is a local daily newspaper that covers news and information in Coachella Valley, CA. Coverage includes local and national news, sports, business and lifestyle issues affecting the local community.; Full Page Mono: 106.75; Full Page Colour: 337.06
Currency: US Dollars
DAILY NEWSPAPER

Desert Sun Newspapers
Owner: Gannett Co., Inc.
Editorial: 750 N Gene Autry Trl, Palm Springs, California 92262-5463. **T:** 1 760 322-8889
W: http://www.desertsun.com **Circ:** 38000 Not Audited
Editor: William Dean; **Editor:** Jamie Lee Pricer
NEWSPAPER

DeSoto Times Tribune
Owner: P.H. Publishing LLC
Editorial: 2445 Highway 51 S, Hernando, Mississippi 38632-1734. **T:** 1 662 429-6397
E: editor@desototimestribune.com
W: http://www.desototimes.com **Circ:** 8500 Not Audited
Publisher: Cyndi Pittman; **News Editor:** Terri Smith
Editorial Profile: DeSoto Times Tribune is a local, daily newspaper serving DeSoto County, MS. It provides information on news and events of importance to the local community.; Full Page Mono: 11.48
Currency: US Dollars
DAILY NEWSPAPER

Detroit Free Press
Owner: Gannett Co., Inc.
Editorial: 615 W Lafayette Blvd, Detroit, Michigan 48226-3124. **T:** 1 313 222-6400
E: localnews@freepress.com
W: http://www.freep.com
Freq: Daily; **Circ:** 175703 Not Audited
Publisher & Editor: Paul Anger; **City Night Editor:** Sally Tato
Editorial Profile: Detroit Free Press is a general-interest daily newspaper written for the general public in Detroit. Founded in 1831 as the weekly Democratic Free Press and Michigan Intelligencer, the publication is one of the largest daily newspapers in the country. It has won eight Pulitzer Prizes. Coverage includes business, automotive, consumer, health and technology. Articles consist of news and trend stories, product announcements and reviews, case studies, company profiles, personality profiles and interviews. The publication has daily deadlines in the afternoon. It is best to contact staff editors and reporters before 3pm ET. The paper is distributed via home delivery on Thursdays, Fridays and Sundays. It is available daily on newsstands.; Full Page Mono: 411.00; Full Page Colour: 2514.68
Currency: US Dollars
DAILY NEWSPAPER

Detroit Free Press
Editorial: 120 E Lenawee St, Lansing, Michigan 48919-0001. **T:** 1 517 372-8660
DAILY NEWSPAPER

Detroit Free Press
Editorial: 6200 Metropolitan Pkwy, Sterling Heights, Michigan 48312-1022.
T: 1 586 826-7260
DAILY NEWSPAPER

Detroit Free Press
Editorial: 1100 New York Ave NW, Ste 200E, Washington, District Of Columbia 20005-6116.
T: 1 202 906-8203
DAILY NEWSPAPER

The Detroit Jewish News
Owner: Detroit Jewish News LLC
Editorial: 29200 Northwestern Hwy, Ste 110, Southfield, Michigan 48034.
T: 1 248 354-6060 **W:** http://www.jnonline.us
Freq: Thu; **Circ:** 23000 Not Audited
Publisher: Arthur Horwitz; **Editor in Chief:** Robert Sklar
Editorial Profile: The Detroit Jewish News is a weekly newspaper serving the Jewish residents of Detroit. It covers local, national

and global news with an emphasis on events in Israel. It also features articles on all aspects of Jewish life, from the arts to care for the elderly.; Full Page Mono: 37.50
Currency: US Dollars
NEWSPAPER

Detroit Lakes Newspapers
Owner: Forum Communications Co.
Editorial: 511 Washington Ave, Detroit Lakes, Minnesota 56501-3007. **T:** 1 218 847-3151
W: http://www.dl-online.com **Circ:** 38000 Not Audited
Editor: Nate Bowe; **Publisher:** Dennis Winskowski
NEWSPAPER

The Detroit News
Owner: MediaNews Group
Editorial: 615 W Lafayette Blvd, Detroit, Michigan 48226-3124. **T:** 1 313 222-2300
W: http://www.detroitnews.com
Freq: Mon thru Fri; **Circ:** 113489 Not Audited
News Editor: Marti Davenport; **Editor & Publisher:** Jon Wolman; **Editor & Publisher:** Jon Wolman
Editorial Profile: Detroit News is a general-interest daily newspaper written for the general public in Detroit and was founded in 1873 as The Evening News. The paper covers business, science, automotive, consumer, health and technology. The paper is distributed via home delivery on Thursdays, Fridays and Saturdays. It will be available daily on newsstands; Full Page Mono: 206.80; Full Page Colour: 237.81
Currency: US Dollars
DAILY NEWSPAPER

Detroit News
Editorial: 529 14th Street NW, Suite 969, Washington, District Of Columbia 20045.
T: 1 202 662-8733
DAILY NEWSPAPER

The Detroit News
Editorial: Boji Tower, 124 W. Allegan St, Suite 1112, Lansing, Michigan 48933.
T: 1 517 371-3660
E: lansing@detroitnews.com
DAILY NEWSPAPER

Detroit News - Investigative Team
Editorial: 2 Woodward Ave, Detroit, Michigan 48226-3437. **T:** 1 313 222-2513
Editorial Profile: This bureau houses The Detroit News' Investigative and Special Projects team.
DAILY NEWSPAPER

DeVaul Publishing, Inc.
Editorial: 429 N Market Blvd, Chehalis, Washington 98532. **T:** 1 360 748-6848
W: http://www.devaulpublishing.com
Circ: 14966 Not Audited
NEWSPAPER

Devils Lake Journal
Owner: Fortress Investment Group, LLC
Editorial: 516 4th St, Devils Lake, North Dakota 58301-2502. **T:** 1 701 662-2127
E: news@devilslakejournal.com
W: http://www.devilslakejournal.com
Freq: Daily; **Circ:** 3600 Not Audited
Editor: Louise Oleson; **Publisher:** Kathy Svidal
Editorial Profile: Devils Lake Journal is a local newspaper serving the Devils Lake, ND area. It provides information on local news, events, sports and weather.; Full Page Mono: 12.10; Full Page Colour: 48.02
Currency: US Dollars
DAILY NEWSPAPER

El Dia
Editorial: 6331 26th St, Berwyn, Illinois 60402-2631. **T:** 1 708 652-6397
E: eldia@eldianews.com
W: http://www.eldianews.com
Freq: Fri; **Circ:** 60000 Not Audited
Editor: Ana Maria Montes de Oca; **Publisher:** Jorge Montes de Oca
Editorial Profile: El Dia's editorial mission is to provide the Spanish community with information on community activities and current events. The publication is written for the Old Spanish community of Cicero, IL. Deadlines are on Wednesdays at 5pm CT.; Full Page Mono: 29.62; Full Page Colour: 1876.25
Currency: US Dollars
NEWSPAPER

The Dialog
Owner: Catholic Press Inc.
Editorial: 1925 Delaware Ave, Wilmington, Delaware 19806-2301. **T:** 1 302 573-3109
E: news@thedialog.org
W: http://thedialog.org/
Freq: Fri; **Circ:** 26000 Not Audited
Editor: Mike Lang; **Publisher:** W. Francis Malooly; **Editor:** Joseph Ryan
Editorial Profile: The Dialog is a weekly Catholic newspaper serving the Catholic community of Delaware and the Eastern Maryland.; Full Page Mono: 42.70; Full Page Colour: 100.00
Currency: US Dollars
NEWSPAPER

El Diario de El Paso
Owner: Editora Paso del Norte
Editorial: 1801 Texas Ave, El Paso, Texas 79901-1811. **T:** 1 915 838-1600
E: newsroom@diariousa.com
W: http://www.diariousa.com
Freq: Daily; **Circ:** 20000 Not Audited
Editorial Profile: EL Diario de El Paso is a daily, Spanish-language newspaper serving the Hispanic community in El Paso, TX. It covers international and local news, sports, arts & entertainment, social events and real estate.; Full Page Mono: 224.00; Full Page Colour: 260.00
Currency: US Dollars
DAILY NEWSPAPER

Diario La Estrella
Owner: McClatchy Newspapers
Editorial: 400 W 7th St, Fort Worth, Texas 76102-4701
W: http://www.diariolaestrella.com
Freq: Fri; **Circ:** 100000 Not Audited
Editorial Profile: Diario La Estrella is a weekly, Spanish-language newspaper serving the Hispanic community throughout Dallas and Fort Worth, TX.; Full Page Mono: 15.16; Full Page Colour: 658.00
Currency: US Dollars
NEWSPAPER

Diario Las Américas
Owner: :as Americas Multimedia, LLC
Editorial: 888 Brickell Ave Fl 5, Miami, Florida 33131-2913. **T:** 1 305 633-3341
E: diariolasamericas@gmail.com
W: http://www.diariolasamericas.com
Freq: Daily; **Circ:** 63445 Not Audited
Publisher: Horacio Aguirre
Editorial Profile: Diario Las Americas is a regional daily newspaper published for Spanish speaking residents of Miami. It covers international, national and local news, as well as arts & entertainment.; Full Page Mono: 36.20; Full Page Colour: 1200.00
Currency: US Dollars
DAILY NEWSPAPER

El Diario/La Prensa
Owner: ImpreMedia LLC
Editorial: 1 Metrotech Ctr, Brooklyn, New York 11201-3948. **T:** 1 212 807-4600
E: metro@eldiariony.com
W: http://www.eldiariony.com
Freq: Daily; **Circ:** 46872 Not Audited
Legal Affairs Editor: Candida Portugues; **Publisher:** Rossana Rosado
Editorial Profile: El Diario/La Prensa is a daily newspaper written for Spanish communities of New York. The editorial mission of the newspaper is to provide the Spanish communities of New York with cultural news and information.; Full Page Mono: 49.87; Full Page Colour: 168.39
Currency: US Dollars
DAILY NEWSPAPER

El Diario/La Prensa
Editorial: 1 Police Plz, New York, New York 10038-1403. **T:** 1 212 406-3990
E: metro@eldiariony.com
Bureau Chief: Gloria Medina
DAILY NEWSPAPER

Dickinson County News
Owner: Rust Communications
Editorial: 3000 18th St Highway 9 West, Suite 400, Spirit Lake, Iowa 51360-1242.
T: 1 712 336-1211
E: dcn@dickinsoncountynews.com
W: http://www.dickinsoncountynews.com
Freq: 2 Times/Week; **Circ:** 17450 Not Audited
Publisher: Paula Buenger
Editorial Profile: Dickinson County News is written for the residents of Dickinson County, IA and surrounding areas. It covers local news, events and sports. Deadlines are at noon on Fridays before the Wednesday edition and at noon on Wednesdays before the Saturday edition.
NEWSPAPER

The Dickinson Press
Owner: Forum Communications Co.
Editorial: 1815 1st St W, Dickinson, North Dakota 58601-2463. **T:** 1 701 225-8111
E: newsroom@thedickinsonpress.com
W: http://www.thedickinsonpress.com
Freq: Daily; **Circ:** 6486 Not Audited
Publisher: Harvey Brock
Editorial Profile: Dickinson Press is a daily newspaper serving the Dickinson, ND community. It covers local and national news, lifestyle, business and government.; Full Page Mono: 11.25; Full Page Colour: 70.00
Currency: US Dollars
DAILY NEWSPAPER

Dig Magazine
Owner: University Media Group
Editorial: 5261 Highland Rd #167, Ste 167, Baton Rouge, Louisiana 70808.
T: 1 225 248-1229
E: editor@digbatonrouge.com
W: http://digbatonrouge.com
Freq: Wed; **Circ:** 20000 Not Audited
Editorial Profile: Dig Magazine is a free, weekly newspaper serving the areas immediately surrounding Louisiana State University's campus in Baton Rouge, LA. The paper is independently-owned and in no way affiliated with the university. It covers campus news, events, sports and features relevant to the student population. The production schedule follows that of the university and usually halts for portions of December, January and May.; Full Page Mono: 11.91
Currency: US Dollars
NEWSPAPER

The Dispatch
Owner: Halifax Media Holdings LLC
Editorial: 30 E 1St Ave, Lexington, North Carolina 27292-3302. **T:** 1 336 249-3981
E: news@the-dispatch.com
W: http://www.the-dispatch.com
Freq: Daily; **Circ:** 7191 Not Audited
Radio & Television Editor: Michelle Moore; **Publisher:** Steve Skaggs
Editorial Profile: The Dispatch is a daily local newspaper for Lexington, NC. The publication covers local news, business, lifestyle, sports and entertainment stories.; Full Page Mono: 23.00; Full Page Colour: 300.00
Currency: US Dollars
DAILY NEWSPAPER

The Dispatch
Owner: Tribune-Review Publishing Co.
Editorial: 116 E Market St, Blairsville, Pennsylvania 15717. **T:** 1 724 459-6100
W: http://www.pittsburghlive.com/x/blairsvilledispatch
Freq: Fri; **Circ:** 14000 Not Audited
Editor: Jeffrey Himler; **Publisher:** Richard Scaife
Editorial Profile: The Disptach is written for the residents of Blairsville, PA. It covers community news and events, national and international news and sports.; Full Page Mono: 15.18
Currency: US Dollars
NEWSPAPER

Dispatch/Argus
Owner: Small Newspaper Group
Editorial: 1720 5th Ave, Moline, Illinois 61265-7907. **T:** 1 309 764-4344
E: press@qconline.com
W: http://www.qconline.com
Editor: Jackie Chesser; **Niche Editor:** Laura Fraembs; **Publisher & Editor:** Gerald Taylor
Editorial Profile: Dispatch/Argus publishes both the Dispatch and the Rock Island Argus in Moline, IL.
DAILY NEWSPAPER

Dispatch-Post USA
Owner: Missouri Minority Press Service, Inc.
Editorial: 8401 New Jersey Ave., Kansas City, Kansas 66112. **T:** 1 913 481-4727
E: dispatchpostusanewspaper@gmail.com
Freq: Thu; **Circ:** 30000 Not Audited
Editorial Profile: Dispatch-Post USA provides weekly news updates to the African-American communities of Missouri. Local community news is covered, as well as some national news.; Full Page Mono: 15.86
Currency: US Dollars
NEWSPAPER

Diversity Media Group
Owner: Diversity Media Group Inc.
Editorial: 1301 Lafeyette St., St. 202, Fort Wayne, Indiana 46802. **T:** 1 260 420-8580
Circ: 34500
Editor: Vince Robinson; **Editor:** Vince Robinson; **Editor:** Vince Robinson
NEWSPAPER

Dodge City Daily Globe
Owner: GateHouse Media Inc.
Editorial: 705 N 2nd Ave, Dodge City, Kansas 67801-4410. **T:** 1 620 225-4151
E: dcnews@dodgeglobe.com
W: http://www.dodgeglobe.com
Freq: Daily; **Circ:** 7000 Not Audited
News Editor: Nancy Calderon
Editorial Profile: Dodge City Daily Globe is a local newspaper for the Dodge City, KS area. The newspaper covers local news, business, sports and arts & entertainment stories. The newspaper also covers national and statewide stories if they have a direct impact on the newspaper's readership. All inquiries should be addressed to the managing editor. Deadlines for the publication are by noon CT the day before issue date.; Full Page Mono: 9.87; Full Page Colour: 210.00
Currency: US Dollars
DAILY NEWSPAPER

The Dominion Post
Owner: The West Virginia Newspaper Publishing Company
Editorial: 1251 Earl L Core Rd, Morgantown, West Virginia 26505-6298. **T:** 1 304 292-6301
E: newsroom@dominionpost.com
W: http://www.dominionpost.com
Freq: Daily; **Circ:** 20458 Not Audited
Editor: Geri Ferrara; **Campus Life Editor:** Michael Janney; **Publisher:** David Raese;
Editor: Ron Rittenhouse
Editorial Profile: The Dominion Post is a local daily newspaper published for the residents of Northern West Virginia. It covers local news and events. The lead time varies.; Full Page Mono: 34.91; Full Page Colour: 575.00
Currency: US Dollars
DAILY NEWSPAPER

Door County Advocate
Owner: Gannett Co., Inc.
Editorial: 235 N 3rd Ave, Sturgeon Bay, Wisconsin 54235-2417. **T:** 1 920 743-3321
E: advocate@doorcountyadvocate.com
W: http://www.godoorcounty.com
Freq: Sat; **Circ:** 10500 Not Audited
Editor: Warren Bluhm; **Publisher:** Kevin Corrado
Editorial Profile: Door County Advocate is a twice-weekly newspaper serving residents of Door County, WI. Each edition covers county news, sports, births, deaths and public announcements, opinion articles, classified advertising and television listings. The weekday edition also contains local business news and a section called Community. Community provides columns submitted by neighborhood freelance writers, along with stories about the local YMCA, Door County Library, schools and senior centers. The weekend edition of the paper carries a section titled Family, which celebrates local peoples' accomplishments in school, service clubs and elsewhere in addition to wedding and anniversary announcements. The Family section relies heavily on reader-submitted photographs and information.; Full Page Mono: 14.00
Currency: US Dollars
NEWSPAPER

Dorchester Star
Owner: Chesapeake Publishing and Printing
Editorial: 511 Poplar St, Cambridge, Maryland 21613. **T:** 1 410 228-0222
W: http://www.dorchesterstar.com
Freq: Fri; **Circ:** 11000 Not Audited
Editor: Gale Dean; **Publisher:** David Fike;
Editor: Dustin Holt
Editorial Profile: Dorchester Star's editorial mission is to provide local news and event information for residents of Dorchester County, MD.; Full Page Mono: 11.25
Currency: US Dollars
NEWSPAPER

Dos Mundos
Editorial: 902A Southwest Blvd, Kansas City, Missouri 64108-2341. **T:** 1 816 221-4747
E: newsstaff@dosmundos.com
W: http://www.dosmundos.com
Freq: Thu; **Circ:** 20000 Not Audited
Editor: Clara Reyes; **Publisher:** Manuel Reyes
Editorial Profile: Dos Mundos delivers news to the Hispanic community of Kansas City, MO.; Full Page Mono: 14.00; Full Page Colour: 2184.00
Currency: US Dollars
NEWSPAPER

The Dothan Eagle
Owner: BH Media Group
Editorial: 227 N Oates St, Dothan, Alabama 36303-4555. **T:** 1 334 792-3141
E: news@dothaneagle.com
W: http://www.dothaneagle.com
Freq: Daily; **Circ:** 24134 Not Audited
City Editor: Kendall Clinton; **City Editor:**

Kendall Clinton; **City Editor:** Kendall Clinton
Editorial Profile: The Dothan Eagle is a daily newspaper written for residents of Dothan, AL. The paper covers local and national news, sports and weather.; Full Page Mono: 46.00; Full Page Colour: 375.00
Currency: US Dollars
DAILY NEWSPAPER

Dothan Progress
Owner: BH Media Group
Editorial: 227 N Oates St, Dothan, Alabama 36303-4555. **T:** 1 334 792-3141
E: news@dothaneagle.com
W: http://www2.dothaneagle.com/dea/dothan_progress/
Freq: Thu; **Circ:** 25000 Not Audited
Editorial Profile: Dothan Progress is written for the residents of Dothan, Headland and Ashford, AL. It covers local news, education, entertainment and food.; Full Page Mono: 11.50
Currency: US Dollars
NEWSPAPER

Douglas County Post-Gazette
Editorial: 2929 N 204th St, Suite 117, Elkhorn, Nebraska 68022. **T:** 1 402 289-2329
E: editor@dcpostgazette.com
W: http://www.dcpostgazette.com
Freq: Tue; **Circ:** 14100 Not Audited
Publisher: Penny Overmann; **Editor:** Mary Lou Rodgers; **Editor:** Mary Lou Rodgers
Editorial Profile: Douglas County Post-Gazette is a local weekly newspaper. Its editorial mission is to be the best local news source for the communities of Elkhorn, Waterloo, Bennington, and Valley, NE. Deadlines are on Fridays at 9am CT.; Full Page Mono: 16.25; Full Page Colour: 1550.50
Currency: US Dollars
NEWSPAPER

Douglas County Publishing
Editorial: 215 Main St, Corsica, South Dakota 57328-2240. **T:** 1 605 946-5489
E: globe@siouxvalley.net **Circ:** 3000 Not Audited
Editorial Profile: Douglas County Publishing is a local newspaper in Corsica, SD.
NEWSPAPER

Douglas County Sentinel
Owner: Paxton Media Group
Editorial: 8501 Bowden St, Douglasville, Georgia 30134-1705. **T:** 1 770 942-6571
W: http://www.douglascountysentinel.com
Freq: Daily; **Circ:** 3666 Not Audited
Publisher: Cathy New
Editorial Profile: Douglas County Sentinel's editorial mission is to bring to the citizens of Douglas news which directly affects and impacts their lives.; Full Page Mono: 20.00; Full Page Colour: 150.00
Currency: US Dollars
DAILY NEWSPAPER

The Douglas Enterprise
Editorial: 1823 Peterson Ave S, Douglas, Georgia 31535. **T:** 1 912 384-2323
E: dougent@windstream.net
W: http://www.douglasenterprise.net
Circ: 28000 Not Audited
Editor: Tracy Mayo
Editorial Profile: All mail must be sent to the P.O. box address.
NEWSPAPER

Dowagiac Daily News
Owner: Boone/Narragansett Publishing
Editorial: 205 Spaulding St, Dowagiac, Michigan 49047-1474. **T:** 1 269 782-2101
W: http://www.dowagiacnews.com
Freq: Daily; **Circ:** 1586 Not Audited
Publisher: Bryan Clapper; **Editor:** John Eby
Editorial Profile: Dowagiac Daily News is written for residents of Dowagiac, MI. The paper covers local news, sports, business and entertainment.; Full Page Mono: 12.80
Currency: US Dollars
DAILY NEWSPAPER

The Downey Patriot
Editorial: 8301 Florence Ave, Ste 100, Downey, California 90240. **T:** 1 562 904-3668
E: news@thedowneypatriot.com
W: http://www.thedowneypatriot.com
Freq: Thu; **Circ:** 25000 Not Audited
Publisher: Jennifer Dekay-Givens
Editorial Profile: The Downey Patriot is a community newspaper serving Downey, CA and the surrounding areas. It includes local news, sports, business, health news, opinion and community events.; Full Page Mono: 19.00
Currency: US Dollars
NEWSPAPER

Downtown Denver News
Editorial: 1550 Larimer St, Ste 223, Denver, Colorado 80202-1602. **T:** 1 303 292-6397
E: lododdnews@earthlink.net
W: http://www.downtowndenvernews.com
Freq: Monthly; **Circ:** 20000 Not Audited
Editorial Profile: Downtown Denver News is a monthly, local newspaper written for the residents of Denver. It is published on the 10th of each month. The deadline falls on the fifth of each month prior to the issue date.; Full Page Mono: 9.75; Full Page Colour: 2600.00
Currency: US Dollars
NEWSPAPER

Downtown News
Editorial: 1264 W 1st St, Los Angeles, California 90026. **T:** 1 213 481-1448
E: realpeople@downtownnews.com
W: http://www.ladowntownnews.com
Freq: Mon; **Circ:** 47000 Not Audited
Editorial Profile: Downtown News is a weekly newspaper for the people who work in downtown Los Angeles. Its editorial mission is to provide news about business, politics, arts and culture.; Full Page Mono: 44.00; Full Page Colour: 7428.00
Currency: US Dollars
NEWSPAPER

DPA - Deutsche Presse-Agentur - New York Bureau
Editorial: United Nations, Room S-352, New York, New York 10017. **T:** 1 646 797-2852
Bureau Chief: Chris Melzer
Editorial Profile: This is the New York bureau of Deutsche Presse-Agenture, based in Hamburg, Germany.
DAILY NEWSPAPER

Draugas
Owner: Lithuanian Catholic Press Society Inc.
Editorial: 4545 W. 63rd St., Chicago, Illinois 60629-5589. **T:** 1 773 585-9500
E: redakcija@draugas.org
W: http://www.draugas.org
Freq: Daily; **Circ:** 3000
Editor in Chief: Dalia Cidzikaite
Editorial Profile: Draugas is a daily newspaper publishing Tuesday through Saturday that delivers news, events and features to Lithuanian-speaking communities throughout the world. There is no publisher for the paper.; Full Page Mono: 7.00
Currency: US Dollars
DAILY NEWSPAPER

Dring Publishing
Editorial: 1952 Railroad Ave, Arcadia, Louisiana 71001. **T:** 1 318 263-2922
E: news@bienvilledemocrat.com **Circ:** 12100 Not Audited
NEWSPAPER

Du Quoin Evening Call
Owner: GateHouse Media Inc.
Editorial: 9 N Division St, Du Quoin, Illinois 62832. **T:** 1 618 542-2133
E: dqnews@frontier.com
W: http://www.duquoin.com
Freq: Mon thru Fri; **Circ:** 3800 Not Audited
News Editor: Kathy Kopshever
Editorial Profile: Du Quoin Evening Call provides local news to readers in Du Quoin, IL and the surrounding areas. All mail must be sent to the P.O. box address.; Full Page Mono: 9.75; Full Page Colour: 100.00
Currency: US Dollars
DAILY NEWSPAPER

Duarte View
Owner: Duarte Chamber of Commerce
Editorial: 1634 3rd St., Duarte, California 91010. **T:** 1 626 357-3333
W: http://www.duartechamber.com
Freq: Bi-Monthly; **Circ:** 10000 Not Audited
Publisher: Diana Burckhard; **Editor:** Jim Kirchner
Editorial Profile: Duarte View is a free, bi-monthly newspaper published by the Duarte Chamber of Commerce and mailed to residents and businesses in Duarte, Bradbury and portions of Monrovia and Irwindale, CA. It contains news about community residents, schools, city information and local businesses.; Full Page Mono: 10.52
Currency: US Dollars
NEWSPAPER

Dubois-Spencer Counties Publishing
Owner: DSC Publishing Co. Inc.
Editorial: 113 W 6th St, Ferdinand, Indiana 47532. **T:** 1 812 367-2041
E: ferdnews@psci.net **Circ:** 5100 Not Audited
Editorial Profile: Dubois-Spencer Counties Publishing is a weekly community publisher serving the residents of Ferdinand and Spencer in Indiana.
NEWSPAPER

Duluth Budgeteer News
Owner: Forum Communications
Editorial: 424 W 1St St, Duluth, Minnesota 55802-1516. **T:** 1 218 723-5212
E: budgeteer@duluthbudgeteer.com
W: http://www.duluthnewstribune.com/event/group/group/Budgeteer
Freq: Sun; **Circ:** 40000 Not Audited
Editor: Naomi Yaeger
Editorial Profile: Duluth Budgeteer News is published weekly for residents of Duluth, MN. The newspaper covers area news, sports and arts & entertainment.; Full Page Mono: 42.41; Full Page Colour: 2890.00
Currency: US Dollars
NEWSPAPER

Duluth News-Tribune
Owner: Forum Communications Co.
Editorial: 424 W 1St St, Duluth, Minnesota 55802-1516. **T:** 1 218 723-5300
E: news@duluthnews.com
W: http://www.duluthnewstribune.com
Freq: Daily; **Circ:** 40933 Not Audited
Publisher: Ken Browall; **Editor:** Robin Washington
Editorial Profile: Duluth (MN) News-Tribune is daily newspaper serving the residents of Lake Superior and Duluth, MN that covers news, sports, entertainment and community events.; Full Page Mono: 82.85; Full Page Colour: 400.00
Currency: US Dollars
DAILY NEWSPAPER

The Duncan Banner
Owner: Community Newspaper Holdings, Inc.
Editorial: 1001 W Elm Ave, Duncan, Oklahoma 73533-4746. **T:** 1 580 255-5354
E: editor@duncanbanner.com
W: http://duncanbanner.com
Freq: Daily; **Circ:** 8960 Not Audited
Publisher: Edward Darling; **Editor:** Jeff Kaley
Editorial Profile: The Duncan Banner is a daily newspaper that provides local and national news for residents in the Duncan, OK and surrounding areas.; Full Page Mono: 14.45; Full Page Colour: 17.45
Currency: US Dollars
DAILY NEWSPAPER

The Dundalk Eagle
Owner: Kimbel Publication Inc.
Editorial: 4 N Center Pl, Dundalk, Maryland 21222. **T:** 1 410 288-6060
E: info@dundalkeagle.net
W: http://www.dundalkeagle.com
Freq: Thu; **Circ:** 19000 Not Audited
Editor: Steve Matrazzo; **Publisher:** Mary Oelke; Full Page Mono: 19.60
Currency: US Dollars
NEWSPAPER

The Dunwoody Crier
Owner: Crier Newspapers, LLC
Editorial: 5064 Nandina Ln Ste C, Dunwoody, Georgia 30338-4115. **T:** 1 770 451-4147
E: thecrier@mindspring.com
W: http://www.thecrier.net
Freq: Wed; **Circ:** 23000 Not Audited
Editorial Profile: The Dunwoody Crier is a local newspaper written for residents of Dunwoody, GA. The newspaper covers local news, sports, weather, business and arts & entertainment.; Full Page Mono: 31.76; Full Page Colour: 31.76
Currency: US Dollars
NEWSPAPER

Duowei News
Owner: Chinese Media Net Inc. (CMN)
Editorial: 6 E 46th St Rm 302, New York, New York 10017-2432. **T:** 1 212 219-3892
E: newsdesk@dwnews.com
W: http://www.dwnews.com
Freq: Fri; **Circ:** 20000 Not Audited
Publisher: Bettina Yang
Editorial Profile: Duowei News is a Chinese-language weekly covering national and international news. It also covers local news, life in North America, arts & entertainment and real estate.; Full Page Mono: 30.00
Currency: US Dollars
NEWSPAPER

The Durango Herald
Owner: Ballantine Communications, Inc.
Editorial: 1275 Main Ave, Durango, Colorado 81301-5137. **T:** 1 970 247-3504
E: herald@durangoherald.com
W: http://www.durangoherald.com
Freq: Daily; **Circ:** 6736 Not Audited
Publisher: Richard Ballantine; **City Editor:** Katie Burford; **Editor:** Don Lindley; **News Editor:** Amy Maestas
Editorial Profile: The Durango Herald covers local and regional news for the residents of Durango, CO.; Full Page Mono: 18.50; Full Page Colour: 450.00
Currency: US Dollars
DAILY NEWSPAPER

Durant Daily Democrat
Owner: Heartland Publications
Editorial: 200 W Beech St, Durant, Oklahoma 74701. **T:** 1 580 924-4388
E: editor@durantdemocrat.com
W: http://www.durantdemocrat.com
Freq: Daily; **Circ:** 5500 Not Audited
Publisher: Chris Allen
Editorial Profile: Durant Daily Democrat is the local, daily newspaper published for the Durant, OK area. The newspaper covers local news, sports and lifestyle topics. All inquiries should be addressed to the editor.; Full Page Mono: 9.86; Full Page Colour: 225.00
Currency: US Dollars
DAILY NEWSPAPER

Dyersburg State Gazette
Owner: Rust Communications
Editorial: 294 Highway 51 Bypass, Dyersburg, Tennessee 38024. **T:** 1 731 285-4091
W: http://www.stategazette.com
Freq: Mon thru Fri; **Circ:** 7000 Not Audited
Publisher & Editor: Sheila Rouse
Editorial Profile: Dyersburg State Gazette has been serving Northwest Tennessee since 1865 and today stands as the largest information medium in the region. With coverage focused exclusively on local people and local events, in recent years the paper has expanded into regional prominence with an award-winning news staff and a skilled and creative advertising department. It is written for residents of Dyer County, TN and surrounding areas.; Full Page Mono: 11.80; Full Page Colour: 14.13
Currency: US Dollars
DAILY NEWSPAPER

Dziennik Zwiazkowy
Owner: Alliance Printers and Publishers Inc.
Editorial: 5711 N Milwaukee Ave, Chicago, Illinois 60646-6215. **T:** 1 773 763-3343
E: dziennik@zwiazkowy.com
W: http://www.dziennikzwiazkowy.com
Freq: Mon thru Fri; **Circ:** 25000 Not Audited
Editor: Wojtek Bialasiewicz; **Editor:** Peter Domaraezki
Editorial Profile: Polish Daily News' editorial mission is to familiarize immigrants from Poland, Russia, Lithuania and the Ukraine with American culture, such as the laws and the politics in Washington, D.C. The newspaper, written in Polish, also works to maintain Polish traditions.; Full Page Mono: 12.00; Full Page Colour: 150.00
Currency: US Dollars
DAILY NEWSPAPER

E.A. MacKay Enterprises
Owner: E.A. MacKay Enterprise
Editorial: 116 S Main St, Lombard, Illinois 60148. **T:** 1 630 627-7010
E: lombardian@sbcglobal.net
W: http://members.aol.com/lombardian/homepage.html **Circ:** 21500 Not Audited
Editor: Jane Charmelo; **Editor:** Chris Fox
NEWSPAPER

The Eagle
Owner: Evening Post Publishing Co.
Editorial: 1729 Briarcrest Dr, Bryan, Texas 77802-2712. **T:** 1 979 776-4444
E: news@theeagle.com
W: http://www.theeagle.com
Freq: Daily; **Circ:** 19132 Not Audited
Editor: Kelly Brown; **News Editor:** Elizabeth Webb
Editorial Profile: The Eagle provides readers with local, regional, and national news coverage. The newspaper is distributed throughout eight counties in the Brazos Valley, TX. The newspaper also covers business, education, politics, religion, sports, entertainment, lifestyle, and classifieds.; Full Page Mono: 40.35; Full Page Colour: 510.00
Currency: US Dollars
DAILY NEWSPAPER

The Eagle
Owner: Associated Newspapers
Editorial: 502 Forest Ave, Plymouth, Michigan 48170-1752. **T:** 1 734 467-1900
E: editor@journalgroup.com
W: http://www.associatednewspapers.net
Freq: Thu; **Circ:** 15000 Not Audited

Editorial Profile: The Eagle is a community newspaper for residents of Western Wayne County, MI.; Full Page Mono: 11.70
Currency: US Dollars
NEWSPAPER

Eagle Herald
Owner: Bliss Communications Inc.
Editorial: 1809 Dunlap Ave, Marinette, Wisconsin 54143-1706. **T:** 1 715 735-6611
E: news@eagleherald.com
W: http://www.ehextra.com
Freq: Daily; **Circ:** 9200 Not Audited
Editorial Profile: Eagle Herald is a daily newspaper published for the residents of Marinett, WI. It covers news and events in the local community.; Full Page Mono: 24.75; Full Page Colour: 132.07
Currency: US Dollars
DAILY NEWSPAPER

Eagle Newspapers
Owner: Eckenroth Publications, Inc.
Editorial: 1116 10th St, Coronado, California 92118. **T:** 1 619 437-8800
E: editor@eaglenewsca.com
W: http://www.eaglenewsca.com **Circ:** 19000 Not Audited
Editor: Dean Eckenroth; **Publisher:** Dean Eckenroth
NEWSPAPER

Eagle Newspapers
Owner: Community Media Group LLC
Editorial: 2501 James St Ste 100, Syracuse, New York 13206-1115. **T:** 1 315 434-8889
E: newsroom@eaglenewsonline.com
W: http://www.eaglenewsonline.com
Circ: 3760 Not Audited
Editor: Ned Campbell; **Editor:** Jason Emerson; **Editor:** Michael Masucci; **Editor:** Ami Olson; **Editor:** Pierce Smith; **Publisher:** Dave Tyler
NEWSPAPER

Eagle River Publications
Owner: Delphos Herald Inc.
Editorial: 425 Mill St, Eagle River, Wisconsin 54521-8002. **T:** 1 715 479-4421
E: erpub@nnex.net
W: http://www.vcnewsreview.com **Circ:** 11230 Not Audited
Publisher: Kurt Krueger; **Editor:** Gary Ridderbusch
NEWSPAPER

Eagle Times
Owner: Eagle Publications, Inc.
Editorial: 401 River Rd, Claremont, New Hampshire 3743. **T:** 1 603 543-3100
E: news@eagletimes.com
Freq: Daily; **Circ:** 7793 Not Audited
Editorial Profile: Eagle Times is a daily newspaper that services Southwestern New Hampshire and Vermont.; Full Page Mono: 17.00; Full Page Colour: 205.00
Currency: US Dollars
DAILY NEWSPAPER

The Eagle-Tribune
Owner: Community Newspaper Holdings, Inc.
Editorial: 100 Turnpike St, North Andover, Massachusetts 1845. **T:** 1 978 946-2000
W: http://www.eagletribune.com
Freq: Mon thru Fri; **Circ:** 28509 Not Audited
Publisher: Karen Andreas; **Haverhill Editor:** Bill Cantwell; **New Hampshire Editor:** Jo-Anne MacKenzie; **City Editor:** Warren Talbot
Editorial Profile: The Eagle-Tribune in North Andover, MA is published daily for residents of New Hampshire and Massachusetts and covers local, national and international news, arts, weather and sports.; Full Page Mono: 40.65; Full Page Colour: 525.00
Currency: US Dollars
DAILY NEWSPAPER

Earlville Post Newspapers
Editorial: 107 Rail Rd, Earlville, Illinois 60518. **T:** 1 815 246-4600 **E:** editor@earlvillepost.com
Circ: 3500 Not Audited
Editor: Andrea Bloom; **Publisher:** Stuart Bloom
NEWSPAPER

The Early Bird
Owner: Ball Publishing Company
Editorial: 5312 Sebring Warner Rd, Greenville, Ohio 45331. **T:** 1 937 548-3330
E: publisher@earlybirdpaper.com
W: http://www.earlybirdpaper.com
Freq: Sun; **Circ:** 27558 Not Audited
Publisher: Carol Ball
Editorial Profile: The Early Bird is a weekly newspaper established in 1968, written for the residents of County Target, OH. It covers news and events in the local community. Deadlines

are Thursdays at noon CT.; Full Page Mono: 65.00
Currency: US Dollars
NEWSPAPER

Early County News
Owner: Early County News, Inc.
Editorial: 529 College St, Blakely, Georgia 39823. **T:** 1 229 723-4376
E: ecnews@windstream.net
W: http://www.earlycountynews.com
Freq: Wed; **Circ:** 11400
Editor: William Fleming
Editorial Profile: The Early County News is a weekly community newspaper serving residents of Early County, GA. Deadlines for the publication fall on Fridays at 5pm ET.; Full Page Mono: 6.23
Currency: US Dollars
NEWSPAPER

East Area Publishing
Editorial: 165 2nd St SW, Conde, South Dakota 57434. **T:** 1 605 382-5627
E: eastarea@nvc.net **Circ:** 1198 Not Audited
NEWSPAPER

East Bay Express
Owner: East Bay Publishing LLC
Editorial: 620 3rd St, Oakland, California 94607-3551. **T:** 1 510 879-3700
E: editor@eastbayexpress.com
W: http://www.eastbayexpress.com
Freq: Wed; **Circ:** 50000 Not Audited
Publisher: Jody Colley
Editorial Profile: East Bay Express in Oakland, CA is a weekly newspaper for the residents of the East Bay, CA area, covering local news and events.; Full Page Mono: 20.30
Currency: US Dollars
NEWSPAPER

East Bay Newspapers - Tiverton
Owner: East Bay Newspapers
Editorial: 1745 Main Rd, Tiverton, Rhode Island 02878-4523. **T:** 1 401 683-1000
W: http://www.eastbayri.com **Circ:** 9308 Not Audited
Publisher: Matthew Hayes
NEWSPAPER

East Bay Newspapers-East Providence
Owner: East Bay Newspapers
Editorial: 1 Bradford St, Bristol, Rhode Island 02809-1906. **T:** 1 401 434-7210
W: http://www.eastbayri.com **Circ:** 14634 Not Audited
Editor: Josh Bickford; **Publisher:** Matthew Hayes
NEWSPAPER

The East County Californian
Owner: East County Community Newspapers, Inc.
Editorial: 119 N Magnolia Ave, El Cajon, California 92020-3903. **T:** 1 619 441-0400
E: info@eccalifornian.com
W: http://www.eccalifornian.com
Freq: Thu; **Circ:** 32500 Not Audited
Publisher: John Moreno; **Editor:** Iris Neal
Editorial Profile: The East County Californian serves the cities of El Cajon, Santee, La Mesa, Lemon Grove, and the communities of Spring Valley, Lakeside, Blossom Valley, Flinn Springs, Rancho San Diego, Casa de Oro, Dehesa, Dulzura, and Crest all, CA. Coverage includes local news, sports, business, arts and entertainment, food, and business.; Full Page Mono: 91.80
Currency: US Dollars
NEWSPAPER

East County Gazette
Editorial: 1130 Broadway, El Cajon, California 92021-4805. **T:** 1 619 444-5774
E: gazettenews@sbcglobal.net
W: http://www.eastcountygazette.com
Freq: Thu; **Circ:** 20000 Not Audited
Editorial Profile: East County Gazette is a weekly newspaper written for the residents of East County, CA.; Full Page Mono: 10.50
Currency: US Dollars
NEWSPAPER

East County Times
Owner: MediaNews Group
Editorial: 1700 Cavallo Rd, Antioch, California 94509. **T:** 1 925 757-2525
E: ccnnewsrelease@bayareanewsgroup.com
W: http://www.contracostatimes.com
Freq: Daily; **Circ:** 17050 Not Audited
Editor: Craig Lazzeretti; **Editor:** Stephen Trousdale
Editorial Profile: East County Times is a daily newspaper serving residents of Antioch, Bay Point, Bethel Island, Brentwood, Byron,

Discovery Bay, Knightsen, Oakley and Pittsburg, CA. It cover local news, events, politics, schools, sports, editorial and features of interest to readers in East Contra Costa County. The paper is delivered directly to residents' homes Mondays through Saturdays. The Sunday edition is circulated as a supplemental section within The Contra Costa Times.; Full Page Mono: 360.00; Full Page Colour: 1467.00
Currency: US Dollars
DAILY NEWSPAPER

The East County Times
Editorial: 513 Eastern Blvd, Baltimore, Maryland 21221. **T:** 1 410 780-3303
E: ecteditorial@comcast.net
W: http://www.eastcountytimesonline.com
Freq: Thu; **Circ:** 45000 Not Audited
Editor: Allison McAlister; **Publisher:** George Wilbanks
Editorial Profile: The East County Times is a weekly newspaper that was founded in 1970. The paper's editorial mission is to uplift the community and neighborhood in which we live to encourage people to make their homes here and work here. The publication is written for all ages and was formerly known as Essex Times. This is a 48-page tabloid newspaper.; Full Page Mono: 12.60
Currency: US Dollars
NEWSPAPER

East Hampton Star
Owner: East Hampton Star Inc.
Editorial: 153 Main St, East Hampton, New York 11937. **T:** 1 631 324-0002
E: editor@easthamptonstar.com
W: http://www.easthamptonstar.com
Freq: Thu; **Circ:** 15200 Not Audited
Editor: David Rattray; **Publisher:** Helen Rattray
Editorial Profile: East Hampton Star is a local weekly newspaper for the residents of East Hampton, NY. It covers news and events in the local community.; Full Page Mono: 28.00
Currency: US Dollars
NEWSPAPER

East Oregonian
Owner: East Oregonian Publishing Co.
Editorial: 211 SE Byers Ave, Pendleton, Oregon 97801-2346. **T:** 1 541 276-2211
E: eonews@eastoregonian.com
W: http://www.eastoregonian.com
Freq: Daily; **Circ:** 7890 Not Audited
Publisher & Editor: Tom Brown
Editorial Profile: East Oregonian is published daily for the residents of Pendelton, OR and surrounding areas. The newspaper covers local news, business, sports and community events.; Full Page Mono: 18.83; Full Page Colour: 58.67
Currency: US Dollars
DAILY NEWSPAPER

East Side Daily News
Editorial: 11400 Woodland Ave, Cleveland, Ohio 44104-2636. **T:** 1 216 721-1674
E: esdn1@yahoo.com
W: http://www.eastsidedailynews.com
Freq: Fri; **Circ:** 20000 Not Audited
Editorial Profile: East Side Daily News is written for the African American residents of Cleveland, OH. It covers news and events in the African American community.; Full Page Mono: 25.00
Currency: US Dollars
NEWSPAPER

The East Tennessee Catholic
Owner: Diocese of Knoxville
Editorial: 805 Northshore Drive Southwest, Knoxville, Tennessee 37922.
T: 1 865 584-3307 **W:** http://etcatholic.org
Freq: Monthly; **Circ:** 22000
Editor: Bill Brewer; **Publisher:** Richard Stika
Editorial Profile: The East Tennessee Catholic is a community newspaper for the Diocese of Knoxville, TN.; Full Page Mono: 21.05
Currency: US Dollars
NEWSPAPER

East Texas Review
Editorial: 517 S Mobberly Ave, Longview, Texas 75602-1827. **T:** 1 903 236-0406
E: graphics@easttexasreview.com
W: http://www.easttexasreview.com
Freq: Thu; **Circ:** 10000 Not Audited
Editor: Joycelyne Fadojutimi; **Publisher:** Robert Fadojutimi
Editorial Profile: East Texas Review is a weekly community newspaper serving Longview, TX.; Full Page Mono: 42.50
Currency: US Dollars
NEWSPAPER

East Valley Tribune
Owner: 10/13 Communications
Editorial: 1620 W Fountainhead Pkwy Ste 219, Tempe, Arizona 85282-1848.
T: 1 480 898-6500 **E:** newstips@evtrib.com
W: http://www.eastvalleytribune.com
Freq: Fri; **Circ:** 91942
Editorial Profile: East Valley Tribune is a newspaper covering local, national and international news. It serves suburban Phoenix, specifically the communities of Ahwatukee, Apache Junction, Chandler, Gilbert, Mesa, Queen Creek and Tempe, AZ. The paper also offers a section specifically about Scottsdale. It is printed Wednesday, Friday and Saturday but is available online 7 days a week.; Full Page Mono: 59.59; Full Page Colour: 624.18
Currency: US Dollars
NEWSPAPER

Eastern Arizona Courier, Inc.
Owner: Wick Communications Inc.
Editorial: 301 E US Highway 70 Suite A, Safford, Arizona 85546. **T:** 1 928 428-2560
W: http://www.eacourier.com
Freq: Sun; **Circ:** 7859
Publisher: Monica Watson
NEWSPAPER

The Eastern Gazette
Editorial: 21 Main St, Dexter, Maine 4930.
T: 1 207 924-7402
E: gazette@easterngazette.com
W: http://www.easterngazette.com
Freq: Fri; **Circ:** 17500 Not Audited
Editorial Profile: The Eastern Gazette is published weekly for the residents of Dexter, ME and surrounding areas. The newspaper covers local news and community events.; Full Page Mono: 12.00; Full Page Colour: 75.00
Currency: US Dollars
NEWSPAPER

Eastern Group Publications, Inc.
Owner: Eastern Group Publications
Editorial: 111 South Avenue 59, Los Angeles, California 90042. **T:** 1 323 341-7970
E: service@egpnews.com
W: http://egpnews.com **Circ:** 104000 Not Audited
Publisher: Dolores Sanchez
Editorial Profile: Eastern Group Publications is a weekly community newspaper publisher serving the residents of Los Angeles, Brooklyn, Belvedere and City Terrace, CA.
NEWSPAPER

Eastern Shore Post
Editorial: 25248 Lankford Hwy, Onley, Virginia 23418. **T:** 1 757 789-7678
W: http://www.easternshorepost.com
Freq: Fri; **Circ:** 13000
Editor: Cheryl Nowak
Editorial Profile: Eastern Shore Post is weekly community newspaper serving residents of Onley, VA, with a focus on local news, sports, and events.
NEWSPAPER

Eastern Wake News
Owner: McClatchy Newspapers
Editorial: 110 N Arendell Ave, Zebulon, North Carolina 27597-2602. **T:** 1 919 269-6101
W: http://www.easternwakenews.com
Freq: Wed; **Circ:** 21600 Not Audited
Publisher: Felicia Gressette
Editorial Profile: Eastern Wake News is a weekly newspaper covering Knightdale, Wendell, Zebulon and neighboring communities like Middlesex, Pilot, Archer Lodge, Lizard Lick, Hopkins, Shotwell, Pearces, Eagle Rock and Bunn, NC. It is a source for in-depth coverage of issues that affect the area: news, photos, honor rolls and schools; exclusive reports and photos from recreation teams; town government coverage; and more stories and photos of the Carolina Mudcats and high school sports than any other source.; Full Page Mono: 27.45; Full Page Colour: 418.00
Currency: US Dollars
NEWSPAPER

Eastland/Callahan County Newspapers
Owner: Eastland/Callahan County Newspapers
Editorial: 215 S Seaman St, Eastland, Texas 76448. **T:** 1 254 629-1707
W: http://www.e-cinc.com **Circ:** 5006 Not Audited
Editor: Paula Carpenter; **Editor:** Margaret Hetrick; **Editor:** LaDonna Latham
NEWSPAPER

Eastside Voice
Editorial: 195 N Shortridge Rd, Ste D, Indianapolis, Indiana 46219-8909.
T: 1 317 356-2222
W: http://www.eastsidevoicenews.com
Freq: Fri; **Circ:** 20000
Editor in Chief: Ethel Winslow
Editorial Profile: Eastside Voice is a weekly community newspaper serving neighborhoods in Eastern Indianapolis. Each edition includes local news stories, columns, a calendar of events, puzzles and games and comics. Special sections include school zone, financial focus, senior lifestyle and health and fitness. The publication launched in March 2009.; Full Page Mono: 14.00
Currency: US Dollars
NEWSPAPER

Easy Reader
Owner: 2100 Trust LLC
Editorial: 832 Hermosa Ave, Hermosa Beach, California 90254-4116. **T:** 1 310 372-4611
E: easyreader@easyreadernews.com
W: http://www.easyreadernews.com
Freq: Thu; **Circ:** 50000 Not Audited
Editorial Profile: Easy Reader is published weekly for the residents of Manhattan Beach, El Segundo, Redondo Beach and Hermosa Beach, CA. The newspaper covers local news, sports, entertainment and community events.; Full Page Mono: 40.00
Currency: US Dollars
NEWSPAPER

Ebony
Owner: Johnson Publishing Company, Inc.
Editorial: 1270 Avenue of the Americas Fl 21, New York, New York 10020-1700.
T: 1 212 397-4500
Editorial Profile: Written as an African American oriented consumer interest magazine. Editorial coverage explores topics ranging from education and history to politics, literature and arts, business, personalities, civil rights, sports entertainment, music and social events.
NEWSPAPER

Echo Press
Owner: Forum Communications
Editorial: 225 7th Ave E, Alexandria, Minnesota 56308. **T:** 1 320 763-3133
E: echo@echopress.com
W: http://www.echopress.com
Freq: Fri; **Circ:** 10500 Not Audited
Editor: Tara Bitzan
Editorial Profile: Echo Press is a twice weekly newspaper for the residents of Douglas County, MN. It covers news and events in the local community. Deadlines are on Mondays and Wednesdays at 10am ET. The outlet offers RRS (Real Simple Syndication).; Full Page Mono: 12.40
Currency: US Dollars
NEWSPAPER

Echo Publishing & Printing
Owner: Morris Communications
Editorial: 506 James St., Brainerd, Minnesota 56401. **T:** 1 218 829-4705
E: news@pequotlakesecho.com
W: http://www.pineandlakes.com **Circ:** 5454 Not Audited
Publisher: Pete Mohs; **Editor:** Nancy Vogt
NEWSPAPER

Les Echos - New York Bureau
Owner: Groupe les Echos
Editorial: 1330 Avenue Of The Americas, 14th Floor, New York, New York 10019.
T: 1 212 641-6500 **W:** http://www.lesechos.fr
Bureau Chief: Pierre de Gasquet
Editorial Profile: This is the New York bureau for Les Echos newspaper in Paris.
DAILY NEWSPAPER

ECM Publishers, Inc.
Owner: ECM Publishers, Inc.
Editorial: 880 15th St SW, Forest Lake, Minnesota 55025-1313. **T:** 1 651 464-4601
Circ: 42075 Not Audited
Publisher: Julian Andersen; **Editor:** Clint Riese
NEWSPAPER

El Eco de Virginia-Weekly
Editorial: 204 Brackenridge Ave, Norfolk, Virginia 23505-4322. **T:** 1 757 625-1341
E: elecodeva@yahoo.com
W: http://www.ecohispanic.com
Freq: Wed; **Circ:** 30000 Not Audited
Editorial Profile: El Eco de Virginia-Weekly is a Spanish-language newspaper written for Hispanic residents of Norfolk, VA and the surrounding area.; Full Page Mono: 27.62
Currency: US Dollars
NEWSPAPER

Ecorse Telegram
Owner: Gina C. Wilson
Editorial: 10748 W Jefferson Ave, River Rouge, Michigan 48218-1232.
T: 1 313 928-2955
E: telegram@telegramnews.net
W: http://www.telegramnews.net
Freq: Thu; **Circ:** 12000 Not Audited
Editorial Profile: Ecorse Telegram is published weekly for the residents of Ecorse, MI and surrounding areas. The newspaper covers local news, sports and community events.; Full Page Mono: 20.00
Currency: US Dollars
NEWSPAPER

Ecuador News
Editorial: 6403 Roosevelt Ave, 2nd Fl, Woodside, New York 11377-3643.
T: 1 718 205-7014 **E:** ecuanews@inch.com
W: http://www.ecuadornews.com.ec
Freq: Wed; **Circ:** 45000 Not Audited
Editorial Profile: Ecuador News in Woodside, NY is a weekly newspaper written for Ecuadorian and Hispanic communities in New York, New Jersey and other U.S. cities.; Full Page Mono: 21.54
Currency: US Dollars
NEWSPAPER

Ed Print
Owner: EdPrint, Inc.
Editorial: 13342 NE 175th St, Woodinville, Washington 98072. **T:** 1 425 483-0606
E: editor@woodinville.com
W: http://www.nwnews.com **Circ:** 30200 Not Audited
Editor: Lisa Allen; **Publisher:** Julie Bosely; **Editor:** Karen Diefendorf
Editorial Profile: Ed Print is a community newspaper publisher in Woodinville, WA.
NEWSPAPER

Edward A. Sherman Publishing Co.
Editorial: 101 Malbone Rd, Newport, Rhode Island 2840. **T:** 1 401 849-3300 **Circ:** 15000 Not Audited
Editor: Richard Alexander; **Editor:** Janine Weisman; **Editor:** Janine Weisman; **Editor:** Janine Weisman
Editorial Profile: Edward A. Sherman Publishing Co. is a weekly community newspaper publisher serving the residents of Newport, RI.
NEWSPAPER

Edwardsville Intelligencer
Owner: Hearst Newspapers
Editorial: 117 N 2nd St, Edwardsville, Illinois 62025. **T:** 1 618 656-4700
E: citydesk@edwpub.net
W: http://www.theintelligencer.com
Freq: Daily; **Circ:** 4288 Not Audited
Publisher: Denise Von Der Haar
Editorial Profile: Edwardsville Intelligencer is published daily for the residents of Edwardsville, IL and surrounding areas. The newspaper provides information about local news, business, sports and community events.; Full Page Mono: 17.60
Currency: US Dollars
DAILY NEWSPAPER

Effingham Daily News
Owner: Community Newspaper Holdings, Inc.
Editorial: 201 N Banker St, Effingham, Illinois 62401-2304. **T:** 1 217 347-7151
E: editor@effinghamdailynews.com
W: http://www.effinghamdailynews.com
Freq: Mon thru Fri; **Circ:** 9588
Publisher: Steven Raymond
Editorial Profile: Effingham Daily News is is published daily for the residents of Effingham, IL an surrounding areas. The newspaper covers local news, sports, business, entertainment and lifestyles.; Full Page Mono: 16.00; Full Page Colour: 55.81
Currency: US Dollars
DAILY NEWSPAPER

Effingham Now
Owner: Morris Communications
Editorial: 293 S Columbia Ave, Rincon, Georgia 31326-9027. **T:** 1 912 826-1290
W: http://savannahnow.com/effinghamnow
Freq: Sun; **Circ:** 12500 Not Audited
Editor: Deann Komanecky; **Publisher:** Michael Traynor
Editorial Profile: Effingham Now is a newspaper distributed three days a week to the subscribers of the Savannah (GA) Morning News and residents of Effingham County, GA. Please do not send any mail to the street address.; Full Page Mono: 9.66; Full Page Colour: 125.00
Currency: US Dollars
NEWSPAPER

El Dorado News-Times
Owner: News-Times Publishing Co.
Editorial: 111 N Madison Ave, El Dorado, Arkansas 71730-6124. **T:** 1 870 862-6611
E: editorial@eldoradonews.com
W: http://www.eldoradonews.com
Freq: Daily; **Circ:** 7476 Not Audited
Publisher: Walter Hussman; **Editor:** Lauren Martin
Editorial Profile: El Dorado News-Times is a daily newspaper published for El Dorado, AR. The paper covers local news and events. It combines with the Camden (AR) News and the Magnolia (AR) Banner-News on Sundays.; Full Page Mono: 18.85; Full Page Colour: 297.00
Currency: US Dollars
DAILY NEWSPAPER

El Dorado Times
Owner: GateHouse Media Inc.
Editorial: 114 N Vine St, El Dorado, Kansas 67042-2089. **T:** 1 316 321-1120
E: eldoradotimes@eldoradotimes.com
W: http://www.eldoradotimes.com
Freq: Daily; **Circ:** 3950 Not Audited
Publisher: Kent Bush; **News Editor:** Julie Curtis
Editorial Profile: El Dorado Times is a daily newspaper published in the town of El Dorado, KS and distributed throughout the area. The paper covers local news and events for residents of the town.; Full Page Mono: 9.00; Full Page Colour: 11.00
Currency: US Dollars
DAILY NEWSPAPER

El Paso Times
Owner: MediaNews Group
Editorial: 500 W Overland Ave Ste 150, El Paso, Texas 79901-1086. **T:** 1 915 546-6100
E: borderland@elpasotimes.com
W: http://www.elpasotimes.com
Freq: Daily; **Circ:** 65002 Not Audited
Editor: Robert Moore; **Publisher:** Sergio Salinas
Editorial Profile: El Paso Times is a local, daily newspaper published for the residents of El Paso, TX and Southern New Mexico. It covers news, sports, business, lifestyle and community events. Lead time for submissions vary with the content.; Full Page Mono: 296.79; Full Page Colour: 456.42
Currency: US Dollars
DAILY NEWSPAPER

El Paso Times
Editorial: 1005 Congress Ave, Austin, Texas 78701-2463. **T:** 1 512 479-6606
DAILY NEWSPAPER

El Paso Times
Editorial: 490 Old Santa Fe Trl, Santa Fe, New Mexico 87501-2749. **T:** 1 505 820-6898
Bureau Chief: Milan Simonich
DAILY NEWSPAPER

El Segundo Herald Newspapers
Owner: Herald Publications
Editorial: 312 E Imperial Ave, El Segundo, California 90245. **T:** 1 310 322-1830
E: pr@heraldpublications.com
W: http://www.heraldpublications.com
Circ: 50000 Not Audited
Editor: Heidi Maerker; **Publisher:** Richard Van Vranken
NEWSPAPER

Elgin Newspapers
Owner: Newspapers of Fayette County, Inc.
Editorial: 227 Center St, Elgin, Iowa 52141.
T: 1 563 426-5591
E: elginecho@alpinecom.net
W: http://fayettecountynewspapers.com
Circ: 4273 Not Audited
Editor: Jessica Duren
NEWSPAPER

Elite News
Editorial: 2349 Cedar St., Dallas, Texas 75203.
T: 1 214 372-6500 **E:** elitearticles@aol.com
W: http://www.dfwelitenews.com
Freq: Fri; **Circ:** 45000
Editorial Profile: Elite News is written for predominantly African American churches in northern Texas and provides its readers with the following sections: Local and National News, Sports, Editorials, Community Leader Profiles, Church Activities, Health and Fitness, Business Consumer Tips, Classified and Employment Opportunities and Community Calendar.; Full Page Mono: 35.00
Currency: US Dollars
NEWSPAPER

Elizabethton Star
Owner: Elizabethton Newspapers Inc.
Editorial: 300 N Sycamore St, Elizabethton, Tennessee 37643-2742. **T:** 1 423 542-4151
W: http://www.starhq.com
Freq: Mon thru Fri; **Circ:** 7257 Not Audited
Editor in Chief: Brian Reese
Editorial Profile: Elizabethton Star is the daily newspaper for Carter County and Elizabethton County, TN. It is a general newspaper that covers local as well as regional news from Northeast Tennessee.; Full Page Mono: 15.00; Full Page Colour: 245.00
Currency: US Dollars
DAILY NEWSPAPER

Elk City Daily News
Owner: Family Corporation
Editorial: 206 W Broadway Ave, Elk City, Oklahoma 73644-4742. **T:** 1 580 225-3000
E: news@ecdailynews.com
W: http://ecdailynews.com
Freq: Daily; **Circ:** 5740 Not Audited
Editor: Cheryl Overstreet; **Publisher:** Larry Wade
Editorial Profile: Elk City Daily News is published for the residents of Elk City, OK and surrounding areas. The paper provides information on local news and community events. Deadlines are one day prior to issue date.; Full Page Mono: 10.70; Full Page Colour: 920.10
Currency: US Dollars
DAILY NEWSPAPER

Elk Grove Citizen
Owner: Herburger Publications, Inc.
Editorial: 8970 Elk Grove Blvd, Elk Grove, California 95624-1946. **T:** 1 916 685-3945
E: egnews@herburger.net
W: http://www.egcitizen.com
Freq: Fri; **Circ:** 10350 Not Audited
Publisher: David Herburger; **Editor:** Cameron MacDonald
Editorial Profile: Elk Grove Citizen is written for residents of Elk Grove, CA. It covers local news and events.; Full Page Mono: 9.50
Currency: US Dollars
NEWSPAPER

The Elkhart Truth
Owner: Truth Publishing
Editorial: 421 S 2nd St, Elkhart, Indiana 46516-3238. **T:** 1 574 294-1661
E: newsroom@elkharttruth.com
W: http://www.etruth.com
Freq: Daily; **Circ:** 15896 Not Audited
Publisher: Brandon Erlacher
Editorial Profile: The Elkhart Truth is a daily newspaper for Elkhart, IN. The main goal of the paper is to be the dominant source of local news. The publication is written for residents of Elkhart County and the surrounding area. Topics covered include news about local schools, local government, and community organizations.; Full Page Mono: 15.64
Currency: US Dollars
DAILY NEWSPAPER

Elko Daily Free Press
Owner: Lee Enterprises, Inc.
Editorial: 3720 E Idaho St, Elko, Nevada 89801-4611. **T:** 1 775 738-3118
E: news@elkodaily.com
W: http://elkodaily.com
Freq: Mon thru Fri; **Circ:** 6700 Not Audited
Editorial Profile: Elko Daily Free Press is a newspaper serving residents of Elko, NV and its surrounding area. It covers news, events, school news, sports, business, health and features of interest to local residents. Deadlines are two days prior to publication at noon PT.; Full Page Mono: 15.30; Full Page Colour: 440.00
Currency: US Dollars
DAILY NEWSPAPER

Elliott Publishing, Inc.
Owner: Elliott Publishing Co. Inc
Editorial: 103 E Hannibal St, Liberty, Illinois 62347. **T:** 1 217 645-3033
E: libertyb@adams.net
W: http://www.elliott-publishing.com
Circ: 3625
Publisher: Jim Elliott; **Editor:** Marcia Elliott; Full Page Mono: 6.25
Currency: US Dollars
NEWSPAPER

The Ellsworth American
Owner: Ellsworth American, Inc.
Editorial: 30 Water St, Ellsworth, Maine 4605.
T: 1 207 667-2576
E: news@ellsworthamerican.com
W: http://www.ellsworthamerican.com
Freq: Thu; **Circ:** 10355 Not Audited
Publisher: Alan Baker; **Publisher:** Alan Baker; **Publisher:** Alan Baker; **Publisher:** Alan Baker

Editorial Profile: Ellsworth American is a weekly newspaper written for residents of Hancock County, ME. Deadlines for the publication are Mondays at 5pm ET.; Full Page Mono: 17.85
Currency: US Dollars
NEWSPAPER

Ellsworth Reporter
Owner: Morris Multimedia, Inc.
Editorial: 304 N Douglas Ave, Ellsworth, Kansas 67439-3218. **T:** 1 785 472-5085
E: indy@eaglecom.net
W: http://www.indyrepnews.com
Freq: Weekly; **Circ:** 3200 Not Audited
Editor: Linda Mowery-Denning
NEWSPAPER

Ellwood City Ledger
Owner: Beaver Newspapers Inc.
Editorial: 835 Lawrence Ave, Ellwood City, Pennsylvania 16117-5908. **T:** 1 724 758-5573
E: eclnews@ellwoodcityledger.com
W: http://www.ellwoodcityledger.com
Freq: Mon thru Fri; **Circ:** 3341 Not Audited
Publisher: Alan Buncher
Editorial Profile: Ellwood City Ledger is published daily for the residents of Ellwood City, PA and surrounding areas. The newspaper offers local, state and national news, sports, business, lifestyles and entertainment.; Full Page Mono: 15.23; Full Page Colour: 17.23
Currency: US Dollars
DAILY NEWSPAPER

Ely Times & Eureka Sentinel Newspapers
Owner: Battleborn Media LLC
Editorial: 515 Murry St., Ely, Nevada 89301. **T:** 1 775 289-4491 **E:** elytimes@gmail.com
W: http://www.elynews.com
Freq: Fri; **Circ:** 3146 Not Audited; Full Page Mono: 22.75
Currency: US Dollars
NEWSPAPER

Embarcadero Publishing - Palo Alto
Owner: Embarcadero Publishing Co.
Editorial: 450 Cambridge Ave, Palo Alto, California 94306-1507. **T:** 1 650 326-8210
E: editor@paweekly.com **Circ:** 59000
Editor: Jocelyn Dong; **Publisher:** Tom Gibboney; **Publisher:** William Johnson
Editorial Profile: Embarcadero Publshing in Palo Alto, CA publishes The Almanac, Mountain View Voice and Palto Alto Weekly.
NEWSPAPER

Embarcadero Publishing - Pleasanton
Owner: Embarcadero Publishing Co.
Editorial: 5506 Sunol Blvd Ste 100, Pleasanton, California 94566-7779.
T: 1 925 600-0840
W: http://embarcaderomediagroup.com
Editor: Jeremy Walsh
Editorial Profile: Embarcadero Publishing - Pleasanton produces hyperlocal community news, including Pleasanton (CA) Weekly in print, as well as the online-only Danville (CA) Express and San Ramon (CA) Express.
NEWSPAPER

Emmetsburg Democrat & Reporter
Owner: Ogden Newspapers
Editorial: 1122 Broadway St, Ste B, Emmetsburg, Iowa 50536. **T:** 1 712 852-2323
W: http://www.emmetsburgnews.com
Circ: 5200 Not Audited
Publisher: Dan McCain; **Editor:** Jane Whitmore
NEWSPAPER

Empire Publishing Corporation
Editorial: 1525 Central Ave, Far Rockaway, New York 11691. **T:** 1 516 594-4000
E: lijeworld@aol.com **Circ:** 80000 Not Audited
Editor In Chief: Jerome Lippman
NEWSPAPER

Empire State Weeklies
Editorial: 2010 Empire Blvd, Webster, New York 14580-1915. **T:** 1 585 671-1533
E: websterherald@empirestateweeklies.com
Circ: 4800 Not Audited
Editor: Mike Sorenson
NEWSPAPER

The Emporia Gazette
Owner: White Corporation, Inc.
Editorial: 517 Merchant St, Emporia, Kansas 66801. **T:** 1 620 342-4800
E: newsroom@emporiagazette.com
W: http://www.emporiagazette.com
Freq: Mon thru Fri; **Circ:** 5857
Editorial Profile: The Emporia Gazette's editorial mission is to provide readers with a complete daily package of local and regional news, plus the latest top stories from the state, nation and world. The publication is written for the communities of Lyon, Chase, Coffey, Greenwood, Morris and Osage counties in Kansas. It covers local and national news, sports, editorials, food, film reviews, youth columns, business news, agricultural news, Emporia State University news, and television listings.; Full Page Mono: 10.56; Full Page Colour: 215.00
Currency: US Dollars
DAILY NEWSPAPER

Enfoque Deportivo
Editorial: 13227 Noblecrest Dr, Houston, Texas 77041-1871. **T:** 1 713 785-7191
E: enfoque@sbcglobal.net
W: http://www.enfoquedeportivo.com
Freq: Bi-Weekly; **Circ:** 10000
Editor: Maritza Reyes; **Publisher:** William Jose Reyes
Editorial Profile: Enfoque Deportivo is a local community newspaper for the residents of Houston and the surrounding communities.; Full Page Mono: 17.00
Currency: US Dollars
NEWSPAPER

Engle Publishing Company
Editorial: 1425 W Main St, Mount Joy, Pennsylvania 17552. **T:** 1 717 653-1833
E: news@engleonline.com
W: http://www.engleonline.com **Circ:** 398678 Not Audited
Publisher: Charles Engle; **Editor:** Francine Fulton
NEWSPAPER

Englewood Sun
Editorial: 120 W Dearborn St, Englewood, Florida 34223-3237. **T:** 1 941 681-3000
W: http://www.sun-herald.com
Freq: Daily; **Circ:** 8400 Not Audited
Publisher: David Dunn-Rankin; **Editor:** Dana Sanchez
Editorial Profile: Englewood Sun is written for the residents of Englewood, FL.; Full Page Mono: 13.70
Currency: US Dollars
DAILY NEWSPAPER

Enid News and Eagle
Owner: Community Newspaper Holdings, Inc.
Editorial: 227 W Broadway Ave, Enid, Oklahoma 73701. **T:** 1 580 233-6600
E: info@enidnews.com
W: http://enidnews.com
Freq: Daily; **Circ:** 12288 Not Audited
Publisher: Jeff Funk
Editorial Profile: Enid News and Eagle is a local weekly newspaper serving the residents of Enid, OK and the surrounding area. The newspaper covers local and national news, sports, arts & entertainment, editorial, business and community events. Deadlines are two days before issue dates.; Full Page Mono: 25.75; Full Page Colour: 31.85
Currency: US Dollars
DAILY NEWSPAPER

Enlace
Owner: San Diego Union-Tribune, LLC
Editorial: 1669 Brandywine Ave, Chula Vista, California 91911-6073. **T:** 1 619 293-1039
E: editorial@mienlace.com
W: http://www.vidalatinasd.com
Freq: Fri; **Circ:** 112982
Editor: Lilia O'Hara
Editorial Profile: Enlace is a weekly newspaper providing Local and Community News to the Hispanic and Spanish-speaking communities in San Diego, CA and Tijuana, Baja California, Mexico.
NEWSPAPER

Ennis Daily News
Owner: Fackelman Newspapers
Editorial: 213 N Dallas St, Ennis, Texas 75119-4096. **T:** 1 972 875-3801
W: http://www.ennisdailynews.com
Freq: Mon thru Fri; **Circ:** 3930 Not Audited
Publisher: Ben Brooks
Editorial Profile: Ennis Daily News is a local newspaper serving the residents of Ennis, TX and the surrounding communities. The newspaper covers local news, sports, arts & entertainment, weather, business and community events.; Full Page Mono: 9.00; Full Page Colour: 150.00
Currency: US Dollars
DAILY NEWSPAPER

The Enquirer-Journal
Owner: Paxton Media Group
Editorial: 500 W Jefferson St, Monroe, North Carolina 28112-4657. **T:** 1 704 289-1541
E: news@theej.com
W: http://www.enquirerjournal.com
Freq: Daily; **Circ:** 6523 Not Audited
Publisher: Marvin Enderle
Editorial Profile: The Enquirer-Journal is a local daily newspaper serving the residents of Union County, NC. The newspaper covers local and national news, sports, arts, editorial, business and community events.; Full Page Mono: 19.50; Full Page Colour: 290.00
Currency: US Dollars
DAILY NEWSPAPER

The Enterprise
Owner: Gazette Newspapers Inc.
Editorial: 23125 Camden Way, California, Maryland 20619. **T:** 1 301 862-2111
W: http://www.somdnews.com/enterprise
Freq: Fri; **Circ:** 16000 Not Audited
Publisher: Karen Acton; **Editor:** Rick Boyd
Editorial Profile: The Enterprise is a local weekly newspaper written for the residents of Lexington Park, MD and surrounding areas. The publication covers local news, sports, area schools and community events.; Full Page Mono: 14.79
Currency: US Dollars
NEWSPAPER

The Enterprise
Owner: GateHouse Media Inc.
Editorial: 1324 Belmont St, Brockton, Massachusetts 02301-4435.
T: 1 508 586-6200
E: newsroom@enterprisenews.com
W: http://www.enterprisenews.com
Freq: Mon thru Fri Not Audited
Editor: Chazy Dowaliby
Editorial Profile: The Enterprise is a daily newspaper serving residents living South of Boston, including the community of Brockton, MA. It covers international, national and local news, sports, business, editorials, arts & entertainment and feature stories.; Full Page Mono: 42.60
Currency: US Dollars
DAILY NEWSPAPER

Enterprise and Pioneer Newspapers
Owner: Hometown Publishing, LLC
Editorial: 3341 Los Padres Drive, Frazier Park, California 93225. **T:** 1 661 245-3794
W: http://www.mountainenterprise.com
Circ: 7000 Not Audited
Publisher: Gary Meyer
NEWSPAPER

Enterprise Ledger
Owner: BH Media Group
Editorial: 106 N Edwards St, Enterprise, Alabama 36330-2524. **T:** 1 334 347-9533
E: news@eprisenow.com
W: http://www.eprisenow.com
Freq: Daily; **Circ:** 10372 Not Audited
Editorial Profile: Enterprise Ledger is a local newspaper serving the residents of Enterprise and Coffee County, AL. It covers local and national news, sports, entertainment, technology, food, weather, obituaries and business.; Full Page Mono: 19.75; Full Page Colour: 230.00
Currency: US Dollars
DAILY NEWSPAPER

Enterprise Publishing - Seward
Owner: Enterprise Publishing Co.
Editorial: 129 S 6Th St, Seward, Nebraska 68434-2003. **T:** 1 402 643-3676
Freq: Weekly
Editor: Jill Martin
Editorial Profile: The Enterprise Publishing Co. publishes two newspapers in Seward, Nebraska: The Seward County (NE) Independent and The Sentinel in Friend, NE.
NEWSPAPER

Enterprise Publishing Company, Inc.
Owner: Enterprise Publishing Co.
Editorial: 138 N 16th St, Blair, Nebraska 68008. **T:** 1 402 426-2121
E: news@enterprisepub.com
W: http://www.enterprisepub.com **Circ:** 9505 Not Audited
Editor: Doug Barber; **Publisher:** Mark Rhoades; **Editor:** Melissa Rice
NEWSPAPER

Enterprise-Journal
Owner: Emmerich Newspapers Inc.
Editorial: 112 Oliver Emmerich Dr, McComb, Mississippi 39648. **T:** 1 601 684-2421
E: news@enterprise-journal.com
W: http://www.enterprise-journal.com
Freq: Daily; **Circ:** 8088 Not Audited
News Editor: Karen Freeman
Editorial Profile: Enterprise-Journal covers all news relevant to Southwest Mississippi. The editorial content of the newspaper includes local news, sports, lifestyle, outdoors and family.; Full Page Mono: 18.81
Currency: US Dollars
DAILY NEWSPAPER

The Epoch Times
Editorial: 50 Cragwood Rd Suite 305, South Plainfield, New Jersey 7080.
T: 1 732 548-0380 **E:** nj@epochtimes.com
W: http://epochtimes.com
Freq: Fri; **Circ:** 20000 Not Audited
Editorial Profile: Epoch Times is a Chinese-American weekly newspaper. They distribute an English as well as a Chinese version.; Full Page Mono: 15.00
Currency: US Dollars
NEWSPAPER

Epoch Times
Owner: Epoch Times International
Editorial: 34 W 27th St Fl 5, New York, New York 10001-6909. **T:** 1 212 239-2808
E: nyc_news@epochtimes.com
W: http://www.theepochtimes.com **Circ:** 90000
Editor-in-Chief: John Nania
Editorial Profile: Epoch Times is a Chinese-American Daily newspaper.; Full Page Mono: 27.00; Full Page Colour: 44.30
Currency: US Dollars
DAILY NEWSPAPER

Epoch Times-Chicago Edition
Owner: Tu (Andrew)
Editorial: Epoch Times, Chicago, 3249 S. Halsted St., Chicago, Illinois 60608.
T: 1 312 808-9410
E: midwest@epochtimes.com
W: http://www.theepochtimes.com
Freq: Fri; **Circ:** 16000 Not Audited
Editor: Stacey Tang; **Publisher:** Andrew Tu
Editorial Profile: Epoch Times-Chicago Edition is a free newspaper for American and Chinese-American residents and businesses in Chicago. Their mission is to enrich local communities with news and perspectives on current events which are often overlooked by mainstream media, especially by outlets inside China. It strives to present an alternative and uncensored view to the propaganda generated by the People's Republic of China.; Full Page Mono: 25.70
Currency: US Dollars
NEWSPAPER

The Erickson Tribune
Owner: Erickson Retirement Communities
Editorial: 703 Maiden Choice Ln, Catonsville, Maryland 21228-3632. **T:** 1 410 242-2880
E: editor@erickson.com
W: http://www.ericksontribune.com
Freq: Monthly; **Circ:** 477000
Editor: Deborah Dasch; **Editor:** Deborah Dasch
Editorial Profile: The Erickson Tribune is a monthly newspaper distributed to residents of Erickson Retirement Communities in Baltimore (MD) and the surrounding area. Each issue explores current events and topics of interest in a newspaper format. It also contains feature stories on a wide range of topics along with sections devoted to health, food, computers and technology, crosswords and contests. Much of the editorial content comes from wire services. The newsletter is overseen by the retirement communities' internal marketing department.; Full Page Mono: 387.81
Currency: US Dollars
NEWSPAPER

Erie Times-News
Owner: Times Publishing Inc.
Editorial: 205 W 12Th St, Erie, Pennsylvania 16534-0002 **E:** newsdesk@timesnews.com
W: http://www.goerie.com
Freq: Daily; **Circ:** 43617 Not Audited
Publisher: Rosanne Cheeseman
Editorial Profile: Erie Times-News is published daily for the residents of Erie, PA, and the surrounding communities. The newspaper covers local and national news, sports, opinions, entertainment, business and community events. In October 2000, Morning News and Erie Daily Times merged into Erie Times-News.; Full Page Mono: 76.22; Full Page Colour: 235.20
Currency: US Dollars
DAILY NEWSPAPER

ESP Publications
Editorial: 27 W Main St, Smithtown, New York 11787. **T:** 1 631 265-3500
E: messenger127e@aol.com **Circ:** 32500 Not Audited
Editorial Profile: ESP Publications is a weekly community newspaper publisher serving the

residents of Brookhaven, Ronkonkoma, Smithtown, Patchogue and Medford, NY.
NEWSPAPER

El Especial
Editorial: 3510 Bergenline Ave, Union City, New Jersey 07087-4775. **T:** 1 201 348-1959
E: news@elespecial.com
W: http://www.elespecial.com
Freq: Tue; **Circ:** 295000 Not Audited
Publisher: Antonio Ibarria; **Editor:** José Sibaja
Editorial Profile: El Especial provides news, information and entertainment to Latin Americans nationwide. This paper does not offer black and white advertising.; Full Page Colour: 23.50
Currency: US Dollars
NEWSPAPER

El Especial
Editorial: 175 Fontainebleau Blvd, Ste 2J2, Miami, Florida 33172. **T:** 1 305 225-3742
E: adsmiami@elespecial.com
Freq: Fri; **Circ:** 25000 Not Audited
Publisher: Antonio Ibarria; **Editor:** José Sibaja
Editorial Profile: El Especial is a weekly Spanish newspaper. The publication provides the Hispanic community in Miami with local news, business, politics, education, sports and arts & entertainment.; Full Page Colour: 55.95
Currency: US Dollars
NEWSPAPER

El Especialito
Editorial: 3510 Bergenline Ave, Union City, New Jersey 07087-4775. **T:** 1 201 348-1959
W: http://www.elespecial.com **Circ:** 295000
NEWSPAPER

Essex Reporter & Colchester Sun Newspapers
Owner: Lynn Publication
Editorial: 42 Severance Green #108, Colchester, Vermont 5446. **T:** 1 802 878-5282
Circ: 19000 Not Audited
Editor: Jason Starr
NEWSPAPER

Estherville Daily News
Owner: Ogden Newspapers
Editorial: 10 N 7th St, Estherville, Iowa 51334-2232. **T:** 1 712 362-2622
W: http://www.esthervilledailynews.com
Freq: Mon thru Fri; **Circ:** 2282 Not Audited
Publisher: Glen Caron; **Publisher:** Glen Caron; **Publisher:** Glen Caron
Editorial Profile: Estherville Daily News is a local daily newspaper serving the residents of Estherville, IA and the surrounding area. The newspaper covers local news, editorial, sports, arts & entertainment, business and community events.; Full Page Mono: 5.30; Full Page Colour: 65.00
Currency: US Dollars
DAILY NEWSPAPER

La Estrella de Tucson
Owner: Lee Enterprises, Inc.
Editorial: 4850 S Park Ave, Tucson, Arizona 85714. **T:** 1 520 573-4419
E: laestrella@azstarnet.com
W: http://www.laestrelladetucson.com
Freq: Fri; **Circ:** 40000 Not Audited
Publisher: John Humenik; **Editor:** Ernesto Portillo
Editorial Profile: La Estrella de Tucson is a weekly newspaper aimed at Spanish-speaking and bilingual Hispanics in southern Arizona. It is published by the Arizona Daily Star and operates from its offices.; Full Page Mono: 24.20
Currency: US Dollars
NEWSPAPER

Eugene Weekly
Editorial: 1251 Lincoln St, Eugene, Oregon 97401. **T:** 1 541 484-0519
E: office@eugeneweekly.com
W: http://www.eugeneweekly.com
Freq: Thu; **Circ:** 39850 Not Audited
Editor: Ted Taylor
Editorial Profile: Eugene Weekly is a local newspaper serving the residents of Eugene, OR and the surrounding area. The newspaper covers local news, opinions, environmental issues, arts & entertainment and community events. It also contains personal and classified ads. Deadlines are Fridays before issue date.; Full Page Mono: 25.55; Full Page Colour: 1565.00
Currency: US Dollars
NEWSPAPER

Eureka Springs Independent
Editorial: 178A W Van Buren, Eureka Springs, Arkansas 72632-3655. **T:** 1 479 253-6101
E: newsdesk@eurekaspringsindependent.com
W: http://www.eurekaspringsindependent.com
Freq: Wed
Editor: Mary Pat Boian
Editorial Profile: Eureka Springs Independent is a weekly community newspaper covering local news, events, opinion, sports and features for Eureka Springs, AR and Carroll County, AR residents.
NEWSPAPER

The Evangelist
Owner: Albany Catholic Press Association, Inc.
Editorial: 40 N Main Ave, Albany, New York 12203. **T:** 1 518 453-6688
W: http://www.evangelist.org
Freq: Thu; **Circ:** 47000 Not Audited
Publisher: Howard Hubbard; **Editor:** Christopher Ringwald
Editorial Profile: The Evangelist's editorial mission is to provide Catholic news to 14 counties surrounding Albany, NY. The publication is written for members of the Roman Catholic Diocese of Albany, NY. It contains Catholic news, local parish features, daily scripture readings, people in the news and a community calendar.; Full Page Mono: 25.85
Currency: US Dollars
NEWSPAPER

Evanston RoundTable
Owner: Evanston RoundTable LLC
Editorial: 1124 Florence Ave Ste 3, Evanston, Illinois 60202-5829. **T:** 1 847 864-7741
E: info@evanstonroundtable.com
W: http://www.evanstonroundtable.com
Freq: Bi-Weekly; **Circ:** 18000 Not Audited
Editorial Profile: Evanston RoundTable is a free, bi-weekly newspaper serving residents of Evanston, IL. It covers local news, traffic, arts & entertainment, business, lifestyle, opinions, schools and sports.; Full Page Mono: 25.00
Currency: US Dollars
NEWSPAPER

The Evansville Courier & Press
Owner: E.W. Scripps Co.
Editorial: 300 E Walnut St, Evansville, Indiana 47713-1938. **T:** 1 812 424-7711
E: courier@courierpress.com
W: http://www.courierpress.com
Freq: Daily; **Circ:** 44554 Not Audited
Editor: Tim Ethridge; **Editor:** Tim Ethridge; **Editor:** Tim Ethridge; **Editor:** Tim Ethridge; **Publisher:** Jack Pate; **Editor:** Leah Ward
Editorial Profile: The Evansville Courier & Press is a local daily newspaper serving the residents of Evansville, IN and the Indiana, Kentucky and Illinois tri-state area. The newspaper covers regional and local news, sports, arts & entertainment, business, health, law enforcement and politics. Press releases can be sent by mail or by e-mail.; Full Page Mono: 134.25; Full Page Colour: 446.57
Currency: US Dollars
DAILY NEWSPAPER

The Evansville Courier & Press
Editorial: 200 W Washington St Ste M7, Indianapolis, Indiana 46204-2754.
T: 1 317 631-7405
Bureau Chief: Chelsea Schneider Kirk
DAILY NEWSPAPER

The Evening Leader
Owner: Horizon Publications
Editorial: 102 E Spring St, Saint Marys, Ohio 45885. **T:** 1 419 394-7414
W: http://www.theeveningleader.com
Freq: Daily; **Circ:** 5412 Not Audited
Publisher: Gayle Masonbrink
Editorial Profile: The Evening Leader is a local daily newspaper serving the residents of Auglaize County, OH. The newspaper covers local news, sports, police, entertainment, business and community events.; Full Page Mono: 14.09; Full Page Colour: 259.09
Currency: US Dollars
DAILY NEWSPAPER

The Evening News
Owner: GateHouse Media Inc.
Editorial: 109 Arlington St, Sault Sainte Marie, Michigan 49783-1942. **T:** 1 906 632-2235
E: edit@sooeveningnews.com
W: http://www.sooeveningnews.com
Freq: Daily; **Circ:** 6996 Not Audited
Editor: Scott Brand; **Editor:** Kenn Filkins; **Publisher:** Howard Kaiser; **Editor:** Jack Storey; **Editor:** Brenda Weber
Editorial Profile: The Evening News is a local daily newspaper serving the residents of Chippewa County, Luce County and Macaneau County, MI. The newspaper mainly covers local and world news, sports, lifestyle, business, health and community events.; Full Page Mono: 15.85; Full Page Colour: 195.50
Currency: US Dollars
DAILY NEWSPAPER

Evening Post Publishing Company
Owner: Evening Post Publishing Co.
Editorial: 104 E Doty Ave, Summerville, South Carolina 29483-6300. **T:** 1 843 572-0511
W: http://www.journalscene.com **Circ:** 22000
Editor: Frank Johnson; **Publisher:** Steve Wagenlander
NEWSPAPER

The Evening Sun
Owner: Snyder Communications Corporation
Editorial: 29 Lackawanna Ave, Norwich, New York 13815-1404. **T:** 1 607 334-3276
E: news@evesun.com
W: http://www.evesun.com
Freq: Daily; **Circ:** 4500 Not Audited
Publisher: Richard Snyder
Editorial Profile: The Evening Sun is a local daily newspaper serving the residents of Chenango County, NY. The newspaper mainly covers local news, sports, editorial, arts & entertainment, business and community events.; Full Page Mono: 12.05; Full Page Colour: 225.00
Currency: US Dollars
DAILY NEWSPAPER

The Evening Sun
Owner: MediaNews Group
Editorial: 135 Baltimore St, Hanover, Pennsylvania 17331-3142. **T:** 1 717 637-3736
E: news@eveningsun.com
W: http://www.eveningsun.com
Freq: Daily; **Circ:** 18632 Not Audited
News Editor: Craig Paskoski
Editorial Profile: The Evening Sun is a local daily newspaper serving the residents of York County and Adams County, PA. The newspaper covers local and national news, sports, entertainment, style, editorial and community events.; Full Page Mono: 45.58; Full Page Colour: 529.94
Currency: US Dollars
DAILY NEWSPAPER

The Evening Telegram
Owner: Fortress Investment Group, LLC
Editorial: 111 Green St, Herkimer, New York 13350-1958. **T:** 1 315 866-2220
W: http://www.herkimertelegram.com
Freq: Daily; **Circ:** 6657 Not Audited
Editorial Profile: The Evening Telegram is a daily, local newspaper written for the local residents of Herkimer, NY. The newspaper covers local news and events.; Full Page Mono: 10.66; Full Page Colour: 310.00
Currency: US Dollars
DAILY NEWSPAPER

Evening Times
Owner: Ricketson Newspapers Inc.
Editorial: 1010 State Highway 77, Marion, Arkansas 72364-9007. **T:** 1 870 735-1010
W: http://www.theeveningtimes.com
Freq: Daily; **Circ:** 7385 Not Audited
Publisher: Alex Coulter
Editorial Profile: Evening Times provides local news for Crittenden County and Eastern Arkansas.; Full Page Mono: 13.92; Full Page Colour: 345.00
Currency: US Dollars
DAILY NEWSPAPER

The Evening Tribune
Owner: Fortress Investment Group, LLC
Editorial: 85 Canisteo St, Hornell, New York 14843. **T:** 1 607 324-1425
E: news@eveningtribune.com
W: http://www.eveningtribune.com
Freq: Daily; **Circ:** 7562 Not Audited
Editor: John Anderson; **Publisher:** Tom Connors
Editorial Profile: The Evening Tribune is a local daily newspaper serving residents of Hornell, NY and the surrounding Canisteo Valley area. The newspaper covers local and world news, sports, entertainment, health and business. Deadlines fall one day prior to issue date.; Full Page Mono: 9.65; Full Page Colour: 200.00
Currency: US Dollars
DAILY NEWSPAPER

Everett Leader Herald News Gazette
Editorial: 28 Church St, Everett, Massachusetts 02149-2799.
T: 1 617 387-4570
E: everettleader@comcast.net
Freq: Thu; **Circ:** 15000 Not Audited
Publisher: Joseph Curnane; **Editor:** Jennifer Didonato
Editorial Profile: Everett Leader Herald News Gazette is a community newspaper targeted at the residents of Everett, MA.; Full Page Mono: 10.00
Currency: US Dollars
NEWSPAPER

Evergreen Newspapers, Inc.
Owner: Landmark Community Newspapers, Inc.
Editorial: 27902 Meadow Dr Unit 200, Evergreen, Colorado 80439-2106.
T: 1 303 674-5534 **E:** news@evergreenco.com
Circ: 10050 Not Audited
Editor: Doug Bell; **News Editor:** Chris Ferguson; **Editor:** Ian Neligh; **Publisher:** Tim Zeman
Editorial Profile: Evergreen Newspapers, Inc. produces the Clear Creek Courant in Idaho Springs, ID, the High Timber Times in Conifer, CO, the Columbine (CO) Courier and the Canyon Courier in Evergreen, CO, where the main offices are located. The editorial staff is shared and moves between the offices as needed.
NEWSPAPER

EWA Publications
Editorial: 2446 E 65th St, Brooklyn, New York 11234. **T:** 1 718 763-7034
E: editman1000@yahoo.com **Circ:** 523000 Not Audited
Publisher: Kenneth Brown; **Editor:** Kevin Browne
NEWSPAPER

The Examiner
Owner: GateHouse Media Inc.
Editorial: 410 S Liberty St, Independence, Missouri 64050-3805. **T:** 1 816 254-8600
E: localnews@examiner.net
W: http://www.examiner.net Not Audited
Editor: Jeff Fox; **Editor:** Jeff Fox
Editorial Profile: The Examiner is published for the residents of Independence and Blue Springs, MO. The newspaper covers local and national news, sports, politics, arts & entertainment and education.; Full Page Mono: 30.50; Full Page Colour: 283.00
Currency: US Dollars
NEWSPAPER

The Examiner
Editorial: 795 Willow St, Beaumont, Texas 77701-1829. **T:** 1 409 832-1400
E: mail@theexaminer.com
W: http://www.theexaminer.com
Freq: Fri; **Circ:** 30000 Not Audited
News Editor: Jerry Jordan
Editorial Profile: The Examiner is a weekly newspaper serving the residents of Beaumont, TX. It contains local news, community events, sports, schools, businesses and features of interest to local readers.; Full Page Mono: 23.50
Currency: US Dollars
NEWSPAPER

Examiner Publications, Inc.
Owner: Examiner Publications, Inc.
Editorial: 4N781 Gerber Rd, Bartlett, Illinois 60103. **T:** 1 630 830-4145
E: news@examinerpublications.com
W: http://www.examinerpublications.com
Freq: Wed; **Circ:** 37800 Not Audited
Editor: Bruce Leighty; **Publisher:** Randall Petrik
Editorial Profile: Please only send local news press releases that are relevant to the paper's local coverage. Press releases that do not involve the town are not useful. Please visit the Web site to gain a better perspective of what they consider local news.; Full Page Mono: 45.00
Currency: US Dollars
NEWSPAPER

El Exito
Owner: Latin American Press
Editorial: 1904 Silver Birch Ln, Las Vegas, Nevada 89104-4252. **T:** 1 702 431-1904
W: http://www.elexitolasvegas.com
Freq: Fri; **Circ:** 10000 Not Audited
Editorial Profile: El Exito is a free weekly newspaper published in Spanish and English, providing News coverage for the Hispanic community in Las Vegas, NV. It is published on Fridays and is available in print and online.; Full Page Mono: 18.00
Currency: US Dollars
NEWSPAPER

Explorer Newspapers, Inc.
Owner: Thirteenth Street Media Inc.
Editorial: 7225 N. Mona Lisa Road, Tucson, Arizona 85747. **T:** 1 520 797-4384
E: editor@explorernews.com
W: http://www.explorernews.com

Freq: Wed; **Circ:** 47475 Not Audited
News Editor: Thelma Grimes
Editorial Profile: Explorer Newspapers, Inc. in Tucson, AZ covers local news, business, government, sports, recreation, arts and entertainment.; Full Page Mono: 39.85
Currency: US Dollars
NEWSPAPER

Exponent Telegram

Owner: Clarksburg Publishing Company
Editorial: 324 Hewes Ave, Clarksburg, West Virginia 26301-2744. **T:** 1 304 626-1400
E: news@exponent-telegram.com
W: http://www.exponent-telegram.com
Freq: Daily; **Circ:** 14557 Not Audited
Editor: Danny Carpenter; **Publisher:** William Highland
Editorial Profile: Exponent Telegram's editorial mission is to provide local news and sports to the community. It is written for residents of North Central West Virginia.; Full Page Mono: 20.40; Full Page Colour: 300.00
Currency: US Dollars
DAILY NEWSPAPER

The Express

Owner: Ogden Newspapers
Editorial: 9 W Main St, Lock Haven, Pennsylvania 17745-1276. **T:** 1 570 748-6791
E: news@lockhaven.com
W: http://www.lockhaven.com
Freq: Daily; **Circ:** 7366
Editor: Lana Muthler; **Publisher:** Robert Rolley
Editorial Profile: The Express is the daily newspaper for Lock Haven, PA. It is a general interest newspaper that covers local, national, and international news and events.; Full Page Mono: 14.50; Full Page Colour: 99.00
Currency: US Dollars
DAILY NEWSPAPER

Express

Owner: Washington Post Co.
Editorial: 1150 15th St NW Bldg LENNOX5, Washington, District Of Columbia 20071-0001.
T: 1 202 334-6800 **E:** inbox@readexpress.com
W: http://www.washingtonpost.com/express
Freq: Mon thru Fri; **Circ:** 179118 Not Audited
Editor: Daniel Caccavaro
Editorial Profile: Express is a free commuter daily newspaper targeting readers and commuters in the Washington, D.C. metro area. It is provided complimentary in the Sunday edition. The editorial mix includes national, international and local news. Designed and owned by The Washington Post, the paper reaches readers whose busy schedules prevent them from reading newspapers frequently, mainly between the ages of 18 and 34. Much of the editorial content is pulled from wire services and the paper operates with a minimal staff.; Full Page Mono: 104.00; Full Page Colour: 121.00
Currency: US Dollars
DAILY NEWSPAPER

Express News

Editorial: W130N10437 Washington Dr, Germantown, Wisconsin 53022.
T: 1 262 238-6397
E: thomasj@discoverhometown.com
W: http://www.discoverhometown.com
Circ: 60500 Not Audited
NEWSPAPER

Express-Star

Owner: Community Newspaper Holdings, Inc.
Editorial: 302 N 3rd St, Chickasha, Oklahoma 73018-2618. **T:** 1 405 224-2600
E: editor@chickashanews.com
W: http://chickashanews.com
Freq: Daily; **Circ:** 4600 Not Audited
Editorial Profile: Express-Star is the local newspaper for the Chickasha, OK area. Feature stories focus on local, regional and national events. The paper is written to inform the community of any news, events or interesting human interest stories. Deadlines are daily at noon CT.; Full Page Mono: 9.45; Full Page Colour: 12.45
Currency: US Dollars
DAILY NEWSPAPER

The Express-Times

Owner: Newhouse Newspapers
Editorial: 30 N 4th St, Easton, Pennsylvania 18042-3528. **T:** 1 610 258-7171
E: news@express-times.com
W: http://www.lehighvalleylive.com/expresstimes
Freq: Daily; **Circ:** 31878 Not Audited
Editorial Profile: The Express-Times in Easton, PA is published daily for residents in Northampton County and parts of Lehigh County, PA. The paper covers both local and national news, sports, business,

entertainment, lifestyle and events.; Full Page Mono: 66.00; Full Page Colour: 215.51
Currency: US Dollars
DAILY NEWSPAPER

El Extra

Editorial: 1214 Gardenview Dr, Dallas, Texas 75217-4311. **T:** 1 214 309-0990
E: pressrelease@elextranewspaper.com
W: http://www.elextranewspaper.com
Freq: Thu; **Circ:** 20370 Not Audited
Editorial Profile: El Extra is published weekly for the Hispanic community of the Dallas metropolitan area. The newspaper provides local, national and international news, business, politics and community events. Deadlines are on Tuesdays at 1pm CT.; Full Page Mono: 23.00; Full Page Colour: 126.38
Currency: US Dollars
NEWSPAPER

Extra

Owner: City-Suburban Community Newspapers, Inc.
Editorial: 3906 W North Ave, Chicago, Illinois 60647-4618. **T:** 1 773 252-3534
E: editor@extranews.net
W: http://www.extranews.net
Freq: Thu; **Circ:** 63413 Not Audited
Publisher: Mila Tellez
Editorial Profile: Extra is a weekly community newspaper serving the Hispanic residents of Chicago and the surrounding suburbs.; Full Page Mono: 45.51
Currency: US Dollars
NEWSPAPER

El Extra

Owner: Freedom Communications Inc.
Editorial: 1400 E Nolana Ave, McAllen, Texas 78504-6111. **T:** 1 956 683-4161
Freq: Fri; **Circ:** 43000 Not Audited
Editor: G. Zulema Baez-Ahumada
Editorial Profile: El Extra is a weekly Spanish-language newspaper covering local news and events.; Full Page Mono: 9.28
Currency: US Dollars
NEWSPAPER

The Facts

Owner: Southern Newspapers, Inc.
Editorial: 720 S Main St, Clute, Texas 77531-5411. **T:** 1 979 265-7411
E: news@thefacts.com
W: http://www.thefacts.com
Freq: Daily; **Circ:** 16027 Not Audited
Editorial Profile: The Facts is written for Brazorian county community readers. in and around Brazorian County.; Full Page Mono: 14.50; Full Page Colour: 375.00
Currency: US Dollars
DAILY NEWSPAPER

Facts

Editorial: 1112 34th Ave, Seattle, Washington 98122-5139. **T:** 1 206 324-0552
E: justthefacts@nwfacts.com
W: http://nwfacts.com
Freq: Wed; **Circ:** 100000 Not Audited
Editorial Profile: Facts provides community news to residents of Tacoma and Seattle, WA.; Full Page Mono: 22.50
Currency: US Dollars
NEWSPAPER

Fairbanks Daily News-Miner

Owner: MediaNews Group
Editorial: 200 N Cushman St, Fairbanks, Alaska 99701-2858. **T:** 1 907 456-6661
E: newsroom@newsminer.com
W: http://newsminer.com
Freq: Daily; **Circ:** 13767 Not Audited
Publisher: Marti Buscaglia; **News Editor:** Jeff Richardson
Editorial Profile: Fairbanks Daily News-Miner is published daily for the residents of Fairbanks, AK and surrounding areas. The newspaper covers local and regional news, business, sports, lifestyles and entertainment.; Full Page Mono: 25.88; Full Page Colour: 685.00
Currency: US Dollars
DAILY NEWSPAPER

The Fairfax County Times

Owner: Post-Newsweek Media, Inc.
Editorial: 11710 Plaza America Drive, Ste 420, Reston, Virginia 20190-3360.
T: 1 703 437-5400
W: http://www.fairfaxtimes.com
Freq: Wed; **Circ:** 140000 Not Audited
Publisher: Karen Acton; **Editor:** Steve Cahill
Editorial Profile: The Fairfax County Times is a weekly newspaper serving Fairfax County, VA. It is dedicated to providing local news coverage with an emphasis on people, events, sports, businesses, government, real estate

and entertainment. Deadlines are at 3pm ET. It was previously published through multiple regional editions, but as of September 2008 has been under a single edition.; Full Page Mono: 50.00; Full Page Colour: 140.00
Currency: US Dollars
NEWSPAPER

Fairfield Ledger

Owner: Inland Industries Inc.
Editorial: 112 E Broadway Ave, Fairfield, Iowa 52556-3202. **T:** 1 641 472-4129
E: ffledger@lisco.com
W: http://www.goldentrianglenewspapers.com
Freq: Mon thru Fri; **Circ:** 3010 Not Audited
Editor: Andy Hallman; **Editor:** Julie Johnston;
Publisher: Jeff Wilson
Editorial Profile: Fairfield Ledger is a local daily newspaper serving the Fairfield, IA area. It provides residents of the local community with information on local news and events in and around the Fairfield and Jefferson county communities. Editorial submissions must be received by noon CT the day prior to publication.; Full Page Mono: 10.88; Full Page Colour: 38.57
Currency: US Dollars
DAILY NEWSPAPER

Fairfield Towne Crier

Editorial: 1594 Stonewall Dr, Newark, Ohio 43055. **T:** 1 740 344-7555
E: freedomptg@roadrunner.com
W: http://www.fairfieldtownecrier.com
Freq: Bi-Weekly; **Circ:** 35000 Not Audited
Editor: Edward Heaton; **Editor:** Edward Heaton; **Editor:** Edward Heaton; **Publisher:** Esther McMillen-Heaton; **Publisher:** Esther McMillen-Heaton
Editorial Profile: Fairfield Towne Crier in Newark, OH s a community newspaper covering local news and events. The paper has two editions, the Fairfield Towne Crier and the Eastern Towne Crier, that are published every other week.; Full Page Mono: 13.00
Currency: US Dollars
NEWSPAPER

Fairmont Photo Press

Owner: BuddBay Media LLC
Editorial: 112 E 1st St, Fairmont, Minnesota 56031. **T:** 1 507 238-9456
W: http://www.fairmontphotopress.com
Freq: Wed; **Circ:** 11829 Not Audited
Editor: Sherman Kumba
Editorial Profile: Fairmont Photo Press is a local weekly newspaper written for the Fairmont, MN, community.; Full Page Mono: 11.50
Currency: US Dollars
NEWSPAPER

Fairmont Sentinel

Owner: Ogden Newspapers
Editorial: 64 Downtown Plz, Fairmont, Minnesota 56031-1733. **T:** 1 507 235-3303
E: news@fairmontsentinel.com
W: http://www.fairmontsentinel.com
Freq: Mon thru Fri; **Circ:** 4586 Not Audited
Publisher: Gary Andersen; **Editor:** Lee Smith
Editorial Profile: Fairmont Sentinel is a local daily newspaper serving the Fairmont, MN area. It is written for residents of surrounding counties. The newspaper provides residents of the local community with information on local news and events in and around the Fairmont community. Contact the publication for the circulation information and advertisement rates.; Full Page Mono: 19.55; Full Page Colour: 150.00
Currency: US Dollars
DAILY NEWSPAPER

Falls Church News-Press

Owner: Benton Communications
Editorial: 200 Little Falls St Ste 508, Falls Church, Virginia 22046-4302.
T: 1 703 532-3267 **E:** fcnp@fcnp.com
W: http://www.fcnp.com
Freq: Thu; **Circ:** 25000 Not Audited
Editor In Chief: Nicholas Benton
Editorial Profile: Falls Church News-Press is a weekly community newspaper servicing the residents of Falls Church, VA.; Full Page Mono: 38.50
Currency: US Dollars
NEWSPAPER

Falmouth Publishing Company

Editorial: 50 Depot Ave, Falmouth, Massachusetts 2540. **T:** 1 508 548-4700
W: http://www.capenews.net **Circ:** 19809 Not Audited
Editor: John Paradise
Editorial Profile: Falmouth Publishing Company (aka Enterprise Newspapers)

publishes the Falmouth Enterprise, the Mashpee Enterprise, the Sandwich Enterprise, the Bourne Enterprise, and the Barnstable Enterprise.
NEWSPAPER

Fannin Sentinel

Owner: Owen (Elaine) & Owen (James)
Editorial: 29 State St., Blue Ridge, Georgia.
T: 1 706 258-3406
E: fanninsentinel.lisag@gmail.com
W: http://fanninsentinel.com
Freq: Thu
Editorial Profile: Fannin Sentinel is a community newspaper serving Fannin County, GA, including local news and community events.
NEWSPAPER

Faribault Daily News

Owner: Huckle Media LLC
Editorial: 514 Central Ave N, Faribault, Minnesota 55021-4304. **T:** 1 507 333-3100
E: editor@faribault.com
W: http://www.faribault.com
Freq: Daily; **Circ:** 6495 Not Audited
Editorial Profile: Faribault Daily News is written for the residents of Rice County, MN. It reports on local and national news and events of interest.; Full Page Mono: 17.90; Full Page Colour: 370.00
Currency: US Dollars
DAILY NEWSPAPER

Farmer-Record Newspapers

Owner: Shelby Daily Globe, Inc.
Editorial: 43 E Main St, New London, Ohio 44851. **T:** 1 419 929-3411
W: http://www.sdgnewsgroup.com **Circ:** 12400 Not Audited
Publisher: Scott Gove; **Editor:** Jim Souslin;
Editor: Terry Wilson
NEWSPAPER

Farmer's Weekly Review

Owner: Farmer's Weekly Review Inc.
Editorial: 100 Manhattan Rd, Joliet, Illinois 60433. **T:** 1 815 727-4811
E: farmersweekly@sbcglobal.net
Freq: Thu; **Circ:** 14200 Not Audited
Editorial Profile: Farmer's Weekly Review is written to inform residents of Will County, IL and the surrounding area of local farming news.; Full Page Mono: 11.25
Currency: US Dollars
NEWSPAPER

Farragut Press

Owner: Republic Newspapers, Inc.
Editorial: 11863 Kingston Pike, Knoxville, Tennessee 37934-3833. **T:** 1 865 675-6397
E: editor@farragutpress.com
W: http://www.farragutpress.com
Freq: Thu; **Circ:** 16325 Not Audited
Editorial Profile: Farragut Press is a local paper providing news to the community of Farragut, TN.; Full Page Mono: 12.65
Currency: US Dollars
NEWSPAPER

The Fayette Advertiser

Owner: Roll Media
Editorial: 203 Main St, Fayette, Missouri 65248-1306. **T:** 1 660 248-2235
E: news@fayettenews.com
W: http://www.fayettenewspapers.com
Freq: 2 Times/Week; **Circ:** 3800 Not Audited
Publisher: Patrick Roll
Editorial Profile: Publishes the Fayette Advertiser and the Fayette Democrat-Leader.
NEWSPAPER

Fayetteville Free Weekly

Owner: Stephens Media
Editorial: 212 N East Ave, Fayetteville, Arkansas 72701-5225. **T:** 1 479 521-4550
W: http://www.freeweekly.com
Freq: Thu; **Circ:** 12000 Not Audited
Editor: Richard Davis
Editorial Profile: Fayetteville Free Weekly is a community newspaper written for the residents of Fayetteville, AR.; Full Page Mono: 9.00
Currency: US Dollars
NEWSPAPER

The Fayetteville Observer

Owner: Fayetteville Publishing Co.
Editorial: 458 Whitfield St, Fayetteville, North Carolina 28306-1614. **T:** 1 910 323-4848
E: news@fayobserver.com
W: http://www.fayobserver.com
Freq: Daily; **Circ:** 41371 Not Audited
Publisher: Charles Broadwell
Editorial Profile: The Fayetteville (NC) Observer provides coverage of local and regional news, the military, arts &

entertainment, lifestyle news, sports and business. Lead times vary depending on the section and type of news involved.; Full Page Mono: 51.50; Full Page Colour: 235.01
Currency: US Dollars
DAILY NEWSPAPER

Federal Hill Gazette
Owner: Renaissance Communications
Editorial: 55 Bradford St, Providence, Rhode Island 02903-1677. **T:** 1 401 521-2701
W: http://www.thefederalhillgazette.com
Freq: Monthly; **Circ:** 20000 Not Audited
Editor: Mark Press
Editorial Profile: Federal Hill Gazette is a community newspaper published for the residents of Providence, RI.; Full Page Mono: 12.85; Full Page Colour: 13.04
Currency: US Dollars
NEWSPAPER

Federal Way Mirror
Owner: Black Press
Editorial: 31919 1st Ave S Ste 101, Federal Way, Washington 98003-5258.
T: 1 253 925-5565
E: editor@fedwaymirror.com
W: http://www.federalwaymirror.com
Freq: Sat; **Circ:** 30400 Not Audited
Publisher: Rudi Alcott; **Editor:** Carrie Rodriguez
Editorial Profile: Federal Way Mirror is a local newspaper that covers local legislation, news and events for residents of Federal Way, WA. Deadlines are Mondays and Wednesdays before issue date. All editorial correspondence should be sent to the street address. All advertising correspondence should be sent to Federal Way Mirror, c/o Sound Publishing, 7869 NE Day Rd., Bainbridge Island, WA 98110.; Full Page Mono: 27.50
Currency: US Dollars
NEWSPAPER

Le Figaro - New York Bureau
Owner: FigaroMedias
Editorial: United Nations Headquarters, Room S-360, New York, New York 10017.
T: 1 646 863-2151
Editorial Profile: This is the New York Bureau for Le Figaro based in Paris, France.
DAILY NEWSPAPER

FilAm Star
Editorial: 1028 Mission St, San Francisco, California 94103-2813. **T:** 1 415 593-5955
E: fastad@filamstar.net
W: http://www.filamstar.net/
Editor: Jun Ilagan
Editorial Profile: FilAm Star is a bi-weekly publication that keeps San Franciscans up-to-date with news and features in the Bay Area and the Philippines. The paper can be found in Asian/American stores, supermarkets and restaurants. The paper's reach extends from Sacramento to all of Silicon Valley. The online edition is updated regularly. It was first published in 2007.
NEWSPAPER

The Filipino Express
Owner: Filipino Express, Inc.
Editorial: 2711 John F Kennedy Blvd, Jersey City, New Jersey 7306. **T:** 1 201 434-1114
E: filexpress@aol.com
W: http://www.filipinoexpress.com
Freq: Fri; **Circ:** 25000 Not Audited
Editorial Profile: The Filipino Express is a weekly publication for the Filipino-American community. The paper brings residents news, opinions, entertainment, real estate/business, sports and classifieds.; Full Page Mono: 100.00
Currency: US Dollars
NEWSPAPER

Filipino Press
Editorial: 600 E 8th St, Ste 3, National City, California 91950-2400. **T:** 1 619 477-0940
W: http://www.filipinopress.com
Freq: Sat; **Circ:** 25000 Not Audited
Editorial Profile: Filipino Press is a weekly newspaper that is written for the Filipino residents in the San Diego area.; Full Page Mono: 12.69
Currency: US Dollars
NEWSPAPER

The Filipino Reporter
Owner: Filipino Reporter Enterprises, Inc.
Editorial: 350 5th Ave, Ste 1007, New York, New York 10118-0600. **T:** 1 212 967-5784
E: filipinoreporter@aol.com
W: http://www.filipinoreporter.us
Freq: Fri; **Circ:** 25000
News Editor: Edmund Silvestre
Editorial Profile: The Filipino Reporter is a weekly newspaper written for Filipino Americans in the tri-state area of New York, New Jersey and Connecticut. The newspaper covers news, entertainment, sports and immigration.; Full Page Mono: 11.00
Currency: US Dollars
NEWSPAPER

Fillmore County Journal
Editorial: 136 Saint Anthony St N, Preston, Minnesota 55965. **T:** 1 507 765-2151
E: news@fillmorecountyjournal.com
W: http://www.fillmorecountyjournal.com
Freq: Mon; **Circ:** 12000 Not Audited
Editorial Profile: The Fillmore County Journal is a free local newspaper written to share stories and news with the local community.; Full Page Mono: 11.29
Currency: US Dollars
NEWSPAPER

Financial Times (New York)
Owner: Financial Times
Editorial: 330 Hudson St Fl 8, New York, New York 10013-1014. **T:** 1 212 641-6500
E: main.news@ft.com **W:** http://www.ft.com
Circ: 305685
Editor in Chief: Lionel Barber
Editorial Profile: New York Bureau for the Financial Times, covering the latest news & current affairs, politics, finance and business in New York for the newspaper.; Full Page Mono: 280.48; Full Page Colour: 348.13
Currency: US Dollars
DAILY NEWSPAPER

Financial Times (San Francisco)
Owner: Financial Times
Editorial: 251 Post St Ste 200, San Francisco, California 94108-5021. **T:** 1 415 445-5600
Editorial Profile: San Francisco bureau for the Financial Times covering the latest news & current affairs, politics, finance and business in San Francisco for the newspaper.
DAILY NEWSPAPER

Financial Times (Washington DC)
Editorial: 1023 15th St NW Ste 700, Washington, District Of Columbia 20005-2631.
T: 1 202 434-0972
Bureau Chief: Megan Murphy
Editorial Profile: Washington Bureau for the Financial Times, covering the latest news & current affairs, politics, finance and business in Washington for the newspaper.
DAILY NEWSPAPER

Finanz und Wirtschaft - New York Bureau
Owner: Verlag Finanz und Wirtschaft AG
Editorial: 301 W 22nd St #68, New York, New York 10011-2615. **T:** 1 212 529-1455
E: newyork@fuw.ch **W:** http://www.fuw.ch
Circ: 38354 Not Audited
Editorial Profile: Covers business, finance and economy.
NEWSPAPER

Finger Lakes Community Newspapers
Editorial: 109 N Cayuga St, Ithaca, New York 14850-4341. **T:** 1 607 277-7000 **Circ:** 7495 Not Audited
Publisher: Jim Bilinski
NEWSPAPER

Finger Lakes Times
Owner: Community Media Group
Editorial: 218 Genesee St, Geneva, New York 14456. **T:** 1 315 789-3333
E: fltimes@fltimes.com
W: http://www.fltimes.com
Freq: Daily; **Circ:** 14017 Not Audited
Publisher: Paul Barrett
Editorial Profile: Finger Lakes Times is published daily for the residents of Geneva, NY and surrounding areas. The newspaper covers local and state news, business, sports, lifestyles and entertainment.; Full Page Mono: 20.50; Full Page Colour: 355.00
Currency: US Dollars
DAILY NEWSPAPER

Five Cities Times Press-Recorder Publishing
Owner: Lee Enterprises, Inc.
Editorial: 260 Station Way, Ste F, Arroyo Grande, California 93420. **T:** 1 805 925-2691
Circ: 15200 Not Audited
Publisher: Cynthia Schur
NEWSPAPER

The Flagship
Owner: Flagship
Editorial: 1510 Gilbert St, Norfolk, Virginia 23511-2738. **T:** 1 757 322-2865
E: news@flagshipnews.com
W: http://www.flagshipnews.com
Freq: Thu; **Circ:** 40000 Not Audited
Publisher: Laura Baxter; **Editor:** Molly Burgess
Editorial Profile: The Flagship is a weekly newspaper that serves members of the U.S. Navy and their families in the Norfolk, VA area it includes the latest news and events of the Navy and other branches of the military.; Full Page Mono: 19.09
Currency: US Dollars
NEWSPAPER

Flathead Beacon
Owner: Povich (Maury)
Editorial: 217 Main St, Kalispell, Montana 59901-4453. **T:** 1 406 257-9220
E: news@flatheadbeacon.com
W: http://www.flatheadbeacon.com
Freq: Wed; **Circ:** 25000 Not Audited
Editor in Chief: Kellyn Brown
Editorial Profile: Flathead Beacon is a weekly community newspaper for the residents of Flathead Valley, MT and the surrounding areas. The paper does not offer black and white ads.; Full Page Mono: 18.33; Full Page Colour: 25.00
Currency: US Dollars
NEWSPAPER

The Flint Journal
Owner: MLive Media Group
Editorial: 540 S Saginaw St Ste 101, Flint, Michigan 48502-1804. **T:** 1 810 766-6100
E: flnews@mlive.com
W: http://www.mlive.com/flintjournal
Freq: Fri; **Circ:** 39900
Editor: Marjory Raymer; **Editor:** Marjory Raymer
Editorial Profile: The Flint Journal is written for the residents of Flint, MI. It covers local and world news, local events, sports, travel, food and music.; Full Page Mono: 60.42; Full Page Colour: 69.48
Currency: US Dollars
NEWSPAPER

Florence Mining Newspapers
Editorial: 601 Central Ave,, Florence, Wisconsin 54121. **T:** 1 715 528-3276
E: upnorth2@borderlandnet.net
W: http://www.florenceminingnews.com
Circ: 3000 Not Audited
NEWSPAPER

Florence Morning News
Owner: HB Media Group
Editorial: 310 S Dargan St, Florence, South Carolina 29506-2537. **T:** 1 843 317-6397
E: news@scnow.com
W: http://www.scnow.com
Freq: Daily; **Circ:** 28631 Not Audited
News Editor: Kim Ginfrida
Editorial Profile: Florence Morning News is a local newspaper serving the residents of Florence, SC. It includes news, weather, sports and lifestyles.; Full Page Mono: 50.00; Full Page Colour: 54.50
Currency: US Dollars
DAILY NEWSPAPER

Florida Catholic Newspaper Group
Owner: Florida Catholic Inc. (The)
Editorial: 50 E Robinson St, Ste G, Orlando, Florida 32801. **T:** 1 407 373-0075
E: news@thefloridacatholic.org
W: http://www.thefloridacatholic.org
Freq: Weekly; **Circ:** 151900 Not Audited
Editor: Bob Reddy
Editorial Profile: Florida Catholic Newspaper Group publishes the official newspaper for the Roman Catholic Archdiocese of Miami and the Dioceses of Orlando, Palm Beach, Pensacola-Tallahassee, St. Petersburg, and Venice, FL and shares in the mission of proclaiming religious news by providing information, education and a forum for discussion. Its mission is to provide objective, accurate, current information about the church and events that reflect the lives and activities of its readers. It only features news about Catholicism and Florida. All pitches and press materials should be submitted through the paper's main e-mail address.
NEWSPAPER

Florida Sentinel-Bulletin
Editorial: 2207 E 21st Ave, Tampa, Florida 33605-2099. **T:** 1 813 248-1921
E: editor@flsentinel.com
W: http://flsentinel.com
Freq: Fri; **Circ:** 21600
Publisher: Sybil Kay Andrews-Wells; **Editor:** Gwendolyn Hayes
Editorial Profile: Florida Sentinel Bulletin is a local newspaper serving the African American community in the Tampa, FL area. The editorial mission is to keep the community informed of news and events relevant to African Americans. The newspaper covers both local and national news. Florida Sentinel Bulletin is published twice a week on Tuesday and Friday.; Full Page Mono: 14.00
Currency: US Dollars
NEWSPAPER

The Florida Star
Editorial: 1225 W Beaver St, Jacksonville, Florida 32204. **T:** 1 904 766-8834
E: info@thefloridastar.com
W: http://www.thefloridastar.com
Freq: Fri; **Circ:** 10500 Not Audited
Editor in Chief: Clara McLaughlin
Editorial Profile: The Florida Star is a local newspaper serving the African-American community in Jacksonville, FL.; Full Page Mono: 15.00
Currency: US Dollars
NEWSPAPER

Florida Sun
Editorial: 2700 Catalina Dr, Orlando, Florida 32805-5808. **T:** 1 407 423-1156
E: sunreview@aol.com
W: http://www.floridasunreview.com
Freq: Thu; **Circ:** 10000 Not Audited
Editorial Profile: Florida Sun is published weekly for the residents of Orlando, FL and surrounding areas. The newspaper covers local news, entertainment and community events.; Full Page Mono: 17.50
Currency: US Dollars
NEWSPAPER

The Florida Times-Union
Owner: Morris Multimedia, Inc.
Editorial: 1 Riverside Ave, Jacksonville, Florida 32202-4917. **T:** 1 904 359-4111
W: http://www.jacksonville.com
Freq: Daily; **Circ:** 84321 Not Audited
Editor: Frank Denton; **Editor:** Carole Fader; **Publisher:** Mark Nusbaum
Editorial Profile: Founded in 1865, The Florida Times-Union is a general-interest, broadsheet newspaper with an emphasis on local area coverage, with some national and international wire coverage. It covers area news, politics, crime, professional and collegiate sports and arts and culture, maintaining bureaus in several Florida and Georgia locations. The paper also produces skirt! magazine's Jacksonville edition and a host of weekly feature sections. It launched its Web arm in 1996, which became jacksonville.com in 1997. The publication aims to be the primary news and information source for Northeast Florida residents.; Full Page Mono: 236.00; Full Page Colour: 784.37
Currency: US Dollars
DAILY NEWSPAPER

The Florida Times-Union
Editorial: 3375 Community Rd, Brunswick, Georgia 31520-2867. **T:** 1 912 264-0405
Editorial Profile: Do NOT send faxes!
DAILY NEWSPAPER

Florida Times-Union Military Publications
Owner: Morris Multimedia, Inc.
Editorial: 1 Riverside Ave, Jacksonville, Florida 32202-4917. **T:** 1 904 359-4168 **Circ:** 32000
Editor: Paige Gnann; **Publisher:** Mark Nusbaum; **Editor:** Clark Pierce; **Editor:** Bill Wesselhoff
Editorial Profile: Florida Times-Union Military Publications in Jacksonville, FL include The Periscope; Jax Air News; and The Mirror.
NEWSPAPER

Florida Today
Owner: Gannett Co., Inc.
Editorial: One Gannett Plaza, Melbourne, Florida 32940. **T:** 1 321 242-3500
W: http://www.floridatoday.com
Freq: Daily; **Circ:** 54021 Not Audited
Publisher: Jeff Kiel; **Editor:** John McCarthy
Editorial Profile: Florida Today serves Brevard County, FL and the area surrounding Cape Canaveral, FL. It also publishes five weekly and four monthly community newspapers, which cater to the distinct neighborhoods within Brevard County.; Full Page Mono: 116.08; Full Page Colour: 124.58
Currency: US Dollars
DAILY NEWSPAPER

Florida Today
Editorial: 240 Interstate Ct SE, Palm Bay, Florida 32909-3998. **T:** 1 321 409-1422
DAILY NEWSPAPER

Florida Weekly
Owner: Florida Media Group LLC
Editorial: 4300 Ford Street Ext, Ste 105, Fort Myers, Florida 33916-9318. **T:** 1 239 333-2135
E: news@floridaweekly.com
W: http://www.floridaweekly.com
Freq: Thu; **Circ:** 63000 Not Audited
Editor: Betty Wells
Editorial Profile: Florida Weekly is published for the residents of Fort Myers, FL and West Palm Peach, FL. It covers news, entertainment, dining, business and real estate.; Full Page Mono: 30.00
Currency: US Dollars
NEWSPAPER

Flyer Group
Owner: Community Newspaper Holdings, Inc.
Editorial: 8109 Kingston St Ste 500, Avon, Indiana 46123-8211. **T:** 1 317 272-5800
W: http://www.flyergroup.com **Circ:** 52000
Publisher: Harold Allen; **Editor:** Kathy Linton
Editorial Profile: Flyer Group in Avon, IN is a community newspaper publisher.
NEWSPAPER

Focus
Editorial: #2 Leslie Dr, Brodheadsville, Pennsylvania 18322. **T:** 1 570 992-9300
E: thefocus@ptd.net
Freq: Fri; **Circ:** 25000 Not Audited
Editorial Profile: Focus is a publication for residents in Monroe County, PA. It covers local news, dining, entertainment, health and fitness, home improvement, real estate and automotive. It is distributed to more than 40 towns.; Full Page Mono: 9.00
Currency: US Dollars
NEWSPAPER

Focus Daily News
Owner: Focus Newspapers
Editorial: 1337 Marilyn Ave, Desoto, Texas 75115-6414. **T:** 1 972 223-9175
E: focuseditor@sbcglobal.net
W: http://focusdailynews.com
Freq: Daily; **Circ:** 34323 Not Audited
Editorial Profile: Focus Daily News is written for the residents of DeSoto, Cedar Hill, Lancaster and Duncanville, TX. It covers local news, weather, sports, business and arts & entertainment.; Full Page Mono: 43.00; Full Page Colour: 150.00
Currency: US Dollars
DAILY NEWSPAPER

Foliage Enterprises, Inc.
Editorial: 400 N Park Ave, Apopka, Florida 32712-4152. **T:** 1 407 886-2777
W: http://www.theapopkachief.com
Circ: 14000 Not Audited
Editor: John Peery; **Publisher:** John Ricketson
NEWSPAPER

Folio Weekly
Editorial: 9456 Philips Hwy Ste 11, Jacksonville, Florida 32256-1342.
T: 1 904 260-9770
E: themail@folioweekly.com
W: http://www.folioweekly.com
Freq: Tue; **Circ:** 51000 Not Audited
Editor: Jeffrey Billman; **Publisher:** David Brennan
Editorial Profile: Folio Weekly is published for the residents of Northeastern Florida. The publication provides news, arts and entertainment and other feature articles.; Full Page Mono: 35.00
Currency: US Dollars
NEWSPAPER

Fontana Herald News
Owner: Century Group (The)
Editorial: 16981 Foothill Blvd, Ste N, Fontana, California 92335-3573. **T:** 1 909 822-2231
W: http://www.fontanaheraldnews.com
Freq: Fri; **Circ:** 11500 Not Audited
Publisher: Grace Barnett; **Editor:** Russell Ingold
Editorial Profile: Fontana Herald News is a local newspaper serving the residents of Fontana, CA. It includes information on local news, weather, sports, business, and entertainment. Deadlines for the publication are two days before issue date.; Full Page Mono: 19.65
Currency: US Dollars
NEWSPAPER

The Foothills Focus
Owner: The Foothills Focus, LLC.
Editorial: 46641 N Black Canyon Hwy, New River, Arizona 85087-6941. **T:** 1 623 465-5808
W: http://www.thefoothillsfocus.com
Freq: Wed; **Circ:** 30000
Editor: Mark Buckhout
Editorial Profile: The Foothills Focus offers local news, sports and events to residents of the northeast and northwest Valley communities in Arizona, including Anthem, Cave Creek, Carefree, Desert Hills, Diamond Creek Estates, Dove Valley Estates, Dove Valley Ranch, Mountain Gate, New River, North Phoenix, North Scottsdale, Tramonto, Tatum Ranch and Tatum Highlands.; Full Page Mono: 43.70
Currency: US Dollars
NEWSPAPER

Foothills Media Group
Owner: Journal Register Company
Editorial: 59 Field St, Torrington, Connecticut 06790-4942. **T:** 1 860 489-3121
W: http://www.foothillsmediagroup.com
Editorial Profile: Foothills Media Group in Torrington, CT is a community newspaper publisher associated with the daily paper, The Register Citizen, and produces several weekly newspapers serving various towns in Connecticut, including The Avon (CT) News. All papers publish on Wednesdays, and have a lead time of one week.
NEWSPAPER

Foothills Sentry
Owner: Bennyhoff (Anita)
Editorial: 10642 Morada, Orange, California 92869. **T:** 1 714 532-4406
E: foothillssentry@socal.rr.com
W: http://www.foothillssentry.com
Freq: Monthly; **Circ:** 45804 Not Audited
Editorial Profile: Foothills Sentry in Orange, CA is a monthly community newspaper serving the residents of Villa Park, East and Central Orange, North Tustin, Silverado, and Modjeska Canyons, CA. The newspaper features local news, politics and lifestyle stories.; Full Page Mono: 19.00; Full Page Colour: 23.00
Currency: US Dollars
NEWSPAPER

The Foothills Sun-Gazette
Editorial: 120 N E St, Exeter, California 93221-1729. **T:** 1 559 592-3171
E: news@thesungazette.com
W: http://www.thesungazette.com
Freq: Wed; **Circ:** 21225 Not Audited
Editorial Profile: The Foothills Sun-Gazette is a weekly newspaper serving the foothill communities of Exeter, CA. The publication provides information on community news, events, sports, business and education. Deadlines are on Tuesdays at noon ET.; Full Page Mono: 12.93
Currency: US Dollars
NEWSPAPER

The Forecaster
Owner: Lewiston Daily Sun Inc.
Editorial: 5 Fundy Rd, Falmouth, Maine 04105-1774. **T:** 1 207 781-3661
E: editor@theforecaster.net
W: http://www.theforecaster.net
Freq: Weekly; **Circ:** 69500 Not Audited
Editor: Mo Mehlsak; **Publisher:** Karen Rajotte
Editorial Profile: The Forecaster provides local coverage to the Greater Portland, ME area. It publishes the Forecaster North, Forecaster South, Forecaster Portland City and Forecaster Mid-Coast Editions on a weekly basis.
NEWSPAPER

Forest Blade Publishing Company
Owner: Smith Newspapers
Editorial: 416 W Moring St, Swainsboro, Georgia 30401. **T:** 1 478 237-9971
E: news@forest-blade.com
W: http://www.forest-blade.com **Circ:** 15985 Not Audited
Publisher: Gail Williamson
NEWSPAPER

Forrest City Times Herald
Owner: Times-Herald Publishing Co., Inc.
Editorial: 222 N Izard St, Forrest City, Arkansas 72335. **T:** 1 870 633-3130
E: fctimes@thnews.com
W: http://www.thnews.com
Freq: Daily; **Circ:** 5000 Not Audited
Publisher: Weston Lewey
Editorial Profile: Forrest City Times Herald is a daily newspaper serving Forrest City, AR and the surrounding area. Sections include news, sports, arts & entertainment and opinions.; Full Page Mono: 11.64; Full Page Colour: 250.00
Currency: US Dollars
DAILY NEWSPAPER

Forsyth County News
Editorial: 302 Veterans Memorial Blvd, Cumming, Georgia 30040-2644.
T: 1 770 887-3126 **E:** editor@forsythnews.com
W: http://www.forsythnews.com
Freq: Daily; **Circ:** 12500 Not Audited
Editor: Kevin Atwill; **Editor:** Kevin Atwill; **Editor:** Kevin Atwill; **Publisher:** John Hall
Editorial Profile: The Forsyth County News is a local newspaper serving the residents of Forsyth County, GA. It includes information on local news, weather, sports, business, and entertainment. Reporters will often covering general news as needed, regardless of their usual beats.; Full Page Mono: 16.45; Full Page Colour: 38.37
Currency: US Dollars
DAILY NEWSPAPER

Fort Bend Herald & Texas Coaster
Owner: Hartman Newspapers, Inc.
Editorial: 1902 4th St, Rosenberg, Texas 77471-5140. **T:** 1 281 342-4474
E: newsroom@fbherald.com
W: http://www.fbherald.com
Freq: Daily; **Circ:** 8200
Editorial Profile: Fort Bend Herald & Texas Coaster is a local, daily newspaper serving the Fort Bend, TX area. The paper's editorial mission is to print the news that affects people in the community. It covers local news and sports.; Full Page Mono: 15.50; Full Page Colour: 275.00
Currency: US Dollars
DAILY NEWSPAPER

Fort Bend Star
Editorial: 4655 Techniplex Dr, Ste 300, Stafford, Texas 77477. **T:** 1 281 690-4200
E: starnews@fortbendstar.com
W: http://www.fortbendstar.com
Freq: Wed; **Circ:** 62094 Not Audited
Publisher: Beverly Carter; **Editor:** Jean Sandlin
Editorial Profile: Fort Bend Star is published weekly for the residents of Fort Bend County, TX. The newspaper covers local news, sports, business news, education, arts & entertainment and community events.; Full Page Mono: 23.50; Full Page Colour: 3960.50
Currency: US Dollars
NEWSPAPER

Fort Campbell Courier
Editorial: 2574 23rd St, Fort Campbell, Kentucky 42223-5307. **T:** 1 270 798-6090
E: courier.editor@conus.army.mil
W: http://www.fortcampbellcourier.com
Freq: Thu; **Circ:** 24000 Not Audited
Publisher: Bob Jenkins; **Editor in Chief:** Kimberly Lewis
Editorial Profile: Fort Campbell Courier is a local newspaper that serves members of the Army in Fort Campbell, KY.; Full Page Mono: 12.00
Currency: US Dollars
NEWSPAPER

Fort Collins Coloradoan
Owner: Gannett Co., Inc.
Editorial: 1300 Riverside Ave, Fort Collins, Colorado 80524-4353. **T:** 1 970 493-6397
E: news@coloradoan.com
W: http://www.coloradoan.com
Freq: Daily; **Circ:** 19547 Not Audited
News Editor: Rebecca Powell
Editorial Profile: Fort Collins Coloradoan is a local newspaper serving the residents of Fort Collins, CO. It includes information on local news, weather, sports, business and entertainment.; Full Page Mono: 59.40; Full Page Colour: 73.80
Currency: US Dollars
DAILY NEWSPAPER

Fort Drum Mountaineer
Editorial: 1012 S. Riva Ridge Lodge, Fort Drum, New York 13602. **T:** 1 315 772-5469
E: drum.pao@conus.army.mil
W: http://www.drum.army.mil
Freq: Thu; **Circ:** 10000 Not Audited
Editorial Profile: The Fort Drum Mountaineer is a local newspaper serving the military and their families in Fort Drum, NY.; Full Page Mono: 24.55; Full Page Colour: 79.13
Currency: US Dollars
NEWSPAPER

Fort Hood Herald
Owner: Mayborn Enterprises
Editorial: 1809 Florence Rd, Killeen, Texas 76541-8977. **T:** 1 254 634-2125
E: news@kdhnews.com
Freq: Thu; **Circ:** 40000 Not Audited
Publisher: Sue Mayborn; **Editor:** Rose Thayer
Editorial Profile: Fort Hood Herald is a weekly newspaper serving the military personnel of Fort Hood and residents of Kileen, TX. In addition to newsstand availability, the paper is also inserted into the Killeen (TX) Daily Herald, with which it shares offices.; Full Page Mono: 8.73
Currency: US Dollars
NEWSPAPER

Fort Hood Sentinel
Owner: Mayborn Enterprises
Editorial: Fort Hood U.S. Army Base, 1001 Rim W105 Corps Public Affairs Office, Fort Hood, Texas 76544. **T:** 1 254 287-2436
W: http://www.forthoodsentinel.com
Freq: Thu; **Circ:** 26500 Not Audited
Editor: Todd Pruden
Editorial Profile: Fort Hood Sentinel is a free, weekly newspaper serving military personnel and civilian employees and residents of the U.S. Army Base in Fort Hood, TX.; Full Page Mono: 12.00
Currency: US Dollars
NEWSPAPER

Fort Jackson Leader
Owner: Camden Media Co.
Editorial: 4394 Strom Thurmond Blvd., Fort Jackson, South Carolina 29207.
T: 1 803 751-7045 **E:** fjleader@gmail.com
W: http://www.fortjacksonleader.com
Freq: Thu; **Circ:** 15000 Not Audited
Editor: Susanne Kappler; **Publisher:** Mike Mischner
Editorial Profile: Fort Jackson Leader is a military newspaper in Camden, SC. The paper covers community news, events and sports.; Full Page Mono: 14.70
Currency: US Dollars
NEWSPAPER

Fort Lee Traveller
Owner: Military Newspapers of Virginia
Editorial: 114 Charlotte Ave Suite A, Colonial Heights, Virginia 23834-3007.
T: 1 804 526-8656
E: leeeeditor@conus.army.mil
W: http://www.fortleetraveller.com
Freq: Thu; **Circ:** 11000 Not Audited
Publisher: Laura Baxter; **Editor:** Patrick Buffett
Editorial Profile: Fort Lee Traveller is written for soldiers, civilians, family members and retirees of the U.S. Army. It covers news and feature articles about the Fort Lee, VA community.; Full Page Mono: 12.24
Currency: US Dollars
NEWSPAPER

Fort Mill Times
Owner: McClatchy Newspapers
Editorial: 124 Main St, Fort Mill, South Carolina 29715-1739. **T:** 1 803 547-2353
E: news@fortmilltimes.com
W: http://www.fortmilltimes.com
Freq: Wed; **Circ:** 19135 Not Audited
Publisher: Debbie Ables; **Editor:** Michael Harrison
Editorial Profile: Fort Mill Times is a local newspaper for Fort Mill, Tega Cay and Indian Land, SC. The publication features local and national news, weather, sports, business and entertainment. The newspaper also includes news about local schools, government, community and church activities. Deadlines are on Fridays at noon ET.; Full Page Mono: 16.70; Full Page Colour: 1257.00
Currency: US Dollars
NEWSPAPER

Fort Morgan Times
Owner: MediaNews Group
Editorial: 329 Main St, Fort Morgan, Colorado 80701-2108. **T:** 1 970 867-5651
E: fmtimes@fmtimes.com
W: http://www.fortmorgantimes.com
Freq: Daily; **Circ:** 3925 Not Audited
Editor: John La Porte
Editorial Profile: Fort Morgan Times is a local daily newspaper serving the residents of Fort Morgan, CO. The publication features local news, weather, sports, economy and business, and entertainment.; Full Page Mono: 10.75
Currency: US Dollars
DAILY NEWSPAPER

Fort Polk Guardian
Owner: News Leader, Inc.
Editorial: 7033 Magnolia Dr., Leesville, Louisiana 71459-5329. **T:** 1 337 531-4033
E: kimberly.reischling@us.army.mil
W: http://www.fortpolkguardian.com
Freq: Fri; **Circ:** 13000 Not Audited
Editor: Jean Dubiel; **Editor in Chief:** Kimberly Reischling
Editorial Profile: Fort Polk Guardian is a local newspaper serving military personnel and their families in Fort Polk, LA. Press releases should go to the Editor in Chief directly.; Full Page Mono: 23.87
Currency: US Dollars
NEWSPAPER

The Fort Scott Tribune
Owner: Rust Communications
Editorial: 12 E Wall St, Fort Scott, Kansas 66701-1423. **T:** 1 620 223-1460
E: editor@fstribune.com
W: http://www.fstribune.com
Freq: Mon thru Fri; **Circ:** 3200 Not Audited
Publisher: Julie Simpson
Editorial Profile: The Fort Scott Tribune is a local newspaper serving the residents of Fort Scott, KS. It includes information on local news, weather, sports, business and entertainment. The weekend edition, entitled the Sunday Herald-Tribune, is combined with the Nevada (MO) Daily Mail's weekend edition and is distributed to residents in both Vernon County, MO, and Bourbon County, KS.; Full Page Mono: 6.25; Full Page Colour: 150.00
Currency: US Dollars
DAILY NEWSPAPER

Fort Worth Star-Telegram
Owner: McClatchy Newspapers
Editorial: 808 Throckmorton St, Fort Worth, Texas 76102-6315. **T:** 1 817 390-7400
E: newsroom@star-telegram.com
W: http://www.star-telegram.com
Freq: Daily; **Circ:** 173833 Not Audited
Editorial Profile: Fort Worth Star-Telegram, founded in 1906, is distributed in 23 North Texas counties in and around the Fort Worth, TX area. The Fort Worth Star-Telegram is a newspaper written for the general public. It offers regional and national news, and provides its readers with information on business, real estate, arts & entertainment, and sports. The business section offers breaking news, investigative reports, news and news analysis, features, columns and profiles. The Star-Telegram is a morning edition paper.; Full Page Mono: 455.00; Full Page Colour: 492.10
Currency: US Dollars
DAILY NEWSPAPER

Fort Worth Weekly
Editorial: 3311 Hamilton Ave, Fort Worth, Texas 76107. **T:** 1 817 321-9700
E: feedback@fwweekly.com
W: http://www.fwweekly.com
Freq: Wed; **Circ:** 60000 Not Audited
Publisher: Lee Newquist; **Editor:** Gayle Reaves
Editorial Profile: Fort Worth Weekly serves the residents of Fort Worth, TX. It provides coverage of news, sports, entertainment and other lifestyle stories.; Full Page Mono: 32.09
Currency: US Dollars
NEWSPAPER

Fortville-McCordsville Reporter & New Palestine Press
Owner: Home News Enterprises
Editorial: 22 W New Rd, Greenfield, Indiana 46140-1090. **T:** 1 317 462-5528
Editor: Scott Slade; **Editor:** Scott Slade
NEWSPAPER

The Forum
Owner: Forum Communications Co.
Editorial: 101 5th St N, Fargo, North Dakota 58102-4826. **T:** 1 701 235-7311
E: news@forumcomm.com
W: http://www.in-forum.com
Freq: Daily; **Circ:** 39824 Not Audited
Publisher: Bill Marcil; **News Editor:** Dave Roepke; **Editor:** Matt Von Pinnon
Editorial Profile: The Forum is a daily newspaper published for readers in the sister cities of Fargo, ND and Morehead, MN. The editorial content covers local and regional news, government, politics, business, technology, sports, entertainment and agriculture.; Full Page Mono: 57.89; Full Page Colour: 188.20
Currency: US Dollars
DAILY NEWSPAPER

Forum
Editorial: 600 E Boulevard Ave, Bismarck, North Dakota 58505-0601. **T:** 1 701 255-5607
DAILY NEWSPAPER

Forum Communications
Editorial: 312 Oak St, Farmington, Minnesota 55024. **T:** 1 651 460-6606 **Circ:** 4400 Not Audited
Editor: Nathan Hansen; **Editor:** Nathan Hansen; **Publisher:** Steve Messick
NEWSPAPER

Forum Publishing Group, Inc.
Owner: Tribune Company
Editorial: 1701 Green Rd, Pompano Beach, Florida 33064-1074. **T:** 1 954 698-6397
W: http://www.sun-sentinel.com/services/newspaper/fpg/ **Circ:** 599098 Not Audited
Editor: Kari Barnett; **Editor:** Alan Goch; **Editor:** Barbara Negron; **Editor:** Daniel White
NEWSPAPER

Forum South
Owner: BJP Publications
Editorial: 15519 Lahn St, Howard Beach, New York 11414-2858. **T:** 1 718 845-3221
E: forumwest@gmail.com
W: http://theforumnewsgroup.com
Freq: Thu; **Circ:** 60000 Not Audited
Publisher: Patricia Adams; **Editor in Chief:** Anna Gustafson
Editorial Profile: Forum South is a free weekly newspaper serving Queens County, NY. It offers local news, world events, lifestyle topics, food, health, sports and education. Deadlines are on Mondays.; Full Page Mono: 40.00
Currency: US Dollars
NEWSPAPER

The Forward Newspapers
Owner: Forward Association (The)
Editorial: 125 Maiden Ln, New York, New York 10038-4912. **T:** 1 212 889-8200
E: newsdesk@forward.com
W: http://www.forward.com
Freq: Fri; **Circ:** 29428 Not Audited
Editorial Profile: The Forward began publishing in 1897 as a daily Yiddish newspaper, but now publishes weekly on Fridays, with a Yiddish version that publishes bi-weekly. The paper still publishes in Yiddish and began an English version in 1990. The newspaper covers news, politics and culture in the Jewish world. Please ONLY send press materials with a Jewish angle. Publications were previously known as The Jewish Daily Forward.
NEWSPAPER

Foster's Daily Democrat
Owner: Foster Publishing Co. (George J.)
Editorial: 150 Venture Dr, Dover, New Hampshire 03820-5913. **T:** 1 603 742-4455
E: news@fosters.com
W: http://www.fosters.com
Freq: Daily; **Circ:** 19023 Not Audited
Publisher: Therese Foster; **Editor:** Jeremiah Turner
Editorial Profile: Foster's Daily Democrat is a daily newspaper published for the residents of Southeastern New Hampshire. The newspaper provides information on local news, weather, sports, business and events.; Full Page Mono: 20.95; Full Page Colour: 435.00
Currency: US Dollars
DAILY NEWSPAPER

Fostoria Review Times
Owner: Findlay Publishing Company (The)
Editorial: 113 E Center St, Fostoria, Ohio 44830-2905. **T:** 1 419 435-6641
E: rtnews@reviewtimes.com
W: http://www.reviewtimes.com
Freq: Daily; **Circ:** 3790 Not Audited
News Editor: Joel Sensenig; **News Editor:** Joel Sensenig
Editorial Profile: Fostoria Times Review is a local newspaper serving the residents of Fostoria, OH. It includes information on local and national news, weather, sports, business, and entertainment.; Full Page Mono: 10.40; Full Page Colour: 175.00
Currency: US Dollars
DAILY NEWSPAPER

Foto News
Owner: Journal Community Publishing Group
Editorial: 807 E 1st St, Merrill, Wisconsin 54452. **T:** 1 715 536-7121
W: http://www.merrillfotonews.com
Freq: Wed; **Circ:** 16400 Not Audited
Editor: Collin Lueck
Editorial Profile: Foto News is a weekly community newspaper written for residents in Merrill, WI and surrounding areas.; Full Page Mono: 25.40
Currency: US Dollars
NEWSPAPER

Frankfurter Allgemeine - New York Bureau
Owner: Frankfurter Allgemeine Zeitung GmbH
Editorial: 125 North 10th St, #S5B, Brooklyn, New York 11211-1169. **T:** 1 718 599-2750
W: http://www.faz.net
Editorial Profile: This is the New York bureau for Frankfurter Allgemeine Zeitung in Frankfurt, Germany.
DAILY NEWSPAPER

Franklin Banner-Tribune
Editorial: 115 Wilson St, Franklin, Louisiana 70538. **T:** 1 337 828-3706
E: editor@banner-tribune.com
W: http://www.banner-tribune.com
Freq: Daily; **Circ:** 3231 Not Audited
Publisher: Allan Von Werder
Editorial Profile: Franklin Banner-Tribune is a newspaper for the residents of Franklin, Louisiana. The publication offers articles on local news, entertainment and events, sports, tourism, and weather.; Full Page Mono: 6.84; Full Page Colour: 300.00
Currency: US Dollars
DAILY NEWSPAPER

The Franklin County Times
Owner: Franklin County Newspapers, Inc.
Editorial: 14131 Highway 43, Russellville, Alabama 35653-2847. **T:** 1 256 332-1881
W: http://www.franklincountytimes.com
Freq: Sat; **Circ:** 13000 Not Audited
Editorial Profile: Franklin County Times is a newspaper serving the residents of Franklin County, Alabama. The publication offers articles on local and national news, sports, and events. The lead time for Franklin County Times is two days.; Full Page Mono: 12.07
Currency: US Dollars
NEWSPAPER

The Franklin Group
Owner: Sun Media Group
Editorial: 187 Wilton Rd, Farmington, Maine 04938-6120. **T:** 1 207 778-2075
E: info@thefranklinjournal.com **Circ:** 7500 Not Audited
Editor: Greg Davis; **Publisher:** Edward Snook
NEWSPAPER

The Frederick News-Post
Owner: Randall Family LLC.
Editorial: 351 Ballenger Center Dr, Frederick, Maryland 21703-7095. **T:** 1 301 662-1177
E: citydesk@newspost.com
W: http://www.fredericknewspost.com
Freq: Daily; **Circ:** 27661 Not Audited
Editorial Profile: The Frederick (MD) News-Post is a daily newspaper that covers local news, current events and sports.; Full Page Mono: 25.50; Full Page Colour: 350.00
Currency: US Dollars
DAILY NEWSPAPER

Free Bird Times
Owner: Free Bird Times Publishing Co.
Editorial: 11 Robinhood Ave, Middleboro, Massachusetts 2346. **T:** 1 508 923-9966
E: freebirdtimes@comcast.net
W: http://www.freebirdtimes.com
Freq: Monthly; **Circ:** 45000 Not Audited
Editorial Profile: Free Bird Times is a monthly newspaper published and distributed free to the residents of Middleboro, MA and surrounding communities. The newspaper covers local news, community events, and lifestyle topics. It is dedicated to reporting, "the pleasant and good life that exists" in the local area. Deadlines for submissions fall on the first Wednesday of the month prior to issue date.; Full Page Mono: 7.20
Currency: US Dollars
NEWSPAPER

The Free Lance-Star
Owner: Free Lance-Star Publishing Co. (The)
Editorial: 616 Amelia St, Fredericksburg, Virginia 22401-3887. **T:** 1 540 374-5000
E: newsroom@freelancestar.com
W: http://www.fredericksburg.com
Freq: Daily; **Circ:** 38711 Not Audited
Editor: Richard Amrhine; **Publisher:** Nicholas Cadwallender; **Editor:** Phil Jenkins; **Editor:** Phil Jenkins; **Editor:** Phil Jenkins; **Editor:** Phil Jenkins; **Editor:** Katherine Shapleigh
Editorial Profile: The Free Lance-Star is a daily newspaper serving the residents of Fredericksburg, VA and surrounding counties. It offers articles on local news, national news, events and business.; Full Page Mono: 27.40; Full Page Colour: 96.15
Currency: US Dollars
DAILY NEWSPAPER

The Free Press
Owner: Community Newspaper Holdings, Inc.
Editorial: 418 S 2nd St, Mankato, Minnesota 56001-3784. **T:** 1 507 344-6397
E: editor@mankatofreepress.com
W: http://mankato-freepress.com
Freq: Daily; **Circ:** 20481 Not Audited
Publisher: Jim Santori
Editorial Profile: The Free Press is published daily for residents of South Central Minnesota. The newspaper covers local news, weather, sports and community events. Feature articles cover business, education, arts & entertainment, lifestyle and other topics of interest to area residents. The lead time for editorial submissions is 3pm CT daily.; Full Page Mono: 24.73; Full Page Colour: 338.00
Currency: US Dollars
DAILY NEWSPAPER

The Free Press
Owner: Halifax Media Holdings LLC
Editorial: 2103 N Queen St, Kinston, North Carolina 28501-1695. **T:** 1 252 527-3191
W: http://www.kinston.com
Freq: Daily; **Circ:** 11358 Not Audited
Editorial Profile: The Free Press covers local community news, sports and weather. The publication is written for the residents of Kinston, NC.; Full Page Mono: 15.38; Full Page Colour: 430.00
Currency: US Dollars
DAILY NEWSPAPER

Free Press
Owner: Cooke Communications LLC
Editorial: 91731 Overseas Hwy, Tavernier, Florida 33070-2649. **T:** 1 305 853-7277
E: freepress@keysnews.com
W: http://www.keysnews.com
Freq: Wed; **Circ:** 12800 Not Audited
Editor: Dan Campbell; **Publisher:** Paul Clarin
Editorial Profile: Free Press is a weekly local newspaper covering local news and community events. There are two editions of the paper. One is sent to Key Largo and Homestead, FL, and the other is sent to Islamorada and Tavernier, FL. The two issues are identical in content and have the same staff. Circulation figures are the combination of the two different editions.; Full Page Mono: 14.73
Currency: US Dollars
NEWSPAPER

The Free Press
Owner: The Free Press, Inc.
Editorial: 8 N Main St, Ste 101, Rockland, Maine 4841. **T:** 1 207 596-0055
E: freepress@freepressonline.com
W: http://www.freepressonline.com
Freq: Thu; **Circ:** 12000 Not Audited
Publisher: Alice McFadden; **Editor:** Patricia Poe
Editorial Profile: The Free Press is a weekly newspaper serving midcoast Maine. It covers community news, shopping, dining and entertainment.; Full Page Mono: 10.65
Currency: US Dollars
NEWSPAPER

The Free Press Newspapers
Owner: G.W. Communications
Editorial: 111 S Water St, Wilmington, Illinois 60481-1373. **T:** 1 815 476-7966
E: fpnnews@cbcast.com
W: http://www.freepressnewspapers.com
Freq: Wed; **Circ:** 23043 Not Audited
Publisher: Eric Fisher; **Editor:** Ann Gill; **Editor:** Pam Monson
Editorial Profile: The Fress Press Newspapers provide local coverage for the residents of Kankakee County, Grundy County and Southern Will County, IL.; Full Page Mono: 19.00
Currency: US Dollars
NEWSPAPER

Free Times
Owner: Portico Publications, Ltd.
Editorial: 1534 Main St, Columbia, South Carolina 29201-2808. **T:** 1 803 765-0707
W: http://www.free-times.com
Freq: Wed; **Circ:** 35000 Not Audited
Editor: Dan Cook; **Publisher:** Eric Hancock; **News Editor:** Eva Moore
Editorial Profile: Free Times is published weekly for residents of Columbia, SC and surrounding communities. The publication offers articles on local and national news, events and entertainment, including music, movies and theater.; Full Page Mono: 22.20; Full Page Colour: 1340.00
Currency: US Dollars
NEWSPAPER

Freedom Communications - Willows
Owner: Freedom Communications Inc.
Editorial: 130 N Butte St Ste A, Willows, California 95988-2836. **T:** 1 530 934-6800
Circ: 2477 Not Audited
Editor: Steve Miller; **Publisher:** Paula Patton
NEWSPAPER

The Freeman
Owner: Conley Publishing Group
Editorial: 801 N Barstow St, Waukesha, Wisconsin 53186-4801. **T:** 1 262 542-2500
E: news@conleynet.com
W: http://www.gmtoday.com
Freq: Daily; **Circ:** 12371 Not Audited
Editor: Lee Fensin; **Publisher:** Philip Paige; **Editor:** Bill Yorth
Editorial Profile: The Freeman is a daily newspaper published for residents of

Waukesha, WI and surrounding areas. It covers local news and events.; Full Page Mono: 29.76; Full Page Colour: 184.92
Currency: US Dollars
DAILY NEWSPAPER

Freeman's Journal & Hometown Oneonta
Editorial: 21 Railroad Ave, Cooperstown, New York 13326-1169. **T:** 1 607 547-6103
W: http://allotsego.homestead.com/index.html
Circ: 15500
NEWSPAPER

Freestone County Times
Owner: Freestone County Times, Inc.
Editorial: 401 E Commerce St, Fairfield, Texas 75840-1603. **T:** 1 903 389-6397
E: news@freestonecountytimes.com
W: http://www.freestonecountytimes.com
Freq: Tue
Editor: Karen Leidy; **Publisher:** Scott Marsters
Editorial Profile: The Freestone County Times is a weekly newspaper providing Local News coverage to the communities in Freestone County, TX.
NEWSPAPER

Fremont Tribune
Owner: Lee Enterprises, Inc.
Editorial: 135 N Main St, Fremont, Nebraska 68025-5673. **T:** 1 402 721-5000
E: tribnews@ftrib.com
W: http://fremonttribune.com
Freq: Daily; **Circ:** 6550 Not Audited
News Editor: Tammy McKeighan
Editorial Profile: Fremont Tribune is a local daily newspaper serving the residents of Fremont, NE and its surrounding communities. The publication offers local and national news, events, health, business and entertainment.; Full Page Mono: 19.75; Full Page Colour: 380.00
Currency: US Dollars
DAILY NEWSPAPER

The Fresno Bee
Owner: McClatchy Newspapers
Editorial: 1626 E St, Fresno, California 93786-0001. **T:** 1 559 441-6111
E: metro@fresnobee.com
W: http://www.fresnobee.com
Freq: Daily; **Circ:** 101181 Not Audited
Editorial Profile: The Fresno Bee is written for the general public in the Fresno, CA area. Major news focuses are business, technology, state news, national news, local news, international news, lifestyle, sports and entertainment.; Full Page Mono: 230.25; Full Page Colour: 252.00
Currency: US Dollars
DAILY NEWSPAPER

The Fresno Bee
Editorial: 700 12th St NW, Washington, District Of Columbia 20005-3945.
T: 1 202 383-0006
DAILY NEWSPAPER

The Fresno Bee
Editorial: 525 W Main St, Visalia, California 93291-6116. **T:** 1 559 622-2400
E: southvalley@fresnobee.com
DAILY NEWSPAPER

Front Page and Chronicle Newspapers
Owner: Real Times, Inc.
Editorial: 479 Ledyard St, Detroit, Michigan 48201-2641. **T:** 1 313 963-5522
E: chronicle4@aol.com
W: http://www.michronicle.com **Circ:** 70000 Not Audited
Publisher: Hiram Jackson
NEWSPAPER

Front Page Group Inc.
Editorial: 2703 S Park Ave, Lackawanna, New York 14218. **T:** 1 716 823-8222
E: newsroomfpg@wny.twcbc.com
Freq: Weekly; **Circ:** 10500 Not Audited
Editorial Profile: Front Page-Lackawanna Edition is a tabloid newspaper serving the residents of Lackawanna, NY. The publication offers articles on local news and community events.; Full Page Colour: 820.00
Currency: US Dollars
NEWSPAPER

Front Range Guardian
Owner: Gannett Co., Inc.
Editorial: 205 River Dr S, Great Falls, Montana 59405-1854. **T:** 1 406 791-1444
E: mstergionis@greatfallstribune.com
W: http://www.greatfallstribune.com
Freq: Fri; **Circ:** 12000 Not Audited
Publisher: Jim Strauss; **Editor:** Mark Sturgeones
Editorial Profile: Front Range Guardian is a military publication written for the military personnel of the Malmstrom Air Force Base.; Full Page Mono: 14.05
Currency: US Dollars
NEWSPAPER

The Frontline
Editorial: 112 Vilseck Rd Suite 109, Fort Stewart, Georgia 31314. **T:** 1 912 767-5669
E: usarmy.stewart.3-id.list.pao-frontline-news-desk@mail.mil
W: http://www.stewart.army.mil
Freq: Thu; **Circ:** 25000
Editorial Profile: The Frontline is written for the army community of Fort Stewart, GA.; Full Page Mono: 13.00
Currency: US Dollars
NEWSPAPER

Fulda Newspapers
Editorial: 118 N St Paul Ave, Fulda, Minnesota 56131-1156. **T:** 1 507 425-2303
E: text@fuldafreepress.net
W: http://www.fuldafreepress.net **Circ:** 12320 Not Audited
Editorial Profile: Fulda Newspapers is a local newspaper providing the community of Fulda, MN with news.
NEWSPAPER

The Fulton Sun
Owner: Wehco Media Inc.
Editorial: 115 E 5th St, Fulton, Missouri 65251. **T:** 1 573 642-7272
E: news@fultonsun.com
W: http://www.fultonsun.com
Freq: Daily; **Circ:** 4500 Not Audited
Editor: Karen Atkins; **Editor:** Kevin Smith
Editorial Profile: Fulton Sun is a newspaper serving the residents of Fulton, MO. The publication offers articles on local news and community events. Deadlines for the publication are 10am CT the day before issue date.; Full Page Mono: 7.30; Full Page Colour: 10.30
Currency: US Dollars
DAILY NEWSPAPER

La Gaceta
Owner: La Gaceta Publishing Inc.
Editorial: 3210 E 7th Ave, Tampa, Florida 33605. **T:** 1 813 248-3921
E: lagaceta@tampabay.rr.com
W: http://www.lagacetanewspaper.com
Freq: Fri; **Circ:** 18110 Not Audited
Editorial Profile: La Gaceta is written for the Spanish, Italian and English residents in Tampa, FL. It covers local news and events.; Full Page Mono: 11.00
Currency: US Dollars
NEWSPAPER

The Gadsden Times
Owner: Halifax Media Holdings LLC
Editorial: 401 Locust St, Gadsden, Alabama 35901-3737. **T:** 1 256 549-2000
E: news@gadsdentimes.com
W: http://www.gadsdentimes.com
Freq: Daily; **Circ:** 13473 Not Audited
Publisher: Glen Porter
Editorial Profile: The Gadsden Times is published daily for residents of Gadsden, AL and surrounding communities. The publication covers local, national and international news, weather, sports, religion and community events. Feature articles cover business, education, arts & entertainment, lifestyle and other information of interest to community residents.; Full Page Mono: 39.50
Currency: US Dollars
DAILY NEWSPAPER

Gainesville Daily Register
Owner: Community Newspaper Holdings, Inc.
Editorial: 306 E California St, Gainesville, Texas 76240. **T:** 1 940 665-5511
W: http://www.gainesvilleregister.com
Freq: Mon thru Fri; **Circ:** 5902 Not Audited
Editor: Delania Trigg
Editorial Profile: Gainesville Daily Register is a newspaper serving residents of Gainesville, TX. The publication covers local news and community events. Deadlines are one day prior to issue date at 10:30am MT.; Full Page Mono: 9.90; Full Page Colour: 330.00
Currency: US Dollars
DAILY NEWSPAPER

Gainesville Guardian
Owner: New York Times Regional Newspaper Group
Editorial: 2700 SW 13th St, Gainesville, Florida 32608-2015. **T:** 1 352 337-0376
E: news@gainesvilleguardian.com
W: http://www.gainesvilleguardian.com
Freq: Thu; **Circ:** 10000 Not Audited
Publisher: James Doughton; **Editor:** Carolyn Palmer
Editorial Profile: Gainesville Guardian is a community newspaper written for the African American community of Gainsville, FL. The paper covers local news, events, businesses, schools, sports and feature stories.; Full Page Mono: 14.35
Currency: US Dollars
NEWSPAPER

The Gainesville Sun
Owner: Halifax Media Holdings LLC
Editorial: 2700 SW 13th St, Gainesville, Florida 32608-2015. **T:** 1 352 374-5000
E: voice@gvillesun.com
W: http://www.gainesville.com
Freq: Daily; **Circ:** 26477 Not Audited
Publisher: James Doughton
Editorial Profile: The Gainesville Sun provides news and information to North Central Florida. As of November 2008, the publication has some combined operations with the Star-Banner in Ocala, FL.; Full Page Mono: 120.30; Full Page Colour: 792.00
Currency: US Dollars
DAILY NEWSPAPER

Gainesville Voice
Owner: New York Times Company (The)
Editorial: 2700 SW 13th St, Gainesville, Florida 32608-2015. **T:** 1 352 374-5000
W: http://blogs.gainesvillevoice.com
Freq: Thu; **Circ:** 15000 Not Audited
Publisher: James Doughton; **Editor:** Carolyn Palmer
Editorial Profile: Gainesville Voice is a local newspaper written for the residents of Gainesville, FL. Deadlines are on Thursdays at 4pm ET.; Full Page Mono: 14.44; Full Page Colour: 125.00
Currency: US Dollars
NEWSPAPER

Galion Inquirer
Owner: Ohio Community Media LLC.
Editorial: 129 Harding Way E, Galion, Ohio 44833-1902. **T:** 1 419 468-1117
E: editor@galioninquirer.com
W: http://www.galioninquirer.com
Freq: Fri; **Circ:** 3860 Not Audited
Editor: Rachel Mendell; **Publisher:** Vicki Taylor
Editorial Profile: Galion Inquirer is a local daily newspaper serving the residents of Galion, OH and surrounding areas. It covers local news and community events. Deadlines are the day before issue date.; Full Page Mono: 9.15; Full Page Colour: 16.30
Currency: US Dollars
NEWSPAPER

Gallipolis Daily Tribune
Owner: Heartland Publications
Editorial: 825 3rd Ave, Gallipolis, Ohio 45631-1624. **T:** 1 740 446-2342
W: http://www.mydailytribune.com
Freq: Daily; **Circ:** 4466 Not Audited
Publisher: Sammy Lopez
Editorial Profile: Gallipolis Daily Tribune is a newspaper serving the residents of Gallipolis, OH. The publication covers local and national news, events, sports, business, and lifestyles. On Sundays, the paper joins with its sister newspaper, The Daily Sentinel in Pomeroy, OH to produce the Sunday Times-Sentinel. Advertising deadlines are two days prior to publication.; Full Page Mono: 11.35; Full Page Colour: 180.00
Currency: US Dollars
DAILY NEWSPAPER

The Galt Herald
Owner: Herburger Publications, Inc.
Editorial: 604 N Lincoln Way, Galt, California 95632-8601. **T:** 1 209 745-1551
W: http://www.thegaltherald.com
Freq: Wed; **Circ:** 11700 Not Audited
Publisher: David Herburger; **Editor:** Bonnie Rodriguez
Editorial Profile: The Galt Herald provides news and information for the residents of Galt, CA and Southern Sacramento County. Deadlines are Mondays before the issue date.; Full Page Mono: 9.50
Currency: US Dollars
NEWSPAPER

The Galveston County Daily News
Owner: Walls Investment Co.
Editorial: 8522 Teichman Rd, Galveston, Texas 77554-9119. **T:** 1 409 683-5200
E: newsroom@galvnews.com
W: http://www.galvestondailynews.com
Freq: Daily; **Circ:** 27456 Not Audited
Publisher: Patrick Graham; **News Editor:** Dave Mathews
Editorial Profile: The Galveston (TX) County Daily News provides news and information for the residents of Galveston County, TX.; Full Page Mono: 29.00; Full Page Colour: 425.00
Currency: US Dollars
DAILY NEWSPAPER

Gambit Weekly
Owner: Gambit Communications, Inc.
Editorial: 3923 Bienville St, New Orleans, Louisiana 70119. **T:** 1 504 486-5900
E: response@gambitweekly.com
W: http://www.bestofneworleans.com
Freq: Tue; **Circ:** 40000 Not Audited
Editor: Kevin Allman; **Publisher:** Margo DuBos
Editorial Profile: Gambit Weekly is a weekly newspaper covering the New Orleans arts & entertainment scene, as well as politics and culture. The publication provides an alternative view of New Orleans' diverse communities.; Full Page Mono: 169.00; Full Page Colour: 3262.00
Currency: US Dollars
NEWSPAPER

La Ganga Especial
Owner: MediaNews Group
Editorial: 23 E Beach St, Ste 205, Watsonville, California 95076. **T:** 1 831 724-6564
E: contacto@lagangaonline.com
W: http://www.lagangaonline.com
Freq: Fri; **Circ:** 25000 Not Audited
Editorial Profile: La Ganga, part of the Bay Area News Group, publishes a variety of lifestyle stories for 70 cities along the Central Coast of California.; Full Page Mono: 45.00
Currency: US Dollars
NEWSPAPER

Gannett Newspapers - Delaware
Owner: Gannett Co., Inc.
Editorial: 618 Beam St, Salisbury, Maryland 21801-7803. **T:** 1 302 537-1881
E: newshub@delmarvanow.com
W: http://www.delmarvanow.com **Circ:** 40000 Not Audited
Editor: Alyson Cunningham; **Editor:** Laren Hughes-Hall
Editorial Profile: Gannett Newspapers - Delaware provides Community and Local News coverage for the in the Delaware-Maryland-Virginia tri-state area (Delmarva).
NEWSPAPER

Gannett Newspapers - Maryland
Owner: Gannett Co., Inc.
Editorial: 12417 Ocean Gtwy Ste 7A, Ocean City, Maryland 21842-9522.
T: 1 410 213-9442
E: newshub@delmarvanow.com
W: http://www.delmarvanow.com **Circ:** 60230
Editor: Kamlesh Desai; **Editor:** Lauren Hughes
NEWSPAPER

Gannett Newspapers - Virginia
Owner: Gannett Co., Inc.
Editorial: 23079 Courthouse Ave, Accomac, Virginia 23301-1505. **T:** 1 757 787-1200
E: newshub@delmarvanow.com
W: http://www.delmarvanow.com **Circ:** 20500 Not Audited
Editor: Ted Shockley
NEWSPAPER

Garden City Telegram
Owner: Harris Enterprises
Editorial: 310 N 7th St, Garden City, Kansas 67846-5521. **T:** 1 620 275-8500
E: newsroom@gctelegram.com
W: http://www.gctelegram.com
Freq: Daily; **Circ:** 7437 Not Audited
News Editor: Derek Thompson
Editorial Profile: Garden City Telegram provides news and information for the residents of southwest Kansas.; Full Page Mono: 14.88; Full Page Colour: 295.00
Currency: US Dollars
DAILY NEWSPAPER

The Garden Island
Owner: Lee Enterprises, Inc.
Editorial: 3-3137 Kuhio Hwy, Lihue, Hawaii 96766-1141. **T:** 1 808 245-3681
E: editor@thegardenisland.com
W: http://thegardenisland.com
Freq: Daily; **Circ:** 10873 Not Audited
Editor in Chief: Bill Buley
Editorial Profile: The Garden Island is published daily for the residents of Lihue, HI and surrounding areas. The newspaper covers local and national news, business, sports, lifestyles and entertainment.; Full Page Mono: 24.00; Full Page Colour: 280.00
Currency: US Dollars

DAILY NEWSPAPER

Gardena Valley News
Owner: Verdugo (Edward)
Editorial: 15005 S Vermont Ave, Gardena, California 90247-3004. **T:** 1 310 329-6351
E: gvnedit@yahoo.com
W: http://www.gardenavalleynews.org
Freq: Thu; **Circ:** 10000 Not Audited
Editor: Gary Kohatsu
Editorial Profile: Gardena Valley News is a local newspaper that provides news and information for the Gardena, CA area. Regular features include local news, arts & entertainment, community events and sports.; Full Page Mono: 9.00
Currency: US Dollars
NEWSPAPER

The Gardner News
Owner: Gardner News, Inc. (The)
Editorial: 309 Central St, Gardner, Massachusetts 01440-3839.
T: 1 978 632-8000
E: editorial@thegardnernews.com
W: http://www.thegardnernews.com
Freq: Daily; **Circ:** 4657 Not Audited
Publisher: Alberta Bell; **Editor:** Dan Kittredge
Editorial Profile: The Gardner News is a local daily newspaper that provides news and information for the Gardner, MA area. Lead time for the Tuesday business special is the previous Friday.; Full Page Mono: 8.25; Full Page Colour: 1332.00
Currency: US Dollars
DAILY NEWSPAPER

The Gardner News
Owner: Gardner News LLC
Editorial: 136 E Main St, Gardner, Kansas 66030-1310. **T:** 1 913 856-7615
E: submissions@gardnernews.com
W: http://www.gardnernews.com
Freq: Weekly; **Circ:** 10000 Not Audited
Publisher: Mark Humble; **Editor:** Danedri Thompson
Editorial Profile: Gardner News is a community newspaper serving Gardner, KS, including local news, sports and community events.; Full Page Mono: 14.00
Currency: US Dollars
NEWSPAPER

Garner-Cleveland Record
Owner: McClatchy Newspapers
Editorial: 228 E Market St, Smithfield, North Carolina 27577-3918. **T:** 1 919 836-5703
E: garnercleveland@newsobserver.com
W: http://www.garnercleveland.com
Freq: Sun
Editor: Scott Bolejack
Editorial Profile: Garner-Cleveland Record is a weekly newspaper providing Local News coverage for the residents of Garner and Johnston County, NC.
NEWSPAPER

Garrett County Weekender
Owner: Community Newspaper Holdings, Inc.
Editorial: 19 Baltimore St, Cumberland, Maryland 21502. **T:** 1 301 722-4600
E: gcweekender@times-news.com
W: http://www.times-news.com
Freq: Fri; **Circ:** 16000 Not Audited
Publisher: Larry Effingham
Editorial Profile: Garrett County Weekender is a local weekly newspaper that provides news and information to the communities of Garrett County, MD. Deadlines are on Tuesdays at noon ET.; Full Page Mono: 9.31; Full Page Colour: 1132.02
Currency: US Dollars
NEWSPAPER

The Gary Crusader
Owner: Chicago Crusader Newspaper
Editorial: 1549 Broadway, Gary, Indiana 46407. **T:** 1 219 885-4357
E: garycrusadernews@aol.com
W: http://www.garycrusader.com
Freq: Thu; **Circ:** 56519 Not Audited
Editorial Profile: The Gary Crusader is a weekly newspaper written for African Americans in Northwest Indiana. The newspaper covers employment, equal rights, social justice, sports and entertainment. The publication is a sister publication of the Chicago Crusader, which covers the same topics in the Chicago area.
NEWSPAPER

Gaston Gazette
Owner: Halifax Media Holdings LLC
Editorial: 1893 Remount Rd, Gastonia, North Carolina 28054-7413. **T:** 1 704 869-1700
E: info@gastongazette.com
W: http://www.gastongazette.com
Freq: Daily; **Circ:** 20961 Not Audited
Editor: Hunter Bretzius; **Publisher:** Julie Moreno
Editorial Profile: Gaston Gazette is published daily for residents of Gaston, Lincoln, and Cleveland counties, NC and York County, SC. The newspaper covers local news, weather, sports and community events. Feature articles cover business, politics, education, arts & entertainment and lifestyle. The lead time and deadlines for the publication vary.; Full Page Mono: 21.70; Full Page Colour: 500.00
Currency: US Dollars
DAILY NEWSPAPER

GateHouse Media - Canandaigua, NY
Owner: GateHouse Media Inc.
Editorial: 73 Buffalo St, Canandaigua, New York 14424. **T:** 1 585 394-0770
E: messenger@messengerpostmedia.com
W: http://www.mpnnow.com **Circ:** 60100 Not Audited
News Editor: Paul Gangarossa; **Publisher:** Richard Procida
Editorial Profile: GateHouse Media - Canandaigua, NY is a weekly newspaper publisher serving the residents of Monroe County, NY.
NEWSPAPER

GateHouse Media - Canton, OH
Owner: GateHouse Media Inc.
Editorial: 500 Market St. S. Suite B., Canton, Ohio 44702. **T:** 1 330 899-2872
E: suburbanite@thesuburbanite.com
W: http://www.thesuburbanite.com
Circ: 46200
Editor: Erin Pustay; **Publisher:** Chris White
Editorial Profile: GateHouse Media of Canton, OH publishes several local papers in and around Ohio, including the Repository, the Times-Reporter, the Surburbanite and the Independent.
NEWSPAPER

GateHouse Media - Chester, IL
Owner: GateHouse Media Inc.
Editorial: 624 State St, Chester, Illinois 62233-1634. **T:** 1 618 826-2385
W: http://www.randolphcountyheraldtribune.com
Freq: Weekly; **Circ:** 4366 Not Audited
NEWSPAPER

GateHouse Media - Concord, MA
Owner: GateHouse Media Inc.
Editorial: 150 Baker Avenue Ext Ste 101, Concord, Massachusetts 01742-2126.
T: 1 978 371-5200
W: http://www.wickedlocal.com **Circ:** 44338 Not Audited
Editor: Holly Camero; **Editor in Chief:** Kathleen Cordeiro; **Publisher:** Chuck Goodrich; **Editor:** Eileen Kennedy; **Editor:** Jennifer Martinage; **Editor:** Jason McEntire; **Editor:** Joyce Pellino Crane; **News Editor:** Sam Perkins; **Editor:** Kathie Ragsdale; **Editor:** Kathleen Ragsdale; **Editor:** Melissa Russell; **Editor:** Margaret Smith; **Editor:** Kevin Zimmerman
NEWSPAPER

GateHouse Media - Danvers, MA
Owner: GateHouse Media Inc.
Editorial: 75 Sylvan St Ste B3, Danvers, Massachusetts 01923-2763.
T: 1 978 739-1300
Freq: Weekly; **Circ:** 25110 Not Audited
Editor in Chief: Peter Chianca; **Publisher:** Kirk Davis; **Editor:** Nell Escobar Coakley; **Editor:** Jane Fosberry Enos; **Editor:** Jane Fosberry Enos; **Editor:** Mike Gaffney; **Editor:** Rosemary Herbert; **Editor:** Nathan Lamb; **Editor:** Daniel MacAlpine; **Editor:** Kathryn O'Brien; **Editor:** Jeff Pope; **Editor:** Katrina Powell; **Editor:** Matthew Reid; **Editor:** Sarah Thomas
NEWSPAPER

GateHouse Media - Dover, DE
Owner: GateHouse Media Inc.
Editorial: 1196 S Little Creek Rd, Dover, Delaware 19901-4727. **T:** 1 302 678-3616
Editorial Profile: GateHouse Media, of Dover, DE, owns and operates weekly newspapers throughout the state. The papers include the Dover Post and the Milford Beacon.
NEWSPAPER

GateHouse Media - Eldora, IA
Owner: GateHouse Media Inc.
Editorial: 1513 Edgington Ave, Eldora, Iowa 50627. **T:** 1 641 939-5051 **Circ:** 4400 Not Audited
Publisher: John Butters; **Editor:** Rick Patrie
NEWSPAPER

GateHouse Media - Framingham, MA
Owner: GateHouse Media Inc.
Editorial: 33 New York Ave, Framingham, Massachusetts 01701-8857.
T: 1 508 626-4412
E: metrowest@wickedlocal.com
W: http://www.wickedlocal.com **Circ:** 14711 Not Audited
Editor: Paul Crocetti; **Editor:** Glenda Hazard; **Editor:** Glenda Hazard; **Editor In Chief:** Richard Lodge; **Editor In Chief:** Richard Lodge; **Editor In Chief:** Richard Lodge; **Editor In Chief:** Richard Lodge; **Editor:** Phil Maddocks; **Editor:** Phil Maddocks; **Editor:** Phil Maddocks; **Editor:** Alison McCall; **Editor:** Sara Mulkeen; **Editor:** Joe O'Connell; **Editor:** Michael Wyner
NEWSPAPER

GateHouse Media - Geneseo, IL
Owner: GateHouse Media Inc.
Editorial: 108 W 1st St, Geneseo, Illinois 61254. **T:** 1 309 944-2119
W: http://geneseorepublic.com **Circ:** 6700 Not Audited
Editor: Doug Boock; **Editor:** Mindy Carls; **Editor:** Mindy Carls; **Editor:** Lisa Depies; **Publisher:** Dee Evans
NEWSPAPER

GateHouse Media - Hingham, MA
Owner: GateHouse Media Inc.
Editorial: 73 South St, Hingham, Massachusetts 2043. **T:** 1 781 749-0031
W: http://www.wickedlocal.com **Circ:** 7253 Not Audited
Editor: Mary Ford; **Publisher:** Mark Olivieri
NEWSPAPER

GateHouse Media - Lexington, MA
Owner: GateHouse Media Inc.
Editorial: 9 Meriam St, Lexington, Massachusetts 02420-5300.
T: 1 781 674-7740 **Circ:** 31207 Not Audited
Editor in Chief: Kathleen Cordeiro; **Editor:** Emily Costello; **Publisher:** Chuck Goodrich; **Editor:** Andrew Levin; **Editor:** Christine Warren
Editorial Profile: Publishes the Belmont Citizen-Herald, Winchester Star, Burlington Union, Arlington Advocate and Lexington Minuteman for the Lexington, Massachusetts area.
NEWSPAPER

GateHouse Media - Marblehead
Owner: GateHouse Media Inc.
Editorial: 11 State St, Marblehead, Massachusetts 01945-3592
W: http://www.wickedlocal.com
Publisher: Kirk Davis; **Editor:** George Derringer; **Editor:** George Derringer; **Editor:** Kris Olson; **Editor in Chief:** Marlene Switzer; **Editor in Chief:** Marlene Switzer
NEWSPAPER

GateHouse Media - Marshfield, MA
Owner: GateHouse Media Inc.
Editorial: 165 Enterprise Dr, Marshfield, Massachusetts 2050. **T:** 1 781 837-3500
E: marshfield@wickedlocal.com
W: http://www.townonline.com **Circ:** 26725 Not Audited
Editor: Seth Jacobson; **Editor in Chief:** Gregory Mathis; **Editor in Chief:** Gregory Mathis; **Publisher:** Mark Olivieri; **Editor:** Dave Palana; **Editor:** Nancy White
NEWSPAPER

GateHouse Media - Mount Shasta, CA
Owner: GateHouse Media Inc.
Editorial: 924B N Mount Shasta Blvd, Mount Shasta, California 96067-8700.
T: 1 530 926-5214
E: news@mtshastanews.com
W: http://www.mtshastanews.com **Circ:** 6500 Not Audited
Publisher: Genny Axtman; **Editor:** Steve Gerace; **Editor:** Steve Gerace
NEWSPAPER

GateHouse Media - Needham, MA
Owner: GateHouse Media Inc.
Editorial: 254 2nd Ave, Needham, Massachusetts 2494. **T:** 1 781 433-8200
W: http://www.wickedlocal.com **Circ:** 28621 Not Audited
Editor: Max Bowen; **Editor:** Cathy Brauner; **Editor:** Erin Clossey; **Editor:** Erin Clossey; **Editor:** Julie Cohen; **Editor:** Jesse Floyd; **Publisher:** Chuck Goodrich; **Editor:** Art Illman; **Editor In Chief:** Richard Lodge; **Editor In Chief:** Richard Lodge; **Editor In Chief:** Richard Lodge; **Editor In Chief:** Richard Lodge; **Editor:** Phil Salisbury; **Editor:** Valentina Zic

Editorial Profile: The online version for the weekly papers is Townonline.com at MA-DI260.
NEWSPAPER

GateHouse Media - Newton, IL
Owner: GateHouse Media Inc.
Editorial: 700 W Washington St, Newton, Illinois 62448-1129. **T:** 1 618 783-2324
E: news@pressmentor.com
W: http://www.pressmentor.com **Circ:** 8100 Not Audited
Editor: Vanette King; **Publisher:** Kerry Kocher
NEWSPAPER

GateHouse Media - Orleans, MA
Owner: GateHouse Media Inc.
Editorial: 5 Namskaket Rd, Orleans, Massachusetts 2653. **T:** 1 508 255-2121
W: http://www.wickedlocal.com/capecod
Circ: 17953 Not Audited
Editor: Maureen Goodwin; **Editor:** Doug Karlson; **Publisher:** Mark Olivieri; Full Page Mono: 16.75
Currency: US Dollars
NEWSPAPER

GateHouse Media - Peoria, IL
Owner: GateHouse Media Inc.
Editorial: 1 News Plz, Peoria, Illinois 61643-0001. **T:** 1 309 692-6600 **Circ:** 24044 Not Audited
Editor: Marianne Gillespie; **Editor:** Adam Larck; **Editor:** Sean McGowan
Editorial Profile: Publishes Woodford Times, Chillicothe Times-Bulletin, East Peoria Times-Courier, Morton Times-News and Washington Times-Reporter.
NEWSPAPER

GateHouse Media - Plymouth, MA
Owner: GateHouse Media Inc.
Editorial: 182 Standish Ave, Plymouth, Massachusetts 2360. **T:** 1 508 591-6600
E: ocm@wickedlocal.com
W: http://home.wickedlocal.com **Circ:** 48400 Not Audited
Editor: Beth Doyle; **Editor:** Sarah Glaser; **Editor in Chief:** Gregory Mathis; **Editor in Chief:** Gregory Mathis; **Editor:** Frank Mulligan; **Publisher:** Mark Olivieri; **Editor:** David Smith
NEWSPAPER

GateHouse Media - Prescott, AR
Owner: GateHouse Media Inc.
Editorial: 100 E Elm St, Prescott, Arkansas 71857-2128. **T:** 1 870 887-2002
W: http://www.picayune-times.com
Editor: Wendy Ledbetter
NEWSPAPER

GateHouse Media - Raynham, MA
Owner: GateHouse Media Inc.
Editorial: 370 Paramount Dr Ste 3, Raynham, Massachusetts 02767-5419.
T: 1 508 967-3500 **W:** http://wickedlocal.com
Circ: 56136 Not Audited
Editor: Stuart Green; **Editor:** Stuart Green; **Editor:** Stuart Green; **Publisher:** Mark Olivieri; **Editor:** Donna Whitehead
NEWSPAPER

GateHouse Media - Ripley, WV
Owner: GateHouse Media Inc.
Editorial: 305 Church St N, Ripley, West Virginia 25271-1205. **T:** 1 304 372-4222
E: editor@jacksonnewspapers.com
W: http://www.jacksonnewspapers.com
Circ: 26200 Not Audited
Editor: Greg Matics; **Publisher:** Jennifer Patterson
Editorial Profile: Gatehouse Media is an outlet publication providing the community of Ripley, WV with weekly newspapers.
NEWSPAPER

GateHouse Media - Shawneetown, IL
Owner: GateHouse Media Inc.
Editorial: 288 N Lincoln Blvd E, Shawneetown, Illinois 62984. **T:** 1 618 269-3147
E: gallatin@yourclearwave.com **Circ:** 2557 Not Audited
NEWSPAPER

GateHouse Media - Somerville, MA
Owner: GateHouse Media Inc.
Editorial: 80 Central St., Somerville, Massachusetts 2144. **T:** 1 781 396-1982
W: http://www.townonline.com **Circ:** 12218 Not Audited
Editor: Nell Escobar Coakley; **Editor:** Nell Escobar Coakley; **Editor in Chief:** Jesse Floyd; **Publisher:** Chuck Goodrich; **Editor:** Steven Ryan; **Editor in Chief:** Marlene Switzer; **Editor in Chief:** Marlene Switzer
NEWSPAPER

GateHouse Media - Weymouth, MA
Owner: GateHouse Media Inc.
Editorial: 91 Washington St, Weymouth, Massachusetts 2188. **T:** 1 781 682-4850
W: http://home.wickedlocal.com **Circ:** 9472 Not Audited
Editor in Chief: Gregory Mathis; **Editor in Chief:** Gregory Mathis; **Publisher:** Mark Olivieri
NEWSPAPER

GateHouse Media - Yarmouth Port, MA
Owner: GateHouse Media Inc.
Editorial: 923 Route 6A Unit G, Yarmouth Port, Massachusetts 02675-2159.
T: 1 508 888-0000
W: http://www.wickedlocal.com/yarmouth
Circ: 42131 Not Audited
Editor: John Basile; **Publisher:** Mark Olivieri
NEWSPAPER

Gateway Press - East Office
Owner: Gateway Newspapers
Editorial: 460 Rodi Rd, Penn Hills, Pennsylvania 15235-4547. **T:** 1 412 856-7400
W: http://www.gatewaynewspapers.com
Circ: 41332 Not Audited
Editor: Brian Estadt; **Editor:** Brian Estadt; **Publisher:** Richard Scaife; **Editor:** Nafari Vanaski
NEWSPAPER

Gateway Press - West Office
Owner: Trib Total Media
Editorial: 503 Martindale St, Pittsburgh, Pennsylvania 15212-5746. **T:** 1 412 388-5800
W: http://www.gatewaynewspapers.com
Circ: 10564 Not Audited
Editor: Bob Pastin; **Editor:** Bob Pastin; **Editor:** Bob Pastin; **Publisher:** Richard Scaife; **Editor:** Jim Spezialetti
NEWSPAPER

Gazeta Brazilian News
Owner: Vuelma (Zigomar)
Editorial: 4390 N Federal Hwy Ste 207, Fort Lauderdale, Florida 33308-5200.
T: 1 954 938-9292 **E:** news@gazetanews.com
W: http://www.gazetanews.com
Freq: Thu; **Circ:** 16000
Editor in Chief: Fernanda Cirino; **Publisher:** Zigomar Vuelma
Editorial Profile: Launched in 1994, offers entertainment, sports, politics, society and general interest news for the Brazilian community in Florida.; **Full Page Mono:** 5.92; **Full Page Colour:** 11.11
Currency: US Dollars
NEWSPAPER

Gazeta Wyborcza - Washington, DC Bureau
Owner: Agora SA
Editorial: 400 N Capitol St NW Ste 750, Washington, District Of Columbia 20001-1536.
T: 1 202 887-8330 **W:** http://www.wyborcza.pl
Freq: Daily
Editorial Profile: This is the Washington, D.C. bureau of Gazeta Wyborcza in Warszawa, Poland.
DAILY NEWSPAPER

The Gazette
Owner: Gazette Company (The)
Editorial: 500 3rd Ave Se, Cedar Rapids, Iowa 52401-1608. **T:** 1 319 398-8313
E: news@sourcemedia.net
W: http://thegazette.com
Freq: Daily; **Circ:** 40657 Not Audited
Editorial Profile: The Gazette is a daily morning newspaper published in Cedar Rapids, IA. It provides Cedar Rapids and 16 counties in Eastern Iowa with local, regional, national and international news, sports, business, entertainment coverage and "information that is important to the readers.";
Full Page Mono: 78.17; **Full Page Colour:** 97.71
Currency: US Dollars
DAILY NEWSPAPER

The Gazette
Owner: Anschutz Corp.
Editorial: 30 E Pikes Peak Ave Ste 100, Colorado Springs, Colorado 80903-1580.
T: 1 719 632-5511 **W:** http://www.gazette.com
Freq: Daily; **Circ:** 53260 Not Audited
Editor: Joe Hight; **Publisher:** Dan Steever
Editorial Profile: The Gazette is a daily newspaper published for the residents of Colorado Springs, CO. It was founded in 1872 as The Out West. The newspaper's goal is to inform and connect all residents of the area to the world and to bolster the relationship between the military and non-military

communities.; **Full Page Mono:** 116.56; **Full Page Colour:** 226.46
Currency: US Dollars
DAILY NEWSPAPER

The Gazette
Editorial: 319 E 5th St, Des Moines, Iowa 50309-1927. **T:** 1 515 243-7220
Bureau Chief: Rod Boshart; **Bureau Chief:** Rod Boshart
DAILY NEWSPAPER

The Gazette
Editorial: 200 S Clinton St, Ste 201, Iowa City, Iowa 52240-4028. **T:** 1 319 339-3155
E: iowacity@gazcomm.com
DAILY NEWSPAPER

The Gazette
Owner: Acorn Media Services, LLC
Editorial: 1406 Main St, East Hartford, Connecticut 6108. **T:** 1 860 289-6468
E: editor@ehgazette.com
W: http://www.ehgazette.com
Freq: Thu; **Circ:** 15000 Not Audited
Editor: Bill Doak
Editorial Profile: The Gazette is a weekly newspaper, covering local sports, government, news, and entertainment for residents of East Hartford, CT.; **Full Page Mono:** 19.18
Currency: US Dollars
NEWSPAPER

Gazette
Editorial: 1335 W Harrison St, Chicago, Illinois 60607-3318. **T:** 1 312 243-4288
E: info@gazettechicago.com
W: http://www.gazettechicago.com
Freq: Fri; **Circ:** 17000 Not Audited
Editorial Profile: Gazette is a community newspaper serving Near West/Tri-Taylor, University Village/UIC South Campus, West Loop, South Loop, West Haven, Bridgeport/Armour Square, Bronzeville, Chinatown, West Town, and Heart of Chicago communities of Chicago, IL. The paper is published the first Friday of each month.; **Full Page Mono:** 50.00
Currency: US Dollars
NEWSPAPER

Gazette Newspaper
Editorial: 7014 Mill Rd, Brecksville, Ohio 44141. **T:** 1 440 526-7977
E: production1@gazette-news.com
W: http://www.gazette-news.com
Freq: Bi-Weekly; **Circ:** 12000 Not Audited
Editor: Joyce McFadden
Editorial Profile: The Gazette Newspaper is a bi-weekly publication that covers Brecksville, Broadview Heights, Independence, Parma and Seven Hills in Ohio.; **Full Page Mono:** 15.00
Currency: US Dollars
NEWSPAPER

Gazette Newspapers
Owner: West Coast Media News, LLC
Editorial: 5225 E 2nd St, Long Beach, California 90803. **T:** 1 562 433-2000
E: editor@gazettes.com
W: http://www.gazettes.com **Circ:** 67000
Publisher: Simon Grieve
Editorial Profile: Gazette Newspapers are a source of community news in the southeast corridor of Long Beach, CA. Go to http://www.gazettes.com/calendar/ for calendar & event listings.
NEWSPAPER

Gazette Newspapers
Editorial: 46 W Jefferson St, Jefferson, Ohio 44047. **T:** 1 440 576-9125
E: news@gazettenews.com
W: http://gazettenews.com
Freq: Weekly; **Circ:** 14600 Not Audited
Editor: Doris Cook; **Editor:** Doris Cook; **Editor:** Martha Sorhan; **Editor:** Kathy Wnoroski; **Editor:** Kathy Wnoroski; **Full Page Mono:** 18.75
Currency: US Dollars
NEWSPAPER

Gazette Newspapers
Owner: AGC Printing & Design, Inc.
Editorial: 207 Atlantic Ave, Blue Point, New York 11715-1409. **T:** 1 631 363-0154
E: gazettecentral@yahoo.com
W: http://bayportbluepointgazette.com/
Circ: 13000
NEWSPAPER

Gazette Newspapers-Montgomery County
Owner: Gazette Newspapers Inc.
Editorial: 9030 Comprint Ct, Gaithersburg, Maryland 20877-1307. **T:** 1 301 948-3120
E: montgomery@gazette.net
W: http://www.gazette.net **Circ:** 289868 Not

Audited
Publisher: Karen Acton; **Editor:** Douglas Tallman
Editorial Profile: Gazette Newspapers-Montgomery County is a weekly community newspaper publisher serving the residents of Damascus, Clarksburg, Germantown, Boyds, Poolesville, Olney, Bethesda, Chevy, Kensington, Potomac, North Potomac, Rockville, Aspen Hill, Gaithersburg, Montgomery Village, Burtonsville, Silver Spring, Takoma and Wheaton, MD.
NEWSPAPER

Gazette Newspapers-Prince George's County
Owner: Gazette Newspapers, Inc.
Editorial: 13501 Virginia Manor Rd, Laurel, Maryland 20707-6515. **T:** 1 240 473-7500
E: princegeorges@gazette.net
W: http://www.gazette.net **Circ:** 204493 Not Audited
Editor: Vanessa Harrington
NEWSPAPER

Gazette Publications, Inc.
Editorial: 7 Harris Ave, Jamaica Plain, Massachusetts 2130. **T:** 1 617 524-2626
Circ: 23420
Editor: Andy Zagastizabal
Editorial Profile: Gazette Publications, Inc. is a weekly community newspaper publisher serving the residents of Jamaica Plain and Mission Hill, MA.
NEWSPAPER

Gazette van Detroit
Editorial: 18740 E. 13 Mile Rd., Roseville, Michigan 48066-1378
E: editor@gazettevandetroit.com
W: http://www.gazettevandetroit.com
Freq: Bi-Weekly
Editor in Chief: Elisabeth Khan
Editorial Profile: Gazette van Detroit is a community newspaper.
NEWSPAPER

GCA Publishing Company, Inc.
Editorial: 2323 Crestmoor Rd, Nashville, Tennessee 37215. **T:** 1 615 298-1500
E: news@gcanews.com
W: http://www.gcanews.com **Circ:** 33200 Not Audited
Publisher: Gary Cunningham; **Publisher:** Gary Cunningham; **Publisher:** Gary Cunningham
Editorial Profile: GCA Publishing Company, Inc. is a weekly community newspaper written for the residents of Nashville, Green Hills, Belle Meade and West Meade, TN.
NEWSPAPER

Genesee County Herald
Owner: Genesee County Herald Inc.
Editorial: G10098 N Dort Hwy, Clio, Michigan 48420. **T:** 1 810 686-3840
E: editor@myherald.net **Circ:** 3800 Not Audited
Publisher: Michael Harrington; **Editor:** Craig Nelson
NEWSPAPER

Geneva Publications
Editorial: 506 S Commerce St, Geneva, Alabama 36340-2421. **T:** 1 334 684-2280
E: news@genevareaper.com
W: http://www.oppnewsonline.com/23250/1964/1/home **Circ:** 3665 Not Audited
Publisher: Brenda Pujol; **Editor:** Cheryl Withrow
NEWSPAPER

Georgetown Media Group
Owner: Georgetown Media Group
Editorial: 1054 Potomac St NW, Washington, District Of Columbia 20007.
T: 1 202 338-4833
E: editorial@georgetowner.com **Circ:** 50000 Not Audited
Editor: Robert Devaney
Editorial Profile: The Georgetown Media Group publishes The Georgetowner and Downtowner, two free, bi-weekly tabloid-style, newspapers. The publications specialize in lifestyle, focusing on the arts, real estate, education, dining, health, beauty, fashion, society and with a special In Country section featuring Virginia's horse country. The two publications can be found in areas throughout metro DC, Northern Virginia and Maryland.
NEWSPAPER

Georgetown/Auburn Papers
Editorial: 2775 Miners Flat Rd, Georgetown, California 95634-9345. **T:** 1 530 333-4481
E: editor@gtgazette.com **Circ:** 2800 Not Audited
Editor: Rebecca Murphy

Editorial Profile: Georgetown/Auburn Papers is a local newspaper for the community of Georgetown, CA.
NEWSPAPER

The Georgia Bulletin
Editorial: 2401 Lake Park Dr Se, Smyrna, Georgia 30080-8862. **T:** 1 404 920-7430
E: editor@georgiabulletin.org
W: http://www.georgiabulletin.org
Freq: Thu; **Circ:** 80000 Not Audited
Publisher: Wilton Gregory; **Editor:** Gretchen Keiser
Editorial Profile: The Georgia Bulletin is the official newspaper of the Archdiocese of Atlanta and covers local Catholic news and feature stories. Deadlines are on the Thursday before the issue date.; **Full Page Mono:** 14.00
Currency: US Dollars
NEWSPAPER

Germantown Newspapers, Inc.
Editorial: 6661 Germantown Ave, Philadelphia, Pennsylvania 19119-2251. **T:** 1 215 438-4000
E: editor@germantownnewspapers.com
W: http://www.germantownnewspapers.com
Circ: 32000 Not Audited
Editorial Profile: Germantown Newspapers Inc. in Philadelphia, PA publishes the Independent Voice for the residents of Northwest Philadelphia.
NEWSPAPER

Gettysburg Times
Owner: Times & News Publishing Co.
Editorial: 1570 Fairfield Rd, Gettysburg, Pennsylvania 17325-7252. **T:** 1 717 334-1131
E: news@gburgtimes.com
W: http://www.gettysburgtimes.com
Freq: Daily; **Circ:** 9001 Not Audited
Publisher: Harry Hartman; **Editor:** B.J. Small
Editorial Profile: Gettysburg Times is a daily newspaper published Monday through Saturday for the residents of Adams County, PA. It provides news and information. Lead time and deadlines vary.; **Full Page Mono:** 14.92; **Full Page Colour:** 18.72
Currency: US Dollars
DAILY NEWSPAPER

Gilbert Publishing
Editorial: 15624 Betroit Ave, Gilbert, Minnesota 55741-5007. **T:** 1 218 741-4445
E: esgh@dz.net
NEWSPAPER

The Gilbert Times
Owner: Heartland Publications
Editorial: 100 Block East 3rd Avenue, Williamson, West Virginia 25661.
T: 1 304 235-4242
W: http://www.gilberttimes.net
Freq: Wed; **Circ:** 15000 Not Audited
Publisher: D.Gaither Perry; **Editor:** Lorretta Tackett
Editorial Profile: The Gilbert Times is a weekly paper distributed throughout Gilbert, WV and surrounding areas. It features stories on community news and events, education, sports and local businesses.; **Full Page Mono:** 10.00
Currency: US Dollars
NEWSPAPER

Gillette News-Record
Owner: Gillette News-Record
Editorial: 1201 W 2nd St, Gillette, Wyoming 82716-3301. **T:** 1 307 682-9306
E: news@gillettenewsrecord.com
W: http://www.gillettenewsrecord.com
Freq: Daily; **Circ:** 6900 Not Audited
Editorial Profile: Gillette News-Record is a daily newspaper for residents of Gillette and Campbell County, WY. Published daily except Saturday, the publication covers local news, sports, government, business, health, lifestyles and education information. Deadlines are daily at 9am MT.; **Full Page Mono:** 14.30; **Full Page Colour:** 175.00
Currency: US Dollars
DAILY NEWSPAPER

Gladstone Dispatch
Owner: NPG Newspapers
Editorial: 104 N. Main St., Liberty, Missouri 64068-1640. **T:** 1 816 781-4941
E: gladstonenews@npgco.com
W: http://gladstonedispatch.com
Freq: Thu
Editorial Profile: Gladstone Dispatch is a weekly community newspaper serving residents of Gladstone, MO with community news, sports, education, opinion and events.
NEWSPAPER

Glasgow Daily Times
Owner: Community Newspaper Holdings, Inc.

Editorial: 100 Commerce Dr, Glasgow, Kentucky 42141-1192. **T:** 1 270 678-5171
W: http://glasgowdailytimes.com
Freq: Daily; **Circ:** 5448 Not Audited
Editor: James Brown; **Editor:** James Brown; **Publisher:** Keith Ponder
Editorial Profile: Glasgow Daily Times is a daily newspaper for the residents of Glasgow, KY and the surrounding area. Regular features include local news, sports, business and education. Deadlines are at noon CT on the day prior to publication.; Full Page Mono: 13.44; Full Page Colour: 125.00
Currency: US Dollars
DAILY NEWSPAPER

Glastonbury Citizen, Inc.
Editorial: 87 Nutmeg Ln, Glastonbury, Connecticut 06033-2353. **T:** 1 860 633-4691
Circ: 35085 Not Audited
Editor: Mike Thompson
NEWSPAPER

The Gleaner
Owner: E.W. Scripps Co.
Editorial: 455 Klutey Park Plaza Dr, Henderson, Kentucky 42420-5213.
T: 1 270 827-2000 **E:** news@thegleaner.com
W: http://www.courierpress.com/news/gleaner/
Freq: Daily; **Circ:** 8047 Not Audited
Editor: Tom Lovett
Editorial Profile: The Gleaner is a local, daily newspaper serving residents of Henderson, KY. It covers local news and events, business, sports, obituaries and social issues.; Full Page Mono: 16.26; Full Page Colour: 90.00
Currency: US Dollars
DAILY NEWSPAPER

Glen Rose Newspaper
Editorial: 615 Ne Big Bend Trl, Glen Rose, Texas 76043-4866. **T:** 1 254 897-4536
E: editor@glenrosenewspaper.com
W: http://www.glenrosenewspaper.com
Editorial Profile: Glen Rose Newspaper is a weekly newspaper providing Local News coverage to residents in Somervell County and Glen Rose, TX.
NEWSPAPER

Glendale News-Press
Owner: Tribune Company
Editorial: 202 W 1st St, Los Angeles, California 90012-4299. **T:** 1 818 637-3200
W: http://www.glendalenewspress.com
Freq: Daily; **Circ:** 20000 Not Audited
Editor: Dan Evans
Editorial Profile: Glendale News-Press is published for the residents of Glendale, La Crescenta, La Canada Flintridge and Montrose, CA. The newspaper covers local news, sports, education, business, politics, crime and community events. It is distributed inside the Los Angeles Times and is available, free of charge, at select news racks throughout the area. It shares offices with the Burbank Leader. On Sundays, the paper combines with the Burbank Leader to put out a Sunday issue, the Sunday News-Press & Leader.; Full Page Mono: 23.00; Full Page Colour: 250.00
Currency: US Dollars
DAILY NEWSPAPER

Glenwood Springs Post Independent
Owner: Swift Newspapers
Editorial: 824 Grand Ave, Glenwood Springs, Colorado 81601-3557. **T:** 1 970 945-8515
E: news@postindependent.com
W: http://www.postindependent.com
Freq: Daily; **Circ:** 10000 Not Audited
Publisher: Michael Bennett; **Editor:** Randy Essex
Editorial Profile: Glenwood Springs Post Independent is a daily newspaper written to provide news and information to the residents of Glenwood Springs, CO and surrounding communities. Sections include news, sports, arts & entertainment and letters to the editor.; Full Page Mono: 35.78; Full Page Colour: 139.28
Currency: US Dollars
DAILY NEWSPAPER

The Globe
Editorial: 1825 Jackson St, Sioux City, Iowa 51105. **T:** 1 712 255-2550
W: http://www.catholicglobe.org
Freq: Thu; **Circ:** 26000 Not Audited
Editor: Joanne Fox; **Publisher:** Walker Nickless
Editorial Profile: Sioux City Globe is the official newspaper of the Diocese of Sioux City, IA. It covers local news and events for the area Catholic community. The lead time varies between 10 days and two weeks.; Full Page Mono: 12.70
Currency: US Dollars
NEWSPAPER

The Globe
Owner: Landmark Military Newspapers
Editorial: 1122 Henderson Drive, Jacksonville, North Carolina 28540. **T:** 1 910 4517421
W: http://www.camplejeuneglobe.com
Freq: Thu; **Circ:** 30000 Not Audited
Editorial Profile: The Globe is a free, weekly newspaper serving military personnel and civilian employees and residents of the Camp Lejeune Marine Corps Base, NC. Although the paper is printed and distributed by Landmark Military Newspapers of North Carolina, all editorial content is provided by military personnel. Deadlines are Wednesdays at 11am ET.; Full Page Mono: 22.16; Full Page Colour: 310.00
Currency: US Dollars
NEWSPAPER

Globe Gazette
Owner: Lee Enterprises, Inc.
Editorial: 300 N Washington Ave, Mason City, Iowa 50401-3222. **T:** 1 641 421-0500
E: news@globegazette.com
W: http://www.globegazette.com
Freq: Daily; **Circ:** 12689 Not Audited
Publisher: Howard Query; **Editor:** Jane Reynolds; **News Editor:** Bob Steenson; **Editor:** Tom Thoma
Editorial Profile: Globe Gazette is a published daily for the residents of Mason City, IA and surrounding areas. The newspaper covers local news, business and sports.; Full Page Mono: 26.25
Currency: US Dollars
DAILY NEWSPAPER

Globe Newspapers
Owner: News Media Corp.
Editorial: 298 N Pine St, Globe, Arizona 85501. **T:** 1 928 425-7121
W: http://www.silverbelt.com **Circ:** 10900
Publisher: Marc Marin; **Editor:** Holly Sow
NEWSPAPER

Gloucester Daily Times
Owner: Community Newspaper Holdings, Inc.
Editorial: 36 Whittemore St, Gloucester, Massachusetts 01930-2581.
T: 1 978 283-7000
E: gdt@gloucestertimes.com
W: http://www.gloucestertimes.com
Freq: Mon thru Fri; **Circ:** 6341 Not Audited
Editor: Raymond Lamont; **Editor:** Raymond Lamont; **Editor:** Raymond Lamont; **Editor:** Gail McCarthy
Editorial Profile: Gloucester Daily Times is a daily local newspaper serving the residents of Gloucester, MA and surrounding communities. It covers sports, business and local news. The publication's Web site offers a searchable database with purchase of the daily newspaper.; Full Page Mono: 21.50
Currency: US Dollars
DAILY NEWSPAPER

Gloucester-Mathews Gazette-Journal
Owner: Tidewater Newspapers Inc.
Editorial: 6625 Main St, Gloucester, Virginia 23061. **T:** 1 804 693-3101
E: info@gazettejournal.net
W: http://www.gazettejournal.net
Freq: Thu; **Circ:** 11331 Not Audited
Publisher: Elsa Verbyla
Editorial Profile: Gloucester-Mathews Gazette-Journal is a local newspaper written for the residents of Gloucester, VA. The paper covers local news and events. Deadlines are on Tuesdays at noon ET.; Full Page Mono: 9.50; Full Page Colour: 1396.00
Currency: US Dollars
NEWSPAPER

Gold Nugget Publications
Owner: Gold Nugget Publications, Inc.
Editorial: 169 W Jackson St, Virden, Illinois 62690-1269. **T:** 1 217 965-3355
E: editor@gnnews.net
W: http://www.gnnews.net
Freq: Wed; **Circ:** 6100
Editor: Lisa Rascher; **Editor:** Janice Smith; **Editor:** Sandy Webb; **Publisher:** Julie Westerhausen; Full Page Mono: 8.00
Currency: US Dollars
NEWSPAPER

The Gold Standard
Owner: United States Army
Editorial: Building 1109, Wing D; 6th Street, Fort Knox, Kentucky 40121-5199.
T: 1 502 624-8728
W: http://www.fkgoldstandard.com
Freq: Thu; **Circ:** 20000 Not Audited
Editorial Profile: The Gold Standard is written for military and retirees.; Full Page Mono: 12.66
Currency: US Dollars
NEWSPAPER

Goldsboro News-Argus
Owner: Buchheit News Management
Editorial: 310 N Berkeley Blvd, Goldsboro, North Carolina 27534. **T:** 1 919 778-2211
E: news@newsargus.com
W: http://www.newsargus.com
Freq: Mon thru Fri; **Circ:** 14736 Not Audited
Editor: Renee Carey; **Publisher:** Hal Tanner
Editorial Profile: Goldsboro News-Argus is published daily for the residents of Wayne County, NC. The newspaper covers local news, sports and Seymour Johnson Air Force base news. Sections and departments regularly featured include business, church, classified, editorials, entertainment, lifestyle, sports and weather. Editorial deadlines are daily at 10:30am ET. The newspaper accepts non-disclosure agreements on a case-by-case basis.; Full Page Mono: 24.60; Full Page Colour: 495.00
Currency: US Dollars
DAILY NEWSPAPER

Good News Florida
Owner: Blackstone Media Group
Editorial: 5601 Powerline Rd., Fort Lauderdale, Florida 33309. **T:** 1 954 564-5378
W: http://goodnewsfl.org
Freq: Monthly; **Circ:** 65000
Publisher: Grif Blackstone; **Editor:** Shelly Pond
Editorial Profile: Good News is the largest Christian news publication in Florida with the goal of delivering " relevant truth on God, life, relationships, and more".
NEWSPAPER

Good Times Weekly of Santa Cruz County
Owner: Mainstreet Media Group
Editorial: 1205 Pacific Ave Ste 301, Santa Cruz, California 95060-3936.
T: 1 831 458-1100 **E:** letters@gtweekly.com
W: http://www.goodtimessantacruz.com
Freq: Thu; **Circ:** 40000 Not Audited
News Editor: Jacob Pierce; **Publisher:** Ron Slack
Editorial Profile: Good Times Weekly of Santa Cruz County is written for residents in Santa Cruz, CA. It is Santa Cruz County's guide to entertainment and events, presents news of ongoing local interest and reflects the voice, character and spirit of the unique community. It is available free of charge but limited to one copy per reader. Deadlines are Fridays before publication.; Full Page Mono: 12.00
Currency: US Dollars
NEWSPAPER

The Goshen News
Owner: Community Newspaper Holdings, Inc.
Editorial: 114 S Main St, Goshen, Indiana 46526-3734. **T:** 1 574 533-2151
E: news@goshennews.com
W: http://www.goshennews.com
Freq: Daily; **Circ:** 9470
Editorial Profile: The Goshen News is published for the residents of Goshen, IN and surrounding areas. It provides information on local news, sports and weather.; Full Page Mono: 24.00; Full Page Colour: 75.48
Currency: US Dollars
DAILY NEWSPAPER

Gosport
Owner: U.S. Navy
Editorial: 150 Hase Rd, Pensacola, Florida 32508-1051. **T:** 1 850 452-4466
W: http://www.gosportpensacola.com
Freq: Fri; **Circ:** 25000 Not Audited
Editor: Scott Hallford
Editorial Profile: Gosport is written for the civilian community and military community surrounding the Pensacola Naval Air Station. It provides base news and information.; Full Page Mono: 15.04
Currency: US Dollars
NEWSPAPER

Gowanda News
Owner: Metro Group Inc.
Editorial: 49 W Main St, Gowanda, New York 14070-1305. **T:** 1 716 532-2288
Freq: Sun; **Circ:** 11462 Not Audited
Publisher: Bernard Bradpiece; **Editor:** Mary Pankow; **Editor:** Mary Pankow; **Editor:** Mary Pankow
Editorial Profile: Gowanda News is a weekly newspaper serving the residents of Gowanda, NY and its surrounding areas. The paper serves as a news provider and as a consumer's magazine.; Full Page Mono: 8.23
Currency: US Dollars
NEWSPAPER

Grand County Newspapers
Owner: Swift Newspapers
Editorial: 424 E Agate Ave, Granby, Colorado 80446. **T:** 1 970 887-3334
E: news@skyhidailynews.com
W: http://www.skyhidailynews.com
Circ: 15500 Not Audited
NEWSPAPER

Grand Forks Herald
Owner: Forum Communications Co.
Editorial: 375 2nd Ave N, Grand Forks, North Dakota 58203-3707. **T:** 1 701 780-1100
E: info@gfherald.com
W: http://www.grandforksherald.com
Freq: Daily; **Circ:** 26611 Not Audited
Editor: Brad Dokken
Editorial Profile: Grand Forks Herald is a local daily newspaper written for residents of Grand Forks, ND. The newspaper covers local and statewide news, sports, and entertainment, as well as community events.; Full Page Mono: 46.88; Full Page Colour: 524.00
Currency: US Dollars
DAILY NEWSPAPER

Grand Haven Tribune
Owner: Grand Haven Publishing Company
Editorial: 101 N 3rd St, Grand Haven, Michigan 49417-1209. **T:** 1 616 842-6400
E: news@grandhaventribune.com
W: http://www.grandhaventribune.com
Freq: Mon thru Fri; **Circ:** 8567 Not Audited
Publisher: Paul Bedient; **Editor:** Marie Havenga; **Publisher:** Kevin Hook; **News Editor:** Becky Vargo
Editorial Profile: Grand Haven Tribune is published daily for the residents of Grand Haven, MI and surrounding areas. The newspaper covers local news, sports, arts & entertainment and community events.; Full Page Mono: 18.68; Full Page Colour: 218.68
Currency: US Dollars
DAILY NEWSPAPER

The Grand Island Independent
Owner: Omaha World-Herald Co.
Editorial: 422 W 1st St, Grand Island, Nebraska 68801. **T:** 1 308 646-0590
E: ask@theindependent.com
W: http://www.theindependent.com
Freq: Daily; **Circ:** 18446 Not Audited
Publisher: Don Smith
Editorial Profile: Grand Island Independent is published daily for the residents of Grand Island, NE. The newspaper covers local news, sports, business news, arts & entertainment and community events.; Full Page Mono: 25.73; Full Page Colour: 375.00
Currency: US Dollars
DAILY NEWSPAPER

Grand Junction Free Press
Owner: Swift
Editorial: 145 N 4th St, Grand Junction, Colorado 81501-2541. **T:** 1 970 243-2200
W: http://www.gjfreepress.com
Freq: Fri; **Circ:** 14000
Publisher: Kim Burner
Editorial Profile: Grand Junction Free Press is a daily newspaper written for the community of Grand Junction, CO.; Full Page Mono: 15.00
Currency: US Dollars
NEWSPAPER

Grand Rapids Press
Owner: MLive Media Group
Editorial: 169 Monroe Ave NW Ste 100, Grand Rapids, Michigan 49503-2632.
T: 1 616 222-5400 **E:** grnews@mlive.com
W: http://www.mlive.com/grpress
Freq: Daily; **Circ:** 82021
Editorial Profile: Founded in 1892, Grand Rapids Press is a daily broadsheet covering West Michigan and outlying areas. It is an afternoon paper, therefore it is often best to contact members of the editorial staff in the late afternoon, rather than in the morning or at mid-day.; Full Page Mono: 92.55; Full Page Colour: 305.65
Currency: US Dollars
DAILY NEWSPAPER

Grand Rapids Press
Owner: MLive Media Group
Editorial: 217 N Sycamore St, Lansing, Michigan 48933. **T:** 1 517 487-8888
Editorial Profile: Known as the Booth Newspapers Bureau, this office contributes to all eight of the Booth-owned dailies, including: the Ann Arbor News, Bay City Times, Flint Journal, Grand Rapids Press, Jackson Citizen Patriot, Kalamazoo Gazette, Muskegon Chronicle and the Saginaw News all in

Michigan. To reach any one or all of the above papers, please make only one submission of press materials.
DAILY NEWSPAPER

The Grand Traverse Insider
Owner: Morning Star Publishing Company
Editorial: 415 Cass Street, Traverse City, Michigan 49684-2537. **T:** 1 231 486-0072
E: news@grandtraverseinsider.com
W: http://www.grandtraverseinsider.com
Freq: Sun; **Circ:** 41900
Editor: Dave Lein
Editorial Profile: Grand Traverse Insider is a weekly newspaper providing Local and Community News coverage for the Grand Traverse, Leelanau and Benzie counties, MI.; Full Page Mono: 19.60; Full Page Colour: 20.56
Currency: US Dollars
NEWSPAPER

Granite Publishing
Editorial: 346 S Houston St, Aransas Pass, Texas 78336-2515. **T:** 1 361 758-5391
Circ: 4300
NEWSPAPER

Grant County News & Carson Press
Editorial: 119 Main Street, Elgin, North Dakota 58533. **T:** 1 701 584-2900
E: gcn@westriv.com
Freq: Weekly; **Circ:** 2460 Not Audited
Editorial Profile: Grant County News and Carson Press are weekly newspapers serving the residents of Elgin, North Dakota. The publications cover local news and community events. Deadlines are the Friday before issue date.
NEWSPAPER

Grant County News & Express
Owner: Landmark Community Newspapers, Inc.
Editorial: 129 S Main St Ste B, Dry Ridge, Kentucky 41035-9406. **T:** 1 859 824-3343
E: gceditorial@grantky.com
W: http://www.grantky.com **Circ:** 18424 Not Audited
Editor: Jamie Baker-Nantz; **Editor:** Jamie Baker-Nantz; **Publisher:** Ken Stone
NEWSPAPER

Grants Pass Daily Courier
Owner: Courier Publishing Company
Editorial: 409 Se 7Th St, Grants Pass, Oregon 97526-3003. **T:** 1 541 474-3700
E: news@thedailycourier.com
W: http://www.thedailycourier.com
Freq: Mon thru Fri; **Circ:** 11321 Not Audited
Editor: Jeff Duewel; **Publisher:** Dennis Mack; **Editor:** Dennis Roler; **News Editor:** Patricia Snyder; **News Editor:** Patricia Snyder; **News Editor:** Patricia Snyder; **News Editor:** Patricia Snyder
Editorial Profile: Grants Pass Daily Courier is published daily for the residents of Grants Pass, OR. The newspaper covers local and state news, sports, business and entertainment.; Full Page Mono: 10.95; Full Page Colour: 325.00
Currency: US Dollars
DAILY NEWSPAPER

Granville Newspapers
Owner: Gannett Co., Inc.
Editorial: 110 E Elm St, Granville, Ohio 43023-1462. **T:** 1 740 587-3397
W: http://www.granvillesentinel.com
Circ: 12794
NEWSPAPER

Grapevine Independent
Owner: Messenger Publishing Group
Editorial: 7144 Fair Oaks Blvd, Carmichael, California 95608-6434. **T:** 1 916 773-1111
E: publisher@mpg8.com
W: http://www.rcgrapevine.com
Freq: Fri; **Circ:** 11000 Not Audited
Editorial Profile: Grapevine Independent covers news and sports in Rancho Cordova and Eastern Sacramento County, CA.; Full Page Mono: 12.75
Currency: US Dollars
NEWSPAPER

Grapevine Newspaper
Editorial: 3638 E Landis Ave, Vineland, New Jersey 08361-3046. **T:** 1 856 457-7815
E: letters@grapevinenewspaper.com
W: http://www.grapevinenewspaper.com
Freq: Wed; **Circ:** 20000
Editorial Profile: Grapevine Newspaper was founded in early 2008. It is a weekly community newspaper published every Wednesday, serving the residents of Vineland, NJ and Cumberland County, NJ.; Full Page Mono: 31.00; Full Page Colour: 106.00
Currency: US Dollars
NEWSPAPER

The Graphic
Owner: Schurz Communications Inc.
Editorial: 319 State St, Petoskey, Michigan 49770-2746. **T:** 1 231 347-2544
E: petoskeynews@petoskeynews.com
W: http://www.thegraphicweekly.com
Freq: Thu; **Circ:** 14000 Not Audited
Publisher: Douglas Caldwell; **Editor:** Sheri McWhirter-O'Donnell
Editorial Profile: The Graphic is a free, weekly newspaper serving residents of Petoskey, MI and the surrounding communities of Mackinac Island, Atwood, Gaylord and Carlevoix, MI. The paper covers news and information, shopping, new food, drinks and activities, events, arts and weird and unusual jobs. It shares its offices and editorial staff with the Petoskey News-Review.; Full Page Mono: 15.85
Currency: US Dollars
NEWSPAPER

Graves Publishing Co.
Editorial: 418 N Main St, Nashville, Arkansas 71852-2006. **T:** 1 870 845-2010
E: editor@nashvillenews.org
W: http://www.nashvillenews.org **Circ:** 6387 Not Audited
Editor: Danielle Cummings; **Publisher:** Mike Graves; **Editor:** Jim Penson
NEWSPAPER

Great Bend Tribune
Owner: Morris Multimedia, Inc.
Editorial: 2012 Forest Ave, Great Bend, Kansas 67530-4014. **T:** 1 620 792-1211
E: email@gbtribune.com
W: http://www.gbtribune.com
Freq: Daily; **Circ:** 6195 Not Audited
Publisher: Mary Hoisington
Editorial Profile: Great Bend Tribune is published for the residents of Great Bend, KS and surrounding areas. It provides information on news, sports and community events.; Full Page Mono: 12.06; Full Page Colour: 18.06
Currency: US Dollars
DAILY NEWSPAPER

Great Falls Tribune
Owner: Gannett Co., Inc.
Editorial: 205 River Dr S, Great Falls, Montana 59405-1854. **T:** 1 406 791-1444
E: tribcity@greatfallstribune.com
W: http://www.greatfallstribune.com
Freq: Daily; **Circ:** 22628 Not Audited
Editorial Profile: Great Falls Tribune is written for the community and the surrounding area of Great Falls, MT. The publication covers local news, agriculture, outdoors, sports and community events.; Full Page Mono: 48.20; Full Page Colour: 655.00
Currency: US Dollars
DAILY NEWSPAPER

Great Lakes Bulletin
Owner: NorthWest News Group
Editorial: 2601A Paul Jones Street, Grayslake, Illinois 60088. **T:** 1 847 688-4808
E: editor.bulletin@yahoo.com
W: http://cnic.navy.mil/greatlakes
Freq: Fri; **Circ:** 14000 Not Audited
Editor: Paul Engstrom; **Publisher:** John Rung
Editorial Profile: Great Lakes Bulletin is a weekly newspaper aimed at naval personnel and residents of the Naval Training Center in Great Lakes, IL. Features include local news, military information, recreation, health, wellness and weather. Deadlines are on Mondays at 4pm 6T.; Full Page Mono: 12.00
Currency: US Dollars
NEWSPAPER

Great Lakes Pilot
Owner: Enrico & Mary Capogrossoa
Editorial: E22029 Everette, Grand Marais, Michigan 49839. **T:** 1 906 494-2391
E: editor@thegreatlakespilot.com
W: http://www.thegreatlakespilot.com
Freq: Monthly; **Circ:** 30000 Not Audited
Editorial Profile: Great Lakes Pilot is a monthly newspaper that provides information on the unique history, attractions and lifestyles surrounding the Great Lakes area in Michigan. It focuses on folklore, fables, features, and humor of the Great Lakes States.; Full Page Mono: 20.00
Currency: US Dollars
NEWSPAPER

Great Plains Examiner
Editorial: 209 Aspen Ave, Bismarck, North Dakota 58503-0204. **T:** 1 701 202-8748
W: http://www.greatplainsexaminer.com
Freq: Monthly; **Circ:** 10000
Publisher: Gary Emineth
Editorial Profile: The Great Plains Examiner covers local news, politics and business in Bismarck and Mandan in North Dakota. It focuses on high-quality journalism with a host of veteran writers providing in-depth coverage of area communities. Launched in June 2011 but relaunched under new ownership in December 2012, the paper is published monthly and is available by carrier delivery rack or mail.; Full Page Mono: 12.92; Full Page Colour: 15.00
Currency: US Dollars
NEWSPAPER

Greater Meadowbrook News
Owner: Greater Meadowbrook News
Editorial: 2320 Oakland Blvd Ste 207, Fort Worth, Texas 76103-3239. **T:** 1 817 413-0019
E: meadowbrooknews@sbcglobal.net
W: http://www.greatermeadowbrooknews.com
Freq: Bi-Weekly; **Circ:** 21000
Editorial Profile: Greater Meadowbrook News offers local news and information for residents and businesses of East Forth Worth, West Arlington and Richland Hills, TX.; Full Page Mono: 25.00; Full Page Colour: 25.00
Currency: US Dollars
NEWSPAPER

Greater Media Newspapers
Owner: Greater Media Inc.
Editorial: 198 Route 9 North, Manalapan, New Jersey 7726. **T:** 1 732 358-5200
W: http://www.gmnews.com **Circ:** 207339 Not Audited
NEWSPAPER

Greater Tulsa Reporter Newspapers
Owner: Union Boundary, Inc.
Editorial: 7116 S Mingo Rd, Suite 103, Tulsa, Oklahoma 74133. **T:** 1 918 254-1515
E: info@gtrnews.com
W: http://www.gtrnews.com **Circ:** 37500 Not Audited
Editorial Profile: Greater Tulsa Reporter Newspapers is a publisher delivering community newspapers to Tulsa, OK.
NEWSPAPER

Greek News
Owner: Greek News Inc.
Editorial: 3507 23rd Ave, Astoria, New York 11105-2204. **T:** 1 718 545-4888
E: info@greeknewsonline.com
W: http://www.greekamerican.com
Freq: Mon; **Circ:** 16000 Not Audited
Editorial Profile: Greek News is a weekly newspaper and provides news and events listings, along with cultural programs information to members of the Greek-American community. Contact the publication for advertisement rates.; Full Page Mono: 7.88
Currency: US Dollars
NEWSPAPER

Green Banner Publications
Owner: Green Banner Publications, Inc
Editorial: 490 E State Road 60, Pekin, Indiana 47165. **T:** 1 812 967-3176
E: sales@gbpnews.com
W: http://www.gbpnews.com **Circ:** 63145 Not Audited
Editor: Marcus Amos; **Editor:** George Browning; **Publisher:** Joe Green; **Editor:** Janna Ross; **Editor:** Janna Ross
Editorial Profile: Green Banner Publications in Pekin, IN publishes The Banner-Gazette, The Scottsburg Giveaway, The Scott County Journal & The Chronicle, The Leader and The Washington County Edition. The publications provide community news coverage for Scott, Washington and Clark Counties, IN.
NEWSPAPER

Green Bay Press-Gazette
Owner: Gannett Co., Inc.
Editorial: 435 E Walnut St, Green Bay, Wisconsin 54301-5001. **T:** 1 920 435-4411
E: localnews@greenbaypressgazette.com
W: http://www.greenbaypressgazette.com
Freq: Daily; **Circ:** 39751 Not Audited
Publisher: Kevin Corrado
Editorial Profile: Green Bay Press-Gazette is a local daily newspaper written for residents of Green Bay and Northeastern Wisconsin. The newspaper covers local, national and world news, sports, business, lifestyle, arts & entertainment and community events.; Full Page Mono: 87.30; Full Page Colour: 287.86
Currency: US Dollars
DAILY NEWSPAPER

Green Valley News and Sun Publishing
Owner: Wick Communications Inc.
Editorial: 18705 S. I-19 Frontage Rd, Ste 125, Green Valley, Arizona 85614.
T: 1 520 625-5511 **E:** editorial@gvnews.com
W: http://www.gvnews.com **Circ:** 19000 Not Audited
Publisher: Rebecca Bradner; **Editor:** Dan Shearer
Editorial Profile: Santa Cruz Valley Sun is a weekly newspaper serving residents of Sahuarita, Green Valley, Amado, Tubac, Patagonia and Sonoita in Arizona. It is distributed free. It covers local news, sports and events.
NEWSPAPER

Greenbelt News Review
Owner: Greenbelt Co-operative Publishing Assn.
Editorial: 15 Crescent Rd, Ste 100, Greenbelt, Maryland 20770. **T:** 1 301 474-4131
E: newsreview@greenbelt.com
W: http://www.greenbeltnewsreview.com
Freq: Thu; **Circ:** 10000 Not Audited
Publisher: Eileen Farnham; **News Editor:** Elaine Skolnik; **Editor:** Mary Lou Williamson
Editorial Profile: Greenbelt News Review ONLY covers news and events concerning residents of Greenbelt, MD. The paper does not accept or use regional events and news and cannot use anything that is not in its coverage area.; Full Page Mono: 12.15
Currency: US Dollars
NEWSPAPER

Greene County Dailies - Community Newspapers
Owner: Ohio Community Media LLC.
Editorial: 1836 West Park Square, Bellbrook, Ohio 45385. **T:** 1 937 372-4444
W: http://www.tcnewsnet.com
Editorial Profile: Greene County Dailies - Community Newspapers publishes the Beavercreek News-Current and the Sugarcreek-Bellbrook Times, covering Local News for the areas southeast of Dayton, OH.
NEWSPAPER

Greene County Daily World
Owner: Rust Communications
Editorial: 79 Main St S, Linton, Indiana 47441. **T:** 1 812 847-4487
W: http://www.gcdailyworld.com
Freq: Fri; **Circ:** 6300 Not Audited
Publisher: Randy List; **Editor:** Chris Pruett
Editorial Profile: Greene County Daily World is a weekday newspaper serving residents of Greene County, including Bloomfield and Linton, IN. It provides local, world and national news with sports, business, health and entertainment articles. The Daily World also contains public notices, community events, obituaries and classifieds. It was created in January 2006, when two local daily newspapers, the Linton Daily Citizen and the Evening World in Bloomfield, IN, were combined into a single publication. Deadlines are at 11am ET two days prior to issue date.; Full Page Mono: 7.85; Full Page Colour: 90.00
Currency: US Dollars
NEWSPAPER

Greene County Newspaper Group
Owner: Ohio Community Media LLC.
Editorial: 30 S Detroit St, Xenia, Ohio 45385-3502. **T:** 1 937 372-4444
E: editor@xeniagazette.com
Freq: Daily; **Circ:** 8224 Not Audited
Editor: Charles Caperton; **Editor:** Amanda Crowe
DAILY NEWSPAPER

Greene Publishing, Inc.
Owner: Greene Publishing Inc.
Editorial: 1695 N State Road 53, Madison, Florida 32340-1548. **T:** 1 850 973-4141
E: greenepub@greenepublishing.com
W: http://www.greenepublishing.com
Circ: 7000
Editor: Jacob Bembry; **Publisher:** Emerald Greene
Editorial Profile: Greene Publishing, Inc. is a community newspaper publisher serving the residents of Tallahassee, FL and Thomasville, GA.
NEWSPAPER

Greeneville Sun
Owner: Jones Media, Inc.
Editorial: 121 W Summer St, Greeneville, Tennessee 37743-4923. **T:** 1 423 638-4181
E: gsun@xtn.net
W: http://www.greenevillesun.com
Freq: Daily; **Circ:** 13039 Not Audited
Editor: John Jones; **Editor:** Kathy Knight

Editorial Profile: Greeneville Sun is a local daily newspaper written for residents of Greenville and Green County, TN. The publication's mission is to provide its readers with information about local news and events.; Full Page Mono: 28.75; Full Page Colour: 93.57
Currency: US Dollars
DAILY NEWSPAPER

Greensburg Daily News
Owner: Community Newspaper Holdings, Inc.
Editorial: 135 S Franklin St, Greensburg, Indiana 47240-2023. **T:** 1 812 663-3111
E: news@greensburgdailynews.com
W: http://www.greensburgdailynews.com
Freq: Mon thru Fri; **Circ:** 5100 Not Audited
Publisher: Laura Welborn
Editorial Profile: Greensburg Daily News provides local and community news, including education, business and local sports coverage for the residents of Greensburg and Decatur County, IN.; Full Page Mono: 17.20; Full Page Colour: 75.00
Currency: US Dollars
DAILY NEWSPAPER

Greenville Daily Advocate
Owner: Ohio Community Media
Editorial: 428 S Broadway St, Greenville, Ohio 45331-1926. **T:** 1 937 548-3151
E: pressrelease@dailyadvocate.com
W: http://www.dailyadvocate.com
Freq: Fri; **Circ:** 7000 Not Audited
Editor: Christine Chalmers; **Publisher:** David Compton
Editorial Profile: Greenville Daily Advocate's editorial mission is to be committed to the community and to provide its readers with local news and information. The publication is written for Darke county residents.; Full Page Mono: 16.50; Full Page Colour: 175.00
Currency: US Dollars
NEWSPAPER

The Greenville News
Owner: Gannett Co., Inc.
Editorial: 305 S Main St, Greenville, South Carolina 29601-2605. **T:** 1 864 298-4100
E: localnews@greenvillenews.com
W: http://www.greenvilleonline.com
Freq: Daily; **Circ:** 45370 Not Audited
Publisher: Steve Brandt
Editorial Profile: The Greenville News aims to provide Greenville, SC, and its surrounding communities, which include Pickens, Anderson and Spartanburg counties, with local, regional and national news. The paper became a part of Gannett when the company bought Multimedia in December 1995.; Full Page Mono: 160.25; Full Page Colour: 540.87
Currency: US Dollars
DAILY NEWSPAPER

The Greenville News
Editorial: 517 Amherst Ave, Columbia, South Carolina 29205-2601. **T:** 1 803 256-7367
DAILY NEWSPAPER

Greenville Record-Argus
Editorial: 10 Penn Ave, Greenville, Pennsylvania 16125. **T:** 1 724 588-5000
Freq: Daily; **Circ:** 5400 Not Audited
Publisher: Steve Gargasz
Editorial Profile: Greenville Record-Argus is published daily for the residents of Greenville, PA and surrounding areas. The publication is a general interest newspaper covering local news, weather, sports, education, business, arts & entertainment and other information of interest to the local community.; Full Page Mono: 14.00
Currency: US Dollars
DAILY NEWSPAPER

Greenwich Citizen
Owner: Hearst Corporation
Editorial: 1455 E Putnam Ave, Ste 102, Old Greenwich, Connecticut 06870-1360.
T: 1 203 625-4460 **E:** gcitizen@bcnnew.com
W: http://www.greenwichcitizen.com
Freq: Fri; **Circ:** 12516 Not Audited
Publisher: Michelle McAbee; **Editor:** Jim Wolfe
Editorial Profile: Greenwich Citizen is a weekly newspaper published for the residents of Greenwich, CT. The newspaper is comprised of three main sections: News, which includes local/regional news, sports, living, police reports and obituaries; classifieds, which includes CT Job Hunter and CT Auto Pix; and features, which includes a weather section.; Full Page Mono: 20.00
Currency: US Dollars
NEWSPAPER

Greenwich Post
Owner: Hersam Acorn Newspapers
Editorial: 10 Corbin Dr, Floor 3, Darien, Connecticut 6820. **T:** 1 203 861-9191
E: editor@greenwich-post.com
W: http://www.greenwich-post.com
Freq: Thu; **Circ:** 16000 Not Audited
Editor: Maggie Caldwell; **Publisher:** Thomas Nash
Editorial Profile: Greenwich Post is published weekly for the residents of Greenwich, CT and surrounding areas. The newspaper covers local news and community events. Deadlines are Tuesdays at noon ET.; Full Page Mono: 12.60
Currency: US Dollars
NEWSPAPER

Greenwich Time
Owner: Hearst Corporation
Editorial: 1455 E Putnam Ave, Old Greenwich, Connecticut 06870-1360. **T:** 1 203 625-4400
E: letters.greenwichtime@scni.com
W: http://www.greenwichtime.com
Freq: Daily; **Circ:** 5616 Not Audited
Publisher: Henry B. Haitz
Editorial Profile: Greenwich Time covers news in Southern Connecticut. Its coverage includes local news, sports, business news and entertainment.; Full Page Mono: 76.10; Full Page Colour: 525.00
Currency: US Dollars
DAILY NEWSPAPER

Greenwood Commonwealth
Owner: Emmerich Newspapers Inc.
Editorial: 329 Highway 82 W, Greenwood, Mississippi 38930-6538. **T:** 1 662 453-5312
E: commonwealth@gwcommonwealth.com
W: http://www.gwcommonwealth.com
Freq: Mon thru Fri; **Circ:** 5741 Not Audited
Publisher: Tim Kalich; **News Editor:** David Monroe
Editorial Profile: Greenwood Commonwealth's editorial mission is to provide its readers with the finest in local news and information about the Greenwood, MS community.; Full Page Mono: 14.90; Full Page Colour: 340.00
Currency: US Dollars
DAILY NEWSPAPER

The Greer Citizen
Owner: Hometown News, Inc.
Editorial: 105 Victoria St, Greer, South Carolina 29651. **T:** 1 864 877-2076
E: ads@greercitizen.com
W: http://www.greercitizen.com
Freq: Thu; **Circ:** 11000 Not Audited
Editor: Joel Fitzpatrick; **Publisher:** Don Wilder
Editorial Profile: The Greer Citizen is a weekly newspaper serving residents of Greer, SC. It provides local news, sports, government issues and other pertinent information. The deadlines are on Tuesdays at noon ET.; Full Page Mono: 8.00
Currency: US Dollars
NEWSPAPER

The Gresham Outlook
Owner: Community Newspapers Inc.
Editorial: 1190 NE Division St, Gresham, Oregon 97030. **T:** 1 503 665-2181
W: http://greshamoutlook.com/news/index.php
Freq: Monthly; **Circ:** 10000 Not Audited
News Editor: Steve Brown
Editorial Profile: Gresham Outlook is a community newspaper serving the residents of Multnomah County, including the communities of Gresham, Troutdale, Fairview and Wood Village, OR. It covers local news, schools, businesses, sports, people, government and features.; Full Page Mono: 13.59; Full Page Colour: 95.00
Currency: US Dollars
NEWSPAPER

Griffin Daily News
Owner: Paxton Media Group
Editorial: 323 E Solomon St, Griffin, Georgia 30223-3315. **T:** 1 770 227-3276
W: http://www.griffindailynews.com
Freq: Daily; **Circ:** 6936 Not Audited
Publisher: David Clevenger; **Editor:** John Sullivan
Editorial Profile: Griffin Daily News is published for the residents of Griffin, GA, and surrounding areas. The paper covers local and state news, business, sports and entertainment.; Full Page Mono: 20.60; Full Page Colour: 370.00
Currency: US Dollars
DAILY NEWSPAPER

The Grizzly & Life
Editorial: 42007 Fox Farm Road #3B, Big Bear Lake, California 92315. **T:** 1 909 866-3456
W: http://www.bigbeargrizzly.net **Circ:** 18700 Not Audited
Editor: Judi Bowers; **Editor:** Judi Bowers;
Publisher: Jerry Wright
NEWSPAPER

Grosse Pointe News
Owner: Point News Group
Editorial: 21316 Mack Ave, Grosse Pointe Woods, Michigan 48236-1047.
T: 1 313 882-6900
E: editor@grossepointenews.com
W: http://www.grossepointenews.com
Freq: Thu; **Circ:** 12500 Not Audited
Publisher: Robert Liggett; **Editor:** Joe Warner
Editorial Profile: Grosse Pointe News is a community newspaper written for residents of Grosse Pointe and Harper Woods, MI.; Full Page Mono: 25.00
Currency: US Dollars
NEWSPAPER

The Grove Sun Daily
Owner: Macquarie Media Group
Editorial: 16 W 3rd St, Grove, Oklahoma 74344-3223. **T:** 1 918 786-2228
E: news@grovesun.com
W: http://www.grovesun.com
Freq: Daily; **Circ:** 6000 Not Audited
Publisher: Cheryl Franklin; **Editor:** Kirsten Mustain
Editorial Profile: The Grove Sun Daily is written for the residents of Grove, OK. It covers local news, events, sports and weather.; Full Page Mono: 7.50; Full Page Colour: 100.00
Currency: US Dollars
DAILY NEWSPAPER

Grupo Bogota, Inc.
Editorial: 198 W Chew Ave, Philadelphia, Pennsylvania 19120-2465. **T:** 1 215 424-1200
E: gbogota@aol.com
W: http://www.gbogota.com **Circ:** 65000 Not Audited
Publisher: Ricardo Hurtado; **Editor:** Fernando Mendez
NEWSPAPER

GT Enterprises
Editorial: 102 E Robbins St, Graettinger, Iowa 51342. **T:** 1 712 859-3780 **E:** grtimes@rvtc.net
Circ: 1350 Not Audited
Editorial Profile: GT Enterprises is a local newspaper providing news to the community of Graettinger, IA.
NEWSPAPER

The Guardian - Washington, DC Bureau
Owner: Guardian Media Group plc
Editorial: 900 17th St NW Ste 250, Washington, District Of Columbia 20006-2524.
T: 1 202 223-2486
Editorial Profile: This is the Guardian's bureau in Washington, DC.
DAILY NEWSPAPER

The Guardian and Observer - New York Bureau
Owner: Guardian Media Group plc
Editorial: 49 W 27th St, New York, New York 10001-6936. **T:** 1 212 614-1257
Editorial Profile: This is the New York bureau for the Guardian and Observer.
DAILY NEWSPAPER

Guide News
Editorial: 800 W Church Rd, Mechanicsburg, Pennsylvania 17055-3179.
T: 1 717 766-0211 2
E: guidenews@frycomm.com
Freq: Monthly; **Circ:** 161000 Not Audited
Editor: Linda Jastron; **Publisher:** Ted Schope
Editorial Profile: Guide News is a weekly newspaper written for the residents of Mechanicsburg, PA. The newspaper covers local news and advertisements. Deadlines are on Thursdays at 4pm ET.; Full Page Mono: 10.55
Currency: US Dollars
NEWSPAPER

Guidon
Owner: Gannett
Editorial: 320 Illinois Ave, Fort Leonard Wood, Missouri 65473. **T:** 1 573 336-5487
E: guidoneditor@myguidon.com
W: http://www.myguidon.com
Freq: Thu; **Circ:** 10000 Not Audited
Editorial Profile: Guidon is a military publication for members of the U.S. Army and headquartered in the Public Affairs Office at Fort Leanard Wood, where all editorial content is edited and approved.; Full Page Mono: 10.40
Currency: US Dollars
NEWSPAPER

Gujarat Times
Owner: Parikh Worldwide Media, LLC
Editorial: 37 W 20Th St Ste 1009, New York, New York 10011-3714. **T:** 1 212 206-7361
E: info@gujarattimesusa.com
W: http://www.gujarattimesusa.com
Freq: Fri; **Circ:** 15000 Not Audited
Publisher: Sudhir Parikh
Editorial Profile: Gujarat Times is written for Gujarati-speaking members of the Indian community in the United States. Provides news and events coverage.; Full Page Mono: 20.00
Currency: US Dollars
NEWSPAPER

Gulf Breeze News
Owner: Newell (Lisa) & Papajohn (Vici)
Editorial: 913 Gulf Breeze Pkwy, Gulf Breeze, Florida 32561-4754. **T:** 1 850 932-8986
E: news@gulfbreezenews.com
W: http://www.gulfbreezenews.com
Freq: Thu; **Circ:** 12900 Not Audited
Editorial Profile: Gulf Breeze News is a weekly community newspaper serving residents of Gulf Breeze, FL.; Full Page Mono: 30.00
Currency: US Dollars
NEWSPAPER

Gulf Coast Good News
Editorial: 336 Rodenberg Ave, Biloxi, Mississippi 39531. **T:** 1 228 435-2456
E: gulfcoastgoodnews@cableone.net
W: http://www.goodnewsusa.org
Freq: Monthly; **Circ:** 25000 Not Audited
Publisher: James Black
Editorial Profile: Gulf Coast Good News' editorial mission is to promote a climate for positive growth on the Gulf Coast community by focusing on events and situations that exemplify good news, celebrating the efforts and accomplishments of individuals and businesses actively involved in the support of the community, and encouraging a sense of cooperation among its people. The publication seeks to build a coalition of all people who have a similar vision and genuine desire to make the Mississippi Gulf Coast a better place to live, work and raise children. Their belief is that promoting good news rather than bad, printing positive media instead of negative, can have a unifying, cohesive effect on the citizens of the area and that this promotion of good will is the essence of God's message of love to all people. Deadlines for the publication are on the 10th of every month.; Full Page Mono: 18.00
Currency: US Dollars
NEWSPAPER

The Gulf Coast Newspapers - Fairhope
Owner: Crescent Publishing Co., LLC
Editorial: 325 Fairhope Ave, Fairhope, Alabama 36532-2317. **T:** 1 251 928-2321
W: http://www.gulfcoastnewstoday.com
Freq: Sat; **Circ:** 3000 Not Audited
Publisher: Sudie Gambrell; **Editor:** Mike Odom
Editorial Profile: The Fairhope Courier is written for residents of Fairhope, AL. Issued on Wednesdays and Saturdays, the paper contains local news, information about government, education, sports and arts & entertainment. Deadlines are at 10am CT.; Full Page Mono: 6.30
Currency: US Dollars
NEWSPAPER

Gulf Coast Newspapers-Daphne
Owner: Crescent Publishing Co., LLC
Editorial: 1805 Main St, Daphne, Alabama 36526-4543. **T:** 1 251 928-2321
W: http://www.gulfcoastnewstoday.com
Circ: 10500 Not Audited
Publisher: Sudie Gambrell; **Editor:** Mike Odom
NEWSPAPER

Gulf Coast Newspapers-Foley
Owner: Crescent Publishing Co., LLC
Editorial: 217 N McKenzie St, Foley, Alabama 36535-3533. **T:** 1 251 943-2151
W: http://www.gulfcoastnewstoday.com
Circ: 6250 Not Audited
Publisher: Sudie Gambrell; **Editor:** Cathy Higgins
NEWSPAPER

Gulf Pine Catholic
Owner: Catholic Diocese of Biloxi
Editorial: 1790 Popps Ferry Rd, Biloxi, Mississippi 39532. **T:** 1 228 702-2126
E: gulfpinecatholic@biloxidiocese.org
W: http://www.gulfpinecatholic.com
Freq: Bi-Weekly; **Circ:** 17800 Not Audited
Editor: Terry Dickson; **Publisher:** Roger Morin
Editorial Profile: Gulf Pine Catholic's mission is to spread the gospel through contemporary

means of communication. The publication serves the Catholic Family in the Diocese of Biloxi. Deadlines for the publication are every Friday.; Full Page Mono: 10.00
Currency: US Dollars
NEWSPAPER

The Gulfport Gabber

Editorial: 1419 49th St S, Gulfport, Florida 33707-4301. **T:** 1 727 321-6965
E: news@thegabber.com
W: http://www.thegabber.com
Freq: Thu; **Circ:** 14000 Not Audited
Editorial Profile: The Gulfport Gabber is a local weekly newspaper written for residents of Gulfport, FL and the surrounding communities. The publication's mission is to provide readers with information about local news, community events, and in-depth classifieds.; Full Page Mono: 23.00
Currency: US Dollars
NEWSPAPER

Guymon Daily Herald

Owner: Horizon Publications
Editorial: 515 N Ellison St, Guymon, Oklahoma 73942. **T:** 1 580 338-3355
W: http://www.guymondailyherald.com
Freq: Daily; **Circ:** 2332 Not Audited
Publisher: Allison Gipe
Editorial Profile: Guymon Daily Herald is written for residents of Guymon, OK and surrounding communities. It covers local news, weather, sports, arts & entertainment and business.; Full Page Mono: 8.38; Full Page Colour: 75.00
Currency: US Dollars
DAILY NEWSPAPER

The Gwinnett Citizen

Owner: The Snellville Citizen, Inc.
Editorial: 719 Scenic Hwy, Ste D, Lawrenceville, Georgia 30046.
T: 1 770 963-3699
E: info@gwinnettcitizen.com
W: http://www.gwinnettcitizen.com
Freq: Monthly; **Circ:** 15000 Not Audited
Editorial Profile: The Gwinnett Citizen Online serves the residents of Gwinnett County, GA with local news, information, political updates and events. The Web site also provides daily news updates and a community events calendar. The Web site has a printed counterpart, The Gwinnett Citizen, but features original content. Editors do not honor or sign non-disclosure agreements. The editorial lead time varies.; Full Page Mono: 28.00
Currency: US Dollars
NEWSPAPER

Gwinnett Daily Post

Owner: Southern Community Newspapers Inc.
Editorial: 725 Old Norcross Rd, Lawrenceville, Georgia 30046-4317. **T:** 1 770 963-9205
E: news@gwinnettdailypost.com
W: http://www.gwinnettdailypost.com/
Freq: Daily; **Circ:** 59425 Not Audited
Publisher: J.K. Murphy
Editorial Profile: Gwinnett Daily Post is a daily local newspaper published for residents of Gwinnett County, GA and surrounding areas. The newspaper covers all local news, weather and sports. Mailings should be sent to the PO address.; Full Page Mono: 83.67; Full Page Colour: 268.86
Currency: US Dollars
DAILY NEWSPAPER

Hagadone Corporation

Owner: Hagadone Corp.
Editorial: 105 W Lynch, Plains, Montana 59859. **T:** 1 406 826-3402
W: http://www.vp-mi.com Circ: 2016 Not Audited
Publisher: Dan Drewry; **Editor:** Justyna Tomtas
Editorial Profile: Hagadone Corporation is a community newspaper publisher producing two titles, Clark Fork Valley Press and Mineral Independent, serving readers in Sanders and Mineral County, MT.
NEWSPAPER

Hagedorn Communications

Editorial: 135 Dreiser Loop, Bronx, New York 10475-2704. **T:** 1 718 320-3071
W: http://www.bxnews.net Circ: 39300 Not Audited
Publisher: Chris Hagedorn
NEWSPAPER

Hairenik Weeklies

Owner: Hairenik Association, Inc.
Editorial: 80 Bigelow Ave, Watertown, Massachusetts 2472. **T:** 1 617 926-3974
E: manager@hairenik.com
W: http://www.hairenik.com

Editor: Zaven Torikian
Editorial Profile: Hairenik Weeklies publishes weekly newspapers that covering news and events that affect the Armenian community. They primarily cover the East Coast region, but also include content relating to the local Boston area. They target the Armenian community and those who have an interest in that community, such as congressmen and professors of Armenian studies. The word "hairenik" means "fatherland" in Armenian. The English version is called Armenian Weekly. The Armenian version, called Hairenik Weekly, is written in Armenian script. There are significant editorial differences between the two versions. The Web site has sample articles from each version. The lead time is one week.
NEWSPAPER

The Haitian Times

Editorial: 495 Flatbush Ave Fl 2, Brooklyn, New York 11225-3706. **T:** 1 646 770-2687
E: thehaitiantimes@gmail.com
W: http://www.haitiantimes.com
Freq: Wed; **Circ:** 15000 Not Audited
Editorial Profile: The Haitian Times is written for Haitian Americans living in New York City and the surrounding areas. The articles focus on news about Haiti and New York. The publication covers sports, arts & entertainment, business, and features on prominent Haitians throughout the United States. The editorial deadlines are Fridays prior to the issue date.; Full Page Mono: 13.00; Full Page Colour: 2435.94
Currency: US Dollars
NEWSPAPER

Hallettsville Publishing Company

Editorial: 108 S Texana St, Hallettsville, Texas 77964. **T:** 1 361 798-2481
E: tribuneherald@sbcglobal.net Circ: 8300 Not Audited
Publisher: Buddy Preuss; **Editor:** David True
NEWSPAPER

Halston Media

Owner: Halston Media, LLC
Editorial: 360 Underhill Ave, the Grace Building, Yorktown Heights, New York 10598-4558 **W:** http://www.halstonmedia.com
Freq: Thu
Publisher: Brett Freeman; **Editor:** Bryan Fumagalli
Editorial Profile: Halston Media is a community newspaper publisher in Yorktown Heights, NY, producing the Mahopac (NY) News, The Somers (NY) Record and Yorktown (NY) News.
NEWSPAPER

Hamlin County Publishing

Editorial: 123 E Main St, Castlewood, South Dakota 57223. **T:** 1 605 793-2293
E: hcp@itctel.com Circ: 2687 Not Audited
NEWSPAPER

Hamodia

Editorial: 207 Foster Ave, Brooklyn, New York 11230. **T:** 1 718 853-9094
E: info@hamodia.com
W: http://www.hamodia.com
Freq: Daily; **Circ:** 159931 Not Audited
Editorial Profile: Hamodia is an independently owned, local, daily newspaper serving the Jewish community throughout the New York metro area. The newspaper covers a variety of local news and events, and also features public affairs, international news and cultural topics of interest. The lead times and deadlines for the publication vary.; Full Page Mono: 18.00; Full Page Colour: 625.00
Currency: US Dollars
DAILY NEWSPAPER

The Hampton Roads Voice

Owner: Green (Jack)
Editorial: 2501 Marshall Ave, Newport News, Virginia 23607. **T:** 1 757 244-5654
E: editor@voicenewspaper.com
W: http://www.voicenewspaper.com
Freq: Thu; **Circ:** 16000 Not Audited
Editor: Algeree Johnson
Editorial Profile: The Hampton Roads Voice is a free weekly African-American newspaper covering News from, by and about African-Americans. It is distributed the Richmond and Hampton Roads metropolitan areas, including Chesterfield, Henrico, Hanover, New Kent, Charles City, Powhatan, Petersburg, Hopewell, Prince Edward, Nottoway, Newport News, Hampton, Williamsburg, Portsmouth and Virginia Beach.; Full Page Mono: 27.17
Currency: US Dollars
NEWSPAPER

The Hanahan, Goose Creek & North Charleston News

Editorial: 1231 Yeamans Hall Rd, Hanahan, South Carolina 29410-2745
E: hanahancom@aol.com
Freq: Wed; **Circ:** 14000 Not Audited
Editorial Profile: The Hanahan, Goose Creek & North Charleston News is a community newspaper for the residents of North Charleston, SC.; Full Page Mono: 10.00
Currency: US Dollars
NEWSPAPER

Hancock-Henderson Quill Inc.

Owner: Rodeffer, (Dessa)
Editorial: 102 N Broadway St, Stronghurst, Illinois 61480-5023. **T:** 1 309 924-1871
E: quill@hcil.net
W: http://www.quillnewspaper.com Circ: 2850
Publisher: Dessa Rodeffer
NEWSPAPER

Handelsblatt - New York Bureau

Editorial: 33 Irving Pl Fl 10, New York, New York 10003-2332. **T:** 49 180 536-5365
W: http://www.handelsblatt.com
Freq: Daily
Editorial Profile: This is the New York bureau of Handelsblatt in Dusseldorf, Germany.
DAILY NEWSPAPER

Handley Herald

Owner: McClatchy Newspapers
Editorial: 2401 Halbert St, Fort Worth, Texas 76112-5507
Freq: Monthly; **Circ:** 54000
Editor: William Ludwig
Editorial Profile: Handley Herald is a community newspaper for the residents of Fort Worth (TX) and the surrounding communities.; Full Page Mono: 12.87
Currency: US Dollars
NEWSPAPER

The Hanford Sentinel

Owner: Lee Enterprises, Inc.
Editorial: 300 W 6th St, Hanford, California 93230-4518. **T:** 1 559 582-0471
W: http://www.hanfordsentinel.com
Freq: Mon thru Fri; **Circ:** 7448 Not Audited
Editorial Profile: The Hanford Sentinel is the local newspaper for the Hanford, CA area. The newspaper covers local news, business, sports, agriculture and news from their local state prisons and the U.S. Navy master jet base. The newspaper also covers national stories that have a direct impact on its readership.; Full Page Mono: 32.50; Full Page Colour: 386.00
Currency: US Dollars
DAILY NEWSPAPER

Hannibal Courier-Post

Owner: GateHouse Media Inc.
Editorial: 200 N 3Rd St, Hannibal, Missouri 63401-3504. **T:** 1 573 221-2800
W: http://www.hannibal.net
Freq: Daily; **Circ:** 4853 Not Audited
Editor: Mary Lou Montgomery; **Publisher:** David Stringer
Editorial Profile: Hannibal Courier-Post is published for the residents of Hannibal, MO and surrounding areas. The newspaper covers local news, politics, sports, business and arts & entertainment. It also covers national stories that have an impact on the newspaper's readership.; Full Page Mono: 15.10; Full Page Colour: 140.00
Currency: US Dollars
DAILY NEWSPAPER

Harbor Country News

Owner: Paxton Media Group
Editorial: 121 W. Michigan, Michigan City, Indiana 46360. **T:** 1 269 469-1410
E: harborcountrynews@yahoo.com
W: http://www.harborcountry-news.com
Freq: Thu; **Circ:** 13500 Not Audited
Publisher: Bill Hackney; **Editor:** David Johnson
Editorial Profile: Harbor Country News is the local newspaper for the regions of New Buffalo, Three Oaks and Bridgeman, MI. It covers local news, business, sports and arts & entertainment, as well as national and statewide stories if they have a direct impact on the readership. Deadlines are on Fridays at 5pm ET.; Full Page Mono: 10.50
Currency: US Dollars
NEWSPAPER

Hardin County News

Owner: Beaumont Enterprise-Hearst Newspapers
Editorial: 522 N Main St, Lumberton, Texas 77657-7351. **T:** 1 409 755-4912
E: hardincounty@beaumontenterprise.com
W: http://www.beaumontenterprise.com/

community-news/hcn
Freq: Wed; **Circ:** 21000 Not Audited
Editor: Jay Cockrell; **Publisher:** Bill Offill
Editorial Profile: Hardin County News is a weekly local newspaper for Hardin County, TX. The newspaper covers local news, business, sports, religion, education and arts & entertainment stories. The newspaper also covers national and statewide stories if they have a direct impact on the newspaper's readership. All inquiries should be addressed to the editor. Deadlines are Fridays at 5pm CT for the Wednesday issue.; Full Page Mono: 10.00
Currency: US Dollars
NEWSPAPER

The Harlan Daily Enterprise

Owner: Heartland Publications
Editorial: 1548 S US Highway 421, Harlan, Kentucky 40831-2501. **T:** 1 606 573-4510
W: http://www.harlandaily.com
Freq: Mon thru Fri; **Circ:** 6581 Not Audited
Editorial Profile: The Harlan Daily Enterprise is a local, daily newspaper that provides local news coverage for residents of Harlan, KY. The paper covers local news, business, sports and arts & entertainment, as well as state and national news that has a direct impact on the newspaper's readership. Deadlines are at 1pm ET.; Full Page Mono: 14.29; Full Page Colour: 275.00
Currency: US Dollars
DAILY NEWSPAPER

Harlan Newspapers

Owner: Tribune Newspapers Inc
Editorial: 1114 7th St, Harlan, Iowa 51537.
T: 1 712 755-3111
E: news2@harlanonline.com
W: http://www.harlanonline.com Circ: 10216 Not Audited
Editor: Bob Bjoin; **Editor:** Mike Oeffner; **Editor:** Kim Wegener
NEWSPAPER

Harrisburg Daily Newspapers

Owner: GateHouse Media Inc.
Editorial: 35 S Vine St, Harrisburg, Illinois 62946-1725. **T:** 1 618 253-7146
E: hbgnews@yourclearwave.com
W: http://www.dailyregister.com
Freq: Daily; **Circ:** 7070 Not Audited
Publisher: Kevin Haezebroeck
DAILY NEWSPAPER

Harrison Daily Times

Owner: Neighbor Newspapers
Editorial: 111 W Rush Ave, Harrison, Arkansas 72601-4218. **T:** 1 870 741-2325
E: news@harrisondaily.com
W: http://www.harrisondaily.com
Freq: Daily; **Circ:** 10439 Not Audited
Publisher: Ronnie Bell; **Editor:** Dwain Lair;
Editor: Dwain Lair
Editorial Profile: Harrison Daily Times is published Monday through Friday and on Sunday. The newspaper is distributed to five Arkansas counties and parts of Southern Missouri. It covers local and regional news, business, sports, consumer interest, finance, lifestyles and community events. Send information to PO Box address only.; Full Page Mono: 13.15; Full Page Colour: 130.00
Currency: US Dollars
DAILY NEWSPAPER

Harrison News-Herald

Owner: Schloss Media, Inc.
Editorial: 144 S Main St, Cadiz, Ohio 43907-1133. **T:** 1 740 942-2118
E: info@harrisonnewsherald.com
W: http://www.harrisonnewsherald.com
Freq: Sat; **Circ:** 15600 Not Audited
Editorial Profile: Harrison News-Herald is published weekly for the Harrison County and Cadiz, OH area. The newspaper covers local news, sports, business and arts & entertainment. It also covers national stories if they have a local impact.; Full Page Mono: 9.95
Currency: US Dollars
NEWSPAPER

The Hartford Courant

Owner: Tribune Company
Editorial: 285 Broad St, Hartford, Connecticut 06105-3785. **T:** 1 860 241-6200
W: http://www.courant.com
Freq: Daily; **Circ:** 120473 Not Audited
Publisher: Nancy Meyer
Editorial Profile: The Hartford Courant is a daily, general-interest broadsheet newspaper written for the general public in the Hartford, CT area. Its mission is to provide news and information to a general readership.; Full Page Mono: 280.00; Full Page Colour: 925.19

Currency: US Dollars
DAILY NEWSPAPER

The Hartford Courant
Editorial: 101 Phoenix Ave, Enfield, Connecticut 06082-4471
DAILY NEWSPAPER

The Hartford Courant
Editorial: 200 Adams St, Manchester, Connecticut 06042-1915
DAILY NEWSPAPER

The Hartford Courant
Editorial: 373 E Main St, Middletown, Connecticut 06457-4556
DAILY NEWSPAPER

Hartford Publications
Owner: Hartford Publications
Editorial: 563 Franklin Ave, Hartford, Connecticut 06114-3019. T: 1 860 296-6128
E: hartfordpubs@aol.com
W: http://www.greaterhartford.com
Editor: Kelley Bates
NEWSPAPER

Hartselle Enquirer/Morgan Countian
Owner: Boone Newspapers, Inc.
Editorial: 407 Chestnut St Nw, Hartselle, Alabama 35640-2407. T: 1 256 773-6566
E: news@hartselleenquirer.com
W: http://www.hartselleenquirer.com
Circ: 7000
Publisher: Randy Garrison
NEWSPAPER

The Harvest
Owner: Diocese of Great Falls/Billings
Editorial: 121 23rd St S, Great Falls, Montana 59401-3939 E: vicargeneral@diocesegfb.org
W: http://diocesegfb.org/harvest_449.html
Freq: Bi-Monthly; Circ: 18000
Editor: Jay Peterson; Publisher: Michael Warfel
Editorial Profile: The Harvest is a bi-monthly newspaper for the Diocese of Great Falls/Billings, MT.; Full Page Mono: 19.25
Currency: US Dollars
NEWSPAPER

The Hastings Tribune
Owner: Seaton Newspapers
Editorial: 908 W 2Nd St, Hastings, Nebraska 68901-5063. T: 1 402 462-2131
E: tribune@hastingstribune.com
W: http://www.hastingstribune.com
Freq: Daily; Circ: 10811 Not Audited
Editorial Profile: The Hastings Tribune is a local, daily newspaper for the Hastings, NE area. The newspaper does not publish an edition on Sundays. It covers local news, business, sports and arts & entertainment. It also covers national and statewide stories if they have a direct impact on the newspaper's readership.; Full Page Mono: 12.95; Full Page Colour: 55.13
Currency: US Dollars
DAILY NEWSPAPER

Hattiesburg American
Owner: Gannett Co., Inc.
Editorial: 825 N Main St, Hattiesburg, Mississippi 39401-3433. T: 1 601 582-4321
E: news@hattiesburgamerican.com
W: http://www.hattiesburgamerican.com
Freq: Daily; Circ: 8421 Not Audited
Editorial Profile: Hattiesburg American is the daily newspaper for the Hattiesburg, MS area. The newspaper covers local news, business, sports, and arts & entertainment stories. The newspaper also covers national and statewide stories if they have a direct impact on the newspaper's readership. All inquiries should be addressed to the executive editor.; Full Page Mono: 28.25; Full Page Colour: 98.09
Currency: US Dollars
DAILY NEWSPAPER

Hattiesburg Publishing Inc.
Owner: Emmerich Newspapers Inc.
Editorial: 103 N 40th Ave, Hattiesburg, Mississippi 39401-6606. T: 1 601 268-2331
W: http://www.hubcityspokes.com Circ: 10400 Not Audited
NEWSPAPER

Havre Daily News
Owner: Havre Daily News, Inc.
Editorial: 119 2nd St, Havre, Montana 59501-3507. T: 1 406 265-6795
E: news@havredailynews.com
W: http://www.havredailynews.com
Freq: Mon thru Fri; Circ: 4280 Not Audited
Editorial Profile: Havre Daily News is published for the residents of Havre, MT and

surrounding areas. It focuses on local news, sports, agriculture, business, editorials and arts & entertainment. It also includes national stories if they have an impact on the newspaper's readership.; Full Page Mono: 10.50; Full Page Colour: 4.00
Currency: US Dollars
DAILY NEWSPAPER

Hawaii Army Weekly
Owner: Gannett Co., Inc.
Editorial: Public Affairs Office, USAG-HI, 314 Sasaoka St, Schofield Barracks, Hawaii 96857. T: 1 808 656-3155
E: editor@hawaiiarmyweekly.com
W: http://www.hawaiiarmyweekly.com
Freq: Fri; Circ: 15300 Not Audited
News Editor: Sarah Pacheco
Editorial Profile: Hawaii Army Weekly provides news and information for and about the United States Army Base in Achifield Barracks, HI. The weekly newspaper is published for soldiers, their family members and civilians. Deadlines are on Fridays prior to issue date.; Full Page Mono: 13.21
Currency: US Dollars
NEWSPAPER

Hawaii Hochi
Owner: Shizuoka Shimbun
Editorial: 917 Kokea St, Honolulu, Hawaii 96817-4528. T: 1 808 845-2255
E: oioi@hawaii.rr.com
Freq: Daily; Circ: 3000 Not Audited
Editor in Chief: Noriyoshi Kanaizumi;
Publisher: Paul Yempuku
Editorial Profile: Japanese & English language.; Full Page Mono: 16.20
Currency: US Dollars
DAILY NEWSPAPER

The Hawk Eye
Owner: Harris Enterprises
Editorial: 800 S Main St, Burlington, Iowa 52601-5870. T: 1 319 754-8461
E: news@thehawkeye.com
W: http://www.thehawkeye.com
Freq: Daily; Circ: 18777 Not Audited
Editor: John Gaines
Editorial Profile: The Hawk Eye is the daily local newspaper for the Des Moines, Lee, Henry, Jefferson, Washington, Louisa and Van Buren counties of Iowa. The newspaper covers local news, arts & entertainment, sports and business stories.; Full Page Mono: 21.28; Full Page Colour: 290.00
Currency: US Dollars
DAILY NEWSPAPER

Al Hayat - New York Bureau
Editorial: United Nations Building, 16th Fl, New York, New York 10017.
T: 1 212 486-0576
DAILY NEWSPAPER

Haynes Publishing Company
Editorial: 310 Washington, Saint Francis, Kansas 67756. T: 1 785 332-3162
E: sf.herald@nwkansas.com Circ: 1671 Not Audited
NEWSPAPER

The Hays Daily News
Owner: Harris Enterprises
Editorial: 507 Main St, Hays, Kansas 67601-4228. T: 1 785 628-1081
W: http://www.hdnews.net
Freq: Daily; Circ: 12514 Not Audited
Editorial Profile: The Hays Daily News is written for the residents of Hays, KS and surrounding areas. The newspaper covers local news, sports, weather, politics and community events.; Full Page Mono: 16.07; Full Page Colour: 330.00
Currency: US Dollars
DAILY NEWSPAPER

Headlight Newspapers
Owner: Fisher's Publishing Co.
Editorial: 908 W Broadway St, Morrilton, Arkansas 72110-3329. T: 1 501 354-2451
E: pjch@suddenlinkmail.com
W: http://www.headlightnews.com
Freq: Wed; Circ: 6800 Not Audited
Publisher: David Fisher; Editor: Larry Miller;
Full Page Mono: 13.00
Currency: US Dollars
NEWSPAPER

The Healdsburg Tribune & Windsor Times
Owner: Sonoma West Publishers
Editorial: 5 Mitchell Ln, Healdsburg, California 95448. T: 1 707 838-9211
E: news@sonomawest.com Circ: 7100 Not Audited
Publisher: Rollie Atkinson; Editor: Greg

Clementi; Editor: Kerrie Russell
NEWSPAPER

Hellenic Times
Editorial: 823 11th Ave, Fl 5, New York, New York 10019. T: 1 212 986-6881
E: hellenictimes@aol.com
Freq: Fri; Circ: 15000 Not Audited
Editor In Chief: James Kapsalis
Editorial Profile: Hellenic Times serves Greek Americans and those interested in the Greek American community. The newspaper contains news and features that are relevant and of interest to the Greek American community.; Full Page Mono: 9.00
Currency: US Dollars
NEWSPAPER

The Hellenic Voice
Owner: Mosaic Communications Group
Editorial: 80 Hayden Ave Ste 110, Lexington, Massachusetts 02421-7962.
T: 1 781 402-0027
E: editor@thehellenicvoice.com
W: http://www.thehellenicvoice.com
Freq: Wed; Circ: 20000 Not Audited
News Editor: Steve Crowe
Editorial Profile: The Hellenic Voice is a weekly newspaper seeking to establish a greater awareness of the social and economic advancement of all Hellenes, while recognizing, unifying and strengthening the Hellenic values and the power the community has to enhance its future.; Full Page Mono: 11.64
Currency: US Dollars
NEWSPAPER

Henderson Daily Dispatch
Owner: Paxton Media Group
Editorial: 304 S Chestnut St, Henderson, North Carolina 27536-4225.
T: 1 252 436-2700
E: news@hendersondispatch.com
W: http://www.hendersondispatch.com
Freq: Daily; Circ: 6261 Not Audited
News Editor: Allie Rae Mauser
Editorial Profile: Henderson Daily Dispatch is the daily newspaper of Henderson and Vance counties, NC. It covers local and national news, lifestyle and sports. Deadlines are daily at 7pm ET.; Full Page Mono: 19.02; Full Page Colour: 175.81
Currency: US Dollars
DAILY NEWSPAPER

Henderson Daily News
Owner: Hartman Newspapers, Inc.
Editorial: 1711 US Highway 79 S, Henderson, Texas 75654-4509. T: 1 903 657-2501
W: http://www.hendersondailynews.com
Freq: Daily; Circ: 6039 Not Audited
Editorial Profile: Henderson Daily News covers community news for the residents of the Henderson, TX area. Deadlines are 11am CT one day prior to the issue date.; Full Page Mono: 9.43; Full Page Colour: 11.52
Currency: US Dollars
DAILY NEWSPAPER

Hendersonville Star-News
Owner: Gannett Co., Inc.
Editorial: 1 Examiner Ct, Gallatin, Tennessee 37066-7111. T: 1 615 824-8480
E: hsnnews@mtcngroup.com
W: http://www.hendersonvillestarnews.com
Freq: Fri; Circ: 18500 Not Audited
Editor: Sarah Kingsbury
Editorial Profile: Hendersonville Star-News is a free publication written for residents of Sumner County, TN. It covers local news, sports, and events. Deadlines for the publication are Monday for the Wednesday issue and Wednesday for the Friday issue.; Full Page Mono: 17.00
Currency: US Dollars
NEWSPAPER

Henrico Citizen
Owner: T3 Media, LLC
Editorial: 4807 Hermitage Rd, Ste 204, Richmond, Virginia 23227. T: 1 804 262-1700
E: citizen@henricocitizen.com
W: http://www.henricocitizen.com
Freq: Bi-Weekly; Circ: 17500 Not Audited
Editor: Tom Lappas
Editorial Profile: Henrico Citizen is a bi-weekly newspaper written for the residents of Richmond, VA.; Full Page Mono: 40.00
Currency: US Dollars
NEWSPAPER

Henry Daily Herald
Owner: Southern Community Newspapers Inc.
Editorial: 38 Sloan St, McDonough, Georgia 30253-3102. T: 1 770 957-9161
W: http://www.henryherald.com

Freq: Daily; Circ: 39909 Not Audited
Publisher: Bonnie Pratt; Editor: Jim Zachary
Editorial Profile: Henry Daily Herald is a newspaper written for residents of Henry County, GA. It covers local news, sports, government, education, business and events. It combines its coverage with the Clayton News Daily in Jonesboro, GA on Saturdays.; Full Page Mono: 10.55
Currency: US Dollars
DAILY NEWSPAPER

Henry Newspapers
Editorial: 709 3rd St, Henry, Illinois 61537.
T: 1 309 364-3250 E: henrynews@verizon.net
Circ: 3750
Editor: Doug Ziegler
NEWSPAPER

The Herald
Owner: Jasper Herald Company
Editorial: 216 E 4th St, Jasper, Indiana 47546-3102. T: 1 812 482-2424
E: news@dcherald.com
W: http://www.dcherald.com
Freq: Mon thru Fri; Circ: 10500 Not Audited
Editor: Dawn Mazur
Editorial Profile: The Herald is published daily for resident of Jasper, IN and surrounding areas. The newspaper covers local and national news, sports, business and entertainment.; Full Page Mono: 11.40
Currency: US Dollars
DAILY NEWSPAPER

The Herald
Owner: Community Newspaper Holdings, Inc.
Editorial: 52 S Dock St, Sharon, Pennsylvania 16146. T: 1 724 981-6100
E: edletters@sharonherald.com
W: http://www.sharonherald.com
Freq: Daily; Circ: 15250 Not Audited
Editor: Nancy Ash; Editor: James Raykie;
Editor: Michael Roknick; Publisher: Sharon Sorg; Editor: Joe Wiercinski
Editorial Profile: The Herald is the leading daily newspaper in the Mercer County, PA. area. It covers the Mercer County and the Shenango Valley as well as the adjacent towns in the New Wilmington/Volant area. The newspaper covers loca and national news, business, sports, religion, education, lifestyle and entertainment.; Full Page Mono: 39.32; Full Page Colour: 54.44
Currency: US Dollars
DAILY NEWSPAPER

The Herald
Owner: McClatchy Newspapers
Editorial: 132 W Main St, Rock Hill, South Carolina 29730-4430. T: 1 803 329-4000
W: http://www.heraldonline.com
Freq: Daily; Circ: 22317 Not Audited
Publisher: Debbie Abels; Editor: Paul Osmundson; News Editor: Chris Sherk
Editorial Profile: The Herald is a daily newspaper serving the counties of York, Chester and Lancaster, SC. The publication covers local news, community events, sports and lifestyles. Deadlines are the day prior to issue date.; Full Page Mono: 43.82; Full Page Colour: 134.90
Currency: US Dollars
DAILY NEWSPAPER

The Herald
Owner: Black Press Ltd.
Editorial: 1213 California St, Everett, Washington 98201-3445. T: 1 425 339-3000
E: newstips@heraldnet.com
W: http://www.heraldnet.com
Freq: Daily; Circ: 39477 Not Audited
News Editor: Mark Carlson; Publisher: David Davisman
Editorial Profile: The Herald is written for residents of Snohomish and Island counties in Washington. It features world, national, state and local news, sports, opinion and the economy. It also provides its readers with a lifestyle section each day of the week.; Full Page Mono: 71.04; Full Page Colour: 1180.00
Currency: US Dollars
DAILY NEWSPAPER

The Herald
Editorial: 1803 Barnard St, Savannah, Georgia 31401-8066. T: 1 912 232-4505
E: news@savannahherald.net
Freq: Wed; Circ: 12000 Not Audited
Editorial Profile: The Herald is written for the African American community in Savannah, GA. The paper features social events, editorial columns and a church section. Deadlines are on Mondays at noon ET.; Full Page Mono: 12.00; Full Page Colour: 1107.00
Currency: US Dollars
NEWSPAPER

The Herald
Owner: McClatchy Newspapers
Editorial: 228 E Market St, Smithfield, North Carolina 27577-3918. **T:** 1 919 934-2176
W: http://www.theherald-nc.com
Freq: Wed; **Circ:** 30400 Not Audited
Editor: D. Best; **Editor:** D. Best; **Editor:** D. Best; **Editor:** D. Best; **Publisher:** Felicia Gressette
Editorial Profile: The Herald is a published weekly for the residents of Smithfield, NC and surrounding areas. The newspaper covers local news, sports, business and arts & entertainment.; Full Page Mono: 37.68; Full Page Colour: 418.00
Currency: US Dollars
NEWSPAPER

The Herald
Owner: McClatchy Newspapers
Editorial: 103 W Stewart, Puyallup, Washington 98371-4369. **T:** 1 253 841-2481
W: http://www.puyallupherald.com
Freq: Wed; **Circ:** 25000 Not Audited
Publisher: George Le Masurier; **Editor:** Brian McLean
Editorial Profile: The Herald, formerly known as the Pierce County Herald, is a weekly newspaper serving the residents of Puyallup, South Hill, Sumner, Bonney Lake and Edgewood, WA. Deadlines are on Mondays at noon PT.; Full Page Mono: 9.50
Currency: US Dollars
NEWSPAPER

Herald & Journal Newspapers
Editorial: 119 6th St, Hawley, Minnesota 56549. **T:** 1 218 483-3306
E: news@claycountyunion.net **Circ:** 5200 Not Audited
Editor: Marc Ness; **Publisher:** Eugene Prim
NEWSPAPER

Herald & Review
Owner: Lee Enterprises, Inc.
Editorial: 601 E William St, Decatur, Illinois 62523-1190. **T:** 1 217 429-5151
E: hrnews@herald-review.com
W: http://www.herald-review.com
Freq: Daily; **Circ:** 25026 Not Audited
Editorial Profile: Herald & Review is written for residents of Decatur, IL and the surrounding area. It covers, local news, weather, sports, politics, religion, business, entertainment, law, education, health, opinion and lifestyles in the Decatur, IL area.; Full Page Mono: 50.80; Full Page Colour: 165.77
Currency: US Dollars
DAILY NEWSPAPER

The Herald Bulletin
Owner: Community Newspaper Holdings, Inc.
Editorial: 1133 Jackson St, Anderson, Indiana 46016. **T:** 1 765 622-1212
E: newsroom@heraldbulletin.com
W: http://www.theheraldbulletin.com
Freq: Daily; **Circ:** 19809 Not Audited
Publisher: Henry Bird
Editorial Profile: The Herald Bulletin is a daily newspaper written for Madison, Delaware, Hamilton and Henry counties, IN. The newspaper covers local and national news, sports, business, community news and obituaries. Deadlines are at 5pm ET.; Full Page Mono: 30.50; Full Page Colour: 32.50
Currency: US Dollars
DAILY NEWSPAPER

The Herald Company of Oklahoma Inc.
Editorial: 439 W Main St, Healdton, Oklahoma 73438. **T:** 1 580 229-0147
E: healdtonherald@att.net **Circ:** 2580
Publisher: Christi Blakemore
Editorial Profile: Publishes the Wilson Post-Democrat and the Healdton Herald.
NEWSPAPER

Herald Democrat
Owner: Stephens Media Group
Editorial: 603 S Sam Rayburn Fwy, Sherman, Texas 75090-7258. **T:** 1 903 893-8181
E: news@heralddemocrat.com
W: http://www.heralddemocrat.com
Freq: Daily; **Circ:** 17000 Not Audited
Editor: Jonathan Cannon; **Publisher:** John Wright
Editorial Profile: Herald Democrat is written for the residents of Sherman, TX. It covers local news, weather, sports, business and entertainment.; Full Page Mono: 27.30; Full Page Colour: 28.30
Currency: US Dollars
DAILY NEWSPAPER

Herald Journal
Owner: Community Media Group
Editorial: 114 S Main St, Monticello, Indiana 47960-2328. **T:** 1 574 583-5121
E: editor@rensselaerrepublican.com
W: http://www.newsbug.info/monticello_herald_journal/
Freq: Daily; **Circ:** 4500 Not Audited
Publisher: Don Hurd; **Editor:** Trent Wright
Editorial Profile: Herald Journal is a local newspaper written for the residents of Monticello, IN. The newspaper is published daily Monday through Saturday. There is no Sunday edition. The publication covers local news, sports, education/schools and business in the Monticello, IN area. Deadlines are at noon CT.; Full Page Mono: 14.50; Full Page Colour: 49.66
Currency: US Dollars
DAILY NEWSPAPER

The Herald Journal
Owner: Pioneer Newspapers
Editorial: 75 W 300 N, Logan, Utah 84321-3971. **T:** 1 435 752-2121
E: hjnews@hjnews.com
W: http://www.hjnews.com
Freq: Daily; **Circ:** 15533 Not Audited
News Editor: Chuck Nunn; **Publisher:** Mike Starn
Editorial Profile: The Herald Journal is written for the residents of the Logan, UT area. It covers local and city news, sports, arts & entertainment and other relevant topics of interest.; Full Page Mono: 14.47; Full Page Colour: 280.00
Currency: US Dollars
DAILY NEWSPAPER

Herald Monthly
Owner: Chinese Christian Herald Crusades
Editorial: 48 Allen St, New York, New York 10002-5304. **T:** 1 718 799-8248
E: herald@cchc.org **W:** http://www.cchc.org
Freq: Monthly; **Circ:** 510000 Not Audited
Editorial Profile: Herald Monthly is a community newspaper serving the Christian Chinese community.; Full Page Mono: 50.00
Currency: US Dollars
NEWSPAPER

The Herald News
Owner: GateHouse Media Inc.
Editorial: 207 Pocasset St, Fall River, Massachusetts 2722. **T:** 1 508 676-8211
E: news@heraldnews.com
W: http://www.heraldnews.com
Freq: Daily; **Circ:** 12128 Not Audited
Publisher: Lisa Strattan; **Editor In Chief:** Lynne Sullivan; **Editor In Chief:** Lynne Sullivan
Editorial Profile: The Herald News is a daily newspaper serving Fall River, MA and the surrounding area. It covers news, sports, business and lifestyle.; Full Page Mono: 35.00
Currency: US Dollars
DAILY NEWSPAPER

The Herald News
Owner: Rhea County Publishing Co.
Editorial: 3687 Rhea County Hwy, Dayton, Tennessee 37321. **T:** 1 423 775-6111
E: news@rheaheraldnews.com
W: http://www.rheaheraldnews.com
Freq: Sun; **Circ:** 13700 Not Audited
Publisher: Sarah Jane Locke
Editorial Profile: The Herald News is a local newspaper published for the residents in Rhea County, TN. The newspaper covers local news, events, sports, business and weather.; Full Page Mono: 17.35
Currency: US Dollars
NEWSPAPER

Herald Newspapers
Owner: Seawave Corporation
Editorial: 1508 Route 47, Rio Grande, New Jersey 08242-1413. **T:** 1 609 886-8600
E: newsdesk@cmcherald.com
W: http://www.capemaycountyherald.com
Circ: 33100
Publisher: Arthur Hall
Editorial Profile: Herald Newspapers is a community newspaper publisher serving the residents of Cape May County in NJ.
NEWSPAPER

Herald Newspapers, Inc.
Editorial: 1435 E Hyde Park Blvd, Chicago, Illinois 60615-3009. **T:** 1 773 643-8533
E: hpherald@aol.com
W: http://www.hpherald.com **Circ:** 33000 Not Audited
Editor: Gabriel Piemonte; **Publisher:** Bruce Sagan
Editorial Profile: Herald Newspapers, Inc. is a publication delivering local newspapers to Chicago, IL.
NEWSPAPER

Herald Publications
Owner: Better Newspapers Inc.
Editorial: 314 E Church St, Mascoutah, Illinois 62258. **T:** 1 618 566-8282
E: heraldpubs@heraldpubs.com
W: http://www.heraldpubs.com
Freq: Thu; **Circ:** 9000 Not Audited
Editor: Keith Gillett; **Editor:** Pamela Rensing
Editorial Profile: Publishes the Fairview Heights Tribune, the Clinton County News, the Mascoutah Herald, and the Scott Flier.; Full Page Mono: 10.47
Currency: US Dollars
NEWSPAPER

Herald Publications - Arthur
Owner: Better Newspapers Inc.
Editorial: 113 E Illinois St, Arthur, Illinois 61911-1331. **T:** 1 217 543-2151 **Circ:** 6700 Not Audited
Publisher: Greg Hoskins
Editorial Profile: Herald Publications - Arthur publishes two community weeklies that serve residents in Douglas, Piatt and Macon counties in Illinois. It's corporate offices are in Mascoutah, IL.
NEWSPAPER

Herald Publications - Villa Grove
Editorial: 5 7 S Main St, Villa Grove, Illinois 61956-1522. **T:** 1 217 832-4201
E: vgnews@mchsi.com **Circ:** 4200 Not Audited
Publisher: Greg Hoskins; **Editor:** Nate Thompson; Full Page Mono: 4.85
Currency: US Dollars
NEWSPAPER

Herald Publishing Co.
Owner: Courier Herald Publishing Company
Editorial: 4075 W Main St, Soperton, Georgia 30457-2325. **T:** 1 912 529-6624 **Circ:** 5081 Not Audited
Editor: Jonathon Finley; **Publisher:** Griffin Lovett; **Editor:** Betty McCoy
Editorial Profile: The Herald Publishing Company Newspapers prefer to be contacted via e-mail.
NEWSPAPER

Herald Republican
Owner: KPC Media Group Inc.
Editorial: 45 S Public Sq, Angola, Indiana 46703-1970. **T:** 1 260 665-3117
W: http://www.heraldrepublicanonline.com
Freq: Daily; **Circ:** 4027
Publisher: Terry Housholder; **Editor:** Michael Marturello; **Editor:** Amy Oberlin
Editorial Profile: Herald Republican provides news and information for Steuben County, IN.; Full Page Mono: 12.81; Full Page Colour: 46.80
Currency: US Dollars
DAILY NEWSPAPER

Herald Times Reporter
Owner: Gannett Co., Inc.
Editorial: 902 Franklin St, Manitowoc, Wisconsin 54220-4514. **T:** 1 920 684-4433
E: htrnews@htrnews.com
W: http://www.htrnews.com
Freq: Daily; **Circ:** 9274 Not Audited
News Editor: Russ Budzisz; **Publisher:** Kevin Corrado
Editorial Profile: Herald Times Reporter is a daily newspaper that serves the residents of Manitowoc, WI. It covers national, state and local news, business, community events, editorials, features, arts & entertainment and sports. It shares offices with the weekly Lakeshore Chronicle.; Full Page Mono: 37.40; Full Page Colour: 50.81
Currency: US Dollars
DAILY NEWSPAPER

Herald/Country Market
Owner: B&B Publishing Co., Inc.
Editorial: 500 Brown Blvd, Bourbonnais, Illinois 60914. **T:** 1 815 933-1131
E: news@bbherald.com
W: http://www.bbherald.com
Freq: Weekly; **Circ:** 36000
Publisher: Toby Olszewski
Editorial Profile: The Herald and the Country Market are weekly publications mailed each Tuesday to residents of Bourbonnais, Bradley, Manteno Village, Aroma Park, Beecher, Grant Park, Hirscher, Manhattan, Momence, Peotone, St. Anne, rural Routes 1 and 17 in Wilmington, and other surrounding areas.; Full Page Mono: 16.00
Currency: US Dollars
NEWSPAPER

The Herald-Banner
Owner: Community Newspaper Holdings, Inc.
Editorial: 2305 King St, Greenville, Texas 75401-3257. **T:** 1 903 455-4220
W: http://www.heraldbanner.com
Freq: Daily; **Circ:** 8283 Not Audited
Publisher: Lisa Chappell; **Editor:** Caleb Slinkard
Editorial Profile: The Herald-Banner is a local daily newspaper written for the residents of Greenville, TX. The newspaper covers local, national and international news, sports and features. The outlet offers RSS (Really Simple Syndication).; Full Page Mono: 15.96; Full Page Colour: 270.00
Currency: US Dollars
DAILY NEWSPAPER

Herald-Banner Publications
Owner: Community Newspaper Holdings, Inc.
Editorial: 2305 King St, Greenville, Texas 75401. **T:** 1 903 455-4220
W: http://www.heraldbanner.com
Freq: Weekly; **Circ:** 19200 Not Audited
Publisher: Lisa Chappell; **Editor:** David Wilfong
NEWSPAPER

Herald-Citizen
Owner: Cookeville Newspapers Inc.
Editorial: 1300 Neal St, Cookeville, Tennessee 38501-4330. **T:** 1 931 526-9715
E: editor@herald-citizen.com
W: http://www.herald-citizen.com
Freq: Daily; **Circ:** 9352 Not Audited
Publisher: Mike DeLapp; **Editor:** Buddy Pearson
Editorial Profile: Herald-Citizen is written for the residents of Cookeville and Putnam County, TN. The newspaper is published daily except for Saturday. It covers local news, sports, lifestyles, education, religion, business and entertainment. The paper does NOT accept press releases or submissions. Deadlines are 11am ET the day before issue date.; Full Page Mono: 12.35; Full Page Colour: 106.00
Currency: US Dollars
DAILY NEWSPAPER

The Herald-Dispatch
Owner: Champion Industries Inc.
Editorial: 946 5th Ave, Huntington, West Virginia 25701. **T:** 1 304 526-4000
E: news@herald-dispatch.com
W: http://www.herald-dispatch.com
Freq: Daily; **Circ:** 26601 Not Audited
News Editor: Don Willis
Editorial Profile: The Herald-Dispatch is published for the residents of Huntington, WV, Southern Ohio, and Eastern Kentucky. The daily newspaper covers local news, sports, entertainment, police, education, health and religion.; Full Page Mono: 82.73; Full Page Colour: 496.85
Currency: US Dollars
DAILY NEWSPAPER

The Herald-Mail
Owner: Schurz Communications Inc.
Editorial: 100 Summit Ave, Hagerstown, Maryland 21740-5509. **T:** 1 301 733-5131
E: news@herald-mail.com
W: http://www.herald-mail.com
Freq: Daily; **Circ:** 23637 Not Audited
Publisher: Andy Bruns
Editorial Profile: The Herald-Mail is a local morning newspaper. It is published for the residents of the Washington County, MD tri-state area, which includes Washington and Frederick counties, MD; Fulton and Franklin counties, PA; Berkeley, Jefferson and Morgan counties, WV; and Frederick County, VA.; Full Page Mono: 24.42; Full Page Colour: 34.42
Currency: US Dollars
DAILY NEWSPAPER

The Herald-News
Owner: Shaw Media
Editorial: 2175 Oneida St, Joliet, Illinois 60435-6560. **T:** 1 815 280-4101
E: news@theherald-news.com
W: http://www.theherald-news.com
Freq: Mon thru Fri; **Circ:** 33310 Not Audited
News Editor: Bob Okon; **Editor:** Kate Schott
Editorial Profile: The Herald-News is a daily newspaper written for the residents of Joliet, IL and the suburban communities of Chicago. The paper covers local news, business, sports and lifestyle.; Full Page Mono: 33.00; Full Page Colour: 300.00
Currency: US Dollars
DAILY NEWSPAPER

Herald-News Publishers, Inc.
Editorial: 408 Main St, Wolf Point, Montana 59201-1534. **T:** 1 406 653-2222
E: herald@nemont.net
W: http://www.wolfpointherald.com/
Circ: 1817 Not Audited
Publisher: Darla Shumway; Full Page Mono: 19.11; Full Page Colour: 120.00

Currency: US Dollars
NEWSPAPER

El Heraldo News
Editorial: 4532 Columbia Ave, Dallas, Texas 75226-1016. **T:** 1 214 827-9700
E: editorial@elheraldonews.com
W: http://www.elheraldonews.com
Freq: Fri; **Circ:** 25000 Not Audited
Publisher: Asminda Rayo; **Editor:** Francisco Rayo
Editorial Profile: El Heraldo News is a Spanish-language newspaper serving the Dallas metro area. It contains local, national and international news, sports and entertainment stories of interest to the local Hispanic population.; Full Page Mono: 25.00
Currency: US Dollars
NEWSPAPER

The Herald-Palladium
Owner: Paxton Media Group
Editorial: 3450 Hollywood Rd, Saint Joseph, Michigan 49085-9155. **T:** 1 269 429-2400
E: localnews@heraldpalladium.com
W: http://www.heraldpalladium.com
Freq: Daily; **Circ:** 11659 Not Audited
Publisher: David Holgate; **News Editor:** Steve Jewell
Editorial Profile: The Herald-Palladium is a daily newspaper focused on reporting the news in Southwest Michigan. The paper features local news, business, sports, world, health, stock market and entertainment news.; Full Page Mono: 29.16; Full Page Colour: 475.00
Currency: US Dollars
DAILY NEWSPAPER

Herald-Standard
Owner: Calkins Media
Editorial: 8 E Church St #18, Uniontown, Pennsylvania 15401-3563. **T:** 1 724 439-7500
E: hsnews@heraldstandard.com
W: http://www.heraldstandard.com
Freq: Daily; **Circ:** 20636 Not Audited
Publisher: Bob Pinarski
Editorial Profile: Herald Standard is a local newspaper for the residents of Uniontown, PA. The editorial content covers local news, sports, community events and entertainment.; Full Page Mono: 44.95; Full Page Colour: 264.71
Currency: US Dollars
DAILY NEWSPAPER

Herald-Star
Owner: Ogden Newspapers
Editorial: 401 Herald Sq, Steubenville, Ohio 43952-2090. **T:** 1 740 283-4711
E: newsroom@heraldstaronline.com
W: http://www.heraldstaronline.com
Freq: Daily; **Circ:** 9228 Not Audited
Publisher: Alex Marshall; **News Editor:** Fred Rossano
Editorial Profile: Herald-Star is a daily, local newspaper serving the Steubenville, OH area. Local, national and international news are covered, as well as sports, entertainment and lifestyle information.; Full Page Mono: 31.19; Full Page Colour: 484.56
Currency: US Dollars
DAILY NEWSPAPER

Herald-Star Newspapers
Owner: Ogden Newspapers
Editorial: 401 Herald Sq, Steubenville, Ohio 43952. **T:** 1 740 283-4711
E: newsroom@heraldstaronline.com
W: http://www.heraldstaronline.com
Circ: 32555 Not Audited
Publisher: Alex Marshall
NEWSPAPER

The Herald-Sun
Owner: Paxton Media Group
Editorial: 2828 Pickett Rd, Durham, North Carolina 27705-5613. **T:** 1 919 419-6500
E: news@heraldsun.com
W: http://www.heraldsun.com
Freq: Daily; **Circ:** 21367 Not Audited
Editor: Bob Ashley; **Publisher:** Rick Bean
Editorial Profile: The Herald-Sun is a local, daily newspaper written primarily for residents of Durham, Orange, Granville, Person, and Chatham Counties in North Carolina. The newspaper covers, local, national, and international news, as well as sports, entertainment, business, religion, health, and technology. Contact the publication for lead time and deadlines.; Full Page Mono: 72.45; Full Page Colour: 460.53
Currency: US Dollars
DAILY NEWSPAPER

The Herald-Times
Owner: Schurz Communications Inc.
Editorial: 1900 S Walnut St, Bloomington, Indiana 47401. **T:** 1 812 332-4401
W: http://www.heraldtimesonline.com
Freq: Daily; **Circ:** 20415 Not Audited
Publisher: E. Mayer Maloney; **News Editor:** Janice Rickert; **Editor:** Robert Zaltsberg
Editorial Profile: The Herald-Times is a daily newspaper written for residents of the Bloomington, IN area. It covers local news, sports and entertainment in. The publication combines with The Times-Mail and The Reporter-Times for the Sunday edition called the Hoosier Times.; Full Page Mono: 32.17; Full Page Colour: 417.00
Currency: US Dollars
DAILY NEWSPAPER

Hereford Brand
Owner: Roberts Publishing Company
Editorial: 313 Lee Ave, Hereford, Texas 79045-5341. **T:** 1 806 364-2030
E: hbnews@wtrt.net
Freq: Daily; **Circ:** 2500 Not Audited
Editorial Profile: Hereford Brand is a daily newspaper published for the residents of Deaf Smith County and Hereford, TX. It provides local news coverage Tuesday through Saturday. No editions are published on Sunday or Monday.; Full Page Mono: 7.00; Full Page Colour: 200.00
Currency: US Dollars
DAILY NEWSPAPER

Heritage Newspapers - Saline
Owner: Journal Register Company
Editorial: 106 W Michigan Ave, Saline, Michigan 48176-1325. **T:** 1 734 429-7380
W: http://www.heritage.com
Freq: Weekly; **Circ:** 7500 Not Audited
Publisher: Jim O'Rourke
NEWSPAPER

Heritage Newspapers - Southgate
Owner: Journal Register Company
Editorial: 1 Heritage Dr Ste 100, Southgate, Michigan 48195-3047. **T:** 1 734 246-0800
E: editor@thenewsherald.com
W: http://www.heritage.com **Circ:** 123220 Not Audited
Editor: Lena Khzouz
NEWSPAPER

Hernando Today
Owner: Media General Inc.
Editorial: 15299 Cortez Blvd, Brooksville, Florida 34613-6005. **T:** 1 352 544-5200 4
W: http://www.hernandotoday.com
Freq: Daily; **Circ:** 16103 Not Audited
Publisher: Duane Chichester; **Editor:** Julio Ochoa
Editorial Profile: Hernando Today is a daily newspaper serving Hernando County, FL and its surrounding areas. The publication is a general newspaper covering sports, local and national news, opinion, entertainment, travel, leisure, health, fitness and classifieds.; Full Page Mono: 23.05; Full Page Colour: 77.28
Currency: US Dollars
DAILY NEWSPAPER

Hersam Acorn Newspapers - Ridgefield
Owner: Hersam Acorn Newspapers
Editorial: 16 Bailey Ave, Ridgefield, Connecticut 06877-4512. **T:** 1 203 894-3332
W: http://www.acorn-online.com **Circ:** 11763 Not Audited
Editor: Kim Donnelly; **Publisher:** Thomas Nash; **Editor:** Jeanette Ross; **Editor:** Susan Wolf
NEWSPAPER

Hersam Acorn Newspapers - Shelton
Owner: Hersam Acorn Newspapers
Editorial: 1000 Bridgeport Ave., Shelton, Connecticut 6484. **T:** 1 203 926-2080
W: http://www.hersamacorn.com **Circ:** 93953 Not Audited
Editor: Bill Bloxsom; **Editor:** Kate Czaplinski; **Editor:** Jill Dion; **Editor:** Jill Dion; **Editor:** Brad Durrell; **Editor:** Don Eng; **Editor:** Susan Hunter; **Editor:** John Kovach; **Publisher:** Thomas Nash; **Editor:** Kait Shea
NEWSPAPER

Hesperia Star
Owner: Freedom Communications Inc.
Editorial: 15550 Main St Ste C11, Hesperia, California 92345-3492. **T:** 1 760 956-7827
E: editor@hesperiastar.com
W: http://www.hesperiastar.com
Freq: Tue; **Circ:** 20000 Not Audited
Editor: Peter Day; **Publisher:** Stephan Wingert; Full Page Mono: 17.25
Currency: US Dollars
NEWSPAPER

The Hibbing Daily Tribune
Owner: American Consolidated Media
Editorial: 2142 1st Ave, Hibbing, Minnesota 55746-3759. **T:** 1 218 262-1011
E: news@hibbingdailytribune.net
W: http://www.hibbingmn.com
Freq: Daily; **Circ:** 4535 Not Audited
Editor: Kelly Grinsteinner
Editorial Profile: The Hibbing Daily Tribune is published for the residents of Hibbling, MN and surrounding areas. The newspaper covers local news, sports, government and weather. The paper's Monday edition only appears on the Web site.; Full Page Mono: 17.15; Full Page Colour: 150.00
Currency: US Dollars
DAILY NEWSPAPER

Hickory Daily Record
Owner: World Media Enterprises, Inc.
Editorial: 1100 Park Place, Hickory, North Carolina 28602. **T:** 1 828 322-4510
E: news@hickoryrecord.com
W: http://www.hickoryrecord.com
Freq: Daily; **Circ:** 16740 Not Audited
Editor: Scott Bryan; **Publisher:** Eric Millsaps
Editorial Profile: Hickory Daily Record is written for the residents of Hickory, NC. It covers news, business, sports, entertainment and community issues.; Full Page Mono: 21.58; Full Page Colour: 182.25
Currency: US Dollars
DAILY NEWSPAPER

Hickory Focus
Editorial: 264 1st Ave NW, Hickory, North Carolina 28601-6103. **T:** 1 828 322-1036
E: focusnews@centurylink.net
W: http://www.focusnewspaper.com
Freq: Thu; **Circ:** 37500 Not Audited
Publisher: Tammy Panther
Editorial Profile: Hickory (NC) Focus is a free, weekly newspaper serving eight counties and providing reviews, feature stories and a directory.; Full Page Mono: 8.63; Full Page Colour: 650.00
Currency: US Dollars
NEWSPAPER

High Country Press
Editorial: 130 N Depot St, Boone, North Carolina 28607. **T:** 1 828 264-2262
E: news@highcountrypress.com
W: http://www.highcountrypress.com
Freq: Thu; **Circ:** 10000 Not Audited
Editorial Profile: High Country Press serves the residents of Watauga and Avery, NC. The weekly newspaper covers local news, sports, business and community events.; Full Page Mono: 6.00
Currency: US Dollars
NEWSPAPER

High Plains Daily Leader
Editorial: 218 S Kansas Ave, Liberal, Kansas 67901-3704. **T:** 1 620 626-0840
E: news@hpleader.com
W: http://www.hpleader.com
Freq: Mon thru Fri; **Circ:** 7000 Not Audited
Editor: Larry Phillips; **Publisher:** Earl Watt
Editorial Profile: High Plains Daily Leader is a 14-page daily broadsheet newspaper serving the residents of Liberal, KA.; Full Page Mono: 13.00; Full Page Colour: 123.60
Currency: US Dollars
DAILY NEWSPAPER

High Point Enterprise
Owner: Paxton Media Group
Editorial: 210 Church Ave, High Point, North Carolina 27262-4806. **T:** 1 336 888-3500
W: http://www.hpe.com
Freq: Daily; **Circ:** 16043 Not Audited
Publisher: Rick Bean; **Editor:** Sonny Hedgecock; **Editor:** Megan Ward
Editorial Profile: High Point Enterprise is a daily newspaper serving High Point, NC and the surrounding communities. It covers local news, government, business, lifestyle and sports stories. It also covers national stories if they have an impact on the readership. The lead time for the publication varies.; Full Page Mono: 31.24; Full Page Colour: 495.00
Currency: US Dollars
DAILY NEWSPAPER

Highland Community News
Owner: Century Group (The)
Editorial: 27268 Baseline St, Highland, California 92346-3163. **T:** 1 909 862-1771
E: news@highlandnews.net
W: http://www.highlandnews.net
Freq: Fri; **Circ:** 15000 Not Audited
Editor: Charles Roberts; **Publisher:** Jane Smith
Editorial Profile: Highland Community News is a local weekly newspaper serving the Highland, CA area. The publication focuses on local, community-related news and events.; Full Page Mono: 17.70
Currency: US Dollars
NEWSPAPER

Highlands Star/Barbers Hill
Owner: Grafikpress Corp.
Editorial: 5906 Star Ln, Houston, Texas 77057. **T:** 1 281 328-9605
W: http://www.starcouriernews.com
Circ: 10000 Not Audited
NEWSPAPER

Highlands Today
Owner: Media General Inc.
Editorial: 315 US Highway 27 N, Sebring, Florida 33870-2148. **T:** 1 863 386-5800
E: highlandstoday@highlandstoday.com
W: http://www.highlandstoday.com
Freq: Daily; **Circ:** 4373 Not Audited
Editor: Richard Hensley; **Editor:** Richard Hensley; **Publisher:** Tina McClelland Gottus; **News Editor:** Bill Rogers; **News Editor:** Bill Rogers
Editorial Profile: Highlands Today launched in August 1996, with a distinct focus on local news in Highlands, Hardee and DeSoto, FL. Advertising deadlines are at 5pm ET.; Full Page Mono: 27.42; Full Page Colour: 93.55
Currency: US Dollars
DAILY NEWSPAPER

Hill Country & Four Points Newspapers
Owner: Granite Publications
Editorial: 103 Woods Ln, Cedar Park, Texas 78613. **T:** 1 512 259-4449
W: http://www.hillcountrynews.com
Circ: 28000 Not Audited
Editor: Scott Coleman
NEWSPAPER

Hill Country Community Journal
Editorial: 303 Earl Garrett St, Kerrville, Texas 78028-4529. **T:** 1 830 257-2828
E: journal@ktc.com
W: http://www.hccommunityjournal.com
Freq: Wed
Editorial Profile: Hill Country Community Journal is a weekly newspaper providing Local News coverage to the residents of Kerrville, TX.
NEWSPAPER

Hillsboro Argus, Inc.
Owner: Newhouse Newspapers
Editorial: 150 SE 3rd Ave, Hillsboro, Oregon 97123-4019. **T:** 1 503 648-1131
W: http://www.oregonlive.com/argus
Circ: 31008 Not Audited
Editor: Tom Maurer; **Editor:** Samantha Swindler
NEWSPAPER

Hillsdale Daily News
Owner: GateHouse Media Inc.
Editorial: 2764 W Carleton Rd, Hillsdale, Michigan 49242-9191. **T:** 1 517 437-7351
E: editor@thedailyreporter.com
W: http://www.hillsdale.net
Freq: Daily; **Circ:** 7095 Not Audited
Publisher: David Ferro; **News Editor:** Amanda VanAuker
Editorial Profile: Hillsdale Daily News is published for the residents of Hillsdale, MI. The newspaper covers local news, weather, sports and community events. Feature articles cover business developments, education, arts & entertainment and lifestyle. Deadlines are two days prior to issue date.; Full Page Mono: 12.00; Full Page Colour: 126.00
Currency: US Dollars
DAILY NEWSPAPER

Hilltop Times
Owner: Ogden Publishing Corp.
Editorial: 322 Standard Way, Ogden, Utah 84404-1371. **T:** 1 801 629-5220
E: hilltop.times@hill.af.mil
W: http://www.hilltoptimes.com
Freq: Thu; **Circ:** 17500 Not Audited
Editor: Mary Lou Gorny
Editorial Profile: Hilltop Times is geared toward servicemen and families of Hill Air Force Base, UT. The publication covers base news, sports, and event listings. Deadlines are on Thursdays prior to the issue date at 3pm MT.; Full Page Mono: 18.61
Currency: US Dollars
NEWSPAPER

Hinds Ledger
Owner: Gannett Co., Inc.
Editorial: 201 S Congress St, Jackson, Mississippi 39201-4202. **T:** 1 601 360-4642
W: http://www.northeastledger.com

Circ: 40000 Not Audited
Editor: Annie Oeth; **Editor:** Annie Oeth; **Editor:** Annie Oeth; **Editor:** Annie Oeth
NEWSPAPER

The Hippo

Editorial: 49 Hollis St, Manchester, New Hampshire 03101-1239. **T:** 1 603 625-1855
E: news@hippopress.com
W: http://www.hippopress.com
Freq: Thu; **Circ:** 36000 Not Audited
Publisher: Jody Reese
Editorial Profile: The Hippo is published weekly for the residents of Manchester, NH and surrounding areas. The newspaper covers local news, sports and entertainment.; Full Page Mono: 45.00
Currency: US Dollars
NEWSPAPER

El Hispanic News

Owner: Brilliant Media LLC
Editorial: 6700 N New York Ave Ste 212, Portland, Oregon 97203-2836.
T: 1 503 228-3139
E: info@elhispanicnews.com
W: http://www.elhispanicnews.com
Freq: Thu; **Circ:** 20000 Not Audited
Publisher: Melanie Davis
Editorial Profile: El Hispanic News is a weekly publication written for the Hispanic community of Portland, OR. The publication focuses on Pacific Northwest news, national news, international news, sports, people and business. Deadlines are the day before issue date. The publication does not publish an editorial calendar.; Full Page Mono: 22.00; Full Page Colour: 2593.00
Currency: US Dollars
NEWSPAPER

El Hispano

Owner: El Hispano
Editorial: 1903 21st St, Sacramento, California 95814. **T:** 1 916 442-0267
E: blarenas2@yahoo.com
Freq: Wed; **Circ:** 15000 Not Audited
Editorial Profile: El Hispano's editorial mission is to inform and transform the image of the Latino community in Sacramento, CA. The publication covers issues such as sports, local news and entertainment. The newspaper is published primarily in Spanish but does have an English section as well.; Full Page Mono: 15.29
Currency: US Dollars
NEWSPAPER

El Hispano

Owner: Lopez Publications, Inc.
Editorial: 50 N State Rd, Springfield, Pennsylvania 19064-1332. **T:** 1 484 472-6059
W: http://www.el-hispano.com
Freq: Thu; **Circ:** 16500 Not Audited
Editor: Sara Lopez; **News Editor:** James Smith
Editorial Profile: El Hispano's editorial mission is to inform the Hispanic communities of Southeastern Pennsylvania and Northeastern New Jersey about local and national news and events. Editorial deadlines are on Mondays.; Full Page Mono: 30.00
Currency: US Dollars
NEWSPAPER

El Hispano

Owner: EMES Publications, Inc.
Editorial: 1200 Del Mar Pkwy, Aurora, Colorado 80010. **T:** 1 303 340-0303
E: hispano@roes.net
W: http://www.elhispanonewspaper.com
Freq: Thu; **Circ:** 20000 Not Audited
Editorial Profile: El Hispano is a Spanish-language newspaper providing news and information to the residents of Aurora, Colorado.; Full Page Mono: 45.05
Currency: US Dollars
NEWSPAPER

El Hispano News

Editorial: 2102 Empire Central, Dallas, Texas 75235-4302. **T:** 1 214 357-2186
E: graphics@elhispanonews.com
W: http://www.elhispanonews.com
Freq: Thu; **Circ:** 20081 Not Audited
Editor: Aldo Barbosa
Editorial Profile: El Hispano News is a local newspaper written for the Hispanic community in Dallas. The paper covers healthcare, education, immigration, politics, business, sports and arts & entertainment.; Full Page Mono: 26.00
Currency: US Dollars
NEWSPAPER

Hispanos Unidos

Owner: AH/HU Associates, Inc.

Editorial: 411 W 9th Ave, Escondido, California 92025-5034. **T:** 1 760 740-9561
E: info@hispanosnews.com
W: http://www.hispanosnews.com/HUnews
Freq: Fri; **Circ:** 26000 Not Audited
Editor: Jaime Castaneda; **Publisher:** Ana Hannegan
Editorial Profile: Hispanos Unidos is published weekly for the residents of San Diego and Riverside, CA. The newspaper focuses on showing a better picture of the Hispanic issues and community. Coverage includes local, national and international news, sports, business and social issues.; Full Page Mono: 24.00; Full Page Colour: 375.00
Currency: US Dollars
NEWSPAPER

Hmong Times

Editorial: 962 University Ave W, Saint Paul, Minnesota 55104-4703. **T:** 1 651 224-9395
E: hmongtimes@gmail.com
W: http://www.hmongtimes.com
Freq: Bi-Weekly; **Circ:** 15000 Not Audited
Editorial Profile: Hmong Times is published bi-monthly for the Hmong community of Minnesota.; Full Page Mono: 18.00
Currency: US Dollars
NEWSPAPER

Hmong Today

Editorial: 704 University Ave W, Ste 201, Saint Paul, Minnesota 55104-4803.
T: 1 651 489-0021 **E:** hmongtoday@gmail.com
W: http://www.hmongtoday.com
Freq: Bi-Monthly; **Circ:** 15000 Not Audited
Editorial Profile: Hmong Today is a bi-weekly newspaper serving the Hmong community in St. Paul, MN. Newspaper content includes local news, sports, health, living, politics and business. Deadlines are on Fridays.; Full Page Mono: 19.79; Full Page Colour: 470.00
Currency: US Dollars
NEWSPAPER

Hobbs Daily News-Sun

Owner: Shearman Newspapers
Editorial: 201 N Thorp St, Hobbs, New Mexico 88240-6058. **T:** 1 575 393-2123
W: http://www.hobbsnews.com
Freq: Daily; **Circ:** 7564 Not Audited
Editorial Profile: Hobbs Daily News-Sun is a local newspaper serving residents of Lea County, NM. The publication covers news, local government, education, business, sports and community events.; Full Page Mono: 11.25; Full Page Colour: 325.00
Currency: US Dollars
DAILY NEWSPAPER

Hockessin Community News

Owner: GateHouse Media Inc.
Editorial: 24 W Main St, Hockessin, Delaware 19709. **T:** 1 302 378-9531
E: editor@communitypub.com
W: http://www.hockessincommunitynews.com/
Freq: Sun
News Editor: Ben Mace
Editorial Profile: Hockessin Community News offers local news and information to residents in and around Hockessin, Pike Creek and Brandywine (New Castle County), Delaware.
NEWSPAPER

Hola Noticias

Owner: Norsan Media
Editorial: 4565 Saint Augustine Rd Suite A, Jacksonville, Florida 32207-7229.
T: 1 904 448-6969
E: tuopinion@holanoticias.com
W: http://www.holanoticias.com
Freq: Wed; **Circ:** 10000 Not Audited
Editorial Profile: Hola Noticias is a weekly Spanish-language newspaper written for the Hispanic residents of Jacksonville, FL and the surrounding areas.; Full Page Mono: 17.72
Currency: US Dollars
NEWSPAPER

Holdrege Daily Citizen

Owner: Holdrege Daily Citizen, Inc.
Editorial: 418 Garfield St, Holdrege, Nebraska 68949-2219. **T:** 1 308 995-4441
E: holdregecitizennews@gmail.com
Freq: Daily; **Circ:** 3174 Not Audited
Editor: Tunney Price
Editorial Profile: Holdrege Daily Citizen is a local newspaper serving the residents of Holdrege, NE. The publication covers local news and community events. Deadlines are daily at 1pm CT.; Full Page Mono: 8.00; Full Page Colour: 330.00
Currency: US Dollars
DAILY NEWSPAPER

The Holland Sentinel

Owner: GateHouse Media Inc.

Editorial: 54 W 8th St, Holland, Michigan 49423. **T:** 1 616 546-4200
W: http://www.hollandsentinel.com
Freq: Daily; **Circ:** 11516 Not Audited
Publisher: Peter Esser
Editorial Profile: The Holland Sentinel is a daily local newspaper serving residents of Holland, MI. The publication covers news, entertainment, sports, business, religion and community events.; Full Page Mono: 15.74; Full Page Colour: 106.50
Currency: US Dollars
DAILY NEWSPAPER

Holly Media Group, Inc.

Editorial: 3237 Ranch Rd, Wimberley, Texas 78676-5371. **T:** 1 512 268-0562
W: http://hollymedia.newspaperdirect.com
Circ: 7608 Not Audited
Editor: Anne Drabicky; **Publisher:** Leslie Stearns
NEWSPAPER

Hollywood Gazette

Editorial: 3363 Sheridan St, Ste 209, Hollywood, Florida 33021-3658.
T: 1 954 962-8180
W: http://www.hollywoodgazette.com
Freq: Monthly; **Circ:** 30000 Not Audited
Editorial Profile: Hollywood (FL) Gazette offers a blend of healthy lifestyle features, municipal news and neighborhood happenings. The paper does not wish to receive press releases via e-mail.; Full Page Mono: 6.80
Currency: US Dollars
NEWSPAPER

Hollywood Star

Editorial: 2000 Ne 42Nd Ave, Pmb 142, Portland, Oregon 97213-1305.
T: 1 503 282-9392 **E:** hstareditorial@aol.com
W: http://hollywoodstarnews.info
Freq: Monthly; **Circ:** 23000 Not Audited
Publisher: Mary DeHart; **Editor:** Nancy Woods
Editorial Profile: Hollywood Star is published monthly for the residents of Portland, OR and surrounding areas. The newspaper provides information and local news and arts & entertainment.; Full Page Mono: 9.49
Currency: US Dollars
NEWSPAPER

Home & Away, Irish Voice

Editorial: 875 Avenue Of The Americas, Rm 2100, New York, New York 10001-3586.
T: 1 212 684-3366
W: http://www.irishvoice.com **Circ:** 97000 Not Audited
Editor: Debbie McGoldrick; **Publisher:** Niall O'Dowd
NEWSPAPER

Home News Tribune

Owner: Gannett Co., Inc.
Editorial: 35 Kennedy Blvd, East Brunswick, New Jersey 8816. **T:** 1 732 246-5500
E: hntmetro@mycentraljersey.com
W: http://www.mycentraljersey.com
Freq: Daily; **Circ:** 21725 Not Audited
Editor: Paul Grzella
Editorial Profile: Home News Tribune is published daily for the residents of East Brunswick, NJ. The newspaper covers local news, business and community events.; Full Page Mono: 225.86; Full Page Colour: 1481.56
Currency: US Dollars
DAILY NEWSPAPER

Home Reporter Publications

Owner: Brooklyn Media Group
Editorial: 9733 4th Ave, Brooklyn, New York 11209-8104. **T:** 1 718 238-6600
E: editorial@homereporternews.com
W: http://www.homereporternews.com
Circ: 20203 Not Audited
Editor in Chief: Helen Klein
NEWSPAPER

Homestead Publishing Co.

Owner: Tribune Company
Editorial: 139 N Main St Ste 203, Bel Air, Maryland 21014-8800. **T:** 1 410 838-4451
E: news@theaegis.com
W: http://www.baltimoresun.com/explore/harford/publications/the-aegis/ **Circ:** 120410 Not Audited
NEWSPAPER

Hometown Life Newspapers

Owner: Gannett Co., Inc.
Editorial: 101 N Lafayette St, South Lyon, Michigan 48178-2070. **T:** 1 248 437-2011
W: http://www.hometownlife.com
Freq: Weekly; **Circ:** 19200
Editorial Profile: Hometown Life Newspapers produces four Gannett Michigan weeklies:

Novi News, Northville Record, South Lyon Herald and Milford Times.; Full Page Mono: 14.35; Full Page Colour: 17.43
Currency: US Dollars
NEWSPAPER

Hometown Media Group

Owner: Hometown Media Group, LLC
Editorial: 200 William St, Rye Brook, New York 10573-4643. **T:** 1 914 653-1000
E: publisher@hometwn.com
W: http://www.hometwn.com **Circ:** 38301 Not Audited
Editor in Chief: Christian Falcone; **Publisher:** Howard Sturman
NEWSPAPER

Hometown News

Owner: Jubilee (Janet)
Editorial: 4229 1st Ave, Tucker, Georgia 30084-4496. **T:** 1 770 493-3003
E: htnewsatlanta@yahoo.com
W: http://www.hometownnewsatlanta.com
Circ: 120000 Not Audited
Publisher: Janet Jubilee; **Editor:** Adina Solomon
Editorial Profile: Hometown News Inc. is a community newspaper publisher offering six monthly newspapers serving news to communities outside Atlanta, including the Brookhaven Buzz, Decatur Dispatch, Lilburn Living, Norcross News, Ponce Press and Tucker Times.
NEWSPAPER

Hometown News

Owner: Hometown News, L.C.
Editorial: 5059 Turnpike Feeder Rd, Fort Pierce, Florida 34951-2246. **T:** 1 772 465-5656
E: info@hometownnewsol.com
W: http://www.myhometownnews.net
Circ: 78000 Not Audited
Publisher: Vernon Smith
NEWSPAPER

Hometown News Brevard County

Owner: Hometown News, L.C.
Editorial: 380 N Wickham Rd, Ste F, Melbourne, Florida 32935. **T:** 1 321 242-1013
E: brevnews@hometownnewsol.com
W: http://www.myhometownnews.net
Circ: 176443 Not Audited
Publisher: Vernon Smith
NEWSPAPER

Hometown News South Daytona

Owner: Hometown News, L.C.
Editorial: 2400 S Ridgewood Ave, Ste 22, South Daytona, Florida 32119-3073.
T: 1 386 322-5900
E: info@hometownnewsol.com
W: http://myhometownnews.net **Circ:** 46000
Editor: Cecil Brumley; **Editor:** Cecil Brumley; **Editor:** Cecil Brumley; **Editor:** Cecil Brumley;
Publisher: Vernon Smith
NEWSPAPER

Hometown Weekly

Owner: Hometown Publications LLC
Editorial: 29 Janes Ave, Medfield, Massachusetts 2052. **T:** 1 508 359-2200
E: news@hometownweekly.net
W: http://www.hometownweekly.net
Circ: 38263 Not Audited
Editor: Sarah Coppinger
Editorial Profile: Hometown Weekly is a weekly community newspaper written for the residents of Medfield, MA.; Full Page Mono: 16.00
Currency: US Dollars
NEWSPAPER

Hometown/Tribune Publishing

Editorial: 570 Holt Ave, Holtville, California 92250. **T:** 1 760 356-2995
E: holtvillenews@aol.com
W: http://www.imperialvalleynews.com
Circ: 11200 Not Audited
Publisher: Steven Larson
NEWSPAPER

The Homewood Star

Owner: Starnes Publishing
Editorial: 3 Office Park Circle, Suite 316, Birmingham, Alabama 35223.
T: 1 205 313-1780
W: http://www.thehomewoodstar.wordpress.com
Freq: Monthly; **Circ:** 14000
Editor: Ashley Berkery; **Publisher:** Dan Starnes
Editorial Profile: The Homewood Star is a monthly, community newspaper written for the residents of Homewood, AL.; Full Page Colour: 6.55
Currency: US Dollars
NEWSPAPER

Honolulu Star-Advertiser
Owner: Black Press
Editorial: 500 Ala Moana Blvd Ste 7210, Honolulu, Hawaii 96813-4927.
T: 1 808 529-4700
W: http://www.staradvertiser.com
Freq: Daily; **Circ:** 272856 Not Audited
News Editor: Stephanie Kendrick
Editorial Profile: Honolulu Star-Advertiser is a daily newspaper published for the residents of Honolulu and its surrounding communities. The publication covers local, regional, state, national, and international news, as well as sports, business and entertainment news.; Full Page Mono: 160.00; Full Page Colour: 225.00
Currency: US Dollars
DAILY NEWSPAPER

Hood County News
Editorial: 1501 S Morgan St, Granbury, Texas 76048. **T:** 1 817 573-7066
W: http://www.hcnews.com
Freq: Sat; **Circ:** 12200 Not Audited
Editor: Roger Enlow; **Editor:** Rick Mauch;
Publisher: Jerry Tidwell
Editorial Profile: Hood County News is written for the residents of Granbury, TX. It covers local events that are newsworthy, interesting or otherwise important to the Granbury community.; Full Page Mono: 10.50; Full Page Colour: 706.14
Currency: US Dollars
NEWSPAPER

The Hook
Owner: Better Publications LLC
Editorial: 100 2nd St NW, Charlottesville, Virginia 22902-5193. **T:** 1 434 295-8700
E: editor@readthehook.com
W: http://www.readthehook.com
Freq: Thu; **Circ:** 21000 Not Audited
Editor: Courteney Stuart; Full Page Mono: 8.15
Currency: US Dollars
NEWSPAPER

Ho'okele
Owner: Oahu Publishing
Editorial: Navy Region Hawaii Public Affairs Office, 850 Ticonderoga Suite 110, Pearl Harbor, Hawaii 96860-4884.
T: 1 808 473-2888
E: editor@hookelenews.com
W: http://www.hookelenews.com
Freq: Fri; **Circ:** 16800
Editorial Profile: Ho'okele is a free weekly newspaper, published every Friday, written for the naval personnel at Navy Region Hawaii and published by the Honolulu Star-Advertiser. It contains stories, news, events and articles pertaining to Navy Region Hawaii. Deadlines for the publication are Friday the week before issue date.; Full Page Mono: 13.21
Currency: US Dollars
NEWSPAPER

The Hoosier Topics
Editorial: 1 N Main St, Cloverdale, Indiana 46120-8538. **T:** 1 765 795-4438
E: htopics@ccrtc.com
W: http://www.countryconnect.com/htopics/htopics.html
Freq: Tue; **Circ:** 20000 Not Audited
Editorial Profile: The Hoosier Topics is a free, weekly newspaper written for and about Cloverdale, Greencastle, Quincy, Poland, Eminence, Reelsville, Putnamville, Coatesville, Stilesville, Fillmore, Roachdale, Bainbridge and Spencer, IN. It covers local news, community events, businesses, sports, schools and editorials. Deadlines are at noon ET.; Full Page Mono: 6.45
Currency: US Dollars
NEWSPAPER

Hoover Sun
Owner: Hoover Sun LLC
Editorial: 3 Office Park Circle, Suite 316, Birmingham, Alabama 35223.
T: 1 205 313-1780 **W:** http://hooversun.com
Freq: Monthly; **Circ:** 22000
Publisher: Dan Starnes; **Editor:** Rebecca Walden
Editorial Profile: Hoover Sun is a monthly community newspaper serving residents of Hoover, AL with local news, sports, schools, opinion, business and events. The paper is direct mailed on the first of each month.
NEWSPAPER

Hope Star
Owner: GateHouse Media Inc.
Editorial: 522 W 3rd St, Hope, Arkansas 71801-5001. **T:** 1 870 777-8841
W: http://www.hopestar.com
Freq: Daily; **Circ:** 3200 Not Audited
Editorial Profile: Hope Star is a daily newspaper serving the residents of Hope, AR

and surrounding areas. The paper covers local, national and international news.; Full Page Mono: 15.65; Full Page Colour: 250.00
Currency: US Dollars
DAILY NEWSPAPER

Hopewell Publishing
Editorial: 516 E Randolph Rd, Hopewell, Virginia 23860-2652. **T:** 1 804 458-8511
E: editor@hopewellnews.com
W: http://www.hopewellnews.com **Circ:** 15000 Not Audited
Publisher: Mike Davis
NEWSPAPER

The Hour
Owner: Hour Publishing Co. (The)
Editorial: 1 Selleck St., Norwalk, Connecticut 6855. **T:** 1 203 846-3281
E: news@thehour.com
W: http://www.thehour.com
Freq: Daily; **Circ:** 13174 Not Audited
Publisher: Chet Valiante
Editorial Profile: The Hour is published daily for the residents of Norwalk, CT and surrounding areas. The newspaper covers local news, community events, historical features, people profiles, arts & entertainment and decorator trends.; Full Page Mono: 52.54; Full Page Colour: 488.75
Currency: US Dollars
DAILY NEWSPAPER

The Hour Publishing Company
Editorial: 1 Selleck St., Norwalk, Connecticut 6855. **T:** 1 203 846-3281
E: news@thehour.com **Circ:** 28000 Not Audited
Publisher: Chet Valiante; **Editor:** Chase Wright
NEWSPAPER

Housatonic Valley Publishing
Owner: Journal Register Company
Editorial: 65 Bank St, New Milford, Connecticut 06776-2701. **T:** 1 860 354-2261
W: http://www.ctcentral.com **Circ:** 31093 Not Audited
NEWSPAPER

Houston Chronicle
Owner: Hearst Newspapers
Editorial: 801 Texas St, Houston, Texas 77002-2904. **T:** 1 713 362-7171
E: citydesk@chron.com
W: http://www.chron.com
Freq: Daily; **Circ:** 370961 Not Audited
News Editor: Charlie Crixell
Editorial Profile: Houston Chronicle is a daily, morning newspaper written for the general public in Texas. The state's largest daily newspaper, it is also the only daily in Houston. The newspaper offers full market coverage focusing on local business news and events, state and national economics, personal finance, government, business, personal computing and technology. Feature topics include the arts, health, beauty, entertainment, fashion, food, lifestyle issues, home, gardening and travel. Types of articles found in the paper include breaking news, trends, features, local company profiles and syndicated columns.; Full Page Mono: 676.00; Full Page Colour: 740.94
Currency: US Dollars
DAILY NEWSPAPER

Houston Chronicle
Editorial: 700 12th St NW Ste 100, Washington, District Of Columbia 20005-3945.
T: 1 202 263-6500
DAILY NEWSPAPER

Houston Chronicle
Editorial: 1005 Congress Ave Ste 1060, Austin, Texas 78701-2469. **T:** 1 512 478-3495
Bureau Chief: Peggy Fikac
Editorial Profile: The San Antonio Express-News' and the Houston Chronicle's Austin burueas merged in 2006, and reporters cover news for both papers.
DAILY NEWSPAPER

Houston Community Newspapers - Cleveland
Owner: Houston Community Newspapers
Editorial: 106 W Hanson St, Cleveland, Texas 77327-4406. **T:** 1 281 592-2626
W: http://www.yourhoustonnews.com
Freq: Weekly; **Circ:** 26950 Not Audited
Editor: Vanesa Brashier
Editorial Profile: Houston Community Newspapers - Cleveland is a weekly community newspaper publisher producing the Cleveland Advocate, Dayton Advocate and Eastex News.
NEWSPAPER

Houston Community Newspapers - Houston
Owner: Houston Community Newspapers
Editorial: 650 FM 1959 Rd, Houston, Texas 77034-5420. **T:** 1 281 378-1920
W: http://www.yourhoustonnews.com
Circ: 30300 Not Audited
Editor: Robert Avery; **Editor:** Jim Molony
Editorial Profile: Houston Community Newspapers publishes the following community newspapers: The Bay Area Citizen; Friendswood Journal; Pearland Journal; Pasadena Citizen; and Deer Park Broadcaster.
NEWSPAPER

Houston Community Newspapers - Houston Tomball Parkway
Owner: Houston Community Newspapers
Editorial: 21901 State Highway 249, Houston, Texas 77070-1546. **T:** 1 281 378-1080
W: http://yourhoustonnews.com **Circ:** 96119 Not Audited
Editor: Roy Kent; **News Editor:** Kimberly Poore
NEWSPAPER

Houston Community Newspapers - Humble
Owner: Houston Community Newspapers
Editorial: 907 E Main St, Humble, Texas 77338-4749. **T:** 1 281 446-1060
W: http://www.yourhoustonnews.com
Freq: Weekly; **Circ:** 91063 Not Audited
Editor: Melecio Franco
Editorial Profile: Houston Community Newspapers - Humble is a weekly community newspaper publisher producing Observer Newspapers for Humble, Kingwood, Atascocita, Lake Houston and East Montgomery County.; Full Page Colour: 1679.00
Currency: US Dollars
NEWSPAPER

Houston Community Newspapers - Sugar Land
Owner: Houston Community Newspapers
Editorial: 7613 Katy Fwy, Houston, Texas 77024-2026. **T:** 1 281 378-1900
W: http://www.yourhoustonnews.com
Circ: 129012 Not Audited
Publisher: Richard Davis; **News Editor:** David Taylor
Editorial Profile: Houston Communications LLC is the publisher of community newspapers throughout the Houston metropolitan area. The Sugar Land office is the home of the Sugar Land Sun, Fort Bend Sun, The Rancher, Memorial Examiner, West University Examiner, Bellaire Examiner and River Oaks Examiner.
NEWSPAPER

Houston Forward Times Publishing
Editorial: 4411 Almeda Rd, Houston, Texas 77004-4901. **T:** 1 713 526-4727
E: forwardtimes@forwardtimes.com
W: http://www.forwardtimes.com
Freq: Weekly; **Circ:** 138080 Not Audited
Editorial Profile: Houston Forward Times Publishing serves the African American community in Houston. It covers community accomplishments, news and events.
NEWSPAPER

Houston Home Journal
Owner: Sun Multimedia, Inc.
Editorial: 1210 Washington St, Perry, Georgia 31069-2556. **T:** 1 478 987-1823
W: http://www.hhjnews.com
Freq: Daily; **Circ:** 14774 Not Audited
Publisher: Daniel Evans
Editorial Profile: Houston Home Journal is a daily newspaper serving Perry, GA and the surrounding area.; Full Page Mono: 10.00; Full Page Colour: 100.00
Currency: US Dollars
DAILY NEWSPAPER

Houston Press
Owner: Voice Media Group
Editorial: 1621 Milam St Ste 100, Houston, Texas 77002-8059. **T:** 1 713 280-2400
E: letters@houstonpress.com
W: http://www.houstonpress.com
Freq: Thu; **Circ:** 84043 Not Audited
Editor: Margaret Downing; **Editor:** Margaret Downing; **Publisher:** Stuart Folb
Editorial Profile: Houston Press is the metropolitan weekly that has become one of Houston's most respected and most read newspapers. The Press is dedicated to hard-hitting journalism, smart criticism, lively features and good old-fashioned muckraking.; Full Page Mono: 28.69
Currency: US Dollars
NEWSPAPER

Houston Sun
Editorial: 1520 Isabella St, Houston, Texas 77004-4042. **T:** 1 713 524-0786
E: info@houstonsun.com
W: http://www.houstonsun.com/
Freq: Fri
Editorial Profile: Houston Sun is a weekly newspaper providing Local and Community News coverage to the African-American community residing in Houston, TX.
NEWSPAPER

Hoy
Owner: Tribune Company
Editorial: 435 N Michigan Ave Fl 22, Chicago, Illinois 60611-7552. **T:** 1 312 527-8400
E: hola@vivelohoy.com
W: http://www.vivelohoy.com
Freq: Mon thru Fri; **Circ:** 75000 Not Audited
Publisher: John Trainor
Editorial Profile: Hoy is a free, daily Spanish-language newspaper published by the Tribune Company. It publishes three geographic editions, Chicago, New York and Los Angeles. Each edition covers local, national and international news of interest to Hispanic populations in the local area. Sports, business news and entertainment news are also covered. Each daily edition also contains special sections: Mondays include Sports and Education; Tuesdays feature a Trips section; Wednesdays offer a Health section; Thursdays feature Style and Fashion, Real Estate and Home sections; and on Fridays, an Auto section is included. Vida Hoy is the weekend supplement covering restaurants, events, music, TV, movies and other entertainment news and features. The Wall Street Journal provides an eight-page financial section on Thursdays. Additionally, Hoy dedicates region-specific pages each day to news from Central America, South America, Mexico, Puerto Rico and the Caribbean.; Full Page Mono: 55.73; Full Page Colour: 112.65
Currency: US Dollars
DAILY NEWSPAPER

Hoy
Owner: Tribune Company
Editorial: 202 W 1st St Fl 3, Los Angeles, California 90012-4299. **T:** 1 213 237-3001
E: hola@vivelohoy.com
W: http://www.hoylosangeles.com
Freq: Fri; **Circ:** 348000
Editor: Alejandro Maciel; **Publisher:** Roaldo Moran
Editorial Profile: Hoy is a free, weekly Spanish-language newspaper. The Los Angeles edition is split into four zoned editions, which include the areas of Los Angeles, Orange County, San Gabriel/Inland Empire and San Fernando Valley, CA. Each edition covers local, national and international news of interest to Hispanic populations in the local area. Sports, business news and entertainment news are also covered. Advertising deadlines are at 2pm PT two days prior to publication.; Full Page Mono: 49.21; Full Page Colour: 550.00
Currency: US Dollars
NEWSPAPER

Hubbell Publishing Co.
Editorial: 214 E Partridge St, Metamora, Illinois 61548-9691. **T:** 1 309 321-0285
E: herald@mtco.com **Circ:** 21000 Not Audited
NEWSPAPER

Hubin Publishing
Editorial: 201 Main St S, Hector, Minnesota 55342-1237. **T:** 1 320 848-2248
E: newsmir@hcctel.net **Circ:** 2250 Not Audited
Editor: Jake Dornseif; **Publisher:** John Hubin
Editorial Profile: Publishes the News-Mirror and the Bird Island Union.
NEWSPAPER

The Hudson Reporter Newspapers
Owner: Hudson Reporter Associates LP
Editorial: 1400 Washington St, Hoboken, New Jersey 07030-5558. **T:** 1 201 798-7800
E: editorial@hudsonreporter.com
W: http://www.hudsonreporter.com
Freq: Weekly; **Circ:** 42305 Not Audited
Editor In Chief: Caren Matzner
Editorial Profile: The Hudson Reporter Newspapers are local newspapers serving residents of the Hudson County, NJ. The publications focus on local news and community events.
NEWSPAPER

Hudson Valley Freedom Press
Owner: Hudson Valley Freedom Press LLC
Editorial: 144 Main St., Cold Spring, New York 10516. **T:** 1 845 265-2468 **Circ:** 6000
Publisher: Elizabeth Ailes
NEWSPAPER

The Hudson Valley Press

Editorial: 343 Broadway, Newburgh, New York 12550-5301. **T:** 1 845 562-1313
E: news@hvpress.net
W: http://www.hvpress.net
Freq: Wed; **Circ:** 31800 Not Audited
Editorial Profile: The Hudson Valley Press in Newburgh, NY is a local publication which is written for the Latino and African American communities in Ulster, Putnam, Dutchess and Sullivan counties. The newspaper is published on a weekly basis and covers local news, sports, entertainment and cultural stories. The editorial deadline for the publication is Monday at 5pm ET.; Full Page Mono: 29.00
Currency: US Dollars
NEWSPAPER

Huether Brothers Publishing

Owner: Tim Huether
Editorial: US Hwy 18, Mission, South Dakota 57555. **T:** 1 605 856-4469
E: tribnews@gwtc.net
W: http://www.trib-news.com **Circ:** 2775 Not Audited
Publisher: Tim Huether
NEWSPAPER

Hugo Daily News

Owner: Hugo Publishing Company
Editorial: 128 E Jackson St, Hugo, Oklahoma 74743. **T:** 1 580 326-3311
W: http://www.hugonews.com
Freq: Daily; **Circ:** 2900 Not Audited
Publisher: Stan Stamper
Editorial Profile: Hugo Daily News is a local, daily newspaper serving residents in Choctaw County and Northeastern Oklahoma. The publication covers local and community news, events and people. Deadlines are at noon CT.; Full Page Mono: 6.00; Full Page Colour: 210.00
Currency: US Dollars
DAILY NEWSPAPER

Huntington Beach Independent

Owner: Times Community News
Editorial: 1375 Sunflower Ave, Costa Mesa, California 92626-1665. **T:** 1 714 966-4600
E: hbindependent@latimes.com
W: http://www.hbindependent.com
Freq: Thu; **Circ:** 21447 Not Audited
Editor: John Canalis
Editorial Profile: Huntington Beach Independent is written for residents of Huntington Beach, CA. It covers local news and events. Deadlines are on Tuesdays.; Full Page Mono: 29.90; Full Page Colour: 1431.00
Currency: US Dollars
NEWSPAPER

The Huntington County Tab

Editorial: 1670 Etna Ave, Huntington, Indiana 46750-4132. **T:** 1 260 356-1107
E: tabnewsroom@comcast.net
W: http://www.huntingtoncountytab.com
Freq: Mon; **Circ:** 15500 Not Audited
Editor: Cindy Klepper
Editorial Profile: Huntington County Tab's editorial mission is to serve the people of Huntington County and offer them the foremost in enlightening news information. This local publication is written for Huntington residents. Articles include news, travel, weather and community events. Deadlines for the publication are one week before issue date.; Full Page Mono: 7.25
Currency: US Dollars
NEWSPAPER

Huntington Herald-Press

Owner: Paxton Media Group
Editorial: 7 N Jefferson St, Huntington, Indiana 46750-2839. **T:** 1 260 356-6700
E: hpnews@h-ponline.com
W: http://www.h-ponline.com
Freq: Daily; **Circ:** 7169 Not Audited
Publisher: Andy Eads; **Editor:** Rebecca Sandlin
Editorial Profile: Huntington Herald-Press is published daliy for the residents of Huntington, IN and surrounding areas. It covers local news and community events.; Full Page Mono: 18.00; Full Page Colour: 210.00
Currency: US Dollars
DAILY NEWSPAPER

Huntsville Item

Owner: Community Newspaper Holdings, Inc.
Editorial: 1409 10th St, Huntsville, Texas 77320-3805. **T:** 1 936 295-5407
W: http://itemonline.com
Freq: Daily; **Circ:** 6940 Not Audited
Editorial Profile: Huntsville Item is a daily newspaper published for the residents of Huntsville, TX. It provides information on local news and events. Deadlines for the publication

are the day before issue date.; Full Page Mono: 19.50; Full Page Colour: 21.51
Currency: US Dollars
DAILY NEWSPAPER

The Huntsville Times

Owner: Advance Publications, Inc.
Editorial: 200 West Side Square Ste 100, Huntsville, Alabama 35801-5623.
T: 1 256 532-4000 **E:** hsvnews@al.com
W: http://www.al.com/huntsville
Freq: Daily; **Circ:** 38241 Not Audited
Editorial Profile: The Huntsville Times is a daily newspaper that covers weather, news, sports, entertainment, classified ads, politics, travel guides and Alabama commerce.; Full Page Mono: 80.73; Full Page Colour: 264.21
Currency: US Dollars
DAILY NEWSPAPER

The Huntsville Times

Editorial: 836 Washington Ave, Montgomery, Alabama 36104-3839. **T:** 1 334 269-2804
E: htimes@htimes.com
W: http://www.htimes.com
DAILY NEWSPAPER

Huron Daily Tribune

Owner: Hearst Newspapers
Editorial: 211 N Heisterman St, Bad Axe, Michigan 48413-1291. **T:** 1 989 269-6461
E: pgardner@hearstnp.com
W: http://www.michiganshumb.com
Freq: Daily; **Circ:** 6461 Not Audited
News Editor: Kate Hessling; **Editor:** Dave Shane; **Editor:** Dave Shane
Editorial Profile: Huron Daily Tribune is written for residents of Huron, MI. It covers a wide range of topics including local sports, news and entertainment. Deadlines are at 8:30am CT daily.; Full Page Mono: 19.30; Full Page Colour: 275.00
Currency: US Dollars
DAILY NEWSPAPER

Huron Plainsman

Owner: News Media Corp.
Editorial: 49 3rd St SE, Huron, South Dakota 57350-2015. **T:** 1 605 352-6401
W: http://www.plainsman.com
Freq: Daily; **Circ:** 5230 Not Audited
Publisher: Mark Davis
Editorial Profile: Huron Plainsman is a daily newspaper dedicated to bringing forth all of the pertinent local and national news. The publication is written for residents of Huron, SD and surrounding areas. Deadlines are at 3pm MT. The outlet offers RSS (Really Simple Syndication).; Full Page Mono: 14.70; Full Page Colour: 19.23
Currency: US Dollars
DAILY NEWSPAPER

Hürriyet - New York Bureau

Editorial: United Nations, Room 344-B, New York, New York 10017. **T:** 1 212 963-7141
Editorial Profile: This is the New York bureau for Hürriyet, which is based in Istanbul, Turkey.
DAILY NEWSPAPER

The Hutchinson News

Owner: Harris Enterprises
Editorial: 300 W 2nd Ave, Hutchinson, Kansas 67501-5211. **T:** 1 620 694-5700
W: http://www.hutchnews.com
Freq: Daily; **Circ:** 30653 Not Audited
Editor: Sandra Milburn; **News Editor:** Jason Probst
Editorial Profile: The Hutchinson News is a daily newspaper written for the residents of Wichita, Canton and Hutchinson, KS. The newspaper covers local and national news.; Full Page Mono: 27.47; Full Page Colour: 94.55
Currency: US Dollars
DAILY NEWSPAPER

Idaho Catholic Register

Owner: Roman Catholic Diocese of Boise
Editorial: 1501 S Federal Way, Boise, Idaho 83705-2588. **T:** 1 208 342-1311
W: http://www.catholicidaho.org/en/diocesanoffices/communicationsicr/pages/communicationsicr.aspx
Freq: Bi-Weekly; **Circ:** 13150 Not Audited
Editor: Michael Brown; **Publisher:** Michael P. Driscoll
Editorial Profile: Idaho Catholic Register covers Catholicism, religious and social issues. It hopes to inform, unify, inspire and educate the Catholic population. Deadlines for the publication are two weeks before the issue date.; Full Page Mono: 12.65
Currency: US Dollars
NEWSPAPER

Idaho Mountain Express

Owner: Express Publishing, Inc.
Editorial: 591 First Ave N, Ketchum, Idaho 83340. **T:** 1 208 726-8060
E: news@mtexpress.com
W: http://www.mtexpress.com
Freq: 2 Times/Week; **Circ:** 13500 Not Audited
Editor: Greg Foley; **Publisher:** Pam Morris
Editorial Profile: Idaho Mountain Express appears twice weekly for people around the Sun Valley, ID resort area. The paper covers local news, sports and arts. It contains a calendar of regional events. Deadlines for the publication are one week before issue date.; Full Page Mono: 17.30
Currency: US Dollars
NEWSPAPER

Idaho Press-Tribune

Owner: Pioneer Newspapers
Editorial: 1618 N Midland Blvd, Nampa, Idaho 83651-1751. **T:** 1 208 467-9251
E: newsroom@idahopress.com
W: http://www.idahopress.com
Freq: Daily; **Circ:** 21065 Not Audited
Publisher: Matt Davison
Editorial Profile: Idaho Press-Tribune is published daily for the residents of Nampa, ID. The newspaper covers local and national news, sports, business, politics, education, lifestyles and entertainment.; Full Page Mono: 19.48; Full Page Colour: 20.55
Currency: US Dollars
DAILY NEWSPAPER

Idaho State Journal

Owner: Pioneer Newspapers
Editorial: 305 S Arthur Ave, Pocatello, Idaho 83204. **T:** 1 208 232-4161
E: reporters@journalnet.com
W: http://www.journalnet.com
Freq: Daily; **Circ:** 18149 Not Audited
Editor: Doug Lindley; **Publisher:** Andy Pennington
Editorial Profile: Idaho State Journal is a daily newspaper written for residents of Idaho. Topics covered include news, events, weather, sports, politics and business.; Full Page Mono: 25.95; Full Page Colour: 390.00
Currency: US Dollars
DAILY NEWSPAPER

The Idaho Statesman

Owner: McClatchy Newspapers
Editorial: 1200 N Curtis Rd, Boise, Idaho 83706-1239. **T:** 1 208 377-6200
E: newsroom@idahostatesman.com
W: http://www.idahostatesman.com
Freq: Daily; **Circ:** 43335 Not Audited
Editor: Holly Anderson
Editorial Profile: The Idaho Statesman is written for residents in the Boise, ID, area. The paper covers local, regional, state, national and international news, as well as sports, business, arts & entertainment and special reports. It was founded as a weekly newspaper in 1864. The paper does not publish a holiday gift guide.; Full Page Mono: 94.65; Full Page Colour: 318.63
Currency: US Dollars
DAILY NEWSPAPER

Identidad Latina

Editorial: 593 Farmington Ave, Hartford, Connecticut 6105. **T:** 1 860 231-9891
E: news@identidadlatina.com
W: http://www.identidadlatina.com
Freq: Bi-Weekly; **Circ:** 15000
Editor: Jorge Alatrista; **Publisher:** Ruth Espinoza
Editorial Profile: Identidad Latina is a community newspaper serving the Hispanic community of Hartford, CT.; Full Page Mono: 18.70
Currency: US Dollars
NEWSPAPER

Illinois Times

Owner: Central Illinois Communications Inc.
Editorial: 1320 S State St, Springfield, Illinois 62704. **T:** 1 217 753-2226
E: editor@illinoistimes.com
W: http://www.illinoistimes.com
Freq: Thu; **Circ:** 30000 Not Audited
Editor: Fletcher Farrar; **Publisher:** Sharon Whalen
Editorial Profile: Illinois Times is published weekly for residents of Springfield, IL and surrounding communities. It is an alternative to the mainstream media for arts and local news. It covers local news, community events, arts & entertainment and nightlife. Please send editorial submissions and press materials to the main e-mail address.; Full Page Mono: 6.25
Currency: US Dollars
NEWSPAPER

Illyria

Owner: Ekrem Newspaper, L.L.C.
Editorial: 481 8Th Ave Ste 536, New York, New York 10001-1809. **T:** 1 212 868-2224
E: info@illyriapress.com
W: http://www.illyriapress.com
Freq: Fri; **Circ:** 10000 Not Audited
Editor: Ruben Avxhiu; **Publisher:** Vebi Bharami
Editorial Profile: Illyria is an Albanian American newspaper in New York. It covers events in Albania, Kosovo, the Albanian territories of Macedonia, Montenegro and the diaspora. The paper is written for Albanian Americans and those interested in the politics and history of Albania and the former Yugoslavia.; Full Page Mono: 5.93
Currency: US Dollars
NEWSPAPER

Image/Newstand Newspapers

Editorial: 117 E 2nd St, Holden, Missouri 64040. **T:** 1 816 732-5552
E: holdenimage@embarqmail.com
W: http://www.holdenimage.com **Circ:** 12300 Not Audited
Publisher: John Roberts; **Editor:** Steve Sullins
NEWSPAPER

Impacto Latin News

Editorial: 225 W 35Th St Ste 305, New York, New York 10001-1904. **T:** 1 212 807-0400
E: media@impactony.com
W: http://www.impactony.com
Freq: Wed; **Circ:** 56450 Not Audited
Editor in Chief: Jason Smith; **Publisher:** Gail Smith Carillo
Editorial Profile: Impacto Latin News is a local weekly newspaper serving the Latin communities of New York. It covers community, national, international news, sports coverage and movie reviews. Deadlines are on Fridays at noon ET.; Full Page Mono: 49.75; Full Page Colour: 13834.00
Currency: US Dollars
NEWSPAPER

Impacto USA

Owner: Los Angeles Newspaper Group
Editorial: 21250 Hawthorne Blvd Ste 170, Torrance, California 90503-5514.
T: 1 562 499-1415
W: http://www.impactousa.com
Freq: Sat; **Circ:** 250000
Editor: Jose Fuentes
Editorial Profile: Impacto USA is a community newspaper written for the residents of Torrance, CA and the surrounding areas.; Full Page Mono: 147.50
Currency: US Dollars
NEWSPAPER

Imperial Valley Press

Owner: Schurz Communications Inc.
Editorial: 205 N 8th St, El Centro, California 92243-2301. **T:** 1 760 337-3400
W: http://www.ivpressonline.com
Freq: Daily; **Circ:** 11125 Not Audited
Publisher: Gerard Delaney; **Editor in Chief:** Richard Montenegro Brown; **Editor in Chief:** Richard Montenegro Brown
Editorial Profile: Imperial Valley Press is a daily newspaper published for the residents of Imperial County, CA and surrounding areas. Topics covered include local, national and world news, sports, weather, entertainment and health news.; Full Page Mono: 26.35; Full Page Colour: 495.00
Currency: US Dollars
DAILY NEWSPAPER

Impulso

Editorial: 6645 Southside Dr, Los Angeles, California 90022-4715. **T:** 1 323 721-9773
E: impulso@sbcglobal.net
W: http://www.impulsonoticias.com
Freq: Weekly; **Circ:** 10000
Editor: Mireya Olivera
Editorial Profile: Impulso is a weekly Spanish-language newspaper. It is written for the Oaxacan immigrant community in Los Angeles. Topics covered include community news, education, immigration and healthcare.; Full Page Mono: 12.50
Currency: US Dollars
NEWSPAPER

The IND

Owner: IND Media Group LLC
Editorial: 551 Jefferson St, Lafayette, Louisiana 70501. **T:** 1 337 988-4607
E: indbox@theind.com
W: http://www.theind.com
Freq: Monthly; **Circ:** 24000 Not Audited
Editorial Profile: The IND is a local newspaper serving the community of Lafayette, LA. The newspaper appears in two sections. The first offers news and features on business, politics

and other timely issues. The second covers arts, culture and lifestyle.; Full Page Mono: 66.00
Currency: US Dollars
NEWSPAPER

Independence Reporter
Owner: Reporter Publishing Company, Inc.
Editorial: 320 N 6th St, Independence, Kansas 67301-3129. **T:** 1 620 331-3550
Freq: Daily; **Circ:** 7918 Not Audited
Editor: Brian Thomas
Editorial Profile: Independence Reporter is a bi-weekly newspaper published for Independence, KS. Coverage includes news, weather, sports, business and arts & entertainment.; Full Page Mono: 6.93; Full Page Colour: 195.00
Currency: US Dollars
DAILY NEWSPAPER

The Independent
Owner: Community Newspaper Holdings, Inc.
Editorial: 224 17th St, Ashland, Kentucky 41101-7606. **T:** 1 606 326-2600
W: http://dailyindependent.com
Freq: Daily; **Circ:** 12066 Not Audited
Publisher: Eddie Blakeley; **Editor:** Mark Maynard; **Editor:** Mark Maynard; **Editor:** Mark Maynard; **Editor:** Mark Maynard; **Editor:** Lee Ward; Full Page Mono: 29.40; Full Page Colour: 380.00
Currency: US Dollars
DAILY NEWSPAPER

Independent
Owner: Gallup Independent Co. (The)
Editorial: 500 N Ninth St, Gallup, New Mexico 87301-5379. **T:** 1 505 863-6811
W: http://www.gallupindependent.com
Freq: Daily; **Circ:** 12584 Not Audited
Publisher: Robert Zollinger
Editorial Profile: Independent is written for Navajo Indians and other residents of Gallup, NM. All press releases and other related correspondence must be mailed to the P.O. Box address. Deadlines for the publication are daily at 6:30am MT.; Full Page Mono: 21.00
Currency: US Dollars
DAILY NEWSPAPER

The Independent
Owner: GateHouse Media Inc.
Editorial: 50 North Ave NW, Massillon, Ohio 44647-5497. **T:** 1 330 833-2631
E: indenews@indeonline.com
W: http://www.indeonline.com
Freq: Daily; **Circ:** 8854 Not Audited
Editor: Robert McCune; **Editor:** Joe Shaheen; **Editor:** Joe Shaheen; **Publisher:** Chris White
Editorial Profile: The Independent is published daily for the residents of Massillon, OH and surrounding areas. The paper focuses on local news, sports, business, education and city life.; Full Page Mono: 19.75; Full Page Colour: 295.00
Currency: US Dollars
DAILY NEWSPAPER

The Independent
Editorial: 2250 1st St, Livermore, California 94550. **T:** 1 925 447-8700
E: editmail@compuserve.com
W: http://www.independentnews.com
Freq: Thu; **Circ:** 33000 Not Audited
Editor: Janet Armantrout; **Publisher:** Joan Kinney Seppala
Editorial Profile: The Independent provides local news coverage to residents of Livermore, Pleasanton and Sunol, CA. Deadlines are at 5pm PT on the Friday prior to the issue date.; Full Page Mono: 26.10
Currency: US Dollars
NEWSPAPER

The Independent
Owner: East Hampton Independent News Company Inc.
Editorial: 74 Montauk Hwy, Unit 19, East Hampton, New York 11937-3268.
T: 1 631 324-2500 **E:** news@indyeastend.com
W: http://www.indyeastend.com
Freq: Wed; **Circ:** 19769 Not Audited
Publisher: Jim Mackin; **News Editor:** Kitty Merrill; **Editor in Chief:** Rick Murphy; **Editor in Chief:** Rick Murphy
Editorial Profile: The Independent is a weekly newspaper serving the communities of East Hampton, South Hampton, Riverhead, Southold and Shelter Island, NY. It covers community news, events, sports, business and features of interest to local readers. Deadlines are at noon ET.; Full Page Mono: 55.44; Full Page Colour: 350.00
Currency: US Dollars
NEWSPAPER

The Independent
Owner: Independent Publishing Company
Editorial: 40 N 300 E Ste 103, Saint George, Utah 84770-2900. **T:** 1 435 656-1555
E: independent@infowest.com
W: http://www.suindependent.com
Freq: Fri; **Circ:** 21000
Editor: Cami Cox; **Publisher:** Josh Warburton
Editorial Profile: The Independent is a monthly newspaper providing Arts & Entertainment News and Listings to the residents of Saint George, UT and the greater Southern Utah area.
NEWSPAPER

The Independent - (New York)
Editorial: 1450 Broadway Rm 702, New York, New York 10018-2272. **T:** 1 212 308-4539
Editorial Profile: This is the New York bureau for The Independent in London.
DAILY NEWSPAPER

Independent & Sun
Editorial: 1022 Grass Valley Rd, Winnemucca, Nevada 89445-4045. **T:** 1 866 644-5011
Circ: 18500
NEWSPAPER

Independent News
Editorial: 124 Palafox Pl, Pensacola, Florida 32502-5630. **T:** 1 850 438-8115
E: info@inweekly.net
W: http://www.inweekly.net
Freq: Thu; **Circ:** 25000 Not Audited
Editorial Profile: Independent News is a local newspaper written for the residents of Pensacola, FL.; Full Page Mono: 25.54; Full Page Colour: 50.00
Currency: US Dollars
NEWSPAPER

The Independent News
Owner: News-Gazette Inc.
Editorial: 137 N. Walnut St., Danville, Illinois 61832. **T:** 1 217 443-8484
E: indnews@news-gazette.com
W: http://www.the-independent-news.com
Freq: Wed; **Circ:** 16000 Not Audited
Editor: Vicki Delhaye; **Publisher:** John Foreman
Editorial Profile: The Independent News is a weekly, community newspaper serving residents of Georgetown and surrounding areas in Vermilion County, IL. It contains local news, events and feature stories.; Full Page Mono: 10.25
Currency: US Dollars
NEWSPAPER

The Independent News
Owner: Two Rivers Publishing Co. Inc
Editorial: 25 Saint Anthony Ln, Florissant, Missouri 63031. **T:** 1 314 831-4645
E: independentnws@aol.com
W: http://www.flovalleynews.com
Freq: Thu; **Circ:** 28400 Not Audited
News Editor: Carol Arnett
Editorial Profile: The Independent News is a weekly publication covering news and events for the cities of Florissant and Hazelwood, MO. Topics include local sports, community news, events, city politics and features.; Full Page Mono: 12.50
Currency: US Dollars
NEWSPAPER

The Independent Newspaper Group
Owner: Callery Press, Inc.
Editorial: 385 Broadway, Suite 105, Revere, Massachusetts 2151. **T:** 1 617 523-9490
E: editor@beaconhilltimes.com **Circ:** 21300 Not Audited
Editorial Profile: The Independent Newspaper Group is a weekly, community newspaper publisher serving residents of Boston.
NEWSPAPER

Independent Newspapers
Owner: Edward A. Sherman Publishing Co.
Editorial: 230 Robinson St, Wakefield, Rhode Island 02879-3500. **T:** 1 401 789-6000
Circ: 10500 Not Audited
Editor: Betty Cotter; **Editor:** Laura Kelly
Editorial Profile: Independent Newspapers is a community newspaper publisher in Wakefield, RI, and produces South County Independent, and The North-East Independent.
NEWSPAPER

The Independent Newspapers
Owner: Rock Valley Publishing LLC
Editorial: 240 N West Ave, Elmhurst, Illinois 60126-2543. **T:** 1 630 834-8244
E: questpublishing@aol.com
W: http://www.theindependentnewspapers.com
Freq: Thu; **Circ:** 12000
Publisher: Pete Cruger
Editorial Profile: The Elmhurst (IL) Independent is a weekly community newspaper serving residents of Elmhurst, IL, including local news, sports, events, entertainment, opinion, police reports and obituaries. All editorial inquiries should be sent to the main e-mail address.
NEWSPAPER

Independent Newspapers - Apache Junction
Owner: Independent Newsmedia Inc
Editorial: 2066 Apache Trl Suite 110, Apache Junction, Arizona 85120. **T:** 1 480 982-7799
W: http://arizona.newszap.com **Circ:** 64500 Not Audited
Publisher: Bret McKeanad; **Editor:** Terrance Thornton
Editorial Profile: Independent Newspapers in Apache Junction, Az publishes the Apache Junction/Gold Canyon Independent; East Mesa Independent; Gilbert Independent and the Queen Creek -San Tan Valley Independent. Deadlines are at noon MT.
NEWSPAPER

Independent Newspapers - Scottsdale
Owner: Independent Newsmedia Inc
Editorial: 23043 N 16th Ln, Phoenix, Arizona 85027-1331. **T:** 1 623 445-2777
W: http://www.arizona.newszap.com
Circ: 23000 Not Audited
Publisher: Bret McKeand; **Editor:** Terrance Thornton
Editorial Profile: Independent Newspapers - Scottsdale is a weekly community newspaper publisher serving the residents of Scottsdale, Phoenix and Paradise Valley, AZ.
NEWSPAPER

Independent Newspapers - Sun City
Owner: Independent Newsmedia Inc
Editorial: 17220 N Boswell Blvd, Ste L101, Sun City, Arizona 85373-2065.
T: 1 623 972-6101 **E:** wvnews@newszap.com
W: http://arizona.newszap.com/westvalley
Circ: 85000 Not Audited
Publisher: Charlene Bisson; **News Editor:** Rusty Bradshaw; **News Editor:** Jeff Grant
Editorial Profile: Independent Newspapers is a community newspaper publisher in Sun City, AZ.
NEWSPAPER

Independent Newspapers, Inc. - Clewiston
Owner: Independent Newspapers, Inc.
Editorial: 820 W Sugarland Hwy, Clewiston, Florida 33440-2700. **T:** 1 863 983-9148
W: http://www.newszap.com/ini **Circ:** 8000 Not Audited
Editor: Jose Zaragoza
NEWSPAPER

Independent Newspapers, Inc. - La Belle
Editorial: 22 Fort Thompson Ave, La Belle, Florida 33935. **T:** 1 863 675-2541 **Circ:** 10500 Not Audited
Publisher: Tom Bird; **Editor:** Patty Brant
NEWSPAPER

Independent Record
Owner: Lee Enterprises, Inc.
Editorial: 317 N Cruse Ave, Helena, Montana 59601-5003. **T:** 1 406 447-4000
E: irstaff@helenair.com
W: http://www.helenair.com
Freq: Daily; **Circ:** 12541 Not Audited
News Editor: Leah Gilman; **Editor:** Greg Lemon; **Publisher:** Tyler Miller
Editorial Profile: Independent Record is a daily newspaper published for the residents of Helena, MT and surrounding areas. It covers local, state and national news, weather, sports and community events.; Full Page Mono: 20.62; Full Page Colour: 279.00
Currency: US Dollars
DAILY NEWSPAPER

Independent Tribune
Owner: World Media Enterprises, Inc.
Editorial: 363 Church St N Ste 140, Concord, North Carolina 28025-4578.
T: 1 704 782-3155
E: news@independenttribune.com
W: http://www.independenttribune.com
Freq: Fri; **Circ:** 16910
Publisher: Jon Dunham
Editorial Profile: Independent Tribune is a weekly newspaper written for the communities of Concord and Kannapolis, NC. It covers local news, sports and lifestyle stories.; Full Page Mono: 16.17; Full Page Colour: 23.88
Currency: US Dollars
NEWSPAPER

The Independent Weekly
Owner: City of Roses Newspaper Co.
Editorial: 302 E Pettigrew St Ste 300, Durham, North Carolina 27701-3796.
T: 1 919 286-1972 **E:** editors@indyweek.com
W: http://www.indyweek.com
Freq: Wed; **Circ:** 45000 Not Audited
Editor: Lisa Sorg; **Publisher:** Sioux Watson
Editorial Profile: Independent Weekly is written for residents of Durham, NC. It covers local news, social issues, arts & entertainment, music and lifestyle.; Full Page Mono: 31.00; Full Page Colour: 1900.21
Currency: US Dollars
NEWSPAPER

The Index-Journal
Owner: Index Journal (The)
Editorial: 610 Phoenix St, Greenwood, South Carolina 29646. **T:** 1 864 223-1411
W: http://www.indexjournal.com
Freq: Daily; **Circ:** 12817 Not Audited
Publisher: Judith Mundy Burns
Editorial Profile: The Index-Journal is a daily newspaper for Greenwood, SC and the surrounding community. It covers local and national news, lifestyle, business and sports.; Full Page Mono: 22.00; Full Page Colour: 300.00
Currency: US Dollars
DAILY NEWSPAPER

India Abroad
Owner: India Abroad Publishing, Inc.
Editorial: 42 Broadway, Fl 18, Ste 1836, New York, New York 10004-1617.
T: 1 212 929-1727
E: editorial@indiaabroad.com
W: http://www.indiaabroad.com
Freq: Fri; **Circ:** 38000 Not Audited
Editor in Chief: Nikhil Lakshman
Editorial Profile: India Abroad in New York is published weekly for members of the Indian American Center for Political Awareness. The newspaper covers all social and political issues affecting the Indian community in America. The publication's editorial mission is to increase awareness in the Indian American community and encourage participation in American democracy. Deadlines for the publication are on Tuesdays.; Full Page Mono: 46.00
Currency: US Dollars
NEWSPAPER

India Globe
Editorial: 27025 McPherson Square Station, Washington, District Of Columbia 20038.
T: 1 202 271-1100 **E:** indiaglobe@hotmail.com
Freq: Weekly; **Circ:** 10000 Not Audited
Editorial Profile: India Globe is a weekly community newspaper distributed to the Indian residents of Washington, D.C. and the surrounding areas.; Full Page Mono: 300.00
Currency: US Dollars
NEWSPAPER

India Journal
Owner: Premier Media Inc.
Editorial: 13353 Alondra Blvd Ste 115, Santa Fe Springs, California 90670-5588.
T: 1 562 802-9720
E: editorial@indiajournal.com
W: http://www.indiajournal.com
Freq: Fri; **Circ:** 20500 Not Audited
Publisher: Navneet Chugh; **News Editor:** Nimmi Raghunathan; **Editor:** Mohinder Singh; **Editor:** Mohinder Singh
Editorial Profile: India Journal is a weekly newspaper that serves southern California's South Asian community. It features local news, sports and entertainment. Editorial deadlines are on Mondays. Advertising deadlines are on Fridays.; Full Page Mono: 4.75
Currency: US Dollars
NEWSPAPER

INDIA New England
Owner: Mishra Group, Inc. (The)
Editorial: 1344 Maine St., Waltham, Massachusetts 2451. **T:** 1 781 373-3220
E: editorial@mishragroup.com
W: http://www.indianewengland.com
Freq: Bi-Weekly; **Circ:** 12000 Not Audited
Editor: Martin Desmarais; **Editor in Chief:** Terry Egan
Editorial Profile: India New England is written for the Indo-American community throughout New England. It covers business, entrepreneurship, cultural and community news and events.; Full Page Mono: 22.65
Currency: US Dollars
NEWSPAPER

India This Week/Express India
Editorial: 7908 Kennewick Ave Apt 101, Takoma Park, Maryland 20912-7413.
T: 1 301 445-0200
E: indiathisweekeditorial@gmail.com
Circ: 22000
NEWSPAPER

India Tribune
Editorial: 3302 W Peterson Ave, Chicago, Illinois 60659. **T:** 1 773 588-5077
W: http://www.indiatribune.com
Freq: Sat; **Circ:** 40000 Not Audited
Editor: J.V. Rao; **Publisher:** Eric Shah
Editorial Profile: India Tribune, an English weekly newspaper, was launched in 1977 in Chicago to serve the Asian Indian settlers in the USA. It is published in three editions: Chicago, New York and Atlanta. The publication is written for the Indian community in the United States. The lead time for India Tribune is one week.; **Full Page Mono:** 25.71
Currency: US Dollars
NEWSPAPER

India West
Owner: India West Publications
Editorial: 933 Macarthur Blvd, San Leandro, California 94577-3062. **T:** 1 510 383-1140
E: news@indiawest.com
W: http://www.indiawest.com
Freq: Fri; **Circ:** 150000 Not Audited
Editor: Bina Murarka; **Editor:** Bina Murarka;
Publisher: Ramesh Murarka
Editorial Profile: India West is a weekly newspaper published for the Indian American community in San Leandro, CA and the surrounding area. The paper covers news, local events, business, sports, religion, lifestyle and entertainment. Some articles are also reprinted from Indianlifeandstyle.com, an online-only magazine targeting the Indian American community.; **Full Page Mono:** 30.00; **Full Page Colour:** 2100.00
Currency: US Dollars
NEWSPAPER

Indiana Gazette
Owner: Community Newspaper Holdings, Inc.
Editorial: 899 Water St, Indiana, Pennsylvania 15701-1700. **T:** 1 724 465-5555
W: http://www.indianagazette.com
Freq: Daily; **Circ:** 12380
Publisher: Michael Donnelly
Editorial Profile: Indiana Gazette is a daily newspaper published for the residents of Indiana, PA and surrounding areas. The publication focuses on small-town journalism. It covers local news, sports, arts & entertainment and letters to the editor. Deadlines are daily at 10pm ET.; **Full Page Mono:** 16.98; **Full Page Colour:** 159.95
Currency: US Dollars
DAILY NEWSPAPER

Indiana Herald
Editorial: 2170 N Illinois St, Indianapolis, Indiana 46202. **T:** 1 317 923-8291
E: herald1@earthlink.net
W: http://www.indianaherald.com
Freq: Fri; **Circ:** 25000 Not Audited
Editorial Profile: Indiana Herald is a weekly, community newspaper serving the African-American and multi-ethnic population in Indianapolis. It covers local and national news, sports, arts & entertainment and community events.; **Full Page Mono:** 19.14
Currency: US Dollars
NEWSPAPER

Indiana Newspaper Group
Owner: MC Communications, Inc.
Editorial: 407 E Main St, Gas City, Indiana 46933-1532. **T:** 1 765 674-0070 **Circ:** 14000 Not Audited
Publisher: Greg LeNeave; **Editor:** Rachel Terry
NEWSPAPER

Indiana WEEKENDER
Editorial: 6433 E Washington St, Ste 155, Indianapolis, Indiana 46219-6678.
T: 1 317 322-3315
E: indianaweekender@aol.com
W: http://www.indianaweekender.com
Freq: Bi-Weekly; **Circ:** 50000
Editorial Profile: Indiana WEEKENDER started in 1989 in Shelbyville, IN. It was a four-page paper known as the Shelby Weekly and covered Shelby, Rush, and Decatur counties. In 1990, the paper became the Shelby Tri-County Weekly, increased to eight pages, and added Bartholomew and Hancock counties. During the course of the last 12 years the paper has grown and increased its circulation into eight counties. The paper features a TV Section, Dining Out, Job Services, Nightlife, Entertainment, Sports, Bingo, Auto Market,

and Real Estate sections. Deadlines are on Wednesdays at noon ET.; **Full Page Mono:** 15.00
Currency: US Dollars
NEWSPAPER

The Indianapolis Recorder
Owner: George P. Stewart Publishing Co.
Editorial: 2901 N Tacoma Ave, Indianapolis, Indiana 46218-2737. **T:** 1 317 924-5143
E: newsroom@indyrecorder.com
W: http://www.indianapolisrecorder.com
Freq: Fri; **Circ:** 13300 Not Audited
Editorial Profile: The Indianapolis Recorder's editorial mission is to empower and enlighten the African American community of Indianapolis. Deadline for the publication is one week before issue date.; **Full Page Mono:** 30.00
Currency: US Dollars
NEWSPAPER

The Indianapolis Star
Owner: Gannett Co., Inc.
Editorial: 307 N Pennsylvania St, Indianapolis, Indiana 46204-1819. **T:** 1 317 444-4000
E: startips@indystar.com
W: http://www.indystar.com
Freq: Daily; **Circ:** 140343 Not Audited
Publisher: Karen Crotchfelt; **Editor:** Jeff Taylor
Editorial Profile: The Indianapolis Star is a 60+ page, four-color broadsheet read by the general public of Indiana. According to its publishers, the mission of Indianapolis Newspapers Inc. "is to be central Indiana's primary provider of news and information. To accomplish our mission, we will publish accurate, fair, and complete products of news, information, and opinion." The publication provides coverage of arts & entertainment, travel, real estate, health & fitness, automotive, city and state news, and sports. The paper runs business stories every day and publishes BusinessMonday, which contains in-depth, expanded business coverage with a local slant. The Indianapolis Star was founded in 1903. In 1995, the newspaper merged with its evening competitor, the Indianapolis News. The two were published separately until 1999, when the News was discontinued. The Holiday Gift Guide is an advertorial product and ONLY grants paid placement.; **Full Page Mono:** 323.00; **Full Page Colour:** 360.32
Currency: US Dollars
DAILY NEWSPAPER

The Indianapolis Star
Editorial: 1100 New York Ave NW Ste 200E, Washington, District Of Columbia 20005-6116.
T: 1 202 906-8100
Editorial Profile: The Indianapolis Star is owned by Gannett Newspapers. This bureau is also referred to as the Gannett News Service Washington, DC office.
DAILY NEWSPAPER

The Indianapolis Star
Editorial: 13095 Publishers Dr, Fishers, Indiana 46038-8826. **T:** 1 317 444-5500
Editorial Profile: This bureau covers news and issues in Indiana's Hamilton, Boone, and Southern Madison counties, as well as the Pike, Washington and Lawrence townships in Marion County. This is also referred to as the North bureau.
DAILY NEWSPAPER

The Indianapolis Star
Editorial: 65 Airport Pkwy Ste 130, Greenwood, Indiana 46143-1439.
T: 1 317 444-2700
DAILY NEWSPAPER

La Informacion Newspapers
Owner: Martinez (Lina)
Editorial: 6065 Hillcroft St Ste 400B, Houston, Texas 77081-1013. **T:** 1 713 272-0100
W: http://www.lainformacion.us **Circ:** 200000 Not Audited
Editor: Emilio Martinez-Paula; **Editor:** Emilio Martinez-Paula; **Editor:** Emilio Martinez-Paula
NEWSPAPER

El Informador
Owner: Community Newspaper Holdings, Inc.
Editorial: 308 S Thornton Ave, Dalton, Georgia 30720. **T:** 1 706 272-7740
E: elinformador@daltoncitizen.com
W: http://elinformadoronline.com
Freq: Wed; **Circ:** 10000
Publisher: William Bronson; **Editor:** Alexis Perez; **Full Page Mono:** 10.00
Currency: US Dollars
NEWSPAPER

El Informador del Valle
Editorial: 44917 Golf Center Pkwy, Ste 3, Indio, California 92201-7301.
T: 1 760 342-7558 **E:** elinformads@yahoo.com
W: http://www.chpg1.org
Freq: Sun; **Circ:** 40000 Not Audited
Editorial Profile: El Informador del Valle is a Spanish-language newspaper for Indio, CA. It provides the Hispanic community with information on local news, arts & entertainment and more.; **Full Page Mono:** 15.00
Currency: US Dollars
NEWSPAPER

The Ingleside Light
Editorial: 855 Head St, San Francisco, California 94132-2813. **T:** 1 415 215-4246
E: publisher@inglesidelight.com
W: http://www.inglesidelight.com
Freq: Monthly; **Circ:** 12000
Editorial Profile: The Ingleside Light is an independent newspaper providing Community News to the residents of San Francisco's Ingleside neighborhood and serving the south central region of the city, including McLaren Park, Brooks Park and Ocean Avenue.
NEWSPAPER

Inglewood Today
Owner: Brown (Willie)
Editorial: 9111 S La Cienega Blvd, Ste 100, Inglewood, California 90301.
T: 1 310 670-9600
W: http://www.inglewoodtoday.com
Freq: Thu; **Circ:** 25000 Not Audited
Publisher: Willie Brown
Editorial Profile: Inglewood Today is a free, weekly community paper that serves the residents, businesses and local government of Inglewood, CA. The tabloid paper covers community news, events, politics, school districts, businesses and locally-related editorials. Some national news issues and happenings are also covered, if they are relevant to local readers. The paper encourages article contributions from area residents. The lead time is Mondays at noon PT.; **Full Page Mono:** 49.50
Currency: US Dollars
NEWSPAPER

Inland Empire Community Newspapers
Editorial: 1809 Commercenter W, San Bernardino, California 92408-3303.
T: 1 909 381-9898 **E:** iecn1@mac.com
W: http://www.iecn.com **Circ:** 20000 Not Audited
NEWSPAPER

Inland Register
Owner: Roman Catholic Diocese of Spokane
Editorial: 1023 W Riverside Ave, Spokane, Washington 99201-1103. **T:** 1 509 358-7340
E: inlandregister@dioceseofspokane.org
W: http://www.dioceseofspokane.org
Freq: Monthly; **Circ:** 12000 Not Audited
Publisher: Blase Cupich; **Editor:** Eric Meisfjord
Editorial Profile: The Inland Register is a community newspaper serving the Catholic community of Spokane, WA. It is published 17 times per year.; **Full Page Mono:** 15.20
Currency: US Dollars
NEWSPAPER

Inland Valley Daily Bulletin
Owner: MediaNews Group
Editorial: 2041 E 4th St, Ontario, California 91764-2605. **T:** 1 909 987-6397
W: http://www.dailybulletin.com
Freq: Daily; **Circ:** 60096 Not Audited
Editorial Profile: Inland Valley Daily Bulletin serves a 13-city region around Ontario, CA, stretching from Kellogg Hill in the west to Rialto in the east, Mount Baldy in the north to the southern towns of Chino and Chino Hills. This paper is a part of the Los Angeles Newspaper Group, a subsidiary of MediaNews Group. It covers local, regional, state, national and international news, as well as business, sports, entertainment and special features.; **Full Page Mono:** 651.00; **Full Page Colour:** 2121.48
Currency: US Dollars
DAILY NEWSPAPER

Inland Valley News
Owner: Inland Valley News, Inc.
Editorial: 2009 Porter Field Way Ste C, Upland, California 91786-1106.
T: 1 909 985-0072
E: info@inlandvalleynews.com
W: http://www.inlandvalleynews.com
Freq: Thu; **Circ:** 18000 Not Audited
Editorial Profile: Inland Valley News is written for the African American community living in

the Inland Valley area of Southern California.; **Full Page Mono:** 24.90
Currency: US Dollars
NEWSPAPER

The Inlander
Editorial: 1227 W. Summit Parkway, Spokane, Washington 99201. **T:** 1 509 325-0634
E: totheeditor@inlander.com
W: http://www.inlander.com
Freq: Thu; **Circ:** 47000 Not Audited
Editor: Jacob Fries
Editorial Profile: The Inlander in Spokane, WA is published weekly and covers local news, weather, sports, arts, features and community events.; **Full Page Mono:** 49.00
Currency: US Dollars
NEWSPAPER

Inner City
Owner: Penfield Communication
Editorial: 50 Fitch St, New Haven, Connecticut 6515. **T:** 1 203 387-0354
Freq: Wed; **Circ:** 20000 Not Audited
Editorial Profile: Inner City's editorial mission is to cover local news, sports, government, arts & entertainment for residents of greater Bridgeport and New Haven, CT.; **Full Page Mono:** 55.00
Currency: US Dollars
NEWSPAPER

The Inquirer & Mirror
Owner: GateHouse Media Inc.
Editorial: 1 Old South Rd, Nantucket, Massachusetts 02554-2836.
T: 1 508 228-0001 **E:** newsroom@inkym.com
W: http://www.ack.net
Freq: Thu; **Circ:** 11300 Not Audited
Editorial Profile: The Inquirer & Mirror is written for the residents of Nantucket, MA. It covers local news, events and weather.; **Full Page Mono:** 19.89
Currency: US Dollars
NEWSPAPER

Inquiring News
Owner: Hales (Reggie)
Editorial: 51 Gilbert Ave, Bloomfield, Connecticut 06002-3824. **T:** 1 860 983-7587
E: inqnews@aol.com
W: http://www.inqnews.com
Freq: Wed; **Circ:** 55000 Not Audited
Editorial Profile: Inquiring News is a local, community newspaper serving residents of Hartford, New Haven, Bridgeport, Springfield and Waterbury, CT. The paper includes local news, business, sports, arts & entertainment and community events.; **Full Page Mono:** 35.82
Currency: US Dollars
NEWSPAPER

The Inquisitor
Owner: Danny Lawler Enterprises, LLC
Editorial: 7781 Highway 1, Shreveport, Louisiana 71107. **T:** 1 318 929-5152
E: news@cmaaccess.com
W: http://www.theinquisitor.com
Freq: Fri; **Circ:** 36000 Not Audited
Editorial Profile: The Inquisitor in Shreveport, LA is a weekly newspaper that covers local news, events, business, politics and lifestyle for residents of Caddo and Bossier parishes.; **Full Page Mono:** 10.00
Currency: US Dollars
NEWSPAPER

Inside Publications
Owner: Inside Publications
Editorial: 6221 N Clark St, Chicago, Illinois 60660-1207. **T:** 1 773 465-9700
E: insidepublicationschicago@gmail.com
W: http://www.insideonline.com **Circ:** 50000
Editorial Profile: Inside Publications is a local newspaper providing the community of Chicago, IL with news.
NEWSPAPER

Insider News Wisconsin
Editorial: 3001 Douglas Ave, Racine, Wisconsin 53402-4101
E: insiderwisconsin@yahoo.com
W: http://www.insiderwisconsin.com
Freq: Bi-Weekly; **Circ:** 35000 Not Audited
Editorial Profile: Insider News is a free, bi-weekly newspaper serving Racine, WI and surrounding communities. It covers local news, events, schools, business, government and features of interest to local readers.; **Full Page Mono:** 32.00
Currency: US Dollars
NEWSPAPER

Insight News
Owner: Insight News, Inc.

Editorial: 1815 Bryant Ave N, Minneapolis, Minnesota 55411-3212. **T:** 1 612 588-1313
E: info@insightnews.com
W: http://www.insightnews.com
Freq: Mon; **Circ:** 35000 Not Audited
Editor in Chief: Al McFarlane; **Publisher:** Batala-Ra McFarlane
Editorial Profile: Insight News is written for African American residents of Minneapolis. It covers information, instruction and inspiration in a user-friendly, culturally relevant way. It provides preferred access to African American consumers for businesses, agencies and organizations.; Full Page Mono: 69.81
Currency: US Dollars
NEWSPAPER

The Intelligencer
Owner: Calkins Media
Editorial: 333 N Broad St, Doylestown, Pennsylvania 18901-3407. **T:** 1 215 345-3000
E: intell_news@phillyburbs.com
W: http://www.theintell.com
Freq: Mon thru Fri; **Circ:** 24447 Not Audited
Editorial Profile: The Intelligencer is a daily newspaper for the residents of Doylestown, PA and surrounding areas. The newspaper covers local news, sports, events, entertainment, business and politics.; Full Page Mono: 33.73; Full Page Colour: 38.73
Currency: US Dollars
DAILY NEWSPAPER

Intelligencer Journal/Lancaster New Era
Owner: Lancaster Newspapers, Inc.
Editorial: 8 W King St, Lancaster, Pennsylvania 17603-3824. **T:** 1 717 291-8811
E: news@lnpnews.com
W: http://www.lancasteronline.com
Freq: Daily; **Circ:** 72091 Not Audited
News Editor: Jon Ferguson; **Editor:** Peter Mekeel; **News Editor:** Randy Montgomery
Editorial Profile: Intelligencer Journal/ Lancaster New Era is a daily paper published for the residents of Lancaster County, PA and surrounding communities. The newspaper covers local, national and international news, weather, sports, and community events. Feature articles cover business developments, education, politics, arts & entertainment, and lifestyle. It previously was two separate publications, the Lancaster Intelligencer and the Lancaster New Era.; Full Page Mono: 89.00; Full Page Colour: 294.39
Currency: US Dollars
DAILY NEWSPAPER

Intelligencer/News-Register
Owner: Ogden Newspapers
Editorial: 1500 Main St, Wheeling, West Virginia 26003-2826. **T:** 1 304 233-0100
W: http://www.news-register.net **Circ:** 15847
Publisher: Ogden Nutting
DAILY NEWSPAPER

The Inter-Mountain
Owner: Ogden Newspapers
Editorial: 520 Railroad Ave, Elkins, West Virginia 26241. **T:** 1 304 636-2121
E: newsroom@theintermountain.com
W: http://www.theintermountain.com
Freq: Daily; **Circ:** 8606 Not Audited
Editor: Edgar Kelley; **Editor:** Linda Skidmore; **Publisher:** Don Smith
Editorial Profile: The Inter-Mountain is a local daily newspaper written for residents of Randolph County, WV and the six surrounding counties. The newspaper covers local news and events in central West Virginia. The lead time for the newspaper is one week.; Full Page Mono: 21.87; Full Page Colour: 71.70
Currency: US Dollars
DAILY NEWSPAPER

Intermountain Catholic
Owner: Catholic Diocese of Salt Lake City
Editorial: 27 C St, Salt Lake City, Utah 84103. **T:** 1 801 328-8641 **E:** icnews@icatholic.org
W: http://www.icatholic.org
Freq: Fri; **Circ:** 14500 Not Audited
Editor: Marie Mischel; **Publisher:** John Wester
Editorial Profile: Intermountain Catholic is a weekly newspaper that provides news and information for the Diocese of Salt Lake City.; Full Page Mono: 20.00
Currency: US Dollars
NEWSPAPER

Intermountain Jewish News
Editorial: 1177 Grant St Ste 200, Denver, Colorado 80203-2362. **T:** 1 303 861-2234
E: email@ijn.com **W:** http://www.ijn.com
Freq: Fri; **Circ:** 50000 Not Audited
Editorial Profile: Intermountain Jewish News's editorial mission is to provide news and information of interest to the Jewish population of Colorado, New Mexico, Wyoming, Utah and Montana.; Full Page Mono: 68.63
Currency: US Dollars
NEWSPAPER

InTowner
Owner: InTowner Publishing Corp.
Editorial: 1730B Corcoran St NW, Washington, District Of Columbia 20009.
T: 1 202 234-1717
W: http://www.intowner.com
Freq: Monthly; **Circ:** 30000 Not Audited
Editorial Profile: InTowner is a local newspaper targeted only to the residents of the following neighborhoods: Adams Morgan, Mt. Pleasant, Columbia Heights; Dupont, Scott, Thomas and Logan Circles; Mt. Vernon Square/Pennsylvania Quarter, Shaw, U Street. The paper runs on the second Friday of the month and is only interested in community happenings. No city or regional information is accepted. Send press materials by e-mail or mail, but not by fax. Only e-mails with clear, specific subject lines will be opened.; Full Page Mono: 19.00
Currency: US Dollars
NEWSPAPER

Investor's Business Daily
Owner: Data Analysis, Inc.
Editorial: 12655 Beatrice St, Los Angeles, California 90066-7300. **T:** 1 310 448-6000
E: ibdnews@investors.com
W: http://www.investors.com
Freq: Mon thru Fri; **Circ:** 158955 Not Audited
News Editor: Ed Carson; **News Editor:** Ed Carson; **Editor:** Wesley Mann; **Publisher:** William O'Neil
Editorial Profile: Investor's Business Daily is a daily business newspaper aimed at senior executives, professionals and entrepreneurs, as well as individual and professional investors. The newspaper provides national business news, new management and investment ideas, and proprietary information used to make business and investment decisions, including stock data such as industry group rankings, relative strength, earnings per share ranking, volume percentage change and accumulation distribution. The paper is distributed Mondays through Fridays.; Full Page Mono: 167.12; Full Page Colour: 246.86
Currency: US Dollars
DAILY NEWSPAPER

Investor's Business Daily
Editorial: 1270 Oakmead Pkwy Ste 208, Sunnyvale, California 94085-4041.
T: 1 408 720-2129
DAILY NEWSPAPER

Investor's Business Daily
Editorial: 1001 Connecticut Ave NW, Ste 415, Washington, District Of Columbia 20036-5587.
T: 1 202 728-2150
DAILY NEWSPAPER

Investor's Business Daily
Editorial: 145 W 45th St Rm 1101, New York, New York 10036-4018. **T:** 1 212 626-7676
DAILY NEWSPAPER

Iola Register
Owner: Iola Register Publishing, Inc.
Editorial: 302 S Washington Ave, Iola, Kansas 66749-3255. **T:** 1 620 365-2111
E: editorial@iolaregister.com
W: http://www.iolaregister.com
Freq: Daily; **Circ:** 3842 Not Audited
Editor: Bob Johnson; **Editor:** Jocelyn Sheets
Editorial Profile: Iola Register is a local newspaper serving Allen County and the communities of Iola, Gas, Humboldt, Moran, LaHarpe and Colony, KS.; Full Page Mono: 9.65; Full Page Colour: 82.50
Currency: US Dollars
DAILY NEWSPAPER

Ionia Sentinel Standard
Owner: GateHouse Media Inc.
Editorial: 114 N Depot St, Ionia, Michigan 48846-1688. **T:** 1 616 527-2100
E: newsroom@sentinel-standard.com
W: http://www.sentinel-standard.com
Freq: Daily; **Circ:** 3100 Not Audited
News Editor: Karen Bota
Editorial Profile: Ionia Sentinel Standard is written for residents of Ionia County, MI and surrounding areas. It cover local news and information.; Full Page Mono: 14.75; Full Page Colour: 190.00
Currency: US Dollars
DAILY NEWSPAPER

Iowa Bystander and El Communicador Newspapers
Owner: IPS Media LLC.
Editorial: 1922 Ingersoll Ave, Des Moines, Iowa 50309. **T:** 1 515 770-1218 **Circ:** 10500 Not Audited
Publisher: Jerald Bratley; **Editor:** Jonathan Narcisse
NEWSPAPER

Iowa City Press-Citizen
Owner: Gannett Co., Inc.
Editorial: 1725 N Dodge St, Iowa City, Iowa 52245-9589. **T:** 1 319 337-3181
E: newsroom@press-citizen.com
W: http://www.press-citizen.com
Freq: Mon thru Fri; **Circ:** 9836 Not Audited
Editorial Profile: Iowa City Press-Citizen is published daily for the residents of Iowa City, IA and surrounding areas. The newspaper covers local and state news, business, sports, lifestyles and entertainment.; Full Page Mono: 41.64; Full Page Colour: 425.00
Currency: US Dollars
DAILY NEWSPAPER

Iowa County Newspapers
Owner: Gannett Co., Inc.
Editorial: 100 W Main St, Marengo, Iowa 52301. **T:** 1 319 642-5506
E: publish@netins.net **Circ:** 13307 Not Audited
Publisher: Dan DeBettignies; **Editor:** J.O. Parker
NEWSPAPER

Iowa Information, Inc.
Editorial: 227 9th St, Sheldon, Iowa 51201.
T: 1 712 324-5347
E: editor@iowainformation.com **Circ:** 7900 Not Audited
Editor: Jeff Grant; **Publisher:** Peter Wagner
NEWSPAPER

Ipswich Tribune
Editorial: 103 Main, Ipswich, South Dakota 57451. **T:** 1 605 426-6471
E: news.iptribune@midconetwork.com
Circ: 1600 Not Audited
Publisher: Dwain Gibson; **Editor:** Tena Gibson; **Editor:** Tena Gibson
NEWSPAPER

Iranians Newspaper
Owner: Washington Iranians Media, Inc.
Editorial: 43861 Arborvitae Dr, Ashburn, Virginia 20147. **T:** 1 703 724-9680
E: iranians@iraniansnewspaper.com
W: http://www.iraniansnewspaper.com
Freq: Weekly; **Circ:** 120000 Not Audited
Editor: Taghi Mokhtar
Editorial Profile: Iranians Newspaper is published weekly in Persian. The newspaper serves the Iranian community of the United States. It provides information on developments within the Iranian community and other topics of importance to Iranians.; Full Page Mono: 12.50
Currency: US Dollars
NEWSPAPER

Irish Echo
Editorial: 11 Hanover Sq, Fl 13, New York, New York 10005-2874. **T:** 1 212 482-4818
E: letters@irishecho.com
W: http://www.irishecho.com
Freq: Wed; **Circ:** 62000 Not Audited
Publisher: Mairtin O'Muilleoir
Editorial Profile: Irish Echo, founded in 1928, is the largest circulation Irish American newspaper in the United States. It covers arts & leisure, business and sports. The deadlines are 4pm ET every Friday.; Full Page Mono: 32.70
Currency: US Dollars
NEWSPAPER

Irish Emigrant
Editorial: 1412 Broadway Fl 22, New York, New York 10018-9241. **T:** 1 212 871-0111 200
E: editors@irishcentral.com
W: http://www.irishcentral.com **Circ:** 20000 Not Audited
Publisher: Connell Gallagher; **Editor:** Kate Hickey
NEWSPAPER

The Irish Examiner
Editorial: 60 E 42nd St Ste 1462, New York, New York 10165-1462. **T:** 1 212 994-8042
E: info@irishexaminerusa.com
W: http://www.irishexaminerusa.com
Freq: Wed; **Circ:** 45000 Not Audited
Editor: Grahame Curtis; **Publisher:** Paddy McCarthy
Editorial Profile: The Irish Examiner is a weekly, nationally distributed tabloid newspaper based in Long Island City, NY, serving Irish American readers throughout the United States. The paper includes Irish and Irish American news, including arts & entertainment, travel, fashion & beauty trends, business news from American companies in Ireland and Irish companies in America and Irish and Irish American opinions and analysis. Advertising deadlines are on Fridays at 4pm ET.; Full Page Mono: 30.00
Currency: US Dollars
NEWSPAPER

Irish Examiner - New York Bureau
Editorial: 131 E 66th St, New York, New York 10065-6147. **T:** 1 212 734-8844
Editorial Profile: This is the New York bureau of the Irish Examiner.
DAILY NEWSPAPER

The Irish Herald
Editorial: 223 Victoria Rd, Burlingame, California 94010-2845. **T:** 1 650 344-3765
E: editor@irish-herald.com
W: http://www.irish-herald.com
Freq: Monthly; **Circ:** 34000 Not Audited
Editorial Profile: The Irish Herald is a weekly newspaper serving Irish residents of Burlingame, CA and surrounding areas. The paper's editorial mission is to inform and entertain the Irish population with international and local Irish news, entertainment listings, music and book reviews, advice on immigration, real estate, business and finance, travel stories and sports updates.; Full Page Mono: 37.50
Currency: US Dollars
NEWSPAPER

Iron Mountain Advertiser
Owner: Ogden Newspapers
Editorial: 421 S Stephenson Ave, Iron Mountain, Michigan 49801-3454.
T: 1 906 774-3708
E: advertiser@ironmountainadvertiser.com
Freq: Tue; **Circ:** 20600 Not Audited
Editor: Joe Edelbeck; Full Page Mono: 17.00
Currency: US Dollars
NEWSPAPER

Ironton Tribune
Owner: Boone Newspapers Inc.
Editorial: 2903 S 5th St, Ironton, Ohio 45638-2866. **T:** 1 740 532-1441
E: news@irontontribune.com
W: http://www.irontontribune.com
Freq: Daily; **Circ:** 5486 Not Audited
Editor: Jessica St. James
Editorial Profile: Ironton Tribune's editorial mission is to provide news for the community of Ironton, OH. The publication contains sports, entertainment, news and events on a local scale. The paper is published every day except Saturday.; Full Page Mono: 16.50; Full Page Colour: 175.00
Currency: US Dollars
DAILY NEWSPAPER

Isanti County News
Owner: ECM Publishers, Inc.
Editorial: 234 Main St S, Cambridge, Minnesota 55008. **T:** 1 763 689-1981
E: editor.countynews@ecm-inc.com
W: http://www.isanticountynews.com
Freq: Wed; **Circ:** 12472 Not Audited
Publisher: Julian Andersen; **Editor:** Rachel Kytonen
Editorial Profile: Isanti County News is a weekly newspaper serving Isanti, Cambridge and Braham counties, MN. It provides the local community with information on news, events, sports and weather.; Full Page Mono: 10.10
Currency: US Dollars
NEWSPAPER

The Island Packet
Owner: McClatchy Newspapers
Editorial: 10 Buck Island Rd, Bluffton, South Carolina 29910-5937. **T:** 1 843 706-8100
E: newsroom@islandpacket.com
W: http://www.islandpacket.com
Freq: Daily; **Circ:** 19512 Not Audited
Publisher: Sara Johnson Borton
Editorial Profile: The Island Packet is a daily newspaper published for the residents of Southern Beaufort County, including Bluffton and Hilton Head Island, SC. It focuses on local news and events, business, real estate, editorial and feature articles. The paper is published the last Thursday of every month and items are due by the 15th of the month prior. Deadlines are on Mondays at 5pm ET.; Full Page Mono: 40.00; Full Page Colour: 265.00
Currency: US Dollars
DAILY NEWSPAPER

Island Sand Paper
Editorial: 1661 Estero Blvd Ste 4A, Fort Myers Beach, Florida 33931-2846. **T:** 1 239 463-4461
E: islandsandpaper@earthlink.net
W: http://www.islandsandpaper.com
Freq: Fri; **Circ:** 10000 Not Audited
Publisher: Bob Layfield; **Editor:** Missy Layfield
Editorial Profile: The Island Sand Paper is a weekly newspaper serving residents and businesses in Ft. Myers Beach, Florida. "By Islanders, For Islanders" is their motto and readers are assured of seeing the inside scoop on what's happening on and around the island. The paper covers local news, events, politics, features, editorials, businesses and profiles of community members. Advertising deadlines are Wednesdays at 5 pm ET.; Full Page Mono: 10.13
Currency: US Dollars
NEWSPAPER

Island Sun
Editorial: 1640 Periwinkle Way, Ste 2, Sanibel, Florida 33957. **T:** 1 239 395-1213
E: press@islandsunnews.com
W: http://www.islandsunnews.com
Freq: Fri; **Circ:** 11000 Not Audited
Editorial Profile: Island Sun is a weekly newspaper written for the communities of Lee County, FL.; Full Page Mono: 8.65; Full Page Colour: 545.00
Currency: US Dollars
NEWSPAPER

The Islander
Editorial: 5404 Marina Dr, Holmes Beach, Florida 34217. **T:** 1 941 778-7978
E: news@islander.org
W: http://www.islander.org
Freq: Wed; **Circ:** 17000 Not Audited
Editorial Profile: The Islander is a weekly newspaper bringing local news to the residents of Holmes Beach, FL. It covers topics related to business, health, sports and events.; Full Page Mono: 12.00
Currency: US Dollars
NEWSPAPER

Issaquah Press, Inc.
Owner: Seattle Times Company
Editorial: 45 Front St S, Issaquah, Washington 98027-3820. **T:** 1 425 392-6434
E: isspress@isspress.com
Freq: Weekly; **Circ:** 48400 Not Audited
Publisher: Deborah Berto; **Editor:** Ari Cetron;
Editor: Tim Pfarr
NEWSPAPER

Issaquah/Sammamish Reporter
Owner: Black Press
Editorial: 2700 Richards Rd Ste 201, Bellevue, Washington 98005-4200. **T:** 1 425 391-0363
E: news@issaquahreporter.com
W: http://www.issaquahreporter.com
Circ: 32000
Editor: Craig Groshart; **Publisher:** William Shaw
NEWSPAPER

Isthmus
Owner: Isthmus Publishing Company, Inc.
Editorial: 101 King St, Madison, Wisconsin 53703-3313. **T:** 1 608 251-5627
E: edit@isthmus.com
W: http://www.thedailypage.com
Freq: Thu; **Circ:** 60000 Not Audited
Publisher: Vincent O'Hern; **Editor:** Dean Robbins
Editorial Profile: Isthmus is written for residents in Madison, WI. It covers local news and events. Deadlines fall on Mondays at 5pm CT.; Full Page Mono: 63.97; Full Page Colour: 2350.00
Currency: US Dollars
NEWSPAPER

Italian Tribune
Editorial: 7 N Willow St, Ste 8C, Montclair, New Jersey 7042. **T:** 1 973 860-0101
E: mail@italiantribune.com
W: http://www.italiantribune.com
Freq: Thu; **Circ:** 97000 Not Audited
Editor: Joseph Cannavo; **Publisher:** A.J. Buddy Fortunato
Editorial Profile: Italian Tribune is a community newspaper serving Italian Americans in the Northeast. The paper focuses on current events and happenings of interest in the Italian American community.; Full Page Mono: 16.52
Currency: US Dollars
NEWSPAPER

L' Italo Americano
Owner: L'Italo American Foundation
Editorial: 10631 Vinedale St, Sun Valley, California 91352-2825. **T:** 1 626 359-7715
E: info.italoamericano@gmail.com
W: http://www.italoamericano.com
Freq: Thu; **Circ:** 30000 Not Audited
Publisher: Robert Barbera; **Editor in Chief:** Simone Schiavinato
Editorial Profile: L'Italo Americano provides news coverage and features for Italian-Americans in Sun Valley, CA and surrounding areas. The weekly publication covers news and events within the Italian-American community.; Full Page Mono: 10.00; Full Page Colour: 1100.00
Currency: US Dollars
NEWSPAPER

The Item
Owner: Osteen Publishing Co.
Editorial: 20 N Magnolia St, Sumter, South Carolina 29150. **T:** 1 803 774-1200
E: news@theitem.com
W: http://www.theitem.com
Freq: Daily; **Circ:** 18640 Not Audited
Editor: Dennis Brunson; **Publisher:** Jack Osteen
Editorial Profile: The Item's editorial mission is to provide news, sports and events coverage for the Sumter, SC area.; Full Page Mono: 17.50; Full Page Colour: 295.00
Currency: US Dollars
DAILY NEWSPAPER

The Ithaca Journal
Owner: Gannett Co., Inc.
Editorial: 123 W State St, Ithaca, New York 14850-5479. **T:** 1 607 272-2321
E: ijnews@gannett.com
W: http://www.theithacajournal.com
Freq: Daily; **Circ:** 9050 Not Audited
Publisher: Sherman Bodner
Editorial Profile: The Ithaca Journal provides the communities of Ithaca and Tompkins County, NY with local news and information, sports, education, crime and weather. Deadlines are at noon ET.; Full Page Mono: 42.85; Full Page Colour: 1750.00
Currency: US Dollars
DAILY NEWSPAPER

Ithaca Times
Owner: Newski Inc.
Editorial: 109 N Cayuga St, Ithaca, New York 14850-4341. **T:** 1 607 277-7000
E: front@ithacatimes.com
W: http://www.ithacatimes.com
Freq: Wed; **Circ:** 20382 Not Audited
Publisher: Jim Bilinski
Editorial Profile: Ithaca Times is a local weekly newspaper written for residents of Tompkins County, NY and surrounding areas. The newspaper covers local and national news, community events, sports and arts & entertainment. Deadlines for the publication are Fridays the week before issue date.; Full Page Mono: 29.00
Currency: US Dollars
NEWSPAPER

j. - The Jewish News Weekly of Northern California
Owner: San Francisco Jewish Community Publications Inc.
Editorial: 225 Bush St, Ste 1480, San Francisco, California 94104.
T: 1 415 263-7200 **E:** info@jweekly.com
W: http://www.jweekly.com
Freq: Fri; **Circ:** 19000 Not Audited
Editor: Sue Fishkoff; **Publisher:** Steven Gellman
Editorial Profile: J. - The Jewish News Weekly of Northern California is a community newspaper targeted at the Jewish community of San Francisco.; Full Page Mono: 168.25
Currency: US Dollars
NEWSPAPER

Jacksboro Newspapers
Owner: Graham Newspapers, Inc.
Editorial: 212 N Church St, Jacksboro, Texas 76458. **T:** 1 940 567-2616
E: editor@jacksboronewspapers.com
W: http://www.jacksboronewspapers.com
Circ: 3798 Not Audited
Publisher: Robert Krecklow
Editorial Profile: Jacksboro Newspapers was founded in June 1880 by J.N. Rodgers and his two daughters. Jacksboro Newspapers provides the community of Jacksboro with local news.
NEWSPAPER

The Jackson Citizen Patriot
Owner: MLive Media Group
Editorial: 214 S Jackson St, Jackson, Michigan 49201. **T:** 1 517 787-2300
E: janews@mlive.com
W: http://www.mlive.com/jackson
Freq: Daily; **Circ:** 15985 Not Audited
Editorial Profile: The Jackson Citizen Patriot is a daily newspaper written for the residents of Jackson, MI. The publication covers local news, sports, weather and events. The Lansing, MI bureau contributes to all eight of the MLive-owned dailies, including: the Ann Arbor News, Bay City Times, Flint Journal, Grand Rapids Press, Jackson Citizen Patriot, Kalamazoo Gazette, Muskegon Chronicle and the Saginaw News.; Full Page Mono: 40.40
Currency: US Dollars
DAILY NEWSPAPER

Jackson County Floridan
Owner: World Media Enterprises, Inc.
Editorial: 4403 Constitution Ln, Marianna, Florida 32448-4472. **T:** 1 850 526-3614
E: editorial@jcfloridan.com
W: http://www.jcfloridan.com
Freq: Fri; **Circ:** 4392 Not Audited
Editorial Profile: Jackson County Floridian is a community newspaper covering local and national news, weather and sports for the residents of Jackson County, FL.; Full Page Mono: 23.00; Full Page Colour: 220.00
Currency: US Dollars
NEWSPAPER

Jackson Hole Daily
Owner: Jackson Hole Magazine
Editorial: 1225 Maple Way, Jackson, Wyoming 83002. **T:** 1 307 733-2047
E: daily@jhnewsandguide.com
W: http://www.jhnewsandguide.com
Freq: Mon thru Fri; **Circ:** 8000 Not Audited
Editor: Kevin Huelsmann; **Publisher:** Michael Sellett
Editorial Profile: Jackson Hole Daily is a free newspaper distributed at outlets throughout Teton and Lincoln counties, WY and Teton Valley, ID. It offers news and information to local residents and visitors on topics such as local, state, regional, national, world, sports, business, entertainment and syndicated comics and features. Readership fluctuates dramatically during the summer and winter seasons due to increased circulation at restaurants and hospitality locations. Jackson Hole Daily shares its editorial staff and offices with its sister publication, the Jackson Hole News & Guide, a weekly paid-subscription newspaper. Do not send duplicate press materials to both publications. Deadlines are at 5pm MT two days prior to issue date.; Full Page Mono: 10.20; Full Page Colour: 120.00
Currency: US Dollars
DAILY NEWSPAPER

Jackson Hole News & Guide
Owner: Jackson Hole Magazine
Editorial: 1225 Maple Way, Jackson, Wyoming 83001. **T:** 1 307 732-7063
E: editor@jhnewsandguide.com
W: http://www.jhnewsandguide.com
Freq: Wed; **Circ:** 11000 Not Audited
Editor: Angus Thuermer
Editorial Profile: Jackson Hole News & Guide is a local, weekly newspaper written for the residents of Jackson and Teton County, WY. It features local news, community events, arts & entertainment, sports, society, health and business. The paper shares its editorial staff and offices with its sister publication, the Jackson Hole Daily. Please do not send duplicate press materials to both publications. E-mail submissions or send them to the PO Box address. Deadlines are on Fridays at 5pm MT.; Full Page Mono: 19.45; Full Page Colour: 80.00
Currency: US Dollars
NEWSPAPER

The Jackson Sun
Owner: Gannett Co., Inc.
Editorial: 245 W Lafayette St, Jackson, Tennessee 38301-6148. **T:** 1 731 427-3333
E: contactus@jacksonsun.com
W: http://www.jacksonsun.com
Freq: Daily; **Circ:** 17829 Not Audited
Editor: Tom Bohs; **Publisher:** Roy Heatherly
Editorial Profile: The Jackson Sun is written for the surrounding communities of Jackson, TN. It covers local news of 13 counties.; Full Page Mono: 61.75; Full Page Colour: 210.93
Currency: US Dollars
DAILY NEWSPAPER

Jacksonville Daily Progress
Owner: Community Newspaper Holdings, Inc.
Editorial: 525 E Commerce St, Jacksonville, Texas 75766-4909. **T:** 1 903 586-2236
E: editor@jacksonvilleprogress.com
W: http://www.jacksonvilleprogress.com
Freq: Daily; **Circ:** 3900 Not Audited
Editor: Amy Brocato Pearson; **Publisher:** Lange Svehlak
Editorial Profile: Jacksonville Daily Progress is a local daily newspaper written for residents of Jacksonville, TX and the surrounding areas. It is a general interest newspaper that covers local news, sports, finances, health, entertainment and events.; Full Page Mono: 8.80; Full Page Colour: 225.00
Currency: US Dollars
DAILY NEWSPAPER

Jacksonville Free Press
Owner: Jacksonville Free Press
Editorial: 903 Edgewood Ave W, Jacksonville, Florida 32208. **T:** 1 904 634-1993
E: jfreepress@aol.com
W: http://www.jacksonvillefreepress.com
Freq: Thu; **Circ:** 47300 Not Audited
Editor: Charles Griggs; **Publisher:** Rita Perry;
Editor: Sylvia Perry
Editorial Profile: Jacksonville Free Press is a weekly newspaper published by Jacksonville Free Press. The editorial content covers positive African-American news as well as other races. Contact the newspaper for deadline and lead time information.; Full Page Mono: 38.50
Currency: US Dollars
NEWSPAPER

Jacksonville Journal-Courier
Owner: Civitas LLC
Editorial: 235 W State St, Jacksonville, Illinois 62650-2092. **T:** 1 217 245-6121
E: news@myjournalcourier.com
W: http://www.myjournalcourier.com
Freq: Daily; **Circ:** 8260 Not Audited
Editor: David Bauer; **Publisher:** Kent Kilpatrick
Editorial Profile: Jacksonville Journal-Courier is published for the residents of Jacksonville, IL and surrounding areas. The newspaper cover local and regional news, business, sports, lifestyles and entertainment.; Full Page Mono: 20.57; Full Page Colour: 69.82
Currency: US Dollars
DAILY NEWSPAPER

J-Ad Graphics
Owner: J-Ad Graphics
Editorial: 1351 N M 43 Hwy, Hastings, Michigan 49058-8499. **T:** 1 269 945-9554
E: ads@j-adgraphics.com
W: http://j-adgraphics.com
Freq: Weekly; **Circ:** 132742 Not Audited
News Editor: Jeanne Boss; **News Editor:** John Hendler; **News Editor:** Doug VanderLaan
Editorial Profile: J-Ad Graphics is a community newspaper publisher and printing service offering several weekly community newspapers to Central Michigan communities, including The Hastings Banner, The (Hastings) Reminder, The Sun & News, Maple Valley News, Lakewood News, Lowell Ledger and the Ad-visor & Chronicle.
NEWSPAPER

The Jamestown Sun
Owner: Forum Communications Co.
Editorial: 121 3rd St NW, Jamestown, North Dakota 58401. **T:** 1 701 252-3120
E: js@jamestownsun.com
W: http://www.jamestownsun.com
Freq: Daily; **Circ:** 6234 Not Audited
Publisher: Rob Keller
Editorial Profile: The Jamestown Sun is a daily newspaper published Monday through Saturday that provides local news coverage for residents of the town. Deadlines are typically two days before an item's publication date.; Full Page Mono: 13.60; Full Page Colour: 180.00
Currency: US Dollars
DAILY NEWSPAPER

Janesville Argus/Waseca County News
Owner: Huckle Media LLC
Editorial: 213 2Nd St Nw, Waseca, Minnesota 56093-2401. **T:** 1 507 835-3380
W: http://www.southernminn.com **Circ:** 4390
NEWSPAPER

The Janesville Gazette
Owner: Bliss Communications Inc.
Editorial: 1 S Parker Dr, Janesville, Wisconsin 53545. **T:** 1 608 754-3311
E: newsroom@gazettextra.com
W: http://www.gazettextra.com
Freq: Daily; **Circ:** 17224
Editor: Scott Angus; **Publisher:** Skip Bliss;
Editor: Ann Fiore
Editorial Profile: The Janesville Gazette is a newspaper published daily for the residents of Rock and Walworth counties and the surrounding areas in southern Wisconsin. The newspaper covers local, national and international news, weather, sports and community events.; Full Page Mono: 46.00; Full Page Colour: 611.00
Currency: US Dollars

DAILY NEWSPAPER

Japanese Daily Sun
Editorial: 20817 S Western Ave, Torrance, California 90501-1804. **T:** 1 310 222-8788
E: jps753@aol.com
Freq: Mon thru Fri; **Circ:** 15000 Not Audited
Editor: Tomomi Kanemaru; **Editor:** Ty Makino
Editorial Profile: The Japanese Daily Sun is a daily tabloid paper containing various news, entertainment and sports stories.; Full Page Mono: 240.00; Full Page Colour: 1200.00
Currency: US Dollars
DAILY NEWSPAPER

Jennings Daily News
Owner: Fackelman Newspapers
Editorial: 238 Market St, Jennings, Louisiana 70546. **T:** 1 337 824-3011
E: jdnnews@bellsouth.net
W: http://www.jenningsdailynews.net
Freq: Daily; **Circ:** 5000 Not Audited
Editor: Rebecca Chaisson; **Publisher:** Dona Smith
Editorial Profile: Jennings Daily News covers local news and events of the Jeff Davis Parish for residents of Jennings, LA.; Full Page Mono: 10.59; Full Page Colour: 15.30
Currency: US Dollars
DAILY NEWSPAPER

Jersey & Courier Times
Editorial: 285 W Side Ave Suite 250, Jersey City, New Jersey 07305-1130.
T: 1 201 333-6885 **Circ:** 94800
NEWSPAPER

Jersey County Journal
Owner: Campbell Publications
Editorial: 832 S State St, Jerseyville, Illinois 62052. **T:** 1 618 498-1234
E: jcjnews@campbellpublications.net
W: http://www.jerseycountyjournal.com
Freq: Wed; **Circ:** 10700 Not Audited
Editorial Profile: Jersey County Journal is a weekly community newspaper written for the residents of Jerseyville, IL.; Full Page Mono: 10.06
Currency: US Dollars
NEWSPAPER

The Jersey Journal
Owner: Newhouse Newspapers
Editorial: 30 Journal Sq, Jersey City, New Jersey 07306-4101. **T:** 1 201 653-1000
W: http://www.nj.com/jjournal
Freq: Daily; **Circ:** 13093 Not Audited
Publisher: Kendrick Ross; **Editor:** Agustin Torres
Editorial Profile: The Jersey Journal is published daily for the residents of Jersey City, NJ and surrounding areas. The newspaper covers local and state news, business, sports, lifestyles and entertainment.; Full Page Mono: 47.06; Full Page Colour: 135.00
Currency: US Dollars
DAILY NEWSPAPER

Jersey Shore Newsmagazines
Editorial: 1816 Long Beach Blvd, Surf City, New Jersey 08008-5461. **T:** 1 609 494-5900
W: http://www.thesandpaper.net **Circ:** 69710 Not Audited
Editor: Anita Josephson; **Publisher:** Curt Travers
Editorial Profile: Jersey Shore Newsmagazines is a weekly community newspaper publisher serving the residents of Ocean County and Surf City, NJ.
NEWSPAPER

The Jewish Advocate
Editorial: 15 School St, Boston, Massachusetts 02108-4307.
T: 1 617 367-9100
E: editorial@thejewishadvocate.com
W: http://www.thejewishadvocate.com
Freq: Fri; **Circ:** 30000 Not Audited
Publisher: Yitzchok Aharon Korff; **Editor:** J. Michael Whalen
Editorial Profile: The Jewish Advocate is published weekly for members of the Jewish community in Boston. The publication aims to provide detailed information on all local, national and international issues relevant to the Jewish religion, culture and community.; Full Page Mono: 37.05
Currency: US Dollars
NEWSPAPER

Jewish Community Voice
Editorial: 1301 Springdale Rd, #250, Cherry Hill, New Jersey 08003-2763.
T: 1 856 751-9500 217 **E:** jvoice@jfedsnj.org
W: http://www.jewishvoicesnj.org
Freq: Bi-Weekly; **Circ:** 12500 Not Audited
Publisher: Sally Grossman; **Editor:** David Portnoe
Editorial Profile: Jewish Community Voice is a community newspaper written for the Jewish community in and around Cherry Hill, NJ.; Full Page Mono: 30.25
Currency: US Dollars
NEWSPAPER

Jewish Exponent
Owner: Jewish Publishing Group
Editorial: 2100 Arch St Fl 4, Philadelphia, Pennsylvania 19103-1300. **T:** 1 215 832-0700
W: http://www.jewishexponent.com
Freq: Thu; **Circ:** 30000 Not Audited
Editorial Profile: Jewish Exponent in Philadelphia, PA is a weekly newspaper for the Jewish community that covers local, national and international news; offers an opinion section about all the important issues of the day; features about people and institutions in the community; weekly pages for kids, teens and college students; and arts, books, business, science, health, travel, food and dining.; Full Page Mono: 38.59
Currency: US Dollars
NEWSPAPER

The Jewish Georgian
Editorial: 8495 Dunwoody Pl Bldg 9, Ste 100, Atlanta, Georgia 30350-3366.
T: 1 404 236-8911 **E:** jewishga@bellsouth.net
W: http://jewishgeorgian.com
Freq: Bi-Monthly; **Circ:** 16000 Not Audited
Editorial Profile: The Jewish Georgian is a free, bi-monthly newspaper serving the Jewish community in the Atlanta metro area and key cities throughout the state of Georgia. It specializes in human-interest stories about trail-blazing Georgians in such fields as government, politics, community affairs, business, the arts, sports, law and medicine. Copies can be found at synagogues, community centers, organizations and schools.; Full Page Mono: 9.17
Currency: US Dollars
NEWSPAPER

The Jewish Herald
Owner: American Jewish Publishing Corporation
Editorial: 1689 46th St, Brooklyn, New York 11204. **T:** 1 718 972-4000
Freq: Thu; **Circ:** 340000 Not Audited
Editorial Profile: The Jewish Herald is written for the Jewish community nationwide. It focuses on informing the Jewish community about world and local news, features, commentary, events, lifestyle, religion and other topics of general interest.; Full Page Mono: 75.00; Full Page Colour: 600.00
Currency: US Dollars
NEWSPAPER

Jewish Journal - Boston North
Owner: North Shore Jewish Press, LTD
Editorial: 27 Congress St Ste 501, Salem, Massachusetts 01970-5577.
T: 1 978 745-4111 **E:** pr@jewishjournal.org
W: http://www.jewishjournal.org
Freq: Bi-Weekly; **Circ:** 13000 Not Audited
Editor: Susan Jacobs; **Publisher:** Barbora Schneider
Editorial Profile: Jewish Journal - Boston North is written for Jewish residents in Northeastern Massachusetts. It covers international, national and local news, arts & entertainment and health.; Full Page Mono: 24.53
Currency: US Dollars
NEWSPAPER

The Jewish Journal of Greater Los Angeles
Owner: The Jewish Journal
Editorial: 3580 Wilshire Blvd Ste 1510, Los Angeles, California 90010-2516.
T: 1 213 368-1661
E: editor@jewishjournal.com
W: http://www.jewishjournal.com
Freq: Fri; **Circ:** 50000 Not Audited
Editorial Profile: The Jewish Journal of greater Los Angeles is a non-profit community weekly newspaper serving the city's Jewish community. Coverage includes news, business, events, arts and entertainment, and other information relevant to the Jewish community. It was founded in 1985.; Full Page Mono: 47.50; Full Page Colour: 3375.00
Currency: US Dollars
NEWSPAPER

The Jewish Post of New York
Owner: Link Marketing & Promotions, Inc.
Editorial: 31 E 32nd St, Ste 300, New York, New York 10016-5509. **T:** 1 212 563-9219
E: jewishpost@yahoo.com
W: http://www.jewishpost.com

Freq: Fri; **Circ:** 55000 Not Audited
Publisher: Henry Levy; **Publisher:** Henry Levy;
Editor: Scott Levy
Editorial Profile: The Jewish Post of New York is published for members of the New York Jewish community. The editorial content includes local Jewish news, international news, community events, travel, business and the arts.; Full Page Mono: 42.00
Currency: US Dollars
NEWSPAPER

The Jewish Press
Owner: Jewish Press, Inc.
Editorial: 4915 16th Ave, Brooklyn, New York 11204-1115. **T:** 1 718 330-1100
E: ads@jewishpress.com
W: http://www.jewishpress.com
Freq: Wed; **Circ:** 250000 Not Audited
Editor: Chumi Friedman; **Publisher:** Naomi Mauer
Editorial Profile: The Jewish Press is a weekly newspaper published in Brooklyn, NY. The paper covers local, national and international news of interest to the Jewish community in New York and abroad. The publication's coverage includes politics, opinions, special features, Torah lessons and Jewish lifestyle articles. The newspaper is distributed nationally and internationally.; Full Page Mono: 91.00
Currency: US Dollars
NEWSPAPER

Jewish Press
Owner: The Jewish Press Group of Tampa Bay
Editorial: 1101 Belcher Rd S, Ste H, Largo, Florida 33771. **T:** 1 727 535-4400
E: jewishpress@aol.com
W: http://www.jewishpresstampabay.com
Circ: 11700 Not Audited
Publisher: Jim Dawkins
NEWSPAPER

The Jewish Star
Owner: The Jewish Star LLC
Editorial: 2 Endo Blvd, Garden City, New York 11530-6707. **T:** 1 516 632-5205
E: pressreleases@thejewishstar.com
W: http://www.thejewishstar.com
Freq: Fri; **Circ:** 13000 Not Audited
Editorial Profile: The Jewish Star is a weekly newspaper serving the Orthodox Jewish communities of the South Shore in New York.; Full Page Mono: 30.37
Currency: US Dollars
NEWSPAPER

Jewish Times
Editorial: 21 W Delilah Rd, Pleasantville, New Jersey 08232-1403. **T:** 1 609 407-0909
E: jwishtimes@aol.com
W: http://www.jewishtimes-sj.com
Freq: Fri; **Circ:** 15000 Not Audited
Editor: Gerald Etter; **Publisher:** Shy Kramer;
Full Page Mono: 15.30
Currency: US Dollars
NEWSPAPER

The Jewish Voice & Herald
Owner: Jewish Alliance of Greater Rhode Island
Editorial: 401 Elmgrove Ave, Providence, Rhode Island 02906-3451. **T:** 1 401 421-4111
W: http://jvhri.org
Freq: Bi-Weekly; **Circ:** 10000 Not Audited
Editorial Profile: The Jewish Voice covers news and opinions of interest to Jewish residents in Rhode Island and Southeastern Massachusetts. Deadlines for submissions are on Mondays at 4pm ET.; Full Page Mono: 20.00
Currency: US Dollars
NEWSPAPER

The Jewish Week, Inc.
Owner: Jewish Week, Inc. (The)
Editorial: 1501 Broadway, Ste 505, New York, New York 10036. **T:** 1 212 921-7822
W: http://www.thejewishweek.com
Freq: Weekly; **Circ:** 98100 Not Audited
Editorial Profile: The Jewish Week, Inc., an independent community newspaper, is recognized widely as the largest and most respected Jewish newspaper in America. It has five regional editions including Manhattan, Long Island, Queens, Westchester/The Bronx, and Brooklyn/Staten Island. In covering the Jewish world, from Midtown to the Mideast, The Jewish Week reports on news, trends, features, and analysis from Israel as well as from throughout the New York metropolitan area. Deadlines are one week prior to the issue date.
NEWSPAPER

JH Weekly
Editorial: 567 W Broadway, Jackson, Wyoming 83001. **T:** 1 307 732-0299
E: editor@planetjh.com **W:** http://planetjh.com
Freq: Wed; **Circ:** 12000 Not Audited
Editorial Profile: JH Weekly is a Local News and Entertainment weekly newspaper.; Full Page Mono: 11.24
Currency: US Dollars
NEWSPAPER

Jobe Publishing - Horse Cave
Owner: Jobe Publishing Inc.
Editorial: 570 S Dixie St, Horse Cave, Kentucky 42749. **T:** 1 270 786-2679
E: print@scrtc.com
W: http://www.jpinews.com **Circ:** 22750 Not Audited
Editor: Candace Geralds; **Editor:** Candace Geralds; **Publisher:** Jeff Jobe; **Editor:** Jerry Matera; **Editor:** Jerry Matera
NEWSPAPER

Jobe Publishing - Morgantown
Owner: Jobe Publishing Inc.
Editorial: 120 E Ohio St, Morgantown, Kentucky 42261. **T:** 1 270 526-4151
W: http://www.jpinews.com **Circ:** 10900 Not Audited
Publisher: Diane Dyer; **Editor:** C. Josh Givens
Editorial Profile: Cave Country Newspapers-Morgantown is a community newspaper publisher serving the residents of Morgantown, KY.
NEWSPAPER

Johnlor Publishing, Inc.
Editorial: 20 Medford Ave, Route 112, Patchogue, New York 11772-1220.
T: 1 631 475-1000 **Circ:** 18350 Not Audited
Editor: Liz Finnegan; **Editor:** Linda Leuzzi; **Publisher:** John Tuthill
Editorial Profile: Johnlor Publishing, Inc. in Patchogue, NY publishes the community newspapers Islip Bulletin, Suffolk County News and Long Island Advance. The Islip Bulletin and Suffolk County share editorial staff, while the Long Island Advance has a separate editor and reporter.
NEWSPAPER

The Johnson City News & Neighbor
Owner: The Shopping News, LLC
Editorial: 1114 Sunset Dr Ste 1, Johnson City, Tennessee 37604-2969. **T:** 1 423 979-1300
E: newsandneighbor@charter.net
W: http://www.newsandneighboronline.com
Freq: Sat; **Circ:** 30797 Not Audited
Editorial Profile: The Johnson City News & Neighbor is a community newspaper for residents of Johnson City, TN.; Full Page Mono: 17.95
Currency: US Dollars
NEWSPAPER

Johnson City Press
Owner: Sandusky Newspapers Inc.
Editorial: 204 W Main St, Johnson City, Tennessee 37604-6212. **T:** 1 423 929-3111
E: newsroom@johnsoncitypress.com
W: http://www.johnsoncitypress.com
Freq: Daily; **Circ:** 24358 Not Audited
News Editor: Sam Watson; **Publisher:** Justin Wilcox
Editorial Profile: Johnson City Press is a daily newspaper written for residents of Johnson City, TN and the surrounding area. The newspaper covers local news, sports, business, entertainment, lifestyles and events. Deadlines are everyday at midnight ET.; Full Page Mono: 30.00; Full Page Colour: 419.00
Currency: US Dollars
DAILY NEWSPAPER

The Joint Based Journal
Owner: Comprint Military Publications
Editorial: 20 Macdill Blvd SW, Ste 219, Washington, District Of Columbia 20032-7711.
T: 1 202 767-1837
W: http://www.dcmilitary.com/section/news08
Freq: Fri; **Circ:** 15000 Not Audited
Editor: Kimberly Bamber; **Publisher:** John Rives
Editorial Profile: The Joint Based Journal is a free, weekly publication serving the Bolling Air Force Base in Washington, D.C.; Full Page Mono: 19.16; Full Page Colour: 21.17
Currency: US Dollars
NEWSPAPER

Jones Media Enterprises
Editorial: 412 S 16th St, Waco, Texas 76706.
T: 1 254 753-3871 **Circ:** 4535 Not Audited
Editorial Profile: The publication does not want to receive press materials.
NEWSPAPER

The Joplin Globe
Owner: Community Newspaper Holdings, Inc.
Editorial: 117 E 4th St, Joplin, Missouri 64801-2302. **T:** 1 417 623-3480
W: http://www.joplinglobe.com
Freq: Daily; **Circ:** 19606 Not Audited
Publisher: Michael Beatty; **Editor:** Carol Stark
Editorial Profile: The Joplin Globe is a daily newspaper published in Joplin, MO. Founded in 1986, the paper provides in-depth news coverage and features for residents of Southwest Missouri, as well as over 90 surrounding communities in 14 counties.; Full Page Mono: 31.95; Full Page Colour: 39.05
Currency: US Dollars
DAILY NEWSPAPER

Joplin Herald
Owner: Community Newspaper Holdings, Inc.
Editorial: 117 E 4th St, Joplin, Missouri 64801-2302. **T:** 1 417 623-3480
W: http://www.joplinglobe.com
Freq: Wed; **Circ:** 10000
Publisher: Michael Beatty; **Editor:** Carol Stark
Editorial Profile: Joplin Herald is a free, weekly newspaper serving residents of Joplin, MO. It covers local news, events and features. It is published from the offices of The Joplin (MO) Globe and mailed directly to residents' homes. Editorial lead times and advertising deadlines are at 5pm CT.; Full Page Mono: 12.00
Currency: US Dollars
NEWSPAPER

La Jornada Latina
Owner: Gate West Coast Ventures, LLC
Editorial: 4412 Carver Woods Dr Ste 200, Cincinnati, Ohio 45242-5539.
T: 1 513 891-1000 **E:** editor@tsjnews.com
W: http://www.tsjnews.com
Freq: Fri; **Circ:** 15000 Not Audited
Editor in Chief: Leyla Pena; **Publisher:** Brian Wiles
Editorial Profile: La Jornada Latina is distributed to local businesses and areas heavy in Hispanic population in the Greater Cincinnati, Northern Kentucky and Dayton regions. It includes local community and organizational news, local editorial content, special events, sports and entertainment.; Full Page Mono: 30.38
Currency: US Dollars
NEWSPAPER

O Jornal
Owner: GateHouse Media Inc.
Editorial: 10 Purchase St, Fall River, Massachusetts 2720. **T:** 1 508 678-3844
E: editorial@ojornal.com
W: http://www.ojornal.com
Freq: Fri; **Circ:** 14500 Not Audited
Editor: Lurdes DaSilva; **Publisher:** Ric Oliveira
Editorial Profile: O Jornal is a weekly newspaper that covers Portuguese culture in English and Portuguese. The paper is a bilingual community newspaper distributed in Massachusetts and Rhode Island.; Full Page Mono: 16.50
Currency: US Dollars
NEWSPAPER

The Journal
Owner: Ogden Newspapers
Editorial: 303 N Minnesota St, New Ulm, Minnesota 56073-1733. **T:** 1 507 359-2911
E: news@nujournal.com
W: http://www.nujournal.com
Freq: Daily; **Circ:** 6204 Not Audited
Publisher: Bruce Fenske; **Editor:** Kevin Sweeney; **News Editor:** Donna Weber
Editorial Profile: The Journal is a daily local newspaper covering news in southern Minnesota, including Brown and Sibley counties. The publication covers local, sports and community news.; Full Page Mono: 27.11
Currency: US Dollars
DAILY NEWSPAPER

The Journal
Owner: Ogden Newspapers
Editorial: 207 W King St, Martinsburg, West Virginia 25401-3211. **T:** 1 304 263-8931
E: news@journal-news.net
W: http://www.journal-news.net
Freq: Daily; **Circ:** 16911 Not Audited
Publisher: Craig Bartoldson; **Editor:** Don Smith
Editorial Profile: The Journal is a local daily newspaper serving the residents of Berkley, Jefferson, and Morgan counties in West Virginia. It covers local, state and national news, sports, entertainment and community events.; Full Page Mono: 24.90; Full Page Colour: 320.00
Currency: US Dollars
DAILY NEWSPAPER

The Journal
Owner: Comprint Military Publications
Editorial: 8901 Rockville Pike, Bethesda, Maryland 20889. **T:** 1 301 295-5727
W: http://www.dcmilitary.com/section/news11
Freq: Thu; **Circ:** 12000 Not Audited
Publisher: John Rives
Editorial Profile: The Journal is a weekly communtiy newspaper located in Bethesda, MD. It's main focus is on military personnal and lifestyle.; Full Page Mono: 19.16
Currency: US Dollars
NEWSPAPER

The Journal
Owner: Macon Chronicle-Herald
Editorial: 204 W Bourke St, Macon, Missouri 63552. **T:** 1 660 385-3121
E: chnews@centurytel.net
W: http://www.maconch.com
Freq: Mon; **Circ:** 11000
Editor: Terri Hackett; **Publisher:** Pat Quinly
Editorial Profile: The Journal is a community newspaper written for the residents of Macon, MO.; Full Page Mono: 9.90
Currency: US Dollars
NEWSPAPER

The Journal
Owner: Minnesota Premier Publications
Editorial: 1115 Hennepin Ave, Minneapolis, Minnesota 55403-1705. **T:** 1 612 825-9205
W: http://www.journalmpls.com
Freq: Bi-Weekly; **Circ:** 30000 Not Audited
Editor: Sarah McKenzie
Editorial Profile: The Journal, also known as the Skyway News, is a local weekly newspaper serving Minneapolis and Saint Paul, MN. Its editorial mission is to provide the connection between the two cities. It provides information on news, events and arts of interest to the local community.; Full Page Mono: 48.59; Full Page Colour: 2022.00
Currency: US Dollars
NEWSPAPER

The Journal
Owner: Eagle Media
Editorial: 210 W North 1st St, Seneca, South Carolina 29678-3250. **T:** 1 864 882-2375
E: life@upstatetoday.com
W: http://www.upstatetoday.com
Freq: Daily; **Circ:** 9500 Not Audited
Editor: Norman Cannada; **Publisher:** Michael Leonard
Editorial Profile: The Journal is a daily local newspaper written for residents in and around Oconee County and Clemson County, SC including Seneca and Clemson, SC. It covers local news, events, politics, sports, weather, features and news from the local colleges and universities.; Full Page Mono: 14.50; Full Page Colour: 80.00
Currency: US Dollars
DAILY NEWSPAPER

Journal & Courier
Owner: Gannett Co., Inc.
Editorial: 217 N 6th St, Lafayette, Indiana 47901-1448. **T:** 1 765 423-5511
E: editor@journalandcourier.com
W: http://www.jconline.com
Freq: Daily; **Circ:** 23974 Not Audited
Publisher: Gary Suisman
Editorial Profile: Journal & Courier is a daily newspaper published in Lafayette, IN. It is distributed in ten counties in west-central Indiana. The paper covers local and regional news, as well as business, lifestyle, sports, and entertainment. It is available in print form, online, and in Spanish once a month as Journal and Courier en Espanol.; Full Page Mono: 55.11
Currency: US Dollars
DAILY NEWSPAPER

Journal & Topics Newspapers
Owner: Wessell Family
Editorial: 622 Graceland Ave, Des Plaines, Illinois 60016-4519. **T:** 1 847 299-5511
E: journalnews@mail.com
W: http://www.journal-topics.com **Circ:** 70166 Not Audited
Editor: Todd Wessell
NEWSPAPER

The Journal Gazette
Owner: Journal Gazette Company (The)
Editorial: 600 W Main St, Fort Wayne, Indiana 46802-1408. **T:** 1 260 461-8773
E: jgnews@jg.net
W: http://www.journalgazette.net
Freq: Daily; **Circ:** 43000 Not Audited
Publisher: Julie Inskeep; **Editor:** Craig Klugman
Editorial Profile: The Journal Gazette is a daily morning newspaper in Fort Wayne, IN that operates in conjunction with The News-Sentinel, the afternoon newspaper of the city. The papers have combined their business operations such as circulation, advertising, marketing and production, but the newsrooms work separately. The paper covers any news-related stories and particularly focuses on Northeast Indiana. Special sections also appear in the Fort Wayne News-Sentinel.; Full Page Mono: 150.35; Full Page Colour: 517.33
Currency: US Dollars
DAILY NEWSPAPER

The Journal Gazette
Editorial: 529 14th St NW, Washington, District Of Columbia 20045-1002.
T: 1 202 879-6710
DAILY NEWSPAPER

The Journal Gazette
Editorial: 200 W Washington St, Indianapolis, Indiana 46204-2728. **T:** 1 317 686-0901
Bureau Chief: Niki Kelly
DAILY NEWSPAPER

Journal Gazette/Times-Courier
Owner: Lee Enterprises, Inc.
Editorial: 700 Broadway Ave E Ste 9, Mattoon, Illinois 61938-4617. **T:** 1 217 235-5656
E: editorial@jg-tc.com
W: http://www.jg-tc.com
Freq: Daily; **Circ:** 11337 Not Audited
Editorial Profile: Journal Gazette/Times-Courier is published daily for residents of Mattoon, IL and Charleston, IL and surrounding areas. The publication is a general interest newspaper covering local news, weather, sports, education, business, arts & entertainment and other information of interest to the local community.
DAILY NEWSPAPER

Journal Inquirer
Owner: Elizabeth Ellis
Editorial: 306 Progress Dr, Manchester, Connecticut 06042-2299. **T:** 1 860 646-0500
E: news@journalinquirer.com
W: http://www.journalinquirer.com
Freq: Daily; **Circ:** 27338
Publisher: Elizabeth Ellis
Editorial Profile: The Journal Inquirer was founded in 1968 and serves residents of north central Connecticut. The paper covers local news and events for 17 towns in the area of the state.; Full Page Mono: 56.00; Full Page Colour: 400.00
Currency: US Dollars
DAILY NEWSPAPER

The Journal News
Owner: Gannett Co., Inc.
Editorial: 1133 Westchester Ave Ste N-110, White Plains, New York 10604-3511.
T: 1 914 694-9300 **E:** metro@lohud.com
W: http://www.lohud.com
Freq: Daily; **Circ:** 58573 Not Audited
Editor: Scott Faubel; **Publisher:** Janet Hasson
DAILY NEWSPAPER

Journal News
Owner: Malone (Susan)
Editorial: 6219 W 63Rd St, Chicago, Illinois 60638-5134. **T:** 1 773 586-1300
E: myjournalnews@aol.com
Freq: Wed; **Circ:** 20000 Not Audited
Editorial Profile: Journal News' editorial mission is to inform people of news and events in South Damen.; Full Page Mono: 9.80
Currency: US Dollars
NEWSPAPER

The Journal News - Rockland Edition
Owner: Gannett Co., Inc.
Editorial: 1 Crosfield Ave, West Nyack, New York 10994-2222. **T:** 1 845 578-2424
E: letters@lohud.com
W: http://www.lohud.com
Freq: Daily; **Circ:** 23545 Not Audited
Editor: Caryn McBride
Editorial Profile: The Journal News-Rockland Edition is published daily for residents of West Nyack, NY.; Full Page Mono: 200.00
Currency: US Dollars
DAILY NEWSPAPER

Journal Newspapers
Editorial: 211 Main St, White Haven, Pennsylvania 18661. **T:** 1 570 443-9131
E: hellojournal@gmail.com **Circ:** 23000 Not Audited
Publisher: Clara Holder; **Editor in Chief:** Ruth Isenberg; **Editor in Chief:** Ruth Isenberg
NEWSPAPER

The Journal Newspapers
Owner: Barron Communications
Editorial: 306 E Newmark Ave, Monterey Park, California 91755-2908. **T:** 1 626 572-7450
E: news@sgvjournal.com
W: http://www.sgvjournal.com **Circ:** 10000 Not Audited
NEWSPAPER

Journal Press, Inc.
Owner: Jessica Herrink
Editorial: 10250 Kings Hwy, King George, Virginia 22485-3429. **T:** 1 540 775-2024
E: news@journalpress.com
W: http://www.journalpress.com **Circ:** 16000 Not Audited
Editor: Jessica Herrink; **Publisher:** Ruth Herrink
NEWSPAPER

Journal Publications
Editorial: 431 S Main St, Hillsboro, Illinois 62049. **T:** 1 217 532-3933
E: thejournal-news@consolidated.net
W: http://www.thejournal-news.net **Circ:** 8108 Not Audited
NEWSPAPER

Journal Register Company-Kennett Square
Owner: Journal Register Company
Editorial: 250 N Bradford Ave, West Chester, Pennsylvania 19382-1912. **T:** 1 610 444-6590
E: kennettpaper@gmail.com
W: http://www.southernchestercountyweeklies.com/ **Circ:** 9500 Not Audited
Editor: Chris Barber; **Editor:** Chris Barber; **Editor:** Chris Barber; **Editor:** Fran Kaye
Editorial Profile: Journal Register Company-Kennett Square publishes the Avon Grove Sun and The Kennet Paper weekly newspapers, providing Local News coverage to Kennett Square, Chadds Ford, Avon Grove and Oxford, PA communities.
NEWSPAPER

Journal Review
Owner: PTS, Inc.
Editorial: 119 N Green St, Crawfordsville, Indiana 47933-1708. **T:** 1 765 362-1200
E: rop@jrpress.com
W: http://www.journalreview.com
Freq: Daily; **Circ:** 7891 Not Audited
Publisher: Shawn Storie
Editorial Profile: Journal Review is a daily newspaper published in Crawfordsville, IN. The paper covers local news and events for local residents and the surrounding area, including parts of Hendrix, Boone, Montgomery and Putnam Counties, IN.; Full Page Mono: 15.90; Full Page Colour: 250.00
Currency: US Dollars
DAILY NEWSPAPER

Journal Star
Owner: GateHouse Media Inc.
Editorial: 1 News Plz, Peoria, Illinois 61643-0001. **T:** 1 309 686-3000 **E:** news@pjstar.com
W: http://www.pjstar.com
Freq: Daily; **Circ:** 57658 Not Audited
Publisher: Ken Mauser
Editorial Profile: Journal Star is a daily newspaper written for the residents of Peoria, IL. The newspaper covers local news and events, business, sports and arts & entertainment. The newspaper also covers national and state news.; Full Page Mono: 88.74; Full Page Colour: 291.70
Currency: US Dollars
DAILY NEWSPAPER

The Journal Times
Owner: Lee Enterprises, Inc.
Editorial: 212 4th St, Racine, Wisconsin 53403-1005. **T:** 1 262 634-3322
W: http://www.journaltimes.com
Freq: Daily; **Circ:** 23209 Not Audited
News Editor: Tom Farley; **Editor:** Rob Golub; **Publisher:** Mark Lewis
Editorial Profile: The Journal Times is a daily newspaper serving Racine, WI. The newspaper covers local news sports, business, health, fitness, real estate and arts & entertainment. Press releases can be sent by e-mail. Deadlines for the editorial submissions is one week prior to the issue date.; Full Page Mono: 46.75; Full Page Colour: 288.17
Currency: US Dollars
DAILY NEWSPAPER

Journal Tribune
Owner: Beacon Press Inc.
Editorial: 457 Alfred St, Biddeford, Maine 04005-9447. **T:** 1 207 282-1535
E: jtcommunity@journaltribune.com
W: http://www.journaltribune.com
Freq: Daily; **Circ:** 4558 Not Audited
Editorial Profile: Journal Tribune is the only daily newspaper in York County, ME. It serves

readers in Wells and Old Orchard Beach, ME and its readership extends west to the New Hampshire border. The paper covers local news, sports and arts & entertainment.; Full Page Mono: 16.25; Full Page Colour: 300.00
Currency: US Dollars
DAILY NEWSPAPER

Journal/Bugle Newspapers
Editorial: 706 7th St, Britton, South Dakota 57430. T: 1 605 448-2281
E: journal@brittonsd.com
W: http://www.marshallcountyjournal.com
Circ: 2350 Not Audited
Editorial Profile: Both paper's share a website which is headed the Marshall County Journal. It contains news stories from the Britton Journal and the Langford Bugle print editions.
NEWSPAPER

Journal/Gazette Publishing
Owner: Central Iowa Publishing
Editorial: 409 Main St, Bayard, Iowa 50029. T: 1 712 651-2321 E: ciapub@netins.net
W: http://iowanewspapersonline.com
Circ: 3359 Not Audited
Editorial Profile: Journal/Gazette Publishing is a community newspaper publisher serving the residents of Des Moines, IA.
NEWSPAPER

Journal-Advocate
Owner: MediaNews Group
Editorial: 504 N 3rd St, Sterling, Colorado 80751-3203. T: 1 970 522-1990
W: http://www.journal-advocate.com
Freq: Daily; **Circ:** 4796 Not Audited
Publisher: David McClain
Editorial Profile: Journal-Advocate is a daily newspaper published for the residents of Sterling, CO and surrounding areas. It provides information on local and state news, government, politics and community events.; Full Page Mono: 14.00; Full Page Colour: 16.00
Currency: US Dollars
DAILY NEWSPAPER

Journal-News
Owner: Cox Media Group, Inc.
Editorial: 228 Court St, Hamilton, Ohio 45011-2820. T: 1 513 863-8200
W: http://www.journal-news.com
Freq: Daily; **Circ:** 19956 Not Audited
Editor: Kevin Aldridge
Editorial Profile: Journal-News is a daily morning newspaper serving the residents of Butler County, OH since 1886. It contains news and advertising and serves as a forum for community issues. It has also been recognized as the best daily in Ohio in its circulation class by the Ohio Society of Professional Journalists.; Full Page Mono: 21.50; Full Page Colour: 25.50
Currency: US Dollars
DAILY NEWSPAPER

Journal-Register
Owner: Community Newspaper Holdings, Inc.
Editorial: 543 Main St, Medina, New York 14103-1420. T: 1 585 798-1400
E: thejournalregister@mail.com
W: http://www.journal-register.com
Freq: Daily; **Circ:** 1316 Not Audited
Editorial Profile: Journal-Register is published daily Monday through Friday, and serves residents in Eastern Orleans County, NY. The editorial mission is to provide the best community coverage. The newspaper covers mostly local news, although national news are sometimes included. The managing editor is the main PR contact. Send press releases by fax. Deadlines for the publication are one day before issue date.; Full Page Mono: 9.76; Full Page Colour: 5.00
Currency: US Dollars
DAILY NEWSPAPER

The Journal-Standard
Owner: GateHouse Media Inc.
Editorial: 27 S State Ave, Freeport, Illinois 61032-4210. T: 1 815 232-1171
E: frontdoor@journalstandard.com
W: http://www.journalstandard.com
Freq: Daily; **Circ:** 7016 Not Audited
Editorial Profile: The Journal-Standard is published daily for the residents of Freeport, IL and surrounding areas. The newspaper covers local and national news, community events, sports and business news.; Full Page Mono: 16.00; Full Page Colour: 2076.90
Currency: US Dollars
DAILY NEWSPAPER

Joyce Media, Inc.
Editorial: 3413 Soledad Canyon Rd, Acton, California 93510. T: 1 661 269-1169

E: help@joycemediainc.com
W: http://www.joycemediainc.com Circ: 19940 Not Audited
Editor: Gayle Joyce; **Editor:** Gayle Joyce;
Editor: Gayle Joyce; **Publisher:** John Joyce
NEWSPAPER

Juice
Editorial: 715 Locust St, Des Moines, Iowa 50309-3703. T: 1 515 284-8080
E: info@dmjuice.com W: http://dmjuice.com
Freq: Wed; **Circ:** 40000 Not Audited
Editor: Sarah Day Owen
Editorial Profile: Juice wants to be the definitive guide for young residents in the Des Moines, IA area. It includes information on dining and shopping, arts & entertainment and career advice for young professionals.; Full Page Mono: 14.26
Currency: US Dollars
NEWSPAPER

Junction City Daily Union
Owner: Montgomery Communications, Inc.
Editorial: 222 W 6Th St, Junction City, Kansas 66441-3047. T: 1 785 762-5000
E: m.editor@thedailyunion.net
W: http://www.thedailyunion.net
Freq: Daily; **Circ:** 4313 Not Audited
Editorial Profile: Junction City Daily Union is written for residents of Junction City, Fort Riley, Grandview Plaza, Milford, Chapman, Wakefield, Ogden, Herington, Woodbine, Dwight, White City, Parker Ville and Alta Vista, KS. It covers local news, business, politics, sports, people and community events.; Full Page Mono: 8.60; Full Page Colour: 200.00
Currency: US Dollars
DAILY NEWSPAPER

Juneau Empire
Owner: Morris Multimedia, Inc.
Editorial: 3100 Channel Dr, Juneau, Alaska 99801-7814. T: 1 907 586-3740
E: editor@juneauempire.com
W: http://www.juneauempire.com
Freq: Daily; **Circ:** 4190
Publisher: Mark Bryan
Editorial Profile: Juneau Empire is published Monday through Friday afternoon and Sunday morning for readers in the Juneau, AK area. The newspaper covers local, national and international news, sports, business and arts.; Full Page Mono: 25.85; Full Page Colour: 475.00
Currency: US Dollars
DAILY NEWSPAPER

The Jupiter Courier
Owner: E.W. Scripps Co.
Editorial: 1939 S Federal Hwy, Stuart, Florida 34994-3915. T: 1 561 745-3311
W: http://www.tcpalm.com
Freq: Sun; **Circ:** 25000
Editorial Profile: The Jupiter Courier in Stuart, FL is a local newspaper for the residents of Jupiter, Tequesta, and Juno Beach, FL areas. The publication reports only on local news and community events. It offers a TMC edition on Wednesday. Press releases should be mailed or faxed to the office. The staff understands that public relations companies send out more than one copy of the same item, however they do not wish to receive the same press release eight times.; Full Page Mono: 21.89
Currency: US Dollars
NEWSPAPER

Kaechele Publications
Owner: Kaechele, (Cheryl)
Editorial: 231 Trowbridge St Ste 17, Allegan, Michigan 49010-1330. T: 1 269 673-5534
E: editor@allegannews.com
W: http://www.allegannews.com Circ: 5384 Not Audited
Publisher: Cheryl Kaechele; **Editor:** Ryan Lewis; **Editor:** Scott Sullivan; **Editor:** Scott Sullivan
NEWSPAPER

Kahoka Newspapers
Editorial: 178 W Main St, Kahoka, Missouri 63445. T: 1 660 727-3395
E: themedia@centurytel.net
W: http://www.nemonews.net Circ: 4400 Not Audited
Editor: Mike Scott
NEWSPAPER

Kalamazoo Gazette
Owner: MLive Media Group
Editorial: 300 S Kalamazoo Mall, Kalamazoo, Michigan 49007-4800. T: 1 269 345-3511
E: kznews@mlive.com
W: http://www.mlive.com/kzgazette
Freq: Daily; **Circ:** 31881 Not Audited

Editorial Profile: Kalamazoo (MI) Gazette covers local, national and international news. The lead time and deadlines for this publication vary. Contact the newspaper for details. It is published in the same office as the Kalamazoo Gazette Weeklies.; Full Page Mono: 105.60; Full Page Colour: 168.75
Currency: US Dollars
DAILY NEWSPAPER

KaMai Forum
Editorial: 1108 Vincent Way, Glendale, California 91205-3621. T: 1 818 956-0551
E: kamaiforum@aol.com
Freq: Semi-Monthly; **Circ:** 15000 Not Audited
Editorial Profile: KaMai Forum's editorial mission is to keep readers updated on news concerning Japanese-Americans. It focuses on community, national, and international news relating to the Japanese.; Full Page Mono: 18.00
Currency: US Dollars
NEWSPAPER

Kanawha-Putnam Ad Mailer
Owner: Valley Publications
Editorial: 6050 State Route 34, Winfield, West Virginia 25213. T: 1 304 755-0270
W: http://www.kpadmailer.com
Freq: Sun; **Circ:** 113000 Not Audited
Publisher: Jim Spanner
Editorial Profile: Kanawha-Putnam Ad Mailer is written for residents of the Kanawha and Putnam counties in West Virginia. Deadlines are on Wednesdays.; Full Page Mono: 27.50
Currency: US Dollars
NEWSPAPER

Kane County Chronicle
Owner: Shaw Media
Editorial: 333 N Randall Rd Ste 2, Saint Charles, Illinois 60174-1500. T: 1 630 232-9222
E: editorial@kcchronicle.com
W: http://www.kcchronicle.com
Freq: Daily; **Circ:** 10346 Not Audited
Editor: Kathy Gresey; **Publisher:** J. Thomas Shaw
Editorial Profile: Kane County Chronicle reports on local and national news for Kane County, IL.; Full Page Mono: 20.95
Currency: US Dollars
DAILY NEWSPAPER

The Kane Republican
Owner: Horizon Publications
Editorial: 200 N Fraley St, Kane, Pennsylvania 16735-1177. T: 1 814 837-6000
E: krnews1@zitomedia.net
W: http://www.kanerepublican.com
Freq: Daily; **Circ:** 1973 Not Audited
Editor: Joseph Bell; **Publisher:** Darlene Coder
Editorial Profile: The Kane Republican is a daily local paper serving the residents of Mckean County, PA. The paper covers local news, government, education, athletics and community events. Deadlines fall on the day prior to the issue date at 2pm ET.; Full Page Mono: 7.90; Full Page Colour: 9.20
Currency: US Dollars
DAILY NEWSPAPER

Kansas City Globe
Owner: Jordon Communications Company
Editorial: 615 E 29th St, Kansas City, Missouri 64109. T: 1 816 531-5253
E: kcglobe@swbell.net
W: http://www.thekcglobe.com
Freq: Thu; **Circ:** 10500 Not Audited
Editorial Profile: Kansas City Globe is published weekly for the African American community in Kansas City, MO. The newspaper covers local news, sports, features, business and community events. Deadlines are on Mondays at noon CT.; Full Page Mono: 22.84; Full Page Colour: 2870.00
Currency: US Dollars
NEWSPAPER

Kansas City Hispanic News
Owner: Arce Communications
Editorial: 2918 Southwest Blvd, Kansas City, Missouri 64108-3615. T: 1 816 472-5246
E: kchnews@swbell.net
W: http://www.kchispanicnews.com
Freq: Thu; **Circ:** 14000 Not Audited
Publisher: Joe Arce; **News Editor:** Ramona Arce; **Editor:** Jose Faus
Editorial Profile: Kansas City Hispanic News is a local newspaper serving residents in the metropolitan Kansas City, MO area. The newspaper is published in English and Spanish, and reports on local and national news, features, business and finance. The newspaper's main audience is Hispanic men and women. The editorial deadline is the

Friday before publication.; Full Page Mono: 14.00; Full Page Colour: 1700.00
Currency: US Dollars
NEWSPAPER

The Kansas City Star
Owner: McClatchy Newspapers
Editorial: 1729 Grand Blvd, Kansas City, Missouri 64108-1413. T: 1 816 234-4636
W: http://www.kansascity.com
Freq: Daily; **Circ:** 176197 Not Audited
News Editor: Charles Howland
Editorial Profile: The Kansas City Star is a 80+ page daily, broadsheet newspaper that was founded in 1880 covering local, regional, national and international news. Its mission is to be the "area's preeminent communications company because of a commitment to one ideal: Building our community through knowledge." The paper does not publish a Holiday Gift Guide.; Full Page Mono: 149.00; Full Page Colour: 178.80
Currency: US Dollars
DAILY NEWSPAPER

The Kansas City Star
Editorial: 300 SW 10th Ave, Topeka, Kansas 66612-1504. T: 1 785 354-1388
DAILY NEWSPAPER

The Kansas City Star
Editorial: State Capitol Building #118A, Jefferson City, Missouri 65101. T: 1 573 634-3565
DAILY NEWSPAPER

Kansas State Globe
Owner: Jordan Publishing Co.
Editorial: 7506 Nebraska Ave, Kansas City, Kansas 66112. T: 1 913 481-4727
E: ksglobe@sbcglobal.net
W: http://www.minoritypressserviceinc.com
Freq: Thu; **Circ:** 25600 Not Audited
Editor: David Jordan
Editorial Profile: The Dispatch Post USA is a weekly newspaper serving African-American residents in the Kansas City, KS area. Each edition covers local and state news, lifestyle features, arts & entertainment, sports, and other information of interest to the African-American community. Deadlines are on Mondays at 5pm CT.; Full Page Mono: 18.00
Currency: US Dollars
NEWSPAPER

Kauppalehti - New York Bureau
Owner: Kauppalehti Oy
Editorial: 225 Garfield Pl, Apt 2, Brooklyn, New York 11215-2264. T: 1 347 725-4172
W: http://www.kauppalehti.fi Circ: 81337 Not Audited
Editorial Profile: This is the New York office for the Kauppalehti which is based in Finland.
DAILY NEWSPAPER

Kearney Hub
Owner: Omaha World-Herald Co.
Editorial: 13 E 22nd St, Kearney, Nebraska 68847-5404. T: 1 308 237-2152
E: news@kearneyhub.com
W: http://www.kearneyhub.com
Freq: Daily; **Circ:** 11285 Not Audited
Editor: Lori Guthard; **Editor:** Brad Norton
Editorial Profile: Kearney Hub is a local daily newspaper published in Kearney, NE. The newspaper, founded in 1888, covers local and national news, sports, education, agriculture and business for the Southeastern Nebraska area. Fax or e-mail press releases to the assistant managing editor.; Full Page Mono: 15.20; Full Page Colour: 56.26
Currency: US Dollars
DAILY NEWSPAPER

The Keene Sentinel
Owner: Keene Publishing Co.
Editorial: 60 West St, Keene, New Hampshire 03431-3373. T: 1 603 352-1234
E: news@keenesentinel.com
W: http://www.sentinelsource.com
Freq: Daily; **Circ:** 8928 Not Audited
Editor: Bill Bilodeau; **Publisher:** Thomas Ewing; **News Editor:** Benjamin Yelle
Editorial Profile: The Keene Sentinel is a daily, local newspaper published for residents of the Keene, NH area. The editorial content of the newspaper covers local news, community events, sports, arts & entertainment, education and health.; Full Page Mono: 13.60; Full Page Colour: 305.00
Currency: US Dollars
DAILY NEWSPAPER

Keene Sentinel Weeklies
Editorial: 60 West St, Keene, New Hampshire 03431-3373. T: 1 603 352-1234
E: news@keenesentinel.com

W: http://www.sentinelsource.com
Freq: Weekly; **Circ:** 9000 Not Audited
Publisher: Thomas Ewing; Full Page Mono: 13.60
Currency: US Dollars
NEWSPAPER

Kendall County Record Inc.
Editorial: 222 S Bridge St, Yorkville, Illinois 60560-1502. **T:** 1 630 553-7034
E: news@kendallcountyrecord.com
Circ: 22227 Not Audited
Editor: John Etheredge; **Publisher:** Jeff Farren; **Editor:** Kathy Farren
NEWSPAPER

Kennebec Journal
Owner: Maine Today Media Inc.
Editorial: 274 Western Ave, Augusta, Maine 04330-4976. **T:** 1 207 623-3811
W: http://www.kjonline.com
Freq: Daily; **Circ:** 8648 Not Audited
Editorial Profile: Kennebec Journal is a daily newspaper serving the residents of Augusta, ME and surrounding areas. The newspaper covers local and national news, sports, entertainment, business and community events.; Full Page Mono: 58.37; Full Page Colour: 638.14
Currency: US Dollars
DAILY NEWSPAPER

Kenosha News
Owner: United Communications Corp.
Editorial: 5800 7th Ave, Kenosha, Wisconsin 53140-4131. **T:** 1 262 657-1000
E: newsroom@kenoshanews.com
W: http://www.kenoshanews.com
Freq: Daily; **Circ:** 20354 Not Audited
Publisher: Kenneth Dowdell; **Editor:** Jon Losness
Editorial Profile: Kenosha News is a daily newspaper serving residents of Kenosha County, WI. The newspaper provides news, community events, entertainment and sports.; Full Page Mono: 25.75; Full Page Colour: 38.55
Currency: US Dollars
DAILY NEWSPAPER

Kent County Daily Times
Owner: R.I.S.N. Operations Inc.
Editorial: 1353 Main St, West Warwick, Rhode Island 02893-3859. **T:** 1 401 821-7400
W: http://www.ricentral.com
Freq: Mon thru Fri; **Circ:** 2930 Not Audited
Publisher: Nanci Batson; **Editor:** Jeremiah Ryan
Editorial Profile: Kent County Daily Times is a daily newspaper serving Kent County, RI. It provides local, regional, national and international news. It also contains sports, entertainment, education, business and feature stories. Advertising deadlines are at 3pm ET three days prior to publication.; Full Page Mono: 14.03; Full Page Colour: 480.00
Currency: US Dollars
DAILY NEWSPAPER

Kent Reporter
Owner: Black Press
Editorial: 19426 68th Ave S, Ste A, Kent, Washington 98032. **T:** 1 253 872-6600
E: letters@kentreporter.com
W: http://www.kentreporter.com
Freq: Fri; **Circ:** 27000 Not Audited
Editor: Mark Klaas; **Publisher:** Polly Shepherd
Editorial Profile: Kent (WA) Reporter is a weekly newspaper that covers local news, sports, business, arts & entertainment and community events.; Full Page Mono: 27.50
Currency: US Dollars
NEWSPAPER

Kenton Times
Owner: Barnes Newspapers (Ray)
Editorial: 201 E Columbus St, Kenton, Ohio 43326-1599. **T:** 1 419 674-4066
W: http://www.kentontimes.com
Freq: Daily; **Circ:** 7200 Not Audited
Publisher: Jeff Barnes; **Editor:** Tim Thomas
Editorial Profile: Kenton Times is the local newspaper for residents of Kenton, OH and the surrounding area. The newspaper covers the local news, sports, government, and events that are of interest to the community.; Full Page Mono: 8.50; Full Page Colour: 255.00
Currency: US Dollars
DAILY NEWSPAPER

The Kentucky Enquirer
Owner: Gannett Co., Inc.
Editorial: 226 Grandview Dr, Fort Mitchell, Kentucky 41017-2702. **T:** 1 859 578-5555
E: kynews@enquirer.com
W: http://www.nky.com
Freq: Daily; **Circ:** 21495 Not Audited
Editor: Steve Wilson
Editorial Profile: The Kentucky Enquirer is a supplement to the Cincinnati Enquirer and its coverage includes the three Northern counties of Kentucky.; Full Page Mono: 58.00; Full Page Colour: 60.00
Currency: US Dollars
DAILY NEWSPAPER

Kentucky New Era
Owner: Kentucky New Era, Inc.
Editorial: 1618 E 9th St, Hopkinsville, Kentucky 42240-4430. **T:** 1 270 886-4444
E: editor@kentuckynewera.com
W: http://www.kentuckynewera.com
Freq: Mon thru Fri; **Circ:** 7361 Not Audited
Publisher: Taylor Hayes; **Editor:** Eli Pace
Editorial Profile: Kentucky New Era is a daily newspaper published for the residents of Christian, Todd, Caldwell and Trigg County, KY. The newspaper provides information on local and national news. Send all press releases to the managing editor.; Full Page Mono: 11.00; Full Page Colour: 195.00
Currency: US Dollars
DAILY NEWSPAPER

Kentucky Publishing Inc.
Editorial: 1540 McCracken Rd., Paducah, Kentucky 42001. **T:** 1 270 442-7389
W: http://www.ky-news.com **Circ:** 26600 Not Audited
Publisher: Greg LeNeave; **Editor:** Kelly Paul
NEWSPAPER

Kernersville News
Owner: Carteret Publishing Company
Editorial: 300 E Mountain St, Kernersville, North Carolina 27284. **T:** 1 336 993-2161
E: news@kernersvillenews.com
W: http://www.kernersvillenews.com
Freq: Sat; **Circ:** 23950 Not Audited
Editorial Profile: Kernersville News is a local newspaper written for the residents of Kernersville, NC. The paper covers schools, local government, health, arts & entertainment, lifestyle, recreation, crafts, sports, real estate and community events. Deadlines are one day prior to the issue day at noon ET.; Full Page Mono: 24.50
Currency: US Dollars
NEWSPAPER

Kerrville Daily Times
Owner: Southern Newspapers, Inc.
Editorial: 429 Jefferson St, Kerrville, Texas 78028-4412. **T:** 1 830 896-7000
E: news@dailytimes.com
W: http://dailytimes.com
Freq: Daily; **Circ:** 7852 Not Audited
Editor: Christina Knott
Editorial Profile: Kerrville Daily Times is published daily for residents in Kerr County, TX. The newspaper covers local and national news, sports, business and lifestyle.; Full Page Mono: 16.30; Full Page Colour: 320.00
Currency: US Dollars
DAILY NEWSPAPER

KerWest, Inc.
Editorial: 14693 W Whitesbridge Ave, Kerman, California 93630. **T:** 1 559 846-6689
E: kerwest@msn.com
W: http://www.kerwestnewspapers.com
Circ: 12200 Not Audited
NEWSPAPER

Ketchikan Daily News
Owner: Pioneer Printing Co., Inc.
Editorial: 501 Dock St, Ketchikan, Alaska 99901-6411. **T:** 1 907 225-3157
W: http://www.ketchikandailynews.com
Freq: Daily; **Circ:** 3200 Not Audited
Publisher: Tena Williams
Editorial Profile: Ketchikan Daily News covers a mix of local, state, national and international news serving the residents of Ketchikan and other parts of Southeast Alaska. The newspaper is published every day except Sunday.; Full Page Mono: 16.20; Full Page Colour: 320.00
Currency: US Dollars
DAILY NEWSPAPER

Kewaunee County Star-News
Editorial: 203 Ellis St, Kewaunee, Wisconsin 54216-1051. **T:** 1 920 388-3175
E: editorial@gokewauneecounty.com
W: http://www.kewauneecountynews.com
Freq: Sat; **Circ:** 10000 Not Audited
Editor: Warren Bluhm; **Publisher:** Kevin Corrado
Editorial Profile: Kewaunee County Star-News, launched September 18, 2010, is a local weekly newspaper serving residents of Kewaunee County, WI. The paper covers general news, business, sports, education and arts & entertainment.; Full Page Mono: 13.00
Currency: US Dollars
NEWSPAPER

The Key West Citizen
Owner: Cooke Communications LLC
Editorial: 3420 Northside Dr, Key West, Florida 33040-4254. **T:** 1 305 292-7777
E: editor@keysnews.com
W: http://www.keysnews.com
Freq: Daily; **Circ:** 8468 Not Audited
Publisher: Paul Clarin; **News Editor:** Sandra Frederick
Editorial Profile: The Key West Citizen is a local daily newspaper serving the residents of Key West, FL and surrounding areas. The publication covers local news events, weather, sports, business and arts & entertainment.; Full Page Mono: 26.08
Currency: US Dollars
DAILY NEWSPAPER

Key West Keynoter
Editorial: 2720A N Roosevelt Blvd, Key West, Florida 33040-3926. **T:** 1 305 296-6989
W: http://www.keysnet.com
Freq: Sat; **Circ:** 35000 Not Audited
Editor: Larry Kahn; **Publisher:** Wayne Markham
Editorial Profile: Key West Keynoter is a local newspaper written for the residents of Key West, FL.; Full Page Mono: 27.85
Currency: US Dollars
NEWSPAPER

Keynoter Newspapers
Owner: Keynoter Publishing Company Inc.
Editorial: 3015 Overseas Hwy, Marathon, Florida 33050. **T:** 1 305 743-5551
E: keynoter@keynoter.com
W: http://www.keysnet.com **Circ:** 43000 Not Audited
Editor: Larry Kahn; **Publisher:** Wayne Markham
Editorial Profile: Keynoter Newspapers is a community newspaper publisher serving residents of Marathon, FL.
NEWSPAPER

Khaas Baat Newspaper
Owner: Khaas Baat Communications
Editorial: 18313 Cypress Stand Cir, Tampa, Florida 33647-1816. **T:** 1 813 758-1786
E: editor@khaasbaat.com
W: http://www.khaasbaat.com
Freq: Monthly; **Circ:** 10000 Not Audited
Editorial Profile: Khaas Baat Newspaper is a free monthly publication serving Florida's Indian-American community since August 2004. The paper reports on local news, health, business, books, movies, automotive and lifestyle stories, and other topics affecting the Indian-American community. The paper is distributed the first week of the month. Press materials must be submitted by the 20th of the previous month.; Full Page Mono: 6.59; Full Page Colour: 130.00
Currency: US Dollars
NEWSPAPER

Killeen Daily Herald
Owner: Mayborn Enterprises
Editorial: 1809 Florence Rd, Killeen, Texas 76541-8977. **T:** 1 254 634-2125
E: news@kdhnews.com
W: http://www.kdhnews.com
Freq: Daily; **Circ:** 16534 Not Audited
Publisher: Sue Mayborn
Editorial Profile: Killeen Daily Herald is written for residents in Killeen, Fort Hood, Harker Heights and Copper's Cove, TX. It covers, local, national and state news, arts & entertainment, lifestyles, sports and courts. It shares offices with the Fort Hood Herald. Press releases should be e-mailed or faxed to the managing editor.; Full Page Mono: 24.93; Full Page Colour: 85.13
Currency: US Dollars
DAILY NEWSPAPER

Kingman Daily Miner
Owner: Western Newspapers, Inc.
Editorial: 3015 Stockton Hill Rd, Kingman, Arizona 86401-4162. **T:** 1 928 753-6397
E: editorial@kingmandailyminer.com
W: http://www.kingmandailyminer.com
Freq: Daily; **Circ:** 7595 Not Audited
Publisher: Robin Mauser; **Editor:** Rich Thurlow
Editorial Profile: Kingman Daily Miner is a newspaper written for the residents of Kingman, AZ. It provides local news, weather and sports.; Full Page Mono: 17.07; Full Page Colour: 57.37
Currency: US Dollars
DAILY NEWSPAPER

Kingsport Daily News
Editorial: 310 E Sullivan St, Kingsport, Tennessee 37660. **T:** 1 423 246-4800
E: sd@kingsportdailynews.com
W: http://www.chartertn.net/dailynews
Freq: Daily; **Circ:** 7800 Not Audited
Editor: Pete Dykes; **Publisher:** Steven Dykes; **Editor:** Jean Fletcher
Editorial Profile: Kingsport Daily News is dedicated to the service of God, our country and its readers. The publication is written for community members of Kingsport, TN.; Full Page Mono: 17.50; Full Page Colour: 52.50
Currency: US Dollars
DAILY NEWSPAPER

Kingsport Times-News
Owner: Sandusky Newspapers Inc.
Editorial: 701 Lynn Garden Dr, Kingsport, Tennessee 37660-5607. **T:** 1 423 246-8121
E: news@timesnews.net
W: http://www.timesnews.net
Freq: Daily; **Circ:** 34230 Not Audited
Publisher: Keith Wilson
Editorial Profile: Kingsport Times-News' editorial mission is to be the watchdog of the community, and to provide local news and information to its readers. The publication is written for Hawkins County and Southwest Virginia.; Full Page Mono: 55.00; Full Page Colour: 294.90
Currency: US Dollars
DAILY NEWSPAPER

Kirkland Reporter
Owner: Black Press
Editorial: 11630 Slater Ave NE Suite 8/9, Kirkland, Washington 98034.
T: 1 425 822-9166
E: editor@kirklandreporter.com
W: http://www.kirklandreporter.com
Freq: Wed; **Circ:** 26350 Not Audited
Editor: Matt Phelps
Editorial Profile: Kirkland Reporter is a weekly newspaper for residents of Kirkland, WA. It began publishing in 1978 and was acquired by Pacific Publishing in 1991. It was sold in April 2007 to Black Press Ltd.; Full Page Mono: 27.50; Full Page Colour: 395.00
Currency: US Dollars
NEWSPAPER

Kirksville Daily Express & News
Owner: GateHouse Media
Editorial: 110 E Mcpherson St, Kirksville, Missouri 63501-3506. **T:** 1 660 665-2808
E: dailyexpresseditor@gmail.com
W: http://www.kirksvilledailyexpress.com
Freq: Daily; **Circ:** 4270 Not Audited
Editorial Profile: Kirksville Daily Express & News is written for residents of Kirksville, MO. It covers local, national and international news, sports, food and health.; Full Page Mono: 10.05
Currency: US Dollars
DAILY NEWSPAPER

The Kirtland Air Force Base Nucleus
Owner: Fig Publications
Editorial: 377 ABW/PA Nucleus, 2000 Wyoming Blvd. SE Ste. A13, Kirtland, New Mexico 87117. **T:** 1 505 892-8080
E: 77abw.nucleus@kirtland.af.mil
W: http://www.kafbnucleus.com
Freq: Fri; **Circ:** 10000 Not Audited
Publisher: Rockford Hayes
Editorial Profile: The Kirtland Air Force Base Nucleus is a free, weekly newspaper serving the military personnel, civilian employees and residents of Kirtland Air Force Base, NM. It provides readers with local news and information pertinent to the local community and military members in the United States and abroad. Although it is owned by Wick Communications, which handles printing and advertising, all editorial content is supplied by military staff members. Editorial submissions are due to the base's Public Affairs office on Fridays at 9am CT and advertising is due on Fridays at 5pm CT.; Full Page Mono: 19.80
Currency: US Dollars
NEWSPAPER

Kitsap Sun
Owner: E.W. Scripps Co.
Editorial: 545 5th St, Bremerton, Washington 98337. **T:** 1 360 377-3711
E: sunnews@kitsapsun.com
W: http://www.kitsapsun.com
Freq: Daily; **Circ:** 28262 Not Audited
Editorial Profile: Kitsap Sun in Bremerton, WA provides local news, events and sports coverage.; Full Page Mono: 50.09; Full Page Colour: 352.32
Currency: US Dollars
DAILY NEWSPAPER

Kitsap Sun Weekly Newspapers
Owner: E.W. Scripps Co.
Editorial: 545 5th St, Bremerton, Washington 98337. **T:** 1 360 377-3711 **Circ:** 48043 Not Audited
Publisher: Rob White
NEWSPAPER

Kitsap Weekly Newspapers
Owner: Black Press
Editorial: 3888 NW Randall Way, Ste 100, Silverdale, Washington 98383-7847.
T: 1 360 308-9161 **Circ:** 39895 Not Audited
Editor: Kassie Korich; **Editor:** Greg Skinner; **Publisher:** Rob White
NEWSPAPER

Klamath Falls Herald and News
Owner: Pioneer Newspapers
Editorial: 2701 Foothills Blvd, Klamath Falls, Oregon 97603-3785. **T:** 1 541 885-4410
E: news@heraldandnews.com
W: http://www.heraldandnews.com
Freq: Daily; **Circ:** 14947 Not Audited
Publisher: Heidi Wright
Editorial Profile: Klamath Falls Herald and News is published daily for the residents of Klamath Falls, OR and surrounding areas. The newspaper covers local news, business, sports, entertainment and community events.; Full Page Mono: 27.25; Full Page Colour: 48.93
Currency: US Dollars
DAILY NEWSPAPER

The Knox County Neighbors
Owner: GateHouse Media Inc.
Editorial: 140 S Prairie St, Galesburg, Illinois 61401. **T:** 1 309 344-3800
W: http://www.galesburg.com/the_paper
Freq: Wed; **Circ:** 23000 Not Audited
Editor: Lisa Coon; **Editor:** Lisa Coon; **News Editor:** Tom Martin; **Publisher:** Tony Scott
Editorial Profile: Knox County Neighbors is a weekly newspaper serving residents of Knox County, IL and the community of Alpha, IL. It covers local news, community events, sports, business, features, editorials, education, entertainment, health and women's issues. In each edition, the paper will feature a local profile of a community leader, a community volunteer, a senior citizen, a community military veteran or personnel, a teacher or student and a coach or athlete. Advertising and editorial deadlines are on Fridays at 5pm CT.; Full Page Mono: 8.90
Currency: US Dollars
NEWSPAPER

Knoxville County FOCUS
Editorial: 2620 Cedar Ln, Knoxville, Tennessee 37918-2311. **T:** 1 865 686-9970
E: staff@knoxfocus.com
W: http://www.knoxfocus.com
Freq: Mon; **Circ:** 13000 Not Audited
Editor: Marianne Dedmon; **Publisher:** Steve Hunley
Editorial Profile: Knoxville/Knox County FOCUS provides residents of Knoxville, TN and surrounding communities with information about local news, government, sports, education, and entertainment. The paper is published every Wednesday.; Full Page Mono: 12.44; Full Page Colour: 1140.00
Currency: US Dollars
NEWSPAPER

The Knoxville Journal
Owner: Premiere Publishing
Editorial: 1717 N Broadway St, Knoxville, Tennessee 37917-5836. **T:** 1 865 546-5353
E: news@theknoxvillejournal.com
W: http://www.theknoxvillejournal.com
Freq: Thu; **Circ:** 45000 Not Audited
Editorial Profile: The Knoxville Journal is a community newspaper circulated throughout Knox, Anderson, Blount, Sevier, Loudon and Campbell, TN counties.; Full Page Mono: 12.50
Currency: US Dollars
NEWSPAPER

The Knoxville News Sentinel
Owner: E.W. Scripps Co.
Editorial: 2332 News Sentinel Dr, Knoxville, Tennessee 37921-5766. **T:** 1 865 523-3131
E: news@knoxnews.com
W: http://www.knoxnews.com
Freq: Daily; **Circ:** 84187 Not Audited
Editorial Profile: The Knoxville News Sentinel is a daily newspaper for Knoxville and Eastern Tennessee residents. Coverage includes breaking news, business, arts & entertainment, lifestyle and sports.; Full Page Mono: 179.57; Full Page Colour: 258.48
Currency: US Dollars
DAILY NEWSPAPER

The Knoxville News Sentinel
Editorial: 1090 Vermont Ave NW, Washington, District Of Columbia 20005-4905.
T: 1 202 408-2727
DAILY NEWSPAPER

The Knoxville News Sentinel
Editorial: Legislative Plaza Room 28, 6th and Union St., Nashville, Tennessee 37243-0001.
T: 1 615 242-7782
Bureau Chief: Tom Humphrey; **Bureau Chief:** Tom Humphrey; **Bureau Chief:** Tom Humphrey
DAILY NEWSPAPER

The Knoxville News Sentinel
Editorial: 100 Tulsa Rd, Oak Ridge, Tennessee 37830-3207. **T:** 1 865 481-3625
Bureau Chief: Bob Fowler; **Bureau Chief:** Bob Fowler; **Bureau Chief:** Bob Fowler; **Bureau Chief:** Bob Fowler
Editorial Profile: All mail should be sent to the main office in Knoxville, TN.
DAILY NEWSPAPER

Kodiak Daily Mirror
Owner: MediaNews Group
Editorial: 1419 Selig St, Kodiak, Alaska 99615-6450. **T:** 1 907 486-3227
E: info@kodiakdailymirror.com
W: http://www.kodiakdailymirror.com
Freq: Daily; **Circ:** 3000 Not Audited
Publisher: Richard Harris
Editorial Profile: Kodiak Daily Mirror is a local paper serving residents of Kodiak, AK and surrounding villages. Coverage includes local news, sports and features.; Full Page Mono: 12.75; Full Page Colour: 101.69
Currency: US Dollars
DAILY NEWSPAPER

Kokomo Perspective
Owner: Wilson Media Group
Editorial: 209 N Main St, Kokomo, Indiana 46901-4623. **T:** 1 765 452-0055
E: editor@kokomoperspective.com
W: http://www.kokomoperspective.com
Freq: Wed; **Circ:** 31000
Publisher: Don Wilson
Editorial Profile: Kokomo Perspective is published weekly for the residents of Kokomo, IN and surrounding areas. The newspaper covers local news, opinions and community events.; Full Page Mono: 16.95
Currency: US Dollars
NEWSPAPER

Kokomo Tribune
Owner: Community Newspaper Holdings, Inc.
Editorial: 300 N Union St, Kokomo, Indiana 46901-4612. **T:** 1 765 459-3121
E: ktnews@kokomotribune.com
W: http://kokomotribune.com
Freq: Daily; **Circ:** 19925 Not Audited
Publisher: Robyn McCloskey
Editorial Profile: Kokomo Tribune is published daily for the residents of Howard County, IN. The newspaper covers local, national, and international news, as well as topics such as sports, business, agriculture, and education.; Full Page Mono: 44.50; Full Page Colour: 145.92
Currency: US Dollars
DAILY NEWSPAPER

The Korea Daily
Owner: JMNet USA
Editorial: 690 Wilshire Pl, Los Angeles, California 90005-3930. **T:** 1 213 368-2500
Freq: Daily
Bureau Chief: Chang Yeon Hwa
DAILY NEWSPAPER

The Korea Daily - Chicago
Owner: JMNet USA
Editorial: 790 Busse Rd, Elk Grove Village, Illinois 60007-2118. **T:** 1 847 228-7200
E: edited.chicago@koreadaily.com
W: http://www.koreadaily.com
Freq: Mon thru Fri; **Circ:** 100000 Not Audited
Editor in Chief: Julie Kim; **Publisher:** Hyun Kee Kwon
Editorial Profile: Korea Daily is a daily newspaper serving the Korean community of Chicago. Associated with Joongang Media Network.; Full Page Mono: 31.53; Full Page Colour: 40.55
Currency: US Dollars
DAILY NEWSPAPER

Korea Daily - Los Angeles
Owner: JMNet USA
Editorial: 690 Wilshire Pl, Los Angeles, California 90005-3930. **T:** 1 213 368-2500
W: http://www.koreadaily.com
Freq: Daily; **Circ:** 72000 Not Audited
Editor in Chief: Sung-Tae Kim; **Publisher:** Intek Park
Editorial Profile: Korea Daily is a daily newspaper providing news to the Korean community in Los Angeles. Associated with Joongang Media Network.; Full Page Mono: 8.27
Currency: US Dollars
DAILY NEWSPAPER

The Korea Daily - New York
Owner: JMNet USA
Editorial: 4327 36th St, Long Island City, New York 11101-1703. **T:** 1 718 361-7700
E: nyopinion@koreadaily.com
W: http://www.koreadaily.com
Freq: Daily; **Circ:** 58750 Not Audited
Editor in Chief: Hyun Sang Lee
Editorial Profile: Korea Daily news is a Korean language newspaper for residents in and around New York City. Associated with Joongang Media Network.; Full Page Mono: 23.27; Full Page Colour: 4511.00
Currency: US Dollars
DAILY NEWSPAPER

Korea Times Chicago Edition
Editorial: 3720 W Devon Ave, Lincolnwood, Illinois 60712-1102. **T:** 1 847 626-0388
E: jjh@koreatimes.com
W: http://chi.koreatimes.com
Freq: Mon thru Fri; **Circ:** 50000 Not Audited
Editorial Profile: Korea Times Chicago Edition is a daily, Korean-language paper serving the residents of Chicago. It provides local, national and international news.; Full Page Mono: 13.20; Full Page Colour: 50.00
Currency: US Dollars
DAILY NEWSPAPER

Korea Times DC Edition
Editorial: 7601 Little River Tpke, Annandale, Virginia 22003-2601. **T:** 1 703 941-8001
E: edit@koreatimesdc.com
W: http://dc.koreatimes.com
Freq: Daily; **Circ:** 50000
Editor: Pae Park
Editorial Profile: Korea Times DC Edition in Annandale, VA is a daily newspaper serving the Korean population in Virginia and the District of Columbia.; Full Page Mono: 9.70; Full Page Colour: 77.66
Currency: US Dollars
DAILY NEWSPAPER

Korea Times Los Angeles Edition
Editorial: 4525 Wilshire Blvd, Los Angeles, California 90010. **T:** 1 323 692-2000
W: http://www.koreatimes.com
Freq: Daily; **Circ:** 70000 Not Audited
Publisher: Jae Min Chang; **Editor:** Chris Kim
Editorial Profile: Korea Times Los Angeles Edition (Hankook Ilbo) has been an integral part of the Korean American community since its founding in 1967. In partnership with Korean American communities nationwide, the Times seeks to provide hard news, which is presented from a culturally informed perspective. The paper is the most established Korean daily newspaper in the United States, in that it is the longest-running paper and the largest in terms of circulation. The paper features headline news from Korea and around the world, as well as coverage of breaking news in the United States.; Full Page Mono: 22.00; Full Page Colour: 3528.00
Currency: US Dollars
DAILY NEWSPAPER

Korea Times New York Edition
Editorial: 4222 27th St, Long Island City, New York 11101. **T:** 1 718 482-1122
W: http://www.koreatimes.com
Freq: Mon thru Fri; **Circ:** 45000 Not Audited
Publisher: Jae Min Chang; **Editor in Chief:** Chang Yeon
Editorial Profile: Korea Times New York Edition covers local, regional, national and international news. It is geared toward a Korean audience. The ad rate provided is for the smallest size black-and-white ad available. The color rate is only offered for the front page, which is also for the smallest size available.; Full Page Mono: 11.60; Full Page Colour: 28.98
Currency: US Dollars
DAILY NEWSPAPER

Korea Times San Francisco Edition
Owner: Korea Daily News, Inc.
Editorial: 8134 Capwell Dr, Oakland, California 94621. **T:** 1 510 777-1111
E: ktnews247@yahoo.com
W: http://sf.koreatimes.com
Freq: Daily; **Circ:** 30000 Not Audited
Publisher: Michael Kang
Editorial Profile: Korean Times San Francisco is published daily for the Asian residents of San Francisco. The edition covers local news, arts & entertainment and sports and is written in Korean.; Full Page Mono: 8.51; Full Page Colour: 25.94
Currency: US Dollars
DAILY NEWSPAPER

Korea Times Seattle Edition
Owner: Korea Times USA (The)
Editorial: 12532 Aurora Ave N, Seattle, Washington 98133-8036. **T:** 1 206 622-2229
W: http://www.koreatimes.com
Freq: Daily; **Circ:** 10000 Not Audited
Editorial Profile: The Korea Times is the oldest independent and most influential English daily in Korea, has served as Korea's bridge to the world since November 1, 1950.; Full Page Mono: 40.00
Currency: US Dollars
DAILY NEWSPAPER

Korean Phila Times
Owner: KoreanPhila Times Inc.
Editorial: 103 Township Line Rd, Rockledge, Pennsylvania 19046-5127. **T:** 1 215 740-2218
W: http://juganphila.com
Freq: Fri; **Circ:** 15000
Editor: Justin Lee
Editorial Profile: Korean Phila Times is a weekly community newspaper serving the Korean-American community in the Philadelphia area, including Montgomery County, Delaware County, Bucks County, Southern New Jersey and Delaware.; Full Page Mono: 6.95; Full Page Colour: 11.30
Currency: US Dollars
NEWSPAPER

Koreaworld
Owner: The Koreaworld, Inc.
Editorial: 9610 Long Point Rd, Ste 340, Houston, Texas 77055-4259.
T: 1 713 827-0063
E: mykoreaworld@yahoo.com
Freq: Fri; **Circ:** 12000 Not Audited
Editorial Profile: Koreaworld is a weekly, Korean-language newspaper serving the Korean-American communities of Houston, Austin and San Antononio. The paper features Korean politics, economics, entertainment and other news.; Full Page Mono: 2.60
Currency: US Dollars
NEWSPAPER

KPC Media Group - Auburn
Owner: KPC Media Group Inc.
Editorial: 118 W 9th St, Auburn, Indiana 46706-2225. **T:** 1 260 357-4123 **Circ:** 4100 Not Audited
Editor: Sue Carpenter; **Publisher:** Terry Housholder; **Editor:** Jeff Jones
Editorial Profile: The Butler Bulletin and the Garrett Clipper both have their own PO Box mailing address.
NEWSPAPER

Kwik Konnection Printing & Publishing, Inc.
Editorial: 213 W Main St, Staunton, Illinois 62088. **T:** 1 618 635-3172
E: ads@kwikkonnection.com
W: http://www.kwikkonnection.com **Circ:** 9000 Not Audited
Editor: William Napper
NEWSPAPER

The Kyocharo News
Editorial: 1260 B St, Hayward, California 94541-2955. **T:** 1 510 728-1236
E: sundaytopic@yahoo.com
W: http://www.asianmediaguide.com
Freq: Sat; **Circ:** 17000 Not Audited
Editorial Profile: The Kyocharo News is published in Korean to provide news and information concerning the Korean American population. The publication provides local Korean American community news, national and international headlines, news from Korea and a section dealing with women's issues and interests. Deadlines are noon PT on Fridays.; Full Page Mono: 3.81
Currency: US Dollars
NEWSPAPER

L & M Publications
Owner: L & M Publications Inc.
Editorial: 1840 Merrick Ave, Merrick, New York 11566. **T:** 1 516 378-5320
E: lmpub@optonline.net
W: http://www.merricklife.com **Circ:** 10476 Not Audited
Editor: Paul Laursen; **Publisher:** Linda Toscano
Editorial Profile: L & M Publications is a community newspaper publisher servicing the residents of New York, Northern NJ and Long Island, NY.
NEWSPAPER

L.A. Web Inc. Newspapers
Owner: L.A. Web, Inc.
Editorial: 9639 Telstar Ave, El Monte, California 91731-3003. **T:** 1 626 453-8800
W: http://www.chinesedaily.com **Circ:** 85000 Not Audited
DAILY NEWSPAPER

La Canada Flintridge Outlook Weeklies
Editorial: 800 Foothill Blvd, La Canada Flintridge, California 91011-3336.
T: 1 818 790-7500
E: outlooknews@outlooknewspapers.com
W: http://www.lacanadaoutlook.com
Circ: 22500 Not Audited
NEWSPAPER

La Canada Valley Sun
Owner: Tribune Company
Editorial: 202 W 1st St, Los Angeles, California 90012-4299. **T:** 1 818 790-8774
E: lcnews@valleysun.net
W: http://www.lacanadaonline.com
Freq: Thu; **Circ:** 10000 Not Audited
Editor: Carol Cormaci; **Editor:** Dan Evans
Editorial Profile: La Canada Valley Sun is a weekly, community newspaper serving areas in and surrounding La Canada, CA. Coverage includes local news, events, sports, religion, entertainment, schools and editorials. Please use the news release form on their website or e-mail all press releases to the appropriate editor or reporter. Valley Sun newspapers will NOT accept materials that are faxed or mailed. Deadlines for calendar submissions are on Mondays at 11 a.m. PT.; Full Page Mono: 24.50
Currency: US Dollars
NEWSPAPER

La Crosse Tribune
Owner: Lee Enterprises, Inc.
Editorial: 401 3rd St N, La Crosse, Wisconsin 54601. **T:** 1 608 782-9710
E: news@lacrossetribune.com
W: http://www.lacrossetribune.com
Freq: Daily; **Circ:** 24263 Not Audited
Publisher: Russell Cunningham; **News Editor:** Keith O'Donnell; **Editor:** Scott Rada
Editorial Profile: La Crosse Tribune is a daily newspaper written for the residents of La Crosse, WI. It covers local news, sports, entertainment, events and health. The lead time varies according to topic.; Full Page Mono: 38.28; Full Page Colour: 247.00
Currency: US Dollars
DAILY NEWSPAPER

La Follette Press Publications
Owner: Landmark Community Newspapers, Inc.
Editorial: 225 N 1st St, La Follette, Tennessee 37766. **T:** 1 423 562-8468
E: stories@lafollettepress.com
W: http://www.lafollettepress.com **Circ:** 11000 Not Audited
Editor: Brent Schanding
NEWSPAPER

La Jolla Light
Owner: Mainstreet Media Group
Editorial: 565 Pearl St Ste 300, La Jolla, California 92037-5051. **T:** 1 858 459-4201
W: http://lajollalight.com
Freq: Thu; **Circ:** 20047 Not Audited
Editor: Susan DeMaggio; **Editor:** Susan DeMaggio; **Editor:** Susan DeMaggio; **Editor:** Susan DeMaggio; **Publisher:** Phyllis Pfeiffer
Editorial Profile: La Jolla Light is dedicated to delivering local news, business, sports, entertainment and religious news to the community of La Jolla, CA.; Full Page Mono: 32.95
Currency: US Dollars
NEWSPAPER

La Junta Tribune-Democrat
Owner: GateHouse Media Inc.
Editorial: 422 Colorado Ave, La Junta, Colorado 81050-2336. **T:** 1 719 384-4475
E: eevans@ljtdmail.com
W: http://www.lajuntatribunedemocrat.com
Freq: Daily; **Circ:** 3800 Not Audited
Editorial Profile: La Junta Tribune-Democrat is a local newspaper written for the residents of La Junta, CO. It provides information on local news, weather and sports.; Full Page Mono: 8.25; Full Page Colour: 60.00
Currency: US Dollars
DAILY NEWSPAPER

The La Porte Herald-Argus
Owner: Paxton Media Group
Editorial: 701 State St, La Porte, Indiana 46350. **T:** 1 219 362-2161
E: ha@heraldargus.com
W: http://www.heraldargus.com
Freq: Daily; **Circ:** 5581 Not Audited
Publisher: Bill Hackney; **Editor:** Kim King
Editorial Profile: The La Porte Herald-Argus's editorial mission is to deliver news, weather, sports, and entertainment information to its readers. The publication is written for residents of LaPorte, IN.; Full Page Mono: 15.46; Full Page Colour: 98.46
Currency: US Dollars
DAILY NEWSPAPER

LA Watts Times
Owner: Blackwell Company
Editorial: 3800 Crenshaw Blvd, Los Angeles, California 90008-1813. **T:** 1 323 299-3800
W: http://www.lawattstimes.com
Freq: Thu; **Circ:** 25500 Not Audited
Publisher: Danny Bakewell
Editorial Profile: L.A. Watts Times is a local weekly newspaper written for the African American community in Los Angeles County, CA. The paper publishes information on education, business, health, legal, financial, entertainment, career and employment opportunities as well as many current and historical topics.; Full Page Mono: 58.24; Full Page Colour: 4560.00
Currency: US Dollars
NEWSPAPER

LA Weekly
Owner: Voice Media Group
Editorial: 3861 Sepulveda Blvd, Culver City, California 90230-4605. **T:** 1 310 574-7100
W: http://www.laweekly.com
Freq: Thu; **Circ:** 170504 Not Audited
Editor: Sarah Fenske
Editorial Profile: LA Weekly is published every Thursday for the young, affluent residents of Los Angeles. The publication covers news, entertainment, art, culture and lifestyle. Sections include Calendar, Picks, Scoring the Clubs, News, Film, Music, Theater, Art, Books, Radio, Politics, Dining and Cyber. Submit releases to the appropriate section editor. The editorial deadline falls on Monday at noon PT.; Full Page Mono: 84.00
Currency: US Dollars
NEWSPAPER

Laconia Daily Sun
Editorial: 65 Water St, Laconia, New Hampshire 03246-3378. **T:** 1 603 527-9299
E: news@laconiadailysun.com
W: http://www.laconiadailysun.com
Freq: Daily; **Circ:** 14000 Not Audited
Publisher: Mark Guerringue
Editorial Profile: Laconia Daily Sun is a local daily newspaper written for residents of Laconia, NH and the surrounding area. The publication covers local news and community events. Although there is no set deadline for press release submissions, it is suggested that they be sent one to two days prior to the issue date. After 80 years as an afternoon paper, it switched to morning circulation in November 2006.; Full Page Mono: 6.00; Full Page Colour: 100.00
Currency: US Dollars
DAILY NEWSPAPER

Ladue News
Owner: Lee Enterprises, Inc.
Editorial: 8811 Ladue Rd, Ste D, Saint Louis, Missouri 63124-2084. **T:** 1 314 863-3737
E: pressreleases@laduenews.com
W: http://www.laduenews.com
Freq: Fri; **Circ:** 42500 Not Audited
Editor in Chief: Trish Muyco-Tobin; **Publisher:** Justin Nangle
Editorial Profile: Ladue News is written for residents in the St. Louis, MO area. It covers news and events.; Full Page Mono: 2.05
Currency: US Dollars
NEWSPAPER

The Lafourche Gazette
Owner: Legendre (Earl P.)
Editorial: 12958 E Main St, Larose, Louisiana 70373-1450. **T:** 1 985 693-7229
E: lafgazette@thelafourchegazette.com
W: http://www.thelafourchegazette.com
Freq: Sun; **Circ:** 15300 Not Audited
Editor: Vicki Chaisson; **Publisher:** Earl Legendre
Editorial Profile: The Lafourche Gazette's editorial mission is to be a free news source for the local communities of Lafourche and Larose, LA.; Full Page Mono: 14.92
Currency: US Dollars
NEWSPAPER

LaGrange Daily News
Owner: Heartland Publications
Editorial: 105 Ashton St, Lagrange, Georgia 30240-3111. **T:** 1 706 884-7311
E: editor@lagrangenews.com
W: http://www.lagrangenews.com
Freq: Daily; **Circ:** 10280 Not Audited
Publisher: John Clark; **Editor:** Tim Epperson
Editorial Profile: LaGrange Daily News is published daily for the residents of Lagrange, GA and surrounding areas. The newspaper cover local and state news, business, sports, lifestyle and entertainment.; Full Page Mono: 12.45; Full Page Colour: 75.63
Currency: US Dollars
DAILY NEWSPAPER

LaGrange Publishing Company
Editorial: State Road 9 S & County Rd 100 S,, Lagrange, Indiana 46761. **T:** 1 260 463-2166
E: lagpubco@kuntrynet.com
W: http://www.lagrangepublishing.com
Circ: 34300 Not Audited
Publisher: William Connelly; **Editor:** Guy Thompson
NEWSPAPER

Laguna Beach Independent
Owner: Firebrand Media LLC.
Editorial: 250 Broadway St, Laguna Beach, California 92651-1807. **T:** 1 949 715-4100
E: editor@lbindy.com
W: http://www.lagunabeachindependent.com
Freq: Fri; **Circ:** 15000 Not Audited
Editor in Chief: Andrea Adelson
Editorial Profile: Laguna Beach Independent is a weekly newspaper serving the residents of Laguna Beach, CA.; Full Page Mono: 9.53; Full Page Colour: 880.00
Currency: US Dollars
NEWSPAPER

Lake City Reporter
Owner: Community Newspapers Inc.
Editorial: 180 E Duval St, Lake City, Florida 32055-4085. **T:** 1 386 752-1293
E: news@lakecityreporter.com
W: http://www.lakecityreporter.com
Freq: Daily; **Circ:** 6628 Not Audited
Editor: Robert Bridges; **Publisher:** Todd Wilson
Editorial Profile: Lake City Reporter's editorial mission is to provide the most accurate and fair comprehensive local news coverage to residents of Columbia and surrounding counties. The publication is written for residents of Columbia County, FL.; Full Page Mono: 20.25; Full Page Colour: 225.00
Currency: US Dollars
DAILY NEWSPAPER

Lake Country Publications
Owner: Journal Community Publishing Group
Editorial: 810 Cardinal Ln, Suite 200, Hartland, Wisconsin 53029-2390.
T: 1 262 367-3272 **E:** lakenews@jcpgroup.com
W: http://www.livinglakecountry.com
Freq: Weekly; **Circ:** 10427 Not Audited
Editor in Chief: Scott Peterson
NEWSPAPER

Lake County Journal
Owner: Shaw Media
Editorial: 1100 Washington St, Suite 101, Grayslake, Illinois 60030-1774.
T: 1 847 223-8161
E: lcjedit@lakecountyjournal.com
W: http://www.lakecountyjournal.com
Freq: Thu; **Circ:** 10000 Not Audited
Publisher: John Rung
Editorial Profile: Formerly called the Lake County Journal, Lake County Suburban Life is a weekly newspaper serving residents of Lake County, IL. It offers news, community events, features, arts & entertainment and sports stories.; Full Page Mono: 7.51
Currency: US Dollars
NEWSPAPER

Lake County News-Sun
Owner: Wrapports LLC
Editorial: 1225 Tri State Pkwy, Ste 570, Gurnee, Illinois 60031-9163.
T: 1 847 336-7000
W: http://newssun.suntimes.com
Freq: Daily; **Circ:** 14812 Not Audited
Editor: Rob Elder
Editorial Profile: Lake County News-Sun is a local daily newspaper serving the residents of Lake County, IL. It covers local news, sports, business, entertainment and events.; Full Page Mono: 31.26; Full Page Colour: 106.50
Currency: US Dollars
DAILY NEWSPAPER

Lake County Record-Bee
Owner: MediaNews Group
Editorial: 2150 S Main St, Lakeport, California 95453-5620. **T:** 1 707 263-5636
W: http://www.record-bee.com
Freq: Daily; **Circ:** 4638 Not Audited
Editorial Profile: Lake County Record-Bee's editorial mission is to inform the public of Lake County, CA about local news and information.; Full Page Mono: 13.00; Full Page Colour: 66.24
Currency: US Dollars
DAILY NEWSPAPER

Lake Eufaula Publishing
Owner: Sumner Newspapers Inc.
Editorial: 109 S Main St, Eufaula, Oklahoma 74432. **T:** 1 918 689-2191 **Circ:** 15900 Not Audited
Editor: Jack Fallor; Full Page Mono: 8.00
Currency: US Dollars
NEWSPAPER

Lake Norman Citizen
Editorial: 307 Gilead Rd, Huntersville, North Carolina 28078-6896. **T:** 1 704 948-3348
W: http://www.lakenormancitizen.com
Freq: Fri; **Circ:** 30000
Publisher: Kim Clark; **Editor:** Andy Warfield
Editorial Profile: Lake Norman Citizen is a weekly community newspaper written for the residents of Huntersville, Cornelius and Davidson, NC. The paper began publishing in June 2009.; Full Page Mono: 26.00; Full Page Colour: 100.00
Currency: US Dollars
NEWSPAPER

Lake Norman Publications
Owner: Newsman LLC
Editorial: 209 Delburg St, Davidson, North Carolina 28036-6913. **T:** 1 704 766-2100
W: http://www.lakenormanpublications.com
Circ: 37000 Not Audited
Publisher: Craig Moon
Editorial Profile: Lake Norman Publications in Davidson, NC publishes community newspapers for residents of Union and Mecklenburg County, NC.
NEWSPAPER

Lake Stevens Journal
Owner: Lake Stevens Journal Inc.
Editorial: 1909 Main St, Lake Stevens, Washington 98258. **T:** 1 425 334-9252
E: news@lakestevensjournal.com
W: http://www.lakestevensjournal.com
Freq: Wed; **Circ:** 16000 Not Audited
Publisher: Desiree Cahoon; **Editor:** Pam Stevens
Editorial Profile: Lake Stevens Journal is written for residents of Lake Stevens and Granite Falls, WA. Deadlines are on Thursdays at 5pm PT.; Full Page Mono: 23.00
Currency: US Dollars
NEWSPAPER

Lake Sun Leader
Owner: GateHouse Media Inc.
Editorial: 918 N Business Route 5, Camdenton, Missouri 65020-2648.
T: 1 573 346-2132
E: newsroom@lakesunonline.com
W: http://www.lakenewsonline.com
Freq: Mon thru Fri; **Circ:** 4670 Not Audited
Publisher: John Tucker
Editorial Profile: Lake Sun Leader is a daily newspaper written for the residents of Camdenton, MO. It covers local, national and international news, as well as local recreation, arts, sports and milestones, such as births, deaths and weddings.; Full Page Mono: 8.80; Full Page Colour: 11.80
Currency: US Dollars
DAILY NEWSPAPER

Lake Worth Herald Press, Inc.
Editorial: 130 S H St, Lake Worth, Florida 33460. **T:** 1 561 585-9387
E: lwherald@bellsouth.net
W: http://www.lwherald.com **Circ:** 38000 Not Audited
NEWSPAPER

Lake Wylie Pilot
Owner: McClatchy Newspapers
Editorial: 264 Latitude Ln Ste 102 E-F, Clover, South Carolina 29710-8129.
T: 1 803 831-8166
E: news@lakewyliepilot.com
W: http://www.lakewyliepilot.com
Freq: Tue; **Circ:** 11000 Not Audited
Editor: Catherine Muccigrosso
Editorial Profile: Lake Wylie Pilot provides local news to Lake Wylie, SC and the surrounding counties. Deadlines are on Wednesdays prior to the next issue date.; Full Page Mono: 15.60
Currency: US Dollars
NEWSPAPER

The Lakeland Times

Editorial: 510 Chippewa St, Minocqua, Wisconsin 54548-9395. **T:** 1 715 356-5236
E: editor@lakelandtimes.com
W: http://www.lakelandtimes.com
Freq: Fri; **Circ:** 10000 Not Audited
Editor: Raymond Rivard; **Publisher:** Gregg Walker
Editorial Profile: The Lakeland Times is written for Oneida and Vilas counties, WI.; Full Page Mono: 6.95; Full Page Colour: 558.80
Currency: US Dollars
NEWSPAPER

The Lakelander

Editorial: 1221A N Brazos St, Whitney, Texas 76692-2018. **T:** 1 254 694-4344
E: lakelander@valornet.com
Freq: Wed
Editor: Deanna Eubank; **Publisher:** Ron Eubank
Editorial Profile: The Lakelander is a weekly community newspaper.
NEWSPAPER

The Laker

Owner: Panoramic Publishing Group, LLC
Editorial: 83 Center St, Wolfeboro, New Hampshire 03894-4368. **T:** 1 603 569-5257
E: lkr@thelaker.com
W: http://www.thelaker.com
Freq: Mon; **Circ:** 20000 Not Audited
Editorial Profile: The Laker is a weekly community newspaper serving the Lakes Region in New Hampshire.; Full Page Mono: 3.14; Full Page Colour: 4.09
Currency: US Dollars
NEWSPAPER

Lakeshore Chronicle

Owner: Gannett Co., Inc.
Editorial: 902 Franklin St, Manitowoc, Wisconsin 54220-4514. **T:** 1 920 684-4433
E: htrnews@htrnews.com
W: http://www.htrnews.com
Freq: Sun; **Circ:** 31500 Not Audited
Publisher: Kevin Corrado; **Editor:** Pat Pankratz
Editorial Profile: Lakeshore Chronicle is published twice weekly for residents of Manitowoc County, WI. The publication covers local news, weather, sports and community events. Feature articles cover business, education, arts & entertainment, lifestyle and other topics of importance to community residents. It shares offices and Web site with the daily Herald Times Reporter.; Full Page Mono: 23.52
Currency: US Dollars
NEWSPAPER

Lakeshore Newspapers

Owner: Conley Publishing Group
Editorial: W61N306 Washington Ave Ste L1, Cedarburg, Wisconsin 53012-2451.
T: 1 262 375-5100
E: webmaster@conleynet.com
W: http://www.gmtoday.com **Circ:** 36952 Not Audited
NEWSPAPER

Lakeshore Weekly News

Editorial: 1001 Twelve Oaks Center Dr, Ste 1017, Wayzata, Minnesota 55391-4310.
T: 1 952 473-0890
W: http://www.weeklynews.com
Freq: Tue; **Circ:** 16000 Not Audited
Editor: Joey LeMay
Editorial Profile: Lakeshore Weekly News provides information on news and events to the residents of Wayzata, MN.; Full Page Mono: 31.00
Currency: US Dollars
NEWSPAPER

Lakeway Publishers, Inc.

Owner: Lakeway Publishers, Inc.
Editorial: 20 Business Park Dr, Troy, Missouri 63379. **T:** 1 636 528-9550 **E:** lcjeditor@lcs.net
W: http://www.lakewaypublishers.com
Circ: 16000 Not Audited
Publisher: Pat Whiteside
NEWSPAPER

Lakewood Community News

Editorial: 24 Lakewood Center Mall, Lakewood, California 90712-2418.
T: 1 562 531-9733
E: info@lakewoodchamber.com
W: http://www.lakewoodnews.org
Freq: Monthly; **Circ:** 30000 Not Audited
Publisher: Jodee Kilroy; **Editor:** Robin Vanderwerff
Editorial Profile: Lakewood Community News is a local newspaper written for the residents of Lakewood, CA.; Full Page Mono: 12.67
Currency: US Dollars
NEWSPAPER

Lamorinda Sun

Owner: MediaNews Group
Editorial: 175 Lennon Ln Ste 100, Walnut Creek, California 94598-2466.
T: 1 925 943-8241
E: ccsun@bayareanewsgroup.com
W: http://www.contracostatimes.com
Freq: Fri; **Circ:** 15000 Not Audited
Editor: Sam Richards
Editorial Profile: Lamorinda Sun is a local weekly newspaper serving Lafayette, CA. The paper covers local news, weather, sports, business and arts & entertainment. The paper is a part of the Bay Area News Group subsidiary of MediaNews Group.; Full Page Mono: 28.00
Currency: US Dollars
NEWSPAPER

Lancaster Eagle-Gazette

Owner: Gannett Co., Inc.
Editorial: 138 W Chestnut St, Lancaster, Ohio 43130. **T:** 1 740 654-1321
E: laneg@gannett.com
W: http://www.lancastereaglegazette.com
Freq: Daily; **Circ:** 7687 Not Audited
Editorial Profile: Lancaster Eagle-Gazette covers local news and events for residents of Lancaster (Franklin County), OH. It is written for residents of Lancaster, OH and surrounding area.; Full Page Mono: 29.40; Full Page Colour: 170.40
Currency: US Dollars
DAILY NEWSPAPER

The Lancaster News

Owner: Lancaster Newspapers, Inc.
Editorial: 701 N White St, Lancaster, South Carolina 29720. **T:** 1 803 283-1133
E: news@thelancasternews.com
W: http://www.thelancasternews.com
Circ: 20543 Not Audited
Publisher: Susan Rowell; **Editor:** Barbara Rutledge
NEWSPAPER

Lansing Community Newspapers

Owner: Gannett Co., Inc.
Editorial: 120 E Lenawee St, Lansing, Michigan 48919. **T:** 1 517 377-1112
W: http://www.lsj.com
Freq: Weekly; **Circ:** 149114 Not Audited
Editor: Barbara Modrack; **Editor:** Barbara Modrack
NEWSPAPER

Lansing State Journal

Owner: Gannett Co., Inc.
Editorial: 120 E Lenawee St, Lansing, Michigan 48919-1000. **T:** 1 517 377-1112
E: metro@lsj.com
W: http://www.lansingstatejournal.com
Freq: Daily; **Circ:** 36196 Not Audited
Editorial Profile: Lansing (MI) State Journal is a daily newspaper that covers local news, Michigan state government news, local business, entertainment, high school and Michigan State University athletics, and lifestyle topics.; Full Page Mono: 103.00; Full Page Colour: 352.32
Currency: US Dollars
DAILY NEWSPAPER

Lapeer Area View

Owner: JAMS Media
Editorial: 1521 Imlay City Rd, Lapeer, Michigan 48446-3175. **T:** 1 810 245-9343
E: editor@mihomepaper.com
W: http://www.mihomepaper.com
Freq: Thu; **Circ:** 35000 Not Audited
Editorial Profile: Lapeer Area View is a community newspaper for the residents of Lapeer, MI. It covers local news, weather and sports.; Full Page Mono: 12.19
Currency: US Dollars
NEWSPAPER

Laramie Daily Boomerang

Owner: Wyoming Newspaper Group
Editorial: 320 E Grand Ave, Laramie, Wyoming 82070-3712. **T:** 1 307 742-2176
E: newsone@laramieboomerang.com
W: http://www.laramieboomerang.com
Freq: Daily; **Circ:** 5233 Not Audited
Editorial Profile: Laramie Daily Boomerang is a daily newspaper written for the residents of Laramie, WY and surrounding areas. The newspaper includes coverage of local news, weather, sports, business and lifestyle issues.; Full Page Mono: 13.80; Full Page Colour: 580.00
Currency: US Dollars
DAILY NEWSPAPER

Larchmont Chronicle

Owner: Gilman (Jane)

Editorial: 542 1/2 N Larchmont Blvd, Los Angeles, California 90004. **T:** 1 323 462-2241
W: http://www.larchmontchronicle.com
Freq: Monthly; **Circ:** 76439 Not Audited
Editorial Profile: Larchmont Chronicle is a monthly newspaper, serving the residents of Hancock Park, Windsor Square, Fremont Place, Park LaBrea, Larchmont Village and Miracle Mile, CA. Deadlines are the 15th of every month.; Full Page Mono: 25.40
Currency: US Dollars
NEWSPAPER

Lare Dos

Editorial: 1812 Houston St, Laredo, Texas 78040. **T:** 1 956 791-9950
E: editorial@laredosnews.com
W: http://www.laredosnews.com
Freq: Monthly; **Circ:** 10000 Not Audited
Editorial Profile: Laredos is a local newspaper written for the Hispanic community of Laredo, TX.; Full Page Mono: 65.00
Currency: US Dollars
NEWSPAPER

Laredo Morning Times

Owner: Hearst Newspapers
Editorial: 111 Esperanza Dr, Laredo, Texas 78041-9198. **T:** 1 956 728-2500
E: times@lmtonline.com
W: http://www.lmtonline.com
Freq: Daily; **Circ:** 13153 Not Audited
News Editor: Nick Georgiou; **News Editor:** Nick Georgiou; **Publisher:** William Green
Editorial Profile: Laredo Morning Times is a daily newspaper published in Laredo, TX. It covers local news, business, sports and entertainment. The paper also features a daily Spanish-language news section, Tiemp de Laredo. Deadlines are at 10pm daily.; Full Page Mono: 51.35; Full Page Colour: 162.21
Currency: US Dollars
DAILY NEWSPAPER

Larned Tiller & Toiler Newspapers

Owner: Star Communications Corp.
Editorial: 115 W 5th St, Larned, Kansas 67550. **T:** 1 620 285-3111
E: tiller@star.kscoxmail.com **Circ:** 16750 Not Audited
Publisher: John Settle
NEWSPAPER

Larson Newspapers

Owner: Larson Newspapers, LLC
Editorial: 298 Van Deren Rd, Sedona, Arizona 86336-4826. **T:** 1 928 282-7795
E: editor@larsonnewspapers.com
W: http://www.redrocknews.com **Circ:** 15800 Not Audited
Publisher: Robert Larson
NEWSPAPER

Las Cruces Bulletin

Owner: FIG Publications, LLC
Editorial: 840 N Telshor Blvd Ste E, Las Cruces, New Mexico 88011-8205.
T: 1 575 524-8065
E: editor@lascrucesbulletin.com
W: http://www.lascrucesbulletin.com
Freq: Fri; **Circ:** 20000 Not Audited
Publisher: Richard Coltharp; **News Editor:** Todd Dickson
Editorial Profile: Las Cruces Bulletin's editorial mission is to provide local news first to the residents of the Mesilla Valley, NM. Each issue features exclusive local content, including news, photography, features, sports, business, arts and entertainment, editorials, letters to the editor, local calendars, television listings and classified advertising.; Full Page Mono: 20.00; Full Page Colour: 1303.40
Currency: US Dollars
NEWSPAPER

Las Cruces Sun-News

Owner: MediaNews Group
Editorial: 256 W Las Cruces Ave, Las Cruces, New Mexico 88005-1804. **T:** 1 575 541-5400
W: http://www.lcsun-news.com
Freq: Daily; **Circ:** 26745 Not Audited
Editorial Profile: Las Cruces Sun-News is the local daily newspaper for Las Cruces, NM and the surrounding communities. The editorial content covers local news, sports and business.; Full Page Mono: 34.71; Full Page Colour: 238.82
Currency: US Dollars
DAILY NEWSPAPER

Las Vegas Chinese Daily News

Editorial: 4215 Spring Mountain Rd, Ste B206A, Las Vegas, Nevada 89102.
T: 1 702 312-3998 **W:** http://www.lvcdn.com
Freq: Fri; **Circ:** 20000 Not Audited
Editor: Annie Yen

Editorial Profile: Las Vegas Chinese Daily News provides international and local news, business, real estate, entertainment and lifestyle news to the Las Vegas Chinese community. The paper is written in Mandarin Chinese to appeal to readers from China, Hong Kong, Singapore and Taiwan. The paper teams up with leading news source providers in China and Taiwan. Their mission is to provide objective reporting on the most updated news and events to the growing Asian population. It is distributed to local Chinese retail stores, doctor's offices, supermarkets, libraries and restaurants at no cost to its readers.; Full Page Mono: 11.54
Currency: US Dollars
NEWSPAPER

Las Vegas Chinese News Network

Owner: Las Vegas Chinese News Network Corp.
Editorial: 3552 Wynn Rd, Las Vegas, Nevada 89103-1710. **T:** 1 702 685-6600
E: ad@lvcnn.com **W:** http://www.lvcnn.com
Freq: Fri
Editor in Chief: Mary Lin
Editorial Profile: Las Vegas Chinese News Network is a newspaper that provides Local and Community News coverage for Chinese-speaking residents in the Las Vegas, NV area.
NEWSPAPER

Las Vegas Review-Journal

Owner: Stephens Media
Editorial: 1111 W Bonanza Rd, Las Vegas, Nevada 89106-3545. **T:** 1 702 383-0211
W: http://www.reviewjournal.com
Freq: Daily; **Circ:** 234794 Not Audited
Editorial Profile: Las Vegas Review-Journal is a daily newspaper written for the residents of Las Vegas. It covers local, regional and national news, business, entertainment, health, food, sports and lifestyle. The Las Vegas Sun is circulated daily within the Las Vegas Review-Journal as a six-to-10 page section. The Sun maintains its liberal editorial voice which is independent of the Review-Journal.; Full Page Mono: 234.52; Full Page Colour: 262.51
Currency: US Dollars
DAILY NEWSPAPER

Las Vegas Review-Journal

Editorial: 666 11th St NW Ste 535, Washington, District Of Columbia 20001-4542.
T: 1 202 783-1760
DAILY NEWSPAPER

Las Vegas Review-Journal

Editorial: 102 N Curry St, Carson City, Nevada 89703-4934. **T:** 1 775 687-3900
DAILY NEWSPAPER

Las Vegas Sun

Owner: Greenspun Media Group
Editorial: 2360 Corporate Cir Fl 3, Henderson, Nevada 89074-7723. **T:** 1 702 385-3111
E: letters@lasvegassun.com
W: http://www.lasvegassun.com
Freq: Daily; **Circ:** 34978 Not Audited
Editorial Profile: Las Vegas Sun is a daily newspaper covering local news, business, sports and travel for the Las Vegas community. It is published under a Joint Operating Agreement with the Las Vegas Review-Journal, but remains an independent and separate entity.; Full Page Mono: 225.14; Full Page Colour: 1363.67
Currency: US Dollars
DAILY NEWSPAPER

Las Vegas Sun

Editorial: 101 N Carson St, Carson City, Nevada 89701-3713. **T:** 1 775 687-5032
Bureau Chief: Cy Ryan
DAILY NEWSPAPER

Las Vegas Sun

Editorial: 529 14Th St Nw Ste 1290, Washington, District Of Columbia 20045-2503.
T: 1 202 662-7436
DAILY NEWSPAPER

Las Vegas Tribune

Editorial: 820 E Charleston Blvd, Las Vegas, Nevada 89104-1512. **T:** 1 702 699-8100
E: newsdesk@lasvegastribune.com
W: http://www.lasvegastribune.com
Freq: Wed; **Circ:** 41500 Not Audited
Editorial Profile: Las Vegas Tribune is a weekly newspaper serving residents of Las Vegas. It contains community news and politics, editorials, sports and an entertainment section. Some national news is reported if it is of interest to local readers.; Full Page Mono: 15.00
Currency: US Dollars

NEWSPAPER

Lassen County Times
Owner: Feather Publishing Co.
Editorial: 100 Grand Ave, Susanville, California 96130-4451. **T:** 1 530 257-5321
E: lctimes@lassennews.com
W: http://www.lassennews.com
Freq: Tue; **Circ:** 10525 Not Audited
Publisher: Michael Taborski
Editorial Profile: Lassen County Times is written for the residents of Susanville and Honey Valley Lake, CA. The publication covers local news and community events. Editorial deadlines are on Fridays at noon PT.; Full Page Mono: 8.75
Currency: US Dollars
NEWSPAPER

Latino
Owner: Leon (Wilfredo)
Editorial: 303 N Main St, Mauldin, South Carolina 29662. **T:** 1 864 627-1945
E: editor@latinonewspaper.net
W: http://www.latino4u.net
Freq: Fri; **Circ:** 35000 Not Audited
Editorial Profile: Latino in Mauldin, SC is a Spanish newspaper written for the residents of Greenville, SC and surrounding areas. Its editorial mission is to enhance society by creating, collecting and distributing high quality news, information and entertainment.; Full Page Mono: 10.40
Currency: US Dollars
NEWSPAPER

Latino Communications Network
Owner: Latino Communications Network
Editorial: 1516 E Lake St, Ste 200, Minneapolis, Minnesota 55407.
T: 1 612 729-5900
W: http://www.lcnmedia.com **Circ:** 45000 Not Audited
NEWSPAPER

Latino Press
Owner: Latino Press, Inc.
Editorial: 6301 Michigan Ave, Detroit, Michigan 48210-2954. **T:** 1 313 361-3000
E: editorial@latinodetroit.com
W: http://www.latinodetroit.com
Freq: Thu; **Circ:** 20000 Not Audited
Editorial Profile: Latino Press is published weekly for the Hipanic community in Detroit, MI and surrounding areas. The newspaper covers local news, national news, Mexico news, community events, sports, immigration and education.; Full Page Mono: 57.00
Currency: US Dollars
NEWSPAPER

El Latino San Diego
Owner: Latina Associates Inc.
Editorial: 1550 Broadway, Ste U, Chula Vista, California 91911. **T:** 1 619 426-1491
E: editor@ellatino.net
W: http://www.ellatinoonline.com
Freq: Fri; **Circ:** 80500 Not Audited
Publisher: Mike Cano; **Editor:** Fanny Miller
Editorial Profile: El Latino San Diego is a weekly publication for the Hispanic communities located in Southern California. The publication covers local news and events.; Full Page Mono: 53.50
Currency: US Dollars
NEWSPAPER

El Latino Semanal
Owner: El Latino, Inc.
Editorial: 4404 Georgia Ave, West Palm Beach, Florida 33405. **T:** 1 561 835-4913
E: ellatino@msn.com
W: http://www.ellatino.com
Freq: Fri; **Circ:** 39000 Not Audited
Editor: Miguel Lavin; **Editor:** Olga Vazquez
Editorial Profile: El Latino Semanal is a local newspaper written for the Hispanic community of West Palm Beach, FL. Topics covered include immigration, health, sports and arts & entertainment.; Full Page Mono: 16.00
Currency: US Dollars
NEWSPAPER

Latrobe Bulletin
Owner: Sample News Group
Editorial: 1211 Ligonier St, Latrobe, Pennsylvania 15650-1921. **T:** 1 724 537-3351
E: lb.news@verizon.net
Freq: Daily; **Circ:** 7988 Not Audited
News Editor: Marie McCandless; **Publisher:** Gary Siegel
Editorial Profile: Latrobe Bulletin is a newspaper written for residents of Latrobe, PA. The newspaper, published six days per week, covers local news and events in Latrobe, PA. The lead time varies. Contact the publication for advertising rates. The

publication is not available on World Wide Web.; Full Page Mono: 14.25; Full Page Colour: 150.00
Currency: US Dollars
DAILY NEWSPAPER

Lauderdale County Enterprise
Editorial: 145 E Jackson Ave, Ripley, Tennessee 38063-1556. **T:** 1 731 635-1771
E: enterprisenewspaper@hotmail.com
Freq: Weekly; **Circ:** 5969 Not Audited
Editorial Profile: Lauderdale County Enterprise is written for the general public in Tennessee.; Full Page Colour: 666.00
Currency: US Dollars
NEWSPAPER

Laurel Group Newspapers
Owner: Tribune-Review Publishing Co.
Editorial: 228 Pittsburgh St, Scottdale, Pennsylvania 15683-1735. **T:** 1 724 887-7400
W: http://www.laurelgrouponline.com
Circ: 18626 Not Audited
Editor: Deborah Brehun; **Editor:** Mary Kaufman; **Editor:** Kristie Linden; **Editor:** Paul Paterra; **Publisher:** Richard Scaife; **Editor:** William Zirkle
NEWSPAPER

Laurel Leader-Call
Owner: Gin Creek Publishing
Editorial: 318 N Magnolia St, Laurel, Mississippi 39440-3932. **T:** 1 601 649-9388
W: http://www.leader-call.net
Freq: Daily; **Circ:** 6733 Not Audited
Editorial Profile: Laurel Leader-Call is a daily newspaper for the residents of Laurel County and Jones County, MS. It provides local and national news, business, lifestyle and sports.; Full Page Mono: 12.50; Full Page Colour: 86.14
Currency: US Dollars
DAILY NEWSPAPER

The Laurinburg Exchange
Owner: Heartland Publications
Editorial: 211 W Cronly St, Laurinburg, North Carolina 28352. **T:** 1 910 276-2311
W: http://www.laurinburgexchange.com
Freq: Daily; **Circ:** 8450 Not Audited
Editorial Profile: The Laurinburg Exchange is published daily for the residents of Laurinburg, NC and surrounding areas. The newspaper provides information on local news and community events. Deadlines are at 5pm ET one day prior to issue date.; Full Page Mono: 9.85; Full Page Colour: 250.00
Currency: US Dollars
DAILY NEWSPAPER

Lawndale News
Owner: Lawndale Press, Inc.
Editorial: 5533 W 25th St, Cicero, Illinois 60804-3319. **T:** 1 708 656-6400
E: news@lawndalenews.com
W: http://www.lawndalenews.com
Freq: Thu; **Circ:** 192200 Not Audited
Editor: Ashmar Mandou; **Publisher:** Lynda Nardini
Editorial Profile: Lawndale News is written for the Hispanic residents of Chicago. It covers local news and events. Deadlines are on Thursdays at 5pm CT.; Full Page Mono: 55.00; Full Page Colour: 3810.00
Currency: US Dollars
NEWSPAPER

Lawrence County Advocate
Editorial: 121 N Military Ave, Lawrenceburg, Tennessee 38464. **T:** 1 931 762-1726
E: lawcoadv@bellsouth.net
W: http://www.lawrencecountyadvocate.net
Freq: Sun; **Circ:** 16400 Not Audited
Editor: Sandy Mashburn
Editorial Profile: Lawrence County Advocate is a local newspaper written for residents of Lawrence County, Tennessee. The publication regularly features local news and sometimes features national news.; Full Page Mono: 5.60; Full Page Colour: 691.80
Currency: US Dollars
NEWSPAPER

Lawrence Journal-World
Owner: World Company (The)
Editorial: 645 New Hampshire St, Lawrence, Kansas 66044. **T:** 1 785 843-1000
E: news@ljworld.com
W: http://www.ljworld.com
Freq: Daily; **Circ:** 21245 Not Audited
Editorial Profile: Lawrence Journal-World is a daily newspaper published for the residents of Lawrence, KS and surrounding areas. The publication covers local, national and international news and sports.; Full Page Mono: 27.95; Full Page Colour: 345.00
Currency: US Dollars

DAILY NEWSPAPER

The Lawton Constitution
Owner: Lawton Publishing Company, Inc.
Editorial: 102 SW 3rd St, Lawton, Oklahoma 73501-4031. **T:** 1 580 353-0620
W: http://www.swoknews.com
Freq: Daily; **Circ:** 18937 Not Audited
Publisher: Stephen Bentley; **Editor:** Steve Metzer; **News Editor:** De Ann Patterson
Editorial Profile: The Lawton Constitution is a daily newspaper distributed in the Lawton, OK area. The paper covers local news, recreation, high school sports and community events. National news is taken primarily from the wires. Deadlines are daily at 8pm CT.; Full Page Mono: 19.45; Full Page Colour: 120.61
Currency: US Dollars
DAILY NEWSPAPER

Le Mars Daily Sentinel
Owner: Rust Communications
Editorial: 41 1st Ave NE, Le Mars, Iowa 51031-3535. **T:** 1 712 546-7031
E: sentinel@lemarscomm.net
W: http://www.lemarssentinel.com
Freq: Daily; **Circ:** 2684 Not Audited
Editor: Joanne Glamm; **Publisher:** Randy List
Editorial Profile: Le Mars Daily Sentinel is published daily for the residents of Le Mars, IA and surrounding areas. It covers local and state news, business, sports and entertainment.; Full Page Mono: 10.50; Full Page Colour: 100.00
Currency: US Dollars
DAILY NEWSPAPER

The Leader
Owner: Fortress Investment Group, LLC
Editorial: 34 W Pulteney St, Corning, New York 14830-2211. **T:** 1 607 936-4651 13
W: http://www.the-leader.com
Freq: Daily; **Circ:** 13585 Not Audited
Publisher: Fred Benson
Editorial Profile: The Leader is a daily newspaper published for the residents Corning, Hornell and Bath, NY. It covers local news, sports and public opinions.; Full Page Mono: 22.00; Full Page Colour: 142.66
Currency: US Dollars
DAILY NEWSPAPER

The Leader
Owner: Burge Publishing Corporation
Editorial: 3500 A East T.C. Jester Blvd, Houston, Texas 77292. **T:** 1 713 686-8494
W: http://www.theleadernews.com
Freq: Tue
Editor: Charlotte Aguilar
NEWSPAPER

Leader Group
Owner: Community Newspapers Inc.
Editorial: 1114 Beach Blvd, Jacksonville Beach, Florida 32250. **T:** 1 904 249-9033
W: http://www.beachesleader.com **Circ:** 34600 Not Audited
Editor: Kathleen Hartman; **Publisher:** Tom Wood
NEWSPAPER

Leader Newspapers
Owner: Leader Publishing Inc.
Editorial: 404 Graham Rd, Jacksonville, Arkansas 72076-3813. **T:** 1 501 982-9421
W: http://www.arkansasleader.com **Circ:** 57146 Not Audited
NEWSPAPER

Leader Publications
Editorial: 217 N 4th St, Niles, Michigan 49120-2301. **T:** 1 269 683-2100
W: http://www.leaderpub.com **Circ:** 1260 Not Audited
News Editor: Kimberly Wynn
NEWSPAPER

Leader Publications
Owner: West Side Publishing Co.
Editorial: 3075 Smith Rd Ste 204, Fairlawn, Ohio 44333-4454. **T:** 1 330 665-9595
E: editor@akron.com
W: http://www.akron.com **Circ:** 64997
Publisher: Clark Burns; **Editor:** Kathryn Core
Editorial Profile: Leader Publications is a community newspaper publisher serving Akron, OH and surrounding areas.
NEWSPAPER

Leader Publications
Editorial: 503 N 2nd St, Festus, Missouri 63028. **T:** 1 636 931-7560
E: nvrweakly@aol.com
W: http://www.myleaderpaper.com
Freq: Thu; **Circ:** 58190 Not Audited
Editor: Peggy Bess; **Publisher:** Pam LaPlant; **Editor:** Kim Robertson; **News Editor:** Peggy

Scott
Editorial Profile: Leader Publications provides a local newspaper to the community of Festus, MO.; Full Page Mono: 36.00
Currency: US Dollars
NEWSPAPER

Leader Publishing Company
Editorial: 117 E Walnut St, Salem, Indiana 47167. **T:** 1 812 883-3281 **Circ:** 12300 Not Audited
Editor: Stephanie Ferriell; **Publisher:** Nancy Grossman
NEWSPAPER

Leader Times
Owner: Tribune-Review Publishing Co.
Editorial: 11931 State Route 85, Ste E, Kittanning, Pennsylvania 16201-3741.
T: 1 724 543-1303
E: leadertimes@tribweb.com
W: http://www.pittsburghlive.com/x/leadertimes
Freq: Mon thru Fri; **Circ:** 8104 Not Audited
Publisher: Richard Scaife
Editorial Profile: Leader Times' editorial mission is to be the local source of news and information for Kittanning and Armstrong counties.; Full Page Mono: 200.65; Full Page Colour: 1177.80
Currency: US Dollars
DAILY NEWSPAPER

Leader-Herald
Owner: Ogden Newspapers
Editorial: 8 E Fulton St, Gloversville, New York 12078-3283. **T:** 1 518 725-8616
E: news@leaderherald.com
W: http://www.leaderherald.com
Freq: Daily; **Circ:** 6937 Not Audited
Publisher: Patricia Beck; **Editor:** Bill Trojan
Editorial Profile: Leader-Herald is a daily newspaper published for the residents of Gloversville, NY and surrounding areas. It provides information on local and national news, sports and community events. The lead time varies.; Full Page Mono: 16.95; Full Page Colour: 215.00
Currency: US Dollars
DAILY NEWSPAPER

Leader-Telegram
Owner: Eau Claire Press Company
Editorial: 701 S Farwell St, Eau Claire, Wisconsin 54701-3831. **T:** 1 715 833-9200
E: leadertelegram@ecpc.com
W: http://www.leadertelegram.com
Freq: Daily; **Circ:** 20822 Not Audited
Editor: Andrew Dowd; **Publisher:** Pieter Graaskamp; **Editor:** Steve Kinderman
Editorial Profile: Leader-Telegram is a daily newspaper published for the residents of Eau Claire County, Chippewa Falls, and Menomonie, WI. The publication covers local news, sports, entertainment, government, business news, local schools, religion, food, health, travel, and community events.; Full Page Mono: 33.10; Full Page Colour: 221.51
Currency: US Dollars
DAILY NEWSPAPER

Leader-Times, Inc.
Editorial: 251 North Ave W, Westfield, New Jersey 07090-1499. **T:** 1 908 232-4407
E: press@goleader.com
W: http://www.goleader.com **Circ:** 7600 Not Audited
Publisher: Horace Corbin; **Publisher:** Horace Corbin; **Publisher:** Horace Corbin; **Publisher:** Horace Corbin
Editorial Profile: Leader-times Inc is a local newspaper in Westfield, NJ.
NEWSPAPER

The Leaf-Chronicle
Owner: Gannett Co., Inc.
Editorial: 200 Commerce St, Clarksville, Tennessee 37040-5101. **T:** 1 931 552-1808
W: http://www.theleafchronicle.com
Freq: Daily; **Circ:** 13207 Not Audited
Editorial Profile: The Leaf-Chronicle is a daily newspaper written for the residents of Clarksville, TN. The publication covers local news, sports, business news, local government, education and crime.; Full Page Mono: 35.54; Full Page Colour: 250.00
Currency: US Dollars
DAILY NEWSPAPER

The Leavenworth Times
Owner: GateHouse Media Inc.
Editorial: 422 Seneca St, Leavenworth, Kansas 66048. **T:** 1 913 682-0305
E: news@leavenworthtimes.com
W: http://www.leavenworthtimes.com
Freq: Daily; **Circ:** 6741 Not Audited
Publisher: Steve Curd; **News Editor:** Rimsie

McConiga

Editorial Profile: The Leavenworth Times is a daily newspaper published for the residents of Leavenworth, KS. It covers local news and community events.; Full Page Mono: 13.50; Full Page Colour: 75.88
Currency: US Dollars
DAILY NEWSPAPER

Lebanon Daily News
Owner: MediaNews Group
Editorial: 718 Poplar St, Lebanon, Pennsylvania 17042-6755. **T:** 1 717 272-5611
E: citydesk@ldnews.com
W: http://www.ldnews.com
Freq: Daily; **Circ:** 20606
Publisher: Scott Downs
Editorial Profile: Lebanon Daily News covers international, national, local, business, arts & entertainment and sports news. The publication is geared toward residents of Lebanon, PA and the surrounding area.; Full Page Mono: 29.50; Full Page Colour: 425.00
Currency: US Dollars
DAILY NEWSPAPER

Lebanon Daily Record
Owner: Lebanon Publishing Company
Editorial: 100 E Commercial St, Lebanon, Missouri 65536. **T:** 1 417 532-9131
E: editor@lebanondailyrecord.com
W: http://www.lebanondailyrecord.com
Freq: Daily; **Circ:** 4496 Not Audited
Editor: Julie Turner-Crawford; **Editor:** Julie Turner-Crawford; **Publisher:** Dalton Wright
Editorial Profile: Lebanon Daily Record is published daily for the residents of Lebanon, MO. The newspaper covers local news, sports and community events. Deadlines are at 3pm CT.; Full Page Mono: 8.55; Full Page Colour: 180.00
Currency: US Dollars
DAILY NEWSPAPER

Lebanon Democrat
Owner: Sandusky Newspapers Inc.
Editorial: 402 N Cumberland St, Lebanon, Tennessee 37087-2306. **T:** 1 615 444-3952
E: newsclerk@lebanondemocrat.com
W: http://www.lebanondemocrat.com
Freq: Daily; **Circ:** 6789 Not Audited
Publisher: Jesse Lindsey
Editorial Profile: Lebanon Democrat is a daily, local newspaper targeted at the Lebanon, TN area. The paper covers local news, sports, business and community events. Deadlines are noon CT on Mondays through Thursdays, and at 11am CT on Fridays.; Full Page Mono: 12.25; Full Page Colour: 46.86
Currency: US Dollars
DAILY NEWSPAPER

The Lebanon Reporter
Owner: Community Newspaper Holdings, Inc.
Editorial: 117 E Washington St, Lebanon, Indiana 46052. **T:** 1 765 482-4650
E: news@reporter.net
W: http://www.reporter.net
Freq: Daily; **Circ:** 5000 Not Audited
Publisher: Greta Sanderson
Editorial Profile: The Lebanon Reporter is published daily for the residents of Lebanon, IN and surrounding areas. The newspaper covers local and regional news, business, sports, lifestyles and entertainment.; Full Page Mono: 10.50; Full Page Colour: 39.62
Currency: US Dollars
DAILY NEWSPAPER

The Ledger
Owner: Halifax Media Holdings LLC
Editorial: 300 W Lime St, Lakeland, Florida 33815-4649. **T:** 1 863 802-7000
E: voice@theledger.com
W: http://www.theledger.com
Freq: Daily; **Circ:** 46016 Not Audited
Editor: Lenore Devore; **Editor:** Lenore Devore; **Editor:** Lenore Devore; **Publisher:** Jerome Ferson; **News Editor:** DeWayne Wilson
Editorial Profile: The Ledger in Lakeland, FL covers local and regional news in Polk County, FL and surrounding areas.; Full Page Mono: 116.80; Full Page Colour: 378.47
Currency: US Dollars
DAILY NEWSPAPER

The Ledger
Editorial: 455 6th St NW, Winter Haven, Florida 33881. **T:** 1 863 401-6900
DAILY NEWSPAPER

The Ledger
Editorial: 9 C St, Haines City, Florida 33844-5029. **T:** 1 863 422-6800
DAILY NEWSPAPER

The Ledger
Editorial: 336 E College Ave, Ste 204, Tallahassee, Florida 32301-1573.
T: 1 850 224-8411 **E:** voice@theledger.com
W: http://www.theledger.com
Bureau Chief: Lloyd Dunkelberger
DAILY NEWSPAPER

Ledger Publications, Inc.
Owner: Miller (Tom)
Editorial: 105 Main St, Balsam Lake, Wisconsin 54810-2449. **T:** 1 715 485-3121
E: pcledger@lakeland.ws
W: http://www.pc-ledger.com
Freq: Thu; **Circ:** 3500 Not Audited
Editor: Lynda Olds; **Publisher:** Leslie Waggoner; Full Page Mono: 6.25
Currency: US Dollars
NEWSPAPER

The Ledger-Independent
Owner: Lee Enterprises, Inc.
Editorial: 120 Limestone St, Maysville, Kentucky 41056-1284. **T:** 1 606 564-9091
W: http://www.maysville-online.com
Freq: Mon thru Fri; **Circ:** 5439 Not Audited
Publisher: Robert Hendrickson; **Editor:** Marla Toncray
Editorial Profile: The Ledger-Independent is a daily newspaper published for the residents of Maysville, KY and the surrounding area. It covers local news, sports and community events.; Full Page Mono: 18.57; Full Page Colour: 114.99
Currency: US Dollars
DAILY NEWSPAPER

Lee Newspapers
Owner: Lee Enterprises, Inc.
Editorial: 2045 Grant St, Selma, California 93662. **T:** 1 559 896-1976 **Circ:** 8024 Not Audited
Editorial Profile: Moreover.
NEWSPAPER

Lee's Summit Journal & Blue Springs Journal
Owner: McClatchy Newspapers
Editorial: 415 SE Douglas St, Lee's Summit, Missouri 64063. **T:** 1 816 524-2345
W: http://www.lsjournal.com **Circ:** 30400 Not Audited
NEWSPAPER

Leesburg Today
Owner: American Community Newspapers
Editorial: 5 N King St Suite 103, Leesburg, Virginia 20176-2819. **T:** 1 703 771-8800
W: http://www.leesburgtoday.com
Freq: Fri; **Circ:** 72000 Not Audited
Editorial Profile: Leesburg Today is a weekly newspaper published for the residents of Leesburg, VA. It covers local news, sports, politics, public safety, courts and community events. The news deadline falls on Monday mornings.; Full Page Mono: 23.30
Currency: US Dollars
NEWSPAPER

Leesville Daily Leader
Owner: Fortress Investment Group, LLC
Editorial: 206 E Texas St, Leesville, Louisiana 71446-4056. **T:** 1 337 239-3444
E: news@leesvilledailyleader.com
W: http://www.leesvilledailyleader.com
Freq: Daily; **Circ:** 2759 Not Audited
News Editor: Alix Kunkle; **Publisher:** Suzanne Peveto-Nelson
Editorial Profile: Leesville Daily Leader is a newspaper published for the residents of Leesville, LA. The publication covers local news, sports and community events.; Full Page Mono: 13.46; Full Page Colour: 92.29
Currency: US Dollars
DAILY NEWSPAPER

The Legislative Gazette
Editorial: Empire State Plaza, Concourse Level - Rm106, Albany, New York 12224.
T: 1 518 473-9739
W: http://www.legislativegazette.com
Freq: Tue; **Circ:** 13000 Not Audited
Publisher: Alan Chartock; **Editor:** James Gormley; Full Page Mono: 32.89
Currency: US Dollars
NEWSPAPER

Lehigh Acres Citizen
Owner: Breeze Newspapers
Editorial: 2510 Delprado Blvd, Cape Coral, Florida 33904. **T:** 1 239 368-3944
E: citizen936@hotmail.com
W: http://www.lehighacrescitizen.com
Freq: Wed; **Circ:** 12000 Not Audited
Publisher: Scott Blonde; **Editor:** Mel Toadvine
Editorial Profile: Lehigh Acres Citizen is written for the residents of Lehigh Acres, Alva, Buckingham and East Lee County, FL. It covers community news, sports and events. Deadlines are on Mondays at 5pm ET.; Full Page Mono: 11.62
Currency: US Dollars
NEWSPAPER

Lehigh Acres News-Star
Owner: Gannett Co., Inc.
Editorial: 2442 Dr Martin Luther King Blvd, Fort Myers, Florida 33901-3904.
T: 1 239 344-4721
E: news@lehighnewsstar.com
W: http://news-press.com/lehigh
Freq: Wed; **Circ:** 13000 Not Audited
Editor: Casey Logan; **Editor:** Casey Logan
Editorial Profile: Lehigh Acres News-Star is a weekly newspaper published for the residents of Lehigh Acres, FL. The publication covers local news, sports and community events.; Full Page Mono: 11.43; Full Page Colour: 1277.60
Currency: US Dollars
NEWSPAPER

La Lengua
Owner: E.B.S., Inc.
Editorial: 118 W. Shepherd, Lufkin, Texas 75901. **T:** 1 936 632-8444
E: ebs@suddenlinkmail.com
Freq: Wed; **Circ:** 10000 Not Audited
Editor: Ino Reyes; **Publisher:** Roy Reyes
Editorial Profile: La Lengua is a free, Spanish-language weekly community newspaper serving Lufkin, Nacogdoches and other communities in East Texas. It covers local news, education, government, events and human interest features with a Hispanic angle.; Full Page Mono: 7.00
Currency: US Dollars
NEWSPAPER

LEO Weekly
Owner: Yarmuth (Aaron)
Editorial: 301 E Main St Ste 201, Louisville, Kentucky 40202-1247. **T:** 1 502 895-9770
E: leo@leoweekly.com
W: http://www.leoweekly.com
Freq: Wed; **Circ:** 30000 Not Audited
Publisher: Lauren Feldman
Editorial Profile: LEO Weekly is published weekly for residents of Louisville, KY and surrounding communities. The newspaper reports on a variety of lifestyle topics of interest to area residents, including local news, the arts, government, sports and the environment.; Full Page Mono: 32.02
Currency: US Dollars
NEWSPAPER

Lettera 22 - New York Bureau
Editorial: United Nations, Room 368, New York, New York 10017. **T:** 1 212 963-0937
W: http://www.lettera22.it/index.php
Editorial Profile: This is the New York bureau of Lettera 22, which is based in Roma Italy.
DAILY NEWSPAPER

Lewiston Tribune
Owner: Tribune Publishing Company
Editorial: 505 C St, Lewiston, Idaho 83501.
T: 1 208 743-9411 **E:** city@lmtribune.com
W: http://www.lmtribune.com
Freq: Daily; **Circ:** 24515 Not Audited
Editorial Profile: Lewiston Tribune is a daily newspaper published for the residents of Lewiston, ID. The publication covers local news, sports, business news and community events.; Full Page Mono: 18.44; Full Page Colour: 114.58
Currency: US Dollars
DAILY NEWSPAPER

Lexington Herald-Leader
Owner: McClatchy Newspapers
Editorial: 100 Midland Ave, Lexington, Kentucky 40508-1943. **T:** 1 859 231-3100
W: http://www.kentucky.com
Freq: Daily; **Circ:** 74253 Not Audited
Editor: Peter Baniak; **Publisher:** Rufus Friday
Editorial Profile: Lexington Herald-Leader is a 58-page daily newspaper and a 135-page paper on Sunday. It is a voice for Central and Eastern Kentucky. There are 78 counties in the region, including Fayette, Bourbon, Clark, Jessamine, Madison, Scott and Woodford.; Full Page Mono: 62.10; Full Page Colour: 338.97
Currency: US Dollars
DAILY NEWSPAPER

Lexington Herald-Leader
Editorial: 612A Shelby St, Frankfort, Kentucky 40601-3460. **T:** 1 502 227-4390
DAILY NEWSPAPER

Lexington Herald-Leader
Editorial: 513 Ogden St, Somerset, Kentucky 42501-1739. **T:** 1 606 678-4655
Bureau Chief: Bill Estep
DAILY NEWSPAPER

Liberty Herald & U C Review
Editorial: 10 N Market St, Liberty, Indiana 47353. **T:** 1 765 458-5114
E: info@whitewaterpub.com
W: http://www.thebrookvillenews.com
Circ: 6700 Not Audited
Editor: John Estridge; **Publisher:** Gary Wolf
NEWSPAPER

Libre
Owner: Libre, L.L.C.
Editorial: 2700 SW 8th St, Miami, Florida 33135-4619. **T:** 1 305 643-4200
W: http://www.libreonline.com
Freq: Tue; **Circ:** 15000 Not Audited
Editorial Profile: Libre is a weekly bilingual newspaper written for the residents of Miami. The publication covers local community news, as well as national and international topics of interest.; Full Page Mono: 30.00
Currency: US Dollars
NEWSPAPER

El Líder USA
Editorial: 1813 Balboa Pl, Dallas, Texas 75224-1200. **T:** 1 214 942-4580
E: graphics@elliderusa.com
W: http://www.elliderusa.com
Freq: Thu; **Circ:** 72000 Not Audited
Editor: Francisco Gallegos
Editorial Profile: El Lider USA is written for the residents of Dallas. It covers news and events.; Full Page Mono: 28.00
Currency: US Dollars
NEWSPAPER

Life Newspapers
Owner: McNaughton Newspapers
Editorial: 981 Governor Dr, Ste 101, El Dorado Hills, California 95762. **T:** 1 530 622-1255
E: editor@villagelife.com **Circ:** 32100 Not Audited
NEWSPAPER

Lighthouse
Editorial: 2958 Columbia St, Torrance, California 90503-3806. **T:** 1 310 782-1260
E: lighthouse@us-lighthouse.com
W: http://www.us-lighthouse.com
Freq: Bi-Weekly; **Circ:** 50000 Not Audited
Editor: Tatsuya Kawashima; **Publisher:** Yoichi Komiyama
Editorial Profile: Lighthouse in Torrance, CA is community newspaper serving the Japanese community in and around Torrance, CA.; Full Page Mono: 34.78
Currency: US Dollars
NEWSPAPER

Lillie Suburban Newspapers
Owner: Lillie Suburban Newspapers
Editorial: 2515 7th Ave E, Saint Paul, Minnesota 55109-3004. **T:** 1 651 777-8800
E: news@lillienews.com
W: http://lillienews.com **Circ:** 124405 Not Audited
News Editor: Alex Holmquist; **News Editor:** Johanna Holub; **News Editor:** Patrick Larkin; **News Editor:** Luke Reiter
Editorial Profile: Lillie Suburban Newspapers is a community newspaper publisher in North Saint Paul, MN. The publications are only interested in news that pertains to Minnesota.
NEWSPAPER

The Lima News
Owner: Freedom Communications Inc.
Editorial: 3515 Elida Rd, Lima, Ohio 45807-1538. **T:** 1 419 223-1010
E: info@limanews.com
W: http://www.limaohio.com/
Freq: Daily; **Circ:** 21644 Not Audited
Editor: Jim Krumel; **Editor:** Craig Orosz; **Publisher:** James Shine; **News Editor:** Kiarash Zarezadeh
Editorial Profile: The Lima News is a daily newspaper published for the residents of Lima, OH. It covers local news, sports, education, legal issues, arts & entertainment, local government and community events. Deadlines fall daily at 11:30pm ET prior to the issue date.; Full Page Mono: 53.80; Full Page Colour: 358.84
Currency: US Dollars
DAILY NEWSPAPER

Lincoln Journal Star
Owner: Lee Enterprises, Inc.
Editorial: 926 P St, Lincoln, Nebraska 68508.
T: 1 402 475-4200
E: citydesk@journalstar.com

W: http://www.journalstar.com
Freq: Daily; **Circ:** 54350 Not Audited
Editor: Mark Andersen; **Editor:** Dave Bundy;
Publisher: Ava Thomas
Editorial Profile: Lincoln Journal Star is a daily newspaper written for residents in the Lincoln, NE area. The paper was formerly known as The Lincoln Journal and The Lincoln Star. The paper is a 50+ page newspaper, and its editorial mission is to "provide news, analysis and an open forum for the exchange of ideas and opinions." The paper covers local, regional, state, national and international news, as well as business, entertainment, sports and special reports. It was founded in 1873.; Full Page Mono: 79.05; Full Page Colour: 263.14
Currency: US Dollars
DAILY NEWSPAPER

The Lincoln Journal, Inc.
Owner: Lincoln Journal, Inc.
Editorial: 328 Walnut St, Hamlin, West Virginia 25523. **T:** 1 304 824-5101
E: lincolnjournal@zoominternet.net
Circ: 17557
NEWSPAPER

Lincoln Times-News
Editorial: 119 W Water St, Lincolnton, North Carolina 28092. **T:** 1 704 735-3031
E: news@ltnews.com
W: http://www.lincolntimesnews.com
Freq: Fri; **Circ:** 10500 Not Audited
Publisher: Jerry Leedy
Editorial Profile: Lincoln Times-News is published weekly for the residents of Lincolnton, NC and surrounding areas. The newspaper covers local news and community events.; Full Page Mono: 9.00
Currency: US Dollars
NEWSPAPER

Lincoln Trail Publishing Co.
Owner: CornerStone Media
Editorial: 216 S Central Ave, Casey, Illinois 62420-1726. **T:** 1 217 932-5211 **Circ:** 9150 Not Audited
Editor: JJ Aten; **Publisher:** Charlotte Land;
Editor: Nancy Lawson
NEWSPAPER

Litchfield News-Herald
Owner: Litchfield News-Herald, Inc.
Editorial: 112 E Ryder St, Litchfield, Illinois 62056-2031. **T:** 1 217 324-2121
E: lfdnews@litchfieldil.com
Freq: Daily; **Circ:** 5880 Not Audited
Publisher: John Hanafin; **Publisher:** John Hanafin
Editorial Profile: Litchfield News-Herald is published daily for the residents of Litchfield, IL and surrounding areas. The newspaper covers local news, business, sports and entertainment.; Full Page Mono: 3.80; Full Page Colour: 225.00
Currency: US Dollars
DAILY NEWSPAPER

Litmore Publishing Corp.
Editorial: 81 E Barclay St, Hicksville, New York 11801. **T:** 1 516 931-0012
E: editor@gcnews.com
W: http://www.gcnews.com **Circ:** 37933 Not Audited
Editor: Ann Cadigan
Editorial Profile: Litmore Publishing Corp. is a weekly community newspaper publisher serving the residents of Bethpage, Hicksville, Williston, Syosset and Hyde Park, NY.
NEWSPAPER

The Little Falls Times
Owner: GateHouse Media Inc.
Editorial: 111 Green St, Herkimer, New York 13350-1958. **T:** 1 315 823-3680
E: news@littlefallstimes.com
W: http://www.littlefallstimes.com
Freq: Mon thru Fri; **Circ:** 5053 Not Audited
Publisher: Beth Brewer
Editorial Profile: The Little Falls Times is a local daily newspaper serving the communities of Little Falls, Dolgeville, St. Johnsville, Oppenheim, Fairfield, Middleville and Salisbury, NY. The newspaper covers local and national news, sports, entertainment, health and business.; Full Page Mono: 10.66; Full Page Colour: 90.00
Currency: US Dollars
DAILY NEWSPAPER

Little Saigon News
Editorial: 13861 Seaboard Cir, Garden Grove, California 92843. **T:** 1 714 265-0800
E: saigonnho@gmail.com
Freq: Fri; **Circ:** 10000 Not Audited; Full Page Mono: 10.00

Currency: US Dollars
NEWSPAPER

Livewire Printing Co.
Editorial: 310 2nd St, Jackson, Minnesota 56143. **T:** 1 507 847-3771
E: info@livewireprinting.com **Circ:** 12311
NEWSPAPER

The Living Magazines
Owner: Community Publications, Inc.
Editorial: 179 Fairfield Ave, Bellevue, Kentucky 41073-3410. **T:** 1 859 291-1412
E: pr@livingmagazines.com
W: http://www.livingmagazines.com
Circ: 27900 Not Audited
Editor: Vicki Black; **Editor:** Vicki Black; **Editor:** Grace DeGregorio; **Editor:** Moira Grainger;
Editor: Moira Grainger; **Editor:** Anita Guy;
Editor: Linda Johnson; **Editor:** Linda Johnson;
Publisher: Jim Lied
Editorial Profile: Community Publications Inc. publishes free, monthly news magazines called Fort Mitchell Living, Fort Thomas Living, Hyde Park Living, Indian Hill Living, Sycamore Living and Wyoming Living. Please only send one press release via fax, direct mail or to the main e-mail address. The lead times are by the 10th of the month two months prior to publication. Advertising deadlines are by the 15th of the month two months prior to issue date.
NEWSPAPER

Livingston Chronicle
Owner: McClatchy Newspapers
Editorial: 3033 G St, Merced, California 95340. **T:** 1 209 722-1511
W: http://mercedsunstar.com
Freq: Wed; **Circ:** 10500 Not Audited
Editorial Profile: Livingston Chronicle is a free, weekly newspaper distributed to residents in Livingston, CA and the surrounding area. It is published by the Merced (CA) Sun Star and distributed to its subscribers. The paper only carries local news, events, features and editorials; all national and wire stories are featured within the daily edition of the Merced Sun Star.; Full Page Mono: 11.00
Currency: US Dollars
NEWSPAPER

Livingston County Daily Press & Argus
Owner: Gannett Co., Inc.
Editorial: 323 E Grand River Ave, Howell, Michigan 48843-2322. **T:** 1 517 548-2000
W: http://www.livingstondaily.com
Freq: Mon thru Fri; **Circ:** 9621 Not Audited
Editorial Profile: Livingston County Daily Press & Argus is published for the residents of Livingston County, MI and surrounding areas. It covers local news, sports and events.; Full Page Mono: 33.48; Full Page Colour: 35.26
Currency: US Dollars
DAILY NEWSPAPER

The Livingston Enterprise
Owner: Yellowstone Newspapers
Editorial: 401 S Main St, Livingston, Montana 59047-3418. **T:** 1 406 222-2000
E: news@livent.net
W: http://www.livingstonenterprise.com
Freq: Daily; **Circ:** 3523 Not Audited
News Editor: Dwight Harriman
Editorial Profile: The Livingston Enterprise is a daily afternoon newspaper that offers local, state, national and world news and events. The paper serves residents of towns located on the northern border of Yellowstone National Park, including: Livingston, Gardiner, Clyde Park, Wilsall, Cooke City, MT and surrounding areas. Deadlines are daily at 5pm MT.; Full Page Mono: 7.60; Full Page Colour: 60.00
Currency: US Dollars
DAILY NEWSPAPER

Local Community News
Owner: Local Community Newspapers, LLC
Editorial: 4204 Gardendale St, Ste 201, San Antonio, Texas 78229-3132.
T: 1 210 338-8842
E: tips@salocallowdown.com
W: http://salocallowdown.com
Freq: Monthly; **Circ:** 126300
Publisher: Rick Upton
Editorial Profile: Local Community News is a community newspaper publisher serving the greater San Antonio area with three monthly newspapers divided into zones based on community. The papers are free, and direct-mailed to area residents. All ads are in full color, rates differ by zoned edition.
NEWSPAPER

The Local News
Editorial: 5901 Warner Ave, #429, Huntington Beach, California 92649-4659.
T: 1 714 914-9797 **E:** hbnews1@aol.com
W: http://www.MyHBGold.com
Freq: Bi-Weekly; **Circ:** 20000 Not Audited
Editorial Profile: The Local News is written for people stationed in and around Hamilton Air Force Base in Novato, CA. It covers local and national news stories and events as well as special interests, new product development and humor.; Full Page Mono: 11.54
Currency: US Dollars
NEWSPAPER

Lockhart Post-Register
Editorial: 111 S Church St, Lockhart, Texas 78644. **T:** 1 512 398-4886
E: news@post-register.com
W: http://www.post-register.com
Freq: Thu; **Circ:** 12000 Not Audited
Editor: Kathi Bliss; **Publisher:** Dana Garrett
Editorial Profile: The Lockhart Post-Register provides residents of Lockhart, Texas with local community news, politics, and sports updates weekly.; Full Page Mono: 12.50
Currency: US Dollars
NEWSPAPER

Lockport Union-Sun & Journal
Owner: Community Newspaper Holdings, Inc.
Editorial: 170 East Ave, Lockport, New York 14094-3835. **T:** 1 716 439-9222
W: http://www.lockportjournal.com
Freq: Daily; **Circ:** 6500 Not Audited
Editorial Profile: Lockport Union-Sun & Journal is written for the local residents of Lockport and Eastern Niagara County, NY. The publication covers local news, community events and issues.; Full Page Mono: 23.00; Full Page Colour: 137.29
Currency: US Dollars
DAILY NEWSPAPER

Lodi News-Sentinel
Owner: Lodi News-Sentinel, Inc.
Editorial: 125 N Church St, Lodi, California 95240-2197. **T:** 1 209 369-2761
E: news@lodinews.com
W: http://www.lodinews.com
Freq: Mon thru Fri; **Circ:** 15771 Not Audited
Publisher: Marty Weybret
Editorial Profile: Lodi News-Sentinel is a daily newspaper published for the residents of Lodi, CA and surrounding areas. It covers local and national news, sports, business and entertainment.; Full Page Mono: 23.03; Full Page Colour: 496.94
Currency: US Dollars
DAILY NEWSPAPER

Log Cabin Democrat
Owner: Morris Multimedia, Inc.
Editorial: 1058 Front St, Conway, Arkansas 72032-4356. **T:** 1 501 327-6621
E: editorial@thecabin.net
W: http://www.thecabin.net
Freq: Daily; **Circ:** 10234 Not Audited
Publisher: Alan English
Editorial Profile: Log Cabin Democrat provides local and regional news coverage for much of Faulkner County, AR.; Full Page Mono: 15.15; Full Page Colour: 290.15
Currency: US Dollars
DAILY NEWSPAPER

The Logan Banner
Owner: Community Newspaper Holdings, Inc.
Editorial: 437-447 Stratton St, Logan, West Virginia 25601-3913. **T:** 1 304 752-6950
W: http://www.loganbanner.com
Freq: Daily; **Circ:** 9166 Not Audited
News Editor: Debra Rolen
Editorial Profile: The Logan Banner is a daily newspaper published for the residents of Logan, WV and the surrounding counties of Lincoln, Boone and Mingo. It covers local news, business, lifestyles and sports.; Full Page Mono: 13.45; Full Page Colour: 83.96
Currency: US Dollars
DAILY NEWSPAPER

Logan Daily News
Owner: American Consolidated Media
Editorial: 72 E Main St, Logan, Ohio 43138.
T: 1 740 385-2107
E: publisher@logandaily.com
W: http://www.logandaily.com
Freq: Daily; **Circ:** 4161 Not Audited
Publisher: Lucy Burcham
Editorial Profile: Logan Daily News covers news and events in the Logan, OH community. Send all press releases to the main e-mail address.; Full Page Mono: 14.95; Full Page Colour: 300.00
Currency: US Dollars
DAILY NEWSPAPER

The Lompoc Record
Owner: Lee Enterprises, Inc.
Editorial: 115 N H St, Lompoc, California 93436-6818. **T:** 1 805 736-2313
W: http://www.lompocrecord.com
Freq: Mon thru Fri; **Circ:** 3874 Not Audited
Editor: Marga Cooley; **Publisher:** Cynthia Schur
Editorial Profile: The Lompoc Record publishes every day except Saturdays and provides local news coverage for residents of the Lompoc and Santa Ynez Valleys in California.; Full Page Mono: 25.41; Full Page Colour: 153.88
Currency: US Dollars
DAILY NEWSPAPER

Long Beach Post
Owner: The Long Beach Post, Inc.
Editorial: 5318 E 2Nd St #568, Long Beach, California 90803-5324. **T:** 1 562 248-6314
E: editor@lbpost.com
W: http://www.lbpost.com/print
Freq: Monthly; **Circ:** 25000
Publisher: Deziré Lumachi
Editorial Profile: Long Beach (CA) Post is a monthly newspaper that covers Community News, Business, Lifestyle, Sports, Food, LGBT News and Community Events. The paper is published on the 13th to 15th of reach month. Deadlines are the 8th of each month.; Full Page Mono: 17.02
Currency: US Dollars
NEWSPAPER

Long Beach/Carson/Compton Times Newspaper
Editorial: 121 Linden Ave, Long Beach, California 90802-4990. **T:** 1 562 436-8221
E: lbtimes@aol.com
Freq: Wed; **Circ:** 33000 Not Audited
Editorial Profile: Long Beach/Carson/Compton Times Newspaper is a a weekly, bilingual newspaper serving residents in Long Beach, Carson and Compton, CA. It covers local, regional and national news, editorials, education, business, economic development and family stories. It also profiles prominent African American business leaders and provides Hispanic and Cambodian current events. Deadlines are at noon PT.; Full Page Mono: 28.00
Currency: US Dollars
NEWSPAPER

Long Island Catholic
Owner: RVC Diocese
Editorial: 200 W Centennial Ave, Roosevelt, New York 11575-1937. **T:** 1 516 594-1000
E: editor@licatholic.org
W: http://www.licatholic.org
Freq: Wed; **Circ:** 102000 Not Audited
Editor: Rick Hinshaw
Editorial Profile: Long Island Catholic is a local weekly newspaper written for Catholic residents of Nassau and Suffolk counties, NY. The newspaper covers Catholic news, information, and events, both locally and around the world. Deadlines fall on Fridays prior to the issue date.; Full Page Mono: 63.00
Currency: US Dollars
NEWSPAPER

Long Island Press
Owner: The Morey Organization
Editorial: 575 Underhill Blvd Ste 210, Syosset, New York 11791-3432. **T:** 1 516 284-3300
W: http://www.longislandpress.com
Freq: Thu; **Circ:** 85000 Not Audited
News Editor: Timothy Bolger; **Publisher:** Jed Morey; **Editor in Chief:** Christopher Twarowski
Editorial Profile: Long Island Press, formerly the New Island Ear, covers music and entertainment in the Long Island, NY area. Established in 1978, it is distributed free through record stores, bars, restaurants and movie theaters. The publication focuses particularly on popular music, but also offers limited coverage of other forms of entertainment media, such as films and Web sites. It contains concert and events listings, music and film reviews, classified ads for local musicians and profiles of entertainment personalities. Editorial deadlines are on the second Friday of each month.; Full Page Mono: 31.20
Currency: US Dollars
NEWSPAPER

Long Islander Newspapers
Owner: Tribco, LLC
Editorial: 149 Main St, Huntington, New York 11743. **T:** 1 631 427-7000
E: info@longislandernews.com
W: http://www.longislandernews.com
Circ: 33462 Not Audited
Editor: LuAnn Dallojacono; **Publisher:** Michael

Schenkler
Editorial Profile: Long Islander Newspapers in Huntintgton, NY is a weekly community newspaper publisher serving the residents of Northport, Troy, Long Island and Dix Hills, NY as well as the surrounding areas.
NEWSPAPER

Longboat Key News
Editorial: 5370 Gulf Of Mexico Dr Ste 210, Longboat Key, Florida 34228-2047.
T: 1 941 387-2200 **E:** editorial@lbknews.com
W: http://www.lbknews.com/
Freq: Fri
Editorial Profile: Longboat Key News is weekly newspaper providing Community News, focusing on the residents of Longboat Key and the neighboring areas of St. Armands Key, Bird Key and Lido Key. The newspaper covers Longboat Key town government, Real Estate, Local Business and cultural activities.
NEWSPAPER

The Longboat Observer
Owner: Observer Group Inc.
Editorial: 5570 Gulf Of Mexico Dr, Longboat Key, Florida 34228-1904. **T:** 1 941 383-5509
E: longboatnews@yourobserver.com
W: http://www.yourobserver.com/news/longboat-key/Front-Page
Freq: Thu; **Circ:** 17000 Not Audited
Editorial Profile: Longboat Observer provides local news and community information to Longboat, St. Armands, Lido and Bird Keys, FL.; Full Page Mono: 28.65; Full Page Colour: 100.00
Currency: US Dollars
NEWSPAPER

Longmont Weekly
Owner: Prairie Mountain Publishing)
Editorial: 350 Terry St, Longmont, Colorado 80501-5440. **T:** 1 303 776-2244
W: http://www.longmontweekly.com
Freq: Wed; **Circ:** 16205
Publisher: Dean Lehman
Editorial Profile: Longmont Weekly is a local community newspaper for the residents of Longmont, CO and the surrounding communities. It is based in the same office as the Times-Call. It merged with the Longmont Ledger in 2010.; Full Page Mono: 11.62
Currency: US Dollars
NEWSPAPER

Longview News-Journal
Owner: ASP Westward LP
Editorial: 320 E Methvin St, Longview, Texas 75601. **T:** 1 903 757-3311
E: newsroom@news-journal.com
W: http://www.news-journal.com
Freq: Daily; **Circ:** 20491 Not Audited
Editor: Richard Brack; **Publisher:** Tom Stamper; **News Editor:** Gary Stratton
Editorial Profile: Longview News-Journal is published daily for the residents of Longview, TX and surrounding areas. The newspaper covers local and regional news, business, sports, lifestyles and entertainment.; Full Page Mono: 46.15; Full Page Colour: 275.73
Currency: US Dollars
DAILY NEWSPAPER

Los Alamos Monitor
Owner: Landmark Community Newspapers, Inc.
Editorial: 256 DP Rd, Los Alamos, New Mexico 87544-3233. **T:** 1 505 662-4185
E: lanews@lamonitor.com
W: http://www.lamonitor.com
Freq: Daily; **Circ:** 4751 Not Audited
Editor: John Severance
Editorial Profile: Los Alamos Monitor is a daily paper that provides coverage of local news, weather and sports for residents of the Los Alamos, NM community.; Full Page Mono: 14.16; Full Page Colour: 16.06
Currency: US Dollars
DAILY NEWSPAPER

Los Altos Town Crier
Editorial: 138 Main St, Los Altos, California 94022-2905. **T:** 1 650 948-9000
W: http://www.losaltosonline.com
Freq: Wed; **Circ:** 16500 Not Audited
Editor: Bruce Barton; **Editor:** Pete Borello; **Publisher:** Paul Nyberg
Editorial Profile: Los Altos Town Crier is a weekly paper written for residents of Los Altos, CA. The paper covers local news, sports and weather.; Full Page Mono: 26.02
Currency: US Dollars
NEWSPAPER

Los Angeles Jewish News
Owner: Blazer Communications
Editorial: 16501 Ventura Blvd Ste 504, Encino, California 91436-2047. **T:** 1 818 786-4000
E: info@nationaljewishnews.com
W: http://www.blazermediagroup.com/newspaper.shtml
Freq: Monthly; **Circ:** 106000 Not Audited
Editorial Profile: Los Angeles Jewish News is published monthly by Blazer Communications. The newspaper has local editions in New York, Los Angeles, San Francisco, San Diego, Las Vegas, Miami, northern California, and Orange County, CA. The publication covers news of interest to Jewish people and features articles on travel, recreation, arts and entertainment. The advertising rate listed reflects an ad in the New York edition only.; Full Page Mono: 45.00
Currency: US Dollars
NEWSPAPER

Los Angeles Register
Owner: 2100 Trust LLC
Editorial: 714 W Olympic Blvd Ste 300, Los Angeles, California 90015-1425.
T: 1 877 469-7344
E: newstips@losangelesregister.com
W: http://www.losangelesregister.com
Freq: Daily
Editor: Ron Sylvester; **Editor:** Ron Sylvester
Editorial Profile: Launched in April 2014, the Los Angeles Register is a daily newspaper serving residents of Los Angeles and the surrounding areas, offering local news, entertainment, business, calendar and events, features, arts and entertainment and sports coverage. Contact advertising staff directly for rates. As of September 2014, the print edition has been suspended.
DAILY NEWSPAPER

Los Angeles Sentinel
Editorial: 3800 Crenshaw Blvd, Los Angeles, California 90008-1813. **T:** 1 323 299-3800
W: http://www.lasentinel.net
Freq: Thu; **Circ:** 30000 Not Audited
Publisher: Danny Bakewell; **Editor:** Cheryl Tillman Lee
Editorial Profile: Los Angeles Sentinel is a local, weekly newspaper providing community, business and political news to the African American community in Southern Los Angeles, Orange and San Diego counties, CA. It is Southern California's oldest continually published black newspaper. The paper also contains an insert of Healthy Choices, which focuses on the elimination of certain health problems that affect racial and ethnic minorities.; Full Page Mono: 35.00
Currency: US Dollars
NEWSPAPER

Los Angeles Times
Owner: Tribune Company
Editorial: 202 W 1st St, Los Angeles, California 90012-4299. **T:** 1 213 237-5000
E: newstips@latimes.com
W: http://www.latimes.com
Freq: Daily; **Circ:** 673171 Not Audited
Readers' Representative: Deirdre Edgar; **Publisher:** Eddy Hartenstein; **Editor-in-Chief:** Davan Maharaj; **Bureau Chief:** Tony Perry; **Bureau Chief:** Tony Perry; **Bureau Chief:** Tony Perry
Editorial Profile: Los Angeles Times is a general interest daily newspaper that covers regional, national and international news. The paper uses wire services and reports for certain content areas. In August 2009, Tribune Company formed a national sports content-sharing alliance between its properties, most notably between the Chicago Tribune and the Los Angeles Times. The staff honors news embargoes on a case-by-case basis. For FedEx mailing use: 130 S Broadway, Los Angeles, CA 90012. The outlet offers RSS (Really Simple Syndication).; Full Page Mono: 289.41; Full Page Colour: 361.76
Currency: US Dollars
DAILY NEWSPAPER

Los Angeles Times
Editorial: 220 E 42nd St, New York, New York 10017-5806. **T:** 1 212 448-2839
DAILY NEWSPAPER

Los Angeles Times
Editorial: 1215 K St Ste 1750, Sacramento, California 95814-3948. **T:** 1 916 321-4400
DAILY NEWSPAPER

Los Angeles Times
Editorial: 2224 Running Spring Pl, Encinitas, California 92024-3146. **T:** 1 619 977-6391
Bureau Chief: Tony Perry; **Bureau Chief:** Tony Perry; **Bureau Chief:** Tony Perry
DAILY NEWSPAPER

Los Angeles Times
Editorial: 1375 Sunflower Ave, Costa Mesa, California 92626-1665. **T:** 1 714 966-7715
DAILY NEWSPAPER

Los Cerritos Community News
Owner: Hews (Brian)
Editorial: 13047 Artesia Blvd Ste C102, Cerritos, California 90703-1389.
T: 1 562 407-3873
W: http://loscerritosnews.net
Freq: Fri; **Circ:** 58000 Not Audited
Editor: Jerry Bernstein; **Publisher:** Brian Hews
Editorial Profile: Los Cerritos Community News is a weekly newspaper written for the residents of Cerritos, CA.; Full Page Mono: 21.00
Currency: US Dollars
NEWSPAPER

Los Feliz Ledger
Editorial: 4459 Avocado St, Los Angeles, California 90027-2104. **T:** 1 323 667-9897
W: http://www.losfelizledger.com
Freq: Monthly; **Circ:** 34500 Not Audited
Editorial Profile: Los Feliz Ledger is a free, monthly newspaper serving residents and businesses of Los Feliz, Silver Lake and areas of the Hollywood Hills, CA . The paper covers local news, political issues, schools, community happenings and features. It is distributed directly to residents' homes and is also available for pick-up at area newsstands, retailers and restaurants.; Full Page Mono: 23.75
Currency: US Dollars
NEWSPAPER

Loudoun Times-Mirror
Owner: Times Community Newspapers
Editorial: 9 E Market St, Leesburg, Virginia 20176-3013. **T:** 1 703 777-1111
E: ltmeditor@timespapers.com
W: http://www.loudountimes.com
Freq: Wed; **Circ:** 63013 Not Audited
Publisher: Peter Arundel
Editorial Profile: Loudoun Times-Mirror is a local weekly newspaper written for residents in and around Loudoun County, VA. It covers local news and events, sports, business and features. Deadlines are at 9am ET.; Full Page Mono: 33.00; Full Page Colour: 190.00
Currency: US Dollars
NEWSPAPER

Louisa Publishing
Editorial: 301 James L Hodges Ave S, Wapello, Iowa 52653-1242. **T:** 1 319 523-4631
E: lpc@louisacomm.net **Circ:** 9950 Not Audited
Editor: Rusty Ebert; **Editor:** Evelyn Garmoe; **Editor:** Connie Street; **Editor:** Connie Street
NEWSPAPER

Louisiana State Newspapers
Owner: Louisiana State Newspapers
Editorial: 241 Martin Luther St, Columbia, Louisiana 71418. **T:** 1 318 649-6411
E: caldwellwatchman@bellsouth.net **Circ:** 9400 Not Audited
Editor: Becky Stapleton; **Publisher:** Mary Terry
Editorial Profile: The Post Office Box address should be used for USPS deliveries only. The street address should be used for deliveries by other couriers.
NEWSPAPER

Louisiana State Newspapers-Rayville
Owner: Louisiana State Newspapers
Editorial: 603 Louisa St, Rayville, Louisiana 71269. **T:** 1 318 728-2250
E: lsnbeacon@bellsouth.net **Circ:** 2900 Not Audited
Editor: Daryl Riser; **Editor:** Daryl Riser; **Publisher:** Mary Terry
NEWSPAPER

Lovington Daily Leader
Owner: Wal-Roy Publishing, Inc.
Editorial: 14 W Avenue B, Lovington, New Mexico 88260-4404. **T:** 1 575 396-2844
E: leader@leaco.net
W: http://lovingtonleader.leaco.net
Freq: Daily; **Circ:** 1965 Not Audited
Editorial Profile: Lovington Daily Leader's editorial mission is to provide local news to residents of Lovington, NM. Deadlines for the publication are one week before issue date.; Full Page Mono: 8.00; Full Page Colour: 41.97
Currency: US Dollars
DAILY NEWSPAPER

Lubbock Avalanche-Journal
Owner: Morris Communications
Editorial: 710 Avenue J, Lubbock, Texas 79401-1808. **T:** 1 806 762-8844
W: http://www.lubbockonline.com
Freq: Daily; **Circ:** 27987 Not Audited
Publisher: Steve Beasley; **Editor:** James Bennett
Editorial Profile: Lubbock Avalanche-Journal is written for people in the Lubbock, TX area. It covers local and national news, as well as sports, entertainment, lifestyle, business and opinions. Deadlines for the publication are same day before issue date.; Full Page Mono: 69.95; Full Page Colour: 226.95
Currency: US Dollars
DAILY NEWSPAPER

Ludington Daily News
Owner: Shoreline Media, Inc.
Editorial: 202 N Rath Ave, Ludington, Michigan 49431-1687. **T:** 1 231 845-5181
E: ldn@ludingtondailynews.com
W: http://www.ludingtondailynews.com
Freq: Daily; **Circ:** 6605 Not Audited
Publisher: Jeffrey Evans; **Editor:** Patti Klevorn
Editorial Profile: Ludington Daily News is a daily newspaper published for the residents of Ludington, MI and the surrounding counties of Mason, Manistee, Oceania and Lake. It covers local news and community events. Deadlines are daily at 10am CT.; Full Page Mono: 14.00
Currency: US Dollars
DAILY NEWSPAPER

The Lufkin Daily News
Owner: Southern Newspapers, Inc.
Editorial: 300 Ellis Ave, Lufkin, Texas 75904-3817. **T:** 1 936 632-6631
E: news@lufkindailynews.com
W: http://lufkindailynews.com
Freq: Daily; **Circ:** 10400 Not Audited
Editor: Andy Adams; **Editor:** Denise Hoepfner; **Publisher:** Greg Shrader
Editorial Profile: The Lufkin Daily News is published for the residents of Lufkin, TX and surrounding areas. It provides information on local and national news, finance, sports, features, lifestyles, health and weather.; Full Page Mono: 24.64; Full Page Colour: 152.67
Currency: US Dollars
DAILY NEWSPAPER

Luso-Americano
Editorial: 66 Union St, Newark, New Jersey 7105. **T:** 1 973 344-3200
E: news@lusoamericano.com
W: http://www.lusoamericano.com
Freq: Fri; **Circ:** 28400 Not Audited
Publisher: Antonio Matinho; **News Editor:** Luis Pires
Editorial Profile: Luso-Americano's editorial mission is to serve as a means of social communication among Portuguese communities nationally and internationally. Deadlines are Tuesdays at 10:30am ET for the Wednesday editions, and Thursdays by noon ET for the Friday editions.; Full Page Mono: 10.00
Currency: US Dollars
NEWSPAPER

Lyon-Sioux Press
Owner: New Century Press
Editorial: 310 1st Ave, Rock Rapids, Iowa 51246-1506. **T:** 1 712 472-2525
E: reporter@ncppub.com
W: http://www.ncppub.com **Circ:** 5210 Not Audited
Editor: Jodie Hoogendoorn; **Editor:** Verdona Kelly
NEWSPAPER

M&M Printing Co.
Owner: M&M Printing Co.
Editorial: 210 Woodland Estates Ave, Ruskin, Florida 33570-4591. **T:** 1 813 645-3111
E: editor@observernews.net
W: http://www.observernews.net **Circ:** 48825 Not Audited
Editorial Profile: M&M Printing Co. provides a local newspaper to the community of Ruskin, FL.
NEWSPAPER

Mach Publishing Inc.
Editorial: 127 Avenue C, Snohomish, Washington 98290-2768. **T:** 1 360 568-4121
E: editor.tribune@snoho.com
W: http://www.snoho.com **Circ:** 25500 Not Audited
Publisher: Becky Reed; **Editor:** Jessica Sparks
Editorial Profile: Mach Publishing Inc. the publisher of a local newspaper in Snohomish, WA.
NEWSPAPER

The Macomb Daily
Owner: Journal Register Company
Editorial: 19176 Hall Rd Fl 2, Clinton Township, Michigan 48038-6914.

T: 1 586 469-4510
W: http://www.macombdaily.com
Freq: Daily; **Circ:** 40765 Not Audited
Editorial Profile: The Macomb Daily in Clinton Township, MI is a daily newspaper serving residents of Macomb County, MI. The publication covers local news, sports, business, arts & entertainment and event information for the communities within its distribution area.; Full Page Mono: 97.66; Full Page Colour: 318.02
Currency: US Dollars
DAILY NEWSPAPER

Macon Chronicle-Herald
Owner: GateHouse Media Inc.
Editorial: 204 W Bourke St, Macon, Missouri 63552-1599. **T:** 1 660 385-3121
E: maconch@centurytel.net
W: http://www.maconch.com
Freq: Daily; **Circ:** 2924 Not Audited
Editor: Terri Hackett; **Editor:** Terri Hackett; **News Editor:** Alecia Lassing; **Publisher:** Pat Quinly
Editorial Profile: Macon Chronicle-Herald is published daily for the residents of Macon, MO and surrounding areas. The newspaper covers local news, sports and community events.; Full Page Mono: 8.75; Full Page Colour: 235.00
Currency: US Dollars
DAILY NEWSPAPER

The Macon County News & Shopping Guide
Editorial: 107 Highlands Rd, Franklin, North Carolina 28734. **T:** 1 828 369-6767
E: editor@maconnews.com
W: http://www.maconnews.com
Freq: Thu; **Circ:** 12500 Not Audited
Publisher: Betsey Gooder; **Editor:** Colin Gooder
Editorial Profile: The Macon County News & Shopping Guide is a lcoal newspaper serving the residents of Franklin, NC. The paper covers community news and events.; Full Page Mono: 6.83
Currency: US Dollars
NEWSPAPER

Madelia Community Newspapers
Owner: Christiansen Media, LLC
Editorial: 112 W Main St, Madelia, Minnesota 56062-1440. **T:** 1 507 642-3636
W: http://www.prairiepublishingmn.com/21001/1972/1/home **Circ:** 3110 Not Audited
Editorial Profile: Madelia Community Newspapers is not interested in PR contact or receiving press materials.
NEWSPAPER

Madera Tribune
Owner: Madera Printing and Publishing
Editorial: 2890 Falcon Dr, Madera, California 93637-9287. **T:** 1 559 674-2424
W: http://www.maderatribune.com
Freq: Daily; **Circ:** 4700 Not Audited
News Editor: John Rieping
Editorial Profile: Madera Tribune is a daily newspaper published Monday through Saturday for the residents of Madera, CA and surrounding areas. It covers local news, sports and community events.; Full Page Mono: 14.00; Full Page Colour: 88.98
Currency: US Dollars
DAILY NEWSPAPER

Madison County Herald
Owner: Gannett Co., Inc.
Editorial: 794 Highway 51 Suite B, Madison, Mississippi 39110-9662. **T:** 1 601 853-2899
E: news@mcherald.com
W: http://www.mcherald.com
Freq: Sat; **Circ:** 14042 Not Audited
Editorial Profile: Madison County Herald is written for the residents of Madison County, MS and the surrounding area. It provides information on local news and community events.; Full Page Mono: 14.18; Full Page Colour: 175.00
Currency: US Dollars
NEWSPAPER

The Madison Courier
Owner: Madison Courier, Inc.
Editorial: 310 Courier Sq, Madison, Indiana 47250-9919. **T:** 1 812 265-3641
E: news@madisoncourier.com
W: http://www.madisoncourier.com
Freq: Daily; **Circ:** 8700 Not Audited
Publisher: Jane Jacobs; **Editor:** Elliot Tompkin
Editorial Profile: The Madison Courier, established in 1837 and family owned since 1849, is published Monday through Saturday in Madison, IN. It serves Jefferson and Switzerland counties in Indiana and Trimble and Carroll counties in Kentucky. Deadlines for the publication are at 2pm CT.; Full Page Mono: 12.35; Full Page Colour: 90.17
Currency: US Dollars
DAILY NEWSPAPER

Madison Daily Leader
Editorial: 214 S Egan Ave, Madison, South Dakota 57042-2911. **T:** 1 605 256-4555
E: news@madisondailyleader.com
W: http://www.madisondailyleader.com
Freq: Daily; **Circ:** 3000 Not Audited
Publisher: Jon Hunter
Editorial Profile: Madison Daily Leader's editorial mission is to be the preferred source for news information and advertising. The publication is written for the county of Madison, SD. Deadlines for the publication are at 9am CT of the issue day.; Full Page Mono: 10.40; Full Page Colour: 56.16
Currency: US Dollars
DAILY NEWSPAPER

The Madison Press
Owner: Ohio Community Media LLC.
Editorial: 30 S Oak St, London, Ohio 43140. **T:** 1 740 852-1616
E: editor@madison-press.com
W: http://www.madison-press.com
Freq: Daily; **Circ:** 6500 Not Audited
Editorial Profile: The Madison Press is a daily newspaper written for the residents of Madison County, OH and surrounding areas. It covers local news and community events.; Full Page Mono: 8.85; Full Page Colour: 175.00
Currency: US Dollars
DAILY NEWSPAPER

The Madison Record
Owner: Boone Newspapers Inc.
Editorial: 151 Hughes Rd Ste C, Madison, Alabama 35758-1100. **T:** 1 256 772-6677
E: news@themadisonrecord.com
W: http://www.themadisonrecord.com
Freq: Sat; **Circ:** 10000 Not Audited
Editor: Michael Hansberry
Editorial Profile: The Madison Record is a community newspaper serving Madison, AL with local news, sports, commentary, lifestyle, business, education news and community events.; Full Page Mono: 11.50
Currency: US Dollars
NEWSPAPER

Magnolia Banner-News
Owner: Wehco Media Inc.
Editorial: 130 S Washington, Magnolia, Arkansas 71753-3523. **T:** 1 870 234-5130
E: news@bannernews.net
W: http://www.bannernews.net
Freq: Daily; **Circ:** 4375 Not Audited
Publisher: Walter Hussman
Editorial Profile: Magnolia Banner-News is published daily for the residents of Magnolia, AR and surrounding areas. The newspaper covers local and state news, business, sports, lifestyles and entertainment. It combines with the Camden (AR) News and the El Dorado (AR) News-Times on Sundays.; Full Page Mono: 11.93; Full Page Colour: 275.00
Currency: US Dollars
DAILY NEWSPAPER

Mahogany Revue
Editorial: 903 NE Osceola Ave, Ocala, Florida 34470. **T:** 1 352 368-2002
E: psa@mahoganyrevue.com
W: http://www.mahoganyrevue.com
Freq: Bi-Weekly; **Circ:** 30000 Not Audited
Editorial Profile: Mahogany Revue is published bi-weekly for African Americans and Latin Americans in Ocala, FL. The newspaper provides information on local news and community events. Deadlines are on Thursdays prior to issue date.; Full Page Mono: 13.55; Full Page Colour: 1818.00
Currency: US Dollars
NEWSPAPER

Mail Tribune
Owner: GateHouse Media Inc.
Editorial: 111 N Fir St, Medford, Oregon 97501-2772. **T:** 1 541 776-4411
E: news@mailtribune.com
W: http://www.mailtribune.com
Freq: Daily; **Circ:** 20655 Not Audited
News Editor: Robert Galvin; **Editor in Chief:** Bob Hunter; **Editor:** Bob Pennell; **Publisher:** James Grady Singletary
Editorial Profile: Mail Tribune is dedicated to the people's rights to know. The mission of the publication is to provide quality news and advertising information and services for readers and advertisers. It covers local news, sports, and opinion. The publication is written for adults ages 18 to 65 in the greater part of Oregon. Deadlines for the publication are daily at 5pm PT.; Full Page Mono: 33024.00; Full Page Colour: 39.11
Currency: US Dollars
DAILY NEWSPAPER

Main Line Media News
Owner: Journal Register Company
Editorial: 311 E Lancaster Ave, Ardmore, Pennsylvania 19003. **T:** 1 610 642-4300
W: http://www.mainlinemedianews.com
Circ: 23852 Not Audited
Editorial Profile: Covers community news, sports, business and entertainment from Bala Cynwyd to Malvern counties in Pennsylvania.
NEWSPAPER

Main Street Media San Diego
Owner: Mainstreet Media Group
Editorial: 3702 Via De La Valle #202W, Del Mar, California 92014-4255.
T: 1 858 756-1403 **E:** editor@rsfreview.com
W: http://www.delmartimes.net **Circ:** 44596 Not Audited
Publisher: Phyllis Pfeiffer
Editorial Profile: UT Community Press publishes five weekly newspapers for surrounding area suburbs of San Diego. Four papers are located in the Del Mar, CA office and one, La Jolla Light, is a standalone in La Jolla, CA. The papers cover local news, sports and events.
NEWSPAPER

Main Street Newspapers, Inc.
Editorial: 302 W Main St, Ste B, Christiansburg, Virginia 24073-2981.
T: 1 540 382-6171 **E:** nrv@ourvalley.org
W: http://ourvalley.org **Circ:** 19030 Not Audited
Editor: Aaron Atkins
NEWSPAPER

The Maine Edge
Owner: Edge Media Group
Editorial: 157 Park St Ste 25, Bangor, Maine 04401-5063. **T:** 1 207 942-2901
E: yournews@themaineedge.com
W: http://www.themaineedge.com
Freq: Wed; **Circ:** 18000
Publisher: Michael Fern
Editorial Profile: The Maine Edge is a free weekly newspaper that provides Lifestyle and Cultural Arts coverage to the residents of Bangor, ME, as well as Penobscot and Hancock counties.; Full Page Mono: 32.67
Currency: US Dollars
NEWSPAPER

Mainely Media, LLC
Owner: Mainely Media, LLC
Editorial: 180 Main St, Biddeford, Maine 4005.
T: 1 207 282-4337
W: http://www.mainelymediallc.com
Circ: 93500 Not Audited
Editor: Dan King; **Editor:** Dan King; **Editor:** Dan King; **Publisher:** Chris Miles
NEWSPAPER

Mainline Newspapers
Editorial: 975 Rowena Dr, Ebensburg, Pennsylvania 15931. **T:** 1 814 472-4110
E: mainlinenews@verizon.net
W: http://www.mainlinenewspapers.com
Circ: 11605 Not Audited
Publisher: William Anderson; **Editor:** Justin Eger
NEWSPAPER

Malibu Surfside News
Owner: 22nd Century Media
Editorial: 28990 Pacific Coast Hwy, #C116, Malibu, California 90265-3952.
T: 1 310 457-2112
E: editor@malibusurfsidenews.com
W: http://www.malibusurfsidenews.com
Freq: Thu; **Circ:** 13500 Not Audited
Publisher: Jack Ryan
Editorial Profile: Malibu Surfside News provides local news to the residents of Malibu, CA. Deadlines for the publication are on Tuesdays at noon PT.; Full Page Mono: 15.00
Currency: US Dollars
NEWSPAPER

Malibu Times
Editorial: 3864 Las Flores Canyon Rd, Malibu, California 90265. **T:** 1 310 456-5507
E: malibunews@malibutimes.com
W: http://www.malibutimes.com
Freq: Thu; **Circ:** 12000 Not Audited
Editorial Profile: Malibu Times provides the residents of Malibu, CA with local news, weather and community events. Deadlines are on Tuesdays at 5pm PT.; Full Page Mono: 32.00
Currency: US Dollars
NEWSPAPER

Malone Telegram
Owner: Johnson Newspaper Corp.
Editorial: 469 E Main St, Ste 4, Malone, New York 12953-2128. **T:** 1 518 483-4700
E: news@mtelegram.com
W: http://www.mtelegram.com
Freq: Mon thru Fri; **Circ:** 5346 Not Audited
Editor: Connie Jenkins
Editorial Profile: The Malone Telegram is written for residents of Franklin County, NY. It provides local news concerning the residents of Franklin County, NY. The lead time is the same day.; Full Page Mono: 9.54; Full Page Colour: 60.87
Currency: US Dollars
DAILY NEWSPAPER

Malvern Daily Record
Owner: Horizon Publications
Editorial: 219 Locust St, Malvern, Arkansas 72104-3721. **T:** 1 501 337-7523
E: editor@malvern-online.com
W: http://www.malvern-online.com
Freq: Daily; **Circ:** 4200 Not Audited
Editor: Mark Bivens; **Publisher:** Richard Folds
Editorial Profile: Malvern Daily Record is published daily for the residents of Malvern, AR and surrounding areas. The newspaper covers local and state news, business, sports, lifestyles and entertainment.; Full Page Mono: 11.45; Full Page Colour: 72.13
Currency: US Dollars
DAILY NEWSPAPER

El Mañana
Editorial: 6010 McPherson Rd, Laredo, Texas 78041-6206. **T:** 1 956 712-1122
E: rio@elmanana.com.mx
W: http://www.elmanana.com.mx
Freq: Daily; **Circ:** 25000 Not Audited
Editorial Profile: El Mañana was founded in 1932. It is a Spanish language weekly publication serving the residents of Laredo, TX.; Full Page Mono: 6.45; Full Page Colour: 99.99
Currency: US Dollars
DAILY NEWSPAPER

Manchester Journal
Owner: MediaNews Group
Editorial: 51 Memorial Ave, Manchester Center, Vermont 5255. **T:** 1 802 362-2222
E: news@manchesterjournal.com
W: http://www.manchesterjournal.com
Freq: Fri; **Circ:** 10750 Not Audited
Editor: Brandon Canevari; **Publisher:** Edward Woods
Editorial Profile: Manchester Journal is published weekly for the residents of Manchester Center, VT and surrounding areas. The newspaper covers local news, weather, sports, business, education and entertainment.; Full Page Mono: 13.06
Currency: US Dollars
NEWSPAPER

Manchester Newspapers
Editorial: 14 E Main St, Granville, New York 12832-1334. **T:** 1 518 642-1234
W: http://www.manchesternewspapers.com
Circ: 51600 Not Audited
Publisher: John Manchester
Editorial Profile: Manchester Newspapers is a community newspaper publisher in Granville, NY. It publishes The Granville Sentinel; the Whitehall Times; the North Country Free Press; and the Sentinel/Times Weekender.
NEWSPAPER

The Manhattan Mercury
Owner: Seaton Newspapers
Editorial: 318 N 5th St, Manhattan, Kansas 66502-5971. **T:** 1 785 776-8808
E: news@themercury.com
W: http://www.themercury.com
Freq: Daily; **Circ:** 9424 Not Audited
Editorial Profile: The Manhattan Mercury is published daily for residents of Manhattan, KS and its surrounding areas. The publication is a general interest newspaper, covering local news, sports, weather, business, education, arts and entertainment, and other information of interest to the local community. Deadlines for the publication vary.; Full Page Mono: 13.83; Full Page Colour: 74.06
Currency: US Dollars
DAILY NEWSPAPER

Manhattan Newspaper Group
Owner: Straus News
Editorial: 72 Madison Ave Fl 11, New York, New York 10016-8731. **T:** 1 212 268-8600
E: editorial@manhattanmedia.com
W: http://manhattanmedia.com
Freq: Weekly; **Circ:** 205200 Not Audited
Publisher: Tom Allon
NEWSPAPER

Manila Mail
Owner: Media First Corp.
Editorial: 12 Avalon Dr, Daly City, California 94015. **T:** 1 650 992-5474
E: info@emanilamail.com
W: http://www.emanilamail.com/home.html
Freq: Wed; **Circ:** 25500 Not Audited
Publisher: Ruben Bunag; **Editor:** Benji Solis; **Editor:** Benji Solis; **Editor:** Benji Solis
Editorial Profile: Manila Mail in Daly City, CA is a weekly newspaper serving Filipino American residents in the San Francisco metro area. Published in English, the publication provides readers with local and international news and feature stories that are pertinent to Filipino readers and their culture.; Full Page Mono: 15.00
Currency: US Dollars
NEWSPAPER

Manistee News-Advocate
Owner: Pioneer Newspapers
Editorial: 75 Maple St, Manistee, Michigan 49660. **T:** 1 231 723-3592
E: advocate@pioneergroup.com
W: http://www.manisteenews.com
Freq: Daily; **Circ:** 5000 Not Audited
Editor: Dave Barber; **Publisher:** Marilyn Barker
Editorial Profile: Manistee News-Advocate is a daily newspaper serving Manistee County, MI. It covers local news, sports and events.; Full Page Mono: 11.75; Full Page Colour: 150.00
Currency: US Dollars
DAILY NEWSPAPER

Manly Junction Signal/Northwood Anchor
Owner: Northwood Anchor, Inc. (The)
Editorial: 801 Central Ave, Northwood, Iowa 50459-1519. **T:** 1 641 324-1051 **Circ:** 6700
Editor: Kris Kenison
NEWSPAPER

Mansfield News-Mirror
Owner: McClatchy Newspapers
Editorial: 119 N Main St, Mansfield, Texas 76063. **T:** 1 817 473-4451
W: http://www.mansfieldnewsmirror.com
Freq: Wed; **Circ:** 27000 Not Audited
Editor: Amanda Rogers
Editorial Profile: Mansfield News-Mirror is published twice per week for residents of Tarrant, Johnson, Ellis, and Dallas counties, TX. The publication is a general interest newspaper, covering local news, sports, business, government, education, social, and other information of interest to the local community. The Mansfield News-Mirror is the most complete source of information about Mansfield government and community activities.; Full Page Mono: 15.50
Currency: US Dollars
NEWSPAPER

Manteca Bulletin
Owner: Morris Multimedia, Inc.
Editorial: 531 E Yosemite Ave, Manteca, California 95336-5806. **T:** 1 209 249-3551
E: news@mantecabulletin.com
W: http://www.mantecabulletin.com
Freq: Daily; **Circ:** 6100 Not Audited
Editorial Profile: The Manteca Bulletin is published daily for residents of Manteca, CA and surrounding areas. The publication is a general interest newspaper, covering local news, sports, weather, business, education, arts and entertainment, and other information of interest to the local community.; Full Page Mono: 14.33; Full Page Colour: 53.94
Currency: US Dollars
DAILY NEWSPAPER

Maple Valley Reporter
Owner: Black Press
Editorial: 22035 SE Wax Rd, Ste 20, Maple Valley, Washington 98038. **T:** 1 425 432-1209
E: letters@maplevalleyreporter.com
W: http://www.pnwlocalnews.com
Freq: Sat; **Circ:** 24000 Not Audited
Publisher: Bill Marcum
Editorial Profile: Maple Valley Reporter is a community newspaper written for the residents of Kent, WA.; Full Page Mono: 23.00
Currency: US Dollars
NEWSPAPER

Marco Eagle
Owner: E.W. Scripps Co.
Editorial: 579 E Elkcam Cir, Marco Island, Florida 34145. **T:** 1 239 213-5300
E: mail@marcoeagle.com
W: http://www.marconews.com
Freq: Fri; **Circ:** 10000
Editor: Bill Green
Editorial Profile: Marco Eagle is a community newspaper, serving the residents of Marco Island, FL and its surrounding areas. It covers all aspects of local news, weather, sports, entertainment and community news. It is published by the Naples (FL) Daily News.; Full Page Mono: 15.00
Currency: US Dollars
NEWSPAPER

Marco Island Sun Times
Owner: The Fort Myers News-Press
Editorial: 606 Bald Eagle Dr Ste 201, Marco Island, Florida 34145-2768. **T:** 1 239 394-4050
E: mail@misuntimes.com
W: http://www.marcoislandflorida.com
Freq: Thu; **Circ:** 13500 Not Audited
Editor: Joe Taylor
Editorial Profile: Marco Island Sun Times is a community newspaper written for residents of Marco Island, FL. The paper covers local news, events and sports.; Full Page Mono: 15.00
Currency: US Dollars
NEWSPAPER

Marietta Daily Journal
Owner: Times Journal Inc.
Editorial: 580 S Fairground St Se, Marietta, Georgia 30060-2751. **T:** 1 770 428-9411
E: letters@mdjonline.com
W: http://www.mdjonline.com
Freq: Daily; **Circ:** 14491 Not Audited
Publisher: Otis Brumby; **News Editor:** Leo Hohmann
Editorial Profile: Marietta Daily Journal is a daily newspaper that covers news, events, government and sports for the communities in Cobb County, including Marietta, GA.; Full Page Mono: 26.45; Full Page Colour: 90.06
Currency: US Dollars
DAILY NEWSPAPER

The Marietta Times
Owner: Ogden Newspapers
Editorial: 700 Channel Ln, Marietta, Ohio 45750-2300. **T:** 1 740 373-2121
E: news@mariettatimes.com
W: http://www.mariettatimes.com
Freq: Daily; **Circ:** 7598 Not Audited
News Editor: Evan Bevins
Editorial Profile: The Marietta Times is a daily newspaper that is published for residents of Marietta, OH and surrounding areas. The publication is a general interest newspaper, covering local news, sports, business, education, arts & entertainment and other information of interest to the local community. Deadlines are at 3pm CT.; Full Page Mono: 24.58; Full Page Colour: 175.60
Currency: US Dollars
DAILY NEWSPAPER

Marin Independent Journal
Owner: MediaNews Group
Editorial: 4000 Civic Center Dr Ste 301, San Rafael, California 94903-4129.
T: 1 415 883-8600 **E:** localnews@marinij.com
W: http://www.marinij.com
Freq: Daily; **Circ:** 27027
Publisher: David Rounds; **Editor:** Robert Sterling
Editorial Profile: Marin Independent Journal is a daily newspaper serving the residents of Marin County, CA. It focuses on local news and events ONLY. Regional, state and international stories are covered by wire services. There is no travel section for this paper, so do not send any related stories or pitches.; Full Page Mono: 155.00; Full Page Colour: 955.95
Currency: US Dollars
DAILY NEWSPAPER

Marina Times
Owner: Northside Publications
Editorial: 3053 Fillmore St. Suite 238, San Francisco, California 94123-4009.
T: 1 415 931-0515
W: http://www.marinatimes.com
Freq: Monthly; **Circ:** 20000 Not Audited
Publisher: Earl Adkins; **Editor in Chief:** Susan Dyer Reynolds
Editorial Profile: Marina Times is a monthly newspaper serving residents in San Francisco. It covers local news, weather, sports and community events. Feature articles cover business, education, arts & entertainment, lifestyle and other information of interest to the local community.; Full Page Mono: 18.75
Currency: US Dollars
NEWSPAPER

Marinscope Community Newspapers
Owner: Mallya, (Vijay)
Editorial: 1301 Grant Ave, Novato, California 94945-3143. **T:** 1 415 892-1516
E: editor@marinscope.com
W: http://www.marinscope.com **Circ:** 44942 Not Audited
Editor: Greg Andersen; **Editor:** Soren Hemmila; **Publisher:** Paul Hutceson; **Editor:** Joe Wolfcale
NEWSPAPER

Marion County Newspapers
Owner: Buchanan Communications
Editorial: 307 Elm Ave, South Pittsburg, Tennessee 37380. **T:** 1 423 837-6312
E: mcnews@marioncountynews.net
W: http://www.marioncountynews.net
Freq: Thu; **Circ:** 6400 Not Audited
Publisher: Melissa Brown; Full Page Mono: 8.00
Currency: US Dollars
NEWSPAPER

Marion Daily Republican
Owner: GateHouse Media Inc.
Editorial: 502 W Jackson St, Marion, Illinois 62959-2355. **T:** 1 618 993-2626
W: http://www.dailyrepublicannews.com
Freq: Mon thru Fri; **Circ:** 3069 Not Audited
Publisher: Kevin Haezebroeck; **Editor:** Bill Swinford
Editorial Profile: Marion Daily Republican is published daily for residents of Williamson County, IL and surrounding areas. The publication is a general interest newspaper covering local news, weather, sports, education, business and arts & entertainment.; Full Page Mono: 11.65; Full Page Colour: 67.41
Currency: US Dollars
DAILY NEWSPAPER

The Marion Star
Owner: Gannett Co., Inc.
Editorial: 150 Court St, Marion, Ohio 43302-3093. **T:** 1 740 387-0400
W: http://www.marionstar.com
Freq: Daily; **Circ:** 5943 Not Audited
Publisher: Tom Brennan; **Editor:** John Jarvis
Editorial Profile: The Marion Star is a daily newspaper published for the residents of Marion, OH. It contains local, state, national and international news. Additional sections include sports, opinions, business, technology, travel and lifestyle. Press releases can be submitted through the paper's Web site.; Full Page Mono: 26.80; Full Page Colour: 285.00
Currency: US Dollars
DAILY NEWSPAPER

Marshall County Publishing Company
Owner: Sondag (William)
Editorial: 204 S Washington St, Lacon, Illinois 61540-1445. **T:** 1 309 246-2865
E: sonbtp@aol.com **Circ:** 12300
Editor: William Sondag
NEWSPAPER

The Marshall Democrat-News
Owner: Rust Communications
Editorial: 121 N Lafayette Ave, Marshall, Missouri 65340. **T:** 1 660 886-2233
W: http://www.marshallnews.com
Freq: Daily; **Circ:** 3098 Not Audited
Editor: Rachel Knight
Editorial Profile: The Marshall Democrat-News is a daily newspaper published for the residents of Saline County, MO. It covers local and regional news, sports and community events.; Full Page Mono: 8.66; Full Page Colour: 67.20
Currency: US Dollars
DAILY NEWSPAPER

Marshall Independent
Owner: Ogden Newspapers
Editorial: 508 W Main St, Marshall, Minnesota 56258. **T:** 1 507 537-1551
E: news@marshallindependent.com
W: http://www.marshallindependent.com
Freq: Mon thru Fri; **Circ:** 5304 Not Audited
Editor: Karin Elton; **Publisher:** Russell Labat; **Editor:** Per Peterson
Editorial Profile: Marshall Independent is published daily for residents of Lyon County, MN and surrounding areas. The publication is a general interest newspaper, covering local news, weather, sports, education, business, arts & entertainment and other information of interest to the local community.; Full Page Mono: 19.69
Currency: US Dollars
DAILY NEWSPAPER

Marshall News Messenger
Owner: ASP Westward LP
Editorial: 309 E Austin St, Marshall, Texas 75670-3475. **T:** 1 903 935-7914
E: newsmessenger@marshallnewsmessenger.com **W:** http://www.coxnews.com
Freq: Daily; **Circ:** 5788 Not Audited
Editorial Profile: Marshall News Messenger is published daily for residents of Marshall, TX and surrounding areas. It is a general interest newspaper, covering local news, weather, sports, business, education and other information of interest to local residents. Deadlines are two weeks prior to the issue date.; Full Page Mono: 24.26; Full Page Colour: 39.32
Currency: US Dollars
DAILY NEWSPAPER

Marshfield News-Herald
Owner: Gannett Co., Inc.
Editorial: 111 W 3Rd St, Marshfield, Wisconsin 54449-2811. **T:** 1 715 384-3131
E: areanews@marshfieldnewsherald.com
W: http://www.marshfieldnewsherald.com
Freq: Daily; **Circ:** 8537 Not Audited
Editorial Profile: Marshfield News-Herald is published daily for residents of Marshfield, WI and surrounding areas. The publication is a general interest newspaper, covering local news, weather, sports, business, education, arts & entertainment and other information of interest to the local community. The paper combines with The Daily Tribune in Wisconsin Rapids and the Stevens Point Journal on Sundays. Lead times vary between one and three days.; Full Page Mono: 31.10; Full Page Colour: 357.00
Currency: US Dollars
DAILY NEWSPAPER

Martha's Vineyard Times
Owner: Martha's Vineyard Times Corporation Inc.
Editorial: 30 Beach Rd, Vineyard Haven, Massachusetts 02568-5527.
T: 1 508 693-6100 **E:** mvt@mvtimes.com
W: http://www.mvtimes.com
Freq: Thu; **Circ:** 14000 Not Audited
Editor: Doug Cabral; **Editor:** Doug Cabral
Editorial Profile: Martha's Vineyard Times is written for residents of Martha's Vineyard, MA and surrounding areas. It covers local news and weather, tourist information, arts & entertainment, real estate listings, and tidal and beach updates.; Full Page Mono: 28.00; Full Page Colour: 1700.00
Currency: US Dollars
NEWSPAPER

Martin Publishing, Inc.
Owner: Martin Publishing, Inc.
Editorial: 217 W Market St, Havana, Illinois 62644. **T:** 1 309 543-3311 **Circ:** 7000
Editor: Stacey Creasy; **Publisher:** Robert Martin; **Editor:** Wendy Martin
Editorial Profile: Martin Publishing, Inc. is a community newspaper publisher serving the residents of Mason County, IL.
NEWSPAPER

Martinez News-Gazette
Owner: Gibson Publications
Editorial: 615 Estudillo St, Martinez, California 94553-1119. **T:** 1 925 228-6400
E: martineznews@yahoo.com
W: http://www.martinezgazette.com
Freq: Sun; **Circ:** 14000 Not Audited
Editor: Yael Li-Ron; **Publisher:** David Payne
Editorial Profile: Martinez News-Gazette is a local newspaper written for the residents of Martinez, CA.; Full Page Mono: 7.81
Currency: US Dollars
NEWSPAPER

Martinsville Bulletin
Owner: Matinsville Bulletin, Inc (The)
Editorial: 204 Broad St, Martinsville, Virginia 24112-3799. **T:** 1 276 638-8801
E: info@martinsvillebulletin.com
W: http://www.martinsvillebulletin.com
Freq: Daily; **Circ:** 14205 Not Audited
Publisher: Robert Haskell; **Editor:** Ginny Wray; **Editor:** Mike Wray
Editorial Profile: Martinsville Bulletin is published daily for residents of Martinsville, VA and surrounding areas. It is a general interest newspaper covering local news, weather, sports, business, education and arts & entertainment. Deadlines are at noon ET.; Full Page Mono: 17.72; Full Page Colour: 111.22
Currency: US Dollars
DAILY NEWSPAPER

Maryland Coast Dispatch
Editorial: 10012 Old Ocean City Blvd, Berlin, Maryland 21811-1145. **T:** 1 410 641-4561
E: editor@mdcoastdispatch.com
W: http://www.mdcoastdispatch.com
Freq: Fri; **Circ:** 25000 Not Audited
Editor: Shawn Soper
Editorial Profile: The Maryland Coast Dispatch in Berlin, MD covers local news, sports,

editorials, classifieds and obituaries for Ocean City, Md. and northern Worcester County .; Full Page Mono: 10.18
Currency: US Dollars
NEWSPAPER

Maryland Independent
Owner: Gazette Newspapers Inc.
Editorial: 7 Industrial Park Dr, Waldorf, Maryland 20602. **T:** 1 301 645-9480
W: http://www.somdnews.com/independent
Freq: Fri; **Circ:** 24500 Not Audited
Publisher: Karen Acton; **Editor:** Angela Breck; **Editor:** Angela Breck; **Editor:** Angela Breck
Editorial Profile: Maryland Independent is published twice per week for residents of Charles County, MD and surrounding areas. The publication is a general interest newspaper covering local news, weather, sports, community events and other information of interest to area residents and newcomers. Deadlines are Wednesdays and Fridays at 5pm ET.; Full Page Mono: 24.13; Full Page Colour: 2653.68
Currency: US Dollars
NEWSPAPER

Marysville Globe/Arlington Times
Owner: Black Press/Sound Publishing, Inc.
Editorial: 1085 Cedar Ave, Marysville, Washington 98270-4232. **T:** 1 360 659-1300
W: http://www.pnwlocalnews.com
Freq: Sat; **Circ:** 19653
Publisher: C. Paul Brown; Full Page Mono: 23.45
Currency: US Dollars
NEWSPAPER

Marysville Journal Tribune
Editorial: 207 N Main St, Marysville, Ohio 43040-1161. **T:** 1 937 644-9111
W: http://www.marysvillejt.com
Freq: Daily; **Circ:** 6495 Not Audited
Editor: Ryan Horns
Editorial Profile: The Marysville Journal-Tribune is published daily for residents of Union County, OH, and surrounding areas. The publication is a general interest newspaper, covering local news, weather, sports, education, business, arts, entertainment and other information of interest to the local community. Deadlines for the publication are one week prior to the issue date.; Full Page Mono: 12.25; Full Page Colour: 235.00
Currency: US Dollars
DAILY NEWSPAPER

The Maryville Daily Forum
Owner: GateHouse Media Inc.
Editorial: 111 E Jenkins St, Maryville, Missouri 64468-2318. **T:** 1 660 562-2424
W: http://www.maryvilledailyforum.com
Freq: Daily; **Circ:** 3200 Not Audited
News Editor: Tony Brown
Editorial Profile: The Maryville Daily Forum is published daily for residents of greater Maryville, MO and surrounding areas. The publication is a general interest newspaper, covering local news, weather, sports, education, business and arts & entertainment.; Full Page Mono: 8.60; Full Page Colour: 48.58
Currency: US Dollars
DAILY NEWSPAPER

Il Massaggero - New York Bureau
Editorial: 350 5th Ave, Ste 5915, New York, New York 10118-0110. **T:** 1 212 601-2696
Editorial Profile: This is the New York bureau of Il Massaggero, based in Roma, Italy.
DAILY NEWSPAPER

Mattos Newspapers
Editorial: 1021 Fresno St, Newman, California 95360. **T:** 1 209 862-2222
E: info@mattosnews.com
W: http://www.mattosnews.com **Circ:** 3600 Not Audited
Editor: Dean Harris; **Publisher:** Susan Mattos
NEWSPAPER

The Maui News
Owner: Ogden Newspapers
Editorial: 100 Mahalani St, Wailuku, Hawaii 96793-2529. **T:** 1 808 244-3981
W: http://www.mauinews.com
Freq: Daily; **Circ:** 18134 Not Audited
Publisher: Joseph Bradley; **Editor:** David Hoff; **News Editor:** Lee Imada
Editorial Profile: The Maui News is published daily for residents of Wailuku, HI and surrounding areas. The publication is a general interest newspaper, covering local news, weather, sports, business, education, arts & entertainment and other information of importance to the local community.; Full Page Mono: 35.60; Full Page Colour: 213.03
Currency: US Dollars

DAILY NEWSPAPER

Maui Time Weekly
Editorial: 33 N Market St, Ste 201, Wailuku, Hawaii 96793-1742. **T:** 1 808 244-0777
E: editor@mauitime.com
W: http://www.mauitime.com
Freq: Thu; **Circ:** 18000 Not Audited
Publisher: Thomas Russo
Editorial Profile: Maui Time Weekly is a community newspaper written for the residents of Maui, HI.; Full Page Mono: 121.00
Currency: US Dollars
NEWSPAPER

Maui Weekly
Owner: Hawaii Publications/ Ogden Newspapers
Editorial: 411 Huku Lii Pl Ste 303, Kihei, Hawaii 96753-7062. **T:** 1 808 875-1700
E: office@mauiweekly.com
W: http://www.mauiweekly.com
Freq: Thu; **Circ:** 25000 Not Audited
Publisher: Joseph Bradley; **Editor:** Debra Lordan
Editorial Profile: Maui Weekly is published for residents and visitors of Kihei, HI. The publication is a general interest newspaper covering local news, weather, sports, business, education, arts & entertainment and other information of interest to the local community.; Full Page Mono: 18.00
Currency: US Dollars
NEWSPAPER

Maurer Publishing Co.
Owner: Maurer Publishing LLC
Editorial: 359 Reagon St, Saint Ignace, Michigan 49781-1134. **T:** 1 906 643-9150
W: http://www.stignacenews.com **Circ:** 10100 Not Audited
NEWSPAPER

Maxwell/Gunter Dispatch
Owner: Gannett Co., Inc.
Editorial: 55 LeMay Plaza South, Maxwell A F B, Alabama 36112. **T:** 1 334 953-2601
E: maxwell.dispatch@maxwell.af.mil
W: http://www.maxwellgunterdispatch.com
Freq: Fri; **Circ:** 12500 Not Audited
Editor: Kimberly Wright
Editorial Profile: Maxwell/Gunter Dispatch is a free weekly newspaper serving the Maxwell Air Force Base in Maxwell, AL. It is distributed to base military personnel, civilian family and employees of the base. It covers news and events at the base, along with national and international stories of interest to local military and civilian community members. All editorial content is written by members of the Public Affairs office at the base. Editorial and photography submissions are due on Thursdays at noon ET one week prior to issue date.
NEWSPAPER

Mayfield Messenger
Owner: Mayfield Messenger Corporation
Editorial: 201 N 8th St, Mayfield, Kentucky 42066-1825. **T:** 1 270 247-5223
E: mayfieldmessenger@kyn.twcbc.com
Freq: Daily; **Circ:** 6200 Not Audited
Editor: Jim Abernathy; **Publisher:** Eric Hoffman
Editorial Profile: Mayfield Messenger is published daily for residents of Graves County, KY and surrounding areas. The publication is a general interest newspaper, covering local news, weather, sports, business, education, arts & entertainment and other information of interest to the local community.; Full Page Mono: 8.30; Full Page Colour: 61.77
Currency: US Dollars
DAILY NEWSPAPER

McAlester News-Capital
Owner: Community Newspaper Holdings, Inc.
Editorial: 500 S 2nd St, McAlester, Oklahoma 74501-5806. **T:** 1 918 423-1700
W: http://mcalesternews.com
Freq: Daily; **Circ:** 7500 Not Audited
Publisher: Amy Johns
Editorial Profile: McAlester News-Capital is written for residents of McAlester, OK.; Full Page Mono: 12.75; Full Page Colour: 316.75
Currency: US Dollars
DAILY NEWSPAPER

McCook Daily Gazette
Owner: Rust Communications
Editorial: West 1st and E St, McCook, Nebraska 69001. **T:** 1 308 345-4500
E: editor@mccookgazette.com
W: http://www.mccookgazette.com
Freq: Mon thru Fri; **Circ:** 5661 Not Audited
Editor: Bruce Crosby; **Editor:** Bruce Crosby; **Editor:** Bruce Crosby; **Publisher:** Shary Skiles

Editorial Profile: McCook Daily Gazette provides news to the communities of McCook and the Golden Plains of South Nebraska and Northwest Kansas.; Full Page Mono: 10.20; Full Page Colour: 195.00
Currency: US Dollars
DAILY NEWSPAPER

McCurtain Daily Gazette
Owner: McCurtain County News, Inc. (The)
Editorial: 107 S Central Ave, Idabel, Oklahoma 74745-4847. **T:** 1 580 286-3321
E: paper@mccurtain.com
W: http://www.mccurtain.com
Freq: Daily; **Circ:** 5850 Not Audited
Editor: Bruce Willingham
Editorial Profile: McCurtain Daily Gazette is a local daily newspaper written for the residents of McCurtain County, OK.; Full Page Mono: 7.35; Full Page Colour: 40.74
Currency: US Dollars
DAILY NEWSPAPER

McDonough County Voice
Owner: GateHouse Media Inc.
Editorial: 203 N Randolph St, Macomb, Illinois 61455. **T:** 1 309 833-2114
E: newsroom@mcdonoughvoice.com
W: http://www.mcdonoughvoice.com
Freq: Daily; **Circ:** 6969 Not Audited
Publisher: Lynne Campbell; **Editor:** Jackie Smith
Editorial Profile: McDonough County Voice is a daily newspaper written for residents of Macomb, IL. It covers local, state and world news, sports and business.; Full Page Mono: 14.00; Full Page Colour: 200.00
Currency: US Dollars
DAILY NEWSPAPER

McDowell News
Owner: World Media Enterprises, Inc.
Editorial: 136 N Logan St, Marion, North Carolina 28752-3754. **T:** 1 828 652-3313
E: news@mcdowellnews.com
W: http://www.mcdowellnews.com
Freq: Daily; **Circ:** 5662 Not Audited
Editor: Scott Hollifield; **Publisher:** Lamar Smitherman
Editorial Profile: McDowell News is a daily newspaper published for the residents of McDowell County, including Macon, NC and Greenville, SC. It covers local news and entertainment. Deadlines are daily at 4pm ET.; Full Page Mono: 9.02; Full Page Colour: 33.82
Currency: US Dollars
DAILY NEWSPAPER

McKnight Journal
Owner: Tribune-Review Publishing Co
Editorial: 535 Keystone Dr, Warrendale, Pennsylvania 15086-7538. **T:** 1 724 779-8742
E: mcknightjournal@tribweb.com
W: http://www.yournorthhills.com
Freq: Thu; **Circ:** 16454 Not Audited
Editor: Madelyn Dinnerstein
Editorial Profile: McNight Journal is a local weekly newspaper for residents of Ross Township, McCandless and West View, PA. It covers local news, business, sports and arts & entertainment stories. It also provides national and statewide stories if they have a direct impact on the newspaper's readership. All inquiries should be addressed to the editor. The paper will cease publishing at the end of June 2008.; Full Page Mono: 11.00
Currency: US Dollars
NEWSPAPER

McPherson Sentinel
Owner: GateHouse Media Inc.
Editorial: 301 S Main St, McPherson, Kansas 67460-4830. **T:** 1 620 241-2422
E: sentinel@sbcglobal.net
W: http://www.mcphersonsentinel.com
Freq: Daily; **Circ:** 4000 Not Audited
Publisher: Randy Mitchell
Editorial Profile: McPherson Sentinel provides news for the residents of McPherson County, KS. Deadlines are one day before issue date.; Full Page Mono: 14.00
Currency: US Dollars
DAILY NEWSPAPER

Meadville Newspapers
Owner: Webb (Mary Lou)
Editorial: 100 Main St E, Meadville, Mississippi 39653-9338. **T:** 1 601 384-2484
E: advocate@telepak.net
W: http://www.franklinadvocate.com
Circ: 3400 Not Audited
NEWSPAPER

The Meadville Tribune
Owner: Community Newspaper Holdings, Inc.
Editorial: 947 Federal Ct, Meadville, Pennsylvania 16335-3286. **T:** 1 814 724-6370

E: tribune@meadvilletribune.com
W: http://meadvilletribune.com
Freq: Daily; **Circ:** 10382 Not Audited
Publisher: James Galantis
Editorial Profile: The Meadville Tribune is a daily local newspaper published for Crawford County, PA residents. Regular features include local news, community announcements and sports. Deadlines are at 7pm ET.; Full Page Mono: 25.40; Full Page Colour: 385.00
Currency: US Dollars
DAILY NEWSPAPER

The Mechanicsville Local
Owner: BH Media Group
Editorial: 6400 Mechanicsville Tpke, Mechanicsville, Virginia 23111-4579.
T: 1 804 746-1235 **E:** news@mechlocal.com
W: http://www.mechlocal.com
Freq: Wed; **Circ:** 29864 Not Audited
Editorial Profile: The Mechanicsville Local is a weekly newspaper serving residents of Mechanicsville, VA. It covers local news, community events, sports, editorials and features of interest to area readers. Deadlines are at 5pm ET.; Full Page Mono: 30.00; Full Page Colour: 8.00
Currency: US Dollars
NEWSPAPER

The Mecklenburg Sun
Editorial: 602 Virginia Ave, Clarksville, Virginia 23927-9121. **T:** 1 434 374-8152
E: news@themecklenburgsun.com
W: http://www.sovanow.com
Freq: Wed; **Circ:** 15500 Not Audited
Editorial Profile: Mecklenburg Sun is a local newspaper providing the community of Clarksville, VA with news.; Full Page Mono: 6.00
Currency: US Dollars
NEWSPAPER

Medford Printing
Editorial: 116 1/2 W Cherokee St, Medford, Oklahoma 73759
Editorial Profile: These publications do not accept pitches or press materials, and have requested their contact details not be listed.
NEWSPAPER

Media General Community Newspapers
Owner: Media General
Editorial: 202 S Parker St, Tampa, Florida 33606-2308. **T:** 1 813 259-7600 **Circ:** 47772 Not Audited
Editor: Laura Cone
NEWSPAPER

Media General Newspapers
Owner: Media General Inc.
Editorial: 460 W Main St, Wytheville, Virginia 24382-2207. **T:** 1 276 228-6611
W: http://www.mediageneral.com **Circ:** 8550 Not Audited
Editor: Mark Sage
NEWSPAPER

MediaGlobal News Agency - New York Bureau
Editorial: United Nations Secretariat, Room S-301, New York, New York 10017.
T: 1 609 529-6129 **E:** media@mediaglobal.org
W: http://www.mediaglobal.org
Editorial Profile: This is the New York Bureau for the MediaGlobal News Agency in Princeton Junction, NJ.
DAILY NEWSPAPER

The Medina County Gazette
Owner: Lorain County Printing & Publishing
Editorial: 885 W Liberty St, Medina, Ohio 44256-1312. **T:** 1 330 725-4166
E: areanews@medina-gazette.com
W: http://www.medina-gazette.com
Freq: Daily; **Circ:** 11538 Not Audited
Publisher: George Hudnutt; **News Editor:** Liz Sheaffer
Editorial Profile: The Medina County Gazette provides local news for Medina County, OH.; Full Page Mono: 29.00
Currency: US Dollars
DAILY NEWSPAPER

Memphis Silver Star News
Editorial: 3019 Park Ave, Memphis, Tennessee 38114. **T:** 1 901 452-8828
E: silverstarnews@bellsouth.net
Freq: Wed; **Circ:** 28000 Not Audited
Editorial Profile: Memphis Silver Star News provides news to the African-American community in Memphis, TN. Deadlines are on Fridays.; Full Page Mono: 18.70
Currency: US Dollars
NEWSPAPER

Mennonite World Review

Owner: Mennonite Weekly Review Inc.
Editorial: 129 W 6th St, Newton, Kansas 67114-2117. **T:** 1 316 283-3670
W: http://www.mennoweekly.org
Freq: Mon; **Circ:** 10000 Not Audited
Editor: Paul Schrag; **Publisher:** Robert Schrag
Editorial Profile: Mennonite World Review is a national newspaper that focuses on news and information concerning the North American Mennonite population. The paper includes Mennonite news and activities, ideas for congregations and families, opinions on church issues and current events, editorials, book reviews and Sunday school lesson comments. Editorial deadlines fall on Tuesdays prior to issue dates at noon CT.; Full Page Mono: 22.00; Full Page Colour: 22.00
Currency: US Dollars
NEWSPAPER

El Mensajero

Owner: ImpreMedia LLC
Editorial: 333 Valencia St, San Francisco, California 94103-3547. **T:** 1 415 206-7230 110
E: comentarios@elmensajero.com
W: http://www.impre.com/elmensajero
Freq: Sun; **Circ:** 103800 Not Audited
Editorial Profile: El Mensajero is written for the Latino community of San Francisco. The paper covers local news and sports.; Full Page Mono: 85.00; Full Page Colour: 400.00
Currency: US Dollars
NEWSPAPER

Merced Sun Star

Owner: McClatchy Newspapers
Editorial: 3033 North G St, Merced, California 95340-2108. **T:** 1 209 722-1511
W: http://www.mercedsunstar.com
Freq: Mon thru Fri; **Circ:** 17854 Not Audited
Editorial Profile: Merced Sun-Star's editorial mission is to provide local news and community information for the people of Merced.; Full Page Mono: 42.58; Full Page Colour: 140.24
Currency: US Dollars
DAILY NEWSPAPER

The Mercury

Owner: Digital First Media
Editorial: 24 N Hanover St, Pottstown, Pennsylvania 19464-5410. **T:** 1 610 323-3000
E: mercury@pottsmerc.com
W: http://www.pottsmerc.com
Freq: Daily; **Circ:** 24825 Not Audited
Publisher: Edward Condra; **Editor:** Nancy March; **Editor:** Tony Phyrillas
Editorial Profile: The Mercury is a published daily for readers in the greater Pottstown, PA area. The newspaper provides local news and community event information. News features include lifestyle, sports, business, classifieds and advertising. Some national news is provided by the Associated Press, but the newspaper primarily focuses on keeping its readers aware of news and events occurring in their community.; Full Page Mono: 34.77; Full Page Colour: 48.68
Currency: US Dollars
DAILY NEWSPAPER

Meridian Star

Owner: Community Newspaper Holdings, Inc.
Editorial: 814 22nd Ave, Meridian, Mississippi 39301-5023. **T:** 1 601 693-1551
W: http://www.meridianstar.com
Freq: Daily; **Circ:** 16348 Not Audited
Editor: Ida Brown; **Publisher:** Tim Holder
Editorial Profile: Meridian Star provides local news and information to the residents of Meridian, MS.; Full Page Mono: 29.45; Full Page Colour: 230.00
Currency: US Dollars
DAILY NEWSPAPER

The Mesabi Daily News

Owner: Macquarie Media Group
Editorial: 704 S 7th Ave, Virginia, Minnesota 55792-3086. **T:** 1 218 741-5544
E: mdnedit@mesabidailynews.net
W: http://www.virginiamn.com
Freq: Daily; **Circ:** 9222 Not Audited
Editorial Profile: The Mesabi Daily News provides local news and information to the community of Virginia, MN.; Full Page Mono: 11.41
Currency: US Dollars
DAILY NEWSPAPER

The Messenger

Owner: Ogden Newspapers
Editorial: 713 Central Ave, Fort Dodge, Iowa 50501-3813. **T:** 1 515 573-2141
E: editor@messengernews.net
W: http://www.messengernews.net

Freq: Daily; **Circ:** 11344 Not Audited
Publisher: Larry Bushman
Editorial Profile: The Messenger is a daily newspaper serving Fort Dodge, IA. The newspaper covers local and state news, business, agriculture, sports and entertainment.; Full Page Mono: 23.35; Full Page Colour: 140.00
Currency: US Dollars
DAILY NEWSPAPER

The Messenger

Owner: Paxton Media Group
Editorial: 221 S Main St, Madisonville, Kentucky 42431-2567. **T:** 1 270 824-3300
E: newsroom@the-messenger.com
W: http://www.the-messenger.com
Freq: Fri; **Circ:** 7422 Not Audited
Publisher: Rick Welch
Editorial Profile: The Messenger is a local newspaper serving the residents of Madisonville, KY and the surrounding area. The publication covers local news, sports and community events. Deadlines are four working days in advance.; Full Page Mono: 17.23; Full Page Colour: 290.00
Currency: US Dollars
NEWSPAPER

The Messenger

Owner: Diocese of Covington, KY.
Editorial: 402 E 21st St, Covington, Kentucky 41014. **T:** 1 859 392-1570
E: messenger@covingtondiocese.org
W: http://www.covingtondiocese.org
Freq: Fri; **Circ:** 27000 Not Audited
Editor: Tim Fitzgerald; **Publisher:** Roger Foys; Full Page Mono: 13.00
Currency: US Dollars
NEWSPAPER

The Messenger

Editorial: 246 W Main St, Hillsboro, New Hampshire 3244. **T:** 1 603 464-3388
E: granitequill@mcttelecom.com
W: http://www.themessengernh.com
Freq: Fri; **Circ:** 17000 Not Audited
Editor: Joyce Bosse; **Publisher:** Leigh Bosse
Editorial Profile: The Messenger is written for residents of Hillsboro, NH. It covers local news and community events. Deadlines are on Mondays at 5pm ET.; Full Page Mono: 9.00
Currency: US Dollars
NEWSPAPER

Messenger Publications

Editorial: 104 S Robinson St, Miles, Texas 76861. **T:** 1 325 468-3611 **Circ:** 1000 Not Audited
NEWSPAPER

Messenger Publishing Group

Owner: Messenger Publishing Group
Editorial: 7405 Greenback Ln, #129, Citrus Heights, California 95610-5603.
T: 1 916 773-1111 **E:** publisher@mpg8.com
W: http://www.mpg8.com **Circ:** 41000 Not Audited
Editorial Profile: Messenger Publishing Group publishes bi-monthly and weekly newspapers to the residents of Placer County and Sacramento County. It publishes the Carmichael Times, American River Messenger, Mercury, Citrus Heights Messenger, Placer Sentinel, Orangevale Sun, Sacramento Oracle, Arden Advocate, Auburn Sentinel, Natomas Messenger and Granite Bay Mirror.
NEWSPAPER

Metro Boston

Owner: Seabay Media Holdings LLC.
Editorial: 234 Congress St Fl 4, Boston, Massachusetts 02110-2470.
T: 1 617 210-7905 **E:** letters@metro.us
W: http://www.metro.us/boston
Freq: Daily; **Circ:** 137953 Not Audited
Editorial Profile: Metro Boston is a commuter daily newspaper serving commuters and residents of Boston. It reports national, regional and worldwide news, sports and arts & entertainment.; Full Page Mono: 168.96; Full Page Colour: 185.76
Currency: US Dollars
DAILY NEWSPAPER

The Metro Courier

Editorial: 314 Walton Way, Augusta, Georgia 30901-2436. **T:** 1 706 724-6556
E: metrocourier@comcast.net
Freq: Thu; **Circ:** 28700 Not Audited
Editorial Profile: The Metro Courier's editorial mission is to address the issues and concerns of the African-American community in Augusta. The publication is written for the African American communities of Augusta, GA.; Full Page Mono: 16.50
Currency: US Dollars

NEWSPAPER

Metro Group Inc.

Owner: Strategic Publications LLC
Editorial: 75 Boxwood Ln, Cheektowaga, New York 14227-2707. **T:** 1 716 668-5223
E: edit@metrowny.com
W: http://www.metrowny.com **Circ:** 282051 Not Audited
Publisher: Gerard Grabowski; **Editor:** Matt Ondesko
NEWSPAPER

The Metro Herald

Owner: Davis Communications Group
Editorial: 901 N Washington St, Alexandria, Virginia 22314-5509. **T:** 1 703 548-8891
W: http://www.metroherald.com
Freq: Fri; **Circ:** 16481 Not Audited
Editorial Profile: The Metro Herald is a local newspaper written for the African American community of Alexandria, VA.; Full Page Mono: 30.11
Currency: US Dollars
NEWSPAPER

Metro New York

Owner: Seabay Media Holdings LLC.
Editorial: 120 Broadway Fl 6, New York, New York 10271-1100. **T:** 1 212 457-7790
E: letters@metro.us
W: http://www.metro.us/newyork
Freq: Mon thru Fri; **Circ:** 293216 Not Audited
Editorial Profile: Metro New York is a commuter daily newspaper that is distributed for free each weekday. It is designed and packaged for young, urban, active and well-educated audiences and provides readers with the news that they need, condensed into a 15-minute read. Local, national and international news reports are combined with the latest entertainment listings and reviews.; Full Page Mono: 385.95; Full Page Colour: 1184.34
Currency: US Dollars
DAILY NEWSPAPER

Metro North Media, Inc.

Editorial: 5752 Fieldston Rd, Bronx, New York 10471-2508. **T:** 1 718 543-5200
E: bxny@aol.com **Circ:** 53500 Not Audited
Editor: John DeSio; **Publisher:** Andrew Wolf
Editorial Profile: Metro North Media Inc. in the Bronx, NY publishes the Riverdale Review and the Bronx Press-Review.
NEWSPAPER

Metro North Newspapers

Owner: Jackalope Publishing
Editorial: 8710 Grant St, Thornton, Colorado 80229-4716. **T:** 1 303 426-6000
W: http://www.great8newspapers.com
Circ: 51200 Not Audited
Editorial Profile: Metro North Newspapers is a community newspaper publisher in Highlands Ranch, CO.
NEWSPAPER

Metro Philadelphia

Owner: Seabay Media Holdings LLC.
Editorial: 30 S 15th St, the Graham Building, Philadelphia, Pennsylvania 19102-4826.
T: 1 215 717-2600
W: http://www.metro.us/philadelphia
Freq: Daily; **Circ:** 116509 Not Audited
Editorial Profile: Philadelphia Metro is a free, commuter daily newspaper that is distributed to commuters and residents throughout the Philadelphia metropolitan area. It targets young professionals and is intended to be read during a 15-minute morning commute. The newspaper has concise articles that focus on local, national and international news, lifestyle, sports and arts & entertainment stories.; Full Page Colour: 76.83
Currency: US Dollars
DAILY NEWSPAPER

Metro Pulse

Owner: E.W. Scripps Co.
Editorial: 602 S Gay St Fl 2, Knoxville, Tennessee 37902-1605. **T:** 1 865 522-5399
E: editor@metropulse.com
W: http://www.metropulse.com
Freq: Thu; **Circ:** 37500 Not Audited
Publisher: Paul Abraham; **Editor:** Coury Turczyn
Editorial Profile: Metro Pulse in Knoxville, TN is a weekly newspaper that covers local news, arts & entertainment and community events.; Full Page Mono: 9.00
Currency: US Dollars
NEWSPAPER

Metro San Diego Communications Inc.

Owner: REP Publishing, Inc

Editorial: 1250 6th Ave. 12th Floor, San Diego, California 92101. **T:** 1 619 906-4104
W: http://www.sandiegometro.com
Circ: 16000 Not Audited
Publisher: Rebeca Page; **Publisher:** Kevin Specht; **Editor:** Taunya Specht
NEWSPAPER

Metro Silicon Valley

Owner: Metro Publishing Group
Editorial: 550 S 1st St, San Jose, California 95113-2806. **T:** 1 408 298-8000
E: letters@metronews.com
W: http://www.metronews.com
Freq: Wed; **Circ:** 70000
Publisher: Dan Pulcrano
Editorial Profile: Metro is a weekly newspaper published by Metro Publishing Group, for the residents of Silicon Valley, CA. The newspaper covers local news, business, entertainment and music.; Full Page Mono: 50.83
Currency: US Dollars
NEWSPAPER

Metro Times

Owner: Times Shamrock Group
Editorial: 1200 Woodward Heights Blvd, Ferndale, Michigan 48220. **T:** 1 313 961-4060
E: letters@metrotimes.com
W: http://www.metrotimes.com
Freq: Wed; **Circ:** 68891 Not Audited
Publisher: Chris Keating; **Editor in Chief:** Valerie Vande Panne
Editorial Profile: Metro Times is a local, weekly newspaper serving the tri-county area surrounding Detroit, MI. It provides information on news, events, and arts and entertainment of interest to the local community. In May 2014, the publication merged with fellow alternative newsweekly Real Detroit Weekly.; Full Page Mono: 54.12
Currency: US Dollars
NEWSPAPER

Metroland

Owner: Lou Communications, Inc.
Editorial: 419 Madison Ave, Albany, New York 12210. **T:** 1 518 463-2500
E: metroland@metroland.net
W: http://www.metroland.net
Freq: Thu; **Circ:** 40000 Not Audited
Editorial Profile: Metroland in Albany, NY is a weekly newspaper that covers local news, sports, arts & entertainment, fashion, food and travel.; Full Page Mono: 24.46
Currency: US Dollars
NEWSPAPER

Metropolis Newspapers

Owner: Paxton Media Group
Editorial: 111 E 5th St, Metropolis, Illinois 62960. **T:** 1 618 524-2141
W: http://www.metropolisplanet.com
Circ: 15950 Not Audited
Editor: Linda Kennedy
NEWSPAPER

Metropolitan News Company

Owner: Grace Communications, Inc.
Editorial: 210 S Spring St, Los Angeles, California 90012. **T:** 1 213 346-0033
E: news@metnews.com
W: http://www.mnc.net **Circ:** 43230 Not Audited
Publisher: Roger Grace
NEWSPAPER

MetroWest Daily News

Owner: GateHouse Media Inc.
Editorial: 33 New York Ave, Framingham, Massachusetts 1701. **T:** 1 508 626-3800
E: metrowest@wickedlocal.com
W: http://www.metrowestdailynews.com
Freq: Daily; **Circ:** 14222 Not Audited
Editor in Chief: Richard Lodge; **Editor in Chief:** Richard Lodge; **Editor in Chief:** Richard Lodge; **Editor in Chief:** Richard Lodge
Editorial Profile: MetroWest Daily News is published for the residents of Boston and its Western suburbs. It covers regional, state, business, technology, sports, health, lifestyle and arts. The publication honors embargoes and accepts non-disclosure agreements. Advertisings deadlines are at 4pm ET.; Full Page Mono: 41.25
Currency: US Dollars
DAILY NEWSPAPER

MetroWest Publishing

Owner: Landmark Community Newspapers, Inc.
Editorial: 139 N Main St, Brighton, Colorado 80601. **T:** 1 303 659-2522 200
E: news@metrowestnewspapers.com
W: http://www.metrowestfyi.com **Circ:** 26625 Not Audited
Publisher: Allen Messick

NEWSPAPER

El Mexicano

Owner: Zapari (Fernando)
Editorial: 2301 Fairfield Ave, Ste 102, Fort Wayne, Indiana 46807. **T:** 1 260 456-6843
E: elmexica@earthlink.net
W: http://www.elmexicanonews.com
Freq: Fri; **Circ:** 10000 Not Audited
Editorial Profile: El Mexicano is a free, monthly, Spanish-language newspaper. It is distributed the first Friday of each month at newsstands, restaurants and businesses with a large Hispanic clientèle throughout Fort Wayne, South Bend, Ligonier and the surrounding area, including communities in southern Michigan. It covers regional and international news, events, sports and entertainment of interest to a Hispanic audience.; Full Page Mono: 12.00
Currency: US Dollars
NEWSPAPER

The Mexico Ledger

Owner: Fortress Investment Group, LLC
Editorial: 300 N Washington St, Mexico, Missouri 65265-2775. **T:** 1 573 581-1111
E: news@mexicoledger.com
W: http://www.mexicoledger.com
Freq: Mon thru Fri; **Circ:** 4049 Not Audited
Editor: Brenda Fike; **Publisher:** Joe May; **News Editor:** Janeen Sims
Editorial Profile: The Mexico Ledger is a daily newspaper that serves Mexico and Audrain counties, as well as portions of Boone, Callaway, Montgomery, Monroe and Ralls counties, MO. It provides all the news, events and happenings. Deadlines are at 9am CT.; Full Page Mono: 13.00; Full Page Colour: 210.00
Currency: US Dollars
DAILY NEWSPAPER

The Miami Herald

Owner: McClatchy Newspapers
Editorial: 3511 NW 91st Ave, Doral, Florida 33172-1216. **T:** 1 305 350-2111
W: http://www.miamiherald.com
Freq: Daily; **Circ:** 141188 Not Audited
Editor: Amy Driscoll
Editorial Profile: The Miami Herald, published daily, is a general interest broadsheet newspaper written for the general public in the greater Miami area. The publication aims to provide readers with breaking news and features and other general information. It includes partnerships with several community publications and features a number of neighborhood sub-domains on its Web site.; Full Page Mono: 283.00; Full Page Colour: 310.62
Currency: US Dollars
DAILY NEWSPAPER

The Miami Herald

Editorial: 2010 NW 150th Ave, Pembroke Pines, Florida 33028-2805. **T:** 1 954 538-7102
E: browardnews@miamiherald.com
DAILY NEWSPAPER

The Miami Herald

Editorial: 104350 Overseas Hwy Apt A205, Key Largo, Florida 33037-2940.
T: 1 305 742-9687
DAILY NEWSPAPER

The Miami Herald

Editorial: 336 E College Ave Ste 201, Tallahassee, Florida 32301-1559.
T: 1 850 222-3095
Bureau Chief: Mary Ellen Klas
DAILY NEWSPAPER

The Miami Laker

Owner: Graham Companies (The)
Editorial: 15450 New Barn Rd, Ste 103, Miami Lakes, Florida 33014. **T:** 1 305 817-4028
E: miamilaker1@aol.com
Freq: Bi-Monthly; **Circ:** 16500 Not Audited
Editorial Profile: The Miami Laker is a twice-monthly community publication geared towards the residents of the greater Miami Lakes area. The publication focuses on those local issues that impact the lives of their readership. Deadlines for the publication are 10 days before issue date.; Full Page Mono: 17.25; Full Page Colour: 1050.00
Currency: US Dollars
NEWSPAPER

Miami New Times

Owner: Voice Media Group
Editorial: 4500 Biscayne Blvd Ste 200, Miami, Florida 33137-3227. **T:** 1 305 576-8000
E: editorial@miaminewtimes.com
W: http://www.miaminewtimes.com
Freq: Wed; **Circ:** 69501 Not Audited
Editor: Chuck Strouse

Editorial Profile: Miami New Times is a weekly newspaper written for residents and tourists in the Miami area. The newspaper covers local news and events, business, politics, social issues, travel and other news of interests to the local community.; Full Page Mono: 24.20
Currency: US Dollars
NEWSPAPER

Miami News Record

Owner: Macquarie Media Group
Editorial: 14 1st Ave NW, Miami, Oklahoma 74354-6224. **T:** 1 918 542-5533
E: news@miaminewsrecord.com
W: http://www.miaminewsrecord.com
Freq: Fri; **Circ:** 6000 Not Audited
Publisher: Jim Abruzzo; **Editor:** Jim Ellis
Editorial Profile: Miami News Record is a daily publication, with the exception of Monday and offers news stories, events listings and general coverage. The publication is geared towards residents in and around Miami, OK.; Full Page Mono: 12.75; Full Page Colour: 80.00
Currency: US Dollars
NEWSPAPER

The Miami Times

Editorial: 900 NW 54th St, Miami, Florida 33127. **T:** 1 305 694-6210
W: http://www.miamitimesonline.com
Freq: Wed; **Circ:** 17178 Not Audited
Publisher: Rachel Reeves; **Publisher:** Rachel Reeves
Editorial Profile: The Miami Times is written for Miami's African American community. It provides news, cultural and lifestyle information.; Full Page Mono: 47.75
Currency: US Dollars
NEWSPAPER

Miami's Community Newspapers

Owner: Your Hometown Newspapers, Inc.
Editorial: 6796 SW 62nd Ave, South Miami, Florida 33143-3306. **T:** 1 305 669-7355
W: http://www.communitynewspapers.com
Circ: 127000 Not Audited
Editor: Ron Beasley; **Editor:** David Berkowitz; **Editor:** Dan Palmer; **Editor:** Dan Palmer; **Editor:** Dan Palmer; **Editor:** Dan Palmer; **Editor:** Dick Yager; **Editor:** Dick Yager; **Editor:** Dick Yager
Editorial Profile: Miami's Community Newspapers in South Miami, FL serves communities in the North Miami Beach, North Miami and North Bay Village areas of Broward and Dade Counties, FL. It distributes free newspapers featuring community news, events, business, health, entertainment and sports stories.
NEWSPAPER

The Michigan Catholic

Owner: Archdiocese of Detroit
Editorial: 305 Michigan Ave, Detroit, Michigan 48226. **T:** 1 313 224-8000
E: themichigancatholic@aod.org
W: http://www.aodonline.org
Freq: Bi-Weekly; **Circ:** 22000 Not Audited
Publisher: Allen Vigneron
Editorial Profile: The Michigan Catholic is a weekly newspaper written for senior citizens in the Detroit area. The publication's editorial mission is to provide news and information on local, national, and international Catholic issues.; Full Page Mono: 17.00; Full Page Colour: 960.00
Currency: US Dollars
NEWSPAPER

The Michigan Citizen

Editorial: 1055 Trumbull St, Detroit, Michigan 48216-1938. **T:** 1 313 963-8282
E: editor@michigancitizen.com
W: http://www.michigancitizen.com
Freq: Thu; **Circ:** 55100 Not Audited
Publisher: Catherine Kelly
Editorial Profile: The Michigan Citizen is a weekly newspaper published for the residents of Detroit. The paper covers local news and events, arts & entertainment, cartoons and other topics of general interest.; Full Page Mono: 27.30
Currency: US Dollars
NEWSPAPER

Micromedia Publications

Owner: Micromedia Publications, Inc.
Editorial: 15 Union Ave, Lakehurst, New Jersey 8733. **T:** 1 732 657-7344
W: http://www.micromediapubs.com
Circ: 105000 Not Audited
News Editor: Eric San Juan; **Publisher:** Stewart Swan
NEWSPAPER

Mid Valley Publishing - Reedley

Editorial: 1130 G St, Reedley, California 93654. **T:** 1 559 638-2244
W: http://www.reedleyexponent.com
Circ: 13100 Not Audited
Publisher: Fred Hall; **Editor:** Doug Hoagland; **Editor:** George Villagrana
Editorial Profile: Mid Valley Publishing - Reedley is a weekly community newspaper publisher serving the residents of Reedley, Orange Cove and Parlier, CA.
NEWSPAPER

Mid Valley Publishing - Sanger

Editorial: 740 N St, Sanger, California 93657.
T: 1 559 875-2511
E: sangerherald@gmail.com
W: http://www.reedleyexponent.com
Circ: 3700 Not Audited
Publisher: Fred Hall; **Publisher:** Fred Hall; **Editor:** Dick Sheppard; **Editor:** Kathy Williams
NEWSPAPER

The Middletown Press

Owner: Journal Register Company
Editorial: 386 Main Street Ext Fl 4, Middletown, Connecticut 06457-4406.
T: 1 860 347-3331
E: letters@middletownpress.com
W: http://www.middletownpress.com
Freq: Mon thru Fri; **Circ:** 6114 Not Audited
Editor: John Berry; **Publisher:** Matt DeRienzo
Editorial Profile: The Middletown Press is a local daily newspaper which provides readers in Middlesex County, CT with local, regional and national news. News features include sports, business, lifestyle, entertainment and classifieds. It combines with The Bristol (CT)Press and The Herald in New Britain, CT on Sundays.; Full Page Mono: 21.41
Currency: US Dollars
DAILY NEWSPAPER

Midland Daily News

Owner: Hearst Newspapers
Editorial: 124 S McDonald St, Midland, Michigan 48640-5161. **T:** 1 989 835-7171
E: info@mdn.net
W: http://www.ourmidland.com
Freq: Daily; **Circ:** 10003 Not Audited
Editor: John Telfer
Editorial Profile: Midland Daily News strives to be a thorough source of local area news and information for its Midland, MI readership.; Full Page Mono: 31.00; Full Page Colour: 700.00
Currency: US Dollars
DAILY NEWSPAPER

Midland Reporter-Telegram

Owner: Hearst Newspapers
Editorial: 201 E Illinois Ave, Midland, Texas 79701-4852. **T:** 1 432 682-5311
W: http://www.mrt.com
Freq: Daily; **Circ:** 15294 Not Audited
Editor: Stewart Doreen; **News Editor:** Trevor Hawes; **News Editor:** Trevor Hawes; **Editor:** Mella McEwen; **Publisher:** Dave Wedel
Editorial Profile: Midland Reporter-Telegram is a community newspaper that covers national and international events and news. It is published daily for residents of the Midland, TX area. Deadlines for the publication are 5pm MT.; Full Page Mono: 27.65; Full Page Colour: 375.00
Currency: US Dollars
DAILY NEWSPAPER

Midsouth Newspapers

Editorial: Highway 195 East, Haleyville, Alabama 35565-0430. **T:** 1 205 486-9461
E: nwanews@centurytel.net
W: http://www.mytrpaper.com **Circ:** 21000 Not Audited
Publisher: Horace Moore
NEWSPAPER

The Mid-South Tribune

Owner: A J M Enterprises Inc.
Editorial: 1801 Edward Ave, Memphis, Tennessee 38107-3015
E: blackinfohwy@prodigy.net
W: http://blackinformationhighway.wordpress.com
Freq: Fri; **Circ:** 24402 Not Audited
Editorial Profile: The Mid-South Tribune is a weekly newspaper written for the African American and Hispanic population in Memphis, TN. The newspaper covers news, business, sports and entertainment. Due to the enormous amount of e-mail the newspaper receives, the staff requests that all business, economic, or Internet news be e-mailed, and they request a phone and fax not be listed.; Full Page Mono: 25.00
Currency: US Dollars
NEWSPAPER

Mid-Valley News

Owner: Private Owner
Editorial: 11401 Valley Blvd, Masterson Building Suite 200B, El Monte, California 91731. **T:** 1 626 443-1753
W: http://midvalleynews.com
Freq: Wed; **Circ:** 30000 Not Audited
Editorial Profile: Mid-Valley News is a weekly newspaper serving the San Gabriel Valley, CA area. It provides information on local news, sports and lifestyles.; Full Page Mono: 13.00
Currency: US Dollars
NEWSPAPER

Mid-Valley Publications

Editorial: 2221 K St, Merced, California 95340-3868. **T:** 1 209 358-5311
E: info@midvalleypub.com
W: http://www.mercedcountytimes.net
Circ: 29200
Editorial Profile: Mid-Valley Publications in Winton, CA, publishes the following weekly newspapers: El Tiempo in Winton, CA; Merced (CA) County Times; Hilmar (CA) Times; Waterford (CA) News; and Atwater-Winton (CA) Times.
NEWSPAPER

The Mid-Valley Town Crier

Owner: Freedom Communications Inc.
Editorial: 401 S Iowa Ave, Weslaco, Texas 78596-6255. **T:** 1 956 969-2543
W: http://www.midvalleytowncrier.com
Freq: Sun; **Circ:** 22500
Publisher: John Greider
Editorial Profile: The Mid-Valley Town Crier is written for the residents of Weslaco, TX. It covers local news and events.; Full Page Mono: 11.79; Full Page Colour: 1587.99
Currency: US Dollars
NEWSPAPER

The MidWeek

Owner: Shaw Media
Editorial: 1586 Barber Greene Rd, Dekalb, Illinois 60115-7900. **T:** 1 815 756-4841
E: readit@midweeknews.com
W: http://www.midweeknews.com
Freq: Wed; **Circ:** 28000 Not Audited
Publisher: Don Bricker
Editorial Profile: The Midweek in Dekalb, IL is a weekly community newspaper that covers local news and events.; Full Page Mono: 35.12
Currency: US Dollars
NEWSPAPER

MidWeek Publications

Editorial: 500 Ala Moana Blvd Ste 7500, Honolulu, Hawaii 96813-4930.
T: 1 808 628-3791
W: http://www.midweek.com **Circ:** 300000 Not Audited
Editor in Chief: Don Chapman; **Publisher:** Ron Nagasawa
NEWSPAPER

Midwest Buy Line

Editorial: 522 Beltrami Ave Suite 115, Bemidji, Minnesota 56601-3136. **T:** 1 218 759-1139
Freq: Sat; **Circ:** 19600 Not Audited
Editorial Profile: Midwest Buy Line is a weekly newspaper serving residents in a 50-mile radius of Bemidji, MN. It covers local news and events in the area. Deadlines are on Wednesdays.; Full Page Mono: 10.95
Currency: US Dollars
NEWSPAPER

Mile High Newspapers

Owner: Jackalope Publishing
Editorial: 110 N Rubey Dr, Unit 120, Golden, Colorado 80403. **T:** 1 303 279-5541
E: newsroom@milehighnews.com
W: http://www.milehighnews.com **Circ:** 56775 Not Audited
NEWSPAPER

Miles City Star

Owner: Yellowstone Newspapers
Editorial: 818 Main St, Miles City, Montana 59301-3221. **T:** 1 406 234-0450
E: mceditor@midrivers.com
W: http://www.milescitystar.com
Freq: Daily; **Circ:** 3300 Not Audited
Editor: Elaine Forman; **Editor:** Denise Hartse; **Publisher:** Dan Killoy
Editorial Profile: Miles City Star is a daily newspaper serving the community of Miles City, MT. The publication provides readers with news stories, events listings, sports coverage and advertising.; Full Page Mono: 7.96; Full Page Colour: 51.48
Currency: US Dollars
DAILY NEWSPAPER

The Milford Daily News

Owner: GateHouse Media Inc.

Editorial: 159 S Main St, Milford, Massachusetts 01757-3287.
T: 1 508 634-7500
E: milforddailynews@wickedlocal.com
W: http://www.milforddailynews.com
Freq: Daily; **Circ:** 4851 Not Audited
Editor in Chief: Richard Lodge; **Editor in Chief:** Richard Lodge; **Editor in Chief:** Richard Lodge; **Editor in Chief:** Richard Lodge
Editorial Profile: The Milford Daily News is a daily newspaper serving residents of Milford, MA. It covers local news, sports and arts. Advertising deadlines are at 4pm ET.; Full Page Mono: 23.06; Full Page Colour: 425.00
Currency: US Dollars
DAILY NEWSPAPER

The Military Press
Owner: Military Press Group
Editorial: 9715 Carroll Center Rd, Ste 104, San Diego, California 91262.
T: 1 858 537-2280
E: editor@militarypress.com
W: http://www.militarypress.com
Freq: Bi-Weekly; **Circ:** 100000 Not Audited
Publisher: Richard Matz; **Editor:** Trevor Watson
Editorial Profile: The Military Press is a newspaper written for military personnel in San Diego. The paper covers military news, sports and entertainment.; Full Page Mono: 22.29; Full Page Colour: 297.29
Currency: US Dollars
NEWSPAPER

Mill Creek View Newspaper
Owner: Fillbrook & Associates
Editorial: 16212 Bothell Everett Hwy Ste F-313, Mill Creek, Washington 98012-1603.
T: 1 425 357-0549
E: millcreekview@frontier.com
Freq: Bi-Weekly; **Circ:** 14000 Not Audited
Publisher: Fred Fillbrook
Editorial Profile: Mill Creek View Newspaper is a bi-weekly newspaper for the residents of Mill Creek, WA. The newspaper provides coverage on topics such as local news, sports, arts & entertainment and community events.; Full Page Mono: 15.00
Currency: US Dollars
NEWSPAPER

Miller Publishing
Editorial: 114 W 3rd St, Miller, South Dakota 57362. **T:** 1 605 853-3575
E: news@themillerpress.com
W: http://www.themillerpress.com **Circ:** 2475 Not Audited
Publisher: Mike Caviness; **News Editor:** Ruth Moller; **News Editor:** Ruth Moller
NEWSPAPER

Miller Publishing Company
Owner: Miller Publishing Co.
Editorial: 230 S 2nd St, Miamisburg, Ohio 45342-2925. **T:** 1 947 866-3331 **Circ:** 14900 Not Audited
Publisher: Don Miller; **Editor:** Steve Sandlin; **Editor:** Steve Sandlin; **Editor:** Steve Sandlin; **Editor:** Steve Sandlin
NEWSPAPER

Milton Newspapers, Inc.
Owner: Halifax Media Group LLC
Editorial: 6629 Elva St, Milton, Florida 32570-4735. **T:** 1 850 623-2120
E: news@srpressgazette.com
W: http://www.srpressgazette.com **Circ:** 22800 Not Audited
Publisher: Jim Fletcher; **Editor:** Bill Gamblin
NEWSPAPER

The Milwaukee Community Journal
Editorial: 3612 N Dr Martin Luther King Dr, Milwaukee, Wisconsin 53212.
T: 1 414 265-5300
E: editorial@communityjournal.net
W: http://www.communityjournal.net
Freq: Fri; **Circ:** 61350 Not Audited
Editor: Tom Mitchell; **Editor:** Tom Mitchell; **Publisher:** Patricia Pattillo
Editorial Profile: The Milwaukee Community Journal is a publication that specializes in covering news and information on a local and national level. It strives to serve its readership with the necessary information to keep them informed of pertinent events and happenings.; Full Page Mono: 34.00
Currency: US Dollars
NEWSPAPER

Milwaukee Courier
Editorial: 6310 N Port Washington Rd, Milwaukee, Wisconsin 53217-4300.
T: 1 414 449-4860
E: milwaukeecourier@aol.com
W: http://www.milwaukeecourieronline.com
Circ: 80000 Not Audited
Publisher: Jerrel Jones; **Editor:** Lynda Jones
NEWSPAPER

Milwaukee Journal Sentinel
Owner: Journal Communications
Editorial: 333 W State St, Milwaukee, Wisconsin 53203-1305. **T:** 1 414 224-2000
E: jsmetro@journalsentinel.com
W: http://www.jsonline.com
Freq: Daily; **Circ:** 191153 Not Audited
Editorial Profile: Milwaukee Journal Sentinel is written for the residents of Milwaukee and surrounding areas. It covers local, state, national and international news, as well as business, entertainment, sports and lifestyle. The paper is the product of a 1995 merger between the Milwaukee Journal, founded in 1882, and the Milwaukee Sentinel, founded in 1837. The paper uses wire services, including the Associated Press, Reuters, Bloomberg News and Dow Jones News Service for much of its national and international news. In August 2009, the paper joined a national sports content-sharing alliance with several other papers across the country.; Full Page Mono: 166.00; Full Page Colour: 197.54
Currency: US Dollars
DAILY NEWSPAPER

Milwaukee Journal Sentinel
Editorial: National Press Building #940, Washington, District Of Columbia 20045.
T: 1 202 662-7290
DAILY NEWSPAPER

Milwaukee Journal Sentinel
Editorial: 10 E Doty St Ste 200, Madison, Wisconsin 53703-3354. **T:** 1 608 258-2262
DAILY NEWSPAPER

Milwaukee Journal Sentinel
Editorial: 1801 Dolphin Drive, Waukesha, Wisconsin 53186-1430. **T:** 1 262 650-0270
E: jswauk@journalsentinel.com
DAILY NEWSPAPER

The Milwaukee Times Weekly
Editorial: 1936 N Dr Martin Luther King Dr, Milwaukee, Wisconsin 53212-3642.
T: 1 414 263-5088 **E:** miltimes@gmail.com
Freq: Thu; **Circ:** 20000 Not Audited
Editor: Jacquelyn Heath; **Publisher:** Lynda Jackson Conyers
Editorial Profile: The Milwaukee Times Weekly is a weekly newspaper serving the African American community in Milwaukee and its surrounding areas. It covers national and local news, sports, lifestyle, opinions and community events.; Full Page Mono: 15.00
Currency: US Dollars
NEWSPAPER

Minden Press-Herald
Owner: Specht Newspapers Inc.
Editorial: 203 Gleason St, Minden, Louisiana 71055-3455. **T:** 1 318 377-1866
W: http://www.press-herald.com
Freq: Daily; **Circ:** 5398 Not Audited
Editorial Profile: Minden Press-Herald is a daily newspaper serving the Minden, LA area. The publication features news and events listings as well as coverage of local sports and politics. Deadlines are at 11am CT the day before publication. Advertising in the Minden Press-Herald will also run in the Bossier Press-Tribune and the Bossier Banner Progress.; Full Page Mono: 9.50; Full Page Colour: 250.00
Currency: US Dollars
DAILY NEWSPAPER

Mineral Daily News-Tribune
Owner: GateHouse Media Inc.
Editorial: 21 Shamrock Drive, Keyser, West Virginia 26726-3202. **T:** 1 304 788-3333
E: newsroom@newstribune.info
W: http://www.newstribune.info
Freq: Mon thru Fri; **Circ:** 6000 Not Audited
Publisher: David Boden
Editorial Profile: Mineral Daily News-Tribune is a daily newspaper written for the residents of Potomac Valley, WV. Do not contact the publication via fax.; Full Page Mono: 8.06; Full Page Colour: 29.03
Currency: US Dollars
DAILY NEWSPAPER

Mineral Wells Index
Owner: Community Newspaper Holdings, Inc.
Editorial: 300 SE 1st St, Mineral Wells, Texas 76067-5331. **T:** 1 940 325-4465
E: editor@mineralwellsindex.com
W: http://mineralwellsindex.com
Freq: Daily; **Circ:** 3500 Not Audited
Editorial Profile: Mineral Wells Index is a daily newspaper providing local news coverage for the Mineral Wells and Palo Pinto County, TX area.; Full Page Mono: 12.50; Full Page Colour: 345.00
Currency: US Dollars
DAILY NEWSPAPER

Ming Pao Free Daily
Owner: Ming Pao Enterprise Corporation Ltd.
Editorial: 4331 33rd St, Long Island City, New York 11101-2316. **T:** 1 718 786-2888
E: mpdailynews@yahoo.com
W: http://www.mingpaony.com
Freq: Daily; **Circ:** 35000 Not Audited
Editorial Profile: Ming Pao Free Daily is a daily newspaper published for Chinese Americans. The publication covers news, business and entertainment in the United States.; Full Page Mono: 123.20; Full Page Colour: 1088.00
Currency: US Dollars
DAILY NEWSPAPER

The Mining Journal
Owner: Ogden Newspapers
Editorial: 249 W Washington St, Marquette, Michigan 49855-4321. **T:** 1 906 228-2500
W: http://www.miningjournal.net
Freq: Daily; **Circ:** 10268 Not Audited
Publisher: Jim Reevs; **News Editor:** Dan Weingarten
Editorial Profile: The Mining Journal is a daily newspaper published for the residents of Michigan's Upper Peninsula. The publication provides local and national news as well as sports, weather, obituaries and classifieds.; Full Page Mono: 21.65; Full Page Colour: 240.00
Currency: US Dollars
DAILY NEWSPAPER

Miniondas
Owner: Velasquez Publishing Inc.
Editorial: 17291 Irvine Blvd. Suite 255, Tustin, California 92780. **T:** 1 714 668-1010
E: editorial@miniondas.com
W: http://www.miniondas.com
Freq: Thu; **Circ:** 60000 Not Audited
Editor: Jesus Morales; **Publisher:** Sergio Velasquez
Editorial Profile: Miniondas provides local news coverage for the Spanish speaking community in Orange County, CA.; Full Page Mono: 20.70
Currency: US Dollars
NEWSPAPER

Minnesota Spokesman-Recorder
Owner: Williams-Dillard (Tracey)
Editorial: 3744 4th Ave S, Minneapolis, Minnesota 55409-1327. **T:** 1 612 827-4021
W: http://www.spokesman-recorder.com
Freq: Thu; **Circ:** 10000 Not Audited
Editor in Chief: Vickie Evans-Nash; **Publisher:** Tracey Williams-Dillard
Editorial Profile: Minnesota Spokesman-Recorder provides local news for the African American community in Minneapolis. Deadlines are on Fridays at noon CT.; Full Page Mono: 45.92
Currency: US Dollars
NEWSPAPER

Minority Communicator News Group
Owner: Minority Community News Group
Editorial: 90 W Campus View Blvd, Columbus, Ohio 43235-1447. **T:** 1 614 781-1160
E: tceditor@aol.com
W: http://communicatornews.homestead.com
Freq: Weekly; **Circ:** 153000 Not Audited
Publisher: Jack Harris
Editorial Profile: Minority Communicator News publishes regional editions of The Communicator, which covers community news with a focus on relevance to Central Ohio's African American population. Editions for Columbus, Cleveland, Cincinnati and Dayton are available.; Full Page Mono: 27.78; Full Page Colour: 32.54
Currency: US Dollars
NEWSPAPER

Minot Daily News
Owner: Ogden Newspapers
Editorial: 301 4th St SE, Minot, North Dakota 58701-4066. **T:** 1 701 857-1900
E: news@minotdailynews.com
W: http://www.minotdailynews.com
Freq: Daily; **Circ:** 13459 Not Audited
Publisher: Steve Herron; **Editor:** Bryan Obenchain; **Editor:** Bryan Obenchain
Editorial Profile: Minot Daily News is a daily newspaper for Minot, ND and the surrounding areas. The newspaper covers local news, sports, business, lifestyle and politics. The intended readership of the publication are local community residents with an interest in current local issues.; Full Page Mono: 38.95; Full Page Colour: 470.00
Currency: US Dollars
DAILY NEWSPAPER

Minuteman/County Times Publications - Westport, CT
Owner: Journal Register Company
Editorial: 40 Sargent Dr, New Haven, Connecticut 06511-6111. **T:** 1 203 789-5200
W: http://www.ctcentral.com **Circ:** 38000 Not Audited
Editor: Tom Henry; **Editor:** Donna Saracco
NEWSPAPER

The Mirror
Owner: Diocese of Springfield-Cape Girardeau
Editorial: 601 S Jefferson Ave, Springfield, Missouri 65806. **T:** 1 417 866-0841
W: http://www.the-mirror.org
Freq: Fri; **Circ:** 17000 Not Audited
Editor: Leslie Eidson; **Publisher:** James Vann Johnston
Editorial Profile: The Mirror is the newspaper of the Catholic Diocese of Springfield-Cape Girardeau, MO. It written for southern Missouri Catholics. The Mirror strives to provide current diocesan content to southern Missouri Catholics, as well as create a sense of Catholic community.; Full Page Mono: 13.50
Currency: US Dollars
NEWSPAPER

Mirror Media Group
Owner: Mirror Media Group, INC
Editorial: 3435 Ocean Park Blvd Ste 210, Santa Monica, California 90405-3315.
T: 1 310 577-6507
Freq: Thu; **Circ:** 25000 Not Audited
Editor-in-Chief: Brenton Garen
Editorial Profile: Santa Monica Mirror is written for residents in and around Santa Monica, CA, including the towns of Pacific Palisades, Brentwood, Marina del Ray, Venice, West Los Angeles, Malibu, Playa del Rey and Mar Vista. It reflects the concerns of the community, thematically focusing on housing issues, agenda items and topics before the city council, local notables and school successes. Deadlines are on Fridays at noon.; Full Page Mono: 28.00
Currency: US Dollars
NEWSPAPER

The Mirror Newspapers
Editorial: 113 W Wayne St, Maumee, Ohio 43537. **T:** 1 419 893-8135
E: info@themirrornewspaper.com
W: http://www.themirrornewspaper.com
Circ: 19695 Not Audited
NEWSPAPER

The Mission News Group
Owner: Mission News Group
Editorial: 23472 Vista Del Verde Ste 6, Coto de Caza, California 92679-3930.
T: 1 949 589-9990
W: http://missionviejonewsgroup.com
Circ: 104700 Not Audited
Editorial Profile: The Mission News Group is a community newspaper publisher that services the residents of Los Angeles, Long Beach, and Santa Ana, CA.
NEWSPAPER

Mission Publishing Group
Owner: Mission Publishing Group, LLC
Editorial: 6549 Mission Gorge Rd., #199, San Diego, California 92120. **T:** 1 619 283-9747
W: http://scoopsandiego.com
Editor: Doug Curlee; **Publisher:** Jim Madaffer; **Editor:** David Ogul; **Editor:** Jeremy Ogul
Editorial Profile: San Diego Community News Network produces three monthly community newspapers covering the San Diego metropolitan area: Mission Times Courier, La Mesa Courier and Mission Valley News, as well as the combined Web site, Scoop San Diego.
NEWSPAPER

The Mississippi Link
Owner: Mississippi Link Inc.
Editorial: 2659 Livingston Rd, Jackson, Mississippi 39213. **T:** 1 601 896-0084
W: http://www.mississippilink.com
Freq: Thu; **Circ:** 17000
Editor: Gail Brown; **Publisher:** Jackie Hampton
Editorial Profile: The Mississippi Link is a local, weekly newspaper providing news for and about the Jackson, MS area. It covers local news, sports, editorials, city notices, arts & entertainment and classified advertising.; Full Page Mono: 18.00
Currency: US Dollars
NEWSPAPER

Mississippi Press
Owner: Advance Publications, Inc.
Editorial: 906 Convent Ave, Pascagoula, Mississippi 39567-4334. **T:** 1 228 762-1111
E: msnews@themississippipress.com
W: http://www.gulflive.com/mississippipress
Freq: Daily; **Circ:** 15050 Not Audited
Editorial Profile: Mississippi Press provides news and information to the residents of Gautier, MS.; Full Page Mono: 13.00; Full Page Colour: 15.61
Currency: US Dollars
DAILY NEWSPAPER

Missoula Independent
Owner: Independent Publishing Corp.
Editorial: 317 S Orange St, Missoula, Montana 59801-1810. **T:** 1 406 543-6609
E: frontdesk@missoulanews.com
W: http://missoulanews.bigskypress.com
Freq: Thu; **Circ:** 20000 Not Audited
Publisher: Lynne Foland
Editorial Profile: Missoula Independent is written for residents of Missoula, MT. Its editorial mission is to provide news and information about current politics and culture of Western Montana. Deadlines are on Mondays by 5pm MT.; Full Page Mono: 29.48
Currency: US Dollars
NEWSPAPER

Missoulian
Owner: Lee Enterprises, Inc.
Editorial: 500 S Higgins Ave, Missoula, Montana 59801-2736. **T:** 1 406 523-5200
E: newsdesk@missoulian.com
W: http://www.missoulian.com
Freq: Daily; **Circ:** 22197 Not Audited
Editor: Sherry Devlin; **News Editor:** Justin Grigg; **Publisher:** Jim McGowan
Editorial Profile: Missoulian provides local news coverage for the Western Montana area. Missoulian keeps readers informed of the latest local and regional news, business, education, health, foods and the outdoors.; Full Page Mono: 52.00; Full Page Colour: 375.00
Currency: US Dollars
DAILY NEWSPAPER

Missouri Dakota Publishing Inc.
Owner: Bridge City Publishing, Inc.
Editorial: 110 S Exene St, Gettysburg, South Dakota 57442. **T:** 1 605 765-2464
E: pcnews@pottercountynews.com **Circ:** 5000
Editor: Nancy Anderson; **Publisher:** Larry Atkinson; **Editor:** Molly McRoberts
NEWSPAPER

Missourian Publishing Co.
Owner: Missourian Publishing Company (The)
Editorial: 14 W Main St, Washington, Missouri 63090-2518. **T:** 1 636 239-7701
E: washnews@emissourian.com
W: http://www.emissourian.com
Freq: 2 Times/Week; **Circ:** 33108 Not Audited
Editor: Gregg Jones
Editorial Profile: Missourian Publishing Co. publishes two editions twice a week. The papers cover regional news, politics, events, sports and weather. The editions are written for residents of Washington, St. Clair and Union, MO. It also publishes a senior citizens magazine called the Senior Life Times. The deadline for the editorial submissions are on Mondays at 4pm CT and for the weekend news on Thursdays at 4pm CT.; Full Page Colour: 1404.90
Currency: US Dollars
NEWSPAPER

Mitchell Newspapers, Inc.
Owner: Trib Publications, Inc.
Editorial: 13 S Scott St, Camilla, Georgia 31730-1705. **T:** 1 229 336-5265
E: camillaenterprise@camillaga.net **Circ:** 10100 Not Audited
NEWSPAPER

Moab Sun News
Editorial: 30 S 100 E, Moab, Utah 84532-2664. **T:** 1 435 259-6261
W: http://moabsunnews.com
Freq: Thu
Editor: Veronica Harvey; **Publisher:** Andrew Mirrington
Editorial Profile: Moab Sun News is a free weekly community newspaper serving residence of Moab, UT. The paper began publishing in April 2012.
NEWSPAPER

Moberly Monitor-Index & Evening Democrat
Owner: GateHouse Media Inc.
Editorial: 218 N Williams St, Moberly, Missouri 65270-1566. **T:** 1 660 263-4123

E: moberlymonitor@socket.net
W: http://www.moberlymonitor.com
Freq: Mon thru Fri; **Circ:** 4029 Not Audited
Publisher: Rod Dixon; **Editor:** Drew Van Dyke
Editorial Profile: Moberly Monitor-Index & Evening Democrat is written for residents in Moberly, MO. It covers local news, national news, business and sports. Deadlines are at noon CT.; Full Page Mono: 14.20; Full Page Colour: 150.00
Currency: US Dollars
DAILY NEWSPAPER

Mobile Press-Register
Owner: Advance Publications, Inc.
Editorial: 401 N Water St, Mobile, Alabama 36602-4015. **T:** 1 251 219-5400
E: mobilenews@al.com
W: http://www.al.com/mobile
Freq: Daily; **Circ:** 66044 Not Audited
Editorial Profile: Mobile Press-Register is Alabama's oldest newspaper, founded in 1813 and published continuously since then. It is a daily publication serving residents of Mobile and Baldwin counties, AL, with information on hard and local news, sports, business & finance, entertainment, events, lifestyle and weather. Deadlines are at noon ET two days prior to publication.; Full Page Mono: 114.02; Full Page Colour: 124.49
Currency: US Dollars
DAILY NEWSPAPER

Mode
Editorial: 1120 N 3Rd St, Harrisburg, Pennsylvania 17102-2018. **T:** 1 717 234-6633
E: modenews@harrisburgpa.com
Freq: Monthly
Editorial Profile: Mode is a monthly community newspaper serving Harrisburg, PA.
NEWSPAPER

The Modesto Bee
Owner: McClatchy Newspapers
Editorial: 1325 H St, Modesto, California 95354. **T:** 1 209 578-2000
W: http://www.modbee.com
Freq: Daily; **Circ:** 60106 Not Audited
Editorial Profile: The Modesto Bee, formerly known as Morning Herald News, was founded in 1849. The newspaper's editorial mission is to provide news, information and service that exceeds customers' expectations every day.; Full Page Mono: 110.00; Full Page Colour: 2087.14
Currency: US Dollars
DAILY NEWSPAPER

The Modesto Bee
Editorial: 700 12th St NW, Ste 1000, Washington, District Of Columbia 20005-3994. **T:** 1 202 383-6000
DAILY NEWSPAPER

Mohave Valley Daily News
Owner: Brehm Communications, Inc.
Editorial: 2435 S Miracle Mile, Bullhead City, Arizona 86442-7311. **T:** 1 928 763-2505
W: http://www.mohavedailynews.com
Freq: Mon thru Fri; **Circ:** 8240 Not Audited
Editor: Bill McMillen; **Publisher:** Chuck Rathbun
Editorial Profile: Mohave Valley Daily News is a local daily newspaper serving the Mohave Valley and Bullhead City, AZ. The publication provides information on news, events, sports and weather for the area.; Full Page Mono: 25.10; Full Page Colour: 399.00
Currency: US Dollars
DAILY NEWSPAPER

Mohawk Valley Media
Owner: Journal Register Company
Editorial: 130 Broad St, Oneida, New York 13421. **T:** 1 315 363-5100
E: editorial@mohawkvalleymedia.com
W: http://www.romeobserver.com **Circ:** 20000 Not Audited
Publisher: Phil Austin
NEWSPAPER

El Mojave
Owner: Freedom Communications Inc.
Editorial: 13891 Park Ave, Victorville, California 92392. **T:** 1 760 241-7744
W: http://www.laprensadelmojave.com
Freq: Sat; **Circ:** 10000 Not Audited
Editor: Kay Lovato; **Publisher:** Stephan Wingert
Editorial Profile: El Mojave is a community newspaper written for the residents of Victorville, CA and the surrounding areas.; Full Page Mono: 9.25
Currency: US Dollars
NEWSPAPER

Molinegocios USA
Editorial: 100 W Broad St Ste 107, Hazleton, Pennsylvania 18201-6304. **T:** 1 570 501-2177
Freq: Monthly
Editor: Cathy Arroyo
Editorial Profile: Molinegocios USA is a weekly newspaper providing Local and Community News coverage for the Hispanic community in Northwest Pennsylvania.
NEWSPAPER

Mon Valley Messenger
Owner: Haniford Enterprises, LLC
Editorial: 1373 Meadowlark Dr, Pittsburgh, Pennsylvania 15243-1217. **T:** 1 412 249-8177
E: info@monvalleymessenger.com
W: http://www.monvalleymessenger.com
Freq: Monthly
Publisher: Douglas Haniford; **Editor:** Christen Stroh
Editorial Profile: Mon Valley Messenger is a monthly community newspaper providing news to the surrounding areas of Pittsburgh, Pennsylvania. Mon Valley Messenger aims at providing business information and offering local businesses a forum for advertising products and services. Mon Valley Messenger covers hometown news, features and local happenings.
NEWSPAPER

Monadnock Shopper News
Owner: Mitchell Shakour
Editorial: 445 West St, Keene, New Hampshire 3431. **T:** 1 603 352-5250
E: shopper@shoppernews.com
W: http://www.shoppernews.com
Freq: Wed; **Circ:** 42750 Not Audited
Editorial Profile: Monadnock Shopper News is published weekly for the residents of Keene, NH. The newspaper provides local news, business, sports, entertainment, real estate and a shopping guide.; Full Page Mono: 17.13
Currency: US Dollars
NEWSPAPER

Monday Morning Newspapers Group
Owner: Springer Publishing Co., Inc.
Editorial: 31201 Chicago Rd S, Ste A101, Warren, Michigan 48093-5500.
T: 1 586 939-6800
E: news@detroitautoscene.com
W: http://www.detroitautoscene.com
Circ: 27600 Not Audited
Publisher: Bill Springer; **Editor:** Jim Stickford
NEWSPAPER

Le Monde - West Hollywood Bureau
Editorial: 1123 N Flores St, Apt 16, West Hollywood, California 90069.
T: 1 323 654-5070
DAILY NEWSPAPER

Monett Times
Owner: Rust Communications
Editorial: 505 E Broadway St, Monett, Missouri 65708-2333. **T:** 1 417 235-3135
E: editor@monett-times.com
W: http://www.monett-times.com **Circ:** 4100
Publisher: Jacob Brower; **Editor:** Lisa Schlichtman
Editorial Profile: Monett Times is a daily newspaper that provides local news coverage for residents of Monett, MO. In addition to news, the publication also covers sports, business and arts and entertainment. The paper is written for the general local community.; Full Page Mono: 5.95; Full Page Colour: 120.00
Currency: US Dollars
DAILY NEWSPAPER

The Monitor
Owner: Freedom Communications Inc.
Editorial: 1400 E Nolana Ave, McAllen, Texas 78504. **T:** 1 956 683-4000
W: http://www.themonitor.com
Freq: Daily; **Circ:** 39467 Not Audited
Editor: Queenie Pemelton
Editorial Profile: The Monitor in McAllen, TX is a local daily newspaper that covers local news, sports, business and events.; Full Page Mono: 50.22; Full Page Colour: 551.00
Currency: US Dollars
DAILY NEWSPAPER

The Monitor
Owner: Diocese of Trenton
Editorial: 701 Lawrenceville Rd, Trenton, New Jersey 8648. **T:** 1 609 406-7404
E: monitor@dioceseoftrenton.org
W: http://www.dioceseoftrenton.org
Freq: Thu; **Circ:** 20000 Not Audited
Publisher: John Smith; **News Editor:** Mary Stadnyk
Editorial Profile: The Monitor is the weekly newspaper written for Catholics in the Trenton,

NJ area. Its editorial mission is to keep members up-to-date on the news and events of the Diocese of Trenton. It covers news, activities, anniversaries and events of local parishes and the Diocese.; Full Page Mono: 32.00; Full Page Colour: 1560.00
Currency: US Dollars
NEWSPAPER

The Monitor
Owner: Page Publications
Editorial: 20121 Cox Rd, Sutherland, Virginia 23885. **T:** 1 804 733-8636
E: dmmonitor@earthlink.net
Freq: Wed; **Circ:** 10080 Not Audited
Editorial Profile: The Monitor is a local weekly newspaper serving residents of the Petersburg, VA area. The publication covers local news and community events. Deadlines are 5pm ET the Friday before issue date.; Full Page Mono: 7.00
Currency: US Dollars
NEWSPAPER

Monitor/Lake Area Leader
Owner: MediaOne LLC
Editorial: 1316 S 3rd St., Mabank, Texas 75147. **T:** 1 903 887-4511
E: publisher@themonitor.net
W: http://www.themonitor.net **Circ:** 31000 Not Audited
Publisher: John Buzzetta
Editorial Profile: Monitor/Lake Area Leader in Mabank, TX publishes The Monitor and The Lake Area Leader, both community newspapers that cover local news and events.
NEWSPAPER

The Monmouth Journal
Owner: Monmouth Journal, LLC (The)
Editorial: 46 English Plz, Ste D, Red Bank, New Jersey 7701. **T:** 1 732 747-7007
E: editorial@themonmouthjournal.com
W: http://www.themonmouthjournal.com
Freq: Fri; **Circ:** 10000 Not Audited
Editorial Profile: The Monmouth Journal is published weekly for the residents of Red Bank, NJ and surrounding areas. The newspaper covers local news and community events.; Full Page Mono: 7.00
Currency: US Dollars
NEWSPAPER

Monroe County Publishers, Inc.
Owner: MCP Inc.
Editorial: 1302 River Road, Sparta, Wisconsin 54656-1713. **T:** 1 608 269-3186
E: mcp2006@centurytel.net
W: http://www.spartanewspapers.com
Circ: 9850
Editor: William Gleiss; **Editor:** Patrick Mulvaney
Editorial Profile: Monroe County Publishers, Inc. provides the community of Sparta, WI with news.
NEWSPAPER

Monroe Dispatch
Owner: Monroe Dispatch Corporation
Editorial: 1005 Powell St, Monroe, Louisiana 71203. **T:** 1 318 325-2858
E: mdispatch@yahoo.com
Freq: Thu; **Circ:** 12250 Not Audited
Publisher: Frank DeTiege; **Editor:** Irma Hall DeTiege
Editorial Profile: Monroe Dispatch is a weekly newspaper published for the African American communities of Monroe, LA. The newspaper covers local news, lifestyles, interests and concerns. Editorial deadlines are on Mondays at 6pm CT.; Full Page Mono: 11.50
Currency: US Dollars
NEWSPAPER

Monroe Free Press
Editorial: 216 Collier St, Monroe, Louisiana 71201. **T:** 1 318 388-1310
E: monroefreepress@prodigy.net
W: http://www.monroefreepress.com
Freq: Thu; **Circ:** 14000 Not Audited
Editorial Profile: Monroe Free Press is a local newspaper written for the African American community of Monroe, LA. The paper serves as an advocate for minorities, working people and women's issues. The paper also provides local news and sports coverage. Deadlines are Mondays at 5pm CT.; Full Page Mono: 17.00
Currency: US Dollars
NEWSPAPER

The Monroe News
Owner: Monroe Publishing Company
Editorial: 20 W 1st St, Monroe, Michigan 48161-2333. **T:** 1 734 242-1100
E: newsmail@monroenews.com
W: http://www.monroenews.com

Freq: Daily; **Circ:** 15098 Not Audited
Publisher: Lonnie Peppler-Moyer; **Editor:** Deborah Saul
Editorial Profile: Monroe News is a daily newspaper that provides local news coverage for the Monroe County, MI area. The paper's editorial mission is to enhance the lives of its readers through information. All inquiries and press releases should be directed to the news editor by e-mail, or to the editorial department fax at 734-242-0937.; Full Page Mono: 23.26; Full Page Colour: 26.76
Currency: US Dollars
DAILY NEWSPAPER

The Monroe Times
Owner: Bliss Communications Inc.
Editorial: 1065 4th Ave W, Monroe, Wisconsin 53566-1318. **T:** 1 608 328-4202
W: http://www.themonroetimes.com
Freq: Daily; **Circ:** 5985 Not Audited
Publisher: Skip Bliss; **Editor:** Mary Jane Grenzow; **News Editor:** Andrew Hellpap
Editorial Profile: The Monroe Times is a local daily newspaper serving the residents of Green and Lafayette counties in Southern Wisconsin. The newspaper covers local and regional news, sports, entertainment, business and community events. Deadlines are at 9am CT the day before issue date.; Full Page Mono: 30.91; Full Page Colour: 105.28
Currency: US Dollars
DAILY NEWSPAPER

Montana Standard
Owner: Lee Enterprises, Inc.
Editorial: 25 W Granite St, Butte, Montana 59701-9218. **T:** 1 406 496-5500
E: editor@mtstandard.com
W: http://www.mtstandard.com
Freq: Daily; **Circ:** 36300 Not Audited
Editor: Matt Christensen; **Publisher:** Tyler Miller
Editorial Profile: Montana Standard is a daily newspaper reporting local, national and international news to the residents of southern Montana.; Full Page Mono: 33.00; Full Page Colour: 208.23
Currency: US Dollars
DAILY NEWSPAPER

Montecito Journal
Editorial: 1206 Coast Village Cir Ste D, Montecito, California 93108-2710.
T: 1 805 565-1860
E: news@montecitojournal.net
W: http://www.montecitojournal.net
Freq: Wed; **Circ:** 12000 Not Audited
Editorial Profile: Montecito Journal is written for the residents of Montecito, CA. It covers local fashion, design, travel, real estate, restaurants and business.; Full Page Mono: 28.75
Currency: US Dollars
NEWSPAPER

The Monterey County Herald
Owner: MediaNews Group
Editorial: 8 Upper Ragsdale Dr, Monterey, California 93940-5730. **T:** 1 831 372-3311
E: editors@montereyherald.com
W: http://www.montereyherald.com
Freq: Daily; **Circ:** 22524 Not Audited
Editor: Donald Miller; **Editor:** Donald Miller; **Editor:** Donald Miller; **Editor:** Donald Miller;
Publisher: Gary Omernick
Editorial Profile: The Monterey County Herald is a daily newspaper serving Salinas, Carmel and Monterey County, CA. It covers local news, entertainment, business and sports.; Full Page Mono: 70.30; Full Page Colour: 754.00
Currency: US Dollars
DAILY NEWSPAPER

Monterey County Weekly
Owner: Milestone Communications
Editorial: 668 Williams Ave, Seaside, California 93955-5736. **T:** 1 831 394-5656
E: mail@mcweekly.com
W: http://www.montereycountyweekly.com
Freq: Thu; **Circ:** 40000 Not Audited
Publisher: Erik Cushman
Editorial Profile: Monterey County Weekly is published weekly for the residents of Seaside, CA and surrounding areas. The newspaper covers local news, sports and community events.; Full Page Mono: 26.84; Full Page Colour: 2164.00
Currency: US Dollars
NEWSPAPER

Montgomery Advertiser
Owner: Gannett Co., Inc.
Editorial: 425 Molton St, Montgomery, Alabama 36104-3523. **T:** 1 334 262-1611
W: http://www.montgomeryadvertiser.com
Freq: Daily; **Circ:** 26521 Not Audited
Editorial Profile: Montgomery Advertiser's editorial mission is to be the number one source for news, information, and advertising needs for the Montgomery, AL metropolitan area. This publication provides a forum for diverse opinions, serves as a force for positive change, and acts as a watchdog for the public interest and the First Amendment.; Full Page Mono: 99.99; Full Page Colour: 326.73
Currency: US Dollars
DAILY NEWSPAPER

Montgomery Communications, Inc.
Editorial: 222 W 6th St, Junction City, Kansas 66441-3047. **T:** 1 785 762-5000
W: http://www.thedailyunion.net **Circ:** 23105 Not Audited
NEWSPAPER

The Montgomery County Sentinel
Owner: Montgomery Sentinel Publishing, Inc.
Editorial: 22 W Jefferson St Ste 309, Rockville, Maryland 20850-4259.
T: 1 301 838-0788
W: http://www.thesentinel.com
Freq: Thu; **Circ:** 10000 Not Audited
Publisher: Lynn Kapiloff; **Editor:** Brian Karem
Editorial Profile: The Montgomery County Sentinel is published weekly for the residents of Rockville, MD and surrounding areas. The newspaper covers local news and community events.; Full Page Mono: 18.00
Currency: US Dollars
NEWSPAPER

Montgomery News
Owner: Pelorus Inc.
Editorial: 2106 Us Highway 206, Belle Mead, New Jersey 08502-4007. **T:** 1 908 874-0020
E: editor@montynews.com
W: http://www.montynews.com
Freq: Monthly; **Circ:** 20900 Not Audited
Editorial Profile: Montgomery News in Belle Mead, NJ is a community newspaper serving Montgomery Township and Rocky Hill, NJ.; Full Page Mono: 23.70
Currency: US Dollars
NEWSPAPER

Montgomery Newspapers
Owner: Journal Register Company
Editorial: 290 Commerce Dr, Fort Washington, Pennsylvania 19034-2400. **T:** 1 215 542-0200
E: editorial@montgomerynews.com
W: http://www.montgomerynews.com
Circ: 24966 Not Audited
News Editor: Scott Roman; **News Editor:** Meghan Ross; **Publisher:** Elizabeth Wilson
Editorial Profile: Montgomery Newspapers covers local news and events in Montgomery County and Bucks County, Pa. It publishers Ambler Gazette, Colonial News, Glenside News & Globe News & Times Chronicle, Montgomery Life, North Penn Life, Perkasie News-Herald, Public Spirit & Willow Grove Guide, Roxborough Review, Souderton Independent, Springfield Sun and Spring-Ford Reporter & Valley Item.
NEWSPAPER

Montgomery Publishing Inc.
Owner: Emmerich Newspapers Inc.
Editorial: 401 Summit St, Winona, Mississippi 38967-2240. **T:** 1 662 283-1131
W: http://www.winonatimes.com **Circ:** 4400 Not Audited
NEWSPAPER

Montgomery Publishing, LLC
Editorial: 1633 W Main St, Salem, Virginia 24153-3115. **T:** 1 540 389-9355
W: http://www.ourvalley.org **Circ:** 11700 Not Audited
Editor: Meg Hibbert; **Editor:** Ed McCoy
NEWSPAPER

Montrose Daily Press
Owner: Wick Communications Inc.
Editorial: 3684 N Townsend Ave, Montrose, Colorado 81401-5949. **T:** 1 970 249-3444
E: editor@montrosepress.com
W: http://www.montrosepress.com
Freq: Daily; **Circ:** 5472 Not Audited
Publisher: Francis Wick
Editorial Profile: Montrose Daily Press is a local newspaper serving the residents of Montrose, CO. It includes information on local news, weather, sports, business and arts & entertainment.; Full Page Mono: 13.00; Full Page Colour: 275.00
Currency: US Dollars
DAILY NEWSPAPER

Moon Valley Tattler
Owner: Moon Valley Tattler, LLC
Editorial: 13236 N 7th St, #4304, Phoenix, Arizona 85022. **T:** 1 602 765-0902
E: info@mvtattler.com
W: http://www.moonvalleytattler.com
Freq: Monthly; **Circ:** 17000 Not Audited
Editor: Jax Designs; **Publisher:** Dawn Trapp
Editorial Profile: Moon Valley Tattler is a monthly newspaper serving residents of the North and Moon valleys in Phoenix.; Full Page Mono: 3.77
Currency: US Dollars
NEWSPAPER

Moorefield Examiner & The Weekender Newspapers
Owner: Heishman (Phoebe)
Editorial: 132 S Main St, Moorefield, West Virginia 26836-1102. **T:** 1 304 530-6397
E: examiner@hardynet.com
W: http://www.moorefieldexaminer.com
Circ: 9076 Not Audited
NEWSPAPER

The Mooresville Tribune
Owner: World Media Enterprises, Inc.
Editorial: 147 E Center Ave, Mooresville, North Carolina 28115-2513.
T: 1 704 664-5554
E: news@mooresvilletribune.com
W: http://www.mooresvilletribune.com
Freq: Fri; **Circ:** 10767 Not Audited
Publisher: Tim Dearman; **Editor:** Dale Gowing; **Editor:** Karen Kistler
Editorial Profile: The Mooresville Tribune is a community newspaper serving residents of Mooresville, NC, including local news, sports, commentary, entertainment and community events.; Full Page Mono: 9.22
Currency: US Dollars
NEWSPAPER

The Morning Call
Owner: Tribune Company
Editorial: 101 N 6th St, Allentown, Pennsylvania 18101-1403.
T: 1 610 820-6500 3 **E:** news@mcall.com
W: http://www.mcall.com
Freq: Daily; **Circ:** 79726 Not Audited
Publisher: Timothy Ryan; **Editor:** Diane Stoneback; **Editor:** Diane Stoneback; **Editor:** Diane Stoneback
Editorial Profile: The Morning Call is a daily newspaper published in nine counties in Pennsylvania. It covers arts & entertainment, food, sports, travel, television, features, business and local, national and international news.; Full Page Mono: 106.00; Full Page Colour: 343.90
Currency: US Dollars
DAILY NEWSPAPER

The Morning Call
Editorial: Main Capitol, Bldg 524, Harrisburg, Pennsylvania 17120-0001. **T:** 1 717 783-7305
DAILY NEWSPAPER

Morning Journal
Owner: Ogden Newspapers
Editorial: 308 Maple St, Lisbon, Ohio 44432-1205. **T:** 1 330 424-9541
E: news@mojonews.com
W: http://www.morningjournalnews.com
Freq: Daily; **Circ:** 8482 Not Audited
Publisher: Larry Dorschner; **Editor:** Dennis Spalvieri; **Editor:** Dorma Tolson
Editorial Profile: Morning Journal is a daily newspaper providing news for Lisbon, OH.; Full Page Mono: 26.75
Currency: US Dollars
DAILY NEWSPAPER

The Morning Journal
Owner: Journal Register Company
Editorial: 1657 Broadway, Lorain, Ohio 44052-3439. **T:** 1 440 245-6901
E: news@morningjournal.com
W: http://www.morningjournal.com
Freq: Daily; **Circ:** 23500 Not Audited
Editor: Tom Skoch; **Publisher:** Jeff Sudbrook
Editorial Profile: The Morning Journal is a daily newspaper serving the residents of Lorain, Erie, Huron and Cuyahoga County, OH. It includes information on local news, weather, sports, business and entertainment.; Full Page Mono: 68.75; Full Page Colour: 251.70
Currency: US Dollars
DAILY NEWSPAPER

The Morning News
Owner: Stephens Media Group
Editorial: 2560 N Lowell Rd, Springdale, Arkansas 72764-1818. **T:** 1 479 751-6200
E: news@nwaonline.com
W: http://www.nwaonline.com
Freq: Daily; **Circ:** 28448 Not Audited
Editor: Spencer Tirey
Editorial Profile: The Morning News is a daily newspaper that covers local events and news for the residents in Springdale and Bentonville, AR.; Full Page Mono: 17.50
Currency: US Dollars
DAILY NEWSPAPER

The Morning News
Owner: Horizon Publications
Editorial: 34 N Ash St, Blackfoot, Idaho 83221-2101. **T:** 1 208 785-1100
E: mnews@cableone.net
W: http://www.am-news.com
Freq: Daily; **Circ:** 4250 Not Audited
Publisher: Leonard Martin
Editorial Profile: The Morning News provides local news to the Blackfoot, ID community. The newspaper covers local news, business, sports and arts & entertainment stories.; Full Page Mono: 14.50; Full Page Colour: 150.00
Currency: US Dollars
DAILY NEWSPAPER

Morning Sentinel
Owner: Maine Today Media Inc.
Editorial: 31 Front St, Waterville, Maine 04901-6648. **T:** 1 207 873-3341
W: http://www.onlinesentinel.com
Freq: Daily; **Circ:** 11106 Not Audited
Editorial Profile: Morning Sentinel is a local newspaper serving the residents of Waterville, ME. It includes information on local news, weather, sports, business and entertainment.; Full Page Mono: 60.33; Full Page Colour: 657.28
Currency: US Dollars
DAILY NEWSPAPER

Morning Star Publications
Owner: Richardson (Bryant)
Editorial: 951 Norman Eskridge Hwy, Seaford, Delaware 19973-1719. **T:** 1 302 629-9788
E: editor@mspublications.com **Circ:** 7600 Not Audited
Publisher: Bryant Richardson; **Editor:** Daniel Richardson
Editorial Profile: Mornings Star Publications is a community newspaper publisher serving the residents of Salisbury, MD.
NEWSPAPER

The Morning Sun
Owner: GateHouse Media Inc.
Editorial: 701 N Locust St, Pittsburg, Kansas 66762. **T:** 1 620 231-2600
W: http://www.morningsun.net
Freq: Daily; **Circ:** 8145 Not Audited
Publisher: Steve Wade
Editorial Profile: The Morning Sun is a local newspaper serving the residents of Pittsburg. KS. It includes information on local news, weather, sports, business and arts & entertainment.; Full Page Mono: 15.30; Full Page Colour: 185.00
Currency: US Dollars
DAILY NEWSPAPER

Morning Sun
Owner: Journal Register Company
Editorial: 711 W Pickard St, Mount Pleasant, Michigan 48858-1585. **T:** 1 989 779-6000
E: news@michigannewspapers.com
W: http://www.themorningsun.com
Freq: Daily; **Circ:** 10958 Not Audited
Editorial Profile: Morning Sun is a regional newspaper serving the residents of Gratiot County, Isabella County, and Southern Clare County, MI. It includes information on local news, weather, sports, business and arts & entertainment.; Full Page Mono: 17.45
Currency: US Dollars
DAILY NEWSPAPER

The Morning Times
Owner: Sample News Group
Editorial: 201 N Lehigh Ave, Sayre, Pennsylvania 18840. **T:** 1 570 888-9643
W: http://www.morning-times.com
Freq: Mon thru Fri; **Circ:** 6000 Not Audited
Editor: Lisa Howeler; **Editor:** Lisa Howeler;
Publisher: Kelly Luvison
Editorial Profile: The Morning Times is published daily for residents of Sayre, Athens and South Waverly, PA and Waverly, NY. The newspaper covers local news, sports and community events.; Full Page Mono: 12.54; Full Page Colour: 280.00
Currency: US Dollars
DAILY NEWSPAPER

Morris Daily Herald
Owner: Shaw Media
Editorial: 1804 Division St, Morris, Illinois 60450. **T:** 1 815 942-3221
E: news@morrisdailyherald.com
W: http://www.morrisdailyherald.com

Freq: Daily; **Circ:** 6867 Not Audited
Publisher: Gerry Burke; **Editor:** Kate Schott;
Editor: T.G. Smith
Editorial Profile: Morris Daily Herald is a local newspaper serving the residents of Morris, IL. It includes information on local news, weather, sports, business and arts & entertainment.; Full Page Mono: 16.10; Full Page Colour: 46.76
Currency: US Dollars
DAILY NEWSPAPER

Morris Multimedia, Inc.
Editorial: 122 S 3rd Ave, Oakdale, California 95361. **T:** 1 209 847-3021
E: ads@oakdaleleader.com **Circ:** 22700 Not Audited
NEWSPAPER

Morrison County Record
Owner: ECM Publishers, Inc.
Editorial: 216 1st St SE, Little Falls, Minnesota 56345-3004. **T:** 1 320 632-2345
E: mcr@mcrecord.com
W: http://www.mcrecord.com
Freq: Sun; **Circ:** 19212 Not Audited
Publisher: Julian Andersen; **News Editor:** Terry Lehrke
Editorial Profile: Morrison County Record is a local newspaper serving the residents of Morrison County, MN. It covers local news, weather, sports, business and arts & entertainment. Deadlines fall on the Wednesday before publication.; Full Page Mono: 9.10
Currency: US Dollars
NEWSPAPER

Moscow Pullman Daily News
Owner: TPC Holdings
Editorial: 409 S Jackson St, Moscow, Idaho 83843-2251. **T:** 1 208 882-5561
E: editor@dnews.com
W: http://www.dnews.com
Freq: Daily; **Circ:** 7500 Not Audited
News Editor: Devin Rokyta
Editorial Profile: Moscow Pullman Daily News is published for the residents of Moscow, Whitman County and Latah County, ID. The newspaper covers local news, weather, sports, arts & entertainment and business.; Full Page Mono: 13.64; Full Page Colour: 42.58
Currency: US Dollars
DAILY NEWSPAPER

Moulton Advertiser
Owner: Moulton Advertiser Inc.
Editorial: 659 Main St, Moulton, Alabama 35650-1512. **T:** 1 256 974-1114
E: editor@moultonadvertiser.com
W: http://www.moultonadvertiser.com
Freq: Thu; **Circ:** 13500 Not Audited
Publisher: Clint Shelton
Editorial Profile: Moulton Advertiser is a local newspaper serving the residents of Moulton, AL. It includes information on local news, weather, sports, business and entertainment. Deadlines are on Mondays.; Full Page Mono: 10.85
Currency: US Dollars
NEWSPAPER

Moultrie News
Owner: Evening Post Publishing Co.
Editorial: 134 Columbus St, Charleston, South Carolina 29403-4809. **T:** 1 843 849-1778
E: editor@moultrienews.com
W: http://www.moultrienews.com
Freq: Wed; **Circ:** 28225 Not Audited
Editor: Sully Witte; **Editor:** Sully Witte
Editorial Profile: Moultrie News is the weekly local newspaper written for the residents of Mount Pleasant, SC and the surrounding area. The newspaper aims to bring the general news, events and information of the community to its residents.; Full Page Mono: 15.00
Currency: US Dollars
NEWSPAPER

The Moultrie Observer
Owner: Community Newspaper Holdings, Inc.
Editorial: 25 N Main St, Moultrie, Georgia 31768-3861. **T:** 1 229 985-4545
W: http://www.moultrieobserver.com
Freq: Daily; **Circ:** 7485 Not Audited
Editorial Profile: The Moultrie Observer is published daily for the residents of Moultrie, GA and surrounding areas. The newspaper covers local and regional news, sports, education, lifestyles and entertainment.; Full Page Mono: 21.05; Full Page Colour: 294.00
Currency: US Dollars
DAILY NEWSPAPER

Moundsville Daily Echo
Owner: Self-Owned

Editorial: 715 Lafayette Ave, Moundsville, West Virginia 26041. **T:** 1 304 845-2660
Freq: Daily; **Circ:** 3805 Not Audited
Editorial Profile: The Moundsville Daily Echo is a local newspaper serving the residents of Moundsville, WV. It includes information on local news, weather, sports, business, and entertainment.; Full Page Mono: 4.17
Currency: US Dollars
DAILY NEWSPAPER

Mount Airy News
Owner: Heartland Publications
Editorial: 319 N Renfro St, Mount Airy, North Carolina 27030-3838. **T:** 1 336 786-4141
E: mtanews@civitasmedia.com
W: http://www.mtairynews.com
Freq: Daily; **Circ:** 11017 Not Audited
Editorial Profile: Mount Airy News is a local newspaper written for residents of Surry County, NC. The newspaper is published from Sunday through Saturday mornings and covers local news, sports, business and events. The deadline for submissions is generally three days prior to the issue date.; Full Page Mono: 11.40; Full Page Colour: 90.00
Currency: US Dollars
DAILY NEWSPAPER

Mount Pleasant Daily Tribune
Owner: Palmer Media
Editorial: 1705 Industrial Rd, Mount Pleasant, Texas 75455-2235. **T:** 1 903 572-1705
E: news@dailytribune.net
W: http://www.dailytribune.net
Freq: Daily; **Circ:** 5000 Not Audited
Editorial Profile: Mount Pleasant Daily Tribune is published for the residents of Titus, Franklin, Camp and Morris counties, TX. It covers news, sports, education, healthcare, business, lifestyle and arts & entertainment.; Full Page Mono: 15.00; Full Page Colour: 230.00
Currency: US Dollars
DAILY NEWSPAPER

Mount Pleasant News
Owner: Inland Media Inc.
Editorial: 215 W Monroe St, Mount Pleasant, Iowa 52641-2110. **T:** 1 319 385-3131
E: pub@mpnews.net
W: http://www.mpnews.net
Freq: Daily; **Circ:** 2450 Not Audited
News Editor: Brooks Taylor
Editorial Profile: Mount Pleasant News is a local newspaper serving the residents of Mount Pleasant, IA. It includes information on local news, weather, sports, business and entertainment.; Full Page Mono: 10.84; Full Page Colour: 210.00
Currency: US Dollars
DAILY NEWSPAPER

Mount Vernon News
Owner: Progressive Communications
Editorial: 18 E Vine St, Mount Vernon, Ohio 43050-3200. **T:** 1 740 397-5333
W: http://www.mountvernonnews.com
Freq: Daily; **Circ:** 9099 Not Audited
Publisher: Kay Culbertson; **Editor:** Cheryl Splain
Editorial Profile: Mount Vernon News is a local newspaper serving the residents of Mount Vernon, Fredericktown, Centerburg, Gambier, Danville, Sparta, Bladensburg and Utica, OH. It includes information on local news, weather, sports, business and entertainment.; Full Page Mono: 15.00
Currency: US Dollars
DAILY NEWSPAPER

Mount Vernon Voice
Editorial: 8808A Pear Tree Village Ct, Alexandria, Virginia 22309-4221.
T: 1 703 360-0080
E: mountvernonvoice@aol.com
W: http://www.mountvernonvoice.com
Freq: Wed; **Circ:** 12000 Not Audited; Full Page Mono: 19.50
Currency: US Dollars
NEWSPAPER

Mountain City Publishing Company
Editorial: 112 N Watauga Ln, Lookout Mountain, Tennessee 37350.
T: 1 423 822-6397 **E:** mtncpub@bellsouth.net
Circ: 9500 Not Audited
Publisher: William Parker; **Editor:** Ferris Robinson
NEWSPAPER

Mountain Democrat
Owner: McNaughton Newspapers
Editorial: 1360 Broadway, Placerville, California 95667-5902. **T:** 1 530 622-1255
E: mtdemo@mtdemocrat.net

W: http://www.mtdemocrat.com
Freq: Daily; **Circ:** 12544 Not Audited
Editor: Michael Raffety
Editorial Profile: Mountain Democrat is a local newspaper serving the residents of El Dorado County, CA since 1854. Regular features include local news, weather, sports, business, and entertainment.; Full Page Mono: 22.50; Full Page Colour: 73.87
Currency: US Dollars
DAILY NEWSPAPER

Mountain Home News Publishing
Owner: Rust Communications
Editorial: 195 S 3rd E, Mountain Home, Idaho 83647. **T:** 1 208 587-3331
W: http://www.mountainhomenews.com
Freq: Wed; **Circ:** 16300
Editorial Profile: Mountain Home News Publishing is a community newspaper publisher servicing the residents of Boise, ID.; Full Page Mono: 10.55
Currency: US Dollars
NEWSPAPER

Mountain Mail
Owner: Arkansas Valley Publishing
Editorial: 125 E 2nd St, Salida, Colorado 81201-2114. **T:** 1 719 539-6691
W: http://www.themountainmail.com
Freq: Daily; **Circ:** 4000 Not Audited
Editorial Profile: Mountain Mail is a daily local newspaper serving the residents of Salida, CO and surrounding areas. The publication features local news, weather, sports, business, and entertainment.; Full Page Mono: 8.50; Full Page Colour: 70.00
Currency: US Dollars
DAILY NEWSPAPER

The Mountain Press
Owner: Paxton Media Group
Editorial: 119 River Bend Dr, Sevierville, Tennessee 37876-1943. **T:** 1 865 428-0746
E: editor@themountainpress.com
W: http://www.themountainpress.com
Freq: Daily; **Circ:** 8400 Not Audited
Editor: Jason Davis; **Publisher:** Jana Thomasson
Editorial Profile: The Mountain Press is a local newspaper serving the residents of Sevier County, TN. It includes information on local news, weather, sports, business and entertainment. Deadlines are the same day as the issue date.; Full Page Mono: 21.11; Full Page Colour: 320.00
Currency: US Dollars
DAILY NEWSPAPER

The Mountain Sun
Owner: Southern Newspapers, Inc.
Editorial: 429 Jefferson St, Kerrville, Texas 78028-4412. **T:** 1 830 896-7000
E: news@dailytimes.com
W: http://dailytimes.com
Freq: Wed
Editorial Profile: The Mountain Sun is Kerrville Daily Times free weekly community newspaper. The newspaper covers local and national news, sports, business and lifestyle.
NEWSPAPER

The Mountain Times
Owner: Outer Limits Publishing, LLC
Editorial: 5465 Route 4, Killington, Vermont 5751. **T:** 1 802 422-2398
E: editor@mountaintimes.info
W: http://www.mountaintimes.info
Freq: Thu; **Circ:** 10500 Not Audited
Editorial Profile: Mountain Times is a regional weekly newspaper serving the residents of Central Vermont. The publication features local news, weather, sports, business and entertainment. Deadlines are on Fridays prior to issue date. The paper cannot accept attachments. Please include information in the body of the e-mail.; Full Page Mono: 10.70
Currency: US Dollars
NEWSPAPER

Mountain Times & Watauga Democrat
Owner: Jones Media, Inc.
Editorial: 474 Industrial Park Dr, Boone, North Carolina 28607-3937. **T:** 1 828 264-6397
E: newspaper@mountaintimes.com
Circ: 28503
Publisher: Gene Fowler
NEWSPAPER

Mountain Xpress
Owner: Green Line Media, Inc.
Editorial: 2 Wall St, Asheville, North Carolina 28801-2721. **T:** 1 828 251-1333
E: news@mountainx.com
W: http://www.mountainx.com

Freq: Wed; **Circ:** 26175 Not Audited
Publisher: Jeff Fobes
Editorial Profile: Mountain Xpress is a local newspaper written for the residents of Asheville, NC. The paper covers local news, weather, sports, business and arts & entertainment.; Full Page Mono: 30.00; Full Page Colour: 1103.27
Currency: US Dollars
NEWSPAPER

Mountaineer
Editorial: 6101 Wetzel Ave Bldg 430 Rm 260, Fort Carson, Colorado 80913-4156.
T: 1 719 526-4144
E: fcmountaineer@hotmail.com
W: http://www.csmng.com/mountaineer
Freq: Fri; **Circ:** 20000 Not Audited
Editor: Devin Fisher
Editorial Profile: Mountaineer is a weekly newspaper published in the interest of the 7th Infantry Division and the Fort Carson, CO community. Editorial coverage includes local news, sports, arts, events, health and nutrition.; Full Page Mono: 18.82; Full Page Colour: 1330.00
Currency: US Dollars
NEWSPAPER

Mshale
Editorial: 333 Washington Ave N Ste 300, Minneapolis, Minnesota 55401-1353
E: editor@mshale.com
W: http://www.mshale.com
Freq: Monthly; **Circ:** 18000 Not Audited
Publisher: Tom Gitaa
Editorial Profile: Mshale is a local, monthly newspaper serving African American residents of Minneapolis. The paper covers news, business, arts & entertainment, technology, politics and information of interest to the African American community.; Full Page Mono: 12.41
Currency: US Dollars
NEWSPAPER

Mukilteo Beacon
Owner: Beacon Publishing, Inc.
Editorial: 806 5th St, Mukilteo, Washington 98275. **T:** 1 425 347-5634
E: editor@mukilteobeacon.com
W: http://www.mukilteobeacon.com
Freq: Wed; **Circ:** 10000 Not Audited
Publisher: Paul Archipley; **Editor:** Rebecca Carr
Editorial Profile: Mukilteo Beacon is published weekly for the residents of Mukilteo, WA and surrounding areas. The newspaper covers local news, government and sports.; Full Page Mono: 18.50
Currency: US Dollars
NEWSPAPER

The Mullet Wrapper
Editorial: 901 E 24Th Ave, Gulf Shores, Alabama 36542-3115. **T:** 1 850 492-5221
E: mulletwrapper@gulftel.com
W: http://mulletwrapper.com
Freq: Bi-Weekly; **Circ:** 18000 Not Audited
Editorial Profile: Mullet Wrapper is a local, community newspaper serving residents of Perdido Key and Pensacola, FL as well as parts of Alabama. The paper includes local news and information of interest to its readers.; Full Page Mono: 11.00; Full Page Colour: 75.00
Currency: US Dollars
NEWSPAPER

Mulvane Newspapers
Editorial: 204 W Main St, Mulvane, Kansas 67110-1765. **T:** 1 316 777-4233 **Circ:** 2750 Not Audited
Editor: Michael Robinson
NEWSPAPER

Muncie Times
Editorial: 1304 N Martin Luther King, Muncie, Indiana 47303-3107. **T:** 1 765 741-0037
E: themuncietimes@comcast.net
Freq: Bi-Weekly; **Circ:** 10000 Not Audited
Editor: Tendayi Kumbula; **Publisher:** Bea Moten-Foster
Editorial Profile: Muncie Times is a local newspaper serving the African-American community in Muncie, IN and surrounding areas. The publication's editorial mission is to provide their readers with current news and information. The publication covers news and events that affect their readers. Deadlines are on Fridays.; Full Page Mono: 8.50
Currency: US Dollars
NEWSPAPER

El Mundo
Editorial: 760 N Eastern Ave Ste 110, Las Vegas, Nevada 89101-2888.

T: 1 702 649-8553
E: elmundopaper@ureach.com
W: http://www.elmundo.net
Freq: Fri; Circ: 29765 Not Audited
Editor: Valdemar Gonzalez
Editorial Profile: El Mundo is a weekly, Spanish-language community newspaper. Deadlines for press releases are Tuesdays by 2pm PT.; Full Page Mono: 16.50; Full Page Colour: 1488.00
Currency: US Dollars
NEWSPAPER

El Mundo
Owner: El Mundo Communications Co.
Editorial: 11410 Ne 124Th St #441, Kirkland, Washington 98034-4305. T: 1 800 797-4544
E: info@elmundous.com
W: http://www.elmundous.com
Freq: Thu; Circ: 20000 Not Audited
Publisher: Martha Montoya
Editorial Profile: El Mundo is written for the Hispanic community in Wenatchee, WA. It covers news and current events occurring in Mexico.; Full Page Mono: 14.00
Currency: US Dollars
NEWSPAPER

El Mundo
Owner: Banner Publications, Inc.
Editorial: 408 S Huntington Ave, Boston, Massachusetts 2130. T: 1 617 522-5060
W: http://www.elmundoboston.com
Freq: Thu; Circ: 30000 Not Audited
Editorial Profile: El Mundo is a weekly newspaper that provides local and national news to Hispanic communities around Boston. The newspaper also provides weekly features in business, politics, education, health and sports. Deadlines are on Mondays at 2pm ET.; Full Page Mono: 25.00; Full Page Colour: 2350.00
Currency: US Dollars
NEWSPAPER

El Mundo
Editorial: 2112 E Cesar Chavez St, Austin, Texas 78702. T: 1 512 476-8636
E: info@elmundonewspaper.com
W: http://www.elmundonewspaper.com
Freq: Thu; Circ: 40000 Not Audited
Editor: Roberto Angulo
Editorial Profile: El Mundo in Austin, TX is a weekly Spanish newspaper that covers local news and events in a region that includes Round Rock, Georgetown, Cedar Park, Lockhart, Bastrop, Buda, and Kyle. Deadlines are on Mondays prior to publication.; Full Page Mono: 25.00; Full Page Colour: 23.00
Currency: US Dollars
NEWSPAPER

Mundo Hispanico
Owner: Atlanta Journal-Constitution (The)
Editorial: 6455 Best Friend Rd, Norcross, Georgia 30071-2914. T: 1 404 881-0441
E: editorial@mundohispanico.com
W: http://www.mundohispanico.com
Freq: Thu; Circ: 71500 Not Audited
Editor: Rodrigo Cervantes; Publisher: Anibal Torres
Editorial Profile: Mundo Hispanico is a local newspaper written for the Hispanic population of Atlanta. The newspaper covers local news, sports and arts & entertainment. Deadlines are on Mondays prior to issue date.; Full Page Mono: 40.13
Currency: US Dollars
NEWSPAPER

Mundo Hispano
Owner: Mundo Hispano-Hispanic World, Inc.
Editorial: 5306 Ballard Dr, Knoxville, Tennessee 37918-3904. T: 1 865 548-1148
E: info@mundohispanotn.com
W: http://www.mundohispanotn.com
Freq: Monthly; Circ: 20000 Not Audited
Editorial Profile: Mundo Hispano is a local newspaper written for the Hispanic community of Knoxville, TN. The newspaper covers local news, sports, arts & entertainment, religion and culture.; Full Page Mono: 15.00
Currency: US Dollars
NEWSPAPER

Mundo Hispano - Utah
Owner: Falcon Enterprise
Editorial: 9131 S Monroe Plaza Way, Ste C, Sandy, Utah 84070-4608. T: 1 801 569-3338
E: editor@mymundohispano.com
W: http://www.munhispano.com
Freq: Semi-Monthly; Circ: 10000 Not Audited
Publisher: Gladys Gonzalez; Editor: Sandra Plazas; Full Page Mono: 29.00
Currency: US Dollars
NEWSPAPER

The Murfreesboro Post
Editorial: 2955 S Rutherford Blvd Ste I, Murfreesboro, Tennessee 37130-0719.
T: 1 615 869-0800
E: online@murfreesboropost.com
W: http://www.murfreesboropost.com
Freq: Sun; Circ: 25000 Not Audited
Publisher: Ron Fryar
Editorial Profile: The Murfreesboro Post is a community-based weekly newspaper serving the households and businesses of the Mufreesboro market. Daily breaking news is offered on the Web site.; Full Page Mono: 23.00
Currency: US Dollars
NEWSPAPER

Murphysboro American
Owner: GateHouse Media Inc.
Editorial: 1400 Walnut St, Murphysboro, Illinois 62966. T: 1 618 684-5833
W: http://www.murphysboroamerican.com
Freq: Thu; Circ: 10750 Not Audited
Editor: Jessica Miles
Editorial Profile: Murphysboro American is written for residents of Murphysboro, IL. It covers local news, sports, entertainment and event listings. Deadlines are on Tuesdays and Thursdays at 5pm CT.; Full Page Mono: 10.52
Currency: US Dollars
NEWSPAPER

Murray Ledger & Times
Owner: Murray Newspapers Inc.
Editorial: 1001 Whitnell Ave, Murray, Kentucky 42071. T: 1 270 753-1916
E: mlt@murrayledger.com
W: http://www.murrayledger.com
Freq: Mon thru Fri; Circ: 7159 Not Audited
Publisher: Alice Rouse; Editor: Greg Travis
Editorial Profile: Murray Ledger & Times is a daily newspaper published for the residents of Murray, KY and the surrounding area. It covers local news, sports and business.; Full Page Mono: 10.50; Full Page Colour: 125.00
Currency: US Dollars
DAILY NEWSPAPER

Muscatine Journal
Owner: Lee Enterprises, Inc.
Editorial: 301 E 3rd St, Muscatine, Iowa 52761-4116. T: 1 563 263-2331
E: news@muscatinejournal.com
W: http://www.muscatinejournal.com
Freq: Mon thru Fri; Circ: 5127
Publisher: Steven Jameson
Editorial Profile: Muscatine Journal is a local daily newspaper written for residents of Muscatine, IA. The publication's editorial mission is to attract as many readers as possible by providing the most up-to-date information about local news and events.; Full Page Mono: 13.00
Currency: US Dollars
DAILY NEWSPAPER

Muskegon Chronicle
Owner: MLive Media Group
Editorial: 500 W Western Ave Ste 100, Muskegon, Michigan 49440-1000.
T: 1 231 683-2329 E: munews@mlive.com
W: http://www.mlive.com/chronicle
Freq: Daily; Circ: 21722 Not Audited
Editorial Profile: Muskegon Chronicle is a local daily newspaper written for residents of Muskegon, MI and the surrounding area. The publication's editorial mission is to provide current news and information to the community. Editorial deadlines are daily at 8:30am CT.; Full Page Mono: 98.30; Full Page Colour: 775.00
Currency: US Dollars
DAILY NEWSPAPER

Muskogee Daily Phoenix
Owner: Community Newspaper Holdings, Inc.
Editorial: 214 Wall St, Muskogee, Oklahoma 74401-6644. T: 1 918 684-2888
E: news@muskogeephoenix.com
W: http://www.muskogeephoenix.com
Freq: Daily; Circ: 9079 Not Audited
Editor: Mike Kays; Publisher: Randy Mooney
Editorial Profile: Muskogee Daily Phoenix's editorial mission is to bring the eight area counties local and national news, sports and features. The publication is written for the eight counties in northeast Oklahoma.; Full Page Mono: 34.67; Full Page Colour: 349.00
Currency: US Dollars
DAILY NEWSPAPER

Muslim Journal
Owner: Muslim Journal Enterprises, Inc.
Editorial: 231 E. 51st St., Chicago, Illinois 60615. T: 1 773 952-8177
E: muslimjrnl@comcast.net
W: http://muslimjournal.net
Freq: Fri; Circ: 10000 Not Audited
Editorial Profile: Muslim Journal is written for the Muslim communities in the United States, Australia and the Middle East. It covers political and social issues of interest to the Muslim community. Deadlines are on Tuesdays at 5pm CT.; Full Page Mono: 15.00
Currency: US Dollars
NEWSPAPER

The Muslim Observer
Owner: Muslim Media Network
Editorial: 29004 W 8 Mile Rd, Farmington Hills, Michigan 48336. T: 1 248 426-7777
E: submissions@muslimobserver.com
W: http://www.muslimobserver.com
Freq: Thu; Circ: 10000 Not Audited
Editor in Chief: Aslam Abdullah; Publisher: A.S. Nakadar
Editorial Profile: The Muslim Observer is a weekly newspaper tabloid covering international, national and community news for Muslims. Based in Wisconsin, it distributed across the United States including South Florida and the Detroit, Houston, Chicago and San Francisco metro areas.; Full Page Mono: 5.71
Currency: US Dollars
NEWSPAPER

My Backyard
Editorial: 34 Rosewood Ave, South Attleboro, Massachusetts 02703-5913.
T: 1 508 212-4454
E: mybackyard@comcast.net
W: http://www.mybackyardnews.com
Freq: Semi-Monthly; Circ: 13000 Not Audited
Editor: James Hanley
Editorial Profile: My Backyard is a weekly newspaper written for residents of Rhode Island and Southeastern Massachusetts, including East Providence, Pawtucket, Lincoln, Central Falls and Cumberland, RI and Attleboro, MA. The paper is publised the 1st and 3rd Friday each month.; Full Page Mono: 10.00
Currency: US Dollars
NEWSPAPER

My Barrington Life
Owner: Shaw Media
Editorial: 7717 S. Route 31, Crystal Lake, Illinois 60014. T: 1 815 459-4040
E: tips@nwherald.com
W: http://www.mybarringtonlife.com
Freq: Thu; Circ: 17000
Editorial Profile: My Barrington Life is a weekly community newspaper serving residents of Barrington, IL with community news, business, sports, events and opinion. The publication is mailed free to Barrington-area residents and businesses.; Full Page Mono: 7.09
Currency: US Dollars
NEWSPAPER

Mystic River Press
Owner: Sun Publishing Company
Editorial: 15 Holmes St, Mystic, Connecticut 06355-2651. T: 1 860 536-9577
E: news@themysticriverpress.com
W: http://www.thewesterlysun.com
Freq: Thu; Circ: 10815 Not Audited
Editorial Profile: Mystic River Press is a local, weekly newspaper serving residents of of Mystic, Groton, and Stonington, CT. Its editorial mission is to provide readers with the latest news and information. Deadlines are on Mondays.; Full Page Mono: 12.50
Currency: US Dollars
NEWSPAPER

N&W Media
Owner: N&W Media
Editorial: 100 E. Jackson, Willard, Missouri 65781. T: 1 417 751-2322
E: editor@crosscountrytimes.com Circ: 3550
Editorial Profile: N&W Media is a community newspaper publisher servicing the residents of Springfield, MO.
NEWSPAPER

La Nacion Hispana
Owner: Hispanic Marketing, Inc.
Editorial: 1601 Cedar Lane Rd, Ste 15, Greenville, South Carolina 29617.
T: 1 864 246-4110
W: http://www.lanacionhispana.com
Freq: Wed; Circ: 10000 Not Audited
Editorial Profile: La Nacion Hispana is written for Hispanic residents of Greenville, SC. It covers community, national and international news, sports, weather and lifestyles. Deadlines are Fridays.; Full Page Mono: 10.44
Currency: US Dollars
NEWSPAPER

El Nacional de Oklahoma
Editorial: 304 SW 25th St, Oklahoma City, Oklahoma 73109-5922. T: 1 405 632-4531
E: noticias@elnacionalmedia.net
W: http://www.noticiasoklahoma.com
Freq: Thu; Circ: 65000 Not Audited
Editorial Profile: El Nacional de Oklahoma is a Spanish language newspaper written for Hispanics in and around Oklahoma City, OK.; Full Page Mono: 15.50
Currency: US Dollars
NEWSPAPER

Nadig Newspapers
Owner: Nadig Press
Editorial: 4937 N Milwaukee Ave, Chicago, Illinois 60630-2114. T: 1 773 286-6100
E: news@nadignewspapers.com
W: http://www.nadignewspapers.com
Circ: 24000 Not Audited
Editor: Randy Erickson
Editorial Profile: Nadig newspapers serves the Far Northwest Side of Chicago and the surrounding suburbs providing local and community news.; Full Page Mono: 43.00
Currency: US Dollars
NEWSPAPER

The Napa Valley Register
Owner: Lee Enterprises, Inc.
Editorial: 1615 2nd St, Napa, California 94559-2818. T: 1 707 226-3711
W: http://www.napavalleyregister.com
Freq: Daily; Circ: 11659
Publisher: Brenda Speth
Editorial Profile: The mission of Napa Valley Register is to provide news and information to the residents of Napa Valley, CA. The publication is written for residents of Napa Valley, CA and surrounding areas. The paper is delivered early in the morning to all subscribers and newsstands, seven days a week.; Full Page Mono: 23.90; Full Page Colour: 27.40
Currency: US Dollars
DAILY NEWSPAPER

Naples Daily News
Owner: E.W. Scripps Co.
Editorial: 1100 Immokalee Rd, Naples, Florida 34110-4810. T: 1 239 262-3161
E: news@naplesnews.com
W: http://www.naplesnews.com
Freq: Daily; Circ: 71907 Not Audited
Editor: Manny Garcia
Editorial Profile: Naples Daily News is a local newspaper published for the residents of Naples and Collier County, FL. The newspaper covers local and national news, business, arts & entertainment, events and sports.; Full Page Mono: 80.55; Full Page Colour: 265.65
Currency: US Dollars
DAILY NEWSPAPER

Naples Florida Weekly
Owner: Florida Media Group LLC
Editorial: 2025 J&C Blvd, Suite 5, Naples, Florida 34109. T: 1 239 325-1960
E: info@floridaweekly.com
W: http://www.floridaweekly.com
Freq: Thu; Circ: 18000
Publisher: Pason Gaddis
Editorial Profile: Naples Florida Weekly, launched October 2, 2008, is a weekly newspaper written for residents of Naples and Collier County, FL. It covers news, arts & entertainment, dining, regional business and real estate.; Full Page Mono: 15.44
Currency: US Dollars
NEWSPAPER

Nashoba Publications Inc.
Owner: Fitchburg Publishing Co.
Editorial: 78 Barnum Rd, Ayer, Massachusetts 1434. T: 1 978 772-0777
E: editor@nashobapub.com
W: http://www.nashobapublishing.com
Circ: 25009 Not Audited
Editorial Profile: Please send all postal correspondence to the PO address.
NEWSPAPER

Nashville Scene
Owner: Southcomm, Inc.
Editorial: 210 12th Ave S Ste 100, Nashville, Tennessee 37203-4046. T: 1 615 244-7989
E: editor@nashvillescene.com
W: http://www.nashvillescene.com
Freq: Thu; Circ: 48714 Not Audited
Editor: Jim Ridley; Publisher: Mike Smith
Editorial Profile: Nashville Scene is a weekly newspaper published for the residents of Nashville, TN and surrounding areas. The publication covers local news and community events.; Full Page Mono: 46.47; Full Page Colour: 2882.00
Currency: US Dollars

NEWSPAPER

Nassau Border Papers, Inc.
Editorial: 139 Tulip Ave, Floral Park, New York 11001. **T:** 1 516 775-2700 **Circ:** 28700 Not Audited
NEWSPAPER

Natchez Democrat
Owner: Boone Newspapers Inc.
Editorial: 503 N Canal St, Natchez, Mississippi 39120. **T:** 1 601 442-9101
E: newsroom@natchezdemocrat.com
W: http://www.natchezdemocrat.com
Freq: Daily; **Circ:** 10500 Not Audited
Publisher: Kevin Cooper; **Editor:** Stephen Hemelt
Editorial Profile: Natchez Democrat's editorial mission is to provide news and information to the people of Natchez, MS and surrounding areas. The publication is written for the people of Natchez and Vidalia, MS and those that live on the Mississippi-Louisiana boarder. The publication covers all topics of interest to the local community.; Full Page Mono: 22.50; Full Page Colour: 255.00
Currency: US Dollars
DAILY NEWSPAPER

Natchitoches Times
Owner: Natchitoches Times
Editorial: 904 South Dr, Natchitoches, Louisiana 71457. **T:** 1 318 352-3618
E: news@natchitochestimes.com
W: http://www.natchitochestimes.com
Freq: Daily; **Circ:** 4000 Not Audited
Editor: Carolyn Roy; **Publisher:** Lovan Thomas
Editorial Profile: Natchitoches Times' editorial mission is to provide news and information to its readers. The publication is written for the residents of Natchitoches, LA. The publication covers current news and events.; Full Page Mono: 11.64
Currency: US Dollars
DAILY NEWSPAPER

National Herald
Editorial: 3710 30th St, Long Island City, New York 11101. **T:** 1 718 784-5255
E: info@thenationalherald.com
W: http://www.thenationalherald.com
Freq: Daily; **Circ:** 80000 Not Audited
Editorial Profile: National Herald is published daily for Greek communities in New York and Massachusetts. The newspaper covers local, national and international news, business, culture and entertainment.; Full Page Mono: 36.97; Full Page Colour: 40.30
Currency: US Dollars
DAILY NEWSPAPER

Native American Times
Owner: Snell (Lisa)
Editorial: 14113 Ranch Acres Dr, Tahlequah, Oklahoma 74464-0383. **T:** 1 918 708-5838
E: info@nativetimes.com
W: http://www.nativetimes.com
Freq: Weekly; **Circ:** 10000 Not Audited
Editorial Profile: Native American Times is a local newspaper published weekly for the Native American residents of Tulsa, OK and surrounding areas. It provides news coverage that is specifically tailored to the Native American perspective with the understanding of special issues, such as as sovereign rights, civil rights and government-to-government relationships with the federal government.; Full Page Mono: 17.00
Currency: US Dollars
NEWSPAPER

Navajo County Publishers
Editorial: 200 E Hopi Dr, Holbrook, Arizona 86025. **T:** 1 928 524-6203
E: tribunenews@cableone.net
W: http://www.azjournal.com **Circ:** 8801 Not Audited
Publisher: Matthew Barger; **Editor:** Francie Payne
Editorial Profile: Navajo County Publishers produces Silver Creek Herald in Snowflake, AZ and the Holbrook (AZ) Tribune-News.
NEWSPAPER

Navajo Times
Owner: Navajo Times Publishing Co., Inc.
Editorial: Highway 264 Route 12, Window Rock, Arizona 86515. **T:** 1 928 871-1130
E: editor@navajotimes.com
W: http://www.navajotimes.com
Freq: Thu; **Circ:** 24000 Not Audited
Publisher: Tom Arviso; **Editor:** Candace Begody
Editorial Profile: Navajo Times is a local newspaper published weekly for the Native American population of Window Rock, AZ and surrounding areas. It covers local news,

government and community events.; Full Page Mono: 14.00
Currency: US Dollars
NEWSPAPER

Navajo-Hopi Observer
Owner: Western Newspapers, Inc.
Editorial: 2717 N 4th St Ste 110, Flagstaff, Arizona 86004-1813. **T:** 1 928 226-9696
E: nhoeditorial@nhonews.com
W: http://www.nhonews.com
Freq: Wed; **Circ:** 15000 Not Audited
Publisher: Doug Wells
Editorial Profile: Navajo-Hopi Observer is published weekly for the Native American Indians of Flagstaff, AZ. The publication informs the Navajo and Hopi, who live on reservations, about local news, government and community events. Deadlines are on Thursdays at 4pm MT.; Full Page Mono: 14.10
Currency: US Dollars
NEWSPAPER

Navarro County Times
Editorial: 111 W 3Rd Ave Ste D, Corsicana, Texas 75110-4685. **T:** 1 903 874-1888
E: news@navarrocountytimes.com
NEWSPAPER

The Navigator & Journal-Register Newspapers
Owner: Reppert Publications
Editorial: 19 W Main St, Albion, Illinois 62806-1006. **T:** 1 618 445-2355
Freq: Weekly; **Circ:** 17200 Not Audited
Editor: Duane Crays; **Publisher:** Patrick Seil; **Publisher:** Patrick Seil
Editorial Profile: The Navigator & Journal-Register is written for residents that live in and around Albion, IL. The publication covers news and events.
NEWSPAPER

La Nazione - New York Bureau
Editorial: United Nations Headquarters, Room S-306, New York, New York 10017.
T: 1 212 963-7159
Editorial Profile: New York Bureau of La Nazione covering United States news and current affairs including politics, economics, sport and entertainment.
DAILY NEWSPAPER

Nearby News
Owner: Times Media Group
Editorial: 3200 N Hayden Rd Ste 210, Scottsdale, Arizona 85251-6654.
T: 1 480 654-4460 **E:** info@nearbynews.com
W: http://www.nearbynews.com **Circ:** 30000 Not Audited
Editor: Christina Fuoco-Karasinski; **Publisher:** Frank Hamilton
Editorial Profile: Nearby News in Scottsdale, AZ provides local news and information to nine communities in the East Valley, in North Scottsdale and in North Chandler.
NEWSPAPER

Neighbor Newspapers
Owner: Neighbor Newspapers
Editorial: 225 N Clay St, Marshfield, Missouri 65706-1652. **T:** 1 417 859-2013
E: news@marshfieldmail.com
W: http://www.marshfieldmail.com **Circ:** 21900 Not Audited
Publisher: Dave Berry
NEWSPAPER

Neighbor Newspapers
Owner: Neighbor Newspapers
Editorial: 116 N 2nd Ave, Ozark, Missouri 65721. **T:** 1 417 581-3541 **Circ:** 7200 Not Audited
Publisher: Dave Berry; **Editor:** Ryan Bowling; **Editor:** Donna Osborn
NEWSPAPER

Neighbor Newspapers
Owner: LI Media Group LLC
Editorial: 565 Broadhollow Road, Farmingdale, New York 11735. **T:** 1 631 226-2636
W: http://www.theneighbornewspapers.com
Circ: 667919 Not Audited
Publisher: Jeff Lambert; **Editor:** Jamie Lynn Ryan
NEWSPAPER

Neighbor Newspapers - Cobb
Editorial: 580 S Fairground St Se, Marietta, Georgia 30060-2751. **T:** 1 770 428-9411
E: mdjnews@mdjonline.com
W: http://www.neighbornewspapers.com
Circ: 99950 Not Audited
Publisher: Otis Brumby
NEWSPAPER

Neighbor Newspapers - Dekalb
Editorial: 10930 Crabapple Road, Suite 9, Roswell, Georgia 30075. **T:** 1 770 454-9388
E: dekalb@neighbornewspapers.com
W: http://www.neighbornewspapers.com
Circ: 49200 Not Audited
Publisher: Otis Brumby; **Editor:** LaTria Garnigan
NEWSPAPER

Neighbor Newspapers - North Fulton
Owner: Neighbor Newspapers
Editorial: 10930 Crabapple Rd, Roswell, Georgia 30075-5813. **T:** 1 770 993-7400
E: nfulton@neighbornewspapers.com
W: http://www.neighbornewspapers.com
Freq: Weekly; **Circ:** 47980 Not Audited
Publisher: Otis Brumby
Editorial Profile: Neighbor Newspapers, based in Marietta, GA, produces weekly newspapers serving metro Atlanta's suburban communities.
NEWSPAPER

Neighbor Newspapers - Northside Atlanta
Owner: Neighbor Newspapers, Inc.
Editorial: 5290 Roswell Rd Ste M, Atlanta, Georgia 30342-1978. **T:** 1 404 256-3100
E: nside@neighbornewspapers.com
W: http://www.neighbornewspapers.com
Circ: 35086
Publisher: Otis Brumby; **News Editor:** Everett Catts
Editorial Profile: Neighbor Newspapers - Northside Atlanta is a community newspaper publisher servicing the residents of Atlanta, as well as Sandy Springs and Marietta, GA.
NEWSPAPER

Neighbor Newspapers - South Metro
Owner: Neighbor Newspapers
Editorial: 5442 Frontage Rd, Ste 130, Forest Park, Georgia 30297. **T:** 1 404 363-8484
E: smetro@neighbornewspapers.com
W: http://www.neighbornewspapers.com
Freq: Weekly; **Circ:** 97775 Not Audited
Editor: Bill Baldowski; **Publisher:** Otis Brumby; **Editor:** Mary Cosgrove
NEWSPAPER

The Neighbor Newspapers - West Metro
Owner: Neighbor Newspapers
Editorial: 4471 Jimmy Lee Smith Pkwy Ste 200&201C, Hiram, Georgia 30141-2725.
T: 1 770 445-9401
W: http://www.neighbornewspapers.com
Circ: 46125
Publisher: Otis Brumby; **Editor:** Monica Burge; **Editor:** Tom Spigolon
Editorial Profile: The Neighbor Newspapers - West Metro in Hiram, GA publishes the Paulding Neighbor, the Douglas Neighbor and the Bartow Neighbor.
NEWSPAPER

Neighbor Newspapers-Owasso
Owner: Neighbor Newspapers
Editorial: 202 E 2nd Ave Ste 101, Owasso, Oklahoma 74055-3131. **T:** 1 918 272-1155
W: http://owassoreporter.com **Circ:** 6300 Not Audited
Editor: Vicki Albright; **Publisher:** Mike Brown
NEWSPAPER

Neighbor Newspapers-Sand Springs
Owner: Neighbor Newspapers
Editorial: 303 N McKinley Ave, Sand Springs, Oklahoma 74063. **T:** 1 918 245-6634
W: http://www.neighbor-newspapers.com
Circ: 6200 Not Audited
Publisher: Mike Brown
NEWSPAPER

Neighbor to Neighbor News, Inc.
Editorial: 710 Main St, East Aurora, New York 14052. **T:** 1 716 652-0320
E: eanews@eastaurorany.com
W: http://www.eastaurorany.com **Circ:** 5600
Publisher: Grant Hamilton; **Editor:** Jeremy Morlock
Editorial Profile: Neighbor to Neighbor News, Inc. is a community newspaper publisher servicing the residents of Buffalo and Niagara Falls, NY.
NEWSPAPER

The Neighborhood Leader
Owner: Jaramogi Communications
Editorial: 2227 N Broad St, Philadelphia, Pennsylvania 19132-4502. **T:** 1 267 970-5632
E: neighborhoodlead@aol.com
Freq: Bi-Weekly; **Circ:** 20000
Editorial Profile: Neighborhood Leader is a local community newspaper for the residents

of Philadelphia and the surrounding communities.; Full Page Mono: 14.84
Currency: US Dollars
NEWSPAPER

The Neighborhood News/Garfield Heights Tribune
Owner: Psenicka (Ellen)
Editorial: 8613 Garfield Blvd, Garfield Heights, Ohio 44125-1317. **T:** 1 216 441-2141
E: nnews1923@aol.com
W: http://www.theneighborhoodnews.com
Freq: Wed; **Circ:** 15000 Not Audited
Editorial Profile: Neighborhood News/Garfield Heights Tribune is a local weekly newspaper in Garfield Heights, OH. The publication's editorial mission is to provide news and information to the community. The publication is written for the communities in Garfield Heights and Southeast Ohio. The paper covers all news and events that affect the community.; Full Page Mono: 10.00
Currency: US Dollars
NEWSPAPER

Neighborhood Publications Inc.
Owner: Union Leader Corp.
Editorial: 100 William Loeb Dr, Manchester, New Hampshire 03109-5309.
T: 1 603 314-0447
E: editor@yourneighborhoodnews.com
W: http://www.newhampshire.com/section/newhampshire14 **Circ:** 64050 Not Audited
Editor: Christine Heiser; **Editor:** Christine Heiser; **Editor:** Christine Heiser; **Editor:** Sarah LeBrun; **Editor:** Jerry Liptak
NEWSPAPER

Neighbors
Owner: R.I.S.N. Operations Inc.
Editorial: 75 Main St, Woonsocket, Rhode Island 2895. **T:** 1 401 767-8535
E: news@woonsocketcall.com
W: http://www.woonsocketcall.com
Freq: Fri; **Circ:** 32000 Not Audited
Publisher: Mary Lynn Bosiak
Editorial Profile: Neighbors is a free community newspaper which covers local news, events and activities.; Full Page Mono: 3.00
Currency: US Dollars
NEWSPAPER

Neosho Daily News
Owner: GateHouse Media Inc.
Editorial: 1006 W Harmony St, Neosho, Missouri 64850-1631. **T:** 1 417 451-1520
W: http://www.neoshodailynews.com
Freq: Mon thru Fri; **Circ:** 3474 Not Audited
Editor: John Ford; **News Editor:** Todd Higdon; **Publisher:** Rick Rogers; **Publisher:** Rick Rogers; **Publisher:** Rick Rogers; **Publisher:** Rick Rogers
Editorial Profile: Neosho Daily News is a local daily newspaper serving Neosho, MO and the surrounding area. It provides information on news and events of interest to the local community.; Full Page Mono: 10.75; Full Page Colour: 50.00
Currency: US Dollars
DAILY NEWSPAPER

Ness Press Inc.
Editorial: 122 Main St N, Fordville, North Dakota 58231. **T:** 1 701 229-3641
E: nesspres@polarcomm.com **Circ:** 3310 Not Audited
NEWSPAPER

Nevada Appeal
Owner: Swift Newspapers
Editorial: 580 Mallory Way, Carson City, Nevada 89701-5360. **T:** 1 775 882-2111
E: editor@nevadaappeal.com
W: http://www.nevadaappeal.com
Freq: Fri; **Circ:** 16707 Not Audited
Publisher: Mark Raymond
Editorial Profile: Nevada Appeal is a local, daily newspaper serving Carson City, NV and the surrounding area. It covers news, events, sports and weather. Lead time varies.; Full Page Mono: 35.80; Full Page Colour: 112.28
Currency: US Dollars
NEWSPAPER

Nevada Daily Mail
Owner: Rust Communications
Editorial: 131 S Cedar St, Nevada, Missouri 64772-3309. **T:** 1 417 667-3344
E: editor@nevadadailymail.com
W: http://www.nevadadailymail.com
Freq: Mon thru Fri; **Circ:** 2600 Not Audited
Editor: Ralph Pokorny; **Publisher:** Julie Simpson
Editorial Profile: Nevada Daily Mail is a local newspaper serving Bourbon County and Nevada, MO. It provides information, news,

community events, sports, business and entertainment. The weekend edition, entitled the Sunday Herald-Tribune, is combined with the Fort Scott (KS) Tribune's weekend edition and is distributed to residents in both Vernon County, MO and Bourbon County, KS.; Full Page Mono: 9.85; Full Page Colour: 150.00
Currency: US Dollars
DAILY NEWSPAPER

Nevada Journal & Tri-County Times Newspapers
Owner: Stephens Media
Editorial: 922 Lincoln Hwy, Nevada, Iowa 50201-1722. **T:** 1 515 382-2161 **Circ:** 6105 Not Audited
NEWSPAPER

New Age-Examiner Newspapers
Owner: Times Shamrock Group
Editorial: 16 E Tioga St, Tunkhannock, Pennsylvania 18657. **T:** 1 570 836-2123
E: news@wcexaminer.com
W: http://www.newage-examiner.com
Circ: 20419 Not Audited
NEWSPAPER

New Armenia Daily
Editorial: 815 S Central Ave, Ste 31, Glendale, California 91204. **T:** 1 818 246-6468
E: newarmeniadaily@aol.com
Freq: Daily; **Circ:** 8000 Not Audited
Editorial Profile: New Armenia Daily is a daily newspaper for Armenian Americans in the Glendale, CA area. The editorial mission is to provide news about Armenia to Armenians living in the United States.; Full Page Mono: 1.88
Currency: US Dollars
DAILY NEWSPAPER

New Braunfels Herald-Zeitung
Owner: Southern Newspapers, Inc.
Editorial: 707 Landa St, New Braunfels, Texas 78130. **T:** 1 830 625-9144
E: news@herald-zeitung.com
W: http://herald-zeitung.com
Freq: Daily; **Circ:** 8000 Not Audited
Publisher: James Rainey
Editorial Profile: New Braunfels Herald-Zeitung is a local newspaper written for residents of Comal County, TX. The newspaper covers local news, sports and community events.; Full Page Mono: 10.50; Full Page Colour: 250.00
Currency: US Dollars
DAILY NEWSPAPER

New Britain Herald
Owner: Central Connecticut Communications
Editorial: 1 Court St Fl 4, New Britain, Connecticut 06051-2262. **T:** 1 860 225-4601
W: http://www.newbritainherald.com
Freq: Daily; **Circ:** 4356 Not Audited
Editorial Profile: New Britain Herald covers local news, sports and information for residents of New Britain, CT. It combines with The Bristol (CT) Press on Sundays. It shares offices with Imprint Newspapers, a parent publisher of three community weeklies.; Full Page Mono: 29.48
Currency: US Dollars
DAILY NEWSPAPER

New Castle News
Owner: Community Newspaper Holdings, Inc.
Editorial: 27 N Mercer St, New Castle, Pennsylvania 16101. **T:** 1 724 654-6651
E: nceditor@ncnewsonline.com
W: http://www.ncnewsonline.com
Freq: Daily; **Circ:** 13272
Publisher: Lawrence Corvi; **Editor:** Mitch Olszak
Editorial Profile: New Castle News is published daily for the residents of New Castle, PA and surrounding areas. The newspaper covers local and state news, business, sports, lifestyles and entertainment.; Full Page Mono: 35.75; Full Page Colour: 295.00
Currency: US Dollars
DAILY NEWSPAPER

New City
Owner: New City Communications, Inc.
Editorial: 47 W Polk St Ste 100-223, Chicago, Illinois 60605-2000. **T:** 1 312 243-8786
E: editorial@newcity.com
W: http://www.newcity.com
Freq: Thu; **Circ:** 40000 Not Audited
Editorial Profile: New City is published weekly for young adults in Chicago and surrounding communities. The newspaper mainly covers arts & entertainment, but also focuses on topics of interest to young adult audiences, including politics, subcultures, work, money, travel, health & fitness, love, sex, fashion and

shopping. They prefer pitches be sent to topic specific editors.; Full Page Mono: 37.00
Currency: US Dollars
NEWSPAPER

The New Fillmore
Editorial: 2130 Fillmore St, Ste 202, San Francisco, California 94115-2224.
T: 1 415 441-6070 **E:** editor@newfillmore.com
W: http://www.newfillmore.com
Freq: Monthly; **Circ:** 20000 Not Audited
Editor: Barbara Repa; **Publisher:** Thomas Reynolds
Editorial Profile: The New Fillmore is a monthly San Francisco neighborhood newspaper serving residents in Pacific Heights, the Fillmore and Japantown. It covers local people, community events, food, entertainment, health and fitness. News submissions must be received by the 12th of the month prior to publication. Advertising deadlines are on the 15th of the month prior to distribution.; Full Page Mono: 30.00
Currency: US Dollars
NEWSPAPER

The New Hampshire Union Leader
Owner: Nackey S. Loeb School of Communications Inc.
Editorial: 100 William Loeb Dr, Manchester, New Hampshire 03109-5309.
T: 1 603 668-4321 **E:** news@unionleader.com
W: http://www.unionleader.com
Freq: Daily; **Circ:** 37912 Not Audited
Editor: Sandra Bradley; **Publisher:** Joseph McQuaid
Editorial Profile: The New Hampshire Union Leader is published daily for residents of Manchester, NH and surrounding communities. The newspaper covers local, regional and national news as well as local recreation, entertainment, lifestyle and travel. The newspaper's Sunday edition is called the New Hampshire Sunday News.; Full Page Mono: 51.15; Full Page Colour: 170.50
Currency: US Dollars
DAILY NEWSPAPER

The New Hampshire Union Leader
Editorial: State House Room 116, Concord, New Hampshire 03301-4951.
T: 1 603 225-3500
DAILY NEWSPAPER

New Haven Register
Owner: Journal Register Company
Editorial: 40 Sargent Dr, New Haven, Connecticut 06511-6111. **T:** 1 203 789-5200
W: http://www.nhregister.com
Freq: Daily; **Circ:** 70255 Not Audited
Editorial Profile: New Haven Register is Connecticut's second largest daily newspaper. The publication provides readers throughout New Haven, CT and the surrounding areas with local, regional and national news.; Full Page Mono: 113.47; Full Page Colour: 340.39
Currency: US Dollars
DAILY NEWSPAPER

New Jersey Herald
Owner: Quincy Newspapers, Inc.
Editorial: 2 Spring St, Newton, New Jersey 07860-2057. **T:** 1 973 383-1500
E: newsroom@njherald.com
W: http://www.njherald.com
Freq: Daily; **Circ:** 11814
Publisher: Jack Findley; **Editor:** Kathy Stevens
Editorial Profile: New Jersey Herald is published daily for the residents of Sussex County, NJ. The newspaper covers local and regional news, business, sports, lifestyles and entertainment.; Full Page Mono: 24.76; Full Page Colour: 81.83
Currency: US Dollars
DAILY NEWSPAPER

New Jersey Hills Media Group - Chester
Owner: Parker Publications
Editorial: 530 Main St, Chester, New Jersey 07930-2669. **T:** 1 908 879-4100
W: http://newjerseyhills.com **Circ:** 16600 Not Audited
Editor: Mike Condon; **Editor:** Patricia Claire Robinson
NEWSPAPER

New Jersey Hills Media Group - Clinton
Owner: Parker Publications
Editorial: 14 E Main St, Clinton, New Jersey 08809-1394. **T:** 1 908 647-1187
W: http://newjerseyhills.com **Circ:** 23131 Not Audited
NEWSPAPER

New Jersey Jewish Media Group
Owner: Jewish Media Group
Editorial: 1086 Teaneck Rd, Teaneck, New Jersey 07666-4854. **T:** 1 201 837-8818
E: pr@jewishmediagroup.com
W: http://www.jstandard.com **Circ:** 58500 Not Audited
Publisher: James Janoff; **Editor:** Joanne Palmer
NEWSPAPER

New Jersey Jewish Newspapers
Owner: Jewish Times (The)
Editorial: 901 State Route 10, Whippany, New Jersey 07981-1105. **T:** 1 973 887-3900
E: editorial@njjewishnews.com
W: http://www.njjewishnews.com **Circ:** 48000 Not Audited
Editor in Chief: Andrew Silow-Carroll
Editorial Profile: New Jersey Jewish News in Whippany, NJ, covers news and events pertinent to Jewish communities in Greater Middlesex County, Greater Monmouth County, and Princeton Mercer Bucks, NJ counties. Published by the Jewish Federation of Greater MetroWest NJ, the North Jersey Jewish News has five editions.
NEWSPAPER

New Journal & Guide
Editorial: 974 Norfolk Sq, Norfolk, Virginia 23502. **T:** 1 757 543-6531
E: njguide@gmail.com
W: http://www.njournalg.com
Freq: Thu; **Circ:** 15000 Not Audited
Editorial Profile: New Journal and Guide is a weekly newspaper written for the African-American community of Norfolk, Virginia Beach, Chesapeake, Suffolk, Portsmouth, Hampton, and Newport News, VA. The newspaper aims to bring its readers information on local, national and international news and events.; Full Page Mono: 15.60
Currency: US Dollars
NEWSPAPER

New Milford Spectrum
Owner: Hearst Corporation
Editorial: 45B Main St, New Milford, Connecticut 06776-2807. **T:** 1 860 354-2273
W: http://www.newmilfordspectrum.com
Freq: Fri; **Circ:** 20614 Not Audited
Editor: Norm Cummings; **Publisher:** Shawn Palmer
Editorial Profile: New Milford Spectrum is a weekly newspaper for the town of New Milford, CT. The paper provides local information on current events, movies, entertainment, recreation and specialty columns.; Full Page Mono: 17.51
Currency: US Dollars
NEWSPAPER

The New Orleans Advocate
Owner: Capital City Press LLC
Editorial: 329 Baronne Street, New Orleans, Louisiana 70112. **T:** 1 504 636-7400
W: http://www.theneworleansadvocate.com
Freq: Daily
News Editor: Kenneth Duhe; **News Editor:** Kenneth Duhe
Editorial Profile: New Orleans Advocate is a Daily Newspaper providing Local, Community, Metro and City, Arts & Entertainment, Society, Sports and Business coverage for the residents of the New Orleans, LA metro area.
DAILY NEWSPAPER

New Orleans Data News Weekly
Owner: Data Enterprises, Inc.
Editorial: 3501 Napoleon Ave, New Orleans, Louisiana 70125-4843. **T:** 1 504 821-7421
E: datanews@bellsouth.net
W: http://www.ladatanews.com
Freq: Sat; **Circ:** 20000 Not Audited
Editor: Edwin Buggage; **Publisher:** Terry Jones
Editorial Profile: New Orleans Data News Weekly is a local weekly newspaper serving African-American residents in the New Orleans, LA area. The publication provides information on news and events of interest to the local community. The lead time for New Orleans Data News Weekly is one week.; Full Page Mono: 22.76
Currency: US Dollars
NEWSPAPER

New Pittsburgh Courier
Owner: Real Times, Inc.
Editorial: 315 E Carson St, Pittsburgh, Pennsylvania 15219-1202. **T:** 1 412 481-8302
E: newsroom@newpittsburghcourier.com
W: http://www.newpittsburghcourier.com
Freq: Wed; **Circ:** 10000 Not Audited
Publisher: Rod Doss
Editorial Profile: New Pittsburgh Courier is a weekly newspaper written for the African

American community in Western Pennsylvania. It covers local news and community events of interest to African Americans.; Full Page Mono: 26.52
Currency: US Dollars
NEWSPAPER

New Tampa Neighborhood News
Owner: Coary
Editorial: 15345 Amberly Dr, Tampa, Florida 33647-2144. **T:** 1 813 910-2575
E: info@ntneighborhoodnews.com
W: http://ntneighborhoodnews.com
Freq: Monthly; **Circ:** 35000 Not Audited
Editorial Profile: New Tampa Neighborhood News is a monthly newspaper serving the residents of New Tampa and Wesley Chapel, FL. The publication contains news, sports, school updates, business updates, transportation and roadway issues, and other information of interest to the readership.; Full Page Mono: 13.62
Currency: US Dollars
NEWSPAPER

New Times
Owner: New Times Media Group
Editorial: 1010 Marsh St, San Luis Obispo, California 93401. **T:** 1 805 546-8208
E: letters@newtimesslo.com
W: http://www.newtimesslo.com
Freq: Thu; **Circ:** 40000 Not Audited
Publisher: Bob Rucker
Editorial Profile: New Times is published weekly for the residents of San Luis Obispo County, CA and surrounding areas. The newspaper covers local news, community events and lifestyle. Deadlines are on Fridays prior to issue date.; Full Page Mono: 11.98
Currency: US Dollars
NEWSPAPER

The New Town Press
Editorial: 421 Stone Meeting House Rd, Woolwich Township, New Jersey 08085-3609.
T: 1 856 467-3113
E: newtownpress@comcast.net
W: http://www.newtownpress.com
Freq: Fri; **Circ:** 14000 Not Audited
Editorial Profile: The New Town Press is a local monthly newspaper serving the Woolwich Township, NJ area. It provides information on local news and events of interest to the community. Deadlines for the publication are three weeks before issue date. Please contact the editor in chief with any further inquiries.; Full Page Mono: 11.75
Currency: US Dollars
NEWSPAPER

New Ulm Shopper Post Review
Editorial: 514 3rd North St, New Ulm, Minnesota 56073-1705. **T:** 1 507 359-2091
E: nushopper@nujournal.com
Freq: Tue; **Circ:** 16500 Not Audited
Editorial Profile: New Ulm Shopper Post Review is written for residents of New Ulm, MN and surrounding areas. It provides information on news and events of interest to the local community.; Full Page Mono: 5.45
Currency: US Dollars
NEWSPAPER

The New Vision
Owner: Roman Catholic Diocese of Tuscon
Editorial: 111 S Church Ave, Tucson, Arizona 85701-1602. **T:** 1 520 792-3410
W: http://www.newvisiononline.org
Freq: Monthly; **Circ:** 35000
Editorial Profile: The New Vision is a Catholic community newspaper serving the Roman Catholic Diocese of Tuscon, AZ.; Full Page Mono: 20.00
Currency: US Dollars
NEWSPAPER

New World Publications
Owner: Catholic Archdiocese of Chicago
Editorial: 835 N Rush St, Chicago, Illinois 60611-2030. **T:** 1 312 534-7777
E: editorial@catholicnewworld.com
W: http://www.catholicnewworld.com
Circ: 108000 Not Audited
Editor: Joyce Duriga; **Publisher:** Francis George
Editorial Profile: New World Publications' mission is to be the key source of information about the Catholic church in Chicago. It provides news, analysis and commentary about the church at the world, national and local levels and about issues of concern to the Catholic community. It acts as an instrument of evangelization by providing current information and guidance in matters of faith, morals and spiritual life.
NEWSPAPER

New York Amsterdam News
Owner: Am News Corp.
Editorial: 2340 Frederick Douglass Blvd, New York, New York 10027. **T:** 1 212 932-7400
W: http://www.amsterdamnews.com
Freq: Wed; **Circ:** 12587 Not Audited
Editor: Nayabe Arinde
Editorial Profile: New York Amsterdam News covers the African-American community in and around New York City. Includes news and events from the community, social issues and business. Also contains an insert of Healthy Choices, which focuses on the elimination of certain health problems that affect racial and ethnic minorities.; Full Page Mono: 62.39; Full Page Colour: 4516.30
Currency: US Dollars
NEWSPAPER

New York Awam
Owner: New York Awam Inc.
Editorial: 373 Broadway, Rm D20, New York, New York 10013-3928. **T:** 1 212 219-1331
E: nypawam@aol.com
W: http://newyorkawam.org
Freq: Fri; **Circ:** 50000 Not Audited
Editorial Profile: New York AWAM is a weekly, Urdu-language newspaper based out of New York.; Full Page Mono: 60.00
Currency: US Dollars
NEWSPAPER

New York Beacon
Owner: Smith Haj Group
Editorial: 237 W 37Th St Rm 201, New York, New York 10018-6779. **T:** 1 212 213-8585
E: newyorkbeacon@yahoo.com
W: http://www.newyorkbeacon.net
Freq: Thu; **Circ:** 71000 Not Audited
Editorial Profile: New York Beacon is a weekly general newspaper serving the Bronx, Brooklyn, Manhattan, Queens, Staten Island, Westchester and Long Island, NY as well as New Jersey and Connecticut. The newspaper covers sports, personalities, entertainment, health, local and world news and events.; Full Page Mono: 65.70
Currency: US Dollars
NEWSPAPER

The New York Carib News
Owner: Carib News Corporation
Editorial: 35 W 35Th St Ste 705, New York, New York 10001-2205. **T:** 1 212 944-1991
E: info@nycaribnews.com
W: http://www.nycaribnews.com
Freq: Wed; **Circ:** 67000 Not Audited
Editor: Michael Roberts; **Publisher:** Karl Rodney
Editorial Profile: Launched in 1983, The New York Carib News, a 50-page tabloid-sized newspaper, is published weekly for the Caribbean-American community of New York City. The publication covers local news, sports, fashion, travel, community events and lifestyle information from and about the Caribbean. Deadlines are on Fridays at 6pm ET.; Full Page Mono: 80.00; Full Page Colour: 5670.00
Currency: US Dollars
NEWSPAPER

New York Journal
Owner: General Media Strategies, Inc.
Editorial: 500 W 39th St, 3rd Fl, New York, New York 10018-1105. **T:** 1 212 586-4141
E: blacknewswatch@aol.com
Freq: Thu; **Circ:** 69000 Not Audited
Editorial Profile: The New York Journal is a weekly newspaper serving the African American community in New York. The bulk of the paper's staff consists of contributors and freelance writers.; Full Page Mono: 60.00; Full Page Colour: 61.60
Currency: US Dollars
NEWSPAPER

The New York Observer
Owner: Observer Media Group, LLC
Editorial: 321 W 44th St, New York, New York 10036-5404. **T:** 1 212 755-2400
E: editorial@observer.com
W: http://www.observer.com
Freq: Wed; **Circ:** 60312 Not Audited
Editor in Chief: Ken Kurson; **Publisher:** Jared Kushner; **Editor:** Guelda Voien
Editorial Profile: The New York Observer is written for residents of New York City. Topics are mostly political in nature.; Full Page Mono: 210.61; Full Page Colour: 1391.00
Currency: US Dollars
NEWSPAPER

New York Post
Owner: News America Publishing Inc.
Editorial: 1211 Avenue of the Americas, New York, New York 10036-8701.

T: 1 212 930-8000 8
W: http://www.nypost.com
Freq: Daily; **Circ:** 477314 Not Audited
Editor in Chief: Col Allan; **Publisher:** Jesse Angelo
Editorial Profile: New York Post is a tabloid-format newspaper aimed at the general public in the New York City area. The publication covers local and regional news, business, sports, entertainment, celebrities, fashion and travel.; Full Page Mono: 1014.24; Full Page Colour: 1301.55
Currency: US Dollars
DAILY NEWSPAPER

New York Post
Editorial: 529 14th St NW Ste 1114, Washington, District Of Columbia 20045-2101. **T:** 1 202 393-1787
DAILY NEWSPAPER

New York Post
Editorial: 9 City Hall, New York, New York 10007-1200. **T:** 1 212 566-2367
DAILY NEWSPAPER

The New York Times
Owner: New York Times Company (The)
Editorial: 620 8th Ave, New York, New York 10018-1618. **T:** 1 212 556-1234
E: news-tips@nytimes.com
W: http://www.nytimes.com
Freq: Daily; **Circ:** 2149012 Not Audited
Publisher: Arthur Ochs Sulzberger
Editorial Profile: The New York Times offers the latest news from around the world. There are several different editions of the paper for Eastern and national regions. The paper gets much of its content and reporting from its many bureaus. The foreign desk is responsible for correspondents and stringers around the world. The paper offers DealBook pages Tuesdays through Fridays, with content corresponding with the DealBook blog. Daily deadlines are usually between 5pm and 6pm ET. The paper does not accept artwork. This outlet covers TCommerce (Television Commerce).; Full Page Mono: 823.00; Full Page Colour: 1067.00
Currency: US Dollars
DAILY NEWSPAPER

The New York Times - Atlanta
Editorial: 2107 N Decatur St., Ste 419, Decatur, Georgia 30033. **T:** 1 404 584-8645
Bureau Chief: Richard Fausset
DAILY NEWSPAPER

The New York Times - Chicago
Editorial: 111 E Wacker Dr Ste 3020, Chicago, Illinois 60601-4803. **T:** 1 312 552-7200
Bureau Chief: Monica Davey
DAILY NEWSPAPER

The New York Times - City Hall Bureau
Editorial: 1 City Hall, Rm 9, New York, New York 10007-1212. **T:** 1 212 556-1947
DAILY NEWSPAPER

The New York Times - Houston
Editorial: 440 Louisiana St, Ste 1510, Houston, Texas 77002. **T:** 1 713 752-2006
Bureau Chief: Manny Fernandez
DAILY NEWSPAPER

The New York Times - Los Angeles
Editorial: 5900 Wilshire Blvd Ste 910, Los Angeles, California 90036-5027.
T: 1 323 658-8984
Bureau Chief: Adam Nagourney
DAILY NEWSPAPER

The New York Times - Miami
Editorial: 100 Biscayne Blvd Ste 3020, Miami, Florida 33132-2305. **T:** 1 305 358-6066
Bureau Chief: Lizette Alvarez
DAILY NEWSPAPER

The New York Times - NYPD
Editorial: 1 Police Plz, Ste 202C, New York, New York 10038-1403. **T:** 1 212 556-1337
DAILY NEWSPAPER

The New York Times - San Francisco
Editorial: 201 Spear St Suite 1560, San Francisco, California 94105-1961.
T: 1 415 836-6700 **E:** sfburo@nytimes.com
Bureau Chief: Norimitsu Onishi
Editorial Profile: The bureau prefers all staff to be contacted by e-mail.
DAILY NEWSPAPER

The New York Times - United Nations
Editorial: Secretariat Bldg Rm 453 UN, New York, New York 10017-0000.
T: 1 212 556-7161
DAILY NEWSPAPER

The New York Times - Washington D.C.
Editorial: 1627 I St NW, Washington, District Of Columbia 20006-4007. **T:** 1 202 862-0300
DAILY NEWSPAPER

The Newnan Times-Herald
Owner: Thomasson Family
Editorial: 16 Jefferson St, Newnan, Georgia 30263-1913. **T:** 1 770 253-1576
E: editor@newnan.com
W: http://www.times-herald.com
Freq: Daily; **Circ:** 11860 Not Audited
Editor: Ellen Corker; **Editor:** Winston Skinner
Editorial Profile: The Newnan Times-Herald is written for residents of Newnan, GA. It covers local news and events.; Full Page Mono: 17.85; Full Page Colour: 100.00
Currency: US Dollars
DAILY NEWSPAPER

Newport Beach Independent
Owner: Firebrand Media LLC
Editorial: 1834 Newport Blvd, Costa Mesa, California 92627-5045. **T:** 1 949 715-4100
W: http://www.newportbeachindy.com
Circ: 25500
Editor: Christopher Trela
Editorial Profile: Founded in June 2009, this newspaper aims to fill the vacuum created by relentless cuts made to local news coverage. Provides news, commentary and information about Newport Beach, CA and Costa Mesa, CA.; Full Page Colour: 11.07
Currency: US Dollars
NEWSPAPER

Newport Daily Express
Owner: Horizon Publications
Editorial: 178 Hill St, Newport, Vermont 5855.
T: 1 802 334-6568
W: http://newportvermontdailyexpress.com
Freq: Mon thru Fri; **Circ:** 4290 Not Audited
Publisher: Ken Wells
Editorial Profile: Newport Daily Express serves the residents of Newport, VT and its surrounding areas. The paper provides information on local news and events of interest to the community.; Full Page Mono: 10.45; Full Page Colour: 11.99
Currency: US Dollars
DAILY NEWSPAPER

Newport Daily Express
Editorial: United Nations, Room C-322, New York, New York 10017. **T:** 1 212 560-4312
Editorial Profile: This is the New York bureau of the Newport Daily Express, which is based in Newport, VT.
DAILY NEWSPAPER

The Newport Daily News
Owner: Sherman Publishing Co.
Editorial: 101 Malbone Rd, Newport, Rhode Island 2840. **T:** 1 401 849-3300
E: newsroom@newportri.com
W: http://www.newportdailynews.com
Freq: Daily; **Circ:** 11678 Not Audited
Publisher: William Lucey; **News Editor:** Harvey Peters
Editorial Profile: The Newport Daily News is a local newspaper serving Newport, RI and the surrounding area. The newspaper provides information on news and events of interest to the local community. Advertising deadlines are at 4pm ET.; Full Page Mono: 22.00; Full Page Colour: 325.00
Currency: US Dollars
DAILY NEWSPAPER

Newport Miner & Gem State Miner Newspapers
Owner: Willenbrock II (Frederick J.)
Editorial: 421 S Spokane, Newport, Washington 99156. **T:** 1 509 447-2433
E: theminer@povn.com
W: http://www.pendoreillerivervalley.com
Circ: 6500 Not Audited
NEWSPAPER

Newport This Week
Editorial: 86 Broadway, Newport, Rhode Island 02840-2750. **T:** 1 401 847-7766
E: news@newportthisweek.net
W: http://newport-now.com
Freq: Thu; **Circ:** 13800 Not Audited
Editorial Profile: Newport This Week, is a weekly newspaper written for the residents of Newport, RI. The editorial content includes

community news and events, sports, weather, editorials and a community guide. The editorial lead time is on Mondays at 5pm ET. Advertising deadlines are at noon ET.; Full Page Mono: 14.00
Currency: US Dollars
NEWSPAPER

The News & Advance
Owner: BH Media Group
Editorial: 101 Wyndale Dr, Lynchburg, Virginia 24501-6710. **T:** 1 434 946-7195
E: news@newsadvance.com
W: http://www.newsadvance.com
Freq: Daily; **Circ:** 27338 Not Audited
Publisher: Terry Jamerson
Editorial Profile: News & Advance is a daily newspaper. Publication coverage includes local news, business, lifestyle and political information. The newspaper is intended for a readership of residents of Lynchburg, VA and surrounding areas.; Full Page Mono: 56.10; Full Page Colour: 806.10
Currency: US Dollars
DAILY NEWSPAPER

News & Citizen, Inc.
Owner: News & Citizen, Inc.
Editorial: 417 Brooklyn St, Morrisville, Vermont 05661-8510. **T:** 1 802 888-2212
E: news@newsandcitizen.com
W: http://www.newsandcitizen.com
Circ: 18925 Not Audited
Publisher: Bradley Limoge; **Editor:** J.B. McKinley
NEWSPAPER

The News & Observer
Owner: McClatchy Newspapers
Editorial: 215 S McDowell St, Raleigh, North Carolina 27601-1331. **T:** 1 919 829-4500
E: metroeds@newsobserver.com
W: http://www.newsobserver.com
Freq: Daily; **Circ:** 121441 Not Audited
Editorial Profile: The News & Observer is a daily newspaper serving the Research Triangle of Raleigh, Durham, and Chapel Hill. The newspaper was started in the 1800s and was family-owned until 1997, when it was purchased by The McClatchy Company. The News & Observer runs seven days a week and includes national, regional, and local news, as well as sports, health, business, technology, and lifestyle information. Health and science, education, home, arts, auto, money, and business coverage run daily. In addition to the Research Triangle area, The News & Observer reaches Orange, Wake, Johnston, and Harnett counties. There is no editorial calendar available and deadlines are ongoing.; Full Page Mono: 290.86; Full Page Colour: 322.54
Currency: US Dollars
DAILY NEWSPAPER

The News & Observer
Editorial: 505 W Franklin St, Chapel Hill, North Carolina 27516-2315. **T:** 1 919 932-2000
E: orange@newsobserver.com
Bureau Chief: Mark Schultz; **Bureau Chief:** Mark Schultz; **Bureau Chief:** Mark Schultz
DAILY NEWSPAPER

News & Observer Weeklies - Chapel Hill
Owner: McClatchy Newspapers
Editorial: 505 W Franklin St, Chapel Hill, North Carolina 27516-2315. **T:** 1 919 932-2011
Circ: 92300 Not Audited
Publisher: Orage Quarles; **Editor:** Mark Schultz; **Editor:** Mark Schultz; **Editor:** Mark Schultz
NEWSPAPER

News & Record
Owner: BH Media Group
Editorial: 200 E Market St, Greensboro, North Carolina 27401-2910. **T:** 1 336 373-7000
W: http://www.news-record.com
Freq: Daily; **Circ:** 49496 Not Audited
News Editor: Cathy Frail
Editorial Profile: News & Record is a daily newspaper published for the residents of Greensboro, NC. It began as two smaller papers, The Daily Record and The Greensboro Daily News. The Daily Record was founded in 1890, The Greensboro Daily News in 1909. In 1982, the two papers merged and became a strictly morning paper and established its current name. It serves to inform Greensboro, Guilford, Randolph, Rockingham, Alamance, and Davidson, NC counties, the so-called Triad area, about current events, local and national news, culture, sports and world affairs. It is published in four different editions, which are all geared toward their respective area of distribution.; Full Page Mono: 89.73; Full Page Colour: 297.00

Currency: US Dollars
DAILY NEWSPAPER

News & Record
Editorial: 203 E Harris Pl, Eden, North Carolina 27288-5329. **T:** 1 336 627-4881
DAILY NEWSPAPER

News and Eagle
Owner: KBA News, LLC
Editorial: 306 N Main St, New Carlisle, Ohio 45344-1839. **T:** 1 937 845-1709
E: input@newcarlisleohio.net **Circ:** 3600
Publisher: Dale Grimm
NEWSPAPER

The News and Tribune
Owner: Community Newspaper Holdings, Inc.
Editorial: 221 Spring St, Jeffersonville, Indiana 47130-3353. **T:** 1 812 283-6636
E: newsroom@newsandtribune.com
W: http://newsandtribune.com
Freq: Daily; **Circ:** 9725 Not Audited
Publisher: Bill Hanson; **Editor:** Shea Van Hoy
Editorial Profile: The News and Tribune is written for the residents of Clark and Floyd County, IN. It covers local news, sports, lifestyle and community events. The paper is published Tuesday through Sunday.; Full Page Mono: 18.50; Full Page Colour: 150.00
Currency: US Dollars
DAILY NEWSPAPER

The News and Tribune
Editorial: 303 Scribner Dr, New Albany, Indiana 47150. **T:** 1 812 206-6397 **Circ:** 8389 Not Audited; Full Page Mono: 18.50; Full Page Colour: 150.00
Currency: US Dollars
DAILY NEWSPAPER

News Barometer
Editorial: 30344 Overseas Hwy, Big Pine Key, Florida 33043. **T:** 1 305 872-0106
E: bigpinenews@aol.com
W: http://www.newsbarometer.com
Freq: Fri; **Circ:** 10000 Not Audited
Editorial Profile: News Barometer is a local weekly newspaper serving the residents of Big Pine, FL. The publication covers local news and community events. Deadlines are Tuesdays at noon ET.; Full Page Mono: 7.00; Full Page Colour: 616.00
Currency: US Dollars
NEWSPAPER

News Chief
Owner: Halifax Media Holdings LLC
Editorial: 455 6th St NW, Winter Haven, Florida 33881-4061. **T:** 1 863 401-6900
E: news@newschief.com
W: http://www.newschief.com
Freq: Daily; **Circ:** 2979 Not Audited
Publisher: Jerome Ferson
Editorial Profile: News Chief is a local daily newspaper serving the residents of Polk County, FL and its surrounding communities. The newspaper covers local and national news, business, entertainment and sports.; Full Page Mono: 16.20; Full Page Colour: 150.00
Currency: US Dollars
DAILY NEWSPAPER

News Chronicle Company, Inc.
Owner: Sample News Group
Editorial: 22 E King St, Shippensburg, Pennsylvania 17257-1308. **T:** 1 717 532-4101
E: nceditor@gmail.com **W:** http://shipnc.com
Circ: 6800 Not Audited
Publisher: Joe Beegle
Editorial Profile: News Chronicle Company, Inc. is a community newspaper publisher servicing the residents of Harrisburg and Carlisle, PA.
NEWSPAPER

The News Courier
Owner: Community Newspaper Holdings, Inc.
Editorial: 410 W Green St, Athens, Alabama 35611-2518. **T:** 1 256 232-2720
W: http://www.enewscourier.com
Freq: Daily; **Circ:** 5970 Not Audited
Publisher: Ann Laurence
Editorial Profile: The News Courier is a local daily newspaper serving the residents of Athens, AL and the surrounding communities. It covers local news and community events.; Full Page Mono: 11.47; Full Page Colour: 39.50
Currency: US Dollars
DAILY NEWSPAPER

The News Democrat
Owner: Ohio Community Media LLC.
Editorial: 111 E State St, Georgetown, Ohio 45121-1412. **T:** 1 937 378-6161

E: info@newsdemocrat.com
W: http://www.newsdemocrat.com
Freq: Weekly; **Circ:** 26385 Not Audited
Editorial Profile: The News-Democrat, located in Georgetown, OH, publishes local weekly newspapers serving in and around Brown County, OH.
NEWSPAPER

News Extra
Owner: Media General Inc.
Editorial: 310 S Dargan St, Florence, South Carolina 29506. **T:** 1 843 317-6397
W: http://www.scnow.com
Freq: Wed; **Circ:** 12500 Not Audited
Publisher: Mark Laskowski; **Editor:** Matt Tate
Editorial Profile: News Extra is a supplemental publication of Morning News, circulated to residents of Florence, SC. The newspaper covers news, community events, sports and arts & entertainment.; Full Page Mono: 6.00
Currency: US Dollars
NEWSPAPER

News For You
Owner: New Readers Press
Editorial: 104 Marcellus St., Syracuse, New York 13204. **T:** 1 315 422-9121
E: nrp@proliteracy.org
W: http://www.newsforyouonline.com
Freq: Wed; **Circ:** 67387 Not Audited
Editor: Tracy Carman
Editorial Profile: News for You is a weekly newspaper circulated nationally to schools. It is written at the reading level of four to six. Each issue includes the top news of the week, world news, national news, people in the news and special features such as A Look at Work, Health News and The Law. The publication does not accept press releases or advertisements.
NEWSPAPER

The News Gazette
Owner: Community Media Group
Editorial: 224 W Franklin St, Winchester, Indiana 47394-1808. **T:** 1 765 584-4501
E: newsgazette@comcast.net
W: http://www.winchesternewsgazette.com
Freq: Daily; **Circ:** 2500 Not Audited
Editorial Profile: The News Gazette is a daily newspaper published for residents of Winchester, IN. The paper covers local news, sports and business.; Full Page Mono: 10.45; Full Page Colour: 135.00
Currency: US Dollars
DAILY NEWSPAPER

The News Gram
Editorial: 2543 Del Rio Blvd, Eagle Pass, Texas 78852. **T:** 1 830 773-8610
E: elgram@hilconet.com
W: http://www.thenewsgramonline.net
Freq: Fri; **Circ:** 3000 Not Audited
Editorial Profile: The News Gram is a daily, Spanish-English bilingual newspaper serving the residents of Eagle Pass, TX, which is a community near San Antonio. The publication covers local news and events. The deadline to submit press releases is 2pm CT.; Full Page Mono: 7.35; Full Page Colour: 150.00
Currency: US Dollars
NEWSPAPER

The News Herald
Owner: Halifax Media Holdings LLC
Editorial: 501 W 11th St, Panama City, Florida 32401-2330. **T:** 1 850 747-5000
E: pcnhnews@pcnh.com
W: http://www.newsherald.com
Freq: Mon thru Fri; **Circ:** 30829 Not Audited
Editor: Mike Cazalas; **Editor:** Robert Cooper; **Publisher:** Alan Davis
Editorial Profile: The News Herald is a daily newspaper that serves the Panama City, FL area. The newspaper covers local news, business, sports, lifestyle, business, government, military and community events.; Full Page Mono: 60.69
Currency: US Dollars
DAILY NEWSPAPER

The News Herald
Owner: World Media Enterprises, Inc.
Editorial: 301 Collett St, Morganton, North Carolina 28655-3322. **T:** 1 828 437-2161
E: news@morganton.com
W: http://www.morganton.com
Freq: Daily; **Circ:** 10160 Not Audited
Editor: Kyle Phipps; **Publisher:** Lamar Smitherman
Editorial Profile: The News Herald is a daily newspaper serving the Morganton, NC area. It includes local news, sports, lifestyle, business and arts & entertainment. The paper covers national news stories only if they have an impact on the readers.; Full Page Mono: 13.58

Currency: US Dollars
DAILY NEWSPAPER

News Herald/Greene County News
Owner: Hudson-Catskill Newspaper Corp.
Editorial: 164 Main St, Ravena, New York 12143-1112. **T:** 1 518 756-2030
E: ravenaclass@thedailymail.net
W: http://www.thedailymail.net **Circ:** 3700 Not Audited
Publisher: Heather Bagshaw; **Editor:** Hilary Hawke; **Editor:** Melanie Lekoceinc
Editorial Profile: News Herald/Greene County News provides Local News coverage to Greene County and Albany County communities.
NEWSPAPER

News India (U.S.A.) Inc.
Owner: Parikh Worldwide Media LLC
Editorial: 37 W 20th St Ste 1009, New York, New York 10011-3714. **T:** 1 212 675-7515
E: editor@newsindiatimes.com
W: http://www.newsindiatimes.com
Freq: Fri; **Circ:** 14400 Not Audited
Editor: Sunil Adam; **Publisher:** Sudhir Parikh
Editorial Profile: Parikh Worldwide Media LLC is the largest Indian-American publishing group in the United States. The group publishes "News India Times," a national weekly newspaper and "Desi Talk in New York," a weekly newspaper serving the New York-New Jersey-Connecticut region.; Full Page Mono: 40.00
Currency: US Dollars
NEWSPAPER

News Journal
Owner: Gannett Co., Inc.
Editorial: 70 W 4th St, Mansfield, Ohio 44903-1676. **T:** 1 419 522-3311
E: yournews@mansfieldnewsjournal.com
W: http://www.mansfieldnewsjournal.com
Freq: Daily; **Circ:** 16733 Not Audited
Editor: Dave Polcyn
Editorial Profile: News Journal is a daily newspaper written for the residents of Mansfield, OH to provide local news coverage and community information.; Full Page Mono: 38.70; Full Page Colour: 415.00
Currency: US Dollars
DAILY NEWSPAPER

The News Journal
Owner: Gannett Co., Inc.
Editorial: 950 W Basin Rd, New Castle, Delaware 19720-1008. **T:** 1 302 324-2500
E: newsdesk@delawareonline.com
W: http://www.delawareonline.com
Freq: Daily; **Circ:** 76246 Not Audited
Editorial Profile: The News Journal is a daily broadsheet newspaper covering regional, national and international news for the New Castle, DE area.; Full Page Mono: 155.76; Full Page Colour: 494.54
Currency: US Dollars
DAILY NEWSPAPER

The News Journal
Editorial: 116 E Water St, Dover, Delaware 19901-3614. **T:** 1 302 734-7577
DAILY NEWSPAPER

The News Journal
Owner: Swartz Media
Editorial: 312 Railroad Ave, Florence, South Carolina 29506. **T:** 1 843 667-9656
E: tnj@florencenewsjournal.com
W: http://www.florencenewsjournal.com
Freq: Wed; **Circ:** 20500 Not Audited
Editor: Brenda Harrison; **Publisher:** Don Swartz
Editorial Profile: The News Journal is a local newspaper written for the residents of Florence, SC.; Full Page Mono: 15.75
Currency: US Dollars
NEWSPAPER

News Korea Weekly
Owner: News Korea Texas Inc.
Editorial: 2000 Royal Ln, Ste 200, Dallas, Texas 75229. **T:** 1 972 247-9111
W: http://www.wnewskorea.com
Freq: Fri; **Circ:** 10500 Not Audited
Publisher: Timothy Choe; **Editor:** Yun Choi
Editorial Profile: News Korea Weekly is a free community newspaper providing regional and local news to the Korean American populations of many cities in Texas. The paper is distributed in the Dallas/Ft. Worth area as well as Austin, Houston, San Antonio and Killeen, TX.; Full Page Mono: 4.30; Full Page Colour: 6.45
Currency: US Dollars
NEWSPAPER

The News Leader
Owner: Gannett Co., Inc.
Editorial: 11 N Central Ave, Staunton, Virginia 24401-4212. **T:** 1 540 885-7281
E: getpublished@newsleader.com
W: http://www.newsleader.com
Freq: Daily; **Circ:** 14675 Not Audited
Publisher: Roger Watson
Editorial Profile: The News Leader is published daily for the residents of Staunton, VA and surrounding areas. The newspaper covers local, regional and national news, sports and community events.; Full Page Mono: 39.95; Full Page Colour: 1070.00
Currency: US Dollars
DAILY NEWSPAPER

News Leader
Owner: Community Newspapers Inc.
Editorial: 511 Ash St, Fernandina Beach, Florida 32034. **T:** 1 904 261-3696
W: http://www.fbnewsleader.com
Freq: Fri; **Circ:** 12200 Not Audited
Publisher: Foy Maloy; **Editor:** Michael Parnell
Editorial Profile: News Leader is a newspaper serving the residents of Fernandina Beach, FL. The publication covers local news, community events and sports.; Full Page Mono: 19.27
Currency: US Dollars
NEWSPAPER

News Leader Newspapers
Owner: Lakeway Publishers of Florida
Editorial: 637 8th St, Clermont, Florida 34711-2159. **T:** 1 352 242-9818
E: thenewsleader@cfl.rr.com **Circ:** 84000 Not Audited
Publisher: Jodi Marano
Editorial Profile: News Leader Newspapers in Clermont, FL publishes the Clermont News Leader, the four Corners News Leader and the Sumter Shopper.
NEWSPAPER

The News Press
Owner: Community Newspaper Holdings, Inc.
Editorial: 211 W 9th Ave, Stillwater, Oklahoma 74074-4406. **T:** 1 405 372-5000
E: editor@stwnewspress.com
W: http://www.stillwater-newspress.com
Freq: Daily; **Circ:** 6804 Not Audited
Publisher: Jeff Funk
Editorial Profile: The News Press is published daily for the residents of Stillwater, OK and surrounding areas. The newspaper covers local and national news, sports, entertainment, business, lifestyle and community events.; Full Page Mono: 10.70; Full Page Colour: 225.00
Currency: US Dollars
DAILY NEWSPAPER

News Publishing
Editorial: 419 M St, Neligh, Nebraska 68756. **T:** 1 402 887-4840
E: nelighnews@frontiernet.net **Circ:** 2800 Not Audited
NEWSPAPER

News Publishing Company - Ringgold
Editorial: 7513 Nashville St, Ringgold, Georgia 30736. **T:** 1 706 935-2621
E: catoosacountynews@catoosanews.com
W: http://www.catoosanews.com **Circ:** 8745 Not Audited
Editor: Misty Martin-Chastain
NEWSPAPER

News Publishing Company, Inc.
Editorial: 1126 Mills St, Black Earth, Wisconsin 53515. **T:** 1 608 767-3655
E: pmr@newspubinc.com
W: http://www.newspubinc.com **Circ:** 64099 Not Audited
Editor: Michael Carignan; **Editor:** John Donaldson; **Editor:** Matt Geiger; **Editor:** Gary Schuetz
NEWSPAPER

The News Reporter
Owner: News Reporter Company Inc.
Editorial: 127 W Columbus St, Whiteville, North Carolina 28472-4023.
T: 1 910 642-4104
W: http://www.whiteville.com
Freq: Mon; **Circ:** 10483 Not Audited
Editor: Dan Biser; **News Editor:** Clara Cartrette; **Publisher:** James High; **Editor:** Les High
Editorial Profile: News Reporter is a weekly newspaper serving the residents of Whiteville, NC.; Full Page Mono: 12.12
Currency: US Dollars
NEWSPAPER

News Sun
Owner: KPC Media Group Inc.

Editorial: 102 N Main St, Kendallville, Indiana 46755-1714. **T:** 1 260 347-0400
W: http://www.kpcnews.com/
Freq: Daily; **Circ:** 7934
Publisher: Terry Housholder
Editorial Profile: News Sun is written for the residents of Kendallville, IN. It covers local news, national news, local sports, events, politics and agriculture. Deadlines are at 5pm CT.; Full Page Mono: 14.70; Full Page Colour: 30.14
Currency: US Dollars
DAILY NEWSPAPER

News Tribune
Owner: Daily News Tribune, Inc.
Editorial: 426 2nd St, La Salle, Illinois 61301-2334. **T:** 1 815 223-3200
E: ntnews@newstrib.com
W: http://www.newstrib.com
Freq: Mon thru Fri; **Circ:** 17626 Not Audited
Publisher: Joyce McCullough; **News Editor:** Craig Sterrett; **News Editor:** Craig Sterrett
Editorial Profile: News Tribune is published daily for the residents of La Salle, IL and the surrounding area. The newspaper covers local news, sports, lifestyles, business and community events.; Full Page Mono: 24.00; Full Page Colour: 345.00
Currency: US Dollars
DAILY NEWSPAPER

News Tribune
Owner: Wehco Media Inc.
Editorial: 210 Monroe St, Jefferson City, Missouri 65101. **T:** 1 573 636-3131
E: editor@newstribune.com
W: http://www.newstribune.com
Freq: Daily; **Circ:** 15021
Editorial Profile: News Tribune is a local daily newspaper serving the residents of Jefferson City, MO. It provides information on local news, events, sports and weather. Deadlines are at 11pm CT one day prior to issue date.; Full Page Mono: 10.09; Full Page Colour: 180.00
Currency: US Dollars
DAILY NEWSPAPER

The News Tribune
Owner: McClatchy Newspapers
Editorial: 1950 S State St, Tacoma, Washington 98405-2817. **T:** 1 253 597-8742
E: newstips@thenewstribune.com
W: http://www.thenewstribune.com
Freq: Daily; **Circ:** 65264 Not Audited
Publisher: David Zeeck
Editorial Profile: The News Tribune is a daily newspaper reaching readers in Tacoma and Pierce County, WA. The paper covers sports with the following sections: Baseball, basketball, football, golf/tennis, hockey, college, UW Huskies and WSU Cougars. It covers business with market summaries and a Fortune 500 list. In addition, it covers government, crime and environmental issues. Arts & entertainment includes comics, puzzles, computers, food and restaurant coverage, family issues, travel and TV listings. Public opinion is represented in the following sections: Editorials, endorsements, letters and writers tips. The paper also covers technology issues in the greater South Puget Sound region. Deadlines are at noon PT three days before issue date.; Full Page Mono: 162.80; Full Page Colour: 498.86
Currency: US Dollars
DAILY NEWSPAPER

The News Tribune
Editorial: 1417 Columbia St SW, Olympia, Washington 98501-2342. **T:** 1 360 786-1826
DAILY NEWSPAPER

The News Virginian
Owner: BH Media Group
Editorial: 1300 W Main St, Waynesboro, Virginia 22980-2414. **T:** 1 540 949-8213
E: enewstips@newsvirginian.com
W: http://www.newsvirginian.com
Freq: Daily; **Circ:** 6344 Not Audited
Editorial Profile: The News Virginian is a daily newspaper covering Waynesboro, Staunton, Augusta County and Nelson County, VA and the surrounding areas. Topics include community events, business and sports.; Full Page Mono: 23.85; Full Page Colour: 390.00
Currency: US Dollars
DAILY NEWSPAPER

News-Banner
Owner: News Banner Publications, Inc.
Editorial: 125 N Johnson St, Bluffton, Indiana 46714-1907. **T:** 1 260 824-0224
E: newsroom@news-banner.com
W: http://www.news-banner.com

Freq: Daily; **Circ:** 5059 Not Audited
Publisher: Mark Miller
Editorial Profile: News-Banner is published Monday through Saturday for the residents of Bluffton, IN and surrounding areas. It cover local news and community events. Deadlines are at noon CT one day prior to issue date.; Full Page Mono: 11.80; Full Page Colour: 240.00
Currency: US Dollars
DAILY NEWSPAPER

News-Bulletin Times
Editorial: 501 Madrid St, Castroville, Texas 78009. **T:** 1 830 538-2556
E: cornerstonenews@sbcglobal.net **Circ:** 5200 Not Audited
Publisher: Natalie Spencer
NEWSPAPER

Newsday
Owner: Cablevision Systems Corp.
Editorial: 235 Pinelawn Rd, Melville, New York 11747-4226. **T:** 1 631 843-2700
W: http://www.newsday.com
Freq: Daily; **Circ:** 443362 Not Audited
Publisher: Gordon McLeod
Editorial Profile: Newsday is a daily tabloid covering local, national and international news, business, sports and features. Its mission is to provide breaking news and news analysis to the general public. The paper won a 1997 Pulitzer Prize for Spot News and a 2002 Best in Business Breaking News award from the Society of American Business Editors and Writers.; Full Page Mono: 522.12; Full Page Colour: 52.20
Currency: US Dollars
DAILY NEWSPAPER

Newsday
Editorial: 1090 Vermont Ave NW, Washington, District Of Columbia 20005-4905.
T: 1 202 408-2715
DAILY NEWSPAPER

Newsday
Editorial: State Capitol LCA Pressroom, 3rd Floor, Albany, New York 12224.
T: 1 518 465-2311
Bureau Chief: Yancey Roy
DAILY NEWSPAPER

Newsday
Editorial: 633 E Main St, Riverhead, New York 11901-7013. **T:** 1 631 727-7333
Bureau Chief: Mitchell Freedman
DAILY NEWSPAPER

Newsday
Editorial: 225 Cadman Plz E Rm 695, Brooklyn, New York 11201-1832.
T: 1 718 624-6880
DAILY NEWSPAPER

Newsday
Editorial: 100 Supreme Court Dr, Mineola, New York 11501-4815
DAILY NEWSPAPER

The News-Dispatch
Owner: Paxton Media Group
Editorial: 121 W Michigan Blvd, Michigan City, Indiana 46360-3267. **T:** 1 219 874-7211
E: news@thenewsdispatch.com
W: http://www.michigancityin.com
Freq: Daily; **Circ:** 5965 Not Audited
Publisher: Bill Hackney; **Editor:** Amanda Haverstick
Editorial Profile: The News-Dispatch is published daily for the residents of Michigan City, IN and surrounding areas. The newspaper covers news, sports, business, events, entertainment, health and lifestyles.; Full Page Mono: 15.10
Currency: US Dollars
DAILY NEWSPAPER

The News-Enterprise
Owner: Landmark Community Newspapers, Inc.
Editorial: 408 W Dixie Ave, Elizabethtown, Kentucky 42701-2499. **T:** 1 270 769-1200
E: ne@thenewsenterprise.com
W: http://www.thenewsenterprise.com
Freq: Daily; **Circ:** 12257 Not Audited
News Editor: Jeff D'Alessio; **Publisher:** Chris Ordway; **Editor:** Ben Sheroan
Editorial Profile: The News-Enterprise is written for the community of Elizabethtown, KY.; Full Page Mono: 18.82; Full Page Colour: 348.82
Currency: US Dollars
DAILY NEWSPAPER

News-Enterprise
Owner: CommunityMedia Corporation
Editorial: 11110 Los Alamitos Blvd, Ste 101, Los Alamitos, California 90720-3602.
T: 1 562 431-1397
W: http://newsenterprise.net/
Freq: Wed; **Circ:** 30000 Not Audited
Editor: Ted Apodaca; **Publisher:** Lon Wahlberg
Editorial Profile: News-Enterprise is a newspaper serving the residents of Los Alamitos, Rossmoor, Cypress, La Palma, Seal Beach, Hawaiian Gardens and El Dorado Estates, CA. The publication covers local news and community events. Deadlines for the publication are Fridays at 5pm PT.; Full Page Mono: 16.00
Currency: US Dollars
NEWSPAPER

The News-Gazette
Owner: News-Gazette Inc.
Editorial: 15 E Main St, Champaign, Illinois 61820-3641. **T:** 1 217 351-5252
E: news@news-gazette.com
W: http://www.news-gazette.com
Freq: Daily; **Circ:** 41969
Editor: George Dobrik; **Publisher:** John Foreman
Editorial Profile: The News-Gazette is a newspaper serving the residents of Champaign, IL and its surrounding area. The publication covers local news, events, sports, arts & entertainment and business.; Full Page Mono: 47.53
Currency: US Dollars
DAILY NEWSPAPER

News-Gazette Community Newspapers
Owner: News-Gazette Inc.
Editorial: 303 E Main St Ste D, Mahomet, Illinois 61853-7424. **T:** 1 217 586-2512
Freq: Wed; **Circ:** 2300 Not Audited
Editor: Amelia Benner; **Publisher:** John Foreman
Editorial Profile: News-Gazette Community Newspapers is written for community of Mahomet, IL. The lead time for Mahomet Citizen is the same day.
NEWSPAPER

The News-Herald
Owner: Journal Register Company
Editorial: 7085 Mentor Ave, Willoughby, Ohio 44094. **T:** 1 440 951-0000
E: editor@news-herald.com
W: http://www.news-herald.com
Freq: Daily; **Circ:** 40238 Not Audited
Editor: Janet Podolak; **Editor:** Janet Podolak; **Publisher:** Jeff Sudbrook
Editorial Profile: The News-Herald provides local news, national news and sports coverage for the Northeast Ohio area.; Full Page Mono: 48.05; Full Page Colour: 705.00
Currency: US Dollars
DAILY NEWSPAPER

NewsHopper
Editorial: 2215 S 6Th St, Brainerd, Minnesota 56401-5549. **T:** 1 218 772-0300
E: hopper@emily.net
W: http://www.newshopper.net
Freq: Sat; **Circ:** 25000 Not Audited
Editorial Profile: NewsHopper is a local newspaper written for the residents of Aitkin, MN.; Full Page Mono: 12.50
Currency: US Dollars
NEWSPAPER

The News-Item
Owner: Times-Shamrock Communications
Editorial: 707 N Rock St, Shamokin, Pennsylvania 17872. **T:** 1 570 644-6397
E: editorial@newsitem.com
W: http://www.newsitem.com
Freq: Daily; **Circ:** 8163 Not Audited
Editor: Andy Heintzelman; **Publisher:** Henry Nyce
Editorial Profile: The News-Item provides local news and feature articles to residents in Northumberland County, PA.; Full Page Mono: 15.65; Full Page Colour: 520.00
Currency: US Dollars
DAILY NEWSPAPER

Newsleaders
Owner: Von Meyer Publishing, Inc.
Editorial: 32 1st Ave NW, Saint Joseph, Minnesota 56374-4524. **T:** 1 320 363-7741
E: news@thenewsleaders.com
W: http://www.thenewsleaders.com
Freq: Weekly; **Circ:** 11683
Editorial Profile: Newsleaders is a local newspaper in Saint Joseph, MN.
NEWSPAPER

The News-Messenger
Owner: Gannett Co., Inc.
Editorial: 1700 Cedar St, Fremont, Ohio 43420-1114. **T:** 1 419 332-5511
E: newsdesk@thenews-messenger.com
W: http://www.thenews-messenger.com
Freq: Daily; **Circ:** 5172
Editorial Profile: The News-Messenger is a daily newspaper serving the residents of Sandusky County and Fremont, OH. The publication covers local news, community events and sports.; Full Page Mono: 29.20; Full Page Colour: 325.00
Currency: US Dollars
DAILY NEWSPAPER

Newspaper Publishers LLC
Owner: Einstein (Don)
Editorial: 1035 Conklin Rd, Conklin, New York 13748-1102. **T:** 1 607 775-0472
E: deinstein@stny.rr.com
W: http://www.wecoverthetowns.com
Circ: 4000 Not Audited
Publisher: Don Einstein
NEWSPAPER

The News-Press
Owner: Gannett Co., Inc.
Editorial: 2442 Dr Martin Luther King Blvd, Fort Myers, Florida 33901-3904.
T: 1 239 335-0200
E: mailbag@news-press.com
W: http://www.news-press.com
Freq: Daily; **Circ:** 60197 Not Audited
Publisher: Mei-Mei Chan
Editorial Profile: The News-Press, located in Fort Myers, FL, was founded in 1884 by Stafford Cleveland. The newspaper joined the Gannett family in 1971. It publishes three different daily morning editions that are tailored to their respective distribution locations. These are Cape Coral, the area's largest city; Bonita Springs and South Lee County; and Fort Myers and surrounding Lee County. The newspaper covers local and regional, business, sports, lifestyles and entertainment news.; Full Page Mono: 115.80; Full Page Colour: 392.73
Currency: US Dollars
DAILY NEWSPAPER

News-Press
Editorial: 24850 Old 41 Rd, Bonita Springs, Florida 34135-7021. **T:** 1 239 992-1345
DAILY NEWSPAPER

News-Record
Owner: Gannett Co., Inc.
Editorial: 307 S Commercial St Ste 202, Neenah, Wisconsin 54956-5700.
T: 1 920 729-6622
E: information@newsrecord.net
W: http://www.newsrecord.net
Freq: Wed; **Circ:** 23900 Not Audited
Publisher: Genia Lovett; **Editor:** Rachel Rausch
Editorial Profile: News-Record is a local newspaper written for the residents of Neenah, WI. The paper covers news, sports and arts & entertainment. This outlet offers RSS (Really Simple Syndication.); Full Page Mono: 15.35
Currency: US Dollars
NEWSPAPER

News-Register
Owner: News-Register Publishing Co.
Editorial: 611 NE 3rd St, McMinnville, Oregon 97128. **T:** 1 503 472-5114
E: news@newsregister.com
W: http://www.newsregister.com
Freq: Sat; **Circ:** 10921 Not Audited
News Editor: Ty Walker; **Editor:** Racheal Winter
Editorial Profile: News-Register is published weekly for the residents of McMinnville, OR and surrounding areas. The newspaper covers local news, sports and community events.; Full Page Mono: 19.05
Currency: US Dollars
NEWSPAPER

News-Republican
Owner: Stephens Media
Editorial: 2136 Mamie Eisenhower Ave, Boone, Iowa 50036-4437. **T:** 1 515 432-1234
E: news@newsrepublican.com
W: http://www.newsrepublican.com
Freq: Daily; **Circ:** 2400 Not Audited
Editor in Chief: Greg Eckstrom; **Publisher:** Claudia Lovin
Editorial Profile: News-Republican is a newspaper covering local news, sports and community events for the residents of Boone, IA. The advertising deadline is at noon CT.; Full Page Mono: 7.90; Full Page Colour: 185.00
Currency: US Dollars

DAILY NEWSPAPER

The News-Review
Owner: Swift Newspapers
Editorial: 345 NE Winchester St, Roseburg, Oregon 97470. **T:** 1 541 672-3321
E: newsdesk@nrtoday.com
W: http://www.nrtoday.com
Freq: Daily; **Circ:** 18287 Not Audited
Editor: Vicki Menard; **Publisher:** Mark Raymond
Editorial Profile: The News-Review is a daily published for the residents of Roseburg, OR. It covers news and events in the local community.; Full Page Mono: 30.90; Full Page Colour: 605.00
Currency: US Dollars
DAILY NEWSPAPER

The News-Sentinel
Owner: Ogden Newspapers
Editorial: 600 W Main St, Fort Wayne, Indiana 46802. **T:** 1 260 461-8439
W: http://www.news-sentinel.com
Freq: Mon thru Fri; **Circ:** 13409
Publisher: Michael Christman; **Editor:** Kerry Hubartt
Editorial Profile: The News-Sentinel is a daily newspaper covering local news, features, business and sports for the residents of Fort Wayne, IN. The paper has special sections that print throughout the week: Business Monday covers the world of business and guides readers through workplace and industry news on Mondays; Food offers recipes and suggestions on cooking on Tuesdays; Home & Style offers gardening and home improvement advice on Saturdays; Prep Sports Monday provides in depth coverage of high school sport on Mondays; Ticket! is a weekend arts & entertainment guide for the area around Fort Wayne, IN that prints on Thursdays.; Full Page Mono: 71.04; Full Page Colour: 97.04
Currency: US Dollars
DAILY NEWSPAPER

The News-Star
Owner: Gannett Co., Inc.
Editorial: 411 N 4th St, Monroe, Louisiana 71201-6743. **T:** 1 318 322-5161
E: news@thenewsstar.com
W: http://www.thenewsstar.com
Freq: Daily; **Circ:** 26000 Not Audited
News Editor: Mark Henderson; **Publisher:** David Petty
Editorial Profile: The News-Star is a daily newspaper serving residents of northeastern Louisiana. Their mission is to provide accurate and comprehensive news, advertising and public service information to readers in a timely fashion every day of the year.; Full Page Mono: 81.48; Full Page Colour: 595.00
Currency: US Dollars
DAILY NEWSPAPER

The News-Sun
Owner: Harbor Point Media LLC
Editorial: 2227 US Highway 27 S, Sebring, Florida 33870. **T:** 1 863 385-6155
E: editor@newssun.com
W: http://www.newssun.com
Freq: Fri; **Circ:** 17000 Not Audited
Editor: Scott Dressel
Editorial Profile: The News-Sun in Sebring, FL is a weekly newspaper serving residents of Highlands County, FL. Coverage includes local news, features, lifestyle, sports and business.; Full Page Mono: 16.39
Currency: US Dollars
NEWSPAPER

Newstime
Owner: Lakeway Publishers, Inc.
Editorial: 11102 Veterans Memorial Pkwy, Lake Saint Louis, Missouri 63367-1113.
T: 1 636 625-3081 **E:** newstime@centurytel.net
W: http://www.hometown-online.net
Freq: Sat; **Circ:** 17000
Publisher: Carol Clark; **Editor:** Tim Hager
Editorial Profile: Newstime is a local community newspaper written for the residents of Lake Saint Louis, MO and the surrounding communities.; Full Page Mono: 10.50; Full Page Colour: 60.50
Currency: US Dollars
NEWSPAPER

The News-Times
Owner: Hearst Corporation
Editorial: 333 Main St, Danbury, Connecticut 06810-5818. **T:** 1 203 744-5100
E: news@newstimes.com
W: http://www.newstimes.com
Freq: Daily; **Circ:** 15658 Not Audited
Editor: Art Cummings; **Publisher:** Henry B. Haitz

Editorial Profile: The News-Times is a daily newspaper written for the residents of Danbury, CT. It covers news, sports, entertainment, features and opinion. They prefer all press releases be sent to the main fax number, which reaches the newsroom directly.; Full Page Mono: 46.57; Full Page Colour: 399.00
Currency: US Dollars
DAILY NEWSPAPER

The News-Times
Owner: Community Media Whitewater Valley Publishing
Editorial: 123 S Jefferson St, Hartford City, Indiana 47348-2270. **T:** 1 765 348-0110
E: newstimes@comcast.net
W: http://www.hartfordcitynewstimes.com
Freq: Mon thru Fri; **Circ:** 740 Not Audited
Editorial Profile: The News-Times, formerly known as Hartford City News Times, is written for residents of Hartford City, IN. The newspaper covers local news, business, sports and arts & entertainment. The newspaper also covers national and statewide stories if they have a direct impact on the newspaper's readership.; Full Page Mono: 8.00; Full Page Colour: 20.00
Currency: US Dollars
DAILY NEWSPAPER

News-Times
Owner: News Media Corp.
Editorial: 831 NE Avery St, Newport, Oregon 97365. **T:** 1 541 265-8571
W: http://www.newportnewstimes.com
Freq: Fri; **Circ:** 10300 Not Audited
Editor: Steve Card
Editorial Profile: News-Times is published weekly for residents of Lincoln County, OR and surrounding areas. It covers local news, sports, business, entertainment and events.; Full Page Mono: 19.76
Currency: US Dollars
NEWSPAPER

News-Topic
Owner: Paxton Media Group
Editorial: 123 Pennton Ave NW, Lenoir, North Carolina 28645-4373. **T:** 1 828 758-7381
W: http://www.newstopic.net
Freq: Daily; **Circ:** 7646 Not Audited
Editor: Guy Lucas
Editorial Profile: News-Topic is a daily newspaper published for the residents of Caldwell County, NC. The publication covers local news, sports, arts and entertainment, and community events. It is best to send releases at least one week in advance of the event, and it is preferable to send them in two weeks prior.; Full Page Mono: 19.00; Full Page Colour: 196.44
Currency: US Dollars
DAILY NEWSPAPER

Newton Citizen
Owner: Southern Community Newspapers Inc.
Editorial: 969 S Main St NE, Conyers, Georgia 30012-4501. **T:** 1 770 483-7108
E: news@newtoncitizen.com
W: http://www.newtoncitizen.com
Freq: Daily; **Circ:** 16170 Not Audited
Publisher: J.K. Murphy; **Editor:** Alice Queen
Editorial Profile: Newton Citizen is published daily for the residents of Covington, GA and surrounding areas. The newspaper provides information on local and regional news and community events.; Full Page Mono: 18.04; Full Page Colour: 57.40
Currency: US Dollars
DAILY NEWSPAPER

Newton Daily News
Owner: Shaw Media
Editorial: 200 1st Ave E, Newton, Iowa 50208-3716. **T:** 1 641 792-3121
E: newsroom@newtondailynews.com
W: http://www.newtondailynews.com
Freq: Daily; **Circ:** 5800 Not Audited
Publisher: Dan Goetz
Editorial Profile: Newton Daily News is published daily for the residents of Newton, IA and surrounding areas. It provides local news and information on community events.; Full Page Mono: 10.20; Full Page Colour: 150.00
Currency: US Dollars
DAILY NEWSPAPER

Newton Kansan
Owner: GateHouse Media Inc.
Editorial: 121 W 6Th St, Newton, Kansas 67114-2117. **T:** 1 316 283-1500
E: news@thekansan.com
W: http://www.thekansan.com
Freq: Daily; **Circ:** 7513 Not Audited
News Editor: James Jordan; **Publisher:** Randy Mitchell

Editorial Profile: Newton Kansan is a local daily newspaper written for residents of Newton, KS and the surrounding area. The newspaper covers local news, business, sports and arts & entertainment stories. The newspaper also covers national and statewide stories if they have a direct impact on the newspaper's readership.; Full Page Mono: 16.08; Full Page Colour: 200.00
Currency: US Dollars
DAILY NEWSPAPER

Nguoi Viet Daily News
Owner: Nguoi Viet Inc.
Editorial: 14771 Moran St, Westminster, California 92683. **T:** 1 714 892-9414
E: nv2@nguoi-viet.com
W: http://www.nguoi-viet.com
Freq: Daily; **Circ:** 18000 Not Audited
Editor: Giao Pham; **Publisher:** Dat Phan
Editorial Profile: Nguoi Viet Daily News provides news and information to the Vietnamese community in the United States, particularly those living in California. The publication was the first Vietnamese language daily newspaper written outside of Vietnam. Advertising deadlines are at 2pm PT.; Full Page Mono: 16.50; Full Page Colour: 1173.00
Currency: US Dollars
DAILY NEWSPAPER

Niagara Frontier Publications
Editorial: 1859 Whitehaven Rd, Grand Island, New York 14072-1803. **T:** 1 716 773-7676
W: http://www.wnypapers.com **Circ:** 31350 Not Audited
Editor: Larry Austin; **Editor:** Susan Campbell; **Publisher:** Skip Mazenauer
Editorial Profile: Niagara Frontier Publications in Grand Island, NY is a publisher of community newspapers.
NEWSPAPER

Niagara Gazette
Owner: Community Newspaper Holdings, Inc.
Editorial: 310 Niagara St, Niagara Falls, New York 14303-1141. **T:** 1 716 282-2311
W: http://www.niagara-gazette.com
Freq: Daily; **Circ:** 10498 Not Audited
Publisher: Peter Mio
Editorial Profile: Niagara Gazette is a daily, local newspaper for the area surrounding Niagara Falls, NY. The newspaper covers local news, business, sports, finance, health and arts & entertainment. It also covers national and statewide stories if they have a direct impact on the newspaper's readership. Deadlines are between 12:30pm and 1pm ET.; Full Page Mono: 34.72
Currency: US Dollars
DAILY NEWSPAPER

Nielson Publishing Inc.
Editorial: 164 S Elm St, Avoca, Iowa 51521. **T:** 1 712 343-2154
E: avocajh@iowatelecom.net **Circ:** 2750 Not Audited
Publisher: Donald Nielson; **Editor:** Richard Price
NEWSPAPER

NikkeiWest
Editorial: 123 E San Carlos St, Ste 521, San Jose, California 95112. **T:** 1 408 998-0920
E: editor@nikkeiwest.com
W: http://www.nikkeiwest.com
Freq: Bi-Weekly; **Circ:** 12000 Not Audited
Editorial Profile: NikkeiWest is for Japanese Americans residing in northern California. The editorial content includes local and national news, events, sports, history and other topics of general interest.; Full Page Mono: 6.50; Full Page Colour: 1700.00
Currency: US Dollars
NEWSPAPER *

Niles Daily Star
Owner: Leader Publications
Editorial: 217 N 4th St, Niles, Michigan 49120-2399. **T:** 1 269 683-2101
E: leader.news@leaderpub.com
W: http://www.nilesstar.com
Freq: Daily; **Circ:** 1970 Not Audited
Publisher: Bryan Clapper; **News Editor:** Kimberly Wynn
Editorial Profile: Niles Daily Star is published daily for the residents of Niles, MI and surrounding areas. The newspaper covers local and regional news, business, sports and entertainment.; Full Page Mono: 9.45
Currency: US Dollars
DAILY NEWSPAPER

NJN Publishing - Flemington
Owner: Advance Publications Inc.
Editorial: 8 Minneakoning Rd, Flemington, New Jersey 8822. **T:** 1 908 782-4747

W: http://www.nj.com/hunterdon **Circ:** 151548
Publisher: Joseph Gioioso; **Editor:** Michael Kelly; **News Editor:** Beth Wade; **News Editor:** Beth Wade
Editorial Profile: NJN Publishing is a weekly community newspaper publisher serving the residents of New Jersey.
NEWSPAPER

NJToday.net
Owner: CMD Media
Editorial: 1139 E Jersey St Ste 503, Elizabeth, New Jersey 07201-2444. **T:** 1 908 352-3100
E: news@njtoday.net
W: http://www.njtoday.net
Freq: Fri; **Circ:** 35000 Not Audited
Editor: Paul Hadsall; **Publisher:** Lisa McCormick
Editorial Profile: NJToday.net is a weekly newspaper serving Union and Middlesex County, NJ, and distributed throughout the area. The paper covers news and events of interest to local residents.; Full Page Mono: 40.00
Currency: US Dollars
NEWSPAPER

Nogales International & Weekly Bulletin
Owner: Wick Communications Inc.
Editorial: 268 W View Point Dr, Nogales, Arizona 85621-4114. **T:** 1 520 375-5760
W: http://www.nogalesinternational.com/the_bulletin **Circ:** 6300 Not Audited
Editorial Profile: Nogales International and Weekly Bulletin are sister newspapers covering Santa Cruz County, AZ. Nogales International is the flagship paper, publishing on Tuesdays and Fridays, while the Weekly Bulletin publishes Wednesdays.
NEWSPAPER

Nor Gyank
Editorial: 825 E Colorado St, Glendale, California 91205-1221. **T:** 1 818 240-9996
E: sevshen@aol.com
Freq: Tue; **Circ:** 10500 Not Audited; Full Page Mono: 5.45
Currency: US Dollars
NEWSPAPER

Nordmark Publishing
Owner: Nordmark Publishing
Editorial: 22 Central Ave., Suite 1, Beach, North Dakota 58621. **T:** 1 701 872-3755
E: goldenandbillings@gmail.com **Circ:** 1600 Not Audited
Publisher: Jason Nordmark
NEWSPAPER

Norfolk Daily News
Owner: Huse Publishing
Editorial: 525 W Norfolk Ave, Norfolk, Nebraska 68701-5236. **T:** 1 402 371-1020
E: editor@norfolkdailynews.com
W: http://www.norfolkdailynews.com
Freq: Daily; **Circ:** 14553 Not Audited
Publisher: Jerry Huse; **Editor:** Kent Warneke
Editorial Profile: Norfolk Daily News is a local newspaper for the Norfolk, NE area. The newspaper covers local, national and statewide news, business, sports and arts & entertainment. All inquiries should be addressed to the editor.; Full Page Mono: 21.75; Full Page Colour: 476.00
Currency: US Dollars
DAILY NEWSPAPER

Normal Newspapers
Owner: Pyne, (Edward)
Editorial: 1702 W College Ave Ste G, Normal, Illinois 61761-2793. **T:** 1 309 454-5476
E: thenormalite@gmail.com **Circ:** 5900 Not Audited
Editor: Patty Fye; **Publisher:** Edward Pyne
NEWSPAPER

The Norman Transcript
Owner: Community Newspaper Holdings, Inc.
Editorial: 215 E Comanche St, Norman, Oklahoma 73069. **T:** 1 405 321-1800
E: news@normantranscript.com
W: http://www.normantranscript.com
Freq: Daily; **Circ:** 9500 Not Audited
Publisher: Terry Connor; **Editor:** Deb Parker
Editorial Profile: The Norman Transcript is a local daily newspaper that provides information on local news and topics of interest to residents of Norman, OK and surrounding communities. Coverage includes Oklahoma news, sports, business, real estate, editorials, outdoor news, arts & entertainment, lifestyles, religion, seniors, features, columnists, food, family, health, garden and more.; Full Page Mono: 16.75; Full Page Colour: 295.00
Currency: US Dollars

DAILY NEWSPAPER

North Adams Transcript
Owner: MediaNews Group
Editorial: 124 American Legion Dr, North Adams, Massachusetts 01247-3942.
T: 1 413 663-3741 **E:** news@thetranscript.com
W: http://www.thetranscript.com
Freq: Daily; **Circ:** 5127 Not Audited
Publisher: Robert Chapman; **Editor:** Michael Foster; **Publisher:** Peter Lynch
Editorial Profile: North Adams Transcript is a daily newspaper published Monday through Saturday for the residents of North Adams, MA and surrounding areas. The paper covers local news and events. Send press releases by e-mail to the editor. Deadlines are one week prior to issue date.; Full Page Mono: 20.25; Full Page Colour: 279.00
Currency: US Dollars
DAILY NEWSPAPER

North Attleborough Free Press
Owner: GateHouse Media Inc.
Editorial: 31 N Washington St, North Attleboro, Massachusetts 02760-1682.
T: 1 508 699-6755 **E:** news@nafreepress.com
W: http://www.nafreepress.com
Freq: Wed; **Circ:** 17000 Not Audited
Editorial Profile: North Attleborough Free Press is written for residents in North Attleborough, MA. It covers local news and events. Deadlines for the paper are on Fridays prior to the issue date at noon ET.; Full Page Mono: 10.00
Currency: US Dollars
NEWSPAPER

North Augusta Today
Owner: Morris Communications
Editorial: 725 Broad St, Augusta, Georgia 30901-1336. **T:** 1 706 724-0851
W: http://natoday.augusta.com
Freq: Weekly; **Circ:** 17000
Editorial Profile: North Augusta Today is a free weekly community newspaper under the Augusta (GA) Chronicle banner, and includes local news, sports, education and community events for the North Augusta, GA community.
NEWSPAPER

North Avenue News
Owner: Cooper (Ellen)
Editorial: 70 Cumberland Rd, Burlington, Vermont 05408-2465. **T:** 1 802 864-7530
E: noavenews@aol.com
Freq: Monthly; **Circ:** 16050 Not Audited
Publisher: Cliff Cooper; **Editor:** Ellen Cooper
Editorial Profile: North Avenue News is a community newspaper serving the residents of Burlington, VT. It covers local news and community events.; Full Page Mono: 10.50
Currency: US Dollars
NEWSPAPER

North Bay Bohemian
Owner: Metro Publishing Group
Editorial: 847 5Th St, Santa Rosa, California 95404-4526. **T:** 1 707 527-1200
W: http://www.bohemian.com
Freq: Wed; **Circ:** 25000 Not Audited
Editor: Stett Holbrook; **Publisher:** Rosemary Olson
Editorial Profile: North Bay Bohemian in Santa Rosa, CA is a weekly newspaper that covers local news, business, entertainment and sports in Sonoma, Napa and Marin counties.; Full Page Mono: 32.76
Currency: US Dollars
NEWSPAPER

North Central News
Owner: Blanc (Tara)
Editorial: 5308 N 12th St Ste 402, Phoenix, Arizona 85014-2927. **T:** 1 602 277-2742
E: editor@northcentralnews.net
W: http://www.northcentralnews.net
Freq: Monthly; **Circ:** 26000 Not Audited
Publisher: Tara Blanc; **Editor:** Teri Carnecelli
Editorial Profile: North Central News is a local newspaper written for the residents of Phoenix.; Full Page Mono: 34.00; Full Page Colour: 39.30
Currency: US Dollars
NEWSPAPER

North Country This Week
Owner: Shumway (Gordon C.)
Editorial: 19 Depot St, Potsdam, New York 13676-1143. **T:** 1 315 265-1000
E: news@northcountrynow.com
W: http://www.northcountrynow.com
Freq: Wed; **Circ:** 10258 Not Audited
News Editor: Craig Freilich; **Publisher:** William Shumway
Editorial Profile: North Country This Week is the weekly, local newspaper for St. Lawrence County, NY. The newspaper covers local news, business, sports and arts & entertainment stories. The newspaper also covers national and statewide stories if they have a direct impact on the newspaper's readership.; Full Page Mono: 11.60
Currency: US Dollars
NEWSPAPER

North County Sun
Owner: Print Zone
Editorial: 7040 Avenida Encinas #104-115, Carlsbad, California 92011-4652.
T: 1 760 635-9100
E: info@hotinnorthcounty.com
W: http://www.hotinnorthcounty.com
Freq: Bi-Monthly
Editorial Profile: North County Sun is a bi-monthly publication providing restaurant, local event and entertainment coverage to the residents and visitors of North County, CA, with some coverage of Greater San Diego.
NEWSPAPER

North Fort Myers Neighbor
Owner: Breeze Newspapers
Editorial: 2787 N Tamiami Trl, North Fort Myers, Florida 33903-2213. **T:** 1 239 656-5248
E: nfmneighbor@breezenewspapers.com
W: http://www.breezenewspapers.com
Freq: Wed; **Circ:** 24000 Not Audited
Publisher: Scott Blonde; **Editor:** Andrea Galabinski
Editorial Profile: North Fort Myers Neighbor is a weekly newspaper written for residents of North Fort Myers, FL. It covers community events, school news and sports, business profiles, real estate, human interest stories and government issues that affect local residents. Editorial and advertising deadlines are on Fridays at 5pm ET.; Full Page Mono: 11.62
Currency: US Dollars
NEWSPAPER

North Georgia News
Editorial: 266 Cleveland St, Blairsville, Georgia 30512-8537. **T:** 1 706 745-6343
E: ngnews@windstream.net
W: http://www.nganews.com
Freq: Wed; **Circ:** 10800 Not Audited
Editor: Norman Cooper; **Publisher:** Kenneth West
Editorial Profile: North Georgia News is a local newspaper written for the residents of Blairsville, GA. The paper covers local news, business, sports and arts & entertainment.; Full Page Mono: 9.50
Currency: US Dollars
NEWSPAPER

North Haven Citizen
Owner: Record-Journal Publishing Company
Editorial: 11 Crown St, Meriden, Connecticut 6450. **T:** 1 203 235-1661
E: news@thenorthhavencitizen.com
W: http://www.thenorthhavencitizen.com
Freq: Fri; **Circ:** 11500 Not Audited
Editor: Kyle Swartz; **Publisher:** Eliot White
Editorial Profile: North Haven Citizen is written for the residents of North Haven, CT. It seeks to provide the readers with community news and information through stories on local news, sports, community groups, businesses, politics and schools. It encourages the submissions of photos, stories, events, schedules, press releases and birth and wedding announcements.; Full Page Mono: 11.35
Currency: US Dollars
NEWSPAPER

North Jersey Community Newspapers - Community News Editions
Owner: North Jersey Media Group
Editorial: 12-38 River Rd, Fair Lawn, New Jersey 07410-1802. **T:** 1 201 703-8793
E: communitynews@northjersey.com
Freq: Wed; **Circ:** 78404 Not Audited
Publisher: Janice Friedman; **Editor:** Richard Mardekian
NEWSPAPER

North Jersey Community Newspapers - Essex Division-East
Owner: North Jersey Media Group Inc.
Editorial: 90 Centre St, Nutley, New Jersey 7110. **T:** 1 973 667-2100 **Circ:** 10131 Not Audited
Editor: Mollie Gray; **Publisher:** Kathleen Hivish; **Editor:** Owen Proctor
NEWSPAPER

North Jersey Community Newspapers - Ridgewood
Owner: North Jersey Media Group Inc.
Editorial: 41 Oak St, Ridgewood, New Jersey 07450-3805. **T:** 1 201 612-5400
E: ridgewoodnews@northjersey.com
W: http://www.northjersey.com **Circ:** 71125 Not Audited
Publisher: Janice Friedman; **Editor:** Ed Virgin; **Editor:** Trudy Walz; **Editor:** Trudy Walz; **Editor:** Trudy Walz; **Editor:** Trudy Walz
NEWSPAPER

North Jersey Community Newspapers - West Paterson
Owner: North Jersey Media Group Inc.
Editorial: 1 Garret Mountain Plz, Woodland Park, New Jersey 7424. **T:** 1 973 569-7393
E: today@northjersey.com
W: http://www.northjersey.com **Circ:** 30873 Not Audited
Publisher: Mike Lawson; **Editor:** Christa Limone
NEWSPAPER

North Jersey Media Group - Cresskill
Owner: North Jersey Media Group Inc.
Editorial: 210 Knickerbocker Rd Ste 1200, Cresskill, New Jersey 07626-1801.
T: 1 201 894-6700
W: http://www.northjersey.com **Circ:** 105496 Not Audited
Editor: Chris Lang; **Editor:** William Slossar
NEWSPAPER

North Jersey Media Group - Kinnelon
Owner: North Jersey Media Group Inc.
Editorial: 509 Main St, Butler, New Jersey 7405. **T:** 1 973 283-5600
W: http://www.northjersey.com **Circ:** 60757 Not Audited
Editor: Jai Agnish; **Editor:** Matt Fagan; **Editor:** Matt Fagan; **Editor:** Matt Fagan; **Publisher:** Mike Lawson; **Editor:** Donna Rolando; **Editor:** Rebecca Scanlan
Editorial Profile: North Jersey Media Group - Kinnelon is a community newspaper publisher in Butler, NJ.
NEWSPAPER

North Jersey Media Group - Rockaway
Owner: North Jersey Media Group Inc.
Editorial: 100 Commons Way, Rockaway, New Jersey 7866. **T:** 1 973 586-8190
E: neighbor@northjersey.com
W: http://www.northjersey.com **Circ:** 88413 Not Audited
Editor: Ellen Fox Tamblyn; **Publisher:** Mike Lawson; **Editor:** Trish Reynolds
NEWSPAPER

North Jersey Prospector
Owner: North Jersey Prospector, Inc.
Editorial: 479 Grove St, Clifton, New Jersey 07013-3134. **T:** 1 973 365-1111
Freq: Thu; **Circ:** 88200
Publisher: Alex Bidnik; **Editor:** Madeline Bogee; **News Editor:** Viktor Glowa; **Editor:** Harold Leib; **Editor:** Ronald Watterston
Editorial Profile: North Jersey Prospector is a weekly community newspaper written for residents of Clifton, NJ and surrounding areas.; Full Page Mono: 10.64
Currency: US Dollars
NEWSPAPER

North Kitsap Herald
Owner: Black Press
Editorial: 18887 State Highway 305 NE, Ste 700, Poulsbo, Washington 98370.
T: 1 360 779-4464
E: editor@northkitsapherald.com
W: http://www.northkitsapherald.com
Freq: Fri; **Circ:** 12800 Not Audited
Publisher: Donna Etchey; **Editor:** Richard Walker
Editorial Profile: North Kitsap Herald is a community newspaper serving the Poulsbo, Kingston, Suquamish, Hansville, Indianola and Little Boston, WA area. The paper offers local news, features, editorial and sports. Send all editorial correspondence to the PO Box address. Send advertising correspondence to North Kitsap Herald, c/o Sound Publishing, 7689 NE Day Rd., Bainbridge Island, WA 98110. Ads will also run in the paper's sister publications, including Bainbridge Island Review, Bremerton Patriot and Port Orchard Independent.; Full Page Mono: 18.70
Currency: US Dollars
NEWSPAPER

North Lawndale Community News
Owner: Strategic Human Services
Editorial: 1211 S Western Ave, Ste 203, Chicago, Illinois 60608-1152.
T: 1 312 492-9090 **E:** webmaster@nlcn.org
W: http://www.nlcn.org
Freq: Weekly; **Circ:** 15000
Editorial Profile: North Lawndale Community News is published weekly for African-American residents of Chicago.; Full Page Mono: 30.00
Currency: US Dollars
NEWSPAPER

North Myrtle Beach Times
Owner: Polly Lowman
Editorial: 203 Highway 17 N, North Myrtle Beach, South Carolina 29582-2937.
T: 1 843 249-3525 **E:** nmbtimes@sc.rr.com
W: http://www.nmbtimes.com
Freq: Thu; **Circ:** 12400 Not Audited
Editor: Polly Lowman
Editorial Profile: North Myrtle Beach Times is a local newspaper written for the residents of North Myrtle Beach, SC.; Full Page Mono: 8.00
Currency: US Dollars
NEWSPAPER

The North Platte Telegraph
Owner: Omaha World-Herald Co.
Editorial: 621 N Chestnut St, North Platte, Nebraska 69101. **T:** 1 308 532-6000
E: editor@nptelegraph.com
W: http://www.nptelegraph.com
Freq: Daily; **Circ:** 10653 Not Audited
Publisher: Peter Rogers
Editorial Profile: The North Platte Telegraph is the daily newspaper of North Platte, NE and the surrounding communities. It covers local news, sports, lifestyle, farming and legal stories. They also cover national stories if they have an impact on the readership.; Full Page Mono: 16.55; Full Page Colour: 365.00
Currency: US Dollars
DAILY NEWSPAPER

North Port Sun
Owner: Sun Coast Media Group Inc.
Editorial: 13487 Tamiami Trl, North Port, Florida 34287-1211. **T:** 1 941 429-3000
W: http://www.sun-herald.com
Freq: Daily; **Circ:** 5500 Not Audited
Publisher: David Dunn-Rankin; **Editor:** Lorraine Schneeberger
Editorial Profile: North Port Sun is a daily newspaper serving the local population of North Port, Fl. The newspaper includes coverage of local news events, business, lifestyle, real estate, and sports that impact the local readers. The publication is intended for readers in North Port, FL and surrounding communities.; Full Page Mono: 12.95
Currency: US Dollars
DAILY NEWSPAPER

North Raleigh News & Midtown Raleigh News
Owner: McClatchy Newspapers
Editorial: 215 S McDowell St, Raleigh, North Carolina 27601-1331
E: nrnews@newsobserver.com
Freq: Weekly
Editor: Amy Seeley
NEWSPAPER

North Shore Today
Editorial: 17 W John St Unit 1, Hicksville, New York 11801-1045. **T:** 1 516 496-4300
E: events@northshoretoday.com
W: http://www.northshoretoday.com
Freq: Wed; **Circ:** 150000
Editor: Rachel Schlau
Editorial Profile: North Shore Today is a weekly community newspaper featuring fashion and community events, and news, and dining reviews.
NEWSPAPER

The North Shore Weekend
Owner: JWC Media
Editorial: 445 Sheridan Rd Ste 100, Highwood, Illinois 60040-1317.
T: 1 847 926-0911
W: http://www.northshoreweekend.com
Freq: Weekly
Editor in Chief: David Sweet
Editorial Profile: North Shore Weekend is a weekly newspaper covering the North Shore region in the Chicagoland area.
NEWSPAPER

North Valley Community News
Owner: Decision Publications
Editorial: 9401 Reseda Blvd, Ste 100, Northridge, California 91324-2980.
T: 1 818 534-1797
E: info@decisionpublications.com
W: http://www.northvalleycommunitynews.com
Freq: Bi-Weekly; **Circ:** 40000 Not Audited
Editorial Profile: Community Connection is a weekly newspaper written for the residents of Northridge, Granada Hills, Porter Ranch and Chatsworth, CA.; Full Page Mono: 43.75

Currency: US Dollars
NEWSPAPER

Northeast and North Forest Newspapers
Owner: Grafikpress Corp.
Editorial: 5327 Aldine Mail Rd, Houston, Texas 77039. **T:** 1 281 449-9945
E: nenewsroom@aol.com
W: http://www.nenewsroom.com **Circ:** 45000 Not Audited
Publisher: Gilbert Hoffman; **Editor:** Mr. Luke
Editorial Profile: Northeast and North Forest Newspapers cover the local area ONLY. They do not want to be contacted via e-mail.
NEWSPAPER

The Northeast Mississippi Daily Journal
Owner: Journal Publishing Company
Editorial: 1242 S Green St, Tupelo, Mississippi 38804-6301. **T:** 1 662 842-2611
E: djnews@djournal.com
W: http://nems360.com
Freq: Daily; **Circ:** 29642 Not Audited
Publisher: Billy Crews; **Editor:** Lloyd Gray; **Editor:** Lloyd Gray; **Editor:** Lloyd Gray
Editorial Profile: The Northeast Mississippi Daily Journal in Tupelo, MS provides local news, sports, business, entertainment and lifestyle coverage to residents of Northeast Mississippi.; Full Page Mono: 35.19; Full Page Colour: 400.00
Currency: US Dollars
DAILY NEWSPAPER

Northeast News
Editorial: 5715 St. John Ave., Kansas City, Missouri 64123. **T:** 1 816 241-0765
E: northeastnews@socket.net
W: http://northeastnews.net
Freq: Wed; **Circ:** 12450
Publisher: Michael Bushnell; **Editor:** Leslie Collins
Editorial Profile: Northeast News is a weekly community newspaper covering the northeast Kansas City area, including local news, sports, features and community events.; Full Page Mono: 9.00
Currency: US Dollars
NEWSPAPER

Northeast News & Tribune
Owner: Tampa Tribune/Media General Inc.
Editorial: 413 Hedgeway Dr, Valrico, Florida 33594-3117. **T:** 1 813 731-8026
Freq: Wed; **Circ:** 13054 Not Audited
Editorial Profile: Northeast News & Tribune is a local newspaper serving the residents of Tampa, FL and surrounding areas. The publication covers local news and community events. Deadlines are on Wednesdays at noon ET.; Full Page Mono: 17.30
Currency: US Dollars
NEWSPAPER

Northeast Ohio Media Group
Owner: Advance Publications, Inc.
Editorial: 1660 West 2nd St Suite 3200, Cleveland, Ohio 44113. **T:** 1 216 999-5000
W: http://www.neohiomediagroup.com/products/sun-news/
Freq: Weekly; **Circ:** 124614 Not Audited
Editorial Profile: Northeast Ohio Media Group produces the weekly Sun Newspapers, and are sister company of The Plain Dealer and Cleveland.com.
NEWSPAPER

Northeaster and North News
Editorial: 2844 Johnson St NE, Minneapolis, Minnesota 55418-3056. **T:** 1 612 788-9003
E: contact@nenorthnews.com
W: http://nenorthnews.com **Circ:** 63500 Not Audited
Editor: Kerry Ashmore
Editorial Profile: Northeaster and North News in Minneapolis, MN is a community newspaper publisher.
NEWSPAPER

Northend Agent's, LLC
Editorial: 680 Blue Hills Ave, Hartford, Connecticut 6112. **T:** 1 860 827-1010
E: northendagents@aol.com
W: http://www.northendagentsnewspaper.com
Freq: Wed; **Circ:** 40000 Not Audited
Editor: John Allen
Editorial Profile: Northend Agent's, LLC is a weekly newspaper which provides its readers with the latest in news and information. It cover local news, community news, and lifestyle issues in the Hartford, CT area.; Full Page Mono: 15.30; Full Page Colour: 1600.00
Currency: US Dollars
NEWSPAPER

The Northern Cross
Owner: Diocese of Duluth
Editorial: 2830 E 4th St, Duluth, Minnesota 55812. **T:** 1 218 724-9111
W: http://www.dioceseduluth.org
Freq: Fri; **Circ:** 30000 Not Audited
Editor: Kyle Eller; **Editor:** Kyle Eller; **Publisher:** Paul Sirba
Editorial Profile: The Northern Cross is a monthly newspaper for the Diocese of Duluth, MN. It is mailed on the first Friday of the month. It strives to keep Catholics in the Arrowhead area of Minnesota well informed about their faith.; Full Page Mono: 45.00; Full Page Colour: 145.00
Currency: US Dollars
NEWSPAPER

Northern Express
Editorial: 830 Cottage View Dr, Ste 204, Traverse City, Michigan 49684.
T: 1 231 947-8787
E: info@northernexpress.com
W: http://www.northernexpress.com
Freq: Mon; **Circ:** 33000 Not Audited
Editorial Profile: Northern Express is written for residents of Traverse City, MI. Its mission is to provide readers with the latest in local nightlife, news, opinions, events and happenings.; Full Page Mono: 19.80
Currency: US Dollars
NEWSPAPER

The Northern Light
Owner: Point Roberts Press, Inc.
Editorial: 225 Marine Dr, Ste 200, Blaine, Washington 98230-4001. **T:** 1 360 332-1777
E: editor@thenorthernlight.com
W: http://www.thenorthernlight.com
Freq: Thu; **Circ:** 10300 Not Audited
Managing Director: Kathy McGee
Editorial Profile: The Northern Light is a community newspaper serving the towns of Blaine and Birch Bay, WA, and the surrounding areas. It includes local news, features, sports and community events.; Full Page Mono: 23.00
Currency: US Dollars
NEWSPAPER

The Northern Nevada Catholic
Owner: Diocese of Reno
Editorial: 290 S Arlington Ave Ste 200, Reno, Nevada 89501-1713. **T:** 1 775 326-9410
W: http://www.dioceseofreno.org/userpages/NND_Catholic.aspx
Freq: Bi-Monthly; **Circ:** 145000
Editor: Maureen Angel; **Publisher:** Randolph Calvo
Editorial Profile: Northern Nevada Catholic is published for the Diocese of Reno.
NEWSPAPER

Northern Virginia Daily
Owner: Shenandoah Publishing House Inc.
Editorial: 152 N Holliday St, Strasburg, Virginia 22657. **T:** 1 540 465-5137
W: http://www.nvdaily.com
Freq: Daily; **Circ:** 13318 Not Audited
Editor: Linda Ash; **Editor:** Rich Cooley
Editorial Profile: Northern Virginia Daily provides the latest in local news and information to local residents of Strasburg, VA. The newspaper covers local news, events, sports, business, arts & entertainment and lifestyles.; Full Page Mono: 16.45; Full Page Colour: 370.00
Currency: US Dollars
DAILY NEWSPAPER

Northern Wyoming Daily News
Owner: McCraken Newspapers
Editorial: 201 N 8th St, Worland, Wyoming 82401. **T:** 1 307 347-3241
W: http://www.wyodaily.com
Freq: Daily; **Circ:** 4000 Not Audited
Editorial Profile: Northern Wyoming Daily News is written for residents of the Worland, WY area. It covers local news.; Full Page Mono: 8.78; Full Page Colour: 120.00
Currency: US Dollars
DAILY NEWSPAPER

Northland Neighbors
Owner: McClatchy Newspapers
Editorial: 17 W 12th St, Columbus, Georgia 31901-5254. **T:** 1 706 324-5526
E: neighbors@ledger-enquirer.com
Freq: Wed; **Circ:** 51000
Editor: Marcia McAllister
Editorial Profile: Northland Neighbors is a weekly paper that is inserted in the Columbus (GA) Ledger-Enquirer and is also distributed on racks throughout North Columbus and South Harris County, GA. Coverage is highly localized and features stories about youth, sports, recreation, family, home, dining and entertainment.; Full Page Mono: 17.00
Currency: US Dollars
NEWSPAPER

Northside Sun
Owner: Emmerich Newspapers Inc.
Editorial: 246 Briarwood Dr, #101, Jackson, Mississippi 39206. **T:** 1 601 957-1122
E: sun@northsidesun.com
W: http://www.northsidesun.com
Freq: Thu; **Circ:** 11000 Not Audited
Publisher: Wyatt Emmerich; **Editor:** Jimmye Sweat
Editorial Profile: Northside Sun's mission is to provide its readers with the local news and information. The publication is written for residents of northern Mississippi.; Full Page Mono: 18.30
Currency: US Dollars
NEWSPAPER

Northwest Arkansas Times
Owner: Stephens Media Group
Editorial: 212 N East Ave, Fayetteville, Arkansas 72701-5225. **T:** 1 479 442-1700
W: http://www.nwaonline.com
Freq: Daily; **Circ:** 13958 Not Audited
Publisher: Jeff Jeffus
Editorial Profile: Northwest Arkansas Times is a daily newspaper serving Northwest Arkansas and surrounding areas. The publication covers news, sports, opinions, academics, business, health, agriculture and living. The outlet offers RSS (Really Simple Syndication).; Full Page Mono: 44.10; Full Page Colour: 475.00
Currency: US Dollars
DAILY NEWSPAPER

The Northwest Examiner
Owner: Classen (Allan)
Editorial: 2825 NW Upshur St, Suite C, Portland, Oregon 97210-2285.
T: 1 503 241-2353 **E:** allan@nwexaminer.com
W: http://www.nwexaminer.com
Freq: Monthly; **Circ:** 35000 Not Audited
Editorial Profile: The Northwest Examiner in Portland, OR is a monthly newspaper that covers local news and governments, sports, editorials, community events and features.; Full Page Mono: 11.46
Currency: US Dollars
NEWSPAPER

Northwest Florida Daily News
Owner: Halifax Media Holdings LLC
Editorial: 200 Racetrack Rd NW, Fort Walton Beach, Florida 32547-1645. **T:** 1 850 863-1111
E: news@nwfdailynews.com
W: http://www.nwfdailynews.com
Freq: Daily; **Circ:** 35775 Not Audited
Publisher: Tom Conner; **Editor:** Colin Lipnicky
Editorial Profile: Northwest Florida Daily News is a local daily newspaper serving residents of Fort Walton, Navarre and Crestview, FL.; Full Page Mono: 50.00; Full Page Colour: 159.83
Currency: US Dollars
DAILY NEWSPAPER

Northwest Guardian
Owner: McClatchy Newspapers
Editorial: Fort Lewis MIlitary Base, Building 2026B, Fort Lewis, Washington 98433.
T: 1 253 967-0171
E: nwgeditor@thenewstribune.com
W: http://www.nwguardian.com
Freq: Fri; **Circ:** 20700 Not Audited
Publisher: Charles Jacoby; **Editor:** David Kuhns; **Editor:** David Kuhns
Editorial Profile: Northwest Guardian is a community newspaper that serves active military personnel, civilians and employees of the army base in Fort Lewis, WA. Although the paper is printed and distributed by The News Tribune in Tacoma, WA all editorial content is created by military staff. Contact The News Tribune for advertising inquiries by phone at (253)597-8742, or by mail at: PO Box 11000; Tacoma, WA 98411.; Full Page Mono: 35.85
Currency: US Dollars
NEWSPAPER

Northwest Herald
Owner: Shaw Media
Editorial: 7717 S Il Route 31, Crystal Lake, Illinois 60014-8132. **T:** 1 815 459-4040
E: news@nwherald.com
W: http://www.nwherald.com
Freq: Daily; **Circ:** 27206 Not Audited
News Editor: Kevin Lyons; **Publisher:** John Rung; **Editor:** Jason Schaumburg
Editorial Profile: Northwest Herald is published daily for the residents of Crystal Lake, IL and surrounding areas. The newspaper covers local and state news, bussiness, sports and entertainment.; Full Page Mono: 31.42; Full Page Colour: 142.15
Currency: US Dollars
DAILY NEWSPAPER

Northwest Indiana Catholic Newspaper
Owner: Diocese of Gary
Editorial: 9292 Broadway, Merrillville, Indiana 46410-7047. **T:** 1 219 769-9292
E: nwic@dcgary.org
W: http://www.nwicatholic.com
Freq: Sun; **Circ:** 15000
Editorial Profile: Northwest Indiana Catholic Newspaper is a community newspaper for the Diocese of Gary, In.; Full Page Mono: 10.14
Currency: US Dollars
NEWSPAPER

Northwest Observer
Owner: PS Communications Inc.
Editorial: 1616 Nc Highway 68 N, Oak Ridge, North Carolina 27310-9667.
T: 1 336 644-7035 **E:** info@nwobserver.com
W: http://www.nwobserver.com
Freq: Fri; **Circ:** 13000 Not Audited
Publisher: Patti Stokes
Editorial Profile: Northwest Observer is a weekly newspaper serving the Oak Ridge, NC area.; Full Page Mono: 58.82
Currency: US Dollars
NEWSPAPER

Northwest Signal
Owner: Bryan Publishing Company
Editorial: 595 E Riverview Ave, Napoleon, Ohio 43545-1865. **T:** 1 419 592-5055
W: http://www.northwestsignal.net
Freq: Daily; **Circ:** 4784 Not Audited
Publisher: Christopher Cullis; **News Editor:** Brian Koeller; **Editor:** Jen Lazenby; **Editor:** Sheila Naveau
Editorial Profile: Northwest Signal is a local newspaper published Monday through Friday and serving the residents of the Northwest portion of Ohio. Each edition covers local, state, and national news, community event listings, entertainment updates and local weather and sports reports. Deadlines are at 9:30am on the day before issue date.; Full Page Mono: 11.00; Full Page Colour: 210.00
Currency: US Dollars
DAILY NEWSPAPER

Norwalk Reflector
Owner: Sandusky Newspapers Inc.
Editorial: 61 E Monroe St, Norwalk, Ohio 44857-1532. **T:** 1 419 668-3771
E: news@norwalkreflector.com
W: http://www.norwalkreflector.com
Freq: Daily; **Circ:** 8053 Not Audited
Publisher: Andrew Prutsok; **News Editor:** Matthew Roche
Editorial Profile: Norwalk Reflector is a daily newspaper published for the residents of Norwalk, OH. It covers the latest news and information. Deadlines are two days prior to issue date.; Full Page Mono: 13.00; Full Page Colour: 210.00
Currency: US Dollars
DAILY NEWSPAPER

Norwood News
Owner: Mosholu Preservation Corp.
Editorial: 3400 Reservoir Oval E, Bronx, New York 10467-3102. **T:** 1 718 324-4998
E: norwoodnews@norwoodnews.org
W: http://www.norwoodnews.org
Freq: Bi-Weekly; **Circ:** 15000 Not Audited
Editor in Chief: David Cruz
Editorial Profile: Norwood News is a local newspaper serving Bronx, NY, including Norwood, Bedford Park, and Fordham Bedford since 1988. The publication offers information about local news and community events.; Full Page Mono: 12.78
Currency: US Dollars
NEWSPAPER

The Notes
Owner: LaBrie (Mark) & LaBrie (Andrew)
Editorial: 33 Yarmouth Crossing Dr, Yarmouth, Maine 04096-6740. **T:** 1 207 846-4112
E: news@thenotes.org
W: http://www.thenotes.org
Freq: Tue; **Circ:** 11500 Not Audited
Editorial Profile: The Notes is a community newspaper serving Yarmouth, ME with local news and community events.; Full Page Mono: 9.30
Currency: US Dollars
NEWSPAPER

Noticia
Owner: L.I. Media Communications Inc.
Editorial: 53 E Merrick Rd Ste 353, Freeport, New York 11520-4056. **T:** 1 516 223-5678
E: editorial@noticiali.com
W: http://www.noticiali.com

WORLD NEWS MEDIA

Freq: Wed; **Circ:** 48500 Not Audited
Editor in Chief: Elaina Lopez
Editorial Profile: Noticia is a Spanish newspaper serving Long Island, NY and the five boroughs.The publication provides information on local news, community events and entertainment.; Full Page Mono: 13.00
Currency: US Dollars
NEWSPAPER

La Noticia
Editorial: 5936 Monroe Rd, Charlotte, North Carolina 28212. **T:** 1 704 568-6966
E: editor@lanoticia.com
W: http://www.lanoticia.com
Freq: Wed; **Circ:** 21000 Not Audited
Editor: Diego Barahona; **Publisher:** Hilda Gurdian
Editorial Profile: La Noticia is written for Hispanic residents in Asheville and Charlotte, NC. It covers local, national and international news, sports, real estate, entertainment, politics, education and business.; Full Page Mono: 37.82; Full Page Colour: 45.28
Currency: US Dollars
NEWSPAPER

Noticias Libres
Owner: Wehco Media Inc.
Editorial: 212 N East Ave, Fayetteville, Arkansas 72701. **T:** 1 479 571-6431
E: noticiaslibres@nwanews.com
W: http://www.nwanews.com/nl
Freq: Thu; **Circ:** 15000 Not Audited
Publisher: Jeff Jeffus
Editorial Profile: Noticias Libres is a free Spanish-language newspaper serving the Hispanic community in Northwest Arkansas, including the communities of Springdale, Rogers, Fayetteville and Siloam Springs. It provides news, sports and entertainment stories.; Full Page Mono: 10.00
Currency: US Dollars
NEWSPAPER

Noticias Libres
Owner: Wehco Media Inc.
Editorial: 400 E 11th St, Chattanooga, Tennessee 37403. **T:** 1 423 756-6900
W: http://www.noticiaslibres.com
Freq: Thu; **Circ:** 12000 Not Audited
Editor: Luis Carrasco
Editorial Profile: Noticias Libres is a local, weekly newspaper serving Hispanic and Spanish-speaking residents of Tennessee and North Georgia. The paper includes local news and information pertaining to the local Hispanic community. The paper shares an office with the Chattanooga (TN) Times Free Press.; Full Page Mono: 7.50; Full Page Colour: 50.00
Currency: US Dollars
NEWSPAPER

Noticiero Colombiano Hispano
Editorial: 437 Linden Ave, Elizabeth, New Jersey 7202. **T:** 1 908 351-9390
E: noticolomb@aol.com
W: http://www.noticierohispano.com
Freq: Wed; **Circ:** 62000 Not Audited
Editorial Profile: Noticiero Colombiano Hispano is written for Colombian residents in Elizabeth, NJ. It covers news, arts & entertainment and Hispanic culture. Monthly supplements include special articles on automobiles, tourism, real estate and health.; Full Page Mono: 30.00
Currency: US Dollars
NEWSPAPER

Noticiero Semanal
Owner: Freedom Communications Inc.
Editorial: 115 E Oak Ave, Porterville, California 93257-3807. **T:** 1 559 784-5000
E: recorder@portervillerecorder.com
W: http://www.noticierosemanal.com
Freq: Thu; **Circ:** 30000 Not Audited
Editor: Sonia Fuentes
Editorial Profile: Noticiero Semanal in Porterville, CA is a Spanish-language newspaper that covers local news and community events.; Full Page Mono: 46.00
Currency: US Dollars
NEWSPAPER

Novedades News
Editorial: 121 S Zang Blvd, Dallas, Texas 75208-4530. **T:** 1 214 943-2932
E: editorial@novedadesnews.com
W: http://www.novedadesnews.com
Freq: Wed; **Circ:** 38000 Not Audited
Editorial Profile: Novedades News' editorial mission is to provide news and information to the Hispanic community of Dallas. Deadlines are on Fridays.; Full Page Mono: 22.00; Full Page Colour: 740.00
Currency: US Dollars
NEWSPAPER

Nowy Dziennik
Owner: Bicentennial Publishing Corporation
Editorial: 70 Outwater Ln, Garfield, New Jersey 07026-3847. **T:** 1 212 594-2266
E: listy@dziennik.com
W: http://www.dziennik.com
Freq: Daily; **Circ:** 28000 Not Audited
Editor: Jan Latus; **Editor:** Jan Latus
Editorial Profile: Nowy Dziennik is a daily newspaper published in New Jersey. The publication's editorial mission is to provide its readers with the latest news and information. The publication is written for Polish-speaking people, and those originating from Poland, of New York and surrounding areas.; Full Page Mono: 10.00
Currency: US Dollars
DAILY NEWSPAPER

NRG Connecticut
Owner: NRG Inc.
Editorial: 740 N Main St, Ste W, West Hartford, Connecticut 6117.
T: 1 860 231-2424
E: editorial@jewishledger.com
W: http://www.jewishledger.com **Circ:** 37000 Not Audited
Editor: Stacey Dresner; **Publisher:** N. Richard Greenfield; **Editor:** Judie Jacobson
NEWSPAPER

Nuestra Comunidad
Owner: Gannett Co., Inc.
Editorial: 891 E Oak Rd, Vineland, New Jersey 08360-2311. **T:** 1 856 563-5206
W: http://www.sjcomunidad.com
Freq: Fri; **Circ:** 20000 Not Audited
Editor: Pablo Mansilla
Editorial Profile: Nuestra Comunidad is a weekly community newspaper for the residents of Vineland, NJ. It covers sports, arts & entertainment, politics, health, environment, technology and youth.; Full Page Mono: 6.56
Currency: US Dollars
NEWSPAPER

Nueva America
Owner: Hispanic Millenium Media, Corp.
Editorial: 990 Suffolk Ave, Brentwood, New York 11717-4502. **T:** 1 631 231-6222
E: nuameric@aol.com
W: http://www.nuevamericany.com
Freq: Thu; **Circ:** 75000
Editor: Claudia Canales; **Editor:** Claudia Canales; **Editor:** Claudia Canales; **Publisher:** Ivan Guerrero
Editorial Profile: Nueva America is published weekly for the Latino population of Long Island, NY and surrounding areas. The publication contains community and national news of interest to the readers. A local events calendar is also included. The publication does not have a Web site. The lead time and deadlines vary.; Full Page Mono: 8.00
Currency: US Dollars
NEWSPAPER

El Nuevo Coqui
Editorial: 258 Clifton Ave, Newark, New Jersey 07104-1907. **T:** 1 973 481-3233
E: glorin@optonline.net
Freq: Thu; **Circ:** 18000 Not Audited
Editorial Profile: El Nuevo Coqui is a weekly Spanish language newspaper serving the Puerto Rican residents of Newark, NJ. It covers features and local news.; Full Page Mono: 12.00
Currency: US Dollars
NEWSPAPER

El Nuevo Herald
Owner: McClatchy Newspapers
Editorial: 3511 NW 91st Ave, Doral, Florida 33172-1216. **T:** 1 305 376-3535
W: http://www.elnuevoherald.com
Freq: Daily; **Circ:** 51356 Not Audited
Publisher: David Landsberg
Editorial Profile: El Nuevo Herald is the primary Spanish newspaper in South and Central Florida, since its launch in 1987. Coverage includes local and national news, sports and arts & entertainment.; Full Page Mono: 115.00; Full Page Colour: 442.69
Currency: US Dollars
DAILY NEWSPAPER

El Nuevo Heraldo
Owner: Freedom Communications Inc.
Editorial: 1135 E Van Buren St, Brownsville, Texas 78520-7055. **T:** 1 956 542-4301
W: http://www.elnuevoheraldo.com
Freq: Daily; **Circ:** 7162 Not Audited
Publisher: Daniel Cavazos
Editorial Profile: El Nuevo Heraldo is written for the residents of Brownsville, TX. It covers local news and events.; Full Page Mono: 8.95; Full Page Colour: 551.00
Currency: US Dollars
DAILY NEWSPAPER

El Nuevo Patria
Owner: Patria Media Foundation Inc.
Editorial: 1393 Sw 1St St Ste 400, Miami, Florida 33135-2321. **T:** 1 305 698-8787
E: patrianews@aol.com
W: http://elnuevopatria.com/
Freq: Fri; **Circ:** 30000 Not Audited
Publisher: Eladio Jose Armesto; **Editor In Chief:** Carlos Díaz Luján
Editorial Profile: El Nuevo Patria is a local, Hispanic newspaper serving the residents of South Florida. It includes information on local news, weather, sports, business and entertainment.; Full Page Mono: 19.25; Full Page Colour: 325.00
Currency: US Dollars
NEWSPAPER

Nuevo Siglo
Editorial: 7137 N Armenia Ave Ste B, Tampa, Florida 33604-5263
E: nuevosiglonews@gmail.com
W: http://www.nuevosiglotampa.com
Freq: Thu; **Circ:** 27000 Not Audited
Editorial Profile: Nuevo Siglo in Tampa, FL is a local publication dedicated to the Hispanic community of Hillsborough County, FL.; Full Page Mono: 12.00
Currency: US Dollars
NEWSPAPER

Nuevo Siglo
Owner: Bandia (Ezequiel)
Editorial: 2644 W 47th St, Chicago, Illinois 60632-1350. **T:** 1 773 890-1656
E: ns@nuevosiglonews.com
W: http://www.nuevosiglonews.com
Freq: Fri; **Circ:** 30000 Not Audited
Editorial Profile: Nuevo Siglo is a weekly newspaper written for Spanish-speaking residents of Chicago.; Full Page Mono: 52.00
Currency: US Dollars
NEWSPAPER

Number Nine Media Inc
Owner: Number Nine Media Inc.
Editorial: 1837 Camino Del Llano, Belen, New Mexico 87002. **T:** 1 505 864-4472
E: vcnb@news-bulletin.com
W: http://www.news-bulletin.com **Circ:** 45000 Not Audited
Editor: Clara Garcia; **Publisher:** Dave Puddu
NEWSPAPER

Nutfield Publishing
Owner: Nutfield Publishing
Editorial: 2 Litchfield Rd, Londonderry, New Hampshire 3053. **T:** 1 603 537-2760
E: ads@nutpub.net **W:** http://www.nutpub.net
Freq: Thu; **Circ:** 28407 Not Audited
Editor: Leslie O'Donnell
Editorial Profile: Nutfield Publishing, of Londonderry, NH, produces newspapers that serve the communities of Londonderry, Derry, East Derry, Chester, Sandown, Hampstead and East Hampstead.; Full Page Mono: 32.10
Currency: US Dollars
NEWSPAPER

NUVO
Owner: NUVO, Inc.
Editorial: 3951 N Meridian St Ste 200, Indianapolis, Indiana 46208-4078.
T: 1 317 254-2400 **E:** editors@nuvo.net
W: http://www.nuvo.net
Freq: Wed; **Circ:** 45000 Not Audited
News Editor: Rebecca Townsend
Editorial Profile: NUVO is written for the residents of Indianapolis and surrounding areas. The newspaper is published every Wednesday and covers politics, culture, cuisine, arts & entertainment, music reviews and a community calendar of events. The best day to reach the paper is on Fridays between 9 a.m. and 5 p.m. The outlet offers RSS (Really Simple Syndication).; Full Page Mono: 48.52; Full Page Colour: 2875.00
Currency: US Dollars
NEWSPAPER

NY Japion
Editorial: 411 Lafayette St, 3rd Fl, New York, New York 10003-7032. **T:** 1 212 431-9970
E: reader@nyjapion.com
W: http://www.ejapion.com
Freq: Fri; **Circ:** 23000 Not Audited
Editorial Profile: NY Japion is a free community newspaper serving New York City's Japanese-American community.; Full Page Mono: 60.00
Currency: US Dollars
NEWSPAPER

The Oak Ridger
Owner: GateHouse Media Inc.
Editorial: 785 Oak Ridge Tpke, Oak Ridge, Tennessee 37830. **T:** 1 865 482-1021
E: oakridge@oakridger.com
W: http://www.oakridger.com
Freq: Daily; **Circ:** 7700 Not Audited
Publisher: Darrell Richardson; **Editor:** Donna Smith
Editorial Profile: The Oak Ridger's editorial mission is to provide its readers with current local news and events. It is written for residents of Oak Ridge and Anderson Counties, TN. Deadlines are one day prior to the issue date. The outlet offers RSS (Really Simple Syndication).; Full Page Mono: 14.60; Full Page Colour: 190.00
Currency: US Dollars
DAILY NEWSPAPER

The Oakland Press
Owner: Journal Register Company
Editorial: 48 W Huron St, Pontiac, Michigan 48342-2101. **T:** 1 248 332-8181
W: http://www.theoaklandpress.com
Freq: Daily; **Circ:** 45859 Not Audited
News Editor: Matt Myftiu
Editorial Profile: The Oakland Press in Pontiac, MI is a daily newspaper for the residents of Oakland County, MI that covers the day's events, from the goings-on in local communities, schools, police departments and courts to the political events in the nation's capitol. It provides local, regional, state and national news, as well as sports, business, features, special reports and entertainment coverage. It strives to "deliver quality products and services that exceed our customers' expectations." Deadlines are three days prior to issue date.; Full Page Mono: 240.47; Full Page Colour: 351.00
Currency: US Dollars
DAILY NEWSPAPER

Oberlin & Amherst Newspapers
Owner: Civitas Media
Editorial: 42 S Main St, Oberlin, Ohio 44074-1627. **T:** 1 440 775-1611
E: news@theoberlinnews.com **Circ:** 4000 Not Audited
Editor: Jason Hawk; **Publisher:** Tom Hutson
NEWSPAPER

El Observador
Editorial: 99 N 1st St, Ste 100, San Jose, California 95113. **T:** 1 408 938-1700
W: http://www.el-observador.com
Freq: Fri; **Circ:** 84000 Not Audited
Editor: Rosario Vital; **Editor:** Rosario Vital; **Editor:** Rosario Vital
Editorial Profile: El Observador is a weekly bilingual publication that covers sports, entertainment, local, national and international news for Santa Clara, San Mateo and Encino, CA. It covers both Hispanic and American community issues. Deadlines are on Fridays prior to issue date.; Full Page Mono: 30.00
Currency: US Dollars
NEWSPAPER

El Observador Utah
Owner: Deseret Management Corp.
Editorial: 55 N 300 W Ste 500, Salt Lake City, Utah 84101-3502. **T:** 1 801 236-6000
E: pdark@elobservadorutah.com
W: http://observadordeutah.com
Freq: Sat; **Circ:** 10000
Editor: Patricia Dark
Editorial Profile: El Observador Utah is a local community paper for the Spanish communities of Utah including Ogden, Layton, Clearfield, Keysville, Bountiful, Centerville, Farmington, North Salt Lake, Salt Lake City, West Valley City, Kearns, Taylorsville, West Jordan, Sandy, American Fork, Orem and Provo.; Full Page Mono: 23.33
Currency: US Dollars
NEWSPAPER

Observer
Owner: Ogden Newspapers
Editorial: 8-10 E 2nd St, Dunkirk, New York 14048-1600. **T:** 1 716 366-3000
E: editorial@observertoday.com
W: http://www.observertoday.com
Freq: Daily; **Circ:** 6889 Not Audited
News Editor: Bill Hammond; **News Editor:** Bill Hammond
Editorial Profile: Observer is a daily community newspaper serving the residents of Northern Chautauqua County, NY. The newspaper covers local news, sports, entertainment, editorial, business and

community events.; Full Page Mono: 27.52; Full Page Colour: 372.52
Currency: US Dollars
DAILY NEWSPAPER

The Observer
Owner: Western Communications Inc.
Editorial: 1406 5th St, La Grande, Oregon 97850-2402. **T:** 1 541 963-3161
W: http://www.lagrandeobserver.com
Freq: Daily; **Circ:** 6029 Not Audited
Publisher: Kari Borgen; **Editor:** Andrew Cutler; **Editor:** Jeff Petersen
Editorial Profile: La Grande Observer is a daily newspaper for the residents of La Grande, OR. It covers news and events in the local community. The lead time for La Grande Observer is three days. Deadline for the publication is three days before issue date.; Full Page Mono: 12.70; Full Page Colour: 36.39
Currency: US Dollars
DAILY NEWSPAPER

(The) Observer
Owner: Deerfield Publishing
Editorial: 201 N Federal Hwy, Ste 103, Deerfield Beach, Florida 33441.
T: 1 954 428-9045
E: observernews@comcast.net
W: http://www.observernewspaperonline.com
Freq: Thu; **Circ:** 30000 Not Audited
Publisher: David Eller; **Editor:** Diane Emeott
Editorial Profile: The Observer is published weekly for the residents of Broward County, FL. The newspaper provides information about local news, sports, education and community events.; Full Page Mono: 9.50
Currency: US Dollars
NEWSPAPER

The Observer
Editorial: 39 Seeley Ave, Kearny, New Jersey 07032-1806. **T:** 1 201 991-1600
E: editorial@theobserver.com
W: http://www.theobserver.com
Freq: Wed; **Circ:** 32500
Editor: Karen Zautyk
Editorial Profile: The Observer is published weekly for the residents of Kearny, NJ and surrounding areas. The newspaper covers local news, sports and community events.; Full Page Mono: 18.00
Currency: US Dollars
NEWSPAPER

The Observer
Owner: Rio Rancho Observer, LLC
Editorial: 1594 Sara Rd SE, Rio Rancho, New Mexico 87124-1862. **T:** 1 505 892-8080
E: editor@rrobserver.com
W: http://www.rrobserver.com
Freq: Sun; **Circ:** 23500 Not Audited
Publisher: Rockford Hayes
Editorial Profile: The Observer is a community newspaper that serves Rio Rancho, NM and the surrounding communities on the west side of Albuquerque, NM. It includes news, sports and information about the people who make up the community. The news deadlines for the Wednesday edition are Mondays at noon and for Fridays the deadlines are Wednesdays at noon MT.; Full Page Mono: 18.00
Currency: US Dollars
NEWSPAPER

The Observer - New York Bureau
Editorial: 2 Bank St, Apt 1, New York, New York 10014. **T:** 1 212 614-8576
Editorial Profile: This is the New York bureau for The Observer of London.
DAILY NEWSPAPER

Observer & Eccentric Newspapers - Detroit
Owner: Gannett Co., Inc.
Editorial: 615 W Lafayette Blvd, Detroit, Michigan 48226-3124. **T:** 1 586 826-7494
W: http://www.hometownlife.com **Circ:** 158439 Not Audited
Editor: Brad Kadrich; **Editor:** Susan Mason; **Editor:** Larry Ruehlen; **Editor:** Karen Smith
Editorial Profile: Observer & Eccentric Newspapers offer local news, sports and events to residents of suburban Detroit. It has other offices in Sterling Heights, MI and Plymouth, MI, where main reception is maintained. All news faxes go to the Detroit newsroom.
NEWSPAPER

Observer & Eccentric Newspapers - Sterling Heights
Owner: Gannett Co., Inc
Editorial: 6200 Metropolitan Pkwy, Sterling Heights, Michigan 48312-1022.

T: 1 586 826-7494
W: http://www.hometownlife.com
Editor: Sandy Armbruster
Editorial Profile: Observer & Eccentric Newspapers offer local news, sports and events to residents of suburban Detroit. It has other offices in Detroit, MI and Plymouth, MI, where main reception is maintained. All news faxes go to the Detroit newsroom.
NEWSPAPER

The Observer Group Newspapers of Southern California
Editorial: 1219 20th St, Bakersfield, California 93301. **T:** 1 661 324-9466
E: observernews@gmail.com **Circ:** 97315 Not Audited
NEWSPAPER

The Observer News Enterprise
Owner: Horizon Publications
Editorial: 309 N College Ave, Newton, North Carolina 28658-3255. **T:** 1 828 464-0221
E: onenews@observernewsonline.com
W: http://www.observernewsonline.com
Freq: Mon thru Fri; **Circ:** 3000 Not Audited
Publisher: Michael Willard
Editorial Profile: The Observer News Enterprise is a newspaper that provides local news coverage for the Catawba County communities of Newton, Conover, Maiden, Claremont and Catawba, NC. The five-day newspaper comes out at noon ET each day with coverage of government activity, police and courts news, business developments, education and area sports. It also contains feature stories that highlight the people and places of Catawba County.; Full Page Mono: 9.80; Full Page Colour: 75.00
Currency: US Dollars
DAILY NEWSPAPER

Observer Newspapers
Owner: The Observer Group Inc.
Editorial: 1970 Main St, Sarasota, Florida 34236. **T:** 1 941 366-3468
W: http://www.yourobserver.com
Freq: Weekly
News Editor: Pam Eubanks; **Publisher:** Matt Walsh
NEWSPAPER

Observer-Dispatch
Owner: GateHouse Media Inc.
Editorial: 221 Oriskany St E, Utica, New York 13501-1201. **T:** 1 315 792-5000
E: news@uticaod.com
W: http://www.uticaod.com
Freq: Daily; **Circ:** 26637 Not Audited
News Editor: Fran Perritano
Editorial Profile: Observer-Dispatch is published daily for residents of Utica, NY and surrounding communities. The newspaper covers local and national news, as well as community events. Feature articles cover business, politics, education, arts & entertainment, lifestyle and other information of interest to those in the Mohawk Valley.; Full Page Mono: 66.47; Full Page Colour: 69.47
Currency: US Dollars
DAILY NEWSPAPER

Observer-Reporter
Owner: Observer Publishing Comapny
Editorial: 122 S Main St, Washington, Pennsylvania 15301. **T:** 1 724 222-2200
E: newsroom@observer-reporter.com
W: http://www.observer-reporter.com
Freq: Daily; **Circ:** 29539 Not Audited
Editor: Park Burroughs; **Editor:** Park Burroughs; **Editor:** Brad Hundt; **Editor:** Brad Hundt; **Editor:** Brad Hundt; **Editor:** Brad Hundt; **Publisher:** Thomas Northrop; **Editor:** Linda Ritzer
Editorial Profile: Observer-Reporter is a local daily newspaper written for residents of Washington and Greene counties, PA. The newspaper covers local news, sports, business, religion and events.; Full Page Mono: 42.50; Full Page Colour: 225.00
Currency: US Dollars
DAILY NEWSPAPER

OC Weekly
Owner: Voice Media Group
Editorial: 2975 Red Hill Ave Ste 150, Costa Mesa, California 92626-1203.
T: 1 714 550-5900
W: http://www.ocweekly.com
Freq: Thu; **Circ:** 69693 Not Audited
Editor: Gustavo Arellano; **Publisher:** Kurtis Barton
Editorial Profile: OC Weekly is published for the residents of Orange County, CA and surrounding areas. The newspaper covers local and national news, music, arts, politics and sports.; Full Page Mono: 22.50

Currency: US Dollars
NEWSPAPER

Ocean City Sentinel
Owner: Sample Media, Inc.
Editorial: 112 E 8th St, Ocean City, New Jersey 08226-3736. **T:** 1 609 399-5411
E: sentinelnews@comcast.net
W: http://www.oceancitysentinel.com
Freq: Thu; **Circ:** 10000 Not Audited
Editorial Profile: Ocean City Sentinel serves residents of Ocean City, NJ. The paper focuses on local news, sports and community events.; Full Page Mono: 14.57
Currency: US Dollars
NEWSPAPER

Ocean City Today
Owner: Flag Publications
Editorial: 8200 Coastal Hwy, Ocean City, Maryland 21842. **T:** 1 410 723-6397
E: editor@oceancitytoday.net
W: http://www.oceancitytoday.net
Freq: Fri; **Circ:** 18000 Not Audited
Editorial Profile: Ocean City Today is a weekly newspaper serving the Maryland coast.; Full Page Mono: 11.50; Full Page Colour: 75.00
Currency: US Dollars
NEWSPAPER

The Ocean County Signal
Owner: Ocean Signal Media Group, LLC
Editorial: 195 Lehigh Ave Ste 1, Lakewood, New Jersey 08701-4555
W: http://www.oceancountysignal.com/
Freq: Daily
Editorial Profile: The Ocean County Signal is a daily newspaper covering Local News for the residents of Ocean County, NJ. Coverage includes Business and Community News, Events, Opinions, Politics, Schools, Sports and Towns in addition to other local topics. They do not accept pitching or press materials and have requested that their contact information not be listed.; Full Page Mono: 1000.00; Full Page Colour: 1195.00
Currency: US Dollars
DAILY NEWSPAPER

The Oconee Leader
Owner: Peecher Communcations LLC
Editorial: 46 Greensboro Hwy, Watkinsville, Georgia 30677-2514. **T:** 1 706 310-1104
E: editor@theoconeeleader.com
W: http://www.theoconeeleader.com/
Freq: Thu; **Circ:** 12500
Editorial Profile: The Oconee Leader is a weekly community newspaper covering local news and events in Oconee County, GA.; Full Page Mono: 1000.00; Full Page Colour: 1125.00
Currency: US Dollars
NEWSPAPER

Odessa American
Owner: Freedom Communications Inc.
Editorial: 222 E 4th St, Odessa, Texas 79761.
T: 1 432 337-6262 **E:** oanews@oaoa.com
W: http://www.oaoa.com
Freq: Daily; **Circ:** 18324 Not Audited
Publisher: Patrick Canty
Editorial Profile: Odessa American is a daily newspaper written for residents of Odessa, TX. The newspaper covers local news, sports and entertainment in the Permian Basin area.; Full Page Mono: 28.89; Full Page Colour: 395.00
Currency: US Dollars
DAILY NEWSPAPER

Oelwein Daily Register
Owner: Community Newspaper Group
Editorial: 25 1st St SE, Oelwein, Iowa 50662-2314. **T:** 1 319 283-2144
E: news@oelweindailyregister.com
W: http://www.oelweindailyregister.com
Freq: Daily; **Circ:** 2690 Not Audited
Publisher: Deb Weigel
Editorial Profile: Oelwein Daily Register is published daily for residents of Olewein, IA and surrounding areas. The publication is a general interest newspaper, covering local news, weather, sports, education, business, arts & entertainment and other information of interest to the local community.; Full Page Mono: 18.60; Full Page Colour: 250.00
Currency: US Dollars
DAILY NEWSPAPER

La Oferta
Owner: La Oferta Newspaper Inc.
Editorial: 1376 N 4th St, San Jose, California 95112. **T:** 1 408 436-7850
E: info@laoferta.com
W: http://www.laoferta.com
Freq: Fri; **Circ:** 21000 Not Audited

Editorial Profile: La Oferta targets a bilingual Hispanic market within Santa Clara, San Mateo, Contra Costa, Alameda and San Francisco, CA. It covers news, community events, editorials, business and features relevant to the Spanish-speaking population in Southern California.; Full Page Mono: 29.75; Full Page Colour: 3780.00
Currency: US Dollars
NEWSPAPER

Ogdensburg Journal
Owner: St. Lawrence County Newspapers, Inc.
Editorial: 308 Isabella St, #312, Ogdensburg, New York 13669-1407. **T:** 1 315 393-1003
E: journal@ogd.com **W:** http://www.ogd.com
Freq: Mon thru Fri; **Circ:** 5500 Not Audited
Editorial Profile: Ogdensburg Journal is a weekday newspaper serving residents of Ogdensburg, NY, and surrounding communities. It covers local and regional news, sports, arts & entertainment, events, editorials and features of interest to local readers.; Full Page Mono: 9.75; Full Page Colour: 140.00
Currency: US Dollars
DAILY NEWSPAPER

The Ogle County Life
Editorial: 311 Washington St, Oregon, Illinois 61061. **T:** 1 815 732-2156
W: http://www.oglecountylife.com
Freq: Mon; **Circ:** 12700
Editor: Tina Ketter
Editorial Profile: The Ogle County Life is a community newspaper written for residents of Oregon, IL.; Full Page Mono: 18.70
Currency: US Dollars
NEWSPAPER

Ogle County Newspapers
Owner: Shaw Media
Editorial: 121 S 4th St, Ste A, Oregon, Illinois 61061. **T:** 1 815 732-6166
E: oglenews@essex1.com
W: http://www.oglecountynews.com
Circ: 4850 Not Audited
Publisher: Earleen Hinton; **Editor:** Vinde Wells
NEWSPAPER

Okaloosa Publishing Company
Owner: Halifax Media Holdings LLC
Editorial: 295 W James Lee Blvd, Crestview, Florida 32536-3313. **T:** 1 850 682-6524
E: okpublishing@crestviewbulletin.com
W: http://www.crestviewbulletin.com
Circ: 13500
Publisher: Jason Mobley; **Editor:** Michael Stewart
NEWSPAPER

The Oklahoma Eagle
Editorial: 624 E Archer St, Tulsa, Oklahoma 74120. **T:** 1 918 582-7124
E: news@theoklahomaeagle.net
Freq: Thu; **Circ:** 15000 Not Audited
Editorial Profile: The Oklahoma Eagle is written for the African-American community of Tulsa, OK.; Full Page Mono: 15.50
Currency: US Dollars
NEWSPAPER

Oklahoma Gazette
Owner: Gazette Media Inc.
Editorial: 3701 N Shartel Ave, Oklahoma City, Oklahoma 73118-7102. **T:** 1 405 528-6000
W: http://www.okgazette.com
Freq: Wed; **Circ:** 57500 Not Audited
Editorial Profile: Oklahoma Gazette is a free weekly newspaper for the residents of central Oklahoma. The newspaper's mission is to analyze elements that affect the quality of life in central Oklahoma; to stimulate thought and participation with information and opinion on entertainment opportunities and social needs; to expose conditions and actions that detract from our quality of life; and to recognize those individuals and actions that deserve commendation within the community. The lead time varies per issue.; Full Page Mono: 75.24; Full Page Colour: 2232.00
Currency: US Dollars
NEWSPAPER

The Oklahoman
Owner: Anschutz Corp.
Editorial: 9000 Broadway Ext, Oklahoma City, Oklahoma 73114-3708. **T:** 1 405 475-3311
W: http://www.newsok.com
Freq: Daily; **Circ:** 117180 Not Audited
Editorial Profile: The Oklahoman is a general-interest broadsheet newspaper serving readers in the Oklahoma City area. Business is covered in a daily business section, which also appears on Sunday. A large part of The Oklahoman's business coverage focuses on the oil industry. Types of articles included in the business

section are short news items, company news, industry news, and trend stories.; Full Page Mono: 384.95; Full Page Colour: 2677.83
Currency: US Dollars
DAILY NEWSPAPER

The Oklahoman
Editorial: 529 14th St NW Ste 914, Washington, District Of Columbia 20045-1901; Full Page Mono: 112.56
Currency: US Dollars
DAILY NEWSPAPER

Okmulgee Daily Times
Owner: Sumner Newspapers Inc.
Editorial: 114 E 7th St, Okmulgee, Oklahoma 74447-4606. **T:** 1 918 756-3600
E: okmulgeedailytimes@yahoo.com
W: http://www.okmulgeecountynewssource. com
Freq: Daily; **Circ:** 4483 Not Audited
Editor: Herman Brown; **Publisher:** Derek Sumner
Editorial Profile: Okmulgee Daily Times is a daily newspaper written for the residents of Okmulgee, OK.; Full Page Mono: 9.25; Full Page Colour: 150.00
Currency: US Dollars
DAILY NEWSPAPER

The Olathe News
Owner: The McClatchy Company
Editorial: 1729 Grand Blvd, Kansas City, Missouri 64108-1413. **T:** 1 816 234-4636
W: http://www.theolathenews.com
Freq: Bi-Weekly; **Circ:** 25000
Editorial Profile: The Olathe News is a bi-weekly community news edition of the Kansas City Star written for the residents of Johnson County, KS. Covers local news, sports, opinion and entertainment.
NEWSPAPER

Old Towne Orange Plaza Review
Editorial: 134 S Glassell St, Orange, California 92866-1434. **T:** 1 714 771-6919
W: http://www.orangereview.com
Freq: Bi-Monthly
Editorial Profile: Old Towne Orange Plaza Review provides community news and Old Towne city center coverage for residents of Orange, CA.
NEWSPAPER

Olney Daily Mail
Owner: GateHouse Media Inc.
Editorial: 206 S Whittle Ave, Olney, Illinois 62450. **T:** 1 618 393-2931
E: news@olneydailymail.com
W: http://www.olneydailymail.com
Freq: Daily; **Circ:** 4300 Not Audited
Editor: Mark Allen; **Publisher:** Ray McGrew
Editorial Profile: Olney Daily Mail is published daily for the residents of Olney, IL and surrounding areas. The newspaper covers local news, business, arts & entertainment, sports, health and government.; Full Page Mono: 18.01; Full Page Colour: 225.00
Currency: US Dollars
DAILY NEWSPAPER

The Olympian
Owner: McClatchy Newspapers
Editorial: 111 Bethel St NE, Olympia, Washington 98506-4365. **T:** 1 360 754-5400
E: news@theolympian.com
W: http://www.theolympian.com
Freq: Daily; **Circ:** 21621 Not Audited
Publisher: George Le Masurier
Editorial Profile: The Olympian is a local daily newspaper written for residents of Olympia, WA. The newspaper covers local news, sports, education, business, entertainment and politics.; Full Page Mono: 67.00; Full Page Colour: 900.00
Currency: US Dollars
DAILY NEWSPAPER

Omaha Star
Owner: Washington, (Marguerita)
Editorial: 2216 N 24th St, Omaha, Nebraska 68110-2213. **T:** 1 402 346-4041
W: http://www.omahastarinc.com
Freq: Thu; **Circ:** 30000 Not Audited
Editorial Profile: Omaha Star is written for the African-American community in Omaha, NE, and the surrounding areas. Deadlines for the publication are Tuesdays by noon before issue date.; Full Page Mono: 18.00
Currency: US Dollars
NEWSPAPER

Omaha World-Herald
Owner: MediaNews Group
Editorial: 1314 Douglas St Ste 700, Omaha, Nebraska 68102-1811. **T:** 1 402 444-1000
E: news@owh.com

W: http://www.omaha.com
Freq: Daily; **Circ:** 125748 Not Audited
Editorial Profile: Omaha World-Herald is a daily, general interest broadsheet newspaper written for readers in the greater Omaha, NE, area. Coverage includes business, technology, working, entertainment, home, living, sports and local, regional and national news.; Full Page Mono: 177.00; Full Page Colour: 591.60
Currency: US Dollars
DAILY NEWSPAPER

Omaha World-Herald
Editorial: 529 14th St NW Ste 1009, Washington, District Of Columbia 20045-2001.
T: 1 202 662-7270
Bureau Chief: Joseph Morton
DAILY NEWSPAPER

Omaha World-Herald
Editorial: 635 S 14th St Ste 320, Lincoln, Nebraska 68508-2701. **T:** 1 402 473-9580
Bureau Chief: Paul Hammel
DAILY NEWSPAPER

On Common Ground News
Editorial: 1240 Sigman Rd, Ste 107, Conyers, Georgia 30012. **T:** 1 678 526-1910
E: editor@ocgnews.com
W: http://www.ocgnews.com
Freq: Bi-Weekly; **Circ:** 30000 Not Audited
Editorial Profile: On Common Ground News is a bi-weekly newspaper written for the residents of DeKalb County, GA. The newspaper covers local news, education, business, arts & entertainment, health and real estate. It is issued on the 1st and 15th of each month.; Full Page Mono: 53.00
Currency: US Dollars
NEWSPAPER

One Nation News
Owner: Black Heart Publishing Inc.
Editorial: 1614 Harmon Pl Ste 203, Minneapolis, Minnesota 55403-1964.
T: 1 763 205-6751
E: info@onenationnews.com
W: http://www.onenationnews.com
Freq: Wed; **Circ:** 10000 Not Audited
Publisher: Joe Bryson; **Editor:** Kay Hansen
Editorial Profile: One Nation News is a weekly newspaper serving the African-American residents in the Twin Cities in Minnesota. It is published every Wednesday.; Full Page Mono: 59.00
Currency: US Dollars
NEWSPAPER

The Oneida
Editorial: 579A Main St, Oneida, New York 13421. **T:** 1 315 829-8399
E: info@oneida-nation.org
W: http://www.oneidaindiannation.com
Freq: Bi-Monthly; **Circ:** 62000 Not Audited
Publisher: Ray Halbritter; **Editor:** Jim Heines
Editorial Profile: The Oneida is an American Indian weekly newspaper that focuses on news, weather, business and other information important to the residents of Oneida, NY. They do not accept advertising. They do not accept press releases outside their community.
NEWSPAPER

The Oneida Daily Dispatch
Owner: Journal Register Company
Editorial: 130 Broad St, Oneida, New York 13421-1696. **T:** 1 315 363-5100
E: newsroom@oneidadispatch.com
W: http://www.oneidadispatch.com
Freq: Mon thru Fri; **Circ:** 6715
Publisher: Jan Dewey; **Editor:** Kurt Wanfried;
Editor: Kurt Wanfried
Editorial Profile: The Oneida Daily Dispatch is written for Oneida and Madison County residents in New York.; Full Page Mono: 16.29
Currency: US Dollars
DAILY NEWSPAPER

Opelika-Auburn News
Owner: BH Media Group
Editorial: 2901 Society Hill Rd, Opelika, Alabama 36804-4850. **T:** 1 334 749-6271
E: editors@oanow.com
W: http://www.oanow.com
Freq: Daily; **Circ:** 12748 Not Audited
Editorial Profile: Opelika-Auburn News is a daily newspaper published for the residents of Opelika, AL and surrounding areas. It provides local and national news and information.; Full Page Mono: 31.93; Full Page Colour: 34.43
Currency: US Dollars
DAILY NEWSPAPER

La Opinion
Owner: La Opinion Co, Inc.
Editorial: 404 College Ave, Jacksonville, Texas 75766-2244. **T:** 1 903 586-0827

E: laopinion@suddenlinkmail.com
Freq: Bi-Monthly; **Circ:** 10000
Editor: Judith Cantua
Editorial Profile: La Opinion is a bi-monthly community newspaper servicing Spanish speaking communities of Western Texas.; Full Page Mono: 15.00
Currency: US Dollars
NEWSPAPER

La Opinión
Owner: ImpreMedia LLC
Editorial: 700 S Flower St Ste 3000, Los Angeles, California 90017-4217.
T: 1 213 622-8332
W: http://www.laopinion.com
Freq: Daily; **Circ:** 113489 Not Audited
Publisher: Monica Lozano; **Editor:** Reynaldo Mena
Editorial Profile: La Opinión is a daily Spanish language newspaper for the Hispanic community of the Los Angeles area. It provides residents with information on local news, weather, sports and more. It maintains a commitment to diversity and immigration, as well as other issues specific to the Los Angeles Latino community. The paper is one of the most widely read and longest running Spanish-language newspapers in the country. It was first published in 1926. Previously focused on Mexico and Mexican and Mexican-American issues, the paper now serves a broader Hispanic readership with coverage of news and cultural topics from Central and South America, Cuba, Puerto Rico and The United States, in addition to international wire content. It is the recipient of a 2006 Jose Ortega y Gasset Award from El Pais newspaper in Spain. Contact the paper via Metro & News Editor.; Full Page Mono: 94.31; Full Page Colour: 1934.23
Currency: US Dollars
DAILY NEWSPAPER

Orange County Neighborhood Newspapers Inc.
Owner: CommunityMedia Corporation
Editorial: 9559 Valley View St, Cypress, California 90630. **T:** 1 714 220-0292
Circ: 73500 Not Audited
Editor: Travis Perkins
NEWSPAPER

Orange County Publishing Co., Inc.
Owner: Orange County Publishing
Editorial: 131 N West Court St, Paoli, Indiana 47454. **T:** 1 812 723-2572
E: ocpinc@ocpnews.com
Freq: Weekly; **Circ:** 18009 Not Audited
Publisher: Art Hampton; Full Page Mono: 716.00
Currency: US Dollars
NEWSPAPER

The Orange County Register
Owner: 2100 Trust LLC
Editorial: 625 N Grand Ave, Santa Ana, California 92701-4347. **T:** 1 877 469-7344
E: local@ocregister.com
W: http://www.ocregister.com
Freq: Daily; **Circ:** 681512 Not Audited
Editorial Profile: The Orange County Register is published daily for the residents of Orange County, CA and surrounding areas. The newspaper covers local news and community events. Advertising rates reflect Monday, Tuesday and Wednesday. Rates for Thursday, Friday and Saturday are higher.; Full Page Mono: 361.85; Full Page Colour: 386.73
Currency: US Dollars
DAILY NEWSPAPER

The Orange County Register - Anaheim
Editorial: 1771 S Lewis St, Anaheim, California 92805-6439. **T:** 1 714 704-3700
E: orangecitynews@ocregister.com
DAILY NEWSPAPER

The Orange County Register - Laguna Woods
Editorial: 24351 El Toro Rd, Laguna Woods, California 92637-4901. **T:** 1 949 837-5200
DAILY NEWSPAPER

The Orange County Register - Lake Forest
Editorial: 22481 Aspan St, Lake Forest, California 92630-1630. **T:** 1 949 454-7300
DAILY NEWSPAPER

The Orange County Register - San Clemente
Editorial: 95 Avenida Del Mar, San Clemente, California 92672-4013. **T:** 1 949 492-5135
W: http://www.ocregister.com/sections/

city-pages/sanjuancapistrano/
DAILY NEWSPAPER

Orange County Register Community Newspapers
Owner: 2100 Trust LLC
Editorial: 625 N Grand Ave, Santa Ana, California 92701-4347. **T:** 1 877 469-7344
W: http://www.ocregister.com
Editor: Susan Gill Vardon
NEWSPAPER

Orange County Register Community Newspapers - North
Owner: 2100 Trust LLC
Editorial: 1771 S Lewis St, Anaheim, California 92805-6439. **T:** 1 714 634-1567
W: http://www.ocregister.com **Circ:** 135863 Not Audited
NEWSPAPER

Orange County Register Community Newspapers - South
Owner: 2100 Trust LLC
Editorial: 22481 Aspan St, Lake Forest, California 92630. **T:** 1 949 454-7300
W: http://www.ocregister.com **Circ:** 126078 Not Audited
Editor: Freda Freeman; **Editor:** Nellene Teubner
NEWSPAPER

Oregon Coast Today
Owner: East Oregonian Publishing Co.
Editorial: 820 Se Highway 101 Suite A, Lincoln City, Oregon 97367-2773.
T: 1 541 921-0413
E: news@oregoncoasttoday.com
W: http://www.oregoncoasttoday.com
Freq: Fri; **Circ:** 17500
Editor: Patrick Alexander
Editorial Profile: Oregon Coast Today is a free weekly newspaper providing Local and Community News coverage for the residents of Newport, Lincoln City, Yachats, Tillamook, Pacific City and Depoe Bay, OR.
NEWSPAPER

The Oregon Sentinel
Editorial: Oregon Military Dept, Public Affairs, AGPA Rm 204, Salem, Oregon 997309.
T: 1 503 584-3917 **E:** agpa@mil.state.or.us
W: http://www.oregon.gov/
Freq: Semi-Monthly; **Circ:** 15000 Not Audited
Editor: Jeff Thompson
Editorial Profile: The Oregon Sentinel is a free semi-monthly publication providing news and features about the Oregon National Guard. It changed its name from Azuwur in 2003. The paper does not accept advertising.
NEWSPAPER

The Oregonian
Owner: Oregonian Media Group
Editorial: 1320 SW Broadway, Portland, Oregon 97201-3411. **T:** 1 503 221-8327 5
E: newsroom@oregonian.com
W: http://www.oregonlive.com
Freq: Daily; **Circ:** 142882 Not Audited
Publisher: N. Christian Anderson
Editorial Profile: The Oregonian is a newspaper written for the general public in the Portland, OR area. It offers regional and national news and provides its readers with information on business, real estate, arts, entertainment, and sports. The business section offers breaking news, investigative reports, news and news analysis, features, columns and profiles on business in Oregon. The editorial staff only wants to receive information that pertains to Oregon businesses. The staff won a 2007 Pulitzer Prize for Breaking News.; Full Page Mono: 263.70; Full Page Colour: 913.84
Currency: US Dollars
DAILY NEWSPAPER

The Oregonian
Editorial: 365 Warner Milne Rd, Oregon City, Oregon 97045-4073. **T:** 1 503 294-5920
E: south@oregonian.com
DAILY NEWSPAPER

The Oregonian
Editorial: 1675 SW Marlow Ave, Portland, Oregon 97225-5104. **T:** 1 503 294-5950
E: west@oregonian.com
Bureau Chief: Tom Maurer
DAILY NEWSPAPER

The Oregonian
Editorial: 900 Court St NE Ste 43, Salem, Oregon 97301-4045. **T:** 1 503 221-8234
E: politics@oregonian.com
DAILY NEWSPAPER

Orlando Sentinel
Owner: Tribune Company
Editorial: 633 N Orange Ave, Orlando, Florida 32801-1300. **T:** 1 407 420-5000
E: news@orlandosentinel.com
W: http://www.orlandosentinel.com
Freq: Daily; **Circ:** 173542 Not Audited
Publisher: Howard Greenberg
Editorial Profile: Orlando Sentinel is a daily newspaper written for the general public in Orlando and East Central Florida, including the counties of Brevard, Flagler, Lake, Marion, Orange, Osceola, Seminole, Sumter and Volusia. Deadlines are two days prior to publication.; Full Page Mono: 387.00; Full Page Colour: 1948.19
Currency: US Dollars
DAILY NEWSPAPER

Orlando Sentinel
Editorial: 336 E College Ave Ste 105, Tallahassee, Florida 32301-1554.
T: 1 850 222-5564
DAILY NEWSPAPER

Orlando Sentinel
Editorial: 1898 E Burleigh Blvd, Tavares, Florida 32778-4366. **T:** 1 352 742-5920
E: lake@orlandosentinel.com
Bureau Chief: Jerry Fallstrom
DAILY NEWSPAPER

The Orlando Times
Owner: Calvin Collins, Jr.
Editorial: 4403 Vineland Rd Ste B5, Orlando, Florida 32811-7362. **T:** 1 407 841-3052
E: keepupwiththetimes@gmail.com
W: http://www.orlando-times.com
Freq: Thu; **Circ:** 10000 Not Audited
Publisher: Calvin Collins; **Publisher:** Calvin Collins
Editorial Profile: The Orlando Times is geared toward the African American residents of Orlando, FL and surrounding areas in central Florida. Topics covered in the newspaper include education, religion, local news and information of interest to the black community residing in Orlando, FL.; Full Page Mono: 18.50
Currency: US Dollars
NEWSPAPER

Orlando Weekly
Owner: Times Shamrock Group
Editorial: 1505 E Colonial Dr, STE 200, Orlando, Florida 32803-4705.
T: 1 407 377-0400
E: letters@orlandoweekly.com
W: http://www.orlandoweekly.com
Freq: Thu; **Circ:** 45000 Not Audited
Publisher: Graham Jarrett; **Editor:** Erin Sullivan
Editorial Profile: Orlando (FL) Weekly covers local news, politics, music, arts & entertainment, dining, social issues and community events.; Full Page Mono: 63.00
Currency: US Dollars
NEWSPAPER

Oroville Mercury-Register
Owner: MediaNews Group
Editorial: 2124 5th Ave, Oroville, California 95965-3400. **T:** 1 530 533-3131
W: http://www.orovillemr.com
Freq: Daily; **Circ:** 7000 Not Audited
Editor: David Little
Editorial Profile: Oroville Mercury-Register is a daily newspaper serving the residents of Oroville, CA and the Greater Mid-Valley area. It covers local news, sports, opinion, features and business.; Full Page Mono: 67.03
Currency: US Dollars
DAILY NEWSPAPER

Osage Valley Newspapers
Owner: Standard Herald, Inc.
Editorial: 205 S Main St, Windsor, Missouri 65360-1869. **T:** 1 660 647-2121 **Circ:** 6800
Editor: Colby Gordon; **Editor:** Frank Mercer
NEWSPAPER

Osceola News-Gazette
Owner: Florida Sun Publications
Editorial: 108 Church St, Kissimmee, Florida 34741. **T:** 1 407 846-7600
E: display@osceolanewsgazette.com
W: http://www.osceolanewsgazette.com
Freq: Sat; **Circ:** 39000 Not Audited
Editor in Chief: Brian McBride; **Publisher:** Matt Plocha
Editorial Profile: Osceola News-Gazette in Kissimmee, FL covers local news, sports, arts and entertainment, opinion and community events. Deadlines are three days prior to issue date; Full Page Mono: 20.35; Full Page Colour: 1491.00
Currency: US Dollars
NEWSPAPER

El Osceola Star
Editorial: 220 E Monument Ave, Ste C, Kissimmee, Florida 34741. **T:** 1 407 933-0174
E: starnews@aol.com
W: http://www.elosceolastar.com
Freq: Fri; **Circ:** 15000 Not Audited
Editor: Bill Hansen
Editorial Profile: El Osceola Star is a local newspaper written for the Hispanic residents of Kissimmee, FL. Advertising deadlines are Mondays at 5PM ET.; Full Page Mono: 14.00
Currency: US Dollars
NEWSPAPER

Oshkosh Northwestern
Owner: Gannett Co., Inc.
Editorial: 224 State St Floor 3, Oshkosh, Wisconsin 54901-4868. **T:** 1 920 235-7700
E: oshkoshnews@thenorthwestern.com
W: http://www.thenorthwestern.com
Freq: Daily; **Circ:** 12526 Not Audited
Publisher: Thomas Cooper
Editorial Profile: Oshkosh Northwestern is published daily for the residents of Oshkosh, WI and surrounding areas. The newspaper covers local and regional news, sports, entertainment, business and community events.; Full Page Mono: 49.90; Full Page Colour: 312.36
Currency: US Dollars
DAILY NEWSPAPER

Oskaloosa Herald
Owner: Community Newspaper Holdings, Inc.
Editorial: 1901 A Ave W, Oskaloosa, Iowa 52577-1971. **T:** 1 641 672-2581
E: oskynews@oskyherald.com
W: http://www.oskaloosaherald.com
Freq: Daily; **Circ:** 3320 Not Audited
Editor: Duane Nollen; **Publisher:** Deb Van Engelenhoven
Editorial Profile: Oskaloosa Herald is published daily for the residents of Oskaloosa, IA and surrounding areas. The newspaper covers local news, sports, agriculture, government and lifestyle features.; Full Page Mono: 8.17; Full Page Colour: 75.00
Currency: US Dollars
DAILY NEWSPAPER

Osprey Observer Inc.
Owner: Osprey Observer Inc.
Editorial: 900 Lithia Pinecrest Rd, Brandon, Florida 33511. **T:** 1 813 657-2418
E: editor@ospreyobserver.com
W: http://www.ospreyobserver.com
Circ: 86000 Not Audited
Editor: Harley Gilmore
Editorial Profile: Osprey Observer Inc. in Brandon, FL is a community newspaper publisher that serves the residents of Tampa, St. Petersburg and Clearwater, FL.
NEWSPAPER

Ossian Journal-News
Owner: News-Banner Publications
Editorial: 1002 Dehner Dr, Ossian, Indiana 46777. **T:** 1 260 622-4108
E: ossianj@adamswells.com
W: http://www.news-banner.com **Circ:** 9802 Not Audited
NEWSPAPER

Osteen Publishing Company - Ponte Vedra
Owner: Osteen Publishing Company
Editorial: 1102 A1A North, Unit 108, Ponte Vedra Beach, Florida 32082.
T: 1 904 285-8831 **E:** pvrecorder@opcfla.com
W: http://www.pontevedrarecorder.com
Circ: 35000
Publisher: Susan Griffin; **Editor:** Kelly Hould
NEWSPAPER

Osteen Publishing Group
Owner: Osteen Publishing Group
Editorial: 3513 U.S. Hwy. 17, Fleming Island, Florida 32003. **T:** 1 904 264-3200
W: http://www.claytodayonline.com
Circ: 12000 Not Audited
Publisher: Jon Cantrell
NEWSPAPER

The Oswego County Weeklies
Editorial: 80 N Jefferson St, Mexico, New York 13114-3000. **T:** 1 315 963-7813
E: ocweeklies@cnymail.com **Circ:** 34567 Not Audited
Publisher: Mark Backus
Editorial Profile: The Oswego County Weeklies is a community newspaper publisher n Mexico, NY.
NEWSPAPER

Ottawa Herald
Owner: Harris Enterprises
Editorial: 104 S Cedar St, Ottawa, Kansas 66067-2392. **T:** 1 785 242-4700
E: news@ottawaherald.com
W: http://www.ottawaherald.com
Freq: Daily; **Circ:** 6100 Not Audited
Editorial Profile: Ottawa Herald is published daily for the residents of Franklin County, KS and surrounding areas. The newspaper covers news, sports, business and weather.; Full Page Mono: 9.18; Full Page Colour: 135.00
Currency: US Dollars
DAILY NEWSPAPER

Ottumwa Courier
Owner: Community Newspaper Holdings, Inc.
Editorial: 213 E 2nd St, Ottumwa, Iowa 52501-2940. **T:** 1 641 684-4611
E: news@ottumwacourier.com
W: http://www.ottumwa.com
Freq: Daily; **Circ:** 11772 Not Audited
Publisher: Dave Balcom; **Editor:** James Grob
Editorial Profile: Ottumwa Courier is written for residents of Ottumwa, IA. It covers local news, sports, entertainment, health, state and national news.; Full Page Mono: 20.25; Full Page Colour: 275.00
Currency: US Dollars
DAILY NEWSPAPER

Our Time Press
Owner: Greaves (David)
Editorial: 679 Lafayette Ave, Brooklyn, New York 11216. **T:** 1 718 599-6828
E: editors@ourtimepress.com
W: http://www.ourtimepress.com
Freq: Thu; **Circ:** 20000 Not Audited
Editorial Profile: Our Time Press is an African-American owned and operated free tabloid-sized paper published in Brooklyn, New York.; Full Page Mono: 75.00
Currency: US Dollars
NEWSPAPER

Our Town
Owner: Straus News
Editorial: 36 Ridge St, Pearl River, New York 10965-2407. **T:** 1 845 735-1342
E: news@ourtownnews.com
W: http://www.ourtownnews.com
Freq: Wed; **Circ:** 14400 Not Audited
Editorial Profile: Our Town is a weekly newspaper serving the residents of Rockland and Northern Bergen, NY.; Full Page Mono: 14.35
Currency: US Dollars
NEWSPAPER

Our Town News
Owner: South Florida Media Group
Editorial: 3665 Park Central Blvd. North, Pompano Beach, Florida 33069.
T: 1 954 973-3330
W: http://www.theourtownnews.com
Freq: Thu; **Circ:** 49073 Not Audited
Editorial Profile: Our Town News covers local news, events and interests for the people of Coral Springs, Parkland, West Boca, Coconut Creek and Margate, FL.; Full Page Mono: 21.50
Currency: US Dollars
NEWSPAPER

Out & About Nashville
Owner: Out & About Nashville, Inc.
Editorial: 3951 Moss Rose Dr, Nashville, Tennessee 37216-2925. **T:** 1 615 596-6210
E: news@outandaboutnashville.com
W: http://www.outandaboutnashville.com
Freq: Monthly; **Circ:** 15000
Publisher: Jerry Jones
Editorial Profile: Out & About Nashville, launched in 2002, is a community newspaper written for the Nashville and Knoxville, TN gay, lesbian, bi-sexual and transgender community. It provides local news coverage as well as coverage of business, politics, entertainment, features and sports.; Full Page Mono: 23.86
Currency: US Dollars
NEWSPAPER

Outlook
Owner: Horizon Publications
Editorial: 309 N College Ave, Newton, North Carolina 28658-3255. **T:** 1 828 464-0221
E: onenews@observernewsonline.com
W: http://www.observernewsonline.com
Freq: Thu; **Circ:** 10000 Not Audited
Editor: Barbara Burns; **Publisher:** Michael Willard
Editorial Profile: Outlook is a free, weekly publication that emphasizes positive news about Catawba County, NC. From feature stories to arts & entertainment and the social scene, it is filled with local names and people. Published by The Observer News Enterprise, Outlook is included in every Thursday edition of the daily newspaper and is also available at area newsstands and businesses.; Full Page Mono: 7.50
Currency: US Dollars
NEWSPAPER

Over the Mountain Journal
Editorial: 2016 Columbiana Rd, Birmingham, Alabama 35216. **T:** 1 205 823-9646
W: http://www.otmj.com
Freq: Bi-Weekly; **Circ:** 40000 Not Audited
Editor: Keysha Drexel
Editorial Profile: Over the Mountain Journal in Birmingham, AL is a bi-weekly newspaper that covers local news, community events and lifestyle topics of interest to the surrounding communities. Deadlines are three weeks prior to the issue date.; Full Page Mono: 50.00; Full Page Colour: 2500.00
Currency: US Dollars
NEWSPAPER

Owatonna People's Press
Owner: Huckle Media LLC
Editorial: 135 W Pearl St, Owatonna, Minnesota 55060-2316. **T:** 1 507 451-2840
E: news@owatonna.com
W: http://www.owatonna.com
Freq: Daily; **Circ:** 6597 Not Audited
Editorial Profile: Owatonna People's Press is a local daily newspaper serving the residents of Owatonna, MN and the surrounding area. The newspaper mainly covers local news, sports, and community events. The paper accepts advertising at an open rate of $13.50 per column inch.; Full Page Mono: 17.90; Full Page Colour: 370.00
Currency: US Dollars
DAILY NEWSPAPER

Owego Pennysaver
Owner: Times Shamrock Group
Editorial: 183 Front St, Owego, New York 13827-1520. **T:** 1 607 687-2434
E: opennysaver@stny.rr.com
W: http://www.owegopennysaver.com
Freq: Sun; **Circ:** 20023 Not Audited
Editor: Wendy Post; **Publisher:** Greg Zyla
Editorial Profile: Owego Pennysaver is a local weekly newspaper serving the residents of Tioga County, NY and the Northeastern portion of Bradford County, PA. The newspaper is comprised mainly of advertising, but it also contains some local news and features of interest to the local community. Deadlines are on Wednesday mornings.; Full Page Mono: 14.12
Currency: US Dollars
NEWSPAPER

Owensboro Messenger-Inquirer
Owner: Paxton Media Group
Editorial: 1401 Frederica St, Owensboro, Kentucky 42301-4804. **T:** 1 270 926-0123
E: news@messenger-inquirer.com
W: http://www.messenger-inquirer.com
Freq: Daily; **Circ:** 22876 Not Audited
Publisher: Bob Morris
Editorial Profile: Owensboro Messenger-Inquirer is a daily newspaper for residents of a seven-county area in Kentucky and Southern Indiana. The publication covers local news, events and sports. The editorial deadline is one day prior to the issue date.; Full Page Mono: 34.47; Full Page Colour: 550.00
Currency: US Dollars
DAILY NEWSPAPER

Oxford Eagle
Owner: Oxford Eagle, Inc.
Editorial: 916 Jackson Ave E, Oxford, Mississippi 38655-3636. **T:** 1 662 234-4331
E: news@oxfordeagle.com
W: http://www.oxfordeagle.com
Freq: Daily; **Circ:** 6000 Not Audited
News Editor: Jon Scott
Editorial Profile: Oxford Eagle is a daily newspaper serving the residents of Lafayette County, MS. The newspaper provides news and sports coverage to the local community.; Full Page Mono: 9.55; Full Page Colour: 264.55
Currency: US Dollars
DAILY NEWSPAPER

Oxford Public Ledger
Editorial: 200 W Spring St, Oxford, North Carolina 27565-3247. **T:** 1 919 693-2646
E: opl@earthlink.net
Freq: Mon; **Circ:** 13000 Not Audited
Editor: Al Carson
Editorial Profile: Oxford Public Ledger aims to provide local news and information to residents of Oxford County, NC. The deadlines are Tuesday at noon ET for the Thursday

publication and Friday at 5pm ET for the Monday publication.; Full Page Mono: 6.50
Currency: US Dollars
NEWSPAPER

PA Focus
Owner: Ogden Newspapers
Editorial: 114 Lee Ave, Weirton, West Virginia 26062. **T:** 1 304 748-0606
W: http://www.pafocus.com
Freq: Thu; **Circ:** 13600 Not Audited
Publisher: Alex Marshall
Editorial Profile: PA Focus is a weekly newspaper serving residents of Florence, Paris, Midway, McDonald, Burgettstown, Slovan and Avella, PA. It covers local news, businesses, sports, schools and community events.; Full Page Mono: 7.47
Currency: US Dollars
NEWSPAPER

Pacific Publishing Company
Owner: Pacific Publishing Co. Inc.
Editorial: 636 S Alaska St, Seattle, Washington 98108-1727. **T:** 1 206 461-1300
W: http://www.pacificpublishingcompany.com
Circ: 40000 Not Audited
Editor: Vera Chan-Pool; **Editor:** Vera Chan-Pool; **Editor:** Vera Chan-Pool; **Editor:** Vera Chan-Pool; **Publisher:** Mike Dillon
Editorial Profile: Pacific Publishing Co. in Seattle, WA publishes City Living Seattle, Madison Park Times and Queen Anne News & Magnolia News.
NEWSPAPER

Pacific Sun
Owner: Heinen (Bob)
Editorial: 835 4th St Ste B, San Rafael, California 94901-3260. **T:** 1 415 485-6700
E: letters@pacificsun.com
W: http://www.pacificsun.com
Freq: Fri; **Circ:** 22000 Not Audited
Publisher: Bob Heinen
Editorial Profile: Pacific Sun is a local weekly newspaper serving the residents of Marin County, CA, and Sonoma County, CA. It is an independent, alternative paper and content focuses on local news, entertainment, lifestyle and politics. The lead time for the paper varies per article.; Full Page Mono: 29.90
Currency: US Dollars
NEWSPAPER

Packet Publications - Allentown
Owner: Princeton Packet, Inc. (The)
Editorial: 34 S Main St, Allentown, New Jersey 8501. **T:** 1 609 924-3244
E: editor@pacpub.com
W: http://www.centraljersey.com **Circ:** 12339 Not Audited
Editor: Aubrey Huston; **Publisher:** James Kilgore
NEWSPAPER

Packet Publications - Princeton
Owner: Princeton Packet, Inc. (The)
Editorial: 300 Witherspoon St, Princeton, New Jersey 08542-3401. **T:** 1 609 924-3244
E: feedback@centraljersey.com
W: http://www.centraljersey.com **Circ:** 12680 Not Audited
Editor: Aubrey Huston; **Editor:** David Kilby; **Publisher:** James Kilgore; **Editor:** Charlie Kim
Editorial Profile: Packet Publications in Princeton, NJ, publishes 11 community weekly papers, 7 TMC weekly publications, 1 lifestyle glossy magazine, and centraljersey.com. The Princeton Packet is the most widely read of their newspapers.
NEWSPAPER

Paden Publishing, LLC
Editorial: 3 Foundry St, Ste 1, Greene, New York 13778. **T:** 1 607 656-4511
E: hometownnews@frontiernet.net
W: http://www.tritownnews.com **Circ:** 3550 Not Audited
Editor: Pete Mansheffer; **Publisher:** Kenneth Paden
NEWSPAPER

The Paducah Sun
Owner: Paxton Media Group
Editorial: 408 Kentucky Ave, Paducah, Kentucky 42003-1567. **T:** 1 270 575-8600
E: news@paducahsun.com
W: http://www.paducahsun.com
Freq: Daily; **Circ:** 20616 Not Audited
News Editor: Ron Clark; **News Editor:** Ron Clark; **News Editor:** Ron Clark; **News Editor:** Ron Clark; **Editor:** Adam Shull
Editorial Profile: The Paducah Sun is a daily newspaper serving Paducah, KY and the surrounding area. It covers news, business, sports, entertainment, outdoors and religion.; Full Page Mono: 30.27

Currency: US Dollars
DAILY NEWSPAPER

Pakistan Post
Editorial: 16922 Hillside Ave, Jamaica, New York 11432. **T:** 1 718 739-2976
E: thepakistanpost@gmail.com
W: http://www.pakistanpost.net
Freq: Wed; **Circ:** 81000 Not Audited
Editorial Profile: Pakistan Post is a community newspaper targeted at the Pakistani community of Jamaica, NY.; Full Page Mono: 35.00
Currency: US Dollars
NEWSPAPER

Pakistan Publications
Owner: Pakistan Publications, Inc. (The)
Editorial: 6666 Harwin Dr, Ste 365, Houston, Texas 77036-2263. **T:** 1 713 914-0786
E: pakistanchronicle@gmail.com
W: http://www.pakistanchronicle.com
Freq: Weekly; **Circ:** 90000 Not Audited
Publisher: Nasreen Khan
Editorial Profile: Pakistan Publications publishes three weekly newspapers targeting South Asians and Muslims in the United States: The Pakistan Journal, which publishes in Urdu; The Pakistan Chronicle, which publishes in English, and the South Asian Chronicle, which also publishes in English.; Full Page Mono: 20.00
Currency: US Dollars
NEWSPAPER

Palatka Daily News
Owner: Community Newspapers Inc.
Editorial: 1825 Saint Johns Ave, Palatka, Florida 32177-4400. **T:** 1 386 312-5200
E: palatkadailynews@yahoo.com
W: http://www.palatkadailynews.com
Freq: Daily; **Circ:** 10300 Not Audited
Editor: Andy Hall; **Publisher:** Rusty Starr; **Editor:** Larry Sullivan
Editorial Profile: Palatka Daily News is a local newspaper serving the Palatka, FL community. The publication is published daily. It covers local news, sports and events.; Full Page Mono: 23.22
Currency: US Dollars
DAILY NEWSPAPER

Palestine Herald-Press
Owner: Community Newspapers Holdings, Inc.
Editorial: 519 N Elm St, Palestine, Texas 75801-2927. **T:** 1 903 729-0281
E: palestineherald@gmail.com
W: http://www.palestineherald.com
Freq: Daily; **Circ:** 7645 Not Audited
Publisher: Gary Connor
Editorial Profile: Palestine Herald-Press is published daily for the residents of Palestine, TX and surrounding areas. The newspaper covers local news, sports and community events.; Full Page Mono: 10.30; Full Page Colour: 100.00
Currency: US Dollars
DAILY NEWSPAPER

Palisadian Post
Owner: Smolinisky (Alan)
Editorial: 881 Alma Real Dr Site 213, Pacific Palisades, California 90272-3731. **T:** 1 310 454-1321 **E:** info@palipost.com
W: http://www.palisadespost.com
Freq: Thu; **Circ:** 15000 Not Audited
Editor in Chief: Frances Sharpe; **Publisher:** Alan Smolinisky
Editorial Profile: Palisadian Post is a local newspaper written for the residents of Pacific Palisades, CA. The paper covers local news and community events.; Full Page Mono: 28.05
Currency: US Dollars
NEWSPAPER

Palladium-Item
Owner: Gannett Co., Inc.
Editorial: 1175 N A St, Richmond, Indiana 47374-3226. **T:** 1 765 962-1575
E: palitem@pal-item.com
W: http://www.pal-item.com
Freq: Daily; **Circ:** 9927
News Editor: Millie Martin
Editorial Profile: Palladium-Item is a daily newspaper serving the greater Richmond, IN area. It covers local and national news, sports, politics and agricultural news.; Full Page Mono: 41.28; Full Page Colour: 481.00
Currency: US Dollars
DAILY NEWSPAPER

The Palladium-Times
Owner: Sample News Group
Editorial: 140 W 1st St, Oswego, New York 13126. **T:** 1 315 343-3800
E: editor@palltimes.com

W: http://www.pall-times.com
Freq: Daily; **Circ:** 8507 Not Audited
Publisher: Jon Spaulding; **Editor:** Harrison Wilde
Editorial Profile: The Palladium-Times is published daily for the residents of Oswego, NY and surrounding areas. The newspapers covers local and national news.; Full Page Mono: 17.00; Full Page Colour: 375.00
Currency: US Dollars
DAILY NEWSPAPER

Palm Beach Daily News
Owner: Cox Media Group, Inc.
Editorial: 265 Royal Poinciana Way, Palm Beach, Florida 33480-4041. **T:** 1 561 820-3800
W: http://www.palmbeachdailynews.com
Freq: Daily; **Circ:** 7126 Not Audited
Editorial Profile: Palm Beach Daily News is a sister publication to the Palm Beach Post. The newspaper covers local news, entertainment, politics and events of interest to residents of Palm Beach, FL. From mid-June through mid-September, this publication switches to a bi-weekly with print editions on Thursdays and Sundays.; Full Page Mono: 59.28; Full Page Colour: 1573.00
Currency: US Dollars
DAILY NEWSPAPER

The Palm Beach Post
Owner: Cox Media Group, Inc.
Editorial: 2751 S Dixie Hwy, West Palm Beach, Florida 33405-1233. **T:** 1 561 820-4400
E: pbmetro@pbpost.com
W: http://www.palmbeachpost.com
Freq: Daily; **Circ:** 105335 Not Audited
Editorial Profile: The Palm Beach Post is a metropolitan daily newspaper with bureaus throughout the state of Florida covering local, state, national and international news.; Full Page Mono: 192.67; Full Page Colour: 238.41
Currency: US Dollars
DAILY NEWSPAPER

The Palm Beach Post
Editorial: 2915 S Congress Ave, Delray Beach, Florida 33445-7338. **T:** 1 561 279-3450
DAILY NEWSPAPER

The Palm Beach Post
Editorial: 1838 Park Ln S, Jupiter, Florida 33458-8077. **T:** 1 561 820-3030
DAILY NEWSPAPER

The Palm Beach Post
Editorial: 336 E College Ave Ste 202, Tallahassee, Florida 32301-1551.
T: 1 850 224-1368
DAILY NEWSPAPER

The Palm Beach Post
Editorial: 901 Sansburys Way, Royal Palm Beach, Florida 33411-3600. **T:** 1 561 820-3627
DAILY NEWSPAPER

The Palm Beach Post
Editorial: 400 N Capitol St NW Ste 750, Washington, District Of Columbia 20001-1536.
T: 1 202 777-7090
Editorial Profile: This is the Washington D.C. bureau of The Palm Beach Post.
DAILY NEWSPAPER

Palo Verde Valley & Quartzsite Times
Owner: Western Newspapers, Inc.
Editorial: 153 S Broadway, Blythe, California 92225. **T:** 1 760 922-3181
E: editor@paloverdevalleytimes.com
W: http://www.paloverdevalleytimes.com
Freq: 2 Times/Week; **Circ:** 5000
Publisher: Debbie Hoel
NEWSPAPER

Palos Verdes Peninsula News
Owner: MediaNews Group
Editorial: 609 Deep Valley Dr., Suite 229, Rolling Hills Estates, California 90274.
T: 1 310 377-6877 **W:** http://www.pvnews.com
Freq: Thu; **Circ:** 18400 Not Audited
Publisher: Julia Parton; **Editor in Chief:** Mary Scott
Editorial Profile: Palos Verdes Peninsula News is a twice-weekly newspaper serving the Palos Verdes Peninsula, including Palos Verdes Estates, Rolling Hills Estates, Rolling Hills and Rancho Palos Verdes, CA. It covers local news, business, sports, health, entertainment and community events. An edition of the paper is circulated for free to non-subscribers in the area on the third Saturday of each month.; Full Page Mono: 22.54; Full Page Colour: 117.00
Currency: US Dollars
NEWSPAPER

Palouse Living
Editorial: 409 S Jackson St, Moscow, Idaho 83843-2251. **T:** 1 208 882-5561
E: editor@dnews.com
W: http://www.dnews.com
Freq: Tue; **Circ:** 10500 Not Audited
Editorial Profile: Palouse Living is a weekly publication serving non-subscribers to the Moscow (ID) Pullman Daily News in Pullman, WA, and Moscow, ID. It contains only advertising and does not accept press releases or other editorial submissions.; Full Page Mono: 6.18
Currency: US Dollars
NEWSPAPER

The Pampa News
Owner: PTS, Inc.
Editorial: 403 W Atchison Ave, Pampa, Texas 79065. **T:** 1 806 669-2525
W: http://www.thepampanews.com
Freq: Daily; **Circ:** 4578 Not Audited
Editor: Timothy Howsare; **Publisher:** Randall Pribble
Editorial Profile: The Pampa News is a community newspaper serving the Pampa, TX area. The publication covers local news, sports, an oil and gas report and community events.; Full Page Mono: 12.80; Full Page Colour: 170.00
Currency: US Dollars
DAILY NEWSPAPER

Pamplin Media Group
Owner: Pamplin Media Group
Editorial: 6605 SE Lake Rd, Portland, Oregon 97222-2161. **T:** 1 503 226-6397 **Circ:** 165700 Not Audited
Publisher: Angela Fox; **Editor:** Jessie Kirk; **Editor:** Ray Pitz; **News Editor:** Raymond Rendleman; **Publisher:** John Schrag
NEWSPAPER

Panamericano Hoy
Editorial: 2350 Nantucket Ln, Elgin, Illinois 60123-8579 **E:** editor@colombiahoy.net
W: http://colombiahoy.net
Freq: Monthly
Editorial Profile: Focuses on the Latino and Colombian population and the positive impact they are having on communities. Discusses News, Events, Sports, and Culture topics.
NEWSPAPER

Panorama
Editorial: 7080 Hollywood Blvd, Ste 504, Los Angeles, California 90028. **T:** 1 323 463-7224
E: pmgnews@sbcglobal.net
W: http://www.kmnb.com
Freq: Wed; **Circ:** 60000
Publisher: Eugene Levin; **Editor:** Irene Parker
Editorial Profile: Panorama is a Russian language newspaper serving the Russian community of Los Angeles.; Full Page Mono: 11.97
Currency: US Dollars
NEWSPAPER

Panorama Hispano
Editorial: 266 Elmwood Ave, Suite 927, Buffalo, New York 14222. **T:** 1 716 228-7498
E: phnews@msn.com
W: http://www.panoramahispanoonline.com
Freq: Monthly; **Circ:** 20000 Not Audited
Editorial Profile: Panorama Hispano is a free monthly Spanish-language newspaper serving community news to the upstate New York Hispanic communities in Buffalo, Fredonia, Dunkirk, Jamestown and Rochester.; Full Page Mono: 13.28
Currency: US Dollars
NEWSPAPER

The Pantagraph
Owner: Lee Enterprises, Inc.
Editorial: 301 W Washington St, Bloomington, Illinois 61701-3803. **T:** 1 309 829-9000
E: newsroom@pantagraph.com
W: http://www.pantagraph.com
Freq: Daily; **Circ:** 30900 Not Audited
Editor: Mark Pickering
Editorial Profile: The Pantagraph is a local daily newspaper published for residents in central Illinois. The newspaper covers local, national and international news, sports, business, and community events.; Full Page Mono: 73.88; Full Page Colour: 112.63
Currency: US Dollars
DAILY NEWSPAPER

Pantagraph Regional Newspapers - West
Owner: Lee Enterprises, Inc.
Editorial: 1926 S Main St, Eureka, Illinois 61530. **T:** 1 309 467-3314
E: newsroom@mtc.com
W: http://www.pantagraph.com/wcj **Circ:** 2585

Editor: Jeff Wiseman; **Editor:** Cheryl Wolfe
NEWSPAPER

The Paper
Owner: Boma (Mark) & Boma (Mary)
Editorial: 204 E Chippewa St, Dwight, Illinois 60420. **T:** 1 815 584-1901
E: thepaper1901@sbcglobal.net
W: http://thepaper1901.com
Freq: Wed; **Circ:** 10000 Not Audited
Editorial Profile: The Paper is a community newspaper serving the following communities: Dwight, Gardner, Mazon, Odell, Reddick, Campus, Essex, Cullom, Kempton, Buckingham, Union Hill, Ransom, Blackstone, Cabery, Sauneminm Emington, Kinsman, Verona, Braceville, Herscher and South Wilmington, IL. It contains stories on community news, events, schools, government, sports, business and features.; Full Page Mono: 8.60
Currency: US Dollars
NEWSPAPER

The Paper
Editorial: 3643 Grand Ave, Ste A, San Marcos, California 92078-2336. **T:** 1 760 747-7119
E: thepaper@cox.net
W: http://www.thecommunitypaper.com
Freq: Thu; **Circ:** 24000
Editorial Profile: The Paper is a local community newspaper for the residents ot San Marcos, CA and the surrounding communities.; Full Page Mono: 19.13
Currency: US Dollars
NEWSPAPER

Paper of Montgomery County
Editorial: 101 W Main St, Ste 300, Crawfordsville, Indiana 47933.
T: 1 765 361-0100
E: news@thepaper24-7.com
W: http://www.thepaper24-7.com
Freq: Mon thru Fri; **Circ:** 1500 Not Audited
Editorial Profile: The Paper of Montgomery County is written for the residents of Crawfordsville, IN.; Full Page Mono: 8.00; Full Page Colour: 26.16
Currency: US Dollars
DAILY NEWSPAPER

The Paper of Wabash County
Editorial: Junction 13 + 24 Bypass, Wabash, Indiana 46992. **T:** 1 260 563-8326
E: ads@thepaperofwabash.com
W: http://www.thepaperof wabash.com
Freq: Tue; **Circ:** 16225 Not Audited
Publisher: Wayne Rees; **Editor:** Brent Swan
Editorial Profile: The Paper Of Wabash County is a community newspaper serving the residents of Wabash County, IN.; Full Page Mono: 6.85
Currency: US Dollars
NEWSPAPER

The Papers Incorporated
Owner: Baumgartner (Ronald)
Editorial: 206 S Main St, Milford, Indiana 46542-3004. **T:** 1 574 658-4111
W: http://www.the-papers.com **Circ:** 58203 Not Audited
Publisher: Ron Baumgartner; **Editor in Chief:** Jeri Seely
Editorial Profile: The Papers, Inc. is a printing and publishing company based in Milford, IN.
NEWSPAPER

Paraglide
Editorial: Public Affairs Office Xviii Airborne Corps Pao, Imse-Brg-Pa, Fort Bragg, North Carolina 28310-5000. **T:** 1 910 432-5007
E: paraglidebragg@gmail.com
W: http://paraglideonline.net
Freq: Thu
Editor: Sandy Aubrey
Editorial Profile: Paraglide is a weekly community newspaper serving Fort Bragg, NC, with local news, sports, and features of interest to the military community.
NEWSPAPER

Paragould Daily Press
Owner: Paxton Media Group
Editorial: 1401 W Hunt St, Paragould, Arkansas 72450. **T:** 1 870 239-8562
E: newsinfo@paragoulddailypress.com
W: http://www.paragoulddailypress.com
Freq: Daily; **Circ:** 5539 Not Audited
Editor: Steve Gillespie
Editorial Profile: Paragould Daily Press is a daily newspaper serving Paragould and Greene County, AR. The publication covers local news and sports. Features content is taken almost exclusively from wire services.; Full Page Mono: 8.75; Full Page Colour: 160.00
Currency: US Dollars
DAILY NEWSPAPER

Paris Beacon-News
Owner: Edgar County Newspapers Inc.
Editorial: 218 N Main St, Paris, Illinois 61944-1738. **T:** 1 217 465-6424
E: news@parisbeacon.com
W: http://www.parisbeacon.com
Freq: Daily; **Circ:** 5400 Not Audited
Editorial Profile: Paris Beacon-News is a daily newspaper serving the residents of Paris, IL. It covers local news, sports and community events.; Full Page Mono: 10.00; Full Page Colour: 200.00
Currency: US Dollars
DAILY NEWSPAPER

The Paris News
Owner: Southern Newspapers, Inc.
Editorial: 5050 SE Loop 286, Paris, Texas 75460-6576. **T:** 1 903 785-8744
E: editor@theparisnews.com
W: http://theparisnews.com
Freq: Daily; **Circ:** 10000 Not Audited
Editorial Profile: The Paris News is a local newspaper written for residents of the Red River region in Texas. The newspaper covers local news, sports and events.; Full Page Mono: 18.00; Full Page Colour: 295.00
Currency: US Dollars
DAILY NEWSPAPER

Paris Post-Intelligencer
Owner: Paris Publishing Co., Inc.
Editorial: 208 E Wood St, Paris, Tennessee 38242-4139. **T:** 1 731 642-1162
E: parispi@parispi.net
W: http://www.parispi.net
Freq: Daily; **Circ:** 8050 Not Audited
News Editor: Ken Walker
Editorial Profile: Paris Post-Intelligencer provides local news to Henry County, TN.; Full Page Mono: 9.85
Currency: US Dollars
DAILY NEWSPAPER

The Park Press
Editorial: 2218 Banchory Rd, Winter Park, Florida 32792-4702. **T:** 1 407 644-6760
E: info@theparkpress.com
W: http://www.theparkpress.com
Freq: Monthly
Publisher: Rick Cable; **Editor:** Tricia Cable
Editorial Profile: The Park Press is a monthly newspaper that provides Local and Community News coverage to the residents of Winter Park, FL.
NEWSPAPER

Parkersburg News and Sentinel
Owner: Ogden Newspapers
Editorial: 519 Juliana St, Parkersburg, West Virginia 26101-5135. **T:** 1 304 485-1891
E: editorial@newsandsentinel.com
W: http://www.newsandsentinel.com
Freq: Daily; **Circ:** 21878 Not Audited
Editor: Jesse Mancini; **Publisher:** Jim Spanner
Editorial Profile: Parkersburg News and Sentinel is a daily newspaper serving the area surrounding Parkersburg, West Virginia. The paper covers local news, business, sports, society and community events. Press releases should be sent to the managing editor regardless of content. Deadlines are one day prior to publication.; Full Page Mono: 79.57; Full Page Colour: 487.30
Currency: US Dollars
DAILY NEWSPAPER

Parkston Advance, Inc.
Editorial: 205 W Main St, Parkston, South Dakota 57366. **T:** 1 605 928-3111
E: advance@santel.net
W: http://www.parkstonadvance.com
Circ: 1550 Not Audited
Publisher: Scott Ehler; **Editor:** Elizabeth Grosz
NEWSPAPER

Parsons Sun
Owner: Family Media, Inc.
Editorial: 220 S 18th St, Parsons, Kansas 67357. **T:** 1 620 421-2000
E: news@parsonssun.com
W: http://www.parsonssun.com
Freq: Daily; **Circ:** 6286 Not Audited
Publisher: Shanna Guiot
Editorial Profile: Parsons Sun is a daily newspaper serving residents of Southeast Kansas. It covers local news, sports and business.; Full Page Mono: 10.50; Full Page Colour: 140.00
Currency: US Dollars
DAILY NEWSPAPER

Pasadena Star-News
Owner: MediaNews Group
Editorial: 911 E Colorado Blvd, Pasadena, California 91106-1772. **T:** 1 626 578-6300
E: news.star-news@sgvn.com
W: http://www.pasadenastarnews.com
Freq: Daily; **Circ:** 24880 Not Audited
Editor: Frank Girardot
Editorial Profile: Pasadena Star-News is a daily newspaper serving the residents of Pasadena, CA and surrounding communities. This paper is a part of the Los Angeles Newspaper Group, a subsidiary of MediaNews Group. The paper's coverage includes news, sports, business and features. The paper is published 48 weeks out of the year.; Full Page Mono: 651.00; Full Page Colour: 2121.50
Currency: US Dollars
DAILY NEWSPAPER

Pasadena Weekly
Owner: Southland Publishing
Editorial: 50 S De Lacey Ave, Ste 200, Pasadena, California 91105.
T: 1 626 584-1500
W: http://www.pasadenaweekly.com
Freq: Thu; **Circ:** 30000 Not Audited
Publisher: Jon Guynn; **Editor:** Kevin Uhrich
Editorial Profile: Pasadena (CA) Weekly covers local news, sports, business, politics and community events.; Full Page Mono: 26.02; Full Page Colour: 1694.00
Currency: US Dollars
NEWSPAPER

The Pasadena/San Gabriel Valley Journal
Editorial: 1541 N Lake Ave, Pasadena, California 91104-2374. **T:** 1 626 798-3972
W: http://www.pasadenajournal.com
Freq: Thu; **Circ:** 12000 Not Audited
Editorial Profile: The Pasadena/San Gabriel Valley Journal is a weekly publication serving the African American community within the towns of Pasadena, Altadena, and San Gabriel Valley, CA. The publication covers local news, national news, arts & entertainment and community events. Deadlines are on Fridays at noon PT.; Full Page Mono: 30.00
Currency: US Dollars
NEWSPAPER

Pascack Press
Owner: Press Group, INC
Editorial: 192 3rd Ave Ste 14, Westwood, New Jersey 07675-2100. **T:** 1 201 664-2105
E: pascackpress@thepressgroup.net
Freq: Mon
Editor: Tom Clancey
Editorial Profile: Pascack Press is a weekly newspaper providing Local and Community News coverage for the residents of the Emerson, Hillsdale, Montvale, Park Ridge, River Vale, Township of Washington, Westwood and Woodcliff Lake, NJ region.
NEWSPAPER

Pascack Valley Community Life
Owner: North Jersey Media Group Inc.
Editorial: 372 Kinderkamack Rd, Westwood, New Jersey 07675-1653. **T:** 1 201 664-2501
E: pvcommunitylife@northjersey.com
W: http://www.pvcommunitylife.com
Freq: Thu; **Circ:** 23298 Not Audited
Editor: Kevin Glynn
Editorial Profile: Pascack Valley Community Life is a member of North Jersey Community Newspapers-Bergen Division. It is a weekly, community newspaper serving residents of Pascack Valley, NJ (Montvale, Park Ridge, Woodcliff Lake, Hillsdale, Westwood, River Vale, Washington Township and Emerson). It covers local news, events, schools, sports, business and features stories.; Full Page Mono: 13.60
Currency: US Dollars
NEWSPAPER

Paso Robles Newspapers Inc.
Owner: News Media Corp.
Editorial: 502 First St, Ste C, Paso Robles, California 93446-3742. **T:** 1 805 237-6060
W: http://www.pasoroblespress.com
Circ: 14400 Not Audited
Publisher: Jason Cross; **Publisher:** Jason Cross; **Editor:** Brian Williams
NEWSPAPER

Pataskala Post
Editorial: 190 E Broad St, Pataskala, Ohio 43062-7104. **T:** 1 740 964-6226
E: pataskalapost@earthlink.net
Freq: Thu; **Circ:** 11152 Not Audited
Editorial Profile: Pataskala Post covers local news, the city council, the school board, high school sports and community events.; Full Page Mono: 6.45
Currency: US Dollars
NEWSPAPER

The Patriot Ledger
Owner: GateHouse Media Inc.
Editorial: 400 Crown Colony Dr, Quincy, Massachusetts 02169-0930.
T: 1 617 786-7000 **E:** newsroom@ledger.com
W: http://www.patriotledger.com
Freq: Daily; **Circ:** 28670
Editor: Chazy Dowaliby
Editorial Profile: The Patriot Ledger in Quincy, MA is a daily regional newspaper covering news, sports and entertainment.; Full Page Mono: 63.54; Full Page Colour: 220.05
Currency: US Dollars
DAILY NEWSPAPER

Patriot Publications
Owner: GateHouse Media Inc.
Editorial: 15 W Pearl St, Coldwater, Michigan 49036-1912. **T:** 1 517 278-2318
W: http://www.thedailyreporter.com **Circ:** 3500 Not Audited
Publisher: David Ferro
NEWSPAPER

The Patriot-News
Owner: Newhouse Newspapers
Editorial: 2020 Technology Pkwy Ste 300, Mechanicsburg, Pennsylvania 17050-9412.
T: 1 717 255-8100 **E:** newstips@pennlive.com
W: http://www.patriot-news.com
Freq: Daily; **Circ:** 70380 Not Audited
Editorial Profile: The Patriot-News is a daily newspaper written for the residents of Harrisburg, PA and surrounding areas. The publication focuses on Pennsylvania-related news stories, but maintains a broad approach to reporting important national and international news. The special feature sections include recreation, weddings, sports and travel.; Full Page Mono: 58.00; Full Page Colour: 94.45
Currency: US Dollars
DAILY NEWSPAPER

The Patriot-News
Editorial: Main Capitol, Room 524, Harrisburg, Pennsylvania 17120-0001. **T:** 1 717 255-4106
DAILY NEWSPAPER

Pauls Valley Democrat
Owner: Community Newspaper Holdings, Inc.
Editorial: 108 S Willow St, Pauls Valley, Oklahoma 73075-3834. **T:** 1 405 238-6464
E: sfisher@pvdemocrat.com
W: http://www.pvdemocrat.com
Freq: Daily; **Circ:** 2474 Not Audited
Editorial Profile: Pauls Valley Democrat is a daily newspaper serving the residents of Pauls Valley, OK. The publication focuses on local news, sports and business.; Full Page Mono: 7.25; Full Page Colour: 9.75
Currency: US Dollars
DAILY NEWSPAPER

Paw Prints Publishing
Editorial: 3285 S 1050 W, Westville, Indiana 46391. **T:** 1 219 785-2234
E: wvindicator@aol.com **Circ:** 4000 Not Audited
Editor: Gaylen Armstrong
NEWSPAPER

Pawnee Republican
Editorial: 600 G St, Pawnee City, Nebraska 68420. **T:** 1 402 852-2575
E: news@pawneenews.com
W: http://www.pawneenews.com
Freq: Thu; **Circ:** 13000
Editor: Paula Jasa; **Editor:** Carol Sisco
Editorial Profile: Pawnee Republican is the official newspaper of Pawnee County, NE. Its coverage area includes Pawnee County and the surrounding communities, including the school districts of Pawnee City, Lewston Consolidated and Humboldt Table Rock Steinauer.; Full Page Mono: 7.50
Currency: US Dollars
NEWSPAPER

The Paxton Herald
Editorial: 101 Lincoln St, Harrisburg, Pennsylvania 17112. **T:** 1 717 545-9540
E: thepaxtonherald@verizon.net
W: http://www.thepaxtonherald.com
Freq: Wed; **Circ:** 22000 Not Audited
Editorial Profile: The Paxton Herald is a weekly newspaper serving Lancaster, Northern York, Perry and Cumberland counties, PA. The publication is in a "long tabloid format" and covers local news and community events.; Full Page Mono: 6.95
Currency: US Dollars
NEWSPAPER

Paxton Media Group - High Point
Owner: Paxton Media Group
Editorial: 210 Church Ave, High Point, North Carolina 27262-4806. **T:** 1 336 472-9500
Circ: 23600 Not Audited

Publisher: Rick Bean; **Editor:** Kathy Stuart
NEWSPAPER

Peach Publications
Owner: Peach Publishing Co. Inc.
Editorial: 109 Anderson Ave, Fort Valley, Georgia 31030-4141. **T:** 1 478 825-2432
W: http://theleadertribune.net **Circ:** 12100 Not Audited
News Editor: Victor Kulkosky; **Publisher:** Judy Robinson
NEWSPAPER

Peak Publications
Owner: Peak Publications, Inc.
Editorial: 208 S 3rd St, Raton, New Mexico 87740. **T:** 1 575 445-2721 **Circ:** 5000 Not Audited
NEWSPAPER

Pecos River Dispatch
Editorial: 815 S Grand St, Rankin, Texas 79778-9800. **T:** 1 432 693-2873
E: dispatchrankin@hotmail.com
Freq: Thu
NEWSPAPER

Pekin Daily Times
Owner: GateHouse Media Inc.
Editorial: 20 S 4th St, Pekin, Illinois 61554.
T: 1 309 346-1111
E: community@pekintimes.com
W: http://www.pekintimes.com
Freq: Daily; **Circ:** 12537
Editor: Josh Bradshaw; **Publisher:** Gregg Ratliff; **Editor:** Michelle Teheux
Editorial Profile: Pekin Daily Times is published daily for the residents of Pekin, IL and surrounding areas. The newspaper covers local news, sports, entertainment and community events.; Full Page Mono: 21.00; Full Page Colour: 72.04
Currency: US Dollars
DAILY NEWSPAPER

Peninsula Clarion
Owner: Morris Multimedia, Inc.
Editorial: 150 Trading Bay Dr, Ste 1, Kenai, Alaska 99611-7716. **T:** 1 907 283-7551
E: news@peninsulaclarion.com
W: http://www.peninsulaclarion.com
Freq: Daily; **Circ:** 4799 Not Audited
Publisher: Vitto Kleinschmidt; **Editor:** Will Morrow
Editorial Profile: Peninsula Clarion is a daily newspaper written for residents of Alaska's Kenai Peninsula. The publication covers news, sports, business, arts & entertainment, outdoor recreation and community events.; Full Page Mono: 21.40; Full Page Colour: 300.00
Currency: US Dollars
DAILY NEWSPAPER

Peninsula Daily News
Owner: Horvitz Newspapers, Inc.
Editorial: 150 S 5th Ave, Sequim, Washington 98382-2915. **T:** 1 360 452-2345
E: news@peninsuladailynews.com
W: http://www.peninsuladailynews.com
Freq: Daily; **Circ:** 12444 Not Audited
News Editor: Michael Foster
Editorial Profile: Peninsula Daily News is a local newspaper serving residents of Washington's Olympic Peninsula. The publication covers local news, sports, business, education and community events.; Full Page Mono: 28.12; Full Page Colour: 91.70
Currency: US Dollars
DAILY NEWSPAPER

Peninsula Gateway
Owner: McClatchy Newspapers
Editorial: 3555 Erickson St, Gig Harbor, Washington 98335. **T:** 1 253 851-9921
E: gatewayeditor@gateline.com
W: http://www.gateline.com
Freq: Wed; **Circ:** 20000 Not Audited
Editor: Brian McLean
Editorial Profile: Peninsula Gateway is published weekly for the residents of Gig Harbor, WA. The publication covers local news, sports, business, lifestyle and community events. Deadlines are on Fridays at 5pm PT.; Full Page Mono: 20.90
Currency: US Dollars
NEWSPAPER

Peninsula Warrior
Owner: Military Newspapers of Virginia
Editorial: 150 W Brambleton Ave, Norfolk, Virginia 23510-2018. **T:** 1 757 878-4920
E: pw@militarynews.com
W: http://www.peninsulawarrior.com
Freq: Fri; **Circ:** 14000 Not Audited
Publisher: Laura Baxter; **Editor:** Matthew

Miller
Editorial Profile: Peninsula Warrior is written for the Langley Air Force Base and Armed Forces communities in Hampton Roads, VA, producing two editions, for Air Force and Army.; Full Page Mono: 17.77
Currency: US Dollars
NEWSPAPER

Penn-Franklin News Publishing Co.
Editorial: 4021 Old William Penn Hwy, Murrysville, Pennsylvania 15668.
T: 1 724 327-3471
E: news@penn-franklin.com
W: http://www.penn-franklin.com **Circ:** 6000 Not Audited
Editorial Profile: The Penn-Franklin News Publishing Co. publishes the Penn-Franklin News, the Penn-Trafford News and the Delmont-Salem News. They only accept local news tips. They do NOT accept e-mail attachments.
NEWSPAPER

Penobscot Bay Press
Editorial: 69 Main St, Stonington, Maine 4681.
T: 1 207 367-2200
E: cis@penobscotbaypress.com
W: http://www.penobscotbaypress.com
Circ: 5880
Editor: R. Nathaniel Barrows
Editorial Profile: Penobscot Bay Press is a community newspaper publisher servicing the residents of Bangor, ME.
NEWSPAPER

Pensacola News Journal
Owner: Gannett Co., Inc.
Editorial: 101 E Romana St, Pensacola, Florida 32502-5652. **T:** 1 850 435-8500
E: news@pnj.com **W:** http://www.pnj.com
Freq: Daily; **Circ:** 32254 Not Audited
Editorial Profile: Pensacola News Journal is a daily regional newspaper for Northwest Florida and Southern Alabama. The publication offers investigative reports as well as information on health, education, arts & entertainment, news, food, recreation and sports.; Full Page Mono: 153.34; Full Page Colour: 502.20
Currency: US Dollars
DAILY NEWSPAPER

The Pensacola Voice
Owner: Pensacola Voice, Inc. (The)
Editorial: 213 E Yonge St, Pensacola, Florida 32503. **T:** 1 850 434-6963
E: info@pensacolavoice.com
W: http://www.pensacolavoice.com
Freq: Thu; **Circ:** 10000 Not Audited
Editorial Profile: Pensacola Voice is a newspaper serving the African American community of Pensacola, FL. The publication covers news, sports, entertainment, health and religion. It also provides news of importance for and relating to African Americans. Deadlines are Tuesdays at noon ET.; Full Page Mono: 26.00
Currency: US Dollars
NEWSPAPER

Pentagram
Owner: Comprint Military Publications
Editorial: 204 Lee Ave, Bldg 59, Fort Myer, Virginia 22211-1103. **T:** 1 703 696-5401
E: pentagram@conus.army.mil
W: http://www.dcmilitary.com/section/news10
Freq: Fri; **Circ:** 24000 Not Audited
Editor: Courtney Dock-Abuhl; **Publisher:** John Rives
Editorial Profile: Pentagram is written to provide news and event information to the Fort Meyers, VA military community. Deadlines are on Fridays.; Full Page Mono: 39.62
Currency: US Dollars
NEWSPAPER

People Newspapers
Owner: City Newspapers, LP
Editorial: 750 N Saint Paul St Ste 2100, Dallas, Texas 75201-3214. **T:** 1 214 739-2244
E: editor@peoplenewspapers.com
W: http://www.peoplenewspapers.com
Freq: Weekly; **Circ:** 23500 Not Audited
Publisher: Patricia Martin
Editorial Profile: People Newspapers is a weekly newspaper publisher in Northern Dallas. The papers cover news, sports, entertainment, arts, politics and features in the North Dallas area. The target audience is affluent readers in the community.
NEWSPAPER

People of God
Owner: Archdiocese of Santa Fe
Editorial: 4000 Saint Josephs Pl NW, Albuquerque, New Mexico 87120.
T: 1 505 831-8180 **E:** cradigan@archdiosf.org

W: http://www.archdiocesesantafe.org
Freq: Monthly; **Circ:** 43000 Not Audited
Editor: Celine Baca Radigan; **Editor:** Celine Baca Radigan; **Editor:** Celine Baca Radigan;
Editor: Celine Baca Radigan; **Publisher:** Michael Sheehan
Editorial Profile: People of God is a monthly newspaper published by the Archdiocese of Santa Fe, NM. The paper contains community and Catholic church news and events The paper is available for pick-up at Catholic churches throughout the area during the second week of each month, except July. Lead times are the 10th of the month prior to publication. Advertising should be submitted to Templeton Marketing Services by the 15th of the month prior to distribution.; Full Page Mono: 14.74
Currency: US Dollars
NEWSPAPER

El Periodico U.S.A.
Owner: Spanish Point, Inc.
Editorial: 801 E Fir Ave, McAllen, Texas 78501. **T:** 1 956 631-5628
E: usa1@sc2000.net
W: http://www.elperiodicousa.com
Freq: Wed; **Circ:** 55000 Not Audited
Publisher: Kathy Letelier
Editorial Profile: El Periodico U.S.A. provides national news and information for and about the Hispanic population across the country. Deadlines are on Fridays at noon CT.; Full Page Mono: 25.00; Full Page Colour: 3024.00
Currency: US Dollars
NEWSPAPER

Perry Daily Journal
Owner: Perry Publishing and Broadcasting
Editorial: 714 Delaware St, Perry, Oklahoma 73077-6425. **T:** 1 580 336-2222
W: http://www.pdjnews.com
Freq: Daily; **Circ:** 3250 Not Audited
Publisher: Phillip Reid
Editorial Profile: Perry Daily Journal is a local newspaper serving residents of Perry County, OK. The publication covers news, sports, arts & entertainment and community events.; Full Page Mono: 10.42; Full Page Colour: 103.00
Currency: US Dollars
DAILY NEWSPAPER

Perry Newspapers
Editorial: 123 S Jefferson St, Perry, Florida 32347. **T:** 1 850 584-5513
E: newsdesk@perrynewspapers.com
W: http://www.perrynewspapers.com
Circ: 10200 Not Audited
Publisher: Donald Lincoln
Editorial Profile: Perry Newspapers is a weekly community newspaper publisher serving the residents of Perry, FL.
NEWSPAPER

Peru Tribune
Owner: Paxton Media Group
Editorial: 26 W 3rd St, Peru, Indiana 46970-2155. **T:** 1 765 473-6641
W: http://www.perutribune.com
Freq: Daily; **Circ:** 7292 Not Audited
Editor: Matt Hutton; **Publisher:** Misty Sharp
Editorial Profile: Peru Tribune is published for the residents of Peru and Miami County, IN. The newspaper covers local and state news, business, sports, lifestyles and entertainment.; Full Page Mono: 18.00; Full Page Colour: 210.00
Currency: US Dollars
DAILY NEWSPAPER

Peshtigo Times
Editorial: 841 Maple St, Peshtigo, Wisconsin 54157-1341. **T:** 1 715 582-4541
E: news@peshtigotimes.com
W: http://www.peshtigotimes.com
Freq: Wed; **Circ:** 10450 Not Audited
Editorial Profile: The Peshtigo Times is a local newspaper serving the residents of Wisconsin's Marinette and Oconto Counties, WI, and Menominee County, MI. It covers local news, sports, education and community events. Deadlines are at 10am CT.; Full Page Mono: 7.20
Currency: US Dollars
NEWSPAPER

Petersburg Observer Newspapers
Editorial: 235 E Sangamon Ave, Petersburg, Illinois 62675. **T:** 1 217 632-2236
E: observer@gcctv.com **Circ:** 4600 Not Audited
NEWSPAPER

Petoskey News-Review
Owner: Schurz Communications Inc.
Editorial: 319 State St, Petoskey, Michigan 49770-2746. **T:** 1 231 347-2544

E: petoskeynews@petoskeynews.com
W: http://www.petoskeynews.com
Freq: Daily; **Circ:** 9789 Not Audited
News Editor: Rachel Brougham; **Publisher:** Douglas Caldwell
Editorial Profile: Petoskey News-Review is an evening weekday newspaper serving residents of Petoskey, Harbor Springs and Traverse City, MI. Coverage includes local and national news, sports and entertainment. It shares its offices and editorial staff with The Graphic, a free, weekly newspaper serving Petoskey, MI and surrounding communities. The lead time for submissions varies depending on content.; Full Page Mono: 15.85; Full Page Colour: 55.88
Currency: US Dollars
DAILY NEWSPAPER

Pharos-Tribune
Owner: Community Newspaper Holdings, Inc.
Editorial: 517 E Broadway, Logansport, Indiana 46947-3154. **T:** 1 574 722-5000
E: ptnews@pharostribune.com
W: http://www.pharostribune.com
Freq: Daily; **Circ:** 9303 Not Audited
News Editor: Sarah Einselen; **Publisher:** Robyn McCloskey
Editorial Profile: Pharos-Tribune is a local daily newspaper serving residents of Logansport, Cass County and Central Indiana since 1844. The publication covers news, sports and community events taking place in and around Logansport. Regular features include local news, government, education and business. Deadlines are on the day of publication at 10:15am CT.; Full Page Mono: 16.50; Full Page Colour: 57.87
Currency: US Dollars
DAILY NEWSPAPER

Philadelphia Daily News
Owner: Interstate General Media
Editorial: 801 Market St Ste 300, Philadelphia, Pennsylvania 19107-3183. **T:** 1 215 854-5908
W: http://www.phillydailynews.com
Freq: Daily; **Circ:** 79863 Not Audited
Editor: Michael Days
Editorial Profile: Philadelphia Daily News, established in 1925, is a tabloid newspaper written specifically for Philadelphia residents. Emphasizing local news and events, its editorial content provides in-depth coverage of community, government, economic and business issues. Coverage extends to national and international news in the U.S. and World sections. Articles include features, breaking news, columns and accent features focusing on subjects such as careers and money. The paper does not publish a Holiday Gift Guide. The black and white advertising rate is a combination rate for this paper and the Philadelphia Inquirer. Calendar listings are handled through a third party company, Event Source. When sending information via mail to the paper, clearly designate that it is for the newsroom.; Full Page Mono: 145.00; Full Page Colour: 2141.69
Currency: US Dollars
DAILY NEWSPAPER

Philadelphia Daily News
Editorial: Press Office State Capital Bldg, Ste 524-E, Harrisburg, Pennsylvania 17108.
T: 1 717 783-9666
DAILY NEWSPAPER

The Philadelphia Inquirer
Owner: Interstate General Media
Editorial: 801 Market St Fl 3, Philadelphia, Pennsylvania 19107-3126.
T: 1 215 854-2000 4502
W: http://www.inquirer.com
Freq: Daily; **Circ:** 330485 Not Audited
News Editor: Brian Leighton; **Editor:** Bill Marimow
Editorial Profile: Philadelphia Inquirer is a broadsheet newspaper written for residents in the Philadelphia area. It covers local, national and international news, as well as local zoned coverage of the suburbs and surrounding regions, business, technology, features, entertainment and sports. The paper won a 1997 Pulitzer Prize for Explanatory Journalism. Calendar listings are handled through a third party company, Event Source.; Full Page Mono: 857.00; Full Page Colour: 2215.60
Currency: US Dollars
DAILY NEWSPAPER

Philadelphia Inquirer
Editorial: 53 Haddonfield Rd, Cherry Hill, New Jersey 08002-4802. **T:** 1 856 779-3840
DAILY NEWSPAPER

Philadelphia Inquirer
Editorial: 125 W State St, Trenton, New Jersey 08608-1101. **T:** 1 609 292-5775

DAILY NEWSPAPER

Philadelphia Inquirer
Editorial: 524 State Capitol Building Fl E, Harrisburg, Pennsylvania 17120-0020
DAILY NEWSPAPER

Philadelphia Inquirer
Editorial: 800 River Rd Route 23, Conshohocken, Pennsylvania 19428-2632.
T: 1 610 313-8000
DAILY NEWSPAPER

The Philadelphia Sunday Sun
Owner: Philadelphia Sun Group (The)
Editorial: 6661 Germantown Ave, Philadelphia, Pennsylvania 19119-2251. **T:** 1 215 848-7864
E: infosundaysun@yahoo.com
W: http://www.philasun.com
Freq: Sun; **Circ:** 20000 Not Audited
Editor: J. Whyatt Mondesire
Editorial Profile: The Philadelphia Sunday Sun is published weekly for the residents of Philadelphia and surrounding areas. The newspaper provides information on local news and community events. Deadlines are on Wednesdays at noon ET.; Full Page Mono: 47.20
Currency: US Dollars
NEWSPAPER

The Philadelphia Tribune
Owner: The Philadelphia Tribune, Co.
Editorial: 520 S 16th St, Philadelphia, Pennsylvania 19146-1565. **T:** 1 215 893-4050
E: newsroom@phillytrib.com
W: http://www.phillytrib.com
Freq: Fri; **Circ:** 23090 Not Audited
News Editor: Johann Calhoun
Editorial Profile: The Philadelphia Tribune is written for the African American residents of Philadelphia, Delaware County and parts of Montgomery County, PA. It covers local news, sports, arts & entertainment, crime, health, business news, religion, politics and community events. The Sunday circulation is 10,380, Tuesday is 14,177 and Friday is 7,792.; Full Page Mono: 117.15
Currency: US Dollars
NEWSPAPER

Philadelphia Weekly
Owner: Review Publishing
Editorial: 1500 Sansom St Fl 3, Philadelphia, Pennsylvania 19102-2800. **T:** 1 215 563-7400
W: http://www.philadelphiaweekly.com
Freq: Wed; **Circ:** 100326 Not Audited
Editor-in-Chief: Stephen Segal; **Editor-in-Chief:** Stephen Segal; **Editor-in-Chief:** Stephen Segal; **Editor-in-Chief:** Stephen Segal
Editorial Profile: Philadelphia Weekly is published for the residents of Philadelphia, Southern New Jersey and Northern Delaware. Founded in 1971, this alternative newspaper focuses on the entertainment scene in Philadelphia as well as local and national news, government and politics.; Full Page Mono: 46.00; Full Page Colour: 3474.00
Currency: US Dollars
NEWSPAPER

Philippine News
Editorial: 1818 Gilbreth Rd, St 220, Burlingame, California 94010-1225.
T: 1 650 552-9775 **E:** feedback@gmanews.tv
W: http://www.philippinenews.com
Freq: Fri; **Circ:** 64000
Editor: Cherie Querol Moreno
Editorial Profile: Philippine News is published weekly for the Filipino American community of Southern San Francisco. The newspaper provides information on local news, business, culture, arts & entertainment and community events.; Full Page Mono: 35.00
Currency: US Dollars
NEWSPAPER

Phoenix New Times
Owner: Voice Media Group
Editorial: 1201 E Jefferson St, Phoenix, Arizona 85034-2300. **T:** 1 602 271-0040
E: feedback@newtimes.com
W: http://www.phoenixnewtimes.com
Freq: Thu; **Circ:** 140000 Not Audited
Editor: Rick Barrs; **Publisher:** Kurtis Barton
Editorial Profile: Phoenix New Times is a weekly newspaper published for the residents of Phoenix, Arizona. The paper focuses on news, culture, music, film, dining, and local events. The lead time and deadlines for this publication vary. Contact the publication for updated advertising rates.; Full Page Mono: 44.99
Currency: US Dollars
NEWSPAPER

Photo Star
Owner: Bunner, (Judith E.)
Editorial: 307 State St., Willshire, Ohio 45898.
T: 1 419 495-2696
E: photostarnews@frontier.com
Freq: Wed; **Circ:** 11200 Not Audited
Editor: Judith Bunner; **Editor:** Judith Bunner
Editorial Profile: Photo Star is a local newspaper serving residents of the Willshire, OH area. The publication covers local news and community events.; Full Page Mono: 8.50; Full Page Colour: 725.00
Currency: US Dollars
NEWSPAPER

The Picayune
Owner: Victory Publishing, LTD.
Editorial: 1007 Avenue K, Marble Falls, Texas 78654. **T:** 1 830 693-7152
E: info@thepicayune.com
W: http://www.thepicayunetv.com/
Freq: Wed; **Circ:** 24409 Not Audited
Editorial Profile: The Picayune is a local newspaper serving residents of Picayune and areas around Marble Falls, TX. It covers local news, community events, sports and features of interest to local readers. It shares its editorial staff with its sister daily paper, the River Cities Daily Tribune in Marble Falls, TX. Deadlines are on Mondays at noon CT.; Full Page Mono: 12.49
Currency: US Dollars
NEWSPAPER

Picayune Item
Owner: Community Newspaper Holdings, Inc.
Editorial: 17 Richardson Ozona Rd, Picayune, Mississippi 39466-7865. **T:** 1 601 798-4766
E: picayuneitem@bellsouth.net
W: http://www.picayuneitem.com
Freq: Daily; **Circ:** 4343 Not Audited
Publisher: Tom Andrews
Editorial Profile: Picayune Item is a daily newspaper serving the residents of Pearl River County, MS and surrounding areas. It covers local news, education, sports and community events.; Full Page Mono: 11.33
Currency: US Dollars
DAILY NEWSPAPER

Pickens County News & LINK
Owner: Gannett Co., Inc.
Editorial: 305 S Main St, Greenville, South Carolina 29601-2605. **T:** 1 864 298-4100
Circ: 75000 Not Audited
Publisher: Steve Brandt; **Editor:** Terry Cregar;
Editor: Ron DeKett
Editorial Profile: Pickens County News & LINK is a community newspaper publisher in Greenville, SC.
NEWSPAPER

Picket Fence Media
Editorial: 34932 Calle Del Sol Ste B, Capistrano Beach, California 92624-1664.
T: 1 949 388-7700 **Circ:** 41500
Editorial Profile: Picket Fence Media is a local newspaper providing news to the community of Capistrano Beach, CA.
NEWSPAPER

Picket News
Owner: Courtney, (John)
Editorial: 25 E Antietam St, Hagerstown, Maryland 21740-5659. **T:** 1 301 766-7097
E: editor@picketnews.com
W: http://www.picketnews.com
Freq: Sun; **Circ:** 12000 Not Audited
Publisher: John Courtney; **Editor:** Jennifer Leese
Editorial Profile: Picket News is published weekly for the residents of Hagerstown, MD and surrounding areas. The newspaper covers local and county news, sports, health and entertainment.; Full Page Mono: 18.00
Currency: US Dollars
NEWSPAPER

PICT Partnership
Owner: Douthit Communications Inc.
Editorial: 158 Lear Rd, Avon Lake, Ohio 44012-1908. **T:** 1 440 933-5100
E: news@westlifenews.com
W: http://www.2presspapers.com
Freq: Wed; **Circ:** 19500 Not Audited
Publisher: Harold Douthit; Full Page Mono: 14.50
Currency: US Dollars
NEWSPAPER

Pierce County Community Newspaper Group
Editorial: 4412 6th Ave, Ste 4, Tacoma, Washington 98406-3500. **T:** 1 253 759-5773
E: news@tacomaweekly.com **Circ:** 54000 Not Audited
Editor: John Larson; **Publisher:** John Weymer
Editorial Profile: Pierce County Community Newspaper Group is a weekly newspaper publisher in Fife, WA.
NEWSPAPER

Pilcher Publishing
Editorial: 116 Clark St, Lowell, Indiana 46356.
T: 1 219 696-7711 **E:** lowelltrib@comcast.net
W: http://www.thelowelltribune.com **Circ:** 6000 Not Audited
Publisher: Matt Pilcher; **Editor:** Jackie Smith
Editorial Profile: Pilcher Publishing is a weekly community newspaper publisher serving the residents of Ceder Lake and Lowell, IN. Send press releases via fax, not email.
NEWSPAPER

The Pilot
Owner: Roman Catholic Archdiocese of Boston
Editorial: 66 Brooks Dr, Braintree, Massachusetts 02184-3839.
T: 1 617 779-3782
E: editorial@pilotcatholicnews.com
W: http://www.pilotcatholicnews.com
Freq: Fri; **Circ:** 24000 Not Audited
Editor: Antonio Enrique; **Publisher:** Seán O'Malley
Editorial Profile: The Pilot is a weekly newspaper written for members of the Roman Catholic Archdiocese of Boston. The paper covers local news and issues pertaining to the Roman Catholic Church.; Full Page Mono: 25.00; Full Page Colour: 1980.00
Currency: US Dollars
NEWSPAPER

The Pilot
Owner: The Pilot LLC
Editorial: 145 W Pennsylvania Ave, Southern Pines, North Carolina 28387-5428.
T: 1 910 692-7271 **W:** http://www.thepilot.com
Freq: Fri; **Circ:** 15000 Not Audited
Editor: Steve Bouser; **Editor:** John Nagy;
Publisher: David Woronoff
Editorial Profile: The Pilot is a local newspaper written for residents of Pinehurst, Southern Pines and the rest of the Sandhills in NC. The newspaper, published three days a week, covers local news and events. The lead time varies. Deadlines for The Pilot are noon ET on Thursdays for the Monday issue, Mondays for the Wednesday issue or Wednesdays for the Friday issue.; Full Page Mono: 15.00
Currency: US Dollars
NEWSPAPER

The Pilot-News
Owner: Horizon Publications
Editorial: 214 N Michigan St, Plymouth, Indiana 46563-2135. **T:** 1 574 936-3101
E: news@thepilotnews.com
W: http://www.thepilotnews.com
Freq: Daily; **Circ:** 7250 Not Audited
Publisher: Rick Kreps
Editorial Profile: The Pilot-News is published for residents of Marshall County, IN and surrounding areas. The newspapers covers local and state news, business, sports, lifestyles and entertainment.; Full Page Mono: 10.20; Full Page Colour: 100.00
Currency: US Dollars
DAILY NEWSPAPER

Pine Bluff Commercial
Owner: Stephens Media
Editorial: 300 S Beech St, Pine Bluff, Arkansas 71601-4039. **T:** 1 870 534-3400
E: pbcnews@pbcommercial.com
W: http://www.pbcommercial.com
Freq: Daily; **Circ:** 11500 Not Audited
Editor: Sandra Hope
Editorial Profile: Pine Bluff Commercial is a daily newspaper written for residents in Southeast Arkansas. The paper covers local, regional and community news. The Monday edition of the paper is called PBC Today and is in tabloid format.; Full Page Mono: 17.60; Full Page Colour: 250.00
Currency: US Dollars
DAILY NEWSPAPER

Pine Creek Journal
Owner: Tribune-Review Publishing Co.
Editorial: 535 Keystone Dr, Warrendale, Pennsylvania 15086-7538. **T:** 1 724 779-8742
W: http://www.yournorthhills.com/pinecreekjournal
Freq: Thu; **Circ:** 26000 Not Audited
Editor: Dave McElhinny; **Editor:** Dave McElhinny; **Editor:** Dave McElhinny; **Editor:** Dave McElhinny; **Publisher:** Richard Scaife
Editorial Profile: Pine Creek Journal is a local weekly newspaper serving residents of Seneca Valley and Pine Creek, PA. It covers local news, business, sports and arts & entertainment stories. It also provides national and statewide stories if they have a direct impact on the newspaper's readership. All inquiries should be addressed to the editor.; Full Page Mono: 14.97
Currency: US Dollars
NEWSPAPER

The Pineapple
Owner: Delray Beach Pineapple, LLC
Editorial: 777 NE 5th Ave Suite D-151, Delray Beach, Florida 33483-5360. **T:** 1 561 299-1430
E: info@delraypineapple.com
W: http://pineapplenewspaper.com
Freq: Monthly; **Circ:** 10000
Editorial Profile: The Pineapple is a monthly newspaper providing Local and Community News coverage for the residents of the Delray Beach, FL. It covers upcoming events, emerging artists and musicians, new business developments, educational and recreational opportunities.; Full Page Colour: 995.00
Currency: US Dollars
NEWSPAPER

The Pinnacle
Owner: Mainstreet Media Group
Editorial: 350 6th St, Ste 102, Hollister, California 95023-3882. **T:** 1 831 637-6300
E: editor@pinnaclenews.com
W: http://www.pinnaclenews.com
Freq: Fri; **Circ:** 17400 Not Audited
Editor: Kollin Kosmicki
Editorial Profile: The Pinnacle is published weekly for residents of Hollister, CA and surrounding areas. The newspaper covers local news, business, sports, lifestyles and entertainment.; Full Page Mono: 20.00
Currency: US Dollars
NEWSPAPER

Pioneer
Owner: Pioneer Newspapers
Editorial: 115 N Michigan Ave, Big Rapids, Michigan 49307-1401. **T:** 1 231 796-4831
E: info@pioneergroup.com
W: http://www.bigrapidsnews.com
Freq: Daily; **Circ:** 5966 Not Audited
Editor in Chief: David Clark; **Publisher:** John Norton
Editorial Profile: Pioneer is a daily newspaper written for the residents of Big Rapids and Mecosta County, MI.; Full Page Mono: 15.75; Full Page Colour: 165.00
Currency: US Dollars
DAILY NEWSPAPER

Pioneer Group
Editorial: 115 N Michigan Ave, Big Rapids, Michigan 49307-1401. **T:** 1 231 796-4831
E: info@pioneergroup.com
W: http://www.pioneergroup.net **Circ:** 33645 Not Audited
Editor: Bob Allen; **Publisher:** John Norton
NEWSPAPER

Pioneer Press
Owner: Wrapports LLC
Editorial: 350 N Orleans St, Chicago, Illinois 60654-1975. **T:** 1 312 321-3000
W: http://pioneerlocal.suntimes.com
Freq: Weekly; **Circ:** 121562 Not Audited
News Editor: Marah Altenberg; **News Editor:** Charles Berman; **News Editor:** Charles Berman; **News Editor:** Rich Bird; **Editor:** Jennifer Fisher
Editorial Profile: Placing an ad in just one paper is not an option, the advertising rate provided is based on an estimated group rate. Single ads can be placed in the Glencoe News for the rate listed.
NEWSPAPER

Piqua Daily Call
Owner: Ohio Community Media LLC.
Editorial: 310 Spring St, Piqua, Ohio 45356-2334. **T:** 1 937 773-2721
E: editorial@dailycall.com
W: http://www.dailycall.com
Freq: Daily; **Circ:** 6567 Not Audited
Publisher: Frank Beeson; **Editor:** Susan Hartley
Editorial Profile: Piqua Daily Call is published for the residents of Piqua, OH and surrounding areas. The newspaper covers local and state news, business, sports, lifestyles and entertainment. Deadlines are at 1pm the day prior to issue date.; Full Page Mono: 15.25; Full Page Colour: 49.64
Currency: US Dollars
DAILY NEWSPAPER

The Pitch
Owner: SouthComm Inc.
Editorial: 1627 Main St, Kansas City, Missouri 64108-1368. **T:** 1 816 561-6061
E: tips@pitch.com **W:** http://www.pitch.com

Freq: Wed; **Circ:** 40000 Not Audited
Publisher: Joel Hornbostel; **Editor:** Scott Wilson
Editorial Profile: The Pitch in Kansas City, MO is a weekly newspaper providing in-depth local news, lifestyle and arts & entertainment coverage.; Full Page Mono: 45.00
Currency: US Dollars
NEWSPAPER

Pittsburgh Catholic
Editorial: 135 1st Ave, Ste 200, Pittsburgh, Pennsylvania 15222. **T:** 1 412 471-1252
E: info@pittsburghcatholic.org
W: http://www.pittsburghcatholic.org
Freq: Fri; **Circ:** 111750 Not Audited
Editor: William Cone
Editorial Profile: Pittsburgh Catholic serves as an instrument of education by presenting readers with accurate news and information about the church on a local, national and universal level. Its main goal is to provide a forum for expression of views, in a manner consistent with the teachings of the church and the principle of respect for others. The weekly newspaper is written for Catholics in the six county Diocese of Pittsburgh. Deadlines are at noon ET on Fridays, one week before issue date.; Full Page Mono: 58.00; Full Page Colour: 3780.60
Currency: US Dollars
NEWSPAPER

Pittsburgh City Paper
Owner: Steel City Media
Editorial: 650 Smithfield St, Pittsburgh, Pennsylvania 15222-3902. **T:** 1 412 316-3342
E: info@steelcitymedia.com
W: http://www.pittsburghcitypaper.ws
Freq: Wed; **Circ:** 72000 Not Audited
News Editor: Charlie Deitch; **Publisher:** Michael Frischling; **Editor:** Chris Potter
Editorial Profile: Pittsburgh City Paper is a local weekly newspaper serving residents of the Pittsburgh area. It features local news, sports, arts & entertainment and event listings.; Full Page Mono: 54.10
Currency: US Dollars
NEWSPAPER

Pittsburgh Post-Gazette
Owner: Block Communications Inc.
Editorial: 34 Blvd of the Allies, Pittsburgh, Pennsylvania 15222-1204. **T:** 1 412 263-1100
W: http://www.post-gazette.com
Freq: Daily; **Circ:** 166609 Not Audited
Editorial Profile: Founded in 1786, the Pittsburgh Post-Gazette is a 70+ page broadsheet newspaper written for the general public in Pittsburgh and western Pennsylvania. The publication's mission statement is "to serve the community, our readers and advertisers as the region's indispensable source of news, advertising, and information." Business coverage in the publication includes local, regional and national news, features, investor information, personal finance tips, and technology information.; Full Page Mono: 303.90; Full Page Colour: 334.38
Currency: US Dollars
DAILY NEWSPAPER

Pittsburgh Post-Gazette
Editorial: 524E Main Capitol Building, Harrisburg, Pennsylvania 17120-0022.
T: 1 717 787-4254
DAILY NEWSPAPER

Pittsburgh Post-Gazette
Editorial: 5360 Progress Blvd, Bethel Park, Pennsylvania 15102-2546. **T:** 1 412 851-1512
DAILY NEWSPAPER

Pittsburgh Post-Gazette
Editorial: 235 Hope St, Carnegie, Pennsylvania 15106-3655. **T:** 1 412 722-0085
DAILY NEWSPAPER

Pittsburgh Post-Gazette
Editorial: 230 Executive Dr, Cranberry Twp, Pennsylvania 16066-6415. **T:** 1 724 772-4799
DAILY NEWSPAPER

Pittsburgh Tribune-Review
Owner: Tribune-Review Publishing Co.
Editorial: 503 Martindale St, Pittsburgh, Pennsylvania 15212-5746. **T:** 1 412 321-6460
W: http://triblive.com
Freq: Daily; **Circ:** 198963 Not Audited
Editor: Frank Craig; **Publisher:** Richard Scaife
Editorial Profile: Pittsburgh Tribune-Review began publishing on December 17, 1992. It is a daily newspaper covering Pittsburgh. It contains business, entertainment, style and regional, national and international news. The newspaper has several regional editions, including the Tribune-Review. Online content is

held on TribLIVE.com.; Full Page Mono: 200.65; Full Page Colour: 1244.72
Currency: US Dollars
DAILY NEWSPAPER

Pittsburgh Tribune-Review
Editorial: State Capital Bldg, Floor E Room 524, Harrisburg, Pennsylvania 17120-0001.
T: 1 717 787-1405
DAILY NEWSPAPER

Pittsburgh Tribune-Review
Editorial: 622 Cabin Hill Dr, Greensburg, Pennsylvania 15601-1657. **T:** 1 724 838-5143
DAILY NEWSPAPER

Pittsburgh Tribune-Review
Owner: Tribune Review Publishing Co
Editorial: 127 W Apple St, Connellsville, Pennsylvania 15425-3132
Editor: Rose Snyder
DAILY NEWSPAPER

Pittsburgh Union
Editorial: 1719 Liberty Ave, Pittsburgh, Pennsylvania 15222. **T:** 1 412 281-8533
Freq: Bi-Weekly; **Circ:** 11000 Not Audited
Editor: Anna D'Alo; **Publisher:** Larry Frediani
Editorial Profile: Pittsburgh Union is written for The Italian Sons and Daughters of America, a fraternal organization located mainly in Pennsylvania, New York, Ohio, West Virginia, Illinois, Indiana and Florida. The newspaper covers news and events regarding The Italian Sons and Daughters of America. There is no e-mail nor Web site for Pittsburgh Union. Advertising is not accepted.
NEWSPAPER

El Placazo
Editorial: 1300 Chihuahua St, San Antonio, Texas 78207. **T:** 1 210 226-7466
E: cristina@sananto.org
W: http://www.sananto.org
Freq: Monthly; **Circ:** 96000 Not Audited
Editorial Profile: El Placazo is published to educate and train youth in all aspects of newspaper production and develop the artistic, writing and cognitive skills of youth participants. The paper also allows community residents to voice, document and express their creativity, history, social concerns and thoughts through the submission and publication of poetry, articles and artwork. It is community-operated and designed as an educational tool for youth, adult and elder residents interested in newspaper production. Does not accept advertising.
NEWSPAPER

Placer Herald
Owner: Brehm Communications, Inc.
Editorial: 5055 Pacific St, Rocklin, California 95677-2707. **T:** 1 916 624-9713
W: http://www.placerherald.com
Freq: Thu; **Circ:** 14350 Not Audited
Editor: Krissi Khokhobashvili
Editorial Profile: Placer Herald is a local weekly newspaper written for the residents of Rocklin, CA. Deadlines are at 5pm PT on Fridays.; Full Page Mono: 24.00
Currency: US Dollars
NEWSPAPER

The Plain Dealer
Owner: Advance Publications, Inc.
Editorial: 1660 W 2nd St, Cleveland, Ohio 44113-1454. **T:** 1 216 999-5000
E: metrodesk@plaind.com
W: http://www.cleveland.com/plaindealer
Freq: Daily; **Circ:** 283954 Not Audited
Editor: Debra Adams Simmons; **Reader Representative:** Ted Diadiun
Editorial Profile: The Plain Dealer is a broadsheet daily newspaper distributed in Cuyahoga County, OH and covers local/metro, international, consumer, health, and business news. Monday's edition carries the Personal Finance section focusing on investments, savings, and spending money. The Tuesday Business section offers a look at business developments locally and around the world. In addition, on Tuesday, the Everywoman section deals with work, home, and the social concerns of women. Inside & Out, the paper's home and garden section, is published on Thursday. Friday Magazine features dining and local events in Northeast Ohio every Friday. In August 2009, the paper joined a national sports content-sharing alliance with several other papers across the country. The newspaper publishes seven times a week and provides home delivery three days a week, including Sunday.; Full Page Mono: 520.00; Full Page Colour: 1686.42
Currency: US Dollars
DAILY NEWSPAPER

The Plain Dealer
Editorial: 1625 K St NW, Washington, District Of Columbia 20006-1604
DAILY NEWSPAPER

The Plain Dealer
Editorial: 155 E Broad St, Columbus, Ohio 43215-3609. **T:** 1 614 228-8200
E: state@plaind.com
Bureau Chief: Robert Higgs
DAILY NEWSPAPER

Plain Dealer & Sun, Inc.
Editorial: 528 E O&M Ave, North Vernon, Indiana 47265. **T:** 1 812 346-3973
E: pds@northvernon.com
W: http://www.plaindealer-sun.com
Circ: 13500 Not Audited
Editor: Sharon Hamilton; **Editor:** Sharon Hamilton; **Publisher:** Barbara King; **Editor:** Bryce Mayer
NEWSPAPER

Plain Press
Editorial: 2012 W 25Th St Ste 500, Cleveland, Ohio 44113-4131. **T:** 1 216 621-3060
E: plainpress@gmail.com
W: http://plainpress.wordpress.com
Freq: Monthly; **Circ:** 21000 Not Audited
Editor: Deborah Sadlon
Editorial Profile: Plain Press is a monthly paper written for the residents of the near west side of Cleveland, OH.; Full Page Mono: 18.50
Currency: US Dollars
NEWSPAPER

Plaindealer Publishing
Owner: Lee Enterprises, Inc.
Editorial: 707 S 13th St, Tekamah, Nebraska 68061. **T:** 1 402 374-2226
E: support@midwestmessenger.com
W: http://www.midwestmessenger.com
Circ: 128767 Not Audited
Publisher: Joe Zink
NEWSPAPER

The Plains Reporter
Owner: Wick Communications Inc.
Editorial: 14 4th St W, Williston, North Dakota 58801. **T:** 1 701 572-2165
E: news@willistonherald.com
W: http://www.willistonherald.com
Freq: Wed; **Circ:** 15100 Not Audited
Publisher: Mitzi Moe
Editorial Profile: The Plains Reporter is a local weekly newspaper written for the residents of Williston, ND and the surrounding area.; Full Page Mono: 9.10
Currency: US Dollars
NEWSPAPER

Plainview Daily Herald
Owner: Hearst Newspapers
Editorial: 820 Broadway St, Plainview, Texas 79072-7316. **T:** 1 806 296-1300
W: http://www.myplainview.com
Freq: Daily; **Circ:** 8000 Not Audited
Editor: Doug McDonough; **Editor:** Doug McDonough
Editorial Profile: Plainview Daily Herald is a local daily newspaper written for the residents of Hale, Castro, Swisher, Briscoe, Lamb, and Floyd Counties in Texas. The newspaper primarily covers the local news, sports, features and lifestyles of Plainview, TX.; Full Page Mono: 18.21; Full Page Colour: 300.00
Currency: US Dollars
DAILY NEWSPAPER

El Planeta
Owner: Phoenix Media/Communications Group (The)
Editorial: 311 Highland Ave., Somerville, Massachusetts 2144. **T:** 1 617 379-2016
E: editor@elplaneta.com
W: http://www.elplaneta.com
Freq: Thu; **Circ:** 50000 Not Audited
Editorial Profile: El Planeta in Chelsea, MA is a weekly Spanish-language newspaper serving the Latino population in the Boston metro area and throughout New England. The paper covers regional, national and international news, politics, sports and arts & entertainment. Copies are distributed via subscriptions, picked-up at retailers and newsstands or they are handed out. Advertising deadlines are on Fridays at 5pm ET.; Full Page Mono: 22.00; Full Page Colour: 150.00
Currency: US Dollars
NEWSPAPER

Plant City Courier & Tribune
Owner: Media General Inc.
Editorial: 933 Chad Ln, Tampa, Florida 33619-4331. **T:** 1 813 627-4727

W: http://plantcity.tbo.com
Freq: Wed; **Circ:** 10700
Editor: Dave Nicholson; **Editor:** Dave Nicholson; **Editor:** Dave Nicholson; **Editor:** Dave Nicholson
Editorial Profile: Plant City Courier & Tribune is a local newspaper written for the residents of Plant City, FL. The newspaper covers local news. Deadlines are on Thursdays at 4pm ET.; Full Page Mono: 15.60
Currency: US Dollars
NEWSPAPER

Platte County Citizen
Owner: Stubbs Publishing Company
Editorial: 331 Main St, Platte City, Missouri 64079-8451. **T:** 1 816 858-5154
E: newsdesk1@plattecountycitizen.com
W: http://www.plattecountycitizen.com
Freq: Wed; **Circ:** 11850 Not Audited
Editorial Profile: Platte County Citizen is a local weekly newspaper written for the residents of Platte County, MO. The paper offers comprehensive and complete coverage of the Platte County Commission, Sheriff's Department and municipal governments in Platte City, Weston, Camden Point, Dearborn and Edgerton, MO. The newspaper also features local coverage of Platte County R-3, West Platte R-2 and North Platte R-1 School Districts, including reports from Board of Education meetings and other school-related events and activities. The paper also covers local high school sports, including results and features on all Pirate, Bluejay and Panthers teams. The newspaper strives to provide its readers with not only timely news stories, but also features about the people and places that make the northern Platte County area unique and special.; Full Page Mono: 10.00
Currency: US Dollars
NEWSPAPER

Platte County Newspapers
Owner: News Media Corp.
Editorial: 1007 8th St, Wheatland, Wyoming 82201. **T:** 1 307 322-2627
E: pceditor@pcrecordtimes.com
W: http://www.pcrecordtimes.com **Circ:** 6930 Not Audited
Editor: Amber Ningen; **Publisher:** Jeff Robertson
NEWSPAPER

Pocahontas Record-Democrat, Buena Vista County Journal & Laurens Sun Newspapers
Editorial: 218 N Main St, Pocahontas, Iowa 50574-1624. **T:** 1 712 335-3553
E: publisher@pokyrd.com **Circ:** 7195 Not Audited
NEWSPAPER

Pocono Record
Owner: GateHouse Media Inc.
Editorial: 511 Lenox St, Stroudsburg, Pennsylvania 18360-1516. **T:** 1 570 421-3000
W: http://www.poconorecord.com
Freq: Daily; **Circ:** 11617 Not Audited
Publisher: Joe Vanderhoof
Editorial Profile: Pocono Record's editorial mission is to provide the leading source of information in the Pocono Mountain area in Pennsylvania. The newspaper strives to provide an accurate, balanced, and fair news report. Pocono Record will exercise leadership, professionalism, and social responsibility for the betterment of the community. The local daily newspaper is written for residents in Monroe County and the Pocono Mountain area in Pennsylvania. Pocono Record covers local, national, and international news.; Full Page Mono: 24.25; Full Page Colour: 324.25
Currency: US Dollars
DAILY NEWSPAPER

Point Pleasant Register
Owner: Heartland Publications
Editorial: 200 Main St, Point Pleasant, West Virginia 25550. **T:** 1 304 675-1333
E: news@mydailyregister.com
W: http://www.mydailyregister.com
Freq: Daily; **Circ:** 3918 Not Audited
Publisher: Sammy Lopez
Editorial Profile: Point Pleasant Register is a local newspaper written for the residents of Point Pleasant, WV. The paper covers local news, sports, business and lifestyle.; Full Page Mono: 11.35; Full Page Colour: 38.23
Currency: US Dollars
DAILY NEWSPAPER

Polk County Publishing
Owner: Polk County Publishing Co.
Editorial: 100 E Calhoun St, Livingston, Texas 77351. **T:** 1 936 327-4357

E: enterprise@easttexasnews.com
W: http://www.easttexasnews.com **Circ:** 31048 Not Audited
Editor: Martha Charrey; **Publisher:** Alvin Holley; **Editor:** Greg Peak; **Editor:** Kim Popham; **Editor:** Jim Powers; **Editor:** Darlene Pyle
NEWSPAPER

Pomerado Newspapers
Owner: MainStream Media Group LLC
Editorial: 14023 Midland Rd, Poway, California 92064-3959. **T:** 1 858 218-7200
E: news@pomeradonews.com
W: http://www.pomeradonews.com
Circ: 32000 Not Audited
Editor: Steve Dreyer; **Publisher:** Douglas Manchester
NEWSPAPER

The Pomeroy Daily Sentinel
Owner: Heartland Publications
Editorial: 200 Main St., Point Pleasant, West Virginia 25550. **T:** 1 304 675-1333
E: mdsnews@mydailysentinel.com
W: http://www.mydailysentinel.com
Freq: Daily; **Circ:** 3471 Not Audited
Publisher: Sammy Lopez
Editorial Profile: The Pomeroy Daily Sentinel is a daily newspaper serving the residents of Pomeroy and Middleport, OH. It contains world, national, state and local news, events, sports and editorial coverage. The paper is especially interested in receiving articles and photographs concerning new employees, promotions, club activities, civic organization programs, birthdays, anniversaries, weddings and engagements, honors and awards. On Sundays, the paper joins with its sister newspaper, the Gallipolis (OH) Daily Tribune to produce the Sunday Times-Sentinel.; Full Page Mono: 10.05; Full Page Colour: 180.00
Currency: US Dollars
DAILY NEWSPAPER

The Pompano Pelican
Editorial: 1500 E Atlantic Blvd, Ste A, Pompano Beach, Florida 33060.
T: 1 954 783-8700
W: http://www.pompanopelican.com
Freq: Fri; **Circ:** 15000 Not Audited
Editorial Profile: The Pompano Pelican's editorial mission is to produce the news that people need to know and want to know. It is focused on the local community and is written for residents of Pompano Beach, FL. Deadlines are noon ET, Wednesdays before issue date.; Full Page Mono: 12.00
Currency: US Dollars
NEWSPAPER

The Ponca City News
Owner: Ponca City Publishing Company
Editorial: 300 N 3rd St, Ponca City, Oklahoma 74601-4336. **T:** 1 580 765-3311
E: news@poncacitynews.com
W: http://www.poncacitynews.com
Freq: Daily; **Circ:** 7436 Not Audited
Editor: Fred Hilton; **Editor:** Bob Patterson
Editorial Profile: The Ponca City News is a daily newspaper written for the residents of Ponca City, OK. The paper cover local news, education, sports, business and lifestyles.; Full Page Mono: 12.00; Full Page Colour: 240.00
Currency: US Dollars
DAILY NEWSPAPER

El Popular
Owner: El Popular, Inc.
Editorial: 404 Truxtun Ave, Bakersfield, California 93301-5316. **T:** 1 661 398-1000
E: news@elpopularnews.com
W: http://www.elpopularnews.com
Freq: Fri; **Circ:** 24000 Not Audited
Editorial Profile: El Popular is a local weekly newspaper serving western Kern County, CA. It covers local community news, upcoming events, local sports, health, food and arts & entertainment. It also contains the section Our Culture.; Full Page Mono: 17.50
Currency: US Dollars
NEWSPAPER

Porcupine Press
Owner: Porcupine Press, Inc.
Editorial: E3720 Munising St, Chatham, Michigan 49816. **T:** 1 906 439-5111
W: http://www.upmag.net
Freq: Monthly; **Circ:** 25000 Not Audited
Editor: Michael Van Den Branden
Editorial Profile: Porcupine Press is written for residents in the upper peninsula of Michigan. Deadlines for the publication are due by the 15th of the month before the issue date.; Full Page Mono: 15.36
Currency: US Dollars
NEWSPAPER

Port Arthur News
Owner: Community Newspaper Holdings, Inc.
Editorial: 3501 Turtle Creek Dr, Port Arthur, Texas 77642-8053. **T:** 1 409 721-2400
E: panews@panews.com
W: http://www.panews.com
Freq: Daily; **Circ:** 10859 Not Audited
Editor: Roger Cowles; **Publisher:** Rich Macke
Editorial Profile: The Port Arthur News is published daily for the residents of Jefferson County, TX. It delivers local news and information to residents of Jefferson County, TX. Topics covered also include national news, financial news, town hall news, arts and entertainment and health news.; Full Page Mono: 35.00; Full Page Colour: 300.00
Currency: US Dollars
DAILY NEWSPAPER

Port Clinton News Herald
Owner: Gannett Co., Inc.
Editorial: 115 W 2Nd St, Port Clinton, Ohio 43452-1012. **T:** 1 419 734-3141
E: newsherald@thenews-messenger.com
W: http://www.portclintonnewsherald.com
Freq: Daily; **Circ:** 2190 Not Audited
Editorial Profile: Port Clinton News Herald is published for the residents in Ottawa County and Port Clinton, OH. It covers local and county news, features, business and community events. The paper dates back to 1865. After undergoing many name and ownership changes, the Port Clinton Herald and the Daily News merged in 1969 to become the News Herald.; Full Page Mono: 19.20; Full Page Colour: 215.00
Currency: US Dollars
DAILY NEWSPAPER

Port Orchard Independent
Owner: Black Press
Editorial: 2950 SE Mile Hill Dr, Port Orchard, Washington 98366-2958. **T:** 1 360 876-4414
W: http://www.portorchardindependent.com
Freq: Fri; **Circ:** 18300 Not Audited
Publisher: Rich Peterson; **Editor:** Jeff Rhodes
Editorial Profile: Port Orchard Independent is a weekly newspaper written for the residents of Port Orchard, WA and surrounding areas. The paper covers local news, business, sports and community events. Deadlines are at noon PT prior to issue date. Send all editorial correspondence to the PO Box address. Send advertising correspondence to Port Orchard Independent, c/o Sound Publishing, 7689 NE Day Rd., Bainbridge Island, WA 98110. Ads will also run in the paper's sister publications, including Bainbridge Island Review, Bremerton Patriot and North Kitsap Herald.; Full Page Mono: 22.40
Currency: US Dollars
NEWSPAPER

Port Publications, Inc.
Owner: Port Publications, Inc.
Editorial: 125 E Main St, Port Washington, Wisconsin 53074-1915. **T:** 1 262 284-3494
E: news@ozaukeepress.com
W: http://www.ozaukeepress.com/ **Circ:** 19300
NEWSPAPER

Portage Daily Register
Owner: Capital Newspapers
Editorial: 1640 La Dawn Dr, Portage, Wisconsin 53901-8822. **T:** 1 608 745-3500
E: pdr-news@capitalnewspapers.com
W: http://www.wiscnews.com/portagedailyregister
Freq: Daily; **Circ:** 4369 Not Audited
Editor: Kerry Lechner
Editorial Profile: Portage Daily Register is published daily for the residents of Portage, Columbia and Market counties, WI. The newspaper provides local news and information.; Full Page Mono: 29.20; Full Page Colour: 93.76
Currency: US Dollars
DAILY NEWSPAPER

Portales News-Tribune
Owner: Freedom Communications Inc.
Editorial: 101 E 1st St, Portales, New Mexico 88130. **T:** 1 575 356-4481 **E:** pnt@yucca.net
W: http://www.pntonline.com
Freq: Daily; **Circ:** 2200 Not Audited
Publisher: Ray Sullivan
Editorial Profile: Portales News-Tribune is published daily for the residents of Portales, NM. The newspaper focuses on news, sports, business and features about the community. Deadlines are daily at 10pm MT.; Full Page Mono: 9.75; Full Page Colour: 247.20
Currency: US Dollars
DAILY NEWSPAPER

Porterville Recorder
Owner: Rhode Island Suburban Newspapers, Inc.
Editorial: 115 E Oak Ave, Porterville, California 93257-3807. **T:** 1 559 784-5000
E: recorder@portervillerecorder.com
W: http://www.portervillerecorder.com
Freq: Daily; **Circ:** 9118 Not Audited
Editorial Profile: Porterville Recorder is written for residents of Southeastern Tulare County, CA.; Full Page Mono: 34.00; Full Page Colour: 225.00
Currency: US Dollars
DAILY NEWSPAPER

Portland Daily Sun
Owner: Portland News Club, LLC.
Editorial: 181 State St, Portland, Maine 04101-3701. **T:** 1 207 699-5801
E: news@portlanddailysun.me
W: http://www.portlanddailysun.me
Freq: Daily; **Circ:** 15000
Publisher: Mark Guerringue
Editorial Profile: Portland Daily Sun is a free publication distributed Tuesday through Saturday for the residents of Portland, ME and the surrounding areas.; Full Page Mono: 1.00
Currency: US Dollars
DAILY NEWSPAPER

Portland Mercury
Owner: Index Publishing LLC
Editorial: 115 Sw Ash St Ste 600, Portland, Oregon 97204-3549. **T:** 1 503 294-0840
E: news@portlandmercury.com
W: http://www.portlandmercury.com
Freq: Thu; **Circ:** 42500 Not Audited
Publisher: Rob Crocker; **Editor:** William Humphrey
Editorial Profile: Portland Mercury is a free weekly arts, entertainment, and culture newspaper. It is targeted at 20-somethings in Portland, OR and its surrounding areas. The paper offers extensive entertainment listings, music reviews, political news and local news. It is also filled with humorous parodies of the news.; Full Page Mono: 41.78
Currency: US Dollars
NEWSPAPER

Portland Observer
Owner: Northwest Print Inc.
Editorial: 4747 NE M L King Blvd, Portland, Oregon 97211. **T:** 1 503 288-0033
E: news@portlandobserver.com
W: http://www.portlandobserver.com
Freq: Wed; **Circ:** 39534 Not Audited
Editor: Mike Leighton
Editorial Profile: Portland Observer is a weekly newspaper written for residents of Portland, OR. Deadlines are 5pm PT, Friday before issue date. Contact the publication for advertisement rates.; Full Page Mono: 70.00
Currency: US Dollars
NEWSPAPER

The Portland Phoenix
Owner: Phoenix Media/Communications Group (The)
Editorial: 16 York St Ste 102, Portland, Maine 04101-4564. **T:** 1 207 773-8900
E: submit@phx.com
W: http://www.thephoenix.com/portland
Freq: Fri; **Circ:** 44500 Not Audited
Publisher: Stephen Mindich
Editorial Profile: The Portland (ME) Phoenix is written for residents of Maine and New Hampshire. It covers local news, events and entertainment. Deadlines are on Tuesdays at 5pm ET.; Full Page Mono: 13.33
Currency: US Dollars
NEWSPAPER

Portland Press Herald
Owner: Maine Today Media Inc.
Editorial: 1 City Ctr Stop 5, Portland, Maine 04101-4009. **T:** 1 207 791-6650
E: news@mainetoday.com
W: http://www.pressherald.com
Freq: Daily; **Circ:** 37776 Not Audited
Editorial Profile: Portland Press Herald is a daily newspaper for residents of Portland that covers business, sports, entertainment, news, real estate and travel. The Sunday edition is named the Maine Sunday Telegram. Editorial lead times vary according to specific section.; Full Page Mono: 84.00; Full Page Colour: 266.64
Currency: US Dollars
DAILY NEWSPAPER

Portsmouth Daily Times
Owner: Heartland Publications
Editorial: 637 6th St, Portsmouth, Ohio 45662-3924. **T:** 1 740 353-3101
E: pdtnews@civitasmedia.com
W: http://www.portsmouth-dailytimes.com
Freq: Daily; **Circ:** 13733 Not Audited
Editorial Profile: Portsmouth Daily Times is a local newspaper serving the residents of Portsmouth, OH. The paper covers local news, sports, entertainment and lifestyle. Deadlines are at 10pm ET the day prior to the issue date.; Full Page Mono: 18.75; Full Page Colour: 255.00
Currency: US Dollars
DAILY NEWSPAPER

Portsmouth Herald
Owner: GateHouse Media Inc.
Editorial: 111 NH Ave, Portsmouth, New Hampshire 03801-2864. **T:** 1 603 436-1800
E: news@seacoastonline.com
W: http://www.seacoastonline.com
Freq: Daily; **Circ:** 11348 Not Audited
Editor: Deb Cram; **Editor:** Christine French; **Publisher:** John Tabor
Editorial Profile: Portsmouth Herald is a local, daily newspaper providing news to residents of Portsmouth, NH. It is based in the same office as Seacost Newspapers, publisher of multiple community weeklies. Deadlines are at 5pm ET.; Full Page Mono: 26.00; Full Page Colour: 465.00
Currency: US Dollars
DAILY NEWSPAPER

Portuguese Times
Editorial: 1501 Acushnet Ave, New Bedford, Massachusetts 02746-2223.
T: 1 508 997-3118 **E:** ptimes@aol.com
W: http://www.portuguesetimes.com
Freq: Wed; **Circ:** 16000 Not Audited
Editorial Profile: Portuguese Times provides news to the Portuguese community. Portuguese Times is written for Portuguese-Americans and Portuguese people across the United States.; Full Page Mono: 10.00
Currency: US Dollars
NEWSPAPER

The Post & Mail
Owner: Horizon Publications
Editorial: 927 W Connexion Way, Columbia City, Indiana 46725-1031. **T:** 1 260 244-5153
E: news@thepostandmail.com
W: http://www.thepostandmail.com
Freq: Daily; **Circ:** 3583 Not Audited
Publisher: Rick Kreps
Editorial Profile: The Post & Mail provides local news, sports and events coverage for the Columbia City, IN area.; Full Page Mono: 9.20; Full Page Colour: 100.00
Currency: US Dollars
DAILY NEWSPAPER

The Post and Courier
Owner: Evening Post Publishing Co.
Editorial: 134 Columbus St, Charleston, South Carolina 29403-4809. **T:** 1 843 577-7111
W: http://www.postandcourier.com
Freq: Daily; **Circ:** 85723 Not Audited
Publisher: P.J. Browning
Editorial Profile: The Post and Courier was established in 1926 when The Daily Courier and The Evening Post combined. The newspaper kept separate staffs until the 1970s. In 1991 it was determined that the highest readership was for the morning edition so the evening edition stopped production. The news department is separated into four main areas: metro desk, copy desk, sports and features. The paper does not publish an editorial calendar.; Full Page Mono: 167.87; Full Page Colour: 491.63
Currency: US Dollars
DAILY NEWSPAPER

Post Community Newspapers
Editorial: 154 E Center St, Shelley, Idaho 83274-1302. **T:** 1 208 357-7661
E: news@theshelleypioneer.com
W: http://theshelleypioneer.com **Circ:** 4000
Publisher: Roger Plathow; **Editor:** Shirley Thompson
NEWSPAPER

Post Eagle
Owner: Post Publishing Co.
Editorial: 800 Van Houten Ave, Clifton, New Jersey 07013-2035. **T:** 1 973 473-5414
E: posteagle@aol.com
W: http://www.posteaglenewspaper.com
Freq: Wed; **Circ:** 10000 Not Audited
Editorial Profile: Post Eagle is published weekly for the residents of Clifton, NJ and surrounding areas. The newspaper covers local news, sports and community events.; Full Page Mono: 11.00
Currency: US Dollars
NEWSPAPER

Post Falls Press
Owner: Hagadone Corp.

Editorial: 201 N 2nd St, Coeur D Alene, Idaho 83814-2803. **T:** 1 208 664-8176
W: http://www.postfallspress.com
Freq: Daily; **Circ:** 3729 Not Audited
Editor: Mark Nelke; **Publisher:** Jim Thompson
Editorial Profile: Post Falls Press is written for the residents of Post Falls, ID. It combines with the Coeur d'Alene Press on Sunday.; Full Page Mono: 32.67; Full Page Colour: 415.00
Currency: US Dollars
DAILY NEWSPAPER

Post News Group
Owner: Post News Group
Editorial: 405 14th St, Oakland, California 94612-2715. **T:** 1 510 287-8200
E: pressrelease@postnewsgroup.com
W: http://postnewsgroup.com **Circ:** 52500 Not Audited
Publisher: Paul Cobb; **Editor:** Ken Epstein; **Editor:** Victor Martinez
Editorial Profile: Post News Group in Oakland, CA is a weekly community newspaper publisher serving the residents of Oakland, Richmond, San Francisco and Berkeley, CA.
NEWSPAPER

The Post Newspapers
Owner: Post Newspapers (The)
Editorial: 5164 Normandy Park Dr Ste 100, Medina, Ohio 44256-5903. **T:** 1 330 721-7678
E: news@thepostnewspapers.com
W: http://www.thepostnewspapers.com
Freq: Sat; **Circ:** 108600
Publisher: Bruce Trogdon
Editorial Profile: The Post Newspapers offer local news and information in nine different community newspapers in the Medina, Ohio area.; Full Page Mono: 2998.00; Full Page Colour: 3597.60
Currency: US Dollars
NEWSPAPER

Post Newspapers, Inc.
Owner: MediaNews Group
Editorial: 59 Marylinn Dr, Milpitas, California 95035. **T:** 1 408 262-2454 **Circ:** 70900 Not Audited
Editor: Rob Devincenzi
Editorial Profile: Post Newspapers Inc. in Milpitas, CA publishes the Berryessa Sun, Fremont Bulletin, Milpitas Post and Newark Connection.
NEWSPAPER

Post Register
Owner: Post Company
Editorial: 333 Northgate Mile, Idaho Falls, Idaho 83401. **T:** 1 208 522-1800
E: news@postregister.com
W: http://www.postregister.com
Freq: Daily; **Circ:** 25139 Not Audited
News Editor: Bryce Glenn; **Publisher:** Roger Plothow
Editorial Profile: Post Register is a daily local newspaper serving the Idaho Falls, ID area. Local, national and international news is covered, as well as lifestyle, entertainment and sports features.; Full Page Mono: 24.85; Full Page Colour: 315.00
Currency: US Dollars
DAILY NEWSPAPER

Post-Bulletin
Owner: Small Newspaper Group
Editorial: 18 1st Ave SE, Rochester, Minnesota 55904. **T:** 1 507 285-7600
E: news@postbulletin.com
W: http://www.postbulletin.com
Freq: Mon thru Fri; **Circ:** 38200 Not Audited
Publisher: Randy Chapman
Editorial Profile: Post-Bulletin in Rochester, MN is a daily newspaper that offers in-depth national and local news, including health, politics, entertainment, sports, technology, lifestyle, home, faith, food, and a section Teen Beat, specifically devoted to teenagers in the area.; Full Page Mono: 55.10; Full Page Colour: 50.25
Currency: US Dollars
DAILY NEWSPAPER

The Post-Crescent
Owner: Gannett Co., Inc.
Editorial: 306 W Washington St, Appleton, Wisconsin 54911-5452. **T:** 1 920 733-4411
E: pcnews@postcrescent.com
W: http://www.postcrescent.com
Freq: Daily; **Circ:** 35986
Publisher: Genia Lovett
Editorial Profile: The Post-Crescent is written for residents of Appleton, WI, and the surrounding counties. The newspaper covers news, sports, arts & entertainment, jobs and community information relevant to the area. Please send all correspondence to the PO

Box.; Full Page Mono: 83.10; Full Page Colour: 133.79
Currency: US Dollars
DAILY NEWSPAPER

The Post-Crescent
Editorial: 307 S Commercial St, Neenah, Wisconsin 54956-5700. **T:** 1 920 729-6622
Bureau Chief: Rachel Rausch
DAILY NEWSPAPER

Post-Gazette
Editorial: 5 Prince St, Boston, Massachusetts 02113-2443. **T:** 1 617 227-8929
E: postgazette@aol.com
W: http://www.bostonpostgazette.com
Freq: Fri; **Circ:** 25900 Not Audited
Editorial Profile: Post-Gazette in Boston is a community newspaper that covers local news and events pertinent to the Italian-American community in New England. Deadlines are Wednesdays at noon ET.; Full Page Mono: 20.00
Currency: US Dollars
NEWSPAPER

The Post-Journal
Owner: Ogden Newspapers
Editorial: 15 W 2nd St, Jamestown, New York 14701-5215. **T:** 1 716 487-1111
E: editorial@post-journal.com
W: http://www.post-journal.com
Freq: Daily; **Circ:** 12226 Not Audited
Publisher: Michael Bird; **Editor:** Chris Murphy; **Editor:** John Whittaker
Editorial Profile: The Post-Journal is written for residents of Chautauqua and Cattaraugus County, NY, and Warren County, PA. Deadlines are daily at 5pm ET.; Full Page Mono: 50.44; Full Page Colour: 47.54
Currency: US Dollars
DAILY NEWSPAPER

Postlatino
Owner: Postlatino LLC
Editorial: 147 Jefferson Ln, East Hartford, Connecticut 06118-2110. **T:** 1 860 760-0522
E: info@postlatino.com
W: http://postlatino.com
Freq: Monthly
Editor: Maria Lino
Editorial Profile: Postlatino is a community newspaper serving the Hispanic population in East Hartford, CT and the greater New England area, including local, regional, state, national and world news as it concerns the Latin American community.
NEWSPAPER

The Post-Report
Owner: Community Newspaper Holdings, Inc.
Editorial: 801 N Kanawha St, Beckley, West Virginia 25801. **T:** 1 304 255-4400
W: http://www.register-herald.com
Freq: Thu; **Circ:** 20222 Not Audited
Publisher: Frank Wood
Editorial Profile: A community newspaper for the Beckley West Virginia area.; Full Page Mono: 10.54
Currency: US Dollars
NEWSPAPER

The Post-Standard
Owner: Newhouse Newspapers
Editorial: 101 N Salina St, Syracuse, New York 13202-1030. **T:** 1 315 470-0011
E: citynews@syracuse.com
W: http://www.syracuse.com/poststandard
Freq: Daily; **Circ:** 96835 Not Audited
Curator: Brian Cubbison; **News Curator:** Sonja Meyer Duntley; **Curator:** Dan Padovano
Editorial Profile: The Post-Standard is a daily broadsheet newspaper distributed in the Syracuse, NY area. It covers Central New York news, politics, education, sports and entertainment, as well as regional, national and international news. The paper was founded in 1829 as the Onondaga Standard.; Full Page Mono: 167.98; Full Page Colour: 509.46
Currency: US Dollars
DAILY NEWSPAPER

The Post-Standard
Editorial: 3900 Fairfax Dr, Arlington, Virginia 22203-1661. **T:** 1 571 970-3751
DAILY NEWSPAPER

The Post-Star
Owner: Lee Enterprises, Inc.
Editorial: Lawrence and Cooper Streets, Glens Falls, New York 12801-3749.
T: 1 518 792-3131
W: http://www.poststar.com
Freq: Daily; **Circ:** 23525 Not Audited
Editor: Bob Condon; **Publisher:** Rick Emanuel

Editorial Profile: The Post-Star is a local daily newspaper written for residents of Saratoga County, Washington County and Warren County, NY.; Full Page Mono: 28.38
Currency: US Dollars
DAILY NEWSPAPER

Post-Tribune
Owner: Wrapports LLC
Editorial: 350 N Orleans St, Chicago, Illinois 60654-1975. **T:** 1 219 648-3000
W: http://posttrib.suntimes.com
Freq: Daily; **Circ:** 26850 Not Audited
News Editor: Jon Gard; **Publisher:** Lisa Tatina
Editorial Profile: Post-Tribune is a division of the Chicago Sun-Times and a part of Hollinger International, Inc. newspapers. The publication is a daily newspaper operating out of Merrillville, IN, in the vicinity of Gary, IN. It serves Gary and its surrounding communities and provides local, regional, and state news, as well as sports and entertainment news for the area. The newspaper maintains an online version of its daily edition at www.post-trib.com.; Full Page Mono: 93.86; Full Page Colour: 313.70
Currency: US Dollars
DAILY NEWSPAPER

Poteau Daily News & Sun
Owner: Horizon Publications
Editorial: 804 N Broadway St, Poteau, Oklahoma 74953-3503. **T:** 1 918 647-3188
E: editor@poteaudailynews.com
W: http://www.poteaudailynews.com
Freq: Fri; **Circ:** 3900 Not Audited
Editor: Kim Ross; **Publisher:** Robert Shearon
Editorial Profile: Poteau Daily News & Sun is a local daily newspaper written for the residents of LeFlore County, OK. The newspaper covers news, business, sports, and arts & entertainment.; Full Page Mono: 7.82; Full Page Colour: 9.57
Currency: US Dollars
NEWSPAPER

The Potrero View
Editorial: 2325 3rd St, Ste 344, San Francisco, California 94107.
T: 1 415 626-8723 **E:** office@potreroview.net
W: http://www.potreroview.net
Freq: Monthly; **Circ:** 10000 Not Audited
Editorial Profile: The Potrero View is a weekly neighborhood newspaper for the Portrero Hill area of San Francisco, CA. The publication contains neighborhood news and events for its residents and visitors. Contact the publication for advertising rates and editorial submission guidelines. The Web site of the publication is under construction.; Full Page Mono: 17.40
Currency: US Dollars
NEWSPAPER

Pottsville Republican & Herald
Owner: Times-Shamrock Communications
Editorial: 111 Mahantongo St, Pottsville, Pennsylvania 17901-3008. **T:** 1 570 622-3456
E: nuzdesk@republicanherald.com
W: http://www.republicanherald.com
Freq: Daily; **Circ:** 20378 Not Audited
Editor in Chief: Peter Banko; **News Editor:** Leanne Bush; **Publisher:** Henry Nyce
Editorial Profile: Pottsville Republican & Herald is a local newspaper written for residents of Schuylkill County, PA. The newspaper covers local news and events.; Full Page Mono: 40.00; Full Page Colour: 265.00
Currency: US Dollars
DAILY NEWSPAPER

Poughkeepsie Journal
Owner: Gannett Co., Inc.
Editorial: 85 Civic Center Plz, Poughkeepsie, New York 12601-2498. **T:** 1 845 454-2000
E: newsroom@poughkee.gannett.com
W: http://www.poughkeepsiejournal.com
Freq: Daily; **Circ:** 22191 Not Audited
Publisher: Barry Rothfeld
Editorial Profile: Poughkeepsie Journal is a daily newspaper serving the residents of the Poughkeepsie, NY area. Coverage includes local and city news, business, editorials, sports and lifestyle.; Full Page Mono: 72.80; Full Page Colour: 753.00
Currency: US Dollars
DAILY NEWSPAPER

Powdersville Post & Easley Progress
Owner: Heartland Publications
Editorial: 205 Russell St, Easley, South Carolina 29640. **T:** 1 864 855-0355
E: news@theeasleyprogress.com **Circ:** 17000 Not Audited
Editor: Lonnie Adamson; **Publisher:** Ty Ramsdale
NEWSPAPER

The Prairie Advocate
Owner: Acres of Sky Communications, Inc.
Editorial: 446 S Broad St, Lanark, Illinois 61046. **T:** 1 815 493-2560
E: pa@pacc-news.com
W: http://www.pacc-news.com
Freq: Wed; **Circ:** 15800 Not Audited
Editor: Lynn Kocal; **Publisher:** Thomas Kocal
Editorial Profile: The Prairie Advocate is a weekly local newspaper written for residents of Carroll County, IL. The publication is a general interest newspaper covering local news and community events. Deadlines are noon CT Fridays before issue date.; Full Page Mono: 18.00
Currency: US Dollars
NEWSPAPER

The Prairie Catholic
Owner: Diocese of New Ulm
Editorial: 1400 6Th St N, New Ulm, Minnesota 56073-2057. **T:** 1 507 359-2966
W: http://www.dnu.org/news
Freq: Monthly; **Circ:** 26000
Editor: Christine Clancy; **Publisher:** John LeVoir; **Editor in Chief:** Dan Rossini
Editorial Profile: The Prairie Catholic is a newspaper written for the Diocese of New Ulm, MN. The paper does not accept outside advertising.
NEWSPAPER

Prairie Mountain Publishing Boulder Dailies
Owner: MediaNews Group
Editorial: 5450 Western Ave, Boulder, Colorado 80301-2709. **T:** 1 303 442-1202
Circ: 41634
Editor: Jenn Fields; **Editor:** Kevin Kaufman; **Publisher:** Albert Manzi
DAILY NEWSPAPER

The Prairie Post & Sun Country
Owner: Forum Communications Co.
Editorial: 121 3rd St NW, Jamestown, North Dakota 58401-3127. **T:** 1 701 952-8432
Circ: 42525
Publisher: Bruce Henke; **Editor:** Kathy Steiner
NEWSPAPER

Prairie Publications
Owner: Gannett Co., Inc.
Editorial: 414 E 4th St, Dell Rapids, South Dakota 57022. **T:** 1 605 428-5441 **Circ:** 4398 Not Audited
Publisher: Randell Beck; **Editor:** Jill Meier; **Editor:** Luke Tatge
Editorial Profile: Prairie Publications is a local newspaper in Dell Rapids, SD.
NEWSPAPER

Pratt Tribune
Owner: Fortress Investment Group, LLC
Editorial: 320 S Main St, Pratt, Kansas 67124-2706. **T:** 1 620 672-5511
W: http://www.pratttribune.com
Freq: Mon thru Fri; **Circ:** 2000 Not Audited
Editor: Carol Bronson; **Editor:** Conrad Easterday; **Publisher:** Keith Lippoldt
Editorial Profile: Pratt Tribune is a daily newspaper that is written for residents of Pratt, KS. Articles include news, weather, travel and sports.; Full Page Mono: 8.95; Full Page Colour: 100.00
Currency: US Dollars
DAILY NEWSPAPER

Precinct Reporter Group
Editorial: 1677 W Base Line St, San Bernardino, California 92411-1685.
T: 1 909 889-0597
E: news@precinctreporter.com
W: http://www.precinctreporter.com
Circ: 80000
NEWSPAPER

La Prensa
Owner: ImpreMedia LLC
Editorial: 685 S Ronald Reagan Blvd, Longwood, Florida 32750-6435.
T: 1 407 767-0070
W: http://www.laprensafl.com
Freq: Thu; **Circ:** 35000 Not Audited
Publisher: Dora Casanova de Toro; **Editor in Chief:** Iza Montalvo
Editorial Profile: La Prensa Newspaper's editorial mission is to provide a voice for the Spanish residents Longwood, FL. The publication includes topics of fashion, beauty, community news, national and local news, health news and immigration topics. The lead time for La Prensa Newspaper is one week.; Full Page Mono: 35.36
Currency: US Dollars
NEWSPAPER

La Prensa
Editorial: 1704 E 5th St, Ste 103, Austin, Texas 78702-4482. **T:** 1 512 478-3090
E: laprensanews@aol.com
W: http://www.laprensaofaustin.com
Freq: Thu; **Circ:** 20000 Not Audited
Editorial Profile: La Prensa is a local newspaper written for the residents of Austin, TX.; Full Page Mono: 18.25
Currency: US Dollars
NEWSPAPER

La Prensa de Chicago
Editorial: 4518 W Fullerton Ave, Chicago, Illinois 60639-1934. **T:** 1 773 521-7286
E: info@laprensachicago.com
W: http://www.laprensaus.com
Freq: Fri
Editor: Diego Giraldo; **Publisher:** Martha González
Editorial Profile: La Prensa de Chicago is a weekly newspaper providing Local and Community News for the Hispanic and Spanish-speaking community in Chicago, IL.
NEWSPAPER

La Prensa de Colorado
Owner: La Prensa de Colorado
Editorial: 7280 Irving St Ste A-106, Westminster, Colorado 80030-4933.
T: 1 303 287-4105
E: news@laprensadecolorado.com
W: http://www.laprensadecolorado.com
Freq: Fri; **Circ:** 10000
News Editor: Germán Gónzalez
Editorial Profile: La Prensa de Colorado is a weekly Spanish-language newspaper providing Local and Community News coverage for the residents of Westminster, CO.
NEWSPAPER

La Prensa de Houston
Editorial: 7100 Regency Square Blvd Ste 217, Houston, Texas 77036-3187.
T: 1 713 334-4959
E: editorial@prensadehouston.com
W: http://www.prensadehouston.com
Freq: Weekly; **Circ:** 96500
Editor in Chief: Lorely De Leon
Editorial Profile: La Prensa de Houston is a weekly publication in Spanish committed to providing international, national and local advertisers with the best medium to reach Spanish-speaking consumers in the Houston metropolitan and suburban areas with more than 3,700 points of distribution. Each issue features a balanced content of news, reports, business information and entertainment for the entire family.
NEWSPAPER

La Prensa De San Antonio
Owner: Duran Duran Industries
Editorial: 230 N Medina St, San Antonio, Texas 78207-3022. **T:** 1 210 242-7900
W: http://www.laprensasa.com
Freq: Sun; **Circ:** 60581 Not Audited
Editor in Chief: Nina Duran; **Publisher:** Tino Duran
Editorial Profile: La Prensa De San Antonio is a bilingual newspaper written for the Hispanic community of San Antonio. The newspaper aims to encourage the community by reporting on positive news stories, as well as cultural issues and entertainment news and information.; Full Page Mono: 21.00
Currency: US Dollars
NEWSPAPER

La Prensa en Iowa
Owner: Lopez (Lorena)
Editorial: 109 S Main St, Denison, Iowa 51442-1958. **T:** 1 712 790-1563
E: info@laprensaiowa.com
W: http://www.laprensaiowa.com
Freq: Bi-Weekly
Editorial Profile: La Prensa en Iowa is a bi-weekly community newspaper serving the Hispanic population of Western Iowa, including Storm Lake, Denison, Carroll, Perry, Des Moines, and Ames. The paper includes local, national, and international news, as well as sports, health, and immigration news.; Full Page Mono: 6.81; Full Page Colour: 8.27
Currency: US Dollars
NEWSPAPER

Prensa Hispana
Owner: Hispanic Press
Editorial: 809 E Washington St, Ste 209, Phoenix, Arizona 85034. **T:** 1 602 256-2443
E: prensanews@prensahispana.com
W: http://www.prensahispanaaz.com
Freq: Wed; **Circ:** 65000 Not Audited
Editorial Profile: Prensa Hispana is a regional newspaper for the Hispanic community of Arizona. It covers international, national and local news, sports, art and events.; Full Page Mono: 25.00; Full Page Colour: 4830.00
Currency: US Dollars
NEWSPAPER

La Prensa Hispana
Owner: HIM, Inc.
Editorial: 45102 Smurr St, Indio, California 92201-4404. **T:** 1 760 342-2565
W: http://www.laprensahispananewspaper.com
Freq: Fri; **Circ:** 46500 Not Audited
Editorial Profile: La Prensa Hispana is a bilingual newspaper written for residents in Indio, CA.; Full Page Mono: 35.00
Currency: US Dollars
NEWSPAPER

La Prensa Hispana-L.A.
Owner: OSA Communications
Editorial: 815 S Central Ave, Ste 12B, Glendale, California 91204. **T:** 1 818 500-8103
E: laprensahispana@aol.com
W: http://laprensahispanala.com
Freq: Weekly; **Circ:** 60000 Not Audited
Editorial Profile: La Prensa Hispana-L.A. covers the concerns of the Hispanic community in California.; Full Page Mono: 21.50
Currency: US Dollars
NEWSPAPER

La Prensa Latina
Owner: Mendelson and Associates
Editorial: 995 S Yates Rd, Ste 3, Memphis, Tennessee 38119. **T:** 1 901 751-2100
E: sidney@laprensalatina.com
W: http://www.laprensalatina.com
Freq: Sun; **Circ:** 37000 Not Audited
Editor: Vivian Fernandez; **Publisher:** Sidney Mendelson
Editorial Profile: La Prensa Latina in Memphis, TN is a local newspaper written for Hispanic residents and covers community news, sports, social events, education, arts & entertainment and features.; Full Page Mono: 14.49
Currency: US Dollars
NEWSPAPER

La Prensa Ohio/Michigan
Owner: Aztlan Communications, Inc.
Editorial: 616 Adams St, Toledo, Ohio 43604-1420. **T:** 1 419 870-6565
E: laprensa1@yahoo.com
W: http://www.laprensa1.com
Freq: Wed; **Circ:** 13000 Not Audited
Editorial Profile: La Prensa is a weekly, bilingual newspaper serving the Latino and Hispanic communities in Northern Ohio, including Toledo and Cleveland, and Southern Michigan, including Detroit. It provides readers with community news about education, people, politics and events. It also offers in-depth cultural articles on literature, art, poetry, dance, travel and Tejano music. It is distributed to Latino dining and entertainment establishments, retail and specialty stores, hotels, museums, libraries, universities and other educational facilities. The paper is also available by paid subscription. Advertising deadlines are at 11am ET.; Full Page Mono: 15.00; Full Page Colour: 15.79
Currency: US Dollars
NEWSPAPER

La Prensa San Diego
Editorial: 651 3rd Ave Ste C, Chula Vista, California 91910-5720. **T:** 1 619 425-7400
E: laprensa@ix.netcom.com
W: http://www.laprensa-sandiego.org
Freq: Fri; **Circ:** 35000 Not Audited
Editorial Profile: La Prensa San Diego in Chula Vista, CA is a weekly newspaper that aims to be the voice of the Mexican-American and Latino communities. Deadline for the publication is on Tuesday at 5pm PT prior to Friday publication.; Full Page Mono: 28.00
Currency: US Dollars
NEWSPAPER

Prescott Newspapers
Owner: Prescott Newspapers, Inc.
Editorial: 8307 E State Route 69, Prescott Valley, Arizona 86312-2001.
T: 1 928 445-3333
E: editorial@prescottaz.com
W: http://www.dcourier.com **Circ:** 27330 Not Audited
Publisher: Kelly Soldwedel; **Editor:** Tim Wiederaenders
Editorial Profile: Prescott Newspapers in Prescott Valley, AZ publishes the Chino Valley Review and the Prescott Valley Tribune.
NEWSPAPER

Presidio Sentinel
Owner: Presidio Communications
Editorial: 325 W Washington St Suite 2-181, San Diego, California 92103-1946.
T: 1 619 296-8731 **E:** ppsentinel@aol.com
W: http://www.presidiosentinel.com
Freq: Monthly; **Circ:** 15500
Editorial Profile: Presidio Sentinel is published monthly for the residents of San Diego, CA. The newspaper covers local news and community events.; Full Page Mono: 16.08
Currency: US Dollars
NEWSPAPER

Presque Isle Newspapers
Editorial: 104 S 3rd St, Rogers City, Michigan 49779. **T:** 1 989 734-2105
E: editor@piadvance.com
W: http://www.piadvance.com **Circ:** 5850 Not Audited
Publisher: Richard Lamb; **Publisher:** Richard Lamb; **Publisher:** Richard Lamb; **Publisher:** Richard Lamb
NEWSPAPER

The Press
Owner: Sullivan (Beth)
Editorial: 1538 Main St, Speedway, Indiana 46224-6527. **T:** 1 317 241-4345
E: thepress@sbcglobal.net
Freq: Wed; **Circ:** 4700 Not Audited
Editor: A.J. Nelson; **Publisher:** Beth Sullivan
Editorial Profile: The Press is a local newspaper providing community news and events for residents of Speedway, IN. Coverage includes local events and sports, business and arts & entertainment news.; Full Page Mono: 12.00
Currency: US Dollars
NEWSPAPER

The Press - Lehigh Valley Press
Owner: Times News, Inc - A Pencor Company
Editorial: 1633 N 26th St, Allentown, Pennsylvania 18104-1805. **T:** 1 610 740-0944
W: http://www.tnonline.com **Circ:** 24009 Not Audited
Editor: Johanna Billings; **Editor:** Debra Galbraith; **Publisher:** Scott Masenheimer; **Editor:** Debra Palmieri; **Editor:** George Taylor; **Editor:** George Taylor; **Editor:** George Taylor
Editorial Profile: East Penn Publishing is a weekly community newspaper publisher serving the residents of Parkland, Whitehall, Coplay, Northampton, Salisbury and Catasauqua, PA as well as the surrounding areas. The advertising rate provided is based on a placement in all eight papers.
NEWSPAPER

Press & Sun-Bulletin
Owner: Gannett Co., Inc.
Editorial: 33 Lewis Rd, Binghamton, New York 13905-1040. **T:** 1 607 798-1234
E: bgm-newsroom@gannett.com
W: http://www.pressconnects.com
Freq: Daily; **Circ:** 29809 Not Audited
Publisher: Sherman Bodner
Editorial Profile: Press & Sun-Bulletin was created in 1985 by the merger of the Evening Press and the morning Sun-Bulletin. It serves readers in Broome, Tioga, Chenango, Delaware and Otsego counties in New York, and Susquehanna and Bradford counties in Pennsylvania. Coverage includes local and regional news, national news affecting the paper's readers, sports, business, lifestyle and arts & entertainment. The lead time varies depending on the section and type of news involved.; Full Page Mono: 107.52; Full Page Colour: 321.62
Currency: US Dollars
DAILY NEWSPAPER

The Press Democrat
Owner: Halifax Media Holdings LLC
Editorial: 427 Mendocino Ave, Santa Rosa, California 95401-6313. **T:** 1 707 546-2020
W: http://www.pressdemocrat.com
Freq: Daily; **Circ:** 53521 Not Audited
Publisher: Bruce Kyse
Editorial Profile: The Press Democrat is a local, daily newspaper based in Santa Rosa, CA, with additional bureaus in Petaluma and Ukiah, CA. The paper covers local, regional and national news of interest to residents of Northern California. Pitches are preferred via e-mail.; Full Page Mono: 113.00; Full Page Colour: 374.71
Currency: US Dollars
DAILY NEWSPAPER

The Press Democrat
Editorial: 205 Keller St, Ste 102, Petaluma, California 94952-2886. **T:** 1 707 762-7297
DAILY NEWSPAPER

The Press Democrat
Editorial: 445 N State St, Ukiah, California 95482-4490. **T:** 1 707 462-6473
DAILY NEWSPAPER

Press Journal
Owner: E.W. Scripps Co.
Editorial: 1801 Us Highway 1, Vero Beach, Florida 32960-5415. **T:** 1 772 562-2315
E: yesdesk@scripps.com
W: http://www.tcpalm.com
Freq: Daily; **Circ:** 29610 Not Audited
Editor: Mark Tomasik; **Editor:** Mark Tomasik; **Editor:** Mark Tomasik; **Editor:** Mark Tomasik;
Publisher: Thomas Weber
Editorial Profile: Press Journal in Vero Beach, FL is a daily newspaper published for residents of Indian River County, FL and surrounding communities. The newspaper covers local news, sports, events, business and lifestyle.; Full Page Mono: 39.77; Full Page Colour: 260.00
Currency: US Dollars
DAILY NEWSPAPER

The Press Newspapers
Owner: DCI
Editorial: 1550 Woodville Rd, Millbury, Ohio 43447-9619. **T:** 1 419 836-2221
E: news@presspublications.com
W: http://www.presspublications.com
Freq: Mon; **Circ:** 33977 Not Audited
News Editor: Kelly Kaczala; **News Editor:** Larry Limpf; Full Page Mono: 33.32
Currency: US Dollars
NEWSPAPER

Press Newspapers of Delaware County
Owner: 21st Century Media
Editorial: 1914 Parker Dr., Holmes, Pennsylvania 19043. **T:** 1 610 583-4432
E: press@delconewsnetwork.com
W: http://www.delconewsnetwork.com
Circ: 4757
NEWSPAPER

The Press of Atlantic City
Owner: Abarta, Inc.
Editorial: 11 Devins Ln, Pleasantville, New Jersey 08232-4107. **T:** 1 609 272-7000
E: newstips@pressofac.com
W: http://www.pressofatlanticcity.com
Freq: Daily; **Circ:** 68542 Not Audited
Publisher: Mark Blum
Editorial Profile: The Press of Atlantic City is a daily newspaper distributed in Atlantic City, NJ and the surrounding area. The newspaper covers local government, education, business and community news, as well as entertainment, sports and lifestyle. Business coverage focuses heavily on the area's legal gambling industry. The newspaper's staff covers local and state news only; national news is taken almost exclusively from wire services.; Full Page Mono: 81.00; Full Page Colour: 265.51
Currency: US Dollars
DAILY NEWSPAPER

The Press of Atlantic City
Editorial: 1 S Main St, Cape May Court House, New Jersey 08210-2249. **T:** 1 609 463-6710
Bureau Chief: W.F. Keough; **Bureau Chief:** W.F. Keough
DAILY NEWSPAPER

The Press of Atlantic City
Editorial: Statehouse 125 W State St, Trenton, New Jersey 8625. **T:** 1 609 292-4935
DAILY NEWSPAPER

The Press of Atlantic City
Editorial: 22 W Landis Ave, Ste F, Vineland, New Jersey 08360-8134. **T:** 1 856 794-5110
E: wkeough@pressofac.com
Editorial Profile: All mail should be sent to the main office.
DAILY NEWSPAPER

Press Publications
Editorial: 4779 Bloom Ave, White Bear Lake, Minnesota 55110-2764. **T:** 1 651 407-1200
E: news@presspubs.com
W: http://www.presspubs.com **Circ:** 55547
Publisher: Carter Johnson; Full Page Mono: 22.00
Currency: US Dollars
NEWSPAPER

Press Publishing Company
Owner: Press Publishing Co.
Editorial: 3245 Garrett Rd, Drexel Hill, Pennsylvania 19026-2338. **T:** 1 610 259-4141
E: mail@presspublishing.org
Freq: Weekly; **Circ:** 14500 Not Audited

NEWSPAPER

Press-Banner
Owner: Tracy Press
Editorial: 5215 Scotts Valley Dr, Ste F, Scotts Valley, California 95066. **T:** 1 831 438-2500
E: pbeditor@pressbanner.com
W: http://www.pressbanner.com
Freq: Fri; **Circ:** 20000 Not Audited
Editor: Peter Burke
Editorial Profile: Press Banner is a weekly local newspaper serving residents of Lorenzo Valley and Scotts Valley, CA. The newspaper covers local news, sports and community events.; Full Page Mono: 13.00
Currency: US Dollars
NEWSPAPER

Press-Enterprise
Owner: Press-Enterprise, Inc.
Editorial: 3185 Lackawanna Ave, Bloomsburg, Pennsylvania 17815. **T:** 1 570 784-2121
E: news@pressenterprise.net
W: http://www.pressenterpriseonline.com
Freq: Daily; **Circ:** 21260 Not Audited
Editor: Linda Dancho; **Editor:** James Sachetti
Editorial Profile: Press-Enterprise is a daily newspaper serving Bloomsburg, PA and the surrounding communities. The newspaper provides residents with the latest information on news, weather and sports.; Full Page Mono: 24.92; Full Page Colour: 34.12
Currency: US Dollars
DAILY NEWSPAPER

The Press-Enterprise
Owner: 2100 Trust LLC
Editorial: 3450 14th St, Riverside, California 92501-3862. **T:** 1 951 684-1200
E: news@pe.com **W:** http://www.pe.com
Freq: Daily; **Circ:** 137581 Not Audited
Publisher: Mike Burns
Editorial Profile: The Press-Enterprise, established in 1878, is a general interest newspaper serving the Riverside and San Bernardino counties in Southern California.; Full Page Mono: 199.00; Full Page Colour: 649.38
Currency: US Dollars
DAILY NEWSPAPER

The Press-Enterprise
Editorial: 474 W Esplanade Ave, San Jacinto, California 92583-5006. **T:** 1 951 763-3400
DAILY NEWSPAPER

The Press-Enterprise
Editorial: 925 L St Ste 312, Sacramento, California 95814-3703. **T:** 1 916 445-9973
Bureau Chief: John Bender
DAILY NEWSPAPER

The Press-Enterprise
Editorial: 27740 Jefferson Ave Ste 380, Temecula, California 92590-2608.
T: 1 951 375-3701
E: news@pressenterprise.net
W: http://www.pe.com/southwest
Editorial Profile: The Press-Enterprise/The Press Southwest covers the communities of Murrieta, Menifee, Temecula, Wildomar, Lake Elsinore, Canyon Lake and Perris.
DAILY NEWSPAPER

Press-Republican
Owner: Community Newspaper Holdings, Inc.
Editorial: 170 Margaret St, Plattsburgh, New York 12901-1899. **T:** 1 518 561-2300
E: news@pressrepublican.com
W: http://www.pressrepublican.com
Freq: Daily; **Circ:** 14804 Not Audited
Editor: Lois Clermont; **Editor:** Lois Clermont; **News Editor:** Suzanne Moore; **Publisher:** Robert Parks
Editorial Profile: Press-Republican's editorial mission is to be the leading print and online news source. The publication is written for Clinton, Franklin and Essex counties of Northeastern New York.; Full Page Mono: 30.76; Full Page Colour: 38.56
Currency: US Dollars
DAILY NEWSPAPER

Press-Telegram
Owner: MediaNews Group
Editorial: 300 Oceangate, Long Beach, California 90802-6801. **T:** 1 562 435-1161
E: ptnews@presstelegram.com
W: http://www.presstelegram.com
Freq: Daily; **Circ:** 77334 Not Audited
Editorial Profile: Press-Telegram is a daily newspaper distributed in the Long Beach, CA area, South of Downtown Los Angeles. This paper is a part of the Los Angeles Newspaper Group, a subsidiary of Media News Group. It covers local business, political and community news, as well as entertainment and recreation, lifestyle, travel and high school, collegiate and professional sports. Although the newspaper covers national business and political news, the newspaper's staff covers local news only; national news is taken almost exclusively from the Associated Press and other wire services. The advertising rates listed are for ads in the Los Angeles Newspaper Group, as paper specific ads cannot be purchased.; Full Page Mono: 651.00; Full Page Colour: 2121.48
Currency: US Dollars
DAILY NEWSPAPER

Press-Tribune Publishing
Owner: Brehm Communications, Inc.
Editorial: 188 Cirby Way, Roseville, California 95678. **T:** 1 916 786-8746
W: http://www.thepresstribune.com
Freq: Sat; **Circ:** 31000 Not Audited
Editor: Scott Anderson; **Publisher:** Todd Frantz
NEWSPAPER

Price County Publications
Owner: American Consolidated Media
Editorial: 115 N Lake Ave, Phillips, Wisconsin 54555-1220. **T:** 1 715 339-3036
E: news@thephillipsbee.com
W: http://www.pricecountydaily.com
Circ: 7300 Not Audited
Editor: Seth Carlson; **Editor:** Eric Knudson
Editorial Profile: Price County Publications is a weekly newspaper for the residents of Price County, WI. It covers local news and events.
NEWSPAPER

The Pride of the Prairie
Owner: Pride Publications
Editorial: 2018 2nd St, Bowdle, South Dakota 57428. **T:** 1 608 281-0421
E: bowdlepride@gmail.com
W: http://www.pridepublications.net/pride.html
Freq: Weekly
Editorial Profile: The Pride of the Prairie is a weekly newspaper providing Local News and Community News for the residents of Bowdle, SD.
NEWSPAPER

Prime Publishers Inc.
Owner: Prime Publishers Inc.
Editorial: 744 Main St S Ste 90, Woodbury, Connecticut 06798-3732. **T:** 1 203 262-6631
E: newsdesk@ctvoices.com
W: http://www.voicesnews.com **Circ:** 64205 Not Audited
Publisher: Rudy Mazurosky; **Editor:** Pattie Wesley
NEWSPAPER

Prime Time Military Newspapers
Owner: Hearst Corporation (The)
Editorial: 2203 S Hackberry, San Antonio, Texas 78210-4119. **T:** 1 210 534-8848
E: fshnewsleader@gmail.com **Circ:** 136789 Not Audited
Editor: Shannon Carabajal; **Editor:** Steve Elliott
Editorial Profile: Prime Time Military Newspapers provides local news coverage for military and civilian personnel at Ft. Sam Houston and Kelly, Lackland, Brooks Air Force Bases in the San Antonio, TX area.
NEWSPAPER

Prime Time Newspapers
Owner: Prime Time Newspapers Inc.
Editorial: 301 Avenue E, San Antonio, Texas 78205. **T:** 1 210 250-3000
W: http://www.mysanantonio.com
Circ: 201610 Not Audited
Editor: Lauri Eaton; **Editor:** Steve Elliott; **Editor:** Scott Mahon; **Editor:** Edmond Ortiz
NEWSPAPER

The Prince George's Post
Editorial: 15207 Marlboro Pike, Upper Marlboro, Maryland 20772-3111.
T: 1 301 627-0900 **W:** http://www.pgpost.com
Freq: Thu; **Circ:** 10000 Not Audited
Editorial Profile: The Prince George's Post is written for the African-American community of Prince George County, MD.; Full Page Mono: 21.00
Currency: US Dollars
NEWSPAPER

Prince George's Sentinel
Owner: Berlyn Inc.
Editorial: 9458 Lanham Severn Rd, Seabrook, Maryland 20706. **T:** 1 301 306-9500
E: editor-pg@thesentinel.com
W: http://www.thesentinel.com
Freq: Thu; **Circ:** 23000 Not Audited
Publisher: Lynn Kapiloff
Editorial Profile: Prince George's Sentinel is written for residents of Prince George County, MD. The publication provides news on community events, sports, business and local entertainment.; Full Page Mono: 34.92
Currency: US Dollars
NEWSPAPER

Princeton Daily Clarion
Owner: Brehm Communications, Inc.
Editorial: 100 N Gibson St, Princeton, Indiana 47670-1800. **T:** 1 812 385-2525
E: news@pdclarion.com
W: http://www.tristate-media.com/pdclarion
Freq: Daily; **Circ:** 6800 Not Audited
Publisher: Gary Blackburn; **Editor:** Andrea Howe; **Editor:** Andrea Howe; **Editor:** Andrea Howe; **Editor:** Andrea Howe
Editorial Profile: Princeton Daily Clarion is published daily for the residents of Gibson County, IN and surrounding areas. The newspaper covers local and state news, business, sports, lifestyles and entertainment.; Full Page Mono: 14.35; Full Page Colour: 160.00
Currency: US Dollars
DAILY NEWSPAPER

Printer's Inc.
Editorial: 111 N 3rd St, Beresford, South Dakota 57004. **T:** 1 605 763-2006
E: republic@bmtc.net **Circ:** 3592 Not Audited
NEWSPAPER

Printer's Inc.
Owner: Printer's Inc.
Editorial: 209 S Main Ave, Wagner, South Dakota 57380. **T:** 1 605 384-5616
E: announcer@hcinet.net
W: http://www.announceronline.com
Circ: 8670 Not Audited
NEWSPAPER

El Progreso Hispano
Editorial: 756 Tyvola Rd Ste 102, Charlotte, North Carolina 28217-3535.
T: 1 704 529-6624 **E:** ehispano@bellsouth.net
W: http://www.elprogresohispano.com
Freq: Bi-Weekly; **Circ:** 27000 Not Audited
Editorial Profile: El Progresso Hispano is a bi-weekly Spanish-language newspaper written for residents in Charlotte, NC.; Full Page Mono: 250.00
Currency: US Dollars
NEWSPAPER

The Progress
Owner: Progressive Publishing Co.
Editorial: 206 E Locust St, 2NDFL Fl, Clearfield, Pennsylvania 16830.
T: 1 814 765-5581
E: news@theprogressnews.com
W: http://www.theprogressnews.com
Freq: Daily; **Circ:** 11680 Not Audited
Editor: Jill Golden; **Publisher:** Margaret Krebs
Editorial Profile: The Progress is written for the residents of Clearfield, PA and the surrounding area. It covers local news and community events. Deadlines are at 7am ET the day before publication date.; Full Page Mono: 18.73; Full Page Colour: 22.21
Currency: US Dollars
DAILY NEWSPAPER

The Progress News
Editorial: 410 Main St, Emlenton, Pennsylvania 16373. **T:** 1 724 867-2435
W: http://www.progressnews.net
Freq: Tue; **Circ:** 14000 Not Audited
Editorial Profile: The Progress News provides local news and information for the residents of Venengo, Clarion, Butler and Armstrong County, PA.; Full Page Mono: 10.00
Currency: US Dollars
NEWSPAPER

The Progress-Index
Owner: Scranton Times
Editorial: 15 Franklin St, Petersburg, Virginia 23803-4503. **T:** 1 804 732-3456
E: newsroom@progress-index.com
W: http://www.progress-index.com
Freq: Daily; **Circ:** 10830 Not Audited
Publisher: Cindy Morgan
Editorial Profile: The Progress-Index's editorial mission is to provide local news to the residents of Petersburg, VA and surrounding towns. The newspaper covers various local news and events, lifestyle, business, and other topics of general interest.; Full Page Mono: 24.75; Full Page Colour: 380.00
Currency: US Dollars
DAILY NEWSPAPER

The Progressor-Times
Editorial: 1198 E Findlay St, Carey, Ohio 43316-9760. **T:** 1 419 396-7567
E: news@theprogressortimes.com
W: http://theprogressortimes.com **Circ:** 4000 Not Audited
NEWSPAPER

Providence En Espanol
Editorial: 280 Broadway, Providence, Rhode Island 02903-3007. **T:** 1 401 454-3004
W: http://www.providenceenespanol.com
Freq: Fri; **Circ:** 25000 Not Audited
Editorial Profile: Providence (RI) en Espanol was founded in 1999 as the only weekly newspaper serving Rhode Island's Latino population. It is published every Friday.; Full Page Mono: 35.00
Currency: US Dollars
NEWSPAPER

The Providence Journal
Owner: GateHouse Media Inc.
Editorial: 75 Fountain St, Providence, Rhode Island 02902-0050. **T:** 1 401 277-7000 2
E: news@providencejournal.com
W: http://www.providencejournal.com
Freq: Daily; **Circ:** 74396 Not Audited
Publisher: Howard Sutton
Editorial Profile: The Providence Journal is a general interest broadsheet newspaper written for the general public in the Providence, RI area. It is America's oldest major daily newspaper of general circulation in continuous publication. Its mission is "to publish an independent and profitable newspaper of unquestioned integrity devoted to the dissemination of local, state, national, and international news of interest and importance, and to do so in a manner noted for its excellence on a national scale while ever maintaining an outspoken voice for the welfare of Rhode Islanders."; Full Page Mono: 300.30; Full Page Colour: 2866.26
Currency: US Dollars
DAILY NEWSPAPER

Providence Phoenix
Owner: Phoenix Media/Communications Group (The)
Editorial: 150 Chestnut St, Providence, Rhode Island 02903-4637. **T:** 1 401 273-6397
W: http://providence.thephoenix.com
Freq: Thu; **Circ:** 68000 Not Audited
News Editor: Philip Eil; **Publisher:** Stephen Mindich
Editorial Profile: Providence Phoenix is written for the residents of Providence, RI. It covers local news and arts & entertainment.; Full Page Mono: 23.92; Full Page Colour: 3189.00
Currency: US Dollars
NEWSPAPER

Public Opinion
Owner: MediaNews Group
Editorial: 77 N 3rd St, Chambersburg, Pennsylvania 17201-1803. **T:** 1 717 264-6161
E: newsdesk@publicopinionnews.com
W: http://www.publicopiniononline.com
Freq: Daily; **Circ:** 16271 Not Audited
Editor: Becky Bennett; **Publisher:** Sara Glines
Editorial Profile: Public Opinion is published daily for the residents of Chambersburg, PA and surrounding areas. The newspaper covers local news, sports, entertainment and business news.; Full Page Mono: 38.00; Full Page Colour: 47.50
Currency: US Dollars
DAILY NEWSPAPER

The Pueblo Chieftain
Owner: Star Journal Publishing Corporation
Editorial: 825 W 6th St, Pueblo, Colorado 81003-2313. **T:** 1 719 544-3520
E: city@chieftain.com
W: http://www.chieftain.com
Freq: Mon thru Fri; **Circ:** 35192 Not Audited
News Editor: Stan Nelson
Editorial Profile: The Pueblo Chieftain is published daily for residents of Pueblo, CO and surrounding communities. The newspaper covers local news, weather, sports, and community events. Feature articles cover business developments, politics, education, arts & entertainment and lifestyle. Please use the main e-mail address for all press materials.; Full Page Mono: 71.50; Full Page Colour: 216.82
Currency: US Dollars
DAILY NEWSPAPER

El Pueblo Latino
Owner: MassPublishing Co. LLC
Editorial: 1860 Main St, Springfield, Massachusetts 01103-1000.
T: 1 413 788-1213
E: elpueblolatino@repub.com
Freq: Thu; **Circ:** 11500 Not Audited
Publisher: Anita Rivera; **Editor:** Lucilla Santana; **Editor:** Lucilla Santana

Editorial Profile: El Pueblo Latino is a free, weekly newspaper serving Latinos and Spanish-speaking residents and businesses in Western Massachusetts. It covers Latino community leaders, news, events, businesses and features. It is available for pick-up at local retailers, libraries, schools and restaurants. Deadlines are on Tuesdays at 5pm ET.; Full Page Mono: 13.00
Currency: US Dollars
NEWSPAPER

Pueblo Publishers, Inc.
Editorial: 7122 N 59th Ave, Glendale, Arizona 85301-2436. **T:** 1 623 842-6000 **Circ:** 20000 Not Audited
Editor: Carolyn Dryer; **Publisher:** William Toops
Editorial Profile: Pueblo Publishers, Inc. is a weekly community newspaper publisher serving the residents of Glendale and Peoria, AZ.
NEWSPAPER

Pueblo West View
Editorial: 825 W 6th St, Pueblo, Colorado 81003-2313. **T:** 1 719 547-9606
E: comments@pueblowestview.com
W: http://www.chieftain.com/pueblo_west_view/
Freq: Thu; **Circ:** 12000 Not Audited
Editor: Christine Casillas; **Publisher:** Robert Rawlings
Editorial Profile: Pueblo West View is a community newspaper targeted at the residents of Pueblo, CO.; Full Page Mono: 12.45
Currency: US Dollars
NEWSPAPER

Pulaski County Press
Owner: Pulaski County Press, Inc.
Editorial: 114 W Main St, Winamac, Indiana 46996. **T:** 1 574 946-6628
E: news@pulaskijournal.com
W: http://www.pulaskijournal.com **Circ:** 12200 Not Audited
Editorial Profile: Pulaski County Press produces The Pulaski County Journal and The Independent, serving the Pulaski County, IN area.
NEWSPAPER

Pulse-Journal Newspapers
Owner: Cox Media Group, Inc.
Editorial: 7320 Yankee Rd, Liberty Township, Ohio 45044-9168. **T:** 1 513 829-7900
E: butlercountynews@coxohio.com
W: http://www.pulsejournal.com **Circ:** 68733 Not Audited
Editor: Kevin Aldridge; **Editor:** Jennifer Collins
NEWSPAPER

El Punto Semanal
Owner: EC Hispanic Media
Editorial: 11205 Imperial Hwy, Norwalk, California 90650-2229
W: http://www.elpuntosemanal.com
Freq: Monthly
Publisher: Martha De La Torre
Editorial Profile: El Punto Semanal is a monthly newspaper that provides Local and Community News coverage to the Latino community of greater Los Angeles.
NEWSPAPER

Punxsutawney Spirit
Owner: Horizon Publications
Editorial: 510 Pine St, Punxsutawney, Pennsylvania 15767-1404. **T:** 1 814 938-8740
E: editor@punxsutawneyspirit.com
W: http://www.punxsutawneyspirit.com
Freq: Mon thru Fri; **Circ:** 5105 Not Audited
Publisher: Mary Jude Troupe; **Editor in Chief:** Zak Lantz
Editorial Profile: Punxsutawney Spirit is a local daily newspaper written for residents in Punxsutawney, PA and provides local news and information.; Full Page Mono: 12.00; Full Page Colour: 150.00
Currency: US Dollars
DAILY NEWSPAPER

Purcellville Gazette
Owner: Weber (Ben)
Editorial: 130 N 21St St, Purcellville, Virginia 20132-3077. **T:** 1 540 662-0852
E: editor@purcellvillegazette.com
W: http://www.purcellvillegazette.com
Freq: Fri; **Circ:** 20000
Editorial Profile: Purcellville Gazette is a local newspaper serving residents of Purcellville, VA and the surrounding areas.; Full Page Mono: 9.62
Currency: US Dollars
NEWSPAPER

Pure News USA
Editorial: 1701 S College St, Springfield, Illinois 62704. **T:** 1 217 528-5588
E: tellit@purenews.com
W: http://www.purenews.com
Freq: Monthly; **Circ:** 50000 Not Audited
Editorial Profile: Pure News USA in Sprinfield, IL is a monthly newspaper written for historical African-American churches, universities and businesses nationwide.; Full Page Mono: 25.00
Currency: US Dollars
NEWSPAPER

Puro Futbol
Editorial: 4248 Lake Park Ave, Gurnee, Illinois 60031-3035. **T:** 1 847 858-7493
E: info@purofutbolonline.com
W: http://www.purofutbolonline.com
Freq: Wed; **Circ:** 15000 Not Audited
Editor in Chief: Oscar Zepeda
Editorial Profile: Puro Futbol is Spanish-language weekly newspaper written for the amateur, youth and professional soccer teams in Northern Illinois. The paper includes player statistics, league information and team biographies.; Full Page Mono: 11.23; Full Page Colour: 40.00
Currency: US Dollars
NEWSPAPER

Putnam County Press
Owner: Hall (Don)
Editorial: 928 S Lake Blvd, Mahopac, New York 10541-3242. **T:** 1 845 628-8400
E: putnampress@aol.com
Freq: Weekly; **Circ:** 12400 Not Audited
Editorial Profile: Putnam County Press is a local weekly newspaper written for residents of Putnam County, NY. Deadlines are Friday at noon ET.
NEWSPAPER

Putnam Town Crier & Northeast Ledger
Editorial: 158 Main St, Ste 9, Putnam, Connecticut 6260. **T:** 1 860 933-3744
E: ptcrier@gmail.com
W: http://www.putnamtowncrier.com
Freq: Thu; **Circ:** 12000 Not Audited
Editorial Profile: Putnam Town Crier & Northeast Ledger is a community newspaper that targets the area of Putnam, CT.; Full Page Mono: 9.00
Currency: US Dollars
NEWSPAPER

QST Publications
Owner: Quattenbaum (Caroline) & Quattenbaum (Russell)
Editorial: 628 Glover Ave, Enterprise, Alabama 36330-2014. **T:** 1 334 393-2969
E: news@southeastsun.com
W: http://www.southeastsun.com **Circ:** 22000 Not Audited
Publisher: Russell Quattlebaum
NEWSPAPER

Quad-City Times
Owner: Lee Enterprises, Inc.
Editorial: 500 E 3rd St, Davenport, Iowa 52801. **T:** 1 563 383-2200
E: newsroom@qctimes.com
W: http://www.qctimes.com
Freq: Daily; **Circ:** 40247 Not Audited
Publisher: Julie Bechtel; **Editor:** Kevin Schmidt
Editorial Profile: Quad-City Times is a daily newspaper serving the residents of Davenport, IA and surrounding communities. Local and national news, sports, entertainment and lifestyle information are included.; Full Page Mono: 79.59; Full Page Colour: 275.88
Currency: US Dollars
DAILY NEWSPAPER

Quad-City Times
Editorial: 321 E Walnut St, Ste 160, Des Moines, Iowa 50309. **T:** 1 515 422-9061
Bureau Chief: Charlotte Eby
DAILY NEWSPAPER

Quantico Sentry
Owner: BH Media Group
Editorial: 3250 Catlin Ave, Quantico, Virginia 22134-5109. **T:** 1 703 784-2741
E: sentry.quantico@usmc.mil
W: http://www.quantico.usmc.mil
Freq: Thu; **Circ:** 11000 Not Audited
Publisher: John Rives; **Editor:** David White
Editorial Profile: Quantico Sentry is published for the Marine Corp and residents of Quantico, VA. It covers local news and information.; Full Page Mono: 16.10
Currency: US Dollars
NEWSPAPER

Que Pasa
Owner: Latino Communications
Editorial: 3025 Waughtown St Ste G, Winston Salem, North Carolina 27107-1679. **T:** 1 336 784-9004
W: http://www.quepasamedia.com
Freq: Thu; **Circ:** 67000 Not Audited
Publisher: Jose Isasi
Editorial Profile: Que Pasa is a community newspaper which provides Hispanic readers with local and national news. The publication has two editions; one is distributed throughout the Greensboro, NC area and the other is distributed throughout the Raleigh-Durham, NC area. All contents are the same except for editorials. Other features include sports, entertainment, business, education and classifieds. The deadline for press releases is the Friday prior to issue date.; Full Page Mono: 28.00
Currency: US Dollars
NEWSPAPER

Que Pasa Mi Gente
Owner: Latino Communications
Editorial: 7508 E Independence Blvd Ste 109, Charlotte, North Carolina 28227-9409. **T:** 1 704 319-5044
E: editor@quepasamedia.com
W: http://www.quepasa-migente.com
Freq: Tue
Publisher: Julio Suarez; **News Editor:** Eloy Tupayachi
Editorial Profile: Previously two separate publications, Mi Gente and Que Pasa Charlotte. Offers local news and information to Spanish-speaking residents of Mecklenburg, Gaston, Union, Cabarrus, Iredell, Lincoln, Rowan, Catawba and Burke Counties in North Carolina and York and Lancaster Counties in South Carolina.; Full Page Mono: 34.89; Full Page Colour: 34.89
Currency: US Dollars
NEWSPAPER

Que Pasa Raleigh
Owner: Winston-Salem Media
Editorial: 4600 New Bern Ave Ste 101, Raleigh, North Carolina 27610-1881. **T:** 1 919 645-1680
W: http://www.quepasamedia.com
Freq: Thu; **Circ:** 25000 Not Audited
Publisher: Jose Isasi; **News Editor:** Eloy Tupayachi
Editorial Profile: Que Pasa is a weekly Spanish language newspaper written for the residents of Raleigh, NC.; Full Page Mono: 12.60
Currency: US Dollars
NEWSPAPER

Queens Chronicle
Owner: Mark I Publications, Inc.
Editorial: 6233 Woodhaven Blvd, Rego Park, New York 11374-3731. **T:** 1 718 205-8000
E: ads@qchron.com
W: http://www.queenschronicle.com
Circ: 160000 Not Audited
Editor in Chief: Peter Mastrosimone; **Publisher:** Mark Weidler
Editorial Profile: Queens Chronicles publishes eight different editions of the Queens Chronicle newspapers with a combined circulation of 160,000. The papers cover local and national news, weather, sports, and community events. Feature articles cover business developments, local politics, education, arts and entertainment, lifestyle, and other topics of interest to local residents. Do not send any materials unless they have a Queens connection.
NEWSPAPER

Queens Gazette Publishing
Owner: Service Publications Inc.
Editorial: 4216 34th Ave, Astoria, New York 11101-1110. **T:** 1 718 361-6161
E: qgazette@aol.com
W: http://www.qgazette.com **Circ:** 90000 Not Audited
Editorial Profile: Queens Gazette Publishing in Astoria, NY publishes Western Queens Gazette, Queens Gazette and Eastern Queens Gazette.
NEWSPAPER

Queens Ledger Newspaper Group
Owner: Queens Ledger Greenpoint Star, Inc.
Editorial: 6960 Grand Ave, Maspeth, New York 11378. **T:** 1 718 639-7000
E: news@queensledger.com
W: http://www.queensledger.com **Circ:** 99453
Editorial Profile: Queens Ledger Newspaper Group is a weekly community newspaper publisher serving the resident of Queens and Brooklyn, NY.
NEWSPAPER

Queens Times
Owner: C.T. Publishing, Corp.
Editorial: 4808 111th St, Corona, New York 11368. **T:** 1 718 592-2196
E: editor@queenstimes.com
W: http://www.queenstimes.com
Freq: Thu; **Circ:** 90000 Not Audited
Editorial Profile: Queens Times's editorial mission is to be an informative and positive news source. The publication is written for residents of Queens, NY. Founded in 1995, the Queens Times is a 16-page tabloid publication.; Full Page Mono: 20.90
Currency: US Dollars
NEWSPAPER

Queens Tribune Newspapers
Owner: Tribco, LLC
Editorial: 15050 14th Rd, Whitestone, New York 11357-2609. **T:** 1 718 357-7400
E: news@queenstribune.com
W: http://www.queenstribune.com
Circ: 171000 Not Audited
Editor in Chief: Steven Ferrari; **Publisher:** Michael Schenkler
NEWSPAPER

Quincy Herald-Whig
Owner: Quincy Newspapers, Inc.
Editorial: 130 S 5th St, Quincy, Illinois 62301-3916. **T:** 1 217 223-5100 **E:** whig@whig.com
W: http://www.whig.com
Freq: Daily; **Circ:** 16278 Not Audited
Editor: Gerri Berendzen; **Editor:** Holly Wagner
Editorial Profile: Quincy Herald-Whig is published daily for the residents of Quincy, IL and surrounding areas. The newspaper covers local news, sports, community events, health and lifestyles.; Full Page Mono: 30.46; Full Page Colour: 107.68
Currency: US Dollars
DAILY NEWSPAPER

The Quiviran
Editorial: 348 Terrace Trl W, Lake Quivira, Kansas 66217-8697
E: leanna@thequiviran.com
W: http://www.quiviran.com/
Freq: Monthly
Editorial Profile: The Quiviran is a community newspaper dedicated to news stories for Lake Quivira, KS.
NEWSPAPER

Quotidiano Nazionale - New York Bureau
Editorial: United Nations, Room 306, New York, New York 10017. **T:** 1 212 963-7159
Editorial Profile: New York bureau of QN - Quotidiano Nazionale covering United States regional and national news and current affairs including economics, politics, sports, cars, lifestyle, entertainment, culture and technology.
DAILY NEWSPAPER

R.F.D. News
Owner: Gazette Publishing Co.
Editorial: 107 N Sandusky St, Bellevue, Ohio 44811-1425. **T:** 1 419 483-7410
E: rfdnews@bizwoh.rr.com
Freq: Semi-Monthly; **Circ:** 68572 Not Audited; Full Page Mono: 2652.48
Currency: US Dollars
NEWSPAPER

Rafu Shimpo
Editorial: 138 Astronaut E S Onizuka St, Los Angeles, California 90012-3810.
T: 1 213 629-2231 **E:** info@rafu.com
W: http://www.rafu.com
Freq: Daily; **Circ:** 21000 Not Audited
Publisher: Michael Komai
Editorial Profile: Rafu Shimpo is a daily newspaper published for the Japanese American community in Los Angeles. The editorial content covers general interest articles, including local news, sports, personalities and events.; Full Page Mono: 9.06
Currency: US Dollars
DAILY NEWSPAPER

Raleigh Downtowner
Editorial: 516 E Jones St, Raleigh, North Carolina 27601-1138
W: http://www.raleighdowntowner.com
Freq: Monthly; **Circ:** 72000 Not Audited
Publisher: Crash Gregg
Editorial Profile: Raleigh Downtowner is a monthly, community newspaper featuring community and local government news and feature stories. It is run in conjunction with the Raleigh Chronicle. The outlet has requested that no contact details be listed.; Full Page Mono: 73.22; Full Page Colour: 76.43

Currency: US Dollars
NEWSPAPER

The Raleigh Telegram
Owner: The Raleigh Telegram
Editorial: 64 TW Alexander Drive, Durham, North Carolina 27709. **T:** 1 919 760-3110
E: raleightelegram@yahoo.com
W: http://www.raleightelegram.com
Freq: Weekly
Editorial Profile: The Raleigh Telegram is a weekly newspaper providing Local and Community News coverage to the residents of the Raleigh-Durham and Chapel Hill, NC area.
NEWSPAPER

Ramona Sentinel
Owner: Mainstreet Media Group
Editorial: 425 10Th St Ste A, Ramona, California 92065-3936. **T:** 1 760 789-1350
E: news@ramonasentinel.com
W: http://www.ramonasentinel.com
Freq: Thu; **Circ:** 14000 Not Audited
Publisher: Jeff Mitchell; **Editor:** Maureen Robertson
Editorial Profile: Ramona Sentinel is a local, weekly newspaper serving residents of Ramona, CA. It focuses on local sports and community news.; Full Page Mono: 16.66
Currency: US Dollars
NEWSPAPER

Randall Publishing Corporation
Editorial: 8803 Sudley Rd Ste 201, Manassas, Virginia 20110-4718. **T:** 1 703 369-5253
E: editor@observernow.com **Circ:** 70000 Not Audited
Editorial Profile: Randall Publishing Corp. in Manassas, VA is a community newspaper publisher.
NEWSPAPER

Rankin Ledger
Owner: Gannett Co., Inc.
Editorial: 201 S Congress St, Jackson, Mississippi 39201-4202. **T:** 1 601 360-4600
E: news@rankinledger.com
W: http://www.rankinledger.com
Freq: Sat; **Circ:** 48000 Not Audited
Editorial Profile: Rankin Ledger in Jackson, MS is a weekly newspaper that covers local news and events.; Full Page Mono: 17.50
Currency: US Dollars
NEWSPAPER

Rapid City Journal
Owner: Lee Enterprises, Inc.
Editorial: 507 Main St, Rapid City, South Dakota 57701-2733. **T:** 1 605 394-8300
E: news@rapidcityjournal.com
W: http://www.rapidcityjournal.com
Freq: Daily; **Circ:** 23202 Not Audited
Publisher: Shannon Brinker; **News Editor:** Doug Demmons
Editorial Profile: Rapid City Journal is published daily for residents of Rapid City, SD and surrounding areas. The publication is a general interest newspaper, covering local news, weather, sports, business, education, arts and entertainment, and other information of interest to the local community. Deadlines are daily at 9am MT. Emails sent to the main email address should not include attachments.; Full Page Mono: 87.20; Full Page Colour: 625.00
Currency: US Dollars
DAILY NEWSPAPER

Rare Reminder & The Chronicle
Owner: Rare Reminder, Inc. (The)
Editorial: 222 Dividend Rd, Rocky Hill, Connecticut 06067-3740. **T:** 1 860 563-9386
Circ: 86526
Editor: Kate Kelleher; **Publisher:** Jim Klatt
Editorial Profile: Rare Reminder & The Chronicle in Rocky Hill, CT is a community newspaper publisher.
NEWSPAPER

Ravalli Republic
Owner: Lee Enterprises, Inc.
Editorial: 232 W Main St, Hamilton, Montana 59840-2552. **T:** 1 406 363-3300
E: editor@ravallirepublic.com
W: http://www.ravallinews.com
Freq: Daily; **Circ:** 6345 Not Audited
Editorial Profile: The Ravalli Republic is a daily newspaper serving the residents of Hamilton, MT. Articles are about local news, weather, sports and events. Deadlines are 24 hours prior to issue date.; Full Page Mono: 13.78; Full Page Colour: 200.00
Currency: US Dollars
DAILY NEWSPAPER

Rawlins Daily Times
Owner: Rawlins Newspapers Inc.

Editorial: 522 W Buffalo St, Rawlins, Wyoming 82301-5623. **T:** 1 307 324-3411
W: http://www.rawlinstimes.com
Freq: Daily; **Circ:** 3600 Not Audited
Publisher: Holly Dabb; **Editor:** Kathy Johnson
Editorial Profile: Rawlins Daily Times covers local news, sports and community events for residents of Rawlins and Carbon County, WY. It has been serving south central Wyoming since 1889.; Full Page Mono: 8.67; Full Page Colour: 154.35
Currency: US Dollars
DAILY NEWSPAPER

La Raza
Owner: ImpreMedia LLC
Editorial: 225 W Ohio St Fl 3, Chicago, Illinois 60654-7898. **T:** 1 312 870-7000
E: agenda@laraza.com
W: http://www.laraza.com
Freq: Sun; **Circ:** 153345 Not Audited
Editorial Profile: La Raza's editorial mission is to be the organ of accountability for the Hispanic community in Chicago. Coverage in the weekly newspaper includes local, city and national news, as well as business and finance, arts & entertainment and health news.; Full Page Mono: 97.50; Full Page Colour: 108.86
Currency: US Dollars
NEWSPAPER

La Raza de Noroeste
Owner: Washington Post Co.
Editorial: 1213 California St, Everett, Washington 98201-3445. **T:** 1 425 673-6633
E: editor@nuestronoroeste.com
W: http://www.larazanw.com
Freq: Fri; **Circ:** 24000 Not Audited
Editorial Profile: La Raza de Noroeste is a local, weekly Spanish language newspaper serving Hispanic residents of Everett and Puget Sound, WA. The paper includes strong Mexican content and Mexican news by region. It also focuses on arts & entertainment and Hispanic-related news in the community, such as education and schools, police issues and immigration. The paper also features profiles of successful Hispanics, Mexican sports like soccer and content with newcomer relevance, such as how to behave in public places and how to access the government and other public services.; Full Page Mono: 25.95
Currency: US Dollars
NEWSPAPER

RC News
Owner: RCN Corporation
Editorial: 207 E Government St, Brandon, Mississippi 39042-3151. **T:** 1 601 825-8333
E: rankincn@aol.com **Circ:** 23400 Not Audited
NEWSPAPER

Reader & Perico
Editorial: 2314 Main St, Omaha, Nebraska 68107. **T:** 1 402 341-7323
E: news@thereader.com
W: http://www.thereader.com
Editorial Profile: Reader & Perico in Omaha, NE publishes the following community newspapers: El Perico and The Reader.
NEWSPAPER

The Reading Chronicle
Owner: Woburn Daily Times, Inc.
Editorial: 531 Main St, Reading, Massachusetts 01867-3134.
T: 1 781 944-2200
E: readingchronicle@comcast.net
W: http://homenewshere.com
Freq: Daily
Editor: Paul Feely; **Publisher:** Peter Haggerty
Editorial Profile: The Reading Chronicle covers community news for the residents of Reading, MA and Wakefield, MA. Coverage includes local news, editorials, lifestyles, sports, state and national news.
DAILY NEWSPAPER

Reading Eagle
Owner: Reading Eagle Company
Editorial: 345 Penn St, Reading, Pennsylvania 19601-4029. **T:** 1 610 371-5000
E: news@readingeagle.com
W: http://www.readingeagle.com
Freq: Daily; **Circ:** 45818 Not Audited
Editor: Harry Deitz; **Editor:** Harry Deitz; **Publisher:** William Flippin; **News Editor:** Ron Southwick
Editorial Profile: Reading Eagle is written for residents of the Reading and Berks County, PA. It covers local, regional, state, national and international news, as well as sports, business, entertainment and special news features.; Full Page Mono: 27.39; Full Page Colour: 75.29
Currency: US Dollars

DAILY NEWSPAPER

Real Change
Editorial: 96 S Main St., Seattle, Washington 98121-2207. **T:** 1 206 441-3247
E: webmaster@realchangenews.org
W: http://www.realchangenews.org
Freq: Wed; **Circ:** 12000 Not Audited
Publisher: Timothy Harris; **Editor:** Amy Roe
Editorial Profile: Real Change is published twice a month for and by the homeless community of Seattle and surrounding areas. The newspaper publishes the views of poor and homeless people and their advocates. Its editorial mission is to organize, educate, and build alliances to find community-based solutions to homelessness and poverty in Seattle and nationwide. Each issue contains 32 pages of quality journalism, poetry, opinion, art and photography, much of it produced by the poor and homeless themselves. It also shares book and film reviews, interviews and other feature stories with members of the International Network of Streetpapers.; Full Page Mono: 90.00
Currency: US Dollars
NEWSPAPER

The Record
Owner: Journal Register Company
Editorial: 501 Broadway, Troy, New York 12180-3324. **T:** 1 518 270-1200
E: newsroom@troyrecord.com
W: http://www.troyrecord.com
Freq: Daily; **Circ:** 8406 Not Audited
Editor: James Franco; **Editor:** Lisa Robert Lewis; **Editor:** Lisa Robert Lewis; **Editor:** Lisa Robert Lewis
Editorial Profile: The Record is a local daily newspaper for residents of Troy, NY and the surrounding area. It provides coverage of local news, sports, schools and community information, arts & entertainment, business and travel.; Full Page Mono: 37.74; Full Page Colour: 320.00
Currency: US Dollars
DAILY NEWSPAPER

The Record
Owner: GateHouse Media Inc.
Editorial: 530 E Market St, Stockton, California 95202. **T:** 1 209 943-6397
E: newsroom@recordnet.com
W: http://www.recordnet.com
Freq: Daily; **Circ:** 27266 Not Audited
Publisher: Roger Coover
Editorial Profile: The Record serves the Stockton, CA metro area. The publication offers local, state, national and world news as well as sports, business, entertainment and classifieds. It was established in 1896.; Full Page Mono: 108.33; Full Page Colour: 328.83
Currency: US Dollars
DAILY NEWSPAPER

Record
Editorial: 1200 S Shelby St, Louisville, Kentucky 40203. **T:** 1 502 636-0296
E: record@archlou.org
W: http://www.archlou.org/therecord
Freq: Thu; **Circ:** 64000 Not Audited
News Editor: Glenn Rutherford
Editorial Profile: The Record is a weekly publication run by the Archdiose of Louisville.; Full Page Mono: 20.00
Currency: US Dollars
NEWSPAPER

Record & Banner
Editorial: 3203 Highway 367 N, Bald Knob, Arkansas 72010. **T:** 1 501 724-0398
E: wcrecord@centurytel.net **Circ:** 5500 Not Audited
NEWSPAPER

The Record & Herald News
Owner: North Jersey Media Group Inc.
Editorial: 1 Garret Mountain Plz, Woodland Park, New Jersey 07424-3320.
T: 1 973 569-7000
E: newsroom@northjersey.com
W: http://www.northjersey.com
Freq: Daily; **Circ:** 160571
Editor in Chief: Martin Gottlieb; **News Editor:** Scott Muller
Editorial Profile: The Record & Herald News are two daily newspapers, available only in a combined edition, and are not available separately.; Full Page Mono: 263.30; Full Page Colour: 275.80
Currency: US Dollars
DAILY NEWSPAPER

The Record Newspapers
Editorial: 333 W Round Bunch Rd, Bridge City, Texas 77611. **T:** 1 409 735-5305
E: therecordnews@sbcglobal.net **Circ:** 34000

Not Audited
Editor: Nicole Gibbs; **Publisher:** Karen Gros
Editorial Profile: The Record Newspapers of Bridge City, TX, publishes weeklies with news and events of local interest to residents of Orange County, TX.
NEWSPAPER

Record Newspapers, Inc.
Editorial: 325 S McCoy St, Granville, Illinois 61326. **T:** 1 815 339-2321 **Circ:** 3850
Editorial Profile: Record Newspapers, Inc. is a community newspaper publisher serving the residents of Peoria and Bloomington, IL.
NEWSPAPER

Record Publishing Company
Editorial: 1050 W Main St, Kent, Ohio 44240-2006. **T:** 1 330 541-9400
W: http://www.recordpub.com **Circ:** 107805 Not Audited
Publisher: David Dix; **Editor:** Jamie Gerard; **Editor:** Phil Keren; **Editor:** Eric Marotta; **Editor:** Andrew Schunk
Editorial Profile: Record Publishing Company in Kent, OH is a community newspaper publisher.
NEWSPAPER

Record Searchlight
Owner: E.W. Scripps Co.
Editorial: 1101 Twin View Blvd, Redding, California 96003-1531. **T:** 1 530 243-2424
E: letters@redding.com
W: http://www.redding.com
Freq: Daily; **Circ:** 18250 Not Audited
Editor: Damon Arthur; **Editor:** Silas Lyons
Editorial Profile: Record Searchlight is written for residents of Redding, CA and surrounding areas. It offers a balance of news emphasizing local issues and pays attention to public spending, growth, development, government and literacy. In addition to helping victims of earthquakes and firestorms, it sponsors events and activities in the community. The outlet offers RSS (Really Simple Syndication).; Full Page Mono: 53.50; Full Page Colour: 495.00
Currency: US Dollars
DAILY NEWSPAPER

Record-Courier
Owner: Dix Communications
Editorial: 126 N Chestnut St, Ravenna, Ohio 44266-2254. **T:** 1 330 541-9400
E: editor@recordpub.com
W: http://www.recordpub.com
Freq: Daily; **Circ:** 17406 Not Audited
Editor: Roger DiPaolo; **Publisher:** David Dix; **News Editor:** Chad Murphy; **Editor:** Diane Smith
Editorial Profile: Record-Courier provides news and information to the Canton County and Portage County, OH area. Deadlines are 8pm ET the day before the issue date.; Full Page Mono: 18.12; Full Page Colour: 27.62
Currency: US Dollars
DAILY NEWSPAPER

The Recorder
Owner: Newspapers of New England
Editorial: 14 Hope St, Greenfield, Massachusetts 1301. **T:** 1 413 772-0261
E: newsinfo@recorder.com
W: http://www.recorder.com
Freq: Daily; **Circ:** 11995 Not Audited
Editor: Tim Blagg
Editorial Profile: The Recorder is a daily newspaper published primarily for the residents of Greenfield, MA, as well as some parts of Franklin County, MA. Coverage includes local news, community events, arts & entertainment and sports. Deadlines are daily at 9pm ET.; Full Page Mono: 15.98; Full Page Colour: 280.00
Currency: US Dollars
DAILY NEWSPAPER

The Recorder
Owner: William J. Kline & Sons, Inc.
Editorial: 1 Venner Rd, Amsterdam, New York 12010. **T:** 1 518 843-1100
E: news@recordernews.com
W: http://www.recordernews.com
Freq: Daily; **Circ:** 8116 Not Audited
Publisher: Kevin McClary
Editorial Profile: The Recorder provides national and local news for residents of Montgomery and Fulton counties, NY. It covers national and local news, sports, community happenings, opinions and arts.; Full Page Mono: 14.95; Full Page Colour: 250.00
Currency: US Dollars
DAILY NEWSPAPER

Recorder Community Newspapers - Caldwell
Owner: Recorder Community Newspapers
Editorial: 10 Brookside Ave, Caldwell, New Jersey 07006-5600. **T:** 1 973 226-8900
W: http://newjerseyhills.com **Circ:** 19000 Not Audited
Editor: Paula Brown; **Editor:** Lorie Russo Greenspan
NEWSPAPER

Recorder Community Newspapers - Madison
Owner: New Jersey Hills Media Group
Editorial: 155 Main St, Madison, New Jersey 07940-2156. **T:** 1 973 377-2000
W: http://www.newjerseyhills.com **Circ:** 16410 Not Audited
Editor: Garry Herzog; **Editor:** Garry Herzog; **Editor:** Jim Lent; **Editor:** Jim Lent; **Editor:** Jim Lent; **Editor:** Jim Lent; **Editor:** P.C. Robinson
NEWSPAPER

Record-Herald
Owner: Ohio Community Media
Editorial: 320 Washington Sq, Washington Court House, Ohio 43160-1751.
T: 1 740 335-3611 **E:** info@recordherald.com
W: http://www.recordherald.com
Freq: Daily; **Circ:** 5533 Not Audited
Editorial Profile: Record-Herald is daily newspaper published for residents of Fayette County, OH and surrounding areas. The publication is a general interest newspaper, covering local news, weather, sports, business, education, arts & entertainment and other information of interest to the local community. It also publishes the South Central Ohio Shoppers Guide on Sundays.; Full Page Mono: 12.25; Full Page Colour: 90.00
Currency: US Dollars
DAILY NEWSPAPER

Record-Journal
Owner: Record-Journal Publishing Company
Editorial: 11 Crown St, Meriden, Connecticut 06450-5713. **T:** 1 203 235-1661
E: newsroom@record-journal.com
W: http://www.myrecordjournal.com
Freq: Daily; **Circ:** 19541 Not Audited
Editor: Michael Misarski; **Publisher:** Eliot White
Editorial Profile: Record-Journal is a weekly newspaper serving the residents of Meriden and Wallingford, CT. The publication covers news, local events and sports.; Full Page Mono: 50.50; Full Page Colour: 220.00
Currency: US Dollars
DAILY NEWSPAPER

Red Latina
Editorial: 4422 Woodson Rd, Saint Louis, Missouri 63134-3702. **T:** 1 314 772-3515
E: redlatinastl@hotmail.com
W: http://www.redlatinastl.com
Freq: Bi-Weekly; **Circ:** 15000 Not Audited
Editorial Profile: Red Latina is written for the Hispanic community of Saint Louis, MO.; Full Page Mono: 11.43
Currency: US Dollars
NEWSPAPER

Red Oak Express
Owner: Landmark Community Newspapers, Inc.
Editorial: 2012 Commerce Dr, Red Oak, Iowa 51566. **T:** 1 712 623-2566
E: news@redoakexpress.com
W: http://www.redoakexpress.com
Freq: Tue; **Circ:** 11480 Not Audited
Editorial Profile: Red Oak Express is published weekly for residents of Red Oak, IA and surrounding areas. The publication covers local news, weather, sports, education, business, arts & entertainment and other information of interest to the local community. Deadlines for the publication are Thursdays at 5pm CT.; Full Page Mono: 11.73
Currency: US Dollars
NEWSPAPER

Red Wing Newspapers
Owner: Red Wing Publishing
Editorial: 250 Prairie Center Dr, Ste 211, Eden Prairie, Minnesota 55344-7911.
T: 1 952 934-5045
W: http://www.edenprairienews.com
Circ: 27150 Not Audited
Editor: Karla Wennerstrom; **Editor:** Karla Wennerstrom; **Editor:** Karla Wennerstrom
NEWSPAPER

RedEye
Owner: Tribune Company
Editorial: 435 N Michigan Ave, Chicago, Illinois 60611-4066. **T:** 1 312 222-4970
E: redeye@tribune.com
W: http://www.redeyechicago.com
Freq: Mon thru Fri; **Circ:** 200000 Not Audited
Publisher: Tony Hunter; **News Editor:** Jim Walsh
Editorial Profile: RedEye is a free, commuter daily newspaper that is owned by the Chicago Tribune. It offers a unique approach to news and entertainment and targets urban commuters in metro Chicago. The paper, designed for a 20-minute read, features everything from top news stories and sports to celebrity gossip. The publication is also coupled with Metromix.com, the Tribune's online entertainment guide.; Full Page Mono: 113.76; Full Page Colour: 113.76
Currency: US Dollars
DAILY NEWSPAPER

Redlands Daily Facts
Owner: MediaNews Group
Editorial: 700 Brookside Ave, Redlands, California 92373-5102. **T:** 1 909 793-3221
E: editor@inlandnewspapers.com
W: http://www.redlandsdailyfacts.com
Freq: Mon thru Fri; **Circ:** 7012 Not Audited
Editorial Profile: Redlands Daily Facts is a local daily newspaper written for residents of Redlands, CA and surrounding areas. This paper is a part of the Los Angeles Newspaper Group, a subsidiary of Media News Group. The publication is a general interest newspaper that covers local news, weather, sports, education, business, arts and entertainment, and other information of interest to the local community.; Full Page Mono: 15.00; Full Page Colour: 24.08
Currency: US Dollars
DAILY NEWSPAPER

Redmond Reporter
Owner: Black Press
Editorial: 8105 166Th Ave Ne Ste 102, Redmond, Washington 98052-3999.
T: 1 425 867-0353
E: editor@redmond-reporter.com
W: http://www.redmond-reporter.com/
Freq: Fri; **Circ:** 25000
Editor: Andy Nystrom
Editorial Profile: Redmond Reporter is a local, weekly newspaper serving residents of Redmond, WA. The paper includes local news, sports, business, arts & entertainment and community events.; Full Page Mono: 27.50
Currency: US Dollars
NEWSPAPER

Reed Print, Inc.
Editorial: 406 Central Ave, Shafter, California 93263-2156. **T:** 1 661 746-4942 **Circ:** 11175 Not Audited
Publisher: Don Reed; **Publisher:** Frank Reed; **Editor:** Jamie Stewart
Editorial Profile: Reed Print, Inc. is a local newspaper in Shafter, CA.
NEWSPAPER

The Reflector
Owner: Case Publishing Inc.
Editorial: 20 NW 20th Ave, Battle Ground, Washington 98604. **T:** 1 360 687-5151
E: news@thereflector.com
W: http://www.thereflector.com
Freq: Wed; **Circ:** 28000 Not Audited
Editor: Ken Vance; **Publisher:** Steve Walker
Editorial Profile: The Reflector in Battle Ground, WA is published weekly for the residents of Clark County, WA and surrounding areas. The newspaper provides information on local news and community events. All mail must be sent to the PO Box.; Full Page Mono: 15.10
Currency: US Dollars
NEWSPAPER

Reflejos
Owner: Paddock Publications
Editorial: 155 E Algonquin Rd, Arlington Heights, Illinois 60005-4617.
T: 1 847 427-4300 **E:** copy@reflejos.com
W: http://www.reflejos.com
Freq: Sun; **Circ:** 100000 Not Audited
Editor: Marco Ortiz; **Publisher:** Doug Ray
Editorial Profile: Reflejos is a free, weekly, bilingual newspaper serving the suburban Chicago Latino community. Its focus is motivational, educational and inspirational news in the Cook, DuPage, Kane, Lake and McHenry counties. Deadlines are at 5pm CT.; Full Page Mono: 34.88
Currency: US Dollars
NEWSPAPER

The Register Citizen
Owner: Journal Register Company
Editorial: 190 Water St, Torrington, Connecticut 06790-5325. **T:** 1 860 489-3121
E: editor@registercitizen.com
W: http://www.registercitizen.com
Freq: Daily; **Circ:** 5211 Not Audited
Editor: John Berry
Editorial Profile: The Register Citizen is a daily newspaper that provides readers with local, regional and national news coverage. The newspaper focuses on local community news. Daily features include sports, business, entertainment, lifestyle and classifieds.; Full Page Mono: 19.35
Currency: US Dollars
DAILY NEWSPAPER

Register Publications, Inc.
Owner: Delphos Herald Inc.
Editorial: 126 W High St, Lawrenceburg, Indiana 47025. **T:** 1 812 537-0063
E: newsroom@registerpublications.com
Freq: Weekly; **Circ:** 14538 Not Audited
Publisher: Tom Brooker; **Editor:** Jim Buchberger
NEWSPAPER

Register Star
Owner: Johnson Newspaper Corp.
Editorial: 364 Warren St, Hudson, New York 12534-2419. **T:** 1 518 828-1616
E: editorial@registerstar.com
W: http://www.registerstar.com
Freq: Daily; **Circ:** 3381 Not Audited
Editorial Profile: Register Star is a local daily newspaper intended to serve the needs of the general public in Hudson, NY and the surrounding counties.; Full Page Mono: 14.51; Full Page Colour: 300.00
Currency: US Dollars
DAILY NEWSPAPER

The Register-Guard
Owner: Guard Publishing Company
Editorial: 3500 Chad Dr, Eugene, Oregon 97408-7426. **T:** 1 541 485-1234
E: rgnews@registerguard.com
W: http://www.registerguard.com
Freq: Daily; **Circ:** 53891 Not Audited
News Editor: Chris Frisella
Editorial Profile: The Register-Guard is published daily for residents of Eugene, OR and surrounding communities. It covers local news, weather, sports and community events. Feature articles cover business, lifestyle, arts & entertainment, education and other topics of interest to area residents.; Full Page Mono: 168.95; Full Page Colour: 249.15
Currency: US Dollars
DAILY NEWSPAPER

The Register-Guard
Editorial: 444 Kingwood St, Florence, Oregon 97439-9361. **T:** 1 541 902-9030
DAILY NEWSPAPER

The Register-Guard
Editorial: State Capitol Press Room, Salem, Oregon 97301-0001. **T:** 1 503 363-3451
DAILY NEWSPAPER

The Register-Herald
Owner: Community Newspaper Holdings, Inc.
Editorial: 801 N Kanawha St, Beckley, West Virginia 25801. **T:** 1 304 255-4400
E: rhnews@register-herald.com
W: http://www.register-herald.com
Freq: Daily; **Circ:** 22355 Not Audited
Editor: Mary Stillwell; **Publisher:** Frank Wood
Editorial Profile: The Register-Herald is for the residents of Southern West Virginia. It covers national news, local news, sports, events and politics.; Full Page Mono: 39.68
Currency: US Dollars
DAILY NEWSPAPER

The Register-Mail
Owner: GateHouse Media Inc.
Editorial: 140 S Prairie St, Galesburg, Illinois 61401-4636. **T:** 1 309 343-7181
E: news@register-mail.com
W: http://www.galesburg.com
Freq: Daily; **Circ:** 9785
Editor: Tom Martin; **Publisher:** Tony Scott
Editorial Profile: The Register-Mail is a daily newspaper published for the residents of Galesburg, IL and surrounding areas.; Full Page Mono: 20.59; Full Page Colour: 230.00
Currency: US Dollars
DAILY NEWSPAPER

The Register-News
Owner: Community Newspaper Holdings, Inc.
Editorial: 911 Broadway St, Mount Vernon, Illinois 62864-4008. **T:** 1 618 242-0113
E: your.news@register-news.com
W: http://www.register-news.com
Freq: Daily; **Circ:** 9155 Not Audited
Publisher: Bob Dennis
Editorial Profile: The Register-News is published daily for the residents of Mount Vernon, IL abd surrounding areas. The newspaper covers local news, sports, business and entertainment.; Full Page Mono: 13.86; Full Page Colour: 46.79
Currency: US Dollars
DAILY NEWSPAPER

Reidsville Review & Eden News
Owner: BH Media Group
Editorial: 1921 Vance St, Reidsville, North Carolina 27320-3254
E: news@reidsvillereview.com
W: http://www.newsadvance.com/rockingham_now
Freq: Daily; **Circ:** 6477
Publisher: Steve Kaylor
DAILY NEWSPAPER

Reminder Press, Inc.
Editorial: 130 Old Town Rd, Vernon, Connecticut 06066-2322. **T:** 1 860 875-3366
W: http://www.courant.com/reminder-news/
Freq: Weekly; **Circ:** 242019 Not Audited
Publisher: Ken Hovland; Full Page Colour: 977.40
Currency: US Dollars
NEWSPAPER

Reminder Publications Inc.
Owner: Reminder Publications Inc.
Editorial: 280 N Main St, East Longmeadow, Massachusetts 01028-1868.
T: 1 413 525-6661
E: news@reminderpublications.com
W: http://www.thereminder.com **Circ:** 51700 Not Audited
Editorial Profile: Reminder Publications Inc. is a local newspaper in East Longmeadow, MA.
NEWSPAPER

Reno Gazette-Journal
Owner: Gannett Co., Inc.
Editorial: 955 Kuenzli St, Reno, Nevada 89502. **T:** 1 775 788-6200 **E:** tips@rgj.com
W: http://www.rgj.com
Freq: Daily; **Circ:** 37704 Not Audited
Publisher: John Maher; **Editor:** Kelly Scott
Editorial Profile: Reno Gazette-Journal is a local, daily newspaper providing Reno, NV residents with local and world-wide news coverage. The paper includes local and national news, sports, technology, business, outdoors and special reports.; Full Page Mono: 271.34; Full Page Colour: 400.74
Currency: US Dollars
DAILY NEWSPAPER

Reno News & Review
Owner: Chico Community Publishing, Inc.
Editorial: 708 N Center St, Reno, Nevada 89501. **T:** 1 775 324-4440
E: renoletters@newsreview.com
W: http://www.newsreview.com/reno/home
Freq: Thu; **Circ:** 21726 Not Audited
Editor: Brian Burghart; **Editor:** Kelley Lang; **News Editor:** Dennis Myers; **Publisher:** Jeff von Kaenel
Editorial Profile: Reno News & Review is published weekly for the residents of Reno, NV and surrounding areas. The newspaper offers community news, arts & entertainment and event listings. Do not send press releases via fax.; Full Page Mono: 65.09
Currency: US Dollars
NEWSPAPER

Rensselaer Republican
Owner: Community Media Group
Editorial: 117 N Van Rensselaer St, Rensselaer, Indiana 47978. **T:** 1 219 866-5111
E: editor@rensselaerrepublican.com
W: http://www.newsbug.info/rensselaer_republican/
Freq: Daily; **Circ:** 2088 Not Audited
Editorial Profile: Rensselaer Republican is published daily for the residents of Rennsselaer, IN and surrounding areas. The newspaper covers local news, business, sports, lifestyles and entertainment.; Full Page Mono: 13.00; Full Page Colour: 250.00
Currency: US Dollars
DAILY NEWSPAPER

Renton Reporter
Owner: Black Press
Editorial: 19426 68th Ave S Ste A, Kent, Washington 98032-1193. **T:** 1 425 255-3484
E: letters@rentonreporter.com
W: http://www.rentonreporter.com
Freq: Fri; **Circ:** 31000 Not Audited
Editor: Brian Beckley; **Publisher:** Ellen Morrison
Editorial Profile: Renton (WA) Reporter is a weekly newspaper that covers local news, politics, sports and arts & entertainment.; Full Page Mono: 27.50
Currency: US Dollars

NEWSPAPER

The Reporter
Owner: MediaNews Group
Editorial: 916 Cotting Ln, Vacaville, California 95688-9338. **T:** 1 707 448-6401
E: newsroom@thereporter.com
W: http://www.thereporter.com
Freq: Daily; **Circ:** 17248 Not Audited
Publisher: Jim Gleim
Editorial Profile: The Reporter is a daily newspaper written for the residents of Northern Solano County, CA. The newspaper covers local news and events, public safety, education, county government, business in the area and courts.; Full Page Mono: 35.85; Full Page Colour: 896.00
Currency: US Dollars
DAILY NEWSPAPER

The Reporter
Owner: Journal Register Company
Editorial: 307 Derstine Ave, Lansdale, Pennsylvania 19446-3532. **T:** 1 215 855-8440
E: citydesk@thereporteronline.com
W: http://www.thereporteronline.com
Freq: Daily; **Circ:** 8480 Not Audited
Publisher: Edward Condra
Editorial Profile: The Reporter is a daily newspaper written for the residents of Lansdale, PA. It covers various local news for the Lansdale, PA region, including sports, arts and entertainment, business and lifestyle topics.; Full Page Mono: 27.00; Full Page Colour: 620.00
Currency: US Dollars
DAILY NEWSPAPER

The Reporter
Owner: Gannett Co., Inc.
Editorial: N6637 Rolling Meadows Dr, Fond du Lac, Wisconsin 54937-9471.
T: 1 920 922-4600
W: http://www.fdlreporter.com
Freq: Mon thru Fri; **Circ:** 9322 Not Audited
News Editor: Peggy Breister
Editorial Profile: The Reporter is a local, daily newspaper published by Gannett Newspapers for the residents of Fond Du Lac, WI and the surrounding area. It includes local, regional and national news.; Full Page Mono: 49.90; Full Page Colour: 158.77
Currency: US Dollars
DAILY NEWSPAPER

The Reporter
Editorial: 1088 S Main St, Akron, Ohio 44301.
T: 1 330 535-7061 **E:** reporter14@juno.com
Freq: Sat; **Circ:** 35000 Not Audited
Editorial Profile: The Reporter is a weekly community newspaper written for residents of Akron, OH. Its main focus is on local news with an emphasis on the African American Community.; Full Page Mono: 28.50
Currency: US Dollars
NEWSPAPER

The Reporter
Owner: McClatchy Newspapers
Editorial: 91655 Overseas Hwy, Tavernier, Florida 33070-2558. **T:** 1 305 852-3216
W: http://www.keysnet.com
Freq: Fri; **Circ:** 13000 Not Audited
Editor: David Goodhue; **Publisher:** Wayne Markham
Editorial Profile: The Reporter is a local newspaper written for the residents of Tavernier, FL. The newspaper covers local and national news, weather, sports and community events.; Full Page Mono: 10.28
Currency: US Dollars
NEWSPAPER

The Reporter Group
Owner: Jewish Federation of Broome County
Editorial: 500 Clubhouse Rd, Vestal, New York 13850-4700. **T:** 1 607 724-2360
E: treporter@aol.com
W: http://www.thereportergroup.org
Freq: Bi-Weekly; **Circ:** 17027 ABC-Audit Bureau of Circulations
Editorial Profile: The Reporter Group is a community newspaper publisher serving the Jewish communities of New York, Pennsylvania and Connecticut.
NEWSPAPER

The Reporter Newspapers
Owner: Regional Publishing Corp.
Editorial: 12247 S Harlem Ave, Palos Heights, Illinois 60463-1431. **T:** 1 708 448-6161
E: thereporter@comcast.net
W: http://www.thereporteronline.net
Circ: 72684
Publisher: Amy Richards; **Editor:** Jeff Vorva
Editorial Profile: The Reporter Newspapers is a community newspaper publisher serving the residents of Chicago, Naperville and Joliet, IL.
NEWSPAPER

Reporter Newspapers
Owner: Springs Publishing, LLC
Editorial: 6065 Roswell Rd Ne Ste 225, Atlanta, Georgia 30328-4012.
T: 1 404 917-2200
E: publisher@reporternewspapers.net
W: http://www.reporternewspapers.net
Circ: 66000 Not Audited
Editor: Joe Earle; **Publisher:** Steve Levene
Editorial Profile: Reporter Newspapers in Sandy Springs, GA is a community newspaper publisher serving the residents of Atlanta.
NEWSPAPER

Reporter Press, LLC-Stowe Reporter and Waterbury Record
Owner: Reporter Press, LLC
Editorial: 49 School St, Stowe, Vermont 5672.
T: 1 802 253-2101
Freq: Weekly; **Circ:** 9300 Not Audited
Publisher: A. Biddle Duke
NEWSPAPER

El Reportero Nacional
Owner: El Reportero News Media Inc.
Editorial: 4800 Wadsworth Blvd, Ste 205, Wheat Ridge, Colorado 80033.
T: 1 303 432-3650
E: elreportero@qwestoffice.net
Freq: Wed; **Circ:** 18000 Not Audited
Editor: Tony Flores
Editorial Profile: El Reportero Nacional is a weekly Spanish-language newspaper serving the Hispanic community in and around Denver. It provides local, national and international news along with articles on Spanish culture, education and local events.; Full Page Colour: 74.72
Currency: US Dollars
NEWSPAPER

The Reporter-Times
Owner: Schurz Communications Inc.
Editorial: 60 S Jefferson St, Martinsville, Indiana 46151. **T:** 1 765 342-3311
W: http://www.reporter-times.com
Freq: Daily; **Circ:** 4849
News Editor: Ronald Hawkins
Editorial Profile: The Reporter-Times is a local daily newspaper written for residents in Morgan County, IN. The publication's editorial mission is to strive for accuracy in local reporting. The publication combines with The Times-Mail and The Herald-Times for the Sunday edition called the Hoosier Times.; Full Page Mono: 14.31; Full Page Colour: 230.00
Currency: US Dollars
DAILY NEWSPAPER

The Repository
Owner: GateHouse Media Inc.
Editorial: 500 Market Ave S, Canton, Ohio 44702-2112. **T:** 1 330 580-8300
E: newsroom@cantonrep.com
W: http://www.cantonrep.com
Freq: Daily; **Circ:** 51190
Publisher: Chris White
Editorial Profile: The Repository is a daily newspaper that supplies news coverage to residents of the Canton, OH area. The editorial content covers local and regional news, business, entertainment, sports and arts.; Full Page Mono: 70.95; Full Page Colour: 231.64
Currency: US Dollars
DAILY NEWSPAPER

The Republic
Owner: Home News Enterprises
Editorial: 333 2nd St, Columbus, Indiana 47201-6709. **T:** 1 812 372-7811
E: editorial@therepublic.com
W: http://www.therepublic.com
Freq: Daily; **Circ:** 17000 Not Audited
Editor: Tom Jekel; **Publisher:** Charles Wells
Editorial Profile: The Republic is a daily newspaper. The newspaper is written for residents of Brown, Jackson, Bartholomew, Decatur, and Jennings Counties in Indiana. The newspaper covers local news, sports, entertainment and events. The lead time varies.; Full Page Mono: 25.56; Full Page Colour: 348.00
Currency: US Dollars
DAILY NEWSPAPER

The Republican
Owner: Newhouse Newspapers
Editorial: 1860 Main St, Springfield, Massachusetts 01103-1000.
T: 1 413 788-1000 **E:** news@repub.com
W: http://www.masslive.com
Freq: Daily; **Circ:** 58564 Not Audited
Editorial Profile: The Republican was formerly the Springfield Union-News and is published daily for residents of Springfield, MA and surrounding communities in western Massachusetts. It covers local and national news, political news, arts & entertainment and sports.; Full Page Mono: 85.48; Full Page Colour: 283.06
Currency: US Dollars
DAILY NEWSPAPER

The Republican
Editorial: Press Gallery at The State House, Room 455, Boston, Massachusetts 2133.
T: 1 617 722-2790
DAILY NEWSPAPER

Republican Valley Review
Editorial: 11 John St Ofc B, Alma, Nebraska 68920-2153. **T:** 1 308 928-9982
E: republicanreview@yahoo.com
Freq: Weekly
Editor: Rhonda Hogeland
Editorial Profile: The Republican Valley Review offers local news and information for residents in and around Alma, Nebraska.
NEWSPAPER

Republican-Times
Owner: Rogers Printing Company, Inc. (W.B.)
Editorial: 122 E 8Th St, Trenton, Missouri 64683-2183. **T:** 1 660 359-2212
E: rtimes@lyn.net
W: http://www.republican-times.com
Freq: Daily; **Circ:** 3197 Not Audited
Publisher: Wendell Lenhart; **Editor:** Diane Lowrey
Editorial Profile: Republican-Times is a weekly community newspaper written for the residents of Trenton, MO. The paper covers local news and events.; Full Page Mono: 6.30; Full Page Colour: 8.30
Currency: US Dollars
DAILY NEWSPAPER

The Resident
Editorial: 252 S Broad St, Pawcatuck, Connecticut 6379. **T:** 1 860 608-0467
E: editor@theresident.com
W: http://www.theresident.com
Freq: Bi-Weekly; **Circ:** 30000 Not Audited
Editorial Profile: The Resident in Pawcatuck, CT is a bi-weekly newspaper written that covers local news and events, including the regional casino industry.; Full Page Mono: 31.00
Currency: US Dollars
NEWSPAPER

Resumen Newspaper
Owner: Res-News Corporation Inc.
Editorial: 138-42 90 Ave Ste F1, Jamaica, New York 11435-4104. **T:** 1 718 899-8603
E: rojas123@aol.com
W: http://www.resumen.8m.net
Freq: Fri; **Circ:** 32000 Not Audited
Editor: Jairo Casas
Editorial Profile: Resumen Newspaper is a weekly publication that covers local, national and international news, entertainment, sports, editorial columns and opinions. The paper primarily targets the Spanish-speaking residents of Southern New York and Northern New Jersey. Deadlines are on Wednesdays.; Full Page Mono: 14.00
Currency: US Dollars
NEWSPAPER

The Revere Independent Newspaper Group
Owner: Independent Newspaper Group
Editorial: 385 Broadway Suite 105, Revere, Massachusetts 2151. **T:** 1 781 485-0588
Circ: 50100 Not Audited
Editor: John Lynds; **Publisher:** Stephen Quigley; **Editor:** Joshua Resnek; **Editor in Chief:** Cary Shuman
Editorial Profile: The Revere Independent Newspaper Group is a weekly community newspaper publisher serving the residents of Revere, Charlestown, East Boston, Chelsea, Winthrop, Lynn and Everett, MA.
NEWSPAPER

The Review
Owner: Ogden Newspapers
Editorial: 210 E 4th St, East Liverpool, Ohio 43920-3144. **T:** 1 330 385-4545
E: newsroom@reviewonline.com
W: http://www.reviewonline.com
Freq: Daily; **Circ:** 5735 Not Audited
Editor: Jim Mackey; **Publisher:** Tammie McIntosh
Editorial Profile: The Review is a local daily newspaper serving the residents of the Ohio, West Virginia, and Pennsylvania tri-state area. The newspaper covers local news, sports, entertainment, business, weather, lottery and community events.; Full Page Mono: 13.55; Full Page Colour: 225.00
Currency: US Dollars
DAILY NEWSPAPER

Review Newspapers
Owner: Review Publishing
Editorial: NW Corner of 12th and Porter, Philadelphia, Pennsylvania 19148.
T: 1 215 336-2500
E: editor@southphillyreview.com
W: http://www.southphillyreview.com
Circ: 119000 Not Audited
Publisher: John Gallo; **Editor:** Bill Gelman
NEWSPAPER

Review-Roxborough
Owner: Journal Register Company
Editorial: 6220 Ridge Ave, Philadelphia, Pennsylvania 19128. **T:** 1 215 483-7300
E: reviewnews@gmail.com
W: http://www.roxreview.com
Freq: Wed; **Circ:** 15000 Not Audited
Editorial Profile: Review-Roxborough is a weekly newspaper serving the Roxborough, Manayunk, Andorra, Wissahickon and East Falls sections of the Philadelphia area. Editorial deadlines are on Fridays at noon ET. Advertising deadlines are on Mondays at 4pm ET. Deadlines are a day earlier when holidays fall on a Friday or Monday.; Full Page Mono: 26.76
Currency: US Dollars
NEWSPAPER

Revista de Victoria
Owner: Alvarez, (Emett)
Editorial: 2001 E. Sabine, Ste. 107, Victoria, Texas 77901-4373. **T:** 1 361 578-9686
E: revista@att.net
W: http://www.revistadevictoria.com
Freq: Monthly; **Circ:** 10000 Not Audited
Editorial Profile: Revista de Victoria is a monthly newspaper serving the Hispanic community in Victoria, TX.; Full Page Mono: 21.15
Currency: US Dollars
NEWSPAPER

RFD News Group
Editorial: 205 N Elk St, Elkton, South Dakota 57026-2124. **T:** 1 605 542-4831
E: rfdnews@mchsi.com
W: http://www.rfdnewsgroup.com **Circ:** 1850 Not Audited
Editor: Paul Ekern; **Editor:** Robin Mulvey; **Publisher:** C.J. Schumacher; **Editor:** Jane Utech
NEWSPAPER

RH Weekly
Owner: Prairie Mountain Publishing)
Editorial: 201 E 5th St, Loveland, Colorado 80537-5605. **T:** 1 970 669-5050
Freq: Wed; **Circ:** 15000
Publisher: Dean Lehman; **Editor:** Jeff Stahla
Editorial Profile: RH Weekly is a local community newspaper for the residents of Loveland, CO and the surrounding communities.; Full Page Mono: 8.93
Currency: US Dollars
NEWSPAPER

Rhode Island Catholic
Owner: Diocese of Providence
Editorial: 184 Broad St, Providence, Rhode Island 2903. **T:** 1 401 272-1010
E: editor@thericatholic.com
W: http://thericatholic.com
Freq: Thu; **Circ:** 30000 Not Audited
Editor: Rick Snizek; **Publisher:** Thomas Tobin
Editorial Profile: Rhode Island Catholic in Providence, RI is a weekly newspaper that covers news and events of interest to the Catholic community.; Full Page Mono: 19.00
Currency: US Dollars
NEWSPAPER

RIA Novosti - New York Bureau
Editorial: United Nations, Room S-301, New York, New York 10017. **T:** 1 646 509-3421
Editorial Profile: This is the New York Bureau of RIA Novosti based out of London, United Kingdom.
DAILY NEWSPAPER

Richards Publishing Company, Inc.
Editorial: 2nd and Main St, Gonvick, Minnesota 56644. **T:** 1 218 487-5225
E: richards@gvtel.com **Circ:** 5300 Not Audited
Editor: Corrine Richards; **Publisher:** Richard Richards
NEWSPAPER

Richmond County Daily Journal
Owner: Heartland Publications

Editorial: 105 E Washington St, Rockingham, North Carolina 28379-3639.
T: 1 910 997-3111
E: news@yourdailyjournal.com
W: http://www.yourdailyjournal.com
Freq: Daily; **Circ:** 8439 Not Audited
Publisher: Rick Bacon; **Editor:** Corey Friedman
Editorial Profile: Richmond County Daily Journal is published 5 days a week for the residents of Rockingham, NC and surrounding areas. The newspaper covers local and state news, business, education, sports and arts & entertainment. It offers a combined Saturday and Sunday edition called the Daily Journal Weekender.; Full Page Mono: 14.50; Full Page Colour: 295.00
Currency: US Dollars
DAILY NEWSPAPER

Richmond Free Press
Owner: Paradigm Communications, Inc.
Editorial: 422 E Franklin St, Richmond, Virginia 23219. **T:** 1 804 644-0496
E: news@richmondfreepress.com
W: http://www.richmondfreepress.com
Freq: Thu; **Circ:** 36905 Not Audited
Editorial Profile: Richmond Free Press is written for the residents of Richmond, VA. It covers local news and events.; Full Page Mono: 32.60
Currency: US Dollars
NEWSPAPER

Richmond Register
Owner: Community Newspaper Holdings, Inc.
Editorial: 380 Big Hill Ave, Richmond, Kentucky 40475. **T:** 1 859 623-1669
E: editor@richmondregister.com
W: http://www.richmondregister.com
Freq: Daily; **Circ:** 4060
Publisher: Ann Laurence; **Editor:** Bill Robinson
Editorial Profile: The Richmond Register is written for residents of Madison County, KY. The publication delivers local and national news to the area. The Register reports on local events and human interest stories from the surrounding communities. The lead time is three days.; Full Page Mono: 12.96; Full Page Colour: 255.00
Currency: US Dollars
DAILY NEWSPAPER

Richmond Times-Dispatch
Owner: BH Media Group
Editorial: 300 E Franklin St, Richmond, Virginia 23219-2214. **T:** 1 804 649-6000
E: news@timesdispatch.com
W: http://www.timesdispatch.com
Freq: Daily; **Circ:** 99802 Not Audited
Editor: Daniel Finnegan; **Publisher:** Thomas Silvestri
Editorial Profile: Richmond Times-Dispatch is a 50+ page, four-color broadsheet newspaper written for the general public in the Richmond, VA area. The Business section is featured daily, covering local and national business stories, daily stock market rates, real estate, chemicals, manufacturing, retail, utilities, finance and healthcare. Articles include features, breaking news, trends, analysis, profiles and investigative stories.; Full Page Mono: 211.00; Full Page Colour: 671.09
Currency: US Dollars
DAILY NEWSPAPER

The Richmond Voice
Owner: Jack J. Green
Editorial: 205 E Clay St, Richmond, Virginia 23219. **T:** 1 804 644-9060
E: richmond.voice@verizon.net
W: http://www.voicenewspaper.com
Freq: Wed; **Circ:** 39400 Not Audited
Publisher: Jack Green; **Publisher:** Jack Green; **Publisher:** Jack Green; **Editor:** Algeree Johnson
Editorial Profile: The Richmond (VA) Voice is a weekly newspaper that targets African Americans and covers local and national news as well as community events.; Full Page Mono: 54.34
Currency: US Dollars
NEWSPAPER

Richner Communications, Inc.
Editorial: 2 Endo Blvd, Garden City, New York 11530. **T:** 1 516 569-4000
E: feedback@liherald.com
W: http://www.liherald.com **Circ:** 89534 Not Audited
Editor: Jeff Bessen; **Editor:** Scott Brinton; **Editor:** Scott Brinton; **Editor:** Scott Brinton; **Editor:** Alex Costello; **Editor:** Chris Engelhardt; **Editor:** Hector Flores; **Editor:** Jean Graham; **Editor:** Mary Malloy; **Editor:** Douglas Miller; **Editor:** Douglas Miller; **Editor:** Douglas Miller; **Editor:** Judy Rattner; **Editor:** Anthony Rifalto; **Editor:** David Weingrad

Editorial Profile: Richner Communications Inc. in Garden City, NY publishes 15 community newspapers in the Nassau County, NY.
NEWSPAPER

Ridgway Record
Owner: Horizon Publications
Editorial: 325 Main St, Ste A, Ridgway, Pennsylvania 15853-8019. **T:** 1 814 773-3161
E: ridgwayrecord@shop-right.com
W: http://www.ridgwayrecord.com
Freq: Mon thru Fri; **Circ:** 3150 Not Audited
Publisher: Darlene Coder
Editorial Profile: Ridgway Record is dedicated to providing the most local news possible to residents of Ridgeway, PA. It delivers local news and events weekly to the community.; Full Page Mono: 8.15; Full Page Colour: 115.00
Currency: US Dollars
DAILY NEWSPAPER

The Rio Grande Catholic
Owner: Diocese of El Paso
Editorial: 499 Saint Matthews St, El Paso, Texas 79907-4214. **T:** 1 915 872-8414
E: riogrande@elpasodiocese.org
W: http://www.riograndecatholic.org
Freq: Monthly; **Circ:** 28000
Publisher: Mark Joseph Seitz; **Editor:** Andrew Sparke
Editorial Profile: The Rio Grande Catholic is a monthly newspaper written for the Diocese of El Paso in Texas.; Full Page Mono: 22.00
Currency: US Dollars
NEWSPAPER

Rio Grande Sun
Owner: Sun Publishing, Inc.
Editorial: 123 N Railroad Ave, Espanola, New Mexico 87532. **T:** 1 505 753-2126
E: rgsun@cybermesa.com
W: http://www.riograndesun.com
Freq: Thu; **Circ:** 11126 Not Audited
Editor: Kevin Bersett; **Publisher:** Robert Trapp
Editorial Profile: Rio Grande Sun is a local weekly newspaper for the residents of Rio Arriba and Northern Santa Fe County, NM. The publication covers local news, events, sports, arts & entertainment and education. The editorial deadlines are Mondays at 5pm MT.; Full Page Mono: 9.50
Currency: US Dollars
NEWSPAPER

Ripley Publishing Company, Inc.
Editorial: 115 S Washington St, Versailles, Indiana 47042-9455. **T:** 1 812 689-6364
E: publication@ripleynews.com
W: http://www.ripleynews.com **Circ:** 9600 Not Audited
Publisher: Linda Chandler; **Editor:** Mary Mattingly
NEWSPAPER

Rising Publications
Editorial: 25 Warburton Ave, Yonkers, New York 10701-7079. **T:** 1 914 965-4000
E: risingmediagroup@gmail.com
W: http://www.risingmediagroup.com
Freq: Fri; **Circ:** 54496 Not Audited
Editor In Chief: Dan Murphy; **Publisher:** Nick Sprayregen
Editorial Profile: Rising Publications in Yonkers, NY publishes the following community newspapers: North Castle Rising; Pelham Rising; Rye Rising: Yonkers Rising; Sound View Rising; Harrison Rising; Eastchester Rising; Westchester Rising; and Mt. Vernon Rising.
NEWSPAPER

River Cities Daily Tribune
Owner: Victory Publishing, LTD.
Editorial: 1007 Avenue K, Marble Falls, Texas 78654-5039. **T:** 1 830 693-7152
E: info@thepicayune.com
W: http://www.highlandlakeslive.com
Freq: Daily; **Circ:** 4300 Not Audited
Editorial Profile: River Cities Daily Tribune is a local daily newspaper serving residents of Marble Falls, TX. It covers local news, community events, sports and features of interest to local readers. It shares its editorial staff with its sister weekly paper, the Picayune Tribune. Deadlines are at 4:30pm CT.; Full Page Mono: 6.53; Full Page Colour: 43.29
Currency: US Dollars
DAILY NEWSPAPER

River Cities' Reader
Editorial: 532 W 3rd St, Davenport, Iowa 52801. **T:** 1 563 324-0049
E: info@rcreader.com
W: http://www.rcreader.com

Freq: Bi-Weekly; **Circ:** 22000 Not Audited
Editor: Kathleen McCarthy; **Publisher:** Todd McGreevy; **Publisher:** Todd McGreevy
Editorial Profile: River Cities' Reader is a weekly newspaper for the residents of Davenport, IA. The editorial mission is to report the local news of Davenport as well as provide comprehensive and critical arts, music, and culture coverage.; Full Page Mono: 20.09
Currency: US Dollars
NEWSPAPER

River Publishing
Editorial: 308 W Cedar St, Brinkley, Arkansas 72021-2710. **T:** 1 870 734-1056 **Circ:** 10100 Not Audited
Publisher: Katie Jacques; **Publisher:** Katie Jacques; **Publisher:** Katie Jacques; **Editor:** Trisha Rogers
NEWSPAPER

River Valley Newspapers
Owner: River Valley Newspaper Group
Editorial: 401 N. Third St., La Crosse, Wisconsin 54601-3281. **T:** 1 608 782-9710
E: information@lee.net
W: http://www.rivervalleynewspapers.com
Circ: 6988 Not Audited
Editor: Randy Erickson
NEWSPAPER

The Riverdale Press
Owner: Richner Communications
Editorial: 6155 Broadway, Bronx, New York 10471-3153. **T:** 1 718 543-6065
E: newsroom@riverdalepress.com
W: http://www.riverdalepress.com
Freq: Thu; **Circ:** 10000 Not Audited
Editorial Profile: The Riverdale Press is a weekly newspaper for residents of the Northwest Bronx, NY area. The editorial mission is to provide the community with accurate and up-to-date local news and information. Deadlines for the publication are on Mondays before issue date.; Full Page Mono: 30.10; Full Page Colour: 2986.20
Currency: US Dollars
NEWSPAPER

Riverfront Times
Owner: Voice Media Group
Editorial: 6358 Delmar Blvd Ste 200, Saint Louis, Missouri 63130-4718.
T: 1 314 754-5966
E: feedback@riverfronttimes.com
W: http://www.riverfronttimes.com
Freq: Thu; **Circ:** 50000 Not Audited
Editor: Paul Friswold; **Editor:** Chad Garrison
Editorial Profile: Riverfront Times is a weekly newspaper published for the residents of St. Louis and surrounding areas. It covers local news, culture, arts & entertainment and weather.; Full Page Mono: 47.43; Full Page Colour: 10.05
Currency: US Dollars
NEWSPAPER

Riverside Review
Editorial: 215 Military Rd, Buffalo, New York 14207. **T:** 1 716 877-8400
W: http://www.buffaloreview.com
Freq: Wed; **Circ:** 12000 Not Audited
Editorial Profile: Riverside Review is a weekly newspaper for the residents of northwest Buffalo, NY. It covers news and events in the local community.; Full Page Mono: 9.00
Currency: US Dollars
NEWSPAPER

Riverton Ranger
Editorial: 421 E Main St, Riverton, Wyoming 82501-4438. **T:** 1 307 856-2244
E: ranger@wyoming.com
W: http://www.dailyranger.com
Freq: Daily; **Circ:** 7214 Not Audited
Editor: Wayne Nicholls
Editorial Profile: Riverton Ranger is a local daily newspaper for the residents of Freemont County, WY. The publication covers news and events in the local community. Deadlines are at noon, MT one day prior to issue date.; Full Page Mono: 10.95; Full Page Colour: 150.00
Currency: US Dollars
DAILY NEWSPAPER

Roane Newspapers
Editorial: 204 Franklin St, Kingston, Tennessee 37763. **T:** 1 865 376-3481
E: newsroom@roanecounty.com
W: http://www.roanecounty.com **Circ:** 15987 Not Audited
Editor: Terri Likens; **Publisher:** Johnny Teglas
NEWSPAPER

The Roanoke Times
Owner: BH Media Group

Editorial: 201 Campbell Ave SW, Roanoke, Virginia 24011-1105. **T:** 1 540 981-3100
E: news@roanoke.com
W: http://www.roanoke.com
Freq: Daily; **Circ:** 62619 Not Audited
Publisher: Debbie Meade
Editorial Profile: The Roanoke Times is a daily newspaper serving Roanoke and 19 surrounding counties in Southwest Virginia. It provides readers with information on the latest local and national news, sports, weather, arts & entertainment, technology, health, business, automotive, political and other news. The paper also publishes the New River Valley Current, which serves readers in the Christiansburg-Blacksburg, VA area and surrounding New River Valley counties. Local tab publications are inserted into the regular newspaper for zoned news and advertising. The paper also publishes Blue Ridge Business Journal, Blue Ridge Sports Journal and Blue Ridge Employment Weekly.; Full Page Mono: 45.83; Full Page Colour: 57.29
Currency: US Dollars
DAILY NEWSPAPER

The Roanoke Times
Editorial: 1111 E Main St, Richmond, Virginia 23219-3531. **T:** 1 804 239-8337
DAILY NEWSPAPER

The Roanoke Times
Editorial: 110 Peppers Ferry Rd, Christiansburg, Virginia 24073.
T: 1 540 381-1668 **E:** newriver@roanoke.com
DAILY NEWSPAPER

The Robesonian
Owner: Heartland Publications
Editorial: 2175 N Roberts Ave, Lumberton, North Carolina 28358-2867.
T: 1 910 739-4322
W: http://www.robesonian.com
Freq: Daily; **Circ:** 12562 Not Audited
Publisher: M. Joseph Craig; **Editor:** Donnie Douglas
Editorial Profile: The Robesonian is a daily newspaper serving the residents of Robeson County, NC. It covers news and events in the local community.; Full Page Mono: 19.95; Full Page Colour: 72.06
Currency: US Dollars
DAILY NEWSPAPER

Robins Rev-Up
Editorial: 620 North St., Bldg 905, Warner Robins, Georgia 31098-2255.
T: 1 478 468-2137
W: http://www.robins.af.mil/library/rev.asp
Freq: Fri; **Circ:** 15000 Not Audited
Editor: Lanorris Askew; **Publisher:** Rick Brewer
Editorial Profile: Robins Rev-Up is a weekly paper written for current and former members of the U.S. military services. Deadlines are Mondays at 4pm ET.; Full Page Mono: 13.00
Currency: US Dollars
NEWSPAPER

Robinson Daily News
Owner: Lewis Newspapers
Editorial: 302 S Cross St, Robinson, Illinois 62454-2137. **T:** 1 618 544-2101
E: news@robdailynews.com
W: http://www.robdailynews.com
Freq: Daily; **Circ:** 5262 Not Audited
Editor: Greg Bilbrey; **Editor:** Randy Harrison; **Publisher:** Kathleen Lewis
Editorial Profile: Robinson Daily News is a local daily newspaper written for Crawford County, IL.; Full Page Mono: 9.50; Full Page Colour: 195.00
Currency: US Dollars
DAILY NEWSPAPER

Robinson Newspapers
Owner: Robinson Newspapers
Editorial: 14006 1st Ave S, Suite B, Burien, Washington 98168. **T:** 1 206 708-1378
W: http://www.robinsonnews.com
Freq: Weekly; **Circ:** 49000 Not Audited
Editor: Eric Mathison; **Editor:** Eric Mathison; **Editor:** Eric Mathison; **Publisher:** Jerry Robinson
NEWSPAPER

Robson Publishing
Editorial: 9532 E Riggs Rd, Sun Lakes, Arizona 85248-7463. **T:** 1 480 895-4506
E: advertising@robson.com
W: http://www.robsonpublishing.com
Circ: 29500 Not Audited
Publisher: Linda Gosnel; **Editor:** Linda Robson; **Editor:** Linda Robson
Editorial Profile: Robson Publishing is a publication that provides the community of Sun Lakes, AZ with community newspapers.

NEWSPAPER

Rochester Catholic Press

Owner: Rochester Catholic Press Association, Inc.
Editorial: 1150 Buffalo Rd, Rochester, New York 14624. **T:** 1 585 529-9530
E: info@catholiccourier.com
W: http://www.catholiccourier.com
Freq: Monthly; **Circ:** 107109
Publisher: Salvatore Matano; Full Page Mono: 102.00
Currency: US Dollars
NEWSPAPER

Rochester Democrat and Chronicle

Owner: Gannett Co., Inc.
Editorial: 55 Exchange Blvd, Rochester, New York 14614-2001. **T:** 1 585 232-7100
E: infodesk@democratandchronicle.com
W: http://www.democratandchronicle.com
Freq: Daily; **Circ:** 94103 Not Audited
Editorial Profile: Rochester Democrat and Chronicle began in 1833 as The Balance. Soon after, the name changed to the Daily Democrat. In 1870, the paper combined with the two-year-old Chronicle to become the Rochester Democrat and Chronicle. The newspaper aims to "be the highest valued source of news, information and advertising services in the Greater Rochester market." It was awarded Gannett's Outstanding Achievement Award for best overall performance in 1997. The paper features major local, regional, national and world news. Local stories come from around the city and surrounding suburbs. Business coverage includes national and world economic news, stock listings, and features on its "big three" local companies (Kodak, Xerox, B&L), as well as start-ups and entrepreneurs. Rochester Living, the lifestyle and feature section, was redesigned in 1996 and focuses on a different informational topic every day of the week: Sunday features arts, travel, and books; Monday features health; Tuesday features relationships; Wednesday features personal finance; Thursday features family; Friday features entertainment; and Saturday features home. Sports coverage includes news from around the region and nation.; Full Page Mono: 480.75; Full Page Colour: 1522.02
Currency: US Dollars
DAILY NEWSPAPER

Rochester Sentinel

Owner: Sentinel Corporation (The)
Editorial: 118 E 8th St, Rochester, Indiana 46975-1508. **T:** 1 574 223-2111
E: news@rochsent.com
W: http://www.rochsent.com
Freq: Daily; **Circ:** 3900 Not Audited
Editor: Mike Kenny; **Publisher:** Sarah Overmyer Wilson; **Editor:** W.S. Wilson
Editorial Profile: Rochester Sentinel is published daily for the residents of Rochester, IN and surrounding areas. The newspaper covers local and state news, business, sports, lifestyles and entertainment.; Full Page Mono: 7.44; Full Page Colour: 110.00
Currency: US Dollars
DAILY NEWSPAPER

The Rochester Times

Editorial: 1 Old Dover Rd Ste, Rochester, New Hampshire 03867-3438. **T:** 1 603 332-2300
E: thetimes@fosters.com
W: http://www.fosters.com/apps/pbcs.dll/section?category=ROCTIMES
Freq: Thu; **Circ:** 15000 Not Audited
Editor: John Nolan
Editorial Profile: The Rochester Times is a weekly newspaper published for the residents of Rock County, NE. The publication features local news and community events. The news deadline falls on Tuesday at noon CT.; Full Page Mono: 10.80
Currency: US Dollars
NEWSPAPER

The Rock River Times

Owner: Rock River Times Inc. (The)
Editorial: 128 N Church St, Rockford, Illinois 61101-1002. **T:** 1 815 964-9767
E: contact@rockrivertimes.com
W: http://www.rockrivertimes.com
Freq: Wed; **Circ:** 22000 Not Audited
Editorial Profile: The Rock River Times is a weekly newspaper written for residents of Illinois and Madison, WI. The publication focuses on local news and events, but it also covers state, national and international news. News deadlines are on Thursdays at 4pm CT. The best days to contact reporters and editors are Tuesdays, Wednesdays and Thursdays between 10am and 5pm CT. The publication prefers to receive press materials via mail, fax

and e-mail, in that order.; Full Page Mono: 9.08; Full Page Colour: 10.72
Currency: US Dollars
NEWSPAPER

Rock Valley Publishing, LLC.

Editorial: 11512 N 2nd St, Machesney Park, Illinois 61115. **T:** 1 815 877-4044
E: info@rvpublishing.com
W: http://www.rvpublishing.com
Freq: Weekly; **Circ:** 12463 Not Audited
Editor: Melanie Bradley; **Publisher:** Pete Cruger
NEWSPAPER

The Rockaway Times

Owner: Boyle (Kevin) & Adams (Patricia)
Editorial: 11404 Beach Channel Dr, Rockaway Park, New York 11694-2211.
T: 1 718 634-3030
E: news@rockawaytimes.com
W: http://rockawaytimes.com
Freq: Thu; **Circ:** 10000
Editorial Profile: Launched June 26, 2014, The Rockaway Times is a free, weekly community newspaper covering news, events, arts and entertainment in the Rockaways, a Queens neighborhood in New York.
NEWSPAPER

Rockdale Citizen

Owner: Southern Community Newspapers Inc.
Editorial: 969 S Main St NE, Conyers, Georgia 30012-4501 **E:** news@rockdalecitizen.com
W: http://www.rockdalecitizen.com
Freq: Daily; **Circ:** 6599 Not Audited
Editor: Jay Jones; **Editor:** Jay Jones; **Editor:** Jay Jones; **Editor:** Jay Jones; **Publisher:** Alice Queen
Editorial Profile: Rockdale Citizen is a daily newspaper for the residents of Conyers, GA. The paper combines with the Newton Citizen on weekends.; Full Page Mono: 29.62; Full Page Colour: 375.00
Currency: US Dollars
DAILY NEWSPAPER

Rockford Register Star

Owner: GateHouse Media Inc.
Editorial: 99 E State St, Rockford, Illinois 61104-1009. **T:** 1 815 987-1200
E: local@rrstar.com **W:** http://www.rrstar.com
Freq: Daily; **Circ:** 61640 Not Audited
Publisher: Josh Trust
Editorial Profile: Rockford Register Star serves the Rockford, IL area by delivering news and local information to the city and surrounding communities. It is distributed to the Rock River Valley in Northwest Illinois. In addition to the city of Rockford, it serves suburban and regional readers in Loves Park, Machesney Park, Roscoe, Rockton and South Beloit, Winnebago County; Belvidere and other towns in Boone County; Byron, Oregon, and other communities in Ogle County, IL. They do not publish an editorial calendar.; Full Page Mono: 128.03; Full Page Colour: 403.71
Currency: US Dollars
DAILY NEWSPAPER

The Rockford Squire

Owner: Altena & Roger Allen (Beth)
Editorial: 331 Northland Dr NE, Rockford, Michigan 49341-1025. **T:** 1 616 866-4465
W: http://www.rockfordsquire.com
Freq: Thu; **Circ:** 11000 Not Audited
Editorial Profile: The Rockford Squire is a weekly newspaper for the residents of Rockford, MI. It covers news and events in the local community.; Full Page Mono: 8.50
Currency: US Dollars
NEWSPAPER

Rockingham Publishing Company

Owner: Rockingham Publishing Company
Editorial: 231 S Liberty St, Harrisonburg, Virginia 22801-3621. **T:** 1 540 574-6229
W: http://www.dnronline.com
Freq: Weekly; **Circ:** 53600 Not Audited
Editor: Travis Long; **Publisher:** Peter Yates; Full Page Mono: 9.40
Currency: US Dollars
NEWSPAPER

Rockland County Times

Owner: Citizen Publishing Co.
Editorial: 119 Main St, Nanuet, New York 10954. **T:** 1 845 627-1414
E: editor@rocklandcountytimes.com
W: http://www.rocklandcountytimes.com
Freq: Thu; **Circ:** 12000 Not Audited
Publisher: Ken Herndon; **Publisher:** Armand Miele
Editorial Profile: Rockland County Times is a local weekly newspaper for the residents of Rockland County, NY. The publication covers

information on news and events occurring in the local community.; Full Page Mono: 11.18
Currency: US Dollars
NEWSPAPER

Rockland Jewish Reporter

Editorial: 450 W Nyack Rd, West Nyack, New York 10994-1754. **T:** 1 845 362-4200
E: admin@jewishrockland.org
Freq: Monthly; **Circ:** 12000 Not Audited
Editor: Marla Cohen
Editorial Profile: Rockland Jewish Reporter is a community newspaper published for the Jewish residents of West Nyack, NY.; Full Page Mono: 26.00
Currency: US Dollars
NEWSPAPER

Rockland Review

Owner: Angel Media & Publishing Co.
Editorial: 26 Snake Hill Rd, West Nyack, New York 10994. **T:** 1 845 727-4114
E: rocklandreview@optonline.net
W: http://www.rocklandreviewnews.com
Freq: Fri; **Circ:** 25000 Not Audited
Publisher: Joseph Miele; **Editor:** Jeannine Ripa
Editorial Profile: Rockland Review is a community newspaper written for the residents of West Nyack, NY.; Full Page Mono: 16.00
Currency: US Dollars
NEWSPAPER

Rocky Ford Daily Gazette

Owner: Rocky Ford Publishing Company
Editorial: 912 Elm Ave, Rocky Ford, Colorado 81067-1249. **T:** 1 719 254-3351
E: news@rockyforddailygazette.com
Freq: Daily; **Circ:** 3300 Not Audited
Editorial Profile: Rocky Ford Daily Gazette is a local newspaper serving the residents of Crowley and Otero County, CO. The newspaper covers local news, sports and community events.; Full Page Mono: 6.10; Full Page Colour: 85.00
Currency: US Dollars
DAILY NEWSPAPER

Rocky Mount Telegram

Owner: Cooke Communications, LLC
Editorial: 1000 Hunter Hill Rd, Rocky Mount, North Carolina 27804-1727.
T: 1 252 446-5161
W: http://www.rockymounttelegram.com
Freq: Daily; **Circ:** 14059 Not Audited
Editor: Jeff Herrin; **Publisher:** Mark Wilson
Editorial Profile: Rocky Mount Telegram is published daily for the residents of Rocky Mount, NC. It covers news and events in the local community.; Full Page Mono: 22.36; Full Page Colour: 345.00
Currency: US Dollars
DAILY NEWSPAPER

The Rolesville Buzz

Editorial: 104-D S. Main St., Rolesville, North Carolina 27571. **T:** 1 919 554-4797
E: news@rolesvillebuzz.com
W: http://rolesvillebuzz.com
Freq: Monthly; **Circ:** 16000
Editorial Profile: The Rolesville (NC) Buzz is a monthly community newspaper serving residents of Rolesville and Wake Forest, NC with local news, sports and community events. Issues are mailed free to area residents on the first of each month.; Full Page Mono: 11.71
Currency: US Dollars
NEWSPAPER

Rolla Daily News

Owner: GateHouse Media Inc.
Editorial: 101 W 7Th St, Rolla, Missouri 65401-3243. **T:** 1 573 364-2468
E: news@therolladailynews.com
W: http://www.therolladailynews.com
Freq: Daily; **Circ:** 5021 Not Audited
Publisher: Floyd Jernigan
Editorial Profile: Rolla Daily New is a daily newspaper for the residents of Rolla, MO. It covers news and events in the local community. Deadlines are the same day as the issue date.; Full Page Mono: 12.05; Full Page Colour: 150.00
Currency: US Dollars
DAILY NEWSPAPER

rolling out UrbanStyle Weekly

Owner: Steed Media Group
Editorial: 770 English Ave NW, Atlanta, Georgia 30318-8400. **T:** 1 404 635-1313
E: editorial@rollingout.com
W: http://www.rollingout.com
Freq: Weekly; **Circ:** 1201817 Not Audited
Publisher: Munson Steed

Editorial Profile: rolling out UrbanStyle Weekly is a newspaper that offers African Americans mainstream reviews of celebrities, entertainment, movies, politics and society. The newspaper is involved in the transformation of urban America by shaping and perpetuating the continuity of African American culture. The paper provides African Americans with instructions on how to live and with paradigms of what they can aspire to be. The paper is distributed in all major cities throughout the United States.
NEWSPAPER

Rolling Thunder Express

Editorial: 134A Main St, Newport, Maine 04953-3105. **T:** 1 207 368-2028
E: info@rollingthunderexpress.com
W: http://www.rollingthunderexpress.com
Freq: Mon; **Circ:** 16200 Not Audited
Publisher: Sylvia Angel-Currier
Editorial Profile: Rolling Thunder Express is a local weekly newspaper serving the residents of Newport, Corinna, East Newport, Detroit, Dixmont, Exeter, Cambridge, Parkman, Hartland, St. Albans, Garland, Stetson, Burnham, Ripley, Abbot, Willimantic, Pittsfield, Dexter, Palmyra, Etna, Plymouth, Guilford, Sangerville, Blanchard, Harmony, Carmel, Clinton, Dover-Foxcroft, Levant, Unity, Canaan, Monson, East Corinth, Troy, Athens and Greenville, ME. The newspaper mainly covers local news, sports, entertainment, education and community events.; Full Page Mono: 6.87
Currency: US Dollars
NEWSPAPER

Rome News-Tribune

Owner: News Publishing Company
Editorial: 305 E 6th Ave, Rome, Georgia 30161. **T:** 1 706 298-5252
E: romenewstribune@rn-t.com
W: http://www.romenews-tribune.com
Freq: Daily; **Circ:** 14466 Not Audited
Publisher: Otis Raybon
Editorial Profile: Rome News-Tribune is a local daily newspaper serving the Rome, GA area. It's mission is to provide vital information to the communities it serves through growth, leadership and innovation.; Full Page Mono: 23.86; Full Page Colour: 275.00
Currency: US Dollars
DAILY NEWSPAPER

Roswell Daily Record

Editorial: 2301 N Main St, Roswell, New Mexico 88201-6452. **T:** 1 575 622-7710
W: http://www.rdrnews.com
Freq: Daily; **Circ:** 11600 Not Audited
Publisher: Charles Fischer; **Editor:** Andrew Poertner; **News Editor:** Peg Tremper
Editorial Profile: Roswell Daily Record is a daily newspaper for the residents of Roswell, NM. It covers news and events in the local community.; Full Page Mono: 15.20; Full Page Colour: 50.25
Currency: US Dollars
DAILY NEWSPAPER

Round Rock Leader/Pflugerville Pflag

Owner: Cox Media Group, Inc.
Editorial: 1015 S Mays St, Round Rock, Texas 78664-6745. **T:** 1 512 255-5827
Freq: Weekly; **Circ:** 14700
Editor: Brad Stutzman
NEWSPAPER

Royalton Recorder

Editorial: 13737 State Rd, North Royalton, Ohio 44133-3907. **T:** 1 440 237-2235
E: rrnews@aol.com
W: http://www.nroyaltonchamber.com
Freq: Semi-Monthly; **Circ:** 14500 Not Audited
Editor: Maria Magnelli
Editorial Profile: Royalton Recorder is a community newspaper written for the residents of North Royalton, OH. It covers news and events in the local community. Deadlines for the publication are one week before the issue date.; Full Page Mono: 55.00
Currency: US Dollars
NEWSPAPER

Rumbo de Houston

Owner: ImpreMedia LLC
Editorial: 9950 Westpark Dr Ste 326, Houston, Texas 77063-5199.
T: 1 713 579-3700
W: http://www.impre.com/rumbo
Freq: Fri; **Circ:** 50000 Not Audited
Editorial Profile: Rumbo de Houston is a free Spanish-language tabloid published weekly for the Hispanic community in the Houston metro area. It covers local and community news, including education, personal finance and

health. It also offers in-depth national, international news, sports and entertainment, with particular emphasis on Mexico and Latin America. Rumbo comes from the Spanish word often associated with the Latin American phrase meaning "heading north" and, by implication, heading to move up in life.; Full Page Mono: 65.22
Currency: US Dollars
NEWSPAPER

Rumores
Owner: Hispanic Publishing Group
Editorial: 429 N Bristol St, Santa Ana, California 92703. **T:** 1 714 547-8283
E: editorial@rumoresnews.com
Freq: Wed; **Circ:** 30000 Not Audited
Editorial Profile: Rumores in Santa Ana, CA targets the Spanish-speaking community and covers local news, arts & entertainment, health and general interest topics.; Full Page Mono: 10.00
Currency: US Dollars
NEWSPAPER

Rural Virginian
Owner: Media General Inc.
Editorial: 685 Rio Road West, Charlottesville, Virginia 22901. **T:** 1 434 978-7216
E: rv@dailyprogress.com
W: http://www.ruralvirginian.com
Freq: Wed; **Circ:** 14000 Not Audited
Editor: Terry Karnes
Editorial Profile: Rural Virginian is a weekly newspaper for the residents of Charlottesville, VA. It covers community news and events.; Full Page Mono: 15.50
Currency: US Dollars
NEWSPAPER

Rural-Urban Record
Editorial: 24487 Squire Rd, Columbia Station, Ohio 44028. **T:** 1 440 236-8982
E: news@rural-urbanrecord.com
W: http://www.rural-urbanrecord.com
Freq: Mon; **Circ:** 22274 Not Audited
Editorial Profile: Rural-Urban Record is written for the residents of Columbia Station, OH and surrounding areas. It covers news and events in the local community. Deadlines are on Wednesdays at 5pm ET.; Full Page Mono: 14.50
Currency: US Dollars
NEWSPAPER

Russell County Newspapers Inc.
Owner: Times Journal Inc.
Editorial: 120 Wilson St, Russell Springs, Kentucky 42642. **T:** 1 270 866-3191
E: news@russellcountynewspapers.com
W: http://www.russellcountynewspapers.com
Circ: 14500 Not Audited
Editor: Derek Aaron; **Publisher:** Patsy Judd
NEWSPAPER

Russian Bazaar
Editorial: 224 Kings Hwy Floor 2, Brooklyn, New York 11223-1240. **T:** 1 718 266-4444
E: rusbazaar@yahoo.com
W: http://www.russian-bazaar.com
Freq: Thu; **Circ:** 19000
Editorial Profile: Russian bazaar is a weekly community newspaper for the Russian community of Brooklyn, NY.; Full Page Mono: 7.20
Currency: US Dollars
NEWSPAPER

The Russian World
Owner: Russian World Newspaper
Editorial: 11410 Ne 124Th St Ste 292, Kirkland, Washington 98034-4305.
T: 1 425 821-3741
E: russianworld@russianreklama.net
W: http://www.russianworldnewspaper.org
Freq: Mon; **Circ:** 10000
Editor In Chief: Alex Cherkasov
Editorial Profile: The Russian World is a bi-weekly newspaper and is distributed throughout Washington State, Portland, OR and in Vancouver, British Columbia.; Full Page Mono: 5.05
Currency: US Dollars
NEWSPAPER

Russkaya Reklama
Owner: Courier-Life
Editorial: 2699 Coney Island Ave, Brooklyn, New York 11235. **T:** 1 718 769-3000
E: reklama2000@yahoo.com
W: http://www.rusrek.com
Freq: Fri; **Circ:** 40000 Not Audited
Publisher: Paul Smukler; **Editor:** Michael Tripolsky
Editorial Profile: Russkaya Reklama is a Russian-language paper distributed in Brooklyn, NY.; Full Page Mono: 10.37; Full Page Colour: 62.22
Currency: US Dollars
NEWSPAPER

Ruston Daily Leader
Owner: Fackelman Newspapers
Editorial: 212 W Park Ave, Ruston, Louisiana 71270-4314. **T:** 1 318 255-4353
E: newsroom@rustonleader.com
W: http://www.rustonleader.com
Freq: Daily; **Circ:** 5718 Not Audited
Editor: Buddy Davis; **Publisher:** Rick Hohlt
Editorial Profile: Ruston Daily Leader is published daily for the residents of Lincoln Parish, LA. The newspaper covers local news, sports, lifestyles, arts & entertainment and community events.; Full Page Mono: 10.65; Full Page Colour: 175.00
Currency: US Dollars
DAILY NEWSPAPER

Rutland Herald
Owner: Herald Association, Inc. (The)
Editorial: 27 Wales St, Rutland, Vermont 05701-4027. **T:** 1 802 747-6121
E: pressreleases@rutlandherald.com
W: http://www.rutlandherald.com
Freq: Daily; **Circ:** 12569 Not Audited
Editor: Alan Keays; **News Editor:** Patty Minichiello; **Publisher:** R. John Mitchell;
Bureau Chief: Louis Porter
Editorial Profile: Rutland Herald is a daily newspaper serving residents of Central and Southern Vermont. News coverage includes community events, breaking news, sports, opinion, home and garden, and business. Contact the newspaper for lead time and deadline information.; Full Page Mono: 24.30; Full Page Colour: 152.27
Currency: US Dollars
DAILY NEWSPAPER

The Rye Record
Editorial: 17 Elm Pl, Rye, New York 10580.
T: 1 914 925-0540 **E:** ryerecordweb@aol.com
W: http://www.ryerecord.com
Freq: Bi-Weekly; **Circ:** 10000 Not Audited
Publisher: Robin Jovanovich
Editorial Profile: The Rye Record provides local news and events to the Rye, NY community.; Full Page Mono: 25.00
Currency: US Dollars
NEWSPAPER

Rzeczpospolita - Virginia Bureau
Owner: Presspublica
Editorial: 1557 Dunterry Pl, Mc Lean, Virginia 22101-4316. **T:** 1 703 827-0359
Freq: Daily
Editorial Profile: This is the McLean, VA bureau of Rzeczpospolita in Warsaw, Poland.
DAILY NEWSPAPER

SabaH
Editorial: 5003 Gravois Ave, Saint Louis, Missouri 63116-2307. **T:** 1 314 351-0201
E: sabahbos@aol.com
W: http://www.sabahusa.com
Freq: Mon; **Circ:** 50000 Not Audited
Editorial Profile: SabaH, which means sunrise, is a Bosnian-language newspaper in Saint Louis, MO that provides political news from the Balkans. It also covers events of interest to Bosnian-Americans in the U.S., especially in St. Louis, Chicago, New York, Detroit, Grand Rapids, MI, and other cities with large Bosnian populations. It is distributed throughout the U.S. and Canada.; Full Page Mono: 150.00
Currency: US Dollars
NEWSPAPER

Sabine Index/Around the Bend
Owner: Thomas (Lovan B.)
Editorial: 875 San Antonio Ave, Many, Louisiana 71449. **T:** 1 318 256-3495
W: http://www.thesabineindex.com
Editorial Profile: The Sabine Index and Around the Bend are published for the communities of Sabine Parrish, LA.
NEWSPAPER

Sac-Osage Publishing
Editorial: 3rd & Pine St, Osceola, Missouri 64776. **T:** 1 417 646-2211
E: sacosagenews@centurytel.net **Circ:** 7950 Not Audited
NEWSPAPER

The Sacramento Bee
Owner: McClatchy Newspapers
Editorial: 2100 Q St, Sacramento, California 95816-6816. **T:** 1 916 321-1000
W: http://www.sacbee.com
Freq: Daily; **Circ:** 191608 Not Audited
Editorial Profile: The Sacramento Bee is a broadsheet newspaper with an emphasis on local coverage. It is written for the residents of the Sacramento, CA area. It covers local news and business, as well as local and regional entertainment, sports, lifestyle, politics, crime, and arts and culture. The paper's mission is to be the region's leading media company, providing a trusted and valued source of news and information to the communities they serve.; Full Page Mono: 350.00; Full Page Colour: 1260.00
Currency: US Dollars
DAILY NEWSPAPER

Sacramento Bee - Capitol Bureau
Editorial: 925 L St Ste 600, Sacramento, California 95814-3763. **T:** 1 916 321-1199
Bureau Chief: Dan Smith
DAILY NEWSPAPER

Sacramento News & Review
Owner: Chico Community Publishing, Inc.
Editorial: 1124 Del Paso Blvd, Sacramento, California 95815-3607. **T:** 1 916 498-1234
E: sactonewstips@newsreview.com
W: http://www.newsreview.com/sacramento/home
Freq: Thu; **Circ:** 85000 Not Audited
Editorial Profile: Sacramento News & Review is written for residents of the Sacramento, CA area. The publication provides news, community arts & entertainment, a calendar of events and several special features, including the annual Women's Issues in October.; Full Page Mono: 8.40
Currency: US Dollars
NEWSPAPER

Sacramento Observer
Editorial: 2330 Alhambra Blvd, Sacramento, California 95817. **T:** 1 916 452-4781
W: http://www.sacobserver.com
Freq: Thu; **Circ:** 49090 Not Audited
Editor: Larry Lee; **Editor:** Larry Lee
Editorial Profile: Sacramento Observer delivers local, national and international news aimed toward the African-American population of Sacramento, CA. The weekly newspaper provides information on sports, business, religion, health issues, government, education and the economy. Within the SOUL section, readers can find articles about entertainment, shopping, poetry, literature and stories about local and national influential African-Americans. The paper also publishes a calendar of events, a real estate guide and several columns. Send all press releases directly to the editors.; Full Page Mono: 90.00; Full Page Colour: 6370.00
Currency: US Dollars
NEWSPAPER

The Saginaw News
Owner: MLive Media Group
Editorial: 100 S Michigan Ave Ste 3, Saginaw, Michigan 48602-2054. **T:** 1 989 752-7171
E: sanews@mlive.com
W: http://www.mlive.com/saginawnews
Freq: Fri; **Circ:** 19126
Editorial Profile: The Saginaw News is a newspaper published for the residents of Saginaw County, MI. The publication covers local news, sports, law enforcement, courts, education, politics, government and community events. The Lansing, MI bureau contributes to all eight of the MLive Media Group publications, including: The Ann Arbor News, Bay City Times, Flint Journal, Grand Rapids Press, Jackson Citizen Patriot, Kalamazoo Gazette, Muskegon Chronicle and The Saginaw News. Press releases should be sent by fax and are due at least seven days prior to publication. Deadlines for the publication are not set, but items are generally needed by two days before issue date. Circulation for the Thursday edition is 25,789, for the Friday Edition it is 26,119 and for Sunday it is 37,223.; Full Page Mono: 43.25; Full Page Colour: 182.00
Currency: US Dollars
NEWSPAPER

Saigon Tex News
Editorial: 815 Birdsall St, Houston, Texas 77007-5105. **T:** 1 713 626-2600
E: warner@saigontexnews.com
W: http://saigontexnews.com/
Freq: Thu
NEWSPAPER

Saigon Times
Editorial: 9234 Valley Blvd, Rosemead, California 91770-1922. **T:** 1 626 288-2696
E: sgtimes@aol.com
W: http://www.saigontimesusa.com
Freq: Fri; **Circ:** 20000 Not Audited
Editor: Hap Thai; **Publisher:** Cam Tran
Editorial Profile: Saigon Times is a weekly newspaper written for the Vietnamese-speaking residents of Rosemead, CA.; Full Page Mono: 11.23
Currency: US Dollars
NEWSPAPER

Salem News
Owner: Community Newspaper Holdings, Inc.
Editorial: 32 Dunham Rd, Beverly, Massachusetts 01915-1895.
T: 1 978 922-1234 **E:** sn@ecnnews.com
W: http://www.salemnews.com
Freq: Mon thru Fri; **Circ:** 16855 Not Audited
Editor: David Olson; **Editor:** David Olson
Editorial Profile: Salem News is written for the residents of Salem, MA. The publication covers local news, sports, police, courts, money, health, home, family and community events.; Full Page Mono: 40.95; Full Page Colour: 470.00
Currency: US Dollars
DAILY NEWSPAPER

Salem News
Owner: Ogden Newspapers
Editorial: 161 N Lincoln Ave, Salem, Ohio 44460-2903. **T:** 1 330 332-4601
E: salemnews@salemnews.net
W: http://www.salemnews.net
Freq: Daily; **Circ:** 3998 Not Audited
Editor: John Celidonio; **Publisher:** Beth Volosin
Editorial Profile: Salem News delivers community news to the residents of Columbiana County, OH.; Full Page Mono: 21.80
Currency: US Dollars
DAILY NEWSPAPER

Salem Times Commoner Newspapers
Editorial: 120 S Broadway Ave, Salem, Illinois 62881-1610. **T:** 1 618 548-3330
E: stceditor@salemtc.net **Circ:** 20300 Not Audited
NEWSPAPER

Salem Weekly
Editorial: 1342 Capitol St NE, Salem, Oregon 97301-7849. **T:** 1 503 540-0022
E: editors@willamettelive.com
W: http://www.willamettelive.com
Freq: Bi-Weekly
Editor: Shawn Estes; **Publisher:** A.P. Walther
Editorial Profile: Salem Weekly is an alternative, free weekly newspaper offering local news, thought and culture to the greater Salem, OR area.
NEWSPAPER

Salina Journal
Owner: Harris Enterprises
Editorial: 333 S 4th St, Salina, Kansas 67401-3903. **T:** 1 785 823-6363 **E:** news@salina.com
W: http://www.salina.com
Freq: Daily; **Circ:** 28004 Not Audited
Editorial Profile: Salina Journal is published daily for residents of Salina and northwestern Kansas. The newspaper covers local news, weather, sports and community events. Feature articles cover business, education, lifestyle and arts & entertainment.; Full Page Mono: 21.95; Full Page Colour: 456.00
Currency: US Dollars
DAILY NEWSPAPER

The Salinas Californian
Owner: Gannett Co., Inc.
Editorial: 123 W Alisal St, Salinas, California 93901-2644. **T:** 1 831 424-2221
E: newsroom@thecalifornian.com
W: http://www.thecalifornian.com
Freq: Mon thru Fri; **Circ:** 7362 Not Audited
Editor: Katharine Ball; **Publisher:** Amy Pack
Editorial Profile: The Salinas Californian is published daily for residents of Salinas Valley, CA. The newspaper covers local news, weather, sports, and community events. Feature articles cover business, education, arts and entertainment, lifestyle, and other information of interest to community residents.; Full Page Mono: 59.19; Full Page Colour: 690.00
Currency: US Dollars
DAILY NEWSPAPER

The Saline Courier
Owner: Horizon Publications
Editorial: 321 N Market St, Benton, Arkansas 72015-3734. **T:** 1 501 315-8228
W: http://www.bentoncourier.com
Freq: Daily; **Circ:** 6563 Not Audited
Editor: Brent Davis; **Publisher:** Terri Leifeste

Editorial Profile: The Saline Courier is a daily local newspaper serving Saline County, AR. It is published in the evening Monday through Friday and in the morning on Saturday and Sunday.; Full Page Mono: 14.55; Full Page Colour: 46.90
Currency: US Dollars
DAILY NEWSPAPER

Salisbury Post
Owner: Evening Post Publishing Co.
Editorial: 131 W Innes St, Salisbury, North Carolina 28144-4338. **T:** 1 704 633-8950
E: news@salisburypost.com
W: http://www.salisburypost.com
Freq: Daily; **Circ:** 16046
Publisher: Greg Anderson; **Editor:** Elizabeth Cook
Editorial Profile: Salisbury Post is published daily for the residents of Rowan County, NC. The newspaper covers local news, sports, education and community events.; Full Page Mono: 31.80; Full Page Colour: 399.00
Currency: US Dollars
DAILY NEWSPAPER

Salmon Press - Lancaster
Owner: Salmon Press LLC
Editorial: 79 Main St, Lancaster, New Hampshire 03584-3027. **T:** 1 603 788-4939
W: http://www.newhampshirelakesandmountains.com
Circ: 9200
Publisher: Frank Chilinski; **Editor:** Art McGrath
NEWSPAPER

Salmon Press - Meredith
Owner: Salmon Press LLC
Editorial: 5 Water St, Meredith, New Hampshire 03253-6233. **T:** 1 603 279-4516
W: http://www.newhampshirelakesandmountains.com
Circ: 14965 Not Audited
Editor: Brendan Berube; **Publisher:** Frank Chilinski; **Editor:** Erin Plummer
NEWSPAPER

Salmon Press - Wolfeboro
Owner: Salmon Press LLC
Editorial: Clark Plaza, 35 Center St, Wolfeboro, New Hampshire 3896.
T: 1 603 569-3126
W: http://www.newhampshirelakesandmountains.com
Circ: 10500 Not Audited
Editor: Thomas Beeler; **Publisher:** Frank Chilinski; **Editor:** Joshua Spalding
NEWSPAPER

Salt Lake City Weekly
Owner: Copperfield Publishing, Inc.
Editorial: 248 S Main St, Salt Lake City, Utah 84101-2001. **T:** 1 801 575-7003
W: http://www.cityweekly.net
Freq: Thu; **Circ:** 60000 Not Audited
Publisher: John Saltas; **Editor:** Jerre Wroble
Editorial Profile: Salt Lake City Weekly is published for the residents of Salt Lake City, UT and surrounding areas. The newspaper covers local news and entertainment.; Full Page Mono: 67.20
Currency: US Dollars
NEWSPAPER

The Salt Lake Tribune
Owner: MediaNews Group
Editorial: 90 S 400 W Ste 700, Salt Lake City, Utah 84101-1431. **T:** 1 801 257-8742
E: news@sltrib.com **W:** http://www.sltrib.com
Freq: Daily; **Circ:** 177132 Not Audited
Editorial Profile: The Salt Lake Tribune is the largest and most widely read daily newspaper in Utah. It was founded in 1872. The Tribune is published for a general consumer audience. Articles include features, breaking news, trends, analyses, profiles, and investigative stories. Topics covered also include entertainment, health, food and drink, sports, and reviews.; Full Page Mono: 218.00; Full Page Colour: 327.45
Currency: US Dollars
DAILY NEWSPAPER

The Salt Lake Tribune
Editorial: 529 14th St NW Ste 1255, Washington, District Of Columbia 20045-2201.
T: 1 202 662-8925
DAILY NEWSPAPER

Salt River Journal
Editorial: 200 N 3Rd St, Hannibal, Missouri 63401-3504. **T:** 1 573 221-2800
E: webmaster@courierpost.com
W: http://www.hannibal.net
Freq: Wed; **Circ:** 10100 Not Audited
Publisher: David Stringer
Editorial Profile: Salt River Journal is a weekly newspaper published for the residents of Hannibal, MO and surrounding communities. The publication covers hunting and fishing news and information.; Full Page Mono: 7.36
Currency: US Dollars
NEWSPAPER

El Salvador Dia a Dia
Editorial: 3325 Wilshire Blvd, Ste 739, Los Angeles, California 90010. **T:** 1 213 674-8549
E: diaadianews@yahoo.com
W: http://www.diaadia.com.pa
Freq: Fri; **Circ:** 40000 Not Audited
Editorial Profile: El Salvador Dia A Dia is a community newspaper written for the Spanish-speaking residents of Los Angeles.; Full Page Mono: 25.00
Currency: US Dollars
NEWSPAPER

Sampan
Owner: Asian American Civic Association
Editorial: 87 Tyler St, 5th Fl, Boston, Massachusetts 02111-1833.
T: 1 617 426-9492 **E:** news@sampan.org
W: http://www.sampan.org
Freq: Bi-Weekly; **Circ:** 10000 Not Audited
Editor: Cody Yiu
Editorial Profile: Sampan is the only Chinese-English bilingual newspaper in the New England area. It is published on the first and third Friday of each month primarily for the Asian-American community in the greater New England area. The newspaper offers information on news and events in the area. Deadlines are on Fridays before the publication day.; Full Page Mono: 12.00
Currency: US Dollars
NEWSPAPER

Sampson Independent
Owner: Heartland Publications
Editorial: 303 W Elizabeth St, Clinton, North Carolina 28328-4426. **T:** 1 910 592-8137
W: http://www.clintonnc.com
Freq: Daily; **Circ:** 7000 Not Audited
Editor: Sherry Matthews; **Publisher:** Jules Molenda
Editorial Profile: Sampson Independent is a daily newspaper published for the residents of Warsaw, Faison, Wallace, Sampson, Duplin, Harnett and Cumberland, NC. The newspaper covers local news, sports, business, lifestyles, education, agriculture, religion, arts & entertainment, courts, crime and community events.; Full Page Mono: 15.10; Full Page Colour: 335.00
Currency: US Dollars
DAILY NEWSPAPER

The Sampson Weekly
Editorial: 404 Sunset Ave, Clinton, North Carolina 28328-3942. **T:** 1 910 590-2102
E: info@thesampsonweekly.com
W: http://www.thesampsonweekly.com
Freq: Thu
Editor: Melvin Henderson
Editorial Profile: The Sampson Weekly is a weekly newspaper that provides Local and Community News coverage to the residents of Clinton, NC and Sampson County.
NEWSPAPER

Sam's Good News
Owner: Sammy G. Media Corp.
Editorial: 162 N Main St, Stony Brook Plaza, Rutland, Vermont 5701. **T:** 1 802 773-4040
E: samsgoodnews@aol.com
W: http://www.samsgoodnews.com
Freq: Wed; **Circ:** 11000 Not Audited
Editor: Rosemary Finley; **Editor:** Rosemary Finley; **Publisher:** Samuel Gorruso
Editorial Profile: Sam's Good News' editorial mission is to provide good, positive news and information to the people in Vermont communities. The newspaper has 500 distribution points, including some in New York state. Topics include local news, real estate, business, horoscopes and sports in addition to other relevant topics. Deadline for submission of press releases falls on Friday prior to the issue date.; Full Page Mono: 12.00; Full Page Colour: 1344.00
Currency: US Dollars
NEWSPAPER

San Angelo Standard-Times
Owner: E.W. Scripps Co.
Editorial: 34 W Harris Ave, San Angelo, Texas 76903-5838. **T:** 1 325 659-8200
E: standard@gosanangelo.com
W: http://www.gosanangelo.com
Freq: Daily; **Circ:** 18299 Not Audited
Publisher: Jeff DeLoach; **Editor:** Michael Kelly
Editorial Profile: San Angelo Standard-Times is a daily newspaper published for the residents of San Angelo, TX. The publication covers local news, sports, business, agriculture, city and county government, police, education, health and community events.; Full Page Mono: 41.41; Full Page Colour: 420.00
Currency: US Dollars
DAILY NEWSPAPER

San Antonio Current
Owner: Times Shamrock Group
Editorial: 915 Dallas St, San Antonio, Texas 78215-1433. **T:** 1 210 227-0044
E: sacalendar@sacurrent.com
W: http://www.sacurrent.com
Freq: Wed; **Circ:** 46613 Not Audited
Editor in Chief: Callie Enlow
Editorial Profile: San Antonio (TX) Current is a local alternative weekly newspaper focusing on investigative reports, alternative news, entertainment and lifestyle.; Full Page Mono: 51.03; Full Page Colour: 2250.00
Currency: US Dollars
NEWSPAPER

San Antonio Express-News
Owner: Hearst Newspapers
Editorial: 301 Avenue E, San Antonio, Texas 78205-2006. **T:** 1 210 250-3000
W: http://www.mysanantonio.com
Freq: Daily; **Circ:** 146463 Not Audited
Editor in Chief: Mike Leary; **Editor:** Tracy Lehmann; **Editor:** Tracy Lehmann; **Editor:** Tracy Lehmann; **Editor:** Tracy Lehmann;
Editor: Richard Marini; **Editor:** Richard Marini; **Editor:** Richard Marini; **Publisher:** John McKeon
Editorial Profile: San Antonio Express-News is written for residents in the Southwest. The paper covers local, regional, national and international news, as well as business, technology, books, features, travel, home, garden and sports. It was founded in 1866. The Internet version of the paper is MySA.com.; Full Page Mono: 364.11; Full Page Colour: 387.27
Currency: US Dollars
DAILY NEWSPAPER

San Antonio Express-News
Editorial: 700 12th St NW Ste 1000, Washington, District Of Columbia 20005-3994.
T: 1 202 263-6400
DAILY NEWSPAPER

San Antonio Express-News
Editorial: 1005 Congress Ave, Austin, Texas 78701-2463. **T:** 1 512 478-3495
Bureau Chief: Peggy Fikac
Editorial Profile: The San Antonio Express-News' and the Houston Chronicle's Austin bureaus merged in 2006, and reporters cover news for both papers.
DAILY NEWSPAPER

San Antonio Observer
Owner: Observer Newspaper Group
Editorial: 3427 Belgium Ln, San Antonio, Texas 78219. **T:** 1 210 212-6397
W: http://www.saobserver.com
Freq: Wed; **Circ:** 60000 Not Audited
Editorial Profile: San Antonio Observer is a community newspaper written for the residents of San Antonio, TX.; Full Page Mono: 50.00
Currency: US Dollars
NEWSPAPER

San Bernardino Sun City Newspapers
Owner: MediaNews Group
Editorial: 290 N D St Ste 102, San Bernardino, California 92401-1734.
T: 1 909 889-9666 **W:** http://www.sbsun.com
Circ: 137250 Not Audited
Editorial Profile: Produced by the San Bernardino (CA) Sun, City Newspapers consist of five weekly newspapers that target specific communities throughout the area. Each newspaper is inserted within the Friday edition of the San Bernardino (CA) Sun and also mailed to selected non-subscribers on Saturdays. The papers cover the lifestyles and events of the communities and residents in the area. They rely heavily on readers' submissions of photos and stories concerning neighborhood news, volunteerism, community events, hobbies and youth sports.; Full Page Mono: 651.00
Currency: US Dollars
NEWSPAPER

San Diego City News
Owner: JRAD Media Corporation
Editorial: 550 Marina Parkway, PMB 47, Chula Vista, California 91910. **T:** 1 888 407-1541
E: info@sdcitynews.com
W: http://www.sdcitynews.com
Freq: Fri
Editorial Profile: San Diego City News is weekly newspaper providing Local and Community News to the residents of San Diego, CA.
NEWSPAPER

San Diego CityBeat
Owner: Southland Publishing
Editorial: 3047 University Ave Ste 202, San Diego, California 92104-3039.
T: 1 619 281-7526 **E:** editor@sdcitybeat.com
W: http://www.sdcitybeat.com
Freq: Wed; **Circ:** 50000 Not Audited
Publisher: Kevin Hellman; **Editor:** David Rolland
Editorial Profile: San Diego CityBeat is an alternative weekly newspaper distributed throughout San Diego County.; Full Page Mono: 16.61; Full Page Colour: 1185.00
Currency: US Dollars
NEWSPAPER

San Diego Community Newspaper Group
Owner: Mannis Communications, Inc.
Editorial: 1621 Grand Ave Ste C, San Diego, California 92109-4458. **T:** 1 858 270-3103
W: http://www.sdnews.com **Circ:** 62000 Not Audited
Editor: Kendra Hartmann; **Publisher:** Julie Hoisington
Editorial Profile: San Diego Community Newspaper Group is a community newspaper publisher servicing the residents of Sand Diego.
NEWSPAPER

San Diego Downtown News
Owner: sdCNN
Editorial: 3737 5th Ave Ste 201, San Diego, California 92103-4217. **T:** 1 619 519-7775
W: http://sandiegodowntownnews.com
Circ: 18000
Editor: Morgan Hurley; **Publisher:** David Mannis
Editorial Profile: San Diego Downtown News is a monthly community newspaper serving downtown San Diego, including the Columbia, Core/Civic, Cortez Hill, East Village, Gaslamp/Horton Plaza, Little Italy and Marina neighborhoods. The paper includes local news, business, entertainment, opinion, and event calendars.
NEWSPAPER

San Diego Jewish Journal
Owner: Ross (Mark) & Edelstein (Mark)
Editorial: 5665 Oberlin Dr Ste 204, San Diego, California 92121-1739. **T:** 1 858 638-9818
W: http://www.sdjewishjournal.com
Freq: Monthly; **Circ:** 20000 Not Audited
Editor: Alanna Berman
Editorial Profile: San Diego Jewish Journal is a monthly community newspaper serving the Jewish community in San Diego, Palm Springs and Temecula Valley, CA. It includes local, national and international news of interest to the Jewish community.; Full Page Mono: 33.88
Currency: US Dollars
NEWSPAPER

San Diego Monitor News
Editorial: 3570 Olive St, Lemon Grove, California 91945-1737. **T:** 1 619 668-1007
E: sdmnews@aol.com
Freq: Sat; **Circ:** 15000 Not Audited
Editorial Profile: San Diego Monitor News is published twice a month for residents of San Diego. The publication covers local news, sports and community events. Deadlines for the publication are Tuesdays.; Full Page Mono: 15.50
Currency: US Dollars
NEWSPAPER

San Diego Reader
Editorial: 1703 India St, San Diego, California 92101-2517. T: 1 619 235-3000
E: info@sandiegoreader.com
W: http://www.sandiegoreader.com
Freq: Thu; **Circ:** 130000 Not Audited
News Editor: Matt Potter
Editorial Profile: San Diego Reader is a weekly newspaper written for the residents of San Diego. The newspaper cover local news, arts and entertainment, politics and events.; Full Page Mono: 89.45; Full Page Colour: 5254.00
Currency: US Dollars
NEWSPAPER

San Diego Uptown News
Owner: sdCNN
Editorial: 3737 5th Ave, Ste 201, San Diego, California 92103-4217. **T:** 1 619 519-7775
W: http://sduptownnews.com
Freq: Bi-Weekly; **Circ:** 22000
Editor: Morgan Hurley; **Publisher:** David Mannis
Editorial Profile: San Diego Uptown News is a free, bi-weekly newspaper serving the communities of Mission Hills, Bankers Hill, Hillcrest, University Heights, North Park, South Park, Normal Heights, Kensington and surrounding areas.; Full Page Mono: 20.41
Currency: US Dollars
NEWSPAPER

The San Diego Voice & Viewpoint
Editorial: 3619 College Ave, San Diego, California 92115-7041. **T:** 1 619 266-2233
E: news@sdvoice.info
W: http://sdvoice.info/index1.htm
Freq: Thu; **Circ:** 30000 Not Audited
Editorial Profile: The San Diego Voice & Viewpoint is written for the residents of San Diego. Deadlines for the paper are Mondays prior to issue date.; Full Page Mono: 26.00
Currency: US Dollars
NEWSPAPER

San Diego Yu-Yu
Owner: International Times Corp.
Editorial: 4655 Ruffner St, Ste 290, San Diego, California 92111. **T:** 1 858 576-9016
E: info@sandiegoyuyu.com
W: http://www.sandiegoyuyu.com
Freq: Bi-Weekly; **Circ:** 10000 Not Audited
Publisher: Noriko Sato
Editorial Profile: San Diego Yu-Yu is a Japanese-language newspaper serving Japanese communities in San Diego, Los Angeles, San Jose and Orange County, CA.; Full Page Mono: 19.81
Currency: US Dollars
NEWSPAPER

The San Fernando Sun
Owner: San Fernando Valley Sun Newspapers, Inc.
Editorial: 601 S Brand Blvd, Ste 202, San Fernando, California 91340-4950.
T: 1 818 365-3111
W: http://www.sanfernandosun.com
Freq: Thu; **Circ:** 10000 Not Audited
Editorial Profile: The San Fernando Sun is a local newspaper published every Thursday by San Fernando Valley Sun Newspaper. It is published for the residents of the San Fernando, CA area. The newspaper covers local news, sports, social and community events and business.; Full Page Mono: 19.00
Currency: US Dollars
NEWSPAPER

San Francisco Bay Guardian
Owner: San Francisco Newspaper Co.
Editorial: 835 Market St. Suite 558, San Francisco, California 94104-4248.
T: 1 415 255-3100 **E:** news@sfbg.com
W: http://www.sfbg.com
Freq: Wed; **Circ:** 95000 Not Audited
Publisher: Mark Bieschke; **Editor:** Steven Jones; **Publisher:** Glenn Zuehls
Editorial Profile: San Francisco Bay Guardian is a weekly newspaper published for the residents of San Francisco. The publication covers local news, politics, the environment, consumer issues, arts & entertainment, criminal justice, education, health and women's issues.; Full Page Mono: 71.20
Currency: US Dollars
NEWSPAPER

San Francisco Bay View
Owner: San Francisco Bay View Inc.
Editorial: 4917 3rd St, San Francisco, California 94124. **T:** 1 415 671-0789
E: editor@sfbayview.com
W: http://www.sfbayview.com
Freq: Monthly; **Circ:** 20000 Not Audited
Editor: Mary Ratcliff; **Publisher:** Willie Ratcliff
Editorial Profile: San Francisco Bay View is a monthly newspaper published for the African American community of San Francisco. The newspaper features news and views of urgent concern to the Black community, both locally and throughout the diaspora - from business and politics to arts and entertainment.; Full Page Mono: 15.00
Currency: US Dollars
NEWSPAPER

San Francisco Chronicle
Owner: Hearst Newspapers
Editorial: 901 Mission St, San Francisco, California 94103-2905. **T:** 1 415 777-1111
E: metro@sfchronicle.com
W: http://www.sfchronicle.com
Freq: Daily; **Circ:** 211779 Not Audited
Publisher: Jeffrey Johnson
Editorial Profile: San Francisco Chronicle is the largest newspaper in northern California and the second largest in the Western United States. It is a regional, daily newspaper with circulation that stretches from the Oregon border to Santa Barbara and includes the Silicon Valley.; Full Page Mono: 691.92; Full Page Colour: 2198.27
Currency: US Dollars
DAILY NEWSPAPER

San Francisco Chronicle
Editorial: 700 12th St NW, Washington, District Of Columbia 20005-3945.
T: 1 202 263-6565
Bureau Chief: David McCumber
DAILY NEWSPAPER

San Francisco Chronicle
Editorial: 3 Television Cir, Sacramento, California 95814-0750
DAILY NEWSPAPER

San Francisco Examiner
Owner: San Francisco Newspaper Co.
Editorial: 835 Market St. Suite 550, San Francisco, California 94104-4248.
T: 1 415 359-2600
E: newstips@sfexaminer.com
W: http://www.sfexaminer.com
Freq: Mon thru Fri; **Circ:** 75009 Not Audited
Editor in Chief: Michael Howerton; **Publisher:** Glenn Zuehls
Editorial Profile: San Francisco Examiner is a free commuter newspaper targeting affluent urban readers in the San Francisco Metro area. With its heavy use of graphics and succinct articles, it delivers coverage of world and local events on the day they happen. The front page unveils breaking news; other sections include the Beyond the Bay, Arts & Culture and Sports. The paper is delivered to homes Thursdays and Sundays but is available by single-copy Monday through Friday and Sundays.; Full Page Mono: 117.84; Full Page Colour: 136.84
Currency: US Dollars
DAILY NEWSPAPER

San Gabriel Valley Newspaper Group
Owner: MediaNews Group
Editorial: 1210 N Azusa Canyon Rd, West Covina, California 91790. **T:** 1 626 962-8811
E: news.tribune@sgvn.com
W: http://www.sgvtribune.com
Freq: Weekly; **Circ:** 139000 Not Audited
Editorial Profile: San Gabriel Valley Newspaper Group covers local stories and features for the communities of San Gabriel Valley, CA.; Full Page Mono: 100.25
Currency: US Dollars
NEWSPAPER

San Gabriel Valley Tribune
Owner: MediaNews Group
Editorial: 1210 N Azusa Canyon Rd, West Covina, California 91790-1003.
T: 1 626 657-0982 **E:** news.tribune@sgvn.com
W: http://www.sgvtribune.com
Freq: Daily; **Circ:** 56513 Not Audited
Editorial Profile: San Gabriel Valley Tribune is a daily newspaper serving the communities of West Covina, Monrovia, Temple City, Altadena, Arcadia, El Monte, CA and surrounding cities and towns. This paper is a part of the Los Angeles Newspaper Group, a subsidiary of Media News Group. The paper's coverage includes news, sports, business, features, and real estate.; Full Page Mono: 62.39; Full Page Colour: 396.83
Currency: US Dollars
DAILY NEWSPAPER

San Jose Mercury News
Owner: MediaNews Group
Editorial: 750 Ridder Park Dr, San Jose, California 95131-2432. **T:** 1 408 920-5000
E: themerc@mercurynews.com
W: http://www.mercurynews.com
Freq: Daily; **Circ:** 581532 Not Audited
Editorial Profile: San Jose Mercury News is a daily newspaper covering Silicon Valley, CA, including Santa Clara County, Southern Alameda County, Southern San Mateo County and Scotts Valley. The paper is read by a large number of high-tech professionals in the area. It serves its readership by presenting a variety of local business news, including many computer company stories and interviews. Coverage also includes news, business, consumer and technology. Consumer coverage includes lifestyles, health, food, fashion, arts & entertainment and travel. The outlet offers RSS (Really Simple Syndication).; Full Page Mono: 788.00; Full Page Colour: 12514.00
Currency: US Dollars
DAILY NEWSPAPER

San Jose Mercury News
Editorial: 1215 K St Ste 930, Sacramento, California 95814-3946. **T:** 1 916 441-4601
Editorial Profile: This bureau is shared with the Contra Costa Times.
DAILY NEWSPAPER

San Juan Sun
Owner: MediaNews Group
Editorial: 201 N Allen Ave, Farmington, New Mexico 87401-6212. **T:** 1 505 325-4545
Freq: Wed; **Circ:** 15000 Not Audited
Publisher: John Elchert; **Editor:** Troy Turner
Editorial Profile: San Juan Sun is written for the residents of San Juan County, NM. The publication features advertisements, as well as some news briefs. Deadlines are on Mondays at 3:30pm MT.; Full Page Mono: 6.70; Full Page Colour: 2927.96
Currency: US Dollars
NEWSPAPER

San Marcos Daily Record
Owner: Community Newspaper Holdings, Inc.
Editorial: 1910 S Interstate 35, San Marcos, Texas 78666-5901. **T:** 1 512 392-2458
W: http://www.sanmarcosrecord.com
Freq: Daily; **Circ:** 6464 Not Audited
News Editor: Anita Miller
Editorial Profile: San Marcos Daily Record is a daily newspaper published for the residents of San Marcos, TX. The publication covers local news, sports, and community events.; Full Page Mono: 11.70; Full Page Colour: 350.00
Currency: US Dollars
DAILY NEWSPAPER

San Marino Tribune
Editorial: 1441 San Marino Ave, San Marino, California 91108. **T:** 1 626 792-6397
W: http://www.sanmarinotribune.com
Freq: Thu; **Circ:** 15000 Not Audited
Editor: Winston Chua; **Editor:** Mitch Lehman; **Publisher:** Clifton Smith
Editorial Profile: San Marino Tribune is a weekly, local paper serving the residents of the San Marino, CA. It covers local news and sports, lifestyles, events, entertainment calendars, home and garden tips and dining reviews. Deadlines are on Wednesdays at noon PT.; Full Page Mono: 20.00; Full Page Colour: 1432.00
Currency: US Dollars
NEWSPAPER

San Mateo County Times
Owner: MediaNews Group
Editorial: 477 9Th Ave Ste 110, San Mateo, California 94402-1858. **T:** 1 650 348-4321
E: bangcirc@bayareanewsgroup.com
W: http://www.mercurynews.com/san-mateo-county-times
Freq: Daily; **Circ:** 24915 Not Audited
Editorial Profile: San Mateo County Times is a local, daily newspaper covering the municipalities in San Mateo County, CA. The paper includes local news specific to San Mateo County as well as County Coastline and the North and South County cities. The paper also offers complete local, college and professional sports coverage, social and entertainment news, and local business reporting. The paper is a part of the Bay Area News Group subsidiary of MediaNews Group.; Full Page Mono: 140.00; Full Page Colour: 449.30
Currency: US Dollars
DAILY NEWSPAPER

San Patricio Publishing Company
Owner: Tracy (Jim & John)
Editorial: 117 S Rachal St, Sinton, Texas 78387. **T:** 1 361 364-1270
E: editor@sanpatpublishing.com
W: http://www.sanpatpublishing.com
Circ: 3100 Not Audited
Editor: Jesse Horton; **Editor:** Johnnie Sue Littleton; **Publisher:** John Tracy
NEWSPAPER

The Sand Mountain Reporter
Owner: Southern Newspapers, Inc.
Editorial: 1603 Progress Dr, Albertville, Alabama 35950-8547. **T:** 1 256 840-3000
E: news@sandmountainreporter.com
W: http://www.sandmountainreporter.com
Freq: Sat; **Circ:** 10628 Not Audited
Publisher: Ben Shurett
Editorial Profile: The Sand Mountain Reporter is published three times a week for the residents of Albertville, AL. The newspaper covers local news, sports and community events. Deadlines fall on the day prior to publication at at 10am CT.; Full Page Mono: 10.90
Currency: US Dollars
NEWSPAPER

The Sandspur
Owner: Fayetteville Publishing Co.
Editorial: 458 Whitfield St, Fayetteville, North Carolina 28306-1614. **T:** 1 910 323-4848
W: http://www.sandspuronline.com
Freq: Wed; **Circ:** 68000 Not Audited
Publisher: Charles Broadwell; **Editor:** Kim Hasty; **Editor:** Kim Hasty
Editorial Profile: The Sandspur is published weekly for the residents of Fayetteville, NC. The newspaper covers community news, business, people profiles, education, religion and outdoor recreation.; Full Page Mono: 16.45
Currency: US Dollars
NEWSPAPER

Sandusky Register
Owner: Sandusky Newspapers Inc.
Editorial: 314 W Market St, Sandusky, Ohio 44870-2410. **T:** 1 419 625-5500
W: http://www.sanduskyregister.com
Freq: Daily; **Circ:** 18652 Not Audited
Publisher: Doug Phares
Editorial Profile: Sandusky Register is a daily newspaper published for the residents of Sandusky, OH. The publication covers local news, sports, and community events. They ONLY accept news items relating to north-central Ohio. They will NOT accept national press releases or product information.; Full Page Mono: 23.06; Full Page Colour: 317.20
Currency: US Dollars
DAILY NEWSPAPER

The Sanford Herald
Owner: Paxton Media Group
Editorial: 208 Saint Clair Ct, Sanford, North Carolina 27330-3916. **T:** 1 919 708-9000
E: news@sanfordherald.com
W: http://www.sanfordherald.com
Freq: Daily; **Circ:** 8162 Not Audited
News Editor: Jennifer Gentile; **Editor:** R.V. Hight; **Publisher:** Bill Horner
Editorial Profile: The Sanford Herald is published daily for the residents of Sanford, NC and surrounding areas. The newspaper provides information about local news, business, sports, lifestyle and entertainment. The paper will publish national news stories only if it has a direct impact on the local area.; Full Page Mono: 13.65
Currency: US Dollars
DAILY NEWSPAPER

Santa Barbara Independent
Editorial: 122 W Figueroa St, Santa Barbara, California 93101. **T:** 1 805 965-5205
E: news@independent.com
W: http://www.independent.com
Freq: Thu; **Circ:** 40000 Not Audited
Editor In Chief: Marianne Partridge
Editorial Profile: The Santa Barbara (CA) Independent is a weekly newspaper published for the residents of Santa Barbara County, CA. The publication covers local news, arts, entertainment, business news, politics, and sports. Contact the publication for advertisement rates. The news deadline falls on Monday at noon PT.; Full Page Mono: 34.00
Currency: US Dollars
NEWSPAPER

Santa Barbara Latino
Owner: Ampersand Publishing Company
Editorial: 715 Anacapa St, Santa Barbara, California 93101-2203. **T:** 1 805 564-5200
W: http://www.elmexicanosb.com
Freq: Bi-Weekly; **Circ:** 15000 Not Audited
Editor: Alejandro Parra
Editorial Profile: Santa Barbara Latino is a bi-weekly newspaper written for the Spanish-speaking residents between Carpinteria and Lompoc in Santa Barbara, CA. It shares an office with the Santa Barbara News-Press. Topics include local news, community events, opinion, education, immigration, sports, arts & entertainment. Advertising deadlines are 3pm PT on Wednesdays.; Full Page Mono: 19.00
Currency: US Dollars
NEWSPAPER

Santa Barbara News-Press
Owner: Ampersand Publishing Company
Editorial: 715 Anacapa St, Santa Barbara, California 93101. **T:** 1 805 564-5200
W: http://www.newspress.com
Freq: Daily; **Circ:** 26200 Not Audited
Editor: Scott Steepleton

Editorial Profile: Santa Barbara News-Press is a daily newspaper serving the Santa Barbara, CA area. The publication covers local news, business, entertainment, lifestyle and sports.; Full Page Mono: 63.86; Full Page Colour: 550.00
Currency: US Dollars
DAILY NEWSPAPER

The Santa Clara Weekly
Editorial: 3000 Scott Blvd, Ste 105, Santa Clara, California 95054-3321.
T: 1 408 243-2000
E: scweekly@ix.netcom.com
W: http://www.santaclaraweekly.com
Freq: Wed; **Circ:** 40000 Not Audited
Editor: Angie Tolliver
Editorial Profile: The Santa Clara Weekly is published for the residents of Santa Clara, CA and surrounding areas. The newspaper covers local news, sports and community events. It is distributed via newstands and local businesses. The paper also publishes a color edition once a month that is distributed directly to the homes of area residents. The color edition has a circulation of 31,000 and is issued on the second to last Wednesday of each month. The news deadline for both editions is Fridays the week prior to publication.; Full Page Mono: 37.33
Currency: US Dollars
NEWSPAPER

Santa Cruz Sentinel
Owner: MediaNews Group
Editorial: 1800 Green Hills Rd Ste 210, Scotts Valley, California 95066-4985.
T: 1 831 423-4242
W: http://www.santacruzsentinel.com
Freq: Daily; **Circ:** 23465 Not Audited
News Editor: Donald Fukui; **Publisher:** Michael Jung; **Editor:** Donald Miller; **Editor:** Donald Miller; **Editor:** Donald Miller; **Editor:** Donald Miller
Editorial Profile: Santa Cruz Sentinel is a daily newspaper written for the residents of Santa Cruz, CA. The newspaper covers local news, sports, education, arts & entertainment, business and events. It only covers Santa Cruz County in California. Do NOT send pitches without a strong Santa Cruz tie.; Full Page Mono: 40.56; Full Page Colour: 133.37
Currency: US Dollars
DAILY NEWSPAPER

Santa Cruz Weekly
Owner: Metro Publishing, Inc.
Editorial: 115 Cooper St, Santa Cruz, California 95060. **T:** 1 831 457-9000
E: contact@santacruzweekly.com
W: http://www.santacruzweekly.com/
Freq: Wed; **Circ:** 25000 Not Audited
Editor: Steve Palopoli; **Publisher:** Debra Whizin
Editorial Profile: Santa Cruz Weekly is a weekly newspaper. The publication is an arts & entertainment guide for the greater Santa Cruz, CA area. Coverage includes Web, books, art, music, events, theater, dining, movies, reviews and local news features.
NEWSPAPER

The Santa Fe New Mexican
Owner: Robin Martin
Editorial: 202 E Marcy St, Santa Fe, New Mexico 87501-2021. **T:** 1 505 983-3303
E: newsroom@sfnewmexican.com
W: http://www.santafenewmexican.com
Freq: Daily; **Circ:** 19228 Not Audited
Publisher: Ginny Sohn
Editorial Profile: The Santa Fe New Mexican is a daily newspaper published for the residents of Santa Fe, NM. The publication covers local news, sports, business news, travel, health, science, food, the outdoors, arts & entertainment and community events. The outlet offers RSS (Really Simple Syndication).; Full Page Mono: 29.75; Full Page Colour: 34.75
Currency: US Dollars
DAILY NEWSPAPER

Santa Fe Reporter
Owner: City of Roses Newspaper Co.
Editorial: 132 E Marcy St, Santa Fe, New Mexico 87501-2054. **T:** 1 505 988-5541
E: editor@sfreporter.com
W: http://www.sfreporter.com
Freq: Wed; **Circ:** 22000 Not Audited
Publisher: Jeff Norris
Editorial Profile: Santa Fe Reporter is a weekly newspaper published for the residents of Santa Fe, NM. The publication covers local news, arts, culture and community events.; Full Page Mono: 41.45
Currency: US Dollars
NEWSPAPER

The Santa Maria Sun
Owner: Santa Maria Sun LLC
Editorial: 2540 Skyway Dr, Santa Maria, California 93455-1514. **T:** 1 805 347-1968
E: mail@santamariasun.com
W: http://www.santamariasun.com
Freq: Thu; **Circ:** 19000 Not Audited
Editor: Ryan Miller
Editorial Profile: The Santa Maria Sun is a local weekly newspaper published for the residents of Santa Maria, CA. The publication covers local news, arts & entertainment, business, crime, sports, religion, cultural and social issues, local politics, education, agriculture, health and environmental issues. Deadlines are on Tuesdays.; Full Page Mono: 17.96; Full Page Colour: 1228.00
Currency: US Dollars
NEWSPAPER

Santa Maria Times
Owner: Lee Enterprises, Inc.
Editorial: 3200 Skyway Dr, Santa Maria, California 93455-1824. **T:** 1 805 925-2691
W: http://www.santamariatimes.com
Freq: Daily; **Circ:** 10749 Not Audited
Editor: Marga Cooley; **Publisher:** Cynthia Schur
Editorial Profile: Santa Maria Times is published daily for the residents of Santa Maria, CA. The publication covers local news, sports and community events. The newspaper shares a staff with Times-Press-Recorder and Adobe Press.; Full Page Mono: 25.70
Currency: US Dollars
DAILY NEWSPAPER

Santa Monica Daily Press
Editorial: 1640 5th St Ste 218, Santa Monica, California 90401-3325. **T:** 1 310 458-7737
W: http://www.smdp.com
Freq: Daily; **Circ:** 10450 Not Audited
Publisher: Ross Furukawa; **Editor in Chief:** Matthew Hall
Editorial Profile: Santa Monica Daily Press is a local daily tabloid-size newspaper serving Santa Monica, CA and the surrounding area. It provides residents with information on news and events of interest to the community.; Full Page Mono: 20.00; Full Page Colour: 95.00
Currency: US Dollars
DAILY NEWSPAPER

Santa Monica Observer
Owner: Outlook of Santa Monica LLC
Editorial: 1844 Lincoln Blvd, Santa Monica, California 90404-4506. **T:** 1 310 452-9900
E: editor@smobserver.com
W: http://www.smobserver.com
Freq: Mon; **Circ:** 22000
Publisher: David Ganezer; **Editor-in-Chief:** Rebecca James
Editorial Profile: Santa Monica Observer focuses on Santa Monica, CA and adjoining communities, such as Pacific Palisades, Brentwood, West Los Angeles and Venice, CA.; Full Page Mono: 12.00
Currency: US Dollars
NEWSPAPER

Sapulpa Daily Herald
Owner: Sumner Newspapers Inc.
Editorial: 16 S Park St, Sapulpa, Oklahoma 74066-4220. **T:** 1 918 224-5185
W: http://www.sapulpaheraldonline.com
Freq: Daily; **Circ:** 4501 Not Audited
Editor: Eric Bruce; **Publisher:** Darren Sumner
Editorial Profile: Sapulpa Daily Herald is a daily newspaper written for the residents of Sapulpaa, OK. The paper covers national and local news, sports and arts & entertainment.; Full Page Mono: 19.00; Full Page Colour: 62.10
Currency: US Dollars
DAILY NEWSPAPER

Sarasota Herald-Tribune
Owner: Halifax Media Holdings LLC
Editorial: 1741 Main St, Sarasota, Florida 34236-5812. **T:** 1 941 953-7755
E: advocate@heraldtribune.com
W: http://www.heraldtribune.com
Freq: Daily; **Circ:** 73698 Not Audited
Publisher: Patrick Dorsey
Editorial Profile: Sarasota Herald-Tribune is a daily general-interest newspaper serving Sarasota, Manatee and Charlotte counties on Florida's Gulf Coast. The paper has been published continuously since 1925. Articles include features, breaking news, trends, analyses, profiles and investigative stories.; Full Page Mono: 185.38; Full Page Colour: 538.51
Currency: US Dollars
DAILY NEWSPAPER

Sarasota Herald-Tribune
Editorial: 300 Tamiami Trl S, Venice, Florida 34285-2451. **T:** 1 941 486-3068
DAILY NEWSPAPER

Sarasota Herald-Tribune
Editorial: 2025 Lakewood Ranch Blvd, Bradenton, Florida 34211-4946.
T: 1 941 745-7823
DAILY NEWSPAPER

Saratoga Today
Owner: Saratoga Publishing LLC
Editorial: 5 Case St, Saratoga Springs, New York 12866-3501. **T:** 1 518 581-2480
W: http://www.saratogatodaynewspaper.com
Freq: Fri; **Circ:** 10000 Not Audited
Editorial Profile: Saratoga Today is a free community newspaper published weekly for residents of Saratoga Springs and communities such as Ballston Spa, Malta, Milton, Wilton, Schuylerville and Greenfield, NY. It provides local news, sports and community events happening in the area. It is distributed at news racks, convenience stores and retailers in the distribution area.; Full Page Mono: 21.45
Currency: US Dollars
NEWSPAPER

The Saratogian
Owner: Journal Register Company
Editorial: 20 Lake Ave, Saratoga Springs, New York 12866. **T:** 1 518 584-4242
E: news@saratogian.com
W: http://www.saratogian.com
Freq: Daily; **Circ:** 6475 Not Audited
Publisher: Michael O'Sullivan
Editorial Profile: The Saratogian is a daily local newspaper serving the residents of Saratoga Springs and Saratoga County, NY. The publication covers local news, national news, lifestyle, sports, and features a weekly entertainment calendar. Press releases can be faxed to the appropriate staff member according to topic.; Full Page Mono: 35.22; Full Page Colour: 536.00
Currency: US Dollars
DAILY NEWSPAPER

Sarcoxie Publishing Co.
Editorial: 101 N 6th, Sarcoxie, Missouri 64862. **T:** 1 417 548-3311
E: fstop@centurytel.net **Circ:** 3096
Editorial Profile: Sarcoxie Publishing Co. publishes the Sarcoxie Record, the Jasper County Citizen and Pierce City Leader-Journal, providing local coverage for Jasper County communities and Pierce City, MO.
NEWSPAPER

Sauk Valley Newspapers
Owner: Sauk Valley Newspapers
Editorial: 3200 E Lincolnway, Sterling, Illinois 61081-1773. **T:** 1 815 625-3600
E: news@svnmail.com
W: http://www.saukvalley.com
Freq: Mon thru Fri; **Circ:** 16521
Publisher: Trevis Mayfield
Editorial Profile: Sauk Valley Newspapers publishes newspapers covering Dixon, Sterling and Rock Falls, IL.
DAILY NEWSPAPER

Savanna Newspapers
Editorial: 315 Main St, Savanna, Illinois 61074. **T:** 1 815 273-2277 **E:** savtj@grics.net
Circ: 12900 Not Audited
NEWSPAPER

Savannah Morning News
Owner: Morris Communications
Editorial: 1375 Chatham Pkwy, Savannah, Georgia 31405-0301. **T:** 1 912 236-9511
W: http://www.savannahnow.com
Freq: Daily; **Circ:** 30698 Not Audited
Newsroom Administrator: Chris Thompson; **Publisher:** Michael Traynor
Editorial Profile: Savannah Morning News is a regional daily morning newspaper published for the residents of Savannah, GA and the surrounding communities. It has a very strict anti-spam policy in place. Please contact the paper for specific information about e-mailing reporters on staff.; Full Page Mono: 95.00; Full Page Colour: 620.23
Currency: US Dollars
DAILY NEWSPAPER

Savannah Tribune, Inc.
Editorial: 1805 Martin Luther King Jr Blvd, Savannah, Georgia 31415. **T:** 1 912 233-6128
W: http://www.savannahtribune.com
Circ: 23000 Not Audited
NEWSPAPER

SCENE
Owner: Moran Marketing Group
Editorial: 445 Broad St, Menasha, Wisconsin 54952-3146. **T:** 1 920 418-1777
W: http://www.scenenewspaper.com
Freq: Monthly; **Circ:** 40000 Not Audited
Publisher: Jim Moran
Editorial Profile: SCENE is a news, arts & entertainment newspaper targeting 19 to 45 year old readers in the Fox Cities, Green Bay, Oshkosh WI, and the surrounding areas. It was founded in 1990 and was called the Valley Scene. In 2000, James Moran of the Moran Marketing Group became the new owner and changed the paper's name to SCENE. Deadlines for display ads are the 20th of the month prior to the issue's publication.; Full Page Mono: 11.90; Full Page Colour: 13.10
Currency: US Dollars
NEWSPAPER

Schneps Publications Inc.
Editorial: 38-15 Bell Blvd, Bayside, New York 11361. **T:** 1 718 224-5863 **Circ:** 95000 Not Audited
NEWSPAPER

Schwans Publications, Inc.
Editorial: 135 S Main St, Salem, South Dakota 57058. **T:** 1 605 425-2361
E: tschwans@triotel.net **Circ:** 2600 Not Audited
NEWSPAPER

SCN Communications Group
Owner: SCN Communications
Editorial: 7196 Cooley Lake Rd, Waterford, Michigan 48327-4113. **T:** 1 248 360-6397
E: editor@scnmail.com **Circ:** 79000
Publisher: James Fancy
NEWSPAPER

Scoop U.S.A.
Editorial: 942 N Watts St, Philadelphia, Pennsylvania 19123-1000. **T:** 1 215 232-5974
E: phillyscoop@aol.com
W: http://www.scoopusanewspaper.com
Freq: Fri; **Circ:** 35000 Not Audited
Editor: R. Sonny Driver
Editorial Profile: Scoop U.S.A. is a weekly community newspaper providing community news and public service announcements to residents in Philadelphia.; Full Page Mono: 22.00; Full Page Colour: 2712.00
Currency: US Dollars
NEWSPAPER

The Scotsman Press
Editorial: 750 W Genesee St, Syracuse, New York 13204-2306. **T:** 1 315 472-7825
W: http://www.scotsmanonline.com
Circ: 197000 Not Audited
NEWSPAPER

The Scottish Banner
Editorial: 13799 Park Blvd, #271, Seminole, Florida 33776. **T:** 1 866 5445157
E: mail@scottishbanner.com
W: http://www.scottishbanner.com
Freq: Monthly; **Circ:** 33089 Not Audited
Editorial Profile: The Scottish Banner is a community newspaper for the Scottish community in the United States.; Full Page Mono: 16.17
Currency: US Dollars
NEWSPAPER

Scottsboro Daily Sentinel
Owner: Southern Newspapers, Inc.
Editorial: 701 Veterans Dr, Scottsboro, Alabama 35768-2132. **T:** 1 256 259-1020
E: dsnews@thedailysentinel.com
W: http://www.thedailysentinel.com
Freq: Daily; **Circ:** 4200 Not Audited
Publisher: Brad Shurett
Editorial Profile: Scottsboro Daily Sentinel is a local newspaper published daily except for Saturday and Monday. The newspaper covers local news, sports, education, and government for all of Jackson County, AL.; Full Page Mono: 9.20; Full Page Colour: 204.20
Currency: US Dollars
DAILY NEWSPAPER

The Scout & Eastern Colorado News Newspapers
Owner: I-70 Publishing Company Inc.
Editorial: 1522 Main St, Strasburg, Colorado 80136-7507. **T:** 1 303 622-9796
E: dclaussen@i-70scout.com
W: http://www.i-70scout.com
Freq: Fri; **Circ:** 8000 Not Audited; Full Page Mono: 13.62
Currency: US Dollars
NEWSPAPER

The Scuppernong Reminder
Owner: Washington News Media
Editorial: 217 N Market St, Washington, North Carolina 27889
Freq: Weekly
Editor: Jurgen Boerema; **Publisher:** Ashley VanSant
Editorial Profile: The Scuppernong Reminder is a Washington Newsmedia LLC publication covering Tyrrell County and eastern Washington County in Washington, NC.
NEWSPAPER

Sea Coast Echo
Owner: BSL Newspapers, Inc.
Editorial: 124 Court St, Bay Saint Louis, Mississippi 39520. **T:** 1 228 467-5474
W: http://www.seacoastecho.com
Freq: Sat; **Circ:** 18700 Not Audited
News Editor: Geoff Belcher; **News Editor:** Geoff Belcher
Editorial Profile: Sea Coast Echo is a local newspaper written for residents of Bay Saint Louis, MS. Published twice weekly, the newspaper covers the local news, sports and business in the Bay Saint Louis, MS area. Deadlines are three days prior to issue date.; Full Page Mono: 12.50
Currency: US Dollars
NEWSPAPER

Seacoast Newspapers
Owner: GateHouse Media Inc.
Editorial: 111 NH Ave, Portsmouth, New Hampshire 03801-2864. **T:** 1 603 436-1800
E: news@seacoastonline.com
W: http://www.seacoastonline.com
Circ: 56397
Editor: Aaron Sanborn; **Publisher:** John Tabor
Editorial Profile: Seacoast Newspapers offers several community, weekly newspapers to residents in and around Portsmouth, NH. It is based in the same office as the Portsmouth (NH) Herald.
NEWSPAPER

The Seattle Times
Owner: Seattle Times Co.
Editorial: 1000 Denny Way, Seattle, Washington 98109-5340. **T:** 1 206 464-2111 4
W: http://seattletimes.com
Freq: Daily; **Circ:** 262087 Not Audited
Editor: Kathy Best; **Publisher:** Frank Blethen
Editorial Profile: The Seattle Times is a daily newspaper covering local, national and international news, as well as business, technology, real estate, travel, food, features, entertainment and sports. The Sunday issue is combined with the Seattle Post-Intelligencer. It was founded in 1896.; Full Page Mono: 425.50; Full Page Colour: 4365.00
Currency: US Dollars
DAILY NEWSPAPER

Seattle Times
Editorial: 529 14th St NW, Washington, District Of Columbia 20045-1002.
T: 1 202 662-7455
DAILY NEWSPAPER

Seattle Weekly
Owner: Sound Publishing
Editorial: 307 3rd Ave S Fl 2, Seattle, Washington 98104-2684. **T:** 1 206 623-0500
E: news@seattleweekly.com
W: http://www.seattleweekly.com
Freq: Wed; **Circ:** 75000 Not Audited
Editor in Chief: Mark Baumgarten; **Publisher:** Ken Stocker
Editorial Profile: Seattle Weekly is a newspaper published every Friday for the residents of Seattle, WA. The newspaper covers national and local news, entertainment, events, education, politics, and business. Seattle Weekly publishes an extensive calendar listing. Contact the publication for advertising information.; Full Page Mono: 47.00
Currency: US Dollars
NEWSPAPER

Security Council Report - New York Bureau
Editorial: 1 Dag Hammarskjold Plz Fl 21, New York, New York 10017-2201.
T: 1 212 759-5186
E: contact@securitycouncilreport.org
Editorial Profile: This is the New York Bureau of the Security Council Report association.
DAILY NEWSPAPER

The Sedalia Democrat
Owner: Freedom Communications Inc.
Editorial: 700 S Massachusetts Ave, Sedalia, Missouri 65301-4548. **T:** 1 660 826-1000
E: news@sedaliademocrat.com
W: http://www.sedaliademocrat.com
Freq: Mon thru Fri; **Circ:** 7602
Publisher: Lynn Kidd
Editorial Profile: The Sedalia Democrat is a daily newspaper serving the Sedalia, MO area. The paper covers local news, entertainment and recreation, lifestyle, and high school sports. Regional and national news, as well as collegiate and professional sports coverage, is taken solely from the wires.; Full Page Mono: 17.44; Full Page Colour: 232.88
Currency: US Dollars
DAILY NEWSPAPER

Seguin Daily News
Owner: Guadalupe Media, LTD.
Editorial: 609 E Court St, Seguin, Texas 78155-5713. **T:** 1 830 379-2234
W: http://www.seguintoday.com
Freq: Mon thru Fri; **Circ:** 3500 Not Audited
Editorial Profile: Seguin Daily News is written for the residents of Seguin, TX. News topics include community, farm, religion, health, military, home & garden and a local citizen profile.; Full Page Mono: 2.34
Currency: US Dollars
DAILY NEWSPAPER

Seguin Gazette-Enterprise
Owner: Southern Newspapers, Inc.
Editorial: 1012 Schriewer, Seguin, Texas 78155-7497. **T:** 1 830 379-5441
E: editor@seguingazette.com
W: http://www.seguingazette.com
Freq: Daily; **Circ:** 3991 Not Audited
Publisher: Neice Bell; **News Editor:** Jessica Sanders
Editorial Profile: Seguin Gazette-Enterprise is published Tuesday through Friday and Sunday in the morning. The editorial mission is to provide news and sports information to the county. The paper primarily covers local news for the residents of Seguin and Guadalupe County, TX. Send press releases to the news editor by e-mail.; Full Page Mono: 12.00; Full Page Colour: 285.00
Currency: US Dollars
DAILY NEWSPAPER

The Selma Times-Journal
Owner: Boone Newspapers Inc.
Editorial: 1018 Water Ave, Selma, Alabama 36701-4667. **T:** 1 334 875-2110
E: news@selmatimesjournal.com
W: http://www.selmatimesjournal.com
Freq: Daily; **Circ:** 10043 Not Audited
News Editor: Rick Couch; **Publisher:** Dennis Palmer; **Editor:** Tim Reeves
Editorial Profile: The Selma Times-Journal is written for residents in Selma and The Black Belt, AL. It covers a mixture of national and local news and sports.; Full Page Mono: 23.45; Full Page Colour: 176.45
Currency: US Dollars
DAILY NEWSPAPER

La Semana
Owner: Newspan Media
Editorial: 6601 Tarnef Dr Ste 200, Houston, Texas 77074-3634. **T:** 1 713 774-4652
W: http://www.semananews.com
Freq: Sun; **Circ:** 140000 Not Audited
Publisher: Mario Duenas; **Editor in Chief:** Marina Gil
Editorial Profile: La Semana is a weekly Sunday newspaper serving the Hispanic population of Houston.; Full Page Mono: 56.40; Full Page Colour: 3542.50
Currency: US Dollars
NEWSPAPER

La Semana
Editorial: 903 Albany St, Boston, Massachusetts 2119. **T:** 1 617 427-6212
E: wcea2000@aol.com
W: http://www.lasemanawceatv.com
Freq: Thu; **Circ:** 12000 Not Audited
Editorial Profile: La Semana is a free weekly Spanish-language newspaper distributed on Thursdays throughout Massachusetts and Rhode Island. The publication covers Latin American news and editorial content, as well as local and some national news for the Hispanic community in the metropolitan Boston area.; Full Page Mono: 16.00
Currency: US Dollars
NEWSPAPER

La Semana del Metroplex
Editorial: 2305 Fall River Dr, Arlington, Texas 76006-5705. **T:** 1 817 704-3270
W: http://www.lasemanatx.com
Freq: Fri; **Circ:** 20000 Not Audited
Editorial Profile: La Semana del Metroplex is a weekly bilingual publication written for residents of Fort Worth, TX.; Full Page Mono: 45.00
Currency: US Dollars
NEWSPAPER

La Semana Del Sur
Owner: Guillermo Rojas
Editorial: 100 W 5th St, Ste 701, Tulsa, Oklahoma 74103. **T:** 1 918 744-9502
W: http://www.lasemanadelsur.com
Freq: Wed; **Circ:** 15000 Not Audited; Full Page Mono: 9.00
Currency: US Dollars
NEWSPAPER

Semana News
Owner: NEWSPAN Media Corp.
Editorial: 6601 Tarnef Dr Ste 200, Houston, Texas 77074-3634. **T:** 1 713 774-4652
W: http://www.semananews.com
Freq: Sun; **Circ:** 125000 Not Audited
Editor in Chief: Marina Gil
Editorial Profile: Focuses on the Hispanic community in the Houston area. Reports on local and national headlines, including lifestyle pertinent to Spanish speaking families. Highlights on everything from sports to people active in community life.; Full Page Mono: 5132.40; Full Page Colour: 6143.28
Currency: US Dollars
NEWSPAPER

Semanario Argentino
Editorial: 20900 ME 30 Ave #200, Aventura, Florida 33160. **T:** 1 786 277-5148
W: http://www.eldiarioargentino.com
Freq: Tue; **Circ:** 43000
Editor: María Amelia Castro; **Publisher:** Oscar Posedente
Editorial Profile: Seminario Argentino is a weekly that provides news and information to the Argentine and Hispanic community of South Florida.
NEWSPAPER

Seminole Producer
Editorial: 121 N Main St, Seminole, Oklahoma 74868-4627. **T:** 1 405 382-1100
E: news@seminoleproducer.com
W: http://www.seminoleproducer.com
Freq: Daily; **Circ:** 5400 Not Audited
Editorial Profile: Seminole Producer is published daily for the residents of Seminole County, OK. The newspaper covers local news, sports and community events. Deadlines are one day prior to issue date at 10am CT.; Full Page Mono: 6.30; Full Page Colour: 70.00
Currency: US Dollars
DAILY NEWSPAPER

The Sentinel
Owner: Lee Enterprises, Inc.
Editorial: 457 E North St, Carlisle, Pennsylvania 17013-2655. **T:** 1 717 243-2611
E: frontdoor@cumberlink.com
W: http://www.cumberlink.com
Freq: Daily; **Circ:** 15156
Publisher: Mark Heintzelman
Editorial Profile: The Sentinel is a daily newspaper serving residents in Cumberland County, PA. The publication covers local, national, state and international news, sports, entertainment and community announcements. Press releases should be faxed to the appropriate editor. Deadlines for the publication are before 8am ET the day of publication.; Full Page Mono: 29.50; Full Page Colour: 34.95
Currency: US Dollars
DAILY NEWSPAPER

The Sentinel
Owner: Ogden Newspapers
Editorial: 352 6th St, Lewistown, Pennsylvania 17044-1213. **T:** 1 717 248-6741
E: sentinel@lewistownsentinel.com
W: http://www.lewistownsentinel.com
Freq: Daily; **Circ:** 9008 Not Audited
Publisher: Ruth Eddy
Editorial Profile: The Sentinel is published six days a week Monday through Saturday. It covers a wide variety of topics including national and local news, seniors, outdoors, government, entertainment, sports, health, business, schools, religion and agriculture. Press releases can be sent by fax to the appropriate editor. The newspaper coves six central Pennsylvania counties.; Full Page Mono: 18.88; Full Page Colour: 280.00
Currency: US Dollars
DAILY NEWSPAPER

Sentinel & Enterprise
Owner: MediaNews Group
Editorial: 808 Main St, Fitchburg, Massachusetts 01420-3153.
T: 1 978 343-6911
E: news@sentinelandenterprise.com
W: http://www.sentinelandenterprise.com
Freq: Daily; **Circ:** 15514 Not Audited
Publisher: Mark O'Neil
Editorial Profile: Sentinel & Enterprise is a daily local newspaper serving residents of Central Massachusetts. The newspaper covers local news, national news, business, obituaries and sports. Lead time varies.; Full Page Mono: 28.00; Full Page Colour: 200.00
Currency: US Dollars
DAILY NEWSPAPER

El Sentinel del Sur del la Florida
Owner: Tribune Company
Editorial: 6501 Nob Hill Rd, Tamarac, Florida 33321-6422. **T:** 1 954 356-4000
E: agenda@elsentinel.com
W: http://www.sun-sentinel.com/elsentinel
Freq: Sat; **Circ:** 118177 Not Audited
Publisher: Howard Greenberg; **Editor:** Deborah Ramirez
Editorial Profile: El Sentinel del Sur del la Florida is a free, weekly Spanish-language newspaper serving Hispanic residents in Broward and Palm Beach counties, including the city of Fort Lauderdale, FL. It covers local, national and international news pertinent to the Hispanic community. Other features include sports, lifestyle, food, events and a classifieds section. It is published from the offices of the South Florida Sun-Sentinel. Deadlines are on Tuesdays at 5pm ET.; Full Page Mono: 32.00; Full Page Colour: 1200.00
Currency: US Dollars
NEWSPAPER

Sentinel News
Editorial: 3677 N Highway 126 Ste C5, Ogden, Utah 84404-9493. **T:** 1 801 731-9191
E: mgeditor@sentinelnews.net
W: http://www.sentinelnews.net
Freq: Bi-Monthly; **Circ:** 16200 Not Audited
Publisher: Reed Mackley
Editorial Profile: Sentinel News is a weekly newspaper written for the residents between Farr West and North Ogden in Weber County, UT.; Full Page Mono: 38.00
Currency: US Dollars
NEWSPAPER

El Sentinel Orlando
Owner: Tribune Company
Editorial: 633 N Orange Ave, Orlando, Florida 32801-1300. **T:** 1 407 420-5000
W: http://www.orlandosentinel.com/elsentinel
Freq: Sat; **Circ:** 99150 Not Audited
Editor: Rafael Palacio
Editorial Profile: El Sentinel Orlando is a free, weekly Spanish-language newspaper serving Hispanic residents in Orange, Seminole, Osceola, Lake and West Volusia, FL counties, which includes the cities of Orlando, Daytona Beach and Melbourne, FL. It covers local, national and international news pertinent to the Hispanic community. Other features include sports, lifestyle, food, events and a classifieds section. The paper is home delivered to local Hispanics and is also available for pick-up at area businesses. It is published from the offices of the Orlando Sentinel. Advertising rates are a combination run with the Orlando Sentinel. Deadlines are on Thursdays at noon ET before publication.; Full Page Mono: 31.00
Currency: US Dollars
NEWSPAPER

The Sentinel Printing & Publishing Co.
Editorial: 145 S L St, Dinuba, California 93618. **T:** 1 559 591-4632
E: dinubasentinel@sbcglobal.net **Circ:** 21518
Editor: Kevin Geaney; **Editor:** Linda Renn
NEWSPAPER

Sentinel Weekly News
Owner: GG Publications, Inc.
Editorial: 1307B W 6th St, Ste 119C, Corona, California 92882. **T:** 1 951 737-9784
E: sentinelweekly@aol.com
Freq: Wed; **Circ:** 11000 Not Audited
Editor: Ellisa May Lendennie; **Publisher:** Gary Lendennie
Editorial Profile: Sentinel Weekly News is written for the residents of Corona, CA. It covers local news.; Full Page Mono: 125.00
Currency: US Dollars
NEWSPAPER

The Sentinel-Echo
Owner: Community Newspaper Holdings, Inc.
Editorial: 123 W 5th St, London, Kentucky 40741-1837. **T:** 1 606 878-7400
W: http://www.sentinel-echo.com
Freq: Fri; **Circ:** 10000 Not Audited
Editor: Carrie Dillard; **Publisher:** Willie Sawyers

Editorial Profile: Sentinel-Echo is a local newspaper serving residents of the town London and Laurel county, KY. The newspaper is published three times a week on Monday, Wednesday, and Friday. Sentinel-Echo covers local and community news for the area. Press releases should be e-mailed to the managing editor.; Full Page Mono: 7.90
Currency: US Dollars
NEWSPAPER

The Sentinel-Record
Owner: Wehco Media Inc.
Editorial: 300 Spring St, Hot Springs National Park, Arkansas 71901-4148.
T: 1 501 623-7711 **W:** http://www.hotsr.com
Freq: Daily; **Circ:** 13893 Not Audited
Publisher: Walter Hussman
Editorial Profile: The Sentinel-Record is a daily newspaper serving residents of Hot Springs National Park, AR and adjoining towns. The publication covers local news, business, lifestyles, arts & entertainment and sports.; Full Page Mono: 30.75; Full Page Colour: 98.99
Currency: US Dollars
DAILY NEWSPAPER

Sentinel-Tribune
Owner: The Sentinel Co.
Editorial: 300 E Poe Rd, Bowling Green, Ohio 43402-1329. **T:** 1 419 352-4611
E: letters@sentinel-tribune.com
W: http://www.sent-trib.com
Freq: Daily; **Circ:** 10550 Not Audited
Publisher: Thomas Haswell; **Editor:** Jan Larson McLaughlin; **Editor:** Debbie Rogers
Editorial Profile: Sentinel-Tribune is a daily newspaper serving residents of Wood County, OH. It covers local and national news, arts & entertainment, education, farming, lifestyles, real estate, religion and sports. Advertising deadlines are at 5pm ET.; Full Page Mono: 14.10; Full Page Colour: 250.00
Currency: US Dollars
DAILY NEWSPAPER

Sereechai Newspaper
Editorial: 1253 Vine St Ste 16A, Los Angeles, California 90038-1682. **T:** 1 323 465-7550
E: sereechai@sbcglobal.net
W: http://www.sereechai.com
Freq: Sat; **Circ:** 15000
Publisher: Teck Bna-Snenguraiparn; **Editor:** Somchet Phayakarit
Editorial Profile: Sereechai is a Thai newspaper written for the residents of the greater Los Angeles area. Includes community and international news, arts and entertainment, lifestyle and society, law and editorial sections.; Full Page Mono: 7.00
Currency: US Dollars
NEWSPAPER

Sesh Communications Newspapers
Owner: Sesh Communications Newspapers
Editorial: 3440 Burnet Ave, Ste 130, Cincinnati, Ohio 45229-2833.
T: 1 513 961-3331 **W:** http://seshnow.com
Circ: 28800 Not Audited
Publisher: Jan-Michele Lemon Kearney; **Editor-in-Chief:** Dan Yount
NEWSPAPER

Seven Days
Owner: Da Capo Publishing
Editorial: 255 S Champlain St, Burlington, Vermont 5401. **T:** 1 802 865-1020
W: http://www.sevendaysvt.com
Freq: Wed; **Circ:** 34000 Not Audited
Editorial Profile: Seven Days is a weekly arts newspaper serving residents in the greater Burlington, Middlebury, Montpelier, Stow, The Mad River Valley, Rutland, St. Albans and Plattsburgh, VT areas. The newspaper covers music, film and art and contains a calendar listing local events. Deadlines for the publication are on Thursdays by 5pm ET.; Full Page Mono: 26.44
Currency: US Dollars
NEWSPAPER

SF Weekly
Owner: San Francisco Newspaper Co.
Editorial: 835 Market St. Suite 550, San Francisco, California 94104-4248.
T: 1 415 536-8100 **E:** feedback@sfweekly.com
W: http://www.sfweekly.com
Freq: Wed; **Circ:** 50000 Not Audited
Publisher: Glenn Zuehls
Editorial Profile: SF Weekly is an award-winning news and arts weekly for the San Francisco area. It provides residents with information on local news, arts & entertainment, cultural affairs and much more.; Full Page Mono: 103.95; Full Page Colour: 128.95

Currency: US Dollars
NEWSPAPER

Shaw Media - Downers Grove, IL
Owner: Shaw Media
Editorial: 1101 31st St, Suite 260, Downers Grove, Illinois 60515-5515. **T:** 1 630 368-1100
W: http://www.mysuburbanlife.com
Freq: Weekly; **Circ:** 43689 Not Audited
Editor: David Good; **News Editor:** Alex Soulier; **News Editor:** Ryan Terrell
Editorial Profile: Shaw Media - Downers Grove, IL is a weekly community newspaper publisher serving the residents of Berwyn, Brookfield, La Grange, Lemont and Riverside, IL. The circulation provided for each weekly newspaper published is a combination total.; Full Page Colour: 2594.00
Currency: US Dollars
NEWSPAPER

Shaw Media - St. Charles, IL
Owner: Shaw Media
Editorial: 333 N Randall Rd Ste 2, Saint Charles, Illinois 60174-1500.
T: 1 630 232-9222
W: http://www.mysuburbanlife.com
Circ: 29775 Not Audited
Publisher: J. Thomas Shaw
NEWSPAPER

Shawano Leader
Owner: BlueLine Media Holdings
Editorial: 1464 E Green Bay St, Shawano, Wisconsin 54166-2258. **T:** 1 715 526-2121
E: editor@shawanoleader.com
W: http://www.shawanoleader.com
Freq: Daily; **Circ:** 6505 Not Audited
Publisher: Greg Mellis
Editorial Profile: Shawano Leader is a local daily newspaper serving the residents of Shawano County, WI. The newspaper mainly covers local and world news, sports, financial and community events. Deadlines for the publication are at 10am CT the day before issue date.; Full Page Mono: 16.78; Full Page Colour: 135.00
Currency: US Dollars
DAILY NEWSPAPER

The Shawnee News-Star
Owner: GateHouse Media Inc.
Editorial: 215 N Bell Ave, Shawnee, Oklahoma 74801. **T:** 1 405 273-4200
E: newsroom@news-star.com
W: http://www.news-star.com
Freq: Daily; **Circ:** 7175 Not Audited
Publisher: Brian Blansett; **Editor:** Ed Blochowiak
Editorial Profile: The Shawnee News-Star is a local newspaper serving the residents of Shawnee, OK. It includes information on local news, weather, sports, business and arts & entertainment.; Full Page Mono: 10.00
Currency: US Dollars
DAILY NEWSPAPER

The Sheboygan Press
Owner: Gannett Co., Inc.
Editorial: 632 Center Ave, Sheboygan, Wisconsin 53081-4621. **T:** 1 920 457-7711
E: news@sheboyganpress.com
W: http://www.sheboyganpress.com
Freq: Daily; **Circ:** 13170
Editorial Profile: The Sheboygan Press is a local daily newspaper written for residents of Sheboygan, WI. The newspaper covers local news, sports, and events as well as national news that effects the residents of Sheboygan, WI.; Full Page Mono: 42.50; Full Page Colour: 300.00
Currency: US Dollars
DAILY NEWSPAPER

Shelby County Reporter
Owner: Shelby County Newspapers, Inc.
Editorial: 115 N Main St, Columbiana, Alabama 35051. **T:** 1 205 669-3131
W: http://www.shelbycountyreporter.com
Freq: Wed; **Circ:** 33900 Not Audited
Editor: Jan Griffey
Editorial Profile: Shelby County Reporter is a weekly newspaper serving the residents of Shelby County, AL. The publication covers local news and community events. Deadlines are on Mondays at 10am ET.; Full Page Mono: 21.10
Currency: US Dollars
NEWSPAPER

Shelby Globe
Owner: Shelby Daily Globe, Inc.
Editorial: 37 W Main St, Shelby, Ohio 44875.
T: 1 419 342-4276
W: http://www.sdgnewsgroup.com
Freq: Daily; **Circ:** 4200 Not Audited
Publisher: Scott Gove; **Editor:** Jodi Myers;

Editor: Chuck Ridenour
Editorial Profile: The Shelby Daily Globe is a local newspaper serving the residents of Shelby, OH. It includes information on local news, weather, sports, business, and entertainment. The lead time and deadline are the same day as issue date. Contact the publication for advertising rates.; Full Page Mono: 11.35
Currency: US Dollars
DAILY NEWSPAPER

The Shelby Star
Owner: Halifax Media Holdings LLC
Editorial: 315 E Graham St, Shelby, North Carolina 28150-5452. **T:** 1 704 484-7000
E: shelbystar@shelbystar.com
W: http://www.shelbystar.com
Freq: Daily; **Circ:** 11982 Not Audited
Publisher: Skip Foster
Editorial Profile: The Shelby Star is a local newspaper serving the residents of Shelby, NC. It includes information on local news, weather, sports, business and entertainment.; Full Page Mono: 22.75; Full Page Colour: 77.35
Currency: US Dollars
DAILY NEWSPAPER

Shelbyville Daily Union
Owner: CNHI
Editorial: 100 W Main St, Shelbyville, Illinois 62565-1652. **T:** 1 217 774-2161
E: news@shelbyvilledailyunion.com
W: http://www.shelbyvilledailyunion.com
Freq: Daily; **Circ:** 3200 Not Audited
Publisher: Paul Semple
Editorial Profile: Shelbyville Daily Union is a local daily newspaper serving Shelbyville, Windsor, Findlay, Moweaqua and Stewardson, IL. The newspaper covers community news, politics, sports and entertainment. Advertising deadlines are at noon CT the day before issue date.; Full Page Mono: 6.65; Full Page Colour: 75.00
Currency: US Dollars
DAILY NEWSPAPER

Shelbyville News
Owner: Paxton Media Group
Editorial: 123 E Washington St, Shelbyville, Indiana 46176. **T:** 1 317 398-6631
E: shelbynews@shelbynews.com
W: http://www.shelbynews.com
Freq: Daily; **Circ:** 8655 Not Audited
Publisher: Rachael Raney; **Editor:** Andrea Smithson
Editorial Profile: The Shelbyville Times is a local newspaper serving the residents of Shelbyville, IN. It includes information on local news, weather, sports, business, and entertainment. This publication serves the local community of Shelbyville, IN. The staff prefers to be contacted via e-mail.; Full Page Mono: 17.00; Full Page Colour: 230.00
Currency: US Dollars
DAILY NEWSPAPER

Shelbyville Times-Gazette
Owner: Rust Communications
Editorial: 323 E Depot St, Shelbyville, Tennessee 37160-4027. **T:** 1 931 684-1200
E: editor@t-g.com **W:** http://www.t-g.com
Freq: Daily; **Circ:** 7385 Not Audited
Publisher: Hugh Jones
Editorial Profile: Shelbyville Times-Gazette is a local newspaper serving the residents of Shelbyville, TN.; Full Page Mono: 9.14; Full Page Colour: 250.00
Currency: US Dollars
DAILY NEWSPAPER

Shelton-Mason County Journal Inc.
Owner: Shelton-Mason County Journal Inc.
Editorial: 227 W Cota St, Shelton, Washington 98584-2263. **T:** 1 360 426-4412
E: pr@masoncounty.com
W: http://masoncounty.com
Freq: Thu; **Circ:** 17022 Not Audited
Publisher: Kari Sleight
Editorial Profile: Shelton-Mason County Journal is a local newspaper serving the residents of Shelton, WA. It includes information on local news, weather, sports, business and entertainment.
NEWSPAPER

Shepherd Express
Owner: Alternative Publications Employees Cooperative
Editorial: 207 E Buffalo St Ste 410, Milwaukee, Wisconsin 53202-5712.
T: 1 414 276-2222 **E:** editor@shepex.com
W: http://www.expressmilwaukee.com
Freq: Thu; **Circ:** 60650 Not Audited
Editorial Profile: Shepherd Express is written for the residents of Milwaukee. It provides

coverage of local music, arts and culture. It also includes listing of local events in the area.; Full Page Mono: 16.95
Currency: US Dollars
NEWSPAPER

The Shepherd of the Hills Gazette
Owner: Shepherd of the Hills Historical Society
Editorial: 118 State Dr, Hollister, Missouri 65672-4987. **T:** 1 417 332-1099
W: http://www.shepherdgazette.com
Freq: Quarterly; **Circ:** 150000 Not Audited
Editorial Profile: The Shepherd of the Hills Gazette provides entertainment news, area events and show reviews for the Branson, MO area, and is distributed five times each year.; Full Page Colour: 61.38
Currency: US Dollars
NEWSPAPER

Sherburne County Citizen
Owner: Meyer Publications
Editorial: 14054 Bank St, Becker, Minnesota 55308-8865. **T:** 1 763 261-5880
E: citizennewspaper@sherbtel.net
W: http://www.citizennewspaper.com
Freq: Sat; **Circ:** 11200 Not Audited
Editorial Profile: Sherburne County Citizen is a local newspaper serving the residents of Sherburne County, MN. It includes information on local news, weather, sports, business and entertainment.; Full Page Mono: 10.05
Currency: US Dollars
NEWSPAPER

Sher-E-Panjab
Owner: Singh (Baldev)
Editorial: 2477 Poppy St, East Meadow, New York 11554-5211. **T:** 1 516 783-1001
E: mail@sher-e-panjab.com
W: http://www.sher-e-panjab.com
Freq: Fri; **Circ:** 14500 Not Audited
News Editor: Aman Hammi
Editorial Profile: Sher-E-Panjab is a weekly Panjabi (Indian language) newspaper published for the residents of New York, NY.; Full Page Mono: 12.00
Currency: US Dollars
NEWSPAPER

Sheridan Press
Owner: Sheridan Newspapers, Inc.
Editorial: 144 E Grinnell St, Sheridan, Wyoming 82801-3933. **T:** 1 307 672-2431
W: http://www.thesheridanpress.com
Freq: Daily; **Circ:** 6750 Not Audited
Publisher: Steven Woody
Editorial Profile: Sheridan Press is a local newspaper serving the residents of Sheridan, WY. It includes information on local news, weather, sports, business and entertainment.; Full Page Mono: 14.00; Full Page Colour: 89.81
Currency: US Dollars
DAILY NEWSPAPER

Sherman Publications, Inc.
Owner: Sherman Publications Inc.
Editorial: 666 S Lapeer Rd, Oxford, Michigan 48371. **T:** 1 248 628-4801
E: shermanpub@aol.com
W: http://www.oxfordleader.com **Circ:** 37600 Not Audited
Editor: C.J. Carnacchio; **Editor:** Phil Custadio; **Editor:** David Fleet; **Publisher:** Jim Sherman; **Editor:** Dan Shriner
Editorial Profile: Sherman Publications, Inc. publishes The Citizen, The Clarkston News, The Lake Orion Review, The Oxford Leader, providing local coverage for the Oxford, Lake Orion, Clarkston, Ortonville/Brandon and Goodrich, MI communities.
NEWSPAPER

Shippensburg Sentinel
Owner: Lee Enterprises, Inc.
Editorial: 81 W King St, Shippensburg, Pennsylvania 17257-1224. **T:** 1 717 530-2444
W: http://www.cumberlink.com
Freq: Sat; **Circ:** 13500
Publisher: Mark Heintzelman
Editorial Profile: Shippensburg Sentinel is published twice weekly for residents of Shippensburg, PA.; Full Page Mono: 7.09
Currency: US Dollars
NEWSPAPER

Shop Right
Owner: Horizon Publications
Editorial: 325 Main St Ste A, Ridgway, Pennsylvania 15853-8019. **T:** 1 814 776-2121
E: ridgwayrecord@shop-right.com
W: http://www.ridgewayrecord.com
Freq: Mon; **Circ:** 27111
Editor: Joe Bell; **Publisher:** Darlene Coder

Editorial Profile: Shop Right in Ridgway, PA is a weekly newspaper that covers community news and events.; Full Page Mono: 11.60
Currency: US Dollars
NEWSPAPER

The Shoppers Guide
Owner: Gazette Newspapers
Editorial: 6 E Main St, Everett, Pennsylvania 15537-1256. **T:** 1 814 623-1151
E: shopperguide@embarqmail.com
W: http://www.bedfordgazette.com
Freq: Sat; **Circ:** 26027 Not Audited
Editorial Profile: The Shoppers Guide is a weekly community newspaper serving residents of the Everett, PA area. It covers local news, sports and entertainment.; Full Page Mono: 10.25
Currency: US Dollars
NEWSPAPER

The Shopping News of Lancaster County
Owner: Hocking Printing Co., Inc.
Editorial: 615 E Main St, Ephrata, Pennsylvania 17522-2537. **T:** 1 717 738-1151
E: snews@ptd.net **W:** http://www.snews.com
Freq: Tue; **Circ:** 38000 Not Audited
Editorial Profile: The Shopping News of Lancaster County in Ephrata, PA is a weekly newspaper that covers local news and events.; Full Page Mono: 12.50
Currency: US Dollars
NEWSPAPER

Shore Publishing - Madison
Owner: Shore Publishing LLC
Editorial: 724 Boston Post Rd, Ste 202, Madison, Connecticut 6443.
T: 1 203 245-1877
E: news@shorepublishing.com
W: http://www.shorepublishing.com
Circ: 70102 Not Audited
Publisher: Lisa Miksis
Editorial Profile: Shore Publishing - Madison (CT) offers superior local news coverage delivered to every home and business every week. The publications feature informative articles about issues that are important to local residents and affect their daily lives, including weekly resident profiles and regular reports on town projects, boards, and committees. News coverage is complemented by columns from state senators, local authors, and naturalists, letters to the editor, opinion pieces and submissions from readers.
NEWSPAPER

Shoreline Publishing
Owner: Shapiro (Edward)
Editorial: 629 Fifth Ave Ste 213, Pelham, New York 10803-3708. **T:** 1 914 738-7869
E: prod@shorelinepub.com
W: http://www.shorelinepub.com **Circ:** 47303 Not Audited
Publisher: Edward Shapiro
Editorial Profile: Shoreline Publishing provides a local newspaper for Pelham, NY.
NEWSPAPER

Shoreline Times
Owner: Shore Line Newspaper Group
Editorial: 40 Sargent Dr, New Haven, Connecticut 06511-6111. **T:** 1 203 789-5200
E: shorelinetimes@ctcentral.com
W: http://www.shorelinetimes.com
Freq: Fri; **Circ:** 30902 Not Audited
Editor: Susan Braden
Editorial Profile: The Shoreline Times is a weekly community newspaper focusing on news along the shoreline of New Haven, CT.; Full Page Mono: 31.85
Currency: US Dollars
NEWSPAPER

Shoshone News-Press
Owner: Hagadone Corp.
Editorial: 620 E Mullan Ave, Osburn, Idaho 83849. **T:** 1 208 752-1120
W: http://www.shoshonenewspress.com
Freq: Daily; **Circ:** 4006 Not Audited
Publisher: Dan Drewry
Editorial Profile: Shoshone News-Press is a local newspaper serving the residents of Shoshone County, ID. The paper includes information on local news, weather, sports, business and entertainment.; Full Page Mono: 13.83; Full Page Colour: 200.00
Currency: US Dollars
DAILY NEWSPAPER

Siam Media Weekly Thai Newspaper
Owner: Siam Media, Inc.
Editorial: 9266 Valley Blvd, Rosemead, California 91770. **T:** 1 626 307-9119
E: siammedia@gmail.com
W: http://www.siammedia.org
Freq: Fri; **Circ:** 10000 Not Audited
Editorial Profile: Siam Media Weekly Thai Newspaper provides news and information for and about the Thai and Southeast Asian community living in the United States. Deadlines are on Fridays at 6pm PT.; Full Page Mono: 2.07
Currency: US Dollars
NEWSPAPER

Sicangu Sun Times
Editorial: BIA Hwy I, Rosebud, South Dakota 57570. **T:** 1 605 747-2280
E: suntimes@goldenwest.net
Freq: Semi-Monthly; **Circ:** 15000 Not Audited
Editorial Profile: Sicangu Sun Times is a local newspaper serving the Native American residents of Rosebud, SD. It includes information on local news, weather, sports, business and entertainment.; Full Page Mono: 9.00
Currency: US Dollars
NEWSPAPER

The Sidney Daily News
Owner: Ohio Community Media LLC.
Editorial: 1451 N Vandemark Rd, Sidney, Ohio 45365-3547. **T:** 1 937 498-8088
W: http://www.sidneydailynews.com
Freq: Daily; **Circ:** 13141 Not Audited
Publisher: Jeff Billiel; **Editor:** Melanie Speicher
Editorial Profile: The Sidney Daily News is a daily, local paper serving the residents of the Sidney, OH area. It covers local news, sports, entertainment and lifestyle information as well as comprehensive event listings.; Full Page Mono: 18.90; Full Page Colour: 27.90
Currency: US Dollars
DAILY NEWSPAPER

Sie7e Dias
Editorial: 2555 Porter Lake Dr Ste 107, Sarasota, Florida 34240-7865.
T: 1 941 341-0000 **E:** periodico@7dias.us
W: http://www.7dias.us
Freq: Sat; **Circ:** 23000 Not Audited
Editorial Profile: Sie7E Dias is a local newspaper written for the Hispanic community of Sarasota, Pinellas, FL.; Full Page Mono: 17.00
Currency: US Dollars
NEWSPAPER

Sierra Sun
Owner: Swift Newspapers
Editorial: 12315 Deerfield Dr, Truckee, California 96161-0510. **T:** 1 530 587-6061
E: editor@sierrasun.com
W: http://www.sierrasun.com
Freq: 2 Times/Week; **Circ:** 5871 Not Audited
Editor: Kevin MacMillan
Editorial Profile: Sierra Sun is a community newspaper serving residents of Truckee, Tahoe City, Sqaw Valley and Kings Beach, CA. It covers regional and local news, sports, editorials and lifestyle stories. Tahoe World, an arts, entertainment and recreation guide to the North Shore area, is inserted into the paper on Wednesdays.; Full Page Mono: 13.00; Full Page Colour: 16.00
Currency: US Dollars
NEWSPAPER

Sierra Vista Herald/Bisbee Daily Review
Owner: Wick Communications Inc.
Editorial: 102 Fab Ave, Sierra Vista, Arizona 85635-1784. **T:** 1 520 458-9440
E: svhnews@transedge.com
W: http://www.svherald.com **Circ:** 10876 Not Audited
Publisher: Philip Vega
DAILY NEWSPAPER

Siglo 21
Editorial: 316 Essex St, Ste 305, Lawrence, Massachusetts 01840-1422.
T: 1 978 687-2652 **E:** editor@siglo21.com
W: http://www.siglo21.com
Freq: Daily; **Circ:** 25000 Not Audited
Publisher: Victor Gonzalez; **Editor:** Roberto Rodriguez
Editorial Profile: Siglo 21 is written for Hispanic residents of the New England area. It covers local, national and international news, sports, entertainment, health and business. There is also an English insert available allowing a multi-generational audience.; Full Page Mono: 30.00; Full Page Colour: 138.54
Currency: US Dollars
DAILY NEWSPAPER

Siglo21
Editorial: 200 S A St, Oxnard, California 93030-5717. **T:** 1 805 240-2070
W: http://www.misiglo21.com
Freq: Thu; **Circ:** 20000
Editor: Luis Ayala
Editorial Profile: Siglo21 is a Spanish-language weekly that integrates local news, entertainment and sports stories with even more in-depth reports from the nation, Mexico and Latin America.; Full Page Mono: 8.57
Currency: US Dollars
NEWSPAPER

The Signal
Owner: Morris Multimedia, Inc.
Editorial: 24000 Creekside Rd, Santa Clarita, California 91355-1726. **T:** 1 661 259-1234
E: citydesk@signalscv.com
W: http://www.the-signal.com
Freq: Daily; **Circ:** 9329 Not Audited
Publisher: Randy Morton
Editorial Profile: The Signal is a local daily newspaper written for residents of northern Los Angeles County, including the communities of Santa Clarita, Agua Dolce, Canyon Country, Castaic, Newhall, Saugus, Stevenson Ranch, Valencia and Val Verde, CA. It covers local news, schools, business, sports, editorials, community events and arts & entertainment.; Full Page Mono: 39.90; Full Page Colour: 127.46
Currency: US Dollars
DAILY NEWSPAPER

The Signal
Owner: U.S. Army Signal Center
Editorial: 520 Chamberlain Ave Bldg 209, Fort Gordon, Georgia 30905-5735.
T: 1 706 791-7069
E: thesignal@conus.army.mil
W: http://www.fortgordonsignal.com
Freq: Fri; **Circ:** 18000 Not Audited
Publisher: Roy Chalker
Editorial Profile: The Signal is a free weekly civilian enterprise newspaper published for all personnel at Fort Gordon, GA.; Full Page Mono: 10.75
Currency: US Dollars
NEWSPAPER

The Signal Tribune
Owner: Strichart (Neena)
Editorial: 939 E 27Th St, Signal Hill, California 90755-2703. **T:** 1 562 427-8678
E: newspaper@signaltribune.com
W: http://www.signaltribune.com
Freq: Thu; **Circ:** 25000 Not Audited
Editorial Profile: The Signal Tribune covers news and events for the community of Signal Hill, CA.; Full Page Mono: 18.00
Currency: US Dollars
NEWSPAPER

Silicon Valley Community Newspapers
Owner: MediaNews Group
Editorial: 1095 The Alameda, San Jose, California 95126-3142. **T:** 1 408 200-1000
W: http://www.mercurynews.com/san-jose-neighborhoods **Circ:** 148779 Not Audited
Editor: Chris Vongsarath
NEWSPAPER

Silicon Valley Community Newspapers - Los Gatos
Owner: MediaNews Group
Editorial: 1095 The Alameda, San Jose, California 95126-3142. **T:** 1 408 200-1050
W: http://www.mercurynews.com/my-town
Circ: 29750 Not Audited
Editor: Dick Sparrer
NEWSPAPER

Silver City Daily Press & Independent
Owner: Independent Publishing Co./Christina Ely Owner
Editorial: 300 W Market St, Silver City, New Mexico 88061-4956. **T:** 1 575 388-1576
E: tely@silvercitydailypress.net
W: http://www.scdailypress.com
Freq: Daily; **Circ:** 9072 Not Audited
Publisher: Tina Ely; **Editor:** Dean Thompson
Editorial Profile: Silver City Daily Press & Independent serves the residents of Silver City, NM. It covers local news, weather, sports, business and entertainment.; Full Page Mono: 16.25; Full Page Colour: 17.25
Currency: US Dollars
DAILY NEWSPAPER

Silver City Sun-News
Owner: MediaNews Group
Editorial: 208 W Broadway St, Silver City, New Mexico 88061. **T:** 1 575 538-5893
W: http://www.scsun-news.com
Freq: Daily; **Circ:** 2200 Not Audited
Editor: Christine Steele
Editorial Profile: Silver City Sun-News is a daily newspaper serving the residents of Silver City, NM. It covers news, sports, features, business and opinion articles. It shares some of its editorial content with the Las Cruces (NM) Sun-News.; Full Page Mono: 9.50; Full Page Colour: 50.00
Currency: US Dollars
DAILY NEWSPAPER

Simpson Publishing Co., Inc.
Owner: Emmerich Newspapers Inc.
Editorial: 206 Main Ave N, Magee, Mississippi 39111. **T:** 1 601 849-3434
E: mcourier@bellsouth.net
W: http://www.mageecourier-countynews.com
Circ: 6450 Not Audited
Editorial Profile: Simpson Publishing Co., Inc. provides local news to the community of Magee, MS.
NEWSPAPER

Sing Tao Daily
Owner: Sing Tao Newspapers Ltd.
Editorial: 188 Lafayette St, New York, New York 10013. **T:** 1 212 431-9030
E: editor@nysingtao.com
W: http://www.nysingtao.com
Freq: Daily; **Circ:** 55000 Not Audited
Editor: Lotus Chau; **Editor:** Alice Lee;
Publisher: Robin Mui
Editorial Profile: Sing Tao Daily is a daily newspaper published for the members of the Chinese speaking community. The newspaper covers local, regional, national and international news as well as entertainment, business and finance and lifestyle issues.; Full Page Mono: 6.00; Full Page Colour: 8.40
Currency: US Dollars
DAILY NEWSPAPER

Sing Tao Daily
Owner: Sing Tao Newspapers (S.F.) Ltd.
Editorial: 5000 Shoreline Ct Ste 300, South San Francisco, California 94080-1956.
T: 1 650 808-8800 **E:** editor@singtaousa.com
W: http://www.singtaousa.com
Freq: Daily; **Circ:** 10000 Not Audited
Bureau Chief: Wesley Chu; **Publisher:** Tim Lau; **Editor in Chief:** Joseph Leung
Editorial Profile: Sing Tao Daily is a newspaper covering local, national and international news relevant to Chinese Americans in the San Francisco Bay area. Advertising deadlines are at noon PT.; Full Page Mono: 7.50; Full Page Colour: 11.00
Currency: US Dollars
DAILY NEWSPAPER

Sing Tao Daily - Boston Edition
Editorial: 130 Lincoln St, Boston, Massachusetts 2111. **T:** 1 617 426-9642
E: singtaoboston@yahoo.com
Freq: Daily
Bureau Chief: Klysler Yen
DAILY NEWSPAPER

Sing Tao Daily - Chicago Edition
Editorial: 2109 S China Pl, B, Chicago, Illinois 60616-1536. **T:** 1 312 842-3191
E: chicago@nysingtao.com
Bureau Chief: Michelle Teo
DAILY NEWSPAPER

Sing Tao Daily - Los Angeles Edition
Editorial: 17059 Green Dr, City of Industry, California 91745-1812. **T:** 1 626 956-8210
E: editor@singtaola.com
DAILY NEWSPAPER

Sing Tao Daily - San Francisco Edition
Owner: Sing Tao Newspapers Ltd.
Editorial: 625 Kearny St, San Francisco, California 94108-1849. **T:** 1 415 989-7111
DAILY NEWSPAPER

The Sioux City Journal
Owner: Lee Enterprises, Inc.
Editorial: 515 Pavonia St, Sioux City, Iowa 51101-2245. **T:** 1 712 293-4250
E: frontdoor@siouxcityjournal.com
W: http://www.siouxcityjournal.com
Freq: Daily; **Circ:** 27951 Not Audited
Editor: Chris Coates; **Editor:** Chris Coates;
Editor: Chris Coates; **Editor:** Chris Coates;
Publisher: Ron Peterson
Editorial Profile: The Sioux City Journal is a daily local newspaper serving the residents of Sioux City, IA and the surrounding area. The newspaper covers news, sports, government, politics and entertainment.; Full Page Mono: 56.15; Full Page Colour: 219.11
Currency: US Dollars
DAILY NEWSPAPER

Sioux Valley News
Owner: Sioux Valley News
Editorial: 126 E Main St, Anthon, Iowa 51004. **T:** 1 712 373-5571 **Circ:** 2150 Not Audited
NEWSPAPER

Siskiyou Daily News
Owner: GateHouse Media Inc.
Editorial: 309 S Broadway St, Yreka, California 96097-2905. **T:** 1 530 842-5777
E: news@siskiyoudaily.com
W: http://www.siskiyoudaily.com
Freq: Daily; **Circ:** 6061 Not Audited
Publisher: Matt Guthrie; **Editor:** Jim Luksic
Editorial Profile: Siskiyou Daily News is a local daily newspaper serving Siskiyou County, CA and the surrounding area. It provides information on news and events of interest to the local community.; Full Page Mono: 15.95; Full Page Colour: 285.00
Currency: US Dollars
DAILY NEWSPAPER

Skagit Valley Community Newspapers - Mount Vernon
Owner: Skagit Valley Publishing Co.
Editorial: 1215 Anderson Rd, Mount Vernon, Washington 98274-7615. **T:** 1 360 424-3251
E: weeklyeditor@skagitpublishing.com
W: http://www.goskagit.com **Circ:** 17839
Editor: Kathy Boyd
Editorial Profile: Skagit Valley Newspapers - Mount Vernon offers local and community news to residents in and around Mount Vernon. It shares offices with the Skagit Valley Herald.
NEWSPAPER

Skagit Valley Herald
Owner: Skagit Valley Publishing Co.
Editorial: 1215 Anderson Rd, Mount Vernon, Washington 98274-7615. **T:** 1 360 424-3251
E: news@skagitvalleyherald.com
W: http://www.goskagit.com
Freq: Daily; **Circ:** 17231 Not Audited
Publisher: Heather Hernandez; **Editor:** Colette Weeks
Editorial Profile: Skagit Valley Herald is a local daily newspaper serving Mount Vernon, WA and the surrounding area. It provides information on news and events of interest to the local community, as well as sports, entertainment and community issues.; Full Page Mono: 23.45
Currency: US Dollars
DAILY NEWSPAPER

Skagit Valley Newspapers
Owner: Skagit Valley Publishing Co.
Editorial: 901 6th St, Anacortes, Washington 98221. **T:** 1 360 293-3122
E: feedback@goanacortes.com
W: http://www.goskagit.com **Circ:** 8724 Not Audited
Editor: Kimberly Jacobson; **Editor:** Elaine Walker
NEWSPAPER

The Skanner
Owner: The Skanner Newspaper Group
Editorial: 415 N Killingsworth St, Portland, Oregon 97217-2440. **T:** 1 503 285-5555
E: info@theskanner.com
W: http://www.theskanner.com
Freq: Thu; **Circ:** 30000 Not Audited
Publisher: Bernie Foster; **News Editor:** Brian Stinson
Editorial Profile: The Skanner is written for African American residents of Portland, OR. It covers local news and events.; Full Page Mono: 69.50
Currency: US Dollars
NEWSPAPER

The Skanner
Editorial: 415 N Killingsworth St, Portland, Oregon 97217-2440. **T:** 1 503 285-5555
E: seattle@theskanner.com
W: http://www.theskanner.com
Freq: Thu; **Circ:** 20000 Not Audited
Publisher: Bernie Foster; Full Page Mono: 69.50
Currency: US Dollars
NEWSPAPER

Skywrighter
Owner: Cox Media Group
Editorial: 5215 Thurlow St, Bldg 70, Area C, Wright Patterson AFB, Ohio 45433-5547. **T:** 1 937 522-3251
E: 88abw.skywrighter@wpafb.af.mil
W: http://www.skywrighter.com
Freq: Fri; **Circ:** 16000 Not Audited
Editor: Jim Tyler; **Publisher:** Julia Wallace
Editorial Profile: Skywrighter is a local weekly newspaper serving Wright-Patterson Air Force Base and the surrounding area. It provides the community with information on news and events related to the base and the local community.; Full Page Mono: 16.00
Currency: US Dollars
NEWSPAPER

Smith Communications
Editorial: 100 N Jefferson Ave, Eatonton, Georgia 31024. **T:** 1 706 485-3501
E: msgr@msgr.com **W:** http://www.msgr.com
Circ: 17800 Not Audited
Editor: Ron Bridgeman; **Editor:** Elizabeth Neal; **Publisher:** Mark Smith
NEWSPAPER

The Smithtown News, Inc.
Editorial: 1 Brooksite Dr, Smithtown, New York 11787. **T:** 1 631 265-2100
E: info@smithtownnews.com **Circ:** 37740 Not Audited
Editor: David Ambro; **Publisher:** Bernard Paley
NEWSPAPER

Smoky Mountain News
Editorial: 34 Church St, Waynesville, North Carolina 28786-5709. **T:** 1 828 452-4251
E: news@smokymountainnews.com
W: http://www.smokymountainnews.com
Freq: Wed; **Circ:** 16000 Not Audited
News Editor: Becky Johnson
Editorial Profile: Smoky Mountain News is a weekly newspaper covering Haywood, Jackson, Macon and Swain counties in NC. It features hard news, editorials on local issues and an extensive arts, entertainment, books and outdoors section. The paper caters to both residents and tourists. Deadlines for editorial content and advertising are Thursdays at 3 p.m. ET for the following week's publication.; Full Page Mono: 12.00
Currency: US Dollars
NEWSPAPER

Sneak Preview - Ashland
Editorial: 2305 Ashland St, Ste C, Ashland, Oregon 97520-3777. **T:** 1 541 482-0368
E: sneakpre@mind.net
W: http://www.sneakpre.com **Circ:** 44000
Editorial Profile: Sneak Preview - Ashland is a monthly community newspaper publisher serving the residents of Ashland, OR.
NEWSPAPER

Snyder County Times
Editorial: 405 E Main St, Middleburg, Pennsylvania 17842-1215. **T:** 1 570 837-6065
E: scuc@ptd.net
W: http://www.thesnydercountytimes.com
Freq: Fri; **Circ:** 16108 Not Audited
Publisher: Susan Weaver
Editorial Profile: Snyder County Times is a weekly newspaper written for the residents of Snyder County, PA. The newspaper aims to bring its readers information on local news, politics, education, sports and community events.; Full Page Mono: 8.00
Currency: US Dollars
NEWSPAPER

Snyder Daily News
Owner: McQueen (Roy)
Editorial: 3600 College Ave, Snyder, Texas 79549-4637. **T:** 1 325 573-5486
E: sdn@snydertex.com
W: http://www.snyderdailynews.com
Freq: Daily; **Circ:** 4688 Not Audited
Editor: Shirley Gorman; **Publisher:** Roy McQueen; **News Editor:** Jeff West
Editorial Profile: Snyder Daily News is written for residents of Snyder, TX and the surrounding area. It covers local news, sports and community events.; Full Page Mono: 8.75; Full Page Colour: 255.00
Currency: US Dollars
DAILY NEWSPAPER

El Sol
Owner: Gannett Co., Inc.
Editorial: 123 W Alisal St, Salinas, California 93901-2644. **T:** 1 831 424-2221
E: mivozenelsol@thecalifornian.com
W: http://www.elsoldesalinas.com
Freq: Sat; **Circ:** 20000 Not Audited
Editorial Profile: El Sol is a weekly, Spanish-language newspaper serving the Hispanic community in Monterey, Santa Cruz and San Benito counties, CA. It is published by the staff of the Salinas (CA) Californian daily newspaper. Deadlines for Saturday's edition are on Thursdays at noon PT. Send press releases to the editor directly.; Full Page Mono: 38.69
Currency: US Dollars
NEWSPAPER

El Sol de Cleveland
Owner: RB Publishing & Media Services
Editorial: 3157 W 105th St, Cleveland, Ohio 44111. **T:** 1 216 535-9388
E: elsoldecleveland@att.net
W: http://www.elsoldecleveland.com
Freq: Semi-Monthly; **Circ:** 25000 Not Audited
Editorial Profile: El Sol de Cleveland is a semi-monthly newspaper serving the Latino community in and around Cleveland. It is available for pick-up at local retailers, restaurants, community centers and newsstands.; Full Page Mono: 9.00
Currency: US Dollars
NEWSPAPER

El Sol de la Florida
Editorial: 980 E Osceola Pkwy, Kissimmee, Florida 34744-1615. **T:** 1 407 483-5851
E: admin@elsoldelaflorida.com
W: http://www.elsoldelaflorida.com
Freq: Weekly; **Circ:** 65000
Editorial Profile: El Sol de la Florida is a weekly newspaper providing Local and Community News coverage for the Hispanic community in Miami-Dade, Broward y Palm Beach, as well Orlando, Kissimmee, Tampa and Fort Myers, FL.; Full Page Mono: 21.95
Currency: US Dollars
NEWSPAPER

El Sol de Yakima
Owner: Seattle Times Co.
Editorial: 114 N 4th St, Yakima, Washington 98901-2707. **T:** 1 509 249-6181
E: adsmailbox@yakimaherald.com
W: http://elsoldeyakima.com
Freq: Thu; **Circ:** 13250 Not Audited
Editor: Joseph Trevino; Full Page Mono: 14.71
Currency: US Dollars
NEWSPAPER

El Sol Del Valle Imperial
Editorial: 280 Campillo St Ste D, Calexico, California 92231-3200. **T:** 1 760 353-8711
E: meza1120@yahoo.com
Freq: Fri; **Circ:** 12000 Not Audited
Editorial Profile: El Sol Del Valle Imperial is a spanish newspaper written for the residents of El Centro, CA. Call ahead before sending them a fax.; Full Page Mono: 24.00
Currency: US Dollars
NEWSPAPER

El Sol News
Editorial: 1 Bank St, Ste 304, Stamford, Connecticut 6901. **T:** 1 203 323-8400
E: info@elsolnews.com
W: http://www.elsolnews.com
Freq: Fri; **Circ:** 50000 Not Audited
Editor: Raul Arteaga
Editorial Profile: El Sol News is a weekly newspaper written for the Hispanic community of Stamford, CT.; Full Page Mono: 14.00
Currency: US Dollars
NEWSPAPER

Le Soleil de la Floride
Owner: Griffon Graphics
Editorial: 2117 Hollywood Blvd, Hollywood, Florida 33020. **T:** 1 954 922-1800
E: info@lesoleildelafloride.com
W: http://www.lesoleildelafloride.com
Freq: Monthly; **Circ:** 25000 Not Audited
Editor: Yves Beauchamp; **Publisher:** Louis St-Laurent
Editorial Profile: Le Soleil de la Floride is a local weekly newspaper written for residents of Southern Florida and Quebec. It also covers tourism-related information, which acts as a resource guide to the tourist-readers. The publication provides local and national news coverage for its readers.; Full Page Mono: 50.00
Currency: US Dollars
NEWSPAPER

Somos Frontera
Owner: MediaNews Group
Editorial: 500 W Overland, El Paso, Texas 79901. **T:** 1 915 546-6100
W: http://www.somosfrontera.com
Freq: Sat; **Circ:** 50000 Not Audited
Editor: Juan Antonio Rodriguez
Editorial Profile: Somos Frontera is a local, weekly Spanish-language newspaper serving Hispanic and Spanish-speaking residents of El Paso, TX. The paper includes local news, business, sports, arts & entertainment and other information. It is published out of the same office as the El Paso (TX) Times and shares some of its staff.; Full Page Mono: 24.15
Currency: US Dollars
NEWSPAPER

Sonoma Valley Sun Newspapers
Editorial: 158 W Napa St, Sonoma, California 95476. **T:** 1 707 933-0101
E: news@sonomasun.com
W: http://news.sonomaportal.com **Circ:** 22700 Not Audited
Editor: Jody Purdom
NEWSPAPER

Sonoran News
Owner: Conestoga Merchants Inc.
Editorial: 6812 E Cave Creek Rd, Ste 1, Cave Creek, Arizona 85331. **T:** 1 480 488-2021
E: news@sonorannews.com
W: http://www.sonorannews.com
Freq: Bi-Weekly; **Circ:** 44000 Not Audited
Editorial Profile: Sonoran News is published weekly and distributed free of charge to more than 38,000 homes and businesses throughout the Cave Creek, Carefree, Desert Hills, New River, Tatum Ranch, Rio Verde, N. Phoenix and N. Scottsdale areas including Anthem, Desert Mountain, Terravita, Legend Trail, Winfield, Tramonto, Troon, Boulders and Pinnacle Peak. Deadlines are 5pm Thursday for advertising and 5pm Friday for editorial material.; Full Page Mono: 32.00
Currency: US Dollars
NEWSPAPER

Soundoff!
Editorial: 4409 Llewellyn Ave, Fort Meade, Maryland 20755. **T:** 1 301 677-6806
E: joyce.p.brayboy.civ@mail.mil
W: http://www.ftmeade.army.mil
Freq: Thu; **Circ:** 11946 Not Audited
Editor: Joyce Brayboy
Editorial Profile: Soundoff! provides local news, sports and entertainment information to the military personnel of Fort Meade, MD and people in the surrounding county.; Full Page Mono: 46.86
Currency: US Dollars
NEWSPAPER

South Arkansas Sunday News
Owner: Wehco Media Inc.
Editorial: 111 N Madison Ave, El Dorado, Arkansas 71730-6124. **T:** 1 870 862-6611
E: editorial@eldoradonews.com
W: http://www.eldoradonews.com
Freq: Sun; **Circ:** 12041 Not Audited
Publisher: Walter Hussman
Editorial Profile: South Arkansas Sunday News is a weekly newspaper covering El Dorado, AR and surrounding communities.; Full Page Mono: 25.65
Currency: US Dollars
NEWSPAPER

South Belt-Ellington Leader
Editorial: 11555 Beamer Rd, Houston, Texas 77089-2357. **T:** 1 281 481-5656
E: mynews@southbeltleader.com
W: http://www.southbeltleader.com
Freq: Thu
Editorial Profile: The South Belt-Ellington Leader is a weekly community newspaper.
NEWSPAPER

South Bend Tribune
Owner: Schurz Communications Inc.
Editorial: 225 W Colfax Ave, South Bend, Indiana 46626-1000. **T:** 1 574 235-6161
E: sbtnews@sbtinfo.com
W: http://www.southbendtribune.com
Freq: Daily; **Circ:** 47928 Not Audited
Editorial Profile: South Bend Tribune provides local and regional news coverage. The paper covers business news, sports and arts & entertainment.; Full Page Mono: 64.02; Full Page Colour: 1110.00
Currency: US Dollars
DAILY NEWSPAPER

South Bend Tribune
Editorial: 123 Lincolnway W, Mishawaka, Indiana 46544-2010. **T:** 1 574 235-6561
E: mishawaka@sbtinfo.com
DAILY NEWSPAPER

South Bergenite
Owner: North Jersey Media Group Inc.
Editorial: 9 Lincoln Ave, Rutherford, New Jersey 7070. **T:** 1 201 933-4416
E: southbergenite@northjersey.com
W: http://www.northjersey.com/towns/south-bergen
Freq: Thu; **Circ:** 26327 Not Audited
Publisher: Janice Friedman; **Editor:** Jamie Winters; **Editor:** Jamie Winters
Editorial Profile: South Bergenite is a weekly newspaper for residents of Rutherford, East Rutherford, Lyndhurst, Carlstadt, North Arlington and Meadowlands, NJ. The newspaper covers local news, business, sports and arts & entertainment. The newspaper also covers national and statewide stories if they have a direct impact on the

newspaper's readership.; Full Page Mono: 20.59
Currency: US Dollars
NEWSPAPER

South Boston Online
Editorial: 700 E Broadway, South Boston, Massachusetts 2127. **T:** 1 617 269-5550
E: mail@southbostononline.com
W: http://www.southbostononline.com
Freq: Thu; **Circ:** 13000 Not Audited
Editorial Profile: South Boston Online is written for the residents in South Boston. It covers news, events, people and politics. Deadlines are on Tuesdays.; Full Page Mono: 12.50
Currency: US Dollars
NEWSPAPER

South County Leader
Owner: Neighbor News
Editorial: 103 N Cabaniss Ave, Bixby, Oklahoma 74008-4401. **T:** 1 918 366-4655
E: news@southcountyleader.com
W: http://www.southcountyleader.com
Freq: Thu
Publisher: Jamey Honeycutt; **News Editor:** Jo-Ann Jennings
Editorial Profile: South County Leader is a weekly newspaper that provides Local and Community News to the residents of Bixby, OK.
NEWSPAPER

South County Newspapers, LLC.
Owner: News Media Corp.
Editorial: 522 Broadway St, Ste A, King City, California 93930. **T:** 1 831 385-4880
E: editor@southcountynewspapers.com
Circ: 5500 Not Audited
Publisher: Jason Cross; **Publisher:** Jason Cross
Editorial Profile: South County Newspapers, LLC. is a weekly community newspaper publisher serving the residents of King City, Gonzales, Greenfield and Soledad, CA.
NEWSPAPER

South County Publications
Editorial: 110 N 5th St, Auburn, Illinois 62615-1449. **T:** 1 217 438-6155
W: http://www.southcountypublications.com
Circ: 10275 Not Audited
Editor: Byron Painter; **Editor:** Joe Pritchett
NEWSPAPER

South Dade News Leader
Owner: Calkins-Media
Editorial: 205 N Flagler Ave, Homestead, Florida 33030-6130. **T:** 1 305 245-2311
W: http://www.southdadenewsleader.com
Freq: Thu; **Circ:** 12000 Not Audited
Editorial Profile: South Dade News Leader is a local newspaper serving South Dade, FL and the surrounding area. The publication provides information on news and events of interest to the local community. The lead time for the publication varies depending on the material.; Full Page Mono: 18.90
Currency: US Dollars
NEWSPAPER

The South End News & Bay Windows Publications
Editorial: 28 Damrell St Ste 204, Boston, Massachusetts 02127-3077.
T: 1 617 464-7280
E: news.baywindows@gmail.com
W: http://www.baywindows.com **Circ:** 39000 Not Audited
NEWSPAPER

South Florida Sun Sentinel
Owner: Tribune Company
Editorial: 500 E Broward Blvd, Fort Lauderdale, Florida 33394-3000.
T: 1 954 356-4000
W: http://www.sun-sentinel.com
Freq: Daily; **Circ:** 162721 Not Audited
News Editor: Dana Banker; **News Editor:** Dana Banker; **Publisher:** Howard Greenberg; **Editor:** Howard Saltz
Editorial Profile: South Florida Sun Sentinel is a daily, broadsheet newspaper written for the general public in Southern Florida, particularly in Palm Beach, Broward and Dade counties. The Business Section offers features, breaking news, and cover stories on various business issues. The Monday edition offers the Weekly Business section, a tabloid-sized pull-out featuring articles on business, personal finance and the economic pulse of various regional areas. Articles include software reviews and South Florida Web sites in the Technology section; Business Leads, TeachSmart, People on the Move, and columns in the Your Business section; trade growth and networking in the International Business section; Savings Game, IRA investing and columns in the Personal Finance section; industry trends; and cover stories. Society Scene is published Wednesdays in the paper and covers charity happenings. Other topics included in Sun Sentinel are art, books, food, music and travel.; Full Page Mono: 196.00; Full Page Colour: 225.40
Currency: US Dollars
DAILY NEWSPAPER

South Florida Sun Sentinel
Editorial: 333 SW 12th Ave, Deerfield Beach, Florida 33442-3107. **T:** 1 561 243-6600
Editorial Profile: The bureau is physically located in Delray Beach, Palm Beach County. All mail correspondence for the office must be sent to the address in Deerfield Beach, FL. Due to safety precautions, mail will not be accepted at the Delray office.
DAILY NEWSPAPER

South Florida Sun Sentinel
Editorial: 6501 Nob Hill Rd, Tamarac, Florida 33321-6422. **T:** 1 954 572-2050
DAILY NEWSPAPER

South Florida Sun Sentinel
Editorial: 336 E College Ave Ste 105, Tallahassee, Florida 32301-1554.
T: 1 850 224-6214
DAILY NEWSPAPER

South Florida Sun Times
Editorial: 305 NW 10th Ter, Hallandale Beach, Florida 33009. **T:** 1 954 458-0635
E: sfsuntimes@aol.com
W: http://www.southfloridasun.net
Freq: Thu; **Circ:** 60000 Not Audited
Editor: Larry Bluestein; **Publisher:** Craig Farquhar
Editorial Profile: South Florida Sun Times is a local newspaper written for the residents of Hallandale, FL.; Full Page Mono: 23.00
Currency: US Dollars
NEWSPAPER

South Florida Times
Editorial: 3020 Ne 32Nd Ave Ste 200, Fort Lauderdale, Florida 33308-7233.
T: 1 954 356-9360
W: http://www.sfltimes.com
Freq: Fri; **Circ:** 26000 Not Audited
Publisher: Robert Beatty
Editorial Profile: South Florida Times is distributed every Friday throughout Broward County, FL. The newspaper focuses on local news and events that are important to the African American community. Features include business, politics, lifestyle, entertainment and sports. Deadlines are on Wednesdays at noon ET.; Full Page Mono: 34.95; Full Page Colour: 3876.00
Currency: US Dollars
NEWSPAPER

South Haven Tribune
Owner: Paxton Media Group
Editorial: 255 Center St, South Haven, Michigan 49090-1362. **T:** 1 269 637-1104
E: news@southhaventribune.com
Freq: Sun; **Circ:** 14000 Not Audited
Editor: Becky Burkert; **Publisher:** David Holgate
Editorial Profile: South Haven Tribune is a community newspaper serving South Haven, MI and the surrounding area. The publication provides information on news and events of interest to the local community. Deadlines are Wednesdays at 5pm CT.; Full Page Mono: 11.36
Currency: US Dollars
NEWSPAPER

South Jersey Times
Owner: Newhouse Newspapers
Editorial: 93 5th St, Salem, New Jersey 08079-1041. **T:** 1 856 935-1500
E: news@southjerseymedia.com
W: http://www.nj.com/salem
Freq: Daily; **Circ:** 7811 Not Audited
Editor: Sean Leary; **Publisher:** Ceil Smith; Full Page Mono: 26.10; Full Page Colour: 96.34
Currency: US Dollars
DAILY NEWSPAPER

South Jersey Times
Owner: Newhouse Newspapers-Advance Publications
Editorial: 309 S Broad St, Woodbury, New Jersey 08096-2406. **T:** 1 856 845-3300
W: http://www.nj.com/southjerseytimes/
Freq: Daily; **Circ:** 24125 Not Audited
Editor: William Gallo; **Editor:** Cindy Hepner
Editorial Profile: South Jersey Times is a daily newspaper published by South Jersey Newspapers. The newspaper provides readers in Salem County, Gloucester County, and Cumberland, NJ with local and national news. Other features include lifestyle, entertainment, sports, business and classifieds.; Full Page Mono: 85.00; Full Page Colour: 89.09
Currency: US Dollars
DAILY NEWSPAPER

South Lake Press
Owner: Harbor Point Media LLC
Editorial: 212 E Main St, Leesburg, Florida 34748-5227. **T:** 1 352 394-2183
W: http://www.southlakepress.com
Freq: Fri; **Circ:** 40000 Not Audited
Publisher: Rich Pinder
Editorial Profile: South Lake Press is a local newspaper serving Clermont, Minneola, Groveland, Mascotte and Montverde in Lake County, FL. The publication provides information on news, sports, arts & entertainment and events of interest to the local community.; Full Page Mono: 11.25
Currency: US Dollars
NEWSPAPER

South Marion Citizen
Editorial: 8810 Sw Highway 200 Unit 104, Ocala, Florida 34481-7824. **T:** 1 352 854-3986
W: http://www.smcitizen.com
Freq: Fri; **Circ:** 15000 Not Audited
Editor: Jim Clark; **Publisher:** Gerry Mulligan
Editorial Profile: South Marion Citizen is a local newspaper written for the residents of Ocala, FL.; Full Page Mono: 14.87
Currency: US Dollars
NEWSPAPER

The South Pittsburgh Reporter
Editorial: 813 E Warrington Ave, Pittsburgh, Pennsylvania 15210. **T:** 1 412 481-0266
E: news@sopghreporter.com
W: http://sopghreporter.com
Freq: Tue; **Circ:** 12000 Not Audited
Editorial Profile: The South Pittsburgh Reporter is a local newspaper for the residents of Pittsburgh.; Full Page Mono: 8.10
Currency: US Dollars
NEWSPAPER

South Shore Tribune
Owner: Frank G Naudus
Editorial: 4 California Pl N, Island Park, New York 11558-2215. **T:** 1 516 431-5628
E: info@litribune.com
W: http://www.litribune.com
Freq: Weekly; **Circ:** 32366 Not Audited
Editorial Profile: South Shore Tribune is a local newspaper published every Thursday. It is published for the residents of the South Shore of Long Island, NY. The newspaper covers local news, sports, entertainment, and lifestyle issues.
NEWSPAPER

South Texas Catholic
Owner: Roman Catholic Diocese of Corpus Christi
Editorial: 620 Lipan St, Corpus Christi, Texas 78401. **T:** 1 361 693-6605
E: stc@diocesecc.org
W: http://southtexascatholic.com
Freq: Fri; **Circ:** 46000 Not Audited
Editor: Alfredo Cardenas; **Publisher:** Michael Mulvey
Editorial Profile: South Texas Catholic in Corpus Christi, TX is a monthly newspaper serving the local Catholic community.; Full Page Mono: 22.98; Full Page Colour: 22.98
Currency: US Dollars
NEWSPAPER

South Whidbey Record/Whidbey News-Times
Owner: Sound Publishing, Inc.
Editorial: 107 S Main St Ste E101, Coupeville, Washington 98239-3569. **T:** 1 360 221-5300
Editorial Profile: The Whidbey News-Times/ Whidbey Examiner provide Local and Community News coverage for Whidbey Island, WA. The Whidbey News-Times covers North and Central Whidbey Island, from Greenbank to Deception Pass. The Whidbey Examiner is a weekly newspaper serving the community of Coupewille, WA.
NEWSPAPER

Southbridge Evening News
Owner: Stonebridge Press
Editorial: 25 Elm St, Southbridge, Massachusetts 01550-2605.
T: 1 508 764-4325
W: http://www.southbridgeeveningnews.com
Freq: Mon thru Fri; **Circ:** 4098 Not Audited
Publisher: Frank Chilinski; **Editor:** Adam Minor
Editorial Profile: The Southbridge Evening News is a local daily newspaper written for residents of Southbridge, MA and the surrounding towns. The newspaper covers local news, sports, arts and entertainment, business, and national stories if they have a direct impact on the readership.; Full Page Mono: 15.00
Currency: US Dollars
DAILY NEWSPAPER

The Southeast Christian Outlook
Editorial: 920 Blankenbaker Pkwy, Louisville, Kentucky 40243-1845. **T:** 1 502 253-89950
W: http://southeastoutlook.org/
Freq: Thu; **Circ:** 70000
Editor: Brent Adams
Editorial Profile: The Southeast Christian Outlook is a weekly publication serving the members of the Southeast Christian Church in Louisville, Kentucky. It features a Devotions section, as well as articles concerning the Christian religion in the context of Global, American, Kentucky, and Louisville life.
NEWSPAPER

Southeast Missourian
Owner: Rust Communications
Editorial: 301 Broadway St, Cape Girardeau, Missouri 63701-7330. **T:** 1 573 335-6611
E: news@semissourian.com
W: http://www.semissourian.com
Freq: Mon thru Fri; **Circ:** 11216 Not Audited
Editor: Bob Miller; **Publisher:** Jon Rust
Editorial Profile: Southeast Missourian is a local daily newspaper devoted to keeping the residents of Southeastern Missouri informed about the news of their community. The articles in the newspaper focus on local news, arts, sports and business, as well as national stories that have an impact on the readership.; Full Page Mono: 19.28; Full Page Colour: 330.00
Currency: US Dollars
DAILY NEWSPAPER

Southern Chinese Daily News - Houston Edition
Owner: Southern Newspapers, Inc.
Editorial: 11122 Bellaire Blvd, Houston, Texas 77072-2608. **T:** 1 281 498-4310
E: wealee@aol.com
W: http://www.scdaily.com
Freq: Daily; **Circ:** 25000 Not Audited
Editor: Jun Gai; **Publisher:** Wea Lee
Editorial Profile: Southern Chinese Daily News-Houston Edition is a daily newspaper that serves the Chinese community of Houston.; Full Page Mono: 34.00
Currency: US Dollars
DAILY NEWSPAPER

Southern Cross
Owner: Roman Catholic Diocese of Savannah
Editorial: 601 E Liberty St, Savannah, Georgia 31401. **T:** 1 912 201-4100
E: southerncross@diosav.org
W: http://www.southerncross.diosav.org
Freq: Thu; **Circ:** 28000 Not Audited
Publisher: Gregory Hartmayer; **Editor:** Michael Johnson
Editorial Profile: Southern Cross in Savannah, GA is published weekly and covers news of interest to Catholics. Deadlines are on Fridays prior to issue date.; Full Page Mono: 12.00
Currency: US Dollars
NEWSPAPER

The Southern Cross
Owner: Roman Catholic Bishop of San Diego
Editorial: 3888 Paducah Dr, San Diego, California 92117. **T:** 1 858 490-8266
E: socross@diocese-sdiego.org
W: http://www.thesoutherncross.org
Freq: Monthly; **Circ:** 28400 Not Audited
Publisher: Robert Brom
Editorial Profile: The Southern Cross is the official newspaper of the archdiocese of San Diego, CA. The publication comes out monthly and deals with matters of local news which effect its readers.; Full Page Mono: 30.00; Full Page Colour: 1596.00
Currency: US Dollars
NEWSPAPER

Southern Dutchess News
Editorial: 84 E Main St, Wappingers Falls, New York 12590. **T:** 1 845 297-3723
E: newsplace@aol.com
W: http://sdutchessnews.com
Freq: Weekly; **Circ:** 15000 Not Audited
Editor: Kate Goldsmith; **Editor:** Melina Makris;
Publisher: Al Osten
NEWSPAPER

The Southern Illinoisan
Owner: Lee Enterprises, Inc.
Editorial: 710 N Illinois Ave, Carbondale, Illinois 62901-1283. **T:** 1 618 529-5454

E: news@southernillinoisan.com
W: http://www.thesouthern.com
Freq: Daily; **Circ:** 23099 Not Audited
Editor: Gary Metro; **Publisher:** John Pfeifer; **Editor:** Cara Recine; **Editor:** Les Winkeler
Editorial Profile: The Southern Illinoisan is published daily for the residents of Carbondale, IL and surrounding areas. The newspaper covers local news, business, sports and community events.; Full Page Mono: 45.40; Full Page Colour: 79.91
Currency: US Dollars
DAILY NEWSPAPER

Southern Lakes Newspapers LLC.
Owner: Southern Lakes Newspapers LLC
Editorial: 700 N Pine St, Burlington, Wisconsin 53105-1472. **T:** 1 262 728-3411
W: http://www.waterfordpost.com **Circ:** 4875 Not Audited
Publisher: Jack Cruger; **Editor in Chief:** Ed Nadolski
NEWSPAPER

Southern Lakes Newspapers LLC. - Burlington
Editorial: 700 N Pine St, Burlington, Wisconsin 53105-1261. **T:** 1 262 763-3511
E: delavaneditor@southernlakesnewspapers.com
W: http://www.southernlakesnewspapers.com
Circ: 14800 Not Audited
Publisher: Jack Cruger; **Editor in Chief:** Ed Nadolski
NEWSPAPER

Southern Lakes Newspapers LLC. - Elkhorn
Owner: Southern Lakes Newspapers LLC
Editorial: 11 W Walworth St, Elkhorn, Wisconsin 53121-1736. **T:** 1 262 723-2921
E: elkinde@elkhornindependent.com
W: http://www.mywalworthcounty.com
Freq: Thu
Publisher: Jack Cruger
NEWSPAPER

Southern Rhode Island Newspapers
Editorial: 187 Main St., Wakefield, Rhode Island 2879. **T:** 1 401 789-9744
W: http://www.ricentral.com
Publisher: Nanci Batson; **Editor:** James Bessette; **Editor:** Jeremiah Ryan
Editorial Profile: Southern Rhode Island is a community newspaper publisher, affiliated with the Kent County Daily Times, and publishes five papers: The Narragansett Times, The Standard-Times, The East Greenwich Pendulum, The Chariho Times, and The Coventry Courier.
NEWSPAPER

The Southington Citizen
Owner: Record-Journal Publishing Company
Editorial: 11 Crown St, Meriden, Connecticut 06450-5713. **T:** 1 860 620-5960
E: news@thesouthingtoncitizen.com
W: http://www.southingtoncitizen.com
Freq: Fri; **Circ:** 22000
Editor: Nick Carroll; **Publisher:** Eliot White
Editorial Profile: The Southington Citizen is published weekly for the residents of Southington, CT and surrounding areas. The newspaper covers local news and community events.; Full Page Mono: 12.20
Currency: US Dollars
NEWSPAPER

Southshore Press
Owner: South Shore Press Inc.
Editorial: 2 Coraci Blvd, Ste 7, Shirley, New York 11967-4833. **T:** 1 631 878-7800
E: sspress2000@aol.com
Freq: Wed; **Circ:** 45000 Not Audited
Editor: Jeannie Kubik
Editorial Profile: South Shore Press in Shirley, NY, is a weekly newspaper that covers local news and events.; Full Page Mono: 220.00
Currency: US Dollars
NEWSPAPER

Southside Pride
Owner: Felien Publishing
Editorial: 3200 Chicago Ave, Minneapolis, Minnesota 55407. **T:** 1 612 822-4662
E: editor@southsidepride.com
W: http://www.southsidepride.com
Freq: Monthly; **Circ:** 48000 Not Audited
Editorial Profile: Southside Pride is a monthly community newspaper delivered free to homes and businesses in South Minneapolis. The newspaper covers local news, business, sports, religious events/issues and arts & entertainment stories. The newspaper also covers national and statewide stories if they have a direct impact on the newspaper's readership. Southside Pride has three different editions that cover different areas of South Minneapolis. These are: Phillips-Powderhorn (27,000 papers delivered on the first Monday of the month), Nokomis (23,000 papers delivered on the second Monday of the month) and Riverside (25,000 papers delivered on the third Monday of the month).; Full Page Mono: 20.00; Full Page Colour: 1450.00
Currency: US Dollars
NEWSPAPER

Southside Times
Owner: Times-Leader Publications LLC
Editorial: 7670 US 31 S., Indianapolis, Indiana 46227. **T:** 1 317 300-8782
E: news@ss-times.com
W: http://www.ss-times.com
Freq: Thu; **Circ:** 21500 Not Audited
Editor: Nicole Davis; **Publisher:** Roger Huntzinger
Editorial Profile: Southside Times is written for the residents of the south side of Indianapolis and Greenwood in Johnson County, IN. It is a weekly local newspaper that covers local news, sports, business and entertainment stories. Deadlines are at 10am ET.; Full Page Mono: 15.30
Currency: US Dollars
NEWSPAPER

The Southsider Voice
Editorial: 6025 Madison Ave., Suite B, Indianapolis, Indiana 46227-1160.
T: 1 317 781-0023
E: news@southsidervoice.com
W: http://www.southsidervoice.com
Freq: Wed; **Circ:** 25000
Publisher: Kelly Sawyers; **Editor:** Denise Summers
Editorial Profile: The Southsider Voice, launched in February 2009, is a community weekly newspaper that serves residents of Indianapolis's south side. It offers local news, sports and arts & entertainment.; Full Page Mono: 4.16; Full Page Colour: 4.85
Currency: US Dollars
NEWSPAPER

The Southtown Star
Owner: Wrapports LLC
Editorial: 350 N Orleans St Fl 10, Chicago, Illinois 60654-1700. **T:** 1 708 633-4800
E: news@southtownstar.com
W: http://southtownstar.suntimes.com
Freq: Mon thru Fri; **Circ:** 34542 Not Audited
Editor: Joe Biesk
Editorial Profile: The Southtown Star is a daily newspaper written for the residents of South and West portions of the greater Chicago area. The newspaper covers local news, business, entertainment, sports and events.; Full Page Mono: 118.00; Full Page Colour: 185.70
Currency: US Dollars
DAILY NEWSPAPER

Southwest Daily News
Owner: Fortress Investment Group, LLC
Editorial: 716 E Napoleon St, Sulphur, Louisiana 70663-3402. **T:** 1 337 527-7075
E: sdneditorial@yahoo.com
W: http://www.sulphurdailynews.com
Freq: Daily; **Circ:** 3077 Not Audited
Editor: Marilyn Monroe; **Publisher:** Suzanne Peveto-Nelson
Editorial Profile: Southwest Daily News is a daily newspaper, locally written for residents of Southwestern Louisiana. The newspaper covers local news, business, sports and arts & entertainment stories. The newspaper also covers national and statewide stories if they have a direct impact on the newspaper's readership. All inquiries should be addressed to the editor. Deadlines are at noon CT the day before publication.; Full Page Mono: 14.39
Currency: US Dollars
DAILY NEWSPAPER

Southwest Messenger Press
Editorial: 3840 147th St, Midlothian, Illinois 60445. **T:** 1 708 388-2425
E: spressnews@aol.com **Circ:** 73829 Not Audited
Publisher: Margaret Lysen; **Editor:** Lori Taylor
Editorial Profile: Southwest Messenger Press in Midlothian, IL is a community newspaper publisher.
NEWSPAPER

Southwest Orlando Bulletin
Owner: Kearney Publishing Corporation
Editorial: 7901 Kingspointe Pkwy, Ste 28, Orlando, Florida 32819. **T:** 1 407 351-1573
E: info@kearneypublishing.com
W: http://www.southwestorlandobulletin.com
Freq: Bi-Monthly; **Circ:** 43000 Not Audited
Publisher: Brenda Kearney; **Editor:** Lisa Sagers
Editorial Profile: Southwest Orlando Bulletin is published bi-monthly for the residents of Orlando, FL. The newspaper provdes information about local news, community events, birth and wedding announcements, fundraising and education.; Full Page Mono: 72.00
Currency: US Dollars
NEWSPAPER

Southwest Suburban Publishing
Owner: Red Wing Publishing
Editorial: 327 Marschall Rd, Shakopee, Minnesota 55379. **T:** 1 952 440-1234
Circ: 14700 Not Audited
Editor: Lori Carlson; **Publisher:** Laurie Hartmann; **Editor:** Amy Lyon
Editorial Profile: Southwest Suburban Publishing is a weekly community newspaper publisher serving the residents of Prior Lake and Savage, MN.
NEWSPAPER

Southwest Sun
Owner: Emmerich Newspapers Inc.
Editorial: 112 Oliver Emmerich Dr, McComb, Mississippi 39648-6330. **T:** 1 601 684-2421
W: http://www.enterprise-journal.com
Freq: Wed; **Circ:** 11600 Not Audited
Editorial Profile: Southwest Sun is a weekly newspaper written for the residents of McComb, MS. It covers local, statewide and national news, business, sports and arts & entertainment.; Full Page Mono: 16.45
Currency: US Dollars
NEWSPAPER

The Southwest Times
Owner: Southwest Publishers, Inc.
Editorial: 34 5th St NE, Pulaski, Virginia 24301. **T:** 1 540 980-5220
W: http://www.southwesttimes.com
Freq: Fri; **Circ:** 5200 Not Audited
Publisher: Kay Kline; **Editor:** Melinda Williams
Editorial Profile: The Southwest Times' editorial mission is to deliver local news and community information to its readers in Pulaski County, Western Wythe County, Radford and Western Montgomery, VA.; Full Page Mono: 12.00; Full Page Colour: 250.00
Currency: US Dollars
NEWSPAPER

Spanish Journal
Editorial: 611 W National Ave, Ste 316, Milwaukee, Wisconsin 53204.
T: 1 414 643-5683
E: spanishjournalads@yahoo.com
Freq: Thu; **Circ:** 20000 Not Audited
Editor: Robert Miranda; **Publisher:** Rhonda Welch
Editorial Profile: Spanish Journal is a Spanish-language publication written for the Hispanic-American residents of Milwaukee.; Full Page Mono: 1.65
Currency: US Dollars
NEWSPAPER

Spartanburg Herald-Journal
Owner: Halifax Media Holdings LLC
Editorial: 189 W Main St, Spartanburg, South Carolina 29306-2334. **T:** 1 864 582-4511
E: goupstate@shj.com
W: http://www.goupstate.com
Freq: Daily; **Circ:** 34067 Not Audited
Publisher: Kevin Drake
Editorial Profile: Spartanburg (SC) Herald-Journal serves readers in the state's upstate region and covers local and regional news, business, sports, arts & entertainment and community news. The outlet offers RSS (Really Simple Syndication).; Full Page Mono: 98.95; Full Page Colour: 353.57
Currency: US Dollars
DAILY NEWSPAPER

Speakin' Out News
Editorial: 115 Wholesale Ave NE, Huntsville, Alabama 35811. **T:** 1 256 551-1020
W: http://www.speakinoutnews.info
Freq: Wed; **Circ:** 25676 Not Audited
Editorial Profile: Speakin' Out News is an African-American publication written for residents of Huntsville, AL. It covers local news, business, sports, health, religion and arts & entertainment. Deadlines are on Mondays at noon CT.; Full Page Mono: 25.00; Full Page Colour: 2996.00
Currency: US Dollars
NEWSPAPER

Spectator
Owner: GateHouse Media Inc.
Editorial: 85 Canisteo St, Hornell, New York 14843. **T:** 1 607 324-1425
E: news@eveningtribune.com
W: http://www.eveningtribune.com
Freq: Sun; **Circ:** 14500 Not Audited
Editor: John Anderson; **Publisher:** Tom Connors
Editorial Profile: Spectator is written for the residents of Hornell, NY. It covers local news, business, sports and arts & entertainment stories. It also covers national and statewide stories if they have a direct impact on the newspaper's readership. All inquiries should be addressed to the editor.; Full Page Mono: 9.65
Currency: US Dollars
NEWSPAPER

The Spectator & Fall River Spirit
Owner: GateHouse Media Inc.
Editorial: 780 County St, Somerset, Massachusetts 02726-5001.
T: 1 508 674-4656
W: http://www.southcoasttoday.com
Circ: 16000 Not Audited
Editor: George Austin
NEWSPAPER

The Spectrum
Owner: Gannett Co., Inc.
Editorial: 275 E Saint George Blvd, Saint George, Utah 84770-2986. **T:** 1 435 674-6200
W: http://www.thespectrum.com
Freq: Daily; **Circ:** 18456 Not Audited
Editor: Todd Seifert; **Publisher:** Donnie Welch
Editorial Profile: The Spectrum is a daily local newspaper serving the residents of St. George, UT. The newspaper covers local and national news, sports and other topics of interest to the readers.; Full Page Mono: 18.60; Full Page Colour: 515.00
Currency: US Dollars
DAILY NEWSPAPER

Spencer Daily Reporter
Owner: Rust Communications
Editorial: 310 E Milwaukee St, Spencer, Iowa 51301-4569. **T:** 1 712 262-6610
E: news@spencerdailyreporter.com
W: http://www.spencerdailyreporter.com
Freq: Daily; **Circ:** 3900 Not Audited
Publisher: Paula Buenger; **Editor:** Randy Cauthron
Editorial Profile: Spencer Daily Reporter is written for the community of Spencer, IA. The publication provides local news, sports, agriculture, and community events coverage.; Full Page Mono: 8.40; Full Page Colour: 215.00
Currency: US Dollars
DAILY NEWSPAPER

Spencer Evening World
Owner: Spencer Evening World, Inc.
Editorial: 114 E Franklin St, Spencer, Indiana 47460-1877. **T:** 1 812 829-2255
W: http://www.spencereveningworld.com
Freq: Daily; **Circ:** 3800 Not Audited
Editor: Travis Curry; **Publisher:** John Gillaspy
Editorial Profile: Spencer Evening World is a local daily newspaper serving residents of Owen County, IN. It covers local news, lifestyle and community events. Advertising deadlines are at 5pm the day before publication. News deadlines are at 10am ET the day of issue.; Full Page Mono: 5.50; Full Page Colour: 85.00
Currency: US Dollars
DAILY NEWSPAPER

Spencer Newspapers, Inc.
Editorial: 210 E Main St, Spencer, West Virginia 25276-1602. **T:** 1 304 927-2360
Circ: 5417 Not Audited
Editor: Jim Cooper; **Publisher:** David J. Hedges
NEWSPAPER

The Spokesman-Review
Owner: Cowles Publishing Company
Editorial: 999 W Riverside Ave, Spokane, Washington 99201-1006. **T:** 1 509 459-5000
E: news@spokesman.com
W: http://www.spokesman.com
Freq: Daily; **Circ:** 59807 Not Audited
Publisher: Stacey Cowles
Editorial Profile: The Spokesman-Review is a daily newspaper written for the general public of the Spokane, WA area. The business section includes articles on technology, employment, growth and development, agriculture, economy, logging, media and mining. Articles include trends, breaking news, analyses, profiles and investigative stories. Additional articles include travel, genealogy, books, theater and music. The paper has won the Best in Business Award by the Society of

American Business Editors and Writers.; Full Page Mono: 109.25; Full Page Colour: 997.75
Currency: US Dollars
DAILY NEWSPAPER

The Spokesman-Review
Editorial: 608 Northwest Blvd, Coeur D Alene, Idaho 83814-2174. **T:** 1 208 765-7100
E: idaho@spokesman.com
DAILY NEWSPAPER

The Spokesman-Review
Editorial: 13208 E Sprague Ave, Spokane, Washington 99216-0844. **T:** 1 509 927-2170
DAILY NEWSPAPER

The Spokesman-Review
Editorial: 2601 W Hillway Dr, Boise, Idaho 83702-0937. **T:** 1 208 336-2854
E: news@spokesman.com
DAILY NEWSPAPER

Spotlight Newspapers
Owner: Eagle Media Partners LP
Editorial: 125 Adams St, Delmar, New York 12054. **T:** 1 518 439-4949
E: news@spotlightnews.com
W: http://www.spotlightnews.com
Freq: Weekly; **Circ:** 58395 Not Audited
Publisher: John McIntyre
NEWSPAPER

The Springfield News-Leader
Owner: Gannett Co., Inc.
Editorial: 651 N Boonville Ave, Springfield, Missouri 65806. **T:** 1 417 836-1100
E: webeditor@news-leader.com
W: http://www.news-leader.com
Freq: Daily; **Circ:** 30201 Not Audited
Publisher: Linda Ramey-Greiwe
Editorial Profile: The Springfield (MO) News-Leader is a daily, general interest publication written for residents of Southwest Missouri. The publication covers news, business, sports and arts & entertainment.; Full Page Mono: 100.33; Full Page Colour: 120.84
Currency: US Dollars
DAILY NEWSPAPER

Springfield News-Sun
Owner: Cox Media Group, Inc.
Editorial: 202 N Limestone St, Springfield, Ohio 45503-4202. **T:** 1 937 328-0300
E: cssprinqfield.csspringfield@coxinc.com
W: http://www.springfieldnewssun.com
Freq: Daily; **Circ:** 16232 Not Audited
Editor: Ben McLaughlin
Editorial Profile: Springfield News Sun is published daily for residents of Springfield, OH. The newspaper covers local and national news, sports and arts & entertainment. Deadlines are on Mondays at noon ET.; Full Page Mono: 36.25; Full Page Colour: 103.19
Currency: US Dollars
DAILY NEWSPAPER

The Springfield Paper
Owner: Penda Publishing
Editorial: 1026 N Plum St, Springfield, Ohio 45504-2108. **T:** 1 937 327-9017
E: editor@pendapublishing.com
W: http://www.thespringfieldpaper.com
Freq: Wed; **Circ:** 50000
Editorial Profile: The Springfield Paper is a weekly newspaper providing Local News, Community News, Sports and Lifestyle coverage to the residents of Springfield, OH and Clark County. The newspaper also focuses on religious news pertaining to the area.
NEWSPAPER

Springhill Press
Owner: Loven Thomas
Editorial: 403 Butler St, Springhill, Louisiana 71075-2735. **T:** 1 318 539-3511
E: nattimes@wnonline.net
Freq: Thu; **Circ:** 30000 Not Audited
Editorial Profile: Springhill (LA) Press is a weekly newspaper that covers local news, events, sports, politics and social issues. Deadlines are on Fridays.; Full Page Mono: 6.25; Full Page Colour: 717.00
Currency: US Dollars
NEWSPAPER

St. Albans Messenger
Owner: Vermont Media Publishing Co.
Editorial: 281 N Main St, Saint Albans, Vermont 05478-2503. **T:** 1 802 524-9771
E: news@samessenger.com
W: http://www.samessenger.com
Freq: Daily; **Circ:** 5000 Not Audited
Editorial Profile: St. Albans Messenger provides Franklin County, VT residents with local news, sports and coverage of community events.; Full Page Mono: 14.25; Full Page Colour: 48.75
Currency: US Dollars
DAILY NEWSPAPER

The St. Augustine Record
Owner: Morris Multimedia, Inc.
Editorial: 1 News Pl, Saint Augustine, Florida 32086-6520. **T:** 1 904 829-6562
E: editor@staugustine.com
W: http://www.staugustine.com
Freq: Daily; **Circ:** 17607 Not Audited
Publisher: Ron Davidson; **Editor:** Kathy Nelson
Editorial Profile: The St. Augustine Record is published daily for the residents of St. Augustine, FL and surrounding areas. The newspaper covers local and state news, business, sports, lifestyles and entertainment.; Full Page Mono: 23.00
Currency: US Dollars
DAILY NEWSPAPER

The St. Bernard News
Owner: Roberson Advertising
Editorial: 3010 Lausat St, Metairie, Louisiana 70001. **T:** 1 504 832-1481
E: editor@thestbernardnews.com
W: http://thestbernardnews.com/
Freq: Wed; **Circ:** 21075 Not Audited
Editor: Bobby Giroir; **Publisher:** Michael Roberson
Editorial Profile: The St. Bernard News is published weekly for the residents of Metairie, LA and the surrounding St. Bernard Parish area. The newspaper covers local news and community events.; Full Page Mono: 12.95
Currency: US Dollars
NEWSPAPER

St. Clair Times
Owner: Consolidated Publishing
Editorial: 1911 Martin St S, Ste 7, Pell City, Alabama 35128. **T:** 1 205 884-3400
W: http://www.dailyhome.com/stclair/dh-stclair.htm
Freq: Thu; **Circ:** 33700 Not Audited
Editor: Jimmy Creed
Editorial Profile: St. Clair Times in Pell City, AL is a weekly newspaper that covers local news and events.; Full Page Mono: 8.75
Currency: US Dollars
NEWSPAPER

St. Cloud Times
Owner: Gannett Co., Inc.
Editorial: 3000 7Th St N, Saint Cloud, Minnesota 56303-3108. **T:** 1 320 255-8700
E: newsroom@stcloudtimes.com
W: http://www.sctimes.com
Freq: Daily; **Circ:** 19984 Not Audited
Publisher: Scott Johnson; **News Editor:** Kate Kompas
Editorial Profile: St. Cloud Times is written for the residents of Saint Cloud, MN. It includes local, business, sports and recreational news.; Full Page Mono: 59.04; Full Page Colour: 220.27
Currency: US Dollars
DAILY NEWSPAPER

St. Cloud Visitor
Editorial: 305 7th Ave N, Ste 206, Saint Cloud, Minnesota 56303-3600. **T:** 1 320 251-3022
E: news@stcloudvisitor.org
W: http://www.stcdio.org
Freq: Bi-Weekly; **Circ:** 44500 Not Audited
Publisher: John Kinney; **Editor:** Joe Towalski
Editorial Profile: St. Cloud Visitor provides news to the Catholic residents of central Minnesota. Coverage includes religious issues and events.; Full Page Mono: 25.00; Full Page Colour: 1181.00
Currency: US Dollars
NEWSPAPER

St. Joseph News-Press
Owner: NPG Newspapers
Editorial: 825 Edmond St, Saint Joseph, Missouri 64501-2737. **T:** 1 816 271-8500
W: http://www.newspressnow.com
Freq: Daily; **Circ:** 23596 Not Audited
Publisher: David Bradley
Editorial Profile: St. Joseph News-Press is a daily newspaper covering over twenty counties in Northwest Missouri. The publication covers local news, events, lifestyle, business, and political issues affecting the area. The newspaper is written for a readership of local community residents.; Full Page Mono: 54.57; Full Page Colour: 176.03
Currency: US Dollars
DAILY NEWSPAPER

St. Lawrence County Newspapers
Owner: St. Lawrence County Newspapers, Inc.
Editorial: 308 Isabella St, Ogdensburg, New York 13669-1409. **T:** 1 315 393-1000
Circ: 25629 Not Audited
NEWSPAPER

St. Louis American
Editorial: 2315 Pine St., Saint Louis, Missouri 63103. **T:** 1 314 533-8000
W: http://www.stlamerican.com
Freq: Thu; **Circ:** 70000 Not Audited
Publisher: Donald Suggs; **Publisher:** Donald Suggs; **Publisher:** Donald Suggs; **Publisher:** Donald Suggs
Editorial Profile: St. Louis American is a weekly newspaper geared toward African-Americans. Topics covered include news, religion, entertainment, sports and profiles of successful local African-Americans in business, healthcare or public service. The paper was founded in 1928.; Full Page Mono: 68.00
Currency: US Dollars
NEWSPAPER

St. Louis Argus
Owner: The Saint Louis Argus Publishing Company
Editorial: 4595 Martin Luther King Blvd, Saint Louis, Missouri 63113. **T:** 1 314 531-1323
E: media@argusstl.com
W: http://www.stlouisargus.com
Freq: Thu; **Circ:** 33000 Not Audited
Publisher: Eddie Hasan; **Editor:** Eric Wilson; **Editor:** Eric Wilson
Editorial Profile: St. Louis Argus is a weekly newspaper featuring articles on entertainment, travel, leisure, editorial, events, classifieds, sports, news and opinion.; Full Page Mono: 21.68
Currency: US Dollars
NEWSPAPER

The St. Louis Evening Whirl
Owner: Thomas Publishing Co. Inc.
Editorial: 4244 McPherson Ave, Saint Louis, Missouri 63108-2908. **T:** 1 678 778-2616
E: info@thewhirlonline.com
W: http://www.thewhirlonline.com
Freq: Mon; **Circ:** 52500 Not Audited
Publisher: Barry Thomas
Editorial Profile: The St. Louis Evening Whirl is written for residents of Saint Louis, Jefferson and Saint Charles counties, MO, as well as Saint Clair, Madison and Bond counties, IL, and focuses heavily on crime in the area.; Full Page Mono: 31.75
Currency: US Dollars
NEWSPAPER

St. Louis Jewish Light
Editorial: 6 Millstone Campus Dr Ste 3010, Saint Louis, Missouri 63146-6603.
T: 1 314 743-3660
E: news@thejewishlight.com
W: http://www.stljewishlight.com
Freq: Wed; **Circ:** 12000 Not Audited
Editor: Ellen Futterman; **Editor:** Ellen Futterman; **Publisher:** Larry Levin
Editorial Profile: St. Louis Jewish Light is published for Jewish residents of St. Louis. The paper covers local news, community events and announcements.; Full Page Mono: 45.00
Currency: US Dollars
NEWSPAPER

St. Louis Metro Sentinel Journal
Owner: Metro Publishing Group, Inc.
Editorial: 2002 St. Louis Ave., Saint Louis, Missouri 63106. **T:** 1 314 531-2101
E: metrosentinel@sbcglobal.net
W: http://www.metrosentineljournal.com
Freq: Thu
Editorial Profile: St. Louis Metro Sentinel Journal is a weekly community newspaper serving the St. Louis African-American community with relevant news and editorials.
NEWSPAPER

St. Louis Post-Dispatch
Owner: Lee Enterprises, Inc.
Editorial: 900 N Tucker Blvd, Saint Louis, Missouri 63101-1069. **T:** 1 314 340-8000
E: metro@post-dispatch.com
W: http://www.stltoday.com
Freq: Daily; **Circ:** 186820 Not Audited
Editor: Gilbert Bailon; **Publisher:** Kevin Mowbray
Editorial Profile: Founded by Joseph Pulitzer in 1878, the St. Louis Post-Dispatch is a daily four-color broadsheet newspaper that covers regional, national, and international news. The platform of the publication, according to Pulitzer, is that it "will always fight for progress and reform, never tolerate injustice or corruption, always fight demagogues of all parties, never belong to any party, always oppose privileged classes and public plunderers, never lack sympathy with the poor, always remain devoted to the public welfare, never be satisfied with merely printing news, always be drastically independent, never be afraid to attack wrong, whether by predatory plutocracy or predatory poverty." Other topics covered in the publication include music, travel, theater, arts, food, and books. The publication's staff does not accept unsolicited e-mail attachments due to virus dangers. All calendar and event items should be submitted through http://events.stltoday.com/listings.; Full Page Mono: 313.12; Full Page Colour: 597.42
Currency: US Dollars
DAILY NEWSPAPER

St. Louis Post-Dispatch
Editorial: 1025 Connecticut Ave NW, Washington, District Of Columbia 20036-5405. **T:** 1 202 298-6880
DAILY NEWSPAPER

St. Louis Post-Dispatch
Editorial: 190 Spring Dr, Saint Charles, Missouri 63303-3255. **T:** 1 636 255-7201
E: stcharles@post-dispatch.com
Bureau Chief: Fred Ehrlich
DAILY NEWSPAPER

St. Louis Post-Dispatch
Editorial: 200 S Bemiston Ave, Clayton, Missouri 63105-1915. **T:** 1 314 863-2812
DAILY NEWSPAPER

St. Louis Post-Dispatch
Editorial: 1200 Market St Rm 130, Saint Louis, Missouri 63103-2862
DAILY NEWSPAPER

St. Louis Review
Editorial: 20 Archbishop May Dr, Saint Louis, Missouri 63119. **T:** 1 314 792-7500
W: http://www.stlouisreview.com
Freq: Fri; **Circ:** 86000 Not Audited
Publisher: Robert Hermann
Editorial Profile: St. Louis Review is a newspaper published by the Archdiocese of St. Louis and should be only sent appropriate material. The publication is not generally open to receiving PR materials, as they are a niche publication strictly covering the Catholic Church in St. Louis.; Full Page Mono: 25.75
Currency: US Dollars
NEWSPAPER

The St. Lucie News Tribune
Owner: E.W. Scripps Co.
Editorial: 600 Edwards Rd, Fort Pierce, Florida 34982-6295. **T:** 1 772 461-2050
E: yesdesk@scripps.com
W: http://www.tcpalm.com
Freq: Daily; **Circ:** 35739 Not Audited
Publisher: Bob Brunjes; **Editor:** Mike Canan; **Editor:** Mike Graham; **Editor:** Mike Graham; **Editor:** Mark Tomasik; **Editor:** Mark Tomasik; **Editor:** Mark Tomasik; **Editor:** Mark Tomasik
Editorial Profile: The St. Lucie News Tribune shares staff and editorial content with the Stuart (FL) News. The newspaper covers local news and community events. Other sister publications include the Jupiter (FL) Courier, Vero Beach (FL) Press Journal, and Sebastian (FL) Sun.; Full Page Mono: 176.90; Full Page Colour: 260.00
Currency: US Dollars
DAILY NEWSPAPER

St. Paul Papers
Editorial: 406 Howard Ave, Saint Paul, Nebraska 68873-2124. **T:** 1 308 754-4401
Circ: 2904 Not Audited
NEWSPAPER

St. Paul Pioneer Press
Owner: MediaNews Group
Editorial: 345 Cedar St, Saint Paul, Minnesota 55101-1004. **T:** 1 651 222-1111
E: news@pioneerpress.com
W: http://www.twincities.com
Freq: Daily; **Circ:** 239968 Not Audited
Publisher: Guy Gilmore
Editorial Profile: Founded in 1849, The St. Paul Pioneer Press is a daily, 60+ page, four-color broadsheet newspaper written for the general audience of Minnesota and Wisconsin. It aims to be the "leading provider of news and information for an audience that spans the Twin Cities, parts of Minnesota, and a large part of Wisconsin." It covers national and regional news, editorials, sports, business and technology. Consumer issues covered include fashion, food, health, travel, arts and entertainment, music, movies and theater. Outside of the St. Paul area the paper is known as the Minnesota Pioneer Press.; Full Page Mono: 242.00; Full Page Colour: 4200.00
Currency: US Dollars
DAILY NEWSPAPER

St. Paul Pioneer Press
Editorial: 400 S 4th St, Minneapolis, Minnesota 55415-1411. **T:** 1 612 338-6516
DAILY NEWSPAPER

St. Paul Publishing Co.
Editorial: 1643 Robert St S, #60B, West St. Paul, Minnesota 55118-3903.
T: 1 651 457-1177
E: sppc@stpaulpublishing.com
W: http://www.stpaulpublishing.com
Circ: 37250
Editorial Profile: St. Paul Publishing Co. is a local newspaper providing news to the community of St. Paul, MN.
NEWSPAPER

Stafford County Sun
Owner: BH Media Group
Editorial: 306 Garrisonville Rd, Stafford, Virginia 22554. **T:** 1 540 659-4466
E: info@staffordcountysun.com
W: http://www.staffordcountysun.com
Freq: Fri; **Circ:** 20000 Not Audited
Editorial Profile: Stafford County Sun is written for residents of Stafford County, VA. It covers local news and information, community events and stories of interest to area readers.; Full Page Mono: 12.00; Full Page Colour: 205.00
Currency: US Dollars
NEWSPAPER

The Stamford Star
Editorial: 202 E Hamilton St, Stamford, Texas 79553-4730. **T:** 1 325 773-5100
W: http://www.stamfordspirit.com
Freq: Thu
Editor: Cheyenne Bereuter
Editorial Profile: Covers news, sports and events in the Stamford, Texas area.
NEWSPAPER

La Stampa - Los Angeles Bureau
Editorial: 600 N Sweetzer Ave, Los Angeles, California 90048-2102. **T:** 39 048 662-0016
W: http://www.lastampa.it
Editorial Profile: This is the Los Angeles Bureau for La Stampa, based out of Milano, Italy.
DAILY NEWSPAPER

La Stampa - New York Bureau
Owner: EDIT
Editorial: 7 Times Sq Ste 4307, New York, New York 10036-6508. **T:** 1 212 207-0908
E: maurizio.molinari@lastampa.it
W: http://www.lastampa.it
Editorial Profile: This is the New York Bureau for La Stampa, based out of Milano, Italy.
DAILY NEWSPAPER

The Standard
Owner: Tri-State Media
Editorial: 204 W Locust St, Boonville, Indiana 47601-3005. **T:** 1 812 897-2330
E: newsroom@warricknews.com
W: http://warricknews.com
Freq: Thu
NEWSPAPER

The Standard Banner
Owner: Jefferson County Standard Publishing Co., Inc.
Editorial: 122 W Old Andrew Johnson Hwy, Jefferson City, Tennessee 37760-1945.
T: 1 865 475-2081
E: news@standardbanner.com
W: http://www.standardbanner.com
Freq: Thu; **Circ:** 63420 Not Audited
Editorial Profile: Standard-Banner is a local community newspaper for the residents of Jefferson City, TN and the surrounding communities.; Full Page Mono: 7.90
Currency: US Dollars
NEWSPAPER

Standard Democrat
Owner: DA Publishing, LLC
Editorial: 205 S New Madrid St, Sikeston, Missouri 63801. **T:** 1 573 471-1137
E: news@standard-democrat.com
W: http://www.standard-democrat.com
Freq: Mon thru Fri; **Circ:** 4888 Not Audited
Publisher: Michael Jensen
Editorial Profile: Standard Democrat is a daily newspaper of Sikeston, MO and the surrounding areas. The newspaper covers local and national news, sports, business, lifestyle, and local events. It is intended for a readership of community subscribers.; Full Page Mono: 11.53; Full Page Colour: 350.00
Currency: US Dollars
DAILY NEWSPAPER

Standard-Examiner
Owner: Ogden Publishing Corp.
Editorial: 332 Standard Way, Ogden, Utah 84404-1371. **T:** 1 801 625-4200
W: http://www.standard.net
Freq: Daily; **Circ:** 52750 Not Audited
Publisher: Charles Horton
Editorial Profile: Standard-Examiner covers local, regional and national news for the Ogden, Layton, Kaysville, Davis and Cache, UT area. Deadlines are at 8pm MT before issue date. It was first published as The Standard in 1888.; Full Page Mono: 46.93; Full Page Colour: 51.40
Currency: US Dollars
DAILY NEWSPAPER

Standard-Journal
Owner: Sample News Group
Editorial: 21 N Arch St, Milton, Pennsylvania 17847-1211. **T:** 1 570 742-9671
E: newsroom@standard-journal.com
W: http://www.standard-journal.com
Freq: Daily; **Circ:** 3245 Not Audited
Editor: Chris Brady; **Publisher:** Amy Moyer
Editorial Profile: Standard-Journal is a local daily newspaper published for the residents of Lewisburg, PA. The publication covers local news, sports and community events.; Full Page Mono: 15.00; Full Page Colour: 300.00
Currency: US Dollars
DAILY NEWSPAPER

Standard-Speaker
Owner: Times-Shamrock Communications
Editorial: 21 N Wyoming St, Hazleton, Pennsylvania 18201-6098. **T:** 1 570 455-3636
E: editorial@standardspeaker.com
W: http://www.standardspeaker.com
Freq: Daily; **Circ:** 20008 Not Audited
Publisher: Scott Lynett
Editorial Profile: Standard-Speaker is a daily newspaper written for residents of Hazelton, PA and surrounding areas. The publication covers local news, sports and community events.; Full Page Mono: 22.58; Full Page Colour: 265.00
Currency: US Dollars
DAILY NEWSPAPER

The Standard-Times
Owner: GateHouse Media Inc.
Editorial: 25 Elm St, New Bedford, Massachusetts 02740-6228.
T: 1 508 997-7411 **E:** newsroom@s-t.com
W: http://www.southcoasttoday.com
Freq: Daily; **Circ:** 20276 Not Audited
Publisher: Mary Harrington; **Editor:** Susan Pawlak-Seaman; **Editor in Chief:** Robert Unger
Editorial Profile: The Standard-Times is a daily newspaper located in New Bedford, MA. The features include sports, religion, social issues, education, career, healthcare and lifestyle. The lead time is two weeks. Contact the publication for advertising rates.; Full Page Mono: 47.50; Full Page Colour: 187.03
Currency: US Dollars
DAILY NEWSPAPER

Stanwood/Camano News
Owner: Pinkham (Dave) & Pinkham (Pam)
Editorial: 9005 271st St NW, Stanwood, Washington 98292. **T:** 1 360 629-2155
E: newsroom@scnews.com
W: http://www.scnews.com
Freq: Tue; **Circ:** 18675 Not Audited
Editorial Profile: Stanwood/Camano News is written for the residents of Snohomish and Island Counties, WA. The newspaper covers local news and community events, as well as general news stories of interest to its readership.; Full Page Mono: 17.80
Currency: US Dollars
NEWSPAPER

Star
Owner: KPC Media Group Inc.
Editorial: 118 W 9th St, Auburn, Indiana 46706. **T:** 1 260 925-2611
W: http://www.dekalbstar.com
Freq: Daily; **Circ:** 6255
Publisher: Terry Housholder; **Editor:** David Kurtz
Editorial Profile: The Evening Star provides news and information for the Auburn, IN area. Deadlines are the day before issue date.; Full Page Mono: 3.40; Full Page Colour: 55.30
Currency: US Dollars
DAILY NEWSPAPER

The Star
Owner: Northstar Media
Editorial: 930 Cleveland St S, Cambridge, Minnesota 55008-1785. **T:** 1 763 689-1181
E: news@cambridgemn.com
W: http://www.northstarmedia.net
Freq: Sat; **Circ:** 16000 Not Audited
Publisher: Keith Hansen; **Editor:** Linda Noyce
Editorial Profile: Star is a local community newspaper published for the residents of Cambridge, MN. and the surrounding communities.; Full Page Mono: 10.50
Currency: US Dollars
NEWSPAPER

Star Beacon
Owner: Community Newspaper Holdings, Inc.
Editorial: 4626 Park Ave, Ashtabula, Ohio 44004-6933. **T:** 1 440 998-2323
W: http://www.starbeacon.com
Freq: Daily; **Circ:** 11424 Not Audited
Editor: Neil Frieder; **Publisher:** Jim Frustere
Editorial Profile: Star Beacon provides news to the residents of Ashtabula, OH. Deadlines are at noon ET.; Full Page Mono: 25.08; Full Page Colour: 305.00
Currency: US Dollars
DAILY NEWSPAPER

Star Community Newspapers
Owner: Star Community Newspapers, LLC
Editorial: 624 Krona Dr, Plano, Texas 75074-8300. **T:** 1 972 398-4200
W: http://www.scntx.com **Circ:** 73000 Not Audited
Editorial Profile: Star Community Newspapers houses editorial operations for community weeklies serving residents in and around Plano, Allen, Mesquite, Rowlett, Carrollton, Coppell, Flower Mound, Lewisville, Southlake, The Colony, McKinney, Frisco, Celina and Little Elm, TX. It shares offices with the Plano Star-Courier.; Full Page Mono: 15.00
Currency: US Dollars
NEWSPAPER

STAR Community Publishing Group
Owner: DSA Community Publishing
Editorial: 25 Deshon Dr, Melville, New York 11747. **T:** 1 516 393-9300
E: promotions@starcpg.com
W: http://www.starcpg.com
Freq: No Frequency Established;
Circ: 1484066 Not Audited
Editor: Barbara Fisher; **Publisher:** Mike Gates
Editorial Profile: Star Community Publishing Group publishes newspapers for people interested in shopping in Nassau, Suffolk, Brooklyn, Queens and Staten Island, NY. The publication does not accept press releases.
NEWSPAPER

Star Courier
Owner: GateHouse Media Inc.
Editorial: 105 E Central Blvd, Kewanee, Illinois 61443-2245. **T:** 1 309 852-2181
E: editor@starcourier.com
W: http://www.starcourier.com
Freq: Fri; **Circ:** 6200 Not Audited
Publisher: Dee Evans; **Editor:** Mike Landis
Editorial Profile: Star Courier is published daily for the residents of Kewanee, IL and surrounding areas. The newspaper covers local news, business, sports, education and community events.; Full Page Mono: 10.45
Currency: US Dollars
NEWSPAPER

Star Herald/Hills Crescent Newspapers
Owner: Tollefson Publishing
Editorial: 117 W Main St, Luverne, Minnesota 56156. **T:** 1 507 283-2333
W: http://www.star-herald.com **Circ:** 3840 Not Audited
Editor: Lori Ehde; **Publisher:** Roger Tollefson
NEWSPAPER

Star News
Owner: ECM Publishers, Inc.
Editorial: 506 Freeport Ave NW Ste A, Elk River, Minnesota 55330-4755.
T: 1 763 441-3500
E: print.elkriver@ecm-inc.com
W: http://erstarnews.com
Freq: Sat; **Circ:** 20600 Not Audited
Publisher: Julian Andersen; **Editor:** Jim Boyle; **Editor:** Bruce Strand
Editorial Profile: Star News is a community newspaper published in Elk River, MN. The paper covers local news and events for residents of the town and the surrounding area. Deadlines are Fridays at 10am CT prior to issue date.; Full Page Mono: 17.00
Currency: US Dollars
NEWSPAPER

The Star of Zion
Editorial: 3225 W Sugar Creek Rd, Charlotte, North Carolina 28269-7314.
T: 1 704 599-4630
E: sozbusiness@yahoo.com
Freq: Monthly; **Circ:** 10000 Not Audited
Editorial Profile: The Star of Zion covers news and events of the A.M.E. Zion Church.; Full Page Mono: 12.00
Currency: US Dollars
NEWSPAPER

The Star Press
Owner: Gannett Co., Inc.
Editorial: 345 S High St, Muncie, Indiana 47305. **T:** 1 765 747-5700
E: news@muncie.gannett.com
W: http://www.thestarpress.com
Freq: Daily; **Circ:** 20941 Not Audited
Editorial Profile: The Star Press is a regional newspaper of East Central Indiana. The paper covers national, as well as local news stories. Coverage also includes, sports, business and cultural items. The main goal of the paper is to provide the most accurate and up-to-date news and information for their readers.; Full Page Mono: 38.49; Full Page Colour: 146.49
Currency: US Dollars
DAILY NEWSPAPER

Star Publishing Group
Owner: Graham Newspapers, Inc.
Editorial: 319 N Burleson Blvd, Burleson, Texas 76028-3907. **T:** 1 817 295-0486
W: http://www.thestargroup.com **Circ:** 15950 Not Audited
Editor: Mike Eskridge; **Editor:** Paul Gnadt; **Editor:** Paul Gnadt; **Publisher:** Robb Krecklow; **Editor:** Candice McMichen; **Editor:** Candy McMichen; **Editor:** Brian Porter
Editorial Profile: Star Publishing Group is a community newspaper publisher servicing the residents of Dallas, as well as Fort Worth and Arlington, TX.
NEWSPAPER

Star Register Publications
Owner: Wrapports LLC
Editorial: 112 W Clark St, Crown Point, Indiana 46307. **T:** 1 219 663-4212 **Circ:** 3264 Not Audited
Publisher: Lisa Tatina
Editorial Profile: Star Register Publications produces the Crown Point (IN) Star and the Cedar Lake-Lowell (IN) Star, both affiliated with the Post-Tribune in Merrilville, IN.
NEWSPAPER

Star Tribune
Owner: Taylor Corp.
Editorial: 425 Portland Ave, Minneapolis, Minnesota 55415-1699. **T:** 1 612 673-4000
E: releases@startribune.com
W: http://www.startribune.com
Freq: Daily; **Circ:** 301494 Not Audited
Publisher: Michael Klingensmith
Editorial Profile: Star Tribune is a broadsheet written for the general public in the Twin Cities. There are separate Minneapolis and St. Paul editions. Although they focus on news in their respective regions, both editions offer the same international, national, state, metro and consumer news. In August 2009, the paper joined a national sports content-sharing alliance with several other papers across the country.; Full Page Mono: 267.00; Full Page Colour: 309.50
Currency: US Dollars
DAILY NEWSPAPER

Star Tribune
Editorial: 1090 Vermont Ave NW, Washington, District Of Columbia 20005-4905
DAILY NEWSPAPER

Star Tribune
Editorial: 101 W Burnsville Pkwy Ste 101, Burnsville, Minnesota 55337-2571.
T: 1 952 882-4938
DAILY NEWSPAPER

Star Tribune
Editorial: 75 Rev Dr Martin Luther King Jr Blvd, Saint Paul, Minnesota 55155-1605.
T: 1 651 222-1636
DAILY NEWSPAPER

Star Tribune
Editorial: 8360 City Centre Dr Ste 130, Woodbury, Minnesota 55125-3381.
T: 1 651 925-5040
Editorial Profile: The Star Tribune bureau located in Woodbury, MN is also known as the Eastern Suburbs bureau.
DAILY NEWSPAPER

Star-Banner
Owner: Halifax Media Holdings LLC
Editorial: 2121 SW 19th Avenue Rd, Ocala, Florida 34471-7752. **T:** 1 352 867-4010
E: calendar@starbanner.com
W: http://www.ocala.com

Freq: Daily; **Circ:** 28651 Not Audited
Publisher: James Doughton
Editorial Profile: Ocala (FL) Star-Banner is a daily morning newspaper providing news coverage to readers in Marion County, FL. The paper provides coverage of local and regional news, government, politics, business, entertainment, education, and real estate. As of November 2008, they have some combined operations with the Gainesville (FL) Sun.; Full Page Mono: 93.61; Full Page Colour: 302.55
Currency: US Dollars
DAILY NEWSPAPER

The Star-Democrat
Owner: ACM / Chesapeake Publishing and Printing
Editorial: 29088 Airpark Dr, Easton, Maryland 21601-7000. **T:** 1 410 822-1500
E: stardem@chespub.com
W: http://www.stardem.com
Freq: Daily; **Circ:** 16398 Not Audited
News Editor: Kelley Allen; **Publisher:** David Fike
Editorial Profile: The Star-Democrat is published daily for the residents of Talbot, MD. The newspaper covers local news and community events.; Full Page Mono: 24.90; Full Page Colour: 255.00
Currency: US Dollars
DAILY NEWSPAPER

Star-Gazette
Owner: Gannett Co., Inc.
Editorial: 201 Baldwin St, Elmira, New York 14901. **T:** 1 607 734-5151
E: sgnews@gannett.com
W: http://www.stargazette.com
Freq: Daily; **Circ:** 13289 Not Audited
Publisher: Sherman Bodner
Editorial Profile: Star-Gazette is a daily local newspaper serving residents of Elmira, NY and surrounding communities. The newspaper covers local and national news, weather, sports and community events. Feature articles cover business developments, local and national politics, education, arts & entertainment and lifestyle.; Full Page Mono: 62.50; Full Page Colour: 665.00
Currency: US Dollars
DAILY NEWSPAPER

Star-Herald
Owner: Omaha World-Herald Co.
Editorial: 1405 Broadway, Scottsbluff, Nebraska 69361-3151. **T:** 1 308 632-9000
E: news@starherald.com
W: http://www.starherald.com
Freq: Daily; **Circ:** 12311 Not Audited
Editor: Steve Frederick; **Publisher:** Jim Holland
Editorial Profile: Star-Herald is the daily newspaper of Scottsbluff, NE and the surrounding region. It covers local and national news, lifestyle and sports. Lead time varies.; Full Page Mono: 20.78; Full Page Colour: 78.03
Currency: US Dollars
DAILY NEWSPAPER

Starkville Daily News
Owner: Horizon Publications
Editorial: 304 E Lampkin St, Starkville, Mississippi 39759-2910. **T:** 1 662 323-1642
E: news@starkvilledailynews.com
W: http://www.starkvilledailynews.com
Freq: Daily; **Circ:** 7875 Not Audited
Publisher: Donald Norman; **Editor:** Zack Plair
Editorial Profile: Starkville Daily News is the successor to the Starkville News (established in 1901) and the East Mississippi Times (established in 1867), which were consolidated in 1926. It has been published daily since October 31, 1960. The publication is written for residents of Starkville, MS. The lead time for Starkville Daily News is same day. Deadlines for the publication end two days prior to the issue date.; Full Page Mono: 10.25; Full Page Colour: 325.00
Currency: US Dollars
DAILY NEWSPAPER

Starkville Dispatch
Owner: Commercial Dispatch Publishing Company
Editorial: 101 S Lafayette St, Ste 16, Starkville, Mississippi 39759-2914.
T: 1 661 323-2424
W: http://www.thestarkvilledispatch.com
Freq: Daily; **Circ:** 2500
Editorial Profile: The Starkville Dispatch is printed for the residents of Starkville, MS. It shares much of its content with the Commercial Dispatch in Columbus, MS.; Full Page Mono: 12.90
Currency: US Dollars
DAILY NEWSPAPER

The Star-Ledger
Owner: Newhouse Newspapers
Editorial: 1 Star Ledger Plz, Newark, New Jersey 07102-1227. **T:** 1 973 392-4141
E: metro@starledger.com
W: http://www.nj.com/starledger
Freq: Daily; **Circ:** 296466 Not Audited
Publisher: Richard Vezza; **Editor:** Kevin Whitmer
Editorial Profile: The Star-Ledger is a 95+ page, four-color broadsheet written for the general public in the New Jersey area. The newspaper aims to serve the greater New Jersey region. The business section is featured daily, covering local and national business stories, daily stock market rates, and real estate. The largest business sections appear in the Tuesday and Sunday editions. Articles include features, breaking news, trends, analyses, profiles, and investigative stories.; Full Page Mono: 506.34; Full Page Colour: 551.02
Currency: US Dollars
DAILY NEWSPAPER

The Star-Ledger
Editorial: 50 W State St, Trenton, New Jersey 08608-1220. **T:** 1 609 989-0012
E: trenton@starledger.com
DAILY NEWSPAPER

The Star-Ledger
Editorial: 1305 Campus Pkwy Ste 200, Wall Township, New Jersey 07753-6813.
T: 1 732 919-0381
Bureau Chief: Laura Craven
DAILY NEWSPAPER

Star-Mercury Publications
Owner: Grimes Publications
Editorial: 3051 Roosevelt Hwy, Manchester, Georgia 31816. **T:** 1 706 846-3188
Circ: 11600 Not Audited
Editor: Jim Grimes; **Editor:** Rob Richardson
NEWSPAPER

Star-News
Owner: Halifax Media Holdings LLC
Editorial: 1003 S 17th St, Wilmington, North Carolina 28401-8023. **T:** 1 910 343-2000
E: breakingnews@starnewsonline.com
W: http://www.starnewsonline.com
Freq: Daily; **Circ:** 35339 Not Audited
Publisher: Robert Gruber
Editorial Profile: Star-News is a daily newspaper aimed at providing local, national and global news coverage to the Wilmington, NC area. The paper's sections include local news, sports, entertainment, business, leisure and marketplace.; Full Page Mono: 152.38; Full Page Colour: 226.41
Currency: US Dollars
DAILY NEWSPAPER

The Star-News
Owner: San Diego Neighborhood Newspapers, Inc.
Editorial: 296 3rd Ave, Chula Vista, California 91910-2701. **T:** 1 619 427-3000
W: http://www.thestarnews.com
Freq: Fri; **Circ:** 33750 Not Audited
Publisher: Margo Caffrey; **Editor:** Carlos Davalos
Editorial Profile: Star News is a weekly newspaper providing Local News coverage to the residents of Chula Vista, National City, Bonita, East Lake and Otay Ranch, CA. Coverage includes local news and events, business, sports and social issues.; Full Page Mono: 20.25
Currency: US Dollars
NEWSPAPER

El Starous News
Owner: Observer Newspaper Group
Editorial: 3427 Belgium Ln, San Antonio, Texas 78219-2501. **T:** 1 210 212-6397
E: taylor2039@aol.com
Freq: Wed
Editor: Waseem Ali
Editorial Profile: El Starous News provides Local News coverage to the African-American Community in San Antonio, TX.
NEWSPAPER

The Star-Republican
Owner: Ohio Community Media LLC.
Editorial: 761 S. Nelson Ave., Wilmington, Ohio 45177. **T:** 1 937 382-2574
E: info@wnewsj.com
W: http://www.wnewsj.com
Freq: Mon; **Circ:** 18000 Not Audited
Publisher: Pam Stricker
Editorial Profile: The Star-Republican is a local newspaper serving Clinton County, OH, including Blanchester and Wilmington, OH,

including local news, sports, commentary and entertainment.; Full Page Mono: 15.75
Currency: US Dollars
NEWSPAPER

The State
Owner: McClatchy Newspapers
Editorial: 1401 Shop Rd, Columbia, South Carolina 29201-4843. **T:** 1 803 771-6161
E: state@thestate.com
W: http://www.thestate.com
Freq: Daily; **Circ:** 57163 Not Audited
Editorial Profile: The State is a daily four-color newspaper serving residents of Columbia, SC. The newspaper focuses on coverage of state and local matters instead of national stories. According to the publishers, "our readers have a greater opportunity to affect what happens at the state and local level than at the national level." The newspaper includes the following sections: Business, Classifieds, Columnists, Features, Opinion, Local News, Sports, Weather and Obituaries. The paper contains a strong local focus on politics and the government. As explained by the publishers, the aim of the newspaper is "to place the news in context, and to help readers have a deeper understanding of the issues." The publication is a 2002 winner of the Best in Business award, given by the Society of American Business Editors and Writers.; Full Page Mono: 164.06; Full Page Colour: 531.81
Currency: US Dollars
DAILY NEWSPAPER

The State Journal
Owner: Dix Communications
Editorial: 1216 Wilkinson Blvd, Frankfort, Kentucky 40601-1243. **T:** 1 502 227-4556
W: http://www.state-journal.com
Freq: Daily; **Circ:** 8633 Not Audited
News Editor: Shannon Brock; **Editor:** Phil Case; **Editor:** Dan Liebman; **Publisher:** Ann Maenza
Editorial Profile: The State Journal is written for residents of Frankfort, KY. It covers local news, sports, business, education and events.; Full Page Mono: 11.50; Full Page Colour: 190.00
Currency: US Dollars
DAILY NEWSPAPER

The State Journal-Register
Owner: GateHouse Media Inc.
Editorial: 1 Copley Plz, Springfield, Illinois 62701-1927. **T:** 1 217 788-1300
E: sjr@sj-r.com **W:** http://www.sj-r.com
Freq: Daily; **Circ:** 37171 Not Audited
Publisher: Walt Lafferty
Editorial Profile: The State Journal-Register is a daily newspaper for residents of Springfield, IL and the central part of the state. The publication covers local and national news, sports, business and arts & entertainment.; Full Page Mono: 223.50; Full Page Colour: 327.21
Currency: US Dollars
DAILY NEWSPAPER

Stateline Publications
Owner: Grabinoski (Kristin)
Editorial: 520 6Th St, Armstrong, Iowa 50514-7711. **T:** 1 712 868-3460
E: krisg@armstrongjournal.com **Circ:** 1886 Not Audited
Editor: Dorothy Cronk; **Publisher:** Kristin Grabinoski; **Editor:** Kim Meyer
Editorial Profile: Stateline Publications publishes The Ringsted Dispatch, Swea City Herald-Press and Armstrong Journal. It provides Local News coverage for Emmet County and Kossuth County, IA communities.
NEWSPAPER

Staten Island Advance
Owner: Newhouse Newspapers
Editorial: 950 W Fingerboard Rd, Staten Island, New York 10305-1453.
T: 1 718 981-1234 **E:** citydesk@siadvance.com
W: http://www.silive.com
Freq: Daily; **Circ:** 30632 Not Audited
Publisher: Caroline Diamond Harrison; **Editor:** Brian Laline; **Editor:** Brian Laline; **Editor:** Brian Laline; **News Editor:** Richard Ryan
Editorial Profile: Staten Island Advance is a daily regional newspaper for residents of Staten Island, NY. The paper features business, sports, living, entertainment and national, regional and local news. The paper's travel section found in the Sunday paper is provided by The Star-Ledger, a sister publication. The mission of the publication is to provide the most accurate and comprehensive news for the readers with the highest of journalistic integrity.; Full Page Mono: 65.89; Full Page Colour: 211.05
Currency: US Dollars
DAILY NEWSPAPER

Staten Island Advance
Editorial: 9 City Hall, New York, New York 10007-1200. **T:** 1 718 304-7307
DAILY NEWSPAPER

Statesboro Herald
Owner: Morris Multimedia, Inc.
Editorial: 1 Proctor St, Statesboro, Georgia 30458-1387. **T:** 1 912 764-9031
W: http://www.statesboroherald.net
Freq: Daily; **Circ:** 8544 Not Audited
Editorial Profile: Statesboro Herald is written for the residents of Bulloch County, GA. The outlet offers RSS (Really Simple Syndication).; Full Page Mono: 13.04; Full Page Colour: 195.00
Currency: US Dollars
DAILY NEWSPAPER

Statesman Journal
Owner: Gannett Co., Inc.
Editorial: 280 Church St NE, Salem, Oregon 97301-3734. **T:** 1 503 399-6611
E: newsroom@statesmanjournal.com
W: http://www.statesmanjournal.com
Freq: Daily; **Circ:** 30066 Not Audited
Publisher: Steve Silberman
Editorial Profile: The Statesman Journal is a daily newspaper published for the residents of Salem, OR and surrounding areas. The newspaper covers local and state news, business, sports, lifestyles and entertainment.; Full Page Mono: 92.09; Full Page Colour: 124.48
Currency: US Dollars
DAILY NEWSPAPER

Statesville Record & Landmark
Owner: World Media Enterprises, Inc.
Editorial: 222 E Broad St, Statesville, North Carolina 28677-5325. **T:** 1 704 873-1451
E: news@statesville.com
W: http://www.statesville.com
Freq: Daily; **Circ:** 13269 Not Audited
Publisher: Tim Dearman; **Editor:** Dave Ibach
Editorial Profile: Statesville Record & Landmark is written for residents of Statesville, NC.; Full Page Mono: 12.07
Currency: US Dollars
DAILY NEWSPAPER

Steamboat Pilot & Today
Owner: WorldWide Ltd. Liability Co.
Editorial: 1901 Curve Plaza, Steamboat Springs, Colorado 80487. **T:** 1 970 879-1502
W: http://www.steamboatpilot.com
Freq: Daily; **Circ:** 9738 Not Audited
News Editor: Nicole Miller; **Publisher:** Suzanne Schlicht
Editorial Profile: Steamboat Pilot & Today is a local newspaper for residents of Steamboat Springs, CO. The paper covers local news, business, sports and arts & entertainment. It also covers national and statewide stories if they have a direct impact on the newspaper's readership.; Full Page Mono: 12.52
Currency: US Dollars
DAILY NEWSPAPER

Stephens Media - Cabot
Owner: Stephens Media
Editorial: 903 S Pine St, Cabot, Arkansas 72023. **T:** 1 501 843-3534
W: http://www.pulaskinews.net **Circ:** 14065 Not Audited
Editor: Mark Buffalo; **Publisher:** Dennis Byrd; **Editor:** Greg Rayburn
NEWSPAPER

Stephens Media Group-Van Alstyne
Owner: Stephens Media
Editorial: 209 N Dallas St, Van Alstyne, Texas 75495. **T:** 1 903 482-5253 **Circ:** 17500 Not Audited
Editor: Jeremy Corley; **Editor:** Jeremy Corley; **Editor:** Jeremy Corley; **Publisher:** John Wright
NEWSPAPER

Stephenville Empire-Tribune
Owner: American Consolidated Media
Editorial: 590 E South Loop, Stephenville, Texas 76401-5310. **T:** 1 254 965-3124
E: news@empiretribune.com
W: http://www.yourstephenvilletx.com
Freq: Daily; **Circ:** 4384 Not Audited
Publisher: Rochelle Stidham
Editorial Profile: Stephenville Empire-Tribune's editorial mission is to be the premiere source of local information to the residents of Erath County, TX. Deadlines are at 2pm CT the day before publication. Deadlines for Sunday's edition are at noon CT the Friday before.; Full Page Mono: 14.65; Full Page Colour: 125.00
Currency: US Dollars
DAILY NEWSPAPER

The Steuben Courier-Advocate
Owner: GateHouse Media Inc.
Editorial: 10 W Steuben St, Bath, New York 14810. **T:** 1 607 776-2121
E: scanewsassistant@stny.rr.com
W: http://www.steubencourier.com
Freq: Sun; **Circ:** 10800 Not Audited
Publisher: Karen Causer; **Editor:** Mary Perham
Editorial Profile: Steuben Courier-Advocate is written for the residents of Steuben County, NY.; Full Page Mono: 7.20
Currency: US Dollars
NEWSPAPER

Steubenville Register
Owner: Roman Catholic Diocese of Steubenville
Editorial: 422 Washington St, Steubenville, Ohio 43952. **T:** 1 740 282-3631
E: register@diosteub.org
W: http://www.diosteub.org
Freq: Bi-Weekly; **Circ:** 16300 Not Audited
Editor: Pat Defrancis; **Publisher:** Kurt Kemo
Editorial Profile: Steubenville Register's editorial mission is to inform about the Catholic church locally and internationally. The publication is written for the Catholic residents in 13 counties in Ohio.; Full Page Mono: 7.25
Currency: US Dollars
NEWSPAPER

Stevens Point Journal
Owner: Gannett Co., Inc.
Editorial: 1200 3rd St, Stevens Point, Wisconsin 54481-2855. **T:** 1 715 344-6100
E: news@stevenspointjournal.com
W: http://www.stevenspointjournal.com
Freq: Daily; **Circ:** 8259 Not Audited
Editorial Profile: Combines with The Daily Tribune in Wisconsin Rapids and the Marshfield News-Herald on Sundays.; Full Page Mono: 31.10; Full Page Colour: 357.00
Currency: US Dollars
DAILY NEWSPAPER

Stillwater Gazette
Owner: ECM Publishers, Inc.
Editorial: 1931 Curve Crest Blvd W, Stillwater, Minnesota 55082-6063. **T:** 1 651 439-3130
W: http://www.stillwatergazette.com
Freq: 3 Times/Week; **Circ:** 22819
Publisher: Mark Berriman
Editorial Profile: The Stillwater Gazette is a group of local newspapers that provides Local News coverage of the St. Croix Valley region. They do not accept any press info that is not related to Minnesota.
NEWSPAPER

Stillwater Valley Advertiser
Owner: Arens Publications
Editorial: 395 S High St, Covington, Ohio 45318-1121. **T:** 1 937 473-2028
E: production@woh.rr.com
W: http://www.arenspub.com
Freq: Wed; **Circ:** 10378 Not Audited
Editor: Jean Devlin; **Publisher:** Gary Godfrey
Editorial Profile: Stillwater Valley Advertiser is written for residents of Covington, OH.; Full Page Mono: 11.62
Currency: US Dollars
NEWSPAPER

The Stokes News & The Weekly Independent
Owner: Heartland Publications
Editorial: 1072 N Main St, Walnut Cove, North Carolina 27052-9312. **T:** 1 336 591-8191
W: http://www.thestokesnews.com
Freq: Thu; **Circ:** 6920 Not Audited
Editor: Shannon Fenner
NEWSPAPER

Stonebridge Press Newspapers
Editorial: 25 Elm St, Southbridge, Massachusetts 1550. **T:** 1 508 764-4325
W: http://www.theheartofmassachusetts.com/
Circ: 49320 Not Audited
Publisher: Frank Chilinski; **Editor:** David Dore; **Editor:** Adam Minor
Editorial Profile: Stonebridge Press Newspapers is a weekly community newspaper publisher serving the residents of Spencer, Webster, Auburn, Sturbridge, Charlton and Southbridge, MA.
NEWSPAPER

The Stranger
Owner: Index Publishing LLC
Editorial: 1535 11th Ave, Fl 3, Seattle, Washington 98122. **T:** 1 206 323-7101
E: editor@thestranger.com
W: http://www.thestranger.com
Freq: Thu; **Circ:** 80000 Not Audited
Editor: Christopher Frizzelle; **News Editor:** Dominic Holden; **Publisher:** Tim Keck
Editorial Profile: Stranger is a tabloid weekly publication written for the residents of Seattle. The newspaper covers news on recent events.; Full Page Mono: 25.60
Currency: US Dollars
NEWSPAPER

Straus News
Editorial: 20 West Ave, Chester, New York 10918. **T:** 1 845 469-9000
E: nyoffice@strausnews.com
W: http://www.strausnews.com **Circ:** 35943 Not Audited
Publisher: Jeanne Straus
Editorial Profile: Straus News is a community newspaper publisher headquartered in Chester, NY.
NEWSPAPER

Straus News
Editorial: 1A Main St Ste 9, Sparta, New Jersey 07871-1909. **T:** 1 973 300-0890
E: njoffice@strausnews.com
W: http://www.strausnews.com **Circ:** 50723 Not Audited
Publisher: Jeanne Straus
NEWSPAPER

Street Sense
Editorial: 1317 G St NW, Washington, District Of Columbia 20005-3102. **T:** 1 202 347-2006
E: info@streetsense.org
W: http://www.streetsense.org
Freq: Bi-Weekly; **Circ:** 12000 Not Audited
Editor in Chief: Mary Otto
Editorial Profile: Street Sense is published bi-weekly on Wednesday for the residents of Washington, D.C. The newspaper is written and published by homeless men and women as part of a mission to help them earn income. It explores issues related to poverty, homelessness and other social problems.; Full Page Mono: 25.00
Currency: US Dollars
NEWSPAPER

StreetWise
Owner: Streetwise, Inc.
Editorial: 4454 N Broadway St Suite 350, Chicago, Illinois 60640-5660.
T: 1 773 334-6600
E: pressreleases@streetwise.org
W: http://www.streetwise.org
Freq: Wed; **Circ:** 13000 Not Audited
Editor: Suzanne Hanney; **Publisher:** Jim LoBianco
Editorial Profile: StreetWise was founded to meet a vitally important area of need among the homeless of Chicago. Through its operation of a street newspaper, the organization seeks to empower men and women who are homeless, or at risk of becoming so, as they work toward gainful employment. The newspaper provides news and information for the Chicago area.; Full Page Mono: 9.56
Currency: US Dollars
NEWSPAPER

Stuart News
Owner: E.W. Scripps Co.
Editorial: 1939 Se Federal Hwy, Stuart, Florida 34994-3915. **T:** 1 772 287-1550
E: yesdesk@scripps.com
W: http://www.tcpalm.com
Freq: Daily; **Circ:** 69287 Not Audited
News Editor: Joshua Pearl; **News Editor:** Joshua Pearl; **Editor:** Mark Tomasik; **Editor:** Mark Tomasik; **Editor:** Mark Tomasik; **Editor:** Mark Tomasik; **Publisher:** Thomas Weber
Editorial Profile: Stuart News is published daily for residents of Stuart, FL and surrounding communities. The publication covers local news, features and community events. The newspaper has several sister publications including The Port St. Lucie (FL) News, Fort Pierce (FL) Tribune, Vero Beach (FL) Press Journal, and the Sebastian (FL) Sun. Press releases should be directed to the appropriate editor.; Full Page Mono: 171.75; Full Page Colour: 1710.00
Currency: US Dollars
DAILY NEWSPAPER

Stumpf Publishing
Editorial: 924 Whitewater Ave., Saint Charles, Minnesota 55972. **T:** 1 507 932-3663
E: sceditor@stumpfpublishing.net **Circ:** 6200 Not Audited
Editor: Laura Berndt; **Editor:** Cheryl Nymann
NEWSPAPER

Sturgis Journal
Owner: Liberry
Editorial: 209 John St, Sturgis, Michigan 49091-1459. **T:** 1 269 651-5407
E: newsroom@sturgisjournal.com
W: http://www.sturgisjournal.com
Freq: Daily; **Circ:** 7000 Not Audited
Editor: Candice Phelps; **Publisher:** Dan Tollefson
Editorial Profile: Sturgis Journal is published daily for the residents of Sturgis, MI and surrounding areas. The newspaper covers local and regional news, business, sports, lifestyles and entertainment.; Full Page Mono: 12.50; Full Page Colour: 235.00
Currency: US Dollars
DAILY NEWSPAPER

Stuttgart Daily Leader
Owner: GateHouse Media Inc.
Editorial: 111 W 6th St, Stuttgart, Arkansas 72160-4243. **T:** 1 870 673-8533
E: editor@stuttgartdailyleader.com
W: http://www.stuttgartdailyleader.com
Freq: Daily; **Circ:** 2552 Not Audited
Editorial Profile: Stuttgart Daily Leader is written for residents of Stuttgart, AR. It covers local news, sports and entertainment.; Full Page Mono: 12.50; Full Page Colour: 200.00
Currency: US Dollars
DAILY NEWSPAPER

Style Weekly
Owner: Landmark Media Enterprises, LLC
Editorial: 1313 E Main St, Richmond, Virginia 23219. **T:** 1 804 358-0825
E: info@styleweekly.com
W: http://www.styleweekly.com
Freq: Wed; **Circ:** 35100 Not Audited
News Editor: Scott Bass; **Publisher:** Lori Collier Waran; **News Editor:** Tina Griego; **Editor in Chief:** Jason Roop; **Editor in Chief:** Jason Roop
Editorial Profile: Style Weekly is a weekly newspaper that provides news and information with a slant toward recreation for the Richmond, VA area. The papers covers local news, sports, entertainment and events.; Full Page Mono: 27.62
Currency: US Dollars
NEWSPAPER

Suburban Flint Newspaper Group
Owner: Newhouse Newspapers
Editorial: 200 E 1st St, Flint, Michigan 48502. **T:** 1 810 766-6100 **E:** fj@flintjournal.com
W: http://www.flintjournal.com **Circ:** 93645 Not Audited
NEWSPAPER

Suburban Journals - Madison County
Owner: Lee Enterprises, Inc.
Editorial: 2 Eastport Executive Drive, Collinsville, Illinois 62234. **T:** 1 618 344-0264
E: metroeastnews@yourjournal.com
W: http://www.stltoday.com/suburban-journals/illinois **Circ:** 55105 Not Audited
NEWSPAPER

Suburban Journals - St. Charles County
Owner: Lee Enterprises, Inc.
Editorial: 14522 S Outer 40 Rd, Town and Country, Missouri 63017-5737.
T: 1 314 821-1110
E: goodnews@yourjournal.com
W: http://www.stltoday.com/suburban-journals
Circ: 79988 Not Audited
Editor: Janice Denham
NEWSPAPER

The Suburban News
Editorial: 5724 Main Rd, Hunlock Creek, Pennsylvania 18621. **T:** 1 570 675-6397
E: ads@nepafreeads.com
W: http://www.nepafreeads.com
Freq: Thu; **Circ:** 10000 Not Audited
Editorial Profile: The Suburban News is a weekly newspaper published for the residents of Back Mountain, PA and the surrounding cities.; Full Page Mono: 15.75
Currency: US Dollars
NEWSPAPER

Suburban News
Owner: Midlands Newspapers, Inc.
Editorial: 604 Fort Crook Rd N, Bellevue, Nebraska 68005-4557. **T:** 1 402 773-7300
W: http://www.omaha.com **Circ:** 8450
Publisher: Shon Barenklau; **Editor:** Vince Mancuso
NEWSPAPER

Suburban Newspapers, Inc.
Editorial: 7820 Wyatt Dr, Fort Worth, Texas 76108. **T:** 1 817 246-2473 **Circ:** 30000 Not Audited
Editor: Charlsea Littlefield; **Editor:** Courtney Thompson; **Publisher:** Bo Underwood
Editorial Profile: Suburban Newspapers, Inc. is a local newspaper in Fort Worth, TX.
NEWSPAPER

Suburban Washington Newspapers
Owner: American Community Newspapers, LLC
Editorial: 6564 Loisdale Ct, Springfield, Virginia 22150-1827. **T:** 1 703 738-2520
E: news@sungazette.net
W: http://www.sungazette.net
Freq: Weekly; **Circ:** 67949 Not Audited
Editor: Scott McCaffrey
NEWSPAPER

Suffolk News-Herald
Owner: Boone Newspapers Inc.
Editorial: 130 S Saratoga St, Suffolk, Virginia 23434. **T:** 1 757 539-3437
W: http://www.suffolknewsherald.com
Freq: Daily; **Circ:** 3930 Not Audited
Editorial Profile: Suffolk News-Herald provides news and information for the Suffolk, VA area.; Full Page Mono: 21.74; Full Page Colour: 350.00
Currency: US Dollars
DAILY NEWSPAPER

Sullivan Daily Times
Owner: Pierce Publishing Co Inc.
Editorial: 115 W Jackson St, Sullivan, Indiana 47882. **T:** 1 812 268-6356
W: http://www.sullivan-times.com
Freq: Daily; **Circ:** 4300 Not Audited
Publisher: Nancy Gettinger; **Editor:** Pete Wilson
Editorial Profile: Sullivan Daily Times provides news and information for Sullivan, IN. Deadlines are at noon CT on the issue date.; Full Page Mono: 7.25; Full Page Colour: 240.00
Currency: US Dollars
DAILY NEWSPAPER

Sulphur Springs News-Telegram
Owner: Echo Publishing Company
Editorial: 401 Church St, Sulphur Springs, Texas 75483. **T:** 1 903 885-8663
E: news@ssecho.com
W: http://www.ssnewstelegram.com
Freq: Daily; **Circ:** 5500 Not Audited
News Editor: Faith Huffman; **News Editor:** Faith Huffman; **News Editor:** Faith Huffman; **News Editor:** Faith Huffman; **Publisher:** Scott Keys
Editorial Profile: Sulphur Springs News-Telegram is a local daily newspaper written for residents of Sulphur Springs, TX. The newspaper primarily covers local news. Deadlines are at noon CT the day prior to publication.; Full Page Mono: 11.48; Full Page Colour: 358.00
Currency: US Dollars
DAILY NEWSPAPER

Summit Daily News
Owner: Swift Newspapers
Editorial: 40 W Main St, Frisco, Colorado 80443. **T:** 1 970 668-3998
E: news@summitdaily.com
W: http://www.summitdaily.com
Freq: Daily; **Circ:** 12000 Not Audited
Publisher: Matt Sandberg
Editorial Profile: Summit Daily News provides news and information for the Frisco, CO area.; Full Page Mono: 10.75
Currency: US Dollars
DAILY NEWSPAPER

The Sun
Owner: Paxton Media Group
Editorial: 518 Carson St, Jonesboro, Arkansas 72401-3128. **T:** 1 870 935-5525
E: newsroom@jonesborosun.com
W: http://www.jonesborosun.com
Freq: Daily; **Circ:** 19830 Not Audited
Publisher: David Mosesso; **Editor in Chief:** Roy Ockert; **Editor in Chief:** Roy Ockert; **Editor in Chief:** Roy Ockert; **Editor in Chief:** Roy Ockert; **Editor:** Sherry Pruitt; **News Editor:** Brian Smith; **News Editor:** Brian Smith; **News Editor:** Brian Smith; **News Editor:** Brian Smith; **Editor:** Chris Wessel
Editorial Profile: The Sun is published daily for the residents of Jonesboro, AR and surrounding areas. The newspaper covers local and state news, sports, lifestyles and entertainment.; Full Page Mono: 27.25; Full Page Colour: 3440.25
Currency: US Dollars
DAILY NEWSPAPER

The Sun
Owner: MediaNews Group
Editorial: 290 N D St Ste 102, San Bernardino, California 92401-1734.
T: 1 909 889-9666 **W:** http://www.sbsun.com
Freq: Daily; **Circ:** 52281 Not Audited

Editorial Profile: The Sun is a daily newspaper that serves San Bernadino, CA. This paper is a part of the Los Angeles Newspaper Group, a subsidiary of Media News Group. The publication features local, regional, state, national and international news, as well as sports, business and entertainment.; Full Page Mono: 651.00; Full Page Colour: 2121.48
Currency: US Dollars
DAILY NEWSPAPER

The Sun
Owner: MediaNews Group
Editorial: 491 Dutton St, Lowell, Massachusetts 01854-4289.
T: 1 978 458-7100
W: http://www.lowellsun.com
Freq: Daily; **Circ:** 45648 Not Audited
Editor: James Campanini
Editorial Profile: The Sun is a daily newspaper covering news for all of Northern Middlesex County and parts of Northern Essex County, MA and Southern New Hampshire. Coverage includes local news, politics, sports, lifestyle and entertainment.; Full Page Mono: 54.30; Full Page Colour: 179.61
Currency: US Dollars
DAILY NEWSPAPER

The Sun & Country Messenger Newspapers
Editorial: 108 Cascade St, Osceola, Wisconsin 54020. **T:** 1 715 294-2314
W: http://www.osceolasun.com **Circ:** 4100
Editor: Phillip Bock; **Publisher:** Randi Smith
NEWSPAPER

The Sun Chronicle
Owner: United Communications Corp.
Editorial: 34 S Main St, Attleboro, Massachusetts 02703-2920.
T: 1 508 222-7000
E: news@thesunchronicle.com
W: http://www.thesunchronicle.com
Freq: Daily; **Circ:** 12486 Not Audited
Publisher: Oreste D'Arconte; **Editor:** Mike Kirby
Editorial Profile: The Sun Chronicle is a daily newspaper for the Attleboro, MA area. It provides news, special reports, features, opinions, sports and announcements.; Full Page Mono: 16.33; Full Page Colour: 395.00
Currency: US Dollars
DAILY NEWSPAPER

Sun Coast Media Newspapers
Owner: Sun Coast Media Group Inc.
Editorial: 190 S Florida Ave, Bartow, Florida 33830-4701. **T:** 1 863 533-4183
E: news@polkcountydemocrat.com
W: http://www.polkcountydemocrat.com
Circ: 16651 Not Audited
Publisher: Derek Dunn-Rankin; **Publisher:** Jim Gouvellis; **Editor:** Jeff Roslow
NEWSPAPER

Sun Herald
Owner: McClatchy Newspapers
Editorial: 205 Debuys Rd, Gulfport, Mississippi 39507. **T:** 1 228 896-2100
E: mynews@sunherald.com
W: http://www.sunherald.com
Freq: Daily; **Circ:** 28966 Not Audited
Editor: Paul Hampton; **Editor:** Paul Hampton; **Editor:** Paul Hampton; **Editor:** Paul Hampton; **Editor:** Scott Hawkins; **Publisher:** Glen Nardi
Editorial Profile: Sun Herald is a daily newspaper for the residents of Biloxi, MS. The publication covers news, people and events nationally, as well as local news along the Mississippi Coast.; Full Page Mono: 57.12; Full Page Colour: 191.36
Currency: US Dollars
DAILY NEWSPAPER

Sun Journal
Owner: Lewiston Sun Journal, Inc.
Editorial: 104 Park St, Lewiston, Maine 04240-0304. **T:** 1 207 784-5411
E: editor@sunjournal.com
W: http://www.sunjournal.com
Freq: Daily; **Circ:** 33516 Not Audited
Publisher: James Costello; **Editor:** Denise Scammon
Editorial Profile: Sun Journal in Lewiston, ME is a daily newspaper covering local news and events.; Full Page Mono: 43.80; Full Page Colour: 350.00
Currency: US Dollars
DAILY NEWSPAPER

Sun Journal
Owner: Halifax Media Holdings LLC
Editorial: 3200 Wellons Blvd, New Bern, North Carolina 28562-5234. **T:** 1 252 638-8101
W: http://www.newbernsj.com
Freq: Daily; **Circ:** 12234 Not Audited
Publisher: Vernon DeBolt; **Editor:** Eddie Fitzgerald
Editorial Profile: Sun Journal is a daily newspaper for New Bern, NC and the surrounding communities. The newspaper covers local news, arts and entertainment, sports, business, and lifestyle stories. Contact the publication for circulation information and advertisements rates.; Full Page Mono: 17.00; Full Page Colour: 495.00
Currency: US Dollars
DAILY NEWSPAPER

The Sun News
Owner: McClatchy Newspapers
Editorial: 914 Frontage Rd E, Myrtle Beach, South Carolina 29577-6700.
T: 1 843 626-8555
E: sneditors@thesunnews.com
W: http://www.thesunnews.com
Freq: Daily; **Circ:** 38304 Not Audited
Editor: Caroline Evans
Editorial Profile: The Sun News is a daily newspaper published for the residents of Myrtle Beach, SC and surrounding areas. It provides information on local news and community events.; Full Page Mono: 59.05; Full Page Colour: 202.39
Currency: US Dollars
DAILY NEWSPAPER

The Sun News
Owner: Metro Group Inc.
Editorial: 141 Buffalo St, Hamburg, New York 14075-5010. **T:** 1 716 649-4040
E: news@thesunnews.net
W: http://www.thesunnews.net
Freq: Thu; **Circ:** 10500 Not Audited
Publisher: Jerry Grabowski; **Editor:** Jessie Owen
Editorial Profile: The Sun provides news and information for suburban Buffalo, NY. The deadlines are at 5pm ET on Thursdays.; Full Page Mono: 9.52; Full Page Colour: 510.00
Currency: US Dollars
NEWSPAPER

The Sun Newspapers
Owner: Community Media Corporation
Editorial: 216 Main St, Seal Beach, California 90740. **T:** 1 562 430-7555
E: sun@sunnews.com
W: http://www.sunnews.org
Freq: Thu; **Circ:** 32000 Not Audited
Publisher: Lindsay Evans; **Editor:** Donna Leedy
Editorial Profile: The Sun Newspapers is a local paper serving the residents and tourists of the communities of Seal Beach, Huntington Harbour, Rossmoor/Los Alamitos and Sunset Beach, CA. It contains local news, entertainment, events, sports and lifestyle features. It also provides comprehensive event listings and information on travel services.; Full Page Mono: 20.80
Currency: US Dollars
NEWSPAPER

Sun Newspapers
Owner: ECM Publishers, Inc.
Editorial: 10917 Valley View Rd, Eden Prairie, Minnesota 55344-3730
W: http://ecmpublishers.com **Circ:** 54253 Not Audited
NEWSPAPER

The Sun Newspapers - Central Jersey
Owner: Elauwit LLC
Editorial: 20 Nassau St Ste 26A, Princeton, New Jersey 08542-4509. **T:** 1 609 751-0245
W: http://cj.sunne.ws
Freq: Wed; **Circ:** 24100
Editor: Alan Bauer; **Publisher:** Dan McDonough
Editorial Profile: Sun & Telegram Newspapers - Central Jersey publishes the Hopewell Sun, the Montgomery Sun and the Lawrence Sun, providing Local and Community News to the residents of Mercer County, Somerset County and Middlesex County, NJ.; Full Page Mono: 8.00
Currency: US Dollars
NEWSPAPER

The Sun Newspapers - South Jersey
Owner: Elauwit LLC
Editorial: 108 Kings Hwy E, Haddonfield, New Jersey 08033-2099. **T:** 1 856 427-0933
E: info@elauwitmedia.com
W: http://sj.sunne.ws **Circ:** 74600 Not Audited
Editor: Alan Bauer; **Publisher:** Dan McDonough
NEWSPAPER

The Sun Patriot Newspapers
Owner: ECM Publishers, Inc.
Editorial: 8 S Elm St, Waconia, Minnesota 55387-1412. **T:** 1 952 442-4414
W: http://sunpatriot.com **Circ:** 14191
Publisher: Julian Andersen
Editorial Profile: The Sun Patriot Newspapers is a community newspaper publisher servicing the residents Waconia, Minneapolis and St. Paul, MN.
NEWSPAPER

Sun Post News
Owner: Freedom Communications Inc.
Editorial: 625 N Grand Ave, Santa Ana, California 92701-4347. **T:** 1 949 492-5122
E: sunpostnews@ocregister.com
W: http://www.ocregister.com/community
Freq: Fri; **Circ:** 10667 Not Audited
Editor: Rob Vardon
Editorial Profile: Sun Post News is a newspaper serving residents of San Clemente, CA, that is published three times per week.; Full Page Mono: 16.14; Full Page Colour: 197.00
Currency: US Dollars
NEWSPAPER

Sun Press & News Publications
Owner: Press & News Publications
Editorial: 33 2nd St NE, Osseo, Minnesota 55369. **T:** 1 763 425-3323
E: sunpressnews@acnpapers.com
W: http://www.pressnews.com **Circ:** 36320 Not Audited
Editorial Profile: Sun Press & News Publications is a local newspaper for the community of Osseo, MN.
NEWSPAPER

Sun Publishing Company
Owner: Record-Journal Publishing Company
Editorial: 99 Mechanic St, Pawcatuck, Connecticut 06379-2132. **T:** 1 401 348-1000
E: advertising@thewesterlysun.com
W: http://www.thewesterlysun.com
Circ: 31729 Not Audited
Publisher: Eliot White
NEWSPAPER

Sun Thisweek Newspapers
Owner: ECM Publishers, Inc.
Editorial: 15322 Galaxie Ave Ste 219, Apple Valley, Minnesota 55124-3150.
T: 1 952 846-2011
W: http://www.sunthisweek.com **Circ:** 66346 Not Audited
Editor: Laura Adelmann; **Publisher:** Julian Andersen; **Editor:** John Gessner; **Editor:** John Gessner; **Editor:** John Gessner; **Editor:** John Gessner; **Editor:** Andrew Miller
Editorial Profile: Sun ThisWeek Newspapers, of Apple Valley, MN, provide news, information, entertainment, sports and events to residents of the following communities: Burnsville, Apple Valley, Farmington, Rosemont, Lakeville, and Dakota County.
NEWSPAPER

Sun Times
Owner: Nester (Robert)
Editorial: 300 N Main St, Chelsea, Michigan 48118-1502. **T:** 1 734 562-2325
E: info@thesuntimesnews.com
Freq: Tue; **Circ:** 23727 Not Audited
Publisher: Robert Nester; **Editor:** Wendy Wood
Editorial Profile: Sun Times is a weekly publication that provides news and information to the residents of Chelsea, MI. Articles cover news, weather and sports.; Full Page Mono: 10.00
Currency: US Dollars
NEWSPAPER

Sunbury News
Editorial: 18 E William St, Delaware, Ohio 43015. **T:** 1 740 363-1161
E: snnews@sunburynews.com
W: http://www.sunburynews.com
Freq: Thu; **Circ:** 10000 Not Audited
Editor: Gary Henry; **Editor:** Gary Henry; **Editor:** Gary Henry; **Publisher:** Scott Koon
Editorial Profile: Sunbury News is a local weekly newspaper written for residents of the Big Walnut school district in Delaware, OH. The newspaper covers local news, sports and events. Deadlines are on Mondays at noon ET.; Full Page Mono: 5.20
Currency: US Dollars
NEWSPAPER

Suncoast News - New Port Richey
Owner: Media General Inc.
Editorial: 8069 Regency Park Boulevard, Port Richey, Florida 34668. **T:** 1 727 815-1000
W: http://www.suncoastnews.com
Freq: 2 Times/Week; **Circ:** 147245 Not Audited
Publisher: Duane Chichester; **Editor:** Robert Hibbs
Editorial Profile: Suncoast News is published twice a week for the residents of west Pasco County, FL. The newspaper covers local news, sports, entertainment and community events. Deadlines for the publication vary.
NEWSPAPER

The Suncook Valley Sun
Editorial: 21 Broadway St, Pittsfield, New Hampshire 3263. **T:** 1 603 435-6291
E: svsun@aol.com
W: http://www.suncookvalleysun.com
Freq: Wed; **Circ:** 11000 Not Audited
Publisher: Arthur Morse
Editorial Profile: The Suncook Valley Sun provides news for residents of Pittsfield, NH. Deadlines are on Thursdays at 4:30pm ET.; Full Page Mono: 9.50
Currency: US Dollars
NEWSPAPER

Sundance Times Newspapers
Editorial: 311 Main St., Sundance, Wyoming 82729. **T:** 1 307 283-3411
W: http://www.sundancetimes.com **Circ:** 2300 Not Audited
NEWSPAPER

Sunday Dispatch
Owner: Wilkes-Barre Publishing Co.
Editorial: 109 New St, Pittston, Pennsylvania 18640. **T:** 1 570 655-1418
E: sd@psdispatch.com
Freq: Sun; **Circ:** 14000
Editor: Edward Ackerman
Editorial Profile: Sunday Dispatch is a local, weekly newspaper written for residents of Pittston, PA. The publication provides coverage of local news, sports, arts & entertainment and events. Deadlines are at 5pm ET.; Full Page Mono: 11.27
Currency: US Dollars
NEWSPAPER

The Sunday Independent
Owner: Flores (Michael)
Editorial: 1907 W M 21, Owosso, Michigan 48867-9317. **T:** 1 989 723-1118
E: news@owossoindependent.com
W: http://www.owossoindependent.com
Freq: 2 Times/Week; **Circ:** 31574 Not Audited
Publisher: Michael Flores
Editorial Profile: The Sunday Independent is a community newspaper providing news and information for the Owosso, MI area.; Full Page Mono: 27.85; Full Page Colour: 28.69
Currency: US Dollars
NEWSPAPER

Sunday News
Owner: Lancaster Newspapers, Inc.
Editorial: 8 W King St, Lancaster, Pennsylvania 17603-3824. **T:** 1 717 291-8811
E: sunnews@lnpnews.com
W: http://www.lancasteronline.com/pages/paper/sundaynews
Freq: Sun; **Circ:** 101702 Not Audited
Editorial Profile: Sunday News is a weekly newspaper published for the residents of Lancaster, PA and surrounding areas. It provides local and state news and information on community events.; Full Page Mono: 58.00
Currency: US Dollars
NEWSPAPER

The SunPost Weekly
Owner: SunPost Media, Inc.
Editorial: 720 Ne 69Th St Apt 11N, Miami, Florida 33138-5756. **T:** 1 305 482-1785
W: http://www.sunpostweekly.com
Freq: Thu; **Circ:** 40000 Not Audited
Editorial Profile: The Sunpost is published for the residents of Miami Beach, FL and its surrounding communities. The editorial content includes local and national news, weather, sports, lifestyle, events and other topics of interest to the community.; Full Page Mono: 20.86
Currency: US Dollars
NEWSPAPER

Sun-Reporter Publishing Company
Owner: Sun Reporter Publishing
Editorial: 1791 Bancroft Ave, San Francisco, California 94124. **T:** 1 415 671-1000
E: sunmedia97@aol.com
W: http://www.sunreporter.com **Circ:** 170452 Not Audited
Editor: Gail Berkley
Editorial Profile: Sun-Reporter Publishing Company provides newspapers in the San Francisco Bay area which focus on news that

truly affects the lives and families throughout the black community.
NEWSPAPER

Sun-Telegraph
Owner: Stevenson Newspapers
Editorial: 817 12th Ave, Sidney, Nebraska 69162-1625. **T:** 1 308 254-2818
W: http://www.suntelegraph.com
Freq: Daily; **Circ:** 2350 Not Audited
Editorial Profile: Sun-Telegraph provides news and information for the Sidney, NE area.; Full Page Mono: 9.50; Full Page Colour: 75.00
Currency: US Dollars
DAILY NEWSPAPER

Super Express USA
Owner: Media Express USA
Editorial: 111 John St. Floor 28, New York, New York 10038. **T:** 1 212 227-5800
E: reklama@seusa.info **W:** http://www.se.pl
Freq: Mon thru Fri; **Circ:** 20000
Editorial Profile: Super Express USA is a daily newspaper published in Polish, and the largest newspaper serving the Polish-American audience in the United States, with editions for New York and Chicago. The U.S. edition is a division of the Super Express tabloid in Poland. News from Poland is featured, along with features on Polish-American everyday life.
DAILY NEWSPAPER

Superior Publishing Company
Owner: Superior Publishing Co., Inc.
Editorial: 148 E 3rd St, Superior, Nebraska 68978-1705. **T:** 1 402 879-3291
E: tse@superiorne.com
W: http://superiorne.com **Circ:** 3000 Not Audited
Editorial Profile: Superior (NE) Publishing Company produces the community newspapers Superior Express and the Jewell County Record.; Full Page Mono: 4.50
Currency: US Dollars
NEWSPAPER

Suplemento
Editorial: 7055 Yarmouth Ave, Reseda, California 91335-4827. **T:** 1 818 708-8407
E: director@elsuplemento.com
W: http://www.elsuplemento.com
Freq: Monthly; **Circ:** 24000
Editorial Profile: El Suplemento is a monthly newspaper that provides Local and Community News coverage to the Argentinean community in the Los Angeles, CA and Southern California.
NEWSPAPER

Sussex County Post
Owner: Independent Newspapers Inc.
Editorial: 37A N Walnut St, Milford, Delaware 19963-1445. **T:** 1 302 629-5505
E: sussexpost@newszap.com
W: http://www.newszap.com/SussexPost/
Freq: Thu; **Circ:** 18800
Editorial Profile: Sussex Post provides news and information for East Sussex County, DE. The editorial lead time and advertising deadlines are on Fridays at 5pm ET.; Full Page Mono: 10.16
Currency: US Dollars
NEWSPAPER

Suwannee Democrat/Mayo Free Press
Owner: Community Newspaper Holdings, Inc.
Editorial: 211 Howard St E, Live Oak, Florida 32064-3208. **T:** 1 386 362-1734
E: nf.editorial@gaflnews.com
W: http://www.suwanneedemocrat.com
Circ: 7098
Publisher: Myra Regan; **Editor:** Jeff Waters
NEWSPAPER

Svet
Owner: Svet Russian Media Group
Editorial: 350 E Dundee Rd, Ste 206, Wheeling, Illinois 60090-3104.
T: 1 847 243-0838 **E:** svet@svet.com
W: http://www.svet.com
Freq: Mon thru Fri; **Circ:** 7500 Not Audited
Editor in Chief: Alexander Etman; **Editor in Chief:** Alexander Etman; **Editor in Chief:** Alexander Etman; **Publisher:** Emily Etman
Editorial Profile: Svet is a free, daily newspaper published in the Russian language and serving the Russian community throughout the Chicago metro area. Since 1992, the paper has provided local and international news and features of interest to the Russian-American population. The Saturday edition, called Saturday Plus Weekly is devoted to photo stories, featuring the rich and famous here and abroad, with helpful hints on where to go and what to do in and around Chicago. The paper is available for pick-up at newsstands throughout Chicago.; Full Page Mono: 10.67
Currency: US Dollars
DAILY NEWSPAPER

Swarner Communications
Owner: Swarner, (Ken & Ron)
Editorial: 8312 Custer Rd SW, Lakewood, Washington 98499-2526. **T:** 1 253 584-1212
E: feedback@weeklyvolcano.com
W: http://www.northwestmilitary.com
Circ: 69250 Not Audited
NEWSPAPER

Sweetwater Reporter
Owner: Horizon Publications
Editorial: 112 W 3rd St, Sweetwater, Texas 79556. **T:** 1 325 236-6677
E: editor@sweetwaterreporter.com
W: http://www.sweetwaterreporter.com
Freq: Daily; **Circ:** 4176 Not Audited
Editor: Tatiana Rodriguez
Editorial Profile: Sweetwater Reporter provides news and information for Nolan County, TX and surrounding communities. Published daily except Saturdays, the lead time and deadline for the weekdays are 10am CT on the issue date. For the Sunday edition, editorial submissions must be in by 10am CT Saturday.; Full Page Mono: 10.75; Full Page Colour: 250.00
Currency: US Dollars
DAILY NEWSPAPER

Syracuse New Times
Owner: Brod (William)
Editorial: 1415 W Genesee St, Syracuse, New York 13204-2119. **T:** 1 315 422-7011
E: editorial@syracusenewtimes.com
W: http://www.syracusenewtimes.com
Freq: Wed; **Circ:** 40000 Not Audited
Publisher: William Brod; **Editor in Chief:** Larry Dietrich; **Editor in Chief:** Larry Dietrich
Editorial Profile: Syracuse (NY) New Times provides local news, sports and arts & entertainment coverage.; Full Page Mono: 50.33
Currency: US Dollars
NEWSPAPER

The Tablet
Owner: Tablet Publishing Company
Editorial: 310 Prospect Park W, Brooklyn, New York 11215. **T:** 1 718 965-7333
W: http://www.thetablet.org
Freq: Sat; **Circ:** 72000
Publisher: Nicholas DiMarzio; **Editor:** Ed Wilkinson
Editorial Profile: The Tablet is written for the Catholic residents in Brooklyn, NY. It covers news about the Catholic religion.; Full Page Mono: 35.67; Full Page Colour: 2950.00
Currency: US Dollars
NEWSPAPER

Tahlequah Daily Press
Owner: Community Newspaper Holdings, Inc.
Editorial: 106 W 2nd St, Tahlequah, Oklahoma 74464-4724. **T:** 1 918 456-8833
E: news@tahlequahdailypress.com
W: http://www.tahlequahdailypress.com
Freq: Daily; **Circ:** 6881 Not Audited
Editorial Profile: Tahlequah Daily Press is a newspaper serving the community of Tahlequah, OK. The publication covers local news, sports and community events. Deadlines are at 11am CT the day before publication.; Full Page Mono: 8.50; Full Page Colour: 85.00
Currency: US Dollars
DAILY NEWSPAPER

Tahoe Mountain News
Editorial: 963 3rd St, South Lake Tahoe, California 96150-4301. **T:** 1 530 542-7033
E: tahoemountainnews@gmail.com
Freq: Monthly; **Circ:** 10000 Not Audited
Publisher: Taylor Flynn; **Editor:** Heather Gould
Editorial Profile: Tahoe Mountain News is a newspaper serving the residents of South Lake Tahoe, CA and the surrounding area. The publication covers local news and community events. The paper only accepts press releases and submissions pertaining to the local area. It is published on the tenth of each month, and deadlines are the first of the month. All mail must be sent to P.O. Box address.; Full Page Mono: 7.39
Currency: US Dollars
NEWSPAPER

Tahoe World
Owner: Swift Newspapers
Editorial: 3090 North Lake Blvd, Tahoe City, California 96145. **T:** 1 530 583-3488
E: editor@sierrasun.com
W: http://www.tahoe.com
Freq: Wed; **Circ:** 14000 Not Audited
Editor: Kevin MacMillan
Editorial Profile: Tahoe World is a free, weekly source for arts, entertainment, dining and recreation in the North Shore, including Truckee, Tahoe City, Squaw Valley and Kings Beach, CA. It provides residents and tourists with stories that celebrate the Tahoe lifestyle, including a calendar of events, live music and movie reviews, local columnists, outdoor activities and feature articles. It is inserted within the Sierra Sun daily newspaper in Truckee, CA, and the North Lake Tahoe Bonanza paper in Incline Village, NV. It is also available at newsstands throughout the area. All mail must be sent to the PO Box. Advertising deadlines are at noon PT.; Full Page Mono: 16.00
Currency: US Dollars
NEWSPAPER

Tailwind
Owner: Daily Republic
Editorial: 400 Brennan Cir, Travis AFB, California 94535-5001. **T:** 1 707 424-0131
E: tailwind@travis.af.mil
W: http://www.travis.af.mil
Freq: Fri; **Circ:** 10040 Not Audited
Editor: Madelyn Ottem
Editorial Profile: Tailwind is the official news publication of Travis Air Force Base in Travis, CA. The newspaper is written for members of the base and covers local news, base news, events, information and sports. It is put out by The Daily Republic, though the Air Force is still responsible for all content. The editorial deadline is Fridays at 4:30pm PT.; Full Page Mono: 13.00
Currency: US Dollars
NEWSPAPER

Taiwan Daily
Editorial: 2646 Durfee Ave #168, El Monte, California 91732-3472
W: http://www.taiwandaily.net
Freq: Daily
Editor in Chief: Dexing Yan
Editorial Profile: Taiwan Daily is a daily newspaper in traditional Chinese published in North America. It covers Taiwan news, United States and Community, Leisure and Living, Sports, and Advertisements. All its Taiwan news is provided by Liberty Times, which is thought to take a Pan Green pro-independence political stance. As is characteristic of Taiwan Paparazzi, articles usually are featured comprehensive biographies covering celebrities' height and weight, as well as provocative pictures of strippers and celebrity relations.
DAILY NEWSPAPER

Take 5
Editorial: 16810 E Avenue Of The Fountains Ste 113, Fountain Hills, Arizona 85268-8495.
T: 1 480 889-2335
W: http://www.take5az.com/indexwebzine.html
Freq: Bi-Weekly; **Circ:** 14000 Not Audited
Editorial Profile: Take 5 is a free, entertainment and news guide serving the residents of Fountain Hills and North Scottsdale, AZ. It covers local outdoor activities, festivals, events, music and dining.; Full Page Mono: 16.50
Currency: US Dollars
NEWSPAPER

Takoma Voice
Owner: Takoma Publishing, Inc.
Editorial: 7040 Carroll Ave, Ste 2, Takoma Park, Maryland 20912-4465.
T: 1 301 891-6744 **E:** editor@takoma.com
W: http://www.takoma.com
Freq: Monthly; **Circ:** 40000 Not Audited
Editorial Profile: Takoma Voice is a local monthly newspaper serving the residents of Takoma Park, MD and the surrounding community. The publication covers local news and community events. Deadlines are on the 15th of the month prior to issue date.; Full Page Mono: 25.00
Currency: US Dollars
NEWSPAPER

Tallahassee Capital Outlook
Owner: Holmes, Jr. (Rev. Dr. R.B.)
Editorial: 1363 East Tennessee Street, Tallahassee, Florida 32308. **T:** 1 850 877-0105
E: info@capitaloutlook.com
W: http://www.capitaloutlook.com
Freq: Thu; **Circ:** 12000 Not Audited
Editor: Tiffany Harris; **Publisher:** R.B. Holmes
Editorial Profile: Tallahassee Capital Outlook is a newspaper serving African American residents of Tallahassee, FL. The publication covers local and national news, sports, and community events.; Full Page Mono: 33.00
Currency: US Dollars
NEWSPAPER

Tallahassee Democrat
Owner: Gannett Co., Inc.
Editorial: 277 N Magnolia Dr, Tallahassee, Florida 32301-2664. **T:** 1 850 599-2100
E: letters@tallahassee.com
W: http://www.tallahassee.com
Freq: Daily; **Circ:** 29181 Not Audited
Editorial Profile: Tallahassee Democrat is a daily newspaper published for the residents of Tallahassee and Lèon County, FL. The paper covers local news, business, city and state government, entertainment, high school and college sports, lifestyle, and entertainment.; Full Page Mono: 103.25; Full Page Colour: 339.98
Currency: US Dollars
DAILY NEWSPAPER

Tallahassee Democrat
Editorial: 336 E College Ave, Tallahassee, Florida 32301-1551. **T:** 1 850 671-6547
W: http://www.tallahassee.com
Freq: Daily
DAILY NEWSPAPER

Tama/Grundy Publishing Inc.
Owner: Marshalltown Newspaper Inc.
Editorial: 220 W 3rd St, Tama, Iowa 52339.
T: 1 641 484-2841
E: editor@tamatoledonews.com
W: http://www.tamatoledonews.com
Circ: 6400 Not Audited
Publisher: Mike Schlesinger; **Editor:** John Speer
NEWSPAPER

Tampa Bay Newspapers
Owner: Times Publishing Co.
Editorial: 9911 Seminole Blvd, Seminole, Florida 33772-2536. **T:** 1 727 397-5563
E: editorial@tbnweekly.com
W: http://www.tbnweekly.com **Circ:** 162350 Not Audited
Publisher: Dan Autrey; **Editor:** Alexandra Lundahl; **Editor:** Bob McClure; **Editor:** Juliana Torres
NEWSPAPER

Tampa Bay Times
Owner: Poynter Institute for Media Studies
Editorial: 490 1st Ave S Fl 4, Saint Petersburg, Florida 33701-4204.
T: 1 727 893-8111 **E:** local@tampabay.com
W: http://www.tampabay.com
Freq: Daily; **Circ:** 317270 Not Audited
Publisher: Joe DeLuca
Editorial Profile: Tampa Bay Times is a general-interest broadsheet newspaper written for readers in the greater St. Petersburg, Tampa, and Clearwater, FL. The mission of the newspaper is to provide news and information to the general public.; Full Page Mono: 770.00; Full Page Colour: 2431.86
Currency: US Dollars
DAILY NEWSPAPER

Tampa Bay Times
Editorial: 1100 Connecticut Ave NW, Washington, District Of Columbia 20036-4101.
T: 1 202 463-0571
Bureau Chief: Alex Leary
DAILY NEWSPAPER

Tampa Bay Times
Editorial: 15365 Cortez Blvd, Brooksville, Florida 34613-6174. **T:** 1 352 754-6100
E: hernando@tampabay.com
Bureau Chief: Mike Konrad; **Bureau Chief:** Mike Konrad
DAILY NEWSPAPER

Tampa Bay Times
Editorial: 710 Court St, Clearwater, Florida 33756-5508. **T:** 1 727 446-6397
DAILY NEWSPAPER

Tampa Bay Times
Editorial: 11321 US Highway 19, Port Richey, Florida 34668-1416. **T:** 1 727 869-6238
E: pasco@sptimes.com
Bureau Chief: Bill Stevens; **Bureau Chief:** Bill Stevens
DAILY NEWSPAPER

Tampa Bay Times
Editorial: 336 E College Ave Ste 303, Tallahassee, Florida 32301-1560.
T: 1 850 224-7263
Bureau Chief: Steve Bousquet
DAILY NEWSPAPER

Tampa Bay Times
Editorial: 1000 N Ashley Dr, Tampa, Florida 33602-3716. **T:** 1 813 226-3300

E: tampanews@tampabay.com; Full Page Mono: 5.00
Currency: US Dollars
DAILY NEWSPAPER

Tampa Bay Times
Editorial: 11268 Winthrop Main St, Riverview, Florida 33578-4266. **T:** 1 813 661-2425
E: local@sptimes.com
Bureau Chief: Ernest Hooper
DAILY NEWSPAPER

Tampa Bay Times
Editorial: 26240 Golden Maple Loop, Wesley Chapel, Florida 33544-6304.
T: 1 813 909-4606
DAILY NEWSPAPER

The Tampa Tribune
Owner: Revolution Capital Group
Editorial: 200 S Parker St, Tampa, Florida 33606-2308. **T:** 1 813 259-7600
E: news@tampatrib.com
W: http://www.tampatrib.com
Freq: Daily; **Circ:** 198543 Not Audited
Publisher: Brian Burns; **Editor:** Ken Koehn
Editorial Profile: The Tampa Tribune is a daily broadsheet that focuses on local, national, and international news which affects west central Florida. It is a morning paper and is one of the top 50 papers in the United States in terms of circulation. Regular sections include the Main News section, containing "international, national, and state news, as well as major regional and local stories;" the Florida/Metro section, covering "hard news about Florida and the Tampa Bay metro area;" the Business & Finance section, focusing on local and national news of importance, and containing expanded feature coverage on Sunday; and the sports section.; Full Page Mono: 330.00; Full Page Colour: 445.50
Currency: US Dollars
DAILY NEWSPAPER

The Tampa Tribune
Editorial: 2560 Gulf To Bay Blvd Ste 100, Clearwater, Florida 33765-4421
DAILY NEWSPAPER

The Tampa Tribune
Editorial: 4450 Pet Ln Bldg 2, Lutz, Florida 33559-6307
DAILY NEWSPAPER

Taos News
Owner: Watkin (Robin)
Editorial: 226 Albright St, Taos, New Mexico 87571-6312. **T:** 1 575 758-2241
E: publish@taosnews.com
W: http://www.taosnews.com
Freq: Thu; **Circ:** 11020 Not Audited
Publisher: Chris Baker; **Editor:** Rick Romancito
Editorial Profile: Taos News is a local, weekly newspaper serving the community of Taos, NM. The publication covers local news, community events, lifestyle, education, business and other topics of general interest. Deadlines are on Fridays at noon MT.; Full Page Mono: 16.40
Currency: US Dollars
NEWSPAPER

Taunton Daily Gazette
Owner: GateHouse Media Inc.
Editorial: 5 Cohannet St, Taunton, Massachusetts 02780-3903.
T: 1 508 880-9000
E: newsroom@tauntongazette.com
W: http://www.tauntongazette.com
Freq: Daily; **Circ:** 5642 Not Audited
Publisher: Lisa Strattan; **Editor In Chief:** Lynne Sullivan; **Editor In Chief:** Lynne Sullivan
Editorial Profile: Taunton Daily Gazette is a local daily newspaper for the residents of Taunton, MA and the surrounding area. The publication covers local and national news, community events and sports.; Full Page Mono: 22.95; Full Page Colour: 250.00
Currency: US Dollars
DAILY NEWSPAPER

Taylor Daily Press
Owner: Blackland Publications
Editorial: 211 W 3rd St, Taylor, Texas 76574-3518. **T:** 1 512 352-8535
E: news@taylordailypress.net
W: http://www.taylordailypress.net
Freq: Mon thru Fri; **Circ:** 5300 Not Audited
Editorial Profile: Taylor Daily Press is a newspaper serving the residents of Taylor, TX. The publication covers local news, entertainment, sports and community events.; Full Page Mono: 8.75; Full Page Colour: 200.00
Currency: US Dollars

DAILY NEWSPAPER

Tazewell County Free Press
Editorial: 1249 Front St, Richlands, Virginia 24641. **T:** 1 276 963-0127
E: freepres@netscope.net
Freq: Wed; **Circ:** 13500 Not Audited
Editorial Profile: Tazewell County Free Press is a newspaper serving the residents of Tazewell County, VA. The publication covers local news and community events. Deadlines are on Mondays at 5pm ET.; Full Page Mono: 8.00
Currency: US Dollars
NEWSPAPER

tbt*
Owner: Poynter Institute for Media Studies
Editorial: 490 1st Ave S Fl 4, Saint Petersburg, Florida 33701-4204.
T: 1 727 893-8477
E: tbteditors@tampabay.com
W: http://www.tampabay.com/tbt
Freq: Mon thru Fri; **Circ:** 40000 Not Audited
Publisher: Joe DeLuca
Editorial Profile: tbt*, launched as a weekly newspaper in September 2004, also known as the Tampa Bay Times, is a free, commuter and alternative daily newspaper that is distributed each weekday. It contains concise versions of the day's local and national news, along with sports, entertainment and consumer features. It provides restaurant reviews, movie listings and information about places to go and things to do in the area. The Friday edition features a special entertainment pullout section. Advertising deadlines are at noon ET.; Full Page Mono: 44.00; Full Page Colour: 66.26
Currency: US Dollars
DAILY NEWSPAPER

El Tecolote
Editorial: 2958 24th St, San Francisco, California 94110. **T:** 1 415 648-1045
W: http://www.eltecolote.org
Freq: Bi-Weekly; **Circ:** 10000 Not Audited
Editorial Profile: El Tecolote is a bilingual, bi-monthly newspaper for the Latino population of the San Francisco Bay area. 10,000 copies are distributed freely throughout sites in the Mission District and East Bay. Its primary goal, according to the newspaper's mission statement, is "to provide a vehicle of information and organization to the Chicano/Latino communities of the Bay Area, articulating it's social, cultural, political and economic needs through our ongoing and timely coverage of issues." It has also established itself as an effective training ground for aspiring Latino journalists. The paper was founded in 1970 by Juan Gonzales as part of a project in his La Raza studies class at San Francisco State University. It is the longest running Spanish/English bilingual newspaper in California and remains a centerpiece to Mission District arts, culture and community. It is mostly staffed by volunteers and is a member of the San Francisco Neighborhood Newspaper Association and founding member New America Media.; Full Page Mono: 16.25
Currency: US Dollars
NEWSPAPER

Tehachapi News, Inc.
Owner: Moorehouse (Ginger)
Editorial: 411 N Mill St, Tehachapi, California 93561-1351. **T:** 1 661 822-6828
E: editorial@tehachapinews.com
W: http://www.tehachapinews.com
Circ: 23500 Not Audited
NEWSPAPER

Telegram & Gazette
Owner: Halifax Media Holdings LLC
Editorial: 100 Front St, Worcester, Massachusetts 01608-1425.
T: 1 508 793-9100 **E:** newstips@telegram.com
W: http://www.telegram.com
Freq: Daily; **Circ:** 74027 Not Audited
Publisher: Bruce Gaultney
Editorial Profile: Established in 1866, the Telegram & Gazette is a daily broadsheet providing local, national, and international news coverage to the Worcester, MA area. The Telegram & Gazette is a morning paper. The publication's coverage includes technology, real estate, business news, food, travel, music, the arts, and lifestyle topics.; Full Page Mono: 124.54; Full Page Colour: 133.92
Currency: US Dollars
DAILY NEWSPAPER

The Telegraph
Owner: McClatchy Newspapers
Editorial: 120 Broadway, Macon, Georgia 31201-3444. **T:** 1 478 744-4200

W: http://www.macon.com
Freq: Daily; **Circ:** 36960 Not Audited
News Editor: Ben Yoder
Editorial Profile: The Telegraph is a daily newspaper that covers local and regional news. It includes sports, lifestyle, arts & entertainment and business. The paper also produces editions specifically for Houston and Peach Counties, GA.; Full Page Mono: 81.30; Full Page Colour: 274.50
Currency: US Dollars
DAILY NEWSPAPER

The Telegraph
Owner: Civitas Media, LLC
Editorial: 111 E Broadway, Alton, Illinois 62002-6218. **T:** 1 618 463-2500
E: telegraph@thetelegraph.com
W: http://www.thetelegraph.com
Freq: Daily; **Circ:** 24032 Not Audited
Publisher: Jim Shrader; **Editor:** Bob Strickley
Editorial Profile: The Telegraph is a local daily newspaper for residents of Madison, Jersey, Calhoun, Macoupin, and Greene Counties, IL.; Full Page Mono: 45.33; Full Page Colour: 149.36
Currency: US Dollars
DAILY NEWSPAPER

The Telegraph
Owner: Independent Publications Inc.
Editorial: 17 Executive Dr, Hudson, New Hampshire 03051-4903. **T:** 1 603 882-2741
W: http://www.nashuatelegraph.com
Freq: Daily; **Circ:** 14473 Not Audited
Editor: Sandy Bucknam; **Publisher:** Gregory Pohl; **Editor:** Jonathan Van Fleet
Editorial Profile: The Telegraph is a daily newspaper for residents of Nashua, NH and Southern New Hampshire. The paper covers local news, weather, sports, community events, business, education, arts & entertainment, lifestyle and other information of interest to community residents.; Full Page Mono: 35.10; Full Page Colour: 120.85
Currency: US Dollars
DAILY NEWSPAPER

The Telegraph
Editorial: 16 Green St Ste B, Warner Robins, Georgia 31093-2606. **T:** 1 478 923-5650
News Editor: Ryan Gilchrest
Editorial Profile: The Telegraph, formerly The Macon Telegraph, maintains its own office and shares its editorial staff with the main office in Macon, GA. The bureau covers Houston County news, information and events.
DAILY NEWSPAPER

Telegraph Herald
Owner: Woodward Communications, Inc.
Editorial: 801 Bluff St, Dubuque, Iowa 52001-4647. **T:** 1 563 588-5611
E: thonline@wcinet.com
W: http://www.thonline.com
Freq: Daily; **Circ:** 24586 Not Audited
Publisher: James Normandin
Editorial Profile: Telegraph Herald is a general interest daily newspaper covering topics such as news, employment, education, tourism, recreation, holidays, events, special interests, sports, business, health and family. The weekend edition prints on Saturday.; Full Page Mono: 1.83
Currency: US Dollars
DAILY NEWSPAPER

Telegraph Newspapers
Owner: Brehm Communications, Inc.
Editorial: 921 Sutter St, Ste 100, Folsom, California 95630-2441. **T:** 1 916 985-2581
W: http://www.goldcountrymedia.com
Circ: 23600 Not Audited
NEWSPAPER

Telluride Daily Planet
Editorial: 307 E Colorado, Telluride, Colorado 81435. **T:** 1 970 728-9788
E: editor@telluridedailyplanet.com
W: http://www.telluridenews.com
Freq: Daily; **Circ:** 3150 Not Audited
Editor: Katie Klingsporn
Editorial Profile: Telluride Daily Planet is a daily local paper serving residents in the Telluride, CO area.; Full Page Mono: 11.00; Full Page Colour: 14.00
Currency: US Dollars
DAILY NEWSPAPER

Telluride Watch
Editorial: 125 West Pacfic Ave, Telluride, Colorado 81435-2042. **T:** 1 970 728-4496
E: editor@telluridewatch.com
W: http://www.telluridewatch.com
Freq: Thu; **Circ:** 10000
Publisher: Seth Cagin; **Editor:** Marta Tarbell

Editorial Profile: Telluride Watch is published twice a week for the residents of Telluride, CO. All materials must be sent to the PO Box address.; Full Page Mono: 13.00
Currency: US Dollars
NEWSPAPER

Tempe-Chandler Wrangler News
Editorial: 2145 E Warner Rd, Ste 102, Tempe, Arizona 85284. **T:** 1 480 966-0845
E: editor@wranglernews.com
W: http://www.wranglernews.com
Freq: Bi-Weekly; **Circ:** 20000 Not Audited
Editorial Profile: The Tempe-Chandler Wrangler News is a bi-weekly community newspaper serving the residents of Tempe, AZ.; Full Page Mono: 10.00
Currency: US Dollars
NEWSPAPER

Temple Daily Telegram
Owner: Mayborn Enterprises
Editorial: 10 S 3rd St, Temple, Texas 76501-7619. **T:** 1 254 778-4444 **E:** tdt@tdtnews.com
W: http://www.temple-telegram.com
Freq: Daily; **Circ:** 17181 Not Audited
Editorial Profile: Temple Daily Telegram is a newspaper serving the residents of Temple, Texas. The publication covers local news, community events, business, and sports.; Full Page Mono: 24.50; Full Page Colour: 536.00
Currency: US Dollars
DAILY NEWSPAPER

Tempo News
Editorial: 2826 Leonard Reid Ave, Sarasota, Florida 34234-6231. **T:** 1 941 359-1065
E: temponews@comcast.net
W: http://www.temponewsflorida.com
Freq: Thu; **Circ:** 40000 Not Audited
Editor: Inez Hunter; **Publisher:** Johnny Hunter
Editorial Profile: Tempo News is published weekly for the African-American communities of Manatee and Sarasota, FL. The newspaper provides information about local news, cultural issues and community events.; Full Page Mono: 15.00
Currency: US Dollars
NEWSPAPER

The Tennessean
Owner: Gannett Co., Inc.
Editorial: 1100 Broadway, Nashville, Tennessee 37203-3116. **T:** 1 615 259-8000
E: local@tennessean.com
W: http://www.tennessean.com
Freq: Daily; **Circ:** 95771 Not Audited
Editorial Profile: The Tennessean covers local and regional news, as well as entertainment, lifestyle, sports and business.; Full Page Mono: 188.00; Full Page Colour: 1250.00
Currency: US Dollars
DAILY NEWSPAPER

The Tennessean
Editorial: 1100 New York Ave NW Ste 200E, Washington, District Of Columbia 20005-6116.
T: 1 703 854-8943
W: http://www.tennessean.com/
DAILY NEWSPAPER

The Tennessean
Editorial: 512 Autumn Springs Ct Ste D, Franklin, Tennessee 37067-2847.
T: 1 615 771-5400 **E:** wam@tennessean.com
W: http://www.tennessean.com/section/WILLIAMSON
Editor: Mark Cook; **Editor:** Mark Cook
Editorial Profile: The Franklin County bureau staff of the Tennessean publishes the Review Appeal, a free, a weekly, community newspaper. The Review Appeal is available to all local residents for pick-up at various locations throughout Williamson County, TN. It is also inserted within The Tennessean to its subscribers on Wednesdays. Content focuses on local news and community events and issues. Other features include sports, business, education, entertainment, lifestyle, politics and classifieds.
DAILY NEWSPAPER

Tennessee Register
Owner: Diocese of Nashville
Editorial: 2400 21st Ave S, Nashville, Tennessee 37212. **T:** 1 615 783-0750
E: tnregister@dioceseofnashville.com
W: http://www.dioceseofnashville.com/tnregister.pdf
Freq: Bi-Weekly; **Circ:** 19000 Not Audited
Publisher: David Choby; **Editor In Chief:** Rick Musacchio
Editorial Profile: Tennessee Register is a local newspaper written for the residents of Nashville, TN.; Full Page Mono: 15.42
Currency: US Dollars
NEWSPAPER

The Tennessee Tribune

Owner: Perry & Perry & Associates
Editorial: 1501 Jefferson St, Nashville, Tennessee 37208-3016. **T:** 1 615 321-3268
E: info@tntribune.com
W: http://tntribune.com
Freq: Weekly; **Circ:** 45000 Not Audited
Editorial Profile: Focused on issues of interest to members of the black community. Included are regular departments on health, entertainment, business, education, society, and history. Reviews on books, fashion, and travel are also covered.; Full Page Mono: 3078.00; Full Page Colour: 2673.00
Currency: US Dollars
NEWSPAPER

Terrell Tribune

Owner: Hartman Newspapers, Inc.
Editorial: 150 9th St, Terrell, Texas 75160-3061. **T:** 1 972 563-6476
E: editor@terrelltribune.com
W: http://www.terrelltribune.com
Freq: Daily; **Circ:** 6200 Not Audited
Publisher: Mike Elswick
Editorial Profile: Terrell Tribune is published daily for the residents of Terrell, TX and surrounding areas. The newspaper covers local and state news, business, sports, lifestyles and entertainment. Editorial deadlines are daily at noon CT.; Full Page Mono: 10.00; Full Page Colour: 330.00
Currency: US Dollars
DAILY NEWSPAPER

Tester

Owner: Comprint Military Publications
Editorial: 22268 Cedar Point Rd Bldg 409, Patuxent River, Maryland 20670-1154.
T: 1 301 757-6748 **E:** webmaster@gazette.net
W: http://www.dcmilitary.com/section/news14
Freq: Thu; **Circ:** 15000 Not Audited
Editor: Christine Basham; **Editor:** Christine Basham; **Publisher:** John Rives
Editorial Profile: Tester provides news and information for the Patuxent Naval Air Test Center. The weekly newspaper is read by the Patuxent Naval Air Test Center personnel.; Full Page Mono: 19.16; Full Page Colour: 2572.64
Currency: US Dollars
NEWSPAPER

Texarkana Gazette

Owner: Wehco Media Inc.
Editorial: 315 Pine St, Texarkana, Texas 75501-5683. **T:** 1 903 794-3311
W: http://www.texarkanagazette.com
Freq: Daily; **Circ:** 24352 Not Audited
News Editor: Andrea Miller; **Editor:** Les Minor
Editorial Profile: Texarkana Gazette is the daily newspaper for the community of Texarkana, TX. The publication covers local news, sports, entertainment and community events. Deadlines are at 9am CT.; Full Page Mono: 26.84; Full Page Colour: 33.27
Currency: US Dollars
DAILY NEWSPAPER

Thang Long

Editorial: 18 Faulkner St, Apt 1, Dorchester, Massachusetts 02122-1339.
T: 1 617 436-4036 **E:** nvietnam04@yahoo.com
W: http://www.conong.com
Freq: Tue; **Circ:** 22000 Not Audited
Editor: Charles Nguyen; **Publisher:** Cuong Nguyen
Editorial Profile: Thang Long is a Vietnamese-language publication written for the Vietnamese community in Boston and the surrounding area. The newspaper focuses on local, national and international news. It also covers entertainment and business issues.; Full Page Mono: 8.33
Currency: US Dollars
NEWSPAPER

TheMash

Owner: Tribune Company
Editorial: 435 N Michigan Ave Fl 4, Chicago, Illinois 60611-7547. **T:** 1 312 222-4726
E: themash@tribune.com
W: http://www.themash.com
Freq: Thu; **Circ:** 65000
Publisher: Tony Hunter; **Editor:** Phillip Thompson
Editorial Profile: TheMash is a free weekly newspaper serving Chicago high school readers. Editorial content includes sports, current events and pop culture. The paper is distributed Thursdays at all Chicago public high schools and is written largely by CPS high school students. The paper launched in September 2008.; Full Page Mono: 62.37
Currency: US Dollars
NEWSPAPER

Thief River Falls Times, Inc.

Owner: MCM Media, LLC
Editorial: 324 Main Ave N, Thief River Falls, Minnesota 56701. **T:** 1 218 681-4450
W: http://www.trftimes.com
Freq: Weekly; **Circ:** 28250 Not Audited
Editor: Dave Hill; **Publisher:** Randal Hultgren
Editorial Profile: Thief River Falls Times, Inc. provides local news and sports for the residents of Thief River Falls, MN.
NEWSPAPER

Thikana

Owner: Prometheus International, Inc.
Editorial: 1135 45Th Ave, Long Island City, New York 11101-5109. **T:** 1 718 472-0700
E: wthikana@aol.com
W: http://www.thikana.net
Freq: Fri; **Circ:** 30000
Editor: Muhammad Rahman
Editorial Profile: Thikana is a weekly community newspaper serving the Bengali American population in New York City and is published in Bengali, the official language of Bangladesh. It contains local, national and international news of importance to readers.
NEWSPAPER

This Week

Owner: Lee Enterprises, Inc.
Editorial: 600 Lyon St S, Albany, Oregon 97321. **T:** 1 541 926-2211
Freq: Wed; **Circ:** 17500 Not Audited
Editorial Profile: This Week is a weekly newspaper written for the residents of Albany, OR.; Full Page Mono: 5.50
Currency: US Dollars
NEWSPAPER

This Week From Indian Country Today

Owner: Four Directions Media
Editorial: 590 Madison Ave Ste 1864, New York, New York 10022-2524.
T: 1 315 829-8355 **E:** editor@ictmn.com
W: http://www.indiancountrytodaymedianetwork.com
Freq: Wed
Editor: Theresa Braine; **Editor:** Ken Polisse
Editorial Profile: This Week From Indian Country Today magazine features stories and perspectives from Native American journalists that include news, entertainment, business, politics and education.
NEWSPAPER

ThisWeek Community Newspapers

Owner: Dispatch Printing Company (The)
Editorial: 7801 N Central Dr, Lewis Center, Ohio 43035-9407. **T:** 1 740 888-6100
E: editorial@thisweeknews.com
W: http://www.thisweeknews.com
Freq: Weekly; **Circ:** 323534 Not Audited
News Editor: Julanne Hohbach
Editorial Profile: ThisWeek Community Newspapers publishes more than 20 local papers in the Columbus, OH region. All are distributed for free to subscribers of the Columbus Dispatch.
NEWSPAPER

Thomasville Times-Enterprise

Owner: Community Newspaper Holdings, Inc.
Editorial: 106 South St, Thomasville, Georgia 31792-6061. **T:** 1 229 226-2400
W: http://www.timesenterprise.com
Freq: Daily; **Circ:** 7927 Not Audited
Publisher: Norman Bankston; **Editor:** Clint Thompson
Editorial Profile: Thomasville Times-Enterprise's editorial mission is to provide news and information to the Thomasville, GA community.; Full Page Mono: 22.05; Full Page Colour: 340.00
Currency: US Dollars
DAILY NEWSPAPER

Thousandsticks Newspapers

Editorial: 22009 Main St, Hyden, Kentucky 41749. **T:** 1 606 672-3399 **Circ:** 7300 Not Audited
NEWSPAPER

Three Rivers Commercial-News

Owner: Three Rivers Commercial, Inc.
Editorial: 124 N Main St, Three Rivers, Michigan 49093-1559. **T:** 1 269 279-7488
E: news@threeriversnews.com
W: http://www.threeriversnews.com
Freq: Daily; **Circ:** 2940 Not Audited
Publisher: Dirk Milliman
Editorial Profile: Three Rivers Commercial-News provides local news and sports coverage for the Three Rivers, MI area.; Full Page Mono: 11.07; Full Page Colour: 275.00
Currency: US Dollars
DAILY NEWSPAPER

Three Rivers Publishing Inc.

Editorial: 501 E Washington St, Cuba, Missouri 65453. **T:** 1 573 885-7460
E: news@cubafreepress.com
W: http://www.threeriverspublishing.com
Circ: 3600 Not Audited
Editor: Chris Case
NEWSPAPER

ThumbPrint News

Editorial: 8061 Marsh Rd, Algonac, Michigan 48001. **T:** 1 810 794-2300
E: thumbprintnews@comcast.net
W: http://www.thumbprintnews.com
Freq: Monthly; **Circ:** 30000
Publisher: Allen Kodet; **Editor:** Diane Kodet
Editorial Profile: ThumbPrint News offers local news and features to residents of Clay Township, Oakland, Sanilac, St. Clair, Tuscola, Genessee, Huron, Lapeer and Macomb, MI. News tips must be received by the 10th of the month previous to the month of publication. It was established in October 2009.; Full Page Mono: 11.90
Currency: US Dollars
NEWSPAPER

Thunder Prairie Publishing

Owner: Nichols (Nanalee)
Editorial: 161 Main, Deport, Texas 75435.
T: 1 903 652-4205 **E:** tppub@1starnet.com
Circ: 4905 Not Audited
NEWSPAPER

The Thunderbolt

Editorial: 14185 W Falcon, Luke Air Force Base, Phoenix, Arizona 85309.
T: 1 623 856-6055
E: luke.thunderbolt@luke.af.mil
W: http://www.aerotechnews.com/lukeafb/
Freq: Fri; **Circ:** 15000 Not Audited
Editor: Deborah Leuthold
Editorial Profile: Thunderbolt is the official newspaper of Luke Air Force Base, AZ. The weekly publication features the latest news on the base, the people, the events, and includes a mix of local and Air Force news, features, sports, and community happenings. Thunderbolt is published by Pueblo Publishers, Inc., a private firm in no way connected with the US Air Force, under exclusive written contract with the 56th Support Group, Luke Air Force Base, AZ. This commercial enterprise Air Force newspaper is an authorized publication for members of the US military services. Contents of the "Thunderbolt" are not necessarily the official views of, or endorsed by, the US government, the Department of Defense, or the Department of the Air Force.; Full Page Mono: 15.70; Full Page Colour: 984.00
Currency: US Dollars
NEWSPAPER

El Tiempo

Owner: Vegas Review Journal (Las)
Editorial: 1111 W Bonanza Rd, Las Vegas, Nevada 89106. **T:** 1 702 387-2972
W: http://www.eltiempolv.com
Freq: Fri; **Circ:** 50000 Not Audited
Editor: Hernando Amaya
Editorial Profile: El Tiempo is an independent product of the Las Vegas Review-Journal. It is written for Latinos. Send press releases to the editor directly.; Full Page Mono: 45.00
Currency: US Dollars
NEWSPAPER

El Tiempo Latino

Owner: Washington Post Co.
Editorial: 1150 15Th St Nw, Washington, District Of Columbia 20071-0001.
T: 1 202 334-9100
W: http://www.eltiempolatino.com
Freq: Fri; **Circ:** 49945 Not Audited
Publisher: Alberto Avendano; **Editor:** Miguel Guilarte; **Editor:** Miguel Guilarte
Editorial Profile: El Tiempo Latino in Washington, DC is a weekly Spanish newspaper that covers local, national and international news for the Hispanic community in the metropolitan region, including Arlington, VA.; Full Page Mono: 30.00
Currency: US Dollars
NEWSPAPER

Tifton Gazette

Owner: Community Newspaper Holdings, Inc.
Editorial: 211 Tift Ave N, Tifton, Georgia 31794-4463. **T:** 1 229 382-4321
E: ttg.editorial@gaflnews.com
W: http://www.tiftongazette.com
Freq: Daily; **Circ:** 9500 Not Audited
News Editor: Steve Carter
Editorial Profile: Tifton Gazette provides local news and sports coverage for the Tifton, GA

area.; Full Page Mono: 21.70; Full Page Colour: 294.00
Currency: US Dollars
DAILY NEWSPAPER

Tilden Newspapers

Editorial: 202 E 2nd St, Tilden, Nebraska 68781. **T:** 1 402 368-5315
E: tildencitizen@cableone.net **Circ:** 15750 Not Audited
Editor: Donna Smith; **Publisher:** Verlyn Thomas
NEWSPAPER

Tiloben Publishing Co.

Editorial: 2600 S Jackson St, Seattle, Washington 98144. **T:** 1 888 909-3070
W: http://www.seattlemedium.com **Circ:** 64500 Not Audited
Editor: Chris Bennet
NEWSPAPER

The Times

Owner: Morris Multimedia Inc.
Editorial: 345 Green St NW, Gainesville, Georgia 30501. **T:** 1 770 532-1234
E: news@gainesvilletimes.com
W: http://www.gainesvilletimes.com
Freq: Daily; **Circ:** 22000 Not Audited
Publisher: Dennis Stockton
Editorial Profile: The Times was founded in 1947. It provides daily news, including features, entertainment, business and sports for the residents of Gainesville, GA.; Full Page Mono: 23.12; Full Page Colour: 402.00
Currency: US Dollars
DAILY NEWSPAPER

The Times

Owner: Small Newspaper Group
Editorial: 110 W Jefferson St, Ottawa, Illinois 61350-5010. **T:** 1 815 433-2000
E: newsroom@mywebtimes.com
W: http://www.mywebtimes.com
Freq: Mon thru Fri; **Circ:** 15850 Not Audited
Editor: Mike Murphy; **Publisher:** John Newby
Editorial Profile: The Times, formerly known as the Daily Times, is a newspaper serving the Ottawa community, and the surrounding areas of Lasselle County, IL. They do not want to receive ANYTHING via fax.; Full Page Mono: 18.90; Full Page Colour: 230.00
Currency: US Dollars
DAILY NEWSPAPER

The Times

Owner: Paxton Media Group
Editorial: 251 E Clinton St, Frankfort, Indiana 46041. **T:** 1 765 659-4622
E: news@ftimes.com
W: http://www.ftimes.com
Freq: Daily; **Circ:** 6000 Not Audited
Publisher: Sharon Bardonner
Editorial Profile: The Times is a local, weekly newspaper for the residents of Frankfort, IN. The paper includes news, weather, travel, sports and community events.; Full Page Mono: 18.00; Full Page Colour: 210.00
Currency: US Dollars
DAILY NEWSPAPER

The Times

Owner: Newhouse Newspapers
Editorial: 413 River View Plaza, Trenton, New Jersey 8618. **T:** 1 609 989-5454
E: news@njtimes.com
W: http://www.nj.com/times
Freq: Daily; **Circ:** 31971 Not Audited
Editor in Chief: Matt Dowling; **Publisher:** Sheila Gallagher-Montone
Editorial Profile: The Times is published daily and distributed throughout Mercer County, NJ. The newspaper provides readers with local and national news. Readers will also find other features, such as sports, business, education, entertainment, lifestyle, community and classifieds.; Full Page Mono: 62.42; Full Page Colour: 270.57
Currency: US Dollars
DAILY NEWSPAPER

The Times

Owner: R.I.S.N. Operations Inc.
Editorial: 23 Exchange St, Pawtucket, Rhode Island 02860-2059. **T:** 1 401 722-4000
E: editor@pawtuckettimes.com
W: http://www.pawtuckettimes.com
Freq: Daily; **Circ:** 5068 Not Audited
Publisher: Mary Lynn Bosiak
Editorial Profile: The Times is a local daily newspaper for the residents of Pawtucket, Central Falls, Lincoln, East Providence and Cumberland, RI and Seekonk and Attleboro, MA. The publication covers local news and community events.; Full Page Mono: 21.71; Full Page Colour: 23.44
Currency: US Dollars

DAILY NEWSPAPER

The Times
Owner: Lee Enterprises, Inc.
Editorial: 601 W. 45th Ave, Munster, Indiana 46321-2875. **T:** 1 219 933-3200
E: newstips@nwitimes.com
W: http://www.nwitimes.com
Freq: Daily; **Circ:** 85889 Not Audited
Publisher: Christopher White
Editorial Profile: The Times is a daily newspaper that serves Munster, IN; Lake County, IN; the Southern part of Cook County, IL; the west end of Porter County, IN; and the Northwest portion of LaPorte County, IN. The publication covers local, state, national and international news, as well as sports, business and arts & entertainment.; Full Page Mono: 90.75; Full Page Colour: 108.90
Currency: US Dollars
DAILY NEWSPAPER

The Times
Owner: Gannett Co., Inc.
Editorial: 222 Lake St, Shreveport, Louisiana 71101-3738. **T:** 1 318 459-3200
E: shreveporttimes@gannett.com
W: http://www.shreveporttimes.com
Freq: Daily; **Circ:** 36111 Not Audited
Publisher: Donald Bailey
Editorial Profile: The Times, founded in 1872, is a daily, morning broadsheet newspaper distributed in Northwestern Louisiana. It covers local, regional and national news, as well as local sports, religion, politics, entertainment and lifestyle stories. Contact the appropriate section editor with press releases and general questions. The lead time varies, but can be as short as one day. Advertising is due by 5pm CT.; Full Page Mono: 145.00; Full Page Colour: 368.77
Currency: US Dollars
DAILY NEWSPAPER

The Times
Owner: The Paper of Montgomery County
Editorial: 641 Westfield Rd, Noblesville, Indiana 46060-1323. **T:** 1 317 773-9960
E: news@thetimes24-7.com
W: http://www.thenoblesvilletimes.com
Freq: Daily; **Circ:** 7074 Not Audited
Publisher: Tim Timmons
Editorial Profile: Noblesville Daily Times is a local newspaper published for the residents of Arcadia, Atlanta, Carmel, Cicero, Fishers, Noblesville, Sheridan and Westfield in Hamilton County, Indiana. It covers community events, local news, education, government, weather and sports. Deadlines are on Thursdays at noon ET. The paper does not publish on Tuesdays or Sundays.; Full Page Mono: 11.50; Full Page Colour: 14.71
Currency: US Dollars
DAILY NEWSPAPER

The Times
Editorial: 2080 N Main St, Crown Point, Indiana 46307-2002. **T:** 1 219 662-5300
DAILY NEWSPAPER

The Times
Editorial: 1111 Glendale Blvd, Valparaiso, Indiana 46383-3724. **T:** 1 219 462-5151
Bureau Chief: John Scheibel
Editorial Profile: The Valparaiso bureau staff put out the paper's zoned edition, The Vidette Times.
DAILY NEWSPAPER

The Times
Editorial: 3410 Delta Dr, Portage, Indiana 46368-5120. **T:** 1 219 762-4334
DAILY NEWSPAPER

The Times
Owner: Strickbine Publishing Inc.
Editorial: 3200 N Hayden Rd Ste 210, Scottsdale, Arizona 85251-6654.
T: 1 480 348-0343
E: info@timespublications.com
W: http://www.timespublications.com
Freq: Monthly; **Circ:** 113000 Not Audited
Editorial Profile: Times is a monthly newspaper providing Local and Community News coverage for the residents of North Valley, Scottsdale, Northeast Phoenix, Glendale, Gilbert, Chandler, East Mesa and Ahwatukee, AZ.
NEWSPAPER

The Times
Editorial: 150 W Market St Ste 135, Indianapolis, Indiana 46204-2841.
T: 1 317 637-9078
Bureau Chief: Dan Carden
DAILY NEWSPAPER

The Times & Democrat
Owner: Lee Enterprises, Inc.
Editorial: 1010 Broughton St, Orangeburg, South Carolina 29115-5962.
T: 1 803 533-5500
E: news@timesanddemocrat.com
W: http://thetandd.com
Freq: Daily; **Circ:** 13259 Not Audited
Editor: Lee Harter; **Editor:** Lee Harter;
Publisher: Cathy Hughes
Editorial Profile: The Times & Democrat is a daily newspaper written for the residents of Central South Carolina. It covers local news, sports, features and events. Deadlines are the day prior to publication between 6pm and 8pm ET.; Full Page Mono: 18.23; Full Page Colour: 571.00
Currency: US Dollars
DAILY NEWSPAPER

The Times & Los Tiempos
Owner: Lancaster Management Inc.
Editorial: 16 S Kansas Ave, Liberal, Kansas 67901-3732. **T:** 1 620 624-2541 **Circ:** 15489
NEWSPAPER

The Times (Washington)
Owner: News UK
Editorial: 529 14th St NW Ste 446, Washington, District Of Columbia 20045-1413.
T: 1 202 347-7659
W: http://www.thetimes.co.uk
Editorial Profile: The Times of London offers a U.S. edition. The staff in this Washington office, as well as the London staff contribute to the U.S. edition. Please pitch reporting staff at both locations.
DAILY NEWSPAPER

The Times Argus
Owner: Times Argus
Editorial: 540 N Main St, Barre, Vermont 05641-2504. **T:** 1 802 479-0191 3
E: news@timesargus.com
W: http://www.timesargus.com
Freq: Daily; **Circ:** 7216 Not Audited
Publisher: R. John Mitchell; **Editor:** Steven Pappas
Editorial Profile: The Times Argus written for the residents of Barre, VT. It covers local news, sports and state government.; Full Page Mono: 13.98; Full Page Colour: 40.83
Currency: US Dollars
DAILY NEWSPAPER

Times Argus
Editorial: 112 Main St, Montpelier, Vermont 05602-2908. **T:** 1 802 223-3335
W: http://www.timesargus.com
DAILY NEWSPAPER

Times Beacon Record Newspapers
Editorial: 185 Main St, Setauket, New York 11733-2803. **T:** 1 631 751-7744
E: news@tbrnewspapers.com
W: http://www.northshoreoflongisland.com
Circ: 53888 Not Audited
Editor: Elena Glowatz; **Editor:** Patricia Kalish
Editorial Profile: Publishes The Port Times Record, The Times of Northport, The Times of Huntington, The Times of Middle Country, The Village Times Herald, The Village Beacon Record, and The Times of Smithtown.
NEWSPAPER

Times Community News Group
Owner: Times Shamrock Group
Editorial: 149 Penn Ave, Scranton, Pennsylvania 18503. **T:** 1 570 348-9185
Circ: 63210 Not Audited
Editor: Chris Cornell; **Publisher:** Timothy Holmes; **Editor:** Shannon Keith; **Editor:** Shannon Keith; **Editor:** Shannon Keith
NEWSPAPER

Times Community Newspapers
Editorial: 300 Stony Brook Ct, Newburgh, New York 12550. **T:** 1 845 561-0170
W: http://www.timescommunitypapers.com
Circ: 8500 Not Audited
NEWSPAPER

Times Community Newspapers - Warrenton
Owner: Times Community Newspapers
Editorial: 39 Culpeper St, Warrenton, Virginia 20186-3319. **T:** 1 540 347-4222
W: http://www.timescommunity.com
Circ: 55114 Not Audited
Editorial Profile: Times Community Newspapers- Warrenton (VA) serve residents of Culpeper County, Fauquier County and Prince William County, VA.
NEWSPAPER

Times Community Newspapers–Vandalia
Owner: Civitas Media
Editorial: 69 N Dixie Dr Ste E, Vandalia, Ohio 45377-2060. **T:** 1 937 890-6030
W: http://www.tcnewsnet.com **Circ:** 13000 Not Audited
NEWSPAPER

The Times Group - New London
Owner: Day Publishing Co.
Editorial: 47 Eugene Oneill Dr., New London, Connecticut 6320. **T:** 1 860 440-1150
W: http://www.theday.com **Circ:** 79063 Not Audited
Publisher: Gary Farrugia; **Editor:** Marisa Nadolny
NEWSPAPER

Times Herald
Owner: Bradford Publishing Co.
Editorial: 639 Norton Dr, Olean, New York 14760-1498. **T:** 1 716 372-3121
E: news@oleantimesherald.com
W: http://www.oleantimesherald.com
Freq: Daily; **Circ:** 10083 Not Audited
Publisher: Jim Bonn
Editorial Profile: Times Herald is a daily newspaper based in Olean, NY. It covers community news, sports, births and deaths, business, weather and other news for St. Bonaventure University and Cattaraugus, Allegany, McKean, Potter and Cameron Counties.; Full Page Mono: 22.27
Currency: US Dollars
DAILY NEWSPAPER

Times Herald
Owner: Journal Register Company
Editorial: 410 Markley St, Norristown, Pennsylvania 19401-4617. **T:** 1 610 272-2500
W: http://www.timesherald.com
Freq: Daily; **Circ:** 10138 Not Audited
Publisher: Edward Condra; **Editor:** Stan Huskey
Editorial Profile: Times Herald is published daily for the residents of Norristown, PA and surrounding areas. The newspaper provides information about local, national and global news, business, sports, entertainment and features.; Full Page Mono: 41.55; Full Page Colour: 690.00
Currency: US Dollars
DAILY NEWSPAPER

Times Herald
Owner: Gannett Co., Inc.
Editorial: 911 Military St, Port Huron, Michigan 48060-5448. **T:** 1 810 985-7171
E: timesherald@gannett.com
W: http://www.thetimesherald.com
Freq: Daily; **Circ:** 15016
Editor: Michael Eckert; **Editor:** Michael Eckert; **Editor:** Michael Eckert; **Editor:** Michael Eckert
Editorial Profile: Times Herald is published daily for the residents of Port Huron, MI and surrounding areas. The newspaper covers local and state news, business, sports, lifestyles and entertainment.; Full Page Mono: 40.55
Currency: US Dollars
DAILY NEWSPAPER

Times Herald-Record
Owner: GateHouse Media Inc.
Editorial: 40 Mulberry St, Middletown, New York 10940-6302. **T:** 1 845 343-2181
E: news@th-record.com
W: http://www.recordonline.com
Freq: Daily; **Circ:** 45859 Not Audited
Publisher: Joe Vanderhoof
Editorial Profile: Times Herald-Record is a daily newspaper serving residents of the Hudson Valley and the Catskills, NY. The newspaper covers local, national and international news, as well as business, sports, arts & entertainment, editorials and community events.; Full Page Mono: 105.20; Full Page Colour: 344.45
Currency: US Dollars
DAILY NEWSPAPER

Times Herald-Record
Editorial: 1170 Route 17M, Ste 4, Chester, New York 10918. **T:** 1 845 783-2764
DAILY NEWSPAPER

Times Herald-Record
Editorial: 34 John St, Kingston, New York 12401-3822. **T:** 1 845 340-4910
DAILY NEWSPAPER

Times Herald-Record
Editorial: 479 Broadway, Monticello, New York 12701-1756. **T:** 1 845 794-3712
DAILY NEWSPAPER

Times Herald-Record
Editorial: 831 Little Britain Rd, New Windsor, New York 12553-5518. **T:** 1 845 562-2555
DAILY NEWSPAPER

The Times Leader
Owner: Ogden Newspapers
Editorial: 200 S 4th St, Martins Ferry, Ohio 43935-1312. **T:** 1 740 633-1131
E: timesleader@timesleaderonline.com
W: http://www.timesleaderonline.com
Freq: Daily; **Circ:** 10389 Not Audited
Publisher: Lori Figurski
Editorial Profile: The Times Leader is a daily, local newspaper for the Martins Ferry, OH area. It covers local news, sports, business, government and lifestyle stories. The paper also covers national stories if they are of interest to the readership.; Full Page Mono: 22.92; Full Page Colour: 255.00
Currency: US Dollars
DAILY NEWSPAPER

The Times Leader
Owner: Wilkes-Barre Publishing Co.
Editorial: 15 N Main St, Wilkes-Barre, Pennsylvania 18711-0250. **T:** 1 570 829-7100
W: http://www.timesleader.com
Freq: Daily; **Circ:** 33632 Not Audited
News Editor: Joe Healey
Editorial Profile: The Times Leader in Wilkes-Barre, PA serves Northeastern PA and covers local and national news, sports, arts & entertainment, business and lifestyle topics.; Full Page Mono: 63.03; Full Page Colour: 495.00
Currency: US Dollars
DAILY NEWSPAPER

Times Media Inc.
Owner: Bellou (William)
Editorial: 1900 Camden Ave, San Jose, California 95124. **T:** 1 408 494-7000
E: times@timesmediainc.com
W: http://www.timesmediainc.com **Circ:** 55000 Not Audited
Publisher: William Bellou
Editorial Profile: Times Media Inc. is the local newspaper providing the community of San Jose, CA with news.
NEWSPAPER

The Times News
Owner: Pencor Services
Editorial: 594 Blakeslee Boulevard Dr W, Lehighton, Pennsylvania 18235-9754.
T: 1 610 377-2051
E: tnonline@postoffice.ptd.net
W: http://www.tnonline.com
Freq: Daily; **Circ:** 11623
Publisher: Fred Masenheimer; **Editor:** Emmett McCall; **Editor in Chief:** Bob Urban
Editorial Profile: The Times News is a daily newspaper serving the counties of Carbon, Schuylkill, Lehigh, Monroe and Northampton, PA. The publication not only covers local news in each county, but state-wide news as well. Sections include news, sports, calendars, announcements and classified ads.; Full Page Mono: 10.95; Full Page Colour: 19.24
Currency: US Dollars
DAILY NEWSPAPER

Times Newsweekly
Owner: Ridgewood Times Printing and Publishing Company, Inc.
Editorial: 6071 Woodbine St, Ridgewood, New York 11385-3242. **T:** 1 718 821-7500
E: info@timesnewsweekly.com
W: http://www.timesnewsweekly.com
Freq: Thu; **Circ:** 30000 Not Audited
Editorial Profile: Times Newsweekly is written for the residents of Queens, NY. It covers local news and events.; Full Page Mono: 10.50
Currency: US Dollars
NEWSPAPER

Times Observer
Owner: Ogden Newspapers
Editorial: 205 Pennsylvania Ave W, Warren, Pennsylvania 16365-2412. **T:** 1 814 723-8200
E: editorial@timesobserver.com
W: http://www.timesobserver.com
Freq: Daily; **Circ:** 8798 Not Audited
Publisher: Bob Patchen
Editorial Profile: Times Observer's editorial mission is to provide local, national, and international news and information. This publication serves residents of Warren County, PA. Deadline for Warren Times Observer is the day before issue date.; Full Page Mono: 21.62; Full Page Colour: 30.18
Currency: US Dollars
DAILY NEWSPAPER

The Times of Acadiana
Owner: Gannett Co., Inc.

Editorial: 1100 Bertrand Dr, Lafayette, Louisiana 70506-4110. **T:** 1 337 289-6300
E: calendar@theadvertiser.com
W: http://www.theadvertiser.com/section/acadiana
Freq: Thu; **Circ:** 29500 Not Audited
Editor: Cindy McCurry-Ross
Editorial Profile: The Times of Acadiana is a free, alternative news magazine covering entertainment, recreation, politics, culture, food and business in Lafayette, LA, and the surrounding Acadiana region of southern Louisiana. Columns review movies, music, the arts, food and wine, books and sporting events.; Full Page Mono: 21.05
Currency: US Dollars
NEWSPAPER

Times of India - Maryland Bureau
Editorial: 7505 Alfred Dr, Silver Spring, Maryland 20910-5203. **T:** 1 917 332-7105
DAILY NEWSPAPER

Times Publishing Group
Owner: Patrice Edwards
Editorial: 9601 Soquel Dr, Aptos, California 95003-4163. **T:** 1 831 688-7549
E: info@cyber-times.com
W: http://www.tpgonlinedaily.com **Circ:** 36000 Not Audited
Publisher: Patrice Edwards; **Publisher:** Patrice Edwards; **Publisher:** Patrice Edwards; **Publisher:** Patrice Edwards; **Editor:** Noel Smith
NEWSPAPER

Times Publishing Newspapers
Owner: Times Publishing Newspapers, Inc.
Editorial: 341 Rumpf Ave, Langhorne, Pennsylvania 19047-5523. **T:** 1 215 702-3405
W: http://www.timespub.com
Freq: Monthly; **Circ:** 115716
Publisher: Donna Allen; **Editor:** Mark Allen
Editorial Profile: Times Publishing Newspapers, Inc. publishes eight monthly newspapers providing Local and Community News coverage to the residents of Bucks County, PA, Publications are The Morrisville Times, Yardley Voice, Newtown Gazette, Northampton Herald, Langhorne Ledger, Southampton Spirit, New Hope News and the Doylestown Observer.
NEWSPAPER

The Times Record
Owner: Sample News Group
Editorial: 3 Business Pkwy, Brunswick, Maine 4011. **T:** 1 207 729-3311
E: news@timesrecord.com
W: http://www.timesrecord.com
Freq: Daily; **Circ:** 7722 Not Audited
News Editor: Daryl Madore; **Publisher:** Chris Miles
Editorial Profile: The Times Record serves the mid-Coastal Maine area. It focuses on local news and sports.; Full Page Mono: 16.50; Full Page Colour: 300.00
Currency: US Dollars
DAILY NEWSPAPER

Times Record
Owner: Stephens Media
Editorial: 3600 Wheeler Ave, Fort Smith, Arkansas 72901-6621. **T:** 1 479 785-7700
E: press@swtimes.com
W: http://www.swtimes.com
Freq: Daily; **Circ:** 35378 Not Audited
Bureau Chief: Dennis Byrd; **Editor:** Judi Hansen; **Editor:** Jay Harshaw; **Publisher:** Gene Kincy
Editorial Profile: Times Record is a daily newspaper for the residents of Fort Smith, AR.; Full Page Mono: 40.98; Full Page Colour: 137.70
Currency: US Dollars
DAILY NEWSPAPER

Times Record News
Owner: E.W. Scripps Co.
Editorial: 1301 Lamar St, Wichita Falls, Texas 76301-7032. **T:** 1 940 767-8341
W: http://www.timesrecordnews.com
Freq: Daily; **Circ:** 22448 Not Audited
Publisher: Dwayne Bivona; **Editor:** Deanna Watson
Editorial Profile: Times Record News is a daily newspaper written for the residents of Wichita Falls, TX. The newspaper covers current news and events. The deadline for the publication is 5pm CT, the day before issue date.; Full Page Mono: 38.91; Full Page Colour: 184.20
Currency: US Dollars
DAILY NEWSPAPER

Times Recorder
Owner: Gannett Co., Inc.

Editorial: 34 S 4th St, Zanesville, Ohio 43701-3417. **T:** 1 740 452-4561
E: trnews@zanesvilletimesrecorder.com
W: http://www.zanesvilletimesrecorder.com
Freq: Daily; **Circ:** 11186 Not Audited
Editorial Profile: Times Recorder is a daily newspaper providing News and Current Affairs information for the residents of Muskingum County and Zanesville, OH.; Full Page Mono: 35.50; Full Page Colour: 335.00
Currency: US Dollars
DAILY NEWSPAPER

Times Square Chronicles
Owner: Bowling (Suzanna) & Basch (David)
Editorial: 461 W 49th St Apt 1B, New York, New York 10019-7285. **T:** 1 212 245-1071
E: info@t2conline.com
W: http://t2conline.com
Freq: Monthly
Editorial Profile: Times Square Chronicles is a monthly community newspaper covering Arts and Entertainment News, relevant Breaking News in the Times Square area and National News of relevance to those in the area. The coverage area is 39th to 59th Streets, from 6th Street to the Hudson River.
NEWSPAPER

Times Union
Owner: Capital Newspapers
Editorial: 645 Albany Shaker Rd, Albany, New York 12211-1158. **T:** 1 518 454-5694
E: tucitydesk@timesunion.com
W: http://www.timesunion.com
Freq: Daily; **Circ:** 55281 Not Audited
Publisher: George Hearst; **Editor:** Rex Smith
Editorial Profile: Times Union is a daily newspaper serving the capital region of New York, which includes Albany, Schenectady, Troy, Rensselaer and Saratoga ONLY. It provides readers with the latest news, weather, entertainment and sports information. The paper dates back to 1856. After a merger with a competitor, the Evening Union, the Times Union was forged in 1891. In 1937, Hearst took over the newspaper and ended 72 years of afternoon publication by moving the Times Union into the morning field. The paper will no longer accept event listings submitted by phone, fax, email or traditional mail. Print calendars will only include those events submitted online. To submit, go to http://events.timesunion.com/ and follow the directions. There is a help page at the site should you need assistance.; Full Page Mono: 175.00; Full Page Colour: 1155.00
Currency: US Dollars
DAILY NEWSPAPER

The Times Weekly
Owner: C & C Publications
Editorial: 254 E Cass St, Joliet, Illinois 60432. **T:** 1 815 723-0325
E: timesweekly@sbcglobal.net
W: http://timesweeklynewspaper.tripod.com
Freq: Thu; **Circ:** 28000 Not Audited
Editorial Profile: The Times Weekly provides news and information on topics that affect African Americans in the Joliet, IL community.; Full Page Mono: 46.12
Currency: US Dollars
NEWSPAPER

Times West Virginian
Owner: MediaNews Group
Editorial: 300 Quincy St, Fairmont, West Virginia 26554-3136. **T:** 1 304 367-2500
E: timeswv@timeswv.com
W: http://www.timeswv.com
Freq: Daily; **Circ:** 11372 Not Audited
Publisher: Kelly Miller; **News Editor:** Cliff Nichols; **Editor:** John Veasey
Editorial Profile: Times West Virginian is published daily for the residents of Marion County, WV. The newspaper covers local and state news, business, sports, lifestyles and entertainment.; Full Page Mono: 20.05; Full Page Colour: 24.05
Currency: US Dollars
DAILY NEWSPAPER

Times/Ledger Newspapers
Owner: News Corporation Ltd.
Editorial: 4102 Bell Blvd, 2nd Fl, Bayside, New York 11361. **T:** 1 718 229-0300
E: timesledgernews@cnglocal.com
W: http://www.timesledger.com **Circ:** 46975 Not Audited
NEWSPAPER

Times-Beacon Newspapers
Owner: Gannett Co., Inc.
Editorial: 3601 Highway 66, Neptune, New Jersey 7754. **T:** 1 609 597-3211
E: tbeacon@app.com
W: http://www.timesbeacon.com **Circ:** 15877

Not Audited
Publisher: Thomas Donovan
NEWSPAPER

TimesDaily
Owner: Tennessee Valley Printing Co. Inc.
Editorial: 219 W Tennessee St, Florence, Alabama 35630-5455. **T:** 1 256 766-3434
E: vent@timesdaily.com
W: http://www.timesdaily.com
Freq: Daily; **Circ:** 21349 Not Audited
Publisher: Darrell Sandlin
Editorial Profile: TimesDaily is a newspaper written for the residents of Northwest Alabama. It covers local news, sports, entertainment and events.; Full Page Mono: 59.15; Full Page Colour: 190.42
Currency: US Dollars
DAILY NEWSPAPER

Times-Gazette
Owner: Ohio Community Media LLC.
Editorial: 209 S High St, Hillsboro, Ohio 45133-1496. **T:** 1 937 393-3456
E: info@timesgazette.com
W: http://www.timesgazette.com
Freq: Daily; **Circ:** 4667 Not Audited
Publisher: Gary Abernathy; **Editor:** Steve Roush
Editorial Profile: Times-Gazette is written for the residents of Highland County, OH. It covers local news and sports. Deadlines are at 4:30pm ET the day before publication.; Full Page Mono: 10.30; Full Page Colour: 195.00
Currency: US Dollars
DAILY NEWSPAPER

Times-Georgian
Owner: Paxton Media Group
Editorial: 901 Hays Mill Rd, Carrollton, Georgia 30117-9576. **T:** 1 770 834-6631
W: http://www.times-georgian.com
Freq: Daily; **Circ:** 8019 Not Audited
Editor: Bruce Browning; **News Editor:** Amy Lavender; **Publisher:** Leonard Woolsey
Editorial Profile: Times-Georgian's editorial mission is to report current news and information to the public. It is written for the residents of Carroll County and Harallson County, GA and covers current news and events that affect the community. Deadlines are one day before issue date.; Full Page Mono: 20.00; Full Page Colour: 150.00
Currency: US Dollars
DAILY NEWSPAPER

The Times-Herald
Owner: MediaNews Group
Editorial: 440 Curtola Pkwy, Vallejo, California 94590-6923. **T:** 1 707 644-1141
W: http://www.timesheraldonline.com
Freq: Daily; **Circ:** 15782 Not Audited
Publisher: Jim Gleim
Editorial Profile: The Times-Herald is the local daily newspaper written for the residents of Vallejo, Benicia and American County, CA and the surrounding communities. The newspaper covers international, national and local news, sports, events and arts & entertainment.; Full Page Mono: 26.50; Full Page Colour: 625.00
Currency: US Dollars
DAILY NEWSPAPER

The Times-Herald
Owner: Herald Publishing Company
Editorial: 508 N Court St, Carroll, Iowa 51401-2747. **T:** 1 712 792-3573
E: newspaper@carrollspaper.com
W: http://www.carrollspaper.com
Freq: Daily; **Circ:** 6525 Not Audited
Editor: Larry Devine
Editorial Profile: The Times-Herald is a local, daily newspaper serving Carroll, IA and surrounding communities.; Full Page Mono: 6.10
Currency: US Dollars
DAILY NEWSPAPER

Times-Journal
Owner: Southern Newspapers, Inc.
Editorial: 811 Greenhill Blvd NW, Fort Payne, Alabama 35967-3675. **T:** 1 256 845-2550
E: news@times-journal.com
W: http://www.times-journal.com
Freq: Daily; **Circ:** 5897 Not Audited
Editorial Profile: Times-Journal is a local daily newspaper serving Fort Payne, AL. The paper covers local news, weather, sports and opinion.; Full Page Mono: 9.40; Full Page Colour: 40.44
Currency: US Dollars
DAILY NEWSPAPER

The Times-Mail
Owner: Schurz Communications Inc.
Editorial: 813 16th St, Bedford, Indiana 47421. **T:** 1 812 275-3355

W: http://www.tmnews.com
Freq: Mon thru Fri; **Circ:** 9000
Editor in Chief: Scott Schurz
Editorial Profile: The Times-Mail's editorial mission is to provide news and information to the public with a heavy emphasis on local events, personalities and trends that affect the residents of south central Indiana. The publication combines with The Times-Mail and The Reporter-Times for the Sunday edition called the Hoosier Times.; Full Page Mono: 17.83; Full Page Colour: 310.00
Currency: US Dollars
DAILY NEWSPAPER

The Times-News
Owner: Lee Enterprises, Inc.
Editorial: 132 Fairfield St W, Twin Falls, Idaho 83301-5492. **T:** 1 208 733-0931 3
E: frontdoor@magicvalley.com
W: http://www.magicvalley.com
Freq: Daily; **Circ:** 15275 Not Audited
Editor: Autumn Agar
Editorial Profile: The Times-News is a daily newspaper serving the community of Twin Falls, ID and surrounding southern Idaho communities, including Jerome and Burley, ID and Gooding County, ID. The newspaper includes national and local news, business, sports and lifestyle sections.; Full Page Mono: 26.84; Full Page Colour: 420.00
Currency: US Dollars
DAILY NEWSPAPER

Times-News
Owner: Halifax Media Holdings LLC
Editorial: 707 S Main St, Burlington, North Carolina 27215-5844. **T:** 1 336 227-0131
W: http://www.thetimesnews.com
Freq: Daily; **Circ:** 18141 Not Audited
Editor: Brent Lancaster; **Publisher:** Paul Mauney; **Editor:** Madison Taylor
Editorial Profile: Times-News is published daily for residents of Burlington, NC and surrounding communities. The newspaper covers local, national, and international news, weather, sports and community events. Feature articles cover business developments, politics, education, arts & entertainment, lifestyle and other topics of interest to the local community.; Full Page Mono: 24.37; Full Page Colour: 460.00
Currency: US Dollars
DAILY NEWSPAPER

Times-News
Owner: Halifax Media Holdings LLC
Editorial: 106 Henderson Crossing Plz, Hendersonville, North Carolina 28792-2879. **T:** 1 828 692-0505
E: tnnews@hendersonvillenews.com
W: http://www.blueridgenow.com
Freq: Daily; **Circ:** 11374 Not Audited
Editorial Profile: Times-News is a daily newspaper serving the Hendersonville, NC region. The publication covers local news, sports and community events.; Full Page Mono: 25.73; Full Page Colour: 450.00
Currency: US Dollars
DAILY NEWSPAPER

The Times-Picayune
Owner: Newhouse Newspapers
Editorial: 365 Canal St Ste 3100, New Orleans, Louisiana 70130-6509.
T: 1 504 299-3518 **W:** http://www.nola.com
Freq: Daily; **Circ:** 27455 Not Audited
Recruiting Analyst: James Smith
Editorial Profile: The Times-Picayune is a 70+ page, four-color broadsheet newspaper, published for the New Orleans general consumer audience. The business section, entitled Money, is featured daily, covering local and national business stories, daily stock market rates, and real estate. Articles include features, breaking news, trends, analyses, profiles, reviews, and investigative stories. Topics covered include entertainment, travel, health, food and drink, technology, and sports. As of October 1, 2012, The Times-Picayune is no longer publishing seven days a week, but produces expanded editions on Wednesday, Friday and Sunday, and much of the editorial staff's focus has shifted to their digital platform, NOLA.com.; Full Page Mono: 186.20; Full Page Colour: 622.60
Currency: US Dollars
DAILY NEWSPAPER

The Times-Picayune
Editorial: 700 12th St NW, Ste 1000, Washington, District Of Columbia 20005-3994
DAILY NEWSPAPER

The Times-Picayune
Editorial: 2520 Belle Chasse Hwy, Gretna, Louisiana 70053-6767. **T:** 1 504 826-3781

DAILY NEWSPAPER

The Times-Picayune
Editorial: 301 W Airline Hwy Ste 103, La Place, Louisiana 70068-3823.
T: 1 985 652-0950
DAILY NEWSPAPER

The Times-Picayune
Editorial: 4013 N I 10 Service Rd W, Metairie, Louisiana 70002-6718. **T:** 1 504 883-7050
DAILY NEWSPAPER

The Times-Picayune
Editorial: 2070 Gause Blvd E, Slidell, Louisiana 70461-5431. **T:** 1 985 645-2850
DAILY NEWSPAPER

The Times-Picayune
Editorial: 301 Main St. Suite 101, Baton Rouge, Louisiana 70801. **T:** 1 225 342-7315
DAILY NEWSPAPER

The Times-Picayune
Editorial: 1001 N Highway 190, Covington, Louisiana 70433-8962. **T:** 1 985 898-4825
DAILY NEWSPAPER

The Times-Reporter
Owner: GateHouse Media Inc.
Editorial: 629 Wabash Ave Nw, New Philadelphia, Ohio 44663-4145.
T: 1 330 364-5577
E: news@timesreporter.com
W: http://www.timesreporter.com
Freq: Daily; **Circ:** 16300 Not Audited
Editor: Melissa Griffy Seeton; **News Editor:** Joe Wright
Editorial Profile: The Times Reporter is a daily newspaper written for residents of the Dover and New Philadelphia, OH area. The editorial mission is to provide news and information to the public. The deadlines are 5pm ET the day before issue date.; Full Page Mono: 25.95; Full Page Colour: 360.00
Currency: US Dollars
DAILY NEWSPAPER

Times-Republic
Owner: Community Media Group
Editorial: 1492 E Walnut St, Watseka, Illinois 60970-1806. **T:** 1 815 432-5227
E: watseka@intranix.com
W: http://www.newsbug.info/watseka_times_republic.com
Freq: Daily; **Circ:** 2890 Not Audited
Publisher: Don Hurd
Editorial Profile: The Times-Republic is written for the communities in Iroquois County, IL.; Full Page Mono: 9.35
Currency: US Dollars
DAILY NEWSPAPER

Times-Republican
Owner: Marshalltown Newspaper Inc.
Editorial: 135 W Main St, Marshalltown, Iowa 50158-5800. **T:** 1 641 753-6611
E: news@timesrepublican.com
W: http://www.timesrepublican.com
Freq: Daily; **Circ:** 6737
Publisher: Mike Schlesinger
Editorial Profile: Times-Republican is a daily newspaper serving Central Iowa. Articles include news, weather, travel, sports and local events.; Full Page Mono: 24.52; Full Page Colour: 209.52
Currency: US Dollars
DAILY NEWSPAPER

Times-Review Newspapers
Owner: Times-Review Newspapers
Editorial: 7785 Main Rd, Mattituck, New York 11952-1518. **T:** 1 631 298-3200
E: editor@timesreview.com
W: http://timesreview.com **Circ:** 17900 Not Audited
Editor: Tim Kelly; **Publisher:** Andrew Olsen; **Editor:** Michael White
NEWSPAPER

The Times-Sentinel Newspapers
Editorial: 125 N Main St, Goddard, Kansas 67052-8871. **T:** 1 316 540-0500
W: http://www.tsnews.com **Circ:** 22300
Editorial Profile: Times-Sentinel Newspapers provides Local and Community News coverage for the Kansas communities of Cheney, Clearwater, Garden Plain and Goddard.
NEWSPAPER

Times-Shamrock Group
Owner: Times-Shamrock Media Group
Editorial: 24 S Main St, Montrose, Pennsylvania 18801. **T:** 1 570 278-6397
W: http://www.independentweekender.com
Circ: 19650 Not Audited
Editor: Robert Baker; **Editor:** Robert Baker; **Editor:** Robert Baker
NEWSPAPER

Times-Standard
Owner: MediaNews Group
Editorial: 930 6th St, Eureka, California 95501.
T: 1 707 441-0500
E: editor@times-standard.com
W: http://www.times-standard.com
Freq: Daily; **Circ:** 18284 Not Audited
Publisher: Dave Kuta
Editorial Profile: Times-Standard is published daily for the residents of Eureka, CA and surrounding areas. The newspaper covers local and state news, business, sports, lifestyles and entertainment. The paper no longer prints Monday editions, but is available online.; Full Page Mono: 33.00; Full Page Colour: 625.00
Currency: US Dollars
DAILY NEWSPAPER

The Times-Tribune
Owner: Community Newspaper Holdings, Inc.
Editorial: 201 N Kentucky Ave, Corbin, Kentucky 40701-1529. **T:** 1 606 528-2464
E: newsroom@thetimestribune.com
W: http://www.thetimestribune.com
Freq: Mon thru Fri; **Circ:** 9464 Not Audited
Editorial Profile: The Times-Tribune is a daily newspaper published for the residents of Southeastern Kentucky. The paper covers local news, sports, business and lifestyle.; Full Page Mono: 12.15; Full Page Colour: 250.00
Currency: US Dollars
DAILY NEWSPAPER

The Times-Tribune
Owner: Times-Shamrock Communications
Editorial: 149 Penn Ave, Scranton, Pennsylvania 18503. **T:** 1 570 348-9100
E: newsroom@timesshamrock.com
W: http://www.thetimes-tribune.com
Freq: Daily; **Circ:** 41769 Not Audited
Editorial Profile: The Times-Tribune is published daily for the residents of Scranton, PA and surrounding areas. The newspaper provides information about local and national news, business, sports, lifestyles and entertainment.; Full Page Mono: 60.22; Full Page Colour: 189.15
Currency: US Dollars
DAILY NEWSPAPER

Tinker Take Off
Owner: Dolan Media Company
Editorial: 7460 Arnold St, Ste 125, Tinker AFB, Oklahoma 73145. **T:** 1 405 739-7624
E: tinker.takeoff@tinker.af.mil
W: http://www.tinkertakeoff.com
Freq: Fri; **Circ:** 18000 Not Audited
Editor: Micah Garbarino
Editorial Profile: Tinker Take Off is weekly newspaper written for employees and retirees of Tinker Air Force Base in Oklahoma City. The publication covers all news that affects the lives of the people on Tinker Air Force Base.; Full Page Mono: 17.50
Currency: US Dollars
NEWSPAPER

Tinker Take Off
Owner: Journal Record Publishing Company
Editorial: 72nd Air Base Wing Headquarters, Bldg 460, Rm 125, Oklahoma City, Oklahoma.
T: 1 405 739-5780
E: tinker.takeoff@tinker.af.mil
W: http://journalrecord.com/tinkertakeoff
Freq: Fri
Editor: April McDonald
Editorial Profile: Tinker Take Off is a weekly community newspaper serving Tinker Air Force Base in Oklahoma City, OK.
NEWSPAPER

Tinnen Publishing
Editorial: 102 E Maple St, Plattsburg, Missouri 64477. **T:** 1 816 539-2111
E: leader@centurytel.net **Circ:** 21362 Not Audited
Publisher: Steve Tinnen
Editorial Profile: Tinnen Publishing is a weekly community newspaper publisher serving the residents of Kansas City, MO.
NEWSPAPER

Tioga Publishing
Owner: Community Media Group
Editorial: 6 W 2nd St, Coudersport, Pennsylvania 16915. **T:** 1 814 274-8044
Circ: 10000
Editor: Brent Addleman; **Publisher:** James Monks
NEWSPAPER

Tioga Publishing - Wellsboro
Owner: Community Media Group
Editorial: 25 East Ave, Wellsboro, Pennsylvania 16901-1618. **T:** 1 570 724-2287
W: http://www.tiogapublishing.com **Circ:** 6700 Not Audited
Editor: Natalie Kennedy; **Publisher:** James Monks
NEWSPAPER

Tipton County Tribune
Owner: Elwood Publishing Co.
Editorial: 116 S Main St, Ste A, Tipton, Indiana 46072. **T:** 1 765 675-2115
E: tiptontribune@elwoodpublishing.com
W: http://www.elwoodpublishing.com
Freq: Daily; **Circ:** 3000 Not Audited
Publisher: Robert Nash
Editorial Profile: Tipton County Tribune is published daily for the residents of Tipton, IN and surrounding areas. The newspaper covers local and state news, business, sports, lifestyles and entertainment.; Full Page Mono: 9.95; Full Page Colour: 150.00
Currency: US Dollars
DAILY NEWSPAPER

Titusville Herald
Owner: Titusville Herald, Inc.
Editorial: 209 W Spring St, Titusville, Pennsylvania 16354-1687. **T:** 1 814 827-3634
E: news@titusvilleherald.com
W: http://www.titusvilleherald.com
Freq: Daily; **Circ:** 4000 Not Audited
Editorial Profile: Titusville Herald provides news for residents of Titusville, PA. It covers local news and events that effect the community. Deadlines are two days before issue date.; Full Page Mono: 9.60; Full Page Colour: 255.00
Currency: US Dollars
DAILY NEWSPAPER

T-News Weekly
Owner: New York Times Company (The)
Editorial: 315 28th Ave, Tuscaloosa, Alabama 35401-1022. **T:** 1 205 345-0505
Freq: Wed; **Circ:** 21934 Not Audited
Editor: Lauren Barrera; **Publisher:** Timothy Thompson
Editorial Profile: T-News Weekly is a free publication mailed to non-subscribers of the Tuscaloosa News and distributed to area newstands. The paper features stories of local interest, neighborhood announcements, growth projects, school activities, entertainment and events. It also contains the week's major news headlines and a classified section.; Full Page Mono: 7.50; Full Page Colour: 160.00
Currency: US Dollars
NEWSPAPER

Today's Catholic
Owner: Diocese of Fort Wayne – South Bend
Editorial: 915 S Clinton St, Fort Wayne, Indiana 46802. **T:** 1 260 456-2824
E: editor@fw.diocesefwsb.org
W: http://www.diocesefwsb.org
Freq: Sun; **Circ:** 52000 Not Audited
Editor: Tim Johnson; **Publisher:** Kevin Rhoades
Editorial Profile: Today's Catholic is a local catholic newspaper for residents of Fort Wayne, IN and the surrounding counties. It provides local and national news of interest to the Catholic community, and comes out once a week on Sundays.; Full Page Mono: 15.00
Currency: US Dollars
NEWSPAPER

Today's Catholic Newspaper
Owner: Archdiocese of San Antonio
Editorial: 2718 W Woodlawn Ave, San Antonio, Texas 78228-5124.
T: 1 210 734-1692
W: http://www.satodayscatholic.com
Freq: Bi-Weekly; **Circ:** 30000
Publisher: Gustavo Garcia-Siller; **Editor:** Jordan McMorrough
Editorial Profile: Today's Catholic Newspaper is written for the Archdiocese of San Antonio.; Full Page Mono: 14.44
Currency: US Dollars
NEWSPAPER

Today's News-Herald
Owner: River City Newspapers, L.L.C.
Editorial: 2225 Acoma Blvd W, Lake Havasu City, Arizona 86403-2995. **T:** 1 928 453-4237
E: news@havasunews.com
W: http://www.havasunews.com
Freq: Daily; **Circ:** 10000 Not Audited
Editor: Pam Ashley
Editorial Profile: Today's News-Herald is a weekly newspaper serving residents of Lake Havasu City, AZ and surrounding communities. The newspaper covers local and national news, community events, weather and sports.; Full Page Mono: 20.36; Full Page Colour: 69.86
Currency: US Dollars
DAILY NEWSPAPER

Toledo Free Press
Editorial: 605 Monroe St, Toledo, Ohio 43604-1015. **T:** 1 419 241-1700
E: news@toledofreepress.com
W: http://www.toledofreepress.com
Freq: Sun; **Circ:** 72000 Not Audited
Editor in Chief: Michael Miller; **Editor in Chief:** Michael Miller; **Editor in Chief:** Michael Miller; **Editor in Chief:** Michael Miller
Editorial Profile: Toledo Free Press supports local and regional growth in Northwest Ohio and Southeast Michigan. The paper supports hometown growth initiatives through insightful news coverage and objective editorials. Free Style, a monthly magazine, is inserted into the paper and covers makeup, hairstyles and clothing. The Star, an arts & entertainment section, is inserted into the paper on Wednesdays.; Full Page Mono: 62.00; Full Page Colour: 62.79
Currency: US Dollars
NEWSPAPER

The Toledo Journal
Editorial: 3021 Douglas, Toledo, Ohio 43606-5001. **T:** 1 419 472-4521 **E:** toljour@aol.com
W: http://www.thetoledojournal.com
Freq: Wed; **Circ:** 63000 Not Audited
Editor: Myron Stewart; **Publisher:** Sandra Stewart
Editorial Profile: The Toledo Journal's editorial mission is to provide news and information to the African American community in Toledo, Sylvania, Oregon and Springfield Township, OH. It covers national and local news and events that affect its readers.; Full Page Mono: 23.40; Full Page Colour: 502.00
Currency: US Dollars
NEWSPAPER

Tolosa Press
Owner: Central Coast News Group, LLC
Editorial: 615 Clarion Ct Ste 2, San Luis Obispo, California 93401-8197.
T: 1 805 543-6397
W: http://www.tolosapress.com **Circ:** 80000 Not Audited
Editor: Neil Farrell; **Publisher:** Mary Gardner; **Editor:** Theresa Wilson
Editorial Profile: Tolosa Press is a local newspaper providing the community of San Luis Obispo, CA with news.
NEWSPAPER

The Tolucan Times and Canyon Crier
Owner: Ticor
Editorial: 10701 Riverside Dr, Toluca Lake, California 91602. **T:** 1 818 762-2171
E: editorial@tolucantimes.com
W: http://www.tolucantimes.com
Freq: Wed; **Circ:** 40000 Not Audited
Editorial Profile: The Tolucan Times and Canyon Crier is a local weekly newspaper serving residents of Glendale, Burbank, North Hollywood, NoHo Arts District, Universal City, Toluca Lake, Valley Village, Studio City, Sherman Oaks and Encino, CA. Advertising deadlines are at noon PT.; Full Page Mono: 30.00
Currency: US Dollars
NEWSPAPER

Tomah Journal Newspapers
Owner: Lee Enterprises, Inc.
Editorial: 903 Superior Ave, Ste 3, Tomah, Wisconsin 54660. **T:** 1 608 372-4123
E: tomahnews@lee.net
W: http://www.tomahjournal.com **Circ:** 10600 Not Audited
Publisher: Chris Hardie; **Editor:** Steve Rundio; **Editor:** Steve Rundio
Editorial Profile: Tomah Journal Newspapers is a weekly community newspaper publisher serving the residents of Tomah, WI.
NEWSPAPER

The Tomball Magnolia Tribune
Owner: Armadillo Advertising Inc.
Editorial: 517 W Main St, Tomball, Texas 77375. **T:** 1 281 255-6397
E: news@tribunenews.com
W: http://www.tribunenews.com
Freq: Mon; **Circ:** 53652 Not Audited
Publisher: Nancy Nygaard; **Editor:** Brian Walzel
Editorial Profile: The Tomball Magnolia Tribune is published weekly for the residents of Tomball, TX and surrounding areas. The newspaper covers local news and community events.; Full Page Mono: 22.70

Currency: US Dollars
NEWSPAPER

The Tonawanda News

Owner: Community Newspaper Holdings, Inc.
Editorial: 435 River Rd, North Tonawanda, New York 14120. **T:** 1 716 693-1000
E: newsroom@tonawanda-news.com
W: http://www.tonawanda-news.com
Freq: Daily; **Circ:** 3819 Not Audited
Publisher: Peter Mio
Editorial Profile: Tonawanda News is written for residents of Tonawanda, NY. The publication strictly covers local news and events. They do NOT accept any pitches without a local angle.; Full Page Mono: 17.22
Currency: US Dollars
DAILY NEWSPAPER

Tonopah Times-Bonanza & Goldfield News Newspapers

Owner: Stephens Media
Editorial: 150 Main St, Tonopah, Nevada 89049. **T:** 1 775 482-3365 **Circ:** 3200 Not Audited
Editor: Matt Ward; **Publisher:** Marie Wujek
Editorial Profile: Tonopah Times-Bonanza & Goldfield News Newspapers is a local newspaper in Tonopah, NV.
NEWSPAPER

Topeka Capital-Journal

Owner: Morris Communications
Editorial: 616 SE Jefferson St, Topeka, Kansas 66607-1137. **T:** 1 785 295-1111
E: news@cjonline.com
W: http://www.cjonline.com
Freq: Daily; **Circ:** 26468 Not Audited
Editor: Steve Thompson
Editorial Profile: Topeka Capital-Journal is published daily for residents of Topeka, KS and surrounding communities. The newspaper covers state government, as well as regional news in 23 Northeast Kansas counties.; Full Page Mono: 81.89; Full Page Colour: 1250.00
Currency: US Dollars
DAILY NEWSPAPER

Topsail Advertiser

Owner: Halifax Media Holdings LLC
Editorial: 206A S. Topsail Dr., Surf City, North Carolina 28445. **T:** 1 910 328-3033
W: http://www.topsailadvertiser.com
Freq: Thu
Publisher: Elliott Potter
Editorial Profile: Topsail Advertiser is a weekly community newspaper serving Pender, Onslow, and New Hanover counties, NC. The paper includes local news and community events.
NEWSPAPER

The Town Common

Owner: Maravalli (Marc)
Editorial: 77 Wethersfield St, Rowley, Massachusetts 01969-1713.
T: 1 978 948-8696
E: editor@thetowncommon.com
W: http://www.thetowncommon.com
Freq: Wed; **Circ:** 18000 Not Audited
Editorial Profile: The Town Common serves the residents within the Triton Regional School district and the towns of Rowley, Newbury, Salisbury, Byfield and Plum Island, MA. Coverage includes local news, events and school and community happenings.; Full Page Mono: 23.80
Currency: US Dollars
NEWSPAPER

The Town Courier

Editorial: 309 Main St., Gaithersburg, Maryland. **T:** 1 301 330-0132
E: news@towncourier.com
W: http://www.towncourier.com
Freq: Bi-Weekly; **Circ:** 14500
Editorial Profile: The Town Courier is a bi-weekly community newspaper serving Gaithersburg, MD and the surrounding areas, including local news, business, education, sports, opinion and features. The paper publishes a Gaithersburg, MD edition on the 1st and 3rd Fridays of each month, and an Urbana, MD edition on the 4th Friday of each month.; Full Page Mono: 10.28; Full Page Colour: 14.05
Currency: US Dollars
NEWSPAPER

Town Crier

Owner: Flannery Publications
Editorial: 203 NE 1st St, Winlock, Washington 98596. **T:** 1 360 785-3151
E: towncrier@flannerypubs.com
W: http://www.flannerypubs.com
Freq: Wed; **Circ:** 12000 Not Audited
Editor: Kim Collucci; **Publisher:** Patrick Myers

Editorial Profile: The Town Crier is a local weekly newspaper written for the residents of Lewis County, WA. The publication covers local news, sports, and community events. Editorial deadlines are on Fridays at noon PT.; Full Page Mono: 8.90
Currency: US Dollars
NEWSPAPER

Town Crier

Editorial: 218 Genesee St, Geneva, New York 14456-2323. **T:** 1 315 789-5186
E: info@thetowncrier.com
Freq: Daily; **Circ:** 3800 Not Audited
Editorial Profile: Town Crier services the Finger Lakes region of New York with news, events and more.; Full Page Mono: 80.00
Currency: US Dollars
DAILY NEWSPAPER

Town Crier Community Newspapers

Owner: Ogden Newspapers
Editorial: 200 Franklin St Se, Warren, Ohio 44483-5711. **T:** 1 330 629-6200
W: http://www.towncrieronline.com
Freq: Weekly; **Circ:** 20000 Not Audited
Editor: Amy Wilson
Editorial Profile: Town Crier's editorial mission is to provide news and information that affects the community. The publication is written for the residents of Boardman, OH and surrounding areas.
NEWSPAPER

Town Crier Newspapers

Owner: Woburn Daily Times, Inc.
Editorial: 1 Arrow Dr, Woburn, Massachusetts 01801-2039. **T:** 1 978 658-2346 100
E: office@yourtowncrier.com
W: http://www.homenewshere.com
Freq: Thu; **Circ:** 6900 Not Audited
Publisher: Peter Haggerty; **News Editor:** Jayne Miller
NEWSPAPER

The Town Line

Owner: Town Line, Inc. (The)
Editorial: 16 Jones Brook Xing, South China, Maine 4358. **T:** 1 207 445-2234
E: townline@fairpoint.net
W: http://www.townline.org
Freq: Thu; **Circ:** 15000 Not Audited
Editor: Roland Hallee
Editorial Profile: The Town Line is a weekly newspaper serving the towns of Albion, China, Palermo, Vassalboro, Windsor and Winslow, ME. The editorial deadline is Mondays at 4pm ET.; Full Page Mono: 12.50
Currency: US Dollars
NEWSPAPER

Town Reminder

Owner: Turley Publications, Inc.
Editorial: 138 College St, Ste 2, South Hadley, Massachusetts 01075-1576.
T: 1 413 536-5333
E: townreminder@turley.com
W: http://www.townreminderonline.com
Freq: Fri; **Circ:** 11800
Editor: Aimee Henderson; **Publisher:** Patrick Turley
Editorial Profile: Town Reminder is published weekly for the residents of South Hadley, MA. The newspaper covers local news, sports and community events.; Full Page Mono: 11.50; Full Page Colour: 1360.00
Currency: US Dollars
NEWSPAPER

The Town Talk

Owner: Gannett Co., Inc.
Editorial: 1201 3rd St, Alexandria, Louisiana 71301. **T:** 1 318 487-6397
W: http://www.thetowntalk.com
Freq: Daily; **Circ:** 16029 Not Audited
News Editor: Randy Benson
Editorial Profile: The Town Talk is a daily newspaper serving Alexandria, LA and the surrounding area. It covers news, sports, features, business, technology and entertainment.; Full Page Mono: 39.80; Full Page Colour: 210.18
Currency: US Dollars
DAILY NEWSPAPER

Town Talk Newspapers

Owner: Journal Register Company
Editorial: 1914 Parker Ave, Holmes, Pennsylvania 19043-1414. **T:** 1 610 583-4432
W: http://www.delconewsnetwork.com
Circ: 48650 Not Audited
Publisher: Richard Crowe; **Editor:** Christina Parker
NEWSPAPER

Town Times

Owner: Record-Journal Publishing Company

Editorial: 488 Main St, Middlefield, Connecticut 06455-1210. **T:** 1 860 349-8000
E: news@towntimes.com
W: http://www.towntimes.com
Freq: Fri; **Circ:** 10000 Not Audited
Publisher: Eliot White; **Editor:** Stephanie Wilcox
Editorial Profile: Town Times is a weekly newspaper serving Durham, Middlefield and Rockfall, CT.; Full Page Mono: 15.30
Currency: US Dollars
NEWSPAPER

Town Topics

Editorial: 305 Witherspoon St, Princeton, New Jersey 08542-3454. **T:** 1 609 924-2200
E: pressreleases@towntopics.com
W: http://www.towntopics.com
Freq: Wed; **Circ:** 15500 Not Audited
Editorial Profile: Town Topics is a weekly newspaper that concentrates on events and people in Princeton Borough and Township, NJ. Deadlines are on Fridays.; Full Page Mono: 14.95; Full Page Colour: 1173.60
Currency: US Dollars
NEWSPAPER

The Town-Crier Newspaper

Owner: Newspaper Publishers, Inc.
Editorial: 12794 W Forest Hill Blvd Ste 31, Wellington, Florida 33414-4758.
T: 1 561 793-7606 **E:** news@gotowncrier.com
W: http://www.gotowncrier.com **Circ:** 35500 Not Audited
Publisher: Barry Manning
Editorial Profile: Town-Crier Newspaper is a local newspaper for the community of Wellington, FL.
NEWSPAPER

TP Printing Company

Owner: TP Printing Company
Editorial: 103 W Spruce St, Abbotsford, Wisconsin 54405. **T:** 1 715 223-2342
E: tp@tpprinting.com
W: http://www.centralwinews.com **Circ:** 5300 Not Audited
Publisher: Carol O'Leary; **Editor:** Peter Weinschenk
NEWSPAPER

Tracy Press

Owner: Tracy Press
Editorial: 145 W 10th St, Tracy, California 95376-3903. **T:** 1 209 835-3030
E: tpnews@tracypress.com
W: http://www.tracypress.com
Freq: Fri; **Circ:** 19904 Not Audited
Editor: Michael Langley
Editorial Profile: Tracy Press strives to provide its readers with comprehensive coverage of local news and information, while keeping a keen eye toward national events and happenings.; Full Page Mono: 24.20; Full Page Colour: 33.85
Currency: US Dollars
NEWSPAPER

Traverse City Record-Eagle

Owner: Community Newspaper Holdings, Inc.
Editorial: 120 W Front St, Traverse City, Michigan 49684-2280. **T:** 1 231 946-2000
W: http://www.record-eagle.com
Freq: Daily; **Circ:** 17383 Not Audited
News Editor: Glenn Puit; **News Editor:** Mike Tyree
Editorial Profile: Traverse City Record-Eagle is a daily morning newspaper that circulates in 13 counties in lower Northwest Michigan. Newspaper coverage includes local news, sports, weather, lifestyle and business. The intended readership of the newspaper is local community residents.; Full Page Mono: 31.83; Full Page Colour: 37.08
Currency: US Dollars
DAILY NEWSPAPER

The Trentonian

Owner: Journal Register Company
Editorial: 600 Perry St, Trenton, New Jersey 08618-3934. **T:** 1 609 989-7800
E: editor@trentonian.com
W: http://www.trentonian.com
Freq: Daily; **Circ:** 23145 Not Audited
Publisher: Edward Condra
Editorial Profile: The Trentonian is a daily newspaper published for the residents of Trenton, NJ and the Mercer, Burlington and Bucks areas. The newspaper covers local news, business, sports and lifestyle information.; Full Page Mono: 167.43
Currency: US Dollars
DAILY NEWSPAPER

Triad City Beat

Owner: Beat Media, Inc.

Editorial: 1451 S. Elm-Eugene St., Greensboro, North Carolina 27406.
T: 1 336 256-9320
W: http://triad-city-beat.com
Freq: Wed
Publisher: Allen Broach; **Editor in Chief:** Brian Clarey
Editorial Profile: Launched in March 2014, Triad City Beat is a hyperlocal alternative newsweekly, covering community news and culture in Greensboro, High Point and Winston-Salem, NC.; Full Page Mono: 10.26; Full Page Colour: 12.31
Currency: US Dollars
NEWSPAPER

Triad Publications, LLC

Editorial: 51119 Omaha St, Osseo, Wisconsin 54758. **T:** 1 715 597-3313
E: tcnc@triadpubc.biz
W: http://www.triadpubs.biz **Circ:** 2600 Not Audited
Publisher: Chad Nyseth
NEWSPAPER

Triangle News Leader

Owner: Independent Publications Inc.
Editorial: 4645 N Highway 19A, 19A, Mount Dora, Florida 32757-2039. **T:** 1 352 589-8811
W: http://www.trianglenewsleader.com
Freq: Wed; **Circ:** 31100 Not Audited
Editor: Linda Briody; **Publisher:** Donna Covert
Editorial Profile: Triangle News Leader is a community newspaper written for the residents of Mount Dora, FL. It covers local news, health, education, events and entertainment.; Full Page Mono: 75.00; Full Page Colour: 11.33
Currency: US Dollars
NEWSPAPER

The Triangle Tribune

Owner: Charlotte Post Publishing Co.
Editorial: 115 Market St Ste 360H, Durham, North Carolina 27701-3241.
T: 1 919 688-9408 22
E: editor@triangletribune.com
W: http://www.triangletribune.com
Freq: Sun; **Circ:** 10000 Not Audited
Publisher: Gerald Johnson
Editorial Profile: The Triangle Tribune is published for African-American residents of Raleigh and Durham, NC. The newspaper covers local news, weather, sports and community events of interest to members of the African American community in the "Triangle."; Full Page Mono: 24.00
Currency: US Dollars
NEWSPAPER

The Tribeca Trib

Editorial: 401 Broadway, New York, New York 10013-3005. **T:** 1 212 219-9709
W: http://www.tribecatrib.com
Freq: Monthly; **Circ:** 16000
Editorial Profile: The Tribeca Trib is published 11 times a year and is written for residents of New York.; Full Page Mono: 20.19
Currency: US Dollars
NEWSPAPER

TribLocal

Owner: Tribune Company
Editorial: 435 N. Michigan Ave., Chicago, Illinois 60611. **T:** 1 312 527-8138
E: triblocaltips@tribune.com
W: http://www.chicagotribune.com/news/local/suburbs/
Freq: Thu; **Circ:** 220000
Bureau Chief: Patrick Regan
Editorial Profile: TribLocal is a weekly community newspaper that is circulated alongside the Chicago Tribune. Each edition of the paper is hyper-local, focusing on individual neighborhoods or suburbs of Chicago. The weekly publication is comprised of 16 local editions. The online edition provides local news coverage for 80 locations via 42 online outlets. This content is user generated and posted on the Web site. A minority of the content is comprised of relevant local stories written by staff members of the Chicago Tribune. The print editions are as follows: Arlington Heights; Park Ridge/Des Plaines; Northbrook/Glenview; Lake Zurich/Mundelein; Highland Park/Deerfield; Libertyville/Lake Forest; Wilmette/Winnetka; Orland Park/Homer Glen; and Tinley Park/Lincoln-Way.
NEWSPAPER

La Tribuna de New Jersey

Editorial: 300 36th St, Union City, New Jersey 07087-4724. **T:** 1 201 617-1360
Freq: Bi-Weekly; **Circ:** 53000 Not Audited
Editorial Profile: La Tribuna de New Jersey is a bi-monthly newspaper written for Hispanic residents and others interested in the Hispanic

culture in Union City, NJ. The newspaper focuses on general news and Hispanic affairs.; Full Page Mono: 19.80
Currency: US Dollars
NEWSPAPER

La Tribuna Hispana - USA
Editorial: 48 Main St, 2nd Fl, Hempstead, New York 11550. **T:** 1 516 486-6457
E: editorial@latribunahispana.com
W: http://www.latribunahispana.com
Freq: Wed; **Circ:** 49000 Not Audited
Editorial Profile: La Tribuna Hispana - USA is published weekly for New York's Spanish-speaking residents. The newspaper covers news, arts & entertainment, religion, family, politics and community events. Deadlines fall on Tuesdays at noon ET.; Full Page Mono: 25.50
Currency: US Dollars
NEWSPAPER

The Tribune
Owner: McClatchy Newspapers
Editorial: 3825 S Higuera St, San Luis Obispo, California 93401-7438. **T:** 1 805 781-7800
E: newsroom@thetribunenews.com
W: http://www.sanluisobispo.com
Freq: Daily; **Circ:** 29353 Not Audited
Publisher: Bruce Ray
Editorial Profile: The Tribune is a daily newspaper serving the San Luis Obispo, CA area. The publication covers local news, business, events and sports.; Full Page Mono: 32.20; Full Page Colour: 470.00
Currency: US Dollars
DAILY NEWSPAPER

The Tribune
Owner: Swift Newspapers
Editorial: 501 8th Ave, Greeley, Colorado 80631-3913. **T:** 1 970 352-0211
W: http://www.greeleytribune.com
Freq: Daily; **Circ:** 18200 Not Audited
Editor: Randy Bangert; **Publisher:** Bart Smith
Editorial Profile: The Tribune is a daily local newspaper for residents of Greeley and Weld County, CO. Its mission is to provide its readers with community news, events and information.; Full Page Mono: 28.23; Full Page Colour: 30.23
Currency: US Dollars
DAILY NEWSPAPER

The Tribune
Owner: Stephens Media
Editorial: 317 5th St, Ames, Iowa 50010-6101. **T:** 1 515 232-2160
E: news@amestrib.com
W: http://www.amestrib.com
Freq: Daily; **Circ:** 10000 Not Audited
Editor: Michael Crumb; **Editor:** Alexandra Hayne; **Publisher:** Geoff Schumacher
Editorial Profile: The Tribune is published daily for the residents of Ames, IA and surrounding areas. The newspaper covers local and state news, business, sports, lifestyles and entertainment.; Full Page Mono: 17.20; Full Page Colour: 154.80
Currency: US Dollars
DAILY NEWSPAPER

The Tribune
Owner: Home News Enterprises
Editorial: 100 Saint Louis Ave, Seymour, Indiana 47274-2304. **T:** 1 812 522-4871
W: http://www.tribtown.com
Freq: Daily; **Circ:** 8400 Not Audited
Editor: Dan Davis; **Publisher:** Charles Wells
Editorial Profile: The Seymour Daily Tribune is a local newspaper serving the residents of Seymour, IN. It includes information on local news, weather, sports, business, and entertainment.; Full Page Mono: 13.44; Full Page Colour: 250.00
Currency: US Dollars
DAILY NEWSPAPER

Tribune
Owner: Horizon Publications
Editorial: 104 N Main St, Deer Park, Washington 99006. **T:** 1 509 276-5043
W: http://www.dptribune.biz
Freq: Wed; **Circ:** 12447 Not Audited
Editor: Thomas Costigan
Editorial Profile: The Tribune is a weekly newspaper providing Local News coverage for the residents for Deer Park, WA.; Full Page Mono: 8.50
Currency: US Dollars
NEWSPAPER

Tribune
Editorial: 173 Coquina Ave, Ormond Beach, Florida 32174-3303. **T:** 1 434 979-0373
E: tribune54@gmail.com
Freq: Thu; **Circ:** 12000 Not Audited

Editorial Profile: Tribune is published weekly for members of the African American community in Charlottesville, VA. The newspaper covers local news, community events and social issues. Deadlines for the publication are on Tuesdays.; Full Page Mono: 16.94
Currency: US Dollars
NEWSPAPER

Tribune 2000 Newspapers
Owner: Johnson (Lawrence & Cindy)
Editorial: 757 H St, Burwell, Nebraska 68823-4110. **T:** 1 308 346-4504
E: bwtrib@tribune2000.com
W: http://www.tribune2000.com **Circ:** 2661
Editor: Cindy Johnson; **Publisher:** Lawrence Johnson
NEWSPAPER

Tribune and Record
Owner: Forum Communications, Co.
Editorial: 607 Pacific Ave, Morris, Minnesota 56267-1942. **T:** 1 320 589-2525
Publisher: Sue Dieter; **Publisher:** Sue Dieter;
Publisher: Sue Dieter; **Publisher:** Sue Dieter;
Editor: Katie Erdman; **Editor:** Kim Ukura
NEWSPAPER

Tribune Chronicle
Owner: Ogden Newspapers
Editorial: 240 Franklin St Se, Warren, Ohio 44483-5761. **T:** 1 330 841-1600
E: news@tribune-chronicle.com
W: http://www.tribtoday.com
Freq: Mon thru Fri; **Circ:** 21844 Not Audited
Publisher: Charles Jarvis; **Editor:** Frank Robinson
Editorial Profile: Tribune Chronicle strives to give its vast readership comprehensive coverage of all the local area news and information that impacts the lives of those in and around Warren, OH.; Full Page Mono: 65.45; Full Page Colour: 785.00
Currency: US Dollars
DAILY NEWSPAPER

The Tribune Newspapers
Owner: Hartburg Publications
Editorial: 18525 W Lake Houston Pkwy, Ste 102, Humble, Texas 77346. **T:** 1 281 540-8742
W: http://www.ourtribune.com
Freq: Wed; **Circ:** 55000 Not Audited
Editorial Profile: The Tribune Newspapers is a weekly newspaper serving the Humble, TX community. Deadlines are Thursdays at 5pm, CT.; Full Page Mono: 26.50
Currency: US Dollars
NEWSPAPER

Tribune Papers
Owner: Tribune Papers, Inc. (The)
Editorial: 1 Boston Way, Asheville, North Carolina 28803-2653. **T:** 1 828 277-1760
W: http://www.thetribunepapers.com/
Circ: 25000
Publisher: David Morgan; **Editor:** Clint Parker;
Editor: Clint Parker
NEWSPAPER

Tribune Publications
Owner: Horgan (Daniel)
Editorial: 277 Commercial St, Malden, Massachusetts 02148-6708.
T: 1 781 321-8000
E: editor@maldennews.com
Freq: Daily; **Circ:** 15569 Not Audited
Editor: Stephen Freker; **Publisher:** Daniel Horgan
DAILY NEWSPAPER

Tribune Publishing Company
Editorial: 395 W Broadway, Boston, Massachusetts 2127. **T:** 1 617 268-3440
E: editor@southbostonnews.com
W: http://www.southbostoninfo.com
Circ: 30400 Not Audited
Publisher: Daniel Horgan; **Editor:** Alice O'Leary
NEWSPAPER

Tribune Star
Owner: Community Newspaper Holdings, Inc.
Editorial: 222 S 7th St, Terre Haute, Indiana 47807-3601. **T:** 1 812 231-4200
E: community@tribstar.com
W: http://www.tribstar.com
Freq: Daily; **Circ:** 16978 Not Audited
Editor: Max Jones; **Publisher:** William Riley;
News Editor: Zach Taylor
Editorial Profile: Tribune Star is a daily newspaper covering local, regional, and national news, weather, and sports. The newspaper serves Vigo, Clay, Sullivan, Greene, Parke, and Vermillion IN, and Edgar, Clark, and Crawford, IL.; Full Page Mono: 40.27; Full Page Colour: 45.50

Currency: US Dollars
DAILY NEWSPAPER

The Tribune-Democrat
Owner: Community Newspaper Holdings, Inc.
Editorial: 425 Locust St, Johnstown, Pennsylvania 15901-1817. **T:** 1 814 532-5199
E: tribdem@tribdem.com
W: http://www.tribdem.com
Freq: Daily; **Circ:** 27525 Not Audited
Editor: Eric Knopsnyder; **Publisher:** Robin Quillon
Editorial Profile: The Tribune-Democrat is a daily newspaper serving the residents of Johnstown and west central Pennsylvania. It features news, business, sports and editorials.; Full Page Mono: 48.25; Full Page Colour: 655.00
Currency: US Dollars
DAILY NEWSPAPER

Tribune-Herald
Owner: Stephens Media Group
Editorial: 355 Kinoole St, Hilo, Hawaii 96720-2945. **T:** 1 808 935-6621
W: http://www.hawaiitribune-herald.com
Freq: Daily; **Circ:** 16503 Not Audited
Editorial Profile: Tribune-Herald is a daily newspaper that delivers news and events to the Big Island, HI area.; Full Page Mono: 30.50; Full Page Colour: 550.00
Currency: US Dollars
DAILY NEWSPAPER

Tribune-Review
Owner: Tribune-Review Publishing Co.
Editorial: 503 Martindale St, Pittsburgh, Pennsylvania 15212-5746. **T:** 1 724 834-1151
E: release@tribweb.com
W: http://www.pittsburghlive.com
Freq: Daily; **Circ:** 198963 Not Audited
Editor: Susan McFarland; **Publisher:** Richard Scaife
Editorial Profile: Tribune-Review is a daily newspaper that covers news from Greensburg, PA and the counties of Westmoreland, Fayette and Indiana. It contains business, entertainment, style and regional, national and international news. The newspaper has several regional editions, including the Pittsburgh Tribune-Review.; Full Page Mono: 96.37; Full Page Colour: 141.37
Currency: US Dollars
DAILY NEWSPAPER

Tribune-Times
Owner: Greenville News/Gannett
Editorial: 305 S Main St, Greenville, South Carolina 29601. **T:** 1 864 298-4100
E: tletters@tribunetimes.com
W: http://www.tribunetimes.com
Freq: Wed; **Circ:** 43525 Not Audited
Publisher: Steve Brandt
Editorial Profile: Tribune-Times is a weekly publication written for residents of Greenville, SC. It mainly focuses on local news and sports.; Full Page Mono: 19.65
Currency: US Dollars
NEWSPAPER

Tri-City Herald
Owner: McClatchy Newspapers
Editorial: 333 W Canal Dr, Kennewick, Washington 99336. **T:** 1 509 582-1500
E: news@tricityherald.com
W: http://www.tri-cityherald.com
Freq: Daily; **Circ:** 27163 Not Audited
Publisher: Gregg McConnell
Editorial Profile: Tri-City Herald is the local daily newspaper for the residents of Kennewick, WA. Coverage includes local news, sports, arts & entertainment, food, nutrition, lifestyle and weather.; Full Page Mono: 60.64; Full Page Colour: 215.96
Currency: US Dollars
DAILY NEWSPAPER

Tri-City Printers
Editorial: 320 W 8th St, Cozad, Nebraska 69130. **T:** 1 308 784-3644
E: news@tricitytrib.com
W: http://www.tricitytrib.com **Circ:** 3750 Not Audited
NEWSPAPER

Tri-City Voice
Owner: What's Happening Inc.
Editorial: 39737 Paseo Padre Pkwy, Fremont, California 94538-2996. **T:** 1 510 494-1999
E: tricityvoice@aol.com
W: http://www.tricityvoice.com
Freq: Fri; **Circ:** 25500 Not Audited
Editorial Profile: Tri-City Voice in Fremont, CA is a weekly community newspaper covering the cities of Fremont, Newark, Union City, Hayward, Sunol, and Milpitas, CA. Through a blend of local coverage of sports, culture and

art & entertainment, the newspaper has become an essential resource for understanding, exploring, and celebrating the area's heritage. Tri-City Voice speaks with a distinctive voice to a large multicultural audience. It is distributed to over 2,500 locations including community centers, government offices, libraries, all major businesses, high-end apartments, hotels, restaurants, medical centers, recreational facilities, schools, and high traffic retail locations, in addition to our subscribers. Deadlines are on Thursdays at 5 pm PT.; Full Page Mono: 18.82; Full Page Colour: 400.00
Currency: US Dollars
NEWSPAPER

Tri-County Herald
Owner: News Leader Co. Inc.
Editorial: 620 W Carl Hubbell Blvd, Meeker, Oklahoma 74855. **T:** 1 405 279-2363
E: news@tricountyherald.com
W: http://www.okemahnewsleader.com/77278/1578/online-editiontricounty-herald
Freq: Fri
Editorial Profile: Tri-County Herald is a weekly community newspaper serving Meeker, Harrah, McLoud and Newalla, OK with community news, events and sports coverage.
NEWSPAPER

Tri-County Newspapers
Editorial: 217 S Alvaredo Ave, Belle, Missouri 65013. **T:** 1 573 859-3328 **E:** kjl@socket.net
Circ: 5300 Not Audited
Publisher: Kurt Lewis; **Editor:** Ron Lewis
NEWSPAPER

Tri-County Publications
Owner: Mullin (Mitch)
Editorial: 111 W Ada Ave, Wilburton, Oklahoma 74578-2416. **T:** 1 918 465-3851
E: tricountypubinc@sbcglobal.net
Freq: Thu; **Circ:** 4400 Not Audited
Publisher: Mitch Mullin; Full Page Mono: 6.00
Currency: US Dollars
NEWSPAPER

Tri-County Publishing, Inc.
Owner: Tri County Publishing, Inc.
Editorial: 3 Banner Row, Mc Kenzie, Tennessee 38201. **T:** 1 731 352-3323
E: banner@mckenziebanner.com
W: http://mckenziebanner.com **Circ:** 10000 Not Audited
Editor: Joel Washburn; **Editor:** Joel Washburn;
Publisher: Ramona Washburn
Editorial Profile: Tri-County Publishing, Inc. is a community newspaper publisher that services the residents of Jackson, TN.
NEWSPAPER

Tri-County Sentry
Owner: Hunt Communications, LLC
Editorial: 1200 N Ventura Rd, Ste G, Oxnard, California 93030-3804. **T:** 1 805 983-0015
E: sentry1234@aol.com
W: http://www.tricountysentry.com
Freq: Fri; **Circ:** 10000 Not Audited
Editorial Profile: Tri-County Sentry is a local newspaper written for the African Amercian community of Oxnard, CA.; Full Page Mono: 21.50
Currency: US Dollars
NEWSPAPER

Tri-County Sunday
Owner: McLean Publishing Co.
Editorial: 500 Jeffers St, Du Bois, Pennsylvania 15801. **T:** 1 814 371-4200
W: http://www.thecourierexpress.com
Freq: Sun; **Circ:** 16500
Editor: Joy Norwood
Editorial Profile: The Tri-County Sunday is the Sunday delivered version of the Courier-Express. The Tri-County Sunday covers the topics and areas as the Courier-Express, and is published at the same offices.
NEWSPAPER

Tri-County Times
Owner: Rockman Communications
Editorial: 256 N Fenway Dr, Fenton, Michigan 48430-2699. **T:** 1 810 629-8282
E: news@tctimes.com
W: http://www.tctimes.com
Freq: 2 Times/Week; **Circ:** 22898 Not Audited
Publisher: Craig Rockman; **Editor:** Sharon Stone; **Editor:** Dave Troppens
Editorial Profile: Tri-County Times is a community-based publication that looks to give its followers comprehensive coverage of local area news and events. The lead time is two days. Deadline is two days before the publication date.; Full Page Mono: 28.56
Currency: US Dollars
NEWSPAPER

Tri-State Defender
Owner: Real Times Media, Inc.
Editorial: 203 Beale St, Ste 200, Memphis, Tennessee 38103. **T:** 1 901 523-1818
E: editorial@tri-statedefender.com
W: http://www.tri-statedefender.com
Freq: Thu; **Circ:** 36000 Not Audited
Editorial Profile: Tri-State Defender is a local weekly newspaper written for residents in and around Memphis, TN. The publication strives to provide its readership with comprehensive coverage of local area news and information. Deadlines are Mondays at 5pm ET.; Full Page Mono: 32.07
Currency: US Dollars
NEWSPAPER

Troy Daily News
Owner: Ohio Community Media LLC.
Editorial: 224 S Market St, Troy, Ohio 45373-3300. **T:** 1 937 335-5634
E: editorial@tdnpublishing.com
W: http://www.tdn-net.com
Freq: Daily; **Circ:** 10568 Not Audited
Publisher: Frank Beeson
Editorial Profile: Troy Daily News (TDN) is a daily newspaper serving residents of Troy, OH and surrounding communities. It covers local, national and international news, weather, and sports. Feature articles cover business, politics, health, education, arts & entertainment, lifestyle, and other topics of interest to members of the local community.; Full Page Mono: 18.85; Full Page Colour: 27.85
Currency: US Dollars
DAILY NEWSPAPER

Troy Messenger
Owner: Boone Newspapers Inc.
Editorial: 918 S Brundidge St, Troy, Alabama 36081-3213. **T:** 1 334 566-4270
W: http://www.troymessenger.com
Freq: Daily; **Circ:** 2814 Not Audited
Editorial Profile: Troy Messenger is a daily newspaper written for residents of Troy and Pike County, AL.; Full Page Mono: 12.50; Full Page Colour: 200.00
Currency: US Dollars
DAILY NEWSPAPER

Troy-Somerset Gazette
Owner: Gazette Newspapers, Inc.
Editorial: 1903 E Wattles Rd, Troy, Michigan 48085-5083. **T:** 1 248 524-4868
W: http://www.troy-somersetgazette.com
Freq: Mon; **Circ:** 25000 Not Audited
Publisher: Claire Weber
Editorial Profile: Troy-Somerset Gazette in Troy, MI is a community newspaper that covers local news and events. Deadlines for the publication are Mondays at 5pm ET.; Full Page Mono: 15.60
Currency: US Dollars
NEWSPAPER

The Trussville Tribune
Owner: ADLAB Communications
Editorial: 5850 Valley Rd Ste 90, Trussville, Alabama 35235-8683. **T:** 1 205 533-8664
E: news@trussvilletribune.com
W: http://www.trussvilletribune.com
Freq: Wed
Publisher: Scott Buttram
Editorial Profile: The Trussville Tribune is a weekly newspaper providing Local and Community News coverage to the residents of Trussville, AL.
NEWSPAPER

Tryon Daily Bulletin
Editorial: 16 N Trade St, Tryon, North Carolina 28782. **T:** 1 828 859-9151
E: news@tryondailybulletin.com
W: http://www.tryondailybulletin.com
Freq: Daily; **Circ:** 4993 Not Audited
Editor: Samantha Hurst; **Publisher:** Betty Ramsey
Editorial Profile: Tryon Daily Bulletin is a daily newspaper serving residents of Tryon, NC and surrounding communities. The newspaper covers local, national and international news, weather, sports, business, education, health, politics and arts & entertainment.; Full Page Mono: 7.60
Currency: US Dollars
DAILY NEWSPAPER

Tu Decides/You Decide
Owner: Tu Decides Media
Editorial: 7601 W Clearwater Ave Ste 407, Kennewick, Washington 99336-1677.
T: 1 509 591-0495
E: info@tudecidesmedia.com
W: http://www.tudecidesmedia.com
Freq: Fri; **Circ:** 20000 Not Audited
Editorial Profile: Tu Decides/You Decide is a weekly bilingual newspaper for the residents of Kennewick, WA and the surrounding areas. It covers local news, events, arts & entertainment and religion.; Full Page Mono: 17.68
Currency: US Dollars
NEWSPAPER

Tucson Weekly
Owner: 10/13 Communications
Editorial: 3280 E Hemisphere Loop Ste 180, Tucson, Arizona 85706-5027.
T: 1 520 294-1200
E: mailbag@tucsonweekly.com
W: http://www.tucsonweekly.com
Freq: Thu; **Circ:** 46300 Not Audited
Editor: Dan Gibson; **Publisher:** Tom Lee
Editorial Profile: Tucson Weekly is a weekly newspaper serving residents of Tucson, AZ and surrounding communities. The newspaper covers local, national, and international news, weather, sports, and events. Feature articles cover business, politics, health, education, arts and entertainment, lifestyle, and other topics of interest to the local community. Deadlines for the publication are one week prior to the issue date. The outlet offers RSS (Real Simple Syndication).; Full Page Mono: 90.90
Currency: US Dollars
NEWSPAPER

Tulare Advance-Register
Owner: Gannett Co., Inc.
Editorial: 330 N West St, Tulare, California 93274. **T:** 1 559 735-3200
E: tularenews@visaliatimesdelta.com
W: http://www.tulareadvanceregister.com
Freq: Mon thru Fri; **Circ:** 5874
Publisher: Amy Pack
Editorial Profile: Tulare Advance-Register is written for residents in Tulare and the surrounding Tulare County, CA. It covers local news and events only, and takes regional and national coverage entirely from wire services. Tulare Advance-Register shares much of its content and staff with sister publication Visalia Times-Delta in neighboring Visalia, CA.; Full Page Mono: 54.09
Currency: US Dollars
DAILY NEWSPAPER

Tullahoma Newspapers
Owner: Lakeway Publishers, Inc.
Editorial: 505 Lake Way Pl, Tullahoma, Tennessee 37388. **T:** 1 931 455-4545
E: tnased@lcs.net
W: http://www.tullahomanews.com
Circ: 17900 Not Audited
NEWSPAPER

Tulsa World
Owner: BH Media Group
Editorial: 315 S Boulder Ave, Tulsa, Oklahoma 74103-3401. **T:** 1 918 581-8300
E: news@tulsaworld.com
W: http://www.tulsaworld.com
Freq: Daily; **Circ:** 73924 Not Audited
Publisher: Bill Masterson; **News Editor:** Mike Strain
Editorial Profile: Tulsa World is written for the greater metropolitan Tulsa, OK, region. Coverage includes local, regional and national news, business, entertainment, sports and features. The paper does not publish an editorial calendar.; Full Page Mono: 115.00; Full Page Colour: 122.94
Currency: US Dollars
DAILY NEWSPAPER

Tulsa World
Editorial: State Capitol Bldg, Rm 430, Oklahoma City, Oklahoma 73105.
T: 1 405 528-2465
Bureau Chief: Barbara Hoberock
DAILY NEWSPAPER

Turkish Journal - New York Bureau
Editorial: United Nations, Room S-362, New York, New York 10017. **T:** 1 212 963-0935
W: http://ww.turkishjournal.com
Editorial Profile: This is the New York Bureau for Turkish Journal which is based in Istanbul, Turkey.
DAILY NEWSPAPER

Turley Publications, Inc.
Owner: Turley Publications, Inc.
Editorial: 24 Water St, Palmer, Massachusetts 01069-1885. **T:** 1 413 283-8393
W: http://www.turley.com **Circ:** 38404 Not Audited
Editor: Charles Bennett; **Editor:** Paula Killough; **Publisher:** Patrick Turley
NEWSPAPER

TurleyCT Community Publications
Owner: TurleyCT Community Publications
Editorial: 540 Hopmeadow St, Simsbury, Connecticut 06070-2496. **T:** 1 860 651-4700
W: http://www.turleyct.com **Circ:** 142700 Not Audited
Editor: Mark Jahne; **Editor:** Nancy Thompson; **Publisher:** Keith Turley; **Editor:** Lynn Woike
Editorial Profile: TurleyCT Community Publications features community newspaper mailed to households in West Hartford, Avon, Burlington, Canton, Farmington, Rocky Hill, Newington, Wethersfield, and Glastonury, and Simsbury, CT. The publications cover local news with a focus on events, town meetings, schools, sports and business.
NEWSPAPER

Turner Publishing
Owner: Turner Publishing Inc.
Editorial: 5 Fern St, Turner, Maine 4282.
T: 1 207 225-2076
E: articles@turnerpublishing.net
W: http://www.turnerpublishing.net
Circ: 161406 Not Audited
NEWSPAPER

Turnstile Media Group
Owner: Turnstile Media Group
Editorial: 1500 Park Center Dr, Orlando, Florida 32835-5705. **T:** 1 407 515-2605
W: http://www.wpmobserver.com
Freq: Thu; **Circ:** 5000 Not Audited
Publisher: Tracy Craft
Editorial Profile: Turnstile Media Group newspapers are published for the residents of Winter Park and Maitland, FL.; Full Page Mono: 14.00
Currency: US Dollars
NEWSPAPER

Turtle Creek News
Editorial: 1812 N Haskell Ave, Ste 200, Dallas, Texas 75204. **T:** 1 214 887-0737
Freq: Fri; **Circ:** 25000 Not Audited
Publisher: Lance Brennan; **Editor:** Chris Libby
Editorial Profile: Turtle Creek News is a local newspaper written for the residents of Dallas. Do not send press releases to the paper by fax.; Full Page Mono: 30.00
Currency: US Dollars
NEWSPAPER

The Tuscaloosa News
Owner: Halifax Media Holdings LLC
Editorial: 315 28th Ave, Tuscaloosa, Alabama 35401-1022. **T:** 1 205 345-0505
E: news@tuscaloosanews.com
W: http://www.tuscaloosanews.com
Freq: Daily; **Circ:** 25678 Not Audited
Publisher: Timothy Thompson
Editorial Profile: The Tuscaloosa News's editorial mission is to provide local and national news for the residents of the Tuscaloosa, AL area.; Full Page Mono: 49.25
Currency: US Dollars
DAILY NEWSPAPER

Tuscumbia Newspapers
Editorial: 106 W 5th St, Tuscumbia, Alabama 35674-2412. **T:** 1 256 383-8471
E: colbertcountyreporter@earthlink.net
Circ: 5700 Not Audited
NEWSPAPER

Twin City Times
Owner: Steele (Laurie)
Editorial: 33 Dunn St, Auburn, Maine 04210-6822. **T:** 1 207 795-5017
E: editor@twincitytimes.com
W: http://www.twincitytimes.com
Freq: Thu; **Circ:** 34697 Not Audited
Publisher: Laurie Steele; **Editor-in-Chief:** Peter Steele
Editorial Profile: The Twin City Times is a community newspaper written for the residents of Auburn, ME and the surrounding areas.; Full Page Mono: 19.00
Currency: US Dollars
NEWSPAPER

Twin Valley Publications
Editorial: 10 S Main St, West Alexandria, Ohio 45381. **T:** 1 937 839-4733
E: twinvpub@infinet.com
W: http://twinvalleypublications.com
Circ: 8000 Not Audited
NEWSPAPER

The Two River Times
Editorial: 75 W. Front Street, Red Bank, New Jersey 07701-1531. **T:** 1 732 219-5788
E: editor@tworivertimes.com
W: http://trtnj.com
Freq: Thu; **Circ:** 10000 Not Audited
Editor: Michelle Kuhn; **Publisher:** Ellen McCarthy
Editorial Profile: Two River Times provides local residents of Red Bank, NJ with local news and information.; Full Page Mono: 11.90
Currency: US Dollars
NEWSPAPER

Tyler Morning Telegraph
Owner: T.B. Butler Publishing Co., Inc.
Editorial: 410 W Erwin St, Tyler, Texas 75702.
T: 1 903 597-8111 **E:** opinion@tylerpaper.com
W: http://www.tylerpaper.com
Freq: Daily; **Circ:** 22556 Not Audited
Publisher: C. Nelson Clyde; **News Editor:** Jeremy Scott
Editorial Profile: Tyler Morning Telegraph is published daily for the residents of Tyler, TX and surrounding areas. The newspaper covers local and state news, business, sports, lifestyles and entertainment.; Full Page Mono: 28.33; Full Page Colour: 400.00
Currency: US Dollars
DAILY NEWSPAPER

The U.P. Catholic
Owner: Catholic Diocese of Marquette
Editorial: 1004 Harbor Hills Dr, Marquette, Michigan 49855-8851. **T:** 1 906 227-9131
E: jfee@dioceseofmarquette.org
W: http://www.dioceseofmarquette.org
Freq: Bi-Weekly; **Circ:** 20662 Not Audited
Editor: John Fee
Editorial Profile: The U.P. Catholic is a bi-weekly newspaper published on the first and third Fridays of each month by the Catholic Diocese of Marquette, MI. Its mission is to unite all Catholic households in the Upper Peninsula with the Diocesan Church through a newspaper that brings residents news and information that broaden their perspectives, leading to greater closeness to Christ as they live with faith in their daily lives.; Full Page Mono: 13.98
Currency: US Dollars
NEWSPAPER

U.S. 1 Newspaper
Editorial: 12 Roszel Rd, Princeton, New Jersey 08540-6234. **T:** 1 609 452-7000
E: info@princetoninfo.com
W: http://www.princetoninfo.com
Freq: Wed; **Circ:** 19000 Not Audited
Editorial Profile: U.S. 1 Newspaper is a business focused publication written for professionals in the greater Princeton, NJ area.; Full Page Mono: 14.10
Currency: US Dollars
NEWSPAPER

UJP News
Owner: U.S. Japan Publications NY Inc.
Editorial: 147 W 35th Street Ste 1705, Rm 1101, New York, New York 10001.
T: 1 212 252-8833 **E:** mail@ujp.com
W: http://www.ujp.com
Freq: Monthly; **Circ:** 40000 Not Audited
Editorial Profile: UJP News is a Japanese economic newspaper.; Full Page Mono: 100.00
Currency: US Dollars
NEWSPAPER

Ukiah Daily Journal
Owner: MediaNews Group
Editorial: 590 S School St, Ukiah, California 95482-5438. **T:** 1 707 468-3500
E: udj@pacific.net
W: http://www.ukiahdailyjournal.com
Freq: Daily; **Circ:** 5006 Not Audited
Publisher: Kevin McConnell; **Editor:** K.C. Meadows
Editorial Profile: The Ukiah Daily Journal's mission is to provide its readers with the latest in local news and information. The publication is written for the residents of Ukiah, CA and its surrounding area.; Full Page Mono: 16.00; Full Page Colour: 2323.43
Currency: US Dollars
DAILY NEWSPAPER

The Ukrainian Weekly & Svoboda
Owner: Ukrainian National Association, Inc.
Editorial: 2200 State Rt 10, Parsippany, New Jersey 07054-5304. **T:** 1 973 292-9800
Circ: 16000
Editor in Chief: Roma Hadzewycz
Editorial Profile: The Ukrainian Weekly is community newspaper published every Fridays covering Ukrainian news, culture, and events.
NEWSPAPER

Ulster Publishing Co. - Kingston
Owner: Ulster Publishing
Editorial: 322 Wall St, Kingston, New York 12401-3820. **T:** 1 845 334-8200
W: http://www.ulsterpublishing.com
Circ: 17400 Not Audited
Editor: Dan Barton; **Editor:** Will Dendis; **Editor:** Brian Hollander; **Publisher:** Geddy

Sveikauskas
NEWSPAPER

Ultima Nota
Editorial: 4768 Broadway, New York, New York 10034-4916. **T:** 1 917 567-8565
W: http://www.ultimanota.com
Freq: Weekly
Editorial Profile: Ultima Nota is a weekly newspaper providing Local and Community News coverage to the Hispanic community in New Jersey, New York and Connecticut.
NEWSPAPER

Unidos en el Sur de California
Owner: 2100 Trust LLC
Editorial: 523 N Grand Ave, Santa Ana, California 92701-4345. **T:** 1 951 368-9330
E: laprensaeditors@pe.com
W: http://www.unidossc.com
Freq: Fri; **Circ:** 323476
Editorial Profile: Unidos en el Sur de California is a weekly Spanish language community newspaper serving the Latino population in Southern California with news (Noticias), sports (Deportes) and NEXT, a bilingual entertainment guide. Four zoned editions are offered, serving Orange County, Inland Southern California, Coachella Valley and Los Angeles.
NEWSPAPER

The Union
Owner: Swift Newspapers
Editorial: 464 Sutton Way, Grass Valley, California 95945-4102. **T:** 1 530 273-9561
E: letters@theunion.com
W: http://www.theunion.com
Freq: Mon thru Fri; **Circ:** 16571 Not Audited
Publisher: Dave Schmall
Editorial Profile: The Union is a daily newspaper covering western Nevada County, CA, including Nevada City and Grass Valley. The publication covers local news, sports, community news, local events and entertainment.; Full Page Mono: 26.46; Full Page Colour: 295.00
Currency: US Dollars
DAILY NEWSPAPER

Union City Daily Messenger
Editorial: 613 E Jackson St, Union City, Tennessee 38261-5239. **T:** 1 731 885-0744
E: ucdm@ucmessenger.com
W: http://www.ucmessenger.com
Freq: Daily; **Circ:** 8000 Not Audited
Editor: David Critchlow; **Publisher:** David Critchlow
Editorial Profile: Union City Daily Messenger is a local newspaper written for the residents of Union City, TN. It covers local news and events.; Full Page Mono: 8.50; Full Page Colour: 55.38
Currency: US Dollars
DAILY NEWSPAPER

Union Daily Times
Owner: Heartland Publications
Editorial: 100 Times Blvd, Union, South Carolina 29379. **T:** 1 864 427-1234
W: http://www.uniondailytimes.com
Freq: Daily; **Circ:** 6409 Not Audited
Editor: Charles Warner
Editorial Profile: Union Daily Times is written for the residents of Union, SC and surrounding areas. The newspaper covers lcoal and state news, business, sports, education, lifestyles and entertainment.; Full Page Mono: 11.95; Full Page Colour: 80.00
Currency: US Dollars
DAILY NEWSPAPER

The Union Democrat
Owner: Western Communications Inc.
Editorial: 84 S Washington St, Sonora, California 95370. **T:** 1 209 532-7151
W: http://www.uniondemocrat.com
Freq: Mon thru Fri; **Circ:** 8753 Not Audited
Editor: Craig Cassidy; **Publisher:** Gary Piech
Editorial Profile: The Union Democrat's editorial mission is to serve the community by providing the latest in local news and information. The publication is written for residents of Mother Lode, Yosemite, and the Sierra Nevada.; Full Page Mono: 21.00; Full Page Colour: 455.00
Currency: US Dollars
DAILY NEWSPAPER

Union Star and Reporter Newspapers
Owner: Womack Publishing Company Inc.
Editorial: 241 Main St, Brookneal, Virginia 24528. **T:** 1 434 376-2795
E: news@theunionstar.com
W: http://www.wpcva.com/brookneal
Freq: Weekly; **Circ:** 5600 Not Audited
Publisher: Chad Harrison; **Editor:** James Meadows
Editorial Profile: Union Star and Reporter Newspapers is written for residents of Charlotte, Campbell and Halifax Counties, VA. The deadlines for advertising are on Mondays at noon ET. The editorial deadlines are on Fridays at 5pm ET.
NEWSPAPER

Union-Finley Messenger
Owner: Haniford Enterprises LLC
Editorial: 1373 Meadowlark Dr, Pittsburgh, Pennsylvania 15243. **T:** 1 412 249-8177
E: news@unionfinley.com
W: http://www.unionfinley.com
Freq: Monthly; **Circ:** 17000 Not Audited
Publisher: Douglas Haniford
Editorial Profile: Union-Finley Messenger is a monthly newspaper written for the residents of Finleyville, PA and the surrounding area. It covers local news and events. It was launched in June 2004.; Full Page Mono: 8.00
Currency: US Dollars
NEWSPAPER

Union-Recorder
Owner: Community Newspaper Holdings, Inc.
Editorial: 165 Garrett Way NW, Milledgeville, Georgia 31061-2371. **T:** 1 478 452-0567
E: newsroom@unionrecorder.com
W: http://www.unionrecorder.com
Freq: Daily; **Circ:** 7500 Not Audited
Publisher: Keith Barlow
Editorial Profile: Union-Recorder provides its readers with the latest in local news and information in the Milledgeville, GA area. Please contact them only with information of local interest.; Full Page Mono: 14.40; Full Page Colour: 270.00
Currency: US Dollars
DAILY NEWSPAPER

Upstate Newspapers, Inc.
Owner: Keowee Publications, Inc.
Editorial: 100 E Main St, Westminster, South Carolina 29693-1715. **T:** 1 864 647-5404
E: westnews@bellsouth.net **Circ:** 6300 Not Audited
Editor: Ashton Hester; **Editor:** Ashton Hester; **Editor:** Ashton Hester; **Editor:** Rolann Lee; **Publisher:** Robert Tribble
NEWSPAPER

Urban Spectrum
Editorial: 2727 Welton St, Denver, Colorado 80205-2913. **T:** 1 303 292-6446
E: DenverUrbanSpectrum@urbanspectrum.net
W: http://www.denverurbanspectrum.com
Freq: Monthly; **Circ:** 25000 Not Audited
Publisher: Rosalind Harris
Editorial Profile: Urban Spectrum is a free, monthy newspaper published since 1987 for the multi-cultural residents of Denver. The paper is written primarily for African American and Latino American communities. It covers movie and play critiques, top-selling music artists, community notes and features local and national columnists.; Full Page Mono: 48.00; Full Page Colour: 1880.00
Currency: US Dollars
NEWSPAPER

Urbana Daily Citizen
Owner: Ohio Community Media LLC.
Editorial: 220 E Court St, Urbana, Ohio 43078-1805. **T:** 1 937 652-1331
E: editor@urbanacitizen.com
W: http://www.urbanacitizen.com
Freq: Mon thru Fri; **Circ:** 5616 Not Audited
Publisher: Lane Moon
Editorial Profile: Urbana Daily Citizen is a local newspaper written for residents of Champaign County, OH. The newspaper covers local news, sports and events.; Full Page Mono: 12.15; Full Page Colour: 300.00
Currency: US Dollars
DAILY NEWSPAPER

Urdu Times USA
Owner: Urdu Media Network, Inc.
Editorial: 16920 Hillside Ave, Jamaica, New York 11432-4435. **T:** 1 718 297-8700
E: urdutimesny@aol.com
W: http://www.urdutimesusa.com
Freq: Thu; **Circ:** 17000
Editorial Profile: The Urdu Times USA is a weekly newspaper providing Community News coverage for the Indian, Pakastani and Urdu-speaking community in the United States.; Full Page Mono: 20.00
Currency: US Dollars
NEWSPAPER

Urdu Times USA - Chicago
Owner: Urdu Media Network, Inc.
Editorial: 7450 Skokie Blvd, Skokie, Illinois 60077-3374. **T:** 1 773 274-3100
E: urdutimes@hotmail.com
W: http://www.urdutimesusa.com/chicago
Freq: Thu; **Circ:** 10000
Bureau Chief: Tariq Khawaja
Editorial Profile: The Urdu Times USA is a weekly newspaper providing Community News coverage for the Indian, Pakastani and Urdu-speaking community in the Chicago, IL area.; Full Page Mono: 20.00
Currency: US Dollars
NEWSPAPER

Urdu Times USA - Texas
Owner: Urdu Media Network, Inc.
Editorial: 2326 Robinsons Fry, Sugar Land, Texas 77479-1321. **T:** 1 832 755-7200
W: http://www.urdutimesusa.com
Freq: Thu
Bureau Chief: Waqar Hussain
Editorial Profile: The Urdu Times USA is a weekly newspaper providing Community News coverage for the Indian, Pakastani and Urdu-speaking community in the Houston, TX area.; Full Page Mono: 20.00
Currency: US Dollars
NEWSPAPER

USA Today
Owner: Gannett Co., Inc.
Editorial: 7950 Jones Branch Dr, Mc Lean, Virginia 22107-0002. **T:** 1 703 854-3400
E: newstips@usatoday.com
W: http://www.usatoday.com
Freq: Mon thru Fri; **Circ:** 3255157 Not Audited
Editor in Chief: David Callaway
Editorial Profile: USA Today is a national, general interest newspaper covering consumer-driven and general interest topics. There are many trend stories and profiles, as well as news from around the world. Coverage also includes business, technology, entertainment, travel, movie and book reviews, television, food, fashion, health and sports. The paper is broken down into the sections News, Money, Sports, Life, Travel, Tech and Weather. It also makes heavy use of color and graphics. Lead times vary for departments and reporters. The ad rates in their media kit are based on modular sizes. Editors and reporters honor non-disclosure agreements on a case-by-case basis. They also publish an e-Edition copy of the print publication and a Saturday-Sunday e-edition called USA Today EXTRA. It was founded in 1982.; Full Page Mono: 1006.89; Full Page Colour: 1595.32
Currency: US Dollars
DAILY NEWSPAPER

USA Today
Editorial: 6060 Center Dr Ste 900, Los Angeles, California 90045-8854.
T: 1 310 444-2100
DAILY NEWSPAPER

USA Today
Editorial: 535 Madison Ave Fl 20, New York, New York 10022-4214
DAILY NEWSPAPER

USA Today
Editorial: 100 Pine St Ste 250, San Francisco, California 94111-5104. **T:** 1 415 901-5380
DAILY NEWSPAPER

USA Today
Editorial: 1575 Eye St NW Ste 350, Washington, District Of Columbia 20005-1114.
T: 1 202 906-8150
DAILY NEWSPAPER

USAfrica The Newspaper
Owner: USAfrica Communications
Editorial: 8303 Southwest Fwy, Ste 100, Houston, Texas 77074. **T:** 1 713 270-5500
E: usafrica247@gmail.com
W: http://www.usafricaonline.com
Freq: Monthly; **Circ:** 75000 Not Audited
Editorial Profile: USAfrica The Newspaper serves the growing community of immigrant Africans, African Americans and residents of Houston.; Full Page Mono: 113.64
Currency: US Dollars
NEWSPAPER

U-T San Diego
Owner: The San Diego Union-Tribune, LLC
Editorial: 350 Camino De La Reina, San Diego, California 92108-3003.
T: 1 619 299-3131
W: http://www.utsandiego.com
Freq: Daily; **Circ:** 222541 Not Audited
Editor: Jeff Light; **Publisher:** Douglas Manchester
Editorial Profile: U-T San Diego is published daily for the residents of San Diego County, CA and surrounding areas. The newspaper offers comprehensive news and features of local happenings and the regional business economy. The outlet offers RSS (Really Simple Syndication). When sending mail, please note: 5260 Anna Ave, San Diego, CA 92110 is a corrected address UPS puts on packages. This address is only used for UPS packages, and is not the main or mailing address for the paper. The paper was previously titled The San Diego Union-Tribune.; Full Page Mono: 473.00; Full Page Colour: 3975.00
Currency: US Dollars
DAILY NEWSPAPER

U-T San Diego
Editorial: 925 L St Ste 1190, Sacramento, California 95814-3704. **T:** 1 916 445-2934
DAILY NEWSPAPER

U-T San Diego
Editorial: 3156 Vista Way Ste 301, Oceanside, California 92056-3622. **T:** 1 760 752-6750
DAILY NEWSPAPER

UWeekly
Owner: 614 Media Group
Editorial: 458 E Main St, Columbus, Ohio 43215-5344. **T:** 1 614 488-4400 17
E: editor@uweekly.com
W: http://www.uweekly.com
Freq: Wed; **Circ:** 16000 Not Audited
Editor: Chelsea Castle; **Publisher:** Wayne Lewis
Editorial Profile: UWeekly is a weekly newspaper serving the areas in and around Ohio State University's campus in Columbus, OH. The paper is independently-owned and not affiliated with the university. It covers campus news, events, sports music, movies, television shows, technology and gadgets and features relevant to the student population. The production schedule usually halts for portions of December and June. Send pitches by e-mail.; Full Page Mono: 10.00
Currency: US Dollars
NEWSPAPER

V Novom Svete
Editorial: 55 Broad St, 20th Fl, New York, New York 10004-2501. **T:** 1 212 482-0303
E: editor@vnsnews.com
W: http://www.vnsnews.com
Freq: Thu; **Circ:** 47500 Not Audited
Editor: Davit Guy
Editorial Profile: V Novom Svete in New York is a weekly newspaper serving the Russian and Russian American Community.; Full Page Mono: 100.00
Currency: US Dollars
NEWSPAPER

Vacation News
Editorial: 3797 Highway 54, Osage Beach, Missouri 65065-2138. **T:** 1 573 348-4577
Freq: Bi-Weekly; **Circ:** 11500 Not Audited
Editor: Charis Patris; **Publisher:** John Tucker
Editorial Profile: Vacations News is a bi-weekly community newspaper written for residents of Osage Beach, MO.; Full Page Mono: 6.52
Currency: US Dollars
NEWSPAPER

Vail Daily
Owner: Swift Newspapers
Editorial: 40780 US Hwy 6 & 24, Avon, Colorado 81620. **T:** 1 970 949-0555
E: newsroom@vaildaily.com
W: http://www.vaildaily.com
Freq: Daily; **Circ:** 13000 Not Audited
Editor: Caramie Schnell
Editorial Profile: Vail Daily is a local daily newspaper written for the local residents and tourists of Vail, CO. The publication covers local news, community events, sports, arts & entertainment, editorials and advertisements. Use the street address when mailing items through UPS and Fedex, and use the PO box when mailing items through USPS.; Full Page Mono: 97.59
Currency: US Dollars
DAILY NEWSPAPER

The Valdosta Daily Times
Owner: Community Newspaper Holdings, Inc.
Editorial: 201 N Troupe St, Valdosta, Georgia 31601-5774. **T:** 1 229 244-1880
W: http://www.valdostadailytimes.com
Freq: Daily; **Circ:** 13595 Not Audited
Publisher: Sandy Sanders
Editorial Profile: The Valdosta Daily Times's editorial mission is to provide news about Valdosta, GA and its surrounding counties in

South Florida and North Georgia.; Full Page Mono: 27.30; Full Page Colour: 500.00
Currency: US Dollars
DAILY NEWSPAPER

Valley Advocate
Owner: Newspapers of New England
Editorial: 115 Conz St, Northampton, Massachusetts 1060. **T:** 1 413 529-2840
E: editor@valleyadvocate.com
W: http://www.valleyadvocate.com
Freq: Thu; **Circ:** 40000 Not Audited
Editor In Chief: Tom Vannah
Editorial Profile: Valley Advocate is written for residents of Hampden, Hampshire, Franklin and Berkshire counties in Massachusetts. It covers news, lifestyle, arts & entertainment and community events. Its editorial mission is to provide an alternative to the mainstream press with articles written for an audience of primarily young, educated college graduates.; Full Page Mono: 40.74
Currency: US Dollars
NEWSPAPER

Valley Breeze Newspapers
Owner: Breeze Publications
Editorial: 6 Blackstone Valley Pl Ste 204, Lincoln, Rhode Island 02865-1112.
T: 1 401 334-9555 **E:** news@valleybreeze.com
W: http://www.valleybreeze.com **Circ:** 35500
Editor in Chief: Marcia Green; **News Editor:** Nancy O'Halloran; **Publisher:** Tom Ward
NEWSPAPER

Valley Bugler
Owner: Valley Bugler Newspaper, Inc
Editorial: 705 Vandercook Way, Longview, Washington 98632-4016. **T:** 1 360 414-1246
E: editor@valleybugler.com
W: http://www.valleybugler.com
Freq: Monthly
Editorial Profile: Valley Bugler is a monthly newspaper providing Local and Community News coverage to the residents of Longview, WA.; Full Page Mono: 15.00; Full Page Colour: 26.40
Currency: US Dollars
NEWSPAPER

The Valley Catholic
Owner: Diocese of San Jose
Editorial: 1150 N 1st St, Ste 100, San Jose, California 95112-4966. **T:** 1 408 983-0260
E: valleycatholic@dsj.org
W: http://www.valleycatholiconline.com
Freq: Monthly; **Circ:** 65000
Editor: Roberta Ward
Editorial Profile: The Valley Catholic is a monthly newspaper for the Diocese of San Jose, CA.; Full Page Mono: 26.50
Currency: US Dollars
NEWSPAPER

The Valley Chronicle
Owner: Century Group (The)
Editorial: 2091 W Florida Ave, Ste 140, Hemet, California 92545. **T:** 1 951 652-6529
E: info@thevalleychronicle.com
W: http://www.thevalleychronicle.com
Freq: Fri; **Circ:** 40000 Not Audited
Publisher: Eric Buskirk
Editorial Profile: The Valley Chronicle is published twice a month for the residents of Hemet, San Jacinto, Valle Vista and Winchester, CA. The editorial content includes local news, business, sports, arts and events.; Full Page Mono: 27.00; Full Page Colour: 2775.00
Currency: US Dollars
NEWSPAPER

Valley City Times-Record
Owner: Horizon Publications
Editorial: 146 3rd St NE, Valley City, North Dakota 58072-3047. **T:** 1 701 845-0463
W: http://www.times-online.com
Freq: Daily; **Circ:** 2355 Not Audited
Editor: Paul Riemerman
Editorial Profile: Valley City Times-Record is the daily newspaper for Valley City, ND and the surrounding communities. It covers local news, sports and lifestyle topics in the region.; Full Page Mono: 9.95; Full Page Colour: 180.00
Currency: US Dollars
DAILY NEWSPAPER

Valley Community Newspapers, Inc.
Editorial: 2709 Riverside Blvd, Sacramento, California 95818. **T:** 1 916 429-9901
E: editor@valcomnews.com
W: http://www.valcomnews.com **Circ:** 60000 Not Audited
Editorial Profile: Valley Community Newspapers, Inc. is a community newspaper publisher serving the Sacramento, CA area.

NEWSPAPER

The Valley Courier
Owner: Alamosa Newspapers, Inc.
Editorial: 2205 State Ave, Alamosa, Colorado 81101-3500. **T:** 1 719 589-2553
E: news@alamosanews.com
W: http://www.alamosanews.com
Freq: Daily; **Circ:** 5700 Not Audited
Publisher: Keith Cerny; **Editor:** Lloyd Engen
Editorial Profile: The Valley Courier serves the businesses and residents of Alamosa, CO with local and regional news.; Full Page Mono: 14.30; Full Page Colour: 80.00
Currency: US Dollars
DAILY NEWSPAPER

The Valley Dispatch
Owner: MediaNews Group
Editorial: 491 Dutton St, Lowell, Massachusetts 01854-4221.
T: 1 978 458-7100
W: http://www.thevalleydispatch.com
Freq: Daily; **Circ:** 14500 Not Audited
Editor: David McArdle
Editorial Profile: The Valley Dispatch is a newspaper for residents of Lowel, MA. Deadlines are at noon ET.; Full Page Mono: 12.00; Full Page Colour: 51.71
Currency: US Dollars
DAILY NEWSPAPER

Valley Free Press
Editorial: 1586 Barber Greene Rd, Dekalb, Illinois 60115-7900. **T:** 1 815 756-4841
E: vfpnews@vfpnews.com
W: http://www.vfpnews.com
Freq: Tue; **Circ:** 13200 Not Audited
Editor: Debbie Behrends; **Publisher:** Don Bricker
Editorial Profile: Valley Free Press is published weekly for the residents of Sandwich, IL and surrounding areas. The newspaper covers local news, sports and community events.; Full Page Mono: 7.00
Currency: US Dollars
NEWSPAPER

Valley Independent
Owner: Tribune-Review Publishing Co.
Editorial: Eastgate 19, Monessen, Pennsylvania 15062-1368. **T:** 1 724 684-5200
E: valley@tribweb.com
W: http://www.pittsburghlive.com/x/valleyindependent
Freq: Daily; **Circ:** 13211 Not Audited
Editor: Joe Abramowitz; **News Editor:** Carl Hill; **Publisher:** Richard Scaife
Editorial Profile: Valley Independent is a local newspaper written for the residents of Washington, Fayette, and West Moreland Counties in Pennsylvania. The newspaper covers local news, sports, and events.; Full Page Mono: 29.14; Full Page Colour: 38.11
Currency: US Dollars
DAILY NEWSPAPER

The Valley Journals
Editorial: 584 W 83605, Midvale, Utah 84070. **T:** 1 801 254-5974
E: info@myutahjournals.com
W: http://www.valleyjournals.com
Circ: 318200 Not Audited
Editor: Tom Haraldsen; **Editor:** Crystal Liechty; **Publisher:** Boyd Petersen; **Editor:** Linda Petersen; **Editor:** Kim Wells
NEWSPAPER

Valley Morning Star
Owner: Freedom Communications Inc.
Editorial: 1310 S Commerce St, Harlingen, Texas 78550-7711. **T:** 1 956 430-6200
W: http://www.valleystar.com
Freq: Daily; **Circ:** 18439 Not Audited
Publisher: Tyler Patton; **Editor:** Marci Ponce
Editorial Profile: Valley Morning Star is published daily for residents of Harlingen, TX and surrounding communities. The newspaper covers local news, weather, sports, features, business, politics, arts & entertainment, lifestyle and community events.; Full Page Mono: 46.25; Full Page Colour: 551.00
Currency: US Dollars
DAILY NEWSPAPER

Valley News
Owner: Newspapers of New England
Editorial: 24 Interchange Dr, West Lebanon, New Hampshire 3784. **T:** 1 603 298-8711
E: news@vnews.com
W: http://www.vnews.com
Freq: Daily; **Circ:** 16522 Not Audited
News Editor: Martin Frank; **Editor:** Jeffrey Good; **News Editor:** John Gregg; **Editor:** Ernie Kohlsaat; **Editor:** John Lippman; **Editor:** John Lippman; **Publisher:** Dan McClory

Editorial Profile: Valley News is a local, daily newspaper serving residents of Grafton County, NH and White River Junction, VT. The paper covers local news, business, community events and sports.; Full Page Mono: 25.52; Full Page Colour: 85.25
Currency: US Dollars
DAILY NEWSPAPER

Valley News & Village News Newspapers
Owner: Village News, Inc.
Editorial: 127 W Elder St, Fallbrook, California 92028. **T:** 1 760 723-7319
W: http://www.myvalleynews.com **Circ:** 24525
NEWSPAPER

Valley News Dispatch
Owner: Tribune-Review Publishing Co.
Editorial: 210 E 4th Ave, Tarentum, Pennsylvania 15084. **T:** 1 724 224-4321
W: http://www.pittsburghlive.com/x/valleynewsdispatch
Freq: Daily; **Circ:** 28135 Not Audited
Editorial Profile: Valley News Dispatch is a local daily newspaper written for the Tarentum, PA community. The publication focuses on local, regional, and national news coverage.; Full Page Mono: 49.28
Currency: US Dollars
DAILY NEWSPAPER

Valley News Group
Editorial: 23009 Ventura Blvd, Woodland Hills, California 91364. **T:** 1 818 223-9545
E: wnrcnews@instanet.com
W: http://www.valleynewsgroup.com
Circ: 35000 Not Audited
Editor: Theda Reichman
Editorial Profile: Valley News Group is written for the residents of Woodland Hills, CA. It covers local news and events.
NEWSPAPER

Valley Newspapers
Owner: Valley Newspapers Holdings, LP
Editorial: 1811 N 23rd St, McAllen, Texas 78501. **T:** 1 956 682-2423
E: otc@valleytowncrier.com
W: http://www.valleytowncrier.com
Freq: Weekly; **Circ:** 123710 Not Audited
Editor: Brad Nibert; **Editor:** Brad Nibert; **Editor:** Brad Nibert; **Editor:** Brad Nibert; Full Page Colour: 2265.00
Currency: US Dollars
NEWSPAPER

Valley Post
Owner: E.W. Scripps Co.
Editorial: 1101 Twin View Blvd., Redding, California 96003. **T:** 1 530 365-2797
E: news@andersonvalleypost.com
W: http://www.andersonvalleypost.com
Freq: Wed; **Circ:** 12000 Not Audited
Editor: George Winship
Editorial Profile: Valley Post is a local weekly newspaper written for residents of Anderson, CA and the surrounding area. Editorial deadlines are Thursdays before the issue date.; Full Page Mono: 13.00
Currency: US Dollars
NEWSPAPER

Valley Publications
Editorial: 104 E Fifth St, Cochrane, Wisconsin 54622-7138. **T:** 1 608 248-2451
E: recorder@mwt.net **Circ:** 3028 Not Audited
Editor: Faith McFarlim; **Publisher:** Gary Stumpf; Full Page Mono: 6.40
Currency: US Dollars
NEWSPAPER

Valley Publishing
Owner: News Media Corp.
Editorial: 835 1st Ave, Monte Vista, Colorado 81144. **T:** 1 719 852-3531
E: valleypubs@amigo.net **Circ:** 3993 Not Audited
Publisher: Jennifer Alonzo; **Editor:** Sylvia Lobato
NEWSPAPER

Valley Publishing Co.
Editorial: 613 7th St, Prosser, Washington 99350. **T:** 1 509 786-1711
W: http://www.valleypublishing.us **Circ:** 5800 Not Audited
Publisher: Danielle Fournier; **Editor:** Mike Marino
NEWSPAPER

Valley Ranger
Editorial: 200 S Court St, Lewisburg, West Virginia 24901. **T:** 1 304 645-1206
E: wvdailynews@suddenlinkmail.com
Freq: Sun; **Circ:** 23953 Not Audited
Editor: Tonya Sizemoore; **Publisher:** Judy

Steele
Editorial Profile: The Valley Ranger (Tmc)'s editorial mission is to provide its readers with news and information. The publication is written for local residents of the Greenbrier Valley, WV area. A Web site is not available.; Full Page Mono: 10.50
Currency: US Dollars
NEWSPAPER

The Valley Times-News
Editorial: 220 N 12th St, Lanett, Alabama 36863-6422. **T:** 1 334 644-8100
W: http://www.valleytimes-news.com
Freq: Daily; **Circ:** 8000 Not Audited
Editor: Scott Sickler
Editorial Profile: The Valley Times-News is written for the residents of Lanett, AL.; Full Page Mono: 9.50; Full Page Colour: 300.00
Currency: US Dollars
DAILY NEWSPAPER

Valley Voice
Owner: Reiter's Newspaper Group, Inc.
Editorial: 19360 Rinaldi St, Ste 502, Porter Ranch, California 91326. **T:** 1 310 429-0484
E: yourvalleyvoice@hotmail.com
W: http://www.evalleyvoice.com
Freq: Monthly; **Circ:** 10000 Not Audited
Editorial Profile: Valley Voice is a local, monthly newspaper serving residents of the North Central San Fernando Valley, CA. The paper includes local news and information relevant to the local community. The paper prints the last Wednesday of the month.; Full Page Mono: 28.00
Currency: US Dollars
NEWSPAPER

Valley Wide Newspapers
Owner: Pryke (Raymond)
Editorial: 16925 Main St Ste A, Hesperia, California 92345-6038. **T:** 1 760 244-0021
E: valleywide@valleywidenews.com
W: http://www.valleywidenewspaper.com
Circ: 25900 Not Audited
Editorial Profile: Valley Wide Newspapers is a weekly newspaper publisher serving the residents of Apple Valley, Hesperia, Adelanto and Victorville, CA.
NEWSPAPER

Valley/Pymatuning Area News
Editorial: 46 W Jefferson St, Jefferson, Ohio 44047-1028. **T:** 1 440 576-9115
Editor: Dorris Cook; **Publisher:** Bob Halsted
NEWSPAPER

Van Buren Publishing
Owner: Stephens Media
Editorial: 100 N 11th St, Van Buren, Arkansas 72956. **T:** 1 479 474-5215
W: http://www.pressargus.com **Circ:** 17731 Not Audited
Editor: Kenneth Fry; **Publisher:** Gene Kincy
NEWSPAPER

Van Wert Times-Bulletin
Owner: Ohio Community Media LLC.
Editorial: 700 Fox Rd, Van Wert, Ohio 45891-2485. **T:** 1 419 238-2285
E: info@timesbulletin.com
W: http://www.timesbulletin.com
Freq: Daily; **Circ:** 7000 Not Audited
Publisher: Kirk Dougal; **Editor:** Ed Gebert; **Editor:** Sherry Missler
Editorial Profile: Van Wert Times-Bulletin is written for the community residents in and around Van Wert, OH. It covers community news, events, schools, sports, businesses, agriculture and editorials.; Full Page Mono: 12.50; Full Page Colour: 135.00
Currency: US Dollars
DAILY NEWSPAPER

Van Zandt Newspapers, L.L.C.
Owner: Van Zandt Newspapers, LLC
Editorial: 109 N 5th St, Wills Point, Texas 75169. **T:** 1 903 873-2525 **E:** vznews@aol.com
W: http://www.vanzandtnewspapers.com
Circ: 17100 Not Audited
Publisher: John Buzzetta; **Editor:** Julie Vaughan
NEWSPAPER

Vanguard Newspapers
Owner: Vangaurd Publishing LLC
Editorial: 106 E 1st St, Sumner, Iowa 50674-1430. **T:** 1 563 578-3351 **Circ:** 2720 Not Audited
Editorial Profile: Vanguard Newspapers publish the Sumner Gazette, Tripoli Leader and Fredericksburg Review.
NEWSPAPER

Vecherniy New York
Owner: Lesti Publishing Corp.

Editorial: 1529 Voorhies Ave, Brooklyn, New York 11235-3912. **T:** 1 718 615-1210
E: lestitv@yahoo.com
W: http://www.vechny.com
Freq: Fri; **Circ:** 20000
Editor in Chief: Menarais Shekinskaya; **Publisher:** Boris Zaturensky; Full Page Mono: 10.00
Currency: US Dollars
NEWSPAPER

Venango Newspapers
Owner: Venango Newspapers Inc.
Editorial: 1510 W 1St St, Oil City, Pennsylvania 16301-3211. **T:** 1 814 676-7444
E: info.thederrick@gmail.com
W: http://www.thederrick.com
Publisher: Ned Cowart; **Editor:** Cindi Power
Editorial Profile: Venango Newspapers includes The Derrick and The News-Herald, which cover local news for the residents of Venango County, Pennsylvania.
DAILY NEWSPAPER

El Venezolano
Editorial: 8390 NW 53rd St, Ste 318, Doral, Florida 33166-4699. **T:** 1 305 717-3206
E: info@elvenezolanonews.com
W: http://elvenezolanonews.com
Freq: Thu; **Circ:** 20000 Not Audited
Editor: Oswaldo Munoz
Editorial Profile: El Venezolano is a local newspaper written for the Hispanic community of Doral, FL.; Full Page Mono: 140.00
Currency: US Dollars
NEWSPAPER

Venezuela al Dia
Editorial: 8245 NW 36th St, Ste 3, Doral, Florida 33166-6636. **T:** 1 786 221-2191
W: http://www.venezuelaaldia.com
Freq: Weekly; **Circ:** 10000 Not Audited
Editor: Armando Chirinos
Editorial Profile: Venezuela al Dia is a newspaper serving the Venezuelan community abroad in Miami and the surrounding area. It includes international and national news, sports, editorial and entertainment stories of interest to Venezuelan readers.; Full Page Mono: 30.00
Currency: US Dollars
NEWSPAPER

Venice Gondolier Sun
Owner: Sun Coast Media Group Inc.
Editorial: 200 E Venice Ave, Venice, Florida 34285-1941. **T:** 1 941 207-1000
W: http://www.venicegondolier.com
Freq: Sat; **Circ:** 31000 Not Audited
Publisher: Lang Capasso; **Editor:** Bob Mudge
Editorial Profile: Venice Gondolier Sun is a local newspaper that is published for the residents of Sarasota County in Florida. The publication covers local news, events, business, entertainment and sports.; Full Page Mono: 19.30
Currency: US Dollars
NEWSPAPER

Ventura Breeze
Editorial: 1575 Spinnaker Dr, #105B-393, Ventura, California 93001. **T:** 1 805 653-0143
E: publisher@venturabreeze.com
W: http://www.venturabreeze.com
Freq: Bi-Weekly; **Circ:** 11000 Not Audited
Editorial Profile: Ventura Breeze is a local community newspaper written for the residents of Ventura, CA. The paper covers local news, governments, schools, business, arts & entertainment, local events and weather. Send all press materials to the main e-mail address.; Full Page Mono: 20.00
Currency: US Dollars
NEWSPAPER

Ventura County Reporter
Owner: Southland Publishing
Editorial: 700 E Main St, Ventura, California 93001-2906. **T:** 1 805 648-2244
W: http://www.vcreporter.com
Freq: Thu; **Circ:** 33000 Not Audited
Publisher: David Comden; **Editor:** Michael Sullivan
Editorial Profile: Ventura (CA) County Reporter is an alternative weekly publication that provides in-depth features, investigative reporting and arts & entertainment coverage.; Full Page Mono: 28.33
Currency: US Dollars
NEWSPAPER

Ventura County Star
Owner: E.W. Scripps Co.
Editorial: 550 Camarillo Center Dr, Camarillo, California 93010-7700. **T:** 1 805 437-0000
W: http://www.vcstar.com
Freq: Daily; **Circ:** 47604 Not Audited
Editor: John Moore; **Editor:** John Moore; **Editor:** John Moore; **Editor:** John Moore
Editorial Profile: Ventura County Star is a local daily newspaper serving the residents of Ventura County, CA. The publication features local news, weather, sports, business, and entertainment.; Full Page Mono: 128.00; Full Page Colour: 425.13
Currency: US Dollars
DAILY NEWSPAPER

Verde Valley Newspapers Inc.
Owner: Western Newspapers, Inc.
Editorial: 116 S Main St, Cottonwood, Arizona 86326. **T:** 1 928 634-2241
E: editorial@verdevalleynews.com
W: http://www.verdevnews.com **Circ:** 21522 Not Audited
Editor: Dan Engler; **Publisher:** Pam Miller
NEWSPAPER

The Vermont News Guide
Owner: Hersam Acorn Newspapers
Editorial: 99 Bonnet St, Manchester Center, Vermont 05255-8919. **T:** 1 802 362-3535
E: vng@hersamacornvt.com
W: http://www.vermontnews-guide.com
Freq: Wed; **Circ:** 14919 Not Audited
Editor: Liz Schafer; **Publisher:** Renee Tassone
Editorial Profile: The Vermont News Guide is a weekly publication which announces surrounding area up and coming events in the Manchester Center, VT region. Deadlines for the publication are on Thursdays.; Full Page Mono: 10.65
Currency: US Dollars
NEWSPAPER

The Vermont Standard
Owner: Vermont Standard Inc.
Editorial: 466 Rt 4 W, Woodstock, Vermont 5091. **T:** 1 802 457-1313
E: info@thevermontstandard.com
W: http://www.thevermontstandard.com
Freq: Thu; **Circ:** 13600 Not Audited
Publisher: Phillip Camp
Editorial Profile: The Vermont Standard is a community newspaper for the residents of Woodstock, VT.; Full Page Mono: 8.25
Currency: US Dollars
NEWSPAPER

Vernon Daily Record
Owner: North Central Texas Publishing Company
Editorial: 3214 Wilbarger St, Vernon, Texas 76384. **T:** 1 940 552-5454
E: vdr@vernonrecord.com
W: http://www.vernonrecord.com
Freq: Daily; **Circ:** 4546 Not Audited
Publisher: Larry Crabtree; **News Editor:** Daniel Walker
Editorial Profile: Vernon Daily Record's editorial mission is to provide daily news coverage to its readers. Deadlines are by 10am CT the day before.; Full Page Mono: 7.90; Full Page Colour: 150.00
Currency: US Dollars
DAILY NEWSPAPER

Vernon Publishing - Eldon
Owner: Vernon Publishing, Inc.
Editorial: 415 S Maple St, Eldon, Missouri 65026-1856. **T:** 1 573 392-5658
W: http://www.vernonpublishing.com
Circ: 5850 Not Audited
Editor: Tim Flora; **Editor:** Tim Flora; **Publisher:** Trevor Vernon
NEWSPAPER

Vernon Publishing - Versailles
Owner: Vernon Publishing, Inc.
Editorial: 104 W Jasper St, Versailles, Missouri 65084-1020. **T:** 1 573 378-5441
E: leader-statesman@vernonpublishing.com
W: http://www.vernonpublishing.com
Circ: 12750 Not Audited
Editor: Bryan Jones; **Publisher:** Dane Vernon
NEWSPAPER

Vero Beach Hometown News
Owner: Hometown News, L.C.
Editorial: 1020 Old Dixie Hwy, Vero Beach, Florida 32960-4359. **T:** 1 772 569-6767
E: veronews@hometownnewsol.com
W: http://www.myhometownnews.net
Freq: Fri; **Circ:** 18900 Not Audited
Publisher: Vernon Smith; Full Page Mono: 19.25
Currency: US Dollars
NEWSPAPER

Vevay Newspapers, Inc.
Editorial: 111 W Market St, Vevay, Indiana 47043. **T:** 1 812 427-2311
E: news@vevaynewspapers.com
W: http://www.vevaynewspapers.com
Freq: Weekly; **Circ:** 3573 Not Audited
Editor: Patrick Lanman; **Publisher:** Don Wallis; Full Page Colour: 850.00
Currency: US Dollars
NEWSPAPER

The Vici Vision
Owner: McCormick (Jennifer)
Editorial: 107 1/2 E Broadway, Vici, Oklahoma. **T:** 1 580 995-3425
E: vicichamber@vicihorizon.com
W: http://vicivision.wordpress.com
Freq: Thu
Editorial Profile: The Vici Vision is a weekly community newspaper serving residents of Vici, OK with community news and events coverage.
NEWSPAPER

Vicksburg Post
Owner: Vicksburg Printing and Publishing Co.
Editorial: 1601F N Frontage Rd, Vicksburg, Mississippi 39180-5149. **T:** 1 601 636-4545
E: newsreleases@vicksburgpost.com
W: http://www.vicksburgpost.com
Freq: Daily; **Circ:** 12254 Not Audited
Publisher: Jeff Schumacher
Editorial Profile: Vicksburg Post is a daily newspaper which covers local news, business, sports and arts & entertainment for the residents of Vicksburg, MS. The newspaper, established in 1883, was awarded the Pulitzer Prize.; Full Page Mono: 17.78; Full Page Colour: 210.00
Currency: US Dollars
DAILY NEWSPAPER

Victoria Advocate
Owner: Victoria Advocate Publishing Co.
Editorial: 311 E Constitution St, Victoria, Texas 77901-8197. **T:** 1 361 575-1451
E: newsroom@vicad.com
W: http://www.victoriaadvocate.com
Freq: Daily; **Circ:** 25405 Not Audited
Editor: Chris Cobler; **Editor:** Becky Cooper; **Editor:** Becky Cooper; **Editor:** Becky Cooper; **Editor:** Becky Cooper; **Publisher:** John Roberts; **Editor:** Frank Tilley
Editorial Profile: Victoria Advocate is a daily newspaper written for residents of Victoria, TX. It covers business, sports, arts & entertainment, features and news stories.; Full Page Mono: 61.40; Full Page Colour: 855.00
Currency: US Dollars
DAILY NEWSPAPER

Vida
Editorial: 130 Palm Dr, Oxnard, California 93030. **T:** 1 805 483-1008
E: vidanews@aol.com
Freq: Thu; **Circ:** 35000 Not Audited
Editor: Ramon Arceo; **Editor:** John Dearinger; **Editor:** Lucy Gomez; **Publisher:** Manuel Munoz; **Editor:** Carlos Olea; **Editor:** Nancy Reed; **Editor:** Loury Smith; **Editor:** Jose Valencia
Editorial Profile: Vida is written for Hispanic and Latino residents throughout Southern California. It features local and national news, in addition to sports, business, lifestyles and arts & entertainment coverage. The deadlines are on Fridays.; Full Page Mono: 47.50; Full Page Colour: 3500.00
Currency: US Dollars
NEWSPAPER

Vida en el Valle
Owner: McClatchy Newspapers
Editorial: 1626 E St, Fresno, California 93706. **T:** 1 559 441-6780
E: noticias@vidaenelvalle.com
W: http://www.vidaenelvalle.com
Freq: Wed; **Circ:** 172000 Not Audited
Publisher: Valerie Bender; **Editor:** Juan Esparza; **Editor:** Juan Esparza
Editorial Profile: Vida en el Valle is a weekly newspaper which provides news of importance to the Latino community of the central San Joaquin Valley, CA. The newspaper covers topics such as education, politics, business, sports and arts & entertainment. The paper promotes cultural contributions of Latinos in the Valley.; Full Page Mono: 136.40; Full Page Colour: 1241.00
Currency: US Dollars
NEWSPAPER

Vida Latina
Owner: Mundial Group, Inc.
Editorial: 113 W 28th St Rm 2A, New York, New York 10001-6113. **T:** 1 770 698-9992
E: vidalatina@mundialgroup.net
Freq: Monthly; **Circ:** 55226 Not Audited
Editor: Roberto Abramowitz; **Publisher:** Felix Senzion; **Editor:** Carlos Torres Bujanda
Editorial Profile: Vida Latina is a Spanish-language newspaper that is distributed throughout the Southeastern United States. It covers entertainment, health, immigration, features, sports and community news.; Full Page Mono: 44.00
Currency: US Dollars
NEWSPAPER

La Vida News/The Black Voice
Owner: T&P Publishing Co.
Editorial: 5601 Bridge St, Ste 300, Fort Worth, Texas 76112-2355. **T:** 1 817 543-2095
E: newsdesk@lavidanewstheblackvoice.com
W: http://lavidanewstheblackvoice.com
Freq: Thu; **Circ:** 39700 Not Audited
Editorial Profile: La Vida News/The Black Voice is a weekly community newspaper serving the African-American community in Fort Worth, TX and the surrounding areas. The paper was founded in 1957.; Full Page Mono: 47.00
Currency: US Dollars
NEWSPAPER

Vida Nueva/Tidings
Owner: Catholic Archdiocese of Los Angeles
Editorial: 3424 Wilshire Blvd, Los Angeles, California 90010-2263. **T:** 1 213 637-7360
Editor: Victor Aleman; **Publisher:** José H. Gómez; **Editor in Chief:** John David Long-Garcia; **Editor:** Mike Nelson
NEWSPAPER

Vien-Dong Daily News
Owner: Vietnamese America Media Corporation
Editorial: 14891 Moran St, Westminster, California 92683-5535. **T:** 1 714 379-2851
E: viendong@aol.com
W: http://www.viendongdaily.com
Freq: Daily; **Circ:** 25000
Editorial Profile: Vien-Dong Daily News is a daily newspaper for Vietnamese-speaking residents in and around Los Angeles and Orange County, CA. It also publishes a weekly edition on Saturdays culling regionally specific news from each week for residents of San Diego, CA. The paper launched in 1993.; Full Page Mono: 9.00; Full Page Colour: 655.50
Currency: US Dollars
DAILY NEWSPAPER

Viet Bao Daily News
Editorial: 14841 Moran St, Westminster, California 92683. **T:** 1 714 894-2500
E: info@vietbao.com
W: http://www.vietbao.com
Freq: Daily; **Circ:** 20000 Not Audited
Editor: Phan Tan Hai; **Publisher:** Hoabinh Le-Munzer; **Editor:** Kha Nguyen
Editorial Profile: Viet Bao Daily News serves the Vietnamese community in Southern California. The editorial mission is to keep the Vietnamese communities informed of local news and events, business, lifestyle, politics, education and entertainment.; Full Page Mono: 4.07; Full Page Colour: 1700.00
Currency: US Dollars
DAILY NEWSPAPER

Viet Bao Houston
Editorial: 11528 Bellaine Blvd #F, Houston, Texas 77072-4925. **T:** 1 281 933-0999
E: houston@vietbao.com
W: http://www.vietbao.com
Freq: Fri; **Circ:** 15000
Editor: Van Le
Editorial Profile: Viet Bao is a Vietnamese language publication founded in 1993. The Houston edition is published every Friday.; Full Page Mono: 3.29; Full Page Colour: 6.97
Currency: US Dollars
NEWSPAPER

Viet Nam Moi
Editorial: 8060 Boone Rd, Houston, Texas 77072-4925. **T:** 1 281 933-9283
Freq: Sat; **Circ:** 10000
Editorial Profile: Viet Nam Moi is a weekly newspaper written for the Vietnamese community. Advertising rates available upon request.
NEWSPAPER

Viet Tide
Editorial: 9315 Bolsa Ave #620, Westminster, California 92683-5902. **T:** 1 714 262-7028
E: baoviettide@yahoo.com
Freq: Fri; **Circ:** 20000 Not Audited
Editorial Profile: Viet Tide is a community newspaper providing Community News coverage for the Vietnamese community in Westminster, CA.; Full Page Mono: 10.50
Currency: US Dollars
NEWSPAPER

Vietnam - The Daily News
Owner: Pacific Press Corporation
Editorial: 2350 S 10th St, San Jose, California 95112-4109. **T:** 1 408 292-3422
E: vnnb@vietnamdaily.com
W: http://www.vietnamdaily.com
Freq: Fri; **Circ:** 13000 Not Audited
Editorial Profile: Vietnam - The Daily News is a daily paper focusing on the Vietnamese community of California.; Full Page Mono: 4.61; Full Page Colour: 23.54
Currency: US Dollars
NEWSPAPER

The Vietnam Post & Thuongmoi Viet Nam
Editorial: 10515 Harwin Dr, Ste 120, Houston, Texas 77036-1533. **T:** 1 713 777-4900
E: vietnampost@aol.com
W: http://www.thevietnampost.com
Circ: 74000
Editor: Angelo Hoang; **Publisher:** Missy Nguyan
Editorial Profile: The Vietnam Post & Thuongmoi Viet Nam are free Vietnamese-language newspapers serving the Asian communities of the greater Houston area. They are also distributed on international flights to Asia.
NEWSPAPER

View Newspapers
Owner: Stephens Media Group
Editorial: 1111 W Bonanza Rd, Las Vegas, Nevada 89106-3545. **T:** 1 702 383-0264
W: http://www.viewnews.com **Circ:** 511000 Not Audited
Editor: Ginger Meurer
NEWSPAPER

The Villadom Times Newspapers
Owner: Villadom Time Inc. (The)
Editorial: 333 Godwin Ave, Midland Park, New Jersey 07432-1533. **T:** 1 201 652-0744
E: editorial@villadom.com
W: http://www.villadom.com **Circ:** 47461 Not Audited
Editor: Jennifer Crusco; **Editor:** Jennifer Crusco; **Editor:** Jennifer Crusco
Editorial Profile: The Villadom Times Newspapers is a community newspaper publisher in Midland Park, NJ. The paper has four editions covering four zones: Wyckoff/Franklin Lakes/Midland Park; Mahwah and Ramsey; Ridgewood and Glen Rock; and Saddle River/Upper Saddle River/Allendale/Ho-Ho-Kus /Waldwick.
NEWSPAPER

Village & Southwest Newspapers
Owner: Responsive Newspapers, L.P.
Editorial: 5160 Spruce St, Bellaire, Texas 77401. **T:** 1 713 668-9293
E: mynews@village-southwest-news.com
W: http://village-southwest-news.com
Circ: 40000 Not Audited
NEWSPAPER

Village Living
Owner: Starnes Publishing
Editorial: 3 Office Park Circle, Suite 316, Birmingham, Alabama 35223.
T: 1 205 313-1780
W: http://villagelivingonline.wordpress.com
Freq: Monthly; **Circ:** 13500
Editor: Jennifer Gray; **Publisher:** Dan Starnes
Editorial Profile: Village Living is a monthly newspaper providing Local and Community News coverage to the members of Mountain Brook, AL
NEWSPAPER

Village News
Editorial: 4607 W Hundred Rd, Chester, Virginia 23831. **T:** 1 804 751-0421
E: news@villagepublishing.com
W: http://www.villagenewsonline.com
Freq: Wed; **Circ:** 12000 Not Audited
Publisher: Linda Fausz; **Editor:** Mark Fausz; Full Page Mono: 13.73; Full Page Colour: 20.40
Currency: US Dollars
NEWSPAPER

Village View Publications, Inc.
Owner: Dixon (Annette)
Editorial: 1160 S Michigan Ave Apt 1306, Chicago, Illinois 60605-3701.
T: 1 708 425-1910 **E:** vvnew@sbcglobal.net
W: http://vvnew.com
Freq: Bi-Weekly; **Circ:** 25000
Editorial Profile: Village View Publications is the Publisher of four free bi-weekly community newspapers covering the South and far-South suburban Chicagoland: B-MAC - Blue Island/Midlothian/Alsip/Crestwood; Suburban-Oak Lawn/Burbank/Justice/Hickory Hills/Evergreen Park; South Suburban - Chicago Ridge/Worth/Palos Hills/Palos Park/Palos Heights; Far South -Oak Forest/Orland Park/Tinley Park. Covers local news, community events, local business, schools, sports, arts & entertainment, travel, food and restaurant reviews.; Full Page Mono: 25.00
Currency: US Dollars
NEWSPAPER

The Village Voice
Owner: Voice Media Group
Editorial: 80 Maiden Ln Rm 2105, New York, New York 10038-4893. **T:** 1 212 475-3300
W: http://www.villagevoice.com
Freq: Wed; **Circ:** 210000 Not Audited
Editor: Tom Finkel; **Publisher:** Josh Fromson
Editorial Profile: The Village Voice was founded in 1955. Called "the father of alternative weeklies," the Village Voice "introduced free-form, high-spirited, and passionate journalism." The weekly covers New York politics, national politics, and the arts. This publication is known as the "writer's paper." Deadlines are on Monday evenings. The editorial department accepts non-disclosure agreements on a case by case basis.; Full Page Mono: 14.57; Full Page Colour: 2531.00
Currency: US Dollars
NEWSPAPER

The Villager
Owner: Houston Community Newspapers
Editorial: 1600 Lake Front Cir, The Woodlands, Texas 77380-3613.
T: 1 281 378-1040
W: http://www.yourhoustonnews.com/woodlands
Freq: Thu; **Circ:** 39900 Not Audited
Publisher: Ray Biggerstaff; **Editor:** Andy Dubois
Editorial Profile: The Villager is a weekly newspaper written for the surrounding communities of The Woodlands Spring, TX area. The paper covers local and regional news.; Full Page Mono: 22.24
Currency: US Dollars
NEWSPAPER

Villager
Editorial: 757 Snelling Ave S, Saint Paul, Minnesota 55116-2250. **T:** 1 651 699-1462
E: news@myvillager.com
W: http://www.myvillager.com
Freq: Bi-Weekly; **Circ:** 60000 Not Audited
Publisher: Michael Mischke
Editorial Profile: Villager is a local newspaper serving Saint Paul, MN. The publication features general interest news, local news and community events.; Full Page Mono: 43.75
Currency: US Dollars
NEWSPAPER

The Villager Newspaper Group
Editorial: 8933 E Union Ave Ste 230, Greenwood Village, Colorado 80111-1357.
T: 1 303 773-8313
E: news@villagerpublishing.com
W: http://www.villagerpublishing.com
Freq: Weekly; **Circ:** 21700 Not Audited
Editorial Profile: The Villager Newspaper Group is a weekly community newspaper publisher serving the residents of Greenwood Village, CO.
NEWSPAPER

The Villages Daily Sun
Owner: Villages Media Group
Editorial: 1100 Main St, The Villages, Florida 32159-7719. **T:** 1 352 753-1119
E: dailyedit@aol.com
W: http://www.thevillagesdailysun.com
Freq: Daily; **Circ:** 48979 Not Audited
Publisher: Phillip Markward
Editorial Profile: The Villages Daily Sun is published daily for the residents of the Villages, a retirement community in The Villages, FL. It covers local news, sports, features and community events. Advertising deadlines are at 3pm ET.; Full Page Mono: 21.50; Full Page Colour: 190.00
Currency: US Dollars
DAILY NEWSPAPER

Vincennes Sun-Commercial
Owner: Paxton Media Group
Editorial: 702 Main St, Vincennes, Indiana 47591-2910. **T:** 1 812 886-9955
E: vscnews@suncommercial.com
W: http://www.suncommercial.com
Freq: Daily; **Circ:** 8841
Publisher: Vickie Palmer; **News Editor:** Jenny Peter
Editorial Profile: Vincennes Sun-Commercial's editorial mission is to be the best source of local news and information including accuracy and fairness. Vincennes Sun-Commercial is written for residents of Knox County, IN.; Full Page Mono: 17.23; Full Page Colour: 285.00
Currency: US Dollars
DAILY NEWSPAPER

The Vindicator
Owner: Vindicator Printing Company
Editorial: 107 Vindicator Sq, Youngstown, Ohio 44503-1136. **T:** 1 330 747-1471
E: news@vindy.com **W:** http://www.vindy.com
Freq: Daily; **Circ:** 39776 Not Audited
Editor: Todd Franko; **Publisher:** Betty Jagnow
Editorial Profile: The Vindicator is a daily newspaper providing news coverage for readers in the greater Youngstown, OH area. The newspaper focuses on events and people in the community. Other features include area sports coverage, business news, local entertainment, lifestyle and classified ads. The newspaper is published daily except on Saturday.; Full Page Mono: 73.86; Full Page Colour: 243.13
Currency: US Dollars
DAILY NEWSPAPER

Vineyard Gazette
Editorial: 34 S Summer St, Edgartown, Massachusetts 2539. **T:** 1 508 627-4311
E: news@mvgazette.com
W: http://www.mvgazette.com
Freq: Fri; **Circ:** 12500 Not Audited
Publisher: Jane Seagrave; **Editor:** Julia Wells
Editorial Profile: Vineyard Gazette is written for the residents of Martha's Vineyard, MA. Deadlines are on Mondays and Wednesdays prior to issue date.; Full Page Mono: 23.50
Currency: US Dollars
NEWSPAPER

Vinita Daily Journal
Owner: Wetherford News
Editorial: 138 S Wilson St, #140, Vinita, Oklahoma 74301-3730. **T:** 1 918 256-6422
E: vdjnews@cableone.net
W: http://www.vdjonline.com
Freq: Daily; **Circ:** 4331 Not Audited
Editor: David Burgess; **Editor:** Brenda Haskell; **Publisher:** John Link
Editorial Profile: Vinita Daily Journal is a daily newspaper serving the residents of Vinita, OK and the surrounding areas. The newspaper covers local news, business, sports and arts & entertainment stories. It also covers national and statewide stories if they have a direct impact on the newspaper's readership. All inquiries should be addressed to the editor. Deadlines are at 2pm CT the day before issue date.; Full Page Mono: 12.12; Full Page Colour: 90.00
Currency: US Dollars
DAILY NEWSPAPER

The Virginia Gazette
Owner: Tribune Company
Editorial: 216 Ironbound Rd, Williamsburg, Virginia 23188. **T:** 1 757 220-1736
E: editor@vagazette.com
W: http://www.vagazette.com
Freq: Sat; **Circ:** 19500 Not Audited
Editor: Rusty Carter; **Editor:** Rusty Carter; **Editor:** Rusty Carter; **Editor:** Rusty Carter; **Publisher:** Bill O'Donovan
Editorial Profile: The Virginia Gazette is published twice a week for the residents of Williamsburg, VA. It covers local news, sports, opinion, events, education, opinion and legal notices.; Full Page Mono: 18.53; Full Page Colour: 2083.00
Currency: US Dollars
NEWSPAPER

Virginian Review
Owner: Covington Virginian, Inc.
Editorial: 128 N Maple Ave, Covington, Virginia 24426-1545. **T:** 1 540 962-2121
E: virginianreview@aol.com
W: http://www.thevirginianreview.com
Freq: Daily; **Circ:** 6379 Not Audited
Editorial Profile: Virginian Review is a local newspaper serving the residents of Covington, Clifton Forge, Allegheny County, and Bath County, VA. The publication features local news, sports, weather, real estate, tourism, education, health services and other pertinent information for the area.; Full Page Mono: 9.25; Full Page Colour: 220.00
Currency: US Dollars
DAILY NEWSPAPER

The Virginian-Pilot
Owner: Landmark Media Enterprises, LLC
Editorial: 150 W Brambleton Ave, Norfolk, Virginia 23510-2018. **T:** 1 757 446-2000
W: http://www.pilotonline.com
Freq: Daily; **Circ:** 126053 Not Audited
Editor in Chief: Denis Finley
Editorial Profile: The Virginian-Pilot is a daily newspaper serving the Hampton Roads community of Virginia which includes 12 cities and counties. It covers food, business, technology, real estate, entertainment and travel. Do NOT send press releases for product promotions or product reviews. The Virginian-Pilot is ONLY interested in news concerning Virginia and, moreover, the Hampton Roads communities. Press releases should be sent to the appropriate journalists and editors.; Full Page Mono: 223.00; Full Page Colour: 708.58
Currency: US Dollars
DAILY NEWSPAPER

The Virginian-Pilot
Editorial: 921 Battlefield Blvd N, Chesapeake, Virginia 23320-4803. **T:** 1 757 222-5200
E: clipper@pilotonline.com
DAILY NEWSPAPER

The Virginian-Pilot
Editorial: 1111 E Main St Fl 3, Richmond, Virginia 23219-3573. **T:** 1 804 697-1560
DAILY NEWSPAPER

The Virginian-Pilot
Editorial: 157 N Main St Ste B, Suffolk, Virginia 23434-4565. **T:** 1 757 222-5550
E: thesun@pilotonline.com
DAILY NEWSPAPER

The Virginian-Pilot
Editorial: 4549 Commerce St Ste 101, Virginia Beach, Virginia 23462-3370.
T: 1 757 222-5100
DAILY NEWSPAPER

Visalia Times-Delta
Owner: Gannett Co., Inc.
Editorial: 330 N West St, Visalia, California 93291-6000. **T:** 1 559 735-3200
E: news@visaliatimesdelta.com
W: http://www.visaliatimesdelta.com
Freq: Daily; **Circ:** 15557 Not Audited
Editor: Mike Hazelwood; **Publisher:** Amy Pack
Editorial Profile: Visalia Times-Delta is a daily newspaper covering local news and sports in Visalia and the surrounding Tulare County, CA. The paper covers local news and events only, and takes regional and national coverage entirely from wire services.; Full Page Mono: 60.31; Full Page Colour: 900.00
Currency: US Dollars
DAILY NEWSPAPER

La Vision de Georgia
Editorial: 1394 Indian Trail Lilburn Rd Ste 202, Norcross, Georgia 30093-2678.
T: 1 770 963-7521
W: http://www.lavisionnewspaper.com
Freq: Fri; **Circ:** 40000 Not Audited
Editor: Nadja Castillo; **Publisher:** Victoria Chacon
Editorial Profile: La Vision de Georgia in Norcross, GA is s a free weekly newspaper for the Hispanic community in the metropolitan Atlanta area. It covers community, national and Latin American news.; Full Page Mono: 16.67; Full Page Colour: 95.00
Currency: US Dollars
NEWSPAPER

Vision Hispana
Editorial: 1151 Harbor Bay Pkwy, Alameda, California 94502-6540. **T:** 1 510 865-6274
E: contact@visionhispanausa.com
W: http://www.visionhispanausa.com/
Editorial Profile: Vision Hispana is a a community newspaper informing the citizens of Alameda, CA on local news, events, education, health & safety and travel in regards to the Hispanic community. The paper was founded in 2003.
NEWSPAPER

Vita.mn
Owner: McClatchy Newspapers
Editorial: 425 Portland Ave, Minneapolis, Minnesota 55488-1511. **T:** 1 612 673-4000
W: http://www.vita.mn
Freq: Thu; **Circ:** 50000 Not Audited
Editor: Simon Groebner
Editorial Profile: Vita.mn is a free, weekly newspaper serving primarily 25- to 34-year-old residents of Minneapolis. The paper is entertainment-focused and targeted toward people on the go. Coverage includes fashion and video games, theater, music and restaurant reviews, and a relationship column.; Full Page Mono: 32.00
Currency: US Dollars
NEWSPAPER

Vocero Hispano
Owner: Vocero Hispano, Inc.

Editorial: 335 Chandler St, Ste 8, Worcester, Massachusetts 01602-3441.
T: 1 508 792-1942 **E:** voceronews@aol.com
W: http://www.vocerohispano.com
Freq: Fri; **Circ:** 20000 Not Audited
Editorial Profile: Vocero Hispano, published weekly, focuses on news within the Hispanic communities across Massachusetts. The paper covers local news, business, sports and arts & entertainment stories.; Full Page Mono: 18.00
Currency: US Dollars
NEWSPAPER

El Vocero Hispano
Editorial: 2818 Vineland Ave Se, Grand Rapids, Michigan 49508-1453.
T: 1 616 246-6023
E: elvocero@elvoceromi.com
W: http://www.elvocerous.com
Freq: Fri; **Circ:** 25000 Not Audited
Editorial Profile: El Vocero Hispano in Grand Rapids, MI is written for the Hispanic communities in Michigan. The newspaper covers community news, cultural events and services and national news of interest to Hispanic communities.; Full Page Mono: 13.00; Full Page Colour: 1200.00
Currency: US Dollars
NEWSPAPER

Voice Media
Owner: Voice Media
Editorial: 1511 Ritchie Hwy Ste 304, Arnold, Maryland 21012-2471
Editor: Hayley Gable Bowerman
Editorial Profile: Voice Media is a community newspaper publisher serving Anne Arundel County in Maryland, and produces three monthly papers: the Pasadena (MD) Voice, the Severna Park (MD) Voice, and the Arundel Voice. The editorial staff is shared, though there are separate PO boxes for each publication.
NEWSPAPER

The Voice Newspapers
Owner: Journal Register Company
Editorial: 51180 Bedford St, New Baltimore, Michigan 48047-2533. **T:** 1 586 716-8100
E: editor@voicenews.com
W: http://www.voicenews.com **Circ:** 74336 Not Audited
Publisher: Jeff Parra; **Editor:** Jeff Payne
Editorial Profile: The Voice Newspapers in New Baltimore, MI is a publisher of community newspapers.
NEWSPAPER

The Voice Newspapers
Owner: Megamedia Enterprises Inc.
Editorial: 5236 W North Ave, Chicago, Illinois 60639. **T:** 1 773 889-0880
E: tvoicenews@gmail.com **Circ:** 30000 Not Audited
Editorial Profile: The Voice Newspapers in Chicago publishes The Garfield-Lawndale Voice and The Austin Voice, both weekly neighborhood newspapers.
NEWSPAPER

The Voice of the Southwest
Owner: Roman Catholic Diocese of Gallup
Editorial: 711 S Puerco Dr, Gallup, New Mexico 87301-6178. **T:** 1 505 863-4406
W: http://www.dioceseofgallup.org/voice.php
Freq: Bi-Monthly; **Circ:** 10500
Publisher: James Wall
Editorial Profile: The Voice of the Southwest is bi-monthly paper for the Diocese of Gallup, NM.; Full Page Mono: 35.00
Currency: US Dollars
NEWSPAPER

Voice of the Valley
Editorial: 23745 225Th Way Se Ste 203, Maple Valley, Washington 98038-5294.
T: 1 425 432-9696 **E:** voice9696@comcast.net
W: http://www.voiceofthevalley.com
Freq: Tue; **Circ:** 17300 Not Audited
Editorial Profile: Voice of the Valley covers news for the local residents of Maple Valley, WA. The lead time for Voice of the Valley is two to three weeks, depending on the story.; Full Page Mono: 16.00; Full Page Colour: 1080.00
Currency: US Dollars
NEWSPAPER

The Voice-Tribune
Owner: Blue Equity
Editorial: 735 E Main St, Louisville, Kentucky 40202-1005. **T:** 1 502 897-8900
E: circ@voice-tribune.com
W: http://www.voice-tribune.com
Freq: Thu; **Circ:** 13301 Not Audited
Editorial Profile: The Voice-Tribune provides community news for Jefferson County and Eastern Louisville, KY.; Full Page Mono: 31.50
Currency: US Dollars
NEWSPAPER

Vondrak Publishing Co.
Editorial: 5639 W 63rd St, Chicago, Illinois 60638-5513. **T:** 1 773 476-4800
E: vonpub@aol.com
W: http://www.swnewsherald.com **Circ:** 61500 Not Audited
Editor: Joseph Boyle; **Publisher:** James Vondrak
Editorial Profile: Southwest Community News Group in Summit, IL is a community newspaper publisher.
NEWSPAPER

Voyager Media
Owner: Voyager Media Group, Inc.
Editorial: 23856 W Andrew Rd, Plainfield, Illinois 60585-8770. **T:** 1 815 436-2431
W: http://www.buglenewspapers.com
Circ: 64200 Not Audited
Editorial Profile: Voyager Media in Plainfield, IL is a publisher of community newspapers.
NEWSPAPER

La Voz
Owner: Cruz (Andres)
Editorial: 560 E Third St, Lexington, Kentucky 40508-1738. **T:** 1 859 621-2106
E: info@lavozky.com
W: http://www.lavozky.com
Freq: Bi-Weekly; **Circ:** 10000 Not Audited
Editorial Profile: La Voz is a Spanish-language newspaper written for residents of Lexington, KY.; Full Page Mono: 12.00
Currency: US Dollars
NEWSPAPER

La Voz
Owner: The Voice Publishing Corp.
Editorial: 1020 Kipling Rd, Elizabeth, New Jersey 07208-1039. **T:** 1 908 352-6654
E: lavoznj@aol.com
W: http://www.lavoznj.com
Freq: Bi-Weekly; **Circ:** 38000 Not Audited
Publisher: Daniel Garcia; **Editor:** Virginia Iturralde
Editorial Profile: La Voz in Elizabeth, NJ is a bi-weekly Spanish-language newspaper written for Spanish-speaking residents in the region.; Full Page Mono: 12.40
Currency: US Dollars
NEWSPAPER

La Voz Arizona
Owner: Gannett Co., Inc.
Editorial: 200 E Van Buren St, Phoenix, Arizona 85004-2238. **T:** 1 602 444-3800
W: http://www.lavozarizona.com
Freq: Fri; **Circ:** 60000 Not Audited
Editor: Elvia Diaz; **Editor:** Elvia Diaz; **Publisher:** Elvira Espinoza
Editorial Profile: La Voz Arizona is a free Spanish-language newspaper serving Hispanic residents in Phoenix, Mesa, Tempe and West Valley, AZ. It covers local news, sports and community events. It shares offices with the Arizona Republic.; Full Page Mono: 54.28; Full Page Colour: 150.00
Currency: US Dollars
NEWSPAPER

Voz da Comunidade
Owner: Massachusetts Alliance of Portguese Speakers
Editorial: 1046 Cambridge St., Cambridge, Massachusetts 2139. **T:** 1 617 864-7600
W: http://www.maps-inc.org/news/newsletter
Freq: Quarterly
Editorial Profile: Voz da Communidade is a quarterly, bilingual newsletter published by MAPS, the Massachusetts Alliance of Portugese Speakers, a non-profit agency dedicated to providing health and social services to Portugese-American residents of Massachusetts. The newsletter contains relevant news items for this community, including events and recognition.
NEWSPAPER

La Voz De Dalton
Owner: Palacios Communications
Editorial: 737 Riverbend Rd, Dalton, Georgia 30721. **T:** 1 706 272-0113 **E:** lavoz@optilink.us
W: http://www.lavozgroup.com
Freq: Thu; **Circ:** 15000 Not Audited
Editorial Profile: La Voz is a bilingual English and Spanish newspaper covering News for the Hispanic community residing in the Dalton, GA area.; Full Page Mono: 17.00; Full Page Colour: 150.00
Currency: US Dollars
NEWSPAPER

La Voz de Houston
Owner: Hearst Newspapers
Editorial: 801 Texas St, Houston, Texas 77002-2904. **T:** 1 713 362-7171
W: http://www.chron.com/news/spanish
Freq: Wed; **Circ:** 100000 Not Audited
Editor: Aurora Losada; **Publisher:** Alejandro Sánchez
Editorial Profile: La Voz de Houston is a weekly newspaper published in Spanish. The paper provides Hispanic readers with local, national and international news with an emphasis on Hispanics and the news that affects them. Deadlines for press releases are Fridays at 5pm CT.; Full Page Mono: 89.00; Full Page Colour: 219.00
Currency: US Dollars
NEWSPAPER

La Voz de Indiana
Editorial: 2911 W Washington St, Indianapolis, Indiana 46222.
T: 1 317 423-0957
E: press@lavozdeindiana.com
W: http://www.lavozdeindiana.com
Freq: Bi-Monthly; **Circ:** 20000 Not Audited
Editor: Claudia Cuartas
Editorial Profile: La Voz de Indiana is written for the Hispanic residents of Indianapolis with international and regional news, events, cultural and feature stories. It is circulated to every major city in the state of Indiana and as far North as Detroit, East to Columbus and Dayton, OH, South to Lexington, KY and West to various cities in Illinois. Press releases should be in both English and Spanish and include a high resolution photograph.; Full Page Mono: 15.89
Currency: US Dollars
NEWSPAPER

La Voz De La Calle
Owner: The Voice Publishing Corp.
Editorial: 4696 E 10th Ct, Hialeah, Florida 33013. **T:** 1 305 687-5555
E: lavozdelacalle@bellsouth.net
W: http://www.lavozdelacalle.net
Freq: Fri; **Circ:** 25000 Not Audited
Editor: Victor Benitez; **Editor:** Julio Martinez; **Editor:** Rosa Martinez; **Editor:** Richard Patron; **Editor:** Jose Puig; **Editor:** Ana Rodriguez; **Editor:** Arelis Rodriguez; **Publisher:** Vincent Rodriguez; **News Editor:** Raul Tapanez Estrella
Editorial Profile: La Voz De La Calle is a weekly newspaper published for the Spanish-speaking Latin American community in Hialeah, FL. The newspaper is printed in Spanish and provides local, state and national news to its readers. Deadlines are on Wednesdays at noon ET.; Full Page Mono: 30.00; Full Page Colour: 30.00
Currency: US Dollars
NEWSPAPER

La Voz Hispana
Editorial: 159 E 116th St, New York, New York 10029. **T:** 1 212 348-8270
E: discomund@aol.com
W: http://www.lavozhispanany.com
Freq: Thu; **Circ:** 68000 Not Audited
Publisher: Nick Lugo
Editorial Profile: La Voz Hispana is a weekly newspaper which is printed in Spanish. The newspaper is distributed throughout New York City every Thursday. La Voz Hispana provides the Hispanic communities with local and national news. Other features include education, business, politics, entertainment, sports, and classifieds.; Full Page Mono: 32.00
Currency: US Dollars
NEWSPAPER

La Voz Hispana
Editorial: 51 Elm St Ste 307, New Haven, Connecticut 06510-2049. **T:** 1 203 865-2272
E: info@lavozhispanact.com
W: http://www.lavozhispanact.com
Freq: Weekly; **Circ:** 35000 Not Audited
Editor: Abelardo King; **Publisher:** Sully Saneaux
Editorial Profile: La Voz Hispana is a community newspaper serving the Hispanic community in and around New Haven, CT.; Full Page Mono: 11.65
Currency: US Dollars
NEWSPAPER

La Voz Hispana
Owner: La Voz Hispana
Editorial: 3552 Sullivant Ave, Columbus, Ohio 43204. **T:** 1 614 274-5505
E: lavozh@yahoo.com
W: http://www.lavozhispana.com
Freq: Fri; **Circ:** 20000 Not Audited
Editor: Cynthia Aguilar; **Publisher:** Alejandro Flores
Editorial Profile: La Voz Hispana is a local newspaper providing news to the community of Columbus, OH.; Full Page Mono: 45.00
Currency: US Dollars
NEWSPAPER

La Voz Hispanic
Editorial: 710 N 4Th Ave Ste A, Pasco, Washington 99301-3705. **T:** 1 509 547-6640
E: lavoz@bmi.net
W: http://www.lavozhispanicnews.com
Freq: Thu; **Circ:** 16000 Not Audited
Editor: Francisco Alveraz; **Publisher:** David Cortinas
Editorial Profile: La Voz Hispanic is a weekly Spanish-language community newspaper.; Full Page Mono: 14.60
Currency: US Dollars
NEWSPAPER

Voz Latina
Editorial: 1823 S Park St, Madison, Wisconsin 53713-1213. **T:** 1 608 255-0611
E: normalopez78@hotmail.com
Freq: Bi-Weekly; **Circ:** 10000 Not Audited
Editor: Rada Marcelo; **Publisher:** Luis Montoto
Editorial Profile: Voz Latina is a local newspaper written for the residents of Madison, WI.; Full Page Mono: 10.50
Currency: US Dollars
NEWSPAPER

La Voz Nueva
Owner: La Voz Publishing Company, Inc
Editorial: 4047 Tejon St, Denver, Colorado 80211-2214. **T:** 1 303 936-8556
E: news@lavozcolorado.com
W: http://www.lavozcolorado.com
Freq: Wed; **Circ:** 30000 Not Audited
Editorial Profile: La Voz Nueva is a weekly newspaper distributed throughout Denver. The newspaper is bilingual but is geared toward the Latino community. It provides regional news.; Full Page Mono: 21.00
Currency: US Dollars
NEWSPAPER

Wabash Plain Dealer
Owner: Paxton Media Group
Editorial: 123 W Canal St, Wabash, Indiana 46992-3042. **T:** 1 260 563-2131
E: news@wabashplaindealer.com
W: http://www.wabashplaindealer.com
Freq: Daily; **Circ:** 6108 Not Audited
Publisher: Misty Sharp
Editorial Profile: Wabash Plain Dealer is published daily for the residents of Wabash County, IN and surrounding areas. The newspaper provides information on news and community events.; Full Page Mono: 18.00; Full Page Colour: 225.00
Currency: US Dollars
DAILY NEWSPAPER

Waco Tribune-Herald
Owner: Robinson Media Co.
Editorial: 900 Franklin Ave, Waco, Texas 76701-1906. **T:** 1 254 757-5757
E: news@wacotrib.com
W: http://www.wacotrib.com
Freq: Daily; **Circ:** 29117 Not Audited
Editorial Profile: Waco Tribune-Herald is a daily newspaper for the residents of the Waco County, TX. It covers national and local news and events. Deadlines are the same day as the issue date. The outlet offers RSS (Really Simple Syndication).; Full Page Mono: 55.51; Full Page Colour: 487.00
Currency: US Dollars
DAILY NEWSPAPER

The Wake Weekly
Owner: Allen Publishing LLC
Editorial: 229 E Owen Ave, Wake Forest, North Carolina 27587. **T:** 1 919 556-3182
E: news@wakeweekly.com
W: http://www.wakeweekly.com
Freq: Thu; **Circ:** 10000 Not Audited
Publisher: Todd Allen
Editorial Profile: The Wake Weekly is a community newspaper for the residents of Wake Forest, NC. The paper covers local news, business, sports and arts & entertainment in zip codes 27587, 27571, 27614, 27616, 27525, 27596, 27549.; Full Page Mono: 11.00
Currency: US Dollars
NEWSPAPER

Wakefield Daily Item
Owner: Wakefield Item Co.
Editorial: 26 Albion St, Wakefield, Massachusetts 01880-2803.
T: 1 781 245-0080
E: news@wakefieldItem.com
W: http://www.wakefielditem.com

Freq: Mon thru Fri; **Circ:** 4556 Not Audited
Publisher: Glenn Dolbeare; **Editor:** Peter Rossi; **Editor:** Peter Rossi
Editorial Profile: Wakefield Daily Item is published daily for residents of Wakefield, MA and surrounding communities. The newspaper covers local news, weather, sports and community events. Feature artivles cover business, arts and entertainment and lifestyle.; Full Page Mono: 20.00; Full Page Colour: 225.00
Currency: US Dollars
DAILY NEWSPAPER

Waldron Mansfield Papers

Editorial: 200 S Main St, Waldron, Arkansas 72958. **T:** 1 479 637-4161
W: http://www.waldronnews.com **Circ:** 4375 Not Audited
NEWSPAPER

The Wall Street Journal

Owner: News Corporation Ltd.
Editorial: 1211 Avenue of the Americas Fl 4, New York, New York 10036-0003.
T: 1 212 416-2000 **E:** newseditors@wsj.com
W: http://online.wsj.com
Freq: Daily; **Circ:** 2294093 Not Audited
News Editor: Lisa Kalis; **News Editor:** Tom Loftus; **News Editor:** Richard Taliaferro; **News Editor:** Robert Walzer
Editorial Profile: The Wall Street Journal is considered the most widely-read periodical in the nation's business and investment community. Information in the paper is also distributed to many Dow Jones outlets, including news service and specialized financial and commodity reports. The paper produces tabloid-style supplements that appear several times each year called The Wall Street Journal Reports. Report topics include small business, world business, telecommunications, technology, executive pay and personal finance. Several sections appear throughout the week, including the Personal Journal, which covers health, automotive, technology and personal finance, a Greater New York metro section, which provides general consumer news content for their New York City readership and WSJ Weekend, which features lifestyle related news, cultural coverage and reviews. National supplement The Sunday Journal provides business content from the paper to business sections of many external daily newspapers. The lead time for feature and news coverage is one day to one week. The lead time for The Wall Street Journal Reports is three to five months, although stories are often developed during the two or three months immediately preceding the issue. The lead time for Marketplace and Enterprise is two months. Deadlines are at 5:30pm ET for in-depth business and Marketplace stories and 3pm ET for shorter stories. The paper does not publish a Holiday Gift Guide.; Full Page Mono: 2073.71; Full Page Colour: 2654.40
Currency: US Dollars
DAILY NEWSPAPER

The Wall Street Journal

Editorial: 407 N Maple Dr Ste 104, Beverly Hills, California 90210-3818.
T: 1 424 204-4827
Bureau Chief: Ethan Smith
DAILY NEWSPAPER

The Wall Street Journal

Editorial: 201 California St Fl 10, San Francisco, California 94111-5002.
T: 1 415 986-6886
News Editor: Michael Totty; **News Editor:** Michael Totty
DAILY NEWSPAPER

The Wall Street Journal

Editorial: 1025 Connecticut Ave NW Ste 800, Washington, District Of Columbia 20036-5419.
T: 1 202 862-9200
Editor: Autumn Brewington; **News Editor:** Mary Lu Carnevale
DAILY NEWSPAPER

The Wall Street Journal

Editorial: 1201 W Peachtree St NW Ste 2550, Atlanta, Georgia 30309
DAILY NEWSPAPER

The Wall Street Journal

Editorial: 1 S Wacker Dr, Chicago, Illinois 60606-4614. **T:** 1 312 750-4000
Bureau Chief: Jason Dean
DAILY NEWSPAPER

The Wall Street Journal

Editorial: 53 State St Ste 1201, Boston, Massachusetts 02109-3000.

T: 1 617 654-6700
DAILY NEWSPAPER

The Wall Street Journal

Editorial: 2000 Town Ctr Ste 750, Southfield, Michigan 48075-1127. **T:** 1 248 204-5500
DAILY NEWSPAPER

The Wall Street Journal

Editorial: 500 Grant St Ste 2750, Pittsburgh, Pennsylvania 15219-2509. **T:** 1 412 553-6900
Bureau Chief: Clare Ansberry
DAILY NEWSPAPER

The Wall Street Journal

Editorial: 1201 Elm St Ste 5050, Dallas, Texas 75270-2141. **T:** 1 214 951-7100
E: lonestar.bureau@wsj.com
DAILY NEWSPAPER

The Wall Street Journal

Editorial: 600 Travis St, Houston, Texas 77002-3009. **T:** 1 713 227-5440
E: lonestar.bureau@wsj.com
DAILY NEWSPAPER

Walla Walla Union-Bulletin

Owner: Seattle Times Co.
Editorial: 112 S 1st Ave, Walla Walla, Washington 99362-3011. **T:** 1 509 525-3300
W: http://www.union-bulletin.com
Freq: Daily; **Circ:** 12921 Not Audited
Editor: Rick Doyle
Editorial Profile: Walla Walla Union-Bulletin provides news for the local community. It is written for readers of all ages in Walla Walla, WA. Deadlines are five days before issue date.; Full Page Mono: 23.20; Full Page Colour: 486.00
Currency: US Dollars
DAILY NEWSPAPER

Walnut Creek Journal

Editorial: 2640 Shadelands Dr, Walnut Creek, California 94598-2513. **T:** 1 925 943-8241
E: wcjournal@cctimes.com
W: http://www.contracostatimes.com/walnutcreekjournal
Freq: Thu; **Circ:** 17651
Editor: Sam Richards; Full Page Mono: 15.65
Currency: US Dollars
NEWSPAPER

The Walton and Loganville Tribune Newspapers

Owner: Southern Newspapers, Inc.
Editorial: 124 N Broad St, Monroe, Georgia 30655. **T:** 1 770 267-8371
E: tribstaff@waltontribune.com
W: http://waltontribune.com **Circ:** 17300 Not Audited
Publisher: Brian Arrington
NEWSPAPER

The Walton Sun

Owner: Halifax Media Holdings LLC
Editorial: 5597 Highway 98 W, Ste 203, Santa Rosa Beach, Florida 32459-5363.
T: 1 850 267-4555 **E:** news@waltonsun.com
W: http://www.waltonsun.com
Freq: Sat; **Circ:** 12000 Not Audited
Editor: William Hatfield
Editorial Profile: The Walton Sun is written for residents and visitors of Walton County, FL.; Full Page Mono: 10.36
Currency: US Dollars
NEWSPAPER

The Wanderer

Owner: Wanderer Printing Co.
Editorial: 201 Ohio St, Saint Paul, Minnesota 55107-2003. **T:** 1 651 224-5733
E: editorial@thewandererpress.com
W: http://www.thewandererpress.com
Freq: Thu; **Circ:** 17000 Not Audited
Editor: Alphonse Matt
Editorial Profile: The Wanderer is a weekly newspaper written for residents in Saint Paul, MN and surrounding areas.; Full Page Mono: 14.00
Currency: US Dollars
NEWSPAPER

Wapakoneta Daily News

Owner: Horizon Publications
Editorial: 520 Industrial Dr, Wapakoneta, Ohio 45895-9200. **T:** 1 419 738-2128
W: http://www.wapakdailynews.com
Freq: Mon thru Fri; **Circ:** 5300 Not Audited
Publisher: Dianna Epperly
Editorial Profile: Wapakoneta Daily News strives to provide news and information to the residents of Wapakoneta, OH. Please send all mail correspondence to the PO Box address.; Full Page Mono: 13.34; Full Page Colour: 294.00

Currency: US Dollars
DAILY NEWSPAPER

Washington Chinese News

Owner: Lee & Lee Washington, Inc.
Editorial: 5848 Hubbard Dr, Rockville, Maryland 20852-4820. **T:** 1 301 984-8988
E: news@wchns.com
W: http://www.wchns.com
Freq: Sat; **Circ:** 15000 Not Audited
Publisher: Ray Hwang; **Editor:** Yen Lin; **Editor:** Ching Shu
Editorial Profile: Washington Chinese News is a community newspaper written for Chinese Americans in Rockville, MD.; Full Page Mono: 5.75
Currency: US Dollars
NEWSPAPER

Washington City Paper

Owner: SouthComm, Inc.
Editorial: 1400 I St NW Ste 900, Washington, District Of Columbia 20005-6527.
T: 1 202 332-2100
E: mail@washingtoncitypaper.com
W: http://www.washingtoncitypaper.com
Freq: Fri; **Circ:** 83000 Not Audited
Publisher: Amy Austin; **Editor:** Mike Madden
Editorial Profile: Washington City Paper is written for those living in or around Washington, D.C. The newspaper's editorial mission is to provide information regarding city life and arts & entertainment for single people, ages 20 to 50.; Full Page Mono: 25.44
Currency: US Dollars
NEWSPAPER

Washington County News

Owner: Gray and Gray Inc.
Editorial: 81 Grenade Ave, Chatom, Alabama 36518. **T:** 1 251 847-2599
W: http://www.washcountynews.com
Freq: Fri; **Circ:** 11500 Not Audited
Publisher: Willie Gray; **Editor:** Barry Hendrix
Editorial Profile: Washington County News is a local, weekly newspaper written for the residents of Chatom, AL.; Full Page Mono: 9.00
Currency: US Dollars
NEWSPAPER

Washington Daily News

Owner: Washington Newsmedia, LLC
Editorial: 217 N Market St, Washington, North Carolina 27889. **T:** 1 252 946-2144
E: news@wdnweb.com
W: http://www.wdnweb.com
Freq: Daily; **Circ:** 8736 Not Audited
Editorial Profile: Washington Daily News's editorial mission is to report local news to the community of Washington, NC. The paper is focused towards all age groups and all topics concerning the general public. The lead time for Washington Daily News is same day.; Full Page Mono: 11.00; Full Page Colour: 424.00
Currency: US Dollars
DAILY NEWSPAPER

Washington Evening Journal

Owner: Inland Media Comapny, Inc.
Editorial: 111 N Marion Ave, Washington, Iowa 52353. **T:** 1 319 653-2191
W: http://www.washjrnl.com
Freq: Daily; **Circ:** 3850 Not Audited
News Editor: David Holte
Editorial Profile: Washington Evening Journal is a local daily newspaper written for the residents of Washington County, IA. The publication focuses on local news of Washington County, but national news is also included if it applies to the community.; Full Page Mono: 10.88; Full Page Colour: 34.61
Currency: US Dollars
DAILY NEWSPAPER

Washington Hispanic

Owner: Washington Hispanic, Inc.
Editorial: 8455 Colesville Rd Ste 700, Silver Spring, Maryland 20910-3318.
T: 1 202 667-8881
E: info@washingtonhispanic.com
W: http://www.washingtonhispanic.com
Freq: Fri; **Circ:** 45000 Not Audited
Editor: Nelly Carrion
Editorial Profile: Washington Hispanic is an independent weekly Spanish-language newspaper which serves the Washington metropolitan area. The publication's goal is to inform the area's Hispanic community as well as other community groups about local, national, and international news and events. The lead time for Washington Hispanic is three days.; Full Page Mono: 40.00
Currency: US Dollars
NEWSPAPER

The Washington Informer

Editorial: 3117 Martin Luther King Jr Ave SE, Washington, District Of Columbia 20032.
T: 1 202 561-4100
E: news@washingtoninformer.com
W: http://www.washingtoninformer.com
Freq: Thu; **Circ:** 17000 Not Audited
Publisher: Denise Rolark-Barnes; **Publisher:** Denise Rolark-Barnes
Editorial Profile: The Washington Informer is a weekly newspaper covering news, issues and features relating to the African American community of Washington, D.C. Deadlines are on Mondays at 5pm ET. The editorial staff asks that all press materials be directed to the main e-mail address.; Full Page Mono: 37.98; Full Page Colour: 2311.00
Currency: US Dollars
NEWSPAPER

Washington Jewish Week

Owner: Washington Jewish Week, LLC
Editorial: 11426 Rockville Pike, Ste 236, Rockville, Maryland 20852. **T:** 1 301 230-2222
E: wjweek@aol.com
W: http://www.washingtonjewishweek.com
Freq: Thu; **Circ:** 10000 Not Audited
Publisher: Craig Burke
Editorial Profile: Washington Jewish Week is a weekly newspaper that covers social issues affecting the Jewish communities of Washington, D.C., Maryland and northern Virginia.; Full Page Mono: 23.60
Currency: US Dollars
NEWSPAPER

Washington Park Profile

Editorial: 617 E Jewell Ave, Denver, Colorado 80210-4038. **T:** 1 303 778-8021
E: wpprofile@qwestoffice.net
W: http://www.washingtonparkprofile.com
Freq: Monthly; **Circ:** 16000 Not Audited
Editor: Eileen Abbattista; **Editor:** Eileen Abbattista; **Publisher:** Paul Kashmann
Editorial Profile: The Washington Park Profile is a monthly newspaper written for residents of the communities surrounding Denver. The publication covers local news of the city and national news if it applies to the area. Deadlines for editorial submissions are the fourth Wednesdays of the month prior to the issue date.; Full Page Mono: 20.74
Currency: US Dollars
NEWSPAPER

The Washington Post

Owner: Washington Post Co.
Editorial: 1150 15th St NW, Washington, District Of Columbia 20071-0001.
T: 1 202 334-6000
W: http://www.washingtonpost.com
Freq: Daily; **Circ:** 436601 Not Audited
Bureau Chief: Anthony Faiola; **Editor:** Matthew McFarland; **Editor:** Frances Sellers; **News Editor:** Barbara Vobejda; **Publisher:** Katharine Weymouth
Editorial Profile: The Washington Post focuses on news from the nation's capital, including national business, political issues, commerce, federal regulations and finance. There is also coverage of sports, entertainment, features, local and world news. It has a content share agreement for technology stories from The Verge. Lead times vary. All local bureaus, with the exception of Annapolis and Richmond, will be closing in early 2012.; Full Page Mono: 909.00; Full Page Colour: 994.60
Currency: US Dollars
DAILY NEWSPAPER

The Washington Post

Editorial: 1001 E Main St Ste 203, Richmond, Virginia 23219-3536. **T:** 1 804 649-7575
DAILY NEWSPAPER

The Washington Post

Editorial: 526 King St Ste 515, Alexandria, Virginia 22314-3143. **T:** 1 703 518-3000
DAILY NEWSPAPER

The Washington Post

Editorial: 305 Harrison St SE, Leesburg, Virginia 20175-3729. **T:** 1 703 771-4102
E: lextra@washpost.com
DAILY NEWSPAPER

The Washington Post

Editorial: 3 Church Cir, Annapolis, Maryland 21401-1932 **E:** aaextra@washpost.com
DAILY NEWSPAPER

The Washington Post

Editorial: 4020 University Dr, Fairfax, Virginia 22030-6802. **T:** 1 703 383-5100
E: fxliving@washpost.com
DAILY NEWSPAPER

The Washington Post
Editorial: 9500 Arena Dr, Largo, Maryland 20774-3701. **T:** 1 301 618-1720
E: pgextra@washpost.com
DAILY NEWSPAPER

The Washington Post
Editorial: 51 Monroe St, Rockville, Maryland 20850-2419. **T:** 1 301 294-2600
E: mocoextra@washpost.com
Editorial Profile: This bureau publishes the Montgomery Extra print edition of the Washington Post.
DAILY NEWSPAPER

The Washington Post
Editorial: 9420 Battle St, Manassas, Virginia 20110-5432. **T:** 1 703 392-1303
DAILY NEWSPAPER

Washington Sun
Editorial: 830 Kennedy St NW Ste B2, Washington, District Of Columbia 20011-2948.
T: 1 202 882-1021
E: thewashingtonsun@aol.com
W: http://thewashingtonsun.com
Freq: Thu; **Circ:** 55000 Not Audited
Editorial Profile: Washington Sun is published weekly for members of the African American community throughout the United States. The newspaper covers local, national and international news, social issues and other topics of interest to African Americans.; Full Page Mono: 16.80
Currency: US Dollars
NEWSPAPER

The Washington Times
Owner: The Washington Times LLC
Editorial: 3600 New York Ave NE, Washington, District Of Columbia 20002-1947.
T: 1 202 636-3000
W: http://www.washingtontimes.com
Freq: Mon thru Fri; **Circ:** 31838 Not Audited
Editor: John Solomon
Editorial Profile: The Washington Times is a general interest daily newspaper that offers coverage of the greater Washington, D.C. area. Its mission is to provide readers with breaking news and news analysis. It offers a complete listing of the day's important scheduled events, a daily congressional briefing and an international briefing about happenings in the diplomatic community. Send all press materials directly to the Managing Editor, that address is configured to be a general inbox for the newsroom.
DAILY NEWSPAPER

The Washington Times - National Weekly Edition
Owner: Washington Times, LLC
Editorial: 3600 New York Ave NE, Washington, District Of Columbia 20002-1947.
T: 1 202 636-3000
W: http://www.washingtontimes.com
Freq: Sun; **Circ:** 79000 Not Audited
Editorial Profile: The Washington Times - National Weekly edition was founded in 1994. Send all press materials directly to the Managing Editor, that address is configured to be a general inbox for the newsroom.; Full Page Mono: 1800.00; Full Page Colour: 2400.00
Currency: US Dollars
NEWSPAPER

Washington Times-Herald
Owner: Community Newspaper Holdings, Inc.
Editorial: 102 E Van Trees St, Washington, Indiana 47501-2943. **T:** 1 812 254-0480
W: http://www.washtimesherald.com
Freq: Daily; **Circ:** 6849
Publisher: Harold Allen; **Editor:** Melody Brunson; **Editor:** Kelly Overton
Editorial Profile: Washington Times-Herald is published daily for residents of Washington, IN and the surrounding area. The newspaper covers local and state news, business, sports, lifestyles and entertainment.; Full Page Mono: 10.90
Currency: US Dollars
DAILY NEWSPAPER

Waterbury Republican-American
Owner: American-Republican Inc.
Editorial: 389 Meadow St, Waterbury, Connecticut 06702-1808. **T:** 1 203 574-3636
E: releases@rep-am.com
W: http://www.rep-am.com
Freq: Daily; **Circ:** 38797 Not Audited
News Editor: Greg Hanisek; **News Editor:** Greg Hanisek; **News Editor:** Greg Hanisek; **News Editor:** Greg Hanisek
Editorial Profile: Waterbury Republican-American was founded in 1844. Its editorial mission is to provide local, national and

international news to the residents of Waterbury, CT.; Full Page Mono: 55.65; Full Page Colour: 183.41
Currency: US Dollars
DAILY NEWSPAPER

Waterbury Republican-American
Editorial: 101 Main St, Torrington, Connecticut 06790-5306. **T:** 1 860 489-4615
DAILY NEWSPAPER

Waterbury Republican-American
Editorial: 207 Playhouse Cor, Southbury, Connecticut 06488-2265. **T:** 1 203 264-5554
Bureau Chief: Chris Gardner
DAILY NEWSPAPER

The Waterloo-Cedar Falls Courier
Owner: Lee Enterprises, Inc.
Editorial: 501 Commercial St, Waterloo, Iowa 50701-5413. **T:** 1 319 291-1400
E: newsroom@wcfcourier.com
W: http://www.wcfcourier.com
Freq: Mon thru Fri; **Circ:** 38732
Publisher: David Braton; **News Editor:** Pat Kinney; **Editor:** Dennis Magee; **Editor:** Nancy Raffensperger Newhoff
Editorial Profile: Waterloo-Cedar Falls Courier is a daily, local newspaper for the Waterloo/Cedar Falls, IA area. The newspaper covers local news, business, sports and arts & entertainment stories. It also covers national and statewide stories if they have a direct impact on the newspaper's readership.; Full Page Mono: 43.13; Full Page Colour: 475.00
Currency: US Dollars
DAILY NEWSPAPER

Watertown Daily Times
Owner: Johnson Newspaper Corp.
Editorial: 260 Washington St, Watertown, New York 13601-3301. **T:** 1 315 782-1000
E: news@wdt.net
W: http://www.watertowndailytimes.com
Freq: Daily; **Circ:** 18319 Not Audited
Editor: Judy Jacobs; **Editor:** Mary Kaskan
Editorial Profile: Watertown Daily Times is a daily newspaper written for residents of Northern New York. The newspaper covers local, state, and national news, events and sports.; Full Page Mono: 12.72; Full Page Colour: 185.00
Currency: US Dollars
DAILY NEWSPAPER

Watertown Daily Times
Owner: Times Publishing Company
Editorial: 113 W Main St, 115115, Watertown, Wisconsin 53094. **T:** 1 920 261-5161
E: news1@wdtimes.com
W: http://www.wdtimes.com
Freq: Daily; **Circ:** 9510 Not Audited
Editor: James Clifford
Editorial Profile: Watertown Daily Times is a local newspaper written for residents in Watertown, WI. The newspaper covers local, national and international news, sports and community events.; Full Page Mono: 11.65; Full Page Colour: 185.00
Currency: US Dollars
DAILY NEWSPAPER

Watertown Public Opinion
Owner: United Communications Corp.
Editorial: 120 3rd Ave NW, Watertown, South Dakota 57201-2311. **T:** 1 605 886-6901
E: news@thepublicopinion.com
W: http://www.thepublicopinion.com
Freq: Daily; **Circ:** 11228
News Editor: Wayne Hammond; **Editor:** Roger Merriam; **Editor:** Terry O'Keefe; **Publisher:** Mark Roby
Editorial Profile: Watertown Public Opinion is a daily newspaper written for residents of Watertown, SD and surrounding areas. The newspaper covers local and regional news, sports, education, lifestyles and entertainment.; Full Page Mono: 25.00; Full Page Colour: 190.00
Currency: US Dollars
DAILY NEWSPAPER

Watertown Town Times
Owner: Prime Publishers Inc.
Editorial: 469 Main St, Watertown, Connecticut 06795-2628. **T:** 1 860 274-8851
E: newsdept@towntimesnews.com
W: http://www.towntimesnews.com
Freq: Thu; **Circ:** 17000 Not Audited
Editor: James Dreher; **Publisher:** Rudy Mazurosky; **Editor:** James Taylor
Editorial Profile: Watertown Town Times is written for the residents of Watertown, CT and the surrounding area. It covers local and national news. Deadlines are on Fridays.; Full Page Mono: 15.96
Currency: US Dollars

NEWSPAPER

Waupaca Publishing
Owner: Journal Register Company
Editorial: 600 Industrial Dr, Waupaca, Wisconsin 54981-8814. **T:** 1 715 258-5546
W: http://www.waupacanow.com **Circ:** 12190
Editor: Robert Cloud; **Editor:** Sharon Van Ryzin
Editorial Profile: Waupaca Publishing prints the Waupauca County Post East and West editions.
NEWSPAPER

Wausau Daily Herald
Owner: Gannett Co., Inc.
Editorial: 800 Scott St, Wausau, Wisconsin 54403-4951. **T:** 1 715 842-2101
E: announcements@wdhprint.com
W: http://www.wausaudailyherald.com
Freq: Daily; **Circ:** 13978 Not Audited
Publisher: Michael Beck
Editorial Profile: Wausau Daily Herald is a local daily newspaper written for residents of Marathon County and Lincoln County, WI. Deadlines are at 8am CT.; Full Page Mono: 40.80; Full Page Colour: 719.30
Currency: US Dollars
DAILY NEWSPAPER

The Wave and Los Angeles Independent Newspaper Group
Owner: Equal Access Media Inc.
Editorial: 3731 Wilshire Blvd Suite 840, Los Angeles, California 90015-1008.
T: 1 323 556-5720
W: http://www.laindependent.com
Freq: Weekly; **Circ:** 298435 Not Audited
Publisher: Pluria Marshall
NEWSPAPER

The Wave Inc.
Owner: Hartman Newspapers, Inc.
Editorial: 107 E Austin St, Port Lavaca, Texas 77979-4402. **T:** 1 361 552-9788
E: news@plwave.com
W: http://www.portlavacawave.com
Freq: Sat; **Circ:** 4400 Not Audited; Full Page Mono: 9.00
Currency: US Dollars
NEWSPAPER

Wave of Long Island
Owner: Wave Publishing Co.
Editorial: 8808 Rockaway Beach Blvd, Rockaway Beach, New York 11693.
T: 1 718 634-4000
W: http://www.rockawave.com
Freq: Fri; **Circ:** 12300 Not Audited
Publisher: Susan Locke
Editorial Profile: Wave of Long Island is a local newspaper that serves the residents of Rockaway Beach, NY. It covers local news, weather and sports.; Full Page Mono: 20.00; Full Page Colour: 760.00
Currency: US Dollars
NEWSPAPER

Wave Publishing Company
Editorial: 165 S 100 W, Heber City, Utah 84032-2001. **T:** 1 435 654-1471
E: editor@wasatchwave.com
W: http://www.wasatchwave.com **Circ:** 5900 Not Audited
NEWSPAPER

Waverly Newspapers
Owner: Community Media Group
Editorial: 311 W Bremer Ave, Waverly, Iowa 50677. **T:** 1 319 352-3334
E: news@waverlynewspapers.com
W: http://www.waverlynewspapers.com
Circ: 12800 Not Audited
Editor: Anelia Dimitrova
NEWSPAPER

Waxahachie Daily Light
Owner: Waxahachie Newspapers Inc.
Editorial: 200 W Marvin Ave, Waxahachie, Texas 75165-3040. **T:** 1 972 937-3310
W: http://www.thedailylight.com
Freq: Mon thru Fri; **Circ:** 5027 Not Audited
Publisher: Jeffrey Para; **Editor:** Neal White
Editorial Profile: Waxahachie Daily Light, founded in 1867, has been providing news for Waxahachie, TX and the surrounding communities for more than 133 years. Its focus is providing readers with local news - the events and people of note in Ellis County, TX. Deadlines are at 10am CT.; Full Page Mono: 9.70; Full Page Colour: 175.00
Currency: US Dollars
DAILY NEWSPAPER

Waxahachie Newspapers, Inc.
Owner: American Consolidated Media

Editorial: 200 W Marvin Ave, Waxahachie, Texas 75165. **T:** 1 972 937-3310
W: http://www.waxahachiedailylight.com
Circ: 4800 Not Audited
Editor: Paul Gauntt; **Publisher:** Jeffrey Para; **Editor:** Neal White
Editorial Profile: Waxahachie Newspapers, Inc. has been providing news for the Waxahachie, TX and surrounding communities since 1867. The papers' focus is to provide readers with local news, events and people of note in the community. All mail must be sent to the P.O. address.
NEWSPAPER

Waycross Journal-Herald
Owner: Waycross Journal-Herald Inc.
Editorial: 400 Isabella St, Waycross, Georgia 31501. **T:** 1 912 283-2244
E: newsroom@wjhnews.com
W: http://www.wjhnews.com
Freq: Daily; **Circ:** 10100 Not Audited
Editor: Scott Cooper; **Editor:** Jack Williams; **Publisher:** Roger Williams
Editorial Profile: Waycross Journal-Herald is the official legal organ of Ware County, GA. The daily paper that has been serving Waycross County, GA and the surrounding area since 1875.; Full Page Mono: 15.00; Full Page Colour: 200.00
Currency: US Dollars
DAILY NEWSPAPER

Wayne County News
Editorial: 310 Central Ave, Wayne, West Virginia 25570-9602. **T:** 1 304 272-3433
W: http://www.waynecountynews.com
Freq: Daily; **Circ:** 5100 Not Audited
Editorial Profile: Wayne County News is written for residents of Wayne County, WV and the surrounding area. The publication aims to bring local news to the community.; Full Page Mono: 11.75
Currency: US Dollars
DAILY NEWSPAPER

Wayne County Newspapers, Inc.
Editorial: 205 W Jackson St, Corydon, Iowa 50060-1418. **T:** 1 641 872-1234
W: http://www.corydontimes.com **Circ:** 3000 Not Audited
Publisher: Rhonda Bennett; **Editor:** Willa Clark
NEWSPAPER

The Wayne Independent
Owner: Fortress Investment Group, LLC
Editorial: 220 8th St, Honesdale, Pennsylvania 18431-1854. **T:** 1 570 253-3055
W: http://www.wayneindependent.com
Freq: Daily; **Circ:** 4297 Not Audited
Publisher: Michelle Hessling
Editorial Profile: The Wayne Independent is written for the residents of Wayne County, PA. Deadlines are two days before publication date at 5pm ET.; Full Page Mono: 15.25; Full Page Colour: 19.02
Currency: US Dollars
DAILY NEWSPAPER

Waynedale News
Editorial: 2700 Lower Huntington Rd, Fort Wayne, Indiana 46809. **T:** 1 219 747-4535
E: news@waynedalenews.com
W: http://www.waynedalenews.com
Freq: Bi-Weekly; **Circ:** 11000 Not Audited
Editorial Profile: The Waynedale News is a free, bi-weekly newspaper written for the residents of southwest Fort Wayne, IN, including the communities of Waynedale, Wildwood, Foster Park, Time Corners, Coventry, Zanesville and surrounding areas. It covers local news, businesses, schools, government, sports, editorials and features of interest to area readers.; Full Page Mono: 13.00
Currency: US Dollars
NEWSPAPER

Waynesboro Record Herald
Owner: Fortress Investment Group, LLC
Editorial: 30 Walnut St, Waynesboro, Pennsylvania 17268. **T:** 1 717 762-2151
W: http://www.therecordherald.com
Freq: Mon thru Fri; **Circ:** 9928 Not Audited
Editor: Shawn Hardy; **Publisher:** Pat Patterson
Editorial Profile: Waynesboro Record Herald is written for the residents of Waynesboro, PA and the surrounding area. It brings local news, sporting events and general community events to the residents of the area. Deadlines are at 10:30am ET the day of publication.; Full Page Mono: 14.90; Full Page Colour: 56.21
Currency: US Dollars
DAILY NEWSPAPER

Wayuga Community Newspapers, Inc.

Editorial: 6784 W Main St, Red Creek, New York 13143. **T:** 1 315 754-6229
E: star@wayuga.com **Circ:** 5500 Not Audited
Editor: Louise Broach; **Publisher:** Angelo Palermo
NEWSPAPER

Weatherford Daily News

Editorial: 118 S Broadway St, Weatherford, Oklahoma 73096. **T:** 1 580 772-3301
E: wdn@wdnonline.com
W: http://www.wdnonline.com
Freq: Daily; **Circ:** 4893 Not Audited
Publisher: Phillip Reid
Editorial Profile: Weatherford Daily News is the daily newspaper for Weatherford, OK. The newspaper focuses on local news and events for the area's residents. Sections include news, sports, public records, community calendar, school calendar and classified ads.; Full Page Mono: 13.74; Full Page Colour: 85.00
Currency: US Dollars
DAILY NEWSPAPER

Weatherford Democrat

Owner: Community Newspaper Holdings, Inc.
Editorial: 512 Palo Pinto St, Weatherford, Texas 76086-4197. **T:** 1 817 594-7447
E: editor@weatherforddemocrat.com
W: http://www.weatherforddemocrat.com
Freq: Daily; **Circ:** 6500 Not Audited
Publisher: Julie Killion; **Editor:** David May
Editorial Profile: Weatherford Democrat's editorial mission is to provide the local news and information to Weatherford and Parker County residents. The deadline for the publication is the day before issue date by 10am CT.; Full Page Mono: 12.50; Full Page Colour: 250.00
Currency: US Dollars
DAILY NEWSPAPER

Weatherford Telegram

Owner: McClatchy Newspapers
Editorial: 112 S Main St, Weatherford, Texas 76086-4320. **T:** 1 817 594-9902
W: http://www.weatherfordtelegram.net
Freq: Wed; **Circ:** 34000
Publisher: Lance Winter
Editorial Profile: Weatherford Telegram is published weekly for the residents of Weatherford, TX and surrounding areas. The newspaper cover local news, sports, lifestyles, religion and community events.; Full Page Mono: 24.07
Currency: US Dollars
NEWSPAPER

Webster County Publishing Company, Inc.

Owner: Webster County Publishing Co. Inc.
Editorial: 221 S Commercial St, Seymour, Missouri 65746-8743. **T:** 1 417 935-2257
E: citizen190@gmail.com
W: http://www.webstercountycitizen.com
Circ: 5116 Not Audited
NEWSPAPER

Webster-Kirkwood Times, Inc.

Editorial: 122 W Lockwood Ave, 2nd Fl, Saint Louis, Missouri 63119. **T:** 1 314 968-2699
E: newsroom@timesnewspapers.com
W: http://www.timesnewspapers.com
Circ: 72400 Not Audited
Publisher: Dwight Bitikofer; **Editor In Chief:** Don Corrigan
NEWSPAPER

Wedgwood Shopping News

Editorial: 6001 Granbury Rd, Fort Worth, Texas 76133. **T:** 1 817 292-2260
E: wsn@mesh.net
Freq: Bi-Weekly; **Circ:** 25000 Not Audited
Publisher: Carla Duke
Editorial Profile: Wedgwood Shopping News is a local newspaper serving the residents of Fort Worth, TX. The paper includes local news, a shopping guide, profiles on advertisers and community information.; Full Page Mono: 10.60
Currency: US Dollars
NEWSPAPER

Wednesday Journal Publishing Co.

Editorial: 141 S Oak Park Ave, Oak Park, Illinois 60302-2972. **T:** 1 708 524-8300
W: http://www.wjinc.com **Circ:** 59350 Not Audited
News Editor: Terry Dean; **Publisher:** Dan Haley; **Editor:** Jean Lotus
NEWSPAPER

The Weekender

Owner: Sentinel-Standard Inc.

Editorial: 114 N Depot St, Ionia, Michigan 48846. **T:** 1 616 527-2100
W: http://www.sentinel-standard.com
Freq: Sun; **Circ:** 23500 Not Audited
Publisher: Cindy Conrad; **Editor:** Lori Kilchermann
Editorial Profile: The Weekender is a local daily newspaper written for citizens of Ionia County, MI. The publication provides coverage of local news and events, as well as national and international news that pertains to the community.; Full Page Mono: 14.75
Currency: US Dollars
NEWSPAPER

The Weekly

Owner: Paper of Montgomery Co. (The)
Editorial: 101 W Main St, Ste 300, Crawfordsville, Indiana 47933.
T: 1 765 361-0100
E: news@thepaper24-7.com
W: http://www.thepaper24-7.com
Freq: Tue; **Circ:** 12500 Not Audited
Editorial Profile: The Weekly provides local and national news to Montgomery, Fountain, Park and Putman counties, IN. It shares its editorial staff and offices with The Paper of Montgomery County.; Full Page Mono: 16.00
Currency: US Dollars
NEWSPAPER

The WEEKLY

Owner: Chapel Hill Media Inc.
Editorial: 190 Finley Golf Course Rd, Chapel Hill, North Carolina 27517-4473.
T: 1 919 933-1551
W: http://www.chapelhillweekly.com
Freq: Thu
Editor: Evan Markfield; **Publisher:** Dan Shannon
Editorial Profile: The WEEKLY is a community newspaper focusing on local news in Chapel Hill, NC.; Full Page Mono: 10.40
Currency: US Dollars
NEWSPAPER

Weekly & Beacon

Owner: Northeast Publishing
Editorial: 491 Main St, Bangor, Maine 04401-6296. **T:** 1 207 990-8139
E: beacon@bangordailynews.com
W: http://www.maineville.com
Editor: Ardeana Hamlin; **Publisher:** Richard Warren
NEWSPAPER

Weekly Alibi

Owner: NuCity Publications
Editorial: 413 Central Ave Nw, Albuquerque, New Mexico 87102-3219. **T:** 1 505 346-0660
E: alibi@alibi.com **W:** http://www.alibi.com
Freq: Thu; **Circ:** 45000 Not Audited
Editorial Profile: Weekly Alibi in Albuquerque, NM is a weekly newspaper that covers local news and events.; Full Page Mono: 80.96
Currency: US Dollars
NEWSPAPER

The Weekly Challenger

Owner: Weekly Challenger, Inc
Editorial: 2500 Dr Martin Luther King Jr St S, Ste F, Saint Petersburg, Florida 33705.
T: 1 727 896-2922
E: editor@theweeklychallenger.com
W: http://www.theweeklychallenger.com
Freq: Thu; **Circ:** 25000 Not Audited
Editorial Profile: The Weekly Challenger in Saint Petersburg, FL is published weekly for African American residents of north central Florida, Tampa and Saint Petersburg, FL. The newspaper covers local news, weather, sports and community events. Feature articles cover African American history, business, politics, education, arts & entertainment and lifestyle. The publication is a member of the National Newspaper Publishers Association Inc.; Full Page Mono: 28.00; Full Page Colour: 325.00
Currency: US Dollars
NEWSPAPER

The Weekly Citizen

Editorial: 308 S Thornton Ave, Dalton, Georgia 30720. **T:** 1 706 217-6397
E: sitefeedback@daltoncitizen.com
W: http://daltondailycitizen.com
Freq: Mon; **Circ:** 19800
News Editor: Daniel Olson
Editorial Profile: The Weekly Citizen is published weekly for the citizens of Dalton, GA and the surrounding communities.; Full Page Mono: 6.00
Currency: US Dollars
NEWSPAPER

The Weekly News

Owner: Armijo Newspapers & Public Relations

Editorial: 14144 Central Ave. #B, Chino, California 91710. **T:** 1 909 464-1200
W: http://www.anapr.com/category/the-weekly-news/
Freq: Fri
Editor: Sarah Armijo
Editorial Profile: The Weekly News is a weekly newspaper providing Local and Community News coverage to the residents of the communities of Walnut, Diamond Bar, Chino Hills, Rowland Heights and Phillips Ranch, CA.
NEWSPAPER

Weekly News Publishing

Owner: Suburban Publishing
Editorial: 10 1st Ave, Peabody, Massachusetts 1960. **T:** 1 978 532-5880
E: editor@weeklynews.net
W: http://www.weeklynews.net **Circ:** 20000 Not Audited
Editor: Jeff Shmase
Editorial Profile: Weekly News Publishing is a community newspaper publisher serving the communities of Peabody, MA and Lynnfield, MA with the Peabody (MA) Weekly News and the Winfield (MA) Weekly News.
NEWSPAPER

Weekly Press and Review Newspapers

Editorial: 218 S 45th St, Philadelphia, Pennsylvania 19104-2919. **T:** 1 215 222-2846
W: http://www.weeklypress.com **Circ:** 30000 Not Audited
NEWSPAPER

The Weekly Sentinel

Editorial: 952 Post Rd Unit 10, Wells, Maine 04090-4142. **T:** 1 207 646-8448
E: editor@theweeklysentinel.com
W: http://www.theweeklysentinel.com
Freq: Fri; **Circ:** 37962
Editorial Profile: The Weekly Sentinel is a community newspaper for the residents of Wells, ME and the surrounding communities.; Full Page Mono: 12.00
Currency: US Dollars
NEWSPAPER

Weekly Surge

Editorial: 914 Frontage Rd E, Myrtle Beach, South Carolina 29577-6700.
T: 1 843 443-2462
W: http://www.weeklysurge.com
Freq: Thu; **Circ:** 25000 Not Audited
Editor: Kent Kimes
Editorial Profile: Weekly Surge is an alternative newspaper serving the residents of Myrtle Beach, SC. The paper includes arts & entertainment, news, local events, politics and lifestyle information.; Full Page Mono: 25.00; Full Page Colour: 12.06
Currency: US Dollars
NEWSPAPER

The Weekly Villager

Owner: Villager Newspapers
Editorial: 10661 Highland Ave, Garrettsville, Ohio 44231-1104. **T:** 1 330 527-5761
E: news@weeklyvillager.com
W: http://www.weeklyvillager.com
Freq: Thu; **Circ:** 15000 Not Audited
Editorial Profile: The Weekly Villager is a free, weekly newspaper serving the communities of Garretsville, Newton Falls, Burton and Middlefield, OH. It covers local news, events, entertainment and features.; Full Page Mono: 7.50
Currency: US Dollars
NEWSPAPER

The Weirs Times

Owner: Weirs Publishing Co., Inc.
Editorial: 515 Endicott St N, Laconia, New Hampshire 03246-1725. **T:** 1 603 366-8463
E: info@weirs.com **W:** http://www.weirs.com
Freq: Thu; **Circ:** 30000 Not Audited
Publisher: Robert Lawton; **Editor:** Brendan Smith
Editorial Profile: The Weirs Times is a local newspaper written for residents of Laconia, NH. The newspaper covers local news, sports, business, entertainment, and events.; Full Page Mono: 12.30
Currency: US Dollars
NEWSPAPER

Weirton Daily Times

Owner: Ogden Newspapers
Editorial: 401 Herald Sq, Steubenville, Ohio 43952-2059. **T:** 1 304 748-0606
E: newsroom@heraldstaronline.com
W: http://www.weirtondailytimes.com
Freq: Daily; **Circ:** 4143 Not Audited
Publisher: Alex Marshall
Editorial Profile: Weirton Daily Times is a daily newspaper that provides local, national

and international news for the residents of Weirton, WV.; Full Page Mono: 48.44; Full Page Colour: 312.61
Currency: US Dollars
DAILY NEWSPAPER

Welch Publishing Company

Editorial: 117 E 2nd St, Perrysburg, Ohio 43551. **T:** 1 419 874-4491
E: publisher@perrysburg.com
W: http://perrysburg.com **Circ:** 35125
Editor: Deb Buker
Editorial Profile: Welch Publishing Company, of Perrysburg, OH, publishes local newspapers in the state of Ohio, including: the Perrysburg Messenger Journal; Rossford Record Journal; Holland-Springfield Journal, and Point and Shoreland Journal.
NEWSPAPER

Wellington Daily News

Owner: Fortress Investment Group, LLC
Editorial: 113 W Harvey Ave, Wellington, Kansas 67152-3840. **T:** 1 620 326-3326
W: http://www.wellingtondailynews.com
Freq: Daily; **Circ:** 2900 Not Audited
Editorial Profile: Wellington Daily News is published daily for the residents of Wellington, KS and surrounding areas. The newspaper covers local and state news, business, sports, lifestyles and arts & entertainment.; Full Page Mono: 9.00; Full Page Colour: 11.00
Currency: US Dollars
DAILY NEWSPAPER

Wells Newspapers

Owner: Sadie Wells
Editorial: 100 S Thayer St, Spencer, Nebraska 68777-9784. **T:** 1 402 589-1010
E: advocate@nntc.net **Circ:** 1729 Not Audited
NEWSPAPER

Wellsville Daily Reporter

Owner: Fortress Investment Group, LLC
Editorial: 159 N Main St, Wellsville, New York 14895-1158. **T:** 1 585 593-5300
W: http://www.wellsvilledaily.com
Freq: Daily; **Circ:** 4500 Not Audited
Editor: John Anderson; **Publisher:** Oak Duke
Editorial Profile: Wellsville Daily Reporter is written to bring local news to Alleghany County, NY.; Full Page Mono: 8.50; Full Page Colour: 100.00
Currency: US Dollars
DAILY NEWSPAPER

Wenatchee World

Owner: World Publishing Co.
Editorial: 14 N Mission St, Wenatchee, Washington 98801-2240. **T:** 1 509 663-5161
E: newsroom@wenworld.com
W: http://www.wenatcheeworld.com
Freq: Daily; **Circ:** 19356 Not Audited
News Editor: John Taylor
Editorial Profile: Wenatchee World is a daily newspaper that covers regional news for Wenatchee, WA. The newspaper features topics such as local business, recreation, arts and entertainment, sports, business, agriculture, community, classifieds, government, transportation, family, faith and health.; Full Page Mono: 32.10; Full Page Colour: 103.46
Currency: US Dollars
DAILY NEWSPAPER

West 10 Newspapers

Owner: West 10 Newspapers
Editorial: 2850 Stage Village Cv, Ste 5, Bartlett, Tennessee 38134-4682.
T: 1 901 388-1500 **Circ:** 40000
Editor: Dawn Boone; **Editor:** Graham Sweeney
NEWSPAPER

West Bend Daily Times & Hartford Times Press

Editorial: 100 S 6th Ave, West Bend, Wisconsin 53095-3309. **T:** 1 262 338-0622
W: http://www.gmtoday.com
Publisher: Philip Paige
DAILY NEWSPAPER

West Branch Communications

Owner: West Branch Communications, Inc.
Editorial: 102 N Market St, Solon, Iowa 52333-7702. **T:** 1 319 624-2233
E: hybrid@southslope.net **Circ:** 1800 Not Audited
Publisher: Doug Lindner; **Editor:** Lori Lindner
NEWSPAPER

West Central Publishing

Editorial: 206 George St, Saint Marys, West Virginia 26170-1024. **T:** 1 304 684-2424
E: news@oracleandleader.com
W: http://oracleandleader.com **Circ:** 13000
NEWSPAPER

West Central Tribune
Owner: Forum Communications Co.
Editorial: 2208 Trott Ave Sw, Willmar, Minnesota 56201-2723. **T:** 1 320 235-1150
E: news@wctrib.com
W: http://www.wctrib.com
Freq: Daily; **Circ:** 16846 Not Audited
Publisher: Steve Ammermann; **Editor:** Kelly Boldan; **News Editor:** Susan Lunneborg
Editorial Profile: West Central Tribune is a daily newspaper written for the residents of Willmar, MN. It covers local news, business, community news, entertainment and sports.; Full Page Mono: 21.57; Full Page Colour: 463.00
Currency: US Dollars
DAILY NEWSPAPER

West Coast Jewish News
Owner: Sunset Publications
Editorial: 1908 Pomona Ave, Ste D, Costa Mesa, California 92627-6233.
T: 1 949 650-1638
E: sunsetpublishing@aol.com
Freq: Monthly; **Circ:** 18000 Not Audited
Editor: Steve Gold; **Publisher:** Avi Melman
Editorial Profile: West Coast Jewish News is a monthly newspaper written to bring local news to Orange and Los Angeles counties, CA. The publication is written for people of Jewish faith.; Full Page Mono: 28.62
Currency: US Dollars
NEWSPAPER

West County Times
Owner: MediaNews Group
Editorial: 4301 Lakeside Dr, Richmond, California 94806-5281. **T:** 1 510 758-8400
E: ccnnewsrelease@bayareanewsgroup.com
W: http://www.contracostatimes.com/west-county-times
Freq: Daily; **Circ:** 33000 Not Audited
Editor: Kathleen Kirkwood
Editorial Profile: West County Times in Richmond, CA is a daily newspaper that covers news, sports, arts & entertainment and more.; Full Page Mono: 57.00
Currency: US Dollars
DAILY NEWSPAPER

West Georgia Newspapers
Owner: Paxton Media Group
Editorial: 604A Alabama Ave S, Bremen, Georgia 30110-2302. **T:** 1 770 537-2434
Circ: 14600 Not Audited
Editor: Bruce Browning; **Publisher:** Leonard Woolsey
NEWSPAPER

West Hartford News
Owner: Journal Register Company
Editorial: 386 Main St, 4th Fl, Middletown, Connecticut 06457-3360. **T:** 1 860 347-3331
E: westhartfordnews@ctcentral.com
W: http://www.westhartfordnews.com
Freq: Thu; **Circ:** 13000 Not Audited
Publisher: Daniel Moriarty; **Editor:** Viktoria Sundquist
Editorial Profile: West Hartford News is a weekly newspaper for residents of West Hartford, CT.; Full Page Mono: 15.65
Currency: US Dollars
NEWSPAPER

West Hawaii Today
Owner: Stephens Media Group
Editorial: 75-5580 Kuakini Hwy, Kailua Kona, Hawaii 96740-1647. **T:** 1 808 329-9311
E: wht@aloha.net
W: http://www.westhawaiitoday.com
Freq: Daily; **Circ:** 10446 Not Audited
Editorial Profile: West Hawaii Today is written for Kailua-Kona, HI and the surrounding areas.; Full Page Mono: 23.00; Full Page Colour: 405.00
Currency: US Dollars
DAILY NEWSPAPER

West Nebraska Register
Editorial: 2708 Old Fair Rd, Grand Island, Nebraska 68803. **T:** 1 308 382-4660
W: http://www.gidiocese.org/wnr
Freq: Semi-Monthly; **Circ:** 18000 Not Audited
Publisher: William Deninger; **Editor:** Mary Parlin
Editorial Profile: West Nebraska Register is written for Catholics in Grand Island, NE. It covers local news as well as organizational news from the Diocese of Grand Island.; Full Page Mono: 8.56
Currency: US Dollars
NEWSPAPER

West Of
Editorial: 829 Savannah Hwy, Ste C, Charleston, South Carolina 29407-7282.
T: 1 843 766-9378 **W:** http://www.westof.net
Freq: Tue; **Circ:** 25000
Editorial Profile: West Of is a free, weekly newspaper that serves the West Ashley community of Charleston, SC. It covers local news, opinions, schools, arts & entertainment, dining and sports as well as features a calendar of events.; Full Page Mono: 5.23
Currency: US Dollars
NEWSPAPER

West Plains Daily Quill
Owner: Quill Press Company, Inc.
Editorial: 125 Jefferson Ave, West Plains, Missouri 65775-2753. **T:** 1 417 256-9191
W: http://home.centurytel.net/westplainsdailyquill
Freq: Mon thru Fri; **Circ:** 6922 Not Audited
Editorial Profile: West Plains Daily Quill is published weekly for residents of Howell County, MO. The newspaper covers local news and community events.; Full Page Mono: 12.10; Full Page Colour: 250.00
Currency: US Dollars
DAILY NEWSPAPER

West Seattle Herald Inc.
Owner: Robinson Newspapers
Editorial: 14006 1St Ave S Suite B, Burien, Washington 98168-3402. **T:** 1 206 932-0300
E: wseditor@robinsonnews.com
W: http://www.westseattleherald.com
Circ: 15200 Not Audited
Publisher: Gerald Robinson; **Editor:** Ken Robinson
NEWSPAPER

West Sherburne Tribune
Editorial: 13602 Jefferson St Ne, Ham Lake, Minnesota 55304-6926. **T:** 1 763 263-3602
E: westrib@sherbtel.net
W: http://www.westsherburnetribune.com
Freq: Sat; **Circ:** 12370 Not Audited
Editorial Profile: West Sherburne Tribune is written for residents of Sherburne County, MN in the Big Lake area. Deadlines are on Thursdays by noon CT.; Full Page Mono: 10.10
Currency: US Dollars
NEWSPAPER

West Shore News/Bigfork Eagle Publications
Owner: Hagadone Corp.
Editorial: 8299 Mt Highway 35, Bigfork, Montana 59911-3583. **T:** 1 406 837-5131
Circ: 4500 Not Audited
Editor: David Reese; **Publisher:** Rick Weaver
NEWSPAPER

West Side Community News
Owner: Community Papers, Inc.
Editorial: 608 S Vine St, Indianapolis, Indiana 46241. **T:** 1 317 241-7363
E: commnews@in-motion.net
Freq: Wed; **Circ:** 25000 Not Audited
Editorial Profile: West Side Community News is published weekly for the residents of Indianapolis, IN and surrounding areas. The newspaper covers local news, sports and community events. Deadlines for the publications are on Fridays at noon CT.; Full Page Mono: 19.00
Currency: US Dollars
NEWSPAPER

West Suburban Journal
Owner: Trottie Publishing Inc.
Editorial: 9930 Derby Ln Ste 101, Westchester, Illinois 60154-3770.
T: 1 708 344-5975
W: http://www.westsuburbanjournal.com
Freq: Thu; **Circ:** 10000 Not Audited
Publisher: Nicole Trottie
Editorial Profile: West Suburban Journal is a free, weekly newspaper that serves residents of the near and far west Chicago suburbs. It features hard-hitting news, profiles and entertainment stories.; Full Page Mono: 15.27
Currency: US Dollars
NEWSPAPER

West Suburban Publishing Group
Owner: Wrapports LLC
Editorial: 350 N. Orleans, 10 South, Chicago, Illinois 60504-8295. **T:** 1 630 978-8880
News Editor: Dan Cassidy; **News Editor:** Bob Oswald
Editorial Profile: The West Suburban Publishing Group publishes the Aurora Beacon-News, the Elgin Courier-News and the Naperville Sun.
DAILY NEWSPAPER

West Tennessee Catholic
Owner: Diocese of Memphis
Editorial: 5825 Shelby Oaks Dr, Memphis, Tennessee 38134-7316. **T:** 1 901 373-1200
E: wtc.editor@cc.cdom.org
W: http://www.cdom.org
Freq: Weekly; **Circ:** 12400
Publisher: J. Terry Steib
Editorial Profile: West Tennessee Catholic is a weekly paper written for the Diocese of Memphis, TN.; Full Page Mono: 0.36
Currency: US Dollars
NEWSPAPER

The West Texas Angelus
Owner: Catholic Diocese of San Angelo (The)
Editorial: 804 Ford St, San Angelo, Texas 76905. **T:** 1 325 651-7500
W: http://www.sanangelodiocese.org
Freq: Monthly; **Circ:** 20000 Not Audited
Editor: Jimmy Patterson; **Publisher:** Michael Pfeifer
Editorial Profile: The West Texas Angelus is written for the parishioners of the Catholic Dioceses of San Angelo, TX.; Full Page Mono: 5.50
Currency: US Dollars
NEWSPAPER

West Valley News
Editorial: 8378 Sale Ave, West Hills, California 91304-3339. **T:** 1 818 883-3374
E: editorial@westvalleynews-sfv.com
W: http://www.westvalleynews-sfv.com
Freq: Monthly
Editorial Profile: West Valley News is a monthly community newspaper serving the San Fernando Valley. The paper primarily focuses on business and community news; Full Page Mono: 15.00; Full Page Colour: 15.58
Currency: US Dollars
NEWSPAPER

West Valley View
Owner: West Valley View Inc.
Editorial: 1050 E Riley Dr, Avondale, Arizona 85323-2002. **T:** 1 623 535-8439
E: editor@westvalleyview.com
W: http://www.westvalleyview.com
Freq: 2 Times/Week; **Circ:** 79846 Not Audited
Publisher: Elliott Freireich; **Editor:** Mike Russo
Editorial Profile: West Valley View is written for the residents of Litchfield Park, AZ and surrounding areas including Avondale, Buckeye, Goodyear and Tolleson, AZ. The newspaper covers local news and community events. Deadlines are on Fridays before issue date.; Full Page Mono: 39.22
Currency: US Dollars
NEWSPAPER

West Virginia Daily News
Owner: Moffitt Newspapers
Editorial: 200 S Court St, Lewisburg, West Virginia 24901. **T:** 1 304 645-1206
E: wvdailynews@suddenlinkmail.com
Freq: Mon thru Fri; **Circ:** 4200 Not Audited
Editor: Bill Frye; **Publisher:** Judy Steele
Editorial Profile: West Virginia Daily News's editorial mission is to keep the area informed about what's going on in the local community. The publication is written for Lewisburg, WV and the immediate surrounding area.; Full Page Mono: 6.85; Full Page Colour: 120.00
Currency: US Dollars
DAILY NEWSPAPER

West Virginia Standard Newspapers
Owner: Unger Enterprises
Editorial: 2222 2Nd Ave, Nitro, West Virginia 25143-1770. **T:** 1 304 743-6731
E: editor@putnamstandard.com
W: http://www.theputnamstandard.com
Circ: 93000 Not Audited
Editor: Jack Bailey
NEWSPAPER

The West Volusia Beacon
Owner: Mustard Seed Publishing Inc.
Editorial: 110 W New York Ave, Deland, Florida 32720-5416. **T:** 1 386 734-4622
E: info@beacononlinenews.com
W: http://www.beacononlinenews.com
Freq: Mon; **Circ:** 14050 Not Audited
Editorial Profile: The West Volusia Beacon is a local newspaper serving West Volusia County, FL. It provides the local community with information on news, events, sports and weather.; Full Page Mono: 16.25
Currency: US Dollars
NEWSPAPER

West Windsor & Plainsboro News
Editorial: 12 Roszel Rd Ste C205, Princeton, New Jersey 08540-6234. **T:** 1 609 243-9119
W: http://www.wwpinfo.com
Freq: Bi-Weekly; **Circ:** 12000
NEWSPAPER

The Westerly Sun
Owner: Record-Journal Publishing Company
Editorial: 56 Main St, Westerly, Rhode Island 02891-2155. **T:** 1 401 348-1000
E: editorial@thewesterlysun.com
W: http://www.thewesterlysun.com
Freq: Daily; **Circ:** 8665 Not Audited
News Editor: Angela Algier; **Editor:** Adrienne Altobelli
Editorial Profile: The Westerly Sun is a local, daily newspaper serving the Westerly, RI and Stonington, CT areas. The paper covers local news, sports and entertainment. It is the main source of local news and advertising in Southern Rhode Island and Southeastern Connecticut.; Full Page Mono: 18.11; Full Page Colour: 300.00
Currency: US Dollars
DAILY NEWSPAPER

Western Recorder
Owner: Kentucky Baptist Convention
Editorial: 13420 Eastpoint Centre Dr, Louisville, Kentucky 40223-4160.
T: 1 502 489-3535
W: http://www.westernrecorder.org
Freq: Tue; **Circ:** 25000 Not Audited
Editor: Todd Deaton
Editorial Profile: Western Recorder is written for Baptists and Christians in Kentucky. It covers Christian issues, church issues and mission reports.; Full Page Mono: 30.00
Currency: US Dollars
NEWSPAPER

Western States Weeklies Inc.
Editorial: 6153 Fairmount Ave Ste 220, San Diego, California 92120-3436.
T: 1 619 280-2985
W: http://www.navydispatch.com **Circ:** 48000 Not Audited
Editorial Profile: Western States Weeklies Inc. in San Diego, CA is a weekly community newspaper publisher serving the Navy communities of San Diego, Ventura, Long Beach, Mira Mesa and Scripps Ranch, CA.
NEWSPAPER

Western Wayne Newspapers
Owner: Janis Buhl
Editorial: 26 W Church St, Cambridge City, Indiana 47327. **T:** 1 765 478-5448
E: westernwaynenews@frontier.com
W: http://www.western-wayne-news.com
Circ: 3150 Not Audited
NEWSPAPER

The Westfield News
Owner: Allbritton Communications Co.
Editorial: 62 - 64 School St, Westfield, Massachusetts 01085-2890.
T: 1 413 562-4181
E: pressreleases@thewestfieldnews.com
W: http://thewestfieldnews.com
Freq: Daily; **Circ:** 5300 Not Audited
Editor: Daniel Moriarty
Editorial Profile: Westfield News is a local daily newspaper distributed nightly Monday through Friday. The Saturday edition is a morning paper. It delivers local news and event information to the Westfield, MA community. Deadline is approximately a week before issue date.; Full Page Mono: 12.80; Full Page Colour: 375.00
Currency: US Dollars
DAILY NEWSPAPER

Westfield Publications
Editorial: 39 E Main St, Westfield, New York 14787. **T:** 1 716 326-3163
W: http://www.westfieldrepublican.com
Circ: 2450
Editor: Jenna Loughlin
NEWSPAPER

Westside Gazette
Editorial: 545 NW 7th Ter, Fort Lauderdale, Florida 33311. **T:** 1 954 525-1489
E: wgazette@bellsouth.net
W: http://www.thewestsidegazette.com
Freq: Thu; **Circ:** 30000 Not Audited
Publisher: Bobby Henry; **Editor:** Pamela Henry-Lewis
Editorial Profile: Westside Gazette is a weekly newspaper offering insight into news and events that affect African-Americans in Broward County, FL.; Full Page Mono: 32.87
Currency: US Dollars
NEWSPAPER

Westside News Inc.
Editorial: 1835 N Union St, Spencerport, New York 14559-1153. **T:** 1 585 352-3411
W: http://www.westsidenewsonline.com
Circ: 33065 Not Audited
Editor: Evelyn Dow; **Editor:** Evelyn Dow;
Publisher: Keith Ryan
Editorial Profile: Westside News in Spencerport, NY is a community newspaper

WORLD NEWS MEDIA

publisher whose publications include the Suburban News North Edition; the Suburban News West Edition; the Suburban News South Edition; and the Hamlin-Clarkson Herald.
NEWSPAPER

Westside Observer
Editorial: 2090 Castro St, San Francisco, California 94131. **T:** 1 415 517-6331
W: http://www.westsideobserver.com
Freq: Monthly; **Circ:** 20000 Not Audited
Publisher: Mitch Bull
Editorial Profile: Westside Observer is written for the general public in San Francisco.; Full Page Mono: 25.00
Currency: US Dollars
NEWSPAPER

Westside Weekly
Editorial: 6253 Pine St, Philadelphia, Pennsylvania 19143-1027. **T:** 1 215 474-7411
E: westsidepa@aol.com
W: http://www.westsidepa.com
Freq: Sat; **Circ:** 13000 Not Audited
Editorial Profile: Westside Weekly is a community newspaper written for the residents of West Philadelphia.; Full Page Mono: 15.00
Currency: US Dollars
NEWSPAPER

Westword
Owner: Voice Media Group
Editorial: 969 Broadway, Denver, Colorado 80203-2705. **T:** 1 303 296-7744
E: editorial@westword.com
W: http://www.westword.com
Freq: Thu; **Circ:** 68000 Not Audited
Editor: Patricia Calhoun; **Publisher:** Scott Tobias
Editorial Profile: Westword is a weekly alternative newspaper started to inform young, active people of Denver. Every week, the new edition is distributed to college classrooms, coffeehouses, corporate offices and at the state capitol. It generally does not accept press releases, unless it is of particular interest to the local audience. Contact the editorial department for further inquiries.; Full Page Mono: 43.70; Full Page Colour: 46.23
Currency: US Dollars
NEWSPAPER

The Wetumpka Herald Newspapers
Owner: Tallapoosa Publishers, Inc.
Editorial: 300 Green St, Wetumpka, Alabama 36092-2507. **T:** 1 334 567-7811
E: news@thewetumpkaherald.com
W: http://www.thewetumpkaherald.com
Circ: 6963 Not Audited
NEWSPAPER

WG News + Arts
Owner: Gould (Genia)
Editorial: 330 Wythe Ave. #8B, Brooklyn, New York 11249. **T:** 1 917 304-6213
E: info@thewgnews.com
W: http://thewgnews.com
Freq: Monthly; **Circ:** 13500
Editorial Profile: WG News + Arts is a monthly community newspaper covering the Williamsburg and Greenspoint communities in Brooklyn, focusing on local art, music, food, real estate, environment, politics, fashion and theater.; Full Page Mono: 16.09
Currency: US Dollars
NEWSPAPER

Wharton Co. Newspapers, Inc.
Owner: Wharton County Newspapers
Editorial: 115 W Burleson St, Wharton, Texas 77488. **T:** 1 979 532-8840
W: http://www.journal-spectator.com
Circ: 6025
News Editor: Barry Halvorson; Full Page Mono: 7.00
Currency: US Dollars
NEWSPAPER

What's Happening! Community Newspapers
Owner: Chamber Publications, Ltd.
Editorial: 314 McHenry Rd Ste A, Buffalo Grove, Illinois 60089-2430. **T:** 1 847 419-8819
E: editorial@whatshappeningonline.com
W: http://www.whatshappeningonline.com
Freq: Monthly; **Circ:** 64459
NEWSPAPER

The Wheel
Owner: Military Newspapers of Virginia
Editorial: 213 Calhoun St, Fort Eustis, Virginia 23604-1645. **T:** 1 757 878-4920
E: wheel5@militarynews.com
W: http://www.forteustiswheel.com
Freq: Thu; **Circ:** 10500
Publisher: Laura Baxter; **Editor:** Zach Shelby

Editorial Profile: The Wheel is a military newspaper in Fort Eustis, VA. The paper covers military news, community news and sports.; Full Page Mono: 9.68
Currency: US Dollars
NEWSPAPER

Wherry Publishing, Inc.
Editorial: 503 King, Cottonwood, Idaho 83522. **T:** 1 208 962-3851
E: cotchron@camasnet.com
W: http://www.cottonwoodchronicle.com
Circ: 1927 Not Audited
NEWSPAPER

White Mountain Publishing Co.
Owner: Kramer Publications
Editorial: 3191 S White Mountain Rd, Show Low, Arizona 85901. **T:** 1 928 537-5721
E: postmaster@wmicentral.com
W: http://www.wmicentral.com **Circ:** 25174 Not Audited
Editorial Profile: White Mountain Publishing Co. publishes the White Mountain Independent for the Show Low, Pinetop-Lakeside, Snowflake-Taylor, Springville-Eager, St. Johns, Heber/Overgaard, AZ areas, including Local and Community News coverage for the local Navajo and Apache communities.
NEWSPAPER

Whitewater Publications, Inc.
Editorial: 531 Main St, Brookville, Indiana 47012-1407. **T:** 1 765 647-4221
E: info@whitewaterpub.com **Circ:** 6250 Not Audited
Editor: John Estridge; **Publisher:** Gary Wolf
NEWSPAPER

Whittier Daily News
Owner: MediaNews Group
Editorial: 7612 Greenleaf Ave, Whittier, California 90602-1625. **T:** 1 562 698-0955
E: news.wdn@sgvn.com
W: http://www.whittierdailynews.com
Freq: Daily; **Circ:** 14367 Not Audited
Editor: Andrew Landeros
Editorial Profile: Whittier Daily News is a daily newspaper written for the residents of Whittier, CA. This paper is a part of the Los Angeles Newspaper Group, a subsidiary of MediaNews Group. It covers local news, sports, business, features and arts & entertainment in Whittier and Southeast Los Angeles.; Full Page Mono: 651.00; Full Page Colour: 2121.50
Currency: US Dollars
DAILY NEWSPAPER

The Wichita Eagle
Owner: McClatchy Newspapers
Editorial: 825 E Douglas Ave, Wichita, Kansas 67202-3512. **T:** 1 316 268-6000
E: wenews@wichitaeagle.com
W: http://www.kansas.com
Freq: Daily; **Circ:** 60454 Not Audited
Editor: Sherry Chisenhall; **Publisher:** Kim Nussbaum
Editorial Profile: The Wichita Eagle is a daily newspaper covering Wichita, KS and the surrounding area. The paper covers local and national news, sports, business and the arts. The best way to contact the paper is by fax. The editorial deadline varies depending on the section. The lead times vary depending on the story. The editorial department accepts non-disclosure agreements on a case-by-case basis.; Full Page Mono: 76.85; Full Page Colour: 431.25
Currency: US Dollars
DAILY NEWSPAPER

The Wichita Eagle
Editorial: 300 SW 10th Ave, Topeka, Kansas 66612-1504. **T:** 1 785 296-3006
DAILY NEWSPAPER

Wick Communications, Inc.
Owner: Wick Communications Inc.
Editorial: 5751 E Mayflower Ct, Wasilla, Alaska 99654. **T:** 1 907 352-2250
E: valleylife@frontiersman.com
W: http://www.frontiersman.com **Circ:** 11143 Not Audited
NEWSPAPER

Wilber Newspapers
Editorial: 113 W 3rd St, Wilber, Nebraska 68465. **T:** 1 402 821-2586
E: wilberrepublican@windstream.net
Circ: 2300 Not Audited
NEWSPAPER

The Wilkes Journal-Patriot
Owner: Carter-Hubbard Publishing Co., Inc.
Editorial: 711 Main St, North Wilkesboro, North Carolina 28659. **T:** 1 336 838-4117

W: http://www.journalpatriot.com
Freq: Fri; **Circ:** 15200 Not Audited
Editor: Charles Williams
Editorial Profile: The Wilkes Journal-Patriot is a community newspaper covering local news and events for the residents of Wilkes County, NC. Send press information by fax or to the main e-mail address.; Full Page Mono: 7.59
Currency: US Dollars
NEWSPAPER

Wilkes-Barre Independent Gazette
Editorial: 253 S. Main Street, Wilkes-Barre, Pennsylvania. **T:** 1 570 266-8086
E: betsy@vote4betsy.com
W: http://www.wbindependentgazette.com/
Freq: Weekly
Publisher: Lou Jasikoff
Editorial Profile: The Wilkes-Barre (PA) Independent Gazette is a a community newspaper composed of local news, commentary, letters to the editor, classifieds, puzzles and press releases.
NEWSPAPER

Willamette Week
Owner: City of Roses Newspaper Co.
Editorial: 2220 NW Quimby St, Portland, Oregon 97210. **T:** 1 503 243-2122
E: info@wweek.com
W: http://www.wweek.com
Freq: Wed; **Circ:** 90000 Not Audited
Publisher: Richard Meeker; **Editor:** Aaron Mesh; **Editor:** Mark Zusman; **Editor:** Mark Zusman
Editorial Profile: Willamette Week is a weekly publication for the residents of Portland, OR and the surrounding areas. The readership tends to be younger, based on the liberal news and views in the newspaper. Half of the publication deals with local news while the other half deals with local arts and culture. Deadlines for the publication are 10 days prior to the issue date.; Full Page Mono: 39.96; Full Page Colour: 3700.00
Currency: US Dollars
NEWSPAPER

Williams Publishing Company
Editorial: 107 N Main St, Greensboro, Georgia 30642. **T:** 1 706 453-7988
E: editor@heraldjournal.net **Circ:** 6200 Not Audited
Publisher: Carey Williams
NEWSPAPER

Williamson County Sun, Inc.
Owner: Thurmond (Clark)
Editorial: 707 S Main St, Georgetown, Texas 78626. **T:** 1 512 930-4824
E: letters@countysun.com
W: http://www.wilcosun.com **Circ:** 21800 Not Audited
Editor: Andrew Mclemore
NEWSPAPER

Williamson Daily News
Owner: Heartland Publications
Editorial: 100 E 3rd Ave, Williamson, West Virginia 25661-3620. **T:** 1 304 235-4242
W: http://www.williamsondailynews.com
Freq: Daily; **Circ:** 10578 Not Audited
Editor: Lorretta Tackett
Editorial Profile: Williamson Daily News is a daily newspaper written for the residents of Mingo and Logan County, WV as well as Pike and Martin County, KY. The newspaper covers local news, events, sports and entertainment. Deadlines for the publication are 6pm ET the day prior to issue date.; Full Page Mono: 9.85; Full Page Colour: 300.00
Currency: US Dollars
DAILY NEWSPAPER

Williamson Herald
Owner: MainStreet Media
Editorial: 1117 Columbia Ave, Franklin, Tennessee 37064-3616. **T:** 1 615 790-6465
E: news@williamsonherald.com
W: http://www.williamsonherald.com
Freq: Thu; **Circ:** 15000 Not Audited
Publisher: Derby Jones
Editorial Profile: Williamson Herald is a local newspaper serving residents of Williamson County, TN. The paper covers local news, lifestyle stories and sports. Deadlines are on Mondays at noon ET.; Full Page Mono: 14.00
Currency: US Dollars
NEWSPAPER

Williamsport Sun-Gazette
Owner: Ogden Newspapers
Editorial: 252 W 4th St, Williamsport, Pennsylvania 17701. **T:** 1 570 326-1551
E: news@sungazette.com
W: http://www.sungazette.com

Freq: Daily; **Circ:** 23575 Not Audited
Editor: Laura Janssen; **Publisher:** Bernie Oravec; **Editor:** Dave Troisi
Editorial Profile: Williamsport Sun-Gazette is published daily for residents of Williamsport, PA and surrounding communities. The newspaper covers local and national news, weather, sports and community events. Feature articles cover business developments, politics, education, arts & entertainment and lifestyle. Deadlines are the day prior to the issue date at 5pm ET.; Full Page Mono: 40.00; Full Page Colour: 305.00
Currency: US Dollars
DAILY NEWSPAPER

Williston Daily Herald
Owner: Wick Communications Inc.
Editorial: 14 4th St W, Williston, North Dakota 58801-5308. **T:** 1 701 572-2165
E: news@willistonherald.com
W: http://www.willistonherald.com
Freq: Daily; **Circ:** 4134 Not Audited
News Editor: Jerry Burnes; **Publisher:** Mitzi Moe
Editorial Profile: Williston Daily Herald is a daily newspaper written for residents of Williston, ND and the surrounding areas. The paper covers local news and events. There is no Saturday edition. The paper is affiliated with the Plains Reporter.; Full Page Mono: 12.60; Full Page Colour: 103.00
Currency: US Dollars
DAILY NEWSPAPER

Wilmington Journal
Editorial: 412 S 7th St, Wilmington, North Carolina 28401-5214. **T:** 1 910 762-5502
E: wilmjourn@aol.com
W: http://www.wilmingtonjournal.com
Freq: Thu; **Circ:** 10000 Not Audited
Editorial Profile: Wilmington Journal is a weekly newspaper written for residents of Wilmington, NC. The newspaper covers local and national news. Deadlines are at 5pm ET on the Tuesday before issue date.; Full Page Mono: 20.00; Full Page Colour: 1207.00
Currency: US Dollars
NEWSPAPER

Wilmington News-Journal
Owner: Ohio Community Media LLC.
Editorial: 761 S Nelson Ave, Wilmington, Ohio 45177-2517. **T:** 1 937 382-2574
E: info@wnewsj.com
W: http://www.wnewsj.com
Freq: Daily; **Circ:** 7292 Not Audited
Editor: Lora Abernathy; **Publisher:** Pam Stricker
Editorial Profile: Wilmington News-Journal is written for residents of Clinton County, OH. Deadlines are at 4pm ET. The Monday shopper edition of the paper is called the Star Republican. The paper was established in 1837.; Full Page Mono: 15.50; Full Page Colour: 22.31
Currency: US Dollars
DAILY NEWSPAPER

Wilson County News
Owner: WCN, Inc.
Editorial: 1012 C St, Floresville, Texas 78114. **T:** 1 830 216-4519 **E:** reader@wcn-online.com
W: http://www.wilsoncountynews.com
Freq: Wed; **Circ:** 11000 Not Audited
Editor: Nannette Kilbey-Smith; **Publisher:** Elaine Kolodziej
Editorial Profile: Wilson County News's editorial mission is to provide accurate and fair news and information to the community. The paper is written for residents of Wilson County, TX. Deadlines for Wilson County News are noon CT, Thursday before issue date.; Full Page Mono: 11.75
Currency: US Dollars
NEWSPAPER

Wilson Daily Times
Owner: The Wilson Times Company
Editorial: 2001 Downing St SW, Wilson, North Carolina 27893-4611. **T:** 1 252 243-5151
E: editor@wilsontimes.com
W: http://www.wilsontimes.com
Freq: Mon thru Fri; **Circ:** 12320
Publisher: Morgan Dickerman; **Editor:** Jon Jimison
Editorial Profile: Wilson Daily Times is a local daily newspaper serving residents of Wilson, NC and surrounding communities. The newspaper covers local, state, and national news, weather, sports and community events. Feature articles cover business developments, education, politics, arts & entertainment and lifestyle. The editorial lead time for the publication varies. Deadlines for the publication are one day prior to the issue date.; Full Page Mono: 13.23; Full Page Colour: 350.00

Currency: US Dollars
DAILY NEWSPAPER

Win Awenen Nisitotung
Editorial: 531 Ashmun St, Sault Sainte Marie, Michigan 49783-1907. **T:** 1 906 632-6398
W: http://www.saulttribe.com
Freq: Monthly; **Circ:** 19000 Not Audited
Editorial Profile: Win Awenen Nisitotung is a community newspaper written for the Sault Tribe of Chippewa Indians in Sault Sainte Marie, MI.; Full Page Mono: 8.50
Currency: US Dollars
NEWSPAPER

The Winchester Star
Owner: Byrd Newspapers
Editorial: 2 N Kent St, Winchester, Virginia 22601-5098. **T:** 1 540 667-3200
E: news@winchesterstar.com
W: http://www.winchesterstar.com
Freq: Daily; **Circ:** 19417 Not Audited
Publisher: Thomas Byrd
Editorial Profile: Winchester Star is written for residents of Frederick County, VA.; Full Page Mono: 20.40; Full Page Colour: 24.27
Currency: US Dollars
DAILY NEWSPAPER

Winchester Sun
Owner: Schurz Communications Inc.
Editorial: 20 Wall St, Winchester, Kentucky 40391-1975. **T:** 1 859 744-3123
E: news@winchestersun.com
W: http://www.winchestersun.com
Freq: Daily; **Circ:** 7300 Not Audited
Publisher: Scott Schurz
Editorial Profile: Winchester Sun is written for the community of Winchester, KY. The publication covers local news, sports and community events.; Full Page Mono: 11.25
Currency: US Dollars
DAILY NEWSPAPER

The Windsock
Owner: Ellis Publishing Co.
Editorial: PSC Box 8013, MCAS Public Affairs Office, Cherry Point, North Carolina 28533.
T: 1 252 466-4241
E: cherry.point.windsock@gmail.com
W: http://www.usmc.mil/unit/mcascherrypoint/pages/default.aspx
Freq: Thu; **Circ:** 11000 Not Audited
Editor: Samantha Arrington; **Editor:** Stacey Swann
Editorial Profile: The Windsock provides news and information for and about the Marines stationed at the USMC Air Base at Cherry Point, NC and members of the surrounding community.; Full Page Mono: 12.70
Currency: US Dollars
NEWSPAPER

The Windy City Word
Editorial: 5090 W Harrison St, Chicago, Illinois 60644. **T:** 1 773 378-0261
E: windycityword02@yahoo.com
Freq: Thu; **Circ:** 20000 Not Audited
Editor: Jocelyn Denson; **Editor:** Jocelyn Denson; **Publisher:** Mary Denson
Editorial Profile: The Windy City Word is written for the residents of Chicago's West Side.; Full Page Mono: 45.00
Currency: US Dollars
NEWSPAPER

Winfield Courier
Owner: Winfield Publishing Co.
Editorial: 201 E 9th Ave, Winfield, Kansas 67156-2817. **T:** 1 620 221-1050
E: courier@winfieldcourier.com
W: http://www.winfieldcourier.com
Freq: Mon thru Fri; **Circ:** 4522
Publisher: Lloyd Craig
Editorial Profile: Winfield Courier is published daily for residents of Cowley County, KS and surrounding areas. The newspaper covers local and state news, business, sports, lifestyles and arts & entertainment.; Full Page Mono: 7.40; Full Page Colour: 165.00
Currency: US Dollars
DAILY NEWSPAPER

Wingspread
Owner: Hearst Corporation (The)
Editorial: 1150 5th St East, Randolph AFB, Universal City, Texas 78150.
T: 1 210 652-5760
E: 502abw.pa.wingspread@us.af.mil
W: http://www.randolph.af.mil/news
Freq: Fri; **Circ:** 10725 Not Audited
Editor: Precious Yett
Editorial Profile: Wingspread is a weekly military newspaper serving the military and civilian community at Randolph Air Force Base in Texas. It covers news and issues relevant to the people at the base, which itself is known as the "Showplace of the Air Force" due to its extensive and famous training school for pilots. The base is the headquarters of the U.S. Air Force's Education and Training command and home to the 12th Flying Training Wing, the 19th Air Force, the Air Force Personnel center, the Recruiting Service headquarters, the Air Force Services Agency and the Air Force Management Engineering Agency. Stories and photographs for publication may be faxed, e-mailed or turned in on a disc. It is published by Prime Time Military Newspapers in San Antonio, TX, where all of it's corporate staff are located. Deadlines are on Thursdays at noon CT.; Full Page Mono: 19.06
Currency: US Dollars
NEWSPAPER

Winnebago Indian News
Editorial: 100 Bluff Ave, Winnebago, Nebraska 68071-9787. **T:** 1 402 878-3221
E: winnebagoindiannews@yahoo.com
W: http://www.winnebagotribe.com/winnebago_indian_news.html
Freq: Bi-Weekly
Editor: Jerome Lapointe
Editorial Profile: Winnebago Indian News is a bi-weekly newspaper offering news and information for the Winnebago Tribe of Nebraska.; Full Page Mono: 7.00
Currency: US Dollars
NEWSPAPER

Winona Daily News
Owner: Lee Enterprises, Inc.
Editorial: 902 E 2nd St Ste 110, Winona, Minnesota 55987-6512. **T:** 1 507 453-3500
E: news@winonadailynews.com
W: http://www.winonadailynews.com
Freq: Daily; **Circ:** 7885 Not Audited
Editor: Jerome Christenson; **Publisher:** Russell Cunningham; **Editor:** Darrell Ehrlick
Editorial Profile: Winona Daily News is written for surrounding communities of Winona, MN.; Full Page Mono: 22.92; Full Page Colour: 300.00
Currency: US Dollars
DAILY NEWSPAPER

Winona Post
Editorial: 64 E 2Nd St, Winona, Minnesota 55987-3409. **T:** 1 507 452-1262
E: winpost@winonapost.com
W: http://www.winonapost.com
Freq: Sun; **Circ:** 23782 Not Audited
Editor: Frances Edstrom; **Publisher:** John Edstrom; **News Editor:** Sarah Squires
Editorial Profile: Winona Post is written for surrounding communities of Winona, MN. It provides residents with information on news and events of interest to the local communities. Deadlines for the Wednesday edition are on the Monday prior to the issue date at noon CT. Deadlines for the Sunday edition are on the Thursday prior to the issue date at noon CT.; Full Page Mono: 18.27
Currency: US Dollars
NEWSPAPER

Winston-Salem Chronicle
Owner: Consolidated Media
Editorial: 617 N Liberty St, Winston-Salem, North Carolina 27101-2912.
T: 1 336 722-8624 **E:** news@wschronicle.com
W: http://www.wschronicle.com
Freq: Thu; **Circ:** 10000 Not Audited
Publisher: Ernest Pitt; **Editor:** Kevin Walker
Editorial Profile: Winston-Salem Chronicle is written for African-American community of Forsyth County, NC. Deadlines are at 5pm ET on Mondays.; Full Page Mono: 16.20
Currency: US Dollars
NEWSPAPER

Winston-Salem Journal
Owner: World Media Enterprises, Inc.
Editorial: 418 N Marshall St, Winston Salem, North Carolina 27101-2815.
T: 1 336 727-7211 **E:** news@wsjournal.com
W: http://www.journalnow.com
Freq: Daily; **Circ:** 48252 Not Audited
Editorial Profile: Winston-Salem Journal is a daily newspaper with a primary coverage area of Forsyth County, and nine other counties in Northwest North Carolina including Alleghany, Ashe, Davidson, Davie, Stokes, Surry, Watuaga, Wilkes and Yadkin. The paper features local, state and national news, business, arts & entertainment, sports and classifieds. The paper uses a percentage rate for color advertisements.; Full Page Mono: 109.00; Full Page Colour: 136.25
Currency: US Dollars
DAILY NEWSPAPER

The Winter Texan Times
Owner: Brunson (James)
Editorial: 1217 N Conway Ave, Mission, Texas 78572-4112. **T:** 1 956 580-7800
E: news@wintertexantimes.com
W: http://www.wintertexantimes.com
Freq: Thu; **Circ:** 25000
News Editor: Kathy Olivarez
Editorial Profile: The Winter Texan Times is distributed free of charge to Mobile Home and RV Parks Valleywide, from Mission to Brownsville, including the following: Mission - McAllen - Pharr - San Juan - Alamo - Edinburg - Donna - Weslaco - Mercedes La Feria - Harlingen - San Benito - Los Fresnos - Port Isabel - South Padre Island - Brownsville.; Full Page Mono: 30.00
Currency: US Dollars
NEWSPAPER

Wisconsin Newspress, Inc.
Editorial: 113 E Mill St, Plymouth, Wisconsin 53073-1703. **T:** 1 920 893-6411
E: reply@plymouth-review.com
W: http://www.plymouth-review.com
Circ: 32405 Not Audited
Editor: Greg Ceilley; **Editor:** Emmitt Feldner; **Editor:** Sue Mroz; **Editor:** Jeff Pederson
Editorial Profile: Wisconsin Newspress Inc. in Plymouth, WI publishes The Sheboygan Falls News, The Review and The Beacon.
NEWSPAPER

Wisconsin State Journal
Owner: Capital Newspapers
Editorial: 1901 Fish Hatchery Rd, Madison, Wisconsin 53713-1248. **T:** 1 608 252-6100
W: http://www.madison.com/wsj
Freq: Daily; **Circ:** 81286 Not Audited
Editor: John Smalley
Editorial Profile: Wisconsin State Journal covers national, regional and local news as well as sports and politics.; Full Page Mono: 106.50; Full Page Colour: 187.63
Currency: US Dollars
DAILY NEWSPAPER

Wisconsin State Journal
Editorial: State Capital Press Room, Madison, Wisconsin 53701 **W:** http://www.madison.com
Editorial Profile: The reporters in this bureau work out of the state capital press room.
DAILY NEWSPAPER

Wise Newspapers, Inc.
Editorial: 203 E Harrison St, De Quincy, Louisiana 70633-3545. **T:** 1 337 786-8004
E: dequincynews@centurytel.net
W: http://www.dequincynews.com **Circ:** 6200 Not Audited
Editorial Profile: Wise Newspapers, Inc. is a local newspaper providing news for the community of De Quincy, LA.
NEWSPAPER

The Witness
Owner: Archdiocese of Dubuque
Editorial: 1229 Mount Loretta Ave, Dubuque, Iowa 52003. **T:** 1 563 588-0556
E: dbqcwo@arch.pvt.k12.ia.us
W: http://www.arch.pvt.k12.ia.us/witness/
Freq: Sun; **Circ:** 11970 Not Audited
Publisher: Jerome Hanus; **Editor:** Carol Hoverman
Editorial Profile: The Witness serves the Catholic Diocese of Dubuque, IA. Its editorial mission is to inform people of news from Rome and the Pope. Deadlines are on Mondays at noon CT.; Full Page Mono: 12.35
Currency: US Dollars
NEWSPAPER

WNS Publications
Owner: Komlanc Jr. (Anthony)
Editorial: 100 E Main St, Morrison, Illinois 61270. **T:** 1 815 772-7244
E: sentinel@whitesidesentinel.com
W: http://www.whitesidesentinel.com
Circ: 5500 Not Audited
Editor: Jerry Lindsey; **Publisher:** Sue Patten
Editorial Profile: WNS Publications is a community newspaper publisher serving the residents of Davenport, IA, Rock Island and Moline, IL.
NEWSPAPER

Womack Publishing
Owner: Womack Publishing Company Inc.
Editorial: 206 E Main St, Jamestown, North Carolina 27282-9532. **T:** 1 336 841-4933
E: jamestownnews@northstate.net
W: http://www.womacknewspapers.com/jamestownnews **Circ:** 9000 Not Audited
NEWSPAPER

Wood Land Publishing Inc.
Editorial: 2404 S Park Ave, Pearland, Texas 77581-4234. **T:** 1 281 485-7501
W: http://www.thereporternews.com
Circ: 12500 Not Audited
Editor: David Davis
NEWSPAPER

Woodmen Edition
Owner: Walter Publishing Co.
Editorial: 620 Southpointe Ct, Colorado Springs, Colorado 80906-3897.
T: 1 719 578-5112
W: http://www.waltpub.com
Freq: Fri; **Circ:** 16000
Editorial Profile: Contains community news for Colorado Springs, CO area residents.; Full Page Mono: 13.00
Currency: US Dollars
NEWSPAPER

Woodside Herald
Editorial: 4311 Greenpoint Ave, Sunnyside, New York 11104-2605. **T:** 1 718 729-3772
E: woodsideherald@aol.com
W: http://www.woodsideherald.com
Freq: Fri; **Circ:** 16000 Not Audited
Editorial Profile: Woodside Herald is written for residents of Sunnyside, Woodside and Long Island City, NY. Deadlines are on Mondays at 5pm ET.; Full Page Mono: 18.00
Currency: US Dollars
NEWSPAPER

Woodward News
Owner: Community Newspaper Holdings, Inc.
Editorial: 904 Oklahoma Ave, Woodward, Oklahoma 73801-4660. **T:** 1 580 256-2200
W: http://www.woodwardnews.net
Freq: Daily; **Circ:** 5000 Not Audited
Publisher: Sheila Gay; **Editor:** Johnny McMahan
Editorial Profile: Woodward News is written for residents of Woodward County, OK. Deadlines are 5pm CT, the prior day before issue date.; Full Page Mono: 10.12; Full Page Colour: 170.00
Currency: US Dollars
DAILY NEWSPAPER

Worcester Mag
Owner: Holden Landmark Co.
Editorial: 101 Water St, Ste 3, Worcester, Massachusetts 01604-5033.
T: 1 508 749-3166
W: http://www.worcestermagazine.com
Freq: Thu; **Circ:** 30500 Not Audited
Editor: Brittany Durgin; **Publisher:** Kathy Real
Editorial Profile: Worcester Mag is a weekly local newspaper of Worcester Publishing Ltd. The publication covers a mix of investigative reporting, issue analysis, personality profiles and opinion columns for readers in the Worcester, MA community. The newspaper also reaches readers in central Massachusetts and some Boston suburbs. Regular features include news, opinion, in-depth cover stories, an arts & entertainment section containing dedicated music, culture and film/video pages and a comprehensive events calendar.; Full Page Colour: 2960.00
Currency: US Dollars
NEWSPAPER

The Working Waterfront
Owner: Island Institute
Editorial: 386 Main St, Rockland, Maine 4841.
T: 1 207 594-9209
E: inquiry@islandinstitute.org
W: http://www.workingwaterfront.com
Freq: Monthly; **Circ:** 50000 Not Audited
Editor: Tom Groening
Editorial Profile: Working Waterfront in Rockland, ME is community newspaper that covers local news and events.; Full Page Mono: 69.00
Currency: US Dollars
NEWSPAPER

The World
Owner: Lee Enterprises, Inc.
Editorial: 350 Commercial Ave, Coos Bay, Oregon 97420-2269. **T:** 1 541 269-1222
E: theworldnews@theworldlink.com
W: http://www.theworldlink.com
Freq: Mon thru Fri; **Circ:** 7808 Not Audited
Editor: Larry Campbell
Editorial Profile: The World is published daily for the residents of Coos Bay, OR and surrounding areas. The newspaper covers news, national news, sports, outdoors, home and garden, business, coast life and entertainment. It is published daily except on Sunday, Labor Day, or Christmas.; Full Page Mono: 30.20; Full Page Colour: 97.27
Currency: US Dollars
DAILY NEWSPAPER

The World
Editorial: 403 US Route 302, Barre, Vermont 5641. **T:** 1 802 479-2582
E: editor@vt-world.com
W: http://www.vt-world.com
Freq: Wed; **Circ:** 21707 Not Audited
Editor: Laura Rappold
Editorial Profile: The World is published weekly for the residents of Barre, VT and surrounding areas. The publication provides information about local news and community events.; Full Page Mono: 11.00
Currency: US Dollars
NEWSPAPER

The World Company Bonner Springs
Owner: World Company (The)
Editorial: 128 Oak St, Bonner Springs, Kansas 66012-1046. **T:** 1 785 843-1000 **Circ:** 2200 Not Audited
Publisher: Tamara Hand
NEWSPAPER

World Journal: Los Angeles Edition
Editorial: 1588 Corporate Center Dr, Monterey Park, California 91754-7624.
T: 1 323 268-4982
E: citydesk-la@worldjournal.com
W: http://la.worldjournal.com
Editor In Chief: Shyh-Yaw Chen
Editorial Profile: World Journal: Los Angeles Edition is a daily community newspaper.
DAILY NEWSPAPER

World Journal: New York Edition
Owner: World Journal Inc.
Editorial: 14107 20th Ave, Whitestone, New York 11357-3062. **T:** 1 718 746-8889
E: citydesk@worldjournal.com
W: http://www.worldjournal.com/ny
Freq: Daily; **Circ:** 75000 Not Audited
Editor: Claire Chen; **Editor in Chief:** Tyson Won
Editorial Profile: World Journal: New York Edition is a Chinese-language newspaper published daily for residents in North America. The paper covers political and social developments in China, Hong Kong, Taiwan, and Southeast Asia, as well as business, sports, arts & entertainment and sports news.; Full Page Mono: 11.42; Full Page Colour: 24.63
Currency: US Dollars
DAILY NEWSPAPER

World Journal: San Francisco Edition
Owner: World Journal Inc.
Editorial: 231 Adrian Rd, Millbrae, California 94030-3102. **T:** 1 650 692-9936
W: http://www.worldjournal.com/sf
Freq: Daily; **Circ:** 250000 Not Audited
Editor: Yu-Ru Chen; **Editor:** Luna Shi; **Publisher:** Pili Wang
Editorial Profile: World Journal: San Francisco Edition is a local daily newspaper written for the Chinese and Chinese-American community of San Francisco and surrounding areas.; Full Page Mono: 6.70; Full Page Colour: 10.00
Currency: US Dollars
DAILY NEWSPAPER

World Journal: Texas Edition
Owner: World Journal Inc.
Editorial: 5855 Sovereign Dr Ste C, Houston, Texas 77036-2337. **T:** 1 713 771-4363
E: wji111@yahoo.com
W: http://epapertx.chineseworld.com/
Freq: Daily; **Circ:** 20000 Not Audited
Editor: Giin Horng; Full Page Mono: 132.00; Full Page Colour: 291.60
Currency: US Dollars
DAILY NEWSPAPER

Worldwest Ltd., Liability Co.
Owner: Worldwest LLC
Editorial: 708 N Beeline Hwy, Payson, Arizona 85541. **T:** 1 928 474-5251
E: editor@payson.com
W: http://www.paysonroundup.com
Circ: 11000 Not Audited
Editor: Pete Aleshire; **Publisher:** John Naughton
NEWSPAPER

Worrall Community Newspapers
Owner: Worrall Community Newspapers Inc.
Editorial: 1291 Stuyvesant Ave, Union, New Jersey 07083-3823. **T:** 1 908 686-7700
E: editorial@thelocalsource.com
W: http://www.localsource.com **Circ:** 24550 Not Audited
Editor: Stacey Eaton; **Editor:** Yael Katzwer; **Publisher:** David Worrall
NEWSPAPER

Wynne Progress Inc.
Editorial: 702 Falls Blvd N, Wynne, Arkansas 72396. **T:** 1 870 238-2375
E: wynnenews@cablelynx.com **Circ:** 27000 Not Audited
Publisher: David Boger; **Editor:** James Jennings
Editorial Profile: Wynne Progress Inc. providing news to the community of Wynne, AR.
NEWSPAPER

Wyoming Tribune-Eagle
Owner: Cheyenne Newspapers, Inc.
Editorial: 702 W Lincolnway, Cheyenne, Wyoming 82001-4397. **T:** 1 307 634-3361
E: news@wyomingnews.com
W: http://www.wyomingnews.com
Freq: Daily; **Circ:** 14061 Not Audited
News Editor: Mark Borgard; **Publisher:** L. Michael McCraken
Editorial Profile: Wyoming Tribune-Eagle is a daily newspaper that is written for surrounding communities of Cheyenne, WY. The newspaper covers local news, events, business, entertainment, and sports stories.; Full Page Mono: 22.50; Full Page Colour: 80.06
Currency: US Dollars
DAILY NEWSPAPER

Yakima Herald-Republic
Owner: Seattle Times Co.
Editorial: 114 N 4th St, Yakima, Washington 98901-2707. **T:** 1 509 248-1251
E: news@yakima-herald.com
W: http://www.yakima-herald.com
Freq: Daily; **Circ:** 36186 Not Audited
Editor: Bob Crider; **News Editor:** Jeff Garretson
Editorial Profile: Yakima Herald-Republic is a local daily newspaper written for the residents of Yakima, WA. The newspaper covers the local news, business, entertainment and sports, as well as national and limited international stories.; Full Page Mono: 40.87; Full Page Colour: 683.00
Currency: US Dollars
DAILY NEWSPAPER

Yankton Daily Press & Dakotan
Owner: Yankton Media Inc.
Editorial: 319 Walnut St, Yankton, South Dakota 57078. **T:** 1 605 665-7811
E: newsroom@yankton.net
W: http://www.yankton.net
Freq: Mon thru Fri; **Circ:** 8303 Not Audited
Editorial Profile: Yankton Daily Press & Dakotan is published daily for the residents of Yankton, SD and surrounding areas. The newspaper covers local and regional news, business, sports, education and entertainment.; Full Page Mono: 18.36; Full Page Colour: 60.03
Currency: US Dollars
DAILY NEWSPAPER

Yated Ne'Eman
Editorial: 53 Olympia Ln, Monsey, New York 10952-2829. **T:** 1 845 369-1600
E: editor@yated.com
W: http://www.yated.com
Freq: Wed; **Circ:** 33000 Not Audited
Publisher: Pinchos Lipschultz; **Editor:** Avi Yishai
Editorial Profile: Yated Ne'Eman is a newspaper written for the Haredi Jewish community in and around Monsey, NY.; Full Page Mono: 6.25
Currency: US Dollars
NEWSPAPER

Yelp & Yosemite Sun Newspapers
Owner: Lucenup Media
Editorial: 30651 Holiday Dr, Coarsegold, California 93614. **T:** 1 559 658-5419
W: http://www.theyelp.com **Circ:** 10000 Not Audited
NEWSPAPER

YES! Weekly
Owner: Womack Newspapers Inc
Editorial: 5500 Adams Farm Ln Ste 204, Greensboro, North Carolina 27407-7059.
T: 1 336 316-1231
W: http://www.yesweekly.com
Freq: Wed; **Circ:** 43000 Not Audited
Editor: Jeff Sykes
Editorial Profile: YES! Weekly in Greensboro, NC is an alternative newspaper that focuses on the cultural, political and artistic aspects of the Triad, which includes High Point and Winston-Salem, NC. Targeted to young professionals, it strives to be the conscience of the community, a recorder of history, a voice for all citizens and an advocate of the good. Deadlines are on Mondays.; Full Page Mono: 30.00
Currency: US Dollars
NEWSPAPER

Yevreiski Mir
Editorial: 1100 Coney Island Ave, Ste 400, Brooklyn, New York 11230. **T:** 1 718 434-0900
W: http://www.evreimir.com
Freq: Tue; **Circ:** 14000 Not Audited
Editorial Profile: Yevreiski Mir is a community newspaper written for Russian-speaking Jewish residents of Brooklyn, NY and the surrounding areas.; Full Page Mono: 6.72
Currency: US Dollars
NEWSPAPER

York Daily Record
Owner: MediaNews Group
Editorial: 1891 Loucks Rd, York, Pennsylvania 17408-9708. **T:** 1 717 771-2000
E: news@ydr.com **W:** http://www.ydr.com
Freq: Daily; **Circ:** 53725 Not Audited
Editor: James McClure; **Editor:** James McClure; **Editor:** James McClure; **Editor:** James McClure
Editorial Profile: York Daily Record is written for the residents of York County, PA. It covers national and local news, sports, business and events. The Sunday edition of the paper is called York Sunday News.; Full Page Mono: 83.35; Full Page Colour: 269.82
Currency: US Dollars
DAILY NEWSPAPER

The York Dispatch
Owner: Buckner News Alliance
Editorial: 205 N George St, York, Pennsylvania 17401. **T:** 1 717 854-1575
E: news@yorkdispatch.com
W: http://www.yorkdispatch.com
Freq: Daily; **Circ:** 22275 Not Audited
Editor: Lori Goodlin; **Publisher:** David Martens
Editorial Profile: The York Dispatch is a daily, evening newspaper serving the York, PA area. The paper covers local news, business, entertainment, sports and lifestyle. On Sundays, it combines with the York Daily Record. The lead time is two weeks and the absolute deadline is one week before issue date.; Full Page Mono: 87.10; Full Page Colour: 146.19
Currency: US Dollars
DAILY NEWSPAPER

York News-Times
Owner: Omaha World-Herald Co.
Editorial: 327 N Platte Ave, York, Nebraska 68467. **T:** 1 402 362-4478
E: news@yorknewstimes.com
W: http://www.yorknewstimes.com
Freq: Daily; **Circ:** 4328 Not Audited
Publisher: Greg Awtry
Editorial Profile: York News-Times is a local daily newspaper written for residents of York, NE. The publication's editorial mission is to report the local news of York, NE.; Full Page Mono: 12.50; Full Page Colour: 119.00
Currency: US Dollars
DAILY NEWSPAPER

York Weekly Record
Owner: MediaNews Group
Editorial: 1891 Loucks Rd, York, Pennsylvania 17408. **T:** 1 717 771-2000 **E:** weekly@ydr.com
W: http://www.ydr.com
Freq: Fri; **Circ:** 69250 Not Audited
Publisher: Sara Glines; **Editor:** Cathy Hirko; **Editor:** Cathy Hirko; **Editor:** Cathy Hirko; **Editor:** Cathy Hirko
Editorial Profile: Weekly Record's editorial mission is to serve and inform Southern York County, PA. The paper is affiliated with the York Daily Record and is distributed to their subscribers via mail. It covers community news and events, sports, education and local government.; Full Page Mono: 15.00
Currency: US Dollars
NEWSPAPER

Yucaipa/Calimesa News Mirror
Owner: Century Group (The)
Editorial: 35154 Yucaipa Blvd, Yucaipa, California 92399-4339. **T:** 1 909 797-9101
E: news@newsmirror.net
W: http://www.newsmirror.net
Freq: Fri; **Circ:** 20200 Not Audited
Publisher: Toebe Bush; **Editor:** Claire Teeters; **Editor:** Claire Teeters; **Editor:** Claire Teeters
Editorial Profile: Yucaipa/Calimesa News Mirror is a weekly newspaper serving residents of Yucaipa, Calimesa and Oak Glen, CA. It emphasizes local news and covers breaking news, crimes, public announcements and civic events.; Full Page Mono: 17.70
Currency: US Dollars
NEWSPAPER

The Yuma Sun
Owner: Freedom Communications Inc.
Editorial: 2055 S Arizona Ave, Yuma, Arizona 85364-6596. **T:** 1 928 783-3333
E: newsroom@yumasun.com
W: http://www.yumasun.com
Freq: Daily; **Circ:** 15932 Not Audited
Publisher: Joni Brooks; **Editor:** Roxanne Molenar; **News Editor:** Rob Powell; **Editor:** Terry Ross
Editorial Profile: The Yuma Sun is a daily newspaper serving the Yuma, AZ area. The publication covers local news, sports, lifestyle and entertainment for the residents of Yuma.; Full Page Mono: 30.01; Full Page Colour: 797.00
Currency: US Dollars
DAILY NEWSPAPER

Zion-Benton News
Owner: United Communications Corp.
Editorial: 2711 Sheridan Rd, Ste 202, Zion, Illinois 60099. **T:** 1 847 746-9000
E: zion@kenoshanews.com
W: http://www.zion-bentonnews.com
Freq: Thu; **Circ:** 21800 Not Audited
Publisher: Frank Misureli; **Editor:** Mona Shannon
Editorial Profile: Zion-Benton News is a community newspaper for the residents of Beach Park, Winthrop Harbor and Zion, IL.; Full Page Mono: 10.75
Currency: US Dollars
NEWSPAPER

NEWS SERVICE/SYNDICATE

Accuracy in Media
Owner: Accuracy in Media, Inc.
Editorial: 4350 E West Hwy Ste 555, Bethesda, Montgomery, Maryland 20814-4582.
T: 1 202 364-4401 **E:** info@aim.org
W: http://www.aim.org
Editor: Roger Aronoff; **Publisher:** Don Irvine
Editorial Profile: Accuracy in Media is a non-profit, grassroots citizens watch dog of the news media that critiques botched and bungled news stories and sets the record straight on important issues that have received slanted coverage. Column focus is on examples of media bias, distortion and erroneous coverage.
NEWS SERVICE/SYNDICATE

AccuWeather
Owner: AccuWeather, Inc.
Editorial: 385 Science Park Rd, State College, Pennsylvania 16803-2215. **T:** 1 814 235-8600
W: http://www.accuweather.com
Editorial Profile: AccuWeather provides a portfolio of products and services via the Internet, in print and behind the scenes for millions of people worldwide. It services 300,000 paying customers in media, business, government and institutions, and millions more through AccuWeather.com. It also provides content to more than 10,000 Internet sites, including CNN Interactive, ABC's owned and operated stations, The Washington Post and The New York Times.
NEWS SERVICE/SYNDICATE

African American Newswire
T: 1 413 221-7931 **E:** info@unityfirst.com
W: http://www.unityfirst.com
Editorial Profile: African American Newswire is a news service that reaches communities of color, including community-based organizations, business and professional groups, social associations and spiritual outlets across the country.
NEWS SERVICE/SYNDICATE

Agence France-Presse
Editorial: 1500 K St NW Ste 600, Washington, District Of Columbia 20005-1200.
T: 1 202 289-0700 **E:** afp-us@afp.com
W: http://www.afp.com
Editorial Profile: Founded in 1835, this international news service is headquartered in Paris. It serves thousands of radio, TV, magazine, newspaper and company subscribers around the globe. Journalists are based in 165 countries providing top quality international service tailored for the specific needs of clients in each region.
NEWS SERVICE/SYNDICATE

Agence France-Presse
Editorial: 747 3rd Ave, Fl 35, New York, New York 10017. **T:** 1 212 735-9204
E: nyeco@afp.com
Bureau Chief: Brigitte Dusseau
NEWS SERVICE/SYNDICATE

Agence France-Presse
Editorial: 6430 W Sunset Blvd Ste 702, Hollywood, California 90028-7910.
T: 1 323 463-0675 **E:** afpla@afp.com
News Editor: Robert Woollard
NEWS SERVICE/SYNDICATE

Agence France-Presse
Editorial: 20 N Wacker Dr Ste 2610, Chicago, Illinois 60606-3004. **T:** 1 312 527-5510
NEWS SERVICE/SYNDICATE

Agence France-Presse
Editorial: 100 Biscayne Blvd, Ste 3030, Miami, Florida 33132-2305. **T:** 1 305 679-9965
Editorial Profile: This is the Miami office of Agence France-Presse, an international news service.
NEWS SERVICE/SYNDICATE

Agence France-Presse
Editorial: United Nations Building, Library Bldg, 405 E 42nd St., New York, New York 10017. **T:** 1 212 759-8183
NEWS SERVICE/SYNDICATE

Agence France-Presse
Editorial: 753 Central Ave, Alameda, California 94501-3457. **T:** 1 510 263-8420
Bureau Chief: Glenn Chapman
NEWS SERVICE/SYNDICATE

Agencia EFE
Owner: EFE, S.A.
Editorial: 529 14th St NW Ste 1252, Washington, District Of Columbia 20045-2202.
T: 1 202 745-7692 **W:** http://www.efe.com
Editorial Profile: Agencia EFE serves as a source of news for Hispanic Americans and Hispanic media in the United States and around the world. The daily online news wire publishes stories in Spanish, with some copy available in English. The English Language Service in Coral Gables, FL, translates high profile stories into English. Correspondents cover a variety of news of interest to Hispanic people including health, immigration, politics, business and entertainment.
NEWS SERVICE/SYNDICATE

Agencia EFE
Editorial: 5959 Blue Lagoon Dr Suite 308, Miami, Florida 33126-2052. **T:** 1 305 262-7575
Editorial Profile: This is the Maimi bureau for the news service.
NEWS SERVICE/SYNDICATE

Agencia EFE
Editorial: 25 W 43rd St, Ste 1114, New York, New York 10036-7410. **T:** 1 212 867-5757
Bureau Chief: Rafael Cañas
Editorial Profile: This is the New York bureau for Agencia EFE.
NEWS SERVICE/SYNDICATE

Agencia EFE
T: 1 787 723-6023 **E:** redacpr@efe.com
Editorial Profile: This is the Puerto Rico bureau for Agencia EFE.
NEWS SERVICE/SYNDICATE

AgeVenture News Service
Editorial: 19432 Preserve Dr, Boca Raton, Palm Beach, Florida 33498-4818.
T: 1 561 866-8251
E: ageventurenewsservice@demko.com
W: http://www.demko.com
Editorial Profile: AgeVenture News Service reports news and trends in health, wellness, life-expectancy and longevity research. Profiles new products and services designed to promote successful aging and active retirement. Reviews books, movies, dvds and computer programs based on themes related to fitness, boomers, aging and retirement planning and lifestyles.
NEWS SERVICE/SYNDICATE

Alan Lavine Inc.
Editorial: 10199 Willow Ln, Palm Beach Gardens, Florida 33410-5141.
T: 1 561 630-7112 **E:** mwliblav@gmail.com
W: http://www.moneycouple.com
Editorial Profile: Alan Lavine Inc. specializes in news about mutual funds, banking, real estate and personal finance. Columns often appear in the Boston Herald, Pittsburgh-Post Gazette, the Palm Beach (FL) Daily News, Scripps Howard newspapers in Florida, Savannah Now, Dow Jones Marketwatch, Treasure Coast Business Journal, Mutual Funds Interactive, Yahoo! Finance, Mutual Fund Interactive, FOXNews.com, the Appeal-Democrat, Investor's Business Daily and The Oregonian, Dow Jones Retirement Weekly, Financial Advisor Magazine, and Registered

Rep Magazine. Targets both affluent and middle income readers and attempts to help people make financial decisions.
NEWS SERVICE/SYNDICATE

Alsop, Jonathon
Editorial: 336 Washington St, Brookline, Massachusetts 2445. **T:** 1 617 784-7150
E: jon@invinoveritas.com
W: http://bostonwineschool.com
Editorial Profile: Jonathan Alsop's self-syndicated wine column takes an iconoclastic look at the world of wine, including wine tasting, vineyard and winery news.
NEWS SERVICE/SYNDICATE

AlterNet
Owner: Independent Media Institute
Editorial: 1881 Harmon St, Berkeley, California 94703-2415. **T:** 1 415 284-1420
E: info@alternet.org
W: http://www.alternet.org
Editorial Profile: AlterNet is a non-profit organization devoted to promoting and strengthening the independent press. About 45 stories a week are syndicated on the virtual newswire. Categories include: news and features; media culture review; essays, columns and opinions; shorts; arts & entertainment and books and authors. Coverage often includes new media and technology, political commentary, the environment, sex, personal essays and noteworthy literary writing. More than 200 media outlets subscribe.
NEWS SERVICE/SYNDICATE

American Baptist News Service
Editorial: 588 N. Gulphrd, King of Prussia, Pennsylvania 19406. **T:** 1 610 768-2322
E: news@abc-usa.org
W: http://www.abc-usa.org
Editorial Profile: The American Baptist News Service provides information on events and developments in the American Baptist Churches USA.
NEWS SERVICE/SYNDICATE

American Chemical Society News Service
Editorial: 1155 16th St NW, Washington, District Of Columbia 20036-4839.
T: 1 202 872-4400 **E:** newsroom@acs.org
W: http://www.chemistry.org
Editor: Michael Bernstein
Editorial Profile: American Chemical Society News Service provides expert commentary on a variety of topics related to the chemical sciences. Also distributes news briefs and features on many of the research findings presented at its national meetings and in its numerous scientific journals.
NEWS SERVICE/SYNDICATE

American Federation of Teachers
Owner: American Federation of Teachers
Editorial: 555 New Jersey Ave NW, Washington, District Of Columbia 20001-2079.
T: 1 202 879-4430 **E:** online@aft.org
W: http://www.aft.org
Editor in Chief: Roger Glass; **Editor in Chief:** Roger Glass
Editorial Profile: Monthly review and opinion column focusing on current issues affecting education, children and labor/management relations. Monthly radio spots are also done on the same subject matter.
NEWS SERVICE/SYNDICATE

American Lawyer Media
Owner: ALM Media Properties, LLC
Editorial: 120 Broadway 5th Floor, New York, New York 10271-1101. **T:** 1 212 457-9408
W: http://www.alm.com
Editorial Profile: American Lawyer Media is the nation's leading source of news and information for the legal industry. The news service owns and publishes 33 award-winning national and regional legal trade newspapers and magazines, including The American Lawyer and The National Law Journal. Other services for legal professionals include book, custom and newsletter publishing, court verdict and settlement reporting, production of legal trade shows and conferences, educational seminars and distribution of content related to the legal industry.
NEWS SERVICE/SYNDICATE

American-International News Syndicate
Editorial: 695 Olive Rd, Santa Barbara, California 93108. **T:** 1 805 969-5848
Editorial Profile: The syndicate's main features, Ask The Expert and The Discriminating Traveler, cover restaurants, food, new books, art and luxury travel news.

The features explore spas, wines and cruises and syndicated to 25 newspapers across the country.
NEWS SERVICE/SYNDICATE

Amok
T: 1 415 730-5610 **W:** http://www.amok.com
Editorial Profile: The author looks at news and issues affecting America's ethnic minorities, with special emphasis on Asian-Americans. He also includes coverage of sports, politics, movies, entertainment, public policy, Washington events, California, high-tech, computers and the Internet.
NEWS SERVICE/SYNDICATE

Ampersand Communications
Editorial: 2311 S Bayshore Drive, Miami, Florida 33133-4728. **T:** 1 305 285-2200
E: amprsnd@aol.com
W: http://www.ampersandcom.com
Editorial Profile: Self-syndicated columns offer information on a variety of topics, including consumer and business travel, food, health, book reviews, environmental issues, house and home, pets and senior lifestyles. They appear in many major daily newspapers, magazines, trade journals, and through online syndication.
NEWS SERVICE/SYNDICATE

Anadolu Agency - New York Bureau
Editorial: 821 United Nations Plz Fl 6, New York, New York 10017-3520.
T: 1 212 980-5211 **E:** newyork@aa.com.tr
W: http://www.aa.com.tr/en/
Editorial Profile: This is the New York Bureau of Anadolu Agency in Turkey.
NEWS SERVICE/SYNDICATE

Anne Gilbert Enterprises
Editorial: 5808 Royal Club Dr, Boynton Beach, Palm Beach, Florida 33437-4264.
T: 1 561 364-5798
Editorial Profile: Offers feature stories as well as a column with either b/w or color photos on antiques and the travel involved in finding them.
NEWS SERVICE/SYNDICATE

ANSA - New York Bureau
Editorial: 42 W 76Th St Apt 1B, New York, New York 10023-8705. **T:** 1 971 251-5498
W: http://www.ansa.it
Editorial Profile: This is the New York bureau for ANSA, based in Rome, Italy.
NEWS SERVICE/SYNDICATE

ANSA Italian News Agency - New York Bureau
Editorial: 866 United Nations Plz Rm 410, New York, New York 10017-1831.
T: 1 212 319-6802 **E:** ansa.newyork@ansa.it
W: http://www.ansa.it
Editorial Profile: This is the New York bureau of ANSA Italian News Agency.
NEWS SERVICE/SYNDICATE

AP Financial News
Owner: Associated Press, Inc.
Editorial: 450 W 33rd St, 14th Fl, New York, New York 10001-2603. **T:** 1 212 621-7190
E: apfinancial@ap.org **W:** http://www.ap.org
Editorial Profile: AP Financial News is a news service of the Associated Press geared toward providing news more quickly for individual investors who use the Web for public company information. It offers expanded financial coverage and includes corporate earnings reports. This site offers RSS (Really Simple Syndication).
NEWS SERVICE/SYNDICATE

APA - Austria Presse Agentur - New York Bureau
Owner: APA-Austria Presse Agentur
Editorial: 340 E 64Th St Apt 16G, New York, New York 10065-7516. **T:** 1 212 755-5236
W: http://www.journale.apa.at/cms/journale
Editorial Profile: This is the New York bureau of APA - Austria Presse Agentur in Wien, Austria.
NEWS SERVICE/SYNDICATE

Arab Writers Group Syndicate
Owner: Hanania Enterprises Ltd.
Editorial: 15139 Windsor Dr, Orland Park, Illinois 60462. **T:** 1 312 933-9855
W: http://rayhanania.wordpress.com/
Publisher: Ray Hanania; **Publisher:** Ray Hanania
Editorial Profile: Arab Writers Group Syndicate offers opinion and editorial columns on issues connected to the Middle East. The columns range from political commentary to humorous satire. Each is written from an Arab

perspective. The syndicate also reviews books on the Middle East, Arab, Jewish, Israeli, Christian, Muslim and Islamic topics.
NEWS SERVICE/SYNDICATE

Army News Service
T: 1 703 602-8134 **E:** arnews@smc.army.mil
W: http://www.army.mil/news
Editor: Gary Sheftick
Editorial Profile: Army News Service keeps the United States Army's obligation of informing the American people and the Army of the latest Army news, including news on policies and combat updates.
NEWS SERVICE/SYNDICATE

Army Times News Service
Editorial: 6883 Commercial Dr, Springfield, Virginia 22159. **T:** 1 703 750-8643
E: armylet@armytimes.com
W: http://www.armytimes.com
News Editor: Cathy Walser
Editorial Profile: Army Times News Service offers exclusive, original, in-depth news and analysis about an Army career, pay and benefits and issues impacting professional advancement. It also has community information and active lifestyle features of interest to Army personnel and their families. There are over 18 supplements during the year, including valuable military resource guides, a special annual historical issue, military healthcare specials and important second career and educational supplements.
NEWS SERVICE/SYNDICATE

Arts & Leisure News Service
Editorial: 115 E 82Nd St Apt 3B, New York, New York 10028-0878. **T:** 1 212 772-1625
E: artsandleisure@yahoo.com
W: http://www.artsandleisurenews.com
Editorial Profile: Arts & Leisure News Service covers the popular culture scene including, travel, food, wine, theater, music, dance, celebrities, movies and everything that deals with entertainment and leisure time. It goes out nationally with the potential of reaching 11 million people.
NEWS SERVICE/SYNDICATE

Ask Jerry
T: 1 202 244-2222 **E:** askjerry@earthlink.net
Editorial Profile: Eclectic, entertaining consumer advice column featured in daily newspapers throughout the United States. Ask Jerry solutions appear in the Features, Business and Sunday magazine sections, where millions of readers learn to find the unobtainable and solve the impossible.
NEWS SERVICE/SYNDICATE

Assist News Service
Editorial: 23591 El Toro Rd, Lake Forest, California 92630-4774. **T:** 1 949 472-0974
E: danjuma1@aol.com
W: http://www.assistnews.net
Editorial Profile: Assist News Service offers news on religious happenings around the world, focusing on international news from a Christian perspective.
NEWS SERVICE/SYNDICATE

Associated Baptist Press
W: http://www.abpnews.com
Editorial Profile: Associated Baptist Press provides daily coverage of Baptist news, news from the nation's capital and other general news and information of concern to Christians in the United States and around the world. Their mission is to serve Christ by providing credible and compelling information about matters of faith. The coverage includes religion, liberty, morality and ethical issues. It is a news cooperative and tries to develop a network of reporters and news outlets that provide a steady source of news.
NEWS SERVICE/SYNDICATE

Associated Designs
Editorial: 1100 Jacobs Dr, Eugene, Oregon 97402-1983. **T:** 1 541 461-2082
E: info@associateddesigns.com
W: http://www.associateddesigns.com
Editor: Rick McAlexander
Editorial Profile: Associated Designs home plans are created by talented designers with more than 50 years of combined home design experience. Weekly columns feature plans that are published in newspapers around the country. Since the company was founded, more than 60,000 home plans have been sold.
NEWS SERVICE/SYNDICATE

Associated Press
Owner: Associated Press, Inc.
Editorial: 450 W 33rd St Fl 14, New York, New York 10001-2626. **T:** 1 212 621-1500

E: apnyc@ap.org **W:** http://www.ap.org
Editor: Damian Troise
Editorial Profile: Founded in 1848, Associated Press is an international news organization offering news, photos, graphics, audio and video for 1,700 newspapers and 5,000 radio and television outlets in the United States as well as newspaper, radio and television subscribers internationally. There are bureaus worldwide representing over one hundred countries. It features a massive digital photo network, a continuously updated online news service, a television news service and one of the largest radio networks in the United States. Daybook items for New York City should go to the alternate email.
NEWS SERVICE/SYNDICATE

Associated Press
Owner: Associated Press, Inc.
Editorial: 101 Marietta St NW, Suite 2450, Atlanta, Georgia 30303-2720.
T: 1 404 522-8971 **E:** apatlanta@ap.org
W: http://www.apsouthatlantic.org
News Editor: Jim Van Anglen
Editorial Profile: South Daybook department items for regional South coverage can be sent to the South Daybook Department e-mail.
NEWS SERVICE/SYNDICATE

Associated Press
Owner: Associated Press, Inc.
Editorial: 184 High St, Floor 3, Boston, Massachusetts 2110. **T:** 1 617 357-8100
E: apboston@ap.org
NEWS SERVICE/SYNDICATE

Associated Press
Owner: Associated Press, Inc.
Editorial: 10 S Wacker Dr Ste 2500, Chicago, Illinois 60606-7491. **T:** 1 312 781-0500
E: chifax@ap.org
Bureau Chief: George Garties
Editorial Profile: This is a central bureau for Illinois coverage. Daybook items should go to the main e-mail address.
NEWS SERVICE/SYNDICATE

Associated Press
Owner: Associated Press, Inc.
Editorial: 1103 Schrock Rd, Ste 300, Columbus, Ohio 43229-1179.
T: 1 614 885-2727 **E:** apcolumbus@ap.org
W: http://www.ap.org/ohio
Bureau Chief: Eva Parziale
NEWS SERVICE/SYNDICATE

Associated Press
Owner: Associated Press, Inc.
Editorial: 4851 Lyndon B Johnson Fwy Ste 300, Dallas, Texas 75244-6047.
T: 1 972 991-2100 **E:** aptexas@ap.org
Bureau Chief: Dale Leach
NEWS SERVICE/SYNDICATE

Associated Press
Owner: Associated Press, Inc.
Editorial: 1444 Wazee St Ste 130, Denver, Colorado 80202-1395. **T:** 1 303 825-0123
E: apdenver@ap.org
Bureau Chief: Jim Clarke
NEWS SERVICE/SYNDICATE

Associated Press
Owner: Associated Press, Inc.
Editorial: 300 River Place Dr Ste 2400, Detroit, Michigan 48207-5064.
T: 1 313 259-0650 **E:** apmichigan@ap.org
Bureau Chief: Eva Parziale
NEWS SERVICE/SYNDICATE

Associated Press
Owner: Associated Press, Inc.
Editorial: 16945 Northchase Dr Ste 2110, Houston, Texas 77060-2151.
T: 1 281 872-8900 **E:** aptexas@ap.org
Bureau Chief: Dale Leach
NEWS SERVICE/SYNDICATE

Associated Press
Owner: Associated Press, Inc.
Editorial: 215 W Pershing Rd Ste 221, Kansas City, Missouri 64108-4316. **T:** 1 816 421-4844
E: apkansascity@ap.org
W: http://www.apkansascity.org
Bureau Chief: Kia Breaux; **News Editor:** Chris Clark
NEWS SERVICE/SYNDICATE

Associated Press
Owner: Associated Press, Inc.
Editorial: 221 S Figueroa St Ste 300, Los Angeles, California 90012-2552.
T: 1 213 626-1200 **E:** losangeles@ap.org
W: http://www.ap.org/states/california
Bureau Chief: Anthony Marquez

Editorial Profile: This is a central bureau for California coverage. Daybook items should go to the main e-mail address.
NEWS SERVICE/SYNDICATE

Associated Press
Owner: Associated Press, Inc.
Editorial: 9100 NW 36th St. Suite 111, Doral, Florida 33178-2435. **T:** 1 305 594-5825
E: miami@ap.org **W:** http://www.ap.org/florida
Bureau Chief: Jim Baltzelle
NEWS SERVICE/SYNDICATE

Associated Press
Owner: Associated Press, Inc.
Editorial: 1835 Market St Ste 1700, Philadelphia, Pennsylvania 19103-2945.
T: 1 215 561-1133 **E:** phillyap@ap.org
W: http://www.ap.org/states/pennsylvania
Bureau Chief: Sally Hale
NEWS SERVICE/SYNDICATE

Associated Press
Owner: Associated Press, Inc.
Editorial: 3131 Elliott Ave Ste 750, Seattle, Washington 98121-1095. **T:** 1 206 682-1812
E: apseattle@ap.org
W: http://www.ap.org/states/northwest
NEWS SERVICE/SYNDICATE

Associated Press
Editorial: 1100 13th St NW Ste 500, Washington, District Of Columbia 20005-4051.
T: 1 202 641-9000 **E:** apwashington@ap.org
Bureau Chief: Sally Buzbee; **News Editor:** Eugene Kim; **News Editor:** David Pace; **News Editor:** Ron Powers; **News Editor:** Libby Quaid; **News Editor:** Matt Yancey
Editorial Profile: Daybook items for the D.C. area should be sent to the main e-mail address.
NEWS SERVICE/SYNDICATE

Associated Press
Owner: Associated Press, Inc.
Editorial: 303 2nd St Ste 680, San Francisco, California 94107-6304. **T:** 1 415 495-1708
E: sanfrancisco@ap.org
W: http://www.ap.org/california
Bureau Chief: John Raess
NEWS SERVICE/SYNDICATE

Associated Press
Owner: Associated Press, Inc.
Editorial: 251 N Illinois St Ste 1600, Indianapolis, Indiana 46204-1943.
T: 1 317 639-5501 **E:** indy@ap.org
Bureau Chief: George Garties; **News Editor:** Jeni O'Malley
NEWS SERVICE/SYNDICATE

Associated Press
Owner: Associated Press, Inc.
Editorial: 218 N Charles St Suite 330, Baltimore, Maryland 21201-4021.
T: 1 410 837-8315 **E:** midatlsups@ap.org
W: http://www.ap.org/maryland
Bureau Chief: Dorothy Abernathy; **News Editor:** Amanda Kell
NEWS SERVICE/SYNDICATE

Associated Press
Owner: Associated Press, Inc.
Editorial: 425 Portland Ave 3rd Floor, Minneapolis, Minnesota 55488.
T: 1 612 332-2727 **E:** apminneapolis@ap.org
W: http://www.ap.org/states/minnesota
News Editor: Doug Glass; **Bureau Chief:** Michelle Morgante
Editorial Profile: This is a central bureau for Minnesota coverage. Daybook items should go to the main e-mail address.
NEWS SERVICE/SYNDICATE

Associated Press
Owner: Associated Press, Inc.
Editorial: 700 W Saint Clair Ave Ste 318, Cleveland, Ohio 44113-1226.
T: 1 216 771-2172 **E:** apcolumbus@ap.org
W: http://www.ap.org/ohio
Bureau Chief: Eva Parziale
NEWS SERVICE/SYNDICATE

Associated Press
Owner: Associated Press, Inc.
Editorial: 2200 4th Ave N, Birmingham, Alabama 35203-3802. **T:** 1 205 251-4221
W: http://www.apsouthatlantic.org
NEWS SERVICE/SYNDICATE

Associated Press
Owner: Associated Press, Inc.
Editorial: 201 Monroe St Ste 1940, Montgomery, Alabama 36104-3721.
T: 1 334 262-5947 **E:** moge@ap.org
W: http://www.apsouthatlantic.org

News Editor: Jim Van Anglen
NEWS SERVICE/SYNDICATE

Associated Press
Owner: Associated Press, Inc.
Editorial: 1850 N Central Ave Ste 640, Phoenix, Arizona 85004-4573.
T: 1 602 258-8934 **E:** aparizona@ap.org
W: http://www.aparizona.org
NEWS SERVICE/SYNDICATE

Associated Press
Owner: Associated Press, Inc.
Editorial: 10810 Executive Center Dr Ste 308, Little Rock, Arkansas 72211-4388.
T: 1 501 225-3668 **E:** pebbles@ap.org
W: http://www.ap.org/arkansas
News Editor: Kelly Kissel; **News Editor:** Kelly Kissel; **Bureau Chief:** Dale Leach
NEWS SERVICE/SYNDICATE

Associated Press
Owner: Associated Press, Inc.
Editorial: 505 5th Ave Ste 1000, Des Moines, Iowa 50309-2315. **T:** 1 515 243-3281
E: apdesmoines@ap.org
W: http://www.ap.org/iowa
Bureau Chief: Kia Breaux; **News Editor:** Scott McFetridge
NEWS SERVICE/SYNDICATE

Associated Press
Owner: Associated Press, Inc.
Editorial: 525 W Broadway, Louisville, Kentucky 40202-2206. **T:** 1 502 583-7718
E: aplouisville@ap.org
W: http://www.ap.org/kentucky
Bureau Chief: Adam Yeomans
NEWS SERVICE/SYNDICATE

Associated Press
Owner: Associated Press, Inc.
Editorial: 1515 Poydras St Ste 2500, New Orleans, Louisiana 70112-3716.
T: 1 504 523-3931 **E:** nrle@ap.org
W: http://www.ap.org/states/louisiana
Bureau Chief: Dale Leach; **News Editor:** Brian Schwaner
NEWS SERVICE/SYNDICATE

Associated Press
Owner: Associated Press, Inc.
Editorial: 909 N 96th St Ste 104, Omaha, Nebraska 68114-2508. **T:** 1 402 391-0031
E: omahane@ap.org
News Editor: Scott McFetridge; **Bureau Chief:** Michelle Morgante
NEWS SERVICE/SYNDICATE

Associated Press
Owner: Associated Press, Inc.
Editorial: 50 W State St Ste 1114, Trenton, New Jersey 08608-1220. **T:** 1 609 392-3622
E: aptrenton@ap.org
W: http://www.ap.org/states/nj/index.html
Bureau Chief: Sally Hale
NEWS SERVICE/SYNDICATE

Associated Press
Owner: Associated Press, Inc.
Editorial: 5130 San Francisco Rd NE Ste A, Albuquerque, New Mexico 87109-4618.
T: 1 505 822-9022 **E:** apalbuquerque@ap.org
W: http://www.apnewmexico.org
NEWS SERVICE/SYNDICATE

Associated Press
Owner: Associated Press, Inc.
Editorial: 4800 Six Forks Rd Ste 210, Raleigh, North Carolina 27609-5245.
T: 1 919 510-8937 **E:** apraleigh@ap.org
W: http://www.apsouthatlantic.org
News Editor: Tim Rogers
NEWS SERVICE/SYNDICATE

Associated Press
Owner: Associated Press, Inc.
Editorial: 312 Elm St, C/O the Cincinnati Enquirer, Cincinnati, Ohio 45202-2739.
T: 1 513 241-2386 **E:** apcolumbus@ap.org
W: http://www.ap.org/ohio
Bureau Chief: Eva Parziale
NEWS SERVICE/SYNDICATE

Associated Press
Owner: Associated Press, Inc.
Editorial: 525 Central Park Dr Ste 202, Oklahoma City, Oklahoma 73105-1707.
T: 1 405 525-2121 **E:** apoklahoma@ap.org
W: http://www.apoklahoma.org
Bureau Chief: Dale Leach
NEWS SERVICE/SYNDICATE

Associated Press
Owner: Associated Press, Inc.

Editorial: 10 Dorrance St Ste 601, Providence, Rhode Island 02903-2018. **T:** 1 401 274-2270
E: approvidence@ap.org
NEWS SERVICE/SYNDICATE

Associated Press
Owner: Associated Press, Inc.
Editorial: 1207 18th Ave South Ste 261A, Nashville, Tennessee 37212.
T: 1 615 373-9988 **E:** apnashville@ap.org
W: http://www.ap.org/states/tennessee
News Editor: Joe Danborn; **Bureau Chief:** Adam Yeomans
NEWS SERVICE/SYNDICATE

Associated Press
Owner: Associated Press, Inc.
Editorial: 111 E. Wisconsin Ave Suite 1925, Milwaukee, Wisconsin 53202.
T: 1 414 225-3580 **E:** apmlw@ap.org
Bureau Chief: George Garties; **News Editor:** Doug Glass
NEWS SERVICE/SYNDICATE

Associated Press
Owner: Associated Press, Inc.
Editorial: 211 King St Ste 205, Charleston, South Carolina 29401-3184.
T: 1 843 722-1660
W: http://www.ap.org/southcarolina
News Editor: Tim Rogers
NEWS SERVICE/SYNDICATE

Associated Press
Owner: Associated Press, Inc.
Editorial: 500 Virginia St E Ste 1150, Charleston, West Virginia 25301-2167.
T: 1 304 346-0897 **E:** chwpr@ap.org
Bureau Chief: Dorothy Abernathy
NEWS SERVICE/SYNDICATE

Associated Press
Owner: Associated Press, Inc.
Editorial: 1100 S Tryon St Ste 101, Charlotte, North Carolina 28203-4298.
T: 1 704 334-4624 **E:** apraleigh@ap.org
W: http://www.apsouthatlantic.org
NEWS SERVICE/SYNDICATE

Associated Press
Owner: Associated Press, Inc.
Editorial: TCU Moudy Building South, Convergence Center, Fort Worth, Texas.
T: 1 817 348-0367
Bureau Chief: Dale Leach
NEWS SERVICE/SYNDICATE

Associated Press
Editorial: 150 W Brambleton Ave, Norfolk, Virginia 23510-2018. **T:** 1 757 625-2047
NEWS SERVICE/SYNDICATE

Associated Press
Owner: Associated Press, Inc.
Editorial: 121 SW Salmon St Ste 1450, Portland, Oregon 97204-2924.
T: 1 503 228-2169 **E:** apportland@ap.org
W: http://www.ap.org/states/northwest
NEWS SERVICE/SYNDICATE

Associated Press
Editorial: 75 Rev Dr Martin Luther King Jr Blvd, Ste B28, Saint Paul, Minnesota 55155-1601. **T:** 1 651 222-4821
E: apminneapolis@ap.org
W: http://www.ap.org/minnesota
Bureau Chief: Michelle Morgante
NEWS SERVICE/SYNDICATE

Associated Press
Editorial: 90 S. 400 St Ste 670, Salt Lake City, Utah 84104. **T:** 1 801 322-3405
E: apsaltlake@ap.org
Bureau Chief: Jim Clarke
NEWS SERVICE/SYNDICATE

Associated Press
Owner: Associated Press, Inc.
Editorial: 490 1st Ave S Suite 2009, Saint Petersburg, Florida 33701-4204.
T: 1 727 823-4721
W: http://www.ap.org/states/florida
NEWS SERVICE/SYNDICATE

Associated Press
Owner: Associated Press, Inc.
Editorial: 825 E Douglas Ave, Wichita, Kansas 67202-3512. **T:** 1 316 263-4601
E: apkansascity@ap.org
W: http://www.apkansascity.org
Bureau Chief: Kia Breaux; **News Editor:** Chris Clark
NEWS SERVICE/SYNDICATE

Associated Press
Owner: Associated Press, Inc.

Editorial: 1215 K St Ste 960, Sacramento, California 95814-3946. **T:** 1 916 448-9555
E: norcal@apcalifornia.org
W: http://www.ap.org/states/california
Bureau Chief: John Raess
NEWS SERVICE/SYNDICATE

Associated Press
Owner: Associated Press, Inc.
Editorial: 11 Stanwix St Ste 1020, Pittsburgh, Pennsylvania 15222-1312. **T:** 1 412 281-3747
E: appittsburgh@ap.org
W: http://www.ap.org/states/pennsylvania
NEWS SERVICE/SYNDICATE

Associated Press
Owner: Associated Press, Inc.
Editorial: 350 Camino De La Reina, San Diego, California 92108-3003.
T: 1 619 231-9365 **E:** losangeles@ap.org
W: http://www.ap.org/states/california
NEWS SERVICE/SYNDICATE

Associated Press
Owner: Associated Press, Inc.
Editorial: 501 N Magnolia Ave, Orlando, Florida 32801-1364. **T:** 1 407 425-4547
W: http://www.ap.org/florida
NEWS SERVICE/SYNDICATE

Associated Press
Editorial: 710 Avenue J, c/o Avalanche Journal, Lubbock, Texas 79401-1808.
T: 1 806 765-0394
Bureau Chief: Dale Leach
NEWS SERVICE/SYNDICATE

Associated Press
Editorial: 1401 Shop Rd Ste B, Columbia, South Carolina 29201-4843.
T: 1 803 799-5510 **E:** apcolumbia@ap.org
W: http://www.apsouthatlantic.org
News Editor: Tim Rogers
NEWS SERVICE/SYNDICATE

Associated Press
Owner: Associated Press, Inc.
Editorial: 10 Columbus Blvd, Fl 9 Ste 23, Hartford, Connecticut 06106-1976.
T: 1 860 246-6876 **E:** aphartford@ap.org
NEWS SERVICE/SYNDICATE

Associated Press
Owner: Associated Press, Inc.
Editorial: 75 Market St, #402, Portland, Maine 04101-5031. **T:** 1 207 772-4157
E: apmaine@ap.org
NEWS SERVICE/SYNDICATE

Associated Press
Owner: Associated Press, Inc.
Editorial: State Capitol Press Room, Springfield, Illinois 62706-0001.
T: 1 217 789-2700 **W:** http://illinois.ap.org
NEWS SERVICE/SYNDICATE

Associated Press
Owner: Associated Press, Inc.
Editorial: 900 N Tucker Blvd, Saint Louis, Missouri 63101-1098. **T:** 1 314 241-2496
E: apkansascity@ap.org
W: http://www.apkansascity.org
Bureau Chief: Kia Breaux
NEWS SERVICE/SYNDICATE

Associated Press
Editorial: 125 S Congress St, Ste 1330, Jackson, Mississippi 39201-3395.
T: 1 601 948-5897 **E:** jkme@ap.org
W: http://www.ap.org/states/mississippi
News Editor: Brian Schwaner; **Bureau Chief:** Adam Yeomans
NEWS SERVICE/SYNDICATE

Associated Press
Owner: Associated Press, Inc.
Editorial: 300 S 4th St Ste 810, Las Vegas, Nevada 89101-6009. **T:** 1 702 382-7440
E: aplasvegas@ap.org
Bureau Chief: Anthony Marquez
NEWS SERVICE/SYNDICATE

Associated Press
Owner: Associated Press, Inc.
Editorial: 50 Park Pl Ste 800, Newark, New Jersey 07102-4305. **T:** 1 973 642-0151
E: aptrenton@ap.org
W: http://www.ap.org/states/nj
NEWS SERVICE/SYNDICATE

Associated Press
Owner: Associated Press, Inc.
Editorial: 600 E Main St, Ste 1250, Richmond, Virginia 23219-2440. **T:** 1 804 643-6646
E: aprichmond@ap.org
W: http://www.ap.org/states/virginia

Bureau Chief: Dorothy Abernathy
NEWS SERVICE/SYNDICATE

Associated Press
Owner: Associated Press, Inc.
Editorial: 750 W 2nd Ave, Ste 102, Anchorage, Alaska 99501-2167.
T: 1 907 272-7549 **E:** apanchorage@ap.org
W: http://www.ap.org/northwest
NEWS SERVICE/SYNDICATE

Associated Press
Owner: Associated Press, Inc.
Editorial: 319 Seward St Ste 12, Juneau, Alaska 99801-1173. **T:** 1 907 586-1515
E: apjuneau@ap.org
W: http://www.ap.org/states/northwest
NEWS SERVICE/SYNDICATE

Associated Press
Owner: Associated Press, Inc.
Editorial: 15 E Main St, c/o News-Gazette, Champaign, Illinois 61820-3625.
T: 1 217 351-4094 **W:** http://illinois.ap.org
NEWS SERVICE/SYNDICATE

Associated Press
Editorial: State Capitol Building, Dover, Delaware 19903. **T:** 1 302 674-3037
W: http://www.ap.org/maryland
NEWS SERVICE/SYNDICATE

Associated Press
Owner: Associated Press, Inc.
T: 1 321 639-8801
W: http://www.ap.org/florida
NEWS SERVICE/SYNDICATE

Associated Press
Owner: Associated Press, Inc.
Editorial: 336 E College Ave, Ste 301, Tallahassee, Florida 32301-1560.
T: 1 850 224-1211
W: http://www.ap.org/florida
NEWS SERVICE/SYNDICATE

Associated Press
Owner: Associated Press, Inc.
Editorial: 500 Ala Moana Blvd, Ste 7-590, Honolulu, Hawaii 96813-4925.
T: 1 808 536-5510 **E:** aphonolulu@ap.org
W: http://www.aphawaii.org
News Editor: Oskar Garcia; **Bureau Chief:** John Raess
NEWS SERVICE/SYNDICATE

Associated Press
Owner: Associated Press, Inc.
Editorial: 101 S Capitol Blvd, Ste 304, Boise, Idaho 83702-7738. **T:** 1 208 343-1894
E: apboise@ap.org
W: http://www.ap.org/northwest
NEWS SERVICE/SYNDICATE

Associated Press
Owner: Associated Press, Inc.
Editorial: Statehouse, Rm. 047GE, 300 SW 10th Street, Topeka, Kansas 66612-1504.
T: 1 785 234-5654 **E:** apkansascity@ap.org
W: http://www.apkansascity.org
NEWS SERVICE/SYNDICATE

Associated Press
Owner: Associated Press, Inc.
Editorial: 165 Cross State Office Bldg., Augusta, Maine 4333. **T:** 1 207 622-3018
E: apmaine@ap.org
NEWS SERVICE/SYNDICATE

Associated Press
Editorial: 100 Summit Ave, c/o Herald-Mail, Hagerstown, Maryland 21740-5509.
T: 1 301 791-5246
W: http://www.ap.org/states/maryland
News Editor: Amanda Kell
NEWS SERVICE/SYNDICATE

Associated Press
Owner: Associated Press, Inc.
Editorial: 120 W Front St, Traverse City, Michigan 49684-2202. **T:** 1 231 929-4180
E: apmichigan@ap.org
W: http://www.ap.org/states/michigan
NEWS SERVICE/SYNDICATE

Associated Press
Owner: Associated Press, Inc.
Editorial: State Capitol #118-B, Jefferson City, Missouri 65101-1556. **T:** 1 573 636-9415
E: apkansascity@ap.org
W: http://www.apkansascity.org
Bureau Chief: Kia Breaux
NEWS SERVICE/SYNDICATE

Associated Press
Owner: Associated Press, Inc.
Editorial: 321 Fuller Ave Fl 2, Helena, Montana 59601-5005. **T:** 1 406 442-7440
E: apmontana@ap.org
W: http://www.ap.org/states/montana
Bureau Chief: Jim Clarke
NEWS SERVICE/SYNDICATE

Associated Press
Owner: Associated Press, Inc.
Editorial: 28 Mountain Rd, Concord, New Hampshire 03301-5480. **T:** 1 603 224-3327
E: apconcord@ap.org
NEWS SERVICE/SYNDICATE

Associated Press
Editorial: 645 Albany Shaker Rd, Albany, New York 12211-1158. **T:** 1 518 458-7821
E: apalbany@ap.org
W: http://www.ap.org/states/newyork
Bureau Chief: Howard Goldberg
NEWS SERVICE/SYNDICATE

Associated Press
Owner: Associated Press, Inc.
Editorial: 541 N Superior St, c/o The Blade, Toledo, Ohio 43660-1000. **T:** 1 419 255-7113
E: apcolumbus@ap.org
W: http://www.ap.org/states/ohio
Bureau Chief: Eva Parziale
NEWS SERVICE/SYNDICATE

Associated Press
Owner: Associated Press, Inc.
Editorial: 315 S Boulder Ave, Tulsa, Oklahoma 74103-3401. **T:** 1 918 584-4346
E: apoklahoma@ap.org
W: http://www.apoklahoma.org
NEWS SERVICE/SYNDICATE

Associated Press
Owner: Associated Press, Inc.
Editorial: Main Capitol, Rm 526, E Floor, Harrisburg, Pennsylvania 17120-0001.
T: 1 717 238-9413
W: http://www.ap.org/pennsylvania
NEWS SERVICE/SYNDICATE

Associated Press
Owner: Associated Press, Inc.
Editorial: 330 N Main Ave, Ste 301, Sioux Falls, South Dakota 57104-6034.
T: 1 605 332-3111 **E:** apsiouxfalls@ap.org
Bureau Chief: Michelle Morgante
NEWS SERVICE/SYNDICATE

Associated Press
Owner: Associated Press, Inc.
Editorial: 535 Stone Cutters Way, Ste 102, Montpelier, Vermont 05602-3796.
T: 1 802 229-0577 **E:** apvermont@ap.org
NEWS SERVICE/SYNDICATE

Associated Press
Owner: Associated Press, Inc.
Editorial: 818 W Riverside Dr., Suite 500, Spokane, Washington 99201.
T: 1 509 624-1258 **E:** apseattle@ap.org
W: http://www.ap.org/northwest
NEWS SERVICE/SYNDICATE

Associated Press
Owner: Associated Press, Inc.
Editorial: 1419 Columbia St. SW, Floor 1, Olympia, Washington 98501.
T: 1 360 753-7222 **E:** apseattle@ap.org
W: http://www.ap.org/northwest
NEWS SERVICE/SYNDICATE

Associated Press
Owner: Associated Press, Inc.
Editorial: 707 E Front Ave, Bismarck, North Dakota 58504-5646. **T:** 1 701 223-8450
E: apbismarck@ap.org
Bureau Chief: Michelle Morgante
NEWS SERVICE/SYNDICATE

Associated Press
Owner: Associated Press, Inc.
Editorial: 320 W 25th St, Ste 310, Cheyenne, Wyoming 82001-3005. **T:** 1 307 632-9351
E: apcheyenne@ap.org
W: http://www.ap.org/wyoming
Bureau Chief: Jim Clarke
NEWS SERVICE/SYNDICATE

Associated Press
Owner: Associated Press, Inc.
Editorial: 119 S Burrowes St, Ste 607, State College, Pennsylvania 16801-3864.
T: 1 814 238-3649
W: http://www.ap.org/states/pennsylvania
NEWS SERVICE/SYNDICATE

Associated Press
Owner: Associated Press, Inc.
Editorial: 5087 E McKinley Ave, Fresno, California 93727-1965. **T:** 1 559 255-7080
E: fresno@ap.org
W: http://www.ap.org/california
NEWS SERVICE/SYNDICATE

Associated Press
Editorial: 40 Sargent Dr, New Haven, Connecticut 06511-6111. **T:** 1 203 964-9270
NEWS SERVICE/SYNDICATE

Associated Press
Owner: Associated Press, Inc.
Editorial: 101 E Romana St, c/o Pensacola News Journal, Pensacola, Florida 32502-5652.
T: 1 850 438-4951
W: http://www.ap.org/states/florida
NEWS SERVICE/SYNDICATE

Associated Press
Owner: Associated Press, Inc.
Editorial: 103 E College St, Ste 208, Iowa City, Iowa 52240. **T:** 1 319 337-5615
W: http://www.ap.org/iowa
Bureau Chief: Kia Breaux
NEWS SERVICE/SYNDICATE

Associated Press
Owner: Associated Press, Inc.
Editorial: 223 W Colfax, South Bend, Indiana 46626-0001. **T:** 1 574 288-1649
NEWS SERVICE/SYNDICATE

Associated Press
Owner: Associated Press, Inc.
Editorial: State Capitol, Rm 243, Frankfort, Kentucky 40601-3490. **T:** 1 502 227-2410
W: http://www.ap.org/states/kentucky
NEWS SERVICE/SYNDICATE

Associated Press
Owner: Associated Press, Inc.
T: 1 225 343-1325
W: http://www.ap.org/states/louisiana/index.html
Bureau Chief: Dale Leach
NEWS SERVICE/SYNDICATE

Associated Press
Owner: Associated Press, Inc.
Editorial: State House, State Circle, Annapolis, Maryland 21404-1471. **T:** 1 410 269-0196
E: midatlsups@ap.org
W: http://www.ap.org/states/maryland
NEWS SERVICE/SYNDICATE

Associated Press
Owner: Associated Press, Inc.
Editorial: 215 S Washington Sq Ste 170, Lansing, Michigan 48933-1889.
T: 1 517 482-8011 **E:** apmichigan@ap.org
W: http://www.facebook.com/AssociatedPressMichigan
NEWS SERVICE/SYNDICATE

Associated Press
Owner: Associated Press, Inc.
Editorial: 1445 K St., Lincoln, Nebraska 68508-3615. **T:** 1 402 476-2525
W: http://www.apnebraska.org
Bureau Chief: Michelle Morgante
NEWS SERVICE/SYNDICATE

Associated Press
Owner: Associated Press, Inc.
Editorial: 102 N Curry St, Carson City, Nevada 89501-2110. **T:** 1 775 687-4190
NEWS SERVICE/SYNDICATE

Associated Press
Owner: Associated Press, Inc.
Editorial: 1 E. Liberty St., Ste 507, Reno, Nevada 89501. **T:** 1 775 322-3639
E: aplasvegas@ap.org
Bureau Chief: Anthony Marquez
NEWS SERVICE/SYNDICATE

Associated Press
Owner: Associated Press, Inc.
Editorial: 11 Devins Ln, c/o The Press, Pleasantville, New Jersey 8232.
T: 1 609 645-2063 **E:** aptrenton@ap.org
W: http://www.ap.org/states/nj/index.html
NEWS SERVICE/SYNDICATE

Associated Press
Owner: Associated Press, Inc.
Editorial: 328 Galisteo St, c/o Albuquerque Tribune, Santa Fe, New Mexico 87501-2606.
T: 1 505 982-1012
W: http://www.apnewmexico.org
News Editor: Linda Ashton
NEWS SERVICE/SYNDICATE

Associated Press
Owner: Associated Press, Inc.
Editorial: 1 News Plz, c/o Buffalo News, Buffalo, New York 14203-2930.
T: 1 716 852-1051 **E:** apalbany@ap.org
W: http://www.ap.org/states/newyork
NEWS SERVICE/SYNDICATE

Associated Press
Owner: Associated Press, Inc.
Editorial: 224 Harrison St, Ste 216, Syracuse, New York 13202-3050. **T:** 1 315 430-5344
E: apalbany@ap.org
W: http://www.ap.org/states/newyork
NEWS SERVICE/SYNDICATE

Associated Press
Owner: Associated Press, Inc.
Editorial: 148 Martine Ave, Ste 237, White Plains, New York 10601-3311.
T: 1 914 946-8841 **E:** apalbany@ap.org
W: http://www.ap.org/states/newyork
NEWS SERVICE/SYNDICATE

Associated Press
Owner: Associated Press, Inc.
Editorial: 900 Court St NE, Ste 43, Salem, Oregon 97301-4045. **T:** 1 503 363-0010
E: apportland@ap.org
W: http://www.ap.org/northwest
NEWS SERVICE/SYNDICATE

Associated Press
Owner: Associated Press, Inc.
Editorial: 1121 Walden Legacy Way, Knoxville, Tennessee 37931-4788 **E:** apnashville@ap.org
W: http://www.ap.org/states/tennessee
NEWS SERVICE/SYNDICATE

Associated Press
Owner: Associated Press, Inc.
Editorial: 1005 Congress Ave, Ste 995, Austin, Texas 78701-2469. **T:** 1 512 472-4004
E: ausstaff@ap.org
Bureau Chief: Dale Leach
NEWS SERVICE/SYNDICATE

Associated Press
Owner: Associated Press, Inc.
Editorial: 300 N. Campbell St., El Paso, Texas 79901-1402. **T:** 1 915 532-1939
W: http://www.facebook.com/AssociatedPressTexas
Bureau Chief: Dale Leach
NEWS SERVICE/SYNDICATE

Associated Press
Owner: Associated Press, Inc.
Editorial: 7950 Jones Branch Dr, c/o USA Today, Mc Lean, Virginia 22107-0001.
T: 1 703 761-0187
NEWS SERVICE/SYNDICATE

Associated Press
Owner: Associated Press, Inc.
Editorial: 119 Martin Luther King Blvd., Madison, Wisconsin 53703.
T: 1 608 255-3679
NEWS SERVICE/SYNDICATE

Associated Press
Owner: Associated Press, Inc.
Editorial: 2751 S Dixie Hwy, c/o Palm Beach Post, West Palm Beach, Florida 33405-1233.
T: 1 561 832-3466 **E:** miami@ap.org
W: http://www.ap.org/states/florida
NEWS SERVICE/SYNDICATE

Associated Press
Owner: Associated Press, Inc.
Editorial: 17291 Irvine Blvd, Ste 263, Tustin, California 92780. **T:** 1 714 573-7888
E: orangecountyca@ap.org
W: http://www.ap.org/california
NEWS SERVICE/SYNDICATE

Associated Press
Owner: Associated Press, Inc.
Editorial: 409 SE 7th St., c/o The Daily Courier, Grants Pass, Oregon 97526.
T: 1 541 476-1722 **E:** apportland@ap.org
W: http://www.ap.org/states/northwest
NEWS SERVICE/SYNDICATE

Associated Press
Owner: Associated Press, Inc.
Editorial: 101 5th St N, Fargo, North Dakota 58102-4826. **T:** 1 701 235-1908
NEWS SERVICE/SYNDICATE

Associated Press
Owner: Associated Press, Inc.
Editorial: 124 S Euclid Ave, Ste 104, Pierre, South Dakota 57501-3171. **T:** 1 605 224-7811
E: apsiouxfalls@ap.org
Bureau Chief: Michelle Morgante
NEWS SERVICE/SYNDICATE

Associated Press
Owner: Associated Press, Inc.
T: 1 518 449-7131 **E:** apalbany@ap.org
W: http://www.ap.org/states/newyork
Editorial Profile: This is the State Capitol bureau for New York State. Daybook items for New York State should go to the main address.
NEWS SERVICE/SYNDICATE

Associated Press
Owner: Associated Press, Inc.
Editorial: 401 N. 28th St., c/o Billings Gazette, Billings, Montana 59101. **T:** 1 406 896-1528
E: apmontana@ap.org
W: http://www.ap.org/states/montana
Bureau Chief: Jim Clarke
NEWS SERVICE/SYNDICATE

Associated Press
T: 1 912 484-5454 **E:** apatlanta@ap.org
W: http://www.apsouthatlantic.org
NEWS SERVICE/SYNDICATE

Associated Press
T: 63 2 525-9217
NEWS SERVICE/SYNDICATE

Associated Press
Owner: Associated Press Inc.
Editorial: 5050 W Tilghman St Ste 115, Allentown, Pennsylvania 18104-9114.
T: 1 610 207-9297
W: http://www.ap.org/states/pennsylvania
NEWS SERVICE/SYNDICATE

Associated Press
Editorial: 17 S High St, Ste 660, Columbus, Ohio 43215-3466. **T:** 1 614 221-5134
E: apcolumbus@ap.org
W: http://www.ap.org/states/ohio
Editorial Profile: This bureau is located in the Columbus, OH Statehouse.
NEWS SERVICE/SYNDICATE

Associated Press
Editorial: 1400 E Nolana Ave, McAllen, Texas 78504-6111. **T:** 1 956 686-6700
NEWS SERVICE/SYNDICATE

Associated Press
Owner: Associated Press
T: 357 2249-2599 **E:** apnicosia@ap.org
NEWS SERVICE/SYNDICATE

Associated Press
T: 962 6 461-4660
Bureau Chief: Jamal Halaby
NEWS SERVICE/SYNDICATE

Associated Press
Owner: Associated Press, Inc.
Editorial: 495 Union Ave, C/O Commerical Appeal, Memphis, Tennessee 38103-3217.
T: 1 865 522-3963
W: http://www.ap.org/states/tennessee/index.html
Editorial Profile: The Memphis Bureau of the Associated Press covers local, regional and national news.
NEWS SERVICE/SYNDICATE

Associated Press
T: 95 1 524-666
NEWS SERVICE/SYNDICATE

Associated Press - United Nations Bureau
Editorial: 405 E 42 St, L-216, New York, New York 10017. **T:** 1 212 963-7106
NEWS SERVICE/SYNDICATE

Associated Press en Espanol
Owner: Associated Press, Inc.
Editorial: 450 W 33rd St, New York, New York 10001. **T:** 1 212 621-1647
W: http://www.ap.org
Editorial Profile: Associated Press en Espanol is a news service that provides a mix of articles translated to Spanish, as well as original Spanish language content.
NEWS SERVICE/SYNDICATE

Athens News Agency - New York Bureau
Editorial: United Nations, Room S-451, New York, New York 10017. **T:** 1 212 963-1708
Editorial Profile: This is the New York bureau for the Athens (Greece) News Agency.
NEWS SERVICE/SYNDICATE

The Auto Advisor Group
Editorial: 14626 Harbor Is, Detroit, Michigan 48215-3110. **T:** 1 941 518-6516
E: bh.autoadvisorgroup@gmail.com
W: http://autoadvisorgroup.blogspot.com
Editor: Bruce Hubbard
Editorial Profile: Columns and features focus on reviews of the best new and used cars, trucks and vans, as well as the best road trips and hotels in the United States.
NEWS SERVICE/SYNDICATE

Auto Digest
Editorial: 2684 34Th St, Washougal, Washington 98671-9156. **T:** 1 831 750-4805
E: adigest1@gmail.com
W: http://www.iveho.com
Editor: Bill Schaffer; **Editor:** Bill Schaffer; **Editor:** Bill Schaffer
Editorial Profile: Auto Digest is a news service that runs four columns a week in a variety of publications throughout the United States. The columns offer reviews and introductions of new cars, car trivia, trends and other auto-related information. Coverage also includes events and other topics relevant to the automotive industry and anyone interested in vehicles. Send all press releases via e-mail to the main e-mail address.
NEWS SERVICE/SYNDICATE

AutoEditor Syndication
Editorial: 2314 Mar East St, Tiburon, California 94920. **T:** 1 415 435-4541
W: http://www.autoeditor.com
Editor: Brian Douglas
Editorial Profile: AutoEditor Syndication includes automotive reviews and weekly auto features.
NEWS SERVICE/SYNDICATE

Automotive Communications Group
Editorial: 3726 Cleveland Ave Nw, Canton, Ohio 44709-2316. **T:** 1 630 842-7827
E: autotalk@aol.com
W: http://www.autotalkvideo.com
Editorial Profile: Automotive Communications Group is a news service that reports new car reviews, information and news on the automotive industry.
NEWS SERVICE/SYNDICATE

Automotive News Syndicate
Editorial: 1155 Gratiot Ave, Detroit, Michigan 48207. **T:** 1 313 446-6000
E: autonews@crain.com
W: http://www.automotivenews.com
Editor in Chief: Keith Crain
Editorial Profile: Automotive News Syndicate is a news and feature service that provides automotive industry news from Crain publications to other media, primarily general circulation newspapers and magazines worldwide.
NEWS SERVICE/SYNDICATE

Automotive Newswire
Editorial: 1513 Rose Virginia Rd, Wyomissing, Pennsylvania 19610. **T:** 1 610 372-6707
W: http://www.autonewswire.net
Editorial Profile: Automotive Newswire is a news service focusing on the automotive industry. It tailors its information for automotive industry executives, engineers and OEM sales personnel. It is delivered daily, by e-mail.
NEWS SERVICE/SYNDICATE

Autowriters Associates Inc.
T: 1 302 998-1650 **E:** info@motormatters.biz
W: http://www.motormatters.biz
Editorial Profile: Autowriters Associates Inc., provides automotive content to print and online media and various automotive-related businesses.
NEWS SERVICE/SYNDICATE

AutoWritersInk
Owner: Schmidt (David)
Editorial: 859 Mosaic Ct, Gahanna, Ohio 43230 **E:** comments@autowritersink.com
W: http://autowritersink.com
Editor: David Schmidt; **Editor:** Patti Schmidt
Editorial Profile: AutoWritersInk is a syndicated news service providing coverage for newspaper automotive sections. They primarily publish in papers owned by Journal Register Corp., comprised of 30 daily and 201 weekly newspapers.
NEWS SERVICE/SYNDICATE

Avanti NewsFeatures
Owner: Fracassa Communications
Editorial: 29106 Palomino Dr, Warren, Michigan 48093-3505
Editor: Hawke Fracassa
Editorial Profile: Avanti NewsFeatures covers a wide variety of general interest topics. There are spotlights on automotive, travel, parenting, books, DVDs, music, games, sporting goods, food, trading cards, computers, politics, home products and tools. Editorial content is posted to their aWeb site, as well as distributed to the Macomb Observer, the Oakland Observer, MI Dog, The Blade, the Metro Observer and the Downriver Observer.
NEWS SERVICE/SYNDICATE

Baptist Press
Editorial: 901 Commerce St, Nashville, Tennessee 37203. **T:** 1 615 782-8617
E: bpress@sbc.net **W:** http://www.bpnews.net
Editor: Art Toalston
Editorial Profile: Founded in 1946, this is a news service of the Southern Baptist Convention. Stories go out to 40 state Baptist newspapers with a combined readership of 1.16 million. There are also offices in Richmond, VA; Atlanta; and Washington.
NEWS SERVICE/SYNDICATE

Bay City News Service
Editorial: 1390 Market St, San Francisco, California 94102-5398. **T:** 1 415 552-8900
E: baycitynews@pacbell.net
W: http://www.baycitynews.com
Editorial Profile: Bay City News Service is a regional, general interest news wire service which operates 24 hours a day gathering information from in and around the greater San Francisco Bay area. Established in 1979, it provides a real-time news report delivered directly to media organizations, Web sites, public relations firms, government agencies and more than 100 newsrooms via a satellite, dedicated phone line and Internet network.
NEWS SERVICE/SYNDICATE

Best Buys in Wine
Editorial: 1406 Thomas Pl, Fort Worth, Tarrant, Texas 76107-2432. **T:** 1 817 732-4758
E: reniesteves@msn.com
W: http://www.cuisineconcepts.org
Editorial Profile: Best Buys in Wine features commentary on wine and spirits of good value, reviews of recent releases, overviews of individual wineries, and seasonal and holiday suggestions. Also includes announcements of festivals, food pairings, gadget information, wine school information, book reviews and interviews. Focuses on wine and food through travel and the amenities whether it be historical highlights, rural charm or city magnetism.
NEWS SERVICE/SYNDICATE

BestWire
Editorial: 1 Ambest Rd, Oldwick, New Jersey 8858. **T:** 1 908 439-2200
E: editor_bw@ambest.com
W: http://www.ambest.com
News Editor: Mark Dobrow; **Editor:** Caroline Saucer; **Editor:** Caroline Saucer
Editorial Profile: BestWire offers insurance industry news on earnings, litigation, state rate actions, mergers and acquisitions, industry trends, legislative actions and upcoming industry conferences and events. The service accepts press releases from insurers, state insurance departments, insurance trade groups and consulting and equity analysis companies.
NEWS SERVICE/SYNDICATE

Biofile
Editorial: 995 Teaneck Rd, Apt 3N, Teaneck, New Jersey 07666-4543. **T:** 1 201 833-2350
E: mrbiofile@aol.com
W: http://www.thebiofile.com
Editorial Profile: Biofile is a news service that offers biographies of high-profile athletes, as well as interviews with celebrities and television personalities.
NEWS SERVICE/SYNDICATE

Biopharm Insight
Owner: Pearson PLC
Editorial: 330 Hudson St Fl 4, New York, New York 10013-1014. **T:** 1 212 500-1384
W: http://www.biopharminsight.com
Editorial Profile: Biopharm Insight, a Financial Times Group publication, launched in September 2007. It publishes real-time news and data concerning the most price sensitive issues in the global pharmaceutical market. Built for financial professionals, the wire covers product approvals, litigation, licensing deals and mergers and acquisitions. Its clients are financial professionals who subscribe to the news service, and the articles found online can also be sent to clients' e-mail and BlackBerry. Online content is available through a paid subscription and through

mergermarket.com. Print weekly prints in the Financial Times.
NEWS SERVICE/SYNDICATE

Black Press Service, Inc.
Editorial: 375 Fifth Ave. 3rd Flr, New York, New York 10016. **T:** 1 212 686-6850
E: news@blackradionetwork.com
W: http://www.minoritynews.net
Editor: Roy Thompson; **Editor:** Roy Thompson; **Editor:** Roy Thompson
Editorial Profile: Specializes in news and features with a minority perspective. Syndicated to about 170 minority-oriented print and broadcast news outlets.
NEWS SERVICE/SYNDICATE

Bloomberg News
Owner: Bloomberg L.P.
Editorial: 731 Lexington Ave, New York, New York 10022-1331. **T:** 1 212 617-2300
E: release@bloomberg.net
W: http://www.bloomberg.com
News Editor: Nathaniel Baker; **Editor:** Max Berley; **Editor:** Lisa Beyer; **Editor:** Mary Duenwald; **Editor:** Mary Duenwald; **News Editor:** Andrew Dunn; **Editor:** Paula Dwyer; **Editor:** James Greiff; **Editor:** Tobin Harshaw; **Editor:** Timothy Lavin; **News Editor:** Joe Sabo; **Editor:** Brendan Walsh; **Editor:** Frank Wilkinson; **Editor in Chief:** Matthew Winkler; **Editor:** Chapin Wright
Editorial Profile: Bloomberg News is an international wire service, including print, television, radio and Internet, that provides news, data and analysis to business and media professionals around the world. Bloomberg publishes over 6,000 stories on an average day, syndicating to over 450 newspapers worldwide with a combined circulation of 80 million people. The service is part of Bloomberg Financial Markets and covers business, financial and economic issues, as well as technology, international, national, political, entertainment and sports news. In 2010, they launched a government platform, Bloomberg Government. In 2011, they launched their first opinion section, Bloomberg View.
NEWS SERVICE/SYNDICATE

Bloomberg News
Editorial: 1399 New York Ave NW Fl 11, Washington, District Of Columbia 20005-4749.
T: 1 202 624-1956
Bureau Chief: Jonathan Allen; **News Editor:** Mark Rohner; **Editor:** Bennett Roth
NEWS SERVICE/SYNDICATE

Bloomberg News
Editorial: 2001 Ross Ave Suite 350, Dallas, Texas 75201-3018. **T:** 1 214 954-9430
E: release@bloomberg.net
NEWS SERVICE/SYNDICATE

Bloomberg News
Editorial: 111 S Wacker Dr Ste 4950, Chicago, Illinois 60606-4418. **T:** 1 312 443-5900
NEWS SERVICE/SYNDICATE

Bloomberg News
Editorial: 100 Summer St Ste 2810, Boston, Massachusetts 02110-2108.
T: 1 617 210-4600 **E:** release@bloomberg.net
Bureau Chief: Tom Moroney
NEWS SERVICE/SYNDICATE

Bloomberg News
Editorial: 27777 Franklin Rd Ste 1510, Southfield, Michigan 48034-8265.
T: 1 248 827-2950
Bureau Chief: Jeff Green
NEWS SERVICE/SYNDICATE

Bloomberg News
Editorial: 235 Peachtree St NE Ste 2210, Atlanta, Georgia 30303-1406.
T: 1 404 507-1300
Bureau Chief: Anita Sharpe; **Bureau Chief:** Anita Sharpe
NEWS SERVICE/SYNDICATE

Bloomberg News
Editorial: 1201 N Market St Fl 12, Wilmington, Delaware 19801-1147. **T:** 1 302 661-7600
News Editor: Cecile Daurat; **News Editor:** Cecile Daurat; **Bureau Chief:** Jef Feeley
NEWS SERVICE/SYNDICATE

Bloomberg News
Editorial: 1420 5th Ave, Seattle, Washington 98101-4087. **T:** 1 206 913-4540
Bureau Chief: Peter Robison
NEWS SERVICE/SYNDICATE

Bloomberg News
Editorial: 3 Pier Ste 101, San Francisco, California 94111-2036. **T:** 1 415 617-7100
News Editor: Greg Chang; **Editor:** Dan Reichl; **News Editor:** Vivek Shankar; **Bureau Chief:** Jeff Taylor
NEWS SERVICE/SYNDICATE

Bloomberg News
Editorial: 6500 Wilshire Blvd Ste 2360, Los Angeles, California 90048-4916.
T: 1 323 782-4220
Bureau Chief: Anthony Palazzo; **Editor:** Lester Pimentel
NEWS SERVICE/SYNDICATE

Bloomberg News
Editorial: 811 Main St Ste 4650, Houston, Texas 77002-6227. **T:** 1 713 547-8400
Bureau Chief: Richard Stubbe
NEWS SERVICE/SYNDICATE

Bloomberg News
Editorial: 770 L St, Ste 950, Sacramento, California 95814-3361. **T:** 1 415 912-2960
NEWS SERVICE/SYNDICATE

Bloomberg News
Editorial: 121 SW Salmon St, Portland, Oregon 97204-2908. **T:** 1 503 471-1358
NEWS SERVICE/SYNDICATE

Bloomberg News
T: 27 112861900
E: johannesburg@bloomberg.net
Bureau Chief: Antony Sguazzin
NEWS SERVICE/SYNDICATE

Bloomberg News
Editorial: 125 W State St, Trenton, New Jersey 08608-1101. **T:** 1 609 394-0736
Bureau Chief: Stacie Sherman
NEWS SERVICE/SYNDICATE

Bloomberg News
Owner: Bloomberg L.P.
Editorial: 120 N Washington Sq Ste 805, Lansing, Michigan 48933-1619
NEWS SERVICE/SYNDICATE

Bloomberg News
Editorial: 1111 Brickell Ave Fl 11, Miami, Florida 33131-3122. **T:** 1 305 579-4330
Bureau Chief: Bill Faries
NEWS SERVICE/SYNDICATE

Bulletin News Network
Editorial: 11190 Sunrise Valley Dr, Ste 130, Reston, Virginia 20191-4375.
T: 1 703 483-6100
E: editorial@bulletinnews.com
W: http://www.bulletinnews.com
Editor: Mark Gabor; **Publisher:** Paul Roellig
Editorial Profile: Founded in 1990, Bulletin News Network offers customized business and political intelligence to top-level corporate and government decision makers. They cater to large corporations and federal agencies seeking to inform their top executives on all the latest developments concerning their organization, competitors and industry.
NEWS SERVICE/SYNDICATE

Cagle Cartoons
Editorial: 906 Chelham Way, Santa Barbara, California 93108-1049. **T:** 1 805 969-2829
W: http://www.cagla.com
Editorial Profile: Cagle Cartoons features political cartoons and syndicated political columns. All of them are available for purchase to be used in any publication.
NEWS SERVICE/SYNDICATE

Cal Sport Media
Editorial: 35557 Trevino Trl, Beaumont, California 92223-6203. **T:** 1 310 775-7595
E: info@calsportmedia.com
W: http://www.calsportmedia.com
Editorial Profile: Cal Sport Media is a photo wire service covering athletes and sporting events in California and the West Coast.
NEWS SERVICE/SYNDICATE

Capital News Service
Owner: Phillip Merrill College of Journalism, University of Marylan
Editorial: 529 14th St NW, Ste 950, Washington, District Of Columbia 20045-1926.
T: 1 202 628-1677
W: http://merrill.umd.edu/cns
Editorial Profile: Capital News Service serves as a source of Maryland state and federal government news for 14 daily newspapers and wire services, more than 60 weekly and monthly newspapers and newsletters, a news-radio station, a statewide public television network and several online services. The news service is operated by the Philip Merrill College of Journalism at the University of Maryland, College Park. It is only in operation during the months school is in session, from August to May. Students' stories have appeared in The Washington Post, The Baltimore Sun and The Washington Times.
NEWS SERVICE/SYNDICATE

Capital News Service
Editorial: 48 Maryland Ave, Ste 301, Annapolis, Maryland 21401.
T: 1 410 626-1008
Bureau Chief: Rafael Lorente; **Bureau Chief:** Rafael Lorente; **Bureau Chief:** Rafael Lorente
NEWS SERVICE/SYNDICATE

Capitol Media Services
Editorial: Press Room 1820 W Washington St, Phoenix, Arizona 85007-2812.
T: 1 602 390-1850 **E:** capmedia@hotmail.com
Editorial Profile: Content centers on political, legal and business issues and syndicates to daily and weekly newspapers throughout the state, as well as radio stations.
NEWS SERVICE/SYNDICATE

Caruba, Alan
Editorial: 28 W 3Rd St Apt 1321, South Orange, New Jersey 07079-1786.
T: 1 973 763-6392 **E:** acaruba@aol.com
W: http://www.caruba.com
Editorial Profile: Provides different focuses each month of the best novels, books on business and finance, cookbooks, religion, history, biographies, health and other comparable topics. The news service started in the 1960s, first as a weekly newspaper column, later as a monthly column and now on the Internet.
NEWS SERVICE/SYNDICATE

Catholic News Service
Editorial: 3211 4th St NE, Washington, District Of Columbia 20017.
T: 1 202 541-3250 **E:** cns@catholicnews.com
W: http://www.catholicnews.com
News Editor: James Lackey; **Editor in Chief:** Anthony Spence
Editorial Profile: The mission of Catholic News Service is to spread the Gospel and report the news that affects Catholics in their everyday lives. It is the oldest and largest news wire service specializing in reporting on religion, and is the primary source of national and world news that appears in the United States Catholic press. It is also a leading source of news for Catholic print and broadcast media throughout the world. It was created in 1920 by the bishops of the United States but is editorially independent.
NEWS SERVICE/SYNDICATE

CCA Press
Editorial: 111 E Chestnut St, Suite 29J, Chicago, Illinois 60611-6006.
T: 1 312 642-3453
Editorial Profile: CCA Press is a syndicate that covers national and international news and politics.
NEWS SERVICE/SYNDICATE

Center for Investigative Reporting
Editorial: 2130 Center St Ste 103, Berkeley, California 94704-1384. **T:** 1 510 809-3160
E: center@cironline.org **W:** http://cironline.org
Editorial Profile: Founded in 1977, the Center for Investigative Reporting is the nation's oldest nonprofit investigative news organization, producing multimedia reporting that has impact and is relevant to people's lives.
NEWS SERVICE/SYNDICATE

The Center for Investigative Reporting
Editorial: 126 Post St, San Francisco, California 94108-4713. **T:** 1 415 821-8520
W: http://cironline.org/
Editorial Profile: The Center for Investigative Reporting San Francisco office, formerly The Bay Citizen, launched in May 2010 as a non-profit, publicly supported news organization offering original coverage of Bay Area civic and community news. It focuses on government and public policy, education, the arts and cultural affairs, the environment, food, wine and neighborhood news. The organization also provides content for The New York Times' Bay Area edition.
NEWS SERVICE/SYNDICATE

The Center for Investigative Reporting
Editorial: 925 L St Ste 150, Sacramento, California 95814-3703. **T:** 1 916 504-4085
W: http://cironline.org/
Editorial Profile: Founded in 1977, the Center for Investigative Reporting is the nation's oldest nonprofit investigative news organization, producing multimedia reporting that has impact and is relevant to people's lives. Serves as the State Legislature bureau for news service.
NEWS SERVICE/SYNDICATE

The Center for Investigative Reporting
Editorial: 625 N Grand Ave, Santa Ana, California 92701-4347. **T:** 1 714 796-3536
W: http://cironline.org/
Editorial Profile: Founded in 1977, the Center for Investigative Reporting is the nation's oldest nonprofit investigative news organization, producing multimedia reporting that has impact and is relevant to people's lives. This is the Santa Ana office of CIR.
NEWS SERVICE/SYNDICATE

Chad, Norman
Editorial: 12747 Pacific Ave. #1, Los Angeles, California 90066 **E:** asktheslouch@aol.com
Editorial Profile: He writes a weekly sports-based syndicated column called Couch Slouch. Each column closes with the feature Ask the Slouch; if a reader's question is selected, the reader wins $1.25 in cash. "Pay the man, Shirley," is frequently cited as a response to readers who have fulfilled the comedy quotient for their particular question. His column has become infamous for many references to his ex-wives and his strong dislike of what he terms "showboating in poker."
NEWS SERVICE/SYNDICATE

China News Service
Editorial: 15 E 40th St, Rm 801, New York, New York 10016. **T:** 1 212 481-2510
W: http://www.chinanews.com.cn
Editorial Profile: China News Service is a government owned news service distributing China-related news to outlets around the world. It covers national and international news, business, politics, life, culture and sports.
NEWS SERVICE/SYNDICATE

The Christian Science Monitor News Service
Editorial: 210 Massachusetts Ave, Boston, Massachusetts 02115-3012.
T: 1 617 450-2300
E: syndication@csmonitor.com
W: http://www.csmonitor.com
Editor: Marshall Ingwerson
Editorial Profile: This syndicate covers international and United States news and features.The syndicate has been the recipient of seven Pulitzer Prizes and more than a dozen Overseas Press Club awards.
NEWS SERVICE/SYNDICATE

Cinematters
Editorial: 48 N Huntington Ct, Richmond Hill, Georgia 31324-3069. **T:** 1 912 756-6122
E: laura@cinematters.com
W: http://www.cinematters.com
Editorial Profile: Cinematters is a nationally syndicated column that tries to help parents bring big-screen lessons to life for children to enjoy, understand and apply to their lives. They use newly-released family films to provide readers with creative and simple ideas to spark family bonding. It appears in newspapers, regional parenting magazines and on select parenting Web sites.
NEWS SERVICE/SYNDICATE

City News Service, Inc.
Editorial: 11400 W Olympic Blvd, Los Angeles, California 90064-1550.
T: 1 310 481-0404 **E:** news@socalnews.com
W: http://www.socalnews.com
Editor: Lori Streifler
Editorial Profile: City News Service, Inc. is America's largest regional news service. It provides Southern California news 24 hours a day to print and broadcast media outlets. Specifically, it covers news in Los Angeles, Orange, Riverside and San Diego counties, including goverment, crime, court and entertainment stories.
NEWS SERVICE/SYNDICATE

The Classified Guys
Editorial: 12 Bates Pl, Danbury, Connecticut 06810-6803. **T:** 1 888 712-7070
E: comments@classifiedguys.com
W: http://www.classifiedguys.com
Editorial Profile: The Classified Guys produces products and services that help newspapers generate more revenue from their classified sections. Their product line includes

being the largest supplier of garage sale kits and car selling kits in North America.
NEWS SERVICE/SYNDICATE

Cleveland Clinic News Service
Editorial: 9500 Euclid Ave Jjn4-01, Cleveland, Ohio 44195-0001. **T:** 1 216 444-0141
W: http://my.clevelandclinic.org/news_service/contact.aspx
News Producer: Dave Grendzynski
Editorial Profile: Cleveland Clinic News Service provides reliable information from one of the nation's top academic medical centers. Provides daily stories with two sound bites and b-roll. Also releases Patient Feature Stories and provides video upon request to media outlets.
NEWS SERVICE/SYNDICATE

Commercial Real Estate Direct
Owner: FM Financial Publishing, LLC
Editorial: 12 Terry Dr Ste 102, Newtown, Pennsylvania 18940-1875. **T:** 1 215 504-2860
W: http://www.crenews.com
Editorial Profile: Founded in 1999, Commercial Real Estate Direct tries to bring high-end news and information to professionals in the commercial real estate industry. Since it is a complex industry, people must understand who is raising equity, from whom and for what. They also have to know who is providing debt and at what cost.
NEWS SERVICE/SYNDICATE

Community Features
Editorial: 1733 Dawsonville Hwy, Gainesville, Georgia 30501-1531. **T:** 1 770 287-3798
E: commfeat@charter.net
W: http://www.communityfeatures.com
Editor: Bill Johnson; **Editor:** Bill Johnson
Editorial Profile: Contains religious features for religion pages that are designed to encourage people to worship regularly. Also sells church pages and bible verse pages for newspapers.
NEWS SERVICE/SYNDICATE

Computing With Kids
Editorial: 903 Falls Bridge Ln, Great Falls, Virginia 22066-1347. **T:** 1 703 444-9005
E: jinny@computingwithkids.com
W: http://www.computingwithkids.com
Editor in Chief: Jinny Gudmundsen
Editorial Profile: Computing With Kids is a weekly online magazine and syndicated column. It provides reviews of children's software, video games, Web sites and smart toys. It issues BEST PICK Awards for the outstanding products in each category. The column appears in USAToday.com and Gannett newspapers.
NEWS SERVICE/SYNDICATE

Content That Works
Editorial: 4410 N Ravenswood Ave Ste 101, Chicago, Illinois 60640-5873.
T: 1 773 728-8351
E: editorial@contentthatworks.com
W: http://www.contentthatworks.com
Editorial Profile: Content That Works creates original content that helps its local media partners build audiences, drive revenue and strengthen brands. More than 1000 local media organizations use CTW content in print or online, including CTW's fully designed print publications, individual stories or online feeds. Primary topics covered by the outlet include real estate, jobs/careers, automotive, home decorating/home improvement, bridal, parenting, health & wellness, 50-plus, food, couponing, eco-wise, holiday entertaining, holiday decorating, holiday gift guides and holiday PixelGrams.
NEWS SERVICE/SYNDICATE

ConTexto Latino
Owner: Metro Creative Graphics, Inc.
Editorial: 519 8Th Ave, New York, New York 10018-6506. **T:** 1 212 947-5100
W: http://mcg.metrocreativeconnection.com/publish/contextolatino
Editorial Profile: ConTexto Latino is a comprehensive Hispanic editorial features service. Provides publishers with ready-to-run features to enhance their print and online publications and help with efforts to expand into niche and specialty publications.
NEWS SERVICE/SYNDICATE

Continental News Service
Editorial: 501 W Broadway, Plaza A PMB#265, San Diego, California 92101-3562.
T: 1 858 492-8696
E: continentalnewsservice@yahoo.com
W: http://continentalnewsservice.com
Editor In Chief: Gary Salamone
Editorial Profile: Travel destination stories and food features/recipes are offered along with investigative reports and coverage of unreported news. Also publishes Continental Newstime magazine and an online children's newspaper.
NEWS SERVICE/SYNDICATE

Cook, A.J.
Editorial: 6785 Slash Pine Cv, Memphis, Tennessee 38119. **T:** 1 901 754-8925
W: http://www.taxfables.com
Editorial Profile: True-to-life reports on affairs of taxpayers and tax dodgers from thousands of IRS cases which Cook reviews. He reports on ever-changing tax pictures for lifestyles of most readers and for lifestyles they dream about. Offers tips on year-round tax planning to build wealth for the lowest-bracket taxpayers on up.
NEWS SERVICE/SYNDICATE

Creators Syndicate
Editorial: 737 3rd St, Hermosa Beach, Los Angeles, California 90254-4714.
T: 1 310 337-7003 **E:** info@creators.com
W: http://www.creators.com
Editorial Profile: Creators Syndicate distributes a variety of features, including advice, lifestyle and opinion columns, as well as comics and editorial cartoons. Send press releases by fax or e-mail. Press releases will be forwarded to the appropriate contact. The service was founded in 1987.
NEWS SERVICE/SYNDICATE

Cricket Communications, Inc.
T: 1 610 924-9158 **E:** crcktinc@aol.com
Editor: Mark Battersby
Editorial Profile: Cricket Communications, Inc., provides features, columns and special reports on tax, financial and money management topics for medium-size businesses and their owners/shareholders and operators.
NEWS SERVICE/SYNDICATE

Critics Inc.
Editorial: 6724 Perimeter Loop Rd, Ste 310, Dublin, Ohio 43017-3202. **T:** 1 614 408-3865
E: comments@critics.com
W: http://www.criticsinc.com
Editorial Profile: Critics Inc. serves as a source of new film and video criticism for nationwide media outlets. For each movie, the staff presents a wrap-up review as well as ratings from 15 prominent critics. Ultimately, the editors paint a picture of the national critical consensus. They also offer a dueling critics portion, including two quotes, one from the critic who gave the highest rating and one from the critic giving the lowest rating.
NEWS SERVICE/SYNDICATE

Cronkite News Service
Owner: Arizona State University
Editorial: 555 N Central Ave Ste 302, Phoenix, Arizona 85004-1248. **T:** 1 602 496-5020
E: cronkitenews@asu.edu
W: http://cronkitenews.asu.edu
Editorial Profile: Cronkite News Service features stories, photos and video packages about Arizona issues. The news service is a part of Arizona State University and serves as a professional experience for the students of the Walter Cronkite School of Journalism and Mass Communication.
NEWS SERVICE/SYNDICATE

Cronkite News Service - Washington, D.C.
Owner: Arizona State University
Editorial: 1834 Connecticut Ave Nw, Washington, District Of Columbia 20009-5732.
T: 1 202 684-2400 **E:** cronkitedc@asu.edu
Bureau Chief: Steve Crane
NEWS SERVICE/SYNDICATE

Curt Schleier Reviews
Editorial: 646 Jones Rd, Rivervale, Bergen, New Jersey 07675-6034. **T:** 1 201 391-7135
E: writa1@verizon.net
Editorial Profile: Curt Schleier Reviews focuses on author and celebrity interviews, book industry news, book reviews, DVD and CD-ROM reviews and television reviews.
NEWS SERVICE/SYNDICATE

Cuyler News Service
T: 1 518 465-1745 **E:** efmnews@aol.com
Editorial Profile: Founded in 1956, Cuyler News Service is an independent wire service, providing in-depth news on legislative and financial issues from the New York's capitol in Albany, NY.
NEWS SERVICE/SYNDICATE

Dave Goodwin & Associates
T: 1 305 865-0158
Editor: Dave Goodwin
Editorial Profile: Dave Goodwin & Associates target the consumer with Q&A, commentary, and compiled information on money matters, insurance and travel.
NEWS SERVICE/SYNDICATE

Dave Says
Editorial: 1749 Mallory Ln, Brentwood, Tennessee 37027-2931. **T:** 1 615 371-8881
E: davesays@daveramsey.com
W: http://www.daveramsey.com/davesays/
Editor: David Taylor
Editorial Profile: Dave Says column is a compilation of transcripts from calls taken on The Dave Ramsey Show radio program, which focuses on life and how it happens to revolve around money. Ramsey's common sense advice helps people change their lives by getting out of debt and building wealth.
NEWS SERVICE/SYNDICATE

Davidson, Jim
Editorial: 2 Bentley Dr, Conway, Arkansas 72034-9602. **T:** 1 800 242-2618
W: http://www.jimdavidsoncolumn.com
Editorial Profile: This is a self-syndicated weekly column offering practical and down to earth ideas and concepts for everyday life. He stresses traditional values, hard work and high moral standards. It is syndicated to around 250 newspapers.
NEWS SERVICE/SYNDICATE

The Diet Detective
Editorial: 17 E 17th St, Fl 4, New York, New York 10003-1943. **T:** 1 212 367-7575
W: http://www.dietdetective.com
Editorial Profile: Charles Stuart Platkin's Diet Detective is the largest syndicated nutrition and fitness column in the United States. It appears in more than 100 daily newspapers including Rochester (NY) Democrat & Chronicle, Omaha (NE) World-Herald, The State, Honolulu (HI) Advertiser and more. The author works with an in-house team of registered dietitians and fitness professionals, as well as additional expert sources from around the country to investigate timely topics in nutrition, food, weight control and fitness.
NEWS SERVICE/SYNDICATE

Dow Jones Capital Markets Report
Owner: News Corporation Ltd.
Editorial: 1211 Avenue Of The Americas Fl 5, New York, New York 10036-8706.
T: 1 212 416-2000
E: spotnews@priority.dowjones.com
W: http://www.dowjones.com/salesandtrading/product-cmr.asp
Editorial Profile: Newsletter delivering global fixed-income market coverage. Includes commentary on all major markets, ratings and economic news.
NEWS SERVICE/SYNDICATE

Dow Jones Commodities News Service
Owner: News Corporation Ltd.
Editorial: 1211 Avenue Of The Americas, Fl 5, New York, New York 10036-8706.
T: 1 212 416-2000
E: spotnews@priority.dowjones.com
W: http://www.djnewswires.com
Editorial Profile: Dow Jones Commodities News Service is owned by Dow Jones and is dedicated to delivering the most complete commodity and futures coverage in the industry. Includes grains, livestock and futures markets coverage.
NEWS SERVICE/SYNDICATE

Dow Jones Corporate Filings Alert
Owner: News Corporation Ltd.
Editorial: 1025 Connecticut Ave NW, Ste 1100, Washington, District Of Columbia 20036-5405. **T:** 1 202 862-7100
W: http://www.djnewswires.com
Editorial Profile: Dow Jones Corporate Filings Alert is a news service delivering coverage on news uncovered in SEC filings and bankruptcy courts.
NEWS SERVICE/SYNDICATE

Dow Jones Emerging Markets Report
Owner: News Corporation Ltd.
Editorial: 1211 Avenue Of The Americas, Fl 5, New York, New York 10036-8706.
T: 1 212 416-2000
E: spotnews@priority.dowjones.com
W: http://www.djnewswires.com
Editor: Charles Roth
Editorial Profile: Dow Jones Emerging Markets Report delivers coverage on emerging markets throughout the Americas and in other regions of the world. Includes commentary on all major markets, ratings and economic news.
NEWS SERVICE/SYNDICATE

Dow Jones Newswires
Owner: News Corporation Ltd.
Editorial: 1211 Avenue of the Americas, New York, New York 10036-8701.
T: 1 212 416-2000
E: spotnews@priority.dowjones.com
W: http://www.djnewswires.com
Editorial Profile: Dow Jones Newswires provides news for financial professionals in the equities, fixed-income, foreign exchange, energy and stock markets. Dow Jones Newswires provides real-time business news and information to approximately 438,000 financial professionals around the world. The division also offers news for financial firms' Web sites and Dow Jones Newsletters' sector-specific content. Dow Jones & Company also publishes The Wall Street Journal and its international and online editions, Barron's and the Far Eastern Economic Review, Dow Jones Indexes and the Ottaway group of community newspapers.
NEWS SERVICE/SYNDICATE

Dow Jones Newswires
Editorial: 1025 Connecticut Ave NW Ste 800, Washington, District Of Columbia 20036-5419.
T: 1 202 862-9200
NEWS SERVICE/SYNDICATE

Dow Jones Newswires
Editorial: 1 S Wacker Dr, Chicago, Illinois 60606-4614. **T:** 1 312 750-4000
NEWS SERVICE/SYNDICATE

Dow Jones Newswires
Editorial: 1835 Market St Ste 450, Philadelphia, Pennsylvania 19103-2939.
T: 1 215 656-8285
NEWS SERVICE/SYNDICATE

Dow Jones Newswires
Editorial: 2000 Town Ctr Ste 750, Southfield, Michigan 48075-1127. **T:** 1 248 204-5500
NEWS SERVICE/SYNDICATE

Dow Jones Newswires
Editorial: 600 Travis St, Houston, Texas 77002-3009. **T:** 1 713 227-5440
NEWS SERVICE/SYNDICATE

Dow Jones Newswires
T: 971 43314260
E: djnews.dubai@dowjones.com
News Editor: Marcus Wright
Editorial Profile: This bureau operates as the Arabic-language Zawya Dow Jones News Service. Produced jointly by Dow Jones Newswires and ABQ Zawya, it is the English and Arabic-language news service covering the Middle East's financial markets. It provides news, commentary and analysis, covering public, private and state-owned enterprises, as well as those companies looking to join the region's stock markets. It also covers regional stock markets and mergers and acquisitions activity; government privatizations and budgetary moves; economic trends and infrastructure tenders.
NEWS SERVICE/SYNDICATE

Dow Jones Newswires
Editorial: 201 California St Fl 10, San Francisco, California 94111-5002.
T: 1 415 986-6886
Editor: Cassandra Sweet
NEWS SERVICE/SYNDICATE

DTN News Service
Owner: Telvent
Editorial: 9110 W Dodge Rd, Ste 300, Omaha, Nebraska 68114-3316. **T:** 1 800 485-4000
E: agnews@telventdtn.com
W: http://www.dtnprogressivefarmer.com
News Editor: Anthony Greder; **Editor in Chief:** Greg Horstmeier
Editorial Profile: Founded in 1984, DTN News Service delivers 24-hour information about agriculture, refined fuels, commodities, futures trading, public safety, aviation, turf, recreation, construction and transportation. It is the leading business-to-business provider of real-time market, news and weather information services to agriculture, energy trading markets and other weather-sensitive industries. They deliver on-demand market information, commodity cash prices, industry news and in-depth analysis, and location-specific weather to over 120,000 subscribers for agriculture, refined fuels and trading markets.
NEWS SERVICE/SYNDICATE

Earth Talk
Editorial: 28 Knight St, Norwalk, Connecticut 6851. **T:** 1 203 854-5559
E: info@emagazine.com
W: http://www.emagazine.com/
Editorial Profile: Earth Talk provides a weekly question and answer column focused on environmental issues. It is distributed to more than 1,100 publications nationwide.
NEWS SERVICE/SYNDICATE

Edit International
Editorial: 251 W 92nd St, Apt 4A1, New York, New York 10025. **T:** 1 212 721-5100
W: http://www.editinternational.com
Editorial Profile: Edit International offers feature news to newspapers and magazines worldwide. The topics they look at include technology, warfare, terrorism, science, medicine, travel and human interest. The writers are published in over 30 languages.
NEWS SERVICE/SYNDICATE

Editor's Copy Syndicate
Editorial: 423 Flat Top Mountain Rd, Fairview, North Carolina 28730-9696.
T: 1 828 628-1994
Editorial Profile: Editor's Copy Syndicate offers a variety of consumer interest columns on such topics as the current fashion season, kitchen hints and television. It also covers the Washington scene with non-partisan commentary on various issues and regulations.
NEWS SERVICE/SYNDICATE

Editor's Copy Syndicate
Editorial: 3803 Pin Oaks St, Sarasota, Florida 34232. **T:** 1 941 366-2169
Editorial Profile: Editor's Copy Syndicate covers recent news on politics and the Washington scene.
NEWS SERVICE/SYNDICATE

Elfman, Doug
Editorial: 3674 Wild Springs St, Las Vegas, Nevada 89129-5051. **T:** 1 702 336-2625
E: elfmonster@yahoo.com
W: http://www.dougelfman.com
Editorial Profile: Syndication packages include the weekly column, briefs, Top 10 lists and high-resolution photos. The editorial objective is to reach both video gamers, parents, adult gamers and general-interest newspaper readers. Weekly adult readership is in the millions in print and online. The Game Dork column appears in more than 20 daily newspapers including the Las Vegas Review-Journal, The Kansas City Star; the Times-Picayune in New Orleans; and The Commercial Appeal in Memphis, TN.
NEWS SERVICE/SYNDICATE

Emirates News Agency - New York Bureau
Editorial: United Nations, Room L-0221 E, New York, New York 10017.
T: 1 212 963-0923
Editorial Profile: This is the New York bureau of Emirates News Agency, which is based in Abu Dhabi, United Arab Emirates.
NEWS SERVICE/SYNDICATE

Engelbert Wine & Food Service
Editorial: 3204 Sawmill Rd, Newtown Square, Delaware, Pennsylvania 19073-1901.
T: 1 610 353-4870 **E:** herbeng@juno.com
W: http://www.tastevingroup.com
Editorial Profile: Provides print, radio and TV commentary on selecting wines to compliment foods, understanding wine labels, wine and health, cooking with wine and interviews with wine makers and wine personalities.
NEWS SERVICE/SYNDICATE

Entertainment Report
Editorial: 322 Mall Blvd, Ste 237, Monroeville, Pennsylvania 15146. **T:** 1 412 371-1399
E: entrpt@aol.com
Editor: Doris Alma; **Editor:** Doris Alma; **Editor:** Doris Alma; **Editor:** Jane Otis; **Editor:** Jane Otis; **Editor:** Jane Otis; **Editor:** Alan Petrucelli; **Editor:** Alan Petrucelli; **Editor:** Alan Petrucelli; **Editor:** Bill Self; **Editor:** Bill Self; **Editor:** Bill Self
Editorial Profile: Entertainment Report provides entertainment and travel news with features on music, films, books, science, health, food, lifestyles, children and home decoration. It covers new product reviews in radio, television and print mediums. The music, book and DVD news and review column is part of the Dow Jones Newswires. 156 papers carry their content. Their website is currently being updated.
NEWS SERVICE/SYNDICATE

Environment News Service
Owner: Naturalist Com Inc.
T: 1 206 605-3757
W: http://www.ens-newswire.com
Editor in Chief: Sunny Lewis
Editorial Profile: Environment News Service is a daily international wire service. Its mission is to provide late-breaking environmental news in a fair and balanced manner. Contributors around the world cover issues and events that affect the environment. They do not want to be contacted via mail.
NEWS SERVICE/SYNDICATE

Episcopal News Service
Editorial: 815 2nd Ave, New York, New York 10017-4559. **T:** 1 212 716-6000
E: newsline@episcopalchurch.org
W: http://www.episcopalchurch.org/ens
Editor: Matthew Davies
Editorial Profile: Episcopal News Service provides news about the Episcopal Church in the United States and the Anglican Communion worldwide.
NEWS SERVICE/SYNDICATE

Executive Intelligence Review News Services
Editorial: 729 15th St NW, Washington, District Of Columbia 20005-2105.
T: 1 703 777-9451 **E:** eirns@larouchepub.com
W: http://www.larouchepub.com
Editor: Nancy Spannaus
Editorial Profile: Serves as a source of economic and political news for media outlets and clients worldwide. Columns about international affairs and environmentalism also are included. Bureaus of the service are located in European and South American cities. A major empahsis is placed on economic and political intelligence for policy makers internationally.
NEWS SERVICE/SYNDICATE

Eyes on Mississippi
T: 1 601 366-4089
Editorial Profile: Political commentary drawing on 60 years of covering Mississippi politics, government and social change. Self-syndicated to 15 newspapers.
NEWS SERVICE/SYNDICATE

FairWarning
Editorial: 17514 Ventura Blvd Ste 103, Encino, California 91316-3892. **T:** 1 818 453-8785
W: http://www.fairwarning.org
Editor: Myron Levin
Editorial Profile: FairWarning is a non-profit news organization that aims to provide in-depth, investigative reporting on issues such as health, saftey and corporate conduct. It launched in March 2010.
NEWS SERVICE/SYNDICATE

Family Features Editorial Syndicate, Inc.
Editorial: 5825 Dearborn St, Mission, Kansas 66202-2745. **T:** 1 913 722-0055
E: support@familyfeatures.com
W: http://www.familyfeatures.com
Editorial Profile: Established in 1974, Family Features Editorial Syndicate provides consumer food and beverages coverage to newspapers and Web sites. It offers cooking advice columns, recipes and general food features to more than 2,400 newspapers and other publications.
NEWS SERVICE/SYNDICATE

Fashion Wire Daily
Owner: Fashion Wire Daily, LLC
Editorial: 71 W. 23rd St, 17th Floor, New York, New York 10010-4102.
T: 1 212 792-8282
E: fwd@fashionwiredaily.com
W: http://www.fashionwiredaily.com
Editorial Profile: Fashion Wire Daily is an international newswire and Web site aimed at fashion, arts and entertainment professionals. The site's editorial mission is to supply media subscribers around the world with breaking stories, features, articles and photos for syndication. They do NOT accept submissions for publication on the Fashion Wire Daily website.
NEWS SERVICE/SYNDICATE

Featurewell
Editorial: 238 W 4th St, New York, New York 10014-2610. **T:** 1 212 924-2283
E: featurewell@featurewell.com
W: http://www.featurewell.com
Editorial Profile: Featurewell syndicates both original and non-original content covering culture, business, technology, sports, sex, science, food, health, entertainment, travel and politics to both print and online outlets. It serves as a global marketplace offering articles and photos from some of the world's finest journalists.
NEWS SERVICE/SYNDICATE

Federal Information & News Dispatch, Inc.
Editorial: 5900 Princess Garden Pkwy, Ste 230, Lanham, Maryland 20706-2948.
T: 1 301 429-5944 **E:** agenda@find-inc.com
W: http://www.find-inc.com
Bureau Chief: C. Patrick Thorne; **Bureau Chief:** C. Patrick Thorne; **Bureau Chief:** C. Patrick Thorne
Editorial Profile: Federal Information & News Dispatch, Inc., serves as a source of government and business news for major news services, online services and other media and business outlets. Their clients include Lexis-Nexis, Dow Jones Factiva, the Denver Post, NewsEdge, the National Journal and Federal News Service, among others.
NEWS SERVICE/SYNDICATE

Federal News Service
Owner: Federal News Service, Inc.
Editorial: 1000 Vermont Ave NW, Ste 500, Washington, District Of Columbia 20005-4903.
T: 1 202 347-1400 **E:** info@fednews.com
W: http://www.fednews.com
Bureau Chief: Kirk Hanneman
Editorial Profile: Founded in 1985, Federal News Service offers real-time verbatim transcripts of Congressional hearings, government briefings, speeches, press conferences and other newsmaker events to news bureaus and other governmental and nongovernmental organizations through its Washington Transcription subscription service. The transcripts are sent out within 24 hours. FNS also offers on-demand transcription, translation and media monitoring services. There are also offices in Moscow and Jerusalem that do regional transcription work.
NEWS SERVICE/SYNDICATE

Feeley News Bureau
Editorial: 3141 Washington Ave, Wilmette, Illinois 60091-2082. **T:** 1 847 251-7191
Bureau Chief: Jim Feeley; **Bureau Chief:** Jim Feeley; **Editor:** Jim Limper; **News Editor:** Barry Stockton
Editorial Profile: Feeley News Bureau provides news and features daily to more than 1100 print publications with a rated 86.3 million readership and more than 900 electronic media outlets. Primary focus includes leisure, entertainment, travel, sports and product reviews. Business news briefs, product and trade show coverage also are available.
NEWS SERVICE/SYNDICATE

Fenten, D.X.
Editorial: 27 Bowdon Rd, Greenlawn, Suffolk, New York 11740-1901. **T:** 1 631 271-3199
E: dxf7777@aol.com
Editorial Profile: Self-syndicated weekly column explores the ins and outs of the world of computers, personal and otherwise.
NEWS SERVICE/SYNDICATE

Fenton, Lois
Editorial: 721 Shore Acres Dr, Mamaroneck, Westchester, New York 10543-4214.
T: 1 914 698-0721 **E:** lois.fenton@prodigy.net
W: http://www.thefentons.com/Lois
Editorial Profile: Fenton offers men's dress columns and seminars. She shows men how to dress for business and business casual occasions, as well as what to wear for weekend getaways and black-tie events. The information is aimed at the average reader. The columns are self-syndicated weekly to about 10 newspapers.
NEWS SERVICE/SYNDICATE

Fleet Hometown News Center
Owner: Armed Forces
Editorial: 9420 3rd Ave, Ste 100, Norfolk, Virginia 23511. **T:** 1 757 322-1073
E: fleethometownnews@navy.mil
W: https://www.chinfo.navy.mil/fhtnc/index.html
Editorial Profile: Designed to increase national awareness of the activities of United States sailors, marines and coast guardsmen through written stories and documented images about them to hometown markets. Includes positive news stories to friends and family of US serviceman in their hometown.
NEWS SERVICE/SYNDICATE

FNA News
T: 1 801 355-3336 **E:** rng2@utah.edu
W: http://www.fnanews.com
Editor: Cindy Richie
Editorial Profile: FNA News was formed in March 1980, in Salt Lake City, and has been responsible for bringing many stories to the front page of attention in the Salt Lake City metro area, as well as the nation and beyond. See fnanews.com to see what the news agency does.
NEWS SERVICE/SYNDICATE

Food Nutrition Health News Service
Editorial: 1712 Taylor St NW, Washington, District Of Columbia 20011-5313.
T: 1 202 723-2477
E: goody.solomon@verizon.net
W: http://www.fnhnews.com
Editorial Profile: This service features articles about food issues, food regulations, legislation regarding food safety and labeling, food trends such as products and consumption, health, nutrition and the environment. Please do not fax this news service.
NEWS SERVICE/SYNDICATE

The French News Agency
Editorial: 18661 Woodbank Way, Saratoga, California 95070. **T:** 1 408 538-0457
W: http://www.thefrenchnewsagency.com
Bureau Chief: Jean-Baptiste Su
Editorial Profile: Established in 2006, the French News Agency is a media and research company providing interactive news, market intelligence and consulting services focused on the world of business and technology. It serves as a source of news, photos, graphics, audio/podcasts and videos for major business and online publications in both France and the United States. The agency provides distinctive news services, research and analysis in all formats (text, photos, videos, podcasts, etc.) with reports that are accurate, balanced and informed.
NEWS SERVICE/SYNDICATE

Fuel Injection
Editorial: 35308 Stellwagen St, Wayne, Michigan 48184-2368. **T:** 1 734 678-0712
W: http://www.fuel-infection.com
Editorial Profile: Fuel Injection is a self-syndicated automotive column by Christopher Jackson. It aims to be a resource for those who are addicted to cars. All of the information provided is general opinion. New cars are added about once a month.
NEWS SERVICE/SYNDICATE

Funeral Wire
Editorial: 860 F Ave, Ste 104, Plano, Texas 75074-6865. **T:** 1 972 398-7998
W: http://www.funeralwire.com
Editor: Melanie Laubach
Editorial Profile: Funeral Wire is the leading source for deathcare industry news. Includes information on cemeteries, cremation, funerals, grieving and education for the deathcare industry. Press Releases can be submitted directly through the website.
NEWS SERVICE/SYNDICATE

GamerLive.TV
Editorial: 205-13th St, Penthouse, San Francisco, California 94103.
T: 1 310 801-6750 **W:** http://www.gamerlive.tv
Editorial Profile: GamerLive.TV is the exclusive provider of gaming content for Tribune syndication to newspapers and websites across the country. Provides video game and lifestyle content as well as video, community and interactive services. Delivers up-to-date content on the latest games, platforms and trends.
NEWS SERVICE/SYNDICATE

Gannett ContentOne
Owner: Gannett Co., Inc.
Editorial: 7950 Jones Branch Dr, Mc Lean, Virginia 22107-0002. **T:** 1 703 854-5800
E: gnscopydesk@gns.gannett.com
W: http://www.gannett.com
Editorial Profile: Formerly Gannett News Service and offers wire stories for news outlets around the world. It has operations in 41 states and the District of Columbia, which includes 85 newspapers, as well as in Guam, the United Kingdom, Canada, Belgium, Germany, Hong Kong and Singapore. Headquartered in McLean, VA, it mainly serves as a Washington bureau, but also covers national news, sports, lifestyle and entertainment.
NEWS SERVICE/SYNDICATE

Gannett ContentOne
Owner: Gannett Co., Inc.

Editorial: 150 State St Ste 202, Albany, New York 12207-1626. **T:** 1 518 436-9781
Editorial Profile: This is the Albany, NY office of Gannett ContentOne, a news service that offers wire stories for news outlets around the world.
NEWS SERVICE/SYNDICATE

Gannett ContentOne
Editorial: 333 State Capitol Dr, Rm G-251, Baton Rouge, Louisiana 70802-5256.
T: 1 225 387-6506
Bureau Chief: Mike Hasten
NEWS SERVICE/SYNDICATE

Gannett ContentOne
Editorial: 336 E College Ave, Ste 200, Tallahassee, Florida 32301. **T:** 1 850 508-1740
Bureau Chief: Paul Flemming
NEWS SERVICE/SYNDICATE

Gannett ContentOne
Editorial: 1100 New York Ave NW Ste 200, Washington, District Of Columbia 20005-3934.
T: 1 703 854-5800 2
NEWS SERVICE/SYNDICATE

GateHouse News Service
Editorial: Press Room State Capitol, Springfield, Illinois 62706-0001.
T: 1 217 788-1518 **E:** statehouse@sj-r.com
W: http://www.sj-r.com
Editorial Profile: Gatehouse News Service provides stories on Illinois politics, government and healthcare for the GateHouse newspapers in Illinois, including the Rockford (IL) Register-Star, Peoria (IL) Journal-Star and Star Courier in Kewanee, IL.
NEWS SERVICE/SYNDICATE

GateHouse News Service
Editorial: 1101 31st St, Ste 185, Downers Grove, Illinois 60515-5583. **T:** 1 630 368-1100
E: national@gatehousemedia.com
W: http://www.gatehousenewsservice.com
Editor: Lisa Glowinski
Editorial Profile: Gatehouse News Service is a print and online content resource that is available to local newspapers throughout the country. Their own publications primarily have circulations under 50,000 and follow the events of each town with a dedicated team. This original content is then offered to other local publications. The service offers articles, columns, photos, graphics, political cartoons and Internet content such as video clips.
NEWS SERVICE/SYNDICATE

Gelman Feature Syndicate
T: 1 607 498-4700
Editorial Profile: Gelman Feature Syndicate is a self-syndicated weekly commentary about anything of a strange, interesting or off-beat nature.
NEWS SERVICE/SYNDICATE

Getty Images
Owner: Getty Images, Inc.
Editorial: 75 Varick St, New York, New York 10013-1917. **T:** 1 646 613-4000
E: pressreleases@gettyimages.com
W: http://www.gettyimages.com
Editorial Profile: Getty Images provides photos from major news, arts & entertainment, sports, political events any other newsworthy event. There are also travel shots and celebrities. It is syndicated to more than 20 countries and is also available to 1,800 newspapers via Newscom.
NEWS SERVICE/SYNDICATE

Glenmoor Enterprises Media Group
Editorial: 75 N Main St, #203, Willits, California 95490-3107. **T:** 1 707 367-4608
E: glenmoorent@yahoo.com
W: http://www.autoreviewsplus.com
Editor in Chief: Ron Moorhead
Editorial Profile: Information provided by this group includes auto road tests, auto industry news, auto Q & A, travel features, lifestyle features outdoor adventures and recreational vehicle adventures.
NEWS SERVICE/SYNDICATE

Global Horizons Syndicate
Editorial: 1330 New Hampshire Ave NW, Apt 609, Washington, District Of Columbia 20036-6311. **T:** 1 202 966-8636
Editor: Pam Ebert
Editorial Profile: Column covers everything concerning the environment including pollution, energy, health and political issues.
NEWS SERVICE/SYNDICATE

Global Information Network
Editorial: 146 W 29th St Rm 7E, New York, New York 10001-8201. **T:** 1 212 244-3123
E: ipsgin@igc.org
W: http://www.globalinformationnetwork.com
Editorial Profile: Global Information Network supplies a daily service of unique global and national news and features, spotlighting emerging economies and developing countries, prepared by journalists from the regions. Special areas of coverage: Africa, Asia and Latin America. Development news that's timely, insightful, balanced and fact-checked. Offers text to print media and content for online services.
NEWS SERVICE/SYNDICATE

Global Security Newswire
Owner: Atlantic Media Company
Editorial: 600 New Hampshire Ave NW, Washington, District Of Columbia 20037-2403.
T: 1 202 454-8942
E: gsn@nationaljournal.com
W: http://www.globalsecuritynewswire.org
Editor: Chris Schneidmiller
Editorial Profile: Founded in 2001, Global Security Newswire's mission is to strengthen global security by reducing the risk of use and preventing the spread of nuclear, biological and chemical weapons. It hopes to raise public awareness, serve as a catalyst for new thinking and take direct action to reduce these threats. The Web site hopes to give people access to the facts about these threats because issues need to be debated beyond the experts and policy-makers.
NEWS SERVICE/SYNDICATE

Globe Photos
Owner: Whelan (Mary Beth)
Editorial: 24 Edmore Ln S, West Islip, New York 11795-4016. **T:** 1 631 661-3131
E: info@globephotos.com
W: http://www.globephotos.com
Editorial Profile: Globe Photos is a news service that provides specialized coverage of the entertainment industry to a variety of markets, including multimedia, television, film, advertising, corporate, editorial and publishing industries. It maintains a comprehensive stock photography archive.
NEWS SERVICE/SYNDICATE

Globe Syndicate
Editorial: 9090 Wagner Creek Rd, Talent, Jackson, Oregon 97540. **T:** 1 541 944-2418
W: http://www.globesyndicate.com
Editorial Profile: Globe Syndicate offers columns on a variety of topics including family values, healthcare, living with a disability, general commentaries and editorials.
NEWS SERVICE/SYNDICATE

The Gold Sheet
Editorial: 4717 Van Nuys Blvd, Fl 3, Sherman Oaks, Los Angeles, California 91403-2100.
T: 1 800 798-4653
E: goldshee@goldsheet.com
W: http://www.goldsheet.com
Editor: Gary Olshan
Editorial Profile: The Gold Sheet is a sports information newsletter covering football and basketball. It offers insight and analysis on teams across the nation. For football coverage, there is comprehensive pointspread coverage, college and pro power ratings, statistical reviews and detailed reports on injuries and lineup changes. There are also reports on college games with in-depth analysis of each game.
NEWS SERVICE/SYNDICATE

Goldsborough, Reid
Editorial: 756 Suffolk Rd, Rydal, Pennsylvania 19046-3426 **E:** reidgoldsborough@gmail.com
W: http://www.reidgold.com/
Editorial Profile: This is a nationally-syndicated bi-weekly column focusing on personal computers and related technology, including software, hardware and the Internet. The focus is on issues and trends. Do not send press releases about personnel changes or company acquisitions.
NEWS SERVICE/SYNDICATE

Golf Publishing Syndicate
Editorial: 2743 Saxon St, Allentown, Pennsylvania 18103-2825. **T:** 1 610 437-4982
E: info@galvgolf.com
W: http://www.galvgolf.com
Editor: Karl Gilbert
Editorial Profile: Golf Publishing Syndicate offers features on golf equipment, golf etiquette, learning how to play better golf and professional golf analysis.
NEWS SERVICE/SYNDICATE

Gongwer News Service
Editorial: 17 S High St, Suite 630, Columbus, Ohio 43215-3413. **T:** 1 614 221-1992
E: gongwer@gongwer-oh.com
W: http://www.gongwer-oh.com
Editor: Kent Cahlander
Editorial Profile: Gongwer News Service provides comprehensive, accurate, timely and balanced daily news reports on the activities of state government, with a particular emphasis on legislative activities. The news service provides subscribers with a complete package of information about Ohio's state government, including real time e-mail alerts and bill tracking.
NEWS SERVICE/SYNDICATE

Gongwer News Service
Editorial: 124 W Allegan St, Ste 1200, Lansing, Michigan 48933-1737.
T: 1 517 482-3500 **E:** gongwer@gongwer.com
W: http://www.gongwer.com
Editor: Zachary Gorchow; **Publisher:** John Lindstrom
Editorial Profile: The Lansing bureau of Gongwer News Service provides The Michigan Report, a comprehensive, accurate, timely report on the activities of state government, with a particular emphasis on legislative activities.
NEWS SERVICE/SYNDICATE

Gotta Love It
Editorial: 2050 Mark Twain Cir, Bethlehem, Pennsylvania 18017-1531. **T:** 1 610 570-9827
W: http://www.fpfc.org
Editorial Profile: Gotta Love It is a weekly, self-syndicated food column. It deals with food and beverage products, cookbooks and interesting new recipes.
NEWS SERVICE/SYNDICATE

Graham News Service
Editorial: 2770 W 5Th St Apt 20G, Brooklyn, New York 11224-4216. **T:** 1 718 372-1920
E: grahamnews@aol.com
Editor: Paula Royce Graham
Editorial Profile: Graham News Service offers commentary, features and profiles on a number of topics including films, fashion, beauty, lifestyles, home furnishings, interior design, food, wine, restaurants and travel. Do NOT send faxes to the phone number! They do not have a fax machine.
NEWS SERVICE/SYNDICATE

Grochowski, John
T: 1 312 321-2351
E: jgrochowski@suntimes.com
W: http://www.casinoanswerman.com
Editorial Profile: John Grochowski self-syndicates a weekly, casino column that runs in several Midwest newspapers. His column is sometimes labeled as The Casino Answer Man.
NEWS SERVICE/SYNDICATE

Guidry News Service
Editorial: 4001 Fannin St, Suite 4432, Houston, Texas 77004-4077.
T: 1 409 763-6397
W: http://www.guidrynews.com
Editorial Profile: Guidry News Service publishes Gulf Coast E-news, a newsletter delivered by e-mail five days a week; the Online News Station, a news magazine covering events impacting the Gulf Coast region of Texas and Louisiana; and The Guidry News Gazette, published weekly on its Web site. It primarily focuses on coverage in Houston, Galveson, Beaumont, Port Arthur, Kemah, Bay Area Houston and the surrounding areas. Topics covered include Government & Politics, Education, Arts & Entertainment, Ports, Obituaries, Opinion & Editorial, Business & Industry, Faith & Values, Gardening, Economics, Weather, and Events.
NEWS SERVICE/SYNDICATE

Hamilton, Argus
Editorial: 930 Palm Ave, Apt 132, West Hollywood, California 90069.
T: 1 818 386-9552 **E:** argusjokes@aol.com
W: http://www.argushamilton.com
Editorial Profile: This self-syndicated column appears on the Internet and in over 100 newspapers across the United States. The author offers a humorous look at timely topics from Washington and around the country.
NEWS SERVICE/SYNDICATE

Hannah News Service
Editorial: 21 W Broad St, Ste 1050, Columbus, Ohio 43215-4188.
T: 1 614 228-3113
E: pressreleases@hannah.com
W: http://hannah.com
Publisher: Judith Bird; **Editor:** Paul Teasley
Editorial Profile: Hannah News Service covers state government and the state house, including legislative, healthcare and education news.
NEWS SERVICE/SYNDICATE

Have Fun at the Movies
Editorial: 10717 Bushire Dr, Dallas, Texas 75229-5330. **T:** 1 214 536-9399
Editorial Profile: A consumer guide to a wide range of good films, DVDs and videos. The weekly column recommends only the best first run theater releases, classic movies, videos, children's films, golden oldies, outstanding foreign films and independent films. Syndicated to more than 30 newspapers.
NEWS SERVICE/SYNDICATE

Health Behavior News Service
Editorial: 2000 Florida Ave NW, Ste 210, Washington, District Of Columbia 20009-1231.
T: 1 202 387-2829 **E:** hbns-editor@cfah.org
W: http://www.cfah.org/hbns
Editor: Kelly Malcom
Editorial Profile: Health Behavior News Service is a resource for the news media and public to find the best and most recent evidence-based scientific research to help people make decisions about their health and healthcare. They monitor articles in peer-reviewed journals and research by non-profit, public- and private-sector producers of systematic evidence reviews.
NEWS SERVICE/SYNDICATE

Health Promotion Features
Editorial: 1802 N Carson St Ste 108-2550, Carson City, Nevada 89701-1265.
T: 1 775 887-0670
Editor: John Yacenda; **Editor:** John Yacenda
Editorial Profile: As a subsidiary of Health Care Strategies, Inc., the columns focus on general health promotion and nutrition. Specialty features address the mental and physical training needs of recreational/amateur athletes, and explore the common concerns of men and women in relationships.
NEWS SERVICE/SYNDICATE

Hearst News Service
Editorial: 700 12th St NW Ste 100, Washington, District Of Columbia 20005-3945.
T: 1 202 263-6400 **W:** http://www.hearst.com
Bureau Chief: David McCumber
Editorial Profile: Hearst News Service combines daily stories from each Hearst newspaper, along with contributions from its own Washington staff, and transmits them to the group's daily newspapers and subscribers to the New York Times News Service. The Washington staff regularly covers the White House, Congress, the economy and national security.
NEWS SERVICE/SYNDICATE

The Hechinger Report
Editorial: 475 Riverside Dr, New York, New York 10115-0002
E: hechinger@tc.columbia.edu
W: http://hechingerreport.org/
Editor: Liz Willen
Editorial Profile: The Hechinger Report is a non-profit news organization that is focused on producing in-depth education journalism. Working with in-house and freelance reporters, The Report covers education issues, including investigative reporting, detailed analysis, and occasionally featuring opinion from some of the leading thinkers in education. These stories appear nationwide in newspapers and on websites, as well as on the Hechinger Report's website. The Hechinger Report is an independently funded unit of Teachers College at Columbia University.
NEWS SERVICE/SYNDICATE

High Country News
Editorial: 119 Grand Ave, Paonia, Colorado 81428-9905. **T:** 1 970 527-4898
E: editor@hcn.org **W:** http://www.hcn.org
Editorial Profile: High Country News reports on the West's natural resources, public lands and changing communities. It covers 11 Western states, from the Great Plains to the northwest, and from the northern Rockies to the desert southwest. It offers environmental news, analysis and commentary on water, logging, wildlife, grazing, public lands, economic growth and other issues changing the face of the West.
NEWS SERVICE/SYNDICATE

Hispanic Link News Service
Editorial: 1420 N St NW, Washington, District Of Columbia 20005. **T:** 1 202 234-0280
W: http://www.hispaniclink.org

Editor: Carlos Ericksen
Editorial Profile: Founded in 1980, Hispanic Link News Service syndicates news analysis, opinion and feature columns to more than 350 print, broadcast and news media, plus universities and individuals in leadership positions throughout the Americas in English and Spanish. The mission is to give exposure to the views and expertise of Hispanic authorities in all fields; educate a general audience on Hispanic interests, issues, and perspectives; create a national showcase for Hispanic writing talent; and provide a conduit for Hispanic writers and experts in and beyond the United States to exchange information, views, and ideas.
NEWS SERVICE/SYNDICATE

Hollister Kids

Editorial: 3 E Wynnewood Rd, Wynnewood, Pennsylvania 19096-1917. **T:** 1 484 829-0024
E: contactus@hollisterkids.com
W: http://www.hollisterkids.com
Publisher: Peter Landry
Editorial Profile: Hollister Kids offers educational supplements for newspapers in education programs. It features try to reach, teach and entertain young readers and their families with a new topic every week.
NEWS SERVICE/SYNDICATE

Hollywood News Service

Editorial: 13636 Ventura Blvd, Ste 303, Sherman Oaks, Los Angeles, California 91423-3700. **T:** 1 818 990-5945
E: editor@newscalendar.com
W: http://www.newscalendar.com
Editor in Chief: Carolyn Fox
Editorial Profile: Hollywood News Calendar offers information for covering the entertainment industry, including which celebrities are available for interviews, what celebrities are going to which parties, where the premieres are being held or when a celebrity is appearing in court. It is sent out Monday through Friday to subscribers.
NEWS SERVICE/SYNDICATE

Home Improvement Time Inc.

Editorial: 7425 Steubenville Pike, Oakdale, Allegheny, Pennsylvania 15071-9311. **T:** 1 412 787-2881
W: http://www.homeimprovementtime.com
Editor: Carole Stewart
Editorial Profile: Founded in 1966, Home Improvement Time Inc. offers editors and webmasters access to non-copyrighted editorial content focusing on home improvement and energy management topics. It offers three online home improvement, in-and-around-the-house camera ready feature editions per year, via industry sponsors, to daily and weekly newspapers and news sources. Each edition has about 50 stories and/or photos.
NEWS SERVICE/SYNDICATE

Homeland Security News Wire

Editorial: 220 Old Country Rd Ste 200, Mineola, New York 11501-4208.
T: 1 202 318-1567 **E:** info@newswirepubs.com
W: http://www.homelandsecuritynewswire.com
Editorial Profile: Homeland Security News Wire is designed for executives, investors and senior decision makers involved in the homeland security market. It provides daily reports on trends, technologies and emerging market directions, and is international in its coverage and readership. Issues covered include biodefense and food supply safety, biometrics and identity authentication, border security, business continuity and disaster recovery, critical infrastructure and IT security, detection, emergency response and management, homeland security budget, intelligence, surveillance, training and simulation technologies and transportation security.
NEWS SERVICE/SYNDICATE

Hot Topics Publications Inc.

Owner: Carroll (Ned) & Carroll (Debby)
T: 1 215 635-1120 **E:** hottopics@comcast.net
W: http://www.hottopicshotserials.com
Editor: Ned Carroll
Editorial Profile: Hot Topics Publications provides materials for educational environments. The products include 16-page tabloid supplements with full color covers and teacher's guides. Experienced teachers help write lesson plans so that editors and reporters can get an intuitive product.
NEWS SERVICE/SYNDICATE

Hughes, Mike

Editorial: 1149 Woodside Dr, Haslett, Michigan 48840-9780. **T:** 1 517 339-5051

E: hughestvmike@aol.com
W: http://mikehughes.tv
Editorial Profile: This self-syndicated column covers television. It provides readers with reviews and previews of upcoming television programs.
NEWS SERVICE/SYNDICATE

Icon Sports Media

Owner: XML Team Solutions
Editorial: 531-A North Hollywood Way #221, Burbank, California 91505. **T:** 1 818 334-8796
W: http://www.iconsportsmedia.com
Editorial Profile: Icon Sports Media is a digital photography wire service.
NEWS SERVICE/SYNDICATE

IDG News Service

Owner: International Data Group
Editorial: 1 Exeter Plaza, 15th Floor, Boston, Massachusetts 2116. **T:** 1 617 239-7841
E: idgnews@idg.com **W:** http://www.idg.com
Editor in Chief: Elizabeth Heichler; **Editor in Chief:** Elizabeth Heichler
Editorial Profile: IDG News Service is a technology media, research and event company. The parent company, International Data Group, publishes more than 300 magazines and newspapers. It is updated six days a week, 24 hours a day, and has correspondents worldwide, covering their respective markets. The mission of the service is to provide major breaking news stories to its affiliates, including the majority of news stories that run in IDG publications and Web sites around the world.
NEWS SERVICE/SYNDICATE

IDG News Service

Owner: International Data Group
Editorial: 906 Philip Powers Dr, Laurel, Maryland 20707-3510. **T:** 1 301 604-6250
E: idgnews@idg.com
Editorial Profile: IDG News Service provides readers with information on technology, online media, print publishing, market research and events.
NEWS SERVICE/SYNDICATE

IDG News Service

Owner: International Data Group
Editorial: 501 2nd St, Ste 600, San Francisco, California 94107-4133. **T:** 1 415 974-7432
E: idgnews@idg.com
W: http://www.idgnews.com
Bureau Chief: James Niccolai
Editorial Profile: IDG News Service is a technology media, research and event company. The parent company, International Data Group, publishes more than 300 magazines and newspapers. It is updated six days a week, 24 hours a day, and has correspondents worldwide, covering their respective markets. The mission of the service is to provide major breaking news stories to its affiliates, including the majority of news stories that run in IDG publications and Web sites around the world.
NEWS SERVICE/SYNDICATE

IDG News Service

Owner: International Data Group
Editorial: 224 W 4th St Ste 200, New York, New York 10014-3188. **T:** 1 212 400-0524
E: idgnews@idg.com
NEWS SERVICE/SYNDICATE

IDG News Service

Owner: International Data Group
Editorial: 19367 SW 79 Place, Miami, Florida 33157. **T:** 1 305 964-5184
E: idgnews@idg.com
NEWS SERVICE/SYNDICATE

IDG News Service

Owner: International Data Group
T: 31 20 758-5955 **E:** idgnews@idg.com
NEWS SERVICE/SYNDICATE

IDG News Service

Owner: International Data Group
T: 61 2 9902-2719
NEWS SERVICE/SYNDICATE

Independence Feature Syndicate

Editorial: 727 E. 16th Ave., Denver, Colorado 80203. **T:** 1 303 279-6536 **E:** info@i2i.org
W: http://www.i2i.org
Publisher: Jon Caldara
Editorial Profile: This syndicate is in a variety of publications and provides citizens of Colorado and the nation with specific recommendations to help resolve important issues. Issues include improving the educational system, healthcare costs, economic freedom and controlling violent crime. It offers issue papers and editorials.

They are interested in pieces focused on Colorado or Colorado localities.
NEWS SERVICE/SYNDICATE

Inman News Features

Editorial: 1100 Marina Village Pkwy Ste 102, Alameda, California 94501-6471.
T: 1 510 658-9252 **E:** press@inman.com
W: http://www.inman.com
Editorial Profile: Founded in 1983, Inman News Features is a real estate news service and syndicate based in the San Francisco Bay area. It is a daily news feed and reports on residential and commercial real estate, including market trends, emerging technologies and news for homebuyers and sellers. Editorial content is licensed to over 250 newspapers and 50,000 Web sites.
NEWS SERVICE/SYNDICATE

Inter Press Service

Editorial: 529 14th St NW, Washington, District of Columbia 20045-1002.
T: 1 202 662-7160 **E:** ipswas@igc.org
W: http://www.ipsnews.net
Editor in Chief: Ramesh Jaura
Editorial Profile: Inter Press Service covers news from Third World countries and tries to give a voice to the voiceless, promote information on development issues and help create a better balance and flow of international news. There are news features, analysis and expert commentaries on events and global processes affecting the economic, social and political development of peoples and nations, especially in Africa, Asia, the Arab World, the Caribbean and Latin America. There is a focus on the gap between rich and poor, human rights, international trade negotiations, refugees and international migration patterns, conflict and peace-keeping, population issues and the international debt crisis.
NEWS SERVICE/SYNDICATE

Inter Press Service

Editorial: UN Plaza, United Nations Rm L-214, New York, New York 10017.
T: 1 212 963-6156
Editorial Profile: This is the New York bureau of the news service.
NEWS SERVICE/SYNDICATE

International Fashion Syndicate

Editorial: 35 Park Ave, New York, New York 10016. **T:** 1 646 742-9307 **E:** info@fgi.org
Editorial Profile: International Fashion Syndicate syndicates Clotheslines, a weekly question-and-answer fashion advice feature that includes tips on the latest trends and designers.
NEWS SERVICE/SYNDICATE

International News Features Network

Editorial: 415 E 52nd St, New York, New York 10022-6424. **T:** 1 212 753-2939
E: generalstrategics@msn.com
Editor: Edward Mahoney
Editorial Profile: International News Features Network offers print and broadcast media clients packaged features covering a variety of general interest topics, such as travel, book reviews, food, personal finance, entertainment, medical/health and the arts.
NEWS SERVICE/SYNDICATE

Interpress of London and New York

Editorial: 90 Riverside Dr, New York, New York 10024-5306. **T:** 1 212 873-0772
Editor in Chief: Jeffrey Blyth
Editorial Profile: Interpress of London and New York includes consumer information on new products, commentary on travel trends in the United States and on all aspects of American media, Q&A about home computers and the latest news on the music scene, records, film, video and books.
NEWS SERVICE/SYNDICATE

Investigative Newsource

Owner: San Diego State University
Editorial: 5500 Campanile Dr, San Diego, California 92182-0001. **T:** 1 619 594-5100
W: http://inewsource.org
Editorial Profile: Investigative Newsource is a non-profit news service at San Diego State University, providing investigative journalism to the citizens of San Diego and Imperial County, CA, and is partnered with KPBS, the PBS-NPR affiliate in San Diego.
NEWS SERVICE/SYNDICATE

ITAR-TASS

Editorial: 529 14th St NW, Ste 1004, Washington, District Of Columbia 20045.
T: 1 202 662-7080 **E:** washtass@gmail.com
W: http://www.itar-tass.com
Bureau Chief: Andrei Sitov

Editorial Profile: ITAR-TASS (Information Telegraph Agency of Russia) is the successor to the Soviet era TASS news service. It was originally formed in 1904 as the official news agency of the Russian state. The service has 74 bureaus within Russia and the CIS, with another 65 offices in 62 countries abroad.
NEWS SERVICE/SYNDICATE

ITAR-TASS

Editorial: 780 3rd Ave, 19th Fl, New York, New York 10017. **T:** 1 212 245-4250
E: itar@aol.com
NEWS SERVICE/SYNDICATE

ITAR-TASS - United Nations Bureau

Editorial: 405 E 42nd Street, United Nations Rm C-312, New York, New York 10017.
T: 1 212 688-6764
Editorial Profile: This is the ITAR-TASS United Nations bureau.
NEWS SERVICE/SYNDICATE

J Features

T: 1 781 383-6688 **E:** jfeatures@aol.com
Editorial Profile: J Features offers consumer-oriented money management help, focusing on mutual funds, investments and personal finance that is especially helpful information for non-traditional business page readers.
NEWS SERVICE/SYNDICATE

Jacobi, Dana

Editorial: 460 E 79th St, New York, New York 10021-1443. **T:** 1 212 744-0939
E: djacobi@aol.com
W: http://www.danajacobi.com
Editorial Profile: The column targets mainstream readers interested in good food and healthful eating. Please only send press releases that are strictly related to food.
NEWS SERVICE/SYNDICATE

James Srodes News Service Inc.

Editorial: 1754 Park Rd NW, Washington, District Of Columbia 20010.
T: 1 202 232-5312 **E:** srodesnews@msn.com
W: http://www.jamessrodes.com
Bureau Chief: James Srodes
Editorial Profile: There are news features focusing on broad economic policy, the World Bank and financial issues affecting business and commerce internationally.
NEWS SERVICE/SYNDICATE

Jandon Features

Editorial: 2319 S 105Th Ave, Omaha, Douglas, Nebraska 68124-1821. **T:** 1 402 502-4367
W: http://midwestgardening.com
Editorial Profile: Jandon Features provides weekly columns and seasonal features that focus on gardening and landscaping in the Midwest. It also includes product reviews. It is syndicated to daily and weekly newspapers in cities from Ohio to Nebraska, including Chicago, Milwaukee, Omaha, NE, Sioux City, IA, and Peoria, IL.
NEWS SERVICE/SYNDICATE

Jiji Press America

Owner: JIJI Press LTD.
Editorial: 120 W 45th St, Suite 1401, New York, New York 10036-4041.
T: 1 646 231-6300 **E:** edit@jijiusa.com
W: http://www.jiji.com
Editorial Profile: JiJi Press America is a Japanese wire service serving newspapers in Japan on varied topics with emphasis on financial and business news.
NEWS SERVICE/SYNDICATE

JiJi Press America

Editorial: 300 W Adams St, Ste 322, Chicago, Illinois 60606-5109. **T:** 1 312 750-1415
W: http://www.jiji.com
Bureau Chief: Kenzo Matsuoka
Editorial Profile: This is the Chicago bureau of JiJi Press America.
NEWS SERVICE/SYNDICATE

JiJi Press America

Editorial: 21250 Hawthorne Blvd, Ste 700, Torrance, California 90503-5514.
T: 1 310 792-7442 **E:** jijila@jijiusa.com
Bureau Chief: Yoshihisa Tamura
Editorial Profile: This is the Torrance, CA, bureau for the news service.
NEWS SERVICE/SYNDICATE

Jiji Press America

Editorial: 529 14th St NW, Ste 550, Washington, District Of Columbia 20045-1500.
T: 1 202 783-4330
E: jijipressdc@nationalpress.com
Bureau Chief: Yoshiki Kishida

Editorial Profile: This is the Washington bureau of JiJi Press America.
NEWS SERVICE/SYNDICATE

John Maginnis

Owner: Maginnis (John)
E: lapolitics@cox.net
W: http://www.lapolitics.com
Editorial Profile: Maginnis is self-syndicated columnist covering Louisiana Politics and Government for several outlets in Louisiana, and has been covering the subject since 1972, also in his weekly newsletter, LaPolitics Weekly. He is the author of "The Last Hayride" (1984) and "Cross to Bear" (1992). He was inducted into the LSU Manship School of Communications Hall of Fame in 2000.
NEWS SERVICE/SYNDICATE

Journal Press Syndicate

Editorial: 545 W End Ave, New York, New York 10024-2713. **T:** 1 212 580-8559
E: ijbnyc@aol.com
Editor: Irwin Breslauer
Editorial Profile: Journal Press Syndicate offers columns, features, commentary and opinion on a wide range of consumer interest topics from healthcare to travel and from parenting to personal finance.
NEWS SERVICE/SYNDICATE

JTA

Owner: Jewish Telegraphic Agency
Editorial: 24 W. 30 Street, 4th Fl, New York, New York 10001. **T:** 1 212 643-1890
E: newsdesk@jta.org **W:** http://www.jta.org
Editorial Profile: The Jewish Telegraphic Agency is a news service covering domestic and international news of interest to Jewish people. It hopes to provide accurate reports and informative analysis of the issues and news developments, including coverage of political, economic and social developments affecting Jews around the world.
NEWS SERVICE/SYNDICATE

JTA

Editorial: 1025 Vermont Ave NW, Ste 504, Washington, District Of Columbia 20005-3578. **T:** 1 202 737-0935 **E:** newsdesk@jta.org
W: http://www.jta.org
Bureau Chief: Ron Kampeas
Editorial Profile: JTA is a global news service serving the Jewish community.
NEWS SERVICE/SYNDICATE

Kaiser Health News

Owner: Kaiser Family Foundation (Henry J.)
Editorial: 1330 G St NW, Washington, District Of Columbia 20005-3004. **T:** 1 202 347-5270
E: khnnews@kff.org
W: http://www.kaiserhealthnews.org
Editor in Chief: John Fairhall; **Editor:** Stephanie Stapleton
Editorial Profile: Kaiser Health News launched in early 2009. It is an independent news service that focuses on the nation's healthcare system and related political and policy issues. The news service provides in-depth stories on developments, initiatives and debates in the healthcare system. In addition to reporting, the news service features columns, video, graphics and multimedia elements. News content is also provided online.
NEWS SERVICE/SYNDICATE

Keister-Williams Newspaper Services, Inc.

Editorial: 1807 Emmet St N, Ste 6B, Charlottesville, Virginia 22901.
T: 1 434 293-4709 **E:** kw@kwnews.com
W: http://www.kwnews.com
Editor: Carol Lindsay
Editorial Profile: Keister-Williams Newspaper Services, Inc., offers a weekly feature with daily Bible readings for the newspapers it serves. The features are non-denominational messages to encourage church attendance.
NEWS SERVICE/SYNDICATE

Kid Scoop

Owner: Vicki Whiting
T: 1 707 996-6077 **E:** thescoop@kidscoop.com
W: http://www.kidscoop.com
Editorial Profile: Kid Scoop provides award-winning internationally syndicated print and online content full of educational puzzles, games and fun for young readers aged 5 to 13. Every week there are two or more Newspapers in Education lessons that direct readers to other parts of the newspaper. There is also a weekly writing prompt that encourages children to get something published. It is designed to make reading the newspaper fun and engaging.
NEWS SERVICE/SYNDICATE

King Features Syndicate

Owner: Hearst Corporation (The)
Editorial: 300 W 57th St, Fl 15, New York, New York 10019-5238. **T:** 1 212 969-7550
E: kfswriters@hearst.com
W: http://www.kingfeatures.com
Editorial Profile: King Features Syndicate is a member of Hearst Entertainment and Syndication Group, which combines Hearst Corporation's cable network partnerships, television programming activities and newspaper syndication and merchandise licensing operations. It is a premier distributor of comics, columns, editorial cartoons, puzzles and games, distributing in print and online some 150 features to nearly 5,000 newspapers around the globe. Its columns cover business, personal finance, commentary, entertainment, lifestyle, advice, health, fitness and sports.
NEWS SERVICE/SYNDICATE

King Features Weekly Service

Owner: Hearst Corporation (The)
Editorial: 628 Virginia Dr, Orlando, Florida 32803-1858. **T:** 1 407 894-7300
W: http://ww3.rbma.com
Editorial Profile: King Features Weekly Service is a features syndicator to weekly, monthly and college newspapers, with more than 1,300 subscribers nationwide. It offers weekly packages with more than 75 comics, puzzles, columns and features. Features include color comics, a weekly Sudoku puzzle, cartoons, a birding graphic, a bible trivia quiz, a cooking/celebrities feature and a police log review.
NEWS SERVICE/SYNDICATE

Knight, Bill

W: http://billknightcolumn.blogspot.com
Editorial Profile: Knight is a self-syndicated opinion columnist for some Illinois-based GateHouse Media newspapers, including the Daily Register in Canton, IL and the Pekin (IL) Daily Times. He writes two columns a week on various subjects, of both national and Illinois state significance, and is also a commentator for Tri-States Public Radio, WIUM-FM 91.3, which also features his columns on their web site.
NEWS SERVICE/SYNDICATE

Knight, Tom

Editorial: 8302 6th Ave, Brooklyn, New York 11209-4556. **T:** 1 718 836-0936
Editorial Profile: Focus is on baseball nostalgia. Self-syndicated weekly to six newspapers.
NEWS SERVICE/SYNDICATE

Kuwait News Agency - United Nations Bureau

Editorial: 405 E 42nd St, United Nations Library, Rm S-0314B, New York, New York 10017-3507. **T:** 1 917 456-7830
E: newyork.kuna@gmail.com
W: http://www.kuna.net.kw
Editorial Profile: This is the United Nations bureau of the Kuwait News Agency.
NEWS SERVICE/SYNDICATE

Kuwait News Agency - Washington Bureau

Editorial: 529 14th St NW, Ste 906, Washington, District Of Columbia 20045-1901. **T:** 1 202 347-5554 **W:** http://www.kuna.net.kw
Bureau Chief: Shorouk Sadeqi
Editorial Profile: Serves as the U.S. national politics bureau.
NEWS SERVICE/SYNDICATE

Kyodo News

Editorial: 747 3rd Ave Rm 1803, New York, New York 10017-2869. **T:** 1 212 508-5460
E: kni@kyodonews.com
W: http://www.kyodonews.com
Bureau Chief: Yasushi Funatsu
Editorial Profile: Founded in 1945, Kyodo is based in Japan and has bureaus all over the world. It is a Japanese news agency independent of government, political and commercial interests. It provides a Japanese-language news service that is distributed to virtually all newspapers and broadcast networks in Japan, as well as English and Chinese language services that reach news agencies, newspapers, and radio and television broadcasters in various parts of the world.
NEWS SERVICE/SYNDICATE

Kyodo News

Editorial: 250 E 1st St Ste 302, Los Angeles, California 90012-3819. **T:** 1 213 680-9448
E: kyodolosangeles@gmail.com
Bureau Chief: Masahiro Watanabe

Editorial Profile: This is the Los Angeles bureau for Kyodo News.
NEWS SERVICE/SYNDICATE

Kyodo News

Editorial: 747 3rd Ave Rm 1801, New York, New York 10017-2869. **T:** 1 212 508-5460
Editorial Profile: This is the United Nations bureau for the news service.
NEWS SERVICE/SYNDICATE

Lasky, Jane

Editorial: 1009 Coronado Terrace, Los Angeles, California 90026. **T:** 1 213 819-5054
Editorial Profile: This self-syndicated column appears in about 35 daily newspapers. It focuses on travel trends, hotel news, airline updates and cultural etiquette. Most readers are business travelers, future business travelers and armchair travelers. It also provides travel insights through anecdotes and insider's tips.
NEWS SERVICE/SYNDICATE

Lempert, Phil

Editorial: 3015 Main St, Ste 320, Santa Monica, California 90405-6402.
T: 1 310 392-0448
W: http://www.supermarketguru.com
Editorial Profile: This syndicated column covers trends and products in the food industry, including new foods, diet tips, healthy eating and recipes. There is analysis and the author identifies and explains trends to both industry and consumers in a thought provoking manner.
NEWS SERVICE/SYNDICATE

Lisa Miller Film Preview

Editorial: 824 Marsh Ave, Reno, Nevada 89509-1945
W: http://www.lisamillerfilmpreview.com
Editorial Profile: Lisa Miller Film Preview offers the lastest movie entertainment news and provides in-depth reviews of new movie releases.
NEWS SERVICE/SYNDICATE

Listening Inc.

Editorial: 152 S Illinois St, Hobart, Lake, Indiana 46342. **T:** 1 219 947-5478
E: listeninginc@comcast.net
W: http://www.listeninginc.com
Bureau Chief: Richard Bennett
Editorial Profile: Listening Inc. distributes a variety of weekly columns by a husband and wife writing team. The columns offer advice and lifestyle information about remarriage, step-family living, attention deficit disorder and the challenges of mid-life.
NEWS SERVICE/SYNDICATE

Literary Features Syndicate

Editorial: 92 East St, North Grafton, Massachusetts 01536-1806.
T: 1 508 839-4404
W: http://literarykids.tumblr.com
Publisher: Constance Basbanes
Editorial Profile: Literary Features Syndicate offers profiles of authors, a children's book review package, seasonal choices and the author's thoughts of certain works. There are also links to his various appearances and guest spots, as well as quotes about his works. He also writes about all matters concerning books collecting, book culture and the future of the medium.
NEWS SERVICE/SYNDICATE

Long News Service

Editorial: 2103B Pompton Dr, Austin, Texas 78757-8216. **T:** 1 512 478-5663
Editor: Bill Kidd
Editorial Profile: Long News Service provides articles and information relating to state government, politics and business developments to several daily newspapers in Texas. It also syndicates to some national publications dealing primarily with education, healthcare, law enforcement, insurance and workers compensation matters.
NEWS SERVICE/SYNDICATE

Lubavitch News Service

Editorial: 770 Eastern Pkwy, Brooklyn, New York 11213. **T:** 1 718 774-4000
E: info@lubavitch.com
W: http://lubavitch.com
Editor in Chief: Baila Olidort
Editorial Profile: Lubavitch News Service is the official news network of the Chabad Lubavitch movement. It provides news and information about Jewish life worldwide. The news service was founded in 1958.
NEWS SERVICE/SYNDICATE

Lutheran News Service

Editorial: 8765 W Higgins Rd, Chicago, Illinois 60631. **T:** 1 773 380-2958 **E:** news@elca.org
W: http://www.elca.org/news
Editorial Profile: Lutheran News Service is a news service of the Evangelical Lutheran Church in America. Reports on the church's ministries and provides stories about its people and their faith to journalists, religion writers and columnists, as well as other members of the media.
NEWS SERVICE/SYNDICATE

LVESN: Las Vegas Entertainment & Sports Newswire

W: http://www.lvesn.com
Editorial Profile: LVESN: Las Vegas Entertainment and Sports Newswire covers sports and entertainment news from the Las Vegas area, including coverage of hotels, restaurants, trade shows, conventions, movies, TV, music, fashion, beauty, sports and gaming news.
NEWS SERVICE/SYNDICATE

Lynch-Hudson, Regina

Editorial: 1865 River Falls Dr, Roswell, Georgia 30076-5114. **T:** 1 770 998-9911
E: thewritepublicist@earthlink.net
W: http://www.thewritepublicist.com
Editorial Profile: The columns serve as a source for minority and African-American news publicizing people, places, products and performances. Targeting black media nationwide, Doing Biz In seeks to share unique, inspiring business stories. Regina's A-List Abodes focuses on cultural travel venues including restaurants and resorts and yet another features auto reviews.
NEWS SERVICE/SYNDICATE

Maghreb Arabe Press - United Nations Bureau

Editorial: 405 E 42nd St, United Nations Rm S-486, New York, New York 10017.
T: 1 212 963-4068
Editorial Profile: This is the United Nations bureau of Maghreb Arabe Press in Morocco.
NEWS SERVICE/SYNDICATE

MAI Photo/News Agency, Inc.

Editorial: 6601 Ashmere Ln, Centreville, Virginia 20120-3753. **T:** 1 703 968-0030
E: staff@maiphoto.com
W: http://maiphoto.com
News Editor: David Gatley
Editorial Profile: Provides news and photos covering national security, the military and politics. Encompasses the State Department, United States Congress, the Department of Defense and the White House.
NEWS SERVICE/SYNDICATE

Marion Joyce Syndicate

Editorial: 52 Sagamore Rd, Bronxville, New York 10708-1544. **T:** 1 914 961-2020
Editorial Profile: Daily and weekly features, plus coupons, on national consumer brands covering a variety of topics: food, health, nutrition, household products, entertainment, travel, etc. Participants are major consumer service and product manufacturers.
NEWS SERVICE/SYNDICATE

Market News International

Owner: Market News International Inc.
Editorial: 40 Fulton St, 5th Floor, New York, New York 10038-1850. **T:** 1 212 669-6400
W: http://mninews.marketnews.com
Editorial Profile: Market News International is a news service that offers a broad selection of market news reports on major economies, monetary policy, currencies, bonds and derivatives. These stories are the same exclusive and incisive coverage successful traders and fund managers count on for their edge in the fast-moving global markets. The focus is on political and economic news briefs and features for professionals in the fixed income and foreign exchange markets.
NEWS SERVICE/SYNDICATE

Market News International

Owner: Market News International Inc.
Editorial: 529 14th St NW, Ste 1100, Washington, District Of Columbia 20045-1503.
T: 1 202 371-2121
Bureau Chief: Denny Gulino
NEWS SERVICE/SYNDICATE

Market News International

Owner: Market News International Inc.
Editorial: Chicago Mercantile Exchange, 30 South Wacker Dr., Chicago, Illinois 60604.
T: 1 708 784-1849
Bureau Chief: Alyce Andres-Frantz
NEWS SERVICE/SYNDICATE

Mature Life Features

Editorial: 3911 Kendall St, San Diego, California 92109-6130. **T:** 1 858 483-3412
W: http://maturelifefeatures.com
Editor in Chief: Cecil Scaglione; **Editor in Chief:** Cecil Scaglione
Editorial Profile: Mature Life Features syndicates articles and photos for the 40+ year old population. It offers news briefs, features and commentary on a wide range of topics, including personal finance, lifestyles, automobiles, health, travel, gaming and national news.
NEWS SERVICE/SYNDICATE

Mavrix Photo

Owner: Mavrix Photo Inc.
Editorial: 8605 Santa Monica Blvd, West Hollywood, California 90069-4109.
T: 1 323 289-2371
W: http://www.mavrixphoto.com
Editorial Profile: Mavrix Photo is a global celebrity news photo agency, located both in Miami Beach and Los Angeles.
NEWS SERVICE/SYNDICATE

McClatchy Newspapers

Owner: McClatchy Newspapers
Editorial: 700 12th St NW Ste 1000, Washington, District of Columbia 20005-3994.
T: 1 202 383-6000 **E:** web@mcclatchydc.com
W: http://www.mcclatchydc.com
News Editor: Mike Bold
Editorial Profile: Serves as the Washington bureau for all 30 McClatchy daily newspapers. It also oversees the operations of 8 international bureaus and contributes stories to their affiliated news service, McClatchy-Tribune Information Services.
NEWS SERVICE/SYNDICATE

McClatchy-Tribune Information Services

Owner: McClatchy/Tribune
Editorial: 700 12th St NW, Washington, District Of Columbia 20005-3945.
T: 1 202 383-6095
W: http://www.mctdirect.com
Editor-in-Chief: Debra Leithauser
Editorial Profile: McClatchy-Tribune Information Services provides news and feature stories, photos, print and Web news, feature graphics, illustrations, caricatures and paginated news products to news organizations around the world. The service relies on America's top newspapers for its content and does not accept outside articles for distribution. Content includes health, science, weather information, business, lifestyle topics and more. With contributions from more than 70 newspapers plus its own staff in the United States and Europe, its services appear in more than 1,000 newspapers worldwide and is represented on leading online services.
NEWS SERVICE/SYNDICATE

McManus Syndicate

Editorial: 9311 Harrington Dr, Potomac, Montgomery, Maryland 20854-4510.
T: 1 301 469-5870
W: http://www.marriagesavers.org
Editor: Harriet McManus
Editorial Profile: McManus Syndicate covers religious and ethical issues with a focus on improving and stabilizing marriages. It also hopes to prepare people for lifelong marriages, strengthen existing marriages and restore troubled marriages. There are also reports on major events with a moral component and suggests ways to raise ethical standards.
NEWS SERVICE/SYNDICATE

MCT Campus

Editorial: 700 12th St NW, Ste 1000, Washington, District Of Columbia 20005-3994.
T: 1 202 383-6022
E: campus@mctinfoservices.com
W: http://www.mctcampus.com
Editor: Wes Albers
Editorial Profile: This is a national news service for college newspapers that is devoted to covering the college scene with reports, articles, cartoons and features, as well as contemporary story ideas.
NEWS SERVICE/SYNDICATE

Meadowlands Media Group

Editorial: 20 Nevins St., Rutherford, New Jersey 07070-2819. **T:** 1 201 978-8524
Editor: Catherine Salfino
Editorial Profile: Meadowlands Media Group syndicates fantasy sports columns for football and baseball.
NEWS SERVICE/SYNDICATE

Media General News Service

Editorial: 333 E Franklin St, Richmond, Virginia 23219. **T:** 1 804 649-6000
E: news@timesdispatch.com
W: http://www.mgnewsservice.com
Editorial Profile: Media General News Service offers various feature stories from Media General newspapers, as well as syndication products on home, garden, celebrities, food and travel. The company's publishing assets include three metropolitan newspapers: The Tampa (FL) Tribune, the Richmond (VA) Times-Dispatch and the Winston-Salem (NC) Journal. They also include 22 daily community newspapers in Virginia, North Carolina, Florida, Alabama and South Carolina and more than 100 weekly newspapers and other publications.
NEWS SERVICE/SYNDICATE

Media Page, Inc.

T: 1 310 838-1436
E: newsdesk@mediapage.com
W: http://www.mediapage.com
Editor: Carol Kravitz
Editorial Profile: Media Page, Inc., supplies breaking news stories and emergency communications between public service agencies and the media to all of the major television and radio stations in Southern California. Contact the news service by e-mail.
NEWS SERVICE/SYNDICATE

MediaGlobal News Agency

Editorial: United Nations Building, 2nd Floor, New York, New York 10017.
T: 1 609 529-6129
W: http://www.mediaglobal.org
Bureau Chief: Naosherwan Nalavala
Editorial Profile: MediaGlobal News Agency is an organization that focuses their editorial content on the global south, humanitarian efforts and global development. This news service is based in New York, New York.
NEWS SERVICE/SYNDICATE

Medill News Service

Owner: Medill News Service
Editorial: 1325 G St NW, Suite 730, Washington, District Of Columbia 20005-3104.
T: 1 202 347-8700 **E:** medilldc@gmail.com
W: http://www.medilldc.net
Editor: Matt Mansfield; **Editor:** Josh Meyer; **Bureau Chief:** Ellen Shearer
Editorial Profile: Medill News Service is comprised of graduate journalism students at Northwestern University. The program begins on a smaller scale in Evanston, while the Washington, D.C. operation is the more advanced level. Students in Washington, D.C. report on federal politics and government, "focusing on how public policy affects people's lives," and specializes in investigative reporting with multimedia coverage.
NEWS SERVICE/SYNDICATE

Medill News Service

Owner: Medill News Service
Editorial: 105 W Adams St, Ste 200, Chicago, Illinois 60603-6202. **T:** 1 312 503-4100
W: http://news.medill.northwestern.edu/chicago
Editorial Profile: The focus of the Chicago-based Medill News Service is on business, economy, science, medicine and urban affairs in the Chicagoland area, and specifically partners with Chicago media outlets such as the Daily Herald, and The Times of Munster.
NEWS SERVICE/SYNDICATE

Mengenhauser, Jane

Editorial: 8905 Camfield Dr, Alexandria, Virginia 22308-2819. **T:** 1 703 360-5062
E: janemeng@cox.net
Editorial Profile: Self-syndicated features on a variety of foods and culinary history. Includes seasonal recipes and features on fund-raising for community groups, such as PTAs, booster clubs, churches, libraries, garden clubs and choirs.
NEWS SERVICE/SYNDICATE

Merrell Enterprises

Editorial: 2610 Garfield St NW, Washington, District Of Columbia 20008-4104.
T: 1 202 265-1925
E: jesse@jessehmerrell.com
Editorial Profile: Focus is on political commentary on current events/news from a moral/religious perspective.
NEWS SERVICE/SYNDICATE

Metro Feature Syndicate

Owner: Metro Publishing Group
Editorial: 626 McCarthy Dr, New Milford, New Jersey 07646-1029. **T:** 1 201 385-2000
E: metropub@aol.com
W: http://www.travelwritersjournal.net
Editorial Profile: Metro Feature Syndicate is a news service that targets weekly newspapers in the metropolitan New York and New Jersey areas. The service provides various columns to weekly newspapers in these areas. The news service contains articles on skiing, travel, book reviews and theatre. Bob and Sandy Nesoff also write a weekly travel column for New York City Resident Magazine, Courier Publications (Queens, Brooklyn, Long Island), Cruising Squared, Cruise Critic, and Paick.com. They are also travel columnists for L'Chaim Magazine published by North Jersey Media.
NEWS SERVICE/SYNDICATE

MIC Insurance Services

Editorial: 170 Kinnelon Rd Rm 11, Kinnelon, New Jersey 07405-2324. **T:** 1 973 492-2828
W: http://www.micinsurance.com
Editorial Profile: MIC Insurance Services appears in several newspapers in New Jersey each Sunday. It provides news about long term care, individual and group health, and medicine and medigap insurances. Sometimes there is analysis of different coverages. Overall, it tries to help readers understand the world of health insurance.
NEWS SERVICE/SYNDICATE

Middle East News Agency - New York Bureau

Editorial: United Nations, Room 301, New York, New York 10017. **T:** 1 212 963-7131
Editorial Profile: This is the New York bureau of Middle East News Agency, based in Cairo, Egypt.
NEWS SERVICE/SYNDICATE

Midnight Trader

Owner: MidnightTrader Inc.
Editorial: 4804 Montgomery Ln, Suite 201, Bethesda, Maryland 20814-5302.
T: 1 888 559-0073
E: editorial@midnighttrader.com
W: http://www.midnighttrader.com
Editorial Profile: Midnight Trader provides public company news, data and market analysis focused on the after-hours markets. It offers real-time extended-hours coverage of stocks moving after-hours and likely to move in the following regular session. The goal of the news service is to provide opportunities for readers to be better prepared for the extended-hours trading session by staying ahead of Wall Street with live pre-market stock trading news from 6:45am to 10am EST, and late breaking after-hours coverage from 3:30pm to 8pm ET. The service is subscription-based.
NEWS SERVICE/SYNDICATE

Midwest Features Syndicate

T: 1 608 274-8925 **E:** info@roadstraveled.com
W: http://www.midwestfeatures.com
Editorial Profile: Midwest Features Syndicate produces a weekly travel column whose content emphasizes, but is not limited to, Wisconsin and its border cities. Also produces other travel and Midwest features for various publications. Stock photography on file.
NEWS SERVICE/SYNDICATE

Military Update

T: 1 703 830-6863 **E:** milupdate@aol.com
W: http://www.militaryupdate.com
Editorial Profile: The weekly news column reaches two million readers and covers breaking news affecting the lives of service members and their families, including analysis of issues affecting pay, benefits and lifestyles of active duty members, retirees and reservists. It is intended for daily newspapers near military bases.
NEWS SERVICE/SYNDICATE

Milligan Syndicate

Editorial: 515 Shady Ln, Barrington, Illinois 60010-4144. **T:** 1 847 381-1593
Editor: Annie Milligan; **Editor:** Molly Milligan
Editorial Profile: The primary focus is on home decorating, home services, entertainment and etiquette. Also features reviews of books covering home design, interior design, decorating and gardening.
NEWS SERVICE/SYNDICATE

Missouri News Horizon

Editorial: 1025 Northeast Dr, Jefferson City, Missouri 65109-2579
E: mnhnews@missouri-news.org
W: http://missouri-news.org
Editorial Profile: Missouri News Horizon is a News Service covering Missouri news. Topics include agriculture, budget and taxes, business, education, environment,

government, military, politics and regulation as well as news from around the Midwest.
NEWS SERVICE/SYNDICATE

Moisés Naím

Editorial: 1779 Massachusetts Ave. NW, Washington, District of Columbia 20036.
T: 1 202 939-2262 **E:** mbetheil@ceip.org
W: http://www.moisesnaim.com
Editorial Profile: Moisés Naím is a syndicated columnist covering both national and international politics for outlets in the United States, Spain, Italy and Latin America. His column appears in The New York Times, The Financial Times, The Washington Post, Newsweek, Time, Foreign Policy and Foreign Affairs. All contact should be directed to his publicist.
NEWS SERVICE/SYNDICATE

Money & Markets

Owner: Associated Press, Inc.
Editorial: 450 W 33rd St, New York, New York 10001. **T:** 1 212 621-1924 **E:** stocks@ap.org
W: http://www.ap.org/markets
Editor: Joyce Rosenberg
Editorial Profile: Money & Markets is an off-shoot of the Associated Press and provides analytical, forward-looking financial data in the form of graphs, data and reports. The service offers modular, customized business and financial sections and is distributed in newspapers nationwide. It is designed to offer the quick-paced changes of the financial world in both print and online content formats. The service also offers Money & Markets Extra, which is geared towards newspapers' weekend editions.
NEWS SERVICE/SYNDICATE

Morem, Sue

T: 1 763 557-4998 **E:** info@suemorem.com
W: http://www.suemorem.com
Editorial Profile: This nationally syndicated column helps people get the jobs of their dreams, present themselves with enthusiasm in every social situation, dazzle company presidents and clients alike with their people skills, out-shine the competition and epitomize the look of career success.
NEWS SERVICE/SYNDICATE

Morris News Service

Owner: Morris Communications Corp., LLC
Editorial: 229 Peachtree St NE, Ste 202 International Tower, Atlanta, Georgia 30303-1601. **T:** 1 404 589-8424
E: mnews@morris.com
W: http://www.morrisnewsservice.com
Editorial Profile: Morris News Service provides news on government and political concerns affecting the Southeast. It serves more than 35 daily newspapers in Florida, Georgia and Texas.
NEWS SERVICE/SYNDICATE

Mortgage News Co.

Editorial: 141 North Rd, Cromwell, Connecticut 6416. **T:** 1 860 685-0082
E: epeat@mortgagenews.com
Editorial Profile: Mortgage News Co. distributes Earl Peattie's column about real estate and mortgages. The news service does NOT want to be contacted.
NEWS SERVICE/SYNDICATE

Motor News Media Corporation

Owner: Motor News Media
Editorial: 3321 109th St, Urbandale, Iowa 50322-8105. **T:** 1 515 986-1155
E: motornewsmedia@live.com
W: http://www.motornewsmedia.com
Editorial Profile: This is a customer-focused news service that provides automotive news, features and photos to educate and entertain readers. It serves approximately 120 newspaper and Web site clients in 38 states. The writers offer the latest trends, concepts, designs and hints for readers. They also produce an annual new vehicle preview that covers over 300 specific vehicles and 35 nameplates with approximately 1,900 pictures.
NEWS SERVICE/SYNDICATE

Movie Choices for Kids

Editorial: 160 W 77th St, New York, New York 10024-6912. **T:** 1 212 799-6146
Editorial Profile: The weekly column gives all the information a parent needs to make informed decisions about movies for their children.
NEWS SERVICE/SYNDICATE

National Gay/Lesbian Bisexual Transgender Travel Desk

Editorial: 301 Mount Rose St Apt 20, Reno, Nevada 89509-3373. **T:** 1 775 348-7990

E: nglbttraveldesk@gmx.com
Editor: Sylvia Seltzer
Editorial Profile: The news service covers travel news affecting gays, lesbians, bisexuals and transgenders around the country. It offers free travel articles for alternative and traditional publications who want gay-friendly stories but are unable to afford a travel editor. It includes stories on cities, states, attractions and travel throughout North America and features reviews of travel books. Reporters work with tourist associations, bed & breakfasts, restaurants, hotels, attractions, motels, public transit systems and convention & visitor bureaus. Stories appear in alternative and traditional publications nationwide and sometimes in international publications. They do NOT want to get any information by mail.
NEWS SERVICE/SYNDICATE

National News Bureau
Editorial: 3343 W School House Ln, Philadelphia, Pennsylvania 19129-5517. **T:** 1 215 849-9016
Editor: Debra Cruz
NEWS SERVICE/SYNDICATE

Natural Resources News Service
Owner: Public Education Center
Editorial: The National Press Building 529, 14th St. NW Ste. 962, Washington, District Of Columbia 20045. **T:** 1 202 466-4310
E: info@publicedcenter.org
W: http://www.dcbureau.org/category/natural-resources-news-service
Editor: Joseph Trento; **Editor:** Susan Trento
Editorial Profile: Natural Resources News Service covers environmental issues such as air and water pollution, toxins, habitat protection and reclamation, public land management and environmental regulation.
NEWS SERVICE/SYNDICATE

New America Media
Owner: Pacific News Service
Editorial: 209 9th St Ste 200, San Francisco, California 94103-6800. **T:** 1 415 503-4170
W: http://www.newamericamedia.org
Editor: Paul Kleyman; **Editor:** Paul Kleyman; **Editor:** Andrew Lam; **Korean Media Monitor:** Aruna Lee
Editorial Profile: New America Media syndicates daily stories through the Associated Press wire to subscribing mainstream and community newspapers across the country. It serves as a conduit for youth, ethnic and other voices that aren't heard as much in mainstream media. It offers feature-length commentary, news analysis and investigative reporting about topics such as immigration, civil liberties threats and hybrid identities.
NEWS SERVICE/SYNDICATE

New Car News Syndicate
Editorial: 41 Quercus Circle, Little Rock, Arkansas 72223. **T:** 1 501 425-9737
E: carnews@aol.com
Editorial Profile: New Car News Syndicate provides news and information on automotive trends. Geared toward auto shoppers, the publication features car and truck testing, brand reviews and product reviews.
NEWS SERVICE/SYNDICATE

New York German Press
Editorial: 11 Broadway, Ste 851, New York, New York 10004-1306. **T:** 1 212 269-3438
E: info@newyorkgermanpress.com
W: http://www.newyorkgermanpress.com
Editor: Jens Korte
Editorial Profile: New York German Press is the main independent press agency covering the United States financial markets for German language media. The agency covers developments in the United States securities market as well as the broader aspects of the United States economy.
NEWS SERVICE/SYNDICATE

New York Reporters
Editorial: 244 5th Ave Suite H247, New York, New York 10001-7604. **T:** 1 212 340-1098
E: mail@newyorkreporters.com
W: http://www.newyorkreporters.com
Editor in Chief: Harald Weiss
Editorial Profile: New York Reporters is a German-language news service that provides lifestyle, business and technology stories for European subscribers in Germany, Austria and Switzerland. It streams news 24 hours a day, seven days a week. Content comes from writers attending trade seminars, workshops and conferences, as well as from Internet conferences and news releases. It reaches 25 European magazines and newspapers. It is an active member of the Association of American

Business Correspondents, the Foreign Press Center of New York and the Financial Writer Association of New York.
NEWS SERVICE/SYNDICATE

The New York Times News Service/ Syndicate
Owner: New York Times Company (The)
Editorial: 620 8th Ave, New York, New York 10018-1618. **T:** 1 212 556-1927
E: nytns@nytimes.com
W: http://www.nytsyn.com
Editorial Profile: The New York Times News Service/Syndicate offers a variety of nationally syndicated columnists and content from The New York Times and other newspapers and wire services to its subscribers. There are columns, special features and book excerpts from many different countries and points of view. It Serves more than 2,000 clients on five continents and transmits material in English and Spanish. It works closely with The New York Times News Service and transmits material in English and Spanish.
NEWS SERVICE/SYNDICATE

News Service of Florida
Editorial: 336 E College Ave, Tallahassee, Florida 32301-1551. **T:** 1 850 656-6400
W: http://www.newsserviceflorida.com
Publisher: Ruth Herrle
Editorial Profile: The News Service of Florida is an independent wire service providing journalists, lobbyists, government officials and other civic leaders with comprehensive information about the activities of Florida state government.
NEWS SERVICE/SYNDICATE

News-Features Syndicate
T: 1 212 229-1111
E: newsfeatsyndicate@gmail.com
Editor: Caroline Howe
Editorial Profile: News-Features Syndicate offers its varied media clients in-depth stories on a variety of subjects, including book reviews, celebrity profiles, human interest, style, fashion, trends, technology, media and consumerism. Veteran journalists and experienced freelancers around the globe are members of the team servicing publications across the country.
NEWS SERVICE/SYNDICATE

NewsPortraits Syndicate
T: 1 201 342-2985
Editorial Profile: NewsPortraits Syndicate offers commentary on the interplay of government, politics, economics, national and foreign affairs. It includes interviews and profiles of personalities in these areas and covers topics of interest to teenagers. The service is not equipped to syndicate outside contributions.
NEWS SERVICE/SYNDICATE

Newswatch Feature Service
T: 1 949 645-4504
E: newswatch@earthlink.net
Editorial Profile: Newswatch Feature Service is an independent news feature service providing editorial content, including articles, photo features, pictorials, column pieces and special sections, to national trade, technical, professional and consumer magazines. It specializes in covering technology, public safety, entertainment and travel.
NEWS SERVICE/SYNDICATE

Nielsen Entertainment News Wire
Editorial: 5055 Wilshire Blvd, Fl 7, Los Angeles, California 90036-6100.
T: 1 323 525-2335
Bureau Chief: Angela Dawson
NEWS SERVICE/SYNDICATE

NNPA News Service
Editorial: 3200 13th St NW, Washington, District Of Columbia 20010-2410.
T: 1 202 319-1291
W: http://www.blackpressusa.com
Editorial Profile: Founded during World War II, the NNPA News Service is a national black news service that distributes investigative reports, news and feature articles, as well as political and social commentary to its member papers.
NEWS SERVICE/SYNDICATE

Northwest Auto News Service
Editorial: 4213 Glen Terra Dr Se, Olympia, Washington 98503-7165. **T:** 1 360 438-3825
E: lhall@nwautonews.com
Editor: Lynne Hall
Editorial Profile: Northwest Auto News Service is a newspaper syndicate that focuses on the automotive industry. Topics covered

include new-car test drives and feature articles ranging from car care to technology. It syndicates to several newspapers and Web sites, including The Oregonian in Portland, OR; The News Tribune in Tacoma, WA; the Peninsula Gateway in Gig Harbor, WA; The Sequim (WA) Gazette; The Forks (WA) Forum; the Port Townsend (WA) News; the Mountain Mail in Salida, CO; The Chaffee County Times in Buena Vista, CO; and the Herald Democrat in Leadville, CO as well as MSN Autos and NBCNews.com.
NEWS SERVICE/SYNDICATE

Notimex - Miami Bureau
Editorial: 3191 Coral Way Ste 501, Coral Gables, Florida 33145-3227.
T: 1 305 445-0716
NEWS SERVICE/SYNDICATE

NYCity News Service
Owner: CUNY Graduate School of Journalism
Editorial: 219 W. 40th St., New York, New York 10018. **T:** 1 646 758-7700
W: http://nycitynewsservice.com
Editorial Profile: NYCity News Service is a Web-based news service operated by the CUNY Graduate School of Journalism in New York City, with content primarily provided by attending students, overseen by faculty. The focus of coverage is local New York City news. Content is distributed to media outlets internationally.
NEWS SERVICE/SYNDICATE

On Computers
Editorial: 1630 Chicago Ave Apt 1513, Evanston, Illinois 60201-4595.
T: 1 847 570-9881
W: http://www.oncomp.com
Editorial Profile: On Computers is a weekly syndicated column that features the latest in computer and technology news. Coverage includes computer hardware and software, new technology in phones and cameras, video games, Web sites and Web services, technology trends, books, user studies and surveys and GPS.
NEWS SERVICE/SYNDICATE

OneWorld United States
Editorial: 1721 20Th St Nw, Washington, District Of Columbia 20009-1104.
T: 1 202 509-9781 **E:** useditors@oneworld.net
W: http://www.oneworld.net
Editorial Profile: Launched in 2000, One World United States aggregates breaking news for use by non-governmental organizations, human rights groups and international charities. Drawing from hundreds of non-profit sources, the news service offers comprehensive coverage of health, economic, political and social issues around the world.
NEWS SERVICE/SYNDICATE

O'Toole, Thomas J. and Joanne R.
Editorial: 4603 Wood St, Willoughby, Ohio 44094-5821. **T:** 1 440 942-5455
E: traveljournalists@hotmail.com
Editorial Profile: Their column focuses on travel including features and photo essays of destinations, attractions and historic sites, as well as occasional profiles related to travel or outdoors. Self-syndicated weekly to more than 250 newspaper, magazine and online outlets.
NEWS SERVICE/SYNDICATE

Outdoor News Service
T: 1 909 887-3444 **E:** odwriter@verizon.net
W: http://www.outdoornewsservice.com
Editor: Jim Matthews
Editorial Profile: Outdoor News Service offers news about Southern California fishing reports, waterfowl coverage, outdoor packages and columns that are distributed to daily newspapers and Internet sites throughout the region for use on outdoor pages. It is syndicated to about 11 daily papers.
NEWS SERVICE/SYNDICATE

Pacific Perspectives
Editorial: 11372 Bunche Hall, Los Angeles, California 90095-1487. **T:** 1 310 825-9110
W: http://blogs.lmu.edu/asiamedia
Editorial Profile: Discusses news from the Asia Pacific region, as well as all aspects of the media in Asia, including its role in regional and national economies, societies and political debate. Columns are syndicated to several national and international publications including The South China Morning Post, Mainichi Shimbun, the China Times, the Korea Times, the Khaleej Times, the Seattle Times, the San Diego Business Journal and the Straits Times.
NEWS SERVICE/SYNDICATE

Parent to Parent
Editorial: 2464 Taylor Rd, Ste 131, Wildwood, Missouri 63040-1222. **T:** 1 877 236-7793
E: mail2ptp@parenttoparent.com
W: http://www.parenttoparent.com
Editor: Jodie Lynn; **Editor:** Jodie Lynn; **Editor:** Jodie Lynn; **Editor:** Jodie Lynn
Editorial Profile: Parent to Parent is a weekly column that covers parenting, family, health and education, ranging from pre-pregnancy to teens, and up to age 21, as well as products for moms and dads. Annual spring, summer, back to school and holiday gift guides are offered from March 1 to December 13; correlate dates accordingly via season. The column is syndicated nationally and internationally to Canada, Hong Kong and Australia. It also appears in various parenting publications online and in print.
NEWS SERVICE/SYNDICATE

Pilarski, Mark
T: 1 231 499-6919
W: http://www.markpilarski.com
Editorial Profile: Mark Pilarski syndicate offers the Deal Me In weekly column, as well as a host of casino and gambling resources, including additional columns, gaming strategy audio files, quizzes, quotes and various other tips and techniques. It has provided content to media outlets such as Casino City Times, The Detroit News, Reno Gazette Journal, Biloxi Sun Herald, Nevada Appeal, Shreveport Times, Sacramento Bee, Fresno Bee and others.
NEWS SERVICE/SYNDICATE

Plain Label Press
T: 1 636 207-9880
E: lower79124@mypacks.net
W: http://creativeon-line.com/syndicate
Editorial Profile: Plain Label Press is a specialty syndicate serving both print and online publications. It offers a family of humorous features that try and stray from the mainstream.
NEWS SERVICE/SYNDICATE

Platts Global Alert
Owner: McGraw-Hill Companies
Editorial: 2 Penn Plz Fl 25, New York, New York 10121-0101. **T:** 1 212 904-3070
E: releases@platts.com
W: http://www.platts.com
Editorial Profile: Platts Global Alert is an energy news and information provider. It aims to help global energy markets enhance their performance through such offerings as independent industry news and price benchmarks. There are 15 offices worldwide that cover the oil, natural gas, electricity, nuclear power, coal, petrochemical and metals markets.
NEWS SERVICE/SYNDICATE

Platts Global Alert
Owner: McGraw-Hill Companies
Editorial: Heritage Plaza, 1111 Bagby St., Houston, Texas 77002. **T:** 1 713 658-9261
NEWS SERVICE/SYNDICATE

Platts Global Alert
Owner: McGraw-Hill Companies
Editorial: 1200 G St Nw Ste 1000, Washington, District Of Columbia 20005-3845.
T: 1 202 383-2000
Editor: Jasmin Melvin
NEWS SERVICE/SYNDICATE

Platts Global Alert
Owner: McGraw-Hill Companies
T: 44 20 71767000
NEWS SERVICE/SYNDICATE

Polaris Images
Editorial: 259 W 30th St. 14th Floor, New York, New York 10001-2809.
T: 1 212 967-5656
E: team@polarisimages.com
W: http://www.polarisimages.com
Editorial Profile: Polaris Images represents photographers and distributes photographs to media industries worldwide.
NEWS SERVICE/SYNDICATE

Prensa Latina - New York Bureau
Editorial: United Nations, Room L-0240, New York, New York 10017
W: http://www.plenglish.com
Editorial Profile: This is the New York Bureau of Prensa Latina, which is based in Havana, Cuba.
NEWS SERVICE/SYNDICATE

Presbyterian News Service
Editorial: 100 Witherspoon St, Louisville, Kentucky 40202-6300. **T:** 1 502 569-5000
W: http://www.pcusa.org/pcnews

Editor: Jerry Van Marter
Editorial Profile: This is the official news agency of the Presbyterian Church. They gather and disseminate news and information about the denomination and its work to church members, church officials, religious and secular media, and the public. Their editorial freedom allows them to fairly report on all aspects of the church, both good and bad.
NEWS SERVICE/SYNDICATE

Press Associates Union News Service
Editorial: 2605 P St Nw Ste A, Washington, District Of Columbia 20007-5029.
T: 1 202 898-4825
E: paiunionnews@yahoo.com
W: http://www.paiunionnews.com
Editor in Chief: Mark Gruenberg
Editorial Profile: Press Associates Union News Service provides stories and columns that discuss a wide range of work related topics, including Washington politics, policy from labor's view, major court decisions, union activism, economics, job safety and health. It also includes story-related photos and graphics.
NEWS SERVICE/SYNDICATE

Press Trust of India - New York Bureau
Editorial: S 450 United Nations, New York, New York 10017. **T:** 1 212 963-7127
W: http://ptinews.com
NEWS SERVICE/SYNDICATE

Press Trust of India - Washington Bureau
Editorial: 5705 Brewer House Cir Apt 302, Rockville, Maryland 20852-5425.
T: 1 917 817-0859 **W:** http://www.ptinews.com
NEWS SERVICE/SYNDICATE

Project Vision 21
Editorial: 18121 E Hampden Ave 120-C, Aurora, Colorado 80013-3590.
T: 1 720 936-1769
E: info@newsandservices.com
W: http://www.newsandservices.com
Editorial Profile: Project Vision 21 provides daily news and information, in English and in Spanish, about the Hispanic community in Colorado and neighboring states. Its information is used by local, regional and national media outlets. Stories have appeared in at least 30 newspapers in the United States and in several Latin American countries and on at least 45 Web sites. They have also been used by Denver area radio and television stations.
NEWS SERVICE/SYNDICATE

Pulliam Weston, Liz
Editorial: 3940 Laurel Canyon Blvd, Studio City, California 91604-3709
W: http://www.asklizweston.com
Editorial Profile: Liz Pulliam Weston writes a nationally syndicated question and answer column appears in newspapers throughout the country, including the Los Angeles Times, the Palm Beach (FL) Post, the Portland (OR) Oregonian, Stars & Stripes and others.
NEWS SERVICE/SYNDICATE

Punch In International Syndicate
Editorial: 400 E 59th St Apt 9F, New York, New York 10022-2344. **T:** 1 212 755-4363
E: press@punchin.com
W: http://www.punchin.com
Editor: Bob Bowman
Editorial Profile: Punch In International Syndicate features free food, wine, travel and entertainment information to residents in the New York City area as well as nationally and internationally. The Web site has columns on travel, restaurants and Broadway shows, as well as music and movie reviews. It is syndicated electronically to Web sites, radio, newspapers and magazines worldwide.
NEWS SERVICE/SYNDICATE

Purcell, Tom
T: 1 571 216-6265 **E:** tom@tompurcell.com
W: http://www.tompurcell.com
Editorial Profile: Purcell is a self-syndicated humor columnist who touches on the controversies of public policy as well as complications of everyday existence. He offers stories about issues and events, and delivers suggested truths and common sense through satire. The column runs 680 words per week and appears in over a dozen newspapers.
NEWS SERVICE/SYNDICATE

Q Syndicate
Owner: Q Syndicate, LLC

Editorial: 11920 Farmington Rd, Livonia, Michigan 48150-1724. **T:** 1 734 290-7200 22
E: qsyndicate@pridesource.com
W: http://www.qsyndicate.com
Editor: Chris Azzopardi
Editorial Profile: Q Syndicate offers content and community to the gay and lesbian press. Features include travel, entertainment, sports, editorial cartoons, puzzles, movies and more.
NEWS SERVICE/SYNDICATE

Racing Information Service
Editorial: 6141 Sunset Ln, Indianapolis, Indiana 46228-1455. **T:** 1 317 251-4371
W: http://www.ris-news.com
Chicago Bureau Chief: Dave Chess
Editorial Profile: Racing Information Service is the oldest and largest interactive newswire dedicated to motor sports. It covers every form of auto racing and motorcycles worldwide, including NASCAR, Formula One, GP2, Champ Car, IRL, SCCA, Professional Sports Car Racing, AMA, World of Outlaws, USAC, BTCC, FIA GT, IKF and karting. It also provides racing book, software and movie reviews. It serves around 150 newspapers, several magazines and electronic outlets.
NEWS SERVICE/SYNDICATE

Raia, James
Editorial: 122 43rd St, Sacramento, California 95819. **T:** 1 916 455-8389
W: http://www.byjamesraia.com
Editorial Profile: This is a site offering columns about car reviews. Columns are picked up by various media outlets.
NEWS SERVICE/SYNDICATE

Rautzhan, Kendal
Editorial: 118 S 5th St, Lewisburg, Pennsylvania 17837-1810. **T:** 1 570 898 2929
E: kendal@sunlink.net
W: http://www.greatestbooksforkids.com
Editorial Profile: Books to Borrow...Books to Buy is a syndicated weekly column providing parenting and educational tips to get books and kids connected. The primary emphasis stresses the importance of adults reading to children everyday and also providing reflective thought on the role of a parent to a child. The column is followed by children's book reviews. Syndicated to more than 45 newspapers across the country. The companion website, Greatest Books for Kids features numerous additional chidren's book reviews.
NEWS SERVICE/SYNDICATE

Real Estate Matters Syndicate
Editorial: 361 Park Ave Ste 200, Glencoe, Illinois 60022-1585. **T:** 1 847 242-0550
E: thinkglink@aol.com
W: http://www.thinkglink.com
Editorial Profile: This self-syndicated column provides homeowners with the information they need to proceed with confidence when buying, selling, renovating or refinancing their home. It focuses on a wide range of timely national topics, including discrimination, mortgage financing, buyer brokerage, disclosure and property taxes. It appears in more than 30 newspapers.
NEWS SERVICE/SYNDICATE

Red Line Report
Editorial: 11 Patch Ln, Lake Placid, New York 12946-1631. **T:** 1 518 523-4289
E: kyle@redlinereport.com
W: http://redlinereport.com
Editorial Profile: Weekly humorous hockey column that looks at the National Hockey League, Major Junior and International Leagues.
NEWS SERVICE/SYNDICATE

Red Square Media
Editorial: 200 Riverside Blvd Ste 26E, New York, New York 10069-0904
E: info@rsqmc.com
W: http://www.redsquaremediacorp.com
Editorial Profile: Provides American celebrity, fashion, and entertainment news geared towards the Russian market. Features video interviews for television and online, written interviews and stories for online Russian magazine publications. Coverage of red carpet events, charity events and fundraisers, festivals, film premieres and screenings, fashion events, and more. Interviews are done in English and then Russian subtitles or translation is added later.
NEWS SERVICE/SYNDICATE

Reel to Real Celebrity Profiles
Editorial: 8643 N Fielding Rd, Milwaukee, Wisconsin 53217-2427. **T:** 1 414 352-7998
W: http://www.reeltoreal.com
Editor: David Fantle; **Publisher:** Tom Johnson

Editorial Profile: This is a self-syndicated weekly column featuring two-on-one, face-to-face interviews with show business personalities and celebrities. They mainly do in-depth features about those in the entertainment industry. The column runs in dozens of publications throughout the country.
NEWS SERVICE/SYNDICATE

Reinfeld, Hesh
Editorial: 6329 Crombie St, Pittsburgh, Pennsylvania 15217. **T:** 1 412 421-8379
W: http://www.heshreinfeld.com
Editorial Profile: The column aims to tap into readers' sense of humor and retain the respectability of a serious business publication. It is syndicated in the Central New York Business Journal, Las Vegas Business Press and the Treasure Coast Business Journal. The column started in the Central New York Business Journal.
NEWS SERVICE/SYNDICATE

Religion News Service
Owner: Religion News Association
Editorial: 529 14Th St Nw Ste 1009, Washington, District Of Columbia 20045-2001.
T: 1 202 463-8777 **E:** info@religionnews.com
W: http://www.religionnews.com
Editor: Kevin Eckstrom; **Editor:** Kevin Eckstrom; **Editor:** Kevin Eckstrom; **Editor:** Kevin Eckstrom
Editorial Profile: Religion News Service offers news about religion, ethics, spirituality and moral issues. There is a network of correspondents around the world providing news and information on all faiths and religious movements. They hope to provide intelligent, objective coverage of all religions, including Judaism, Christianity, Islam, Asian religions and private spirituality.
NEWS SERVICE/SYNDICATE

Reuters
Owner: Thomson Reuters
Editorial: 3 Times Sq, New York, New York 10036-6564. **T:** 1 646 223-4000
E: nyc.equities.newsroom@news.reuters.com
W: http://www.reuters.com
Stringer: Kathy Finn; **Stringer:** Tim Ghianni
Editorial Profile: Founded in 1851, Reuters offers 24-hour coverage of global happenings for professionals around the world. With 196 editorial bureaus in 130 countries and 2,400 editorial staff members, it covers international news, regional news, politics, social issues, health, business, sports and media. The news service also provides text, graphics, pictures, in-depth news analysis, features and profiles. They also offer a complimentary newsletter, Reuters Washington Extra, that includes the outlet's most popular stories of the day with an introductory from the Washington bureau chief.
NEWS SERVICE/SYNDICATE

Reuters
Editorial: 1 N Dearborn St Ste 500, Chicago, Illinois 60602-4349. **T:** 1 312 408-8500
Bureau Chief: David Greising
NEWS SERVICE/SYNDICATE

Reuters
Editorial: 633 W 5th St, Los Angeles, California 90071-2005. **T:** 1 213 380-2014
Bureau Chief: Ron Grover; **Bureau Chief:** Ron Grover
NEWS SERVICE/SYNDICATE

Reuters
Editorial: 1333 H St NW, Washington, District Of Columbia 20005-4707. **T:** 1 202 898-8300
Bureau Chief: Marilyn Thompson; **News Editor:** Karey Wutkowski
NEWS SERVICE/SYNDICATE

Reuters
Editorial: 1155 Brewery Park Blvd Ste 250, Detroit, Michigan 48207-2640.
T: 1 313 202-6920
E: detroitnewsroom@reuters.com
Bureau Chief: Paul Lienert
NEWS SERVICE/SYNDICATE

Reuters
Editorial: 5201 Blue Lagoon Dr, Miami, Florida 33126-2064. **T:** 1 305 810-2688
E: miami.newsroom@thomsonreuters.com
NEWS SERVICE/SYNDICATE

Reuters
Editorial: 5525 Golden Bear Dr, Overland Park, Kansas 66223-3350. **T:** 1 913 663-2658
NEWS SERVICE/SYNDICATE

Reuters
Editorial: 500 Dallas St, Houston, Texas 77002-4800. **T:** 1 713 210-8500
NEWS SERVICE/SYNDICATE

Reuters
Editorial: 3340 Peachtree Rd NE, Atlanta, Georgia 30326-1023. **T:** 1 404 720-2891
Editorial Profile: The majority of the correspondents from this bureau spend their time on the road. Contact them via email.
NEWS SERVICE/SYNDICATE

Reuters
Editorial: 22 Thomson Pl, Boston, Massachusetts 02210-1212.
T: 1 617 856-4401
NEWS SERVICE/SYNDICATE

Reuters
Editorial: 1351 E Eyre St, Philadelphia, Pennsylvania 19125-3303. **T:** 1 215 922-1086
NEWS SERVICE/SYNDICATE

Reuters
Editorial: 600 University St, Seattle, Washington 98101-1176. **T:** 1 206 674-3531
NEWS SERVICE/SYNDICATE

Reuters
Editorial: 425 Market St Fl 5, San Francisco, California 94105-2403. **T:** 1 415 677-2500
NEWS SERVICE/SYNDICATE

Reuters
T: 27 117753155 **W:** http://af.reuters.com
NEWS SERVICE/SYNDICATE

Reuters
T: 92 51 281-0017
Bureau Chief: Maria Golovnina
NEWS SERVICE/SYNDICATE

Reuters
Editorial: 7500 N Dobson Rd, Scottsdale, Arizona 85256-2718. **T:** 1 866 885-0688
NEWS SERVICE/SYNDICATE

Reuters
T: 966 1 464-1480
NEWS SERVICE/SYNDICATE

Reuters
T: 973 17538111
NEWS SERVICE/SYNDICATE

Reuters
T: 20 2 5577150
Bureau Chief: Michael Georgy
NEWS SERVICE/SYNDICATE

Reuters
T: 965 2243 1920
NEWS SERVICE/SYNDICATE

Reuters
T: 216 7 178-7711 **W:** http://www.reuters.com
Bureau Chief: Christian Lowe
NEWS SERVICE/SYNDICATE

Reuters
Editorial: 401 N Tryon St Suite 264, Charlotte, North Carolina 28202-2196.
T: 1 704 998-2506
NEWS SERVICE/SYNDICATE

Reuters
Editorial: 1750 Creekside Oaks Dr Ste 100, Sacramento, California 95833-3647.
T: 1 916 576-6200
NEWS SERVICE/SYNDICATE

Reuters
Editorial: 1601 Elm St, Dallas, Texas 75201-4701. **T:** 1 214 953-0001
NEWS SERVICE/SYNDICATE

Reuters - United Nations Bureau
Editorial: United Nations #C-316, New York, New York 10017. **T:** 1 212 355-7424
Bureau Chief: Patrick Worsnip
Editorial Profile: This bureau is based at the United Nations.
NEWS SERVICE/SYNDICATE

Reuters America
Owner: Thomson Reuters
Editorial: 3 Times Sq, New York, New York 10036-6564. **T:** 1 646 223-4000
W: http://www.thomsonreuters.com
Editorial Profile: Reuters America serves as a domestic news and information service. If provides state-by-state general and political news. Other topics covered include

professional and college sports, business news and financial data as well as entertainment, lifestyle and feature stories. Its launch was announced in mid-December 2010.
NEWS SERVICE/SYNDICATE

Reuters Health Information
Owner: Thomson Reuters
Editorial: 3 Times Sq, New York, New York 10036-6564. **T:** 1 646 223-4716
E: healtheditor@thomsonreuters.com
W: http://www.reutershealth.com
Editorial Profile: Reuters Health provides medical and healthcare news. They try to offer unbiased, authoritative, timely and dependable news. They use an international staff from bureaus around the world to produce stories for their three news wires: Reuters Health eLine, Reuters Medical News and Reuters Health Industry Briefing. Pitches should be sent via the main e-mail. They ask that PR professionals not pitch them via phone.
NEWS SERVICE/SYNDICATE

Reuters Life!
Editorial: 3 Times Sq, New York, New York 10036. **T:** 1 646 223-4000
Editorial Profile: Reuters Life! is a wire of lifestyle stories that covers news and trends in the fields of entertainment, celebrities, leisure, lifestyles, health, the environment and odd news. It carries approximately 60 stories a day, about 20 of which are exclusive to Reuters Life! clients.
NEWS SERVICE/SYNDICATE

Rex Features
Editorial: 316 N Labrea Ave, Los Angeles, California 90036. **T:** 1 323 954-8400
W: http://www.rexusa.com
Editorial Profile: This is the Los Angeles bureau of Rex Features. It serves as a photo press agency and also offers feature articles on various topics including travel, human interest, animals, science and technology, general interest and offbeat news.
NEWS SERVICE/SYNDICATE

Rinker, Harry
Editorial: 22 Stillwater Cir, Brookfield, Connecticut 06804-1146. **T:** 1 484 695-5628
W: http://www.harryrinker.com
Editorial Profile: This is a self-syndicated Q&A column focusing on collectibles made after 1920 and offers appraisal and consulting advice in the antiques and collectibles field. It attempts to offer the widest range of antiques and collectibles informational services possible. The column appears in more than 10 publications nationwide.
NEWS SERVICE/SYNDICATE

Risk & Compliance Journal
Owner: News Corporation Ltd.
Editorial: 1211 Avenue of the Americas, New York, New York 10036-8701
E: riskjournal@wsj.com
W: http://online.wsj.com/public/page/risk-compliance-journal.html
Editor: Ben DiPietro
Editorial Profile: Risk & Compliance Journal is a News and Information Service that provides news coverage of a wide span of governance, risk and compliance issues, including analysis of laws and regulations, the risks of global market and trademark expansion, and practical guidance on how companies and corporate boards can uphold their corporate reputations.
NEWS SERVICE/SYNDICATE

Robertson Treatment
Editorial: 1750 Powder Springs Rd SW, Marietta, Georgia 30064-4850.
T: 1 323 878-2399
E: gilspeaks@robertsontreatment.com
W: http://www.robertsontreatment.com
Editor: Gil Robertson
Editorial Profile: Robertson Treatment takes an in-depth look at the entertainment community and travel and concentrates on breakthrough African American artists, as well as issues affecting people of color in the entertainment world. The column is syndicated throughout the country to over 30 African American news weeklies and has a readership around 3 million.
NEWS SERVICE/SYNDICATE

Roll Call Report Syndicate
Editorial: 1822 Corcoran St NW, Washington, District Of Columbia 20009-1608.
T: 1 202 667-9760
W: http://www.rollcallvotes.com
Editorial Profile: Roll Call Report Syndicate syndicate provides congressional voting reports to U.S. newspapers and online media. They want to help constituents track federal lawmakers' votes and hold them accountable for their stands. They provide coverage that voters, political reporters, editorial boards, activist groups and others can use to monitor the beliefs and goals of their representatives and senators. It was founded in July 1973. They do not want to be contacted.
NEWS SERVICE/SYNDICATE

Roth Content Services
T: 1 414 455-2091 **E:** info@rothcontent.com
W: http://rothcontent.com
Editor: Jay Roth; **Editor:** Jay Roth; **Editor:** Jay Roth; **Editor:** Jay Roth
Editorial Profile: Roth Content Services provides publications with small to medium circulations with up-to-date reviews focusing on business and technology products, services, books as well as specialty content on a contracted basis.
NEWS SERVICE/SYNDICATE

Saddle Ridge Communications
T: 1 304 686-2630
Editorial Profile: Weekly columns, which are syndicated to 20 newspapers, cover anecdotes, information and occasional commentaries on conservation issues, ecology and the environment, natural wildlife history and back-to-nature travel destinations.
NEWS SERVICE/SYNDICATE

Saenger Syndicate
Editorial: 2121 Star Ln, Alpine, California 91901-2868. **T:** 1 619 445-4105
E: editor@reviewexpress.com
W: http://www.classicmovieguide.com
Editor: Diana Saenger
Editorial Profile: Founded in 1990, Saenger Syndicate offers reviews of film, books and DVDs and celebrity interviews appear in print and online media of weekly and monthly publications. They cover all markets, from children to adults.
NEWS SERVICE/SYNDICATE

Sallan, Bruce
Editorial: 1317 Santa Barbara St, Santa Barbara, California 93101-2016.
T: 1 818 648-0748 **E:** bruce@brucesallan.com
W: http://www.brucesallan.com
Editorial Profile: Bruce Sallan is a self-syndicated columnist who focuses on fatherhood and single-parent issues ranging from teen parenting to dating.
NEWS SERVICE/SYNDICATE

Salon Media Group
Editorial: 870 Market St Ste 528, San Francisco, California 94102-3023.
T: 1 415 645-9200 **E:** editorial@salon.com
W: http://www.salon.com
Editor: Andrew Leonard
Editorial Profile: Offers syndication of Salon.com's daily articles. Subscribers can access 6-12 stories a day, six days a week. Coverage includes breaking news, lifestyles, entertainment, business, books, technology, health, politics, gossip, sports, culture and more.
NEWS SERVICE/SYNDICATE

Saudi Press Agency
Editorial: 601 New Hampshire Ave NW, Washington, District Of Columbia 20037.
T: 1 800 453-3177
E: news@saudipressagency.com
W: http://www.spa.gov.sa/english
Bureau Chief: Naila Al-Sowayel
Editorial Profile: This is the Washington bureau for the Saudi Press Agency and is the main bureau for the service's coverage of the United States.
NEWS SERVICE/SYNDICATE

Saudi Press Agency
Editorial: 405 E 42nd St, United Nations Rm S-301, New York, New York 10017.
T: 1 212 308-2412
Editorial Profile: This is the United Nations bureau of the Saudi Press Agency.
NEWS SERVICE/SYNDICATE

Savvy Senior
T: 1 405 360-4228 **E:** editor@savvysenior.org
W: http://www.savvysenior.org
Editor: Jim Miller
Editorial Profile: Savvy Senior is a nationally syndicated newspaper column that offers valuable resources to seniors and the families who support them. It also provides tips and information through a resource book, a weekly radio show and regular television features on PBS, CNN Headline Newsand the NBC Today show. The column started in 2002 and now has more than 400 daily newspapers and other clients.
NEWS SERVICE/SYNDICATE

Selacia
Editorial: 171 Pier Ave, Santa Monica, California 90405-5311. **T:** 1 310 915-2884
W: http://www.selacia.com
Editorial Profile: This is a self-syndicated feature column focusing on alternative health, personal growth, lifestyle issues, technology, spirituality, social issues and female empowerment. Her features appear in numerous publications, including Mount Shasta Magazine, Let's Live, Cosmic Link, Whole Life Times and Whole Life News. She also reviews books and Web sites on spirituality and personal growth.
NEWS SERVICE/SYNDICATE

Senior Wire News Service
Editorial: 2377 Elm St, Denver, Colorado 80207. **T:** 1 303 355-3882
E: clearmountain@tde.com
W: http://www.seniorwire.net
Editorial Profile: Started in 1990, Senior Wire News Service offers content aimed specifically at mature publications and readers. It provides senior and boomer-oriented news, including features, health, psychology, sports, beauty, humor, travel and grandparenting. Topics include legislation, health, finances, travel, aging, commentary and advice. Stories appear in publications across the United States, Canada and Mumbai, India. Primary topics should include: legislation, health, finances, travel and aging gracefully commentary and advice.
NEWS SERVICE/SYNDICATE

Smoots, Elizabeth
Editorial: 5735 27th Ave NE, Seattle, Washington 98105-5511. **T:** 1 206 434-2173
E: doctor@practicalprevention.com
W: http://www.practicalprevention.com
Editorial Profile: Practical Prevention provides sensible tips to help readers of all ages stay healthy. The 600-word weekly column is available in a variety of engaging formats and focuses on healthy lifestyles, not disease treatment.
NEWS SERVICE/SYNDICATE

So It Goes
Editorial: 165 N 5th St, Apt 208, Port Hueneme, California 93041. **T:** 1 805 236-3746
W: http://www.jasonlove.com
Editorial Profile: Jason Love provides a weekly humor column to publications and Web sites nationwide. The column, which grew out of Love's stand-up comedy and cartoons, won an award from the National Society of Newspaper Columnists.
NEWS SERVICE/SYNDICATE

South Florida News Service
Owner: Florida International University
Editorial: School of Journalism and Mass Com, Florida International University, 3000 NE 151st St, North Miami, Florida 33181.
T: 1 305 919-5624
W: http://journalism.FIU.edu
News Editor: Allan Richards
Editorial Profile: Launched in January 2009, South Florida News Service provides local South Florida news, written by journalism students at Florida International University. Content is provided to the Sun Sentinel, The Miami Herald, The Palm Beach Post and The Scripps Treasure Coast newspapers in Stuart.
NEWS SERVICE/SYNDICATE

Southern California Focus
Editorial: 1720 Oak St, Santa Monica, Los Angeles, California 90405-4804.
T: 1 310 452-3918 **E:** tdelias@aol.com
Editor: Thomas Elias; **Editor:** Thomas Elias
Editorial Profile: Southern California Focus offers commentary on public affairs and any issue that affects California: political, business, economical, ecological, science, books, education, transportation, etc. Syndicated bi-weekly to 94 newspapers.
NEWS SERVICE/SYNDICATE

Southern Ohio News Media
Editorial: 9935 Fite Ave, Hamersville, Ohio 45130-8792. **T:** 1 513 317-8430
E: southernohionews@aol.com
Editor: Matt Ernst
Editorial Profile: Launched in 2008, Southern Ohio News Media covers Southern Ohio, Northern Kentucky and Southeastern Indiana.
NEWS SERVICE/SYNDICATE

Splash Newswire
Owner: Corbis Corporation
Editorial: 333 Washington Blvd, Ste 508, Marina del Rey, California 90292-5136.
T: 1 310 821-2666
E: newsdesk@splashnews.com
W: http://www.splashnews.com
Editorial Profile: Offers photos of celebrity sightings with commentary. Its main offices are based in London.
NEWS SERVICE/SYNDICATE

Sports Advisor Features
Owner: Trius Publishing, Inc.
T: 1 619 825-9770
E: drpete@drpeteandersen.com
W: http://www.drpeteandersen.com
Editorial Profile: Sports Advisor Features is a news service providing sports advice and information. It includes information and features about how to use mental skills training to enhance physical and academic performance.
NEWS SERVICE/SYNDICATE

The Sports Network
Owner: Sports Network (The)
Editorial: 2200 Byberry Rd Ste 200, Hatboro, Pennsylvania 19040-3739. **T:** 1 215 441-8444
E: comments@sportsnetwork.com
W: http://www.sportsnetwork.com
Editorial Profile: The Sports Network is a sports news and information Web site for sports fans. The site offers up-to-the minute news and scores, pre- and post-game reports, analysis, features, league, team, individual player and associated other statistics, injuries, odds and weather reports. It provides live coverage of the NBA, MLB, NHL, NFL, golf, soccer, tennis, auto racing and horse racing.
NEWS SERVICE/SYNDICATE

Starcott Media Services
Editorial: 6906 Royalgreen Dr, Cincinnati, Hamilton, Ohio 45244-4004.
T: 1 513 231-6034 **E:** contact@dulley.com
W: http://www.dulley.com
Editorial Profile: Started in 1982, and syndicated to over 400 newspapers and magazines, this Q&A column covers a broad range of money-saving topics, including air conditioning units, furnaces, fireplaces, energy-efficient light bulbs, solar window heaters, water conservation, geodesic dome homes, refrigerators and landscaping. There is detailed information about a variety of topics but presented in a way that average readers can understand.
NEWS SERVICE/SYNDICATE

Stark's News Service
Owner: J-C Communications Co., Inc.
Editorial: 318 W Adams St Ste 1406, Chicago, Illinois 60606-5173. **T:** 1 312 236-5122
E: sns@starks-news.com
W: http://www.starks-news.com
Editorial Profile: Stark's News Service is a source of late-breaking news, statistics and up-to-the-minute market outlooks about cars, trucks, farm and construction machinery. The features focus on the business of production, sales and inventory and are published twice a month in the newsletter.
NEWS SERVICE/SYNDICATE

State House News Service
Editorial: State House, Rm 458, Boston, Massachusetts 2133. **T:** 1 617 722-2439
E: news@statehousenews.com
W: http://www.statehousenews.com
Editor: Michael Norton
Editorial Profile: State House News Service offers daily coverage of the legislative happenings on Beacon Hill. It offers news without a political slant or bias. Stories appear in papers throughout Massachusetts, including the Massachusetts Institute for a New Commonwealth, which jointly operates the 02133.org Web site.
NEWS SERVICE/SYNDICATE

State Net
Editorial: 2101 K St, Sacramento, California 95816-4920. **T:** 1 916 444-0840
E: info@statenet.com
W: http://www.statenet.com
Editor: Rich Ehisen
Editorial Profile: State Net offers data, legislative intelligence and in-depth reporting for people who care about the actions of government. It monitors every bill in the 50 states, District of Columbia, Congress and every state agency regulation.
NEWS SERVICE/SYNDICATE

Steyn, Mark
E: mailbox@steynonline.com
W: http://www.steynonline.com
Editorial Profile: This column covers politics, arts and culture and can be read each week throughout much of the English-speaking world. In the United States, his column appears in newspapers from The Washington Times to The Evening Bulletin in Philadelphia, The Orange County Register in California to Black & White in Birmingham, Alabama. It also appears in The Jerusalem Post, The Australian, Investigate and Hawke's Bay Today in New Zealand; and more occasionally in The Wall Street Journal and (translated into Italian) Il Foglio.
NEWS SERVICE/SYNDICATE

Stoneberg, Diana
Editorial: 417 N 10Th St, Grover Beach, California 93433-1745. **T:** 1 805 801-0915
E: info@gadgetgrrl.com
W: http://www.gadgetgrrl.com
Editorial Profile: The service presents technology in a fun and entertaining way, including the latest technologies, games, electronics, appliances, toys, music, MP3, consumer electronics, wireless devices and the Internet. The author looks at all the latest and biggest technology gadgets. Her columns run both online, including TheStreet.com and housekeeping channel.com, as well as in print with a circulation of about 3 million readers. Gadget Grrl is appears on TV News and Talk Shows featuring the latest consumer electronics services and apps. She also hosts a daily podcast.
NEWS SERVICE/SYNDICATE

The Straight Dope
Owner: Atalaya Capital Management
Editorial: 11 E Illinois St, Chicago, Illinois 60611. **T:** 1 312 828-0350
W: http://www.straightdope.com
Editorial Profile: The Straight Dope is a nationally distributed column and newsletter that answers questions about scientific phenomena and complicated or interesting questions. It appears mostly in alternative weekly newspapers.
NEWS SERVICE/SYNDICATE

Strange But True
Editorial: 1237 Rae Rd, Lyndhurst, Ohio 44124-1409. **T:** 1 440 460-0330
E: strangetrue@cs.com
Editorial Profile: Strange But True is a self-syndicated lifestyle or magazine column featuring strange but true stories. It has been syndicated to more than 75 papers on six continents. Each column features questions submitted by readers that are answered by the writers. Its focus is to provide readers answers to everything you wondered about (and some things you never wanted to know).
NEWS SERVICE/SYNDICATE

Suddenly Senior
Editorial: 2431 Canadian Way, Apt 21, Clearwater, Florida 33763. **T:** 1 727 726-0066
E: suddenlysenior@gmail.com
W: http://www.suddenlysenior.com
Editorial Profile: This is a seniors column for everyone over 50 who feels too young to be getting old. It includes humor, nostalgia, health and senior advocacy news. The Web site strives to be the most trusted senior site on the Internet. It is syndicated to over 84 newspapers with a combined circulation of 3.1 million.
NEWS SERVICE/SYNDICATE

Sun-Times Media Wire
Editorial: 350 N Orleans St, Chicago, Illinois 60654-1975. **T:** 1 312 321-2147
E: wire@suntimes.com
Editor: Jeff Mayes
Editorial Profile: Sun-Times Media Wire is a service launched by the Chicago Sun-Times. It delivers news and notices from organizations to print and electronic media serving the area. It serves as a hub for consideration of releases, meeting notices, event announcements and other important information. It specializes in breaking news in and around Chicago 24 hours per day.
NEWS SERVICE/SYNDICATE

Talk Radio News Service
Editorial: 236 Massachusetts Ave Ne Ste 306, Washington, District Of Columbia 20002-4980.
T: 1 202 337-5322
E: bookings@talkradionews.com
W: http://www.talkradionews.com
Bureau Chief: Ellen Ratner
Editorial Profile: Talk Radio News Service is a news booking and host service dedicated to serving the talk radio community. It provides local talk radio stations, producers, hosts and their listeners with up-to-date information and behind the scenes scoops from the nation's capitol.
NEWS SERVICE/SYNDICATE

The Talk Radio News Service
Editorial: 1 United Nations Plz Floor 2Ndl-241, New York, New York 10017-3514.
T: 1 212 715-0830
Editorial Profile: This is the United Nations bureau for Talk Radio News Service.
NEWS SERVICE/SYNDICATE

The Talk Radio News Service
Editorial: 1120 Avenue Of The Americas Fl 13, New York, New York 10036-6700.
T: 1 212 993-5899 2000
Bureau Chief: Ari Zoldan
Editorial Profile: This is the New York, NY bureau.
NEWS SERVICE/SYNDICATE

Targeted News Service
Editorial: 7723 Harwood Pl, Springfield, Virginia 22152. **T:** 1 703 304-1897
E: editor@targetednews.com
W: http://www.targetednews.com
Editor: Myron Struck
Editorial Profile: Targeted News Service is an editorial services company providing focused news products. It offers a wide range of news and support services to newspapers. The news service assists in gathering a wide range of raw government and congressional documents documents and makes that information available directly to newspapers and other end-users in a targeted manner.
NEWS SERVICE/SYNDICATE

This is True
Owner: This is True Inc.
T: 1 970 626-6030
W: http://www.thisistrue.com
Editorial Profile: This is True provides humorous commentary on the news and reports on bizarre-but-true news items from legitimate printed news sources from around the world.
NEWS SERVICE/SYNDICATE

This Side of 60
T: 1 316 283-2309 **E:** thisside60@cox.net
W: http://www.visit-snider.com
Editorial Profile: This Side of 60 is an upbeat column focusing on empowerment in aging for readers 40 and up. An award-winning healthcare writer, her column appears in 50 papers in 40 states.
NEWS SERVICE/SYNDICATE

Trade News Service
Editorial: 3701 State Route 21, Canandaigua, New York 14424-9020. **T:** 1 585 396-0027
E: tns@rochester.rr.com
W: http://www.fats-and-oils.com
Editor: Dennis Maxfield; **Editor:** Dennis Maxfield; **Editor:** Dennis Maxfield
Editorial Profile: Weekly information service for producers, traders and consumers of edible and inedible fats and oils. Included are price histories, import/export data and numerous news and statistical reports for the trade.
NEWS SERVICE/SYNDICATE

Travel Arts Syndicate
Editorial: 377 Rector Pl, Apt 10H, New York, New York 10280-1436. **T:** 1 212 807-7509
E: travelarts1@aol.com
W: http://www.travelartssyndicate.com
Editor in Chief: Terese Loeb Kreuzer
Editorial Profile: The Travel Arts Syndicate provides edited, fact-checked, camera ready copy from some of the world's most experienced travel writers.
NEWS SERVICE/SYNDICATE

Travels with Lonely Planet
Owner: Lonely Planet Publications
Editorial: 150 Linden St, Oakland, California 94607-2538. **T:** 1 510 250-6400
E: pressusa@lonelyplanet.com
W: http://www.lonelyplanet.com
Editorial Profile: Travels with Lonely Planet is a syndicated column offering travel information and destinations from around the world. It runs in media outlets around the world and its columns are pulled from its pool of authors.
NEWS SERVICE/SYNDICATE

Tribune Content Agency
Owner: Tribune Company
Editorial: 435 N Michigan Ave Ste 1400, Chicago, Illinois 60611-7551.
T: 1 312 222-4444
W: http://www.tmsfeatures.com
Editorial Profile: Tribune Content Agency is a leading media content company that provides syndicated information and entertainment products to print, electronic and on-air media worldwide. It is a subsidiary of Tribune Company.
NEWS SERVICE/SYNDICATE

Tribune Content Agency
Editorial: 40 Media Dr, Queensbury, New York 12804-4086. **T:** 1 518 792-9914
NEWS SERVICE/SYNDICATE

Tribune Content Agency - Specialty Products
Owner: Tribune Company
Editorial: 435 N Michigan Ave Ste 1400, Chicago, Illinois 60611-7551.
T: 1 312 527-8200
W: http://www.tmsspecialtyproducts.com
Editorial Profile: Tribune Content Agency - Specialty Products writes, designs and edits print content for newspaper classified and editorial special sections. It offers single stories, as well as complete advertorial sections. Niche content is created to target specific demographics, readers and advertisers. Employment and careers, entertainment and lifestyles packages are published weekly, and dozens of topic-specific special sections are available annually, quarterly or by request.
NEWS SERVICE/SYNDICATE

Tribune Washington News Bureau
Owner: Tribune Company
Editorial: 1090 Vermont Ave NW, Washington, District Of Columbia 20005-4905.
T: 1 202 824-8200
Bureau Chief: David Lauter; **Editor:** Edmund Sanders
Editorial Profile: Serves as the Washington bureau for all Tribune Company newspapers.
NEWS SERVICE/SYNDICATE

Triv Guy
Editorial: 282 Spring Dr, Spartanburg, South Carolina 29302-3248. **T:** 1 864 621-7129
E: trivia@writeme.com
W: http://www.holytrivia.com
Editorial Profile: The column started in 1999. Wilson Casey, a Guiness World Record holder also known as the Triv Guy, provides topical multiple choice trivia questions and answers. His column runs seven times a week, 365 days a year. He writes a biblical trivia column once a week; the other six days, the column features trivia of a general nature. It is syndicated in over 500 newspapers.
NEWS SERVICE/SYNDICATE

TV Times/New England Motorsports Syndication
Editorial: 27 Bayberry Dr Apt 2, Sharon, Massachusetts 02067-1334.
T: 1 781 784-7857
W: http://www.enterprisenews.com/tracktalk
Editor: Lou Modestino; **Editor:** Lou Modestino; **Editor:** Lou Modestino; **Editor:** Lou Modestino
Editorial Profile: Serves as a source of motorsport news including listings of all weekend activities on television, cable and satellite channels. The columns are sent out weekly via e-mail. Off-season coverage includes new drivers and products, as well as the latest motorsport gossip. New England racing and schedules are included and cover what's happening in New England year-round.
NEWS SERVICE/SYNDICATE

U-Bild Newspaper Features
Editorial: 3800 Oceanic Dr, Ste 107, Oceanside, California 92056-5836.
T: 1 818 785-6368 **W:** http://www.u-bild.com
Editor: Jeffrey Reeves
Editorial Profile: Founded in 1948, U-Bild Newspaper Features offers woodworking plans that are ideal for woodworkers and do-it-yourselfers of all skill levels. The unique trace, saw and assemble designs feature simple-to-follow patterns that allow even beginners to achieve professional results. The column is syndicated to about 200 newspapers.
NEWS SERVICE/SYNDICATE

UKOPIA
Editorial: 3325 Wilshire Blvd, Suite 1238, Los Angeles, California 90010. **T:** 1 213 386-7755
E: info@ukopia.com
W: http://www.ukopia.com
Editorial Profile: Provides current events and news for Koreans living in the United States. Also features information on sports, politics, economy, lifestyle, entertainment and education.
NEWS SERVICE/SYNDICATE

United Methodist News Service
Editorial: 810 12th Ave S, Nashville, Tennessee 37203. **T:** 1 615 742-5470
E: newsdesk@umcom.org
W: http://umns.umc.org
Editorial Profile: Founded in 1940, United Methodist News Service gathers news about the United Methodist Church for dissemination to the religious and secular media. It seeks to assure that the United Methodist Church is reflected in the media as fairly and accurately as possible.
NEWS SERVICE/SYNDICATE

United Nations News Service
Editorial: Office of the Spokesman/Sec General, United Nations S-378, New York, New York 10017. **T:** 1 212 963-7162
E: inquiries@un.org
W: http://www.un.org/news
Editorial Profile: United Nations News Service provides current information on the office of the Secretary General and United Nations missions around the globe. Updates are available in English, French, Spanish, Chinese and Russian. They do NOT want to be contacted.
NEWS SERVICE/SYNDICATE

United Press International
Owner: News World Communications, Inc.
Editorial: 1133 19th St NW, Washington, District Of Columbia 20036-3604.
T: 1 202 898-8000 **E:** nationaldesk@upi.com
W: http://www.upi.com
Editorial Profile: United Press International, since 1907, has been a leading provider of critical information to media outlets, businesses, governments and researchers worldwide. Covering a wide range of topics, UPI's journalists provide in-depth reports and analysis of global issues affecting business and policy decisions, short news bulletins, and a headline service. Products include original content in English, Spanish and Arabic text and photos. Headquarters are in Washington, with offices in Hong Kong; London; Santiago, Chile; Seoul, South Korea; and Tokyo.
NEWS SERVICE/SYNDICATE

United Press International
Editorial: 25348 Via Pacifica, Valencia, California 91355-2634. **T:** 1 661 670-8023
Editorial Profile: This is the West Coast bureau of United Press International. All releases should be in the form of email and sent to the News Editor.
NEWS SERVICE/SYNDICATE

Universal Uclick
Owner: Andrews McMeel Universal
Editorial: 1130 Walnut St, Kansas City, Jackson, Missouri 64106-2109.
T: 1 816 581-7300 **E:** press@amuniversal.com
W: http://universaluclick.com
Editor: Lee Salem
Editorial Profile: Universal Uclick offers a lineup of features, from insightful and provocative commentary to useful and delightful lifestyle, consumer and entertainment information, advice and opinion on a wide range of topics including: parenting, advice, food and recipes, fashion, healthcare, computers, home remodeling, business, personal finance, entertainment and travel, plus comic strips, comic panels and editorial cartoons.
NEWS SERVICE/SYNDICATE

University of Miami News Service
Editorial: 5100 Brunson Dr, Coral Gables, Florida 33146-2413. **T:** 1 305 284-6943
Editorial Profile: University of Miami News Service is run by the University of Miami School of Communication. Student reporters cover news features in South Florida, including sports events and business news.
NEWS SERVICE/SYNDICATE

USA Today Sports Images
Owner: Gannett Co., Inc.
Editorial: 1440 Broadway, New York, New York 10018-2301. **T:** 1 646 937-5480
E: info@usatodaysportsimages.com
W: http://www.usatodaysportsimages.com
Editorial Profile: USA Today Sports Images is a global leader in premium digital media content creation and distribution to media companies worldwide. It offers some of the industry's premium sports content to exceed the demand of the digital media world's ever changing needs. Its content is distributed on deadline for editorial usage and accessed via their Web site or direct wire feed to our creative professional clients.

NEWS SERVICE/SYNDICATE

Veterinary Information Network News Service
Owner: Veterinary Information Network, Inc.
Editorial: 777 W Covell Blvd, Davis, California 95616-5916. **T:** 1 530 756-4881
E: news@vin.com **W:** http://news.vin.com
Editor: Jennifer Fetterman
Editorial Profile: News wire focusing on veterinary news.
NEWS SERVICE/SYNDICATE

Vietnam News Agency - United Nations Bureau
Editorial: Room C-319, United Nations, New York, New York 10017. **T:** 1 212 963-7616
Editorial Profile: This is the United Nations bureau of the Vietnam News Agency, which is based in Hanoi, Vietnam.
NEWS SERVICE/SYNDICATE

The Washington Post Writers Group
Owner: Washington Post Co.
Editorial: 1150 15th St NW, Washington, District Of Columbia 20071-0001.
T: 1 202 334-6375
W: http://www.postwritersgroup.com
Editorial Profile: The Washington Post Writers Group provides features with an emphasis on national and international political and social commentary with both liberal and conservative viewpoints. General features cover personal finance, book reviews, real estate and movie reviews.
NEWS SERVICE/SYNDICATE

Western News Service
Editorial: 866 Oneonta Dr, Los Angeles, California 90065-4125. **T:** 1 323 256-3625
E: jim.thompson@wnsnews.com
Editorial Profile: Western News Service offers information about national and international news, travel features and technology. It is used by more than 35 newspapers and 350 radio stations.
NEWS SERVICE/SYNDICATE

Whitegate Features Syndicate
Editorial: 71 Faunce Dr, Providence, Rhode Island 2906. **T:** 1 401 274-2149
Editorial Profile: Founded in 1988, Whitegate Features Syndicate offers feature columns on a variety of topics, including food, wine, gardening, beauty, entertainment, fashion, dining, home decorating, lifestyle issues, health and travel. It also provides reviews of books, software and music CDs. Articles are syndicated to more than 200 newspapers around the world.
NEWS SERVICE/SYNDICATE

Williams, Armstrong
Editorial: 201 Massachusetts Ave NE, Ste C-1, Washington, District Of Columbia 20002-4988.
T: 1 202 546-5400 **E:** arightside@aol.com
W: http://www.armstrongwilliams.com
Editorial Profile: This self-syndicated column provides intelligent and value-oriented commentary on American culture and politics with a reputation for taking tough political issues and making them personal for its readers. It is from a conservative and Christian perspective.
NEWS SERVICE/SYNDICATE

Winning Investing
Editorial: 411 Palmer Ave, Aptos, California 95003-5209. **T:** 1 831 685-1932
E: wisales@winninginvesting.com
W: http://www.winninginvesting.com
Editorial Profile: Winning Investing describes how professionals employ fundamental analysis strategies to pinpoint the best stocks and mutual funds.
NEWS SERVICE/SYNDICATE

WireImage
Editorial: 75 Varick St, 5th Fl, New York, New York 10013-1917. **T:** 1 646 613-5580
E: nydesk@wireimage.com
W: http://www.wireimage.com
Editor: Pancho Bernasconi
Editorial Profile: WireImage is a photography news service reaching professional publishing, broadcast and online media. They also provide photo and press release distribution through other newswires, including the Associated Press, Reuters Pictures, Business Wire, Gannett News Service and The New York Times News Service. Photos can be delivered to either a broad or targeted list of media outlets.
NEWS SERVICE/SYNDICATE

WireImage
Editorial: 6300 Wilshire Blvd, 16th Floor, Los Angeles, California 90048-5204.
T: 1 323 202-4101 **E:** ladesk@wireimage.com
W: http://www.wireimage.com
Editorial Profile: Wire Image is a top ranking digital photo agency and wire service for entertainment photography.
NEWS SERVICE/SYNDICATE

WorkWise
Editorial: 1284 Main St, Crete, Illinois 60417-2145 **E:** culp@workwise.net
W: http://www.workwise.net
Editorial Profile: WorkWise offers two syndicated columns:The WorkWise commentary, syndicated since 1994, covers emerging trends in the workplace, on-the-job issues, job hunting and small business. The job-hunting Work Wise Interactive, syndicated since 2004, features two Q&As with lighthearted BlogTips, to which sources contribute humorous information about the job-hunting process. Both columns have appeared in publications and broadcasts such as The Modesto Bee, The Fresno Bee, The Miami Herald, The Hartford Courant, The San Antonio Express-News, The Houston Chronicle, The Roanoke Times, the Northwest Indiana Times and The Stamford Advocate.
NEWS SERVICE/SYNDICATE

World Features Syndicate
Editorial: 5842 Sagebrush Rd, La Jolla, San Diego, California 92037. **T:** 1 858 456-6215
E: info@worldfeaturessyndicate.com
W: http://www.worldfeaturessyndicate.com
Editor: Ronald Sataloff
Editorial Profile: World Features Syndicate distributes quick-hitting, themed lists of off-beat information, usually two to four column inches. The columns cover a number of topics: sports, music, general interest, business, history and animals.
NEWS SERVICE/SYNDICATE

World News Syndicate, Ltd.
Owner: Lane (Nancy)
Editorial: 519 Alameda St, Altadena, Los Angeles, California 91001-2904.
T: 1 323 469-2333
Editor: Nancy Lane
Editorial Profile: World News Syndicate provides information and reviews of new music, books, CDs, DVDs as well as political, automotive, religious and health and beauty topics. Also, features news and gossip from Hollywood and the film world. Monthly columns are sent to roughly 164 smaller newspapers across the country and Canada including minority publications. Will be launching a travel and entertainment supplement and website in July 2013.
NEWS SERVICE/SYNDICATE

WorldWatch Affairs Syndicate
Editorial: 14421 Charter Rd, Jamaica, Queens, New York 11435-6386. **T:** 1 718 591-7246
E: jjmcolumn@att.net
Editor: John Metzler; **Editor:** John Metzler;
Editor: John Metzler
Editorial Profile: WorldWatch Affairs Syndicate is a weekly roundup of key diplomatic, defense and developmental issues filed from the United Nations and abroad. Self-syndicated to 16 newspapers and premium Web sites.
NEWS SERVICE/SYNDICATE

World-Wire
Editorial: 620 Vineyard, Suite 303, Seattle, Washington 98110. **T:** 1 800 637-3178
W: http://www.world-wire.com
Editor in Chief: Sunny Lewis
Editorial Profile: World-Wire provides press releases from environmentally relevant organizations and corporations that keeps readers up to date on this fast-changing field.
NEWS SERVICE/SYNDICATE

Xinhua News Agency - Los Angeles Bureau
Editorial: 66 W La Sierra Dr, Arcadia, California 91007. **T:** 1 626 202-8227
W: http://www.xinhuanet.com
Editorial Profile: This is the Los Angeles bureau of the news agency, which is based in China and covers international and political news.
NEWS SERVICE/SYNDICATE

Xinhua News Agency - New York Bureau
Editorial: 1540 Broadway, 44th Floor, New York, New York 10036-4039.
T: 1 718 335-8388 **E:** xinhua.ny@gmail.com
W: http://www.xinhuanet.com/english/
Bureau Chief: Zeng Hu
Editorial Profile: Xinhua News Agency is based in China and covers international and political news.
NEWS SERVICE/SYNDICATE

Xinhua News Agency - United Nations Bureau
Editorial: Room L-238, UN Headquarters, New York, New York 10017
W: http://www.xinhuanet.com/english
Bureau Chief: Zhenqiu Gu
Editorial Profile: This is the United Nations bureau of the Xinhua News Agnecy based in Beijing.
NEWS SERVICE/SYNDICATE

Xinhua News Agency - Washington, DC Bureau
Editorial: 529 14th St NW Ste F2, Washington, District Of Columbia 20045-1207.
T: 1 202 661-8181
NEWS SERVICE/SYNDICATE

Zimmerman, Sandy
T: 1 702 731-6491
E: sandyzimm2003@yahoo.com
W: http://www.discovertheultimate.com
Editorial Profile: Zimmerman writes the Best in Las Vegas and Best in the World columns, covering Shows, Entertainment, Dining, Spas, Famous Chefs, Openings, Interviews and Reviews. She is syndicated with over 1,000 newspapers and magazines around the world.
NEWS SERVICE/SYNDICATE

Zuma Press
Editorial: 408 N El Camino Real, San Clemente, California 92672-4717.
T: 1 949 481-3747 **E:** zinfo@zumapress.com
W: http://www.zumapress.com
Editorial Profile: Zuma Press covers local and international news, sports, entertainment, in-depth investigative stories, features and travel.
NEWS SERVICE/SYNDICATE

BROADCASTING

RADIO STATIONS

KAAA-AM
Owner: Cameron Broadcasting Inc.
Editorial: 2350 Miracle Mile Ste 300, Bullhead City, Arizona 86442-7505. **T:** 1 928 763-5586
E: news@cameronbroadcasting.com
W: http://www.talkatoz.com
Editorial Profile: KAAA-AM is a commercial station owned by Cameron Broadcasting Inc. The format of the station is news and talk programming. KAAA-AM broadcasts to the Bullhead City, AZ area at 1230 AM.

KAAB-AM
Owner: WRD Entertainment Inc.
Editorial: 920 Harrison St, Batesville, Arkansas 72501. **T:** 1 870 793-4196
Editorial Profile: KAAB-AM is a commercial station owned by WRD Entertainment Inc. The format of the station is classic hits music. KAAB-AM broadcasts to the Batesville, AR area at 1130 AM.

KAAK-FM
Owner: Cherry Creek Radio
Editorial: 20 3rd St N, Ste 231, Great Falls, Montana 59401. **T:** 1 406 761-7600
W: http://www.k99radio.com
Editorial Profile: KAAK-FM is a commercial station owned by Cherry Creek Radio. The format for the station is hot adult contemporary. KAAK-FM broadcasts to the Great Falls, MT area at 98.8 FM.

KAAM-AM
Owner: DJRD Broadcasting LLC
Editorial: 3201 Royalty Row, Irving, Texas 75062-4943. **T:** 1 972 445-1700
E: kaam@kaamradio.com
W: http://www.kaamradio.com
Editorial Profile: KAAM-AM is a commercial station owned by DJRD Broadcasting LLC. The format of the station is adult standards. KAAM-AM broadcasts to the Dallas-Fort Worth area at 770 AM.

KAAN-AM
Owner: Goodradio.TV LLC
Editorial: 1212 S 25th St, Bethany, Missouri 64424-2602. **T:** 1 660 425-6380
W: http://www.northwestmoinfo.com
Editorial Profile: KAAN-AM is a commercial station owned by Goodradio.TV LLC. The format of the station is oldies. KAAN-AM broadcasts to the Bethany, MO at 870 AM.

KAAN-FM
Owner: Goodradio.TV LLC
Editorial: Highway 69 South, Bethany, Missouri 64424. **T:** 1 660 425-6380
W: http://www.northwestmoinfo.com
Editorial Profile: KAAN-FM is a commercial station owned by Goodradio.TV LLC. The format of the station is country music. KAAN-FM broadcasts to the Kansas City, MO area at 95.5 FM.

KAAP-FM
Owner: Cherry Creek Radio
Editorial: 231 N Wenatchee Ave, Wenatchee, Washington 98801. **T:** 1 509 665-6565
E: newswenatchee@cherrycreekradio.com
W: http://www.applefm.com
Editorial Profile: KAAP-FM is a commercial station owned by Cherry Creek Radio. The format of the station is adult contemporary music. KAAP-FM broadcasts to the Wenatchee, WA area at 99.5 FM.

KAAQ-FM
Owner: Eagle Radio Inc.
Editorial: 1210 W 10th St, Alliance, Nebraska 69301-2804. **T:** 1 308 762-1400
W: http://www.panhandlepost.com
Editorial Profile: KAAQ-FM is a commercial station owned by Eagle Radio Inc. The format of the station is contemporary country. KAAQ-FM broadcasts to the Alliance, NE area at 105.9 FM.

KAAR-FM
Owner: Cherry Creek Radio
Editorial: 750 Dewey Blvd, Butte, Montana 59701-3200. **T:** 1 406 494-1030
W: http://www.925kaar.com
Editorial Profile: KAAR-FM is a commercial station owned by Cherry Creek Radio. The format for the station is contemporary country. KAAR-FM broadcasts to the Butte, MT area at 92.5 FM.

KAAT-FM
Owner: Casa Media Partners, LLC
Editorial: 320 W Bedford Ave, Ste 201, Fresno, California 93711. **T:** 1 559 436-1031
Editorial Profile: KAAT-FM is a commercial station owned by Casa Media Partners, LLC. The format of the station is Hispanic programming. KAAT-FM broadcasts to the Oakhurst, CA area at 103.1 FM.

KAAY-AM
Owner: Cumulus Media Inc
Editorial: 700 Wellington Hills Rd, Little Rock, Arkansas 72211-2026. **T:** 1 501 401-0200
W: http://www.1090kaay.com
Editorial Profile: KAAY-AM is a commercial station owned by Cumulus Media Inc. The format of the station is Christian talk. KAAY-AM broadcasts to the Little Rock, AR area at 1090 AM.

KAAZ-FM
Owner: Appaloosa Broadcasting
Editorial: 302 S 2nd St, Ste 204, Laramie, Wyoming 82070. **T:** 1 307 745-5208
Editorial Profile: KAAZ-FM is a commercial station owned by Appaloosa Broadcasting. The format of the station is rock. KAAZ-FM broadcasts to the Laramie, WY area at 98.7 FM.

KABC-AM
Owner: Cumulus Media Inc
Editorial: 3321 S La Cienega Blvd, Los Angeles, California 90016-3114.
T: 1 310 840-4900 **E:** kabcpress@gmail.com
W: http://www.kabc.com
Editorial Profile: KABC-AM is a commercial station owned by Cumulus Media Inc. The format of the station is news and talk. KABC-AM broadcasts to the Los Angeles area at 790 AM.

KABD-FM
Owner: Dakota Broadcasting, LLC
Editorial: 426 N Highway 281 Ste 4, Aberdeen, South Dakota 57401-1864.
T: 1 605 725-5551
W: http://www.dakotabroadcasting.com

KABF-FM
Owner: Arkansas Broadcasting Foundation
Editorial: 2101 Main St, Little Rock, Arkansas 72206-1527. **T:** 1 501 372-6119
W: http://www.kabf.org
Editorial Profile: KABF-FM is a non-commercial community station owned by the Arkansas Broadcasting Foundation. The format of the station is variety. KABF-FM broadcasts to the Little Rock, AR area at 88.3 FM.

KABG-FM
Owner: American General Media
Editorial: 4125 Carlisle Blvd NE, Albuquerque, New Mexico 87107-4806. **T:** 1 505 878-0980
W: http://www.big985.com
Editorial Profile: KABG-FM is a commercial station owned by American General Media. The format of the station is classic hits. KABG-FM broadcasts to the Albuquerque, NM area at 98.5 FM.

KABI-AM
Owner: Morris Communications
Editorial: 200 N Broadway St, Abilene, Kansas 67410. **T:** 1 785 823-1111
W: http://www.ksallink.com/kabi
Editorial Profile: KABI-AM is a commercial station owned by Morris Communications. The format of the station is adult standards. KABI-AM broadcasts to the Abilene, KS area at 1560 AM.

KABQ-AM
Owner: Clear Channel Media and Entertainment
Editorial: 5411 Jefferson St NE, Ste 100, Albuquerque, New Mexico 87109.
T: 1 505 830-6400 **W:** http://www.abqtalk.com
Editorial Profile: KABQ-AM is a commercial station owned by Clear Channel Media and Entertainment. The format of the station is talk. KABQ-AM broadcasts to the Albuquerque, NM area at 1350 AM.

KABQ-FM
Owner: Clear Channel Media and Entertainment
Editorial: 5411 Jefferson St NE, Ste 100, Albuquerque, New Mexico 87109.
T: 1 505 830-6400
W: http://www.classiccountry1047.com
Editorial Profile: KABQ-FM is a commercial station owned by Clear Channel Media and Entertainment. The format of the station is classic country. KABQ-FM broadcasts to the Albuquerque, NM area at 104.7 FM.

KABU-FM
Owner: Dakota Circle Tipi, Inc.
Editorial: 7889 Highway 57, Saint Michael, North Dakota 58370-9000. **T:** 1 701 766-4095
E: kabu@stellarnet.com
W: http://www.nv1.org/kabu.html

KABW-FM
Owner: Doud Media Group LLC
Editorial: 1740 N 1st St, Abilene, Texas 79603-7401. **T:** 1 325 437-9596
W: http://www.95q.fm
Editorial Profile: KABW-FM is a commercial station owned by Doud Media Group LLC. The format of the station is country. KABW-FM broadcasts in the Abilene, TX area at 95.1 FM.

KABX-FM
Owner: Mapleton Radio, LLC
Editorial: 1020 W Main St, Merced, California 95340-4521. **T:** 1 209 723-2191
W: http://www.975kabx.com
Editorial Profile: KABX-FM is a commercial station owned by Mapleton Radio, LLC. The format of the station is adult contemporary. KABX-FM broadcasts to the Merced, Ca area at 97.5 FM.

KABZ-FM
Owner: Signal Media Inc.
Editorial: 2400 Cottondale Ln, Little Rock, Arkansas 72202. **T:** 1 501 661-1037
W: http://www.1037thebuzz.com
Editorial Profile: KABZ-FM is a commercial station owned by Signal Media Inc. The format of the station is sports. KABZ-FM broadcasts in the Little Rock, AR area at 103.7 FM.

KACC-FM
Owner: Alvin Community College
Editorial: 3110 Mustang Rd, Alvin, Texas 77511-4807. **T:** 1 281 756-3766
W: http://www.kaccradio.com
Editorial Profile: KACC-FM is a non-commercial station owned by Alvin Community College. The format of the station is rock/album-oriented rock. KACC-FM broadcasts to the Alvin, TX area at 89.7 FM.

KACH-AM
Owner: White(Alan & Nelada)
Editorial: 1633 N Radio Station Rd, Preston, Idaho 83263-4706. **T:** 1 208 852-1340
E: kach@kachradio.com
W: http://www.kachradio.com
Editorial Profile: KACH-AM is a commercial station owned by Alan & Nelada White. The format of the station is adult contemporary. KACH-AM broadcasts to the Preston, ID area at 1340 AM.

KACI-AM
Owner: Bicoastal Media LLC
Editorial: 719 E 2Nd St, The Dalles, Oregon 97058-2417. **T:** 1 541 296-2211
W: http://www.gorgeradio.com
Editorial Profile: KACI-AM is a commercial station owned by Bicoastal Media LLC. The format of the station is news and talk. KACI-AM broadcasts to The Dalles, OR area at 1300 AM.

KACI-FM
Owner: Bicoastal Media LLC
Editorial: 719 E 2Nd St Ste 203, The Dalles, Oregon 97058-2417. **T:** 1 541 296-2211
W: http://www.935kaci.com
Editorial Profile: KACI-FM is a commercial station owned by Bicoastal Media LLC. The format of the station is classic hits music. KACI-FM broadcasts to the Portland, OR area at 97.7 FM.

KACL-FM
Owner: Townsquare Media, Inc.
Editorial: 4303 Memorial Hwy, Mandan, North Dakota 58554-4711. **T:** 1 701 663-6411
W: http://www.cool987fm.com
Editorial Profile: KACL-FM is a commercial station owned by Townsquare Media, Inc. The format of the station is classic hits. KACL-FM broadcasts to the Minot-Bismarck, ND area at 98.7 FM.

KACO-FM
Owner: Perry Publishing & Broadcasting Inc.
Editorial: 115 W Broadway St, Anadarko, Oklahoma 73005-2805. **T:** 1 405 247-6682
E: anadarkospots@perrybroadcasting.net
W: http://www.superstarcountry985.com
Editorial Profile: KACO-FM is a commercial station owned by Perry Publishing & Broadcasting Inc. The format of the station is country music. KACO-FM broadcasts to the Anadarko, OK area at 98.5 FM.

KACQ-FM
Owner: Witcher(Ronald K.)
Editorial: 505 N Key Ave, Lampasas, Texas 76550-1850. **T:** 1 512 556-6193
E: management@lampasasradio.com
W: http://www.lampasasradio.com

KACS-FM
Owner: Chehalis Valley Educational Foundation
Editorial: 2451 NE Kresky Ave, Unit A, Chehalis, Washington 98532.
T: 1 360 740-9436 **E:** kacs@kacs.org
W: http://www.kacs.org
Editorial Profile: KACS-FM is a non-commercial station owned by Chehalis Valley Educational Foundation. The format of the station is contemporary Christian music and religious programming. KACS-FM broadcasts to the Seattle area at 90.5 FM.

KACT-AM
Owner: Zia Broadcasting
Editorial: 2125 N US Highway 385, Andrews, Texas 79714-9106. **T:** 1 432 523-2845
E: kact1055@windstream.net
W: http://www.kactradio.com
Editorial Profile: KACT-AM is a commercial station owned by Zia Broadcasting. The format of the station is talk. KACT-AM broadcasts to the Andrews, TX area at 1360 AM.

KACT-FM
Owner: Zia Broadcasting
Editorial: 2125 N US Highway 385, Andrews, Texas 79714. **T:** 1 432 523-2845
E: kact1055@windstream.net
W: http://www.kactradio.com

KACU-FM
Owner: Abilene Christian University
Editorial: 1201 E Ambler Ave, Abilene, Texas 79601. **T:** 1 325 674-2441 **E:** info@kacu.org
W: http://www.kacu.org
Editorial Profile: KACU-FM is a non-commercial station owned by Abilene Christian University. The format of the station is variety, featuring news and music. KACU-FM broadcasts in the Abilene, TX area at 89.7 FM.

KACV-FM
Owner: Amarillo College
Editorial: 2408 S Jackson St, Amarillo, Texas 79109. **T:** 1 806 371-5222
E: kacvfm90@actx.edu
W: http://www.kacvfm.org
Editorial Profile: KACV-FM is a non-commercial station owned by Amarillo College. The format of the station is variety. KACV-FM broadcasts to the Amarillo, TX area at 89.9 FM.

KACY-FM
Owner: Tornado Alley Communications LLC
Editorial: 106 N Summit St, Arkansas City, Kansas 67005. **T:** 1 620 442-1102
E: studio@1025theriver.com
W: http://1025theriver.com
Editorial Profile: KACY-FM is a commercial station owned by Tornado Alley Communications LLC. The format of the station is classic hits. KACY-FM broadcasts to the Arkansas City, KS area at 102.5 FM.

KACZ-FM
Owner: Manhattan Broadcasting
Editorial: 2414 Casement Rd, Manhattan, Kansas 66502. **T:** 1 785 776-1350
W: http://www.z963.com
Editorial Profile: KACZ-FM is a commercial station owned by Manhattan Broadcasting. The format of the station is Top 40/CHR music. KACZ-FM broadcasts in the Manhattan, KS area at 96.3 FM.

KADA-AM
Owner: Chickasaw Nation
Editorial: 1019 N Broadway Ave, Ada, Oklahoma 74820. **T:** 1 580 332-1212
E: score@cableone.net
W: http://www.kadaradio.net
Editorial Profile: KADA-AM is a commercial station owned by Chickasaw Nation. The format of the station is sports and talk. KADA-AM broadcasts in the Ada, OK area adults at 1230 AM.

KADA-FM
Owner: Chickasaw Nation
Editorial: 1019 N Broadway Ave, Ada, Oklahoma 74820-2036. **T:** 1 580 436-1616
E: kada@cableone.net
W: http://www.kadaradio.net
Editorial Profile: KADA-FM is a commercial station owned by Chickasaw Nation. The format of the station is adult contemporary music. KADA-FM broadcasts to the Ada, OK area at 99.3 FM.

KADI-AM
Owner: Vision Communications Inc.
Editorial: 5431 W Sunshine St, Brookline Station, Missouri 65619-9433.
T: 1 417 831-0995 **E:** traffickadi@gmail.com
W: http://www.1340kadi.com
Editorial Profile: KADI-AM is a commercial station owned by Vision Communications Inc. The format of the station is Conservative news talk. KADI-AM broadcasts to the Brookline Station, MO area at 1340 AM.

KADI-FM
Owner: Vision Communications Inc.
Editorial: 5431 W Sunshine St, Brookline Station, Missouri 65619-9433.
T: 1 417 831-0995 **W:** http://www.99hitfm.com
Editorial Profile: KADI-FM is a commercial station owned by Vision Communications Inc. The format of the station is contemporary Christian music. KADI-FM broadcasts to the Springfield, MO area at 99.5 FM.

KADR-AM
Owner: Design Homes Inc.
Editorial: 24493 Highway 128, Elkader, Iowa 52043-8038. **T:** 1 563 245-1400
E: kctn@alpinecom.net
W: http://www.hitsandfavorites.com/home.asp?callsign=KADR-AM
Editorial Profile: KADR-AM is a commercial station owned by Design Homes Inc. The format of the station is adult contemporary. KADR-AM broadcasts to the Cedar Rapids, IA area at 1400 AM.

KADS-AM
Owner: Paragon Communications Inc.
Editorial: 220 S Pioneer Rd, Elk City, Oklahoma 73644-4926. **T:** 1 580 225-9696
E: kecoproduction@cableone.net
W: http://www.thesportsanimal.com
Editorial Profile: KADS-AM is a commercial station owned by Paragon Communications Inc. The format of the station is sports. KADS-AM broadcasts to the Elk City, OK area at 1240 AM.

KADU-FM
Owner: Heartland Christian Broadcasters Inc.
Editorial: 4090 Highway 11, International Falls, Minnesota 56649. **T:** 1 218 285-7398
E: staff@psalm995.org
W: http://www.psalm995.org
Editorial Profile: KADU-FM is a non-commercial station owned by Heartland Christian Broadcasters Inc. The format of the station is contemporary Christian. KADU-FM broadcasts to Hibling, MN at 90.1 FM.

KADV-FM
Owner: Central Valley Christian Academy
Editorial: 1300 S Woodland St, Visalia, California 93277-4214. **T:** 1 855 427-7664
E: info@mypromisefm.com
W: http://www.mypromisefm.com
Editorial Profile: KADV-FM is a non-commercial station owned by Central Valley Christian Academy. The format of the station is Christian music and teachings. KADV-FM broadcasts to the Ceres, CA area at 90.5 FM.

KAEH-FM
Owner: Casa Media Partners, LLC
Editorial: 650 S E St, San Bernardino, California 92408-1902. **T:** 1 909 381-0969
Editorial Profile: KAEH-FM is a commercial station owned by Casa Media Partners, LLC. The format of the station is regional Mexican programming. KAEH-FM broadcasts to the San Bernardino, CA area at 100.9 FM.

KAFC-FM
Owner: Christian Broadcasting Inc.
Editorial: 6401 E Northern Lights Blvd, Anchorage, Alaska 99504. **T:** 1 907 222-4826
W: http://www.kafc.org
Editorial Profile: KAFC-FM is a commercial station owned by the Christian Broadcasting Inc. The format of the station is contemporary Christian music. KAFC-FM broadcasts in the Anchorage, AK area at 93.7 FM.

KAFE-FM
Owner: Saga Communications
Editorial: 2219 Yew Street Rd, Bellingham, Washington 98229-8855. **T:** 1 360 734-9790
E: kafe@kafe.com **W:** http://www.kafe.com
Editorial Profile: KAFE-FM is a commercial station owned by Saga Communications, dba Cascade radio Group. The format of the station is Lite Rock/Lite AC music. KAFE-FM broadcasts to the Bellingham, WA area at 104.1 FM.

KAFF-AM
Owner: Guyann Corp.
Editorial: 1117 W Route 66, Flagstaff, Arizona 86001-6213. **T:** 1 928 774-5231
E: news@kaff.com
W: http://www.country935.com
Editorial Profile: KAFF-AM is a commercial station owned by Guyann Corp. The format of the station is classic country. KAFF-AM broadcasts in the Flagstaff, AZ area at 930 AM.

KAFF-FM
Owner: Guyann Corp.
Editorial: 1117 W Route 66, Flagstaff, Arizona 86001. **T:** 1 928 774-5231
W: http://www.kaff.com
Editorial Profile: KAFF-FM is a commercial station owned by Guyann Corp. The format of the station is contemporary country music. KAFF-FM broadcasts to the Flagstaff, AZ area at 92.9 FM.

KAFM-FM
Owner: Grand Valley Public Radio Co. Inc.
Editorial: 1310 Ute Ave, Grand Junction, Colorado 81501-4620. **T:** 1 970 241-8801
E: kafm@kafmradio.org
W: http://www.kafmradio.org
Editorial Profile: KAFM-FM is a non-commercial station owned by Grand Valley Public Radio Co. Inc. The format of the station is variety. KAFM-FM broadcasts to the Grand Junction, CO area at 88.1 FM.

KAFR-FM
Owner: American Family Association
Editorial: 107 Park Gate Dr, Tupelo, Mississippi 38801-3010. **T:** 1 662 844-8888
E: comments@afr.net **W:** http://www.afr.net
Editorial Profile: KAFR-FM is a non-commercial station owned by American Family Association. The format of the station is contemporary Christian music and talk. KAFR-FM broadcasts to the Willis, TX area at 88.3 FM.

KAFX-FM
Owner: Townsquare Media, LLC
Editorial: 1216 S 1st St, Lufkin, Texas 75901.
T: 1 936 639-4455 **W:** http://www.kfox95.com
Editorial Profile: KAFX-FM is a commercial station owned by Townsquare Media, LLC. The format of the station is hot adult contemporary. KAFX-FM broadcasts to the Lufkin, TX area at 95.5 FM.

KAFY-AM
Owner: Favorita Broadcasting(La)
Editorial: 4043 Geer Rd, Hughson, California 95326-9798. **T:** 1 209 883-8760
E: lafavorita@lafavorita.net

W: http://www.lafavorita.net
Editorial Profile: KAFY-AM is a commercial station owned by La Favorita Broadcasting. The format of the station is Hispanic religious. KAFY-AM broadcasts to the Hughson, CA area at 1100 AM.

KAGB-FM
Owner: Pacific Media Group
Editorial: 75-5852 Alii Dr. Suite B1 & B2, Lagoon Tower, Kailua Kona, Hawaii 96740-1310. **T:** 1 808 329-6633
W: http://www.kaparadio.com
Editorial Profile: KAGB-FM is a commercial station owned by Pacific Media Group. The format of the station is Hawaiian AC. The station airs locally in the Kona, HI area at 99.1 FM.

KAGC-AM
Owner: Bryan Broadcasting
Editorial: 2700 Rudder Freeway South, Suite 5000, College Station, Texas 77845. **T:** 1 979 695-9595
E: christianfamilyradio@yahoo.com
W: http://www.kagcradio.com
Editorial Profile: KAGC-AM is a commercial station owned by Bryan Broadcasting. The format of the station is religious programming. KAGC-AM broadcasts to the College Station, TX area at 1510 AM.

KAGE-AM
Owner: KAGE Inc.
Editorial: 752 Bluffview Cir, Winona, Minnesota 55987. **T:** 1 507 452-4000
W: http://www.winonaradio.com
Editorial Profile: KAGE-AM is a commercial station owned by KAGE Inc. The format of the station is country music. KAGE-AM broadcasts to the Winona, MN area at 1380 AM.

KAGE-FM
Owner: KAGE Inc.
Editorial: 752 Bluffview Cir, Winona, Minnesota 55987. **T:** 1 507 452-4000
W: http://www.winonaradio.com
Editorial Profile: KAGE-FM is a commercial station owned by KAGE Inc. The format of the station is adult contemporary. KAGE-FM broadcasts to the Winona, MN area at 95.3 FM.

KAGG-FM
Owner: Clear Channel Media and Entertainment
Editorial: 1716 Briarcrest Dr, Ste 150, Bryan, Texas 77802. **T:** 1 979 268-9696
W: http://www.aggie96.com
Editorial Profile: KAGG-FM is a commercial station owned by Clear Channel Media and Entertainment. The format of the station is country music. KAGG-FM broadcasts to the Bryan, TX area at 96.1 FM.

KAGH-AM
Owner: Ashley County Broadcasters
Editorial: 117 E Wellfield Road, Crossett, Arkansas 71635. **T:** 1 870 364-2181
E: kagh@windstream.net
W: http://www.crossettradio.com
Editorial Profile: KAGH-AM is a commercial statio owned by Ashley County Broadcasters. The format of the station is Classic Hits. KAGH-AM broadcasts to the Crossett, AR area at 800 AM.

KAGH-FM
Owner: Ashley County Broadcasters
Editorial: 117 E Wellfield Road, Crossett, Arkansas 71635. **T:** 1 870 364-2182
E: kagh@windstream.net
W: http://www.crossettradio.com
Editorial Profile: KAGH-FM is a commercial station owned by Ashley County Broadcasters. The format of the station is contemporary country. KAGH-FM broadcasts to the Crossett, AR area at 104.9 FM.

KAGI-AM
Owner: State of Oregon
Editorial: 1250 Siskiyou Blvd, Ashland, Oregon 97520-5001. **T:** 1 541 552-6301
E: jprinfo@sou.edu **W:** http://www.ijpr.org
Editorial Profile: KAGI-AM is a non-commercial station owned by State of Oregon. The format of the station is news and talk. KAGI-AM broadcasts to the Grant Pass, OR area at 930 AM.

KAGJ-FM
Owner: Snow College
Editorial: 150 College Ave, Ephraim, Utah 84627. **T:** 1 435 283-7425
W: http://www.snow.edu/~kage/
Editorial Profile: KAGJ-FM is a non-commercial station owned by Snow College.

The format of the station is rock alternative music. KAGJ-FM broadcasts to the Ephraim, UT area area at 89.5 FM.

KAGL-FM
Owner: Noalmark Broadcasting Corp.
Editorial: 2525 N West Ave, El Dorado, Arkansas 71730. **T:** 1 870 863-6126
E: newsroom@totalradio.us
W: http://www.eagle933.com
Editorial Profile: KAGL-FM is a commercial station owned by Noalmark Broadcasting Corp. The format of the station is classic rock. KAGL-FM broadcasts to the El Dorado, AR area at 93.3 FM.

KAGM-FM
Owner: American General Media
Editorial: 4125 Carlisle Blvd NE, Albuquerque, New Mexico 87107-4806. **T:** 1 505 878-0980
W: http://power1067.com
Editorial Profile: KAGM-FM is a commercial station owned by American General Media. The format of the station is urban contemporary. KAGM-FM broadcasts to the Albuquerque, NM area at 106.7 FM.

KAGO-AM
Owner: Basin Mediactive, LLC
Editorial: 404 Main St Ste 4, Klamath Falls, Oregon 97601-6021. **T:** 1 541 882-8833
E: news@mybasin.com
W: http://www.mybasin.com
Editorial Profile: KAGO-AM is a commercial station owned by Basin Mediactive, LLC. The format of the station is news and talk. KAGO-AM broadcasts in the Klamath Falls, OR area at 1150 AM.

KAGO-FM
Owner: Basin Mediactive, LLC
Editorial: 404 Main St Ste 4, Klamath Falls, Oregon 97601-6021. **T:** 1 541 882-8833
E: news@mybasin.com
W: http://www.99-5therock.com
Editorial Profile: KAGO-FM is a commercial station owned by Basin Mediactive, LLC. The format of the station is rock music. KAGO-FM broadcasts to the Klamath Falls, OR area at 99.5 FM.

KAGU-FM
Owner: Gonzaga University Telecom Association
Editorial: 502 E Boone Ave, Spokane, Washington 99258. **T:** 1 509 313-6660
Editorial Profile: KAGU-FM is a non-commercial station owned by Gonzaga University Telecom Association. The format of the station is classical. KAGU-FM broadcasts to the Spokane, WA area at 88.7 FM.

KAGY-AM
Owner: Spotlight Broadcasting of New Orleans LLC
Editorial: 409 Duke St, Morgan City, Louisiana 70380. **T:** 1 985 384-1430
E: KAGYradio@gmail.com
W: http://www.kagyradio.com
Editorial Profile: KAGY-AM is a commercial station owned by Spotlight Broadcasting of New Orleans LLC. The format of the station is variety. KAGY-AM broadcasts to the Port Sulphur, LA area at 1510 AM.

KAHE-FM
Owner: Rocking M Radio
Editorial: 2601 Central Ave, Dodge City, Kansas 67801-6200. **T:** 1 620 225-8080
W: http://mykansasradio.todayinkansas.com
Editorial Profile: KAHE-FM is a commercial station owned by Rocking M Radio. The format of the station is oldies music. KAHE-FM broadcasts to the Dodge City, KS area at 95.5 FM.

KAHI-AM
Owner: KAHI Corporation
Editorial: 985 Lincoln Way, Ste 103, Auburn, California 95603-5255. **T:** 1 530 885-5636
E: info@kahi.com **W:** http://www.kahi.com
Editorial Profile: KAHI-AM is a commercial station owned by KAHI Corporation. The format of the station is variety. KAHI-AM broadcasts to the Sacramento, CA area at 950 AM.

KAHL-AM
Owner: San Antonio Radio Works
Editorial: 8023 Vantage Dr, Ste 840, San Antonio, Texas 78230. **T:** 1 210 341-1310
E: info@call1310.com
W: http://www.call1310.com
Editorial Profile: KAHL-AM is a commercial station owned by San Antonio Radio Works. The format of the station is adult standards.

KAHL-AM broadcasts to the San Antonio area at 1310 AM.

KAHM-FM
Owner: Southwest Broadcasting
Editorial: 510 Henry St, Prescott, Arizona 86301-2670. **T:** 1 928 445-7800
E: prescott@kahm.info
W: http://www.kahm.info
Editorial Profile: KAHM-FM is a commercial station owned by Southwest Broadcasting. The format of the station is easy listening music. KAHM-FM broadcasts to the Phoenix area at 102.1 FM.

KAHR-FM
Owner: Eagle Bluff Enterprises
Editorial: 932 County Road 448, Poplar Bluff, Missouri 63901-9018. **T:** 1 573 686-3700
E: frn@tcmax.net **W:** http://todaysbesthits.com
Editorial Profile: KAHR-FM is a commercial station owned by Eagle Bluff Enterprises. The format of the station is Jack FM - Adult Hits. KAHR-FM broadcasts to the Poplar Bluff, MO area at 96.7 FM.

KAHS-AM
Owner: Catholic Radio Network
Editorial: 1612 SW River Rd, El Dorado, Kansas 67042. **T:** 1 316 320-1360
E: kahs@kahs.kscoxmail.com
W: http://www.1360kahs.com
Editorial Profile: KAHS-AM is a commercial station owned by Catholic Radio Network. The format of the station is religious, featuring Catholic programming. KAHS-AM broadcasts to the El Dorado, KS area at 1360 AM.

KAHZ-AM
Owner: Multicultural Radio Broadcasting Inc.
Editorial: 747 E Green St, Pasadena, California 91101-2145. **T:** 1 626 844-1600
W: http://www.am1300.com
Editorial Profile: KAHZ-AM is a commercial station owned by Multicultural Radio Broadcasting Inc. The format of the station is Chinese news and talk. KAHZ-AM broadcasts to the greater Los Angeles area at 1300 AM.

KAIM-FM
Owner: Salem Communications
Editorial: 1160 N King St, Honolulu, Hawaii 96817. **T:** 1 808 533-0065
W: http://www.thefishhawaii.com
Editorial Profile: KAIM-FM is a commercial station owned by Salem Communications. The format of the station is contemporary Christian. KAIM-FM broadcasts to the Honolulu area at 95.5 FM.

KAIQ-FM
Owner: Entravision Communications Corp.
Editorial: 1220 Broadway, Ste 600, Lubbock, Texas 79401. **T:** 1 806 763-6051
W: http://www.tricolor955.com
Editorial Profile: KAIQ is owned by Entravision Communications. It's format is Hispanic. It broadcasts locally on 95.5 FM.

KAIR-AM
Owner: KNZA, Inc.
Editorial: 200 N 5th St, Atchison, Kansas 66002-2413. **T:** 1 913 367-1470
E: kairradio@gmail.com **W:** http://kairfm.com
Editorial Profile: KAIR-AM is a commercial station owned by KNZA, Inc. The format of the station is classic country. KAIR-AM broadcasts to the Atchison, KS area at 1470 AM.

KAIR-FM
Owner: KNZA, Inc.
Editorial: 200 N 5th St, Atchison, Kansas 66002. **T:** 1 913 367-1470
E: kairradio@gmail.com
W: http://www.kairfm.com
Editorial Profile: KAIR-FM is a commercial station owned by KNZA, Inc. The format of the station is contemporary country music. KAIR-FM broadcasts to the Atchison, KS, area at 93.7 FM.

KAIS-FM
Owner: Educational Media Foundation
Editorial: 5700 W Oaks Blvd, Rocklin, California 95765-3719. **T:** 1 916 251-1600
W: http://www.klove.com
Editorial Profile: KAIS-FM is a non-commercial station owned by Educational Media Foundation. The format of the station is contemporary Christian rock music. KAIS-FM broadcasts to the Tracy, CA area at 90.7.

KAJA-FM
Owner: Clear Channel Media and Entertainment

Editorial: 6222 W Interstate 10, San Antonio, Texas 78201-2013. **T:** 1 210 736-9700
W: http://www.kj97.com
Editorial Profile: KAJA-FM is a commercial station owned by Clear Channel Media and Entertainment. The format for the station is contemporary country. KAJA-FM broadcasts to the San Antonio area at 97.3 FM.

KAJC-FM
Owner: Calvary Chapel Monmouth-Independence
Editorial: 1399 Monmouth St, Independence, Oregon 97351-1126. **T:** 1 503 837-1000
E: kajc@kajcfm.com **W:** http://www.kajcfm.org
Editorial Profile: KAJC-FM is a non-commercial station owned by Calvary Chapel Monmouth-Independence. The format of the station is Contemporary Christian music and Christian teaching programming. KAJC-FM broadcasts to the Salem, OR area at 90.1 FM.

KAJE-FM
Owner: Convergent Broadcasting
Editorial: 826 S Padre Island Dr, Corpus Christi, Texas 78416-2506. **T:** 1 361 814-3800
W: http://www.1073jakefm.com
Editorial Profile: KAJE-FM is a commercial station owned by Convergent Broadcasting. The format of the station is classic hits. KAJE-FM broadcasts to the Corpus Christi, TX area at 107.3 FM.

KAJM-FM
Owner: Sierra H Broadcasting, Inc.
Editorial: 7434 E Stetson Dr, Ste 255, Scottsdale, Arizona 85251. **T:** 1 480 994-9100
W: http://www.mega1043.com
Editorial Profile: KAJM-FM is a commercial station owned by Sierra H Broadcasting, Inc. The format of the station is rhythmic oldies music. KAJM-FM broadcasts in the Scottsdale, AZ area at 104.3 FM.

KAJN-FM
Owner: Agape Broadcasting Foundation Inc.
Editorial: 110 W 3rd St, Crowley, Louisiana 70526. **T:** 1 337 783-1560 **E:** barryt@kajn.com
W: http://www.kajn.com
Editorial Profile: KAJN-FM is a commercial station owned by Agape Broadcasting Foundation Inc. The format of the station is contemporary Christian music, news and talk. KAJN-FM broadcasts to Lafayette, LA at 102.9 FM.

KAJO-AM
Owner: Grants Pass Broadcasting Corp.
Editorial: 888 Rogue River Hwy, Grants Pass, Oregon 97527-5209. **T:** 1 541 476-6608
E: news@kajo.com **W:** http://www.kajo.com
Editorial Profile: KAJO-AM is a commercial station owned by Grants Pass Broadcasting Corp. The format of the station is adult standards music and talk. KAJO-AM broadcasts in the Grants Pass, OR area at 1270 AM.

KAJR-FM
Owner: RM Broadcasting LLC
Editorial: 75153 Merle Dr Ste G, Palm Desert, California 92211-5197. **T:** 1 760 568-4550
W: http://959theoasis.com
Editorial Profile: KAJR-FM is a commercial station owned by RM Broadcasting LLC. The format of the station is Lite AC. KAJR-FM broadcasts to the Palm Springs, CA area at 95.9 FM.

KAJX-FM
Owner: Roaring Fork Public Radio Inc.
Editorial: 110 E Hallam St, Ste 134, Aspen, Colorado 81611. **T:** 1 970 920-9000
W: http://www.aspenpublicradio.org
Editorial Profile: KAJX-FM is a non-commercial station owned by Roaring Fork Public Radio Inc. The format of the station is news, classical and jazz. KAJX-FM broadcasts to the Aspen, CO area at 91.5 FM.

KAKC-AM
Owner: Clear Channel Media and Entertainment
Editorial: 2625 S Memorial Dr, Tulsa, Oklahoma 74129. **T:** 1 918 388-5100
W: http://www.1300kakc.com
Editorial Profile: KAKC-AM is a commercial station owned by Clear Channel Media and Entertainment. The format of the station is sports. KAKC-AM broadcasts to the Tulsa, OK area at 1300 AM.

KAKJ-FM
Owner: Delta Force II Radio
Editorial: 700 W Martin Luther King Jr Dr, Ste 2, West Helena, Arkansas 72390.
T: 1 870 572-9506 **E:** force2@sbcglobal.net

W: http://www.force2radio.com
Editorial Profile: KAKJ-FM is a commercial station owned by Delta Force II Radio. The format of the station is oldies, blues and gospel. KAKJ-FM broadcasts to the West Helena, AR area at 105.3 FM.

KAKK-AM
Owner: De La Hunt Broadcasting
Editorial: Highway 34 West, Walker, Minnesota 56470. **T:** 1 218 547-4000
W: http://www.kkradionetwork.com
Editorial Profile: KAKK-AM is a commercial station owned by De La Hunt Broadcasting. The format of the station is oldies. KAKK-AM broadcasts to the Walker, MN area at 1570 AM.

KAKN-FM
Owner: Assn. of Free Lutheran Congregations Mission Corp.
Editorial: Mile 2 Alaska Peninsula Highway, Naknek, Alaska 99633-9999.
T: 1 907 246-7492 **E:** kakn@kakn.org
W: http://www.kaknradio.org
Editorial Profile: KAKN-FM is a commercial station owned by Assn. of Free Lutheran Congregations Mission Corp. The format of the station is contemporary Christian and gospel music. KAKN-FM broadcasts to the Naknek, AK area at 100.9 FM.

KAKQ-FM
Owner: Clear Channel Media and Entertainment
Editorial: 546 9th Ave, Fairbanks, Alaska 99701. **T:** 1 907 450-1000
W: http://www.101magic.com
Editorial Profile: KAKQ-FM is a commercial station owned by Clear Channel Media and Entertainment. The format for the station is hot adult contemporary. KAKQ-FM broadcasts to the Fairbanks, AK area at 101.1 FM.

KAKS-FM
Owner: Hog Radio, Inc.
Editorial: 2250 W Sunset Ave, Ste 3, Springdale, Arkansas 72762-5187.
T: 1 479 303-2034
E: thehog@hogsportsradio.com
W: http://www.hogsnow.com
Editorial Profile: KAKS-FM is a commercial station owned by Hog Radio, Inc. The format of the station is sports. KAKS-FM broadcasts to the Fayetteville, AR area at 99.5 FM.

KAKT-FM
Owner: Mapleton Radio, LLC
Editorial: 1438 Rossanley Dr, Medford, Oregon 97501-1751. **T:** 1 541 779-1550
W: http://www.1051hankfm.com
Editorial Profile: KAKT-FM is a commercial station owned by Mapleton Radio, LLC. The format of the station is country music. KAKT-FM broadcasts in the Medford, OR area at 105.1 FM.

KALA-FM
Owner: St. Ambrose University
Editorial: 518 W Locust St, Davenport, Iowa 52803-2829. **T:** 1 563 333-6219
E: kala@sau.edu **W:** http://www.sau.edu/kala
Editorial Profile: KALA-FM is a non-commercial station owned by St. Ambrose University. The format of the station is variety. KALA-FM broadcasts to the Davenport, IA on 88.5 FM.

KALC-FM
Owner: Entercom Communications Corp.
Editorial: 4700 S Syracuse St, Ste 1050, Denver, Colorado 80237. **T:** 1 303 967-2700
W: http://www.alice1059.com
Editorial Profile: KALC-FM is a commercial station owned by Entercom Communications Corp. The format of the station is hot adult contemporary. KALC-FM broadcasts to the Denver area at 105.9 FM.

KALD-FM
Owner: Houston Christian Broadcasters
Editorial: 2424 South Blvd, Houston, Texas 77098-5110. **T:** 1 713 520-5200
W: http://www.khcb.org
Editorial Profile: KALD-FM is a non-commercial station owned by Houston Christian Broadcasters. The format of the station is Christian programming and music. KALD-FM broadcasts to the Caldwell, TX area at 91.9 FM.

KALE-AM
Owner: Ingstad Radio Washington, LLC
Editorial: 4304 W 24Th Ave Suite 200, Kennewick, Washington 99338-2320.
T: 1 509 783-0783
Editorial Profile: KALE-AM is a commercial station owned by Ingstad Radio Washington, LLC. The format of the station is classic country. KALE-AM broadcasts to the Kennewick, WA area at 960 AM.

KALF-FM
Owner: Mapleton Radio, LLC
Editorial: 1459 Humboldt Rd, Ste D, Chico, California 95928. **T:** 1 530 899-3600
Editorial Profile: KALF-FM is a commercial station owned by Mapleton Radio, LLC. The format of the station is country music. KALF-FM broadcasts to the Chico, CA area at 95.7 FM.

KALI-AM
Owner: Multicultural Radio Broadcasting Inc.
Editorial: 747 E Green St Fl 4, Pasadena, California 91101-2145. **T:** 1 626 844-8882
W: http://www.mrbi.net
Editorial Profile: KALI-AM is a commercial station owned by Multicultural Radio Broadcasting Inc. The format of the station Spanish religious. KALI-AM broadcasts to the Pasadena, CA area at 900 AM. The station does not accept press releases.

KALI-FM
Owner: Multicultural Radio Broadcasting Inc.
Editorial: 747 E Green St Fl 4, Pasadena, California 91101-2145. **T:** 1 626 844-8882
Editorial Profile: KALI-FM is a commercial station owned by Multicultural Radio Broadcasting Inc. The format of the station is primarily adult standards, and features a variety of ethnic and multicultural programming, most of it being Vietnamese. KALI-FM broadcasts to the Pasadena, CA area at 106.3 FM.

KALK-FM
Owner: East Texas Broadcasting Inc.
Editorial: Highway 67 West 1 Mile, Mount Pleasant, Texas 75455. **T:** 1 903 577-9770
W: http://www.easttexasradio.com
Editorial Profile: KALK-FM is a commercial station owned by East Texas Broadcasting Inc. The format of the station is adult hits. KALK-FM broadcasts to the Mount Pleasant, TX area at 97.7 FM.

KALL-AM
Owner: Broadway Media
Editorial: 9256 S State St, Sandy, Utah 84070-2604. **T:** 1 801 956-4121
W: http://espn.kall700sports.com
Editorial Profile: KALL-AM is a commercial station owned by Broadway Media Group. The format of the station is sports. KALL-AM broadcasts to the Salt Lake City area at 700 AM.

KALM-AM
Owner: E-Communications, LLC
Editorial: Highway 63 North, Thayer, Missouri 65791. **T:** 1 417 264-7211
E: kkountry@kkountry.com
W: http://www.am1290thegift.com
Editorial Profile: KALM-AM is a commercial station owned by E-Communications, LLC. The format of the station is gospel. KALM-AM broadcasts to the Thayer, MO area at 1290 AM.

KALP-FM
Owner: Big Ben Broadcasters Inc.
Editorial: 500 E Hendryx Dr, Alpine, Texas 79830. **T:** 1 432 837-2144
W: http://www.bigbendradio.com
Editorial Profile: KALP-FM is a commercial station owned by Big Ben Broadcasters Inc. The format of the station is country. KALP-FM broadcasts to the Alpine, TX area at 92.7 FM.

KALQ-FM
Owner: Community Broadcasting Co.
Editorial: 292 Santa Fe Ave, Alamosa, Colorado 81101-2810. **T:** 1 719 589-6644
W: http://www.kgiwkalq.com
Editorial Profile: KALQ-FM is a commercial station owned by Community Broadcasting Co. The format of the station is country. KALQ-FM broadcasts to the Alamosa, CO area at 93.5 FM.

KALS-FM
Owner: Your Network of Praise Inc.
Editorial: 106 Cooperative Way Ste 102, Kalispell, Montana 59901-9506.
T: 1 406 752-5257 **E:** onair@ynop.org
W: http://www.ynop.org

KALU-FM
Owner: Langston University
Editorial: Hwy 33 Sanford, Room 304, Langston, Oklahoma 73050.
T: 1 877 466-2231
W: http://www.langston.edu/campus_life/langston_university/kalu.aspx
Editorial Profile: KALU-FM is a non-commercial college educational station owned by Langston University. The format of the station is variety. KALU-FM broadcasts to the Langston University campus and Langston, OK area at a frequency of 89.3 FM.

KALV-AM
Owner: MM & K of Alva, Inc.
Editorial: Highway 281 North, Alva, Oklahoma 73717. **T:** 1 580 327-1430
E: kalvradio@yahoo.com
Editorial Profile: KALV-AM is a commercial station owned by MM & K of Alva, Inc. The format of the station is oldies. KALV-AM broadcasts to the Alva, OK area at 1430 AM.

KALW-FM
Owner: San Francisco Unified School District
Editorial: 500 Mansell St, San Francisco, California 94134-1858. **T:** 1 415 841-4121
E: news@kalw.org **W:** http://www.kalw.org
Editorial Profile: KALW-FM is a non-commercial station owned by the San Francisco Unified School District. The format of the station is news and talk. KALW-FM broadcasts to the San Francisco area at 91.7 FM.

KALX-FM
Owner: University of California
Editorial: 26 Barrows Hall, Spc 5650, Berkeley, California 94720. **T:** 1 510 642-1111
E: mail@kalx.berkeley.edu
W: http://kalx.berkeley.edu
Editorial Profile: KALX-FM is a non-commercial station owned by the University of California. The format of the station is college variety. KALX-FM broadcasts to the Berkeley, CA area at 103.6 FM.

KALZ-FM
Owner: Clear Channel Media and Entertainment
Editorial: 83 E Shaw Ave, Fresno, California 93710-7620. **T:** 1 559 230-4300
W: http://www.powertalk967.com
Editorial Profile: KALZ-FM is a commercial station owned by Clear Channel Media and Entertainment. The format of the station is news and talk. KALZ-FM broadcasts to the Fresno, CA, area at 96.7 FM.

KAMA-AM
Owner: Univision Communications Inc.
Editorial: 2211 E Missouri Ave Ste 300, El Paso, Texas 79903-3837. **T:** 1 915 544-9797
W: http://univisionamerica.univision.com
Editorial Profile: KAMA-AM is commercial station owned by Univision Communications Inc. The format of the station is Hispanic news and talk. KAMA-AM broadcasts to the El Paso, TX area at 750 AM.

KAMA-FM
Owner: Univision Communications Inc.
Editorial: 5100 Southwest Fwy, Houston, Texas 77056-7308. **T:** 1 713 965-2400
W: http://1049tumusica.univision.com
Editorial Profile: KAMA-FM is a commercial station owned by Univision Communications Inc. The format is Hispanic hits. KAMA-FM broadcasts to the Houston area at 104.9 FM.

KAMB-FM
Owner: Central Valley Broadcasting
Editorial: 90 E 16th St, Merced, California 95340. **T:** 1 209 723-1015
E: kamb@celebrationradio.com
W: http://www.celebrationradio.com
Editorial Profile: KAMB-FM is a non-commercial station owned by Central Valley Broadcasting. The format of the station is contemporary Christian music and talk. KAMB-FM broadcasts in the Merced, CA area at 101.5 FM.

KAMD-FM
Owner: Radio Works Inc.
Editorial: 612 Fairview Road, Camden, Arkansas 71701. **T:** 1 870 836-9567
E: radioworks@cablelynx.com
W: http://www.k97online.com
Editorial Profile: KAMD-FM is a commercial station owned by Radio Works Inc. The format of the station is adult contemporary music. KAMD-FM broadcasts in the Camden, AR area at 97.1 FM.

KAMJ-FM
Owner: Sudbury Broadcasting Group
Editorial: 125 S 2nd St, Blytheville, Arkansas 72315. **T:** 1 870 762-2093

KAML-AM
Owner: SIGA Broadcasting Corp.
Editorial: 1568 County Road 345, Kenedy, Texas 78119-5229. **T:** 1 830 583-2990
E: kaml990am@gmail.com
W: http://ww.kaml990.com
Editorial Profile: KAML-AM is a commercial station owned by SIGA Broadcasting Corp. The format for the station is country. KAML-AM broadcasts to the Kenedy, TX area at 990 AM.

KAML-FM
Owner: Legend Communications
Editorial: 2810 Southern Dr, Gillette, Wyoming 82718-9369. **T:** 1 307 686-2242
E: news@basinsradio.com
W: http://www.basinsradio.com
Editorial Profile: KAML-FM is a commercial station owned by Legend Communications. The format of the station is hot adult contemporary. KAML-FM broadcasts to the Gillette, WY area at 97.3 FM.

KAMO-FM
Owner: Cumulus Media Inc.
Editorial: 4209 N Frontage Rd, Fayetteville, Arkansas 72703-5002. **T:** 1 479 521-5566
W: http://www.nashfm943.com
Editorial Profile: KAMO-FM is a commercial station owned by Cumulus Media Inc. The format of the station is country music. KAMO-FM broadcasts to the Fayetteville, AR area at 94.3 FM.

KAMP-FM
Owner: CBS Radio
Editorial: 5670 Wilshire Blvd Ste 200, Los Angeles, California 90036-5657.
T: 1 323 971-9710 **E:** amp@ampradio.com
W: http://amp.cbslocal.com
Editorial Profile: KAMP-FM is a commercial station owned by CBS Radio. The format of the station is Top 40/CHR. KAMP-FM broadcasts to the Los Angeles area at 97.1 FM.

KAMQ-AM
Owner: Hughes Broadcasting
Editorial: 1609 Radio Blvd, Carlsbad, New Mexico 88220. **T:** 1 575 887-7563
W: http://www.carlsbadradio.com
Editorial Profile: KAMQ-AM is a commercial station owned by Hughes Broadcasting. The format of the station is sports. KAMQ-AM broadcasts to the Carlsbad, NM area at 1240 AM.

KAMS-FM
Owner: E-Communications, LLC
Editorial: Highway 63 North, Thayer, Missouri 65791. **T:** 1 417 264-7211
E: news@kkountry.com
W: http://www.kkountry.com
Editorial Profile: KAMS-FM is a commercial station owned by E-Communications, LLC. The format of the station is contemporary country. KAMS-FM broadcasts to the Thayer, MO area at 95.1 FM.

KAMU-FM
Owner: Texas A & M University
Editorial: Texas A & M University, 4244 Tamu, College Station, Texas 77843-4244.
T: 1 979 845-5613 **E:** kamu-fm@tamu.edu
W: http://www.kamu.tamu.edu
Editorial Profile: KAMU-FM is a non-commercial station owned by Texas A & M University. The format of the station is news, classical and jazz. KAMU-FM broadcasts to the College Station, TX area at 90.9 FM.

KAMX-FM
Owner: Entercom Communications Corp.
Editorial: 4301 Westbank Dr, 3rd Fl, Austin, Texas 78746-6568. **T:** 1 512 327-9595
W: http://www.mix947.com
Editorial Profile: KAMX-FM is a commercial station owned by Entercom Communications Corp. The format of the station is hot adult contemporary. KAMX-FM broadcasts to the Austin, TX area at 94.7 FM.

KAMY-FM
Owner: Family Life Broadcasting, Inc.
Editorial: 7204 Joliet Ave, Ste C, Lubbock, Texas 79423-1136. **T:** 1 800 776-1070
W: http://www.myflr.org
Editorial Profile: KAMY-FM is a non-commercial station owned by Family Life Broadcasting, Inc. The format of the station is Christian programming and music. KAMY-FM broadcasts to the Lubbock, TX area at 90.1 FM.

KAMZ-FM
Owner: Tahoka Radio LLC
Editorial: 1220 Broadway, Ste 1035, Lubbock, Texas 79401. T: 1 806 741-0701
Editorial Profile: KAMZ-FM is a commercial station owned by Tahoka Radio LLC. The format of the station is regional Mexican. KAMZ-FM broadcasts to the Lubbock, TX area at 103.5 FM.

KANA-AM
Owner: Butte Broadcasting Inc.
Editorial: 105 Main St, Anaconda, Montana 59711. T: 1 406 563-8011
E: mail@kbowkopr.com
Editorial Profile: KANA-AM is a commercial station owned by Butte Broadcasting Inc. The format for the station is classic rock. KANA-AM broadcasts to the Anaconda, MT area at 580 AM.

KAND-AM
Owner: New Century Broadcasting
Editorial: 701 South Main St, Corsicana, Texas 75110. T: 1 903 874-7421
W: http://www.kandradio.com
Editorial Profile: KAND-AM is a commercial station owned by New Century Broadcasting. The format is country. KAND-AM broadcasts to the Corsicana, TX area at 1340 AM.

KANE-AM
Owner: Coastal Broadcasting of Larose Inc.
Editorial: 800 S Lewis St Ste 204D, New Iberia, Louisiana 70560-4854.
T: 1 337 365-3434 E: kane@kane1240.com
W: http://www.kane1240.com
Editorial Profile: KANE-AM is a commercial station owned by Coastal Broadcasting of Larose Inc. The format of the station is variety. KANE-AM broadcasts to the Lafayette, LA area at 1240 AM.

KANI-AM
Owner: Martin Broadcasting
Editorial: 215 E Milam St, Wharton, Texas 77488. T: 1 979 532-4141
E: kaniam1500@yahoo.com
Editorial Profile: KANI-AM is a commercial station owned by Martin Broadcasting. The format of the station is gospel music and religious talk programming. KANI-AM broadcasts to the Wharton, TX area at 1500 AM.

KANN-AM
Owner: Faith Communications Corp.
Editorial: 2201 S 6th St, Las Vegas, Nevada 89104-2962. T: 1 702 731-5452
E: info@sosradio.net
W: http://www.sosradio.net
Editorial Profile: KANN-AM is a non-commercial station owned by Faith Communications Corp. The format of the station is contemporary Christian music. KANN-AM broadcasts to the Syracuse, UT, area at 1120 AM.

KANO-FM
Owner: Hawaii Public Radio
Editorial: 738 Kaheka St, Ste 101, Honolulu, Hawaii 96814. T: 1 808 955-8821
E: news@hawaiipublicradio.org
W: http://www.hawaiipublicradio.org
Editorial Profile: KANO-FM is a non-commercial station owned by Hawaii Public Radio. The format of the station is news, talk, and classical music. KANO-FM broadcasts to the Honolulu, HI area at 91.1 FM.

KANS-FM
Owner: Kansas Radio Inc.
Editorial: 918 Graham St, Emporia, Kansas 66801. T: 1 620 343-9393
E: thewave@ksradio.com
W: http://www.ksradio.com
Editorial Profile: KANS-FM is a commercial station owned by Kansas Radio Inc. The format of the station is Lite Rock/Lite AC music. KANS-FM broadcasts in the Emporia, KS area at 99.5 FM.

KANT-FM
Owner: Appaloosa Broadcasting
Editorial: 2109 E 10th St, Cheyenne, Wyoming 82001-5219. T: 1 307 638-8921
Editorial Profile: KANT-FM is a commercial station owned by Appaloosa Broadcasting. The format of the station is adult hits. KANT-FM broadcasts to the Guernsey, WY area at 104.1 FM.

KANU-FM
Owner: University of Kansas
Editorial: 1120 W 11th St, Lawrence, Kansas 66044-2902. T: 1 785 864-4530
W: http://kansaspublicradio.org

Editorial Profile: KANU-FM is a non-commercial station owned by the University of Kansas. The format of the station is news, classical and jazz music. KANU-FM broadcasts to the Kansas City, MO, area at 91.5 FM.

KANW-FM
Owner: Albuquerque Public Schools
Editorial: 2020 Coal Ave SE, Albuquerque, New Mexico 87106-4318. T: 1 505 242-7163
W: http://www.kanw.com
Editorial Profile: KANW-FM is a non-commercial station owned by Albuquerque Public Schools. The format of the station is Hispanic variety. KANW-FM broadcasts to the Albuquerque, NM area at 89.1 FM.

KANY-FM
Owner: Jodesha Broadcasting Inc.
Editorial: 1520 Simpson Ave, Aberdeen, Washington 98520-4708. T: 1 206 439-1188
E: laestaciondelafamilia@gmail.com
W: http://laestaciondelafamilia.org
Editorial Profile: KANY-FM is a commercial station owned by Jodesha Broadcasting Inc. The format of the station is Spanish Contemporary Christian. KANY-FM broadcasts to the Aberdeen, WA area at 93.7 FM.

KANZ-FM
Owner: Kanza Society Inc.
Editorial: 210 N 7th St, Garden City, Kansas 67846. T: 1 620 275-7444 E: hppr@hppr.org
W: http://www.hppr.org
Editorial Profile: KANZ-FM is a non-commercial station owned by Kanza Society Inc. The format of the station is news and classical. KANZ-FM broadcasts to the Garden City, KS area at 91.1 FM.

KAOC-FM
Owner: Simmons Media Group
Editorial: 1403 3Rd St, Langdon, North Dakota 58249-2232. T: 1 701 256-1080
W: http://www.maverick105fm.com
Editorial Profile: KAOC-FM is a commercial station owned by Simmons Media Group. The format of the station is contemporary country. KAOC-FM broadcasts to the Langdon, ND area at 105.1 FM.

KAOD-FM
Owner: Red Rock Radio Corp.
Editorial: 501 S Lake Ave, Ste 200, Duluth, Minnesota 55802. T: 1 218 728-9500
E: production@redrockradio.org
W: http://www.95kqds.com
Editorial Profile: KAOD-FM is a commercial station owned by Red Rock Radio Corp. The format of the station is classic rock music. KAOD-FM broadcasts to the Duluth, MN area at 106.7 FM.

KAOI-AM
Owner: Visionary Related Entertainment
Editorial: 1900 Main St, Wailuku, Hawaii 96793-1900. T: 1 808 244-9145
E: kaoi@kaoi.net W: http://www.kaoi.net
Editorial Profile: KAOI-AM is commercial station owned by Visionary Related Entertainment. The format of the station is news, talk and sports. KAOI-AM broadcasts to the Wailuku, HI area at 1110 AM.

KAOI-FM
Owner: Visionary Related Entertainment
Editorial: 1900 Main St, Wailuku, Hawaii 96793-1900. T: 1 808 244-9145
E: kaoi@kaoi.net W: http://www.kaoi.net
Editorial Profile: KAOI-FM is a commercial station owned by Visionary Related Entertainment. The format of the station is AAA-Adult Album Alternative. KAOI-FM broadcasts to the Wailuku, HI area at 95.1 FM.

KAOK-AM
Owner: Cumulus Media Inc.
Editorial: 425 Broad St, Lake Charles, Louisiana 70601. T: 1 337 439-3300
W: http://www.kaok.com
Editorial Profile: KAOK-AM is a commercial station owned by Cumulus Media Inc. The format of the station is news and talk. KAOK-AM broadcasts to the Lake Charles, LA area at 1400 AM.

KAOL-AM
Owner: Kanza Inc.
Editorial: 102 N Mason St, Carrollton, Missouri 64633-2159. T: 1 660 542-0404
W: http://kaolradio.com
Editorial Profile: KAOL-AM is a commercial station owned by Kanza Inc. The format of the station is classic country. KAOL-AM broadcasts to the Carrollton, MO area at 1410 AM.

KAOR-FM
Owner: University of South Dakota
Editorial: Al Neuharth Media Center, Room 205, Vermillion, South Dakota 57069.
T: 1 605 677-5477 E: kaor@usd.edu
W: http://www.kaor.org
Editorial Profile: KAOR-FM is a non-commercial station owned by the University of South Dakota. The format of the station is rock alternative. KAOR-FM broadcasts to the Vermillion, SD area at 91.1 FM.

KAOS-FM
Owner: Evergreen State College
Editorial: 2700 Evergreen Pkwy Nw, Olympia, Washington 98505-0001. T: 1 360 867-6895
E: kaos@evergreen.edu
W: http://www.kaosradio.org
Editorial Profile: KAOS-FM is a non-commercial station owned by Evergreen State College. The format of the station is variety. KAOS-FM broadcasts to the Olympia, WA area at 89.3 FM.

KAOX-FM
Owner: Simmons Media Group
Editorial: 436 Fossil Butte Dr, Kemmerer, Wyoming 83101. T: 1 307 877-4422

KAOY-FM
Owner: New West Broadcasting
Editorial: 1145 Kilauea Ave, Hilo, Hawaii 96720-4203. T: 1 808 935-5461
W: http://www.kwxx.com
Editorial Profile: KAOY-FM is a commercial station owned by New West Broadcasting. The format of the station is a variety of Hawaiian music. KAOY-FM broadcasts to the Kona, HI at 101.5 FM.

KAPA-FM
Owner: Pacific Media Group
Editorial: 75-5852 Alii Dr, Ste B1 & B2 Beachbuilding, Kailua Kona, Hawaii 96740-1310. T: 1 808 329-6633
E: studio@kaparadio.com
W: http://www.kaparadio.com
Editorial Profile: KAPA-FM is a commercial station owned by Pacific Media Group. The format of the station is Hawaiian AC. KAPA-FM's target audience is listeners, ages 18 to 64, in the Hilo, HI area. The station airs locally at 100.3 FM.

KAPB-FM
Owner: Gay(Tom)
Editorial: 520 Chester St, Marksville, Louisiana 71351-2844. T: 1 318 253-9331
E: kapbfm977@gmail.com
W: http://www.kapbfm.com
Editorial Profile: KAPB-FM is a commercial station owned by Tom Gay. The format of the station is country. KAPB-FM broadcasts to the Marksville, LA area at 97.7 FM.

KAPE-AM
Owner: Withers Broadcasting of Missouri, LLC
Editorial: 901 S Kingshighway St, Cape Girardeau, Missouri 63703-8003.
T: 1 573 339-7000 E: news@withersradio.net
W: http://kaperadio1550.com
Editorial Profile: KAPE-AM is a commercial station owned by Withers Broadcasting of Missouri, LLC. The format of the station is news and talk. KAPE-AM broadcasts to the Cape Girardeau, MO area at 1550 AM.

KAPL-AM
Owner: Applegate Media Inc.
Editorial: 7590 Highway 238, Jacksonville, Oregon 97530-9140. T: 1 541 899-5275
E: staff@kaplradio.com
W: http://www.kaplradio.org
Editorial Profile: KAPL-AM is a non-commercial station owned by the Applegate Media Inc. The format of the station is religious talk and music. KAPL-AM broadcasts in the Jacksonville, OR area at 1300 AM.

KAPN-FM
Owner: Brazos Valley Communications LLC
Editorial: 1240 E Villa Maria Rd, Bryan, Texas 77802-2519. T: 1 979 776-1240
W: http://www.1073theplanet.com
Editorial Profile: KAPN-FM is a commercial station owned by Brazos Valley Communications LLC. The format of the station is hot adult contemporary. KAPN-FM broadcasts to the Brenham, TX area at 107.3 FM.

KAPR-AM
Owner: Sonora Broadcasting, LLC
Editorial: 3222 S Richey Ave, Tucson, Arizona 85713-5498. T: 1 520 790-2440
E: info@kvoi.com W: http://www.kvoi.com/

Editorial Profile: KAPR-AM is a commercial station owned by Sonora Broadcasting, LLC. The format of the station is talk. KAPR-AM broadcasts to the Tucson, AZ area at 930 AM.

KAPS-AM
Owner: J & J Broadcasting, Inc.
Editorial: 2029 Freeway Dr, Mount Vernon, Washington 98273-5470. T: 1 360 424-7676
E: kapsradio@gmail.com
W: http://www.kapsradio.com
Editorial Profile: KAPS-AM is a commercial station owned by J & J Broadcasting, Inc. The format of the station is contemporary country. KAPS-AM broadcasts to the Seattle area at 660 AM.

KAPW-FM
Owner: Reynolds Radio Inc.
Editorial: 212 Old Grande Blvd, Tyler, Texas 75703-4226. T: 1 903 581-5259
E: spots@theblaze.cc
W: http://www.power993.fm
Editorial Profile: KAPW-FM is a commercial station owned by Reynolds Radio Inc. The format is Bilingual Top 40/CHR. KAPW-FM broadcasts to the Tyler, TX area at 99.3 FM.

KAQA-FM
Owner: Kekahu Foundation Inc.
Editorial: 4520D Hanalei Plantation Rd, Princeville, Hawaii 96722-5420.
T: 1 808 826-7774 E: kkcr@kkcr.org
W: http://www.kkcr.org
Editorial Profile: KAQA-FM is a non-commercial station owned by Kekahu Foundation Inc. The format of the station is variety. KAQA-FM broadcasts to the Princeville, HI area at 90.9 FM.

KARA-FM
Owner: Educational Media Foundation
Editorial: 5700 W Oaks Blvd, Rocklin, California 95765. T: 1 916 251-2142
W: http://www.air1.com
Editorial Profile: KARA-FM is a non-commercial station owned by Educational Media Foundation. The format of the station is contemporary Christian. KARA-FM broadcasts to the Rocklin, CA.

KARB-FM
Owner: Eastern Utah Broadcasting
Editorial: 1899 N. Carbonville Rd, Price, Utah 84501. T: 1 435 637-1167
W: http://www.castlecountryradio.com
Editorial Profile: KARB-FM is a commercial station owned by Eastern Utah Broadcasting. The format of the station is contemporary country. KARB-FM broadcasts to the Salt Lake City area at 98.3 FM.

KARI-AM
Owner: Way Broadcasting Inc.
Editorial: 4840 Lincoln Rd, Blaine, Washington 98230-9602. T: 1 360 371-5500
E: info@kari55.com W: http://www.kari55.com
Editorial Profile: KARI-AM is a commercial station owned by Way Broadcasting Inc. The format of the station is gospel and religious programming. KARI-AM broadcasts to the Blaine, WA area at 550 AM.

KARL-FM
Owner: KMHL Broadcasting Corp.
Editorial: 1414 E College Dr, Marshall, Minnesota 56258. T: 1 507 532-2282
E: info@marshallradio.net
W: http://1051karl.com
Editorial Profile: KARL-FM is a commercial station owned by KMHL Broadcasting Corp. The format of the station is contemporary country music. KARL-FM broadcasts to the Marshall, MN area at 105.1 FM.

KARM-FM
Owner: Harvest Broadcasting Company, Inc.
Editorial: 1300 S Woodland St, Visalia, California 93277-4214. T: 1 559 627-5276
E: info@mypromisefm.com
W: http://www.mypromisefm.com
Editorial Profile: KARM-FM is a non-commercial station owned by Harvest Broadcasting Company, Inc. The format of the station is Christian teaching. KARM-FM broadcasts to the Visalia, CA area at 89.7 FM.

KARN-AM
Owner: Cumulus Media Inc
Editorial: 700 Wellington Hills Rd, Little Rock, Arkansas 72211-2026. T: 1 501 401-0200
W: http://www.sportsanimal920.com
Editorial Profile: KARN-AM is a commercial station owned by Cumulus Media Inc. The format of the station is sports. KARN-AM broadcasts in the Little Rock, AR area at 920 AM

KARN-FM
Owner: Cumulus Media Inc
Editorial: 700 Wellington Hills Rd, Little Rock, Arkansas 72211-2026. **T:** 1 501 401-0200
W: http://www.karnnewsradio.com
Editorial Profile: KARN-FM is a commercial station owned by Cumulus Media Inc. The format of the station is news and talk. KARN-FM broadcasts to the Little Rock, AR area at 102.5 FM.

KARP-FM
Owner: Iowa City Broadcasting Co.
Editorial: 20132 Highway 15 N, Hutchinson, Minnesota 55350-5642. **T:** 1 320 587-2140
E: info@karpradio.com
W: http://www.karpradio.com
Editorial Profile: KARP-FM is a commercial station owned by Iowa City Broadcasting Co.The format of the station is classic country. KARP-FM broadcasts to the Hutchinson, MN area at 106.9 FM.

KARS-AM
Owner: American General Media
Editorial: 4125 Carlisle Blvd NE, Albuquerque, New Mexico 87107-4806. **T:** 1 505 878-0980
W: http://www.area102.9.com
Editorial Profile: KARS-AM is a commercial station owned by American General Media. The format of the station is a modern rock. KARS-AM broadcasts to the Belen, NM area at 840 AM.

KARS-FM
Owner: Fort Collins /Lafayette Divestiture Trust (The)
Editorial: 600 Main St, Windsor, Colorado 80550-5133. **T:** 1 970 674-2700
W: http://www.rock1029.com
Editorial Profile: KARS-FM is a commercial station owned by Fort Collins /Lafayette Divestiture Trust (The). The format of the station is rock/album oriented rock. KARS-FM broadcasts in the Cheyenne, WY area with a booster in Fort Collins, CO at 102.9 FM.

KART-AM
Owner: Lee Family Broadcasting
Editorial: 47 N 100 W, Jerome, Idaho 83338-5403. **T:** 1 208 324-8181
E: traffic@leeradio.net
Editorial Profile: KART-AM is a commercial station owned by Lee Family Broadcasting. The format of the station is country music. KART-AM broadcasts to the Jerome, ID area at 1400 AM.

KARU-FM
Owner: Educational Media Foundation
Editorial: 7301 Broadway Ext, Ste 131, Oklahoma City, Oklahoma 73116-9038.
T: 1 405 708-5683
Editorial Profile: KARU-FM is a non-commercial station owned by Educational Media Foundation. The format of the station is contemporary Christian. KWRI-FM broadcasts to the Cache, OK area at 88.9 FM.

KARV-AM
Owner: KERM Inc.
Editorial: 201 W 2nd St, Russellville, Arkansas 72801. **T:** 1 479 968-1184
E: karv_kyel@yahoo.com
Editorial Profile: KARV-AM is a commercial station owned by KERM Inc. The format of the station is news and talk. KARV-AM broadcasts in the Russellville, AR, area at 610 AM.

KARV-FM
Owner: KERM Inc.
Editorial: 201 W 2nd St, Russellville, Arkansas 72801. **T:** 1 479 968-1184
Editorial Profile: KARV-FM is a commercial station owned by KERM Inc. The format of the station is news and talk. KARV-FM broadcasts to the Ola, AR, area at 101.3 FM.

KARX-FM
Owner: Cumulus Media Inc.
Editorial: 301 S Polk St, Ste 100, Amarillo, Texas 79101. **T:** 1 806 342-5200
E: karx957@hotmail.com
W: http://www.957thekar.com
Editorial Profile: KARX-FM is a commercial station owned by Cumulus Media Inc. The format of the station is classic rock. KARX-FM broadcasts to the Amarillo, TX area at 95.7 FM.

KARY-FM
Owner: New Northwest Broadcasters LLC
Editorial: 1200 Chesterly Dr, Ste 160, Yakima, Washington 98902. **T:** 1 509 248-2900
W: http://www.cherryfm.com
Editorial Profile: KARY-FM is owned by New Northwest Broadcasters. The format of the station is oldies. KARY-FM broadcasts to the Yakima, WA area at 100.9 FM.

KARZ-FM
Owner: KMHL Broadcasting Corp.
Editorial: 1414 E College Dr, Marshall, Minnesota 56258-2027. **T:** 1 507 532-2282
E: info@marshallradio.net
W: http://1075karz.com
Editorial Profile: KARZ-FM is a commercial station owned by KMHL Broadcasting Corp. The format of the station is rock. KARZ-FM broadcasts to the Marshall, MN area at 107.5 FM.

KASA-AM
Owner: Herrera(Moises)
Editorial: 1445 W Baseline Rd, Phoenix, Arizona 85041-7010. **T:** 1 602 276-4241
Editorial Profile: KASA-AM is a commercial station owned by Moises Herrera. The format of the station is Hispanic Christian programming. KASA-AM broadcasts in the Phoenix area at 1540 AM.

KASB-FM
Owner: Bellevue School District No.405
Editorial: 10416 Wolverine Way, Bellevue, Washington 98004-4622. **T:** 1 425 4567101
E: congerb@kasbfm.com
W: http://kasbfm.com
Editorial Profile: KASB-FM is a non-commercial station owned by Bellevue School District No.405. The format of the station is variety. KASB-FM broadcasts to the Bellevue, WA area at 89.9 FM.

KASE-FM
Owner: Clear Channel Media and Entertainment
Editorial: 3601 S Congress Ave, Austin, Texas 78704-7250. **T:** 1 512 684-7300
W: http://www.kase101.com
Editorial Profile: KASE-FM is a commercial station owned by Clear Channel Media and Entertainment. The format of the station is contemporary country music. KASE-FM broadcasts to the Austin, TX area at 100.7 FM.

KASF-FM
Owner: Adams State College
Editorial: 208 Edgemont Blvd, Alamosa, Colorado 81101-2373. **T:** 1 719 587-7862
E: kasf909FM@gmail.com
W: http://kasf.asf.adams.edu
Editorial Profile: KASF-FM is a non-commercial station owned by Adams State College. The format of the station is college variety. KASF-FM broadcasts to the Alamosa, CO area at 90.9 FM.

KASH-FM
Owner: Clear Channel Media and Entertainment
Editorial: 800 E Dimond Blvd, Ste 3-370, Anchorage, Alaska 99515. **T:** 1 907 522-1515
E: news@650keni.com
W: http://www.kashcountry1075.com
Editorial Profile: KASH-FM is a commercial station owned by Clear Channel Media and Entertainment. The format of the station is contemporary country music. KASH-FM broadcasts to the Anchorage, AK area at 107.5 FM.

KASI-AM
Owner: Clear Channel Media and Entertainment
Editorial: 415 Main St, Ames, Iowa 50010.
T: 1 515 232-1430
W: http://www.1430kasi.com
Editorial Profile: KASI-AM is a commercial station owned by Clear Channel Media and Entertainment. The format of the station is news, sports and talk. KASI-AM broadcasts to the Ames, IA area at 1430 AM.

KASL-AM
Owner: Cook Brothers Broadcasting, LLC
Editorial: 2208 W Main St, Newcastle, Wyoming 82701-2331. **T:** 1 307 746-4433
E: news@kaslradio.com
W: http://www.kaslradio.com
Editorial Profile: KASL-AM is a commercial station owned by Cook Brothers Broadcasting, LLC. The format of the station is classic country. KASL-AM broadcasts to the Newcastle, WY area at 1240 AM.

KASM-AM
Owner: StarCom LLC
Editorial: 35223 238th Ave, Albany, Minnesota 56307-9798. **T:** 1 320 845-2184
E: studio@kasmradionetwork.com
W: http://www.kasmwqpm.com
Editorial Profile: KASM-AM is a commercial station owned by StarCom LLC. The format of the station is agricultural and talk. KASM-AM broadcasts in the St. Cloud, MN area at 1150 AM.

KASO-AM
Owner: Greenwood Acres Baptist Church
Editorial: 410 Lakeshore Dr, Minden, Louisiana 71055-2139. **T:** 1 318 377-1240
E: kasoradio@yahoo.com
W: http://www.kaso1240.com
Editorial Profile: KASO-AM is commercial station owned by Fred Caldwell. The format of the station is classic hits. KASO-AM broadcasts to the Minden, LA area at 1240 AM.

KASR-FM
Owner: Creative Sports Media Inc.
Editorial: 1072 Markham St, Ste 300, Conway, Arkansas 72032-4310. **T:** 1 501 327-6611
E: kasr@sbcglobal.net **W:** http://www.kasr.com
Editorial Profile: KASR-FM is a non-commercial station owned by Creative Sports Media Inc. The format of the station is sports. KASR-FM broadcasts to the Conway, AR area at 92.7 FM.

KASS-FM
Owner: Mount Rushmore Broadcasting Inc.
Editorial: 218 N Wolcott St, Casper, Wyoming 82601-1923. **T:** 1 307 265-1984
E: mrbnews@wyoming.com
Editorial Profile: KASS-FM is a commercial station owned by Mount Rushmore Broadcasting Inc. The format for the station is rock. KASS-FM broadcasts to the Casper, WY area at 106.9 FM.

KAST-AM
Owner: Ohana Media Group
Editorial: 285 SW Main Ct, Ste 200, Warrenton, Oregon 97146-9457.
T: 1 503 861-6620
W: http://www.kast1370.com
Editorial Profile: KAST-AM is a commercial station owned by Ohana Media Group. The format of the station is news and talk. KAST-AM broadcasts in the Astoria, OR area at 1370 AM.

KASU-FM
Owner: Arkansas State University
Editorial: 104 Cooley St, State University, Arkansas 72467-9999. **T:** 1 870 972-2200
E: kasu@astate.edu
W: http://www.kasu.astate.edu
Editorial Profile: KASU-FM is a non-commercial station owned by Arkansas State University. The format of the station is variety. KSAU-FM broadcasts to the State University, AR area at 91.9 FM.

KASV-FM
Owner: Top 'O Texas Educational Broadcasting Foundation
Editorial: 1084 Coronado Cir, Borger, Texas 79007-2502. **T:** 1 806 359-8855
E: kjrt@kingdomkeys.org
W: http://www.kingdomkeys.org
Editorial Profile: KASV-FM is a non-commercial station owned by Top 'O Texas Educational Broadcasting Foundation. The format of the station is Christian music and talk programming. The station broadcasts locally to the Borger, TX area at a frequency of 88.3 FM.

KATA-AM
Owner: Bicoastal Media LLC
Editorial: 5640 S Broadway St, Eureka, California 95503-6905. **T:** 1 707 442-2000
E: eurekanews@bicoastalmedia.com
W: http://www.kata1340.com
Editorial Profile: KATA-AM is a commercial station owned by Bicoastal Media LLC. The format of the station is sports. KATA-AM broadcasts to the Eureka, CA area at 1340 AM.

KATB-FM
Owner: Christian Broadcasting Inc.
Editorial: 6401 E Northern Lights Blvd, Anchorage, Alaska 99504. **T:** 1 907 333-5282
W: http://www.katb.org
Editorial Profile: KATB-FM is a non-commercial station owned by Christian Broadcasting Inc. The format of the station is Christian. KATB-FM broadcasts to the Anchorage, AK area at 89.3 FM.

KATC-FM
Owner: Cumulus Media Inc
Editorial: 6805 Corporate Dr, Colorado Springs, Colorado 80919-1976.
T: 1 719 593-2700
W: http://www.catcountry951.com
Editorial Profile: KATC-FM is a commercial station owned by Cumulus Media Inc. The format of the station is contemporary country. KATC-FM broadcasts to the Colorado Springs, CO area at 95.1 FM.

KATD-AM
Owner: Multicultural Radio Broadcasting Inc.
Editorial: 44 Gough St Ste 301, San Francisco, California 94103-5424.
T: 1 415 978-5378 **E:** kiqi1010@gmail.com
W: http://www.kiqi1010am.com
Editorial Profile: KATD-AM is a commercial station owned by Multicultural Radio Broadcasting Inc. The format of the station is Hispanic. KATD-AM broadcasts to the San Francisco area at 990 AM.

KATE-AM
Owner: Three Eagles Communications Co.
Editorial: 1633 W Main St, Albert Lea, Minnesota 56007-1868. **T:** 1 507 373-2338
W: http://www.myalbertlea.com
Editorial Profile: KATE-AM is a commercial station owned by Three Eagles Communications Co. The format of the station is talk. KATE-AM broadcasts to the Rochester, MN and Mason City, IA areas at 1450 AM.

KATF-FM
Owner: Radio Dubuque Inc.
Editorial: 346 W 8th St, Dubuque, Iowa 52001-4627. **T:** 1 563 690-0800
E: katfm@katfm.com
W: http://www.katfm.com
Editorial Profile: KATF-FM is a commercial station owned by Radio Dubuque Inc. The format for the station is adult contemporary music. KATF-FM broadcasts to the Cedar Rapids, IA area at 92.9 FM.

KATH-AM
Owner: Chatham Hill Foundation, Inc.
Editorial: 8828 N Stemmons Fwy, Ste 106, Dallas, Texas 75247. **T:** 1 214 951-0132
W: http://grnonline.info
Editorial Profile: KATH-AM is a commercial station owned by Chatham Hill Foundation, Inc. The format of the station is religious. KATH-AM broadcasts to the Dallas area at 1000 AM.

KATI-FM
Owner: Zimmer Radio Group
Editorial: 3109 S 10 Mile Dr, Jefferson City, Missouri 65109. **T:** 1 573 893-5696
W: http://www.943kat.com
Editorial Profile: KATI-FM is a commercial station owned by Zimmer Radio Group. The format of the station is contemporary country music. KATI-FM broadcasts to the Jefferson City, MO area at 94.3 FM.

KATJ-FM
Owner: El Dorado Broadcasting
Editorial: 12370 Hesperia Rd, Victorville, California 92395-7719. **T:** 1 760 241-1313
W: http://www.katcountry1007.com
Editorial Profile: KATJ-FM is a commercial station owned by El Dorado Broadcasting. The format of the station is country music. KATJ-FM broadcasts to the Victorville, CA area at 100.7 FM.

KATK-AM
Owner: Hughes Broadcasting
Editorial: 1609 Radio Blvd, Carlsbad, New Mexico 88220. **T:** 1 575 887-7563
W: http://www.carlsbadradio.com
Editorial Profile: KATK-AM is a commercial station owned by Hughes Broadcasting. The format of the station is classic hits. KATK-AM broadcasts to the Carlsbad, NM area at 740 AM.

KATK-FM
Owner: Hughes Broadcasting
Editorial: 1609 Radio Blvd, Carlsbad, New Mexico 88220-6427. **T:** 1 575 885-2151
W: http://www.carlsbadradio.com
Editorial Profile: KATK-FM is a commercial station owned by Hughes Broadcasting. The format of the station is country. KATK-FM broadcasts to the Carlsbad, NM area at 92.1 FM.

KATL-AM
Owner: Star Printing Co.
Editorial: 818 Main St, Miles City, Montana 59301. **T:** 1 406 234-7700
E: katlradio@katlradio.com
W: http://www.katlradio.com
Editorial Profile: KATL-AM is a commercial station owned by Star Printing Co. The format of the station is adult contemporary music. KATL-AM broadcasts in the Miles City, MT area at 770 AM.

KATM-FM

Owner: Cumulus Media Inc
Editorial: 3136 Boeing Way, Stockton, California 95206. **T:** 1 209 766-5103
W: http://www.katm.com
Editorial Profile: KATM-FM is a commercial station owned by Cumulus Media Inc. The format of the station is country music. KATM-FM broadcasts in the Modesto, CA area at 103.3 FM.

KATO-AM

Owner: McMurray Communications Inc.
Editorial: 3335 W 8th St, Thatcher, Arizona 85552. **T:** 1 928 428-1230
E: traffic@mcmurrayradio.com
W: http://www.mysouthernaz.com
Editorial Profile: KATO-AM is a commercial station owned by McMurray Communications Inc. The format of the station is news and talk. KATO-AM broadcasts in the Safford, AZ area at 1230 AM.

KATO-FM

Owner: Radio Mankato
Editorial: 59346 Madison Ave, Mankato, Minnesota 56001-8518. **T:** 1 507 345-4537
E: news@ktoe.com
W: http://www.radiomankato.com

KATP-FM

Owner: Townsquare Media, LLC
Editorial: 6214 W 34th Ave, Amarillo, Texas 79109-4006. **T:** 1 806 355-9777
W: http://blakefm.com
Editorial Profile: KATP-FM is a commercial station owned by Townsquare Media, LLC. The format of the station is contemporary country. KATP-FM broadcasts to the Amarillo, TX, area at 101.9 FM.

KATQ-AM

Owner: Radio Int'l/KATQ Broadcast Association Inc.
Editorial: 112 E 3rd Ave, Plentywood, Montana 59254-2223. **T:** 1 406 765-1480
E: katq@nemont.net
W: http://www.katqradio.com
Editorial Profile: KATQ-AM is a commercial station owned by Radio Int'l/KATQ Broadcast Association Inc. The format of the station is classic country. KATQ-AM broadcasts to the Plentywood, MT area at 1070 AM.

KATQ-FM

Owner: Radio Int'l/KATQ Broadcast Association Inc.
Editorial: 112 E 3rd Ave, Plentywood, Montana 59254-2223. **T:** 1 406 765-1480
E: katq@nemont.net
W: http://www.katqradio.com
Editorial Profile: KATQ-FM is a commercial station owned by Radio Int'l/KATQ Broadcast Assoc. Inc. The format of the station is classic rock. KATQ-FM broadcasts in the Plentywood, MT area at 100.1 FM.

KATR-FM

Owner: Media Logic LLC
Editorial: 519 W Main St, Sterling, Colorado 80751-3059. **T:** 1 970 521-2732
E: medialogic@kci.net
W: http://www.katcountry983.com
Editorial Profile: KATR-FM is a commercial station owned by Media Logic LLC. The format of the station is contemporary country. KATR-FM broadcasts to the Denver area at 98.3 FM.

KATS-FM

Owner: Townsquare Media, LLC
Editorial: 4010 Summitview Ave, Yakima, Washington 98908. **T:** 1 509 972-3461
E: katsfm@gmail.com
W: http://www.katsfm.com
Editorial Profile: KATS-FM is a commercial station owned by Townsquare Media, LLC. The format of the station is rock/album-oriented rock. KATS-FM broadcasts to the Yakima, WA area at 94.5 FM.

KATT-FM

Owner: Cumulus Media Inc
Editorial: 4045 NW 64th St, Ste 600, Oklahoma City, Oklahoma 73116.
T: 1 405 848-0100 **W:** http://www.katt.com
Editorial Profile: KATT-FM is a commercial station owned by Cumulus Media Inc. The format of the station is rock music. KATT-FM broadcasts to the Oklahoma City area at 100.5 FM.

KATW-FM

Owner: Pacific Empire Radio Corp.
Editorial: 403 Capitol St, Lewiston, Idaho 83501-1815. **T:** 1 208 743-6564
E: wecare@catfm.com
W: http://www.catfm.com

Editorial Profile: KATW-FM is a commercial station owned by Pacific Empire Radio Corp. The format of the station is hot adult contemporary music. KATW-FM broadcasts to the Lewiston, ID area at 101.5 FM.

KATX-FM

Owner: High Plains Radio Network
Editorial: 2900 W Washington St, Stephenville, Texas 76401-3734.
T: 1 254 629-2621 **E:** katx@hprnetwork.com
W: http://www.hprnetwork.com/index_central.html
Editorial Profile: KATX-FM is an commercial station owned by High Plains Radio Network. The format of the station is classic rock. ATX-FM broadcasts to the Eastland, TX area at 97.7 FM.

KATY-FM

Owner: All Pro Broadcasting Inc.
Editorial: 27431 Enterprise Cir W, Temecula, California 92590-4833. **T:** 1 951 506-1222
W: http://www.1013katy.com
Editorial Profile: KATY-FM is a commercial station owned by All-Pro Broadcasting Inc. The format of the station is adult contemporary music. KATY-FM broadcasts to the Temecula, CA area at 101.3 FM.

KATZ-AM

Owner: Clear Channel Media and Entertainment
Editorial: 1001 Highlands Plaza Dr W, Ste 100, Saint Louis, Missouri 63110.
T: 1 314 333-8000
W: http://www.gospel1600.com
Editorial Profile: KATZ-AM is a commercial station owned by Clear Channel Media and Entertainment. The format of the station is gospel music. KATZ-AM broadcasts to the St. Louis area at 1600 AM.

KAUD-FM

Owner: University of Missouri
Editorial: 409 Jesse Hall Univ Of Missouri, Columbia, Missouri 65211-0001.
T: 1 573 882-3431 **E:** news@kbia.org
W: http://www.kbia.org
Editorial Profile: KAUD-FM is a non-commercial station owned by University of Missouri. The format of the station is news and classical music. KAUD-FM broadcasts to the Mexico, MO area at 90.5.

KAUJ-FM

Owner: Simmons Broadcasting, Inc.
Editorial: 856 W 12th St, Grafton, North Dakota 58237. **T:** 1 701 352-0431
W: http://www.walshcountydailynews.com
Editorial Profile: KAUJ-FM is a commercial station owned by the Simmons Broadcasting, Inc. The format of the station is oldies. KAUJ-FM broadcasts to the Fargo, ND area at 100.9 FM.

KAUM-FM

Owner: Baum(James G.)
Editorial: West Highway 80, Colorado City, Texas 79512. **T:** 1 325 728-5530
E: kvmckaum@sbcglobal.net
W: http://www.tsnradio.com
Editorial Profile: KAUM-FM is a commercial station owned by James G. Baum. The format of the station is country music. KAUM-FM broadcasts in the Colorado City, TX area at 107.1 FM.

KAUR-FM

Owner: Minnesota Public Radio
Editorial: 2001 S Summit Ave 2001 Smt S, Sioux Falls, South Dakota 57197-0001.
T: 1 605 274-4388 **W:** http://kaur.augie.edu

KAUS-AM

Owner: Three Eagles Communications Co.
Editorial: 18431 State Highway 105, Austin, Minnesota 55912-6147. **T:** 1 507 437-7666
E: kaus@kaus.com
W: http://www.myaustinminnesota.com
Editorial Profile: KAUS-AM is a commercial station owned by Three Eagles Communications Co. The format of the station is news, sports and talk. KAUS-AM broadcasts to the Austin, MN area at 1480 AM.

KAUS-FM

Owner: Three Eagles Communications Co.
Editorial: 18431 State Highway 105, Austin, Minnesota 55912. **T:** 1 507 437-7666
W: http://www.myaustinminnesota.com
Editorial Profile: KAUS-FM is a commercial station owned by Three Eagles Communications Co. The format of the station is country music. KAUS-FM broadcasts to the Austin, MN area at 99.9 FM.

KAUU-FM

Owner: Patrick Communications
Editorial: 515 S 700 E Ste 1C, Salt Lake City, Utah 84102-2802. **T:** 1 801 412-6040
Editorial Profile: KAUU-FM is a commercial station is brokered by Patrick Communications and operated by SLC Divestiture Trust I. The format of the station is classic rock. KAUU-FM broadcasts to the Salt Lake City area at 105.1 FM.

KAVA-AM

Owner: Latino Communications
Editorial: 600 Grant St, Ste 600, Denver, Colorado 80203. **T:** 1 303 733-5266
Editorial Profile: KAVA-AM is a commercial station owned by Latino Communications. The format of the station is news/talk. KAVA-AM broadcasts to the Denver area at 1480 AM.

KAVL-AM

Owner: RZ Radio LLC
Editorial: 570 E Avenue Q9, Palmdale, California 93550-4655. **T:** 1 661 947-3107
W: http://www.foxsports610.com
Editorial Profile: KAVL-AM is a commercial station owned by RZ Radio LLC. The format of the station is sports. KAVL-AM broadcasts in the Lancaster, CA area at 610 AM.

KAVP-AM

Owner: Western Slope Communications
Editorial: 751 Horizon Ct Ste 225, Grand Junction, Colorado 81506-8767.
T: 1 970 241-6460
E: production@wscradio.net
W: http://wscradio.net
Editorial Profile: KAVP-AM is a commercial station owned by Western Slope Communications. The format of the station is sports/talk. KAVP-AM broadcasts to the Grand Junction-Montrose, CO area at 1450 AM.

KAVV-FM

Owner: Stereo 97 Inc.
Editorial: 156 W 5th St, Benson, Arizona 85602-6508. **T:** 1 520 290-9797
W: http://www.cavefm.com
Editorial Profile: KAVV-FM is a commercial station owned by Stereo 97 Inc. The format of the station is country. KAVV-FM broadcasts to the Tucson, AZ area at 97.7 FM.

KAVW-FM

Owner: American Family Association
Editorial: 107 Park Gate Dr, Tupelo, Mississippi 38801-3010. **T:** 1 662 844-8888
E: comments@afr.net **W:** http://www.afr.net
Editorial Profile: KAVW-FM is the Tupelo, Mississippi American Family Radio station.

KAVX-FM

Owner: Lufkin Educational Broadcasting Foundation
Editorial: 151 Holmes Rd, Lufkin, Texas 75904. **T:** 1 936 639-5673
E: 919kavx@kavx.org **W:** http://www.kavx.org
Editorial Profile: KAVX-FM is a non-commercial station owned by Lufkin Educational Broadcasting Foundation. The format of the station is religious talk. KAVX-FM broadcasts to the Lufkin, TX area at 91.9 FM.

KAWC-AM

Owner: Arizona Western College
Editorial: 2020 S Avenue 8 E, Yuma, Arizona 85365-6900. **T:** 1 928 344-7690
E: info@kawc.org **W:** http://www.kawc.org
Editorial Profile: KAWC-AM is a non-commercial station owned by Arizona Western College. The format of the station is variety. KAWC-AM broadcasts to the Yuma, AZ area at 1320 AM.

KAWC-FM

Owner: Arizona Western College
Editorial: 2020 S Avenue 8 E, Yuma, Arizona 85365-6900. **T:** 1 928 344-7690
E: info@kawc.org **W:** http://www.kawc.org
Editorial Profile: KAWC-FM is a non-commercial station owned by Arizona Western College. The format of the station is news and talk. KAWC-FM broadcasts in the Yuma, AZ area at 88.9 FM.

KAWL-AM

Owner: MWB Broadcasting LLC
Editorial: 1309 Road 11, York, Nebraska 68467. **T:** 1 402 362-4433
E: kawl@kawlam.com
W: http://www.kawlam.com
Editorial Profile: KAWL-AM is a commercial station owned by MWB Broadcasting LLC. The format of the station is oldies. KAWL-AM broadcasts to the Lincoln, NE area at 1370 AM.

KAWO-FM

Owner: Townsquare Media, LLC
Editorial: 827 E Park Blvd Ste 100, Boise, Idaho 83712-7783. **T:** 1 208 344-6363
W: http://www.wow1043.com
Editorial Profile: KAWO-FM is a commercial station owned by Townsquare Media, LLC. The format of the station is contemporary country. KAWO-FM broadcasts to the Boise, ID area at 104.3 FM.

KAWW-AM

Owner: Crain Media Group LLC
Editorial: 111 N Spring St, Searcy, Arkansas 72143. **T:** 1 501 268-7123
E: production@crainmedia.com
W: http://www.crainmedia.com
Editorial Profile: KAWW-AM is a commercial station owned by Crain Media Group LLC. The format of the station is news, talk and sports. KAWW-AM broadcasts in the Heber Springs, AR area at 1370 AM.

KAWZ-FM

Owner: Calvary Chapel Twin Falls
Editorial: 4002 N 3300 E, Twin Falls, Idaho 83301. **T:** 1 208 734-4357
E: feedback@csnradio.com
W: http://www.csnradio.com
Editorial Profile: KAWZ-FM is a non commercial station owned by Calvary Chapel Twin Falls. The format of the station is religious music and talk. KAWZ-FM broadcasts in the Twin Falls, ID area at 89.9 FM.

KAXA-FM

Owner: Thomas Gebhart's Reddog Media
Editorial: 814 Harper Rd, Kerrville, Texas 78028-2979. **T:** 1 830 896-8380
Editorial Profile: KAXA-FM is a commercial station owned by Thomas Gebhart's Reddog Media. The format of the station is classic rock music, featuring sounds from the 50s, 60s and 70s. KAXA-FM broadcasts to the Kerrville, TX area at a frequency of 103.7 FM.

KAXE-FM

Owner: Northern Community Radio Inc.
Editorial: 260 NE 2nd St, Grand Rapids, Minnesota 55744. **T:** 1 218 326-1234
E: kaxe@kaxe.org **W:** http://www.kaxe.org
Editorial Profile: KAXE-FM is a non-commercial station owned by Northern Community Radio Inc. The format of the station is variety. KAXE-FM broadcasts in the Grand Rapids, MN area at 91.7 FM.

KAXL-FM

Owner: Skyride Unlimited Inc.
Editorial: 110 S Montclair St, Ste 205, Bakersfield, California 93309.
T: 1 661 832-2800 **E:** kaxl@kaxl.com
W: http://www.kaxl.com
Editorial Profile: KAXL-FM's format is Contemporary Christian/ Inspirational. Their target audience is 18-54.

KAYD-FM

Owner: Cumulus Media Inc.
Editorial: 755 S 11th St, Ste 102, Beaumont, Texas 77701. **T:** 1 409 833-9421
W: http://www.kayd.com
Editorial Profile: KAYD-FM is a commercial station owned by Cumulus Media Inc. The format of the station is country music. KAYD-FM broadcasts to the Beaumont, TX area at 101.7 FM.

KAYE-FM

Owner: Northern Oklahoma College
Editorial: 1220 E Grand Ave, Tonkawa, Oklahoma 74653-4022. **T:** 1 580 628-6446
W: http://www.north-ok.edu
Editorial Profile: KAYE-FM is a non-commercial station owned by Northern Oklahoma College. The format of the station is rock alternative. KAYE-FM broadcasts to the Tonkawa, OK area at 90.7 FM.

KAYH-FM

Owner: Bott Broadcasting Co.
Editorial: 2201 S Thompson St, Ste C7, Springdale, Arkansas 72764.
T: 1 479 750-7893
W: http://www.bottradionetwork.com
Editorial Profile: KAYH-FM is a non-commercial station owned by Bott Broadcasting Co. The format of the station is Christian. KAYH-FM broadcasts to Fayetteville, AR and its surrounding areas at 89.3 FM.

KAYL-AM

Owner: Community First Broadcasting
Editorial: 606 1/2 Lake Ave, Storm Lake, Iowa 50588-1875. **T:** 1 712 732-3520
E: production@stormlakeradio.com
W: http://www.stormlakeradio.com

Editorial Profile: KAYL-AM is a commercial station owned by Community First Broadcasting. The format of the station is Spanish Adult Hits. KAYL-AM broadcasts to the Storm Lake, IA area at 990 AM.

KAYL-FM
Owner: Community First Broadcasting
Editorial: 606 1/2 Lake Ave, Storm Lake, Iowa 50588. **T:** 1 712 732-3520
E: production@stormlakeradio.com
W: http://www.kaylradio.com
Editorial Profile: KAYL-FM is a commercial station owned by Community First Broadcasting. The format of the station is adult contemporary music. KAYL-FM broadcasts to the Storm Lake, IA area at 101.7 FM.

KAYO-FM
Owner: Morris Communications
Editorial: 5431 E Mayflower Ln, Ste 3, Wasilla, Alaska 99654-7891.
T: 1 907 631-0493
W: http://www.countrylegends1009.com
Editorial Profile: KAYO-FM is a commercial station owned by Morris Communications. The format of the station is classic country. KAYO-FM broadcasts to the Wasilla, AK area at 100.9.

KAYQ-FM
Owner: Valkyrie Broadcasting Inc.
Editorial: 1649 Commercial St, Warsaw, Missouri 65355-3060. **T:** 1 660 438-7343
E: kayqtraffic@embarqmail.com
Editorial Profile: KAYQ-FM is a commercial station owned by Valkyrie Broadcasting Inc. The format of the station is classic country. KAYQ-FM broadcasts to the Warsaw, MO area at 97.1 FM.

KAYS-AM
Owner: Eagle Radio Inc.
Editorial: 2300 Hall St, Hays, Kansas 67601-3062. **T:** 1 785 625-2578
E: haysnews@eagleradio.net
W: http://www.kaysradio.com
Editorial Profile: KAYS-AM is a commercial station owned by Eagle Radio Inc. The format of the station is oldies. KAYS-AM broadcasts to the Hays, KS area at 1400 AM.

KAYX-FM
Owner: Bott Broadcasting Co.
Editorial: 111 W Main St, Richmond, Missouri 64085-1709. **T:** 1 816 470-9925
E: comments@bottradionetwork.com
W: http://www.bottradionetwork.com
Editorial Profile: KAYX-FM is a commercial station owned by Bott Broadcasting Co. The format of the station is Christian and religious programming. KAYX-FM broadcasts to the Richmond, MO area at 92.5 FM.

KAZA-AM
Owner: Radio Fiesta Corporation
Editorial: 1820 Cochrane Rd, Morgan Hill, California 95037-9029. **T:** 1 805 928-1030
W: http://radiovidaabundante.com
Editorial Profile: KAZA-AM is a commercial station owned by Radio Fiesta Corporation. The format of the station is Hispanic contemporary Christian and religious music. KAZA-AM broadcasts to the San Jose, CA area at 1290 AM.

KAZC-FM
Owner: South Central Oklahoma Christian Broadcasting Inc.
Editorial: 20750 State Hwy 1W, Ada, Oklahoma 74820-5421. **T:** 1 580 332-0902
E: email@thegospelstation.com
W: http://www.thegospelstation.com
Editorial Profile: KAZC-FM is a non-commercial station owned by South Central Oklahoma Christian Broadcasting Inc. The format of the station is gospel. KAZC-FM broadcasts to the Ada, OK area at 88.3 FM.

KAZE-FM
Owner: Reynolds Radio Inc.
Editorial: 212 Grande Blvd, Ste B100, Tyler, Texas 75703. **T:** 1 903 845-5259
E: spots@theblaze.cc
W: http://www.theblaze.fm
Editorial Profile: KAZE-FM is a commercial station owned by Reynolds Radio Inc. The format of the station is urban contemporary. KAZE-FM broadcasts to Tyler, TX area at 106.9 FM and is a simulcast of KBLZ-FM.

KAZF-FM
Owner: Bernal(Paulino)
Editorial: 4501 N McColl Rd, McAllen, Texas 78504-2431. **T:** 1 956 781-5528
Editorial Profile: KAZF-FM is a commercial station owned by Paulino Bernal. The format of the station is Hispanic contemporary Christian programming. KAZF-FM broadcasts to the McAllen, TX area at 91.9 FM.

KAZG-AM
Owner: Hubbard Radio, LLC
Editorial: 4343 E Camelback Rd Ste 200, Phoenix, Arizona 85018-2756.
T: 1 480 941-1007 **W:** http://kazg1440.com
Editorial Profile: KAZG-AM is a commercial station owned by Hubbard Radio, LLC. The format of the station is oldies. KAZG-AM broadcasts to the Phoenix area at 1440 AM.

KAZI-FM
Owner: Austin Community Radio
Editorial: 8906 Wall St Ste 203, Austin, Texas 78754-4542. **T:** 1 512 836-9544
W: http://www.kazifm.org
Editorial Profile: KAZI-FM is a commercial station owned by Austin Community Radio. The format of the station is variety. KAZI-FM broadcasts to the Austin, TX community at 88.7 FM.

KAZM-AM
Owner: Tabback Broadcasting Company
Editorial: 3400 W Highway 89A, Sedona, Arizona 86336-4914. **T:** 1 928 282-4154
E: news@kazmradio.com
W: http://www.kazmradio.com
Editorial Profile: KAZM-AM is a commercial station owned by the Tabback Broadcasting Company. The format of the station is news, talk and sports. KAZM-AM broadcasts to the Phoenix area at 780 AM.

KAZN-AM
Owner: Multicultural Radio Broadcasting Inc.
Editorial: 747 E Green St, Pasadena, California 91101-2145. **T:** 1 626 568-1300
W: http://www.am1300.com
Editorial Profile: KAZN-AM is a commercial station owned by Multicultural Radio Broadcasting Inc. The format of the station is a variety of Chinese music and talk. KAZN-AM broadcasts to the Pasadena, CA area at 1300 AM.

KAZR-FM
Owner: Saga Communications
Editorial: 1416 Locust St, Des Moines, Iowa 50309-3014. **T:** 1 515 280-1350
W: http://www.lazer1033.com
Editorial Profile: KAZR-FM is a commercial station owned by Saga Communications. The format of the station is rock music. KAZR-FM broadcasts to the Des Moines, IA area at 103.3 FM.

KAZU-FM
Owner: California State University-Monterey Bay
Editorial: 100 Campus Center, Blvd 201, Seaside, California 93955. **T:** 1 831 582-5298
W: http://www.kazu.org
Editorial Profile: KAZU-FM is a non-commercial station owned by California State University-Monterey Bay. The format of the station is news and talk. KAZU-FM broadcasts to the Pacific Grove, CA area at 90.3 FM.

KAZX-FM
Owner: Clear Channel Media and Entertainment
Editorial: 200 E Broadway, Farmington, New Mexico 87401-6418. **T:** 1 505 325-1716
W: http://www.star1029.com
Editorial Profile: KAZX-FM is a commercial station owned by Clear Channel Media and Entertainment. The format of the station is Top 40/CHR music. KAZX-FM broadcasts to the Farmington, NM area at 102.9 FM.

KAZY-FM
Owner: Appaloosa Broadcasting
Editorial: 2109 E 10th St, Cheyenne, Wyoming 82001. **T:** 1 307 638-8921
E: traffic@1049krrr.com
W: http://www.937kazy.com
Editorial Profile: KAZY-FM is a commercial station owned by Appaloosa Broadcasting. The format of the station is rock. KAZY-FM broadcasts to the Laramie, WY area at 93.7 FM.

KBAA-FM
Owner: Adelante Media Group
Editorial: 500 Media Pl, Sacramento, California 95815. **T:** 1 916 368-6300
Editorial Profile: KBAA-FM is a commercial station owned by Adelante Media Group. The format of the station is Spanish AC. KBAA-FM broadcasts to the Grass Valley, CA area at 103.3 FM.

KBAC-FM
Owner: Hutton Broadcasting, LLC
Editorial: 2502 Camino Entrada Ste C, Santa Fe, New Mexico 87507-4911.
T: 1 505 471-1067
W: http://www.santafe.com/kbac
Editorial Profile: KBAC-FM is a commercial station owned by Hutton Broadcasting, LLC. The format of the station is adult album alternative music. KBAC-FM broadcasts to the Santa Fe, NM area at 98.1 FM.

KBAD-AM
Owner: Lotus Communications Corp.
Editorial: 8755 W Flamingo Rd, Las Vegas, Nevada 89147-8667. **T:** 1 702 876-1460
E: lotussignup@yahoo.com
W: http://www.werlv.com/pages/1695802.php
Editorial Profile: KBAD-AM is a commercial station owned by Lotus Communications Corp. The format of the station is sports. KBAD-AM broadcasts in the Las Vegas area at 920 AM.

KBAI-AM
Owner: Saga Communications
Editorial: 2219 Yew Street Rd, Bellingham, Washington 98229. **T:** 1 360 734-9790
E: kgmi@kgmi.com
W: http://www.930kbai.com
Editorial Profile: KBAI-AM is a commercial station owned by Saga Communications. The format of the station is progressive talk. KBAI-AM broadcasts to the Bellingham, WA area at 930 AM.

KBAJ-FM
Owner: Red Rock Radio Corp.
Editorial: 501 S Lake Ave, Ste 200, Duluth, Minnesota 55802-2392. **T:** 1 218 728-9500
W: http://www.95kqds.com
Editorial Profile: KBAJ-FM is a commercial station owned by Red Rock Radio Corp. The format of the station is classic rock music. KMAJ-FM broadcasts to the Deer River, MN area and is a simulcast of KQDS-FM in Duluth, MN.

KBAM-AM
Owner: Bicoastal Media LLC
Editorial: 1130 14th Ave, Longview, Washington 98632-3017. **T:** 1 360 425-1500
W: http://www.kbamcountry.com
Editorial Profile: KBAM-AM is a commercial station owned by Bicoastal Media LLC. The format of the station is country music. KBAM-AM broadcasts in the Portland, OR area at 1270 AM.

KBAQ-FM
Owner: Maricopa Community Colleges
Editorial: 2323 W 14th St, Tempe, Arizona 85281-6948. **T:** 1 480 833-1122
E: mail@kbaq.org **W:** http://www.kbaq.org
Editorial Profile: KBAQ-FM is a non-commercial station owned by Maricopa Community Colleges. The format of the station is classical music. KBAQ-FM broadcasts to the Tempe, AZ area at 89.5 FM.

KBAR-AM
Owner: Lee Family Broadcasting
Editorial: 113 Shoshone St N, Twin Falls, Idaho 83301-6150. **T:** 1 208 436-4757
Editorial Profile: KBAR-AM is a commercial station owned by Lee Family Broadcasting. The primary format of the station is news/talk, and it also airs oldies music. KBAR-AM broadcasts to the Twin Falls area in Idaho at a frequency of 1230 AM.

KBAR-FM
Owner: Victoria RadioWorks Inc.
Editorial: 3613 N Main St, Victoria, Texas 77901. **T:** 1 361 576-6114
E: vrw@suddenlinkmail.com
Editorial Profile: KBAR-FM is a commercial station owned by Victoria RadioWorks Inc. The format of the station is rock alternative. KBAR-FM broadcasts to the Victoria, TX area at 100.9 FM.

KBAT-FM
Owner: Townsquare Media, Inc.
Editorial: 11300 State Highway 191 Bldg 2, Midland, Texas 79707-1367.
T: 1 432 563-5499 **E:** contact@kbat.com
W: http://www.kbat.com
Editorial Profile: KBAT-FM a commercial station owned by Townsquare Media, Inc. The format of the station is rock music. KBAT-FM broadcasts to the Midland, TX area at 99.9 FM.

KBAY-FM
Owner: Digity LLC
Editorial: 190 Park Center Plz Ste 200, San Jose, California 95113-2223.
T: 1 408 287-5775 **W:** http://www.kbay.com
Editorial Profile: KBAY-FM is a commercial station owned by Digity LLC. The format of the station is Lite Rock/Lite AC. KBAY-FM broadcasts to the San Francisco area at 94.5 FM.

KBAZ-FM
Owner: Townsquare Media, LLC
Editorial: 3250 S Reserve St, Ste 200, Missoula, Montana 59801. **T:** 1 406 728-9300
W: http://www.963theblaze.com
Editorial Profile: KBAZ-FM is a commercial station owned by Townsquare Media, LLC. The format of the station is rock alternative. KBAZ-FM broadcasts to the Missoula, MT area at 96.3 FM.

KBBD-FM
Owner: Mapleton Communications LLC
Editorial: 1601 E 57th Ave, Spokane, Washington 99223. **T:** 1 509 448-1000
W: http://www.1039bobfm.com
Editorial Profile: KBBD-FM is a a commercial station owned by Mapleton Communications LLC. The format of the station is Adult Hits.

KBBE-FM
Owner: Davies Communications Inc.
Editorial: 411 E Euclid St, McPherson, Kansas 67460. **T:** 1 620 241-1504
E: oldies96.7@midkansasradio.com
W: http://www.midkansasradio.com
Editorial Profile: KBBE-FM is a commercial station owned by Davies Communication Inc. The format of the station is oldies music. KBBE-FM broadcasts to the McPherson, KS area at 96.7 FM.

KBBG-FM
Owner: Afro-American Community Broadcasting Inc
Editorial: 918 Newell St, Waterloo, Iowa 50703-2720. **T:** 1 319 234-1441
E: lou@kbbg.org **W:** http://www.kbbgfm.org
Editorial Profile: KBBG-FM is a non-commercial station owned by Afro-American Community Broadcasting Inc. The format of the station is educational. KBBG-FM broadcasts to the Cedar Rapids, IA area at 88.1 FM.

KBBI-AM
Owner: Kachemak Bay Broadcasting Inc.
Editorial: 3913 Kachemak Way, Homer, Alaska 99603. **T:** 1 907 235-7721 **E:** dorle@kbbi.org
W: http://www.kbbi.org
Editorial Profile: KBBI-AM is a non-commercial station owned by Kachemak Bay Broadcasting Inc. The format of the station is variety. KBBI-AM broadcasts to the Homer, AK area at 890 AM.

KBBK-FM
Owner: NRG Media LLC
Editorial: 4343 O St, Lincoln, Nebraska 68510. **T:** 1 402 475-4567
W: http://www.b1073.com
Editorial Profile: KBBK-FM is a commercial station owned by NRG Media. The format of the station is hot adult contemporary. KBBK-FM broadcasts to the Lincoln, NE area at 107.3 FM.

KBBM-FM
Owner: Cumulus Media Inc.
Editorial: 503 Old 63 N, Columbia, Missouri 65201-6305. **T:** 1 573 449-4141
W: http://www.nashfm100.com
Editorial Profile: KBBM-FM is a commercial station owned by Cumulus Media Inc. The format of the station is contemporary country. KBBM-FM broadcasts to the Columbia, MO area at 100.1 FM.

KBBN-FM
Owner: Custer County Broadcasting Inc.
Editorial: Highway 2 and Callaway Road, Broken Bow, Nebraska 68822.
T: 1 308 872-5881
E: info@sandhillsexpress.com
W: http://www.kbbn.com
Editorial Profile: KBBN-FM is a commercial station owned by Custer County Broadcasting Inc. The format of the station is classic rock. KBBN-FM broadcasts to the Broken Bow, NE area at 95.3 FM.

KBBO-AM
Owner: New Northwest Broadcasters LLC
Editorial: 1200 Chesterly Dr, Ste 160, Yakima, Washington 98902. **T:** 1 509 248-2900
W: http://www.talk980kusa.com
Editorial Profile: KBBO-AM is a commercial station owned by New Northwest Broadcasters LLC. The format of the station is news and

talk. KBBO-AM broadcasts in the Yakima, WA area at 980 AM.

KBBO-FM
Owner: Ohana Media Group
Editorial: 833 Gambell St, Anchorage, Alaska 99501-3756. **T:** 1 907 344-4045
W: http://www.921bob.fm
Editorial Profile: KBBO-FM is a commercial station owned by Ohana Media Group. The format of the station is adult hits. KBBO-FM broadcasts to the Anchorage, AK area at 92.1 FM.

KBBQ-FM
Owner: Cumulus Media Inc.
Editorial: 4209 N Frontage Rd, Fayetteville, Arkansas 72703-5002. **T:** 1 479 452-0681
W: http://www.1027thevibe.com
Editorial Profile: KBBQ-FM is a commercial station owned by Cumulus Media Inc. The format of the station is rhythmic Top 40/CHR. KBBQ-FM broadcasts to Fort Smith, AR area at 102.7 FM.

KBBR-AM
Owner: Bicoastal Media LLC
Editorial: 320 Central Ave, Ste 519, Coos Bay, Oregon 97420. **T:** 1 541 267-2121
E: southcoastpsa@bicoastalmedia.com
W: http://www.1340kbbr.com
Editorial Profile: KBBR-AM is a commercial station owned by Bicoastal Media LLC. The format of the station is progressive news and talk. KBBR-AM broadcasts to the Coos Bay, OR area at 1340 AM.

KBBS-AM
Owner: Legend Communications
Editorial: 1221 Fort St, Buffalo, Wyoming 82834. **T:** 1 307 684-7070 **E:** kbbs@vcn.com
W: http://1450amkbbs.com
Editorial Profile: KBBS-AM is a commercial station owned by Legend Communications. The format of the station is classic country. KBBS-AM broadcasts to the Buffalo, WY area at 1450 AM.

KBBT-FM
Owner: Univision Communications Inc.
Editorial: 12451 Network Blvd Ste 140, San Antonio, Texas 78249-3336.
T: 1 210 610-4300
W: http://www.thebeatsa.com
Editorial Profile: KBBT-FM is a commercial station owned by Univision Communications Inc. The format for the station is urban contemporary. KBBT-FM broadcasts to the San Antonio area at 98.5 FM.

KBBU-FM
Owner: Adelante Media Group
Editorial: 903 Kansas Ave Ste R, Modesto, California 95351-1558. **T:** 1 209 526-5352
Editorial Profile: KBBU-FM is a commercial station owned by Adelante Media Group. The format of the station is regional Mexican. KBBU-FM broadcasts to the Modesto, CA area at 93.9.

KBBW-AM
Owner: Williams(Steve)
Editorial: 1019 Washington Ave, Waco, Texas 76701-1256. **T:** 1 254 757-1010
E: info@1010kbw.com
W: http://www.kbbw.com
Editorial Profile: KBBW-AM is a commercial station owned by Steve Williams. The format of the station is Christian talk. KBBW-AM broadcasts to the Waco, TX area at 1010 AM.

KBBX-FM
Owner: Connoisseur Media LLC
Editorial: 11128 John Galt Blvd, Ste 25, Omaha, Nebraska 68137-2385.
T: 1 402 884-0968 **W:** http://radiolobo977.com
Editorial Profile: KBBX-FM is a commercial station owned by Connoisseur Media LLC. The format of the station is regional Mexican. KBBX-FM broadcasts to Omaha, NE at 97.7 FM.

KBBY-FM
Owner: Cumulus Media Inc.
Editorial: 1376 Walter St, Ventura, California 93003-5658. **T:** 1 805 642-8595
W: http://www.b951.com
Editorial Profile: KBBY-FM is a commercial station owned by Cumulus Media Inc. The format of the station is hot adult contemporary music. KBBY-FM broadcasts to the Ventura, CA area at 95.1 FM.

KBBZ-FM
Owner: Bee Broadcasting Inc.

Editorial: 2432 US Highway 2 E, Kalispell, Montana 59901. **T:** 1 406 755-8700
E: b985@beebroadcasting.com
W: http://www.kbbz.com
Editorial Profile: KBBZ-FM is a commercial station owned by Bee Broadcasting, Inc. The format of the station is classic rock. KBBZ-FM broadcasts to the Kalispell, MT area at 98.5 FM.

KBCE-FM
Owner: JWBP Broadcasting, LLC
Editorial: 1605 Murray St, Ste 111, Alexandria, Louisiana 71301-6875.
T: 1 318 445-0800
W: http://www.b102jamz.com
Editorial Profile: KBCE-FM is commercial station owned by JWBP Broadcasting, LLC. The format of the station is urban adult contemporary music. KBCE-FM broadcasts to the Alexandria, LA area at 102.3 FM.

KBCH-AM
Owner: Pacific West Broadcasting Inc.
Editorial: 800 SE Highway 101, Ste C, Lincoln City, Oregon 97367. **T:** 1 541 265-2266
E: news@ybcradio.com
W: http://www.kbcham.com
Editorial Profile: KBCH-AM is a commercial station owned by Pacific West Broadcasting Inc. The format of the station is adult standards music, news and talk. KBCH-FM broadcasts to Lincoln City, OR at 1400 AM.

KBCK-AM
Owner: Toole(Robert Cummings)
Editorial: 302 Missouri Ave, Deer Lodge, Montana 59722. **T:** 1 406 846-1100
E: riverradio@bresnan.net
Editorial Profile: KBCK-AM is a commercial station owned by Robert Cummings Toole. The format of the station is news, sports and country. KBCK-AM broadcasts to the Deer Lodge, MT area at 1400 AM.

KBCL-AM
Owner: Barnabas Center Ministries
Editorial: 316 Gregg St, Shreveport, Louisiana 71104. **T:** 1 318 861-1070
E: kbcl_radio@bellsouth.net
W: http://www.praise1070.org
Editorial Profile: KBCL-AM is a commercial station owned by Barnabas Center Ministries. The format of the station is Christian talk programming. KBCL-AM broadcasts to the Shreveport, LA area at 1070 AM.

KBCN-FM
Owner: Pearson Broadcasting
Editorial: 101 Bluebird St, Harrison, Arkansas 72601-1908. **T:** 1 870 743-1157
W: http://www.espnarkansas.net
Editorial Profile: KBCN-FM is a commercial station owned by Pearson Broadcasting. The format of the station is sports talk. KBCN-FM is the ESPN Radio affiliate for the Harrison, AR area and broadcasts locally at 104.3 FM.

KBCO-FM
Owner: Clear Channel Media and Entertainment
Editorial: 4695 S Monaco St, Denver, Colorado 80237-3403. **T:** 1 303 444-5600
W: http://www.kbco.com
Editorial Profile: KBCO-FM is a commercial station owned by Clear Channel Media and Entertainment. The format of the station is adult album alternative. KBCO-FM broadcasts to the Boulder, CO area at 97.3 FM.

KBCQ-AM
Owner: Majestic Communications
Editorial: 5206 W 2nd St, Roswell, New Mexico 88201-8839. **T:** 1 575 622-6450
W: http://www.am1230kbcq.com
Editorial Profile: KBCQ-AM is a commercial station owned by Majestic Communications. The format of the station is classic hits. KBCQ-AM broadcasts to the Roswell, NM area at 1230 AM.

KBCQ-FM
Owner: Majestic Communications
Editorial: 5206 W 2nd St, Roswell, New Mexico 88201-8839. **T:** 1 575 622-6450
E: production@roswellradio.net
W: http://www.q971fm.com
Editorial Profile: KBCQ-FM is a commercial station owned by Majestic Communications. The format of the station is Top 40/CHR music. KBCQ-FM broadcasts to the Roswell, NM area at 97.1 FM.

KBCR-AM
Owner: Cool Radio, LLC
Editorial: 2110 Mount Werner Cir, Steamboat Springs, Colorado 80487-9009.

T: 1 970 879-2270 **W:** http://www.kbcr.com
Editorial Profile: KBCR-AM is a commercial station owned by Cool Radio, LLC. The format of the station is local talk. KBCR-AM broadcasts to the Steamboat Springs, CO area at 1230 AM.

KBCR-FM
Owner: Cool Radio, LLC
Editorial: 2110 Mount Werner Rd, Steamboat Springs, Colorado 80487. **T:** 1 970 879-2270
E: kbcr@nctelecom.net
W: http://www.kbcr.com
Editorial Profile: KBCR-FM is a commercial station owned by Cool Radio, LLC. The format of the station is classic and contemporary country. KBCR-FM broadcasts to the Steamboat Springs, CO area at 96.9 FM.

KBCS-FM
Owner: Bellevue Community College
Editorial: 3000 Landerholm Cir Se, Bellevue, Washington 98007-6406. **T:** 1 425 564-2427
E: office@kbcs.fm **W:** http://www.kbcs.fm
Editorial Profile: KBCS-FM is a non-commercial station owned by Bellevue Community College. The format of the station is variety. KBCS-FM broadcasts to the Bellevue, WA area at 91.3 FM.

KBCU-FM
Owner: Bethel College
Editorial: 300 E 27th St, North Newton, Kansas 67117-8061. **T:** 1 316 284-5273
E: kbcu@bethelks.edu
W: http://www.bethelks.edu/kbcu

KBCV-AM
Owner: Bott Broadcasting Co.
Editorial: 500 W Main St Ste 103A, Branson, Missouri 65616-2862. **T:** 1 417 336-1570
E: comments@bottradionetwork.com
W: http://www.bottradionetwork.com
Editorial Profile: KBCV-AM is a non-commercial station owned by Bott Broadcasting Co. The format of the station is religious and talk. KBCV-AM broadcasts to Branson, MO and surrounding areas at 1570 AM.

KBCW-FM
Owner: University of Central Oklahoma
Editorial: 100 N University Dr, Edmond, Oklahoma 73034. **T:** 1 405 974-3333
E: kcscfm@uco.edu
W: http://www.kcscfm.com
Editorial Profile: KBCW-FM is a non-commercial station owned by the University of Central Oklahoma. The format of the station is classical music. KBCW-FM broadcasts to the McAlester, OK area at 91.9 FM and is a simulcast of KCSC-FM.

KBCY-FM
Owner: Cumulus Media Inc.
Editorial: 2525 S Danville Dr, Abilene, Texas 79605. **T:** 1 325 793-9700
W: http://www.kbcy.com
Editorial Profile: KBCY-FM is a commercial station owned by Cumulus Media Inc. The format of the station is country. KBCY-FM broadcasts to the Abilene, TX area at a frequency of 99.7.

KBDB-FM
Owner: Forks Broadcasting, Inc.
Editorial: 260 Cedar Ave, Forks, Washington 98331-9605. **T:** 1 360 374-6233
E: news@forksbroadcasting.com
W: http://www.twilight967.com
Editorial Profile: KBDB-FM is a commercial station owned by Forks Broadcasting, Inc. The format of the station is adult contemporary. KBDB-FM broadcasts to the Forks, WA area at 96.7 FM.

KBDN-FM
Owner: Bicoastal Media LLC
Editorial: 320 Central Ave, Ste 519, Coos Bay, Oregon 97420. **T:** 1 541 267-2121
E: southcoastpsa@bicoastalmedia.com
W: http://www.kbdn.com
Editorial Profile: KBDN-FM is a commercial station owned by Bicoastal Media LLC. The format of the station is country. KBDN-FM broadcasts to the Coos Bay, OR area at 96.5 FM.

KBDR-FM
Owner: Border Media Partners LLC
Editorial: 107 Calle Del Norte, Ste 212, Laredo, Texas 78041. **T:** 1 956 725-1000
W: http://www.bmpradio.com
Editorial Profile: KBDR-FM is a commercial station owned by Border Media Partners LLC. The format of the station is Regional Mexican.

KBDR-FM broadcasts to the Loredo, TX area on 100.5 FM.

KBDS-FM
Owner: Radio Campesina Bakersfield, Inc.
Editorial: 6313 Schirra Ct Ste 313, Bakersfield, California 93313-2174.
T: 1 661 837-0745
W: http://www.campesina.com
Editorial Profile: KBDS-FM is a commercial station owned by Radio Campesina Bakersfield, Inc. The format of the station is Regional Mexican. KBDS-FM broadcasts to the Bakersfield, CA area at 103.9 FM.

KBDV-FM
Owner: Baldridge-Dumas Communications Inc.
Editorial: 605 San Antonio Ave, Many, Louisiana 71449-3018. **T:** 1 318 256-0555
E: kwlv@bellsouth.net
Editorial Profile: KBDV-FM is a commercial station owned by Baldridge-Dumas Communications Inc. The format of the station is adult contemporary. KBDV-FM broadcasts to the Shreveport, LA area at 92.7 FM.

KBDY-FM
Owner: Toga Radio, LLC
Editorial: 106 N First St, Saratoga, Wyoming 82331. **T:** 1 307 326-8642
E: traffic@bigfoot99.com
Editorial Profile: KBDY-FM is a commercial station owned by Toga Radio LLC. The format of the station is country. KBDY-FM broadcasts to the Saratoga, WY at 102.1 FM. The station does not air PSAs, but does accept local community event announcements via email to traffic@bigfoot99.com.

KBDZ-FM
Owner: Donze Communications Inc.
Editorial: 122 Perry Plz, Ste D, Perryville, Missouri 63775-4203. **T:** 1 573 547-8005
E: suntimesnews@charter.net
W: http://www.kbdz931.com
Editorial Profile: KBDZ-FM is a commercial station owned by Donze Communications Inc. The format of the station is contemporary country. KBDZ-FM broadcasts to the Perryville, MO area at 93.1 FM.

KBEA-FM
Owner: Townsquare Media
Editorial: 1229 Brady St, Davenport, Iowa 52803-4616. **T:** 1 563 326-2541
W: http://www.b100.net
Editorial Profile: KBEA-FM is a commercial station owned by Townsquare Media. The format of the station is Top 40/CHR. The station broadcasts to the Davenport, IA area at 99.7 FM.

KBEB-FM
Owner: Clear Channel Media and Entertainment
Editorial: 1545 River Park Dr Ste 500, Sacramento, California 95815-4693.
T: 1 916 929-5325
W: http://www.b925country.com/main.html
Editorial Profile: KBEB-FM is a commercial station owned by Clear Channel Media and Entertainment. The format of the station is contemporary country. KFBK-FM broadcasts to the Sacramento, CA area at 92.5 FM.

KBEC-AM
Owner: Phillips (Jim)
Editorial: 711 Ferris Ave, Waxahachie, Texas 75165-2585. **T:** 1 972 923-1390
E: info@kbec.com **W:** http://www.kbec.com
Editorial Profile: KBEC-AM is a commercial station owned by Phillips (Jim). The format of the station is country, specifically Classic Texas music. KBEC-AM broadcasts to the Waxahachie, TX area at 1390 AM.

KBED-AM
Owner: Cumulus Media Inc.
Editorial: 755 S 11th St, Ste 102, Beaumont, Texas 77701. **T:** 1 409 951-2500
W: http://www.lagrand1450.com
Editorial Profile: KBED-AM is a commercial station owned by Cumulus Media Inc. The format of the station is regional Mexican. KBED-AM broadcasts to the Beaumont, TX area at 1510 AM.

KBEE-FM
Owner: Cumulus Media Inc
Editorial: 434 W Bearcat Dr, Salt Lake City, Utah 84115-2520. **T:** 1 801 485-6700
W: http://www.b987.com
Editorial Profile: KBEE-FM is a commercial station owned by Cumulus Media Inc. The format for the station is Top 40/CHR. KBEE-FM broadcasts to the Salt Lake City area at 98.7 FM.

KBEL-AM
Owner: Box Broadcasting Corp.
Editorial: 813 E Lincoln Rd, Idabel, Oklahoma 74745-7816. **T:** 1 580 286-6642
E: kbel967@yahoo.com
Editorial Profile: KBEL-AM is a commercial station owned by Box Broadcasting Corp. The format of the station is news/talk. KBEL-AM broadcasts to the Idabel, OK area at 1240 AM.

KBEL-FM
Owner: Box Broadcasting Corp.
Editorial: 813 E Lincoln Rd, Idabel, Oklahoma 74745-7816. **T:** 1 580 286-6642
E: kbel967@yahoo.com
W: http://www.kbelradio.com
Editorial Profile: KBEL-FM is a commercial station owned by Box Broadcasting Corp. The format of the station is country music. KBEL-FM broadcasts to the Idabel, OK area at 96.7 FM.

KBEM-FM
Owner: Minneapolis Public Schools
Editorial: 1555 James Ave N, Minneapolis, Minnesota 55411. **T:** 1 612 668-1735
E: studio@jazz88fm.com
W: http://www.jazz88fm.com
Editorial Profile: KBEM-FM is a non-commercial station owned by Minnesota Public Schools. The format of the station is jazz. KBEM-FM broadcasts to the Minneapolis area at 88.5 FM.

KBEQ-FM
Owner: Wilks Broadcast Group
Editorial: 508 Westport Rd, Kansas City, Missouri 64111-3012. **T:** 1 816 753-4000
W: http://www.q104kc.com
Editorial Profile: KBEQ-FM is a commercial station owned by Wilks Broadcast Group. The format of the station is contemporary country music. KBEQ-FM broadcasts to the Kansas City, MO area on 104.3 FM.

KBER-FM
Owner: Cumulus Media Inc
Editorial: 434 Bearcat Dr, Salt Lake City, Utah 84115. **T:** 1 801 485-6700
W: http://www.kber.com
Editorial Profile: KBER-FM is a commercial station owned by Cumulus Media Inc. The format of the station is rock/album-oriented rock. KBER-FM broadcasts to the Salt Lake City area at 101.1 FM.

KBET-AM
Owner: Royce International Broadcasting Corporation
Editorial: 6725 Via Austi Pkwy Fl 2, Las Vegas, Nevada 89119-3507.
T: 1 760 341-0123 **W:** http://790talknow.com
Editorial Profile: KBET-AM is a commercial station owned by Royce International (dba Silver State Broadcasting, LLC). The format of the station is Conservative talk programming. KBET-AM broadcasts to the Las Vegas area at 790 AM.

KBEV-FM
Owner: Dead-Air Broadcasting Co.
Editorial: 610 N Montana St, Dillon, Montana 59725. **T:** 1 406 683-2800
E: deadair@kdbm-kbev.com
W: http://www.kdbmkbev.com

KBEW-AM
Owner: KBEW, Inc.
Editorial: 705 E Leland Pkwy, Blue Earth, Minnesota 56013. **T:** 1 507 526-2181
E: kbew@bevcomm.net
Editorial Profile: KBEW-AM is a commercial station owned by KBEW, Inc. The format of the station is oldies music. KBEW-AM broadcasts to the Blue Earth, MN area at 1560 AM.

KBEW-FM
Owner: KBEW, Inc.
Editorial: 705 E Leland Pkwy, Blue Earth, Minnesota 56013. **T:** 1 507 526-2181
E: kbew@bevcomm.net
Editorial Profile: KBEW-FM is a commercial station owned by KBEW, Inc. The format of the station is country music. KBEW-FM broadcasts to the Blue Earth, MN area at 98.1 FM.

KBEY-FM
Owner: Victory Publishing Company, Ltd.
Editorial: 2108 US Highway 281 Ste A, Marble Falls, Texas 78654-4361. **T:** 1 830 693-5551
W: http://www.kbeyfm.com
Editorial Profile: KBEY-FM is a commercial station owned by Two Way Communications, LLC. The format of the station is classic country. KBEY-FM broadcasts to the Austin, TX area at 103.9 FM.

KBEZ-FM
Owner: Journal Broadcast Group
Editorial: 4590 E 29Th St, Tulsa, Oklahoma 74114-6208. **T:** 1 918 743-7814
W: http://www.929bob.com
Editorial Profile: KBEZ-FM is a commercial station owned by Journal Broadcast Group. The format of the station is adult hits. KBEZ-FM broadcasts to the Tulsa, OK area at 92.9 FM.

KBFB-FM
Owner: Radio One Inc.
Editorial: 13331 Preston Rd, Ste 1180, Dallas, Texas 75240. **T:** 1 972 331-5400
W: http://thebeatdfw.com
Editorial Profile: KBFB-FM is a commercial station owned by Radio One Inc. The format of the station is rhythmic Top 40/CHR music. KBFB-FM broadcasts to the Dallas area at 97.9 FM.

KBFC-FM
Owner: Forrest City Broadcasting Co.
Editorial: 501 E Broadway St, Forrest City, Arkansas 72335-3801. **T:** 1 870 633-1252
E: radio@arkansas.net **W:** http://arkradio.com
Editorial Profile: KBFC-FM is a commercial station owned by Forrest City Broadcasting Co. The format of the station is classic and contemporary country. KBFC-FM broadcasts to the Forrest City, AR area at 93.5 FM.

KBFF-FM
Owner: Alpha Broadcasting
Editorial: 1211 SW 5th Ave Ste 600, Portland, Oregon 97204-3706. **T:** 1 503 243-7595
W: http://www.live955.com
Editorial Profile: KBFF-FM is a commercial station owned by Alpha Broadcasting. The format of the station is Hot AC. KBFF-FM broadcasts to the Portland, OR area at 95.5 FM.

KBFI-AM
Owner: Blue Sky Broadcasting Inc.
Editorial: 327 S Marion Ave, Sandpoint, Idaho 83864. **T:** 1 208 263-2179
Editorial Profile: KBFI-AM is a commercial station owned by Blue Sky Broadcasting. The format of the station is news, sports and talk. KBFI-AM broadcast to the Sandpoint, ID area at 1450 AM.

KBFL-AM
Owner: Meyer Communications
Editorial: 3000 E Chestnut Expy, Springfield, Missouri 65802. **T:** 1 417 862-3751
W: http://www.kbflfm.com
Editorial Profile: KBFL-AM is a commercial station owned by Meyer Communications. The format of the station is adult standards. KBFL-AM broadcasts to the Springfield, MO area at 1060 AM.

KBFL-FM
Owner: Meyer Communications
Editorial: 3000 E Chestnut Expy, Springfield, Missouri 65802. **T:** 1 417 862-3751
W: http://www.kbflfm.com
Editorial Profile: KBFL-FM is a commercial station owned by Meyer Communications. The format of the station is adult standards. KBFL-FM broadcasts to the Springfield, MO area at 99.9 FM.

KBFM-FM
Owner: Clear Channel Media and Entertainment
Editorial: 901 E Pike Blvd, Weslaco, Texas 78596. **T:** 1 956 973-9202
W: http://www.wild104.net
Editorial Profile: KBFM-FM is a commercial station owned by Clear Channel Media and Entertainment. The format of the station is Top 40/CHR music. KBFM-FM broadcasts to the Weslaco, TX area at 104.1 FM.

KBFO-FM
Owner: Armada Media Corp.
Editorial: 3304 S Highway 281, Aberdeen, South Dakota 57401-8792. **T:** 1 605 229-3632
E: aberdeenproduction@hubcityradio.com
W: http://www.hubcityradio.com/point
Editorial Profile: KBFO-FM is a commercial station owned by Armada Media Corp. The format of the station is hot adult contemporary. KBFO-FM broadcasts to the Aberdeen, SD area at 106.7 FM.

KBFP-AM
Owner: Clear Channel Media and Entertainment
Editorial: 1100 Mohawk St Ste 280, Bakersfield, California 93309-7417.
T: 1 661 322-9929
W: http://www.comedy800.com/main.html
Editorial Profile: KBFP-AM is a commercial station owned by Clear Channel Media and Entertainment. The format of the station is comedy. KBFP-AM broadcasts to the Bakersfield, CA area at 800 AM.

KBFP-FM
Owner: Clear Channel Media and Entertainment
Editorial: 1100 Mohawk St, Ste 280, Bakersfield, California 93309.
T: 1 661 322-9929
W: http://www.lapreciosa1053.com
Editorial Profile: KBFP-FM is a commercial station owned by Clear Channel Media and Entertainment. The format of the station is Hispanic oldies. KBFP-FM broadcasts to the Bakersfield, CA area at 105.3 FM.

KBFS-AM
Owner: Ultimate Caps, Inc.
Editorial: 707 Harding St, Belle Fourche, South Dakota 57717. **T:** 1 605 892-2571
E: kbfs@mato.com **W:** http://www.kbfs.com
Editorial Profile: KBFS-AM is a commercial station owned by Ultimate Caps, Inc. The format of the station is news, sports and country music. KBFS-AM broadcasts to the Belle Fourche, SD area at 1450 AM.

KBFX-FM
Owner: Clear Channel Media and Entertainment
Editorial: 800 E Dimond Blvd, Ste 3-370, Anchorage, Alaska 99515. **T:** 1 907 522-1515
W: http://www.1005thefox.com
Editorial Profile: KBFX-FM is a commercial station owned by Clear Channel Media and Entertainment. The format of the station is classic rock music. KBFX-FM broadcasts to the Anchorage, AK area at 100.5 FM.

KBGA-FM
Owner: University of Montana
Editorial: 208 University Ctr, Missoula, Montana 59812-0001. **T:** 1 406 243-6758
E: news@kbga.org **W:** http://www.kbga.org
Editorial Profile: KBGA-FM is a non-commercial station owned by University of Montana. The format of the station is variety. KBGA-FM broadcasts to the Missoula, MT area at 89.9 FM.

KBGB-FM
Owner: Crain Media Group, LLC
Editorial: 111 N Spring St, Searcy, Arkansas 72143-7712. **T:** 1 501 268-7123
W: http://www.crainmedia.com
Editorial Profile: KBGB-FM is a commercial station owned by Crain Media Group, LLC. The format of the station is contemporary country. KBGB-FM broadcasts to the Kensett, AR area at a frequency of 105.7 FM.

KBGG-AM
Owner: Cumulus Media Inc
Editorial: 4143 109th St, Urbandale, Iowa 50322-7925. **T:** 1 515 331-9200
W: http://www.1700thechamp.com
Editorial Profile: KBGG-AM is a commercial station owned by Cumulus Media Inc. The format of the station is sports. KBGG-AM broadcasts to the Des Moines, IA area at 1700 AM.

KBGL-FM
Owner: Hull Broadcasting
Editorial: 1200 Baker Ave, Great Bend, Kansas 67530-4523. **T:** 1 620 792-3647
W: http://www.kbglfm.com
Editorial Profile: KBGL-FM is a commercial station owned by Hull Broadcasting. The format of the station is CHR. KBGL-FM broadcasts to the Great Bend, KS area on 106.9 FM.

KBGN-AM
Owner: Wilson(Nelson & Karen)
Editorial: 3303 E Chicago St, Caldwell, Idaho 83605. **T:** 1 208 459-3635
E: kbgn@kbgnradio.com
W: http://www.kbgnradio.com
Editorial Profile: KBGN-AM is a commercial station owned by Nelson and Karen Wilson. The format of the station is Christian music and talk. KBGN-AM broadcasts to the Caldwell, ID area at 1060 AM.

KBGO-FM
Owner: Clear Channel Media and Entertainment
Editorial: 314 W State Highway 6, Waco, Texas 76712. **T:** 1 254 776-3900
W: http://www.oldies95online.com
Editorial Profile: KBGO-FM is a commercial station owned by Clear Channel Media and Entertainment. The format of the station is oldies. KBGO-FM broadcasts to the Waco, TX area at 95.7 FM.

KBGX-FM
Owner: Mahalo Broadcasting
Editorial: 74-5605 Luhia St, Ste B7, Kailua Kona, Hawaii 96740. **T:** 1 808 329-8090
E: info@lava105.com
W: http://www.lava105.com
Editorial Profile: KBGX-FM is a commercial station owned by Maholo Broadcasting. The format for the station is oldies. KBGX-FM broadcasts to Kailua Kona, HI area at 105.3 FM.

KBGY-FM
Owner: Milestone Radio II LLC
Editorial: 14443 Armstrong Blvd Nw, Ramsey, Minnesota 55303-7284. **T:** 1 612 721-4000
Editorial Profile: KBGY-FM is a commercial station owned by Milestone Radio II LLC. The format for the station is regional Mexican. The station airs locally at 107.5 FM.

KBHB-AM
Owner: New Rushmore Radio
Editorial: 1612 Junction Ave Ste 1, Sturgis, South Dakota 57785-2166. **T:** 1 605 347-4455
E: info@kbhbradio.com
W: http://www.kbhbradio.com
Editorial Profile: KBHB-AM is a commercial station owned by New Rushmore Radio. The format of the station is an eclectic mix of country music, news and agriculture reporting. KBHB-AM broadcasts to the Rapid City, SD area at 810 AM.

KBHC-AM
Owner: Southwest Arkansas Radio
Editorial: 1513 S 4th St, Nashville, Arkansas 71852. **T:** 1 870 845-3601
E: swarkradio@hotmail.com
W: http://www.southwestarkansasradio.com
Editorial Profile: KBHC-AM is a commercial station owned by Southwest Arkansas Radio. The format of the station is regional Mexican music. KBHC-AM broadcasts to the Nashville, AR area at 1260 AM.

KBHE-FM
Owner: State Board for Educational Television
Editorial: 555 N Dakota St, Vermillion, South Dakota 57069. **T:** 1 605 677-5861
E: news@sdpb.org **W:** http://www.sdpb.org
Editorial Profile: KBHE-FM is a non-commercial station owned by the State Board for Educational Television. The format of the station is news and classical. KBHE-FM broadcasts to the Vermillion, SD area at 89.3 FM.

KBHH-FM
Owner: Farmworker Educational Radio Network, Inc.
Editorial: 6313 Schirra Ct, Bakersfield, California 93313-2174. **T:** 1 661 837-0745
W: http://www.campesina.com
Editorial Profile: KBHH-FM is a commercial station owned by Farmworker Educational Radio Network, Inc. The format of the station is Regional Mexican music. KBHH-FM broadcasts to the Kerman, CA area at a frequency of 95.3 FM.

KBHI-FM
Owner: Dana Withers
Editorial: 125 S Kingshighway St, Sikeston, Missouri 63801-2943. **T:** 1 573 471-2000
Editorial Profile: KBHI-FM is a commercial station owned by Dana Withers. The format of the station is rock music. KBHI-FM broadcasts to the Sikeston, MO area at 107.1 FM.

KBHL-FM
Owner: Christian Heritage Broadcasting
Editorial: 402 E Pike St, Osakis, Minnesota 56360-8346. **T:** 1 320 859-3000
E: mail@praisefm.org
W: http://www.praisefm.org
Editorial Profile: KBHL-FM is a non-commercial station owned by Christian Heritage Broadcasting. The format of the station is contemporary Christian music. KBHL-FM broadcasts in the Osakis, MN area at 103.9 FM.

KBHP-FM
Owner: Omni Broadcasting Co.
Editorial: 502 Beltrami Ave NW, Bemidji, Minnesota 56601. **T:** 1 218 444-1500
W: http://www.kb101fm.com
Editorial Profile: KBHP-FM is a commercial station owned by Omni Broadcasting Co. The

format of the station is country music. KBHP-FM broadcasting in the Bemidji, MN area at 101.1 FM.

KBHR-FM
Owner: Parallel Broadcasting Inc.
Editorial: 649 W Country Club, Big Bear City, California 92314. T: 1 909 584-5247
E: news@kbhr933.com
W: http://www.kbhr933.com
Editorial Profile: KBHR-FM is a commercial station owned by Parallel Broadcasting Inc. The format of the station is adult album alternative. KBHR-FM broadcasts to the Big Bear City, CA area at 93.3 FM.

KBHT-FM
Owner: M & M Broadcasters
Editorial: 5501 Bagby Ave, Waco, Texas 76711-2300. T: 1 254 772-0930
W: http://www.1049thebeatonline.com
Editorial Profile: KBHT-FM is a commercial station owned by M & M Broadcasters. The format of the station is rhythmic and urban CHR. KBHT-FM broadcasts to the Waco, TX area at 104.9 FM.

KBHU-FM
Owner: Black Hills State University
Editorial: 1200 University St, Unit 9003, Spearfish, South Dakota 57799.
T: 1 605 642-6265
E: thebuzzfm@thebuzzfm.net
W: http://www.thebuzzfm.net
Editorial Profile: KBHU-FM is a non-commercial station owned by Black Hills State University. The format of the station is rock alternative. KBHU-FM broadcasts to the Spearfish, SD area at 89.1 FM.

KBHW-FM
Owner: Heartland Christian Broadcasters Inc.
Editorial: 4090 Highway 11, International Falls, Minnesota 56649. T: 1 218 285-7398
E: studio@psalm995.org
W: http://www.psalm995.org
Editorial Profile: KBHW-FM is a non-commercial station owned by Heartland Christian Broadcasters Inc. The format of the station is contemporary Christian music. KBHW-FM broadcasts to the International Falls, MN area at 99.5 FM.

KBHZ-FM
Owner: Christian Heritage Broadcasting
Editorial: 402 E Pike St, Osakis, Minnesota 56360-8346. T: 1 320 859-3000
E: mail@praisefm.org **W:** http://praisefm.org
Editorial Profile: KBHZ-FM is a non-commercial station owned by Christian Heritage Broadcasting. The format of the station is contemporary Christian music and talk. KBHZ-FM broadcasts to the Osakis, MN area at 91.9 FM.

KBIA-FM
Owner: University of Missouri
Editorial: 409 Jesse Hall Univ Of Missouri, Columbia, Missouri 65211. T: 1 573 882-3431
E: news@kbia.org **W:** http://www.kbia.org
Editorial Profile: KBIA-FM is a non-commercial station owned by the University of Missouri. The format of the station is news and classical music. KBIA-FM broadcasts to the Columbia, MO area at 91.3 FM.

KBIB-AM
Owner: Hispanic Community College
Editorial: 290 N Santa Clara Rd, Marion, Texas 78124-2047. T: 1 830 914-2083
Editorial Profile: KBIB-AM is a non-commercial station owned by Hispanic Community College. The format of the station is Hispanic religious programming. KBIB-AM broadcasts to the Marion, TX area at 1000 AM.

KBIC-FM
Owner: Christian Ministries of the Valley Inc.
Editorial: 2720 W Business 83, Weslaco, Texas 78596-1225. T: 1 956 968-7777
E: informacion@radiovida.com
W: http://www.radiovida.com
Editorial Profile: KBIC-FM is a commercial station owned by Christian Ministries of the Valley Inc. The format of the station is Hispanic religious programming. KBIC-FM broadcasts to the Weslaco, TX area at 105.7 FM.

KBIF-AM
Owner: Gore-Overgaard Broadcasting Inc.
Editorial: 3401 W Holland Ave, Fresno, California 93722-4197. T: 1 559 222-0900
E: kbif@900kbif.com **W:** http://900kbif.com
Editorial Profile: KBIF-AM is a commercial station owned by Gore-Overgaard

Broadcasting Inc. The format of the station is Asian and Indian variety. KBIF-AM broadcasts to the Fresno, CA area at 900 AM.

KBIG-FM
Owner: Clear Channel Media and Entertainment
Editorial: 3400 W Olive Ave Ste 550, Burbank, California 91505-5544. T: 1 818 559-2252
W: http://www.1043myfm.com
Editorial Profile: KBIG-FM is a commercial station owned by Clear Channel Media and Entertainment. The format of the station is hot adult contemporary. KBIG-FM broadcasts to the Los Angeles area at 104.3 FM.

KBIK-FM
Owner: Tallgrass Broadcasting, LLC
Editorial: 309 N Penn Ave, Independence, Kansas 67301-3325. T: 1 620 331-3000
W: http://www.indy1029.com
Editorial Profile: KBIK-FM is a commercial station owned by Tallgrass Broadcasting, LLC. The format is contemporary country. KBIK-FM broadcasts to the Independence, KS area at 102.9 FM.

KBIM-AM
Owner: Noalmark Broadcasting Corp.
Editorial: 1301 N Main St, Roswell, New Mexico 88201-5013. T: 1 575 623-9100
E: kevin@kbimradio.com
W: http://www.kbim910.com
Editorial Profile: KBIM-AM is a commercial station owned by Noalmark Broadcasting Corp. The format of the station is news and talk. KBIM-AM broadcasts to the Roswell, NM area at 910 AM.

KBIM-FM
Owner: Noalmark Broadcasting Corp.
Editorial: 1301 N Main St, Roswell, New Mexico 88201-5013. T: 1 575 623-9100
W: http://www.kbim949.com
Editorial Profile: KBIM-FM is a commercial station owned by Noalmark Broadcasting Corp. The format of the station is contemporary country. KBIM-FM broadcasts to the Roswell, NM area at 94.9 FM.

KBIP-FM
Owner: Tallgrass Broadcasting, LLC
Editorial: 309 Penn St, Independence, Kansas 67301. T: 1 620 331-3000
W: http://www.tallgrassnation.com
Editorial Profile: KBIP-FM is a commercial station owned by Tallgrass Broadcasting, LLC. The format of the station is news and talk. KBIP-FM broadcasts to the Elk City, KS area at 94.9 FM.

KBIQ-FM
Owner: Salem Communications
Editorial: 7150 Campus Dr Ste 150, Colorado Springs, Colorado 80920-3157.
T: 1 719 531-5438
W: http://www.kbiqradio.com
Editorial Profile: KBIQ-FM is a commercial station owned by Salem Communications. The format of the station is contemporary Christian. KBIQ-FM broadcasts to the Colorado Springs, CO area at 102.7 FM.

KBIU-FM
Owner: Cumulus Media
Editorial: 425 Broad St, Lake Charles, Louisiana 70601. T: 1 337 439-3300
W: http://www.kbiu.com
Editorial Profile: KBIU-FM is a commercial station owned by Cumulus Media. The format of the station is adult contemporary. KBIU-FM broadcasts to the Lake Charles, LA area at a frequency of 103.3 FM.

KBIX-AM
Owner: Stephens Media Group
Editorial: 2448 E 81st St, Ste 5500, Tulsa, Oklahoma 74137. T: 1 918 492-2660
E: kxoj@kxoj.com
W: http://www.thesportsanimal.com
Editorial Profile: KBIX-AM is a commercial station owned by Stephens Media Group. The format of the station is sports. KBIX-AM broadcasts to the Muskogee, OK area at 1490 AM.

KBIZ-AM
Owner: Ottumwa Radio.
Editorial: 416 Main Street, Ottumwa, Iowa 52501. T: 1 641 684-5563
W: http://www.kbizam.com
Editorial Profile: KBIZ-AM is a commercial station owned by Ottumwa Radio. The format for the station is talk. KBIZ-AM broadcasts to the Ottumwa, IA/Kirksville, MO area at 1240 AM.

KBJA-AM
Owner: United Broadcasting Company, Inc.
Editorial: 10348 S Redwood Rd, South Jordan, Utah 84095-9339. T: 1 801 254-7699
E: super@kbja1640.com
W: http://www.kbja1640.com
Editorial Profile: KBJA-AM is a commercial station owned by United Broadcasting Company, Inc. The format of the station is Spanish language news talk and sports. KBJA-AM broadcasts in the Salt Lake City area at 1640 AM.

KBJD-AM
Owner: Salem Communications
Editorial: 3131 S Vaughn Way, Ste 601, Aurora, Colorado 80014. T: 1 303 750-5687
E: news@710knus.com
W: http://www.1650radioluz.com
Editorial Profile: KBJD-AM is a commercial station owned by Salem Communications. The format of the station is Spanish Christian. KBJD-AM broadcasts to the Aurora, CO area at 1650 AM.

KBJM-AM
Owner: Media Associates Inc.
Editorial: 500 1st Ave E, Lemmon, South Dakota 57638. T: 1 605 374-5747
E: kbjm1400@sdplains.com
W: http://kbjm.com
Editorial Profile: KBJM-AM is a commercial station owned by Media Associates Inc. The format of the station is classic country. KBJM-AM broadcasts to the Lemmon, SD area at 1400 AM.

KBJS-FM
Owner: Shivery(Bob)
Editorial: 406 Nacogdoches St, Jacksonville, Texas 75766. T: 1 903 586-5257
E: info@kbjs.org **W:** http://www.kbjs.org

KBJT-AM
Owner: KBJT, Inc.
Editorial: 303 N Spring St, Fordyce, Arkansas 71742-3317. T: 1 870 352-7137
E: kbjt@coatesmedia.com
W: http://www.kbjtkq.com
Editorial Profile: KBJT-AM is a commercial station owned by KBJT, Inc. The format of the station is news and talk. KBJT-AM broadcasts in the Fordyce, AR area at 1590 AM.

KBKB-AM
Owner: Pritchard Broadcasting Co.
Editorial: 610 N 4Th St Ste 300, Burlington, Iowa 52601-5059. T: 1 319 752-5402
E: news@burlingtonradio.com
W: http://www.1360kbkb.com
Editorial Profile: KBKB-AM is a commercial station owned by Pritchard Broadcasting Co. The format of the station is classic country. KBKB-AM broadcasts to the Burlington, IA area at 1360 AM.

KBKB-FM
Owner: Titan Broadcasting LLC
Editorial: 610 N 4Th St Ste 310, Burlington, Iowa 52601-5059. T: 1 319 752-2701
W: http://www.1017thebull.com
Editorial Profile: KBKB-FM is a commercial station owned by Titan Broadcasting LLC. The format of the station is country. KBKB-FM broadcasts to the Burlington, IA area at 107.1 FM.

KBKG-FM
Owner: Adkins(Jim)
Editorial: 501 Bryan Ave, Corning, Arkansas 72422-3262. T: 1 870 857-6646
E: lite93fm@isainet.com
Editorial Profile: KBKG-FM is a commercial station owned by Jim Adkins. The format of the station is classic hits. KBKG-FM broadcasts to the Corning, AR area at 93.5 FM.

KBKK-FM
Owner: Mapleton Communications
Editorial: 92 W Shamrock Ave, Pineville, Louisiana 71360-6435. T: 1 318 487-1035
W: http://www.1055kbuck.com
Editorial Profile: KBKK-FM is a commercial station owned by Opus Broadcasting of Alexandria, LLC. The format of the station is country music. KBKK-FM broadcasts to the Alexandria, LA area at 105.5 FM.

KBKL-FM
Owner: Townsquare Media, Inc.
Editorial: 315 Kennedy Ave, Grand Junction, Colorado 81501-7552. T: 1 970 242-7788
E: kool1079@cumulus.com
W: http://kool1079.com
Editorial Profile: KBKL-FM is a commercial station owned by Townsquare Media, Inc. The

format of the station is oldies music. KBKL-FM broadcasts in the Grand Junction, CO area at 107.9 FM.

KBKR-AM
Owner: Pacific Empire Communications
Editorial: 2510 East Cove Ave, La Grande, Oregon 97850-3911. T: 1 541 963-4121
E: supertalk@eoni.com
W: http://www.supertalk1450.com
Editorial Profile: KBKR-AM is a commercial station owned by Pacific Empire Communications. The format of the station is talk. KLBM-AM broadcasts in the La Grande, OR area at 1490 AM and is a simulcast of KLBM-AM.

KBKS-FM
Owner: Clear Channel Media and Entertainment
Editorial: 645 Elliott Ave W #400, Seattle, Washington 98119-3911. T: 1 206 494-2000
E: pd@kissfmseattle.com
W: http://www.kissfmseattle.com
Editorial Profile: KBKS-FM is a commercial station owned by Clear Channel Media and Entertainment. The format of the station is Top 40/CHR. KBKS-FM broadcasts to the Seattle area at 106.1 FM.

KBKW-AM
Owner: Jodesha Broadcasting Inc.
Editorial: 1520 Simpson Ave, Aberdeen, Washington 98520. T: 1 360 533-3000
E: news@kbkw.com **W:** http://www.kbkw.com
Editorial Profile: KBKW-AM is a commercial station owned by Jodesha Broadcasting Inc. The format of the station is news and talk. KBKW-AM broadcasts to the Aberdeen, WA area at 1450 AM.

KBKY-FM
Owner: KM Communications Inc.
Editorial: 2855 G St, Merced, California 95340-2133. T: 1 209 385-9994
Editorial Profile: KBKY-FM is a commercial station owned by KM Communications Inc. The format of the station is Spanish religious. KBKY-FM broadcasts to the Merced, CA area at 94.1 FM.

KBKZ-FM
Owner: Phillips Broadcasting Inc
Editorial: 100 Fisher Dr, Trinidad, Colorado 81082-3919. T: 1 719 846-3355
E: kcrt@comcast.net
W: http://www.kcrtradio.com/kbkz
Editorial Profile: KBZK-FM is a commercial station owned by Phillips Broadcasting Inc. The format of the station is contemporary country. KBZK-FM broadcasts to the Trinidad, CO area at 96.5 FM.

KBLA-AM
Owner: Multicultural Radio Broadcasting Inc.
Editorial: 747 E Green St Fl 4, Pasadena, California 91101-2145. T: 1 626 844-8882
Editorial Profile: KBLA-AM is a commercial station owned by Multicultural Radio Broadcasting Inc. The format of the station is variety. KBLA-AM broadcasts to the Los Angeles area at 900 AM. The station does not accept press releases.

KBLB-FM
Owner: BL Broadcasting Inc.
Editorial: 13225 Dogwood Dr, Baxter, Minnesota 56425-8669. T: 1 218 828-1244
W: http://www.todaysbestcountry.com
Editorial Profile: KBLB-FM is a commercial station owned by BL Broadcasting Inc. The format of the station is contemporary country music. KBLB-FM broadcasts in the Minneapolis area at 93.3 FM.

KBLC-FM
Owner: Houston Christian Broadcasters
Editorial: 2424 South Blvd, Houston, Texas 77098-5110. T: 1 713 520-5200
E: email@khcb.org **W:** http://www.khcb.org
Editorial Profile: KBLC-FM is non-commercial station owned by Houston Christian Broadcasters. The format of the station is Christian music and religious talk. KBLC-FM broadcasts to the Fredericksburg Houston area at 91.5 FM and simulcasts on KHCB-FM.

KBLD-FM
Owner: Calvary Chapel of Tri-Cities
Editorial: 10611 W Clearwater Ave, Kennewick, Washington 99336-8621.
T: 1 509 619-7007 E: kbldthetree@gmail.com
W: http://www.kbld.com
Editorial Profile: KBLD-FM is a non-commercial station owned by Calvary Chapel of Tri-Cities. The format of the station is

Christian music and talk. KBLD-FM broadcasts in the Kennewick, WA area at 91.7 FM.

KBLE-AM
Owner: Sacred Heart Radio
Editorial: 7357 148Th Ave Ne, Redmond, Washington 98052-4148. **T:** 1 425 867-2340
E: info@sacredheartradio.org
W: http://www.sacredheartradio.org
Editorial Profile: KBLE-AM is a non-commercial station owned by Sacred Heart Radio. The format of the station is religious. KBLE-AM broadcasts to the Kirkland, WA area at 1050 AM.

KBLF-AM
Owner: Huth Broadcasting Inc.
Editorial: 756 Hickory St, Red Bluff, California 96080. **T:** 1 530 527-1490
E: kblfam@yahoo.com
W: http://www.kblfam.com
Editorial Profile: KBLF-AM is a commercial station owned by Huth Broadcasting Inc. The format of the station is adult standards. KBLF-AM broadcasts to the Red Bluff, CA area at 1490 AM.

KBLG-AM
Owner: Connoisseur Media LLC
Editorial: 2075 Central Ave, Billings, Montana 59102. **T:** 1 406 248-7777
W: http://www.kblg910.com
Editorial Profile: KBLG-AM is a commercial station owned by Connoisseur Media LLC. The format of the station is news, talk and sports. KBLG-AM broadcasts in the Billings, MT area at 910 AM.

KBLI-AM
Owner: Riverbend Communications LLC
Editorial: 400 W Sunnyside Rd, Idaho Falls, Idaho 83402-4613. **T:** 1 208 523-3722
W: http://www.eastidahonews.com
Editorial Profile: KBLI-AM is a commercial station owned by Riverbend Communications LLC. The format of the station is news and talk. KBLI-AM broadcasts to the Idaho Falls, ID area at 630 AM.

KBLJ-AM
Owner: Cherry Creek Radio
Editorial: 116 Dalton Ave, La Junta, Colorado 81050. **T:** 1 719 384-5456 **E:** kblj@secom.net
W: http://www.cherrycreekradio.com
Editorial Profile: KBLJ-AM is a commercial station owned by Cherry Creek Radio. The format of the station is oldies. KBLJ-AM broadcasts to the La Junta, CO area at 1400 AM.

KBLL-AM
Owner: Cherry Creek Radio
Editorial: 110 E Broadway St, Helena, Montana 59601-4232. **T:** 1 406 442-6620
E: kbllam@cherrycreekradio.com
W: http://www.kbllradio.com
Editorial Profile: KBLL-AM is a commercial station owned by Cherry Creek Radio. The format of the station is news and talk. KBLL-AM broadcasts in the Helena, MT area at 1240 AM.

KBLL-FM
Owner: Cherry Creek Radio
Editorial: 110 E Broadway St, Helena, Montana 59601-4232. **T:** 1 406 442-4490
Editorial Profile: KBLL-FM is a commercial station owned by Cherry Creek Radio. The format of the station is country music. KBLL-FM broadcasts in the Helena, MT area at 99.5 FM.

KBLP-FM
Owner: South Central Broadcasting & Advertising
Editorial: 204 S Main St, Lindsay, Oklahoma 73052-5634. **T:** 1 405 756-4438
W: http://www.kblpradio.com
Editorial Profile: KBLP-FM is a commercial station owned by South Central Oklahoma Broadcasting & Advertising. The format of the station is country music. KBLP-FM broadcasts to the Oklahoma City area at 105.1 FM.

KBLQ-FM
Owner: Cache Valley Radio Inc.
Editorial: 810 W 200 N, Logan, Utah 84321. **T:** 1 435 752-1390 **E:** kblq@cvradio.com
W: http://www.q92.fm
Editorial Profile: KBLQ-FM is a commercial station owned by Cache Valley Radio Inc. The format of the station is adult contemporary music. KBLQ-FM broadcasts to the Salt Lake City area at 92.9 FM.

KBLR-FM
Owner: R & R Broadcasting, Inc.
Editorial: 5011 Capitol Ave, Omaha, Nebraska 68132-2921. **T:** 1 402 342-2000
Editorial Profile: KBLR-FM is a commercial station owned by R & R Broadcasting, Inc.The format of the show is country music. KBLR-FM broadcasts to the Blair, NE area at 97.3 FM.

KBLS-FM
Owner: Morris Communications
Editorial: 200 N Broadway St, Abilene, Kansas 67410. **T:** 1 785 263-3422
W: http://www.sunny1025.com
Editorial Profile: KBLS-FM is a commercial station owned by Morris Communications. The format of the station is adult contemporary music. KBLS-FM broadcasts in the Salina, KS area at 102.5 FM.

KBLT-FM
Owner: Radio Cactus LTD.
Editorial: 1010 Garner Field Rd, Uvalde, Texas 78801. **T:** 1 830 278-3693
E: kbradioranch@hotmail.com
W: http://www.kbnu.fm
Editorial Profile: KBLT-FM is a commercial station owned by Radio Cactus LTD. The format of the station is country music. KBLT-FM broadcasts to the Uvalde, TX area at 104.3 FM.

KBLU-AM
Owner: El Dorado Broadcasting
Editorial: 755 W 28th St, Yuma, Arizona 85364. **T:** 1 928 344-4980
W: http://www.kbluam.com
Editorial Profile: KBLU-AM is a commercial station owned by El Dorado Broadcasting. The format of the station is news, sports and talk. KBLU-AM broadcasts to the Yuma, AZ area at 560 AM.

KBLX-FM
Owner: Entercom Communications Corp.
Editorial: 201 3Rd St Ste 1200, San Francisco, California 94103-3143.
T: 1 415 777-0965
E: kblxcomments@entercom.com
W: http://www.kblx.com
Editorial Profile: KBLX-FM is a commercial station owned by Entercom Communications Corp.. The format of the station is urban adult contemporary music. KBLX-FM broadcasts to the San Francisco area at 102.9 FM.

KBLY-AM
Owner: Riverbend Communications LLC
Editorial: 400 W Sunnyside Rd, Idaho Falls, Idaho 83402-4613. **T:** 1 208 785-1400
W: http://www.eastidahonews.com
Editorial Profile: KBLY-AM is a commercial station owned by Riverbend Communications LLC. The format of the station is news and talk. KBLY-AM broadcasts to the Idaho Falls, ID area at 1260 AM.

KBLZ-FM
Owner: Reynolds Radio Inc.
Editorial: 212 Grande Blvd Ste B100, Tyler, Texas 75703-4201. **T:** 1 903 581-5259
W: http://www.theblaze.fm
Editorial Profile: KBLZ is a commercial station owned by Reynolds Radio Inc. The format of the station is urban contemporary music. KBLZ-FM broadcasts to Tyler, TX at 102.7 FM.

KBMB-AM
Owner: Entravision Communications Corp.
Editorial: 501 N 44th St, Phoenix, Arizona 85008-6526. **T:** 1 602 776-1400
W: http://www.espnradio710am.com
Editorial Profile: KBMB-AM is a commercial station owned by Entravision Communications Corp. The format of the station is Hispanic sports programming. KBMB-AM broadcasts to the Phoenix area at 710 AM.

KBME-AM
Owner: Clear Channel Media and Entertainment
Editorial: 2000 West Loop S, Houston, Texas 77027-3513. **T:** 1 713 212-8000
W: http://www.sports790.com
Editorial Profile: KBME-AM is a commercial station owned by Clear Channel Media and Entertainment. The format of the station is sports. KBME-AM broadcasts to the Houston area at 790 AM.

KBMG-FM
Owner: Adelante Media Group
Editorial: 2722 S Redwood Rd, Salt Lake City, Utah 84119-8409. **T:** 1 801 908-8777
W: http://www.adelantemediagroup.com
Editorial Profile: KBMG-FM is a commercial station owned by Adelante Media Group. The format of the station is Bilingual Top 40/CHR. KBMG-FM broadcasts to the Salt Lake City area at 106.1 FM.

KBMP-FM
Owner: Bott Broadcasting Co.
Editorial: 10550 Barkley St Ste 100, Overland Park, Kansas 66212-1824. **T:** 1 913 642-7770
E: comments@bottradionetwork.com
W: http://www.bottradionetwork.com
Editorial Profile: KBMP-FM is a commercial station owned by Bott Broadcasting Co. The format of the station is religious programming. KBMP-FM broadcasts to the Overland Park, KS area at 90.5 FM.

KBMQ-FM
Owner: Media Ministries, Inc.
Editorial: 130 Art Alley Ste C, Monroe, Louisiana 71201-6749. **T:** 1 318 387-1230
E: info@kbmq.org **W:** http://www.kbmq.org
Editorial Profile: KBMQ-FM is a non-commercial station owned by Media Ministries, Inc. The format of the station is Contemporary Christian. KBMQ-FM broadcasts to the Monroe, LA area at a frequency of 88.7 FM.

KBMR-AM
Owner: Clear Channel Media and Entertainment
Editorial: 3500 E Rosser Ave, Bismarck, North Dakota 58501-3376. **T:** 1 701 255-1234
E: kbmr@clearchannel.com
W: http://www.kbmr.com
Editorial Profile: KBMR-AM is a commercial station owned by Clear Channel Media and Entertainment. The format of the station is country music. KBMR-AM broadcasts to the Bismarck, ND area at 1130 AM.

KBMV-FM
Owner: E-Communications LLC.
Editorial: 10 Court Sq, West Plains, Missouri 65775-3444. **T:** 1 417 255-2548
E: eckman@centurytel.net
Editorial Profile: KBMV-FM is a commercial station owned by E-Communications LLC. The format of the station is Christian music and talk. KBMV-FM broadcasts to the Springfield, MO area at 107.1 FM.

KBMW-AM
Owner: L & L Radio
Editorial: 605 Dakota Ave, Wahpeton, North Dakota 58075-4331. **T:** 1 701 642-8747
E: studio@kbmwam.com
W: http://www.kbmwam.com
Editorial Profile: KBMW-AM is a commercial station owned by L & L Radio. The format of the station is news and talk. KBMW-AM broadcasts to the Wahpeton, ND area at 1450 AM.

KBMX-FM
Owner: Townsquare Media, LLC
Editorial: 14 E Central Entrance, Duluth, Minnesota 55811. **T:** 1 218 727-4500
W: http://www.mix108.com
Editorial Profile: KBMX-FM is a commercial station owned by Townsquare Media, LLC. The format of the station is hot adult contemporary. KBMX-FM broadcasts to the Duluth, MN area at 107.7 FM.

KBNA-FM
Owner: Univision Communications Inc.
Editorial: 2211 E Missouri Ave, Ste 300, El Paso, Texas 79903-3837. **T:** 1 915 544-9797
W: http://www.univision.com/content/channel.jhtml?chid=10068&schid=10081
Editorial Profile: KBNA-FM is a commercial station owned by Univision Communications Inc. The format of the station is regional Mexican. KBNA-FM broadcasts to the El Paso, TX area at 97.5 FM.

KBND-AM
Owner: Combined Communications
Editorial: 63088 Ne 18Th St Ste 200, Bend, Oregon 97701-7102. **T:** 1 541 382-5263
E: news@kbnd.com **W:** http://www.kbnd.com
Editorial Profile: KBND-AM is a commercial station owned by Combined Communications. The format for the station is news and talk. KBND-AM broadcasts to the Bend, OR area at 1110 AM.

KBNH-AM
Owner: Harney County Radio, LLC
Editorial: 69470 S Egan Rd, Burns, Oregon 97720-2537. **T:** 1 541 573-2055
E: info@kbnh1230.com
W: http://kbnh1230.com
Editorial Profile: KBNH-AM is a commercial station owned by Harney County Radio, LLC. The format of the station is classic country with a mix of hits from every decade. KBNH-AM broadcasts to the Burns, OR area at 1230 AM.

KBNJ-FM
Owner: World Radio Network, Inc.
Editorial: 3766 Saturn Rd, Corpus Christi, Texas 78413. **T:** 1 361 855-0975
E: dj@kbnj.org **W:** http://www.kbnj.org
Editorial Profile: KBNJ-FM is a non-commercial station owned by World Radio Network, Inc. The format is contemporary Christian music and talk. KBNJ-FM broadcasts in the Corpus Christi, TX area at 91.7 FM.

KBNL-FM
Owner: Inspiracom
Editorial: 1620 E Plum St, Laredo, Texas 78043-1023. **T:** 1 956 724-9211
E: kbnl@inspiracom.org
W: http://www.kbnl.org
Editorial Profile: KBNL-FM is a non-commercial station owned by Inspiracom. The format is contemporary Christian and Hispanic. KBNL-FM broadcasts to the Laredo, TX area at 89.9 FM.

KBNN-AM
Owner: Goodradio.TV LLC
Editorial: 18553 Gentry Rd, Lebanon, Missouri 65536. **T:** 1 417 532-9111
E: kjel@regionalradio.com
W: http://www.regionalradio.com
Editorial Profile: KBNN-AM is a commercial station owned by Goodradio.TV LLC. The format of the station is news and talk. KBNN-AM broadcasts in the Lebanon, MO area at 750 AM.

KBNO-AM
Owner: Latino Communications
Editorial: 600 Grant St, Ste 600, Denver, Colorado 80203-3540. **T:** 1 303 733-5266
W: http://www.radioquebueno.com
Editorial Profile: KBNO-AM is a commercial station owned by Latino Communications. The format of the station is Hispanic programming. KBNO-AM broadcasts to the Denver area at 1280 AM.

KBNP-AM
Owner: Second Amendment Foundation
Editorial: 278 SW Arthur St, Portland, Oregon 97201-4745. **T:** 1 503 223-6769
E: spots@kbnp.com **W:** http://www.kbnp.com
Editorial Profile: KBNP-AM is a commercial station owned by Second Amendment Foundation. The format of the station is business talk. KBNP-AM broadcasts to Portland, OR, at 1410 AM.

KBNR-FM
Owner: World Radio Network, Inc.
Editorial: 901 Mexico Blvd, Brownsville, Texas 78520. **T:** 1 956 542-6933 **E:** kbnr@lwrn.org
W: http://www.radiokbnr.org
Editorial Profile: KBNR-FM is a non-commercial station owned by World Radio Network, Inc. The format is Hispanic religious talk and music. KBNR-FM broadcasts to the Brownsville, TX area at 88.3 FM.

KBNU-FM
Owner: Radio Cactus LTD.
Editorial: 1010 Garner Field Rd, Uvalde, Texas 78801-4810. **T:** 1 830 278-3693
E: kbradioranch@hotmail.com
W: http://www.kbnu.fm
Editorial Profile: KBNU-FM is a commercial station owned by Radio Cactus LTD. The format of the station is country. KBNU-FM broadcasts to the San Antonio area at 93.9 FM.

KBNV-FM
Owner: American Family Association
Editorial: 107 Parkgate Dr, Tupelo, Mississippi 38801. **T:** 1 662 844-8888
E: comments@afr.net **W:** http://www.afr.net

KBNW-AM
Owner: Horizon Broadcasting Group
Editorial: 854 NE 4th St, Bend, Oregon 97701-4711. **T:** 1 541 383-3825
E: news@horizonbroadcastinggroup.com
W: http://www.newsradiocentraloregon.com
Editorial Profile: KBNW-AM is a commerical station owned by Horizon Broadcast Group. The format for the station is news and talk. KBNW-AM broadcasts to the Bend, OR area at 1340 AM.

KBOA-AM
Owner: Pollack Broadcasting Co.
Editorial: 1303 Southwest Drive, Kennett, Missouri 63857. **T:** 1 573 888-4616
W: http://www.kboaradio.com
Editorial Profile: KBOA-AM is a commercial station owned by Pollack Broadcasting Co. The format of the station is adult standards. KBOA-AM broadcasts to the Kennett, MO area at 1540 AM.

KBOA-FM
Owner: Pollack Broadcasting Co.
Editorial: 1303 Southwest Drive, Kennett, Missouri 63857. **T:** 1 573 888-4616
E: ktmo@semoradio.com
W: http://www.kboaradio.com
Editorial Profile: KBOA-FM is a commercial station owned by Pollack Broadcasting Co. The format of the station is hot adult contemporary music. KBOA-FM broadcasts to the Kennett, MO area at 105.5 FM.

KBOB-FM
Owner: Townsquare Media
Editorial: 1229 Brady St, Davenport, Iowa 52803-4616. **T:** 1 563 326-2541
E: quadcities.prod@cumulus.com
W: http://www.rock1049.net
Editorial Profile: KBOB-FM is a commercial station owned by Townsquare Media. The format of the station is rock music. KBOB-FM broadcasts to the Davenport, IA area at 104.9 FM.

KBOC-FM
Owner: Liberman Broadcasting Inc.
Editorial: 2410 Gateway Dr, Irving, Texas 75063-2727. **T:** 1 972 652-2900
W: http://lazeta.estrellatv.com
Editorial Profile: KBOC-FM is a commercial station owned by Liberman Broadcasting Inc. The format of the station is Regional Mexican, featuring regional Mexican music. KBOC-FM broadcasts to the Dallas area at 98.3 FM.

KBOE-AM
Owner: Jomast Corp.
Editorial: 2172 230Th St, Oskaloosa, Iowa 52577-9113. **T:** 1 641 673-3493
E: news@kboeradio.com
W: http://www.kboeradio.com
Editorial Profile: KBOE-AM is a commercial station owned by Jomast Corp. The format of the station is country. KBOE-AM broadcasts to the Oskaloosa, IA area at 740 AM.

KBOE-FM
Owner: Jomast Corp.
Editorial: 2172 230th St, Oskaloosa, Iowa 52577-9113. **T:** 1 641 673-3493
E: kboe@kboeradio.com
W: http://www.kboeradio.com
Editorial Profile: KBOE-FM is a commercial station owned by Jomast Corp. The format of the station is contemporary country. KBOE-FM broadcasts to the Oskaloosa, IA area at 104.9 FM.

KBOI-AM
Owner: Cumulus Media Inc
Editorial: 1419 W Bannock St, Boise, Idaho 83702-5234. **T:** 1 208 336-3670
E: 670@news.com
W: http://www.670kboi.com
Editorial Profile: KBOI-AM is a commercial station owned by Cumulus Media Inc. The format of the station is news, talk and sports. KBOI-AM broadcasts to the Boise, ID area at 670 AM.

KBON-FM
Owner: Marx (Rose Ann)
Editorial: 109 S 2nd St, Eunice, Louisiana 70535. **T:** 1 337 546-0007
E: 101.1@kbon.com **W:** http://www.kbon.com
Editorial Profile: KBON-FM is a commercial station owned by Rose Ann Marx. The format of the station is classic country. KBON-FM broadcasts in the Lafayette, LA area at 101.1 FM.

KBOO-FM
Owner: KBOO Foundation
Editorial: 20 SE 8th Ave, Portland, Oregon 97214-1257. **T:** 1 503 231-8032
W: http://www.kboo.fm
Editorial Profile: KBOO-FM is a non-commercial station owned by KBOO Foundation. The format of the station is variety. KBOO-FM broadcasts to the Portland, OR area at 90.7 FM.

KBOS-FM
Owner: Clear Channel Media and Entertainment
Editorial: 83 E Shaw Ave, Ste 150, Fresno, California 93710-7622. **T:** 1 559 230-4300
W: http://www.b95forlife.com
Editorial Profile: KBOS-FM is a commercial station owned by Clear Channel Media and Entertainment. The format of the station is rhythmic Top 40/CHR. KBOS-FM broadcasts to the Fresno, CA area at 94.9 FM.

KBOT-FM
Owner: Leighton Enterprises Inc.
Editorial: 1340 Richwood Rd, Detroit Lakes, Minnesota 56501. **T:** 1 218 847-5624
E: kdlmkbot@lakesnet.net
W: http://www.catchthewave1041.com
Editorial Profile: KBOT-FM is a commercial station owned by Leighton Enterprises Inc. The format of the station is adult contemporary. KBOT-FM broadcasts in the Detroit Lakes, MN area at 104.1 FM.

KBOV-AM
Owner: Great Country Broadcasting Inc.
Editorial: South Highway 395, Bishop, California 93514. **T:** 1 760 873-6324
E: kibskbov@yahoo.com
W: http://www.kibskbov.com
Editorial Profile: KBOV-AM is a commercial station owned by Great Country Broadcasting Inc. The format of the station is classic hits. KBOV-AM broadcasts to the Bishop, CA area at 1230 AM.

KBOW-AM
Owner: Butte Broadcasting Inc.
Editorial: 660 Dewey Blvd, Butte, Montana 59701. **T:** 1 406 494-7777
E: mail@kbowkopr.com
W: http://www.kbow550.net
Editorial Profile: KBOW-AM is a commercial station owned by Butte Broadcasting Inc. The format for the station is country music, news and sports. KBOW-AM broadcasts to the Butte, MT area at 550 AM.

KBOX-FM
Owner: American General Media
Editorial: 2325 Skyway Dr, Santa Maria, California 93455-1137. **T:** 1 805 922-1041
W: http://www.1041pirateradio.com
Editorial Profile: KBOX-FM is a commercial station owned by American General Media. The format of the station is adult hits. KBOX-FM broadcasts to the Santa Barbara, CA area at 104.1 FM.

KBOY-FM
Owner: Mapleton Radio, LLC
Editorial: 1438 Rossanley Dr, Medford, Oregon 97501-1751. **T:** 1 541 779-1550
W: http://www.957kboy.com
Editorial Profile: KBOY-FM is a commercial station owned by Mapleton Radio, LLC. The format of the station is classic rock music. KBOY-FM broadcasts in the Medford, OR area at 95.7 FM.

KBOZ-AM
Owner: Reier Broadcasting Company Inc.
Editorial: 5445 Johnson Rd, Bozeman, Montana 59718. **T:** 1 406 587-9999
E: news@kboz.com **W:** http://www.kboz.com
Editorial Profile: KBOZ-AM is a commercial station owned by Reier Broadcasting Co., Inc. The format of the station is news and talk. KBOZ-AM broadcasts in the Bozeman, MT area at 1090 AM.

KBOZ-FM
Owner: Reier Broadcasting Company Inc.
Editorial: 5445 Johnson Rd, Bozeman, Montana 59718. **T:** 1 406 587-9999
E: news@kboz.com **W:** http://www.kboz.com
Editorial Profile: KBOZ-FM is a commercial station owned by the Reier Broadcasting Co., Inc. The format of the station is country music. KBOZ-FM broadcasts in the Bozeman, MT area at 99.9 FM.

KBPA-FM
Owner: Emmis Communications Corp.
Editorial: 8309 N Interstate Hwy 35, Austin, Texas 78753. **T:** 1 512 832-4000
W: http://www.hibob.fm
Editorial Profile: KBPA-FM is a commercial station owned by Emmis Communications Corp. The format of the station is adult hits. KBPA-FM broadcasts to the Austin, TX area at 103.5 FM.

KBPC-FM
Owner: KBPC, LLC
Editorial: 112 E Pecan St Ste 1212, San Antonio, Texas 78205-1531.
T: 1 936 544-9350 **E:** news@kbpcfm.com
W: http://www.kbpcfm.com
Editorial Profile: KBPC-FM is a commercial station owned by KBPC, LLC and operated by Allied Broadcasting. The format of the station is country music. KBPC-FM broadcasts to the East Texas area at 93.5 FM.

KBPI-FM
Owner: Clear Channel Media and Entertainment
Editorial: 4695 S Monaco St, Denver, Colorado 80237. **T:** 1 303 713-8000
W: http://www.kbpi.com
Editorial Profile: KBPI-FM is a commercial station owned by Clear Channel Media and Entertainment. The format of the station is rock. KBPI-FM broadcasts to the Denver area at 106.7 FM.

KBPN-FM
Owner: Minnesota Public Radio
Editorial: 501 W College Dr, #402, Brainerd, Minnesota 56401. **T:** 1 218 829-1072
E: newsroom@mpr.org
W: http://minnesota.publicradio.org/radio/stations/kbpnkbpr
Editorial Profile: KBPN-FM is a non-commercial station owned by Minnesota Public Radio. The station of the station is news and talk. KBPN-FM broadcasts to the Brainerd, MN area at 88.3 FM.

KBPR-FM
Owner: Minnesota Public Radio
Editorial: 501 W College Dr, #402, Brainerd, Minnesota 56401. **T:** 1 218 829-1072
E: newsroom@mpr.org
W: http://minnesota.publicradio.org/radio/stations/kbpnkbpr/
Editorial Profile: KBPR-FM is a non-commercial station owned by Minnesota Public Radio. The format of the station is classical. KBPR-FM broadcasts to the Brainerd, MN area at 90.7 FM.

KBPS-AM
Owner: Portland Public School District
Editorial: 515 Ne 15Th Ave, Portland, Oregon 97232-2897. **T:** 1 503 916-5828
W: http://kbps.am
Editorial Profile: KBPS-AM is a non-commercial station owned by the Portland Public School District. The format of the station features children's programming from 8 a.m. to 3 p.m., and then is controlled by students from 3 p.m. to 5 p.m. under an oldies music format. KBPS-AM broadcasts to the Portland, OR area at 1450 AM.

KBPY-FM
Owner: Chadrad Communications, Inc
Editorial: 226 Bordeaux St, Chadron, Nebraska 69337-2393. **T:** 1 308 432-5545
E: kbpy@chadrad.com
Editorial Profile: KBPY-FM is a commercial station owned by Chadrad Communications, Inc. The format of the station is rock/album-oriented rock. KBPY-FM is licensed to the Hay Springs, NE area broadcasting at a frequency of 107.7 FM.

KBQB-FM
Owner: Results Radio Group
Editorial: 856 Manzanita Ct, Chico, California 95926. **T:** 1 530 342-2200
E: friendsofbob@927bobfm.com
W: http://www.927bobfm.com
Editorial Profile: KBQB-FM is a commercial station owned by Results Radio Group. The format of the station is adult hits. KBQB-FM broadcasts to the Chico, CA area at 92.7 FM.

KBQI-FM
Owner: Clear Channel Media and Entertainment
Editorial: 5411 Jefferson St NE, Ste 100, Albuquerque, New Mexico 87109.
T: 1 505 830-6400
W: http://www.bigi1079.com
Editorial Profile: KBQI-FM is a commercial station owned by Clear Channel Media and Entertainment. The format of the station is contemporary country. KBQI-FM broadcasts to the Albuquerque, NM area at 107.9 FM.

KBRB-AM
Owner: Sandhills Broadcasting
Editorial: 122 E 2nd St, Ainsworth, Nebraska 69210. **T:** 1 402 387-1400 **E:** kbrb@sscg.net
W: http://www.kbrbradio.com
Editorial Profile: KBRB-AM is a commercial station owned by Sandhills Broadcasting. The format of the station is country. KBRB-AM broadcasts to the Ainsworth, NE area at 1400 AM.

KBRB-FM
Owner: Sandhills Broadcasting
Editorial: 122 E 2nd St, Ainsworth, Nebraska 69210. **T:** 1 402 387-1400 **E:** kbrb@sscg.net
W: http://www.kbrbradio.com
Editorial Profile: KBRB-FM is a commercial station owned by Sandhills Broadcasting. The format of the station is classic rock. KBRB-FM broadcasts to the Ainsworth, NE area at 92.7 FM.

KBRC-AM
Owner: J & J Broadcasting, Inc.
Editorial: 2029 Freeway Dr, Mount Vernon, Washington 98273-5470. **T:** 1 360 424-1430
E: kapskbrc@yahoo.com
W: http://www.kbrcradio.com
Editorial Profile: KBRC-AM is a commercial station owned by J & J Broadcasting, Inc. The format of the station is classic hits. KBRC-AM broadcasts to the Mount Vernon, WA area at 1430 AM.

KBRD-AM
Owner: BJ & Skip's For The Music Foundation
Editorial: 1849 Abernethy Rd NE, Olympia, Washington 98516-3710. **T:** 1 360 491-6800
E: kbrdpsa@gmail.com
W: http://www.apikai.com/kbrd
Editorial Profile: KBRD-AM is a non-commercial station owned by BJ & Skip's For The Music Foundation. The format of the station is adult standards. KBRD-AM broadcasts to the Olympia, WA area at 680 AM. Please note that they do NOT accept PSAs from outside of Thurston County, WA.

KBRE-FM
Owner: Mapleton Radio, LLC
Editorial: 1020 W Main St, Merced, California 95340. **T:** 1 209 723-2191
E: kbre@radiomerced.com
W: http://www.925thebear.com
Editorial Profile: KBRE-FM is a commercial station owned by Mapleton Radio, LLC. The format of the station is rock music. KBRE-FM broadcasts to the Merced, CA area at 92.5 FM.

KBRF-AM
Owner: Results Radio Group
Editorial: 728 Western Ave, Fergus Falls, Minnesota 56537-1095. **T:** 1 218 736-7596
E: contactus@lakesradio.net
W: http://www.lakesradio.net
Editorial Profile: KBRF-AM is a commercial station owned by Results Radio Group. The format of the station is news and talk. KBRF-AM broadcasts to the Fergus Falls, MN area at 1250 AM.

KBRG-FM
Owner: Univision Communications Inc.
Editorial: 750 Battery St, Ste 200, San Francisco, California 94111-1524.
T: 1 415 989-5765
W: http://recuerdo1003.univision.com
Editorial Profile: KBRG-FM is a commercial station owned by Univision Communications Inc. The format of the station is Hispanic oldies. KBRG-FM broadcasts to the San Francisco area at 100.3 FM.

KBRH-AM
Owner: East Baton Rouge School Board
Editorial: 1105 Lee Dr, Baton Rouge, Louisiana 70808-8714. **T:** 1 225 387-1260
Editorial Profile: KBRH-AM is a commercial station owned by East Baton Rouge School Board. The format for the station is blues, R&B and oldies. KBRH-AM broadcasts to the Baton Rouge, LA area at 1260 AM.

KBRI-AM
Owner: East Arkansas Broadcasters Inc.
Editorial: 1501 S. Main St., Wynne, Arkansas 72021. **T:** 1 870 734-1570
Editorial Profile: KBRI-AM is a commercial station owned by East Arkansas Broadcasters Inc. The format of the station is country. KBRI-AM broadcasts to the Wynne, AR area at 1570 AM.

KBRJ-FM
Owner: Morris Communications
Editorial: 301 Arctic Slope Ave, Ste 200, Anchorage, Alaska 99518. **T:** 1 907 344-9622
E: wakeup@kbrj.com **W:** http://www.kbrj.com
Editorial Profile: KBRJ-FM is a commercial station owned by Morris Communications. The format of the station is country. KBRJ-FM broadcasts to the Anchorage, AK area at 104.1 FM.

KBRK-AM
Owner: Three Eagles Communications Co.
Editorial: 227 22nd Ave S, Brookings, South Dakota 57006. **T:** 1 605 692-1430
E: kbrkstudio@brookings.net
W: http://www.brookingsradio.com

Editorial Profile: KBRK-AM is a commercial station owned by Three Eagles Communications Co. The format of the station is adult standards. KBRK-AM broadcasts to the Brookings, SD area at 1430 AM.

KBRK-FM

Owner: Three Eagles Communications Co.
Editorial: 227 22nd Ave S, Brookings, South Dakota 57006. **T:** 1 605 692-1430
E: fmstudio@brookings.net
W: http://www.brookingsradio.com
Editorial Profile: KBRK-FM is a commercial station owned by Three Eagles Communications Co. The format of the station is adult contemporary. KBRK-FM broadcasts to the Brookings, SD area at 93.7 FM.

KBRL-AM

Owner: Armada Media Corp.
Editorial: 1811 W O St, McCook, Nebraska 69001. **T:** 1 308 345-5400
E: production@highplainsradio.net
W: http://www.plainsreporter.com
Editorial Profile: KBRL-AM is a commercial station owned by Armada Media Corp. The format of the station is talk. KBRL-AM broadcasts to the McCook, NE area at 98.5 FM.

KBRQ-FM

Owner: Clear Channel Media and Entertainment
Editorial: 314 W State Highway 6, Waco, Texas 76712. **T:** 1 254 776-3900
W: http://www.1025thebear.com
Editorial Profile: KBRQ-FM is a commercial station owned by Clear Channel Media and Entertainment. The format of the station is rock. KBRQ-FM broadcasts to the Waco, TX area at 102.5 FM.

KBRT-AM

Owner: Crawford Broadcasting Co.
Editorial: 3183 Airway Ave Ste D, Costa Mesa, California 92626-4611. **T:** 1 714 754-4450
E: kbrt@sbcglobal.net
W: http://www.kbrt740.com
Editorial Profile: KBRT-AM is a commercial station owned by Crawford Broadcasting Co. The format of the station is Christian talk. KBRT-AM broadcasts in the Costa Mesa, CA area at 740 AM.

KBRU-FM

Owner: Clear Channel Media and Entertainment
Editorial: 1900 NW Expressway St, Ste 1000, Oklahoma City, Oklahoma 73118.
T: 1 405 858-1400
W: http://www.947thebrew.com
Editorial Profile: KBRU-FM is a commercial station owned by Clear Channel Media and Entertainment. The format of the station is classic rock. KBRU-FM broadcasts to the Oklahoma City area at 94.7 FM.

KBRV-AM

Owner: Flash Broadcasting, LLC
Editorial: 225 S Main St, Soda Springs, Idaho 83276-1627. **T:** 1 208 547-2400
E: mail@kbrvam800.com
W: http://kbrvcountry.com
Editorial Profile: KBRV-AM is a commercial station owned by Flash Broadcasting, LLC. The format of the station is classic and contemporary country music. KBRV-AM broadcasts to the Salt Lake City area at 800 AM.

KBRW-AM

Owner: Silakkuagvik Communications Inc.
Editorial: 1695 Okpik St, Barrow, Alaska 99723-9999. **T:** 1 907 852-6811
W: http://www.kbrw.org
Editorial Profile: KBRW-AM is a non-commercial station owned by Silakkuagvik Communications Inc. The format of the station is variety. KBRW-AM broadcasts to Barrow, AK at 680 AM.

KBRW-FM

Owner: Silakkuagvik Communications Inc.
Editorial: 1695 Okpik St, Barrow, Alaska 99723-9999. **T:** 1 907 852-6811
W: http://www.kbrw.org
Editorial Profile: KBRW-FM is a non-commercial station owned by Silakkuagvik Communications, Inc. The format of the station is talk. KBRW-FM broadcasts to Barrow, AK at 91.9 FM.

KBRX-AM

Owner: Ranchland Broadcasting Co.
Editorial: 251 N Jefferson St, Oneill, Nebraska 68763. **T:** 1 402 336-1612 **E:** news@kbrx.com
W: http://www.kbrx.com

Editorial Profile: KBRX-AM is a commercial station owned by Ranchland Broadcasting Co. The format of the station is oldies. KBRX-AM broadcasts to the Oneill, NE area at 1350 AM.

KBRX-FM

Owner: Ranchland Broadcasting Co.
Editorial: 251 N Jefferson St, Oneill, Nebraska 68763. **T:** 1 402 336-1612 **E:** news@kbrx.com
W: http://www.kbrx.com
Editorial Profile: KBRX-FM is a commercial station owned by Ranchland Broadcasting Co. The format of the station is classic country. KBRX-FM broadcasts to the Oneill, NE area at 102.9 FM.

KBRZ-AM

Owner: Daij Media, LLC
Editorial: 10614 Rockley Rd, Houston, Texas 77099-3514. **T:** 1 281 575-1270
W: http://www.kbrzradio.com
Editorial Profile: KBRZ-AM is a commercial station owned by Daij Media, LLC. The format of the station is variety with an international influence. KBRZ-AM broadcasts to the Houston area at 1460 AM.

KBRZ-FM

Owner: Aleluya Broadcasting Network
Editorial: 1722 Treble Dr, Humble, Texas 77338-5253. **T:** 1 281 446-5725
Editorial Profile: KBRZ-FM is a non-commercial station owned by Aleluya Broadcasting Network. The format of the station is Spanish Contemporary Christian. KBRZ-FM broadcasts to the Victoria, TX area at 89.3 FM.

KBSA-FM

Owner: Louisiana State University
Editorial: 1 University Pl, Shreveport, Louisiana 71115-2301. **T:** 1 318 797-5150
E: listenermail@redriverradio.org
W: http://www.redriverradio.org
Editorial Profile: KBSA-FM is a non-commercial station owned by Louisiana State University. The format of the station is classical music and talk. KBSA-FM broadcasts to the El Dorado, AR area at 90.9 FM.

KBSB-FM

Owner: Bemidji State University
Editorial: 1500 Birchmont Dr NE, Box 11, Bemidji, Minnesota 56601. **T:** 1 218 755-4120
E: fm90@bemidjistate.edu
W: http://www.fm90.org

KBSN-AM

Owner: KSEM Inc.
Editorial: 2241 W Main St, Moses Lake, Washington 98837. **T:** 1 509 765-3441
E: kdrmkbsnbill@hotmail.com
Editorial Profile: KBSN-AM is a commercial station owned by KSEM Inc. The format of the station is news, talk and sports. The station airs in the Moses Lake, WA area on 1470 AM.

KBSO-FM

Owner: Championship Communications
Editorial: 701 Benys Rd, Corpus Christi, Texas 78408-2215. **T:** 1 361 826-5250
E: info@my947country.com
W: http://www.my947country.com
Editorial Profile: KBSO-FM is a commercial station owned by Championship Communications. The format of the station is country. KBSO-FM broadcasts to the Corpus Christi, TX area at 94.7 FM.

KBSR-AM

Owner: Sun Mountain Inc.
Editorial: Rr 1, Hardin, Montana 59034-9801.
T: 1 406 665-2828
W: http://www.bigskyradio.net
Editorial Profile: KBSR-AM is a commercial station owned by Sun Mountain Inc. The format of the station is news, talk and sports. KBSR-AM broadcasts to the Billings, MT area at 1490 AM.

KBST-AM

Owner: Rhattigan Broadcasting
Editorial: 608 Johnson St, Big Spring, Texas 79720-2851. **T:** 1 432 267-6391
E: comments@kbst.com
W: http://www.am.kbst.com
Editorial Profile: KBST-AM is a commercial station owned by Rhattigan Broadcasting. The format of the station is news, talk and sports. KBST-AM broadcasts to the Big Spring, TX area at 1490 AM.

KBST-FM

Owner: Rhattigan Broadcasting
Editorial: 608 Johnson St, Big Spring, Texas 79720. **T:** 1 432 267-6391 **E:** office@kbst.com

W: http://www.943fuse.com
Editorial Profile: KBST-FM is a commercial station owned by Rhattigan Broadcasting. The format of the station is contemporary country. KBST-FM broadcasts to the Big Spring, TX area at 95.7 FM.

KBSU-FM

Owner: Boise State University
Editorial: 1910 University Dr, Boise, Idaho 83725. **T:** 1 208 426-3663
E: boisestatepublicradio@boisestate.edu
W: http://radio.boisestate.edu
Editorial Profile: KBSU-FM is non-commercial station owned by Boise State University. The format of the station is classical music. KBSU-FM broadcasts to the Boise, ID area at 90.3 FM.

KBSX-FM

Owner: Boise State University
Editorial: 1910 University Dr, Boise, Idaho 83725-1915. **T:** 1 208 426-3663
E: boisestatepublicradio@boisestate.edu
W: http://radio.boisestate.edu
Editorial Profile: KBSX-FM is a non-commercial station owned by Boise State University. The format of the station is news and talk programming. KBSX-FM broadcasts to the Boise, ID area at 91.5 FM.

KBSZ-AM

Owner: 1TV.com, Inc.
Editorial: 4301 N 75th St Ste 105, Scottsdale, Arizona 85251-3501. **T:** 1 480 423-1261
W: http://funny973.com
Editorial Profile: KBSZ-AM is a commercial station owned by 1TV.com, Inc. The format of the station is comedy. KBSZ-AM broadcasts to the Apache Junction, AZ area at 1260 AM.

KBTA-AM

Owner: WRD Entertainment Inc.
Editorial: 920 Harrison St, Ste C, Batesville, Arkansas 72501. **T:** 1 870 793-4196
Editorial Profile: KBTA-AM is a commercial station owned by WRD Entertainment Inc. The format of the station is sports. KBTA-AM broadcasts in the Batesville, AR area at 1340 AM.

KBTA-FM

Owner: WRD Entertainment Inc.
Editorial: 920 Harrison St, Ste C, Batesville, Arkansas 72501. **T:** 1 870 793-4196
Editorial Profile: KBTA-FM is a commercial station owned by WRD Entertainment Inc. The format of the station is adult contemporary. KBTA-FM broadcasts to the Batesville, AR area at 99.5 FM.

KBTC-AM

Owner: Media Professionals, Inc.
Editorial: 17647 Highway B, Houston, Missouri 65483. **T:** 1 417 967-3353
W: http://espn1250houston.com
Editorial Profile: KBTC-AM is a commercial station owned by Media Professionals, Inc. The format of the station is sports and talk. KBTC-AM broadcasts to the Houston, MO area at 1250 AM.

KBTE-FM

Owner: Wilks Broadcast Group
Editorial: 33 Briercroft Office Park, Lubbock, Texas 79412. **T:** 1 806 762-3000
W: http://www.1049thebeat.com
Editorial Profile: KBTE-FM is a commercial station owned by Wilks Broadcast Group. The format for the station is urban contemporary music. KBTE-FM broadcasts to the Lubbock, TX, area at 104.9 FM.

KBTK-FM

Owner: Grenax Broadcasting
Editorial: 2409 N 4Th St Ste 101, Flagstaff, Arizona 86004-3735. **T:** 1 928 779-1177
W: http://www.bigtalkerradio.com
Editorial Profile: KBTK-FM is a commercial station owned by Grenax Broadcasting. The format of the station is news and talk. KBTK-FM broadcasts to the Flagstaff, AZ area at 105.1 FM.

KBTM-AM

Owner: East Arkansas Broadcasters Inc.
Editorial: 407 W Parker Rd, Jonesboro, Arkansas 72404. **T:** 1 870 932-8400
W: http://www.kbtm.com
Editorial Profile: KBTM-AM is a commercial station owned by East Arkansas Broadcasters Inc. The format of the station is news, sports and talk. KBTM-AM broadcasts to the Jonesboro, AR area at 1230 AM.

KBTN-AM

Owner: American Media Investments
Editorial: 2510 W 20th St, Joplin, Missouri 64804-0216. **T:** 1 417 451-1420
E: kbtnam@att.net
Editorial Profile: KBTN-AM is a commercial station owned by American Media Investments. The format of the station is country. KBTN-AM broadcasts to the Neosho, MO area at 1420 AM.

KBTN-FM

Owner: American Media Investments
Editorial: 2510 W 20th St, Joplin, Missouri 64804-0216. **T:** 1 417 781-1313
E: production@ami-joplin.com
W: http://kbtnradio.com
Editorial Profile: KBTN-FM is a commercial station owned by American Media Investments. The format of the station is classic country music. KBTN-FM broadcasts in the Joplin, MO area at 99.7 FM.

KBTO-FM

Owner: Programmers Broadcasting Inc.
Editorial: 1120 Highway 5 West, Bottineau, North Dakota 58318. **T:** 1 701 228-5151
E: sunnyradio@hotmail.com
Editorial Profile: KBTO-FM is a commercial station owned by Programmers Broadcasting Inc. The format of the station is country music. KBTO-FM broadcasts to the Minot-Bismarck, ND area at 101.9 FM.

KBTQ-FM

Owner: Univision Communications Inc.
Editorial: 200 S 10th St, Ste 600, McAllen, Texas 78501. **T:** 1 956 631-5499
W: http://recuerdo961.univision.com
Editorial Profile: KBTQ-FM is a commercial station owned by Univision Communications Inc. The format of the station is Hispanic oldies and romantic music. KBTQ-FM broadcasts to the McAllen, TX, area at 96.1 FM.

KBTS-FM

Owner: Rhattigan Broadcasting
Editorial: 608 Johnson St, Big Spring, Texas 79720. **T:** 1 432 267-6391
E: kbstnews@kbst.com
W: http://www.kbst.com
Editorial Profile: KBTS-FM is a commercial station owned by Rhattigan Broadcasting. The format of the station is hot adult contemporary music. KBTS-FM broadcasts to the Big Spring, TX area at 94.3 FM.

KBTT-FM

Owner: Access.1 Communications Corp.
Editorial: 208 N Thomas Dr, Shreveport, Louisiana 71107-6520. **T:** 1 318 222-3122
W: http://www.kbtt.fm
Editorial Profile: KBTT-FM is a commercial station owned by Access.1 Communications Corp. The format of the station is urban contemporary. KBTT-FM broadcasts to the Shreveport, LA area at 103.7 FM.

KBUA-FM

Owner: Liberman Broadcasting Inc.
Editorial: 1845 W Empire Ave, Burbank, California 91504-3402. **T:** 1 818 729-5300
W: http://aquisuena.estrellatv.com
Editorial Profile: KBUA-FM is a commercial station owned by Liberman Broadcasting Inc. The format of the station is regional Mexican music. KBUA-FM broadcasts to the greater Los Angeles area at 94.3 FM.

KBUB-FM

Owner: Better Living Ministries
Editorial: 910 Main St, Brownwood, Texas 76801. **T:** 1 325 646-5993
E: kpsmfm@gmail.com
W: http://www.kpsm.net
Editorial Profile: KBUB-FM is a non-commercial station owned by Better Living Ministries. The format of the station is southern gospel. KBUB-FM broadcasts to the Brownwood, TX area at 90.3 FM.

KBUC-FM

Owner: R Communications, LLC
Editorial: 1201 N Jackson Rd Ste 900, McAllen, Texas 78501-5764.
T: 1 956 992-8895
Editorial Profile: KBUC-FM is a commercial station owned by R Communications, LLC. The format of the station features Tejano music. KBUC-FM broadcasts to the McAllen, TX area at 102.1 FM.

KBUE-FM

Owner: Liberman Broadcasting Inc.
Editorial: 1845 W Empire Ave, Burbank, California 91504-3402. **T:** 1 818 729-5300

W: http://aquisuena.estrellatv.com
Editorial Profile: KBUE-FM is a commercial station owned by Liberman Broadcasting Inc. The format of the station is regional Mexican music. KBUE-FM broadcasts to the Los Angeles area at 105.5 FM.

KBUF-AM
Owner: Armada Media Corp.
Editorial: 1402 E Kansas Ave, Garden City, Kansas 67846. **T:** 1 620 276-2366
E: production@wksradio.com
W: http://www.wksradio.com/kbuf
Editorial Profile: KBUF-AM is a commercial station owned by Armada Media Corp. The format of the station is talk. KBUF-AM broadcasts in the Garden City, KS area at 1030 AM.

KBUK-FM
Owner: KBUK Radio, Inc.
Editorial: 511 FM 155 South, La Grange, Texas 78945. **T:** 1 979 968-3173
E: kvlgkbuk@kvlgkbuk.com
W: http://www.kvlgkbuk.com
Editorial Profile: KBUK-FM is a commercial station owned by KBUK Radio, Inc. The format of the station is classic country music. KBUK-FM broadcasts to the La Grange, TX area at 104.9 FM.

KBUL-AM
Owner: Townsquare Media, LLC
Editorial: 27 N 27Th St, Billings, Montana 59101-2357. **T:** 1 406 248-7827
E: newsradio970@yahoo.com
W: http://www.newsradio970.com
Editorial Profile: KBUL-AM is a commercial station owned by Townsquare Media, LLC. The format of the station is news and talk. KBUL-AM broadcasts in the Billings, MT area at 970 AM.

KBUL-FM
Owner: Cumulus Media Inc
Editorial: 595 E Plumb Ln, Reno, Nevada 89502-3503. **T:** 1 775 789-6700
W: http://www.kbul.com
Editorial Profile: KBUL-FM is a commercial station owned by Cumulus Media Inc. The format of the station is country. KBUL-FM broadcasts to the Reno, NV area at 98.1 FM.

KBUN-AM
Owner: Omni Broadcasting Co.
Editorial: 502 Beltrami Ave NW, Bemidji, Minnesota 56601. **T:** 1 218 444-1500
Editorial Profile: KBUN-AM is a commercial station owned by Omni Broadcasting Co. The format of the station is sports. KBUN-AM broadcasts to the Bemidji, MN area at 1450 AM.

KBUR-AM
Owner: Pritchard Broadcasting Corp.
Editorial: 610 N 4Th St Ste 300, Burlington, Iowa 52601-5059. **T:** 1 319 752-5402
E: info@kbur.com **W:** http://www.kbur.com
Editorial Profile: KBUR-AM is a commercial station owned by Pritchard Broadcasting Corp. The format of the station is news and talk. KBUR-AM broadcasts to the Burlington, IA area at 1490 AM.

KBUS-FM
Owner: East Texas Broadcasting Inc.
Editorial: 2810 Pine Mill Rd, Paris, Texas 75460. **T:** 1 903 785-1068
W: http://www.easttexasradio.com
Editorial Profile: KBUS-FM is a commercial station owned by East Texas Broadcasting Inc. The format of the station is classic rock music. KBUS-FM broadcasts to the Paris, TX area at 101.9 FM.

KBUT-FM
Owner: Crested Butte Mountain Educ. Radio Inc.
Editorial: 508 Maroon Ave, Crested Butte, Colorado 81224. **T:** 1 970 349-5225
E: kbut@kbut.org **W:** http://www.kbut.org
Editorial Profile: KBUT-FM is a commercial station owned by Crested Butte Mountain Educ. Radio Inc. The format of the station is college variety. KBUT-FM broadcasts to the Crested Butte, CO area at 90.3 FM.

KBUX-FM
Owner: Burdette(Maude J.)
Editorial: 16031 Camel Dr, Quartzsite, Arizona 85346. **T:** 1 928 927-5111
E: kbuxradio@hotmail.com
W: http://kbuxradio.tripod.com
Editorial Profile: KBUX-FM is a commercial station owned by Maude Burdette. The format of the station is variety. KBUX-FM brodcasts to the Quartzsite, AZ area at 94.3 FM.

KBUY-AM
Owner: Walton Stations of New Mexico, Inc.
Editorial: 1096 Mechem Dr Ste 230, Ruidoso, New Mexico 88345-7071. **T:** 1 575 258-2222
E: production@kwes.net
W: http://www.kwes.net
Editorial Profile: KBUY-AM is a commercial station owned by Walton Stations of New Mexico, Inc. The format of the station is Classic hits. KBUY-AM broadcasts to the Ruidoso, NM area at 1360 AM.

KBUZ-FM
Owner: American Family Association
Editorial: 2800 SW Wanamaker Rd, Ste 196, Topeka, Kansas 66614. **T:** 1 662 844-8888
E: comments@afr.net **W:** http://www.afa.net
Editorial Profile: KBUZ-FM is a non-commercial station owned by the American Family Association. The format of the station is contemporary Christian. KBUZ-FM broadcasts to the Topeka, KS area at 90.3 FM.

KBVA-FM
Owner: Hendren Communications Inc.
Editorial: 1655 Highway 72 SE, Gravette, Arkansas 72736. **T:** 1 479 787-6411
E: kbva@variety1065.com
W: http://www.variety1065.com
Editorial Profile: KBVA-FM is a commercial station owned by Hendren Communications Inc. The format of the station is classic hits. KBVA-FM broadcasts to the Gravette, AR area at 106.5 FM.

KBVB-FM
Owner: Midwest Communications Inc.
Editorial: 1020 25th St S, Fargo, North Dakota 58103-2312. **T:** 1 701 237-5346
W: http://www.bob95fm.com
Editorial Profile: KBVB-FM is a commercial station owned by Midwest Communications Inc. The format of the station is contemporary country music. KBVB-FM broadcasts to the Fargo, ND area at 95.1 FM.

KBVC-FM
Owner: Three Eagles Communications Co.
Editorial: 7600 County Road 120, Salida, Colorado 81201. **T:** 1 719 539-2575
W: http://www.kbvcfm.com
Editorial Profile: KBVC-FM is a commercial station owned by Three Eagles Communications Co. The format of the station is country. KBVC-FM broadcasts to the Salida, CO area at 104.1 FM.

KBVM-FM
Owner: Catholic Broadcasting Northwest, Inc.
Editorial: 5000 N Willamette Blvd, Portland, Oregon 97203-5743. **T:** 1 503 285-5200
E: info@kbvm.fm **W:** http://www.kbvm.fm
Editorial Profile: KBVM-FM is a non-commercial station owned by Catholic Broadcasting Northwest, Inc. The format of the station is Catholic programming. KBVM-FM broadcasts in the Portland, OR area at 88.3 FM.

KBVR-FM
Owner: State of Oregon
Editorial: 210 Memorial Union E, Corvallis, Oregon 97331. **T:** 1 541 737-6323
W: http://www.kbvr.com

KBVU-FM
Owner: Buena Vista University
Editorial: 610 W 4th St, Storm Lake, Iowa 50588. **T:** 1 712 749-1220
W: http://edge.bvu.edu
Editorial Profile: KBVU-FM is a non-commercial station owned Buena Vista University. The format of the station is rock alternative. KBVU-FM broadcasts to the Storm Lake, IA area at 97.5 FM.

KBWA-FM
Owner: WAY Media Inc.
Editorial: 1707 Main St, Ste 302, Longmont, Colorado 80501. **T:** 1 303 702-9293
W: http://kxwa.wayfm.com
Editorial Profile: KBWA-FM is a commercial station owned by WAY Media Inc. The format of the station is contemporary Christian. KBWA-FM broadcasts to the Brush, CO area on 89.1 FM.

KBWC-FM
Owner: Wiley College
Editorial: 711 Wiley Ave, Marshall, Texas 75670-5151. **T:** 1 903 927-3307
W: http://www.wileyc.edu/studentlife/radio.asp
Editorial Profile: KBWC-FM is a commercial station owned by Wiley College. The format of the station is gospel, R&B oldies and urban contemporary. KBWC-FM broadcasts to the Marshall, TX area at 91.1 FM.

KBWD-AM
Owner: Brown County Broadcasting Co.
Editorial: 300 Carnegie St, Brownwood, Texas 76801-7222. **T:** 1 325 646-3505
E: upfront@koxe.com **W:** http://www.koxe.com
Editorial Profile: KBWD-AM is a commercial station owned by Brown County Broadcasting Co. The format of the station is adult contemporary. KBWD-AM broadcasts to the Brownwood, TX area at 1380 AM.

KBWS-FM
Owner: Armada Media Corp.
Editorial: 509 Veterans Ave, Sisseton, South Dakota 57262. **T:** 1 605 698-3471
E: kbwsstudio@venturecomm.net
W: http://www.bigstoneradio.com
Editorial Profile: KBWS-FM is a commercial station owned by Armada Media Corp. The format of the station is country. KBWS-FM broadcasts to the Sisseton, SD area at a frequency of 102.9 FM.

KBWX-FM
Owner: Clear Channel Media and Entertainment
Editorial: 1001 Highlands Plaza Dr W, Saint Louis, Missouri 63110-1337.
T: 1 314 333-8000
W: http://www.wild1049stl.com
Editorial Profile: KBWX-FM is a commercial station owned by Clear Channel Media and Entertainment. The format of the station is Top 40/CHR. KBWX-FM broadcasts to the St. Louis area at 100.3 FM.

KBXB-FM
Owner: Withers Broadcasting of Southeast Missouri, LLC
Editorial: 125 S Kingshighway St, Sikeston, Missouri 63801-2943. **T:** 1 573 471-2000
W: http://www.b979.net
Editorial Profile: KBXB-FM is a commercial station owned by Withers Broadcasting of Southeast Missouri, LLC. The format of the station is classic country. KBXB-FM broadcasts to Sikeston, MO at 97.9 FM.

KBXI-FM
Owner: Chaparral Broadcasting Inc.
Editorial: 1140 W. Highway 22, Jackson, Wyoming 83301. **T:** 1 307 733-2120
E: psa@billingsmojo925.com
W: http://www.billingsmojo925.com
Editorial Profile: KBXI-FM is a commercial station owned by Chaparral Broadcasting Inc. The format of the station is hybrid of classic rock and adult hits music. KBXI-FM broadcasts in the Park City, MT area at 92.5 FM.

KBXL-FM
Owner: Inspirational Family Radio
Editorial: 1440 S Weideman Ave, Boise, Idaho 83709-1450. **T:** 1 208 377-3790
E: info@myfamilyradio.com
W: http://www.941thevoice.com
Editorial Profile: KBXL-FM is a commercial station owned by Inspirational Family Radio. The format of the station is religious talk. KBXL-FM broadcasts to the Boise, ID area at 94.1 FM.

KBXR-FM
Owner: Cumulus Media Inc.
Editorial: 503 Old 63 N, Columbia, Missouri 65201. **T:** 1 573 449-4141
E: 1023bxr@gmail.com **W:** http://www.bxr.com
Editorial Profile: KBXR-FM is a commercial station owned by Cumulus Media Inc. The format of the station is adult album alternative music. KBXR-FM broadcasts to the Columbia, MO area at 102.3 FM.

KBXT-FM
Owner: Brazos Valley Communications LLC
Editorial: 1240 E Villa Maria Rd, Bryan, Texas 77802. **T:** 1 979 776-1240
W: http://www.1019thebeatfm.com
Editorial Profile: KXBT-FM is a commercial station owned by Brazos Valley Communications LLC. The format of the station is urban contemporary. KXBT-FM broadcasts to the Bryan, TX area on 101.9 FM.

KBXX-FM
Owner: Radio One Inc.
Editorial: 24 Greenway Plz Ste 900, Houston, Texas 77046-2418. **T:** 1 713 623-2108
E: kbxxmusic@gmail.com
W: http://theboxhouston.com
Editorial Profile: KBXX-FM is a commercial station owned by Radio One Inc. The format of the station is rhythmic Top 40/CHR music. KBXX-FM broadcasts in the Houston area at 97.9 FM.

KBYB-FM
Owner: Texarkana Radio Center Licenses, LLC
Editorial: 615 Olive St, Texarkana, Texas 75501-5512. **T:** 1 903 793-4671
W: http://1017hotfm.com
Editorial Profile: KBYB-FM is a commercial station owned by Texarkana Radio Center Licenses, LLC. The format of the station is contemporary country. KBYB-FM broadcasts to the Texarkana, TX area at 101.7 FM.

KBYG-AM
Owner: Pappajohn (David)
Editorial: 2801 Wasson Rd, Big Spring, Texas 79720-6412. **T:** 1 432 263-5294
Editorial Profile: KBYG-AM is a commercial station owned by David Pappajohn. The format of the station is oldies. KBYG-AM broadcasts to the Big Spring, TX area at 1400 AM.

KBYI-FM
Owner: Brigham Young University
Editorial: 102 Ucb, Rexburg, Idaho 83460-1700. **T:** 1 208 496-2050 **E:** kbyi@byui.edu
W: http://www.byui.edu/kbyi
Editorial Profile: KBYI-FM is a non-commercial station owned by Brigham Young University. The format of the station is classical music and news. KBYI-FM broadcasts to the Rexburg, ID area at 94.3 FM.

KBYN-FM
Owner: Favorita Broadcasting(La)
Editorial: 4043 Geer Rd, Hughson, California 95326-9798. **T:** 1 209 883-8760
E: lafavorita@lafavorita.net
W: http://www.lafavorita.net
Editorial Profile: KBYN-FM is a commercial station owned by La Favorita Broadcasting. The format of the station is regional Mexican. KBYN-FM broadcasts to the Arnold, CA area at 95.9 FM.

KBYR-AM
Owner: Ohana Media Group, LLC.
Editorial: 1399 W 34th Ave, Ste 202, Anchorage, Alaska 99503. **T:** 1 907 344-4045
W: http://www.kbyr.com
Editorial Profile: KBYR-AM is a commercial station owned by Ohana Media Group, LLC. The format of the station is news and talk. KBYR-AM broadcasts to the Anchorage, AK area at 700 AM.

KBYU-FM
Owner: Brigham Young University
Editorial: C-302 HFAC, Brigham Young University, Provo, Utah 84604.
T: 1 801 422-8450
W: http://www.classical89.org
Editorial Profile: KBYU-FM is a non-commercial station owned by Brigham Young University. The format of the station is classical music. KBYU-FM broadcasts to the provo, UT area at 89.1 FM.

KBYZ-FM
Owner: Townsquare Media, Inc.
Editorial: 4303 Memorial Hwy, Mandan, North Dakota 58554-4711. **T:** 1 701 663-6411
E: kbyz@cumulus.com
W: http://www.965thefox.com
Editorial Profile: KBYZ-FM is a commercial station owned by Townsquare Media, Inc. The format of the station is classic rock. KBYZ-FM broadcasts to the Mandan, ND area at 96.5 FM.

KBZD-FM
Owner: Tejas Broadcasting
Editorial: 3639 Wolflin Ave, Amarillo, Texas 79102. **T:** 1 806 355-1044
Editorial Profile: KBZD-FM is a commercial station owned by Tejas Broadcasting. The format of the station is Hispanic oldies. KBZD-FM broadcasts to the Amarillo, TX area at 99.7 FM.

KBZE-FM
Owner: Hubcast Broadcasting Inc.
Editorial: 1320 Victor II Blvd, Morgan City, Louisiana 70380-1306. **T:** 1 985 385-6266
W: http://www.kbze.com
Editorial Profile: KBZE-FM is a commercial station owned by Hubcast Broadcasting Inc. The format of the station is urban contemporary. KBZE-FM broadcasts to the Baton Rouge, LA area at 105.9 FM.

KBZM-FM
Owner: Orion Media, LLC
Editorial: 8274 Huffine Ln, Bozeman, Montana 59718-8118. **T:** 1 406 582-1045
W: http://www.montanassuperstation.com
Editorial Profile: KBZM-FM is a commercial station owned by Orion Media, LLC. The

format of the station is classic rock. KBZM-FM broadcasts to the Big Sky, MT area at a frequency of 104.7 FM.

KBZN-FM
Owner: Capitol Broadcasting
Editorial: 257 E 200 S, Ste 400, Salt Lake City, Utah 84111. **T:** 1 801 364-9836
E: comments@kbzn.com
W: http://www.kbzn.com
Editorial Profile: KBZN-FM is a commercial station owned by Capitol Broadcasting. The format of the station is adult contemporary. KBZN-FM broadcasts to the Salt Lake City area at 97.9 FM.

KBZO-AM
Owner: Entravision Communications Corp.
Editorial: 1220 Broadway Ste 600, Lubbock, Texas 79401-3200. **T:** 1 806 763-6051
W: http://www.1460jose.com
Editorial Profile: KBZO-AM is a commercial station owned by Entravision Communications Corp. The format of the station is regional Mexican. KBZO-AM broadcasts to the Lubbock, TX area on 1460 AM.

KBZQ-FM
Owner: Fritsch Jr.(William Richard)
Editorial: 2332 SW Lee Blvd., Lawton, Oklahoma 73505. **T:** 1 580 357-9950
E: kbzq@sbcglobal.net
W: http://www.hitsandfavorites.com
Editorial Profile: KBZQ-FM is a commercial station owned by William Richard Fritsch Jr. The format of the station is adult contemporary music. KBZQ-FM broadcasts to the Lawton, OK area at 99.5 FM.

KBZS-FM
Owner: Townsquare Media, LLC
Editorial: 2525 Kell Blvd, Ste 200, Wichita Falls, Texas 76308. **T:** 1 940 763-1111
W: http://www.1063thebuzz.com
Editorial Profile: KBZS-FM is a commercial station owned by Townsquare Media, LLC. The format of the station is rock music. KBZS-FM broadcasts to the Wichita Falls, TX area at 106.3 FM.

KBZT-FM
Owner: Lincoln Financial Media
Editorial: 1615 Murray Canyon Rd Ste 710, San Diego, California 92108-4321.
T: 1 619 297-9595
W: http://www.fm949sd.com
Editorial Profile: KBZT-FM is a commercial station owned by Lincoln Financial Media. The format of the station is rock alternative music. KBZT-FM broadcasts to the San Diego area at 94.9 FM.

KBZU-FM
Owner: The Last Bastion Station Trust
Editorial: 500 4th St NW, 5th Fl, Albuquerque, New Mexico 87102-5324. **T:** 1 505 767-6761
Editorial Profile: KBZU-FM is a commercial station owned by The Last Bastion Station Trust. The format of the station is classic rock. KBZU-FM broadcasts to the Albuquerque, NM area at 96.3 FM.

KBZY-AM
Owner: Capital Broadcasting Inc.
Editorial: 2659 Commercial St SE, Ste 204, Salem, Oregon 97302. **T:** 1 503 362-1490
E: kbzy@comcast.net **W:** http://www.kbzy.com
Editorial Profile: KBZY-FM is a commercial station owned by Capital Broadcasting Inc. The format of the station is oldies music. KBZY-AM broadcasts to the Salem, OR, area at 1490 AM.

KBZZ-AM
Owner: Americom Broadcasting
Editorial: 961 Matley Ln Ste 120, Reno, Nevada 89502-2119. **T:** 1 775 829-1964
E: info@kbzz.com **W:** http://www.kbzz.com
Editorial Profile: KBZZ-AM is a commercial station owned by Americom Broadcasting. The format for the station is talk. KBZZ-AM broadcasts to the Reno, NV area at 1270 AM.

KCAA-AM
Owner: Broadcast Management Services Inc.
Editorial: 254 Carousel Mall, San Bernardino, California 92401. **T:** 1 909 885-8502
W: http://www.kcaaradio.com
Editorial Profile: KCAA-AM is a commercial station owned by Broadcast Management Services Inc. The format of the station is talk. KCAA-AM broadcasts to the San Bernardino, CA area at 1050 AM.

KCAB-AM
Owner: East Arkansas Broadcasters Inc.
Editorial: 2705 E Parkway Dr, Russellville, Arkansas 72802-2006. **T:** 1 479 968-6816
E: news@rivervalleyradio.com
W: http://www.rivertalk980.com
Editorial Profile: KCAB-AM is a commercial station owned by East Arkansas Broadcasters Inc. The format of the station is news, talk and sports. KCAB-AM broadcasts to the Russellville, AR area at 980 AM.

KCAD-FM
Owner: Clear Channel Media and Entertainment
Editorial: 11291 39th St SW, Dickinson, North Dakota 58601. **T:** 1 701 227-1876
W: http://www.roughridercountry.net
Editorial Profile: KCAD-FM is a commercial station owned by Clear Channel Media and Entertainment. The format of the station is contemporary country. KCAD-FM broadcasts to the Dickinson, ND area at 99.1 FM.

KCAJ-FM
Owner: North Country Media, LLC.
Editorial: 107 Center St W, Roseau, Minnesota 56751-1022. **T:** 1 218 463-0161
E: info@wild102fm.com
W: http://www.kj102.com
Editorial Profile: KCAJ-FM is a commercial station owned byNorth Country Media, LLC. The format of the station is Top 40/CHR, news and sports. KCAJ-FM broadcasts to the Roseau, MN area at 102.2 FM.

KCAL-AM
Owner: Lazer Broadcasting Corp.
Editorial: 1950 S Sunwest Ln, Ste 302, San Bernardino, California 92408-3227.
T: 1 909 384-9750
W: http://www.lamexicana1410.com
Editorial Profile: KCAL-AM is a commercial station owned by Lazer Broadcasting. The format of the station is Spanish oldies. KCAL-AM broadcasts to San Bernardino, CA at 1410 AM.

KCAL-FM
Owner: Anaheim Broadcasting Corp.
Editorial: 1940 Orange Tree Ln, Ste 200, Redlands, California 92374. **T:** 1 909 793-3554
W: http://www.kcalfm.com
Editorial Profile: KCAL-FM is a commercial station owned by Anaheim Broadcasting Corp. The format of the station is rock music. KCAL-FM broadcasts to the Redlands, CA area at 96.7 FM.

KCAM-AM
Owner: Northern Light Network
Editorial: Mile 187 Glenn Highway, Glennallen, Alaska 99588. **T:** 1 907 822-5226
E: kcam@kcam.org **W:** http://www.kcam.org

KCAP-AM
Owner: Cherry Creek Radio
Editorial: 110 E Broadway St, Helena, Montana 59601. **T:** 1 406 442-6620
Editorial Profile: KCAP-AM is a commercial station owned by Cherry Creek Radio. The format for the station is news, sports and talk. KCAP-AM broadcasts to the Helena, MT area at 1340 AM.

KCAQ-FM
Owner: Gold Coast Broadcasting, LLC
Editorial: 2284 S Victoria Ave, Ventura, California 93003-6641. **T:** 1 805 289-1400
E: kvtanews@yahoo.com
W: http://www.q1047.com
Editorial Profile: KCAQ-FM is a commercial station owned by Gold Coast Broadcasting, LLC. The format of the station is Top 40. KCAQ-FM broadcasts to the Ventura, CA area at 104.7 FM.

KCAR-AM
Owner: American Media Investments
Editorial: 203 N Locust St, Clarksville, Texas 75426-3024. **T:** 1 903 427-3861
E: kool985@cebridge.net
Editorial Profile: KCAR-AM is a commercial station owned by American Media Investments. The format of the station is country music. KCAR-AM broadcasts to the Clarksville, TX area at 1350 AM.

KCAR-FM
Owner: American Media Investments
Editorial: 2510 W 20Th St, Joplin, Missouri 64804-0216. **T:** 1 417 781-1313
E: production@ami-joplin.com
Editorial Profile: KCAR-FM is a commercial station owned by American Media Investments. The format of the station is Hot AC. KCAR-FM broadcasts to the Joplin, MO area at 104.3 FM.

KCAS-FM
Owner: Faith Baptist Church Inc.
Editorial: 4301 N Shary Rd, Palmhurst, Texas 78573. **T:** 1 956 424-9098
E: mail@kcasradio.org
W: http://www.kcasradio.org
Editorial Profile: KCAS-FM is a non-commercial station owned by Faith Baptist Church Inc. The format of the station is Contempory Christian/Inspirational. KCAS-FM broadcasts to the Hidalgo, TX area at a frequency of 91.5FM.

KCAT-AM
Owner: Mondy(Elijah)
Editorial: 1207 W 6th Ave, Pine Bluff, Arkansas 71601. **T:** 1 870 534-5001
Editorial Profile: KCAT-AM is a commercial station owned by Elijah Mondy. The format of the station is gospel. KCAT-AM broadcasts in the Pine Bluff, AR at 1340 AM.

KCAW-FM
Owner: Raven Radio Foundation Inc.
Editorial: 2 Lincoln St, Sitka, Alaska 99835-7538. **T:** 1 907 747-5877 **E:** news@kcaw.org
W: http://www.kcaw.org
Editorial Profile: KCAW-FM is non-commercial station owned by Raven Radio Foundation Inc. The format of the station is variety. KCAW-FM broadcasts to the Sitka, AK area at 104.7 FM.

KCBC-AM
Owner: Crawford Broadcasting Co.
Editorial: 10948 Cleveland Ave, Oakdale, California 95361-9709. **T:** 1 209 847-0770
E: kcbcpsa@velociter.net
W: http://www.770kcbc.com
Editorial Profile: KCBC-FM is a non-commercial station owned by Crawford Broadcasting Co. The format of the station is Christian music and talk. KCBC-FM broadcasts to the Sacramento area at 770 AM.

KCBF-AM
Owner: Last Frontier Mediactive, LLC
Editorial: 819 1st Ave, Fairbanks, Alaska 99701-4449. **T:** 1 907 451-5910
W: http://www.820sports.com
Editorial Profile: KCBF-AM is a commercial station owned by Last Frontier Mediactive, LLC. The format of the station is sports. KCBF-AM broadcasts in the Fairbanks, AK area at 880 AM.

KCBI-FM
Owner: First Dallas Media, Inc.
Editorial: 411 Ryan Plaza Dr, Arlington, Texas 76011-3923. **T:** 1 817 792-3800
E: news@kcbi.org **W:** http://www.kcbi.org
Editorial Profile: KCBI-FM is a non-commercial station owned by First Dallas Media, Inc. The format of the station is Christian music, talk and teaching. KCBI-FM broadcasts to the Dallas area at 90.9 FM.

KCBL-AM
Owner: Clear Channel Media and Entertainment
Editorial: 83 E Shaw Ave, Ste 150, Fresno, California 93710. **T:** 1 559 243-4300
W: http://www.foxsportsradio1340.com
Editorial Profile: KCBL-AM is a commercial station owned by Clear Channel Media and Entertainment. The format of the station is sports. KCBL-AM broadcasts to the Fresno, CA area at 1340 AM.

KCBQ-AM
Owner: Salem Communications
Editorial: 9255 Towne Centre Dr Ste 535, San Diego, California 92121-3038.
T: 1 858 535-1210 **E:** info@kcbq.com
W: http://www.kcbq.com
Editorial Profile: KCBQ-FM is a commercial station owned by Salem Communications. The format of the station is news and conservative talk. KCBQ-FM broadcasts to the San Diego area at 1170 AM. Station does not accept PSAs.

KCBR-AM
Owner: DJR Broadcasting
Editorial: 5050 Edison Ave, Ste 218, Colorado Springs, Colorado 80915-3540.
T: 1 719 570-1530
W: http://www.1040kcbr.com
Editorial Profile: KCBR-AM is a commercial station owned by Kona Coast Broadcasting. The format of the station is Christian programming. KCBR-AM broadcasts to the Colorado Springs, CO area at 1040 AM.

KCBS-AM
Owner: CBS Radio
Editorial: 865 Battery St Fl 3, San Francisco, California 94111-1503. **T:** 1 415 765-4000
E: kcbsnewsdesk@cbs.com
W: http://sanfrancisco.cbslocal.com
Editorial Profile: KCBS-AM is a commercial station owned by CBS Radio. The format of the station is news. KCBS-AM broadcasts to the San Francisco area at 740 AM.

KCBS-FM
Owner: CBS Radio
Editorial: 5901 Venice Blvd, Los Angeles, California 90034-1708. **T:** 1 323 937-9331
E: jack@931jackfm.com
W: http://jack.radio.com/
Editorial Profile: KCBS-FM is a commercial station owned by CBS Radio. The format of the station is an eclectic mix of adult hits. KCBS-FM broadcasts to the Los Angeles area at 93.1 FM.

KCBX-FM
Owner: KCBX Inc.
Editorial: 4100 Vachell Ln, San Luis Obispo, California 93401-8113. **T:** 1 805 549-8855
E: 901kcbx@kcbx.org **W:** http://www.kcbx.org
Editorial Profile: KCBX-FM is a non-commercial station owned by KCBX Inc. The format of the station is news and jazz. KCBX-FM broadcasts to the San Luis Obispo, CA area at 90.1 FM.

KCCB-AM
Owner: Adkins(Jim)
Editorial: 501 Bryan Ave, Corning, Arkansas 72422-3262. **T:** 1 870 857-6646
E: lite93fm@isainet.com
Editorial Profile: KCCB-AM is a commercial station owned by Jim Adkins. The format of the station is jazz. KCCB-AM broadcasts to the Corning, AR area at 1260 AM.

KCCC-AM
Owner: Compass Enterprise Inc.
Editorial: 930 N Canal St, Carlsbad, New Mexico 88220-5110. **T:** 1 575 887-5521
Editorial Profile: KCCC-AM is a commercial station owned by Compass Enterprise Inc. The format of the station is oldies. KCCC-AM broadcasts to the Albuquerque, NM area at 930 AM.

KCCD-FM
Owner: Minnesota Public Radio
Editorial: 901 8th St S, Moorhead, Minnesota 56562. **T:** 1 218 287-0666
E: newsroom@mpr.org **W:** http://www.mpr.org
Editorial Profile: KCCD-FM is a non-commercial station owned by Minnesota Public Radio. The format of the station is news and talk programming. KCCD-FM broadcasts to the Moorhead, MN area at 90.3 FM.

KCCK-FM
Owner: Kirkwood Community College
Editorial: 6301 Kirkwood Blvd SW, Cedar Rapids, Iowa 52404. **T:** 1 319 398-5446
E: studio@kcck.org **W:** http://www.kcck.org
Editorial Profile: KCCK-FM is a non-commercial station owned by Kirkwood Community College. The format for the station is jazz. KCCK-FM broadcasts to the Cedar Rapids, IA area at 88.3 FM.

KCCL-FM
Owner: Results Radio Group
Editorial: 298 Commerce Cir, Sacramento, California 95815. **T:** 1 916 576-7333
W: http://www.921khits.com
Editorial Profile: KCCL-FM is a commercial station owned by Results Radio Group. The format of the station is classic hits. KXCL-FM broadcasts to the Sacramento, CA area at 92.1 FM.

KCCM-FM
Owner: Minnesota Public Radio
Editorial: 901 8th St S, Moorhead, Minnesota 56562. **T:** 1 218 287-0666
E: newsroom@mpr.org
W: http://minnesota.publicradio.org/radio/stations/kccdkccm/
Editorial Profile: KCCM-FM is a non-commercial station owned by Minnesota Public Radio. The format of the station is classical music. KCCM-FM broadcasts to the Moorhead, MN area at 91.1 FM.

KCCN-FM
Owner: Summit Media Broadcasting LLC
Editorial: 900 Fort Street Mall Ste 700, Honolulu, Hawaii 96813-3701.
T: 1 808 536-2728
W: http://www.kccnfm100.com
Editorial Profile: KCCN-FM is a commercial owned by Summit Media Broadcasting LLC. The format of the station is Hawaiian

Contemporary Hits. KCCN-FM broadcasts to the Honolulu, HI area at 100.3 FM.

KCCQ-FM

Owner: Clear Channel Media and Entertainment
Editorial: 415 Main St, Ames, Iowa 50010-6099. **T:** 1 515 232-1430
W: http://www.now1051.com/main.html
Editorial Profile: KCCQ-FM is a commercial station owned by Clear Channel Media and Entertainment. The format of the station is Hot AC. KCCQ-FM broadcasts to the Ames, IA area at 105.1 FM.

KCCR-AM

Owner: Riverfront Broadcasting
Editorial: 106 W Capitol Ave, Pierre, South Dakota 57501. **T:** 1 605 224-1240
E: news@todayskccr.com
W: http://www.todayskccr.com
Editorial Profile: KCCR-AM is a commercial station owned by Riverfront Broadcasting. The format of the station is classic hits music and talk. KCCR-AM broadcasts to the Pierre, SD area at 1240 AM.

KCCS-FM

Owner: Colorado College
Editorial: 912 N Weber St, Colorado Springs, Colorado 80903-2921. **T:** 1 719 473-4801
E: news@krcc.org **W:** http://www.krcc.org
Editorial Profile: KCCS-FM is a non-commercial station owned by Colorado College. The format of the station is variety. KCCS-FM broadcasts to the Colorado Springs, CO area at 91.7 FM.

KCCT-AM

Owner: Davila Broadcasting
Editorial: 701 Benys Rd, Corpus Christi, Texas 78408. **T:** 1 361 289-0999
E: rdavila.kcct@gmail.com
Editorial Profile: KCCT-AM is a commercial station owned by Davila Broadcasting. The format of the station is news, talk and classic country. KCCT-AM broadcasts to the Corpus Christi, TX area at 1150 AM.

KCCU-FM

Owner: Cameron University
Editorial: 2800 W Gore Blvd, Lawton, Oklahoma 73505-6320. **T:** 1 580 581-2472
E: kccu@cameron.edu **W:** http://www.kccu.org
Editorial Profile: KCCU-FM is a non-commercial station owned by Cameron University. The format of the station is classical music and talk. KCCU-FM broadcasts to the Lawton, OK area at 89.3 FM.

KCCV-AM

Owner: Bott Broadcasting Co.
Editorial: 10550 Barkley St Ste 112, Overland Park, Kansas 66212-1824. **T:** 1 913 642-7600
E: kccv@bottradionetwork.com
W: http://www.bottradionetwork.com
Editorial Profile: KCCV-AM is a commercial station owned by Bott Broadcasting Co. The format of the station is religious and Christian programming. KCCV-FM broadcasts to the Overland Park, KS area at 760 AM.

KCCV-FM

Owner: Bott Broadcasting Co.
Editorial: 10550 Barkley St, Ste 112, Overland Park, Kansas 66212. **T:** 1 913 642-7600
E: kccv@bottradionetwork.com
W: http://www.bottradionetwork.com
Editorial Profile: KCCV-FM is a commercial station owned by Bott Broadcasting Co. The format of the station is religious and Christian programming. KCCV-FM broadcasts to the Kansas City, MO, area at 92.3 FM.

KCCY-AM

Owner: Clear Channel Media and Entertainment
Editorial: 106 W 24th St, Pueblo, Colorado 81003-2408. **T:** 1 719 545-2080
W: http://www.foxsportspueblo.com
Editorial Profile: KCCY-AM is a commercial station owned by Clear Channel Media and Entertainment. The format of the station is sports. KCCY-AM broadcasts to the Pueblo, CO area at 1350 AM.

KCCY-FM

Owner: Clear Channel Media and Entertainment
Editorial: 2864 S Circle Dr, Ste 150, Colorado Springs, Colorado 80906-7599.
T: 1 719 540-9200 **W:** http://www.y969.com
Editorial Profile: KCCY-FM is a commercial station owned by Clear Channel Media and Entertainment. The format of the station is contemporary country. KCCY-FM broadcasts to the Colorado Springs, CO area at 96.9 FM.

KCDA-FM

Owner: Clear Channel Media and Entertainment
Editorial: 808 E Sprague Ave, Spokane, Washington 99202-2126. **T:** 1 509 242-2400
W: http://www.1031kcda.com
Editorial Profile: KCDA-FM is a commercial station owned by Clear Channel Media and Entertainment. The format of the station is hot adult contemporary music. KCDA-FM broadcasts to the Spokane, WA area at 103.1 FM.

KCDD-FM

Owner: Cumulus Media Inc.
Editorial: 2525 S Danville Dr, Abilene, Texas 79605. **T:** 1 325 793-9700
W: http://www.power103.com
Editorial Profile: KCDD-FM is a commercial station owned by Cumulus Media Inc. The format of the station is Top 40/CHR music. KCDD-FM broadcasts in the Abilene, TX area at 103.7 FM.

KCDQ-FM

Owner: Desert West Air Ranchers Corp.
Editorial: 500 E Fry Blvd, Ste L10, Sierra Vista, Arizona 85635. **T:** 1 520 459-8201
E: info@kkyz.com

KCDU-FM

Owner: Mapleton Radio, LLC
Editorial: 60 Garden Ct Ste 300, Monterey, California 93940-5370. **T:** 1 831 658-5200
E: thebeach1017@yahoo.com
W: http://www.1017thebeach.com
Editorial Profile: KCDU-FM is a commercial station owned by Mapleton Radio, LLC. The format of the station is Top 40/CHR. KCDU-FM broadcasts to the Monterey, CA area at 101.7 FM.

KCDV-FM

Owner: Bayview Communications Inc.
Editorial: 112 Forestry Way, Cordova, Alaska 99574. **T:** 1 907 424-3796
E: email@cordovaradio.com
W: http://www.cordovaradio.com
Editorial Profile: KCDV-FM is a commercial station owned by Bayview Communications Inc. The format of the station is adult contemporary music. KCDV-AM broadcasts in Cordova, AK area at 100.9 FM.

KCDX-FM

Owner: Desert West Air Ranchers Corp.
Editorial: 500 E Fry Blvd, Ste L10, Sierra Vista, Arizona 85635. **T:** 1 520 459-8201
E: info@kkyz.com **W:** http://www.kcdx.com
Editorial Profile: KCDX-FM is a commercial station owned by Desert West Air Ranchers Corp. The format of the station is classic rock. KCDX-FM broadcasts to the Sierra Vista, AZ area at 103.1 FM.

KCDY-FM

Owner: Hughes Broadcasting
Editorial: 1609 Radio Blvd, Carlsbad, New Mexico 88220-6427. **T:** 1 575 887-7563
W: http://www.carlsbadradio.com
Editorial Profile: KCDY-FM is a commercial station owned by Hughes Broadcasting. The format of the station is adult contemporary music. KCDY-FM broadcasts to the Carlsbad, NM area at 104.1 FM.

KCDZ-FM

Owner: Morongo Basin Broadcasting Corp.
Editorial: 6448 Hallee Rd, Ste 5, Joshua Tree, California 92252-1908. **T:** 1 760 366-8471
E: z1077fm@gmail.com
W: http://www.kcdzfm.com
Editorial Profile: KCDZ-FM is a commercial station owned by Morongo Basin Broadcasting Corp. The format of the station is adult contemporary and Top 40/CHR. KCDZ-FM broadcasts to the Joshua Tree, CA area at 107.7 FM.

KCEA-FM

Owner: Sequoia Union High School District
Editorial: 555 Middlefield Rd, Atherton, California 94027. **T:** 1 650 306-8823
W: http://www.kcea.org
Editorial Profile: KCEA-FM is a non-commercial station owned by Sequoia Union High School District. The format of the station is adult standards. KCEA-FM broadcasts to the Atherton, CA area at 89.1 FM.

KCEC-FM

Owner: Campesina Network(La)
Editorial: 670 E 32nd St, Ste 12A, Yuma, Arizona 85365. **T:** 1 928 782-5995
W: http://www.campesina.com
Editorial Profile: KCEC-FM is a commercial station owned by La Campesina Network. The

format of the station is Hispanic. KCEC-FM broadcasts to the Yuma, AZ area on 104.5 FM.

KCED-FM

Owner: Centralia College
Editorial: 600 Centralia College Blvd, Centralia, Washington 98531. **T:** 1 360 736-9391 243

KCEE-AM

Owner: Good News Radio Broadcasting Inc.
Editorial: 3222 S Richey Ave, Tucson, Arizona 85713-5498. **T:** 1 520 790-2440
E: info@690kcee.com
W: http://www.690kcee.com
Editorial Profile: KCEE-AM is a commercial station owned by Good News Radio Broadcasting Inc. The format of the station is adult standards. KCEE-AM broadcasts to the Tucson, AZ area at 690 AM.

KCEG-AM

Owner: Cutforth (Timothy)
Editorial: 516 Main St, Walsenburg, Colorado 81089-2036 **E:** production@socoradio.com
W: http://780kceg.com
Editorial Profile: KCEG-AM is a commercial station owned by Cutforth (Timothy) and operated by SOCO Radio. The format of the station is classic country. KCEG-AM broadcasts to the Colorado Springs, CO area at a frequency of 780 AM.

KCEL-FM

Owner: High Desert Broadcasting LLC
Editorial: 570 E Avenue Q9, Palmdale, California 93550. **T:** 1 661 947-3107
W: http://www.laquebuena961.com
Editorial Profile: KCEL-FM is a commercial station owned by High Desert Broadcasting LLC. The format of the station is regional Mexican. KCEL-FM broadcasts to the Palmdale, CA area at 96.1 FM.

KCEO-AM

Owner: Immaculate Heart Radio Educational Broadcasting
Editorial: 7956 California Ave, Fair Oaks, California 95628-7141. **T:** 1 916 535-0500
W: http://ihradio.com
Editorial Profile: KCEO-AM is a commercial station owned by Immaculate Heart Radio Educational Broadcasting. The format of the station is religious featuring Catholic programming. KCEO-AM broadcasts to the Greater San Diego area at 1000 AM.

KCEP-FM

Owner: Economic Opportunity Board of Clark County
Editorial: 330 W Washington Ave, Las Vegas, Nevada 89106-3327. **T:** 1 702 648-0104
E: info@88kcep.com
W: http://kcep.power88lv.com
Editorial Profile: KCEP-FM is a non-commercial station owned by the Economic Opportunity Board of Clark County. The format of the station is urban contemporary music. KCEP-FM broadcasts to the Las Vegas area at 88.1 FM.

KCEU-FM

Owner: College of Eastern Utah
Editorial: 451 E 400 N, Price, Utah 84501-2626. **T:** 1 435 613-5668 **E:** theedge@ceu.edu
W: http://theedge.ceu.edu
Editorial Profile: KCEU-FM is a non-commercial station owned by College of Eastern Utah. The format of the station is alternative rock. KCEU-FM broadcasts at 89.7 FM to the Price, Utah area.

KCEZ-FM

Owner: Results Radio Group
Editorial: 856 Manzanita Ct, Chico, California 95926-2369. **T:** 1 530 342-2200
W: http://www.power102radio.com
Editorial Profile: KCEZ-FM is a commercial station owned by Results Radio Group. The format of the station is Top 40/CHR. KCEZ-FM broadcasts to the Chico, CA area at 102.1 FM.

KCFA-FM

Owner: Favorita Broadcasting(La)
Editorial: 4043 Geer Rd, Hughson, California 95326. **T:** 1 209 883-8760
E: lafavorita@lafavorita.net
W: http://www.lafavorita.net
Editorial Profile: KCFA-FM is a commercial station owned by La Favorita Broadcasting. The format of the station is regional Mexican music. KCFA-FM broadcasts in the Hughson, CA area at 106.1 FM.

KCFB-FM

Owner: Minnesota Christian Broadcasters Inc.

Editorial: 31287 Brunes St, Pequot Lakes, Minnesota 56472-2761. **T:** 1 218 568-4422
E: news@thewird.mn **W:** http://theword.mn
Editorial Profile: KCFB-FM is a non-commercial station owned by Minnesota Christian Broadcasters Inc. The format of the station is Christian teaching and music. KCFB-FM broadcasts to the St. Cloud, MN area at 91.5 FM.

KCFI-AM

Owner: Coloff Media
Editorial: 721 Shirley St, Cedar Falls, Iowa 50613. **T:** 1 319 277-1918
W: http://www.trueoldieschannel.com
Editorial Profile: KCFI-AM is a commercial station owned by Coloff Media (Fife Communication Company, LLC). The format for the station is oldies. KCFI-AM broadcasts to the Waterloo, IA area at 1250 AM.

KCFJ-AM

Owner: EDI Media
Editorial: Lakeview Highway 395 North, Alturas, California 96101. **T:** 1 530 233-3570
E: englishradio@edimediainc.com
W: http://www.edimediainc.com/english/englishradio
Editorial Profile: KCFJ-AM is a commercial station owned by EDI Media. The format of the station is adult standards. KCFJ-AM broadcasts to the Alturas, CA area at 570 AM.

KCFM-AM

Owner: Coast Broadcasting Inc.
Editorial: 4480 Highway 101, Florence, Oregon 97439. **T:** 1 541 997-9136
E: radiowaves@kcst.com
W: http://www.kcst.com
Editorial Profile: KCFM-AM is a commercial station owned by Coast Broadcasting Inc. The format of the station is adult standards. KCFM-AM broadcasts to the Eugene, OR area at 1250 AM.

KCFN-FM

Owner: American Family Association
Editorial: 720 N Murray St, Wichita, Kansas 67212-4166. **T:** 1 662 884-8888
E: kcfn@afr.net **W:** http://www.afa.net/radio
Editorial Profile: KCFN-FM is a non-commercial station owned by American Family Association. The format of the station is contemporary Christian. KCFN-FM broadcasts in the Wichita, KS area at 91.1 FM.

KCFO-AM

Owner: Friendship Broadcasting, L.P.
Editorial: 5800 E Skelly Dr Ste 150, Tulsa, Oklahoma 74135-6416. **T:** 1 918 622-0970
E: studio@kcfo.com **W:** http://www.kcfo.com
Editorial Profile: KCFO-AM is a commercial station owned by Friendship Broadcasting, L.P. The format of the station is religious programming and talk. KCFO-AM broadcasts to the Tulsa, OK area at 970 AM. KCFO's slogan is "Talk You Can Trust."

KCFP-FM

Owner: Public Broadcasting of Colorado Inc.
Editorial: 7409 S Alton Ct, Centennial, Colorado 80112. **T:** 1 303 871-9191
E: info@cpr.org **W:** http://www.cpr.org
Editorial Profile: KCFP-FM is a non-commercial station owned by Public Broadcasting of Colorado Inc. The format of the station is news and classical. KCFP-FM broadcasts to the Centennial, CO area at 91.9 FM. The station is a simulcast of KVOD-FM.

KCFR-FM

Owner: Public Broadcasting of Colorado Inc.
Editorial: 7409 S Alton Ct, Centennial, Colorado 80112-2301. **T:** 1 303 871-9191
E: info@cpr.org **W:** http://www.cpr.org
Editorial Profile: KCFR-FM is a non-commercial station owned by Public Broadcasting of Colorado Inc. The format of the station is news and talk programming. KCFR-FM broadcasts to the Denver area at 90.1 FM.

KCFV-FM

Owner: St. Louis Community College
Editorial: 3400 Pershall Rd, Saint Louis, Missouri 63135. **T:** 1 314 513-4463
W: http://www.stlcc.edu/kcfv
Editorial Profile: KCFV-FM is a non-commercial station owned by St. Louis Community College. The format of the station is rhythmic Top 40/CHR music. KCFV-FM broadcasts to the St. Louis area at 89.5 FM.

KCFX-FM

Owner: Cumulus Media Inc.
Editorial: 5800 Foxridge Dr, 6th Fl, Mission, Kansas 66202-2333. **T:** 1 913 514-3000

W: http://www.kcfx.com
Editorial Profile: KCFX-FM is a commercial station owned by Cumulus Media Inc. The format of the station is classic rock. KCFX-FM broadcasts to the Kansas, MO area at 101.1 FM.

KCFY-FM
Owner: Relevant Media Inc.
Editorial: 1921 S Rail Ave, Yuma, Arizona 85365. **T:** 1 928 341-9730
E: kcfy@kcfyfm.com
W: http://www.kcfyfm.com
Editorial Profile: KCFY-FM is a non-commercial station owned by Relevant Media Inc. The format of the station is contemporary Christian. KCFY-FM broadcasts to the Yuma, AZ area at 88.1 FM.

KCGB-FM
Owner: Bicoastal Media LLC
Editorial: 1190 22nd St, Hood River, Oregon 97031. **T:** 1 541 386-1511
W: http://www.gorgeradio.com
Editorial Profile: KCGB-FM is a commercial station owned by Bicoastal Media LLC. The format of the station is hot adult contemporary music. KCGB-FM broadcasts to the Portland, OR area at 105.5 FM.

KCGL-FM
Owner: Legend Communications
Editorial: 1949 Mountain View Dr, Cody, Wyoming 82414. **T:** 1 307 578-5000
E: news@bhrnwy.com
W: http://www.mybighornbasin.com

KCGM-FM
Owner: Prairie Communications Inc.
Editorial: 20 Main St, Scobey, Montana 59263. **T:** 1 406 487-2293
E: kcgm@nemont.net
Editorial Profile: KCGM-FM is a commercial station owned by Prairie Communications Inc. The format of the station is country. KCGM-FM broadcasts to the Minot-Bismarck, ND area at 95.7 FM.

KCGN-FM
Owner: Christian Heritage Broadcasting
Editorial: 402 E Pike St, Osakis, Minnesota 56360-8346. **T:** 1 320 859-3000
E: mail@praisefm.org
W: http://www.praisefm.org
Editorial Profile: KCGN-FM is a non-commercial station owned by Christian Heritage Broadcasting. The format of the station is contemporary Christian programming. KCGN-FM broadcasts in the Osakis, MN area at 101.5 FM.

KCGQ-FM
Owner: Max Media
Editorial: 324 Broadway St, Cape Girardeau, Missouri 63701-7331. **T:** 1 573 335-8291
E: realrock@riverradio.net
W: http://www.realrock993.com
Editorial Profile: KCGQ-FM is a commercial station owned by the Max Media. The format of the station is rock/album-oriented rock. KCGQ-FM broadcasts to the Cape Girardeau, MO area at 99.3 FM.

KCGS-AM
Owner: Faith Christian Church
Editorial: 208 Battle St, Marshall, Arkansas 72650-9440. **T:** 1 870 448-5567
E: kcgsam@windstream.net
W: http://www.kcgsam.com
Editorial Profile: KCGS-AM is a commercial station owned by Faith Christian Church. The format of the station is talk. KCGS-AM broadcasts to the Marshall, AR area at 960 AM.

KCGY-FM
Owner: Townsquare Media, LLC
Editorial: 3525 Soldier Springs Rd, Laramie, Wyoming 82070-9017. **T:** 1 307 745-4888
W: http://www.Y95country.com
Editorial Profile: KCGY-FM is a commercial station owned by Townsquare Media, LLC. The format of the station is classic and contemporary country music. KCGY-FM broadcasts to the Laramie, WY area at 95.1 FM.

KCHA-AM
Owner: Coloff Media
Editorial: 207 N Main St, Charles City, Iowa 50616-2016. **T:** 1 641 394-1000
W: http://www.kchaam.com
Editorial Profile: KCHA-AM is a commercial station owned by Coloff Media. The format of the station is oldies. KCHA-AM broadcasts to the Charles City, IA area at 1580 AM.

KCHA-FM
Owner: Coloff Media
Editorial: 207 N Main St, Charles City, Iowa 50616. **T:** 1 641 228-1000
W: http://www.kchafm.com
Editorial Profile: KCHA-FM is a commercial station owned by Coloff Media. The format of the station is adult contemporary. KCHA-FM broadcasts to the Charles City, IA area at 95.9 FM.

KCHE-AM
Owner: J&J Radio Corp.
Editorial: 201 S 5th St, Cherokee, Iowa 51012. **T:** 1 712 225-2511 **E:** kche1@ncn.net
W: http://www.kcheradio.com
Editorial Profile: KCHE-AM is a commercial station owned by J&J Radio Corp. The format of the station is adult standards. KCHE-AM broadcasts to the Cherokee, IA area at 1440 AM.

KCHE-FM
Owner: J&J Radio Corp.
Editorial: 201 S 5th St, Cherokee, Iowa 51012. **T:** 1 712 225-2511
E: news@kcheradio.com
W: http://www.kcheradio.com
Editorial Profile: KCHE-FM is a commercial station owned by the J&J Radio Corp. The format of the station is adult contemporary. KCHE-FM broadcasts to the Cherokee, IA area at 92.1 FM.

KCHH-FM
Owner: Townsquare Media, LLC
Editorial: 27 N 27Th St, Billings, Montana 59101-2357. **T:** 1 406 248-7827
W: http://www.newsradio95.com
Editorial Profile: KCHH-FM is a commercial station owned by Townsquare Media, LLC. The format of the station is news/talk. KCHH-FM broadcasts in the Billings, MT area at 95.5FM.

KCHI-AM
Owner: Leatherman Communications Inc.
Editorial: 421 Washington St, Chillicothe, Missouri 64601. **T:** 1 660 646-4173
E: kchinews@greenhills.net
W: http://www.kchi.com
Editorial Profile: KCHI-AM is a commercial station owned by Leatherman Communications Inc. The format of the station is classic hits. KCHI-AM broadcasts to the Kansas City, MO area at 1010 AM.

KCHI-FM
Owner: Leatherman Communications Inc.
Editorial: 421 Washington St, Chillicothe, Missouri 64601-2521. **T:** 1 660 646-4173
E: kchinews@greenhills.net
W: http://www.kchi.com
Editorial Profile: KCHI-FM is a commercial station owned by Leatherman Communications Inc. The format of the station is classic hits. KCHI-FM broadcasts to the Kansas City, MO area at 98.5 FM.

KCHJ-AM
Owner: Lotus Communications Corp.
Editorial: 5100 Commerce Dr, Bakersfield, California 93309. **T:** 1 661 327-9711
W: http://www.elgallito.com
Editorial Profile: KCHJ-AM is a commercial station owned by Lotus Communications Corp. The format of the station is Hispanic oldies. KCHJ-AM broadcasts to the Bakersfield, CA area at 1010 AM.

KCHK-AM
Owner: Ingstad Brothers Broadcasting, LLC
Editorial: 25821 Langford Ave, New Prague, Minnesota 56071-8864. **T:** 1 952 758-2571
E: production@kchkradio.net
W: http://www.kchkradio.net
Editorial Profile: KCHK-AM is a commercial station owned by Ingstad Brothers Broadcasting, LLC. The primary format of the station is country. KCHK-AM broadcasts to the New Prague, MN area at a frequency of 1350 AM.

KCHL-AM
Owner: Martin Broadcasting
Editorial: 1211 W Hein Rd, San Antonio, Texas 78220-3301. **T:** 1 210 333-0050
W: http://www.kchl.org
Editorial Profile: KCHL-AM is a commercial station owned by Martin Broadcasting. The format of the station is gospel music. KCHL-AM broadcasts to the San Antonio area at 1480 AM.

KCHO-FM
Owner: California State University-Chico
Editorial: 35 Main St, Chico, California 95929. **T:** 1 530 898-5896 **E:** kchonews@csuchico.edu
W: http://www.kcho.org
Editorial Profile: KCHO-FM is a non-commercial station owned by California State University-Chico. The format of the station is classical, jazz and news. KCHO-FM broadcasts to the Chico, CA area at 91.7 FM.

KCHQ-FM
Owner: Rich Broadcasting, LLC
Editorial: 1406 Commerce Way, Idaho Falls, Idaho 83401-1233. **T:** 1 208 233-1133
W: http://www.rivercountryfm.com
Editorial Profile: KCHQ-FM is a commercial station owned by Rich Broadcasting, LLC. The format of the station is contemporary country music. KCHQ-FM broadcasts to the eastern Idaho and western Wyoming areas at 102.1 FM.

KCHR-AM
Owner: South Missouri Broadcasting Co. Inc.
Editorial: 205 E Commercial St, Charleston, Missouri 63834. **T:** 1 573 683-6044
W: http://www.charlestonmo.net
Editorial Profile: KCHR-AM is a commercial station owned by South Missouri Broadcasting Co. Inc. The format of the station is oldies. KCHR-AM broadcasts to the Charleston, MO area at 1350 AM.

KCHS-AM
Owner: GPK Media, LLC
Editorial: 1747 E 3rd Ave, Truth or Consequences, New Mexico 87901-2042. **T:** 1 575 894-2400 **E:** kchs@gpkmedia.com
W: http://www.gpkmedia.com
Editorial Profile: KCHS-AM is a commercial station owned by GPK Media, LLC. The format of the station is country and gospel. KCHS-AM broadcasts to the Truth or Consequences, NM area at 1400 AM.

KCHU-AM
Owner: Terminal Radio Inc.
Editorial: 128 Pioneer Drive, Valdez, Alaska 99686. **T:** 1 907 835-4665 **E:** news@kchu.org
W: http://www.kchu.org
Editorial Profile: KCHU-AM is a non-commercial station owned by Terminal Radio Inc. The format of the station is variety. KATB-FM broadcasts to the Valdez, AK area at 770 AM.

KCHX-FM
Owner: ICA Radio
Editorial: 1330 E 8th St, Ste 207, Odessa, Texas 79761. **T:** 1 432 563-9102
W: http://www.mymix1067.com
Editorial Profile: KCHX-FM is a commercial station owned by ICA Radio. The format of the station is adult contemporary. KCHX-FM broadcasts to the Odessa, TX area at 106.7 FM.

KCHZ-FM
Owner: Cumulus Media Inc.
Editorial: 5800 Foxridge Dr, Ste 600, Mission, Kansas 66202-2335. **T:** 1 913 514-3000
W: http://www.957thevibe.com
Editorial Profile: KCHZ-FM is a commercial station owned by Cumulus Media Inc. The format of the station is rhythmic Top 40/CHR music. KCHZ-FM broadcasts to the Kansas City, MO area at 95.7 FM.

KCID-AM
Owner: SNL Radio, LLC
Editorial: 5601 Cassia St, Boise, Idaho 83705-1836. **T:** 1 208 344-4774
W: http://www.salyluzradio.com
Editorial Profile: KCID-AM is a commercial station owned by SNL Radio, LLC. The format of the station is Spanish Catholic. KCID-AM broadcasts to the Boise, ID area at 1490 AM.

KCIE-FM
Owner: Jicarilla Apache Nation
Editorial: AIE Building, Narrow Gauge Road, Dulce, New Mexico 87528. **T:** 1 575 759-3681
W: http://www.nv1.org/kcie.html
Editorial Profile: KCIE-FM a non-commercial station owned by Jicarilla Apache Nation. The format of the station is a mixed variety of music and talk. KCIE-FM broadcasts to the Albuquerque, NM area at 90.5 FM.

KCIF-FM
Owner: Hilo Christian Broadcasting Corp.
Editorial: 208 Mikahala St, #16, Keaau, Hawaii 96749. **T:** 1 808 982-4356
E: keepchristinfocus@kcifradio.com
W: http://www.kcifhawaii.org
Editorial Profile: KCIF-FM is a non-commercial station owned by Hilo Christian Broadcasting Corp. The format of the station is Christian programming. KCIF-FM broadcasts to the Hilo, HI area at 90.3 FM.

KCII-AM
Owner: Home Broadcasting Inc.
Editorial: 110 E Main St, Washington, Iowa 52353. **T:** 1 319 653-2113
E: news@kciiradio.com
W: http://www.kciiradio.com
Editorial Profile: KCII-AM is a commercial station owned by Home Broadcasting Inc. The format of the station is adult contemporary music and news. KCII-AM broadcasts to the Cedar Rapids, IA area at 1380 AM.

KCII-FM
Owner: Home Broadcasting Inc.
Editorial: 110 E Main St, Washington, Iowa 52353. **T:** 1 319 653-2113
E: kcii@kciiradio.com
W: http://www.kciiradio.com
Editorial Profile: KCII-FM is a commercial station owned by Home Broadcasting Inc. The format of the station is adult contemporary. KCII-FM broadcasts to the Cedar Rapids, IA area at 106.1 FM.

KCIJ-FM
Owner: North Face Broadcasting LLC
Editorial: 213 Renee St, Natchitoches, Louisiana 71457. **T:** 1 318 354-4000
E: kcij@eliteradiogroup.com
W: http://www.106kcij.com
Editorial Profile: KCIJ-FM is a commercial station owned by North Face Broadcasating LLC. The format of the station is adult contemporary. KCIJ-FM broadcasts to the Shreveport, LA area at 106.5 FM.

KCIL-FM
Owner: Sunburst Media-Louisiana, LLC
Editorial: 120 Prevost Dr, Houma, Louisiana 70364-2338. **T:** 1 985 851-1020
W: http://www.c1075.com
Editorial Profile: KCIL-FM is a commercial station owned by Sunburst Media-Louisiana, LLC. The format of the station is contemporary country. KCIL-FM broadcasts to the southern Louisiana area at 96.7.

KCIM-AM
Owner: Carroll Broadcasting Co.
Editorial: 1119 East Plaza Dr, Carroll, Iowa 51401-3838. **T:** 1 712 792-4321
E: kcim@carrollbroadcasting.com
W: http://www.1380kcim.com
Editorial Profile: KCIM-AM is commercial station owned by Carroll Broadcasting Co. The format of the station is classic hits and news. KCIM-AM broadcasts to the Carroll, IA area at 1380 AM.

KCIN-FM
Owner: Cherry Creek Radio
Editorial: 750 Ridgeview Dr, Ste 204, St George, Utah 84770-2697. **T:** 1 435 586-5900
W: http://www.bigkickincountry.com
Editorial Profile: KCIN-FM is a commercial station owned by Cherry Creek Radio. The format of the station is contemporary country. KCIN-FM broadcasts to the Cedar City, UT area at 94.9 FM.

KCIR-FM
Owner: Faith Communications Corp.
Editorial: 1446 Filer Ave E, Twin Falls, Idaho 83301. **T:** 1 208 734-5777
E: info@sosradio.net
W: http://www.sosradio.net
Editorial Profile: KCIR-FM is non-commercial station owned by Faith Communications Corp. The format of the station is contemporary Christian music. KCIR-FM broadcasts in the Twin Falls, ID area at 90.7 FM.

KCIS-AM
Owner: Crista Ministries
Editorial: 19319 Fremont Ave N, Shoreline, Washington 98133. **T:** 1 206 546-7350
E: news@kcisradio.com
W: http://www.kcisradio.com
Editorial Profile: KCIS-AM is a commercial station owned by Crista Ministries. The format of the station is religious and Christian programming. KCIS-AM broadcasts to the Seattle area at 630 AM.

KCIV-FM
Owner: Bott Broadcasting Co.
Editorial: 1031 15th St, Ste 1, Modesto, California 95354. **T:** 1 209 524-8999
E: kciv@bottradionetwork.com
W: http://www.bottradionetwork.com
Editorial Profile: KCIV-FM is a commercial station owned by Bott Broadcasting Co. The format of the station is religious and Christian programming. KCIV-FM broadcasts to the Modesto, CA area at 99.9 FM.

KCIX-FM
Owner: Townsquare Media, LLC
Editorial: 827 E Park Blvd Ste 100, Boise, Idaho 83712-7783. **T:** 1 208 344-6363
W: http://mix106radio.com
Editorial Profile: KCIX-FM is a commercial station owned by Townsquare Media, LLC. The format of the station is hot adult contemporary. KCIX-FM broadcasts to the Boise, ID area at 105.9 FM.

KCJB-AM
Owner: Clear Channel Media and Entertainment
Editorial: 1000 20th Ave SW, Minot, North Dakota 58701. **T:** 1 701 852-4646
E: minotprod@clearchannel.com
W: http://www.kcjb910.com
Editorial Profile: KCJB-AM is a commercial station owned by Clear Channel Media and Entertainment. The format of the station is classic country music. KCJB-AM broadcasts in the Minot, ND area at 910 AM.

KCJC-FM
Owner: East Arkansas Broadcasters Inc.
Editorial: 2705 E Parkway Dr, Russellville, Arkansas 72802-2006. **T:** 1 479 968-6816
E: news@rivervalleyradio.com
W: http://www.rivercountrykcjc.com
Editorial Profile: KCJC-FM is a commercial station owned by East Arkansas Broadcasters Inc. The format of the station is country. KCJC-FM broadcasts in Russellville, AR at 102.3 FM.

KCJF-FM
Owner: MOR Media Inc.
Editorial: 400 Tower Dr, Paragould, Arkansas 72450-4891. **T:** 1 870 236-7627
W: http://www.1039thegame.com
Editorial Profile: KCJF-FM is a commercial station owned by MOR Media Inc. The format of the station is sports. KCJF-FM broadcasts to the Jonesboro, AR area at 103.9 FM.

KCJJ-AM
Owner: River City Radio Inc.
Editorial: 845 Quarry Rd Ste 120, Coralville, Iowa 52241-2206. **T:** 1 319 354-1242
E: kcjjam@gmail.com
W: http://www.1630kcjj.com
Editorial Profile: KCJJ-AM is a commercial station owned by River City Radio Inc. The format for the station is hot adult contemporary and talk. KCJJ-AM broadcasts to the Cedar Rapids, IA area at 1630 AM.

KCJK-FM
Owner: Cumulus Media Inc.
Editorial: 5800 Foxridge Dr, 6th Fl, Mission, Kansas 66202-2333. **T:** 1 913 514-3000
W: http://www.1051jackfm.com
Editorial Profile: KCJK-FM is a commercial station owned by Cumulus Media Inc. The format of the station is Jack FM-Adult Hits. KCJK-FM broadcasts to the Mission, MO area at 105.1 FM.

KCKC-FM
Owner: Wilks Broadcast Group
Editorial: 508 Westport Rd Ste 202, Kansas City, Missouri 64111-3019. **T:** 1 816 753-4000
W: http://kc1021.com
Editorial Profile: KCKC-FM is a commercial station owned by Wilks Broadcast Group. The format of the station is adult contemporary. KCKC-FM broadcasts to the Kansas City, MO area at 102.1 FM.

KCKE-FM
Owner: Lake Area Educational Broadcasting Foundation
Editorial: 128 Possom Hollow Dr, Camdenton, Missouri 65020-6755. **T:** 1 573 346-3200
W: http://www.lifechangingradio.org
Editorial Profile: KCKE-FM is a non-commercial station owned by Lake Area Educational Broadcasting Foundation. The format of the station is contemporary Christian. KCKE-FM broadcasts to the Chillicothe, MO area at a frequency of 90.3 FM.

KCKK-AM
Owner: Hunt Broadcasting
Editorial: 1032 S Union Blvd, Lakewood, Colorado 80228-3373. **T:** 1 303 989-3920
W: http://www.937therock.com
Editorial Profile: KCKK-AM is a commercial station owned by Hunt Broadcasting. The format of the station is adult hits. KCKK-AM broadcasts to the Denver area at 1510 AM.

KCKL-FM
Owner: Lake Country Radio LP
Editorial: 11125 Highway 31 East, Malakoff, Texas 75148. **T:** 1 903 489-1238
E: lakecountry@kcklfm.com
W: http://www.kcklfm.com
Editorial Profile: KCKL-FM is a commercial station owned by Lake Country Radio LP. The format of the station is contemporary country music. KCKL-FM broadcasts in the Malakoff, TX area at 95.9 FM.

KCKM-AM
Owner: Kickin' Country Broadcasting Inc.
Editorial: 1200 S Stockton Ave, Monahans, Texas 79756. **T:** 1 432 943-2588
E: kckm1330@aol.com
W: http://www.kckm1330.com
Editorial Profile: KCKM-AM is a commercial station owned by Kickin' Country Broadcasting Inc. The format of the station is classic country. KCKM-AM broadcasts to the Monahans, TX area at 1330 AM.

KCKN-AM
Owner: Radio Visión Cristiana Management
Editorial: 1700 La Luz Rd, Roswell, New Mexico 88201-8963. **T:** 1 575 622-0658
E: 1020kckn@gmail.com
W: http://www.kckn1020.com
Editorial Profile: KCKN-AM is a commercial station owned by Radio Visión Cristiana Management. The format of the station is Hispanic and religious programming. KCKN-AM broadcasts to the Roswell, NM area at 1020 AM.

KCKX-AM
Owner: Coss, Donald D.
Editorial: 1665 James St, Woodburn, Oregon 97071-3475. **T:** 1 503 769-1460
Editorial Profile: KCKX-AM is a commercial station owned by the Coss, Donald D. The format of the station is Hispanic sports. KCKX-AM broadcasts to the Woodburn, OR area at 1460 AM.

KCKY-AM
Owner: Herrera(Moises)
Editorial: 1445 W Baseline Rd, Phoenix, Arizona 85041. **T:** 1 602 276-4241
Editorial Profile: KCKY-AM is a commercial station owned by Moises Herrera. The format of the station is Hispanic Christian programming. KCKY-AM broadcasts in the Phoenix area at 1150 AM.

KCLB-FM
Owner: Morris Communications
Editorial: 1321 N Gene Autry Trl, Palm Springs, California 92262-5473.
T: 1 760 322-7890 **E:** studio@937kclb.com
W: http://www.937kclb.com
Editorial Profile: KCLB-FM is a commercial station owned by Morris Communications. The format of the station is rock alternative music. KCLB-FM broadcasts to the Palm Springs, CA area at 93.7 FM.

KCLC-FM
Owner: Lindenwood University
Editorial: 209 S Kingshighway St, Saint Charles, Missouri 63301. **T:** 1 636 949-4880
E: fm891@lindenwood.edu
W: http://www.891thewood.com
Editorial Profile: KCLC-FM is a non-commercial station owned by Lindenwood University. The format of the station is adult album alternative music. KCLC-FM broadcasts to the Saint Charles, MO area at 89.1 FM.

KCLD-FM
Owner: Leighton Enterprises Inc.
Editorial: 619 W Saint Germain St, Saint Cloud, Minnesota 56301-3640.
T: 1 320 251-1450
W: http://www.1047kcld.com
Editorial Profile: KCLD-FM is a commercial station owned by Leighton Enterprises Inc. The format of the station is Top 40/CHR music. KCLD-FM broadcasts in the Saint Cloud, MN area at 104.7 FM. Send any press materials to the station's program director.

KCLE-AM
Owner: M&M Broadcasters Ltd.
Editorial: 919 N Main St, Cleburne, Texas 76033-3853. **T:** 1 817 645-6643
W: http://www.sports1460espn.com
Editorial Profile: KCLE-AM is a commercial station owned by M&M Broadcasters Ltd. The format of the station is sports. KCLE-AM broadcasts to the Cleburne, TX area at 1460 AM.

KCLF-AM
Owner: New World Broadcasting Co.
Editorial: 803 Parent St, New Roads, Louisiana 70760. **T:** 1 225 638-6821
W: http://www.kclf1500am.com
Editorial Profile: KCLF-AM is a commercial station owned by New World Broadcasting Co. The format of the station is urban contemporary. KCLF-AM broadcasts to the New Roads, LA area at 1500 AM.

KCLH-FM
Owner: Midwest Family Broadcasting
Editorial: 201 State St, La Crosse, Wisconsin 54601. **T:** 1 608 782-1230
E: email@classichits947.com
W: http://www.classichits947.com
Editorial Profile: KCLH-FM is a commercial station owned by Midwest Family Broadcasting. The format of the station is classic hits. KCLH-FM broadcasts in the La Crosse, WI area at 94.7 FM.

KCLI-AM
Owner: Wright Broadcasting Systems
Editorial: 10040 Highway 54, Weatherford, Oklahoma 73096-3021. **T:** 1 580 772-5939
E: kcli@wrightwradio.com
W: http://www.newstalk1320.com

KCLI-FM
Owner: Wright Broadcasting Systems
Editorial: 10040 Highway 54, Weatherford, Oklahoma 73096-3021. **T:** 1 580 772-5939
E: news@wrightwradio.com
W: http://www.newstalkkcli.com
Editorial Profile: KCLI-FM is a commercial station owned by Wright Broadcasting Systems. The format of the station is news and talk. KCLI-FM broadcasts to Oklahoma City at 99.3 FM.

KCLK-AM
Owner: Pacific Empire Radio Corp.
Editorial: 1859 5Th Ave, Clarkston, Washington 99403-1401. **T:** 1 208 743-6564
E: wecare@catfm.com
Editorial Profile: KCLK-AM is a commercial station owned by Pacific Empire Radio Corp. The format of the station is sports. KCLK-AM broadcasts to the Spokane, WA area at 1430 AM.

KCLK-FM
Owner: Pacific Empire Radio Corp.
Editorial: 403 Capital St, Lewiston, Idaho 83501-1815. **T:** 1 208 743-6564
Editorial Profile: KCLK-FM is a commercial station owned by Pacific Empire Radio Corp. The format of the station is oldies music. KCLK-FM broadcasts to the Spokane, WA area at 94.1 FM.

KCLL-FM
Owner: Foster Communications Co. Inc.
Editorial: 2824 Sherwood Way, San Angelo, Texas 76901. **T:** 1 325 949-2112
E: info@kcll-fm.com
W: http://www.kcll-fm.com
Editorial Profile: KCLL-FM is a commercial station owned by Foster Communications Co. Inc. The format of the station is oldies music. KCLL-FM broadcasts to San Angelo, TX at 100.1 FM.

KCLN-AM
Owner: Prairie Communications LLP
Editorial: 1853 442nd Ave, Clinton, Iowa 52732. **T:** 1 563 243-1390
W: http://www.1390kcln.com
Editorial Profile: KCLN-AM is a commercial station owned by Prairie Communications LLP. The format of the station is adult standards. KCLN-AM broadcasts to the Clinton, IA area at 1390 AM.

KCLQ-FM
Owner: Pearson Broadcasting
Editorial: 18785 Finch Rd, Lebanon, Missouri 65536-7812. **T:** 1 417 532-2962
W: http://www.1079thecoyote.com
Editorial Profile: KCLQ-FM is a commercial station owned by Pearson Broadcasting. The format of the station is contemporary country. KCLQ-FM broadcasts to the Lebanon, MO area at 107.9 FM.

KCLR-FM
Owner: Zimmer Radio Group
Editorial: 3215 Lemone Industrial Blvd, Columbia, Missouri 65201-8248.
T: 1 573 875-1099 **E:** clear99@zrgmail.com
W: http://www.clear99.com
Editorial Profile: KCLR-FM is a commercial station owned by Zimmer Radio Group. The format of the station is contemporary country music. KCLR-FM broadcasts to the Columbia, MO area at 99.3 FM.

KCLT-FM
Owner: Delta Force II Radio
Editorial: 700 W Martin Luther King Jr Dr, Ste 2, West Helena, Arkansas 72390.
T: 1 870 572-9506 **E:** force2@sbcglobal.net
W: http://www.force2radio.com
Editorial Profile: KCLT-FM is a commercial station owned by Delta Force II Radio. The format of the station is urban contemporary, blues and gospel. KCLT-FM broadcasts to the West Helena, AR area at 104.9 FM.

KCLU-AM
Owner: California Lutheran University
Editorial: 60 W Olsen Rd #4400, Thousand Oaks, California 91360-2700.
T: 1 805 493-3900 **E:** kclunews@aol.com
W: http://www.kclu.org
Editorial Profile: KCLU-AM is a non-commercial station owned by California Lutheran University. The format of the station is news. KCLU-AM broadcasts to the Santa Barbara, CA area at 1340 AM.

KCLU-FM
Owner: California Lutheran University
Editorial: 60 W Olsen Rd #4400, Thousand Oaks, California 91360-2700.
T: 1 805 493-3900 **E:** kclunews@aol.com
W: http://www.kclu.org
Editorial Profile: KCLU-FM is a non-commercial station owned by California Lutheran University. The format of the station is news. KCLU-FM broadcasts to Ventura County, CA, area at 88.3 FM.

KCLV-AM
Owner: Zia Broadcasting
Editorial: 710 CR K, Clovis, New Mexico 88101-9149. **T:** 1 575 763-4401
E: kclv@allsups.com
Editorial Profile: KCLV-AM is a commercial station owned by Zia Broadcasting. The format of the station is sports. KCLV-AM broadcasts to the Clovis, NM area at 1240 AM.

KCLV-FM
Owner: Zia Broadcasting
Editorial: 710 CR K, Clovis, New Mexico 88101-9149. **T:** 1 575 763-4401
E: kclv@allsups.com
Editorial Profile: KCLV-FM is a commercial station owned by Zia Broadcasting. The format of the station is contemporary country music. KCLV-FM broadcasts to the Clovis, NM area at 99.1 FM.

KCLW-AM
Owner: Lasting Value Broadcasting Group
Editorial: 115 N Rice St, Hamilton, Texas 76531. **T:** 1 254 386-8804
W: http://www.kclw.com
Editorial Profile: KCLW-AM is a commercial station owned by Lasting Value Broadcasting Group. The format of the station is classic country. KCLW-AM broadcasts to the Hamilton, TX area at 900 AM.

KCLX-AM
Owner: Inland Northwest Broadcasting
Editorial: 1114 N Almon St, Moscow, Idaho 83843-8507. **T:** 1 208 882-2551
E: psa@inlandradio.com
Editorial Profile: KCLX-AM is a commercial station owned by Inland Northwest Broadcasting. The format of the station is classic country. KCLX-AM broadcasts to the Moscow, ID area at 1450 AM.

KCLY-FM
Owner: Taylor Communications
Editorial: 1815 Meadowlark Rd, Clay Center, Kansas 67432. **T:** 1 785 632-5661
E: news@kclyradio.com
W: http://www.kclyradio.com
Editorial Profile: KCLY-FM is a commercial station owned by Taylor Communications. The format of the station is adult contemporary and adult standards music. KCLY-FM broadcasts to the Clay Center, KS area at 100.9 FM.

KCMB-FM
Owner: Elkhorn Media Group
Editorial: 1009 Adams Ave Ste C, La Grande, Oregon 97850-2667. **T:** 1 541 963-3405
W: http://www.1047kcmb.com
Editorial Profile: KCMB-FM is a commercial station owned by Elkhorn Media Group. The format of the station is country. KCMB-FM broadcasts to the La Grande, OR area at 104.7 FM.

KCMC-AM
Owner: Texarkana Radio Center Licenses, LLC
Editorial: 615 Olive St, Texarkana, Texas 75501-5512. **T:** 1 903 793-4671

Editorial Profile: KCMC-AM is a commercial station owned by Texarkana Radio Center Licenses, LLC. The format of the station is classic hits. KCMC-AM broadcasts to the Texarkana, TX area at 940 AM.

KCME-FM
Owner: Cheyenne Mountain PB House Inc.
Editorial: 1921 N Weber St, Colorado Springs, Colorado 80907. **T:** 1 719 578-5263
E: kcme@kcme.org **W:** http://www.kcme.org
Editorial Profile: KCME-FM is a non-commercial station owned by Cheyenne Mountain PB House Inc. The format of the station is classical music. KCME-FM broadcasts to the Colorado Springs, CO area at 88.7 FM.

KCMH-FM
Owner: Christian Broadcasting Group of Mountain Home Inc.
Editorial: 126 S Church St, Mountain Home, Arkansas 72653. **T:** 1 870 425-2525
W: http://www.kcmhradio.com
Editorial Profile: KCMH-FM is a non-commercial station owned by Christian Broadcasting Group of Mountain Home Inc. The format of the station is Christian and religious. KCMH-FM broadcasts to Mountain Home, AR at 91.5 FM.

KCMI-FM
Owner: Christian Media, Inc.
Editorial: 209 E 15th St, Scottsbluff, Nebraska 69361. **T:** 1 308 632-5264
E: contact@kcmifm.com
W: http://www.kcmifm.com
Editorial Profile: KCMI-FM is a commercial station owned by Christian Media, Inc. The format of the station is contemporary Christian music and religious talk. KCMI-FM broadcasts in the Scottsbluff, NE area at 96.9 FM

KCML-FM
Owner: Leighton Enterprises Inc.
Editorial: 619 W Saint Germain St, Saint Cloud, Minnesota 56301-3640.
T: 1 320 251-1450 **W:** http://www.lite999.com
Editorial Profile: KCML-FM is a commercial station owned by Leighton Enterprises Inc. The format of the station is Lite Rock/Lite AC music. KCML-FM broadcasts to the St. Cloud, MN area at 99.9 FM. Send any press materials to the station's program director.

KCMM-FM
Owner: Gallatin Valley Witness Inc.
Editorial: 2050 Amsterdam Rd, Belgrade, Montana 59714. **T:** 1 406 388-4281
W: http://www.kcmmtheone.com
Editorial Profile: KCMM-FM is a commercial station owned by Gallatin Valley Witness Inc. The format of the station is contemporary Christian music and talk. KCMM-FM broadcasts to the Belgrade, MT area at 99.1 FM.

KCMN-AM
Owner: DJR Broadcasting
Editorial: 5050 Edison Ave, Ste 218, Colorado Springs, Colorado 80915-3540.
T: 1 719 570-1530
W: http://www.1530kcmn.com
Editorial Profile: KCMN-AM is a commercial station owned by Kona Coast Broadcasting. The format of the station is adult standards music. KCMN-AM broadcasts to the Colorado Springs, CO area at 1530 AM.

KCMO-AM
Owner: Cumulus Media Inc.
Editorial: 5800 Foxridge Dr, 6th Fl, Mission, Kansas 66202-2333. **T:** 1 913 514-3000
W: http://www.kcmotalkradio710.com
Editorial Profile: KCMO-AM is a commercial station owned by Cumulus Media Inc. The format of the station is news and talk. KCMO-AM broadcasts to the Kansas City, MO area at 710 AM.

KCMO-FM
Owner: Cumulus Media Inc.
Editorial: 5800 Foxridge Dr Fl 6, Mission, Kansas 66202-2347. **T:** 1 913 514-3000
E: news@710kcmo.com
W: http://www.949kcmo.com
Editorial Profile: KCMO-FM is a commercial station owned by Cumulus Media Inc. The format for the station is classic hits. KCMO-FM broadcasts to the Kansas City, MO area at 94.9 FM.

KCMP-FM
Owner: Minnesota Public Radio
Editorial: 480 Cedar St, Saint Paul, Minnesota 55101. **T:** 1 651 290-1500 **E:** 893dj@mpr.org
W: http://minnesota.publicradio.org
Editorial Profile: KCMP-FM is a non-commercial station owned by Minnesota Public Radio. The format of the station is adult album alternative with a significant playlist of local music. KCMP-FM broadcasts to the St. Paul, MN area at 89.3 FM.

KCMQ-FM
Owner: Zimmer Radio Group
Editorial: 3215 Lemone Industrial Blvd, Ste 200, Columbia, Missouri 65201.
T: 1 573 875-1099 **E:** kcmq@zrgmail.com
W: http://www.kcmq.com
Editorial Profile: KCMQ-FM is a commercial station owned by the Zimmer Radio Group. The format of the station is classic rock music. KCMQ-FM broadcasts in the Columbia, MO area at 96.7 FM.

KCMR-FM
Owner: T L C Broadcasting Corp.
Editorial: 600 1st St NW, Ste 101, Mason City, Iowa 50401. **T:** 1 641 424-9300
E: kcmr@kcmrfm.com
W: http://www.kcmrfm.com

KCMS-FM
Owner: Crista Ministries
Editorial: 19319 Fremont Ave N, Shoreline, Washington 98133-3800. **T:** 1 206 546-7350
E: comments@spirit1053.com
W: http://www.spirit1053.com
Editorial Profile: KCMS-FM is a commercial station owned by Crista Ministries. The format of the station is contemporary Christian music. KCMS-FM broadcasts to the Seattle area at 105.3 FM.

KCMT-FM
Owner: Lotus Communications Corp.
Editorial: 3871 N Commerce Dr, Tucson, Arizona 85705-2983. **T:** 1 520 407-4500
W: http://www.kcmt.com
Editorial Profile: KCMT-FM is a commercial station owned by Lotus Communications Corp. The format of the station is regional Mexican music. KCMT-FM broadcasts to the Tucscon, AZ area at 92.1 FM.

KCMX-AM
Owner: Mapleton Radio, LLC
Editorial: 1438 Rossanley Dr, Medford, Oregon 97501. **T:** 1 541 779-1550
W: http://www.kcmxam.com
Editorial Profile: KCMX-AM is a commercial station owned by Mapleton Radio, LLC. The format of the station is news and talk. KCMX-AM broadcasts to the Medford, OR area at 880 AM.

KCMX-FM
Owner: Mapleton Radio, LLC
Editorial: 1438 Rossanley Dr, Medford, Oregon 97501-1751. **T:** 1 541 779-1550
W: http://www.lite102.com
Editorial Profile: KCMX-FM is a commercial station owned by Mapleton Radio, LLC. The format of the station is Lite Rock/Lite AC. KCMX-FM broadcasts to the Medford, OR area at 101.9 FM.

KCMY-AM
Owner: Evans Broadcasting
Editorial: 1960 Idaho St, Carson City, Nevada 89701. **T:** 1 775 884-8000
E: prod@991fmtalk.com
Editorial Profile: KCMY-AM is a commercial station owned by Evans Broadcasting. The format of the station is classic country. KCMY-AM broadcasts to the Reno, NV area at 1300 AM.

KCNA-FM
Owner: Opus Broadcasting Systems Inc.
Editorial: 511 Rossanley Dr, Medford, Oregon 97501. **T:** 1 541 772-0322
E: news@opusradio.com
W: http://www.1027thedrive.com
Editorial Profile: KCNA-FM is a commercial station owned by Opus Broadcasting Systems Inc. The format of the station is classic hits music. KCNA-FM broadcasts to the Medford, OR area at 102.7 FM.

KCNB-FM
Owner: Eagle Communications
Editorial: 331 Main St, Chadron, Nebraska 69337. **T:** 1 308 432-2060
Editorial Profile: KCNB-FM is a commercial station owned by Eagle Communications. The format of the station is adult contemporary. KCNB-FM broadcasts to the Chadron, NE area at 94.7 FM.

KCND-FM
Owner: Prairie Public Broadcasting Inc.
Editorial: 1814 N 15th St, Bismarck, North Dakota 58501. **T:** 1 701 224-1700
E: info@prairiepublic.org
W: http://www.prairiepublic.org
Editorial Profile: KCND-FM is a non-commercial station owned by Prairie Public Broadcasting Inc. The format of the station is news, classical and jazz music. KCND-FM broadcasts to the Bismarck, ND area at 90.5 FM.

KCNI-AM
Owner: Custer County Broadcasting Inc.
Editorial: West Hwy 2, Broken Bow, Nebraska 68822. **T:** 1 308 872-5881
E: info@sandhillsexpress.com
W: http://www.kbbn.com/kcni.php
Editorial Profile: KCNI-AM is a commercial station owned by Custer County Broadcasting Inc. The format of the station is country. KCNI-AM broadcasts to the Broken Bow, NE area at 1280 AM.

KCNO-FM
Owner: EDI Media
Editorial: Lakeview Highway 395 North, Alturas, California 96101. **T:** 1 530 233-3570
E: englishradio@edimediainc.com
W: http://www.edimediainc.com/english/englishradio
Editorial Profile: KCNO-FM is a commercial station owned by EDI Media. The format of the station is classic country. KCNO-FM broadcasts to the Alturas, CA area at 94.5 FM.

KCNP-FM
Owner: Chickasaw Nation
Editorial: 100 East 13th, Ste 220, Ada, Oklahoma 74820. **T:** 1 580 272-5267
W: http://www.kcnpradio.org
Editorial Profile: KCNP-FM is a non-commercial station owned by Chickasaw Nation. The format of the station is community radio, a variety of news, folk, jazz and ethnic programming. KCNP-FM broadcasts to Ada, OK and surrounding areas at 89.5 FM.

KCNQ-FM
Owner: QAB Media LLC
Editorial: 14 Sierra Drive, Kernville, California 93238. **T:** 1 760 376-4500
W: http://www.kcnqonline.com
Editorial Profile: KCNQ-FM is a commercial station owned by QAB Media LLC. The format of the station is country. KCNQ-FM broadcasts to the Kernville, CA area at 102.5 FM.

KCNR-AM
Owner: Free Fire Radio
Editorial: 1326 Market St, Redding, California 96001-0610. **T:** 1 530 605-4565
W: http://www.kcnr1460.com
Editorial Profile: KCNR-AM is owned by Free Fire Radio. The format for the station is talk. KCNR-AM broadcasts to Shasta, CA and surrounding areas at 1460 AM.

KCNT-FM
Owner: Central Community College
Editorial: 550 Technical Blvd, Hastings, Nebraska 68901-8362. **T:** 1 402 461-2580
E: kcntfm@cccneb.edu
Editorial Profile: KCNT-FM is a non-commercial station owned by Central Community College. The format of the station is variety. KCNT-FM broadcasts to the Hastings, NE area at 88.1 FM.

KCNV-FM
Owner: Nevada Public Radio
Editorial: 1289 S Torrey Pines Dr, Las Vegas, Nevada 89146-1004. **T:** 1 702 258-9895
E: info@classical897.org
W: http://www.classical897.org
Editorial Profile: KCNV-FM is a non-commercial station owned by Nevada Public Radio. The format of the station is classical music. KCNV-FM broadcasts to the Las Vegas area at 89.7 FM.

KCNW-AM
Owner: Wilkins Communication Networks Inc.
Editorial: 4535 Metropolitan Ave, Kansas City, Kansas 66106-2551. **T:** 1 913 384-1380
E: kcnw@wilkinsradio.com
W: http://www.wilkinsradio.com
Editorial Profile: KCNW-AM is a commercial station owned by Wilkins Communication Networks Inc. and licensed by Kansas City Radio Inc. The format of the station is religious talk. KCNW-AM broadcasts to the Kansas City, KS area at 1380 AM.

KCNY-FM
Owner: Crain Media Group LLC
Editorial: 1825 E Oak St, Ste 103, Conway, Arkansas 72032-5957. **T:** 1 501 932-0825
W: http://www.y107fm.com
Editorial Profile: KCNY-FM is a commercial station owned by Crain Media Group LLC. The format of the station is contemporary country music. KCNY-FM broadcasts in the Searcy, AR area at 107.1 FM.

KCNZ-AM
Owner: Coloff Media
Editorial: 721 Shirley St, Cedar Falls, Iowa 50613-1513. **T:** 1 319 277-1918
W: http://www.kcnzam.com
Editorial Profile: KCNZ-AM is a commercial station owned by Coloff Media. The format of the station is sports. KCNZ-AM broadcasts to the Cedar Falls, IA area at 1650 AM.

KCOB-AM
Owner: Good Radio TV Co. LLC
Editorial: 1801 N 13th Ave E, Newton, Iowa 50208. **T:** 1 641 792-5262
E: info@kcobradio.com
W: http://myiowainfo.com
Editorial Profile: KCOB-AM is a commercial station owned by Good Radio TV Co. LLC. The format of the station is oldies. KCOB-AM broadcasts to the Netwon, IA area at 1280 AM.

KCOB-FM
Owner: Good Radio TV Co. LLC
Editorial: 1801 N 13th Ave E, Newton, Iowa 50208. **T:** 1 641 792-5262
E: info@kcobradio.com
W: http://www.myiowainfo.com
Editorial Profile: KCOB-FM is a commercial station owned by Good Radio TV Co. LLC. The format of the station is country music. KCOB-FM broadcasts to the Newton, IA area at 95.9 FM.

KCOG-AM
Owner: KCOG, Inc.
Editorial: 402 N 12th St, Centerville, Iowa 52544-1718. **T:** 1 641 437-4242
E: kmgofm@lisco.com
Editorial Profile: KCOG-AM is a commercial station owned by KCOG, Inc. The format of the station is classic hits. KCOG-AM broadcasts to the Centerville, IA area at 1400 AM.

KCOH-AM
Owner: Liberman Broadcasting Inc.
Editorial: 3000 Bering Dr, Houston, Texas 77057-5708. **T:** 1 713 315-3400
E: info@kcohradio.com
W: http://www.kcohradio.com
Editorial Profile: KCOH-AM is a commercial station owned Liberman Broadcasting Inc. The format of the station is urban contemporary. KCOH-AM broadcasts to Houston, TX and surrounding areas at 1230 AM.

KCOL-AM
Owner: Clear Channel Media and Entertainment
Editorial: 4270 Byrd Dr, Loveland, Colorado 80538-7074. **T:** 1 970 461-2560
E: 600kcol@clearchannel.com
W: http://www.600kcol.com
Editorial Profile: KCOL-AM is a commercial station owned by Clear Channel Media and Entertainment. The format of the station is news, sports and talk. KCOL-AM broadcasts to the Fort Collins, CO area at 600 AM.

KCOL-FM
Owner: Clear Channel Media and Entertainment
Editorial: 2885 IH-10 E, Beaumont, Texas 77702. **T:** 1 409 896-5555
E: requests@cool925.com
W: http://www.cool925.com
Editorial Profile: KCOL-FM is a commercial station owned by Clear Channel Media and Entertainment. The format of the station is classic hits. KCOL-FM broadcasts to the Beaumont, TX area at 92.5 FM.

KCOM-AM
Owner: Cherry Creek Radio
Editorial: 218 N Austin St, Comanche, Texas 76442. **T:** 1 325 356-3090
Editorial Profile: KCOM-AM is a commercial station owned by Cherry Creek Radio. The format of the station is classic country. KCOM-AM broadcasts to the Comanche, TX area at 1550 AM.

KCOR-AM
Owner: Univision Communications Inc.

Editorial: 12451 Network Blvd Ste 140, San Antonio, Texas 78249-3336.
T: 1 210 610-4300
W: http://univisionamerica.com
Editorial Profile: KCOR-AM is a commercial station owned by Univision Communications Inc. The format of the station is Hispanic news and talk. KCOR-AM broadcasts to the San Antonio area at 1350 AM.

KCOU-FM
Owner: University of Missouri
Editorial: 2500 MU Student Center, Columbia, Missouri 65201. **T:** 1 573 882-7820
W: http://kcou.fm

KCOW-AM
Owner: Eagle Radio Inc.
Editorial: 1210 W 10th St, Alliance, Nebraska 69301-2804. **T:** 1 308 762-1400
W: http://www.kcowradio.com
Editorial Profile: KCOW-AM is a commercial station owned by Eagle Radio Inc. The format of the station is classic hits. KCOW-AM broadcasts to the Alliance, NE area at 1400 AM.

KCOX-AM
Owner: Cross Texas Media Inc.
Editorial: 1408 E Gibson St, Jasper, Texas 75951-6123. **T:** 1 409 384-4500
W: http://www.1027ktxj.com
Editorial Profile: KCOX-AM is a commercial station owned by Cross Texas Media Inc. The format of the station is conservative talk. KCOX-AM broadcasts in the Jasper, TX area at 1350 AM.

KCOZ-FM
Owner: College of the Ozarks
Editorial: College Of The Ozarks, Point Lookout, Missouri 65726-9999.
T: 1 417 334-6411 **E:** jones@cofo.edu
W: http://www.cofo.edu
Editorial Profile: KCOZ-FM is a non-commercial station owned by College of the Ozarks. The format of the station is contemporary Christian music. KCOZ-FM broadcasts to the Point Lookout, MO area at 91.7 FM.

KCPI-FM
Owner: Three Eagles Communications Co.
Editorial: 1633 W Main St, Albert Lea, Minnesota 56007-1868. **T:** 1 507 373-2338
E: 949thebreeze@albertlea.threeeagles.com
W: http://www.myalbertlea.com
Editorial Profile: KCPI-FM is a commercial station owned by Three Eagles Communications. The format of the station is adult contemporary music. KCPI-FM broadcasts to the Albert Lea, MN area at 94.9 FM.

KCPR-FM
Owner: California Polytechnic State University
Editorial: California Polytechnic University, Graphic Arts Bldg Room 302, San Luis Obispo, California 93407. **T:** 1 805 756-5998
E: traffic.kcpr@gmail.com
W: http://www.kcpr.org
Editorial Profile: KCPR-FM is a non-commercial station owned by California Polytechnic State University. The format of the station is variety. KCPR-FM broadcasts to the San Luis Obispo, CA area at 91.3 FM.

KCPS-AM
Owner: Sandcastle Entertainment
Editorial: 205 S Gear Ave, West Burlington, Iowa 52655. **T:** 1 319 754-6698
E: kcps@aol.com
W: http://www.kcpsradio.com
Editorial Profile: KCPS-AM is a commercial station owned by Sandcastle Entertainment. The format of the station is talk and sports. KCPS-AM broadcasts to the Burlington, IA area at 1150 AM.

KCPW-FM
Owner: Wasatch Public Media
Editorial: 210 E 400 S Ste 7, Salt Lake City, Utah 84111-2849. **T:** 1 801 359-5279
E: news@kcpw.org **W:** http://www.kcpw.org
Editorial Profile: KCPW-FM is a non-commercial station owned by Wasatch Public Media. The format of the station is news and talk. KCPW-FM broadcasts to the Salt Lake City area at 88.3 FM.

KCQL-AM
Owner: Clear Channel Media and Entertainment
Editorial: 200 E Broadway, Farmington, New Mexico 87401. **T:** 1 505 325-1716
W: http://www.foxsports1340.com
Editorial Profile: KCQL-AM is a commercial station owned by Clear Channel Media and Entertainment. The format of the station is sports. KCQL-AM broadcasts to the Farmington, NM area at 1340 AM.

KCQQ-FM
Owner: Clear Channel Media and Entertainment
Editorial: 3535 E Kimberly Rd, Davenport, Iowa 52807-2583. **T:** 1 563 344-7000
E: info@kcqq106.com
W: http://www.q106online.com
Editorial Profile: KCQQ-FM is a commercial station owned by Clear Channel Media and Entertainment. The format of the station is classic rock music. KCQQ-FM broadcasts to the Davenport, IA area at 106.5 FM.

KCRB-FM
Owner: Minnesota Public Radio
Editorial: 405A Beltrami Ave NW, Bemidji, Minnesota 56601. **T:** 1 218 751-8864
E: newsroom@mpr.org
W: http://minnesota.publicradio.org
Editorial Profile: KCRB-FM is a non-commercial station owned by Minnesota Public Radio. The format of the station is classical. KCRB-FM broadcasts to the Bemidji, MN area at 88.5 FM.

KCRC-AM
Owner: Chisholm Trail Broadcasting
Editorial: 316 E Willow Rd, Enid, Oklahoma 73701-1514. **T:** 1 580 237-1390
W: http://www.ctbsports.com
Editorial Profile: KCRC-AM is a commercial station owned by Chisholm Trail Broadcasting. The format of the station is sports. KCRC-AM broadcasts to the Enid, OK area at 1390 AM.

KCRE-FM
Owner: Bicoastal Media LLC
Editorial: 1345 Northcrest Dr, Crescent City, California 95531. **T:** 1 707 464-9561
E: kcre@bicoastalmedia.com
W: http://www.kcrefm.com
Editorial Profile: KCRE-FM is a commercial station owned by Bicoastal Media LLC. The format of the station is adult contemporary. KCRE-FM broadcasts to the Crescent City, CA area at 94.3 FM.

KCRF-FM
Owner: Pacific West Broadcasting Inc.
Editorial: 906 SW Alder St, Newport, Oregon 97365-4712. **T:** 1 541 265-2266
E: news@ybcradio.com
W: http://www.kcrffm.com
Editorial Profile: KCRF-FM is a commercial station owned by Pacific West Broadcasting Inc. The format of the station is classic rock music. KCRF-FM broadcasts in the Newport, OR area at 96.7 FM.

KCR-FM
Owner: San Diego State University
Editorial: 5500 Campanile Dr, San Diego, California 92182. **T:** 1 619 594-7014
W: http://kcr.sdsu.edu
Editorial Profile: KCR-FM is a non-commercial station owned by San Diego State University. The format for the station is college variety. KCR-FM broadcasts to the San Diego area at 98.9 FM.

KCRH-FM
Owner: Chabot-Las Positas Community College
Editorial: 25555 Hesperian Blvd, Hayward, California 94545-2447. **T:** 1 510 723-6954
E: kcrhradio@gmail.com
W: http://www.kcrhradio.com
Editorial Profile: KCRH-FM is a non-commercial station owned by Chabot-Las Positas Community College. The format of the station is variety. KCRH-FM broadcasts to the Hayward, CA area at 89.9 FM.

KCRK-FM
Owner: North Country Broadcasting
Editorial: 187 Mantz Rickey Rd, Colville, Washington 99114-9562. **T:** 1 509 684-5031
E: news@kcvl.com **W:** http://www.kcvl.com
Editorial Profile: KCRK-FM is a commercial station owned by North Country Broadcasting. The format of the station is adult contemporary. KCRK-FM broadcasts to the Spokane, WA area at 92.1 FM.

KCRL-FM
Owner: Community Broadcasting, Inc.
Editorial: 10550 Barkley St Ste 100, Overland Park, Kansas 66212-1824. **T:** 1 800 875-1903
Editorial Profile: KCRL-FM is a commercial station owned by Community Broadcasting, Inc. The format of the station is Christian programming. KCRL-FM broadcasts to the St. Louis, MO area at 90.3 FM.

KCRN-AM
Owner: First Dallas Media, Inc.
Editorial: 17 S Chadbourne St, San Angelo, Texas 76903-5862. **T:** 1 325 655-6917
E: kcrn@kcrn.org **W:** http://www.kcrn.org
Editorial Profile: KCRN-AM is a non-commercial station owned by First Dallas Media inc. The format of the station is contemporary Christian music and religious programming. KCRN-AM broadcasts to the San Angelo, TX area at 1340 AM.

KCRN-FM
Owner: First Dallas Media, INC.
Editorial: 17 S Chadbourne St, Ste 500, San Angelo, Texas 76903. **T:** 1 325 655-6917
E: kcrn@kcrn.org **W:** http://www.kcrn.org
Editorial Profile: KCRN-FM is a non-commercial station owned by First Dallas Media inc. The format of the station is contemporary Christian music and religious programming. KCRN-FM broadcasts to the San Angelo, TX area at 93.9 FM

KCRO-AM
Owner: Salem Communications
Editorial: 11717 Burt St, Ste 202, Omaha, Nebraska 68154. **T:** 1 402 422-1600
W: http://www.kcro.com
Editorial Profile: KCRO-AM is a commercial station owned by Salem Communications. The format of the station is Christian talk. KCRO-AM broadcasts to the Omaha, NE area at 660 AM.

KCRR-FM
Owner: Cumulus Media Inc.
Editorial: 501 Sycamore St Ste 300, Waterloo, Iowa 50703-4651. **T:** 1 319 833-4800
E: kcrr@kcrr.com **W:** http://www.kcrr.com
Editorial Profile: KCRR-FM is a commercial station owned by Cumulus Media Inc. The format for the station is classic rock. KCRR-FM broadcasts to the Cedar Rapids, IA area at 97.7 FM.

KCRS-AM
Owner: ICA Radio
Editorial: 1330 E 8th St, Ste 207, Odessa, Texas 79761. **T:** 1 432 563-9102
E: newstalkkcrs@icabroadcasting.com
W: http://www.newstalkkcrs.com
Editorial Profile: KCRS-AM is a commercial station owned by ICA Radio. The format of the station is news and talk. KCRS-AM broadcasts to the Odessa, TX area at 550 AM.

KCRS-FM
Owner: ICA Radio
Editorial: 1330 E 8th St, Ste 207, Odessa, Texas 79761. **T:** 1 432 563-9102
W: http://www.1033kissfm.net
Editorial Profile: KCRS-FM is a commercial station owned by ICA Radio. The format of the station is Top 40/CHR. KCRS-FM broadcasts to the Odessa, TX area at 103.3 FM.

KCRT-AM
Owner: Phillips Broadcasting Inc.
Editorial: 100 Fisher Dr, Trinidad, Colorado 81082. **T:** 1 719 846-3355
E: kcrt@comcast.net
W: http://www.kcrtradio.com
Editorial Profile: KCRT-AM is a commercial station owned by Phillips Broadcasting Inc. The format of the station is country. KCRT-AM broadcasts to the Trinidad, CO area at 1240 AM.

KCRT-FM
Owner: Phillips Broadcasting Inc.
Editorial: 100 Fisher Dr, Trinidad, Colorado 81082. **T:** 1 719 846-3355
E: kcrt@comcast.net
W: http://www.kcrtradio.com
Editorial Profile: KCRT-FM is a commercial station owned by Phillips Broadcasting Inc. The format of the station is classic rock. KCRT-FM broadcasts to the Trinidad, CO area at 92.5 FM.

KCRV-AM
Owner: Pollack Broadcasting Co.
Editorial: 717 Highway 84, Caruthersville, Missouri 63830. **T:** 1 573 333-1370
E: kcrvradio@att.net
W: http://www.kcrvradio.com/am
Editorial Profile: KCRV-AM is a commercial station owned by Pollack Broadcasting Co. The format of the station is classic country. KCRV-AM broadcasts to the Caruthersville, MO area at 1370 AM.

KCRV-FM
Owner: Pollack Broadcasting Co.
Editorial: 1303 Southwest Drive, Kennett, Missouri 63857. **T:** 1 573 888-4616
E: kcrv@semoradio.com
W: http://www.kcrvradio.com
Editorial Profile: KCRV-FM is a commercial station owned by Pollack Broadcasting Co. The format of the station is oldies. KCRV-FM broadcasts to the Kennett, MO area at 105.1 FM.

KCRW-FM
Owner: Santa Monica College
Editorial: 1900 Pico Blvd, Santa Monica, California 90405. **T:** 1 310 450-5183
E: mail@kcrw.org **W:** http://www.kcrw.com
Editorial Profile: KCRW-FM is a non-commercial station owned by Santa Monica College. The format of the station is college variety. KCRW-FM broadcasts to the Santa Monica, CA area at 89.9 FM.

KCRX-AM
Owner: Casarez Jr.(Rosendo)
Editorial: 200 W 1st St, Ste 801, Roswell, New Mexico 88203-4679. **T:** 1 575 622-1432
E: kcrx1430@hotmail.com
W: http://kcrx.tripod.com
Editorial Profile: KCRX-AM is a commercial station owned by Rosendo Casarez, Jr. The format of the station is classic hits. KCRX-AM broadcasts to the Roswell, NM area at 1430 AM.

KCRX-FM
Owner: Ohana Media Group
Editorial: 285 SW Main Ct, Ste 200, Warrenton, Oregon 97146-9457.
T: 1 503 861-6620
W: http://www.kcrx1023.com
Editorial Profile: KCRX-FM is a commercial station owned by Ohana Media Group. The format of the station is classic rock music. KCRX-FM broadcasts in the Astoria, OR area at 102.3 FM.

KCRZ-FM
Owner: Momentum Broadcasting LP
Editorial: 1401 W Caldwell Ave, Visalia, California 93277. **T:** 1 559 553-1500
E: studio@z1049.com
W: http://www.z1049.com
Editorial Profile: KCRZ-FM is a commercial station owned by Momentum Broadcasting LP. The format of the station is hot adult contemporary. KCRZ-FM broadcasts to the Visalia, CA area at 104.9 FM.

KCSB-FM
Owner: University of California
Editorial: Storke Communications Building, Rm #1055, Santa Barbara, California 93106.
T: 1 805 893-3757 **E:** news@kcsb.org
W: http://www.kcsb.org
Editorial Profile: KCSB-FM is a non-commercial station owned by the University of California. The format of the station is college variety. KCSB-FM broadcasts to the Santa Barbara, CA area at 91.9 FM.

KCSD-FM
Owner: SOUTH DAKOTA BOARD OF DIRECTORS FOR EDUCATIONAL TELECOMMUNICATIONS
Editorial: 1101 W 22nd St, Sioux Falls, South Dakota 57105-1600. **T:** 1 605 331-6690
E: news@sdpb.org **W:** http://www.sdpb.org
Editorial Profile: KCSD-FM is a non-commercial station owned by the University of Sioux Falls. The format of the station is classical, jazz and news. KCSD-FM broadcasts to the Sioux Falls, SD area at 90.9 FM.

KCSF-AM
Owner: Cumulus Media Inc
Editorial: 6805 Corporate Dr Ste 130, Colorado Springs, Colorado 80919-1977.
T: 1 719 593-2700
W: http://www.kcs1300am.com
Editorial Profile: KCSF-AM is a commercial station owned by Cumulus Media Inc. The format of the station is sports and talk. KCSF-AM broadcasts to the Colorado Springs, CO area at 1300 AM.

KCSH-FM
Owner: Lifetalk Radio Inc.
Editorial: 11070 Hwy 10, Ste B, Ellensburg, Washington 98926. **T:** 1 509 964-2061
W: http://www.lifetalk.net
Editorial Profile: KCSH-FM is a non-commercial station owned by Lifetalk Radio Inc. The format of the station is religious. KCSH-FM broadcasts to the Ellensburg, WA area at 88.9 FM.

KCSI-FM
Owner: Hawkeye Communications
Editorial: 1991 Ironwood Ave, Red Oak, Iowa 51566-3204. **T:** 1 712 623-2584
E: kcsi@kcsifm.com
W: http://www.kcsifm.com
Editorial Profile: KCSI-FM is a commercial station owned by Hawkeye Communications. The format of the station is contemporary country music. KCSI-FM broadcasts to the Omaha, NE area at 95.3 FM.

KCSJ-AM
Owner: Clear Channel Media and Entertainment
Editorial: 106 W 24th St, Pueblo, Colorado 81003. **T:** 1 719 545-2080
W: http://www.590kcsj.com
Editorial Profile: KCSJ-AM is a commercial station owned by Clear Channel Media and Entertainment. The format of the station is news and talk. KCSJ-AM broadcasts to the Pueblo, CO area at 590 AM.

KCSM-FM
Owner: San Mateo County Comm. College Dist.
Editorial: 1700 W Hillsdale Blvd, San Mateo, California 94402. **T:** 1 650 574-6586
E: info@kcsm.net **W:** http://www.kcsm.org
Editorial Profile: KCSM-FM is a commercial station owned by San Mateo County Comm. College Dist. The format of the station is jazz. KCSM-FM broadcasts to the San Mateo, CA area at 91.1 FM.

KCSN-FM
Owner: California State University
Editorial: 18111 Nordhoff St, Northridge, California 91330. **T:** 1 818 677-3090
W: http://www.kcsn.org
Editorial Profile: KCSN-FM is a non-commercial station owned by California State University. The format of the station is AAA-Adult Album Alternative. KCSN-FM broadcasts to California State University in Northridge, CA, at 88.5 FM.

KCSP-AM
Owner: Entercom Communications Corp.
Editorial: 7000 Squibb Rd, Mission, Kansas 66202-3233. **T:** 1 913 744-3600
W: http://www.610sports.com
Editorial Profile: KCSP-AM is a commercial station owned by Entercom Communications Corp. The format of the station is sports. KCSP-AM broadcasts to the Kansas City, MO area at 610 AM.

KCSP-FM
Owner: Western Inspirational Broadcasters Inc.
Editorial: 6363 US Highway 50 E, Carson City, Nevada 89701. **T:** 1 775 883-5647
E: info@pilgrimradio.com
W: http://www.pilgrimradio.com
Editorial Profile: KCSP-FM is a non-commercial station owned by Western Inspirational Broadcasters Inc. The format of the station is contemporary Christian programming. KCSP-FM broadcasts to the Carson City, NV area at 90.3 FM.

KCSR-AM
Owner: Chadrad Communications Inc.
Editorial: 226 Bordeaux St, Chadron, Nebraska 69337-2393. **T:** 1 308 432-5545
E: kcsr@chadrad.com
W: http://www.chadrad.com
Editorial Profile: KCSR-AM is a commercial station owned by Chadrad Communications Inc. The format of the station is country music, news and sports. KCSR-AM broadcasts to the Chadron, NE area at 610 AM.

KCSS-FM
Owner: California State University
Editorial: 1 University Cir, Turlock, California 95382-3200. **T:** 1 209 667-3378
E: kcsspromos@gmail.com
W: http://www.kcss.net
Editorial Profile: KCSS-FM is a non-commercial station owned by California State University. The format of the station is rock alternative. KCSS-FM broadcasts to the Turlock, CA area at 91.9 FM.

KCST-FM
Owner: Coast Broadcasting Inc.
Editorial: 4480 Highway 101, Florence, Oregon 97439. **T:** 1 541 997-9136
E: radiowaves@kcst.com
W: http://www.kcst.com
Editorial Profile: KCST-FM is a commercial station owned by Coast Broadcasting Inc. The format of the station is adult contemporary. KCST-FM broadcasts to the Florence, OR area at 106.9 FM.

KCTA-AM
Owner: Broadcasting Corp./Southwest
Editorial: 1602 S Brownlee Blvd, Corpus Christi, Texas 78404. **T:** 1 361 882-7711
E: kctaradio@yahoo.com
W: http://www.kctaradio.com
Editorial Profile: KCTA-AM is a commercial station owned by Broadcasting Corp./ Southwest. The format of the station is Christian music and talk. KCTA-AM broadcasts to the Corpus Christi, TX area at 1030 AM.

KCTC-AM
Owner: Entercom Communications Corp.
Editorial: 5345 Madison Ave, Sacramento, California 95841-3141. **T:** 1 916 334-7777
E: writeus@espn1320.net
W: http://espn1320.net
Editorial Profile: KCTC-AM is a commercial station owned by Entercom Communications Corp. The format for the station is sports. KCTC-AM broadcasts to the Sacramento, CA area at 1320 AM.

KCTE-AM
Owner: Union Broadcasting Inc.
Editorial: 6721 W 121st St, Overland Park, Kansas 66209-2003. **T:** 1 913 344-1500
E: info@810whb.com **W:** http://www.1510.com
Editorial Profile: KCTE-AM is a commercial station owned by Union Broadcasting Inc. The format of the station is talk and sports. KCTE-AM broadcasts in the Kansas City, MO, area at 1510 AM.

KCTI-AM
Owner: Gonzales Communications
Editorial: 615 Saint Paul St, Gonzales, Texas 78629-3551. **T:** 1 830 672-3631
E: kcti@kcti1450.com
W: http://www.kcti1450.com
Editorial Profile: KCTI-AM is a commercial station owned by Gonzales Communications. The format of the station is classic country. KCTI-AM broadcasts to the Gonzales, TX area at 1450 AM.

KCTN-FM
Owner: Design Homes Inc.
Editorial: 24493 Highway 128, Elkader, Iowa 52043-8038. **T:** 1 563 245-1400
E: kctn@alpinecom.net
W: http://www.kctn.com
Editorial Profile: KCTN-FM is a commercial station owned by Design Homes Inc. The format for the station is contemporary country. KCTN-FM broadcasts to the Elkader, IA area at 100.1 FM.

KCTO-AM
Owner: Alpine Broadcasting Corp.
Editorial: 310 S La Frenz Rd, Liberty, Missouri 64068-7944. **T:** 1 816 576-7800
E: kcxl@kc.rr.com
Editorial Profile: KCTO-AM is a commercial station owned by Alpine Broadcasting Corp. The format of the station is Hispanic. KCTO-AM broadcasts to the Cleveland, MO area at 1160 AM.

KCTR-FM
Owner: Townsquare Media, LLC
Editorial: 27 N 27th St, 23rd Fl, Billings, Montana 59101. **T:** 1 406 248-7827
W: http://www.kctr.com
Editorial Profile: KCTR-FM is a commercial station owned by Townsquare Media, LLC. The format of the station is country music. KCTR-FM broadcasts to the Billings, MT area at 102.9 FM.

KCTT-FM
Owner: Mountain Lakes Broadcasting Inc.
Editorial: 620 Highway 5 N, Mountain Home, Arkansas 72653. **T:** 1 870 425-3101
E: news@ktlo.com **W:** http://www.ktlo.com
Editorial Profile: KCTT-FM is a commercial station owned by Mountain Lakes Broadcasting Inc. The format of the station is classic hits. KCTT-FM broadcasts to the Mountain Home, AR area at 101.7 FM.

KCTX-AM
Owner: Boles Broadcasting Co.
Editorial: 1111 16th St NW, Childress, Texas 79201-3417. **T:** 1 940 937-6316
E: kctxradio@gmail.com
Editorial Profile: KCTX-AM is a commercial station owned by Boles Broadcasting Co. The format of the station is oldies and talk. KCTX-AM broadcasts to the Childress, TX area at 1510 AM.

KCTX-FM
Owner: Boles Broadcasting Co.
Editorial: 1111 16th Street NW, Childress, Texas 79201-3417. **T:** 1 940 937-6316
E: kctxradio@gmail.com
Editorial Profile: KCTX-FM is a commercial station owned by Boles Broadcasting Co. The format of the station is classic and contemporary country music. KCTX-FM broadcasts to the Amarillo, TX, area at 96.1 FM.

KCTY-AM
Owner: Wayne Radio Works
Editorial: 85592 574th Ave, Wayne, Nebraska 68787-7043. **T:** 1 402 375-3700
Editorial Profile: KCTY-AM is a commercial station owned by Wayne Radio Works. The format of the station is hot adult contemporary. KCTY-AM broadcasts to the Wayne, NE area at 1590 AM.

KCUA-FM
Owner: Evans Broadcasting
Editorial: 2242 E 1000 S, Roosevelt, Utah 84066-9523. **T:** 1 435 722-5011
E: radio@ubtanet.com
Editorial Profile: KCUA-FM is a commercial station owned by Evans Broadcasting. The format of the station is classic rock. KCUA-FM broadcasts to the Naples, UT area at 92.5 FM.

KCUB-AM
Owner: Cumulus Media Inc
Editorial: 575 W Roger Rd, Tucson, Arizona 85705-2616. **T:** 1 520 887-1000
E: studio@1290amthesource.com
W: http://www.kcubam.com
Editorial Profile: KCUB-AM is a commercial station owned by Cumulus Media Inc. The format of the station is sports and talk. KCUB-AM broadcasts to the Tucson, AZ area at 1290 AM.

KCUE-AM
Owner: Q Media Group, LLC
Editorial: 474 Guernsey Ln, Red Wing, Minnesota 55066. **T:** 1 651 388-7151
Editorial Profile: KCUE-AM is a commercial station owned by Q Media Group, LLC. The format of the station is classic country. KCUE-AM broadcasts in the Minneapolis area at 1250 AM. The station operates under an LMA with Sorenson Broadcasting.

KCUL-AM
Owner: Access.1 Communications Corp.
Editorial: 210 S Broadway Ave, Tyler, Texas 75702-7363. **T:** 1 903 581-9966
Editorial Profile: KCUL-AM is a commercial station owned by Access.1 Communications Corp. The format of the station is sports. KCUL-AM broadcasts to the Shreveport, LA area at 1410 AM.

KCUL-FM
Owner: Access.1 Communications Corp.
Editorial: 210 S Broadway Ave, Tyler, Texas 75702. **T:** 1 903 581-9966
W: http://lainvasora.fm
Editorial Profile: KCUL-FM is a commercial station owned by Access.1 Communications Corp. The format of the station is regional Mexican music. KCUL-FM broadcasts to the Shreveport, LA area at 92.3 FM.

KCUP-AM
Owner: Agpal Broadcasting Inc.
Editorial: 145 N Coast Hwy, Ste D, Newport, Oregon 97365. **T:** 1 541 265-5000
E: info@kcup.net **W:** http://www.kcup.net
Editorial Profile: KCUP-AM is a commercial station owned by Agpal Broadcating Inc. The format of the station is news and talk. KCUP-AM broadcasts to the Newport, OR area at 1230 AM.

KCUR-FM
Owner: University of Missouri
Editorial: 4825 Troost Ave Ste 202, Kansas City, Missouri 64110-2030. **T:** 1 816 235-1551
E: kcur@umkc.edu **W:** http://www.kcur.org
Editorial Profile: KCUR-FM is a non-commercial station owned by the University of Missouri. The format of the station is news and talk. KCUR-FM broadcasts to the Kansas City, MO, area at 89.3 FM.

KCUZ-AM
Owner: Cochise Broadcasting LLC
Editorial: 301 E US Highway 70, #B, Safford, Arizona 85546. **T:** 1 928 428-0916
E: events@saffordradio.com
W: http://www.saffordradio.com
Editorial Profile: KCUZ-AM is a commercial station owned by Cochise Broadcasting LLC. The format of the station is classic rock. KCUZ-AM broadcasts to the Safford, AZ area at 1490 AM.

KCVI-FM
Owner: Riverbend Communications LLC
Editorial: 400 W Sunnyside Rd, Idaho Falls, Idaho 83402-4613. **T:** 1 208 523-3722
W: http://www.kbear.fm
Editorial Profile: KCVI-FM is a commercial station owned by Riverbend Communications LLC. The format of the station is rock. KCVI-FM broadcasts to the Idaho Falls, ID area at 101.5 FM.

KCVJ-FM
Owner: Lake Area Educational Broadcasting Foundation
Editorial: 128 Possum Hollow Dr, Camdenton, Missouri 65020-6755. **T:** 1 573 346-3200
W: http://www.lifechangingradio.org
Editorial Profile: KCVJ-FM is a non-commercial station, owned by Lake Area Educational Broadcasting Foundation.The format of the station is Christian news, music, and talk. KCVJ-FM broadcasts to the Camdenton, MO area at 92.3 FM.

KCVL-AM
Owner: North Country Broadcasting
Editorial: 187 Mantz Rickey Rd, Colville, Washington 99114-9562. **T:** 1 509 684-5031
E: news@kcvl.com **W:** http://www.kcvl.com
Editorial Profile: KCVL-AM is a commercial station owned by North Country Broadcasting. The format of the station is contemporary country music. KCVL-AM broadcasts to the Spokane, WA area at 1240 AM.

KCVM-FM
Owner: Coloff Media
Editorial: 721 Shirley St, Cedar Falls, Iowa 50613. **T:** 1 319 277-1918
E: themix@935themix.com
W: http://935themix.com
Editorial Profile: KCVM-FM is a commercial station owned by Coloff Media. The format of the station is adult contemporary. KCVM-FM broadcasts to the Cedar Falls, IA area at 93.5 FM.

KCVN-FM
Owner: Bott Broadcasting Co.
Editorial: 233 S 13th St, Ste 1520, Lincoln, Nebraska 68508. **T:** 1 402 465-8850
E: kcvn@bottradionetwork.com
W: http://www.bottradionetwork.com
Editorial Profile: KCVN-FM is a commercial station owned by Bott Broadcasting Co. The format of the station is religious. KCVN-FM broadcasts to the Lincoln, NE area at 104.5 FM.

KCVO-FM
Owner: Lake Area Educational Broadcasting Foundation
Editorial: 128 Possum Hollow Dr, Camdenton, Missouri 65020. **T:** 1 573 346-3200
W: http://www.lifechangingradio.org
Editorial Profile: KCVO-FM is a non-commercial station owned by Lake Area Educational Broadcasting Foundation. The format of the station is contemporary Christian music and talk. KCVQ-FM broadcasts to the Camdenton, MO area at 89.7 FM.

KCVQ-FM
Owner: Lake Area Educational Broadcasting Foundation
Editorial: 128 Possum Hollow Dr, Camdenton, Missouri 65020. **T:** 1 573 346-3200
W: http://www.lifechangingradio.org
Editorial Profile: KCVQ-FM is a non-commercial station owned by Lake Area Educational Broadcasting Foundation. The format of the station is Christian news, music, and talk. KCVQ-FM broadcasts to the Camdenton, MO area at 89.7 FM.

KCVR-AM
Owner: Entravision Communications Corp.
Editorial: 6820 Pacific Ave, Ste 3A, Stockton, California 95207-2631. **T:** 1 209 474-0154
W: http://www.maria989.com
Editorial Profile: KCVR-AM is a commercial station owned by Entravision Communications Corp. The format of the station is Hispanic adult hits. KCVR-AM broadcasts to the Stockton, CA area at 1570 AM.

KCVR-FM
Owner: Entravision Communications Corp.
Editorial: 6820 Pacific Ave, Ste 3A, Stockton, California 95207. **T:** 1 209 474-0154
W: http://www.maria989.com
Editorial Profile: KCVR-FM is a commercial station owned by Entravision Communications Corp. The format of the station is Hispanic

adult hits. KCVR-FM broadcasts in Stockton, CA area at 98.9 FM.

KCVS-FM
Owner: VCY America Inc.
Editorial: 3434 W Kilbourn Ave, Milwaukee, Wisconsin 53208-3313. **T:** 1 414 935-3000
E: kcvs@vcyamerica.org
W: http://www.vcyamerica.org
Editorial Profile: KCVS-FM is a non-commercial station owned by VCY America Inc. The format of the station is religious. KCVS-FM broadcasts to the Milwaukee area at 91.7 FM.

KCVT-FM
Owner: Bott Broadcasting Co.
Editorial: 534 S Kansas Ave, Ste 930, Topeka, Kansas 66603. **T:** 1 785 233-9250
E: kcvt@bottradionetwork.com
W: http://www.bottradionetwork.com
Editorial Profile: KCVT-FM is a commercial station owned by Bott Broadcasting Co. The format of the station is Christian news, music and talk. KCVT-FM broadcasts in the Topeka, KS area at 92.5 FM.

KCVV-AM
Owner: Radio Santisimo
Editorial: 1909 7th St, Sacramento, California 95811-7007. **T:** 1 916 442-7389
E: kcvv1240am@radiosantisimosacramento.com
W: http://www.radiosantisimosacramento.com
Editorial Profile: KCVV-AM is a commercial station owned by Radio Santisimo. The format of the station is Spanish-language Catholic programming. KCVV-AM broadcasts to Sacramento, CA, at 1240 AM.

KCVW-FM
Owner: Bott Broadcasting Co.
Editorial: 209 N Meridian Rd, Newton, Kansas 67114-5102. **T:** 1 620 663-0943
E: kcvw@bottradionetwork.com
W: http://www.bottradionetwork.com
Editorial Profile: KCVW-FM is a commercial station owned by Bott Broadcasting Co. The format of the station is religious and Christian programming. KCVW-FM broadcasts to the Newton, KS area at 94.3 FM.

KCVY-FM
Owner: Lake Area Educational Broadcasting Foundation
Editorial: 128 Possum Hollow Dr, Camdenton, Missouri 65020. **T:** 1 573 346-3200
W: http://www.lifechangingradio.org
Editorial Profile: KCVY-FM is a non-commercial station owned by Lake Area Educational Broadcasting Foundation. The format of the station is contemporary Christian music and talk. KCVY-FM broadcasts to the Camdenton, MO area at 89.9 FM.

KCWC-FM
Owner: Central Wyoming College
Editorial: 2660 Peck Ave, Riverton, Wyoming 82501. **T:** 1 307 855-2268
W: http://www.cwc.edu
Editorial Profile: KCWC-FM is a non-commercial station owned by Central Wyoming College. The format of the station is variety. KCWC-FM broadcasts to the Riverton, WY area at 88.1 FM.

KCWD-FM
Owner: Dowdy Broadcasting, Inc.
Editorial: 600 S Pine St, Harrison, Arkansas 72601-5828. **T:** 1 870 741-1402
E: kcwd@windstream.net
W: http://www.kcwdradio.com
Editorial Profile: KCWD-FM is a commercial station owned by Dowdy Broadcasting, Inc. The format of the station is classic hits. KCWD-FM broadcasts to the Harrison, AR area at 96.1 FM.

KCWJ-AM
Owner: Stayton(D.T.)
Editorial: 18920 E Valley View Pkwy Ste C, Independence, Missouri 64055-7020.
T: 1 816 795-6826 **E:** gregharris@kcwj.org
W: http://www.kcwj.org
Editorial Profile: KCWJ-AM is a commercial station owned by D.T. Stayton. The format of the station is religious and gospel programming. KCWJ-AM broadcasts to the Kansas City, MO area at 1030 AM.

KCWM-AM
Owner: Hondo Communications
Editorial: 1605 Avenue K, Hondo, Texas 78861-1838. **T:** 1 830 741-5296
E: kcwm@aol.com **W:** http://www.kcwm.net
Editorial Profile: KCWM-AM is a commercial station owned by Hondo Communications. The

format of the station is classic country. KCWM-AM broadcasts to the Hondo, TX area at 1460 AM.

KCWN-FM
Owner: Crown Broadcasting Inc.
Editorial: 304 Oskaloosa St, Pella, Iowa 50219-2122. **T:** 1 641 628-9999
E: kcwn@kcwnfm.org
W: http://www.kcwnfm.org
Editorial Profile: KCWN-FM is a commercial station owned by Crown Broadcasting Inc. The format of the station is contemporary Christian music. KCWN-FM broadcasts to the Pella, IA area at 99.9 FM.

KCWR-FM
Owner: Owens Productions Inc.(Buck)
Editorial: 3223 N Sillect Ave, Bakersfield, California 93308-6332. **T:** 1 661 326-1011
E: kuzznews@buckowens.com
Editorial Profile: KCWR-FM is a commercial station owned by Buck Owens Productions Inc. The format of the station is classic country music. The station broadcasts to the Bakersfield, CA area at 107.1 FM.

KCWU-FM
Owner: Central Washington University
Editorial: 400 E University Way, Ellensburg, Washington 98926. **T:** 1 509 963-2283
E: news@cwu.edu
W: http://www.881theburg.com
Editorial Profile: KCWU-FM is a non-commercial station owned by Central Washington University. The format of the station is college variety. KCWU-FM broadcasts to the Ellensburg, WA area at 88.1 FM.

KCXL-AM
Owner: Alpine Broadcasting Corp.
Editorial: 310 S La Frenz Rd, Liberty, Missouri 64068. **T:** 1 816 576-7800 **E:** kcxl@kc.rr.com
W: http://www.kcxl.com
Editorial Profile: KCXL-AM is a commercial station owned by Alpine Broadcasting Corp. The format of the station is talk and variety. KCXL-AM broadcasts to the Liberty, MO area at 1140 AM.

KCXR-FM
Owner: KXOJ, Inc.
Editorial: 2448 E 81st St, Ste 5500, Tulsa, Oklahoma 74137-4201. **T:** 1 918 492-2660
E: kxoj@kxoj.com **W:** http://www.kxojnext.com
Editorial Profile: KCXR-FM is a commercial station owned by KXOJ, Inc. The format of the station is contemporary Christian rock and CHR. KCXR-FM broadcasts to the Tulsa, OK area at 100.3 FM.

KCXX-FM
Owner: All Pro Broadcasting Inc.
Editorial: 242 E Airport Dr, Ste 106, San Bernardino, California 92408.
T: 1 909 890-5904 **W:** http://www.x1039.com
Editorial Profile: KCXX-FM is a commercial station owned by All Pro Broadcasting Inc. The format is alternative rock. KCXX-FM broadcasts to the San Bernardino, CA area at 103.9 FM.

KCXY-FM
Owner: Radio Works Inc.
Editorial: 612 Fairview Rd SW, Camden, Arkansas 71701-6554. **T:** 1 870 836-9567
W: http://www.y95online.com
Editorial Profile: KCXY-FM is a commercial station owned by Radio Works Inc. The format of the station is country music. KCXY-FM broadcasts to the Camden, AR area at 95.3 FM.

KCYE-FM
Owner: Beasley Broadcast Group
Editorial: 2920 S Durango Dr, Las Vegas, Nevada 89117-4412. **T:** 1 702 730-0300
W: http://www.kcye.com
Editorial Profile: KCYE-FM is a commercial station owned by Beasley Broadcast Group. The format of the station is country. KCYE-FM broadcasts to the Las Vegas area at 102.7 FM.

KCYK-AM
Owner: MonsterMedia LLC
Editorial: 949 S Avenue B, Yuma, Arizona 85364-3440. **T:** 1 928 782-4321
W: http://outlawcountry1400.com
Editorial Profile: KCYK-AM is a commercial station owned by MonsterMedia LLC. The format of the station is country. KCYK-AM broadcasts in the Yuma, AZ area at 1400 AM.

KCYL-AM
Owner: Witcher(Ronald K.)

Editorial: 505 N Key Ave, Lampasas, Texas 76550. **T:** 1 512 556-6193
E: management@lampasasradio.com
W: http://www.lampasasradio.com

KCYN-FM
Owner: Moab Communications LLC
Editorial: 1030 Bowling Alley Ln, Moab, Utah 84532-3048. **T:** 1 435 259-1035
E: kcyn@kcynfm.com
W: http://www.kcynfm.com
Editorial Profile: KCYN-FM is a commercial station owned by Moab Communications LLC. The format of the station is contemporary country. KCYN-FM broadcasts to the Salt Lake City area at 97.1 FM.

KCYS-FM
Owner: Dave's Broadcasting Corp.
Editorial: 1324 N Holladay Dr, Seaside, Oregon 97138-7132. **T:** 1 503 717-9643
E: kcys@gowebway.com
Editorial Profile: KCYS-FM is a commercial station owned by Dave's Broadcasting Corp. The format of the station is contemporary country music. KCYS-FM broadcasts to the Seaside, OR area at 96.5 FM.

KCYY-FM
Owner: Cox Media Group, Inc.
Editorial: 8122 Datapoint Dr, San Antonio, Texas 78229-3272. **T:** 1 210 615-5400
E: psa@coxradio.com
W: http://www.y100fm.com
Editorial Profile: KCYY-FM is a commercial station owned by Cox Media Group, Inc. The format of the station is country. KCYY-FM broadcasts to the San Antonio area at 100.3 FM.

KCZE-FM
Owner: Coloff Media
Editorial: 207 N Main St, Charles City, Iowa 50616. **T:** 1 641 228-1000
E: kcze@951thebull.com
W: http://www.951thebull.com
Editorial Profile: KCZE-FM is a commercial station owned by Coloff Media. The format of the station is contemporary country. KCZE-FM broadcasts to the Charles City, IA area at 95.1 FM.

KCZO-FM
Owner: Bernal(Paulino)
Editorial: 4501 N McColl Rd, McAllen, Texas 78504-2431. **T:** 1 956 686-6382
Editorial Profile: KCZO-FM is a non-commercial station owned by Paulino Bernal. The format of the station is Hispanic contemporary Christian music. KCZO-FM broadcasts to the McAllen, TX area at 92.1 FM.

KCZQ-FM
Owner: Mega Media Ltd.
Editorial: 116 1st Ave W, Cresco, Iowa 52136.
T: 1 563 547-1000 **E:** superc@iowatelecom.net

KCZZ-AM
Owner: Reyes Media Group
Editorial: 1701 S 55th St, Kansas City, Kansas 66106-2241. **T:** 1 913 287-1480
W: http://reyesmediagroup.com
Editorial Profile: KCZZ-AM is a commercial station owned by Reyes Media Group. The format of the station is Hispanic Top 40/CHR. KCZZ-AM broadcasts to the Kansas City, KS area at 1480 AM.

KDAA-FM
Owner: Mahaffey Enterprises Inc.
Editorial: 1505 Soest Rd, Rolla, Missouri 65401. **T:** 1 573 364-2525
W: http://www.resultsradioonline.com

KDAC-AM
Owner: Bicoastal Media LLC
Editorial: 140 N Main St, Lakeport, California 95453. **T:** 1 707 263-6113
E: kukinews@bicoastalmedia.com
Editorial Profile: KDAC-AM is a commercial station owned by Bicoastal Media LLC. The format of the station is regional Mexican. KDAC-AM broadcasts to the Ukiah, CA area at 1230 AM.

KDAE-AM
Owner: Worship Center of Kingsville(The)
Editorial: 929 N Padre Island Dr, Corpus Christi, Texas 78406. **T:** 1 361 299-1980
W: http://www.radiolibertad.net
Editorial Profile: KDAE-AM is a commercial station owned by The Worship Center of Kingsville. The format of the station is Hispanic religious programming. KDAE-AM

broadcasts to the Corpus Christi, TX area at 1590 AM.

KDAG-FM
Owner: Clear Channel Media and Entertainment
Editorial: 200 E Broadway, Farmington, New Mexico 87401-6418. **T:** 1 505 325-1716
W: http://www.bigdog969.com
Editorial Profile: KDAG-FM is a commercial station owned by Clear Channel Media and Entertainment. The format of the station is classic rock music. KDAG-FM broadcasts to the Albuquerque, NM area at 96.9.

KDAK-AM
Owner: Robert Ingstad Broadcast Group
Editorial: 1255 7th St S, Carrington, North Dakota 58421. **T:** 1 701 652-3151
E: kdakam@daktel.com
W: http://www.newsdakota.com
Editorial Profile: KDAK-AM is a commercial station owned by Robert Ingstad Broadcast Group. The format of the station is country music. KDAK-AM broadcasts to the Carrington, ND area at 1600 AM.

KDAL-AM
Owner: Midwest Communications Inc.
Editorial: 11 E Superior St Ste 380, Duluth, Minnesota 55802-3016. **T:** 1 218 722-4321
E: info@kdal610.com
W: http://www.kdal610.com
Editorial Profile: KDAL-AM is a commercial station owned by Midwest Communications Inc. The format for this station is news and talk. KDAL-AM broadcasts in the Duluth, MN, area at 610 AM.

KDAL-FM
Owner: Midwest Communications Inc.
Editorial: 715 E Central Entrance, Duluth, Minnesota 55811-5596. **T:** 1 218 722-4321
W: http://my957.com
Editorial Profile: KDAL-FM is a commercial station owned by Midwest Communications Inc. The format of the station is adult contemporary. KDAL-FM broadcasts in the Duluth, MN area at 95.7 FM.

KDAM-FM
Owner: Riverfront Broadcasting
Editorial: 202 W 2Nd St, Yankton, South Dakota 57078-4317. **T:** 1 605 665-7892
W: http://www.kdam.fm
Editorial Profile: KDAM-FM is a commercial station owned by Riverfront Broadcasting. The format of the station is rock. KDAM-FM broadcasts to the Yankton, SD area at 94.3 FM.

KDAO-AM
Owner: MTN Broadcasting Inc.
Editorial: 1930 N Center Street Rd, Marshalltown, Iowa 50158. **T:** 1 641 752-4122
E: kdao@kdao.com **W:** http://www.kdao.com
Editorial Profile: KDAO-AM is a commercial station owned by MTN Broadcasting Inc. The format of the station is oldies. KDAO-AM broadcasts to the Marshalltown, IA area on 1190 AM.

KDAO-FM
Owner: MTN Broadcasting Inc.
Editorial: 1930 N Center Street Rd, Marshalltown, Iowa 50158. **T:** 1 641 752-4122
E: kdao@kdao.com **W:** http://www.kdao.com

KDAP-AM
Owner: Henderson (Howard)
Editorial: 2031 N Sulphur Springs Rd, Douglas, Arizona 85607. **T:** 1 520 364-3484
E: kdapfm@yahoo.com
Editorial Profile: KDAP-AM is a commercial station owned by Howard Henderson. The format of the station is Hispanic religious programming. KDAP-AM broadcasts to the Douglas, AZ area at 1450 AM.

KDAP-FM
Owner: Henderson (Howard)
Editorial: 2031 N Sulphur Springs Rd, Douglas, Arizona 85607. **T:** 1 520 364-3484
E: kdapfm@yahoo.com
Editorial Profile: KDAP-FM is a commercial station owned by Henderson (Howard). The format of the station is contemporary country music. KDAP-FM broadcasts to the Tucson, AZ area at 96.5 FM.

KDAQ-FM
Owner: Louisiana State University
Editorial: 1 University Pl, Shreveport, Louisiana 71115-2301. **T:** 1 318 797-5150
E: listenermail@redriverradio.org
W: http://www.redriverradio.org

Editorial Profile: KDAQ-FM is a non-commercial station owned by Louisiana State University. The format of the station is classical, jazz music and news. KDAQ-FM broadcasts to the Shreveport, LA area at 89.9 FM.

KDAR-FM
Owner: Salem Communications
Editorial: 500 E Esplanade Dr Ste 1500, Oxnard, California 93036-0571.
T: 1 805 485-8881 **W:** http://www.kdar.com
Editorial Profile: KDAR-FM is a commercial station owned by Salem Communications. The format of the station is religious talk. KDAR-FM broadcasts to the Oxnard, CA area at 98.3 FM.

KDAT-FM
Owner: Townsquare Media, LLC
Editorial: 425 2nd St SE Fl 4, Cedar Rapids, Iowa 52401-1819. **T:** 1 319 365-9431
E: kdat@kdat.com **W:** http://www.kdat.com
Editorial Profile: KDAT-FM is a commercial station owned by Townsquare Media, LLC. The format of the station is Lite Rock/Lite AC. KDAT-FM broadcasts to the Cedar Rapids, IA area at 104.5 FM.

KDAV-AM
Owner: Renaissance Broadcasting Inc.
Editorial: 1714 Buddy Holly Ave, Lubbock, Texas 79401. **T:** 1 806 744-5859
E: radio@door.net **W:** http://www.kdav.com
Editorial Profile: KDAV-AM is a commercial station owned by Renaissance Broadcasting Inc. The format of the station is oldies. KDAV-AM broadcasts to the Lubbock, TX area at 1590 AM.

KDAY-FM
Owner: Meruelo Group
Editorial: 5055 Wilshire Blvd, Los Angeles, California 90036-6100. **T:** 1 323 337-1600
W: http://www.935kday.com
Editorial Profile: KDAY-FM is a commercial station owned by Meruelo Group. The format of the station is classic hip hop music. DAY-FM broadcasts to the Los Angeles area at 93.5 FM.

KDAZ-AM
Owner: Pan American Broadcasting Company, Inc.
Editorial: 5010 4th St NW, Albuquerque, New Mexico 87107-3908. **T:** 1 505 345-7373
E: dan@am730.com **W:** http://www.am730.cc
Editorial Profile: KDAZ-AM is a non-commercial station owned by Pan American Broadcasting Company, Inc. The format of the station is religious talk programming. KDAZ-AM broadcasts to the Albuquerque, NM area at 730 AM.

KDBB-FM
Owner: MKS Broadcasting Inc.
Editorial: 804 St Joe Drive, Park Hills, Missouri 63601. **T:** 1 573 431-1000
E: news@b104fm.com
W: http://www.b104fm.com
Editorial Profile: KDBB-FM is a commercial station owned by MKS Broadcasting Inc. The format of the station is adult album alternative. KDBB-FM broadcasts to the Park Hills, MO area at 104.3 FM.

KDB-FM
Owner: Santa Monica College
Editorial: 414 E Cota St, Santa Barbara, California 93101-1624. **T:** 1 213 225-7400
E: pressrelease@kusc.org
W: http://www.kusc.org
Editorial Profile: KDB-FM is a commercial station owned by Santa Monica College. The format of the station is classical. KDB-FM broadcasts to the Santa Barbara, CA area at 93.7 FM.

KDBH-FM
Owner: Baldridge-Dumas Communications Inc.
Editorial: 400 Jefferson St, Natchitoches, Louisiana 71457. **T:** 1 318 352-9696
E: production@bdcradio.com
W: http://www.bdcradio.com
Editorial Profile: KDBH-FM is a commercial station owned by Baldridge-Dumas Communications Inc. The format of the station is contemporary country music. KDBH-FM broadcasts to the Natchitoches, LA area at 97.5 FM.

KDBI-FM
Owner: Adelante Media Group
Editorial: 3307 Caldwell Blvd, Ste 102, Nampa, Idaho 83651. **T:** 1 208 463-2900
W: http://www.radiolagrande.com
Editorial Profile: KDBI-FM is a commercial station owned by Adelante Media Group. The format of the station is regional Mexican music. KDBI-FM broadcasts to the Nampa, ID, area at 101.9 FM.

KDBL-FM
Owner: Townsquare Media, LLC
Editorial: 4010 Summitview Ave, Yakima, Washington 98908. **T:** 1 509 972-3461
W: http://www.929thebull.com
Editorial Profile: KDBL-FM is a commercial station owned by Townsquare Media, LLC. The format of the station is contemporary country. KDBL-FM broadcasts to the Yakima, WA area at 92.9 FM.

KDBM-AM
Owner: Dead-Air Broadcasting Co.
Editorial: 610 N Montana St, Dillon, Montana 59725. **T:** 1 406 683-2800
E: deadair@kdbm-kbev.com
W: http://www.kdbmkbev.com
Editorial Profile: KDBM-AM is a commercial station owned by Dead-Air Broadcasting Co. The format for the station is country. KDBM-AM broadcasts to the Dillon, MT area at 1490 AM.

KDBN-FM
Owner: Townsquare Media, Inc.
Editorial: 315 Kennedy Ave, Grand Junction, Colorado 81501-7552. **T:** 1 970 242-7788
W: http://www.95rockfm.com
Editorial Profile: KDBN-FM is a commercial station owned by Townsquare Media, Inc. The format of the station is rock. KDBN-FM broadcasts to the Parachute, CO area at 101.1 FM.

KDBR-FM
Owner: Bee Broadcasting Inc.
Editorial: 2432 US Highway 2 E, Kalispell, Montana 59901. **T:** 1 406 755-8700
E: thebear@beebroadcasting.com
W: http://www.kdbr.com
Editorial Profile: KDBR-FM is a commercial station owned by Bee Broadcasting Inc. The format of the station is contemporary country. KDBR-FM broadcasts to the Kalispell, MT area at 106.7 FM.

KDBS-AM
Owner: Cenla Broadcasting Inc.
Editorial: 1115 Texas Ave, Alexandria, Louisiana 71301. **T:** 1 318 445-1234
W: http://www.espn1410.com
Editorial Profile: KDBS-AM is a commercial station owned by Cenla Broadcasting Inc. The format of the station is sports. KDBS-AM broadcasts to the Alexandria, LA area at 1410 AM.

KDBX-FM
Owner: Three Eagles Communications Co.
Editorial: 227 22nd Ave S, Brookings, South Dakota 57006. **T:** 1 605 692-9125
E: kjjqnews@brookings.net
W: http://www.brookingsradio.com
Editorial Profile: KDBX-FM is a commercial station owned by Three Eagles Communications Co. The format of the station is classic hits. KDBX-FM broadcasts to the Brookings, SD area at 107.1 FM.

KDCC-AM
Owner: Dodge City Community College
Editorial: 3004 N 14th Ave, Dodge City, Kansas 67801. **T:** 1 620 225-6783
W: http://www.dc3.edu
Editorial Profile: KDCC-AM is a non-commercial station owned by Dodge City Community College. The format of the station is sports. KDCC-AM broadcasts to the Dodge City, KS area at 1550.

KDCD-FM
Owner: Four R Broadcasting
Editorial: 3434 Sherwood Way, San Angelo, Texas 76901. **T:** 1 325 947-0899
E: office@lonestar-mdx.com
W: http://www.kdcdradio.com
Editorial Profile: KDCD-FM is a commercial station owned by Four R Broadcasting. The format for the station is classic country. KDCD-FM broadcasts to the San Angelo, TX area at 92.9 FM.

KDCE-AM
Owner: Rio Chama Broadcasting
Editorial: 403 W Pueblo Dr, Espanola, New Mexico 87532-2530. **T:** 1 505 753-2201
E: kdce@zianet.com
W: http://www.kdceradio.com
Editorial Profile: KDCE-AM is a commercial station owned by Rio Chama Broadcasting. The format of the station is Latin music and Spanish news and talk. KDCE-AM broadcasts to the Albuquerque, NM area at 950 AM.

KDCQ-FM
Owner: Bay Cities Building Company Inc.
Editorial: 3120 Broadway St, North Bend, Oregon 97459-2223. **T:** 1 541 269-0929
E: news@kdcq.com **W:** http://www.kdcq.com
Editorial Profile: KDCQ-FM is a commercial station owned by Bay Cities Building Company Inc. The format of the station is classic hits music. KDCQ-FM broadcasts to the North Bend, OR area at 92.9 FM.

KDCR-FM
Owner: Dordt College
Editorial: 498 4th Ave NE, Sioux Center, Iowa 51250. **T:** 1 712 722-0885 **E:** kdcr@dordt.edu
W: http://www.kdcr.dordt.edu
Editorial Profile: KDCR-FM is a non-commercial station owned by Dordt College. The format of the station is Christian music and talk. KDCR-FM broadcasts to the Sioux Center, IA area at 88.5 FM.

KDCZ-FM
Owner: Cumulus Media Inc.
Editorial: 122 4th St SW, Rochester, Minnesota 55902. **T:** 1 507 286-1010
W: http://www.zrock1077.com
Editorial Profile: KDCZ-FM is a commercial station owned by Cumulus Media Inc. The format of the station is rock. KDCZ-FM broadcasts to the Rochester, MN area at 103.9 FM.

KDDB-FM
Owner: Ohana Broadcast Company LLC
Editorial: 1000 Bishop St Ste 200, Honolulu, Hawaii 96813-4203. **T:** 1 808 947-1500
W: http://www.1027dabomb.net
Editorial Profile: KDDB-FM is a commercial station owned by Ohana Broadcast Company LLC. The format of the station is rhythmic Top 40/CHR. KDDB-FM broadcasts to the Honolulu area on 102.7.

KDDD-AM
Owner: PBI, LLC
Editorial: 408 N Dumas Ave, Dumas, Texas 79029-2445. **T:** 1 806 983-5704
E: kflp@kflp.net **W:** http://www.allagnews.com
Editorial Profile: KDDD-AM is a commercial station owned by PBI, LLC. The format of the station is farm and agriculture. KDDD-AM broadcasts to the Dumas-Amarillo, TX area at 800 AM.

KDDD-FM
Owner: PBI, LLC
Editorial: 408 N Dumas Ave, Dumas, Texas 79029. **T:** 1 806 935-4141
E: kddd@cableone.net
W: http://www.kddd953fm.com
Editorial Profile: KDDD-FM is a commercial station owned by PBI, LLC. The format of the station is oldies. KDDD-FM broadcasts to the Dumas, TX area at 95.3 FM.

KDDG-FM
Owner: StarCom LLC
Editorial: 35223 238th Ave, Albany, Minnesota 56307. **T:** 1 320 845-2184
W: http://kasmradio.com
Editorial Profile: KDDG-FM is a commercial station owned by StarCom LLC. The format of the station is classic country. KDDG-FM broadcasts to the Albany, MN area at 105.5 FM.

KDDK-FM
Owner: Radio and Investments, Inc.
Editorial: 59420 Highway 1148, Plaquemine, Louisana 70764-5227. **T:** 1 225 344-2882
E: kddk@bellsouth.net
W: http://www.kddkfm.com
Editorial Profile: KDDK-FM is a commercial station owned by Radio and Investments, Inc. The format of the station is tropical Spanish. KDDK-FM broadcasts to the Addis, LA area at a frequency of 105.5 FM.

KDDQ-FM
Owner: Perry Publishing & Broadcasting Inc.
Editorial: 1701 W Pine Ave, Duncan, Oklahoma 73533. **T:** 1 580 355-1050
W: http://www.perry-pub-broadcasting.com/kddq/

KDDR-AM
Owner: Ingstad Family Media
Editorial: 412 Main Ave, Oakes, North Dakota 58474-1600. **T:** 1 701 742-2187
E: letters@amfmradio.biz
W: http://www.newsdakota.com
Editorial Profile: KDDR-AM is a commercial station owned by Ingstad Family Media. The format of the station is country music. KDDR-AM broadcasts to the Oakes, ND area at 1220 AM.

KDDS-FM
Owner: Adelante Media Group
Editorial: 1400 W Main St, Auburn, Washington 98001. **T:** 1 253 735-9700
W: http://radiolagrande993.com
Editorial Profile: KDDS-FM is a commercial station owned by Adelante Media Group. The format of the station is Hispanic programming. KDDS-FM broadcasts to the Olympia, WA area at 99.3 FM.

KDDX-FM
Owner: Duhamel Broadcasting
Editorial: 2827 E Colorado Blvd, Spearfish, South Dakota 57783-9703. **T:** 1 605 642-5747
W: http://www.xrock.fm
Editorial Profile: KDDX-FM is a commercial station owned by Duhamel Broadcasting. The format of the station is rock. KDDX-FM broadcasts to the Spearfish, SD area at 101.1 FM.

KDDZ-AM
Owner: Walt Disney Co.
Editorial: 12136 W Bayaud Ave, Ste 125, Lakewood, Colorado 80228-2115.
T: 1 303 783-0880
W: http://radio.disney.go.com/music/yourstation/denver/index.html
Editorial Profile: KDDZ-AM is a commercial station owned by Walt Disney Co. The format of the station is children's programming. KDDZ-AM broadcasts to the Denver area at 1690 AM.

KDEC-AM
Owner: Decorah Broadcasting Inc.
Editorial: 110 Highland Dr, Decorah, Iowa 52101-1102. **T:** 1 563 382-4251
E: kdec@kdecradio.net **W:** http://kdecradio.net
Editorial Profile: KDEC-AM is a commercial station owned by Decorah Broadcasting Inc. The format of the station is adult standards, easy listening and news. KDEC-AM broadcasts to the Cedar Rapids, IA area at 1240 AM.

KDEC-FM
Owner: Decorah Broadcasting Inc.
Editorial: 110 Highland Dr, Decorah, Iowa 52101-1102. **T:** 1 563 382-4251
E: kdec@kdecradio.net **W:** http://kdecradio.net
Editorial Profile: KDEC-FM is a commercial station owned by Decorah Broadcasting Inc. The format for the station is adult album alternative. KDEC-FM broadcasts to the Cedar Rapids, IA area at 100.5 FM.

KDEF-AM
Owner: RAMH Corp.
Editorial: 10424 Edith Blvd Ne, Albuquerque, New Mexico 87113-2408. **T:** 1 505 888-1150
Editorial Profile: KDEF-AM is a commercial station owned by the RAMH Corp. The format of the station is sports, featuring Yahoo! Sports radio programming. KDEF-AM broadcasts to the Albuquerque, NM area at 1150 AM.

KDEL-FM
Owner: Southwest Arkansas Media, LLC
Editorial: 601 S 7th St, Arkadelphia, Arkansas 71923-6209. **T:** 1 870 246-9272
W: http://www.arkadelphiaradio.com
Editorial Profile: KDEL-FM is a commercial station owned by Southwest Arkansas Media, LLC. The format of the station is classic rock. KDEL-FM broadcasts to the Arkadelphia, AR area at 100.9 FM.

KDEM-FM
Owner: Luna County Broadcasting
Editorial: 1700 S Gold Ave, Deming, New Mexico 88030-5839. **T:** 1 575 546-9011
E: radio@demingradio.com
W: http://www.demingradio.com
Editorial Profile: KDEM-FM is a commercial station owned by Luna County Broadcasting. The format of the station is adult contemporary music. KDEM-FM broadcasts to the Albuquerque, NM area at 94.3 FM.

KDEP-FM
Owner: Alexandra Communications Inc.
Editorial: 170 3Rd St, Tillamook, Oregon 97141-9489. **T:** 1 503 842-4422
W: http://www.coast105.com
Editorial Profile: KDEP-FM is a commercial station owned by Alexandra Communications Inc. The format is oldies. KDEP-FM broadcasts to the Tillamook, OR at 105.5 FM.

KDES-FM
Owner: R & R Radio Corp.
Editorial: 2100 E Tahquitz Canyon Way, Palm Springs, California 92262. **T:** 1 760 325-2582
W: http://www.kdes.com
Editorial Profile: KDES-FM is a commercial station owned by R & R Radio Corp. The format of the station is oldies. KDES-FM broadcasts to the Palm Springs, CA area at 98.5 FM.

KDET-AM
Owner: Center Broadcasting Company Inc.
Editorial: 307 San Augustine St, Center, Texas 75935. **T:** 1 936 598-3304
Editorial Profile: KDET-AM is a commercial station owned by Center Broadcasting Company Inc. The format for the station is talk. KDET-AM broadcasts to the Shreveport, LA, area at 930 AM.

KDET-FM
Owner: Center Broadcasting Company Inc.
Editorial: 307 San Augustine St, Center, Texas 75935. **T:** 1 936 275-3242
Editorial Profile: KDET-FM is a commercial station owned by Center Broadcasting Company Inc. The format of the station is Spanish talk. KDET-FM broadcasts to the Center, TX area at 92.5 FM.

KDEW-FM
Owner: Arkansas County Broadcasters Inc.
Editorial: 1818 S Buerkle St, Stuttgart, Arkansas 72160-5804. **T:** 1 870 673-1595
E: kdew973@yahoo.com
W: http://www.country973.com
Editorial Profile: KDEW-FM is a commercial station owned by Arkansas County Broadcasters Inc. The format of the station is contemporary country. KDEW-FM broadcasts to the Stuttgart, AR area at 97.3 FM.

KDEX-AM
Owner: Dexter Broadcasting Inc.
Editorial: 20487 State Highway 114, Dexter, Missouri 63841. **T:** 1 573 624-3545
E: kdex1@sbcglobal.net
Editorial Profile: KDEX-AM is a commercial station owned by Dexter Broadcasting Inc. The format of the station is contemporary country. KDEX-AM broadcasts to the Dexter, MO area at 102.3 FM.

KDEX-FM
Owner: Dexter Broadcasting Inc.
Editorial: 20487 State Highway 114, Dexter, Missouri 63841. **T:** 1 573 624-3545
E: kdex1@sbcglobal.net
Editorial Profile: KDEX-FM is a commercial station owned by Dexter Broadcasting Inc. The format of the station is country music. KDEX-FM broadcasts in the Dexter, MO area at 102.3 FM.

KDEY-FM
Owner: Meruelo Group
Editorial: 5055 Wilshire Blvd Ste 720, Los Angeles, California 90036-6107.
T: 1 323 337-1600
W: http://www.935kday.com
Editorial Profile: KDEY-FM is a commercial station owned by Meruelo Group. The format of the station is R&B oldies and classic hip-hop. KDEY-FM broadcasts to the Inland Empire, CA area at 93.5 FM.

KDEZ-FM
Owner: Townsquare Media, Inc.
Editorial: 5100 S Tennis Ln, Sioux Falls, South Dakota 57108-2212. **T:** 1 605 361-0300
W: http://www.easy1001.com
Editorial Profile: KDEZ-FM is a commercial station owned by Townsquare Media, Inc. The format of the station is adult contemporary. KDEZ-FM broadcasts to the Sioux Falls, SD area at 100.1 FM.

KDFM-FM
Owner: Bernal(Paulino)
Editorial: 4501 N McColl Rd, McAllen, Texas 78504. **T:** 1 956 781-5528
W: http://www.nuevaradiocristiana.com
Editorial Profile: KDFM-FM is a commercial station owned by Paulino Bernal. The format of the station is Hispanic contemporary Christian music. KDFM-FM broadcasts to the McAllen, TX area at 103.3 FM.

KDFO-FM
Owner: Clear Channel Media and Entertainment
Editorial: 1100 Mohawk St, Ste 280, Bakersfield, California 93309.
T: 1 661 322-9929
W: http://www.985thefox.com
Editorial Profile: KDFO-FM is a commercial station owned by Clear Channel Media and Entertainment. The format of the station is classic rock. KDFO-FM broadcasts to the Bakersfield, CA area at 98.5 FM.

KDFR-FM
Owner: Family Stations Inc.
Editorial: 2350 NE 44th Ct, Des Moines, Iowa 50317. **T:** 1 515 262-0449 **E:** kdfr@qwest.net
W: http://www.familyradio.com
Editorial Profile: KDFR-FM is a non-commercial station owned by Family Stations Inc. The format of the station is religion. KDFR-FM broadcasts to the Des Moines, IA area at 91.3 FM.

KDFT-AM
Owner: Multicultural Radio Broadcasting Inc.
Editorial: 5801 Marvin D Love Fwy, Ste 409, Dallas, Texas 75237. **T:** 1 972 572-1540
E: kdft-kmny@mrbi.net
W: http://www.kdft540.com
Editorial Profile: KDFT-AM is a commercial station owned by Multicultural Radio Broadcasting Inc. The format of the station is Hispanic religious programming. KDFT-AM broadcasts to the Dallas area at 540 AM.

KDGE-FM
Owner: Clear Channel Media and Entertainment
Editorial: 14001 Dallas Pkwy, Ste 300, Dallas, Texas 75240. **T:** 1 214 866-8000
W: http://www.kdge.com
Editorial Profile: KDGE-FM is a commercial station owned by Clear Channel Media and Entertainment. The format of the station is rock alternative. KDGE-FM broadcasts to the Dallas area at 102.1 FM.

KDGL-FM
Owner: Morris Communications
Editorial: 1321 N Gene Autry Trl, Palm Springs, California 92262. **T:** 1 760 322-7890
W: http://www.theeagle1069.com
Editorial Profile: KDGL-FM is a commercial station owned by Morris Communications. The format of the station is classic hits music. KDGL-FM broadcasts to the Palm Springs, CA area at 106.9 FM.

KDGO-AM
Owner: American General Media
Editorial: 1911 Main Ave Ste 100, Durango, Colorado 81301-5079. **T:** 1 970 247-1240
W: http://www.kdgoam.com
Editorial Profile: KDGO-AM is a commercial station owned by American General Media. The format of the station is news and talk. KDGO-AM broadcasts to the Albuquerque, NM area at 1240 AM.

KDGS-FM
Owner: Entercom Communications Corp.
Editorial: 2120 N Woodlawn St, Ste 352, Wichita, Kansas 67208. **T:** 1 316 685-2121
W: http://www.power939.com
Editorial Profile: KDGS-FM is a commercial station owned by Entercom Communications Corp. The format of the station is rhythmic Top 40/CHR music. KDGS-FM broadcasts to the Wichita, KS area at 93.9 FM.

KDHL-AM
Owner: Townsquare Media, LLC
Editorial: 601 Central Ave N, Faribault, Minnesota 55021-4307. **T:** 1 507 334-0061
W: http://www.kdhlradio.com
Editorial Profile: KDHL-AM is a commercial station owned by Townsquare Media, LLC. The format of the station is country music. KDHL-AM broadcasts to the Faribault, MN area at 920 AM.

KDHN-AM
Owner: Collins Communications Co.
Editorial: 704 W Cleveland St, Dimmitt, Texas 79027. **T:** 1 806 647-4161
E: kdhn1984@yahoo.com
Editorial Profile: KDHN-AM is a commercial station owned by Collins Communications Co. The format of the station is country. KDHN-AM broadcasts to the Dimmitt, TX area at 1470 AM.

KDHT-FM
Owner: Max Media of Colorado
Editorial: 3033 S Parker Rd Ste 700, Aurora, Colorado 80014-2923. **T:** 1 303 872-1500
W: http://www.project107x.com
Editorial Profile: KDHT-FM is a commercial station owned by Max Media of Colorado. The format of the station is alternative rock. KDHT-FM broadcasts to the Aurora, CO area at 107.1 FM.

KDHX-FM
Owner: Double Helix Corporation
Editorial: 3504 Magnolia Ave, Saint Louis, Missouri 63118-1134. **T:** 1 314 664-3955
E: spam@kdhx.org **W:** http://www.kdhx.org
Editorial Profile: KDHX-FM is a non-commercial station owned by Double Helix Corporation. The format of the station is a variety of music and talk. KDHX-FM broadcasts to the St. Louis area at 88.1 FM.

KDIA-AM
Owner: Baybridge Communications
Editorial: 3260 Blume Dr Ste 520, Richmond, California 94806-5715. **T:** 1 510 222-4242
W: http://www.kdia.com
Editorial Profile: KDIA-AM is a non-commercial station owned by Baybridge Communications. The format of the station is Christian talk. KDIA-AM broadcasts in the Richmond, CA area at 1640 AM.

KDIC-FM
Owner: Trustees of Grinnell College
Editorial: 1115 8th Ave, Grinnell, Iowa 50112.
T: 1 641 269-3335 **E:** kdicfm@grinnell.edu
W: http://kdic.grinnell.edu
Editorial Profile: KDIC-FM is a non-commercial station owned by Trustees of Grinnell College. The format of the station is variety. KDIC-FM broadcasts to the Grinnel, IA area at 88.5 FM.

KDIO-AM
Owner: Armada Media Corp.
Editorial: 47 2nd St NW, Ortonville, Minnesota 56278. **T:** 1 320 839-2581
W: http://www.bigstoneradio.com
Editorial Profile: KDIO-AM is a commercial station owned by Armada Media Corp. The format of the station is classic country music and talk. KDIO-AM broadcasts to the Ortonville, MN area at 1350 AM.

KDIS-AM
Owner: Walt Disney Co.
Editorial: 3800 W Alameda Ave, Burbank, California 91505-4300. **T:** 1 818 569-5000
W: http://radio.disney.go.com/music/yourstation/losangeles/index.html
Editorial Profile: KDIS-AM is a commercial station owned by Walt Disney Co. The format of the station is children's music. KDIS-AM broadcasts to the Los Angeles area at 1110 AM.

KDIS-FM
Owner: Salem Communications
Editorial: 415 N McKinley St Ste 610, Little Rock, Arkansas 72205-3168.
T: 1 501 404-6560 **W:** http://faithtalk995.com
Editorial Profile: KDIS-FM a commercial station owned by Salem Communications. The format of the station is Christian talk programming. KDIS-FM broadcasts to the Little Rock, AR area at 99.5 FM.

KDIX-AM
Owner: Starrdak Inc.
Editorial: 119 2nd Ave W, Dickinson, North Dakota 58601. **T:** 1 701 225-5133
E: kdix@kdix.net **W:** http://www.kdix.net
Editorial Profile: KDIX-AM is a commercial station owned by Starrdak Inc. The format of the station is classic hits. KDIX-AM broadcasts to the Dickinson, ND area at 1230 AM.

KDIZ-AM
Owner: Walt Disney Co.
Editorial: 2000 Elm St SE, Minneapolis, Minnesota 55414-2531. **T:** 1 612 617-4000
W: http://radio.disney.go.com/music/yourstation/minneapolis/index.html

KDJE-FM
Owner: Clear Channel Media and Entertainment
Editorial: 10800 Colonel Glenn Rd, Little Rock, Arkansas 72204-8017.
T: 1 501 217-5000
W: http://www.edgelittlerock.com
Editorial Profile: KDJE-FM is a commercial station owned by Clear Channel Media and Entertainment. The format of the station is rock alternative. KDJE-FM broadcasts to the Little Rock, AR area at 100.3 FM.

KDJI-AM
Owner: Petracom
Editorial: 1838 Commerce Dr, Ste A, Lakeside, Arizona 85929. **T:** 1 928 532-3232
Editorial Profile: KDJI-AM is a commercial station owned by Petracom. The format of the station is news and talk. KDJI-AM broadcasts in the Phoenix area at 1270 AM.

KDJK-FM
Owner: Cumulus Media Inc
Editorial: 3136 Boeing Way, Stockton, California 95206. **T:** 1 209 766-5000
E: 104.1thehawk@cumulus.com
W: http://www.104thehawk.com
Editorial Profile: KDJK-FM is a commercial station owned by Cumulus Media Inc. The format of the station is classic rock music. KDJK-FM broadcasts in the Mariposa, CA area at 103.9 FM.

KDJM-FM
Owner: Rocking M Radio
Editorial: 1065 S Range Ave, Colby, Kansas 67701-3505. **T:** 1 785 462-3305
Editorial Profile: KDJM-FM is a commercial station owned by Rocking M Radio. The format of the station is classic country. KJDM-FM broadcasts to the Salina, KS area at a frequency of 101.7 FM.

KDJS-AM
Owner: Iowa City Broadcasting Co.
Editorial: 730 Highway 71 NE, Willmar, Minnesota 56201. **T:** 1 320 231-1600
W: http://www.k-musicradio.com
Editorial Profile: KDJS-AM is a commercial station owned by Iowa City Broadcasting Co. The format of the station is oldies. KDJS-AM broadcasts to the Willmar, MN area at 1590 AM.

KDJS-FM
Owner: Iowa City Broadcasting Co.
Editorial: 730 Highway 71 NE, Willmar, Minnesota 56201. **T:** 1 320 231-1600
W: http://www.k-musicradio.com
Editorial Profile: KDJS-FM is a commercial station owned by Iowa City Broadcasting Co. The format of the station is country music. KDJS-FM broadcasts to the Willmar, MN area at 95.3 FM.

KDJW-AM
Owner: Dale Artho
Editorial: 701 S Pierce St, Ste 101, Amarillo, Texas 79101-2428. **T:** 1 806 350-1360
E: stval@kdjw.org **W:** http://www.kdjw.org
Editorial Profile: KDJW-AM is a commercial station owned by Dale Artho. The format of the station is Catholic talk programming. KDJW-AM broadcasts to the Amarillo, TX area at 1360 AM.

KDKA-AM
Owner: CBS Radio
Editorial: 651 Holiday Dr, Pittsburgh, Pennsylvania 15220-2740. **T:** 1 412 353-1320
E: radionews@kdka.com
W: http://pittsburgh.cbslocal.com/station/newsradio-1020-kdka/
Editorial Profile: KDKA-AM is a commercial station owned by CBS Radio. The format of the station is news and talk programming. KDKA-AM broadcasts to the Pittsburgh area at 1020 AM.

KDKA-FM
Owner: CBS Radio
Editorial: 651 Holiday Dr, 2nd fl, Pittsburgh, Pennsylvania 15220. **T:** 1 412 920-9400
W: http://www.937thefan.com
Editorial Profile: KDKA-FM is a commercial station owned by CBS Radio. The format of the station is sports. KDKA-FM broadcasts to the Pittsburgh area at 93.7 FM.

KDKB-FM
Owner: Hubbard Radio, LLC
Editorial: 1167 W Javelina Ave, Mesa, Arizona 85210-5936. **T:** 1 480 897-9300
W: http://www.kdkb.com
Editorial Profile: KDKB-FM is a commercial station owned by Hubbard Radio, LLC. The format of the station is rock music. KDKB-FM broadcasts to the Mesa, AZ area at 93.3 FM.

KDKD-AM
Owner: Goodradio.TV LLC
Editorial: 2201 N Antioch St, Clinton, Missouri 64735-1119. **T:** 1 660 885-6141
E: pleasants@kdkd.net **W:** http://www.kdkd.net
Editorial Profile: KDKD-AM is a commercial station owned by Goodradio.TV LLC. The format of the station is oldies music. KDKD-AM broadcasts to the Clinton, MO area at 1280 AM.

KDKD-FM
Owner: Goodradio.TV LLC
Editorial: 2201 N Antioch St, Clinton, Missouri 64735-1119. **T:** 1 660 885-6141
E: pleasants@kdkd.net **W:** http://www.kdkd.net
Editorial Profile: KDKD-FM is commercial station owned by Goodradio.TV LLC. The format of the station is contemporary country

music. KDKD-FM broadcasts to the Kansas City, MO area at 95.3 FM.

KDKK-FM
Owner: De La Hunt Broadcasting
Editorial: Highway 34 East, Park Rapids, Minnesota 56470. **T:** 1 218 732-3306
E: kprmkdkk@unitelc.com
W: http://www.kkradionetwork.com
Editorial Profile: KDKK-FM is a commercial station owned by De La Hunt Broadcasting. The format of the station is adult standards music. KDKK-FM in the Park Rapids, MN area at 97.5 FM.

KDKN-FM
Owner: Dockins Broadcast Group
Editorial: 1910 Greenwood Dr #A, Poplar Bluff, Missouri 63901-2430.
T: 1 573 686-1067
W: http://www.1067zone.com
Editorial Profile: KDKN-FM is a commercial station owned by Dockins Broadcast Group. The format of the station is alternative rock music. KDKN-FM broadcasts to the Poplar Bluff, MO area at a frequency of 106.7 FM.

KDKR-FM
Owner: Penfold Communications, Inc.
Editorial: 5617 Diamond Oaks Dr S Ste 200, Fort Worth, Texas 76117-2804.
T: 1 817 831-9130 **W:** http://www.kdkr.org
Editorial Profile: KDKR-FM is a non-commercial station owned by Penfold Communications, Inc. The format of the station is Christian talk and music programming. KDKR-FM broadcasts to the Fort Worth, TX area at 91.3 FM.

KDKS-FM
Owner: Access.1 Communications Corp.
Editorial: 208 N Thomas Dr, Shreveport, Louisiana 71107-6520. **T:** 1 318 222-3122
W: http://www.kdks.fm
Editorial Profile: KDKS-FM is a commercial station owned by Access.1 Communications Corp. The format of the station is urban adult contemporary. KDKS-FM broadcasts to the Shreveport, LA area at 102.1 FM.

KDKT-AM
Owner: Digital Syndicate Network LLC
Editorial: 850 County 21, Beulah, North Dakota 58523-9566. **T:** 1 701 873-2215
E: info@foxsports1410.com
W: http://www.foxsports1410.com
Editorial Profile: KDKT-AM is a commercial station owned by Digital Syndicate Network LLC. The format of the station is sports. KDKT-AM broadcasts in the Beulah, ND area at 1410 AM.

KDLD-FM
Owner: Entravision Communications Corp.
Editorial: 5700 Wilshire Blvd, Ste 250, Los Angeles, California 90036. **T:** 1 323 900-6100
W: http://www.elgato1031.com
Editorial Profile: KDLD-FM is a commercial station owned by Entravision Communications Corp. The format of the station is regional Mexican. KDLD-FM broadcasts to the greater Los Angeles area at 103.1 FM.

KDLE-FM
Owner: Entravision Communications Corp.
Editorial: 5700 Wilshire Blvd, Ste 250, Los Angeles, California 90036. **T:** 1 323 900-6100
W: http://www.elgato1031.com
Editorial Profile: KDLE-FM is a commercial station owned by Entravision Communications Corp. The format of the station is regional Mexican. KDLE-FM broadcasts to the Newport Beach, CA area at 103.1 FM and simulcasts the programming of KDLD-FM.

KDLF-AM
Owner: Latin World Broadcasting
Editorial: 900 8th St, Boone, Iowa 50036-2920. **T:** 1 515 287-0055
Editorial Profile: KDLF-AM is a commercial station owned by Latin World Broadcasting. The format of the station is Hispanic. Christian and religious talk. KDLF-AM broadcasts to the Boone, IA area at 1260 AM.

KDLG-AM
Owner: Dillingham City Schools
Editorial: 565 Seward St, Dillingham, Alaska 99576. **T:** 1 907 842-5281 **E:** info@kdlg.org
W: http://www.kdlg.org
Editorial Profile: KDLG-AM is a non-commercial station owned by Dillingham City Schools. The format of the station is a variety of musical genres, news, and public affairs. KDLG-AM broadcasts to the Dillingham, AK area at 670 AM.

KDLK-FM
Owner: Forum Broadcasting Inc.
Editorial: 107 Center Dr, Del Rio, Texas 78840-3015. **T:** 1 830 775-9583
E: frontdesk@kdlk.com
W: http://www.kdlk.com
Editorial Profile: KDLK-FM is a commercial station owned by Forum Broadcasting Inc. The format of the station is contemporary country music. KDLK-FM broadcasts to the Del Rio, TX area at 94.1 FM.

KDLL-FM
Owner: Pickle Hill Public Broadcasting
Editorial: 14896 Kenai Spur Hwy, Kenai, Alaska 99611-7014. **T:** 1 907 283-8433
W: http://www.kdll.org
Editorial Profile: KDLL-FM is a non-commercial station owned by Pickle Hill Public Broadcasting. The format of the station is news and talk programming. KDLL-FM broadcasts to the Kenai, AK area at 91.9 FM.

KDLM-AM
Owner: Leighton Enterprises Inc.
Editorial: 1340 Richwood Rd, Detroit Lakes, Minnesota 56501. **T:** 1 218 847-5624
E: news@1340kdlm.com
W: http://www.1340kdlm.com
Editorial Profile: KDLM-AM is a commercial station owned by Leighton Enterprises Inc. The format of the station is news, talk, and sports. KDLM-AM broadcasts to the Detroit Lakes, MN area at 1340 AM.

KDLO-FM
Owner: Three Eagles Communications Co.
Editorial: 921 9th Ave SE, Watertown, South Dakota 57201. **T:** 1 605 882-1597
W: http://www.kdlocountry.com
Editorial Profile: KDLO-FM is a commercial station owned by Three Eagles Communications Co. The format of the station is classic country. KDLO-FM broadcasts to the Watertown, SD area at and 96.9 FM.

KDLR-AM
Owner: Double Z Broadcasting Inc.
Editorial: 320 Walnut St W, Devils Lake, North Dakota 58301-3506. **T:** 1 701 662-2161
E: kdlrkdvl@gondtc.com
W: http://www.lrradioworks.com/kdlr.htm
Editorial Profile: KDLR-AM is a commercial station owned by Double Z Broadcasting Inc. The format of the station is country music and news. KDLR-AM broadcasts to the Devils Lake, ND area at 1240 AM.

KDLS-FM
Owner: Latin Broadcasting Company
Editorial: 950 Office Park Rd Ste 212, West Des Moines, Iowa 50265-2548.
T: 1 515 278-4117 **E:** laley105@yahoo.com
Editorial Profile: KDLS-FM is a commercial station owned by Latin Broadcasting Company. The format of the station is Regional Mexican. KDLS-FM broadcasts to the Perry, IA area at a frequency of 105.5 FM.

KDLW-FM
Owner: American General Media
Editorial: 4125 Carlisle Blvd NE, Albuquerque, New Mexico 87107-4806. **T:** 1 505 878-0980
W: http://z1063.com
Editorial Profile: KDLW-FM is a commercial station owned by American General Media. The format of the station is Top 40/CHR. KDLW-FM broadcasts to the Albuquerque, NM area at 106.3 FM.

KDLX-FM
Owner: Visionary Related Entertainment
Editorial: 1900 Main St, Wailuku, Hawaii 96793-1900. **T:** 1 808 244-9145
E: kaoi@kaoi.net

KDLY-FM
Owner: Kenney(Joseph R. and Andrea L.)
Editorial: 1530 Main St, Lander, Wyoming 82520. **T:** 1 307 332-5683
E: radio1@wyoming.com
W: http://www.kdlykove.com
Editorial Profile: KDLY-FM is a commercial station owned by Joseph R. and Andrea L. Kenney. The format for the station is classic hits. KDLY-FM broadcasts to the Casper-Riverton, WY area at 97.5 FM.

KDMA-AM
Owner: Iowa City Broadcasting Co.
Editorial: 4454 Highway 212, Montevideo, Minnesota 56265-4539. **T:** 1 320 269-8815
E: kdmaprod@radiokdma.com
Editorial Profile: KDMA-AM is a commercial station owned by Iowa City Broadcasting Co.. The format of the station is country music. KDMA-AM broadcasts in the Montevideo, MN area at 1460 AM.

KDMG-FM
Owner: Pritchard Broadcasting Co.
Editorial: 1610 N 4th Street, Suite 300, Burlington, Iowa 52601. **T:** 1 319 752-5402
E: bigcountry1031@bigcountry1031.com
W: http://www.bigcountry1031.com
Editorial Profile: KDMG-FM is a commercial station owned by Pritchard Broadcasting Co. The format of the station is country. KDMG-FM broadcasts to the Burlington, IA area at 103.1 FM.

KDMO-AM
Owner: Petersen(Ronald L.)
Editorial: 221 E 4th St, Carthage, Missouri 64836. **T:** 1 417 358-7953
Editorial Profile: KDMO-AM is a commercial station owned by Ronald L. Petersen. The format of the station is adult standards. KDMO-AM broadcasts to the Carthage, MO area at 1490 AM.

KDMS-AM
Owner: El Dorado Broadcasting
Editorial: 1904 W Hillsboro St, El Dorado, Arkansas 71730-6806. **T:** 1 870 863-5121
E: klbqfm@yahoo.com
Editorial Profile: KDMS-AM is a commercial station owned by El Dorado Broadcasting. The format of the station is gospel music and country. KDMS-AM broadcasts in the El Dorado, AR area at 1290 AM.

KDMX-FM
Owner: Clear Channel Media and Entertainment
Editorial: 14001 Dallas Pkwy Ste 300, Dallas, Texas 75240-7369. **T:** 1 214 866-8000
E: psa@ccdallas.com
W: http://www.1029now.com
Editorial Profile: KDMX-FM is a commercial station owned by Clear Channel Media and Entertainment. The format of the station is hot adult contemporary. KDMX-FM broadcasts to the Dallas area at 102.9 FM.

KDNA-FM
Owner: Northwest Communities Education Center
Editorial: 121 Sunnyside Ave, Granger, Washington 98932. **T:** 1 509 854-2222
E: noticias@kdna.org **W:** http://www.kdna.org
Editorial Profile: KDNA-FM is a non-commercial station owned by Northwest Communities Education Center. The format of the station is Hispanic educational programming. KDNA-FM broadcasts to the Granger, WA area at 91.9 FM.

KDND-FM
Owner: Entercom Communications Corp.
Editorial: 5345 Madison Ave, Sacramento, California 95841-3141. **T:** 1 916 334-7777
W: http://www.endonline.com
Editorial Profile: KDND-FM is a commercial station owned by Entercom Communications Corp. The format of the station is Top 40/CHR. KDND-FM broadcasts to the Sacramento, CA area at 107.9 FM.

KDNE-FM
Owner: Doane College Board of Trustees
Editorial: 1014 Boswell Ave, Crete, Nebraska 68333. **T:** 1 402 826-8677 **E:** kdne@doane.edu
W: http://www.doane.edu/FacStaff/Media/KDNE
Editorial Profile: KDNE-FM is a non-commercial station owned by Doane College Board of Trustees. The format of the station is variety. KDNE-FM broadcasts to the Crete, NE area at 91.9 FM.

KDNG-FM
Owner: KUTE Inc.
Editorial: 123 Capote Drive, Ignacio, Colorado 81137. **T:** 1 970 563-0255
W: http://www.ksut.org
Editorial Profile: KDNG-FM is a non-commercial station owned by KUTE Inc. The format of the station is variety. KDNG-FM broadcasts to the Durango, CO area at 89.3 FM.

KDNI-FM
Owner: Northwestern College
Editorial: 1101 E Central Entrance, Duluth, Minnesota 55811. **T:** 1 218 722-6700
W: http://www.life973.com
Editorial Profile: KDNI-FM is a non-commercial station owned by Northwestern College. The format of the station is Christian talk. KDNI-FM broadcasts to the Duluth, MN area at 90.5 FM.

KDNK-FM
Owner: Carbondale Community Access Radio
Editorial: 76 S 2nd St, Carbondale, Colorado 81623. **T:** 1 970 963-0139
W: http://www.kdnk.org
Editorial Profile: KDNK-FM is a commercial station owned by Carbondale Community Access Radio. The format of the station is variety. KDNK-FM broadcasts to the Carbondale, CO area at 88.1 FM.

KDNN-FM
Owner: Clear Channel Media and Entertainment
Editorial: 650 Iwilei Rd Ste 400, Honolulu, Hawaii 96817-5319. **T:** 1 808 550-9200
W: http://www.island985.com
Editorial Profile: KDNN-FM is a commercial station owned by Clear Channel Media and Entertainment. The format for the station is a variety of Hawaiian and reggae music. KDNN-FM broadcasts to the Honolulu area at 98.5 FM.

KDNO-FM
Owner: CarJim LLC
Editorial: 420 Arapahoe St, Thermopolis, Wyoming 82443-2708. **T:** 1 307 864-2119
Editorial Profile: KDNO-FM is a commercial station owned by CarJim LLC. The format of the station is country music. KDNO-FM broadcasts to the Casper, WY area at 101.7 FM.

KDNS-FM
Owner: Dierking Communications
Editorial: 1937 Highway 24, Glen Elder, Kansas 67446-9461. **T:** 1 785 545-3220
E: kdnskzdy@nckcn.com
W: http://kdcountry94.com
Editorial Profile: KDNS-FM is a commercial station owned by Dierking Communications. The format of the station is country music. KDNS-FM broadcasts to the Downs, KS area at 94.1 FM.

KDNW-FM
Owner: Northwestern College
Editorial: 1101 E Central Entrance, Duluth, Minnesota 55811. **T:** 1 218 722-6700
W: http://www.life973.com
Editorial Profile: KDNW-FM is a non-commercial station owned by Northwestern College. The format of the station is contemporary Christian music and talk. KDNW-FM broadcasts to the Duluth, MN area at 97.3 FM.

KDOE-FM
Owner: Payne Radio Group
Editorial: 1600 W Jackson St, Hugo, Oklahoma 74743. **T:** 1 580 326-2555
W: http://kdoe1023.com
Editorial Profile: KDOE-FM is a commercial station owned by Payne Radio Group. The format for the station is adult contemporary. KDOE-FM broadcasts to the Antlers, OK area at 102.3 FM.

KDOG-FM
Owner: Radio Mankato
Editorial: 59346 Madison Ave, Mankato, Minnesota 56001-8518. **T:** 1 507 345-4537
E: news@ktoe.com **W:** http://www.hot967.fm
Editorial Profile: KDOG-FM is a commercial station owned by Radio Mankato. The format of the station is Top 40/CHR. KDOG-FM broadcasts in the Mankato, MN area at 96.7 FM.

KDOK-AM
Owner: Townsquare Media, LLC
Editorial: 3810 Brookside Dr, Tyler, Texas 75701. **T:** 1 903 581-0606
W: http://www.kdok1240.com
Editorial Profile: KDOK-AM is a commercial station owned by Townsquare Media, LLC. The format of the station is Urban Contemporary. KDOK-AM broadcasts to the Tyler, TX area at 1240 AM.

KDOM-AM
Owner: Results Broadcasting, Inc.
Editorial: 1450 Highway 60 71 N, Windom, Minnesota 56101. **T:** 1 507 831-3908
E: kdomnews@windomnet.com
W: http://www.kdomradio.com
Editorial Profile: KDOM-AM is a commercial station owned by Results Broadcasting, Inc. The format of the station is country music. KDOM-AM broadcasts to the Minneapolis area at 1580 AM.

KDOM-FM
Owner: Southwestern Minnesota Radio, Inc.
Editorial: 1450 Highway 60 71 N, Windom, Minnesota 56101. **T:** 1 507 831-3908

E: kdomnews@windomnet.com
W: http://www.kdomradio.com
Editorial Profile: KDOM-FM is a commercial station owned by Southwestern Minnesota Radio, Inc. The format of the station is country music. KDOM-FM broadcasts to the Minneapolis area at 94.3 FM.

KDON-FM

Owner: Clear Channel Media and Entertainment
Editorial: 903 N Main St, Salinas, California 93906. **T:** 1 831 755-8181
W: http://www.kdon.com
Editorial Profile: KDON-FM is a commercial station owned by Clear Channel Media and Entertainment. The format of the station is rhythmic Top 40/CHR music. KDON-FM broadcasts to the Salinas, CA area at 102.5 FM.

KDOT-FM

Owner: Lotus Communications Corp.
Editorial: 2900 Sutro St, Reno, Nevada 89512-1616. **T:** 1 775 329-9261
W: http://www.kdot.com
Editorial Profile: KDOT-FM is a commercial station owned by Lotus Communications Corp. The format of the station is rock. KDOT-FM broadcasts to the Reno, NV area at 104.5 FM.

KDOV-FM

Owner: UCB USA Inc.
Editorial: 1236 Disk Dr, Ste E, Medford, Oregon 97501. **T:** 1 541 776-5368
E: thedove@thedove.us
W: http://www.thedove.us
Editorial Profile: KDOV-FM is a non-commercial station owned by UCB USA Inc. The format of the station is contemporary Christian music and talk programming. KDOV-FM broadcasts in the Medford, OR area at 91.7 FM.

KDOW-AM

Owner: Salem Communications
Editorial: 39138 Fremont Blvd, Fl 3, Fremont, California 94538-1305. **T:** 1 510 713-1100
W: http://www.kdow.biz
Editorial Profile: KDOW-AM is a commercial station owned by Salem Communications. The format of the station is business talk. KDOW-AM broadcasts to the San Francisco and San Jose, CA markets at 1220 AM.

KDPS-FM

Owner: Des Moines Public Schools
Editorial: 1200 Grandview Ave, Des Moines, Iowa 50316. **T:** 1 515 263-2997
E: kdpsradio@gvc.edu
W: http://www.kdpsradio.com
Editorial Profile: KDPS-FM is a non-commercial station owned by Des Moines Public Schools. Weekday programming consists mainly of alternative rock music. KDPS-FM broadcasts to the Central Campus high school and Grand View College students at 88.1 FM.

KDQN-AM

Owner: Bunyard Broadcasting
Editorial: 921 W Collin Raye Dr, De Queen, Arkansas 71832. **T:** 1 870 642-2446
E: numberonecountry@yahoo.com
W: http://www.kdqn.net
Editorial Profile: KDQN-AM is a commercial station owned by Bunyard Broadcasting. The format of the station is Hispanic music and news. KDQN-AM broadcasts to the De Queen, AR area at 1390 AM.

KDQN-FM

Owner: Bunyard Broadcasting
Editorial: 921 W Collin Raye Dr, De Queen, Arkansas 71832. **T:** 1 870 642-2446
E: numberonecountry@yahoo.com
W: http://www.kdqn.net
Editorial Profile: KDQN-FM is a commercial station owned by Bunyard Broadcasting. The format for the station is country music. KDQN-FM broadcasts to the Shreveport, LA area at 92.1 FM.

KDRB-FM

Owner: Clear Channel Media and Entertainment
Editorial: 2141 Grand Ave, Des Moines, Iowa 50312-5303. **T:** 1 515 245-8900
W: http://www.thebusfm.com
Editorial Profile: KDRB-FM is a commercial station owned by Clear Channel Media and Entertainment. The format of the station is adult hits. KDRB-FM broadcasts in the Des Moines, IA area at 100.3 FM.

KDRF-FM

Owner: Cumulus Media Inc

Editorial: 500 4th St NW, 5th Floor, Albuquerque, New Mexico 87102-5324. **T:** 1 505 767-6700 **E:** ed@ed.fm
W: http://www.ed.fm
Editorial Profile: KDRF-FM is a commercial station owned by Cumulus Media Inc. The format of the station is adult hits. KDRF-FM broadcasts to the Albuquerque, NM area at 103.3 FM.

KDRK-FM

Owner: Mapleton Communications LLC
Editorial: 1601 E 57th Ave, Spokane, Washington 99223. **T:** 1 509 448-1000
E: themountain937@yahoo.com
W: http://www.937themountain.com
Editorial Profile: KDRK-FM is a commercial station owned by Mapleton Communications LLC. The format of the station is contemporary country. KDRK-FM broadcasts to the Spokane, WA area at 93.7 FM.

KDRM-FM

Owner: KSEM Inc.
Editorial: 2241 W Main St, Moses Lake, Washington 98837. **T:** 1 509 765-3441
E: kbsnkdrmnews@genext.net
Editorial Profile: KDRM-FM is a commercial station owned by KSEM Inc. The format of the station is hot adult contemporary. KDRM-FM broadcasts to the Spokane, WA area at 99.3 FM.

KDRO-AM

Owner: Benne Media
Editorial: 301 S Ohio Ave, Sedalia, Missouri 65301. **T:** 1 660 826-5005
E: bennemedia@bennemedia.com
W: http://www.kdro.com
Editorial Profile: KDRO-AM is a commercial station owned by Benne Media. The format of the station is classic country music. KDRO-AM broadcasts to the Kansas City, MO area at 1490 AM.

KDRS-AM

Owner: MOR Media Inc.
Editorial: 400 Tower Dr, Paragould, Arkansas 72450-4891. **T:** 1 870 236-7627
Editorial Profile: KDRS-AM is a commercial station owned by MOR Media Inc. The format of the station is Hot AC. KDRS-AM broadcasts to the Paragould, AR area at 1490 AM.

KDRS-FM

Owner: MOR Media Inc.
Editorial: 400 Tower Dr, Paragould, Arkansas 72450. **T:** 1 870 236-7627
W: http://www.neajackfm.com
Editorial Profile: KDRS-FM is a commercial station owned by MOR Media Inc. The format of the station is Jack FM. KDRS-FM broadcasts to the Paragould, AR area at 107.1 FM.

KDRY-AM

Owner: KDRY Radio Inc.
Editorial: 16414 San Pedro Ave Ste 575, San Antonio, Texas 78232-2311.
T: 1 210 545-1100 **E:** am1100@kdry.com
W: http://www.kdry.com
Editorial Profile: KDRY-AM is a commercial station owned by KDRY Radio Inc. The format of the station is religious programming. KDRY-AM broadcasts to the San Antonio area at 1100 AM.

KDSJ-AM

Owner: Goldrush Broadcasting Co.
Editorial: 745 Main St, Deadwood, South Dakota 57732. **T:** 1 605 578-1826
E: kdsj@knology.net
W: http://www.kdsj980.com

KDSK-AM

Owner: KD Radio Inc.
Editorial: 733 E Roosevelt Ave, Grants, New Mexico 87020-2113. **T:** 1 505 285-5598
W: http://kdradio.com
Editorial Profile: KDSK-AM is a commercial station owned by the KD Radio Inc.. The format of the station is oldies. KDSK-AM broadcasts to the Albuquerque, NM area at 1240 AM. The station does not accept pitches.

KDSK-FM

Owner: KD Radio Inc.
Editorial: 733 E Roosevelt Ave, Grants, New Mexico 87020-2113. **T:** 1 505 285-5598
W: http://www.kdsk.com
Editorial Profile: KDSK-FM is a commercial station owned by KD Radio Inc. The format of the station is oldies. KDSK-FM broadcasts to the Grants, NM area at 92.7 FM. The station does not accept pitches.

KDSN-AM

Owner: Mikadety Radio Inc
Editorial: 1530 Ridge Rd, Denison, Iowa 51442. **T:** 1 712 263-3141
E: info@kdsnradio.com
W: http://www.kdsnradio.com
Editorial Profile: KDSN-AM is a commercial station owned by Mikadety Radio Inc. The format of the station is country music. KDSN-AM broadcasts to the Denison, IA area at 1530 AM.

KDSN-FM

Owner: Mikadety Radio Inc
Editorial: 1530 Ridge Rd, Denison, Iowa 51442-1172. **T:** 1 712 263-3141
E: info@kdsnradio.com
W: http://www.kdsnradio.com
Editorial Profile: KDSN-FM is a commercial station owned by Mikadety Radio Inc. The format of the station is adult contemporary music. KDSN-FM broadcasts to the Denison, IA area at 107.1 FM.

KDSP-FM

Owner: Moreland Properties, LLC
Editorial: 10200 E Girard Ave, Bldg. B, Ste. #150, Denver, Colorado 80231-5591.
T: 1 720 248-4000
W: http://www.denverssportsstation.com
Editorial Profile: KDSP-FM is a commercial station owned by Moreland Properties, LLC. The format of the station is sports. KDSP-FM broadcasts to the Denver area at 102.3 FM.

KDSR-FM

Owner: Stephen Marks Enterprises
Editorial: 910 E Broadway, Williston, North Dakota 58801. **T:** 1 701 572-4478
E: kdsr@nemont.net
Editorial Profile: KDSR-FM is a commercial station owned by Stephen Marks Enterprises. The format of the station is adult hits music. KDSR-FM broadcasts to the Williston, ND area at 101.1 FM.

KDSS-FM

Owner: Coates Broadcasting Inc.
Editorial: 466 Aultman St, Ely, Nevada 89301-1551. **T:** 1 775 289-6474
E: kdssfm@sbcglobal.net
Editorial Profile: KDSS-FM is a commercial station owned by Coates Broadcasting Inc. The format of the station is country. KDSS-FM broadcasts to the Salt Lake City area at 92.7 FM.

KDST-FM

Owner: Design Homes Inc.
Editorial: 1931 20th Ave SE, Dyersville, Iowa 52040-9571. **T:** 1 563 875-8193
E: kdst993@iowatelecom.net
W: http://www.realcountryonline.com
Editorial Profile: KDST-FM is a commercial station owned by Design Homes Inc. The format of the station is classic country. KDST-FM broadcasts to the Dyersville, IA area at 99.3 FM.

KDSU-FM

Owner: North Dakota State University
Editorial: 207 5th St N, Fargo, North Dakota 58102. **T:** 1 701 241-6900
E: info@prairiepublic.org
W: http://www.prairiepublic.org
Editorial Profile: KDSU-FM is a non-commercial station owned by North Dakota State University. The format of the station is classical, jazz and news programming. KDSU-FM broadcasts to the Fargo, ND area at 91.9 FM.

KDTD-AM

Owner: Reyes Media Group
Editorial: 1701 S 55th Street, Kansas City, Missouri 66106. **T:** 1 913 287-1480
W: http://www.lagrand1340kc.com
Editorial Profile: KDTD-AM is a commercial station owned by Reyes Media Group. The format of the station is regional Mexican music. KDTD-AM broadcasts to the Kansas City, MO area at 1340 AM.

KDTH-AM

Owner: Radio Dubuque Inc.
Editorial: 346 W 8th St, Dubuque, Iowa 52001-4649. **T:** 1 563 690-0800
E: kdth@kdth.com **W:** http://www.kdth.com
Editorial Profile: KDTH-AM is a commercial station owned by Radio Dubuque Inc. The format of the station is adult standards music, news and talk programming. KDTH-AM broadcasts to the Dubuque, IA area at 1370 AM.

KDTR-FM

Owner: Spanish Peaks Broadcasting, Inc.

Editorial: 2425 W Central Ave, Ste 203, Missoula, Montana 59801. **T:** 1 406 721-6800
W: http://www.trail1033.com
Editorial Profile: KDTR-FM is a commercial station owned by Spanish Peaks Broadcasting, Inc. The format of the station is adult album alternative. KDTR-FM broadcasts to the Missoula, MT area at 103.3 FM.

KDUC-FM

Owner: Dos Costas Communications Corp.
Editorial: 29000 Radio Rd, Barstow, California 92311-1648. **T:** 1 760 256-2121
E: doscostas@yahoo.com
Editorial Profile: KDUC-FM is a commercial station owned by Dos Costas Communications Corp. The format of the station is rhythmic Top 40/CHR music. KDUC-FM broadcasts to the Barstow, CA area at 94.3 FM.

KDUK-FM

Owner: Bicoastal Media LLC
Editorial: 1500 Valley River Dr, Ste 350, Eugene, Oregon 97401. **T:** 1 541 485-1120
W: http://www.kduk.com
Editorial Profile: KDUK-FM is a commercial station owned by Bicoastal Media LLC. The format of the station is Top 40/CHR music. KDUK-FM broadcasts in the Eugene, OR at 104.7 FM.

KDUN-AM

Owner: Sand & Sea Broadcasting LLC
Editorial: 136 N 7th St, Reedsport, Oregon 97467. **T:** 1 541 271-1030
E: kdune@kdune.com
W: http://www.kdune.com

KDUR-FM

Owner: Fort Lewis College
Editorial: 1000 Rim Drive Ft Lewis College, Durango, Colorado 81301-3911.
T: 1 970 247-7634 **E:** kdur@fortlewis.edu
W: http://www.kdur.org
Editorial Profile: KDUR-FM is a non-commercial station owned by Fort Lewis College. The format for the station is free-form. KDUR-FM broadcasts to the Durango, CO area at 91.9 FM.

KDUS-AM

Owner: Hubbard Radio, LLC
Editorial: 1900 W Carmen St, Guadalupe, Arizona 85283-2559. **T:** 1 480 838-0400
W: http://nbcsportsradioam1060.com
Editorial Profile: KDUS-AM is a commercial station owned by Hubbard Radio, LLC. The format of the station is sports. KDUS-AM broadcasts in the Tempe, AZ area at 1060 AM.

KDUT-FM

Owner: Adelante Media Group
Editorial: 2722 S Redwood Rd, Ste 1, Salt Lake City, Utah 84119. **T:** 1 801 908-8777
W: http://radiolagrande1023.com
Editorial Profile: KDUT-FM is a commercial station owned by Adelante Media Group. The format of the station is regional Mexican. KDUT-FM broadcasts to the Salt Lake City area at 102.3 FM.

KDUV-FM

Owner: Community Educational Broadcasting
Editorial: 130 N Kelsey St, Ste H1, Visalia, California 93291. **T:** 1 559 651-4111
E: Spirit@Spirit889.com
W: http://www.spirit889.com
Editorial Profile: KDUV-FM is a non-commercial station owned by Community Educational Broadcasting. The format of the station is contemporary Christian music. KDUV-FM broadcasts to the Visalia, CA area at 88.9 FM.

KDUX-FM

Owner: Morris Communications
Editorial: 1308 Coolidge Rd, Aberdeen, Washington 98520-6317. **T:** 1 360 533-1320
W: http://www.kdux.com
Editorial Profile: KDUX-FM is a commercial station owned by Morris Communications. The format of the station is classic rock music. KDUX-FM broadcasts to the Aberdeen, WA area at 104.7 FM.

KDUZ-AM

Owner: Iowa City Broadcasting Co.
Editorial: 20132 Highway 15 N, Hutchinson, Minnesota 55350. **T:** 1 320 587-2140
E: news@kduz.com **W:** http://www.kduz.com
Editorial Profile: KDUZ-AM is a commercial station owned by Iowa City Broadcasting Co. The format of the station is news, talk and classic country music. KDUZ-AM broadcasts in the Hutchinson, MN area at 1260 AM.

KDVA-FM
Owner: Entravision Communications Corp.
Editorial: 501 N 44th St, Ste 425, Phoenix, Arizona 85008. **T:** 1 602 776-1400
W: http://www.josephoenix.com
Editorial Profile: KDVA-FM is a commercial station owned by Entravision Communications Corp. The format of the station is Hispanic adult hits. KDVA-FM broadcasts to the Phoenix area at 106.9 FM.

KDVL-FM
Owner: Double Z Broadcasting Inc.
Editorial: 320 Walnut St W, Devils Lake, North Dakota 58301-3506. **T:** 1 701 662-2161
E: kdlrkdvl@stellarnet.com
W: http://www.lrradioworks.com
Editorial Profile: KDVL-FM is a commercial station owned by Double Z Broadcasting Inc. The format of the station is classic hits music. KDVL-FM broadcasts to the Fargo, ND area at 102.5 FM.

KDVS-FM
Owner: University of California
Editorial: One Shields Avenue, 14 Lower Freeborn Hall, Davis, California 95616-5224. **T:** 1 530 752-0728 **E:** kdvsnews@gmail.com
W: http://www.kdvs.org
Editorial Profile: KDVS-FM is a non-commercial station owned by University of California. The format of the station is college variety. KDVS-FM broadcasts in the Davis, CA area at 90.3 FM.

KDVV-FM
Owner: Cumulus Media Inc.
Editorial: 825 S Kansas Ave, Ste 100, Topeka, Kansas 66612. **T:** 1 785 272-2122
W: http://www.v100rocks.com
Editorial Profile: KDVV-FM is a commercial station owned by Cumulus Media Inc. The format of the station is rock. KDVV-FM broadcasts to the Topeka, KS area at a frequency of 100.3 FM.

KDWA-AM
Owner: K & M Broadcasting Inc.
Editorial: 514 Vermillion St, Hastings, Minnesota 55033. **T:** 1 651 437-1460
E: news@kdwa.com **W:** http://www.kdwa.com
Editorial Profile: KDWA-AM is a commercial station owned by K&M Broadcasting Inc. The format of the station is news, sports and talk. KDWA-FM broadcasts to the Hastings, MN area at 1460 AM.

KDWB-FM
Owner: Clear Channel Media and Entertainment
Editorial: 1600 Utica Ave S Ste 400, Minneapolis, Minnesota 55416-1480.
T: 1 952 417-3000 **W:** http://www.kdwb.com
Editorial Profile: KDWB-FM is a commercial station owned by Clear Channel Media and Entertainment. The format of the station is Top 40/CHR music. KDWB-FM broadcasts to the Minneapolis area at 101.3 FM.

KDWG-FM
Editorial: 710 S Atlantic St, Dillon, Montana 59725-3511. **T:** 1 406 683-7156
E: kdwg@umwestern.edu
W: http://my.umwestern.edu/kdwg/index.htm
Editorial Profile: KDWG-FM is a non-commercial college station owned by The University of Montana - Western. The format of the station is variety. KDWG-FM broadcasts to the Dillon, MT area at a frequency of 90.9 FM.

KDWI-FM
Owner: University of Northern Iowa
Editorial: University Of Northern Iowa, Cedar Falls, Iowa 50614-0001. **T:** 1 319 273-6400
E: news@iowapublicradio.org
W: http://iowapublicradio.org
Editorial Profile: KDWI-FM is a non-commercial station owned by University of Northern Iowa. The format of the station is a variety of music, news and talk. KDWI-FM broadcasts to the Ottumwa, IA area at 89.1 FM.

KDWM-AM
Owner: Adelante Media Group
Editorial: 706 Butterfield Rd, Yakima, Washington 98901. **T:** 1 509 457-1000

KDWN-AM
Owner: Beasley Broadcast Group
Editorial: 2920 S Durango Dr, Las Vegas, Nevada 89117-4412. **T:** 1 702 730-0300
E: email@bbgi.com **W:** http://www.kdwn.com
Editorial Profile: KDWN-AM is a commercial station owned by Beasley Broadcast Group. The format of the station is sports, news and talk. KDWN-AM broadcasts to the Las Vegas area at 720 AM.

KDWY-FM
Owner: Simmons Media Group
Editorial: 436 Fossil Butte Dr, Kemmerer, Wyoming 83101. **T:** 1 307 877-4422
Editorial Profile: KDWY-FM is a commercial station owned by Simmons Media Group. The format of the station is classic country. KDWY-FM broadcasts to the Kemmerer, WY area at 105.3 FM.

KDWZ-FM
Owner: Midwest Communications Inc.
Editorial: 715 E Central Entrance, Duluth, Minnesota 55811. **T:** 1 218 722-4321
W: http://www.mykdwz.com
Editorial Profile: KDWZ-FM is a commercial station owned by Midwest Communications Inc. The format of the station is Top 40. KDWZ-FM broadcasts to the Duluth, MN area at 102.5 FM.

KDXE-AM
Owner: Simmons Media Group
Editorial: 515 S 700 E Ste 1C, Salt Lake City, Utah 84102-2802. **T:** 1 801 524-2600
Editorial Profile: KDXE-AM is a commercial station owned by Simmons Media Group. The format of the station is Spanish AC. KDXE-AM broadcasts to the Little Rock, AR area at 1380 AM.

KDXT-FM
Owner: Mountain Broadcasting
Editorial: 2600 S Garfield St, Missoula, Montana 59801-7709. **T:** 1 406 541-1071
W: http://107theranch.com
Editorial Profile: KDXT-FM is a commercial station owned by Mountain Broadcasting. The format of the station is classic country. KDXT-FM broadcasts to the Missoula, MT area at 97.9 FM.

KDXU-AM
Owner: Cherry Creek Radio
Editorial: 750 Ridgeview Dr, St George, Utah 84770. **T:** 1 435 673-3579
W: http://www.newstalk890.com
Editorial Profile: KDXU-AM is a commercial station owned by Cherry Creek Radio. The format of the station is news and talk. KDXU-AM broadcasts to the Salt Lake City area at 890 AM.

KDXX-FM
Owner: Univision Communications Inc.
Editorial: 7700 John W Carpenter Fwy Fl 1, Dallas, Texas 75247-4829. **T:** 1 214 525-0400
W: http://maximadallas.univision.com
Editorial Profile: KDXX-FM is a commercial station owned by Univision Communications Inc. The format of the station is Spanish adult contemporary. KDXX-FM broadcasts to the Dallas area at 99.1 FM.

KDXY-FM
Owner: Saga Communications
Editorial: 314 Union St, Jonesboro, Arkansas 72401. **T:** 1 870 933-8800
W: http://www.thefox1049.com
Editorial Profile: KDXY-FM is a commercial station owned by Saga Communications. The format of the station is contemporary country. KDXY-FM broadcasts to the Jonesboro, AR at 104.9 FM.

KDYA-AM
Owner: Bay Bridge Communications
Editorial: 3260 Blume Dr, Ste 520, Richmond, California 94806. **T:** 1 510 222-4242
E: sales@gospel1190.net
W: http://www.gospel1190.net
Editorial Profile: KDYA-AM is a commercial station owned by Bay Bridge Communications. The format of the station is gospel. KDYA-AM broadcasts to the Richmond, CA area at 1190 AM.

KDYK-AM
Owner: Adelante Media Group
Editorial: 706 Butterfield Rd, Yakima, Washington 98901-2021. **T:** 1 509 457-1000
Editorial Profile: KDYK-AM is a commercial station owned by Adelante Media Group. The format of the station is Spanish Adult Hits. KDYK-AM broadcasts to the Yakima, WA area at 1020 AM.

KDYL-AM
Owner: Holiday Broadcasting
Editorial: 3606 S 500 W, Salt Lake City, Utah 84115. **T:** 1 801 262-5624
W: http://www.kdylam.com
Editorial Profile: KDYL-AM is a commercial station owned by Holiday Broadcasting. The format of the station is oldies. KDYL-AM broadcasts to the Salt Lake City area at 1060 AM.

KDYM-AM
Owner: Adelante Media Group
Editorial: 706 Butterfield Rd, Yakima, Washington 98901. **T:** 1 509 457-1000
Editorial Profile: KDYM-AM is a commercial station owned by Adelante Media Group. The format of the station is Spanish AC. KDYM-AM broadcasts to the Yakima, WA area at 1210 AM.

KDYN-AM
Owner: Ozark Communications Inc.
Editorial: 9331 Puddin Ridge Rd, Ozark, Arkansas 72949. **T:** 1 479 667-4567
E: kdyn@centurytel.net
W: http://www.kdyn.com
Editorial Profile: KDYN-AM is a commercial station owned by Ozark Communications Inc. The format of the station is classic country. KDYN-AM broadcasts to the Ozark, AR area at 1540 AM.

KDYN-FM
Owner: Ozark Communications Inc.
Editorial: 9331 Puddin Ridge Rd, Ozark, Arkansas 72949. **T:** 1 479 667-4567
E: kdyn@centurytel.net
W: http://www.kdyn.com
Editorial Profile: KDYN-FM is a commercial station owned by Ozark Communications Inc. The format of the station is classic country music. KDYN-FM broadcasts to the Ozark, AR area at 96.7 FM.

KDZA-FM
Owner: Clear Channel Media and Entertainment
Editorial: 2864 S Circle Dr Ste 300, Colorado Springs, Colorado 80906-4114.
T: 1 719 540-9200
W: http://www.z1079rocks.com
Editorial Profile: KDZA-FM is a commercial station owned by Clear Channel Media and Entertainment. The format of the station is classic rock. KDZA-FM broadcasts to the Pueblo, CO area at 107.9 FM.

KDZN-FM
Owner: Magic Air Communications
Editorial: 210 S Douglas St, Glendive, Montana 59330. **T:** 1 406 377-3377
E: kxgnkdzn@midrivers.com
W: http://www.kxgn.com
Editorial Profile: KDZN-FM is a commercial station owned by Magic Air Communications. The format of the station is contemporary country music. KDZN-FM broadcasts to the Glendive, MT area at 96.5 FM.

KDZR-AM
Owner: Walt Disney Co.
Editorial: 3030 SW Moody Ave, Ste 210, Portland, Oregon 97201-4868.
T: 1 503 228-4322
W: http://www.radiodisney.com/portland
Editorial Profile: KDZR-AM is a commercial station owned by Walt Disney Co. The format of the station is children's entertainment and pop music. KDZR-AM broadcasts to the Portland, OR, area at 1640 AM.

KDZZ-FM
Owner: Cumulus Media Inc.
Editorial: 122 4th St SW, Rochester, Minnesota 55902. **T:** 1 507 286-1010
W: http://www.zrock1077.com
Editorial Profile: KDZZ-FM is a commercial station owned by Cumulus Media Inc. The format of the station is rock. KDZZ-FM broadcasts to the Rochester, MN area at 107.7 FM.

KEAG-FM
Owner: Morris Communications
Editorial: 301 Arctic Slope Ave, Ste 200, Anchorage, Alaska 99518. **T:** 1 907 344-9622
W: http://www.kool973.com
Editorial Profile: KEAG-FM is a commercial station owned by Morris Communications. The format of the station is oldies music. KEAG-FM broadcasts to the Anchorage, AK area at 97.3 FM.

KEAN-FM
Owner: Townsquare Media, LLC
Editorial: 3911 S 1st St, Abilene, Texas 79605. **T:** 1 325 676-7711
W: http://www.keanradio.com
Editorial Profile: KEAN-FM is a commercial station owned by Townsquare Media, LLC. The format of the station is contemporary country music. KEAN-FM broadcasts to the Abliene, TX area at 105.1 FM.

KEAR-AM
Owner: Family Stations Inc.
Editorial: 290 Hegenberger Rd, Oakland, California 94621-1436. **T:** 1 510 568-6200
E: info@familyradio.org
W: http://www.familyradio.com
Editorial Profile: KEAR-AM is a non-commercial station owned by Family Stations Inc. The format of the station is religious. KEAR-AM broadcasts to the greater San Francisco Bay area at 610 AM.

KEAR-FM
Owner: Family Stations Inc.
Editorial: 4135 Northgate Blvd, Ste 1, Sacramento, California 95834-1226.
T: 1 916 641-8191 **E:** info@familyradio.org
W: http://www.familyradio.com
Editorial Profile: KEAR-FM is a non-commercial station owned by Family Stations Inc. The format of the station is religious. KEAR-FM broadcasts to the Sacramento, CA, area at 88.1 FM.

KEAZ-FM
Owner: Crain Media Group LLC
Editorial: 111 N Spring St, Searcy, Arkansas 72143. **T:** 1 501 268-7123
E: production@crainmedia.com
W: http://www.eazy1007.com
Editorial Profile: KEAZ-FM is a commercial station owned by Crain Media Group LLC. The format of the station is adult contemporary. KEAZ-FM broadcasts to the Searcy, AR area at 100.7 FM.

KEBC-AM
Owner: Tyler Media Group Inc.
Editorial: 5101 S Shields Blvd, Oklahoma City, Oklahoma 73129-3217. **T:** 1 405 616-5500
W: http://www.247comedy.com/main.html
Editorial Profile: KEBC-AM is a commercial station owned by Tyler Media Group Inc. The format of the station is comedy. KEBC-AM broadcasts to the Oklahoma City area locally at 1560 AM.

KEBR-AM
Owner: Family Stations Inc.
Editorial: 4135 Northgate Blvd, Ste 1, Sacramento, California 95834-1226.
T: 1 916 641-8191 **E:** info@familyradio.org
W: http://www.familyradio.com
Editorial Profile: KEBR-AM is a non-commercial station owned by Family Stations Inc. The format of the station is religious programming. KEBR-AM broadcasts to the Sacramento, CA area at 1210 AM.

KEBT-FM
Owner: American General Media
Editorial: 1400 Easton Dr, Ste 144-B, Bakersfield, California 93309.
T: 1 661 328-1410
Editorial Profile: KEBT-FM is a commercial station owned by American General Media. The format of the station is regional Mexican. KEBT-FM broadcasts to the Bakersfield, CA area at 96.9 FM.

KECH-FM
Owner: Rich Broadcasting, LLC.
Editorial: 201 S Main St, Hailey, Idaho 83333-8406. **T:** 1 208 788-7118
E: kech95@cox-internet.com
Editorial Profile: KECH-FM is a commercial station owned by Rich Broadcasting, LLC. The format of the station is classic rock and album-oriented rock. KECH-FM broadcasts to the Ketchum, ID area at 95.3 FM.

KECO-FM
Owner: Paragon Communications Inc.
Editorial: 220 S Pioneer Rd, Elk City, Oklahoma 73644. **T:** 1 580 225-9696
E: kecoproduction@cableone.net
W: http://www.kecofm.com
Editorial Profile: KECO-FM is a commercial station owned by Paragon Communications Inc. The format of the station is classic and contemporary country music. KECO-FM broadcasts to the Elk City, OK area at 96.5 FM.

KECR-AM
Owner: Family Stations Inc.
Editorial: 11865 Moreno Ave, Lakeside, California 92040-1110. **T:** 1 619 390-3481
E: info@familyradio.org
W: http://familyradio.com
Editorial Profile: KECR-AM is a non-commercial station owned by Family Stations Inc. The format of the station is religious. KECR-AM broadcasts to the Lakeside, CA area at 910 AM.

KEDA-AM
Owner: D&E Broadcasting
Editorial: 1246 W Laurel Ste 100, San Antonio, Texas 78201-6431.
T: 1 210 226-5254 **E:** kedaradio@yahoo.com
W: http://www.kedaradio.com
Editorial Profile: KEDA-AM is a commercial station owned by D&E Broadcasting. The format of the station is Hispanic programming. KEDA-AM broadcasts to the San Antonio area at 1540 AM.

KEDB-FM
Owner: Honey Creek Broadcasting
Editorial: 402 N 12th St, Centerville, Iowa 52544-1718. **T:** 1 641 856-3996
E: kmgofm@lisco.net **W:** http://www.kedb.fm
Editorial Profile: KEDB-FM is a commercial station owned by Honey Creek Broadcasting. The format of the station is oldies. KEDB-FM broadcasts to the Chariton, IA area at 105.3 FM.

KEDG-FM
Owner: Opus Broadcasting of Alexandria, LLC
Editorial: 92 W Shamrock Ave, Pineville, Louisiana 71360. **T:** 1 318 487-1035
W: http://www.sunny1069fm.com
Editorial Profile: KEDG-FM is a commercial station owned by Opus Broadcasting of Alexandria, LLC. The format of the station is adult contemporary. KEDG-FM broadcasts to the Alexandria, LA area at 106.9 FM.

KEDM-FM
Owner: University of Louisiana at Monroe
Editorial: 250 Stubbs Hall, 401 Bayou Drive, Monroe, Louisiana 71209-0001.
T: 1 318 342-5556 **E:** news@kedm.org
W: http://www.kedm.org
Editorial Profile: KEDM-FM is a non-commercial station owned by University of Louisiana at Monroe. The format of the station is classical, jazz and news. KEDM-FM broadcasts in the Monroe, LA area at 90.3 FM.

KEDO-AM
Owner: Bicoastal Media LLC
Editorial: 1130 14th Ave, Longview, Washington 98632-3017. **T:** 1 360 425-1500
W: http://www.kedoam.com
Editorial Profile: KEDO-AM is a commercial station owned by Bicoastal Media. The format of the station is news and talk. KEDO-AM broadcasts to the Portland, OR area at 1400 AM.

KEDT-FM
Owner: South Texas Public Broadcasting
Editorial: 4455 S Padre Island Dr, Ste 38, Corpus Christi, Texas 78411.
T: 1 361 855-2213 **W:** http://www.kedt.org
Editorial Profile: KEDT-FM is a non-commercial station owned by South Texas Public Broadcasting. The format of the station is classical and jazz. KEDT-FM broadcasts to the Corpus Christi, TX area at 90.3 FM.

KEEH-FM
Owner: Upper Columbia Media
Editorial: 3715 S Grove Rd, Spokane, Washington 99224-5319. **T:** 1 509 456-4870
W: http://www.plr.org
Editorial Profile: KEEH-FM is a non-commercial station owned by Upper Columbia Media. The format of the station is contemporary Christian music. KEEH-FM broadcasts to the Spokane, WA area at 104.9 FM.

KEEL-AM
Owner: Townsquare Media, LLC
Editorial: 6341 W Port Ave, Shreveport, Louisiana 71129. **T:** 1 318 688-1130
E: keel@gapbroadcasting.com
W: http://www.710keel.com
Editorial Profile: KEEL-AM is a commercial station owned by Townsquare Media, LLC. The format of the station is news and talk. KEEL-AM broadcasts to the Shreveport, LA area at 710 AM. The station focuses on local news only and does not wish to receive any guest pitches whatsoever.

KEEP-FM
Owner: Hill Country Broadcasting, LLC
Editorial: 210 Woodcrest St, Fredericksburg, Texas 78624. **T:** 1 830 997-2197
Editorial Profile: KEEP-FM is a commercial station owned by Hill Country Broadcasting, LLC. The format of the station is country. KEEP-FM broadcasts to the Bandera, TX area at 103.1 FM.

KEES-AM
Owner: Salt of the Earth Broadcasting
Editorial: 2737 S Broadway Ave, Tyler, Texas 75701-5413. **T:** 1 903 526-1330
E: kgldradio@yahoo.com
W: http://www.kgld.org
Editorial Profile: KEES-AM is a commercial station owned by Salt of the Earth Broadcasting. The format of the station is urban gospel. KEES-AM broadcasts to the Tyler, Texas area at 1430 AM.

KEEY-FM
Owner: Clear Channel Media and Entertainment
Editorial: 1600 Utica Ave S Ste 400, Saint Louis Park, Minnesota 55416-1480.
T: 1 952 417-3000
E: k102studio@clearchannel.com
W: http://www.k102.com
Editorial Profile: KEEY-FM is a commercial station owned by Clear Channel Media and Entertainment. The format of the station is contemporary country. KEEY-FM broadcasts to the Minneapolis area at 102.1 FM.

KEEZ-FM
Owner: Three Eagles Communications Co.
Editorial: 1807 Lee Blvd, North Mankato, Minnesota 56003-2633. **T:** 1 507 345-4646
W: http://www.myz99.com
Editorial Profile: KEEZ-FM is a commercial station owned by Three Eagles Communications Co. The format of the station is hot adult contemporary music. KEEZ-FM broadcasts to the Mankato, MN area at 99.1 FM.

KEFH-FM
Owner: Alliance Broadcast Communications
Editorial: 207 South Sulley, Clarendon, Texas 79226-0370. **T:** 1 806 874-2296
E: kefh@kool993.net **W:** http://www.kefh.net
Editorial Profile: KEFH-FM is a commercial station owned by Alliance Broadcast Communications. The format of the station is classic hits and some regular oldies music. KEFH-FM broadcasts to the Clarendon, TX area at 99.3 FM.

KEFR-FM
Owner: Family Stations Inc.
Editorial: 13306 Jefferson St, Le Grand, California 95333. **T:** 1 209 389-4659
E: info@familyradio.com
W: http://www.familyradio.com
Editorial Profile: KFRB-FM is a non-commercial station owned by Family Station Inc. The format of the station is religious music and talk. KFRB-FM broadcasts in the Le Grand, CA at 89.9 FM.

KEFX-FM
Owner: CSN International
Editorial: 4002 N 3300 E, Twin Falls, Idaho 83301-0354. **T:** 1 208 734-2049
E: effectradio@hotmail.com
W: http://www.effectradio.com
Editorial Profile: KEFX-FM is a non-commercial station owned by CSN International. The format of the station is Christian rock. KEFX-FM broadcasts to the Twin Falls, ID area at 88.9 FM.

KEGA-FM
Owner: Broadway Media
Editorial: 515 S 700 E Ste 1C, Salt Lake City, Utah 84102-2802. **T:** 1 801 524-2600
W: http://www.1015theeagle.com
Editorial Profile: KEGA-FM is a commercial station owned by Broadway Media. The format of the station is country. KEGA-FM broadcasts to the Salt Lake City area at 101.5 FM.

KEGE-FM
Owner: Rich Broadcasting, LLC
Editorial: 1406 Commerce Way, Idaho Falls, Idaho 83401-1233. **T:** 1 208 233-1133
W: http://www.590kid.com
Editorial Profile: KEGE-FM is a commercial station owned by Rich Broadcasting, LLC. The format of the station is news talk. KEGE-FM broadcasts to the Pocatello, ID area at 92.1 FM.

KEGH-FM
Owner: Simmons Media Group
Editorial: 515 S 700 E, Ste 1C, Salt Lake City, Utah 84102-2802. **T:** 1 801 524-2600
W: http://www.1015theeagle.com
Editorial Profile: KEGH-FM is a commercial station owned by Simmons Media Group. The format of the station is country. KEGH-FM broadcasts to the Salt Lake City area on 106.9 FM.

KEGI-FM
Owner: Saga Communications
Editorial: 314 Union St, Jonesboro, Arkansas 72401-2815. **T:** 1 870 933-8800
W: http://www.eagle1005.com
Editorial Profile: KEGI-FM is a commercial station owned by Saga Communications. The format of the station is rock music. KEGI-FM broadcasts to the Jonesboro, AR area at 100.5 FM.

KEGK-FM
Owner: SMAHH Communications, LLC
Editorial: 64 Broadway N, Fargo, North Dakota 58102-4934. **T:** 1 701 356-1156
E: studio10@theeagle.tv
W: http://www.theeagle.tv
Editorial Profile: KEGK-FM is a commercial station owned by SMAHH Communications, LLC. The format of the station is classic hits. KEGK-FM broadcasts to the Fargo, ND area at 106.9 FM.

KEGL-FM
Owner: Clear Channel Media and Entertainment
Editorial: 14001 Dallas Pkwy, Dallas, Texas 75240-4346. **T:** 1 214 866-8000
W: http://www.kegl.com
Editorial Profile: KEGL-FM is a commercial station owned by Clear Channel Media and Entertainment. The format of the station is rock alternative. KEGL-FM broadcasts to the Dallas area at 97.1 FM.

KEGX-FM
Owner: Ingstad Radio Washington, LLC
Editorial: 4304 W 24Th Ave Suite 200, Kennewick, Washington 99338-2320.
T: 1 509 783-0783
W: http://www.eagle1065.com
Editorial Profile: KEGX-FM is a commercial station owned by Ingstad Radio Washington, LLC. The format of the station is classic rock. KEGX-FM broadcasts to Kennewick, WA area at 106.5.

KEGY-FM
Owner: CBS Radio
Editorial: 8033 Linda Vista Rd, San Diego, California 92111. **T:** 1 858 560-1037
W: http://energy1037.cbslocal.com
Editorial Profile: KEGY-FM is a commercial station owned by CBS Radio. The format of the station is a mix of Top 40/CHR. KEGY-FM broadcasts to the San Diego area at 103.7 FM.

KEHK-FM
Owner: Cumulus Media Inc.
Editorial: 1200 Executive Pkwy, Ste 440, Eugene, Oregon 97401. **T:** 1 541 284-8500
W: http://www.starfm1023.com
Editorial Profile: KEHK-FM is a commercial station owned by Cumulus Media Inc. The format of the station is adult contemporary. KEHK-FM broadcasts to the Eugene, OR area at a frequency of 102.3 FM.

KEIB-AM
Owner: Clear Channel Media and Entertainment
Editorial: 3400 W Olive Ave Ste 550, Burbank, California 91505-5544. **T:** 1 818 559-2252
W: http://www.patriot.la/main.html
Editorial Profile: KEIB-AM is a commercial station owned by Clear Channel Media and Entertainment. The format of the station is liberal talk. KEIB-AM broadcasts to the Los Angeles area on 1150 AM.

KEIN-AM
Owner: Munson Radio Inc.
Editorial: 3313 15th St, Box F, Black Eagle, Montana 59414. **T:** 1 406 761-1310
Editorial Profile: KEIN-AM is a commercial station owned by Munson Radio Inc. The format of the station is adult standards music. KEIN-AM broadcasts in the Great Falls, MT area at 1310 AM.

KEJJ-FM
Owner: J.H. Rees.
Editorial: 219 N Iowa St, Gunnison, Colorado 81230-2478. **T:** 1 970 641-4000
E: gunnisonradio@gmail.com
Editorial Profile: KEJJ-AM is a commercial station owned by J.H. Rees. The format of the station is oldies. KEJJ-AM broadcasts to the Denver area at 98.3 FM.

KEJL-FM
Owner: FiveStar Enterprises LC
Editorial: 1423 W Bender Blvd, Hobbs, New Mexico 88240-9252. **T:** 1 575 393-6000
W: http://hobbsradio.com/eagle
Editorial Profile: KEJL-FM is a commercial station owned by FiveStar Enterprises LC. The format of the station is classic rock. KEJL-FM broadcasts to the Hobbs, NM area at 100.9 FM.

KEJO-AM
Owner: Bicoastal Media LLC
Editorial: 2840 Marion St SE, Albany, Oregon 97322-3978. **T:** 1 541 926-8628
W: http://www.kejoam.com
Editorial Profile: KEJO-AM is a commercial station owned by Bicoastal Media LLC. The format of the station is sports and talk programming. KEJO-AM broadcasts to the Albany, OR area at 1240 AM.

KEJS-FM
Owner: Barton Broadcasting Co.
Editorial: 1607 13th St, Lubbock, Texas 79401-3830. **T:** 1 806 747-5951
E: kejsfm@kejsfm.com
W: http://www.kejsfm.com
Editorial Profile: KEJS-FM is a commercial station owned by Barton Broadcasting Co. The format of the station is Tejano music. The station airs to the Lubbock, TX area at 106.5 FM.

KEJY-AM
Owner: Eureka Broadcasting Inc.
Editorial: 1101 Marsh Rd, Eureka, California 95501-1574. **T:** 1 707 442-5744
Editorial Profile: KEJY-AM is a commercial station owned by Eureka Broadcasting Inc. The format of the station is Spanish Adult Hits. KEJY-AM broadcasts to the Eureka, CA area at 790 AM.

KEKA-FM
Owner: Eureka Broadcasting Inc.
Editorial: 1101 Marsh Rd, Eureka, California 95501-1574. **T:** 1 707 442-5744
W: http://www.keka101.com
Editorial Profile: KEKA-FM is a commercial station owned by Eureka Broadcasting Inc. The format of the station is classic country. KEKA-FM broadcasts to the Eureka, CA area at 101.5 FM.

KEKB-FM
Owner: Townsquare Media, Inc.
Editorial: 315 Kennedy Ave, Grand Junction, Colorado 81501-7552. **T:** 1 970 242-7788
W: http://www.kekbfm.com
Editorial Profile: KEKB-FM is a commercial station owned by Townsquare Media, Inc. The format for the station is country. KEKB-FM broadcasts to the Grand Junction-Montrose, CO area at 99.9 FM.

KEKO-FM
Owner: Cadena Radio Luz Inc.(La)
Editorial: 2702 Pine St, Laredo, Texas 78046-6225. **T:** 1 956 726-4738
Editorial Profile: KEKO-FM is a commercial station owned by La Cadena Radio Luz Inc. The format of the station is Hispanic religious programming. The station airs locally on 101.7 FM.

KELA-AM
Owner: Bicoastal Media LLC
Editorial: 1635 S Gold St, Centralia, Washington 98531-8950. **T:** 1 360 736-3321
W: http://www.kelaam.com
Editorial Profile: KELA-AM is a commercial station owned by Bicoastal Media LLC. The format of the station is news, talk and sports. KELA-AM broadcasts to the Centralia, WA area at 1470 AM.

KELD-AM
Owner: Noalmark Broadcasting Corp.
Editorial: 2525 N West Ave, El Dorado, Arkansas 71730. **T:** 1 870 862-1400
E: newsroom@totalradio.us
W: http://www.totalradio.com/keldam.htm
Editorial Profile: KELD-AM is a commercial station owned by Noalmark Broadcasting Corp. The format of the station is sports. KELD-AM broadcasts to the El Dorado, AR, area at 1400 AM.

KELD-FM
Owner: Noalmark Broadcasting Corp.
Editorial: 2525 N West Ave, El Dorado, Arkansas 71730. **T:** 1 870 863-6126
E: newsroom@totalradio.us
W: http://www.keldfm.com
Editorial Profile: KELD-FM is a commercial station owned by Noalmark Broadcasting Corp. The format of the station is news and talk. KELD-FM broadcasts to the El Dorado, AR area at 106.5 FM.

KELE-AM
Owner: Ozark Media Inc.

Editorial: 800 Hubbard St, Mountain Grove, Missouri 65711-9441. **T:** 1 417 926-4650
Editorial Profile: KELE-AM is a commercial station owned by Ozark Media Inc. The format of the station is news and talk. KELE-AM broadcasts to the Mountain Grove, MO area at 1360 AM.

KELE-FM
Owner: Ozark Media Inc.
Editorial: 800 Hubbard St, Mountain Grove, Missouri 65711-9441. **T:** 1 417 926-4650
W: http://www.925thegrove.com
Editorial Profile: KELE-FM is a commercial station owned by Ozark Media Inc. The format of the station is contemporary country. KELE-FM broadcasts to the Mountain Grove, MO area at 92.5 FM.

KELI-FM
Owner: Townsquare Media
Editorial: 1301 S Abe St, San Angelo, Texas 76903. **T:** 1 325 655-7161
W: http://www.magic987.com
Editorial Profile: KELI-FM is a commercial station owned by Townsquare Media. The format of the station is adult contemporary. KELI-FM broadcasts to the San Angelo, TX area at 98.7 FM.

KELK-AM
Owner: Elko Broadcasting Company
Editorial: 1800 Idaho St, Elko, Nevada 89801. **T:** 1 775 738-1240
E: production@elkoradio.com
W: http://www.elkoradio.com
Editorial Profile: KELK-AM is a commercial station owned by Elko Broadcasting Company. The format of the station is adult contemporary. KELK-AM broadcasts to the Elko, NV area at 1240 AM.

KELN-FM
Owner: Eagle Radio Inc.
Editorial: 1301 E 4th St, North Platte, Nebraska 69101. **T:** 1 308 532-1120
W: http://www.mix97one.com
Editorial Profile: KELN-FM is a commercial station owned by Eagle Radio Inc. The format of the station is adult contemporary music. KELN-FM broadcasts in the North Platte, NE area at 97.1 FM.

KELO-AM
Owner: Midwest Communications
Editorial: 500 S Phillips Ave, Sioux Falls, South Dakota 57104-6825. **T:** 1 605 331-5350
W: http://www.keloam.com
Editorial Profile: KELO-AM is a commercial station owned by Midwest Communications. The format of the station is news and talk. KELO-AM broadcasts in the Sioux Falls, SD area at 1320 AM.

KELO-FM
Owner: Midwest Communications
Editorial: 500 S Phillips Ave, Sioux Falls, South Dakota 57104-6825. **T:** 1 605 331-5350
W: http://www.kelofm.com
Editorial Profile: KELO-FM is a commercial station owned by Midwest Communications. The format of the station is adult contemporary music. KELO-FM broadcasts in the Sioux Falls, SD area at 92.5 FM.

KELP-AM
Owner: McClatchey(Arnie)
Editorial: 6900 Commerce Ave, El Paso, Texas 79915-1102. **T:** 1 915 779-0016
W: http://www.kelpradio.com
Editorial Profile: KELP-AM is a commercial station owned by Arnie McClatchey. The format of the station is religious music and talk. KELP-AM broadcasts to the El Paso, TX area at 1590 AM.

KELQ-FM
Owner: Midwest Communications
Editorial: 500 S Phillips Ave, Sioux Falls, South Dakota 57104-6825. **T:** 1 605 331-5350
W: http://kelo.com
Editorial Profile: KELQ-FM is a commercial station owned by Midwest Communications. The format of the station is news/talk. KELQ-FM broadcasts to the Sioux Falls, SD area at 107.9 FM.

KELU-FM
Owner: Educational Media Foundation
Editorial: 4101 Barbara Loop SE, Ste A, Rio Rancho, New Mexico 87124.
T: 1 505 891-4232 **W:** http://www.klove.com
Editorial Profile: KELU-FM is non-commercial station owned by Educational Media Foundation. The format of the station is contemporary Christian. KELU-FM broadcasts to the Clovis, NM area at 90.3 FM.

KEMC-FM
Owner: Montana State University-Billings
Editorial: 1500 University Dr, Billings, Montana 59101. **T:** 1 406 657-2941
E: mail@ypradio.org **W:** http://ypradio.org
Editorial Profile: KEMC-FM is a non-commercial station owned by Montana State University-Billings. The format of the station is news and public affairs and folk, jazz, and classical music. KEMC-FM broadcasts in the Billings, MT area at 91.7 FM.

KEMX-FM
Owner: ABS Communications, Inc.
Editorial: 2448 E 81st St, Tulsa, Oklahoma 74137-4250. **T:** 1 918 492-2660
E: kxoj@kxoj.com **W:** http://www.kxoj.com
Editorial Profile: KEMX-FM is a commercial station owned by ABS Communications, Inc. The format of the station is contemporary Christian. KEMX-FM broadcasts to the Tulsa, OK area at 94.5 FM.

KENA-AM
Owner: Ouachita Broadcasting Inc.
Editorial: 1600 Reine St S, Mena, Arkansas 71953. **T:** 1 479 394-1450
E: menaradio@allegiance.tv
Editorial Profile: KENA-AM is a commercial station owned by Ouachita Broadcasting Inc. The format of the station is gospel music. KENA-AM broadcasts to the Mena, AR area at 1450 AM.

KENA-FM
Owner: Ouachita Broadcasting Inc.
Editorial: 1600 Reine St S, Mena, Arkansas 71953. **T:** 1 479 394-1450
E: menaradio@allegiance.tv
Editorial Profile: KENA-FM is a commercial station owned by Ouachita Broadcasting Inc. The format of the station is contemporary country. KENA-FM broadcasts to the Mena, AR area at 102.1 FM.

KENC-FM
Owner: Community Radio for Northern Colorado
Editorial: 1901 56Th Ave Ste 200, Greeley, Colorado 80634-2950. **T:** 1 970 378-2579
E: news@kunc.org **W:** http://www.kunc.org
Editorial Profile: KENC-FM is a non-commercial station owned by Community Radio for Northern Colorado. The format of the station is a variety of programming and music. KUNC-FM broadcasts to the Greeley, CO are at 90.7 FM.

KEND-FM
Owner: Pecos Valley Broadcasting Company
Editorial: 317 W Quay Ave, Artesia, New Mexico 88210-2158. **T:** 1 575 746-2751
W: http://www.kendfm.com
Editorial Profile: KEND-FM is a commercial station owned by Pecos Valley Broadcasting Company. The format of the station is classic hits. KEND-FM broadcasts to the Roswell, NM area at 106.5 FM.

KENI-AM
Owner: Clear Channel Media and Entertainment
Editorial: 800 E Dimond Blvd, Ste 3-370, Anchorage, Alaska 99515. **T:** 1 907 522-1515
E: news@650keni.com
W: http://www.650keni.com
Editorial Profile: KENI-AM is a commercial station owned by Clear Channel Media and Entertainment. The format of the station is news and talk programming. KENI-FM broadcasts to the Anchorage, AK area at 650 AM.

KENN-AM
Owner: American General Media
Editorial: 212 W Apache St, Farmington, New Mexico 87401-6235. **T:** 1 505 327-4449
W: http://www.kennradio.com
Editorial Profile: KENN-AM is a commercial station owned by American General Media. The format of the station is news and talk. KENN-AM broadcasts in the Farmington, NM area at 1390 AM.

KENO-AM
Owner: Lotus Communications Corp.
Editorial: 8755 W Flamingo Rd, Las Vegas, Nevada 89147-8667. **T:** 1 702 876-1460
E: lotussignup@yahoo.com
W: http://www.vegasdeportes.com
Editorial Profile: KENO-AM is a commercial station owned by Lotus Communications Corp. The format of the station is Hispanic sports. KENO-AM broadcasts to the Las Vegas area at 1490 AM.

KENR-FM
Owner: Townsquare Media, LLC
Editorial: 3250 S Reserve St Ste 200, Missoula, Montana 59801-8236.
T: 1 406 728-9300
W: http://www.1075zoofm.com
Editorial Profile: KENR-FM is a commercial station owned by Townsquare Media, LLC. The format of the station is adult contemporary. KENR-FM broadcasts to the Missoula, MT area at 107.5 FM.

KENW-FM
Owner: Eastern New Mexico University
Editorial: 52 Broadcast Ctr, Portales, New Mexico 88130. **T:** 1 575 562-2112
E: kenwfm@enmu.edu
W: http://www.kenw.org
Editorial Profile: KENW-FM is a non-commercial station owned by Eastern New Mexico University. The format of the station is classical, news and easy listening. KENW-FM broadcasts to the Portales, NM area on 89.5 FM.

KENZ-FM
Owner: Cumulus Media Inc
Editorial: 434 W Bearcat Dr, Salt Lake City, Utah 84115-2520. **T:** 1 801 485-6700
W: http://www.1019theend.com
Editorial Profile: KENZ-FM is a commercial station owned by Cumulus Media Inc. The format of the station is classic hits music. KENZ-FM broadcasts to the Salt Lake City area at 101.9 FM.

KEOJ-FM
Owner: KXOJ, Inc.
Editorial: 2448 E 81st St Ste 5500, Tulsa, Oklahoma 74137-4201. **T:** 1 918 492-2660
E: kxoj@kxoj.com **W:** http://www.kxoj.com
Editorial Profile: KEOJ-FM is a commercial station owned by KXOJ, Inc. The format for the station is contemporary christian/ inspirational. KEOJ-FM broacasts to the Tulsa, OK area at 101.1 FM.

KEOK-FM
Owner: Payne Radio Group
Editorial: 5686 S Muskogee Ave, Tahlequah, Oklahoma 74464-5487. **T:** 1 918 456-2511
E: info@lakescountry1021.com
W: http://www.lakescountryradio.com
Editorial Profile: KEOK-FM is a commercial station owned by Payne Radio Group. The format of the station is contemporary country. KEOK-FM broadcasts to the Tulsa, OK area at 102.1 FM.

KEOL-FM
Owner: Eastern Oregon University
Editorial: 1 University Blvd, La Grande, Oregon 97850. **T:** 1 541 962-3698
E: 91.7keol@gmail.com
W: http://www.eou.edu/keol
Editorial Profile: KEOL-FM is a non-commercial station owned by Eastern Oregon University. The format of the station is variety. KEOL-FM broadcasts to the La Grande, OR area at 91.7 FM.

KEOM-FM
Owner: Mesquite Independent School District
Editorial: 2600 Motley Dr, #300, Mesquite, Texas 75150-3840. **T:** 1 972 882-7560
W: http://www.keom.fm
Editorial Profile: KEOM-FM is a non-commercial station owned by the Mesquite Independent School District. The format of the station is classic hits music. KEOM-FM broadcasts to the Mesquite, TX area at 88.5 FM.

KEOS-FM
Owner: Brazos Educational Radio
Editorial: 202 E Carson St, Bryan, Texas 77801-1403. **T:** 1 979 779-5367
E: keos@keos.org **W:** http://www.keos.org
Editorial Profile: KEOS-FM is a non-commercial station owned by Brazos Educational Radio. The format of the station is variety. KEOS-FM broadcasts to the Bryan, TX area at 89.1 FM.

KEPC-FM
Owner: Pikes Peak Community College
Editorial: 5675 S Academy Blvd, Colorado Springs, Colorado 80906. **T:** 1 719 502-3128
E: kepc@ppcc.edu
W: http://www.ppcc.edu/kepc
Editorial Profile: KEPC-FM is a non-commercial station owned by Pikes Peak Community College. The format of the station is adult album alternative. KEPC-FM broadcasts to the Colorado Springs, CO area at 89.7 FM.

KEPD-FM
Owner: Adelman Broadcasting Inc.
Editorial: 731 Balsam St, Ridgecrest, California 93555-3510. **T:** 1 760 371-1700
W: http://www.juanfm1049.com
Editorial Profile: KEPD-FM is a commercial station owned by Adelman Broadcasting Inc. The format of the station is Spanish Adult Hits. KEPD-FM broadcasts to the Ridgecrest, CA area at 104.9 FM.

KEPI-FM
Owner: World Radio Network, Inc.
Editorial: 2477 El Indio Hwy, Eagle Pass, Texas 78852-5538. **T:** 1 830 757-0887
E: kepi@lwrn.org **W:** http://www.887kepi.org
Editorial Profile: KEPI-FM is a commercial station owned by World Radio Network, Inc. The format is contemporary Christian. KEPI-FM broadcasts to the San Antonio area at 88.7 FM.

KEPN-AM
Owner: Lincoln Financial Media
Editorial: 7800 E Orchard Rd, Ste 400, Greenwood Village, Colorado 80111-2583.
T: 1 303 321-0950 **W:** http://1600thezone.com
Editorial Profile: KEPN-AM is commercial station owned by Lincoln Financial Media. The format of the station is sports. KEPN-AM broadcasts to the Denver area at 1600 AM.

KEPS-AM
Owner: MBM Radio LLC
Editorial: 127 Kilowatt Dr, Eagle Pass, Texas 78852-3397. **T:** 1 830 773-9247
Editorial Profile: KEPS-AM is a commercial station owned by MBM Radio LLC (dba R Communications). The format of the station is Tejano music. KEPS-AM broadcasts to the Eagle Pass, TX area at 1270 AM.

KEPX-FM
Owner: World Radio Network, Inc.
Editorial: 2477 El Indio Hwy, Eagle Pass, Texas 78852. **T:** 1 830 757-0895
E: kepx@lwrn.org **W:** http://www.kepx.org
Editorial Profile: KEPX-FM is non-commercial station owned by World Radio Network, Inc. The format is Hispanic religious. KEPX-FM broadcasts to the San Antonio, TX area at 89.5 FM.

KERA-FM
Owner: North Texas Public Broadcasting
Editorial: 3000 Harry Hines Blvd, Dallas, Texas 75201. **T:** 1 214 871-1390 **E:** kerafm@kera.org
W: http://www.kera.org
Editorial Profile: KERA-FM is a non-commercial station owned by North Texas Public Broadcasting. The format of the station is news and talk programming. KERA-FM broadcasts to the Dallas area at 90.1 FM.

KERB-AM
Owner: Bernal(Paulino)
Editorial: 4501 N McColl Rd, McAllen, Texas 78504-2431. **T:** 1 956 686-6382
W: http://www.nuevaradiocristiana.com
Editorial Profile: KERB-AM is a commercial station owned by Paulino Bernal. The format of the station is Hispanic contemporary Christian programming. KERB-AM broadcasts to the McAllen, TX area at 600 AM.

KERB-FM
Owner: Bernal(Paulino)
Editorial: 4501 N McColl Rd, McAllen, Texas 78504. **T:** 1 956 781-5528
Editorial Profile: KERB-FM is a non-commercial station owned by Paulino Bernal. The format of the station is Hispanic contemporary Christian programming. KERB-FM broadcasts to the McAllen, TX area at 105.7 FM.

KERI-AM
Owner: American General Media
Editorial: 1400 Easton Dr, Ste 144B, Bakersfield, California 93309.
T: 1 661 328-1410 **W:** http://www.keri.com
Editorial Profile: KERI-AM is a commercial station owned by American General Media. The format of the station is Christian music and talk. KERN-AM broadcasts to the Bakersfield, CA area at 1410 AM.

KERL-FM
Owner: Caldwell Media LLC
Editorial: 2758 Highway 64, Wynne, Arkansas 72396-4061. **T:** 1 870 318-7354
Editorial Profile: KERL-FM is a commercial station owned by Caldwell Media LLC. The format of the station is classic rock. KERL-FM broadcasts to the Wynne, AR at 99.3 FM.

KERM-FM
Owner: Kath Broadcasting, LLC
Editorial: 7060 Radio Rd, Torrington, Wyoming 82240. **T:** 1 307 532-2158
E: news@kgoskerm.com
W: http://kgoskerm.com
Editorial Profile: KERM-FM is a commercial station owned by Kath Broadcasting, LLC. The format of the station is country music. KERM-FM broadcasts in the Torrington, WY area at 98.3 FM.

KERN-AM
Owner: American General Media
Editorial: 1400 Easton Dr, Ste 144B, Bakersfield, California 93309-9412.
T: 1 661 328-1410
W: http://www.kernradio.com
Editorial Profile: KERN-AM is a commercial station owned by American General Media. The format of the station is news and talk. KERN-AM broadcasts to the Bakersfield, CA area at 1180 AM.

KERP-FM
Owner: Rocking M Radio
Editorial: 2601 Central Ave Ste C, Dodge City, Kansas 67801-6212. **T:** 1 620 225-8080
W: http://www.mykansasradio.com
Editorial Profile: KERP-FM is a commercial station owned by Rocking M Radio. The format of the station is contemporary country. KERP-FM broadcasts to the Dodge City, KS area at 96.3 FM.

KERR-AM
Owner: Anderson Radio Broadcasting Inc.
Editorial: 36581 N Reservoir Rd, Polson, Montana 59860-8471. **T:** 1 406 883-5255
E: kerrnews@750kerr.com
W: http://750kerr.com
Editorial Profile: KERR-AM is a commercial station owned by Anderson Radio Broadcasting Inc. The format of the station is classic country. KERR-AM broadcasts to the Polson, MT area at 750 AM.

KERU-FM
Owner: Escuela de la Raza Unida
Editorial: 137 N Broadway, Blythe, California 92225. **T:** 1 760 922-2582
E: keru885@yahoo.com
W: http://www.kerumachi.com
Editorial Profile: KERU-FM is a commercial station owned by Escuela de la Raza Unida. The format of the station is Hispanic and educational programming. KERU-FM broadcasts in the Blythe, CA area at 88.5 FM.

KERV-AM
Owner: Revolution Broadcast Co.
Editorial: 2125 Sidney Baker St, Kerrville, Texas 78028-2551. **T:** 1 830 896-1230
W: http://revfmradio.com
Editorial Profile: KERV-AM is a commercial station owned by Revolution Broadcast Co. The format of the station is talk. KERV-AM broadcasts to the Kerrville, TX area at 1230 AM.

KERX-FM
Owner: Pearson Broadcasting
Editorial: 1912 Church St, Barling, Arkansas 72923-2305. **T:** 1 479 484-7285
Editorial Profile: KERX-FM is a commercial station owned by Pearson Broadcasting. The format of the station is sports. KERX-FM broadcasts to the Barling, AR area at 95.3 FM.

KESA-FM
Owner: Northeast Oklahoma Broadcast Network, Inc.
Editorial: 114 Highway 23 S, Eureka Springs, Arkansas 72632-9153. **T:** 1 479 253-9001
Editorial Profile: KESA-FM is a commercial station owned by Northeast Oklahoma Broadcast Network, Inc. The format of the station is adult contemporary. KESA-FM broadcasts to the Eureka Springs, AR at a frequency of 100.9 FM.

KESC-FM
Owner: University of Southern California
Editorial: 515 S Figueroa St, Ste 2050, Los Angeles, California 90071. **T:** 1 213 225-7400
W: http://www.kusc.org
Editorial Profile: KESC-FM is a commercial station owned by University of Southern California. The format of the station is classical music. KESC-FM broadcasts to the San Luis Obispo, CA area at 99.7 FM.

KESJ-AM
Owner: Eagle Communications
Editorial: 4104 Country Ln, Saint Joseph, Missouri 64506-4921. **T:** 1 816 233-8881
Editorial Profile: KESJ-AM is a commercial station owned by Eagle Communications. The format of the station is sports. KESJ-AM broadcasts to the Saint Joseph, MO area at 1550 AM.

KESM-AM
Owner: Wildwood Communications Inc.
Editorial: 200 Radio Ln, El Dorado Springs, Missouri 64744. **T:** 1 417 876-2741
E: kesm@kesmradio.com
W: http://kesmradio.com
Editorial Profile: KESM-AM is a commercial station owned by Wildwood Communications Inc. The format of the station is classic country and adult contemporary. KESM-AM broadcasts to the El Dorado Springs, MO area at 1580 AM.

KESM-FM
Owner: Wildwood Communications Inc.
Editorial: 200 Radio Ln, El Dorado Springs, Missouri 64744. **T:** 1 417 876-2741
E: kesm@kesmradio.com
W: http://www.kesmradio.com
Editorial Profile: KESM-FM is a commercial station owned by Wildwood Communications Inc. The format of the station is adult contemporary and country music. KESM-FM broadcasts to the El Dorado Spring, MO area at 105.5 FM.

KESN-FM
Owner: Walt Disney Co.
Editorial: 400 Las Colinas Blvd E, Irving, Texas 75039-5579. **T:** 1 214 526-2400
W: http://espn.go.com/dallas/radio
Editorial Profile: KESN-FM is a commercial station owned by Walt Disney Co. and operated by Cumulus Media. The format of the station is sports. KESN-FM broadcasts to the Dallas area at 103.3 FM.

KESO-FM
Owner: MBM Radio Del Rio, LLC
Editorial: 1201 N Jackson Rd, Ste 900, McAllen, Texas 78501. **T:** 1 956 992-8895
Editorial Profile: KESO-FM is a commercial station owned by MBM Radio Del Rio, LLC. The format of the station is Hispanic. KESO-FM broadcasts to the South Padre Island, TX area at 92.7 FM.

KESP-AM
Owner: Cumulus Media Inc
Editorial: 3136 Boeing Way, Stockton, California 95206. **T:** 1 209 766-5103
W: http://www.sportsradio970.com
Editorial Profile: KESP-AM is a commercial station owned by Cumulus Media Inc. The format of the station is sports. KESP-AM broadcasts in the Modesto, CA area at 970 AM.

KESQ-AM
Owner: Gulf-California Broadcast Co.
Editorial: 42650 Melanie Pl, Palm Desert, California 92211-5170. **T:** 1 760 340-7000
Editorial Profile: KESQ-AM is a commercial station owned by Gulf-California Broadcast Co. The format of the station is Regional Mexican music. KESQ-AM broadcasts to the Palm Desert, CA area at 1400 AM.

KESR-FM
Owner: Results Radio Group
Editorial: 1588 Charles Dr, Redding, California 96003. **T:** 1 530 244-9700
W: http://www.1071bobfm.com
Editorial Profile: KESR-FM is a commercial station owned by Results Radio Group. The format of the station is Jack FM-Adult Hits. KESR-FM broadcasts to the Redding, CA area at 107.1 FM.

KESS-FM
Owner: Univision Communications Inc.
Editorial: 7700 John W Carpenter Fwy Fl 1, Dallas, Texas 75247-4829. **T:** 1 214 525-0400
W: http://lajefadallas.univision.com
Editorial Profile: KESS-FM is a commercial station owned by Univision Communications Inc. The format of the station is Regional Mexican. KESS-FM broadcasts to the Dallas area at 107.1 FM.

KEST-AM
Owner: Multicultural Radio Broadcasting Inc.
Editorial: 44 Gough St Ste 301, San Francisco, California 94103-5424.
T: 1 415 978-5378 **E:** kest1450@sbcglobal.net
W: http://www.kestradio.com
Editorial Profile: KEST-AM is a commercial station owned by Multicultural Radio Broadcasting Inc. The format of the station variety featuring multicultural programming. KEST-AM broadcasts to the San Francisco area at 1450 AM.

KESZ-FM
Owner: Clear Channel Media and Entertainment
Editorial: 4686 E Van Buren St Ste 300, Phoenix, Arizona 85008-6967.
T: 1 602 374-6000
W: http://www.kez999.com/main.html
Editorial Profile: KESZ-FM is a commercial station owned by Clear Channel Media and Entertainment. The format of the station is adult contemporary music. KESZ-FM broadcasts in the Phoenix area at 99.9 FM.

KETT-FM
Owner: Armada Media
Editorial: 305 E 4th St, North Platte, Nebraska 69101-6903. **T:** 1 308 532-3344
Editorial Profile: KETT-FM is a commercial station owned by Armada Media. The format of the station is rock. KETT-FM broadcasts to the Scottsbluff, NE area at 99.3 FM.

KETX-AM
Owner: Livingston Telcom Supply, Inc.
Editorial: 115 Radio Rd, Livingston, Texas 77351-7702. **T:** 1 936 327-8916
Editorial Profile: KETX-AM is a commercial station owned by Livingston Telcom Supply, Inc. The format of the station is Adult Contemporary. KETX-AM broadcasts locally to the Livingston, TX area at a frequency of 1440 AM.

KETX-FM
Owner: Livingston Telcom Supply, Inc.
Editorial: 115 Radio Rd, Livingston, Texas 77351-7702. **T:** 1 936 327-8916
E: classichits@livingston.net
W: http://www.923theeagle.com
Editorial Profile: KETX-FM is a commercial station owned by Livingston Telcom Supply, Inc. The format of the station is classic hits. KETX-FM broadcasts in the Livingston, TX area at 92.3 FM.

KEUG-FM
Owner: McKenzie River Broadcasting
Editorial: 925 Country Club Rd, Ste 200, Eugene, Oregon 97401. **T:** 1 541 484-9400
W: http://www.1055bobfm.com
Editorial Profile: KEUG-FM is a commercial station owned by McKenzie River Broadcasting. The format of the station is adult hits. KEUG-FM broadcasts to the Eugene, OR area at 105.5 FM.

KEUN-AM
Owner: Tri-Parish Broadcasting Co.
Editorial: 1237 E Ardoin St, Eunice, Louisiana 70535-6848. **T:** 1 337 457-3041
Editorial Profile: KEUN-AM is a commercial station owned by Tri-Parish Broadcasting Co. The format of the station is talk. KEUN-AM broadcasts to the Lafayette, LA area at 1490 AM.

KEUN-FM
Owner: Tri-Parish Broadcasting Co.
Editorial: 1237 E Ardoin St, Eunice, Louisiana 70535-6848. **T:** 1 337 457-3041
Editorial Profile: KEUN-FM is a commercial station owned by Tri-Parish Broadcasting Co. The format of the station is contemporary country. KEUN-FM broadcasts to the Lafayette, LA area at 105.5.

KEVA-AM
Owner: Sage Brush Broadcasting
Editorial: 568 Airport Road, Evanston, Wyoming 82930. **T:** 1 307 789-9101
E: info@1240keva.com
W: http://www.1240keva.com
Editorial Profile: KEVA-AM is a commercial station owned by Sage Brush Broadcasting. The format of the station is oldies. KEVA-AM broadcasts to the Evanston, WY area at 1240 AM.

KEVT-AM
Owner: One Mart, Corp.
Editorial: 2919 E Broadway Blvd, Tucson, Arizona 85716-5301. **T:** 1 520 272-0105
E: mail@powertalk1210.com
W: http://www.powertalk1210.com
Editorial Profile: KEVT-AM is a commercial station owned by One Mart, Corp. The format of the station is talk. KEVT-AM broadcasts to the Tuscon, AZ area at 1210 AM. The station will start to broadcast its new format on March 1, 2014.

KEWB-FM
Owner: Results Radio Group
Editorial: 1588 Charles Dr, Redding, California 96003. **T:** 1 530 244-9700
W: http://www.power94radio.com
Editorial Profile: KEWB-FM is a commercial station owned by Results Radio Group. The format of the station is rhythmic Top 40/CHR. KEWB-FM broadcasts to the Redding, CA area at 94.7 FM.

KEWF-FM
Owner: BMG Billings
Editorial: 222 N 32nd St, 10th Fl, Billings, Montana 59101. **T:** 1 406 238-1000
E: billings@benedettimedia.com
W: http://www.985thewolf.com
Editorial Profile: KEWF-FM is a commercial station owned by BMG Billings. The format is contemporary country. The station airs int he Billings, MT area at 98.5FM.

KEWI-AM
Owner: Landers Broadcasting Co. Inc.
Editorial: 115 S Main St, Benton, Arkansas 72015-4329. **T:** 1 501 778-6677
Editorial Profile: KEWI-AM is a commercial station owned by Landers Broadcasting Co. Inc. The format of the station is primarily news/talk. KEWI-AM broadcasts to the Benton, AR area at 690 AM.

KEWL-FM
Owner: American Media Investments
Editorial: 1323 College Dr, Texarkana, Texas 75503-3531. **T:** 1 903 793-1109
E: prodcommradio@cableone.net
Editorial Profile: KEWL-FM is a commercial station owned by American Media Investments. The format for the station is classic hits music. KEWL-FM broadcasts to the Texarkana, TX area at 95.1 FM.

KEWU-FM
Owner: Eastern Washington University
Editorial: 104 Radio Tv Building, Cheney, Washington 99004-2437. **T:** 1 509 359-2850
E: jazz@mail.ewu.edu
W: http://www.kewu.ewu.edu
Editorial Profile: KEWU-FM is non-commercial station owned by Eastern Washington University. The format of the station is jazz. KEWU-FM broadcasts to the Spokane, WA area at 89.5 FM.

KEXA-FM
Owner: Wolfhouse Radio Group Inc.
Editorial: 548 E Alisal St, Salinas, California 93905-2760. **T:** 1 831 757-1910
Editorial Profile: KEXA-FM is a commercial station owned by Wolfhouse Radio Group Inc. The format of the station is Spanish Christian. KEXA-FM broadcasts to the Salinas, CA area at 93.9 FM.

KEX-AM
Owner: Clear Channel Media and Entertainment
Editorial: 13333 SW 68th Pkwy Ste 310, Tigard, Oregon 97223-8304.
T: 1 503 323-6400 **E:** news@1190kex.com
W: http://www.1190kex.com
Editorial Profile: KEX-AM is a commercial station owned by Clear Channel Media and Entertainment. The format of the station is news and talk. KEX-AM broadcasts in the Portland, OR area at 1190 AM.

KEXL-FM
Owner: WJAG Inc.
Editorial: 309 Braasch Ave, Norfolk, Nebraska 68701-4113. **T:** 1 402 371-0780
W: http://www.literock97.com
Editorial Profile: KEXL-FM is a commercial station owned by WJAG Inc. The format of the station is Lite Rock/Lite AC. KEXL-FM broadcasts to Norfolk, NE and surrounding areas at 97.5 FM.

KEXO-AM
Owner: Townsquare Media, Inc.
Editorial: 315 Kennedy Ave, Grand Junction, Colorado 81501-7552. **T:** 1 970 242-7788
W: http://www.coloradowest.com/lazeta.cfm
Editorial Profile: KEXO-AM is a commercial station owned by Townsquare Media, Inc. The format for the station is talk. KEXO-AM broadcasts to the Grand Junction-Montrose, CO area at 1230 AM.

KEXP-FM
Owner: University of Washington
Editorial: 113 Dexter Ave N, Seattle, Washington 98109. **T:** 1 206 520-5800
E: info@kexp.org **W:** http://www.kexp.org
Editorial Profile: KEXP-FM is a non-commercial station owned by the University of Washington. The format is adult album

alternative music. KEXP-FM broadcasts in the Seattle area at 90.3 FM.

KEXS-AM
Owner: Catholic Radio Network
Editorial: 201 N Industrial Park Rd, Excelsior Springs, Missouri 64024. **T:** 1 816 630-1090
E: kexs1090am@gmail.com
W: http://www.thecatholicradionetwork.com
Editorial Profile: KEXS-AM is a commercial station owned by Catholic Radio Network. The format of the station is religious Catholic programming and music. KEXS-AM broadcasts to the Kansas City, MO area at 1090 AM.

KEXS-FM
Owner: Catholic Radio Network
Editorial: 201 N Industrial Park Rd, Excelsior Springs, Missouri 64024-1736.
T: 1 816 630-1090
E: catholicradionetwork@gmail.com
W: http://www.thecatholicradionetwork.com
Editorial Profile: KEXS-FM is a commercial station owned by Catholic Radio Network. The format of the station is religious Catholic programming and music. KEXS-FM broadcasts to the Kansas City, MO area at 106.1 FM.

KEXX-FM
Owner: Riviera Broadcast Group
Editorial: 4745 N 7th St Ste 410, Phoenix, Arizona 85014-3669. **T:** 1 602 648-9800
W: http://trendingradio.com
Editorial Profile: KEXX-FM is a commercial station owned by Riviera Broadcast Group. The format of the station is Hot AC. KEXX-FM broadcasts to the Phoenix area at 103.9 FM.

KEYB-FM
Owner: Altus FM Inc.
Editorial: 808 N Main St, Altus, Oklahoma 73521-3116. **T:** 1 580 482-1555
E: keyb@keyb.net **W:** http://www.keyb.net
Editorial Profile: KEYB-FM is a commercial station owned by Altus FM Inc. The format is of the station is country music. KEYB-FM broadcasts to the Altus, OK area at 107.9 FM.

KEYE-AM
Owner: Perryton Radio Inc.
Editorial: Highway 15 West, Perryton, Texas 79070. **T:** 1 806 435-5458
E: info@perryton.info **W:** http://www.keye.net
Editorial Profile: KEYE-AM is a commercial station owned by Perryton Radio Inc. The format of the station is classic country and talk. KEYE-AM broadcasts to the Perryton, TX area at 1400 AM.

KEYE-FM
Owner: Perryton Radio Inc.
Editorial: Highway 15 West, Perryton, Texas 79070. **T:** 1 806 435-5458 **E:** keye@keye.net
W: http://www.keye.net
Editorial Profile: KEYE-FM is a commercial station owned by Perryton Radio Inc.. The format of the station is adult contemporary. KEYE-FM broadcasts to the Perryton, TX area at 93.7 FM.

KEYF-AM
Owner: Mapleton Communications LLC
Editorial: 1601 E 57th Ave, Spokane, Washington 99223-6623. **T:** 1 509 448-1000
Editorial Profile: KEYF-FM is a commercial station owned by Mapleton Communications. The format of the station is adult standards. KEYF-FM broadcasts to the Spokane, WA area at a frequency of 1050 AM.

KEYF-FM
Owner: Mapleton Communications LLC
Editorial: 1601 E 57th Ave, Spokane, Washington 99223. **T:** 1 509 448-1000
W: http://www.1011fmspokane.com
Editorial Profile: KEYF-FM is a commercial station owned by Mapleton Communications LLC. The format of the station is classic hits. KEYF-FM broadcasts to the Spokane, WA area on 101.1 FM.

KEYG-AM
Owner: Wheeler Broadcasting Inc.
Editorial: #1 Radio Road, Grand Coulee, Washington 99133. **T:** 1 509 633-2020
E: keygprod@aol.com
W: http://www.keyg985.com
Editorial Profile: KEYG-AM is a commercial station owned by Wheeler Broadcasting Inc. The format of the station is contemporary country. KEYG-AM broadcasts to the Spokane, WA area 1490 AM.

KEYG-FM
Owner: Wheeler Broadcasting Inc.

Editorial: #1 Radio Road, Grand Coulee, Washington 99133. **T:** 1 509 633-2020
E: keygprod@aol.com
W: http://www.kxa937.com/keygfm.html
Editorial Profile: KEYG-FM is a commercial station owned by Wheeler Broadcasting Inc. The format of the station is classic hits. KEYG-FM broadcasts to the Grand Coulee, WA area at 98.5 FM.

KEYH-AM
Owner: Liberman Broadcasting Inc.
Editorial: 3000 Bering Dr, Houston, Texas 77057-5708. **T:** 1 713 315-3400
Editorial Profile: KEYH-AM is a commercial station owned by Liberman Broadcasting Inc. The format of the station is Hispanic music. KEYH-AM broadcasts to the Houston area at 850 AM.

KEYJ-FM
Owner: Townsquare Media, LLC
Editorial: 3911 S 1st St, Abilene, Texas 79605. **T:** 1 325 676-7711
W: http://www.keyj.com
Editorial Profile: KEYJ-FM is a commercial station owned by Townsquare Media, LLC. The format of the station is rock/album-oriented music. KEYJ-FM broadcasts to the Abilene, TX area at 107.9 FM.

KEYL-AM
Owner: Prairie Broadcasting Inc.
Editorial: 221 Central Ave, Long Prairie, Minnesota 56347. **T:** 1 320 732-2164
E: hotrodfm@rea-alp.com
W: http://www.kxdlhotrodradio.com
Editorial Profile: KEYL-AM is a commercial station owned byPrairie Broadcasting Inc. The format of the station is classic country. KEYL-AM broadcasts to the Long Prairie, MN area at 1400 FM.

KEYN-FM
Owner: Entercom Communications Corp.
Editorial: 2120 N Woodlawn St, Ste 352, Wichita, Kansas 67208. **T:** 1 316 685-2121
W: http://www.keyn.com
Editorial Profile: KEYN-FM is a commercial station owned by Entercom Inc. The format of the station is classic hits. KEYN-FM broadcasts to the Wichita, KS area at 103.7 FM.

KEYQ-AM
Owner: The Association for Community Education Inc.
Editorial: 2310 E Ponderosa Dr, Ste 28, Camarillo, California 93010. **T:** 1 800 260-5676
E: news@nuevavida.com
W: http://www.nuevavida.com
Editorial Profile: KEYQ-AM is a non-commercial station owned by The Association for Community Education Inc. The format of the station is Hispanic religious programming. KEYQ-AM broadcasts to the Camarillo, CA area at 980 AM.

KEYS-AM
Owner: Malkan Interactive Communications
Editorial: 2117 Leopard St, Corpus Christi, Texas 78408. **T:** 1 361 882-7411
W: http://www.espncorpus.com
Editorial Profile: KEYS-AM is a commercial station owned by Malkan Interactive Communications. The format of the station is sports/talk. KEYS-AM broadcasts to the Corpus Christi, TX area at 1440 AM.

KEYW-FM
Owner: Townsquare Media, LLC
Editorial: 2621 W A St, Pasco, Washington 99301. **T:** 1 509 547-9791
W: http://www.keyw.com
Editorial Profile: KEYW-FM is a commercial station owned by Townsquare Media, LLC. The format of the station is hot adult contemporary. KEYW-FM broadcasts to the Pasco, WA area at 98.3 FM.

KEYY-AM
Owner: Biblical Ministries Worldwide
Editorial: 307 S 1600 W, Provo, Utah 84601-3932. **T:** 1 801 374-5210 **E:** mail@keyradio.org
W: http://www.keyy.com
Editorial Profile: KEYY-AM is a non-commercial station owned by Biblical Ministries Worldwide. The format of the station is religious. KEYY-AM broadcasts to the Provo, UT area at 1450 AM.

KEYZ-AM
Owner: Cherry Creek Radio
Editorial: 410 6th St E, Williston, North Dakota 58801-5552. **T:** 1 701 572-5371
W: http://www.keyzradio.com

Editorial Profile: KEYZ-AM is a commercial station owned by Cherry Creek Radio. The format of the station is primarily news, with some classic country. KEYZ-AM broadcasts to the Williston, ND area at 660 AM.

KEZA-FM
Owner: Clear Channel Media and Entertainment
Editorial: 2049 E Joyce Blvd Ste 101, Fayetteville, Arkansas 72703-6395.
T: 1 479 582-1079
W: http://www.magic1079.com
Editorial Profile: KEZA-FM is a commercial station owned by Clear Channel Media and Entertainment. The format of the station is adult contemporary. KEZA-FM broadcasts to the Fayetteville, AR area at 107.9 FM.

KEZE-FM
Owner: Queen B Inc.
Editorial: 500 W Boone Ave, Spokane, Washington 99201. **T:** 1 509 324-4200
W: http://www.hot969.com
Editorial Profile: KEZE-FM is a commercial station owned by Queen B Inc. The format of the station is urban contemporary/Top 40. KEZE-FM broadcasts to the Spokane, WA area at 96.9 FM.

KEZJ-AM
Owner: Boise State University
Editorial: 1910 University Dr, Boise, Idaho 83725-0001. **T:** 1 208 426-3663
W: http://www.radiobilingue.org
Editorial Profile: KEZJ-AM is a non-commercial station owned by Boise State University. The format of the station is Spanish/bilingual news-talk. KESJ-AM broadcasts to the Boise, ID area at 1450 AM.

KEZJ-FM
Owner: Townsquare Media, LLC
Editorial: 415 Park Ave, Twin Falls, Idaho 83301. **T:** 1 208 733-7512
W: http://www.kezj.com
Editorial Profile: KEZJ-FM is a commercial station owned by Townsquare Media, LLC. The format is contemporary country music. The station broadcasts to the Twin Falls, Idaho area 95.7 FM.

KEZK-FM
Owner: CBS Radio
Editorial: 1220 Olive St Fl 3, Saint Louis, Missouri 63103-2324. **T:** 1 314 621-2345
W: http://fresh1025.radio.com
Editorial Profile: KEZK-FM is a commercial station owned by CBS Radio. The format of the station is Adult Contemporary. KEZK-FM broadcasts to the St. Louis area at 102.5 FM.

KEZM-AM
Owner: Merchant Broadcasting Inc.
Editorial: 113 E Napoleon St, Sulphur, Louisiana 70663. **T:** 1 337 527-3611
E: kezm1310am@structurex.net
Editorial Profile: KEZM-AM is a commercial station owned by Merchant Broadcasting Inc. The format of the station is sports. KEZM-AM broadcasts to the Sulphur, LA area at 1310 AM.

KEZN-FM
Owner: CBS Radio
Editorial: 72915 Parkview Dr, Palm Desert, California 92260. **T:** 1 760 340-9383
W: http://www.ez103.com
Editorial Profile: KEZN-FM is a commercial station owned by CBS Radio. The format of the station is adult contemporary. KEZN-FM broadcasts to the Palm Desert, CA area at 103.1 FM.

KEZO-FM
Owner: Journal Broadcast Group
Editorial: 10714 Mockingbird Dr, Omaha, Nebraska 68127-1942. **T:** 1 402 592-5300
W: http://www.z92.com
Editorial Profile: KEZO-FM is a commercial station owned by Journal Broadcast Group. The format of the station is rock. KEZO-FM broadcasts to the Omaha, NE area at 92.3 FM.

KEZP-FM
Owner: Mapleton Communications
Editorial: 92 W Shamrock Ave, Pineville, Louisiana 71360-6435. **T:** 1 318 487-1035
E: red1043kezp@gmail.com
W: http://red1043.com
Editorial Profile: KEZP-FM is a commercial station owned by Opus Broadcasting of Alexandria, LLC. The format of the station is news/talk. KEZP-FM broadcasts to the Alexandria, LA area at 104.3 FM.

KEZR-FM
Owner: Digity LLC
Editorial: 190 Park Center Plz Ste 200, San Jose, California 95113-2223.
T: 1 408 287-5775 **W:** http://mymix1065.com
Editorial Profile: KEZR-FM is a commercial station owned by Digity LLC. The format of the station is hot adult contemporary. KEZR-FM broadcasts to the San Jose, CA area at 106.5 FM.

KEZS-FM
Owner: Max Media
Editorial: 324 Broadway St, Cape Girardeau, Missouri 63701-7331. **T:** 1 573 335-8291
E: k103@riverradio.net
W: http://www.k103fm.com
Editorial Profile: KEZS-FM is a commercial station owned by Max Media. The format of the station is contemporary country. KEZS-FM broadcasts to the Cape Girardeau, MO area at 102.9 FM.

KEZW-AM
Owner: Entercom Communications Corp.
Editorial: 4700 S Syracuse St, Ste 1050, Denver, Colorado 80237-2710.
T: 1 303 967-2700
W: http://www.studio1430.com
Editorial Profile: KEZW-AM is a commercial station owned by Entercom Communications Corp. The format of the station is adult standards. KEZW-AM broadcasts to the Denver area at 1430 AM.

KEZX-AM
Owner: Opus Broadcasting Systems Inc.
Editorial: 511 Rossanley Dr, Medford, Oregon 97501. **T:** 1 541 772-0322
E: news@opusradio.com
W: http://www.sportsradio730.com
Editorial Profile: KEZX-AM is a non-commercial station owned by Opus Broadcasting Systems Inc. The format of the station is sports. KEZX-AM broadcasts to the Medford, OR area at 730 AM.

KEZY-AM
Owner: Hi-Favor Broadcasting LLC
Editorial: 136 S Oak Knoll Ave, Ste 202, Pasadena, California 91101.
T: 1 626 356-4230
W: http://www.nuevavida.com
Editorial Profile: KEZY-AM is a commercial station owned by Hi-Favor Broadcasting LLC. The format of the station is Hispanic and religious. KEZY-AM broadcasts to the Pasadena, CA area at 1240 AM.

KFAB-AM
Owner: Clear Channel Media and Entertainment
Editorial: 5010 Underwood Ave, Omaha, Nebraska 68132-2236. **T:** 1 402 561-2000
W: http://www.kfab.com
Editorial Profile: KFAB-AM is a commercial station owned by Clear Channel Media and Entertainment. The format of the station is news and talk. KFAB-AM broadcasts in the Omaha, NE area at 1110 AM.

KFAE-FM
Owner: Washington State University
Editorial: Murrow Center, Room 382, Pullman, Washington 99164. **T:** 1 509 335-6500
E: nwpr@wsu.edu **W:** http://www.nwpr.org
Editorial Profile: KFAE-FM is a non-commercial station owned by Washington State University. The format classical music and news. KFAE-FM broadcasts to the Kennewick, WA area at 89.1 FM.

KFAI-FM
Owner: Fresh Air Inc.
Editorial: 1808 Riverside Ave, Minneapolis, Minnesota 55454. **T:** 1 612 341-3144
E: newsdepartment@kfai.org
W: http://www.kfai.org
Editorial Profile: KFAI-FM is a non-commercial station owned by Fresh Air Inc. The format of the station is variety. KFAI-FM broadcasts to the Minneapolis area at 90.3 FM.

KFAL-AM
Owner: Zimmer Radio Group
Editorial: 1805 Westminster Ave, Fulton, Missouri 65251. **T:** 1 573 642-3341
E: kfal@zrgmail.com
W: http://www.kfalthebig900.com
Editorial Profile: KFAL-AM is a commercial station owned by Zimmer Radio Group. The format of the station is country music. KFAL-AM broadcasts in the Fulton, MO area at 900 AM.

KFAN-AM

Owner: Clear Channel Media and Entertainment
Editorial: 1530 Greenview Dr SW, Ste 200, Rochester, Minnesota 55902.
T: 1 507 288-3888
W: http://www.fan1270.com
Editorial Profile: KFAN-AM is a commercial station owned by Clear Channel Media and Entertainment. The format of the station is sports. KFAN-AM broadcasts to the Rochester, MN area at 1270 AM.

KFAN-FM

Owner: Hill Country Broadcasting, LLC
Editorial: 210 Woodcrest St, Fredericksburg, Texas 78624. **T:** 1 830 997-2197
W: http://www.knafam.com
Editorial Profile: KFAN-FM is a commercial station owned by Hill Country Broadcasting, LLC. The format of the station is adult album alternative. KFAN-FM broadcasts to the Fredericksburg, TX area at 107.9 FM.

KFAQ-AM

Owner: Journal Broadcast Group
Editorial: 4590 E 29th St, Tulsa, Oklahoma 74114-6208. **T:** 1 918 743-7814
W: http://www.1170kfaq.com
Editorial Profile: KFAQ-AM is a commercial station owned by the Journal Broadcast Group. The format of the station is news and talk. KFAQ-AM broadcasts to the Tulsa, OK area at 1170 AM.

KFAR-AM

Owner: Last Frontier Mediactive, LLC
Editorial: 819 1st Ave Ste A, Fairbanks, Alaska 99701-4449. **T:** 1 907 451-5910
W: http://www.kfar660.com
Editorial Profile: KFAR-AM is a commercial station owned by Last Frontier Mediactive, LLC. The format of the station is news/talk. KFAR-AM broadcasts locally to the Fairbanks, AK area at 660 AM.

KFAT-FM

Owner: Ohana Media Group
Editorial: 833 Gambell St, Anchorage, Alaska 99501-3756. **T:** 1 907 344-4045
W: http://www.kfat929.com
Editorial Profile: KFAT-FM is a commercial station owned by Ohana Media Group. The format of the station is Top 40/CHR. KFAT-FM broadcasts to the Anchorage, AK area at a frequency of 92.9 FM.

KFAV-FM

Owner: Kaspar Broadcasting Co.
Editorial: 1217 N State Highway 47, Warrenton, Missouri 63383-1330.
T: 1 636 377-2300 **E:** kwrekfav@socket.net
W: http://www.kfav.com
Editorial Profile: KFAV-FM is a commercial station owned by Kaspar Broadcasting Co. The format of the station is contemporary country music. KFAV-FM broadcasts to the St. Louis area at 99.9 FM.

KFAX-AM

Owner: Salem Communications
Editorial: 39138 Fremont Blvd, Fremont, California 94538-1316. **T:** 1 510 713-1100
E: comments@kfax.com
W: http://www.kfax.com
Editorial Profile: KFAX-AM is a commercial station owned by Salem Communications. The format of the station is Christian talk. KFAX-AM broadcasts to the San Francisco and San Jose, CA markets at 1100 AM. Please submit PSAs via their website.

KFAY-AM

Owner: Cumulus Media Inc.
Editorial: 4209 N Frontage Rd, Fayetteville, Arkansas 72703-5002. **T:** 1 479 521-5566
E: newstalk1030@cumulus.com
W: http://www.newstalk1030.com
Editorial Profile: KFAY-AM is a commercial station owned by Cumulus Media Inc. The format of the station is news and talk. KFAY-AM broadcasts to the Fayetteville, AR area at 1030 AM.

KFBC-AM

Owner: Montgomery Broadcasting
Editorial: 1806 Capitol Ave, Cheyenne, Wyoming 82001-4530. **T:** 1 307 634-4461
E: production@kfbcradio.com
W: http://kfbcradio.com

KFBD-FM

Owner: Goodradio.TV LLC
Editorial: 313 Old Route 66, Saint Robert, Missouri 65584. **T:** 1 573 336-4913
E: kjpw@regionalradio.com
W: http://www.regionalradio.com

Editorial Profile: KFBD-FM is a commercial station owned by Goodradio.TV LLC. The format of the station is adult contemporary. KFBD-FM broadcasts to the Springfield, MO, area at 97.9 FM.

KFBK-AM

Owner: Clear Channel Media and Entertainment
Editorial: 1545 River Park Dr Ste 500, Sacramento, California 95815-4693.
T: 1 916 929-5325
E: kfbknews@clearchannel.com
W: http://www.kfbk.com
Editorial Profile: KFBK-AM is a commercial station owned by Clear Channel Media and Entertainment. The format of the station is news and talk. KFBK-AM broadcasts to the Sacramento, CA area at 1530 AM.

KFBK-FM

Owner: Clear Channel Media and Entertainment
Editorial: 1545 River Park Dr Ste 500, Sacramento, California 95815-4693.
T: 1 916 929-5325
E: kfbknews@clearchannel.com
W: http://www.kfbk.com
Editorial Profile: KFBK-FM is a commercial station owned by Clear Channel Media and Entertainment. The format of the station is news/talk. KFBK-FM broadcasts to the Sacramento, CA area at 93.1 FM. The station simulcasts KFBK-AM 1530.

KFBN-FM

Owner: Fargo Baptist Church
Editorial: 3303 23rd Ave S, Fargo, North Dakota 58103. **T:** 1 701 232-5500
E: heaven887@cableone.net
W: http://www.kfbn.org
Editorial Profile: KFBN-FM is a non-commercial station owned by Fargo Baptist Church. The format of the station is gospel music and religious programming. KFBN-FM broadcasts to the Fargo, ND area at 88.7 FM.

KFBT-FM

Owner: Clear Channel Media and Entertainment
Editorial: 83 E Shaw Ave, Ste 150, Fresno, California 93710-7622. **T:** 1 559 230-4300
W: http://www.thebeat1037.com
Editorial Profile: KFBT-FM is a commercial station owned by Clear Channel Media and Entertainment. The format of the station is urban contemporary, more specifically "Gen-X Rhythmic." KFBT-FM broadcasts to the Fresno, CA area at 103.7 FM.

KFBW-FM

Owner: Clear Channel Media and Entertainment
Editorial: 13333 SW 68th Pkwy Ste 310, Tigard, Oregon 97223-8304.
T: 1 503 323-6400
W: http://www.1059thebrew.com
Editorial Profile: KFBW-FM is a commercial station owned by Clear Channel Media and Entertainment. The format of the station is classic rock. KFBW-FM broadcasts to the Portland, OR area at 105.9 FM.

KFBX-AM

Owner: Clear Channel Media and Entertainment
Editorial: 546 9th Ave, Fairbanks, Alaska 99701-4902. **T:** 1 907 450-1000
E: kfbx@clearchannel.com
W: http://970kfbx.com
Editorial Profile: KFBX-AM is a commercial station owned by Clear Channel Media and Entertainment. The format of the station is talk. KFBX-AM broadcasts in the Fairbanks, AK area at 970 AM.

KFBZ-FM

Owner: Entercom Communications Corp.
Editorial: 2120 N Woodlawn St, Ste 352, Wichita, Kansas 67208. **T:** 1 316 685-2121
W: http://www.1053thebuzz.com
Editorial Profile: KFBZ-FM is a commercial station owned by Entercom Communications Corp. The format of the station is hot adult contemporary. KFBZ-FM broadcasts to the Wichita, KS area at 105.3 FM.

KFCD-AM

Owner: Bernard Radio
Editorial: 12900 Preston Rd Ste 201, Dallas, Texas 75230-1380. **T:** 1 972 354-1990
W: http://www.kfcd990.com/
Editorial Profile: KFCD-AM is a commercial station owned by Bernard Radio and operated by Principle Broadcasting, LLC. The format of the station is business talk. KFCD-AM broadcasts to the Dallas area at 990 AM.

KFCF-FM

Owner: Fresno Free College Foundation
Editorial: 1449 N Wishon Ave, Fresno, California 93728. **T:** 1 559 233-2221
W: http://www.kfcf.org
Editorial Profile: KFCF-FM is a non-commercial station owned by the Fresno Free College Foundation. The format of the station is variety. KFCF-FM broadcasts in the Fresno, CA area at 88.1 FM.

KFCM-FM

Owner: KFCM Inc.
Editorial: 11 FM 101 Rd, Hardy, Arkansas 72542-0458. **T:** 1 870 856-3249
E: hometownradio@centurytel.net
Editorial Profile: KFCM-FM is a commercial station owned by KFCM Inc. The format of the station is oldies. KFCM-FM broadcasts to the Hardy, AR area at 98.3 FM.

KFDI-FM

Owner: Journal Broadcast Group
Editorial: 4200 N Old Lawrence Rd, Wichita, Kansas 67219. **T:** 1 316 838-9141
E: news@kfdi.com **W:** http://www.kfdi.com
Editorial Profile: KFDI-FM is a commercial station owned by Journal Broadcast Group. The format of the station is contemporary country. KFDI-FM broadcasts to the Wichita, KS area at 101.3 FM.

KFEB-FM

Owner: Eagle Bluff Enterprises
Editorial: 932 County Road 448, Poplar Bluff, Missouri 63901-9018. **T:** 1 573 686-3700
E: frn@tcmax.net
Editorial Profile: KFEB-FM is a commercial station owned by Eagle Bluff Enterprises. The format of the station is rock alternative. KFEB-FM broadcasts to the Poplar Bluff, MO area at 107.5 FM.

KFEG-FM

Owner: Wynne Broadcasting Co.
Editorial: 1338 Oregon Ave, Klamath Falls, Oregon 97601-6540. **T:** 1 541 882-4656
E: webmaster@klamathradio.com
W: http://www.klamathradio.com
Editorial Profile: KFEG-FM is a commercial station owned by Wynne Broadcasting Co. The format of the station is classic rock. KFEG-FM broadcasts to the Klamath Falls, OR area at a frequency of 104.7 FM.

KFEL-AM

Owner: Kansas City Catholic Network, Inc.
Editorial: 3003 N Elizabeth St, Ste D, Pueblo, Colorado 81008-1153. **T:** 1 816 630-1090
W: http://www.thecatholicradionetwork.com
Editorial Profile: KFEL-AM is a commercial station owned by Kansas City Catholic Network, Inc. The format of the station is religious. KFEL-AM broadcasts to the Pueblo, Co area at 970 AM.

KFEQ-AM

Owner: Eagle Communications
Editorial: 4104 Country Ln, Saint Joseph, Missouri 64506-4921. **T:** 1 816 233-8881
W: http://www.680kfeq.com
Editorial Profile: KFEQ-AM is a commercial station owned by Eagle Communications. The format of the station is news and talk. KFEQ-AM broadcasts to the Saint Joseph, MO area at 680 AM.

KFEZ-FM

Owner: Magnus (Edward)
Editorial: 516 Main St, Walsenburg, Colorado 81089-2036 **E:** production@socoradio.com
W: http://easy1013.com
Editorial Profile: KFEZ-FM is a commercial station owned by Magnus (Edward) and operated by SOCO Radio. The format of the station is soft adult contemporary. KFEZ-FM broadcasts to the Greater Southern Colorado area at a frequency of 101.3 FM.

KFFA-AM

Owner: Delta Broadcasting
Editorial: 1360 Radio Dr, Helena, Arkansas 72342. **T:** 1 870 338-8361
E: kffa@arkansas.net **W:** http://www.kffa.com
Editorial Profile: KFFA-AM is a commercial station owned by Delta Broadcasting. The format of the station is classic country and blues. KFFA-AM broadcasts to the Helena, AR area at 1360 AM.

KFFA-FM

Owner: Delta Broadcasting
Editorial: 1360 Radio Dr, Helena, Arkansas 72342. **T:** 1 870 338-8331
E: kffa@arkansas.net **W:** http://www.kffa.com
Editorial Profile: KFFA-FM is a commercial station owned by Delta Broadcasting. The

format of the station is adult contemporary. KFFA-FM broadcasts to the Helena, AR area at 103.1 FM.

KFFB-FM

Owner: Freedom Broadcasting, Inc.
Editorial: 12080 Edgemont Rd, Shirley, Arkansas 72153. **T:** 1 501 884-6812
E: kffb@kffb.com **W:** http://www.kffb.com
Editorial Profile: KFFB-FM is a commercial station owned by Freedom Broadcasting, Inc. The format of the station is adult standards music. KFFB-FM broadcasts to the Shirley, AR area at 106.1 FM.

KFFF-FM

Owner: Clear Channel Media and Entertainment
Editorial: 5010 Underwood Ave, Omaha, Nebraska 68132. **T:** 1 402 561-2000
W: http://www.twister933.com
Editorial Profile: KFFF-FM is a commercial station owned by Clear Channel Media and Entertainment. The format of the station is classic country. KFFF-FM broadcasts to the Omaha, NE area at 93.3 FM.

KFFG-FM

Owner: Cumulus Media Inc.
Editorial: 55 Hawthorne St, San Francisco, California 94105-3906. **T:** 1 415 819-9568
W: http://www.kfog.com
Editorial Profile: KFFG-FM is a commercial station owned by Cumulus Media Inc. The format of the station is adult album alternative. KFFG-FM broadcasts to the San Jose area at 97.7 FM.

KFFK-AM

Owner: Butler Broadcasting
Editorial: 1780 W Holly St, Fayetteville, Arkansas 72703. **T:** 1 479 582-3776
Editorial Profile: KFFK-AM is a commercial station owned by Butler Broadcasting. The format of the station is sports. KFFK-AM broadcasts in the Fayetteville, AR area at 1390 AM.

KFFM-FM

Owner: Townsquare Media, LLC
Editorial: 4010 Summitview Ave, Yakima, Washington 98908. **T:** 1 509 972-3461
W: http://www.kffm.com
Editorial Profile: KFFM-FM is a commercial station owned by Townsquare Media, LLC. The format of the station is Rhythmic Top 40 music. KFFM-FM broadcasts to the Yakima, WA area at 107.3 FM.

KFFN-AM

Owner: Journal Broadcast Group
Editorial: 7280 E Rosewood St, Tucson, Arizona 85710-1350. **T:** 1 520 795-7490
W: http://www.espntucson.com
Editorial Profile: KFFN-AM is a commercial station owned by Journal Broadcast Group. The format of the station is sports. KFFN-AM broadcasts in the Tucson, AZ area at 1490 AM.

KFFX-FM

Owner: Emporia Radio Stations Inc.
Editorial: 1420 C Of E Dr, Emporia, Kansas 66801. **T:** 1 620 342-1400 **E:** kvoe@kvoe.com
W: http://www.kvoe.com
Editorial Profile: KFFX-FM is a commercial station owned by Emporia Radio Stations Inc. The format of the station is hot adult contemporary music. KFFX-FM broadcasts in the Emporia, KS at 104.9 FM

KFGE-FM

Owner: NRG Media LLC
Editorial: 4343 O St, Lincoln, Nebraska 68510-1753. **T:** 1 402 475-4567
E: froggy@froggy981.com
W: http://www.froggy981.com
Editorial Profile: KFGE-FM is a commercial station owned by NRG Media LLC. The format of the station is country. KFGE-FM broadcasts to the Lincoln, NE area at 98.1 FM.

KFGI-FM

Owner: Red Rock Radio Corporation
Editorial: 121 5Th Ave Ne Ste 2, Brainerd, Minnesota 56401-3116. **T:** 1 218 822-3324
Editorial Profile: KFGI-FM is a commercial station owned by Red Rock Radio Corporation. The format of the station is classic rock. KFGI-FM's target audience is adults, ages 18 to 54, in the Minneapolis- St. Paul, MN area.

KFGO-AM

Owner: Midwest Communications

Editorial: 1020 25th St S, Fargo, North Dakota 58103-2312. **T:** 1 701 237-5346
E: kfgo.news@mwcradio.com
W: http://www.kfgo.com
Editorial Profile: KFGO-AM is a commercial station owned by Midwest Communications. The format of the station is news, talk and sports. KFGO-AM broadcasts to the Fargo, ND area at 790 AM.

KFGY-FM
Owner: Sonoma Media Group
Editorial: 1410 Neotomas Ave, Santa Rosa, California 95405-7533. **T:** 1 707 543-0100
W: http://www.froggy929.com
Editorial Profile: KFGY-FM is a commercial station owned by Sonoma Media Group. The format of the station is contemporary country. KGFY-FM broadcasts to the Santa Rosa, CA area at 92.9 FM.

KFH-AM
Owner: Entercom Communications Corp.
Editorial: 2120 N Woodlawn St, Ste 352, Wichita, Kansas 67208. **T:** 1 316 685-2121
E: letters@kfhradio.com
W: http://www.kfhradio.com
Editorial Profile: KFH-AM is a commercial station owned by Entercom Communications Corp. The format of the station is sportstalk programming. KFH-AM broadcasts to the Wichita, KS area at 1240 AM.

KFH-FM
Owner: Entercom Communications Corp.
Editorial: 2120 N Woodlawn St, Ste 352, Wichita, Kansas 67208. **T:** 1 316 685-2121
E: letters@kfhradio.com
W: http://www.kfhradio.com
Editorial Profile: KFH-FM is a commercial station owned by Entercom Communications Corp. The format of the station is sportstalk programming. KFH-FM broadcasts to Wichita, KS area at 98.7 FM.

KFHL-FM
Owner: Mary V. Harris Foundation
Editorial: 2600 Kenwood Rd, Bakersfield, California 93306. **T:** 1 800 617-9673
W: http://www.kfhlradio.com
Editorial Profile: KFHL-FM is a non-commercial station owned by Mary V. Harris Foundation. The format of the station is religious. KFHL-FM broadcasts to the Bakersfield, CA area at 91.7 FM.

KFIA-AM
Owner: Salem Communications
Editorial: 1425 River Park Dr, Ste 520, Sacramento, California 95815.
T: 1 916 924-0710 **W:** http://www.kfia.com
Editorial Profile: KFIA-AM is a commercial station owned by Salem Communications. The format of the station is religious talk. KFIA-AM broadcasts to the Sacramento, CA area at 710 AM.

KFI-AM
Owner: Clear Channel Media and Entertainment
Editorial: 3400 W Olive Ave Ste 550, Burbank, California 91505-5544. **T:** 1 818 559-2252
E: kfinewsdirector@kfi640.com
W: http://www.kfiam640.com
Editorial Profile: KFI-AM is a commercial station owned by Clear Channel Media and Entertainment. The format of the station is news and talk. KFI-AM broadcasts to the Los Angeles area at 640 AM. The station does not accepts PSAs.

KFIG-AM
Owner: Ostlund(John Edwards)
Editorial: 1415 Fulton St, Fresno, California 93721-1609. **T:** 1 559 497-5118
W: http://940espnfresno.com
Editorial Profile: KFIG-AM is a commercial station owned by John Edwards Ostlund. The format of the station is sports. KFIG-AM broadcasts to the Fresno, CA area at 940 AM.

KFIL-AM
Owner: Cumulus Media Inc.
Editorial: 300 Saint Paul St SW, Preston, Minnesota 55965. **T:** 1 507 765-3856
E: production@kfilradio.com
W: http://www.kfilradio.com
Editorial Profile: KFIL-AM is a commercial station owned by Cumulus Media Inc. The format of the station is country and talk. KFIL-AM broadcasts to the Preston, MN area at 1060 AM.

KFIL-FM
Owner: Cumulus Media Inc.
Editorial: 300 Saint Paul St SW, Preston, Minnesota 55965. **T:** 1 507 765-3856
E: production@kfilradio.com
W: http://www.kfilradio.com
Editorial Profile: KFIL-FM is a commercial station owned by Cumulus Media Inc. The format of the station is classic country. KFIL-FM broadcasts in the Preston, MN area at 103.1 FM.

KFIN-FM
Owner: East Arkansas Broadcasters Inc.
Editorial: 407 W Parker Rd, Jonesboro, Arkansas 72404. **T:** 1 870 932-1079
E: kfin@kfin.com **W:** http://www.kfin.com
Editorial Profile: KFIN-FM is a commercial station owned by East Arkansas Broadcasters Inc. The format of the station is contemporary country. KFIN-FM broadcasts to the Jonesboro, AR area at 107.9 FM.

KFIR-AM
Owner: Radio Fiesta Network LLC
Editorial: 28041 Pleasant Valley Rd, Sweet Home, Oregon 97386. **T:** 1 541 367-5117
E: info@kfir720am.com
W: http://www.kfir720am.com
Editorial Profile: KFIR-AM is a commercial station owned by Radio Fiesta Network LLC. The format of the station is primarily talk. KFIR-AM broadcasts to the Sweet Home, OR area at 720 AM.

KFIS-FM
Owner: Salem Communications
Editorial: 6400 SE Lake Rd, Ste 350, Portland, Oregon 97222. **T:** 1 503 786-0600
W: http://www.1041thefish.com
Editorial Profile: KFIS-FM is a commercial station owned by Salem Communications. The format of the station is contemporary Christian music. KFIS-FM broadcasts to the Portland, OR area at 104.1 FM.

KFIT-AM
Owner: Martin Broadcasting
Editorial: 110 Wild Basin Rd, West Lake Hills, Texas 78746-3339. **T:** 1 512 328-8400
E: kfitam@yahoo.com
W: http://gospel1060.com
Editorial Profile: KFIT-AM is a commercial station owned by Martin Broadcasting. The format of the station is gospel music and Hispanic religious programming. KFIT-AM broadcasts to the Austin, TX area at 1060 AM.

KFIV-AM
Owner: Clear Channel Media and Entertainment
Editorial: 2121 Lancey Dr, Modesto, California 95355-3036. **T:** 1 209 551-1306
E: modestopsa@clearchannel.com
W: http://www.powertalk1360.com/main.html
Editorial Profile: KFIV-AM is a commercial station owned by Clear Channel Media and Entertainment. The format of the station is news and talk. KFIV-AM broadcasts to the Modesto, CA area at 1360 AM.

KFIX-FM
Owner: Hull Broadcasting
Editorial: 2300 Hall St, Hays, Kansas 67601-3062. **T:** 1 785 625-2578
E: haysnews@eagleradio.net
W: http://www.kfix.com
Editorial Profile: KFIX-FM is a commercial station owned by Hull Broadcasting. The format of the station is classic rock music. KFIX-FM broadcasts to the Hays, KS area at 96.9 FM.

KFIZ-AM
Owner: RBH Enterprises Inc.
Editorial: 254 Winnebago Dr, Fond du Lac, Wisconsin 54935. **T:** 1 920 921-1071
E: newstip@kfiz.com **W:** http://www.kfiz.com
Editorial Profile: KFIZ-AM is a commercial station owned by RBH Enterprises Inc. The format of the station is news, sports and talk. KFIZ-AM broadcasts to the Fond Du Lac, WI area at 1450 AM.

KFJB-AM
Owner: Marshalltown Broadcasting Inc.
Editorial: 123 W Main St, Marshalltown, Iowa 50158. **T:** 1 641 753-3361
E: news@marshalltownbroadcasting.com
W: http://www.1230kfjb.com
Editorial Profile: KFJB-AM is a commercial station owned by Marshalltown Broadcasting Inc. The format of the station is news and talk. KFJB-AM broadcasts in the Marshalltown, IA area at 1230 AM.

KFJC-FM
Owner: Foothill- De Anza Community College
Editorial: 12345 S El Monte Rd, Los Altos Hills, California 94022-4504.
T: 1 650 949-7260 **E:** info@kfjc.org
Editorial Profile: KFJC-FM is a non-commercial station owned by Foothill- De Anza Community College. The format of the station is variety, including alternative and underground music. KFJC-FM broadcasts to the Los Altos Hills, CA area at 89.7 FM.

KFJZ-AM
Owner: SIGA Broadcasting Corp.
Editorial: 1320 N Shepherd Dr, Houston, Texas 77008-3752. **T:** 1 713 868-5559
Editorial Profile: KFJZ-AM is a commercial station owned by SIGA Broadcasting Corp. The format of the station is Hispanic Christian. KFJZ-AM broadcasts in the Dallas area at AM 870.

KFKA-AM
Owner: Broadcast Media
Editorial: 820 11th Ave, Greeley, Colorado 80631. **T:** 1 970 356-1310
E: info@1310kfka.com
W: http://www.1310kfka.com
Editorial Profile: KFKA-AM is a commercial station owned by Broadcast Media. The station's format is news, sports and talk. KFKA-AM broadcasts to the Greely, CO area at 1310 AM.

KFKF-FM
Owner: Wilks Broadcast Group
Editorial: 508 Westport Rd, Kansas City, Missouri 64111-3012. **T:** 1 816 753-4000
W: http://www.kfkf.com
Editorial Profile: KFKF-FM is a commercial station owned by Wilks Broadcast Group. The format of the station is contemporary country music. KFKF-FM broadcasts to the Kansas City, MO at 94.1 FM.

KFKX-FM
Owner: Hastings College
Editorial: 710 N Turner Ave, Hastings, Nebraska 68901-7621. **T:** 1 402 461-7342
E: kfkx@hastings.edu
W: http://hcmediaonline.org/index.cfm
Editorial Profile: KFKX-FM is a commercial station owned by Hastings College. The format of the station is primarily rock alternative. KFKX-FM broadcasts to the Hastings, NE area at 90.1 FM.

KFLB-AM
Owner: Family Life Radio
Editorial: 808 Tower Dr, Ste 6, Odessa, Texas 79761. **T:** 1 432 580-5352
W: http://www.myflr.org
Editorial Profile: KFLB-AM is a non-commercial station owned by Family Life Radio. The format of the station is contemporary Christian. KFLB-AM broadcasts to the Odessa, TX area at 920 AM.

KFLB-FM
Owner: Family Life Radio
Editorial: 808 Tower Dr Ste 6, Odessa, Texas 79761-4264. **T:** 1 520 742-6976
W: http://www.myflr.org
Editorial Profile: KFRI-FM is a non-commercial station owned by Family Life Radio. The format of the station is contemporary Christian. KFRI-FM broadcasts to the Stanton, TX area at 88.1 FM.

KFLC-AM
Owner: Univision Communications Inc.
Editorial: 7700 John W Carpenter Fwy Fl 1, Dallas, Texas 75247-4829. **T:** 1 214 525-0400
W: http://univisionamerica.com
Editorial Profile: KFLC-AM is a commercial station owned by Univision Communications Inc. The format of the station is Hispanic news and talk programming. KFLC-AM broadcasts to the Dallas area at 1270 AM.

KFLD-AM
Owner: Townsquare Media, LLC
Editorial: 2621 W A St, Pasco, Washington 99301. **T:** 1 509 547-9791
W: http://www.newstalk870.am
Editorial Profile: KFLD-AM is a commercial station owned by Townsquare Media, LLC. The format of the station is news, talk and sports. KFLD-AM broadcasts to the Pasco, WA area at 870 AM.

KFLF-FM
Owner: Fresh Life Church, Inc.
Editorial: 120 2nd St E, Kalispell, Montana 59901-4533. **T:** 1 406 257-3339
W: http://www.freshliferadio.com
Editorial Profile: KFLF-FM is a non-commercial station owned by Fresh Life Church, Inc. The format of the station is religious programming. KFLF-FM broadcasts to the Somers, MT area at 91.3 FM.

KFLG-AM
Owner: Cameron Broadcasting Inc.
Editorial: 2350 Miracle Mile Ste 300, Bullhead City, Arizona 86442-7505. **T:** 1 928 763-5586
E: news@cameronbroadcasting.com
W: http://www.talkatoz.com
Editorial Profile: KFLG-AM is a commercial station owned by Cameron Broadcasting Inc. The format of the station is adult standards. KFLG-AM broadcasts to the Bullhead City, AZ area at 1000 AM.

KFLG-FM
Owner: Cameron Broadcasting Inc.
Editorial: 2350 Miracle Mile Ste 300, Bullhead City, Arizona 86442-7505. **T:** 1 928 763-5586
W: http://www.kflg947.com
Editorial Profile: KFLG-FM is a commercial station owned by Cameron Broadcasting Inc. The format of the station is country music. KFLG-FM broadcasts in the Bullhead City, AZ area at 94.7 FM.

KFLI-FM
Owner: Flinn Broadcasting Corp.
Editorial: 929 Eastline Rd, Searcy, Arkansas 72143-8341. **T:** 1 501 268-1047
W: http://www.flinn.com
Editorial Profile: KFLI-FM is a commercial station owned by Flinn Broadcasting Corp. The format of the station is classic hits. KFLI-FM broadcasts to the Searcy, AR area at 104.7 FM.

KFLN-AM
Owner: Newell Broadcasting
Editorial: 3584 Highway 7, Baker, Montana 59313. **T:** 1 406 778-3371
E: kfln@midrivers.com
W: http://newellbroadcasting.com

KFLO-FM
Owner: Family Life Educational Foundation
Editorial: 2097 N Hearne Ave, Shreveport, Louisiana 71107-7131. **T:** 1 318 550-2000
E: info@miracle891.org
W: http://www.miracle891.org
Editorial Profile: KFLO-FM is a non-commercial station owned by Family Life Educational Foundation. The format of the station is contemporary Christian. KFLO-FM broadcasts to the Shreveport, LA area on 89.1 FM.

KFLP-AM
Owner: Ricketts(Anthony L.)
Editorial: 201 W California St, Floydada, Texas 79235-2700. **T:** 1 806 983-5704
E: kflp@kflp.net **W:** http://www.allagnews.com
Editorial Profile: KFLP-AM is a commercial station owned by Anthony L. Ricketts. The format of the station is agricultural. KFLP-AM broadcasts to the Floydada, TX area at 900 AM.

KFLP-FM
Owner: Ricketts(Anthony L.)
Editorial: 201 W California St, Floydada, Texas 79235. **T:** 1 806 983-5704 **E:** kflp@kflp.net
W: http://www.1061flipfm.com
Editorial Profile: KFLP-FM is a commercial station that is owned by Anthony L. Ricketts. The format of the station is contemporary country music. KFLP-FM broadcasts to the Floydada, TX area at 106.1 FM.

KFLQ-FM
Owner: Family Life Broadcasting, Inc.
Editorial: 300 S Lea Ave, Roswell, New Mexico 88203-4562. **T:** 1 505 296-9100
W: http://www.myflr.org
Editorial Profile: KFLQ-FM is a non-commercial station owned by Family Life Broadcasting, Inc. The format of the station is religious music and talk. KFLQ-FM broadcasts to the Albuquerque, NM area at 91.5 FM.

KFLR-FM
Owner: Family Life Broadcasting, Inc.
Editorial: 7355 N Oracle Rd, Tucson, Arizona 85704-6325. **T:** 1 520 742-6976
W: http://myflr.org
Editorial Profile: KFLR-FM is a non-commercial station owned by Family Life Broadcasting, Inc. The format of the station is religious, family-oriented programming. KFLR-FM broadcasts to the Phoenix area at 90.3 FM.

KFLS-AM
Owner: Wynne Broadcasting Co.
Editorial: 1338 Oregon Ave, Klamath Falls, Oregon 97601-6540. **T:** 1 541 882-4656
W: http://www.klamathradio.com
Editorial Profile: KFLS-AM is a commercial station owned by Wynne Broadcasting Co. The format of the station is news, talk and sports.

KFLS-AM broadcasts to the Klamath Falls, OR area at 1450 AM.

KFLS-FM
Owner: Wynne Broadcasting Co.
Editorial: 1338 Oregon Ave, Klamath Falls, Oregon 97601-6540. **T:** 1 541 882-4656
E: webmaster@klamathradio.com
W: http://www.klamathradio.com
Editorial Profile: KFLS-FM is a commercial station owned by Wynne Broadcasting Co. The format of the station is contemporary country. KFLS-FM broadcasts to the Klamath Falls, OR area at a frequency of 96.5.

KFLT-AM
Owner: Family Life Radio
Editorial: 7355 N Oracle Rd, Ste 102, Tucson, Arizona 85704. **T:** 1 520 742-6976
W: http://www.am830flr.org
Editorial Profile: KFLT-AM is a non-commercial station owned by Family Life Radio. The format of the station is contemporary Christian. KFLT-AM broadcasts to the Tuscon, AZ area at 830 AM.

KFLW-FM
Owner: Ozark Media Inc.
Editorial: 555 Marshall Dr, Saint Robert, Missouri 65584-5601. **T:** 1 573 336-5359
E: studio@kflw989.com
W: http://www.kflw989.com
Editorial Profile: KFLW-FM is a commercial station owned by Ozark Media Inc.. The format of the station is hot adult contemporary music. KFLW-FM broadcasts to the Saint Robert, MO area at 98.9 FM.

KFLX-FM
Owner: Grenax Broadcasting
Editorial: 2409 N 4th St, Ste 101, Flagstaff, Arizona 86004-3735. **T:** 1 928 779-1177
W: http://www.rewindmymusic.com
Editorial Profile: KFLX-FM is a commercial station owned by Grenax Broadcasting. The format of the station is hot adult contemporary. KFLX-FM broadcasts to the Flagstaff, AZ area at 104.1 FM.

KFLY-FM
Owner: Bicoastal Media LLC
Editorial: 1500 Valley River Dr, Ste 350, Eugene, Oregon 97401. **T:** 1 541 485-1120
W: http://www.kflyfm.com
Editorial Profile: KFLY-FM is a commercial station owned by Bicoastal Media LLC. The format of the station is rock alternative music. KFLY-FM broadcasts to the Eugene, OR area at 101.5 FM.

KFMA-FM
Owner: Lotus Communications Corp.
Editorial: 3871 N Commerce Dr, Tucson, Arizona 85705-2983. **T:** 1 520 407-4500
W: http://www.kfma.com
Editorial Profile: KFMA-FM is a commercial station owned by Lotus Communications Corp. The format of the station is rock alternative music. KFMA-FM broadcasts to the Tucson, AZ area at 102.1 FM.

KFMB-AM
Owner: Midwest Television Inc.
Editorial: 7677 Engineer Rd, San Diego, California 92111-1515. **T:** 1 858 571-8888
E: news8@kfmb.com
W: http://www.760kfmb.com
Editorial Profile: KFMB-AM is a commercial station owned by Midwest Television Inc. The format for the station is news and talk. KFMB-AM broadcasts to the San Diego area at 760 AM.

KFMB-FM
Owner: Midwest Television Inc.
Editorial: 7677 Engineer Rd, San Diego, California 92111-1515. **T:** 1 858 292-7600
W: http://www.sandiegojack.com
Editorial Profile: KFMB-FM is a commercial station owned by Midwest Television Inc. The format of the station is adults hits. KFMB-FM broadcasts to the San Diego area at 100.7 FM.

KFMC-FM
Owner: Woodward Broadcasting, Inc.
Editorial: 1371 W Lair Rd, Fairmont, Minnesota 56031. **T:** 1 507 235-5595
E: info@ksum.com **W:** http://www.kfmc.com
Editorial Profile: KFMC-FM is a commercial station owned by Woodward Broadcasting, Inc. The format for the station is classic rock. KFMC-FM broadcasts to the Fairmont, MN area at 106.5 FM.

KFMD-FM
Owner: Hog Radio, Inc.

Editorial: 2250 W Sunset Ave Ste 3, Springdale, Arkansas 72762-5187.
T: 1 479 303-2034
W: http://www.classichits1015.com
Editorial Profile: KFMD-FM is a commercial station owned by Hog Radio, Inc. The format of the station is classic hits. KFMD-FM broadcasts to the Fayetteville, AR area at a frequency of 101.5 FM.

KFMF-FM
Owner: Mapleton of Chico, LLC
Editorial: 1459 Humboldt Rd, Ste D, Chico, California 95928. **T:** 1 530 899-3600
W: http://www.kfm.com
Editorial Profile: KFMF-FM is a commercial station owned by Mapleton of Chico, LLC. The format of the station is classic rock. KFMF-FM broadcasts to the Chico, CA area at 93.9 FM.

KFMI-FM
Owner: Bicoastal Media LLC
Editorial: 5640 S Broadway St, Eureka, California 95503. **T:** 1 707 442-2000
E: eurekanews@bicoastalmedia.com
W: http://www.power963.com
Editorial Profile: KFMI-FM is a commercial station owned by Bicoastal Media LLC. The format of the station is hot adult contemporary. KFMI-FM broadcasts to the Eureka, CA area at 96.3 FM.

KFMJ-FM
Owner: TLP Communications Inc.
Editorial: 516 Stedman St, Ketchikan, Alaska 99901-6629. **T:** 1 907 247-3699
E: kfmj@alaska.fm **W:** http://www.kfmj.com
Editorial Profile: KFMJ-FM is a commercial station owned by TLP Communications. The format of the station is classic hits. KFMJ-FM's target audience is listeners, ages 35 to 100 in the Ketchikan, AK area. The station airs locally on 99.9 FM.

KFMK-FM
Owner: Crista Broadcasting
Editorial: 3600 N Capital of Texas Hwy Ste A200, Austin, Texas 78746-3219.
T: 1 512 329-4400 **E:** info@SPIRIT1059.com
W: http://www.spirit1059.com
Editorial Profile: KFMK-FM is a commercial station owned by Crista Broadcasting. The format of the station is contemporary Christian. KFMK-FM broadcasts to the Austin, TX area at 105.9 FM.

KFML-FM
Owner: Little Falls Radio Corp.
Editorial: 16405 Haven Rd, Little Falls, Minnesota 56345-6400. **T:** 1 320 632-5414
E: news@fallsradio.com
W: http://www.fallsradio.com
Editorial Profile: KFML-FM is a commercial station owned by Little Falls Radio Corp. The format of the station is hot adult contemporary. KFML-FM broadcasts to the Little Falls, MN area at 94.1 FM.

KFMM-FM
Owner: Cochise Broadcasting LLC
Editorial: 301 E US Highway 70, #B, Safford, Arizona 85546. **T:** 1 928 428-0916
W: http://www.saffordradio.com
Editorial Profile: KFMM-FM is a commercial station owned by Cochise Broadcasting LLC. The format of the station is classic rock. KFMM-FM broadcasts to the Phoenix area at 99.1 FM.

KFMN-FM
Owner: FM 97 Associates
Editorial: 1860 Leleiona St, Lihue, Hawaii 96766-9000. **T:** 1 808 246-1197
E: frontdesk@fm97radio.com
W: http://www.fm97radio.com
Editorial Profile: KFMN-FM is a commercial station owned by FM 97 Associates. The format of the station is adult contemporary. KFMN-FM broadcasts to the Greater Lihue, HI area at a frequency of 96.9 FM.

KFMO-AM
Owner: MKS Broadcasting Inc.
Editorial: 804 St Joe Drive, Park Hills, Missouri 63601. **T:** 1 573 431-1000
E: news@b104fm.com
W: http://www.kfmo.com
Editorial Profile: KFMO-AM is a commercial station owned by MKS Broadcasting Inc. The format of the station is news, talk and sports. KFMO-AM broadcasts to the Park Hills, MO area at 1240 AM.

KFMQ-FM
Owner: Clear Channel Media and Entertainment

Editorial: 1632 S Second St, Gallup, New Mexico 87301-5836. **T:** 1 505 863-9391
W: http://www.kfmqrock1061.com
Editorial Profile: KFMQ-FM is a commercial station owned by Clear Channel Media and Entertainment. The format of the station is rock music. KFMQ-FM broadcasts to the Albuquerque, NM area at 106.1 FM.

KFMT-FM
Owner: R & R Broadcasting, Inc.
Editorial: 118 E 5th St, Fremont, Nebraska 68025-5022. **T:** 1 402 721-1340
Editorial Profile: KFMT-FM is a commercial station owned by R & R Broadcasting, Inc. The format of the station is classic rock. KFMT-FM broadcasts to the Fremont, NE area at 105.5.

KFMU-FM
Owner: NRC Broadcasting
Editorial: 2955 Village Dr, Steamboat Springs, Colorado 80487-2143. **T:** 1 970 879-5368
W: http://alwaysmountaintime.com/kfmu
Editorial Profile: KFMU-FM is a commercial station owned by NRC Broadcasting. The format of the station is adult album alternative. KFMU-FM broadcasts to the Steamboat Springs, CO area at 105.5 FM.

KFMW-FM
Owner: Woodward Communications, Inc.
Editorial: 514 Jefferson St, Waterloo, Iowa 50701-5422. **T:** 1 319 234-2200
W: http://www.rock108.com
Editorial Profile: KFMW-FM is a commercial station owned by Woodward Communications, Inc. The format for the station is rock. KFMW-FM broadcasts to the Cedar Rapids, IA area at 107.9 FM.

KFMX-FM
Owner: Townsquare Media, LLC
Editorial: 4413 82nd St, Ste 300, Lubbock, Texas 79424. **T:** 1 806 798-7078
W: http://www.kfmx.com
Editorial Profile: KFMX-FM is a commercial station owned by Townsquare Media, LLC. The format of the station is rock. KFMX-FM broadcasts to the Lubbock, TX area at 95.4 FM.

KFMZ-AM
Owner: Best Broadcast Group
Editorial: 107 S Main St, Brookfield, Missouri 64628-2101. **T:** 1 660 258-3383
E: kzbk@shighway.com
W: http://www.kzbkradio.com
Editorial Profile: KFMZ-AM is a commercial station owned by Best Broadcast Group. The format of the station is hot adult contemporary. KFMZ-AM broadcasts to the Brookfield, MO area at 1470 AM.

KFNA-FM
Owner: Doud Media Group LLC
Editorial: 1740 N 1St St, Abilene, Texas 79603-7401. **T:** 1 325 437-9596
W: http://foxnewsabilene.com
Editorial Profile: KFNA-FM is a commercial station owned by Doud Media Group LLC. The format of the station is top 40/CHR. KFNA-FM broadcasts to Abilene, TX at 96.1 FM.

KFNC-FM
Owner: Cumulus Media Inc.
Editorial: 9801 Westheimer Rd Ste 700, Houston, Texas 77042-3955.
T: 1 713 266-1000
W: http://www.espn975.com
Editorial Profile: KFNC-FM is a commercial station owned by Cumulus Media Inc. The format of the station is sports. KFNC-FM broadcasts to the Houston area at 97.5 FM.

KFNN-AM
Owner: CRC Broadcasting Co.
Editorial: 8145 E Evans Rd Ste 8, Scottsdale, Arizona 85260-3645. **T:** 1 602 241-1510
W: http://www.moneyradio1510.com
Editorial Profile: KFNN-AM is a commercial station owned by CRC Broadcasting Co. The format of the station is financial news and talk. KFNN-AM broadcasts to the Phoenix area on 1510 AM.

KFNO-FM
Owner: Family Stations Inc.
Editorial: 706 W Herndon Ave, Fresno, California 93650-1033. **T:** 1 559 435-4996
E: familyradio@familyradio.org
W: http://www.familyradio.com
Editorial Profile: KFNO-FM is a commercial station owned by Family Stations Inc. The format of the station is Christian programming. KFNO-FM broadcasts to the Fresno, CA area at 90.3 FM.

KFNQ-AM
Owner: CBS Radio
Editorial: 1000 Dexter Ave N Ste 100, Seattle, Washington 98109-3577. **T:** 1 206 805-1090
W: http://seattle.cbslocal.com
Editorial Profile: KFNQ-AM is commercial station owned by CBS Radio. The format of the station is talk. KFNQ-AMbroadcasts in the Seattle area at 1090 AM.

KFNS-AM
Owner: Grand Slam Sports, LLC
Editorial: 8045 Big Bend Blvd Ste 200, Saint Louis, Missouri 63119-2714.
T: 1 314 962-0590 **W:** http://590theman.com
Editorial Profile: KFNS-AM is a commercial station owned by Grand Slam Sports, LLC. The format of the station is talk with a focus on men's interests. KFNS-AM broadcasts to the St. Louis area at 590 AM.

KFNS-FM
Owner: Westplex Broadcasting
Editorial: 30 Tower St, Moscow Mills, Missouri 63362-1139. **T:** 1 636 356-4487
W: http://www.viperrocks.com
Editorial Profile: KFNS-FM is a commercial station owned by Westplex Broadcasting. The format of the station is classic rock. KFNS-FM broadcasts to the St. Louis and Moscow Mills areas at 100.7 FM.

KFNV-FM
Owner: Radio Group(The)
Editorial: 917 Ee Wallace Blvd S, Ferriday, Louisiana 71334. **T:** 1 318 757-4200
E: kfnv@bellsouth.net
W: http://www.kfnvfm.com
Editorial Profile: KFNV-FM is a commercial station owned by The Radio Group. The format of the station is classic hits music. KFNV-FM broadcasts to the Ferriday, LA area at 107.1 FM.

KFNW-AM
Owner: Northwestern College
Editorial: 5702 52nd Ave S, Fargo, North Dakota 58104. **T:** 1 701 282-5910
E: kfnw@kfnw.org **W:** http://www.kfnw.org
Editorial Profile: KFNW-AM is a non-commercial station owned by Northwestern College. The format of the station is contemporary Christian music and talk. KFNW-AM broadcasts to the Fargo, ND area at 1200 AM.

KFNW-FM
Owner: Northwestern College
Editorial: 5702 52nd Ave S, Fargo, North Dakota 58104. **T:** 1 701 282-5910
E: kfnw@kfnw.org **W:** http://www.life979.com
Editorial Profile: KFNW-FM is a non-commercial station owned by Northwestern College. The format of the station is contemporary Christian music and talk. KFNW-FM broadcasts to the Fargo, ND area at 97.9 FM.

KFNX-AM
Owner: Premiere Broadcasting
Editorial: 2001 N 3rd St, Ste 102, Phoenix, Arizona 85004. **T:** 1 602 277-1100
W: http://www.1100kfnx.com
Editorial Profile: KFNX-AM is a commercial station owned by Premiere Broadcasting. The format of the station is news and talk. KFNX-AM broadcasts in the Phoenix area at 1100 AM.

KFNY-AM
Owner: Clear Channel Media and Entertainment
Editorial: 2030 Iowa Ave, Ste A, Riverside, California 92507. **T:** 1 951 784-4210
W: http://www.funny1440.com
Editorial Profile: KFNY-AM is a commercial station owned by Clear Channel Media and Entertainment. The format of the station is all comedy programming. KFNY-AM broadcasts to the Riverside, CA area at 1440 AM.

KFNZ-AM
Owner: Cumulus Media Inc
Editorial: 301 W South Temple, Salt Lake City, Utah 84101-1216. **T:** 1 801 483-1320
W: http://www.1320kfan.com
Editorial Profile: KFNZ-AM is a commercial station owned by Cumulus Media Inc. and is a Yahoo! Sports Radio affiliate. The format of the station is sports. KFNZ-AM broadcasts to the Salt Lake City area at 1320 AM.

KFOG-FM
Owner: Cumulus Media Inc.
Editorial: 55 Hawthorne St, San Francisco, California 94105-3906. **T:** 1 415 995-6800
W: http://www.kfog.com

Editorial Profile: KFOG-FM is a commercial station owned by Cumulus Media Inc. The format of the station is adult album alternative. KFOG-FM broadcasts to the San Francisco area at 104.5 FM.

KFOR-AM

Owner: Three Eagles Communications Co.
Editorial: 3800 Cornhusker Hwy, Lincoln, Nebraska 68504-1533. **T:** 1 402 466-1234
E: kfornews@threeeagles.com
W: http://www.kfor1240.com
Editorial Profile: KFOR-AM is a commercial station owned by Three Eagles Communications Co. The format of the station is news and talk. KFOR-AM broadcasts to the Lincoln, NE area at 1240 AM.

KFOX-AM

Owner: JMK Communications, Inc.
Editorial: 4525 Wilshire Blvd, Fl 3, Los Angeles, California 90010-3845.
T: 1 323 935-0606
W: http://www.radioseoul1650.com
Editorial Profile: KFOX-AM is a commercial station owned by JMK Communications, Inc. The format for the station is Korean programming. KFOX-AM broadcasts to the Los Angeles area at 1650 AM.

KFPR-FM

Owner: California State University
Editorial: 603 N Market St, Redding, California 96003. **T:** 1 530 898-5896
E: kchonews@csuchico.edu
W: http://www.kcho.org
Editorial Profile: KFPR-FM is a non-commercial station owned by California State University. The format of the station is classical, jazz and news. KFPR-FM broadcasts to the Redding, CA area at 88.9 FM.

KFPT-AM

Owner: Fat Dawgs 7 Broadcasting LLC
Editorial: 351 W Cromwell Ave, Fresno, California 93711-6115. **T:** 1 559 447-3570
Editorial Profile: KFPT-AM is a commercial station owned by Fat Dawgs 7 Broadcasting LLC. The format of the station is sports. KFPT-AM broadcasts to the Fresno, CA area at 790 AM.

KFPW-AM

Owner: Pharis Broadcasting Inc.
Editorial: 321 N Greenwood Ave Ste 201, Fort Smith, Arkansas 72901-3453.
T: 1 479 288-1047
W: http://www.sportshog1031.com
Editorial Profile: KFPW-AM is a commercial station owned by Pharis Broadcasting Inc. The format of the station is news and talk. KFPW-AM broadcasts to the Fort Smith, AR area at 1230 AM.

KFPW-FM

Owner: Pharis Broadcasting Inc.
Editorial: 321 N Greenwood Ave Ste 201, Fort Smith, Arkansas 72901-3453.
T: 1 479 288-1047
W: http://www.sportshog1031.com
Editorial Profile: KFPW-FM is a commercial radio station owned by Pharis Broadcasting Inc. The format of the station is rock. KFPW-FM broadcasts to the Fort Smith, AR area on 94.5 FM.

KFQD-AM

Owner: Morris Communications
Editorial: 301 Arctic Slope Ave, Ste 200, Anchorage, Alaska 99518. **T:** 1 907 344-9622
E: news@kfqd.com **W:** http://www.kfqd.com
Editorial Profile: KFQD-AM is a commercial station owned by Morris Communications. The format of the station is news and talk. KFQD-AM broadcasts to the Anchorage, AK area at 750 AM.

KFRA-AM

Owner: Hubcast Broadcasting Inc.
Editorial: 1320 Victor II Blvd, Morgan City, Louisiana 70380-1360. **T:** 1 985 385-6266
W: http://www.kbze.com
Editorial Profile: KFRA-AM is a commercial station owned by Hubcast Broadcasting Inc. The format of the station is urban adult contemporary. KFRA-AM broadcasts to the Morgan City, LA area at 1390 AM.

KFRC-FM

Owner: CBS Radio
Editorial: 865 Battery St Fl 2, San Francisco, California 94111-1503. **T:** 1 415 392-1069
E: kcbsnewsdesk@cbs.com
W: http://www.kcbs.com
Editorial Profile: KFRC-FM is a commercial station owned by CBS Radio. The format of

the station is news. KFRC-FM broadcasts to the San Francisco area at 106.9 FM.

KFRG-FM

Owner: CBS Radio
Editorial: 900 E Washington St, Ste 315, Colton, California 92324-7117.
T: 1 909 825-9525 **E:** webmaster@kfrog.net
W: http://kfrog.radio.com
Editorial Profile: KFRG-FM is a commercial station owned by CBS Radio. The format of the station is country. KFRG-FM broadcasts to the San Bernardino, CA area at 95.1 FM.

KFRH-FM

Owner: Royce International Broadcasting Corporation
Editorial: 73733 Fred Waring Dr, Ste 201, Palm Desert, California 92260-2591.
T: 1 760 341-0123
W: http://www.1043now.com
Editorial Profile: KFRH-FM is a commercial station owned by Royce International Broadcasting Corporation. The format of the station is Top 40/CHR. KFRH-broadcasts to the Las Vegas area at 104.3 FM.

KFRM-AM

Owner: Taylor Communications
Editorial: 1815 Meadowlark Rd, Clay Center, Kansas 67432-8201. **T:** 1 785 632-5661
E: webmaster@kfrm.com
W: http://www.kfrm.com
Editorial Profile: KFRM-AM is a commercial station owned by Taylor Communications. The format of the station is agricultural, news, sports, and talk. KFRM-AM broadcasts to Clay Center, KS area at 550 AM.

KFRN-AM

Owner: Family Stations Inc.
Editorial: 11865 Moreno Ave, Lakeside, California 92040-1110. **T:** 1 800 797-7579
E: kfrn@familyradio.com
W: http://www.familyradio.com
Editorial Profile: KFRN-AM is a non-commercial station owned by Family Stations Inc. The format of the station is religious programming. KFRN-AM broadcasts to the Long Beach, CA area at 1280 AM.

KFRO-FM

Owner: Waller Broadcasting
Editorial: 3400 W Marshall Ave Ste 307, Longview, Texas 75604-5048.
T: 1 903 663-2477
W: http://www.mybreezefm.com
Editorial Profile: KFRO-FM is a commercial station owned by Waller Broadcasting. The format of the station is Top 40/CHR. KFRO-FM broadcasts to the Jacksonville, TX area at 95.3 FM.

KFRQ-FM

Owner: Entravision Communications Corp.
Editorial: 801 N Jackson Rd, McAllen, Texas 78501. **T:** 1 956 661-6000 **E:** kfrq@hiline.net
W: http://www.q945rocks.com
Editorial Profile: KFRQ-FM is a commercial station owned by Entravision Communications Corp. The format of the station is rock. KFRQ-FM broadcasts to the McAllen, TX area at 94.5 FM.

KFRR-FM

Owner: Wilks Broadcast Group
Editorial: 1066 E Shaw Ave, Fresno, California 93710. **T:** 1 559 230-0104
W: http://www.newrock1041.fm
Editorial Profile: KFRR-FM is a commercial station owned by Wilks Broadcast Group. The format of the station is rock alternative. KFRR-FM broadcasts to the Fresno, CA area at 104.1 FM.

KFRU-AM

Owner: Cumulus Media Inc.
Editorial: 503 Old Highway 63 N, Columbia, Missouri 65201-6305. **T:** 1 573 449-4141
W: http://www.kfru.com
Editorial Profile: KFRU-AM is a commercial station owned by Cumulus Media Inc. The format of the station is news and talk. KFRU-AM broadcasts in the Columbia, MO area at 1400 AM.

KFRX-FM

Owner: Three Eagles Communications Co.
Editorial: 3800 Cornhusker Hwy, Lincoln, Nebraska 68504. **T:** 1 402 466-1234
W: http://www.kfrxfm.com
Editorial Profile: KFRX-FM is a commercial station owned by Three Eagles Communications Co. The format of the station is Top 40/CHR. KFRX-FM broadcasts to the Lincoln, NE area at 106.3 FM.

KFRZ-FM

Owner: Wagonwheel Communications Corp.
Editorial: 40 Shoshone Ave, Green River, Wyoming 82935. **T:** 1 307 875-6666
E: mail@theradionetwork.net
W: http://www.theradionetwork.net
Editorial Profile: KFRZ-FM is a commercial station owned by Wagonwheel Communications Corp. The format of the station is classic and contemporary country music. KFRZ-FM broadcasts to the Salt Lake City area at 92.1 FM.

KFSA-AM

Owner: Fred H. Baker
Editorial: 5111 Rogers Ave Ste 650, Fort Smith, Arkansas 72903-2096.
T: 1 749 785-2526 **E:** production@kisr.net
W: http://www.kisr.net
Editorial Profile: KFSA-AM is a commercial station owned by Fred H. Baker. The format of the station is top 40/CHR. KFSA-AM broadcasts in the Fort Smith, AR area at 950 area.

KFSD-AM

Owner: Astor Broadcast Group
Editorial: 2888 Loker Ave E Ste 211, Carlsbad, California 92010-6685. **T:** 1 760 729-1000
E: astorbroadcasting@gmail.com
W: http://www.financialnewsandtalk.com
Editorial Profile: KFSD-AM is a commercial station owned by Astor Broadcast Group (North County Broadcasting Corporation). The format of the station is business news and talk. KFSD-AM broadcasts to the Inland Empire area of Southern California at 1450 AM.

KFSG-AM

Owner: Multicultural Radio Broadcasting Inc.
Editorial: 3463 Ramona Ave, Ste 15, Sacramento, California 95826.
T: 1 916 456-3288
Editorial Profile: KFSG-AM is a commercial station owned by Multicultural Radio Broadcasting Inc. The format of the station is variety, including multicultural programming. KFSG-AM broadcasts to the Sacramento, CA area on 1690 AM.

KFSH-FM

Owner: Salem Communications
Editorial: 701 N Brand Blvd Ste 550, Glendale, California 91203-1235. **T:** 1 714 520-0959
E: fishfeedback@thefish959.com
W: http://www.thefish959.com
Editorial Profile: KFSH-FM is a commercial station owned by Salem Communications. The format of the station is contemporary Christian. KFSH-FM broadcasts to the Los Angeles area at 95.9 FM.

KFSI-FM

Owner: Faith Sound, Inc.
Editorial: 4016 28th St SE, Rochester, Minnesota 55904. **T:** 1 507 289-8585
E: shine@kfsi.org **W:** http://www.kfsi.org

KFSK-FM

Owner: Narrows Broadcasting
Editorial: 404 N 2nd St, Petersburg, Alaska 99833-9999. **T:** 1 907 772-3808
W: http://www.kfsk.org
Editorial Profile: KFSK-FM is a non-commercial station owned by Narrows Broadcasting. The format of the station is variety. KFSK-FM broadcasts to Petersburg, AK at 100.9 FM.

KFSO-FM

Owner: Clear Channel Media and Entertainment
Editorial: 83 E Shaw Ave, Ste 150, Fresno, California 93710-7622. **T:** 1 559 230-4300
W: http://fresno.lapreciosa.com
Editorial Profile: KFSO-FM is a commercial station owned by Clear Channel Media and Entertainment. The format of the station is Hispanic oldies. KFSO-FM's broadcasts to the Fresno, CA area at 92.9 FM.

KFSR-FM

Owner: California State University, Fresno
Editorial: 5201 N Maple Ave, Fresno, California 93740-0001. **T:** 1 559 278-2598
E: 90.7kfsr@gmail.com
W: http://www.csufresno.edu/kfsr
Editorial Profile: KFSR-FM is a non-commercial, student-run station owned by California State University, Fresno. The format of the station is college variety. KFSR-FM's target audience is listeners of all ages interested in diverse music and programming. The station airs locally on 90.7 FM.

KFST-AM

Owner: Fort Stockton Radio Co., Inc.
Editorial: 954 S US Highway 385, Fort Stockton, Texas 79735. **T:** 1 432 336-2228
E: kfst@sbcglobal.net
Editorial Profile: KFST-AM is commercial station owned by Fort Stockton Radio Co., Inc. The format of the station is adult contemporary. KFST-AM broadcasts to the Fort Stockton, TX area at 860 AM.

KFST-FM

Owner: Fort Stockton Radio Co., Inc.
Editorial: 954 S US Highway 385, Fort Stockton, Texas 79735. **T:** 1 432 336-2228
E: kfst@sbcglobal.net
Editorial Profile: KFST-FM is a commercial station owned by Fort Stockton Radio Co., Inc. The format of the station is country and Hispanic music. KFST-FM broadcasts in the Fort Stockton, TX area at 94.3 FM.

KFSZ-FM

Owner: LKCM Radio Group, LP
Editorial: 1117 W Route 66, Flagstaff, Arizona 86001-6213. **T:** 1 928 774-5231
W: http://www.hits1061.com
Editorial Profile: KFSZ-FM is a commercial station owned by LKCM Radio Group, LP. The format of the station is Top 40/CHR. KFSZ-FM broadcasts to the Flagstaff, AZ at a frequency of 106.1 FM.

KFTA-AM

Owner: Lee Family Broadcasting
Editorial: 120 S 300 W, Rupert, Idaho 83350-9667. **T:** 1 208 436-4757
E: traffic@leeradio.net
W: http://www.lafantastica970.com
Editorial Profile: KFTA-AM is a commercial station owned by Lee Family Broadcasting. The format of the station is Regional Mexican music. KFTA-AM broadcasts to the Rupert, ID area at a frequency of 970 AM.

KFTE-FM

Owner: Townsquare Media, LLC
Editorial: 1749 Bertrand Dr, Lafayette, Louisiana 70506. **T:** 1 337 233-6000
W: http://www.planet1051.com
Editorial Profile: KFTE-FM is a commercial station owned by Townsquare Media, LLC. The format of the station rock music. KFTE-FM broadcasts to the Lafayette, LA area at 105.1 FM.

KFTG-FM

Owner: Aleyua Christian Broadcasting
Editorial: 1600 Pasadena Blvd, Pasadena, Texas 77502-2404. **T:** 1 713 589-1336
E: fm@radioaleluya.org
W: http://radioaleluya.org
Editorial Profile: KFTG-FM is a commercial station owned by Aleluya Christian Broadcasting. The format of the station is Hispanic contemporary Christian. KFTG-FM broadcasts to the Pasadena, TX area at 88.1 FM.

KFTI-FM

Owner: Journal Broadcast Group
Editorial: 4200 N Old Lawrence Rd, Wichita, Kansas 67219. **T:** 1 316 838-9141
E: news@kfdi.com
W: http://www.classiccountry923.com
Editorial Profile: KFTI-FM is a commercial station owned by Journal Broadcast Group. The format of the station is classic country. KFTI-FM broadcasts to the Wichita, KS area at 92.3 FM.

KFTK-FM

Owner: Emmis Communications Corp.
Editorial: 800 Saint Louis Union Sta, Saint Louis, Missouri 63103. **T:** 1 314 231-9710
W: http://www.971talk.com
Editorial Profile: KFTK-FM is a commercial station owned by Emmis Communications Corp. The format of the station is news and talk. KFTK-FM broadcasts to the St. Louis area at 97.1 FM.

KFTM-AM

Owner: Media Logic LLC
Editorial: 16041 US Highway 34, Fort Morgan, Colorado 80701. **T:** 1 970 867-5674
E: kftm@medialogicradio.com
W: http://www.kftm.net
Editorial Profile: KFTM-AM is a commercial station owned by Media Logic LLC. The format of the station is adult contemporary music. KFTM-AM broadcasts to the Fort Morgan, CO area at 1400 AM.

KFTT-FM

Owner: Mad Dog Wireless Inc.

Editorial: 2068 McCulloch Blvd N, Lake Havasu City, Arizona 86403-6712.
T: 1 928 855-1051 **W:** http://www.maddog.net
Editorial Profile: KFTT-FM is a commercial station owned by Mad Dog Wireless Inc. The format of the station is oldies. KFTT-FM broadcasts to the Lake Havasu City, AZ area at 107.7 FM.

KFTX-FM
Owner: Quality Broadcasting
Editorial: 1520 S Port Ave, Corpus Christi, Texas 78405. **T:** 1 361 883-5987
W: http://www.kftx.com
Editorial Profile: KFTX-FM is a commercial station owned by Quality Broadcasting. The format of the station is country. KFTX-FM broadcasts to the Corpus Christi, TX area at 97.5 FM.

KFTZ-FM
Owner: Riverbend Communications LLC
Editorial: 400 W Sunnyside Rd, Idaho Falls, Idaho 83402-4613. **T:** 1 208 523-3722
E: onair@z103.fm **W:** http://www.z103.fm
Editorial Profile: KFTZ-FM is a commercial station owned by Riverbend Communications LLC. The format of the station is Top 40/CHR music. KFTZ-FM broadcasts to the Idaho Falls, ID area at 103.3 FM.

KFUN-AM
Owner: Baca Broadcasting LLC
Editorial: One Radio Heights, Las Vegas, New Mexico 87701. **T:** 1 505 425-6766
W: http://www.kfunonline.com
Editorial Profile: KFUN-AM is a commercial station owned by Baca Broadcasting LLC. The format of the station is country and Spanish tejano music. KFUN-AM broadcasts to the Las Vegas, NM area at 1230 AM.

KFUO-AM
Owner: Lutheran Church-Missouri Synod
Editorial: 85 Founders Ln, Saint Louis, Missouri 63105. **T:** 1 314 505-7800
W: http://www.kfuoam.org
Editorial Profile: KFUO-AM is a non-commercial station owned by the Lutheran Church-Missouri Synod. The format of the station is religious music and talk. KFUO-AM broadcasts to the St. Louis area at 850 AM.

KFUT-AM
Owner: Morris Communications
Editorial: 1321 N Gene Autry Trl, Palm Springs, California 92262. **T:** 1 760 322-7890
W: http://www.1270kfut.com
Editorial Profile: KFUT-AM is a commercial station owned by Morris Communications. The format of the station is Spanish-language news, talk and sports programming. KFUT-AM broadcasts to the Palm Springs, CA area at 1270 AM.

KFVR-FM
Owner: Greeley Broadcasting Corp.
Editorial: 2099 U.S. Hwy W, Ste 130-A, Pueblo, Colorado 81008. **T:** 1 719 253-3777
Editorial Profile: KFVR-FM is a commercial station owned by Greeley Broadcasting Corp. The format for the station is classic rock. KFVR-FM broadcasts to the Crescent City, California area at 94.7 FM.

KFWB-AM
Owner: CBS Radio
Editorial: 5670 Wilshire Blvd Ste 200, Los Angeles, California 90036-5657.
T: 1 323 525-0980 **W:** http://kfwbam.com
Editorial Profile: KFWB-AM is a commercial station owned by CBS Radio. The format of the station is news, talk and sports. KFWB-AM broadcasts to the Los Angeles area at 980 AM.

KFWR-FM
Owner: LKCM Radio Group LP
Editorial: 115 W 3rd St, Fort Worth, Texas 76102-7402. **T:** 1 817 332-0959
E: contactus@theranchradio.com
W: http://www.959theranch.com
Editorial Profile: KFWR-FM is a commercial station owned by LKCM Radio Group LP. The format of the station is country music. KFWR-FM broadcasts to the Dallas area at 95.9 FM.

KFXD-AM
Owner: Townsquare Media, LLC
Editorial: 827 E Park Blvd Ste 100, Boise, Idaho 83712-7783. **T:** 1 208 344-6363
W: http://630thefan.com
Editorial Profile: KFXD-AM is a commercial station owned by Townsquare Media, LLC. The format of the station is sports/talk. KFXD-AM broadcasts to the Boise, ID area at 630 AM.

KFXE-AM
Owner: Wennes Communications Stations, Inc.
Editorial: 14 W Main St, Waukon, Iowa 52172. **T:** 1 563 568-3476
E: knei@kneiradio.com
W: http://www.kneiradio.com
Editorial Profile: KFXE-AM is a commercial station owned by Wennes Communications Stations, Inc. The format for the station is sports. KFXE-AM broadcasts to the Waukon, IA area at 1160 AM.

KFXI-FM
Owner: DFWU Inc.
Editorial: 1101 N Broadway St, Marlow, Oklahoma 73055-1123. **T:** 1 580 658-9292
E: kfxi92@att.net **W:** http://www.kfxi.com
Editorial Profile: KFXI-FM is a commercial station owned by DFWU Inc. The format of the station is country music. KFXI-FM broadcasts in the Marlow, OK area at 92.1 FM.

KFXJ-FM
Owner: Journal Broadcast Group
Editorial: 4200 N Old Lawrence Rd, Wichita, Kansas 67219. **T:** 1 316 838-9141
E: news@kfdi.com
W: http://www.1045thefox.com
Editorial Profile: KFXJ-FM is a commercial station owned by Journal Broadcast Group. The format of the station is classic rock. KFXJ-FM broadcasts to the Wichita, KS area at 104.5 FM.

KFXN-AM
Owner: MMTC Broadcasting LLC
Editorial: 1088 Payne Ave, Saint Paul, Minnesota 55130-3739. **T:** 1 651 810-6412
W: http://hmongradioam690.com/
Editorial Profile: KFXN-AM is a commercial station owned by MMTC Broadcasting LLC. The format of the station is Asian American news, music and talk programming, specifically Hmong and Lao American. KFXN-AM broadcasts in the Minneapolis area at 690 AM.

KFXR-AM
Owner: Clear Channel Media and Entertainment
Editorial: 14001 Dallas Pkwy, Dallas, Texas 75240-4346. **T:** 1 214 866-8000
E: psa@ccdallas.com
W: http://www.dfw1190am.com
Editorial Profile: KFXR-AM is a commercial station owned by Clear Channel Media and Entertainment. The format of the station is talk. KFXR-AM broadcasts to the Dallas area at 1190 AM.

KFXR-FM
Owner: Clear Channel Media and Entertainment
Editorial: 1632 S 2nd St, Gallup, New Mexico 87301. **T:** 1 505 863-9391
Editorial Profile: KFXR-FM is a commercial station owned by Clear Channel Media and Entertainment. The format of the station is country. KFXR-FM broadcasts to the Gallup, NM area at 107.3 FM.

KFXS-FM
Owner: New Rushmore Radio
Editorial: 660 Flormann St, Ste 100, Rapid City, South Dakota 57701. **T:** 1 605 343-6161
W: http://www.foxradio.com
Editorial Profile: KFXS-FM is a commercial station owned by New Rushmore Radio. The format of the station is classic rock. KFXS-FM broadcasts to the Rapid City, SD area at 100.3 FM.

KFXX-AM
Owner: Entercom Communications Corp.
Editorial: 0700 SW Bancroft St, Portland, Oregon 97239-4226. **T:** 1 503 223-1441
W: http://www.1080thefan.com
Editorial Profile: KFXX-AM is a commercial station owned by Entercom Communications Corp. The format of the station is sports. KFXX-AM broadcasts to the Portland, OR area at 1080 AM.

KFXX-FM
Owner: Armada Media Corp.
Editorial: 2917 S Colorado St, Ulysses, Kansas 67880-8201. **T:** 1 620 356-1420
Editorial Profile: KFXX-FM is a commercial station owned by Armada Media Corp. The format of the station is regional Mexican. KFXX-FM broadcasts to the Ulysses, KS area at 106.7 FM.

KFXZ-AM
Owner: Delta Media Corporation
Editorial: 3501 NW Evangeline Trwy, Carencro, Louisiana 70520-6240. **T:** 1 337 896-1600
Editorial Profile: KFXZ-FM is a commercial station Delta Media Corporation. The format of the station is Spanish Adult Hits. KFXZ-AM broadcasts to the Lafayette, LA area at 1520 AM.

KFXZ-FM
Owner: Delta Media Corporation
Editorial: 3501 NW Evangeline Trwy, Carencro, Louisiana 70520-6240. **T:** 1 337 896-1600
Editorial Profile: KFXZ-FM is a commercial station owned by Delta Media Corporation. The format of the station is urban adult contemporary, soul and R&B. KFXZ-FM broadcasts to the Lafayette, LA area at 105.9 FM.

KFYI-AM
Owner: Clear Channel Media and Entertainment
Editorial: 4686 E Van Buren St Ste 300, Phoenix, Arizona 85008-6967.
T: 1 602 374-6000
E: kfyinews@clearchannel.com
W: http://www.kfyi.com
Editorial Profile: KFYI-AM is a commercial station owned by Clear Channel Media and Entertainment. The format of the station is news and talk programming. KFYI-AM broadcasts to the Phoenix area at 550 AM.

KFYN-AM
Owner: Vision Media Group
Editorial: 506 N Main St, Bonham, Texas 75418-3718. **T:** 1 903 583-3151
W: http://1420thewarrior.com
Editorial Profile: KFYN-AM is a commercial station owned by Vision Media Group. The format of the station is contemporary country music. KFYN-AM broadcasts to the Bonham, TX area at 1420 AM.

KFYO-AM
Owner: Townsquare Media, LLC
Editorial: 4413 82nd St, Ste 300, Lubbock, Texas 79424. **T:** 1 806 798-7078
E: news@kfyo.com **W:** http://www.kfyo.com
Editorial Profile: KFYO-AM is a commercial station owned by Townsquare Media, LLC. The format of the station is news and talk. KFYO-AM broadcasts to the Lubbock, TX area at 790 AM.

KFYR-AM
Owner: Clear Channel Media and Entertainment
Editorial: 3500 E Rosser Ave, Bismarck, North Dakota 58501. **T:** 1 701 255-1234
E: kfyr@clearchannel.com
W: http://www.kfyr.com
Editorial Profile: KFYR-AM is a commercial station owned by Clear Channel Media and Entertainment. The format of the station is news and talk. KFYR-AM broadcasts to the Bismarck, ND area at 550 AM.

KFYV-FM
Owner: Gold Coast Radio, LLC
Editorial: 2284 S Victoria Ave, Ventura, California 93003-6641. **T:** 1 805 289-1400
W: http://www.live1055.fm
Editorial Profile: KFYV-FM is a commercial station owned by Gold Coast Radio, LLC. The format of the station is Top 40/CHR. KFYV-FM broadcasts to the Ventura, CA area at 105.5 FM.

KFYZ-FM
Owner: Rincon Broadcasting
Editorial: 414 E Cota St, Santa Barbara, California 93101. **T:** 1 805 879-8300
W: http://z945fm.com/main.php
Editorial Profile: KFYZ-FM is a commercial station owned by Rincon Broadcasting. The format of the station is Top 40/CHR. KFYZ-FM broadcasts to the Santa Barbara, CA area at 107.7 FM.

KFZO-FM
Owner: Univision Communications Inc.
Editorial: 7700 John W Carpenter Fwy Fl 1, Dallas, Texas 75247-4829. **T:** 1 214 525-0400
W: http://radioh2odallas.univision.com
Editorial Profile: KFZO-FM is a commercial station owned by Univision Communications Inc. The format of the station is Rhythmic CHR. KFZO-FM broadcasts to the Dallas area at 107.9 FM.

KFZX-FM
Owner: ICA Radio
Editorial: 1330 E 8th St, Ste 207, Odessa, Texas 79761. **T:** 1 432 563-9102
W: http://www.1021jackfm.com
Editorial Profile: KFZX-FM is a commercial station owned by ICA Radio. The format of the station is classic rock. KFZX-FM broadcasts to the Odessa, TX area at 102.1 FM.

KGA-AM
Owner: Mapleton Communications LLC
Editorial: 1601 E 57th Ave, Spokane, Washington 99223. **T:** 1 509 448-1000
W: http://www.1510kga.com
Editorial Profile: KGA-AM is a commercial station owned by Mapleton Communications LLC. The format of the station is sports. KGA-AM broadcasts to the Spokane, WA area at 1510AM.

KGAB-AM
Owner: Townsquare Media, LLC
Editorial: 1912 Capitol Ave, Ste 300, Cheyenne, Wyoming 82001.
T: 1 307 632-4400 **W:** http://www.kgab.com
Editorial Profile: KGAB-AM is a commercial station owned by Townsquare Media, LLC. The format of the station is talk. The station is broadcast to the Cheyenne, WY area at 650 AM.

KGAC-FM
Owner: Minnesota Public Radio
Editorial: 206 S Broadway, Ste 735, Rochester, Minnesota 55904.
T: 1 507 282-0910 **E:** newsroom@mpr.org
W: http://minnesota.publicradio.org/radio/stations/kngakgac
Editorial Profile: KGAC-FM tries to inform, enrich and nourish audiences, assisting them to engage effectively as citizens, enhance their lives, expand their perspectives and strengthen their communities.

KGAF-AM
Owner: Eberhart(Steve)
Editorial: 401 N Radio Hill Rd, Gainesville, Texas 76240-7635. **T:** 1 940 665-5546
E: info@memories1580.com
W: http://www.memories1580.com
Editorial Profile: KGAF-AM is a commercial station owned by Steve Eberhart. The format of the station is oldies. KGAF-AM broadcasts to the Gainesville, TX area at 1580 AM.

KGAK-AM
Owner: KRJG Broadcasting Co.
Editorial: 401 E Coal Ave, Gallup, New Mexico 87301-6001. **T:** 1 505 863-4444
Editorial Profile: KGAK-AM is a commercial station owned by KRJG Broadcasting Co. The format of the station is mixed variety of news and country music. KGAK-AM broadcasts to the Albuquerque, NM area at 1330 AM. The station broadcasts only in the Navajo language.

KGAL-AM
Owner: EADS Broadcasting Corp.
Editorial: 36991 Kgal Dr, Lebanon, Oregon 97355. **T:** 1 541 451-5425 **E:** kgal@kgal.com
W: http://www.kgal.com
Editorial Profile: KGAL-AM is a commercial station owned by EADS Broadcasting Corp. The format of the station is news, sports and talk. KGAL-AM broadcasts to the Albany, OR area at 1580 AM.

KGAM-FM
Owner: Mapleton Communications LLC
Editorial: 1020 W Main St, Merced, California 95340. **T:** 1 209 723-2191
Editorial Profile: KGAM-FM is a commercial station owned by Mapleton Communications LLC. The format of the station is Spanish adult contemporary. KGAM-FM broadcasts to the Fresno-Visalia, CA area at 106.3 FM.

KGAP-FM
Owner: American Media Investments
Editorial: 1323 College Dr, Texarkana, Texas 75503-3531. **T:** 1 903 793-1100
Editorial Profile: KGAP-FM is a commercial station owned by American Media Investments. The format of the station is oldies music. KGAP-FM broadcasts to the Texarkana, TX area at 98.5 FM.

KGAS-AM
Owner: Hanszen Broadcast Group
Editorial: 215 S Market St, Carthage, Texas 75633-2623. **T:** 1 903 693-6668
E: news@kgasradio.com
W: http://www.easttexastoday.com
Editorial Profile: KGAS-AM is a commercial station owned by Hanszen Broadcast Group. The format for the station is sports and talk programming. KGAS-AM broadcasts to the Shreveport, LA area at 1590 AM.

KGAS-FM
Owner: Hanszen Broadcast Group
Editorial: 215 S Market St, Carthage, Texas 75633-2623. **T:** 1 903 693-6668
E: info@kgasradio.com
W: http://www.easttexastoday.com
Editorial Profile: KGAS-FM is a commercial station owned by Hanszen Broadcast Group. The format of the station is country music. KGAS-FM broadcasts to the Shreveport, LA area at 104.3 FM.

KGBA-AM
Owner: Voice of International Christian Evangelism Inc. (The)
Editorial: 605 W State St, El Centro, California 92243. **T:** 1 760 352-9860
E: espanol@kgba.org
W: http://espanol.kgba.org
Editorial Profile: KGBA-AM is a non-commercial station owned by The Voice of International Christian Evangelism Inc. The format of the station is Hispanic and contemporary Christian. KGBA-AM broadcasts to the El Centro, CA area at 1490 AM.

KGBA-FM
Owner: Voice of International Christian Evangelism Inc. (The)
Editorial: 605 W State St, El Centro, California 92243. **T:** 1 760 352-9860 **E:** kgba@kgba.org
W: http://www.kgba.org
Editorial Profile: KGBA-FM is a non-commercial station owned by The Voice of International Christian Evangelism Inc. The format of the station is contemporary Christian. KGBA-FM broadcasts to the El Centro, CA area at 100.1 FM.

KGBB-FM
Owner: Adelman Broadcasting Inc.
Editorial: 731 Balsam St, Ridgecrest, California 93555-3510. **T:** 1 760 371-1700
W: http://www.bobfm1039.com
Editorial Profile: KGBB-FM is a commercial station owned by Adelman Broadcasting Inc. The format of the station is Jack FM-Adult Hits. KGBB-FM broadcasts to the Ridgecrest, CA area at 103.9 FM.

KGBC-AM
Owner: SIGA Broadcasting Corp.
Editorial: 1302 N Shepherd Dr, Houston, Texas 77008-3752. **T:** 1 713 868-5559
E: signbroadcasting@gmail.com
W: http://www.sigabroadcasting.com
Editorial Profile: KGBC-AM is a commercial station owned by SIGA Broadcasting Corp and in an LMA with Pacific Media International. The format of the station is variety of music, news, ethnic programming and Chinese Radio. KGBC-AM broadcasts to the Houston and Galveston, TX areas at 1540 AM.

KGB-FM
Owner: Clear Channel Media and Entertainment
Editorial: 9660 Granite Ridge Dr, Ste 100, San Diego, California 92123. **T:** 1 858 292-2000
W: http://www.101kgb.com
Editorial Profile: KGB-FM is a commercial station owned by Clear Channel Media and Entertainment. The format of the station is classic rock music. KGB-FM broadcasts to the San Diego area at 101.5 FM.

KGBI-FM
Owner: Salem Communications
Editorial: 11717 Burt St Ste 202, Omaha, Nebraska 68154-1500. **T:** 1 402 422-1600
W: http://www.thefishomaha.com
Editorial Profile: KGBI-FM is a commercial station owned by Salem Communications. The format of the station is contemporary Christian music. KGBI-FM broadcasts to the Omaha, NE at 100.7 FM.

KGBN-AM
Owner: Korean Gospel Broadcasting Network
Editorial: 701 N Brand Blvd Ste 550, Glendale, California 91203-1235. **T:** 1 818 956-5552
E: info@kkla.com
Editorial Profile: KGBN-AM is a commercial station owned by Korean Gospel Broadcasting Network. The format of the station is ethnic and multicultural variety. KGBN-AM broadcasts to the Los Angeles area at 1190 AM.

KGBR-FM
Owner: St. Marie Communications Inc.
Editorial: 29795 Ellensburg Ave, #H, Gold Beach, Oregon 97444. **T:** 1 541 247-7211
W: http://www.kgbr.com

KGBT-AM
Owner: Univision Communications Inc.
Editorial: 200 S 10Th St Ste 600, McAllen, Texas 78501-4869. **T:** 1 956 631-5499
W: http://univisionamerica.com
Editorial Profile: KGBT-AM is a commercial station owned by Univision Communications Inc. The format of the station is Spanish news and talk. KGBT-AM broadcasts to the Rio Grande Valley area in Texas at 1530 AM.

KGBT-FM
Owner: Univision Communications Inc.
Editorial: 200 S 10th St, Ste 600, McAllen, Texas 78501-4869. **T:** 1 956 631-5499
W: http://kgbt985.univision.com
Editorial Profile: KGBT-FM is a commercial station owned by Univision Communications Inc. The format of the station is regional Mexican. KGBT-FM broadcasts to the McAllen, TX area at 98.5 FM.

KGBX-FM
Owner: Clear Channel Media and Entertainment
Editorial: 1856 S Glenstone Ave, Springfield, Missouri 65804-2303. **T:** 1 417 890-5555
E: kgbx@kgbx.com **W:** http://www.kgbx.com
Editorial Profile: KGBX-FM is a commercial station owned by Clear Channel Media and Entertainment. The format for the station is adult contemporary. KGBX-FM broadcasts to the Springfield, MO area at 105.9 FM.

KGCB-FM
Owner: Grand Canyon Broadcasters Inc.
Editorial: 3741 Karicio Ln, Prescott, Arizona 86303-6829. **T:** 1 928 776-0909
E: info@radioshine.org
W: http://www.radioshine.org
Editorial Profile: KGCB-FM is a non-commercial station owned by Grand Canyon Broadcasters Inc. The format of the station is contemporary Christian music and religious programming. KGCB-FM broadcasts to the Phoenix area at 90.9 FM.

KGCR-FM
Owner: Praise Network(The)
Editorial: 3410 Road 66, Brewster, Kansas 67732-8907. **T:** 1 785 694-2877
E: kgcr@kgcr.org **W:** http://www.kgcr.org
Editorial Profile: KGCR-FM is a non-commercial station owned by the Praise Network. The format of the station is religious and contemporary Christian programming. KGCR-FM broadcasts to the Brewster, KS area at 107.7 FM.

KGCX-FM
Owner: Sidney Community Broadcasting
Editorial: 213 2nd Ave SW, Sidney, Montana 59270-4019. **T:** 1 406 433-5429
E: kgcxeagle@midrivers.com
W: http://www.radiomontana.net
Editorial Profile: KGCX-FM is a commercial station owned by Sidney Community Broadcasting, a subsidiary of The Marks Radio Group. The format of the station is classic rock. KGCX-FM broadcasts to the Sidney, MT area at a frequency of 93.1 FM.

KGDC-AM
Owner: Two Hearts Communications LLC
Editorial: 30 W Main St, Ste 303, Walla Walla, Washington 99362-2872. **T:** 1 509 525-7878
Editorial Profile: KGDC-AM is a commercial station owned by Two Hearts Communications LLC. The format of the station is news and talk. KGDC-AM broadcasts to the Walla Walla, WA area at 1320 AM.

KGDD-AM
Owner: Bustos Media, LLC
Editorial: 5110 SE Stark St, Portland, Oregon 97215-1751. **T:** 1 503 234-5550
W: http://www.lagrande.mx
Editorial Profile: KGDD-AM is a commercial station owned by Bustos Media, LLC. The format of the station is regional Mexican. KGDD-AM broadcasts to the Portland, OR, area at 1520 AM.

KGED-AM
Owner: Compass Broadcasting, Inc
Editorial: 2171 Ralph Ave, Stockton, California 95206-3625. **T:** 1 559 790-2239
Editorial Profile: KGED-AM is a commercial station owned by Compass Broadcasting, Inc. The format of the station is Christian talk. KGED-AM broadcasts to the Fresno, CA area at 1680 AM.

KGEM-AM
Owner: SNL Radio, LLC
Editorial: 5601 W. Cassia St, Boise, Idaho 83705-1836. **T:** 1 208 344-4774
E: info@saltandlightradio.com
W: http://www.saltandlightradio.com
Editorial Profile: KGEM-AM is a commercial station owned by SNL Radio, LLC. The format of the station is religious. KGEM-AM broadcasts to the Boise, ID area at 1140 AM.

KGEN-AM
Owner: Azteca Broadcasting Corp.
Editorial: 323 E San Joaquin Ave, Tulare, California 93274. **T:** 1 559 686-1370
Editorial Profile: KGEN-AM is a commercial station owned by Azteca Broadcasting Corp. The format of the station is regional Mexican music. KGEN-AM broadcasts in the Tulare, CA area at 1370 AM.

KGEN-FM
Owner: Azteca Broadcasting Corp.
Editorial: 323 E San Joaquin Ave, Tulare, California 93274-4130. **T:** 1 559 686-1370
Editorial Profile: KGEN-FM is a commercial station owned by Azteca Broadcasting Corp. The format of the station is Hispanic. KGEN-FM broadcasts in the Tulare, CA area.

KGEO-AM
Owner: American General Media
Editorial: 1400 Easton Dr Ste 144B, Bakersfield, California 93309-9412.
T: 1 661 328-1410
Editorial Profile: KGEO-AM is a commercial station owned by American General Media. The format of the station is news/talk. KGEO-AM broadcasts to the Bakersfield, CA area at 1230 AM.

KGFF-AM
Owner: Citizen Band Potawatomi Tribe of OK Inc
Editorial: 1570 Gordon Cooper Dr, Shawnee, Oklahoma 74801-9000. **T:** 1 405 273-4390
E: 1450kgff@gmail.com
W: http://www.kgff.com
Editorial Profile: KGFF-AM is a commercial station owned by Citizen Band Potawatomi Tribe of OK Inc. The format of the station is oldies. KGFF-AM broadcasts to the Oklahoma City area at 1450 AM.

KGFJ-FM
Owner: Calvary Chapel of Twin Falls, Inc.
Editorial: 4002 N 3300 E, Twin Falls, Idaho 83301-0354. **T:** 1 208 733-3133
W: http://www.calvarychapeltwinfalls.com/radiotv.php
Editorial Profile: KGFJ-FM is a non-commercial station owned by Calvary Chapel of Twin Falls, Inc. The format of the station is religious teaching. KGFJ-FM broadcasts to the Belt, MT area at a frequency of 88.1 FM.

KGFK-AM
Owner: Leighton Enterprises Inc.
Editorial: 1185 9th St NE, Thompson, North Dakota 58278-9343. **T:** 1 701 772-2204
W: http://www.957theforks.com
Editorial Profile: KGFK-AM is a commercial station owned by Leighton Enterprises Inc. The format of the station is adult contemporary. KGFK-AM broadcasts to the Thompson, ND area at 1590 AM.

KGFL-AM
Owner: King-Sullivan Radio
Editorial: 360 Main St, Clinton, Arkansas 72031. **T:** 1 501 745-4474
E: kgflkhpq@artelco.com
W: http://www.kgflam.com
Editorial Profile: KGFL-AM is a commercial station owned by King-Sullivan Radio. The format of the station is oldies. KGFL-AM broadcasts to the Clinton, AR area at 1110 AM.

KGFM-FM
Owner: American General Media
Editorial: 1400 Easton Dr, Ste 144B, Bakersfield, California 93309-9412.
T: 1 661 328-1410 **E:** listeners@kgfm.com
W: http://www.kgfm.com
Editorial Profile: KGFM-FM is a commercial station owned by American General Media. The format of the station is Lite Rock/Lite AC. KGFM-FM broadcasts to the Bakersfield, CA area at 101.5 FM.

KGFT-FM
Owner: Salem Communications
Editorial: 7150 Campus Dr, Ste 150, Colorado Springs, Colorado 80920-3157.
T: 1 719 531-5438
E: mgoodyear@kbiqradio.com
W: http://www.kgftradio.com
Editorial Profile: KGFT-FM is a commercial station owned by Salem Communications. The format of the station is Christian programming. KGFT-FM broadcasts to the Colorado Springs, CO area at 100.7 FM.

KGFW-AM
Owner: NRG Media LLC
Editorial: 2223 Central Ave, Kearney, Nebraska 68847-5346. **T:** 1 308 698-2100
E: news@kgfw.com **W:** http://www.kgfw.com
Editorial Profile: KGFW-AM is a commercial station owned by NRG Media LLC. The format of the station is news, sports and talk. KGFW-AM broadcasts to the Kearney, NE area at 1340 AM.

KGFX-AM
Owner: James River Broadcasting
Editorial: 214 W Pleasant Dr, Pierre, South Dakota 57501. **T:** 1 605 224-8686
W: http://www.dakotaradiogroup.com
Editorial Profile: KGFX-AM is a commercial station owned by James River Broadcasting. The format of the station is news, talk and country. KGFX-AM broadcasts to the Pierre, SD area at 1060 AM.

KGFX-FM
Owner: James River Broadcasting
Editorial: 214 W Pleasant Dr, Pierre, South Dakota 57501. **T:** 1 605 224-8686
W: http://www.dakotaradiogroup.com/
Editorial Profile: KGFX-FM is a commercial station owned by James River Broadcasting. The format of the station is hot adult contemporary. KGFX-FM broadcasts to the Pierre, SD area at 92.7 FM.

KGFY-FM
Owner: Mahaffey Enterprises Inc.
Editorial: 408 E Thomas Ave, Stillwater, Oklahoma 74075-2648. **T:** 1 405 372-7800
E: stillwaterradio@coxinet.net
W: http://www.stillwaterradio.net
Editorial Profile: KGFY-FM is a commercial station owned by Mahaffey Enterprises Inc. The format of the station is country music. KGFY-FM broadcasts to Oklahoma City at 105.5 FM.

KGGF-AM
Owner: Radio Results Group
Editorial: 306 W 8th St, Coffeyville, Kansas 67337-5829. **T:** 1 620 251-3800
E: kggf.newsinfo@sbcglobal.net
W: http://www.radioresultsgroup.com/id24.html
Editorial Profile: KGGF-AM is a commercial station owned by Radio Results Group. The format of the station is news and talk. KGGF-AM broadcasts to the Tulsa, OK area at 690 AM.

KGGF-FM
Owner: Radio Results Group
Editorial: 200 Arco Pl, Independence, Kansas 67301-3398. **T:** 1 620 331-8444
E: kggf.newsinfo@sbcglobal.net
W: http://www.radioresultsgroup.com/id7.html
Editorial Profile: KGGF-FM is a commercial station owned by Radio Results Group. The format of the station is classic hits. KGGF-FM broadcasts to the Tulsa, OK area at 104.1 FM.

KGGI-FM
Owner: Clear Channel Media and Entertainment
Editorial: 2030 Iowa Ave, Ste A, Riverside, California 92507. **T:** 1 951 684-1991
W: http://www.991kggifm.com
Editorial Profile: KGGI-FM is a commercial station owned by Clear Channel Media and Entertainment. The format of the station is Top 40/CHR. KGGI-FM broadcasts to the Riverside, CA area at 99.1 FM.

KGGL-FM
Owner: Cherry Creek Radio
Editorial: 1600 North Ave W, Ste 101, Missoula, Montana 59801. **T:** 1 406 721-9300
W: http://www.eagle93.com
Editorial Profile: KGGL-FM is a commercial station owned by Cherry Creek Radio. The format of the station is contemporary country music. KGGL-FM broadcasts to the Missoula, MT area at 93.3 FM.

KGGM-FM
Owner: Diebel(Kenneth W.)
Editorial: 1204 Highway 80, Delhi, Louisiana 71232-7502. **T:** 1 318 878-8255
W: http://www.kggmfm.com
Editorial Profile: KGGM-FM is a commercial station owned by Kenneth W. Diebel. The format of the station is southern gospel music. KGGM-FM broadcasts to the Delhi, LA area at 93.5 FM.

KGGN-AM
Owner: Mortenson Broadcasting Co.
Editorial: 1734 E 63rd St, Ste 600, Kansas City, Missouri 64110. **T:** 1 816 333-0092

Editorial Profile: KGGN-AM is a commercial station owned by Mortenson Broadcasting Co. The format of the station is gospel music. KGGN-AM broadcasts to the Kansas City, MO area at 890 AM.

KGGO-FM
Owner: Cumulus Media Inc
Editorial: 4143 109th St, Urbandale, Iowa 50322. **T:** 1 515 331-9200
W: http://www.kggo.com
Editorial Profile: KGGO-FM is a commercial station owned by Cumulus Media Inc. The format of the station is classic rock music. KGGO-FM broadcasts to the Des Moines, IA area at 94.5 FM.

KGGR-AM
Owner: Mortenson Broadcasting Co.
Editorial: 5787 S Hampton Rd, Ste 285, Dallas, Texas 75232. **T:** 1 972 572-5447
W: http://www.kggram.com
Editorial Profile: KGGR-AM is a commercial station owned by the Mortenson Broadcasting Co. The format of the station is gospel music and religious programming. KGGR-AM broadcasts to the Dallas area at 1040 AM.

KGGS-AM
Owner: Steckline Communications
Editorial: 609 E Kansas Plz, Garden City, Kansas 67846-5767. **T:** 1 620 276-3251
W: http://www.kiulradio.com
Editorial Profile: KGGS-AM is a commercial station owned by Steckline Communications. The format of the station is sports. The station airs locally in the Garden City, KS area at 1340 AM.

KGHE-FM
Owner: Grays Harbor Institute
Editorial: 717 Lincoln St, Hoquiam, Washington 98550-1457. **T:** 1 360 580-4001
W: http://www.ghinstitute.org
Editorial Profile: KGHE-FM is a non-commercial community radio station owned by Grays Harbor Institute. The format of the station is variety. KGHE-FM broadcasts to the Elma, WA area at a frequency of 89.1 FM.

KGHL-AM
Owner: BMG Billings
Editorial: 222 N 32nd St, Fl 10, Billings, Montana 59101. **T:** 1 406 238-1000
E: billings@benedettimedia.com
W: http://www.mighty790.com
Editorial Profile: KGHL-AM is a commercial station owned by BMG Billings. The format for the station is classic country. KGHL-AM broadcasts to the Billings, MT area at 790 AM.

KGHM-AM
Owner: Clear Channel Media and Entertainment
Editorial: 1900 NW Expressway, Oklahoma City, Oklahoma 73118-1802.
T: 1 405 840-5271
W: http://www.1340thegame.com/main.html
Editorial Profile: KGHM-AM is a commercial station owned by Clear Channel Media and Entertainment. The format of the station is sports talk. KGHM-AM broadcasts to the Oklahoma City area at 1340.

KGHP-FM
Owner: Peninsula School District #401
Editorial: 14105 Purdy Ln NW, Gig Harbor, Washington 98332. **T:** 1 253 857-3513
E: mail@kghp.org **W:** http://www.kghp.org
Editorial Profile: KGHP-FM is a non-commercial station owned by Peninsula School District #401. The format of the station is variety mix of rock and roll, jazz and reggae. KGHP-FM broadcasts to the Gig Harbor, WA area at 89.9 FM.

KGHR-FM
Owner: TCHSB Inc.
Editorial: Warrior Drive, Tuba City, Arizona 86045-0160. **T:** 1 928 283-5555
E: kghrpublic@ymail.com
Editorial Profile: KGHR-FM is a commercial station owned by TCHSB Inc. The format of the station is variety. KGHR-FM broadcasts to the Tuba City, AZ area at 91.3 FM.

KGHS-AM
Owner: Red Rock Radio Corp.
Editorial: 519 3rd St, International Falls, Minnesota 56649-2317. **T:** 1 218 283-3481
E: production@ksdmradio.com
W: http://www.ksdmradio.com
Editorial Profile: KGHS-AM is a commercial station owned by Red Rock Radio Corp. The format of the station is oldies music. KGHS-FM broadcasts to the International Falls, MN area at 1230 AM.

KGHY-FM
Owner: CCS Radio, Inc.
Editorial: 12021 Palmbeach St, Houston, Texas 77034-3814. **T:** 1 713 941-3676
W: http://www.thegospelhiway.org
Editorial Profile: KGHY-FM is a commercial station owned by CCS Radio, Inc. The format of the station is gospel music. KGHY-FM airs locally on 88.5 FM.

KGIM-AM
Owner: Armada Media Corp.
Editorial: 13541 386th Ave, Aberdeen, South Dakota 57401. **T:** 1 605 229-3632
E: aberdeenproduction@hubcityradio.com
W: http://www.hubcityradio.com
Editorial Profile: KGIM-AM is a commercial station owned by Armada Media Corp. The format of the station is sports. KGIM-AM broadcasts to the Aberdeen, SD area at 1420 AM.

KGIM-FM
Owner: Armada Media Corp.
Editorial: 3304 S Highway 281, Aberdeen, South Dakota 57401-8792. **T:** 1 605 229-3632
E: aberdeenproduction@hubcityradio.com
W: http://www.hubcityradio.com
Editorial Profile: KGIM-FM is a commercial station owned by Armada Media Corp. The format of the station is contemporary country. KGIM-FM broadcasts to the Aberdeen, SD area at 103.7 FM.

KGIR-AM
Owner: Mississippi River Radio
Editorial: 324 Broadway St, Cape Girardeau, Missouri 63701-7331. **T:** 1 573 335-8291
W: http://www.kgir.com
Editorial Profile: KGIR-AM is a commercial station owned by Mississippi River Radio. The format of the station is sports. KGIR-AM broadcasts to the Cape Girardeau, MO area at 1220 AM.

KGIW-AM
Owner: Community Broadcasting Co.
Editorial: 292 Santa Fe Ave, Alamosa, Colorado 81101. **T:** 1 719 589-6644
W: http://www.kgiwkalq.com
Editorial Profile: KGIW-AM is a commercial station owned by Community Broadcasting Co. The format of the station is adult contemporary. KGIW-AM broadcasts to the Alamosa, CO area at 1450 AM.

KGKL-AM
Owner: Townsquare Media
Editorial: 1301 S Abe St, San Angelo, Texas 76903. **T:** 1 325 655-7161
W: http://960kgkl.com
Editorial Profile: KGKL-AM is a commercial station owned by Townsquare Media. The format of the station is news, sports and talk. KGKL-AM broadcasts to the San Angelo, TX area at 960 AM.

KGKL-FM
Owner: Townsquare Media
Editorial: 1301 S Abe St, San Angelo, Texas 76903. **T:** 1 325 655-7161
E: kgkl975@aol.com
W: http://www.975kgkl.com
Editorial Profile: KGKL-FM is a commercial station owned by Townsquare Media. The format of the station is contemporary country. KGKL-FM broadcasts to the San Angelo, TX area at 97.5 FM.

KGKS-FM
Owner: Max Media
Editorial: 324 Broadway St, Cape Girardeau, Missouri 63701-7331. **T:** 1 573 335-8291
W: http://www.kgks.com
Editorial Profile: KGKS-FM is a commercial station owned by Max Media. The format of the station is classic hits. KGKS-FM broadcasts to the Cape Girardeau, MO area at 93.9 FM.

KGLB-AM
Owner: Iowa City Broadcasting Co.
Editorial: 911 Hennepin Ave N, Glencoe, Minnesota 55336-2931. **T:** 1 320 269-8815
Editorial Profile: KGLB-AM is a commercial station owned by Iowa City Broadcasting Co. The format of the station is classic country. KGLB-AM broadcasts to the Minneapolis area at 1310 AM.

KGLC-FM
Owner: Northeast Oklahoma Broadcasting Network
Editorial: 1 N Main St, Miami, Oklahoma 74354-6322. **T:** 1 918 542-1818
E: kgue@sbcglobal.net
Editorial Profile: KGLC-FM is a commercial station owned by Northeast Oklahoma Broadcasting Network. The format for the station is adult contemporary. KGLC-FM broadcasts to the Miami, OK area at 100.9 FM.

KGLD-AM
Owner: Salt of the Earth Broadcasting
Editorial: 2737 S Broadway Ave, Ste 101, Tyler, Texas 75701. **T:** 1 903 526-1330
E: kgldradio@yahoo.com
W: http://www.kgld.org
Editorial Profile: KGLD-AM is a commercial station owned by Salt of the Earth Broadcasting. The format of the station is gospel. KGLD-AM broadcasts to the Tyler, TX area at 1330 AM.

KGLE-AM
Owner: Friends of Christian Radio Inc.
Editorial: 86 Seven Mile Dr, Glendive, Montana 59330. **T:** 1 406 377-3331
E: kgle@midrivers.com **W:** http://www.kgle.org
Editorial Profile: KGLE-AM is a commercial station owned by Friends of Christian Radio Inc. The format of the station is religious. KGLE-AM broadcasts to the Glendive, MT area at 590 AM.

KGLI-FM
Owner: Clear Channel Media and Entertainment
Editorial: 1113 Nebraska St, Sioux City, Iowa 51105. **T:** 1 712 258-5595
W: http://www.kg95.com
Editorial Profile: KGLI-FM is a commercial station owned by Clear Channel Media and Entertainment. The format of the station is hot adult contemporary music. KGLI-FM broadcasts to the Sioux City, IA area at 95.5 FM.

KGLK-FM
Owner: Cox Media Group, Inc.
Editorial: 1990 Post Oak Blvd Ste 2300, Houston, Texas 77056-3847
W: http://www.houstonseagle.com
Editorial Profile: KGLK-FM is a commercial station owned by Cox Media Group, Inc. The format of the station is classic hits. KGLK-FM broadcasts to the Houston area at 107.5 FM.

KGLM-FM
Owner: Butte Broadcasting Inc.
Editorial: 105 Main St, Anaconda, Montana 59711. **T:** 1 406 563-8011
E: mail@kbowkopr.com
Editorial Profile: KGLM-FM is a commercial station owned by Butte Broadcasting Inc. The format of the station is hot adult contemporary music. The station is aired in Anaconda, MT on 97.7 FM.

KGLN-AM
Owner: MBC Grand Broadcasting Inc.
Editorial: 1360 E Sherwood Dr, Grand Junction, Colorado 81501. **T:** 1 970 254-2100
Editorial Profile: KGLN-AM is a commercial station owned by MBC Grand Broadcasting Inc. The format of the station is news and talk. KGLN-AM broadcasts to the Glenwood Springs, CO area at 980 AM.

KGLO-AM
Owner: Three Eagles Communications Co.
Editorial: 341 S Yorktown Pike, Mason City, Iowa 50401. **T:** 1 641 423-1300
W: http://www.kgloam.com

KGLP-FM
Owner: Gallup Public Radio, Inc.
Editorial: 705 Gurley Ave, Gallup, New Mexico 87301-6979. **T:** 1 505 863-7626
E: kglpradio@kglp.org **W:** http://www.kglp.org
Editorial Profile: KGLP-FM is a non-commercial station owned by Gallup Public Radio, Inc. The format for the station is variety. KGLP-FM broadcasts to the Albuquerque, NM area at 91.7 FM.

KGLT-FM
Owner: Montana State University
Editorial: Montana State University, Sub Room 374, Bozeman, Montana 59717-0001.
T: 1 406 994-3001 **W:** http://www.kglt.net
Editorial Profile: KGLT-FM a non-commercial station owned by Montana State University. The format of the station is college variety. KGLT-FM broadcasts in the Bozeman, MT area at 91.9 FM.

KGLU-FM
Owner: Pollack Broadcasting Co.
Editorial: 1303 Southwest Drive, Kennett, Missouri 63857. **T:** 1 573 888-4616
W: http://www.1039thebuzz.com
Editorial Profile: KGLU-FM is a commercial station owned by Pollack Broadcasting Co. The format of the station is adult contemporary. KGLU-FM broadcasts to the Malden, MO area at 103.9 FM.

KGLX-FM
Owner: Clear Channel Media and Entertainment
Editorial: 1632 S Second St, Gallup, New Mexico 87301-5836. **T:** 1 505 863-9391
W: http://991kglx.com
Editorial Profile: KGLX-FM is a commercial station owned by Clear Channel Media and Entertainment. The format of the station is contemporary country. KGLX-FM broadcasts to the Gallup, NM area at 99.1 FM.

KGLY-FM
Owner: Educational Radio Foundation
Editorial: 2721 E Erwin St, Tyler, Texas 75708-2007. **T:** 1 903 593-5863
W: http://www.encouragementfm.com
Editorial Profile: KGLY-FM is a non-commercial station owned by Educational Radio Foundation. The format of the station is religious programming. KGLY-FM broadcasts to the Tyler, TX area at 91.3 FM.

KGME-AM
Owner: Clear Channel Media and Entertainment
Editorial: 4686 E Van Buren St Ste 300, Phoenix, Arizona 85008-6967.
T: 1 602 374-6000
W: http://www.foxsports910.com
Editorial Profile: KGME-AM is a commercial station owned by Clear Channel Media and Entertainment. The format of the station is sports. KGME-AM broadcasts to the Phoenix area at 910 AM.

KGMI-AM
Owner: Saga Communications
Editorial: 2219 Yew Street Rd, Bellingham, Washington 98229. **T:** 1 360 734-9790
E: kgmi@kgmi.com **W:** http://www.kgmi.com
Editorial Profile: KGMI-AM is a commercial station owned by Saga Communications. The format of the station is news and talk. KGMI-AM broadcasts to the Bellingham, WA area at 790 AM.

KGMN-FM
Owner: New West Broadcasting
Editorial: 812 E Beale St, Kingman, Arizona 86401-5925. **T:** 1 928 753-9100
W: http://www.kgmn.net
Editorial Profile: KGMN-FM is a commercial station owned by New West Broadcasting. The format of the station is contemporary country music. KGMN-FM broadcasts in the Phoenix area at 101.1 FM.

KGMO-FM
Owner: Withers Broadcasting of Missouri, LLC
Editorial: 901 S Kingshighway St, Cape Girardeau, Missouri 63703-8003.
T: 1 573 339-7000 **E:** news@withersradio.net
W: http://www.kgmo.com
Editorial Profile: KGMO-FM is a commercial station owned by Withers Broadcasting of Missouri LLC. The format of the station is classic rock. KGMO-FM broadcasts to the Cape Girardeau, MO area at 100.7 FM.

KGMS-AM
Owner: Good News Radio Broadcasting Inc.
Editorial: 3222 S Richey Ave, Tucson, Arizona 85713. **T:** 1 520 790-2440 **E:** info@kvoi.com
W: http://www.kgms.com
Editorial Profile: KGMS-AM is a commercial station owned by Good News Radio Broadcasting Inc. The format of the station is religious programming. KGMS-AM broadcasts to the Tucson, AZ area at 940 AM.

KGMT-AM
Owner: Siebert Communications Inc.
Editorial: 414 4th St, Fairbury, Nebraska 68352. **T:** 1 402 729-3382
Editorial Profile: KGMT-AM is a commercial station owned by Siebert Communications Inc. The format of the station is oldies. KGMT-AM broadcasts to the Fairbury, NE area at 1310 AM.

KGMX-FM
Owner: High Desert Broadcasting LLC
Editorial: 570 E Avenue Q9, Palmdale, California 93550-4655. **T:** 1 661 947-3107
E: psa@highdesertbroadcasting.com
W: http://www.kmix1063.com
Editorial Profile: KGMX-FM-FM is a commercial station owned by High Desert Broadcasting LLC. The format of the station is

adult contemporary. KGMX-FM broadcasts to the Antelope Valley area at 106.3 FM.

KGMY-AM
Owner: Clear Channel Media and Entertainment
Editorial: 1856 S Glenstone Ave, Springfield, Missouri 65804. **T:** 1 417 890-5555
W: http://www.espn1400.com
Editorial Profile: KGMY-AM is a commercial station owned by Clear Channel Media and Entertainment. The format of the station is sports. KGMY-AM broadcasts in the Springfield, MO area at 1400 AM.

KGMZ-FM
Owner: Entercom Communications Corp.
Editorial: 201 3rd St, San Francisco, California 94103-3143. **T:** 1 415 957-0957
W: http://www.957thegame.com
Editorial Profile: KGMZ-FM is a commercial station owned by Entercom Communications Corp. The format of the station is sports. KGMZ-FM broadcasts to the San Francisco area at 95.7 FM.

KGNB-AM
Owner: New Braunfels Communications Inc
Editorial: 1540 Loop 337, New Braunfels, Texas 78130-3352. **T:** 1 830 625-7311
W: http://radionb.com
Editorial Profile: KGNB-AM is a commercial station owned by New Braunfels Communications Inc. The format of the station is classic country and talk. KGNB-AM broadcasts to the New Braunfels, TX area at 1420 AM.

KGNC-AM
Owner: Morris Communications
Editorial: 3505 Olsen Blvd, Ste 117, Amarillo, Texas 79109. **T:** 1 806 355-9801
E: kgnc@kgnc.com
W: http://www.kgncam.com
Editorial Profile: KGNC-AM is a commercial station owned by Morris Communications. The format for the station is news and talk. KGNC-AM broadcasts to the Amarillo, TX area at 710 AM.

KGNC-FM
Owner: Morris Communications
Editorial: 3505 Olsen Blvd, Ste 117, Amarillo, Texas 79109. **T:** 1 806 355-9801
E: kgnc@kgnc.com
W: http://www.kgncfm.com
Editorial Profile: KGNC-FM is a commercial station owned by Morris Communications. The format of the station is country music. KGNC-FM broadcasts to Amarillo, TX at 97.9 FM.

KGNM-AM
Owner: Orama Inc.
Editorial: 2414 S Leonard Rd, Saint Joseph, Missouri 64503. **T:** 1 816 233-2577
E: kgnm@stjoelive.com
W: http://www.kgnmradio.com
Editorial Profile: KGNM-AM is a commercial station owned by Orama Inc. The format for the station is adult contemporary, Christian and talk. KGNM-AM broadcasts to the Saint Joseph, MO area at 1270 AM.

KGNO-AM
Owner: Rocking M Radio
Editorial: 2601 Central Ave Ste C, Dodge City, Kansas 67801-6212. **T:** 1 620 225-8080
W: http://mykansasradio.com
Editorial Profile: KGNO-AM is a commercial station owned by Rocking M Radio. The format of the station is classic country and talk. KGNO-AM broadcasts to the Dodge City, KS area at 1370 AM.

KGNR-FM
Owner: Life Broadcasting Inc.
Editorial: 166 SE Dayton St, John Day, Oregon 97845. **T:** 1 541 575-1840
E: contact@kgnr.org **W:** http://www.kgnr.org

KGNT-FM
Owner: Frandsen Media Company, LLC
Editorial: 810 W 200 N, Logan, Utah 84321. **T:** 1 435 752-1390 **W:** http://www.kool.fm
Editorial Profile: KGNT-FM is a commercial station owned by Frandsen Media Company, LLC. The format of the station is oldies. KGNT-FM broadcasts to the Salt Lake City area at 99.1 FM.

KGNU-AM
Owner: Boulder Community Broadcast Association, Inc.
Editorial: 4700 Walnut St, Boulder, Colorado 80301-2538. **T:** 1 303 449-4885
E: news@kgnu.org **W:** http://www.kgnu.org
Editorial Profile: KGNU-AM is a non-commercial station owned by Boulder Community Broadcast Association, Inc. The format of the station is variety. KGNU-AM broadcasts to the Denver area at 1390 AM. Use the station's news department email address for contact information for author requests. Please submit PSAs through the website.

KGNU-FM
Owner: Boulder Community Broadcast Association, Inc.
Editorial: 4700 Walnut St, Boulder, Colorado 80301-2538. **T:** 1 303 449-4885
E: news@kgnu.org **W:** http://www.kgnu.org
Editorial Profile: KGNU-FM is a non-commercial station owned by Boulder Community Broadcast Association, Inc. The format of the station is variety. KGNU-FM broadcasts to the Boulder, CO area at 88.5 FM. Use the station's news department email address for contact information for author requests. Please submit PSAs through the website.

KGNW-AM
Owner: Salem Communications
Editorial: 2201 6th Ave, Ste 1500, Seattle, Washington 98121-1840. **T:** 1 206 443-8200
E: webmaster@kgnw.com
W: http://www.kgnw.com
Editorial Profile: KGNW-AM is a commercial station owned by Salem Communications. The format of the station is religious music and Christian conservative talk. KGNW-AM broadcasts to the Seattle area at 820 AM.

KGNZ-FM
Owner: Christian Broadcasting Co.
Editorial: 542 Butternut St, Abilene, Texas 79602. **T:** 1 325 673-3045
E: studio@kgnz.com **W:** http://www.kgnz.com
Editorial Profile: KGNZ-FM is a non-commercial station owned by the Christian Broadcasting Co. The format of the station is contemporary Christian music and talk. KGNZ-FM broadcasts in the Abilene, TX area at 88.1 FM.

KGO-AM
Owner: Cumulus Media Inc
Editorial: 55 Hawthorne St, San Francisco, California 94105-3906. **T:** 1 415 995-6800
E: producers@kgoradio.com
W: http://www.kgoradio.com
Editorial Profile: KGO-AM is a commercial station owned by Cumulus Media Inc. The format of the station is news and talk. KGO-AM broadcasts to the San Francisco area at 810 AM.

KGOE-AM
Owner: Bicoastal Media LLC
Editorial: 5640 S Broadway St, Eureka, California 95503. **T:** 1 707 442-2000
E: eurekanews@bicoastalmedia.com
W: http://www.kgoe1480.com
Editorial Profile: KGOE-AM is a commercial station owned by Bicoastal Media LLC. The format for the station is news, talk and sports. KGOE-AM broadcasts to the Eureka, CA area at 1480 AM.

KGOL-AM
Owner: Entravision Communications Corp.
Editorial: 5353 W Alabama St Ste 450, Houston, Texas 77056-5922.
T: 1 713 349-9880
W: http://www.espndeporteshouston.com/
Editorial Profile: KGOL-AM is a commercial station owned by Entravision Communications Corp. The format of the station is Hispanic sports. KGOL-AM broadcasts to the Houston area at 1180 AM.

KGON-FM
Owner: Entercom Communications Corp.
Editorial: 0700 SW Bancroft St, Portland, Oregon 97239-4226. **T:** 1 503 223-1441
W: http://www.kgon.com
Editorial Profile: KGON-FM is a commercial station owned by Entercom Communications Corp. The format of the station is classic rock music. KGON-FM broadcasts to the Portland, OR area at 92.3 FM.

KGOR-FM
Owner: Clear Channel Media and Entertainment
Editorial: 5010 Underwood Ave, Omaha, Nebraska 68132. **T:** 1 402 561-2000
W: http://www.kgor.com
Editorial Profile: KGOR-FM is a commercial station owned by Clear Channel Media and Entertainment. The format of the station is oldies. KGOR-FM broadcasts to the Omaha, NE area at 99.9 FM.

KGOS-AM
Owner: Kath Broadcasting, LLC
Editorial: 7060 Radio Rd, Torrington, Wyoming 82240. **T:** 1 307 532-2158
E: news@kgoskerm.com
W: http://kgoskerm.com
Editorial Profile: KGOS-AM is a commercial station owned by Kath Broadcasting, LLC. The format of the station is country. KGOS-AM broadcasts to the Torrington, WY area at 1490 AM.

KGOT-FM
Owner: Clear Channel Media and Entertainment
Editorial: 800 E Dimond Blvd, Ste 3-370, Anchorage, Alaska 99515. **T:** 1 907 522-1515
W: http://www.kgot.com
Editorial Profile: KGOT-FM is a commercial station owned by Clear Channel Media and Entertainment. The format of the station is Top 40/CHR. KGOT-FM broadcasts to the Anchorage, AK area at 101.3 FM.

KGOU-FM
Owner: University of Oklahoma
Editorial: Copeland Hall, Room 300, Norman, Oklahoma 73019-0001. **T:** 1 405 325-3388
E: news@kgou.org **W:** http://www.kgou.org
Editorial Profile: KGOU-FM is a non-commercial station owned by the University of Oklahoma. The format of the station is jazz, news and talk. KGOU-FM broadcasts to the Norman, OK area at 106.3 FM.

KGOW-AM
Owner: Gow Communications, LLC
Editorial: 5353 W Alabama St Ste 415, Houston, Texas 77056-5942.
T: 1 713 479-5300
W: http://www.ysr1560.com
Editorial Profile: KGOW-AM is a commercial station owned by Gow Communications, LLC. The format of the station is sports. KGOW-AM broadcasts to the Houston area at 1560 AM, and is the flagship station for Sporting News Radio Network.

KGOZ-FM
Owner: Par Broadcast Group
Editorial: 804 Main St, Trenton, Missouri 64683-2044. **T:** 1 660 359-2727
E: news@kttn.com **W:** http://www.kgozfm.com
Editorial Profile: KGOZ-FM is a commercial station owned by Par Broadcast Group. The format of the station is contemporary country. KGOZ-FM broadcasts to the Trenton, MO area at 101.7 FM.

KGPQ-FM
Owner: Pines Broadcasting
Editorial: 279 Midway Rte, Monticello, Arkansas 71655-8605. **T:** 1 870 367-6854
E: pines.radio@sbcglobal.net
Editorial Profile: KGPQ-FM is a commercial station owned by Pines Broadcasting. The format of the station is adult contemporary. KGPQ-FM broadcasts to the Monticello, AR area at 99.9 FM.

KGPZ-FM
Owner: Latto Northland and Broadcasting, Inc.
Editorial: 504 NW 1st Ave Ste 290, Grand Rapids, Minnesota 55744-2668.
T: 1 218 326-7427 **E:** kgpz@paulbunyan.net
W: http://www.kgpzfm.com
Editorial Profile: KGPZ-FM is a commercial station owned by Latto Northland and Broadcasting, Inc. The format of the station is country music. KGPZ-FM broadcasts to the Grand Rapids, MN area at 96.1 FM.

KGRB-FM
Owner: Adelante Media Group
Editorial: 500 Media Pl, Sacramento, California 95815. **T:** 1 916 368-6300
W: http://www.adelantemediagroup.com
Editorial Profile: KGRB-FM is a commercial station owned by Adelante Media Group. The format of the station is regional Mexican. KGRB-FM broadcasts to the Sacramento, CA area at 94.3 FM.

KGRC-FM
Owner: Staradio Corp.
Editorial: 329 Maine St, Quincy, Illinois 62301. **T:** 1 217 224-4102 **E:** real929@staradio.com
W: http://www.real929.com
Editorial Profile: KGRC-FM is a commercial station owned by Starradio Corp. The format of the station is Lite Rock/Lite AC. KGRC-FM broadcasts to the Quincy, IL area at 92.9 FM.

KGRD-FM
Owner: Praise Network(The)
Editorial: 128 S 4th St, Oneill, Nebraska 68763. **T:** 1 402 336-3886
W: http://www.goodnewsgreatmusic.org
Editorial Profile: KGRD-FM is a non-commercial station owned by The Praise Network. The format of the station is Contemporary Christian. KGRD-FM broadcasts to the Oneill, NE area at 105.3 FM.

KGRE-AM
Owner: Greeley Broadcasting Corp.
Editorial: 800 8th Ave Ste 304, Greeley, Colorado 80631-1190. **T:** 1 970 356-1452
E: kgre@msn.com
W: http://www.tigrecolorado.com
Editorial Profile: KGRE-AM is a commercial station owned by Greeley Broadcasting Corp. The format of the station is Hispanic. KGRE-AM broadcasts to the Greeley, CO area at 1450 AM.

KGRG-AM
Owner: Green River Community College
Editorial: 12401 SE 320th St, Auburn, Washington 98092. **T:** 1 253 833-9111
E: programming@kgrg.com
W: http://www.kgrg1.com
Editorial Profile: KGRG-AM is a non-commercial station owned by Green River Community College. The format of the station is a mix of rock alternative and classic rock. KGRG-AM broadcasts to the Auburn, WA area at 1330 AM.

KGRG-FM
Owner: Green River Community College
Editorial: 12401 SE 320th St, Auburn, Washington 98092. **T:** 1 253 833-9111
E: programming@kgrg.com
W: http://www.kgrg.com
Editorial Profile: KGRG-FM is a non-commercial station owned by Green River Community College. The format of the station is rock alternative. KGRG-FM broadcasts to the Auburn, WA area at 89.9 FM.

KGRM-FM
Owner: Grambling State University
Editorial: Washington Johnson Complex, 403 Main Street, 2nd Fl, Grambling, Louisiana 71245-3090. **T:** 1 318 274-6343
W: http://www.gram.edu/life/campus%20media/kgrm
Editorial Profile: KGRM-FM is a non-commercial college station owned by Grambling State University. The format of the station is variety. KGRM-FM broadcasts to the Grambling, LA area at a frequency of 91.5 FM.

KGRN-AM
Owner: Good Radio
Editorial: 909 1/2 Main St, Grinnell, Iowa 50112-2174. **T:** 1 641 236-6106
E: kgrnnews@iowatelecom.net
W: http://www.myiowainfo.com
Editorial Profile: KGRN-AM is commercial station owned by Good Radio. The format of the station is adult contemporary. KGRN-AM broadcasts to the Grinnell, IA area at 1410 AM.

KGRO-AM
Owner: Hughes(Jim)
Editorial: 1701 1/2 N Banks St, Pampa, Texas 79065. **T:** 1 806 669-6809
E: production@kgrokomxradio.com
W: http://www.kgrokomxradio.com
Editorial Profile: KGRO-AM is a commercial station owned by Jim Hughes. The format of the station is adult contemporary. KGRO-AM broadcasts to the Pampa, TX area at 1230 AM.

KGRR-FM
Owner: Radio Dubuque Inc.
Editorial: 346 W 8th St, Dubuque, Iowa 52001-4627. **T:** 1 563 690-0800
W: http://www.973therock.com
Editorial Profile: KGRR-FM is a commercial station owned by Radio Dubuque Inc. The format of the station is rock. KGRR-FM broadcasts to the Dubuque, IA area at 97.3 FM.

KGRS-FM
Owner: Titan Broadcasting LLC
Editorial: 610 N 4Th St Ste 310, Burlington, Iowa 52601-5059. **T:** 1 319 752-2701
W: http://www.thenewmix.com
Editorial Profile: KGRS-FM is a commercial station owned by Titan Broadcasting LLC. The format of the station is hot adult contemporary. KGRS-FM broadcasts to the Burlington, IA area at 107.3 FM.

KGRT-AM
Owner: Adams Radio Group
Editorial: 1355 California Ave, Las Cruces, New Mexico 88001-4130. **T:** 1 575 525-9298
E: radiolc@kgrt.com
W: http://www.kgrt570.com
Editorial Profile: KGRT-AM is a commercial station owned by Adams Radio Group. The format of the station is classic country. KGRT-AM broadcasts to the Las Cruces, NM area at 570 AM.

KGRT-FM
Owner: Adams Radio Group
Editorial: 1355 California Ave, Las Cruces, New Mexico 88001-4130. **T:** 1 575 525-9298
E: radiolc@kgrt.com **W:** http://www.kgrt.com
Editorial Profile: KGRT-FM is a commercial station owned by Adams Radio Group. The format of the station is contemporary country. KGRT-FM broadcasts to the Las Cruces, NM area at 103.9 FM.

KGRV-AM
Owner: Pacific Cascade Communications Corp.
Editorial: 196 SE Main St, Winston, Oregon 97496. **T:** 1 541 679-8185
E: info@kgrv700.net
W: http://www.kgrv700.net

KGRW-FM
Owner: Tejas Broadcasting
Editorial: 3639 Wolflin Ave, Amarillo, Texas 79102-2119. **T:** 1 806 355-1044
Editorial Profile: KGRW-FM is a commercial station owned by Tejas Broadcasting. The format of the station is Hispanic. KGRW-FM broadcasts to the Amarillo, TX area at 104.3 FM.

KGRZ-AM
Owner: Cherry Creek Radio
Editorial: 1600 North Ave W Ste 101, Missoula, Montana 59801-5500.
T: 1 406 728-1450
Editorial Profile: KGRZ-AM is a commercial station owned by Cherry Creek Radio. The format of the station is sports. KGRZ-AM broadcasts to the Missoula, MT area at 1450 AM.

KGSG-FM
Owner: Cherry Creek Radio
Editorial: 2823 W Lewis St, Pasco, Washington 99301-6702. **T:** 1 509 547-1618
W: http://www.groove937.com
Editorial Profile: KGSG-FM is a commercial station owned by Cherry Creek Radio. The format of the station is smooth AC and jazz. KGSG-FM broadcasts to the Pasco, WA area at 93.7 FM.

KGSO-AM
Owner: Steckline Communications
Editorial: 1632 S Maize Rd, Wichita, Kansas 67209. **T:** 1 316 721-8484
W: http://www.kgso.com
Editorial Profile: KGSO-AM is a commercial station owned by Steckline Communications. The format of the station is sports. KGSO-AM broadcasts to Wichita, KS, at 1410 AM.

KGSR-FM
Owner: Emmis Communications Corp.
Editorial: 8309 N Interstate Hwy 35, Austin, Texas 78753-5720. **T:** 1 512 832-4000
W: http://www.kgsr.com
Editorial Profile: KGSR-FM is a commercial station owned by Emmis Communications Corp. The format of the station is adult album alternative music. KGSR-FM broadcasts to the Austin, TX area at 93.3 FM.

KGST-AM
Owner: Lotus Communications Corp.
Editorial: 1110 E Olive Ave, Fresno, California 93728-3535. **T:** 1 559 497-1100
E: production@lotusfresno.com
W: http://www.espn1600am.com
Editorial Profile: KGST-AM is a commercial station owned by Lotus Broadcasting Corp. The format of the station is Mexican Hispanic sports programming. KGST-AM broadcasts to the Fresno, CA area at 1600 AM.

KGSX-FM
Owner: Univision Communications Inc.
Editorial: 12451 Network Blvd Ste 140, San Antonio, Texas 78249-3336.
T: 1 210 610-4300
E: lakalle951@radio.univision.com
W: http://951sanantonio.univision.com
Editorial Profile: KGSX-FM is a commercial station owned by Univision Communications Inc. The format of the station is Hispanic contemporary hits. KGSX-FM broadcasts to the San Antonio area at 95.1 FM.

KGTK-AM
Owner: KITZ Radio Inc.
Editorial: 1700 Se Mile Hill Dr Ste 243, Port Orchard, Washington 98366-3507.
T: 1 360 876-1400 **E:** info@kitz1400.com
W: http://www.kitz1400.com
Editorial Profile: KGTK-AM is a commercial station owned by KITZ Radio Inc. The format of the station is business talk and sports. KGTK-AM broadcasts to the Bellevue, WA area at 920 AM.

KGTL-AM
Owner: Peninsula Communications Inc.
Editorial: 66060 Diamond Ridge Rd, Homer, Alaska 99603-9229. **T:** 1 907 235-6000
E: kwavefm@xyz.net
Editorial Profile: KGTL-AM is a commercial station owned by Peninsula Communications Inc. The format of the station is adult standards and talk. KGTL-AM broadcasts to the Homer, AK area at 620 AM.

KGTM-FM
Owner: Rich Broadcasting, Inc.
Editorial: 544 N Arthur Ave, Pocatello, Idaho 83204-3002. **T:** 1 208 529-6926
W: http://www.star985.com
Editorial Profile: KGTM-FM is a commercial station owned by Rich Broadcasting, Inc. The format of the station is Hot AC. KGTM-FM broadcasts to the Idaho Falls, ID area at 98.1 FM.

KGTO-AM
Owner: Perry Publishing & Broadcasting Inc.
Editorial: 7030 S Yale Ave Ste 302, Tulsa, Oklahoma 74136-5722. **T:** 1 918 494-9886
W: http://thetouch1050.com
Editorial Profile: KGTO-AM is a commercial station owned by Perry Publishing & Broadcasting Inc. The format of the station is R&B oldies. KGTO-AM broadcasts to the Tulsa, OK area at 1050 AM.

KGTS-FM
Owner: Walla Walla University
Editorial: 204 S College Ave, College Place, Washington 99324. **T:** 1 509 527-2991
E: studio@plr.org **W:** http://www.plr.org
Editorial Profile: KGTS-FM is a non-commercial station owned by Walla Walla University. The format of the station is contemporary Christian music and talk. KGTS-FM broadcasts to the College Place, WA area at 93.1 FM.

KGTW-FM
Owner: Alaska Broadcast Communications Inc.
Editorial: 526 Stedman St, Ketchikan, Alaska 99901-6629. **T:** 1 907 225-2193
W: http://ketchikanradio.com
Editorial Profile: KGTW-FM is a commercial station owned by Alaska Broadcast Communications Inc. The format of the station is contemporary country. KGTW-FM broadcasts to the Ketchikan, AK area at 106.7 FM.

KGUA-FM
Owner: Native Media Resource Center
Editorial: 35501 S Highway 1 Unit 50, Gualala, California 95445-9548.
T: 1 707 884-4883
W: http://nativemediaresourcecenter.org
Editorial Profile: KGUA-FM is a non-commercial community station owned by Native Media Resource Center. The format of the station is variety with a focus on Native American news/information and issues in Mendocino County and the Northern tip of Sonoma County. KGUA-FM broadcasts to the Gualala, CA area at 88.3 FM.

KGU-AM
Owner: Salem Communications
Editorial: 1160 N King St, Honolulu, Hawaii 96817-3307. **T:** 1 808 533-0065
W: http://www.760kgu.biz
Editorial Profile: KGU-AM is a commercial station owned by Salem Communications. The format of the station is business talk. KGU-AM broadcasts to the Honolulu area at 760 AM.

KGU-FM
Owner: Salem Communications
Editorial: 1160 N King St, Honolulu, Hawaii 96817. **T:** 1 808 533-0065
W: http://www.995kgufm.com
Editorial Profile: KGU-FM is a commercial station owned by Salem Communications. The format of the station is Religious. KGU-FM broadcasts to the Honolulu area at 99.5 FM.

KGVA-FM
Owner: Fort Belknap College
Editorial: Chippewa and 1st St, Harlem, Montana 59526. **T:** 1 406 353-4656
E: kgvaradiostation@yahoo.com
W: http://www.kgvafm.org

KGVE-FM
Owner: Caleb Corp.
Editorial: 1 W 3rd St, Grove, Oklahoma 74344. **T:** 1 918 786-2211
Editorial Profile: KGVE-FM is a commercial station owned by Caleb Corp. The format of the station is country. KGVE-FM broadcasts to the Tulsa, OK area at 99.3 FM.

KGVL-AM
Owner: Hunt County Radio, LLC
Editorial: 1517 Wolfe City Dr, Greenville, Texas 75401. **T:** 1 903 455-1400
Editorial Profile: KGVL-AM is a commercial station owned by Hunt County Radio, LLC. The format of the station is oldies. KGVL-AM broadcasts to the Greenville, TX area at 1400 AM.

KGVO-AM
Owner: Townsquare Media, LLC
Editorial: 3250 S Reserve St Ste 200, Missoula, Montana 59801-8236.
T: 1 406 728-9300
W: http://newstalkkgvo.com
Editorial Profile: KGVO-AM is a commercial station owned by Townsquare Media, LLC. The format of the station is news and talk. KGVO-AM broadcasts to the Missoula, MT area at 1290 AM.

KGVO-FM
Owner: Townsquare Media, LLC
Editorial: 3250 S Reserve St Ste 200, Missoula, Montana 59801-8236.
T: 1 406 728-9300
W: http://newstalkkgvo.com
Editorial Profile: KGVO-FM is a commercial station owned by Townsquare Media, LLC. The format is news talk. KGVO-FM broadcasts to the Missoula, MT area at 101.5 FM. The station is a simulcast of KGVO-AM.

KGVW-AM
Owner: Gallatin Valley Witness Inc.
Editorial: 2050 Amsterdam Rd, Belgrade, Montana 59714. **T:** 1 406 388-4281
E: cmmevents@yahoo.com
Editorial Profile: KGVW-AM is a commercial station owned by Gallatin Valley Witness Inc. The format for the station is Christian talk, music and news. KGVW-AM broadcasts to the Belgrade, MT area at 640 AM.

KGVY-AM
Owner: KGVY LLC
Editorial: 1510 W Camino Antigua, Sahuarita, Arizona 85629. **T:** 1 520 399-1000
E: kgvynews@kgvy1080.com
W: http://www.kgvy1080.com
Editorial Profile: KGVY-AM is a commercial station owned by KGVY LLC. The format of the station is adult standards. KGVY-AM broadcasts to the Tucson, AZ area at 1080 AM.

KGWA-AM
Owner: Williams Broadcasting LLC
Editorial: 1710 W Willow Rd, Ste 300, Enid, Oklahoma 73703. **T:** 1 580 234-4230
E: production@kofm.com
W: http://www.kofm.com
Editorial Profile: KGWA-AM is a commercial station owned by Williams Broadcasting LLC. The format of the station is news and talk. KGWA-AM broadcasts to the Oklahoma City area at 960 AM.

KGWT-FM
Owner: Hispanic Target Media, Inc.
Editorial: 1524 S Interstate 35, Austin, Texas 78704-8931. **T:** 1 602 283-3293
E: hispanictargetmedia@gmail.com
W: http://www.hispanictargetmedia.info/
Editorial Profile: KGWT-FMis a commercial station owned by Hispanic Target Media, Inc. The format of the station is Hispanic music. KGWT-FM broadcasts locally to the George West, TX area at a frequency of 93.5 FM.

KGWY-FM
Owner: Legend Communications
Editorial: 2810 Southern Dr, Gillette, Wyoming 82718. **T:** 1 307 686-2242
E: news@basinsradio.com
W: http://www.basinsradio.com
Editorial Profile: KGWY-FM is a commercial station owned by Legend Communications. The format of the station is country. KGWY-FM broadcasts to the Denver area at 100.7 FM.

KGY-AM
Owner: KGY Inc.
Editorial: 1700 Marine Dr NE, Olympia, Washington 98501. **T:** 1 360 943-1240
E: news@kgyradio.com
W: http://www.kgyradio.com
Editorial Profile: KGY-AM is a commercial station owned by KGY Inc. The format of the station is adult contemporary music, news and sports. KGY-AM broadcasts to the Seattle area at 1240 AM.

KGYM-AM
Owner: KZIA Inc.
Editorial: 1110 26th Ave SW, Cedar Rapids, Iowa 52404. **T:** 1 319 363-2061
E: info@kgymradio.com
W: http://www.kgymradio.com
Editorial Profile: KGYM-AM is a commercial station owned by KZIA Inc. The format of the station is sports. KGYM-AM broadcasts to the Cedar Rapids, IA area at 1600 AM.

KGYN-AM
Owner: Steckline Communications
Editorial: 2300 N Lelia St, Guymon, Oklahoma 73942. **T:** 1 580 338-1210
E: kgyn@kgynradio.com
W: http://www.kgynradio.com
Editorial Profile: KGYN-AM is a commercial station owned by Steckline Communications. The format of the station is classic country and news. KGYN-AM broadcasts to the Guymon, OK area at 1210 AM.

KGZO-FM
Owner: The Association for Community Education Inc.
Editorial: 2310 E Ponderosa Dr, Ste 28, Camarillo, California 93010. **T:** 1 800 260-5676
W: http://www.nuevavida.com
Editorial Profile: KGZO-FM is a non-commercial station owned by The Association for Community Education Inc. The format of the station is Hispanic religious programming. KGZO-FM broadcasts to the Camarillo, CA area at 90.9 FM.

KHAC-AM
Owner: Western Indian Ministries
Editorial: Highway 264, 02C Hilltop Drive, HC33 Box 40, Gallup, New Mexico 87301.
T: 1 505 371-5587 **E:** khac@westernindian.org
W: http://khac.westernindian.net
Editorial Profile: KHAC-AM is a commercial station owned by Western Indian Ministries. The format of the station is contemporary Christian. KHAC-AM broadcasts to the Rock, AZ area at 880 AM.

KHAK-FM
Owner: Townsquare Media, LLC
Editorial: 425 2nd St SE Fl 4, Cedar Rapids, Iowa 52401-1819. **T:** 1 319 365-9431
E: khak@khak.com **W:** http://www.khak.com
Editorial Profile: KHAK-FM is a commercial station owned by Townsquare Media, LLC. The format of the station is contemporary country. KHAK-FM broadcasts to the Cedar Rapids, IA area at 98.1 FM.

KHAM-FM
Owner: Coloff Media
Editorial: 18643 360th St, Forest City, Iowa 50436-7491. **T:** 1 641 585-1073
Editorial Profile: KHAM-FM is a commercial station owned by Coloff Media. The format of the station is adult contemporary. KHAM-FM broadcasts to the Forest City, IA area at 103.1 FM.

KHAP-FM
Owner: Family Stations Inc.
Editorial: 4135 Northgate Blvd Ste 1, Sacramento, California 95834-1226.
T: 1 866 641-8191
E: familyradio@familyradio.com
W: http://www.familyradio.com
Editorial Profile: KHAP-FM is a non-commercial station owned by Family Stations Inc. The format of the station is religious. KEAR-AM broadcasts to the Sacramento, CA area at 89.1 FM.

KHAQ-FM
Owner: Armada Media Corp.
Editorial: 305 E 4th St, North Platte, Nebraska 69101-6903. **T:** 1 308 534-6650
E: production@huskeradio.com
W: http://www.hawk985.com
Editorial Profile: KHAQ-FM is a commercial station owned by Armada Media Corp. The format of the station is classic rock. KHAQ-FM broadcasts to the McCook, NE area at 98.5 FM.

KHAR-AM
Owner: Morris Communications
Editorial: 301 Arctic Slope Ave, Anchorage, Alaska 99518-3035. **T:** 1 907 344-9622
W: http://www.khar590.com
Editorial Profile: KHAR-AM is a commercial station owned by Morris Communications. The format of the station is sports. KHAR-AM broadcasts to the Anchorage, AK area at 590 AM.

KHAS-AM
Owner: Platte River Radio, Inc.
Editorial: 500 E J St, Hastings, Nebraska 68901. **T:** 1 402 463-1230
E: khaskics@khasradio.com
W: http://www.hastingslink.com
Editorial Profile: KHAS-AM is a commercial station owned by Platte River Radio, Inc. The format of the station is news, talk and AC music. KHAS-AM broadcasts to the Hastings, NE area at 1230 AM.

KHAT-AM
Owner: Appaloosa Broadcasting
Editorial: 302 S 2nd St, Ste 204, Laramie, Wyoming 82070-3650. **T:** 1 307 745-5208
Editorial Profile: KHAT-AM is a commercial station owned by Appaloosa Broadcasting. The format of the station is sports. KHAT-AM broadcasts to the Laramie, WY area on 1210 AM.

KHAY-FM
Owner: Cumulus Media Inc.
Editorial: 1376 Walter St, Ventura, California 93003-5658. **T:** 1 805 642-8595
W: http://www.khay.com
Editorial Profile: KHAY-FM is a commercial station owned by the Cumulus Media Inc. The format of the station is country music. KHAY-FM broadcasts to the Ventura, CA area at 100.7 FM.

KHAZ-FM
Owner: Eagle Radio Inc.
Editorial: 2300 Hall St, Hays, Kansas 67601-3062. **T:** 1 785 625-2578
E: haysnews@eagleradio.net
W: http://www.99kzcountry.com
Editorial Profile: KHAZ-FM is a commercial station owned by Eagle Radio Inc. The format of the station is country. KHAZ-FM broadcasts to the Hays, KS area at 99.5 FM.

KHBC-FM
Owner: Resonate Hawaii, LLC
Editorial: 688 Kinoole St Ste 112, Hilo, Hawaii 96720-3868. **T:** 1 208 837-4104
W: http://www.hawaiiswave.com
Editorial Profile: KHBC-FM is a commercial station owned by Resonate Hawaii, LLC. The format for the station is Hot AC. KHBC-FM broadcasts to the Hilo area at 92.7 FM.

KHBM-AM
Owner: Pines Broadcasting
Editorial: 279 Midway Rte, Monticello, Arkansas 71655. **T:** 1 870 367-6854
E: pines.radio@sbcglobal.net
Editorial Profile: KHBM-AM is a commercial station owned by Pines Broadcasting. The format of the station is adult standards music. KHBM-AM broadcasts in the Monticello, AR area at 1430 AM.

KHBM-FM
Owner: Pines Broadcasting
Editorial: 279 Midway Rte, Monticello, Arkansas 71655-8605. **T:** 1 870 367-6854
E: pines.radio@sbcglobal.net
Editorial Profile: KHBM-FM is a commercial station owned by Pines Broadcasting. The format of the station is classic rock. KHBM-FM broadcasts to the Monticello, AR area at 93.7 FM.

KHBR-AM
Owner: KHBR Radio Inc.
Editorial: 335 Country Club Rd, Hillsboro, Texas 76645. **T:** 1 254 582-3431
E: info@khbrhillsboro.com
W: http://khbrhillsboro.com
Editorial Profile: KHBR-AM is a commercial station owned by KHBR Radio Inc. The format of the station is classic country music. KHBR-AM broadcasts to the Hillsboro, TX, area at 1560 AM.

KHBT-FM
Owner: NRG Media LLC
Editorial: 2196 Montana Ave, Humboldt, Iowa 50548-8625. **T:** 1 515 332-4100
E: thebolt@nrgmedia.com
W: http://www.977thebolt.com
Editorial Profile: KHBT-FM is a commercial station owned by NRG Media LLC. The format of the station is adult contemporary music. KHBT-FM broadcasts to the Humboldt, IA at 97.7 FM.

KHBW-FM
Owner: Houston Christian Broadcasters
Editorial: 2424 South Blvd, Houston, Texas 77098-5110. **T:** 1 713 520-5200
W: http://www.khcb.org/index.html
Editorial Profile: KHBW-FM is a non-commercial station owned by Houston Christian Broadcasters. The format of the station is Christian music and religious talk. KHBW-FM broadcasts to the Brownwood, TX area at 91.7 FM.

KHBZ-FM
Owner: KHOZ LLC
Editorial: 1111 Radio Ave, Harrison, Arkansas 72601-2516. **T:** 1 870 741-2301
Editorial Profile: KHBZ-FM is a commercial station owned by KHOZ LLC. The format of the station is contemporary country. KHBZ-FM broadcasts to the Harrison, AR area at 102.9 FM.

KHCA-FM
Owner: KHCA Inc.
Editorial: 103 N 3rd St, Ste A, Manhattan, Kansas 66502. **T:** 1 785 537-9595
E: angel95fm@hotmail.com
W: http://www.angel95fm.com
Editorial Profile: KHCA-FM is a commercial station owned by KHCA Inc. The format of the station is contemporary Christian music and talk. KHCA-FM broadcasts to the Manhattan, KS area at 95.3 FM.

KHCB-AM
Owner: Houston Christian Broadcasters
Editorial: 2424 South Blvd, Houston, Texas 77098. **T:** 1 713 520-7900
E: amistad@radioamistad.net
W: http://www.khcb.org
Editorial Profile: KHCB-AM is a non-commercial station owned by Houston Christian Broadcasters. The format of the station is Hispanic Christian programming. KHCB-AM broadcasts to the Houston area at 1400 AM.

KHCB-FM
Owner: Houston Christian Broadcasters
Editorial: 2424 South Blvd, Houston, Texas 77098. **T:** 1 713 520-5200 **E:** email@khcb.org
W: http://www.khcb.org
Editorial Profile: KHCB-FM is non-commercial station owned by Houston Christian Broadcasters. The format of the station is Christian music and religious talk. KHCB-FM broadcasts to the Houston area at 105.7 FM.

KHCC-FM
Owner: Hutchinson Community College
Editorial: 815 N Walnut St, Ste 300, Hutchinson, Kansas 67501. **T:** 1 620 662-6646
E: comments@radiokansas.org
W: http://www.radiokansas.org
Editorial Profile: KHCC-FM is a non-commercial station owned by Hutchinson Community College. The format of the station is news and classical music. KHCC-FM broadcasts to the Wichita, KS area at 90.1 FM.

KHCD-FM
Owner: Hutchinson Community College
Editorial: 815 N Walnut St, Ste 300, Hutchinson, Kansas 67501. **T:** 1 620 662-6646
E: comments@radiokansas.org
W: http://www.radiokansas.org
Editorial Profile: KHCD-FM is a non-commercial station owned by Hutchinson Community College. The format of the station is news and classical music. KHCD-FM broadcasts to the Wichita, KS area at 90.1 FM.

KHCM-AM
Owner: Salem Communications
Editorial: 1160 N King St, Honolulu, Hawaii 96817-3307. **T:** 1 808 533-0065
Editorial Profile: KHCM-AM is a commercial station owned by Salem Communications. The format of the station is Chinese programming with blocks of English variety programming. KHCM-AM broadcasts to the Honolulu area at 880 AM.

KHCM-FM
Owner: Salem Communications
Editorial: 1160 N King St, 2nd Fl, Honolulu, Hawaii 96817-3307. **T:** 1 808 533-0065
W: http://www.975countrykhem.com
Editorial Profile: KHCM-FM is a commercial station owned by Salem Communications. The format for the station is classic and contemporary country music. KHCM-FM broadcasts to the Honolulu area at 97.5 FM.

KHCS-FM
Owner: Prairie Avenue Gospel Center
Editorial: 2341 N Duane Rd, Palm Springs, California 92262-3102. **T:** 1 760 864-9620
E: khcs@juno.com **W:** http://www.joy92.org
Editorial Profile: KHCS-FM is a non-commercial station owned by Prairie Avenue Gospel Center. The format of the station is Christian programming. KHCS-FM broadcasts to the Palm Springs, CA area at 91.7 FM.

KHCT-FM
Owner: Hutchinson Community College
Editorial: 815 N Walnut St, Ste 300, Hutchinson, Kansas 67501. **T:** 1 620 662-6646
E: comments@radiokansas.org
W: http://www.radiokansas.org
Editorial Profile: KHCT-FM is a non-commercial station owned by Hutchinson Community College. The format of the station is news and classical music. KHCT-FM broadcasts to the Wichita, KS area at 90.9 FM.

KHDC-FM
Owner: Radio Bilingue Inc.
Editorial: 161 Main St, Ste 4, Salinas, California 93901. **T:** 1 831 757-8039
W: http://www.radiobilingue.org
Editorial Profile: KHDC-FM is a non-commercial station owned by Radio Bilingue Inc. The format of the station is Hispanic variety. KHDC-FM broadcasts to the Salinas, CA area at 90.9 FM.

KHDK-FM
Owner: Pritchard Broadcasting Co.
Editorial: 610 N 4Th St Ste 300, Burlington, Iowa 52601-5059. **T:** 1 319 752-5402
E: hot973@hot973online.com
W: http://www.hot973online.com
Editorial Profile: KHDK-FM is a commercial station owned by Pritchard Broadcasting Co. The format of the station is Top 40/CHR. KHDK-FM broadcasts to the Des Moines, IA area at 97.3 FM.

KHDN-AM
Owner: Sun Mountain Inc.
Editorial: Rr 1, Hardin, Montana 59034-9801. **T:** 1 406 665-2828
W: http://www.bigskyradio.net
Editorial Profile: KHDN-AM is a commercial station owned by Sun Mountain Inc. The format of the station is talk. KHDN-AM broadcasts in the Hardin, MT area at 1230 AM.

KHDR-FM
Owner: Highway Radio Inc.
Editorial: 1611 E Main St, Barstow, California 92311. **T:** 1 760 256-0326
E: highwayradio@highwayradio.com
W: http://www.highwayrock.com
Editorial Profile: KHDR-FM is a commercial station owned by Highway Radio Inc. The format of the station is rock music. KHDR-FM broadcasts to the Barstow, CA area at 96.9 FM.

KHDV-FM
Owner: Mountain Broadcasting
Editorial: 725 Strand Ave, Missoula, Montana 59801-5710. **T:** 1 406 542-1025
E: info@mtnbdc.com
W: http://www.moclub.com
Editorial Profile: KHDV-FM is a commercial station owned by Mountain Broadcasting. The format of the station is oldies. KHDV-FM broadcasts to the Darby, MT area at 107.9 FM.

KHEY-AM
Owner: Clear Channel Media and Entertainment
Editorial: 4045 N Mesa St, El Paso, Texas 79902. **T:** 1 915 351-5400
W: http://www.khey1380.com
Editorial Profile: KHEY-AM is a commercial station owned byClear Channel Media and Entertainment. The format of the station is sports. KHEY-AM broadcasts to the El Paso, TX area at 1380 AM.

KHEY-FM
Owner: Clear Channel Media and Entertainment
Editorial: 4045 N Mesa St, El Paso, Texas 79902. **T:** 1 915 351-5400
E: kheyfm@clearchannel.com
W: http://www.khey.com
Editorial Profile: KHEY-FM is a commercial station owned by Clear Channel Media and Entertainment. The format of the station is country music. KHEY-FM broadcasts to the El Paso, TX area at 96.3 FM.

KHFI-FM
Owner: Clear Channel Media and Entertainment
Editorial: 3601 S Congress Ave, Bldg F, Austin, Texas 78704. **T:** 1 512 684-7300
W: http://www.967kissfm.com
Editorial Profile: KHFI-FM is a commercial station owned by Clear Channel Media and Entertainment. The format of the station is Top 40/CHR music. KHFI-FM broadcasts to the Austin, TX area at 96.7 Kiss FM.

KHFM-FM
Owner: American General Media
Editorial: 4125 Carlisle Blvd NE, Albuquerque, New Mexico 87107-4806. **T:** 1 505 878-0980
W: http://www.classicalkhfm.com
Editorial Profile: KHFM-FM is a commercial station owned by American General Media. The format of the station is classical music. KHFM-FM broadcasts to the Albuquerque, NM area at 95.5 FM.

KHFX-AM
Owner: SIGA Broadcasting Corp.
Editorial: 1302 N Shepherd Dr, Houston, Texas 77008-3752. **T:** 1 713 868-5559
Editorial Profile: KHFX-AM is a commercial station owned by SIGA Broadcasting Corp. The format of the station is Spanish music. KHFX-AM broadcasts to the Cleburne, TX area at 1460 AM.

KHGC-FM
Owner: Cherry Creek Radio
Editorial: 110 E Broadway St, Helena, Montana 59601-4232. **T:** 1 406 4424490
Editorial Profile: KHGC-FM is a commercial station owned by Cherry Creek Radio. The format of the station is classic country. The station airs locally at 98.5 FM.

KHGE-FM
Owner: Clear Channel Media and Entertainment
Editorial: 83 E Shaw Ave, Ste 150, Fresno, California 93710. **T:** 1 559 230-4300
W: http://www.1027thewolf.com
Editorial Profile: KHGE-FM is a commercial station owned by Clear Channel Media and Entertainment. The format of the station is contemporary country music. KHGE-FM broadcasts to the Fresno, CA area at 102.7 FM.

KHGG-AM
Owner: Pharis Broadcasting Inc.
Editorial: 321 N Greenwood Ave, Fort Smith, Arkansas 72901-3453. **T:** 1 479 288-1047
W: http://www.sportshog1031.com
Editorial Profile: KHGG-AM is a commercial station owned by Pharis Broadcasting Inc. The format of the station is sports. KHGG-AM broadcasts to the Fort Smith, AR area at 1580 AM.

KHGG-FM
Owner: Pharis Broadcasting Inc.
Editorial: 321 N Greenwood Ave, Fort Smith, Arkansas 72901-3453. **T:** 1 479 288-1047
W: http://www.sportshog1031.com
Editorial Profile: KHGG-FM is a commercial station owned by Pharis Broadcasting Inc. The format of the station is sports. KHGG-FM broadcasts to the Greenwood, AR area at 103.1 FM.

KHHK-FM
Owner: New Northwest Broadcasters LLC
Editorial: 1200 Chesterly Dr, Ste 160, Yakima, Washington 98902. **T:** 1 509 248-2900
W: http://www.newhot997.com
Editorial Profile: KHHK-FM is a commercial station owned by New Northwest Broadcasters LLC. The format of the station is urban contemporary music. KHHK-FM broadcasts to the Yakima, WA area at 99.7 FM.

KHHL-FM
Owner: Border Media Partners LLC
Editorial: 4050 Eisenhauer Rd, San Antonio, Texas 78218-3409. **T:** 1 210 654-5100
Editorial Profile: KHHL-FM is a commercial station owned by Border Media Partners LLC. The format of the station is Spanish sports. KHHL-FM broadcasts to the San Antonio and Karnes City, TX areas at 103.1.

KHHM-FM
Owner: Entravision Communications Corp.
Editorial: 1436 Auburn Blvd, Sacramento, California 95815-2745. **T:** 1 916 646-4000
W: http://www.hot1035radio.com
Editorial Profile: KHHM-FM is a commercial station owned by Entravision Communications Corp. The format of the station is Top 40/CHR. KHHM-FM broadcasts to the Sacramento, CA area at 103.5 FM.

KHHO-AM
Owner: Clear Channel Media and Entertainment
Editorial: 351 Elliott Ave W Ste 300, Seattle, Washington 98119-4150. **T:** 1 206 494-2000
W: http://www.sportsradiokjr.com
Editorial Profile: KHHO-AM is a commercial station owned by Clear Channel Media and Entertainment. The format of the station is sports. KHHO-AM broadcasts to the Tacoma, WA area at 850 AM.

KHHT-FM
Owner: Clear Channel Media and Entertainment
Editorial: 3400 W Olive Ave Ste 550, Burbank, California 91505-5544. **T:** 1 818 559-2252
E: contacthot@hot923.com
W: http://www.hot923.com
Editorial Profile: KHHT-FM is a commercial station owned by Clear Channel Media and Entertainment. The format of the station is urban adult contemporary and R&B . KHHT-FM broadcasts to the Los Angeles area at 92.3 FM.

KHHZ-FM
Owner: Deer Creek Broadcasting
Editorial: 2654 Cramer Ln, Chico, California 95928. **T:** 1 530 894-4818
W: http://www.khhz.com
Editorial Profile: KHHZ-FM is a commercial station owned by Deer Creek Broadcasting. The format of the station is Hispanic programming. KHHZ-FM broadcasts to the Chico, CA area at 97.7 FM.

KHIB-FM
Owner: Houston Christian Broadcasters
Editorial: 2424 South Blvd, Houston, Texas 77098. **T:** 1 713 520-5200 **E:** email@khcb.org
W: http://www.khcb.org
Editorial Profile: KHIB-FM is a non-commercial station owned by Houston Christian Broadcasters. The format of the station is Christian programming. KHIB-FM broadcasts to the Austin, TX area at 88.5 FM.

KHID-FM
Owner: RGV Educational Broadcasting Inc.
Editorial: 1701 Tennessee St, Harlingen, Texas 78550. **T:** 1 956 421-4111
E: kmbhkhid@aol.com
W: http://www.kmbh.org
Editorial Profile: KHID-FM is a non-commercial station owned by RGV Educational Broadcasting Inc. The format of the station is classical, jazz and news. KHID-FM broadcasts to the Harlingen, TX area at 88.1 FM.

KHIL-AM
Owner: KZLZ LLC
Editorial: 900 W Pattie Rd, Willcox, Arizona 85643-3404. **T:** 1 520 384-4626
W: http://www.xwave1049.com
Editorial Profile: KHIL-AM is a commercial station owned by KZLC LLC. The format of the station is contemporary country. KHIL-AM broadcasts to the Tucson, AZ area at 1250 AM.

KHIP-FM
Owner: Mapleton Radio, LLC
Editorial: 60 Garden Ct, Ste 300, Monterey, California 93940. **T:** 1 831 658-5200
W: http://www.thehippo.com

KHIT-AM
Owner: Lotus Communications Corp.
Editorial: 2900 Sutro St, Reno, Nevada 89512-1616. **T:** 1 775 329-9261
Editorial Profile: KHIT-AM is a commercial station owned by Lotus Communications Corp. The format of the station is Spanish sports. KHIT-AM broadcasts to the Reno, NV area at 1450 AM.

KHIT-FM
Owner: Lotus Communications Corp.
Editorial: 1110 E Olive Ave, Fresno, California 93728. **T:** 1 559 497-1100
E: production@lotusfresno.com
W: http://www.exitos1071.com
Editorial Profile: KHIT-FM is a commercial station owned by Lotus Communications Corp. The format of the station is Spanish AC. KHIT-FM broadcasts to the Fresno, CA area at 107.1 FM.

KHIX-FM
Owner: Ruby Radio Corp.
Editorial: 1750 Manzanita Dr, Ste 1, Elko, Nevada 89801-1600. **T:** 1 775 777-1196
W: http://www.mix96.fm
Editorial Profile: KHIX-FM is a commercial station owned by Ruby Radio Corp. The format of the station is hot adult contemporary. KHIX-FM broadcasts to the Elko, NV area at 96.7 FM.

KHJ-AM
Owner: Liberman Broadcasting Inc.
Editorial: 1845 W Empire Ave, Burbank, California 91504-3402. **T:** 1 818 729-5300
W: http://laranchera.estrellatv.com
Editorial Profile: KHJ-AM is a commercial station owned by Liberman Broadcasting Inc. The format of the station is Hispanic music. KHJ-AM broadcasts to the Los Angeles area at 930 AM.

KHJL-FM
Owner: Amaturo Group
Editorial: 99 Long Ct, Ste 200, Thousand Oaks, California 91360. **T:** 1 805 497-8511
W: http://www.playlist927.com
Editorial Profile: KLSI-FM is a commercial station owned by Amaturo Group. The format of the station is adult contemporary. KLSI-FM broadcasts to the Thousand Oaks, CA area at 92.7 FM. KLSI-FM simulcasts on KJLL-FM.

KHJM-FM
Owner: Covenant Network
Editorial: 4424 Hampton Ave, Saint Louis, Missouri 63109-2232. **T:** 1 314 752-7000
W: http://www.covenantnet.net
Editorial Profile: KHJM-FM is a non-commercial station owned by Covenant Network. The format of the station is religious music and talk. KHJM-FM broadcasts to the Dexter, MO area at 89.1 FM.

KHJZ-FM
Owner: Clear Channel Media and Entertainment
Editorial: 650 Iwilei Rd, Ste 400, Honolulu, Hawaii 96817. **T:** 1 808 550-9200
Editorial Profile: KHJZ-FM is a commercial station owned by Clear Channel Media and Entertainment. The format of the station is rhythmic AC. KHJZ-FM broadcasts to the Honolulu area at 93.9 FM.

KHKA-AM
Owner: Blow Up, LLC
Editorial: 1088 Bishop St Ste LL2, Honolulu, Hawaii 96813-3113. **T:** 1 808 536-2728
Editorial Profile: KHKA-AM is a commercial station owned by Blow Up, LLC. The format of the station is sports. KHKA-AM broadcasts to the Honolulu area at 1500 AM.

KHKE-FM
Owner: University of Northern Iowa
Editorial: University Of Northern Iowa, Cedar Falls, Iowa 50614. **T:** 1 319 273-6400
E: news@iowapublicradio.org
W: http://iowapublicradio.org
Editorial Profile: KHKE-FM is a non-commercial station owned by the University of Northern Iowa. The format for the station is classical. KHKE-FM broadcasts to the Cedar Rapids, IA area at 89.5 FM.

KHKI-FM
Owner: Cumulus Media Inc
Editorial: 4143 109th St, Urbandale, Iowa 50322-7925. **T:** 1 515 331-9200
W: http://www.nashfm973.com
Editorial Profile: KHKI-FM is a commercial station owned by Cumulus Media Inc. The format of the station is contemporary country. KHKI-FM broadcasts to the Urbandale, IA area at 97.3 FM.

KHKK-FM
Owner: Cumulus Media Inc
Editorial: 3136 Boeing Way, Stockton, California 95206. **T:** 1 209 766-5000
E: 104.1thehawk@cumulus.com
W: http://www.104thehawk.com
Editorial Profile: KHKK-FM is a commercial station owned by Cumulus Media Inc. The format of the station is classic rock music. KHKK-FM broadcasts in the Modesto, CA area at 104.1 FM.

KHKL-FM
Owner: Educational Media Foundation
Editorial: 5700 W Oaks Blvd, Rocklin, California 95765. **T:** 1 916 251-2142
E: klove@klove.com **W:** http://www.klove.com
Editorial Profile: Positive & encouraging music focused on loving God & others.

KHKM-FM
Owner: Cherry Creek Radio
Editorial: 1600 North Ave W, Ste 101, Missoula, Montana 59801. **T:** 1 406 728-5000
Editorial Profile: KHKM-FM is a commercial station owned by Cherry Creek Radio. The format of the station is classic country. KHKM-FM broadcasts to the Missoula, MT area at 98.7 FM.

KHKN-FM
Owner: Clear Channel Media and Entertainment
Editorial: 10800 Colonel Glenn Rd, Little Rock, Arkansas 72204. **T:** 1 501 217-5000
W: http://www.949tomfm.com
Editorial Profile: KHKN-FM is a commercial station owned by Clear Channel Media and Entertainment. The format of the station is adult hits. KHKN-FM broadcasts to the Little Rock, AR area at 94.9 FM.

KHKR-AM
Owner: Cherry Creek Radio
Editorial: 750 W. Ridge View Dr., Ste 204, St George, Utah 84770-2697. **T:** 1 435 673-3579
Editorial Profile: KHKR-AM is a commercial station owned by Cherry Creek Radio. The format of the station is classic country. KHKR-AM broadcasts to the St. George, UT area at 1210 AM.

KHKR-FM
Owner: Cherry Creek Radio
Editorial: 110 E Broadway St, Helena, Montana 59601-4232. **T:** 1 406 442-4490
W: http://www.theb104.com
Editorial Profile: KHKR-FM is a commercial station owned by Cherry Creek Radio. The format of the station is hot adult contemporary. KHKR-FM broadcasts in the Helena, MT area at 104.1 FM.

KHKS-FM
Owner: Clear Channel Media and Entertainment
Editorial: 14001 Dallas Pkwy Ste 300, Dallas, Texas 75240-7369. **T:** 1 214 866-8000
W: http://www.1061kissfm.com
Editorial Profile: KHKS-FM is a commercial station owned by Clear Channel Media and Entertainment. The format of the station is Top 40/CHR. KHKS-FM broadcasts to the Dallas area at 106.1 FM.

KHKV-FM
Owner: Houston Christian Broadcasters
Editorial: 2424 South Blvd, Houston, Texas 77098. **T:** 1 713 520-5200
E: amistad@radioamistad.net
W: http://www.khcb.org
Editorial Profile: KHKV-FM is a commercial station owned by Houston Christian Broadcasters. The format of the station is Hispanic Christian programming. KHKV-FM broadcasts to the Houston area at 91.1 FM.

KHKX-FM
Owner: Brazos Communications West, LLC
Editorial: 3303 N Midkiff Rd Ste 115, Midland, Texas 79705-4860. **T:** 1 432 520-9912
W: http://www.kicks99.net
Editorial Profile: KHKX-FM is a commercial station owned by Brazos Communications West, LLC. The format of the station is contemporary country. KHKX-FM broadcasts to the Midland, TX area at 99.1 FM.

KHKZ-FM
Owner: Clear Channel Media and Entertainment
Editorial: 901 E Pike Blvd, Weslaco, Texas 78596. **T:** 1 956 973-9202
W: http://www.hotkiss1063.com
Editorial Profile: KHKZ-FM is a commercial station owned by Clear Channel Media and Entertainment. The format of the station is hot adult contemporary music. KHKZ-FM broadcasts to the Weslaco, TX area at 106.3 FM.

KHLA-FM
Owner: Townsquare Media, LLC
Editorial: 900 N Lake Shore Dr, Lake Charles, Louisiana 70601. **T:** 1 337 433-1641
W: http://929thelake.com
Editorial Profile: KHLA-FM is a commercial station owned by Townsquare Media, LLC. The format of the station is classic hits. KHLA-FM broadcasts to the Lake Charles, LA area at 92.9 FM.

KHLB-FM
Owner: III & W Broadcasting
Editorial: 105 N. Spring St., Mason, Texas 76826 **W:** http://khlbthevoice.com/
Editorial Profile: KHLB-FM is a commercial station owned by III & W Broadcasting. The station broadcasts to the Mason, TX area at 102.5.

KHLL-FM
Owner: Gilliland(Dan)
Editorial: 704 Trenton St, Ste C, West Monroe, Louisiana 71291. **T:** 1 318 323-5994
E: mail@hillradio.com
W: http://www.hillradio.com
Editorial Profile: KHLL-FM is a commercial station owned by Dan Gilliland. The format of the station is contemporary Christian music. KHLL-FM broadcasts in the Monroe, LA area at 100.9 FM.

KHLO-AM
Owner: Pacific Media Group
Editorial: 913 Kanoelehua Ave, Hilo, Hawaii 96720-5116. **T:** 1 808 961-0651
W: http://www.espnhawaii.com
Editorial Profile: KHLO-AM is a commercial station owned by Pacific Media Group. The format of the station is sports. KHLO-AM broadcasts to the Hilo, HI area at 850 AM.

KHLR-FM
Owner: Signal Media of Arkansas, Inc
Editorial: 2400 Cottondale Ln, Little Rock, Arkansas 72202-2020. **T:** 1 501 664-9410
Editorial Profile: KHLR-FM is a commercial station owned by Signal Media of Arkansas, Inc. The format of the station is rhythmic oldies. KHLR-FM broadcasts in the Little Rock, AR area at 106.7 FM.

KHLS-FM
Owner: Sudbury Broadcasting Group
Editorial: 125 S 2nd St, Blytheville, Arkansas 72315-3413. **T:** 1 870 762-2093
W: http://www.thundercountry963.com
Editorial Profile: KHLS-FM is a commercial station owned by Sudbury Broadcasting Group. The format of the station is contemporary country. KHLS-FM broadcasts to the Blytheville, AR area at 96.3 FM.

KHLT-FM
Owner: Smith(Daniel)
Editorial: 2120 N Woodlawn St, Wichita, Kansas 67208-1847. **T:** 1 316 652-9275
Editorial Profile: KHLT-FM is a commercial station owned by Daniel Smith. The format is Adult Contemporary music. KHLT-FM broadcasts to the Wichita, KS area at 92.7 FM.

KHMB-FM
Owner: R & M Broadcasting
Editorial: 203 Fairview Rd, Crossett, Arkansas 71635. **T:** 1 870 364-4700
E: qlite@arkansas.net
W: http://www.qliteradio.com
Editorial Profile: KHMB-FM is a commercial station owned by R & M Broadcasting. The format of the station is lite rock and adult contemporary. KHMB-FM broadcasts to the Crossett, AR area at 99.5 FM.

KHMC-FM
Owner: Lopez(Humberto)
Editorial: 2001 E Sabine St, Ste 101, Victoria, Texas 77901. **T:** 1 361 575-9533
E: majictejano@yahoo.com
W: http://www.majic95fm.com
Editorial Profile: KHMC-FM is a commercial station owned by Humberto Lopez. The format of the station is Hispanic music. KHMC-FM broadcasts in the Victoria, TX area at 95.9 FM.

KHME-FM
Owner: KAGE Inc.
Editorial: 752 Bluffview Cir, Winona, Minnesota 55987. **T:** 1 507 452-4000
W: http://www.winonaradio.com
Editorial Profile: KHME-FM is a commercial station owned by KAGE Inc. The format of the station is adult contemporary. KHME-FM broadcasts to the Winona, MN area at 101.1 FM.

KHMO-AM
Owner: Double O Radio
Editorial: 119 N 3rd St, Hannibal, Missouri 63401-3501. **T:** 1 573 221-3450
W: http://khmoradio.com
Editorial Profile: KHMO-AM is a commercial station owned by Double O Radio. The format of the station is news and talk. KHMO-AM broadcasts to the Quincy, IL area at 1070 AM.

KHMX-FM
Owner: CBS Radio
Editorial: 24 Greenway Plz Ste 1900, Houston, Texas 77046-2428. **T:** 1 713 881-5100
W: http://mix965houston.cbslocal.com
Editorial Profile: KHMX-FM is a commercial station owned by CBS Radio. The format of the station is hot adult contemporary music. KHMX-FM broadcasts to the Houston area at 96.5 FM.

KHMY-FM
Owner: Eagle Radio Inc.
Editorial: 825 N Main St, Hutchinson, Kansas 67501-4605. **T:** 1 620 662-4486
E: khmy@cox.net **W:** http://www.khmyfm.com
Editorial Profile: KHMY-FM is a commercial station owned by Eagle Radio Inc. The format of the station is adult contemporary. KHMY-FM broadcasts to the Hutchinson, KS area at 93.1 FM.

KHND-AM
Owner: Three Way Broadcasting Inc.
Editorial: 718 Lincoln Ave, Harvey, North Dakota 58341. **T:** 1 701 324-4848
E: studio@khnd1470.com
W: http://www.khnd1470.com
Editorial Profile: KHND-AM is a commercial station owned by Three Way Broadcasting Inc. The format of the station is adult contemporary. KHND-AM broadcasts to the Harvey, ND area at 1470 AM.

KHNK-FM
Owner: Bee Broadcasting Inc.
Editorial: 2432 US Highway 2 E, Kalispell, Montana 59901. **T:** 1 406 755-8700
E: hank@myhank.com
W: http://www.myhank.com
Editorial Profile: KHNK-FM is a commercial station owned by Bee Broadcasting, Inc. The format of the station is country music. KHNK-FM broadcasts in the Kalispell, MT area at 95.9 FM.

KHNR-AM
Owner: Salem Communications
Editorial: 1160 N King St, Honolulu, Hawaii 96817. **T:** 1 808 533-0065 **E:** info@khnr.com
W: http://www.khnr.com
Editorial Profile: KHNR-AM is a commercial station owned by Salem Communications. The format of the station is news and talk. KHNR-AM broadcasts to the Honolulu area at 690 AM.

KHNS-FM
Owner: Lynn Canal Broadcasting
Editorial: #1 Theater Drive, Haines, Alaska 99827-1109. **T:** 1 907 766-2020
E: news@khns.org **W:** http://www.khns.org
Editorial Profile: KHNS-FM is a non-commercial station owned by Lynn Canal Broadcasting. The format of the station is free-form, with a wide variety of musical styles, ranging from classic rock to reggae. KHNS-FM broadcasts to Haines, AK at 102.3 FM.

KHOB-AM
Owner: American Asset Management Inc.
Editorial: 1000 E Sanger St, Hobbs, New Mexico 88240-4547. **T:** 1 575 392-9292
E: espnsw@gmail.com
W: http://www.espn1390am.com
Editorial Profile: KHOB-AM is a commercial station owned by American Asset Management Inc. The format is sports. KHOB-AM airs in the Hobbs, NM area at 1390 AM.

KHOC-FM
Owner: Mount Rushmore Broadcasting Inc.
Editorial: 218 N Wolcott St, Casper, Wyoming 82601. **T:** 1 307 265-1984
Editorial Profile: KHOC-FM is a commercial station owned by Mount Rushmore Broadcasting Inc. The format for the station is hot adult contemporary. KHOC-FM broadcasts to the Casper, WY area at 102.5 FM.

KHOE-FM
Owner: Fairfield Educational Radio Station
Editorial: 1000 N 4th St, MR685, Fairfield, Iowa 52557-0001. **T:** 1 641 469-5463
E: khoe@mum.edu **W:** http://www.khoe.org

KHOJ-AM
Owner: Covenant Network
Editorial: 4424 Hampton Ave, Saint Louis, Missouri 63109. **T:** 1 314 752-7000
E: covenantnetwork@juno.com
W: http://www.covenantnet.net
Editorial Profile: KHOJ-AM is a non-commercial station owned by Covenant Network. The format of the station is religious music and talk. KHOJ-AM broadcasts to the St. Louis area at 1460 AM.

KHOK-FM
Owner: Eagle Radio Inc.
Editorial: 1200 Baker Ave, Great Bend, Kansas 67530-4523. **T:** 1 620 792-3647
W: http://www.khokfm.com
Editorial Profile: KHOK-FM is a commercial station owned by Eagle Radio Inc. The format of the station is contemporary country. KHOK-FM broadcasts to the Great Bend, KS area at 100.7 FM.

KHOL-FM
Owner: Jackson Hole Community Radio
Editorial: 155 W Gill Street, Jackson, Wyoming 83001. **T:** 1 307 733-4030
W: http://www.jhcr.org
Editorial Profile: KHOL-FM is a non-commercial station owned by Jackson Hole Community Radio. The format for the station is variety. KHOL-FM broadcasts to the Jackson, WY area at 89.1 FM. The station does not accept pitches and does not wish to be contacted.

KHOM-FM
Owner: E-Communications, LLC
Editorial: 10 Court Sq, West Plains, Missouri 65775-3444. **T:** 1 417 255-2548
E: eckman@centurytel.net
W: http://khomthetrain.com
Editorial Profile: KHOM-FM is a commercial station owned by E-Communications, LLC. The format of the station is classic hits of the 60s, 70s and 80s. KHOM-FM broadcasts to the Springfield, MO area at 100.9 FM.

KHOP-FM
Owner: Cumulus Media Inc
Editorial: 3136 Boeing Way, Stockton, California 95206-4989. **T:** 1 209 766-5000
W: http://www.khop.com
Editorial Profile: KHOP-FM is commercial station owned by Cumulus Media Inc. The format of the station is Top 40/CHR. KHOP-FM broadcasts to the Oakdale, CA area at 95.1 FM.

KHOS-FM
Owner: Revolution Broadcast Co.
Editorial: 680 Highway 277 South, Sonora, Texas 76950. **T:** 1 325 387-3553
E: khoskyxx@verizon.net
W: http://www.revfmradio.com
Editorial Profile: KHOS-FM is a commercial station owned by Revolution Broadcast Co. The format of the station is classic country. KHOS-FM broadcasts to the Sonora, TX area at 92.1 FM.

KHOT-AM
Owner: Immaculate Heart Radio
Editorial: 3256 Penryn Rd, Suite 100, Loomis, California 95650. **T:** 1 916 535-0500
W: http://ihradio.org
Editorial Profile: KHOT-AM is a non-commercial station owned by Immaculate Heart Radio. The format of the station is religious. KHOT-AM broadcasts to the Fresno, CA area at 1250 AM.

KHOT-FM
Owner: Univision Communications Inc.
Editorial: 6006 S 30Th St, Phoenix, Arizona 85042-4802. **T:** 1 602 308-7900
W: http://www.univision.com/content/channel.jhtml?chid=9466&schid=9833
Editorial Profile: KHOT-FM is a commercial station owned by Univision Communications Inc. The format of the station is regional Mexican. KHOT-FM broadcasts to the Phoenix area at 105.9 FM.

KHOV-FM
Owner: Univision Communications Inc.
Editorial: 6006 S 30Th St, Phoenix, Arizona 85042-4802. **T:** 1 602 308-7900
W: http://www.univision.com/content/channel.jhtml?chid=9466&schid=9833
Editorial Profile: KHOV-FM is a commercial station owned by Univision Communications Inc. The format of the station is regional Mexican. KHOV-FM broadcasts to the Phoenix area at 95.7 FM.

KHOW-AM
Owner: Clear Channel Media and Entertainment
Editorial: 4695 S Monaco St, Denver, Colorado 80237-3525. **T:** 1 303 713-8000
W: http://www.khow.com
Editorial Profile: KHOW-AM is a commercial station owned by Clear Channel Media and Entertainment. The format of the station is talk. KHOW-AM broadcasts to the Denver area at 630 AM.

KHOY-FM
Owner: Laredo Catholic Communications Inc.
Editorial: 1901 Corpus Christi St, Laredo, Texas 78043. **T:** 1 956 722-4167
E: khoy@khoy.org **W:** http://www.khoy.org
Editorial Profile: KHOY-FM is a non-commercial station owned by Laredo Catholic Communications Inc. The format of the station is Hispanic religious programming and easy listening. KHOY-FM broadcasts to the Laredo, TX area at 88.1 FM.

KHOZ-AM
Owner: KHOZ LLC
Editorial: 1111 Radio Ave, Harrison, Arkansas 72601-2516. **T:** 1 870 741-2301
Editorial Profile: KHOZ-AM is a commercial station owned by KHOZ LLC. The format of the station is nostalgia music. KHOZ-AM broadcasts to the Harrison, AR area at 900 AM.

KHPA-FM
Owner: Sudbury Broadcasting Group
Editorial: 1600 S Elm St, Hope, Arkansas 71801. **T:** 1 870 777-8868
E: khpafm@supercountry105.com
W: http://www.supercountry105.com
Editorial Profile: KHPA-FM is a commercial station owned by Sudbury Broadcasting Group. The format of the station is contemporary country. KHPA-FM broadcasts to the Hope, AR area at 104.9 FM.

KHPE-FM
Owner: Extra Mile Media Inc.
Editorial: 34545 Highway 20 Se, Albany, Oregon 97322-9731. **T:** 1 541 926-2233
E: production@hope1079.com
W: http://www.hope1079.com
Editorial Profile: KHPE-FM is a commercial station owned by Extra Mile Inc. The format of the station is contemporary Christian music. KHPE-FM broadcasts to the Albany, OR area at 107.9 FM.

KHPO-FM
Owner: Houston Christian Broadcasters
Editorial: 2424 South Blvd, Houston, Texas 77098. **T:** 1 713 520-5200 **E:** email@khcb.org
W: http://www.khcb.org
Editorial Profile: KHPO-FM is a non-commercial station owned by Houston Christian Broadcasters. The format of the station is Christian programming and music. KHPO-FM broadcasts to the Austin, TX area at 91.9 FM.

KHPQ-FM
Owner: King-Sullivan Radio
Editorial: 360 Main St, Clinton, Arkansas 72031. **T:** 1 501 745-4474
E: kgflkhpq@artelco.com
W: http://www.khpq.com
Editorial Profile: KHPQ-FM is a commercial station owned by King-Sullivan Radio. The format of the station is contemporary country. KHPQ-FM broadcasts to the Clinton, AR area at 92.1 FM.

KHPR-FM
Owner: Hawaii Public Radio
Editorial: 738 Kaheka St, Ste 101, Honolulu, Hawaii 96814. **T:** 1 808 955-8821
E: hprnews@hawaiipublicradio.org
W: http://www.hawaiipublicradio.org
Editorial Profile: KHPR-FM is a non-commercial station owned by Hawaii Public Radio. The format of the station is news and classical music. KHPR-FM broadcasts to the Honolulu area at 88.1 FM.

KHPT-FM
Owner: Cox Radio, Inc.
Editorial: 1990 Post Oak Blvd, Ste 2300, Houston, Texas 77056. **T:** 1 713 963-1200
W: http://www.houstonseagle.com
Editorial Profile: KHPT-FM is a commercial station owned by Cox Radio, Inc. The format of the station is classic hits. KHPT-FM broadcasts to the Houston area at 106.9 FM. The station airs KGLK-FM's programming

KHPY-AM
Owner: Van Voorhis (D.L.)
Editorial: 24490 Sunnymead Blvd, Moreno Valley, California 92553-7734.
T: 1 951 247-5479
W: http://www.elsembrador.org
Editorial Profile: KHPY-AM is a non-commercial station owned by Van Voorhis (D.L.). The format of the station is Hispanic religious. KHPY-AM broadcasts to the Moreno Valley, CA area at 1670 AM.

KHQN-AM
Owner: Howell(Robyn)
Editorial: 560 South Orem Blvd, Orem, Utah 84058. **T:** 1 800 776-1913
W: http://khqnradio.com
Editorial Profile: KHQN-AM is a commercial station owned by Robyn Howell. The format of the station is news, sports and talk. KHQN-AM broadcasts to the Salt Lake City area at 1480 AM.

KHQT-FM
Owner: Adams Radio Group
Editorial: 1355 California Ave, Las Cruces, New Mexico 88001-4130. **T:** 1 575 525-9298
W: http://www.hot103.fm
Editorial Profile: KHQT-FM is a commercial station owned by Adams Radio Group. The format of the station is Top 40/CHR. KHQT-FM broadcasts to the Las Cruces, NM area at 103.1 FM.

KHRD-FM
Owner: Results Radio Group
Editorial: 1588 Charles Dr, Redding, California 96003. **T:** 1 530 244-9700
W: http://www.red1031.com
Editorial Profile: KHRD-FM is a commercial station owned by Results Radio Group. The format of the station is classic rock. KHRD-FM broadcasts to the Redding, CA area at 103.1 FM.

KHRK-FM
Owner: Noalmark Broadcasting Corp.
Editorial: 208 Buena Vista Rd, Hot Springs, Arkansas 71913-8208. **T:** 1 501 525-4600
W: http://www.thespurfm.com
Editorial Profile: KHRK-FM is a commercial station owned by Noalmark Broadcasting Corp. The format of the station is contemporary country. KHRK-FM broadcasts to the Hot Springs, AR area at 101.5.

KHRO-AM
Owner: Entravision Communications Corp.
Editorial: 5426 N Mesa St, El Paso, Texas 79912. **T:** 1 915 581-1126
W: http://www.khro1650.com
Editorial Profile: KHRO-AM is a commercial station owned by Entravision Communications Corp. The format of the station is liberal talk. KHRO-AM broadcasts to the El Paso, TX area on 1150 AM.

KHRQ-FM
Owner: Highway Radio Inc.
Editorial: 1611 E Main St, Barstow, California 92311. **T:** 1 760 256-0326
E: highwayradio@highwayradio.com
W: http://www.highwayrock.com
Editorial Profile: KHRQ-FM is a commercial station owned by Highway Radio Inc. The format of the station is rock music. KHRQ-FM broadcasts to the Baker, CA area at 94.9 FM.

KHRS-FM
Owner: Radio Mankato
Editorial: 59346 Madison Ave, Mankato, Minnesota 56001-8518. **T:** 1 507 345-4537
E: news@ktoe.com
W: http://www.kxlp941.com
Editorial Profile: KHRS-FM is a commercial station owned by Radio Mankato. The format of the station is classic rock. KHRS-FM broadcasts to the Mankato, MN area at 105.9 FM.

KHRT-AM
Owner: Faith Broadcasting
Editorial: 3600 County Road 19 S, Minot, North Dakota 58701. **T:** 1 701 852-3789
E: khrt@srt.com **W:** http://www.khrt.com
Editorial Profile: KHRT-AM is a commercial station owned by Faith Broadcasting. The format of the station is gospel music and religious programming. KHRT-AM broadcasts to the Minot, ND area at 1320 AM.

KHRT-FM
Owner: Faith Broadcasting
Editorial: 3600 County Road 19 S, Minot, North Dakota 58701. **T:** 1 701 852-3789
E: khrt@srt.com **W:** http://www.khrt.com
Editorial Profile: KHRT-FM is a commercial station owned by Faith Broadcasting. The format of the station is contemporary Christian. KHRT-AM broadcasts to the Minot-Bismarck, ND area at 106.9 FM.

KHSL-FM
Owner: Deer Creek Broadcasting
Editorial: 2654 Cramer Ln, Chico, California 95928. **T:** 1 530 345-0021
W: http://www.1035theblaze.com
Editorial Profile: KHSL-FM is a commercial station owned by Deer Creek Broadcasting. The format of the station is classic country. KHSL-FM broadcasts in the Chico, CA area at 103.5 FM.

KHSN-AM
Owner: W-7 Broadcasting
Editorial: 320 Central Ave, Ste 519, Coos Bay, Oregon 97420. **T:** 1 541 267-2121
W: http://www.khsn1230.com
Editorial Profile: KHSN-AM is a commercial station owned by W-7 Broadcasting. The

format of the station is sports. KHSN-AM broadcasts to the Coos Bay, OR area at 1230 AM.

KHSS-FM
Owner: Two Hearts Communications LLC
Editorial: 30 W Main St, Ste 303, Walla Walla, Washington 99362-2872. **T:** 1 509 525-7878
E: comments@khssradio.com
W: http://www.khssradio.com
Editorial Profile: KHSS-FM is a commercial station owned by Two Hearts Communications LLC. The format of the station is religious talk. KHSS-FM broadcasts to the Walla Walla, WA area at 100.7 FM.

KHST-FM
Owner: My Town Media, Inc.
Editorial: 412 N Locust St, Pittsburg, Kansas 66762. **T:** 1 620 232-5993
W: http://www.mytown-media.com
Editorial Profile: KHST-FM is a commercial station owned by My Town Media, Inc. The format is classic hits. The station airs in the Pittsburg, KS area at 101.7 FM.

KHSU-FM
Owner: Humboldt State University
Editorial: 1 Harpst St, Arcata, California 95521-8222. **T:** 1 707 826-4807
W: http://www.khsu.org
Editorial Profile: KHSU-FM is a non-commercial station owned by Humboldt State University. The format of the station is variety. KHSU-FM broadcasts to the Arcata, CA area at 90.5 FM.

KHTB-FM
Owner: Cumulus Media Inc
Editorial: 434 W Bearcat Dr, Salt Lake City, Utah 84115-2520. **T:** 1 801 485-6700
W: http://www.949zrock.com
Editorial Profile: KHTB-FM is a commercial station owned by Cumulus Media Inc. The format of the station is alternative rock. KHTB-FM broadcasts to the Salt Lake City area at 94.9 FM.

KHTE-FM
Owner: Crain Media Group LLC
Editorial: 400 Hardin Rd, Little Rock, Arkansas 72211-3502. **T:** 1 501 219-1919
E: production@crainmedia.com
W: http://www.965thevoice.com
Editorial Profile: KHTE-FM is a commercial station owned by Crain Media Group LLC. The format of the station is Conservative Talk. KHTE-FM broadcasts to the Little Rock, AR area at 96.5 FM.

KHTH-FM
Owner: Sonoma Media Group
Editorial: 1410 Neotomas Ave, Santa Rosa, California 95405-7533. **T:** 1 707 543-0100
W: http://www.hot1017online.com
Editorial Profile: KHTH-FM is a commercial station owned by Sonoma Media Group. The station's format is Top 40/CHR. KHTH-FM broadcasts to the San Francisco area at 101.7 FM.

KHTK-AM
Owner: CBS Radio
Editorial: 5244 Madison Ave, Sacramento, California 95841-3004. **T:** 1 916 338-9200
W: http://sacramento.cbslocal.com/station/cbs-sports-1140
Editorial Profile: KHTK-AM is a commercial station owned by CBS Radio. The format of the station is sports. KHTK-AM broadcasts to the Sacramento, CA area at 1140 AM.

KHTN-FM
Owner: Buckley Broadcasting Corp.
Editorial: 510 W 19th St, Merced, California 95340. **T:** 1 209 383-7900
E: hot1047email@aol.com
W: http://www.hot1047fm.com
Editorial Profile: KHTN-FM is a commercial station owned by Buckley Broadcasting Corp. The format of the station is rhythmic Top 40/CHR. KHTN-FM broadcasts to the Merced, CA area at 104.7 FM.

KHTO-FM
Owner: US Stations, LLC
Editorial: 125 Corporate Ter, Hot Springs, Arkansas 71913-7248. **T:** 1 501 525-9700
W: http://www.myhotsprings.com
Editorial Profile: KHTO-FM is a commercial station owned by US Stations, LLC. The format of the station is top 40/CHR. KHTO-FM broadcasts to the Hot Springs, AR area at 96.7 FM.

KHTP-FM
Owner: Entercom Communications Corp.
Editorial: 1100 Olive Way, Seattle, Washington 98101-1873. **T:** 1 206 233-1037
W: http://www.entercomseattle.com
Editorial Profile: KHTP-FM is a commercial station owned by Entercom Communications Corp. The format of the station is rhythmic hot adult contemporary. KHTP-FM broadcasts to the Seattle area at 103.7 FM.

KHTQ-FM
Owner: Queen B Inc.
Editorial: 504 E Sherman Ave, Coeur D Alene, Idaho 83814. **T:** 1 208 664-9271
W: http://www.rock945.com
Editorial Profile: KHTQ-FM is a commercial station owned by Queen B Inc. The format of the station is rock music. KHTQ-FM broadcasts to the Spokane, WA area at 94.5 FM.

KHTR-FM
Owner: Radio Palouse Inc.
Editorial: 1101 Old Wawawai Road, Pullman, Washington 99163. **T:** 1 509 332-6551
E: info@pullmanradio.com
W: http://www.pullmanradio.com
Editorial Profile: KHTR-FM is a commercial station owned by Radio Palouse Inc. The format of the station is classic hits. KHTR-FM broadcasts to the Spokane, WA area at 104.3 FM.

KHTS-AM
Owner: Jeri Lyn Broadcasting Inc.
Editorial: 27225 Camp Plenty Rd, Ste 8, Santa Clarita, California 91351. **T:** 1 661 298-1220
E: info@hometownstation.com
W: http://www.hometownstation.com
Editorial Profile: KHTS-AM is a commercial station owned by Jeri Lyn Broadcasting Inc. The format of the station is adult contemporary music and talk. KHTS-AM broadcasts to Santa Clarita and Lancaster, CA at 1220 AM.

KHTS-FM
Owner: Clear Channel Media and Entertainment
Editorial: 9660 Granite Ridge Dr, Ste 100, San Diego, California 92123. **T:** 1 858 292-2000
W: http://www.channel933.com
Editorial Profile: KHTS-FM is a commercial station owned by Clear Channel Media and Entertainment. The format of the station is Top 40/CHR music. KHTS-FM broadcasts to the San Diego area at 93.3 FM.

KHTT-FM
Owner: Journal Broadcast Group
Editorial: 4590 E 29Th St, Tulsa, Oklahoma 74114-6208. **T:** 1 918 4743-7814
W: http://www.khits.com
Editorial Profile: KHTT-FM is a commercial station owned by Journal Broadcast Group. The format of the station is Top 40/CHR. KHTT-FM broadcasts to the Tulsa, OK area at 106.9 FM.

KHTY-AM
Owner: Clear Channel Media and Entertainment
Editorial: 1100 Mohawk St, Ste 280, Bakersfield, California 93309.
T: 1 661 322-9929
W: http://www.foxsports970am.com
Editorial Profile: KHTY-AM is a commercial station owned by Clear Channel Media and Entertainment. The format of the station is sports. KHTY-AM broadcasts to the Bakersfield, CA, area at 970 AM.

KHUB-AM
Owner: R & R Broadcasting, Inc.
Editorial: 118 E 5th St, Fremont, Nebraska 68025-5022. **T:** 1 402 721-1340
Editorial Profile: KHUB-AM is a commercial station owned by R & R Broadcasting, Inc. The format of the station is news and talk. KHUB-AM broadcasts to the Fremont, NE area at 1340 AM.

KHUM-FM
Owner: Lost Coast Communications
Editorial: 1400 Main St, Ste 104, Ferndale, California 95536. **T:** 1 707 786-5104
E: info@khum.com **W:** http://www.khum.com
Editorial Profile: KHUM-FM is a commercial station owned by Lost Coast Communications. The format for the station is adult album alternative. KHUM-FM broadcasts to the Ferndale, CA area at 104.7 FM.

KHUT-FM
Owner: Eagle Radio Inc.
Editorial: 825 N Main St, Hutchinson, Kansas 67501-4605. **T:** 1 620 662-4486
E: khut.studio@eagleradio.net
W: http://www.hutchinsoncountrystation.com
Editorial Profile: KHUT-FM is commercial station owned by Eagle Radio Inc. The format of the station is contemporary country. KHUT-FM broadcasts to Hutchinson, KS area at 102.9 FM.

KHVH-AM
Owner: Clear Channel Media and Entertainment
Editorial: 650 Iwilei Rd, Ste 400, Honolulu, Hawaii 96817. **T:** 1 808 550-9200
W: http://www.khvh830am.com
Editorial Profile: KHVH-AM is a commercial station owned by Clear Channel Media and Entertainment. The format of the station is news and talk. KHVH-AM broadcasts to the Honolulu area at 830 AM.

KHVL-AM
Owner: HEH Communications LLC
Editorial: 622 Interstate 45 S, Huntsville, Texas 77340. **T:** 1 936 295-2651
W: http://www.khvl.com
Editorial Profile: KHVL-AM is a commercial station owned by HEH Communications LLC. The format of the station is classic hits. KHVL-AM broadcasts to the Huntsville, TX area at 1490 AM.

KHVN-AM
Owner: Mortenson Broadcasting Co.
Editorial: 5787 S Hampton Rd, Ste 285, Dallas, Texas 75232. **T:** 1 214 331-5486
W: http://www.khvnam.com
Editorial Profile: KHVN-AM is a commercial station owned by Mortenson Broadcasting Co. The format of the station is gospel music and religious programming. KHVN-AM broadcasts to the Dallas area at 970 AM.

KHWG-AM
Owner: Media Enterprises Inc.
Editorial: 1050 W Williams Ave, Fallon, Nevada 89406-2634. **T:** 1 775 423-5494
E: khwgradio@gmail.com
W: http://khwgradio.com
Editorial Profile: KHWG-AM is a commercial station owned by Media Enterprises Inc. The format of the station is classic country and oldies. KHWG-AM broadcasts to the Reno, NV area at 750 AM.

KHWG-FM
Owner: Media Enterprises Inc.
Editorial: 1050 W Williams Ave, Fallon, Nevada 89406-2634. **T:** 1 775 423-5494
E: khwg@cccomm.net
W: http://khwgradio.com
Editorial Profile: KHWG-FM is a commercial station owned by Media Enterprises Inc. The format of the station is country. KHWG-FM broadcasts to the Crystal, NV area at 100.1 FM.

KHWI-FM
Owner: Resonate Hawaii, LLC
Editorial: 688 Kinoole St Ste 112, Hilo, Hawaii 96720-3868. **T:** 1 808 959-5700
W: http://www.hawaiiswave.com
Editorial Profile: KHWI-FM is a commercial station owned by Resonate Hawaii, LLC. The format for the station is Hot AC. KHWI-FM broadcasts to the Honolulu area at 92.1 FM.

KHWY-FM
Owner: Highway Radio Inc.
Editorial: 1611 E Main St, Barstow, California 92311. **T:** 1 760 256-0326
E: highwayradio@highwayradio.com
W: http://www.thehighwaystations.com
Editorial Profile: KHWY-FM is a commercial station owned by Highway Radio Inc. The format of the station is dance music. KHWY-FM broadcasts to the Barstow, CA area at 98.9 FM.

KHXS-FM
Owner: Cumulus Media Inc.
Editorial: 2525 S Danville Dr, Abilene, Texas 79605. **T:** 1 325 793-9700
W: http://www.102thebear.com
Editorial Profile: KHXS-FM is a commercial station owned by Cumulus Media Inc. The format of the station is Classic Rock music. KHXS-FM broadcasts in the Abilene, TX area at 102.7 FM.

KHXT-FM
Owner: Townsquare Media, LLC
Editorial: 1749 Bertrand Dr, Lafayette, Louisiana 70506. **T:** 1 337 233-6000
W: http://www.1079ishot.com
Editorial Profile: KHXT-FM is a commercial station owned by Townsquare Media, LLC. The format of the station is rhythmic Top 40/CHR. KHXT-FM broadcasts to the Lafayette, LA area at 107.9 FM.

KHYI-FM
Owner: Metro Broadcasters-Texas, Inc.
Editorial: 12225 Greenville Ave, Dallas, Texas 75243-9362. **T:** 1 972 633-0953
W: http://www.khyi.com
Editorial Profile: KHYI-FM is a commercial station owned by the Metro Broadcasters-Texas, Inc. The format of the station is country music. KHYI-FM broadcasts to the Allen, TX area at 95.3 FM.

KHYL-FM
Owner: Clear Channel Media and Entertainment
Editorial: 1545 River Park Dr Ste 500, Sacramento, California 95815-4693.
T: 1 916 929-5325
W: http://www.v1011fm.com
Editorial Profile: KHYL-FM is a commercial station owned by Clear Channel Media and Entertainment. The format of the station is urban oldies. KHYL-FM broadcasts to the Sacramento, CA area at 101.1 FM.

KHYM-FM
Owner: Great Plains Christian Radio
Editorial: 909 W Carthage, Meade, Kansas 67864. **T:** 1 620 873-2991 **E:** khym@khym.org
W: http://www.khym.org
Editorial Profile: KHYM-FM is a non-commercial station owned by Great Plains Christian Radio. The format of the station is gospel music and religious talk. KHYM-FM broadcasts to the Meade, KS area at 103.9 FM.

KHYT-FM
Owner: Cumulus Media Inc
Editorial: 575 W Roger Rd, Tucson, Arizona 85705. **T:** 1 520 887-1000
W: http://www.khit1075.com
Editorial Profile: KHYT-FM is a commercial station owned by Cumulus Media Inc. The format of the station is classic hits. KHYT-FM broadcasts to the Tucson, AZ area at 107.5 FM.

KHYX-FM
Owner: Ruby Radio Corp.
Editorial: 530 Melarkey St Ste 201, Winnemucca, Nevada 89445-3168.
T: 1 775 625-1027 **W:** http://mix1027.fm
Editorial Profile: KHYX-FM is a commercial station owned by Ruby Radio Corp. The format of the station is Hot AC. KHYX-FM broadcasts to the Winnemucca, NV area at a frequency of 102.7 FM.

KHYY-FM
Owner: Armada Media
Editorial: 305 E 4th St, North Platte, Nebraska 69101-6903. **T:** 1 308 532-3344
Editorial Profile: KHYY-FM is a commercial station owned by Armada Media. The format of the station is contemporary country. KHYY-FM broadcasts to the Scottsbluff, NE area at 106.9 FM.

KHYZ-FM
Owner: Highway Radio Inc.
Editorial: 1611 E Main St, Barstow, California 92311-3239. **T:** 1 760 256-0326
E: highwayradio@highwayradio.com
W: http://www.thehighwaystations.com
Editorial Profile: KHYZ-FM is a commercial station owned by Highway Radio Inc. The format of the station is dance music. KHYZ-FM broadcasts to Mountain Pass, CA and the surrounding area at 99.7FM.

KHZR-FM
Owner: Gateway Creative Broadcasting, Inc
Editorial: 13358 Manchester Rd Ste 100, Des Peres, Missouri 63131-1730.
T: 1 314 909-8569 **E:** info@joyfmonline.org
W: http://boost1019.com
Editorial Profile: KHZR-FM is a non-commercial station owned by Gateway Creative Broadcasting, Inc. The format of the station is Christian CHR. KHZR-FM broadcasts to the St. Louis area at 97.7 FM.

KIAI-FM
Owner: Three Eagles Communications Co.
Editorial: 341 S Yorktown Pike, Mason City, Iowa 50401-4533. **T:** 1 641 423-1300
W: http://www.discovernorthiowa.com/pages/12440227.php
Editorial Profile: KIAI-FM is a commercial station owned by Three Eagles Communications Co. The format of the station

is classic and contemporary country. KIAI-FM broadcasts to the Rochester, MN, and Mason City, IA areas at 93.9 FM.

KIAK-FM
Owner: Clear Channel Media and Entertainment
Editorial: 546 9th Ave, Fairbanks, Alaska 99701. **T:** 1 907 450-1000
E: kiak@clearchannel.com
W: http://www.kiak.com
Editorial Profile: KIAK-FM is a commercial station owned by Clear Channel Media and Entertainment. The format for the station is contemporary country. KIAK-FM broadcasts to the Fairbanks, AK area at 102.5 FM.

KIAM-AM
Owner: Voice for Christ Ministries Inc.
Editorial: 409 East 1st St, Nenana, Alaska 99760-0474. **T:** 1 907 832-5426
E: alaskaradio@vfcm.org
W: http://www.vfcm.org
Editorial Profile: KIAM-AM is a commercial station owned by Voice for Christ Ministries Inc. The format of the station is Christian music and talk. KIAM-AM broadcasts to Nenana, AK 630 AM.

KIAQ-FM
Owner: Three Eagles Communications Co.
Editorial: 200 N 10th St, Fort Dodge, Iowa 50501-3944. **T:** 1 515 955-5656
E: k97@frontiernet.net
W: http://www.threeeagles.com
Editorial Profile: KIAQ-FM is a commercial station owned by Three Eagles Communications Co. The format of the station is contemporary country music. KIAQ-FM broadcasts to the Fort Dodge, IA area at 96.9 FM.

KIBB-FM
Owner: Connoisseur Media LLC
Editorial: 1938 N Woodlawn St Ste 150, Wichita, Kansas 67208-1929.
T: 1 316 558-8800
W: http://www.971bobfm.com
Editorial Profile: KIBB-FM is a commercial station owned by Connoisseur Media LLC. The format of the station is adult hits. KIBB-FM broadcasts to the Wichita, KS area at 97.1 FM.

KIBC-FM
Owner: Burney Educ. Broadcasting Foundation
Editorial: 20410 Marquette St, Burney, California 96013. **T:** 1 530 335-5422
W: http://www.kibcfm.org
Editorial Profile: KIBC-FM is a non-commercial station owned by Burney Educ. Broadcasting Foundation. The format of the station is gospel music and religious programming. KIBC-FM broadcasts to the Burney, CA area at 90.5 FM.

KIBG-FM
Owner: Anderson Radio Broadcasting Inc.
Editorial: 36581 N Reservoir Rd, Polson, Montana 59860-8471. **T:** 1 406 883-5255
E: kerrnews@750kerr.com
W: http://www.thebig100.com
Editorial Profile: KIBG-FM is a commercial station owned by Anderson Radio Broadcasting Inc. The format of the station is classic hits. KIBG-FM airs to the Polson, MT area at 100.7 FM.

KIBR-FM
Owner: Blue Sky Broadcasting Inc.
Editorial: 327 S Marion Ave, Sandpoint, Idaho 83864. **T:** 1 208 263-2179
W: http://www.k102radio.com
Editorial Profile: KIBR-FM is a commercial station owned by Blue Sky Broadcasting Inc. The format of the station is country music. KIBR-FM broadcasts to the Spokane, WA area at 102.5 FM.

KIBS-FM
Owner: Great Country Broadcasting Inc.
Editorial: South Highway 395, Bishop, California 93514. **T:** 1 760 873-6324
E: kibskbov@yahoo.com
W: http://www.kibskbov.com
Editorial Profile: KIBS-FM is a commercial station owned by Great Country Broadcasting Inc. The format of the station is country music. KIBS-FM broadcasts to the Bishop, CA area at 100.7 FM.

KIBT-FM
Owner: Clear Channel Media and Entertainment
Editorial: 2864 S Circle Dr, Ste 300, Colorado Springs, Colorado 80906. **T:** 1 719 540-9200
W: http://www.beatcolorado.com

Editorial Profile: KIBT-FM is a commercial station owned by Clear Channel Media and Entertainment. The format of the station is rhythmic Top 40/CHR. KIBT-FM broadcasts to the Colorado Springs, CO area at 96.1 FM.

KIBX-FM
Owner: Spokane Public Radio Inc.
Editorial: 2319 N Monroe St, Spokane, Washington 99205. **T:** 1 509 328-5729
E: kpbx@kpbx.org **W:** http://www.kpbx.org

KIBZ-FM
Owner: Three Eagles Communications Co.
Editorial: 3800 Cornhusker Hwy, Lincoln, Nebraska 68504. **T:** 1 402 466-1234
E: blaze@kibz.com **W:** http://www.kibz.com
Editorial Profile: KIBZ-FM is a commercial station owned by Three Eagles Communications Co. The format of the station is rock/album-oriented rock. KIBZ-FM broadcasts to the Lincoln, NE area at 104.1 FM.

KICB-FM
Owner: Iowa Central Community College
Editorial: 1 Triton Cir, Fort Dodge, Iowa 50501-5730. **T:** 1 515 576-6049
Editorial Profile: KICB-FM is a non-commercial station owned by Iowa Central Community College. The format of the station is adult album alternative. KICB-FM broadcasts to the Fort Dodge, IA area at 88.1 FM.

KICD-AM
Owner: Saga Communications
Editorial: 2600 Highway Blvd, Spencer, Iowa 51301. **T:** 1 712 262-1240
W: http://www.kicdam.com
Editorial Profile: KICD-AM is a commercial station owned by Saga Communications. The format of the station is news and talk. KICD-AM broadcasts to the Spencer, IA area at 1240 AM.

KICD-FM
Owner: Saga Communications
Editorial: 2600 Highway Blvd, Spencer, Iowa 51301-2140. **T:** 1 712 262-1240
W: http://www.cd1077fm.com
Editorial Profile: KICD-FM is a commercial station owned by Saga Communications. The format of the station is country music. KICD-FM roadcasts to the Spencer, IA area at 107.7 FM.

KICE-AM
Owner: Gross Communications Co.
Editorial: 345 SW Cyber Dr, Ste 101-103, Bend, Oregon 97702-1045. **T:** 1 541 388-3300
W: http://www.espn940.com
Editorial Profile: KICE-AM is a commercial station owned by Gross Communications Co. The format of the station is sports. KICE-AM broadcasts to the Bend, OR area at 940 AM.

KICK-FM
Owner: Double O Radio
Editorial: 408 N 24th St, Quincy, Illinois 62301-3254. **T:** 1 217 223-5292
E: kickfm@hqradio.com
W: http://979kickfm.com
Editorial Profile: KICK-FM is a commercial station owned by Double O Radio. The format of the station is country music. KICK-FM broadcasts to the Quincy, IL area at 97.9 FM.

KICM-FM
Owner: Keystone Broadcasting Corp
Editorial: 115 W Broadway St, Ste 501, Ardmore, Oklahoma 73401. **T:** 1 580 226-9797
W: http://www.thebigstation.net
Editorial Profile: KICM-FM is a commercial station owned by Keystone Broadcasting Corp. The format of the station is contemporary country music. KICM-FM broadcasts to the Ardmore, OK area at 97.7 FM.

KICR-FM
Owner: Blue Sky Broadcasting Inc.
Editorial: 327 S Marion Ave, Sandpoint, Idaho 83864. **T:** 1 208 263-2179
W: http://www.k102radio.com
Editorial Profile: KICR-FM is a commercial station owned by Blue Sky Broadcasting Inc. The format of the station is contemporary country. KICR-FM broadcasts to the Sandpoint, ID area at 102.3 FM.

KICS-AM
Owner: Platte River Radio, Inc.
Editorial: 500 E J St, Hastings, Nebraska 68901. **T:** 1 402 462-5101
E: generalmanager@espnsuperstation.com
W: http://espnsuperstation.com

Editorial Profile: KICS-AM is a commercial station owned by Platte River Radio, Inc. The format of the station is sports. KICS-FM broadcasts in the Hastings, NE area at 1550 AM.

KICT-FM
Owner: Journal Broadcast Group
Editorial: 4200 N Old Lawrence Rd, Wichita, Kansas 67219. **T:** 1 316 838-9141
E: news@kfdi.com **W:** http://www.t95.com
Editorial Profile: KICT-FM is a commercial station owned by Journal Broadcast Group. The format of the station is rock. KICT-FM broadcasts to the Wichita, KS area at 95.1 FM.

KICW-FM
Owner: University of Northern Iowa
Editorial: University Of Northern Iowa, Cedar Falls, Iowa 50614. **T:** 1 319 273-6400
E: news@iowapublicradio.org
W: http://www.iowapublicradio.org
Editorial Profile: KICW-FM is a non-commercial station owned by the University of Northern Iowa. The format of the station is classical. KICW-FM broadcasts to the Cedar Rapids, IA area at 91.1 FM.

KICX-FM
Owner: Armada Media Corp.
Editorial: 1811 W O St, McCook, Nebraska 69001. **T:** 1 308 345-5400
E: production@highplainsradio.net
W: http://www.plainsreporter.com
Editorial Profile: KICX-FM is a commercial station owned by Armada Media Corp. The format of the station is adult contemporary. KICX-FM broadcasts to the McCook, NE area at 98.5 FM.

KICY-AM
Owner: Arctic Broadcasting Association
Editorial: 408 W D St, Nome, Alaska 99762-0820. **T:** 1 907 443-2213 **E:** office@kicy.org
W: http://www.kicy.org
Editorial Profile: KICY-AM is a commercial station owned by Arctic Broadcasting Association. The format of the station is gospel and religion. KICY-AM broadcasts to the Nome, AK area at 850 AM.

KICY-FM
Owner: Arctic Broadcasting Association
Editorial: 408 W D St, Nome, Alaska 99762-0820. **T:** 1 907 443-2213 **E:** office@kicy.org
W: http://www.kicy.org
Editorial Profile: KCIY-FM is a commercial station owned by KICY-FM. The format is gospel and religous music. The station airs at 100.3FM in the Nome, AK area.

KID-AM
Owner: Rich Broadcasting, LLC
Editorial: 1406 Commerce Way, Idaho Falls, Idaho 83401. **T:** 1 208 524-5900
W: http://590kid.com
Editorial Profile: KID-AM is a commercial station owned by Rich Broadcasting, LLC. The format of the station is news and talk. KID-AM broadcasts to the Idaho Falls, ID area at 590 AM.

KIDD-AM
Owner: Buckley Broadcasting Corp.
Editorial: 5 Harris Ct Bldg C, Monterey, California 93940-5751. **T:** 1 831 649-0969
W: http://www.espn630.com
Editorial Profile: KIDD-AM is a commercial station owned by Buckley Broadcasting Corp. The format of the station is sports. KIDD-AM broadcasts to the Monterey, CA area at 630 AM.

KIDE-FM
Owner: Hoopa Valley Tribe
Editorial: Hoopa Valley Shopping Ctr Hwy 96, Hoopa, California 95546. **T:** 1 530 625-4245
W: http://www.hoopa-nsn.gov/departments/kide.htm
Editorial Profile: KIDE-FM is a non-commercial station owned by Hoopa Valley Tribe. The format of the station is variety, Native American programming. KIDE-FM broadcasts in the Hoopa Valley Indian Reservation, CA at 91.3 FM.

KID-FM
Owner: Rich Broadcasting, LLC
Editorial: 1406 Commerce Way, Idaho Falls, Idaho 83401. **T:** 1 208 524-5900
W: http://www.rivercountryfm.com
Editorial Profile: KID-FM is a commercial station owned by Rich Broadcasting, LLC. The format of the station is country music. KID-FM broadcasts in the Idaho Falls, ID area at 96.1 FM.

KIDI-FM
Owner: Emerald Wave Media
Editorial: 718 E Chapel St, Santa Maria, California 93454-4524. **T:** 1 805 928-4334
E: traffic@emeraldwavemedia.com
Editorial Profile: KIDI-FM is a commercial station owned by Emerald Wave Media. The format of the station is regional Mexican. KIDI-FM broadcasts to the Santa Maria, CA area at 105.1 FM.

KIDN-FM
Owner: NRC Broadcasting
Editorial: 2955 Village Dr, Steamboat Springs, Colorado 80487-2143. **T:** 1 970 879-5368
W: http://alwaysmountaintime.com/kidn
Editorial Profile: KIDN-FM is a commercial station owned by NRC Broadcasting. The format of the station is Hot AC. KIDN-FM broadcasts to the Steamboat Springs, CO area on 95.5 FM.

KIDO-AM
Owner: Townsquare Media, LLC
Editorial: 827 E Park Blvd Ste 100, Boise, Idaho 83712-7783. **T:** 1 208 344-6363
W: http://www.kidoam.com
Editorial Profile: KIDO-AM is a commercial station owned by Townsquare Media, LLC. The format of the station is news and talk. KIDO-AM broadcasts to the Boise, ID area at 580 AM.

KIDR-AM
Owner: En Familia, Inc.
Editorial: 3015 N 33rd Dr, Phoenix, Arizona 85017-5204. **T:** 1 602 234-8998
Editorial Profile: KIDR-AM is a commercial station owned by En Familia, Inc. The format of the station is Spanish talk. KIDR-AM broadcasts to the Phoenix area at 740 AM.

KIDS-FM
Owner: Albuquerque Public Schools
Editorial: 2020 Coal Ave SE, Albuquerque, New Mexico 87106. **T:** 1 505 242-7163
Editorial Profile: KIDS-FM is a non-commercial station owned by Albuquerque Public Schools. The format is Hispanic variety. KIDS-FM broadcasts to the Albuquerque, NM area at 88.1 FM.

KIFG-AM
Owner: Times Citizen Communications
Editorial: 406 Stevens St, Iowa Falls, Iowa 50126. **T:** 1 641 648-2521 **E:** kifg@iafalls.com
W: http://www.kifgradio.com
Editorial Profile: KIFG-AM is a commercial station owned by Times Citizen Communications. The format of the station is classic hits. KIFG-AM broadcasts to the Iowa Falls, IA area at 1510 AM.

KIFM-FM
Owner: Lincoln Financial Media
Editorial: 1615 Murray Canyon Rd Ste 710, San Diego, California 92108-4321.
T: 1 619 291-9797
W: http://www.easy981.com
Editorial Profile: KIFM-FM is a commercial station owned by Lincoln Financial Media. The format of the staion is smooth AC. KIFM-FM broadcasts to the San Diego area at 98.1 FM.

KIFS-FM
Owner: Bicoastal Media LLC
Editorial: 3624 Avion Dr, Medford, Oregon 97504. **T:** 1 541 772-4170
W: http://www.107kiss.com
Editorial Profile: KIFS-FM is a commercial station owned by Bicoastal Media LLC. The format of the station is Top 40/CHR music. KIFS-FM broadcasts to the Medford, OR area at 107.5 FM.

KIFT-FM
Owner: NRC Broadcasting
Editorial: 130 Ski Hill Rd, Ste 240, Breckenridge, Colorado 80424.
T: 1 970 453-2234 **W:** http://www.lift106.com
Editorial Profile: KIFT-FM is a commercial station owned by NRC Broadcasting. The format of the station is Top 40. KIFT-FM is licensed to Kremmling, CO and broadcasts to Summit, Grand and Eagle counties at 106.3 FM.

KIFW-AM
Owner: Alaska Broadcast Communications Inc.
Editorial: 611 Lake St, Sitka, Alaska 99835.
T: 1 907 747-5439 **E:** kifw@abcstations.com
W: http://www.kifw.com
Editorial Profile: KIFW-AM is a commercial station owned by Alaska Broadcast Communications Inc. The format of the station is oldies music. KIFW-AM broadcasts to the Sitka, AK area at 1230 AM.

KIFX-FM

Owner: Evans Broadcasting
Editorial: RR 2 Box 2384, 2242 E 1000 S, Roosevelt, Utah 84066-9523.
T: 1 435 722-5011 **E:** radio@ubtanet.com
W: http://www.stormpc.com/fox/foxlink.htm
Editorial Profile: KIFX-FM is a commercial station owned by Evans Broadcasting. The format of the station is adult contemporary. KIFX-FM broadcasts to the Salt Lake City area at 98.5 FM.

KIGC-FM

Owner: William Penn University
Editorial: 201 Trueblood Ave, Oskaloosa, Iowa 52577. **T:** 1 641 673-1095

KIGL-FM

Owner: Clear Channel Media and Entertainment
Editorial: 2049 E Joyce Blvd Ste 101, Fayetteville, Arkansas 72703-6395.
T: 1 479 582-1079
W: http://www.933theeagle.com
Editorial Profile: KIGL-FM is a commercial station owned by Clear Channel Media and Entertainment. The format of the station is classic rock. KIGL-FM broadcasts to the Fayetteville, AR area at 93.3 FM.

KIGN-FM

Owner: Townsquare Media, LLC
Editorial: 1912 Capitol Ave, Ste 300, Cheyenne, Wyoming 82001.
T: 1 307 632-4400 **W:** http://www.kingfm.com
Editorial Profile: KIGN-FM is a commercial station owned by Townsquare Media, LLC. The format of the station is rock music. KIGN-FM broadcasts in the Cheyenne, WY area at 101.9 FM.

KIHK-FM

Owner: Community First Broadcasting, LLC
Editorial: 128 20th St SE, Sioux Center, Iowa 51250. **T:** 1 712 722-1090
E: ksou@siouxcountyradio.com
W: http://www.ksoufm.com
Editorial Profile: KIHK-FM is a commercial station owned by Community First Broadcasting, LLC. The format of the station is classic country. KIHK-FM broadcasts to the Sioux Center, IA area at 106.9 FM.

KIHN-AM

Owner: Little Dixie Broadcasting Co.
Editorial: Highway 70 East, Hugo, Oklahoma 74743. **T:** 1 580 326-6411 **E:** kihn@att.net
Editorial Profile: KIHN-AM is a commercial station owned by Little Dixie Broadcasting Co. The format of the station is variety. KIHN-AM broadcasts in the Hugo, OK area at 1340 AM.

KIHP-AM

Owner: Immaculate Heart Radio
Editorial: 2800 N 44Th St Ste 125, Phoenix, Arizona 85008-1569. **T:** 1 916 535-0500
W: http://ihradio.com
Editorial Profile: KIHP-AM is a commercial station owned by Immaculate Heart Radio. The format of the station is religious and catholic programming. KIHP-AM broadcasts in the Phoenix area at 1310 AM.

KIHR-AM

Owner: Bicoastal Media LLC
Editorial: 1190 22Nd St, Hood River, Oregon 97031-9669. **T:** 1 541 386-1511
W: http://www.kihramfm.com
Editorial Profile: KIHR-AM is a commercial station owned by Bicoastal Media LLC. The format of the station is contemporary country music. KIHR-AM broadcasts to the Portland, OR area at 1340 AM.

KIHT-FM

Owner: Emmis Communications Corp.
Editorial: 800 Saint Louis Union Sta, Saint Louis, Missouri 63103. **T:** 1 314 621-4106
E: feedback@k-hits.com
W: http://www.k-hits.com
Editorial Profile: KIHT-FM is a commercial station owned by Emmis Communications Corp. The format of the station is classic hits music. KIHT-FM broadcasts to the St. Louis area at 96.3 FM.

KIHU-AM

Owner: Immaculate Heart Radio
Editorial: 3256 Penryn Rd Ste 100, Loomis, California 95650-8052. **T:** 1 916 535-0500
W: http://ihradio.com
Editorial Profile: KIHU-FM is a non-commercial station owned by Immaculate Heart Radio. The format is Catholic programming. KIHU-AM broadcasts to the Park City, UT area at 1010 AM.

KIIC-FM

Owner: Waveguide Communications Inc
Editorial: 7 Benton Ave E, Ste 1, Albia, Iowa 52531. **T:** 1 641 932-2112
W: http://www.kiicradio.com
Editorial Profile: KIIC-FM is a commercial station owned by Waveguide Communications Inc. The format of the station is country. KIIC-FM broadcasts to the Albia, IA area at 96.7 FM.

KIID-AM

Owner: Walt Disney Co.
Editorial: 8265 Sierra College Blvd, Ste 312, Roseville, California 95661-9403.
T: 1 916 780-1470

KIIM-FM

Owner: Cumulus Media Inc
Editorial: 575 W Roger Rd, Tucson, Arizona 85705. **T:** 1 520 887-1000
W: http://www.kiimfm.com
Editorial Profile: KIIM-FM is a commercial station owned by Cumulus Media Inc. The format of the station is contemporary country. KIIM-FM broadcasts to the Tucson, AZ area at 99.5 FM.

KIIS-FM

Owner: Clear Channel Media and Entertainment
Editorial: 3400 W Olive Ave Ste 550, Burbank, California 91505-5544. **T:** 1 818 559-2252
W: http://www.kiisfm.com
Editorial Profile: KIIS-FM is a commercial station owned by Clear Channel Media and Entertainment. The format of the station is Top 40/CHR. KIIS-FM broadcasts to the Los Angeles area at 102.7 FM.

KIIX-AM

Owner: Clear Channel Media and Entertainment
Editorial: 4270 Byrd Dr, Loveland, Colorado 80538. **T:** 1 970 482-5991
W: http://www.1410kiix.com
Editorial Profile: KIIX-AM is a commercial station owned by Clear Channel Media and Entertainment. The format of the station is Classic Country. KIIX-AM broadcasts to the Denver area at 1410 AM.

KIIZ-FM

Owner: Clear Channel Media and Entertainment
Editorial: 314 W State Highway 6, Waco, Texas 76712. **T:** 1 254 776-3900
W: http://www.kiiz.com
Editorial Profile: KIIZ-FM is a commercial station owned by Clear Channel Media and Entertainment. The format of the station is urban contemporary. KIIZ-FM broadcasts to the Waco, TX area at 92.3 FM.

KIJN-AM

Owner: Unido Para Christo, Inc.
Editorial: 205 9th St, Farwell, Texas 79325.
T: 1 806 481-3318 **E:** kijn@email.com
Editorial Profile: KIJN-AM is a commercial station owned by Unido Para Christo, Inc. The format of the station is religious programming and Hispanic. KIJN-AM broadcasts to the Farwell, TX area at 1060 AM.

KIJN-FM

Owner: Unido Para Christo, Inc.
Editorial: 205 9th St, Farwell, Texas 79325.
T: 1 806 481-3318
Editorial Profile: KIJN-FM is a commercial station owned by Unido Para Christo, Inc. The format of the station is Spanish language religion. KIJN-FM broadcasts to the Farwell, TX area at 92.3 FM.

KIJV-AM

Owner: Dakota Communications, Ltd.
Editorial: 1726 Dakota Ave S, Huron, South Dakota 57350-4024. **T:** 1 605 352-1933
E: production@kokk.com
W: http://www.performance-radio.com
Editorial Profile: KIJV-AM is a commercial station owned by Dakota Communications, Ltd. The format of the station is CHR. KIJV-AM broadcasts to the Huron, SD area at 1340 AM.

KIKC-AM

Owner: Miles City Forsyth Broadcasting Inc.
Editorial: 210 West Front Street, Forsyth, Montana 59327. **T:** 1 406 346-2711
E: kikc@rangeweb.net **W:** http://kikcamfm.com
Editorial Profile: KIKC-AM is a commercial station owned by Miles City Forsyth Broadcasting Inc. The format of the station is classic country. KIKC-AM broadcasts in the Forsyth, MT area at 1250 AM.

KIKC-FM

Owner: Miles City Forsyth Broadcasting Inc.
Editorial: 210 West Front Street, Forsyth, Montana 59327. **T:** 1 406 346-2711
E: kikc@rangeweb.net
W: http://www.kikcamfm.com
Editorial Profile: KIKC-FM is a commercial station owned by Miles City Forsyth Broadcasting Inc. The format of the station is contemporary country music. KIKC-FM broadcasts to the Forsyth, MT area at 101.3 FM.

KIKD-FM

Owner: Carroll Broadcasting Co.
Editorial: 1119 Plaza Dr, Carroll, Iowa 51401-3838. **T:** 1 712 792-4321
W: http://carrollbroadcasting.com
Editorial Profile: KIKD-FM is a commercial station owned by Carroll Broadcasting Co. The format of the station is contemporary country music. KIKD-FM broadcasts to the Carrol, IA area at 106.7 FM.

KIKF-FM

Owner: Fisher Communications, Inc.
Editorial: 1300 Central Ave W, Great Falls, Montana 59404. **T:** 1 406 761-2800
W: http://www.mykikfm.com

KIKI-AM

Owner: Clear Channel Media and Entertainment
Editorial: 650 Iwilei Rd, Ste 400, Honolulu, Hawaii 96817. **T:** 1 808 550-9200
W: http://www.khbz.com
Editorial Profile: KIKI-AM is a commercial station owned by Clear Channel Media and Entertainment. The format for the station is news and talk. KIKI-AM broadcasts to the Honolulu area at 990 AM.

KIKK-AM

Owner: CBS Radio
Editorial: 24 Greenway Plz, Houston, Texas 77046-2401. **T:** 1 713 881-5100
W: http://houston.cbslocal.com
Editorial Profile: KIKK-AM is commercial station owned by CBS Radio. The format of the station is news, talk and sports. KIKK-AM broadcasts to the Houston area at 650 AM.

KIKN-FM

Owner: Townsquare Media, Inc.
Editorial: 5100 S Tennis Ln, Sioux Falls, South Dakota 57108-2212. **T:** 1 605 361-0300
W: http://www.kikn.com
Editorial Profile: KIKN-FM is a commercial station owned by Townsquare Media, Inc. The format of the station is classic country. KIKN-FM broadcasts to the Sioux Falls, SD area at 100.5 FM.

KIKO-AM

Owner: 1TV.Com, Inc.
Editorial: 4501 Broadway, Miami, Arizona 85539-3800. **T:** 1 928 425-4471
E: kikonews@cableone.net
W: http://kikonews.blogspot.com
Editorial Profile: KIKO-AM is a commercial station owned by 1TV.Com, Inc. The format of the station is primarily news and sports, with oldies and adult contemporary. KIKO-AM broadcasts to the Miami, AZ area at 1340 AM.

KIKO-FM

Owner: 1TV.Com, Inc.
Editorial: 4501 Broadway, Miami, Arizona 85539-3800. **T:** 1 928 425-4471
W: http://funny973.com
Editorial Profile: KIKO-FM is a commercial station owned by 1TV.Com, Inc. The format of the station is comedy. KIKO-FM broadcasts to the Miami, AZ area at 97.3 FM

KIKR-AM

Owner: Cumulus Media Inc.
Editorial: 755 S 11th St, Ste 102, Beaumont, Texas 77701. **T:** 1 409 951-2500
W: http://www.lagrande1450.com
Editorial Profile: KIKR-AM is a commercial station owned by Cumulus Media Inc. The format of the station is Hispanic. KIKR-AM broadcasts to the Beaumont, TX area at 1450 AM.

KIKS-FM

Owner: Iola Broadcasting Inc.
Editorial: 2221 S State St, Iola, Kansas 66749.
T: 1 620 365-3151
E: radiostation@iolaradio.com
W: http://www.iolaradio.com
Editorial Profile: KIKS-FM is a commercial station owned by Iola Broadcasting Inc. The format of the station is contemporary country. KIKS-FM broadcasts to the Iola, KS area at 99.3 FM.

KIKV-FM

Owner: Omni Broadcasting Co.
Editorial: 604 3rd Ave W, Alexandria, Minnesota 56308. **T:** 1 320 762-2154
E: 100.7@kikvfm.com
W: http://www.kikvradio.com
Editorial Profile: KIKV-FM is a commercial station owned by Omni Broadcasting Co. The format of the station is classic country. KIKV-FM broadcasts to the Alexandria, MN area at 100.7 FM.

KIKX-FM

Owner: Locally Owned Radio, LLC
Editorial: 21361 Highway 30, Twin Falls, Idaho 83301. **T:** 1 208 735-8300
E: production@kikx.com
W: http://www.kikx1047.com
Editorial Profile: KIKX-FM is a commercial station owned by Locally Owned Radio, LLC. The format of the station is adult hits. KIKX-FM broadcasts to the Twin Falls, ID area at 104.7 FM.

KIKZ-AM

Owner: Gaines County Broadcasting
Editorial: 105 Nw 11Th St, Seminole, Texas 79360-3301. **T:** 1 432 758-5878
E: kikz-ksem@bajabb.com
W: http://www.kikzksem.ws
Editorial Profile: KIKZ-AM is a commercial station owned by Gaines County Broadcasting. The format of the station is country and Hispanic music. KIKZ broadcasts to the Seminole, TX area at 1250 AM.

KILI-FM

Owner: Lakota Communications Inc.
Editorial: 901 Lamont Lane, Porcupine, South Dakota 57772. **T:** 1 605 867-5002
E: crashwk@hotmail.com
Editorial Profile: KILI-FM is a non-commercial station owned by Lakota Communications Inc. The format of the station is variety. KILI-FM broadcasts to the Rapid City, SD area at 90.1 FM.

KILJ-AM

Owner: Dennison(Paul and Joyce)
Editorial: 2411 Radio Dr, Mount Pleasant, Iowa 52641-8207. **T:** 1 319 385-3111
E: kiljradio@kilj.com **W:** http://www.kilj.com
Editorial Profile: KILJ-AM is a commercial station owned by Paul and Joyce Dennison. The format of the station is classic country music. KILJ-AM broadcasts to the Mount Pleasant, IA area at 1130 AM.

KILJ-FM

Owner: Dennison(Paul and Joyce)
Editorial: 2411 Radio Dr, Mount Pleasant, Iowa 52641-8207. **T:** 1 319 385-8728
E: kiljradio@kilj.com **W:** http://www.kilj.com
Editorial Profile: KILJ-FM is a commercial station owned by Paul and Joyce Dennison. The format of the station is adult standards. KILJ-FM broadcasts to the Mount Pleasant, IA area at 105.5 FM.

KILO-FM

Owner: Bahakel Communications
Editorial: 1805 E Cheyenne Rd, Colorado Springs, Colorado 80906-2868.
T: 1 719 634-4896 **E:** kilostudio@kilo943.com
W: http://www.kilo943.com
Editorial Profile: KILO-FM is a commercial station owned by Bahakel Communications. The format of the station is rock. KILO-FM broadcasts to the Colorado Springs, CO area at 94.3 FM.

KILR-AM

Owner: Jacobson Broadcasting Companies Inc.
Editorial: 3875 150th St, Estherville, Iowa 51334. **T:** 1 712 362-2644
E: kilr@yourstarnet.net
Editorial Profile: KILR-AM is a commercial station owned by Jacobson Broadcasting Companies Inc. The format for the station is talk. KILR-AM broadcasts to the Estherville, IA area at 1070 AM.

KILR-FM

Owner: Jacobson Broadcasting Companies Inc.
Editorial: 3875 150th St, Estherville, Iowa 51334. **T:** 1 712 362-2644
E: kilrradio@hotmail.com
W: http://www.killrradio.com
Editorial Profile: KILR-FM is a commercial station owned by Jacobson Broadcasting Companies Inc. The format of the station is country. KILR-FM broadcasts to the Estherville, IA area at 95.9 FM.

KILT-AM

Owner: CBS Radio
Editorial: 24 Greenway Plz, Houston, Texas 77046-2401. **T:** 1 713 881-5100
W: http://houston.cbslocal.com
Editorial Profile: KILT-AM is a commercial station owned by CBS Radio. The format of the station is sports. KILT-AM broadcasts to the Houston area at 610 AM.

KILT-FM

Owner: CBS Radio
Editorial: 24 Greenway Plz Ste 1900, Houston, Texas 77046-2428. **T:** 1 713 881-5100
W: http://thebull.cbslocal.com
Editorial Profile: KILT-FM is a commercial station owned by CBS Radio. The format of the station is contemporary country. KILT-FM broadcasts to the Houston area at 100.3 FM.

KILV-FM

Owner: Educational Media Foundation
Editorial: 6721 W 121st St Ste 100, Overland Park, Kansas 66209-2031. **T:** 1 888 973-2471
E: info@klove.com **W:** http://www.klove.com
Editorial Profile: KILV-FM is a non-commercial station owned by Educational Media Foundation. The format of the station is contemporary Christian. KILV-FM broadcasts to the Sioux City, IA area at 107.5 FM.

KILX-FM

Owner: Ouachita Broadcasting Inc.
Editorial: 1600 Reine St S, Mena, Arkansas 71953. **T:** 1 479 394-1450
E: menaradio@allegiance.tv
Editorial Profile: KILX-FM is a commercial station owned by Ouachita Broadcasting Inc. The format for the station is hot adult contemporary. KILX-FM broadcasts to the Mena, AR area at 104.1 FM.

KIML-AM

Owner: Legend Communications
Editorial: 2810 Southern Dr, Gillette, Wyoming 82718. **T:** 1 307 686-2242
E: news@basinsradio.com
W: http://www.basinsradio.com
Editorial Profile: KIML-AM is a commercial station owned by Legend Communications. The format of the station is news, talk and sports. KIML-AM broadcasts to the Gillette, WY area at 1270 AM.

KIMM-AM

Owner: Flasen Publishing
Editorial: 11 Main St, Rapid City, South Dakota 57701. **T:** 1 605 342-1150
Editorial Profile: KIMM-AM is a commercial station owned by Flasen Publishing. The format of the station is news/talk. KIMM-AM broadcasts to the Rapid City, SD area at 1150 AM.

KIMN-FM

Owner: Wilks Broadcast Group
Editorial: 720 S Colorado Blvd Ste 1200N, Denver, Colorado 80246. **T:** 1 303 832-5665
W: http://www.mix100.com
Editorial Profile: KIMN-FM is a commercial station owned by Wilks Broadcast Group. The format of the station is hot adult contemporary. KIMN-FM broadcasts to the Denver area at 100.3 FM.

KIMO-FM

Owner: Fisher Communications, Inc.
Editorial: 1300 Central Ave W, Great Falls, Montana 59404. **T:** 1 406 761-2800
Editorial Profile: KIMO-FM is a commercial station owned by Fisher Communications, Inc. The format for the station is adult hits. KIMO-FM broadcasts to the Great Falls, MT area at 107.3 FM.

KIMP-AM

Owner: East Texas Broadcasting Inc.
Editorial: Highway 67 West 1 Mile, Mount Pleasant, Texas 75455. **T:** 1 903 577-9770
W: http://www.easttexasradio.com/kimp.php
Editorial Profile: KIMP-AM is a commercial station owned by East Texas Broadcasting Inc. The format of the station is Spanish Adult Hits. KIMP-AM broadcasts to the Mount Pleasant, TX area at 960 AM.

KIMX-FM

Owner: Appaloosa Broadcasting
Editorial: 302 S 2nd St, Ste 204, Laramie, Wyoming 82070. **T:** 1 307 745-5208
E: imixwyoming@gmail.com
W: http://www.planet967.com
Editorial Profile: KIMX-FM is a commercial station owned by Appaloosa Broadcasting. The format of the station is Top 40/CHR. KIMX-FM broadcasts to the Laramie, WY area at 106.7 FM.

KIMY-FM

Owner: South Central Oklahoma Christian Broadcasting Inc.
Editorial: 20750 State Hwy 1W, Ada, Oklahoma 74820-5424. **T:** 1 580 332-0902
E: email@thegospelstation.com
W: http://www.thegospelstation.com
Editorial Profile: KIMY-FM is a commercial station owned by South Central Oklahoma Christian Broadcasting Inc. The format of the station is gospel music. KIMY-FM broadcasts in the Watonga, OK area at 93.9 FM.

KINA-AM

Owner: Eagle Radio Inc.
Editorial: 1825 S Ohio St, Salina, Kansas 67401. **T:** 1 785 825-4631
W: http://www.910kina.com
Editorial Profile: KINA-AM is a commercial station owned by Eagle Radio Inc. The format of the station is news, talk and sports. KINA-AM broadcasts to the Salina, KS area at 910 AM.

KINB-FM

Owner: The Last Bastion Station Trust, LLC
Editorial: 7725 W Britton Rd Ste B, Oklahoma City, Oklahoma 73132-1508.
T: 1 405 848-0100
Editorial Profile: KINB-FM is a commercial station owned by The Last Bastion Station Trust, LLC. The format of the station is sports. KINB-FM broadcasts locally to the Kingfisher, OK area at 105.3 FM.

KIND-AM

Owner: Tallgrass Broadcasting, LLC
Editorial: 309 N Penn Ave, Independence, Kansas 67301-3325. **T:** 1 620 331-3000
Editorial Profile: KIND-AM is a commercial station owned by Tallgrass Broadcasting, LLC. The format of the station is news and talk. KIND-AM broadcasts to the Independence, KS area at 1010 AM.

KINE-AM

Owner: Cotton Broadcasting
Editorial: 2209 N Padre Island Dr, Corpus Christi, Texas 78408-2432. **T:** 1 361 289-8877
Editorial Profile: KINE-AM is a commercial station owned by Cotton Broadcasting. The format of the station is Hispanic religious programming. KINE-AM broadcasts to the Corpus Christi, TX area at 95.7 FM.

KINE-FM

Owner: Summit Media Broadcasting LLC
Editorial: 900 Fort Street Mall, Honolulu, Hawaii 96813-3721. **T:** 1 808 536-2728
W: http://www.hawaiian105.com
Editorial Profile: KINE-FM is commercial station owned by Summit Media Broadcasting LLC. The format of the station is adult contemporary. KINE-FM broadcasts to the Honolulu area at 105.1 FM.

KING-FM

Owner: Classic Radio Inc.
Editorial: 10 Harrison St, Ste 100, Seattle, Washington 98109-4554. **T:** 1 206 691-2981
E: feedback@king.org **W:** http://www.king.org
Editorial Profile: KING-FM is a commercial station owned by Classic Radio Inc. The format of the station is classical music. KING-FM broadcasts to Seattle at 98.1 FM.

KINI-FM

Owner: St. Francis Mission
Editorial: 100 S Main St, Saint Francis, South Dakota 57572-0419. **T:** 1 605 747-2291
E: kinifm@gwtc.net **W:** http://www.kinifm.com
Editorial Profile: KINI-FM is a non-commercial station owned by St. Francis Mission. The format of the station is variety. KINI-FM broadcasts to the Saint Francis, SD area at 96.1 FM.

KINK-FM

Owner: Alpha Broadcasting
Editorial: 1211 SW 5th Ave Fl 6, Portland, Oregon 97204-3735. **T:** 1 503 517-6000
W: http://kink.fm
Editorial Profile: KINK-FM is a commercial station owned by Alpha Broadcasting. The format of the station is adult album alternative music. KINK-FM broadcasts to the Portland, OR area on 101.9 FM.

KINL-FM

Owner: MBM Radio LLC
Editorial: 127 Kilowatt Dr, Eagle Pass, Texas 78852-3397. **T:** 1 830 773-9247
E: newsep@rcommunications.com
W: http://www.power927.net
Editorial Profile: KINL-FM is a commercial station owned by MBM Radio LLC (dba R Communications). The station's format is hot adult contemporary. KINL-FM broadcasts to the Eagle Pass, TX area at 92.7 FM.

KINN-AM

Owner: Burt Broadcasting Inc.
Editorial: 501 S Florida Ave, Alamogordo, New Mexico 88310. **T:** 1 575 434-1414
E: burtbroadcasting@bbiradio.net
W: http://www.1270kinn.net
Editorial Profile: KINN-AM is a commercial station owned by Burt Broadcasting Inc. The format of the station is talk. KINN-AM broadcasts to the Albuquerque, NM area at 1270 AM.

KINT-FM

Owner: Entravision Communications Corp.
Editorial: 5426 N Mesa St, El Paso, Texas 79912-5421. **T:** 1 915 581-1126
W: http://www.jose939.com
Editorial Profile: KINT-FM is a commercial station owned by Entravision Communications Corp. The format of the station is Regional Mexican. KINT-FM broadcasts to the El Paso, TX, area at 93.9 FM.

KINX-FM

Owner: Fisher Communications, Inc.
Editorial: 1300 Central Ave, Great Falls, Montana 59401-3834. **T:** 1 406 761-2800
W: http://www.kinx1027.com
Editorial Profile: KINX-FM is a commercial station owned by the Fisher Communications, Inc. The format of the station is news and talk. The station airs locally at 102.7 FM.

KINY-AM

Owner: Alaska-Juneau Communications
Editorial: 3161 Channel Dr, Juneau, Alaska 99801-7865. **T:** 1 907 586-3630
E: news@abcstations.com
W: http://www.kinyradio.com
Editorial Profile: KINY-AM is a commercial station owned by Alaska-Juneau Communications. The station's primary format is news/talk/sports. The station airs adult contemporary music programming weekday evenings, Saturday evenings. Sunday mornings feature jazz and blues music. KINY-AM broadcasts to the Juneau, AK area at 800 AM.

KINZ-FM

Owner: My Town Media, Inc.
Editorial: 702 N Plummer Ave, Chanute, Kansas 66720-1463. **T:** 1 620 431-3700
W: http://www.kinz.biz
Editorial Profile: KINZ-FM is a commercial station owned by My Town Media, Inc. The format of the station is classic rock music. KINZ-FM broadcasts to the Chanute, KS area at 95.3 FM.

KIOA-FM

Owner: Saga Communications
Editorial: 1416 Locust St, Des Moines, Iowa 50309. **T:** 1 515 280-1350 **E:** news@kioa.com
W: http://www.kioa.com
Editorial Profile: KIOA-FM is a commercial station owned by Saga Communications. The format of the station is oldies music. KIOA-FM broadcasts to the Des Moines, IA area at 93.3 FM.

KIOC-FM

Owner: Clear Channel Media and Entertainment
Editorial: 2885 IH-10 East, Beaumont, Texas 77702. **T:** 1 409 896-5555
W: http://www.bigdog106.com
Editorial Profile: KIOC-FM is a commercial station owned by Clear Channel Media and Entertainment. The format of the station is rock. KIOC-FM broadcasts to the Beaumont, TX area at 106.1 FM.

KIOD-FM

Owner: GI Family Radio
Editorial: 106 W 8th St, McCook, Nebraska 69001. **T:** 1 308 345-1981
W: http://www.coyote105.com
Editorial Profile: KIOD-FM is a commercial station owned by GI Family Radio. The format of the station is country. KIOD-FM broadcasts to the McCook, NE area at 105.3 FM.

KIOI-FM

Owner: Clear Channel Media and Entertainment
Editorial: 340 Townsend St, San Francisco, California 94107-1633. **T:** 1 415 538-1013
W: http://www.1013.com
Editorial Profile: KIOI-FM is a commercial station owned by Clear Channel Media and Entertainment. The format of the station is hot adult contemporary. KIOI-FM broadcasts to the San Francisco area at 101.3 FM.

KIOK-FM

Owner: Ingstad Radio Washington, LLC
Editorial: 4304 W 24Th Ave Suite 200, Kennewick, Washington 99338-2320.
T: 1 509 783-0783
W: http://www.949thewolfpack.com
Editorial Profile: KIOK-FM is a commercial station owned by Ingstad Radio Washington, LLC. The format of the station is classic and contemporary country. KIOK-FM broadcasts to the Kennewick, WA area at 94.9 FM.

KIOL-AM

Owner: Iola Broadcasting Inc.
Editorial: 2221 S State St, Iola, Kansas 66749.
T: 1 620 365-3151
E: radiostation@iolaradio.com
W: http://www.iolaradio.com
Editorial Profile: KIOL-AM is a commercial station owned by Iola Broadcasting Inc. The format of the station is talk. KIOL-AM broadcasts to the Iola, KS area at 1370 AM.

KION-AM

Owner: Clear Channel Media and Entertainment
Editorial: 903 N Main St, Salinas, California 93906. **T:** 1 831 755-8181
W: http://www.1460kion.com
Editorial Profile: KION-AM is a commercial station owned by Clear Channel Media and Entertainment. The format for the station is news and talk. KION-AM broadcasts to the Salinas, CA area at 1460 AM.

KIOO-FM

Owner: Momentum Broadcasting LP
Editorial: 617 W Tulare Ave, Visalia, California 93277-2552. **T:** 1 559 553-1500
W: http://www.997classicrock.com
Editorial Profile: KIOO-FM is a commercial station owned by Momentum Broadcasting LP. The format of the station is classic rock. KIOO-FM broadcasts to the Visalia, CA area at 99.7 FM.

KIOS-FM

Owner: Omaha Public Schools
Editorial: 3230 Burt St, Omaha, Nebraska 68131-2014. **T:** 1 402 557-2777
E: news@kios.org **W:** http://www.kios.org
Editorial Profile: KIOS-FM is a non-commercial station owned by Omaha Public Schools. The format of the station is news and jazz music. KIOS-FM broadcasts to the Omaha, NE area at 91.5 FM.

KIOT-FM

Owner: Univision Communications Inc.
Editorial: 8009 Marble Ave NE, Albuquerque, New Mexico 87110. **T:** 1 505 262-1142
W: http://www.univision.com
Editorial Profile: KIOT-FM is a commercial station owned by Univision Communications Inc. The format of the station is classic rock music. KIOT-FM broadcasts to the Albuquerque, NM area at 102.5 FM.

KIOU-AM

Owner: Capital City Radio Corp.
Editorial: 2438 E Texas St Ste 7, Bossier City, Louisiana 71111-3737. **T:** 1 318 752-2115

KIOW-FM

Owner: Pilot Knob Broadcasting Inc.
Editorial: 18643 360th St, Forest City, Iowa 50436. **T:** 1 641 585-1073 **E:** kiow@kiow.com
W: http://www.kiow.com
Editorial Profile: KIOW-FM is a commercial station owned by Pilot Knob Broadcasting Inc. The format of the station is variety. KIOW-FM broadcasts to the Forest City, IA area at 107.3 FM.

KIOZ-FM

Owner: Clear Channel Media and Entertainment
Editorial: 9660 Granite Ridge Dr, Ste 100, San Diego, California 92123. **T:** 1 858 292-2000
W: http://www.rock1053.com
Editorial Profile: KIOZ-FM is a commercial station owned by Clear Channel Media and Entertainment. The format of the station is rock. KIOZ-FM broadcasts to the San Diego area at 105.3 FM.

KIPA-AM

Owner: Resonate Hawaii, LLC
Editorial: 688 Kinoole St, Hilo, Hawaii 96720-3877. **T:** 1 808 959-5700
Editorial Profile: KIPA-AM is a commercial station owned by Resonate Hawaii, LLC. The format for the station is news and talk. KIPA-AM broadcasts to the Hilo area at 1060 AM.

KIPO-FM
Owner: Hawaii Public Radio
Editorial: 738 Kaheka St, Ste 101, Honolulu, Hawaii 96814-3726. **T:** 1 808 955-8821
E: admin@hawaiipublicradio.org
W: http://www.hawaiipublicradio.org
Editorial Profile: KIPO-FM is a non-commercial station owned by Hawaii Public Radio. The format of the station is jazz and news. KIPO-FM broadcasts to the Honolulu area at 89.3 FM.

KIPR-FM
Owner: Cumulus Media Inc
Editorial: 700 Wellington Hills Rd, Little Rock, Arkansas 72211-2026. **T:** 1 501 401-0200
W: http://www.power923.com
Editorial Profile: KIPR-FM is a commercial station owned by Cumulus Media Inc. The format of the station is urban contemporary music. KIPR-FM broadcasts to the Little Rock, AR area at 92.3 AM.

KIQI-AM
Owner: Multicultural Radio Broadcasting Inc.
Editorial: 44 Gough St Ste 301, San Francisco, California 94103-5424.
T: 1 415 978-5378 **E:** kiqi1010@gmail.com
W: http://www.kiqi1010am.com
Editorial Profile: KIQI-AM is a commercial station owned by Multicultural Radio Broadcasting Inc. The format of the station is Hispanic news and talk. KIQI-AM broadcasts to the San Francisco area at 1010 AM.

KIQK-FM
Owner: Haugo Broadcasting Inc.
Editorial: 3601 Canyon Lake Dr Ste 1, Rapid City, South Dakota 57702-3901.
T: 1 605 343-0888
E: news@haugobroadcasting.com
W: http://www.kick104.com
Editorial Profile: KIQK-FM is a commercial station owned by Haugo Broadcasting Inc. The format of the station is country. KIQK-FM broadcasts to the Rapid City, SD area at 104.1 FM.

KIQO-FM
Owner: American General Media
Editorial: 3620 Sacramento Dr, San Luis Obispo, California 93401-7215.
T: 1 805 781-2750
E: news@americangeneralmedia.com
W: http://www.thenewq1045.com
Editorial Profile: KIQO-FM is a commercial station owned by American General Media. The format of the station is oldies. KIQO-FM broadcasts to the San Luis Obispo, CA area at 104.5 FM.

KIQQ-AM
Owner: Casa Media Partners, LLC
Editorial: 710 W Old Hwy 58, Barstow, California 92311. **T:** 1 213 745-6224
W: http://www.lamaquinamusical.net
Editorial Profile: KIQQ-AM is a commercial station owned by Casa Media Partners, LLC. The format of the station is Hispanic music. KIQQ-AM broadcasts to the Barstow, CA area at 1310 AM.

KIQQ-FM
Owner: Casa Media Partners, LLC
Editorial: 710 W Old Hwy 58, Barstow, California 92311. **T:** 1 213 745-6224
W: http://www.lamaquinamusical.net
Editorial Profile: KIQQ-FM is a commercial station owned by Casa Media Partners, LLC. The format of the station is Hispanic music. The station airs locally to the Newberry Springs, CA area at 103.7 FM.

KIQX-FM
Owner: Four Corners Broadcasting LLC
Editorial: 190 Turner Dr, Durango, Colorado 81303-8231. **T:** 1 970 259-4444
E: fcb@frontier.net
Editorial Profile: KIQX-FM is a commercial station owned by Four Corners Broadcasting LLC. The format of the station is adult contemporary music. KIQX-FM broadcasts to the Durango, CO area at 101.3 FM.

KIRC-FM
Owner: One Ten Broadcasting Group Inc.
Editorial: 2 E Main St, Shawnee, Oklahoma 74801. **T:** 1 405 878-1803
E: kirc1059@aol.com
Editorial Profile: KIRC-FM is a commercial station owned by One Ten Broadcasting Group Inc. The format of the station is classic country music. KIRC-FM broadcasts to the Shawnee, OK area at 105.9 FM.

KIRK-FM
Owner: Moberly/Macon License Co., LLC
Editorial: 300 W Reed St, Moberly, Missouri 65270. **T:** 1 660 263-1500
E: kresnews@regionalradio.com
W: http://www.centralmoinfo.com
Editorial Profile: KIRK-FM is a commercial station owned by Moberly/Macon License Co., LLC. The format of the station is Classic Hits. KIRK-FM broadcasts to the Moberly, MO area at 99.9 FM.

KIRN-AM
Owner: Lotus Communications Corp.
Editorial: 3301 Barham Blvd Ste 300, Los Angeles, California 90068-1477.
T: 1 323 851-5476
W: http://www.lotuscorp.com
Editorial Profile: KIRN-AM is a commercial station owned by Lotus Communications Corp. The format of the station is Iranian music and talk. The station broadcasts to the Los Angeles area at 670 AM.

KIRO-AM
Owner: Bonneville International Corp.
Editorial: 1820 Eastlake Ave E, Seattle, Washington 98102-3711. **T:** 1 206 726-7000
W: http://mynorthwest.com/category/sports
Editorial Profile: KIRO-AM is a commercial station owned by Bonneville International Corp. The format of the station is sports. KIRO-AM broadcasts to the Seattle area at 710 AM.

KIRO-FM
Owner: Bonneville International Corp.
Editorial: 1820 Eastlake Ave E, Seattle, Washington 98102-3711. **T:** 1 206 726-7000
E: newsdesk@973kiro.com
W: http://www.kiroradio.com
Editorial Profile: KIRO-FM is a commercial station owned by Bonneville International Corp. The format of the station is news and talk. KIRO-FM broadcasts to the Seattle area at 97.3 FM.

KIRQ-FM
Owner: Locally Owned Radio, LLC
Editorial: 21361 Highway 30, Twin Falls, Idaho 83301. **T:** 1 208 735-8300
W: http://www.irock1021.com
Editorial Profile: KIRQ-FM is a commercial station owned by Locally Owned Radio, LLC. The format for the station is rock alternative. KIRQ-FM broadcasts to the Twin Falls, ID area at 102.1 FM.

KIRV-AM
Owner: Centro Cristiano Vida Abundante, Inc.
Editorial: 121 W Alvin Ave, Santa Maria, California 93458-3002. **T:** 1 805 406-9157
W: http://www.radiovidaabundante.com
Editorial Profile: KIRV-AM is a non-commercial station owned by Centro Cristiano Vida Abundante, Inc. The format for the station is Spanish religious programming. KIRV-AM broadcasts to the Fresno, CA area at 1510 AM.

KIRX-AM
Owner: KIRX Inc.
Editorial: 1308 N Baltimore St, Kirksville, Missouri 63501. **T:** 1 660 665-3781
E: kirx@cableone.net
W: http://www.1450kirx.com
Editorial Profile: KIRX-AM is a commercial station owned by KIRX Inc. The format for the station is news, talk and oldies. KIRX-AM broadcasts to the Kirksville, MO area at 1450 AM.

KISC-FM
Owner: Clear Channel Media and Entertainment
Editorial: 808 E Sprague Ave, Spokane, Washington 99202-2126. **T:** 1 509 242-2400
W: http://www.literockkiss.com
Editorial Profile: KISC-FM is a commercial station owned by Clear Channel Media and Entertainment. The format of the station is Lite Rock/Lite AC. KISC-FM broadcasts to the Spokane, WA area at 98.1 FM.

KISD-FM
Owner: Christensen Broadcasting
Editorial: 608 State Highway 30, Pipestone, Minnesota 56164. **T:** 1 507 825-4282
E: kisd@kisdradio.com
W: http://www.kisdradio.com/kisd
Editorial Profile: KISD-FM is a commercial station owned by Christensen Broadcasting. The format of the station is oldies. KISD-FM broadcasts to the Pipestone, MN area at 98.7 FM.

KISF-FM
Owner: Univision Communications Inc.
Editorial: 6767 W Tropicana Ave, Ste 102, Las Vegas, Nevada 89103-4755.
T: 1 702 284-6400
W: http://www.univision.com
Editorial Profile: KISF-FM is a commercial station owned by Univision Communications Inc. The format of the station is regional Mexican. KISF-FM broadcasts to the Las Vegas area at 103.5 FM.

KISL-FM
Owner: Catalina Island Performing Arts Foundation
Editorial: 707 Crescent Ave, Avalon, California 90704. **T:** 1 310 510-7469
E: kisl887@gmail.com **W:** http://www.kisl.org

KISM-FM
Owner: Saga Communications
Editorial: 2219 Yew Street Rd, Bellingham, Washington 98229-8855. **T:** 1 360 734-9790
E: kism@kism.com **W:** http://www.kism.com
Editorial Profile: KISM-FM is a commercial station owned by Saga Communications. The format of the station is classic rock. KISM-FM broadcasts to the Bellingham, WA area at 92.9 FM.

KISN-FM
Owner: Townsquare Media, LLC
Editorial: 125 W Mendenhall St Ste 1, Bozeman, Montana 59715-3500.
T: 1 406 586-2343
W: http://bozemanskissfm.com
Editorial Profile: KISN-FM is a commercial station owned by Townsquare Media, LLC. The format of the station is Top 40/CHR music. KISN-FM broadcasts to the Bozeman, MT area at 96.7 FM.

KISO-FM
Owner: Clear Channel Media and Entertainment
Editorial: 5010 Underwood Ave, Omaha, Nebraska 68132-2236. **T:** 1 402 561-2000
W: http://www.961kissonline.com
Editorial Profile: KISO-FM is a commercial station owned by Clear Channel Media and Entertainment. The format of the station is top 40/CHR. KISO-FM broadcasts to the Omaha, NE area at 96.1 FM.

KISQ-FM
Owner: Clear Channel Media and Entertainment
Editorial: 340 Townsend St, San Francisco, California 94107. **T:** 1 415 538-1013
E: kisslistenerservices@clearchannel.com
W: http://www.981kissfm.com
Editorial Profile: KISQ-FM is a commercial station owned by Clear Channel Media and Entertainment. The format of the station is R&B oldies music. KISQ-FM broadcasts to the San Francisco area at 98.1 FM.

KISR-FM
Owner: Baker Broadcasting
Editorial: 5111 Rogers Ave Ste 650, Fort Smith, Arkansas 72903-2096.
T: 1 479 785-2526 **E:** production@kisr.net
W: http://www.kisr.net
Editorial Profile: KISR-FM is a commercial station owned by Baker Broadcasting. The format of the station is Top 40/CHR music. KISR-FM broadcasts to the Fort Smith, AR area at 93.7 FM.

KISS-FM
Owner: Cox Media Group, Inc.
Editorial: 8122 Datapoint Dr Ste 600, San Antonio, Texas 78229-3446.
T: 1 210 615-5400
W: http://www.kissrocks.com
Editorial Profile: KISS-FM is a commercial station owned by Cox Media Group, Inc. The format of the station is rock/album-oriented rock. KISS-FM broadcasts to the San Antonio area at 99.5 FM.

KIST-FM
Owner: Rincon Broadcasting
Editorial: 414 E Cota St, Santa Barbara, California 93101. **T:** 1 805 879-8300
W: http://www.radiobronco.com
Editorial Profile: KIST-FM is a commercial station owned by Rincon Broadcasting. The format of the station is regional Mexican. KIST-FM broadcasts to the Santa Barbara, CA area at 107.7 FM.

KISU-FM
Owner: Idaho State University
Editorial: 921 S 8Th Ave, Mail Stop 8014, Pocatello, Idaho 83209-0001.
T: 1 208 282-3691 **E:** kisu91@gmail.com
W: http://www.kisu.org
Editorial Profile: KISU-FM is a non-commercial station owned by Idaho State University. The format of the station is variety. KISU-FM broadcasts to the Idaho Falls, ID area at 91.1 FM.

KISV-FM
Owner: American General Media
Editorial: 1400 Easton Dr, Ste 144B, Bakersfield, California 93309-9412.
T: 1 661 328-1410 **E:** news@kernradio.com
W: http://www.hot941.com
Editorial Profile: KISV-FM is a commercial station owned by American General Media. The format of the station is urban contemporary. KISV-FM broadcasts to the Bakersfield, CA area at 94.1 FM.

KISW-FM
Owner: Entercom Communications Corp.
Editorial: 1100 Olive Way, Ste 1650, Seattle, Washington 98101. **T:** 1 206 233-1037
E: hairclub@kisw.com **W:** http://www.kisw.com
Editorial Profile: KISW-FM is a commercial station owned by Entercom Communications Corp. The format of the station is rock and rock alternative music. KISW-FM broadcasts to the Seattle area at 99.9 FM.

KISX-FM
Owner: Townsquare Media, LLC
Editorial: 3810 Brookside Dr, Tyler, Texas 75701. **T:** 1 903 581-0606
W: http://www.hot1073jamz.com
Editorial Profile: KISX-FM is a commercial station owned by Townsquare Media, LLC. The format of the station is urban adult contemporary music. KISX-FM broadcasts in the Tyler, TX, area at 107.3 FM.

KISZ-FM
Owner: American General Media
Editorial: 212 W Apache St, Farmington, New Mexico 87401-6235. **T:** 1 505 327-4449
W: http://www.kisscountry.net
Editorial Profile: KISZ-FM is a commercial station owned by American General Media. The format of the station is country music. KISZ-FM broadcasts to the Albuquerque, NM area at 97.9 FM.

KIT-AM
Owner: Townsquare Media, LLC
Editorial: 4010 Summitview Ave, Ste 200, Yakima, Washington 98908.
T: 1 509 972-3461
W: http://www.1280kitam.com
Editorial Profile: KIT-AM is a commercial station owned by Townsquare Media, LLC. The format of the station is news, sports and talk. KIT-AM broadcasts to the Yakima, WA area at 1280 AM.

KITE-FM
Owner: Victoria RadioWorks Inc.
Editorial: 3613 N Main St, Victoria, Texas 77901. **T:** 1 361 576-6111
E: vrw@suddenlinkmail.com

KITG-FM
Owner: Calvary Chapel of Joplin
Editorial: 4899 E 7th St, Joplin, Missouri 64801-8730. **T:** 1 417 553-0474
W: http://www.kitgradio.com
Editorial Profile: KITG-FM is a non-commercial station owned by Calvary Chapel of Joplin. The format of the station is Christian music and religious teaching. KITG-FM broadcasts to the Sarcoxie, MO area at 89.5 FM.

KITH-FM
Owner: Hochman Hawaii Four, Inc.
Editorial: 4334 Rice St, Ste 206, Lihue, Hawaii 96766-1801. **T:** 1 808 246-4444
W: http://www.hhawaiimedia.com
Editorial Profile: KITH-FM is a commercial station owned by Hochman Hawaii Four, Inc. The format of the station is Island music. KITH-FM broadcasts to the Kauai, HI area at 98.9 FM.

KITI-AM
Owner: Premier Broadcasters, Inc.
Editorial: 1133 Kresky Ave, Centralia, Washington 98531-3773. **T:** 1 360 736-1355
E: newsroom@live95.com
W: http://www.1420kiti.com
Editorial Profile: KITI-AM is a commercial station owned by Premier Broadcasters, Inc. The format of the station is oldies and classic hits music. KITI-AM broadcasts to the Centralia, WA area at 1420 AM.

KITI-FM
Owner: Premier Broadcasters, Inc.

Editorial: 1133 Kresky Ave, Centralia, Washington 98531-3773. **T:** 1 360 736-1355
E: newsroom@live95.com
W: http://www.live95.com
Editorial Profile: KITI-FM is a commercial station owned by Premier Broadcasters, Inc. The format of the station is hot adult contemporary and Top 40. KITI-FM broadcasts to the Centralia, WA area at 95.1 FM.

KITN-FM
Owner: Absolute Communications (dba Radio Werks)
Editorial: 28779 County Highway 35, Worthington, Minnesota 56187.
T: 1 507 372-4829 **E:** info@myradioworks.net
W: http://rockitfm.com
Editorial Profile: KITN-FM is a commercial station owned by Absolute Communications (dba Radio Werks). The format of the station is Classic Rock. KITN-FM broadcasts to the Worthington, MN area at 93.5 FM.

KITO-FM
Owner: Stephens Media Group
Editorial: 2448 E 81st St Ste 5500, Tulsa, Oklahoma 74137-4201. **T:** 1 918 492-2660
E: onair@sportsanimalradio.com
W: http://sportsanimalradio.com
Editorial Profile: KITO-FM is a commercial station owned by Stephens Media Group. The format of the station is sports. KITO-FM broadcasts to the Vinita, OK area at 96.1 FM.

KITS-FM
Owner: CBS Radio
Editorial: 865 Battery St, San Francisco, California 94111-1503. **T:** 1 415 402-6700
W: http://www.live105.com
Editorial Profile: KITS-FM is a commercial station owned by CBS Radio. The format of the station is rock alternative. KITS-FM broadcasts to the San Francisco area at 105.3 FM.

KITX-FM
Owner: Payne Radio Group
Editorial: 1600 W Jackson St, Hugo, Oklahoma 74743. **T:** 1 580 326-2555
E: k955@neto.com **W:** http://www.k955.com
Editorial Profile: KITX-FM is a commercial station owned by Payne Radio Group. The format of the station is country music. KITX-FM broadcasts in the Hugo, OK area at 95.5 FM.

KITZ-AM
Owner: KITZ Radio, Inc.
Editorial: 1700 SE Mile Hill Dr, Ste 243, Port Orchard, Washington 98366.
T: 1 360 876-1400 **E:** info@kitz1400.com
W: http://www.kitz1400.com
Editorial Profile: KITZ-AM is a commercial station owned by KITZ Radio, Inc. The format of the station is business talk and sports. KITZ-AM broadcasts to the Port Orchard, WA area at 1400 AM.

KIUL-AM
Owner: Steckline Communications
Editorial: 609 E Kansas Plz, Garden City, Kansas 67846-5767. **T:** 1 620 276-3251
W: http://www.kiulradio.com
Editorial Profile: KIUL-AM is a commercial station owned by Steckline Communications. The format of the station is news, sports and talk. KIUL-AM broadcasts to Garden City, KS area at 1240 AM.

KIUN-AM
Owner: Pecos Radio Co, Inc.
Editorial: 316 S Cedar St, Pecos, Texas 79772-3211. **T:** 1 432 445-2498
E: kiun@valornet.com
W: http://www.98xfm.com
Editorial Profile: KIUN-AM is a commercial station owned by Pat Parker. The format of the station is Hispanic and classic country. KIUN-AM broadcasts to the Pecos, TX area at 1400 AM.

KIUP-AM
Owner: Four Corners Broadcasting LLC
Editorial: 190 Turner Dr, Unit G, Durango, Colorado 81303-8231. **T:** 1 970 259-4444
E: news@radiodurango.com
W: http://www.radiodurango.com
Editorial Profile: KIUP-AM is a commercial station owned by Four Corners Broadcasting LLC. The format of the station is sports. KIUP-AM broadcasts to the Durango, CO area at 930 AM.

KIVA-AM
Owner: Vanguard Media, LLC
Editorial: 1213 San Pedro Dr NE, Albuquerque, New Mexico 87110-6725.
T: 1 505 899-5029
Editorial Profile: KIVA-AM is a commercial station owned by Vanguard Media, LLC. The format of the station is oldies. KIVA-AM broadcasts to the Albuquerque, NM area at 1600 AM.

KIVY-AM
Owner: Hunt Broadcasting
Editorial: 102 S 5th St, Crockett, Texas 75835.
T: 1 936 544-2171 **E:** spots@kivy.com
W: http://www.kivy.com
Editorial Profile: KIVY-AM is a commercial station owned by Hunt Broadcasting. The format of the station is adult standards, news and talk. KIVY-AM broadcasts to the Crockett, TX area at 1290 AM.

KIVY-FM
Owner: Hunt Broadcasting
Editorial: 102 S 5th St, Crockett, Texas 75835.
T: 1 936 544-2171 **E:** spots@kivy.com
W: http://www.kivy.com
Editorial Profile: KIVY-FM is a commercial station owned by Hunt Broadcasting. The format of the station is country music. KIVY-FM broadcasts to the Crockett, TX area at 92.7 FM.

KIWA-AM
Owner: Sheldon Broadcasting Co. Inc.
Editorial: 411 9th St, Sheldon, Iowa 51201.
T: 1 712 324-2597
E: newstips@kiwaradio.com
W: http://www.kiwaradio.com
Editorial Profile: KIWA-AM is a commercial station owned by Sheldon Broadcasting Co. Inc. The format of the station is country. KIWA-AM broadcasts to the Sheldon, IA area at 1550 AM.

KIWA-FM
Owner: Sheldon Broadcasting Co. Inc.
Editorial: 411 9th St, Sheldon, Iowa 51201.
T: 1 712 324-2597
E: newstips@kiwaradio.com
W: http://www.kiwa-fm.com
Editorial Profile: KIWA-FM is a commercial station owned by Sheldon Broadcasting Co. Inc. The format of the station is classic rock. KIWA-FM broadcasts to the Sheldon, IA area at 105.3 FM.

KIWI-FM
Owner: Lotus Communications Corp.
Editorial: 5100 Commerce Dr, Bakersfield, California 93309. **T:** 1 661 327-9711
W: http://www.radiolobo.com
Editorial Profile: KIWI-FM is a commercial station owned by Lotus Communications Corp. The format of the station is Hispanic programming. KIWI-FM broadcasts to the Bakersfield, CA area at 102.9 FM.

KIWR-FM
Owner: Iowa Western Community College
Editorial: 2700 College Rd, Council Bluffs, Iowa 51503. **T:** 1 712 325-3254
E: 897theriver@iwcc.edu
W: http://www.897theriver.com
Editorial Profile: KIWR-FM is a non-commercial station owned by Iowa Western Community College. The format of the station is rock alternative. KIWR-FM broadcasts to the Omaha, NE area at 89.7 FM.

KIXA-FM
Owner: El Dorado Broadcasting
Editorial: 12370 Hesperia Rd, Ste 16, Victorville, California 92395.
T: 1 760 241-1313
W: http://www.thefox1065.com
Editorial Profile: KIXA-FM is a commercial station owned by El Dorado Broadcasting. The format of the station is classic rock. KIXA-FM broadcasts to Victorville, CA area at 106.5 FM.

KIXB-FM
Owner: Noalmark Broadcasting Corp.
Editorial: 2525 N West Ave, El Dorado, Arkansas 71730. **T:** 1 870 863-6126
E: newsroom@totalradio.us
W: http://www.kix1033.com
Editorial Profile: KIXB-FM is a commercial station owned by Noalmark Broadcasting Corp. The format of the station is classic country. KIXB-FM broadcasts to the El Dorado, AR area at 103.3 FM.

KIXF-FM
Owner: Highway Radio Inc.
Editorial: 1611 E Main St, Barstow, California 92311. **T:** 1 760 256-0326
E: highwayradio@highwayradio.com
W: http://www.highwaycountry.com
Editorial Profile: KIXF-FM is a commercial station owned by Highway Radio Inc. The format of the station is country music. KIXF-FM broadcasts to the Baker, CA area at 101.5 FM.

KIXI-AM
Owner: Hubbard Radio, LLC
Editorial: 3650 131st Ave SE Ste 550, Bellevue, Washington 98006-1334.
T: 1 425 562-8964 **E:** info@kixi.com
W: http://www.kixi.com
Editorial Profile: KIXI-AM is a commercial station owned by Hubbard Radio, LLC. The format of the station is adult standards. KIXI-AM broadcasts to the Bellevue, WA area at 880 AM.

KIXL-AM
Owner: Starboard Media Foundation Inc.
Editorial: 11615 Angus Rd Ste 102, Austin, Texas 78759-4064. **T:** 1 920 884-1460
E: info@relevantradio.com
W: http://www.relevantradio970.com
Editorial Profile: KIXL-AM is a non-commercial station owned by Starboard Media Foundation Inc. The format of the station is religious talk. KIXL-AM broadcasts to the Austin, TX area at 970 AM.

KIXN-FM
Owner: Noalmark Broadcasting Corp.
Editorial: 619 N Turner St, Hobbs, New Mexico 88240-8232. **T:** 1 575 397-4969
E: mail@1radiosquare.com
W: http://www.1radiosquare.com
Editorial Profile: KIXN-FM is a commercial station owned by Noalmark Broadcasting Corp. The format of the station is country. KIXN-FM broadcasts to the Hobbs, NM area at 102.9 FM.

KIXO-FM
Owner: DFWU Inc.
Editorial: 1101 N Broadway St, Marlow, Oklahoma 73055. **T:** 1 580 658-9292
E: kfxi92@att.net
Editorial Profile: KIXO-FM is a commercial station owned by DFWU Inc. The format of the station is country music. KIXO-FM broadcasts to the Marlow, OK area at 106.1 FM.

KIXQ-FM
Owner: Zimmer Radio Group
Editorial: 2702 E 32nd St, Joplin, Missouri 64804. **T:** 1 417 624-1025
W: http://www.kix1025.com
Editorial Profile: KIXQ-FM is a commercial station owned by Zimmer Radio Group. The format of the station is country music. KIXQ-FM broadcasts to the Joplin, MO area at 102.5 FM.

KIXS-FM
Owner: Townsquare Media, LLC
Editorial: 107 N Star Dr, Victoria, Texas 77904. **T:** 1 361 573-0777
W: http://www.kixs.com
Editorial Profile: KIXS-FM is a commercial station owned by Townsquare Media, LLC. The format for the station is contemporary country. KIXS-FM broadcasts to the Victoria, TX area at 107.9 FM.

KIXT-FM
Owner: Prophecy Media Group, LLC (dba Waco Entertainment Group, LLC)
Editorial: 6401 Cobbs Dr, Waco, Texas 76710-2536. **T:** 1 254 772-6104
Editorial Profile: KIXT-FM is a commercial station owned by Prophecy Media Group, LLC (dba Waco Entertainment Group, LLC). The format of the station is contemporary country. KIXT-FM broadcasts to the Waco, TX area at a frequency of 106.7 FM.

KIXV-FM
Owner: Noalmark Broadcasting Corp.
Editorial: 208 Buena Vista Rd, Hot Springs, Arkansas 71913-8208. **T:** 1 501 525-4600
E: spots@klaz.com
Editorial Profile: KIXV-FM is a commercial station owned by Noalmark Broadcasting Corp. The format of the station is rock. KIXV-FM broadcasts to the Hot Springs, AR area at 93.5 FM.

KIXW-AM
Owner: El Dorado Broadcasting
Editorial: 12370 Hesperia Rd, Ste 16, Victorville, California 92395.
T: 1 760 241-1313 **W:** http://www.talk960.com
Editorial Profile: KIXW-AM is a commercial station owned by El Dorado Broadcasting. The format of the station is talk. KIXW-AM broadcasts to Victorville, CA area at 960 AM.

KIXW-FM
Owner: Highway Radio Inc.
Editorial: 1611 E Main St, Barstow, California 92311. **T:** 1 760 256-0326
E: highwayradio@highwayradio.com
W: http://www.highwaycountry.com
Editorial Profile: KIXW-FM is a commercial station owned by Highway Radio Inc. The format of the station is country music. KIXW-FM broadcasts to the Barstow, CA area at 107.3 FM.

KIXX-FM
Owner: Three Eagles Communications Co.
Editorial: 921 9Th Ave Se, Watertown, South Dakota 57201-4960. **T:** 1 605 886-9696
E: kwatnews@watertown.threeeagles.com
W: http://www.96kixx.com
Editorial Profile: KIXX-FM is a commercial station owned by Three Eagles Communications Co. The format of the station is hot adult contemporary. KIXX-FM broadcasts to the Watertown, SD area at 96.1 FM.

KIXY-FM
Owner: Foster Communications Co. Inc.
Editorial: 2824 Sherwood Way, San Angelo, Texas 76901. **T:** 1 325 949-2112
E: advertising@kixyfm.com
W: http://www.kixyfm.com
Editorial Profile: KIXY-FM is commercial station owned by Foster Communications Co. Inc. The format of the station is Top 40/CHR. KIXY-FM broadcasts to the San Angelo, TX area at 94.7 FM.

KIXZ-AM
Owner: Townsquare Media, LLC
Editorial: 6214 W 34th Ave, Amarillo, Texas 79109-4006. **T:** 1 806 355-9777
W: http://www.newsradio940.com
Editorial Profile: KIXZ-AM is a commercial station owned by Townsquare Media, LLC. The format of the station is news and talk. KIXZ-AM broadcasts to the Amarillo, TX area at 940 AM.

KIXZ-FM
Owner: Clear Channel Media and Entertainment
Editorial: 808 E Sprague Ave, Spokane, Washington 99202-2126. **T:** 1 509 242-2400
W: http://www.power961fm.com/main.html
Editorial Profile: KIXZ-FM is a commercial station owned by Clear Channel Media and Entertainment. The format of the station is Country. KIXZ-FM broadcasts to the Spokane, WA area at 96.1 FM.

KIYK-FM
Owner: Cherry Creek Radio
Editorial: 750 Ridgeview Dr, St George, Utah 84770-2665. **T:** 1 435 673-3579
Editorial Profile: KIYK-FM is a commercial station owned by Cherry Creek Radio. The format of the station is hot adult contemporary music. KIYK-FM broadcasts to the St. George, UT area at 107.3 FM.

KIYS-FM
Owner: East Arkansas Broadcasters, Inc
Editorial: 407 W Parker Rd, Jonesboro, Arkansas 72404-8408. **T:** 1 870 934-5000
W: http://www.kissjonesboro.com
Editorial Profile: KIYS-FM is a commercial station owned by East Arkansas Broadcasters, Inc. The format of the station is Top 40/CHR. KRLW-FM broadcasts to the Pocahontas, AR area at 101.7 FM.

KIYU-AM
Owner: Big River Public Broadcasting Corp.
Editorial: 165 Tiger Freeway, Galena, Alaska 99714. **T:** 1 907 656-1488 **E:** raven@kiyu.com
W: http://www.kiyu.com
Editorial Profile: KIYU-AM is a non-commercial station owned by Big River Public Broadcasting Corp. The format of the station is variety. KIYU-AM's target audience is adults, ages 13 to 100, in the Galena, AK area. The station airs locally at 910 AM.

KIYU-FM
Owner: Big River Public Broadcasting Corp.
Editorial: 165 Tiger Freeway, Galena, Alaska 99714. **T:** 1 907 656-1488 **E:** raven@kiyu.com
W: http://www.kiyu.com
Editorial Profile: KIYU-FM is a non-commercial station owned by Big River Public Broadcasting Corp. The format of the station is variety. KIYU-FM broadcasts to the Fairbanks, AK area at 97.1 FM.

KIYX-FM
Owner: Queen B Radio of Wisconsin

Editorial: 51 Means Dr, Platteville, Wisconsin 53818. **T:** 1 608 348-2775
W: http://www.superhits106.com
Editorial Profile: KIYX-FM is a commercial station owned by Queen B Radio of Wisconsin. The format is classic hits.

KIZN-FM
Owner: Cumulus Media Inc
Editorial: 1419 W Bannock St, Boise, Idaho 83702. **T:** 1 208 336-3670 **E:** news@kboi.com
W: http://www.kizn.com
Editorial Profile: KIZN-FM is a commercial station owned by Cumulus Media Inc. The format of the station is contemporary country. KIZN-FM broadcasts to the Boise, ID area at 92.3 FM.

KIZS-FM
Owner: Clear Channel Media and Entertainment
Editorial: 2625 S Memorial Dr, Tulsa, Oklahoma 74129-2601. **T:** 1 918 388-5100
W: http://tulsa.lapreciosa.com
Editorial Profile: KIZS-FM is a commercial station owned by Clear Channel Media and Entertainment. The format of the station is Hispanic oldies. KIZS-FM broadcasts to the Tulsa, OK area at 101.5 FM.

KIZZ-FM
Owner: Clear Channel Media and Entertainment
Editorial: 1000 20th Ave SW, Minot, North Dakota 58701. **T:** 1 701 852-4646
E: minotprod@clearchannel.com
W: http://www.z94radio.com
Editorial Profile: KIZZ-FM is a commercial station owned by Clear Channel Media and Entertainment. The format of the station is Top 40/CHR. KIZZ-FM broadcasts to the Minot-Bismarck, ND area at 93.7 FM.

KJAA-AM
Owner: Taylor (William, D.)
Editorial: 5734 S Mckinney Ave, Globe, Arizona 85501-4361. **T:** 1 928 425-7186
Editorial Profile: KJAA-AM is a commercial station owned by Taylor (William, D.). The format of the station is talk. KJAA-AM broadcasts to the Globe, AZ area at 1240 AM.

KJAB-FM
Owner: Mexico Educational Broadcasting
Editorial: 621 W Monroe St, Mexico, Missouri 65265. **T:** 1 573 581-8606 **E:** kjab@kjab.com
W: http://www.kjab.com
Editorial Profile: KJAB-FM is a non-commercial station owned by Mexico Educational Broadcasting. The format of the station is Christian talk and gospel music. KJAB-FM broadcasts in the Mexico, MO area at 88.3 FM.

KJAC-FM
Owner: Moreland Properties, LLC
Editorial: 10200 E. Girard Ave., Building B, Ste. #150, Denver, Colorado 80231-5591.
T: 1 720 248-4000
W: http://www.denverssportsstation.com
Editorial Profile: KJAC-FM is a commercial station owned by Moreland Properties, LLC. The format of the station is sports. KJAC-FM broadcasts to the Denver area at 105.5 FM.

KJAE-FM
Owner: Pene Broadcasting Inc.
Editorial: 101 Lees Ln, Leesville, Louisiana 71446-3643. **T:** 1 337 239-3402
E: swapshop@kjae935.com
W: http://www.kjae935.com

KJAM-AM
Owner: Three Eagles Communications Co.
Editorial: 101 S Egan Ave, Madison, South Dakota 57042-2841. **T:** 1 605 256-4514
E: kjamnews@madison.threeeagles.com
W: http://www.amazingmadison.com
Editorial Profile: KJAM-AM is a commercial station owned by Three Eagles Communications Co. The format of the station is classic hits. KJAM-FM broadcasts to the Madison, SD area at 1390 AM.

KJAM-FM
Owner: Three Eagles Communications Co.
Editorial: 101 S Egan Ave, Madison, South Dakota 57042-2841. **T:** 1 605 256-4514
E: kjamnews@madison.threeeagles.com
W: http://www.amazingmadison.com
Editorial Profile: KJAM-FM is a commercial station owned by Three Eagles Communications Co. The format of the station is comtemporary country. KJAM-FM broadcasts to the Madison, SD area at 103.1 FM.

KJAN-AM
Owner: Wireless Communications Corp.
Editorial: North Olive St, Atlantic, Iowa 50022.
T: 1 712 243-3920 **E:** kjannews@metc.net
W: http://www.kjan.com
Editorial Profile: KJAN-AM is a commercial station owned by Wireless Communications Corp. The format of the station is adult contemporary. KJAN-AM broadcasts to the Atlantic, IA area at 1220 AM.

KJAQ-FM
Owner: CBS Radio
Editorial: 1000 Dexter Ave N, Ste 100, Seattle, Washington 98109-3577. **T:** 1 206 805-0965
W: http://www.jackseattle.com
Editorial Profile: KJAQ-FM is a commercial station owned by CBS Radio. The format of the station is Jack FM-Adult Hits. KJAQ-FM broadcasts to the Seattle market at 96.5 FM.

KJAS-FM
Owner: Rayburn Broadcasting Co.
Editorial: 765 Hemphill St, Jasper, Texas 75951. **T:** 1 409 384-2626 **E:** sales@kjas.com
W: http://www.kjas.com
Editorial Profile: KJAS-FM is a commercial station owned by Rayburn Broadcasting Co. The format of the station is adult contemporary. KJAS-FM broadcasts to the Jasper, TX area at 107.3 FM.

KJAV-FM
Owner: MBM Radio Del Rio, LLC
Editorial: 1201 N Jackson Rd, McAllen, Texas 78501-5760. **T:** 1 956 992-8895
W: http://www.valleyjack.com
Editorial Profile: KJAV-FM is a commercial station owned by MBM Radio Del Rio, LLC. The format of the station is adult hits. KJAV-FM broadcasts to the McAllen, TX area at 104.9.

KJAX-FM
Owner: Rich Broadcasting, LLC.
Editorial: 1140 West Highway 22, Jackson, Wyoming 83001-9401. **T:** 1 307 733-2120
E: mornings@kjaxfm.com
W: http://www.jacksonholeradio.com
Editorial Profile: KJAX-FM is a commercial station owned by Rich Broadcasting, LLC. The format of the station is classic country. KJAX-FM broadcasts to the Jackson, WY area at 93.3 FM.

KJAY-AM
Owner: Powell(Trudi)
Editorial: 5030 S River Rd, West Sacramento, California 95691. **T:** 1 916 371-5101
Editorial Profile: KJAY-AM is a commercial station owned by Trudi Powell. The format of the station is variety. KJAY-AM broadcasts to the Sacramento, CA area at 1430 AM.

KJBL-FM
Owner: Armada Media Corp.
Editorial: 205 Elm St, Julesburg, Colorado 80737. **T:** 1 970 474-0953
Editorial Profile: KJBL-FM is a commercial station owned by Armada Media Corp. The format of the station is oldies music. KJBL-FM broadcasts to the Julesburg, CO area at 96.5 FM.

KJBN-AM
Owner: Joshua Community Development Corp.
Editorial: 1800 Maple St, North Little Rock, Arkansas 72114. **T:** 1 501 791-1000
W: http://www.kjbn.com
Editorial Profile: KJBN-AM is a commercial station owned by Joshua Community Development Corp. The format of the station is contemporary Christian. KJBN-AM broadcasts to the Little Rock, AR area at 1050 AM.

KJBR-FM
Owner: Educational Media Foundation
Editorial: 6721 W 121st St Ste 100, Overland Park, Kansas 66209-2031. **T:** 1 913 663-9950
W: http://www.air1.com
Editorial Profile: KJBR-FM is a non-commercial station owned by Educational Media Foundation. The format of the station is contemporary Christian. KJBR-FM broadcasts to the Marked Tree, AR area at 93.7 FM.

KJBX-FM
Owner: Saga Communications
Editorial: 314 Union St, Jonesboro, Arkansas 72401. **T:** 1 870 933-8800
W: http://www.themix1067.com
Editorial Profile: KJBX-FM is a commercial station owned by Saga Communications. The format of the station is adult contemporary. KJBX-FM broadcasts to Jonesboro, AR area at 106.7 FM.

KJBZ-FM
Owner: Guerra Enterprises
Editorial: 6402 N Bartlett Ave, Ste 1, Laredo, Texas 78041. **T:** 1 956 726-9393
W: http://z93laredo.com
Editorial Profile: KJBZ-FM is a commercial radio station owned by Guerra Enterprises. The format for the station is Tejano music. KJBZ-FM broadcasts to the Laredo, TX, area at 92.7 FM.

KJCE-AM
Owner: Entercom Communications Corp.
Editorial: 4301 Westbank Dr, 3rd Fl, Austin, Texas 78746. **T:** 1 512 327-9595
W: http://www.talk1370am.com
Editorial Profile: KJCE-AM is a commercial station owned by Entercom Communications Corp. The format of the station is talk. KJCE-AM broadcasts to the Austin, TX area at 1370 AM.

KJCG-FM
Owner: Hi-Line Radio Fellowship
Editorial: 317 1st St, Havre, Montana 59501-3505. **T:** 1 406 265-5845 **E:** info@ynop.org
W: http://www.ynop.org
Editorial Profile: KJCG-FM is a non-commercial station owned by Hi-Line Radio Fellowship. The format of the station is contemporary Christian. The station airs locally at 88.3 FM. KJCG-FM airs KXEI-FM's programming.

KJCK-AM
Owner: Platinum Broadcasting, Inc.
Editorial: 1030 Southwind, Junction City, Kansas 66441. **T:** 1 785 762-5525
E: platinum@kjck.com **W:** http://www.kjck.com
Editorial Profile: KJCK-AM is a commercial station owned by Platinum Broadcasting, Inc. The format of the station is news and talk. KJCK-AM broadcasts to the Junction City, KS area at 1420 AM.

KJCK-FM
Owner: Eagle Communications, Inc.
Editorial: 1030 South Wind, Junction City, Kansas 66441. **T:** 1 785 762-5525
E: powerhits@eagleradio.net
W: http://www.powerhits975.com
Editorial Profile: KJCK-FM is a commercial station owned by Eagle Communications, Inc. The format of the station is Top 40/CHR music. KJCK-FM broadcasts to the Junction City, KS area at 97.5 FM.

KJCR-AM
Owner: Agnus Dei Communications
Editorial: 26 Wyoming Ave, Billings, Montana 59101-1832. **T:** 1 406 294-5250
W: http://www.kjcrradio.com
Editorial Profile: KJCR-AM is a commercial station owned by Agnus Dei Communications. The format of the station is Catholic talk programming. KJCR-AM broadcasts to the Billings, MT area at 1240 AM.

KJCS-FM
Owner: Radio Licensing
Editorial: 1407 N University Dr Ste C, Nacogdoches, Texas 75961-4265.
T: 1 936 564-2900 **E:** info@103thebull.com
W: http://www.103thebull.com
Editorial Profile: KJCS-FM is a commercial station owned by Radio Licensing. The format of the station is classic country. KJCS-FM broadcasts to the Nacogdoches, TX area at 103.3 FM.

KJCU-FM
Owner: Calvary Chapel of Costa Mesa, Inc.
Editorial: 468 S Franklin St, Fort Bragg, California 95437-4803. **T:** 1 707 961-6252
W: http://www.ccfortbragg.com
Editorial Profile: KJCU-FM is a non-commercial station owned by Calvary Chapel of Costa Mesa, Inc. The format of the station is Christian music and religious programming. KJCU-FM broadcasts to the Ft.Bragg, CA area at 89.9 FM.

KJDJ-AM
Owner: Centro Cristiano Vida Abundante, Inc.
Editorial: 121 W Alvin Ave, Santa Maria, California 93458-3002. **T:** 1 805 928-1030
W: http://www.radiovidaabundante.com
Editorial Profile: KJDJ-AM is a non-commercial station owned by Centro Cristiano Vida Abundante, Inc. The format of the station is Spanish religious programming. KJDJ-AM broadcasts to the San Luis Obispo, CA area at a frequency of 1030 AM.

KJDL-AM
Owner: Walker Broadcasting and Communications Inc.
Editorial: 1603 13Th St Ste 210, Lubbock, Texas 79401-3835. **T:** 1 806 744-6864
Editorial Profile: KJDL-AM is a commercial station owned by Walker Broadcasting and Communications Inc. The format of the station is classic country. KJDL-AM broadcasts to the Lubbock, TX area at 1420 AM.

KJDL-FM
Owner: Walker Broadcasting and Communications Inc.
Editorial: 1603 13th St, Lubbock, Texas 79401-3817. **T:** 1 806 744-6864
W: http://www.thereddirtrebel.com
Editorial Profile: KJDL-FM is a commercial station owned by Walker Broadcasting and Communications Inc. The format of the station is country. KJDL-FM broadcasts to the Lubbock, TX area at 105.3 FM.

KJDX-FM
Owner: Sierra Broadcasting Corp.
Editorial: 3015 Johnstonville Rd, Susanville, California 96130. **T:** 1 530 257-2121
E: radioinfo@theradionetwork.com
W: http://www.sierradailynews.com/kjdx.html
Editorial Profile: KJDX-FM is a commercial station owned by Sierra Broadcasting Corp. The format of the station is contemporary country. KJDX-FM broadcasts to the Susanville, CA area at 93.3 FM.

KJDY-AM
Owner: Blue Mountain Broadcasting
Editorial: 413 NW Bridge St, John Day, Oregon 97845. **T:** 1 541 575-1185
E: kjdy@centurytel.net
Editorial Profile: KJDY-AM is a commercial station owned by Blue Mountain Broadcasting. The format of the station is country music. KJDY-AM broadcasts to John Day, OR and the surrounding area on 1400 AM. The station simulcasts on KJDY-FM.

KJDY-FM
Owner: Blue Mountain Broadcasting
Editorial: 413 NW Bridge St, John Day, Oregon 97845. **T:** 1 541 575-1185
E: kjdy@centurytel.net
Editorial Profile: KJDY-FM is a commercial station owned by Blue Mountain Broadcasting. The format for the station is classic and contemporary country. KJDY-FM broadcasts to the John Day, OR area at 94.5 FM.

KJEE-FM
Owner: Evans(James)
Editorial: 302 W Carrillo St, #B, Santa Barbara, California 93101. **T:** 1 805 962-4588
E: kjee929@aol.com **W:** http://www.kjee.com
Editorial Profile: KJEE-FM is a commercial station owned by James Evans. The format of the station is rock alternative. KJEE-FM broadcasts to the Santa Barbara, CA area at 92.9 FM.

KJEF-AM
Owner: Townsquare Media, LLC
Editorial: 900 N Lake Shore Dr, Lake Charles, Louisiana 70601-2120. **T:** 1 337 433-1641
W: http://www.cajunradio.com
Editorial Profile: KJEF-AM is a commercial station owned by Townsquare Media, LLC. The format of the station is cajun and country music. KJEF-AM broadcasts to Lafayette, LA area at 1290 AM.

KJEL-FM
Owner: Goodradio.TV LLC
Editorial: 18553 Gentry Rd, Lebanon, Missouri 65536-5748. **T:** 1 417 532-9111
E: kjel@regionalradio.com
W: http://www.myozarksonline.com
Editorial Profile: KJEL-FM is a commercial station owned by Goodradio.TV LLC. The format of the station is country music. KJEL-FM broadcasts in the Lebanon, MO area at 103.7 FM.

KJET-FM
Owner: Jodesha Broadcasting Inc.
Editorial: 1520 Simpson Ave, Aberdeen, Washington 98520. **T:** 1 360 533-3000
E: news@kbkw.com
W: http://www.1057thejet.com/
Editorial Profile: KJET-FM is a commercial station owned by Jodesha Broadcasting Inc. The format of the station is hot adult contemporary. KJET-FM broadcasts to the Seattle area at 105.7 FM.

KJEZ-FM
Owner: Max Media

Editorial: 1015 W Pine St, Poplar Bluff, Missouri 63901-4839. **T:** 1 573 785-0881
E: z95@riverradio.net
W: http://www.z95thebone.net
Editorial Profile: KJEZ-FM is a commercial station owned by Max Media. The format of the station is rock music. KJEZ-FM broadcasts in the Poplar Bluff, MO area at 94.5 FM.

KJFA-FM
Owner: Univision Communications Inc.
Editorial: 8009 Marble Ave NE, Albuquerque, New Mexico 87110. **T:** 1 505 254-7100
W: http://kjfa.univision.com
Editorial Profile: KJFA-FM is a commercial station owned by Univision Communications Inc. The format of the station is regional Mexican. KKRG-FM broadcasts to the Albuquerque, NM area at 105.1 FM.

KJFF-AM
Owner: Goodradio.TV LLC
Editorial: 1026 Scenic Dr, Festus, Missouri 63028. **T:** 1 636 937-7642
W: http://www.mymoinfo.com
Editorial Profile: KJFF-AM is a commercial station owned by Goodradio.TV LLC. The format of the station is news and talk. KJFF-AM broadcasts to the Festus, MO area at 1400 AM.

KJFM-FM
Owner: Foxfire Communications Inc.
Editorial: 615 Georgia St, Louisiana, Missouri 63353. **T:** 1 573 324-0303
E: kjfmradioeagle102@yahoo.com
W: http://www.kjfmeagle102.net
Editorial Profile: KJFM-FM is a commercial station owned by Foxfire Communications Inc. The format of the station is contemporary country music. KJFM-FM broadcasts to the Louisiana, MO area at 102.1 FM.

KJFX-FM
Owner: Wilks Broadcast Group
Editorial: 1066 E Shaw Ave, Fresno, California 93710. **T:** 1 559 230-0104
W: http://www.957thefox.com
Editorial Profile: KJFX-FM is a commercial station owned by Wilks Broadcast Group. The format of the station is classic rock. KJFX-FM broadcasts to the Fresno, CA area at 95.7 FM.

KJGT-FM
Owner: Jagerita Radio
Editorial: 7575 Corporate Way #B, Eden Prairie, Minnesota 55344-2022
E: news@kjgtfm.org
W: http://kjgtfm.com/Home.html
Editorial Profile: KJGT-FM is a commercial station owned by Jagerita Radio. The format of the station is verity. KJGT-FM broadcasts in the Minneapolis-St. Paul, MN area at 88.3 FM.

KJHK-FM
Owner: University of Kansas
Editorial: 1301 Jayhawk Blvd Rm 472, Lawrence, Kansas 66045-7593.
T: 1 785 864-4745
E: communications@kjhk.org
W: http://www.kjhk.org
Editorial Profile: KJHK-FM is a non-commercial station owned by the University of Kansas. The format of the station is college variety. KJHK-FM broadcasts to the Lawrence, KS area at 90.7 FM.

KJHL-FM
Owner: Great Plains Christian Radio
Editorial: 909 W Carthage, Meade, Kansas 67864. **T:** 1 620 873-2991 **E:** kjil@kjil.com
W: http://www.kjil991.com
Editorial Profile: KJHL-FM is a non-commercial station owned by Great Plains Christian Radio. The format of the station is contemporary Christian music and religious programming. KJHL-FM broadcasts to the Boise City, OK area at 90.9 FM.

KJHM-FM
Owner: Max Media of Colorado
Editorial: 3033 S Parker Rd, Aurora, Colorado 80014-2910. **T:** 1 303 872-1500
W: http://www.jammin1015.com
Editorial Profile: KJHM-FM is a commercial station owned by Max Media of Colorado. The format of the station is rhythmic adult contemporary. KJHM-FM broadcasts to the Aurora, CO area at 101.5 FM.

KJIC-FM
Owner: Community Radio, Inc.
Editorial: 8315 County Road 198, Alvin, Texas 77511. **T:** 1 281 824-1228 **E:** kjic@kjic.org
W: http://www.kjic.org
Editorial Profile: KJIC-FM is a non-commercial station owned by Community Radio, Inc. The format of the station is gospel music. KJIC-FM broadcasts to the Alvin, TX area at 90.5 FM.

KJIL-FM
Owner: Great Plains Christian Radio
Editorial: 909 W Carthage, Meade, Kansas 67864. **T:** 1 620 873-2991 **E:** kjil@kjil.com
W: http://www.kjil991.com
Editorial Profile: KJIL-FM is a non-commercial station owned by Great Plains Christian Radio. The format of the station is contemporary Christian music and religious programming. KJIL-FM broadcasts to the Meade, KS area at 99.1 FM.

KJIM-AM
Owner: Allen Productions(Bob Mark)
Editorial: 4367 Woodlawn Rd, Denison, Texas 75021. **T:** 1 903 893-1197
E: kjim1500am@verizon.net
Editorial Profile: KJIM-AM is a commercial station owned by Bob Mark Allen Productions. The format of the station is adult standards. KJIM-AM broadcasts to the Denison, TX area on 1500 AM.

KJIN-AM
Owner: Sunburst Media-Louisiana, LLC
Editorial: 120 Prevost Dr, Houma, Louisiana 70364-2338. **T:** 1 985 851-1020
Editorial Profile: KJIN-AM is a commercial station owned by Sunburst Media-Louisiana, LLC. The format of the station is sports. KJIN-AM broadcasts to the Houma, LA area at 1490 AM.

KJIR-FM
Owner: Believer's Broadcasting Corp.
Editorial: 220 N 6th St, Quincy, Illinois 62301. **T:** 1 217 221-9410 **E:** thecross@kjir.org
W: http://www.kjir.org

KJIW-FM
Owner: Mondy(Elijah)
Editorial: 204 Moore St, Helena, Arkansas 72342. **T:** 1 870 338-2700
E: news@lordradio.com
W: http://www.kjiwfm.com
Editorial Profile: KJIW-FM is a commercial station owned by Elijah Mondy. The format for the station is Christian and religious programming and gospel music. KJIW-FM broadcasts to the Helena, AR area at 94.5 FM.

KJJD-AM
Owner: Rodriguez-Gallegos Broadcasting Corp.
Editorial: 624 Main St, Longmont, Colorado 80501. **T:** 1 303 651-1199
E: secretaria1170@yahoo.com
W: http://www.laley1170am.com
Editorial Profile: KJJD-AM is a commercial station owned by Rodriguez-Gallegos Broadcasting Corp. The format of the station is Hispanic programming. KJJD-AM broadcasts to the Longmont, CO area at 1170 AM.

KJJJ-FM
Owner: Greeley(Steven M.)
Editorial: 1845 McCulloch Blvd N Ste A14, Lake Havasu City, Arizona 86403-6777.
T: 1 928 855-9336
E: office@myradiocentral.com
W: http://www.kjjjfm.com
Editorial Profile: KJJJ-FM is a commercial station owned by Steven M. Greeley. The format of the station is country. KJJJ-FM broadcasts to Lake Havasu City, AZ at 102.3 FM.

KJJK-AM
Owner: Results Radio Group
Editorial: 728 Western Ave, Fergus Falls, Minnesota 56537-1095. **T:** 1 218 736-7596
E: contactus@lakesradio.net
W: http://family1020.net/family/family.htm
Editorial Profile: KJJK-AM is commercial station owned by Results Radio Group. The format of the station is contemporary Christian. KJJK-AM broadcasts to the Fergus Falls, ND area at 1020 AM.

KJJK-FM
Owner: Results Radio Group
Editorial: 728 Western Ave, Fergus Falls, Minnesota 56537-1095. **T:** 1 218 736-7596
E: contactus@lakesradio.net
W: http://www.lakesradio.net
Editorial Profile: KJJK-FM is a commercial station owned by Results Radio Group. The format of the station is contemporary country music. KJJK-FM broadcasts to the Fergus Falls, ND area at 96.5 FM.

KJJP-FM
Owner: Kanza Society Inc.
Editorial: 104 Sw 6th Ave Suite B-4, Amarillo, Texas 79101-2324. **T:** 1 806 367-9088
E: hppr@hppr.org **W:** http://www.hppr.org
Editorial Profile: KJJP-FM is a non-commercial station owned by Kanza Society Inc. The format of the station is news and classical. KJJP-FM broadcasts to the Amarillo, TX area at 105.7 FM.

KJJQ-AM
Owner: Three Eagles Communications Co.
Editorial: 227 22nd Ave S, Brookings, South Dakota 57006. **T:** 1 605 692-9125
E: kjjqnews@brookings.net
W: http://www.brookingsradio.com
Editorial Profile: KJJQ-AM is a commercial station owned by Three Eagles Communications Co. The format is classic country. The station airs in the Brookings, SD area at 910 AM.

KJJR-AM
Owner: Bee Broadcasting Inc.
Editorial: 2432 US Highway 2 E, Kalispell, Montana 59901. **T:** 1 406 755-8700
E: comments@beebroadcasting.com
W: http://www.beebroadcasting.com
Editorial Profile: KJJR-AM is a commercial station owned by Bee Broadcasting Inc. The format of the station is news and talk. KJJR-AM broadcasts to the Kalispell, MT area at 880 AM.

KJJS-FM
Owner: Hispanic Target Media, Inc.
Editorial: 1524 S Interstate 35, Austin, Texas 78704-8931. **T:** 1 602 283-3293
E: hispanictargetmedia@gmail.com
W: http://www.hispanictargetmedia.info
Editorial Profile: KJJS-FM is a commercial station owned by Hispanic Target Media, Inc. The format of the station is Hispanic music. KJJS-FM broadcasts locally to the Zapata, TX area at a frequency of 103.9 FM.

KJJY-FM
Owner: Cumulus Media Inc
Editorial: 4143 109th St, Urbandale, Iowa 50322. **T:** 1 515 331-9200
W: http://www.kjjy.com
Editorial Profile: KJJY-FM is a commercial station owned by Cumulus Media Inc. The format of the station is country music. KJJY-FM broadcasts to the Des Moines, IA area at 92.5 FM.

KJJZ-FM
Owner: RM Broadcasting LLC
Editorial: 75153 Merle Dr Ste G, Palm Desert, California 92211-5197. **T:** 1 760 568-4550
W: http://www.102kjjz.com
Editorial Profile: KJJZ-FM is a commercial station owned by RM Broadcasting LLC. The format of the station is smooth AC. KJJZ-FM broadcasts to the Palm Springs, CA area at 102.3 FM.

KJKE-FM
Owner: Tyler Media Group Inc.
Editorial: 5101 S Shields Blvd, Oklahoma City, Oklahoma 73129. **T:** 1 405 616-5500
E: jake@jakefm.com
W: http://www.jakefm.com
Editorial Profile: KJKE-FM is a commercial station owned by Tyler Media Group Inc. The format of the station is contemporary country. KJKE-FM broadcasts to the Oklahoma City area at 93.3 FM.

KJKJ-FM
Owner: Clear Channel Media and Entertainment
Editorial: 505 University Ave, Grand Forks, North Dakota 58203-3545. **T:** 1 701 746-1417
W: http://www.kjkj.com
Editorial Profile: KJKJ-FM is a commercial station owned by Clear Channel Media and Entertainment. The format of the station is rock music. KJKJ-FM broadcasts to the Grand Forks, ND area at 107.5 FM.

KJKK-FM
Owner: CBS Radio
Editorial: 4131 N Central Expy, Ste 1000, Dallas, Texas 75204-2121. **T:** 1 214 525-7000
E: jack@jackontheweb.com
W: http://www.jackontheweb.com
Editorial Profile: KJKK-FM is a commercial station owned by CBS Radio. The format of the station is adult hits. KJKK-FM broadcasts to the Dallas area at 100.3 FM. The station has no on air personalities.

KJKS-FM
Owner: Pacific Media Group
Editorial: 311 Ano St, Kahului, Hawaii 96732-1304. **T:** 1 808 877-5566
W: http://www.kissfmmaui.com
Editorial Profile: KJKS-FM is a commercial station owned by Pacific Media Group. The format of the station is adult contemporary. KJKS-FM is licensed to Maui, HI and broadcasts locally at 99.9 FM.

KJLF-FM
Owner: Hi-Line Radio Fellowship
Editorial: 317 1st St, Havre, Montana 59501-3505. **T:** 1 406 265-5845 **E:** info@ynop.org
W: http://www.ynop.org
Editorial Profile: KJLF-FM is a non-commercial station owned by Hi-Line Radio Fellowship. The format of the station is contemporary Christian music and religious. KJLF-FM broadcasts to the Havre, MT area at 90.5 FM.

KJLG-FM
Owner: Great Plains Christian Radio
Editorial: 909 W Carthage St, Meade, Kansas 67864-6406. **T:** 1 620 873-2991
W: http://www.kjil.com
Editorial Profile: KJLG-FM is a non-commercial station owned by Great Plains Christian Radio. The format of the station is contemporary Christian. KJLG-FM broadcasts to the Emporia, KS area at 91.9 FM.

KJLH-FM
Owner: Taxi Productions Inc.
Editorial: 161 N La Brea Ave, Inglewood, California 90301-1707. **T:** 1 310 330-2200
E: production@kjlhradio.com
W: http://www.kjlhradio.com
Editorial Profile: KJLH-FM is a commercial station owned by Taxi Productions Inc. The format is urban adult contemporary. KJLH-FM broadcasts to the Los Angeles area at 102.3 FM.

KJLL-FM
Owner: Amaturo Group
Editorial: 99 Long Ct, Ste 200, Thousand Oaks, California 91360-7400.
T: 1 805 497-8511
W: http://www.playlist927.com
Editorial Profile: KLST-FM is a commercial station owned by Amaturo Group. The format of the station is adult hits. KLST-FM broadcasts to the Thousand Oaks, CA area at 92.7 FM. KLST-FM is a simulcast of KLSI-FM.

KJLO-FM
Owner: Holladay Broadcasting Co.
Editorial: 1109 Hudson Ln, Monroe, Louisiana 71201. **T:** 1 318 388-2323 **E:** kjlo@bayou.com
W: http://www.kjlo.com
Editorial Profile: KJLO-FM is a commercial station owned by Holladay Broadcasting Co. The format of the station is country music. KJLO-FM broadcasts to the Monroe, LA area at 104.1 FM.

KJLS-FM
Owner: Eagle Radio Inc.
Editorial: 2300 Hall St, Hays, Kansas 67601-3062. **T:** 1 785 625-2578
E: haysnews@eagleradio.net
W: http://www.mix103fm.com
Editorial Profile: KJLS-FM is a commercial station owned by Eagle Radio Inc. The format of the station is hot adult contemporary music. KJLS-FM broadcasts to the Hutchinson, KS area at 103.3 FM.

KJLT-AM
Owner: Tri-State Broadcasting Association, Inc.
Editorial: 201 S Bailey Ave, North Platte, Nebraska 69101-5406. **T:** 1 308 532-5515
E: kjlt@kjlt.org **W:** http://www.kjlt.org

KJLT-FM
Owner: Tri-State Broadcasting Association, Inc.
Editorial: 201 S Bailey Ave, North Platte, Nebraska 69101-5406. **T:** 1 308 532-5515
E: kjlt@kjlt.org **W:** http://www.kjlt.org
Editorial Profile: KJLT-FM is a non-commercial station owned by Tri-State Broadcasting Association, Inc. The format of the station is Contemporary Christian. KJLT-FM is licensed to North Platte, NE and broadcasts at a frequency of 94.9 FM.

KJLU-FM
Owner: Lincoln University Curator Board
Editorial: 1004 E Dunklin St, Jefferson City, Missouri 65101-4163. **T:** 1 573 681-5301
W: http://www.lincolnu.edu/web/kjlu/kjlu
Editorial Profile: KJLU-FM is a non-commercial station owned by Lincoln University Curator Board. The format of the

station is urban contemporary and jazz music. KJLU-FM broadcasts in the Jefferson City, MO area at 88.9 FM.

KJLY-FM
Owner: Minn.-Iowa Christian Broadcasting
Editorial: 12089 380th Ave, Blue Earth, Minnesota 56013. **T:** 1 507 526-3233
E: kjly@kjly.com **W:** http://www.kjly.com
Editorial Profile: KJLY-FM is a non-commercial station owned by Minn.-Iowa Christian Broadcasting. The format of the station is Christian talk and music. KJLY-FM broadcasts to the Minneapolis area at 104.5 FM.

KJMA-FM
Owner: La Promesa Foundation
Editorial: 1905 10Th St, Floresville, Texas 78114-2767. **T:** 1 210 821-5050
W: http://grnonline.info
Editorial Profile: KJMA-FM is a non-commercial station owned by La Promesa Foundation. The format of the station is religion with a focus on Catholic programming. KJMA-FM broadcasts to Wilson County, TX residents and the South and Central areas of the state locally at 89.7 FM.

KJMB-FM
Owner: Blythe Radio Inc.
Editorial: 681 N 4th St, Blythe, California 92225. **T:** 1 760 922-7143
E: kjmbfm@hotmail.com
W: http://www.kjmbfm.com
Editorial Profile: KJMB-FM is a commercial station owned by Blythe Radio Inc. The format of the station is adult contemporary. KJMB-FM broadcasts to Blythe, CA at 100.3 FM.

KJMC-FM
Owner: Minority Communications Inc.
Editorial: 1169 25th St, Des Moines, Iowa 50311-4207. **T:** 1 515 279-1811
E: kjmcfm@mchsi.com
W: http://www.kjmcfm.org
Editorial Profile: KJMC-FM is a non-commercial station owned by Minority Communications Inc. The format of the station is urban contemporary music. KJMC-FM broadcasts to the Des Moines, IA area at 89.3 FM.

KJMD-FM
Owner: Pacific Media Group
Editorial: 311 Ano St, Kahului, Hawaii 96732-1304. **T:** 1 808 877-5566
E: studio@dajam983.com
W: http://www.dajam983.com
Editorial Profile: KJMD-FM is a commercial station owned by Pacific Media Group. The format of the station is Rhythmic CHR. KJMD-FM broadcasts to the Kahului, HI area at 98.3 FM.

KJMG-FM
Owner: Holladay Broadcasting Co.
Editorial: 1109 Hudson Ln, Monroe, Louisiana 71201. **T:** 1 318 388-2323 **E:** mail@kmlb.com
W: http://www.majic97.com
Editorial Profile: KJMG-FM is a commercial station owned by Holladay Broadcasting Co. The format of the station is urban adult contemporary. KJMG-FM broadcasts to the Monroe, LA area at 97.3 FM.

KJMH-FM
Owner: Townsquare Media, LLC
Editorial: 900 N Lake Shore Dr, Lake Charles, Louisiana 70601. **T:** 1 337 433-1641
W: http://www.107jamz.com
Editorial Profile: KJMH-FM is a commercial station owned by Townsquare Media, LLC. The format of the station is urban adult contemporary. KJMH-FM broadcasts to the Lake Charles, LA area at 107.5 FM.

KJMJ-AM
Owner: Radio Maria Inc.
Editorial: 601 Washington St, Alexandria, Louisiana 71301. **T:** 1 318 561-6145
E: info.usa@radiomaria.org
W: http://www.radiomaria.us
Editorial Profile: KJMJ-AM is a commercial station owned by Radio Maria Inc. The format of the station is Catholic and religious programming. KJMJ-AM broadcasts to the Shreveport, LA area at 580 AM.

KJMK-FM
Owner: Zimmer Radio, Inc.
Editorial: 2702 E 32nd St, Joplin, Missouri 64804. **T:** 1 417 624-1025
W: http://www.939classichits.com
Editorial Profile: KJMK-FM is a commercial station owned by Zimmer Radio, Inc. The format of the station is classic hits. KJMK-FM broadcasts to the Joplin, MO area at 93.9 FM.

KJML-FM
Owner: American Media Investments
Editorial: 1162 E Highway 126, Pittsburg, Kansas 66762-8712. **T:** 1 620 231-7200
W: http://www.rock1071.com
Editorial Profile: KJML-FM is a commercial station owned by American Media Investments. The format of the station is rock. KJML-FM broadcasts to the Joplin, MO area at 107.1 FM.

KJMM-FM
Owner: Perry Publishing & Broadcasting Inc.
Editorial: 7030 S Yale Ave, Ste 302, Tulsa, Oklahoma 74136-5722. **T:** 1 918 494-9886
E: spots@kjmm.com **W:** http://www.kjmm.com
Editorial Profile: KJMM-FM is a commercial station owned by Perry Publishing & Broadcasting Inc. The format is urban contemporary. KJMM-FM broadcasts to the Tulsa, OK area at 105.3 FM.

KJMN-FM
Owner: Entravision Communications Corp.
Editorial: 1907 Mile High Stadium West Cir, Denver, Colorado 80204-1908.
T: 1 303 832-0050
Editorial Profile: KJMN-FM is a commercial station owned by Entravision Communications Corp. The format of the station is Hispanic adult hits. KJMN-FM broadcasts to the Denver area at 92.1 FM.

KJMO-FM
Owner: Cumulus Media Inc.
Editorial: 1002 Diamond Rdg Ste 300, Jefferson City, Missouri 65109-7901.
T: 1 573 893-5100 **W:** http://www.kjmo.com
Editorial Profile: KJMO-FM is a commercial station owned by Cumulus Media Inc. The format of the station is oldies music. KJMO-FM broadcasts to the Jefferson City, MO area at 97.5 FM.

KJMQ-FM
Owner: Hochman Hawaii Four, Inc.
Editorial: 4334 Rice St, Ste 206, Lihue, Hawaii 96766. **T:** 1 808 246-4444
E: jamz@hhawaiimedia.com
W: http://www.hhawaiimedia.com
Editorial Profile: KJMQ-FM is a commercial station owned by Hochman Hawaii Four, Inc. The format of the station is Top 40/CHR music. KJMQ-FM broadcasts to the Kauai, HI area at 98.1 FM.

KJMS-FM
Owner: Clear Channel Media and Entertainment
Editorial: 2650 Thousand Oaks Blvd Ste 4100, Memphis, Tennessee 38118-2451.
T: 1 901 259-1300 **W:** http://www.v1011.com
Editorial Profile: KJMS-FM is a commercial station owned by Clear Channel Media and Entertainment. The format of the station is urban adult contemporary music. KJMS-FM broadcasts to the Memphis, TN area at 101.1 FM.

KJMT-FM
Owner: Malvern Entertainment Corporation
Editorial: 223 Russell St, Mountain Home, Arkansas 72653-3665. **T:** 1 870 425-4971
W: http://www.mountaintalk97.com
Editorial Profile: KJMT-FM is a commercial station owned by Malvern Entertainment Corporation. The format of the station is news talk. The station airs locally at 97.1 FM.

KJMX-FM
Owner: Bicoastal Media LLC
Editorial: 320 Central Ave, Ste 519, Coos Bay, Oregon 97420. **T:** 1 541 271-3300
W: http://www.kjmxfm.com
Editorial Profile: KJMX-FM is a commercial station owned by Bicoastal Media LLC. The format of the station is classic rock. KJMX-FM broadcasts to the Coos Bay, OR area at 99.5 FM.

KJMY-FM
Owner: Clear Channel Media and Entertainment
Editorial: 2801 Decker Lake Dr, Salt Lake City, Utah 84119. **T:** 1 801 908-1300
W: http://www.my995fm.com
Editorial Profile: KJMY-FM is a commercial station owned by Clear Channel Media and Entertainment. The format of the station is adult contemporary. KJMY-FM broadcasts to the Salt Lake City area at 99.5 FM.

KJMZ-FM
Owner: Perry Publishing & Broadcasting Inc.
Editorial: 1525 SE Flower Mound Rd, Lawton, Oklahoma 73501. **T:** 1 580 355-1050
W: http://www.kjmz.com
Editorial Profile: KJMZ-FM is a commercial station owned by Perry Publishing & Broadcasting Inc. The format of the station is urban contemporary music. KJMZ-FM broadcasts to the Lawton, OK area at 97.9 FM.

KJNA-FM
Owner: Little River Radio Co.
Editorial: 1791 N 2nd St, Jena, Louisiana 71342. **T:** 1 318 992-4155
E: kjnafm@hotmail.com
Editorial Profile: KJNA-FM is a commercial station owned by Little River Radio Co. The format of the station is country music. KJNA-FM broadcasts to the Jena, LA area at 102.7 FM.

KJNO-AM
Owner: Alaska Broadcast Communications Inc.
Editorial: 3161 Channel Dr Ste 2, Juneau, Alaska 99801-7866. **T:** 1 907 586-3630
E: kjno@kjno.com **W:** http://www.kjno.com
Editorial Profile: KJNO-AM is a commercial station owned by Alaska Broadcast Communications Inc. The format of the station is sports programming. KJNO-AM broadcasts to the Ketchikan, AK area at 630 AM.

KJNW-FM
Owner: Northwestern College
Editorial: 15800 Calvary Rd, Kansas City, Missouri 64147-1303. **T:** 1 816 331-8700
W: http://life885.com/category/welcome/
Editorial Profile: KJNW-FM is a non-commercial station owned by Northwestern College. The format of the station is Adult Contemporary Christian music. KJNW-FM broadcasts to the Kansas City, MO area at 88.5 FM.

KJNY-FM
Owner: Mad River Radio
Editorial: 728 7th St Ste 2A, Eureka, California 95501-1158. **T:** 1 707 445-3699
W: http://www.991kissfm.com
Editorial Profile: KJNY-FM is a commercial station owned by Mad River Radio. The format of the station is Top 40/CHR. KJNY-FM broadcasts to the Eureka, CA area at 99.1 FM.

KJNZ-FM
Owner: Cheers Media, Inc.
Editorial: 301 S Tyler Street, Ste. 800, Amarillo, Texas 79101. **T:** 1 806 242-4242
Editorial Profile: KJNZ-FM is a commercial station owned by Cheers Media, Inc. The format of the station is Regional Mexican and Latin Pop. KJNZ-FM broadcasts to the Hereford, TX area at 103.5 FM.

KJOC-AM
Owner: Townsquare Media
Editorial: 1229 Brady St, Davenport, Iowa 52803-4616. **T:** 1 563 326-2541
W: http://espn1170.com
Editorial Profile: KJOC-AM is a commercial station owned by Townsquare Media. The format of the station is sports. KJOC-AM broadcasts to the Davenport, IA area at 1170 AM.

KJOE-FM
Owner: Christensen Broadcasting
Editorial: 2660 Broadway Ave, Slayton, Minnesota 56172. **T:** 1 507 836-6125
E: kjoe@kjoeradio.com
W: http://www.kjoeradio.com/kjoe
Editorial Profile: KJOE-FM is a commercial station owned by Christensen Broadcasting. The format of the station is country music. KJOE-FM broadcasts to the Pipestone, MN area at 106.1 FM.

KJOJ-FM
Owner: Liberman Broadcasting Inc.
Editorial: 3000 Bering Dr, Houston, Texas 77057-5708. **T:** 1 713 315-3400
W: http://houston.laraza.fm
Editorial Profile: KJOJ-FM is a commercial station owned by Liberman Broadcasting Inc. The format of the station is regional Mexican music. KJOJ-FM broadcasts to the Houston area at 103.3 FM.

KJOK-FM
Owner: Altus FM Inc.
Editorial: 808 N Main St, Altus, Oklahoma 73521-3116. **T:** 1 580 482-1555
W: http://www.keyb.net
Editorial Profile: KJOK-FM is a commercial station owned by Altus FM Inc. The format of the station is classic rock music. The station is aired locally on 102.7 FM in Altus, OK.

KJOL-AM
Owner: United Ministries
Editorial: 1354 E Sherwood Dr, Grand Junction, Colorado 81501. **T:** 1 970 254-5565
E: info@kjol.org **W:** http://www.kjol.org
Editorial Profile: KOJA-AM is a non-commercial station owned by United Ministries. The format of the station is religious. KOJA-AM broadcasts to the Grand Junction, CO area at a frequency of 620 AM.

KJON-AM
Owner: Chatham Hill Foundation, Inc.
Editorial: 8828 N Stemmons Fwy, Ste 106, Dallas, Texas 75247. **T:** 1 214 951-0132
W: http://grnonline.info
Editorial Profile: KJON-AM is a commercial station owned by Chatham Hill Foundation, Inc. The format of the station is Hispanic/ Christian programming. KJON-AM broadcasts to the Dallas area at 850 AM.

KJOP-AM
Owner: Immaculate Heart Radio
Editorial: 3256 Penryn Rd, Suite 100, Loomis, California 95650. **T:** 1 916 535-0500
W: http://ihradio.org
Editorial Profile: KJOP-AM is a non-commercial station owned by Immaculate Heart Radio. The format of the station is religious. KJOP-AM broadcasts to the Fresno, CA area at 1240 AM.

KJOT-FM
Owner: Journal Broadcast Group
Editorial: 5257 W Fairview Ave, Ste 260, Boise, Idaho 83706. **T:** 1 208 344-3511
W: http://www.varietyrocks.com
Editorial Profile: KJOT-FM is a commercial station owned by Journal Broadcast Group. The format of the station is variety of rock and adult hits music. KJOT-FM broadcasts to the Boise, ID area at 105.1 FM.

KJOV-FM
Owner: Great Plains Christian Radio
Editorial: 909 W Carthage, Meade, Kansas 67864. **T:** 1 620 873-2991 **E:** kjil@kjil.com
W: http://www.kjil991.com
Editorial Profile: KJOV-FM is a non-commercial station owned by Great Plains Christian Radio. The format of the station is contemporary Christan music. KJOV-FM broadcasts to the Woodward, OK area at 90.7 FM.

KJOX-AM
Owner: Ingstad (James D.)
Editorial: 1200 Chesterly Dr, Ste 160, Yakima, Washington 98902. **T:** 1 509 248-2900
Editorial Profile: KJOX-AM is a commercial station owned by Ingstad (James D.). The format of the station is sports. KJOX-AM broadcasts to the Yakima, WA area at 1340 AM.

KJOY-FM
Owner: Cumulus Media Inc
Editorial: 3136 Boeing Way, Suite #125, Stockton, California 95206. **T:** 1 209 476-1230
W: http://www.993kjoy.com
Editorial Profile: KJOY-FM is a commercial station owned by Cumulus Media Inc. The format of the station is adult contemporary. KJOY-FM broadcasts to the Stockton, CA area at 99.3 FM.

KJOZ-AM
Owner: Daij Media, LLC
Editorial: 1600 Pasadena Blvd, Pasadena, Texas 77502-2404. **T:** 1 713 589-1336
E: fm@radioaleluya.org
W: http://www.radioaleluya.org
Editorial Profile: KJOZ-FM is a commercial station owned by Daij Media, LLC. The format of the station is Spanish Contemporary Christian music programming. Daij Media, LLC broadcasts to the Houston area at 880 AM.

KJPG-AM
Owner: Immaculate Heart Radio
Editorial: 1550 N Fresno St, Fresno, California 93703-3711. **T:** 1 916 535-0500
W: http://ihradio.org
Editorial Profile: KJPG-AM is a commercial station owned by Immaculate Heart Radio. The format of the station is religious programming. KJPG-AM broadcasts to the Bakersfield, CA area at 1050 AM.

KJPW-AM
Owner: DeanRadio.TV LLC

Editorial: 313 Old Route 66, Saint Robert, Missouri 65584. **T:** 1 573 336-4913
E: kjpw@regionalradio.com
W: http://www.myozarksonline.com
Editorial Profile: KJPW-AM is a commercial station owned by DeanRadio.TV LLC. The format of the station is talk programming. KJPW-AM broadcasts to the Waynesville, MO area at 1390 AM.

KJPW-FM
Owner: DeanRadio.TV LLC
Editorial: 313 Old Route 66, Saint Robert, Missouri 65584. **T:** 1 573 336-4913
E: kjpw@regionalradio.com
W: http://www.myozarksonline.com
Editorial Profile: KJPW-FM is a commercial station owned by DeanRadio.TV LLC. The format of the station is talk programming. KJPW-FM broadcasts to the Saint Roberts, MO area at 102.3 FM.

KJQS-AM
Owner: Cumulus Media
Editorial: 434 W Bearcat Dr, Salt Lake City, Utah 84115-2520. **T:** 1 801 485-6700
W: http://www.1320kfan.com
Editorial Profile: KJQS-AM is a commercial station owned by Cumulus Media. The format of the station is sports. KJQS-AM broadcasts to the Salt Lake City area at 1230 AM.

KJQY-FM
Owner: Pueblo Broadcasting Group, LLC
Editorial: 516 Main St, Walsenburg, Colorado 81089-2036. **T:** 1 877 842-6336
E: production@socoradio.com
W: http://power1033.com
Editorial Profile: KJQY-FM is a commercial station owned by Pueblo Broadcasting Group, LLC and operated by SOCO Radio. The format of the station is Top 40/CHR. KJQY-FM broadcasts to the Pueblo County, Colorado area at a frequency of 103.3 FM.

KJR-AM
Owner: Clear Channel Media and Entertainment
Editorial: 351 Elliott Ave W Ste 300, Seattle, Washington 98119-4150. **T:** 1 206 494-2000
W: http://www.sportsradiokjr.com
Editorial Profile: KJR-AM is a commercial station owned by Clear Channel Media and Entertainment. The format of the station is sports. KJR-AM broadcasts to the Seattle area at 950 AM.

KJRB-AM
Owner: Mapleton Communications LLC
Editorial: 1601 E 57Th Ave, Spokane, Washington 99223-6623. **T:** 1 509 448-1000
W: http://www.790kjrb.com
Editorial Profile: KJRB-AM is a commercial station owned by Mapleton Communications LLC. The format of the station is news. KJRB-AM broadcasts to the Spokane, WA area at 790 AM.

KJR-FM
Owner: Clear Channel Media and Entertainment
Editorial: 645 Elliott Ave W Ste 400, Seattle, Washington 98119-3911. **T:** 1 206 494-2000
W: http://www.957kjr.com
Editorial Profile: KJR-FM is a commercial station owned by Clear Channel Media and Entertainment. The format of the station is oldies. KJR-FM broadcasts to the Seattle area at 95.7 FM.

KJRG-AM
Owner: Bott Broadcasting Co.
Editorial: 209 N Meridian Rd, Newton, Kansas 67114. **T:** 1 316 283-4592
E: kjrg@bottradionetwork.com
W: http://www.bottradionetwork.com
Editorial Profile: KJRG-AM is a commercial station owned by Bott Broadcasting Co. The format of the station is religious programming. KJRG-AM broadcasts to the Newton, KS area at 950 AM.

KJRL-FM
Owner: Great Plains Christian Radio
Editorial: 805 S Buckeye Ave, Abilene, Kansas 67410-3211. **T:** 1 785 263-7200
E: radioforlife@kjil.com
W: http://www.kjil1057.com/
Editorial Profile: KJRL-FM is a non-commercial station owned by Great Plains Christian Radio. The format of the station is contemporary Christian music. KJRL-FM broadcasts to the Herington, KS area at 105.7 FM.

KJRN-FM
Owner: Southwestern Adventist University
Editorial: 304 N College Dr, Keene, Texas 76059-2304. **T:** 1 817 202-6788
Editorial Profile: KJRN-FM is a non-commercial station owned by Southwestern Adventist University. The format of the station is contemporary Christian music. KJRN-FM broadcasts to the Keene, TX area at 88.3 FM.

KJRT-FM
Owner: Top 'O Texas Educational Broadcasting Foundation
Editorial: 2615 Paramount Blvd, Amarillo, Texas 79109-3028. **T:** 1 806 359-8855
E: kjrt@kingdomkeys.org
W: http://www.kingdomkeysradio.org
Editorial Profile: KJRT-FM is a non-commercial station owned by Top 'O Texas Educational Broadcasting Foundation. The format of the station is Christian music and talk programming. The station broadcasts locally to the Amarillo, TX area at a frequency of 88.3 FM.

KJRV-FM
Owner: Performance Radio
Editorial: 1726 Dakota Ave S, Huron, South Dakota 57350. **T:** 1 605 352-1933
W: http://www.bigjimrocks.com
Editorial Profile: KJRV-FM is a commercial station owned by Performance Radio. The format of the station is classic rock. KJRV-FM broadcasts to the Huron, SD area at 93.3 FM.

KJSK-AM
Owner: Three Eagles Communications Co.
Editorial: 1418 25th St, Columbus, Nebraska 68601. **T:** 1 402 564-2866
E: kjsk@megavision.com
W: http://www.mycentralnebraska.com
Editorial Profile: KJSK-AM is a commercial station owned by Three Eagles Communications Co. The format of the station is news, sports and talk. KJSK-AM broadcasts to the Columbus, NE area at 900 AM.

KJSN-FM
Owner: Clear Channel Media and Entertainment
Editorial: 2121 Lancey Dr, Modesto, California 95355-3036. **T:** 1 209 551-1306
W: http://www.sunny102fm.com
Editorial Profile: KJSN-FM is a commercial station owned by Clear Channel Media and Entertainment. The format of the station is adult contemporary music. KJSN-FM broadcasts to the Modesto, CA area at 102.3 FM.

KJSR-FM
Owner: Cox Media Group, Inc.
Editorial: 7136 S Yale Ave Ste 500, Tulsa, Oklahoma 74136-6358. **T:** 1 918 493-3434
W: http://www.1033theeagle.com
Editorial Profile: KJSR-FM is a commercial station owned by Cox Media Group, Inc. The format of the station is classic rock. KJSR-FM broadcasts to the Tulsa, OK area at 103.3 FM.

KJTA-FM
Owner: Family Life Radio
Editorial: 1700 N 2nd St, Flagstaff, Arizona 86004-5008. **T:** 1 520 742-6976
W: http://www.myflr.org

KJTH-FM
Owner: Love Station Inc.(The)
Editorial: 6600 W Highway 60, Ponca City, Oklahoma 74601. **T:** 1 580 767-1400
E: mail@thehousefm.com
W: http://www.thehousefm.com
Editorial Profile: KJTH-FM is a non-commercial station owned by The Love Station, Inc. The format of the station is contemporary Christian music. KJTH-FM broadcasts to the Ponca City, OK area at 89.7 FM.

KJTV-AM
Owner: Ramar Communications Inc.
Editorial: 9800 University Ave, Lubbock, Texas 79423-5302. **T:** 1 806 745-3434
W: http://www.am9501007fm.com
Editorial Profile: KJTV-AM is a commercial station owned by Ramar Communications Inc. The format of the station is news, sports and talk. KJTV-AM broadcasts to the Lubbock, TX area at 950 AM.

KJTX-FM
Owner: Wisdom Ministries Inc.
Editorial: 3607 Gilmer Rd, Longview, Texas 75604. **T:** 1 903 759-1243 **E:** kjtxlr@juno.com
W: http://www.kjtx1045fm.com
Editorial Profile: KJTX-FM is a commercial station owned by Wisdom Ministries Inc. The format for the station is contemporary Christian and gospel music. KJTX-FM broadcasts to the Longview, TX area at 104.5 FM.

KJTY-FM
Owner: Family Life Radio
Editorial: 1005 SW 10th Ave, Topeka, Kansas 66604. **T:** 1 520 742-6976
Editorial Profile: KJTY-FM is a non-commercial station owned by Family Life Radio. The format of the station is contemporary Christian and relgious programming. KJTY-FM broadcasts to the Topeka, KS area at 88.1 FM.

KJUG-AM
Owner: Momentum Broadcasting LP
Editorial: 1401 W Caldwell Ave, Visalia, California 93277-7725. **T:** 1 559 553-1500
Editorial Profile: KJUG-AM is a commercial station owned by Momentum Broadcasting LP. The format for the station is Christian/ Inspirational. KJUG-AM broadcasts to the Visalia, CA area at 1270 AM.

KJUG-FM
Owner: Momentum Broadcasting LP
Editorial: 1401 W Caldwell Ave, Visalia, California 93277-7725. **T:** 1 559 553-1500
E: studio@kjug.com **W:** http://www.kjug.com
Editorial Profile: KJUG-FM is a commercial station owned by Momentum Broadcasting LP. The format for the station is contemporary country. KJUG-AM broadcasts to the Visalia, CA area at 106.7 FM.

KJUL-FM
Owner: Summit American Inc.
Editorial: 150 Spectrum Blvd, Las Vegas, Nevada 89101. **T:** 1 702 258-0285
W: http://www.kjul1047.com
Editorial Profile: KJUL-FM is a commercial station owned by Summit American Inc. The format of the station is adult standards. KJUL-FM broadcasts to the Las Vegas area at 104.7 FM.

KJVC-FM
Owner: Hunt (Leon)
Editorial: 805 Polk St, Mansfield, Louisiana 71052-2413. **T:** 1 318 871-5582
E: kjvc@kjvcfm.com
W: http://www.kjvcfm.com
Editorial Profile: KJVC-FM is a commercial station owned by Leon Hunt. The format of the station is contemporary country music. KJVC-FM broadcasts in the Logansport, LA area at 92.7 FM.

KJWL-FM
Owner: Ostlund(John Edwards)
Editorial: 1415 Fulton St, Fresno, California 93721-1609. **T:** 1 559 497-5118
W: http://www.kjwl.com
Editorial Profile: KJWL-FM is a commercial station owned by John Edwards Ostlund. The format of the station is adult contemporary. KJWL-FM broadcasts to the Fresno, CA area at 99.3 FM.

KJWM-FM
Owner: VSS Catholic Communications Inc.
Editorial: 5829 N 60th St, Omaha, Nebraska 68104-1140. **T:** 1 402 571-0200
E: kvss@kvss.com **W:** http://www.kvss.com
Editorial Profile: KJWM-FM is a non-commercial station owned by VSS Catholic Communications Inc. The format of the station is Catholic and religious programming. KJWM-FM broadcasts to the Grand Island, NE area at 91.5 FM.

KJXJ-FM
Owner: Brazos Valley Communications LLC
Editorial: 1240 E Villa Maria Rd, Bryan, Texas 77802. **T:** 1 979 776-1240
W: http://www.rock1039online.com
Editorial Profile: KJXJ-FM is a commercial station owned by Brazos Valley Communications LLC. The format of the station is rock. KJXJ-FM broadcasts to the Waco, TX area at 103.9 FM.

KJXK-FM
Owner: L & L Broadcasting
Editorial: 4050 Eisenhauer Rd, San Antonio, Texas 78218-3409. **T:** 1 210 654-5100
W: http://www.jackfmsa.com
Editorial Profile: KJXK-FM is a commercial station owned by L & L Broadcasting. The format of the station is adult hits. KJXK-FM broadcasts to the San Antonio area at 102.7 FM.

KJXX-AM
Owner: W. Russell Withers
Editorial: 901 S Kingshighway St, Cape Girardeau, Missouri 63703. **T:** 1 573 339-7000
E: kugt@hotmail.com
W: http://www.1170kjxx.com
Editorial Profile: KJXX-AM is a commercial station owned by W Russell Withers. The format of the station is contemporary Christian and adult standards music. KJXX-AM broadcasts to the Cape Girardeau, MO; Paducah, KY; and Harrisburg, IL areas at 1170 AM.

KJYE-AM
Owner: United Ministries
Editorial: 1354 E Sherwood Dr, Grand Junction, Colorado 81501-7546.
T: 1 970 254-5565 **E:** info@kjol.org
W: http://www.kjol.org
Editorial Profile: KJYE-AM is a non-commercial station owned by United Ministries. The format of the station is religious programming. KJYE-AM broadcasts to the Delta, CO area at 1400 AM.

KJYE-FM
Owner: MBC Grand Broadcasting Inc.
Editorial: 1360 E Sherwood Dr, Grand Junction, Colorado 81501. **T:** 1 970 254-2100
E: 92.3thevault@gmail.com
W: http://www.thevault923.com
Editorial Profile: KJYE-FM is a commercial station owned by MBC Grand Broadcasting Inc. The format of the station is classic hits. KJYE-FM broadcasts to the Grand Junction, CO area at 92.3 FM.

KJYL-FM
Owner: Minn-Iowa Christian Broadcasting
Editorial: 103 W Broadway St, Eagle Grove, Iowa 50533-1701. **T:** 1 515 448-4588
E: kjyl@kjyl.org **W:** http://www.kjyl.org
Editorial Profile: KJYL-FM is a non-commercial station owned by Minn-Iowa Christian Broadcasting. The format of the station is gospel music and religious programming. KJYL-FM broadcasts to the Des Moines, IA area at 100.7 FM.

KJYO-FM
Owner: Clear Channel Media and Entertainment
Editorial: 1900 NW Expressway, Ste 1000, Oklahoma City, Oklahoma 73118-1854.
T: 1 405 840-5271
W: http://www.kj103fm.com
Editorial Profile: KJYO-FM is a commercial station owned by Clear Channel Media and Entertainment. The format of the station is Top 40/CHR music. KJYO-FM broadcasts to the Oklahoma City area at 102.7 FM.

KJZA-FM
Owner: St. Paul Bible College
Editorial: 2719 S Dw Ranch Rd, Kingman, Arizona 86401-8611. **T:** 1 855 665-5592
E: kjzafm@yahoo.com **W:** http://www.kjza.org
Editorial Profile: KJZA-FM is a non-commercial station owned by St. Paul Bible College. The format of the station is jazz and news. KJZA-FM broadcasts to the Prescott, AZ area at 89.5 FM.

KJZN-FM
Owner: Wilks Broadcast Group
Editorial: 1066 E Shaw Ave, Fresno, California 93710-7807. **T:** 1 559 230-0104
W: http://www.1055thegame.com
Editorial Profile: KJZN-FM is a commercial station owned by Wilks Broadcast Group. The format of the station is sports. KZJM-FM broadcasts to the Frenso, CA area at 105.5 FM. Send all PSA's via fax.

KJZY-FM
Owner: Redwood Empire Stereocasters
Editorial: 3392 Mendocino Ave, Santa Rosa, California 95403. **T:** 1 707 528-4434
E: jazznotes@kjzy.com **W:** http://www.kjzy.com
Editorial Profile: KJZY-FM is a commercial station owned by Redwood Empire Stereocasters. The format of the station is smooth AC. KJZY-FM broadcasts to the San Francisco area at 93.7 FM.

KJZZ-FM
Owner: Maricopa Community Colleges
Editorial: 2323 W 14Th St, Tempe, Arizona 85281-6948. **T:** 1 480 834-5627
E: mail@kjzz.org **W:** http://www.kjzz.org
Editorial Profile: KJZZ-FM is a commercial station owned by Maricopa Community Colleges. The format of the station is news and jazz. KJZZ-FM broadcasts to the Tempe, AZ area at 91.5 FM.

KKAA-AM
Owner: Family Stations Inc.

Editorial: 3980 S Dakota St, Aberdeen, South Dakota 57401. **T:** 1 510 568-6200
W: http://www.familyradio.com
Editorial Profile: KKAA-AM is a commercial station owned by Family Stations Inc. The format of the station is religious programming. KKAA-FM broadcasts to the Aberdeen, SD area at 1560 AM.

KKAJ-FM
Owner: LKCM Radio Group LP
Editorial: 1205 Northglen St, Ardmore, Oklahoma 73401-1202. **T:** 1 580 226-0421
E: news@sokradio.com
W: http://www.kkaj.com
Editorial Profile: KKAJ-FM is a commercial station owned by LKCM Radio Group LP. The format of the station is contemporary country music. KKAJ-FM broadcasts to the Ardmore, OK area at 95.7 FM.

KKAL-FM
Owner: American General Media
Editorial: 3620 Sacramento Dr, San Luis Obispo, California 93401-7215.
T: 1 805 781-2750
E: news@americangeneralmedia.com
W: http://www.krush925.com
Editorial Profile: KKAL-FM is a commercial station owned by American General Media. The format of the station is hot adult contemporary. KKAL-FM broadcasts in the San Luis Obispo, CA area at 92.5 FM.

KKAM-AM
Owner: Townsquare Media, LLC
Editorial: 4413 82nd St, Ste 300, Lubbock, Texas 79424. **T:** 1 806 798-7078
W: http://www.kkam.com
Editorial Profile: KKAM-AM is a commercial station owned by Townsquare Media, LLC. The format of the station is sports. KKAM-AM broadcasts to the Lubbock, TX area at 1340 AM.

KKAN-AM
Owner: S-Y Communications
Editorial: 205 F St, Phillipsburg, Kansas 67661. **T:** 1 785 543-2151
W: http://www.kkankqma.com
Editorial Profile: KKAN-AM is a commercial station owned by S-Y Communications. The format of the station is adult standards. KKAN-AM broadcasts to the Phillipsburg, KS area at 1490 AM.

KKAQ-AM
Owner: Iowa City Broadcasting Co.
Editorial: 1433 Main Ave N, Thief River Falls, Minnesota 56701. **T:** 1 218 681-4900
E: ktrf@mncable.net **W:** http://ktrf.k2radio.net
Editorial Profile: KKAQ-AM is a commercial station owned by Iowa City Broadcasting Co. The format of the station is classic country. KKAQ-AM broadcasts to the Thief River Falls, MN area at 1460 AM.

KKAT-AM
Owner: Cumulus Media Inc
Editorial: 434 Bearcat Dr, Salt Lake City, Utah 84115. **T:** 1 801 485-6700
W: http://utahsbigtalker.com
Editorial Profile: KKAT-AM is a commercial station owned by Cumulus Media Inc. The format for the station is news and talk. KKAT-AM broadcasts to the Salt Lake City area at 860 AM.

KKBA-FM
Owner: Malkan Interactive Communications
Editorial: 2117 Leopard St, Corpus Christi, Texas 78408-3925. **T:** 1 361 883-3516
W: http://www.927kbay.com
Editorial Profile: KKBA-FM is a commercial station owned by Malkan Interactive Communications. The format of the station is rhythmic adult contemporary. KKBA-FM broadcasts to the Corpus Christi, TX area at 92.7 FM.

KKBB-FM
Owner: Buckley Broadcasting Corp.
Editorial: 3651 Pegasus Dr, Bakersfield, California 93308-6836. **T:** 1 661 393-1900
W: http://www.groove993.com
Editorial Profile: KKBB-FM is a commercial station owned by Buckley Broadcasting Corp. The format of the station is R&B oldies. KKBB-FM broadcasts to the Bakersfield, CA area at 99.3 FM.

KKBC-FM
Owner: Pacific Empire Communications
Editorial: 2510 Cove Ave, La Grande, Oregon 97850. **T:** 1 541 523-4431
W: http://yourboomerradio.com

Editorial Profile: KKBC-FM is a commercial station owned by Pacific Empire Communications. The format of the station is oldies music. KKBC-AM broadcasts to the La Grande, OR area at 95.3 FM.

KKBD-FM
Owner: Clear Channel Media and Entertainment
Editorial: 311 Lexington Ave, Fort Smith, Arkansas 72901. **T:** 1 479 782-8888
W: http://www.bigdog959.com
Editorial Profile: KKBD-FM is a commercial station owned by Clear Channel Media and Entertainment. The format of the station is classic rock. KKBD-FM broadcasts to the Fort Smith, AR area at 95.9 FM.

KKBG-FM
Owner: Pacific Media Group
Editorial: 913 Kanoelehua Ave, Hilo, Hawaii 96720-5116. **T:** 1 808 961-0651
W: http://www.kbigfm.com
Editorial Profile: KKBG-FM is a commercial station owned by Pacific Media Group. The format of the station is adult contemporary. KKBG-FM broadcasts to the Hilo, HI area at 97.9 FM.

KKBI-FM
Owner: JDC Radio Inc.
Editorial: 108 N Broadway St, Broken Bow, Oklahoma 74728-3934. **T:** 1 580 584-3388
E: kkbi@pine-net.com
W: http://www.kkbifm.com
Editorial Profile: KKBI-FM is a commercial station owned by JDC Radio Inc. The format of the station is contemporary country. KKBI-FM broadcasts to the Broken Bow, OK area at 106.1 FM.

KKBJ-AM
Owner: R.P. Broadcasting
Editorial: 2115 Washington Ave S, Bemidji, Minnesota 56601. **T:** 1 218 751-7777
W: http://www.kkbjam.com
Editorial Profile: KKBJ-AM is a commercial station owned by R.P. Broadcasting. The format of the station is news and talk. KKBJ-AM broadcasts in the Minneapolis area at 1360 AM.

KKBJ-FM
Owner: R.P. Broadcasting
Editorial: 2115 Washington Ave S, Bemidji, Minnesota 56601. **T:** 1 218 751-7777
E: news@kkbj.com **W:** http://www.kkbj.com
Editorial Profile: KKBJ-FM is a commercial station owned by R.P. Broadcasting. The format of the station is hot adult contemporary music. KKBJ-FM broadcasts to the Bemidji, MN area at 103.7 FM.

KKBL-FM
Owner: Eagle Broadcasting Inc.
Editorial: 1569 N Central Ave, Monett, Missouri 65708-1104. **T:** 1 417 235-6041
W: http://www.radiotalon.com
Editorial Profile: KKBL-FM is a commercial station owned by Eagle Broadcasting Inc. The format of the station is rock music. KKBL-FM broadcasts to the Monett, MO area at 95.9 FM.

KKBN-FM
Owner: Clarke Broadcasting Corp.
Editorial: 342 S Washington St, Sonora, California 95370. **T:** 1 209 533-1450
W: http://www.kkbnfm.com
Editorial Profile: KKBN-FM is a commercial station owned by Clarke Broadcasting Corp. The format of the station is contemporary country. KKBN-FM broadcasts to the Sonora, CA area at 93.5 FM.

KKBO-FM
Owner: Radio Bismarck, LLC.
Editorial: 3128 E Broadway Ave, Bismarck, North Dakota 58501-5033. **T:** 1 701 751-8000
Editorial Profile: KKBO-FM is a commercial station owned by Radio Bismarck, LLC. The format of the station is country. KKBO-FM broadcasts to the Bismarck, ND area at 105.9 FM.

KKBQ-FM
Owner: Cox Media Group, Inc.
Editorial: 1990 Post Oak Blvd Ste 2300, Houston, Texas 77056-3847.
T: 1 713 961-0093
W: http://www.thenew93q.com
Editorial Profile: KKBQ-FM is a commercial station owned by Cox Media Group, Inc. The format of the station is contemporary country music. KKBQ-FM broadcasts to the Houston area at 92.9 FM.

KKBR-FM
Owner: Town Square Media
Editorial: 27 N 27th St, Billings, Montana 59101-2357. **T:** 1 406 248-7827
E: kkbr971@yahoo.com
W: http://popcrush971.com
Editorial Profile: KKBR-FM is a commercial station owned by Town Square Media. The format of the station is Top 40/CHR. KKBR-FM broadcasts in the Billings, MT area at 97.1 FM.

KKBS-FM
Owner: MLS Communications Inc.
Editorial: 3001 N Highway 64, Guymon, Oklahoma 73942. **T:** 1 580 338-5493
E: kkbs@kkbs.com **W:** http://www.kkbs.com
Editorial Profile: KKBS-FM is a commercial station owned by MLS Communications Inc. The format of the station is rock. KKBS-FM broadcasts to the Guymon, OK area at 92.7 FM.

KKBW-FM
Owner: Clear Channel Media and Entertainment
Editorial: 645 Elliott Ave W Ste 400, Seattle, Washington 98119-3911. **T:** 1 206 494-2000
W: http://www.thebrew1049.com
Editorial Profile: KKBW-FM is a commercial station owned by Clear Channel Media and Entertainment. The format of the station is rock music. KKBW-FM broadcasts to the Seattle area at 104.9 FM.

KKBZ-FM
Owner: Lotus Communications Corp.
Editorial: 1110 E Olive Ave, Fresno, California 93728. **T:** 1 559 497-1100
W: http://www.1051theblaze.com
Editorial Profile: KKBZ-FM is a commercial station owned by Lotus Communications Corp. The format of the station is classic rock. KKBZ-FM broadcasts to the Fresno, CA area at 105.1 FM.

KKCB-FM
Owner: Townsquare Media, LLC
Editorial: 14 E Central Entrance, Duluth, Minnesota 55811. **T:** 1 218 727-4500
W: http://www.kkcb.com
Editorial Profile: KKCB-FM is a commercial station owned by Townsquare Media, LLC. The format of the station is country music. KKCB-FM broadcasts to the Duluth, MN area at 105.1 FM.

KKCD-FM
Owner: Journal Broadcast Group
Editorial: 10714 Mockingbird Dr, Omaha, Nebraska 68127-1942. **T:** 1 402 592-5300
W: http://www.cd1059.com
Editorial Profile: KKCD-FM is a commercial station owned by the Journal Broadcast Group. The format of the station is classic rock. KKCD-FM broadcasts to the Omaha, NE area at 105.9 FM.

KKCH-FM
Owner: NRC Broadcasting
Editorial: 182 Avon Rd, Ste 240, Avon, Colorado 81620-9999. **T:** 1 970 949-0140
W: http://www.mountainjackfm.com
Editorial Profile: KKCH-FM is a commercial station owned by NRC Broadcasting. The format of the station is adult hits. KKCH-FM broadcasts to the Avon, CO area at 92.7 FM.

KKCI-FM
Owner: Rocking M Radio
Editorial: 3023 W 31st St, Goodland, Kansas 67735. **T:** 1 785 899-2309 **E:** kloe@st-tel.net
W: http://www.kloe.com
Editorial Profile: KKCI-FM is a commercial station owned by Rocking M Radio. The format of the station is classic rock. KKCI-FM broadcasts to the Goodland, KS area at 102.5 FM.

KKCJ-FM
Owner: Calvary Chapel of Albuquerque, Inc.
Editorial: 4001 Osuna Rd Ne, Albuquerque, New Mexico 87109-4422. **T:** 1 877 644-2853
E: studio@coreradionetwork.org
W: http://coreradionetwork.org
Editorial Profile: KKCJ-FM is a non-commerical station owned by Calvary Chapel of Albuquerque, Inc. The format of the station is Christian music and religious programming. KKCJ-FM broadcasts to the Cannon AFB, NM area at 90.7 FM.

KKCK-FM
Owner: KMHL Broadcasting Corp.
Editorial: 1414 E College Dr, Marshall, Minnesota 56258. **T:** 1 507 532-2282
E: info@marshallradio.net
W: http://997kkck.com

Editorial Profile: KKCK-FM is a commercial station owned by KMHL Broadcasting Corp. The format of the station is Top 40/CHR music. KKCK-FM broadcasts in the Minneapolis area at 99.7 FM.

KKCL-FM
Owner: Townsquare Media, LLC
Editorial: 4413 82nd St, Ste 300, Lubbock, Texas 79424. **T:** 1 806 798-7078
W: http://www.98kool.com
Editorial Profile: KKCL-FM is a commercial station owned by Townsquare Media, LLC. The format of the station is oldies. KKCL-FM broadcasts to the Lubbock, TX area at 98.1 FM.

KKCM-FM
Owner: Copper Mountain Broadcasting
Editorial: 68474 Twentynine Palms Highway, Twentynine Palms, California 92277.
T: 1 760 362-4264
E: coppermountainbroadcasting@yahoo.com
Editorial Profile: KKCM-FM is a commercial station owned by Copper Mountain Broadcasting. The format of the station is contemporary country. KKCM-FM broadcasts to the Palm Springs, CA area at 92.1 FM.

KKCN-FM
Owner: Townsquare Media
Editorial: 1301 S Abe St, San Angelo, Texas 76903. **T:** 1 325 655-7161
W: http://www.103kkcn.com
Editorial Profile: KKCN-FM is a commercial station owned by Townsquare Media. The format of the station is contemporary country. KKCN-FM broadcasts to the San Angelo, TX area at 103.1 FM.

KKCQ-AM
Owner: Pine to Prairie Broadcasting Inc.
Editorial: 35006 US Highway 2 SE, Fosston, Minnesota 56542. **T:** 1 218 435-1919
E: info@q107fm.com
W: http://www.kkcqradio.com
Editorial Profile: KKCQ-AM is a commercial station owned by Pine to Prairie Broadcasting Inc. The format of the station is talk programming and oldies music. KKCQ-AM broadcasts to the Fosston, MN area at 1480 AM.

KKCQ-FM
Owner: Pine to Prairie Broadcasting Inc.
Editorial: 35006 US Highway 2 SE, Fosston, Minnesota 56542. **T:** 1 218 435-1919
E: info@107fm.com
W: http://www.kkcqnews.blogspot.com
Editorial Profile: KKCQ-FM is a commercial station owned by Pine to Prairie Broadcasting Inc. The format of the station is contemporary country. KKCQ-FM broadcasts to the Fosston, MN area at 96.7 FM.

KKCR-FM
Owner: Kekahu Foundation Inc.
Editorial: 4520D Hanalei Plantation Rd, Princeville, Hawaii 96722-5420.
T: 1 808 826-7774 **E:** kkcr@kkcr.org
W: http://www.kkcr.org
Editorial Profile: KKCR-FM is a non-commercial station owned by Kekahu Foundation Inc. The format of the station is variety. KKCR-FM broadcasts to the Hanalei, HI area at 90.9 FM.

KKCT-FM
Owner: Townsquare Media, Inc.
Editorial: 4303 Memorial Hwy, Mandan, North Dakota 58554-4711. **T:** 1 701 663-6411
W: http://www.hot975fm.com
Editorial Profile: KKCT-FM is a commercial station owned by Townsquare Media, Inc. The format of the station is Top 40/CHR music. KKCT-FM broadcasts to the Bismarck, ND area at 97.5 FM.

KKCW-FM
Owner: Clear Channel Media and Entertainment
Editorial: 13333 SW 68th Pkwy Ste 310, Tigard, Oregon 97223-8304.
T: 1 503 323-6400 **W:** http://www.k103.com
Editorial Profile: KKCW-FM is a commercial station owned by Clear Channel Media and Entertainment. The format of the station is adult contemporary music. KKCW-FM broadcasts to the Portland, OR area at 103.3 FM.

KKCY-FM
Owner: Results Radio Group
Editorial: 1479 Sanborn Rd, Yuba City, California 95993-6042. **T:** 1 530 673-2200
W: http://www.kkcy.com

Editorial Profile: KKCY-FM is a commercial station owned by Results Radio Group. The format of the station is classic country. KKCY-FM broadcasts to the Yuba City, CA area at 103.1 FM.

KKDA-AM
Owner: SKR Partners, LLC
Editorial: 2356 Glenda Ln, Dallas, Texas 75229-3317. **T:** 1 972 620-6296
E: dalkora@dalkora.com
W: http://dalkora.com/
Editorial Profile: KKDA-AM is a commercial station owned by SKR Partners, LLC. The format of the station Korean language programming. KKDA-AM broadcasts to the Grand Prairie, TX area at 730 AM.

KKDA-FM
Owner: Service Broadcasting Corp.
Editorial: 621 NW 6th St, Grand Prairie, Texas 75050-5555. **T:** 1 972 263-9911
W: http://www.myk104.com
Editorial Profile: KKDA-FM is a commercial station owned by Service Broadcasting Corp. The format of the station is urban contemporary music. KKDA-FM broadcasts to the Dallas area at 104.5 FM.

KKDC-FM
Owner: Four Corners Broadcasting LLC
Editorial: 310 Railroad St, Dolores, Colorado 81323. **T:** 1 970 259-4444
W: http://www.radiodolores.com
Editorial Profile: KKDC-FM is a commercial station owned by Four Corners Broadcasting LLC. The format of the station is classic rock. KKDC-FM broadcasts to the Dolores, CO area at 93.3 FM.

KKDD-AM
Owner: Clear Channel Media and Entertainment
Editorial: 2030 Iowa Ave, Riverside, California 92507-7415. **T:** 1 714 350-9702
W: http://radio.disney.go.com/music/yourstation/riverside/index.html
Editorial Profile: KKDD-AM is a commercial station owned by Clear Channel Media and Entertainment. The format of the station is Contemporary Christian. KKDD-AM broadcasts to the San Bernardino-Riverside CA metro area at 1290 AM.

KKDG-FM
Owner: American General Media
Editorial: 1911 Main Ave, Durango, Colorado 81301-5078. **T:** 1 970 247-1240
W: http://99xdurango.com
Editorial Profile: KKDG-FM is a commercial station owned by American General Media. The format of the station is hot adult contemporary. KKDG-FM broadcasts to the Durango, CO area at 99.7 FM.

KKDM-FM
Owner: Clear Channel Media and Entertainment
Editorial: 2141 Grand Ave, Des Moines, Iowa 50312-5303. **T:** 1 515 245-8900
W: http://www.kkdm.com
Editorial Profile: KKDM-FM is a commercial station owned by Clear Channel Media and Entertainment. The format of the station is Top 40/CHR music. KKDM-FM broadcasts to the Des Moines, IA area at 107.5 FM.

KKDO-FM
Owner: Entercom Communications Corp.
Editorial: 5345 Madison Ave, Sacramento, California 95841-3141. **T:** 1 916 334-7777
E: feedback@radio947.net
W: http://www.radio947.net
Editorial Profile: KKDO-FM is a commercial station owned by Entercom Communications Corp. The format of the station is rock alternative. KKDO-FM broadcasts to the Sacramento, CA area at 94.7 FM.

KKDQ-FM
Owner: Iowa City Broadcasting Co.
Editorial: 1433 Main Ave N, Thief River Falls, Minnesota 56701. **T:** 1 218 681-4900
E: jock@mncable.net
W: http://www.trfradio.com
Editorial Profile: KKDQ-FM is a commercial station owned by Iowa City Broadcasting Co. The format of the station is country music. KKDQ-FM broadcasts in the Thief River Falls, MN area at 99.3 FM.

KKDV-FM
Owner: Coast Radio Company Inc.
Editorial: 7901 Stoneridge Dr, Ste 525, Pleasanton, California 94588-3656.
T: 1 925 455-4500
E: spreadstheword@kkdv.com
W: http://kkdv.com
Editorial Profile: KKDV-FM is a commercial station owned by Coast Radio Company Inc. The format of the station is adult contemporary. KKDV-FM broadcasts in the San Francisco, CA area at 92.1 FM.

KKDY-FM
Owner: Central Ozark Radio Network Inc.
Editorial: 983 E Us Highway 160, West Plains, Missouri 65775-4801. **T:** 1 417 256-3131
E: news@ozarkradionetwork.com
W: http://www.kkdy.com
Editorial Profile: KKDY-FM is a commercial station owned by Central Ozark Radio Network Inc. The format of the station is contemporary country music. KKDY-FM broadcasts to the Springfield, MO area at 102.5 FM.

KKDZ-AM
Owner: Walt Disney Co.
Editorial: 200 1st Ave W, Ste 104, Seattle, Washington 98119-4291. **T:** 1 206 281-5300
W: http://www.radiodisney.com/seattle
Editorial Profile: KKDZ-AM is a commercial station owned by Walt Disney Co. The format of the station is family and children's programming. KKDZ-AM broadcasts to the Seattle area at 1250 AM.

KKEA-AM
Owner: Blow Up LLC
Editorial: 900 Fort Street Mall, Ste 700, Honolulu, Hawaii 96813. **T:** 1 808 536-3624
W: http://www.espn1420am.com
Editorial Profile: KKEA-AM is a commercial station owned by Blow Up LLC. The format of the station is sports. KKEA-AM broadcasts to the Honolulu area at 1420 AM.

KKED-FM
Owner: Clear Channel Media and Entertainment
Editorial: 546 9th Ave, Fairbanks, Alaska 99701. **T:** 1 907 450-1000
E: theedge@clearchannel.com
W: http://www.1047theedge.com
Editorial Profile: KKED-FM is a commercial station owned by Clear Channel Media and Entertainment. The format of the station is alternative rock music. KKED-FM broadcasts to the Fairbanks, AK area at 104.7 FM.

KKEG-FM
Owner: Cumulus Media Inc.
Editorial: 4209 N Frontage Rd, Fayetteville, Arkansas 72703-5002. **T:** 1 479 521-5566
W: http://www.983thekeg.com
Editorial Profile: KKEG-FM is a commercial station owned by Cumulus Media Inc. The format of the station is alternative and modern rock music. KKEG-FM broadcasts to the Fayetteville, AR area at 98.3 FM.

KKEN-FM
Owner: Perry Publishing & Broadcasting Inc.
Editorial: 1701 W Pine Ave, Duncan, Oklahoma 73533. **T:** 1 580 355-1050
W: http://perrybroadcasting.net
Editorial Profile: KKEN-FM is a commercial station owned by Perry Publishing & Broadcasting Inc. The format of the station is classic country. KKEN-FM broadcasts to the Duncan, OK area at 97.1 FM.

KKEQ-FM
Owner: Pine to Prairie Broadcasting Inc.
Editorial: 35006 US Highway 2 SE, Fosston, Minnesota 56542-9404. **T:** 1 218 435-1071
E: info@yourqfm.com
W: http://www.yourqfm.com
Editorial Profile: KKEQ-FM is a commercial station owned by Pine to Prairie Broadcasting Inc. The format of the station is contemporary Christian music. KKEQ-FM broadcasts to the Fosston, MN area at 107.1 FM.

KKEX-FM
Owner: Cache Valley Radio Inc.
Editorial: 810 W 200 N, Logan, Utah 84321.
T: 1 435 752-1390 **E:** kkex@cvradio.com
W: http://www.kix96fm.com
Editorial Profile: KKEX-FM is a commercial station owned by Cache Valley Radio Inc. The format of the station is contemporary country. KKEX-FM broadcasts to the Salt Lake City area at 96.7 FM.

KKEZ-FM
Owner: Three Eagles Communications Co.
Editorial: 200 N 10th St, Fort Dodge, Iowa 50501-3925. **T:** 1 515 576-7333
W: http://www.threeeagles.com
Editorial Profile: KKEZ-FM is a commercial station owned by the Three Eagles Communications Co. The format of the station is hot adult contemporary music. KKEZ-FM broadcasts to the Fort Dodge, IA area at 94.5 FM.

KKFD-FM
Owner: DeanRadio.TV LLC
Editorial: 57 1/2 S Court St, Fairfield, Iowa 52556-3287. **T:** 1 641 472-4191
W: http://www.exploreseiowa.com
Editorial Profile: KKFD-FM is a commercial station owned by DeanRadio.TV LLC. The format of the station is classic hits. KKFD-FM broadcasts to the Fairfield, IA area at 95.9 FM.

KKFG-FM
Owner: Clear Channel Media and Entertainment
Editorial: 200 E Broadway, Farmington, New Mexico 87401-6418. **T:** 1 505 325-1716
W: http://www.kool1045.com
Editorial Profile: KKFG-FM is a commercial station owned by Clear Channel Media and Entertainment. The format of the station is classic hits. KKFG-FM broadcasts to the Farmington, NM area at 104.5 FM.

KKFI-FM
Owner: Midcoast Radio Project Inc.
Editorial: 3901 Main St, Kansas City, Missouri 64111-2290. **T:** 1 816 931-3122
W: http://www.kkfi.org
Editorial Profile: KKFI-FM is a non-commercial station owned by Midcoast Radio Project Inc. The format of the station is variety programming. KKFI-FM broadcasts to the Kansas City, MO area at 90.1 FM.

KKFM-FM
Owner: Cumulus Media Inc
Editorial: 6805 Corporate Dr, Ste 130, Colorado Springs, Colorado 80919-1977.
T: 1 719 593-2700 **W:** http://www.kkfm.com
Editorial Profile: KKFM-FM is a commercial station owned by Cumulus Media Inc. The format of the station is classic rock. KKFM-FM broadcasts to the Colorado Springs, CO area at 98.1 FM.

KKFN-FM
Owner: Lincoln Financial Media
Editorial: 7800 E Orchard Rd, Ste 400, Greenwood Village, Colorado 80111.
T: 1 303 321-0950
W: http://www.1043thefan.com
Editorial Profile: KKFN-FM is a commercial station owned by Lincoln Financial Media. The format of the station is sports. KKFN-FM broadcasts to the Greenwood Village, CO area at 104.3 FM.

KKFR-FM
Owner: Riviera Broadcast Group
Editorial: 4745 N 7th St Ste 410, Phoenix, Arizona 85014-3669. **T:** 1 602 648-9800
W: http://www.power983fm.com
Editorial Profile: KKFR-FM is a commercial station owned by Riviera Broadcast Group. The format of the station is urban contemporary music. KKFR-FM broadcasts to the Phoenix area at 98.3 FM. KKFR-FM is in an LMA with Sun City Communications.

KKFS-FM
Owner: Salem Communications
Editorial: 1425 River Park Dr, Ste 520, Sacramento, California 95815-4524.
T: 1 916 924-0710 **E:** info@1039thefish.com
W: http://www.1039thefish.com
Editorial Profile: KKFS-FM is a commercial station owned by Salem Communications. The format of the station is contemporary Christian. KKFS-FM broadcasts to the Sacramento, CA area at 103.9 FM.

KKFT-FM
Owner: Evans Broadcasting
Editorial: 1960 Idaho St, Carson City, Nevada 89701. **T:** 1 775 884-8000
E: prod@991fmtalk.com
W: http://www.991fmtalk.com
Editorial Profile: KKFT-FM is a commercial station owned by Evans Broadcasting. The format of the station is talk. KKFT-FM broadcasts to the Carson City, NV, area at 99.1 FM.

KKGB-FM
Owner: Cumulus Media Inc.
Editorial: 425 Broad St, Lake Charles, Louisiana 70601. **T:** 1 337 439-3300
W: http://www.kkgb.com
Editorial Profile: KKGB-FM is a commercial station owned by Cumulus Media Inc. The format of the station is rock music. KKGB-FM broadcasts to the Lake Charles, LA area at 101.3 FM.

KKGL-FM
Owner: Cumulus Media Inc
Editorial: 1419 W Bannock St, Boise, Idaho 83702. **T:** 1 208 336-3670
W: http://www.96-9theeagle.com
Editorial Profile: KKGL-FM is a commercial station owned by Cumulus Media Inc. The format of the station is classic rock music. KKGL-FM broadcasts to the Boise, ID area at 96.9 FM.

KKGM-AM
Owner: Mortenson Broadcasting Co.
Editorial: 5787 S Hampton Rd, Dallas, Texas 75232-2255. **T:** 1 214 337-5700
W: http://www.kkgmam.com
Editorial Profile: KKGM-AM is a commercial station owned by Mortenson Broadcasting Co. The format of the station is Southern and Bluegrass Gospel. KKGM-AM broadcasts to the Dallas area at 1630 AM.

KKGN-FM
Owner: Radio Ranch Ltd.
Editorial: 3505 Fredericksburg Rd, Kerrville, Texas 78028-9272. **T:** 1 830 896-4990
Editorial Profile: KKGN-FM is a commercial station owned by Radio Ranch Ltd. The format of the station is contemporary country. KKGN-FM broadcasts to the Kerryville, TX area at 96.5 FM.

KKGO-FM
Owner: Mount Wilson FM Broadcasters
Editorial: 1500 Cotner Ave, Los Angeles, California 90025-3303. **T:** 1 310 478-5540
E: mail@gocountry105.com
W: http://mountwilsoninc.com
Editorial Profile: KKGO-FM is a commercial station owned by Mount Wilson FM Broadcasters. The format for the station is contemporary country. KKGO-FM broadcasts to the Los Angeles area at 105.1 FM.

KKGR-AM
Owner: KKGR Inc.
Editorial: 1400 11th Ave, Helena, Montana 59601. **T:** 1 406 443-5237 **E:** kgr@mt.net
Editorial Profile: KKGR-AM is a commercial station owned by KKGR Inc. The format of the station is oldies. KKGR-AM broadcasts to the Helena, MT area at 680 AM.

KKHA-FM
Owner: Tomlinson-Leis Communications L.P.
Editorial: 1713 7th St, Bay City, Texas 77414-5005. **T:** 1 979 323-7771
W: http://www.yoursoutheasttexas.com
Editorial Profile: KKHA-FM is a commercial station owned by Tomlinson-Leis Communications L.P. The format of the station is classic hits. KKHA-FM broadcasts to the Bay City, TX area at 92.5 FM.

KKHB-FM
Owner: Bicoastal Media LLC
Editorial: 5640 S Broadway St, Eureka, California 95503. **T:** 1 707 442-2000
E: eurekanews@bicoastalmedia.com
W: http://www.cool1055.com
Editorial Profile: KKHB-FM is a commercial station owned by Bicoastal Media LLC. The format of the station is oldies. KKHB-FM broadcasts to the Eureka, CA area at 105.5 FM.

KKHH-FM
Owner: CBS Radio
Editorial: 24 Greenway Plz Ste 1900, Houston, Texas 77046-2428. **T:** 1 713 881-5100
W: http://hothits957.cbslocal.com
Editorial Profile: KKHH-FM is a commercial station owned by CBS Radio. The format of the station is Top 40/CHR. KKHH-FM broadcasts to the Houston area at 95.7 FM.

KKHK-FM
Owner: Mapleton Communications LLC
Editorial: 60 Garden Ct, Ste 300, Monterey, California 93940. **T:** 1 831 658-5200
E: bob@955bobfm.com
W: http://www.955bobfm.com
Editorial Profile: KKHK-FM is a commercial station owned by Mapleton Communications LLC. The format of the station is adult hits. KKHK-FM broadcasts to the Monterey, CA area at 95.5 FM.

KKHQ-FM
Owner: Cumulus Media Inc.
Editorial: 501 Sycamore St, Ste 300, Waterloo, Iowa 50703-4651.
T: 1 319 833-4800 **W:** http://www.q923.net
Editorial Profile: KKHQ-FM is a commercial station owned by Cumulus Media Inc. The format of the station is Top 40/CHR. KKHQ-FM

broadcasts to the Waterloo, IA area at 92.3 FM.

KKHR-FM

Owner: Canfin Enterprises Inc.
Editorial: 402 Cypress St, Ste 510, Abilene, Texas 79601. **T:** 1 325 672-5442
W: http://www.radioabilene.com
Editorial Profile: KKHR-FM is a commercial station owned by Canfin Enterprises Inc. The format of the station is Hispanic Top 40/CHR. KKHR-FM broadcasts to the Abilene, TX area at 106.3 FM.

KKHT-FM

Owner: Salem Communications
Editorial: 6161 Savoy Dr, Ste 1200, Houston, Texas 77036-3363. **T:** 1 713 260-3600
E: comments@kkht.com
W: http://www.kkht.com
Editorial Profile: KKHT-FM is a commercial station owned by Salem Communications. The format of the station is religious programming. KKHT-FM broadcasts in the Houston area at 100.7 FM.

KKIA-FM

Owner: Community First Broadcasting
Editorial: 606 1/2 Lake Ave, Storm Lake, Iowa 50588. **T:** 1 712 732-3520
E: production@stormlakeradio.com
W: http://www.stormlakeradio.com
Editorial Profile: KKIA-FM is a commercial station owned by Community First Broadcasting. The format of the station is contemporary country. KKIA-FM broadcasts to the Sioux City, IA area at 92.9 FM.

KKID-FM

Owner: Wheeler (Dave & Carroll)
Editorial: 1415 Forum Dr, Rolla, Missouri 65401-2508. **T:** 1 573 364-4433
E: kkid929fm@kkid929fm.com
W: http://www.kkid929fm.com
Editorial Profile: KKID-FM is a commercial station owned by Dave and Carroll Wheeler. The format of the station is classic rock music. KKID-FM broadcasts to the Springfield, MO area at 92.9 FM.

KKIM-AM

Owner: American General Media
Editorial: 4125 Carlisle Blvd NE, Albuquerque, New Mexico 87107-4806. **T:** 1 505 878-0980
W: http://www.mykkim.com
Editorial Profile: KKIM-AM is a non-commercial station owned by the American General Media. The format of the station is religious talk. KKIM-AM broadcasts to the Albuquerque, NM area at 1000 AM.

KKIN-AM

Owner: Red Rock Radio Corp.
Editorial: 37208 US Highway 169, Aitkin, Minnesota 56431. **T:** 1 218 927-2344
E: kkin@mlecmn.net
W: http://www.kkinradio.com
Editorial Profile: KKIN-AM is a commercial station owned by Red Rock Radio Corp. The format of the station is adult standards music. KKIN-AM broadcasts to the Aitkin, WI area at 94.3 FM.

KKIQ-FM

Owner: Coast Radio Company Inc.
Editorial: 7901 Stoneridge Dr Ste 525, Pleasanton, California 94588-3656.
T: 1 925 455-4500 **E:** programming@kkiq.com
W: http://www.kkiq.com
Editorial Profile: KKIQ-FM is a commercial station owned by the Coast Radio Company Inc. The format of the station is adult contemporary music. KKIQ-FM broadcasts to the Pleasanton, CA area at 101.7 FM.

KKIS-FM

Owner: KSRM, Inc.
Editorial: 40960 K-Beach Rd, Kenai, Alaska 99611. **T:** 1 907 283-8700
E: rken18@radiokenai.com
W: http://www.radiokenai.com
Editorial Profile: KKIS-FM is a commercial station owned by KSRM, Inc. The format of the station is hot adult contemporary. KKIS-FM broadcasts to the Kenai, AK area at 96.5 FM.

KKIT-FM

Owner: DMC Broadcasting Inc.
Editorial: 125 Camino De La Merced Apt A, Taos, New Mexico 87571-5131.
T: 1 575 758-4491
W: http://www.radiointaos.com
Editorial Profile: KKIT-FM is a commercial station owned by DMC Broadcasting Inc. The format of the station is adult hits music. KKIT-

FM broadcasts to the Taos, NM area on 95.9 FM.

KKIX-FM

Owner: Clear Channel Media and Entertainment
Editorial: 2049 E Joyce Blvd Ste 101, Fayetteville, Arkansas 72703-6395.
T: 1 479 582-1079 **W:** http://www.kix104.com
Editorial Profile: KKIX-FM is a commercial station owned by Clear Channel Media and Entertainment. The format of the station is classic country. KKIX-FM broadcasts to the Fayetteville, AR area at 103.9 FM.

KKJG-FM

Owner: American General Media
Editorial: 3620 Sacramento Dr, San Luis Obispo, California 93401-7215.
T: 1 805 781-2750
E: news@americangeneralmedia.com
W: http://www.jugcountry.com
Editorial Profile: KKJG-FM is a commercial station owned by American General Media. The format of the station is contemporary country. KKJG-FM broadcasts to the San Luis Obispo, CA area at 98.1 FM.

KKJK-FM

Owner: Legacy Communications, LLC
Editorial: 3205 W North Front St, Grand Island, Nebraska 68803-4024.
T: 1 308 381-1430
W: http://newsacrossnebraska.com
Editorial Profile: KKJK-FM is a commercial station owned by Legacy Communications, LLC (dba GI Family Radio). The format of the station is Top 40/CHR. KKJK-FM broadcasts to the Grand Island, NE area at 103.1 FM.

KKJL-AM

Owner: San Luis Obispo Broadcasting Inc.
Editorial: 51 Zaca Ln #90, San Luis Obispo, California 93401-7399. **T:** 1 805 543-9400
E: info@kjewel.net **W:** http://www.kjewel.net
Editorial Profile: KKJL-AM is a commercial station owned by San Luis Obispo Broadcasting Inc. The format of the station is adult standards music. KKJL-AM broadcasts in the San Luis Obispo, CA area at 1400 AM.

KKJM-FM

Owner: Gabriel Communications
Editorial: 1310 2nd St N, Sauk Rapids, Minnesota 56379. **T:** 1 320 251-1780
E: friends@spirit929.com
W: http://www.spirit929.com
Editorial Profile: KKJM-FM is a commercial station owned by Gabriel Communications. The format of the station is contemporary Christian. KKJM-FM broadcasts to the Minneapolis area at 92.9 FM.

KKJO-FM

Owner: Eagle Communications
Editorial: 4104 Country Ln, Saint Joseph, Missouri 64506-4921. **T:** 1 816 233-8881
W: http://www.kjo1055.com
Editorial Profile: KKJO-FM is a commercial station owned by Eagle Communications. The format of the station is hot adult contemporary music. KKJO-FM broadcasts in the St. Joseph, MO area at 105.5 FM.

KKJQ-FM

Owner: Armada Media Corp.
Editorial: 1402 E Kansas Ave, Garden City, Kansas 67846. **T:** 1 620 276-2366
E: production@wksradio.com
W: http://www.wksradio.com/q97
Editorial Profile: KKJQ-FM is a commercial station owned by Armada Media Corp. The format of the station is classic country. KKJQ-FM broadcasts to the Garden City, KS area at 97.3 FM.

KKJZ-FM

Owner: California State University-Long Beach
Editorial: 1288 N Bellflower Blvd, Long Beach, California 90815. **T:** 1 562 985-2999
W: http://www.jazzandblues.org
Editorial Profile: KKJZ-FM is a non-commercial station owned by California State University-Long Beach. The format of the station is jazz and blues. KKJZ-FM broadcasts to the Long Beach, CA area at 88.1 FM.

KKKJ-FM

Owner: Wynne Broadcasting Co.
Editorial: 1338 Oregon Ave, Klamath Falls, Oregon 97601-6540. **T:** 1 541 882-4656
E: webmaster@klamathradio.com
W: http://www.klamathradio.com
Editorial Profile: KKKJ-FM is a commercial station owned by Wynne Broadcasting Co. The format of the station is Top 40/CHR. KKKJ-FM

broadcasts to the Klamath Falls, OR area at 105.5 FM.

KKLA-FM

Owner: Salem Communications
Editorial: 701 N Brand Blvd Ste 550, Glendale, California 91203-1235. **T:** 1 818 956-5552
E: info@kkla.com **W:** http://www.kkla.com
Editorial Profile: KKLA-FM is a commercial station owned by Salem Communications. The format of the station is Christian talk. KKLA-FM broadcasts to the Los Angeles area at 99.5 FM.

KKLC-FM

Owner: Educational Media Foundation
Editorial: 5700 W Oaks Blvd, Ste 105, Rocklin, California 95765. **T:** 1 916 251-2142
W: http://www.klove.com
Editorial Profile: KKLC-FM is a commercial station owned by Educational Media Foundation. The format of the station is Christian. KKLC-FM broadcasts to the Mount Shasta, CA area at 107.9 FM.

KKLD-FM

Owner: Yavapai Broadcasting
Editorial: 3405 E Highway 89A, Cottonwood, Arizona 86326-5504. **T:** 1 928 634-2286
E: kkld@myradioplace.com
W: http://www.kkld.com
Editorial Profile: KKLD-FM is a commercial station owned by Yavapai Broadcasting. The format of the station is classic hits. KKLD-FM broadcasts to the Cottonwood, AZ area at 95.9 FM.

KKLE-AM

Owner: Johnson Enterprises Inc.
Editorial: 338 South Kley Dr, Wellington, Kansas 67152. **T:** 1 620 326-3341
E: kley@sutv.com **W:** http://www.kkle.com
Editorial Profile: KKLE-AM is a commercial station owned by Johnson Enterprises Inc. The format of the station is sports. KKLE-AM broadcasts to the Wellington, KS area at 1550 AM.

KKLF-AM

Owner: Volt Radio, LLC
Editorial: 13725 Montfort Dr, Dallas, Texas 75240-4455. **T:** 1 214 526-7400
W: http://247comedy.com
Editorial Profile: KKLF-AM is a commercial station owned by Volt Radio, LLC. The format of the station is comedy radio. KKLF-AM broadcasts to the Dallas area at 1700 AM.

KKLH-FM

Owner: Midwest Family Stations
Editorial: 319B E Battlefield St, Springfield, Missouri 65807-4999. **T:** 1 417 886-5677
W: http://www.1047thecave.com
Editorial Profile: KKLH-FM is a commercial station owned by Midwest Family Stations. The format of the station is classic rock. KKLH-FM broadcasts to the Springfield, MO area on 104.7 FM.

KKLI-FM

Owner: Clear Channel Media and Entertainment
Editorial: 2864 S Circle Dr, Ste 300, Colorado Springs, Colorado 80906. **T:** 1 719 540-9200
W: http://www.klite1063.com
Editorial Profile: KKLI-FM is a commercial station owned by Clear Channel Media and Entertainment. The format of the station is Lite Rock/Lite AC. KKLI-FM broadcasts to the Colorado Springs, CO area at 106.3 FM.

KKLL-AM

Owner: New Life Evangelistic Center, Inc
Editorial: 831 Moffit Street, Joplin, Missouri 64801-3571. **T:** 1 417 781-1100
W: http://www.newlifeevangelisticcenter.org
Editorial Profile: KKLL-AM is a commercial station owned by the New Life Evangelistic Center. The format of the station is contemporary Christian talk and gospel. KKLL-AM broadcasts to the Joplin, MO area at 1100 AM.

KKLN-FM

Owner: Headwaters Media
Editorial: 1605 South 1st St, Kandi Mall, Willmar, Minnesota 56201-4234.
T: 1 320 235-1194 **E:** info@kkln.com
W: http://www.kkln.com
Editorial Profile: KKLN-FM is a commercial station owned by Headwaters Media. The format of the station is rock music. KKLN-FM broadcasts to the Willmar, MN area at 94.1 FM.

KKLO-AM

Owner: New Life Evangelistic Center
Editorial: 481 Muncie Rd, Leavenworth, Kansas 66048-4947. **T:** 1 913 351-1410
W: http://www.hereshelpnet.org
Editorial Profile: KKLO-AM is a commercial station owned by New Life Evangelistic Center. The format of the station is country, contemporary Christian music and gospel. KKLO-AM broadcasts to the Kansas City, MO, metro area at 1410 AM.

KKLR-FM

Owner: Max Media
Editorial: 1015 W Pine St, Poplar Bluff, Missouri 63901-4839. **T:** 1 573 785-0881
E: clear94@riverradio.net
W: http://www.kklr.com
Editorial Profile: KKLR-FM is a commercial station owned by Max Media. The format of the station is contemporary country music. KKLR-FM broadcasts to the Poplar Bluff, MO, area at 94.5 FM.

KKLS-AM

Owner: New Rushmore Radio
Editorial: 660 Flormann St Ste 100, Rapid City, South Dakota 57701-4688.
T: 1 605 343-6161 **W:** http://www.kkls.net
Editorial Profile: KKLS-AM is a commercial station owned by New Rushmore Radio. The format of the station is adult contemporary. KKLS-AM broadcasts to the Rapid City, SD area at 920 AM.

KKLS-FM

Owner: Townsquare Media, Inc.
Editorial: 5100 S Tennis Ln, Sioux Falls, South Dakota 57108-2212. **T:** 1 605 361-0300
W: http://www.hot1047.com
Editorial Profile: KKLS-FM is a commercial station owned by Townsquare Media, Inc. The format of the station is Top 40/CHR music. KKLS-FM broadcasts to the Sioux Falls, SD area at 104.7 FM.

KKLV-FM

Owner: Educational Media Foundation
Editorial: 434 Bearcat Dr, Salt Lake City, Utah 84115. **T:** 1 801 485-6700
W: http://www.klove.com
Editorial Profile: KKLV-FM is a non-commercial station owned by Educational Media Foundation. The format of the station is contemporary Christian. KKLV-FM broadcasts to the Salt Lake City area at 107.5 FM. The station airs programming from K-Love Network.

KKLX-FM

Owner: Legend Communications
Editorial: 1340 Radio Dr, Worland, Wyoming 82401. **T:** 1 307 347-3231
E: kwor@bhrnwy.com
W: http://www.mybighornbasin.com
Editorial Profile: KKLX-FM is a commercial station owned by Legend Communications. The format for the station is hot adult contemporary. KKLX-FM broadcasts to the Worland, WY area at 96.1 FM.

KKLZ-FM

Owner: Beasley Broadcast Group
Editorial: 2920 S Durango Dr, Las Vegas, Nevada 89117-4412. **T:** 1 702 730-0300
W: http://www.963kklz.com
Editorial Profile: KKLZ-FM is a commercial station owned by Beasley Broadcast Group. The format of the station is classic hits. KKLZ-FM broadcasts to the Las Vegas area at 96.3 FM.

KKMA-FM

Owner: Powell Broadcasting Co.
Editorial: 2000 Indian Hills Dr, Sioux City, Iowa 51104. **T:** 1 712 239-2100
W: http://www.kool995.com
Editorial Profile: KKMA-FM is a commercial station owned by Powell Broadcasting Co. The format of the station is classic hits. KKMA-FM broadcasts to the Sioux City, IA area at 99.5 FM.

KKMC-AM

Owner: Monterey County Broadcasters Inc.
Editorial: 30 E San Joaquin St, Ste 105, Salinas, California 93901. **T:** 1 831 424-5562
W: http://www.kkmc.com
Editorial Profile: KKMC-AM is a commercial station owned by Monterey County Broadcasters Inc. The format of the station is Christian talk. KKMC-AM broadcasts to the Salinas, CA area at 880 AM.

KKMG-FM

Owner: Cumulus Media Inc

Editorial: 6805 Corporate Dr, Ste 130, Colorado Springs, Colorado 80919.
T: 1 719 593-2700
W: http://www.989magicfm.com
Editorial Profile: KKMG-FM is a commercial station owned by Cumulus Media Inc. The format of the station is Top 40/CHR. KKMG-FM broadcasts to the Colorado Springs, CO area at 98.9 FM.

KKMI-FM
Owner: Pritchard Broadcasting Co.
Editorial: 610 N 4Th St Ste 300, Burlington, Iowa 52601-5059. **T:** 1 319 752-5402
E: kkmi@935kkmi.com **W:** http://935kkmi.com
Editorial Profile: KKMI-FM is a commercial station owned by Pritchard Broadcasting Co. The format of the station is adult contemporary. KKMI-FM broadcasts to the Burlington, IA area at 93.5 FM.

KKMJ-FM
Owner: Entercom Communications Corp.
Editorial: 4301 Westbank Dr, 3rd Fl, Austin, Texas 78746. **T:** 1 512 327-9595
W: http://www.majic.com
Editorial Profile: KKMJ-FM is a commercial station owned by Entercom Communications Corp. The format of the station is adult contemporary music. KKMJ-FM broadcasts to the Austin, TX area at 99.5 FM.

KKMK-FM
Owner: New Rushmore Radio
Editorial: 660 Flormann St, Ste 100, Rapid City, South Dakota 57701-4688.
T: 1 605 343-6161
W: http://www.newrushmoreradio.com/kkmk
Editorial Profile: KKMK-FM is a commercial station owned by New Rushmore Radio. The format of the station is hot adult contemporary. KKMK-FM broadcasts to the Rapid City, SD area at 93.9 FM.

KKMO-AM
Owner: Salem Communications
Editorial: 2201 6th Ave, Ste 1500, Seattle, Washington 98121. **T:** 1 206 443-8200
W: http://www.radiosol1360.com
Editorial Profile: KKMO-AM is a commercial station owned by Salem Communications. The format of the station is regional Mexican. KKMO-AM broadcasts to the Seattle area at 1360 AM.

KKMR-FM
Owner: Univision Communications Inc.
Editorial: 6006 S 30Th St, Phoenix, Arizona 85042-4802. **T:** 1 602 308-7900
W: http://recuerdophoenix.univision.com
Editorial Profile: KKMR-FM is a commercial station owned by Univision Communications Inc. The format of the station is Spanish Regional/AC. KKMR-FM broadcasts to the Phoenix area at 100.3 FM.

KKMS-AM
Owner: Salem Communications
Editorial: 2110 Cliff Rd, Eagan, Minnesota 55122. **T:** 1 651 405-8800
E: comments@kkms.com
W: http://www.kkms.com
Editorial Profile: KKMS-AM is a commercial station owned by Salem Communications. The format of the station is religious talk. KKMS-AM broadcasts to the Minneapolis area at 980 AM.

KKMT-FM
Owner: Anderson Radio Broadcasting Inc.
Editorial: 36581 N Reservoir Rd, Polson, Montana 59860-8471. **T:** 1 406 883-5255
E: kerrnews@750kerr.com
W: http://750kerr.com
Editorial Profile: KKMT-FM is a commercial station owned by Anderson Radio Broadcasting. The format of the station is classic country music. KKMT-FM broadcasts in the Polson, MT area at 92.3 FM.

KKMV-FM
Owner: Lee Family Broadcasting
Editorial: 120 S 300 W, Rupert, Idaho 83350-9667. **T:** 1 208 436-4757 **W:** http://kat106.com
Editorial Profile: KKMV-FM is a commercial station owned by Lee Family Broadcasting. The format of the station is hot adult contemporary. KKMV-FM broadcasts to the Rupert, ID area at a frequency of 106.1 FM.

KKMX-FM
Owner: Brooke Communications Inc.
Editorial: 1445 W Harvard Ave, Roseburg, Oregon 97471. **T:** 1 541 672-6641
W: http://www.541radio.com
Editorial Profile: KKMX-FM is a commercial station owned by Brooke Communications Inc. The format of the station is adult contemporary. KKMX-FM broadcasts to the Roseburg, OR area at 104.5 FM.

KKMY-FM
Owner: Clear Channel Media and Entertainment
Editorial: 2885 IH-10 East, Beaumont, Texas 77702. **T:** 1 409 896-5555
W: http://www.mix1045.com
Editorial Profile: KKMY-FM is a commercial station owned by Clear Channel Media and Entertainment. The format of the station is Top 40/Rhythmic contemporary music. KKMY-FM broadcasts to the Beaumont, TX area at 104.5 FM.

KKND-FM
Owner: Cumulus Media Inc
Editorial: 201 Saint Charles Ave, Ste 201, New Orleans, Louisiana 70170. **T:** 1 504 581-7002
W: http://www.power1029.com
Editorial Profile: KKND-FM is a commercial station owned by Cumulus Media Inc. The format of the station is rhythmic urban contemporary. KKND-FM broadcasts to New Orleans at 102.9 FM.

KKNE-AM
Owner: Summit Media Broadcasting LLC
Editorial: 900 Fort Street Mall, Honolulu, Hawaii 96813-3721. **T:** 1 808 275-1000
W: http://www.am940hawaii.com
Editorial Profile: KKNE-AM is a commercial station owned by Summit Media Broadcasting LLC. The format of the station is variety. KKNE-AM broadcasts to the Honolulu area at 940 AM.

KKNG-FM
Owner WPA Radio LLC
Editorial: 5101 S Shields Blvd, Oklahoma City, Oklahoma 73129-3217. **T:** 1 405 601-6380
Editorial Profile: KKNG-FM is a commercial station owned by the WPA Radio LLC. The format of the station is Catholic programming. KKNG-FM broadcasts to the Oklahoma City area at 97.3 FM.

KKNI-AM
Owner: Kenai Broadcasting, LLC
Editorial: 851 E Westpoint Dr Ste 301, Wasilla, Alaska 99654-7183.
T: 1 907 373-0222
W: http://www.1430hometownradio.com
Editorial Profile: KKNI-AM is a commercial station owned by Kenai Broadcasting, LLC. The format of the station is news/talk and oldies. KKNI-AM broadcasts to the Wasilla, AK area at 1430 AM.

KKNM-FM
Owner: Tejas Broadcasting
Editorial: 3639 Wolflin Ave, Amarillo, Texas 79102-2119. **T:** 1 806 355-1044
Editorial Profile: KKNM-FM is a commercial station owned by Tejas Broadcasting. The format of the station is classic country. KKNM-FM broadcasts to the Amarillo, TX area at 96.5 FM.

KKNN-FM
Owner: Townsquare Media, Inc.
Editorial: 315 Kennedy Ave, Grand Junction, Colorado 81501-7552. **T:** 1 970 242-7788
W: http://www.95rockfm.com
Editorial Profile: KKNN-FM, is a commercial station owned by Townsquare Media, Inc. The format of the station is rock. KKNN-FM broadcasts to the Grand Junction, CO area at 95.1 FM.

KKNO-AM
Owner: Blakes Enterprises(Robert)
Editorial: 980 Avenue A, Marrero, Louisiana 70072-3228. **T:** 1 504 347-7775
W: http://kkno750.com
Editorial Profile: KKNO-AM is a commercial station owned by Robert Blakes Enterprises. The format of the station is gospel music. KKNO-AM broadcasts locally to the New Orleans area at 750 AM.

KKNS-AM
Owner: El Camino Communications, LLC
Editorial: 1606 Central Ave SE, Albuquerque, New Mexico 87106-4478. **T:** 1 505 255-5015
W: http://www.elcaminoradio.com
Editorial Profile: KKNS-AM is a commercial station owned by El Camino Communications, LLC. The format of the station is regional Mexican. KKNS-AM broadcasts to the Albuquerque, NM area at 1310 AM.

KKNT-AM
Owner: Salem Communications
Editorial: 2425 E Camelback Rd Ste 570, Phoenix, Arizona 85016-4250.
T: 1 602 955-9600
W: http://www.960thepatriot.com
Editorial Profile: KKNT-AM is a commercial station owned by Salem Communications. The format of the station is news and talk. KKNT-AM broadcasts to the Phoenix area at 960 AM.

KKNU-FM
Owner: McKenzie River Broadcasting
Editorial: 925 Country Club Rd, Ste 200, Eugene, Oregon 97401. **T:** 1 541 484-9400
E: bearfox@kknu.com
W: http://www.kknu.com
Editorial Profile: KKNU-FM is a commercial station owned by McKenzie River Broadcasting. The format for the station is contemporary country. KKNU-FM broadcasts to the Eugene, OR area at 93.3 FM.

KKNW-AM
Owner: Hubbard Radio, LLC
Editorial: 3650 131st Ave SE Ste 550, Bellevue, Washington 98006-1334.
T: 1 425 562-8219
E: kknwlistener@1150kknw.com
W: http://1150kknw.com
Editorial Profile: KKNW-AM is a commercial station owned by Hubbard Radio, LLC. The format of the station is alternative news and talk. KKNW-AM broadcasts to the Seattle area at 1150 AM.

KKNX-AM
Owner: Willamette Broadcasting
Editorial: 1142 Willagillespie Rd Ste 28, Eugene, Oregon 97401-6723.
T: 1 541 342-1012 **W:** http://www.radio84.com
Editorial Profile: KKNX-AM is a commercial station owned by Willamette Broadcasting. The format of the station is oldies. KKNX-AM broadcasts to the Eugene, OR area at 840 AM.

KKOA-FM
Owner: Mahalo Broadcasting
Editorial: 74-5605 Luhia St Ste B7, Kailua Kona, Hawaii 96740-1678. **T:** 1 808 329-8090
E: info@lava105.com
W: http://www.koacountry.com
Editorial Profile: KKOA-FM is a commercial station owned by Mahalo Broadcasting. The format of the station is contemporary country. KKOA-FM broadcasts to the Kailua Kona, HI area at 107.7.

KKOB-AM
Owner: Cumulus Media Inc
Editorial: 500 4th St NW, Albuquerque, New Mexico 87102-5324. **T:** 1 505 767-6700
E: newsroom@770kkob.com
W: http://www.770kkob.com
Editorial Profile: KKOB-AM is a commercial station owned by Cumulus Media Inc. The format of the station is news and talk. KKOB-AM broadcasts to the Albuquerque, NM area at 770 AM.

KKOB-FM
Owner: Cumulus Media Inc
Editorial: 500 4th St NW Fl 5, Albuquerque, New Mexico 87102-5324. **T:** 1 505 767-6700
W: http://www.kobfm.com
Editorial Profile: KKOB-FM is a commercial station owned by Cumulus Media Inc. The format of the station is Top 40/CHR. KKOB-FM broadcasts to the Albuquerque, NM area at 93.3 FM.

KKOH-AM
Owner: Cumulus Media Inc
Editorial: 595 E Plumb Ln, Reno, Nevada 89502. **T:** 1 775 789-6700 **E:** info@kkoh.com
W: http://www.kkoh.com
Editorial Profile: KKOH-AM is a commercial station owned by Cumulus Media Inc. The format of the station is news and talk. KKOH-AM broadcasts to the Reno, NV area at 780 AM.

KKOJ-AM
Owner: Kleven Broadcasting Co.
Editorial: 71991 US Highway 71 South, Jackson, Minnesota 56143-3311.
T: 1 507 847-5400 **E:** info@kkoj.com
W: http://www.kkoj.com
Editorial Profile: KKOJ-AM is a commercial station owned by Kleven Broadcasting Co. The format of the station is contemporary country music. KKOJ-AM broadcasts to the Minneapolis area at 1190 AM.

KKOK-FM
Owner: Iowa City Broadcasting Co.
Editorial: 46671 State Highway 28, Morris, Minnesota 56267-4508. **T:** 1 320 589-3131
E: kmrskkok@fedtel.net
W: http://www.kmrskkok.com
Editorial Profile: KKOK-FM is a commercial station owned by the Iowa City Broadcasting Co. The format of the station is contemporary country music. KKOK-FM broadcasts in the Morris, MN area at 95.7 FM.

KKOL-AM
Owner: Salem Communications
Editorial: 2201 6th Ave, Ste 1500, Seattle, Washington 98121-1840. **T:** 1 206 443-8200
E: webmaster@kgnw.com
W: http://www.kkol.com
Editorial Profile: KKOL-AM is a commercial station owned by Salem Communications. The format of the station is business news and talk. KKOL-AM broadcasts to the Seattle area at 1300 AM.

KKOL-FM
Owner: Salem Communications
Editorial: 1160 N King St, Honolulu, Hawaii 96817-3307. **T:** 1 808 533-0065
W: http://www.oldies1079honolulu.com
Editorial Profile: KKOL-FM is a commercial station owned by Salem Communications. The format of the station is oldies. KKOL-FM broadcasts to the Honolulu area at 107.9 FM.

KKON-AM
Owner: Pacific Media Group
Editorial: 75-5852 Alii Dr. Suite B1 & B2, Lagoon Tower, Kailua-Kona, Hawaii 96740.
T: 1 808 961-0651
W: http://www.espnhawaii.com
Editorial Profile: KKON-AM is a commercial station owned by Pacific Media Group. The format of the station is sports. KKON-AM broadcasts to the Kona, HI area at 790 AM.

KKOO-FM
Owner: Treasure Valley Broadcasting
Editorial: 1156 N Orchard St, Boise, Idaho 83706. **T:** 1 208 367-1859
E: production@kweiradio.com
Editorial Profile: KKOO-FM is a commercial station owned by Treasure Valley Broadcasting. The format of the station is stunting as oldies. KKOO-FM broadcasts to the Boise, ID area at 99.5 FM.

KKOR-FM
Owner: Main Street Broadcasting Inc.
Editorial: 255 Cedardale Dr SE, Owatonna, Minnesota 55060-4425. **T:** 1 507 444-9224
W: http://www.kowzonline.com
Editorial Profile: KKOR-FM is a commercial station owned by Main Street Broadcasting Inc. The format of the station is country. KKOR-FM broadcasts to the Owatonna, MN area at 92.1 FM.

KKOT-FM
Owner: Three Eagles Communications Co.
Editorial: 1418 25th St, Columbus, Nebraska 68601-2820. **T:** 1 402 564-2866
W: http://www.mycentralnebraska.com
Editorial Profile: KKOT-FM is a commercial station owned by Three Eagles Communications Co. The format of the station is classic hits. KKOT-FM broadcasts to the Columbus, NE area at 93.5 FM.

KKOV-AM
Owner: Pamplin Broadcasting-Washington, Inc.
Editorial: 6605 Se Lake Rd, Portland, Oregon 97222-2161. **T:** 1 503 223-4321
Editorial Profile: KKOV-AM is a commercial station owned by Pamplin Broadcasting-Washington, Inc. The format of the station is adult standards. KKOV-AM broadcasts to the Portland, OR area at 1550 AM.

KKOW-AM
Owner: American Media Investments
Editorial: 1162 E Highway 126, Pittsburg, Kansas 66762. **T:** 1 620 231-7200
W: http://www.kkowam.com
Editorial Profile: KKOW-AM is a commercial station owned by American Media Investments. The format of the station is country music. KKOW-AM broadcasts in the Pittsburg, KS, area at 860 AM.

KKOW-FM
Owner: American Media Investments
Editorial: 1162 E Highway 126, Pittsburg, Kansas 66762. **T:** 1 620 231-7200
E: kkow@kkowradio.com
W: http://www.kkowfm.com
Editorial Profile: KKOW-FM is a commercial station owned by American Media Investments. The format of the station is contemporary country music. KKOW-FM broadcasts to the Pittsburg, KS, area at 96.9 FM.

KKOY-AM
Owner: My Town Media, Inc.
Editorial: 702 N Plummer Ave, Chanute, Kansas 66720-1463. **T:** 1 620 431-3700
Editorial Profile: KKOY-AM is a commercial station owned by My Town Media, Inc. The format of the station is sports and country. KKOY-AM broadcasts to the Chanute, KS area at 1460 AM.

KKOY-FM
Owner: My Town Media, Inc.
Editorial: 702 N Plummer Ave, Chanute, Kansas 66720. **T:** 1 620 431-3700
W: http://kkoy.com
Editorial Profile: KKOY-FM is a commercial station owned by My Town Media, Inc. The format of the station is top 40/CHR KKOY-FM broadcasts in the Chanute, KS area at 105.5 FM.

KKOZ-AM
Owner: Corum Industries Inc.
Editorial: 303 SE 2nd Avenue, Ava, Missouri 65608. **T:** 1 417 683-4191 **E:** news@kkoz.com
W: http://www.kkoz.com
Editorial Profile: KKOZ-AM is a commercial station owned by Corum Industries Inc. The format of the station is news/talk. KKOZ-AM broadcasts to the Ava, MO area at 1430 AM.

KKOZ-FM
Owner: Corum Industries Inc.
Editorial: 303 Southeast 2nd Avenue, Ava, Missouri 65608-0386. **T:** 1 417 683-4191
E: news@kkoz.com **W:** http://www.kkoz.com
Editorial Profile: KKOZ-FM is a commercial station owned by Corum Industries Inc. The format of the station is news/talk. KKOZ-FM broadcasts to the Springfield, MO area at 92.1 FM.

KKPK-FM
Owner: Cumulus Media Inc
Editorial: 6805 Corporate Dr, Ste 130, Colorado Springs, Colorado 80919.
T: 1 719 593-2700
W: http://www.929peakfm.com
Editorial Profile: KKPK-FM is a commercial station owned by Cumulus Media Inc. The format of the station is adult contemporary. KKPK-FM broadcasts to the Colorado Springs, CO area at 92.9 FM.

KKPL-FM
Owner: Townsquare Media, LLC
Editorial: 600 Main St, Windsor, Colorado 80550-5133. **T:** 1 970 674-2700
W: http://www.999thepoint.com
Editorial Profile: KKPL-FM is a commercial station owned by Townsquare Media, LLC. The format of the station is Hot AC. KKPL-FM broadcasts to the Denver area at 99.9 FM.

KKPN-FM
Owner: Convergent Broadcasting
Editorial: 826 S Padre Island Dr, Corpus Christi, Texas 78416. **T:** 1 361 814-3800
W: http://planet1023.com
Editorial Profile: KKPN-FM is a commercial station owned by Convergent Broadcasting. The format of the station is Top 40/CHR. KKPN-FM broadcasts in Corpus Christi, TX area at 102.3 FM.

KKPR-FM
Owner: Platte River Radio, Inc.
Editorial: 403 E 25th St, Kearney, Nebraska 68847. **T:** 1 308 236-9900
E: generalmanager@kkpr.com
W: http://www.kkpr.com
Editorial Profile: KKPR-FM is a commercial station owned by Platte River Radio, Inc. The format of the station is classic hits. KKPR-FM broadcasts to the Kearney, NE area at 98.9 FM.

KKPS-FM
Owner: Entravision Communications Corp.
Editorial: 801 N Jackson Rd, McAllen, Texas 78501. **T:** 1 956 661-6000 **E:** kkps@hiline.net
W: http://www.quepasa995.com
Editorial Profile: KKPS-FM is a commercial station owned by Entravision Communications Corp. The format of the station is regional Mexican. KKPS-FM broadcasts to the McAllen, TX, area at 99.5 FM.

KKPT-FM
Owner: Signal Media Inc.
Editorial: 2400 Cottondale Ln, Little Rock, Arkansas 72202-2020. **T:** 1 501 664-9410
W: http://www.point941.com
Editorial Profile: KKPT-FM is a commercial station owned by Signal Media Inc. The format of the station is classic rock music. KKPT-FM broadcasts in the Little Rock, AR area at 94.1 FM.

KKPZ-AM
Owner: Crawford Broadcasting Co.
Editorial: 9700 SE Eastview Dr, Happy Valley, Oregon 97086-6975. **T:** 1 503 242-1950
E: info@kkpz.com **W:** http://www.kkpz.com
Editorial Profile: KKPZ-AM is a commercial station owned by Crawford Broadcasting Co. The format of the station is Christian music and programming. KKPZ-AM broadcasts to the Portland, OR area at 1400 AM.

KKQQ-FM
Owner: Three Eagles Communications Co.
Editorial: 227 22nd Ave S, Brookings, South Dakota 57006-2827. **T:** 1 605 692-9125
E: kjjqnews@brookings.net
W: http://www.kcountry102.com
Editorial Profile: KKQQ-FM is a commercial station owned by Three Eagles Communications Co. The format of the station is country music. KKQQ-FM broadcasts to the Brookings, SD area at 102.3 FM.

KKQY-FM
Owner: Eagle Radio Inc.
Editorial: 2300 Hall St, Hays, Kansas 67601-3062. **T:** 1 785 625-2578
E: haysnews@eagleradio.net
W: http://www.hayspost.com/the-country-bull-y102
Editorial Profile: KKQY-FM is a commercial station owned by Eagle Radio Inc. The format of the station is contemporary country music. KKQY-FM broadcasts to Hays, KS at 101.9 FM.

KKRB-FM
Owner: Wynne Broadcasting Co.
Editorial: 1338 Oregon Ave, Klamath Falls, Oregon 97601-6540. **T:** 1 541 882-4656
E: webmaster@klamathradio.com
W: http://www.klamathradio.com
Editorial Profile: KKRB-FM is a commercial station owned by Wynne Broadcasting Co. The format of the station is soft rock. KKRB-FM broadcasts to the Klamath Falls, OR area at a frequency of 106.9 FM.

KKRC-FM
Owner: Tom Ingstad Broadcast Group
Editorial: 4454 Highway 212, Montevideo, Minnesota 56265-4539. **T:** 1 320 269-8815
E: kdmaprod@radiokdma.com
Editorial Profile: KKRC-FM is a commercial station owned by Iowa City Broadcasting Co. The format of the station is oldies music. KKRC-FM broadcasts to the Montevideo, MN area at 93.9 FM.

KKRE-FM
Owner: Altus FM Inc.
Editorial: 808 N Main St, Altus, Oklahoma 73521-3116. **T:** 1 580 482-1555
E: keyb@keyb.net **W:** http://www.keyb.net
Editorial Profile: KKRE-FM is a commercial station owned by Altus FM Inc. The format of the station is oldies music. KKRE-FM broadcasts to the Altus, OK area at 92.5 FM.

KKRG-FM
Owner: Univision Communications Inc.
Editorial: 8009 Marble Ave NE, Albuquerque, New Mexico 87110-7901. **T:** 1 505 254-7100
W: http://www.univision.com/content/channel.jhtml?chid=10014&schid=10027
Editorial Profile: KKRG-FM is a commercial station owned by Univision Communications Inc. The format of the station is Spanish adult contemporary. KKRG-FM broadcasts to the Albuquerque, NM area at 101.3 FM.

KKRK-FM
Owner: Montana Radio Company (The)
Editorial: 516 Fuller Ave, Helena, Montana 59601-3301. **T:** 1 406 442-0400
Editorial Profile: KKRK-FM is a commercial station owned by Montana Radio Company (The). The format of the station is rock music and broadcasts to the Helena, MT area at a frequency of 106.5 FM.

KKRL-FM
Owner: Carroll Broadcasting Co.
Editorial: 1119 East Plaza Dr, Carroll, Iowa 51401-3838. **T:** 1 712 792-4321
E: 937kkrl@carrollbroadcasting.com
W: http://carrollbroadcasting.com
Editorial Profile: KKRL-FM is a commercial station owned by Carroll Broadcasting Co. The format of the station is hot adult contemporary music. KKRL-FM broadcasts to the Carroll, IA area at 93.7 FM.

KKRO-FM
Owner: Educational Media Foundation
Editorial: 5700 W Oaks Blvd, Rocklin, California 95765-3719. **T:** 1 916 251-2142
E: klove@klove.com **W:** http://www.air1.com
Editorial Profile: KLVB-FM is a non-commercial station owned by Educational Media Foundation. The format of the station is Christian CHR/Rock. KKRO-FM broadcasts to the Keizer, OR area at 102.7 FM.

KKRQ-FM
Owner: Clear Channel Media and Entertainment
Editorial: 1 Stephen Atkins Dr, Iowa City, Iowa 52240-8021. **T:** 1 319 354-9500
E: news@kxic.com **W:** http://www.kkrq.com
Editorial Profile: KKRQ-FM is a commercial station owned by Clear Channel Media and Entertainment. The format of the station is classic rock music. KKRQ-FM broadcasts to the Cedar Rapids, IA area at 100.7 FM.

KKRS-FM
Owner: Penfold Communications, Inc.
Editorial: 12720 W Sunset Hwy, Ste C, Airway Heights, Washington 99001-9410.
T: 1 509 244-5577 **E:** kkrs973fm@hotmail.com
Editorial Profile: KKRS-FM is a non-commercial station owned by Penfold Communications, Inc. The station airs a religious format in the Airway Heights, WA area at 97.3 FM.

KKRV-FM
Owner: Morris Communications
Editorial: 1124 N Miller St, Wenatchee, Washington 98801-1541. **T:** 1 509 663-5186
E: johnw@kkrv.com **W:** http://www.kkrv.com
Editorial Profile: KKRV-FM is a commercial station owned by Morris Communications. The format of the station is country. KKRV-FM broadcasts to the Seattle area at 104.7 FM.

KKRX-AM
Owner: Perry Publishing & Broadcasting Inc.
Editorial: 1525 Se Flower Mound Rd, Lawton, Oklahoma 73501-6325. **T:** 1 580 355-1050
W: http://www.perrybroadcasting.net/kxca
Editorial Profile: KKRX-AM is a commercial station owned by Perry Publishing & Broadcasting Inc. The format of the station is sports. KKRX-AMbroadcasts to the Lawton, OK area at 1380 AM.

KKRZ-FM
Owner: Clear Channel Media and Entertainment
Editorial: 13333 SW 68th Pkwy Ste 310, Tigard, Oregon 97223-8304.
T: 1 503 323-6400
W: http://www.z100portland.com
Editorial Profile: KKRZ-FM is a commercial station owned by Clear Channel Media and Entertainment. The format of the station Top 40/CHR music. KKRZ-FM broadcasts to the Portland, OR area at 100.3 FM.

KKSA-AM
Owner: Foster Communications Co. Inc.
Editorial: 2824 Sherwood Way, San Angelo, Texas 76901. **T:** 1 325 949-2112
W: http://www.kksa-am.com
Editorial Profile: KKSA-AM is a commercial station owned by Foster Communications Co. Inc. The format for the station is news, talk and sports. KKSA-AM broadcasts to the San Angelo, TX area at 1260 AM.

KKSD-FM
Owner: Three Eagles Communications Co.
Editorial: 921 9th Ave SE, Watertown, South Dakota 57201-4960. **T:** 1 605 882-1480
E: kwatnews@watertown.threeeagles.com
W: http://gowatertown.net/pages/9121063.php
Editorial Profile: KKSD-FM is a commercial station owned by Three Eagles Communications Co. The format of the station is classic hits. KKSD-FM broadcasts to the Watertown, SD area 104.3 FM.

KKSF-AM
Owner: Clear Channel Media and Entertainment
Editorial: 340 Townsend St, San Francisco, California 94107-1633. **T:** 1 415 356-5500
W: http://www.talk910.com
Editorial Profile: KKSF-AM is a commercial station owned by Clear Channel Media and Entertainment. The format of the station is talk. KKSF-AM broadcasts to the San Francisco area at 910 AM.

KKSI-FM
Owner: O-Town Communications, Inc.
Editorial: 416 E Main St, Ottumwa, Iowa 52501. **T:** 1 641 684-5563
E: info@ottumwaradio.com
W: http://www.kissclassicrock.com
Editorial Profile: KKSI-FM is a commercial station owned by O-Town Communications, Inc. The format of the station is classic rock. KKSI-FM broadcasts to the Ottumwa, IA area at a frequency of 101.5 FM.

KKSM-AM
Owner: Palomar Community College
Editorial: 1140 W Mission Rd, San Marcos, California 92069-1415.
T: 1 760 744-1150 2183
W: http://www.palomar.edu/kksm
Editorial Profile: KKSM-AM is a non-commercial college station owned by Palomar Community College. The format of the station is college variety. KKSM-AM broadcasts to the San Marcos, CA area at AM 1320.

KKSP-FM
Owner: Crain Media Group LLC
Editorial: 400 Hardin Rd, Little Rock, Arkansas 72211-3502. **T:** 1 501 219-1919
Editorial Profile: KKSP-FM is a commercial station owned by Crain Media Group LLc. The format of the station is sports. KKSP-FM broadcasts to the Little Rock, AR area at 93.3 FM.

KKSR-FM
Owner: Ingstad Radio Washington, LLC
Editorial: 4304 W 24th Ave Ste 200, Kennewick, Washington 99338-2320.
T: 1 509 783-0783
W: http://www.cities957.com
Editorial Profile: KKSR-FM is a commercial station owned by Ingstad Radio Washington, LLC. The format of the station is classic hits. KKSR-FM broadcasts to the Kennewick, WA area at 95.7 FM.

KKSS-FM
Owner: Univision Communications Inc.
Editorial: 8009 Marble Ave NE, Albuquerque, New Mexico 87110-7901. **T:** 1 505 254-7100
W: http://www.univision.com/content/channel.jhtml?chid=10014&schid=10159
Editorial Profile: KKSS-FM is a commercial station owned by Univision Communications Inc. The format of the station is rhythmic Top 40/CHR music. KKSS-FM broadcasts to the Albuquerque, NM area at 97.3 FM.

KKST-FM
Owner: Cenla Broadcasting Inc.
Editorial: 1115 Texas Ave, Alexandria, Louisiana 71301. **T:** 1 318 445-1234
W: http://www.kiss987.fm
Editorial Profile: KKST-FM is a commercial station owned by Cenla Broadcasting Inc. The format of the station is urban contemporary music. KKST-FM broadcasts to the Alexandria, LA area at 98.7 FM.

KKSW-FM
Owner: Great Plains Media
Editorial: 3125 W 6th St, Lawrence, Kansas 66049-3101. **T:** 1 785 843-1320
W: http://www.1059kissfm.com
Editorial Profile: KKSW-FM is a commercial station owned by Great Plains Media. The format of the station is Top 40/CHR. KKSW-FM broadcasts to the Lawrence, KS area at 105.9 FM.

KKSY-FM
Owner: Clear Channel Media and Entertainment
Editorial: 600 Old Marion Rd NE, Cedar Rapids, Iowa 52402. **T:** 1 319 395-0530
W: http://www.965kisscountry.com
Editorial Profile: KKSY-FM is a commercial station owned by Clear Channel Media and Entertainment. The format of the station is contemporary country music. KKSY-FM broadcasts in the Cedar Rapids, IA area at 96.5 FM.

KKTC-FM
Owner: DMC Broadcasting Inc.
Editorial: 125A Camino De La Merced Ste A, Taos, New Mexico 87571-5119.
T: 1 575 758-4491
W: http://www.kktctruecountry.com
Editorial Profile: KKTC-FM is a commercial station owned by DMC Broadcasting Inc. The format of the station is contemporary country music. KKTC-FM broadcasts to the Taos, NM area at 99.9 FM.

KKTK-AM
Owner: Freed AM Corp.
Editorial: 3446 Summerhill Rd #B, Texarkana, Texas 75503-3560. **T:** 1 903 255-7942
W: http://www.foxsportstexarkana.com

Editorial Profile: KKTK-AM is a commercial station owned by Freed AM Corp.. The format of the station is sports. KKTK-AM broadcasts to the Texarkana area at 1400 AM.

KKTL-AM
Owner: Townsquare Media, LLC
Editorial: 150 Nichols Ave, Casper, Wyoming 82601. **T:** 1 307 266-5252
E: caspernews@gapbroadcasting.com
W: http://www.1400kktl.com
Editorial Profile: KKTL-AM is a commercial station owned by Townsquare Media, LLC. The format for the station is talk and sports. KKTL-AM broadcasts to the Casper-Riverton, WY area at 1400 AM.

KKTS-FM
Owner: Douglas Broadcasting Inc.
Editorial: 247 Russell Ave, Douglas, Wyoming 82633. **T:** 1 307 358-3636
E: kkty@netcommander.com
W: http://www.kktyonline.com
Editorial Profile: KKTS-FM is a commercial station owned by Douglas Broadcasting Inc. The format of the station is Hot AC. KKTS-FM airs locally at 99.3 FM to the Douglas, WY area.

KKTU-FM
Owner: Lahontan Valley Broadcasting
Editorial: 1155 Gummow Dr, Fallon, Nevada 89406. **T:** 1 775 423-2243
E: kvlv@phonewave.net
Editorial Profile: KKTU-FM is a commercial station owned by Lahontan Valley Broadcasting. The format of the station is adult contemporary. KKTU-FM broadcasts to the Fallon, NV area at 99.5 FM.

KKTX-AM
Owner: Clear Channel Media and Entertainment
Editorial: 501 Tupper Lane Radio Plaza, Corpus Christi, Texas 78417-9736.
T: 1 361 289-0111
W: http://www.1360online.com
Editorial Profile: KKTX-AM is a commercial station owned by Clear Channel Media and Entertainment. The format of the station is news, talk and sports. KKTX-AM broadcasts to the Corpus Christi, TX area at 1360 AM.

KKTX-FM
Owner: Townsquare Media, LLC
Editorial: 3810 Brookside Dr, Tyler, Texas 75701. **T:** 1 903 581-0606
W: http://www.kktx.com
Editorial Profile: KKTX-FM is a commercial station owned by Townsquare Media, LLC. The format of the station is classic rock music. KKTX-FM broadcasts to the Tyler, TX area at 96.1 FM.

KKTY-AM
Owner: Douglas Broadcasting Inc.
Editorial: 247 Russell Ave, Douglas, Wyoming 82633. **T:** 1 307 358-3636
E: kkty@netcommander.com
W: http://www.kktyonline.com
Editorial Profile: KKTY-AM is a commercial station owned by Douglas Broadcasting Inc. The format for the station is oldies. KKTY-AM broadcasts to the Casper-Riverton, WY area at 1470 AM.

KKTY-FM
Owner: Douglas Broadcasting Inc.
Editorial: 247 Russell Ave, Douglas, Wyoming 82633. **T:** 1 307 358-3636
E: kkty@netcommander.com
W: http://kktyonline.com
Editorial Profile: KKTY-FM is a commercial station owned by Douglas Broadcasting Inc. The format for the station is Country. KKTY-AM broadcasts to the Casper-Riverton, WY area at 99.3 FM.

KKTZ-FM
Owner: Dowdy Broadcasting, Inc.
Editorial: 2352 Highway 62 Business, Mountain Home, Arkansas 72653.
T: 1 870 492-6022 **W:** http://www.kktz.net
Editorial Profile: KKTZ-FM is a commercial station owned by Dowdy Broadcasting, Inc. The format of the station is Top 40/CHR. KKTZ-FM broadcasts to the Mountain Home, AR area at 93.5 FM.

KKUA-FM
Owner: Hawaii Public Radio
Editorial: 738 Kaheka St, Ste 101, Honolulu, Hawaii 96814. **T:** 1 808 955-8821
E: news@hawaiipublicradio.org
W: http://www.hawaiipublicradio.org
Editorial Profile: KKUA-FM is a non-commercial station owned by Hawaii Public Radio. The format of the station is news, talk, and classical music. KKUA-FM broadcasts to the Honolulu area at 90.7 FM.

KKUP-FM
Owner: Assurance Sciences Foundation
Editorial: 1241 Franklin Mall, Santa Clara, California 95050-4806. **T:** 1 408 260-2999
E: webmeister@kkup.org
W: http://www.kkup.org
Editorial Profile: KKUP-FM is a non-commercial station owned by Assurance Sciences Foundation. The format of the station is variety. KKUP-FM broadcasts to the Santa Clara, CA area at 91.5 FM.

KKUS-FM
Owner: Access.1 Communications Corp.
Editorial: 210 S Broadway Ave, Tyler, Texas 75702. **T:** 1 903 581-9966
W: http://www.theranch.fm/
Editorial Profile: KKUS-FM is a commercial station owned by Access.1 Communications Corp. The format of the station is classic country. KKUS-FM broadcasts to Tyler, TX at 104.1 FM.

KKUU-FM
Owner: Morris Communications
Editorial: 1321 N Gene Autry Trl, Palm Springs, California 92262. **T:** 1 760 322-7890
W: http://www.927kkuu.com
Editorial Profile: KKUU-FM is a commercial station owned by Morris Communications. The format of the station is rhythmic Top 40/CHR. KKUU-FM broadcasts to the Los Angeles area at 92.7 FM.

KKVR-FM
Owner: Radio Ranch Ltd.
Editorial: 3505 Fredericksburg Rd, Kerrville, Texas 78028-9272. **T:** 1 830 896-4990
Editorial Profile: KKVR-FM is a commercial station owned by Radio Ranch Ltd. The format of the station is oldies KKVR-FM broadcasts to the Kerryville, TX area at 106.1 FM.

KKVU-FM
Owner: Spanish Peaks Broadcasting, Inc.
Editorial: 2425 W Central Ave, Ste 203, Missoula, Montana 59801. **T:** 1 406 721-6800
W: http://www.fresh1045.com
Editorial Profile: KKVU-FM is a commercial station owned by Spanish Peaks Broadcasting, Inc. The format of the station is Top 40/CHR. KKVU-FM broadcasts to the Missoula, MT area at 104.5 FM.

KKVV-AM
Owner: Vegas Broadcasters Inc.(Las)
Editorial: 3185 S Highland Dr Ste 13, Las Vegas, Nevada 89109-1029.
T: 1 702 731-5588 **W:** http://www.kkvv.com
Editorial Profile: KKVV-AM is a commercial station owned by Las Vegas Broadcasters Inc. The format of the station is Christian talk. KKVV-AM broadcasts to the Las Vegas area at 1060 AM.

KKWD-FM
Owner: Cumulus Media Inc
Editorial: 4045 NW 64th St Ste 600, Oklahoma City, Oklahoma 73116-2607.
T: 1 405 848-0100
W: http://www.wild1049hd.com
Editorial Profile: KKWD-FM is a commercial station owned by Cumulus Media Inc. The format of the station is rhythmic Top 40/CHR music. KKWD-FM broadcasts to the Oklahoma City area at 104.9 FM.

KKWF-FM
Owner: Entercom Communications Corp.
Editorial: 1100 Olive Way, Seattle, Washington 98101-1873. **T:** 1 206 233-1037
E: frontdeskmp@entercom.com
W: http://www.1007thewolf.com
Editorial Profile: KKWF-FM is a commercial station owned by Entercom Communications Corp. The format of the station is country. KKWF-FM broadcasts to the Seattle area at 100.7 FM.

KKWK-FM
Owner: Goodradio.TV LLC
Editorial: 607 E Platte Clay Way, Cameron, Missouri 64429-8825. **T:** 1 816 632-6661
W: http://www.northwestmoinfo.com
Editorial Profile: KKWK-FM is a commercial station owned by Goodradio.TV LLC. The format of the station is classic hits. KKWK-FM broadcasts to the Kansas City, MO area at 100.1 FM.

KKWQ-FM
Owner: Border Broadcasting
Editorial: 113 A Lake St Center, Warroad, Minnesota 56763. **T:** 1 218 386-3024
E: kq92@mncable.net
W: http://www.kq92.com
Editorial Profile: KKWQ-FM is a commercial station owned by Border Broadcasting. The format of the station is contemporary country music. KKWQ-FM broadcasts to the Warroad, MN area at 92.5 FM.

KKWS-FM
Owner: BL Broadcasting Inc.
Editorial: 201 1/2 Jefferson St S, Wadena, Minnesota 56482-1531. **T:** 1 218 631-1803
E: kwadkkws@arvig.net
W: http://www.superstationk106.com
Editorial Profile: KKWS-FM is a commercial station owned by BL Broadcasting Inc. The format of the station is contemporary country music. KKWS-FM broadcasts to Wadena, MN at 105.9 FM.

KKXA-AM
Owner: CAAM Partnership (Andy Skotdal)
Editorial: 2707 Colby Ave Ste 1380, Everett, Washington 98201-3568. **T:** 1 425 304-1381
Editorial Profile: KKXA-AM is a commercial station owned by CAAM Partnership (Andy Skotdal). The format of the station is classic country. KAAM-AM broadcasts to the Snohomish, WA area at a frequency of 1520 AM.

KKXK-FM
Owner: Cherry Creek Radio
Editorial: 106 Rose Ln, Montrose, Colorado 81401. **T:** 1 970 249-4546
E: news@coloradoradio.com
W: http://www.coloradoradio.com
Editorial Profile: KKXK-FM is a commercial station owned by Cherry Creek Radio. The format for the station is contemporary country. KKXK-FM broadcasts to the Grand Junction-Montrose, CO area at 94.1 FM.

KKXL-AM
Owner: Clear Channel Media and Entertainment
Editorial: 505 University Ave, Grand Forks, North Dakota 58203. **T:** 1 701 775-0575
W: http://www.1440kkxl.com
Editorial Profile: KKXL-AM is a commercial station owned by Clear Channel Media and Entertainment. The format of the station is sports. KKXL-AM broadcasts to the Grand Forks, ND area at 1440 AM.

KKXL-FM
Owner: Clear Channel Media and Entertainment
Editorial: 505 University Ave, Grand Forks, North Dakota 58203. **T:** 1 701 775-0575
W: http://www.xl93.com
Editorial Profile: KKXL-FM is a commercial station owned by Clear Channel Media and Entertainment. The format of the station is Top 40/CHR music. KKXL-FM broadcasts to the Grand Forks, ND area at 92.9 FM.

KKXS-FM
Owner: Results Radio Group
Editorial: 1588 Charles Dr, Redding, California 96003. **T:** 1 530 244-9700
W: http://xs961.com
Editorial Profile: KKXS-FM is a commercial station owned by Results Radio Group. The format of the station is sports. KKXS-FM broadcasts to the Redding, CA area at 96.1 FM.

KKXT-FM
Owner: North Texas Public Broadcasting
Editorial: 3000 Harry Hines Blvd, Dallas, Texas 75201-1012. **T:** 1 214 871-1390
W: http://kxt.org
Editorial Profile: KKXT-FM is a non-commercial station owned by North Texas Public Broadcasting. The format of the station is adult album alternative. KKXT-FM broadcasts in the Dallas area at 91.7 FM.

KKXX-AM
Owner: Butte Broadcasting Inc.
Editorial: 1363 Longfellow Ave, Chico, California 95926. **T:** 1 530 894-7325
E: info@kkxx.net **W:** http://www.kkxx.net

KKXX-FM
Owner: American General Media
Editorial: 1400 Easton Dr Ste 144B, Bakersfield, California 93309-9412.
T: 1 661 328-1410 **W:** http://www.hits931.com
Editorial Profile: KKXX-FM is a commercial station owned by American General Media. The format of the station is Top 40/CHR. KKXX-FM broadcasts to the Bakersfield, CA area at 93.1 FM.

KKYA-FM
Owner: Riverfront Broadcasting
Editorial: 202 W 2Nd St, Yankton, South Dakota 57078-4317. **T:** 1 605 665-7892
E: production@kk93.com
W: http://www.kk93.com
Editorial Profile: KKYA-FM is a commercial station owned by Riverfront Broadcasting. The format of the station is country. KKYA-FM broadcasts to the Yankton, SD area at 93.1 FM.

KKYN-FM
Owner: Rhattigan Broadcasting
Editorial: 3218 Quincy St, Plainview, Texas 79072-1906. **T:** 1 806 293-2771
W: http://www.kkyn.net
Editorial Profile: KKYN-FM is a commercial station owned by Rhattigan Broadcasting. The format of the station is country music. KKYN-FM broadcasts to the Plainview, TX area at 106.9 FM.

KKYR-FM
Owner: Townsquare Media, LLC
Editorial: 2324 Arkansas Blvd, Texarkana, Arkansas 71854-2016. **T:** 1 870 772-3771
W: http://www.kkyr.com
Editorial Profile: KKYR-FM is a commercial station owned by Townsquare Media, LLC. The format of the station is country, featuring contemporary and classic hits. KKYR-FM broadcasts to the Texarkana, AR area at 102.5 FM.

KKYS-FM
Owner: Clear Channel Media and Entertainment
Editorial: 1716 Briarcrest Dr, Ste 150, Bryan, Texas 77802. **T:** 1 979 846-5597
W: http://www.mix1047.com
Editorial Profile: KKYS-FM is a commercial station owned by Clear Channel Media and Entertainment. The format of the station is hot adult contemporary. KKYS-FM broadcasts to the Bryan, TX area at 104.7 FM.

KKYX-AM
Owner: Cox Media Group, Inc.
Editorial: 8122 Datapoint Dr, Ste 600, San Antonio, Texas 78229-3446.
T: 1 210 615-5400 **W:** http://www.kkyx.com
Editorial Profile: KKYX-AM is a commercial station owned by Cox Media Group, Inc. The format of the station is country. KKYX-AM broadcasts to the San Antonio area at 680 AM.

KKYY-FM
Owner: Powell Broadcasting Co.
Editorial: 2000 Indian Hills Dr, Sioux City, Iowa 51104. **T:** 1 712 239-2100
W: http://www.y1013.net
Editorial Profile: KKYY-FM is a commercial station owned by Powell Broadcasting Co. The format of the station is country. KKYY-FM broadcasts to the Sioux Falls, SD area at 101.3 FM.

KKYZ-FM
Owner: Desert West Air Ranchers Corp.
Editorial: 500 E Fry Blvd, Ste L10, Sierra Vista, Arizona 85635. **T:** 1 520 459-8201
E: info@kkyz.com **W:** http://www.kkyz.com
Editorial Profile: KKYZ-FM is a commercial station owned by Desert West Air Ranchers Corp. The format of the station is oldies music. KKYZ-FM broadcasts to the Tucson, AZ area at 101.7 FM.

KKZN-AM
Owner: Clear Channel Media and Entertainment
Editorial: 4695 S Monaco St, Denver, Colorado 80237-3525. **T:** 1 303 713-8000
W: http://www.realtalk760.com/main.html
Editorial Profile: KKZN-AM is a commercial station owned by Clear Channel Media and Entertainment. The format of the station is talk. KKZN-AM broadcasts to the Denver area at 760 AM.

KKZQ-FM
Owner: High Desert Broadcasting LLC
Editorial: 570 E Avenue Q9, Palmdale, California 93550. **T:** 1 661 947-3107
W: http://www.edge100.com
Editorial Profile: KKZQ-FM is a commercial station owned by High Desert Broadcasting LLC. The format of the station is rock alternative. KKZQ-FM broadcasts to the Palmdale, CA area at 100.1 FM.

KKZX-FM
Owner: Clear Channel Media and Entertainment

Editorial: 808 E Sprague Ave, Spokane, Washington 99202-2126. **T:** 1 509 242-2400
W: http://www.kkzx.com
Editorial Profile: KKZX-FM is a commercial station owned by Clear Channel Media and Entertainment. The format of the station is classic rock. KKZX-FM broadcasts to the Spokane, WA area at 98.9 FM.

KKZY-FM
Owner: Omni Broadcasting Co.
Editorial: 502 Beltrami Ave NW, Bemidji, Minnesota 56601. **T:** 1 218 444-1500
W: http://www.kzyfm955.com
Editorial Profile: KKZY-FM is a commercial station owned by Omni Broadcasting Co. The format of the station is adult contemporary music. KKZY-FM broadcasts to Bemidji, MN at 95.5 FM.

KKZZ-AM
Owner: Gold Coast Radio, LLC
Editorial: 2284 S Victoria Ave Ste 2G, Ventura, California 93003-6626. **T:** 1 805 289-1400
E: psa@goldcoastbroadcasting.com
Editorial Profile: KKZZ-AM is a commercial station owned by Gold Coast Radio, LLC. The format of the station is Spanish news and talk. KKZZ-AM broadcasts to the Ventura, CA area at 1400 AM.

KLAA-AM
Owner: LAA1 LLC
Editorial: 2000 E Gene Autry Way, Anaheim, California 92806-6143. **T:** 1 714 940-2500
W: http://www.am830klaa.com
Editorial Profile: KLAA-AM is a commercial station owned by LAA1 LLC. The format of the station is sports. KLAA-AM broadcasts to the Anaheim, CA area at 830 AM.

KLAA-FM
Owner: Mapleton Communications
Editorial: 92 W Shamrock Ave, Pineville, Louisiana 71360-6435. **T:** 1 318 487-1035
W: http://www.la103.com
Editorial Profile: KLAA-FM is a commercial station owned by Opus Broadcasting of Alexandria, LLC. The format of the station is country music. KLAA-FM broadcasts in the Pineville, LA area at 103.5 FM.

KLAB-FM
Owner: John Brown University
Editorial: 2000 W University St, Siloam Springs, Arkansas 72761-2112.
T: 1 479 524-7360 **E:** klrc@klrc.com
W: http://www.klrc.com
Editorial Profile: KLRC-FM is a non-commercial station owned by John Brown University. The format of the station is religious and contemporary Christian. KLRC-FM broadcasts to the Siloam Springs, AR area at 101.1 FM.

KLAC-AM
Owner: Clear Channel Media and Entertainment
Editorial: 3400 W Olive Ave, Burbank, California 91505-5538. **T:** 1 818 559-2252
W: http://www.am570radio.com
Editorial Profile: KLAC-AM is a commercial station owned by Clear Channel Media and Entertainment. The format of the station is sports. KLAC-AM broadcasts to the Los Angeles area at 570 AM.

KLAD-AM
Owner: Basin Mediactive, LLC
Editorial: 404 Main St Ste 4, Klamath Falls, Oregon 97601-6021. **T:** 1 541 882-8833
E: news@mybasin.com
W: http://www.mybasin.com
Editorial Profile: KLAD-AM is a commercial station owned by Basin Mediactive, LLC. The format of the station is sports talk. KLAD-AM broadcasts to the Klamath Falls, OR area at 960 AM.

KLAD-FM
Owner: Basin Mediactive, LLC
Editorial: 404 Main St Ste 4, Klamath Falls, Oregon 97601-6021. **T:** 1 541 882-8833
E: news@mybasin.com
W: http://www.mybasin.com
Editorial Profile: KLAD-FM is a commercial station owned by New Northwest Broadcasters LLC. The format of the station is country music. KLAD-FM broadcasts to the Klamath Falls, OR area at 92.5 FM.

KLAK-FM
Owner: Digity LLC
Editorial: 1700 Redbud Blvd Ste 185, McKinney, Texas 75069-3270.
T: 1 972 542-9755 **W:** http://www.975klak.com
Editorial Profile: KLAK-FM is a commercial station owned by Digity LLC. The format of the station is adult contemporary music. KLAK-FM broadcasts in the Denison, TX area at 97.5 FM.

KLAL-FM
Owner: Cumulus Media Inc
Editorial: 700 Wellington Hills Rd, Little Rock, Arkansas 72211. **T:** 1 501 401-0200
W: http://www.alice1077.com
Editorial Profile: KLAL-FM is a commercial station owned by Cumulus Media Inc. The format of the station is Top 40/CHR. KLAL-FM broadcasts to the Little Rock, AR area at 107.7 FM.

KLAM-AM
Owner: Bayview Communications Inc.
Editorial: 112 Forestry Way, Cordova, Alaska 99574. **T:** 1 907 424-3796
E: email@cordovaradio.com
W: http://www.cordovaradio.com
Editorial Profile: KLAM-AM is a commercial station owned by Bayview Communications Inc. The format of the station is classic hits. KLAM-AM broadcasts to the Anchorage, AK area at 1450 AM.

KLAN-FM
Owner: Glasgow Broadcasting Corp.
Editorial: 504 2nd Ave S, Glasgow, Montana 59230. **T:** 1 406 228-9336 **E:** kltz@kltz.com
W: http://www.kltz.com
Editorial Profile: KLAN-FM is a commercial station owned by Glascow Broadcasting Corp. The format of the station is adult contemporary. KLAN-FM broadcasts to the Glasgow, MT area at 93.5 FM.

KLAQ-FM
Owner: Townsquare Media, LLC
Editorial: 4180 N Mesa St, El Paso, Texas 79902. **T:** 1 915 544-8864
W: http://www.klaq.com
Editorial Profile: KLAQ-FM is a commercial station owned by Townsquare Media, LLC. The format of the station is rock music. KLAQ-FM broadcasts to the El Paso, TX area at 95.5 FM.

KLAR-AM
Owner: Faith & Power Communications
Editorial: 3320 Anna Ave, Laredo, Texas 78040-1070. **T:** 1 956 723-1300
W: http://www.feypoder.com
Editorial Profile: KLAR-AM is a commercial station owned by Faith & Power Communications. The format of the station is Hispanic religious programming. KLAR-AM broadcasts to the Laredo, TX area at 1300 AM.

KLAT-AM
Owner: Univision Communications Inc.
Editorial: 5100 Southwest Fwy, Houston, Texas 77056-7308. **T:** 1 713 407-1415
W: http://univisionamerica.com
Editorial Profile: KLAT-AM is a commercial station owned by Univision Communications Inc. The format of the station is Hispanic news and talk programming. KLAT-AM broadcasts to the Houston area at 1010 AM.

KLAV-AM
Owner: Lotus Broadcasting Corp
Editorial: 6655 W Sahara Ave Ste C216, Las Vegas, Nevada 89146-0850.
T: 1 702 796-1230
W: http://www.klav1230am.com
Editorial Profile: KLAV-AM is a commercial station owned by Lotus Broadcasting Corp. The format of the station is news and talk. KLAV-AM broadcasts to the Las Vegas area at 1230 AM.

KLAW-FM
Owner: Townsquare Media, LLC
Editorial: 626 SW D Ave, Lawton, Oklahoma 73501. **T:** 1 580 581-3600
E: lawtonpsa@townsquaremedia.com
W: http://www.klaw.com
Editorial Profile: KLAW-FM is a commercial station owned by Townsquare Media, LLC. The format of the station is country music. KLAW-FM broadcasts to the Lawton, OK area at 101.3 FM.

KLAX-FM
Owner: Spanish Broadcasting System
Editorial: 10281 W Pico Blvd, Los Angeles, California 90064-2674. **T:** 1 310 203-0900
W: http://www.979laraza.com
Editorial Profile: KLAX-FM is a commercial station owned by Spanish Broadcasting System. The format of the station is regional Mexican music. KLAX-FM broadcasts to the Los Angeles area at 97.9 FM.

KLAY-AM
Owner: Huntington(Clay)
Editorial: 10025 Lakewood Dr SW, Ste B, Tacoma, Washington 98499.
T: 1 253 581-0324 **E:** klay1180@blarg.net
W: http://www.klay1180.com
Editorial Profile: KLAY-AM is a commercial station owned by Clay Huntington. The format of the station is news and talk. KLAY-AM broadcasts to the Tacoma, WA area at 1180 AM.

KLAZ-FM
Owner: Noalmark Broadcasting Corp.
Editorial: 208 Buena Vista Rd, Hot Springs, Arkansas 71913-8208. **T:** 1 501 525-4600
E: spots@klaz.com **W:** http://www.klaz.com
Editorial Profile: KLAZ-FM is a commercial station owned by Noalmark Broadcasting Corp. The format of the station is Top 40/CHR. KLAZ-FM broadcasts to the Hot Springs, AR area at 105.9 FM.

KLBB-AM
Owner: Endurance Broadcasting LLC
Editorial: 104 Main St N, Stillwater, Minnesota 55082-5076. **T:** 1 651 439-5006
W: http://www.klbbradio.com
Editorial Profile: KLBB-AM is a commercial station owned by Endurance Broadcasting LLC. The format of the station is adult standards music. KLBB-AM broadcasts to the Stillwater, MN area at 1220 AM.

KLBB-FM
Owner: Ramar Communications, Inc.
Editorial: 9800 University Ave, Lubbock, Texas 79423-5302. **T:** 1 806 745-3434
E: info@1077theeagle.fm
W: http://www.1077theeagle.fm
Editorial Profile: KLBB-FM is a commercial station owned by Ramar Communications, Inc. The format of the station is classic hits. KLBB-FM broadcasts to the Lubbock, TX area at a frequency of 107.7 FM.

KLBC-FM
Owner: Texoma Broadcasting Inc.
Editorial: 1418 N 1st Ave, Durant, Oklahoma 74701-2812. **T:** 1 580 924-3100
W: http://www.klbcfm.com
Editorial Profile: KLBC-FM is a commercial station owned by Texoma Broadcasting Inc. The format of the station is country music. KLBC-FM broadcasts in the Durant, OK area at 106.3 FM.

KLBJ-AM
Owner: Emmis Communications Corp.
Editorial: 8309 N Interstate 35, Austin, Texas 78753-5720. **T:** 1 512 832-4000
E: newsroom@emmisaustin.com
W: http://www.newsradioklbj.com
Editorial Profile: KLBJ-AM is a commercial station owned by Emmis Communications Corp. The format of the station is news, sports and talk. KLBJ-AM broadcasts to the Austin, TX area at 590 AM.

KLBJ-FM
Owner: Emmis Communications Corp.
Editorial: 8309 N Interstate Highway 35, Austin, Texas 78753. **T:** 1 512 832-4000
W: http://www.klbjfm.com
Editorial Profile: KLBJ-FM is a commercial station owned by Emmis Communications Corp. The format of the station is rock. KLBJ-FM broadcasts to the Austin, TX area at 93.7 FM.

KLBL-FM
Owner: US Stations, LLC
Editorial: 125 Corporate Ter, Hot Springs, Arkansas 71913-7248. **T:** 1 501 525-9700
E: info@usstations.com
W: http://www.myhotsprings.com
Editorial Profile: KLBL-FM is a commercial station owned by US Stations, LLC. The format of the station is classic country. KLBL-FM broadcasts to the Hot Springs, AR and surrounding areas at 104.5 FM.

KLBM-AM
Owner: Pacific Empire Communications
Editorial: 2510 Cove Ave, La Grande, Oregon 97850-3911. **T:** 1 541 963-4121
E: supertalk@eoni.com
W: http://www.supertalk1450.com
Editorial Profile: KLBM-AM is a commercial station owned by Pacific Empire Communications. The format of the station is talk. KLBM-AM broadcasts in the La Grande, OR area at 1450 AM and simulcasts on KBKR-AM.

KLBN-FM
Owner: Lotus Communications Corp.
Editorial: 1110 E Olive Ave, Fresno, California 93728-3535. **T:** 1 559 497-1100
E: production@lotusfresno.com
W: http://www.1019labuena.com
Editorial Profile: KLBN-FM is a commercial station owned by Lotus Communications Corp. The format of the station is regional Mexican. KLBN-FM broadcasts to the Fresno, CA area at 101.9 FM.

KLBQ-FM
Owner: El Dorado Broadcasting
Editorial: 1904 W Hillsboro St, El Dorado, Arkansas 71730-6806. **T:** 1 870 863-5121
E: klbqfm@yahoo.com
Editorial Profile: KLBQ-FM is a commercial station owned by El Dorado Broadcasting. The format of the station is classic and contemporary country. KLBQ-FM broadcasts to the El Dorado, AR area at 98.7 FM.

KLBS-AM
Owner: Ethnic Radio of Los Banos
Editorial: 401 Pacheco Blvd, Los Banos, California 93635. **T:** 1 209 826-0578
E: pr@klbs.com **W:** http://www.klbs.com
Editorial Profile: KLBS-AM is a commercial station owned by Ethnic Radio of Los Banos. The format of the station is Portuguese news, talk, and music. KLBS-AM broadcasts in the Los Banos, CA area at 1330 AM.

KLBU-FM
Owner: Hutton Broadcasting, LLC
Editorial: 2502 Camino Entrada, Santa Fe, New Mexico 87507-4911. **T:** 1 505 471-1067
W: http://www.santafe.com/juan
Editorial Profile: KLBU-FM is a commercial station owned by Hutton Broadcasting, LLC. The format of the station is Spanish Adult Hits. KLBU-FM broadcasts to the Santa Fe, NM area at 102.9 FM.

KLBW-AM
Owner: Chapel Of Light
Editorial: 1198 Daniels Chapel Rd, New Boston, Texas 75570. **T:** 1 903 628-2561
E: thelight1530@yahoo.com
W: http://www.1530thelight.com
Editorial Profile: KLBW-AM is a commercial station owned by Chapel Of Light. The format of the station is religious music and talk. KLBW-AM broadcasts to the Shreveport, LA area at 1530 AM.

KLCA-FM
Owner: Americom Broadcasting
Editorial: 961 Matley Ln, Ste 120, Reno, Nevada 89502. **T:** 1 775 829-1964
W: http://www.alice965.com
Editorial Profile: KLCA-FM is a commercial station owned by Americom Broadcasting. The format of the station is hot adult contemporary. KLCA-FM broadcasts to the Reno, NV area at 96.5 FM.

KLCB-AM
Owner: Lincoln County Broadcasters Inc.
Editorial: 251 W Cedar St, Libby, Montana 59923. **T:** 1 406 293-6234
E: klcb@frontiernet.net
W: http://www.todaysbestcountryonline.com
Editorial Profile: KLCB-AM is commercial station owned by Lincoln County Broadcasters Inc. The format of the station is contemporary country music. KLCB-AM broadcasts to the Libby, MT area at 1230 AM.

KLCC-FM
Owner: Lane Community College
Editorial: 136 W 8th Ave, Eugene, Oregon 97401-2940. **T:** 1 541 463-6000
E: news@klcc.org **W:** http://www.klcc.org
Editorial Profile: KLCC-FM is a non-commercial station owned by Lane Community College. The format of the station is variety. KLCC-FM broadcasts to the Eugene, OR area at 89.7 FM.

KLCE-FM
Owner: Riverbend Communications LLC
Editorial: 400 W Sunnyside Rd, Idaho Falls, Idaho 83402-4613. **T:** 1 208 528-3722
W: http://www.klce.com
Editorial Profile: KLCE-FM is a commercial station owned by Riverbend Communications LLC. The format of the station is adult contemporary music. KLCE-FM broadcasts to the Idaho Falls, ID area at 97.3 FM.

KLCH-FM
Owner: Q Media Group, LLC
Editorial: 474 Guernsey Ln, Red Wing, Minnesota 55066. **T:** 1 651 388-7151
E: traffic@kwng.com **W:** http://lakehits95.com
Editorial Profile: KLCH-FM is a commercial station owned by Q Media Group, LLC. The

format of the station is oldies. KLCH-FM broadcasts to the Red Wing, MN area at 94.9 FM.

KLCI-FM
Owner: StarCom LLC
Editorial: 14443 Armstrong Blvd NW, Anoka, Minnesota 55303-7284. **T:** 1 763 450-7777
W: http://www.dothebob.com
Editorial Profile: KLCI-FM is a commercial station owned by StarCom LLC. The format of the station is classic country music. KLCI-FM broadcasts to the Princeton, MN area at 106.1 FM.

KLCK-AM
Owner: Haystack Broadcasting, Inc
Editorial: 620 E 3Rd St, The Dalles, Oregon 97058-2506. **T:** 1 541 296-9102
W: http://klck1400.com
Editorial Profile: KLCK-AM is a commercial station owned by Haystack Broadcasting, Inc. The format of the station is talk. KLCK-AM broadcasts to The Dalles, OR area at 1400 AM.

KLCK-FM
Owner: Hubbard Radio, LLC
Editorial: 3650 131st Ave SE Ste 550, Bellevue, Washington 98006-1334.
T: 1 425 373-5536 **E:** info@click989.com
W: http://www.click989.com
Editorial Profile: KLCK-FM is a commercial station owned by Hubbard Radio, LLC. The format of the station is Modern AC. KLCK-FM broadcasts in the Bellevue, WA area at 98.9 FM.

KLCL-AM
Owner: Townsquare Media, LLC
Editorial: 900 N Lake Shore Dr, Lake Charles, Louisiana 70601. **T:** 1 337 433-1641
W: http://cajunradio.net
Editorial Profile: KLCL-AM is a commercial station owned by Townsquare Media, LLC. The format of the station is classic country. KLCL-AM broadcasts to the Lake Charles, LA area at 1470 AM.

KLCM-FM
Owner: Montana Broadcast Communications Inc.
Editorial: 620 NE Main St, Lewistown, Montana 59457-2021. **T:** 1 406 535-3441
E: traffic@kxlo-klcm.com
W: http://www.kxlo-klcm.com
Editorial Profile: KLCM-FM is a commercial station owned by Montana Broadcast Communications Inc. The format of the station is classic and modern rock. KLCM-FM broadcasts to the Lewistown, MT area at 95.9 FM.

KLCN-AM
Owner: Sudbury Broadcasting Group
Editorial: 125 S 2nd St, Blytheville, Arkansas 72315-3413. **T:** 1 870 762-2093
Editorial Profile: KLCN-AM is a commercial station owned by Sudbury Broadcasting Group. The format of the station is news and talk. KLCN-AM broadcasts to the Blytheville, AR area at 910 AM.

KLCU-FM
Owner: Cameron University
Editorial: 2800 W Gore Blvd, Lawton, Oklahoma 73505. **T:** 1 580 581-2472
E: kccu@cameron.edu **W:** http://www.kccu.org
Editorial Profile: KLCU-FM is a non-commercial station owned by Cameron University. The format of the station is news and classical. KLCU-FM broadcasts to the Lawton, OK area at 90.3 FM.

KLCV-FM
Owner: Bott Broadcasting Co.
Editorial: 233 S 13th St, Ste 1520, Lincoln, Nebraska 68508. **T:** 1 402 465-8850
E: klcv@bottradionetwork.com
W: http://www.bottradionetwork.com
Editorial Profile: KLCV-FM is a commercial station owned by Bott Broadcasting Co. The format of the station is Christian news and talk. KLCV-FM broadcasts to the Lincoln, NE area at 88.5 FM.

KLCY-FM
Owner: Ashley Communications
Editorial: 2425 N Vernal Ave, Vernal, Utah 84078-9587. **T:** 1 435 789-1059
W: http://www.klcy.com
Editorial Profile: KLCY-FM is a commercial station owned by Ashley Communications. The format of the station is country. KLCY-FM broadcasts to the Salt Lake City area at 105.9 FM.

KLCZ-FM
Owner: Lewis & Clark State College
Editorial: 500 8th Ave, Lewiston, Idaho 83501-2691. **T:** 1 208 792-2418
W: http://www.klcz.com
Editorial Profile: KLCZ-FM is a non-commercial station owned by Lewis & Clark State College. The format of the station is variety. KLCZ-FM broadcasts to the Lewiston, ID area at 88.9 FM.

KLDC-AM
Owner: Crawford Broadcasting Co.
Editorial: 2821 S Parker Rd Ste 1205, Aurora, Colorado 80014-2708. **T:** 1 303 433-5500
W: http://www.1220kldc.com
Editorial Profile: KLDC-AM is a commercial station owned by Crawford Broadcasting Co. The format of the station is gospel music. KLDC-AM broadcasts to the Denver area at 1220 AM.

KLDG-FM
Owner: Seward County Broadcasting Co.
Editorial: 1410 N Western Ave, Liberal, Kansas 67901. **T:** 1 620 624-3891
W: http://www.kscb.net
Editorial Profile: KLDG-FM is a commercial station owned by Seward County Broadcasting Co. The format of the station is contemporary country music. KLDG-FM broadcasts to the Liberal, KS area at 102.7 FM.

KLDJ-FM
Owner: Townsquare Media, LLC
Editorial: 14 E Central Entrance, Duluth, Minnesota 55811. **T:** 1 218 727-4500
W: http://www.kool1017.com
Editorial Profile: KLDJ-FM is a commercial station owned by Townsquare Media, LLC. The format of the station is classic hits. KLDJ-FM broadcasts to the Duluth, MN area at 101.7 FM.

KLDN-FM
Owner: Louisiana State University
Editorial: 1 University Pl, Shreveport, Louisiana 71115-2301. **T:** 1 318 797-5150
E: listenermail@redriverradio.org
W: http://www.redriverradio.org
Editorial Profile: KLDN-FM is a non-commercial station owned by Louisiana State University. The format of the station is news, talk, jazz and classical music. KLDN-FM broadcasts to the Lufkin, TX area at 88.9 FM.

KLDR-FM
Owner: Grants Pass Broadcasting Corp.
Editorial: 888 Rogue River Hwy, Grants Pass, Oregon 97527-5209. **T:** 1 541 474-7292
E: kldr@kldr.com **W:** http://www.kldr.com
Editorial Profile: KLDR-FM is a commercial station owned by Grants Pass Broadcasting Corp. The format of the station is hot adult contemporary. KLDR-FM broadcasts to the Grants Pass, OR area at 98.3 FM.

KLDY-AM
Owner: Seattle Streaming Radio LLC
Editorial: 7126 Martin Luther King Jr Way S, Ste 201, Seattle, Washington 98118-3595.
T: 1 303 688-5162
Editorial Profile: KLDY-AM is a commercial station owned by Seattle Streaming Radio LLC. The format of the station is Hispanic sports. KLDY-AM broadcasts to the Seattle area at 1280 AM.

KLDZ-FM
Owner: Bicoastal Media LLC
Editorial: 3624 Avion Dr, Medford, Oregon 97504. **T:** 1 541 772-4170
W: http://www.kool103.net
Editorial Profile: KLDZ-FM is a commercial station owned by Bicoastal Media LLC. The format of the station is oldies. KLDZ-FM broadcasts to the Medford, OR area at 103.5 FM.

KLEA-AM
Owner: Lea County Broadcasting
Editorial: Country Club Road, Lovington, New Mexico 88260. **T:** 1 575 396-2244
Editorial Profile: KLEA-AM is a commercial station owned by Lea County Broadcasting. The format of the station is classic country. KLEA-AM broadcasts to the Lovington, NM area at 630 AM.

KLEA-FM
Owner: Lea County Broadcasting
Editorial: 1 Country Club Road, Lovington, New Mexico 88260-0877. **T:** 1 575 396-2244
W: http://www.oldies1017.com
Editorial Profile: KLEA-FM is a commercial station owned by Lea County Broadcasting. The format of the station is oldies music. KLEA-AM broadcasts to the Albuquerque, NM area at 101.7 FM.

KLEB-AM
Owner: Coastal Broadcasting of Larose Inc.
Editorial: 11603 Highway 308, Larose, Louisiana 70373. **T:** 1 985 798-7792
E: klrz@viscom.net **W:** http://www.klrzfm.com
Editorial Profile: KLEB-AM is a commercial station owned by Coastal Broadcasting of Larose Inc. The format of the station is oldies music. KLEB-AM broadcasts to the New Orleans area at 1600 AM.

KLEE-AM
Owner: FMC Broadcasting Inc.
Editorial: 601 W 2nd St, Ottumwa, Iowa 52501. **T:** 1 641 682-8711
E: traffic@tomfmottumwa.com
W: http://www.1480KLEE.com
Editorial Profile: KLEE-AM is a commercial station owned by FMC Broadcasting Inc. The format for the station is oldies. KLEE-AM broadcasts to the Ottumna, IA area at 1480 AM.

KLEF-FM
Owner: Chinook Concert Broadcasters Inc.
Editorial: 4700 Business Park Blvd, Anchorage, Alaska 99503-7176.
T: 1 907 562-4434 **E:** klef@klef.com
W: http://www.klef.com
Editorial Profile: KLEF-FM is a commercial station owned by Chinook Concert Broadcasters Inc. The format of the station is classical. KLEF-FM broadcasts to the Anchorage, AK area at 98.1 FM.

KLEJ-FM
Owner: Acadia Broadcast Partners
Editorial: 320 N Parkerson Ave, Crowley, Louisiana 70526. **T:** 1 337 783-2520
W: http://bayou1067.com
Editorial Profile: KLEJ-FM is a commercial station owned by Acadia Broadcast Partners. The format of the station is Ethnic. KLEJ-FM broadcasts to the Crowley, LA area at 106.7 FM.

KLEM-AM
Owner: Powell Broadcasting Co.
Editorial: 37 2Nd Ave Nw, Le Mars, Iowa 51031-3529. **T:** 1 712 546-4121
E: klemnews@premieronline.net
W: http://www.klem1410.com
Editorial Profile: KLEM-AM is a commercial station owned by Powell Broadcasting Co. The format of the station is adult contemporary music. KLEM-AM broadcasts in the Sioux City, IA area at 1410 AM.

KLEN-FM
Owner: Townsquare Media, LLC
Editorial: 1912 Capitol Ave, Ste 300, Cheyenne, Wyoming 82001.
T: 1 307 632-4400
W: http://www.1063cowboycountry.com
Editorial Profile: KLEN-FM is a commercial station owned by Townsquare Media, LLC. The format for the station is contemporary country. KLEN-FM broadcasts to the Cheyenne, WY area at 106.3 FM.

KLEO-FM
Owner: Pacific Media Group
Editorial: 75-5852 Alii Dr. Suite B1 & B2, Lagoon Tower, Kailua Kona, Hawaii 96740-1310. **T:** 1 808 961-0651
W: http://www.kbigfm.com
Editorial Profile: KLEO-FM is a commercial station owned by Pacific Media Group. The format of the station is adult contemporary music. KLEO-FM broadcasts to the Hilo, HI area at 106.1 FM.

KLER-AM
Owner: Central Idaho Broadcasting
Editorial: 981 Upper Fords Creek Rd, Orofino, Idaho 83544-6217. **T:** 1 208 476-5702
E: klerproduction@kler-radio.com
Editorial Profile: KLER-AM is a commercial station owned by Central Idaho Broadcasting. The format of the station is contemporary country music. KLER-AM broadcasts to the Spokane, WA area at 1300 AM.

KLER-FM
Owner: Central Idaho Broadcasting
Editorial: 981 Upper Fords Creek Rd, Orofino, Idaho 83544-6217. **T:** 1 208 476-5702
E: klerproduction@kler-radio.com
Editorial Profile: KLER-FM is a commercial station owned by Central Idaho Broadcasting. The format of the station is adult contemporary music. KLER-FM broadcasts to the Orofino, ID, area at 95.1 FM.

KLES-FM
Owner: Luna Communications
Editorial: 152101 W County Road 12, Prosser, Washington 99350-7265. **T:** 1 509 786-1310
Editorial Profile: KLES-FM is a commercial station owned by Luna Communications. The format of the station is regional Mexican. KLES-FM broadcasts to the Prosser, WA area at 101.7 FM.

KLEX-AM
Owner: Bott Broadcasting Co.
Editorial: 111 W Main St, Richmond, Missouri 64085. **T:** 1 816 470-9925
E: kayx@bottradionetwork.com
W: http://www.bottradionetwork.com

KLEY-AM
Owner: Johnson Enterprises Inc.
Editorial: 338 S Kley Dr, Wellington, Kansas 67152. **T:** 1 620 326-3341 **E:** kley@sutv.com
W: http://www.kleyam.com
Editorial Profile: KLEY-AM is a commercial station owned by Johnson Enterprises Inc. The format of the station is sports. KLEY-AM broadcasts to the Wellington, KS area at 1130 AM.

KLEY-FM
Owner: L & L Broadcasting
Editorial: 4050 Eisenhauer Rd, San Antonio, Texas 78218-3409. **T:** 1 210 654-5100
W: http://www.vidasanantonio.com
Editorial Profile: KLEY-FM is a commercial station owned by L & L Broadcasting. The format of the station is regional Mexican. KLEY-FM broadcasts to the San Antonio area at 95.7 FM.

KLFC-FM
Owner: Mountaintop Broadcasting Inc.
Editorial: 205 W Atlantic St, Branson, Missouri 65616. **T:** 1 417 334-5532
E: 881fm@klfcradio.com
W: http://www.klfcradio.com
Editorial Profile: KLFC-FM is a non-commercial station owned by Mountaintop Broadcasting Inc. The format of the station is contemporary Christian. KLFC-FM broadcasts to the Branson, MO area at 88.1 FM.

KLFD-AM
Owner: Mid-Minnesota Media LLC
Editorial: 234 N Sibley Ave, Litchfield, Minnesota 55355. **T:** 1 320 693-3281
E: news@klfd1410.com
W: http://www.klfd1410.com
Editorial Profile: KLFD-AM is a commercial station owned by Mid-Minnesota Media LLC. The format of the station is variety. KLDF-AM broadcasts to the Litchfield, MN area at 1410 AM.

KLFE-AM
Owner: Salem Communications
Editorial: 2201 6th Ave, Ste 1500, Seattle, Washington 98121-1840. **T:** 1 206 443-8200
E: webmaster@kgnw.com
W: http://www.1590klfe.com
Editorial Profile: KLFE-AM is a commercial station owned by Salem Communications. The format of the station is talk. KLFE-AM broadcasts to the Seattle area at 1590 AM.

KLFF-FM
Owner: Logos Broadcasting Corp.
Editorial: 560 Higuera St, Ste G, San Luis Obispo, California 93401. **T:** 1 805 541-4343
E: info@klife.org **W:** http://www.klife.org
Editorial Profile: KLFF-FM is a non-commercial station owned by Logos Broadcasting Corp. The format of the station is contemporary Christian. KLFF-FM broadcasts to the San Luis Obispo, CA area at 89.3 FM.

KLFM-FM
Owner: Cherry Creek Radio
Editorial: 20 3rd St N, Ste 231, Great Falls, Montana 59401. **T:** 1 406 761-7600
Editorial Profile: KLFM-FM is a commercial station owned by Cherry Creek Radio. The format of the station is classic hits. KLFM-FM broadcasts to the Great Falls, MT at 92.9 FM.

KLFS-FM
Owner: Educational Media Foundation
Editorial: 6721 W 121st St Ste 100, Overland Park, Kansas 66209-2031. **T:** 1 913 663-9950
W: http://www.klove.com
Editorial Profile: KLFS-FM is a non-commercial station owned by Educational Media Foundation. The format of the station is contemporary Christian. KLFS-FM broadcasts to the Van Buren, AR area at 90.3 FM.

KLFX-FM
Owner: Clear Channel Media and Entertainment
Editorial: 100 W Central Texas Expy, Harker Heights, Texas 76548-2079.
T: 1 254 699-5000
W: http://www.1073rocks.com
Editorial Profile: KLFX-FM is a commercial station that is owned by Clear Channel Media and Entertainment. The station's format is rock music. KLFX-FM broadcasts to the Waco, TX area at 107.3 FM.

KLGA-AM
Owner: NRG Media LLC
Editorial: 2102 80th Ave, Algona, Iowa 50511. **T:** 1 515 295-2475
E: klganews@nrgmedia.com
Editorial Profile: KLGA-AM is a commercial station owned by NRG Media LLC . The format for the station is country music. KLGA-AM broadcasts to the Algona, IA area at 1600 AM.

KLGA-FM
Owner: NRG Media LLC
Editorial: 2102 80th Ave, Algona, Iowa 50511-7134. **T:** 1 515 295-2475
E: klganews@nrgmedia.com
W: http://www.algonaradio.com
Editorial Profile: KLGA-FM is a commercial station owned by NRG Media LLC. The format of the station is adult contemporary. KLGA-FM broadcasts to the Algona, IA area at 92.7 FM.

KLGD-FM
Owner: Vance Communications, LLC
Editorial: 209 S Danville Dr, Abilene, Texas 79605-1464. **T:** 1 325 437-5590
Editorial Profile: KLGD-FM is a commercial station owned byVance Communications, LLC. The format of the station is classic country music. KLGD-FM broadcasts to the Abilene, TX area at 106.9 FM.

KLGL-FM
Owner: Mid-Utah Radio Inc.
Editorial: 1600 W 500 N, Manti, Utah 84642-5503. **T:** 1 435 835-7301
W: http://midutahradio.com/klgl
Editorial Profile: KLGL-FM is a commercial station owned by Mid-Utah Radio Inc. The format of the station is classic hits. KLGL-FM broadcasts to the Salina, UT area at a frequency of 94.5 FM.

KLGN-AM
Owner: Cache Valley Radio Inc.
Editorial: 810 W 200 N, Logan, Utah 84321-3726. **T:** 1 435 752-1390
W: http://www.1390klgn.com
Editorial Profile: KLGN-AM is a commercial station owned by Cache Valley Radio Inc. The format of the station is soft AC. KLGN-AM broadcasts to the Salt Lake City area at 1390 AM.

KLGO-AM
Owner: Genuine Austin Radio
Editorial: 912 S Capital of Texas Hwy Ste 400, West Lake Hills, Texas 78746-6176.
T: 1 512 416-1100 **E:** info@kokefm.com
W: http://kokefm.com
Editorial Profile: KLGO-AM is a commercial station owned by Genuine Austin Radio. The format of the station is progressive country. KLGO-AM broadcasts to the Austin, TX area at 1490 AM.

KLGR-AM
Owner: Three Eagles Communications Co.
Editorial: 639 W Bridge St, Redwood Falls, Minnesota 56283. **T:** 1 507 637-2989
E: klgr@mchsi.com **W:** http://www.myklgr.com
Editorial Profile: KLGR-AM is a commercial station owned by Three Eagles Communications Co. The format of the station is classic country. KLGR-AM broadcasts to the Redwood Falls, MN area at 1490 AM.

KLGR-FM
Owner: Three Eagles Communications Co.
Editorial: 639 W Bridge St, Redwood Falls, Minnesota 56283. **T:** 1 507 637-2989
E: klgr@mchsi.com **W:** http://www.myklgr.com
Editorial Profile: KLGR-FM is a commercial station owned by Three Eagles Communications Co. The format of the station is adult contemporary. KLGR-FM broadcasts to the Redwood Falls, MN area at 97.7 FM.

KLGT-FM
Owner: Legend Communications
Editorial: 324 Coffeen Ave, Sheridan, Wyoming 82801-4809. **T:** 1 307 672-2690
E: klgt@vcn.com
W: http://www.bighornmountainradio.com
Editorial Profile: KLGT-FM is a commercial station owned by Legend Communications. The format of the station is hot country. KLGT-FM broadcasts to the Buffalo, WY area at 92.9 FM.

KLHB-FM
Owner: Tejas Broadcasting
Editorial: 1733 S Brownlee Blvd, Corpus Christi, Texas 78404-3018. **T:** 1 361 883-1600
W: http://www.club983.com
Editorial Profile: KLHB-FM is a commercial station owned by Tejas Broadcasting. The format of the station is Latin oldies music. KLHB-FM broadcasts to the Corpus Christi, TX area at 98.3 FM.

KLHI-FM
Owner: Pacific Media Group
Editorial: 311 Ano St, Kahului, Hawaii 96732-1304. **T:** 1 808 877-5566
W: http://www.native925.com
Editorial Profile: KLHI-FM is a commercial station owned by Pacific Media Group. The format of the station is contemporary island hits. KLHI-FM broadcasts to the Honolulu area at 92.5 FM.

KLHK-FM
Owner: Educational Media Foundation
Editorial: 4111 Barbara Loop Se Ste E1, Rio Rancho, New Mexico 87124-1068.
T: 1 505 352-4028 **W:** http://www.klove.com

KLHT-AM
Owner: Calvary Chapel Honolulu
Editorial: 98-1016 Komo Mai Dr, Aiea, Hawaii 96701. **T:** 1 808 524-1040
E: klht@hawaii.rr.com
W: http://www.calvarychapel.org/honolulu/

KLIC-AM
Owner: Media Ministries, Inc.
Editorial: 130 Art Aly, Monroe, Louisiana 71201-6749. **T:** 1 318 387-1230
W: http://talkradio1230.com
Editorial Profile: KLIC-AM is a commercial station owned by Media Ministries, Inc. The format of the station is oldies. KLIC-AM broadcasts to the Monroe, LA area at 1230 AM.

KLID-AM
Owner: Browning Skidmore Broadcasting Inc.
Editorial: 102 N 11th St, Poplar Bluff, Missouri 63901. **T:** 1 573 686-1600
W: http://www.klidradio.com
Editorial Profile: KLID-AM is a commercial station owned by Browning Skidmore Broadcasting Inc. The format of the station is oldies and talk. KLID-AM broadcasts to the Poplar Bluff, MO area at 1340 AM.

KLIF-AM
Owner: Cumulus Media Inc.
Editorial: 3090 Olive Street West Victory Plaza, Suite 400, Dallas, Texas 75219.
T: 1 214 526-2400 **W:** http://www.klif.com
Editorial Profile: KLIF-AM is a commercial station owned by Cumulus Media Inc. The format of the station is talk programming. KLIF-AM broadcasts to the Dallas area at 570 AM.

KLIF-FM
Owner: Cumulus Media Inc.
Editorial: 3090 Olive St Ste 400, Dallas, Texas 75219-7640. **T:** 1 214 526-7400
W: http://www.i93hits.com
Editorial Profile: KLIF-FM is a commercial station owned by Cumulus Media Inc. The format of the station is Top 40/CHR. KLIF-FM broadcasts to the Dallas area at 93.3 FM.

KLIK-AM
Owner: Cumulus Media Inc.
Editorial: 1002 Diamond Ridge Center, Suite 400, Jefferson City, Missouri 65109.
T: 1 573 893-5100
W: http://www.klik1240.com
Editorial Profile: KLIK-AM is a commercial station owned by Cumulus Media Inc. The format of the station is news and talk. KLIK-AM broadcasts in the Jefferson City, MO area at 1240 AM.

KLIL-FM
Owner: Cajun Broadcasting
Editorial: 10365 Hwy 1, Moreauville, Louisiana 71355. **T:** 1 318 985-2929 **E:** klil@kricket.net
Editorial Profile: KLIL-FM is a commercial station owned by Cajun Broadcasting. The format of the station is oldies music. KLIL-FM broadcasts to the Moreauville, LA, area at 92.1 FM.

KLIN-AM
Owner: NRG Media LLC
Editorial: 4343 O St, Lincoln, Nebraska 68510-1753. **T:** 1 402 475-4567
E: news@klin.com **W:** http://www.klin.com
Editorial Profile: KLIN-AM is a commercial station owned by NRG Media LLC. The format of the station is news, sports and talk. KLIN-AM broadcasts to the Lincoln, NE area at 1400 AM.

KLIO-AM
Owner: Journal Broadcast Group
Editorial: 4200 N Old Lawrence Rd, Wichita, Kansas 67219-3211. **T:** 1 316 838-9141
W: http://espndeportes.espn.go.com/?cc=3888
Editorial Profile: KLIO-AM is a commercial station owned by the Journal Broadcast Group. The format of the station is Spanish language Sports. KLIO-AM broadcasts to the Wichita, KS area at 1070 AM.

KLIP-FM
Owner: Holladay Broadcasting Co.
Editorial: 1109 Hudson Ln, Monroe, Louisiana 71201. **T:** 1 318 388-2323
E: la105@bayou.com
Editorial Profile: KLIP-FM is a commercial station owned by Holladay Broadcasting Co. The format of the station is classic hits music. KLIP-FM broadcasts in the Monroe, LA area at 105.3 FM.

KLIQ-FM
Owner: Platte River Radio, Inc.
Editorial: 500 E J St, Hastings, Nebraska 68901. **T:** 1 402 463-1230
E: thebreeze@kliqfm.com
W: http://www.kliqfm.com
Editorial Profile: KLIQ-FM is a commercial station owned by Platte River Radio, Inc. The format of the station is Lite Rock/Lite AC music. KLIQ-FM broadcasts to the Hastings, NE area at 94.5 FM.

KLIR-FM
Owner: Three Eagles Communications Co.
Editorial: 1418 25th St, Columbus, Nebraska 68601-2820. **T:** 1 402 564-2866
E: klir@columbus.threeeagles.com
W: http://www.mycentralnebraska.com

KLIT-FM
Owner: Nueva Cadena Radio Luz Inc. (La)
Editorial: 2702 Pine St, Laredo, Texas 78046-6225. **T:** 1 956 726-4738
Editorial Profile: KLIT-FM is a commercial station owned by La Nueva Cadena Radio Luz Inc. The format of the station is Hispanic contemporary Christian. The station airs in the Laredo, TX area at 93.3 FM.

KLIV-AM
Owner: Empire Broadcasting Systems Corp.
Editorial: 750 Story Rd, San Jose, California 95122-2604. **T:** 1 408 293-8030
E: news@kliv.com **W:** http://www.kliv.com
Editorial Profile: KLIV-AM is a commercial station owned by Empire Broadcasting Systems Corp. The format of the station is news. KLIV-AM broadcasts to the San Jose, CA area at 1590 AM.

KLIX-AM
Owner: Townsquare Media, LLC
Editorial: 415 Park Ave, Twin Falls, Idaho 83301. **T:** 1 208 733-7512
E: topstory@townsquaremedia.com
W: http://www.newsradio1310.com
Editorial Profile: KLIX-AM is a commercial station owned by Townsquare Media, LLC. The format of the station is news and talk. KLIX-AM broadcasts to the Twin Falls, ID area at 1310 AM.

KLIX-FM
Owner: Townsquare Media, LLC
Editorial: 415 Park Ave, Twin Falls, Idaho 83301. **T:** 1 208 733-7512
W: http://www.kool965.com
Editorial Profile: KLIX-FM is a commercial station owned by Townsquare Media, LLC. The format of the station is oldies. KLIX-FM broadcasts to the Twin Falls, ID area at 96.5 FM.

KLIZ-AM
Owner: BL Broadcasting Inc.
Editorial: 13225 Dogwood Dr, Baxter, Minnesota 56425. **T:** 1 218 828-1244
E: production@brainerd.net
W: http://www.kliz.com
Editorial Profile: KLIZ-AM is a commercial station owned by BL Broadcasting Inc. The format of the station is sports talk. KLIZ-AM broadcasts in the Minneapolis area at 1380 AM.

KLIZ-FM
Owner: BL Broadcasting Inc.
Editorial: 13225 Dogwood Dr, Baxter, Minnesota 56425-8669. **T:** 1 218 828-1244
E: kliz_1075@hotmail.com
W: http://www.theloon.com
Editorial Profile: KLIZ-FM is a commercial station owned by BL Broadcasting Inc. The format of the station is classic rock. KLIZ-FM broadcasts in the Brainerd, MN area at 107.5 FM.

KLJA-FM
Owner: Univision Communications Inc.
Editorial: 10801-2 N Mopac Expy, Austin, Texas 78759. **T:** 1 512 340-7100
W: http://www.univision.com/content/channel.jhtml?chid=10032&schid=10045
Editorial Profile: KLJA-FM is a commercial station owned by Univision Communications Inc. The format of the station is regional Mexican. KLJA-FM broadcasts to the Austin, TX area at 107.7 FM.

KLJR-FM
Owner: Lazer Broadcasting Corp.
Editorial: 200 S A St Ste 400, Oxnard, California 93030-5723. **T:** 1 805 240-2070
E: lazerbroadcasting@radiolazer.com
W: http://www.radiolazer.com
Editorial Profile: KLJR-FM is a commercial station owned by Lazer Broacasting Corp. The format of the station is Spanish adult hits. KLJR-FM broadcasts to the Santa Barbara, CA area at 96.7 FM.

KLJT-FM
Owner: Waller Broadcasting
Editorial: 3400 W Marshall Ave Ste 307, Longview, Texas 75604-5048.
T: 1 903 663-2477 **E:** jjo@mybreezefm.com
W: http://www.mybreezefm.com
Editorial Profile: KLJT-FM is a commercial station owned by Waller Broadcasting. The format of the station is hot adult contemporary. KLJT-FM broadcasts to the Jacksonville, TX area at 102.3 FM.

KLJY-FM
Owner: Gateway Creative Broadcasting, Inc
Editorial: 13358 Manchester Rd Ste 100, Saint Louis, Missouri 63131-1730.
T: 1 314 909-8569 **W:** http://joyfmonline.org
Editorial Profile: KLJY-FM is a non-commercial station owned by Gateway Creative Broadcasting, Inc. The format of the station is Contemporary Christian and talk. The station airs locally on 99.1 FM.

KLJZ-FM
Owner: MonsterMedia LLC
Editorial: 949 S Avenue B, Yuma, Arizona 85364-3440. **T:** 1 928 782-4321
E: todaysbestmusic@z93yuma.com
W: http://www.z93yuma.com
Editorial Profile: KLJZ-FM is a commercial station owned by MonsterMedia LLC. The format of the station is hot adult contemporary music. KLJZ-FM broadcasts in the Yuma, AZ area at 93.1 FM.

KLKA-FM
Owner: American Educational Broadcasting Inc.
Editorial: 3185 S Highland Dr, Las Vegas, Nevada 89109-1092. **T:** 1 702 731-5588
W: http://www.klove.com
Editorial Profile: KLKA-FM is a non-commercial station owned by American Educational Broadcasting Inc and in an LMA with Educational Media Foundation. The format is contemporary Christian music and religious programming from the K-Love Network. KLKA-FM broadcasts to Globe, AZ and surrounding areas at 88.5 FM.

KLKC-AM
Owner: Southeast Kansas Independent Living (SKIL)
Editorial: 1812 Main St, Parsons, Kansas 67357. **T:** 1 620 421-6400
W: http://www.sekinfo.com
Editorial Profile: KLKC-AM is a commercial station owned by Southeast Kansas Independent Living (SKIL). The format of the station is talk and sports. KLKC-AM broadcasts to the Parsons, KS area at 1540 AM.

KLKC-FM
Owner: Southeast Kansas Independent Living (SKIL)
Editorial: 1812 Main St, Parsons, Kansas 67357. **T:** 1 620 421-6400
W: http://www.sekinfo.com
Editorial Profile: KLKC-FM is a commercial station owned by Southeast Kansas

Independent Living (SKIL). The format of the station is adult hits. KLKC-FM broadcasts to the Parsons, KS area at 93.5 FM.

KLKK-FM
Owner: Coloff Media
Editorial: 31 1st St NE, Mason City, Iowa 50401. **T:** 1 641 421-7744
E: klkk@klkkfm.com
W: http://www.klkkfm.com
Editorial Profile: KLKK-FM is a commercial station owned by Coloff Media. The format of the station is classic rock. KLKK-FM broadcasts to the Mason City, IA, area at 103.7 FM.

KLKL-FM
Owner: Access.1 Communications Corp.
Editorial: 208 N Thomas Dr, Shreveport, Louisiana 71107-6520. **T:** 1 318 222-3122
W: http://www.klkl.fm
Editorial Profile: KLKL-FM is a commercial station owned by the Access.1 Communications Corp. The format of the station is oldies. KLKL-FM broadcasts to the Shreveport, LA area at 95.7 FM.

KLKO-FM
Owner: Elko Broadcasting Company
Editorial: 1800 Idaho St, Elko, Nevada 89801-4031. **T:** 1 775 738-1240
E: traffic@elkoradio.com
W: http://www.elkoradio.com
Editorial Profile: KLKO-FM is a commercial station owned by Elko Broadcasting Company. The format of the station is adult hits. KLKO-FM broadcasts to the Salt Lake City area at 93.7 FM.

KLKS-FM
Owner: Minnesota Christian Broadcasters Inc.
Editorial: 31287 Brunes St, Pequot Lakes, Minnesota 56472-2761. **T:** 1 218 568-4422
E: info@mcbiradio.org
W: http://www.100thepulse.org
Editorial Profile: KLKSJ-FM is a non-commercial station owned by Minnesota Christian Broadcasters Inc. The format of the station is contemporary Christian. KLKS-FM broadcasts to the Minneapolis area at 100.1 FM.

KLKY-FM
Owner: Jacobs Radio Programming, LLC
Editorial: 2617 W Falls Ave, Kennewick, Washington 99336-3002. **T:** 1 509 302-9874
W: http://www.urockfm.com
Editorial Profile: KLKY-FM is a commercial station owned by Jacobs Radio Programming, LLC. The format of the station is classic rock. The station airs locally at 96.1 FM.

KLLA-AM
Owner: Pene Broadcasting Inc.
Editorial: 101 Lees Ln, Leesville, Louisiana 71446. **T:** 1 337 239-3403
E: swapshop@kjae935.com
W: http://www.kjae935.com
Editorial Profile: KLLA-AM is a commercial station owned by Pene Broadcasting Co. Inc. The format of the station is oldies. KLLA-AM broadcasts to the Leesville, LA area at 1570 AM.

KLLB-AM
Owner: United Security Financial Inc.
Editorial: 1510 S Richards St, Salt Lake City, Utah 84115-5350. **T:** 1 801 487-0247
E: kllbam@yahoo.com
Editorial Profile: KLLB-AM is a commercial station owned by United Security Financial Inc. The format of the station is gospel music. KLLB-AM broadcasts in the Salt Lake City area.

KLLC-FM
Owner: CBS Radio
Editorial: 865 Battery St Fl 3, San Francisco, California 94111-1503. **T:** 1 415 765-4097
E: studio@radioalice.com
W: http://radioalice.cbslocal.com
Editorial Profile: KLLC-FM is a commercial station owned by CBS Radio. The format of the station is hot adult contemporary music. KLLC-FM broadcasts to the San Francisco area at 97.3 FM.

KLLE-FM
Owner: Univision Communications Inc.
Editorial: 601 W Univision Plz, Fresno, California 93704-1092. **T:** 1 559 430-8500
W: http://www.kallefm.com
Editorial Profile: KLLE-FM is a commercial station owned by Univision Communications Inc. The format of the station is Spanish pop. KLLE-FM broadcasts to the Fresno, CA market at 107.9 FM.

KLLK-AM
Owner: Bicoastal Media LLC
Editorial: 140 N Main St, Lakeport, California 95453. **T:** 1 707 263-6113
E: ukiah@bicoastalspots.com
Editorial Profile: KLLK-AM is a commercial station owned by Bicoastal Media LLC. The format for the station is Hispanic music. KLLK-AM broadcasts to the San Francisco area at 1250 AM.

KLLL-FM
Owner: Wilks Broadcast Group
Editorial: 33 Briercroft Office Park, Lubbock, Texas 79412. **T:** 1 806 762-3000
E: info@klll.com **W:** http://www.klll.com
Editorial Profile: KLLL-FM is a commercial station owned by Wilks Broadcast Group. The format of the station is contemporary country. KLLL-FM broadcasts to the Lubbock, TX area at 96.3 FM.

KLLP-FM
Owner: Rich Broadcasting, LLC
Editorial: 1406 Commerce Way, Idaho Falls, Idaho 83401-1233. **T:** 1 208 233-1133
W: http://www.star985.com
Editorial Profile: KLLP-FM is a commercial station owned by Rich Broadcasting, LLC. The format of the station is hot adult contemporary. KLLP-FM broadcasts to the Pocatello, ID area at 98.5 FM.

KLLT-FM
Owner: Saga Communications
Editorial: 2600 Highway Blvd, Spencer, Iowa 51301. **T:** 1 712 262-3300 **E:** lite1049@ncn.net
W: http://www.lite1049.com
Editorial Profile: KLLT-FM is a commercial station owned by Saga Communications. The format of the station is adult contemporary. KLLT-FM broadcasts to the Spencer, IA area at a frequency of 104.9 FM.

KLLU-FM
Owner: Educational Media Foundation
Editorial: 4111 Barbara Loop Se Ste E1, Rio Rancho, New Mexico 87124-1068.
T: 1 505 352-4028 **W:** http://www.klove.com

KLLY-FM
Owner: Buckley Broadcasting Corp.
Editorial: 3651 Pegasus Dr Ste 107, Bakersfield, California 93308-6836.
T: 1 661 393-1900 **W:** http://www.klly.com
Editorial Profile: KLLY-FM is a commercial station owned by Buckley Broadcasting Corp. The format of the station is Top 40/CHR. KLLY-FM broadcasts to the Bakersfield, CA area at 95.3 FM.

KLLZ-FM
Owner: Omni Broadcasting Co.
Editorial: 502 Beltrami Ave NW, Bemidji, Minnesota 56601. **T:** 1 218 444-1500
W: http://www.z99fm.com
Editorial Profile: KLLZ-FM is a commercial station owned by Omni Broadcasting Co. The format of the station is classic rock music. KLLZ-FM broadcasts to Bemidji, MN at 99.1 FM.

KLMA-FM
Owner: Ojeda Broadcasting Inc.
Editorial: 108 S Willow St, Hobbs, New Mexico 88240-6733. **T:** 1 575 391-9650
E: klmafm@yahoo.com
W: http://www.klmaradio.com
Editorial Profile: KLMA-FM is a commercial station owned by Ojeda Broadcasting Inc. The format of the station is regional Mexican music. KLMA-FM broadcasts in the Hobbs, NM area at 96.5 FM.

KLMG-FM
Owner: Adelante Media Group
Editorial: 500 Media Pl, Sacramento, California 95815-3733. **T:** 1 916 368-6300
W: http://www.latino979.com
Editorial Profile: KLMG-FM is a commercial station owned by Adelante Media Group. The format of the station is Bilingual Top 40/CHR. KLMG-FM broadcasts to the Jackson, CA area at 97.9 FM.

KLMJ-FM
Owner: CD Broadcasting Inc.
Editorial: 1509 4Th St Ne, Hampton, Iowa 50441-1106. **T:** 1 641 456-5656
E: klmj@klmj.com **W:** http://www.klmj.com
Editorial Profile: KLMJ-FM is a commercial station owned by CD Broadcasting Inc. The format of the station is a blend of country and adult contemporary music. KLMJ-FM broadcasts to the Hampton, IA area at 104.9 FM.

KLMM-FM
Owner: Lazer Broadcasting Corp.
Editorial: 312 E Mill St, #302, Santa Maria, California 93454. **T:** 1 805 928-9796
E: lazerbroadcasting@radiolazer.com
W: http://www.radiolazer.com
Editorial Profile: KLMM-FM is a commercial station owned by Lazer Broadcasting Corp. The format of the station is Regional Mexican. KLMM-FM broadcasts to the Santa Maria/Lompoc, CA area at a frequency of 94.1 FM.

KLMP-FM
Owner: Bethesda Christian Broadcasting
Editorial: 1853 Fountain Plaza Dr, Rapid City, South Dakota 57702. **T:** 1 605 342-6822
E: info@klmp.com **W:** http://www.klmp.com
Editorial Profile: KLMP-FM is a non-commercial station owned by Bethesda Christian Broadcasting. The format of the station is religious music and talk. KLMP-FM broadcasts to the Rapid City, SD area on 88.3 FM.

KLMR-AM
Owner: Cherry Creek Radio
Editorial: 7350 US Highway 50, Lamar, Colorado 81052. **T:** 1 719 336-2206
W: http://www.myhometeamsports.com/KLMR.html
Editorial Profile: KLMR-AM is a commercial station owned by Cherry Creek Radio. The format of the station is classic country. KLMR-AM broadcasts to the Lamar, CO area at 920 AM.

KLMR-FM
Owner: Cherry Creek Radio
Editorial: 7350 US Highway 50, Lamar, Colorado 81052. **T:** 1 719 336-2206
W: http://www.myhometeamsports.com/KLMR.html
Editorial Profile: KLMR-FM is a commercial station owned by Cherry Creek Radio. The format of the station is classic hits. KLMR-FM broadcasts to the Lamar, CO area at 93.5 FM.

KLMS-AM
Owner: Three Eagles Communications Co.
Editorial: 3800 Cornhusker Hwy, Lincoln, Nebraska 68504. **T:** 1 402 466-1234
W: http://www.1480klms.com
Editorial Profile: KLMS-AM is a commercial station owned by Three Eagles Communications Co. The format of the station is sports. KLMS-AM broadcasts to the Lincoln, NE area at 1480 AM.

KLMY-FM
Owner: Ohana Media Group
Editorial: 285 SW Main Ct, Warrenton, Oregon 97146-9456. **T:** 1 503 861-6620
W: http://www.ilovemy997.com
Editorial Profile: KLMY-FM is a commercial station owned by Ohana Media Group. The format of the station is Hot AC. KLMY-FM broadcasts to the Astoria, OR area at 99.7 FM.

KLNC-FM
Owner: NRG Media LLC
Editorial: 4343 O St, Lincoln, Nebraska 68510-1753. **T:** 1 402 475-4567
E: comments@1053wow.com
W: http://www.1053wow.com
Editorial Profile: KLNC-FM is a commercial station owned by NRG Media LLC. The format of the station is classic hits. KLNC-FM broadcasts to the Lincoln, NE area at 105.3 FM.

KLNE-FM
Owner: Nebraska Educational Telecommunications Commission
Editorial: 1800 N 33rd St, Lincoln, Nebraska 68503. **T:** 1 402 472-6141
E: radio@netnebraska.org
W: http://netnebraska.org/radio
Editorial Profile: KLNE-FM is a non-commercial station owned by Nebraska Educational Telecommunications Commission. The format of the station is news and classical music. KLNE-FM broadcasts to the Lexington, NE area at 88.7 FM. KLNE-FM's target audience is listeners, ages 18 to 64. KLNE-FM is a simulcast of KUCV-FM, any necessary contact for this station should be done through KUCV-FM.

KLNG-AM
Owner: Wilkins Communication Networks Inc.
Editorial: 120 S 35th St, Ste 2, Council Bluffs, Iowa 51501. **T:** 1 712 323-0100
E: klng@wilkinsradio.com
W: http://www.wilkinsradio.com
Editorial Profile: KLNG-AM is a commercial station owned by Wilkins Communication Networks Inc. The format of the station is Christian talk. KLNG-AM broadcasts to the Omaha, NE area at 1560 AM.

KLNO-FM
Owner: Univision Communications Inc.
Editorial: 7700 John W Carpenter Fwy, Fl 1, Dallas, Texas 75247. **T:** 1 214 525-0400
W: http://laquebuena941.univision.com
Editorial Profile: KLNO-FM is a commercial station owned by Univision Communications Inc. The format of the station is regional Mexican. KLNO-FM broadcasts to the Dallas area at 94.1 FM.

KLNR-FM
Owner: Nevada Public Radio
Editorial: 1289 S Torrey Pines Dr, Las Vegas, Nevada 89146-1004. **T:** 1 702 258-9895
E: info@knpr.org **W:** http://www.knpr.org
Editorial Profile: KLNR-FM is a non-commercial station owned by Nevada Public Radio. The format of the station is news and talk. KLNR-FM broadcasts to the Las Vegas area at 91.7 FM.

KLNV-FM
Owner: Univision Communications Inc.
Editorial: 600 W Broadway Ste 2150, San Diego, California 92101-3389.
T: 1 619 235-0600
W: http://lanueva1065.univision.com
Editorial Profile: KLNV-FM is a commercial station owned by Univision Communications. The format of the station is regional Mexican music. KLNV-FM broadcasts to the San Diego area at 106.5 FM.

KLNZ-FM
Owner: Entravision Communications Corp.
Editorial: 501 N 44th St, Phoenix, Arizona 85008-6526. **T:** 1 602 776-1400
W: http://www.tricolor1035.com
Editorial Profile: KLNZ-FM is a commercial station owned by Entravision Communications Corp. The format of the station is regional Mexican music. KLNZ-FM broadcasts to the Phoenix area at 103.5 FM.

KLOA-AM
Owner: Adelman Broadcasting Inc.
Editorial: 731 Balsam St, Ridgecrest, California 93555-3510. **T:** 1 760 371-1700
W: http://www.adelmanbroadcasting.com
Editorial Profile: KLOA-AM is a commercial station owned by Adelman Broadcasting Inc. The format of the station is oldies. KLOA-AM broadcasts to the Ridgecrest, CA area at 1240 AM.

KLO-AM
Owner: KLO Broadcasting Co.
Editorial: 257 E 200 S Ste 400, Salt Lake City, Utah 84111-2073. **T:** 1 801 364-9836
E: comments@kloradio.com
W: http://www.kloradio.com
Editorial Profile: KLO-AM is a commercial station owned by KLO Broadcasting Co. The format of the station is talk. KLO-AM broadcasts to the Salt Lake City area at 1430 AM.

KLOB-FM
Owner: Entravision Communications Corp.
Editorial: 41601 Corporate Way, Palm Desert, California 92260. **T:** 1 760 341-5837
W: http://www.jose947.com
Editorial Profile: KLOB-FM is a commercial station owned by Entravision Communications Corp. The format of the station is Regional Mexican. KLOB-FM broadcasts to the Palm Desert, CA area at 94.7 FM.

KLOC-AM
Owner: Favorita Broadcasting(La)
Editorial: 4043 Geer Rd, Hughson, California 95326. **T:** 1 209 883-8760
Editorial Profile: KLOC-AM is a commercial station owned by La Favorita Broadcasting. The format of the station is regional Mexican. KLOC-AM broadcasts to Modesto, CA area at 1370.

KLOE-AM
Owner: Melia Communications Inc.
Editorial: 3023 W 31st St, Goodland, Kansas 67735. **T:** 1 785 899-2309 **E:** kloe@st-tel.net
W: http://www.kloe.com
Editorial Profile: KLOE-AM is a commercial station owned by Melia Communications Inc. The format of the station is news, talk and sports. KLOE-AM broadcasts to the Goodland, KS area at 730 AM.

KLOG-AM
Owner: Washington Interstate Broadcasting Inc

Editorial: 506 W Cowlitz Way, Kelso, Washington 98626-1177. **T:** 1 360 636-0110
W: http://www.klog.com
Editorial Profile: KLOG-AM is a commercial station owned by Washington Interstate Broadcasting Inc. The format for the station is sports. KLOG-AM broadcasts to the Kelso, WA area at 1490 AM.

KLOH-AM
Owner: Christensen Broadcasting
Editorial: 608 State Highway 30, Pipestone, Minnesota 56164. **T:** 1 507 825-4282
E: kloh@klohradio.com
W: http://www.klohradio.com
Editorial Profile: KLOH-AM is a commercial station owned by Christensen Broadcasting. The format of the station is country music, talk and news. KLOH-AM broadcasts to the Pipestone, MN area at 1050 AM.

KLOK-AM
Owner: Principle Broadcasting Network, LLC
Editorial: 2905 S King Rd, San Jose, California 95122-1518. **T:** 1 408 440-0851
E: desi1170am@aol.com
W: http://www.klok1170am.com
Editorial Profile: KLOK-AM is a commercial station owned by Principle Broadcasting Network, LLC. The station airs a variety of news, music and talk South Asian programming. KLOK-AM broadcasts to the San Francisco Bay area at 1170 AM.

KLOK-FM
Owner: Entravision Communications Corp.
Editorial: 67 Garden Ct, Monterey, California 93940-5302. **T:** 1 831 333-9735
W: http://www.tricolor995.com
Editorial Profile: KLOK-FM is a commercial station owned by Entravision Communications Corp. The format of the station is Regional Mexican. KLOK-FM broadcasts to the Monterey/Salinas, CA area at a frequency of 99.5 FM.

KLOL-FM
Owner: CBS Radio
Editorial: 24 Greenway Plz, Ste 1900, Houston, Texas 77046-2428.
T: 1 713 881-5100 **W:** http://klol.radio.com
Editorial Profile: KLOL-FM is a commercial station owned by CBS Radio. The format of the station is Hurban. KLOL-FM broadcasts to the Houston area on 101.1 FM.

KLOO-AM
Owner: Bicoastal Media LLC
Editorial: 2840 Marion St SE, Albany, Oregon 97322-3978. **T:** 1 541 926-8628
W: http://www.klooam.com
Editorial Profile: KLOO-AM is a commercial station owned by Bicoastal Media LLC. The format of the station is news and talk. KLOO-AM broadcasts to the Albany, OR area at 1340 AM.

KLOO-FM
Owner: Bicoastal Media LLC
Editorial: 2840 Marion St SE, Albany, Oregon 97322-3978. **T:** 1 541 926-8628
W: http://www.kloofm.com
Editorial Profile: KLOO-AM is a commercial station owned by Bicoastal Media LLC. The format of the station is classic rock. KLOO-AM broadcasts to Albany, OR at 106.3 FM.

KLOQ-FM
Owner: Mapleton Radio, LLC
Editorial: 1020 W Main St, Merced, California 95340-4521. **T:** 1 209 723-2191
W: http://www.radiolobo987.com
Editorial Profile: KLOQ-FM is a commercial station owned by Mapleton Radio, LLC. The format of the station is Hispanic. KLOQ-FM broadcasts to Merced, CA at 98.7 FM.

KLOR-FM
Owner: Team Radio LLC
Editorial: 122 N 3rd St, Ponca City, Oklahoma 74601-4326. **T:** 1 580 762-9930
E: klor@eteamradio.com
W: http://www.eteamradio.com
Editorial Profile: KLOR-FM is a commercial station owned by Team Radio LLC. The format of the station is classic hits. KLOR-FM broadcasts to the Oklahoma City area at 99.3 FM.

KLOS-FM
Owner: Cumulus Media Inc
Editorial: 3321 S La Cienega Blvd, Los Angeles, California 90016-3114.
T: 1 310 840-4800
W: http://www.955klos.com
Editorial Profile: KLOS-FM is a commercial station owned by Cumulus Media Inc. The format of the station is classic rock. KLOS-FM broadcasts to the Los Angeles area at 95.5 FM.

KLOU-FM
Owner: Clear Channel Media and Entertainment
Editorial: 1001 Highlands Plaza Dr W, Saint Louis, Missouri 63110-1337.
T: 1 314 333-8000 **E:** klou@clearchannel.com
W: http://www.klou.com
Editorial Profile: KLOU-FM is a commercial station owned by Clear Channel Media and Entertainment. The format of the station is oldies. KLOU-FM broadcasts to the St. Louis area at 103.3 FM.

KLOW-FM
Owner: Vision Media Group, Inc.
Editorial: 2654 Lamar Ave, Paris, Texas 75460-4847. **T:** 1 903 783-9890
W: http://www.thehotfmrocks.com
Editorial Profile: KLOW-FM is a commercial station owned by Vision Media Group, Inc. The format of the station is Top 40/CHR. KCYY-FM broadcasts to the Paris, TX, Northeast Texas nad South East Oklahoma areas at 98.9 FM.

KLOZ-FM
Owner: Benne Media
Editorial: 160 Highway 42, Kaiser, Missouri 65047. **T:** 1 573 348-1958
W: http://www.todaysbesthits.com
Editorial Profile: KLOZ-FM is a commercial station owned by Benne Media. The format of the station is hot adult contemporary music. KLOZ-FM broadcasts to the Kaiser, MO area at 92.7 FM.

KLPF-AM
Owner: La Promesa Foundation
Editorial: 1903 S Lamesa Rd, Midland, Texas 79701. **T:** 1 432 638-1150
W: http://www.grnonline.com
Editorial Profile: KLPF-AM is a non-commercial station owned by La Promesa Foundation. The format of the station is religious programming with a Catholic emphasis. KLPF-AM broadcasts to the Midland, TX area at 1150 AM.

KLPI-FM
Owner: Louisiana Tech University
Editorial: 100 Wysteria St, Ruston, Louisiana 71272. **T:** 1 318 257-4851
E: general@891klpi.com
Editorial Profile: KLPI-FM is a non-commercial station owned by Louisiana Tech University. The format of the station is variety. KLPI-FM broadcasts to the Ruston, LA area at a frequency of 89.1 FM.

KLPR-FM
Owner: University of Nebraska
Editorial: 905 W 25th St, Kearney, Nebraska 68849-0002. **T:** 1 308 865-8737
E: klpr@unk.edu **W:** http://klpr.unk.edu
Editorial Profile: KLPR-FM is a non-commercial station owned by the University of Nebraska. The format of the station is variety with a primary music format of adult alternative. KLPR-FM broadcasts to the Kearney, NE area on 93.1 FM. This station is student run and only on-air during the school season.

KLPW-AM
Owner: Broadcast Properties
Editorial: 6501 Highway Bb, Washington, Missouri 63090-6085. **T:** 1 636 583-5155
E: news@klpw.com **W:** http://www.klpw.com
Editorial Profile: KLPW-AM is a commercial station owned by Broadcast Properties. The format of the station is news and talk. KLPW-AM broadcasts to the Washington, MO area at 1220 AM.

KLPW-FM
Owner: Marathon Media Group, LLC
Editorial: 5988 Mid Rivers Mall Dr Ste 136, Saint Peters, Missouri 63304-8303.
T: 1 314 808-3870
Editorial Profile: KLPW-FM is a commercial station owned by Marathon Media Group, LLC. The format of the station is sports. KLPW-FM broadcasts in the Elsberry, MO area at 101.7 FM.

KLPX-FM
Owner: Lotus Communications Corp.
Editorial: 3871 N Commerce Dr, Tucson, Arizona 85705-2983. **T:** 1 520 407-4500
W: http://www.klpx.com
Editorial Profile: KLPX-FM is a commercial station owned by Lotus Communications Corp. The format of the station is classic rock. KLPX-FM broadcasts in the Tucson, AZ area at 96.1 FM.

KLPZ-AM
Owner: Learn (Keith Douglas)
Editorial: 816 W 6th St, Parker, Arizona 85344. **T:** 1 928 669-9274
E: info@klpz1380.com
W: http://www.klpz1380.com
Editorial Profile: KLPZ-AM is commercial station owned by Keith Douglas Learn. The format of the station is classic country and talk. KLPZ-AM broadcasts to the Phoenix area at 1380 AM.

KLQB-FM
Owner: Univision Communications Inc.
Editorial: 10801-2 N Mopac Expy, Austin, Texas 78759. **T:** 1 512 419-7100
W: http://www.univision.com/content/channel.jhtml?chid=10032&schid=20932
Editorial Profile: KLQB-FM is a commercial station owned by Univision Communications Inc. The format of the station is regional Mexican. KXBT-FM broadcasts to the Austin, TX area at 104.3 FM.

KLQL-FM
Owner: Three Eagles Communications Co.
Editorial: 1140 150Th Ave, Luverne, Minnesota 56156-4215. **T:** 1 507 283-4444
E: info@luverne.threeeagles.com
W: http://www.oursiouxland.com
Editorial Profile: KLQL-FM is a commercial station owned by Three Eagles Communications. The format of the station is country music. KLQL-FM broadcasts to the Luverne, MN area at 101.1 FM.

KLQM-FM
Owner: Mandatory Broadcasting
Editorial: 2900 W Washington St Ste 73, Stephenville, Texas 76401-3754.
T: 1 254 968-4776 **E:** kwby@hprnetwork.com
W: http://www.hprnetwork.com
Editorial Profile: KLQM-FM is a commercial station owned by Mandatory Broadcasting and operated by High Plains Radio Network. The format of the station is news and sports. KLQM-FM broadcasts to the Stephenville, TX area and nearby communities at 98.5 FM.

KLQP-FM
Owner: Lac Qui Parle Broadcasting Co.
Editorial: 623 W 3rd St, Madison, Minnesota 56256-1325. **T:** 1 320 598-7301
E: klqpfm@farmerstel.net
W: http://www.klqpfm.com
Editorial Profile: KLQP-FM is a commercial station owned by Lac Qui Parle Broadcasting Co. The format of the station is a mix of classic country and classic hits. KLQP-FM broadcasts to the Madison, MN area at 92.1 FM.

KLQT-FM
Owner: Clear Channel Media and Entertainment
Editorial: 5411 Jefferson St NE, Ste 100, Albuquerque, New Mexico 87109.
T: 1 505 830-6400
W: http://www.channel951.com
Editorial Profile: KLQT-FM is a commercial station owned by Clear Channel Media and Entertainment. The format of the station is Top 40/CHR. KLQT-FM broadcasts to the Albuquerque, NM area at 95.1 FM.

KLQV-FM
Owner: Univision Communications Inc.
Editorial: 600 W Broadway, Ste 2150, San Diego, California 92101-3389.
T: 1 619 235-0600
W: http://recuerdo1029.univision.com
Editorial Profile: KLQV-FM is a commercial station owned by Univision Communications Inc. The format of the station is Hispanic oldies and adult hits. KLQV-FM broadcasts to the San Diego area at 102.9 FM.

KLRE-FM
Owner: University of Arkansas
Editorial: 5820 Asher Ave Ste 400, Little Rock, Arkansas 72204-7872.
T: 1 501 569-8485 **W:** http://www.klre.org
Editorial Profile: KLRE-FM is a non-commercial station owned by the University of Arkansas. The format of the station is classical music. KLRE-FM broadcasts in the Little Rock, AR area at 90.5 FM.

KLRG-AM
Owner: Kinlow (Joel, J.)
Editorial: 6400 Scott Hamilton Dr, Little Rock, Arkansas 72209-8538. **T:** 1 727 441-3311
W: http://www.tantalk1340.com
Editorial Profile: KLRG-AM is a commercial station owned by Joel J. Kinlow. The format of the station is news and talk. KLRG-AM broadcasts in the Little Rock, AR area at 880 AM.

KLRH-FM
Owner: Educational Media Foundation
Editorial: 5700 W Oaks Blvd, Rocklin, California 95765. **T:** 1 916 251-2142
W: http://www.klove.com

KLRK-AM
Owner: M & M Broadcasters
Editorial: 5501 Bagby Ave, Waco, Texas 76711-2300. **T:** 1 254 772-0930
Editorial Profile: KLRK-AM is a commercial station owned by M & M Broadcasters. The format of the station is adult hits. KLRK-AM broadcasts to the Waco, TX area at 1590 AM.

KLRQ-FM
Owner: Educational Media Foundation
Editorial: 6721 W 121st St Ste 100, Overland Park, Kansas 66209-2031. **T:** 1 913 663-9950
E: Info@klove.com **W:** http://www.klove.com
Editorial Profile: KLRQ-FM is a non-commercial station owned by Educational Media Foundation. The format of the station is contemporary Christian music. KLRQ-FM broadcasts to the Clinton, MO area at 96.1 FM.

KLRR-FM
Owner: Combined Communications
Editorial: 63088 Ne 18Th St Ste 200, Bend, Oregon 97701-7102. **T:** 1 541 389-1088
E: clear@clear1017.fm
W: http://www.clear1017.fm
Editorial Profile: KLRR-FM is a commercial station owned by Combined Communications. The format of the station is adult album alternative music. KLRR-FM broadcasts to the Bend, OR area at 101.7 FM.

KLRX-FM
Owner: Educational Media Foundation
Editorial: 6721 W 121st St Ste 100, Overland Park, Kansas 66209-2031. **T:** 1 913 663-9950
E: info@klove.com **W:** http://www.klove.com
Editorial Profile: KLRX-FM is a non-commercial station owned by Union Broadcasting Inc. The format of the station is contemporary Christian. KLRX-FM broadcasts to the Kansas City, MO area at 97.3 FM.

KLRZ-FM
Owner: Coastal Broadcasting of Larose Inc.
Editorial: 11603 Highway 308, Larose, Louisiana 70373. **T:** 1 985 798-7792
E: klrz@viscom.net **W:** http://www.klrzfm.com
Editorial Profile: KLRZ-FM is a commercial station owned by Coastal Broadcasting of Larose Inc. The format of the station is variety. KLRZ-FM broadcasts to the Larose, LA area at 100.3 FM.

KLSA-FM
Owner: Louisiana State University
Editorial: 1 University Pl, Shreveport, Louisiana 71115-2301. **T:** 1 318 797-5150
E: listenermail@redriverradio.org
W: http://www.redriverradio.org
Editorial Profile: KLSA-FM is a non-commercial station owned by Louisiana State University. The format of the station is classical, jazz music and news/talk. KLSA-FM broadcasts to the Alexandria, LA area at 90.7 FM.

KLSC-FM
Owner: Max Media
Editorial: 324 Broadway St, Cape Girardeau, Missouri 63701-7331. **T:** 1 573 335-8291
W: http://www.929theriver.com
Editorial Profile: KLSC-FM is a commercial station owned by Max Media. The format of the station is classic hits. KLSC-FM broadcasts to the Cape Girardeau, MO area at a frequency of 92.9 FM.

KLSD-AM
Owner: Clear Channel Media and Entertainment
Editorial: 9660 Granite Ridge Dr, San Diego, California 92123-2688. **T:** 1 858 292-2000
W: http://www.xtrasports1360.com
Editorial Profile: KLSD-AM is a commercial station owned by Clear Channel Media and Entertainment. The format of the station is sports. KLSD-AM broadcasts to the San Diego area at 1360 AM.

KLSE-FM
Owner: Minnesota Public Radio

Editorial: 206 S Broadway, Ste 735, Rochester, Minnesota 55904.
T: 1 507 282-0910 **E:** newsroom@mpr.org
W: http://minnesota.publicradio.org/radio/stations/kzseklse/
Editorial Profile: KLSE-FM is a non-commercial station owned by Minnesota Public Radio. The format of the station is news/talk programming. KLSE-FM broadcasts to the Rochester, MN area at 91.7 FM.

KLSK-FM
Owner: Flinn Broadcasting Corp.
Editorial: 1601 2nd Ave N, Ste 528, Great Falls, Montana 59401-3289.
T: 1 406 727-8200 **W:** http://www.klove.com
Editorial Profile: KLSK-FM is in an LMA with Educational Media Foundation.

KLSM-FM
Owner: Debut Broadcasting Inc.
Editorial: 1601-E N Frontage Rd, Vicksburg, Mississippi 39180-5149. **T:** 1 601 636-2340
W: http://www.1045khits.com
Editorial Profile: KLSM-FM is a commercial station owned by Debut Broadcasting Inc. The format of the station is adult hits. KLSM-FM broadcasts to the Vicksburg, MS area at 104.5 FM.

KLSQ-AM
Owner: Univision Communications Inc.
Editorial: 6767 W Tropicana Ave Ste 102, Las Vegas, Nevada 89103-4755.
T: 1 702 284-6400
W: http://univisionamerica.com
Editorial Profile: KLSQ-AM is a commercial station owned by Univision Communications Inc. The format is Spanish news and talk. KLSQ-AM broadcasts to the Las Vegas area on 870 AM.

KLSR-FM
Owner: Davis Broadcast Company, Inc
Editorial: 114 N 7th St, Memphis, Texas 79245. **T:** 1 806 259-3511
Editorial Profile: KLSR-FM is a commercial station owned by Davis Broadcast Company, Inc. The format of the station is country. KLSR-FM broadcasts to the Memphis, TX area at a frequency of 105.3.

KLSS-FM
Owner: Three Eagles Communications Co.
Editorial: 341 S Yorktown Pike, Mason City, Iowa 50401-4533. **T:** 1 641 423-1300
W: http://www.mystar106.com
Editorial Profile: KLSS-FM is a commercial station owned by Three Eagles Communications Co. The format of the station is adult contemporary. KLSS-FM broadcasts to the Mason City, IA area at 106.1 FM.

KLSU-FM
Owner: Louisiana State University
Editorial B-39 Hodges Hall Lsu, Baton Rouge, Louisiana 70803-0001. **T:** 1 225 578-8688
E: klsupromotions@tigers.lsu.edu
W: http://www.klsu.fm
Editorial Profile: KLSU-FM is a non-commercial station owned by Louisiana State University. The format of the station is college variety. KLSU-FM broadcasts to the Baton Rouge, LA area at 91.1 FM.

KLSY-FM
Owner: Jodesha Broadcasting Inc.
Editorial: 1520 Simpson Ave, Aberdeen, Washington 98520-4708. **T:** 1 360 533-3000
E: info@jodesha.com
W: http://www.bigfoot937.com
Editorial Profile: KLSY-FM is a commercial station owned by Jodesha Broadcasting Inc. The format of the station is contemporary country. KLSY-FM broadcasts to the South Bend, WA area at 107.3 FM.

KLSZ-FM
Owner: Cumulus Media Inc.
Editorial: 4209 N Frontage Rd, Fayetteville, Arkansas 72703-5002. **T:** 1 479 452-0681
W: http://www.rock1007.com
Editorial Profile: KLSZ-FM is a commercial station owned by Cumulus Media Inc. The format of the station is sports. KLSZ-FM broadcasts to the Fort Smith, AR area at 100.7 FM.

KLTA-FM
Owner: Triad Broadcasting, LLC
Editorial: 2720 7th Ave S, Fargo, North Dakota 58103-8710. **T:** 1 701 237-4500
Editorial Profile: KLTA-FM is a commercial station owned by Triad Broadcasting, LLC. The format of the station is adult contemporary music. KLTA-FM broadcasts to the Fargo, ND area at 98.7 FM.

KLTC-AM
Owner: Clear Channel Media and Entertainment
Editorial: 11291 39th St SW, Dickinson, North Dakota 58601. **T:** 1 701 227-1876
E: clearaudio@clearchannel.com
Editorial Profile: KLTC-AM is a commercial station owned by Clear Channel Media and Entertainment. The format of the station is country. KLTC-AM broadcasts to the Dickinson, ND area at 1460 AM.

KLTD-FM
Owner: Townsquare Media, Inc.
Editorial: 608 Moody Ln, Temple, Texas 76504-2952. **T:** 1 254 773-5252
W: http://www.k1017fm.com
Editorial Profile: KLTD-FM is a commercial station owned by Townsquare Media, Inc. The format of the station is classic hits. KLTD-FM broadcasts to the Temple, TX area at 101.7 FM.

KLTE-FM
Owner: Bott Broadcasting Co.
Editorial: 3 Crown Dr, #100, Kirksville, Missouri 63501. **T:** 1 660 627-5583
E: klte@bottradionetwork.com
W: http://www.bottradionetwork.com
Editorial Profile: KLTE-FM is a commercial station owned by Bott Broadcasting Co. The format of the station is Christian talk programming. KLTE-FM broadcasts to the Kirksville, MO area at 107.9 FM.

KLTF-AM
Owner: Little Falls Radio Corp.
Editorial: 16405 Haven Rd, Little Falls, Minnesota 56345-6400. **T:** 1 320 632-2992
E: news@fallsradio.com
W: http://www.fallsradio.com
Editorial Profile: KLTF-AM is a commercial station owned by Little Falls Radio Corp. The format of the station is news, sports, and talk. KLTF-AM broadcasts to the Little Falls, MN area at 960 AM.

KLTG-FM
Owner: Tejas Broadcasting
Editorial: 1733 S Brownlee Blvd, Corpus Christi, Texas 78404-3018. **T:** 1 361 883-1600
E: beach965@gmail.com
W: http://thebeach965fm.com
Editorial Profile: KLTG-FM is a commercial station owned by Tejas Broadcasting. The format of the station is hot adult contemporary music. KLTG-FM broadcasts to the Corpus Christi, TX area at 96.5 FM.

KLTH-FM
Owner: Clear Channel Media and Entertainment
Editorial: 13333 SW 68th Pkwy Ste 310, Tigard, Oregon 97223-8304.
T: 1 503 323-6400
W: http://www.portlandoldies.com
Editorial Profile: KLTH-FM is a commercial station owned by Clear Channel Media and Entertainment. The format of the station is oldies. KLTH-FM broadcasts to the Portland, OR area at 106.7 FM.

KLTI-AM
Owner: Best Broadcast Group
Editorial: 32968 Us Highway 63, Macon, Missouri 63552-4535. **T:** 1 660 385-1560
E: klti@mcmsys.com
W: http://www.kltiradio.com
Editorial Profile: KLTI-AM is a commercial station owned by Best Broadcast Group. The format for the station is classic country. KLTI-AM broadcasts to the Ottumna, IA-Kirksville, MO area at 1560 AM.

KLTI-FM
Owner: Saga Communications
Editorial: 1416 Locust St, Des Moines, Iowa 50309-3014. **T:** 1 515 280-1350
W: http://www.lite1041.com
Editorial Profile: KLTI-FM is a commercial station owned by Saga Communications. The format of the station is adult contemporary. KLTI-FM broadcast to Des Moines, IA at 104.1 FM.

KLTN-FM
Owner: Univision Communications Inc.
Editorial: 5100 Southwest Fwy, Houston, Texas 77056-7308. **T:** 1 713 965-2400
W: http://www.univision.com/content/channel.jhtml?chid=9655&schid=9666
Editorial Profile: KLTN-FM is a commercial station owned by Univision Communications Inc. The format of the station is Mexican regional music. KLTN-FM broadcasts to the Houston area at 102.9 FM.

KLTO-AM
Owner: Forum Broadcasting Inc.
Editorial: 107 Center Dr, Del Rio, Texas 78840-3015. **T:** 1 830 775-9583
Editorial Profile: KLTO-AM is a commercial station owned by Forum Broadcasting Inc. The format of the station is Hispanic Top 40/CHR. KLTO-AM broadcasts to the Del Rio, TX area at 1230 AM.

KLTR-FM
Owner: La Grange Broadcasting
Editorial: 530 W Main St, Brenham, Texas 77833. **T:** 1 979 836-9411
W: http://www.litefm941.com
Editorial Profile: KLTR-FM is a commercial station owned by La Grange Broadcasting. The format of the station is Lite Rock/Lite AC. KLTR-FM broadcasts to the Brenham, TX area at 94.1 FM.

KLTT-AM
Owner: Crawford Broadcasting Co.
Editorial: 2821 S Parker Rd Ste 1205, Aurora, Colorado 80014-2708. **T:** 1 303 433-5500
E: kltt@crawfordbroadcasting.com
W: http://www.670kltt.com
Editorial Profile: KLTT-AM is a commercial station owned by Crawford Broadcasting Co. The format of the station is Christian talk. KLTT-AM broadcasts to the Denver area at 670 AM.

KLTU-FM
Owner: Good News Radio Broadcasting Inc.
Editorial: 3222 S Richey Ave, Tucson, Arizona 85713. **T:** 1 520 790-2440
W: http://www.klove.com
Editorial Profile: KLTU-FM is a commercial station owned by Good News Radio Broadcasting Inc. The format of the station is contemporary Christian. KLTU-FM broadcasts to the Mammoth, AZ area at 88.1 FM. The programming comes from the K-Love Network.

KLTW-FM
Owner: Horizon Broadcasting Group
Editorial: 854 Ne 4Th St, Bend, Oregon 97701-4711. **T:** 1 541 383-3825
E: news@horizonbroadcastinggroup.com
W: http://www.lite951.com
Editorial Profile: KLTW-FM is a commercial station owned by Horizon Broadcasting Group. The format for the station is Lite Rock/Lite AC. KLTW-FM broadcasts to the Bend, OR area at 95.7 FM.

KLTX-AM
Owner: Hi-Favor Broadcasting LLC
Editorial: 136 S Oak Knoll Ave Ste 202, Pasadena, California 91101-2624.
T: 1 626 356-4230
W: http://www.nuevavida.com
Editorial Profile: KLTX-AM is a commercial radio station owned by Hi-Favor Broadcasting LLC. The format of the station is Spanish religious music. KLTX-AM broadcasts to the Pasadena, CA area on 1390 AM.

KLTY-FM
Owner: Salem Communications
Editorial: 6400 N Belt Line Rd, Ste 120, Irving, Texas 75063. **T:** 1 972 870-9949
E: onair@klty.com **W:** http://www.klty.com
Editorial Profile: KLTY-FM is a commercial station owned by Salem Communications, dba Inspiration Media of Texas. The format of the station is contemporary Christian music. KLTY-FM broadcasts to the Dallas area at 94.9 FM.

KLTZ-AM
Owner: Glasgow Broadcasting Corp.
Editorial: 504 2nd Ave S, Glasgow, Montana 59230. **T:** 1 406 228-9336 **E:** kltz@kltz.com
W: http://www.kltz.com
Editorial Profile: KLTZ-AM is a commercial station owned by Glasgow Broadcasting Corp. The format of the station is classic country. KLTZ-AM broadcasts to the Great Falls, MT area at 1240 AM.

KLUA-FM
Owner: Pacific Media Group
Editorial: 75-5852 Alii Dr. Suite B1 & B2, Lagoon Tower, Kailua-Kona, Hawaii 96740.
T: 1 808 961-0651
W: http://www.nativefm.com
Editorial Profile: KLUA-FM is a commercial station owned by Pacific Media Group. The format of the station is contemporary island music. The station airs locally at 93.9 FM.

KLUB-FM
Owner: Townsquare Media, LLC
Editorial: 107 N Star Dr, Victoria, Texas 77904. **T:** 1 361 573-0777
W: http://www.1069therock.com
Editorial Profile: KLUB-FM is a commercial station owned by Townsquare Media, LLC. The format for the station is classic rock. KLUB-FM broadcasts to the Victoria, TX area at 106.9 FM.

KLUC-FM
Owner: CBS Radio
Editorial: 7255 S Tenaya Way Ste 100, Las Vegas, Nevada 89113. **T:** 1 702 253-9800
W: http://www.kluc.com
Editorial Profile: KLUC-FM is a commercial station owned by CBS Radio. The format of the station is urban contemporary. KLUC-FM broadcasts to the Las Vegas area at 98.5 FM.

KLUE-FM
Owner: Stratemeyer Media
Editorial: 203 Main St, Poplar Bluff, Missouri 63901-5831. **T:** 1 573 778-0142
E: stratemeyermedia@yahoo.com
W: http://www.klue103.com
Editorial Profile: KLUE-FM is a commercial station owned by Stratemeyer Media. The format of the station is hot adult contemporary. KLUE-FM broadcasts to the Poplar Bluff, MO area at 103.5 FM.

KLUH-FM
Owner: David Craig Ministries Inc.
Editorial: 1165 County Road 307, Poplar Bluff, Missouri 63901-4887. **T:** 1 573 686-1663
E: info@dcmliferadio.org
W: http://www.dcmliferadio.org/
Editorial Profile: KLUH-FM is a non-commercial station David Craig Ministries Inc. The format of the station is contemporary Christian. KLUH-FM broadcasts to the Poplar Bluff, MO area at 90.3 FM.

KLUK-FM
Owner: Cameron Broadcasting Inc.
Editorial: 2350 Miracle Mile Ste 300, Bullhead City, Arizona 86442-7505. **T:** 1 928 763-5586
E: news@cameronbroadcasting.com
W: http://www.lucky98fm.com
Editorial Profile: KLUK-FM is a commercial station owned by Cameron Broadcasting Inc. The format of the station is classic rock. KLUK-FM broadcasts to the Bullhead City, AZ area at 97.9 FM.

KLUN-FM
Owner: Lazer Broadcasting Corp.
Editorial: 1427 Pine St Ste 3, Paso Robles, California 93446-1766. **T:** 1 805 226-7578
E: lazerbroadcasting@radiolazer.com
W: http://www.radiolazer.com
Editorial Profile: KLUN-FM is a commercial station owned by Lazer Broadcasting Corp. The format of the station is Regional Mexican. KLUN-FM is licensed to Paso Robles, CA and broadcasts to the San Luis Obispo, CA area at a frequency of 103.1 FM.

KLUP-AM
Owner: Salem Communications
Editorial: 9601 McAllister Fwy Ste 1200, San Antonio, Texas 78216-4695.
T: 1 210 344-8481 **E:** webmanager@salem.cc
W: http://www.klup.com
Editorial Profile: KLUP-AM is a commercial station owned by Salem Communications, dba South Texas Broadcasting, Inc. The format of the station is talk. KLUP-AM broadcasts to the San Antonio area at 930 AM.

KLUR-FM
Owner: Cumulus Media Inc.
Editorial: 4302 Call Field Rd, Wichita Falls, Texas 76308. **T:** 1 940 691-2311
W: http://www.klur.com
Editorial Profile: KLUR-FM is a commercial station owned by Cumulus Media Inc. The format of the station is contemporary country music. KLUR-FM broadcasts to the Wichita Falls, TX area at 99.9 FM.

KLUV-FM
Owner: CBS Radio
Editorial: 4131 N Central Expy Ste 1200, Dallas, Texas 75204-2123. **T:** 1 214 525-7000
W: http://kluv.cbslocal.com
Editorial Profile: KLUV-FM is a commercial station owned by CBS Radio. The format is classic hits. KLUV-FM broadcasts to the Dallas area at 98.7 FM.

KLUX-FM
Owner: Diocesan Telecomms. Corp.
Editorial: 1200 Lantana St, Corpus Christi, Texas 78407. **T:** 1 361 289-2487
E: klux@goccn.org **W:** http://www.klux.org
Editorial Profile: KLUX-FM is a non-commercial station owned by Diocesan Telecomms. Corp. The format of the station is

easy listening and religion. KLUX-FM broadcasts to the Corpus Christi, TX area at 89.5 FM.

KLVC-FM
Owner: Educational Media Foundation
Editorial: 5700 W Oaks Blvd, Rocklin, California 95765. **T:** 1 916 251-2142
E: klove@klove.com **W:** http://www.klove.com
Editorial Profile: KLVC-FM is a non-commercial station owned by Educational Media Foundation. The format of the station is contemporary Christian. KLVC-FM broadcasts to the Magalia, CA area at 88.3 FM.

KLVE-FM
Owner: Univision Communications Inc.
Editorial: 655 N Central Ave Ste 2500, Glendale, California 91203-1447.
T: 1 310 846-2800
W: http://iloveklove.univision.com
Editorial Profile: KLVE-FM is a commercial station owned by Univision Communications Inc. The format of the station is Hispanic adult contemporary music. The station airs in the Glendale, CA area on 107.5 FM.

KLVF-FM
Owner: Baca Broadcasting LLC
Editorial: One Radio Heights, Las Vegas, New Mexico 87701. **T:** 1 505 425-6766
Editorial Profile: KLVF-FM is a commercial station owned by Baca Broadcasting LLC. The format of the station is adult contemporary music. KLVF-FM broadcasts to the Albuquerque, NM area at 100.7 FM.

KLVI-AM
Owner: Clear Channel Media and Entertainment
Editorial: 2885 IH-10 East, Beaumont, Texas 77702-1001. **T:** 1 409 896-5555
W: http://www.klvi.com
Editorial Profile: KLVI-AM is a commercial station owned by Clear Channel Media and Entertainment. The format of the station is news, talk and sports. KLVI-AM broadcasts to the Beaumont, TX area at 560 AM.

KLVL-AM
Owner: SIGA Broadcasting Corp.
Editorial: 6161 Savoy Dr Ste 1140, Houston, Texas 77036-3323. **T:** 1 713 787-9922
W: http://www.humtumradio.com
Editorial Profile: KLVL-AM is a commercial station owned by SIGA Broadcasting Corp. The format of the station features a mix of South Asian music, news and talk programming. KLVL-AM broadcasts to the Houston area at 1480 AM.

KLVO-FM
Owner: American General Media
Editorial: 4125 Carlisle Blvd NE, Albuquerque, New Mexico 87107-4806. **T:** 1 505 878-0980
W: http://lainvasora977.com
Editorial Profile: KLVO-FM is a commercial station owned by American General Media. The format of the station is Regional Mexican. KLVO-FM broadcasts to the Albuquerque, NM area at 97.7 FM.

KLVQ-AM
Owner: Lake Country Radio LP
Editorial: 11125 State Highway 31 W, Malakoff, Texas 75148-7158.
T: 1 903 489-1238 **E:** lakecountry@kcklfm.com
W: http://www.kcklfm.com/klvq/
Editorial Profile: KLVQ-AM is a commercial station owned by Lake Country Radio LP. The format of the station is contemporary Christian. KLVQ-AM broadcasts to Malakoff, TX area at 1410 AM.

KLVR-FM
Owner: Educational Media Foundation
Editorial: 5700 W Oaks Blvd, Rocklin, California 95765. **T:** 1 916 251-2142
E: klove@klove.com **W:** http://www.klove.com
Editorial Profile: KLVR-FM is a non-commercial station owned by Educational Media Foundation. The format of the station is contemporary Christian music. KLVR-FM broadcasts to the Middletown, CA area at 91.9 FM.

KLVT-AM
Owner: Cute Boots Broadcasting, LLC
Editorial: 611 N West Ave, Levelland, Texas 79336-3930. **T:** 1 806 894-3134
E: klvtradio@gmail.com
W: http://www.hprnetwork.com
Editorial Profile: KLVT-AM is a commercial station owned by Cute Boots Broadcasting, LLC. The format of the station is news, talk and sports. KLVT-AM broadcasts to the Levelland, TX area at 1230 AM.

KLVV-FM
Owner: Love Station Inc.(The)
Editorial: 6600 W Highway 60, Ponca City, Oklahoma 74601-7926. **T:** 1 580 767-1600
E: mail@klvv.com **W:** http://www.klvv.com
Editorial Profile: KLVV-FM is a non-commercial station owned by The Love Station, Inc. The format of the station is contemporary Christian. KLVV-FM broadcasts to the Ponca City, OK area at 88.7 FM.

KLWB-FM
Owner: Delta Media Corporation
Editorial: 3500 Nw Evangeline Trwy, Carencro, Louisiana 70520-6240. **T:** 1 337 896-1600
E: 1037thegame@gmail.com
W: http://1037thegame.com
Editorial Profile: KLWB-FM is a commercial station owned by Delta Media Corporation. The format of the station is sports/talk. KSLO-FM broadcasts to the Lafayette, LA area at a frequency of 103.7 FM.

KLWN-AM
Owner: Great Plains Media
Editorial: 3125 W 6th St, Lawrence, Kansas 66049-3101. **T:** 1 785 843-1320
W: http://www.klwn.com
Editorial Profile: KLWN-AM is a commercial station owned by Great Plains Media. The format of the station is news, sports and talk programming. KLWN-AM broadcasts to the Lawrence, KS area at 1320 AM.

KLWS-FM
Owner: Washington State University
Editorial: Murrow Center, Room 382, Pullman, Washington 99164. **T:** 1 509 335-6500
E: nwpr@wsu.edu **W:** http://www.nwpr.org
Editorial Profile: KLWS-FM is a non-commercial station owned by Washington State University. The format is news, talk and classical music.. KLWS-FM broadcasts to Ephrata and Moses Lake, WA at 91.5 FM.

KLWT-AM
Owner: Brass Monkey Media LLC
Editorial: 18785 Finch Rd, Lebanon, Missouri 65536-7812. **T:** 1 417 532-2962
Editorial Profile: KLWT-AM is a commercial station owned by Brass Monkey Media LLC. The format of the station is Christian. KLWT-AM broadcasts to the Lebanon, MO area at 1230 AM.

KLXK-FM
Owner: MediaNews Group Inc.
Editorial: 114 E Elm St, Breckenridge, Texas 76424-3613. **T:** 1 254 559-6543
Editorial Profile: KLXK-FM is a commercial station owned by MediaNews Group Inc. The format of the station is country music. KLXK-FM broadcasts in the Breckenridge, TX area at 93.5 FM.

KLXQ-FM
Owner: US Stations, LLC
Editorial: 125 Corporate Ter, Hot Springs, Arkansas 71913. **T:** 1 501 525-9700
W: http://www.myhotsprings.com
Editorial Profile: KLXQ-FM is a commercial station owned by US Stations, LLC. The format of the station is classic rock. KLXQ-FM broadcasts to the Hot Springs, AR area at 101.9 FM.

KLXR-AM
Owner: Quinn(Michael)
Editorial: 1326 Market St, Redding, California 96001. **T:** 1 530 244-5082
E: klxr1230@yahoo.com
Editorial Profile: KLXR-AM is a commercial station owned by Michael Quinn. The format of the station is adult standards music. KLXR-FM broadcasts to the Redding, CA area on 1230 AM.

KLXS-FM
Owner: Riverfront Broadcasting
Editorial: 106 W Capitol Ave, Pierre, South Dakota 57501-2018. **T:** 1 605 224-0095
E: production@todayskccr.com
W: http://pierrecountry.com
Editorial Profile: KLXS-FM is a commercial station owned by Riverfront Broadcasting. The format of the station is contemporary country. KLXS-FM broadcasts to the Pierre, SD area at 95.3 FM.

KLXX-AM
Owner: Townsquare Media, Inc.
Editorial: 4303 Memorial Hwy, Mandan, North Dakota 58554-4711. **T:** 1 701 664-6411
W: http://www.supertalk1270.com
Editorial Profile: KLXX-AM is a commercial station owned by Townsquare Media, Inc. The format of the station is news and talk. KLXX-

AM broadcasts to the Bismarck, ND area at 1270 AM.

KLYC-AM
Owner: Celebrate Life Media, LLC
Editorial: 1975 NE Colvin Ct, McMinnville, Oregon 97128-8404. **T:** 1 503 472-1260
W: http://klyc.us/
Editorial Profile: KLYC-AM is a commercial station owned by Celebrate Life Media, LLC. The format of the station is oldies. KLYC-AM broadcasts to the McMinnville, OR area at 1260 AM.

KLYD-FM
Owner: Snyder Broadcasting Co.
Editorial: 2301 Avenue R, Snyder, Texas 79549. **T:** 1 325 573-9322
Editorial Profile: KLYD-FM is a commercial station owned by Snyder Broadcasting Co. The format of the station is rock alternative. KLYD-FM broadcasts to the Snyder, TX area at 98.9 FM.

KLYK-FM
Owner: Bicoastal Media LLC
Editorial: 1130 14th Ave, Longview, Washington 98632-3017. **T:** 1 360 425-1500
W: http://www.klykradio.com
Editorial Profile: KLYK-FM is a commercial station owned by Bicoastal Media LLC. The format of the station is hot adult contemporary music. KLYK-FM broadcasts to the Portland, OR area at 94.5 FM.

KLYQ-AM
Owner: Townsquare Media, LLC
Editorial: 320 N 1st St, Hamilton, Montana 59840-3516. **T:** 1 406 728-9300
E: contact@klyq.com **W:** http://www.klyq.com
Editorial Profile: KLYQ-AM is a commercial station owned by Townsquare Media, LLC. The format of the station is oldies. KLYQ-AM broadcasts to the Hamilton, MT area at 1240 AM.

KLYR-AM
Owner: Forrester Partnership
Editorial: Highway 64 West, Clarksville, Arkansas 72830. **T:** 1 479 754-3092
W: http://www.klyr.com
Editorial Profile: KLYR-AM is commercial station owned by Forrester Partnership. The format of the station is classic country. KLYR-AM broadcasts in Clarksville, AR area at 1360 AM.

KLYR-FM
Owner: Forrester Partnership
Editorial: Highway 64 West, Clarksville, Arkansas 72830. **T:** 1 479 754-3092
W: http://www.klyr.com
Editorial Profile: KLYR-FM is a commercial station owned by Forrester Partnership. The format of the station is classic country. KLYR-FM broadcasts to the Clarksville, AR area at 92.7 FM.

KLYT-FM
Owner: Calvary Chapel of Albuquerque, Inc.
Editorial: 4001 Osuna Rd NE, Albuquerque, New Mexico 87109. **T:** 1 505 344-9146
E: studio@mystaticradio.com
W: http://www.mystaticradio.com
Editorial Profile: KLYT-FM is a non-commercial station owned by Calvary Chapel of Albuquerque, Inc. The format of the station is contemporary Christian rock and pop music. KLYT-FM broadcasts to the Albuquerque, NM area at 88.3 FM.

KLYV-FM
Owner: Cumulus Media Inc.
Editorial: 5490 Saratoga Rd, Dubuque, Iowa 52002-2593. **T:** 1 563 557-1040
W: http://www.y105music.com
Editorial Profile: KLYV-FM is a commercial station owned by Cumulus Media Inc. The format for the station is Top 40/CHR. KLYV-FM broadcasts to the Cedar Rapids, IA area at 105.3 FM.

KLYY-FM
Owner: Entravision Communications Corp.
Editorial: 5700 Wilshire Blvd, Ste 250, Los Angeles, California 90036. **T:** 1 323 900-6100
W: http://www.jose975.com
Editorial Profile: KLYY-FM is a commercial station owned by Entravision Communications Corp. The format of the station is regional mexican. KLYY-FM broadcasts locally to the Los Angeles area at 97.5 FM.

KLZA-FM
Owner: KNZA, Inc.

Editorial: 1602 Stone St, Falls City, Nebraska 68355. **T:** 1 402 245-6010
E: sunny1013fm@hotmail.com
W: http://www.sunny1013.com
Editorial Profile: KLZA-FM is a commercial station owned by KNZA, Inc. The format of the station is adult contemporary. KLZA-FM broadcasts to the Falls City, NE area at 101.3 FM.

KLZ-AM
Owner: Crawford Broadcasting Co.
Editorial: 2821 S Parker Rd Ste 1205, Aurora, Colorado 80014-2708. **T:** 1 303 433-5500
E: klz@crawfordbroadcasting.com
W: http://www.560thesource.com
Editorial Profile: KLZ-AM is a commercial station owned by Crawford Broadcasting Co. The format of the station is talk. KLZ-AM broadcasts to the Denver area at 560 AM.

KLZK-FM
Owner: Ramar Communications, Inc.
Editorial: 9800 University Ave, Lubbock, Texas 79423. **T:** 1 806 745-3434
W: http://www.973yesfm.com
Editorial Profile: KLZK-FM is a commercial station owned by Ramar Communications, Inc. The format of the station is adult contemporary. KLZK-FM broadcasts to the Lubbock, TX area at a frequency of 97.3 FM.

KLZS-AM
Owner: Eugene Comedy Radio, LLC
Editorial: 471 S A St, Springfield, Oregon 97477-5402
W: http://piratecomedynetwork.com
Editorial Profile: KLZS-AM is a commercial station owned by Eugene Comedy Radio, LLC. The format of the station is comedy. KLZS-AM broadcasts to the Euguene, OR area on 1450 AM.

KLZT-FM
Owner: Emmis Communications Corp.
Editorial: 8309 N Interstate 35, Austin, Texas 78753-5720. **T:** 1 512 481-1071
W: http://www.1071laz.com
Editorial Profile: KLZT-FM is a commercial station owned by Emmis Communications Corp. The format of the station is regional Mexican. KLZT-FM broadcasts in the Austin, TX area at 107.1 FM.

KLZX-FM
Owner: Cache Valley Radio Inc.
Editorial: 810 W 200 N, Logan, Utah 84321.
T: 1 435 752-1390 **E:** klzx@cvradio.com
W: http://www.klzxfm.com
Editorial Profile: KLZX-FM is a commercial station owned by Cache Valley Radio Inc. The format of the station is classic rock. KLZX-FM broadcasts to the Salt Lake City area at 99.9 FM.

KLZZ-FM
Owner: Townsquare Media, LLC
Editorial: 640 Lincoln Ave SE, Saint Cloud, Minnesota 56304. **T:** 1 320 251-4422
W: http://www.1037theloon.com
Editorial Profile: KLZZ-FM is a commercial station owned by Townsquare Media, LLC. The format of the station is classic rock music. KLZZ-FM broadcasts to the Saint Cloud, MN area at 103.7 FM.

KMA-AM
Owner: May Broadcasting
Editorial: 209 N Elm St, Shenandoah, Iowa 51601. **T:** 1 712 246-5270
E: news@kmaland.com
W: http://www.kma960.com
Editorial Profile: KMA-AM is a commercial station owned by May Broadcasting. The format of the station is talk. KMA-AM broadcasts to the Shenandoah, IA area at 960 AM.

KMAD-AM
Owner: Keystone Broadcasting Corp
Editorial: 221 Plaza, Madill, Oklahoma 73446-2250. **T:** 1 580 795-2345
E: kmad1550@yahoo.com
Editorial Profile: KMAD-AM is a commercial station owned by Keystone Broadcasting Corp. The format of the station is country music. KMAD-AM broadcasts to the Madill, OK area at 1550 AM.

KMAD-FM
Owner: Digity LLC
Editorial: 1800 Teague Dr Ste 300, Sherman, Texas 75090-2654. **T:** 1 903 463-6800
W: http://www.madrock1025.com
Editorial Profile: KMAD-FM is a commercial station owned by Digity LLC. The format of the station is rock/album oriented rock.

KMAD-FM broadcasts to Denison, TX and surrounding areas at 102.5 FM.

KMA-FM
Owner: May Broadcasting
Editorial: 209 N Elm St, Shenandoah, Iowa 51601. **T:** 1 712 246-5270
E: news@kmaland.com
W: http://www.kmaland.com
Editorial Profile: KMA-FM is a commercial station owned by May Broadcasting. The format of the station is adult contemporary music. KMA-FM broadcasts to the Shenandoah, IA area at 99.1 FM.

KMAG-FM
Owner: Clear Channel Media and Entertainment
Editorial: 311 Lexington Ave, Fort Smith, Arkansas 72901-3842. **T:** 1 479 782-8888
W: http://www.kmag991.com
Editorial Profile: KMAG-FM is a commercial station owned by Clear Channel Media and Entertainment. The format of the station is classic country. KMAG-FM broadcasts to the Fort Smith, AR area at 99.1 FM.

KMAJ-AM
Owner: Cumulus Media Inc.
Editorial: 825 S Kansas Ave Ste 100, Topeka, Kansas 66612-1233. **T:** 1 785 272-2122
W: http://www.kmaj1440.com
Editorial Profile: KMAJ-AM is a commercial station owned by Cumulus Media Inc. The format of the station is news, talk, and sports. KMAJ-AM broadcasts to the Topeka, KS area at 1440 AM.

KMAJ-FM
Owner: Cumulus Media Inc.
Editorial: 825 S Kansas Ave, Ste 100, Topeka, Kansas 66612. **T:** 1 785 272-2122
W: http://www.kmaj.com
Editorial Profile: KMAJ-FM is a commercial station owned by Cumulus Media Inc. The format of the station is adult contemporary music. KMAJ-FM broadcasts to the Topeka, KS area at 107.7 FM.

KMAL-AM
Owner: Mississippi River Radio
Editorial: 324 Broadway St, Cape Girardeau, Missouri 63701. **T:** 1 573 335-8291
W: http://www.1470kmal.com
Editorial Profile: KMAL-AM is a commercial station owned by Mississippi River Radio. The format of the station is sports. KMAL-AM broadcasts to the Cape Girardeau, MO area at a frequency of 1470 AM.

KMAM-AM
Owner: Bates County Broadcasting Co.
Editorial: 800 E Nursery St, Butler, Missouri 64730. **T:** 1 660 679-4191
E: fm92@embarqmail.com
W: http://www.921kmoe.com
Editorial Profile: KMAM-AM is a commercial station owned by Bates County Broadcasting Co. The format of the station is country. KMAM-AM broadcasts to the Butler, MO area at 1530 AM.

KMAN-AM
Owner: Manhattan Broadcasting
Editorial: 2414 Casement Rd, Manhattan, Kansas 66502. **T:** 1 785 776-1350
E: news@1350kman.com
W: http://www.1350kman.com
Editorial Profile: KMAN-AM is commercial station owned by Manhattan Broadcasting. The format of the station is news, talk, and sports programming. KMAN-AM broadcasts to the Manhattan, KS area on 1350 AM.

KMAQ-AM
Owner: Voy(Dennis W.)
Editorial: 129 N Main St, Maquoketa, Iowa 52060. **T:** 1 563 652-2426
E: kmaq@kmaq.com **W:** http://www.kmaq.com
Editorial Profile: KMAQ-AM is a commercial station owned by Dennis W. Voy. The format of the station is country. KMAQ-AM broadcasts to the Maquoketa, IA area at 1230 AM.

KMAQ-FM
Owner: Voy(Dennis W.)
Editorial: 129 N Main St, Maquoketa, Iowa 52060-2256. **T:** 1 563 652-2426
E: kmaq@kmaq.com **W:** http://www.kmaq.com
Editorial Profile: KMAQ-FM is a commercial station owned by Dennis W. Voy. The format of the station is adult contemporary. KMAQ-FM broadcasts to the Maquoketa, IA area at 95.1 FM.

KMAR-FM
Owner: Boeuf River Broadcasting Co.
Editorial: 1823 Highway 618, Winnsboro, Louisiana 71295. **T:** 1 318 435-5141
E: kmarfm@bellsouth.net
Editorial Profile: KMAR-FM is a commercial station owned by Boeuf River Broadcasting Co. The format of the station is contemporary country. KMAR-FM broadcasts to the Winnsboro, LA area at 95.9 FM.

KMAS-AM
Owner: Olympic Broadcasting Inc.
Editorial: 210 W Cota St, Shelton, Washington 98584-2264. **T:** 1 360 426-1030
E: kmasnews@kmas.com
W: http://kmasnewsradio.com
Editorial Profile: KMAS-AM is a commercial station owned by Olympic Broadcasting Inc. The format of the station is news/talk. KMAS-AM broadcasts to the Seattle area at 1030 AM.

KMAT-FM
Owner: Cordell Communications, Inc
Editorial: 2424 South Blvd, Houston, Texas 77098-5110. **T:** 1 713 520-5200
E: amistad@radioamistad.net
W: http://www.khcb.org
Editorial Profile: KMAT-FM is a non-commercial station owned by Cordell Communications, Inc. The format of the station is Hispanic Christian programming. KMAT-FM broadcasts to the Seadrift/Port O'Connor, TX area at 105.1 FM.

KMAV-FM
Owner: KMSR, Inc.
Editorial: 1000 Main St W, Mayville, North Dakota 58257-1036. **T:** 1 701 786-2335
E: news@kmav.com **W:** http://www.kmav.com
Editorial Profile: KMAV-FM is a commercial station owned by KMSR, Inc. The format of the station is country music. KMAV-FM broadcasts to the Mayville, ND area at 105.5 FM.

KMAX-AM
Owner: Inland Northwest Broadcasting
Editorial: 1114 N Almon St, Moscow, Idaho 83843-8507. **T:** 1 208 882-2551
E: psa@inlandradio.com
Editorial Profile: KMAX-AM is a commercial station owned by Inland Northwest Broadcasting. The format of the station is news, sports and talk. KMAX-AM broadcasts to the Moscow, ID area at 840 AM.

KMAX-FM
Owner: Townsquare Media, LLC
Editorial: 600 Main St, Windsor, Colorado 80550-5133. **T:** 1 970 674-2700
W: http://943loudwire.com
Editorial Profile: KMAX-FM is a commercial station owned by Townsquare Media, LLC. The format of the station is classic rock. KMAX-FM broadcasts to the Windsor, CO area at 94.3 FM.

KMBH-FM
Owner: RGV Educational Broadcasting Inc.
Editorial: 1701 Tennessee St, Harlingen, Texas 78550-8908. **T:** 1 956 421-4111
E: kmbhkhid@aol.com
W: http://www.kmbh.org
Editorial Profile: KMBH-FM is a commercial station owned by RGV Educational Broadcasting Inc. The format of the station is classical, jazz and news. KMBH-FM broadcasts to the Harlingen, TX area at 88.9 FM.

KMBI-AM
Owner: Moody Bible Institute
Editorial: 5408 S Freya St, Spokane, Washington 99223-7114. **T:** 1 509 448-2555
E: kmbi@moody.edu
W: http://www.moodyradionw.fm
Editorial Profile: KMBI-AM is a non-commercial station owned by Moody Bible Institute. The format of the station is religious. KMBI-AM broadcasts to the Spokane, WA area at 1330 AM.

KMBI-FM
Owner: Moody Bible Institute
Editorial: 5408 S Freya St, Spokane, Washington 99223-7114. **T:** 1 509 448-2555
E: kmbi@moody.edu
W: http://www.moodyradionorthwest.fm
Editorial Profile: KMBI-FM is a non-commercial station owned by the Moody Bible Institute. The format of the station is religious. KMBI-FM broadcasts to the Spokane, WA area at 107.9 FM.

KMBL-AM
Owner: Revolution Broadcast Co. of The West
Editorial: 214 Pecan St, Junction, Texas 76849-4141. **T:** 1 325 446-3371
E: chuck@krvl.com
W: http://www.kmblam.com
Editorial Profile: KMBL-AM is a commercial station owned by Revolution Broadcast Co. of The West. The format of the station is classic country. KMBL-AM broadcasts to the Junction, TX area at 1450 AM.

KMBQ-FM
Owner: Spirit of Alaska Broadcasting Inc.
Editorial: 851 E Westpoint Dr Ste 301, Wasilla, Alaska 99654-7183.
T: 1 907 373-0222 **E:** news@kmbq.com
W: http://www.kmbq.com
Editorial Profile: KMBQ-FM is a commercial station owned by Spirit of Alaska Broadcasting Inc. The format of the station is adult contemporary. KMBQ-FM broadcasts to the Wasilla, AK area at 99.7 FM.

KMBR-FM
Owner: Cherry Creek Radio
Editorial: 750 Dewey Blvd, Butte, Montana 59701. **T:** 1 406 494-5895
E: prodbutte@cherrycreekradio.com
W: http://www.955kmbr.com

KMBX-AM
Owner: Entravision Communications Corp.
Editorial: 67 Garden Ct, Monterey, California 93940. **T:** 1 831 333-9735
Editorial Profile: KMBX-AM is a commercial station owned by Entravision Communications Corp. The format of the station is Hispanic religious. KMBX-AM broadcasts to the Monterey, CA area at 700 AM.

KMBZ-AM
Owner: Entercom Communications Corp.
Editorial: 7000 Squibb Rd, Mission, Kansas 66202-3233. **T:** 1 913 744-3600
E: newsboss@kmbz.com
W: http://www.kmbz.com
Editorial Profile: KMBZ-AM is a commercial station owned by Entercom Communications Corp. The format of the station is news, sports and talk programming. KMBZ-AM broadcasts to the Kansas City, MO area at 980 AM.

KMBZ-FM
Owner: Entercom Communications Corp.
Editorial: 7000 Squibb Rd, Mission, Kansas 66202. **T:** 1 913 744-3600
E: news@kmbz.com **W:** http://www.kmbz.com
Editorial Profile: KMBZ-FM is a commercial station owned by Entercom Communications Corp. The format of the station is news/talk. KMBZ-FM broadcasts to the Westwood, KS, area at 98.1 FM.

KMCD-AM
Owner: DeanRadio.TV LLC
Editorial: 57 S Court St, Fairfield, Iowa 52556. **T:** 1 641 472-4191
E: news@fairfieldiowaradio.com
W: http://www.fairfieldiowaradio.com
Editorial Profile: KMCD-AM is a commercial station owned by DeanRadio.TV LLC. The format for the station is classic country. KMCD-AM broadcasts to the Ottumna, IA, Kirksville, MO area at 1570 AM.

KMCH-FM
Owner: Coloff Media
Editorial: 212 E Main St, Manchester, Iowa 52057-1733. **T:** 1 563 927-6249
E: mix947@kmch.com
W: http://www.kmch.com
Editorial Profile: KMCH-FM is a commercial station owned by Coloff Media. The format of the station is adult contemporary and country music. KMCH-FM broadcasts to the Cedar Rapids, IA area at 94.7 FM.

KMCK-FM
Owner: Cumulus Media Inc.
Editorial: 4209 N Frontage Rd, Fayetteville, Arkansas 72703-5002. **T:** 1 479 521-5566
W: http://www.power1057.com
Editorial Profile: KMCK-FM is a commercial station owned by Cumulus Media Inc. The format of the station is Top 40/CHR music, consisting of contemporary pop and rock. KMCK-FM broadcasts to the Fayetteville, AR area at 105.7 FM.

KMCM-FM
Owner: Brazos Communications West, LLC
Editorial: 3303 N Midkiff Rd Ste 115, Midland, Texas 79705-4860. **T:** 1 432 520-9912
W: http://www.97gold.com
Editorial Profile: KMCM-FM is a commercial station owned by Brazos Communications West, LLC. The format of the station is classic hits music. KMCM-FM broadcasts in the Midland, TX, area at 96.9 FM.

KMCN-FM
Owner: Prairie Communications LLP
Editorial: 1853 442nd Ave, Clinton, Iowa 52732. **T:** 1 563 243-1390
W: http://931mac.com
Editorial Profile: KMCN-FM is a commercial station owned by Prairie Communications LLP. The format of the station is adult hits. KMCN-FM broadcasts to the Clinton, IA, area at 94.7 FM.

KMCO-FM
Owner: Southeastern Oklahoma Radio, LLC
Editorial: 1801 E Electric Ave, McAlester, Oklahoma 74501-3824. **T:** 1 918 426-1050
E: info@mcalesterradio.com
W: http://www.mcalesterradio.com
Editorial Profile: KMCO-FM is a commercial station owned by Southeastern Oklahoma Radio, LLC. The format of the station is country music. KMCO-FM broadcasts to the McAlester, OK area at 101.3 FM.

KMCQ-FM
Owner: Queen Cities Broadcasting LLC
Editorial: 553 Roosevelt Ave, Enumclaw, Washington 98022-2990. **T:** 1 214 969-9977
W: http://www.classichitsq1045.com
Editorial Profile: KMCQ-FM is a commercial station owned by Queen Cities Broadcasting LLC. The format of the station is classic hits. KMCQ-FM broadcasts to Enumclaw, WA area at 104.5 FM.

KMCR-FM
Owner: Best Broadcast Group
Editorial: 205 E Norman St, Montgomery City, Missouri 63361-1437. T: 1 573 564-2275
E: kmcr@socket.net
W: http://www.kmcrradio.com
Editorial Profile: KMCR-FM is a commercial station owned by Best Broadcast Group. The format of the station is adult contemporary music. KMCR-FM broadcasts to the Montgomery City, MO area at 103.9 FM.

KMCS-FM
Owner: Prairie Communications LLP
Editorial: 3218 Mulberry Ave, Muscatine, Iowa 52761-2319. **T:** 1 563 263-2442
E: mail@voiceofmuscatine.com
W: http://www.vintage931.com
Editorial Profile: KMCS-FM is a commercial station owned by Prairie Communications LLP. The format of the station is classic rock and blues. KMCS-FM broadcasts to the Muscatine, IA area at 93.1 FM.

KMCV-FM
Owner: Bott Broadcasting Co.
Editorial: 1701 N Bishop Ave Ste 15, Rolla, Missouri 65401-2229. **T:** 1 573 308-1616
W: http://www.bottradionetwork.com
Editorial Profile: KMCV-FM is a non-commercial station owned by Bott Broadcasting Co. The format of the station is religious and Christian programming. KMCV-FM broadcasts to the Rolla, MO area at 89.9 FM.

KMCX-FM
Owner: Clear Channel Media and Entertainment
Editorial: 113 W 4th St, Ogallala, Nebraska 69153-2508. **T:** 1 308 284-3633
W: http://www.kmcx.com/main.html
Editorial Profile: KMCX-FM is a commercial station owned by Clear Channel Media and Entertainment. The format of the station is contemporary country music. KMCX-FM broadcasts to the Ogallala, NE area at 106.5 FM.

KMDL-FM
Owner: Townsquare Media, LLC
Editorial: 1749 Bertrand Dr, Lafayette, Louisiana 70506. **T:** 1 337 233-6000
W: http://www.973thedawg.com
Editorial Profile: KMDL-FM is a commercial station owned by Townsquare Media, LLC. The format of the station is contemporary country music. KMDL-FM broadcasts to the Lafayette, LA area at 97.3 FM.

KMDO-AM
Owner: Fort Scott Broadcasting Co., Inc.
Editorial: 2 N National Ave, Fort Scott, Kansas 66701. **T:** 1 620 223-4500
Editorial Profile: KMDO-AM is a commercial station owned by Fort Scott Broadcasting Co., Inc. The format of the station is talk and sports. KMDO-AM broadcasts to the Fort Scott, KS area at 1600 AM.

KMDR2-FM
Owner: Mad River Radio
Editorial: 728 7th St Ste 2A, Eureka, California 95501-1158. **T:** 1 707 445-3699
W: http://www.1067theedgefm.com
Editorial Profile: KMDR2-FM is owned by Mad River Radio. The format for the station is rock music. KMDR2-FM broadcasts to the Eureka, CA on 106.7 FM. Digital radio technology is used by AM and FM radio stations, via a digital signal embedded in their analog signal, to transmit audio and data.

KMDX-FM
Owner: Four R Broadcasting
Editorial: 3434 Sherwood Way, San Angelo, Texas 76901-3531. **T:** 1 325 947-0899
E: office@lonestar-mdx.com
W: http://www.1061mdx.com
Editorial Profile: KMDX-FM is a commercial station owned by Four R Broadcasting. The format of the station is Rhythmic AC. KMDX-FM broadcasts to the San Angelo, TX area at 106.1 FM.

KMDY-FM
Owner: Cornerstone Community Radio Inc.
Editorial: 521 Main St, Carthage, Illinois 62321-1338. **T:** 1 217 357-3000
E: kmdy@adams.net **W:** http://www.kmdy.org

KMDZ-FM
Owner: Sangre de Cristo Broadcasting Inc.
Editorial: 304 S Grand Ave, Las Vegas, Nevada 87701. **T:** 1 505 426-1967
W: http://967samfm.com
Editorial Profile: KMDZ-FM is a commercial station owned by Sangre de Cristo Broadcasting Inc. The format of the station is adult hits-Jack-FM. KMDZ-FM broadcasts to the Las Vegas area at 96.7 FM.

KMED-AM
Owner: Bicoastal Media LLC
Editorial: 3624 Avion Dr, Medford, Oregon 97504. **T:** 1 541 772-4170
W: http://www.kmed.com
Editorial Profile: KMED-AM is a commercial station owned by Bicoastal Media LLC. The format of the station is news and talk programming. KMED-AM broadcasts to the Medford, OR area at 1440 AM.

KMEL-FM
Owner: Clear Channel Media and Entertainment
Editorial: 340 Townsend St Ste 4, San Francisco, California 94107-1698.
T: 1 415 538-1013 **W:** http://www.kmel.com
Editorial Profile: KMEL-FM is a commercial station owned by Clear Channel Media and Entertainment. The format of the station is urban contemporary music. KMEL-FM broadcasts to the San Francisco area at 106.1 FM.

KMEM-FM
Owner: Tri-Rivers Broadcasting Company, Inc.
Editorial: 650 N Clay St, Memphis, Missouri 63555. **T:** 1 660 465-7225
E: email@kmemfm.com
W: http://www.kmemfm.com
Editorial Profile: KMEM-FM is a commercial station owned by Tri-Rivers Broadcasting Company, Inc. The format of the station is country music. KMEM-FM broadcasts to the Memphis, MO area at 100.5 FM.

KMEN-FM
Owner: Casa Media Partners, LLC
Editorial: 1450 E Bardsley Ave, Tulare, California 93274-5805. **T:** 1 559 687-3170
W: http://www.lamaquinamusical.net
Editorial Profile: KMEN-FM is a commercial station owned by Casa Media Partners, LLC. The format of the station is Hispanic programming. KMEN-FM broadcasts to the Tulare, CA area at 100.5 FM.

KMER-AM
Owner: Simmons Media Group
Editorial: 436 Fossil Butte Dr, Kemmerer, Wyoming 83101. **T:** 1 307 877-4422
Editorial Profile: KMER-AM is a commercial station owned by Simmons Media Group. The format of the station is oldies. KMER-AM broadcasts to the Kemmerer, WY area on 950 AM.

KMET-AM
Owner: Sunset Broadcasting Inc.
Editorial: 700 E Redlands Blvd, Ste U, Redlands, California 92373. **T:** 1 951 849-4644
E: kmet1490talkradio@yahoo.com
W: http://www.1490kmet.com
Editorial Profile: KMET-AM is a commercial station owned by Sunset Broadcasting Inc. The format of the station is news, talk and sports. KMET-AM broadcasts to the Banning, CA area at 1490 AM.

KMEZ-FM
Owner: Cumulus Media Inc
Editorial: 201 Saint Charles Ave, Ste 201, New Orleans, Louisiana 70170. **T:** 1 504 581-7002
W: http://www.oldschool1067.com
Editorial Profile: KMEZ-FM is a commercial station owned by Cumulus Media Inc. The format of the station is urban adult contemporary. KMEZ-FM broadcasts to the New Orleans area at 106.7 FM.

KMFA-FM
Owner: Capitol Broadcasting Association, Inc.
Editorial: 3001 N Lamar Blvd Ste 100, Austin, Texas 78705-2033. **T:** 1 512 476-5632
E: info@kmfa.org **W:** http://www.kmfa.org
Editorial Profile: KMFA-FM is a non-commercial station owned by Capitol Broadcasting Association, Inc. The format of the station is classical music. KMFA-FM broadcasts to the Austin, TX area at 89.5 FM.

KMFG-FM
Owner: Midwest Communications Inc.
Editorial: 807 W 37th St, Hibbing, Minnesota 55746. **T:** 1 218 263-7531
W: http://www.kmfgfm.com
Editorial Profile: KMFG-FM is a commercial station owned by Midwest Communications Inc. The format of the station is classic rock music. KMFG-FM broadcasts in the Hibbing, MN area at 102.9 FM.

KMFM-FM
Owner: Bernal(Paulino)
Editorial: 4501 N McColl Rd, McAllen, Texas 78504-2431. **T:** 1 956 686-6382
Editorial Profile: KMFM-FM is a non-commercial station owned by Paulino Bernal. The format of the station is Hispanic contemporary Christian. KMFM-FM broadcasts to the McAllen, TX area at 100.7 FM.

KMFR-FM
Owner: Hondo Radioworks, LTD
Editorial: 8023 Vantage Dr, Ste 840, San Antonio, Texas 78230. **T:** 1 888 522-7437
Editorial Profile: KMFR-FM is a commercial station owned by Hondo Radioworks, LTD. The format of the station is classic rock. KMFR-FM broadcasts to the San Antonio area at 105.9 FM.

KMFX-AM
Owner: Q Media, LLC
Editorial: 474 Guernsey Ln, Red Wing, Minnesota 55066-7448. **T:** 1 651 388-7151
Editorial Profile: KMFX-AM is a commercial station owned by Q Media, LLC. The format of the station is classic country. KMFX-AM broadcasts to the Wabasha, MN area at a frequency of 1190 AM.

KMFX-FM
Owner: Clear Channel Media and Entertainment
Editorial: 1530 Greenview Dr SW, Ste 200, Rochester, Minnesota 55902.
T: 1 507 288-3888
E: fox1025@clearchannel.com
W: http://www.foxcountry.net
Editorial Profile: KMFX-FM is a commercial station owned by Clear Channel Media and Entertainment. The format of the station is contemporary country. KMFX-FM broadcasts to the Rochester, MN area on 102.5 FM.

KMFY-FM
Owner: Lamke Broadcasting, Inc.
Editorial: 507 SE 11th St, Grand Rapids, Minnesota 55744. **T:** 1 218 999-5699
E: info@kozyradio.com
W: http://www.kmfyradio.com
Editorial Profile: KMFY-FM is a commercial station owned by Lamke Broadcasting, Inc. The format of the station is adult contemporary and lite rock. KMFY-FM broadcasts locally to the Grand Rapids, MN area at a frequency of 96.9 FM.

KMGA-FM
Owner: Cumulus Media Inc
Editorial: 500 4th St NW, 5th Fl, Albuquerque, New Mexico 87102-5324. **T:** 1 505 767-6700
E: kmga@cumulus.com
W: http://www.995magicfm.com
Editorial Profile: KMGA-FM is a commercial station owned by Cumulus Media Inc. The format of the station is adult contemporary. KMGA-FM broadcasts to the Albuquerque, NM area at 99.5 FM.

KMGC-FM
Owner: Radio Works Inc.
Editorial: 612 Fairview Rd SW, Camden, Arkansas 71701. **T:** 1 870 836-9567
E: radioworks@cablelynx.com
W: http://www.magic104online.com
Editorial Profile: KMGC-FM is a commercial station owned by Radio Works Inc. The format of the station is urban contemporary music. KMGC-FM broadcasts to the Camden, AR area at 104.5 FM.

KMGE-FM
Owner: McKenzie River Broadcasting
Editorial: 925 Country Club Rd, Ste 200, Eugene, Oregon 97401. **T:** 1 541 484-9400
W: http://www.kmge.fm
Editorial Profile: KMGE-FM is a commercial station owned by McKenzie River Broadcasting. The format of the station is adult contemporary music. KMGE-FM broadcasts to the Eugene, OR area at 94.5 FM.

KMGI-FM
Owner: Pacific Empire Communications
Editorial: 544 N Arthur Ave, Pocatello, Idaho 83204-3002. **T:** 1 208 233-2121
E: news@102kmgi.com
W: http://www.102kmgi.com
Editorial Profile: KMGI-FM is a commercial station owned by Pacific Empire Communications. The format of the station is rock music. KMGI-FM broadcasts to the Pocatello, ID area at 102.5 FM.

KMGJ-FM
Owner: MBC Grand Broadcasting Inc.
Editorial: 1360 E Sherwood Dr, Grand Junction, Colorado 81501-7546.
T: 1 970 254-2100
W: http://www.931magic.com
Editorial Profile: KMGJ-FM is a commercial station owned by MBC Grand Broadcasting Inc. The format of the station is adult contemporary. KMGJ-FM broadcasts to the Grand Junction, CO area at 93.1 FM.

KMGK-FM
Owner: Branstock Communications Inc.
Editorial: 12 1st St SE, Glenwood, Minnesota 56334. **T:** 1 320 634-5358
E: traffic@kmgk1071.com
W: http://www.kmgk1071.com
Editorial Profile: KMGK-FM is a commercial station owned by Branstock Communications Inc. The format of the station is smooth AC. KMGK-FM broadcasts to the Glenwood, MN area at 107.1 FM.

KMGL-FM
Owner: Tyler Media, LLC
Editorial: 400 E Britton Rd, Oklahoma City, Oklahoma 73114-7515. **T:** 1 405 478-5104
W: http://www.magic104.com
Editorial Profile: KMGL-FM is a commercial station owned by Tyler Media, LLC. The format of the station is adult contemporary music. KMGL-FM broadcasts to the Oklahoma City area at 104.1 FM.

KMGM-FM
Owner: Iowa City Broadcasting Co.
Editorial: 4454 Highway 212, Montevideo, Minnesota 56265-4539. **T:** 1 320 269-8815
E: kdmaprod@radiokdma.com
Editorial Profile: KMGM-FM is a commercial station owned by Iowa City Broadcasting Co. The format of the station is classic rock music. KMGM-FM broadcasts to the Montevideo, MN area at 105.5 FM.

KMGN-FM
Owner: Guyann Corp.
Editorial: 1117 W Route 66, Flagstaff, Arizona 86001-6213. **T:** 1 928 774-5231
W: http://www.939themountain.com
Editorial Profile: KMGN-FM is a commercial station owned by the Guyann Corp. The format of the station is rock. KMGN-FM broadcasts to the Flagstaff, AZ area at 93.9 FM.

KMGO-FM
Owner: KMGO Inc.
Editorial: 402 N 12th St, Centerville, Iowa 52544-1718. **T:** 1 641 856-3996
E: kmgofm@lisco.net
W: http://www.kmgo.com
Editorial Profile: KMGO-FM is a commercial station owned by KMGO Inc. The format of the station is contemporary country. KMGO-FM broadcasts to the Cedar Rapids, IA area at 98.7 FM.

KMGV-FM
Owner: Cumulus Media
Editorial: 1071 W Shaw Ave, Fresno, California 93711-3702. **T:** 1 559 490-9800
W: http://www.mega979.com
Editorial Profile: KMGV-FM is a commercial station owned by Cumulus Media. The format of the station is rhythmic oldies music. KMGV-FM broadcasts to the Fresno, CA area at 97.9 FM.

KMGX-FM
Owner: Gross Communications Co.
Editorial: 345 SW Cyber Dr, Ste 101-103, Bend, Oregon 97702-1045. **T:** 1 541 388-3300
W: http://www.mixradiobend.com
Editorial Profile: KMGX-FM is a commercial station owned by Gross Communications Co. The format of the station is Lite Rock/Lite AC music. KMGX-FM broadcasts to the Bend, OR area at 100.7 FM.

KMGZ-FM
Owner: Broadco of Texas Inc.
Editorial: 1421 Nw Great Plains Blvd Ste C, Lawton, Oklahoma 73505-2843.
T: 1 580 536-9530 **W:** http://www.kmgz.com
Editorial Profile: KMGZ-FM is a commercial station owned by Broadco of Texas Inc. The format of the station is hot adult contemporary music. KMGZ-FM broadcasts in the Lawton, OK area. at 95.3 FM.

KMHA-FM
Owner: Ft. Berthold Communications
Editorial: 601 Lodge Rd, New Town, North Dakota 58763-9400. **T:** 1 701 627-3333
E: kmha@mhanation.com
Editorial Profile: KMHA-FM is a non-commercial station owned by Ft. Berthold Communications. The format of the station is variety. KMHA-FM broadcasts to the New Town, ND area at 91.3 FM.

KMHD-FM
Owner: Oregon Public Broadcasting
Editorial: 7140 SW MacAdam Ave, Portland, Oregon 97219-3013. **T:** 1 503 445-1899
W: http://www.opb.org/kmhd
Editorial Profile: KMHD-FM is a non-commercial station owned by Oregon Public Broadcasting. The format of the station is jazz and blues music. KMHD-FM broadcasts to the Portland, OR area at 89.1 FM.

KMHI-AM
Owner: Impact Radio
Editorial: 1765 Canyon Creek Rd, Mountain Home, Idaho 83647. **T:** 1 208 587-8424
Editorial Profile: KMHI-AM is a commercial station owned by Impact Radio. The format for the station is classic country. KMHI-AM broadcasts to the Mountain Home, ID area at 1240 AM.

KMHK-FM
Owner: Townsquare Media, LLC
Editorial: 27 N 27th St, 23rd Fl, Billings, Montana 59101. **T:** 1 406 248-7827
W: http://www.1037thehawk.com
Editorial Profile: KMHK-FM is a commercial station owned by Townsquare Media, LLC. The format of the station is rock music. KMHK-FM broadcasts in Billings, MT area at 103.7 FM.

KMHL-AM
Owner: KMHL Broadcasting Corp.
Editorial: 1414 E College Dr, Marshall, Minnesota 56258. **T:** 1 507 532-2282
E: info@marshallradio.net
W: http://www.marshallradio.net
Editorial Profile: KMHL-AM is a commercial station owned by KMHL Broadcasting Corp. The format of the station is news, talk, sports and variety music. KMHL-AM broadcasts in the Marshall, MN area at 1400 AM.

KMHM-FM
Owner: Southern Gospetality LLC
Editorial: Route 1, Box 266E, Marble Hill, Missouri 63764-0266. **T:** 1 573 238-1041
E: kmhm1041@clas.net
Editorial Profile: KMHM-FM is a commercial station owned by Southern Gospetality LLC. The format of the station is gospel. KMHM-FM broadcasts to the Marble Hill, MO area at 104.1 FM.

KMHR-AM
Owner: First Western, Inc.
Editorial: 624 3rd St S, Nampa, Idaho 83651-3840. **T:** 1 208 463-1900
Editorial Profile: KMHR-AM is a commercial station owned by First Western, Inc. The format of the station is southern gospel. KMHR-AM airs in the Nampa, ID area at 950 AM.

KMHS-AM
Owner: Coos Bay School District No. 9

Editorial: 10th & Ingersoll, Coos Bay, Oregon 97420-2689. **T:** 1 541 267-1451 **W:** http://www.marshfield.coos-bay.k12.or.us/kmhs/
Editorial Profile: KMHS-AM is a commercial station owned by Coos Bay School District No. 9. The format for the station is classic country. KMHS-AM broadcasts to the Coos Bay, OR area at 1420 AM.

KMHS-FM
Owner: Coos Bay School District No. 9
Editorial: 10th & Ingersoll, Coos Bay, Oregon 97420-2689. **T:** 1 541 267-1451
W: http://www.marshfield.coos-bay.k12.or.us/kmhs/
Editorial Profile: KMHS-FM is a non-commercial station owned by Coos Bay School District No. 9. The format of the station is Top 40/CHR. KMHS-FM broadcasts to the Coos Bay area at 91.3 FM.

KMHT-AM
Owner: Hanszen Broadcast Group
Editorial: 2323 Jefferson Ave, Marshall, Texas 75670. **T:** 1 903 923-8000
E: info@kmhtradio.com
W: http://www.myeasttexasnews.com
Editorial Profile: KMHT-AM is a commercial station owned by Hanszen Broadcast Group. The format of the station is sports. KMHT-AM broadcasts to the Marshall, TX area at 1450 AM.

KMHT-FM
Owner: Hanszen Broadcast Group
Editorial: 2323 Jefferson Ave, Marshall, Texas 75670. **T:** 1 903 923-8000
E: info@kmhtradio.com
W: http://www.kmhtradio.com
Editorial Profile: KMHT-FM is a commercial station owned by Hanszen Broadcast Group. The format of the station is country. KMHT-FM broadcasts to the Marshall, TX area at 103.9 FM.

KMHX-FM
Owner: Sonoma Media Group
Editorial: 1410 Neotomas Ave, Santa Rosa, California 95405-7533. **T:** 1 707 543-0100
W: http://www.mix1049fm.com
Editorial Profile: KMHX-FM is a commercial station owned by Sonoma Media Group. The format of the station is hot adult contemporary music. KMHX-FM broadcasts to the Santa Rosa, CA area at 104.9 FM.

KMIA-AM
Owner: Adelante Media Group
Editorial: 1400 W Main St, Auburn, Washington 98001-5230. **T:** 1 253 735-9700
W: http://kmia.latinosoloexitos.com
Editorial Profile: KMIA-AM is a commercial station owned by Adelante Media Group. The format of the station is Bilingual Top 40/CHR. KMIA-AM broadcasts to the Seattle, WA area at 1210 AM.

KMIC-AM
Owner: Walt Disney Co.
Editorial: 3120 Southwest Fwy Ste 610, Houston, Texas 77098-4521.
T: 1 713 552-1590
W: http://www.radiodisney.com
Editorial Profile: KMIC-AM is a commercial station owned by the Walt Disney Co. The format of the station is children's programming. KMIC-AM broadcasts to the Houston area on 1590 AM.

KMIH-FM
Owner: Mercer Island School District
Editorial: 9100 SE 42nd St, Mercer Island, Washington 98040-4107. **T:** 1 206 236-3296
W: http://hotjamz.org
Editorial Profile: KMIH-FM is a non-commercial station owned by Mercer Island School District. The format of the station is Top 40/CHR. KMIH-FM broadcasts to the Mercer Island, WA area at 88.9 FM.

KMIK-AM
Owner: Walt Disney Co.
Editorial: 4602 E University Dr, Ste 150, Phoenix, Arizona 85034-7423.
T: 1 480 967-1580
W: http://www.radiodisney.com/phoenix
Editorial Profile: KMIK-AM is a commercial station owned by Walt Disney Co. The format of the station is children's programming. KMIK-AM broadcasts to the Phoenix area at 1580 AM.

KMIL-FM
Owner: Fort Bend Broadcasting
Editorial: 901 E 1st St, Cameron, Texas 76520. **T:** 1 254 697-6633 **E:** kmil@kmil.com

W: http://www.kmil.com
Editorial Profile: KMIL-FM is a commercial station owned by Fort Bend Broadcasting. The format of the station is contemporary country music. KMIL-FM broadcasts to the Cameron, TX area at 105.1 FM.

KMIN-AM
Owner: KD Radio Inc.
Editorial: 733 E Roosevelt Ave, Grants, New Mexico 87020-2113. **T:** 1 505 285-5598
W: http://www.kmin980.com
Editorial Profile: KMIN-AM is a commercial station owned by KD Radio Inc. The format of the station is country music. KMIN-AM broadcasts to the Grants, NM area at 980 AM. The station does not accept pitches.

KMIQ-FM
Owner: Cotton Broadcasting
Editorial: 2209 N Padre Island Dr, Corpus Christi, Texas 78408-2432. **T:** 1 361 289-8877
Editorial Profile: KMIQ-FM is a commercial station owned by Cotton Broadcasting. The format of the station is Hispanic programming. KMIQ-FM broadcasts to the Corpus Christi, TX area at 104.9 FM.

KMIS-AM
Owner: Pollack Broadcasting Co.
Editorial: 1303 Southwest Drive, Kennett, Missouri 63857. **T:** 1 573 888-4616
W: http://www.kmisradio.com
Editorial Profile: KMIS-AM is a commercial station owned by Pollack Broadcasting Co. The format of the station is sports. KMIS-AM broadcasts to the Kennett, MO area at 1050 AM.

KMIT-FM
Owner: Saga Communications
Editorial: 501 S Ohlman St, Mitchell, South Dakota 57301. **T:** 1 605 996-9667
E: news@kmit.com **W:** http://www.kmit.com
Editorial Profile: KMIT-FM is a commercial station owned by Saga Communications. The format of the station is contemporary country. KMIT-FM broadcasts to the Mitchell, SD area at 105.9 FM.

KMIX-FM
Owner: Entravision Communications Corp.
Editorial: 6820 Pacific Ave, Ste 3A, Stockton, California 95207-2631. **T:** 1 209 474-0154
W: http://www.tricolor1009.com
Editorial Profile: KMIX-FM is a commercial station owned by Entravision Communications Corp. The format of the station is Regional Mexican. KMIX-FM broadcasts to the Stockton, CA area at 100.9 FM.

KMIY-FM
Owner: Clear Channel Media and Entertainment
Editorial: 3202 N Oracle Rd, Tucson, Arizona 85705. **T:** 1 520 618-2100
W: http://www.my929tucson.com
Editorial Profile: KMIY-FM is a commercial station owned by Clear Channel Media and Entertainment. The format of the station is Hot AC. KMIY-FM broadcasts to the Tuscon, AZ area at 92.9 FM.

KMJ-AM
Owner: Cumulus Media
Editorial: 1071 W Shaw Ave, Fresno, California 93711-3702. **T:** 1 559 490-5800
W: http://www.kmj580.com
Editorial Profile: KMJ-AM is a commercial station owned by Cumulus Media. The format of the station is news and talk. KMJ-AM broadcasts to the Fresno, CA area at 580 AM.

KMJB-FM
Owner: Western Inspirational Broadcasters
Editorial: 6363 Us Highway 50 E, Carson City, Nevada 89701-1410. **T:** 1 775 883-5647
E: info@pilgrimradio.com
W: http://www.pilgrimradio.com
Editorial Profile: KCSP-FM is a non-commercial station owned by Western Inspirational Broadcasters Inc. The format of the station is Christian programming. The station airs locally at 89.1 FM in Hudson, WY, as well as the Riverton and Lander areas, also in Wyoming

KMJE-FM
Owner: Results Radio Group
Editorial: 861 Gray Ave, Yuba City, California 95991-3613. **T:** 1 530 673-2200
W: http://1015khits.com/
Editorial Profile: KMJE-FM is a commercial station owned by Results Radio Group. The format of the station is Spanish Hits. KMJE-FM broadcasts to the Yuba City, CA area at 92.1 FM.

KMJ-FM
Owner: Cumulus Media
Editorial: 1071 W Shaw Ave, Fresno, California 93711-3702. **T:** 1 559 490-5800
W: http://www.kmjnow.com
Editorial Profile: KMJ-FM is a commercial station owned by Cumulus Media. The format of the station is news and talk. KMJ-FM broadcasts to the Fresno, CA area on 105.9 FM.

KMJI-FM
Owner: Townsquare Media, LLC
Editorial: 2324 Arkansas Blvd, Texarkana, Arkansas 71854-2016. **T:** 1 870 772-3771
W: http://www.magic933.com
Editorial Profile: KMJI-FM is a commercial station owned by Townsquare Media, LLC. The format of the station is hot adult contemporary. KMJI-FM broadcasts to the Texarkana, AR area at 93.3 FM.

KMJJ-FM
Owner: Cumulus Media Inc.
Editorial: Cumulus Broadcast Center, 270 Plaza Loop, Bossier City, Louisiana 71111. **T:** 1 318 549-8500
W: http://www.997kmjj.com
Editorial Profile: KMJJ-FM is a commercial station owned by Cumulus Media Inc. The format of the station is urban contemporary music. KMJJ-FM broadcasts to the Shreveport, LA area at 99.7 FM.

KMJK-FM
Owner: Cumulus Media Inc.
Editorial: 5800 Foxridge Dr, Ste 600, Mission, Kansas 66202. **T:** 1 913 514-3000
W: http://www.magic1073.com
Editorial Profile: KMJK-FM is a commercial station owned by Cumulus Media Inc. The format of the station is urban adult contemporary music. KMJK-FM broadcasts to the Kansas City, MO area at 107.3 FM.

KMJM-AM
Owner: Clear Channel Media and Entertainment
Editorial: 600 Old Marion Rd Ne, Cedar Rapids, Iowa 52402-2159. **T:** 1 319 395-0530
W: http://www.1360kmjm.com/main.html
Editorial Profile: KMJM-AM is a commercial station owned by Clear Channel Media and Entertainment. The format of the station is country. KMJM-AM broadcasts to the Cedar Rapids, IA area at 1360 AM.

KMJM-FM
Owner: Clear Channel Media and Entertainment
Editorial: 1001 Highlands Plaza Dr W, Saint Louis, Missouri 63110-1337.
T: 1 314 333-8000 **E:** kmjm@clearchannel.com
W: http://www.kmjm.com
Editorial Profile: KMJM-FM is a commercial station owned by Clear Channel Media and Entertainment. The format of the station is urban adult contemporary music. KMJM-FM broadcasts to the St. Louis area at 100.3 FM.

KMJO-FM
Owner: Midwest Communications
Editorial: 1020 25th St S, Fargo, North Dakota 58103-2312. **T:** 1 701 237-5346
W: http://www.1047popsterfm.com
Editorial Profile: KMJO-FM is a commercial station owned by Midwest Communications. The format of the station is adult hits. KMJO-FM broadcasts to the Fargo, ND area at 104.7 FM.

KMJQ-FM
Owner: Radio One Inc.
Editorial: 24 Greenway Plz, Ste 900, Houston, Texas 77046. **T:** 1 713 623-2108
W: http://myhoustonmajic.com
Editorial Profile: KMJQ-FM is a commercial station owned by Radio One Inc. The format of the station is urban adult contemporary music. KMJQ-FM broadcasts to the Houston area at 102.1 FM.

KMJR-FM
Owner: Tejas Broadcasting
Editorial: 1733 S Brownlee Blvd, Corpus Christi, Texas 78404-3018. **T:** 1 361 883-1600
Editorial Profile: KMJR-FM is a commercial station owned by Tejas Broadcasting. The format of the station is regional Mexican music. KMJR-FM broadcasts in the Corpus Christi, TX area at 105.5 FM.

KMJV-FM
Owner: Wolfhouse Radio Group Inc.
Editorial: 548 E Alisal St, Salinas, California 93905. **T:** 1 831 757-1910

Editorial Profile: KMJV-FM is a commercial station owned by Wolfhouse Radio Group Inc. The format of the station is Hispanic, featuring regional Mexican music. The station airs locally on 106.3 FM.

KMJX-FM
Owner: Clear Channel Media and Entertainment
Editorial: 10800 Colonel Glenn Rd, Little Rock, Arkansas 72204. **T:** 1 501 217-5000
W: http://www.1051thewolf.com
Editorial Profile: KMJX-FM is a commercial station owned by Clear Channel Media and Entertainment. The format of the station is country. KMJX-FM broadcasts to the Little Rock, AR area at 105.1 FM.

KMKF-FM
Owner: Manhattan Broadcasting
Editorial: 2414 Casement Rd, Manhattan, Kansas 66502-6633. **T:** 1 785 776-1350
E: news@1350kman.com
W: http://www.purerock.com
Editorial Profile: KMKF-FM is a commercial station owned by Manhattan Broadcasting. The format of the station is rock music. KMKF-FM broadcasts in the Manhattan, KS area at 101.5 FM.

KMKI-AM
Owner: Walt Disney Co.
Editorial: 13725 Montfort Dr, Dallas, Texas 75240-4455. **T:** 1 972 776-4642
W: http://www.radiodisney.com/dallas
Editorial Profile: KMKI-AM is a commercial station owned by Walt Disney Co. It is the Radio Disney affiliate for the Dallas, TX market. The format of the station is children's programming. KMKI-AM broadcasts to the Greater Dallas area at a frequency of 620 AM.

KMKK-FM
Owner: Ohana Broadcast Company LLC
Editorial: 1000 Bishop St Ste 200, Honolulu, Hawaii 96813-4203. **T:** 1 808 947-1500
Editorial Profile: KMKK-FM is a commercial station owned by Ohana Broadcast Company LLC. The format of the station is a variety of ethnic Hawaiian programming. KMKK-FM broadcasts to the Kaunakakai, HI area at 102.3 FM, but is based in Wailuku, HI.

KMKO-FM
Owner: Three Eagles Communications Co.
Editorial: 1807 Lee Blvd, North Mankato, Minnesota 56003-2633. **T:** 1 507 345-4646
E: info@mankatonewsonline.com
W: http://www.957therockstation.com
Editorial Profile: KMKO-FM is a commercial station owned by Three Eagles Communications Co. The format of the station is AAA. KMKO-FM broadcasts to Mankato, MN area at 95.7 FM.

KMKR-FM
Owner: Lane County School District 4-J
Editorial: 1574 Coburg Rd Ste 237, Eugene, Oregon 97401-4802. **T:** 1 541 790-6686
E: info@krvm.org
Editorial Profile: KRVM-FM is a non-commercial station owned by Lane County School District 4-J. The format of the station is classic country. KRVM-FM broadcasts locally to the Canyonville, OR area at a frequency of 92.3 FM.

KMKS-FM
Owner: Sandlin Broadcasting Co. Inc.
Editorial: 2309 5th St, Bay City, Texas 77414-6220. **T:** 1 979 244-4242 **E:** kmks@kmks.com
W: http://www.kmks.com
Editorial Profile: KMKS-FM is a commercial station owned by Sandlin Broadcasting Co. The format of the station is contemporary country music. KMKS-FM broadcasts to the Matagorda, TX area at 102.5 FM.

KMKT-FM
Owner: Digity LLC
Editorial: 1800 Teague Dr Ste 300, Sherman, Texas 75090-2654. **T:** 1 903 463-6800
W: http://931kmkt.com
Editorial Profile: KMKT-FM is a commercial station owned by Digity LLC. The format of the station is contemporary country music. KMKT-FM broadcasts in the Denison, TX area at 93.1 FM. The station does not produce its own news.

KMKX-FM
Owner: Radio Millennium LLC
Editorial: 1100 Hastings Rd, #B, Ukiah, California 95482-7101. **T:** 1 707 462-4389
E: info@maxrock.com
W: http://www.maxrock.com

Editorial Profile: KMKX-FM is a commercial station owned by Radio Millennium LLC. The format of the station is classic rock. KMKX-FM broadcasts to the San Francisco area at 93.5 FM.

KMKY-AM
Owner: Walt Disney Co.
Editorial: 963 Industrial Rd Ste I, San Carlos, California 94070-4146. **T:** 1 650 637-8800
W: http://radio.disney.go.com/music/yourstation/sanfrancisco/index.html
Editorial Profile: KMKY-AM is a commercial station owned by Walt Disney Co. The format of the station is children. KMKY-AM broadcasts to the San Francisco area at 1310 AM.

KMLA-FM
Owner: Gold Coast Radio, LLC
Editorial: 355 S A St, Oxnard, California 93030-5823. **T:** 1 805 385-5656
E: kmla@lam1037.com
W: http://www.lam1037.com
Editorial Profile: KMLA-FM is a commercial station owned by Gold Coast Radio, LLC. The format of the station is regional Mexican music. KMLA-FM broadcasts to the Los Angeles area at 103.7 FM.

KMLB-AM
Owner: Holladay Broadcasting Co.
Editorial: 1109 Hudson Ln, Monroe, Louisiana 71201. **T:** 1 318 388-2323
E: talk540@bayou.com
W: http://www.kmlb.com
Editorial Profile: KMLB-AM is commercial station owned by Holladay Broadcasting Co. The format of the station is news, talk, and sports. KMLB-AM broadcasts in the Monroe, LA area at 540 AM.

KMLE-FM
Owner: CBS Radio
Editorial: 840 N Central Ave, Phoenix, Arizona 85004-2003. **T:** 1 602 452-1000
W: http://kmle1079.cbslocal.com
Editorial Profile: KMLE-FM is a commercial station owned by CBS Radio. The format of the station is contemporary country. KMLE-FM broadcasts to the Phoenix area at 107.9 FM.

KMLK-FM
Owner: Noalmark Broadcasting Corp.
Editorial: 2525 N West Ave, El Dorado, Arkansas 71730. **T:** 1 870 863-6126
W: http://www.totalradio.com/kmlk.htm
Editorial Profile: KMLK-FM is a commercial station owned by Noalmark Broadcasting Corp. The format of the station is urban adult contemporary. KMLK-FM broadcasts to the El Dorado, AR area at 101.5 FM.

KMLO-FM
Owner: James River Broadcasting
Editorial: 214 W Pleasant Dr, Pierre, South Dakota 57501. **T:** 1 605 224-8686
W: http://www.dakotaradiogroup.com
Editorial Profile: KMLO-FM is a commercial station owned by James River Broadcasting. The format of the station is classic country. KMLO-FM broadcasts to the Pierre, SD area at 100.7 FM.

KMME-FM
Owner: Catholic Broadcasting Northwest, Inc
Editorial: 835 E Park St, Eugene, Oregon 97401-2909. **T:** 1 503 285-5200
Editorial Profile: KMME-FM is a non-commercial station owned by Catholic Broadcasting Northwest, Inc. The format of the station is religious specifically Catholic programming. KMME-FM broadcasts to the Eugene and Springfield areas in Oregon at 100.5 FM.

KMMG-FM
Owner: Adelante Media Group
Editorial: 706 Butterfield Rd, Yakima, Washington 98901-2021. **T:** 1 509 457-1000
Editorial Profile: KMMG-FM is a commercial station owned by Adelante Media Group. The format of the station is Bilingual Top 40/CHR. KMMG-FM broadcasts to the Yakima, WA, area at 96.7 FM.

KMMJ-AM
Owner: Praise Network(The)
Editorial: 723 Turtle Beach, Marquette, Nebraska 68854. **T:** 1 888 920-5665
E: kmmj@kmmj.org **W:** http://www.kmmj.org
Editorial Profile: KMMJ-AM is a non-commercial station owned by The Praise Network. The format of the station is religious music and religious talk. KMMJ-AM broadcasts to the Marquette, NE area at 750 AM.

KMMM-AM
Owner: Rocking M Radio
Editorial: 30129 E US Highway 54, Pratt, Kansas 67124-8304. **T:** 1 620 672-5581
W: http://themighty1290am.com
Editorial Profile: KMMM-AM is a commercial station owned by Rocking M Radio. The format of the station is classic hits. KMMM-AM broadcasts to the Pratt, KS area at 1290 AM.

KMMO-AM
Owner: Missouri Valley Broadcasting Inc.
Editorial: Highway 65 North, Marshall, Missouri 65340. **T:** 1 660 886-7422
E: news@kmmo.com
W: http://www.kmmo.com
Editorial Profile: KMMO-AM is a commercial station owned by Missouri Valley Broadcasting Inc. The format of the station is classic country. KMMO-AM broadcasts to the Kansas City, MO area at 1300 AM.

KMMO-FM
Owner: Missouri Valley Broadcasting Inc.
Editorial: 1070 Lexington Ave., Marshall, Missouri 65340. **T:** 1 660 886-7422
W: http://www.kmmo.com
Editorial Profile: KMMO-FM is a commercial station owned by Missouri Valley Broadcasting Inc. The format of the station is classic country music. KMMO-FM broadcasts to the Kansas City, MO, area at 102.9 FM.

KMMQ-AM
Owner: NRG Media LLC
Editorial: 5011 Capitol Ave, Omaha, Nebraska 68132-2921. **T:** 1 402 342-2000
W: http://1020lapreciosa.com
Editorial Profile: KMMQ-AM is a commercial station owned by NRG Media LLC. The format of the station is regional Mexican. KMMQ-AM broadcasts to the Omaha, NE, area at 1020 AM.

KMMR-FM
Owner: Kielb(Gregory & Claudette)
Editorial: 140 South Second Ave East, Malta, Montana 59538. **T:** 1 406 654-2472
E: kmmrfm@itstriangle.com
W: http://kmmrfm.com
Editorial Profile: KMMR-FM is a commercial station owned by Gregory & Claudette Kielb. The format for the station is contemporary country. KMMR-FM broadcasts to the Malta, MT area at 100.1 FM.

KMMS-AM
Owner: Townsquare Media, LLC
Editorial: 125 W Mendenhall St Ste 1, Bozeman, Montana 59715-3500.
T: 1 406 586-2343 **E:** kmmsam@gmail.com
W: http://www.kmmsam.com
Editorial Profile: KMMS-AM is a commercial station owned by Townsquare Media, LLC. The format of the station is news, talk and sports. KMMS-AM broadcasts in the Bozeman, MT area at 1450 AM.

KMMS-FM
Owner: Townsquare Media, LLC
Editorial: 125 W Mendenhall St, Ste 1, Bozeman, Montana 59715-3500.
T: 1 406 586-2343
W: http://www.mooseradio.com
Editorial Profile: KMMS-FM is a commercial station owned by Townsquare Media, LLC. The format for the station is classic rock. KMMS-FM broadcasts to the Bozeman, MT area at 95.1 FM.

KMMT-FM
Owner: Digerness(Dave & Maryann)
Editorial: 94 Laurel Mountain Road, Mammoth Lakes, California 93546. **T:** 1 760 934-8888
E: kmmtradioworks@yahoo.com
W: http://www.kmmtradio.com
Editorial Profile: KMMT-FM is a commercial station owned by Dave and Maryann Digerness. The format of the station is Adult Top 40. KMMT-FM broadcasts to the Mammoth Lakes, CA area at 106.5 FM.

KMMX-FM
Owner: Wilks Broadcast Group
Editorial: 33 Briercroft Office Park, Lubbock, Texas 79412. **T:** 1 806 762-3000
W: http://www.mix100.net
Editorial Profile: KMMX-FM is a commercial station owned by Wilks Broadcast Group. The format of the station is hot adult contemporary music. KMMX-FM broadcasts to the Lubbock, TX area at 100.3 FM.

KMMY-FM
Owner: Will Payne
Editorial: 1600 W Jackson St, Hugo, Oklahoma 74743-5653. **T:** 1 580 326-2555
E: info@myrock965.com
W: http://www.myrock965.com
Editorial Profile: KMMY-FM is a commercial station owned by Will Payne. The format of the station is active rock. KMMY-FM broadcasts to the Soper, OK area at 96.5 FM.

KMMZ-FM
Owner: PERMIAN BASIN BROADCASTING, LLC
Editorial: 12200 Service Road East, Odessa, Texas 79760. **T:** 1 432 563-2266
E: traffic@lacalienteonline.com
W: http://www.lacalienteonline.com
Editorial Profile: KMMZ-FM is a commercial station owned by PERMIAN BASIN BROADCASTING, LLC. The format of the station is regional Mexican. KMMZ-FM broadcasts to the Odessa, TX area on 101.3 FM.

KMNA-FM
Owner: Casa Media Partners, LLC
Editorial: 152101 W County Road 12, Prosser, Washington 99350-7265. **T:** 1 509 786-1310
Editorial Profile: KMNA-FM is a commercial station owned by Casa Media Partners, LLC. The format of the station is regional Mexican. KMNA-FM broadcasts to the Prosser, WA area at 98.7 FM.

KMNB-FM
Owner: CBS Radio
Editorial: 625 2nd Ave S, Minneapolis, Minnesota 55402-1912. **T:** 1 612 339-1029
W: http://buzn1029.cbslocal.com
Editorial Profile: KMNB-FM is a commercial station owned by CBS Radio. The format of the station is contemporary country music. KMNB-FM broadcasts to the Minneapolis area at 102.9 FM.

KMND-AM
Owner: Townsquare Media, Inc.
Editorial: 11300 State Highway 191 Bldg 2, Midland, Texas 79707-1367.
T: 1 432 563-5499 **W:** http://www.kmnd.com
Editorial Profile: KMND-AM is a commercial station owned by Townsquare Media, Inc. The format of the station is sports. KMND-AM broadcasts to the Midland, TX area at 1510 AM.

KMNR-FM
Owner: University of Missouri
Editorial: 1870 Miner Circle, Rolla, Missouri 65401-2811. **T:** 1 573 341-4272
E: kmnr@mst.edu **W:** http://kmnr.org
Editorial Profile: KMNR-FM is a non-commercial station owned by the University of Missouri. The format is college variety. KMNR-FM broadcasts to the Rolla, MO area at 89.7 FM.

KMNS-AM
Owner: Clear Channel Media and Entertainment
Editorial: 1113 Nebraska St, Sioux City, Iowa 51105-1438. **T:** 1 712 258-5595
E: kmnssports@clearchannel.com
W: http://www.620kmns.com
Editorial Profile: KMNS-AM is a commercial station owned by Clear Channel Media and Entertainment. The format of the station is sports. KMNS-AM broadcasts to the Sioux City, IA area at 620 AM. They do not accept press releases since they get everything for FOX Sports Network.

KMNT-FM
Owner: Bicoastal Media LLC
Editorial: 1635 S Gold St, Centralia, Washington 98531. **T:** 1 360 736-3321
E: kmntryan@gmail.com
W: http://www.kmnt.com
Editorial Profile: KMNT-FM is a commercial station owned by Bicoastal Media LLC. The format of the station is country. KMNT-FM broadcasts to the Centralia, WA area at 104.3 FM.

KMNV-AM
Owner: Davidson Media Group
Editorial: 1516 E Lake St Ste 200, Minneapolis, Minnesota 55407-3579.
T: 1 612 729-5900 **W:** http://laraza1400.com
Editorial Profile: KMNV-AM is a commercial station owned by Davidson Media Group. The format of the station is regional Mexican music. KMNV-AM broadcasts to the Edina, MN area at 1400 AM.

KMNY-AM
Owner: Multicultural Radio Broadcasting Inc.
Editorial: 5801 Marvin D Love Fwy, Ste 409, Dallas, Texas 75237-2319. **T:** 1 972 572-1540
E: kdft-kmny@mrbi.net
W: http://www.lavoz1360dallas.com
Editorial Profile: KMNY-AM is a commercial station owned by Multicultural Radio Broadcasting Inc. The format of the station is Spanish religious programming. KMNY-AM broadcasts to the Dallas area at 1360 AM.

KMOC-FM
Owner: Christian Service Foundation Inc.
Editorial: 1040 W Wenonah Blvd, Wichita Falls, Texas 76309. **T:** 1 940 767-3303
E: kmocfm@wf.net
W: http://www.kmocfm.com
Editorial Profile: KMOC-FM is a non-commercial station owned by The Christian Service Foundation Inc. The format of the station is contemporary Christian music. KMOC-FM broadcasts to the Wichita Falls, TX area at 89.5 FM.

KMOD-FM
Owner: Clear Channel Media and Entertainment
Editorial: 2625 S Memorial Dr, Tulsa, Oklahoma 74129. **T:** 1 918 388-5100
W: http://www.kmod.com
Editorial Profile: KMOD-FM is a commercial station owned by Clear Channel Media and Entertainment. The format is rock. KMOD-FM broadcasts to the Tulsa, OK area at 97.5 FM.

KMOE-FM
Owner: Bates County Broadcasting Co.
Editorial: 800 E Nursery St, Butler, Missouri 64730. **T:** 1 660 679-4191
E: fm92@embarqmail.com
W: http://www.921kmoe.com
Editorial Profile: KMOE-FM is a commercial station owned by Bates County Broadcasting Co. The format of the station is classic country music. KMOE-FM broadcasts to the Kansas City, MO area at 92.1 FM.

KMOG-AM
Owner: Farrell Enterprises LLC
Editorial: 500 E Tyler Pkwy, Payson, Arizona 85541. **T:** 1 928 474-5214
E: news@1420kmog.com
W: http://www.rimcountryradio.com
Editorial Profile: KMOG-AM is a commercial station owned by Farrell Enterprises LLC. The format of the station is country. KMOG-AM broadcasts to the Payson, AZ area at 1420 AM.

KMOJ-FM
Owner: State of Minnesota
Editorial: 2123 W Broadway Ave Ste 200, Minneapolis, Minnesota 55411-1807.
T: 1 612 377-0594 **E:** info@kmojfm.com
W: http://www.kmojfm.com
Editorial Profile: KMOJ-FM is a non-commercial station owned by the State of Minnesota. The format of the station is a variety of African American-centered music and talk. KMOJ-FM broadcasts to the Minneapolis area at 89.9 FM.

KMOK-FM
Owner: Ida-Vend Communications Group
Editorial: 805 Stewart Ave, Lewiston, Idaho 83501. **T:** 1 208 746-5056
Editorial Profile: KMOK-FM is a commercial station owned by Ida-Vend Communications Group. The format of the station is contemporary country music. KMOK-FM broadcasts to the Spokane, WA area at 106.9 FM.

KMOM-FM
Owner: Dakota Broadcasting, LLC
Editorial: 426 N Highway 281 Ste 4, Aberdeen, South Dakota 57401-1864.
T: 1 605 725-5551
W: http://www.dakotabroadcasting.com
Editorial Profile: KMOM-FM is a commercial station owned by Dakota Broadcasting, LLC. The format is country music. KMOM-FM broadcasts to the Aberdeen, SD area at 105.5 FM.

KMON-AM
Owner: Cherry Creek Radio
Editorial: 20 3rd St N, Ste 231, Great Falls, Montana 59401. **T:** 1 406 761-7600
Editorial Profile: KMON-AM is a commercial station owned by Cherry Creek Radio. The format of the station is country music. KMON-AM broadcasts in the Great Falls, MT area at 560 AM.

KMON-FM
Owner: Cherry Creek Radio

Editorial: 20 3rd St N, Ste 231, Great Falls, Montana 59401. **T:** 1 406 761-7600
Editorial Profile: KMON-FM is a commercial station owned by Cherry Creek Radio. The format of the station is contemporary and classic country music. KMON-FM broadcasts to the Great Falls, MT area at 94.5 FM.

KMOO-FM
Owner: Hightower (Ingrid)
Editorial: 2065 N Us Highway 69, Mineola, Texas 75773-3731. **T:** 1 903 569-3823
E: news@kmoo.com **W:** http://www.kmoo.com
Editorial Profile: KMOO-FM is a commercial station owned by Ingrid Hightower. The format of the station is contemporary country. KMOO-FM broadcasts to the Mineola, TX area at 99.9 FM.

KMOQ-FM
Owner: American Media Investments
Editorial: 2510 W 20th St, Joplin, Missouri 64804. **T:** 1 417 781-1313
W: http://www.mynewliferadio.com
Editorial Profile: KMOQ-FM is a commercial station owned by American Media Investments. The format of the station is contemporary Christian and broadcasts to the Joplin, MO area at 105.3 FM.

KMOR-FM
Owner: Armada Media
Editorial: 305 E 4th St, North Platte, Nebraska 69101-6903. **T:** 1 308 532-3344
Editorial Profile: KMOR-FM is a commercial station owned by Armada Media. The format of the station is classic rock. KMOR-FM broadcasts to the Scottsbluff, NE area at 93.3 FM.

KMOU-FM
Owner: Majestic Communication
Editorial: 5206 W 2nd St, Roswell, New Mexico 88201-8839. **T:** 1 575 622-6450
E: production@roswellradio.net
Editorial Profile: KMOU-FM is a commercial station owned by Majestic Communication. The format of the station is country music. KMOU-FM broadcasts to the Roswell, NM area at 104.7 FM.

KMOX-AM
Owner: CBS Radio
Editorial: 1220 Olive St Fl 3, Saint Louis, Missouri 63103-2324. **T:** 1 314 621-2345
E: kmoxnews@kmox.com
W: http://stlouis.cbslocal.com
Editorial Profile: KMOX-AM is a commercial station owned by CBS Radio. The format of the station is news, sports and talk. KMOX-AM broadcasts to the St. Louis area at 1120 AM.

KMOZ-AM
Owner: Bott Broadcasting Co.
Editorial: 1701 N Bishop Ave Ste 15, Rolla, Missouri 65401-2229. **T:** 1 573 647-6285
E: kmoz@bottradionetwork.com
W: http://www.bottradionetwork.com
Editorial Profile: KMOZ-AM is a commercial station owned by Bott Broadcasting Co. The format of the station is Christian talk. KMOZ-AM broadcasts in the Rolla, MO area at 1590 AM.

KMOZ-FM
Owner: MBC Grand Broadcasting Inc.
Editorial: 1360 E Sherwood Dr, Grand Junction, Colorado 81501-7546.
T: 1 970 254-2100
W: http://www.themoose923.com/
Editorial Profile: KMOZ-FM is a commercial station owned by MBC Grand Broadcasting Inc. The format of the station is country. KMOZ-FM broadcasts to the Grand Junction, CO area at 100.7 FM.

KMPA-FM
Owner: Waller Broadcasting
Editorial: 3400 W Marshall Ave Floor 3, Longview, Texas 75604-5035.
T: 1 903 663-2477
W: http://www.kompafm.com
Editorial Profile: KMPA-FM is a commercial station owned by Waller Broadcasting. The format of the station is Spanish Contemporary. KMPA-FM broadcasts to the Longview, TX, area at 103.1 FM.

KMPC-AM
Owner: Radio Korea Media Group
Editorial: 3700 Wilshire Blvd, Ste 1020, Los Angeles, California 90010-3006.
T: 1 213 487-1300 **E:** info@radiokorea.com
W: http://www.radiokorea.com
Editorial Profile: KMPC-AM is a commercial station owned by Radio Korea Media Group. The format of the station is ethnic programming. KMPC-AM broadcasts to the Santa Monica, CA area at 1540 AM.

KMPG-AM
Owner: Promo Radio Corp.
Editorial: 406 Main St, 4th Fl, Watsonville, California 95076-4613. **T:** 1 831 722-4477
Editorial Profile: KMPG-AM is a commercial station owned by Promo Radio Corp. The format of the station is regional Mexican. KMPG-AM broadcasts to the Hollister, CA area at 1520 AM.

KMPO-FM
Owner: Radio Bilingue Inc.
Editorial: 5005 E Belmont Ave, Fresno, California 93727. **T:** 1 559 455-5777
W: http://www.radiobilingue.org
Editorial Profile: KMPO-FM is a non-commercial station owned by Radio Bilingue Inc. The format of the station is Hispanic, featuring a variety of music and talk programming. KMPO-FM's target audience is Hispanic listeners in the Modesto, CA area. KMPO-FM airs at 88.7 FM and is a simulcast of KSJV-FM in Fresno, CA.

KMPR-FM
Owner: Prairie Public Broadcasting
Editorial: 1814 N 15th St, Bismarck, North Dakota 58501-2025. **T:** 1 701 241-6900
W: http://www.prairiepublic.org/radio
Editorial Profile: KMPR-FM is owned by Prairie Public Broadcasting. It is a non-commercial station with a classical and news/talk format that airs locally to the Minot, ND area at 88.9 FM.

KMPS-FM
Owner: CBS Radio
Editorial: 1000 Dexter Ave N, Seattle, Washington 98109-3582. **T:** 1 206 805-0941
E: email@kmps.com **W:** http://www.kmps.com
Editorial Profile: KMPS-FM is a commercial station owned by CBS Radio. The format of the station is contemporary country. KMPS-FM broadcasts to the Seattle area at 94.1 FM.

KMPT-AM
Owner: Townsquare Media, LLC
Editorial: 3250 S Reserve St Ste 200, Missoula, Montana 59801-8236.
T: 1 406 728-9300 **W:** http://www.klcy930.com
Editorial Profile: KMPT-AM is a commercial station owned by Townsquare Media, LLC. The format of the station is progressive talk. KMPT-AM broadcasts to the Missoula, MT area at 930 AM.

KMQA-FM
Owner: Casa Media Partners, LLC
Editorial: 1450 E Bardsley Ave, Tulare, California 93274-5805. **T:** 1 559 687-3170
W: http://www.lamaquinamusical.net
Editorial Profile: KMQA-FM is a commercial station owned by Casa Media Partners, LLC. The format of the station is Hispanic programming. KMQA-FM broadcasts to the Tulare, CA area at 100.5 FM.

KMRB-AM
Owner: Multicultural Radio Broadcasting Inc.
Editorial: 747 E Green St, Ste 208, Pasadena, California 91101. **T:** 1 626 773-1430
W: http://www.am1430.net
Editorial Profile: KMRB-AM is a commercial station owned by Multicultural Radio Broadcasting Inc. The format of the station is variety. KMRB-AM broadcasts to the Pasadena, CA area at 1430 AM.

KMRC-AM
Owner: Spotlight Broadcasting of New Orleans LLC
Editorial: 409 Duke St, Morgan City, Louisiana 70380. **T:** 1 985 384-1430
W: http://www.kmrcradio.com
Editorial Profile: KMRC-AM is a commercial station owned by Spotlight Broadcasting of New Orleans LLC. The format of the station is variety, including Lousiana swamp pop and ethnic Cajun music. KMRC-AM broadcasts to the Morgan City, LA area at 1430 AM.

KMRF-AM
Owner: New Life Evangelistic Center
Editorial: 3208 State Highway Oo, Marshfield, Missouri 65706-2480. **T:** 1 314 421-3020
W: http://www.hereshelpnetwork.org
Editorial Profile: KMRF-AM is a commercial station owned by New Life Evangelistic Center, Inc. The format of the station is religious. KMRF-AM broadcasts to the Greater Springfield, MO area at a frequency of 1510 AM.

KMRJ-FM
Owner: RM Broadcasting LLC
Editorial: 75153 Merle Dr Ste G, Palm Desert, California 92211-5197. **T:** 1 760 568-4550
E: jammin995@markerbroadcasting.com
W: http://www.jammin995fm.com
Editorial Profile: KMRJ-FM is a commercial station owned by RM Broadcasting LLC. The format of the station is Rhythmic AC. KMRJ-FM broadcasts to the Palm Springs, CA area at 99.5 FM.

KMRK-FM
Owner: ICA Radio
Editorial: 1330 E 8th St, Ste 207, Odessa, Texas 79761. **T:** 1 432 563-9102
W: http://www.mycountry961.com
Editorial Profile: KMRK-FM is a commercial station owned by ICA Radio. The format of the station is country. KMRK-FM broadcasts to the Odessa, TX area at 96.1 FM.

KMRN-AM
Owner: Cameron/Bethany Licence Co., LLC
Editorial: 607 E Platte Clay Way, Cameron, Missouri 64429-8825. **T:** 1 816 632-6661
W: http://www.northwestmoinfo.com
Editorial Profile: KMRN-AM is a commercial station owned by Cameron/Bethany Licence Co., LLC. The format of the station is country. KMRN-AM broadcasts to the Cameron, MO, area on 1360 AM.

KMRO-FM
Owner: The Association for Community Education Inc.
Editorial: 2310 E Ponderosa Dr, Ste 28, Camarillo, California 93010. **T:** 1 800 260-5676
E: news@nuevavida.com
W: http://www.nuevavida.com
Editorial Profile: KMRO-FM is a non-commercial station owned by The Association for Community Education Inc. The format of the station is Hispanic religious programming. KMRO-FM broadcasts to the Camarillo, CA area at 90.3 FM.

KMRQ-FM
Owner: Clear Channel Media and Entertainment
Editorial: 2121 Lancey Dr, Modesto, California 95355. **T:** 1 209 551-1306
E: modestopsa@clearchannel.com
W: http://www.rock967.com
Editorial Profile: KMRQ-FM is a commercial station owned by Clear Channel Media and Entertainment. The format of the station is alternative rock. KMRQ-FM broadcasts to the Modesto, CA area at 96.7 FM.

KMRS-AM
Owner: Iowa City Broadcasting Co.
Editorial: 46671 State Highway 28, Morris, Minnesota 56267-4508. **T:** 1 320 589-3131
E: kmrskkok@fedtel.net
W: http://www.kmrskkok.com
Editorial Profile: KMRS-AM is a commercial station owned by Iowa City Broadcasting Co. The format of the station is local news, talk, and sports. KMRS-AM broadcasts to the Morris, MN area at 1230 AM.

KMRX-FM
Owner: Noalmark Broadcasting Corp.
Editorial: 2525 N West Ave, El Dorado, Arkansas 71730. **T:** 1 870 863-6126
W: http://www.totalradio.com/96x.htm
Editorial Profile: KMRX-FM is a commercial station owned by Noalmark Broadcasting Corp. The format of the station is adult contemporary. KMRX-FM broadcasts to the El Dorado, AR area at 96.1 FM.

KMRY-AM
Owner: Sellers Broadcasting Inc.
Editorial: 1957 Blairs Ferry Rd NE, Cedar Rapids, Iowa 52402. **T:** 1 319 393-1450
E: kmry@kmryradio.com
W: http://www.kmryradio.com
Editorial Profile: KMRY-AM is a commercial station owned by Sellers Broadcasting Inc. The format for the station is Classic Hits. KMRY-AM broadcasts to the Cedar Rapids, IA area at 1450 AM.

KMRZ-FM
Owner: Big Thickett Broadcasting Co.
Editorial: 2717 Yellowstone Rd, Rock Springs, Wyoming 82901-2813. **T:** 1 307 362-3793
W: http://www.wyoradio.com
Editorial Profile: KMRZ-FM is a commercial station owned by Big Thickett Broadcasting Co. The format for the station is regional Mexican. KMRZ-FM broadcasts to the Salt Lake City area at 106.7 FM.

KMSA-FM
Owner: Mesa State College
Editorial: 1100 North Ave, Grand Junction, Colorado 81501. **T:** 1 970 248-1442
Editorial Profile: KMSA-FM is a non-commercial station owned by Mesa State College. The format of the station is rock alternative music. KMSA-FM broadcasts in the Grand Rapids, CO area at 91.3 FM.

KMSD-AM
Owner: Armada Media Corp.
Editorial: 15096 SD Highway 15, Milbank, South Dakota 57252-5954. **T:** 1 605 432-5516
E: kmsd@tnics.com
W: http://bigstoneradio.com
Editorial Profile: KMSD-AM is a commercial station owned by Armada Media Corp. The format of the station is classic hits. KMSD-AM broadcasts to the Milbank, SD area at 1510 AM.

KMSE-FM
Owner: Minnesota Public Radio
Editorial: 480 Cedar St, Saint Paul, Minnesota 55101-2217. **T:** 1 651 290-1500
E: 893dj@mpr.org
W: http://www.minnesota.publicradio.org

KMSK-FM
Owner: Minnesota State University-Mankato
Editorial: 1536 Warren St Ste 205, Mankato, Minnesota 56001-6534. **T:** 1 507 389-5678
W: http://www.kmsu.org
Editorial Profile: KMSK-FM is a non-commercial station owned by Minnesota State University-Mankato. The format of the station is college variety. KMSK-FM broadcasts to the Mankato, MN area at 91.3 FM.

KMSM-FM
Owner: University of Montana
Editorial: 1300 W Park Street, Student Union Room 117, Butte, Montana 59701.
T: 1 406 496-1071 **E:** kmsm@mtech.edu
W: http://www.kmsmfm.org

KMSO-FM
Owner: Mountain Broadcasting
Editorial: 725 Strand Ave, Missoula, Montana 59801. **T:** 1 406 542-1025
E: info@mtnbdc.com
W: http://www.moclub.com
Editorial Profile: KMSO-FM is a commercial station owned by Mountain Broadcasting. The format of the station is hot adult contemporary music. KMSO-FM broadcasts to the Missoula, MT area at 102.5 FM.

KMSR-AM
Owner: KMSR, Inc.
Editorial: 1000 Main St W, Mayville, North Dakota 58257-1036. **T:** 1 701 786-2335
E: news@kmav.com **W:** http://www.kmav.com
Editorial Profile: KMSR-AM is a commercial station owned by KMSR, Inc. The format of the station is sports. KMSR-AM broadcasts to the Mayville, ND area at 1520 AM.

KMST-FM
Owner: University of Missouri
Editorial: G6 W Library 400 14th St 400 St, W, Rolla, Missouri 65409-0001.
T: 1 573 341-4386 **E:** kmst@mst.edu
W: http://www.kmst.org
Editorial Profile: KMST-FM is a non-commercial station owned by the University of Missouri. The format of the station is news, talk, and variety. KMST-FM broadcasts to the Rolla, MO area at 88.5 FM.

KMSU-FM
Owner: Minnesota State University-Mankato
Editorial: 1536 Warren St, Mankato, Minnesota 56001-4969. **T:** 1 507 389-5678
W: http://www.mnsu.edu/kmsufm
Editorial Profile: KMSU-FM is a non-commercial station owned by Minnesota State University-Mankato. The format of the station is college variety and news. KMSU-FM broadcasts to the Mankato, MN area at 89.7 FM.

KMSW-FM
Owner: Bicoastal Media LLC
Editorial: 719 E 2nd St, The Dalles, Oregon 97058. **T:** 1 541 296-2211
W: http://www.gorgeradio.com
Editorial Profile: KMSW-FM is a commercial station owned by Bicoastal Media LLC. The format of the station is classic rock music. KMSW-FM broadcasts in the Portland, OR area at 92.7 FM.

KMTA-AM
Owner: Marks Group Inc.

Editorial: 508 Main St, Miles City, Montana 59301. **T:** 1 406 234-5626
W: http://www.kyuskmta.com
Editorial Profile: KMTA-AM is a commercial station owned by Marks Group Inc. The format of the station is oldies. KMTA-AM broadcasts in the Miles City, MT area at 1050 AM.

KMTB-FM
Owner: Southwest Arkansas Radio
Editorial: 1513 S 4th St, Nashville, Arkansas 71852. **T:** 1 870 845-3601
E: swarkradio@hotmail.com
W: http://www.southwestarkansasradio.com
Editorial Profile: KMTB-FM is a commercial station owned by Southwest Arkansas Radio. The format of the station is contemporary country. KMTB-FM broadcasts to the Nashville, AR area at 99.5 FM.

KMTC-FM
Owner: Russellville Educational Broadcasting Foundation
Editorial: 305 Lake Front Drive, Russellville, Arkansas 72802. **T:** 1 479 967-7400
E: kmtc@rccenter.org
W: http://www.kmtcradio.org
Editorial Profile: KMTC-FM is a non-commercial station owned by Russellville Educational Broadcasting Foundation. The format of the station is contemporary Christian music. KMTC-FM broadcasts in the Russellville, AR, area at 91.1 FM.

KMTG-FM
Owner: San Jose Unified School District
Editorial: 1290 Blossom Hill Rd, San Jose, California 95118. **T:** 1 408 535-6310
E: kmtgthestampede@gmail.com
Editorial Profile: KMTG-FM is a non-commercial station owned by San Jose Unified School District. The format of the station is variety. KMTG-FM broadcasts in the San Jose, CA area at 89.3 FM.

KMTH-FM
Owner: Eastern New Mexico University
Editorial: 52 Broadcast Ctr, Portales, New Mexico 88130-7402. **T:** 1 575 562-2112
E: kenwfm@enmu.edu
W: http://www.kenw.org
Editorial Profile: KMTH-FM is a non-commercial station owned by the Eastern New Mexico University. The format of the station is classical and easy listening music, and news. KMTH-FM broadcasts to the Portales, NM area at 98.7 FM.

KMTI-AM
Owner: Barton(Douglas L.)
Editorial: 500 North 1600 West, Manti, Utah 84642. **T:** 1 435 835-7301
E: news@kmtiradio.com
W: http://www.midutahradio.com/kmti
Editorial Profile: KMTI-AM is a commercial station owned by Douglas L. Barton. The format of the station is country. KMTI-AM broadcasts to the Manti, UT area at 650 AM.

KMTK-FM
Owner: Combined Communications
Editorial: 63088 Ne 18Th St Ste 200, Bend, Oregon 97701-7102. **T:** 1 541 382-5263
E: country@mountain997.com
W: http://www.mountain997.com
Editorial Profile: KMTK-FM is a commercial station owned by Combined Communications. The format of the station is contemporary country music. KMTK-FM broadcasts to the Bend, OR area at 99.7 FM.

KMTL-AM
Owner: Domerese(George)
Editorial: 301 Brookswood Rd, Unit 208, Sherwood, Arkansas 72120-4200.
T: 1 501 835-1554
E: kmtl760am@sbcglobal.net
Editorial Profile: KMTL-AM is a commercial station owned by George Domerese. The format of the station is gospel and religious programming. KMTL-AM broadcasts to the Sherwood, AR area at 760 AM.

KMTN-FM
Owner: Rich Broadcasting, LLC.
Editorial: 1140 State Highway 22, Jackson, Wyoming 83001-9401. **T:** 1 307 733-2120
W: http://www.jacksonholeradio.com
Editorial Profile: KMTN-FM is a commercial station owned by Rich Broadcasting, LLC. The format of the station is adult album alternative. KMTN-FM broadcasts to the Jackson, WY area at 96.9 FM.

KMTS-FM
Owner: Colorado West Broadcasting Inc.

Editorial: 3230 S Glen Ave, Unit B2, Glenwood Springs, Colorado 81601. **T:** 1 970 945-9124
E: kmts@kmts.com **W:** http://www.kmts.com
Editorial Profile: KMTS-FM is a commercial station owned by Colorado West Broadcasting Inc. The format of the station is country. KMTS-FM broadcasts to the Denver area at 99.1 FM.

KMTT-AM
Owner: Entercom Communications Corp.
Editorial: 0700 SW Bancroft St, Portland, Oregon 97239-4226. **T:** 1 503 223-1441
W: http://www.1080thefan.com/pages/17659677.php
Editorial Profile: KMTT-AM is a commercial station owned by Entercom Communications Corp. The format of the station is sports. KMTT-AM broadcasts to the Portland, OR area at 910 AM.

KMTX-AM
Owner: Montana Radio Company (The)
Editorial: 516 Fuller Ave, Helena, Montana 59601-3301. **T:** 1 406 442-0400
Editorial Profile: KMTX-AM is a commercial station owned by Montana Radio Company (The). The format of the station is classic hits. KMTX-AM broadcasts to the Helena, MT area at 950 AM.

KMTX-FM
Owner: Montana Radio Company (The)
Editorial: 516 Fuller Ave, Helena, Montana 59601-3301. **T:** 1 406 442-0400
Editorial Profile: KMTX-FM is a commercial station owned by Montana Radio Company (The). The format for the station is adult contemporary. KMTX-FM broadcasts to the Helena, MT area at 105.3 FM.

KMTY-FM
Owner: Armada Media Corp.
Editorial: 613 4th Ave, Holdrege, Nebraska 68949. **T:** 1 308 995-4020
E: kmty@highplainsradio.net
W: http://www.plainsreporter.com
Editorial Profile: KMTY-FM is a commercial station owned by Armada Media Corp. The format of the station is adult hits. KMTY-FM broadcasts to the Lincoln, NE area at 97.7 FM.

KMTZ-FM
Owner: Mountain Broadcasting
Editorial: 725 Strand Ave, Missoula, Montana 59801-5710. **T:** 1 406 542-1025
W: http://www.moclub.com/
Editorial Profile: KMTZ-FM is a commercial station owned by Mountain Broadcasting. The format of the station is hot adult contemporary music. The station airs locally at 107.7 FM.

KMUD-FM
Owner: Redwood Community Radio Inc.
Editorial: 1144 Redway Drive, Redway, California 95560. **T:** 1 707 923-2513
E: news@kmud.org **W:** http://www.kmud.org
Editorial Profile: KMUD-FM is a non-commercial station owned by Redwood Community Radio Inc. The format for the station is variety. KMUD-FM broadcasts to the Redway, CA area at 91.1 FM.

KMUN-FM
Owner: Tillicum Foundation
Editorial: 1445 Exchange St, Astoria, Oregon 97103. **T:** 1 503 325-0010 **E:** news@kmun.org
W: http://www.kmun.org
Editorial Profile: KMUN-FM is a non-commercial station owned by the Tillicum Foundation. The format of the station is variety. KMUN-FM broadcasts to the Astoria, OR area at 91.9 FM.

KMUW-FM
Owner: Wichita State University
Editorial: 3317 E 17th St N, Wichita, Kansas 67208. **T:** 1 316 978-6789 **E:** info@kmuw.org
W: http://www.kmuw.org
Editorial Profile: KMUW-FM is a non-commercial station owned by Wichita State University. The format of the station is news, talk and jazz. KMUW-FM broadcasts to the Wichita, KS area at 89.1 FM.

KMUZ-FM
Owner: Willamette Information, News and Entertainment Service
Editorial: 1313 Mill St Se, Salem, Oregon 97301-6307. **T:** 1 503 967-5689
E: info@kmuz.org **W:** http://www.KMUZ.org
Editorial Profile: KMUZ-FM is a non-commercial community radio station owned by Willamette Information, News and Entertainment Service. The format of the station is variety. KMUZ-FM broadcasts to the

Willamette Valley area in Oregon at a frequency of 88.5 FM.

KMVA-FM
Owner: Trumper Communications
Editorial: 4747 N 7th St Ste 424, Phoenix, Arizona 85014-3663. **T:** 1 602 222-9750
W: http://trendingradio.com
Editorial Profile: KMVA-FM is a commercial station owned by Trumper Communications. The format of the station is Hot AC. KMVA-FM broadcasts to the Phoenix market at 97.5 FM.

KMVI-AM
Owner: Pacific Media Group
Editorial: 311 Ano St, Kahului, Hawaii 96732-1304. **T:** 1 808 877-5566
W: http://www.espn550.com
Editorial Profile: KMVI-AM is a commercial station owned by Pacific Media Group. The format of the station is sports. KMVI-AM broadcasts to the Maui, HI area at 900 AM.

KMVK-FM
Owner: CBS Radio
Editorial: 4131 N Central Expy, Dallas, Texas 75204-2102. **T:** 1 214 525-7000
W: http://lagrande1075.cbslocal.com
Editorial Profile: KMVK-FM is a commercial station owned by CBS Radio. The format of the station is Regional Mexican music. KMVK-FM broadcasts to the Dallas area at 107.5 FM.

KMVL-AM
Owner: Hunt Broadcasting
Editorial: 102 W Main St, Madisonville, Texas 77864. **T:** 1 936 348-9200 **E:** kmvl@kmvl.net
W: http://www.kmvl.net
Editorial Profile: KMVL-AM is a commercial station owned by Hunt Broadcasting. The format of the station is adult standards. KMVL-AM broadcasts to the Madisonville, TX area at 1220 AM.

KMVL-FM
Owner: Hunt Broadcasting
Editorial: 102 W Main St, Madisonville, Texas 77864-1905. **T:** 1 936 348-9200
E: kmvl@kmvl.net **W:** http://www.kmvl.net
Editorial Profile: KMVL-FM is a commercial station owned by Hunt Broadcasting. The format of the station is country. KMVL-FM broadcasts to the Madisonville, TX area at 100.5 FM.

KMVN-FM
Owner: Alaksa Integrated Media
Editorial: 4700 Business Park Blvd Ste 44, Anchorage, Alaska 99503-7176.
T: 1 907 522-1018 **E:** info@movin1057.com
W: http://www.movin1057.com
Editorial Profile: KMVN-FM is a commercial station owned by Alaksa Integrated Media. The format of the station is lite rock/lite ac. KMVN-FM broadcasts to the Anchorage, AK area at 105.7 FM.

KMVP-AM
Owner: Bonneville International Corp.
Editorial: 7740 N 16Th St Ste 200, Phoenix, Arizona 85020-4482. **T:** 1 623 533-3213
W: http://www.gospel860.com
Editorial Profile: KMVP-AM is a commercial station owned by Bonneville International Corp. and in an LMA with AIM Broadcasting. The format of the station is gospel. KMVP-AM broadcasts to the Phoenix area on 860 AM.

KMVQ-FM
Owner: CBS Radio
Editorial: 865 Battery St Fl 2, San Francisco, California 94111-1503. **T:** 1 415 391-9970
W: http://997now.cbslocal.com
Editorial Profile: KMVQ-FM is a commercial station owned by CBS Radio. The format of the station is top 40/CHR. KMVQ-AM broadcasts to the San Francisco area at 99.7 FM.

KMVR-FM
Owner: Bravo Mic Communications, LLC
Editorial: 101 Perkins Dr, Las Cruces, New Mexico 88005. **T:** 1 575 527-1111
E: kmvr@bravomic.com
W: http://www.kmvrfm.com
Editorial Profile: KMVR-FM is a commercial station owned by Bravo Mic Communications, LLC. The format of the station is hot adult contemporary music. KMVR-FM broadcasts to the Las Cruces, NM area at 104.9 FM.

KMVX-FM
Owner: The Radio People
Editorial: 1107 Hudson Ln, Monroe, Louisiana 71201-6033. **T:** 1 318 388-2323

Editorial Profile: KMVX-FM is a commercial station owned by The Radio People. The format of the station is Urban AC. KMVX-FM broadcasts in the Monroe, LA area at 101.9 FM.

KMWB-FM
Owner: New West Broadcasting
Editorial: 1145 Kilauea Ave, Hilo, Hawaii 96720. **T:** 1 808 935-5461
W: http://www.b97hawaii.com
Editorial Profile: KMWB-FM is a commercial station owned by New West Broadcasting. The format of the station is classic hits. KMWB-FM broadcasts to the Hilo, HI area at 93.1 FM. The station simulcasts KNWB-FM.

KMWS-FM
Owner: Washington State University
Editorial: Murrow Center, Room 382, Pullman, Washington 99164. **T:** 1 509 335-6500
E: nwpr@wsu.edu **W:** http://www.nwpr.org
Editorial Profile: KMWS-FM is a non-commercial station owned by Washington State University. The format of the station is news, talk and classical music. KMWS-FM broadcasts to the Mt. Vernon, WA area at 90.1 FM.

KMWX-FM
Owner: Townsquare Media, LLC
Editorial: 3911 S 1st St, Abilene, Texas 79605. **T:** 1 325 676-7711
W: http://www.mymix92.com
Editorial Profile: KMWX-FM is a commercial station owned by Townsquare Media, LLC. The format of the station is adult contemporary music. KMWX-FM broadcasts to the Abilene, TX area at 92.5 FM.

KMWY-FM
Owner: Moody Bible Institute
Editorial: 5408 S Freya St, Spokane, Washington 99223-7114. **T:** 1 509 448-2555
E: kmbi@moody.edu
W: http://www.moodyradionw.fm
Editorial Profile: KMWY-FM is a non-commercial station owned by Moody Bible Institute. The format of the station is religious. KMWY-FM broadcasts to the Jackson, WY area at 91.1 FM.

KMXA-AM
Owner: Entravision Communications Corp.
Editorial: 1907 Mile High Stadium West Cir, Denver, Colorado 80204-1908.
T: 1 303 721-9210
Editorial Profile: KMXA-AM is a commercial station owned by Entravision Communications Corp. The format of the station is Spanish romantica. KMXA-AM broadcasts to the Denver area at 1090 AM.

KMXA-FM
Owner: Clear Channel Media and Entertainment
Editorial: 1000 20th Ave SW, Minot, North Dakota 58701. **T:** 1 701 852-4646
E: minotprod@clearchannel.com
W: http://www.mix999fm.com
Editorial Profile: KMXA-FM is a commercial station owned by Clear Channel Media and Entertainment. The format of the station is hot adult contemporary. KMXA-FM broadcasts to the Minot-Bismarck, ND area at 99.9 FM.

KMXB-FM
Owner: CBS Radio
Editorial: 7255 S. Tenaya Way, Suite 100, Las Vegas, Nevada 89113. **T:** 1 702 257-9400
W: http://www.mix941.fm
Editorial Profile: KMXB-FM is a commercial station owned by CBS Radio. The format of the station is hot adult contemporary. KMXB-FM broadcasts to the Las Vegas area at 94.1 FM.

KMXC-FM
Owner: Townsquare Media, Inc.
Editorial: 5100 S Tennis Ln Ste 200, Sioux Falls, South Dakota 57108-2271.
T: 1 605 339-1140
W: http://www.mix97-3.com
Editorial Profile: KMXC-FM is a commercial station owned by Townsquare Media, Inc. The format of the station is adult contemporary. KMXC-FM broadcasts to the Sioux Falls, SD area at 97.3 FM.

KMXE-FM
Owner: Silver Rock Communications Inc
Editorial: 9 South Broadway, Red Lodge, Montana 59068. **T:** 1 406 446-1199
E: fm99mtn@starband.net
W: http://www.fm99mtn.com
Editorial Profile: KMXE-FM is a commercial station owned by Silver Rock

Communications. The station airs locally on 99.3 FM. The format of the station is oldies, and the target audience is listeners, ages 35 to 100, in the Red Lodge, MT-area.

KMXF-FM
Owner: Clear Channel Media and Entertainment
Editorial: 2049 E Joyce Blvd, Ste 101, Fayetteville, Arkansas 72703.
T: 1 479 582-1079
W: http://www.mix1019.com
Editorial Profile: KMXF-FM is a commercial station owned by Clear Channel Media and Entertainment. The format of the station is Top 40/CHR. KMXF-FM broadcasts to the Fayetteville, AR area at 101.9 FM.

KMXG-FM
Owner: Clear Channel Media and Entertainment
Editorial: 3535 E Kimberly Rd, Davenport, Iowa 52807-2583. **T:** 1 563 344-7000
W: http://www.mix96online.com
Editorial Profile: KMXG-FM is a commercial station owned by Clear Channel Media and Entertainment. The format of the station is adult contemporary music. KMXG-FM broadcasts to the Davenport, IA area at 96.1 FM.

KMXH-FM
Owner: JWBP Broadcasting, LLC
Editorial: 1605 Murray St Ste 111, Alexandria, Louisiana 71301-6875. **T:** 1 318 445-0800
W: http://www.mix939.fm
Editorial Profile: KMXH-FM is a commercial station owned by JWBP Broadcasting, LLC. The format of the station is rhythmic contemporary. KMXH-FM broadcasts to the Alexandria, LA area at a frequency of 93.3 FM.

KMXI-FM
Owner: Deer Creek Broadcasting
Editorial: 2654 Cramer Ln, Chico, California 95928. **T:** 1 530 345-0021
W: http://www.kmxi.com
Editorial Profile: KMXI-FM is a commercial station owned by Deer Creek Broadcasting. The format of the station is adult contemporary. KMXI-FM broadcasts to the Chico, CA area at 95.1 FM.

KMXJ-FM
Owner: Townsquare Media, LLC
Editorial: 6214 W 34th Ave, Amarillo, Texas 79109-4006. **T:** 1 806 355-9777
W: http://www.mix941kmxj.com
Editorial Profile: KMXJ-FM is a commercial station owned by Townsquare Media, LLC. The format of the station is hot adult contemporary. KMXJ-FM broadcasts to the Amarillo, TX area at 94.1 FM.

KMXK-FM
Owner: Townsquare Media, LLC
Editorial: 640 Lincoln Ave SE, Saint Cloud, Minnesota 56304. **T:** 1 320 251-4422
W: http://www.mix949.com
Editorial Profile: KMXK-FM is a commercial station owned by Townsquare Media, LLC. The format of the station is hot adult contemporary music. KMXK-FM broadcasts in the St. Cloud, MN area.

KMXL-FM
Owner: Petersen(Ronald L.)
Editorial: 221 E 4th St, Carthage, Missouri 64836. **T:** 1 417 358-2648
W: http://www.951mikefm.com
Editorial Profile: KMXL-FM is a commercial station owned by Ronald L. Petersen. The format of the station is adult hits. KMXL-FM broadcasts to the Carthage, MO area at 95.1 FM.

KMXN-FM
Owner: Great Plains Media
Editorial: 3125 W 6th St, Lawrence, Kansas 66049. **T:** 1 785 843-1320
W: http://www.bull929.com
Editorial Profile: KMXN-FM is a commercial station owned by Great Plains Media. The format of the station is contemporary country. KMXN-FM broadcasts in the Lawrence, KS at 92.9 FM.

KMXO-AM
Owner: Silva (Ray)
Editorial: 604 N 2nd St, Merkel, Texas 79536.
T: 1 325 928-3060 **E:** kmxo@yahoo.com
Editorial Profile: KMXO-AM is a commercial station owned by Silva (Ray R). The format of the station is Hispanic religious. KMXO-AM broadcasts to the Merkel, TX area at 1500 AM.

KMXP-FM
Owner: Clear Channel Media and Entertainment
Editorial: 4686 E Van Buren St, Phoenix, Arizona 85008-6959. **T:** 1 602 374-6000
W: http://www.mix969.com
Editorial Profile: KMXP-FM is a commercial station owned by Clear Channel Media and Entertainment. The format of the station is hot adult contemporary music. KMXP-FM broadcasts to the Phoenix area at 96.9 FM.

KMXR-FM
Owner: Clear Channel Media and Entertainment
Editorial: 501 Tupper Lane Radio Plaza, Corpus Christi, Texas 78417-9736.
T: 1 361 289-0111
W: http://www.939online.com
Editorial Profile: KMXR-FM is a commercial station owned by Clear Channel Media and Entertainment. The format of the station is oldies music. KMXR-FM broadcasts to the Corpus Christi, TX area at 93.9 FM.

KMXS-FM
Owner: Morris Communications
Editorial: 301 Arctic Slope Ave, Ste 200, Anchorage, Alaska 99518. **T:** 1 907 344-9622
E: winner@kmxs.com
W: http://www.kmxs.com
Editorial Profile: KMXS-FM is a commercial station owned by Morris Communications. The format of the station is hot adult contemporary. KMXS-FM broadcasts to the Anchorage, AK area at 103.1 FM.

KMXT-FM
Owner: Kodiak Island Broadcasting Co., Inc.
Editorial: 620 Egan Way, Kodiak, Alaska 99615. **T:** 1 907 486-3181
W: http://www.kmxt.org
Editorial Profile: KMXT-FM is a non-commercial station owned by Kodiak Island Broadcasting Co., Inc. The format of the station is a variety of music, news, and talk. KMXT-FM broadcasts to Kodiak Island and the Alaska Peninsula at 100.1 FM.

KMXV-FM
Owner: Wilks Broadcast Group
Editorial: 508 Westport Rd, Ste 202, Kansas City, Missouri 64111. **T:** 1 816 753-4000
W: http://www.mix93.com
Editorial Profile: KMXV-FM is a commercial station owned by Wilks Broadcast Group. The format of the station is Top 40/CHR music. KMXV-FM broadcasts to the Kansas City, MO area at 93.3 FM.

KMXW-FM
Owner: Wilks Broadcast Group
Editorial: 300 E 2Nd St Ste 1400, Reno, Nevada 89501-1566. **T:** 1 775 333-0123
W: http://www.renosmix.com
Editorial Profile: KMXW-FM is a commercial station owned by Wilks Broadcast Group. The format of the station is Hot AC. KMXW-FM broadcasts to the Reno, NV area at 100.9 FM.

KMXX-FM
Owner: Entravision Communications Corp.
Editorial: 1803 N Imperial Ave, El Centro, California 92243-1333. **T:** 1 760 482-7777
W: http://www.993tricolor.com
Editorial Profile: KMXX-FM is a commercial station owned by Entravision Communications Corp. The format for the station is Spanish. KMXX-FM broadcasts to the El Centro, CA area at 99.3 FM.

KMXY-FM
Owner: Townsquare Media, Inc.
Editorial: 315 Kennedy Ave, Grand Junction, Colorado 81501-7552. **T:** 1 970 242-7788
W: http://www.mix1043fm.com
Editorial Profile: KMXY-FM is a commercial station owned by Townsquare Media, Inc. The format of the station is hot adult contemporary music. KMXY-FM broadcasts to the Grand Junction, CO area at 104.3 FM.

KMXZ-FM
Owner: Journal Broadcast Group
Editorial: 7280 E Rosewood St, Tucson, Arizona 85710-1350. **T:** 1 520 722-5486
W: http://www.mixfm.com
Editorial Profile: KMXZ-FM is a commercial station owned by Journal Broadcast Group. The format of the station is adult contemporary. KMXZ-FM broadcasts to the Tucson, AZ area at 94.9 FM.

KMYC-AM
Owner: Huth Broadcasting Inc.
Editorial: 1605 Simpson Ln, Marysville, California 95901. **T:** 1 530 742-5555
E: kmyc@syix.com
W: http://www.syix.com/kmyc
Editorial Profile: KMYC-AM is a commercial station owned by Huth Broadcasting Inc. The format of the station is news, sports and talk. KMYC-AM broadcasts in the Sacramento, CA at 1410 AM.

KMYI-FM
Owner: Clear Channel Media and Entertainment
Editorial: 9660 Granite Ridge Dr Ste 100, San Diego, California 92123-2689.
T: 1 858 292-2000
W: http://www.star941fm.com
Editorial Profile: KMYI-FM is a commercial station owned by Clear Channel Media and Entertainment. The format for the station is hot adult contemporary. KMYI-FM broadcasts to the San Diego area at 94.1 FM.

KMYK-FM
Owner: Viper Communications Inc.
Editorial: 5715 Highway 54, Osage Beach, Missouri 65065-3030. **T:** 1 573 348-2772
E: newsroom@krmsradio.com
W: http://www.935rocksthelake.com
Editorial Profile: KMYK-FM is a commercial station owned by Viper Communications Inc. The format of the station is classic rock. KMYK-FM broadcasts to the Osage Beach, MO area at 93.5 FM.

KMYT-FM
Owner: Clear Channel Media and Entertainment
Editorial: 27349 Jefferson Ave, Ste 116, Temecula, California 92590. **T:** 1 951 296-9050
W: http://www.kmyt945.com
Editorial Profile: KMYT-FM is a commercial station owned by Clear Channel Media and Entertainment. The format of the station is smooth AC. KMYT-FM broadcasts to the Temecula, CA area at 94.5 FM.

KMYX-FM
Owner: Campesina Network(La)
Editorial: 6313 Schirra Ct, Bakersfield, California 93313. **T:** 1 661 837-0745
W: http://www.campesina.com
Editorial Profile: KMYX-FM is a commercial station owned by La Campesina Network. The format of the station is regional Mexican. KMYX-FM broadcasts to the Bakersfield, CA area at 92.5 FM.

KMYY-FM
Owner: Opus Media Partners
Editorial: 1200 N 18th St, Ste D, Monroe, Louisiana 71201. **T:** 1 318 387-3922
W: http://realcountry923.com
Editorial Profile: KMYY-FM is a commercial station owned by Opus Media Partners. The format of the station is country music. KMYY-FM broadcasts in the Monroe, LA area at 92.3 FM.

KMYZ-FM
Owner: Stephens Media Group
Editorial: 2448 E 81st St Ste 5500, Tulsa, Oklahoma 74137-4201. **T:** 1 918 492-2660
Editorial Profile: KMYZ-FM is a commercial station owned by Stephens Media Group. The format of the station is rock alternative. KMYZ-FM broadcasts to the Tulsa, OK area at 104.5 FM.

KMZA-FM
Owner: KNZA, Inc.
Editorial: 28 S 4th St, Seneca, Kansas 66538.
T: 1 785 336-6166 **E:** kmza@bbwi.net
W: http://www.kmzafm.com
Editorial Profile: KMZA-FM is a commercial station owned by KNZA, Inc. The format of the station is contemporary country music. KMZA-FM broadcasts in the Seneca, KS area at 92.1 FM.

KMZE-FM
Owner: FM 92 Broadcasters, Inc.
Editorial: 2728 Williams Ave Ste R, Woodward, Oklahoma 73801-5841.
T: 1 580 256-3692 **E:** k101@k101online.com
W: http://www.z92online.com
Editorial Profile: KMZE-FM is a commercial station owned by FM 92 Broadcasters, Inc. The format of the station is news talk and sports. KMZE-FM broadcasts to Oklahoma City, OK area at 92.1 FM.

KMZQ-AM
Owner: Kemp Broadcasting
Editorial: 3999 Las Vegas Blvd S, Las Vegas, Nevada 89119-1001. **T:** 1 702 736-6161
W: http://www.670theq.com
Editorial Profile: KMZQ-AM is a commercial station owned by Kemp Broadcasting. The format of the station is sports. KMZQ-AM broadcasts to the Las Vegas market at 670 AM.

KMZQ-FM
Owner: Kemp Broadcasting
Editorial: 3999 Las Vegas Blvd S, Las Vegas, Nevada 89119-1001. **T:** 1 702 736-6161
W: http://1069theq.com
Editorial Profile: KMZQ-FM is a commercial station owned by Kemp Broadcasting. The format for the station is Hot AC. KMZQ-FM broadcasts to the Las Vegas area at 99.3 FM.

KMZT-AM
Owner: Mount Wilson FM Broadcasters
Editorial: 1500 Cotner Ave, Los Angeles, California 90025. **T:** 1 310 478-5540
E: info@kmzt.com **W:** http://www.kmozart.com
Editorial Profile: KMZT-AM is a commercial station owned by Mount Wilson FM Broadcasters. The format of the station is classical music. KMZT-AM broadcasts to the Los Angeles area at 1260 AM.

KMZU-FM
Owner: Kanza Inc.
Editorial: 102 N Mason St, Carrollton, Missouri 64633-2159. **T:** 1 660 542-0404
E: news@kmzu.com **W:** http://www.kmzu.com
Editorial Profile: KMZU-FM is a commercial station owned by Kanza Inc. The format of the station is contemporary country music and agricultural programming. KMZU-FM broadcasts to the Kansas City, MO area at 100.7 FM.

KMZZ-FM
Owner: Claro Communications Ltd.
Editorial: 400 S Padre Island Dr, Ste 107, Corpus Christi, Texas 78405.
T: 1 361 299-6000
Editorial Profile: KMZZ-FM is a commercial station owned by Claro Communications Ltd. The format of the station is regional Mexican. KMZZ-FM broadcasts to the Corpus Christi, TX area at 106.9 FM.

KNAA-FM
Owner: Northern Arizona University
Editorial: 515 E Pine Knoll, Building 83, Flagstaff, Arizona 86011-0001.
T: 1 928 523-5628 **E:** knau@nau.edu
W: http://www.knau.org
Editorial Profile: KNAA-FM is a non-commercial station owned by Northern Arizona University. The format of the station is classical music and news. KNAA-FM broadcasts to the Flagstaff, AZ area at 90.7 FM.

KNAB-AM
Owner: KNAB Inc.
Editorial: 17534 County Road 49, Burlington, Colorado 80807. **T:** 1 719 346-8600
E: knab@centurytel.net
W: http://www.knabradio.com
Editorial Profile: KNAB-AM is a commercial station owned by KNAB Inc. The format of the station is adult standards. KNAB-AM broadcasts to the Burlington, CO area at 1140 AM.

KNAB-FM
Owner: KNAB Inc.
Editorial: 17534 County Road 49, Burlington, Colorado 80807-9350. **T:** 1 719 346-8600
E: info@knabradio.com
W: http://knabradio.com
Editorial Profile: KNAB-FM is a commercial station owned by KNAB Inc. The format of the station is classic country. KNAB-FM broadcasts to the Denver, CO area at 104.1 FM.

KNAF-AM
Owner: Hill Country Broadcasting, LLC
Editorial: 210 Woodcrest St, Fredericksburg, Texas 78624. **T:** 1 830 997-2197
W: http://www.knafam.com
Editorial Profile: KNAF-AM is a commercial station owned by Hill Country Broadcasting, LLC. The format of the station is classic country. KNAF-AM broadcasts to the San Antonio area at 910 AM.

KNAF-FM
Owner: Hill Country Broadcasting, LLC
Editorial: 210 Woodcrest St, Fredericksburg, Texas 78624. **T:** 1 830 997-2197
W: http://www.knafam.com
Editorial Profile: KNAF-FM is a commercial station owned by Hill Country Broadcasting, LLC. The format of the station is classic and contemporary country. KNAF-FM broadcasts to the San Antonio area at 105.7 FM.

KNAH-FM

Owner: Champlin Broadcasting
Editorial: 4045 NW 64th St Ste 306, Oklahoma City, Oklahoma 73116-2616.
T: 1 633 633-1099
W: http://www.crankhank.com
Editorial Profile: KNAH-FM is a commercial station owned by Champlin Broadcasting. The format of the station is classic country. KNAH-FM broadcasts to the Oklahoma City area at 99.7 FM.

KNAI-FM

Owner: Campesina Network(La)
Editorial: 3602 W Thomas Rd, Ste 6, Phoenix, Arizona 85019. **T:** 1 602 269-3121
E: info@campesinainfo.com
W: http://www.campesina.com
Editorial Profile: KNAI-FM is a commercial station owned by La Campesina Network. The format of the station is regional Mexican. KNAI-FM broadcasts to the Phoenix area at 88.3 FM.

KNAL-AM

Owner: Victoria RadioWorks Inc.
Editorial: 3613 N Main St, Victoria, Texas 77901. **T:** 1 361 576-6114
E: vrw@suddenlinkmail.com
Editorial Profile: KNAL-AM is a commercial station owned by Victoria RadioWorks Inc. The format of the station is adult standards. KNAL-AM broadcasts to the Victoria, TX area at 1410 AM.

KNAM-AM

Owner: MBC Grand Broadcasting Inc.
Editorial: 1360 E Sherwood Dr, Grand Junction, Colorado 81501-7546.
T: 1 970 254-2100
W: http://www.theteam1340.com
Editorial Profile: KNAM-AM is a commercial station owned by MBC Grand Broadcasting Inc. The format of the station is sports. KNAM-AM broadcasts to the Grand Junction, CO area at 1490 AM.

KNAS-FM

Owner: Southwest Arkansas Radio
Editorial: 1513 S 4th St, Nashville, Arkansas 71852. **T:** 1 870 845-3601
E: operations@southwestarkansasradio.com
W: http://www.southwestarkansasradio.com
Editorial Profile: KNAS-FM is a commercial station owned by Southwest Arkansas Radio. The format of the station is adult contemporary. KNAS-FM broadcasts to the Nashville, AR area at 105.5 FM.

KNAU-FM

Owner: Northern Arizona University
Editorial: Building 83 Northern Arizona Univ, Flagstaff, Arizona 86011-0001.
T: 1 928 523-5628 **E:** knau@nau.edu
W: http://www.knau.org
Editorial Profile: KNAU-FM is a non-commercial station owned by Northern Arizona University. The format of the station is classical music and news. KNAU-FM broadcasts to the Flagstaff, AZ area at 88.7 FM.

KNBA-FM

Owner: Koahnic Broadcast Corp.
Editorial: 3600 San Jeronimo Ct, Ste 480, Anchorage, Alaska 99508. **T:** 1 907 793-3500
E: feedback@knba.org **W:** http://www.knba.org
Editorial Profile: KNBA-FM is a non-commercial station owned by Koahnic Broadcast Corp. The format of the station is variety. KNBA-FM broadcasts to the Anchorage, AK area at 90.3 FM.

KNBB-FM

Owner: Communications Capital Managers II of Louisiana LLC
Editorial: 500 N Monroe St, Ruston, Louisiana 71270. **T:** 1 318 255-5000
E: sports@espn977.com
W: http://www.espn977.com
Editorial Profile: KNBB-FM is a commercial station owned by Communications Capital Managers II of Louisiana LLC. The format of the station is sports. KNBB-FM broadcasts to the Ruston, LA area at 99.3 FM.

KNBJ-FM

Owner: Minnesota Public Radio
Editorial: 405A Beltrami Ave NW, Bemidji, Minnesota 56601. **T:** 1 218 751-8864
E: newsroom@mpr.org **W:** http://www.mpr.org
Editorial Profile: KNBJ-FM is a non-commercial station owned by Minnesota Public Radio. The format of the station is news and talk. KNBJ-FM broadcasts to the Bemidji, MN area at 91.3 FM.

KNBR-AM

Owner: Cumulus Media Inc.
Editorial: 55 Hawthorne St Ste 1100, San Francisco, California 94105-3914.
T: 1 415 995-6800 **E:** sports@knbr.com
W: http://www.knbr.com
Editorial Profile: KNBR-AM is a commercial station owned by Cumulus Media Inc. The format of the station is sports. KNBR-AM broadcasts to the San Francisco area at 680 AM.

KNBT-FM

Owner: New Braunfels Communications Inc
Editorial: 1540 Loop 337, New Braunfels, Texas 78130-3352. **T:** 1 830 625-7311
W: http://knbt.fm
Editorial Profile: KNBT-FM is a commercial station owned by New Braunfels Communications Inc. The format of the station is classic country music. KNBT-FM broadcasts to the San Antonio area at 92.1 FM.

KNBU-FM

Owner: Baker University
Editorial: 615 8th St, Baldwin City, Kansas 66006. **T:** 1 785 594-8300
W: http://www.bakeru.edu
Editorial Profile: KNBU-FM is a non-commercial station owned by Baker University. The format of the station is rock alternative. KNBU-FM broadcasts to the Baldwin City, KS area at 89.7 FM.

KNBX-FM

Owner: KCBX Inc.
Editorial: 4100 Vachell Ln, San Luis Obispo, California 93401-8113. **T:** 1 805 549-8855
E: 901kcbx@kcbx.org **W:** http://www.kcbx.org
Editorial Profile: KNBX-FM is a non-commercial station owned by KCBX Inc. The format is classical and jazz music, news and talk. KNBX-FM broadcasts to the San Ardo, CA area at 91.7 FM.

KNBY-AM

Owner: Sudbury Broadcasting Group
Editorial: 2025 McLarty Dr, Newport, Arkansas 72112-4822. **T:** 1 870 523-5891
Editorial Profile: KNBY-AM is a commercial station owned by Sudbury Broadcasting Group. The format of the station is oldies with a focus on 1970s classics. KNBY-AM broadcasts in the Newport, AR area at 1280 AM.

KNBZ-FM

Owner: Armada Media Corp.
Editorial: 3304 S Highway 281, Aberdeen, South Dakota 57401-8792. **T:** 1 605 229-3632
E: aberdeenproduction@hubcityradio.com
W: http://www.hubcityradio.com
Editorial Profile: KNBZ-FM is a commercial station owned by Armada Media Corp. The format of the station is adult hits. KNBZ-FM broadcasts to the Aberdeen, SD area at 97.7 FM.

KNCB-AM

Owner: Collins(Ruby Stinnett)
Editorial: 17525 Highway 1, Vivian, Louisiana 71082-9526. **T:** 1 318 375-3278
Editorial Profile: KNCB-AM is a commercial station owned by Ruby Stinnett Collins. The format of the station is classic country. KNCB-AM broadcasts to the Vivian, LA area at 1320 AM.

KNCB-FM

Owner: Collins(Ruby Stinnett)
Editorial: 17525 Highway 1, Vivian, Louisiana 71082. **T:** 1 318 375-3278
Editorial Profile: KNCB-FM is a commercial station owned by Ruby Stinnett Collins. The format of the station is country music. KNCB-FM broadcasts to the Vivian, LA area at 105.3 FM.

KNCI-FM

Owner: CBS Radio
Editorial: 5244 Madison Ave, Sacramento, California 95841-3004. **T:** 1 916 338-9200
W: http://www.kncifm.com
Editorial Profile: KNCI-FM is a commercial station owned by CBS Radio. The format of the station is contemporary country. KNCI-FM broadcasts to the Sacramento, CA area at 105.1 FM.

KNCK-FM

Owner: KNCK Inc.
Editorial: 1390 West 11th Ave., Concordia, Kansas 66901. **T:** 1 785 243-1414
W: http://www.ncktoday.com
Editorial Profile: KNCK-FM is a commercial station owned by KNCK Inc. The format of the station is hot adult contemporary. KNCK-FM broadcasts to the Concordia, KS area at 94.9 FM.

KNCM-FM

Owner: Minnesota Public Radio
Editorial: 480 Cedar St, Saint Paul, Minnesota 55101-2217. **T:** 1 651 290-1500
E: newsroom@mpr.org
W: http://minnesota.publicradio.org
Editorial Profile: KNCM-FM is a non-commercial station owned by Minnesota Public Radio. The format of the station is classical. KNCM-FM broadcasts to the Appleton, MN area at 88.5 FM.

KNCN-FM

Owner: Clear Channel Media and Entertainment
Editorial: 501 Tupper Lane Radio Plaza, Corpus Christi, Texas 78417-9736.
T: 1 361 289-0111 **W:** http://www.c101.com
Editorial Profile: KNCN-FM is a commercial station owned by Clear Channel Media and Entertainment. The format of the station is album-oriented rock music. KNCN-FM broadcasts to the Corpus Christi, TX area at 101.3 FM.

KNCO-AM

Owner: Nevada County Broadcasters Inc.
Editorial: 1255 E Main St, Grass Valley, California 95945-5766. **T:** 1 530 272-3424
E: news@knco.com **W:** http://www.knco.com
Editorial Profile: KNCO-AM is a commercial station owned by Nevada County Broadcasters Inc. The format of the station is news and talk. KNCO-AM broadcasts in the Grass Valley, CA area at 830 AM.

KNCO-FM

Owner: Nevada County Broadcasters Inc.
Editorial: 1255 E Main St, Grass Valley, California 95945-5766. **T:** 1 530 272-3424
E: news@knco.com
W: http://www.mystarradio.com
Editorial Profile: KNCO-FM is a commercial station owned by Nevada County Broadcasters Inc. The format of the station is adult contemporary. KNCO-FM broadcasts to the Grass Valley, CA area at 94.3 FM.

KNCQ-FM

Owner: Results Radio Group
Editorial: 1588 Charles Dr, Redding, California 96003. **T:** 1 530 244-9700
E: resultsradio@sbcglobal.net
W: http://www.q97country.com
Editorial Profile: KNCQ-FM is a commercial station owned by Results Radio Group. The format of the station is contemporary country. KNCQ-FM broadcasts to the Redding, CA area at 97.3 FM.

KNCR-AM

Owner: Del Rosario Talpa Inc.
Editorial: 2900 Smith Lane, Fortuna, California 95540. **T:** 1 707 725-9363
E: kncr@lanueva1090.com
Editorial Profile: KNCR-AM is a commercial station owned by Del Rosario Talpa Inc. The format of the station is regional Mexican. KNCR-AM broadcasts to the Eureka, CA area at 1090 AM.

KNCT-FM

Owner: Central Texas College
Editorial: Highway 190 West, Killeen, Texas 76541. **T:** 1 254 526-1176
E: knct.music@knct.org
W: http://www.knct.org
Editorial Profile: KNCT-FM is a non-commercial station owned by Central Texas College. The format of the station is easy listening music. KNCT-FM broadcasts to the Killeen, TX area at 91.3 FM.

KNCU-FM

Owner: Pacific West Broadcasting Inc.
Editorial: 906 SW Alder St, Newport, Oregon 97365. **T:** 1 541 265-2266
E: news@ybcradio.com
W: http://www.u92fm.com
Editorial Profile: KNCU-FM is a commercial station owned by Pacific West Broadcasting Inc. The format of the station is country music. KNCU-FM broadcasts in the Newport, OR area at 92.7 FM.

KNCW-FM

Owner: North Cascades Broadcasting
Editorial: 320 Emery Dr, Omak, Washington 98841-9237. **T:** 1 509 826-0100
E: news@komw.net **W:** http://www.komw.net
Editorial Profile: KNCW-FM is a commercial station owned by North Cascades Broadcasting. The format of the station is

country music. KNCW-FM broadcasts to the Spokane, WA area at 92.7 FM.

KNCY-AM

Owner: Riverfront Broadcasting
Editorial: 814 Central Ave, Nebraska City, Nebraska 68410. **T:** 1 402 873-3348
W: http://www.kncycountry.com
Editorial Profile: KNCY-AM is a commercial station owned by Riverfront Broadcasting. The format of the station is classic country. KNCY-AM broadcasts to the Nebraska City, NE area at 1600 AM.

KNCY-FM

Owner: Riverfront Broadcasting
Editorial: 814 Central Ave, Nebraska City, Nebraska 68410-2409. **T:** 1 402 873-3348
W: http://www.kncycountry.com
Editorial Profile: KNCY-FM is a commercial station owned by Riverfront Broadcasting. The format of the station is contemporary country music. KNCY-FM broadcasts to the Auburn, NE area at 103.1 FM.

KNDA-FM

Owner: Rodriguez(Pat & Jessie)
Editorial: 2001 Saratoga Blvd, Corpus Christi, Texas 78417. **T:** 1 361 814-1030
Editorial Profile: KNDA-FM is a commercial station owned by Pat and Jessie Rodriquez. The format of the station is rhythmic Top 40/CHR music. KNDA-FM broadcasts to the Corpus Christi, TX area at 102.9 FM.

KNDC-AM

Owner: Schweitzer Media
Editorial: 505 2nd Ave S, Hettinger, North Dakota 58639. **T:** 1 701 567-2421
E: kndc1490@ndsupernet.com
W: http://www.kndcradio.com
Editorial Profile: KNDC-AM is a commercial station owned by Schweitzer Media. The format of the station is contemporary country. KNDC-AM broadcasts to the Hettinger, ND area at 1490 AM.

KNDD-FM

Owner: Entercom Communications Corp.
Editorial: 1100 Olive Way, Seattle, Washington 98101-1873. **T:** 1 206 285-7625
W: http://www.1077theend.com
Editorial Profile: KNDD-FM is a commercial station owned by Entercom Communications Corp. The format of the station is rock alternative. KNDD-FM broadcasts to the Seattle area at 107.7 FM.

KNDE-FM

Owner: Bryan Broadcasting
Editorial: 2700 Earl Rudder Fwy S, Ste 5000, College Station, Texas 77845.
T: 1 979 846-1150 **E:** radio@knde.com
W: http://www.candy95.com
Editorial Profile: KNDE-FM is a commercial station owned by Bryan Broadcasting. The format of the station is Top 40/CHR. KNDE-FM broadcasts to the College Station, TX area at 95.1 FM.

KNDI-AM

Owner: Jona(Leona)
Editorial: 1734 S King St, Honolulu, Hawaii 96826. **T:** 1 808 946-2844
E: kndiradio@hawaii.rr.com
W: http://www.kndi.com
Editorial Profile: KNDI-AM is a commercial station owned by Leona Jona. The format of the station is variety. KNDI-AM broadcasts to the Honolulu area at 1270 AM.

KNDK-AM

Owner: Simmons Media Group
Editorial: 1403 3rd St, Langdon, North Dakota 58249. **T:** 1 701 256-1080
E: traffic@utma.com
W: http://www.maverick105fm.com
Editorial Profile: KNDK-AM is a commercial station owned by Simmons Media Group. The format of the station is classic country and talk. KNDK-AM broadcasts to the Langdon, ND area at 1080 AM.

KNDK-FM

Owner: KNDK, Inc.
Editorial: 1403 3Rd St, Langdon, North Dakota 58249-2232. **T:** 1 701 256-1080
Editorial Profile: KNDK-FM is a commercial station owned by KNDK, Inc. The format of the station is classic rock. KNDK-FM broadcasts to the Langdon, ND area at 95.7 FM.

KNDN-AM

Owner: Basin Broadcasting Company

Editorial: 1515 W Main St, Farmington, New Mexico 87401-3837. **T:** 1 505 325-1996
Editorial Profile: KNDN-AM is a commercial station owned by Basin Broadcasting Company. The format of the station is a variety of music, news and talk. KNDN-AM broadcasts to the Farmington, NM area at 960 AM.

KNDR-FM
Owner: Central Dakota Enterprises Inc.
Editorial: 1400 3rd St NE, Mandan, North Dakota 58554-3611. **T:** 1 701 663-2345
E: production.kndr@midconetwork.com
W: http://www.kndr.fm
Editorial Profile: KNDR-FM is a non-commercial station owned by Central Dakota Enterprises Inc. The format of the station is contemporary Christian music. KNDR-FM broadcasts to the Mandan, ND area at 104.7 FM.

KNDY-AM
Owner: Dierking Communications
Editorial: 937 Jayhawk Rd, Marysville, Kansas 66508. **T:** 1 785 562-2361
E: kndy@bluevalley.net
W: http://www.kndyradio.com
Editorial Profile: KNDY-AM is a commercial station owned by Dierking Communications. The format of the station is country music. KNDY-AM broadcasts in the Marysville, KS area at 1570 AM.

KNDY-FM
Owner: Dierking Communications
Editorial: 937 Jayhawk Rd, Marysville, Kansas 66508. **T:** 1 785 562-2361
E: kndy@bluevalley.net
W: http://www.kndyradio.com
Editorial Profile: KNDY-FM is a commercial station owned by Dierking Communications. The format of the station is country music. KNDY-FM broadcasts in the Marysville, KS area at 95.5 FM.

KNDZ-FM
Owner: Pacific Cascade Communications Corp.
Editorial: 1139 Hartnell Ave, Redding, California 96002-2113. **T:** 1 530 222-4455
E: info@kvip.org **W:** http://www.kvip.org
Editorial Profile: KNDZ-FM is a non-commercial station owned by Pacific Cascade Communications Corp. The format of the station is Christian and inspirational talk. The station broadcasts to the McKinleyville, CA area at 89.3 FM.

KNEA-AM
Owner: East Arkansas Broadcasters Inc.
Editorial: 403 W Parker Rd, Jonesboro, Arkansas 72404. **T:** 1 870 932-8400
Editorial Profile: KNEA-AM is a commercial station owned by East Arkansas Broadcasters Inc. The format of the station is news and talk. KNEA-AM broadcasts to the Jonesboro, AR area on 970 AM.

KNEB-AM
Owner: Nebraska Rural Radio Association
Editorial: 1928 E Portal Pl, Scottsbluff, Nebraska 69361-2727. **T:** 1 308 632-7121
W: http://www.kneb.com
Editorial Profile: KNEB-AM is a commercial station owned by Nebraska Rural Radio Association. The format for the station is talk and sports. KNEB-AM broadcasts to the Cheyenne, WY, Scottsbluff, NE area at 960 AM.

KNEB-FM
Owner: Nebraska Rural Radio Association
Editorial: 1928 E Portal Pl, Scottsbluff, Nebraska 69361-2727. **T:** 1 308 632-7121
W: http://www.kneb.com
Editorial Profile: KNEB-FM is a commercial station owned by Nebraska Rural Radio Association. The format of the station is contemporary country. KNEB-FM broadcasts to the Cheyenne, WY, Scottsbluff, NE area at 94.1 FM.

KNEC-FM
Owner: Arnold Broadcasting Co Inc.
Editorial: 205 S Main St, Yuma, Colorado 80759-1915. **T:** 1 970 848-2302
E: knec100.9@gmail.com
Editorial Profile: KNEC-FM is a commercial station owned by Arnold Broadcasting Co Inc. The format of the station is adult hits music. KNEC-FM broadcasts to the Yuma, CO area at 100.9 FM.

KNED-AM
Owner: Southeastern Oklahoma Radio, LLC
Editorial: 1801 E Electric Ave, McAlester, Oklahoma 74501. **T:** 1 918 426-1050

E: info@mcalesterradio.com
W: http://www.mcalesterradio.com
Editorial Profile: KNED-AM is a commercial station owned by Southeastern Oklahoma Radio, LLC. The format of the station is classic country. KNED-AM broadcasts to the McAlester, OK area at 1150 AM.

KNEI-FM
Owner: Wennes Communications Stations, Inc.
Editorial: 14 W Main St, Waukon, Iowa 52172. **T:** 1 563 568-3476
E: knei@kneiradio.com
W: http://www.kneiradio.com
Editorial Profile: KNEI-FM is a commercial station owned by Wennes Communications Stations, Inc. The format for the station is country. KNEI-FM broadcasts to the Waukon, IA, area at 103.5 FM.

KNEK-AM
Owner: Cumulus Media Inc
Editorial: 202 Galbert Rd, Lafayette, Louisiana 70506. **T:** 1 337 232-1311
W: http://www.knek.com
Editorial Profile: KNEK-AM is a commercial station owned by Cumulus Media Inc. The format of the station is urban adult contemporary music. KNEK-AM broadcasts to the Lafayette, LA area at 1190 AM.

KNEK-FM
Owner: Cumulus Media Inc
Editorial: 202 Galbert Rd, Lafayette, Louisiana 70506. **T:** 1 337 232-1311
W: http://www.knek.com
Editorial Profile: KNEK-FM is a commercial station owned by Cumulus Media Inc. The format of the station is urban adult contemporary music. KNEK-FM broadcasts to the Lafayette, LA area at 104.7 FM.

KNEL-AM
Owner: Farris Broadcasting
Editorial: 117 S Blackburn St, Brady, Texas 76825-4504. **T:** 1 325 597-2119
E: knel@airmail.net
W: http://www.knelradio.com
Editorial Profile: KNEL-AM is a commercial station owned by Farris Broadcasting. The format for the station is oldies. KNEL-AM broadcasts to the Brady, TX area at 1490 AM.

KNEL-FM
Owner: Farris Broadcasting
Editorial: 117 S Blackburn St, Brady, Texas 76825-4504. **T:** 1 325 597-2119
E: knel@airmail.net
W: http://www.knelradio.com
Editorial Profile: KNEL-FM is a commercial station owned by Farris Broadcasting. The format for the station is classic country. KNEL-FM broadcasts to the San Angelo, TX area at 95.3 FM.

KNEM-AM
Owner: Harbit Communications
Editorial: 414 E Walnut St, Nevada, Missouri 64772. **T:** 1 417 667-3113
E: news@knemknmo.com
W: http://www.knemknmo.com
Editorial Profile: KNEM-AM is a commercial station owned by Harbit Communications. The format of the station is contemporary country music. KNEM-AM broadcasts to the Nevada, MO area at 1240 AM.

KNEN-FM
Owner: Red Beacon Communications LLC
Editorial: 214 N 7th St, Norfolk, Nebraska 68701. **T:** 1 402 371-0100
E: 94rock@94rock.fm
W: http://www.94rock.fm
Editorial Profile: KNEN-FM is a commercial station owned by Red Beacon Communications LLC. The format of the station is classic rock. KNEN-FM broadcasts to the Norfolk, NE area at 94.7 FM.

KNEO-FM
Owner: Sky High Broadcasting Corp.
Editorial: 10827 E Highway 86, Neosho, Missouri 64850-7052. **T:** 1 417 451-5636
E: kneo@kneo.org **W:** http://www.kneo.org
Editorial Profile: KNEO-FM is a non-commercial station owned by Sky High Broadcasting Corp. The format of the station is religious. KNEO-FM broadcasts to the Joplin, MO area at 91.7 FM.

KNES-FM
Owner: J & J Communications Inc.
Editorial: 627 W Commerce St, Fairfield, Texas 75840-1425. **T:** 1 903 389-5637
E: texas99@texas99.com
W: http://www.texas99.com

Editorial Profile: KNES-FM is a commercial station owned by J & J Communications Inc. The format of the station is country music. KNES-FM broadcasts to the Fairfield, TX area at 99.1 FM.

KNET-AM
Owner: Tomlinson-Leis Communications L.P.
Editorial: 800 W Palestine Ave, Palestine, Texas 75801. **T:** 1 903 729-6077
E: news@kyyk.com
W: http://www.youreasttexas.com
Editorial Profile: KNET-AM is a commercial station owned by Tomlinson-Leis Communications L.P. The format of the station is news and talk. KNET-AM broadcasts to the Palestine, TX area at 1450 AM.

KNEU-AM
Owner: Evans Broadcasting
Editorial: 2242 E 1000 S, Roosevelt, Utah 84066-9523. **T:** 1 435 722-5011
E: radio@ubtanet.com
W: http://www.stormpc.com/fox/CntryLink.htm
Editorial Profile: KNEU-AM is a commercial station owned by Evans Broadcasting. The format of the station is country. KNEU-AM broadcasts to the Roosevelt, UT area at 1250 AM.

KNEV-FM
Owner: Cumulus Media Inc
Editorial: 595 E Plumb Ln, Reno, Nevada 89502. **T:** 1 775 789-6700
W: http://www.magic95.com
Editorial Profile: KNEV-FM is a commercial station owned by Cumulus Media Inc. The format of the station is adult contemporary music. KNEV-FM broadcasts in the Reno, NV area at 95.5 FM.

KNEW-AM
Owner: Clear Channel Media and Entertainment
Editorial: 340 Townsend St, San Francisco, California 94107-1633. **T:** 1 415 975-5555
W: http://www.thepatriot960.com
Editorial Profile: KNEW-AM is a commercial station owned by Clear Channel Media and Entertainment. The format of the station is talk. KNEW-AM broadcasts in the San Francisco area at 960 AM.

KNEX-FM
Owner: MBM Radio LLC
Editorial: 307 E 8th St, Del Rio, Texas 78840-3823. **T:** 1 830 775-6291
E: info@rcommunications.com
W: http://www.hot1061.fm
Editorial Profile: KNEX-FM is a commercial station owned by MBM Radio LLC (dba R Communications). The format of the station is Top 40/CHR. KNEX-FM broadcasts to the Laredo, TX area at 106.1 FM.

KNEZ-FM
Owner: Shamrock Communications, Inc.
Editorial: 510 E Plumb Ln, Reno, Nevada 89502-3565. **T:** 1 775 737-4030
W: http://www.knewsreno.com
Editorial Profile: KNEZ-FM is a commercial station owned by Shamrock Communications, Inc. The format of the station is news/talk. KNEZ-FM broadcasts to the Reno, NV area at a frequency of 107.3 FM.

KNFL-AM
Owner: Impact Radio
Editorial: 1910 University Dr, Boise, Idaho 83725-0001. **T:** 1 208 426-3663
W: http://www.espnboise.com
Editorial Profile: KNFL-AM is a commercial station owned by Impact Radio. The station format is sports KNFL-AM broadcasts to the Boise, ID area at 730 AM.

KNFM-FM
Owner: Townsquare Media, Inc.
Editorial: 11300 State Highway 191 Bldg 2, Midland, Texas 79707-1367.
T: 1 432 561-9809
W: http://www.lonestar92.com
Editorial Profile: KNFM-FM is a commercial station owned by Townsquare Media, Inc. The format of the station is contemporary country music. KNFM-FM broadcasts in the Midland, TX area at 92.3 FM.

KNFO-FM
Owner: NRC Broadcasting
Editorial: 402 Aspen Airport Business Ctr, Ste D, Aspen, Colorado 81611. **T:** 1 970 544-9100
W: http://www.kspnradio.com
Editorial Profile: KNFO-FM is a commercial station owned by NRC Broadcasting. The format of the station is news, sports and talk.

KNFO-FM broadcasts to the Aspen, CO area at 106.1 FM.

KNFT-AM
Owner: SkyWest Media, LLC
Editorial: 1560 N Corbin St, Silver City, New Mexico 88061-6526. **T:** 1 575 388-1958
Editorial Profile: KNFT-AM is a commercial station owned by SkyWest Media, LLC. The format of the station is oldies music and talk. KNFT-AM broadcasts to the Silver City, NM area at 950 AM.

KNFT-FM
Owner: SkyWest Media, LLC
Editorial: 1560 N Corbin St, Silver City, New Mexico 88061-6526. **T:** 1 575 538-3396
E: events@silverradio.com
Editorial Profile: KNFT-FM is a commercial station owned by SkyWest Media, LLC. The format of the station is country. KNFT-FM broadcasts to the Silver City, NM area at 102.9 FM.

KNFX-FM
Owner: Clear Channel Media and Entertainment
Editorial: 1716 Briarcrest Dr, Ste 150, Bryan, Texas 77802. **T:** 1 979 268-9696
W: http://www.995thefox.com
Editorial Profile: KNFX-FM is a commercial station owned by Clear Channel Media and Entertainment. The format of the station is classic rock. KNFX-FM broadcasts to the Bryan, TX area at 99.5 FM.

KNGA-FM
Owner: Minnesota Public Radio
Editorial: 206 S Broadway, Ste 735, Rochester, Minnesota 55904.
T: 1 507 282-0910 **E:** newsroom@mpr.org
W: http://www.mpr.org
Editorial Profile: KNGA-FM is a non-commercial station owned by Minnesota Public Radio. The format of the station is news and talk. KNGA-FM broadcasts to the Rochester, MN, Mason City, IA area at 91.7 FM.

KNGL-AM
Owner: Davies Communications Inc.
Editorial: 411 E Euclid St, McPherson, Kansas 67460. **T:** 1 620 241-1504
E: news@midkansasradio.com
W: http://www.midkansasradio.com
Editorial Profile: KNGL-AM is a commercial station owned by Davies Communications Inc. The format of the station is talk. KNGL-AM broadcasts to the McPherson, KS area at 1540 AM.

KNGN-AM
Owner: Kansas Nebraska Good News Broadcasting Corp.
Editorial: 38005 Road 717, McCook, Nebraska 69001-7217. **T:** 1 308 345-2006
W: http://www.kngn.org
Editorial Profile: KNGN-AM is a commercial station owned by Kansas Nebraska Good News Broadcasting Corp. The format of the station is religious programming. KNGN-AM broadcasts to the McCook, NE area at 1360 AM.

KNGT-FM
Owner: Townsquare Media, LLC
Editorial: 900 N Lake Shore Dr, Lake Charles, Louisiana 70601. **T:** 1 337 433-1641
W: http://www.gator995.com
Editorial Profile: KNGT-FM is a commercial station owned by Townsquare Media, LLC. The format of the station is classic country. KNGT-FM broadcasts to the Lake Charles, LA area at 99.5 FM.

KNHC-FM
Owner: Seattle Public Schools
Editorial: 10750 30th Ave NE, Ste 219, Seattle, Washington 98125-7937.
T: 1 206 252-3800
W: http://www.c895worldwide.com
Editorial Profile: KNHC-FM is a non-commercial station owned by Seattle Public Schools. The format of the station is Top 40/CHR music. KNHC-FM broadcasts in the Seattle area at 89.5 FM.

KNHT-FM
Owner: State of Oregon
Editorial: 1250 Siskiyou Blvd, Ashland, Oregon 97520-5001. **T:** 1 541 552-6301
E: jprinfo@sou.edu **W:** http://www.ijpr.org
Editorial Profile: KNHT-FM is a non-commercial station owned by State of Oregon. The format of the station is news and classical music. KNHT-FM broadcasts to the Eureka, CA area at 107.3 FM.

KNIA-AM
Owner: M & H Broadcasting Inc.
Editorial: 1610 N Lincoln St, Knoxville, Iowa 50138. **T:** 1 641 842-3161
E: kniakrls@kniakrls.com
W: http://www.kniakrls.com
Editorial Profile: KNIA-AM is a commercial station owned by M & H Broadcasting Inc. The format of the station is country music. KNIA-AM broadcasts to the Knoxville, IA area at 1320 AM.

KNID-FM
Owner: Chisholm Trail Broadcasting
Editorial: 316 E Willow Rd, Enid, Oklahoma 73701. **T:** 1 580 237-1390
W: http://www.knid.com
Editorial Profile: KNID-FM is a commercial station owned by Chisholm Trail Broadcasting. The format of the station is country music. KNID-FM broadcasts to the Oklahoma City area at 107.1 FM

KNIH-AM
Owner: Immaculate Heart Radio
Editorial: 3256 Penryn Rd Ste 100, Loomis, California 95650-8052. **T:** 1 916 535-0500
E: office@ihradio.com **W:** http://ihradio.com
Editorial Profile: KNIH-AM is a commercial station owned by Immaculate Heart Radio. The format of the station is Catholic radio programming. KNIH-AM broadcasts to the Las Vegas area at 970 AM.

KNIM-AM
Owner: Nodaway Broadcasting Corp
Editorial: 1618 S Main St, Maryville, Missouri 64468. **T:** 1 660 582-2151
E: knim@knimmaryville.com
W: http://www.971thevill.com
Editorial Profile: KNIM-AM is a commercial station owned by Nodaway Broadcasting Corp. The format of the station is country. KNIM-AM broadcasts to the Maryville, MO area at 1580 AM.

KNIN-FM
Owner: Townsquare Media, LLC
Editorial: 2525 Kell Blvd, Ste 200, Wichita Falls, Texas 76308. **T:** 1 940 763-1111
W: http://www.929nin.com
Editorial Profile: KNIN-FM is a commercial station owned by Townsquare Media, LLC. The format of the station is Top 40/CHR. KNIN-FM broadcasts to the Wichita Falls, TX area at 92.9 FM.

KNIS-FM
Owner: Western Inspirational Broadcasters Inc.
Editorial: 6363 US Highway 50 E, Carson City, Nevada 89701. **T:** 1 775 883-5647
E: info@pilgrimradio.com
W: http://www.pilgrimradio.com
Editorial Profile: KNIS-FM is a non-commercial station owned by Western Inspirational Broadcasters Inc. The format of the station is contemporary Christian programming. KNIS-FM broadcasts to the Carson City, NV area at 91.3 FM.

KNIV-FM
Owner: MAV Media, LLC
Editorial: 385 Ironwood Dr, Salt Lake City, Utah 84115-2912. **T:** 1 801 990-8424
W: http://www.mipreferidafm.com
Editorial Profile: KNIV-FM is a commercial station owned by MAV Media, LLC. The format of the station is Regional Mexican. KNIV-FM is licensed to Lyman, WY and broadcasts to the Salt Lake City area at 104.7 FM.

KNIX-FM
Owner: Clear Channel Media and Entertainment
Editorial: 4686 E Van Buren St, Phoenix, Arizona 85008-6959. **T:** 1 602 374-6000
W: http://www.knixcountry.com/main.html
Editorial Profile: KNIX-FM is a commercial station owned by Clear Channel Media and Entertainment. The format of the station is country. KNIX-FM broadcasts to the Phoenix area at 102.5 FM.

KNKK-FM
Owner: Cameron Broadcasting Inc.
Editorial: 2350 Miracle Mile, Bullhead City, Arizona 86442-7505. **T:** 1 928 763-5586
E: news@cameronbroadcasting.com
W: http://www.theknack107.com
Editorial Profile: KNKK-FM is a commercial station owned by Cameron Broadcasting Inc. The format of the station is hot adult contemporary. KNKK-FM broadcasts to the Bullhead City, AZ area at 107.1 FM.

KNKT-FM
Owner: Calvary Chapel of Albuquerque, Inc.
Editorial: 4001 Osuna Rd NE, Albuquerque, New Mexico 87109-4422. **T:** 1 505 344-9146
E: knkt@calvaryabq.org
W: http://www.knkt.com
Editorial Profile: KNKT-FM is a commercial station owned by Calvary Chapel of Albuquerque, Inc. The format of the station is religious and contemporary Christian. KNKT-FM broadcasts to the Albuquerque, NM area at 107.1 FM.

KNLB-FM
Owner: Advance Ministries
Editorial: 510 Acoma Blvd N, Lake Havasu City, Arizona 86403. **T:** 1 928 855-9110
E: info@knlb.com **W:** http://www.knlb.com
Editorial Profile: KNLB-FM is a non-commercial station owned by Advance Ministries. The format of the station is religious music and talk. KNLB-FM broadcasts to Lake Havasu City, AZ at 91.1 FM.

KNLE-FM
Owner: Ixoye Productions Inc.
Editorial: 12703 Research Blvd, Ste 222, Austin, Texas 78759. **T:** 1 512 996-8336
W: http://www.candle88.com
Editorial Profile: KNLE-FM is a commercial station owned by Ixoye Productions Inc. The format of the station is contemporary Christian. KNLE-FM broadcasts to the Austin, TX area at 88.1 FM.

KNLF-FM
Owner: Trumbo(Ron)
Editorial: 440 Lawrence St, Quincy, California 95971. **T:** 1 530 283-4145
E: rtrumbo@gmail.com
W: http://www.knlfradio.com
Editorial Profile: KNLF-FM is a commercial station owned by Ron Trumbo. The format of the station is Christian programming, sports and talk. KNLF-FM broadcasts to the Quincy, CA area at 95.9 FM.

KNLG-FM
Owner: New Life Evangelistic Center
Editorial: 9810 State Road Ae, New Bloomfield, Missouri 65063.
T: 1 573 896-5945
W: http://www.hereshelpnet.org
Editorial Profile: KNLG-FM is a non-commercial station owned by New Life Evangelistic Center. The format of the station is gospel. KNLG-FM broadcasts to the New Bloomfield, MO area at 90.3 FM.

KNLH-FM
Owner: New Life Evangelistic Center, Inc.
Editorial: 1411 Locust St, Saint Louis, Missouri 63103. **T:** 1 314 421-3020
W: http://www.hereshelpnetnetwork.org
Editorial Profile: KNLH-FM is a non-commercial station owned by New Life Evangelistic Center, Inc. The format of the station is contemporary Christian and gospel music. KNLH-FM broadcasts to the St. Louis area at 89.5 FM.

KNLP-FM
Owner: New Life Evangelistic Center, Inc.
Editorial: 2319 Highway 8, Potosi, Missouri 63664. **T:** 1 573 438-4403
W: http://www.hereshelpnetwork.org
Editorial Profile: KNLP-FM is a non-commercial station owned by New Life Evangelistic Center, Inc. The format of the station is gospel and contemporary Christian programming. KNLP-FM broadcasts to the Potosi, MO area at 89.7 FM.

KNLR-FM
Owner: Cowan(Terry A.)
Editorial: 30 SE Bridgeford Blvd, Bend, Oregon 97702-1460. **T:** 1 541 389-8873
E: info@knlr.com **W:** http://www.knlr.com
Editorial Profile: KNLR-FM is a commercial station owned by Terry A. Cowan. The format of the station is contemporary Christian and religious programming. KNLR-FM broadcasts to the Bend, OR area at 95.7 FM.

KNLV-AM
Owner: Sandhills Advertising Corp.
Editorial: 205 S 16th St, Ord, Nebraska 68862. **T:** 1 308 728-3263
E: knlvnews@yahoo.com
W: http://www.knlvradio.com
Editorial Profile: KNLV-AM is a commercial station owned by Sandhills Advertising Corp. The format of the station is oldies music, agricultural news and information. KNLV-AM broadcasts to the Ord, NE area at 1060 AM.

KNLV-FM
Owner: Sandhills Advertising Corp.
Editorial: 205 S 16th St, Ord, Nebraska 68862. **T:** 1 308 728-3263
E: knlvnews@yahoo.com
W: http://www.knlvradio.com
Editorial Profile: KNLV-FM is a commercial station owned by Sandhills Advertising Corp. The format of the station is contemporary country music. KNLV-FM broadcasts to the Ord, NE area at 103.9 FM.

KNLX-FM
Owner: Cowan(Terry A.)
Editorial: 30 SE Bridgeford Blvd, Bend, Oregon 97702-1460. **T:** 1 541 389-8873
E: info@knlr.com **W:** http://www.knlr.com
Editorial Profile: KNLX-FM is a commercial station owned by Terry A. Cowan. The format of the station is contemporary Christian programming. KNLX-FM broadcasts to the Bend, OR area at 104.9 FM.

KNMB-FM
Owner: MTD Inc.
Editorial: 1086 Mechem Dr, Ruidoso, New Mexico 88345. **T:** 1 575 258-9922
E: mtdradio@mtdradio.com
W: http://mtdradio.com
Editorial Profile: KNMB-FM is a commercial station owned by MTD Inc. The format of the station is Hot AC. KNMB-FM broadcasts to the Ruidoso, NM area at 96.7 FM.

KNMI-FM
Owner: Navajo Ministries, Inc.
Editorial: 2103 W Main St, Farmington, New Mexico 87401-3220. **T:** 1 505 327-4357
E: email@verticalradio.org
W: http://www.verticalradio.org
Editorial Profile: KNMI-FM is a non-commercial station owned by Navajo Ministries, Inc. The format of the station is contemporary Christian music. KNMI-FM broadcasts to the Farmington, NM area at 88.9 FM.

KNML-AM
Owner: Cumulus Media Inc
Editorial: 500 4th St NW, Albuquerque, New Mexico 87102-5324. **T:** 1 505 767-6700
W: http://www.610thesportsanimal.com
Editorial Profile: KNML-AM is a commercial station owned by Cumulus Media Inc. The format of the station is sports. KNML-AM broadcasts to the Albuquerque, NM area at 610 AM.

KNMO-FM
Owner: Harbit Communications
Editorial: 414 E Walnut St, Nevada, Missouri 64772. **T:** 1 417 667-3113
E: news@knemknmo.com
W: http://www.knemknmo.com
Editorial Profile: KNMO-FM is a commercial station owned by Harbit Communications. The format of the station is contemporary country. KNMO-FM broadcasts to the Nevada, MO area at a frequency of 97.5 FM.

KNMX-AM
Owner: Sangre de Cristo Broadcasting Inc.
Editorial: 304 S Grand Ave, Las Vegas, New Mexico 87701-3873. **T:** 1 505 426-1967
W: http://lvnradio.com
Editorial Profile: KNMX-AM is a commercial station owned by Sangre de Cristo Broadcasting Inc. The format of the station is variety programming. KNMX-AM broadcasts to the Las Vegas, NM area at 540 AM.

KNMZ-FM
Owner: WP Broadcasting LLC
Editorial: 119 N Canyon Rd, Alamogordo, New Mexico 88310-5910. **T:** 1 575 437-1505
E: krsy@snmradio.com
W: http://www.snmradio.com
Editorial Profile: KNMZ-FM is a commercial station owned by WP Broadcasting LLC. The format of the station is sports. KNMZ-FM broadcasts to the Alamogordo, NM area at 103.7 FM.

KNNB-FM
Owner: White Mountain Apache Tribe
Editorial: Skill Center Road, Whiteriver, Arizona 85941-9999. **T:** 1 928 338-5229
E: knnb@wmat.nsn.us
W: http://www.nv1.org/knnb.html
Editorial Profile: KNNB-FM is a non-commercial station owned by the White Mountain Apache Tribe. The format of the station is a variety of programming. KNNB-FM broadcasts to the Whiteriver, AZ area at 88.1 FM.

KNND-AM
Owner: Schwartzberg Communications Inc.
Editorial: 321 E Main St, Cottage Grove, Oregon 97424. **T:** 1 541 942-2468
E: knnd@knnd.com **W:** http://www.knnd.com
Editorial Profile: KNND-AM is a commercial station owned by Schwartzberg Communications Inc. The format of the station is oldies. KNND-AM broadcasts to the Cottage Grove, OR area at 1400 AM.

KNNG-FM
Owner: Arnold Broadcasting Co Inc.
Editorial: 803 W Main St, Sterling, Colorado 80751-2813. **T:** 1 970 522-1607
E: knng@kci.net
W: http://www.kingfmonline.com
Editorial Profile: KNNG-FM is a commercial station owned by Arnold Broadcasting Co Inc. The format of the station is talk. KNNG-FM broadcasts to the Sterling, CO area at 104.7 FM.

KNNK-FM
Owner: High Plains Radio Network
Editorial: 207 S 25 Mile Ave, Hereford, Texas 79045-6015. **T:** 1 806 363-1005
E: knnk@wtrt.net
W: http://www.knnkradio.com
Editorial Profile: KNNK-FM is a commercial station owned by High Plains Radio Network.The format of the station is religious, news, and talk. KNNK-FM broadcasts to the Amarillo, TX area at 100.5 FM.

KNNN-FM
Owner: Mapleton of Redding, LLC
Editorial: 3360 Alta Mesa Dr, Redding, California 96002. **T:** 1 530 226-9500
W: http://www.reddingradio.com
Editorial Profile: KNNN-FM is a commercial station owned by Mapleton of Redding, LLC. The format of the station is news/talk. KNNN-FM broadcasts to the Redding, CA area at 99.3 FM.

KNNR-AM
Owner: Flinn Broadcasting Corp.
Editorial: 10580 N Mccarran Blvd Ste 115, Reno, Nevada 89503-1896. **T:** 1 775 461-1515
E: productionknnr@gmail.com
Editorial Profile: KNNR-AM is a commercial station owned by Flinn Broadcasting Corp. The station broadcasts to the Reno, NV area at 1400 AM airing a talk format.

KNNS-AM
Owner: Rocking M Radio
Editorial: 5501 10th St, Great Bend, Kansas 67530-6319. **T:** 1 620 792-7108
W: http://centralkansasradio.com
Editorial Profile: KNNS-AM is a commercial station owned by Rocking M Radio. The format of the station is Regional Mexican. KNNS-AM broadcasts to the Great Bend, KS area at 1510 AM.

KNOB-FM
Owner: JYH Broadcasting
Editorial: 3565 Standish Ave, Santa Rosa, California 95407-8139. **T:** 1 707 588-0707
E: bobfm@winecountryradio.net
W: http://www.96xonline.com
Editorial Profile: KNOB-FM is a commercial station owned by JYH Broadcasting. The format of the station is adult hits. KNOB-FM broadcasts to the Santa Rosa, CA area at 96.7 FM.

KNOC-AM
Owner: North Face Broadcasting LLC
Editorial: 213 Renee St, Natchitoches, Louisiana 71457-6225. **T:** 1 318 354-4000
Editorial Profile: KNOC-AM is a commercial station owned by North Face Broadcasting LLC. The format of the station is Urban AC. KNOC-AM broadcasts to the Natchitoches, LA area at 1450 AM.

KNOD-FM
Owner: Wireless Communications Corp.
Editorial: 902 Chatburn Ave, Harlan, Iowa 51537. **T:** 1 712 755-3883
E: knodnews@harlannet.com
W: http://www.knodfm.com
Editorial Profile: KNOD-FM is a commercial station owned by Wireless Communications Corp. The format of the station is oldies music. KNOD-FM broadcasts to the Harlan, IA area at 105.3 FM.

KNOF-FM
Owner: Christian Herritage Broadcasting
Editorial: 910 Elliot Ave, Minneapolis, Minnesota 55404-1322. **T:** 1 612 343-3502
E: mail@praisefm.org
W: http://www.praisefm.org

Editorial Profile: KNOF-FM is a non-commercial station owned by Selby Gospel Broadcasting Corp. The format of the station is gospel and religious programming. KNOF-FM broadcasts to the St. Paul, MN area at 95.3 FM.

KNOG-FM
Owner: World Radio Network, Inc.
Editorial: 150 W 1st St, Nogales, Arizona 85621. **T:** 1 520 287-5206 **E:** knog@lwrn.org
W: http://www.knog.org
Editorial Profile: KNOG-FM is a non-commercial station owned by the World Radio Network, Inc. The format for the station is Hispanic contemporary Christian. KNOG-FM broadcasts to the Tuscon, AZ area at 91.7 FM.

KNOM-AM
Owner: KNOM Radio Mission, Inc.
Editorial: 107 W 3rd Ave, Nome, Alaska 99762. **T:** 1 907 443-5221 **E:** info@knom.org
W: http://www.knom.org
Editorial Profile: KNOM-AM is a non-commercial station owned by the KNOM Radio Mission, Inc. The format of the station is a wide variety of music. KNOM-AM broadcasts to the Nome, AK at 780 AM.

KNOM-FM
Owner: KNOM Radio Mission, Inc.
Editorial: 107 W 3rd Ave, Nome, Alaska 99762. **T:** 1 907 443-5221
W: http://www.knom.org
Editorial Profile: KNOM-FM is a non-commercial radio station owned by the KNOM Radio Mission, Inc. The format of the station is religious programming. KNOM-FM broadcasts in the Nome, AK area at 96.1 FM.

KNON-FM
Owner: Agape Broadcasting Foundation Inc.
Editorial: 5353 Maple Ave, Ste 200, Dallas, Texas 75235-8463. **T:** 1 214 828-9500
E: news@knon.org **W:** http://www.knon.org
Editorial Profile: KNON-FM is a commercial station owned by Agape Broadcasting Foundation Inc. The format of the station is variety. KNON-FM broadcasts to the Dallas area at 89.3 FM.

KNOR-FM
Owner: Liberman Broadcasting Inc.
Editorial: 2410 Gateway Dr, Irving, Texas 75063-2727. **T:** 1 972 652-2900
W: http://larazadallas.estrellatv.com
Editorial Profile: KNOR-FM is a commercial station owned by Liberman Broadcasting Inc. The format of the station is regional Mexican. KNOR-FM broadcasts to the Colleyville, TX area at 93.7 FM.

KNOT-AM
Owner: Guyann Corp.
Editorial: 116 S Alto St, Prescott, Arizona 86303-3604. **T:** 1 928 445-6880
W: http://www.funoldiesnow.com
Editorial Profile: KNOT-AM is a commercial station owned by Guyann Corp. The format of the station is oldies. KNOT-AM broadcasts to the Prescott, AZ area at 1450 AM.

KNOW-FM
Owner: Minnesota Public Radio
Editorial: 480 Cedar St, Saint Paul, Minnesota 55101-2217. **T:** 1 651 290-1500
E: newsroom@mpr.org
W: http://minnesota.publicradio.org
Editorial Profile: KNOW-FM is a non-commercial station owned by Minnesota Public Radio. The format of the station is news and talk. KNOW-FM broadcasts to the St. Paul, MN area at 102.7 FM.

KNOX-AM
Owner: Leighton Enterprises Inc.
Editorial: 1185 9th St NE, Thompson, North Dakota 58278. **T:** 1 701 775-4611
E: live@knoxradio.com
W: http://www.knoxradio.com
Editorial Profile: KNOX-AM is a commercial station owned by Leighton Enterprises Inc. The format of the station is sports, news and talk. KNOX-AM broadcasts to the Thompson, ND area at 1310 AM.

KNOZ-FM
Owner: Rocky III Investments, Inc.
Editorial: 203 Grand Ave, Grand Junction, Colorado 81501-7816. **T:** 1 970 609-1200
E: news@knozfm.com **W:** http://knozfm.com
Editorial Profile: KNOZ-FM is a commercial station owned by Rocky III Investments, Inc. The format of the station is news talk. KNOZ-FM broadcasts to the Grand Junction, CO and surrounding areas at 97.7 FM.

KNPQ-FM
Owner: Eagle Radio Inc.
Editorial: 1301 E 4th St, North Platte, Nebraska 69101. **T:** 1 308 532-1120
W: http://www.knpqcountry.com
Editorial Profile: KNPQ-FM is a commercial station owned by Eagle Radio Inc. The format of the station is country music. KNPQ-FM broadcasts to the North Platte, NE area at 107.3 FM.

KNPR-FM
Owner: Nevada Public Radio
Editorial: 1289 S Torrey Pines Dr, Las Vegas, Nevada 89146. **T:** 1 702 258-9895
E: info@knpr.org **W:** http://www.knpr.org
Editorial Profile: KNPR-FM is a non-commercial station owned by Nevada Public Radio. The format of the station is news and talk. KNPR-FM broadcasts to the Las Vegas area at 89.5 FM.

KNPT-AM
Owner: Yaquina Bay Communications Inc.
Editorial: 906 SW Alder St, Newport, Oregon 97365. **T:** 1 541 265-2266
E: news@ybcradio.com
W: http://www.knptam.com
Editorial Profile: KNPT-AM is a commercial station owned by Yaquina Bay Communications Inc. The format of the station is news and talk. KNPT-AM broadcasts in the Newport, OR area at 1310 AM.

KNRB-FM
Owner: Family Worship Center Church, Inc.
Editorial: Highway 43 S, Atlanta, Texas 78888.
T: 1 225 768-3224 **E:** onair@jsm.org
W: http://www.jsm.org
Editorial Profile: KNRB-FM is a non-commercial station owned by Family Worship Center Church, Inc. The format of the station is religious. KNRB-FM broadcasts to Atlanta, TX at 100.1 FM.

KNRG-FM
Owner: La Grange Broadcasting
Editorial: 325 Radio Ln, Columbus, Texas 78934-3235. **T:** 1 979 732-5766
E: kulmradio@yahoo.com
W: http://www.923knrg.com
Editorial Profile: KNRG-FM is a commercial station owned by La Grange Broadcasting. The format of the station is country music. KNRG-FM broadcasts in the Columbus, TX area at 92.3 FM.

KNRJ-FM
Owner: Sierra H Broadcasting, Inc.
Editorial: 7434 E Stetson Dr, Ste 255, Scottsdale, Arizona 85251. **T:** 1 480 994-9100
W: http://www.azthebeat.com
Editorial Profile: KNRJ-FM is a commercial station owned by Sierra H Broadcasting, Inc. The format of the station is classic hip hop and urban contemporary. KNRJ-FM broadcasts to the Scottsdale, AZ area at 101.1 FM.

KNRK-FM
Owner: Entercom Communications Corp.
Editorial: 0700 SW Bancroft St, Portland, Oregon 97239. **T:** 1 503 223-1441
W: http://www.947.fm
Editorial Profile: KNRK-FM is a commercial station owned by Entercom Communications Corp. The format of the station is rock alternative music. KNRK-FM broadcasts to the Portland, OR area at 94.7 FM.

KNRO-AM
Owner: Mapleton of Redding, LLC
Editorial: 3360 Alta Mesa Dr, Redding, California 96002-2831. **T:** 1 530 226-9500
Editorial Profile: KNRO-AM is a commercial station owned by Mapleton of Redding, LLC. The format of the station is sports. KNRO-AM broadcasts to the Redding, CA area at 1670 AM.

KNRQ-FM
Owner: Cumulus Media
Editorial: 1200 Executive Pkwy Ste 440, Eugene, Oregon 97401-2169.
T: 1 541 284-8500 **W:** http://www.nrq.com
Editorial Profile: KXPC-FM is a commercial station owned by Cumulus Media. The format of the station is rock music. KXPC-FM broadcasts to the Portland, OR area at 103.7 FM.

KNRS-AM
Owner: Clear Channel Media and Entertainment
Editorial: 2801 Decker Lake Dr, Salt Lake City, Utah 84119-2330. **T:** 1 801 908-1300
W: http://www.knrs.com
Editorial Profile: KNRS-AM is a commercial station owned by Clear Channel Media and Entertainment. The format of the station is news/talk. KNRS-AM broadcasts to the Salt Lake City area at 570 AM.

KNRS-FM
Owner: Clear Channel Media and Entertainment
Editorial: 2801 Decker Lake Dr, Salt Lake City, Utah 84119. **T:** 1 801 908-1300
W: http://www.knrs.com
Editorial Profile: KNRS-FM is a commercial station owned by Clear Channel Media and Entertainment. The format of the station is talk. KNRS-FM broadcasts to the Salt Lake City area at 105.7 FM.

KNRV-AM
Owner: New Radio Venture, Inc.
Editorial: 1582 S Parker Rd Ste 204, Denver, Colorado 80231-2716. **T:** 1 303 696-5967
W: http://www.onda1150am.com
Editorial Profile: KNRV-AM is a commercial station owned by New Radio Venture, Inc. The format of the station is Hispanic news and talk. KNRV-AM broadcasts to the Aurora, CO area at 1150 AM.

KNRX-FM
Owner: Townsquare Media
Editorial: 1301 S Abe St, San Angelo, Texas 76903. **T:** 1 325 655-7161
W: http://965therock.com
Editorial Profile: KNRX-FM is a commercial station owned by Townsquare Media. The format of the station is classic rock. KNRX-FM broadcasts to the San Angelo, TX, area at 96.5 FM.

KNRY-AM
Owner: Mount Wilson FM Broadcasters
Editorial: 5 Harris Ct Ste B, Monterey, California 93940-5751. **T:** 1 831 324-0375
E: reception@mountwilsoninc.com
W: http://knry1240.com
Editorial Profile: KNRY-AM is a commercial station owned by Mount Wilson FM Broadcasters. The format of the station is jazz. KNRY-AM broadcasts to the Monterey, CA area at 1240 AM.

KNSG-FM
Owner: Bruce Linder
Editorial: 110 W Central St, Springfield, Minnesota 56087-1404. **T:** 1 507 723-5000
E: info@marshallradio.net
Editorial Profile: KNSG-FM is a commercial station owned by Bruce Linder. The format of the station is adult comtemporary. KNSG-FM broadcasts to the Mankato, MN area at 94.7 FM.

KNSH-AM
Owner: Cumulus Media Inc.
Editorial: 301 S Polk St Ste 100, Amarillo, Texas 79101-1404. **T:** 1 806 342-5200
Editorial Profile: KNSH-AM is a commercial station owned by Cumulus Media Inc. The format of the station is talk. KNSH-AM broadcasts to the Amarillo, TX area at 1550 AM.

KNSH-FM
Owner: Iowa State University
Editorial: 2111 Grand Avenue, Suite 100, Des Moines, Iowa 50312-5393. **T:** 1 515 294-2025
E: news@iowapublicradio.org
W: http://iowapublicradio.org
Editorial Profile: KNSH-FM is a non-commercial station owned by Iowa State University. The format of the station is news and talk. KNSH-FM broadcasts to the Des Moines, IA area at 91.1 FM.

KNSI-AM
Owner: Leighton Enterprises Inc.
Editorial: 619 W Saint Germain St, Saint Cloud, Minnesota 56301-3640.
T: 1 320 251-1450
W: http://www.knsiradio.com
Editorial Profile: KNSI-AM is a commercial station owned by Leighton Enterprises Inc. The format of the station is news and talk. KNSI-AM broadcasts to the St. Cloud, MN area at 1450 AM. Send any press materials to the station's program director.

KNSJ-FM
Owner: Activist San Diego
Editorial: 4246 Wightman St, San Diego, California 92105-2618. **T:** 1 619 283-1100
W: http://knsj.org
Editorial Profile: KNSJ-FM is a non-commercial station owned by Activist San Diego. The format of the station features a variety of news and local music. KNSJ-FM broadcasts to the San Diego area at a frequency of 89.1 FM.

KNSN-AM
Owner: Multicultural Radio Broadcasting Inc.
Editorial: 3033 5th Ave, San Diego, California 92103-5856. **T:** 1 619 543-9100
W: http://www.mrbi.net
Editorial Profile: KNSN-AM is a non-commercial station owned by Multicultural Radio Broadcasting Inc. The format is variety. KNSN-AM broadcasts to the San Diego area at 1240 AM.

KNSP-AM
Owner: BL Broadcasting Inc.
Editorial: 201 1/2 Jefferson St S, Wadena, Minnesota 56482. **T:** 1 218 631-1803
W: http://www.superstationk106.com
Editorial Profile: KNSP-AM is a commercial station owned by BL Broadcasting Inc. The format of the station is country music. KNSP-AM broadcasts to Wadena, MN at 1430 AM.

KNSR-FM
Owner: Minnesota Public Radio
Editorial: 300 Wimmer Hall St John's Univ, Collegeville, Minnesota 56321-9999.
T: 1 320 363-7702 **E:** newsroom@mpr.org
W: http://minnesota.publicradio.org
Editorial Profile: KNSR-FM is a non-commercial station owned by Minnesota Public Radio. The format of the station is news and talk. KNSR-FM broadcasts in the Collegeville, MN area at 88.9 FM.

KNSS-AM
Owner: Entercom Communications Corp.
Editorial: 2120 N Woodlawn St Ste 352, Wichita, Kansas 67208-1881.
T: 1 316 685-2121 **E:** news@knssradio.com
W: http://www.knssradio.com
Editorial Profile: KNSS-AM is a commercial station owned by Entercom Communications Corp. The format of the station is news and talk. KNSS-AM broadcasts in the Wichita, KS area at 1330 AM.

KNST-AM
Owner: Clear Channel Media and Entertainment
Editorial: 3202 N Oracle Rd, Tucson, Arizona 85705-3820. **T:** 1 520 618-2100
W: http://www.knst.com
Editorial Profile: KNST-AM is a commercial station owned by Clear Channel Media and Entertainment. The format of the station is news and talk. KNST-AM broadcasts to the Tucson, AZ area at 790 AM.

KNSW-FM
Owner: Minnesota Public Radio
Editorial: 1450 Collegeway, Worthington, Minnesota 56187-3024. **T:** 1 507 372-2904
E: newsroom@mpr.org
W: http://minnesota.pubicradio.org
Editorial Profile: KNSW-FM is a non-commercial station owned by Minnesota Public Radio. The format of the station is news and talk. KNSW-FM broadcasts to the Worthington, MN area at 91.7 FM.

KNTE-FM
Owner: Liberman Broadcasting Inc.
Editorial: 3000 Bering Dr, Houston, Texas 77057-5708. **T:** 1 713 315-3400
W: http://www.elnorteenlinea.com
Editorial Profile: KNTE-FM is a commercial station owned by Liberman Broadcasting Inc. The format of the station is Regional Mexican. KNTE-FM broadcasts to the Bay City, TX area at a frequency of 101.7 FM.

KNTH-AM
Owner: Salem Communications
Editorial: 6161 Savoy Dr, Ste 1200, Houston, Texas 77036. **T:** 1 713 260-3600
E: comments@1070knth.com
W: http://www.1070knth.com
Editorial Profile: KNTH-AM is a commercial station owned by Salem Communications. The format of the station is news and talk. KNTH-AM broadcasts to the Houston area at 1070 AM.

KNTI-FM
Owner: Bicoastal Media LLC
Editorial: 140 N Main St, Lakeport, California 95453-4815. **T:** 1 707 263-6113
W: http://www.knti.com
Editorial Profile: KNTI-FM is a commercial station owned by Bicoastal Media LLC. The format of the station is adult album alternative. KNTI-FM broadcasts to the Lakeport, CA area at 99.5 FM.

KNTN-FM

Owner: Minnesota Public Radio
Editorial: 901 8th St S, Moorhead, Minnesota 56562. **T:** 1 218 287-0666
E: newsroom@mpr.org
W: http://minnesota.publicradio.org
Editorial Profile: KNTN-FM is non-commercial station owned by Minnesota Public Radio. The format of the station is news and talk programming. KNTN-FM broadcasts to the Moorhead, MN area at 102.7 FM.

KNTR-AM

Owner: Greeley(Steven M.)
Editorial: 1845 McCulloch Blvd N Ste A14, Lake Havasu City, Arizona 86403-6777.
T: 1 928 855-9336
E: office@myradiocentral.com
W: http://kntrtalk.com
Editorial Profile: KNTR-AM is a commercial station owned by Steven M. Greely. The format of the station is sports. KNTR-AM broadcasts to Phoenix area at 980 AM.

KNTS-AM

Owner: Salem Communications
Editorial: 2201 6th Ave, Ste 1500, Seattle, Washington 98121-1840. **T:** 1 206 443-8200
W: http://www.radioluzseattle.com
Editorial Profile: KNTS-AM is a commercial station owned by Salem Communications. The format of the station is Hispanic religious talk. KNTS-AM broadcasts to the Seattle area at 1680 AM.

KNTU-FM

Owner: University of North Texas
Editorial: 1179 Union Circle, Ste 262, Denton, Texas 76201-5826. **T:** 1 940 565-3688
E: kntu@unt.edu **W:** http://www.kntu.com
Editorial Profile: KNTU-FM is a non-commercial station owned by the University of North Texas. The format of the station is jazz music and news. KNTU-FM broadcasts to the Denton, TX area at 88.1 FM.

KNTX-AM

Owner: Henderson Broadcasting Co. LP
Editorial: 7704 FM 1758, State Highway 59 N, Bowie, Texas 76230. **T:** 1 940 872-2288
E: onair@kntxradio.com
W: http://www.kntxradio.com
Editorial Profile: KNTX-AM is a commercial station owned by Henderson Broadcasting Co. LP. The format of the station is oldies music. KNTX-AM broadcasts in the Bowie, TX area at 1410 AM.

KNTY-FM

Owner: Entravision Communications Corp.
Editorial: 1436 Auburn Blvd, Sacramento, California 95815-2745. **T:** 1 916 646-4000
W: http://www.1019thewolf.com
Editorial Profile: KNTY-FM is a commercial station owned by Entravision Communications Corp. The format of the station is contemporary country music. KNTY-FM broadcasts to the Sacramento, CA area at 107.1 FM.

KNUE-FM

Owner: Townsquare Media, LLC
Editorial: 3810 Brookside Dr, Tyler, Texas 75701. **T:** 1 903 581-0606 **W:** http://knue.com
Editorial Profile: KNUE-FM is a commercial station owned by Townsquare Media, LLC. The format of the station is classic and contemporary country. KNUE-FM broadcasts to the Tyler, TX area at 101.5 FM.

KNUI-AM

Owner: Pacific Media Group
Editorial: 311 Ano St, Kahului, Hawaii 96732-1304. **T:** 1 808 877-5566
W: http://knuimaui.com
Editorial Profile: KNUI-AM is a commercial station owned by the Pacific Media Group. The format for the station is news and talk. KNUI-AM broadcasts to the Maui, HI area at 550 AM.

KNUJ-AM

Owner: Ingstad Brothers Broadcasting, LLC
Editorial: 210 1/2 N Minnesota St, New Ulm, Minnesota 56073. **T:** 1 507 359-2921
E: news@knuj.net **W:** http://www.knuj.net
Editorial Profile: KNUJ-AM is a commercial station owned by Ingstad Brothers Broadcasting, LLC. The format for the station is classic country. KNUJ-AM broadcasts to the New Ulm, MN area at 860 AM.

KNUJ-FM

Owner: Ingstad Brothers Broadcasting, LLC
Editorial: 317 N Minnesota St, New Ulm, Minnesota 56073-1876. **T:** 1 507 359-2921
E: knuj@knuj.net **W:** http://www.knuj.net

Editorial Profile: KNUJ-FM is a commercial station owned by Ingstad Brothers Broadcasting, LLC. The format for the station is adult hits. KNUJ-FM broadcasts to the New Ulm, MN area at 107.3 FM.

KNUQ-FM

Owner: Visionary Related Entertainment, Inc
Editorial: 1900 Main St, Wailuku, Hawaii 96793-1900. **T:** 1 808 244-9145
E: kaoi@kaoi.net **W:** http://www.q103maui.com
Editorial Profile: KNUQ-FM is a commercial station owned by Visionary Related Entertainment, Inc. The format of the station is variety featuring roots, rock and reggae music. KNUQ-FM is licensed to the Paauilo, Hawaii area and broadcasts at a frequency of 103.7 FM.

KNUS-AM

Owner: Salem Communications
Editorial: 3131 S Vaughn Way, Ste 601, Aurora, Colorado 80014. **T:** 1 303 750-5687
E: news@salemdenver.com
W: http://www.710knus.com
Editorial Profile: KNUS-AM is a commercial station owned by Salem Communications. The format of the station is news and talk programming. KNUS-AM broadcasts to the Aurora, CO area at 710 AM.

KNUV-AM

Owner: New Radio Venture, Inc.
Editorial: 1582 S Parker Rd, Ste 204, Denver, Colorado 80231-2716. **T:** 1 602 759-1914
Editorial Profile: KNUV-AM is a commercial station owned by New Radio Venture, Inc. The format of the station is Spanish-language talk. KNUV-AM broadcasts to the Phoenix area at 1190 AM.

KNUZ-FM

Owner: La Grange Broadcasting
Editorial: 705 S Live Oak St, San Saba, Texas 76877-6023. **T:** 1 325 372-5225
E: knuz@sansabaradio.com
W: http://www.sansabaradio.com
Editorial Profile: KNUZ-FM is a commercial station owned by La Grange Broadcasting. The format of the station is classic country. KNUZ-FM broadcasts to the San Saba, TX area at 106.1 FM.

KNVO-FM

Owner: Entravision Communications Corp.
Editorial: 801 N Jackson Rd, McAllen, Texas 78501. **T:** 1 956 661-6000
W: http://www.jose1011.com
Editorial Profile: KNVO-FM is a commercial station owned by Entravision Communications Corp. The format of the station is Hispanic Top 40/CHR. KNVO-FM broadcasts to the McAllen, TX area at 101.1 FM.

KNVR-AM

Owner: Henderson(Roy)
Editorial: 705 S Live Oak St, San Saba, Texas 76877. **T:** 1 325 372-5225
E: knuz@sansabaradio.com
W: http://www.sansabaradio.com
Editorial Profile: KNVR-AM is a commercial station owned by Roy Henderson. The format of the station is adult standards. KNVR-AM broadcasts to the Waco, TX area at 1410 AM.

KNWA-AM

Owner: Dowdy Broadcasting, Inc.
Editorial: 600 S Pine St, Harrison, Arkansas 72601-5828. **T:** 1 870 741-1402
E: info@knwaradio.com
W: http://knwaradio.com
Editorial Profile: KNWA-AM is a commercial station owned by Dowdy Broadcasting, Inc. The format of the station is Conservative talk. KNWA-AM broadcasts to the Harrison, AR area at 1600 AM.

KNWB-FM

Owner: New West Broadcasting
Editorial: 1145 Kilauea Ave, Hilo, Hawaii 96720. **T:** 1 808 935-5461
W: http://www.b97hawaii.com
Editorial Profile: KNWB-FM is a commercial station owned by New West Broadcasting. The format of the station is classic hits. KNWB-FM broadcasts to the Hilo, HI area at 97.1 FM. The station simulcasts with KMWB-FM.

KNWC-AM

Owner: Northwestern College
Editorial: 6300 S Tallgrass Ave, Sioux Falls, South Dakota 57108-8107. **T:** 1 605 339-1270
E: knwc@knwc.org **W:** http://www.knwc.org
Editorial Profile: KNWC-AM is a non-commercial station owned by Northwestern College. The format of the station is religious.

KNWC-AM broadcasts to the Sioux Falls, SD area at 1270 AM.

KNWC-FM

Owner: Northwestern College
Editorial: 6300 South Tallgrass Ave, Sioux Falls, South Dakota 57108-8107.
T: 1 605 339-1270 **E:** knwc@knwc.org
W: http://www.knwc.org
Editorial Profile: KNWC-FM is a non-commercial station owned by Northwestern College. The format of the station is contemporary Christian. KNWC-FM broadcasts to the Sioux Falls, SD area 96.5 FM.

KNWD-FM

Owner: Northwestern State University
Editorial: 109 Keyser Hall Northwestern Stat, Natchitoches, Louisiana 71497-0001.
T: 1 318 357-5693 **E:** knwdradio@gmail.com
W: http://knwd.nsula.edu
Editorial Profile: KNWD-FM is a non-commercial station owned by Northwestern State University. The format of the station is variety. KNWD-FM broadcasts to the Natchitoches, LA area at 91.7 FM.

KNWH-AM

Owner: Morris Communications
Editorial: 1321 N Gene Autry Trl, Palm Springs, California 92262. **T:** 1 760 322-7890
W: http://www.knewsradio.com

KNWI-FM

Owner: Northwestern College
Editorial: 3737 Woodland Ave, Suite 111, Des Moines, Iowa 50266. **T:** 1 515 327-1071
E: knwi@desmoines.fm
W: http://www.desmoines.fm
Editorial Profile: KNWI-FM is a non-commercial station owned by Northwestern College. The format of the station is contemporary Christian. KNWI-FM broadcasts to the Des Moines, IA area at 107.1 FM.

KNWM-FM

Owner: Northwestern College
Editorial: 3737 Woodland Ave, Ste 111, Des Moines, Iowa 50266. **T:** 1 515 327-1071
E: knwi@desmoines.fm **W:** http://knwi.nwc.edu
Editorial Profile: KNWM-FM is a non-commercial station owned by Northwestern College. The format of the station is contemporary Christian. KNWM-FM broadcasts to the Des Moines, IA area at 96.1 FM.

KNWO-FM

Owner: Washington State University
Editorial: Murrow Center, Room 382, Pullman, Washington 99164. **T:** 1 509 335-6500
E: nwpr@wsu.edu **W:** http://www.nwpr.org
Editorial Profile: KNWO-FM is a non-commercial station owned by Washington State University. The format of the station is classical, news and talk. KNWO-FM broadcasts to Cottonwood, ID at 90.1 FM.

KNWP-FM

Owner: Washington State University
Editorial: Murrow Comm Ctr Wsu, Room 382, Pullman, Washington 99164.
T: 1 509 335-6500 **E:** nwpr@wsu.edu
W: http://www.nwpr.org
Editorial Profile: KNWP-FM is a non-commercial station owned by Washington State University. The format of the station is classical music and news. KNWP-FM broadcasts to the Port Angeles, WA at 90.1 FM.

KNWQ-AM

Owner: Morris Communications
Editorial: 1321 N Gene Autry Trl, Palm Springs, California 92262. **T:** 1 760 322-7890
W: http://knewsradio.com
Editorial Profile: KNWQ-AM is a commercial station owned by Morris Communications. The format of the station is news and talk. KNWQ-AM broadcasts to the Palm Springs, CA area at 1140 AM.

KNWR-FM

Owner: Washington State University
Editorial: Murrow Center, Room 382, Pullman, Washington 99164. **T:** 1 509 335-6500
E: nwpr@wsu.edu **W:** http://www.nwpr.org
Editorial Profile: KNWR-FM is a non-commercial station owned by Washington State University. The format is news and talk programming. KNWR-FM broadcasts to the Ellensburg and Wenatchee, WA area at 90.7 FM.

KNWS-AM

Owner: Northwestern College

Editorial: 4880 Texas St, Waterloo, Iowa 50702-4742. **T:** 1 319 296-1975
E: info@life1019.com
W: http://www.life1019.com
Editorial Profile: KNWS-AM is a non-commercial station owned by Northwestern College. The format of the station is religious programming. KNWS-AM broadcasts to the Cedar Rapids, IA area at 1090 AM.

KNWS-FM

Owner: Northwestern College
Editorial: 4880 Texas St, Waterloo, Iowa 50702-4742. **T:** 1 319 296-1975
E: info@life1019.com
W: http://www.life1019.com
Editorial Profile: KNWS-FM is a non-commercial station owned by Northwestern College. The format of the station is contemporary Christian. KNWS-FM broadcasts to the Cedar Rapids, IA area at 101.9 FM.

KNWV-FM

Owner: Washington State University
Editorial: Murrow Center, Room 382, Pullman, Washington 99164. **T:** 1 509 335-6500
E: nwpr@wsu.edu **W:** http://www.nwpr.org
Editorial Profile: KNWV-FM is a non-commercial station owned by Washington State University. The format of the station is news and classical music. KNWV-FM broadcasts to the Clarkston, WA/Lewiston, ID area at a frequency of 90.5 FM.

KNWY-FM

Owner: Washington State University
Editorial: Murrow Center, Room 382, Pullman, Washington 99164. **T:** 1 509 335-6500
E: nwpr@wsu.edu **W:** http://www.nwpr.org
Editorial Profile: KNWY-FM is a non-commercial station owned by Washington State University. The format of the station is classical music and news. KNWY-FM broadcasts to the Yakima, WA area at 90.3 FM.

KNWZ-AM

Owner: Morris Communications
Editorial: 1321 N Gene Autry Trl, Palm Springs, California 92262. **T:** 1 760 322-7890
W: http://www.knewsradio.com
Editorial Profile: KNWZ-AM is a commercial station owned by Morris Communications. The format of the station is news and talk. KNWZ-AM broadcasts to the Coachella, CA area at 970 AM.

KNX-AM

Owner: CBS Radio
Editorial: 5670 Wilshire Blvd Ste 200, Los Angeles, California 90036-5657.
T: 1 323 569-1070 **E:** knxnews@cbsradio.com
W: http://losangeles.cbslocal.com/station/knx-1070
Editorial Profile: KNX-AM is a commercial station owned by CBS Radio. The format of the station is news. KNX-AM broadcasts in the Los Angeles area at 1070 AM.

KNXN-AM

Owner: Good News Radio Broadcasting Inc.
Editorial: 3222 S Richey Ave, Tucson, Arizona 85713. **T:** 1 520 790-2440 **E:** info@kvoi.com
W: http://www.kgms.com
Editorial Profile: KNXN-AM is a commercial station owned by Good News Radio Broadcasting Inc. The format of the station is religious programming. KNXN-AM broadcasts to the Sierra Nevada, AZ area at 1470 AM.

KNXR-FM

Owner: United Audio Corporation
Editorial: 1620 Greenview Dr SW, Rochester, Minnesota 55902. **T:** 1 507 288-7700
E: knxrproduction@yahoo.com
Editorial Profile: KNXR-FM is a commercial station owned by United Audio Corporation. The format of the station is easy listening. KNXR-FM broadcasts to the Rochester, MN, Mason City, IA area at 97.5 FM.

KNYD-FM

Owner: Creative Educational Media Corp.
Editorial: 11717 S 129th East Ave, Broken Arrow, Oklahoma 74011-1902.
T: 1 918 455-5693 **E:** mail@oasisnetwork.org
W: http://www.oasisnetwork.org
Editorial Profile: KNYD-FM is a non-commercial station owned by Creative Educational Media Corp. The format of the station is religious talk and gospel music. KNYD-FM broadcasts to the Broken Arrow, OK area at 90.5 FM.

KNYE-FM

Owner: Karen Jackson

Editorial: 1230 Dutch Ford St, Pahrump, Nevada 89048-9105. **T:** 1 775 537-6100
W: http://www.knye.com
Editorial Profile: KNYE-FM is a commercial station owned by Karen Jackson. The format of the station is oldies music and talk. KNYE-FM broadcasts to the Pahrump, NV area at 95.1 FM.

KNYN-FM
Owner: Frandsen (M. Kent)
Editorial: 1044 Main St Ste B, Evanston, Wyoming 82930-3480. **T:** 1 307 789-8116
E: knyn@k-9radio.com **W:** http://k-9radio.com
Editorial Profile: KNYN-FM is a commercial station owned by Frandsen (M. Kent). The format of the station is contemporary country. The station is broadcasts to the Evanston, WY area at 103.9 FM.

KNZA-FM
Owner: KNZA, Inc.
Editorial: 1828 US Highway 73, Hiawatha, Kansas 66434. **T:** 1 785 547-3461
E: knzanews@yahoo.com
W: http://www.knzafm.com
Editorial Profile: KNZA-FM is a commercial station owned by KNZA, Inc. The format of the station is contemporary country music. KNZA-FM broadcasts in the Hiawatha, KS are at 103.9 FM.

KNZR-AM
Owner: Buckley Broadcasting Corp.
Editorial: 3651 Pegasus Dr, Ste 107, Bakersfield, California 93308.
T: 1 661 393-1900 **W:** http://www.knzr.com
Editorial Profile: KNZR-AM is a commercial station owned by Buckley Broadcasting Corp. The format of the station is news and talk. KNZR-AM broadcasts to the Bakersfield, CA area at 1560 AM.

KNZR-FM
Owner: Buckley Broadcasting Corp.
Editorial: 3651 Pegasus Dr, Bakersfield, California 93308-6836. **T:** 1 661 393-1900
W: http://www.knzr.com
Editorial Profile: KNZR-FM is a commercial station owned by Buckley Broadcasting Corp. The format of the station is news and talk. KNZR-FM broadcasts to the Bakersfield, CA area at 97.7 FM. The station is a simulcast of KNZR-AM.

KNZS-FM
Owner: Ad Astra Per Aspera Broadcasting, Inc.
Editorial: 10 E 5Th Ave, Hutchinson, Kansas 67501-6300. **T:** 1 620 665-5758
W: http://www.adastnaradio.net
Editorial Profile: KNZS-FM is a commercial station owned by Ad Astra Per Aspera Broadcasting, Inc. The format for the station is classic rock. KNZS-FM broadcasts to the Wichita-Hutchinson, KS area at 100.3 FM.

KNZZ-AM
Owner: MBC Grand Broadcasting Inc.
Editorial: 1360 E Sherwood Dr, Grand Junction, Colorado 81501-7546.
T: 1 970 254-2100 **E:** news@gjradio.com
W: http://www.1100knzz.com
Editorial Profile: KNZZ-AM is a commercial station owned by MBC Grand Broadcasting Inc. The format of the station is news and talk. KNZZ-AM broadcasts in the Grand Junction, CO area at 1100 AM.

KOA-AM
Owner: Clear Channel Media and Entertainment
Editorial: 4695 S Monaco St, Denver, Colorado 80237. **T:** 1 303 713-8000
E: newsroom@850koa.com
W: http://www.850koa.com
Editorial Profile: KOA-AM is a commercial station owned by Clear Channel Media and Entertainment. The format of the station is news, sports, and talk. KOA-AM broadcasts in the Denver area at 850 AM.

KOAC-AM
Owner: Oregon Public Broadcasting
Editorial: 7140 Sw Macadam Ave, Portland, Oregon 97219-3013. **T:** 1 503 244-9900
E: opbnews@opb.org **W:** http://www.opb.org

KOAK-AM
Owner: Hawkeye Communications
Editorial: 1991 Ironwood Ave, Red Oak, Iowa 51566-3204. **T:** 1 712 623-2584
E: kcsi@kcsifm.com
W: http://www.kcsifm.com
Editorial Profile: KOAK-AM is a commercial station owned by Hawkeye Communications. The format of the station is contemporary country. KOAK-AM broadcasts to the Red Oak, IA area at 1080 AM.

KOAL-AM
Owner: Eastern Utah Broadcasting
Editorial: 1899 N. Carbonville Road, Price, Utah 84501. **T:** 1 435 637-1167
E: news@koal.net
W: http://www.castlecountryradio.com
Editorial Profile: KOAL-AM is a commercial station owned by Eastern Utah Broadcasting. The format of the station is news, sports and talk. KOAL-AM broadcasts to the Salt Lake City area at 750 AM.

KOAN-AM
Owner: IBEW Local 1547 Investments, LLC
Editorial: 4700 Business Park Blvd Bldg E, Anchorage, Alaska 99503-7176.
T: 1 907 522-1018
W: http://www.1080koan.com
Editorial Profile: KOAN-AM is a commercial station owned by IBEW Local 1547 Investments, LLC and managed by Alaska Integrated Media. The format of the station is Sports. KOAN-AM broadcasts to the Anchorage, AK area at 1080 AM.

KOAQ-AM
Owner: Armada Media
Editorial: 305 E 4th St, North Platte, Nebraska 69101-6903. **T:** 1 308 532-3344
Editorial Profile: KOAQ-AM is a commercial station owned by Armada Media. The format is regional Mexican. KOAQ-AM broadcasts to the Scottsbluff, NE area at 690 AM.

KOAS-FM
Owner: Beasley Broadcast Group
Editorial: 2920 S Durango Dr, Las Vegas, Nevada 89117-4412. **T:** 1 702 730-0300
W: http://www.oldschool1057.com/
Editorial Profile: KOAS-FM is a commercial station owned by Beasley Broadcast Group. The format of the station is rhythmic oldies. KOAS-FM broadcasts to the Las Vegas area at 105.7 FM.

KOAZ-AM
Owner: Isleta Radio Co. (Whitman, Martha)
Editorial: 809 Wellesley Dr Ne, Albuquerque, New Mexico 87106-1936. **T:** 1 505 899-5029
E: oasis@1037theoasis.com
W: http://1037theoasis.com
Editorial Profile: KOAZ-AM is a commercial station owned by Isleta Radio Co. (Whitman, Martha). The format of the station is smooth jazz. KOAZ-AM broadcasts to the Greater Albuquerque area at a frequency of 1510 AM.

KOBB-AM
Owner: Reier Broadcasting Company Inc.
Editorial: 5445 Johnson Rd, Bozeman, Montana 59718. **T:** 1 406 587-9999
E: news@kboz.com **W:** http://www.kboz.com
Editorial Profile: KOBB-AM is a commercial station owned by Reier Broadcasting Company Inc. The format of the station is sports. KOBB-AM broadcasts in the Bozeman, MT area at 1230 AM.

KOBB-FM
Owner: Reier Broadcasting Company Inc.
Editorial: 5445 Johnson Rd, Bozeman, Montana 59718. **T:** 1 406 587-9999
E: news@kboz.com **W:** http://www.kboz.com
Editorial Profile: KOBB-FM is a commercial station owned by Reier Broadcasting Company Inc. The format of the station is oldies music. KOBB-FM broadcasts in the Bozeman, MT area at 93.7 FM.

KOBE-AM
Owner: Bravo Mic Communications, LLC
Editorial: 101 Perkins Dr, Las Cruces, New Mexico 88005. **T:** 1 575 527-1111
E: contact@bravomic.com
W: http://www.b1450.com
Editorial Profile: KOBE-AM is a commercial station owned by Bravo Mic Communications, LLC. The format of the station is news, talk and sports. KOBE-AM broadcasts to the Las Cruces, NM area at 1450 AM.

KOBN-FM
Owner: Oregon Public Broadcasting
Editorial: 7140 SW MacAdam Ave, Portland, Oregon 97219-3013. **T:** 1 503 293-1905
E: opbnews@opb.org **W:** http://www.opb.org
Editorial Profile: KOBN-FM is a non-commercial station owned by Oregon Public Broadcasting. The format is news and talk. KOBN-FM broadcasts to the Burns, OR area at 90.1 FM.

KOBO-AM
Owner: Huth Broadcasting Inc.
Editorial: 1605 Simpson Ln, Marysville, California 95901-9747. **T:** 1 530 742-5555
E: kmyc@syix.com
W: http://radiotepeyac.org/RadioTepeyac.php
Editorial Profile: KOBO-AM is a commercial station owned by Huth Broadcasting Inc. The format of the station is regional Mexican. KOBO-AM broadcasts to the Marysville, CA area at 1450 AM.

KOCN-FM
Owner: Clear Channel Media and Entertainment
Editorial: 903 N Main St, Salinas, California 93906. **T:** 1 831 755-8181
W: http://www.koceanradio.com
Editorial Profile: KOCN-FM is a commercial station owned by Clear Channel Media and Entertainment. The format of the station is classic and contemporary R&B. KOCN-FM broadcasts to the Salinas, CA area at a frequency of 105.1 FM.

KOCP-FM
Owner: Gold Coast Radio, LLC
Editorial: 2284 S Victoria Ave, Ventura, California 93003-6641. **T:** 1 805 289-1400
W: http://www.rewind959.com
Editorial Profile: KOCP-FM is a commercial station owned by Gold Coast Radio, LLC. The format of the station is classic hits music. KOCP-FM broadcasts to the Ventura, CA area at 95.9 FM.

KODA-FM
Owner: Clear Channel Media and Entertainment
Editorial: 2000 West Loop S Ste 300, Houston, Texas 77027-3510.
T: 1 713 212-8000
W: http://www.sunny99.com
Editorial Profile: KODA-FM is a commercial station owned by Clear Channel Media and Entertainment. The format of the station is adult contemporary music. KODA-FM broadcasts to the Houston area at 99.1 FM.

KODI-AM
Owner: Legend Communications
Editorial: 1949 Mountain View Dr, Cody, Wyoming 82414. **T:** 1 307 578-5000
E: news@bhrnwy.com
W: http://www.mybighornbasin.com
Editorial Profile: KODI-AM is a commercial station owned by Legend Communications. The format of the station is sports and talk. KODI-AM broadcasts to the Cody, WY area at 1400 AM.

KODJ-FM
Owner: Clear Channel Media and Entertainment
Editorial: 2801 Decker Lake Dr, Salt Lake City, Utah 84119-2330. **T:** 1 801 908-1300
W: http://www.oldies941.com/main.html
Editorial Profile: KODJ-FM is a commercial station owned by Clear Channel Media and Entertainment. The format of the station is classic hits. KODJ-FM broadcasts to the Salt Lake City area at 94.1 FM.

KODL-AM
Owner: Larson-Wynn Inc.
Editorial: 404 E 2nd St, The Dalles, Oregon 97058. **T:** 1 541 296-2101
E: newsroom@kodl.com
W: http://www.kodl.com
Editorial Profile: KODL-AM is a commercial station owned by Larson-Wynn Inc. The format of the station is adult standards. KODL-AM broadcasts to The Dalles, OR area at 1440 AM.

KODM-FM
Owner: Townsquare Media, LLC
Editorial: 11300 State Highway 191 Bldg 2, Midland, Texas 79707-1367.
T: 1 432 561-9809 **E:** kodm@cumulus.com
W: http://www.kodm.com
Editorial Profile: KODM-FM is a commercial station owned by Townsquare Media, LLC. The format of the station is adult contemporary music. KODM-FM broadcasts in the Midland, TX area at 97.9 FM.

KODS-FM
Owner: Americom Broadcasting
Editorial: 961 Matley Ln, Ste 120, Reno, Nevada 89502. **T:** 1 775 829-1964
W: http://www.river1037.com
Editorial Profile: KODS-FM is a commercial station owned by Americom Broadcasting. The format of the station is classic hits. KODS-FM broadcasts to the Reno, NV area at 103.7 FM.

KODY-AM
Owner: Armada Media Corp.
Editorial: 305 E 4th St, North Platte, Nebraska 69101. **T:** 1 308 532-3344
E: production@huskeradio.com
W: http://huskeradio.com
Editorial Profile: KODY-AM is a commercial station owned by Armada Media Corp. The format of the station is news and talk. KODY-AM broadcasts to the North Platte, NE area at 1240 AM

KODZ-FM
Owner: Bicoastal Media LLC
Editorial: 1500 Valley River Dr, Ste 350, Eugene, Oregon 97401. **T:** 1 541 485-1120
W: http://www.kool991.com
Editorial Profile: KODZ-FM is a commercial station owned by Bicoastal Media LLC. The format of the station is classic hits. KODZ-FM broadcasts in the Eugene, OR area at 99.1 FM.

KOEA-FM
Owner: Eagle Bluff Enterprises
Editorial: 116 S Grand Ave, Doniphan, Missouri 63935-1741. **T:** 1 573 686-3700
E: frn@tcmax.net
W: http://foxradionetwork.com
Editorial Profile: KOEA-FM is a commercial station owned by Eagle Bluff Enterprises. The format of the station is classic country. KOEA-FM broadcasts to the Doniphan, MO area at 97.5 FM.

KOEL-AM
Owner: Cumulus Media Inc.
Editorial: 2502 S Frederick Ave, Oelwein, Iowa 50662. **T:** 1 319 283-1234
E: koelam@koel.com **W:** http://www.koel.com
Editorial Profile: KOEL-FM is a commercial station owned by Cumulus Media Inc. The format for the station is agriculture, news, sports and country. KOEL-FM broadcasts to the Cedar Rapids, IA area at 950 AM.

KOEL-FM
Owner: Cumulus Media Inc.
Editorial: 501 Sycamore St, Ste 300, Waterloo, Iowa 50703-4651.
T: 1 319 833-4800 **E:** answers@k985.com
W: http://www.k985.com
Editorial Profile: KOEL-FM is a commercial station owned by Cumulus Media Inc. The format for the station is classic country. KOEL-FM broadcasts to the Waterloo, IA area at 98.5 FM.

KOFC-AM
Owner: Bott Broadcasting Co.
Editorial: 2201 S Thompson St, Ste C7, Springdale, Arkansas 72764.
T: 1 479 750-7707
W: http://www.bottradionetwork.com
Editorial Profile: KOFC-AM is a commercial station owned by Bott Broadcasting Co. The format of the station is religious talk. KOFC-AM broadcasts to the Springdale, AR area at 1250 AM.

KOFE-AM
Owner: Plank (Phillip)
Editorial: 201 N 8th St, Saint Maries, Idaho 83861-1869. **T:** 1 208 245-1240
E: tparrish_kofe@yahoo.com

KOFI-AM
Owner: KOFI Inc.
Editorial: 317 1st Ave E, Kalispell, Montana 59901. **T:** 1 406 755-6690
E: kofi@kofiradio.com
W: http://www.kofiradio.com
Editorial Profile: KOFI-AM is a commercial station owned by KOFI Inc. The format of the station is news and talk. KOFI-AM broadcasts in the Kalispell, MT area at 1180 AM.

KOFM-FM
Owner: Williams Broadcasting LLC
Editorial: 1710 W Willow Rd, Ste 300, Enid, Oklahoma 73703. **T:** 1 580 234-4230
W: http://www.kofm.com
Editorial Profile: KOFM-FM is a commercial station owned by Williams Broadcasting LLC. The format of the station is contemporary country music. KOFM-FM broadcasts to the Oklahoma City area at 103.1 FM.

KOFO-AM
Owner: Brandy Communications
Editorial: 320 E Radio Road, Ottawa, Kansas 66067-9563. **T:** 1 785 242-1220
E: kofo@kofo.com **W:** http://www.kofo.com
Editorial Profile: KOFO-AM is a commercial station owned by Brandy Communications. The format of the station is country. KOFO-AM broadcasts to the Ottawa, KS area at 1220 AM.

WORLD NEWS MEDIA

KOFX-FM
Owner: Entravision Communications Corp.
Editorial: 5426 N Mesa St, El Paso, Texas 79912-5421. **T:** 1 915 581-1126
W: http://www.923thefox.com
Editorial Profile: KOFX-FM is a commercial station owned by Entravision Communications Corp. The format of the station is oldies. KOFX-FM broadcasts to the El Paso, TX area at 92.3 FM.

KOGA-AM
Owner: Clear Channel Media and Entertainment
Editorial: 113 W 4th St, Ogallala, Nebraska 69153-2508. **T:** 1 308 284-3633
W: http://www.930koga.com
Editorial Profile: KOGA-AM is a commercial station owned by Clear Channel Media and Entertainment. The format of the station is adult standards. KOGA-AM broadcasts to the Ogallala, NE area at 930 AM.

KOGA-FM
Owner: Clear Channel Media and Entertainment
Editorial: 113 W 4th St, Ogallala, Nebraska 69153-2508. **T:** 1 308 284-3633
W: http://www.997thelake.com
Editorial Profile: KOGA-FM is a commercial station owned by Clear Channel Media and Entertainment. The format of the station is classic rock. KOGA-FM broadcasts to the Ogallala, NE area at 99.7 FM.

KOGL-FM
Owner: Oregon Public Broadcasting
Editorial: 7140 SW MacAdam Ave, Portland, Oregon 97219-3013. **T:** 1 503 244-3300
E: opbnews@opb.org **W:** http://www.opb.org
Editorial Profile: KOGL-FM is a non-commercial station owned by Oregon Public Broadcasting. The format at the station is news and talk. KOGL-FM broadcasts to the Portland, OR area at 89.3 FM.

KOGM-FM
Owner: Delta Media Corporation
Editorial: 3500 Nw Evangeline Trwy, Carencro, Louisiana 70520-6240. **T:** 1 337 896-1600
E: info@mix1071fm.com
W: http://www.mix1071fm.com
Editorial Profile: KOGM-FM is a commercial station owned by Delta Media Corporation. The format of the station is Hot AC. KOGM-FM broadcasts to the Lafayette, LA area at 107.1 FM.

KOGN-AM
Owner: AM Radio 1490, Inc.
Editorial: 314 S Redwood Rd, Ogden, Utah 84104. **T:** 1 801 886-1550
W: http://lajefautah.com
Editorial Profile: KOGN-AM is a commercial station owned by AM Radio 1490, Inc. The format of the station is regional Mexican music. KOGN-AM broadcasts to the Ogden, UT area at 1490 AM.

KOGO-AM
Owner: Clear Channel Media and Entertainment
Editorial: 9660 Granite Ridge Dr, San Diego, California 92123-2688. **T:** 1 858 292-2000
E: kogo@clearchannel.com
W: http://www.kogo.com/main.html
Editorial Profile: KOGO-AM is a commercial station owned by Clear Channel Media and Entertainment. The format for the station is news and talk. KOGO-AM broadcasts to the San Diego area at 600 AM.

KOGT-AM
Owner: G Cap Communications
Editorial: 5304 Meeks Dr, Orange, Texas 77632. **T:** 1 409 883-4381
W: http://www.kogt.com
Editorial Profile: KOGT-AM is a commercial station owned by G Cap Communications. The format of the station is classic country. KOGT-AM broadcasts to the Orange, TX area at 1600 AM.

KOHI-AM
Owner: Mountain Broadcasting Corp.
Editorial: 36200 Pittsburg Rd, Ste C, Saint Helens, Oregon 97051. **T:** 1 503 397-1600
E: kohi.radio@gmail.com
W: http://am1600kohi.com
Editorial Profile: KOHI-AM is a commercial station owned by Mountain Broadcasting Corp. The format of the station is news, sports and talk. KOHI-AM broadcasts to the Saint Helens, OR area at 1600 AM.

KOHL-FM
Owner: Fremont Newark Community College
Editorial: 43600 Mission Blvd, Fremont, California 94539-5847. **T:** 1 510 659-6221
W: http://www.kohlradio.com
Editorial Profile: KOHL-FM is a non-commercial station owned by Fremont Newark Community College. The format of the station is Top 40/CHR music. KOHL-FM broadcasts in the Fremont, CA area at 89.3 FM.

KOHN-FM
Owner: Tohono O'Odham Nation
Editorial: Business Loop, 86 Main St South, Sells, Arizona 85634. **T:** 1 520 361-5011
E: kohn919@hotmail.com
Editorial Profile: KOHN-FM is a non-commercial station owned by Tohono O'Odham Nation. The format of the station is a ethnic variety format. KOHN-FM broadcasts to the Sells, AZ area at 91.9 FM.

KOHO-FM
Owner: Icicle Broadcasting, Inc.
Editorial: 7475 Koho Pl, Leavenworth, Washington 98826-9023. **T:** 1 509 548-1011
E: news@kohoradio.com
W: http://www.kohoradio.com
Editorial Profile: KOHO-FM is a commercial station owned by Icicle Broadcasting, Inc. The format of the station is adult album alternative. KOHO-FM broadcasts to the Leavenworth, WA area at 101.1 FM.

KOHS-FM
Owner: Alpine School District
Editorial: 175 S 400 E, Orem, Utah 84097. **T:** 1 801 224-9236
Editorial Profile: KQHS-FM is a non-commercial station owned by Alpine School District. The format of the station is rock alternative. KOHS-FM broadcasts to the Salt Lake City area at 91.7 FM.

KOHT-FM
Owner: Clear Channel Media and Entertainment
Editorial: 3202 N Oracle Rd, Tucson, Arizona 85705. **T:** 1 520 618-2100
E: hot983comments@yahoo.com
W: http://www.hot983.com
Editorial Profile: KOHT-FM is a commercial station owned by Clear Channel Media and Entertainments. The format of the station is urban contemporary music. KOHTFM broadcasts to the Tucson, AZ area at 98.3 FM.

KOHU-AM
Owner: West End Radio LLC
Editorial: 80404 Cooney Ln, Hermiston, Oregon 97838-6613. **T:** 1 541 567-6500
W: http://www.gohermiston.com
Editorial Profile: KOHU-AM is a commercial station owned by West End Radio LLC. The format of the station is classic country. KOHU-AM broadcasts to the Hermiston, OR area at 1360 AM.

KOIA-FM
Owner: St. Gabriel Communications, LTD
Editorial: 705 Douglas St Ste 238, Sioux City, Iowa 51101-1043. **T:** 1 712 224-5342
E: fhcradio@fhcradio.com
W: http://www.fhcradio.com
Editorial Profile: KOAI-FM is a non-commercial station owned by St. Gabriel Communications, LTD. The format of the station is Catholic teaching. KOAI-FM broadcasts to the Sioux City, IA area at a frequency of 88.1 FM.

KOIL-AM
Owner: NRG Media LLC
Editorial: 5011 Capitol Ave, Omaha, Nebraska 68132-2921. **T:** 1 402 342-2000
E: omahacares@clearchannel.com
W: http://www.mighty1290.com
Editorial Profile: KOIL-AM is a commercial station owned by NRG Media LLC. The format of the station is news and talk. KOIL-AM broadcasts to the Omaha, NE, area at 1290 AM.

KOIR-FM
Owner: Rio Grande Bible Institute Inc.
Editorial: 4300 S Business Highway 281, Edinburg, Texas 78539-9650. **T:** 1 956 380-3435
E: correo@radioesperanza.com
W: http://www.radioesperanza.com
Editorial Profile: KOIR-FM is a commercial station owned by Rio Grande Bible Institute Inc. The format of the station is religious Spanish music and news. KOIR-FM broadcasts to the Edinburg, TX area at 88.5 FM.

KOIT-FM
Owner: Entercom Communications Corp.
Editorial: 201 3rd St, Ste 1200, San Francisco, California 94103.
T: 1 415 777-0965 **E:** koit@koit.com
W: http://www.koit.com
Editorial Profile: KOIT-FM is a commercial station owned by Entercom Communications Corp. The format is adult contemporary music. KOIT-FM broadcasts to the San Francisco area at 96.5 FM.

KOJM-AM
Owner: New Media Broadcasters
Editorial: 2210 31st St N, Havre, Montana 59501. **T:** 1 406 265-7841
W: http://www.kojm.com
Editorial Profile: KOJM-AM is a commercial station owned by New Media Broadcasters. The format for the station is classic hits. KOJM-AM broadcasts to the Havre, MT area at 610 AM.

KOJY-FM
Owner: Smiley (Doug)
Editorial: 22620 195th St, Bloomfield, Iowa 52537. **T:** 1 641 664-3721
Editorial Profile: KOJY-FM is a commercial station owned by Doug Smiley. The format of the station is southern gospel. KOJY-FM broadcasts to the Bloomfield, IA area at 106.9 FM.

KOKA-AM
Owner: Access.1 Communications Corp.
Editorial: 208 N Thomas St, Shreveport, Louisiana 71107-6520. **T:** 1 318 222-3122
W: http://www.koka.am
Editorial Profile: KOKA-AM is a commercial station owned by Access.1 Communications Corp. The format of the station is gospel music. KOKA-AM broadcasts to the Shreveport, LA area at 980 AM.

KOKB-AM
Owner: Team Radio LLC
Editorial: 102 E Grand Ave, Ponca City, Oklahoma 74601-5207. **T:** 1 580 762-9930
E: tripleplay@eteamradio.com
W: http://www.eteamradio.com
Editorial Profile: KOKB-AM is a commercial station owned by Team Radio LLC. The format of the station is sports. KOKB-AM broadcasts to the Ponca City, OK area at 1580 AM.

KOKC-AM
Owner: Tyler Media, LLC.
Editorial: 400 E Britton Rd, Oklahoma City, Oklahoma 73114-7515. **T:** 1 405 478-5104
W: http://www.kokcradio.com
Editorial Profile: KOKC-AM is a commercial station owned by Tyler Media, LLC. The format of the station is news and talk. KOKC-AM broadcasts to the Oklahoma City area at 1520 AM.

KOKE-AM
Owner: Encino Broadcasting, LLC
Editorial: 9434 Parkfield Dr, Austin, Texas 78758-6227. **T:** 1 512 453-1491
E: spots@austintejas.com
Editorial Profile: KOKE-AM is a commercial station owned by Encino Broadcasting, LLC. The format of the station is regional Mexican. KOKE-AM broadcasts to the Austin, TX area at 1600 AM.

KOKE-FM
Owner: REO Radio Group, LLC
Editorial: 1095 W US Highway 79, Rockdale, Texas 76567-4513. **T:** 1 512 416-1100
W: http://kokefm.com
Editorial Profile: KOKE-FM is a commercial station owned by REO Radio Group, LLC. The format of the station is Progressive Country, a sub-genre of Texas country music. KOKE-FM broadcasts to the Taylor, TX area at 99.3 FM.

KOKF-FM
Owner: Educational Media Foundation
Editorial: 7301 Broadway Ext Ste 131, Oklahoma City, Oklahoma 73116-9038.
T: 1 888 937-2471 **E:** air1@air1.com
W: http://www.air1.com
Editorial Profile: KOKF-FM is a non-commercial station owned by Educational Media Foundation. The format of the station is contemporary Christian. KOKF-FM broadcasts to the Oklahoma City, OK at 90.9 FM.

KOKK-AM
Owner: Performance Radio
Editorial: 1726 Dakota Ave S, Huron, South Dakota 57350. **T:** 1 605 352-1933
W: http://www.performance-radio.com
Editorial Profile: KOKK-AM is a commercial station owned by Performance Radio. The format of the station is contemporary country. KOKK-AM broadcasts to the Huron, SD area at 1210 AM.

KOKL-AM
Owner: Third Day Broadcasting, INC.
Editorial: 100 E 7th St, Okmulgee, Oklahoma 74447-4606. **T:** 1 918 756-3646
E: kokl@sbcglobal.net **W:** http://www.kokl.net
Editorial Profile: KOKL-AM is a commercial station owned by Third Day Broadcasting, INC. The format of the station is country. KOKL-AM broadcasts to the Tulsa, OK area at 1240 AM.

KOKO-AM
Owner: D&H Media, LLC
Editorial: 800 Pca Rd, Warrensburg, Missouri 64093. **T:** 1 660 747-9191
W: http://www.warrensburgradio.com
Editorial Profile: KOKO-AM is a commercial station owned by D&H Media, LLC. The format of the station is oldies music. KOKO-AM broadcasts to the Kansas City, MO, area at 1450 AM.

KOKO-FM
Owner: Big Broadcasting Inc.
Editorial: 2775 E Shaw Ave, Fresno, California 93710. **T:** 1 559 292-9494
W: http://www.koko94.com
Editorial Profile: KOKO-FM is a commercial station owned by Big Broadcasting Inc. The format of the station is a variety of hip-hop and rhythmic oldies. KOKO-FM broadcasts to the Fresno, CA area at 94.3 FM.

KOKP-AM
Owner: Team Radio LLC
Editorial: 122 N 3rd St, Ponca City, Oklahoma 74601-4326. **T:** 1 580 762-9930
E: tripleplay@eteamradio.com
W: http://www.eteamradio.com
Editorial Profile: KOKP-AM is a commercial station owned by Team Radio LLC. The format of the station is sports. KOKP-AM broadcasts to the Ponca City, OK area at 1020.

KOKR-FM
Owner: Sudbury Broadcasting Group
Editorial: 2025 McLarty Dr, Newport, Arkansas 72112-4822. **T:** 1 870 523-5891
E: info@rivercountry967.com
W: http://www.rivercountry967.com
Editorial Profile: KOKR-FM is a commercial station owned by Sudbury Broadcasting Group. The format of the station is contemporary country. KOKR-FM broadcasts to the Newport, AR area at 96.7 FM.

KOKS-FM
Owner: Calvary Broadcasting
Editorial: 2773 Barron Rd, Poplar Bluff, Missouri 63901-1929. **T:** 1 573 686-5080
E: koksradio@mycitycable.com
W: http://www.koks895fm.org
Editorial Profile: KOKS-FM is a non-commercial station owned by Calvary Broadcasting. The format of the station is religious programming. KOKS-FM broadcasts to the Poplar Bluff, MO area at 89.5 FM.

KOKX-AM
Owner: Withers Broadcasting Co.
Editorial: 108 Washington St, Keokuk, Iowa 52632. **T:** 1 319 524-5410
E: krnq963@mchsi.com
W: http://keokukradio.com
Editorial Profile: KOKX-AM is a commercial station owned by Withers Broadcasting Co. The format of the station is adult standards and talk. The station airs in the Keokuk, IA area at 1310 AM.

KOKX-FM
Owner: Withers Broadcasting Co.
Editorial: 108 Washington St, Keokuk, Iowa 52632. **T:** 1 319 524-5410
W: http://keokukradio.com
Editorial Profile: KOKX-FM is a commercial station owned by Withers Broadcasting Co. The format of the station is oldies. KOKX-FM broadcasts to the Koekuk, IA area at 95.3 FM.

KOKY-FM
Owner: Cumulus Media Inc
Editorial: 700 Wellington Hills Rd, Little Rock, Arkansas 72211. **T:** 1 501 401-0200
W: http://www.koky.com
Editorial Profile: KOKY-FM is a commercial station owned by Cumulus Media Inc. The format of the station is urban adult contemporary music. KOKY-FM broadcasts in the Little Rock, AR area at 102.1 FM.

KOKZ-FM
Owner: Woodward Communications, Inc.

Editorial: 514 Jefferson St, Waterloo, Iowa 50701-5422. **T:** 1 319 234-2200
W: http://1057kokz.com
Editorial Profile: KOKZ-FM is a commercial station owned by Woodward Communications, Inc. The format for the station is classic hits music. KOKZ-FM broadcasts to the Cedar Rapids, IA area at 105.7 FM.

KOLA-FM
Owner: Anaheim Broadcasting Corp.
Editorial: 1940 Orange Tree Ln, Ste 200, Redlands, California 92374. **T:** 1 909 793-3554
W: http://www.kolafm.com
Editorial Profile: KOLA-FM is a commercial station owned by Anaheim Broadcasting Corp. The format of the station is classic hits music. KOLA-FM broadcasts to the Redlands, CA area at 99.9 FM.

KOLC-FM
Owner: Americom Broadcasting
Editorial: 961 Matley Ln, Reno, Nevada 89502-2188. **T:** 1 775 829-1964
E: info@tencountry.com
W: http://www.tencountry.com
Editorial Profile: KOLC-FM is a commercial station owned by Americom Broadcasting. The format of the station is contemporary country. KOLC-FM broadcasts to the Reno, NV area at 97.3 FM.

KOLI-FM
Owner: Cumulus Media Inc.
Editorial: 4302 Call Field Rd, Ste D, Wichita Falls, Texas 76308. **T:** 1 940 691-2311
W: http://949theoutlaw.com
Editorial Profile: KOLI-FM is a commercial station owned by Cumulus Media Inc. The format of the station is contemporary country music. KOLI-FM broadcasts to the Wichita Falls, TX area at 94.9 FM.

KOLL-FM
Owner: Vega Broadcasting
Editorial: 2323D S Old Missouri Rd, Springdale, Arkansas 72764-7468.
T: 1 479 756-8686
E: info@ezspanishmedia.com
Editorial Profile: KOLL-FM is a commercial station owned by Vega Broadcasting. The format of the station is Regional Mexican. KOLL-FM broadcasts to the Little Rock, AR area at 106.3 FM.

KOLM-AM
Owner: Cumulus Media Inc.
Editorial: 122 4th St SW, Rochester, Minnesota 55902-3320. **T:** 1 507 286-1010
W: http://pro.kolm-am.tritonflex.com.
Editorial Profile: KOLM-AM is a commercial station owned by Cumulus Media Inc. The format of the station is sports. KOLM-AM broadcasts to the Rochester, MN area at 1520 AM.

KOLU-FM
Owner: Riverview Baptist Christian Schools
Editorial: 4921 W Wernett Rd, Pasco, Washington 99301. **T:** 1 509 547-2062
W: http://www.kolu.com
Editorial Profile: KOLU-FM is a non-commercial station owned by Riverview Baptist Christian Schools. The format of the station is Christian programming. KOLU-FM broadcasts to the Pasco, WA area at 90.1 FM.

KOLV-FM
Owner: Lakeland Broadcasting
Editorial: 1340 North Seventh Street, Willmar, Minnesota 56201. **T:** 1 320 235-1340
E: askus@kwlm.com
W: http://www.bigcountry100.com
Editorial Profile: KOLV-FM is a commercial station owned by Lakeland Broadcasting. The format of the station is contemporary country. KOLV-FM broadcasts in the Minneapolis area at 100.1 FM.

KOLW-FM
Owner: Townsquare Media, LLC
Editorial: 2621 W A St, Pasco, Washington 99301-4702. **T:** 1 509 547-9791
W: http://www.hot975online.com
Editorial Profile: KOLW-FM is a commercial station owned by Townsquare Media, LLC. The format of the station is Rhythmic/CHR. KOLW-FM broadcasts to the Pasco, WA area at 97.5 FM.

KOLY-AM
Owner: James River Broadcasting
Editorial: 118 3rd St E, Mobridge, South Dakota 57601. **T:** 1 605 845-3654
E: koly@amfmradio.biz
W: http://www.dakotaradiogroup.com
Editorial Profile: KOLY-AM is a commercial station owned by James River Broadcasting. The format of the station is adult standards. KOLY-AM broadcasts to the Mobridge, SD area at 1300 AM.

KOLY-FM
Owner: James River Broadcasting
Editorial: 118 3rd St E, Mobridge, South Dakota 57601. **T:** 1 605 845-3654
W: http://www.dakotaradiogroup.com
Editorial Profile: KOLY-FM is a commercial station owned by James River Broadcasting. The format of the station is adult contemporary. KOLY-FM broadcasts to the Mobridge, SD area at 99.5 FM.

KOLZ-FM
Owner: Clear Channel Media and Entertainment
Editorial: 4270 Byrd Dr, Loveland, Colorado 80538-7074. **T:** 1 970 461-2560
W: http://www.koltfm.com
Editorial Profile: KOLZ-FM is a commercial station owned by Clear Channel Media and Entertainment. The format of the station is contemporary country. KOLZ-FM broadcasts in the Cheyenne, WY area at 100.7 FM.

KOMA-FM
Owner: Tyler Media, LLC.
Editorial: 400 E Britton Rd, Oklahoma City, Oklahoma 73114-7515. **T:** 1 405 478-5104
W: http://www.komaradio.com
Editorial Profile: KOMA-FM is a commercial station owned by Tyler Media, LLC. The format of the station is classic hits. KOMA-FM broadcasts to the Oklahoma City area at 92.5 FM

KOMB-FM
Owner: Fort Scott Broadcasting Co., Inc.
Editorial: 2 N National Ave, Fort Scott, Kansas 66701. **T:** 1 620 223-4500
W: http://www.kombfm.com
Editorial Profile: KOMB-FM is a commercial station owned by Fort Scott Broadcasting Co., Inc. The format of the station is oldies. KOMB-FM broadcasts to the Fort Scott, KS area at 103.9 FM.

KOMC-AM
Owner: Earls Broadcasting
Editorial: 202 Courtney St, Branson, Missouri 65616-2434. **T:** 1 417 334-6003
E: mail@krzk.com
W: http://www.hometownradioonline.com
Editorial Profile: KOMC-AM is a commercial station owned by Earls Broadcasting. The format of the station is gospel. KOMC-AM broadcasts to the Branson, MO area at 1220 AM.

KOMC-FM
Owner: Earls Broadcasting
Editorial: 202 Courtney St, Branson, Missouri 65616-2434. **T:** 1 417 334-6003
W: http://www.hometowndailynews.com
Editorial Profile: KOMC-FM is a commercial station owned by Earls Broadcasting. The format of the station is adult standards. KOMC-FM broadcasts to the Springfield, MO area at 100.1 FM.

KOME-FM
Owner: LKCM Radio Group LP
Editorial: 115 W 3rd St, Fort Worth, Texas 76102-7402. **T:** 1 817 332-0959
E: contactus@921hankfm.com
W: http://www.921hankfm.com
Editorial Profile: KOME-FM is a commercial station owned by LKCM Radio Group LP. The format of the station is classic and contemporary country music. KOME-FM broadcasts to the Meridian, TX area at 95.3 FM.

KOMG-FM
Owner: Midwest Family Stations
Editorial: 319B E Battlefield St, Springfield, Missouri 65807. **T:** 1 417 886-5677
W: http://www.1051bob.fm
Editorial Profile: KOMG-FM is a commercial station owned by Midwest Family Stations. The format of the station is country. KOMG-FM broadcasts to the Springfield, MO area at 105.1 FM.

KOMO-AM
Owner: Sinclair Radio of Seattle, LLC
Editorial: 140 4th Ave N, Seattle, Washington 98109-4940. **T:** 1 206 404-4000
E: tips@komo4news.com
W: http://www.komonews.com
Editorial Profile: KOMO-AM is a commercial station owned by Sinclair Radio of Seattle, LLC. The format of the station is news. KOMO-AM broadcasts in the Seattle area at 1000 AM.

KOMO-FM
Owner: Sinclair Radio of Seattle, LLC
Editorial: 140 4th Ave N, Seattle, Washington 98109-4940. **T:** 1 206 404-4000
E: tips@komo4news.com
W: http://www.komonews.com
Editorial Profile: KOMO-FM is a commercial station owned by Sinclair Radio of Seattle, LLC. The format of the station is news and talk. KOMO-FM broadcasts to the Seattle area at 97.7 FM.

KOMP-FM
Owner: Lotus Communications Corp.
Editorial: 8755 W Flamingo Rd, Las Vegas, Nevada 89147-8667. **T:** 1 702 876-1460
W: http://www.komp.com
Editorial Profile: KOMP-FM is a commercial station owned by Lotus Communications Corp. The format of the station is rock music. KOMP-FM broadcasts to the Las Vegas area at 92.3 FM.

KOMR-FM
Owner: Univision Communications Inc.
Editorial: 6006 S 30Th St, Phoenix, Arizona 85042-4802. **T:** 1 602 308-7900
W: http://recuerdophoenix.univision.com
Editorial Profile: KOMR-FM is a commercial station owned by Univision Communications Inc. The format of the station is Spanish Regional/AC. KOMR-FM broadcasts to the Phoenix area at 106.3 FM.

KOMS-FM
Owner: Cumulus Media Inc.
Editorial: 4209 N Frontage Rd, Fayetteville, Arkansas 72703-5002. **T:** 1 479 452-0681
W: http://www.bigcountry1073.com
Editorial Profile: KOMS-FM is a commercial station owned by Cumulus Media Inc. The format of the station is classic country. KOMS-FM broadcasts to the Fort Smith, AR area at 107.3 FM.

KOMT-FM
Owner: Mac Partners
Editorial: 2352 Highway 62 Business, Mountain Home, Arkansas 72653-6847.
T: 1 870 492-6022
Editorial Profile: KOMT-FM is a commercial station owned by Mac Partners. The format of the station is adult contemporary. KOMT-FM broadcasts to the Mountain Home, AR area at 107.5 FM.

KOMW-AM
Owner: North Cascades Broadcasting
Editorial: 320 Emery Dr, Omak, Washington 98841-9237. **T:** 1 509 826-0100
E: news@komw.net **W:** http://www.komw.net
Editorial Profile: KOMW-AM is a commercial station owned by North Cascades Broadcasting. The format of the station is adult standards music. WOMW-AM broadcasts to the Spokane, WA area at 680 AM.

KOMX-FM
Owner: Hughes(Jim)
Editorial: 1701 N Banks St, Pampa, Texas 79065. **T:** 1 806 669-6809
E: production@kgrokomxradio.com
W: http://www.kgrokomxradio.com
Editorial Profile: KOMX-FM is a commercial station owned by Jim Hughes. The format of the station is country. KOMX-FM broadcasts to the Pampa, TX area at 100.3 FM.

KOMY-AM
Owner: Zwerling Broadcasting System Ltd.
Editorial: 2300 Portola Dr, Santa Cruz, California 95062. **T:** 1 831 475-1080
W: http://www.1340komy.com
Editorial Profile: KOMY-AM is commercial station owned by Zwerling Broadcasting System Ltd. The format of the station is adult standards and easy listening. KOMY-AM broadcasts in the Santa Cruz, CA area at 1340 AM.

KONA-AM
Owner: Cherry Creek Radio
Editorial: 2823 W Lewis St, Pasco, Washington 99301-6702. **T:** 1 509 547-1618
E: 610kona@cherrycreekradio.com
W: http://www.610kona.com
Editorial Profile: KONA-AM is a commercial station owned by Cherry Creek Radio. The format of the station is news and talk. KONA-AM broadcasts to the Pasco, WA area at 610 AM.

KONA-FM
Owner: Cherry Creek Radio
Editorial: 2823 W Lewis St, Pasco, Washington 99301-6702. **T:** 1 509 547-1618
W: http://www.mix1053.com
Editorial Profile: KONA-FM is a commercial station owned by Cherry Creek Radio. The format of the station is adult contemporary. KONA-FM broadcasts to the Pasco, WA area at 105.3 FM.

KOND-FM
Owner: Univision Communications Inc.
Editorial: 601 W Univision Plz, Fresno, California 93704-1092. **T:** 1 559 430-8500
W: http://queonda921.univision.com
Editorial Profile: KOND-FM is a commercial station owned by Univision Communications Inc. The format of the station is regional Mexican. KOND-FM broadcasts to the Fresno, CA area at 92.1 FM.

KONE-FM
Owner: Wilks Broadcast Group
Editorial: 33 Briercroft Office Park, Lubbock, Texas 79412. **T:** 1 806 762-3000
W: http://www.rock101.fm
Editorial Profile: KONE-FM is a commercial station owned by Wilks Broadcast Group. The format of the station is classic rock. KONE-FM broadcasts to the Lubbock, TX area at 101.1 FM.

KONI-FM
Owner: Hochman Hawaii Media
Editorial: 300 Ohukai Rd, Ste C318, Kihei, Hawaii 96753-7050. **T:** 1 808 875-8866
E: koni@hawaii.rr.com
W: http://www.hhawaiimedia.com

KONO-AM
Owner: Cox Media Group, Inc.
Editorial: 8122 Datapoint Dr Ste 600, San Antonio, Texas 78229-3446.
T: 1 210 615-5400
W: http://www.kono1011.com
Editorial Profile: KONO-AM is a commercial station owned by Cox Media Group, Inc. The format for the station is sports. KONO-AM broadcasts to the San Antonio area at 860 AM.

KONO-FM
Owner: Cox Media Group, Inc.
Editorial: 8122 Datapoint Dr Ste 600, San Antonio, Texas 78229-3446.
T: 1 210 615-5400
W: http://www.kono1011.com
Editorial Profile: KONO-FM is a commercial station owned by Cox Media Group, Inc. The format for the station is classic hits. KONO-FM broadcasts to the San Antonio area at 101.1 FM.

KONP-AM
Owner: Radio Pacific Inc.
Editorial: 721 E 1st St, Port Angeles, Washington 98362-3600. **T:** 1 360 457-1450
E: info@konp.com **W:** http://www.konp.com
Editorial Profile: KONP-AM is a commercial station owned by Radio Pacific Inc. The format of the station is news, talk and sports. KONP-AM broadcasts to the Port Angeles, WA area at 1450 AM.

KONQ-FM
Owner: Dodge City Community College
Editorial: 3004 N 14th Ave, Dodge City, Kansas 67801. **T:** 1 620 225-6783
W: http://www.dc3.edu
Editorial Profile: KONQ-FM is a non-commercial station owned by Dodge City Community College. The format of the station is variety. KONQ-FM broadcasts to the Dodge City, KS area at a frequency of 91.9 FM.

KONY-FM
Owner: Canyon Media Corporation
Editorial: 204 Playa Della Rosita, Washington, Utah 84780. **T:** 1 435 628-3643
E: kony@infowest.com
W: http://www.999konycountry.com
Editorial Profile: KONY-FM is a commercial station owned by Canyon Media Corporation. The format of the station is contemporary country. KONY-FM broadcasts to the St. George, UT area at 99.9 FM.

KOOC-FM
Owner: Townsquare Media, Inc.
Editorial: 608 Moody Ln, Temple, Texas 76504-2952. **T:** 1 254 773-5252
W: http://www.myb106.com
Editorial Profile: KOOC-FM is a commercial station owned by Townsquare Media, Inc. The format of the station is rhythmic Top 40/CHR

music. KOOC-FM broadcasts to the Temple, TX area at 106.3 FM.

KOOI-FM

Owner: Access.1 Communications Corp.
Editorial: 210 S Broadway Ave, Tyler, Texas 75702. **T:** 1 903 581-9966
W: http://www.kooi.com
Editorial Profile: KOOI-FM is a commercial station owned by Access.1 Communications Corp. The format of the station is adult contemporary. KOOI-FM broadcasts to the Tyler, TX area at 106.5 FM.

KOOK-FM

Owner: Revolution Broadcast Co. of The West
Editorial: 2125 Sidney Baker St, Kerrville, Texas 78028-2551. **T:** 1 830 896-1230
E: production@krvl.com
Editorial Profile: KOOK-FM is a commercial station owned by Revolution Broadcast Co. of The West. The format for the station is classic country music. KOOK-FM broadcasts to the Junction, TX area at 93.5 FM.

KOOL-FM

Owner: CBS Radio
Editorial: 840 N Central Ave, Phoenix, Arizona 85004-2003. **T:** 1 602 776-7000
W: http://kool.cbslocal.com
Editorial Profile: KOOL-FM is a commercial station owned by CBS Radio. The format of the station is classic hits. KOOL-FM broadcasts to the Phoenix area at 94.5 FM.

KOOO-FM

Owner: NRG Media LLC
Editorial: 5011 Capitol Ave, Omaha, Nebraska 68132. **T:** 1 402 342-2000
E: whatever@thebigo1019.com
W: http://www.thebigo1019.com
Editorial Profile: KOOO-FM is a commercial station owned by NRG Media LLC. The format of the station is rock. KOOO-FM is licensed to La Vista, NE and broadcasts to the Omaha, NE area at 101.9 FM.

KOOP-FM

Owner: Texas Educational Broadcasting Co-Op, Inc
Editorial: 3823 Airport Blvd, Ste B, Austin, Texas 78722. **T:** 1 512 472-1369
E: info@koop.org **W:** http://www.koop.org
Editorial Profile: KOOP-FM is a non-commercial station owned by Texas Educational Broadcasting Co-Op, Inc. The format of the station is variety. The station is aired locally on 91.7 FM with a variety format. KOOP-FM's tagline is "Koop 91.7 Community Radio."

KOOQ-AM

Owner: Eagle Radio Inc.
Editorial: 1301 E 4th St, North Platte, Nebraska 69101. **T:** 1 308 532-1120
W: http://www.1410amespn.com
Editorial Profile: KOOQ-AM is commercial station owned by Eagle Radio Inc. The format of the station is sports. KOOQ-AM broadcasts to North Platte, NE at 1410 AM.

KOOR-AM

Owner: Bustos Media, LLC
Editorial: 5110 SE Stark St, Portland, Oregon 97215. **T:** 1 503 234-5550
W: http://www.bustosmediaor.com
Editorial Profile: KOOR-AM is a commercial station owned by Bustos Media, LLC. The format of the station is Spanish news and talk. KOOR-AM broadcasts to the Portland, OR, area at 1010 AM.

KOOS-FM

Owner: Bicoastal Media LLC
Editorial: 320 Central Ave, Ste 519, Coos Bay, Oregon 97420. **T:** 1 541 267-2121
E: southcoastpsa@bicoastalmedia.com
W: http://www.power1073.com
Editorial Profile: KOOS-FM is a commercial station owned by Bicoastal Media LLC. The format of the station is hot adult contemporary music. KOOS-FM broadcasts to the Coos Bay, OR area at 107.3 FM.

KOOV-FM

Owner: M & M Broadcasters, Ltd
Editorial: 5501 Bagby Ave, Waco, Texas 76711-2300. **T:** 1 254 772-0930
W: http://www.929shooterfm.com
Editorial Profile: KOOV-FM is a commercial station owned by M & M Broadcasters, Ltd. The format of the station is Texas country music. KOOV-FM broadcasts to the Waco, TX area at 106.9 FM.

KOOZ-FM

Owner: State of Oregon
Editorial: 1250 Siskiyou Blvd, Ashland, Oregon 97520-5001. **T:** 1 541 552-6301
E: jprinfo@sou.edu **W:** http://www.ijpr.org
Editorial Profile: KOOZ-FM is a non-commercial station owned by State of Oregon. The format of the station is news and classical music. KOOZ-FM broadcasts in the Myrtle Point, OR area at 94.1 FM.

KOPB-AM

Owner: Oregon Public Broadcasting
Editorial: 7140 SW MacAdam Ave, Portland, Oregon 97219-3013. **T:** 1 503 293-1905
E: opbnews@opb.org **W:** http://www.opb.org
Editorial Profile: KOPB-AM is a non-commercial station owned by Oregon Public Broadcasting. The format of the station is news and talk. KOPB-AM broadcasts to the Euguene, OR area at 1600 AM.

KOPB-FM

Owner: Oregon Public Broadcasting
Editorial: 7140 SW Macadam Ave, Portland, Oregon 97219. **T:** 1 503 293-1905
E: opbnews@opb.org **W:** http://www.opb.org
Editorial Profile: KOPB-FM is a non-commercial station owned by Oregon Public Broadcasting. The format of the station is news and talk. KOPB-FM broadcasts to the Portland, OR area at 91.5 FM.

KOPJ-FM

Owner: Lifetalk Radio Inc.
Editorial: 200 Main Ave S, Park Rapids, Minnesota 56470-1518. **T:** 1 800 775-4673
W: http://www.lifetalk.net/
Editorial Profile: KOPJ-FM is a non-commercial station owned by Lifetalk Radio Inc. The station's format is Christian music and religous teaching. KOPJ-FM broadcasts to the Sebaka and Park Rapids, MN areas at 89.3 FM.

KOPN-FM

Owner: New Wave Corporation
Editorial: 915 E Broadway, Columbia, Missouri 65201. **T:** 1 573 874-1139 **E:** mail@kopn.org
W: http://www.kopn.org
Editorial Profile: KOPN-FM is a non-commercial station owned by the New Wave Corporation. The format of the station is variety. KOPN-FM broadcasts to the Columbia, MO area at 89.5 FM.

KOPR-FM

Owner: Butte Broadcasting Inc.
Editorial: 660 Dewey Blvd, Butte, Montana 59701. **T:** 1 406 494-7777
E: mail@kbowkopr.com
W: http://www.kopr94.net
Editorial Profile: KOPR-FM is a commercial station owned by Butte Broadcasting Inc. The format for the station is classic rock. KOPR-FM broadcasts to the Butte, MT area at 94.1 FM.

KOPW-FM

Owner: NRG Media LLC
Editorial: 5011 Capitol Ave, Omaha, Nebraska 68132. **T:** 1 402 342-2000
W: http://www.power1069fm.com
Editorial Profile: KOPW-FM is a commercial station owned by NRG Media LLC. The format of the station is urban contemporary. KOPW-FM broadcasts to the Omaha, NE area on 106.9 FM.

KOPY-AM

Owner: Claro Communications Ltd.
Editorial: 2722 N US Highway 281, Alice, Texas 78332. **T:** 1 361 664-1884
E: claroradio@yahoo.com
Editorial Profile: KOPY-AM is a commercial station owned by Claro Communications Ltd. The format of the station is sports. KOPY-AM broadcasts to the Alice, TX at 1070 AM.

KOPY-FM

Owner: Claro Communications Ltd.
Editorial: 2722 N US Highway 281, Alice, Texas 78332. **T:** 1 361 664-1884
Editorial Profile: KOPY-FM is a commercial station owned by Claro Communications Ltd. The format of the station is Hispanic programming. KOPY-FM broadcasts to the Alice, TX area at 92.1 FM.

KOQL-FM

Owner: Cumulus Media Inc.
Editorial: 503 Old 63 N, Columbia, Missouri 65201. **T:** 1 573 449-4141
W: http://www.q1061.com
Editorial Profile: KOQL-FM is a commercial station owned by Cumulus Media Inc. The format of the station is rhythmic Top 40/CHR

music. KOQL-FM broadcasts to the Columbia, MO area 105.1 FM.

KORA-FM

Owner: Brazos Valley Communications LLC
Editorial: 1240 E Villa Maria Rd, Bryan, Texas 77802. **T:** 1 979 776-1240
W: http://www.korafm.com
Editorial Profile: KORA-FM is a commercial station owned by Brazos Valley Communications LLC. The format of the station is country. KORA-FM broadcasts to the Bryan, TX area at 98.3 FM.

KORC-FM

Owner: Harney County Radio, LLC
Editorial: 69470 S. Egan Road, Burns, Oregon 97720. **T:** 1 541 573-2055
W: http://kbnh1230.com/korc.html
Editorial Profile: KORC-FM is a commercial station owned by Harney County Radio, LLC. The format of the station is soft adult contemporary. KORC-FM broadcasts to the Burns, OR area at 92.7 FM.

KORD-FM

Owner: Townsquare Media, LLC
Editorial: 2621 W A St, Pasco, Washington 99301. **T:** 1 509 547-9791
W: http://www.1027kord.com
Editorial Profile: KORD-FM is a commercial station owned by Townsquare Media, LLC. The format of the station is contemporary country music. KORD-FM broadcasts to the Pasco, WA area at 102.7 FM.

KORE-AM

Owner: Support Christian Broadcasting Inc.
Editorial: 2080 Laura St, Springfield, Oregon 97477. **T:** 1 541 747-5673
E: kore@koreradio.com
W: http://www.koreradio.com
Editorial Profile: KORE-AM is a non-commercial station owned by Support Christian Broadcasting Inc. The format of the station is Christian programming. KORE-AM broadcasts to the Springfield, OR area at 1050 AM.

KORL-FM

Owner: Hochman-McCann Hawaii, Inc.
Editorial: 900 Fort Street Mall, Ste 450, Honolulu, Hawaii 96813. **T:** 1 808 538-1180
E: korlradio001@hawaii.rr.com
W: http://www.hhawaiimedia.net/
Editorial Profile: KORL-FM is a commercial station owned by Hochman-McCann Hawaii, Inc. The format of the station is smooth jazz. KORL-FM broadcasts to the Honolulu, HI area at 101.1 FM. KORL-FM features multicultural brokered programming.

KORN-AM

Owner: Riverfront Broadcasting
Editorial: 319 N Main St, Mitchell, South Dakota 57301. **T:** 1 605 996-1490
E: kornstudio@kornq107.com
W: http://www.1490korn.com
Editorial Profile: KORN-AM is a commercial station owned by Riverfront Broadcasting. The format of the station is news and talk. KORN-AM broadcasts to the Mitchell, SD area at 1490 AM.

KORR-FM

Owner: Idaho Wireless Corp.
Editorial: 436 N Main St, Pocatello, Idaho 83204. **T:** 1 208 234-1290 **E:** spots@kzbq.com
W: http://www.korr104.com
Editorial Profile: KORR-FM is a commercial station owned by Idaho Wirelss Corp. The format of the station is hot adult contemporary. KORR-FM broadcasts to the Pocatello, ID, area at 104.1 FM.

KORT-AM

Owner: 4-K Radio Inc.
Editorial: 612 Pine St, Grangeville, Idaho 83530-1150. **T:** 1 208 983-1230
E: kortoffice@qwestoffice.net
Editorial Profile: KORT-AM is a commercial station owned by 4-K Radio Inc. The format of the station is contemporary country music. KORT-AM broadcasts to the Grangeville, ID area at 1230 AM.

KORT-FM

Owner: 4-K Radio Inc.
Editorial: 612 Pine St, Grangeville, Idaho 83530-1150. **T:** 1 208 983-1230
E: kortoffice@qwestoffice.net
Editorial Profile: KORT-FM is a commercial station owned by 4-K Radio Inc. The format of the station is contemporary country music. KORT-FM broadcasts to the Grangeville, ID area at 92.7 FM.

KORV-FM

Owner: Lake County Radio, LLC
Editorial: 69470 S Egan Rd, Burns, Oregon 97720-2537. **T:** 1 541 573-2055
Editorial Profile: KORV-FM is a commercial station owned by Lake County Radio, LLC. The format of the station is classic hits. KORV-FM broadcasts to the Lakeview, OR area at a frequency of 93.5 FM.

KOSB-FM

Owner: Team Radio LLC
Editorial: 114 W 7th Ave, Stillwater, Oklahoma 74074-4049. **T:** 1 405 377-5325
E: tripleplay@eteamradio.com
W: http://tripleplaysportsradio.com
Editorial Profile: KOSB-FM is a commercial station owned by Team Radio LLC. The format of the station is sports. KOSB-FM broadcasts to the Stillwater, OK area at 105.1 FM.

KOSC-FM

Owner: Classical Public Radio Network, LLC
Editorial: 201 3rd St Ste 1200, San Francisco, California 94103-3143. **T:** 1 415 546-8710
E: feedback@kdfc.com
W: http://www.kdfc.com
Editorial Profile: KOSC-FM is a non-commercial station owned by Classical Public Radio Network, LLC. The format of the station is classical music. KOSC-FM broadcasts locally to the San Francisco area at 90.3 FM.

KOSE-AM

Owner: Sudbury Broadcasting Group
Editorial: 125 S 2nd St, Blytheville, Arkansas 72315. **T:** 1 870 762-2093

KOSF-FM

Owner: Clear Channel Media and Entertainment
Editorial: 340 Townsend St, San Francisco, California 94107-1633. **T:** 1 415 538-1013
W: http://www.big1037fm.com/main.html
Editorial Profile: KOSF-FM is a commercial station owned by Clear Channel Media and Entertainment. The format of the station is classic hits. KOSF-FM broadcasts to the San Francisco area at 103.7 FM.

KOSI-FM

Owner: Entercom Communications Corp.
Editorial: 4700 S Syracuse St, Ste 1050, Denver, Colorado 80237. **T:** 1 303 967-2700
W: http://www.entercomdenver.com
Editorial Profile: KOSI-FM is a commercial station owned by Entercom Communications Corp. The format of the station is Lite Rock/ Lite AC. KOSI-FM broadcasts to the Denver area at 101.1 FM.

KOSN-FM

Owner: Oklahoma State University
Editorial: 303 Paul Miller Building, Stillwater, Oklahoma 74078-4054. **T:** 1 405 744-6352
W: http://www.kosu.org
Editorial Profile: KOSN-FM is a non-commercial station owned by Oklahoma State University. The format of the station is classical music and news. KOSN-FM broadcasts to the Ketchum, OK area at 107.5 FM.

KOSO-FM

Owner: Clear Channel Media and Entertainment
Editorial: 2121 Lancey Dr, Modesto, California 95355-3036. **T:** 1 209 551-1306
E: modestopsa@clearchannel.com
W: http://www.hitradio929.com
Editorial Profile: KOSO-FM is a commercial station owned by Clear Channel Media and Entertainment. The format of the station is Adult CHR. KOSO-FM broadcasts to the Modesto, CA area at 92.9 FM.

KOSP-FM

Owner: Midwest Family Stations
Editorial: 319B E Battlefield St, Springfield, Missouri 65807-4999. **T:** 1 417 886-5677
W: http://www.929thebeat.com
Editorial Profile: KOSP-FM is a commercial station owned by Midwest Family Stations. The format of the station is Top 40/CHR. KOSP-FM broadcasts to the Springfield, MO area at 92.9 FM.

KOSS-AM

Owner: High Desert Broadcasting LLC
Editorial: 570 East Ave Q9, Palmdale, California 93550. **T:** 1 661 947-3107
W: http://www.newstalk1380.com
Editorial Profile: KWJL-AM is a commercial station owned by High Desert Broadcasting LLC. The format of the station is news and talk. KWJL-AM broadcasts to the Palmdale, CA area at 1380 AM.

KOST-FM
Owner: Clear Channel Media and Entertainment
Editorial: 3400 W Olive Ave Ste 550, Burbank, California 91505-5544. **T:** 1 818 559-2252
E: kostpromo@clearchannel.com
W: http://www.kost1035.com
Editorial Profile: KOST-FM is a commercial station owned by Clear Channel Media and Entertainment. The format of the station is soft rock. KOST-FM broadcasts to the Los Angeles area at 103.5 FM.

KOSU-FM
Owner: Oklahoma State University
Editorial: 303 Paul Miller Building, Stillwater, Oklahoma 74078-4054. **T:** 1 405 744-6352
E: kosu@kosu.org **W:** http://www.kosu.org
Editorial Profile: KOSU-FM is a non-commercial station owned by Oklahoma State University. The format of the station is talk and news. KOSU-FM broadcasts to the Oklahoma City area at 91.7 FM.

KOSY-AM
Owner: Townsquare Media, LLC
Editorial: 2324 Arkansas Blvd, Texarkana, Arkansas 71854. **T:** 1 870 772-3771
W: http://www.kosy790.com
Editorial Profile: KOSY-AM is a commercial station owned by Townsquare Media, LLC . The format of the station is gospel music. KOSY-AM broadcasts to the Shreveport, LA area at 790 AM.

KOSY-FM
Owner: Clear Channel Media and Entertainment
Editorial: 2801 Decker Lake Dr, Salt Lake City, Utah 84119-2330. **T:** 1 801 908-1300
W: http://www.rock1065.com
Editorial Profile: KOSY-FM is a commercial station owned by Clear Channel Media and Entertainment. The format of the station is Rock. KOSY-FM broadcasts to the Salt Lake City area at 106.5 FM.

KOTA-AM
Owner: Duhamel Broadcasting
Editorial: 518 Saint Joseph St, Rapid City, South Dakota 57701. **T:** 1 605 342-2000
E: news@kotaradio.com
W: http://kotaradio.com
Editorial Profile: KOTA-AM is a commercial station owned by Duhamel Broadcasting. The format of the station news, sports and talk. KOTA-AM broadcasts to the Rapid City, SD area at 1380 AM.

KOTD-FM
Owner: Oregon Public Broadcasting
Editorial: 7140 SW MacAdam Ave, Portland, Oregon 97219-3013. **T:** 1 503 293-1905
E: opbnews@opb.org **W:** http://www.opb.org
Editorial Profile: KOTD-FM is a non-commercial station owned by Oregon Public Broadcasting. The format of the station is news and talk. KOPB-FM broadcasts to the Portland, OR area at 89.7 FM.

KOTE-FM
Owner: Niemeyer Communications LLC
Editorial: 1275 P Rd, Eureka, Kansas 67045. **T:** 1 620 583-7414 **W:** http://www.kotefm.com
Editorial Profile: KOTE-FM is a commercial station owned by Niemeyer Communications LLC. The format of the station is contemporary country and classic rock music. KOTE-FM broadcasts to the Eureka, KS area at 93.5 FM.

KOTK-AM
Owner: Salem Communications
Editorial: 11717 Burt St, Ste 202, Omaha, Nebraska 68154. **T:** 1 402 422-1600
W: http://www.1420kotk.com
Editorial Profile: KOTK-AM is a commercial station owned by Salem Communication. The format of the station is Hispanic Christian programming. KOTK-AM broadcasts to the Omaha, NE area at 1420 AM.

KOTM-FM
Owner: FMC Broadcasting Inc.
Editorial: 601 W 2nd St, Ottumwa, Iowa 52501. **T:** 1 641 682-8711
E: traffic@tomfmottumwa.com
W: http://www.tomfmottumwa.com
Editorial Profile: KOTM-FM is a commercial station owned by FMC Broadcasting Inc. The format for the station is Top 40/CHR. KOTM-FM broadcasts to the Ottumna, IA area at 97.7 FM.

KOTN-FM
Owner: Arkansas County Broadcasters Inc.
Editorial: 1818 S Buerkle St, Stuttgart, Arkansas 72160-5804. **T:** 1 870 673-1595
Editorial Profile: KAFN-FM is a commercial station owned by Arkansas County Broadcasters Inc. The format of the station is classic country. KAFN-FM broadcasts to the Gould, AR area at 105.5 FM.

KOTO-FM
Owner: San Miguel Educational Fund, Inc.
Editorial: 207 N Pine St, Telluride, Colorado 81435-9999. **T:** 1 970 728-4334
E: news@koto.org **W:** http://www.koto.org
Editorial Profile: KOTO-FM is a non-commercial station owned by San Miguel Educational Fund. The format of the station is variety. KOTO-FM broadcasts to the Telluride, CO area at 91.7 FM.

KOTS-AM
Owner: Luna County Broadcasting
Editorial: 1700 S Gold Ave, Deming, New Mexico 88030-5839. **T:** 1 575 546-9011
E: radio@demingradio.com
W: http://www.demingradio.com
Editorial Profile: KOTS-AM is a commercial station owned by Luna County Broadcasting. The format of the station is classic country. KOTS-AM broadcasts to the Deming, NM area at 1230 AM.

KOTZ-AM
Owner: Kotzebue Broadcasting Inc.
Editorial: 396 Lagoon, Kotzebue, Alaska 99752-9999. **T:** 1 907 442-3434
E: kotzradio@yahoo.com
W: http://www.kotz.org
Editorial Profile: KOTZ-AM is a non-commercial station owned by Kotzebue Broadcasting, Inc. The format of the station is a variety of music and cultural affairs programming. KOTZ-AM broadcasts in the Kotzebue, AK, area at 720 AM.

KOUT-FM
Owner: New Rushmore Radio
Editorial: 660 Flormann St, Ste 100, Rapid City, South Dakota 57701. **T:** 1 605 343-6161
W: http://www.katradio.com
Editorial Profile: KOUT-FM is a commercial station owned by New Rushmore Radio. The format of the station is classic country. KOUT-FM broadcasts to the Rapid City, SD area at 98.7 FM.

KOUU-AM
Owner: Idaho Wireless Corp.
Editorial: 436 N Main St, Pocatello, Idaho 83204-3018. **T:** 1 208 234-1290
E: spots@kzbq.com
Editorial Profile: KOUU-AM is a commercial station owned by Idaho Wireless Corp. The format of the station is classic country. KOUU-AM broadcasts to Pocatello, ID at 1290 AM.

KOUW-FM
Owner: Rich Broadcasting, LLC.
Editorial: 670 W Broadway St, Idaho Falls, Idaho 83402-3333. **T:** 1 208 542-0426
E: kech95@cox-internet.com

KOVC-AM
Owner: Ingstad Family Media
Editorial: 136 Central Ave N, Valley City, North Dakota 58072-2952. **T:** 1 701 845-1490
W: http://www.newsdakota.com
Editorial Profile: KOVC-AM is a commercial station owned by Ingstad Family Media (dba Sioux Valley Broadcasting). The format of the station is classic country. KOVC-AM broadcasts to the Valley City, ND area at 1490 AM.

KOVE-AM
Owner: Kenney(Joseph R. and Andrea L.)
Editorial: 1530 Main St, Lander, Wyoming 82520. **T:** 1 307 332-5683
E: radio1@wyoming.com
W: http://www.kdlykove.com
Editorial Profile: KOVE-AM is a commercial station owned by Joseph R. Kenney and Andrea L. Kenney. The format of the station is country music. KOVE-AM broadcasts to the Lander, WY area at 1330 AM.

KOVE-FM
Owner: Univision Communications Inc.
Editorial: 5100 Southwest Fwy, Houston, Texas 77056-7308. **T:** 1 713 965-2400
W: http://recuerdo1065.univision.com
Editorial Profile: KOVE-FM is a commercial station owned by Univision Communications Inc. The format of the station is Hispanic oldies. KOVE-FM broadcasts to the Houston area at 106.5 FM.

KOVO-AM
Owner: Simmons Media
Editorial: 301 W South Temple, Salt Lake City, Utah 84101. **T:** 1 801 537-1414
W: http://www.1280thezone.com
Editorial Profile: KOVO-AM is a commercial station owned by Simmons Media and managed by Miller Communications Corp. The format of the station is sports talk. KOVO-AM broadcasts to the Salt Lake City, UT area at 960 AM.

KOWB-AM
Owner: Townsquare Media, LLC
Editorial: 3525 Soldier Springs Rd, Laramie, Wyoming 82070. **T:** 1 307 745-4888
W: http://www.kowb1290.com
Editorial Profile: KOWB-AM is a commercial station owned by Townsquare Media, LLC. The format of the station is news, sports and talk. KOWB-AM broadcasts to the Laramie, WY area at 1290 AM.

KOWI-FM
Owner: Iowa State University
Editorial: 2111 Grand Ave Ste 100, Des Moines, Iowa 50312-5393. **T:** 1 515 725-1700
E: info@iowapublicradio.org
W: http://www.iowapublicradio.org
Editorial Profile: KOWI-FM is a non-commercial station owned by Iowa State University. The format of the station is news and talk. KOWI-FM broadcasts to the Ames, IA area at 97.9 FM.

KOWL-AM
Owner: Cherry Creek Radio
Editorial: 276 Kingsbury Grade Ste 203, Stateline, Nevada 89449-9800.
T: 1 775 580-7130
Editorial Profile: KOWL-AM is a commercial station owned by Cherry Creek Radio. The format of the station is news, sports and talk. KOWL-AM broadcasts to the South Lake Tahoe, CA area at 1490 AM.

KOWZ-FM
Owner: Blooming Prairie Farm Radio Inc.
Editorial: 255 Cedardale Dr SE, Owatonna, Minnesota 55060-4425. **T:** 1 507 444-9224
E: kowz@kowzonline.com
W: http://www.kowzfm.com
Editorial Profile: KOWZ-FM is a commercial station owned by Blooming Prairie Farm Radio Inc. The format of the station is adult contemporary music. KOWZ-FM broadcasts to the Owatonna, MN area at 100.9 FM.

KOXE-FM
Owner: Brown County Broadcasting Co.
Editorial: 300 Carnegie St, Brownwood, Texas 76801-7222. **T:** 1 325 646-3505
E: upfront@koxe.com **W:** http://www.koxe.com
Editorial Profile: KOXE-FM is a commercial station owned by Brown County Broadcasting Co. The format of the station is country music. KOXE-FM broadcasts in the Brownwood, TX area at 101.3 FM.

KOXR-AM
Owner: Lazer Broadcasting Corp.
Editorial: 200 S A St Ste 400, Oxnard, California 93030-5723. **T:** 1 805 240-2070
E: lazerbroadcasting@radiolazer.com
W: http://www.radiolazer.com
Editorial Profile: KOXR-AM is a commercial station owned by the Lazer Broacasting Corp. The format of the station is Spanish and talk. KOXR-AM broadcasts to the Santa Barbara, CA area at 910 AM.

KOY-AM
Owner: Clear Channel Media and Entertainment
Editorial: 4686 E Van Buren St, Phoenix, Arizona 85008-6959. **T:** 1 602 374-6000
W: http://www.kfyi.biz/main.html
Editorial Profile: KOY-AM is a commercial station owned by Clear Channel Media and Entertainment. The format of the station is business news and talk. KOY-AM broadcasts to the Phoenix area at 1230 AM.

KOYE-FM
Owner: Access.1 Communications Corp.
Editorial: 210 S Broadway Ave, Tyler, Texas 75702. **T:** 1 903 581-9966
E: tyr@etradiogroup.com
W: http://lainvasora.fm
Editorial Profile: KOYE-FM is a commercial station owned by Access.1 Communications Corp. The format of the station is Hispanic and Top 40/CHR. KOYE-FM broadcasts to the Tyler, TX area at 96.7 FM.

KOYN-FM
Owner: East Texas Broadcasting Inc.
Editorial: 2810 Pine Mill Rd, Paris, Texas 75460. **T:** 1 903 785-1068
E: koyn@easttexasradio.com
W: http://www.easttexasradio.com
Editorial Profile: KOYN-FM is a commercial station owned by East Texas Broadcasting Inc. The format of the station is contemporary country. KOYN-FM broadcasts to the Paris, TX area at 93.9 FM.

KOZA-AM
Owner: Stellar Media, Inc.
Editorial: 1319 S Crane Ave, Odessa, Texas 79763. **T:** 1 432 333-1227
W: http://www.koza1230.com
Editorial Profile: KOZA-AM is a commercial station owned by Stellar Media, Inc. The format of the station is Tejano. KOZA-AM broadcasts to the Odessa, TX area at 1230 AM.

KOZE-AM
Owner: 4-K Radio Inc.
Editorial: 2560 Snake River Ave, Lewiston, Idaho 83501-9717. **T:** 1 208 743-2502
E: chrisripley@koze.com
W: http://www.koze950.com
Editorial Profile: KOZE-AM is a commercial station owned by 4-K Radio Inc. The format of the station is news, sports and talk. KOZE-AM broadcasts to the Spokane, WA area at 950 AM.

KOZE-FM
Owner: 4-K Radio Inc.
Editorial: 2560 Snake River Ave, Lewiston, Idaho 83501-9717. **T:** 1 208 743-2502
Editorial Profile: KOZE-FM is a commercial station owned by 4-K Radio Inc. The format of the station is rock music. KOZE-FM broadcasts to the Lewiston, ID area at 96.5 FM.

KOZI-AM
Owner: Icicle Broadcasting, Inc.
Editorial: 123 E Johnson Ave, Chelan, Washington 98816. **T:** 1 509 682-4033
E: air@kozi.com **W:** http://www.kozi.com
Editorial Profile: KOZI-AM is a commercial station owned by Icicle Broadcasting, Inc. The format of the station is adult standards. KOZI-AM broadcasts to the Chelan, WA area at 1230 AM.

KOZI-FM
Owner: Icicle Broadcasting, Inc.
Editorial: 123 E Johnson Ave, Chelan, Washington 98816. **T:** 1 509 682-4033
E: kozi@kozi.com **W:** http://www.kozi.com
Editorial Profile: KOZI-FM is a commercial station owned by the Icicle Broadcasting, Inc. The format of the station is adult contemporary. KOZI-FM broadcasts to the Chelan, WA area at 93.5 FM.

KOZN-AM
Owner: NRG Media LLC
Editorial: 5011 Capitol Ave, Omaha, Nebraska 68132-2921. **T:** 1 402 342-2000
W: http://www.1620thezone.com
Editorial Profile: KOZN-AM is a commercial station owned by NRG Media LLC. The format of the station is sports. KOZN-AM broadcasts to the Omaha, NE area on 1620 AM.

KOZO-FM
Owner: Creative Educational Media Corp.
Editorial: 301 Gibson Rd, Hollister, Missouri 65672. **T:** 1 417 339-3388
E: mail@oasisnetwork.org
W: http://www.oasisnetwork.org

KOZQ-AM
Owner: Goodradio.TV LLC
Editorial: 313 Old Route 66, Saint Robert, Missouri 65584. **T:** 1 573 336-4913
E: info@goodradio.tv
Editorial Profile: KOZQ-AM is a commerical station owned by Goodradio.TV LLC. The format of the station is adult contemporary. KOZQ-AM broadcasts to the Waynesville, MO area at 1270 AM.

KOZT-FM
Owner: California Radio Partners Inc.
Editorial: 110 S Franklin St, Fort Bragg, California 95437. **T:** 1 707 964-7277
E: thecoast@kozt.com **W:** http://www.kozt.com
Editorial Profile: KOZT-FM is a commercial station owned by California Radio Partners Inc. The format of the station is adult album alternative. KOZT-FM broadcasts to the San Francisco area at 95.3 FM.

KOZY-AM
Owner: Lamke Broadcasting

WORLD NEWS MEDIA

Editorial: 507 SE 11th St, Grand Rapids, Minnesota 55744. **T:** 1 218 999-5699
E: info@kozyradio.com
W: http://www.kozyradio.com
Editorial Profile: KOZY-AM is a commercial station owned by Lamke Broadcasting. The format of the station is oldies music. KOZY-AM broadcasts in the Grand Rapids, MN area at 1320 AM.

KOZY-FM
Owner: Armada Media
Editorial: 2002 Char Ave, Scottsbluff, Nebraska 69361-2255. **T:** 1 308 632-5667
Editorial Profile: KOZY-FM is a commercial station owned by Armada Media. The format of the station is hot AC. KOZY-FM broadcasts to the Scottsbluff, NE area at 101.3 FM.

KOZZ-FM
Owner: Lotus Communications Corp.
Editorial: 2900 Sutro St, Reno, Nevada 89512-1616. **T:** 1 775 329-9261
W: http://www.kozzradio.com
Editorial Profile: KOZZ-FM is a commercial station owned by Lotus Communications Corp. The format of the station is classic rock. KOZZ-FM broadcasts to the Reno, NV area at 105.7 FM.

KPAC-FM
Owner: Texas Public Radio
Editorial: 8401 Datapoint Dr, Ste 800, San Antonio, Texas 78229. **T:** 1 210 614-8977
E: news@tpr.org **W:** http://www.tpr.org
Editorial Profile: KPAC-FM is a non-commercial station owned by Texas Public Radio. The format of the station is classical. KPAC-FM broadcasts to the San Antonio area at 88.3 FM.

KPAE-FM
Owner: Port Allen Educ. Broadcasting Found.
Editorial: 13028 Highway 190 W, Port Allen, Louisiana 70767. **T:** 1 800 324-1108
E: wpaefm@telepak.net
W: http://www.soundradio.org
Editorial Profile: KPAE-FM is a non-commercial station owned by Port Allen Educ. Broadcasting Found. The format of the station is religious programming. KPAE-FM broadcasts to the Port Allen, LA area at 91.5 FM.

KPAK-FM
Owner: Flinn Broadcasting Corp.
Editorial: 543 Main St, Kiowa, Kansas 67070. **T:** 1 580 327-1430 **E:** kpakradio@yahoo.com
W: http://www.kpak.net
Editorial Profile: KPAK-FM is a commercial station owned by Flinn Broadcasting Corp. The format of the station is classic rock. KPAK-FM broadcasts to the Kiowa, KS area at 97.5 FM.

KPAM-AM
Owner: Pamplin Broadcasting-Oregon, Inc.
Editorial: 6605 SE Lake Rd, Portland, Oregon 97222-2161. **T:** 1 503 223-4321
E: news@kpam.com **W:** http://www.kpam.com
Editorial Profile: KPAM-AM is a commercial station owned by Pamplin Broadcasting-Oregon, Inc. The format of the station is talk. KPAM-AM broadcasts to the Portland, OR area at 860 AM.

KPAN-AM
Owner: KPAN Broadcasters
Editorial: 218 E 5th St, Hereford, Texas 79045. **T:** 1 806 364-1860
E: kpan@kpanradio.com
W: http://www.kpanradio.com
Editorial Profile: KPAN-AM is a commercial station owned by KPAN Broadcasters. The format of the station is country and news. KPAN-AM broadcasts to the Hereford, TX area at 860 AM.

KPAN-FM
Owner: KPAN Broadcasters
Editorial: 218 E 5th St, Hereford, Texas 79045. **T:** 1 806 364-1860
E: kpan@kpanradio.com
W: http://www.kpanradio.com
Editorial Profile: KPAN-FM is a commercial station owned by KPAN Broadcasters. The format of the station is country. KPAN-FM broadcasts to the Hereford, TX area at 106.3 FM.

KPAT-FM
Owner: American General Media
Editorial: 2325 Skyway Dr, Ste J, Santa Maria, California 93455. **T:** 1 805 922-1041
W: http://www.957thebeatfm.com
Editorial Profile: KPAT-FM is a commercial station owned by American General Media. The format of the station is urban contemporary. KPAT-FM broadcasts to the Santa Barbara, CA area at 95.7 FM.

KPAW-FM
Owner: Clear Channel Media and Entertainment
Editorial: 4270 Byrd Dr, Loveland, Colorado 80538. **T:** 1 970 461-2560
W: http://www.1079thebear.com
Editorial Profile: KPAW-FM is a commercial station owned by Clear Channel Media and Entertainment. The format of the station is classic rock. KPAW-FM broadcasts to the Loveland, CO area at 107.9 FM.

KPAY-AM
Owner: Deer Creek Broadcasting
Editorial: 2654 Cramer Ln, Chico, California 95928. **T:** 1 530 345-0021
W: http://newstalk1290.wordpress.com
Editorial Profile: KPAY-AM is a commercial station owned by Deer Creek Broadcasting. The format of the station is news and talk. KPAY-AM broadcasts in the Chico, CA area at 1290 AM.

KPBR-FM
Owner: Bott Radio Network
Editorial: 10550 Barkley St Ste 108, Overland Park, Kansas 66212-1824. **T:** 1 913 642-7770
W: http://www.bottradionetwork.com
Editorial Profile: KPBR-FM is a non-commercial station owned by Bott Radio Network. The format of the station is religious. KPBR-FM broadcasts to the Poplar Bluff, MO area at 91.7 FM.

KPBS-FM
Owner: San Diego State University
Editorial: 5200 Campanile Dr, San Diego, California 92182-1901. **T:** 1 619 594-1515
W: http://www.kpbs.org
Editorial Profile: KPBS-FM is a non-commercial station owned by San Diego State University. The format of the station is news, talk and classical. KPBS-FM broadcasts to the San Diego area at 89.5 FM.

KPBX-FM
Owner: Spokane Public Radio Inc.
Editorial: 2319 N Monroe St, Spokane, Washington 99205. **T:** 1 509 328-5729
E: kpbx@kpbx.org **W:** http://www.kpbx.org
Editorial Profile: KPBX-FM is a non-commercial station owned by Spokane Public Radio Inc. The format of the station is news, jazz, folk and classical music. KPBX-FM broadcasts in the Spokane, WA area at 91.1 FM. Do not send any correspondence to the station. The station's public service is exclusively for local arts organizations.

KPBZ-FM
Owner: Spokane Public Radio Inc.
Editorial: 2319 N Monroe St, Spokane, Washington 99205-4548. **T:** 1 509 328-5729
W: http://www.kpbx.org
Editorial Profile: KPBZ-FM is a non-commercial station owned by Spokane Public Radio Inc. The format is news and talk. KPBZ-FM broadcasts to the Spokane, WA area at 90.3 FM.

KPCC-FM
Owner: Pasadena Area Community College District
Editorial: 474 S Raymond Ave, Pasadena, California 91105-2629. **T:** 1 626 583-5100
E: contact@kpcc.org **W:** http://www.scpr.org
Editorial Profile: KPCC-FM is a non-commercial station owned by Pasadena Area Community College District. The format for the station is news and talk. KPCC-FM broadcasts to the Los Angeles area at 89.3 FM.

KPCH-FM
Owner: Red Peach LLC
Editorial: 500 N Monroe St, Ruston, Louisiana 71270-3835. **T:** 1 318 255-5000
E: thepeach993@gmail.com
W: http://www.thepeach993.com
Editorial Profile: KPCH-FM is a commercial station owned by Red Peach LLC. The format of the station is oldies music. KPCH-FM broadcasts to the Ruston, LA area at 99.3 FM.

KPCL-FM
Owner: Voice Ministries of Farmington
Editorial: 1103 W Apache St, Farmington, New Mexico 87401-3806. **T:** 1 505 327-7202
E: kpcl@kpcl.org **W:** http://www.kpcl.org
Editorial Profile: KPCL-FM is a commercial station owned by Voice Ministries of Farmington. The format of the station is contemporary Christian. KPCL-FM broadcasts to the Farmington, NM area at 95.7 FM.

KPCW-FM
Owner: Community Wireless of Park City
Editorial: 460 Swede Alley, Park City, Utah 84060. **T:** 1 435 649-9004 **E:** letters@kpcw.org
W: http://www.kpcw.org
Editorial Profile: KPCW-FM is a non-commercial station owned by Community Wireless or Park City. The format for the station is AAA-adult album alternative, news and talk. KPCW-FM broadcasts to the Park City, UT area at 91.9 FM.

KPDA-AM
Owner: Locally Owned Radio, LLC
Editorial: 21361 Highway 30, Twin Falls, Idaho 83301. **T:** 1 208 735-8300
W: http://www.ktfi1270.com
Editorial Profile: KPDA-AM is a commercial station owned by Locally Owned Radio, LLC. The format of the station is regional Mexican. KPDA-AM broadcasts to the Twin Falls, ID area at 1270 AM.

KPDQ-AM
Owner: Salem Communications
Editorial: 6400 SE Lake Rd, Ste 350, Portland, Oregon 97222. **T:** 1 503 786-0600
W: http://www.kpdq.com
Editorial Profile: KPDQ-AM is a commercial station owned by Salem Communications. The format of the station is Christian talk. KPDQ-AM broadcasts in the Portland, OR area at 800 AM.

KPDQ-FM
Owner: Salem Communications
Editorial: 6400 SE Lake Rd, Ste 350, Portland, Oregon 97222. **T:** 1 503 786-0600
W: http://www.kpdq.fm
Editorial Profile: KPDQ-FM is a commercial station owned by Salem Communications. The format of the station is religious programming. KPDQ-FM broadcasts to the Portland, OR area at 93.9 FM.

KPDR-FM
Owner: Top 'O Texas Educational Broadcasting Foundation
Editorial: 5754 Canyon Dr, Amarillo, Texas 79109-6356. **T:** 1 806 359-8855
E: kjrt@kingdomkeys.org
W: http://www.kingdomkeys.org
Editorial Profile: KPDR-FM is a non-commercial station owned by Top 'O Texas Educational Broadcasting Foundation. The format of the station is Christian music and talk. KPDR-FM broadcasts to the Wheeler/Pampa, TX area at 90.3 FM.

KPEK-FM
Owner: Clear Channel Media and Entertainment
Editorial: 5411 Jefferson St NE, Ste 100, Albuquerque, New Mexico 87109.
T: 1 505 830-6400
W: http://www.1003thepeak.com
Editorial Profile: KPEK-FM is a commercial station owned by Clear Channel Media and Entertainment. The format of the station is hot adult contemporary music. KPEK-FM broadcasts to the Albuquerque, NM area at 100.3 FM.

KPEL-AM
Owner: Townsquare Media, LLC
Editorial: 1749 Bertrand Dr, Lafayette, Louisiana 70506. **T:** 1 337 233-6000
W: http://www.espn1420.com
Editorial Profile: KPEL-AM is a commercial station owned by Townsquare Media, LLC. The format of the station is sports. KPEL-AM broadcasts to the Lafayette, LA area at 1420 AM.

KPEL-FM
Owner: Townsquare Media, LLC
Editorial: 1749 Bertrand Dr, Lafayette, Louisiana 70506. **T:** 1 337 233-6000
W: http://kpel1051news.com
Editorial Profile: KPEL-FM is a local, commercial station owned by Townsquare Media, LLC. The format of the station is news and talk. KPEL-FM broadcasts in the Lafayette, LA area at 96.5 FM.

KPEN-FM
Owner: Peninsula Communications Inc.
Editorial: 66060 Diamond Ridge Rd, Homer, Alaska 99603-9229. **T:** 1 907 235-6000
E: kwavefm@xyz.net

KPER-FM
Owner: Noalmark Broadcasting Corp.
Editorial: 1423 W Bender Blvd, Hobbs, New Mexico 88240-9252. **T:** 1 575 393-1551
W: http://www.hobbsradio.com
Editorial Profile: KPER-FM is a commercial station owned by the Noalmark Broadcasting Corp. The format of the station is countemporary country music. KPER-FM broadcasts to the Albuquerque, NM area at 95.7 FM.

KPET-AM
Owner: KPET Inc.
Editorial: 1 Radio Road, Lamesa, Texas 79331. **T:** 1 806 872-6511 **E:** kpet@pics.net
Editorial Profile: KPET-AM is a commercial station owned by KPET Inc. The format of the station is country music. KPET-AM broadcasts in the Lamesa, TX area at 690 AM.

KPEZ-FM
Owner: Clear Channel Media and Entertainment
Editorial: 3601 S Congress Ave, Austin, Texas 78704-7250. **T:** 1 512 684-7300
W: http://www.thebeatatx.com
Editorial Profile: KPEZ-FM is a commercial station owned by Clear Channel Media and Entertainment. The format of the station is rhythmic Top 40 and urban contemporary. KPEZ-FM broadcasts to the Austin, TX area at 102.3 FM.

KPFA-FM
Owner: Pacifica Foundation, Inc.
Editorial: 1929 Martin Luther King Jr Way, Berkeley, California 94704. **T:** 1 510 848-6767
E: news@kpfa.org **W:** http://www.kpfa.org
Editorial Profile: KPFA-FM is a non-commercial station owned by the Pacifica Foundation, Inc. The format of the station is variety. KPFA-FM broadcasts to the San Francisco area at 94.1 FM.

KPFK-FM
Owner: Pacifica Foundation, Inc.
Editorial: 3729 Cahuenga Blvd West, North Hollywood, California 91604-3584.
T: 1 818 985-2711 **W:** http://www.kpfk.org
Editorial Profile: KPFK-FM is a non-commercial station owned by the Pacifica Foundation, Inc. The format for the station is variety. KPFK-FM broadcasts to the Los Angeles area at 90.7 FM.

KPFM-FM
Owner: Dowdy Broadcasting, Inc.
Editorial: 2352 Highway 62 Business, Mountain Home, Arkansas 72653-6847.
T: 1 870 492-6022 **W:** http://www.kpfm.net
Editorial Profile: KPFM-FM is a commercial station owned by Dowdy Broadcasting, Inc. The format of the station is classic country. KPFM-FM broadcasts to the Mountain Home, AR area at 105.5 FM.

KPFT-FM
Owner: Pacifica Foundation, Inc.
Editorial: 419 Lovett Blvd, Houston, Texas 77006-4018. **T:** 1 713 526-4000
W: http://www.kpft.org
Editorial Profile: KPFT-FM is a non-commercial station owned by Pacifica Foundation, Inc. The format of the station is variety. KPFT broadcasts in the greater Houston area at 90.1 FM.

KPFX-FM
Owner: L & L Radio
Editorial: 2720 7th Ave S, Fargo, North Dakota 58103-8710. **T:** 1 701 237-4500
E: studio@1079thefox.com
W: http://www.1079thefox.com
Editorial Profile: KPFX-FM is a commercial station owned by L & L Radio. The format of the station is classic rock music. KPFX-FM broadcasts in the Fargo, ND area at 107.9 FM.

KPFZ-FM
Owner: Lake County Community Radio
Editorial: 149 N Main St, Lakeport, California 95453-4832. **T:** 1 707 263-3640
E: kpfz@mchsi.com
Editorial Profile: KPFZ-FM is a non-commercial station owned by Lake County Community Radio. The format of the station is variety. KPFZ-FM broadcasts to the Lakeport, CA area at 88.1 FM. Before sending a fax, alert the station with a phone call. They occasionally have to turn the fax machine off.

KPGE-AM
Owner: Lake Powell Communications
Editorial: 91 N 7th Ave, Page, Arizona 86040.
T: 1 928 645-8181 **E:** news@kxaz.com
W: http://www.kxaz.com
Editorial Profile: KPGE-AM is a commercial station owned by Lake Powell Communications. The format of the station is classic country. KPGE-AM broadcasts to the Page, AZ area at 1340 AM.

KPGG-FM
Owner: American Media Investments
Editorial: 1323 College Dr, Texarkana, Texas 75503-3531. **T:** 1 903 793-1100
E: prodcommradio@cableone.net
Editorial Profile: KPGG-FM is a commercial station owned by American Media Investments. The format of the station is classic country. KPGG-FM broadcasts to the Texarkana, TX area at 103.9 FM.

KPGM-AM
Owner: KCD Enterprises Inc.
Editorial: 1200 E. Frank Phillips, Bartlesville, Oklahoma 74005. **T:** 1 918 336-1500
E: kpgm@bartlesvilleradio.com
W: http://www.bartlesvilleradio.com
Editorial Profile: KPGM-AM is a commercial station owned by KCD Enterprises Inc. The format of the station is sports talk. KPGM-AM broadcasts to the Pawhuska, OK area at 1500 AM.

KPGS-FM
Owner: KUTE Inc.
Editorial: 123 Capote Drive, Ignacio, Colorado 81137. **T:** 1 970 563-0255
W: http://www.ksut.org
Editorial Profile: KPGS-FM is a non-commerical station owned by KUTE Inc. The format of the station is variety. KPGS-FM broadcasts to the Ignacio, CO area at 88.1 FM.

KPHI-AM
Owner: Hochman-McCann Hawaii, Inc.
Editorial: 900 Fort Street Mall, Ste 450, Honolulu, Hawaii 96813. **T:** 1 808 538-1180
E: korlradio001@hawaii.rr.com
W: http://www.hhawaiimedia.net
Editorial Profile: KPHI-AM is a commercial station owned by Hochman-McCann Hawaii, Inc. The format of the station is a variety of multicultural music. KPHI-AM broadcasts to the Honolulu area at 1130 AM.

KPHR-FM
Owner: Armada Media Corp.
Editorial: 508 Jenson Ave SE, Watertown, South Dakota 57201. **T:** 1 605 884-3548
E: power106@iw.net
W: http://www.bigstoneradio.com/power106/source
Editorial Profile: KPHR-FM is a commercial station owned by Armada Media Corp. The format of the station is classic rock. KPHR-FM broadcasts to the Watertown, SD area at 106.3 FM.

KPHT-FM
Owner: Clear Channel Media and Entertainment
Editorial: 106 W 24Th St, Pueblo, Colorado 81003-2408. **T:** 1 719 545-2080
W: http://www.kpht955.com
Editorial Profile: KPHT-FM is a commercial station owned by Clear Channel Media and Entertainment. The format of the station is classic hits. KPHT-FM broadcasts to the Pueblo, CO area at 95.5 FM.

KPHW-FM
Owner: Summit Media Broadcasting LLC
Editorial: 900 Fort Street Mall, Honolulu, Hawaii 96813-3721. **T:** 1 808 275-1000
W: http://www.power1043.com
Editorial Profile: KPHW-FM is a commercial station owned by Summit Media Broadcasting LLC. The format of the station is rhythmic Top 40. KPHW-FM broadcasts to the Honolulu, HI area at 104.3 FM.

KPHX-AM
Owner: Continental Broadcasting Corp. of Arizona, Inc.
Editorial: 824 E Washington St, Phoenix, Arizona 85034. **T:** 1 602 257-1351
W: http://www.1480kphx.com
Editorial Profile: KPHX-AM is a commercial station owned by Continental Broadcasting Corp. of Arizona, Inc. The format of the station is liberal talk. KPHX-AM broadcasts to the Phoenix area at 1480 AM.

KPIG-FM
Owner: Mapleton Communications LLC
Editorial: 1110 Main St, Ste 16, Watsonville, California 95076. **T:** 1 831 722-9000
E: sales@kpig.com **W:** http://www.kpig.com
Editorial Profile: KPIG-FM is a commercial station owned by Mapleton Communications LLC. The format of the station is adult album alternative music. KPIG-FM broadcasts to Watsonville, CA area at 107.5 FM.

KPIN-FM
Owner: Rule Communications
Editorial: 219 E Pine St, Ste 112, Pinedale, Wyoming 82941. **T:** 1 307 367-2000
E: kpin@wyoming.com
W: http://www.pinedaleonline.com/kpin
Editorial Profile: KPIN-FM is a commercial station owned by Rule Communications. The format of the station is classic country and oldies. KPIN-FM broadcasts to the Pinedale, WY area at 101.1 FM.

KPIR-AM
Owner: LR Radio Group
Editorial: 1620 Weatherford Hwy, Granbury, Texas 76048. **T:** 1 817 736-0360
W: http://www.kpir.com
Editorial Profile: KPIR-AM is a commercial station owned by LR Radio Group. The format of the station is news, talk and sports. KPIR-AM broadcasts to the Granbury, TX area at 1420 AM.

KPIT-FM
Owner: Jabella Broadcast Network, Inc.
Editorial: 2704 Timberlake Dr, Irving, Texas 75062-8714. **T:** 1 903 855-3460
E: kpit@kpitradio.com
W: http://www.kpitradio.com
Editorial Profile: KPIT-FM is a non-commercial station owned by Jabella Broadcast Network, Inc. The format of the station is Christian Hispanic music and programming. KPIT-FM broadcasts to Pittsburg, TX and surrounding areas at 91.7 FM.

KPJC-AM
Owner: KCCS LLC
Editorial: 3190 Lancaster Dr NE, Salem, Oregon 97305-1350. **T:** 1 503 316-1220
E: radio@t2tn.com
W: http://hebrewnationonline.com/
Editorial Profile: KPJC-AM is a commercial station owned by KCCS LLC. The format of the station is Jewish music and talk. KPJC-AM broadcasts to the Salem, OR area at 1220 AM.

KPKE-AM
Owner: J.H. Rees.
Editorial: 219 N Iowa St, Gunnison, Colorado 81230-2478. **T:** 1 970 641-4000
E: gunnisonradio@gmail.com
Editorial Profile: KPKE-AM is a commercial station owned by J.H. Rees. The format of the station is classic country programming. KPKE-AM broadcasts to the Denver area at 1490 AM.

KPKJ-FM
Owner: Calvary Chapel of Albuquerque, Inc.
Editorial: 4001 Osuna Rd Ne, Albuquerque, New Mexico 87109-4422. **T:** 1 877 644-2853
E: studio@coreradionetwork.org
W: http://coreradionetwork.org
Editorial Profile: KPKJ-FM is a non-commercial station owned by Calvary Chapel of Albuquerque, Inc. The format of the station is Christian music and religious programming. KPKJ-FM broadcasts to the Mentmore, NM area at 88.5 FM.

KPKL-FM
Owner: Spokane Broadcasting Company, LLC
Editorial: 400 South Jef-fer-son St, Suite 304, Spokane, Washington 99204.
T: 1 509 290-6200
W: http://www.kool1071.com
Editorial Profile: KPKL-FM is a commercial station owned by Spokane Broadcasting Company, LLC. The format of the station is classic hits. KPKL-FM broadcasts to the Spokane, WA area at 107.1 FM.

KPKR-FM
Owner: Prescott Valley Broadcasting Co. Inc.
Editorial: 1713 S Kofa Ave Ste E, Parker, Arizona 85344-6401. **T:** 1 928 669-9999
W: http://www.riverratradio.com
Editorial Profile: KPKR-FM is a commercial station owned by Prescott Valley Broadcasting Co. Inc. The format of the station is adult hits. KPKR-FM broadcasts to Prescott Valley and Parker, AZ and its surrounding areas at 95.7 FM.

KPKY-FM
Owner: Rich Broadcasting, LLC
Editorial: 1406 Commerce Way, Idaho Falls, Idaho 83401-1233. **T:** 1 208 233-1133
W: http://949therock.com
Editorial Profile: KPKY-FM is a commercial station owned by Rich Broadcasting, LLC. The format of the station is classic rock. KPKY-FM broadcasts to the Pocatello, ID area at 94.9 FM.

KPLA-FM
Owner: Cumulus Media Inc.
Editorial: 503 Old 63 N, Columbia, Missouri 65201. **T:** 1 573 442-3116
W: http://www.kpla.com
Editorial Profile: KPLA-FM is a commercial station owned by Cumulus Media Inc. The format of the station is adult contemporary. KPLA-FM broadcasts to the Columbia, MO area at 101.5 FM.

KPLD-FM
Owner: Canyon Media Corporation
Editorial: 619 S. Bluff Tower 1 Ste. 300, Saint George, Utah 84780. **T:** 1 435 628-3643
W: http://www.planet941.com
Editorial Profile: KPLD-FM is a commercial station owned by Canyon Media Corporation. The format of the station is hot adult contemporary music. KPLD-FM broadcasts to the St. George, UT area at 105.1 FM.

KPLM-FM
Owner: RM Broadcasting LLC
Editorial: 75153 Merle Dr Ste G, Palm Desert, California 92211-5197. **T:** 1 760 568-4550
E: kplm@markerbroadcasting.com
W: http://www.thebig106.com
Editorial Profile: KPLM-FM is a commercial station owned by RM Broadcasting LLC. The format of the station is country music. KPLM-FM broadcasts to the Palm Springs, CA area at 106.1 FM.

KPLN-FM
Owner: Connoisseur Media LLC
Editorial: 2075 Central Ave, Billings, Montana 59102-4956. **T:** 1 406 248-7777
E: planet@planet1067.com
W: http://www.planet1067.com
Editorial Profile: KPLN-FM is a commercial station owned by Connoisseur Media LLC. The format of the station is Modern AC. KPLN-FM broadcasts to the Billings, MT area at a frequency of 106.7 FM.

KPLO-FM
Owner: James River Broadcasting
Editorial: 214 W Pleasant Dr, Pierre, South Dakota 57501. **T:** 1 605 224-8686
W: http://www.dakotaradiogroup.com
Editorial Profile: KPLO-FM is a commercial station owned by James River Broadcasting. The format of the station is classic country. KPLO-FM broadcasts to the Pierre, SD area at 94.5 FM.

KPLT-AM
Owner: East Texas Broadcasting Inc.
Editorial: 2810 Pine Mill Rd, Paris, Texas 75460. **T:** 1 903 785-1068
E: bud@easttexasradio.com
W: http://www.easttexasradio.com
Editorial Profile: KPLT-AM is a commercial station owned by East Texas Broadcasting Inc. The format of the station is country. KPLT-AM broadcasts to the Paris, TX area at 1490 AM.

KPLT-FM
Owner: East Texas Broadcasting Inc.
Editorial: 2810 Pine Mill Rd, Paris, Texas 75460. **T:** 1 903 785-1068
W: http://www.easttexasradio.com
Editorial Profile: KPLT-FM is a commercial station owned by East Texas Broadcasting Inc. The format of the station is adult contemporary music. KPLT-FM broadcasts to the Paris, TX area at 107.7 FM.

KPLU-FM
Owner: Pacific Lutheran University
Editorial: 12180 Park Ave S, Tacoma, Washington 98447-0001. **T:** 1 253 535-7758
E: news@kplu.org **W:** http://www.kplu.org
Editorial Profile: KPLU-FM is a non-commercial station owned by Pacific Lutheran University. The format of the station is news, jazz and blues music. KPLU-FM broadcasts to the Seattle area at 88.5 FM.

KPLV-FM
Owner: Clear Channel Media and Entertainment
Editorial: 2880 Meade Ave Ste 250, Las Vegas, Nevada 89102-0713.
T: 1 702 238-7300
W: http://www.my931.com/main.html
Editorial Profile: KPLV-FM is a commercial station owned by Clear Channel Media and Entertainment. The format of the station is adult contemporary. KPLV-FM broadcasts to the Las Vegas area at 93.1 FM.

KPLW-FM
Owner: Growing Christian Foundation
Editorial: 606 N Western Ave, Wenatchee, Washington 98801-1204. **T:** 1 509 665-6641
E: kplw@plr.org **W:** http://www.plr.org
Editorial Profile: KPLW-FM is a non-commercial station owned by the Growing Christian Foundation. The format of the station is religious and contemporary Christian music. KPLW-FM broadcasts to the Wenatchee, WA area at 89.9 FM.

KPLX-FM
Owner: Cumulus Media Inc.
Editorial: West Victory Plaza, 3090 Olive Street, Suite 400, Dallas, Texas 75219.
T: 1 214 526-2400
W: http://www.995thewolf.com
Editorial Profile: KPLX-FM is a commercial station owned by Cumulus Media Inc. The format of the station is contemporary country music. KPLX-FM broadcasts to the Dallas area at 99.5 FM.

KPLY-AM
Owner: Lotus Communications Corp.
Editorial: 2900 Sutro St, Reno, Nevada 89512-1616. **T:** 1 775 329-9261
E: kena@kozzradio.com
Editorial Profile: KPLY-AM is a commercial station owned by Lotus Communications Corp. The format of the station is sports. KPLY-AM broadcasts to the Reno, NV area at 630 AM.

KPLZ-FM
Owner: Sinclair Radio of Seattle, LLC
Editorial: 140 4th Ave N, Seattle, Washington 98109-4940. **T:** 1 206 404-4000
E: starcomment@fisherradio.com
W: http://www.star1015.com
Editorial Profile: KPLZ-FM is a commercial station owned by Sinclair Radio of Seattle, LLC. The format of the station is hot adult contemporary. KPLZ-FM broadcasts in the Seattle area at 101.5 FM.

KPMI-AM
Owner: Paskvan Media, Inc.
Editorial: 1410 30Th St Nw Apt 115, Bemidji, Minnesota 56601-4173. **T:** 1 218 751-7777
Editorial Profile: KPMI-FM is a commercial station owned by Paskvan Media, Inc. The format of the station is news/talk. WMIS-FM broadcasts locally to the Bemidji, MN area at 1300 AM.

KPMW-FM
Owner: Rey-Cel Broadcasting, Inc.
Editorial: 230 Hana Hwy Ste 2, Kahului, Hawaii 96732-2313. **T:** 1 808 871-6251
Editorial Profile: KPMW-FM is a commercial station owned by Rey-Cel Broadcasting, Inc. The format of the station is rhythmic Top 40/CHR. The station airs at 105.5 FM from Kahului.

KPMX-FM
Owner: Northeast Colorado Broadcasting, LLC
Editorial: 117 Main St, Sterling, Colorado 80751. **T:** 1 970 522-4800
E: kpmx@necolorado.com
W: http://www.kpmx.com
Editorial Profile: KPMX-FM is a commercial station owned by Northeast Colorado Broadcasting, LLC. The format of the station is hot adult contemporary. KPMX-FM broadcasts to the Sterling, CO area at 105.7 FM.

KPNC-FM
Owner: Team Radio LLC
Editorial: 122 N 3rd St, Ponca City, Oklahoma 74601-4326. **T:** 1 580 767-1101
E: kpnc@eteamradio.com
W: http://www.eteamradio.com
Editorial Profile: KPNC-FM is a commercial station owned by Team Radio LLC. The format of the station is contemporary country music. KPNC-FM broadcasts to the Ponca City, OK area at 100.7 FM.

KPND-FM
Owner: Blue Sky Broadcasting Inc.
Editorial: 327 S Marion Ave, Sandpoint, Idaho 83864. **T:** 1 208 263-2179
W: http://www.953kpnd.com
Editorial Profile: KPND-FM is a commercial station owned by Blue Sky Broadcasting Inc. The format of the station is adult album alternative music. KPND-FM broadcasts to the Spokane, WA area at 95.3 FM.

KPNO-FM
Owner: Praise Network(The)
Editorial: 128 S 4th St, Oneill, Nebraska 68763-1814. **T:** 1 402 336-3886
E: email@goodnewsgreatmusic.org
W: http://www.goodnewsgreatmusic.org
Editorial Profile: KPNO-FM is a non-commercial station owned by The Praise Network. The format of the station is Christian talk and music. KPNO-FM broadcasts to the Norfolk, NE area at 90.9 FM.

KPNS-AM

Owner: Perry Publishing & Broadcasting Inc.
Editorial: 1701 W Pine Ave, Duncan, Oklahoma 73533-2303. **T:** 1 580 255-1350
E: kken@cableone.net
Editorial Profile: KPNS-AM is a commercial station owned by Perry Publishing & Broadcasting Inc. The format of the station is news and talk. KPNS-AM broadcasts to the Duncan, OK area at 1350 AM.

KPNT-FM

Owner: Emmis Communications Corp.
Editorial: 800 Saint Louis Union Sta, Saint Louis, Missouri 63103. **T:** 1 314 231-1057
W: http://www.1057thepoint.com
Editorial Profile: KPNT-FM is a commercial station owned by Emmis Communications Corp. The format of the station is rock alternative. KPNT-FM broadcasts to the St. Louis area at 105.7 FM.

KPNW-AM

Owner: Bicoastal Media LLC
Editorial: 1500 Valley River Dr, Ste 350, Eugene, Oregon 97401. **T:** 1 541 485-1120
W: http://www.kpnw.com
Editorial Profile: KPNW-AM is a commercial owned by Bicoastal Media LLC. The format of the station is news and talk. KPNW-AM broadcasts to the Eugene, OR area at 1120 AM.

KPNY-FM

Owner: Mission Nebraska, Inc.
Editorial: 422 Box Butte Ave, Alliance, Nebraska 69301. **T:** 1 308 762-3473
E: email@mybridgeradio.net
W: http://www.mybridgeradio.net
Editorial Profile: KPNY-FM is a non-commercial station owned by Mission Nebraska, Inc. The format of the station is religious. KPNY-FM broadcasts to the Alliance, NE area at 102.1 FM.

KPOA-FM

Owner: Pacific Media Group
Editorial: 311 Ano St, Kahului, Hawaii 96732-1304. **T:** 1 808 877-5566
W: http://www.kpoa.com
Editorial Profile: KPOA-FM is a commercial station owned by the Pacific Media Group. The format of the station is adult contemporary music. KPOA-FM broadcasts to the Maui, HI area at 93.5 FM.

KPOC-AM

Owner: Combined Media Group
Editorial: 1 Radio Drive, Pocahontas, Arkansas 72455. **T:** 1 870 892-5234
E: kpoc-krlw@centurytel.net
Editorial Profile: KPOC-AM is a commercial station owned by Combined Media Group. The format of the station is news and talk. KPOC-AM broadcasts to the Pocahontas, AR area at 1420 AM.

KPOC-FM

Owner: Combined Media Group
Editorial: 1 Radio Drive, Pocahontas, Arkansas 72455. **T:** 1 870 892-5234
E: kpoc-krlw@centurytel.net
Editorial Profile: KPOC-FM is a commercial station owned by Combined Media Group. The format of the station is adult contemporary. KPOC-FM broadcasts to the Pocahontas, AR at 103.9 FM.

KPOD-AM

Owner: Bicoastal Media LLC
Editorial: 1345 Northcrest Dr, Crescent City, California 95531. **T:** 1 707 464-9561
E: kpod@bicoastalmedia.com
W: http://www.kpod.com
Editorial Profile: KPOD-AM is a commercial station owned by Bicoastal Media LLC. The format of the station is talk, news and sports. KPOD-AM broadcasts in the Crescent City, CA area at 1240 AM.

KPOD-FM

Owner: Bicoastal Media LLC
Editorial: 1345 Northcrest Dr, Crescent City, California 95531. **T:** 1 707 464-9561
E: kpod@bicoastalmedia.com
W: http://www.kpodfm.com
Editorial Profile: KPOD-FM is a commercial station owned by Bicoastal Media LLC. The format of the station is contemporary country music. KPOD-FM broadcasts to the Crescent City, CA area at 97.9 AM.

KPOF-AM

Owner: Pillar of Fire Inc.
Editorial: 3455 W 83rd Ave, Westminster, Colorado 80031. **T:** 1 303 428-0910
E: info@am91.org **W:** http://www.kpof.org

Editorial Profile: KPOF-AM is a non-commercial station owned by Pillar of Fire Inc. The format of the station is Christian programming. KPOF-AM broadcasts to the Denver area at 910 AM.

KPOI-FM

Owner: Ohana Broadcast Company LLC
Editorial: 1000 Bishop St Ste 200, Honolulu, Hawaii 96813-4203. **T:** 1 808 947-1500
W: http://www.kpoifm.com
Editorial Profile: KPOI-FM is a commercial station owned by Ohana Broadcast Company LLC. The format of the station is classic rock. KPOI-FM broadcasts to the Honolulu area at 105.9 FM.

KPOJ-AM

Owner: Clear Channel Media and Entertainment
Editorial: 13333 SW 68th Pkwy Ste 310, Tigard, Oregon 97223-8304.
T: 1 503 323-6400
W: http://www.foxsportsradio620.com
Editorial Profile: KPOJ-AM is a commercial station owned by Clear Channel Media and Entertainment. The format of the station is sports talk. KPOJ-AM broadcasts in the Portland, OR area at 620 AM.

KPOK-AM

Owner: Tri-State Communications, Inc.
Editorial: 11 1/2 N Main St, Bowman, North Dakota 58623-4021. **T:** 1 701 523-3883
E: kpok@ndsupernet.com
W: http://www.kpokradio.com
Editorial Profile: KPOK-AM is a commercial station owned by Tri-State Communications, Inc. The format of the station is contemporary country. KPOK-AM broadcasts to the Bowman, ND area at 1340 AM.

KPOO-FM

Owner: Poor Peoples Radio Inc.
Editorial: 1329 Divisadero St, San Francisco, California 94115. **T:** 1 415 346-5373
E: news@kpoo.com **W:** http://www.kpoo.com
Editorial Profile: KPOO-FM is a non-commercial station owned by Poor Peoples Radio Inc. The format of the station is variety, featuring jazz, blues, reggae, hip hop, gospel, salsa and samba music. KPOO-FM broadcasts to the San Francisco area at 89.5 FM.

KPOS-FM

Owner: Educational Media Foundation
Editorial: 6721 W 121st St Ste 100, Overland Park, Kansas 66209-2031. **T:** 1 913 663-9950
W: http://www.klove.com
Editorial Profile: KPOS-FM is a non-commercial station owned by Educational Media Foundation. The format of the station is contemporary Christian. KPOS-FM broadcasts to the Fouke, AR area at 104.3 FM.

KPOV-FM

Editorial: 501 NW Bond St, Bend, Oregon 97701-3309. **T:** 1 541 322-0863
W: http://www.kpov.org
Editorial Profile: KPOV-FM is a non-commercial station owned by the Women's Civic Improvement League. The format of the station is community radio, featuring news, talk and music programming. KPOV-FM broadcasts to the Bend, OR area at a frequency of 88.9 FM.

KPOW-AM

Owner: MGR Media, LLC
Editorial: 912 Lane 11 1/2, Powell, Wyoming 82435-9222. **T:** 1 307 754-5183
E: kpow@tritel.net
W: http://www.1260kpow.com
Editorial Profile: KPOW-AM is a commercial station owned by MGR Media, LLC. The format of the station is news and talk. KPOW-AM broadcasts to the Powell, WY area at 1260 AM.

KPOW-FM

Owner: Benne Media
Editorial: 301 S Ohio Ave, Sedalia, Missouri 65301. **T:** 1 660 826-5005
W: http://www.power977.com
Editorial Profile: KPOW-FM is a commercial station owned by Benne Media. The format of the station is classic hits. KPOW-FM broadcasts to the Kansas City, MO area at 97.7 FM.

KPPD-FM

Owner: Prairie Public Broadcasting Inc.
Editorial: 1814 N 15th St, Bismarck, North Dakota 58501-2025. **T:** 1 701 224-1700
E: info@prairiepublic.org
W: http://www.prairiepublic.org

Editorial Profile: KPPD-FM is a non-commercial station owned by Prairie Public Broadcasting Inc. The format of the station is news, classical and jazz music. KPPD-FM broadcasts to the Devils Lake, ND area at 91.7 FM and is a simulcast of KCND-FM.

KPPK-FM

Owner: Bicoastal Media LLC
Editorial: 1130 14th Ave, Longview, Washington 98632-3017. **T:** 1 360 425-1500
E: info@kppk98.3.com
W: http://www.kppk98.3.com
Editorial Profile: KPPK-FM is a commercial station owned by Bicoastal Media LLC. The format of the station is adult hits music. KPPK-FM broadcasts in the Portland, OR area at 98.3 FM.

KPPR-FM

Owner: Prairie Public Broadcasting Inc.
Editorial: 207 5th St N, Fargo, North Dakota 58102-4827. **T:** 1 701 241-6900
E: info@prairiepublic.org
W: http://www.prairiepublic.org
Editorial Profile: KPPR-FM is a non-commercial station owned by Prairie Public Broadcasting Inc. The primary format of the station is adult album alternative. KPPR-FM broadcasts to the Fargo, ND area at 89.5 FM.

KPPT-FM

Owner: Agpal Broadcasting Inc.
Editorial: 145 N Coast Hwy, Ste D, Newport, Oregon 97365-3165. **T:** 1 541 265-5000
E: info@bossradio.net
W: http://www.bossradio.net
Editorial Profile: KPPT-FM is commercial station owned by Agpal Broadcasting Inc. The format of the station is classic hits music. KPPT-FM broadcasts to the Newport, OR area at 100.7 FM.

KPPV-FM

Owner: Prescott Valley Broadcasting Co. Inc.
Editorial: 3755 Karicio Ln, Prescott, Arizona 86303-6836. **T:** 1 928 445-8289
W: http://www.kppv.com
Editorial Profile: KPPV-FM is a commercial station owned by Prescott Valley Broadcasting Co. Inc. The format of the station is adult contemporary. KPPV-FM broadcasts to the Prescott, AZ area at 106.7 FM.

KPQ-AM

Owner: Cherry Creek Radio
Editorial: 231 N Wenatchee Ave, Wenatchee, Washington 98801-2009. **T:** 1 509 665-6565
E: newswenatchee@cherrycreekradio.com
W: http://www.kpq.com
Editorial Profile: KPQ-AM is a commercial station owned by Cherry Creek Radio. The format of the station is news, talk and sports. KPQ-AM broadcasts to the Seattle area at 560 AM.

KPQ-FM

Owner: Cherry Creek Radio
Editorial: 231 N Wenatchee Ave, Wenatchee, Washington 98801. **T:** 1 509 665-6565
E: newswenatchee@cherrycreekradio.com
W: http://www.thequake1021.com
Editorial Profile: KPQ-FM is a commercial station owned by Cherry Creek Radio. The format of the station is classic rock. KPQ-FM broadcasts to the Seattle area at 102.1 FM.

KPQX-FM

Owner: New Media Broadcasters
Editorial: 2210 31st St N, Havre, Montana 59501. **T:** 1 406 265-7841 **E:** news@nmbi.com
W: http://www.kpqx.com
Editorial Profile: KPQX-FM is a commercial station owned by New Media Broadcasters. The format for the station is contemporary and classic country. KPQX-FM broadcasts to the Havre, MT area at 92.5 FM.

KPRA-FM

Owner: Family Stations Inc.
Editorial: 4135 Northgate Blvd Ste 1, Sacramento, California 95834-1226.
T: 1 866 641-8191
E: familyradio@familyradio.com
W: http://www.familyradio.com
Editorial Profile: KPRA-FM is a non-commercial radio station owned by Family Stations Inc. The format of the station is religious. KPRA-FM broadcasts to the Sacramento, CA area at 89.5 FM.

KPRB-FM

Owner: Northeast Colorado Broadcasting, LLC
Editorial: 220 State St, Ste 106, Fort Morgan, Colorado 80701. **T:** 1 970 867-7271
E: b106@necolorado.com
W: http://www.b106.com

Editorial Profile: KPRB-FM is a commercial station owned by Northeast Colorado Broadcasting, LLC. The format of the station is adult contemporary. KPRB-FM broadcasts to the Fort Morgan, CO area at 106.3 FM.

KPRC-AM

Owner: Clear Channel Media and Entertainment
Editorial: 2000 West Loop S Ste 300, Houston, Texas 77027-3510.
T: 1 713 212-8000
W: http://www.kprcradio.com/main.html
Editorial Profile: KPRC-AM is a commercial station owned by Clear Channel Media and Entertainment. The format of the station is conservative talk. KPRC-AM broadcasts to the Houston area at 950 AM.

KPRC-FM

Owner: Clear Channel Media and Entertainment
Editorial: 903 N Main St, Salinas, California 93906. **T:** 1 831 755-8181
W: http://salinas.lapreciosa.com/main.html
Editorial Profile: KPRC-FM is a commercial station owned by Clear Channel Media and Entertainment. The format of the station is Hispanic. KPRC-FM broadcasts to the Salinas, CA area on 100.7 FM.

KPRD-FM

Owner: Praise Network(The)
Editorial: 205 E 7th St, Ste 218, Hays, Kansas 67601. **T:** 1 785 628-6300 **E:** kprd@kprd.org
W: http://www.kprd.org
Editorial Profile: KPRD-FM is a non-commercial station owned by The Praise Network. The format of the station is contemporary Christian music and talk. KPRD-FM broadcasts to the Hays, KS area at 88.9 FM.

KPRF-FM

Owner: Townsquare Media, LLC
Editorial: 6214 W 34th Ave, Amarillo, Texas 79109-4006. **T:** 1 806 355-9777
W: http://987jackfm.com
Editorial Profile: KPRF-FM is a commercial station owned by Townsquare Media, LLC. The format of the station is adult hits. KPRF-FM broadcasts to the Amarillo, TX area at 98.7 FM.

KPRI-FM

Owner: Compass Radio of San Diego Inc.
Editorial: 9710 Scranton Rd, Ste 200, San Diego, California 92121-1744.
T: 1 858 678-0102 **E:** info@kprifm.com
W: http://www.kprifm.com
Editorial Profile: KPRI-FM is a commercial station owned by Compass Radio of San Diego Inc. The format of the station is adult album alternative music. KPRI-FM broadcasts to the San Diego area at 102.1 FM.

KPRK-AM

Owner: Townsquare Media, LLC
Editorial: 125 W Mendenhall St, Bozeman, Montana 59715-3586. **T:** 1 406 586-2352
Editorial Profile: KPRK-AM is a commercial station owned by Townsquare Media, LLC. The format of the station is news/talk. KPRK-AM broadcasts locally to the Bozeman, MT area at a frequency of 1340 AM.

KPRL-AM

Owner: North County Communications LLC
Editorial: 531 32nd St, Paso Robles, California 93446. **T:** 1 805 238-1230
E: reception@kprl.com **W:** http://www.kprl.com
Editorial Profile: KPRL-AM is a commercial station owned by North County Communications LLC. The format of the station is sports, news, and talk. KPRL-AM broadcasts to the Paso Robles, CA area at 1230 AM.

KPRO-AM

Owner: Impact Radio, Inc.
Editorial: 7351 Lincoln Ave, Riverside, California 92504-4600. **T:** 1 951 688-1570
E: kproval@aol.com
W: http://www.kpro1570.com
Editorial Profile: KPRO-AM is a commercial station owned by Impact Radio, Inc. The format of the station is religious programming. KPRO-AM broadcasts to the Riverside, CA area at 1570 AM.

KPRP-AM

Owner: Summit Media Broadcasting LLC
Editorial: 900 Fort Street Mall, Honolulu, Hawaii 96813-3721. **T:** 1 808 275-1000
W: http://www.kprpam650.com
Editorial Profile: KPRP-AM is a commercial station owned by Summit Media Broadcasting

LLC. The format of the station is easy listening. KPRP-AM broadcasts to the Honolulu area at 650 AM.

KPRR-FM
Owner: Clear Channel Media and Entertainment
Editorial: 4045 N Mesa St, El Paso, Texas 79902-1526. **T:** 1 915 351-5400
W: http://www.kprr.com
Editorial Profile: KPRR-FM is a commercial station owned by Clear Channel Media and Entertainment. The format of the station is Top 40/CHR music. KPRR-FM broadcasts to the El Paso, TX area at 102.1 FM.

KPRS-FM
Owner: Carter Broadcast Group
Editorial: 11131 Colorado Ave, Kansas City, Missouri 64137-2546. **T:** 1 816 763-2040
E: community@kprs.com
W: http://www.kprs.com
Editorial Profile: KPRS-FM is a commercial station owned by Carter Broadcast Group. The format of the station is urban contemporary and R&B music. KPRS-FM broadcasts to the Kansas City, MO area at 103.3 FM.

KPRT-AM
Owner: Carter Broadcast Group
Editorial: 11131 Colorado Ave, Kansas City, Missouri 64137-2546. **T:** 1 816 763-2040
E: community@kprs.com
W: http://www.kprt.com
Editorial Profile: KPRT-AM is a commercial station owned by Carter Broadcast Group. The format of the station is gospel. KRPT-AM broadcasts to the Kansas City, MO area at 1590 AM.

KPRV-AM
Owner: Coleman Broadcasting
Editorial: Highway 59 South, Poteau, Oklahoma 74953. **T:** 1 918 647-3221
E: kprv@windstream.net
W: http://www.kprvradio.com
Editorial Profile: KPRV-AM is a commercial station owned by Coleman Broadcasting. The format of the station is Adult Standards. KPRV-AM broadcasts to the Poteau, OK area at 1280 AM.

KPRV-FM
Owner: Coleman Broadcasting
Editorial: 22153 Old US Highway 59, Poteau, Oklahoma 74953. **T:** 1 918 647-3221
E: kprv@windstream.net
W: http://www.kprvradio.com
Editorial Profile: KPRV-FM is a commercial station owned by Coleman Broadcasting. The format of the station is lite AC. KPRV-FM broadcasts to the Poteau, OK area at 92.5 FM.

KPRW-FM
Owner: Results Radio Group
Editorial: 235 W Main St, Perham, Minnesota 56573-1448. **T:** 1 218 346-4800
E: contactus@lakesradio.net
W: http://www.lakesradio.net
Editorial Profile: KPRW-FM is a commercial station owned by Results Radio Group. The format of the station is adult contemporary. KPRW-FM broadcasts to the Perham, MN area at 99.5.

KPRZ-AM
Owner: Salem Communications
Editorial: 9255 Towne Centre Dr Ste 535, San Diego, California 92121-3038.
T: 1 858 535-1210 **E:** comments@kprz.com
W: http://www.kprz.com
Editorial Profile: KPRZ-AM is a commercial station owned by Salem Communications. The format of the station is religious talk. KCBQ-AM broadcasts to the San Diego area at 1210 AM.

KPSA-FM
Owner: SkyWest Media, LLC
Editorial: 1560 N Corbin St, Silver City, New Mexico 88061-6526. **T:** 1 575 538-3396
E: events@silvercityradio.com
W: http://www.977theplanet.com
Editorial Profile: KPSA-FM is a commercial station owned by SkyWest Media, LLC. The format of the station is classic rock. KPSA-FM broadcasts to the Silver City, NM area at 97.7 FM.

KPSD-FM
Owner: State Board for Educational Television
Editorial: 555 N Dakota St, Vermillion, South Dakota 57069. **T:** 1 605 677-5861
E: news@sdpb.org **W:** http://www.sdpb.org
Editorial Profile: KPSD-FM is a non-commercial station owned by the State Board for Educational Television. The format of the station is variety. KPSD-FM broadcasts to the Vermillion, SD area at 97.1 FM.

KPSF-AM
Owner: CRC Media West, LLC
Editorial: 75-153 Merle Dr., Unit D, Palm Springs, California 92211. **T:** 1 760 621-0100
W: http://www.moneyradio1510.com
Editorial Profile: KPSF-AM is a commercial station owned by CRC Media West, LLC. The format of the station is business and finance news/talk. KPSF-AM broadcasts to the Palm Springs and Coachella Valley areas of California at a frequency of 1200 AM.

KPSI-AM
Owner: R & R Radio Corp.
Editorial: 2100 E Tahquitz Canyon Way, Palm Springs, California 92262. **T:** 1 760 325-2582
W: http://www.newstalk920.com
Editorial Profile: KPSI-AM is a commercial station owned by R & R Radio Corp. The format of the station is news and talk. KPSI-AM broadcasts to the Palm Springs, CA area at 920 AM.

KPSI-FM
Owner: R & R Radio Corp.
Editorial: 2100 E Tahquitz Canyon Way, Palm Springs, California 92262. **T:** 1 760 325-2582
W: http://www.mix1005.fm
Editorial Profile: KPSI-FM is a commercial station owned by R & R Radio Corp. The format for the station is hot adult contemporary. KPSI-FM broadcasts to the Palm Springs, CA area at 100.5 FM.

KPSL-FM
Owner: Lotus Communications Corp.
Editorial: 5100 Commerce Dr, Bakersfield, California 93309. **T:** 1 661 327-9711
W: http://www.concierto965.com
Editorial Profile: KPSL-FM is a commercial station owned by Lotus Communications Corp. The format of the station is Spanish contemporary music. KPSL-FM broadcasts to the Bakersfield, CA area at 96.5 FM.

KPSM-FM
Owner: Better Living Ministries
Editorial: 910 Main St, Brownwood, Texas 76801. **T:** 1 325 646-5993
E: kpsmfm@gmail.com
W: http://www.kpsm.net
Editorial Profile: KPSM-FM is an commercial station owned by Better Living Ministries. The format of the station is religious programming. The station broadcasts to the Brownwood, TX area at 99.3 FM.

KPSO-FM
Owner: Brooks Broadcasting Corp.
Editorial: 304 E Rice St, Falfurrias, Texas 78355-3624. **T:** 1 361 325-2112
Editorial Profile: KPSO-FM is a commercial station owned by Brooks Broadcasting Corp. The format of the station is Hispanic and tejano music. KPSO-FM broadcasts to the Corpus Christi, TX area at 106.3 FM.

KPST-FM
Owner: Entravision Communications Corp.
Editorial: 41601 Corporate Way, Palm Desert, California 92260-1971. **T:** 1 760 341-5837
Editorial Profile: KPST-FM is a commercial station owned by Entravision Communications Corp. The format of the station is Regional Mexican. KPST-FM broadcasts to the Coachella Valley, CA region locally at 103.5 FM.

KPSZ-AM
Owner: Saga Communications
Editorial: 1416 Locust St, Des Moines, Iowa 50309. **T:** 1 515 280-1350
W: http://www.praise940.com
Editorial Profile: KPSZ-AM is a commercial station owned by Saga Communications. The format of the station is contemporary Christian and religious. KPSZ-AM broadcasts to the Des Moines, IA area at 940 AM.

KPTJ-FM
Owner: Castle Holdings, LLC
Editorial: 209 W Beauregard Ave, San Angelo, Texas 76903-5823
W: http://www.tejano104.com
Editorial Profile: KPTJ-FM is a commercial station owned by Castle Holdings, LLC. The format of the station is Tejano music. KPTJ-FM broadcasts to the Grape Creek, TX area at a frequency of 104.5 FM.

KPTL-FM
Owner: Clear Channel Media and Entertainment
Editorial: 2141 Grand Ave, Des Moines, Iowa 50312-5303. **T:** 1 515 245-8900
W: http://www.alt1063.com/main.html
Editorial Profile: KPTL-FM is a commercial station owned by Clear Channel Media and Entertainment. The format of the station is Modern Rock. KPTL-FM broadcasts to the Des Moines, IA area at 106.3 FM.

KPTR-AM
Owner: R & R Radio Corp.
Editorial: 2100 E Tahquitz Canyon Way, Palm Springs, California 92262. **T:** 1 760 325-2582
W: http://www.kptram1340.com
Editorial Profile: KPTR-AM is commercial station owned by R & R Radio Corp. The format of the station is progressive talk. KPTR-AM broadcasts to the Palm Springs, CA area at 1450 AM.

KPTT-FM
Owner: Clear Channel Media and Entertainment
Editorial: 4695 S Monaco St, Denver, Colorado 80237-3525. **T:** 1 303 713-8000
W: http://www.957theparty.com
Editorial Profile: KPTT-FM is a commercial station owned by Clear Channel Media and Entertainment. The format of the station is Top 40/CHR. KPTT-FM broadcasts to Denver area at 95.7 FM.

KPTX-FM
Owner: Parday Inc.
Editorial: 316 S Cedar St, Pecos, Texas 79772. **T:** 1 432 445-2498
E: kiun@valornet.com
W: http://www.98xfm.com
Editorial Profile: KPTX-FM is a commercial station owned by Parday Inc. The format of the station is adult contemporary. KPTX-FM broadcasts to the Pecos, TX area at 98.3 FM.

KPUA-AM
Owner: New West Broadcasting
Editorial: 1145 Kilauea Ave, Hilo, Hawaii 96720-4203. **T:** 1 808 935-5461
E: news@kpua.net **W:** http://www.kpua.net
Editorial Profile: KPUA-AM is a commercial station owned by New West Broadcasting. The format of the station is news, sports and talk. KPUA-AM broadcasts to the Hilo, HI area at 670 AM.

KPUB-FM
Owner: Northern Arizona University
Editorial: 515 E Pine Knoll, Building 83, Flagstaff, Arizona 86011-0001.
T: 1 928 523-5628 **E:** knau@nau.edu
W: http://www.knau.org
Editorial Profile: KPUB-FM is a non-commercial station owned by Northern Arizona University. The format of the station is news and talk. KPUB-FM broadcasts to the Flagstaff and Page areas in Arizona at a frequency of 91.7 FM.

KPUG-AM
Owner: Saga Communications
Editorial: 2219 Yew Street Rd, Bellingham, Washington 98229-8855. **T:** 1 360 734-9790
E: thezone@kpug1170.com
W: http://www.kpug1170.com
Editorial Profile: KPUG-AM is a commercial station owned by Saga Communications. The format of the station is sports. KPUG-AM broadcasts to the Bellingham, WA area at 1170 AM.

KPUL-FM
Owner: Positive Impact Media Inc.
Editorial: 33365 335th St, Waukee, Iowa 50263. **T:** 1 515 987-9995
E: info@pulse995.com
W: http://www.pulse995.com
Editorial Profile: KPUL-FM is a commercial station owned by Positive Impact Media Inc. The format of the station is contemporary top 40/CHR. KPUL-FM broadcasts to the Des Moines, IA area at 99.5 FM.

KPUR-AM
Owner: Cumulus Media Inc.
Editorial: 301 S Polk St, Amarillo, Texas 79101-1403. **T:** 1 806 342-5200
Editorial Profile: KPUR-AM is a commercial station owned by Cumulus Media Inc. The format of the station is sports. KPUR-AM broadcasts to the Amarillo, TX area at 1440 AM.

KPUR-FM
Owner: Cumulus Media Inc.
Editorial: 301 S Polk St, Ste 100, Amarillo, Texas 79101. **T:** 1 806 342-5200
W: http://www.kpur107.com
Editorial Profile: KPUR-FM is a commercial station owned by Cumulus Media Inc. The format of the station is country. KPUR-FM broadcasts to the Amarillo, TX area at 107.1 FM.

KPUS-FM
Owner: Convergent Broadcasting
Editorial: 826 S Padre Island Dr, Corpus Christi, Texas 78416. **T:** 1 361 814-3800
W: http://classicrock1045.com
Editorial Profile: KPUS-FM is a commercial station owned by Convergent Broadcasting. The format of the station is classic rock. KPUS-FM broadcasts to the Corpus Christi, TX area at a frequency of 104.5 FM.

KPVL-FM
Owner: Postville Chamber of Commerce
Editorial: 207 E Water St, Decorah, Iowa 52101-1803. **T:** 1 563 864-7945
W: http://www.891theblend.org
Editorial Profile: KPVL-FM is a non-commercial station owned by the Postville Chamber of Commerce. The format of the station is variety. KPVL-FM broadcasts to the Cedar Rapids, IA area at 89.1 FM.

KPVR-FM
Owner: Gateway Creative Broadcasting, Inc
Editorial: 30 Tower St, Moscow Mills, Missouri 63362-1139. **T:** 1 636 356-9266
E: info@joyfmonline.org
W: http://boost1019.com
Editorial Profile: KPVR-FM is a commercial station owned by Gateway Creative Broadcasting, Inc. The format of the station is Christian CHR. KPVR-FM broadcasts to the St. Louis area at 94.1 FM.

KPVS-FM
Owner: Pacific Media Group
Editorial: 913 Kanoelehua Ave, Hilo, Hawaii 96720-5116. **T:** 1 808 961-0651
E: studio@nativefm.com
W: http://www.nativefm.com
Editorial Profile: KPVS-FM is a commercial station owned by Pacific Media Group. The format of the station is contemporary island music. KPVS-FM broadcasts to the Hilo, HI area at 95.9 FM.

KPVU-FM
Owner: Prairie View A&M University
Editorial: 130 Hilliard Hall A&M University, Prairie View, Texas 77446-9999.
T: 1 936 261-3750 **E:** kpvu_fm@pvamu.edu
W: http://www.pvamu.edu/kpvu
Editorial Profile: KPVU-FM is a non-commercial station owned by Prarie View A&M University. The format of the station is smooth AC, gospel music, and urban. KPVU-FM broadcasts to the Prairie View, TX area at 91.3 FM.

KPVW-FM
Owner: Entravision Communications Corp.
Editorial: 1907 Mile High Stadium West Cir, Denver, Colorado 80204-1908.
T: 1 303 832-0050
W: http://www.denverhispanicradio.com
Editorial Profile: KPVW-FM is a commercial station owned by Entravision Communications Corp. The format of the station is regional Mexican. KPVW-FM broadcasts to Aspen, Glenwood, CO and the surrounding area at 107.1 FM.

KPWB-AM
Owner: Dockins Broadcast Group
Editorial: 235 Business Hh, Piedmont, Missouri 63957-9410. **T:** 1 573 223-4518
W: http://www.kickincountry105.com
Editorial Profile: KPWB-AM is a commercial station owned by Dockins Broadcast Group. The format of the station is country. KPWB-AM broadcasts to the Piedmont, MO area at a frequency of 1140 AM.

KPWB-FM
Owner: Dockins Broadcast Group
Editorial: 235 Business Hh, Piedmont, Missouri 63957-9410. **T:** 1 573 223-4518
W: http://www.kickincountry105.com
Editorial Profile: KPWB-FM is a commercial station owned by Dockins Broadcast Group. The format of the station is country. KPWB-FM broadcasts to the Piedmont, MO area at 104.9 FM.

KPWR-FM
Owner: Emmis Communications Corp.
Editorial: 2600 W Olive Ave, Burbank, California 91505-4549. **T:** 1 818 953-4200
E: power106info@power106.com
W: http://www.power106.com

Editorial Profile: KPWR-FM is a commercial station owned by Emmis Communications Corp. The format for the station is rhythmic. KPWR-FM broadcasts to the Los Angeles area at 105.9 FM.

KPWW-FM

Owner: Townsquare Media, LLC
Editorial: 2324 Arkansas Blvd, Texarkana, Arkansas 71854. **T:** 1 870 772-3771
W: http://www.power959.com
Editorial Profile: KPWW-FM is a commercial station owned by Townsquare Media, LLC. The format of the station is Top 40/CHR. KPWW-FM broadcasts to the Texarkana, AR area at 95.9 FM.

KPXI-FM

Owner: Hanszen Broadcast Group
Editorial: 1101 Kilgore Dr, Henderson, Texas 75652-5129. **T:** 1 903 655-1800
W: http://www.easttexastoday.com
Editorial Profile: KPXI-FM is a commercial station owned by Hanszen Broadcast Group. The format of the station is country music. KPXI-FM broadcasts to the Tyler, TX area at 100.7 FM.

KPXQ-AM

Owner: Salem Communications
Editorial: 2425 E Camelback Rd Ste 570, Phoenix, Arizona 85016-4250.
T: 1 602 955-9600
W: http://www.faithtalk1360.com
Editorial Profile: KPXQ-AM is a commercial station owned by Salem Communications. The format of the station is religious talk. KPXQ-AM broadcasts to the Phoenix area at 1360 AM.

KPYG-FM

Owner: Mapleton Radio, LLC
Editorial: 795 Brickly Road, San Luis Obispo, California 93401. **T:** 1 831 722-9000
W: http://www.kpig.com
Editorial Profile: KPYG-FM is a commercial station owned by Mapleton Radio, LLC. The format of the station is adult album alternative. KPYG-FM broadcasts to the Watsonville, CA area at 94.9 FM.

KPYK-AM

Owner: Mohnkern Electronics Inc.
Editorial: 1412C W Moore Ave, Terrell, Texas 75160. **T:** 1 972 524-5795
W: http://www.kpyk.com
Editorial Profile: KPYK-AM is a commercial station owned by Mohnkern Electronics Inc. The format of the station is oldies. KPYK-AM broadcasts to Terrell, TX, at 1570 AM.

KPZA-FM

Owner: Noalmark Broadcasting Corp.
Editorial: 619 N Turner St, Hobbs, New Mexico 88240. **T:** 1 575 397-4969
E: kpza@1radiosquare.com
W: http://kpzafm.com
Editorial Profile: KPZA-FM is a commercial station owned by Noalmark Broadcasting Corp. The format of the station is Hispanic. KPZA-FM broadcasts to the Albuquerque, NM area at 103.7 FM.

KPZE-FM

Owner: Pecos Valley Broadcasting Company
Editorial: 317 W Quay Ave, Artesia, New Mexico 88210-2158. **T:** 1 575 746-2751
W: http://www.kpze.com
Editorial Profile: KPZE-FM is a commercial station owned by Pecos Valley Broadcasting Company. The format of the station is regional Mexican music. KPZE-FM broadcasts to the Albuquerque, NM area at 106.1 FM.

KPZK-AM

Owner: Cumulus Media Inc
Editorial: 700 Wellington Hills Rd, Little Rock, Arkansas 72211. **T:** 1 501 401-0200
W: http://www.power923.com
Editorial Profile: KPZK-AM is a commercial station owned by Cumulus Media Inc. The format of the station is urban contemporary. KPZK-AM broadcasts in the Little Rock, AR area at 1250 AM.

KPZK-FM

Owner: Cumulus Media Inc
Editorial: 700 Wellington Hills Rd, Little Rock, Arkansas 72211. **T:** 1 501 401-0200
W: http://www.praisepage.com
Editorial Profile: KPZK-FM is a commercial station owned by Cumulus Media Inc. The format of the station is gospel. KPZK-FM broadcasts to the Little Rock, AR area at 102.5 FM.

KQAC-FM

Owner: All Classical Public Media, Inc.
Editorial: 515 NE 15th Ave, Portland, Oregon 97232. **T:** 1 503 943-5828
E: webmaster@allclassical.org
W: http://www.allclassical.org
Editorial Profile: KQAC-FM is non-commercial station owned by the All Classical Public Media, Inc. The format of the station is classical music. KQAC-FM broadcasts to the Portland, OR area at 89.9 FM.

KQAD-AM

Owner: Three Eagles Communications Co.
Editorial: 1140 150th Ave, Luverne, Minnesota 56156. **T:** 1 507 283-4444
W: http://www.kqad.net
Editorial Profile: KQAD-AM is a commercial station owned by Three Eagles Communications Co. The format of the station is Lite Rock/Lite AC. KQAD-AM broadcasts to the Luverne, MN area at 800 AM.

KQAK-FM

Owner: Horizon Broadcasting Group
Editorial: 854 Ne 4Th St, Bend, Oregon 97701-4711. **T:** 1 541 383-3825
E: kqak1057@horizonbroadcastinggroup.com
W: http://www.kqak.com
Editorial Profile: KQAK-FM is a commercial station owned by the Horizon Broadcasting Group. The format of KQAK-FM is classic hits. The station broadcasts to the Bend, OR area at 105.7 FM.

KQAL-FM

Owner: Winona State University
Editorial: 175 W Mark St, Winona, Minnesota 55987. **T:** 1 507 453-2222
W: http://www.kqal.org
Editorial Profile: KQAL-FM is a non-commercial station owned by Winona State University. The format of the station is rock alternative, classical and jazz. KQAL-FM broadcasts to the Winona, MN area at 89.5 FM.

KQAM-AM

Owner: Steckline Communications
Editorial: 1632 S Maize Rd, Wichita, Kansas 67209-3912. **T:** 1 316 721-8484
W: http://www.kqamradio.com
Editorial Profile: KQAM-AM is a commercial station owned by Steckline Communications. The format of the station is news and talk. KQAM-AM broadcasts to the Wichita, KS area at 1480 AM.

KQAQ-AM

Owner: Hometown Broadcasting Austin, Inc.
Editorial: 109 E Clark St, Albert Lea, Minnesota 56007-2420. **T:** 1 507 373-9600
E: kqaq@classiccountrylegends.com
W: http://www.classiccountrylegends.com
Editorial Profile: KQAQ-AM is a commercial station owned by Hometown Broadcasting, Inc. The format of the station is classic country. KNFX-AM broadcasts to the Rochester, MN area on 970 AM.

KQAV-FM

Owner: High Desert Broadcasting LLC
Editorial: 570 E Avenue Q9, Palmdale, California 93550. **T:** 1 661 947-3107
W: http://www.935thequake.com
Editorial Profile: KQAV-FM is a commercial station owned by High Desert Broadcasting LLC. The format of the station is classic rock. KQAV-FM broadcasts in the Palmdale, CA area at 93.5 FM.

KQAY-FM

Owner: Majestic Communications
Editorial: 902 Date St, Tucumcari, New Mexico 88401-4335. **T:** 1 575 461-0522
E: ktnmkqay@yahoo.com
Editorial Profile: KQAY-FM is a commercial station owned by Majestic Communications. The format of the station is adult contemporary music. KQAY-FM broadcasts to the Tucumcari, NM area at 92.7 FM.

KQAZ-FM

Owner: Country Mountain Airwaves LLC
Editorial: 391 W Deuce Of Clubs Ste C, Show Low, Arizona 85901-5809. **T:** 1 928 532-1010
E: mail@majik101.com
W: http://www.majik101.com
Editorial Profile: KQAZ-FM is a commercial station owned by Country Mountain Airwaves LLC. The format of the station is Lite Rock/Lite AC music. KQAZ-FM broadcasts to the Show Low, AZ and the surrounding areas at 101.7 FM.

KQBA-FM

Owner: Hutton Broadcasting, LLC

Editorial: 2502 Camino Entrada, Santa Fe, New Mexico 87507-4911. **T:** 1 505 471-1067
W: http://www.santafe.com/outlaw
Editorial Profile: KQBA-FM is a commercial station owned by Hutton Broadcasting, LLC. The format of the station is country music. KQBA-FM broadcasts to the Sante Fe, NM area at 107.5 FM.

KQBB-FM

Owner: Center Broadcasting Company Inc.
Editorial: 307 San Augustine St, Center, Texas 75935-3937. **T:** 1 936 598-3304
E: centerbroadcasting@yahoo.com
Editorial Profile: KQBB-FM is a commercial station owned by Center Broadcasting Company Inc. The format of the station is country. KQBB-FM broadcasts to the Center, TX area at 100.5 FM.

KQBK-FM

Owner: Pharis Broadcasting Inc.
Editorial: 321 N Greenwood Ave Ste 201, Fort Smith, Arkansas 72901-3453.
T: 1 479 288-1047
W: http://www.kool1047fm.com
Editorial Profile: KQBK-FM is a commercial station owned by Pharis Broadcasting Inc. The format of the station is oldies. KQBK-FM broadcasts to the Fort Smith, AR area at 104.7 FM.

KQBL-FM

Owner: Impact Radio
Editorial: 5660 E Franklin Rd Ste 200, Nampa, Idaho 83687-5133. **T:** 1 208 465-9966
W: http://www.boisebull.com
Editorial Profile: KQBL-FM is a commercial station owned by Impact Radio. The format of the station is contemporary country. KQBL-FM broadcasts to the Boise, ID area at 100.7 FM.

KQBO-FM

Owner: Sound Investments Unlimited
Editorial: 102 Kctm Fm 103 Rd, Rio Grande City, Texas 78582-9670. **T:** 1 956 487-8224
Editorial Profile: KQBO-FM is a commercial station owned by Sound Investments Unlimited. The format of the station is Hispanic. KQBO-FM broadcasts to the Rio Grande City, TX area at 107.5 FM.

KQBR-FM

Owner: Townsquare Media, LLC
Editorial: 4413 82nd St, Ste 300, Lubbock, Texas 79424. **T:** 1 806 798-7078
W: http://995blakefm.com
Editorial Profile: KQBR-FM is a commercial station owned by Townsquare Media, LLC. The format of the station is contemporary country. KQBR-FM broadcasts to the Lubbock, TX area at 99.5 FM.

KQBT-FM

Owner: Clear Channel Media and Entertainment
Editorial: 2000 West Loop S Ste 300, Houston, Texas 77027-3510.
T: 1 713 212-8000
W: http://www.937thebeathouston.com/main.html
Editorial Profile: KQBT-FM is a commercial station owned by Clear Channel Media and Entertainment. The format of the station is urban contemporary. KQBT-FM broadcasts to the Houston area at 93.7 FM.

KQBU-AM

Owner: Univision Communications Inc.
Editorial: 2211 E Missouri Ave Ste 300, El Paso, Texas 79903-3837. **T:** 1 915 544-9797
W: http://univisionamerica.univision.com
Editorial Profile: KQBU-AM is a commercial station owned by Univision Communications Inc. The format of the station is Hispanic news and talk. KQBU-AM broadcasts to the El Paso, TX area at 920 AM.

KQBU-FM

Owner: Univision Communications Inc.
Editorial: 5100 Southwest Fwy, Houston, Texas 77056. **T:** 1 713 965-2400
W: http://www.quebuena933.com
Editorial Profile: KQBU-FM is a commercial station owned by Univision Communications Inc. The format of the station is regional Mexican. KQBU-FM broadcasts to the Houston area at 93.3 FM.

KQBZ-FM

Owner: Wendlee Broadcasting
Editorial: 600 Fisk Ave, Brownwood, Texas 76801. **T:** 1 325 646-3535
E: breeze@wendlee.com
W: http://www.kqbz-fm.com
Editorial Profile: KQBZ-FM is a commercial station owned by Wendlee Broadcasting. The

format of the station is hot adult contemporary. KQBZ-FM broadcasts to the Brownwood, TX area at 96.9 FM.

KQCB-FM

Owner: Calcomm Stations Oregon LLC
Editorial: 615 Broadway St, Ste 222, Seaside, Oregon 97138. **T:** 1 503 738-8668
W: http://www.musicmatters949.com
Editorial Profile: KQCB-FM is a commercial station owned by Calcomm Stations Oregon LLC. The format of the station is hot adult contemporary music. KQCB-FM broadcasts to the Seaside, OR area at 94.9 FM.

KQCH-FM

Owner: Journal Broadcast Group
Editorial: 10714 Mockingbird Dr, Omaha, Nebraska 68127-1942. **T:** 1 402 592-5300
E: win@cha.com
W: http://www.channel941.com
Editorial Profile: KQCH-FM is a commercial station owned Journal Broadcast Group. The format of the station is Top 40. KQCH-FM broadcasts to the Omaha, NE area at 94.1 FM.

KQCL-FM

Owner: Townsquare Media, LLC
Editorial: 601 Central Ave N, Faribault, Minnesota 55021-4307. **T:** 1 507 334-0061
W: http://www.power96radio.com
Editorial Profile: KQCL-FM is a commercial station owned by Townsquare Media, LLC. The format of the station is classic rock. KQCL-FM broadcasts to the Faribault, MN area at 95.9 FM.

KQCM-FM

Owner: S & H Broadcasting L.L.C.
Editorial: 12370 Hesperia Rd Ste 16, Victorville, California 92395-5808.
T: 1 760 241-1313
W: http://www.kq955.com/main
Editorial Profile: KQCM-FM is a commercial station owned by S & H Broadcasting L.L.C. The format of the station is CHR. KQCM-FM broadcasts to the Victorville, CA area at 105.3 FM.

KQCR-FM

Owner: CD Broadcasting Inc.
Editorial: 1509 4th St NE, Hampton, Iowa 50441. **T:** 1 641 456-5656 **E:** kqcr@kqcr.fm
W: http://www.kqcr.fm
Editorial Profile: KQCR-FM is a commercial station owned by CD Broadcasting Inc. The station's format is adult contemporary music. KQCR-FM broadcasts to the Parkersburg, IA area at 98.9 FM.

KQCS-FM

Owner: Townsquare Media
Editorial: 1229 Brady St, Davenport, Iowa 52803-4616. **T:** 1 563 326-2541
W: http://www.star935fm.com
Editorial Profile: KQCS-FM is a commercial station owned by Townsquare Media. The target audience of the station is adults, ages 18 to 34. The station is aired locally on 93.5 FM. The format of the station is hot adult contemporary. KQCS-FM's tagline is "Star 93.5."

KQCV-AM

Owner: Bott Broadcasting Co.
Editorial: 1919 N Broadway Ave, Oklahoma City, Oklahoma 73103. **T:** 1 405 521-0800
E: kqcv@bottradionetwork.com
W: http://www.bottradionetwork.com
Editorial Profile: KQCV-AM is a commercial station owned by Bott Broadcasting Co. The format of the station is Christian and religious programming. KQCV-AM broadcasts to the Oklahoma City area at 800 AM.

KQCV-FM

Owner: Bott Broadcasting Co.
Editorial: 1919 N Broadway Ave, Oklahoma City, Oklahoma 73103. **T:** 1 405 521-0800
E: kqcv@bottradionetwork.com
W: http://www.bottradionetwork.com
Editorial Profile: KQCV-FM is a commercial station owned by Bott Broadcasting Co. The format for the station is religious and Christian programming. KQCV-FM broadcasts to the Oklahoma City area at 95.1 FM.

KQDI-AM

Owner: Fisher Communications, Inc.
Editorial: 1300 Central Ave W, Great Falls, Montana 59404. **T:** 1 406 761-2800
E: audiogf@q106rocks.com
W: http://www.newstalk1450.com
Editorial Profile: KQDI-AM is a commercial station owned by Fisher Communications, Inc. The format for the station is news and talk.

KQDI-AM broadcasts to the Great Falls, MT area at 1450 AM.

KQDI-FM
Owner: Fisher Communications, Inc.
Editorial: 1300 Central Ave W, Great Falls, Montana 59404. **T:** 1 406 761-2800
W: http://www.q106rocks.com
Editorial Profile: KQDI-FM is a commercial station owned by Fisher Communications, Inc. The format for the station is classic rock. KQDI-FM broadcasts to the Great Falls, MT area at 106.1 FM.

KQDJ-AM
Owner: Ingstad Family Media
Editorial: 2625 8Th Ave Sw, Jamestown, North Dakota 58401-6621. **T:** 1 701 252-1400
W: http://www.newsdakota.com
Editorial Profile: KQDJ-AM is a commercial station owned by Ingstad Family Media. The format of the station is country. KQDJ-AM broadcasts to the Jamestown, ND area at 1400 AM.

KQDJ-FM
Owner: Ingstad Family Media
Editorial: 2625 8Th Ave Sw, Jamestown, North Dakota 58401-6621. **T:** 1 701 252-1400
E: bigdog@daktel.com
W: http://www.newsdakota.com
Editorial Profile: KQDJ-FM is a commercial station owned by Ingstad Family Media. The format of the station is hot adult contemporary music. KQDJ-FM broadcasts to the Jamestown, ND area at 101.1 FM.

KQDL-FM
Owner: Calvary Chapel of Twin Falls, Inc
Editorial: 515 NE 15th Ave, Portland, Oregon 97232-2897. **T:** 1 503 943-5828
W: http://www.csnradio.com
Editorial Profile: KQDL-FM is a non-commercial station owned by Calvary Chapel of Twin Falls, Inc. The format of the station is religious. KQDL-FM broadcasts to Portland, OR and surrounding areas at 90.1 FM.

KQDR-FM
Owner: Prophecy Media Group, LLC (dba Waco Entertainment Group, LLC)
Editorial: 900 Pecan Grove Rd E, Sherman, Texas 75090-1770. **T:** 1 254 868-1073
W: http://1073docfm.com
Editorial Profile: KQDR-FM is a commercial station owned by Prophecy Media Group, LLC. The format of the station is Top 40/CHR. KQDR-FM broadcasts to the Sherman-Denison, TX area.

KQDS-AM
Owner: Red Rock Radio Corp.
Editorial: 501 S Lake Ave, Ste 200, Duluth, Minnesota 55802. **T:** 1 218 728-9500
E: production@redrockradio.org
Editorial Profile: KQDS-AM is a commercial station owned by Red Rock Radio Corp. The format of the station is sports. KQDS-AM broadcasts to the Duluth, MN area at 1490 AM.

KQDS-FM
Owner: Red Rock Radio Corp.
Editorial: 501 S Lake Ave, Ste 200, Duluth, Minnesota 55802. **T:** 1 218 728-9500
E: production@redrockradio.org
W: http://www.95kqds.com
Editorial Profile: KQDS-FM is a commercial station owned by Red Rock Radio Corp. The format of the station is classic rock music. KQDS-FM broadcasts to the Duluth, MN area at 94.9 FM.

KQDY-FM
Owner: Clear Channel Media and Entertainment
Editorial: 3500 E Rosser Ave, Bismarck, North Dakota 58501. **T:** 1 701 255-1234
E: kqdy@clearchannel.com
W: http://www.kqdy.com
Editorial Profile: KQDY-FM is a commercial station owned by Clear Channel Media and Entertainment. The format of the station is contemporary country music. KQDY-FM broadcasts to the Bismarck, ND area at 94.5 FM.

KQED-FM
Owner: KQED, Inc.
Editorial: 2601 Mariposa St, San Francisco, California 94110-1426. **T:** 1 415 553-2129
E: assignmentdesk@kqed.org
W: http://www.kqed.org
Editorial Profile: KQED-FM is a non-commercial station owned by Northern California Public Broadcasting. The format of the station is news and talk. KQED-FM broadcasts to the San Francisco area at 88.5 FM.

KQEG-FM
Owner: Mississippi Valley Broadcasters LLC
Editorial: 1407 2nd Ave N, Onalaska, Wisconsin 54650. **T:** 1 608 782-8335
E: news@lacrosseradiogroup.net
W: http://www.eagle1027.com

KQEI-FM
Owner: KQED Inc.
Editorial: 925 L St, Sacramento, California 95814-3702. **T:** 1 916 446-7119
E: fm@kqed.org **W:** http://www.kqed.org

KQEL-FM
Owner: Burt Broadcasting Inc.
Editorial: 501 S Florida Ave, Alamogordo, New Mexico 88310. **T:** 1 575 434-1414
E: burtbroadcasting@bbiradio.net
W: http://www.1079coolfm.net
Editorial Profile: KQEL-FM is a commercial station owned by Burt Broadcasting Inc. The format of the station is classic hits music. KQEL-FM broadcasts to the Alamogordo, NM area at 107.9 FM.

KQEN-AM
Owner: Brooke Communications Inc.
Editorial: 1445 W Harvard Ave, Roseburg, Oregon 97471-2839. **T:** 1 541 672-6641
W: http://www.541radio.com
Editorial Profile: KQEN-AM is a commercial station owned by Brooke Communications Inc. The format of the station is news, and talk. KQEN-AM broadcasts to the Roseburg, OR area at 1240 AM.

KQEO-FM
Owner: Sand Hill Media
Editorial: 854 Lindsay Blvd, Idaho Falls, Idaho 83402. **T:** 1 208 522-1101
E: arrow@arrow107.com
W: http://www.arrow107.com
Editorial Profile: KQEO-FM is a commercial station owned by Sand Hill Media. The format of the station is classic hits. KQEO-FM broadcasts to the Idaho Falls, ID area at 107.1 FM.

KQEQ-AM
Owner: Hmong American Broadcasting Co.
Editorial: 139 W Olive Ave, Fresno, California 93728-3035. **T:** 1 559 499-1210
W: http://www.thehmongradio.com
Editorial Profile: KQEQ-AM is a commercial radio station owned by Hmong American Broadcasting Co. The format of the station is southern gospel. KQEQ-AM broadcasts to the Fresno, CA, area at 1210 AM.

KQEW-FM
Owner: KBJT, Inc.
Editorial: 303 N Spring St, Fordyce, Arkansas 71742-3317. **T:** 1 870 352-7137
E: kbjt@coatesmedia.com
W: http://www.kbjtkq.com
Editorial Profile: KQEW-FM is a commercial station owned by KBJT, Inc. The format of the station is news, talk and sports programming. KQEW-FM broadcasts to the Fordyce, AR area at 102.3 FM.

KQEZ-FM
Owner: Pacific Empire Radio Corp.
Editorial: 111 Main St, Lewiston, Idaho 83501-2141 **W:** http://www.ezrockradio.com
Editorial Profile: KQEZ-FM is a commercial station owned by Pacific Empire Radio Corp. The format of the station is adult contemporary. KQEZ-FM broadcasts to the Idaho Falls, ID area at 106.3 FM.

KQFC-FM
Owner: Cumulus Media Inc
Editorial: 1419 W Bannock St, Boise, Idaho 83702-5234. **T:** 1 208 336-3670
E: 670@news.com **W:** http://www.98kqfc.com
Editorial Profile: KQFC-FM is a commercial station owned by Cumulus Media Inc. The format of the station is country. KQFC-FM broadcasts to the Boise, ID area at 97.9 FM.

KQFM-FM
Owner: West End Radio LLC
Editorial: 80404 Cooney Ln, Hermiston, Oregon 97838-6613. **T:** 1 541 567-6500
W: http://www.gohermiston.com
Editorial Profile: KQFM-FM is a commercial station owned by West End Radio LLC. The format of the station is oldies. KQFM-FM broadcasts to the Hermiston, OR area at 100.1 FM.

KQFX-FM
Owner: Tejas Broadcasting
Editorial: 3639 Wolflin Ave, Amarillo, Texas 79102-2119. **T:** 1 806 355-1044
Editorial Profile: KQFX-FM is a commercial station owned by Tejas Broadcasting. The format of the station is Hispanic. KQFX-FM broadcasts to the Amarillo, TX area at 104.3 FM.

KQGC-FM
Owner: Educational Media Foundation
Editorial: 4101 Barbara Loop SE, Ste A, Rio Rancho, New Mexico 87124.
T: 1 800 260-5676 **E:** info@nuevavida.com
W: http://nuevavida.com
Editorial Profile: KQGC-FM is a non-commercial station owned by Educational Media Foundation. The format of the station is Hispanic religious. KQGC-FM broadcasts to the Rio Rancho, NM area at 91.1 FM.

KQHK-FM
Owner: Armada Media Corp.
Editorial: 1811 W O St, McCook, Nebraska 69001. **T:** 1 308 345-5400
E: openline@highplainsradio.net
W: http://www.plainsreporter.com
Editorial Profile: KQHK-FM is a commercial station owned by Armada Media Corp. The format of the station is classic rock. KQHK-FM broadcasts to the McCook, NE area at 103.9 FM.

KQHN-FM
Owner: Cumulus Media Inc.
Editorial: Cumulus Broadcast Center, 270 Plaza Loop, Bossier City, Louisiana 71111-4389. **T:** 1 318 549-8500
W: http://www.mixfm973.com
Editorial Profile: KQHN-FM is a commercial station owned by Cumulus Media Inc. The format of the station is CHR music. KQHN-FM broadcasts to the Shreveport, LA area at 97.3 FM.

KQHR-FM
Owner: All Classical Public Media, Inc.
Editorial: 515 NE 15th Ave, Portland, Oregon 97232. **T:** 1 888 306-5277
E: music.info@allclassical.org
W: http://www.allclassical.org
Editorial Profile: KQHR-FM is a non-commercial station owned by All Classical Public Media, Inc. The format of the station is classical music. KQHR-FM broadcasts to Portland, OR and surrounding areas at 88.1 FM.

KQHT-FM
Owner: Clear Channel Media and Entertainment
Editorial: 505 University Ave, Grand Forks, North Dakota 58203. **T:** 1 701 746-1417
W: http://www.961thefox.com
Editorial Profile: KQHT-FM is a commercial station owned by Clear Channel Media and Entertainment. The station's format is classic hits music. KQHT-FM broadcasts to the Grand Forks, ND area at 96.1 FM.

KQIB-FM
Owner: JDC Radio Inc.
Editorial: 108 N Broadway St, Broken Bow, Oklahoma 74728-3934. **T:** 1 580 584-3388
E: kkbi@pine-net.com
W: http://www.kkbifm.com
Editorial Profile: KQIB-FM is a commercial station owned by JDC Radio Inc. The format of the station is hot adult contemporary. KQIB-FM broadcasts to the Broken Bow, OK area at 102.9 FM.

KQIC-FM
Owner: Lakeland Broadcasting
Editorial: 1340 7th St NW, Willmar, Minnesota 56201-0838. **T:** 1 320 235-3535
W: http://www.yourq102.com
Editorial Profile: KQIC-FM is a commercial station owned by Lakeland Broadcasting. The format of the station is hot adult contemporary. KQIC-FM broadcasts in the Willmar, MN area at 102.5 FM.

KQID-FM
Owner: Cenla Broadcasting Inc.
Editorial: 1115 Texas Ave, Alexandria, Louisiana 71301. **T:** 1 318 445-1234
W: http://www.q93fm.com
Editorial Profile: KQID-FM is a commercial station owned by Cenla Broadcasting Inc. The format of the station is Top 40/CHR music. KQID-FM broadcasts in the Alexandria, LA area at 93.1 FM.

KQIE-FM
Owner: LC Media, LP
Editorial: 242 E Airport Dr Ste 106, San Bernardino, California 92408-3408.
T: 1 818 497-4386 **W:** http://kqie1047.com
Editorial Profile: KQIE-FM is a commercial station owned by LC Media, LP. The format of the station is Top 40/CHR. KQIE-FM broadcasts to the Redlands, CA area at 104.7 FM.

KQIZ-FM
Owner: Cumulus Media Inc.
Editorial: 301 S Polk St, Ste 100, Amarillo, Texas 79101. **T:** 1 806 342-5200
W: http://www.931thebeat.com
Editorial Profile: KQIZ-FM is a commercial station owned by Cumulus Media Inc. The format of the station features hip-hop and R&B music programming. KQIZ-FM broadcasts to the Amarillo, TX area at a frequency of 93.1 FM.

KQJK-FM
Owner: Clear Channel Media and Entertainment
Editorial: 1544 River Park Dr Ste 500, Sacramento, California 95815-4602.
T: 1 916 929-5325
W: http://www.jackdotcom.com
Editorial Profile: KQJK-FM is a commercial station owned by Clear Channel Media and Entertainment. The format of the station is adult hits. KQJK-FM broadcasts to the Sacramento, CA area on 93.7 FM.

KQJZ-AM
Owner: Anderson Radio Broadcasting Inc.
Editorial: 36581 N Reservoir Rd, Polson, Montana 59860-8471. **T:** 1 406 883-5255
W: http://www.1340thelounge.com
Editorial Profile: KQJZ-FM is a commercial station owned by Anderson Radio Broadcasting Inc. The format of the station is adult standards. KQJZ-FM broadcasts to the Kalispell, MT area at a frequency of 1340 AM.

KQKI-FM
Owner: Cook(Paul J.)
Editorial: 128 Pluto St, Morgan City, Louisiana 70380. **T:** 1 985 395-2853 **E:** news@kqki.com
W: http://www.kqki.com
Editorial Profile: KQKI-FM is a commercial station owned by Paul J. Cook. The format of the station is country. KQKI-FM broadcasts to the Morgan City, LA area at 95.3 FM.

KQKK-FM
Owner: De La Hunt Broadcasting
Editorial: Highway 34 West, Walker, Minnesota 56484. **T:** 1 218 547-4000
E: kqkkkakk@eot.com
W: http://www.kkradionetwork.com
Editorial Profile: KQKK-FM is a commercial station owned by De La Hunt Broadcasting. The format of the station is aduly contemporary music. KQKK-FM broadcasts to the Walker, MN area at 101.9 FM.

KQKQ-FM
Owner: NRG Media LLC
Editorial: 5011 Capitol Ave, Omaha, Nebraska 68132-2921. **T:** 1 402 342-2000
W: http://www.q985fm.com
Editorial Profile: KQKQ-FM is a commercial station owned by NRG Media LLC. The format of the station is hot adult contemporary music. KQKQ-FM broadcasts to the Omaha, NE area at 98.5 FM.

KQKS-FM
Owner: Lincoln Financial Media
Editorial: 7800 E Orchard Rd Ste 400, Greenwood Village, Colorado 80111-2599.
T: 1 303 270-9776 **W:** http://www.ks1075.com
Editorial Profile: KQKS-FM is a commercial station owned by Lincoln Financial Media. The format of the station is urban contemporary music. KQKS-FM broadcasts to the Denver area at 107.5 FM.

KQKX-FM
Owner: WJAG Inc.
Editorial: 309 Braasch Ave, Norfolk, Nebraska 68701-4113. **T:** 1 402 371-0780
W: http://www.106kix.com
Editorial Profile: KQKX-FM is a commercial station owned by WJAG Inc. The format of the station is country. KQKX-FM broadcasts to the Norfolk, NE area at 106.7 FM.

KQKY-FM
Owner: NRG Media LLC
Editorial: 2223 Central Ave, Kearney, Nebraska 68847. **T:** 1 308 698-2100
E: hits106@gmail.com
W: http://www.kqky.com
Editorial Profile: KQKY-FM is a commercial station owned by NRG Media LLC. The format

WORLD NEWS MEDIA

of the station is Top 40/CHR music. KQKY-FM broadcasts to the Kearney, NE area at 105.9 FM.

KQLA-FM
Owner: Platinum Broadcasting, Inc.
Editorial: US Highway 77 & W Ash St, Junction City, Kansas 66441.
T: 1 785 762-5525 **E:** platinum@kjck.com
W: http://www.qcountry1035.com
Editorial Profile: KQLA-FM is a commercial station owned by Platinum Broadcasting, Inc. The format of the station is country. KQLA-FM broadcasts to the Junction City, KS area at 103.5 FM.

KQLB-FM
Owner: VLB Broadcasting Inc.
Editorial: 401 Pacheco Blvd, Los Banos, California 93635. **T:** 1 209 827-0123
E: pr@kqlb.com **W:** http://www.kqlb.com
Editorial Profile: KQLB-FM is a commercial station owned by VLB Broadcasting Inc. The format of the station is regional Mexican music. KQLB-FM broadcasts in the Los Banos, CA area at 106.9 FM.

KQLK-FM
Owner: Cumulus Media Inc.
Editorial: 425 Broad St, Lake Charles, Louisiana 70601. **T:** 1 337 439-3300
W: http://www.kqlk.com
Editorial Profile: KQLK-FM is a commercial station owned by Cumulus Media Inc. The format of the station is Top 40/CHR. KQLK-FM broadcasts in the Lake Charles, LA area at 97.9 FM.

KQLL-AM
Owner: Summit Media
Editorial: 150 Spectrum Blvd, Las Vegas, Nevada 89101-4860. **T:** 1 702 258-0285
W: http://www.kool1023.com
Editorial Profile: KQLL-AM is a commercial station owned by Summit Media (dba S & R Broadcasting, Inc.). The format of the station is Oldies. KQLL-AM broadcasts to the Las Vegas area at 1280 AM.

KQLM-FM
Owner: Stellar Media, Inc.
Editorial: 1319 S Crane Ave, Odessa, Texas 79763. **T:** 1 432 333-1227
W: http://www.q108fm.com

KQLQ-FM
Owner: Opus Media Partners
Editorial: 1200 N 18th St, Ste D, Monroe, Louisiana 71201. **T:** 1 318 387-3922
W: http://www.hot1031.fm
Editorial Profile: KQLQ-FM is a commercial station owned by Opus Media Partners. The format of the station is Top 40/CHR music. KQLQ-FM broadcasts in the Monroe, LA area at 103.1 FM.

KQLT-FM
Owner: Mount Rushmore Broadcasting Inc.
Editorial: 218 N Wolcott St, Casper, Wyoming 82601. **T:** 1 307 265-1984
Editorial Profile: KQLT-FM is a commercial station owned by Mount Rushmore Broadcasting Inc. The format for the station is country. KQLT-FM broadcasts to the Casper, WY area at 103.7 FM.

KQLV-FM
Owner: Educational Media Foundation
Editorial: 4101 Barbara Loop SE, Rio Rancho, New Mexico 87124-1009. **T:** 1 505 352-4028
E: info@klove.com **W:** http://www.klove.com
Editorial Profile: KQLV-FM is a non-commercial station owned by Educational Media Foundation. The format of the station is contemporary Christian. KQLV-FM broadcasts to the Albuquerque and Santa Fe, NM areas at 90.7 FM.

KQLX-AM
Owner: Great Plains Integrated Marketing Inc.
Editorial: 64 Broadway N, Fargo, North Dakota 58102-4934. **T:** 1 701 683-5287
E: studio@agnews890.com
W: http://www.agnews890.com
Editorial Profile: KQLX-AM is a commercial station owned by Great Plains Integrated Marketing Inc. The format of the station is news. KQLX-AM broadcasts to the Lisbon, ND area at 890 AM.

KQLX-FM
Owner: Great Plains Integrated Marketing Inc.
Editorial: 64 Broadway N, Fargo, North Dakota 58102-4934. **T:** 1 701 683-5287
E: thunderstudio@thunder1061.com
W: http://www.thunder1061.com

Editorial Profile: KQLX-FM is a commercial station owned by Great Plains Integrated Marketing Inc. The format of the station is country. KQLX-FM broadcasts to the Fargo, ND area at 106.1 FM.

KQMA-FM
Owner: S-Y Communications
Editorial: 205 F St, Phillipsburg, Kansas 67661. **T:** 1 785 543-2151
E: radio@kkankqma.com
W: http://www.kkankqma.com
Editorial Profile: KQMA-FM is a commercial station owned by S-Y Communications. The format of the station is hot adult contemporary music and contemporary country music. KQMA-FM broadcasts to the Phillipsburg, KS area at 92.5 FM.

KQMG-AM
Owner: KM Communications Inc.
Editorial: 1812 3rd Ave SE, Independence, Iowa 50644-9884. **T:** 1 319 332-1812
E: kqmgfm@gmail.com
W: http://www.kqmg.org
Editorial Profile: KQMG-AM is a commercial station owned by KM Communications Inc. The format of the station is classic hits. KQMG-AM broadcasts to the Independence, IA area at 1220 AM.

KQMG-FM
Owner: KM Communications Inc.
Editorial: 1812 3rd Ave SE, Independence, Iowa 50644-9884. **T:** 1 319 332-1812
E: kqmgfm@gmail.com
W: http://www.kqmg.org
Editorial Profile: KQMG-FM is a commercial station owned by KM Communications Inc. The format of the station is classic hits. KQMG-FM broadcasts to the Independence, IA area at 95.3 FM.

KQMN-FM
Owner: Minnesota Public Radio
Editorial: 901 8th St S, Moorhead, Minnesota 56562. **T:** 1 218 2847-0666
E: newsroom@mpr.org
W: http://minnesota.publicradio.org/radio/stations/kntnkqmn
Editorial Profile: KQMN-FM is a non-commercial station owned by Minnesota Public Radio. The format of the station is classical music. KQMN-FM broadcasts to the Thief River Falls, MN area at 91.5 FM.

KQMO-FM
Owner: Falcon Broadcasting Inc.
Editorial: 126 S Jefferson Ave, Aurora, Missouri 65605-1635. **T:** 1 417 678-0416
E: kqmo@radiotalon.com
W: http://www.kqmo977.com
Editorial Profile: KQMO-FM is a commercial station owned by Falcon Broadcasting Inc. The format of the station is regional Mexican music. KQMO-FM broadcasts to the Springfield, MO area at 97.7 FM.

KQMQ-FM
Owner: Visionary Related Entertainment
Editorial: 1000 Bishop St Suite 200, Honolulu, Hawaii 96813-4202. **T:** 1 808 947-1500
W: http://931dapaina.com
Editorial Profile: KQMQ-FM is a commercial station owned by Visionary Related Entertainment. The format of the station is reggae. KQMQ-FM broadcasts to Honolulu at 93.1 FM.

KQMR-FM
Owner: Univision Communications Inc.
Editorial: 4745 N 7th St, Phoenix, Arizona 85014-3665. **T:** 1 602 308-7900
W: http://recuerdophoenix.univision.com/
Editorial Profile: KQMR-FM is a commercial station owned by Univision Communications Inc. The format of the station is Hispanic oldies and Hispanic urban. KQMR-FM broadcasts to the Phoenix area on 100.3 FM.

KQMS-AM
Owner: Mapleton of Redding, LLC
Editorial: 3360 Alta Mesa Dr, Redding, California 96002. **T:** 1 530 226-9500
E: news@reddingradio.com
W: http://www.kqms.com
Editorial Profile: KQMS-AM is a commercial station owned by Mapleton of Redding, LLC. The format of the station is news and talk programming. KQMS-AM broadcasts to the Redding, CA area at 1400 AM.

KQMT-FM
Owner: Entercom Communications Corp.
Editorial: 4700 S Syracuse St, Ste 1050, Denver, Colorado 80237. **T:** 1 303 967-2700
W: http://www.995themountain.com

Editorial Profile: KQMT-FM is a commercial station that is owned by Entercom Communications Corp. The format of the station is classic rock. KQMT-FM broadcasts to the Denver area at 99.5 FM.

KQMV-FM
Owner: Hubbard Radio, LLC
Editorial: 3650 131st Ave SE Ste 550, Bellevue, Washington 98006-1334.
T: 1 425 653-9462 **E:** info@movin925.com
W: http://movin925.com
Editorial Profile: KQMV-FM is a commercial station owned by Hubbard Radio, LLC. The format of the station is Top 40. KQMV-FM broadcasts to the Seattle area at 92.5 FM.

KQMY-FM
Owner: Townsquare Media, LLC
Editorial: 4010 Summitview Ave, Yakima, Washington 98908. **T:** 1 509 972-3461
W: http://newstalkkit.com
Editorial Profile: KQMY-FM is a commercial station owned by Townsquare Media, LLC. The format of the station is news/talk. KQMY-FM broadcasts to the Yakima, WA area at 99.3 FM.

KQNA-AM
Owner: Prescott Valley Broadcasting Co. Inc.
Editorial: 3755 Karicio Ln, Prescott, Arizona 86303. **T:** 1 928 445-8289
E: kppv@cableone.net
W: http://www.kqna.com
Editorial Profile: KQNA-AM is a commercial station owned by Prescott Valley Broadcasting Co. Inc. The format of the station is news and talk. KQNA-AM broadcasts to the Prescott, AZ area at 1130 AM.

KQNG-AM
Owner: Ohana Broadcasting, LLC
Editorial: 4271 Halenani St, Lihue, Hawaii 96766. **T:** 1 808 245-9527
E: kong@kongradio.com
W: http://www.kongradio.com
Editorial Profile: KQNG-AM is a commercial radio station that is owned by Ohana Broadcasting, LLC. The format of the station is news, sports and talk. KQNG-AM broadcasts to the Lihue, HI area at 570 AM.

KQNG-FM
Owner: Ohana Broadcast Company
Editorial: 4271 Halenani St, Lihue, Hawaii 96766-1312. **T:** 1 808 245-9527
E: kong@kongradio.com
W: http://www.kongradio.com
Editorial Profile: KQNG-FM is a commercial station owned by Ohana Broadcast Company. The format of the station is Top 40/CHR. KQNG-FM broadcasts to the Lihue, HI area at 93.5 FM.

KQNK-AM
Owner: Dierking Communications
Editorial: 17038 Kqnk Rd, Norton, Kansas 67654-5569. **T:** 1 785 877-3378
E: kqnk@ruraltel.net **W:** http://www.kqnk.com
Editorial Profile: KQNK-AM is a commercial station owned by Dierking Communications. The format of the station is classic rock music. KQNK-AM broadcasts to the Norton, KS area at 1530 AM.

KQNK-FM
Owner: Dierking Communications
Editorial: 17038 Kqnk Rd, Norton, Kansas 67654-5569. **T:** 1 785 877-3378
E: kqnk@ruraltel.net **W:** http://www.kqnk.com
Editorial Profile: KQNK-FM is a commercial station owned by Dierking Communications. The format of the station is classic hits music. KQNK-FM broadcasts to the Norton, KS area at 106.7 FM.

KQNM-AM
Owner: Isleta Radio Co. (Whitman, Martha)
Editorial: 809 Wellesley Dr NE, Albuquerque, New Mexico 87106-1936. **T:** 1 505 899-5029
Editorial Profile: KQNM-AM is a commerical station owned by Isleta Radio Co. (Whitman, Martha). The format of the station is oldies. KQNM-AM can be heard in the Grants, NM area at 1100 AM.

KQNT-AM
Owner: Clear Channel Media and Entertainment
Editorial: 808 E Sprague Ave, Spokane, Washington 99202. **T:** 1 509 242-2400
W: http://www.newstalk590.com
Editorial Profile: KQNT-AM is a commercial station owned by Clear Channel Media and Entertainment. The format of the station is news and talk. KQNT-AM broadcasts to the Spokane, WA area at 590 AM.

KQNU-FM
Owner: Powell Broadcasting Co.
Editorial: 2000 Indian Hills Dr, Sioux City, Iowa 51104-1602. **T:** 1 712 239-2100
E: programming@new1023.com
W: http://www.new1023.com
Editorial Profile: KQNU-FM is a commercial station owned by Powell Broadcasting Co. The format of the station is Top 40/CHR. KQNU-FM broadcasts to the Sioux City, IA area on 102.3 FM.

KQOB-FM
Owner: Cumulus Media Inc
Editorial: 4045 NW 64th St, Ste 600, Oklahoma City, Oklahoma 73116-2607.
T: 1 405 848-0100
W: http://www.969bobfm.com
Editorial Profile: KQOB-FM is a commercial station owned by Cumulus Media Inc. The format is adult hits. KQOB-FM broadcasts to the Oklahoma City area at 96.9 FM.

KQOC-FM
Owner: All Classical Public Media, Inc.
Editorial: 515 NE 15th Ave, Portland, Oregon 97232-2897. **T:** 1 503 943-5828
E: music.info@allclassical.org
W: http://www.allclassical.org
Editorial Profile: KQOC-FM is a non-commercial station owned by All Classical Public Media, Inc. The format of the station is classical music. KQOC-FM broadcasts to Lincoln City, OR and surrounding areas.

KQOD-FM
Owner: Clear Channel Media and Entertainment
Editorial: 2121 Lancey Dr, Modesto, California 95355. **T:** 1 209 551-1306
E: modestopsa@clearchannel.com
W: http://www.mega100online.com
Editorial Profile: KQOD-FM is a commercial station owned by Clear Channel Media and Entertainment. The format of the station is R&B oldies. The station broadcasts to the Modesto, CA area at 100.1 FM

KQOR-FM
Owner: Ouachita Broadcasting Inc.
Editorial: 1600 Reine St S, Mena, Arkansas 71953. **T:** 1 479 394-1450
E: menaradio@allegiance.tv
Editorial Profile: KQOR-FM is a commercial station owned by Ouachita Broadcasting Inc. The format for the station is oldies. KQOR-FM broadcasts to the Mena, AR area at 105.3 FM.

KQPM-FM
Owner: Bicoastal Media LLC
Editorial: 140 N Main St, Lakeport, California 95453-4815. **T:** 1 707 263-6113
W: http://www.kqpm.com
Editorial Profile: KQPM-FM is a commercial station owned by Bicoastal Media LLC. The format of the station is contemporary country. KQPM-FM broadcasts to the San Francisco area at 105.9 FM.

KQPN-AM
Owner: Simmons Media Group
Editorial: 203 Beale St Ste 204, Memphis, Tennessee 38103-3727. **T:** 1 901 452-3094
E: kqpn@730yahoosports.com
W: http://730yahoosports.com
Editorial Profile: KQPN-AM is a commercial station owned by Simmons Media Group. The format of the station is sports. KQPN-AM broadcasts to the Memphis, TN area at 730 AM.

KQPR-FM
Owner: Hometown Broadcasting, Inc.
Editorial: 109 E Clark St, Albert Lea, Minnesota 56007. **T:** 1 507 373-9600
E: kqpr@power96rocker.com
W: http://www.power96rocker.com/
Editorial Profile: KQPR-FM is a commercial station owned by Hometown Broadcasting, Inc. The format of the station is classic rock. KQPR-FM broadcasts to the Rochester, MN - Mason City, IA area at 96.1 FM.

KQPT-FM
Owner: Mapleton of Chico, LLC
Editorial: 1459 Humboldt Rd, Ste D, Chico, California 95928. **T:** 1 530 899-3600
Editorial Profile: KQPT-FM is a commercial station owned by Mapleton of Chico, LLC. The format of the station is Top 40/CHR. KQPT-FM broadcasts to the Chico, CA area at 107.5 FM.

KQQF-FM
Owner: Radio Results Group
Editorial: 306 W 8th St, Coffeyville, Kansas 67337-5829. **T:** 1 620 251-3800
E: kqqf.newsinfo@sbcglobal.net

W: http://www.radioresultsgroup.com
Editorial Profile: KQQF-FM is a commercial station owned by Radio Results Group. The format of the station is Hot AC. KQQF-FM broadcasts to the Tulsa, OK area at 98.9 FM.

KQQK-FM
Owner: Liberman Broadcasting Inc.
Editorial: 3000 Bering Dr, Houston, Texas 77057-5708. **T:** 1 713 315-3400
W: http://www.elnorteenlinea.com
Editorial Profile: KQQK-FM is a commercial station owned by Liberman Broadcasting Inc. The format of the station is regional Mexican. KQQK-FM broadcasts to the Houston area at 107.9 FM.

KQQL-FM
Owner: Clear Channel Media and Entertainment
Editorial: 1600 Utica Ave S, Ste 400, Saint Louis Park, Minnesota 55416-1480.
T: 1 952 417-3000
W: http://www.kool108.com
Editorial Profile: KQQL-FM is a commercial station owned by Clear Channel Media and Entertainment. The format of the station is classic hits. KQQL-FM broadcasts to the Minneapolis area at 107.9 FM.

KQQQ-AM
Owner: Radio Palouse Inc.
Editorial: 1101 Old Wawawai Rd, Pullman, Washington 99163-9002. **T:** 1 509 332-6551
E: news@pullmanradio.com
Editorial Profile: KQQQ-AM is a commercial station owned by Radio Palouse Inc. The format of the station is news, sports and talk. KQQQ-AM broadcasts to the Spokane, WA area at 1150 AM.

KQQZ-AM
Owner: Entertainment Media Trust
Editorial: 6500 W Main St, Belleville, Illinois 62223-3700. **T:** 1 618 394-1430
E: info@kqqz1190am.com
W: http://www.kqqz1190am.com
Editorial Profile: KQQZ-AM is a commercial station owned by Entertainment Media Trust. The format of the station is classic country. KQQZ-AM broadcasts to the St. Louis area at 1190 AM.

KQRA-FM
Owner: Midwest Family Stations
Editorial: 319B E Battlefield St, Springfield, Missouri 65807-4999. **T:** 1 417 886-5677
E: info@q1021.fm **W:** http://www.q1021.fm
Editorial Profile: KQRA-FM is a commercial station owned by Midwest Family Stations. The format of the station is rock alternative. KQRA-FM broadcasts in the Springfield, MO area at 102.1 FM.

KQRC-FM
Owner: Entercom Communications Corp.
Editorial: 7000 Squibb Rd, Mission, Kansas 66202. **T:** 1 913 576-7989
E: kqrc@entercom.com
W: http://www.989therock.com
Editorial Profile: KQRC-FM is a commercial station owned by Entercom Communications Corp. The format for the station is rock music. KQRC-FM broadcasts to the Kansas City, MO area at 98.9 FM.

KQRK-FM
Owner: Anderson Radio Broadcasting Inc.
Editorial: 36581 N Reservoir Rd, Polson, Montana 59860-8471. **T:** 1 406 883-5255
W: http://star92hits.com
Editorial Profile: KQRK-FM is a commercial station owned by Anderson Radio Broadcasting Inc. The format of the station is Top 40/CHR. KQRK-FM is licensed to Pablo, MT and broadcasts locally at 99.7 FM.

KQRL-AM
Owner: Simmons Media Group
Editorial: 5501 Bagby Ave, Waco, Texas 76711. **T:** 1 254 772-0930
Editorial Profile: KRZX-AM is a commercial station owned by Simmons Media Group. The format of the station is country music. KRZX-AM broadcasts in the Waco, TX area at 1580 AM and is a simulcast of KWGW-FM.

KQRN-FM
Owner: Riverfront Broadcasting
Editorial: 319 N Main St, Mitchell, South Dakota 57301. **T:** 1 605 996-1073
E: kornnews@kornq107.com
W: http://www.q107radio.com
Editorial Profile: KQRN-FM is a commercial station owned by Riverfront Broadcasting. The format of the station is hot adult contemporary music. KQRN-FM broadcasts to the Mitchell, SD, area at 107.3 FM.

KQRQ-FM
Owner: Duhamel Broadcasting
Editorial: 518 Saint Joseph St, Rapid City, South Dakota 57701-2717. **T:** 1 605 342-2000
W: http://www.q923radio.com
Editorial Profile: KQRQ-FM is a commercial station owned by Duhamel Broadcasting. The format of the station is classic hits. KQRQ-FM broadcasts to the Rapid City, SD area at a frequency of 92.3 FM.

KQRS-FM
Owner: Cumulus Media Inc
Editorial: 2000 Elm St Se, Minneapolis, Minnesota 55414-2531. **T:** 1 612 617-4000
W: http://www.92kqrs.com
Editorial Profile: KQRS-FM is a commercial station owned by Cumulus Media Inc. The format of the station is classic rock. KQRS-FM broadcasts to the Minneapolis area at 92.5 FM.

KQRT-FM
Owner: Entravision Communications Corp.
Editorial: 500 Pilot Rd Ste D, Las Vegas, Nevada 89119-3624. **T:** 1 702 434-0015
W: http://www.tricolor1051.com
Editorial Profile: KQRT-FM is a commercial station owned by Entravision Communications Corp. The format of the station is Hispanic programming. KQRT-FM broadcasts to the Las Vegas, NV area at 105.1 FM.

KQRV-FM
Owner: Toole(Robert Cummings)
Editorial: 302 Missouri Ave, Deer Lodge, Montana 59722. **T:** 1 406 846-1100
E: riverradio@bresnan.net
Editorial Profile: KQRV-FM is a commercial station owned by Robert Cummings Toole. The format of the station is news, sports and country. KQRV-FM broadcasts to the Deer Lodge, MT area at 96.9 FM.

KQRX-FM
Owner: Brazos Communications West, LLC
Editorial: 3303 N Midkiff Rd Ste 115, Midland, Texas 79705-4860. **T:** 1 432 520-9510
Editorial Profile: KQRX-FM is a commercial station owned by Brazos Communications West, LLC. The format of the station is active rock. KQRX-FM broadcasts in the Midland, TX area at 95.1 FM.

KQSF-FM
Owner: Midwest Communications
Editorial: 500 S Phillips Ave, Sioux Falls, South Dakota 57104-6825. **T:** 1 605 331-5350
W: http://www.q957.com
Editorial Profile: KQSF-FM is a commercial station owned by Midwest Communications. The format of the station is oldies. KQSF-FM broadcasts to the Sioux Falls, SD area at 95.7 FM.

KQSK-FM
Owner: Eagle Communications
Editorial: 331 Main St Ste C, Chadron, Nebraska 69337-2387. **T:** 1 308 432-2060
W: http://www.doubleqcountry.com
Editorial Profile: KQSK-FM is a commercial station owned by Eagle Communications. The format of the station is country music. KQSK-FM broadcasts to the Chadron, NE area at 97.5 FM.

KQSM-FM
Owner: Cumulus Media Inc.
Editorial: 4209 N Frontage Rd, Fayetteville, Arkansas 72703-5002. **T:** 1 479 521-5566
W: http://www.921theticket.com
Editorial Profile: KQSM-FM is a commercial station owned by Cumulus Media Inc. The format of the station is sports. KQSM-FM broadcasts in the Fayetteville, AK area 92.1 FM.

KQSN-FM
Owner: Mur-Thom Broadcasting Inc.
Editorial: 3924 Santa Fe St, Ponca City, Oklahoma 74601-1063. **T:** 1 580 765-5491
E: kixr@kixr.com
Editorial Profile: KQSN-FM is a commercial station owned by Mur-Thom Broadcasting Inc. The format of the station is hot adult contemporary music. KQSN-FM broadcasts to the Ponca City, OK area at 100.1 FM.

KQSP-AM
Owner: Broadcast One, Inc.
Editorial: 919 Lilac Dr N, Minneapolis, Minnesota 55422-4615. **T:** 1 763 230-7602
W: http://www.lapicosa.us
Editorial Profile: KQSP-AM is a commercial station owned by Broadcast One, Inc. The format of the station is Tropical. KQSP-AM broadcasts to the Chaska, MN area at 1530 AM.

KQSR-FM
Owner: El Dorado Broadcasting
Editorial: 755 W 28th St, Yuma, Arizona 85364. **T:** 1 928 344-4980
W: http://www.kqsrfm.com
Editorial Profile: KQSR-FM is a commercial station owned by El Dorado Broadcasting. The format of the station is adult contemporary music. KQSR-FM broadcasts to the Yuma, AZ area at 100.9 FM.

KQSS-FM
Owner: Taylor(William)
Editorial: 5734 S McKinney Ave, Globe, Arizona 85501-4361. **T:** 1 928 425-7186
W: http://www.gila1019.com
Editorial Profile: KQSS-FM is a commercial station owned by William Taylor. The format of the station is contemporary country. KQSS-FM broadcasts to the Globe, AZ area at 98.3 FM.

KQST-FM
Owner: Yavapai Broadcasting
Editorial: 3405 E Highway 89A, Bldg A, Cottonwood, Arizona 86326-5506.
T: 1 928 634-2286
W: http://www.myradioplace.com/q.htm
Editorial Profile: KQST-FM is a commercial station owned by the Yavapai Broadcasting. The format of the station is Top 40/CHR. KQST-FM broadcasts to the Phoenix, AZ area at 102.9 FM.

KQSW-FM
Owner: Big Thicket Broadcasting Co.
Editorial: 2717 Yellowstone Rd, Rock Springs, Wyoming 82901-3261. **T:** 1 307 382-5619
E: wyoradio@wyoradio.com
W: http://www.bestcountryaround.com
Editorial Profile: KQSW-FM is a commercial station owned by Big Thicket Broadcasting Co. The format of the station is classic country. KQSW-FM broadcasts to the Salt Lake City area at 96.5 FM.

KQTA-FM
Owner: Adelante Media Group
Editorial: 3307 Caldwell Blvd, Nampa, Idaho 83651-6402. **T:** 1 208 463-2900
W: http://www.latinosoloexitos.com
Editorial Profile: KQTA-FM is a commercial station owned by Adelante Media Group. The format of the station is Bilingual Top 40/CHR. KQTA-FM broadcasts to the Nampa, ID area at 106.3 FM.

KQTH-FM
Owner: Journal Broadcast Group
Editorial: 7280 E Rosewood St, Tucson, Arizona 85710-1350. **T:** 1 520 722-5486
W: http://www.1041kqth.com
Editorial Profile: KQTH-FM is a commercial station owned by Journal Broadcast Group. The format of the station is news and talk. KQTH-FM broadcasts in the Tucson, AZ area at 104.1 FM.

KQTM-FM
Owner: Team Broadcasting
Editorial: 4131 Barbara Loop SE, Rio Rancho, New Mexico 87124-1362. **T:** 1 505 338-1414
W: http://www.1017theteam.com
Editorial Profile: KQTM-FM is a commercial station owned by Team Broadcasting. The format of the station is sports. KQTM-FM broadcasts to the Albuquerque, NM, area at 101.7 FM.

KQTY-AM
Owner: Zia Broadcasting
Editorial: 113 Union St, Borger, Texas 79007-6019. **T:** 1 806 273-7533
E: kqtyradio@yahoo.com
W: http://www.kqtyradio.com
Editorial Profile: KQTY-AM is a commercial station owned by Zia Broadcasting. The format of the station is news, sports and talk. KQTY-AM broadcasts to the Borger, TX area at 1490 AM.

KQTY-FM
Owner: Zia Broadcasting
Editorial: 113 Union St, Borger, Texas 79007.
T: 1 806 273-7533 **E:** kqtyradio@yahoo.com
W: http://www.kqtyradio.com
Editorial Profile: KQTY-FM is a commercial station owned by Zia Broadcasting. The format of the station is country, Christian, and gospel. KQTY-AM broadcasts to the Borger, TX area at 106.7 FM.

KQTZ-FM
Owner: Monarch Broadcasting
Editorial: 212 W Cypress St, Altus, Oklahoma 73521. **T:** 1 580 482-1450
Editorial Profile: KQTZ-FM is a commercial station owned by Monarch Broadcasting. The format of the station is adult hits music. KQTZ-FM broadcasts to the Altus, OK area at 105.9 FM.

KQUE-AM
Owner: Aleyua Christian Broadcasting
Editorial: 5100 Southwest Fwy, Houston, Texas 77056-7308. **T:** 1 713 965-2400
Editorial Profile: KQUE-AM is a commercial station owned by Aleyua Christian Broadcasting. The format of the station is Hispanic Christian programming. KQUE-AM broadcasts to the Houston area at 980 AM.

KQUL-FM
Owner: Benne Media
Editorial: 160 Highway 42, Kaiser, Missouri 65047. **T:** 1 573 348-1958
W: http://www.cool1027.com
Editorial Profile: KQUL-FM is a commercial station owned by Benne Media. The format of the station is classic hits. KQUL-FM broadcasts in the Kaiser, MO area at 102.7 FM.

KQUR-FM
Owner: Border Media Partners LLC
Editorial: 107 Calle Del Norte, Ste 212, Laredo, Texas 78041. T: 1 956 725-1000
Editorial Profile: KQUR-FM is a commercial station owned by Border Media Partners LLC and operated by MBM Radio Laredo, LLC. The format of the station is Spanish Top 40/CHR. KQUR-FM broadcasts to the Laredo, TX area at 94.9 FM.

KQUS-FM
Owner: US Stations, LLC
Editorial: 125 Corporate Ter, Hot Springs, Arkansas 71913-7248. **T:** 1 501 525-9700
W: http://www.us97country.com
Editorial Profile: KQUS-FM is a commercial station owned by US Stations, LLC. The format of the station is classic country. KQUS-FM broadcasts to the Hot Springs, AR area at 97.5 FM.

KQV-AM
Owner: Calvary Inc.
Editorial: 650 Smithfield St, Ste 620, Pittsburgh, Pennsylvania 15222-3913.
T: 1 412 562-5900 **E:** kqvnews@kqv.com
W: http://www.kqv.com
Editorial Profile: KQV-AM is a commercial station owned by Calvary Inc. The format of the station is news. KQV-AM broadcasts to the Pittsburgh area at 1410 AM.

KQVO-FM
Owner: San Diego State University
Editorial: 695 Highway 111, Calexico, California 92231-3209. **T:** 1 619 594-1515
W: http://www.kpbs.org
Editorial Profile: KQVO-FM is a non-commercial station owned by San Diego State University. The format of the station is news, talk and classical. KQVO-FM broadcasts to Calexico, CA at 97.7 FM.

KQVT-FM
Owner: Townsquare Media, LLC
Editorial: 107 N Star Dr, Victoria, Texas 77904. **T:** 1 361 573-0777
W: http://www.kqvt.com
Editorial Profile: KQVT-FM is a commercial station owned by Townsquare Media, LLC. The format for the station is hot adult contemporary. KQVT-FM broadcasts to the Victoria, TX area at 92.3 FM.

KQWB-AM
Owner: L & L Radio
Editorial: 2720 7th Ave S, Fargo, North Dakota 58103-8710. **T:** 1 701 237-4500
Editorial Profile: KQWB-AM is a commercial station owned by L & L Radio. The format of the station is oldies. KQWB-AM broadcasts in the Fargo, ND area at 1660 AM.

KQWB-FM
Owner: L & L Radio
Editorial: 2720 7th Ave S, Fargo, North Dakota 58103-8710. **T:** 1 701 237-4500
W: http://www.q1051rocks.com
Editorial Profile: KQWB-FM is a commercial station owned by L & L Radio. The format of the station is rock music. KQWB-FM broadcasts in the Fargo, ND area at 105.1 FM.

KQWC-AM

Owner: NRG Media LLC
Editorial: 1020 E 2nd St, Webster City, Iowa 50595. **T:** 1 515 832-1570
W: http://www.kqradio.com
Editorial Profile: KQWC-AM is a commercial station owned by NRG Media LLC. The format of the station is oldies. KQWC-AM broadcasts to the Des Moines, IA area at 1570 AM.

KQWC-FM

Owner: NRG Media LLC
Editorial: 1020 E 2nd St, Webster City, Iowa 50595. **T:** 1 515 832-1570 **E:** kqwc@wmtel.net
W: http://www.kqradio.com
Editorial Profile: KQWC-FM is a commercial station owned by NRG Media LLC. The format is adult contemporary music. KQWC-FM broadcasts to the Webster City, IA area at 95.7 FM.

KQWS-FM

Owner: Washington State University
Editorial: Murrow Center, Room 382, Pullman, Washington 99164. **T:** 1 509 335-6500
E: nwpr@wsu.edu **W:** http://www.nwpr.org
Editorial Profile: KQWS-FM is a non-commercial station owned by Washington State University. The format is news, talk and classical music. KQWS-FM broadcasts to the Omak and Tonasket, WA areas at 90.1 FM, though the station's staff is based in Pullman, WA.

KQXC-FM

Owner: Cumulus Media Inc.
Editorial: 4302 Call Field Rd, Wichita Falls, Texas 76308. **T:** 1 940 691-2311
W: http://www.thehot1039.com
Editorial Profile: KQXC-FM is a commercial station owned by Cumulus Media Inc. The format of the station is rhythmic Top 40. KQXC-FM broadcasts to the Wichita Falls, TX area at 103.9 FM.

KQXF-FM

Owner: Sudbury Broadcasting Group
Editorial: 125 S 2nd St, Blytheville, Arkansas 72315. **T:** 1 870 762-2093
W: http://www.todaysbesthits.com
Editorial Profile: KQXF-FM is a commercial station owned by Sudbury Services. The format of the station is hot adult contemporary. KQXF-FM broadcasts to the Blytheville, AR area at 107.3 FM.

KQXL-FM

Owner: Cumulus Media Inc
Editorial: 650 Wooddale Blvd, Baton Rouge, Louisiana 70806-2930. **T:** 1 225 926-1106
W: http://www.q106dot5.com
Editorial Profile: KQXL-FM is commercial station owned by Cumulus Media Inc. The format of the station is urban adult contemporary music. KQXL-FM broadcasts to the Baton Rouge, LA area at 106.5 FM.

KQXR-FM

Owner: Journal Broadcast Group
Editorial: 5257 W Fairview Ave, Ste 260, Boise, Idaho 83706. **T:** 1 208 344-3511
W: http://www.xrock.com
Editorial Profile: KQXR-FM is a commercial station owned by Journal Broadcast Group. The format of the station is rock music. KQXR-FM broadcasts in the Boise, ID area at 100.3 FM.

KQXT-FM

Owner: Clear Channel Media and Entertainment
Editorial: 6222 NW Interstate Highway 10, San Antonio, Texas 78201. **T:** 1 210 736-9700
W: http://www.q1019.com
Editorial Profile: KQXT-FM is a commercial station owned by Clear Channel Media and Entertainment. The format of the station is adult contemporary. KQXT-FM broadcasts to the San Antonio area at 101.9 FM.

KQXX-FM

Owner: Clear Channel Media and Entertainment
Editorial: 901 E Pike Blvd, Weslaco, Texas 78596. **T:** 1 956 973-9202
W: http://www.kqxx.net
Editorial Profile: KQXX-FM is a commercial station owned by Clear Channel Media and Entertainment. The format of the station is classic rock. KQXX-FM broadcasts to the Weslaco, TX area at 105.5 FM.

KQXY-FM

Owner: Cumulus Media Inc.
Editorial: 755 S 11th St, Ste 102, Beaumont, Texas 77701. **T:** 1 409 951-2500
W: http://www.kqxy.com

Editorial Profile: KQXY-FM is a commercial station owned by Cumulus Media Inc. The format of the station is Top 40/CHR music. KQXY-FM broadcasts to the Beaumont, TX area at 94.1 FM.

KQYB-FM

Owner: Midwest Family Stations
Editorial: 201 State St, La Crosse, Wisconsin 54601. **T:** 1 608 782-1230
W: http://www.kq98.com
Editorial Profile: KQYB-FM is a commercial station owned by Midwest Family Stations. The format of the station is contemporary country. KQYB-FM broadcasts to the La Crosse, WI area at 98.3 FM.

KQYX-AM

Owner: American Media Investments
Editorial: 2510 W 20Th St, Joplin, Missouri 64804-0216. **T:** 1 417 781-1313
E: production@ami-joplin.com
Editorial Profile: KQYX-AM is a commercial station owned by American Media Investments. The format of the station is oldies. KQYX-FM broadcasts to the Joplin, MO area at 1450 AM.

KQZR-FM

Owner: NRC Broadcasting
Editorial: 2955 Village Dr, Steamboat Springs, Colorado 80487-2143. **T:** 1 970 879-5368
W: http://alwaysmountaintime.com/kqzr
Editorial Profile: KQZR-FM is a commercial station owned by NRC Broadcasting. The format of the station is classic rock music. KQZR-FM broadcasts to the Steamboat Springs, CO area at 107.3 FM.

KQZZ-FM

Owner: Double Z Broadcasting Inc.
Editorial: 320 Walnut St W, Devils Lake, North Dakota 58301-3506. **T:** 1 701 662-1797
E: kzzyfm@stellarnet.com
W: http://www.lrradioworks.com
Editorial Profile: KQZZ-FM is a commercial station owned by Double Z Broadcasting Inc. The format of the station is hot adult contemporary music. KQZZ-FM broadcasts to the Devils Lake, ND area at 96.7 FM.

KRAB-FM

Owner: Clear Channel Media and Entertainment
Editorial: 1100 Mohawk St, Ste 280, Bakersfield, California 93309.
T: 1 661 322-9929 **E:** krab@clearchannel.com
W: http://www.krab.com
Editorial Profile: KRAB-FM is a commercial station owned by Clear Channel Media and Entertainment. The format of the station is rock. KRAB-FM broadcasts to the Bakersfield, CA area at 106.1 FM.

KRAE-AM

Owner: Proshop Radio Broadcasting LLC
Editorial: 2232 Dell Range Blvd, Ste 202, Cheyenne, Wyoming 82009.
T: 1 307 637-0301
W: http://www.1480krae.com
Editorial Profile: KRAE-AM is a commercial station owned by Proshop Radio Broadcasting, LLC. The format of the station is oldies. KRAE-AM broadcasts to the Cheyenne, WY area at 1480 AM.

KRAI-FM

Owner: Wild West Radio Inc.
Editorial: 1111 W Victory Way, Craig, Colorado 81625-2950. **T:** 1 970 824-6574
E: krai@krai.com **W:** http://www.krai.com
Editorial Profile: KRAI-FM is a commercial station owned by Wild West Radio Inc. The format of the station is hot adult contemporary. KRAI-FM broadcasts to the Denver area at 93.7 FM

KRAJ-FM

Owner: Adelman Broadcasting Inc.
Editorial: 731 Balsam St, Ridgecrest, California 93555-3510. **T:** 1 760 371-1700
E: traffic@adelmanbroadcasting.com
W: http://www.theheat1009.com
Editorial Profile: KRAJ-FM is a commercial station owned by Adelman Broadcasting Inc. The format of the station is rhythmic contemporary. KRAJ-FM broadcasts to the Ridgecrest, CA area at 100.9 FM.

KRAK-AM

Owner: CBS Radio
Editorial: 11920 Hesperia Rd, Hesperia, California 92345-1851. **T:** 1 760 244-2000
W: http://910cbssports.cbslocal.com
Editorial Profile: KRAK-AM is a commercial station owned by CBS Radio. The format of

the station is sports. KRAK-AM broadcasts to the Hesperia, CA area at 910 AM.

KRAO-FM

Owner: Inland Northwest Broadcasting
Editorial: 1114 N Almon St, Moscow, Idaho 83843-8507. **T:** 1 208 882-2551
E: myradio1025@hotmail.com
Editorial Profile: KRAO-FM is a commercial station owned by Inland Northwest Broadcasting. The format of the station is hot AC. KRAO-FM broadcasts to the Moscow, ID area at 102.5 FM.

KRAQ-FM

Owner: Kleven Broadcasting Co.
Editorial: 71991 US Highway 71 South, Jackson, Minnesota 56143-3311.
T: 1 507 847-5400 **E:** info@kkoj.com
W: http://www.kkoj.com
Editorial Profile: KRAQ-FM is a commercial station owned by Kleven Broadcasting Co. The format of the station is oldies music. KRAQ-FM broadcasts to the Jackson, MN area at 105.7 FM.

KRAV-FM

Owner: Cox Media Group, Inc.
Editorial: 7136 S Yale Ave Ste 500, Tulsa, Oklahoma 74136-6358. **T:** 1 918 493-2400
W: http://www.mix96tulsa.com
Editorial Profile: KRAV-FM is a commercial station owned by Cox Media Group, Inc. The format of the station is adult contemporary. KRAV-FM broadcasts to the Tulsa, OK area at 96.5 FM.

KRAY-FM

Owner: Wolfhouse Radio Group Inc.
Editorial: 548 E Alisal St, Salinas, California 93905-2760. **T:** 1 831 757-1910
W: http://wolfhouseradio.net
Editorial Profile: KRAY-FM is a commercial station owned by Wolfhouse Radio Group Inc. The format of the station is Regional Mexican Hits. KRAY-FM broadcasts to the Salinas, CA area at 103.5 FM.

KRAZ-FM

Owner: Knight Broadcasting Inc.
Editorial: 1101 S Broadway, Ste C, Santa Maria, California 93454-6660.
T: 1 805 688-5798 **W:** http://www.krazfm.com
Editorial Profile: KRAZ-FM is a commercial station owned by Knight Broadcasting Inc. The format of the station is contemporary country. KRAZ-FM broadcasts to the Santa Barbara, CA area at 105.9 FM.

KRBA-AM

Owner: Pentagon Communications, LLC
Editorial: 121 S Cotton Sq, Lufkin, Texas 75904-2933. **T:** 1 936 634-6661
E: traffic@yatesmedia.com
W: http://www.krbaradio.com
Editorial Profile: KRBA-AM is a commerical station owned by Yates Media. The format of the station is classic country, gospel music, news and sports. KRBA-AM broadcasts to the Lufkin, TX area at 1340 AM.

KRBB-FM

Owner: Clear Channel Media and Entertainment
Editorial: 9323 E 37th St N, Wichita, Kansas 67226. **T:** 1 316 494-6600
E: wichitanews@clearchannel.com
W: http://www.b98fm.com
Editorial Profile: KRBB-FM is a commercial station owned by Clear Channel Media and Entertainment. The format of the station is Lite Rock/Lite AC. KRBB-FM broadcasts to the Wichita, KS area at 97.9 FM.

KRBD-FM

Owner: Rainbird Community Broadcasting
Editorial: 123 Stedman St, Ketchikan, Alaska 99901. **T:** 1 907 225-9655 **E:** news@krbd.org
W: http://www.krbd.org
Editorial Profile: KRBD-FM is a commercial station owned by Rainbird Community Broadcasting Corp. The format of the station is variety. KRBD-FM's broadcasts in the Ketchikan, AK area.

KRBE-FM

Owner: Cumulus Media Inc.
Editorial: 9801 Westheimer Rd Ste 700, Houston, Texas 77042-3955.
T: 1 713 266-1000 **W:** http://www.krbe.com
Editorial Profile: KRBE-FM is a commercial station owned byCumulus Media Inc. The format of the station is Top 40/CHR. KRBE-FM broadcasts to the Houston area at 104.1 FM.

KRBI-FM

Owner: Three Eagles Communications Co.
Editorial: 1807 Lee Blvd, North Mankato, Minnesota 56003. **T:** 1 507 345-4646
W: http://www.river105.com
Editorial Profile: KRBI-FM is a commercial station owned by Three Eagles Communications Co. The format of the station is classic hits. KRBI-FM broadcasts to the North Mankato, MN area at 105.5 FM.

KRBL-FM

Owner: Walker Broadcasting and Communications Inc.
Editorial: 1603 13th St, Lubbock, Texas 79401-3817. **T:** 1 806 744-6864
W: http://1057edge.com
Editorial Profile: KRBL-FM is a commercial station owned by Walker Broadcasting and Communications Inc. The format of the station is alternative rock music. KRBL-FM broadcasts to the Lubbock, TX area at 105.7 FM.

KRBS-FM

Owner: Bird Street Media Project
Editorial: 2360 Oro Quincy Hwy, Oroville, California 95966-5226. **T:** 1 530 534-1200
E: krbs@cncnet.com
W: http://www.radiobirdstreet.org

KRBT-AM

Owner: Red Rock Radio Corp.
Editorial: 501 S Lake Ave Ste 200, Duluth, Minnesota 55802-2392. **T:** 1 218 728-9500
W: http://www.krbtam.com
Editorial Profile: KRBT-AM is a commercial station owned by Red Rock Radio Corp.. The format of the station is sports. KRBT-AM broadcasts to the Iron Range areas of Minnesota at 1340 AM.

KRBW-FM

Owner: American Family Association
Editorial: 107 Park Gate Dr, Tupelo, Mississippi 38801-3010. **T:** 1 662 844-8888
E: comments@afr.net **W:** http://www.afr.net
Editorial Profile: KRBW-FM is a non-commercial station owned by American Family Association. The format of the station is Adult contemporary Christian music. KRBW-FM broadcasts to the Ottawa, Kansas area at 90.5 FM.

KRBX-FM

Owner: Boise Community Radio Project, Inc
Editorial: 1020 W Main St Ste 200, Boise, Idaho 83702-5745. **T:** 1 208 424-8166
E: info@radioboise.org
W: http://www.radioboise.org
Editorial Profile: KRBX-FM is a non-commercial community radio station owned by Boise Community Radio Project, Inc. The format of the station is variety. KRBX-FM broadcasts to the Boise, ID area at a frequency of 89.9 FM.

KRBZ-FM

Owner: Entercom Communications Corp.
Editorial: 7000 Squibb Rd, Mission, Kansas 66202-3233. **T:** 1 913 576-7965
W: http://www.965thebuzz.com
Editorial Profile: KRBZ-FM is a commercial station owned by Entercom Communications Corp. The format of the station is rock alternative music. KRBZ-FM broadcasts to the Kansas City, MO area at 96.5 FM.

KRCB-FM

Owner: Rural California Broadcasting Corp.
Editorial: 5850 Labath Ave, Rohnert Park, California 94928-2041. **T:** 1 707 584-2000
E: viewer@krcb.org **W:** http://radio.krcb.org
Editorial Profile: KRCB-FM is a non-commercial station owned by Rural California Broadcasting Corp. The format of the station is variety. KRCB-FM broadcasts to the San Francisco area at 91.1 FM.

KRCC-FM

Owner: Colorado College
Editorial: 912 N Weber St, Colorado Springs, Colorado 80903-2921. **T:** 1 719 473-4801
E: news@krcc.org
W: http://radiocoloradocollege.org
Editorial Profile: KRCC-FM is a non-commercial station owned by Colorado College. The format of the station is variety. KRCC-FM broadcasts to the Colorado Springs, CO area at 91.5 FM.

KRCD-FM

Owner: Univision Communications Inc.
Editorial: 655 N Central Ave, Ste 2500, Glendale, California 91203. **T:** 1 818 500-4500
W: http://recuerdo983.univision.com
Editorial Profile: KRCD-FM is a commercial station owned by Univision Communications

Inc. The format of the station is Hispanic oldies. KRCD-FM broadcasts to the Glendale, CA area at 103.9 FM.

KRCH-FM
Owner: Clear Channel Media and Entertainment
Editorial: 1530 Greenview Dr SW, Ste 200, Rochester, Minnesota 55902.
T: 1 507 288-3888
W: http://www.laser1017.com/main.html
Editorial Profile: KRCH-FM is a commercial station owned by Clear Channel Media and Entertainment. The format of the station is classic rock. KRCH-FM broadcasts to the Rochester, MN area at 101.7 FM.

KRCK-FM
Owner: Royce International Broadcasting Corporation
Editorial: 73733 Fred Waring Dr Ste 201, Palm Desert, California 92260-2591.
T: 1 760 341-0123 **W:** http://www.krck.com
Editorial Profile: KRCK-FM is a commercial station owned by Royce International Broadcasting Corporation. The format of the station is Top 40/CHR. KRCK-FM broadcasts to the Palm Desert, CA area at 97.7 FM.

KRCL-FM
Owner: Listeners Community Radio of Utah Inc.
Editorial: 1971 W North Temple, Salt Lake City, Utah 84116-3046. **T:** 1 801 363-1818
E: fax@krcl.org **W:** http://www.krcl.org
Editorial Profile: KRCL-FM is a non-commercial station owned by Listeners Community Radio of Utah Inc. The format of the station is variety. KRCL-FM broadcasts to the Salt Lake City area at 90.9 FM.

KRCN-AM
Owner: Pilgrim Communications
Editorial: 614 Kimbark St, Longmont, Colorado 80501-4911. **T:** 1 303 776-2323
W: http://www.krcnradio.com
Editorial Profile: KRCN-AM is a commercial station owned by Pilgrim Communications. The format of the station is business news and talk. KRCN-AM broadcasts to the Longmont, CO area at 1060 AM.

KRCO-AM
Owner: Horizon Broadcasting Group
Editorial: 854 NE 4th St, Bend, Oregon 97701.
T: 1 541 447-6770
E: news@horizonbroadcastinggroup.com
W: http://www.krcoam.com
Editorial Profile: KRCO-AM is a commercial station owned by Horizon Broadcasting Group. The format of the station is classic country. KRCO-AM broadcasts in the Prineville, OR area at 690 AM.

KRCQ-FM
Owner: Leighton Broadcasting
Editorial: 1119 Jackson Ave, Detroit Lakes, Minnesota 56501. **T:** 1 218 847-2001
E: krcq@lakesnet.net
W: http://www.realcountry102.com
Editorial Profile: KRCQ-FM is a commercial station owned by Leighton Broadcasting. The format of the station is country. KRCQ-FM broadcasts to the Detroit Lakes, MN area at 102.3 FM.

KRCS-FM
Owner: New Rushmore Radio
Editorial: 660 Flormann St, Ste 100, Rapid City, South Dakota 57701. **T:** 1 605 343-6161
W: http://www.hot931.com
Editorial Profile: KRCS-FM is a commercial station owned by New Rushmore Radio. The format of the station is Top 40/CHR. KRCS-FM broadcasts to the Rapid City, SD area at 93.1 FM.

KRCU-FM
Owner: Southeast Missouri State Univ.
Editorial: 1 University Plz Ms 0300, Cape Girardeau, Missouri 63701-4710.
T: 1 573 651-5070 **E:** comments@krcu.org
W: http://www.krcu.org
Editorial Profile: KRCU-FM is a non-commercial station owned by Southeast Missouri State Univ. The format of the station is classical and news. KRCU-FM broadcasts to the Cape Giradeau, MO area at 90.9 FM.

KRCV-FM
Owner: Univision Communications Inc.
Editorial: 655 N Central Ave, Ste 2500, Glendale, California 91203. **T:** 1 818 500-4500
W: http://recuerdo983.univision.com
Editorial Profile: KRCV-FM is a commercial station owned by Univision Communications Inc. The format of the station is Hispanic oldies. KRCV-FM broadcasts to the Los Angeles area at 98.3 FM.

KRCW-FM
Owner: National Farm Workers Service Center
Editorial: 508 W Lewis St, Pasco, Washington 99301. **T:** 1 509 545-0700
W: http://www.campesina.com
Editorial Profile: KRCW-FM is a commercial station owned by National Farm Workers Service Center. The format of the station is regional Mexican. KRCW-FM broadcasts to the Pasco, WA area at 96.3 FM.

KRCX-FM
Owner: Entravision Communications Corp.
Editorial: 1436 Auburn Blvd, Sacramento, California 95815-2745. **T:** 1 916 646-4000
Editorial Profile: KRCX-FM is a commercial station owned by Entravision Communications Corp. The format of the station is regional Mexican. KRCX-FM broadcasts to the Sacramento, CA area at 99.9 FM.

KRCY-FM
Owner: Mad Dog Wireless Inc.
Editorial: 2068 McCulloch Blvd N, Lake Havasu City, Arizona 86403-6663.
T: 1 928 855-1051 **W:** http://www.maddog.net
Editorial Profile: KRCY-FM is a commercial station owned by Mad Dog Wireless Inc. The format of the station is oldies. KRCY-FM broadcasts to the Lake Havasu City, AZ at 96.7 FM.

KRDA-FM
Owner: Univision Communications Inc.
Editorial: 601 W Univision Plz, Fresno, California 93704-1092. **T:** 1 559 430-8500
W: http://recuerdo1075.com
Editorial Profile: KRDA-FM is a commercial station owned by Univision Communications Inc. The format of the station is Spanish adult hits. KRDA-FM broadcasts in the Fresno, CA, area at 107.5 FM.

KRDD-AM
Owner: Espinoza(Carlos)
Editorial: 170 N Red Bridge Rd, Roswell, New Mexico 88201. **T:** 1 575 623-8111
E: krddam@yahoo.com
Editorial Profile: KRDD-AM is a commercial station owned by Carlos Espinoza. The format of the station is Hispanic adult contemporary music. KRDD-AM broadcasts to the Roswell, NM area at 1320 AM.

KRDE-FM
Owner: Tri-Media, Inc.
Editorial: 800 N Main St, Globe, Arizona 85501. **T:** 1 928 402-9222
E: krde@cableone.net **W:** http://www.krde.com
Editorial Profile: KRDE-FM is a commercial station owned by Tri-Media, Inc.. The format of the station is classic and contemporary country. KRDE-FM broadcasts to the Phoenix area at 94.1 FM.

KRDG-FM
Owner: Mapleton of Redding, LLC
Editorial: 3360 Alta Mesa Dr, Redding, California 96002-2831. **T:** 1 530 226-9500
W: http://www.oldies1053.com
Editorial Profile: KRDG-FM is a commercial station owned by Mapleton of Redding, LLC. The format of the station is oldies music. KRDG-FM broadcasts to the Redding, CA area at 105.3 FM.

KRDJ-FM
Owner: Last Bastion Trust
Editorial: 202 Galbert Rd, Lafayette, Louisiana 70506-1806. **T:** 1 337 232-1311
W: http://www.rock937fm.com
Editorial Profile: KRDJ-FM is a commercial station owned by the Last Bastion Trust. The format of the station is active rock. KRDJ-FM broadcasts to the Lafayette, LA area at 93.7 FM.

KRDM-AM
Owner: Red Mountain Broadcasting, LLC
Editorial: 416 Sw Black Butte Blvd, Redmond, Oregon 97756-2148. **T:** 1 541 548-7621
E: sales@radiolabronca.com
W: http://www.radiolabronca.com
Editorial Profile: KRDM-AM is a commercial station owned by Red Mountain Broadcasting, LLC. The format of the station is Hispanic. KRDM-AM broadcasts to the Redmond, OR area at 1240 AM.

KRDO-AM
Owner: News-Press & Gazette Co.
Editorial: 399 S 8th St, Colorado Springs, Colorado 80905. **T:** 1 719 632-1515
E: krdonews@krdo.com
W: http://www.krdo.com
Editorial Profile: KRDO-AM is a commercial station owned by News-Press & Gazette Co. The format of the station is news and talk. KRDO-AM broadcasts to the Colorado Springs, CO area at 1240 AM.

KRDO-FM
Owner: News-Press & Gazette Co.
Editorial: 399 S 8th St, Colorado Springs, Colorado 80905. **T:** 1 719 632-1515
E: krdonews@krdo.com
W: http://www.krdo.com
Editorial Profile: KRDO-FM is a commercial station owned by News-Press & Gazette Co. The format of the station is news and talk. KRDO-FM broadcasts to the Colorado Springs, CO area at 105.5 FM.

KRDQ-FM
Owner: Rocking M Radio
Editorial: 1065 S Range Ave, Colby, Kansas 67701-3505. **T:** 1 785 462-3305
E: tristateinfo@rockingmradio.com
W: http://nwksradio.com/100-3-kkrd
Editorial Profile: KRDQ-FM is a commercial radio station owned by Rocking M Radio. The format of the station is hot adult contemporary music. KRDQ-FM broadcasts to Colby, KS at 100.3 FM.

KRDS-FM
Owner: Ingstad Brothers Broadcasting, LLC
Editorial: 25821 Langford Ave, New Prague, Minnesota 56071-8864. **T:** 1 952 758-2571
E: production@kchkradio.net
W: http://kchkradio.net
Editorial Profile: KRDS-FM is a commercial station owned by Ingstad Brothers Broadcasting, LLC. The primary format of the station is country music. KRDS-FM broadcasts to the St. Paul, MN area at 95.5 FM.

KRDU-AM
Owner: Clear Channel Media and Entertainment
Editorial: 597 N Alta Ave, Dinuba, California 93618-3202. **T:** 1 559 230-4300
E: krdu@clearchannel.com
W: http://www.krdu1130.com
Editorial Profile: KRDU-AM is a commercial station owned by Clear Channel Media and Entertainment. The format of the station is religious programming. KRDU-AM broadcasts to the Dinuba, CA area at 1130 AM.

KRDX-FM
Owner: Desert West Air Ranchers Corp.
Editorial: 500 E Fry Blvd, Ste L10, Sierra Vista, Arizona 85635. **T:** 1 520 459-8201
E: info@kkyz.com **W:** http://www.fox985.com
Editorial Profile: KRDX-FM is a commercial station owned by Desert West Air Ranchers Corp. The format of the station is oldies music. KRDX-FM broadcasts to the Tucson, AZ area at 98.5 FM.

KRDY-AM
Owner: Salem Communications
Editorial: 9601 McAllister Fwy Ste 1200, San Antonio, Texas 78216-4695.
T: 1 210 344-8481 **E:** am11@krdy.com
W: http://www.krdy.com
Editorial Profile: KRDY-AM is a non-commerical station owned by Salem Communications, dba South Texas Broadcasting, Inc. The format of the station is Spanish Contemporary Christian. The station broadcasts to the San Antonio, TX area at a frequency of 1160 AM.

KRDZ-AM
Owner: Media Logic LLC
Editorial: 32992 US Highway 34, Wray, Colorado 80758-9161. **T:** 1 970 332-4171
E: krdz@medialogicradio.com
W: http://www.krdz.com
Editorial Profile: KRDZ-AM is a commercial station owned by Media Logic LLC. The format of the station is sports and classic hits. KRDZ-AM broadcasts to the Wray, CO area at 1440 AM.

KREB-AM
Owner: Butler Broadcasting
Editorial: 1780 W Holly St, Fayetteville, Arkansas 72703. **T:** 1 479 582-3776
W: http://1190thefan.com
Editorial Profile: KREB-AM is a commercial station owned by Butler Broadcasting. The format of the station is sports and talk. KREB-AM broadcasts to the Fayetteville, AR area at 1190 AM.

KREC-FM
Owner: Cherry Creek Radio
Editorial: 750 West Ridgeview Dr, Ste 204, St George, Utah 84770. **T:** 1 435 673-3579
E: star98fm@cherrycreekradio.com
W: http://www.star98online.com
Editorial Profile: KREC-FM is a commercial station owned by Cherry Creek Radio. The format of the station is adult contemporary. KREC-FM broadcasts to the Salt Lake City area at 98.1 FM.

KRED-FM
Owner: Bicoastal Media LLC
Editorial: 5640 S Broadway St, Eureka, California 95503-6905. **T:** 1 707 442-2000
E: eurekanews@bicoastalmedia.com
W: http://www.kred923.com

KREF-AM
Owner: Metro Radio Group
Editorial: 2020 Alameda St, Norman, Oklahoma 73071-2402. **T:** 1 405 321-1400
E: production@kref.com
W: http://www.sportstalk1400.com
Editorial Profile: KREF-AM is a commercial station owned by Metro Radio Group. The format of the station is sports. KREF-AM broadcasts to the Norman, OK area at 1400 AM.

KREH-AM
Owner: Mass Media Inc.
Editorial: 10613 Bellaire Blvd, Ste 900, Houston, Texas 77072-5221.
T: 1 713 917-0050 **E:** info@daisaigon.com
W: http://www.radiosaigonhouston.com
Editorial Profile: KREH-AM is a commercial station owned by Mass Media Inc. The format of the station is Vietnamese variety. KREH-AM broadcasts to the Houston area at 900 AM.

KREI-AM
Owner: Goodradio.TV LLC
Editorial: 1401 KREI Blvd, Farmington, Missouri 63640-1058. **T:** 1 573 756-6476
W: http://www.mymoinfo.com
Editorial Profile: KREI-AM is a commercial station owned by Goodradio.TV LLC. The format of the station is talk. KREI-AM broadcasts to the St. Louis area at 800 AM.

KREL-AM
Owner: Pilgrim Communications
Editorial: 614 Kimbark St, Longmont, Colorado 80501-4911. **T:** 1 772 770-9000
W: http://www.espn1580.com
Editorial Profile: KREL-AM is a commercial station owned by Pilgrim Communications and operated by SOCO Radio. The format of the station is sports/talk. KREL-AM broadcasts to the Boulder, CO area at 1580 AM.

KREP-FM
Owner: First Republic Broadcasting Corp.
Editorial: 2307 US Highway 81, Belleville, Kansas 66935. **T:** 1 785 527-2266
E: kr-92@nckcn.com
W: http://www.kr92country.com
Editorial Profile: KREP-FM is a commercial station owned by First Republic Broadcasting Corp. The format of the station is country. KREP-FM broadcasts to the Belleville, KS area at 92.1 FM.

KRES-FM
Owner: Moberly/Macon License Co., LLC
Editorial: 300 W Reed St, Moberly, Missouri 65270-1559. **T:** 1 660 263-1500
E: kresnews@regionalradio.com
W: http://www.centralmoinfo.com
Editorial Profile: KRES-FM is a commercial station owned by Moberly/Macon License Co., LLC. The format of the station is country music. KRES-FM broadcasts to the Moberly, MO area at 104.7 FM.

KREU-FM
Owner: Star 92 Company
Editorial: 5111 Rogers Ave Ste 650, Fort Smith, Arkansas 72903-2096.
T: 1 479 785-2526 **E:** production@kisr.net
Editorial Profile: KREU-FM is a commercial station owned by Baker Broadcasting. The format of the station is regional Mexican music. KREU-FM broadcasts to the Fort Smith, AR area at 92.3 FM.

KREV-FM
Owner: Royce International Broadcasting
Editorial: 400 2Nd St Ste 300, San Francisco, California 94107-1448. **T:** 1 415 543-7500
W: http://www.927rev.com
Editorial Profile: KREV-FM is a commercial station owned by Royce International Broadcasting. The format of the station is Top 40/CHR. KREV-FM broadcasts to the San Francisco Bay area at 92.7 FM.

KREW-AM
Owner: Rhattigan Broadcasting
Editorial: 3218 Quincy St, Plainview, Texas 79072-1906. **T:** 1 806 296-2771
Editorial Profile: KREW-AM is a commercial station owned by Rhattigan Broadcasting. The format of the station is sports. KREW-AM broadcasts to the Plainview, TX area at 1400 AM.

KREZ-FM
Owner: Withers Broadcasting Co.
Editorial: 901 S Kingshighway St, Cape Girardeau, Missouri 63703-8003.
T: 1 573 339-7000 **E:** news@withersradio.net
W: http://www.softrock1047.com
Editorial Profile: KREZ-FM is a commercial station owned by Withers Broadcasting Co. The format of the station is adult contemporary. KREZ-FM broadcasts to the Cape Girardeau, MO area at 104.7 FM.

KRFA-FM
Owner: Washington State University
Editorial: Murrow Center, Room 382, Pullman, Washington 99164. **T:** 1 509 335-6500
E: nwpr@wsu.edu **W:** http://www.nwpr.org
Editorial Profile: KRFA-FM is a non commercial station owned by Washington State University. The format is classical music and talk. KFRA-FM broadcasts to the Pullman, WA area at 91.7 FM.

KRFC-FM
Owner: Public Radio for the Front Range
Editorial: 619 S College Ave Ste 4, Fort Collins, Colorado 80524-3068.
T: 1 970 221-5075 **W:** http://www.krfcfm.org
Editorial Profile: KRFC-FM is a non-commercial station owned by Public Radio for the Front Range. The format of the station is variety. KRFC-FM broadcasts to the Fort Collins, CO area at 88.9 FM.

KRFE-AM
Owner: Wilkes(Wade)
Editorial: 6602 Martin Luther King Blvd, Lubbock, Texas 79404. **T:** 1 806 745-1197
W: http://www.am580lubbock.com
Editorial Profile: KRFE-AM is commercial station owned by Wade Wilkes. The format of the station is talk and easy listening. KRFE-AM broadcasts in the Lubbock, TX area at 580 AM.

KRFM-FM
Owner: Petracom
Editorial: 1838 Commerce Dr Ste A, Lakeside, Arizona 85929-7008. **T:** 1 928 368-8100
E: production@whitemountainradio.com
Editorial Profile: KRFM-FM is a commercial station owned by Petracom. The format of the station is hot adult contemporary music. KRFM-FM broadcasts to the Navajo County, AZ at 96.5 FM.

KRFO-AM
Owner: Townsquare Media
Editorial: 245 18th St SE, Owatonna, Minnesota 55060-4062. **T:** 1 507 451-2250
E: krfonews@townsquaremedia.com
W: http://www.krforadio.com
Editorial Profile: KRFO-AM is a commercial station owned by Townsquare Media. The format of the station is oldies music. KRFO-AM broadcasts to the Owatonna, MN area at 1390 AM.

KRFO-FM
Owner: Townsquare Media
Editorial: 245 18th St SE, Owatonna, Minnesota 55060-4062. **T:** 1 507 451-2250
W: http://www.krforadio.com
Editorial Profile: KRFO-FM is a commercial station owned by Townsquare Media. The format of the station is contemporary country music. KRFO-FM broadcasts to the Owatonna, MN area at 104.9 FM.

KRFS-AM
Owner: CK Broadcasting Inc.
Editorial: 630 W 8th St, Superior, Nebraska 68978. **T:** 1 402 879-4741
E: krfsfm@yahoo.com
W: http://www.krfsfm.com
Editorial Profile: KRFS-AM is a commercial station owned by CK Broadcasting Inc. The format of the station is adult contemporary. KRFS-AM broadcasts in the Superior, NE area at 1600 AM.

KRFS-FM
Owner: CK Broadcasting Inc.
Editorial: 630 W 8th St, Superior, Nebraska 68978. **T:** 1 402 879-4741
E: krfsfm@yahoo.com
W: http://www.krfsfm.com
Editorial Profile: KRFS-FM is a commercial station owned by CK Broadcasting Inc. The format of the station is contemporary country music. KRFS broadcasts in the Superior, NE area at 103.9 FM.

KRFX-FM
Owner: Clear Channel Media and Entertainment
Editorial: 4695 S Monaco St, Denver, Colorado 80237. **T:** 1 303 713-8000
W: http://www.thefox.com
Editorial Profile: KRFX-FM is a commercial station owned by Clear Channel Media and Entertainment. The format of the station is classic rock. KRFX-FM broadcasts to the Denver area at 103.5 FM.

KRGE-AM
Owner: Christian Ministries of the Valley Inc.
Editorial: 2720 W Business 83, Weslaco, Texas 78596-1225. **T:** 1 956 968-7777
E: informacion@radiovida.com
W: http://www.radiovida.com
Editorial Profile: KRGE-AM is a commercial station owned by Christian Ministries of the Valley Inc. The format of the station is Spanish Christian music and talk. KRGE-AM broadcasts to the Weslaco, TX area at 1290 AM.

KRGI-AM
Owner: Legacy Communications, LLC
Editorial: 3205 W North Front St, Grand Island, Nebraska 68803-4024.
T: 1 308 381-1430
W: http://www.newsacrossnebraska.com
Editorial Profile: KRGI-AM is a commercial station owned by Legacy Communications, LLC (dba GI Family Radio). The format of the station is news, talk and sports. KRGI-AM broadcasts to the Grand Island, NE area at 1430 AM.

KRGI-FM
Owner: Legacy Communications, LLC
Editorial: 3205 W North Front St, Grand Island, Nebraska 68803-4024.
T: 1 308 381-1430
W: http://www.newsacrossnebraska.com
Editorial Profile: KRGI-FM is a commercial station owned by Legacy Communications, LLC (dba GI Family Radio). The format of the station is country. KRGI-FM broadcasts to the Grand Island, NE area at 96.5 FM.

KRGS-AM
Owner: Western Slope Communications
Editorial: 751 Horizon Ct, Ste 225, Grand Junction, Colorado 81506. **T:** 1 970 241-6460
E: production@wscradio.net
Editorial Profile: KRGS-AM is a commercial station owned by Western Slope Communications. The format of the station is sports. KRGS-AM broadcasts to the Grand Junction, CO area at 960 AM.

KRGT-FM
Owner: Univision Communications Inc.
Editorial: 6767 W Tropicana Ave, Ste 102, Las Vegas, Nevada 89103-4755.
T: 1 702 284-6400
W: http://www.univision.com/content/channel.jhtml?chid=10104&schid=10176
Editorial Profile: KRGT-FM is a commercial station owned by Univision Communications Inc. The format of the station is Hispanic urban AC. KRGT-FM broadcasts to the Las Vegas area at 99.3 FM.

KRGY-FM
Owner: Legacy Communications, LLC
Editorial: 3205 W North Front St, Grand Island, Nebraska 68803-4024.
T: 1 308 381-1430
W: http://newsacrossnebraska.com
Editorial Profile: KRGY-FM is a commercial station owned by Legacy Communications, LLC (dba GI Family Radio). The format of the station is classic rock music. KRGY-FM broadcasts to the Grand Island, NE area at 97.3 FM.

KRHC-AM
Owner: M&M Broadcasters, Ltd
Editorial: 2108 Highway 281 N, Ste A, Marble Falls, Texas 78654. **T:** 1 830 693-5551
Editorial Profile: KRHC-AM is a commercial station owned by M&M Broadcasters, Ltd. The format of the station is country music. KRHC-AM broadcasts to the Austin, TX area at 92.5 FM.

KRHV-FM
Owner: Digerness(Dave & Maryann)
Editorial: 94 Laurel Mountain Rd, Mammoth Lakes, California 93546. **T:** 1 760 934-8888
E: kmmtradioworks@yahoo.com
W: http://www.kmmtradio.com/krhvhome.php
Editorial Profile: KRHV-FM is a commercial station owned by Dave and Maryann Digerness. The format of the station is classic rock. KRHV-FM broadcasts to the Mammoth Lakes, CA area at 93.3 FM.

KRHW-AM
Owner: Withers Broadcasting of Southeast Missouri, LLC
Editorial: 125 S Kingshighway St, Sikeston, Missouri 63801-2943. **T:** 1 573 471-2000
Editorial Profile: KRHW-AM is a commercial station owned by Withers Broadcasting of Southeast Missouri, LLC. The format of the station is country music. KRHW-AM broadcasts to the Sikeston, MO, area at 1520 AM.

KRIA-FM
Owner: Rhattigan Broadcasting
Editorial: 3218 Quincy St, Plainview, Texas 79072. **T:** 1 806 296-2771
E: news@plainviewradio.com
Editorial Profile: KRIA-FM is a commercial station owned by Rhattigan Broadcasting. The format of the station is classic rock. KRIA-FM broadcasts to the Plainview, TX area at 106.9 FM.

KRIB-AM
Owner: Three Eagles Communications Co.
Editorial: 341 S Yorktown Pike, Mason City, Iowa 50401-4533. **T:** 1 641 423-8634
W: http://www.kribradio.com
Editorial Profile: KRIB-AM is a commercial station owned by Three Eagles Communications Co. The format of the station is oldies. KRIB-AM broadcasts to the Rochester, MN and Mason City, IA areas at 1490 AM.

KRIG-FM
Owner: KCD Enterprises Inc.
Editorial: 1200 SE Frank Phillips Blvd, Bartlesville, Oklahoma 74003-4332.
T: 1 918 336-1001
E: radio@bartlesvilleradio.com
W: http://www.bartlesvilleradio.com
Editorial Profile: KRIG-FM is a commercial station owned by KCD Enterprises Inc. The format of the station is country. KRIG-FM broadcasts to the Bartlesville, OK area at 104.9 FM.

KRIK-FM
Owner: Hispanic Target Media, Inc.
Editorial: 406 N Alamo St, Refugio, Texas 78377-2504. **T:** 1 361 526-2497
Editorial Profile: KRIK-FM is a commercial station owned by Hispanic Target Media, Inc. The format of the station is Regional Mexican. KRIK-FM is licensed to Refugio, TX and broadcasts to South Texas including Victoria and Bee counties and surrounding areas.

KRIL-AM
Owner: Townsquare Media, LLC
Editorial: 11300 State Highway 191 Bldg 2, Midland, Texas 79707-1367.
T: 1 432 563-5499 **W:** http://1410kril.com
Editorial Profile: KRIL-AM is a commercial station owned by Townsquare Media, LLC. The format of the station is classic country. KRIL-AM broadcasts to the Midland, TX area at 1410 AM.

KRIO-AM
Owner: Rio Grande Bible Institute Inc.
Editorial: 4300 S Business Highway 281, Edinburg, Texas 78539-9650.
T: 1 956 380-3435
E: correo@radioesperanza.com
W: http://www.radioesperanza.com
Editorial Profile: KRIO-AM is a commercial station owned by Rio Grande Bible Institute Inc. The format of the station is Spanish religious music and news. KRIO-AM broadcasts to the Edinburg, TX area at 910 AM.

KRIO-FM
Owner: Radio Grande Bible Institute Inc.
Editorial: 4300 S Business Highway 281, Edinburg, Texas 78539-9650.
T: 1 956 380-3435
E: correo@radioesperanza.com
W: http://radioesperanza.com
Editorial Profile: KRIO-FM is a non-commerical station owned by Radio Grande Bible Institute Inc. The format of the station is Hispanic music and news. The station broadcasts to the Edinburg, TX area at 97.7 FM.

KRIZ-AM
Owner: Kris Bennett Broadcasting Co.
Editorial: 2600 S Jackson St, Seattle, Washington 98144-2402. **T:** 1 206 323-3070
E: ztwins@aol.com **W:** http://www.ztwins.com
Editorial Profile: KRIZ-AM is a commercial station owned by Kris Bennett Broadcasting Co. The format of the station is talk, gospel and urban contemporary. KRIZ-AM broadcasts to the Seattle, WA area at 1420 AM.

KRJB-FM
Owner: R & J Broadcasting
Editorial: 312 W Main St, Ada, Minnesota 56510. **T:** 1 218 784-2844
W: http://www.krjbradio.com
Editorial Profile: KRJB-FM is a commercial station owned by R & J Broadcasting. The format of the station is country music. KRJB-FM broadcasts to the Ada, MN area at 106.5 FM.

KRJC-FM
Owner: Carlson Communications
Editorial: 1250 Lamoille Hwy, Elko, Nevada 89801-4396. **T:** 1 775 738-9895
W: http://www.krjc.com
Editorial Profile: KRJC-FM is a commercial station owned by Carlson Communications. The format of the station is country. KRJC-FM broadcasts to the Salt Lake City area at 95.3 FM.

KRJM-FM
Owner: R & J Broadcasting
Editorial: 312 W Main St, Ada, Minnesota 56510. **T:** 1 218 784-2844
E: krjmnews@arvig.net
W: http://krjmradio.com
Editorial Profile: KRJM-FM is a commercial station owned by R & J Broadcasting. The format of the station is oldies music. KRJM-FM broadcasts to the Ada, MN area at 101.5 FM.

KRJO-AM
Owner: Holladay Broadcasting Co.
Editorial: 1109 Hudson Ln, Monroe, Louisiana 71201-6003. **T:** 1 318 388-2323
W: http://www.krjo.com
Editorial Profile: KRJO-AM is a commercial station owned by Holladay Broadcasting Co. The format of the station is classic country. KRJO-AM broadcasts in the Monroe, LA area at 1680 AM.

KRJT-FM
Owner: Pacific Empire Communications
Editorial: 2510 Cove Ave, La Grande, Oregon 97850-3911 **W:** http://yourboomerradio.com
Editorial Profile: KRJT-FM is a commercial station owned by Pacific Empire Communications. The format of the station is oldies music. KRJT-FM broadcasts to the Portland, OR area at 105.9 FM.

KRJW-AM
Owner: Wynne Broadcasting Co.
Editorial: 1338 Oregon Ave, Klamath Falls, Oregon 97601-6540. **T:** 1 541 882-4656
E: webmaster@klamathradio.com
W: http://www.klamathradio.com/KRJW/Index.html
Editorial Profile: KRJW-AM is a commercial station owned by Wynne Broadcasting Co. The format of the station is sports talk. The station airs locally at 1240 AM.

KRKC-AM
Owner: King City Communications
Editorial: 1134 San Antonio Dr, King City, California 93930. **T:** 1 831 385-5421
E: krkcdavis@yahoo.com
W: http://www.krkc.com
Editorial Profile: KRKC-AM is a commercial station owned by King City Communications and operated by Radio Del Rey. The format of the station is country. KRKC-AM broadcasts to the King City, CA area at 1490 AM.

KRKC-FM
Owner: Radio Del Rey
Editorial: 1134 San Antonio Dr, King City, California 93930. **T:** 1 831 385-5421
W: http://www.krkc.com
Editorial Profile: KRKC-FM is a commercial station owned by Radio Del Rey. The format of the station is adult contemporary. KRKC-FM broadcasts to the King City, CA area at 102.1 FM.

KRKE-AM
Owner: Vanguard Media, LLC
Editorial: 1213 San Pedro Dr NE, Albuquerque, New Mexico 87110-6725.
T: 1 505 899-5029 **W:** http://koolnm.com

Editorial Profile: KRKE-AM is a commercial station owned by Vanguard Media, LLC. The format of the station is classic hits. KRKE-AM broadcasts to the Albuquerque, NM area at 1550 AM.

KRKH-FM
Owner: Hochman Hawaii Publishing
Editorial: 300 Ohukai Rd, Ste C318, Kihei, Hawaii 96753-7050. **T:** 1 808 875-8866
W: http://hhawaiimedia.com
Editorial Profile: KRKH-FM is a commercial station owned by Hochman Hawaii Publishing. The format of the station is album-oriented rock. KRKH-FM broadcasts to the Maui area at 97.3 FM.

KRKI-FM
Owner: Bandlands Broadcasting
Editorial: 1711 W Main St, Rapid City, South Dakota 57702-2564. **T:** 1 605 721-9005
W: http://www.995espn.com
Editorial Profile: KRKI-FM is a commercial station owned by Bandlands Broadcasting. The format of the station is sports. KRKI-FM broadcasts to the Rapid City, SD area at 99.5 FM.

KRKK-AM
Owner: Big Thickett Broadcasting Co.
Editorial: 2717 Yellowstone Rd, Rock Springs, Wyoming 82901-3261. **T:** 1 307 362-3793
E: wyradio@wyoradio.com
W: http://www.wyoradio.com
Editorial Profile: KRKK-AM is a commercial station owned by Big Thickett Broadcasting Co. The format of the station is talk. KRKK-AM broadcasts to the Rock Springs, WY area at 1360 AM.

KRKN-FM
Owner: O-Town Communications, Inc.
Editorial: 416 E Main St, Ottumwa, Iowa 52501. **T:** 1 641 684-5563
E: info@ottumwaradio.com
W: http://www.ottumwaradio.com
Editorial Profile: KRKN-FM is a commercial station owned by O-Town Communications, Inc. The format of the station is contemporary country. KRKN-FM broadcasts to the Ottumwa, IA area at 104.3 FM.

KRKO-AM
Owner: S.R. Broadcasting Company Inc.
Editorial: 2707 Colby Ave, Ste 1380, Everett, Washington 98201-3568. **T:** 1 425 304-1381
E: rkonews@krko.com
W: http://www.krko.com
Editorial Profile: KRKO-AM is a commercial station owned by S.R. Broadcasting Company Inc. The format of the station is sports. KRKO-AM broadcasts to the Everett, WA area at 1380 AM.

KRKS-AM
Owner: Salem Communications
Editorial: 3131 S Vaughn Way, Ste 601, Aurora, Colorado 80014. **T:** 1 303 750-5687
W: http://www.krks.com
Editorial Profile: KRKS-AM is a commercial station owned by Salem Communications. The format of the station is Christian talk and music. KRKS-AM broadcasts to the Aurora, CO area at 990 AM.

KRKS-FM
Owner: Salem Communications
Editorial: 3131 S Vaughn Way, Ste 601, Aurora, Colorado 80014. **T:** 1 303 750-5687
W: http://www.krks.com
Editorial Profile: KRKS-FM is a commercial station owned by Salem Communications. The format of the station is Christian talk and music. KRKS-AM broadcasts to the Denver, CO area at 94.7 FM.

KRKT-FM
Owner: Bicoastal Media LLC
Editorial: 2840 Marion St SE, Albany, Oregon 97322. **T:** 1 541 926-8628
W: http://www.krkt.com
Editorial Profile: KRKT-FM is a commercial station owned by Bicoastal Media LLC. The format of the station is country music. KRKT-FM broadcasts to Albany, OR at 99.9 FM.

KRKX-FM
Owner: Connoisseur Media LLC
Editorial: 2075 Central Ave, Billings, Montana 59102. **T:** 1 406 248-7777
W: http://www.941ksky.com
Editorial Profile: KRKX-FM is commercial station owned by Connoisseur Media LLC. The format of the station is contemporary country. KRKX-FM broadcasts in the Billings, MT area at 94.1 FM.

KRKY-AM
Owner: NRC Broadcasting
Editorial: 130 Ski Hill Rd, Breckenridge, Colorado 80424. **T:** 1 970 453-2234
Editorial Profile: KRKY-AM is a commercial station owned by NRC Broadcasting. The format of the station is country. KRKY-AM broadcasts to the Breckenridge, CO area at 930 AM.

KRKZ-AM
Owner: Forks Broadcasting, Inc.
Editorial: 260 Cedar Ave, Forks, Washington 98331-9605. **T:** 1 360 374-6220
W: http://www.forks1490.com
Editorial Profile: KRKZ-AM is a commercial station owned by Forks Broadcasting, Inc. The format of the station is news and talk. KRKZ-AM broadcasts to the Forks, WA area at 1490 AM.

KRKZ-FM
Owner: Alexandra Communications Inc.
Editorial: 170 3rd St, Tillamook, Oregon 97141-9489. **T:** 1 503 842-4422
Editorial Profile: KRKZ-FM is a commercial station owned by Alexandra Communications Inc. The format of the station is Top 40/CHR. KRKZ-FM broadcasts to the Astoria, OR area at 94.3 FM.

KRLA-AM
Owner: Salem Communications
Editorial: 701 N Brand Blvd, Glendale, California 91203-1295. **T:** 1 818 956-5552
E: info@krla870.com
W: http://www.am870theanswer.com
Editorial Profile: KRLA-AM is a commercial station owned by Salem Communications. The format of the station is news and talk. KRLA-AM broadcasts to the Los Angeles metro area at 870 AM.

KRLC-AM
Owner: Ida-Vend Communications Group
Editorial: 805 Stewart Ave, Lewiston, Idaho 83501. **T:** 1 208 743-1551
Editorial Profile: KRLC-AM is a commercial station owned by Ida-Vend Communications Group. The format of the station is classic country. KRLC-AM broadcasts to the Spokane, WA area at 1350 AM.

KRLD-AM
Owner: CBS Radio
Editorial: 4131 N Central Expy, Dallas, Texas 75204-2102. **T:** 1 214 525-7000
E: krldeditor@cbs.com **W:** http://www.krld.com
Editorial Profile: KRLD-AM is a commercial station owned by CBS Radio. The format of the station is news and talk programming. KRLD-AM broadcasts to the Dallas area at 1080 AM.

KRLD-FM
Owner: CBS Radio
Editorial: 4131 N Central Expy, Ste 1000, Dallas, Texas 75204-2121. **T:** 1 214 525-7000
W: http://www.1053thefan.com
Editorial Profile: KRLD-FM is a commercial station owned by CBS Radio. The format of the station is sports. KRLD-FM broadcasts to the Dallas area at 105.3 FM.

KRLF-FM
Owner: Living Faith Education Ministries
Editorial: 345 SW Kimball Dr, Pullman, Washington 99163. **T:** 1 509 332-3545
E: krlf@krlf.org **W:** http://www.krlf.org
Editorial Profile: KRLF-FM is a non-commercial station owned by Living Faith Education Ministries. The format of the station is contemporary Christian music. KRLF-FM broadcasts to the Pullman, WA area at 88.5 FM.

KRLI-FM
Owner: Kanza Inc.
Editorial: 102 N Mason St, Carrollton, Missouri 64633-2159. **T:** 1 660 542-0404
E: news@kmzu.com **W:** http://krlicountry.com
Editorial Profile: KRLI-FM is a commercial station owned by the Kanza Inc. The format of the station is country music. The station broadcasts to the Kansas City, MO area at 103.9 FM.

KRLL-AM
Owner: Moniteau Communications Inc.
Editorial: 100A E Buchanan St, California, Missouri 65018. **T:** 1 573 796-3139
E: krllnews@embarqmail.com
Editorial Profile: KRLL-AM is a commercial station owned by Moniteau Communications Inc. The format of the station is classic country. KRLL-AM broadcasts in the California, MO area at 1420 AM.

KRLN-AM
Owner: Royal Gorge Broadcasting LLC
Editorial: 1615 Central Ave, Canon City, Colorado 81212-8578. **T:** 1 719 275-7488
E: krlnnews@gmail.com
Editorial Profile: KRLN-AM is a commercial station owned by Royal Gorge Broadcasting LLC. The format of the station is news/talk. KRLN-AM broadcasts to the Canon City, CO area at 1400 AM.

KRLQ-FM
Owner: Brown (Bill)
Editorial: 1319 N Vienna St, Ruston, Louisiana 71270-2337. **T:** 1 318 255-7941
E: krlq941fm@bellsouth.net
W: http://krlqfm.com
Editorial Profile: KRLQ-FM is a commercial station owned by Bill Brown. The format of the station is classic country. KRLQ-FM broadcasts to the Ruston, LA area at 94.1 FM.

KRLS-FM
Owner: M & H Broadcasting Inc.
Editorial: 1610 N Lincoln St, Knoxville, Iowa 50138. **T:** 1 641 842-3161
E: kniakrls@kniakrls.com
W: http://www.kniakrls.com
Editorial Profile: KRLS-FM is a commercial station owned by M & H Broadcasting Inc. The format of the station is news and music. KRLS-FM broadcasts to the Knoxville, IA area at 92.1 FM.

KRLT-FM
Owner: Cherry Creek Radio
Editorial: 276 Kingsbury Grade, Ste 203, Stateline, Nevada 89449-9800.
T: 1 775 580-7130 **W:** http://www.krltfm.com
Editorial Profile: KRLT-FM is a commercial station owned by Cherry Creek Radio. The format of the station is adult contemporary music. KRLT-FM broadcasts to the South Lake Tahoe, CA area at 93.9 FM.

KRLU-FM
Owner: Educational Media Foundation
Editorial: 4111 Barbara Loop Se Ste E1, Rio Rancho, New Mexico 87124-1068.
T: 1 505 352-4028 **W:** http://www.klove.com

KRLV-AM
Owner: Lotus Broadcasting Corp
Editorial: 6655 W Sahara Ave Ste C216, Las Vegas, Nevada 89146-0850.
T: 1 702 796-1230
W: http://www.krlv1340am.com
Editorial Profile: KRLV-AM is a commercial station owned by Lotus Broadcasting Corp. The format of the station is Hispanic news and talk. KRLV-AM broadcasts to the Las Vegas area at 1340 AM.

KRLW-AM
Owner: Combined Media Group
Editorial: 1 Radio Drive, Pocahontas, Arkansas 72455. **T:** 1 870 892-5234
E: kpoc-krlw@centurytel.net
Editorial Profile: KRLW-AM is a commercial station owned by Combined Media Group. The format of the station is oldies. KRLW-AM broadcasts to the Walnut Ridge, AR area at 1320 AM.

KRMB-FM
Owner: World Radio Network, Inc.
Editorial: 421 E 9th St, Douglas, Arizona 85607. **T:** 1 520 364-5392 **E:** krmc@lwrn.org
W: http://www.worldradionetwork.org/english
Editorial Profile: KRMB-FM is a non-commercial radio station that is owned by the World Radio Network, Inc. The format is Hispanic Christian music. The station airs locally on 90.1 FM.

KRMC-FM
Owner: World Radio Network, Inc.
Editorial: 421 E 9th St, Douglas, Arizona 85607. **T:** 1 520 364-5392 **E:** krmc@lwrn.org
W: http://www.worldradionetwork.com
Editorial Profile: KRMC-FM is a non-commercial station owned by the World Radio Network, Inc. The format is Hispanic Christian music. KRMC-FM broadcasts to the Douglas, AZ area at 91.7 FM.

KRMD-AM
Owner: Cumulus Media Inc.
Editorial: 270 Plaza Loop, Bossier City, Louisiana 71111-4389. **T:** 1 318 549-8500
E: cumulus.shreveport@cumulus.com
W: http://www.supertalk1340.com
Editorial Profile: KRMD-AM is a commercial station owned by Cumulus Media Inc. The format of the station is sports. KRMD-AM broadcasts to the Shreveport, LA area at 1340 AM.

KRMD-FM
Owner: Cumulus Media Inc.
Editorial: 270 Plaza Loop, Cumulus Broadcast Center, Bossier City, Louisiana 71111-4389.
T: 1 318 549-8500
E: krmd.radio@cumulus.com
W: http://www.krmd.com
Editorial Profile: KRMD-FM is a commercial station owned by Cumulus Communications. The format of the station is contemporary country music. KRMD-FM broadcasts to the Shreveport, LA area at 101.1 FM.

KRMG-AM
Owner: Cox Media Group, Inc.
Editorial: 7136 S Yale Ave, Ste 500, Tulsa, Oklahoma 74136. **T:** 1 918 493-7400
E: krmg.news@coxradio.com
W: http://www.krmg.com
Editorial Profile: KRMG-AM is a commercial station owned by Cox Media Group, Inc. The format of the station is news and talk. KRMG-AM broadcasts to the Tulsa, OK area at 740 AM.

KRMG-FM
Owner: Cox Media Group, Inc.
Editorial: 7136 S Yale Ave, Ste 500, Tulsa, Oklahoma 74136. **T:** 1 918 493-7400
E: krmg.news@coxradio.com
W: http://www.krmg.com
Editorial Profile: KRMG-FM is a commercial station owned by Cox Media Group, Inc. The format of the station is news and talk. KRMG-FM broadcasts to the Tulsa, OK area at 102.3 FM.

KRML-AM
Owner: Wisdom Broadcasting Co. Inc.
Editorial: 27200 Rancho San Carlos Rd, Carmel, California 93923-7911.
T: 1 831 244-0102 **W:** http://www.krml.com
Editorial Profile: KRML-AM is a commercial station owned by Wisdom Broadcasting Co. Inc. The format of the station is adult album alternative. KRML-AM broadcasts to the Carmel, CA area at 1410 AM.

KRMO-AM
Owner: Eagle Broadcasting Inc.
Editorial: 126 S Jefferson Ave, Aurora, Missouri 65605-1635. **T:** 1 417 678-0416
E: krmo@radiotalon.com
W: http://www.radiotalon.com
Editorial Profile: KRMO-AM is a commercial station owned by Eagle Broadcasting Inc. The format of the station is sports, talk and agricultural news. KRMO-AM broadcasts to the Springfield, MO, area at 990 AM.

KRMP-AM
Owner: Perry Publishing & Broadcasting Inc.
Editorial: 1528 Ne 23Rd St, Oklahoma City, Oklahoma 73111-3260. **T:** 1 405 427-5877
W: http://okcheartandsoul.com

KRMQ-FM
Owner: Rooney Moon Broadcasting
Editorial: 42437 US 70, Portales, New Mexico 88130. **T:** 1 575 359-1759
E: ksel@rooneymoon.com
W: http://q1015.com
Editorial Profile: KRMQ-FM is a commercial station owned by Rooney Moon Broadcasting. The format of the station is classic hits. KRMQ-FM broadcasts to the Portales, NM area at 101.5 FM.

KRMR-FM
Owner: Rocking M Radio
Editorial: 207 E 7th St Ste 102, Hays, Kansas 67601-4134. **T:** 1 785 628-6108
W: http://centralkansasradio.com/knns-1510
Editorial Profile: KRMR-FM is a commercial station owned by Rocking M Radio. The format of the station is talk. KRMR-FM broadcasts to the Hays, KS area at 105.7 FM.

KRMS-AM
Owner: Viper Communications Inc.
Editorial: 5715 Highway 54, Osage Beach, Missouri 65065-3030. **T:** 1 573 348-2772
E: newsroom@krmsradio.com
W: http://www.krmsradio.com
Editorial Profile: KRMS-AM is a commercial station owned by Viper Communications Inc. The format of the station is news and talk. KRMS-AM broadcasts in the Springfield, MO area at 1150 AM.

KRMW-FM
Owner: Cumulus Media Inc.
Editorial: 4209 N Frontage Rd, Fayetteville, Arkansas 72703-5002. **T:** 1 479 521-5566
W: http://warmnwa.com
Editorial Profile: KRNW-FM is a commercial station owned by Cumulus Media Inc. The

format of the station is adult contemporary music. KRNW-FM broadcasts to the Fayetteville, AR area at 94.9 FM.

KRMX-FM
Owner: M & M Broadcasters
Editorial: 5501 Bagby Ave, Waco, Texas 76711-2300. **T:** 1 254 772-0930
W: http://www.929shooterfm.com
Editorial Profile: KRMX-FM is a commercial station owned by M & M Broadcasters. The format of the station is country music. KRMX-FM airs broadcasts to Waco, TX at 92.9 FM.

KRMY-AM
Owner: Martin's Broadcasting Inc.
Editorial: 314 N 2nd St, Killeen, Texas 76541. **T:** 1 254 628-7070 **E:** krmy@krmyradio.com
W: http://www.krmyradio.com
Editorial Profile: KRMY-AM is a commercial station owned by Martin's Broadcasting Inc. The format of the station is gospel music. KRMY-AM broadcasts to the Killeen, TX area at 1050 AM.

KRNA-FM
Owner: Townsquare Media, LLC
Editorial: 425 2nd St SE Fl 4, Cedar Rapids, Iowa 52401-1819. **T:** 1 319 365-9431
E: krna@krna.com **W:** http://www.krna.com
Editorial Profile: KRNA-FM is a commercial station owned by Townsquare Media, LLC. The format of the station is rock. KRNA-FM broadcasts to the Cedar Rapids, IA area at 94.1 FM.

KRNB-FM
Owner: Service Broadcasting Corp.
Editorial: 621 NW 6th St, Grand Prairie, Texas 75050-5555. **T:** 1 972 263-9911
E: community@krnb.com
W: http://www.krnb.com
Editorial Profile: KRNB-FM is a commercial station owned by Service Broadcasting Corp. The format of the station is urban adult contemporary music. KRNB-FM broadcasts to the Dallas area at 105.7 FM.

KRNE-FM
Owner: Nebraska Educational Telecommunications Commission
Editorial: 1800 N 33rd St, Lincoln, Nebraska 68503. **T:** 1 402 472-6141
E: radio@netnebraska.org
W: http://netnebraska.org/radio
Editorial Profile: KRNE-FM is a non-commercial station owned by Nebraska Educational Telecommunications Commission. The format of the station is news and classical music. KRNE-FM broadcasts to the Merriman, NE area at 91.5 FM.

KRNG-FM
Owner: Sierra Nevada Christian Music Assoc.
Editorial: 360 Pyramid St, Wadsworth, Nevada 89442. **T:** 1 775 575-7777
E: email@renegaderadio.org
W: http://www.renegaderadio.org

KRNH-FM
Owner: Radio Ranch Ltd.
Editorial: 3505 Fredericksburg Rd, Kerrville, Texas 78028-9272. **T:** 1 830 896-4990
E: psa@ranchradiogroup.com
W: http://923theranch.com
Editorial Profile: KRNH-FM is a commercial station owned by Radio Ranch Ltd. The format of the station is country music. KRNH-FM broadcasts to the Kerrville, TX and surrounding communities at 92.3 FM.

KRNK-FM
Owner: Townsquare Media, LLC
Editorial: 150 Nichols Ave, Casper, Wyoming 82601. **T:** 1 307 266-5252
W: http://www.rock967online.com
Editorial Profile: KRNK-FM is a commercial station owned by Townsquare Media, LLC. The format for the station is rock alternative. KRNK-FM broadcasts to the Casper-Riverton, WY area at 96.7 FM.

KRNL-FM
Owner: Cornell College
Editorial: 810 Commons Cir SW, Mount Vernon, Iowa 52314-1000. **T:** 1 319 895-4431
E: krnl@cornellcollege.edu

KRNN-FM
Owner: Capital Community Broadcasting Inc.
Editorial: 360 Egan Dr, Juneau, Alaska 99801. **T:** 1 907 586-1670 **E:** news@ktoo.org
W: http://www.ktoo.org
Editorial Profile: KRNN-FM is a non-commercial station owned by Capital Community Broadcasting Inc. The format of

the station is variety. KRNN-FM broadcasts to the Juneau, AK area at 102.7 FM.

KRNO-FM
Owner: Americom Broadcasting
Editorial: 961 Matley Ln Ste 120, Reno, Nevada 89502-2119. **T:** 1 775 829-1964
E: webmaster@sunny1069.com
W: http://www.sunny1069.com
Editorial Profile: KRNO-FM is a commercial station owned by Americom Broadcasting. The format of the station is adult contemporary. KRNO-FM broadcasts to the Reno, NV area at 106.9 FM.

KRNP-FM
Owner: Armada Media
Editorial: 305 E 4th St, North Platte, Nebraska 69101-6903. **T:** 1 308 532-3344
Editorial Profile: KRNP-FM is a commercial station owned by Armada Media. The format of the station is rock music. The station airs locally to to North Platte, NE area at 100.7 FM.

KRNQ-FM
Owner: Withers Broadcasting Co.
Editorial: 108 Washington St, Keokuk, Iowa 52632. **T:** 1 319 524-5410
E: krnq963@mchsi.com
W: http://www.keokukradio.com
Editorial Profile: KRNQ-FM is a commercial station owned by Withers Broadcasting Co. The format of the station is classic rock. KRNQ-FM broadcasts to the Northeast Missouri, West Central Illinois, and Southeast Iowa listening areas at a frequency of 96.3 FM.

KRNT-AM
Owner: Saga Communications
Editorial: 1416 Locust St, Des Moines, Iowa 50309. **T:** 1 515 280-1350
W: http://www.1350krnt.com
Editorial Profile: KRNT-AM is a commercial station owned by Saga Communications. The format of the station is adult standards and talk. KRNT-AM broadcasts to the Des Moines, IA area at 1350 AM.

KRNU-FM
Owner: University of Nebraska
Editorial: 147 Andersen Hall, University of Nebraska, Lincoln, Nebraska 68588-0466. **T:** 1 402 472-3054 **E:** krnu@unl.edu
W: http://krnu.unl.edu
Editorial Profile: KRNU-FM is a non-commercial station owned by the University of Nebraska. The format of the station is rock alternative. KRNU-FM broadcasts to the Lincoln, NE area at 90.3 FM.

KRNV-FM
Owner: Entravision Communications Corp.
Editorial: 300 S Wells Ave, Ste 12, Reno, Nevada 89502-1670. **T:** 1 775 333-1017
W: http://www.tricolor1021.com
Editorial Profile: KRNV-FM is a commercial station owned by Entravision Communications Corp. The format of the station is Hispanic. KRNV-FM broadcasts to the Reno, NV area at 102.1 FM.

KRNY-FM
Owner: NRG Media LLC
Editorial: 2223 Central Ave, Kearney, Nebraska 68847. **T:** 1 308 698-2100
W: http://www.krny.com
Editorial Profile: KRNY-FM is a commercial station owned by NRG Media LLC. The format of the station is contemporary country. KRNY-FM broadcasts to the Kearney, NE area at 102.3 FM.

KROA-FM
Owner: My Bridge Radio
Editorial: 3347 W Capital Ave, Grand Island, Nebraska 68803-1334. **T:** 1 402 845-6595
E: email@mybridgeradio.net
W: http://www.mybridgeradio.net
Editorial Profile: KROA-FM is a non-commercial station owned by My Bridge Radio. The format of the station is contemporary Christian and religious talk. KROA-FM broadcasts to the Doniphan, NE area at 95.7 FM.

KROB-AM
Owner: Claro Communications Ltd.
Editorial: 400 S Padre Island Dr, Ste 107, Corpus Christi, Texas 78405.
T: 1 361 299-6001
E: krobam1510@sbcglobal.net
Editorial Profile: KROB-AM is a commercial station owned by Claro Communications Ltd. The format of the station is Hispanic programming. KROB-AM broadcasts to the Corpus Christi, TX area at 1510 AM.

KROC-AM
Owner: Cumulus Media Inc.
Editorial: 122 4th St SW, Rochester, Minnesota 55902. **T:** 1 507 286-1010
E: news@kroc.com
W: http://www.krocam.com
Editorial Profile: KROC-AM is a commercial station owned by Cumulus Media Inc. The format of the station is news and talk. KROC-AM broadcasts to the Rochester, MN area at 1340 AM.

KROC-FM
Owner: Cumulus Media Inc.
Editorial: 122 4th St SW, Rochester, Minnesota 55902. **T:** 1 507 286-1010
W: http://www.kroc.com
Editorial Profile: KROC-FM is a commercial station owned by Cumulus Media Inc. The format of the station is Top 40/CHR. KROC-FM broadcasts to the Rochester, MN area at 106.9 FM.

KROD-AM
Owner: Townsquare Media, LLC
Editorial: 4180 N Mesa St, El Paso, Texas 79902. **T:** 1 915 544-9550
W: http://www.krod.com
Editorial Profile: KROD-AM is a commercial station owned by Townsquare Media, LLC. The format of the station is sports. KROD-AM broadcasts in the El Paso, TX area at 600 AM.

KROE-AM
Owner: Lovcom, Inc.
Editorial: 1716 Kroe Ln, Sheridan, Wyoming 82801-9681. **T:** 1 307 672-7421
E: news@sheridan.com
W: http://www.sheridanmedia.com
Editorial Profile: KROE-AM is a commercial station owned by Lovcom, Inc. The format of the station is news, sports and talk. KROE-AM broadcasts to the Sheridan, WY area at 930 AM.

KROF-AM
Owner: Townsquare Media, LLC
Editorial: 1749 Bertrand Dr, Lafayette, Louisiana 70506. **T:** 1 337 233-6000
W: http://www.960thegator.com
Editorial Profile: KROF-AM is a commercial station owned by Townsquare Media, LLC. The format of the station is variety. KROF-AM broadcasts to the Lafayette, LA area at 960 AM.

KROG-FM
Owner: Opus Broadcasting Systems Inc.
Editorial: 511 Rossanley Dr, Medford, Oregon 97501-1771. **T:** 1 541 772-0322
E: news@opusradio.com
W: http://www.969therogue.com
Editorial Profile: KROG-FM is a commercial station owned by Opus Broadcasting Systems Inc. The format of the station is rock alternative music. KROG-FM broadcasts to the Medford, OR area at 96.9 FM.

KROH-FM
Owner: Port Townsend Seventh-Day Adventist Church
Editorial: 1505 Franklin St, Port Townsend, Washington 98368-8121. **T:** 1 360 379-8383
W: http://www.radioofhope.org
Editorial Profile: KROH-FM is a non-commercial station owned by Port Townsend Seventh-Day Adventist Church. The format of the station features religious programming with a Christian focus. KROH-FM is broadcasts to the Port Townsend, WA area at a frequency of 91.1 FM.

KROI-FM
Owner: Radio One Inc.
Editorial: 24 Greenway Plz Ste 900, Houston, Texas 77046-2418. **T:** 1 713 623-2108
W: http://news92fm.com
Editorial Profile: KROI-FM is a commercial station owned by Radio One Inc. The format of the station is news talk. KROI-FM broadcasts to the Houston area at 92.1 FM.

KROK-FM
Owner: Standard Broadcasting Co.
Editorial: 168 Kvvp Dr, Leesville, Louisiana 71446. **T:** 1 337 537-9292
W: http://www.krok.com
Editorial Profile: KROK-FM is a commercial station owned by Standard Broadcasting Co. The format of the station is adult album alternative music. KROK-FM broadcasts to the Leesville, LA area at 95.7 FM.

KROM-FM
Owner: Univision Communications Inc.
Editorial: 12451 Network Blvd Ste 140, San Antonio, Texas 78249-3336.

T: 1 210 610-4300
W: http://estereolatino929.univision.com
Editorial Profile: KROM-FM is a commercial station owned by Univision Communications Inc. The format of the station is regional Mexican. KROM-FM broadcasts to the San Antonio area at 92.9 FM.

KROO-AM
Owner: MediaNews Group Inc.
Editorial: 114 E Elm St, Breckenridge, Texas 76424-3613. **T:** 1 254 559-6543
Editorial Profile: KROO-AM is a commercial station owned by Media News Group Inc. The format of the station is adult contemporary. KROO-AM broadcasts to Breckenridge, TX at 1430 AM.

KROP-AM
Owner: Lardog Communications, LLC (Teresa Goodspeed)
Editorial: 120 S Plaza St, Brawley, California 92227-2428. **T:** 1 760 344-1300
Editorial Profile: KROP-AM is a commercial station owned by Lardog Communications, LLC. The format of the station is conservative talk. The station airs locally at 1300 AM in the El Centro, CA area.

KROQ-FM
Owner: CBS Radio
Editorial: 5901 Venice Blvd, Los Angeles, California 90034-1708. **T:** 1 323 930-1067
E: tips@kroq.com **W:** http://kroq.cbslocal.com
Editorial Profile: KROQ-FM is a commercial station owned by CBS Radio. The format of the station is rock alternative. KROQ-FM broadcasts to the Los Angeles area at 106.7 FM.

KROR-FM
Owner: NRG Media LLC
Editorial: 3532 W Capital Ave, Grand Island, Nebraska 68803. **T:** 1 308 381-1077
W: http://www.rock1015.com

KROS-AM
Owner: KROS Broadcasting Inc.
Editorial: 870 13th Ave N, Clinton, Iowa 52732. **T:** 1 563 242-1252
E: news@krosradio.com
W: http://www.krosradio.com
Editorial Profile: KROS-AM is a commercial station owned by KROS Broadcasting Inc. The format of the station is full service, featuring a mix of adult contemporary music, news, and sports. KROS-AM broadcasts to the Clinton, IA area at 1340 AM.

KROU-FM
Owner: University of Oklahoma
Editorial: University Of Oklahoma, Norman, Oklahoma 73019. **T:** 1 405 325-3388
E: news@kgou.org **W:** http://www.kgou.org

KROX-AM
Owner: Gopher Communications Company
Editorial: 208 S Main St, Crookston, Minnesota 56716-1969. **T:** 1 218 281-1140
E: krox@rrv.net **W:** http://www.kroxam.com
Editorial Profile: KROX-AM is a commercial station owned by Gopher Communications Company. The format of the station is adult contemporary music, sports and news. KROX-AM broadcasts to the Crookston, MN area at 1260 AM.

KROX-FM
Owner: Emmis Communications Corp.
Editorial: 8309 N Interstate Hwy 35, Austin, Texas 78753-5720. **T:** 1 512 836-5769
W: http://www.101x.com
Editorial Profile: KROX-FM is a commercial station owned by Emmis Communications Corp. The format of the station is rock alternative music. KROX-FM broadcasts to the Austin, TX area at 101.5 FM.

KRPA-AM
Owner: Satnam Media Group, Inc.
Editorial: 404 S 1st St Ste 202, Mount Vernon, Washington 98273-3866.
T: 1 604 590-3510 **E:** ssd@radiopunjab.com
W: http://www.radiopunjab.com
Editorial Profile: KRPA-AM is a commercial station owned by Satnam Media Group, Inc. The format of the station features South Asian and Indian focused programming. KRPA-AM broadcasts in the Seattle, WA and Vancouver, BC areas at 1110 AM.

KRPI-AM
Owner: BBC Broadcasting Inc.
Editorial: 5538 Imhoff Rd, Ferndale, Washington 98248. **T:** 1 360 384-5117
E: 1550radio@gmail.com

W: http://www.krpiradio.com
Editorial Profile: KRPI-AM is a commercial station owned by BBC Broadcasting Inc. The format of the station is Indian variety. KRPI-AM broadcasts to the Ferndale, WA area at 1550 AM.

KRPL-AM
Owner: KRPL Inc.
Editorial: 1114 N Almon St, Moscow, Idaho 83843. **T:** 1 208 882-2551
E: reception@idavend.com
Editorial Profile: KRPL-AM is a commercial station owned by KRPL Inc. The format of the station is sports talk. KRPL-AM broadcasts to the Spokane, WA area at 1400 AM.

KRPM-FM
Owner: BMG Billings
Editorial: 222 N 32nd St, Fl 10, Billings, Montana 59101. **T:** 1 406 238-1000
E: billings@benedettimedia.com
W: http://www.magic1075fm.com
Editorial Profile: KRPM-FM is a commercial station owned by BMG Billings. The format of the station is Lite AC/Lite Rock. KRPM-FM broadcasts to the Billings, MT area at 107.5 FM.

KRPR-FM
Owner: Rochester Public Radio
Editorial: 1620 Greenview Dr SW, Rochester, Minnesota 55902-4319. **T:** 1 507 288-2376
Editorial Profile: KRPR-FM is a non-commercial station owned by Rochester Public Radio. The format of the station is classic rock music. KRPR-FM broadcasts to the Rochester, MN area at a frequency of 89.9 FM.

KRPS-FM
Owner: Pittsburg State University
Editorial: 1701 S Broadway St, Pittsburg, Kansas 66762-5856. **T:** 1 620 235-4288
E: krps@pittstate.edu **W:** http://krps.org
Editorial Profile: KRPS-FM is a non-commercial station owned by Pittsburg State University. The format of the station is news, talk, classical, jazz, and folk music. KRPS-FM broadcasts to Pittsburg, KS at 89.9 FM.

KRPT-FM
Owner: Clear Channel Media and Entertainment
Editorial: 6222 W Interstate 10, San Antonio, Texas 78201-2013. **T:** 1 210 736-9700
Editorial Profile: KRPT-FM is a commercial station owned by Clear Channel Media and Entertainment. The format of the station is classic country. KRPT-FM broadcasts to the San Antonio area at 92.5 FM.

KRQB-FM
Owner: Liberman Broadcasting Inc.
Editorial: 1845 Business Center Dr, San Bernardino, California 92408-3467.
T: 1 909 663-1961
W: http://www.quebuena961.com
Editorial Profile: KRQB-FM is a commercial station owned by Liberman Broadcasting Inc. The format of the station is regional Mexican. KRQB-FM broadcasts to the San Bernardino, CA area at 96.1 FM.

KRQC-FM
Owner: Davenport Adventist Radio Inc
Editorial: 4444 W Kimberly Rd, Davenport, Iowa 52806-7107. **T:** 1 563 391-3016
W: http://www.3abnradio.org
Editorial Profile: KRQC-FM is a commercial station owned by Davenport Adventist Radio Inc. The format for the station is Christian music and talk. The target audience of the station is adults, ages 18 to 64. KRQC-FM broadcasts to the Davenport, IA area at 107.9 FM.

KRQK-FM
Owner: American General Media
Editorial: 2325 Skyway Dr, Santa Maria, California 93455-1137. **T:** 1 805 922-1041
W: http://www.1003laley.com
Editorial Profile: KRQK-FM is a commercial station owned by American General Media. The format of the station is Regional Mexican. KRQK-FM broadcasts to the Santa Maria, CA area at 100.3 FM.

KRQN-FM
Owner: Flinn Broadcasting Corp.
Editorial: 425 2nd St SE Fl 4, Cedar Rapids, Iowa 52401-1819. **T:** 1 319 892-3574
W: http://i1071.com
Editorial Profile: KRQN-FM is a commercial station owned by Flinn Broadcasting Corp. and operated by Townsquare Media, LLC. The format of the station is Top 40/CHR. KRQN-FM broadcasts to the Cedar Rapids, IA area at a frequency of 107.1 FM.

KRQQ-FM
Owner: Clear Channel Media and Entertainment
Editorial: 3202 N Oracle Rd, Tucson, Arizona 85705. **T:** 1 520 618-2100
W: http://www.krq.com
Editorial Profile: KRQQ-FM is a commercial station owned by Clear Channel Media and Entertainment. The format of the station is Top 40/CHR. KRQQ-FM broadcasts to the Tucson, AZ area on 93.7 FM.

KRQR-FM
Owner: Results Radio Group
Editorial: 856 Manzanita Ct, Chico, California 95926. **T:** 1 530 342-2200
W: http://www.zrockfm.com
Editorial Profile: KRQR-FM is a commercial station owned by Results Radio Group. The format of the station is rock alternative. KRQR-FM broadcasts to the Chico, CA area at 106.7 FM.

KRQT-FM
Owner: Bicoastal Media LLC
Editorial: 1130 14th Ave, Longview, Washington 98632-3017. **T:** 1 360 425-1500
W: http://www.rocket107.com
Editorial Profile: KRQT-FM is a commercial station owned by Bicoastal Media LLC. The format of the station is classic rock music. KRQT-FM broadcasts to the Portland, OR area at 107.1 FM.

KRQX-FM
Owner: Simmons Media Group
Editorial: 216 W St George Blvd Ste 101, Saint George, Utah 84770-1306.
T: 1 800 603-6035 **E:** mail@demolink.org
W: http://www.x989utah.com
Editorial Profile: KRQX-FM is a commercial station owned by Simmons Media Group. The format of the station is alternative rock. KRQX-FM broadcasts to the St. George, UT area at a frequency of 98.9 FM.

KRRF-FM
Owner: Cumulus Media Inc.
Editorial: 403 E Montecito St, Santa Barbara, California 93101-1759. **T:** 1 805 966-1755
W: http://www.classichits1063.com
Editorial Profile: KRRF-FM is a commercial station owned by Cumulus Media Inc. The format of the station is classic hits. KRRF-FM broadcasts to the Santa Barbara, CA area at 106.3 FM.

KRRG-FM
Owner: Guerra Enterprises
Editorial: 6402 N Bartlett Ave, Ste 1, Laredo, Texas 78041-6448. **T:** 1 956 724-9800
E: livewire@krrg.com **W:** http://bigbuck98.com
Editorial Profile: KRRG-FM is a commercial station owned by Guerra Enterprises. The format of the station is classic country music. KRRG-FM broadcasts to the Laredo, TX, area at 98.1 FM.

KRRK-FM
Owner: Mad Dog Wireless Inc.
Editorial: 2068 Mcculloch Blvd N, Lake Havasu City, Arizona 86403-6712.
T: 1 928 855-1051 **E:** info@maddog.net
W: http://theclassicrockstation.com
Editorial Profile: KRRK-FM is a commercial station owned by Mad Dog Wireless Inc. The format of the station is classic rock music. KRRK-FM broadcasts in the Lake Havasu City, AZ area at 101.1 FM.

KRRM-FM
Owner: Bell (Shirley M.)
Editorial: 225 Rogue River Hwy, Grants Pass, Oregon 97527-5477. **T:** 1 541 479-6497
E: krrm@krrm.com **W:** http://www.krrm.com
Editorial Profile: KRRM-FM is a commercial station owned by Shirley M. Bell. The format of the station is country music and talk. KRRM-FM broadcasts to the Grants Pass, OR area at 94.7 FM.

KRRN-FM
Owner: Entravision Communications Corp.
Editorial: 500 Pilot Rd, Ste D, Las Vegas, Nevada 89119-3624. **T:** 1 702 434-0015
W: http://www.elgato927.com
Editorial Profile: KRRN-FM is a commercial station owned by Entravision Communications Corp. The format of the station is Hispanic. KRRN-FM broadcasts to the Las Vegas area on 92.7 FM.

KRRO-FM
Owner: Midwest Communications
Editorial: 500 S Phillips Ave, Sioux Falls, South Dakota 57104-6825. **T:** 1 605 331-5350
E: krro@krro.com **W:** http://www.krro.com
Editorial Profile: KRRO-FM is a commercial station owned by Midwest Communications. The format of the station is rock/album-oriented rock. KRRO-FM broadcasts to the Sioux Falls, SD area at 103.7 FM.

KRRP-AM
Owner: Hobbs(Francis V.)
Editorial: 163 Catfish Bend Rd, Coushatta, Louisiana 71019-8828. **T:** 1 318 932-7132

KRRQ-FM
Owner: Cumulus Media Inc
Editorial: 202 Galbert Rd, Lafayette, Louisiana 70506. **T:** 1 337 232-1311
W: http://www.krrq.com
Editorial Profile: KRRQ-FM is a commercial station owned by Cumulus Media Inc. The format of the station is urban contemporary. KRRQ-FM broadcasts to the Lafayette, LA area at 95.5 FM.

KRRR-FM
Owner: Appaloosa Broadcasting
Editorial: 2109 E 10th St, Cheyenne, Wyoming 82001. **T:** 1 307 638-8921
E: traffic@1049krrr.com
W: http://www.1049krrr.com
Editorial Profile: KRRR-FM is a commercial station owned by Appaloosa Broadcasting. The format of the station is oldies. KRRR-FM broadcasts to the Cheyenne, WY area at 104.9 FM.

KRRS-AM
Owner: California Broadcasting Company, LLC
Editorial: 965 Stony Point Rd, Santa Rosa, California 95407-7129. **T:** 1 707 545-1460
Editorial Profile: KRRS-AM is a commercial station owned by California Broadcasting Company, LLC. The format of the station is Regional Mexican music. KRRS-AM broadcasts to the Santa Rosa, CA area at 1460 AM.

KRRV-FM
Owner: Cenla Broadcasting Inc.
Editorial: 1115 Texas Ave, Alexandria, Louisiana 71301. **T:** 1 318 445-1234
W: http://www.krrvonline.com
Editorial Profile: KRRV-FM is a commercial station owned by Cenla Broadcasting Inc. The format of the station is country music. KRRV-FM broadcasts to the Alexandria, LA area at 100.3 FM.

KRRW-FM
Owner: Radio Mankato
Editorial: 59346 Madison Ave, Mankato, Minnesota 56001-8518. **T:** 1 507 345-4537
E: news@ktoe.com **W:** http://www.krrw.com
Editorial Profile: KRRW-FM is a commercial station owned by Radio Mankato. The format of the station is country. KRRW-FM broadcasts to the Saint James, MN area at 101.5 FM.

KRRX-FM
Owner: Mapleton of Redding, LLC
Editorial: 3360 Alta Mesa Dr, Redding, California 96002-2831. **T:** 1 530 226-9500
E: news@reddingradio.com
W: http://www.106x.com
Editorial Profile: KRRX-FM is a commercial station owned by Mapleton of Redding, LLC. The format of the station is rock/album-oriented rock. KRRX-FM broadcasts to the Redding, CA area at 106.1 FM.

KRRY-FM
Owner: Double O Radio
Editorial: 408 N 24th St, Quincy, Illinois 62301-3254. **T:** 1 217 223-5292
W: http://www.y101radio.com
Editorial Profile: KRRY-FM is a commercial station owned by Double O Radio. The format of the station is hot adult contemporary. KRRY-FM broadcasts to the Quincy, IL; Hannibal, MO; and Keokuk, IA, area at 100.9 FM.

KRRZ-AM
Owner: Clear Channel Media and Entertainment
Editorial: 1000 20th Ave SW, Minot, North Dakota 58701. **T:** 1 701 852-4646
E: minotprod@clearchannel.com
W: http://www.oldies1390.com
Editorial Profile: KRRZ-AM is a commercial station owned by Clear Channel Media and Entertainment. The format of the station is oldies. KRRZ-AM broadcasts to the Minot-Bismarck, ND area at 1390 AM.

KRSA-AM
Owner: Northern Light Network
Editorial: 11 N 12th St, Petersburg, Alaska 99833-9999. **T:** 1 907 772-3891
E: krsa@krsa.net **W:** http://www.krsa.net
Editorial Profile: KRSA-AM is a commercial station owned by Northern Light Network. The format of the station is variety and Christian programming. KRSA-AM broadcasts to the Petersburg, AK area at 580 AM.

KRSB-FM
Owner: Brooke Communications Inc.
Editorial: 1445 W Harvard Ave, Roseburg, Oregon 97471. **T:** 1 541 672-6641
E: country@bciradio.com
W: http://www.541radio.com
Editorial Profile: KRSB-FM is a commercial station owned by Brooke Communications Inc. The format of the station is contemporary country music. KRSB-FM broadcasts to the Roseburg, OR area at 103.1 FM.

KRSC-FM
Owner: Rogers State University
Editorial: 1701 W Will Rogers Blvd, Claremore, Oklahoma 74017.
T: 1 918 343-7669 **E:** rsuradio@hotmail.com
W: http://www.rsu.edu/rsuradio/index.asp
Editorial Profile: KRSC-FM is a non-commercial station owned by Rogers State University. The format of the station is rock alternative. KRSC-FM broadcasts to the Claremore, OK area at 91.3 FM.

KRSD-FM
Owner: Minnesota Public Radio
Editorial: 2001 S Summit Ave, Sioux Falls, South Dakota 57197. **T:** 1 605 335-6666
W: http://minnesota.publicradio.org/radio/stations/krsd/
Editorial Profile: KRSD-FM is a non-commercial station owned by Minnesota Public Radio. The format of the station is classical music. KRSD-FM broadcasts to the Sioux Falls, SD area at 88.1 FM.

KRSE-FM
Owner: New Northwest Broadcasters LLC
Editorial: 1200 Chesterly Dr, Ste 160, Yakima, Washington 98902. **T:** 1 509 248-2900
W: http://www.1057bobfm.com

KRSH-FM
Owner: Wine Country Radio
Editorial: 3565 Standish Ave, Santa Rosa, California 95407. **T:** 1 707 588-0707
E: studio@krsh.com **W:** http://www.krsh.com
Editorial Profile: KRSH-FM is a commercial station owned by Wine Country Radio. The format of the station is adult album alternative music. KRSH-FM broadcasts to the Santa Rosa, CA area at 95.9 FM.

KRSJ-FM
Owner: Four Corners Broadcasting LLC
Editorial: 190 Turner Dr, Unit G, Durango, Colorado 81303-8231. **T:** 1 970 259-4444
E: news@radiodurango.com
W: http://www.radiodurango.com/krsj.asp
Editorial Profile: KRSJ-FM is a commercial station owned by Four Corners Broadcasting LLC. The format of the station is country music. KRSJ-FM broadcasts to the Albuquerque, NM area at 100.5 FM.

KRSK-FM
Owner: Entercom Communications Corp.
Editorial: 0700 SW Bancroft St, Portland, Oregon 97239-4226. **T:** 1 503 223-1441
W: http://www.1051thebuzz.com
Editorial Profile: KRSK-FM is a commercial station owned by Entercom Communications Corp. The format of the station is hot adult contemporary. KRSK-FM broadcasts in the Portland, OR area at 105.1 FM.

KRSL-AM
Owner: White Communications
Editorial: 1984 N Main St, Russell, Kansas 67665-1236. **T:** 1 785 483-3121
E: comments@krsl.com
W: http://www.krsl.com
Editorial Profile: KRSL-AM is a commercial station owned by White Communications. The format of the station is classic country. KRSL-AM broadcasts to the Russell, KS area at 990 AM.

KRSL-FM
Owner: White Communications
Editorial: 1984 N Main St, Russell, Kansas 67665-1236. **T:** 1 785 483-3121

WORLD NEWS MEDIA

E: comments@krsl.com
W: http://www.krsl.com
Editorial Profile: KRSL-FM is a commercial station owned by White Communications. The format of the station is classic hits. KRSL-FM broadcasts to the Russell, KS area at 95.9 FM.

KRSN-AM
Owner: Sutton (David and Gillian)
Editorial: 3801 Arkansas Ave Ste E, Los Alamos, New Mexico 87544-1600.
T: 1 505 663-1490 **E:** info@krsnam1490.com
W: http://www.krsnam1490.com
Editorial Profile: KRSN-AM is a commercial station owned by David and Gillian Sutton. The format of the station is news, talk information and variety. KRSN-AM broadcasts to the Los Alamos, NM area at 1490 AM.

KRSP-FM
Owner: KSL Broadcasting
Editorial: 55 N 300 W, Salt Lake City, Utah 84101. **T:** 1 801 575-5555
W: http://www.1035thearrow.com
Editorial Profile: KRSP-FM is a commercial station owned by KSL Broadcasting. The format of the station is classic hits. KRSP-FM broadcasts to the Salt Lake City area at 103.5 FM.

KRSQ-FM
Owner: BMG Billings, LLC
Editorial: 222 N 32nd St, Fl 10, Billings, Montana 59101. **T:** 1 406 238-1000
E: billings@benedettimedia.com
W: http://www.hot1019.com
Editorial Profile: KRSQ-FM is a commercial station owned by BMG Billings, LLC. The format is top 40/CHR. The station airs in the Billings, MT area at 101.9FM.

KRSS-FM
Owner: Radio Free Ministries
Editorial: 1500 S 14th St, Clarinda, Iowa 51632-3120. **T:** 1 712 542-2260
W: http://www.krss.me
Editorial Profile: KRSS-FM is a non-commercial station owned by Radio Free Ministries. The format of the station is religious talk and music. KRSS-FM broadcasts to the Omaha, NE area at a frequency of 93.5.

KRST-FM
Owner: Cumulus Media Inc
Editorial: 500 4th St NW Ste 500, Albuquerque, New Mexico 87102-2172.
T: 1 505 767-6700
W: http://www.nashfm923krst.com
Editorial Profile: KRST-FM is a commercial station owned by Cumulus Media Inc. The format for the station is contemporary country. KRST-FM broadcasts to the Albuquerque, NM, area at 92.3 FM.

KRSV-AM
Owner: Western Wyoming Radio Inc.
Editorial: 10399 State Highway 238, Afton, Wyoming 83110. **T:** 1 307 885-5778
E: krsv@silverstar.com

KRSV-FM
Owner: Western Wyoming Radio Inc.
Editorial: 10399 State Highway 238, Afton, Wyoming 83110-9746. **T:** 1 307 885-5778
E: krsv@silverstar.com

KRSW-FM
Owner: Minnesota Public Radio
Editorial: 1450 Collegeway, Worthington, Minnesota 56187-3024. **T:** 1 507 372-2904
W: http://www.minnesota.publicradio.org/radio/stations/knswkrsw/
Editorial Profile: KRSW-FM is a non-commercial station owned by Minnesota Public Radio. The format of the station is classical music. KRSW-FM broadcasts to the Worthington, MN area at 89.3 FM.

KRSX-AM
Owner: Rudex Broadcasting LTD
Editorial: 15000 Seventh St Ste 208E, Victorville, California 92395-3853.
T: 1 760 298-3359 **W:** http://www.krsx.net
Editorial Profile: KRSX-AM is a commercial station owned by Rudex Broadcasting LTD. The format of the station is regional Mexican music. KRSX-AM broadcasts in the Victorville, CA area at 1590 AM.

KRSY-AM
Owner: WP Broadcasting LLC
Editorial: 119 N Canyon Rd, Alamogordo, New Mexico 88310-5910. **T:** 1 575 437-1505
E: krsy@snmradio.com
W: http://snmradio.com/krsyam/index.html
Editorial Profile: KRSY-AM is a commercial station owned by WP Broadcasting LLC. The format of the station is talk. KRSY-AM broadcasts to the Alamogordo, NM area at 1230 AM.

KRSY-FM
Owner: WP Broadcasting LLC
Editorial: 119 N Canyon Rd, Alamogordo, New Mexico 88310-5910. **T:** 1 575 437-1505
E: alamogordo@snmradio.com
W: http://www.snmradio.com
Editorial Profile: KRSY-FM is a commercial station owned by WP Broadcasting LLC. The format of the station is country music. KRSY-FM broadcasts to the Albuquerque, NM area at 92.7 FM.

KRTA-AM
Owner: Opus Broadcasting Systems Inc.
Editorial: 511 Rossanley Dr, Medford, Oregon 97501-1771. **T:** 1 541 772-0322
Editorial Profile: KRTA-AM is a commercial station owned by Opus Broadcasting Systems. The format of the station is regional Mexican music. KRTA-AM broadcasts to the Medford, OR area at 610 AM.

KRTH-FM
Owner: CBS Radio
Editorial: 5670 Wilshire Blvd, Ste 200, Los Angeles, California 90036. **T:** 1 323 936-5784
W: http://kearth101.radio.com
Editorial Profile: KRTH-FM is a commercial station owned by CBS Radio. The format of the station is classic hits. KRTH-FM broadcasts to the Los Angeles area at 101.1 FM.

KRTI-FM
Owner: Good Radio TV Co. LLC
Editorial: 1801 N 13th Ave E, Newton, Iowa 50208-1308. **T:** 1 641 236-5784
E: info@kcobradio.com
W: http://www.myiowainfo.com
Editorial Profile: KRTI-FM is a commercial station owned by Good Radio TV Co. LLC. The format of the station is hot adult contemporary. KRTI-FM broadcasts to the Newton, IA area at 106.7 FM.

KRTN-AM
Owner: Enchanted Air Inc.
Editorial: 1128 State St, Raton, New Mexico 87740-2330. **T:** 1 575 445-3652
E: krtn@bacavalley.com
Editorial Profile: KRTN-AM is a commercial station owned by Enchanted Air Inc. The format of the station is adult contemporary music. KRTN-AM broadcasts to the Albuquerque, NM area at 1490 AM.

KRTN-FM
Owner: Enchanted Air Inc.
Editorial: 1128 State St, Raton, New Mexico 87740-2330. **T:** 1 575 445-3652
E: krtn@bacavalley.com
Editorial Profile: KRTN-FM is a commercial station owned by Enchanted Air Inc. The format of the station is oldies music. KRTN-FM broadcasts to the Albuquerque, NM area at 93.9 FM.

KRTO-FM
Owner: Emerald Wave Media
Editorial: 718 E Chapel St, Santa Maria, California 93454. **T:** 1 805 928-4334
Editorial Profile: KRTO-FM is a commercial station owned by Emerald Wave Media. The format of the station is oldies. KRTO-FM broadcasts to the Santa Maria, CA area at 97.1 FM.

KRTR-FM
Owner: Summit Media Broadcasting LLC
Editorial: 900 Fort Street Mall, Honolulu, Hawaii 96813-3721. **T:** 1 808 275-1000
W: http://www.krater963.com
Editorial Profile: KRTR-FM is a commercial station owned by Summit Media Broadcasting LLC. The format of the station is adult contemporary. KRTR-FM broadcasts to the Honolulu area at 96.3 FM.

KRTS-FM
Owner: Matinee Radio, LLC
Editorial: 111 South Highland Ave., Marfa, Texas 79843. **T:** 1 432 729-4578
W: http://www.marfapublicradio.org
Editorial Profile: KRTS-FM is a non-commercial station owned by Matinee Radio, LLC. The format of the station is variety. KRTS-FM broadcasts to the Odessa-Midland, TX area at 93.5 FM. The station airs programming on KXWT-FM.

KRTU-FM
Owner: Trinity University
Editorial: 1 Trinity Pl, Box 69, San Antonio, Texas 78212. **T:** 1 210 999-8917
E: krtu@trinity.edu **W:** http://www.krtu.org
Editorial Profile: KRTU-FM is a non-commercial station owned by Trinity University. The format of the station is jazz and rock alternative. KRTU-FM broadcasts to the San Antonio area at 91.7 FM.

KRTY-FM
Owner: Empire Broadcasting Systems Corp.
Editorial: 750 Story Rd, San Jose, California 95122. **T:** 1 408 293-8030
W: http://www.krty.com
Editorial Profile: KRTY-FM is a commercial station owned by Empire Broadcasting Systems Corp. The format of the station is contemporary country. KRTY-FM broadcasts to the San Jose, CA area at 95.3 FM.

KRTZ-FM
Owner: American General Media
Editorial: 2402 Hawkins St, Cortez, Colorado 81321-9544. **T:** 1 970 565-6565
E: radio@krtzradio.com
W: http://www.krtzradio.com
Editorial Profile: KRTZ-FM is a commercial station owned by American General Media. The format of the station is adult contemporary music. KRTZ-FM broadcasts to the Albuquerque, NM area at 98.7 FM.

KRUA-FM
Owner: University of Alaska
Editorial: 3211 Providence Dr, PSB Rm 254, Anchorage, Alaska 99508-4614.
T: 1 907 786-6800 **E:** aykrua@uaa.alaska.edu
W: http://www.uaa.alaska.edu/krua

KRUE-AM
Owner: Main Street Broadcasting Inc.
Editorial: 255 Cedardale Dr SE, Owatonna, Minnesota 55060. **T:** 1 507 444-9224
W: http://www.kowzonline.com
Editorial Profile: KRUE-AM is a commercial station owned by Main Street Broadcasting Inc. The format of the station is oldies music. KRUE-AM broadcasts to the Owatonna, MN area at 1170 AM.

KRUF-FM
Owner: Townsquare Media, LLC
Editorial: 6341 W Port Ave, Shreveport, Louisiana 71129. **T:** 1 318 688-1130
W: http://www.k945.com
Editorial Profile: KRUF-FM is a commercial station owned by Townsquare Media, LLC. The format of the station is Top 40/CHR. KRUF-FM broadcasts to the Shreveport, LA area at 94.5 FM.

KRUI-AM
Owner: MTD Inc.
Editorial: 1086 Mechem Dr, Ruidoso, New Mexico 88345-7044. **T:** 1 575 258-9922
W: http://www.mtdradio.com
Editorial Profile: KRUI-AM is a commercial station owned by MTD Inc. The format of the station is talk. KRUI-AM broadcasts to the Ruidoso, NM area at 1490 AM.

KRUI-FM
Owner: Student Broadcasters Inc.
Editorial: 379 IMU, University of Iowa, Iowa City, Iowa 52242. **T:** 1 319 335-9525
E: krui@uiowa.edu **W:** http://www.kruiradio.org
Editorial Profile: KRUI-FM is a non-commercial station owned by Student Broadcasters Inc. The format for the station is college variety. KRUI-FM broadcasts to the Iowa City, IA area at 89.7 FM.

KRUN-AM
Owner: Graham Brothers Communications LLC
Editorial: 1920 Hutchins Ave, Ballinger, Texas 76821. **T:** 1 325 365-5500
E: krun1400@hotmail.com
W: http://www.krunam.com
Editorial Profile: KRUN-AM is a commercial station owned by Graham Brothers Communications LLC. The format of the station is contemporary country. KRUN-AM broadcasts to the Ballinger, TX area at 1400 AM.

KRUP-FM
Owner: McCormick Broadcasting
Editorial: 301 Airport Road, Dillingham, Alaska 99576-9999. **T:** 1 907 842-2333
Editorial Profile: KRUP-FM is a commercial station owned by McCormick Broadcasting. The format of the station is talk. KRUP-FM broadcasts to the Anchorage, AK area at a frequency of 99.1 FM.

KRUS-AM
Owner: Red Peach LLC
Editorial: 500 N Monroe St, Ruston, Louisiana 71270-3835. **T:** 1 318 255-5000
Editorial Profile: KRUS-AM is a commercial station owned by Red Peach LLC. The format of the station is gospel music. KRUS-AM broadcasts to the Ruston, LA area at 1490 AM.

KRUU-FM
Owner: Fairfield Youth Advocacy, Inc.
Editorial: 405 N 2Nd St, Fairfield, Iowa 52556-2467. **T:** 1 641 209-1083
E: news@kruufm.com
W: http://www.kruufm.com
Editorial Profile: KRUU-FM is a non-commercial station owned by Fairfield Youth Advocacy, Inc. The format of the station is news and variety. The station airs locally on 100.1 FM.

KRUZ-FM
Owner: Educational Media Foundation
Editorial: 403 E Montecito St Fl St 3Rda, Santa Barbara, California 93101-1759.
T: 1 805 966-1755 **W:** http://www.kruz.com
Editorial Profile: KRUZ-FM is a commercial station owned by Educational Media Foundation. The format of the station is Christian contemporary. KRUZ-FM broadcasts to the Santa Barbara, CA area at 97.5 FM.

KRVA-FM
Owner: Hunt County Radio
Editorial: 1517 Wolfe City Dr, Greenville, Texas 75401-2111. **T:** 1 903 455-1400
Editorial Profile: KRVA-FM is a commercial station owned by Hunt County Radio. The format of the station is oldies. KRVA-FM broadcasts to the Paris, TX area at 107.1 FM.

KRVB-FM
Owner: Journal Broadcast Group
Editorial: 5257 W Fairview Ave, Ste 260, Boise, Idaho 83706. **T:** 1 208 344-3511
W: http://www.riverinteractive.com
Editorial Profile: KRVB-FM is a commercial station owned by Journal Broadcast Group. The format of the station is adult album alternative music. KRVB-FM broadcasts to the Boise, ID area at 94.9 FM.

KRVC-FM
Owner: Opus Broadcasting Systems Inc.
Editorial: 511 Rossanley Dr, Medford, Oregon 97501. **T:** 1 541 772-0322
W: http://www.hot989.com
Editorial Profile: KRVC-FM is a commercial station owned by Opus Broadcasting Systems Inc. The format of the station is Top 40/CHR. KRVC-FM broadcasts to the Medford, OR area at 98.9 FM.

KRVE-FM
Owner: Clear Channel Media and Entertainment
Editorial: 5555 Hilton Ave, Ste 500, Baton Rouge, Louisiana 70808. **T:** 1 225 231-1860
W: http://www.961theriver.com
Editorial Profile: KRVE-FM is a commercial station owned by Clear Channel Media and Entertainment. The format of the station is Lite Rock/Lite AC. KRVE-FM broadcasts to the Baton Rouge, LA area at 96.1 FM.

KRVF-FM
Owner: LKCM Radio Group LP
Editorial: 214 N Main St, Corsicana, Texas 75110-4620. **T:** 1 903 874-8884
W: http://www.1069theranch.com
Editorial Profile: KRVF-FM is a commercial station owned by LKCM Radio Group LP. The format of the station is classic country. KRVF broadcasts to the Corsicana, TX area at 106.9 FM.

KRVG-FM
Owner: Western Slope Communications
Editorial: 751 Horizon Ct, Ste 225, Grand Junction, Colorado 81506. **T:** 1 970 241-6460
E: production@wscradio.net
Editorial Profile: KRVG-FM is a commercial station owned by Western Slope Communications. The format for the station is classic rock. KRVG-FM broadcasts to the Grand Junction-Montrose, CO area at 95.5 FM.

KRVI-FM
Owner: Journal Broadcast Group
Editorial: 2330 W Grand St, Springfield, Missouri 65802. **T:** 1 417 865-6614
W: http://www.1067theriver.com
Editorial Profile: KRVI-FM is a commercial station owned by Journal Broadcast Group. The format of the station is variety and top 40/

CHR. KRVI-FM broadcasts to the Springfield, MO area at 106.7 FM.

KRVK-FM
Owner: Townsquare Media, LLC
Editorial: 150 Nichols Ave, Casper, Wyoming 82601. **T:** 1 307 266-5252
W: http://www.theriver1079.com
Editorial Profile: KRVK-FM is a commercial station owned by Townsquare Media, LLC. The format of the station is classic rock music. KRVK-FM broadcasts to the Casper, WY area at 107.9 FM.

KRVL-FM
Owner: Revolution Broadcast Co.
Editorial: 2125 Sidney Baker St, Kerrville, Texas 78028-2551. **T:** 1 830 896-1230
E: production@krvl.com
W: http://www.revfmradio.com
Editorial Profile: KRVL-FM is a commercial station owned by Revolution Broadcast Co. The format of the station is classic rock. KRVL-FM broadcasts to the Kerrville, TX area at 94.3 FM.

KRVM-AM
Owner: Lane County School District 4-J
Editorial: 1574 Coburg Rd, Ste 237, Eugene, Oregon 97401-4802. **T:** 1 541 790-6686
W: http://www.ijpr.org
Editorial Profile: KRVM-AM is non-commerical station owned by Lane County School District 4-J. The format for the station is news and talk. WRVM-AM broadcasts to the Eugene, OR area at 1280 AM.

KRVM-FM
Owner: Lane County School District 4-J
Editorial: 1574 Coburg Rd, Ste 237, Eugene, Oregon 97401. **T:** 1 541 790-6686
E: info@krvm.org **W:** http://www.krvm.org
Editorial Profile: KRVM-FM is a non-commercial station owned by School District 4-J. The format of the station is a variety of AAA and blues. KRVM-FM broadcasts to the Eugene, OR area at 91.9 FM.

KRVN-AM
Owner: Nebraska Rural Radio Association
Editorial: 1007 Plum Creek Pkwy, Lexington, Nebraska 68850. **T:** 1 308 324-2371
E: krvnam@krvn.com **W:** http://www.krvn.com
Editorial Profile: KRVN-AM is a commercial station owned by Nebraska Rural Radio Association. The format of the station is agricultural programming and classic country. KRVN-AM broadcasts to the Lexington, NE area at 880 AM.

KRVN-FM
Owner: Nebraska Rural Radio Association
Editorial: 1007 Plum Creek Pkwy, Lexington, Nebraska 68850-2621. **T:** 1 308 324-2371
E: krvnam@krvn.com **W:** http://www.krvn.com
Editorial Profile: KRVN-FM is a commercial station owned by Nebraska Rural Radio Association. The format of the station is classic country. KRVN-FM broadcasts to the Lexington, NE area at 93.1 FM.

KRVO-FM
Owner: Rose Communications, Inc.
Editorial: 2432 US Highway 2 E, Kalispell, Montana 59901. **T:** 1 406 755-8700
E: info@1031theriver.com
W: http://www.1031theriver.com
Editorial Profile: KRVO-FM is a commercial station owned by Rose Communications, Inc. The format of the station is adult album alternative. KRVO-FM broadcasts to the Kalispell, MT area at 103.1 FM.

KRVQ-FM
Owner: QAB Media LLC
Editorial: 14 Sierra Drive, Kernville, California 93238. **T:** 1 760 376-4500
Editorial Profile: KRVQ-FM is a commercial station owned by QAB Media LLC. The format of the station is classic rock. KRVQ-FM broadcasts to the Kernville, CA area at 104.5 FM.

KRVR-FM
Owner: Threshold Communications
Editorial: 961 N Emerald Ave, Ste A, Modesto, California 95351. **T:** 1 209 544-1055
E: theriver@krvr.com **W:** http://www.krvr.com
Editorial Profile: KRVR-FM is a commercial station owned by Threshold Communications. The format of the station is adult hits. KRVR-FM broadcasts to the Modesto, CA area at 105.5 FM.

KRVS-FM
Owner: University of Louisiana at Lafayette
Editorial: Hebrard Blvd Burke Hall U L, Lafayette, Louisiana 70504. **T:** 1 337 482-5787
W: http://www.krvs.org
Editorial Profile: KRVS-FM is a non-commercial station owned by the University of Louisiana at Lafayette. The format of the station is college variety. KRVS-FM broadcasts to the Lafayette, LA, area at 88.7 FM.

KRVV-FM
Owner: Holladay Broadcasting Co.
Editorial: 1109 Hudson Ln, Monroe, Louisiana 71201. **T:** 1 318 388-2323
E: comments@thebeat.net
W: http://www.thebeat.net
Editorial Profile: KRVV-FM is a commercial station owned by Holladay Broadcasting Co. The format of the station is urban contemporary music. KRVV-FM broadcasts to the Monroe, LA area at 100.1 FM.

KRVY-FM
Owner: Iowa City Broadcasting Co.
Editorial: 730 Highway 71 NE, Willmar, Minnesota 56201. **T:** 1 320 231-1600
W: http://www.k-musicradio.com
Editorial Profile: KRVY-FM is a commercial station owned by Iowa City Broadcasting Co. The format of the station is Lite Rock/Lite AC. KRVY-FM broadcasts to the Willmar, MN area at 93.7 FM.

KRVZ-AM
Owner: Country Mountain Airwaves LLC
Editorial: 391 W Deuce Of Clubs, Show Low, Arizona 85901-5809. **T:** 1 928 532-1010
E: traffic@majik101.com
Editorial Profile: KRVZ-AM is a commercial station owned by Country Mountain Airwaves LLC. The format of the station is talk. KRVZ-AM broadcasts to the Phoenix area at 1400 AM.

KRWA-FM
Owner: WAY Media Inc.
Editorial: 1707 Main St, Longmont, Colorado 80501-7407. **T:** 1 303 702-9293
E: comments@wayfm.com
W: http://kxwy.wayfm.com
Editorial Profile: KRWA-FM is a commercial station owned by WAY Media Inc. The format of the station is contemporary Christian. KRWA-FM broadcasts to the Pueblo, CO area at 90.9 FM.

KRWB-AM
Owner: Border Broadcasting
Editorial: 113 A Lake St Center, Warroad, Minnesota 56763. **T:** 1 218 463-1410
E: kq92@mncable.net
W: http://www.1410krwb.com
Editorial Profile: KRWB-AM is a commercial station owned by Border Broadcasting. The format of the station is classic rock. KRWB-AM broadcasts to the Warroad, MN area at 1410 AM.

KRWC-AM
Owner: Donnell Inc.
Editorial: 1472 10th St NW, Buffalo, Minnesota 55313-4443. **T:** 1 763 682-4444
E: info@krwc1360.com
W: http://www.krwc1360.com
Editorial Profile: KRWC-AM is a commercial station owned by Donnell Inc. The format of the station is news and talk. KRWC-AM's broadcasts to Buffalo, MN at 1360 AM.

KRWG-FM
Owner: New Mexico State University
Editorial: 2915 McFie Cir, Rm 121, Las Cruces, New Mexico 88003-1259.
T: 1 575 646-2222 **E:** krwgfm@nmsu.edu
W: http://www.krwg.org
Editorial Profile: KRWG-FM is a non-commercial station owned by New Mexico State University. The format of the station is classical, jazz, news and talk. KRWG-FM broadcasts to the Las Cruces, NM area at 90.7 FM.

KRWK-FM
Owner: Midwest Communications
Editorial: 1020 25th St S, Fargo, North Dakota 58103-2312. **T:** 1 701 237-5346
W: http://www.1019talkfm.com
Editorial Profile: KRWK-FM is a commercial station owned by Midwest Communications. The format of the station is Conservative news/talk. KRWK-FM broadcasts to the Fargo, ND area at 101.9 FM.

KRWM-FM
Owner: Hubbard Radio, LLC
Editorial: 3650 131st Ave SE Ste 550, Bellevue, Washington 98006-1334.
T: 1 425 373-5545
W: http://www.warm1069.com
Editorial Profile: KRWM-FM is a commercial station owned by Hubbard Radio, LLC. The format of the station is Lite Rock/Lite AC music. KRWM-FM broadcasts to the Bellevue, WA area at 106.9 FM.

KRWN-FM
Owner: American General Media
Editorial: 212 W Apache St, Farmington, New Mexico 87401-6235. **T:** 1 505 327-4449
W: http://www.krwn.com
Editorial Profile: KRWN-FM is a commercial station owned by American General Media. The format of the station is modern AC. KRWN-FM broadcasts to the Durango, CO area at 92.9 FM.

KRWP-FM
Owner: Cumulus Media Inc.
Editorial: 1225 S 39 Highway, Stockton, Missouri 65785. **T:** 1 417 276-5253
W: http://krwp1077.com
Editorial Profile: KRWP-FM is a commercial station owned by Cumulus Media Inc. The format of the station is classic country. KRWP-FM broadcasts to the Stockton, MO area at a frequency of 107.7 FM.

KRWQ-FM
Owner: Bicoastal Media LLC
Editorial: 3624 Avion Dr, Medford, Oregon 97504. **T:** 1 541 772-4170
W: http://www.krwq.com
Editorial Profile: KRWQ-FM is a commercial station owned by Bicoastal Media LLC. The format of the station is classic and contemporary country music. KRWQ-FM broadcasts to the Medford, OR area at 100.3 FM.

KRWZ-AM
Owner: Lincoln Financial Media
Editorial: 7800 E Orchard Rd, Ste 400, Greenwood Village, Colorado 80111-2599.
T: 1 303 321-0950
W: http://www.cruisinoldies950.com
Editorial Profile: KRWZ-AM is a commercial station owned by Lincoln Financial Media. The format of the station is oldies. KRWZ-AM broadcasts to the Denver area at 950 AM.

KRXB-FM
Owner: Shaffer Communications Group
Editorial: 110 E Bowie St, Beeville, Texas 78102. **T:** 1 361 358-4941
E: krxbfm@sbcglobal.net
Editorial Profile: KRXB-FM is a commercial station owned by Shaffer Communications Group. The format of the station is classic rock music. KRXB-FM broadcasts to the Beeville, TX area on 107.1 FM.

KRXF-FM
Owner: Gross Communications Co.
Editorial: 345 Sw Cyber Dr Ste 101-103, Bend, Oregon 97702-1045. **T:** 1 541 388-3300
W: http://www.929online.com/
Editorial Profile: KRXF-FM is a commercial station owned by Gross Communications Co. The format of the station is alternative rock music. KRXF-FM broadcasts to the Bend, OR area at 92.9 FM.

KRXL-FM
Owner: KIRX Inc.
Editorial: 1308 N Baltimore St, Kirksville, Missouri 63501. **T:** 1 660 665-9828
E: radionws@cableone.net
W: http://www.945thex.com
Editorial Profile: KRXL-FM is a commercial station owned by KIRX Inc. The format of the station is classic rock music. KRXL-FM broadcasts to the Kirksville, MO area at 94.5 FM.

KRXO-FM
Owner: Tyler Media, LLC
Editorial: 400 E Britton Rd, Oklahoma City, Oklahoma 73114-7515. **T:** 1 405 478-5104
W: http://thefranchiseok.com/
Editorial Profile: KRXO-FM is commercial station owned by Tyler Media, LLC. The format of the station is sports talk. KRXO-FM broadcasts to the Oklahoma City area at 107.7 FM.

KRXP-FM
Owner: Bahakel Communications
Editorial: 1805 E Cheyenne Rd, Colorado Springs, Colorado 80906-2868.
T: 1 719 634-4896
W: http://www.1039rxp.com
Editorial Profile: KRXP-FM is a commercial station owned by Bahakel Communications. The format of the station is rock/album oriented rock. KRXP-FM broadcasts to the Colorado Springs, CO area at 103.9 FM.

KRXQ-FM
Owner: Entercom Communications Corp.
Editorial: 5345 Madison Ave, Sacramento, California 95841. **T:** 1 916 334-7777
W: http://www.krxq.net
Editorial Profile: KRXQ-FM is a commercial station owned by Entercom Communications Corp. The format of the station is rock music. KRXQ-FM broadcasts to the Sacramento, CA area at 98.5 FM.

KRXR-AM
Owner: Juarez(Maria)
Editorial: 501 S Lincoln Ave, Jerome, Idaho 83338. **T:** 1 208 324-9267
Editorial Profile: KRXR-AM is a commercial station owned by Maria Juarez. The format of the station is regional Mexican. KXRX-AM broadcasts to the Jerome, ID area at 1480 AM.

KRXT-FM
Owner: KRXT Inc.
Editorial: 1095 W US Highway 79, Rockdale, Texas 76567. **T:** 1 512 446-6985
E: krxt@krxt985.com
W: http://www.krxt985.com
Editorial Profile: KRXT-FM is a commercial station owned by KRXT Inc. The format of the station is classic country. KRXT-FM broadcasts to the Rockdale, TX area at 98.5 FM.

KRXV-FM
Owner: Highway Radio Inc.
Editorial: 1611 E Main St, Barstow, California 92311. **T:** 1 760 256-0326
E: highwayradio@thehighwayradio.com
W: http://www.thehighwaystations.com
Editorial Profile: KRXV-FM is a commercial station owned by Highway Radio Inc. The format for the station is dance music. KRXV-FM broadcasts to the Barstow, CA area at 98.1 FM.

KRXW-FM
Owner: Minnesota Public Radio
Editorial: 480 Cedar St, Saint Paul, Minnesota 55101-2217. **T:** 1 651 290-1500
E: newsroom@mpr.org
W: http://minnesota.publicradio.org
Editorial Profile: KRXW-FM is a non-commercial station owned by Minnesota Public Radio. The format of the station is news and talk. KRXW-FM broadcasts to the Roseau, MN area at 103.5. KRXW-FM is a simulcast of sister station KNOW-FM.

KRXX-FM
Owner: Kodiak Island Broadcasting Co., Inc.
Editorial: 1315 Mill Bay Rd Ste 1A, Kodiak, Alaska 99615-6411. **T:** 1 907 486-5159
Editorial Profile: KRXX-FM is a commercial station owned by Kodiak Island Broadcasting Co., Inc. The format is Hot AC. KRXX-FM broadcasts to the Kodia, AK area at 101.1 FM.

KRXY-FM
Owner: Olympia Broadcasters, Inc.
Editorial: 2124 Pacific Ave Se, Olympia, Washington 98506-4753. **T:** 1 360 236-1010
E: krxy@krxy.com **W:** http://www.945roxy.com
Editorial Profile: KRXY-FM is a commercial station owned by Olympia Broadcasters, Inc. The format of the station is hot adult contemporary. KRXY-FM broadcasts in the Olympia, WA area at 94.5 FM.

KRYD-FM
Owner: Rocky III Investments, Inc.
Editorial: 475 Water Ave, Montrose, Colorado 81401-3401. **T:** 1 970 263-4100
E: studio@krydradio.com
W: http://www.krydfm.com
Editorial Profile: KRYD-FM is a commercial station owned by Rocky III Investments, Inc. The format of the station is a variety of rock music. KRYD-FM broadcasts to the Norwood, CO and surrounding areas at 104.9 FM. Translator is 92.7 (Grand Junction).

KRYK-FM
Owner: New Media Broadcasters
Editorial: 2210 31st St N, Havre, Montana 59501. **T:** 1 406 265-7841
W: http://www.kryk.com
Editorial Profile: KRYK-FM is a commercial station owned by New Media Broadcasters. The format for the station is hot adult contemporary. KRYK-FM broadcasts to the Havre, MT area at 101.3 FM.

KRYL-FM
Owner: Big Island Broadcasting Co.
Editorial: 900 Fort Street Mall, Ste 450, Honolulu, Hawaii 96813-3780.
T: 1 808 538-1180
W: http://hhawaiimedia.com
Editorial Profile: KRYL-FM is a commercial station owned by Big Island Broadcasting Co. The format of the station is country. KRYL-FM broadcasts to the Haiku, HI area at 106.5.

KRYN-AM
Owner: Adelante Media Group
Editorial: 5110 SE Stark St, Portland, Oregon 97215. **T:** 1 503 234-5550
W: http://www.adelantemediagroup.com
Editorial Profile: KRYN-AM is a commercial station owned by Adelante Media Group. The format of the station is Hispanic oldies. KRYN-AM broadcasts to the Portland, OR area at 1230 AM.

KRYP-FM
Owner: Salem Communications
Editorial: 6400 SE Lake Rd, Ste 350, Portland, Oregon 97222. **T:** 1 503 786-0600
W: http://www.931elrey.com
Editorial Profile: KRYP-FM is a commercial station owned by Salem Communications. The format of the station is regional Mexican music. KRYP-FM broadcasts to the Portland, OR area on 93.1 FM.

KRYS-FM
Owner: Clear Channel Media and Entertainment
Editorial: 501 Tupper Lane Radio Plaza, Corpus Christi, Texas 78417-9736.
T: 1 361 289-0111 **E:** k99@clearchannel.com
W: http://k99country.com
Editorial Profile: KRYS-FM is a commercial station owned by Clear Channel Media and Entertainment. The format of the station is country music. KRYS-FM broadcasts to the Corpus Christi, TX area at 99.1 FM.

KRZA-FM
Owner: ERMAC Inc.
Editorial: 528 9th St, Alamosa, Colorado 81101-3217. **T:** 1 719 589-9057
E: gm@krza.org **W:** http://www.krza.org
Editorial Profile: KRZA-FM is a non-commercial station owned by ERMAC Inc. The format of the station is news and a variety of music and talk programming. KRZA-FM broadcasts in the Denver area at 88.7 FM.

KRZI-AM
Owner: M & M Broadcasters
Editorial: 5501 Bagby Ave, Waco, Texas 76711. **T:** 1 254 772-0930
W: http://www.1660espn.com
Editorial Profile: KRZI-AM is a commercial station owned by M & M Broadcasters. The format of the station is sports. KRZI-AM broadcasts to the Waco, TX area at 1660 AM.

KRZK-FM
Owner: Earls Broadcasting
Editorial: 202 Courtney St, Branson, Missouri 65616-2434. **T:** 1 417 334-6003
W: http://www.hometownradioonline.com
Editorial Profile: KRZK-FM is a commercial station owned by Earls Broadcasting. The format of the station is news/talk. KRZK-FM broadcasts to the Branson, MO area at 106.3 FM.

KRZN-FM
Owner: Connoisseur Media LLC
Editorial: 2075 Central Ave, Billings, Montana 59102. **T:** 1 406 248-7777
W: http://www.963thezone.com
Editorial Profile: KRZN-FM is a commercial station owned by Connoisseur Media LLC. The format of the station is rock alternative music. KRZN-FM broadcasts in the Billings, MT area at 96.3 FM.

KRZQ-FM
Owner: Shamrock Communications, Inc.
Editorial: 510 E Plumb Ln, Reno, Nevada 89502-3565. **T:** 1 775 737-4030
W: http://www.KRZQRadio.com
Editorial Profile: KRZQ-FM is a commercial station owned by Shamrock Communications, Inc. The format of the station is alternative rock music. KRZQ-FM broadcasts locally to the Reno, NV area at a frequency of 104.1 FM.

KRZR-AM
Owner: Clear Channel Media and Entertainment
Editorial: 83 E Shaw Ave, Fresno, California 93710-7620. **T:** 1 559 230-4300
W: http://www.powertalk967.com

Editorial Profile: KRZR-AM is a commercial station owned by Clear Channel Media and Entertainment. The format of the station is news and talk. KRZR-AM broadcasts to the Visalia, CA area at 1400 AM.

KRZY-AM
Owner: Entravision Communications Corp.
Editorial: 2725 Broadbent Pkwy NE, Ste F, Albuquerque, New Mexico 87107.
T: 1 505 342-4141
W: http://www.espndeportes1450.com
Editorial Profile: KRZY-AM is a commercial station owned by Entravision Communications Corp. The station is an ESPN Deportes affiliate. The format of the station is Spanish language sports. KRZY-AM broadcasts to the Albuquerque, NM area at 1450 AM.

KRZY-FM
Owner: Entravision Communications Corp.
Editorial: 2725 Broadbent Pkwy NE, Ste F, Albuquerque, New Mexico 87107.
T: 1 505 342-4141
W: http://www.jose1059.com
Editorial Profile: KRZY-FM is a commercial station owned by Entravision Communications Corp. The format of the station is Hispanic adult hits. KRZY-FM broadcasts to the Albuquerque, NM area at 105.9 FM.

KRZZ-FM
Owner: Spanish Broadcasting System
Editorial: 455 Market St Ste 2300, San Francisco, California 94105-2400.
T: 1 415 543-9330
W: http://www.yosoyraza.com
Editorial Profile: KRZZ-FM is a commercial station owned by Spanish Broadcasting System. The format of the station is Regional Mexican music. KRZZ-FM broadcasts to the San Francisco area at 93.3 FM.

KSAB-FM
Owner: Clear Channel Media and Entertainment
Editorial: 501 Tupper Lane Radio Plaza, Corpus Christi, Texas 78417-9736.
T: 1 361 289-0111 **E:** ksab@clearchannel.com
W: http://www.ksabfm.com
Editorial Profile: KSAB-FM is a commercial station owned by Clear Channel Media and Entertainment. The format for the station is Hispanic. The station broadcasts to the Corpus Christi, TX area at 99.9 FM.

KSAC-FM
Owner: Salem Communications
Editorial: 1425 River Park Dr, Ste 520, Sacramento, California 95815.
T: 1 916 924-0710
W: http://www.money1055.com
Editorial Profile: KSAC-FM is a commercial station owned by Salem Communications. The format of the station is business talk. KSAC-FM broadcasts in the Sacramento, CA area at 105.5 FM.

KSAH-AM
Owner: Border Media Partners LLC
Editorial: 4050 Eisenhauer Rd, San Antonio, Texas 78218-3409. **T:** 1 210 654-5100
Editorial Profile: KSAH-AM is a commercial station owned by Border Media Partners LLC. The format of the station is Spanish language sports/talk. KSAH-AM broadcasts to the San Antonio area at 720 AM.

KSAH-FM
Owner: Border Media Partners LLC
Editorial: 4050 Eisenhauer Rd, San Antonio, Texas 78218-3409. **T:** 1 210 654-5100
Editorial Profile: KSAH-FM is a commercial station owned by Border Media Partners LLC. The format of the station is Hispanic Norteno music. KSAH-FM broadcasts to the San Antonio area at 104.1 FM.

KSAJ-FM
Owner: Morris Communications
Editorial: 200 N Broadway St, Abilene, Kansas 67410-2647. **T:** 1 785 823-1111
W: http://www.ksallink.com
Editorial Profile: KSAJ-FM is a commercial station owned by Morris Communications. The format of the station is oldies music. KSAJ-FM broadcasts to the Salina, KS area at 98.5 FM.

KSAL-AM
Owner: Morris Communications
Editorial: 131 N Santa Fe Ave, Ste 3, Salina, Kansas 67401. **T:** 1 785 823-1111
W: http://www.ksallink.com
Editorial Profile: KSAL-AM is a commercial station owned by Morris Communications. The format of the station is news, talk and sports.

KSAL-AM broadcasts to the Wichita, KS area at 1150 AM.

KSAL-FM
Owner: Morris Communications
Editorial: 131 N Santa Fe Ave, Ste 3, Salina, Kansas 67401-2642. **T:** 1 785 823-1111
W: http://www.ksallink.com
Editorial Profile: KSAL-FM is a commercial station owned by Morris Communications. The format of the station is classic hits. KSAL-FM broadcasts in the Salina, KS at 104.9 FM.

KSAM-AM
Owner: Bee Broadcasting Inc.
Editorial: 2432 US Highway 2 E, Kalispell, Montana 59901. **T:** 1 406 755-8700
E: sam@sam1240.com
W: http://www.beebroadcasting.com
Editorial Profile: KSAM-AM is a commercial station owned by Bee Broadcasting Inc. The format of the station is sports. KSAM-AM broadcasts to the Kalispell, MT area at 1240 AM.

KSAM-FM
Owner: HEH Communications LLC
Editorial: 622 Interstate 45 S, Huntsville, Texas 77340. **T:** 1 936 295-2651
E: ksamnews@yahoo.com
W: http://www.ksam1017.com
Editorial Profile: KSAM-FM is a commercial station owned by HEH Communications LLC. The format of the station is country music. KSAM-FM broadcasts to the Huntsville, TX area at 101.7 FM. Newscasts air throughout the day, CT.

KSAN-FM
Owner: Cumulus Media Inc.
Editorial: 55 Hawthorne St, Ste 1000, San Francisco, California 94105.
T: 1 415 995-6800 **E:** thebone@thebone.net
W: http://www.1077thebone.com
Editorial Profile: KSAN-FM is a commercial station owned by Cumulus Media Inc. The format of the station is classic rock. KSAN-FM broadcasts to the San Francisco area at 107.7 FM.

KSAS-FM
Owner: Townsquare Media, LLC
Editorial: 827 E Park Blvd Ste 100, Boise, Idaho 83712-7783. **T:** 1 208 344-6363
W: http://www.1033kissfm.com
Editorial Profile: KSAS-FM is a commercial station owned by Townsquare Media, LLC. The format of the station is Top 40/CHR music. KSAS-FM broadcasts in the Boise, ID area at 103.5 FM.

KSAU-FM
Owner: Stephen F. Austin State Univ.
Editorial: 1936 North St Boynton Bldg, Nacogdoches, Texas 75961.
T: 1 936 468-4000 **E:** ksau@sfasu.edu
W: http://www.sfasu.edu/ksau

KSAZ-AM
Owner: Radio Casa, Inc.
Editorial: 3291 W Elephant Head Rd, Amado, Arizona 85645-9529. **T:** 1 520 298-6880
W: http://www.radioebenezer580am.com/index.html
Editorial Profile: KSAZ-AM is a commercial station owned by Radio Casa, Inc. The format of the station is Spanish religious. KSAZ-AM broadcasts to the Tucson, AZ area at 580 AM.

KSBH-FM
Owner: KSBH, LLC
Editorial: 213 Renee St, Natchitoches, Louisiana 71457. **T:** 1 318 354-4000
W: http://www.949theriverradio.com
Editorial Profile: KSBH-FM is a commercial station owned by KSBH, LLC. The format of the station is country music. KSBH-FM broadcasts to the Natchitoches, LA area at 94.9 FM.

KSBJ-FM
Owner: KSBJ Educational Foundation
Editorial: 1722 Treble Dr, Humble, Texas 77338. **T:** 1 281 446-5725
W: http://www.ksbj.org
Editorial Profile: KSBJ-FM is a non-commercial station owned by KSBJ Educational Foundation. The format of the station is contemporary Christian. KSBJ-FM broadcasts to the Humble, TX area at 89.3.

KSBL-FM
Owner: Rincon Broadcasting
Editorial: 414 E Cota St, Santa Barbara, California 93101. **T:** 1 805 879-8300
W: http://www.klite.com

Editorial Profile: KSBL-FM is a commercial station owned by Rincon Broadcasting. The format of the station is adult contemporary music. KSBL-FM broadcasts to the Santa Barbara, CA area at 101.7 FM.

KSBN-AM
Owner: KSBN Radio Inc.
Editorial: 7 S Howard St Ste 430, Spokane, Washington 99201-3816. **T:** 1 509 838-4000
E: ksbn@ksbn.net **W:** http://www.ksbn.net
Editorial Profile: KSBN-AM is a commercial station owned by KSBN Radio Inc. The format of the station is business news and talk. KSBN-AM broadcasts to the Spokane, WA area at 1230 AM.

KSBQ-AM
Owner: Lazer Broadcasting Corp.
Editorial: 200 S A St, Oxnard, California 93030-5717. **T:** 1 805 928-9796
W: http://www.radiolazer.com
Editorial Profile: KSBQ-AM is a commercial station owned by the Lazer Broadcasting Corp. The format of the station is regional Mexican. KSBQ-AM broadcasts to the Santa Maria, CA area at 1480 AM.

KSBR-FM
Owner: South Orange County Community College District
Editorial: 28000 Marguerite Pkwy, Mission Viejo, California 92692-3635.
T: 1 949 582-5727 **W:** http://www.ksbr.org
Editorial Profile: KSBR-FM is a non-commercial station owned by the South Orange County Community College District. The format of the station is smooth AC. KSBR-FM broadcasts to the Mission Viejo, CA area at 88.5 FM.

KSBV-FM
Owner: Arkansas Valley Broadcasting LLC.
Editorial: 735 Blake St, Salida, Colorado 81201-2919. **T:** 1 719 539-9377
E: ksbvradio1@gmail.com
W: http://www.ksbv.net
Editorial Profile: KSBV-FM is a commercial station owned by Arkansas Valley Broadcasting LLC. The format of the station is classic rock. KSBV-FM broadcasts to the Salida, CO area at 93.7 FM.

KSBZ-FM
Owner: Alaska Broadcast Communications Inc.
Editorial: 611 Lake St, Sitka, Alaska 99835-7402. **T:** 1 907 747-6626
E: kifw@abcstations.com
Editorial Profile: KSBZ-FM is a commercial station owned by Alaska Broadcast Communications Inc. The format of the station is classic rock. KSBZ-FM broadcasts to the Sitka, AK area at 103.1 FM.

KSCA-FM
Owner: Univision Communications Inc.
Editorial: 655 N Central Ave, Glendale, California 91203-1422. **T:** 1 310 846-2800
W: http://la1019.univision.com
Editorial Profile: KSCA-FM is a commercial station owned by Univision Communications Inc. The format of the station is regional Mexican. KSCA-FM broadcasts to the Glendale, CA area at 101.9 FM.

KSCB-AM
Owner: Seward County Broadcasting Co.
Editorial: 1410 N Western Ave, Liberal, Kansas 67901. **T:** 1 620 624-3891
E: news@kscb.net **W:** http://www.kscb.net
Editorial Profile: KSCB-AM is a commercial station owned by Seward County Broadcasting Co. The format of the station is news, sports and talk. KSCB-AM broadcasts to the Wichita, KS area at 1270 AM.

KSCB-FM
Owner: Seward County Broadcasting Co.
Editorial: 1410 N Western Ave, Liberal, Kansas 67901. **T:** 1 620 624-3891
E: news@kscb.net **W:** http://www.kscb.net
Editorial Profile: KSCB-FM is a commercial station owned by Seward County Broadcasting Co. The format of the station is adult hits. KSCB-FM broadcasts to the Liberal, KS area at 107.5 FM.

KSCH-FM
Owner: East Texas Broadcasting Inc.
Editorial: 930 Gilmer St, Sulphur Springs, Texas 75482-4319. **T:** 1 903 577-9770
W: http://www.easttexasradio.com
Editorial Profile: KSCH-FM is a commercial station owned by East Texas Broadcasting Inc. The format of the station is country music. KSCH-FM broadcasts to the Mount Pleasant, TX area at 95.9 FM.

KSCJ-AM
Owner: Powell Broadcasting Co.
Editorial: 2000 Indian Hills Dr, Sioux City, Iowa 51104. **T:** 1 712 239-2100
E: news@kscj.com **W:** http://www.kscj.com
Editorial Profile: KSCJ-AM is a commercial station owned by Powell Broadcasting Co. The format of the station is news, sports and talk. KSCJ-AM broadcasts to the Sioux City, IA area at 1340 AM.

KSCN-FM
Owner: East Texas Broadcasting Inc.
Editorial: Highway 67 West 1 Mile, Mount Pleasant, Texas 75455. **T:** 1 903 577-9770
W: http://www.easttexasradio.com/starcountry
Editorial Profile: KSCN-FM is a commercial station owned by East Texas Broadcasting Inc. The format of the station is contemporary country. KSCN-FM's broadcasts in the Mount Pleasant, TX area at 96.9 FM.

KSCO-AM
Owner: Zwerling Broadcasting System Ltd.
Editorial: 2300 Portola Dr, Santa Cruz, California 95062. **T:** 1 831 475-1080
W: http://www.ksco.com
Editorial Profile: KSCO-AM is a commercial station owned by Zwerling Broadcasting System Ltd. The format of the station is news and talk. KSCO-AM broadcasts in the Santa Cruz, CA area at 1080 AM.

KSCQ-FM
Owner: SkyWest Media, LLC
Editorial: 1560 N Corbin St, Silver City, New Mexico 88061-6526. **T:** 1 575 538-3396
E: kscq@silvercityradio.com
W: http://www.silvercityradio.com
Editorial Profile: KSCQ-FM is a commercial station owned by SkyWest Media, LCC. The format of the station is adult contemporary. KSCQ-FM broadcasts to the Silver City, NM area at 92.9 FM.

KSCR-AM
Owner: Cumulus Media Inc.
Editorial: 1200 Executive Pkwy, Ste 440, Eugene, Oregon 97401. **T:** 1 541 284-8500
W: http://www.1320inforadio.com
Editorial Profile: KSCR-AM is a commercial station owned by Cumulus Media Inc. The format of the station is business and talk. KSCR-AM broadcasts to the Eugene, OR area at 1320 AM.

KSCS-FM
Owner: Cumulus Media Inc
Editorial: 3090 Olive St, Dallas, Texas 75219-7640. **T:** 1 817 640-1963
W: http://www.kscs.com
Editorial Profile: KSCS-FM is a commercial station owned by Cumulus Media Inc. The format of the station is contemporary country. KSCS-FM broadcasts to the Dallas-Ft. Worth, TX area at 96.3 FM.

KSCV-FM
Owner: Bott Broadcasting Co.
Editorial: 1111 S Glenstone Ave Ste 3-102, Springfield, Missouri 65804-0397.
T: 1 417 864-0901
E: comments@bottradionetwork.com
W: http://www.bottradionetwork.com
Editorial Profile: KSCV-FM is a non-commercial station owned by Bott Broadcasting Co. The format of the station is religious and Christian programming. KSCV-FM broadcasts to the Springfield, MO area at 90.1 FM.

KSDB-FM
Owner: Kansas State University
Editorial: 117 Kansas State Union, Manhattan, Kansas 66505. **T:** 1 785 532-2971
E: radio@ksu.edu
W: http://www.wildcat919.com
Editorial Profile: KSDB-FM is a college station owned by Kansas State University. The format of the station is variety. KSDB-FM broadcasts to the Manhattan, KS area at 91.9 FM.

KSD-FM
Owner: Clear Channel Media and Entertainment
Editorial: 1001 Highlands Plaza Dr W, Saint Louis, Missouri 63110-1337.
T: 1 314 333-8000
W: http://www.937thebull.com
Editorial Profile: KSD-FM is a commercial station owned by Clear Channel Media and Entertainment. The format of the station is contemporary country music. KSD-FM broadcasts to the St. Louis area at 93.7 FM.

KSDL-FM
Owner: Townsquare Media, LLC
Editorial: 2209 S Limit Ave, Sedalia, Missouri 65301-6950. **T:** 1 660 826-1050
W: http://www.923bobfm.com
Editorial Profile: KSDL-FM is a commercial station owned by Townsquare Media, LLC. The format of the station is Jack FM-Adult Hits. KSDL-FM broadcasts to the Sedalia, MO area at 92.3 FM.

KSDM-FM
Owner: Red Rock Radio Corp.
Editorial: 519 3rd St, International Falls, Minnesota 56649. **T:** 1 218 283-3481
E: production@ksdmradio.com
W: http://www.ksdmradio.com
Editorial Profile: KSDM-FM is a commercial station owned by Red Rock Radio Corp. The format of the station is country music. KSDM-FM broadcasts in the International Falls, MN area at 104.1 FM.

KSDN-AM
Owner: Armada Media Corp.
Editorial: 3304 S Highway 281, Aberdeen, South Dakota 57401-8792. **T:** 1 605 229-3632
E: aberdeenproduction@hubcityradio.com
W: http://www.hubcityradio.com
Editorial Profile: KSDN-AM is a commercial station owned by Armada Media Corp. The format of the station is news and talk. KSDN-AM broadcasts to the Aberdeen, SD area at 930 AM.

KSDN-FM
Owner: Armada Media Corp.
Editorial: 3304 S Highway 281, Aberdeen, South Dakota 57401-8792. **T:** 1 605 225-5930
E: aberdeenproduction@hubcityradio.com
W: http://www.hubcityradio.com
Editorial Profile: KSDN-FM is a commercial station owned by Armada Media Corp. The format of the station is classic rock music. KSDN-FM broadcasts to the Aberdeen, SC area at 94.1 FM.

KSDO-AM
Owner: Hi-Favor Broadcasting LLC
Editorial: 344 F St, Ste 200, Chula Vista, California 91910. **T:** 1 626 356-4230
W: http://www.nuevavida.com
Editorial Profile: KSDO-AM is a commercial station owned by Hi-Favor Broadcasting LLC. The format of the station is Spanish language Christian programming. KSDO-AM broadcasts to the Los Angeles area at 1130 AM.

KSDQ-FM
Owner: Sunndale Seventh-Day Adventist Church
Editorial: 6818 Audrain Road 9139, Centralia, Missouri 65240-5906. **T:** 1 573 682-2164
E: ksdqradio@sunnydale.org
W: http://ksdqradio.net
Editorial Profile: KSDQ-FM is a non-commercial station owned by Sunndale Seventh-Day Adventist Church. The station's format features a variety of programming. KSDQ-FM broadcasts to the Centralia, MO area at a frequency of 88.7 FM.

KSDR-AM
Owner: Three Eagles Communications Co.
Editorial: 921 9Th Ave Se, Watertown, South Dakota 57201-4960. **T:** 1 605 886-5747
E: kwatprod@watertown.threeeagles.com
W: http://gowatertown.net
Editorial Profile: KSDR-AM is a commercial station owned by Three Eagles Communications Co. The format of the station is sports and talk. KSDR-AM broadcasts to the Watertown, SD area at 1480 AM.

KSDR-FM
Owner: Three Eagles Communications Co.
Editorial: 921 9Th Ave Se, Watertown, South Dakota 57201-4960. **T:** 1 605 886-5747
E: kwatprod@watertown.threeeagles.com
W: http://gowatertown.net
Editorial Profile: KSDR-FM is a commercial station owned by Three Eagles Communications Co. The format of the station is contemporary country. KSDR-FM broadcasts to the Watertown, SD area at 92.9 FM.

KSDS-FM
Owner: San Diego Community College
Editorial: 1313 Park Blvd, San Diego, California 92101-4712. **T:** 1 619 388-3037
E: info@jazz88.org **W:** http://www.jazz88.org
Editorial Profile: KSDS-FM is a non-commercial station owned by San Diego Community College. The format of the station is jazz, blues and world music. KSDS-FM broadcasts to the San Diego area at 88.3 FM.

KSDW-FM
Owner: Calvary Chapel of Costa Mesa
Editorial: 3000 W Macarthur Blvd Ste 500, Santa Ana, California 92704-7947.
T: 1 714 918-6207
W: http://www.ksdwradio.com
Editorial Profile: KSDW-FM is a non-commercial station owned by Calvary Chapel of Costa Mesa. The format for the station is religious and Christian programming. KSDW-FM broadcasts to Murrieta, CA area at 88.9 FM.

KSDZ-FM
Owner: D.J. Broadcasting Corp.
Editorial: 6492 230th Ln, Gordon, Nebraska 69343-5570. **T:** 1 308 282-2500
E: thetwister@ksdzfm.com
W: http://www.ksdzfm.com
Editorial Profile: KSDZ-FM is a commercial station owned by D.J. Broadcasting Corp. The format of the station is country. KSDZ-FM broadcasts to the Gordon, NE area at 95.5 FM.

KSEA-FM
Owner: Campesina Network(La)
Editorial: 608 E Boronda Rd Ste C, Salinas, California 93906-3129. **T:** 1 831 754-1469
E: paco@campesina.com
W: http://www.campesina.com/ksea
Editorial Profile: KSEA-FM is a commercial station owned by La Campesina Network. The format of the station is regional Mexican. KSEA-FM broadcasts to the Salinas, CA area at 96.3 FM.

KSEC-FM
Owner: La Zeta 957 Co.
Editorial: 2323 S Old Missouri Rd, Springdale, Arkansas 72764-7470. **T:** 1 479 756-8686
E: info@ezspanishmedia.com
W: http://www.ezspanishmedia.com
Editorial Profile: KSEC-FM is a commercial station owned by La Zeta 957 Co. The format of the station is Hispanic programming. KSEC-FM broadcasts to the Rogers, AR area at 95.7 FM.

KSED-FM
Owner: Grenax Broadcasting
Editorial: 2409 N 4th St, Flagstaff, Arizona 86004-3734. **T:** 1 928 779-1177
W: http://www.koltcountry.com
Editorial Profile: KSED-FM is a commercial station owned by Grenax Broadcasting. The format of the station is contemporary country. KSED-FM broadcasts to the Flagstaff, AZ area at 107.5 FM.

KSEF-FM
Owner: Southeast Missouri State Univ.
Editorial: 1 University Plz, MS0300, Cape Girardeau, Missouri 63701-4710.
T: 1 573 651-5070 **E:** comments@krcu.org
W: http://www.krcu.org
Editorial Profile: KSEF-FM is a non-commerical station owned by Southeast Missouri State Univ. The format of the station is classical and news. KSEF-FM broadcasts to the Farmington, MO area on 88.9 FM.

KSEG-FM
Owner: Entercom Communications Corp.
Editorial: 5345 Madison Ave, Sacramento, California 95841-3141. **T:** 1 916 334-9690
W: http://www.eagle969.com
Editorial Profile: KSEG-FM is a commercial station owned by Entercom Communications Corp. The format of the station is classic rock music. KSEG-FM broadcasts to the Sacramento, CA area at 96.9 FM.

KSEH-FM
Owner: Entravision Communications Corp.
Editorial: 1803 N Imperial Ave, El Centro, California 92243-1333. **T:** 1 760 482-7777
E: kwst@entravision.com
W: http://www.jose945.com
Editorial Profile: KSEH-FM is a commercial station owned by Entravision Communications Corp. The format of the station is Hispanic adult hits. KSEH-FM broadcasts to the El Centro, CA area at 94.5 FM.

KSEI-AM
Owner: Pacific Empire Communications
Editorial: 544 N Arthur Ave, Pocatello, Idaho 83204-3002. **T:** 1 208 233-2121
Editorial Profile: KSEI-AM is a commercial station owned by Pacific Empire Communications. The format of the station is sports. KSEI-AM broadcasts to the Pocatello, ID area at 930 AM.

KSEK-AM
Owner: Southeast Kansas Independent Living (SKIL)
Editorial: 202 E Centennial Dr Ste B2, Pittsburg, Kansas 66762-6572.
T: 1 620 232-9912
Editorial Profile: KSEK-AM is a commercial station owned by the Southeast Kansas Independent Living (SKIL). The format of the station is sports. KSEK-AM broadcasts to the Pittsburg, KS area at 1340 AM.

KSEK-FM
Owner: Southeast Kansas Independent Living (SKIL)
Editorial: 202 E Centennial Dr Ste B2, Pittsburg, Kansas 66762-6572.
T: 1 620 232-9912
W: http://www.991urock.com
Editorial Profile: KSEK-FM is a commercial station owned by Southeast Kansas Independent Living (SKIL). The format of the station is classic rock. KSEK-FM broadcasts to the Pittsburg, KS area at 99.1 FM.

KSEL-AM
Owner: Rooney Moon Broadcasting
Editorial: 42437 US 70, Portales, New Mexico 88130. **T:** 1 575 359-1759
E: news@rooneymoon.com
W: http://www.kselcountry.com
Editorial Profile: KSEL-AM is a commercial station owned by Rooney Moon Broadcasting. The format of the station is country. KSEL-AM broadcasts to the Portales, NM area at 1450 AM.

KSEL-FM
Owner: Rooney Moon Broadcasting
Editorial: 42437 US 70, Portales, New Mexico 88130. **T:** 1 575 359-1759
E: news@rooneymoon.com
W: http://www.kselcountry.com
Editorial Profile: KSEL-FM is a commercial station owned by Rooney Moon Broadcasting. The format of the station is contemporary country music. KSEL-AM broadcasts to the Portales, NM area at 105.9 FM.

KSEM-FM
Owner: Gaines County Broadcasting
Editorial: 105 Nw 11Th St, Seminole, Texas 79360-3301. **T:** 1 432 758-5878
E: kikz-ksem@bajabb.com
W: http://www.kikzksem.ws
Editorial Profile: KSEM-FM is a commercial station owned by Gaines County Broadcasting. The format of the station is country and Hispanic music. KSEM-FM broadcasts to Seminole, TX at 106.3 FM.

KSEN-AM
Owner: Townsquare Media, LLC
Editorial: 830 Oilfield Ave, Shelby, Montana 59474-1641. **T:** 1 406 434-5241
E: ksen@gapbroadcasting.com
W: http://www.ksenam.com
Editorial Profile: KSEN-AM is a commercial station owned by Townsquare Media, LLC. The format of the station is oldies. KSEN-AM broadcasts to the Shelby, MT area at 1150 AM.

KSEO-AM
Owner: Texoma Broadcasting Inc.
Editorial: 1418 N 1st Ave, Durant, Oklahoma 74701-2812. **T:** 1 580 924-3100
W: http://www.klbcfm.com
Editorial Profile: KSEO-AM is a commercial station owned by Texoma Broadcasting Inc. The format of the station is news/talk. KSEO-AM broadcasts to the Durant, OK area at 750 AM.

KSEQ-FM
Owner: Buckley Broadcasting Corp.
Editorial: 617 W Tulare Ave, Visalia, California 93277-2552. **T:** 1 559 627-9710
E: promotions@Q97.com
W: http://www.q97.com
Editorial Profile: KSEQ-FM is a commercial station owned by Buckley Broadcasting Corp. The format of the station is Top 40/CHR. KSEQ-FM broadcasts to the Visalia, CA area at 97.1 FM.

KSER-FM
Owner: KSER Foundation
Editorial: 2623 Wetmore Ave, Everett, Washington 98201-2926. **T:** 1 425 303-9070
E: info@kser.org **W:** http://www.kser.org
Editorial Profile: KSER-FM is a non-commercial station owned by KSER Foundation. The format of the station is a variety of news, talk and world music. KSER-FM broadcasts to the Everett, WA area at 90.7 FM.

KSES-FM
Owner: Entravision Communications Corp.

Editorial: 67 Garden Ct, Monterey, California 93940-5302. **T:** 1 831 373-6767 **W:** http://www.jose1071.com
Editorial Profile: KSES-FM is a commercial station owned by Entravision Communications Corp. The format of the station is Hispanic adult hits. KSES-FM broadcasts to the Salinas, CA area at 107.1 FM.

KSEV-AM
Owner: Patrick Broadcasting LP
Editorial: 11451 Katy Fwy, Ste 215, Houston, Texas 77079. **T:** 1 281 588-4800
W: http://www.ksevradio.com
Editorial Profile: KSEV-AM is a commercial station owned by Patrick Broadcasting LP. The format of the station is news and talk. KSEV-AM broadcasts to the Houston area at 700 AM.

KSEY-AM
Owner: Aulabaugh(Mark)
Editorial: #1 Radio Lane, Seymour, Texas 73680. **T:** 1 940 889-2637 **E:** fmksey@aol.com
W: http://www.radioksey.com
Editorial Profile: KSEY-AM is a commercial station owned by Mark Aulabaugh. The format of the station is sports. KSEY-AM broadcasts to the Seymour, TX area at 1230 AM.

KSEY-FM
Owner: Aulabaugh(Mark)
Editorial: #1 Radio Lane, Seymour, Texas 76380. **T:** 1 940 889-2637 **E:** fmksey@aol.com
W: http://www.radioksey.com
Editorial Profile: KSEY-FM is a commercial station owned by Mark Aulabaugh. The format of the station is news, talk and country music. KSEY-FM broadcasts to the Wichita Falls, TX area at 94.3 FM.

KSEZ-FM
Owner: Clear Channel Media and Entertainment
Editorial: 1113 Nebraska St, Sioux City, Iowa 51105. **T:** 1 712 258-5595
W: http://www.z98rocks.com
Editorial Profile: KSEZ-FM is a commercial station owned by Clear Channel Media and Entertainment. The format of the station is classic rock music. KSEZ-FM broadcasts to the Sioux City, IA area at 97.9 FM.

KSFA-AM
Owner: Townsquare Media, LLC
Editorial: 1216 S 1st St, Lufkin, Texas 75901. **T:** 1 936 639-4455
W: http://www.ksfa860.com
Editorial Profile: KSFA-AM is a commercial station owned by Townsquare Media, LLC. The format of the station is news, sports and talk. KSFA-AM broadcasts to the Lufkin, TX area at 860 AM.

KSFC-FM
Owner: Spokane Public Radio Inc.
Editorial: 2319 N Monroe St, Spokane, Washington 99205. **T:** 1 509 328-5729
E: kpbx@kpbx.org **W:** http://www.kpbx.org
Editorial Profile: KSFC-FM is a non-commercial station owned by Spokane Public Radio Inc. The format of the station is news and talk. KSFC-FM broadcasts to the Spokane, WA area at 91.9 FM.

KSFI-FM
Owner: KSL Broadcasting
Editorial: 55 N 300 W, Salt Lake City, Utah 84180-1109. **T:** 1 801 595-1003
W: http://www.fm100.com
Editorial Profile: KSFI-FM is a commercial station owned by KSL Broadcasting. The format of the station is Lite Rock/Lite AC. KSFI-FM broadcasts to the Salt Lake City area at 100.3 FM.

KSFM-FM
Owner: CBS Radio
Editorial: 280 Commerce Cir, Sacramento, California 95815-4212. **T:** 1 916 92368000
W: http://ksfm.cbslocal.com
Editorial Profile: KSFM-FM is a commercial station owned by CBS Radio. The format of the station is rhythmic Top 40. KSFM-FM broadcasts to the Sacramento, CA area at 102.5 FM.

KSFO-AM
Owner: Cumulus Media Inc
Editorial: 55 Hawthorne St Fl 11, San Francisco, California 94105-3906.
T: 1 415 995-6800 **W:** http://www.ksfo.com
Editorial Profile: KSFO-AM is a commercial station owned by Cumulus Media Inc. The format of the station is talk. KSFO-AM broadcasts to the San Francisco area at 560 AM.

KSFQ-FM
Owner: Educational Media Foundation
Editorial: 1750 Saratoga Dr NE, Rio Rancho, New Mexico 87144. **T:** 1 916 251-1600
Editorial Profile: KSFQ-FM is non-commercial station owned by Educational Media Foundation. The format for the station is contemporary christian. KSFQ-FM broadcasts to the Rio Rancho, NM area at 101.1 FM.

KSFR-FM
Owner: Santa Fe Community College
Editorial: 6401 S Richards Ave, Santa Fe, New Mexico 87508. **T:** 1 505 428-1259
E: news@ksfr.org **W:** http://www.ksfr.org
Editorial Profile: KSFR-FM is a non-commercial station owned by Santa Fe Community College. The format of the station is oldies, talk and news. KSFR-FM broadcasts to the Albuquerque, NM area at 90.7 FM.

KSFT-FM
Owner: Clear Channel Media and Entertainment
Editorial: 1113 Nebraska St, Sioux City, Iowa 51105. **T:** 1 712 258-5595
W: http://www.kiss107siouxcity.com
Editorial Profile: KSFT-FM is a commercial station owned by Clear Channel Media and Entertainment. The format of the station is hot adult contemporary. KSFT-FM broadcasts to the Sioux City, IA area at 107.1 FM.

KSFX-FM
Owner: Majestic Communications
Editorial: 5206 W 2nd St, Roswell, New Mexico 88201-8839. **T:** 1 575 622-6450
W: http://1005ksfx.com
Editorial Profile: KSFX-FM is a commercial station owned by Majestic Communications. The format of the station is classic rock. KSFX-FM broadcasts to the Albuquerque, NM area at 100.5 FM.

KSGF-AM
Owner: Journal Broadcast Group
Editorial: 2330 W Grand St, Springfield, Missouri 65802-4900. **T:** 1 417 865-6614
W: http://www.ksgf.com
Editorial Profile: KSGF-AM is a commercial station owned by Journal Broadcast Group. The format of the station is news and talk. KSGF-AM broadcasts to the Springfield, MO area at 1260 AM.

KSGF-FM
Owner: Journal Broadcast Group
Editorial: 2330 W Grand St, Springfield, Missouri 65802. **T:** 1 417 865-6614
W: http://www.ksgf.com
Editorial Profile: KSGF-FM is a commercial station owned by Journal Broadcast Group. The format of the station is news and talk. KSGF-FM broadcasts to the Springfield, MO area at 104.1 FM.

KSGG-AM
Owner: Americom Broadcasting
Editorial: 961 Matley Ln, Reno, Nevada 89502-2188. **T:** 1 775 829-1964
Editorial Profile: KSGG-AM is a commercial station owned by Americom Broadcasting. The format of the station is sports. The station airs in the Reno, NV area at 1230 AM.

KSGL-AM
Owner: Agape Communications
Editorial: 3337 W Central Ave, Wichita, Kansas 67203. **T:** 1 316 942-3231
E: am900@ksgl.com **W:** http://www.ksgl.com
Editorial Profile: KSGL-AM is a commercial station owned by Agape Communications. The format of the station is adult standards. KGSL-AM broadcasts to the Wichita, KS area at 900 AM.

KSGM-AM
Owner: Donze Communications Inc.
Editorial: 21851 White Sands Rd, Sainte Genevieve, Missouri 63670.
T: 1 573 547-8005
E: kbdz@suntimesnews.com
W: http://www.suntimesnews.com
Editorial Profile: KSGM-AM is a commercial station owned by Donze Communications Inc. the format of the station is classic country. KSGM-AM broadcasts to the Sainte Genevieve, MO area at 980 AM.

KSGN-FM
Owner: Good News Radio
Editorial: 2048 Orange Tree Ln, Ste 200, Redlands, California 92374. **T:** 1 909 583-2150
E: info@ksgn.com **W:** http://www.ksgn.com
Editorial Profile: KSGN-FM is a non-commercial station owned by Good News Radio. The format of the station is

contemporary Christian. KSGN-FM broadcasts to the Redlands, CA area at 89.7 FM.

KSGT-AM
Owner: Rich Broadcasting, LLC.
Editorial: 1140 State Highway 22, Jackson, Wyoming 83001-9401. **T:** 1 307 733-2120
W: http://www.jacksonholeradio.com
Editorial Profile: KSGT-AM is a commercial station owned by Rich Broadcasting, LLC. The format of the station is sports. KSGT-AM broadcasts to the Jackson, WY area at 1340 AM.

KSGU-FM
Owner: Nevada Public Radio
Editorial: 1289 S Torrey Pines Dr, Las Vegas, Nevada 89146. **T:** 1 702 258-9895
W: http://www.ksgu.org
Editorial Profile: KSGU-FM is a non-commercial station owned by Nevada Public Radio. The format of the station is classical music, news and talk. KSGU-FM broadcasts to the St. George, UT area on 90.3 FM.

KSHA-FM
Owner: Mapleton of Redding, LLC
Editorial: 3360 Alta Mesa Dr, Redding, California 96002-2831. **T:** 1 530 226-9500
W: http://www.kshasta.com
Editorial Profile: KSHA-FM is a commercial station owned by Mapleton of Redding, LLC. The format of the station is adult contemporary music. KSHA-FM broadcasts to the Redding, CA area at 104.3 FM.

KSHE-FM
Owner: Emmis Communications Corp.
Editorial: 800 Saint Louis Union Sta, Saint Louis, Missouri 63103. **T:** 1 314 621-0095
E: feedback@kshe95.com
W: http://www.kshe95.com
Editorial Profile: KSHE-FM is a commercial station owned by Emmis Communications Corp. The format of the station is rock music. KSHE-FM broadcasts to the St. Louis area at 94.7 FM.

KSHJ-AM
Owner: La Promesa Foundation
Editorial: 11511 Katy Fwy Ste 301, Houston, Texas 77079-1921. **T:** 1 832 786-4500
W: http://www.grnonline.com
Editorial Profile: KSHJ-AM is a commercial station owned by La Promesa Foundation. The format of the station is Catholic radio programming. KSHJ-AM broadcasts to the Houston area at 1430 AM.

KSHK-FM
Owner: Ohana Broadcasting Co.
Editorial: 4271 Halenani St, Lihue, Hawaii 96766. **T:** 1 808 245-9527
E: kong@kongradio.com
W: http://www.kongradio.com
Editorial Profile: KSHK-FM is commercial station owned by Ohana Broadcasting Co. The format of the station is classic rock. KSHK-FM broadcasts to the Lihue, HI area at 103.3 FM.

KSHL-FM
Owner: Linn(Stephanie)
Editorial: 131 NE 15th St, Newport, Oregon 97365. **T:** 1 541 265-6477 **E:** news@kshl.com
W: http://www.kshl.com
Editorial Profile: KSHL-FM is a commercial station owned by Stephanie Linn. The format of the station is country music. KSHL-FM broadcasts in the Newport, OR area at 97.5 FM.

KSHN-FM
Owner: Trinity River Valley Broadcasting
Editorial: 2099 Sam Houston St, Liberty, Texas 77575. **T:** 1 936 336-5793
E: news@kshn.com **W:** http://www.kshn.com
Editorial Profile: KSHN-FM is a commercial station owned by Trinity River Valley Broadcasting. The format of the station is adult contemporary, country and oldies music. KSHN-FM broadcasts to the Liberty, TX area at 99.9 FM.

KSHO-AM
Owner: EADS Broadcasting Corp.
Editorial: 36991 Kgal Dr, Lebanon, Oregon 97355. **T:** 1 541 451-5425 **E:** kgal@kgal.com
W: http://www.ksho.net
Editorial Profile: KSHO-AM is a station owned by EADS Broadcasting Corp. The format of the station is adult standards music. KSHO-FM broadcasts to Albany, OR area at 920 AM.

KSHP-AM
Owner: Las Vegas Radio Co. Inc.(The)

Editorial: 2400 S Jones Blvd Ste 3, Las Vegas, Nevada 89146-3130.
T: 1 702 221-1200 **E:** mail@kshp.com
W: http://www.kshp.com
Editorial Profile: KSHP-AM is a commercial station owned by The Las Vegas Radio Co. Inc. The format of the station is talk. KSHP-AM broadcasts to the Las Vegas area at 1400 AM.

KSHR-FM
Owner: Bicoastal Media LLC
Editorial: 320 Central Ave, Ste 519, Coos Bay, Oregon 97420. **T:** 1 541 267-2121
E: southcoastpsa@bicoastalmedia.com
W: http://www.kshr.com
Editorial Profile: KSHR-FM is a commercial station owned by Bicoastal Media LLC. The format of the station is contemporary country music. KSHR-FM broadcasts to the Coos Bay, OR area at 97.3 FM.

KSHU-FM
Owner: Sam Houston State University
Editorial: Dan Rather Com Bldg, Huntsville, Texas 77341-0001. **T:** 1 936 294-3939
E: thekatkshu@gmail.com
W: http://www.kshu.org
Editorial Profile: KSHU-FM is a non-commercial station owned by Sam Houston State University. The format of the station is college variety. KSHU-FM broadcasts to the Huntsville, TX area at 90.5 FM.

KSIB-AM
Owner: Dave & Kathy Rieck
Editorial: 1409 Highway 34, Creston, Iowa 50801. **T:** 1 641 782-2155
E: news@ksibradio.com
W: http://www.ksibradio.com
Editorial Profile: KSIB-AM is a commercial station owned by Dave & Kathy Rieck. The format of the station is contemporary country music. KSIB-AM broadcasts to the Creston, IA area at 1520 AM.

KSIB-FM
Owner: Dave & Kathy Rieck
Editorial: 1409 Highway 34, Creston, Iowa 50801. **T:** 1 641 782-2155
E: news@ksibradio.com
W: http://www.ksibradio.com
Editorial Profile: KSIB-FM is a commercial station owned by Dave & Kathy Rieck. The format of the station is contemporary country music. KSIB-FM broadcasts to the Creston, IA area at 101.3 FM.

KSID-AM
Owner: KSID Radio Inc.
Editorial: 2306 Legion Park Rd, Sidney, Nebraska 69162. **T:** 1 308 254-5803
W: http://www.ksidradio.com
Editorial Profile: KSID-AM is a commercial station owned by KSID Radio Inc. The format of the station is contemporary country. KSID-AM broadcasts to the Sidney, NE area at 1340 AM.

KSID-FM
Owner: KSID Radio Inc.
Editorial: 2306 Legion Park Rd, Sidney, Nebraska 69162. **T:** 1 308 254-5803
E: ksidprod@ksidradio.com
W: http://www.ksidradio.com
Editorial Profile: KSID-FM is a commercial station owned by KSID Radio Inc. The format of the station is adult contemporary. KSID-FM broadcasts to the Sidney, NE area at 98.7 FM.

KSIG-AM
Owner: Acadia Broadcast Partners
Editorial: 320 N Parkerson Ave, Crowley, Louisiana 70526-5056. **T:** 1 337 783-2520
E: kqis@cox-internet.com
Editorial Profile: KSIG-AM is a commercial station owned by Acadia Broadcast Partners. The format of the station is oldies music. KSIG-AM broadcasts to the Crowley, LA area at 1450 AM.

KSII-FM
Owner: Townsquare Media, LLC
Editorial: 4180 N Mesa St, El Paso, Texas 79902. **T:** 1 915 544-9300 **W:** http://ksii.com
Editorial Profile: KSII-FM is a commercial station owned by Townsquare Media, LLC. The format of the station is hot adult contemporary. KSII-FM broadcasts to the El Paso, TX area at 93.1 FM.

KSIM-AM
Owner: Mississippi River Radio
Editorial: 324 Broadway St, Cape Girardeau, Missouri 63701. **T:** 1 573 335-8291
E: ksim@riverradio.net
W: http://www.1400ksim.com

Editorial Profile: KSIM-AM is a commercial station owned by Mississippi River Radio. The format of the station is news and talk. KSIM-AM broadcasts in the Paducah, MO area at 1400 AM.

KSIR-AM
Owner: Northeast Colorado Broadcasting, LLC
Editorial: 220 State St, Fort Morgan, Colorado 80701-2175. **T:** 1 970 867-7271
E: farm@necolorado.com
W: http://www.ksir.com
Editorial Profile: KSIR-AM is a commercial station owned by Northeast Colorado Broadcasting, LLC. The format of the station agriculture news, talk and sports. KSIR-AM broadcasts in the Denver area at 1010 AM.

KSIS-AM
Owner: Townsquare Media, LLC
Editorial: 2209 S Limit Ave, Sedalia, Missouri 65301-6950. **T:** 1 660 826-1050
W: http://www.ksisradio.com
Editorial Profile: KSIS-AM is a commercial station owned by Townsquare Media, LLC. The format of the station is talk. KSIS-AM broadcasts to the Sedalia, KS, area at 1050 AM.

KSIT-FM
Owner: Big Thickett Broadcasting Co.
Editorial: 2717 Yellowstone Rd, Rock Springs, Wyoming 82901-3261. **T:** 1 307 362-7034
E: wyoradio@wyoradio.com
W: http://www.wyoradio.com
Editorial Profile: KSIT-FM is a commercial station owned by Big Thickett Broadcasting Co. The format of the station is classic rock. KSIT-FM broadcasts to the Salt Lake City area at 99.7 FM.

KSIV-AM
Owner: Bott Broadcasting Co.
Editorial: 1750 S Brentwood Blvd, Ste 811, Saint Louis, Missouri 63144-1344.
T: 1 314 961-1320
E: ksiv@bottradionetwork.com
W: http://www.bottradionetwork.com
Editorial Profile: KSIV-AM is a commercial station owned by Bott Broadcasting Co. The format of the station is religious and Christian programming. KSIV-AM broadcasts to the St. Louis area at 1320 AM.

KSIV-FM
Owner: Bott Broadcasting Co.
Editorial: 1750 S Brentwood Blvd, Ste 811, Saint Louis, Missouri 63144.
T: 1 314 961-1320
E: ksiv@bottradionetwork.com
W: http://www.bottradionetwork.com
Editorial Profile: KSIV-FM is a commercial station owned by Bott Broadcasting Co. The format of the station is religious and Christian programming. KSIV-FM broadcasts to the St. Louis area at 91.5 FM.

KSIW-AM
Owner: Classic Communications Inc.
Editorial: 1922 22nd St, Woodward, Oklahoma 73801. **T:** 1 580 256-1450
E: cciradio@sbcglobal.net
W: http://www.woodwardradio.com
Editorial Profile: KSIW-AM is a commercial station owned by Classic Communications Inc. The format of the station is sports. KSIW-AM broadcasts to the Woodward, OK area at 1450 AM.

KSIX-AM
Owner: SportsRadioCC, LLC
Editorial: 710 Buffalo St, Ste 605, Corpus Christi, Texas 78401. **T:** 1 361 882-5749
W: http://sportsradiocc.com
Editorial Profile: KSIX-AM is a commercial station owned by SportsRadioCC, LLC. The format of the station is sports. KSIX-AM broadcasts to the Corpus Christi, TX area at 1230 AM.

KSIZ-FM
Owner: Buffalo Broadcasting
Editorial: 316 Lawrence Ln, Yreka, California 96097-3210. **T:** 1 530 842-4158
Editorial Profile: KSIZ-FM is a commercial station owned by Buffalo Broadcasting. The format of the station is classic rock. KCWH-FM broadcasts to the Weed/Mount Shasta, CA area at 102.3 FM.

KSJB-AM
Owner: Chesterman Communications Inc.
Editorial: 2400 8th Ave SW, Ste D-1, Jamestown, North Dakota 58401.
T: 1 701 252-3570 **E:** news@ksjbam.com
W: http://www.ksjbam.com

Editorial Profile: KSJB-AM is a commercial station owned by Chesterman Communications Inc. The format of the station is country music and agricultural programming. KSJB-AM broadcasts to the Jamestown, ND area at 600 AM.

KSJE-FM
Owner: San Juan College
Editorial: 4601 College Blvd, Farmington, New Mexico 87402-4609. **T:** 1 505 566-3517
E: ksje@sanjuancollege.edu
W: http://www.ksje.com
Editorial Profile: KSJE-FM is a non-commercial station owned by San Juan College. The format of the station is classical and jazz music. KSJE-FM broadcasts to the Albuquerque, NM area at 90.9 FM.

KSJI-FM
Owner: Good News Ministries, Inc.
Editorial: 13358 Manchester Rd Ste 100, Des Peres, Missouri 63131-1730.
T: 1 314 909-8569 **W:** http://joyfmonline.org
Editorial Profile: KSJI-FM is a non-commercial station owned by Good News Ministries, Inc. The format of the station is Contemporary Christian music. KSJI-FM broadcasts to the St. Louis, MO area at a frequency of 91.1 FM.

KSJJ-FM
Owner: Gross Communications Corporation
Editorial: 345 Sw Cyber Dr Ste 101-103, Bend, Oregon 97702-1045. **T:** 1 541 388-3300
W: http://www.ksjj1029.com
Editorial Profile: KSJJ-FM is a commercial station owned by Gross Communications Corporation. The format of the station is contemporary country. KSJJ-FM broadcasts to the Bend, OR area at a frequency of 102.9 FM.

KSJK-AM
Owner: State of Oregon
Editorial: 1250 Siskiyou Blvd, Ashland, Oregon 97520-5001. **T:** 1 541 552-6301
E: jprinfo@sou.edu **W:** http://www.ijpr.org
Editorial Profile: KSJK-AM is a non-commercial station owned by State of Oregon. The format of the station is news and talk programming. KSJK-AM broadcasts to the Medford, OR area at 1230 AM.

KSJN-FM
Owner: Minnesota Public Radio
Editorial: 480 Cedar St, Saint Paul, Minnesota 55101. **T:** 1 651 290-1500
E: newsroom@mpr.org
W: http://minnesota.publicradio.org
Editorial Profile: KSJN-FM is a non-commercial station owned by Minnesota Public Radio. The format of the station is classical music. KSJN-FM broadcasts to the St. Paul, MN area at 99.5 FM.

KSJO-FM
Owner: Cumulus Media
Editorial: 55 Hawthorne St, San Francisco, California 94105-3906. **T:** 1 415 995-6800
W: http://www.nashfmsjo.com
Editorial Profile: KSJO-FM is a commercial station owned by Cumulus Media. The format of the station is contemporary country. KSJO-FM broadcasts to the San Francisco Bay area at 92.3 FM.

KSJP-FM
Owner: Agnus Dei Communications, Inc.
Editorial: 6300 S Old Village Pl Suite 203, Sioux Falls, South Dakota 57108-2102.
T: 1 605 275-4659
E: kculhane.agnusdei@midconetwork.com
Editorial Profile: KSJP-FM is a commercial station owned by Agnus Dei Communications, Inc. The format of the station is Catholic talk and teaching. KSJP-FM broadcasts to the Aberdeen and Ipswich areas in South Dakota at a frequency of 88.9 FM.

KSJQ-FM
Owner: Eagle Communications
Editorial: 4104 Country Ln, Saint Joseph, Missouri 64506-4921. **T:** 1 816 233-6086
W: http://myqcountry.com
Editorial Profile: KSJQ-FM is a commercial station owned by Eagle Communications. The format of the station is contemporary country. KSJQ-FM broadcasts to the Saint Joseph, MO area at 92.7 FM.

KSJR-FM
Owner: Minnesota Public Radio
Editorial: 300 Wimmer Hall St John's Univ, Collegeville, Minnesota 56321-9999.
T: 1 320 363-7702 **E:** newsroom@mpr.org
W: http://minnesota.publicradio.org/radio/stations/knsrksjr

Editorial Profile: KSJR-FM is a non-commercial station owned by Minnesota Public Radio. The format of the station is classical music. KSJR-FM broadcasts to the Collegeville, MN area at 90.1 FM.

KSJS-FM
Owner: San Jose State University
Editorial: 132 Hugh Gillis Hall, San Jose, California 95192. **T:** 1 408 924-4548
W: http://www.ksjs.org
Editorial Profile: KSJS-FM is a non-commercial station owned by San Jose State University. The format of the station is variety. KSJS-FM broadcasts to the San Jose, CA area on 90.5 FM.

KSJT-FM
Owner: Unica Broadcasting Co. (La)
Editorial: 209 W Beauregard Ave, San Angelo, Texas 76903-5823. **T:** 1 325 655-1717
E: webmaster@tejano104.com
Editorial Profile: KSJT-FM is a commercial station owned by La Unica Broadcasting Co. The format for the station is Spanish adult contemporary. KSJT-FM broadcasts to the San Angelo, TX area at 107.5 AM.

KSJV-FM
Owner: Radio Bilingue Inc.
Editorial: 5005 E Belmont Ave, Fresno, California 93727. **T:** 1 559 455-5777
E: mail@radiobilingue.org
W: http://www.radiobilingue.org
Editorial Profile: KSJV-FM is a non-commercial station owned by Radio Bilingue Inc. The format of the station is Hispanic music and talk. KSJV-FM broadcasts to the Fresno, CA area at 91.5 FM.

KSJZ-FM
Owner: Chesterman Communications Inc.
Editorial: 2400 8th Ave SW, ste 01, Jamestown, North Dakota 58401.
T: 1 701 252-3570 **E:** news@ksjbam.com
W: http://www.ksjzfm.com
Editorial Profile: KSJZ-FM is a commercial station owned by Chesterman Communications Inc. The format of the station is Adult Top 40/CHR music. KSJZ-FM broadcasts to the Jamestown, ND area at 93.3 FM.

KSKA-FM
Owner: Alaska Public Media
Editorial: 3877 University Dr, Anchorage, Alaska 99508-4676. **T:** 1 907 550-8400
E: questions@kakm.org
W: http://www.kska.org
Editorial Profile: KSKA-FM is a non-commercial station owned by Alaska Public Media. The format of the station is news, music and talk. KSKA-FM broadcasts to the Anchorage, AK area at 91.1 FM.

KSKB-FM
Owner: Florida Public Radio, Inc.
Editorial: 104 E 2nd St, Brooklyn, Iowa 52211. **T:** 1 641 522-7202 **E:** kskb@netins.net
Editorial Profile: The station is a non-commercial station owned by Florida Public Radio, Inc. KSKB-FM broadcasts to Des Moines, IA locally at 99.1 FM. The format of the station is religous.

KSKD-FM
Owner: Favorita Broadcasting(La)
Editorial: 4043 Geer Rd, Hughson, California 95326-9798. **T:** 1 209 883-8760
E: lafavorita@lafavorita.net
W: http://www.lafavorita.net
Editorial Profile: KSKD-FM is a commercial station owned by La Favorita Broadcasting. The format of the station is regional Mexican. KSKD-FM broadcasts to the Hughson, CA area at 95.9 FM.

KSKE-AM
Owner: Rocky Mountain Radio
Editorial: 614 Kimbark St, Longmont, Colorado 80501-4911. **T:** 1 303 776-2323
W: http://kvleradio.com
Editorial Profile: KSKE-AM is a commercial station owned by Rocky Mountain Radio. The format of the station is news, talk and sports. KSKE-AM broadcasts to the Longmont, CO area at 1450 AM.

KSKE-FM
Owner: NRC Broadcasting
Editorial: 182 Avon Rd, Ste 240, Avon, Colorado 81620-9999. **T:** 1 970 949-0140
W: http://www.kskeradio.com
Editorial Profile: KSKE-FM is a commercial station owned by NRC Broadcasting. The format of the station is contemporary country.

KSKE-FM broadcasts to the Avon, CO area at 101.7 FM.

KSKG-FM
Owner: Eagle Radio Inc.
Editorial: 1825 S Ohio St, Salina, Kansas 67401. **T:** 1 785 825-4631
W: http://www.999kskg.com
Editorial Profile: KSKG-FM is a commercial station owned by Eagle Radio Inc. The format of the station is contemporary country. KSKG-FM broadcasts to the Salina, KA area at 99.9 FM.

KSKI-FM
Owner: Rich Broadcasting, LLC.
Editorial: 201 S Main St, Hailey, Idaho 83333-8406. **T:** 1 208 788-7118
E: kech95@cox-internet.com
Editorial Profile: KSKI-FM is a commercial station owned by Rich Broadcasting, LLC. The format of the station is AAA-adult album alternative. KSKI-FM broadcasts to the Ketchum, ID area at 94.5.

KSKK-FM
Owner: De La Hunt Broadcasting
Editorial: 11 Bryant Ave SE, Wadena, Minnesota 56482-1543. **T:** 1 218 631-3441
E: kskk@eot.com
W: http://www.kkradionetwork.com
Editorial Profile: KSKK-FM is a commercial station owned by De La Hunt Broadcasting. The format of the station is Lite Rock/Lite AC music and talk. KSKK-FM broadcasts to the Minneapolis area at 94.7 FM.

KSKL-FM
Owner: Armada Media Corp.
Editorial: 1402 E Kansas Ave, Garden City, Kansas 67846. **T:** 1 620 276-2366
E: production@wksradio.com
W: http://www.wksradio.com
Editorial Profile: KSKL-FM is a commercial station owned by Armada Media Corp. The format of the station is classic hits. KSKL-FM broadcasts to the Garden City, KS area at 94.5 FM.

KSKO-AM
Owner: Kuskokwim Public Broadcasting
Editorial: 5 Main St, Mc Grath, Alaska 99627.
T: 1 907 524-3001
W: http://www.kskoradio.org
Editorial Profile: KSKO-AM is a non-commercial station owned by Kuskokwim Public Broadcasting. The format of the station is variety. KSKO-AM broadcasts to the McGrath, AK area at 870 AM.

KSKR-AM
Owner: Brooke Communications Inc.
Editorial: 1445 W Harvard Ave, Roseburg, Oregon 97471-2839. **T:** 1 541 672-6641
W: http://www.541radio.com
Editorial Profile: KSKR-AM is a commercial station owned by Brooke Communications Inc. The format of the station is sports. KSKR-AM broadcasts to the Roseburg, OR area at 1490 AM.

KSKR-FM
Owner: Brooke Communications Inc.
Editorial: 1445 W Harvard Ave, Roseburg, Oregon 97471-2839. **T:** 1 541 672-6641
W: http://www.jelli.com
Editorial Profile: KSKR-FM is a commercial station owned by Brooke Communications Inc. The format of the station is CHR. KSKR-FM broadcasts to the Roseburg, OR area at 100.9 FM.

KSKS-FM
Owner: Cumulus Media
Editorial: 1071 W Shaw Ave, Fresno, California 93711-3702. **T:** 1 559 490-5800
W: http://www.ksks.com
Editorial Profile: KSKS-FM is a commercial station owned by Cumulus Media. The format of the station is country music. KSKS-FM broadcasts to the Fresno, CA area at 93.7 FM.

KSKU-FM
Owner: Ad Astra Per Aspera Broadcasting, Inc.
Editorial: 10 E 5Th Ave, Hutchinson, Kansas 67501-6300. **T:** 1 620 665-5758
W: http://www.adastraradio.net
Editorial Profile: KSKU-FM is a commercial station owned by Ad Astra Per Aspera Broadcasting, Inc. The format of the station is Top 40/CHR. KSKU-FM broadcasts to the Hutchinson, KS area at 94.7 FM.

KSKY-AM
Owner: Salem Communications

Editorial: 6400 N Belt Line Rd, Ste 110, Irving, Texas 75063. **T:** 1 972 870-9949
W: http://www.660amtheanswer.com
Editorial Profile: KSKY-AM is a commercial station owned by Salem Communications. The format of the station is news and talk programming. KSKY-AM broadcasts to the Irving, TX area at 660 AM.

KSKZ-FM
Owner: Armada Media Corp.
Editorial: 1402 E Kansas Ave, Garden City, Kansas 67846. **T:** 1 620 276-2366
E: production@wksradio.com
W: http://www.wksradio.com
Editorial Profile: KSKZ-FM is a commercial station owned by Armada Media Corp. The format of the station is hot adult contemporary. KSKZ-FM broadcasts to the Garden City, KS area at 98.1 FM.

KSL-AM
Owner: KSL Broadcasting
Editorial: 55 N 300 W, Salt Lake City, Utah 84101-3502. **T:** 1 801 575-5555
E: radio.news@ksl.com **W:** http://www.ksl.com
Editorial Profile: KSL-AM is a commercial station owned by KSL Broadcasting. The format of the station is news, sports and talk. KSL-AM broadcasts to the Salt Lake City area at 1160 AM.

KSLC-FM
Owner: Linfield College
Editorial: 900 SE Baker St, McMinnville, Oregon 97128-6808. **T:** 1 503 883-2550
E: kslcmusic@gmail.com
W: http://www.linfield.edu/kslcfm
Editorial Profile: KSLC-FM is a non-commercial college station owned by Linfield College. The format of the station is variety. KSLC-FM broadcasts to the Yamhill County, OR area at 90.3 FM.

KSLD-AM
Owner: KSRM Radio Inc.
Editorial: 40960 K-Beach Rd, Kenai, Alaska 99611-6445. **T:** 1 907 283-8700
E: rken18@radiokenai.com
W: http://www.radiokenai.com
Editorial Profile: KSLD-AM is a commercial station owned by KSRM Radio Inc. The format of the station is sports. KSLD-AM broadcasts to the Kenai, AK, area at 1140 AM.

KSLE-FM
Owner: One Ten Broadcasting Group Inc.
Editorial: 2 E Main St, Shawnee, Oklahoma 74801. **T:** 1 405 878-1803
E: kirc1059@aol.com
Editorial Profile: KSLE-FM is a commercial station owned by One Ten Broadcasting Group Inc. The format of the station is oldies music. KSLE-FM broadcasts to the Shawnee, OK area at 104.7 FM.

KSL-FM
Owner: KSL Broadcasting
Editorial: 55 N 300 W, Salt Lake City, Utah 84101-3502. **T:** 1 801 575-5555
E: talk@ksl.com **W:** http://www.ksl.com
Editorial Profile: KSL-FM is a commercial station owned by KSL Broadcasting. The format of the station is news, sports and talk. KSL-FM broadcasts to the Salt Lake City area at 1160 AM and simulcasts the programming of KSL-AM.

KSLG-FM
Owner: Lost Coast Communications
Editorial: 1400 Main St, Ste 104, Ferndale, California 95536. **T:** 1 707 786-5104
E: psa@kslg.com **W:** http://www.kslg.com
Editorial Profile: KSLG-FM is a commercial station owned by Lost Coast Communications. The format is modern rock. KSLG-FM broadcasts to the Ferndale, CA area at 94.1 FM.

KSLI-AM
Owner: Townsquare Media, LLC
Editorial: 3911 S 1st St, Abilene, Texas 79605. **T:** 1 325 676-7711
W: http://www.1280ksli.com
Editorial Profile: KSLI-AM is a commercial station owned by Townsquare Media, LLC. The format of the station is classic country. KSLI-AM broadcasts to the Abilene, TX area at 1280 AM.

KSLL-AM
Owner: AJB Broadcasting
Editorial: 6 E Main St, Price, Utah 84501-3032. **T:** 1 435 637-1080
E: kusabuzz@gmail.com
W: http://utahsclassicradio.com
Editorial Profile: KSLL-AM is a commercial station owned by AJB Broadcasting. The format of the station is classic rock. KSLL-AM broadcasts to the Price, UT area at 1080 AM.

KSLO-AM
Owner: Delta Media Corporation
Editorial: 216 N Court St, Opelousas, Louisiana 70570-5256. **T:** 1 337 942-2633
W: http://www.ksloradio.com
Editorial Profile: KSLO-AM is a commercial station owned by the Delta Media Corporation. The format of the station is Spanish Adult Hits. KSLO-AM broadcasts to the Opelousas, LA area at 1230 AM.

KSLO-FM
Owner: Delta Media Corporation
Editorial: 3501 NW Evangeline Trwy, Carencro, Louisiana 70520-6240. **T:** 1 337 896-1600
W: http://www.ksloradio.com
Editorial Profile: KSLO-FM is a commercial station owned by Delta Media Corporation. The format of the station is Spanish Adult Hits. KSLO-FM broadcasts to the Lafayette, LA area at a frequency of 105.3 FM.

KSLQ-FM
Owner: Y2K Inc.
Editorial: 511 W 5th St, Washington, Missouri 63090-2205. **T:** 1 636 239-6800
W: http://www.kslq.biz
Editorial Profile: KSLQ-FM is a commercial station owned by Y2K Inc. The format of the station is adult contemporary music. KSLQ-FM broadcasts to the Washington, MO area at 104.5 FM.

KSLR-AM
Owner: Salem Communications
Editorial: 9601 McAllister Fwy, San Antonio, Texas 78216-4681. **T:** 1 210 344-8481
E: kslr@kslr.com **W:** http://www.kslr.com
Editorial Profile: KSLR-AM is a non-commercial station owned by Salem Communications. The format of the station is religious news and talk. KSLR-AM broadcasts to the San Antonio area listeners at 630 AM.

KSLT-FM
Owner: Bethesda Christian Broadcasting
Editorial: 1853 Fountain Plaza Dr, Rapid City, South Dakota 57702-9315. **T:** 1 605 342-6822
E: kslt@kslt.com **W:** http://www.kslt.com
Editorial Profile: KSLT-FM is a commercial station owned by Bethesda Christian Broadcasting. The format of the station is Contemporary Christian. KSLT-FM broadcasts to the Rapid City and Black Hills areas in South Dakota at 107.1 FM.

KSLU-FM
Owner: Southeastern Louisiana University
Editorial: 1220 Seadrive, Vickers Hall, Hammond, Louisiana 70402.
T: 1 985 549-2330 **E:** kslu@selu.edu
W: http://kslu.org
Editorial Profile: KSLU-FM is a non-commercial station owned by Southeastern Louisiana University. The format of the station is adult album alternative. KSLU-FM broadcasts to the Hammond, LA area at 90.9 FM.

KSLV-AM
Owner: San Luis Valley Broadcasting
Editorial: 109 Adams St, Monte Vista, Colorado 81144-1421. **T:** 1 719 852-3581
E: kslv@amigo.net
W: http://www.kslvradio.com
Editorial Profile: KSLV-AM is a commercial station owned by San Luis Valley Broadcasting. The format of the station is country music. KSLV-AM broadcasts to the Monte Vista, CO area at 1240 AM.

KSLV-FM
Owner: San Luis Valley Broadcasting
Editorial: 109 Adams St, Monte Vista, Colorado 81144-1421. **T:** 1 719 852-3581
E: kslv@amigo.net
W: http://www.kslvradio.com
Editorial Profile: KSLV-FM is a commercial station owned by San Luis Valley Broadcasting. The format of the station is adult contemporary. KSLV-FM broadcasts to the Monte Vista and Alamosa, CO areas at 96.5 FM.

KSLX-FM
Owner: Hubbard Radio, LLC
Editorial: 4343 E Camelback Rd Ste 200, Phoenix, Arizona 85018-2756.
T: 1 480 941-1007 **W:** http://www.kslx.com
Editorial Profile: KSLX-FM is a commercial station owned by Hubbard Radio, LLC. The format of the station is classic rock. KSLX-FM broadcasts to the Phoenix area at 100.7 FM.

KSLY-FM
Owner: El Dorado Broadcasting
Editorial: 51 Zaca Ln Ste 100, San Luis Obispo, California 93401-7353.
T: 1 805 545-0101 **W:** http://www.ksly.com
Editorial Profile: KSLY-FM is a commercial station owned by El Dorado Broadcasting. The format of the station is contemporary country. KSLY-FM broadcasts to the San Luis Obispo, CA area at 96.1 FM.

KSLZ-FM
Owner: Clear Channel Media and Entertainment
Editorial: 1001 Highlands Plaza Dr W, Ste 100, Saint Louis, Missouri 63110.
T: 1 314 333-8000 **W:** http://www.z1077.com
Editorial Profile: KSLZ-FM is a commercial station owned by Clear Channel Media and Entertainment. The format of the station is Top 40/CHR music. KSLZ-FM broadcasts to the St. Louis area at 107.7 FM.

KSMA-FM
Owner: Coloff Media
Editorial: 31 1st St NE, Mason City, Iowa 50401. **T:** 1 641 421-7744
E: ksma@987kisscountry.com
W: http://www.987kisscountry.com
Editorial Profile: KSMA-FM is a commercial station owned by Coloff Media. The format of the station is contemporary country. KSMA-FM broadcasts to the Mason City, IA area at 98.7 FM.

KSMB-FM
Owner: Cumulus Media Inc
Editorial: 202 Galbert Rd, Lafayette, Louisiana 70506. **T:** 1 337 232-1311
W: http://www.ksmb.com
Editorial Profile: KSMB-FM is a commercial station owned by Cumulus Media Inc. The format of the station is Top 40/CHR. KSMB-FM broadcasts to the Lafayette, LA area at 94.5 FM.

KSMC-FM
Owner: Saint Mary's College of California
Editorial: 1928 Saint Marys Rd, Moraga, California 94556-2715. **T:** 1 925 631-4772
E: ksmc85@gmail.com
W: http://www.stmarys-ca.edu/ksmc
Editorial Profile: KSMC-FM is a non-commercial station owned by Saint Mary's College of California. The format of the station is variety. KSMC-FM broadcasts to the Moraga, CA area at 89.5 FM.

KSMD-FM
Owner: Crain Media Group LLC
Editorial: 111 N Spring St, Searcy, Arkansas 72143-7712. **T:** 1 501 268-7123
E: production@crainmedia.com
W: http://www.newstalk991.com
Editorial Profile: KSMD-FM is a commercial station owned by Crain Media Group LLC. The format of the station is news, talk and sports. KSMD-FM broadcasts to the Searcy, AR area at 99.1 FM.

KSME-FM
Owner: Clear Channel Media and Entertainment
Editorial: 4270 Byrd Dr, Loveland, Colorado 80538. **T:** 1 970 461-2560
W: http://www.kissfmcolorado.com
Editorial Profile: KSME-FM is a commercial station owned by Clear Channel Media and Entertainment. The format of the station is Top 40/CHR music. KSME-FM broadcasts to the Fort Collins, CO area at 96.1 FM.

KSMF-FM
Owner: State of Oregon
Editorial: 1250 Siskiyou Blvd, Ashland, Oregon 97520-5001. **T:** 1 541 552-6301
E: jprinfo@sou.edu **W:** http://www.ijpr.org
Editorial Profile: KSMF-FM is a non-commercial station owned by the State of Oregon. The format of the station features news and music programming from the Rhythm and News format of Jefferson Public Radio. KSMS-FM broadcasts to the Ashland, OR area at a frequency of 89.1 FM.

KSMG-FM
Owner: Cox Media Group, Inc.
Editorial: 8122 Datapoint Dr, Ste 600, San Antonio, Texas 78229-3446.
T: 1 210 615-5400
W: http://www.magic1053.com
Editorial Profile: KSMG-FM is a commercial station owned by Cox Media Group, Inc. The format of the station is hot adult contemporary music. KSMG-FM broadcasts to the San Antonio area at 105.3 FM.

KSML-AM
Owner: Pentagon Communications, LLC
Editorial: 121 S Cotton Sq, Lufkin, Texas 75904-2933. **T:** 1 936 634-6661
E: traffic@yatesmedia.com
Editorial Profile: KSML-AM is a commercial station owned by Yates Media. The format of the station is news/talk. KSML-AM broadcasts to the Lufkin, TX area at 1260 AM.

KSML-FM
Owner: Pentagon Communications, LLC
Editorial: 121 S Cotton Sq, Lufkin, Texas 75904-2933. **T:** 1 936 634-6661
E: traffic@yatesmedia.com
W: http://www.ksmlradio.com
Editorial Profile: KSML-FM is a commercial station owned by Yates Media. The format of the station is Regional and Tejano. KSML-FM broadcasts to the Palm Desert, CA area at 101.9 FM.

KSMM-AM
Owner: Rocking M Radio
Editorial: 150 Plaza Dr Ste J, Liberal, Kansas 67901-2779. **T:** 1 620 624-8156
E: ksmmproduction@gmail.com
Editorial Profile: KSMM-AM is a commercial station owned by Rocking M Radio. The format of the station is oldies. KSMM-AM broadcasts to Liberal, KS area at 1470 AM.

KSMM-FM
Owner: Rocking M Radio
Editorial: 150 Plaza Dr, Ste J, Liberal, Kansas 67901. **T:** 1 620 624-8156
E: ksmmproduction@gmail.com
Editorial Profile: KSMM-FM is a commercial station owned by Rocking M Radio. The format of the station is regional Mexican. KSMM-FM broadcasts to the Liberal, KS area at 101.5 FM.

KSMO-AM
Owner: KSMO Enterprises
Editorial: 800 S Main St, Salem, Missouri 65560. **T:** 1 573 729-6117
E: ksmoski@fidnet.com
W: http://www.ksmoradio.com

KSMT-FM
Owner: NRC Broadcasting
Editorial: 130 Ski Hill Road, Ste 240, Breckenridge, Colorado 80424.
T: 1 970 453-2234
W: http://www.ksmtradio.com
Editorial Profile: KSMT-FM is a commercial station owned by NRC Broadcasting. The format of the station is adult album alternative. KSMT-FM broadcasts to the Breckenridge, CO area at 102.1 FM.

KSMU-FM
Owner: Missouri State University
Editorial: 901 S National Ave, Springfield, Missouri 65897-0027. **T:** 1 417 836-5878
E: ksmu@missouristate.edu
W: http://ksmu.org
Editorial Profile: KSMU-FM is a non-commercial station owned by Missouri State University. The format of the station is news and classical music. KSMU-FM broadcasts to the Springfield, MO area at 90.3 FM.

KSMX-AM
Owner: El Dorado Broadcasting
Editorial: 2215 Skyway Dr, Santa Maria, California 93455. **T:** 1 805 925-2582
W: http://www.1240ksmx.com
Editorial Profile: KSMX-AM is a commercial station owned by El Dorado Broadcasting. The format of the station is news and talk. KSMX-AM broadcasts to the Santa Maria, CA area at 1240 AM.

KSMX-FM
Owner: Rooney Moon Broadcasting
Editorial: 208 E Grand Ave, Clovis, New Mexico 88101-7531. **T:** 1 575 763-0338
E: news@rooneymoon.com
W: http://www.heymix.com
Editorial Profile: KSMX-FM is a commercial station owned by Rooney Moon Broadcasting. The format of the station is Hot AC. KSMX-FM broadcasts to the Clovis, NM area at a frequency of 107.5 FM.

KSMY-FM
Owner: El Dorado Broadcasting
Editorial: 2215 Skyway Dr, Santa Maria, California 93455. **T:** 1 805 925-2582
W: http://www.elcompa1067.com

Editorial Profile: KSMY-FM is a commercial station owned by El Dorado Broadcasting. The format of the station is Hispanic adult contemporary. KSMY-FM broadcasts to the Santa Maria, CA area at 106.7 FM.

KSNA-FM

Owner: Sand Hill Media
Editorial: 854 Lindsay Blvd, Idaho Falls, Idaho 83402-1820. **T:** 1 208 522-1101
W: http://www.100myfm.com
Editorial Profile: KSNA-FM is a commercial station owned by Sand Hill Media. The format of the station is adult contemporary. KSNA-FM broadcasts to the Idaho Falls, ID area at 100.7 FM.

KSND-FM

Owner: Coss (Donald)
Editorial: 1665 James St, Woodburn, Oregon 97071. **T:** 1 503 981-9400
Editorial Profile: KSND-FM is a commercial station owned by Coss (Donald). The format of the station is Spanish adult hits. KSND-FM broadcasts to the Salem, OR area at 95.1 FM.

KSNE-FM

Owner: Clear Channel Media and Entertainment
Editorial: 2880 Meade Ave Ste 250, Las Vegas, Nevada 89102-0713.
T: 1 702 238-7300
E: vegaspublicservice@clearchannel.com
W: http://www.ksne.com
Editorial Profile: KSNE-FM is a commercial station owned by Clear Channel Media and Entertainment. The format of the station is adult contemporary. KSNE-FM broadcasts to the Las Vegas area at 106.5 FM.

KSNI-FM

Owner: El Dorado Broadcasting
Editorial: 2215 Skyway Dr, Santa Maria, California 93455. **T:** 1 805 925-2582
W: http://www.sunnycountry.com
Editorial Profile: KSNI-FM is a commercial station owned by El Dorado Broadcasting. The format of the station is classic country. KSNI-FM broadcasts to the Santa Maria, CA area at 102.5 FM.

KSNM-FM

Owner: Adams Radio Group
Editorial: 1355 California Ave, Las Cruces, New Mexico 88001-4130. **T:** 1 575 525-9298
E: radiolc@kgrt.com
W: http://www.classichits987.com
Editorial Profile: KSNM-FM is a commercial station owned by Adams Radio Group. The format of the station is classic hits. KSNM-FM broadcasts to the Las Cruces, NM area at a frequency of 98.7 FM.

KSNN-FM

Owner: Cherry Creek Radio
Editorial: 106 Rose Ln, Montrose, Colorado 81401. **T:** 1 970 249-4546
E: news@coloradoradio.com
W: http://coloradoradio.com
Editorial Profile: KSNN-FM is a commercial station owned by Cherry Creek Radio. The format of the station is lite rock. KSNN-FM broadcasts to the Grand Junction-Montrose, CO area at 103.7 FM.

KSNO-FM

Owner: Color Radio Marketing LLC
Editorial: 218 E Valley Rd, El Jebel, Colorado 81623-7735. **T:** 1 970 925-4111
W: http://www.ksno.net/
Editorial Profile: KSNO-FM is a commercial station owned by Colorado West Broadcasting Inc. The format of the station is adult album alternative music. KSNO-FM broadcasts to the Aspen, CO area at 103.5 FM.

KSNP-FM

Owner: My Town Media, Inc.
Editorial: 1910 6th St, Burlington, Kansas 66839. **T:** 1 620 364-8807
W: http://www.977thedawg.com
Editorial Profile: KSNP-FM is a commercial station owned by My Town Media, Inc. The format of the station is classic rock. KSNP-FM broadcasts to the Burlington, KS area at 97.7 FM.

KSNQ-FM

Owner: Townsquare Media, LLC
Editorial: 415 Park Ave, Twin Falls, Idaho 83301. **T:** 1 208 733-7512
W: http://983thesnake.com
Editorial Profile: KSNQ-FM is a commercial station owned by Townsquare Media, LLC. The format of the station is classic rock music. KSNQ-FM broadcasts to the Idaho Falls, ID area at 98.3 FM.

KSNR-FM

Owner: Clear Channel Media and Entertainment
Editorial: 505 University Ave, Grand Forks, North Dakota 58203. **T:** 1 701 746-1417
E: gfprod@clearchannel.com
W: http://www.thecatfm.com
Editorial Profile: KSNR-FM is a commercial station owned by Clear Channel Media and Entertainment. The format of the station is contemporary country. KSNR-FM broadcasts to the Grand Forks, ND area at 92.9 FM.

KSNS-FM

Owner: Florida Public Radio, Inc.
Editorial: 301 S Main St, Medicine Lodge, Kansas 67104. **T:** 1 620 886-3537
W: http://www.krejksns.org
Editorial Profile: KSNS-FM is a non-commercial station owned by Florida Public Radio, Inc. The format of the station is contemporary Christian music. KSNS-FM broadcasts to the Medicine Lodge, KS area at 91.5 FM.

KSNX-FM

Owner: Petracom
Editorial: 27610 N Desierto Dr, Rio Verde, Arizona 85263-6037. **T:** 1 928 362-8100
Editorial Profile: KSNX-FM is a commercial station owned by Petracom. The format of the station is classic hits. KSNX-FM broadcasts to the Heber, AZ area at 105.5 FM.

KSNY-FM

Owner: Snyder Broadcasting Co.
Editorial: 2301 Avenue R, Snyder, Texas 79549. **T:** 1 325 573-9322
W: http://ksnyradio.com
Editorial Profile: KSNY-FM is a commercial station owned by Snyder Broadcasting Co. The format of the station is classic and contemporary country music. KSNY-FM broadcasts to the Snyder, TX area at 101.5 FM.

KSOB-FM

Owner: Rocking M Radio
Editorial: 5501 10th St, Great Bend, Kansas 67530-6319. **T:** 1 620 792-7108
W: http://centralkansasradio.com/kansascountry96
Editorial Profile: KSOB-FM is a commercial station owned by Rocking M Radio. The format of the station is contemporary country. KSOB-FM broadcasts to the Wichita, KS area at 96.7 FM.

KSOC-FM

Owner: Radio One Inc.
Editorial: 13331 Preston Rd Ste 1180, Dallas, Texas 75240-1140. **T:** 1 972 331-5400
W: http://ksoul945.com
Editorial Profile: KSOC-FM is a commercial station owned by Radio One Inc. The format of the station is urban AC and oldies R&B. KSOC-FM broadcasts to the Dallas area at 94.5 FM.

KSOF-FM

Owner: Clear Channel Media and Entertainment
Editorial: 83 E Shaw Ave, Ste 150, Fresno, California 93710. **T:** 1 559 230-4300
W: http://www.softrock989.com
Editorial Profile: KSOF-FM is a commercial station owned by Clear Channel Media and Entertainment. The format of the station is Lite Rock/Lite AC music. KSOF-FM broadcasts in the Fresno, CA area at 98.9 FM.

KSOK-AM

Owner: Cowley County Broadcasting
Editorial: 334 E Radio Ln, Arkansas City, Kansas 67005. **T:** 1 620 442-5400
E: ksok@ksokradio.com
W: http://www.ksokradio.com
Editorial Profile: KSOK-AM is a commercial station owned by Cowley County Broadcasting. The format of the station is classic country. KSOK-AM broadcasts to the Arkansas City, KS area at 1280 AM.

KSOK-FM

Owner: Cowley County Broadcasting
Editorial: 334 E Radio Ln, Arkansas City, Kansas 67005. **T:** 1 620 442-5400
E: ksok@ksokradio.com
W: http://www.ksokradio.com
Editorial Profile: KSOK-FM is a commercial station owned by Cowley County Broadcasting. The format of the station is contemporary country. KSOK-FM broadcasts to the Arkansas City, KS area at 95.9 FM.

KSOL-FM

Owner: Univision Communications Inc.

Editorial: 750 Battery St, Ste 200, San Francisco, California 94111.
T: 1 415 733-5765
W: http://estereosol989.univision.com
Editorial Profile: KSOL-FM is a commercial station owned by Univision Communications Inc. The format of the station is regional Mexican music and news. KSOL-FM broadcasts to the San Francisco area at 98.9.

KSOM-FM

Owner: Meredith Communications LLC
Editorial: 413 Chestnut St, Atlantic, Iowa 50022-1247. **T:** 1 712 243-6885
E: ksomnews@mchsi.com
W: http://www.965ksom.com
Editorial Profile: KSOM-FM is a commercial station owned by Meredith Communications LLC. The format of the station is country. KSOM-FM broadcasts to the Atlantic, IA area at 96.5 FM.

KSON-FM

Owner: Lincoln Financial Media
Editorial: 1615 Murray Canyon Rd Ste 710, San Diego, California 92108-4321.
T: 1 619 291-9797 **E:** ksonstudio@kson.com
W: http://www.kson.com
Editorial Profile: KSON-FM is a commercial station owned by Lincoln Financial Media. The format of the station is country music. KSON-FM broadcasts to the San Diego area at 97.3 FM.

KSOO-AM

Owner: Townsquare Media, Inc.
Editorial: 5100 S Tennis Ln, Sioux Falls, South Dakota 57108-2212. **T:** 1 605 339-1140
W: http://www.ksoo.com
Editorial Profile: KSOO-AM is a commercial station owned by Townsquare Media, Inc. The format of the station is sports, news and talk. KSOO-AM broadcasts to the Sioux Falls, SD area at 1140 AM.

KSOO-FM

Owner: Townsquare Media, Inc.
Editorial: 5100 S Tennis Ln, Sioux Falls, South Dakota 57108-2212. **T:** 1 605 339-1140
W: http://www.espn991.com
Editorial Profile: KSOO-FM is a commercial station owned by Townsquare Media, Inc. The format of the station is sports. KSOO-FM broadcasts to the Sioux Falls, ID area at 99.1 FM.

KSOP-AM

Owner: KSOP Inc.
Editorial: 1285 W 2320 S, West Valley City, Utah 84119-1448. **T:** 1 801 972-1043
W: http://www.cc1370.com
Editorial Profile: KSOP-AM is a commercial station owned by KSOP Inc. The format of the station is classic country. KSOP-AM broadcasts to the West Valley City, UT area at 1370 AM.

KSOP-FM

Owner: KSOP Inc.
Editorial: 1285 W 2320 S, West Valley City, Utah 84119. **T:** 1 801 972-1043
W: http://www.z104country.com
Editorial Profile: KSOP-FM is a commercial station owned by KSOP Inc. The format of the station is contemporary country. KSOP-FM broadcasts to the West Valley City, UT area at 104.3 FM.

KSOQ-FM

Owner: Lincoln Financial Media
Editorial: 1615 Murray Canyon Rd Ste 710, San Diego, California 92108-4321.
T: 1 619 291-9797 **W:** http://www.kson.com
Editorial Profile: KSOQ-FM is a commercial station owned by Lincoln Financial Media. The format of the station is country music. KSOQ-FM broadcasts to the San Diego area at 92.1 FM.

KSOR-FM

Owner: State of Oregon
Editorial: 1250 Siskiyou Blvd, Ashland, Oregon 97520-5001. **T:** 1 541 552-6301
E: jprinfo@sou.edu **W:** http://www.ijpr.org
Editorial Profile: KSOR-FM is a non commercial station owned by State of Oregon. The format of the station features classical music and news programming. KSOR-FM broadcasts to the Medford, OR area at a frequency of 90.5 FM.

KSOS-FM

Owner: Faith Communications Corp.
Editorial: 2201 S 6th St, Las Vegas, Nevada 89104-2962. **T:** 1 702 731-5452
E: info@sosradio.net
W: http://www.sosradio.net

Editorial Profile: KSOS-FM is a non-commerical station owned by Faith Communications Corp. The format of the station contemporary Christian. KSOS-FM broadcasts to the Las Vegas area at 90.5 FM.

KSOU-AM

Owner: Community First Broadcasting, LLC
Editorial: 128 20th St SE, Sioux Center, Iowa 51250. **T:** 1 712 722-1090
E: ksou@siouxcountyradio.com
W: http://siouxcountyradio.com
Editorial Profile: KSOU-AM is a commercial station owned by Community First Broadcasting, LLC. The format of the station is oldies music concentrating on the 1960s and 1970s. KSOU-AM broadcasts to the Sioux Center, IA area at a frequency of 1090 AM.

KSOU-FM

Owner: Community First Broadcasting, LLC
Editorial: 128 20th St SE, Sioux Center, Iowa 51250. **T:** 1 712 722-1090
E: ksou@siouxcountyradio.com
W: http://www.siouxcountyradio.com
Editorial Profile: KSOU-FM is a commercial station owned by Community First Broadcasting, LLC. The format of the station is adult contemporary. KSOU-FM broadcasts to the Sioux Center, IA area at 93.9 FM.

KSPA-AM

Owner: Astor Broadcast Group
Editorial: 8729 9th St, Ste 110, Rancho Cucamonga, California 91730-4312.
T: 1 909 483-1500
W: http://www.financialnewsandtalk.com
Editorial Profile: KSPA-AM is a commercial station owned by Astor Broadcast Group. The format of the station is business news and talk. KSPA-AM broadcasts to the North San Diego, CA and Orange County area at 1510 AM

KSPC-FM

Owner: Pomona College
Editorial: 340 N College Ave, Claremont, California 91711. **T:** 1 909 621-8157
E: news@kspc.org **W:** http://www.kspc.org
Editorial Profile: KSPC-FM is a non-commercial station owned by Pomona College. The format of the station is variety. KSPC-FM broadcasts to the Claremont, CA area at 88.7 FM.

KSPD-AM

Owner: Inspirational Family Radio
Editorial: 1440 S Weideman Ave, Boise, Idaho 83709. **T:** 1 208 377-3790
E: info@myfamilyradio.com
W: http://www.790kspd.com
Editorial Profile: KSPD-AM is a commercial station owned by Inspirational Family Radio. The format of the station is Christian talk programming. KSPD-AM broadcasts to the Boise, ID area at 790 AM.

KSPE-AM

Owner: Rincon Broadcasting
Editorial: 414 E Cota St, Santa Barbara, California 93101. **T:** 1 805 879-8300
W: http://santabarbara.lapreciosa.com
Editorial Profile: KSPE-AM is a commercial station owned by Rincon Broadcasting. The format of the station is Spanish oldies. KSPE-AM broadcasts to the Santa Barbara, CA area at 1490 AM.

KSPI-AM

Owner: Mahaffey Enterprises Inc.
Editorial: 408 E Thomas Ave, Stillwater, Oklahoma 74075-2648. **T:** 1 405 372-7800
E: stillwaterradio@coxinet.net
W: http://www.stillwaterradio.com
Editorial Profile: KSPI-AM is a commercial station owned by Mahaffey Enterprises Inc. The format of the station is sports talk. KSPI-AM broadcasts to the Stillwater, OK area at 780 AM.

KSPI-FM

Owner: Mahaffey Enterprises Inc.
Editorial: 408 E Thomas Ave, Stillwater, Oklahoma 74075-2648. **T:** 1 405 372-7800
E: stillwaterradio@coxinet.net
W: http://www.stillwaterradio.net
Editorial Profile: KSPI-FM is a commercial station owned by Mahaffey Enterprises Inc. The format fo the station is hot adult contemporary. KSPI-FM broadcasts to the Stillwater, Ok area at 93.7 FM.

KSPK-FM

Owner: Mainstreet Broadcasting Company Inc.
Editorial: 516 Main St, Walsenburg, Colorado 81089. **T:** 1 719 738-3636 **E:** info@kspk.com
W: http://www.kspk.com

Editorial Profile: KSPK-FM is a commercial station owned by Mainstreet Broadcasting Company Inc. The format of the station is country. KSPK-FM broadcasts to the Colorado Springs, CO area at 102.3 FM.

KSPL-FM
Owner: Moody Bible Institute
Editorial: 5408 S Freya St, Spokane, Washington 99223. **T:** 1 509 448-2555
E: kmbi@moody.edu
W: http://www.moodyradionorthwest.fm
Editorial Profile: KSPL-FM is a non-commercial station owned by Moody Bible Institute. The format of the station is religious programming. KSPL-FM broadcasts to the Kalispell, MT area at 90.9 FM.

KSPN-AM
Owner: Walt Disney Co.
Editorial: 800 W Olympic Blvd Ste A200, Los Angeles, California 90015-1375.
T: 1 213 284-7100
W: http://espn.go.com/los-angeles/radio/index
Editorial Profile: KSPN-AM is a commercial station owned by Walt Disney Co. The format of the station is sports. KSPN-AM broadcasts to the Los Angeles area at 710 AM.

KSPN-FM
Owner: NRC Broadcasting
Editorial: 402 Aspen Airport Business Ctr, Ste D, Aspen, Colorado 81611-3542.
T: 1 970 925-5776 **E:** kspnfm@gmail.com
W: http://www.kspnradio.com
Editorial Profile: KSPN-FM is a commercial station owned by NRC Broadcasting. The format of the station is adult album alternative. KSPN-FM broadcasts to the Aspen, CO area at 100.1 FM.

KSPO-FM
Owner: Liberty Broadcasting System, LLC
Editorial: 6019 S Crestline St, Spokane, Washington 99223-6823. **T:** 1 509 443-1000
E: acn@acn.cc **W:** http://ww.acn-network.com
Editorial Profile: KSPO-FM is a commercial station owned by Liberty Broadcasting System, LLC. The format of the station is religious. KSPO-FM broadcasts to the Spokane, WA area at 106.5 FM.

KSPQ-FM
Owner: Ozark Radio Network Inc.
Editorial: 983 E US Highway 160, West Plains, Missouri 65775. **T:** 1 417 256-1025
W: http://www.ozarkareanetwork.com
Editorial Profile: KSPQ-FM is a commercial station owned by Ozark Radio Network Inc. The format of the station is adult hits. KSPQ-FM broadcasts to the Springfield, MO area at 93.9 FM.

KSPT-AM
Owner: Blue Sky Broadcasting Inc.
Editorial: 327 S Marion Ave, Sandpoint, Idaho 83864. **T:** 1 208 263-2179
Editorial Profile: KSPT-AM is a commercial station owned by Blue Sky Broadcasting Inc. The format of the station is news, talk, and sports. KSPT-AM broadcasts to the Sandpoint, ID area at 1400 AM.

KSPW-FM
Owner: Journal Broadcast Group
Editorial: 2330 W Grand St, Springfield, Missouri 65802. **T:** 1 417 865-6614
W: http://www.power965jams.com
Editorial Profile: KSPW-FM is a commercial station owned by the Journal Broadcast Group. The format of the station is Top 40/ CHR. KSPW-FM broadcasts to Springfield, MO area at 96.5 FM.

KSPZ-AM
Owner: Sand Hill Media
Editorial: 854 Lindsay Blvd, Idaho Falls, Idaho 83402-1820. **T:** 1 208 522-1101
W: http://www.980thezone.com/index.php
Editorial Profile: KSPZ-AM is a commercial station owned by Sand Hill Media. KSPZ-AM's format is Sports. KSPZ-AM broadcasts to the Idaho Falls, ID area at 980 AM.

KSQL-FM
Owner: Univision Communications Inc.
Editorial: 750 Battery St, Ste 200, San Francisco, California 94111.
T: 1 415 733-5765
W: http://estereosol989.univision.com
Editorial Profile: KSQL-FM is a commercial station owned by Univision Communications Inc. The format of the station is regional Mexican. KSQL-FM broadcasts to the San Francisco area at 98.9 FM.

KSQM-FM
Owner: Sequim Community Broadcasting
Editorial: 577 W Washington St, Ste C, Sequim, Washington 98382-3269.
T: 1 360 681-0000 **E:** news@ksqmfm.com
W: http://www.ksqmfm.com
Editorial Profile: KSQM-FM is a non-commercial station owned by Sequim Community Broadcasting. The format of the station is oldies, adult standards and jazz. KSQM-FM broadcasts to the Sequim, WA area at 91.5 FM.

KSQN-FM
Owner: KLO Broadcasting Co.
Editorial: 515 S 700 E Ste 1C, Salt Lake City, Utah 84102-2802. **T:** 1 801 364-9836
W: http://www.sunny103fm.com
Editorial Profile: KSQN-FM is a commercial station owned by KLO Broadcasting Co. The format of the station is adult contemporary. KSQN-FM broadcasts to the Salt Lake City area at 103.1 FM.

KSQQ-FM
Owner: Morgan Hill Broadcasting
Editorial: 1629 Alum Rock Ave Ste 30, San Jose, California 95116-2418.
T: 1 408 258-9696 **E:** pr@ksqq.com
W: http://www.ksqq.com
Editorial Profile: KSQQ-FM is a commercial station owned by Morgan Hill Broadcasting. The format of the station is ethnic, featuring Portuguese programming. KSQQ-FM broadcasts to the San Jose, CA area at 96.1 FM.

KSQX-FM
Owner: CSSI Non-Profit Educational Broadcasting Corporation
Editorial: 1612 S Main St, Weatherford, Texas 76086. **T:** 1 817 341-8950
E: qxfmnews@yahoo.com
W: http://www.qxfm.com
Editorial Profile: KSQX-FM is a non-commercial station owned by CSSI Non-Profit Educational Broadcasting Corporation. The format of the station is oldies music. KSQX-FM broadcasts to the Dallas-Fort Worth area at 89.1 FM.

KSQY-FM
Owner: Haugo Broadcasting Inc.
Editorial: 3601 Canyon Lake Dr Ste 1, Rapid City, South Dakota 57702-3901.
T: 1 605 343-0888
W: http://www.951ksky.com
Editorial Profile: KSQY-FM is a commercial station owned by Haugo Broadcasting Inc. The format of the station is rock. KSQY-FM broadcasts to Rapid City, SD at 95.1 FM.

KSRA-AM
Owner: Salmon River Communications Inc.
Editorial: 315 Riverfront Dr, Salmon, Idaho 83467. **T:** 1 208 756-2218
E: ksraradio@ksrafm.com
W: http://ksrafm.com
Editorial Profile: KSRA-AM is a commercial station owned by Salmon River Communications Inc. The format of the station is adult contemporary and classic country. KSRA-AM broadcasts to the Salmon, ID area at 960 AM.

KSRA-FM
Owner: Salmon River Communications Inc.
Editorial: 315 Riverfront Dr, Salmon, Idaho 83467. **T:** 1 208 756-2218
E: ksraradio@ksrafm.com
W: http://ksrafm.com
Editorial Profile: KSRA-FM is a commercial radio station owned by Salmon River Communications Inc. The format of the station is classic country and adult contemporary music. KSRA-FM broadcasts to the Salmon, ID area at 92.7 FM.

KSRF-FM
Owner: Ohana Broadcasting, LLC
Editorial: 4271 Halenani St, Lihue, Hawaii 96766-1312. **T:** 1 808 245-9527
E: kong@kongradio.com
W: http://www.surf959fm.com
Editorial Profile: KSRF-FM is a commercial station owned by Ohana Broadcasting, LLC. The format of the station is Hawaiian music. KSRF-FM broadcasts to the Lihue, HI area at 95.9 FM.

KSRG-FM
Owner: State of Oregon
Editorial: 1250 Siskiyou Blvd, Ashland, Oregon 97520-5001. **T:** 1 541 552-6301
E: jprinfo@sou.edu **W:** http://www.ijpr.org
Editorial Profile: KSRG-FM is a commercial station owned by State of Oregon. The format of the station is news, jazz and classical music. KSRG-FM broadcasts to the Ashland, OR area at 88.3. FM.

KSRM-AM
Owner: KSRM Radio Inc.
Editorial: 40960 Kalifornsky Beach Rd, Kenai, Alaska 99611-6445. **T:** 1 907 283-8700
E: info@radiokenai.com
W: http://www.ksrm.com
Editorial Profile: KSRM-AM is a commercial station owned by KSRM Radio Inc. The format of the station is news and talk. KSRM-AM broadcasts to the Kenai, AK area at 920 AM.

KSRN-FM
Owner: Lazer Broadcasting Corp.
Editorial: 1465 Terminal Way, Reno, Nevada 89502. **T:** 1 775 324-4819
W: http://www.radiolazer.com
Editorial Profile: KSRN-FM is a commercial station owned by Lazer Broadcasting Corp. The format of the station is regional Mexican. KSRN-FM broadcasts to the Reno, NV area at 107.7 FM.

KSRO-AM
Owner: Sonoma Media Group
Editorial: 1410 Neotomas Ave, Santa Rosa, California 95405-7533. **T:** 1 707 543-0100
W: http://www.ksro.com
Editorial Profile: KSRO-AM is a commercial station owned Sonoma Media Group. The format of the station is news and talk. KSRO-AM broadcasts to the San Francisco area at 1350 AM.

KSRQ-FM
Owner: Northland Community & Technical College
Editorial: 1101 Highway 1 E, Thief River Falls, Minnesota 56701. **T:** 1 218 683-8588
E: ksrq@northlandcollege.edu
W: http://www.pioneer90.org
Editorial Profile: KSRQ-FM is a non-commercial station owned by Northland Community & Technical College. The format of the station is adult album alternative music. KSRQ-FM broadcasts to the Thief River Falls, MN area at 90.1 FM.

KSRR-AM
Owner: Morey(Robert)
Editorial: 1454 W Business Park Dr, Orem, Utah 84058-2223. **T:** 1 801 224-1400
W: http://kstarradio.wordpress.com
Editorial Profile: KSRR-AM is a commercial station owned by Robert Morey. The format of the station is variety. KSRR-AM broadcasts to the Orem, UT area at 1400 AM.

KSRS-FM
Owner: State of Oregon
Editorial: 1250 Siskiyou Blvd, Ashland, Oregon 97520-5001. **T:** 1 541 552-6301
E: jprinfo@sou.edu **W:** http://www.ijpr.org
Editorial Profile: KSRS-FM is a non-commercial station owned by State of Oregon. The format of the station is news programming and classical music. KSRS-FM broadcasts to the Roseburg, OR area at 91.5 FM.

KSRT-FM
Owner: Lazer Broadcasting Corp.
Editorial: 5510 Skylane Blvd, Ste 102, Santa Rosa, California 95403. **T:** 1 707 284-3069
Editorial Profile: KSRT-FM is a commercial station owned by Lazer Broadcasting Corp. The format of the station is regional Mexican. KSRT-FM broadcasts to the Rohnert Park, CA, area at 107.1 FM.

KSRV-AM
Owner: Idaho Co., Inc.
Editorial: 5660 E Franklin Rd, Suite 200, Nampa, Idaho 83687. **T:** 1 208 921-8430
Editorial Profile: KSRV-AM is a commercial station owned by Idaho Co., Inc (dba Armstrong Radio Group). The format of the station is oldies. KSRV-AM broadcasts to the Boise, ID area at 1380 AM.

KSRV-FM
Owner: Impact Radio
Editorial: 5660 E Franklin Rd, Ste 200, Nampa, Idaho 83687. **T:** 1 208 465-9966
E: bob@impactradiogroup.com
W: http://www.961bobfm.com
Editorial Profile: KSRV-FM is a commercial station owned by Impact Radio. The format of the station is adult hits. KSRV-FM broadcasts to the Boise, ID area at 96.1 FM.

KSRW-FM
Owner: Kessler(Benett)
Editorial: 1280 N Main St, Ste J, Bishop, California 93514-2473. **T:** 1 760 873-5329
W: http://news.sierrawave.net
Editorial Profile: KSRW-FM is a commercial station owned by Benett Kessler. The format of the station is adult contemporary. KSRW-FM broadcasts to the Bishop, CA area at 92.5 FM.

KSRZ-FM
Owner: Journal Broadcast Group
Editorial: 10714 Mockingbird Dr, Omaha, Nebraska 68127-1942. **T:** 1 402 592-5300
E: star@104star.com
W: http://www.104star.com
Editorial Profile: KSRZ-FM is a commercial station owned by Journal Broadcast Group. The format of the station is hot adult contemporary. KSRZ-FM broadcasts to the Omaha, NE area at 104.5 FM.

KSSA-FM
Owner: KBUF Partnership
Editorial: 1402 E Kansas Ave, Garden City, Kansas 67846-5806. **T:** 1 620 225-7161
E: kssaprod@wksradio.com
W: http://www.wksradio.com
Editorial Profile: KSSA-FM is a commercial station owned by KBUF Partnership. The format of the station is regional Mexican. KSSA-FM broadcasts to the Garden City, KS area at 105.9 FM.

KSSB-FM
Owner: Lazer Broadcasting Corp.
Editorial: 251 W Main St, Brawley, California 92227-2201. **T:** 1 760 344-5858
Editorial Profile: KSSB-FM is a commercial station owned by Lazer Broadcasting Corp. The format of the station is Spanish Classic Hits. KSSB-FM broadcasts to the Calipatria, CA area at a frequency of 100.9 FM.

KSSE-FM
Owner: Entravision Communications Corp.
Editorial: 5700 Wilshire Blvd, Ste 250, Los Angeles, California 90036. **T:** 1 323 900-6100
E: comments@superestrella.com
W: http://www.superestrella.com
Editorial Profile: KSSE-FM is a commercial station owned by Entravision Communications Corp. The format of the station is Hispanic Top 40/CHR. KSSE-FM broadcasts to the Los Angeles area at 107.1 FM.

KSSI-FM
Owner: Sound Enterprises
Editorial: 1621 N Downs St, Ridgecrest, California 93555-2429. **T:** 1 760 446-5774
E: kssirock@iwvisp.com
W: http://www.kssifm.com
Editorial Profile: KSSI-FM is a commercial station owned by Sound Enterprises. The format of the station is classic and album-oriented rock. KSSI-FM broadcasts to the Ridgecrest, CA area at 102.7 FM.

KSSK-AM
Owner: Clear Channel Media and Entertainment
Editorial: 650 Iwilei Rd Ste 400, Honolulu, Hawaii 96817-5319. **T:** 1 808 550-9200
W: http://www.ksskradio.com
Editorial Profile: KSSK-AM is a commercial station owned by Clear Channel Media and Entertainment. The format of the station is adult contemporary music and news. KSSK-AM broadcasts to the Honolulu area at 590 AM.

KSSK-FM
Owner: Clear Channel Media and Entertainment
Editorial: 650 Iwilei Rd Ste 400, Honolulu, Hawaii 96817-5319. **T:** 1 808 550-9200
W: http://www.ksskradio.com
Editorial Profile: KSSK-FM is a commercial station owned by Clear Channel Media and Entertainment. The format of the station is adult contemporary music and news. KSSK-FM broadcasts to the Honolulu area at 92.3 FM.

KSSL-FM
Owner: BWB
Editorial: 735 West Panhandle Avenue, Slaton, Texas 79364. **T:** 1 806 828-5775
W: http://www.ksslfm.com
Editorial Profile: KSSL-FM is a non-commercial station owned by BWB. The format of the station is classic country. KSSL-FM broadcasts to the Post, TX area at 107.3 FM.

KSSM-FM
Owner: Townsquare Media, Inc.
Editorial: 608 Moody Ln, Temple, Texas 76504-2952. **T:** 1 254 773-5252

W: http://www.mykiss1031.com
Editorial Profile: KSSM-FM is a commercial station owned by Townsquare Media, Inc. The format of the station is urban contemporary. KSSM-FM broadcasts to the Temple, TX area at 103.1 FM.

KSSN-FM
Owner: Clear Channel Media and Entertainment
Editorial: 10800 Colonel Glenn Rd, Little Rock, Arkansas 72204-8017.
T: 1 501 217-5000 **W:** http://www.kssn.com
Editorial Profile: KSSN-FM is a commercial station owned by Clear Channel Media and Entertainment. The format of the station is country music. KSSN-FM broadcasts to the Little Rock, AR area at 95.7 FM.

KSSR-AM
Owner: Esquibel LLC
Editorial: 2818 Historic Route 66, Santa Rosa, New Mexico 88435-2751. **T:** 1 575 472-5777
W: http://www.kssrradio.com
Editorial Profile: KSSR-AM is a commercial station owned by Esquibel LLC. The station's format is variety. KSSR-AM simulcasts the programming of KKJY-FM to the Albuquerque, NM area at 1340.

KSSR-FM
Owner: Esquibel LLC
Editorial: 2818 Historic Route 66, Santa Rosa, New Mexico 88435-2751. **T:** 1 575 472-5777
E: kssrradio@yahoo.com
W: http://www.kssrradio.com
Editorial Profile: KSSR-FM is a commercial station owned by Esquibel LLC. The format is variety. KSSR-FM airs to the Santa Rosa, NM area at 95.9 FM.

KSSS-FM
Owner: Clear Channel Media and Entertainment
Editorial: 3500 E Rosser Ave, Bismarck, North Dakota 58501-3376. **T:** 1 701 255-1234
E: rock101@clearchannel.com
W: http://www.1015.fm
Editorial Profile: KSSS-FM is a commercial station owned by Clear Channel Media and Entertainment. The format of the station is rock music. KSSS-FM broadcasts to the Bismarck, ND area at 101.5 FM.

KSST-AM
Owner: Hopkins County Broadcasting
Editorial: 717 Shannon Road, Sulphur Springs, Texas 75482. **T:** 1 903 885-3111
E: ksst1230@gmail.com
W: http://www.ksstradio.com
Editorial Profile: KSST-AM is a commercial station owned by Hopkins County Broadcasting. The format of the station is adult standards. KSST-AM broadcasts in the Sulphur Springs, TX area at 1230 AM.

KSSU-FM
Owner: Southeastern Oklahoma State University
Editorial: 1405 N 4th Ave, Pmb 4129, Durant, Oklahoma 74701. **T:** 1 580 745-2906
W: http://homepages.se.edu/kssu
Editorial Profile: KSSU-FM is a non-commercial college station owned by Southeastern Oklahoma State University. The format of the station is variety, featuring Top 40, alternative rock, hip-hop and more. KSSU-FM broadcasts to the Durant, OK area at a frequency of 91.9 FM.

KSSX-FM
Owner: Clear Channel Media and Entertainment
Editorial: 9660 Granite Ridge Dr, San Diego, California 92123-2688. **T:** 1 858 292-2000
W: http://www.957kissfm.com
Editorial Profile: KSSX-FM is a commercial station owned by Clear Channel Media and Entertainment. The station's format is rhythmic oldies. KSSX-FM broadcasts to the San Diego area at 95.7 FM.

KSSZ-FM
Owner: Zimmer Radio Group
Editorial: 3215 Lemone Industrial Blvd, Ste 200, Columbia, Missouri 65201.
T: 1 573 875-1099
W: http://www.theeagle939.com
Editorial Profile: KSSZ-FM is a commercial station owned by the Zimmer Radio Group. The format of the station is talk. KSSZ-FM broadcasts in the Columbia, MO area at 93.9 FM.

KSTA-AM
Owner: Wendlee Broadcasting
Editorial: 600 Fisk Ave, Brownwood, Texas 76801. **T:** 1 325 625-4188
E: ksta1000@gmail.com
W: http://www.colemanradio.com
Editorial Profile: KSTA-AM is a commercial station owned by Wendlee Broadcasting. The format of the station is classic country. KSTA-AM broadcasts in the Coleman, TX area area at 1000 AM.

KSTC-AM
Owner: Arnold Broadcasting Co Inc.
Editorial: 803 W Main St, Sterling, Colorado 80751-2813. **T:** 1 970 522-1607
E: knng@kci.net
W: http://www.kingfmonline.com
Editorial Profile: KSTC-AM is a commercial station owned by Arnold Broadcasting Co Inc. The format of the station is classic hits. KSTC-AM broadcasts to the Sterling, CO area at 1230 AM.

KSTE-AM
Owner: Clear Channel Media and Entertainment
Editorial: 1545 River Park Dr Ste 500, Sacramento, California 95815-4693.
T: 1 916 929-5325 **E:** news@kfbk.com
W: http://www.kste.com
Editorial Profile: KSTE-AM is a commercial station owned by Clear Channel Media and Entertainment. The format of the station is talk. KSTE-AM broadcasts to the Sacramento, CA area at 650 AM.

KSTK-FM
Owner: Wrangell Radio Group Inc.
Editorial: 202 St Michaels Street, Wrangell, Alaska 99929-9999. **T:** 1 907 874-2345
E: info@kstk.org **W:** http://www.kstk.org
Editorial Profile: KSTK-FM is a non-commercial station owned by the Wrangell Radio Group Inc. The format of the station is public radio programming. KSTK-FM broadcasts in the Wrangell, AK area at 101.7 FM.

KSTL-AM
Owner: Crawford Broadcasting Co.
Editorial: 10845 Olive Blvd, Ste 160, Saint Louis, Missouri 63141. **T:** 1 314 878-3600 121
W: http://www.shine690.com
Editorial Profile: KSTL-AM is a commercial station owned by Crawford Broadcasting Co. The format of the station is gospel. KSTL-AM broadcasts to the St. Louis area at 690 AM.

KSTM-FM
Owner: Simpson College
Editorial: 701 N C St, Indianola, Iowa 50125-1201. **T:** 1 515 961-1220
E: kstm@simpson.edu
W: http://kstmfm.wordpress.com
Editorial Profile: KSTM-FM is a non-commercial college station owned by Simpson College. The format of the station is college radio variety. KSTM-FM broadcasts to the Indianola, IA area at a frequency of 88.9 FM.

KSTN-AM
Owner: Knox, Inc.
Editorial: 2171 Ralph Ave, Stockton, California 95206-3625. **T:** 1 209 948-5786
Editorial Profile: KSTN-AM is a commercial station owned by Knox, Inc. The format of the station is contemporary country. KSTN-AM broadcasts to the Stockton, CA area at 1420 AM.

KSTN-FM
Owner: Educational Media Foundation
Editorial: 5700 W Oaks Blvd, Rocklin, California 95765-3719. **T:** 1 916 251-2142
W: http://www.klove.com

KSTP-AM
Owner: Hubbard Broadcasting Inc.
Editorial: 3415 University Ave SE, Minneapolis, Minnesota 55414-3327.
T: 1 651 647-1500 **W:** http://1500espn.com
Editorial Profile: KSTP-AM is a commercial station owned by Hubbard Broadcasting Inc. The format of the station is sports talk. KSTP-AM broadcasts to the Minneapolis area at 1500 AM.

KSTP-FM
Owner: Hubbard Broadcasting Inc.
Editorial: 3415 University Ave SE, Minneapolis, Minnesota 55414.
T: 1 651 642-4141 **W:** http://www.ks95.com
Editorial Profile: KSTP-FM is a commercial station owned by Hubbard Broadcasting Inc. The format of the station is hot adult contemporary music. KSTP-FM broadcasts in the Minneapolis area at 94.5 FM.

KSTR-FM
Owner: MBC Grand Broadcasting Inc.
Editorial: 1360 E Sherwood Dr, Grand Junction, Colorado 81501-7546.
T: 1 970 254-2100 **W:** http://961kstr.com
Editorial Profile: KSTR-FM is a commercial station owned by MBC Grand Broadcasting Inc. The format of the station is classic rock. KSTR-FM broadcasts to the Grand Junction, CO area at 96.1 FM.

KSTT-FM
Owner: El Dorado Broadcasting
Editorial: 51 Zaca Ln, Ste 100, San Luis Obispo, California 93401. **T:** 1 805 545-0101
W: http://www.kstt.com
Editorial Profile: KSTT-FM is a commercial station owned by El Dorado Broadcasting. The format of the station is adult contemporary. KSTT-FM broadcasts to the San Luis Obispo, CA area at 101.3 FM.

KSTV-AM
Owner: Cherry Creek Radio
Editorial: 3209 W Washington, Stephenville, Texas 76401. **T:** 1 254 968-2141
E: kstvnews@gmail.com
W: http://www.kstvfm.com
Editorial Profile: KSTV-AM is a commercial station owned by Cherry Creek Radio, LLC. The format for the station is regional Mexican music. KSTV-AM broadcasts to the Dallas-Fort Worth, TX, area at 1510 AM.

KSTV-FM
Owner: Cherry Creek Radio
Editorial: 3209 W Washington, Stephenville, Texas 76401. **T:** 1 254 968-2141
E: themighty93@gmail.com
W: http://www.kstvfm.com
Editorial Profile: KSTV-FM is a commercial station owned by Cherry Creek Radio. The format of the station is classic country music. KSTV-FM broadcasts to Stephenville, TX at 93.1 FM.

KSTX-FM
Owner: Texas Public Radio
Editorial: 8401 Datapoint Dr, Ste 800, San Antonio, Texas 78229-5903.
T: 1 210 614-8977 **E:** news@tpr.org
W: http://www.tpr.org
Editorial Profile: KSTX-FM is a non-commercial station owned by Texas Public Radio. The format of the station is news and talk. KSTX-FM broadcasts to the San Antonio area at 89.1 FM.

KSTY-FM
Owner: Royal Gorge Broadcasting LLC
Editorial: 1615 Central Ave, Canon City, Colorado 81212-8578. **T:** 1 719 275-7488
E: krlnnews@gmail.com
Editorial Profile: KSTY-FM is a commercial station owned by Royal Gorge Broadcasting LLC. The format of the station is contemporary country. KSTY-FM broadcasts to the Canon City, CO area at 104.5 FM.

KSTZ-FM
Owner: Saga Communications
Editorial: 1416 Locust St, Des Moines, Iowa 50309. **T:** 1 515 280-1350
W: http://www.star1025.com
Editorial Profile: KSTZ-FM is a commercial station owned by Saga Communications. The format of the station is hot adult contemporary music. KSTZ-FM broadcasts to the Des Moines, IA area at 102.5 FM.

KSUA-FM
Owner: University of Alaska Board of Regents
Editorial: 301 Constitution Hall U of Alaska, Fairbanks, Alaska 99775. **T:** 1 907 474-7054
E: ksuagm@gmail.com **W:** http://www.ksua.net
Editorial Profile: KSUA-FM is a non-commercial station owned by the University of Alaska Board of Regents. The format of the station is variety. KSUA-FM broadcasts to the Fairbanks, AK area at 91.5 FM.

KSUB-AM
Owner: Cherry Creek Radio
Editorial: 5 N Main St, Cedar City, Utah 84720. **T:** 1 435 867-8156
W: http://www.ksub590.com
Editorial Profile: KSUB-AM is a commercial station owned by Cherry Creek Radio. The format of the station is talk. KSUB-AM broadcasts in the Cedar City, UT area at 590 AM.

KSUE-AM
Owner: Sierra Broadcasting Corp.
Editorial: 3015 Johnstonville Rd, Susanville, California 96130-8739. **T:** 1 530 257-2121
W: http://www.sierradailynews.com/ksue.html
Editorial Profile: KSUE-AM is a commercial station owned by Sierra Broadcasting Corp. The format of the station is news, talk and sports. KSUE-AM broadcasts to the Susanville, CA area at 1240 AM.

KSUI-FM
Owner: University of Iowa
Editorial: 710 S Clinton St, Iowa City, Iowa 52240-4214. **T:** 1 319 335-5730
E: news@iowapublicradio.org
W: http://iowapublicradio.org
Editorial Profile: KSUI-FM is a non-commercial station owned by the University of Iowa. The format for the station is classical. KSUI-FM broadcasts to the Iowa City, IA area at 91.7 FM.

KSUM-AM
Owner: Woodward Broadcasting, Inc.
Editorial: 1371 W Lair Rd, Fairmont, Minnesota 56031. **T:** 1 507 235-5595
E: info@ksum.com **W:** http://www.ksum.com
Editorial Profile: KSUM-AM is a commercial station owned by Woodward Broadcasting, Inc. The format for the station is country music. KSUM-AM broadcasts to the Fairmont, MN area at 1370 AM.

KSUN-AM
Owner: Marques(Pedro)
Editorial: 714 N 3rd St, Phoenix, Arizona 85004. **T:** 1 602 252-0030
E: ksun@radiofiesta.net
W: http://www.radiofiesta.net
Editorial Profile: KSUN-AM is a commercial station owned by Pedro Marques. The format of the station is Regional Mexican. KSUN-AM broadcasts to the greater Phoenix, AZ area on 1400 AM.

KSUP-FM
Owner: Juneau Alaska Communications, LLC
Editorial: 3161 Channel Dr Ste 2, Juneau, Alaska 99801-7866. **T:** 1 907 506-3630
E: news@abcstations.com
W: http://www.mixfmalaska.com
Editorial Profile: KSUP-FM is a commercial station owned by Juneau Alaska Communications, LLC. The format of the station is hot adult contemporary/AAA. KSUP-FM broadcasts to the Juneau, AK area at 106.3 FM.

KSUT-FM
Owner: KUTE Inc.
Editorial: 123 Capote Dr, Ignacio, Colorado 81137. **T:** 1 970 563-0255
W: http://www.ksut.org
Editorial Profile: KSUT-FM is a commercial station owned by KUTE Inc. The format of the station is a mixed variety of music, news, and talk. KSUT-FM broadcasts to the Ignacio, CO area at 91.3 FM. The station only accepts PSAs through its Web site.

KSUU-FM
Owner: Southern Utah University
Editorial: 351 W Center St, Cedar City, Utah 84720-2470. **T:** 1 435 865-8224
E: ksuu@suu.edu
W: http://www.power91radio.com
Editorial Profile: KSUU-FM is a non-commercial college station owned by Southern Utah University. The format of the station is rock alternative. KSUU-FM broadcasts to the Salt Lake City area at 91.1 FM.

KSUX-FM
Owner: Powell Broadcasting Co.
Editorial: 2000 Indian Hills Dr, Sioux City, Iowa 51104. **T:** 1 712 239-2100
W: http://www.ksux.com
Editorial Profile: KSUX-FM is a commercial station owned by Powell Broadcasting Co. The format of the station is contemporary country music. KSUX-FM broadcasts in the Sioux City, IA area at 101.7 FM.

KSVA-AM
Owner: Lifetalk Radio Inc.
Editorial: 67 Sandia View Lane, Corrales, New Mexico 87048-8731. **T:** 1 505 890-0800
E: office@lifetalk.net **W:** http://www.lifetalk.net
Editorial Profile: KSVA-FM is a commercial station owned by Lifetalk Radio Inc. The format of the station is Christian talk and music. KSVA-FM broadcasts to the Albuquerque, NM area at 920 AM.

KSVC-AM
Owner: Mid-Utah Radio Inc.
Editorial: 390 E Annabella Rd, Richfield, Utah 84701-7084. **T:** 1 435 896-4456
E: news@midutahradio.com
W: http://midutahradio.com/ksvc

Editorial Profile: KSVC-AM is a commercial station owned by Mid-Utah Radio Inc. The format of the station is news, talk and sports. KSVC-AM broadcasts to the Salt Lake City area at 980 AM.

KSVE-AM

Owner: Entravision Communications Corp.
Editorial: 5426 N Mesa St, El Paso, Texas 79912. T: 1 915 581-1126
Editorial Profile: KSVE-AM is a commercial station owned by Entravision Communications Corp. The format of the station is Spanish romantica. KSVE-AM broadcasts to the El Paso, TX area at 1650 AM.

KSVN-AM

Owner: Azteca Broadcasting Corp.
Editorial: 4215 W 4000 S, West Haven, Utah 84401-9631. T: 1 801 430-7699
W: http://www.aztecautah.com/radio.php
Editorial Profile: KSVN-AM is a commercial station owned by Azteca Broadcasting Corp. The format of the station is regional Mexican. KSVN-AM broadcasts to the Salt Lake City area at 730 AM.

KSVP-AM

Owner: Pecos Valley Broadcasting Company
Editorial: 317 W Quay Ave, Artesia, New Mexico 88210-2158. T: 1 575 746-2751
W: http://www.pecosvalleybroadcasting.com
Editorial Profile: KSVP-AM is a commercial station owned by Pecos Valley Broadcasting Company. The format of the station is news, sports and talk. KSVP-AM broadcasts to the Artesia, NM area at 990 AM.

KSVR-FM

Owner: Skagit Valley College
Editorial: 2405 E College Way, Mount Vernon, Washington 98273. T: 1 360 416-7711
E: mail@ksvr.org **W:** http://www.ksvr.org
Editorial Profile: KSVR-FM is a non-commercial station owned by Skagit Valley College. The format of the station is Hispanic variety. KSVR-FM broadcasts to the Mount Vernon, WA area at 91.7 FM.

KSVY-FM

Owner: CommonBond Foundation
Editorial: 164 W Napa St, Sonoma, California 95476-6625. T: 1 707 933-0808
W: http://ksvy.org/
Editorial Profile: KSVY-FM is a non-commercial station owned by the CommonBond Foundation. The format of the station is variety programming. KSVY-FM broadcasts to Sonoma, CA at 91.3 FM.

KSWA-AM

Owner: MediaNews Group Inc.
Editorial: 620 Oak St, Graham, Texas 76450. T: 1 940 549-1330 **E:** news@kwkq-kswa.com
Editorial Profile: KSWA-AM is a commercial station owned by MediaNews Group Inc. The format of the station is classic country. KSWA-AM broadcasts to the Graham, TX area at 1330 AM.

KSWB-AM

Owner: KSWB Licensee LLC
Editorial: 615 Broadway St, Ste 222, Seaside, Oregon 97138-6846. T: 1 503 738-8668
W: http://www.840gold.com
Editorial Profile: KSWB-AM is a commercial station owned by KSWB Licensee LLC. The format of the station is oldies music. KSWB-AM broadcasts to Seaside, OR area at 840 AM.

KSWC-FM

Owner: Southwestern College (The)
Editorial: 100 College St, Winfield, Kansas 67156. T: 1 620 221-3300
E: jinx.radio@sckans.edu
W: http://www.sckans.edu/activities/radiotv-station
Editorial Profile: KSWC-FM is a non-commercial college station owned by Southwestern College (The). The format of the station is CHR. KSWC-FM broadcasts to the Winfield, KS area at a frequency of 100.3 FM.

KSWD-FM

Owner: Bonneville International Corp.
Editorial: 5900 Wilshire Blvd, Ste 1900, Los Angeles, California 90036. T: 1 323 634-1800
E: station@thesoundla.com
W: http://www.thesoundla.com
Editorial Profile: KSWD-FM is a commercial station owned by Bonneville International Corp. The format of the station is adult album alternative. KSWD-FM broadcasts to the Los Angeles area at 100.3 FM.

KSWF-FM

Owner: Clear Channel Media and Entertainment
Editorial: 1856 S Glenstone Ave, Springfield, Missouri 65804. T: 1 417 890-5555
E: studio@1005thewolf.com
W: http://www.1005thewolf.com
Editorial Profile: KSWF-FM is a commercial station owned by Clear Channel Media and Entertainment. The format of the station is country music. KSWF-FM broadcasts to the Springfield, MO area at 100.5 FM.

KSWG-FM

Owner: Circle S Broadcasting Co. Inc.
Editorial: 801 W Wickenburg Way, Wickenburg, Arizona 85390.
T: 1 602 254-6644
W: http://www.963realcountry.com
Editorial Profile: KSWG-FM is a commercial station owned by Circle S Broadcasting Co. Inc. The format of the station is country. KSWG-FM broadcasts to the Wickenburg, AZ area at 96.3 FM.

KSWH-FM

Owner: Henderson State University
Editorial: 1100 Henderson St, Arkadelphia, Arkansas 71999. T: 1 870 230-5185
E: mypulse999@gmail.com
W: http://stuwww.hsu.edu/kswh/blue3column/index.html
Editorial Profile: KSWH-FM is a non-commercial college station owned by Henderson State University. The format of the station is primarily rock and urban music programming. The station broadcasts to the Arkadelphia, AK area at a frequency of 99.9 FM.

KSWI-FM

Owner: Meredith Communications LLC
Editorial: 413 Chestnut St, Atlantic, Iowa 50022-1247. T: 1 712 243-6885
E: info@iowasuperstation.com
W: http://www.ks957online.com
Editorial Profile: KSWI-FM is a commercial station owned by Meredith Communications LLC. The format of the station is classic hits. KSWI-FM broadcasts to the Atlantic, IA area at 95.7 FM.

KSWM-AM

Owner: Falcon Broadcasting Inc.
Editorial: 126 S Jefferson Ave, Aurora, Missouri 65605-1635. T: 1 417 678-0416
W: http://www.kswm940.com
Editorial Profile: KSWM-AM is a commercial station owned by Falcon Broadcasting Inc. The format of the station is news and talk. KSWM-AM broadcasts to the Aurora, CO area at 940 AM.

KSWN-FM

Owner: GI Family Radio
Editorial: 106 W 8th St, McCook, Nebraska 69001. T: 1 308 345-1981
W: http://www.thezone939.com
Editorial Profile: KSWN-FM is a commercial station owned by GI Family Radio. The format of the station is Top 40/CHR. KSWN-FM broadcasts to the McCook, NE area at 93.9 FM.

KSWP-FM

Owner: Lufkin Educational Broadcasting Foundation
Editorial: 151 Holmes Rd, Lufkin, Texas 75904. T: 1 936 639-5673
E: 909kswp@kswp.org
W: http://www.kswp.org
Editorial Profile: KSWP-FM is a non-commercial station owned by Lufkin Educational Broadcasting Foundation. The format of the station is contemporary Christian. KSWP-FM broadcasts to the Lufkin, TX area at 90.9 FM.

KSWV-AM

Owner: Voz Broadcasting Co. Inc.(La)
Editorial: 102 Taos St, Santa Fe, New Mexico 87505-3832. T: 1 505 989-7441
Editorial Profile: KSWV-AM is a commercial station owned by Vox Broadcasting Co. Inc. The format of the station is Hispanic variety and regional Mexican. KSWV-AM broadcasts to the Sante Fe, NM area at 810 AM.

KSWW-FM

Owner: Jodesha Broadcasting Inc.
Editorial: 1520 Simpson Ave, Aberdeen, Washington 98520-4708. T: 1 360 533-3000
E: production@jodesha.com
W: http://www.sunny1021.com
Editorial Profile: KSWW-FM is a commercial station owned by Jodesha Broadcasting Inc. The format of the station is adult contemporary. KSWW-FM broadcasts to the Seattle area at 102.1 FM.

KSXY-FM

Owner: Commonwealth Broadcasting LLC
Editorial: 3565 Standish Ave, Santa Rosa, California 95407. T: 1 707 588-0707
W: http://www.allthehits.fm
Editorial Profile: KSXY-FM is a commercial station owned by Commonwealth Broadcasting LLC. The format of the station is Top 40/CHR. KSXY-FM broadcasts to the Sonoma County, CA area at 100.9 FM.

KSYB-AM

Owner: Amistad Communications
Editorial: 2897 Hilry Huckaby III Avenue, Shreveport, Louisiana 71107.
T: 1 318 222-2744 **E:** ksyb1300@yahoo.com
W: http://www.amistadradiogroup.com
Editorial Profile: KSYB-AM is a commercial station owned by Amistad Communications. The format of the station is gospel. KSYB-AM broadcasts to the Shreveport, LA area at 1300 AM.

KSYC-AM

Owner: State of Oregon
Editorial: 1250 Siskiyou Blvd, Ashland, Oregon 97520-5001. T: 1 541 552-6301
E: jprinfo@sou.edu **W:** http://www.jpr.org
Editorial Profile: KSYC-AM is a non-commercial station owned by State of Oregon. The format of the station is news and talk. KSYC-AM broadcasts to the Yreka, CA area at 1490 AM.

KSYC-FM

Owner: Buffalo Broadcasting
Editorial: 316 Lawrence Ln, Yreka, California 96097-3210. T: 1 530 842-4158
E: traffic@ksyc.net
W: http://www.ksyc1039.com
Editorial Profile: KSYC-FM is a commercial station owned and operated by Buffalo Broadcasting. The format of the station is classic and contemporary country. KSYC-FM broadcasts to the Yreka, CA area at 103.9 FM.

KSYE-FM

Owner: First Dallas Media Inc.
Editorial: 400 E Gladstone Ave, Frederick, Oklahoma 73542. T: 1 866 355-5793
E: news@kcbi.org **W:** http://www.ksye.org
Editorial Profile: KSYE-FM is a non-commercial station owned by the First Dallas Media Inc. The format of the station is religious music and talk. KSYE-FM broadcasts to the Frederick, OK area at 91.5 FM.

KSYL-AM

Owner: Cenla Broadcasting Inc.
Editorial: 1115 Texas Ave, Alexandria, Louisiana 71301. T: 1 318 445-1234
W: http://www.ksyl.com
Editorial Profile: KSYL-AM is a commercial station owned by Cenla Broadcasting Inc. The format of the station is news and talk. KSYL-AM broadcasts to the Alexandria, LA area at 970 AM.

KSYM-FM

Owner: San Antonio College
Editorial: 1300 San Pedro Ave, San Antonio, Texas 78212-4201. T: 1 210 486-5796
E: ksym@alamo.edu
W: http://www.alamo.edu/sac/ksym
Editorial Profile: KSYM-FM is a non-commercial station owned by San Antonio College. The format of the station is adult album alternative and rock alternative. KSYM-FM broadcasts to the San Antonio area at 90.1 FM. Send PSAs to psaksym@hotmail.com.

KSYN-FM

Owner: Zimmer Radio, Inc.
Editorial: 2702 E 32nd St, Joplin, Missouri 64804. T: 1 417 624-1025
W: http://www.ksyn925.com
Editorial Profile: KSYN-FM is a commercial station owned by the Zimmer Radio, Inc. The format of the station is Top 40/CHR music. KSYN-FM broadcasts in the Joplin, MO area at 92.5 FM.

KSYR-FM

Owner: Access.1 Communications Corp.
Editorial: 208 N Thomas Dr, Shreveport, Louisiana 71107-6520. T: 1 318 222-3122
W: http://www.ksyr.fm
Editorial Profile: KSYR-FM is a commercial station owned by Access.1 Communications Corp. The format of the station is regional Mexican music. KSYR-FM broadcasts to the Shreveport, LA area at 92.1 FM.

KSYV-FM

Owner: Knight Broadcasting Inc.
Editorial: 1101 S Broadway, Ste C, Santa Maria, California 93454-6660.
T: 1 805 688-5798 **W:** http://www.mix96.com
Editorial Profile: KSYV-FM is commercial station owned by Knight Broadcasting Inc. The format of the station is adult contemporary. KSYV-FM broadcasts to the Solvang, CA area at 96.7 FM.

KSYZ-FM

Owner: NRG Media LLC
Editorial: 3532 W Capital Ave, Grand Island, Nebraska 68803. T: 1 308 381-1077
W: http://www.1077theisland.com
Editorial Profile: KSYZ-FM is a commercial station owned by NRG Media LLC. The format of the station is adult hits. KSYZ-FM broadcasts to the Grand Island, NE area at 107.7 FM.

KSZL-AM

Owner: Dos Costas Communications Corp.
Editorial: 29000 Radio Rd, Barstow, California 92311-1648. T: 1 760 256-2121
E: doscostas@yahoo.com
Editorial Profile: KSZL-AM is a commercial station owned by Dos Costas Communications Corp. The format of the station is news and talk. KSZL-AM broadcasts to the Barstow, CA area at 1230 AM.

KSZR-FM

Owner: Cumulus Media Inc
Editorial: 575 W Roger Rd, Tucson, Arizona 85705. T: 1 520 887-1000
W: http://allthehitsi975.com
Editorial Profile: KSZR-FM is a commercial station owned by Cumulus Media Inc. The format of the station is Top 40/CHR. KSZR-FM broadcasts to the Tucson, AZ area at 97.5 FM.

KTAA-FM

Owner: Bott Broadcasting Co.
Editorial: 1 Academy Blvd, Big Sandy, Texas 75755-5509. T: 1 913 642-7770 2701
E: comments@bottradionetwork.com
W: http://www.bottradionetwork.com
Editorial Profile: KTAA-FM is a commercial owned by Bott Broadcasting Co. The format of the station is Christian talk. KTAA-FM broadcasts to the Tyler, TX area at 90.7 FM.

KTAC-FM

Owner: Tacoma Broadcasters Inc.
Editorial: 55 Alder St NW, Ste 3, Ephrata, Washington 98823-1696. T: 1 509 754-2000
E: ktac@ktac.com **W:** http://www.ktac.com
Editorial Profile: KTAC-FM is a commercial station owned by Tacoma Broadcasters Inc. The format of the station is religious. KTAC-FM broadcasts to the Ephrata, WA area at 93.9 FM.

KTAD-FM

Owner: Educational Communications of Colorado Springs Inc.
Editorial: 1665 Briargate Blvd Ste 100, Colorado Springs, Colorado 80920-3400. T: 1 719 593-0600 **E:** lightpraise@ktlf.org
W: http://www.ktlf.org
Editorial Profile: KTAD-FM is a non-commercial station owned by Educational Communications of Colorado Springs Inc. The format of the station is religious programming. KTAD-FM broadcasts to the Sterling, CO area on 89.9 FM.

KTAE-AM

Owner: M & M Broadcasters, Ltd.
Editorial: 901 E 1st St, Cameron, Texas 76520. T: 1 281 599-9800
W: http://www.ktae.net
Editorial Profile: KTAE-AM is a commercial station owned by M & M Broadcasters, Ltd. The format of the station is talk. KTAE-AM broadcasts to the Cameron, TX area at 1330 AM.

KTAG-FM

Owner: Legend Communications
Editorial: 1949 Mountain View Dr, Cody, Wyoming 82414. T: 1 307 578-5000
E: news@bhrnwy.com
W: http://www.mybighornbasin.com
Editorial Profile: KTAG-FM is a commercial station owned by Legend Communications. The format of the station is adult contemporary music. KTAG-FM broadcasts to the Cody, WY area at 97.9 FM.

KTAI-FM

Owner: Texas A & M University
Editorial: 700 University Blvd, Kingsville, Texas 78363. T: 1 361 593-3489
E: ktai@tamuk.edu

W: http://www.tamuk.edu/ktai
Editorial Profile: KTAI-FM is a non-commercial station owned by Texas A & M University. The format of the station is variety. KTAI-FM broadcasts to the Kingsville, TX area at 91.1 FM.

KTAK-FM
Owner: Edwards Communications LLC
Editorial: 603 E Pershing Ave, Riverton, Wyoming 82501. **T:** 1 307 856-2251
E: spots@rivertonradio.com
W: http://rivertonradio.com
Editorial Profile: KTAK-FM is a commercial station owned by Edwards Communications LLC. The format for the station is contemporary country. KTAK-FM broadcasts to the Riverton, WY area at 93.9 FM.

KTAL-FM
Owner: Access.1 Communications Corp.
Editorial: 208 N Thomas Dr, Shreveport, Louisiana 71107-6520. **T:** 1 318 222-3122
W: http://www.98rocks.fm
Editorial Profile: KTAL-FM is a commercial station owned by Access.1 Communications Corp. The format of the station is classic rock. KTAL-FM broadcasts to the Shreveport, LA area at 98.1 FM.

KTAM-AM
Owner: Brazos Valley Communications LLC
Editorial: 1240 E Villa Maria Rd, Bryan, Texas 77802. **T:** 1 979 776-1240
Editorial Profile: KTAM-AM is a commercial station owned by Brazos Valley Communications LLC. The format of the regional Mexican. KTAM-AM broadcasts to the Bryan, TX area at 1240 AM.

KTAN-AM
Owner: Cherry Creek Radio
Editorial: 2300 E Busby Dr, Sierra Vista, Arizona 85635. **T:** 1 520 458-4313
E: ktan@cherrycreekradio.com
Editorial Profile: KTAN-AM is a commercial station owned by Cherry Creek Radio. The format of the station is news and talk. KTAN-AM broadcasts in the Sierra Vista, NV area at 1420 AM.

KTAO-FM
Owner: Taos Communications Corp.
Editorial: #9 State Road 150, Taos, New Mexico 87571. **T:** 1 575 758-5826
E: ktao@newmex.com **W:** http://www.ktao.com
Editorial Profile: KTAO-FM is a commercial station owned by Taos Communications Corp. The format of the station is album adult alternative music. KTAO-FM broadcasts to the Albuquerque, NM area at 101.9 FM.

KTAP-AM
Owner: Emerald Wave Media
Editorial: 718 E Chapel St, Santa Maria, California 93454-4524. **T:** 1 805 928-4334
E: traffic@emeraldwavemedia.com
Editorial Profile: KTAP-AM is a commercial station owned by Emerald Wave Media. The format of the station is Hispanic programming and Regional Mexican music. KTAP-AM broadcasts to the Santa Maria, CA area at 1600 AM.

KTAR-AM
Owner: Bonneville International Corp.
Editorial: 7740 N 16th St Ste 200, Phoenix, Arizona 85020-4482. **T:** 1 602 274-6200
E: newsradio620@ktar.com
W: http://arizonasports.com
Editorial Profile: KTAR-AM is a commercial station owned by Bonneville International Corp. The format of the station is sports. KTAR-AM broadcasts in the Phoenix area at 620 AM.

KTAR-FM
Owner: Bonneville International Corp.
Editorial: 7740 N 16th St, Ste 200, Phoenix, Arizona 85020-4482. **T:** 1 602 274-6200
E: newsradio620@ktar.com
W: http://www.ktar.com
Editorial Profile: KTAR-FM is a commercial station owned by Bonneville International Corp. The format of the station is news and talk. KTAR-FM broadcasts to the Phoenix area at 92.3 FM.

KTAT-AM
Owner: Morey Broadcasting LLC
Editorial: 207 W Grand Ave, Frederick, Oklahoma 73542. **T:** 1 580 335-5923
E: kybe959@pldi.net

KTBA-AM
Owner: Western Indian Ministries

Editorial: Highway 264, 02C Hilltop Drive, HC33 Box 40, Gallup, New Mexico 87301. **T:** 1 505 371-5587 **E:** khac@westernindian.org
W: http://www.westernindian.net
Editorial Profile: KTBA-AM is a non-commercial station owned by Western Indian Ministries. The format of the station is contemporary Christian. KTBA-AM broadcasts to the Tuba City, AZ area on 104.9 FM.

KTBB-AM
Owner: Gleiser Communications LLC
Editorial: 1001 E Southeast Loop 323 Ste 455, Tyler, Texas 75701-9600.
T: 1 903 593-2519 **W:** http://www.ktbb.com
Editorial Profile: KTBB-AM is a commercial station owned by Gleiser Communications LLC. The format of the station is news, talk and sports. KTBB-AM broadcasts in the Tyler, TX area at 600 AM.

KTBB-FM
Owner: Gleiser Communications LLC
Editorial: 1001 E Southeast Loop 323, Tyler, Texas 75701-9664. **T:** 1 903 593-2519
E: news@ktbb.com **W:** http://www.ktbb.com
Editorial Profile: KTBB-FM is a commercial station owned by Gleiser Communications LLC. The format of the station is sports. KTBB-FM broadcasts to the Tyler, TX area at 92.1 FM.

KTBG-FM
Owner: Kansas City Public Television
Editorial: 125 E 31st St, Kansas City, Missouri 64108-3216. **T:** 1 816 756-3580
W: http://www.ktbg.fm
Editorial Profile: KTBG-FM is a non-commercial station owned by Kansas City Public Television. The format of the station is adult album alternative. KTBG-FM broadcasts to the Kansas City, MO area at 90.9 FM.

KTBH-FM
Owner: Resonate Hawaii, LLC
Editorial: 688 Kinoole St Ste 112, Hilo, Hawaii 96720-3868. **T:** 1 808 837-4104
E: kaoi@kaoi.net
Editorial Profile: KTBH-FM is a commercial station owned by Resonate Hawaii, LLC. The format of the station is alternative rock. KTBH-FM broadcasts to the Hilo, HI area at 102.1 FM.

KTBI-AM
Owner: Tacoma Broadcasters Inc.
Editorial: 55 Alder St NW, Ste 3, Ephrata, Washington 98823-1696. **T:** 1 509 754-2000
E: ktbi@ktbi.com **W:** http://www.ktbi.com
Editorial Profile: KTBI-AM is a commercial station owned by Tacoma Broadcasters Inc. The format of the station is religious. KTBI-AM broadcasts to the Ephrata, WA area at 810 AM.

KTBL-AM
Owner: Cumulus Media Inc
Editorial: 500 4th St NW, 5th Fl, Albuquerque, New Mexico 87102-5324. **T:** 1 505 767-6700
W: http://www.1050talk.com
Editorial Profile: KTBL-AM is a commercial station owned by Cumulus Media Inc. The format of the station is news and talk. KTBL-AM broadcasts to the Albuquerque, NM area at 1050 AM.

KTBQ-FM
Owner: Townsquare Media, LLC
Editorial: 1216 S 1st St, Lufkin, Texas 75901.
T: 1 936 639-4455 **W:** http://www.q1077.com
Editorial Profile: KTBQ-FM is a commercial station owned by Townsquare Media, LLC. The format of the station is classic rock. KTBQ-FM broadcasts to the Lufkin, TX area at 107.7 FM.

KTBR-AM
Owner: State of Oregon
Editorial: 1250 Siskiyou Blvd, Ashland, Oregon 97520-5001. **T:** 1 541 552-6301
E: jprinfo@sou.edu **W:** http://www.ijpr.org
Editorial Profile: KTBR-AM is a non-commercial station owned by State of Oregon. The format of the station is news and talk programming. KTBR-AM broadcasts to the Roseburg, OR area at 950 AM.

KTBT-FM
Owner: Clear Channel Media and Entertainment
Editorial: 2625 S Memorial Dr, Tulsa, Oklahoma 74129-2601. **T:** 1 918 388-5136
W: http://www.921thebeat.com
Editorial Profile: KTBT-FM is a commercial station owned by Clear Channel Media and Entertainment. The format of the station is Top 40/CHR. KTBT-FM broadcasts to the Tulsa, OK area at 92.1 FM.

KTBZ-AM
Owner: Clear Channel Media and Entertainment
Editorial: 2625 S Memorial Dr, Tulsa, Oklahoma 74129. **T:** 1 918 388-5100
W: http://www.1430thebuzz.com
Editorial Profile: KTBZ-AM is a commercial station owned by Clear Channel Media and Entertainment. The format of the station is sports. KTBZ-AM broadcasts to the Tulsa, OK area at 1430 AM.

KTBZ-FM
Owner: Clear Channel Media and Entertainment
Editorial: 2000 West Loop S, Ste 300, Houston, Texas 77027-3510.
T: 1 713 212-8000 **W:** http://www.thebuzz.com
Editorial Profile: KTBZ-FM is a commercial station owned by Clear Channel Media and Entertainment. The format of the station is rock alternative music. KTBZ-FM broadcasts to the Houston area at 94.5 FM.

KTCC-FM
Owner: Colby Community College
Editorial: 1255 S Range Ave, Colby, Kansas 67701. **T:** 1 785 462-3984

KTCH-FM
Owner: Wayne Radio Works
Editorial: 85592 574th Ave, Wayne, Nebraska 68787-7043. **T:** 1 402 375-3700
E: ktch@ktch.com
W: http://waynedailynews.com
Editorial Profile: KTCH-FM is a commercial station owned by Wayne Radio Works. The format of the station is adult hits. KTCH-FM broadcasts to the Wayne, NE area at 104.9 FM.

KTCK-AM
Owner: Cumulus Media Inc.
Editorial: 3090 Olive St Ste 400, Dallas, Texas 75219-7640. **T:** 1 214 526-2400
W: http://www.theticket.com
Editorial Profile: KTCK-AM is a commercial station owned by Cumulus Media Inc. The format of the station is sports. KTCK-AM broadcasts to the Dallas area at 1310 AM.

KTCL-FM
Owner: Clear Channel Media and Entertainment
Editorial: 4695 S Monaco St, Denver, Colorado 80237. **T:** 1 303 713-8000
W: http://www.area93.com
Editorial Profile: KTCL-FM is a commercial station owned by Clear Channel Media and Entertainment. The format of the station is rock alternative music. KTCL-FM broadcasts to the Denver area at 93.3.

KTCO-FM
Owner: Midwest Communications Inc.
Editorial: 715 E Central Entrance, Duluth, Minnesota 55811-5596. **T:** 1 218 722-4321
E: kdalnews@mwcradio.com
W: http://www.ktcofm.com
Editorial Profile: KTCO-FM is a commercial station owned by Midwest Communications Inc. The format of the station is country music. KTCO-FM broadcasts in the Duluth, MN area at 98.9 FM.

KTCR-AM
Owner: Ingstad (James D.)
Editorial: 830 N Columbia Center Blvd, Ste B2, Kennewick, Washington 99336.
T: 1 509 783-0783
Editorial Profile: KTCR-AM is a commercial station owned by Ingstad (James D.). The format of the station is classic country. KTCR-AM broadcasts to the Kennewick, WA area at 1390 AM.

KTCS-AM
Owner: Big Chief Broadcasting
Editorial: 5304 Highway 45 East, Fort Smith, Arkansas 72916. **T:** 1 479 646-6151
Editorial Profile: KTCS-AM is a commercial station owned by Big Chief Broadcasting. The format of the station is southern gospel music. KTCS-AM broadcasts to the Fort Smith, AR area at 1410 AM.

KTCS-FM
Owner: Big Chief Broadcasting
Editorial: 5304 Highway 45 East, Fort Smith, Arkansas 72916. **T:** 1 479 646-6151
W: http://www.ktcs.com
Editorial Profile: KTCS-FM is a commercial station owned by Big Chief Broadcasting. The format of the station is classic country. KTCS-FM broadcasts to the Fort Smith, AR area at 99.9 FM.

KTCT-AM
Owner: Cumulus Media Inc.
Editorial: 55 Hawthorne St Ste 1100, San Francisco, California 94105-3914.
T: 1 415 995-6800 **E:** sports@knbr.com
W: http://www.knbr.com
Editorial Profile: KTCT-AM is a commercial station owned by Cumulus Media Inc. The format of the station is sports. KTCT-AM broadcasts to the San Francisco area at 1050 AM.

KTCU-FM
Owner: Texas Christian University
Editorial: 2801 S University Dr, Fort Worth, Texas 76129-0001. **T:** 1 817 257-7631
E: ktcu@tcu.edu **W:** http://www.ktcu.net
Editorial Profile: KTCU-FM is a non-commercial station owned by Texas Christian University. The format of the station is variety. KTCU-FM broadcasts in the Dallas area at 88.7 FM.

KTCV-FM
Owner: Kennewick School District No. 17
Editorial: 5929 W Metaline Ave, Kennewick, Washington 99336-1494. **T:** 1 509 222-5670
Editorial Profile: KTCV-FM is a non-commercial station owned by Kennewick School District No. 17. The format of the station is rock alternative. KTCV-FM broadcasts to the Kennewick, WA area at 88.1 FM.

KTCX-FM
Owner: Cumulus Media Inc.
Editorial: 755 S 11th St, Ste 102, Beaumont, Texas 77701. **T:** 1 409 833-9421
W: http://www.ktcx.com
Editorial Profile: KTCX-FM is a commercial station owned by Cumulus Media Inc. The format of the station is urban contemporary music. KTCX-FM broadcasts to the Beaumont, TX area at 102.5 FM.

KTCZ-FM
Owner: Clear Channel Media and Entertainment
Editorial: 1600 Utica Ave S, Ste 400, Minneapolis, Minnesota 55416.
T: 1 952 417-3000 **W:** http://www.cities97.com
Editorial Profile: KTCZ-FM is a commercial station owned by Clear Channel Media and Entertainment. The format of the station is adult album alternative music. KTCZ-FM broadcasts in the Minneapolis area at 97.1 FM.

KTDD-AM
Owner: Clear Channel Media and Entertainment
Editorial: 2030 Iowa Ave, Riverside, California 92507-7415. **T:** 1 951 684-1991
W: http://www.foxsportsradio1350.com
Editorial Profile: KTDD-AM is a commercial station owned by Clear Channel Media and Entertainment. The format of the station is sports. KTDD-AM broadcasts to the Riverside, CA area at 1350 AM.

KTDE-FM
Owner: Four Rivers Broadcasting Inc.
Editorial: 38958 Cypress Way, Gualala, California 95445-8309. **T:** 1 707 884-1000
E: thetide@mcn.org **W:** http://www.ktde.com
Editorial Profile: KTDE-FM is a commercial station owned by Four Rivers Broadcasting Inc. The format of the station is classic rock music. KTDE-FM broadcasts to the Gualala, CA area at 100.5 FM.

KTDH-FM
Owner: Kanza Society Inc.
Editorial: 104 Sw 6Th Ave Suite B-4, Amarillo, Texas 79101-2324. **T:** 1 806 367-9088
W: http://www.hppr.org
Editorial Profile: KTDH-FM is a non-commercial station owned by Kanza Society Inc. The format of the station is news and classical. The station airs locally at 89.3 FM in the Dalhart, TX area.

KTDR-FM
Owner: Grande Broadcasting
Editorial: 307 E 8th St, Del Rio, Texas 78840-3823. **T:** 1 830 775-6291
W: http://www.thebestktdr.com
Editorial Profile: KTDR-FM is a commercial station owned by Grande Broadcasting. The format of the station is adult contemporary. KTDR-FM broadcasts to the Del Rio, TX and surrounding communities at 96.3 FM.

KTDV-FM
Owner: Marshalltown Education Plus, Inc.
Editorial: 1930 N Center Street Rd, Marshalltown, Iowa 50158-9772.

T: 1 641 752-4122 **E:** info@ktdvradio.com
W: http://www.ktdvradio.com
Editorial Profile: KTDV-FM is a non-commercial station owned by Marshalltown Education Plus, Inc. The format of the station is adult contemporary Christian music, news and sports. KTDV-FM broadcasts locally at 91.9 FM.

KTDY-FM
Owner: Townsquare Media, LLC
Editorial: 1749 Bertrand Dr, Lafayette, Louisiana 70506. **T:** 1 337 233-6000
W: http://www.999ktdy.com
Editorial Profile: KTDY-FM is a commercial station owned by Townsquare Media, LLC. The format of the station is adult contemporary music. KTDY-FM broadcasts to the Lafayette, LA area at 99.9 FM.

KTDZ-FM
Owner: Last Frontier Mediactive, LLC
Editorial: 819 1st Ave, Fairbanks, Alaska 99701-4449. **T:** 1 907 451-5910
W: http://www.mytedfm.com
Editorial Profile: KTDZ-FM is a commercial station owned by Last Frontier Mediactive, LLC. The format of the station is adult hits music. KTDZ-FM broadcasts locally to the Fairbanks, AK area at 98.1 FM.

KTEA-FM
Owner: KTEA-FM, LLC
Editorial: 2976 Burton Dr, Cambria, California 93428-4002. **T:** 1 805 924-0103
Editorial Profile: KTEA-FM is a commercial station owned by KTEA-FM, LLC. The format of the station is classic jazz. KTEA-FM broadcasts to the San Luis Obispo, CA area at a frequency of 103.5 FM.

KTEC-FM
Owner: Oregon Institute of Technology
Editorial: 3201 Campus Dr, Klamath Falls, Oregon 97601-8801. **T:** 1 541 885-1840
E: ktec895@gmail.com
W: http://www.oit.edu/ktec
Editorial Profile: KTEC-FM is a non-commercial college station owned by the Oregon Institute of Technology. The station features a free-form format with a variety of programming. KTEC-FM broadcasts to the Klamath Falls, OR area at a frequency of 89.5 FM.

KTEE-FM
Owner: Bicoastal Media LLC
Editorial: 320 Central Ave, Ste 519, Coos Bay, Oregon 97420. **T:** 1 541 267-2121
E: southcoastpsa@bicoastalmedia.com
W: http://www.ktee.com
Editorial Profile: KTEE-FM is a commercial station owned by Bicoastal Media LLC. The format of the station is adult contemporary music. KTEE-FM broadcasts to the Coos Bay, OR area at 94.9 FM.

KTEG-FM
Owner: Clear Channel Media and Entertainment
Editorial: 5411 Jefferson St NE, Ste 100, Albuquerque, New Mexico 87109.
T: 1 505 830-6400
W: http://www.1041theedge.com
Editorial Profile: KTEG-FM is a commercial station owned by Clear Channel Media and Entertainment. The format of the station is rock alternative music. KTEG-FM broadcasts to the Albuquerque, NM area at 104.1 FM.

KTEK-AM
Owner: BUSINESSRADIO HOUSTON LICENSEE LLC
Editorial: 6161 Savoy Dr, Houston, Texas 77036-3308. **T:** 1 713 260-6101
W: http://www.bizradio.com
Editorial Profile: KTEK-AM is a commercial station owned by BUSINESSRADIO HOUSTON LICENSEE LLC. The format of the station is business talk. KTEK-AM broadcasts to the Houston area at 1110 AM.

KTEL-AM
Owner: Capps Broadcast Group
Editorial: 13 1/2 E Main St Ste 202, Walla Walla, Washington 99362-1950.
T: 1 509 522-1383
W: http://www.1490ktel.com
Editorial Profile: KTEL-AM is a commercial station owned by Capps Broadcast Group. The format of the station is sports. KTEL-AM broadcasts to the Walla Walla, WA area at 1490 AM.

KTEM-AM
Owner: Townsquare Media, Inc.

Editorial: 608 Moody Ln, Temple, Texas 76504-2952. **T:** 1 254 773-5252
W: http://www.myktem.com
Editorial Profile: KTEM-AM is a commercial station owned by Townsquare Media, Inc. The format of the station is news and talk. KTEM-AM broadcasts to the Temple, TX area at 1400 AM.

KTEP-FM
Owner: University of Texas
Editorial: 500 W University Ave, Ste 203, El Paso, Texas 79968. **T:** 1 915 747-5152
E: ktep@utep.edu **W:** http://www.ktep.org
Editorial Profile: KTEP-FM is a non-commercial station owned by the University of Texas. The format of the station is classical, jazz and news. KTEP-FM broadcasts to the El Paso, TX area at 88.5 FM.

KTEX-FM
Owner: Clear Channel Media and Entertainment
Editorial: 901 E Pike Blvd, Weslaco, Texas 78596. **T:** 1 956 973-9202
W: http://www.ktex.net
Editorial Profile: KTEX-FM is a commercial station owned by Clear Channel Media and Entertainment. The format of the station is country music. KTEX-FM broadcasts to the Weslaco, TX area at 100.3 FM.

KTEZ-FM
Owner: Baldridge-Dumas Communications Inc.
Editorial: 605 San Antonio Ave, Many, Louisiana 71449. **T:** 1 318 256-0555
E: bdcproduction@bellsouth.net
W: http://www.bdcradio.com
Editorial Profile: KTEZ-FM is a commercial station owned by Baldridge-Dumas Communications Inc. The format for the station is adult contemporary. KTEZ-FM broadcasts to the Many, LA area at 99.9 FM.

KTFC-FM
Owner: Bott Radio Network
Editorial: 1534 Buchanan Ave, Sioux City, Iowa 51106. **T:** 1 712 252-4621
W: http://www.bottradionetwork.com
Editorial Profile: KTFC-FM is a non-commercial station owned by Bott Radio Network. The format of the station is Christian music and talk. KTFC-FM broadcasts to the Sioux City, IA area at 103.3 FM.

KTFG-FM
Owner: Bott Radio Network
Editorial: 1534 Buchanan Ave, Sioux City, Iowa 51106. **T:** 1 712 252-4621
Editorial Profile: KTFG-FM is a non-commercial station owned by Bott Radio Network. The format of the station is Christian and talk. KTFG-FM broadcasts to the Sioux Rapids, IA area at 102.9 FM.

KTFJ-AM
Owner: Swanson(Donald)
Editorial: 1534 Buchanan Ave, Sioux City, Iowa 51106. **T:** 1 712 252-4621
Editorial Profile: KTFJ-AM is a commercial radio station owned by Donald Swanson. The format of the station is religious. KTFJ-AM broadcasts to the Dakota City, IA area at 1250 AM.

KTFM-FM
Owner: Border Media Partners LLC
Editorial: 4050 Eisenhauer Rd, San Antonio, Texas 78218-3409. **T:** 1 210 654-5100
W: http://www.ktfm.com
Editorial Profile: KTFM-FM is a commercial station owned by Border Media Partners LLC. The format of the station is Top 40/CHR. KTFM-FM broadcasts to the San Antonio area at 94.1.

KTFS-AM
Owner: Texarkana Radio Center Licenses, LLC
Editorial: 615 Olive St, Texarkana, Texas 75501-5512. **T:** 1 903 793-4671
W: http://www.kcmc740.com
Editorial Profile: KTFS-AM is a commercial station owned by Texarkana Radio Center Licenses, LLC. The format of the station is sports. KTFS-AM broadcasts to the Texarkana, TX area at 740 AM.

KTFS-FM
Owner: Texarkana Radio Center Licenses, LLC
Editorial: 615 Olive St, Texarkana, Texas 75501-5512. **T:** 1 903 793-4671
Editorial Profile: KTFS-FM is a commercial station owned by Texarkana Radio Center Licenses, LLC. The format of the station is Talk. KTFS-FM broadcasts to the Texarkana, TX area at 107.1 FM.

KTFW-FM
Owner: LKCM Radio Group LP
Editorial: 115 W 3rd St, Fort Worth, Texas 76102. **T:** 1 817 332-0959
E: contactus@921hankfm.com
W: http://www.921hankfm.com
Editorial Profile: KTFW-FM is a commercial station owned by LKCM Radio Group LP. The format of the station is classic and contemporary country music. KTFW-FM broadcasts to the Fort Worth, TX area at 92.1 FM.

KTFX-FM
Owner: Payne Radio Group
Editorial: 401 W Broadway St Ste 301, Muskogee, Oklahoma 74401-6672.
T: 1 918 684-1022
E: production@okiecountry1017.com
W: http://www.okiecountry1017.com
Editorial Profile: KTFX-FM is a commercial station owned by Payne Radio Group. The format of the station is contemporary and classic country. KTFX-FM broadcasts to the Tulsa, OK area at 101.7 FM.

KTGA-FM
Owner: Toga Radio, LLC
Editorial: 106 North First Street, Saratoga, Wyoming 82331. **T:** 1 307 326-8642
E: bigfoot@bigfoot99.com
W: http://www.bigfoot99.com
Editorial Profile: KTGA-FM is a commercial station owned by Toga Radio, LLC. The format of the station is rock and country music. KTGA broadcasts to the Saratoga, WY area at 99.3 FM.

KTGE-AM
Owner: Wolfhouse Radio Group Inc.
Editorial: 548 E Alisal St, Salinas, California 93905. **T:** 1 831 757-1910
Editorial Profile: KTGE-AM is a commercial station owned by Wolfhouse Radio Group Inc. The format of the station is Hispanic oldies. KTGE-AM broadcasts in the Salinas, CA area at 1570 AM.

KTGG-AM
Owner: Spring Arbor University
Editorial: 106 E Main St, Spring Arbor, Michigan 49283. **T:** 1 517 750-6540
E: info@home.fm **W:** http://www.home.fm

KTGL-FM
Owner: Three Eagles Communications Co.
Editorial: 3800 Cornhusker Hwy, Lincoln, Nebraska 68504. **T:** 1 402 466-1234
W: http://ktgl.com
Editorial Profile: KTGL-FM is a commercial station owned by Three Eagles Communications Co. The format of the station is classic rock. KTGL-FM broadcasts to the Lincoln, NE area at 92.9 FM.

KTGO-AM
Owner: Gunn Enterprises, Inc.
Editorial: 301 2nd St SE, Tioga, North Dakota 58852-7302. **T:** 1 701 664-3322
E: news@bakkenbeacon.com
W: http://bakkenbeacon.com
Editorial Profile: KTGO-AM is a commercial station owned by Gunn Enterprises, Inc. The format of the station is talk. KTGO-AM broadcasts to the Tioga, ND area at 1090 AM.

KTGR-AM
Owner: Zimmer Radio Group
Editorial: 3215 Lemone Industrial Blvd, Ste 200, Columbia, Missouri 65201.
T: 1 573 875-1099 **E:** cosmoktgr@yahoo.com
W: http://www.ktgr.com
Editorial Profile: KTGR-AM is a commercial station owned by Zimmer Radio Group. The format of the station is sports. KTGR-AM broadcasts to the Columbia, MO area at 1580 AM.

KTGR-FM
Owner: Zimmer Radio Group
Editorial: 1805 Westminster Ave, Fulton, Missouri 65251. **T:** 1 573 642-3341
E: cosmoktgr@yahoo.com
W: http://www.ktgr.com
Editorial Profile: KTGR-FM is a commercial station owned by Zimmer Radio Group. The format of the station is sports. KTGR-FM broadcasts to the Jefferson City, MO area at 100.5 FM.

KTGS-FM
Owner: South Central Oklahoma Christian Broadcasting Inc.
Editorial: 20750 State Hwy 1W, Ada, Oklahoma 74820-5424. **T:** 1 580 332-0902
E: email@thegospelstation.com
W: http://www.thegospelstation.com

Editorial Profile: KTGS-FM is a non-commercial station owned by South Central Oklahoma Christian Broadcasting Inc. The format for the station is gospel. KTGS-FM broadcasts to the Ada, OK area at 88.3 FM.

KTGV-FM
Owner: Journal Broadcast Group
Editorial: 7280 E Rosewood St, Tucson, Arizona 85710-1350. **T:** 1 520 795-1490
W: http://www.1063thegroove.com
Editorial Profile: KTGV-FM is a commercial station owned by Journal Broadcast Group. The format of the station is rhythmic oldies. KTGV-FM broadcasts to the Tucson, AZ area at 106.3 FM.

KTGX-FM
Owner: Clear Channel Media and Entertainment
Editorial: 2625 S Memorial Dr, Tulsa, Oklahoma 74129-2601. **T:** 1 918 388-5100
W: http://www.1061thetwister.com
Editorial Profile: KTGX-FM is a commercial station owned by Clear Channel Media and Entertainment. The format of the station is contemporary country. KTGX-FM broadcasts to the Tulsa, OK area 106.1 FM.

KTHC-FM
Owner: Cherry Creek Radio
Editorial: 120 E Main St, Sidney, Montana 59270. **T:** 1 406 433-5090
E: power95@midrivers.com
W: http://www.kthcradio.com
Editorial Profile: KTHC-FM is a commercial station owned by Cherry Creek Radio. The format of the station is hot adult contemporary music. KTHC-FM broadcasts to the Sidney, MT area at 95.1 FM.

KTHE-AM
Owner: CarJim LLC
Editorial: 420 Arapahoe St, Thermopolis, Wyoming 82443-2708. **T:** 1 307 864-2119
Editorial Profile: KTHE-AM is a commercial station owned by CarJim LLC. The format of the station is adult contemporary music. KTHE-AM broadcasts to the Thermopolis, WY area at 1240 AM.

KTHH-AM
Owner: Bicoastal Media LLC
Editorial: 2840 Marion St SE, Albany, Oregon 97322. **T:** 1 541 926-8628
W: http://www.comedy990.com
Editorial Profile: KTHH-FM is a commercial station owned by Bicoastal Media LLC. The format of the station is comedy. KTHH-FM broadcasts to the Albany, OR area at 990 AM.

KTHI-FM
Owner: Journal Broadcast Group
Editorial: 5257 W Fairview Ave Ste 260, Boise, Idaho 83706-1766. **T:** 1 208 344-3511
W: http://www.khits.fm
Editorial Profile: KTHI-FM is a commercial station owned by Journal Broadcast Group. The format of the station is classic hits music. KTHI-FM broadcasts to the Boise, ID area at 107.1 FM.

KTHK-FM
Owner: Riverbend Communications LLC
Editorial: 400 W Sunnyside Rd, Idaho Falls, Idaho 83402-4613. **T:** 1 208 523-3722
W: http://www.1055thehawk.com
Editorial Profile: KTHK-FM is a commercial station owned by Riverbend Communications LLC. The format of the station is contemporary country. KTHK-FM broadcasts to the Blackfoot, ID area at 105.5 FM.

KTHN-FM
Owner: Cherry Creek Radio
Editorial: 116 Dalton Ave, La Junta, Colorado 81050. **T:** 1 719 384-5456 **E:** kblj@secom.net
Editorial Profile: KTHN-FM is a commercial station owned by Cherry Creek Radio. The format of the station is country. KTHN-FM broadcasts to the La Junta, CO area at 92.1 FM.

KTHO-AM
Owner: International Aerospace Solutions, Inc.
Editorial: 1001 Heavenly Village Way, South Lake Tahoe, California 96150-7068.
T: 1 530 543-0590 **E:** ktho590@yahoo.com
W: http://www.kthoradio.com
Editorial Profile: KTHO-AM is a commercial station owned by International Aerospace Solutions, Inc. The format of the station is classic rock and talk. KTHO-AM broadcasts to the Lake Tahoe, CA area at 590 AM.

KTHP-FM
Owner: Baldridge-Dumas Communications Inc.
Editorial: 605 San Antonio Ave, Many, Louisiana 71449-3018. **T:** 1 409 787-3399
W: http://www.bdcradio.com
Editorial Profile: KTHP-FM is a commercial station owned by Baldridge-Dumas Communications Inc. The format for the station is classic country. KTHP-FM broadcasts to the Many, LA area at 103.9 FM.

KTHQ-FM
Owner: Country Mountain Airwaves LLC
Editorial: 391 E Deuce Of Clubs Ste C, Show Low, Arizona 85901-4807. **T:** 1 928 532-1010
E: mail@qcountry92.com
W: http://www.qcountry92.com
Editorial Profile: KTHQ-FM is a commercial station owned by Country Mountain Airwaves LLC. The format of the station is contemporary country. KTHQ-FM broadcasts to the Show Low, AZ area at 92.5 FM.

KTHR-FM
Owner: Clear Channel Media and Entertainment
Editorial: 9323 E 37th St N, Wichita, Kansas 67226-2000. **T:** 1 316 494-6600
E: wichitanews@clearchannel.com
W: http://www.1073thebrew.com
Editorial Profile: KTHR-FM is a commercial station owned by Clear Channel Media and Entertainment. The format of the station is classic rock. KTHR-FM broadcasts in the Wichita, KS area at 107.3 FM.

KTHS-AM
Owner: Bunyard Broadcasting
Editorial: #1 Radio Drive, Berryville, Arkansas 72616. **T:** 1 870 423-2147
E: studio@kthsradio.com
W: http://www.kthsradio.com
Editorial Profile: KTHS-AM is a commercial station owned by Bunyard Broadcasting. The format of the station i classic hits. KTHS-AM broadcasts to the Berryville, AR at 1480 AM.

KTHS-FM
Owner: Bunyard Broadcasting
Editorial: #1 Radio Drive, Berryville, Arkansas 72616. **T:** 1 870 423-2147
E: studio@kthsradio.com
W: http://www.kthsradio.com
Editorial Profile: KTHS-FM is a commercial station owned by Bunyard Broadcasting. The format of the station is contemporary country. KTHS-FM broadcasts to the Berryville, AR area at 107.1 FM.

KTHT-FM
Owner: Cox Media Group, Inc.
Editorial: 1990 Post Oak Blvd, Houston, Texas 77056-3818. **T:** 1 713 963-1200
W: http://www.countrylegends971.com
Editorial Profile: KTHT-FM is a commercial station owned by Cox Media Group, Inc. The format of the station is country music. KTHT-FM broadcasts to the Houston area at 97.1 FM.

KTHU-FM
Owner: Results Radio Group
Editorial: 856 Manzanita Ct, Chico, California 95926. **T:** 1 530 342-2200
W: http://chicothunderheads.com
Editorial Profile: KTHU-FM is a commercial station owned by Results Radio Group. The format of the station is classic rock music. KTHU-FM broadcasts to the Chico, CA area at 100.7 FM.

KTHX-FM
Owner: Wilks Broadcast Group
Editorial: 300 E 2Nd St Ste 1400, Reno, Nevada 89501-1566. **T:** 1 775 333-0123
W: http://www.kthxfm.com
Editorial Profile: KTHX-FM is a commercial station owned by Wilks Broadcast Group. The format of the station is adult album alternative. KTHX-FM broadcasts to the Reno, NV area at 100.1 FM.

KTIA-FM
Owner: Truth Broadcasting
Editorial: 900 8th St, Boone, Iowa 50036-2920. **T:** 1 515 432-5014
W: http://www.wtru.com
Editorial Profile: KTIA-FM is a non-commercial station owned by the Truth Broadcasting. The format of the station is Christian and religious talk. KTIA-FM broadcasts to the Boone, IA area at 99.3 FM.

KTIB-AM
Owner: Townsquare Media, LLC
Editorial: 108 Green St, Thibodaux, Louisiana 70301-3048. **T:** 1 985 447-6404
E: ktib640am@gmail.com
W: http://www.ktib640.com
Editorial Profile: KTIB-AM is a commercial station owned by Townsquare Media, LLC. The format of the station is talk, sports and oldies music. KTIB-AM broadcasts to the Thibodaux, LA area at 640 AM.

KTIC-AM
Owner: Nebraska Rural Radio Association
Editorial: 1011 N Lincoln St, West Point, Nebraska 68788-1003. **T:** 1 402 372-5423
W: http://www.kticam.com
Editorial Profile: KTIC-AM is a commercial station owned by Nebraska Rural Radio Association. The format of the station is agriculture and classic country music. KTIC-AM broadcasts to the West Point, NE area at 840 AM.

KTIC-FM
Owner: Nebraska Rural Radio Association
Editorial: 1011 N Lincoln St, West Point, Nebraska 68788. **T:** 1 402 372-5423
W: http://www.1079thebull.com
Editorial Profile: KTIC-FM is a commercial station owned by Nebraska Rural Radio Association. The format of the station is contemporary country. KTIC-FM broadcasts in the West Point, NE area at 107.9 FM.

KTIE-AM
Owner: Salem Communications
Editorial: 701 N Brand Blvd Ste 550, Glendale, California 91203-1235. **T:** 1 818 956-5552
W: http://www.590ktie.com
Editorial Profile: KTIE-AM is a commercial station owned by Salem Communications. The format of the station is news and talk. KTIE-AM broadcasts to the San Bernadino, CA area at 590 AM.

KTIG-FM
Owner: Minnesota Christian Broadcasters Inc.
Editorial: 31287 Brunes St, Pequot Lakes, Minnesota 56472. **T:** 1 218 568-4422
E: info@mcbiradio.org **W:** http://www.ktig.org
Editorial Profile: KTIG-FM is a non-commercial station owned by Minnesota Christian Broadcasters Inc. The format of the station is contemporary Christian music. KTIG-FM broadcasts in the Minneapolis area at 102.7 FM.

KTIJ-FM
Owner: Fuchs Radio Inc.
Editorial: 1515 N Broadway, Hobart, Oklahoma 73651. **T:** 1 580 726-5656
E: thezone@itlnet.net
Editorial Profile: KTIJ-FM is a commercial station owned by Fuchs Radio Inc. The format of the station is Top 40/CHR music. KTIJ-FM broadcasts to the Hobart, OK area at 106.9 FM.

KTIK-AM
Owner: Cumulus Media Inc
Editorial: 1419 W Bannock St, Boise, Idaho 83702-5234. **T:** 1 208 336-3670
E: news@kboi.com **W:** http://www.ktik.com
Editorial Profile: KTIK-AM is a commercial station owned by Cumulus Media Inc. The format of the station is sports. KTIK-AM broadcasts to the Boise, ID area at 1350 AM.

KTIK-FM
Owner: Cumulus Media Inc
Editorial: 1419 W Bannock St, Boise, Idaho 83702-5234. **T:** 1 208 336-3670
W: http://www.ktik.com
Editorial Profile: KTIK-FM is a commercial station owned by Cumulus Media Inc. The format of the station is sports. KTIK-FM broadcasts to the Boise, ID area at 93.1 FM.

KTIL-AM
Owner: Alexandra Communications Inc.
Editorial: 170 3rd St, Tillamook, Oregon 97141-9489. **T:** 1 503 842-4422
W: http://www.ktil-radio.com
Editorial Profile: KTIL-AM is a commercial station owned byAlexandra Communications Inc. The format of the station is news and talk. KTIL-AM broadcasts to Tillamook, OR at 1590 AM.

KTIL-FM
Owner: Alexandra Communications Inc.
Editorial: 170 3rd St, Tillamook, Oregon 97141-9489. **T:** 1 503 842-4422
W: http://www.ktil-radio.com
Editorial Profile: KTIL-FM is a commercial station owned by Alexandra Communications Inc. The format of the station is Cumulus Media's "Real Country." KTIL-FM broadcasts to the Tillamook, OR area at 95.9 FM.

KTIP-AM
Owner: Mayberry Broadcasting Co.
Editorial: 1660 N Newcomb St, Porterville, California 93257. **T:** 1 559 784-1450
E: live@ktip.com **W:** http://www.ktip.com
Editorial Profile: KTIP-AM is a commercial station owned by Mayberry Broadcasting Co. The format of the station is news and talk. KTIP-AM broadcasts in the Porterville, CA area at 1450 AM.

KTIQ-AM
Owner: Mapleton Radio, LLC
Editorial: 1020 W Main St, Merced, California 95340-4521. **T:** 1 209 723-2192
Editorial Profile: KTIQ-AM is a commercial station owned by Mapleton Radio, LLC. The format of the station is Spanish Religious. KTIQ-AM broadcasts to the Merced, CA area at a frequency of 1660 AM.

KTIS-AM
Owner: Northwestern College
Editorial: 3003 Snelling Ave N, Saint Paul, Minnesota 55113-1501. **T:** 1 651 631-5000
E: mail@faithradionet.com
W: http://myfaithradio.com
Editorial Profile: KTIS-AM is a non-commercial station owned by Northwestern College. The format of the station is Christian talk. KTIS-AM broadcasts in the Minneapolis area at 900 AM.

KTIS-FM
Owner: Northwestern College
Editorial: 3003 Snelling Ave N, Saint Paul, Minnesota 55113-1599. **T:** 1 651 631-5000
E: feedback@ktis.fm **W:** http://www.ktis.fm
Editorial Profile: KTIS-FM is a non-commercial station owned by Northwestern College. The format of the station is contemporary Christian music. KTIS-FM broadcasts in the Minneapolis area at 98.5 FM.

KTIX-AM
Owner: Capps Broadcast Group
Editorial: 2003 NW 56th St, Pendleton, Oregon 97801. **T:** 1 541 276-1511
E: 1240ktix@cappsbroadcastgroup.com
W: http://www.1240ktix.com
Editorial Profile: KTIX-AM is a commercial station owned by Capps Broadcast Group. The format of the station is sports. KTIX-AM broadcasts to the Pendleton, OR area at 1240 AM.

KTJJ-FM
Owner: Goodradio.TV LLC
Editorial: 1401 KREI Blvd, Farmington, Missouri 63640-1058. **T:** 1 573 756-6476
W: http://www.mymoinfo.com
Editorial Profile: KTJJ-FM is a commercial station owned by Goodradio.TV LLC. The format of the station is country music. KTJJ-FM broadcasts to the Farmington, MO area at 98.5 FM.

KTJM-FM
Owner: Liberman Broadcasting Inc.
Editorial: 3000 Bering Dr, Houston, Texas 77057-5708. **T:** 1 713 315-3400
W: http://houston.laraza.fm
Editorial Profile: KTJM-FM is a commercial station owned by Liberman Broadcasting. The format of the station is regional Mexican music. KTJM-FM broadcasts to the Beaumont and Port Arthur, TX area at 98.5 FM.

KTJS-AM
Owner: Fuchs Radio Inc.
Editorial: 1515 N Broadway, Hobart, Oklahoma 73651. **T:** 1 580 726-5656
E: thezone@itlnet.net **W:** http://foxradiook.com
Editorial Profile: KTJS-AM is a commercial station owned by Fuchs Radio Inc. The format of the station is classic country. KTJS-AM broadcasts to the Hobart, OK area at 1420 AM.

KTKC-AM
Owner: Hunt(Leon)
Editorial: 226 N Main St, Springhill, Louisiana 71075-3248. **T:** 1 318 539-6000
E: spots@ktkcfm.com
Editorial Profile: KTKC-AM is a commercial station owned by Leon Hunt. The format of the station is news, talk and adult standards music. KTKC-AM broadcasts to the Springhill, LA area at 1460 AM.

KTKC-FM
Owner: Hunt(Leon)
Editorial: 226 N Main St, Springhill, Louisiana 71075-3248. **T:** 1 318 539-6000
E: spots@ktkcfm.com
W: http://www.ktkcfm.com
Editorial Profile: KTKC-FM is a commercial station owned by Leon Hunt. The format of the station is contemporary country. KTKC-FM broadcasts to the Shreveport, LA area at 92.9 FM.

KTKE-FM
Owner: Truckee Tahoe Radio, LLC
Editorial: 12030 Donner Pass Rd, Truckee, California 96161-0449. **T:** 1 530 587-9999
E: info@truckeetahoeradio.com
W: http://www.truckeetahoeradio.com
Editorial Profile: KTKE-FM is a commercial station owned by Truckee Tahoe Radio, LLC. The format of the station is adult album alternative. KTKE-FM broadcasts to the Truckee, CA area at 101.5 FM.

KTKK-AM
Owner: United Broadcasting Company, Inc.
Editorial: 10348 S Redwood Rd, South Jordan, Utah 84095. **T:** 1 801 253-4883
E: webmaster@k-talk.com
W: http://www.k-talk.com
Editorial Profile: KTKK-AM is a commercial station owned by United Broadcasting Company, Inc. The format of the station is talk and news. KTKK-AM broadcasts to the South Jordan, UT area at 630 AM.

KTKL-FM
Owner: Educational Media Foundation
Editorial: 7301 Broadway Ext, Ste 131, Oklahoma City, Oklahoma 73116-9038. **T:** 1 405 708-5683 **W:** http://www.klove.com
Editorial Profile: KTKL-FM is a non-commercial station owned by Educational Media Foundation. The format of the station is contemporary Christian. KTKL-FM broadcasts to the Stigler, OK at 88.5 FM.

KTKN-AM
Owner: Alaska Broadcast Communications Inc.
Editorial: 526 Stedman St, Ketchikan, Alaska 99901-6629. **T:** 1 907 225-2193
W: http://ketchikanradio.com
Editorial Profile: KTKN-AM is a commercial station owned by Alaska Broadcast Communications Inc. The format of the station is talk programming and hot adult contemporary music. KTKN-AM broadcasts to the Ketchikan, AK area at 930 AM.

KTKO-FM
Owner: Beeville Investments, LLC
Editorial: 2300 S Washington St, Beeville, Texas 78102. **T:** 1 361 358-1490
E: kicker106@yahoo.com
Editorial Profile: KTKO-FM is a commercial station owned by Beeville Investments, LLC. The format of the station is contemporary country. KTKO-FM broadcasts to the Beeville, TX area at 105.7 FM.

KTKR-AM
Owner: Clear Channel Media and Entertainment
Editorial: 6222 W Interstate 10, San Antonio, Texas 78201-2013. **T:** 1 210 736-9700
W: http://www.ticket760.com
Editorial Profile: KTKR-AM is a commercial station owned by Clear Channel Media and Entertainment. The format of the station is sports. KTKR-AM broadcasts to the San Antonio area at 760 AM.

KTKS-FM
Owner: Twin Lakes Communications
Editorial: 16875 Highway 52, Barnett, Missouri 65011. **T:** 1 573 378-5669
E: news@lakeradio.net
W: http://www.lakeradio.com
Editorial Profile: KTKS-FM is a commercial station owned by Twin Lakes Communications. The format of the station is classic country music. KTKS-FM broadcasts to the Versailles, MO area at 95.1 FM.

KTKT-AM
Owner: Lotus Communications Corp.
Editorial: 3871 N Commerce Dr, Tucson, Arizona 85705-2983. **T:** 1 520 407-4500
Editorial Profile: KTKT-AM is a commercial station owned by Lotus Communications. The format of the station is Hispanic sports talk. KTKT-AM broadcasts to the Tucson, AZ area on 990 AM.

KTKU-FM
Owner: Alaska Broadcast Communications Inc.
Editorial: 3161 Channel Dr, Juneau, Alaska 99801-7865. **T:** 1 907 586-3630
E: news@abcstations.com
W: http://www.taku105.com
Editorial Profile: KTKU-FM is a commercial station owned by Alaska Broadcast Communications Inc. The format for the

station is country. KTKU-FM broadcasts to the Juneau, AK area at 105.1 FM.

KTKX-FM
Owner: Cox Media Group, Inc.
Editorial: 8122 Datapoint Dr Ste 600, San Antonio, Texas 78229-3446.
T: 1 210 615-5400
W: http://www.x1067fm.com
Editorial Profile: KTKX-FM is a commercial station owned by Cox Media Group, Inc. The format for the station is top 40/CHR. KTKX-FM broadcasts to the San Antonio area at 106.7 FM.

KTKZ-AM
Owner: Salem Communications
Editorial: 1425 River Park Dr Ste 520, Sacramento, California 95815-4524.
T: 1 916 924-0710 **W:** http://www.ktkz.com
Editorial Profile: KTKZ-AM is a commercial station owned by Salem Communications. The format of the station is news and conservative talk. KTKZ-AM broadcasts in the Sacramento, CA area at 1380 AM.

KTLB-FM
Owner: Three Eagles Communications Co.
Editorial: 200 N 10th St, Fort Dodge, Iowa 50501-3925. **T:** 1 515 955-5656
E: k97@frontiernet.net
W: http://www.yourfortdodge.com/pages/15157335.php
Editorial Profile: KTLB-FM is a commercial station owned by Three Eagles Communications. The format of the station is classic hits. KTLB-FM broadcasts to the Fort Dodge, IA area at 105.9 FM.

KTLF-FM
Owner: Educational Communications of Colorado Springs Inc.
Editorial: 1665 Briargate Blvd, Colorado Springs, Colorado 80920-3447.
T: 1 800 428-1201 **E:** lightpraise@ktlf.org
W: http://www.ktlf.org
Editorial Profile: KTLF-FM is a non-commercial station owned by Educational Communications of Colorado Springs Inc. The format of the station is Christian music and religious talk. KTLF-FM broadcasts to the Colorado Springs, CO area at 90.5 FM.

KTLK-AM
Owner: Clear Channel Media and Entertainment
Editorial: 1600 Utica Ave S Ste 400, Minneapolis, Minnesota 55416-1480.
T: 1 952 417-3000
W: http://www.twincitiesnewstalk.com
Editorial Profile: KTLK-AM is a commercial station owned by Clear Channel Media and Entertainment. The format of the station is news/talk. KTLK-AM broadcasts to the Minneapolis area at 1130 AM.

KTLK-FM
Owner: Clear Channel Media and Entertainment
Editorial: 1600 Utica Ave S, Ste 400, Saint Louis Park, Minnesota 55416.
T: 1 952 417-3000 **W:** http://www.kfan.com
Editorial Profile: KTLK-FM is a commercial station owned by Clear Channel Media and Entertainment. The format for the station is sports. KTLK-FM broadcasts to the Minneapolis area at 100.3 FM.

KTLO-AM
Owner: Mountain Lakes Broadcasting Inc.
Editorial: 620 Highway 5 N, Mountain Home, Arkansas 72653. **T:** 1 870 425-3101
E: news@ktlo.com **W:** http://www.ktlo.com
Editorial Profile: KTLO-AM is a commercial station owned by Mountain Lakes Broadcasting Inc. The format is country music. KTLO-AM broadcasts to the Mountain Home, AR area at 1240 AM.

KTLO-FM
Owner: Mountain Lakes Broadcasting Inc.
Editorial: 620 Highway 5 N, Mountain Home, Arkansas 72653-3012. **T:** 1 870 425-3101
E: news@ktlo.com **W:** http://www.ktlo.com
Editorial Profile: KTLO-FM is a commercial station owned by Mountain Lakes Broadcasting Inc. The format of the station is adult standards. KTLO-FM broadcasts to the Mountain Home, AR area at 97.9 FM.

KTLQ-AM
Owner: Payne Radio Group
Editorial: 5686 S Muskogee Ave, Tahlequah, Oklahoma 74464-5487. **T:** 1 918 456-2511
E: info@ktlq1350.com
W: http://www.lakescountry1021.com/page.php?page_id=171
Editorial Profile: KTLQ-AM is a commercial station owned by Payne Radio Group. The format of the station is classic country. KTLQ-AM broadcasts to the Tahlequah, OK area at 1350 AM.

KTLR-AM
Owner: WPA Radio LLC
Editorial: 5101 S Shields Blvd Ste A, Oklahoma City, Oklahoma 73129-3217.
T: 1 405 601-6380 **W:** http://www.ktlr.com
Editorial Profile: KTLR-AM is a commercial station owned by WPA Radio LLC. The format of the station is talk. KTLR-AM broadcasts to the Oklahoma City area at 890 AM.

KTLS-FM
Owner: Chikasaw Nation
Editorial: 1019 N Broadway Ave, Ada, Oklahoma 74820-2036. **T:** 1 580 332-2211
E: score@cableone.net
W: http://www.ktlsradio.com
Editorial Profile: KTLS-FM is a commercial station owned by the Chikasaw Nation. The format of the station is classic rock. KTLS-FM broadcasts in the Ada, OK area at 106.5 FM.

KTLT-FM
Owner: Cumulus Media Inc.
Editorial: 2525 S Danville Dr, Abilene, Texas 79605-6414. **T:** 1 325 793-9700
W: http://www.the98x.com
Editorial Profile: KTLT-FM is a commercial station owned by Cumulus Media Inc. The format of the station is sports. KTLT-FM broadcasts in the Abilene, TX area at 98.1 FM.

KTLU-AM
Owner: Whitehead Enterprises, Inc.
Editorial: 618 N Main St, Rusk, Texas 75785.
T: 1 903 683-5305 **E:** kwrw@mediactr.com
Editorial Profile: KTLU-AM is a commercial station owned by Whitehead Enterprises, Inc. The format of the station is classic hits. KTLU-FM broadcasts to the Rusk, TX area at 1580 AM.

KTLV-AM
Owner: First Choice Broadcasting, Inc.
Editorial: 3336 SE 67th St, Oklahoma City, Oklahoma 73135-1701. **T:** 1 405 672-3886
E: ktlv1220@aol.com
W: http://www.ktlv1220.com
Editorial Profile: KTLV-AM is a commercial station owned by First Choice Broadcasting, Inc. The format of the station is gospel music and religious programming. KTLV-AM broadcasts to the Oklahoma City area at 1220 AM.

KTLW-FM
Owner: Life on the Way Communications, LLC
Editorial: 14820 Sherman Way, Van Nuys, California 91405-2233. **T:** 1 818 779-8484
E: info@lifeontheway.org
W: http://www.ktlw.org
Editorial Profile: KTLW-FM is a non-commercial station owned by Life on the Way Communications, LLC. The format is contemporary Christian. KTLW-FM broadcasts to the Los Angeles area at 88.9 FM.

KTLX-FM
Owner: TLC Education Corp.
Editorial: 2200 25th St, Columbus, Nebraska 68601-2612. **T:** 1 402 564-8548
E: ktlx@frontier.com
Editorial Profile: KTLX-FM is a non-commercial station owned by the TLC Educational Corp. The format of the station is contemporary Christian music and religious programming. KTLX-FM broadcasts to the Columbus, NE area at 91.3 FM.

KTLZ-FM
Owner: Worship Center of Kingsville(The)
Editorial: 929 N Padre Island Dr, Corpus Christi, Texas 78406-1911. **T:** 1 361 299-1992
Editorial Profile: KTLZ-FM is a commercial station owned by The Worship Center of Kingsville. The format of the station is Hispanic religious programming. KTLZ-FM broadcasts to the Cuero, TX area at 89.9 FM.

KTMB-FM
Owner: Ohana Media Group
Editorial: 833 Gambell St, Anchorage, Alaska 99501-3756. **T:** 1 907 344-4045
W: http://www.1021thepeak.com
Editorial Profile: KTMB-FM is a commercial station owned by Ohana Media Group. The format of the station is oldies. KTMB-FM broadcasts to the Anchorage, AK area at 102.1 FM.

KTMC-AM
Owner: Southeastern Oklahoma Radio, LLC
Editorial: 1801 E Electric Ave, McAlester, Oklahoma 74501-3824. **T:** 1 918 426-1050
E: info@mcalesterradio.com
W: http://www.mcalesterradio.com
Editorial Profile: KTMC-AM is a commercial station owned by Southeastern Oklahoma Radio, LLC. The format of the station is adult standards. KTMC-AM broadcasts to the McAlester, OK area at 1400 AM.

KTMC-FM
Owner: Southeastern Oklahoma Radio, LLC
Editorial: 1801 E Electric Ave, McAlester, Oklahoma 74501-3824. **T:** 1 918 426-1050
E: info@mcalesterradio.com
W: http://www.mcalesterradio.com
Editorial Profile: KTMC-FM is a commercial station owned by Southeastern Oklahoma Radio, LLC. The format of the station is classic rock music. KTMC-FM broadcasts to the McAlester, OK area at 105.1 FM.

KTMG-FM
Owner: Guyann Corp.
Editorial: 116 S Alto St, Prescott, Arizona 86303-3604. **T:** 1 928 445-6880
W: http://www.magic991.com
Editorial Profile: KTMG-FM is a commercial station owned by Guyann Corp. The format of the station is Hot AC. KTMG-FM broadcasts to the Prescott, AZ area at 99.1 FM.

KTMM-AM
Owner: MBC Grand Broadcasting Inc.
Editorial: 1360 E Sherwood Dr, Grand Junction, Colorado 81501. **T:** 1 970 254-2100
Editorial Profile: KTMM-AM is a commercial station owned by MBC Grand Broadcasting Inc. The format of the station is sports talk. KTMM-AM broadcasts to the Grand Junction, CO area at 1340 AM.

KTMO-FM
Owner: Pollack Broadcasting Co.
Editorial: 1303 Southwest Drive, Kennett, Missouri 63857. **T:** 1 573 888-4616
W: http://www.ktmoradio.com
Editorial Profile: KTMO-FM is a commercial station owned by Pollack Broadcasting Co. The format of the station is contemporary country music. KTMO-FM broadcasts to the Kennett, MO, area at 106.5 FM.

KTMP-AM
Owner: Creek Broadcasting Corp.
Editorial: 260 N Main St, Heber City, Utah 84032. **T:** 1 435 657-1340
E: ktmp1340am@gmail.com
W: http://www.ktmpradio.com
Editorial Profile: KTMP-AM is a commercial station owned by Creek Broadcasting Corp. The format for the station is classic country. KTMP-AM broadcasts to the Heber City, UT, area at 1340 AM.

KTMQ-FM
Owner: Clear Channel Media and Entertainment
Editorial: 27349 Jefferson Ave, Ste 116, Temecula, California 92590. **T:** 1 951 296-9050
W: http://www.q1033.com
Editorial Profile: KTMQ-FM is a commercial station owned by Clear Channel Media and Entertainment. The format of the station is rock. KTMQ-FM broadcasts to the Temecula, CA area at 103.3 FM.

KTMS-AM
Owner: Rincon Broadcasting
Editorial: 414 E Cota St, Santa Barbara, California 93101. **T:** 1 805 879-8300
W: http://ktms.com
Editorial Profile: KTMS-AM is a commercial station owned by Rincon Broadcasting. The format of the station is news and talk. KTMS-AM broadcasts to the Santa, Barbara, CA, area at 990 AM.

KTMT-AM
Owner: Mapleton Radio, LLC
Editorial: 1438 Rossanley Dr, Medford, Oregon 97501-1751. **T:** 1 541 779-1550
W: http://www.espn580.com
Editorial Profile: KTMT-AM is a commercial station owned by Mapleton Radio, LLC. The format of the station is sports/talk. KTMT-AM broadcasts to the Medford, OR area at 580 AM.

KTMT-FM
Owner: Mapleton Radio, LLC
Editorial: 1438 Rossanley Dr, Medford, Oregon 97501-1751. **T:** 1 541 779-1550
E: mikefm@radiomedford.com
Editorial Profile: KTMT-FM is a commercial station owned by Mapleton Radio, LLC. The format of the station is Top 40/CHR. KTMT-FM broadcasts to the Medford, OR area at 93.7 FM.

KTMX-FM
Owner: MWB Broadcasting LLC
Editorial: 1309 Road 11, York, Nebraska 68467. **T:** 1 402 362-4433
E: ktmx@ktmxfm.com
W: http://www.ktmxfm.com
Editorial Profile: KTMX-FM is a commercial station owned by MWB Broadcasting LLC. The format of the station is adult contemporary music. KTMX-FM broadcasts to the York, NE area at 104.9 FM.

KTMY-FM
Owner: Hubbard Broadcasting Inc.
Editorial: 3415 University Ave SE, Minneapolis, Minnesota 55414.
T: 1 651 642-4107
W: http://www.mytalk1071.com
Editorial Profile: KTMY-FM is a commercial station owned by Hubbard Broadcasting Inc. The format of the station is talk. KTMY-FM broadcasts in the Minneapolis area at 107.1 FM.

KTNA-FM
Owner: Talkeetna Community Radio Inc
Editorial: Second Street, Talkeetna, Alaska 99676. **T:** 1 907 733-1700 **E:** info@ktna.org
W: http://www.ktna.org
Editorial Profile: KTNA-FM is a non-commercial station owned by Talkeetna Community Radio Inc. The format of the station is variety. KTNA-FM broadcasts to the Anchorage, AK area at 88.9 FM.

KTNC-AM
Owner: KNZA, Inc.
Editorial: 1602 Stone St, Falls City, Nebraska 68355-2663. **T:** 1 402 245-2453
E: knza@rainbowtel.net
Editorial Profile: KTNC-AM is a commercial station owned by KNZA, Inc. The format of the station is oldies. KTNC-AM broadcasts to the Falls City, NE area at 1230 AM.

KTNE-FM
Owner: Nebraska Educational Telecommunications Commission
Editorial: 1800 N 33rd St, Lincoln, Nebraska 68503. **T:** 1 402 472-6141
E: radio@netnebraska.org
W: http://netnebraska.org
Editorial Profile: KTNE-FM is a non-commercial station owned by Nebraska Educational Telecommunications Commission. The format of the station is news and classical music. KTNE-FM broadcasts to the Alliance, NE area at 91.1 FM.

KTNF-AM
Owner: Lawson (Chad)
Editorial: 11320 Valley View Rd, Eden Prairie, Minnesota 55344-3613. **T:** 1 952 946-8885
W: http://www.am950radio.com
Editorial Profile: KTNF-AM is a commercial station owned and operated by Lawson (Chad). The format of the station is talk. KTNF-AM broadcasts to the Eden Prairie, MN area at 950 AM.

KTNK-AM
Owner: Knight Broadcasting Inc.
Editorial: 716 E Chapel St, Santa Maria, California 93454-4524. **T:** 1 805 922-7727
E: 1440@knightbroadcasting.com
W: http://www.am1440.com
Editorial Profile: KTNK-AM is a commercial station owned by Knight Broadcasting Inc. The format of the station is news and talk. KTNK-AM broadcasts to the Santa Maria, CA area at 1410 AM.

KTNM-AM
Owner: Majestic Communications
Editorial: 902 Date St, Tucumcari, New Mexico 88401-4335. **T:** 1 575 461-0522
E: ktnmkqay@yahoo.com
Editorial Profile: KTNM-AM is a commercial station owned by Majestic Communications. The format of the station is classic country. KTNM-AM broadcasts to the Tucumcari, NM area at 1400 AM.

KTNN-AM
Owner: Navajo Nation
Editorial: Navajo Shopping Center, Window Rock, Arizona 86515. **T:** 1 928 871-2582
E: webmaster@ktnnonline.com
W: http://www.ktnnonline.com
Editorial Profile: KTNN-AM is a commercial station owned by Navajo Nation. The format of

the station is country music, and Native American music. KTNN-AM broadcasts to the Albuquerque, NM area at 660 AM.

KTNO-AM
Owner: Mortenson Broadcasting Co.
Editorial: 5787 S Hampton Rd, Ste 340, Dallas, Texas 75232. **T:** 1 214 330-5866
W: http://www.ktnoam.com
Editorial Profile: KTNO-AM is a commercial station owned by Mortenson Broadcasting Co. The format of the station is Spanish Contemporary Christian music. KTNO-AM broadcasts to the Dallas area at 1440 AM.

KTNQ-AM
Owner: Univision Communications Inc.
Editorial: 655 N Central Ave, Glendale, California 91203-1422. **T:** 1 818 500-4500
W: http://univisionamerica.com
Editorial Profile: KTNQ-AM is a commercial station owned by Univision Communications. The format for the station is Spanish news and talk. KTNQ-AM broadcasts to the Los Angeles area at 1020 AM.

KTNR-FM
Owner: Multimedios Radio Ola
Editorial: 2702 Pine St, Laredo, Texas 78046.
T: 1 956 726-4738 **W:** http://radiolafm.com
Editorial Profile: KTNR-FM is a non-commercial station owned by Multimedios Radio Ola. The format for the station is Hispanic Christian programming. KTNR-FM broadcasts to the Kennedy, TX area at 92.1 FM.

KTNS-AM
Owner: Casa Media Partners, LLC
Editorial: 40356 Oak Park Way, Oakhurst, California 93644-8872. **T:** 1 559 683-1031
Editorial Profile: KTNS-AM is a commercial station owned by Casa Media Partners, LLC. The format of the station is regional Mexican. KTNS-AM broadcasts to the Oakhurst, CA area at 1060 AM.

KTNT-FM
Owner: Payne Radio Group
Editorial: Highway 69 & Texanna Rd, Eufaula, Oklahoma 74432. **T:** 1 918 689-3663
E: kfox_1025@live.com
W: http://www.kfoxradio.com
Editorial Profile: KTNT-FM is a commercial station owned by Payne Radio Group. The format of the station is contemporary country. KTNT-FM broadcasts to the Eufaula, OK area at 102.5 FM.

KTNX-FM
Owner: Dockins Broadcast Group
Editorial: 235 Business Hh, Piedmont, Missouri 63957-9410. **T:** 1 573 223-4518
Editorial Profile: KTNX-FM is a commercial station owned by Dockins Broadcast Group. The format of the station is adult contemporary. KTNX-FM broadcasts to the Farmington, MO area at 103.9 FM.

KTNY-FM
Owner: Lincoln County Broadcasters Inc.
Editorial: 251 W Cedar St, Libby, Montana 59923. **T:** 1 406 293-6234
E: klcb@frontiernet.net
Editorial Profile: KTNY-FM is a commercial station owned by Lincoln County Broadcasters Inc. The format of the station is Adult hits music. KTNY-FM broadcasts to the Libby, MT area at 101.7 FM.

KTNZ-AM
Owner: Tejas Broadcasting
Editorial: 3639 Wolflin Ave, Amarillo, Texas 79102-2119. **T:** 1 806 355-1044
Editorial Profile: KTNZ-AM is a commercial station owned by Tejas Broadcasting. The format of the station is Sports. KTNZ-AM broadcasts to Amarillo, TX at 1010 AM.

KTOB-AM
Owner: California Broadcasting Company, LLC
Editorial: 965 Stony Point Rd, Santa Rosa, California 95407-7129. **T:** 1 707 974-2834
Editorial Profile: KTOB-AM is a commercial station owned by California Broadcasting Company, LLC. The format of the station is Regional Mexican music. KTOB-AM broadcasts to the Petaluma, CA area at 1490 AM.

KTOE-AM
Owner: Radio Mankato
Editorial: 59346 Madison Ave, Mankato, Minnesota 56001-8518. **T:** 1 507 345-4537
E: news@ktoe.com
W: http://www.katoinfo.com
Editorial Profile: KTOE-AM is a commercial station owned by Radio Mankato. The format for the station is news talk and sports. KTOE-AM broadcasts to the Mankato, MN area at 1420 AM.

KTOH-FM
Owner: Hochman Hawaii One, Inc.
Editorial: 4334 Rice St, Ste. 206, Lihue, Hawaii 96766-1810. **T:** 1 808 246-4444
E: ktoh@hhawaiimedia.com
W: http://roostercountry.com
Editorial Profile: KTOH-FM is a commercial station owned by Hochman Hawaii One, Inc. The format of the station is contemporary country. KTOH-FM broadcasts to the Kauai, HI area at 99.9 FM.

KTOK-AM
Owner: Clear Channel Media and Entertainment
Editorial: 1900 NW Expressway Ste 1000, Oklahoma City, Oklahoma 73118-1854.
T: 1 405 840-5271 **W:** http://www.ktok.com
Editorial Profile: KTOK-AM is a commercial station owned by Clear Channel Media and Entertainment. The format of the station is news and talk. KTOK-AM broadcasts to the Oklahoma City area at 1000 AM.

KTOM-FM
Owner: Clear Channel Media and Entertainment
Editorial: 903 N Main St, Salinas, California 93906. **T:** 1 831 755-8181
W: http://www.ktom.com
Editorial Profile: KTOM-FM is a commercial station owned by Clear Channel Media and Entertainment. The format of the station is contemporary country. KTOM-FM broadcasts to the Salinas, CA area at 92.7 FM.

KTOO-FM
Owner: Capital Community Broadcasting Inc.
Editorial: 360 Egan Dr, Juneau, Alaska 99801.
T: 1 907 586-1670 **E:** news@ktoo.org
W: http://www.ktoo.org
Editorial Profile: KTOO-FM is a non-commercial station owned by Capital Community Broadcasting Inc. The format of the station is news and talk. KTOO-FM broadcasts to the Juneau, AK area at 104.3 FM.

KTOP-AM
Owner: Cumulus Media Inc.
Editorial: 825 S Kansas Ave, Topeka, Kansas 66612-1233. **T:** 1 785 272-2122
W: http://www.ktop1490.com
Editorial Profile: KTOP-AM is a commercial station owned by Cumulus Media Inc. The format of the station is sports. KTOP-AM broadcasts to the Topeka, KS area at 1490 AM.

KTOP-FM
Owner: Cumulus Media Inc.
Editorial: 825 S Kansas Ave, Ste 100, Topeka, Kansas 66612. **T:** 1 785 272-2122
W: http://www.ktopcountry.com
Editorial Profile: KTOP-FM is a commercial station owned by Cumulus Media Inc. The format of the station is country. KTOP-FM broadcasts to the Topeka, KS area at 102.9 FM.

KTOQ-AM
Owner: Haugo Broadcasting Inc.
Editorial: 3601 Canyon Lake Dr, Rapid City, South Dakota 57702-3900. **T:** 1 605 343-0888
W: http://www.ktalkam1340.com
Editorial Profile: KTOQ-AM is a commercial station owned by Haugo Broadcasting Inc. The format of the station is talk programming. KTOQ-AM broadcasts to the Rapid City, SD area at 1340 AM.

KTOX-AM
Owner: Creative Broadcasting Services Inc.
Editorial: 100 Balboa St, Needles, California 92363. **T:** 1 760 326-4500
E: ktox1340@hotmail.com
W: http://www.ktox1340.com
Editorial Profile: KTOX-AM is a commercial station owned by Creative Broadcasting Services, Inc. The format for the station is news and talk. KTOX-AM broadcasts to the Needles, CA area at 1340 AM.

KTOY-FM
Owner: Texarkana Radio Center Licenses, LLC
Editorial: 615 Olive St, Texarkana, Texas 75501-5512. **T:** 1 903 793-4671
W: http://www.ktoy1047.com
Editorial Profile: KTOY-FM is a commercial station owned by Texarkana Radio Center Licenses, LLC. The format of the station is urban adult contemporary. KTOY-FM broadcasts to the Texarkana, TX area at 104.5 FM.

KTOZ-FM
Owner: Clear Channel Media and Entertainment
Editorial: 1856 S Glenstone Ave, Springfield, Missouri 65804-2303. **T:** 1 417 890-5555
W: http://www.alice955.com
Editorial Profile: KTOZ-FM is a commercial station owned by Clear Channel Media and Entertainment. The format of the station is hot AC. KTOZ-FM broadcasts to the Springfield, MO market at 95.5 FM.

KTPF-FM
Owner: Educational Communications of Colorado Springs Inc.
Editorial: 1665 Briargate Blvd, Ste 100, Colorado Springs, Colorado 80920.
T: 1 800 428-1201 **E:** lightpraise@ktlf.org
W: http://www.ktlf.org
Editorial Profile: KTPF-FM is a non-commercial station owned by Educational Communications of Colorado Springs Inc. The format is religious programming. The station airs in the Colorado Sprngs, CO area at 91.3 FM.

KTPI-AM
Owner: RZ Radio LLC
Editorial: 570 E Avenue Q9, Palmdale, California 93550-4655. **T:** 1 661 947-3107
W: http://www.magic1340.com
Editorial Profile: KTPI-AM is a commercial station owned by RZ Radio LLC. The format of the station is adult standards. KTPI-AM broadcasts to the Lancaster, CA area at 1340 AM.

KTPI-FM
Owner: Clear Channel Media and Entertainment
Editorial: 352 E Avenue K4, Lancaster, California 93535-4505. **T:** 1 661 942-1121
W: http://ktpi.com
Editorial Profile: KTPI-FM is a commercial station owned by Clear Channel Media and Entertainment. The format of the station is contemporary country. KTPI-FM broadcasts to the Lancaster, CA area at 97.7 FM.

KTPK-FM
Owner: JMJ Broadcasting Company Inc.
Editorial: 1210 SW Executive Dr, Topeka, Kansas 66615-3850. **T:** 1 785 273-1069
W: http://www.countrylegends1069.com
Editorial Profile: KTPK-FM is a commercial station owned by JMJ Broadcasting Company Inc. The format of the station is classic country. KPTK-FM broadcasts to the Topeka, KS area on 106.9 FM.

KTPL-FM
Owner: Educational Communications of Colorado Springs Inc.
Editorial: 1665 Briargate Blvd, Ste 100, Colorado Springs, Colorado 80920-2555.
T: 1 719 593-0600 **E:** ktpl@ktpl.org
W: http://www.KTPL.org
Editorial Profile: KTPL-FM is a non-commercial station owned by Educational Communications of Colorado Springs Inc. The format of the station is Christian music and religious talk. KTPL-FM broadcasts to the Colorado Springs, CO area at 88.3 FM.

KTPO-FM
Owner: Hellroaring Communications, LLC
Editorial: 327 S Marion Ave, Sandpoint, Idaho 83864-1723. **T:** 1 208 263-2179
W: http://www.953kpnd.com
Editorial Profile: KTPO-FM is a commercial station owned by Hellroaring Communications, LLC. The format of the station is adult album alternative. KTPO-FM broadcasts to the Bonner County area in Idaho at a frequency of 106.7 FM.

KTPR-FM
Owner: Texas Public Radio
Editorial: 8401 Datapoint Dr, Ste 800, San Antonio, Texas 78229-5903.
T: 1 210 614-8977 **E:** news@tpr.org
W: http://www.tpr.org
Editorial Profile: KTPR-FM is a non-commercial station owned by The format of the station is news and talk. The station broadcasts to the San Antonio, TX area at 89.9 FM.

KTPT-FM
Owner: Bethesda Christian Broadcasting
Editorial: 1853 Fountain Plaza Dr, Rapid City, South Dakota 57702. **T:** 1 605 342-6822
E: pointmail@979thepoint.com
W: http://www.979thepoint.com
Editorial Profile: KTPT-FM is a commercial station owned by Bethesda Christian Broadcasting. The format of the station is contemporary Christian. KTPT-FM broadcasts to the Rapid City, SD area at 97.9 FM.

KTPZ-FM
Owner: Locally Owned Radio, LLC
Editorial: 21361 Highway 30, Twin Falls, Idaho 83301-0197. **T:** 1 208 735-8300
W: http://www.ktpz927.com
Editorial Profile: KTPZ-FM is a commercial station owned by Locally Owned Radio, LLC. The format for the station is hot adult contemporary. KTPZ-FM broadcasts to the Twin Falls, ID area at 92.7 FM.

KTQM-FM
Owner: Zia Broadcasting Inc.
Editorial: 710 Cr K, Clovis, New Mexico 88101. **T:** 1 575 762-4411
E: ktqm@plateautel.net
Editorial Profile: KTQM-FM is a commercial station owned by Zia Broadcasting Inc. The format of the station is adult contemporary. KTQM-FM broadcasts to the Clovis, NM area at 99.9 FM.

KTQX-FM
Owner: Radio Bilingue Inc.
Editorial: 5005 E Belmont Ave, Fresno, California 93727. **T:** 1 559 455-5777
W: http://www.radiobilingue.org
Editorial Profile: KTQX-FM is a non-commercial station owned by Radio Bilingue Inc. The format of the station is Hispanic. KTQX-FM broadcasts to the Visalia-Fresno, CA area at 90.1 FM.

KTRA-FM
Owner: Clear Channel Media and Entertainment
Editorial: 200 E Broadway, Farmington, New Mexico 87401. **T:** 1 505 325-1716
W: http://www.102ktra.com
Editorial Profile: KTRA-FM is a commercial station owned by Clear Channel Media and Entertainment. The format of the station is country music. KTRA-FM broadcasts to the Farmington, NM area at 102.1 FM.

KTRB-AM
Owner: Pappas Radio of California, LP
Editorial: 300 Broadway Ste 8, San Francisco, California 94133-4545. **T:** 1 415 713-5526
W: http://espndeportessanfrancisco.com
Editorial Profile: KTRB-AM is a commercial station owned by Pappas Radio of California, LP. The format of the station is Spanish language sports. KTRB-AM broadcasts to the San Francisco area at 860 AM.

KTRC-AM
Owner: Hutton Broadcasting, LLC
Editorial: 2502 Camino Entrada, Santa Fe, New Mexico 87507-4911. **T:** 1 505 471-1067
W: http://www.santafe.com/ktrc
Editorial Profile: KTRC-AM is a commercial station owned by Hutton Broadcasting, LLC. The format of the station is progressive talk. KTRC-AM broadcasts to the Santa Fe, NM area at 1260 AM.

KTRF-AM
Owner: Iowa City Broadcasting Co.
Editorial: 1433 Main Ave N, Thief River Falls, Minnesota 56701. **T:** 1 218 681-1230
E: ktrf@mncable.net **W:** http://ktrf.k2radio.net
Editorial Profile: KTRF-AM is a commercial station owned by Iowa City Broadcasting Co. The format of the station is talk. KTRF-AM broadcasts in the Thief River Falls, MN area at 1230 AM.

KTRG-FM
Owner: Freed AM Corp.
Editorial: 3446 Summerhill Rd #B, Texarkana, Texas 75503-3560. **T:** 1 903 255-7935
Editorial Profile: KTRG-FM is a commercial station owned by Freed AM Corp. The format of the station is sports. KTRG-FM broadcasts to the Texarkana area at a frequency of 94.1 FM.

KTRH-AM
Owner: Clear Channel Media and Entertainment
Editorial: 2000 West Loop S Ste 300, Houston, Texas 77027-3510.
T: 1 713 212-8000 **W:** http://www.ktrh.com
Editorial Profile: KTRH-AM is a commercial station owned by Clear Channel Media and Entertainment. The format of the station is news and talk programming. KTRH-AM broadcasts to the Houston area at 740 AM.

WORLD NEWS MEDIA

KTRI-FM
Owner: Thirteen Forty Productions, Inc.
Editorial: 118 State Dr, Hollister, Missouri 65672-4987. **T:** 1 417 339-1062
Editorial Profile: KTRI-FM is a commercial station owned by Thirteen Forty Productions, Inc. The format of the station is tourist information for the Branson, MO Tri-Lakes area. KTRI-FM broadcasts to the Branson, MO area at 95.9 FM.

KTRN-FM
Owner: Wachter (William B.)
Editorial: 2215 E Harding Ave Ste 7, Pine Bluff, Arkansas 71601-6880.
T: 1 870 536-3282 **E:** ktrn1045fm@yahoo.com
Editorial Profile: KTRN-FM is a commercial station owned by Wachter (William B.). The format of the station is adult contemporary. KTRN-FM broadcasts to the Pine Bluff, AR area at 104.5 FM.

KTRP-AM
Owner: Media Enterprises, LLC
Editorial: 1156 N Orchard St, Boise, Idaho 83706-2234. **T:** 1 208 367-1859
W: http://kweiradio.com
Editorial Profile: KTRP-AM is a commercial station owned by Media Enterprises, LLC. The format of the station is Tejano. KTRP-AM is licensed to Notus, ID and broadcasts to the Boise, ID area.

KTRQ-FM
Owner: East Arkansas Broadcasters Inc.
Editorial: 2758 Highway 64, Wynne, Arkansas 72396-4061. **T:** 1 870 238-8141
E: radiokwyn@cablelynx.com
Editorial Profile: KTRQ-FM is a commercial station owned by East Arkansas Broadcasters Inc. The format of the station is oldies. KTRQ-FM broadcasts to the Wynne, AR area at 102.3 FM.

KTRR-FM
Owner: Townsquare Media, LLC
Editorial: 600 Main St, Windsor, Colorado 80550. **T:** 1 970 674-2700
W: http://www.tri1025.com
Editorial Profile: KTRR-FM is a commercial station owned by Townsquare Media, LLC. The format of the station is adult contemporary. KTRR-FM broadcasts to the Denver area at 102.5 FM.

KTRS-AM
Owner: CH Holdings LLC
Editorial: 638 W Port Plz, Saint Louis, Missouri 63146-3106. **T:** 1 314 453-5500
E: news@ktrs.com **W:** http://www.ktrs.com
Editorial Profile: KTRS-AM is a commercial station owned by CH Holdings LLC. The format of the station is news and talk. KTRS-AM broadcasts to the St. Louis area at 550 AM.

KTRS-FM
Owner: Townsquare Media, LLC
Editorial: 150 Nichols Ave, Casper, Wyoming 82601. **T:** 1 307 266-5252
W: http://www.kisscasper.com
Editorial Profile: KTRS-FM is a commercial station owned by Townsquare Media, LLC. The format for the station is Top 40/CHR. KTRS-FM broadcasts to the Casper-Riverton, WY area at 104.7 FM.

KTRU-FM
Owner: Rice University
Editorial: 6100 Main St, Ley Student Center Rice University, Houston, Texas 77005-1827.
T: 1 713 348-4098 **E:** ktru@ktru.org
W: http://www.ktru.org
Editorial Profile: KTRU-FM is a commercial station owned by Rice University. The format of the station is variety. KTRU-FM broadcasts to the Houston area at 91.7 FM.

KTRW-AM
Owner: Read Broadcasting
Editorial: 6019 S Crestline St, Spokane, Washington 99223-6823. **T:** 1 509 443-1000
E: ktw@fabulous630.com
W: http://www.ktrw.com
Editorial Profile: KTRW-AM is a commercial station owned by Read Broadcasting. The format of the station is news and religion. KTRW-AM broadcasts to the Spokane, WA area at 630 AM.

KTRX-FM
Owner: LKCM Radio Group LP
Editorial: 1205 Northglen St, Ardmore, Oklahoma 73401-1202. **T:** 1 580 226-0421
E: news@sokradio.com
W: http://www.texomarocks.com
Editorial Profile: KTRX-FM is a commercial station owned by LKCM Radio Group LP. The format of the station is classic rock. KTRX-FM broadcasts to the Ardmore, OK area at 92.7 FM.

KTRY-FM
Owner: Redwood Empire Stereocasters
Editorial: 3392 Mendocino Ave, Santa Rosa, California 95403-2213. **T:** 1 707 528-4434
E: holler@ktry.com **W:** http://www.ktry.com
Editorial Profile: KTRY-FM is a commercial station owned by Redwood Empire Stereocasters. The format of the station is country. KTRY-FM broadcasts to the San Francisco area at 106.3 FM.

KTSA-AM
Owner: L & L Broadcasting
Editorial: 4050 Eisenhauer Rd, San Antonio, Texas 78218-3409. **T:** 1 210 654-5100
W: http://www.ktsa.com
Editorial Profile: KTSA-AM is a commercial station owned by L & L Broadcasting. The format of the station is news and talk. KTSA-AM broadcasts to the San Antonio area at 550 AM.

KTSC-FM
Owner: Colorado State University-Pueblo
Editorial: 2200 Bonforte Blvd, Pueblo, Colorado 81001. **T:** 1 719 549-2822
W: http://www.colostate-pueblo.edu/rev89
Editorial Profile: KTSC-FM is a non-commercial station owned by the Colorado State University-Pueblo. The format of the station is urban contemporary. KTSC-FM broadcasts to the Pueblo, CO area at 89.5 FM.

KTSD-FM
Owner: State Board for Educational Television
Editorial: 555 N Dakota St, Vermillion, South Dakota 57069. **T:** 1 605 677-5861
E: news@sdpb.org **W:** http://www.sdpb.org
Editorial Profile: KTSD-FM is a non-commercial station owned by the State Board for Educational Television. The format of the station is news and classical. KTSD-FM broadcasts to the Vermillion, SD area at 91.1 FM.

KTSE-FM
Owner: Entravision Communications Corp.
Editorial: 6820 Pacific Ave, Ste 3A, Stockton, California 95207-2631. **T:** 1 209 474-0154
W: http://www.jose971.com
Editorial Profile: KTSE-FM is a commercial station owned by Entravision Communications Corp. The format of the station is Hispanic adult hits. KTSE-FM broadcasts to the Modesto, CA area at 97.1 FM.

KTSM-AM
Owner: Clear Channel Media and Entertainment
Editorial: 4045 N Mesa St, El Paso, Texas 79902. **T:** 1 915 351-5400
W: http://www.ktsmradio.com
Editorial Profile: KTSM-AM is a commercial station owned by Clear Channel Media and Entertainment. The format of the station is news and talk. KTSM-AM broadcasts to the El Paso, TX area at 690 AM.

KTSM-FM
Owner: Clear Channel Media and Entertainment
Editorial: 4045 N Mesa St, El Paso, Texas 79902. **T:** 1 915 351-5400
W: http://www.sunny999fm.com
Editorial Profile: KTSM-FM is a commercial station owned by Clear Channel Media and Entertainment. The format of the station is Lite Rock/Lite AC music. KTSM-FM broadcasts to the El Paso, TX area at 99.9 FM.

KTSO-FM
Owner: Stephens Media Group
Editorial: 2448 E 81st St Ste 5500, Tulsa, Oklahoma 74137-4201. **T:** 1 918 492-2660
E: studio@941thebreeze.com
W: http://941thebreeze.com
Editorial Profile: KTSO-FM is a commercial station owned by Stephens Media Group. The format of the station is adult contemporary. KTSO-FM broadcasts to the Tulsa, OK area at a frequency of 94.1 FM.

KTSR-FM
Owner: Townsquare Media, LLC
Editorial: 900 N Lake Shore Dr, Lake Charles, Louisiana 70601. **T:** 1 337 433-1641
W: http://kissfm921.com
Editorial Profile: KTSR-FM is a commercial station owned by Townsquare Media, LLC. The format of the station is hot Top 40. KTSR-FM broadcasts to the Lake Charles, LA area at 92.1 FM.

KTST-FM
Owner: Clear Channel Media and Entertainment
Editorial: 1900 NW Expressway, Oklahoma City, Oklahoma 73118-1802.
T: 1 405 840-5271
W: http://www.thetwister.com
Editorial Profile: KTST-FM is a commercial station owned by Clear Channel Media and Entertainment. The format of the station is contemporary country music. KTST-FM broadcasts to the Oklahoma City area at 101.9 FM.

KTSU-FM
Owner: Texas Southern University
Editorial: 3100 Cleburne St, Houston, Texas 77004. **T:** 1 713 313-7591 **E:** ktsufm@tsu.edu
W: http://www.ktsufm.org
Editorial Profile: KTSU-FM is a non-commercial station owned by Texas Southern University. The format of the station is primarily Jazz, gospel and R&B music. KTSU-FM broadcasts to the Houston area at 90.9 FM.

KTSW-FM
Owner: Texas State University-San Marcos
Editorial: 601 University Dr, Rm 106, San Marcos, Texas 78666-4685.
T: 1 512 245-3485 **E:** ktswnews@txstate.edu
W: http://www.ktsw.net
Editorial Profile: KTSW-FM is a non-commercial station owned by Texas State University-San Marcos. The format of the station is college variety. KTSW-FM broadcasts in the San Marcos, TX area at 89.9 FM.

KTSY-FM
Owner: Idaho Conference of Seven Day Adventists
Editorial: 16115 S Montana Ave, Caldwell, Idaho 83607. **T:** 1 208 459-5879
E: family@ktsy.org **W:** http://www.895ktsy.org
Editorial Profile: KTSY-FM is a non-commercial station owned by Idaho Conference of Seventh Day Adventists. The format of the station is contemporary Christian music. KTSY-FM broadcasts to the Boise, ID area at 89.5 FM.

KTTG-FM
Owner: Pearson Broadcasting
Editorial: 1912 Church St, Barling, Arkansas 72923. **T:** 1 479 484-7285
W: http://www.espnarkansas.com
Editorial Profile: KTTG-FM is a commercial station owned by Pearson Broadcasting. The format of the station is sports. KTTG-FM broadcasts to the Fort Smith, AR area at 96.3 FM.

KTTH-AM
Owner: Bonneville International Corp.
Editorial: 1820 Eastlake Ave E, Seattle, Washington 98102. **T:** 1 206 726-7000
E: newsdesk@973kiro.com
W: http://www.mynorthwest.com
Editorial Profile: KTTH-AM is a commercial station owned by Bonneville International Corp. The format of the station is talk. KTTH-AM broadcasts in the Seattle area at 770 AM.

KTTI-FM
Owner: El Dorado Broadcasting
Editorial: 755 W 28th St, Yuma, Arizona 85364. **T:** 1 928 344-4980
W: http://www.951ktti.com
Editorial Profile: KTTI-FM is a commercial station owned by El Dorado Broadcasting. The format of the station is country music. KTTI-FM broadcasts to the Yuma, AZ area at 95.1 FM.

KTTK-FM
Owner: Lebanon Educational Broadcasting Foundation
Editorial: 221 E Commercial St, Lebanon, Missouri 65536-3213. **T:** 1 417 588-1435
E: kttk_radio@fastmail.fm
W: http://www.kttkpowerfm.org
Editorial Profile: KTTK-FM is a non-commercial station owned by Lebanon Educational Broadcasting Foundation. The format of the station is Christian music including Southern Gospel, Christian Country and Gospel Bluegrass. KTTK-FM broadcasts to the Lebanon, MO area at 90.7 FM.

KTTN-AM
Owner: Par Broadcast Group
Editorial: 804 Main St, Trenton, Missouri 64683-2044. **T:** 1 660 359-2727
W: http://www.kttn.com
Editorial Profile: KTTN-AM is a commercial station owned by Par Broadcast Group. The format of the station is Lite Rock/Lite AC. KTTN-AM broadcasts to the Trenton, MO area at 1600 AM.

KTTN-FM
Owner: Par Broadcast Group
Editorial: 804 Main St, Trenton, Missouri 64683-2044. **T:** 1 660 359-2261
W: http://www.kttn.com/kgozfm
Editorial Profile: KTTN-FM is commercial station owned by Par Broadcast Group. The format of the station is classic country. KTTN-FM broadcasts to the Kansas City, MO area at 92.3 FM.

KTTO-AM
Owner: Sacred Heart Radio
Editorial: 7357 148Th Ave Ne, Redmond, Washington 98052-4148. **T:** 1 425 867-2340
E: info@sacredheartradio.org
W: http://www.sacredheartradio.org

KTTR-AM
Owner: Mahaffey Enterprises Inc.
Editorial: 1505 Soest Rd, Rolla, Missouri 65401. **T:** 1 573 364-2525
E: kttrkznn@fidmail.com
W: http://www.resultsradioonline.com
Editorial Profile: KTTR-AM is a commercial station owned by Mahaffey Enterprises Inc. The format of the station is news and talk. KTTR-AM broadcasts to the Rolla, MO area at 1490 AM.

KTTR-FM
Owner: Mahaffey Enterprises Inc.
Editorial: 1505 Soest Rd, Rolla, Missouri 65401. **T:** 1 573 364-2525
E: kttrkznn@fidmail.com
W: http://www.resultsradioonline.com
Editorial Profile: KTTR-FM is a commercial station owned by Mahaffey Enterprises Inc. The format of the station is news and talk. KTTR-FM broadcasts to the Rolla, MO area at 99.7 FM.

KTTS-FM
Owner: Journal Broadcast Group
Editorial: 2330 W Grand St, Springfield, Missouri 65802. **T:** 1 417 865-6614
E: news@ktts.com **W:** http://www.ktts.com
Editorial Profile: KTTS-FM is a commercial station owned by Journal Broadcast Group. The format of the station is contemporary country music. KTTS-FM broadcasts to the Springfield, MO area at 94.7 FM.

KTTT-AM
Owner: Three Eagles Communications Co.
Editorial: 1418 25th St, Columbus, Nebraska 68601. **T:** 1 402 564-2866
W: http://www.mycentralnebraska.com
Editorial Profile: KTTT-AM is a commercial station owned by Three Eagles Communications Co. The format of the station is a variety of ethnic talk programming. KTTT-AM broadcasts in the Columbus, NE area at 1510 AM.

KTTU-FM
Owner: Ramar Communications Inc.
Editorial: 9800 University Ave, Lubbock, Texas 79423. **T:** 1 806 745-3434
E: sports@doublet1043.com
W: http://www.doublet1043.com
Editorial Profile: KTTU-FM is a commercial station owned by Ramar Communications Inc. The format of the station is sports. KTTU-FM broadcasts to the Lubbock, TX area at 104.3 FM.

KTTX-FM
Owner: Whitehead Inc.(Tom S.)
Editorial: 223 E Main St, Brenham, Texas 77833. **T:** 1 979 776-1061 **E:** news@kwhi.com
W: http://www.ktex.com
Editorial Profile: KTTX-FM is a commercial station owned by Tom S. Whitehead Inc. The format of the station is country music. KTTX-FM broadcasts to the Houston area at 106.1 FM.

KTTZ-FM
Owner: Texas Tech University
Editorial: 1901 University Ave, Ste 603B, Lubbock, Texas 79410-1555.
T: 1 806 742-3100 **E:** kohm@ttu.edu
W: http://www.kohm.org
Editorial Profile: KTTZ-FM is a non-commercial station owned by Texas Tech University. The format of the station is classical. KOHM-FM broadcasts to the Lubbock, TX area at 89.1 FM.

KTUB-AM

Owner: Adelante Media Group
Editorial: 2722 S Redwood Rd, Salt Lake City, Utah 84119. **T:** 1 801 908-8777
W: http://www.adelantemediagroup.com
Editorial Profile: KTUB-AM is the ESPN Deportes affiliate in the Salt Lake City, UT market. It is a commercial station owned by Adelante Media Group. The format of the station is Spanish language sports. KTUB-AM broadcasts to the Salt Lake City area at 1600 AM.

KTUC-AM

Owner: Cumulus Media Inc
Editorial: 575 W Roger Rd, Tucson, Arizona 85705. **T:** 1 520 887-1000
W: http://www.1400ktuc.net
Editorial Profile: KTUC-AM is a commercial station owned by Cumulus Media Inc. The format of the station is adult standards music. KTUC-AM broadcasts to the Tucson, AZ area at 1400 AM.

KTUE-AM

Owner: Bernal(Paulino)
Editorial: 4501 N McColl Rd, McAllen, Texas 78504-2431. **T:** 1 956 781-5528
W: http://www.nuevaradiocristiana.com
Editorial Profile: KTUE-AM is a non-commercial station owned by Paulino Bernal. The format of the station is Hispanic contemporary Christian. KTUE-AM broadcasts to the McAllen, TX area at 1260 AM.

KTUF-FM

Owner: KIRX Inc.
Editorial: 1308 N Baltimore St, Kirksville, Missouri 63501. **T:** 1 660 665-9828
E: radiopark@cableone.net
W: http://www.937ktuf.com
Editorial Profile: KTUF-FM is a commercial station owned by KIRX Inc. The format of the station is a mix of classic and contemporary country music. KTUF-FM broadcasts to the Kirksville, MO area at 93.7 FM.

KTUH-FM

Owner: University of Hawaii
Editorial: 2445 Campus Rd, #203, Honolulu, Hawaii 96822. **T:** 1 808 956-7431
W: http://www.ktuh.org
Editorial Profile: KTUH-FM is a non-commercial station owned by the University of Hawaii. The format of the station is variety. The station airs locally on 90.3 FM. KTUH-FM's slogan is "Hawaii's Only Alternative." There are no regularly scheduled newscasts at the station.

KTUI-AM

Owner: Fidelity Broadcasting Inc.
Editorial: 229 Bud St, Sullivan, Missouri 63080. **T:** 1 573 468-5101 **E:** news@ktui.com
W: http://www.ktui.com
Editorial Profile: KTUI-AM is a commercial station owned by Fidelity Broadcasting Inc. The format of the station is news and talk. KTUI-AM broadcasts to the Sullivan, MO area at 1560 AM.

KTUI-FM

Owner: Fidelity Broadcasting Inc.
Editorial: 229 Bud St, Sullivan, Missouri 63080. **T:** 1 573 468-5101 **E:** news@ktui.com
W: http://www.ktui.com
Editorial Profile: KTUI-FM is a commercial station owned by Fidelity Broadcasting Inc. The format of the station is country music and sports. KTUI-FM broadcasts to the Sullivan, MO area at 102.1 FM.

KTUN-FM

Owner: Wildcat Communications LLC
Editorial: 1201 18Th St Ste 250, Denver, Colorado 80202-1869. **T:** 1 970 476-7444
Editorial Profile: KTUN-FM is a commercial station owned by Wildcat Communications LLC. The format for the station is Spanish Hits. KTUN-FM broadcasts to the New Castle, CO area at 94.5 FM.

KTUV-AM

Owner: Birach Broadcasting Corp.
Editorial: 8211 Geyer Springs Rd Ste P6, Little Rock, Arkansas 72209-4909.
T: 1 501 562-2661
Editorial Profile: KTUV-AM is a commercial station owned by Birach Broadcasting Corp. The format of the station is Hispanic programming. KTUV-AM broadcasts to the Little Rock, AR area at 1440 AM.

KTUX-FM

Owner: Townsquare Media, LLC
Editorial: 6341 W Port Ave, Shreveport, Louisiana 71129. **T:** 1 318 688-1130

W: http://www.therockstation99x.com
Editorial Profile: KTUX-FM is a commercial station owned by Townsquare Media, LLC. The format of the station is rock music. KTUX-FM broadcasts to the Shreveport, LA area at 98.9 FM.

KTUZ-AM

Owner: Reunion Broadcasting LLC
Editorial: 7777 S Lewis Ave, Tulsa, Oklahoma 74171-0003. **T:** 1 918 254-7556
W: http://www.quebuenatulsa.com
Editorial Profile: KTUZ-AM is a commercial station owned by Reunion Broadcasting LLC. The format is not available. KTUZ-AM broadcasts to the Tulsa, OK area at 1270 AM.

KTUZ-FM

Owner: Tyler Media Group Inc.
Editorial: 5101 S Shields Blvd, Oklahoma City, Oklahoma 73129-3217. **T:** 1 405 616-5500
E: ktuz@tylermedia.com
W: http://www.ktuz.com
Editorial Profile: KTUZ-FM is a commercial station owned by Tyler Media Group Inc. The format of the station is regional Mexican. KTUZ-FM broadcasts to the Oklahoma City area at 106.7 FM.

KTWA-FM

Owner: O-Town Communications, Inc.
Editorial: 416 Main Street, Ottumwa, Iowa 52501. **T:** 1 641 684-5563
W: http://www.ktwafm.com
Editorial Profile: KTWA-FM is a commercial station owned by O-Town Communications, Inc. The format of the station is adult contemporary. KTWA-FM broadcasts to the Ottumwa, IA area at 92.7 FM.

KTWB-FM

Owner: Backyard Broadcasting
Editorial: 500 S Phillips Ave, Sioux Falls, South Dakota 57104-6825. **T:** 1 605 331-5350
E: ktwb@ktwb.com **W:** http://www.ktwb.com
Editorial Profile: KTWB-FM is a commercial station owned by Backyard Broadcasting. The format of the station is adult contemporary. KTWB-FM broadcasts in the Sioux Falls, SD area at 101.9 FM.

KTWN-FM

Owner: Northern Lights Broadcasting
Editorial: 5300 Edina Industrial Blvd Ste 200, Edina, Minnesota 55439-2907.
T: 1 952 842-7200 **W:** http://www.ktwin.com
Editorial Profile: KTWN-FM is a commercial station owned by Northern Lights Broadcasting. The format of the station is Adult CHR. KTWN-FM broadcasts to the Minneapolis area at 96.3 FM.

KTWO-AM

Owner: Townsquare Media, LLC
Editorial: 150 Nichols Ave, Casper, Wyoming 82601. **T:** 1 307 266-5252
E: caspernews@gapbroadcasting.com
W: http://www.k2radio.com
Editorial Profile: KTWO-AM is a commercial station owned by Townsquare Media, LLC. The format of the station is talk. KTWO-AM broadcasts to the Casper, WY area at 1030 AM.

KTWS-FM

Owner: Combined Communications, Inc.
Editorial: 63088 Ne 18Th St Ste 200, Bend, Oregon 97701-7102. **T:** 1 541 382-5263
W: http://www.thetwins.com
Editorial Profile: KTWS-FM is a commercial station owned by Combined Communications, Inc. The format of the station is classic rock. KTWS-FM broadcasts in the Bend, OR area at 98.3 FM.

KTWV-FM

Owner: CBS Radio
Editorial: 5670 Wilshire Blvd Ste 200, Los Angeles, California 90036-5657.
T: 1 323 937-9283 **E:** wave@ktwv.cbs.com
W: http://947thewave.radio.com
Editorial Profile: KTWV-FM is a commercial station owned by CBS Radio. The format of the station is smooth AC. KTWV-FM broadcasts to the Los Angeles area at 94.7 FM.

KTXC-FM

Owner: Drewry Communications
Editorial: 11320 WCR 127, Midland, Texas 79711. **T:** 1 432 567-9999
W: http://www.laley104fm.com
Editorial Profile: KTXC-FM is a commercial station owned by Drewry Communications. The format for the station is Hispanic programming. KTXC-FM broadcasts to the Midland, TX, area at 104.7 FM.

KTXG-FM

Owner: American Family Association
Editorial: 2600 State Highway 121, Melissa, Texas 75454. **T:** 1 662 844-8888
W: http://www.afr.net
Editorial Profile: KTXG-FM is a non-commercial station owned by American Family Association. The format of the station is contemporary Christian. KTXG-FM broadcasts to the Greenville, TX area at 90.5 FM.

KTXI-FM

Owner: Texas Public Radio
Editorial: 8401 Datapoint Dr, Ste 800, San Antonio, Texas 78229. **T:** 1 210 614-8977
E: news@tpr.org **W:** http://www.tpr.org
Editorial Profile: KTXI-FM is a non-commercial station owned by Texas Public Radio. The format of the station is classical music, news and talk programming. KTXI-FM broadcasts to the San Antonio area at 90.1 FM.

KTXJ-FM

Owner: Cross Texas Media Inc.
Editorial: 1408 E Gibson St, Jasper, Texas 75951-6123. **T:** 1 409 384-4500
E: request@1027ktxj.com
W: http://www.1027ktxj.com
Editorial Profile: KTXJ-FM is a commercial station owned by Cross Texas Media Inc. The format for the station is southern Gospel. KTXJ-FM broadcasts to the Beaumont-Port Arthur, TX, area at 102.7 FM.

KTXK-FM

Owner: Texarkana College
Editorial: 2500 N Robison Rd, Texarkana, Texas 75599. **T:** 1 903 838-4541 3269
W: http://ktxk.org
Editorial Profile: KTXK-FM is a non-commercial station owned by Texarkana College. The format of the station is news/talk and classical. KTXK-FM broadcasts to the Texarkana, TX area at 91.5 FM.

KTXM-FM

Owner: Kremling Enterprises Inc.
Editorial: 111 Main St, Hallettsville, Texas 77964. **T:** 1 361 798-4333
E: txthunderradio@yahoo.com
W: http://www.texasthunderradio.com
Editorial Profile: KTXM-FM is a commercial radio station owned by Kremling Enterprises Inc. The format of the station is contemporary country. KTXM-FM broadcasts to the Hallettsville, TX area at 99.9 FM.

KTXN-FM

Owner: Townsquare Media, LLC
Editorial: 107 N Star Dr, Victoria, Texas 77904-2082. **T:** 1 361 573-0777
W: http://987jack.com
Editorial Profile: KTXN-FM is a commercial station owned by Townsquare Media, LLC. The format of the station is adult hits. KTXN-FM broadcasts to the Victoria, TX area at 98.7 FM.

KTXR-FM

Owner: Meyer Communications
Editorial: 3000 E Chestnut Expy, Springfield, Missouri 65802. **T:** 1 417 862-3751
W: http://www.ktxrfm.com
Editorial Profile: KTXR-FM is a commercial station owned by Meyer Communications. The format of the station is Mainstream AC music. KTXR-FM broadcasts in the Springfield, MO area at 101.3 FM.

KTXT-FM

Owner: Texas Tech University
Editorial: 1901 University Ave, Lubbock, Texas 79410-1544. **T:** 1 806 742-5898
W: http://www.kohm.org
Editorial Profile: KTXT-FM is a non-commercial station owned by Texas Tech University. The format is jazz music. KTXT-FM broadcasts to the Lubbock, TX area at 88.1 FM.

KTXX-FM

Owner: Genuine Austin Radio
Editorial: 912 S Capital of Texas Hwy, West Lake Hills, Texas 78746-5264.
T: 1 512 416-1100
W: http://www.1049thehorn.com
Editorial Profile: KTXX-FM is a commercial station owned by Genuine Austin Radio. The format of the station is sports and classic hits music. KHHL-FM broadcasts to the Austin, TX, area at 104.9 FM.

KTXY-FM

Owner: Zimmer Radio Group
Editorial: 3215 Lemone Industrial Blvd, Ste 200, Columbia, Missouri 65201.
T: 1 573 875-1099 **E:** y107@zrgmail.com

W: http://www.y107.com
Editorial Profile: KTXY-FM is a commercial station owned by the Zimmer Radio Group. The format of the station is Top 40/CHR music. KTXY-FM broadcasts to the Jefferson City, MO area at 106.9 FM.

KTXZ-AM

Owner: Encino Broadcasting, LLC
Editorial: 9434 Parkfield Dr, Austin, Texas 78758-6227. **T:** 1 512 453-1491
E: spots@austintejas.com
Editorial Profile: KTXZ-AM is a commercial station owned by Encino Broadcasting LLC. The format of the station is Hispanic music. KTXZ-AM broadcasts to the Austin, TX area at 1560 AM.

KTYD-FM

Owner: Rincon Broadcasting
Editorial: 414 E Cota St, Santa Barbara, California 93101. **T:** 1 805 879-8300
W: http://www.ktyd.com
Editorial Profile: KTYD-FM is a commercial station owned by Rincon Broadcasting. The format of the station is classic rock. KTYD-FM broadcasts to the Santa Barbara, CA area 99.9 FM.

KTYL-FM

Owner: Townsquare Media, LLC
Editorial: 3810 Brookside Dr, Tyler, Texas 75701. **T:** 1 903 581-0606
W: http://www.mix931fm.com
Editorial Profile: KTYL-FM is a commercial station owned by Townsquare Media, LLC. The format of the station is hot adult contemporary. KTYL-FM broadcasts to the Tyler, TX area at 93.1 FM.

KTZA-FM

Owner: Pecos Valley Broadcasting Company
Editorial: 317 W Quay Ave, Artesia, New Mexico 88210-2158. **T:** 1 575 746-2751
W: http://www.pecosvalleybroadcasting.com
Editorial Profile: KTZA-FM is a commercial station owned by Pecos Valley Broadcasting Company. The format of the station is country music. KTZA-FM broadcasts to the Albuquerque, NM area at 92.9 FM.

KTZN-AM

Owner: Clear Channel Media and Entertainment
Editorial: 800 E Dimond Blvd, Ste 3-370, Anchorage, Alaska 99515. **T:** 1 907 522-1515
W: http://www.550thezone.com
Editorial Profile: KTZN-AM is a commercial station owned by Clear Channel Media and Entertainment. The format of the station is sports. KTZN-AM broadcasts to the Anchorage, AK area at 550 AM.

KTZR-AM

Owner: Clear Channel Media and Entertainment
Editorial: 3202 N Oracle Rd, Tucson, Arizona 85705. **T:** 1 520 618-2100
W: http://lapreciosatucson.com
Editorial Profile: KTZR-AM is a commercial station owned by Clear Channel Media and Entertainment. The format of the station is Spanish Adult Hits. KTZR-AM broadcasts to the Tucson, AZ area at 1450 AM.

KTZZ-FM

Owner: Munson Radio Inc.
Editorial: 3313 15th St, Box F, Black Eagle, Montana 59414. **T:** 1 406 761-1310
Editorial Profile: KTZZ-FM is a commercial station owned by Munson Radio Inc. The format of the station is classic rock music. KTZZ-FM broadcasts in the Great Falls, MT area at 93.7 FM.

KUAC-FM

Owner: University of Alaska
Editorial: 202 Fine Arts Bldg 312 Tanana Dr, University Of Alaska Fairbanks, Fairbanks, Alaska 99775. **T:** 1 907 474-7491
E: comments@kuac.org
W: http://www.kuac.org
Editorial Profile: KUAC-FM is a non-commercial station owned by University of Alaska. The format for the station is a mix of eclectic programming, jazz, classical music and news. KUAC-FM broadcasts to the Fairbanks, AK area at 89.9 FM.

KUAD-FM

Owner: Townsquare Media, LLC
Editorial: 600 Main St, Windsor, Colorado 80550. **T:** 1 970 674-2700
W: http://www.k99.com
Editorial Profile: KUAD-FM is a commercial station owned by Townsquare Media, LLC. The format of the station is country. KUAD-FM

broadcasts to the Windsor, CO area at 99.1 FM.

KUAF-FM
Owner: University of Arkansas
Editorial: 9 S School Ave, Fayetteville, Arkansas 72701-5962. **T:** 1 479 575-2556
E: kuafinfo@uark.edu **W:** http://www.kuaf.com
Editorial Profile: KUAF-FM is a non-commercial station owned by the University of Arkansas. The format of the station is news, classical and jazz music. KUAF-FM broadcasts to the Fayetteville, AR area at 91.3 FM.

KUAI-AM
Owner: Ohana Broadcasting, LLC
Editorial: 4271 Halenani St, Lihue, Hawaii 96766-1312. **T:** 1 808 245-9527
E: kong@kongradio.com
W: http://www.kuai720am.com
Editorial Profile: KUAI-AM is a commercial station owned by Ohana Broadcasting, LLC. The format of the station is contemporary country music. KUAI-AM broadcasts to the Kauai, HI area at 720 AM.

KUAL-FM
Owner: BL Broadcasting Inc.
Editorial: 13225 Dogwood Dr, Baxter, Minnesota 56425-8669. **T:** 1 218 828-1244
E: cooloIdies@cool1035.com
W: http://www.cool1035.com
Editorial Profile: KUAL-FM is a commercial station owned by BL Broadcasting Inc. The format of the station is oldies. KUAL-FM broadcasts to the Brainerd, MN area at 103.5 FM.

KUAR-FM
Owner: University of Arkansas
Editorial: 5820 Asher Ave, Ste 400, Little Rock, Arkansas 72204. **T:** 1 501 569-8485
E: kuar@ualr.edu **W:** http://www.kuar.org
Editorial Profile: KUAR-FM is a non-commercial station owned by the University of Arkansas. The format of the station is news, talk, and jazz music. KUAR-FM broadcasts in the Little Rock, AR at 89.1 FM.

KUAT-FM
Owner: University of Arizona
Editorial: 1423 E University Blvd, #223, Tucson, Arizona 85721-0001.
T: 1 520 621-5828 **E:** cu@kuat.org
W: http://radio.azpm.org
Editorial Profile: KUAT-FM is a non-commercial station owned by the University of Arizona. The format of the station is classical music. KUAT-FM broadcasts to the Tucson, AZ area at 90.5 FM.

KUAZ-AM
Owner: University of Arizona
Editorial: 1423 E University Blvd, #223, Tucson, Arizona 85721-0001.
T: 1 520 621-5828 **E:** cu@kuat.org
W: http://radio.azpm.org/kuaz
Editorial Profile: KUAZ-AM is a non-commercial station owned by University of Arizona. The format of the station is news and jazz music. KUAZ-AM broadcasts to the Southern Arizona area at 1550 AM.

KUAZ-FM
Owner: University of Arizona
Editorial: 1423 E University Blvd, #223, Tucson, Arizona 85721-0001.
T: 1 520 621-5828
E: contactazpm@azpublicmedia.org
W: https://radio.azpm.org/kuaz
Editorial Profile: KUAZ-FM is a non-commercial station owned by the University of Arizona. The format of the station is news and jazz music. KUAZ-FM broadcasts to the Tucson, AZ area listeners at 89.1 FM.

KUBA-AM
Owner: Results Radio Group
Editorial: 1479 Sanborn Rd, Yuba City, California 95993. **T:** 1 530 673-1600
E: office@kubaradio.com
W: http://www.kubaradio.com
Editorial Profile: KUBA-AM is a commercial station owned by Results Radio Group. The format of the station is classic hits and news. KUBA-AM broadcasts to the Sacramento, CA area at 1600 AM.

KUBB-FM
Owner: Buckley Broadcasting Corp.
Editorial: 510 W 19th St, Merced, California 95340. **T:** 1 209 383-7900
E: KUBBemail@aol.com
W: http://www.kubb.com
Editorial Profile: KUBB-FM is a commercial station owned by Buckley Broadcasting Corp. The format of the station is contemporary country. KUBB-FM broadcasts to the Merced, CA area at 96.3 FM.

KUBC-AM
Owner: Cherry Creek Radio
Editorial: 106 Rose Ln, Montrose, Colorado 81401-3823. **T:** 1 970 249-4546
E: news@coloradoradio.com
W: http://www.coloradoradio.com
Editorial Profile: KUBC-AM is a commercial station owned by Cherry Creek Radio. The format of the station is news and talk. KUBC-AM's broadcasts in the Montrose, CO area at 580 AM.

KUBE-FM
Owner: Clear Channel Media and Entertainment
Editorial: 351 Elliott Ave W Ste 300, Seattle, Washington 98119-4150. **T:** 1 206 494-2000
W: http://www.kube93.com
Editorial Profile: KUBE-FM is a commercial station owned by Clear Channel Media and Entertainment. The format of the station is Urban Contemporary music. KUBE-FM broadcasts to the Seattle area at 93.3 FM.

KUBJ-FM
Owner: KSBJ Educational Foundation
Editorial: 1722 Treble Dr, Humble, Texas 77338-5253. **T:** 1 281 446-5725
W: http://www.ksbj.org
Editorial Profile: KUBJ-FM is a non-commercial station owned by KSBJ Educational Foundation. The format of the station is contemporary Christian. KUBJ-FM broadcasts to the Brenham, TX area at 89.7 FM.

KUBL-FM
Owner: Cumulus Media Inc
Editorial: 434 W Bearcat Dr, Salt Lake City, Utah 84115-2520. **T:** 1 801 485-6700
W: http://www.kbull93.com
Editorial Profile: KUBL-FM is a commercial station owned by Cumulus Media Inc. The format of the station is contemporary country. KUBL-FM broadcasts to the Salt Lake City area at 93.3 FM.

KUBO-FM
Owner: Radio Bilingue Inc.
Editorial: 531 Main St #2, El Centro, California 92243. **T:** 1 760 331-8874
W: http://www.radiobilingue.org
Editorial Profile: KUBO-FM is a non-commercial station owned by Radio Bilingue Inc. The format of the station is Hispanic talk. KUBO-FM broadcasts to the El Centro, CA area at 88.7 FM.

KUBQ-FM
Owner: Pacific Empire Communications
Editorial: 2510 Cove Ave, La Grande, Oregon 97850. **T:** 1 541 963-4121 **E:** q98@eoni.com
W: http://www.987kubq.com
Editorial Profile: KUBQ-FM is a commercial station owned by the Pacific Empire Communications. The format of the station is classic rock music. KUBQ-FM broadcasts to La Grande, OR, at 98.7 FM.

KUBR-AM
Owner: Bernal(Paulino)
Editorial: 4501 N McColl Rd, McAllen, Texas 78504-2431. **T:** 1 956 781-5528
Editorial Profile: KUBR-AM is a non-commercial station owned by Paulino Bernal. The format of the station is Hispanic contemporary Christian. KUBR-AM broadcasts to the McAllen, TX area at 1210 AM.

KUBS-FM
Owner: Newport High School
Editorial: 1400 W 5th St, Newport, Washington 99156. **T:** 1 509 447-4931
E: newsportsd@newport.wednet.edu
W: http://www.kubsradio.com/index.htm
Editorial Profile: KUBS-FM is a non-commercial station owned by Newport High School. The format of the station is country. KUBS-FM broadcasts to the Newport, WA area at 91.5 FM.

KUCA-FM
Owner: University of Central Arkansas
Editorial: University Central, Conway, Arkansas 72035-0001. **T:** 1 501 450-3326
Editorial Profile: KUCA-FM is a non-commercial college station owned by University of Central Arkansas. The format of the station is AC. KUCA-FM broadcasts to the Conway, AR area at a frequency of 91.3 FM.

KUCB-FM
Owner: Unalaska Community Broadcasting
Editorial: 5th & Broadway, Unalaska, Alaska 99685. **T:** 1 907 581-1888 **E:** info@kucb.org
W: http://www.kucb.org
Editorial Profile: KUCB-FM is a non-commercial station owned by Unalaska Community Broadcasting. The format of the station is variety. KUCB-FM broadcasts to the Unalaska, AK area at 89.7 FM.

KUCD-FM
Owner: Clear Channel Media and Entertainment
Editorial: 650 Iwilei Rd Ste 400, Honolulu, Hawaii 96817-5319. **T:** 1 808 550-9200
W: http://www.star1019.com
Editorial Profile: KUCD-FM is a commercial station owned by Clear Channel Media and Entertainment. The format of the station is rock alternative. KUCD-FM broadcasts to the Honolulu area at 101.9 FM.

KUCO-FM
Owner: University of Central Oklahoma
Editorial: 100 N University Dr, Edmond, Oklahoma 73034-5207. **T:** 1 405 974-3333
E: kcscfm@uco.edu
W: http://www.kucofm.com
Editorial Profile: KUCO-FM is a non-commercial station owned by the University of Central Oklahoma. The format of the station is classical music. KUCO-FM broadcasts to the Edmond, OK area at 90.1 FM.

KUCR-FM
Owner: University of California - Regents
Editorial: 691 W Linden St Univ Of California, Riverside, California 92507-3919.
T: 1 951 827-3737 **E:** kucrpsa@gmail.com
W: http://www.kucr.org
Editorial Profile: KUCR-FM is a non-commercial station owned by the University of California - Regents. The format for the station is adult contemporary music. KUCR-FM broadcasts to the Riverside, CA area at 88.3 FM.

KUCV-FM
Owner: Nebraska Educational Telecommunications Commission
Editorial: 1800 N 33rd St, Lincoln, Nebraska 68503. **T:** 1 402 472-3611
E: radio@netnebraska.org
W: http://netnebraska.org/radio
Editorial Profile: KUCV-FM is a non-commercial station owned by Nebraska Educational Telecommunications Commission. The format of the station is news and classical music. KUCV-FM broadcasts to the Lincoln, NE area at 91.1 FM.

KUDD-FM
Owner: Broadway Media
Editorial: 515 S 700 E Ste 1C, Salt Lake City, Utah 84102-2802. **T:** 1 801 412-6040
W: http://www.mix1079fm.com
Editorial Profile: KUDD-FM is a commercial station owned by Broadway Media. The format of the station is Top 40/CHR music. KUDD-FM broadcasts in the Salt Lake City area at 107.9 FM.

KUDL-AM
Owner: Entercom Communications Corp.
Editorial: 7000 Squibb Rd, Mission, Kansas 66202-3233. **T:** 1 913 677-8998
W: http://www.kmbz.com
Editorial Profile: KUDL-AM is a commercial station owned by Entercom Communications Corp. The format of the station is business news. KUDL-AM broadcasts to the Kansas City, MO area at 1660 AM.

KUDU-FM
Owner: Lifetalk Radio Inc.
Editorial: 1318 Ak Hwy,, Tok, Alaska 99780.
T: 1 907 883-8343 **W:** http://www.lifetalk.net

KUER-FM
Owner: University of Utah
Editorial: 101 Wasatch Dr #240, Salt Lake City, Utah 84112-1799. **T:** 1 801 581-6625
E: news@kuer.org **W:** http://www.kuer.org
Editorial Profile: KUER-FM is a non-commercial station owned by the University of Utah. The format of the station is news, jazz and talk. KUER-FM broadcasts to the Salt Lake City area at 90.1 FM.

KUFM-FM
Owner: University of Montana
Editorial: U Of Montana Par Tv, Room 180, Missoula, Montana 59812. **T:** 1 406 243-4931
W: http://www.kufm.org
Editorial Profile: KUFM-FM is a non-commercial station owned by University of Montana. The format of the station is news and a variety of music programming. KUFM-FM broadcasts in the Missoula, MT area at 89.1 FM.

KUFO-AM
Owner: Alpha Broadcasting
Editorial: 1211 SW 5th Ave Ste 600, Portland, Oregon 97204-3706. **T:** 1 503 517-6400
E: news@kxl.com
W: http://www.freedom970.com
Editorial Profile: KUFO-AM is a commercial station owned by Alpha Broadcasting. The format of the station is conservative talk. KUFO-AM broadcasts to the Portland, OR area at 970 AM.

KUFW-FM
Owner: National Farm Workers Service Center
Editorial: 400 W Caldwell Ave, Ste C, Visalia, California 93277-7864. **T:** 1 559 622-9401
W: http://www.campesina.com
Editorial Profile: KUFW-FM is a commercial station owned by National Farm Workers Service Center. The format of the station is regional Mexican music. KUFW-FM broadcasts to the Visalia, CA area at 90.5 FM.

KUGN-AM
Owner: Cumulus Media Inc.
Editorial: 1200 Executive Pkwy, Ste 440, Eugene, Oregon 97401. **T:** 1 541 284-8500
E: news@kugn.com **W:** http://www.kugn.com
Editorial Profile: KUGN-AM is a commercial station owned by Cumulus Media Inc. The format of the station is news and talk. KUGN-AM broadcasts in the Eugene, OR area at 590 AM.

KUGR-AM
Owner: Wagonwheel Communications Corp.
Editorial: 40 Shoshone Ave, Green River, Wyoming 82935-5321. **T:** 1 307 875-6666
E: mail@theradionetwork.net
W: http://www.theradionetwork.net
Editorial Profile: KUGR-AM is a commercial station owned by Wagonwheel Communications Corp. The format of the station is adult contemporary music. KUGR-AM broadcasts to the Green River, WY area at 1490 AM.

KUHA-FM
Owner: University of Houston
Editorial: 4343 Elgin Fl 3, Houston, Texas 77204-0002. **T:** 1 713 743-0887
E: communications@kuhf.org
W: http://classical917.org
Editorial Profile: KUHF-FM is a non-commercial station owned by the University of Houston. The format of the station is classical music. KUHF-FM broadcasts to the Houston, TX area at a frequency of 91.7 FM.

KUHC-FM
Owner: Top O'Texas Educations Broadcasting Foundation
Editorial: 116 Hillcrest Dr, Seminole, Oklahoma 74868-5810. **T:** 1 405 380-3516
Editorial Profile: KUHC-FM is a non-commercial station owned by Top O'Texas Educations Broadcasting Foundation. The format of the station is gospel. KUHC-FM broadcasts to the Clayton, NM area and airs locally at 90.5 FM.

KUHF-FM
Owner: University of Houston
Editorial: 4343 Elgin, Fl 3, Houston, Texas 77204. **T:** 1 713 743-0887
E: communications@kuhf.org
W: http://www.kuhf.org
Editorial Profile: KUHF-FM is a non-commercial station owned by the University of Houston. The format of the station is news programming. KUHF-FM broadcasts to the Houston area at 88.7 FM.

KUHL-AM
Owner: Knight Broadcasting Inc.
Editorial: 1101 S Broadway, Ste C, Santa Maria, California 93454. **T:** 1 805 922-7727
E: 1440@knightbroadcasting.com
W: http://www.am1440.com
Editorial Profile: KUHL-AM is a commercial station owned by Knight Broadcasting, Inc. The format of the station is news and talk. KUHL-AM broadcasts to the Santa Maria, CA area at 1410 AM.

KUIC-FM
Owner: Coast Radio Company Inc.
Editorial: 555 Mason Street, Ste 245, Vacaville, California 95688. **T:** 1 707 446-0200
E: news@kuic.com **W:** http://www.kuic.com
Editorial Profile: KUIC-FM is a commercial station owned by Coast Radio Company Inc. The format of the station is adult

contemporary. KUIC-FM broadcasts to the Vacaville, CA area at 95.3 FM.

KUIK-AM
Owner: Westside Radio Inc.
Editorial: 3355 NE Cornell Rd, Hillsboro, Oregon 97124. **T:** 1 503 640-1360
E: amradio@kuik.com **W:** http://www.kuik.com
Editorial Profile: KUIK-AM is a commercial station owned by Westside Radio Inc. The format of the station is news, sports and talk. KUIK-AM broadcasts in the Portland, OR area at 1360 AM.

KUJ-AM
Owner: Alexandra Communications Inc.
Editorial: 45 S Campbell Rd, Walla Walla, Washington 99362-9597. **T:** 1 509 527-1000
W: http://www.kujam.com
Editorial Profile: KUJ-AM is a commercial station owned by Alexandra Communications Inc. The format of the station is news/talk and sports programming. KUJ-AM broadcasts to the Walla Walla, WA area at 1420 AM.

KUJ-FM
Owner: Ingstad Radio Washington, LLC
Editorial: 4304 W 24th Ave Ste 200, Kennewick, Washington 99338-2320.
T: 1 509 783-0783
W: http://www.power991fm.com
Editorial Profile: KUJ-FM is a commercial station owned by Ingstad Radio Washington, LLC. The format of the station is Top 40/CHR. KUJ-FM broadcasts to the Kennewick, WA area at 99.1 FM.

KUJZ-FM
Owner: Cumulus Media Inc.
Editorial: 1200 Executive Pkwy, Eugene, Oregon 97401-2114. **T:** 1 541 284-8500
W: http://www.953thescore.com
Editorial Profile: KUJZ-FM is a commercial station owned by Cumulus Media Inc. The format of the station is sports and talk. KUJZ-FM broadcasts to the Eugene, OR area at 95.3 FM.

KUKA-FM
Owner: Benavides (Jerry)
Editorial: 2722 N Business Highway 281, Alice, Texas 78332. **T:** 1 361 668-6666
W: http://www.kukafm.com
Editorial Profile: KUKA-FM is a commercial station owned by Jerry Benavides. The format of the station is Hispanic. KUKA-FM broadcasts to the Alice, TX area at 105.9 FM.

KUKI-AM
Owner: Bicoastal Media LLC
Editorial: 140 N Main St, Lakeport, California 95453-4815. **T:** 1 707 263-6113
E: kukinews@bicoastalmedia.com
W: http://www.lamaquinamusical.net
Editorial Profile: KUKI-AM is a commercial station owned by Bicoastal Media LLC. The format of the station is Spanish news and talk. KUKI-AM broadcasts to the Ukiah, CA area at 1400 AM.

KUKI-FM
Owner: Bicoastal Media LLC
Editorial: 140 N Main St, Lakeport, California 95453-4815. **T:** 1 707 263-6113
E: kukinews@bicoastalmedia.com
W: http://www.kukifm.com
Editorial Profile: KUKI-FM is a commercial station owned by Bicoastal Media LLC. The format of the station is country music. KUKI-FM broadcasts in the San Francisco area at 103.3 FM.

KUKN-FM
Owner: Washington Interstate Broadcasting Inc
Editorial: 506 W Cowlitz Way, Kelso, Washington 98626. **T:** 1 360 636-0110
W: http://www.kukn.com
Editorial Profile: KUKN-FM is a commercial station owned by Washington Interstate Broadcasting Inc. The format of the station is contemporary country. KUKN-FM broadcasts to the Kelso, WA area at 105.5 FM.

KUKU-AM
Owner: Ozark Radio Network Inc.
Editorial: 983 E Us Highway 160, West Plains, Missouri 65775-4801. **T:** 1 417 256-1025
E: news@ozarkradionetwork.com
W: http://www.ozarknewstalkradio.com/index.php
Editorial Profile: KUKU-AM is a commercial station owned by Ozark Radio Network Inc. The format of the station is news and talk. KUKU-AM broadcasts to the Mountain View, MO area at 1330 AM.

KUKU-FM
Owner: Ozark Radio Network Inc.
Editorial: 983 E Us Highway 160, West Plains, Missouri 65775-4801. **T:** 1 417 256-1025
E: news@ozarkradionetwork.com
W: http://www.bigcountry99.com
Editorial Profile: KUKU-FM is commercial station owned by Ozark Radio Network Inc. The format of the station is classic country. KUKU-FM broadcasts to the Mountain View, MO area at 99.3 FM.

KULE-AM
Owner: Adelante Media Group
Editorial: 910 Basin St SW, Ephrata, Washington 98823. **T:** 1 509 457-1000
Editorial Profile: KULE-AM is a commercial station owned by Adelante Media Group. The format of the station is news and talk programming. KULE-AM broadcasts to the Ephrata, WA area at 730 AM.

KULH-FM
Owner: Resources Management Unlimited Inc.
Editorial: 802 Calhoun St, Chillicothe, Missouri 64601-2205. **T:** 1 660 646-2255
E: 1059thewave@sbcglobal.net
W: http://www.1059thewave.com
Editorial Profile: KULH-FM is a commercial station owned by Resources Management Unlimited Inc. The format of the station is contemporary Christian. KULH-FM broadcasts to the Chillicothe, MO area at 105.9 FM.

KULL-FM
Owner: Townsquare Media, LLC
Editorial: 3911 S 1st St, Abilene, Texas 79605-1639. **T:** 1 325 676-7711
W: http://www.trueoldiesabilene.com
Editorial Profile: KULL-FM is a commercial station owned by Townsquare Media, LLC. The format of the station is classic hits. KFGL-FM broadcasts to the Abilene, TX area at 100.7 FM.

KULM-FM
Owner: La Grange Broadcasting
Editorial: 325 Radio Ln, Columbus, Texas 78934. **T:** 1 979 732-5766
E: kulmradio@yahoo.com
W: http://www.kulmradio.com
Editorial Profile: KULM-FM is a commercial station owned by La Grange Broadcasting. The format of the station is contemporary country music. KULM-FM broadcasts to the Columbus, TX area at 98.3 FM.

KULO-FM
Owner: Omni Broadcasting Co.
Editorial: 604 3rd Ave W, Alexandria, Minnesota 56308. **T:** 1 320 762-2154
E: email@cool943.com
W: http://www.cool943.com
Editorial Profile: KULO-FM is a commercial station owned by Omni Broadcasting Co. The format of the station is oldies. KULO-FM broadcasts to the Alexandria, MN area at 94.3 FM.

KULP-AM
Owner: Wharton County Radio Inc.
Editorial: 515 E Jackson St, El Campo, Texas 77437-4537. **T:** 1 979 543-3303
W: http://www.kulpradio.com
Editorial Profile: KULP-AM is a commercial station owned by Wharton County Radio Inc. The format of the station is classic country. KULP-AM broadcasts to the El Campo, TX area at 1390 AM.

KULV-FM
Owner: Educational Media Foundation
Editorial: 5700 W Oaks Blvd, Rocklin, California 95765. **T:** 1 916 251-2142
W: http://www.klove.com
Editorial Profile: KULV-FM is a commercial station owned by Educational Media Foundation. The format of the station is contemporary Christian. KULV-FM broadcasts to Rocklin, CA at 97.1.

KULY-AM
Owner: Armada Media Corp.
Editorial: 2917 S Colorado St, Ulysses, Kansas 67880-8201. **T:** 1 620 356-1420
W: http://www.wksradio.com
Editorial Profile: KULY-AM is a commercial station owned by Armada Media Corp. The format of the station is country music. KULY-AM broadcasts to the Ulysses, KS area at 1420 AM.

KUMA-AM
Owner: Capps Broadcast Group
Editorial: 2003 NW 56th St, Pendleton, Oregon 97801. **T:** 1 541 276-1511
E: 1290kuma@cappsbroadcastgroup.com

W: http://www.cappsbroadcastgroup.com/1290kuma
Editorial Profile: KUMA-AM is a commercial station owned by Capps Broadcast Group. The format of the station is news and talk. KUMA-AM broadcasts to the Pendleton, OR area at 1290 AM.

KUMA-FM
Owner: Capps Broadcast Group
Editorial: 2003 NW 56th St, Pendleton, Oregon 97801-4593. **T:** 1 541 276-1511
W: http://www.921kuma.com
Editorial Profile: KUMA-FM is a commercial station owned by Capps Broadcast Group. The format of the station is adult contemporary. KUMA-FM airs in the Pendleton, OR area at 92.1 FM.

KUMD-FM
Owner: Regents of the Univ. of MN-Duluth
Editorial: 130 Humanities, 1201 Ordean Ct, Duluth, Minnesota 55812. **T:** 1 218 726-7181
E: kumd@kumd.org **W:** http://www.kumd.org
Editorial Profile: KUMD-FM is a non-commercial station owned by Regents of the Univ. of MN-Duluth. The format of the station is primarily AAA, but also features a variety of other genres including jazz and blues. KUMD-FM broadcasts to the Duluth, MN area at 103.3 FM.

KUMM-FM
Owner: University of Minnesota-Morris
Editorial: 600 E 4th St, Morris, Minnesota 56267. **T:** 1 320 589-6076
W: http://www.kumm.org
Editorial Profile: KUMM-FM is a college station owned by University of Minnesota-Morris. The format of the station is college variety. KUMM-FM broadcasts to the Minneapolis-St. Paul, MN, area at 89.7 FM.

KUMR-FM
Owner: Mid Missouri Media, Inc.
Editorial: 1051 Kingshighway St Ste 6, Rolla, Missouri 65401-2981. **T:** 1 573 308-1045
E: info@mysunny1045.com
W: http://www.mysunny1045.com
Editorial Profile: KUMR-FM is a commercial station owned by Mid Missouri Media, Inc. The format of the station is Lite AC. KUMR-FM broadcasts to the Rolla, MO area at a frequency of 104.5 FM.

KUMU-FM
Owner: Ohana Broadcast Company LLC
Editorial: 1000 Bishop St Ste 200, Honolulu, Hawaii 96813-4203. **T:** 1 808 947-1500
W: http://www.kumu.com
Editorial Profile: KUMU-FM is a commercial station owned by Ohana Broadcast Company LLC. The format of the station is urban adult contemporary. KUMU-FM broadcsts to the Honolulu area at 94.7 FM.

KUMX-FM
Owner: West Central Broadcasting Co Inc.
Editorial: 168 Kvvp Dr, Leesville, Louisiana 71446-5817. **T:** 1 337 537-9000
Editorial Profile: KUMX-FM is a commercial station owned by West Central Broadcasting Co Inc. The format of the station is adult contemporary. KUMX-FM broadcasts to the North Fort Polk, LA area at 106.7 FM.

KUNA-FM
Owner: Gulf-California Broadcast Co.
Editorial: 42650 Melanie Pl, Palm Desert, California 92211-5170. **T:** 1 760 568-6830
Editorial Profile: KUNA-FM is a commercial station owned by Gulf-California Broadcast Co. The format of the station is Regional Mexican. KUNA-FM broadcasts to the Palm Desert, CA area at 96.7 FM.

KUNC-FM
Owner: Community Radio for Northern Colorado
Editorial: 1901 56Th Ave Ste 200, Greeley, Colorado 80634-2950. **T:** 1 970 378-2579
E: news@kunc.org **W:** http://www.kunc.org
Editorial Profile: KUNC-FM is a non-commercial station owned by Community Radio for Northern Colorado. The format of the station is a variety of programming and music. KUNC-FM broadcasts to the Greeley, CO are at 91.5 FM.

KUND-FM
Owner: Prairie Public Broadcasting Inc.
Editorial: 1814 N 15th St, Bismarck, North Dakota 58501-2025. **T:** 1 701 224-1700
E: info@prairiepublic.org
W: http://www.prairiepublic.org
Editorial Profile: KUND-FM is a non-commercial station owned by Prairie Public

Broadcasting Inc. The format of the station is classical and news. KUND-FM broadcasts to the Bismarck, ND area at 89.3 FM.

KUNI-FM
Owner: University of Northern Iowa
Editorial: University Of Northern Iowa, Cedar Falls, Iowa 50614-0001. **T:** 1 319 273-6400
E: news@iowapublicradio.org
W: http://iowapublicradio.org
Editorial Profile: KUNI-FM is a non-commercial station owned by the University of Northern Iowa. The format for the station is adult contemporary, news and talk. KUNI-FM broadcasts to the Cedar Falls, IA area at 90.9 FM.

KUNK-FM
Owner: Hooten Broadcasting Company, LLC
Editorial: 101 Boatyard Dr Ste E, Fort Bragg, California 95437-5700. **T:** 1 707 964-5307
E: traffic@theskunkfm.com
W: http://www.theskunkfm.com
Editorial Profile: KUNK-FM is a commercial station owned by Hooten Broadcasting Company, LLC. The format of the station is adult contemporary. KUNK-FM broadcasts to the Fort Bragg, CA area at 92.7 FM.

KUNM-FM
Owner: University of New Mexico
Editorial: MSC06 3520 Onate Hall 1 University, Albuquerque, New Mexico 87131. **T:** 1 505 277-4806 **E:** news@kunm.org
W: http://www.kunm.org
Editorial Profile: KUNM-FM is a non-commercial station owned by the University of New Mexico. The format of the station is news and variety. KUNM-FM broadcasts to the Albuquerque, NM area at 89.9 FM.

KUNO-AM
Owner: Clear Channel Media and Entertainment
Editorial: 501 Tupper Lane Radio Plaza, Corpus Christi, Texas 78417-9736.
T: 1 361 289-0111
W: http://corpuschristisp.lapreciosa.com
Editorial Profile: KUNO-AM is a commercial station owned by Clear Channel Media and Entertainment. The format of the station is Hispanic oldies. KUNO-AM broadcasts to the Corpus Christi, TX area at 1400 AM.

KUNQ-FM
Owner: Media Professionals, Inc.
Editorial: 17647 Highway B, Houston, Missouri 65483-2818. **T:** 1 417 967-3353
E: traffic@bigcountry99.com
W: http://bigcountry99.com
Editorial Profile: KUNQ-FM is a commercial station owned by Media Professionals, Inc. The format of the station is contemporary and classic country and rock music. KUNQ-FM broadcasts to the Houston, MO area at 99.3 FM.

KUNR-FM
Owner: University of Nevada, Reno
Editorial: University of Nevada Reno, Mail Stop 294, Reno, Nevada 89557.
T: 1 775 327-5867 **E:** news@kunr.org
W: http://www.kunr.org
Editorial Profile: KUNR-FM is a non-commercial station owned by the University of Nevada, Reno. The format of the station is classical, jazz and news. KUNR-FM broadcasts to the Reno, NV area at 88.7 FM.

KUNV-FM
Owner: University of Nevada
Editorial: 4505 S Maryland Pkwy, Las Vegas, Nevada 89154-9900. **T:** 1 702 895-0065
W: http://kunv.unlv.edu
Editorial Profile: KUNV-FM is a non-commercial station owned by the University of Nevada. The format of the station is jazz music and variety programming. KUNV-FM broadcasts to the Las Vegas area at 91.5 FM.

KUNX-AM
Owner: Gold Coast Broadcasting, LLC
Editorial: 2284 S Victoria Ave, Ventura, California 93003-6641. **T:** 1 805 289-1400
E: kvtanews@yahoo.com
W: http://goldcoastbroadcasting.com
Editorial Profile: KUNX-AM is commercial station owned by Gold Coast Broadcasting, LLC. The format is Hispanic news/talk. The station airs in the Ventura, CA area at 1590 AM. KUNX-AM airs programming on KVTA-AM and KKZZ-AM.

KUOA-AM
Owner: Hog Radio, Inc.
Editorial: 2250 W Sunset Ave, Springdale, Arkansas 72762-5148. **T:** 1 479 303-2034

E: thehog@hogsportsradio.com
W: http://www.hogsnow.com
Editorial Profile: KUOA-AM is a commercial station owned by Hog Radio, Inc. The format of the station is talk. KUOA-AM broadcasts to the Springdale, AR area at 1290 AM.

KUOI-FM
Owner: University of Idaho
Editorial: Student Union Bldg Univ Of I, Flr 3, Moscow, Idaho 83844. **T:** 1 208 885-2218
E: news@kuoi.org **W:** http://www.kuoi.org
Editorial Profile: KUOI-FM is a non-commercial station owned by the University of Idaho. The format of the station is college variety. KUOI-FM broadcasts to the Moscow, ID area at 89.3 FM.

KUOL-AM
Owner: Bernal(Paulino)
Editorial: 4501 N McColl Rd, McAllen, Texas 78504. **T:** 1 956 781-5528
W: http://www.nuevaradiocristiana.com
Editorial Profile: KUOL-AM is a commercial station owned by Paulino Bernal. The format of the station is Hispanic contemporary Christian music. KUOL-AM broadcasts to the McAllen, TX area at 1470 AM.

KUOM-AM
Owner: University of Minnesota
Editorial: 610 Rarig Center 330 21st Ave S, Minneapolis, Minnesota 55455-0415.
T: 1 612 625-3500
E: stationmanager@radiok.org
W: http://radiok.cce.umn.edu
Editorial Profile: KUOM-AM is a non-commercial station owned by the University of Minnesota. The format of the station is rock alternative. KUOM-AM broadcasts to the Minneapolis area at 770 AM.

KUOM-FM
Owner: University of Minnesota
Editorial: 610 Rarig Center 330 21st Ave S, Minneapolis, Minnesota 55455-0415.
T: 1 612 625-3500 **E:** news@radiok.org
W: http://www.radiok.org
Editorial Profile: KUOM-FM is a non-commercial station owned by the University of Minnesota. The format is rock alternative. The station airs in the Minneapolis, MN area at 106.5FM.

KUOO-FM
Owner: Community First Broadcasting
Editorial: Highway 9 West, Spirit Lake, Iowa 51360. **T:** 1 712 336-5800
E: news@exploreokoboji.com
W: http://www.kuooradio.com
Editorial Profile: KUOO-FM is a commercial station owned by Community First Broadcasting. The format of the station is adult contemporary music. KUOO-FM broadcasts to the Spirit Lake, IA area at 103.9 FM.

KUOP-FM
Owner: Capital Public Radio
Editorial: 7055 Folsom Blvd, Sacramento, California 95826-2625. **T:** 1 916 278-8900
E: news@capradio.org
W: http://www.capradio.org
Editorial Profile: KUOP-FM is a non-commercial station owned by Capital Public Radio. The format of the station is jazz, news and talk. KUOP-FM broadcasts to the Stockton, CA area at 91.3 FM.

KUOR-FM
Owner: University of Redlands
Editorial: 474 S Raymond Ave, Pasadena, California 91105-2629. **T:** 1 626 583-5100
E: contact@kpcc.org **W:** http://www.scpr.org
Editorial Profile: KUOR-FM is a non-commercial station owned by University of Redlands and operated by Southern California Public Radio. The format of the station is news and talk. KUOR-FM broadcasts to the Long Beach, CA area at 89.1 FM.

KUOW-AM
Owner: University of Washington
Editorial: 4518 University Way NE, Ste 310, Seattle, Washington 98105. **T:** 1 206 543-2710
E: newsroom@kuow.org
W: http://www.kuow.org
Editorial Profile: KUOW-AM is a non-commercial station owned by the University of Washington. The format of the station is news and talk. KUOW-AM broadcasts to the Seattle area at 1340 AM.

KUOW-FM
Owner: University of Washington
Editorial: 4518 University Way NE, Seattle, Washington 98105-4530. **T:** 1 206 543-2710
E: letters@kuow.org **W:** http://www.kuow.org
Editorial Profile: KUOW-FM is a non-commercial station owned by the University of Washington. The format of the station is news and talk programming. KUOW-FM broadcasts to the Seattle area at 94.9 FM.

KUPD-FM
Owner: Hubbard Radio, LLC
Editorial: 1900 W Carmen St, Guadalupe, Arizona 85283-2559. **T:** 1 480 838-0400
W: http://www.98kupd.com
Editorial Profile: KUPD-FM is a commercial station owned by Hubbard Radio, LLC. The format of the station is rock/album-oriented rock music. KUPD-FM broadcasts to the Phoenix area at 97.9 FM.

KUPH-FM
Owner: Central Ozark Radio Network Inc.
Editorial: 6962 Us Highway 60, Mountain View, Missouri 65548-8198.
T: 1 417 934-0969
E: news@ozarkradionetwork.com
W: http://www.thefox969radio.com/index.html
Editorial Profile: KUPH-FM is a commercial station owned by Central Ozark Radio Network Inc. The format of the station is hot adult contemporary. KUPH-FM broadcasts to the Mountain View, MO area at 96.9 FM.

KUPI-FM
Owner: Sand Hill Media
Editorial: 854 Lindsay Blvd, Idaho Falls, Idaho 83402. **T:** 1 208 522-1101
W: http://www.kupi99.com
Editorial Profile: KUPI-FM is a commercial station owned by Sand Hill Media. The format of the station is contemporary country. KUPI-FM broadcasts to the Rexburg, ID area at 99.1 FM.

KUPL-FM
Owner: Alpha Broadcasting
Editorial: 1211 SW 5th Ave Fl 6, Portland, Oregon 97204-3735. **T:** 1 503 517-6400
W: http://www.987thebull.com
Editorial Profile: KUPL-FM is a commercial station owned by Alpha Broadcasting. The format of the station is contemporary country music. KUPL-FM broadcasts in the Portland, OR area at 98.7 FM.

KUPR-FM
Owner: Southern New Mexico Radio Foundation
Editorial: 3001 N Florida Ave, Alamogordo, New Mexico 88310-8711. **T:** 1 575 437-0917
E: kupr917@yahoo.com
W: http://www.kuprradio.com
Editorial Profile: KUPR-FM is a non-commercial community radio station owned by Southern New Mexico Radio Foundation. The format of the station is contemporary christian music. KUPR-FM broadcasts to the Alamogordo, New Mexico area at a frequency of 91.7 FM.

KUPS-FM
Owner: University of Puget Sound
Editorial: 1500 N Warner St Stop 1049, Tacoma, Washington 98416-1049.
T: 1 253 879-3288
E: kupsproduction@pugetsound.edu
W: http://www.kups.net
Editorial Profile: KUPS-FM is a non-commercial station owned by the University of Puget Sound. The format of the station is college variety. KUPS-FM broadcasts to the Seattle area at 90.1 FM.

KUQL-FM
Owner: Saga Communications
Editorial: 501 S Ohlman St, Mitchell, South Dakota 57301. **T:** 1 605 996-9667
W: http://www.kool98.com
Editorial Profile: KUQL-FM is a commercial station owned by Saga Communications. The format of the station is oldies. KUQL-FM broadcasts to the Mitchell, SD area at 98.3 FM.

KUQQ-FM
Owner: Community First Broadcasting
Editorial: Highway 9 West, Spirit Lake, Iowa 51360. **T:** 1 712 336-5800
E: news@exploreokoboji.com
W: http://www.kuqqfm.com
Editorial Profile: KUQQ-FM is a commercial station owned by Community First Broadcasting. The format of the station is classic rock music. KUQQ-FM broadcasts to the Spirit Lake, IA area at 102.1 FM.

KURB-FM
Owner: Cumulus Media Inc
Editorial: 700 Wellington Hills Rd, Little Rock, Arkansas 72211-2026. **T:** 1 501 401-0200
E: b985radio@cumulus.com
W: http://www.b98.com
Editorial Profile: KURB-FM is a commercial station owned by Cumulus Media Inc. The format of the station is hot adult contemporary. KURB-FM broadcasts to the Little Rock, AR area at 98.5 FM.

KURE-FM
Owner: Iowa State University
Editorial: 1199 Friley Hall, Ames, Iowa 50012-0001. **T:** 1 515 294-4332 **E:** kure@kure885.org
W: http://www.kure885.org
Editorial Profile: KURE-FM is a non-commercial college station owned by Iowa State University. The format of the station college variety. KURE-FM broadcasts to the college students at Iowa State University and surrounding areas at 88.5 FM.

KURK-FM
Owner: Wilks Broadcast Group
Editorial: 300 E 2Nd St Ste 1400, Reno, Nevada 89501-1566. **T:** 1 775 333-0123
W: http://www.929thebandit.com
Editorial Profile: KURK-FM is a commercial station owned by Wilks Broadcast Group. The format of the station is classic rock. KURK-FM broadcasts to the Reno, NV area at 92.9 FM.

KURL-FM
Owner: Elenbaas Media Inc.
Editorial: 636 Haugen St, Billings, Montana 59101. **T:** 1 406 245-3121
E: news@kurlradio.com
W: http://www.kurlradio.com
Editorial Profile: KURL-FM is a commercial station owned by Elenbaas Media Inc. The format of the station is religious. KURL-FM broadcasts to the Billings, MT area at 93.3 FM.

KURM-AM
Owner: KERM Inc.
Editorial: 113 E New Hope Rd, Rogers, Arkansas 72758. **T:** 1 479 633-0790
E: news@kurm.net **W:** http://www.kurm.net
Editorial Profile: KURM-AM is a commercial station owned by KERM Inc. The format of the station is news and talk. KURM-AM broadcasts to the Rogers, AR area at 790 AM.

KURM-FM
Owner: KERM Inc.
Editorial: 113 E New Hope Rd, Rogers, Arkansas 72758. **T:** 1 479 633-0790
E: news@kurm.net **W:** http://www.kurm.net
Editorial Profile: KURM-FM is a commercial station owned by KERM Inc. The format of the station is news and talk. KURM-FM broadcasts to the Rogers, AR area at 100.3 FM.

KURQ-FM
Owner: El Dorado Broadcasting
Editorial: 51 Zaca Ln Ste 100, San Luis Obispo, California 93401-7353.
T: 1 805 545-0101
W: http://www.newrock1073.com
Editorial Profile: KURQ-FM is a commercial station owned by El Dorado Broadcasting. The format of the station is rock/album-oriented rock. KURQ-FM broadcasts to the San Luis Obispo, CA area at 107.3 FM.

KURR-FM
Owner: Simmons Media Group
Editorial: 216 W St George Blvd Ste 101, Saint George, Utah 84770-1306.
T: 1 800 603-6035 **E:** mail@demolink.org
Editorial Profile: KURR-FM is a commercial station owned by Simmons Media Group. The format of the station is adult hits. KURR-FM broadcasts to the St. George, UT area at 103.1 FM.

KURV-AM
Owner: MBM Radio Del Rio, LLC
Editorial: 1201 N Jackson Rd, Ste 900, McAllen, Texas 78501-5764.
T: 1 956 992-8895 **E:** news@kurv.com
W: http://www.kurv.com
Editorial Profile: KURV-AM is a commercial station owned by MBM Radio Del Rio, LLC. The format of the station is news and talk. KURV-AM broadcasts to the Edinburg, TX area at 710 AM.

KURY-AM
Owner: Eureka Broadcasting Co., Inc.
Editorial: 605 Railroad St, Brookings, Oregon 97415. **T:** 1 541 469-2111
E: kury@kuryradio.com **W:** http://kury910.com
Editorial Profile: KURY-AM is a commercial station owned by Eureka Broadcasting Co., Inc.The format of the station is adult standards. KURY-AM broadcasts to the Brookings, OR area at 910 AM.

KURY-FM
Owner: Eureka Broadcasting Inc.
Editorial: 605 Railroad St, Brookings, Oregon 97415. **T:** 1 541 469-2111
W: http://kury953.com
Editorial Profile: KURY-FM is a commercial station owned by Eureka Broadcasting Co., Inc. The format of the station is classic hits. KURY-FM broadcasts to the Brookings, OR area at a frequency of 95.3 FM.

KUSA-FM
Owner: AJB Holdings, LLC
Editorial: 6 E Main St, Price, Utah 84501-3032. **T:** 1 435 637-1080
E: kusabuzz@gmail.com
W: http://utahsclassicradio.com
Editorial Profile: KUSA-FM is a commercial station owned by AJB Holdings, LLC. The format of the station is modern adult contemporary. KWSA-FM broadcasts to the Price, UT area at 100.1 FM.

KUSB-FM
Owner: Townsquare Media, Inc.
Editorial: 4303 Memorial Hwy, Mandan, North Dakota 58554-4711. **T:** 1 701 663-6411
W: http://www.uscountryonline.com
Editorial Profile: KUSB-FM is a commercial station owned by Townsquare Media, Inc. The format of the station is country music. KUSB-FM broadcasts to the Bismarck, ND area at 103.3 FM.

KUSC-FM
Owner: University of Southern California
Editorial: 1149 S Hill St Ste H100, Los Angeles, California 90015-2229.
T: 1 213 225-7400 **E:** pressrelease@kusc.org
W: http://www.kusc.org
Editorial Profile: KUSC-FM is a non-commercial station owned by the University of Southern California. The format of the station is classical. KUSC-FM broadcasts to the greater Los Angeles area at 91.5 FM. KUSC-FM does not produce their news content. The station only does interviews related to the arts.

KUSD-FM
Owner: State Board for Educational Television
Editorial: 555 N Dakota St, Vermillion, South Dakota 57069. **T:** 1 605 677-5861
E: news@sdpb.org **W:** http://www.sdpb.org
Editorial Profile: KUSD-FM is a non-commercial station owned by the State Board for Educational Television. The format of the station is news, classical and jazz music. KUSD-FM broadcasts in the Vermillion, SD area at 89.7 FM.

KUSH-AM
Owner: Kelly Media, LLC
Editorial: 3818 E Main St, Cushing, Oklahoma 74023. **T:** 1 918 225-0922
E: kushradio@yahoo.com
W: http://www.1600kush.com
Editorial Profile: KUSH-AM is a commerical station owned by Kelly Media, LLC. The format for the station is news, sports and talk. KUSH-AM broadcasts to the Cushing, OK area at 1600 AM.

KUSJ-FM
Owner: Townsquare Media, Inc.
Editorial: 608 Moody Ln, Temple, Texas 76504-2952. **T:** 1 254 773-5252
W: http://www.myus105.com
Editorial Profile: KUSJ-FM is a commercial station owned by Townsquare Media, Inc.The format of the station is country. KUSJ-FM broadcasts to the Temple, TX area at 105.5 FM.

KUSN-FM
Owner: Radio Results Group
Editorial: 200 Arco Pl, Independence, Kansas 67301-3398. **T:** 1 316 331-8444
E: kggf.newsinfo@sbcglobal.net
W: http://radioresultsgroup.com/radioresultsgroup1_004.htm
Editorial Profile: KUSN-FM is a commercial station owned by Radio Results Group. The format of the station is country music. KUSN-FM broadcasts to the Tulsa, OK area at 98.1 FM.

KUSO-FM
Owner: Flood Communications LLC
Editorial: 214 N 7th St, Ste 1, Norfolk, Nebraska 68701. **T:** 1 402 371-0100
E: us92@us92.com **W:** http://www.us92.com
Editorial Profile: KUSO-FM is a commercial station owned by Flood Communications LLC.

The format of the station is contemporary country. KUSO-FM broadcasts to the Norfolk, NE area at 92.7 FM.

KUSP-FM
Owner: Pataphysical Broadcasting Foundation
Editorial: 203 8th Ave, Santa Cruz, California 95062. **T:** 1 831 476-2800 **E:** kusp@kusp.org **W:** http://www.kusp.org
Editorial Profile: KUSP-FM is a non-commercial station owned by Pataphysical Broadcasting Foundation. The format of the station is variety. KUSP-FM broadcasts to the Santa Cruz, CA area at 88.9 FM.

KUSQ-FM
Owner: Absolute Communications (dba Radio Werks)
Editorial: 28779 County Highway 35, Worthington, Minnesota 56187.
T: 1 507 372-5962 **E:** info@myradioworks.net
W: http://us95.us
Editorial Profile: KUSQ-FM is a commercial station owned by Absolute Communications (dba Radio Werks). The format of the station is contemporary country. KUSQ-FM broadcasts to the Worthington, MN area at 95.1 FM.

KUSU-FM
Owner: Utah State University
Editorial: 43 S Main St, Cache Valley Center for the Arts, Logan, Utah 84321-4560.
T: 1 435 797-3138 **W:** http://www.upr.org
Editorial Profile: KUSU-FM is a non-commercial station owned by Utah State University. The format of the station is classical and news. KUSU-FM broadcasts to the Salt Lake City area at 91.5 FM.

KUTC-FM
Owner: Mid-Utah Radio Inc.
Editorial: 1600 W 500 N, Manti, Utah 84642-5503. **T:** 1 435 835-7301
W: http://midutahradio.com
Editorial Profile: KUTC-FM is a commercial station owned by Mid-Utah Radio Inc. The format of the station is classic hits. KUTC-FM broadcasts to the Richfield, UT area at 93.7 FM.

KUTE-FM
Owner: KUTE Inc.
Editorial: 123 Capote Drive, Ignacio, Colorado 81137. **T:** 1 970 563-0255
W: http://www.ksut.org
Editorial Profile: KUTE-FM is a non-commercial station owned by KUTE Inc. The format of the station is variety. KUTE-FM broadcasts to the Ignacio, CO area at 90.1 FM.

KUT-FM
Owner: University of Texas at Austin
Editorial: 300 W. Dean Keeton (A0704), Austin, Texas 78701-3840. **T:** 1 512 471-1631
E: news@kut.org **W:** http://kut.org
Editorial Profile: KUT-FM is a non-commercial station owned by the University of Texas at Austin. The format of the station is news and talk. KUT-FM broadcasts in the Austin, TX area at 90.5 FM.

KUTI-AM
Owner: Townsquare Media, LLC
Editorial: 4010 Summitview Ave, Yakima, Washington 98908. **T:** 1 509 972-3461
W: http://1460espnyakima.com
Editorial Profile: KUTI-AM is a commercial station owned by Townsquare Media, LLC. The format of the station is sports. KUTI-AM broadcasts in the Yakima, WA at 1460 AM.

KUTR-AM
Owner: Truth Broadcasting
Editorial: 4405 Providence Ln, Winston Salem, North Carolina 27106-3226.
T: 1 336 759-0363 **E:** info@wtru.com
W: http://www.wtru.com
Editorial Profile: KUTR-AM is a commercial station owned by Truth Broadcasting. The format of the station is religious talk. KUTR-AM broadcasts to the Salt Lake City area at 820 AM.

KUTT-FM
Owner: Siebert Communications Inc.
Editorial: 414 4th St, Fairbury, Nebraska 68352. **T:** 1 402 729-3382
E: kutt@diodecom.net
W: http://www.kutt995.com
Editorial Profile: KUTT-FM is a commercial station owned by Siebert Communications Inc. The format of the station is country music. KUTT-FM broadcasts to the Fairbury, NE area at 99.5 FM.

KUTX-FM
Owner: University of Texas at Austin
Editorial: 300 W. Dean Keeton (A0704), Austin, Texas 78701-3840. **T:** 1 512 471-1631
E: kut@kutx.org **W:** http://kutx.org
Editorial Profile: KUTX-FM is a non-commercial station owned by University of Texas at Austin. The station format of the station is AAA. KXBT-FM broadcasts to the Austin, TX area at 98.9 FM.

KUTY-AM
Owner: High Desert Broadcasting LLC
Editorial: 570 E Avenue Q9, Palmdale, California 93550. **T:** 1 661 947-3107
W: http://www.lameramera1470.com/main.php
Editorial Profile: KUTY-AM is a commercial station owned by High Desert Broadcasting LLC. The format of the station is Mexican oldies. KUTY-AM broadcasts to the Los Angeles area at 1470 AM.

KUUB-FM
Owner: Lotus Communications Corp.
Editorial: 2900 Sutro St, Reno, Nevada 89512-1616. **T:** 1 775 329-9261
W: http://www.espn945.com
Editorial Profile: KUUB-FM is a commercial station owned by Lotus Communications Corp. The format of the station is sports/talk. The station broadcasts to the Reno, NV area at 94.5 FM.

KUUL-FM
Owner: Clear Channel Media and Entertainment
Editorial: 3535 E Kimberly Rd, Davenport, Iowa 52807-2583. **T:** 1 563 344-7000
W: http://www.1013kissfm.com
Editorial Profile: KUUL-FM is a commercial station owned by Clear Channel Media and Entertainment. The format of the station is Top 40/CHR. KUUL-FM broadcasts to the Davenport, IA area at 101.3 FM.

KUUU-FM
Owner: Broadway Media
Editorial: 515 S 700 E Ste 1C, Salt Lake City, Utah 84102-2802. **T:** 1 801 524 2600
W: http://www.u92online.com
Editorial Profile: KUUU-FM is a commercial station owned by Broadway Media. The format of the station is urban contemporary. KUUU-FM broadcasts to the Salt Lake City area at 92.5 FM.

KUVA-FM
Owner: MBM Radio Uvalde LLC
Editorial: 1400 Batesville Rd, Uvalde, Texas 78801. **T:** 1 830 278-2555
E: kuva@rcommunications.com
Editorial Profile: KUVA-FM is a commercial station owned by MBM Radio Uvalde LLC. The format of the station is Hispanic music. KUVA-FM broadcasts to the Uvalde, TX area at 102.3 FM.

KUVO-FM
Owner: Kuvo Denver Educational Broadcasting
Editorial: 2900 Welton St, Denver, Colorado 80205-3007. **T:** 1 303 480-9272
E: info@kuvo.org **W:** http://www.kuvo.org
Editorial Profile: KUVO-FM is a non-commercial station owned by Denver Educational Broadcasting. The format of the station is jazz. KUVO-FM broadcasts to the Denver area at 89.3 FM.

KUVR-AM
Owner: Armada Media Corp.
Editorial: 613 4th Ave, Holdrege, Nebraska 68949. **T:** 1 308 995-4020
E: kmty@highplainsradio.net
W: http://www.kuvr.com
Editorial Profile: KUVR-AM is a commercial station owned by Armada Media Corp. The format of the station is oldies music. KUVR-AM broadcasts to the Holdrege, NE area at 1380 AM.

KUWI-FM
Owner: University of Wyoming
Editorial: 1000 E University Ave, Dept 3984, Laramie, Wyoming 82071-2000.
T: 1 307 766-4240 **E:** wprhelp@uwyo.edu
W: http://www.wyomingpublicradio.net
Editorial Profile: KUWI-FM is a non-commercial owned by University of Wyoming. The format of the station is variety. KUWI-FM broadcasts to the Rawlins, WY area at 89.9 FM.

KUWJ-FM
Owner: University of Wyoming
Editorial: 1000 E University Ave, Laramie, Wyoming 82071. **T:** 1 307 766-4240
E: wprhelp@uwyo.edu

W: http://www.wyomingpublicradio.net
Editorial Profile: KUWJ-FM is a non-commercial station owned by the University of Wyoming. The format of the station is jazz music. KUWJ-FM broadcasts to the Laramie, WY area at 90.1 FM.

KUWR-FM
Owner: University of Wyoming
Editorial: 1000 E University Ave, Laramie, Wyoming 82071-2000. **T:** 1 307 766-4240
E: wprhelp@uwyo.edu
W: http://www.wyomingpublicmedia.org
Editorial Profile: KUWR-FM is a non-commercial station owned by University of Wyoming. The format of the station is public radio featuring a mix of news, jazz, AAA music and classical music. KUWR-FM broadcasts to the Laramie, WY area at 91.9 FM.

KUWS-FM
Owner: University of Wisconsin System Board of Regents
Editorial: 1805 Catlin Ave, Superior, Wisconsin 54880-2873. **T:** 1 715 394-8530
W: http://www.kuws.fm
Editorial Profile: KUWS-FM is non-commercial station owned by the University of Wisconsin System Board of Regents. The format of the station is news, talk and variety music. KUWS-FM broadcasts to the Superior, WI area at 91.3 FM.

KUWY-FM
Owner: University of Wyoming
Editorial: 1000 E University Ave, Dept 3984, Laramie, Wyoming 82071. **T:** 1 307 766-4240
E: wprhelp@uwyo.edu
W: http://www.wyomingpublicradio.net
Editorial Profile: KUWY-FM is a non-commercial station owned by the University of Wyoming. The format of the station is classical music. KUWY-FM broadcasts to the Laramie, WY area at 88.5 FM.

KUYI-FM
Owner: Hopi Foundation
Editorial: State Hwy 264, MP 3965, Keams Canyon, Arizona 86034. **T:** 1 928 738-5505
E: info@kuyi.net **W:** http://www.kuyi.net
Editorial Profile: KUYI-FM is a non-commercial station owned by the Hopi Foundation. The format of the station is Native American-based variety programming. KUYI-FM broadcasts to the Keams Canyon, AZ area at 88.1 FM.

KUYO-AM
Owner: Wyoming Christian Broadcasting Co.
Editorial: 1423 S Beverly St, Casper, Wyoming 82609-4131. **T:** 1 307 577-5896
W: http://www.kuyo.com
Editorial Profile: KUYO-AM is a commercial station owned by Wyoming Christian Broadcasting Co. The format of the station is religious and talk. KUYO-AM broadcasts to the Casper-Riverton, WY area at 830 AM.

KUYY-FM
Owner: Community First Broadcasting
Editorial: 2303 W 18th St, Spencer, Iowa 51301. **T:** 1 712 264-1074
W: http://y100-fm.com
Editorial Profile: KUYY-FM is a commercial station owned by Community First Broadcasting, Inc. The format of the station is hot adult contemporary. KUYY-FM broadcasts to the Spencer, IA area at 100.1 FM.

KUZN-FM
Owner: Aleluya Broadcasting Network
Editorial: 912 Curtis Ave, Pasadena, Texas 77502-2402. **T:** 1 713 589-1460
Editorial Profile: KUZN-FM is a commercial station owned by Aleluya Christian Broadcasting. The format of the station is Hispanic contemporary Christian. KUZN-FM broadcasts to the Pasadena, TX area at 88.1 FM.

KUZX-FM
Owner: Entercom Communications Corp.
Editorial: 201 3rd St Ste 1200, San Francisco, California 94103-3143. **T:** 1 415 777-0965
E: comments@myclassical.org
W: http://www.kfox.com
Editorial Profile: KUZX-FM is a commercial station owned by Entercom Communications Corp. The format of the station is classic rock. KUZX-FM broadcasts to the San Francisco area at 102.1 FM.

KUZZ-AM
Owner: Owens Productions Inc.(Buck)
Editorial: 3223 Sillect Ave, Bakersfield, California 93308. **T:** 1 661 326-1011
E: kuzznews@buckowens.com

W: http://www.kuzzradio.com
Editorial Profile: KUZZ-AM is a commercial station owned by Buck Owens Productions Inc. The format of the station is country. KUZZ-AM broadcasts to the Bakersfield, CA area at 550 AM.

KUZZ-FM
Owner: Owens Productions Inc.(Buck)
Editorial: 3223 Sillect Ave, Bakersfield, California 93308. **T:** 1 661 326-1011
E: kuzznews@buckowens.com
W: http://www.kuzzradio.com
Editorial Profile: KUZZ-FM is a commercial station owned by Buck Owens Productions Inc. The format of the station is classic country music. KUZZ-FM broadcasts to the Bakersfield, CA area at 107.9 FM.

KVAB-FM
Owner: Pacific Empire Radio Corp.
Editorial: 403 Capital St, Lewiston, Idaho 83501-1815. **T:** 1 208 743-6564
E: wecare@catfm.com **W:** http://catfm.com
Editorial Profile: KVAB-FM is a commercial station owned by Pacific Empire Radio Corp. The format of the station is classic rock. KVAB-FM broadcasts to the Lewiston, ID at a frequency of 102.9 FM.

KVAK-AM
Owner: North Wave Communications
Editorial: 501 E Bremner St, Valdez, Alaska 99686. **T:** 1 907 835-5825
E: valdeznews@gci.net
W: http://www.kvakradio.com
Editorial Profile: KVAK-AM is a commercial station owned by North Wave Communications. The format of the station is country and variety. KVAK-AM broadcasts to the Valdez, AK area at 1230 AM.

KVAK-FM
Owner: North Wave Communications
Editorial: 501 E Bremner St, Valdez, Alaska 99686. **T:** 1 907 835-5825
E: valdeznews@gci.net
W: http://www.kvakradio.com
Editorial Profile: KVAK-FM is a commercial station owned by North Wave Communications. The format of the station is hot adult contemporary and classic rock. KVAK-FM broadcasts to the Valdez, AK area at 93.3 FM.

KVAN-AM
Owner: Alexandra Communications Inc.
Editorial: 45 Campbell Rd, Walla Walla, Washington 99362-9597. **T:** 1 509 527-1000
Editorial Profile: KVAN-AM is a commercial station owned by Alexandra Communications Inc. The format of the station is Hispanic religious. KVAN-AM broadcasts to the Walla Walla, WA area at 1560 AM.

KVAS-AM
Owner: Ohana Media Group
Editorial: 285 SW Main Ct, Ste. 200, Warrenton, Oregon 97146-9457.
T: 1 503 861-6620
Editorial Profile: KVAS-AM is a commercial station owned by Ohana Media Group. The format of the station is classic country. KVAS-AM broadcasts to the Astoria, OR area at 1230 AM.

KVAS-FM
Owner: Ohana Media Group
Editorial: 285 SW Main Ct, Ste 200, Warrenton, Oregon 97146-9457.
T: 1 503 861-6620
W: http://www.kvas1039.com
Editorial Profile: KVAS-FM is a commercial station owned by Ohana Media Group. The format of the station is country music. KVAS-FM broadcasts in the Astoria, OR area at 103.9 FM.

KVAY-FM
Owner: Bob and Lisa DeLancey
Editorial: 224 S Main St, #203, Lamar, Colorado 81052-2867. **T:** 1 719 336-8734
E: news@kvay.com **W:** http://www.kvay.com
Editorial Profile: KVAY-FM is a commercial station owned by Bob and Lisa DeLancey. The format of the station is contemporary country music. KVAY-FM broadcasts in the Denver and Lamar area, CO at 105.7 FM.

KVBR-AM
Owner: BL Broadcasting Inc.
Editorial: 13225 Dogwood Dr, Baxter, Minnesota 56425-8669. **T:** 1 218 828-1244
E: production@brainerdradio.net
W: http://www.kvbr.com
Editorial Profile: KVBR-AM is a commercial station owned by BL Broadcasting Inc. The

format of the station is news and business talk. KVBR-AM broadcasts to the Baxter, MN area at 1340 AM.

KVCE-AM
Owner: Dallas Broadcasting LLC
Editorial: 6400 N Belt Line Rd Ste 110, Irving, Texas 75063-6065. **T:** 1 214 561-9667
W: http://www.kvceradio.com
Editorial Profile: KVCE-AM is a commercial station owned by Dallas Broadcasting LLC. The format of the station is talk. KVCE-AM broadcasts to the Dallas area at 1160 AM.

KVCK-AM
Owner: Wolftrax Broadcasting LLC
Editorial: 324 Main St, Wolf Point, Montana 59201. **T:** 1 406 653-1900
E: kvck@nemont.net
Editorial Profile: KVCK-AM is a commercial station owned by Wolftrax Broadcasting LLC. The format of the station is classic hits music. KVCK-AM broadcasts to the Wolf Point, MT area at 1450 AM.

KVCK-FM
Owner: Wolftrax Broadcasting LLC
Editorial: 324 Main St, Wolf Point, Montana 59201. **T:** 1 406 653-1900
E: kvck@nemont.net
Editorial Profile: KVCK-FM is a commercial station owned by Wolftrax Broadcasting LLC. The format of the station is country. KVCK-FM broadcasts to the Wolf Point, MT area at 92.7 FM.

KVCL-FM
Owner: Baldridge-Dumas Communications Inc.
Editorial: 304 Kvcl Rd, Winnfield, Louisiana 71483. **T:** 1 318 628-5822
E: kvclradio@yahoo.com
W: http://kvclradio.com
Editorial Profile: KVCL-FM is a commercial station owned by Baldridge-Dumas Communications Inc. The format of the station is country music. KVCL-FM broadcasts to the Winnfield, LA area at 92.1 FM.

KVCR-FM
Owner: San Bernardino Community College
Editorial: 701 S Mount Vernon Ave, San Bernardino, California 92410.
T: 1 909 384-4444 **E:** info@kvcr.org
W: http://www.kvcr.org
Editorial Profile: KVCR-FM is a NPR affiliate, non-commercial station owned by San Bernardino Community College. The format of the station is news and talk. KVCR-FM broadcasts to the San Bernardino, CA area at 91.9 FM.

KVCU-AM
Owner: University of Colorado
Editorial: 1600 Euclid, Boulder, Colorado 80309-0001. **T:** 1 303 492-5031
E: news@radio1190.org
W: http://www.radio1190.org
Editorial Profile: KVCU-AM is a non-commercial station owned by University of Colorado. The format of the station is college variety. KVCU-AM broadcasts to the Boulder, CO area at 1190 AM.

KVCX-FM
Owner: VCY America Inc.
Editorial: 3434 W Kilbourn Ave, Milwaukee, Wisconsin 53208. **T:** 1 414 935-3000
E: kvcx@vcyamerica.org
W: http://www.vcyamerica.org
Editorial Profile: KVCX-FM is a non-commercial station owned by VCY America Inc. The format of the station is religious programming. KVCX-FM broadcasts to the Milwaukee area at 101.5 FM.

KVDG-FM
Owner: La Promesa Foundation
Editorial: 1903 S Lamesa Rd, Midland, Texas 79701. **T:** 1 432 682-5476
W: http://www.grnonline.com
Editorial Profile: KVDG-FM is a non-commercial station owned by La Promesa Foundation. The format for the station is religious talk programming with a Catholic emphasis. KVDG-FM broadcasts to the Midland, TX area at 90.9 FM.

KVDP-FM
Owner: Dry Prong Educational Broadcasting Foundation Inc.
Editorial: 160 Bud Walker Rd, Dry Prong, Louisiana 71423. **T:** 1 318 899-5837
E: kvdpradio@aol.com
Editorial Profile: KVDP-FM is a non-commercial station owned by Dry Prong Educational Broadcasting Foundation Inc. The format of the station is religious programming. KVDP-FM broadcasts in Dry Prong, LA area at 89.1 FM.

KVDU-FM
Owner: Clear Channel Media and Entertainment
Editorial: 929 Howard Ave, New Orleans, Louisiana 70113-1148. **T:** 1 504 679-7300
W: http://www.voodoo104.com
Editorial Profile: KVDU-FM is a commercial station owned by Clear Channel Media and Entertainment. The format of the station is modern AC, with a focus on the 1990s. KVDU-FM broadcasts to the New Orleans area at 104.1 FM.

KVEC-AM
Owner: El Dorado Broadcasting
Editorial: 51 Zaca Ln Ste 100, San Luis Obispo, California 93401-7353.
T: 1 805 545-0101 **E:** news@920kvec.com
W: http://www.920kvec.com
Editorial Profile: KVEC-AM is a commercial station owned by El Dorado Broadcasting. The format of the station is news, talk and sports. KVEC-AM broadcasts in the San Luis Obispo, CA area at 920 AM.

KVEG-FM
Owner: Kemp Broadcasting
Editorial: 3999 Las Vegas Blvd S, Ste K, Las Vegas, Nevada 89119. **T:** 1 702 736-6161
W: http://www.kvegas.com
Editorial Profile: KVEG-FM is a commercial station owned by Kemp Broadcasting. The format of the station is rhythmic Top 40/CHR. KVEG-FM broadcasts to the Las Vegas area at 97.5 FM.

KVEL-AM
Owner: Ashley Communications
Editorial: 2425 N Vernal Ave, Vernal, Utah 84078-9587. **T:** 1 435 789-0920
E: production@kvel.com
W: http://920kvel.com
Editorial Profile: KVEL-AM is a commercial station owned by Ashley Communications. The format of the station is talk, news and sports. KVEL-AM broadcasts to the Salt Lake City area at 920 AM.

KVEN-AM
Owner: Cumulus Media Inc.
Editorial: 1376 Walter St, Ventura, California 93003-5658. **T:** 1 805 642-8595
W: http://www.kven.com
Editorial Profile: KVEN-AM is a commercial station owned by Cumulus Media Inc. The format of the station is sports. KVEN-AM broadcasts to the Ventura, CA area at 1450 AM.

KVER-FM
Owner: World Radio Network, Inc.
Editorial: 4126 N Mesa St, El Paso, Texas 79902. **T:** 1 915 544-9190 **E:** kver@lwrn.org
W: http://www.kver.org
Editorial Profile: KVER-FM is a non-commercial station owned by World Radio Network, Inc. The format is Hispanic religious. KVER-FM broadcasts to the El Paso, TX area at 91.1 FM.

KVET-AM
Owner: Clear Channel Media and Entertainment
Editorial: 3601 S Congress Ave Bldg F, Austin, Texas 78704-7280. **T:** 1 512 684-7300
W: http://www.am1300thezone.com
Editorial Profile: KVET-AM is a commercial station owned by Clear Channel Media and Entertainment. The format of the station is sports. KVET-AM broadcasts to the Austin, TX area at 1300 AM.

KVET-FM
Owner: Clear Channel Media and Entertainment
Editorial: 3601 S Congress Ave, Austin, Texas 78704-7250. **T:** 1 512 684-7300
W: http://www.kvet.com
Editorial Profile: KVET-FM is a commercial station owned by Clear Channel Media and Entertainment. The format of the station is country music. KVET-FM broadcasts to the Austin, TX area at 98.1 FM.

KVFC-AM
Owner: American General Media
Editorial: 2402 Hawkins, Cortez, Colorado 81321. **T:** 1 970 565-6565
W: http://www.kvfcradio.com
Editorial Profile: KVFC-AM is a commercial station owned by American General Media. The format of the station is talk. KVFC-AM broadcasts to the Cortez, CO area at 740 AM.

KVFD-AM
Owner: Three Eagles Communications Co.
Editorial: 200 N 10th St, Fort Dodge, Iowa 50501-3925. **T:** 1 515 955-5656
W: http://www.kvfdam.com
Editorial Profile: KVFD-AM is a commercial station owned by Three Eagles Communications Co. The format of the station is talk. KVFD-AM broadcasts to the Fort Dodge, IA area at 1400 AM.

KVFG-FM
Owner: CBS Radio
Editorial: 11920 Hesperia Rd, Hesperia, California 92345-1851. **T:** 1 760 244-2000
Editorial Profile: KVFG-FM is a commercial station owned by CBS Radio. The format of the station is classic hits. KVFG-FM broadcasts to the Hesperia, CA area at 103.1 FM.

KVFX-FM
Owner: Cache Valley Radio Inc.
Editorial: 810 W 200 N, Logan, Utah 84321-3726. **T:** 1 435 752-1390
E: requests@utahsvfx.com
W: http://www.utahsvfx.com
Editorial Profile: KVFX-FM is a commercial station owned by Cache Valley Radio Inc. The format of the station is Top 40/CHR. KVFX-FM broadcasts to the Salt Lake City area at 94.5 FM.

KVGB-AM
Owner: Eagle Radio Inc.
Editorial: 1200 Baker Ave, Great Bend, Kansas 67530-4523. **T:** 1 620 792-3647
W: http://www.eagleradio.net
Editorial Profile: KVGB-AM is a commercial station owned by Eagle Radio Inc. The format of the station is news, talk and sports. KVGB-AM broadcasts to the Great Bend, KS area at 1590 AM.

KVGB-FM
Owner: Eagle Radio Inc.
Editorial: 1200 Baker Ave, Great Bend, Kansas 67530. **T:** 1 620 792-3647
E: comments@theclassicrockstation.com
W: http://www.b1043.net
Editorial Profile: KVGB-FM is a commercial station owned by Eagle Radio Inc. The format of the station is classic rock. KVGB-FM broadcasts to the Great Bend, KS area at 104.3 FM.

KVGO-FM
Owner: Cumulus Media Inc.
Editorial: 300 Saint Paul St SW, Preston, Minnesota 55965. **T:** 1 507 765-3856
E: production@kfilradio.com
Editorial Profile: KVGO-FM is a commercial station owned by Cumulus Media Inc. The format of the station is oldies. KVGO-FM is licensed to the Spring Valley, MN area and broadcasts locally at a frequency of 104.3 FM.

KVGQ-FM
Owner: Kemp Broadcasting
Editorial: 3999 Las Vegas Blvd S, Las Vegas, Nevada 89119-1001. **T:** 1 702 736-6161
W: http://1069theq.com
Editorial Profile: KVGQ-FM is a commercial station owned by Kemp Broadcasting. The format for the station is Hot AC. KVGQ-FM broadcasts to the Overton, NV area at 106.9 FM.

KVGS-FM
Owner: Beasley Broadcast Group
Editorial: 2920 S Durango Dr, Las Vegas, Nevada 89117-4412. **T:** 1 702 730-0300
E: email@bbgi.com **W:** http://1079bob.com
Editorial Profile: KVGS-FM is a commercial station owned by Beasley Broadcast Group. The format of the station is adult hits. KVGS-FM broadcasts to the Las Vegas area at 107.9 FM.

KVHT-FM
Owner: Culhane Communications Inc.
Editorial: 210 W 3rd St, Yankton, South Dakota 57078. **T:** 1 605 665-2600
E: news@kvht.com **W:** http://www.kvht.com
Editorial Profile: KVHT-FM is a commercial station owned by Culhane Communications Inc. The format of the station is classic hits. KVHT-FM broadcasts to the Yankton, SD area at 106.3 FM.

KVI-AM
Owner: Sinclair Radio of Seattle, LLC
Editorial: 140 4th Ave N Ste 340, Seattle, Washington 98109-4940. **T:** 1 206 404-8000
E: 570kvi@fisherradio.com
W: http://www.kvi.com
Editorial Profile: KVI-AM is a commercial station owned by Sinclair Radio of Seattle, LLC. The format of the station is talk. KVI-AM broadcasts in the Seattle area at 570 AM.

KVIB-FM
Owner: Sun City Communications
Editorial: 4745 N 7th St Ste 410, Phoenix, Arizona 85014-3669. **T:** 1 602 648-9800
W: http://solamenteexitos.com
Editorial Profile: KVIB-FM is a commercial station owned by Sun City Communications. The format of the station is Spanish Hits. KVIB-FM broadcasts to the Phoenix area at 95.1 FM.

KVIC-FM
Owner: Victoria RadioWorks Inc.
Editorial: 3613 N Main St, Victoria, Texas 77901-2607. **T:** 1 361 576-6111
E: vrw@suddenlinkmail.com

KVIK-FM
Owner: Wennes Communications Stations, Inc.
Editorial: 501 W Water St, Decorah, Iowa 52101. **T:** 1 563 382-5863
E: kvik@kvikradio.com
W: http://www.kvikradio.com
Editorial Profile: KVIK-FM is a commercial station owned by Wennes Communications Stations, Inc. The format of the station is classic hits music. KVIK-FM broadcasts to the Decorah, IA area at 104.7 FM.

KVIL-FM
Owner: CBS Radio
Editorial: 4131 N Central Expy Ste 1000, Dallas, Texas 75204-2121. **T:** 1 214 525-7000
W: http://kvil.cbslocal.com
Editorial Profile: KVIL-FM is a commercial station owned by CBS Radio. The format of the station is hot adult contemporary. KVIL-FM broadcasts to the Dallas area at 103.7 FM.

KVIN-AM
Owner: Threshold Communications
Editorial: 961 N Emerald Ave Ste A, Modesto, California 95351-1556. **T:** 1 209 544-1055
E: thevine@kvin.net **W:** http://kvin.net
Editorial Profile: KVIN-AM is a commercial station owned by Threshold Communications. The format of the station is adult standards. KVIN-AM broadcasts to the Modesto, CA area at 920 AM.

KVIP-AM
Owner: Pacific Cascade Communications Corp.
Editorial: 1139 Hartnell Ave, Redding, California 96002-2113. **T:** 1 530 222-4455
E: info@kvip.org **W:** http://www.kvip.org
Editorial Profile: KVIP-AM is a non-commercial station owned by Pacific Cascade Communications Corp. The format of the station is talk. KVIP-AM broadcasts to the Redding, CA area at 540 AM.

KVIP-FM
Owner: Pacific Cascade Communications Corp.
Editorial: 1139 Hartnell Ave, Redding, California 96002-2113. **T:** 1 530 222-4455
E: info@kvip.org **W:** http://www.kvip.org
Editorial Profile: KVIP-FM is a non-commercial station owned by Pacific Cascade Communications Corp. The format of the station is Christian talk. KVIP-FM broadcasts to the Redding, CA area at 98.1 FM.

KVIS-AM
Owner: Northeast Oklahoma Broadcasting Network
Editorial: 1 N Main St, Miami, Oklahoma 74354-6322. **T:** 1 918 542-1818
E: kglc.kvis@yahoo.com
Editorial Profile: KVIS-AM is a commercial station owned by Northeast Oklahoma Broadcasting Network. The format of the station is southern gospel music. KVIS-AM broadcasts in the Miami, OK area at 910 AM.

KVIV-AM
Owner: El Paso Y Juarez Companerismo-Cristiano
Editorial: 6060 Surety Dr Ste 100, El Paso, Texas 79905-2033. **T:** 1 915 565-2999
E: info@kviv1340.com **W:** http://kviv1340.com
Editorial Profile: KVIV-AM is a commercial station owned by El Paso Y Juarez Companerismo-Cristiano. The format of the station is Christian Hispanic religious programming. KVIV-AM broadcasts in the El Paso, TX area at 1340 AM.

KVJM-FM
Owner: Clear Channel Media and Entertainment

Editorial: 1716 Briarcrest Dr, Ste 150, Bryan, Texas 77802-2776. **T:** 1 979 268-9696
W: http://www.kissfm1031.com/main.html
Editorial Profile: KVJM-FM is a commercial station owned by Clear Channel Media and Entertainment. The format of the station is CHR/Top 40. KVJM-FM broadcasts to the Bryan, TX area at 103.1 FM.

KVJY-AM
Owner: MBM Radio Del Rio, LLC
Editorial: 1201 N Jackson Rd Ste 900, McAllen, Texas 78501-5764.
T: 1 956 992-8895
Editorial Profile: KVJY-AM is a commercial station owned by MBM Radio Del Rio, LLC. The format of the station is Spanish News/ Talk. KVJY-AM broadcasts to the McAllen, TX area at 840 AM.

KVKI-FM
Owner: Townsquare Media, LLC
Editorial: 6341 W Port Ave, Shreveport, Louisiana 71129. **T:** 1 318 688-1130
W: http://www.965kvki.com
Editorial Profile: KVKI-FM is a commercial station owned by Townsquare Media, LLC. The format of the station is adult contemporary music. KVKI-FM broadcasts to the Shreveport, LA area at 96.5 FM.

KVKK-AM
Owner: De La Hunt Broadcasting
Editorial: 11 Bryant Ave SE, Wadena, Minnesota 56482-1543. **T:** 1 218 631-3441
E: kskk@eot.com
W: http://www.kkradionetwork.com
Editorial Profile: KVKK-AM is a commercial station owned by De La Hunt Broadcasting. The format of the station is talk. KVKK-AM broadcasts to the Wadena, MN area at 1070 AM.

KVLC-FM
Owner: Bravo Mic Communications, LLC
Editorial: 101 Perkins Dr, Las Cruces, New Mexico 88005. **T:** 1 575 527-1111
W: http://www.101gold.com
Editorial Profile: KVLC-FM is a commercial station owned by Bravo Mic Communications, LLC. The format of the station is oldies. KVLC-FM broadcasts to the Las Cruces, NM area at 101.1 FM.

KVLD-FM
Owner: East Arkansas Broadcasters Inc.
Editorial: 2705 E Parkway Dr, Russellville, Arkansas 72802-2006. **T:** 1 479 968-6816
E: news@rivervalleyradio.com
W: http://sharpe993.com
Editorial Profile: KVLD-FM is a commercial station owned by ast Arkansas Broadcasters Inc. The format of the station is classic rock. KVLD-FM broadcasts to the Russellville, AR area at 99.3 FM.

KVLE-FM
Owner: Pilgrim Communications
Editorial: 1445 State Highway 135, Gunnison, Colorado 81230-9243. **T:** 1 970 648-4365
W: http://www.kvleradio.com
Editorial Profile: KVLE-FM is a commercial station owned by Pilgrim Communications. The format of the station is classic rock. KVLE-FM broadcasts to the Gunnison, CO area at 102.3 FM.

KVLF-AM
Owner: Big Ben Broadcasters Inc.
Editorial: 500 E Hendryx Ave, Alpine, Texas 79830-2108. **T:** 1 432 837-2144
W: http://www.bigbenradio.com
Editorial Profile: KVLF-AM is a commercial station owned by Big Ben Broadcasters Inc. The format of the station is oldies. KVLF-AM broadcasts to the Alpine, TX area at 92.7 FM.

KVLG-AM
Owner: KBUK Radio, Inc.
Editorial: 511 FM 155 South, La Grange, Texas 78945. **T:** 1 979 968-3173
E: kvlgkbuk@kvlgkbuk.com
W: http://www.kvlgkbuk.com
Editorial Profile: KVLG-AM is a commercial station owned by KBUK Radio, Inc. The format of the station in classic country. KVLG-AM broadcasts to the La Grange, TX area at 1570 AM.

KVLI-AM
Owner: QAB Media LLC
Editorial: 14 Sierra Drive, Kernville, California 93238. **T:** 1 760 376-4500
Editorial Profile: KVLI-AM is a commercial station owned by QAB Media LLC. The format of the station is news and talk programming. KVLI-AM broadcasts to the Kernville, CA area at 1140 AM.

KVLK-FM
Owner: Educational Media Foundation
Editorial: 4101 Barbara Loop SE, Ste A, Rio Rancho, New Mexico 87124-1011.
T: 1 505 352-4028 **W:** http://www.klove.com
Editorial Profile: KVLK-FM is a non-commercial station owned by Educational Media Foundation. The format of the station is contemporary Christian. KVLK-FM broadcasts to the Rio Rancho, NM area at 89.5 FM.

KVLL-FM
Owner: Townsquare Media, LLC
Editorial: 1216 S 1st St, Lufkin, Texas 75901.
T: 1 936 639-4455
W: http://www.sunny947fm.com
Editorial Profile: KVLL-FM is a commercial station owned by Townsquare Media, LLC. The format of the station is adult contemporary. KVLL-FM broadcasts to the Lufkin, TX area at 94.7 FM.

KVLO-FM
Owner: Arkansas County Broadcasters, Inc.
Editorial: 1818 S Buerkle St, Stuttgart, Arkansas 72160-5804. **T:** 1 870 673-1595
Editorial Profile: KVLO-FM is a commercial station owned by Arkansas County Broadcasters, Inc. The format of the station is adult hits. KVLO-FM broadcasts to the Little Rock, AR area at 101.7 FM.

KVLT-FM
Owner: American Educational Broadcasting Inc.
Editorial: 2010 SW H K Dodgen Loop, Ste 108, Temple, Texas 76504. **T:** 1 254 791-5251
E: info@kvltfm.com **W:** http://www.klove.com
Editorial Profile: KVLT-FM is a non-commercial station owned by American Educational Broadcasting Inc. The format of the station is contemporary Christian. KVLT-TV broadcasts to the Temple, TX area at 88.5 FM. All programming comes from the K-Love Network.

KVLU-FM
Owner: Lamar University
Editorial: 4400 Martin Luther King Blvd, Beaumont, Texas 77710. **T:** 1 409 880-8164
W: http://www.kvlu.org
Editorial Profile: KVLU-FM is a non-commercial station owned by Lamar University. The format of the station is news, jazz and classical music. KVLU-FM broadcasts in the Beaumont, TX area at 91.3 FM.

KVLV-AM
Owner: Lahontan Valley Broadcasting
Editorial: 1155 Gummow Dr, Fallon, Nevada 89406. **T:** 1 775 423-2243
E: kvlv@phonewave.net
Editorial Profile: KVLV-AM is a commercial station owned by Lahontan Valley Broadcasting. The format of the station is country. KVLV-AM broadcasts to the Fallon, NV area at 980 AM.

KVLW-FM
Owner: American Educational Broadcasting Inc.
Editorial: 2010 SW H K Dodgen Loop, Ste 108, Temple, Texas 76504. **T:** 1 254 791-5251
E: info@kvltfm.com **W:** http://www.klove.com
Editorial Profile: KVLW-FM is a non-commercial station owned by American Educational Broadcasting Inc. The format of the station is contemporary Christian. KVLW-FM broadcasts to the Gatesville, TX area at 88.1 FM. All programming comes from the K-Love Network.

KVLY-FM
Owner: Entravision Communications Corp.
Editorial: 801 N Jackson Rd, McAllen, Texas 78501. **T:** 1 956 661-6000 **E:** kvly@hiline.net
W: http://www.mix1079.net
Editorial Profile: KVLY-FM is a commercial station owned by Entravision Communications Corp. The format of the station is adult contemporary. KVLY-FM broadcasts to the McAllen, TX area at 107.9 FM.

KVMA-AM
Owner: Noalmark Broadcasting Corp.
Editorial: 131 S Jackson, Magnolia, Arkansas 71753-3524. **T:** 1 870 234-5862
E: kvmakvmz@magnoliaradio.com
W: http://www.magnoliaradio.com
Editorial Profile: KVMA-AM is a commercial station owned by Noalmark Broadcasting Corp. The format of the station is country and news. KVMA-AM broadcasts to the Magnolia, AR area at 630 AM.

KVMA-FM
Owner: Cumulus Media Inc.
Editorial: Cumulus Broadcast Center, 270 Plaza Loop, Bossier City, Louisiana 71111.
T: 1 318 549-8500
W: http://www.magic1029fm.com
Editorial Profile: KVMA-FM is a commercial station owned by Cumulus Media Inc. The format of the station is urban adult contemporary music. KVMA-FM broadcasts to the Bossier City, LA area at 102.9 FM.

KVMC-AM
Owner: Baum(James G.)
Editorial: West Highway 80, Colorado City, Texas 79512. **T:** 1 325 728-5530
E: kvmckaum@sbcglobal.net
W: http://www.tsnradio.com
Editorial Profile: KVMC-AM is a commercial station owned by James G. Baum. The format of the station is country music. KVMC-AM broadcasts to the Colorado City, TX area at 1320 AM.

KVML-AM
Owner: Clarke Broadcasting Corp.
Editorial: 342 S Washington St, Sonora, California 95370. **T:** 1 209 533-1450
W: http://www.kvmlam.com/index.php
Editorial Profile: KVML-AM is a commercial station owned by Clarke Broadcasting Corp. The format of the station is news and talk. KVML-AM broadcasts to the Sonora, CA, area at 1450 AM.

KVMN-FM
Owner: Cave City School
Editorial: 620 N Main St, Cave City, Arkansas 72521-9009. **T:** 1 870 283-3309
E: kvmnfm@gmail.com
Editorial Profile: KVMN-FM is a non-commercial station owned by Cave City School. The format of the station is rock and Southern gospel. KVMN-FM broadcasts to the Cave City, AR area at 89.9 FM.

KVMR-FM
Owner: Nevada City Broadcast Group
Editorial: 401 Spring St, Nevada City, California 95959. **T:** 1 530 265-9073
E: news@kvmr.org **W:** http://www.kvmr.org
Editorial Profile: KVMR-FM is a non-commercial station owned by Nevada City Broadcast Group. The format of the station is variety. KVMR-FM broadcasts to the Nevada City, CA area at 89.5 FM.

KVMV-FM
Owner: World Radio Network, Inc.
Editorial: 969 E Thomas Dr, Pharr, Texas 78577-9828. **T:** 1 956 787-9700
E: kvmv@kvmv.org **W:** http://www.kvmv.org
Editorial Profile: KVMV-FM is a non-commercial station owned by World Radio Network, Inc. The format is religious and contemporary Christian. KVMV-FM broadcasts to the Pharr, TX area at 96.9 FM.

KVMX-FM
Owner: Lotus Communications Corp.
Editorial: 5100 Commerce Dr, Bakersfield, California 93309-0684. **T:** 1 661 327-9711
W: http://921kix.com
Editorial Profile: KVMX-FM is a commercial station owned by Lotus Communications Corp. The format of the station is contemporary country. KVMX-FM broadcasts to the Bakersfield, CA area at 92.1 FM.

KVMZ-FM
Owner: Noalmark Broadcasting Corp.
Editorial: 131 S Jackson, Magnolia, Arkansas 71753. **T:** 1 870 234-9901
E: kvmakvmz@magnoliaradio.com
W: http://www.magnoliaradio.com
Editorial Profile: KVMZ-FM is a commercial station owned by Noalmark Broadcasting Corp. The format of the station is contemporary country. KVMZ-FM broadcasts to the Magnolia, AR area at 99.1 FM.

KVNA-AM
Owner: Yavapai Broadcasting
Editorial: 1800 S Milton Rd, Ste 105, Flagstaff, Arizona 86001-6323.
T: 1 928 634-2286
W: http://www.myradioplace.com/am600/am600.htm
Editorial Profile: KVNA-AM is a commercial station owned by Yavapai Broadcasting. The format of the station is news, sports and talk programming. KVNA-AM broadcasts to the Flagstaff, AZ area at 600 AM.

KVNA-FM
Owner: Yavapai Broadcasting
Editorial: 3405 E State Route 89A, Bldg A, Cottonwood, Arizona 86326-5506.
T: 1 928 634-2286
W: http://www.myradioplace.com
Editorial Profile: KLOD-FM is a commercial station owned by Yavapai Broadcasting. The format of the station is adult contemporary. KLOD-FM broadcasts to the Flagstaff, AZ area at 100.1 FM.

KVNE-FM
Owner: Educational Radio Foundation
Editorial: 2721 E Erwin St, Tyler, Texas 75708-2007. **T:** 1 903 593-5863
W: http://www.encouragementfm.com
Editorial Profile: KVNE-FM is a non-commercial station owned by Educational Radio Foundation. The format of the station is contemporary Christian. KVNE-FM broadcasts to the Tyler, TX area at 89.5 FM.

KVNF-FM
Owner: North Fork Valley Public Radio Inc.
Editorial: 233 Grand Ave, Paonia, Colorado 81428. **T:** 1 970 527-4866
W: http://www.kvnf.org
Editorial Profile: KVNF-FM is a non-commercial station owned by North Fork Valley Public Radio Inc. The format of the station is news, jazz and adult album alternative. KVNF-FM broadcasts to the Paonia, CO area at 90.9 FM.

KVNI-AM
Owner: Queen B Inc.
Editorial: 500 W Boone Ave, Spokane, Washington 99201-2404. **T:** 1 509 324-4000

KVNN-AM
Owner: Victoria RadioWorks Inc.
Editorial: 3613 N Main St, Victoria, Texas 77901. **T:** 1 361 576-6111
E: vrw@suddenlinkmail.com
Editorial Profile: KVNN-AM is a commercial station owned by Victoria RadioWorks Inc. The format of the station is news and talk. KVNN-AM broadcasts to the Victoria, TX area at 1340 AM.

KVNO-FM
Owner: Board of Regents of the University of Nebraska
Editorial: 6001 Dodge St, Omaha, Nebraska 68182. **T:** 1 402 554-5866
W: http://www.kvno.org
Editorial Profile: KVNO-FM is a non-commercial station owned by the Board of Regents of the University of Nebraska. The format of the station is classical music. KVNO-FM broadcasts to the Omaha, NE area on 90.7 FM.

KVNR-AM
Owner: Liberman Broadcasting Inc.
Editorial: 13749 Beach Blvd., Westminster, California 92683. **T:** 1 714 918-4444
E: radio@littlesaigonradio.com
W: http://www.littlesaigonradio.com
Editorial Profile: KVNR-AM is a commercial station owned by Liberman Broadcasting Inc. The format of the station is a variety of Asian programming. KVNR-AM broadcasts to the Santa Ana, CA area at 1480 AM.

KVNS-AM
Owner: Clear Channel Media and Entertainment
Editorial: 901 E Pike Blvd, Weslaco, Texas 78596-4937. **T:** 1 956 973-9202
W: http://www.classic1700.com
Editorial Profile: KVNS-AM is a commercial station owned by Clear Channel Media and Entertainment. The format of the station is sports. KVNS-AM broadcasts to the Weslaco, TX area at 1700 AM.

KVNT-AM
Owner: Alaska Integrated Media
Editorial: 4700 Business Park Blvd Bldg E, Anchorage, Alaska 99503-7176.
T: 1 907 522-1018 **E:** traffic@alaskaim.com
W: http://www.1020kvnt.com
Editorial Profile: KVNT-AM is a commercial station owned by Alaska Integrated Media. The format of the station is progressive talk. KVNT-AM broadcasts at a frequency of 1020 AM to the Anchorage, AK area.

KVNU-AM
Owner: Cache Valley Radio Inc.
Editorial: 810 W 200 N, Logan, Utah 84321.
T: 1 435 752-5141
W: http://www.610kvnu.com
Editorial Profile: KVNU-AM is a commercial station owned by Cache Valley Radio Inc. The format of the station is news and talk

programming. KVNU-AM broadcasts to the Logan, UT area at 610 AM.

KVOB-FM
Owner: Rocking M Radio
Editorial: 641 W Cloud St, Salina, Kansas 67401-5618. **T:** 1 785 827-2100
Editorial Profile: KVOB-FM is a commercial station owned by Rocking M Radio. The format of the station is classic rock music. KVOB-FM broadcasts to the Salina, KS area at 95.5 FM.

KVOC-AM
Owner: Mount Rushmore Broadcasting Inc.
Editorial: 218 N Wolcott St, Casper, Wyoming 82601. **T:** 1 307 265-1984
Editorial Profile: KVOC-AM is a commercial station owned by Mount Rushmore Broadcasting Inc. The format of the station is talk. KVOC-AM broadcasts to the Casper, WY area at 1230 AM.

KVOD-FM
Owner: Public Broadcasting of Colorado Inc.
Editorial: 7409 S Alton Ct, Centennial, Colorado 80112-2301. **T:** 1 303 871-9191
E: info@cpr.org **W:** http://www.cpr.org
Editorial Profile: KVOD-FM is a non-commercial station owned by Public Broadcasting of Colorado Inc. The format of the station is classical. KVOD-FM broadcasts to the Centennial, CO area at 88.1 FM.

KVOE-AM
Owner: Emporia Radio Stations Inc.
Editorial: 1420 C Of E Dr, Emporia, Kansas 66801. **T:** 1 620 342-1400 **E:** kvoe@kvoe.com
W: http://www.kvoe.com
Editorial Profile: KVOE-AM is a commercial station owned by Emporia Radio Stations Inc. The format of the station is adult contemporary, news and talk. KVOE-AM broadcasts to the Emporia, KS area at 1400 AM.

KVOE-FM
Owner: Emporia Radio Stations Inc.
Editorial: 1420 C Of E Dr, Emporia, Kansas 66801. **T:** 1 620 342-1400 **E:** kvoe@kvoe.com
W: http://www.kvoe.com
Editorial Profile: KVOE-FM is a commercial station owned by Emporia Radio Stations Inc. The format of the station is country music. KVOE-FM broadcasts to the Emporia, KS area at 101.7 FM.

KVOI-AM
Owner: Good News Radio Broadcasting Inc.
Editorial: 3222 S Richey Ave, Tucson, Arizona 85713-5498. **T:** 1 520 790-2440
E: info@kvoi.com **W:** http://www.kvoi.com
Editorial Profile: KVOI-AM is a commercial station owned by Good News Radio Broadcasting Inc. The format of the station is talk. KVOI-AM broadcasts in Tucson, AZ area at 1030 AM.

KVOK-AM
Owner: Kodiak Island Broadcasting Co., Inc.
Editorial: 1315 Mill Bay Rd Ste 1A, Kodiak, Alaska 99615-6411. **T:** 1 907 486-5159
E: kvok@ak.net **W:** http://www.kvok.com
Editorial Profile: KVOK-AM is a commercial station owned by Kodiak Island Broadcasting Co., Inc. The station's format is contemporary country. KVOK-AM broadcasts to Kodiak, AK, area at 560 AM. This station also operates on 98.7 FM at 250 wattage.

KVOM-AM
Owner: East Arkansas Broadcasters Inc.
Editorial: 1835 Highway 113, Morrilton, Arkansas 72110. **T:** 1 501 354-2484
E: newsroom@kvom.com
W: http://www.kvom.com
Editorial Profile: KVOM-AM is a commercial station owned by East Arkansas Broadcasters Inc. The format of the station is sports. KVOM-AM's broadcasts to the Morrilton, AR area at 800 AM.

KVOM-FM
Owner: East Arkansas Broadcasters Inc.
Editorial: 1835 Highway 113, Morrilton, Arkansas 72110-9009. **T:** 1 501 354-2485
E: newsroom@kvom.com
W: http://www.kvom.com
Editorial Profile: KVOM-FM is a commercial station owned by East Arkansas Broadcasters Inc. The format of the station is country. KVOM-FM broadcasats to the Morrilton, AR area at 101.7 FM.

KVON-AM
Owner: Wine Country Broadcasting Co.
Editorial: 1124 Foster Rd, Napa, California 94558-6520. **T:** 1 707 252-1440
E: psa@kvon.com **W:** http://www.kvon.com
Editorial Profile: KVON-AM is a commercial station owned by Wine Country Broadcasting Co. The format of the station is talk. KVON-AM broadcasts to the San Francisco area at 1440 AM.

KVOO-FM
Owner: Journal Broadcast Group
Editorial: 4590 E 29th St, Tulsa, Oklahoma 74114-6208. **T:** 1 918 743-7814
W: http://www.kvoo.com
Editorial Profile: KVOO-FM is a commercial station owned by the Journal Broadcast Group. The format of the station is contemporary country music. KVOO-FM broadcasts to the Tulsa, OK area at 98.5 FM.

KVOP-AM
Owner: Rhattigan Broadcasting
Editorial: 3218 Quincy St, Plainview, Texas 79072-1906. **T:** 1 806 296-2771
W: http://www.kkyn.net
Editorial Profile: KVOP-AM is a commercial station owned by Rhattigan Broadcasting. The format of the station is news, sports and talk. KVOP-AM broadcasts to the Plainview, TX area at 1090 AM.

KVOQ-AM
Owner: Public Broadcasting of Colorado Inc.
Editorial: 7409 S Alton Ct, Centennial, Colorado 80112-2301. **T:** 1 303 871-9191
E: info@cpr.org **W:** http://www.openaircpr.org
Editorial Profile: KVOQ-AM is a non-commercial station owned by Public Broadcasting of Colorado Inc. The format of the station is indie rock. KVOQ-AM broadcasts to the Denver area at 1340 AM.

KVOR-AM
Owner: Cumulus Media Inc
Editorial: 6805 Corporate Dr, Ste 130, Colorado Springs, Colorado 80919.
T: 1 719 593-2700 **E:** news@kvor.com
W: http://www.kvor.com
Editorial Profile: KVOR-AM is a commercial station owned by Cumulus Media Inc. The format of the station is news and talk. KVOR-AM broadcasts to the Colorado Springs, CO area at 740 AM.

KVOT-AM
Owner: DMC Broadcasting Inc.
Editorial: 125 Camino De La Merced Apt A, Taos, New Mexico 87571-5131.
T: 1 575 758-4491
W: http://www.radiointaos.com
Editorial Profile: KVOT-AM is a commercial station owned by DMC Broadcasting Inc. The format of the station is talk programming. KVOT-AM broadcasts to the Taos, NM area at 1340 AM.

KVOU-FM
Owner: Rhattigan Broadcasting
Editorial: 1400 Batesville Road, Uvalde, Texas 78801. **T:** 1 830 278-2555
E: kvou@rcommunications.com
Editorial Profile: KVOU-FM is a commercial station owned by Rhattigan Broadcasting. The format of the station is country music. KVOU-FM broadcasts to the Uvalde, TX residents at 104.9 FM.

KVOW-AM
Owner: Edwards Communications LLC
Editorial: 603 E Pershing Ave, Riverton, Wyoming 82501. **T:** 1 307 856-2251
W: http://www.ktakradio.com
Editorial Profile: KVOW-AM is a commercial station owned by Edwards Communications LLC. The format for the station is news talk. KVOW-AM broadcasts to the Casper-Riverton, WY area at 1450 AM.

KVOX-AM
Owner: Midwest Communications
Editorial: 1020 25th St S, Fargo, North Dakota 58103-2312. **T:** 1 701 237-5346
E: studio@740thefan.com
W: http://www.740thefan.com
Editorial Profile: KVOX-AM is a commercial station owned by Midwest Communications. The format of the station is sports. KVOX-AM broadcasts to the Fargo, ND area at 740 AM.

KVOX-FM
Owner: James Ingstad Broadcast Group
Editorial: 2720 7th Ave S, Fargo, North Dakota 58103-8710. **T:** 1 701 237-4500
W: http://www.froggyweb.com
Editorial Profile: KVOX-FM is a commercial station owned by James Ingstad Broadcast Group. The format of the station is contemporary country. KVOX-FM broadcasts to the Fargo, ND area at 99.9 FM.

KVPI-AM
Owner: Ville Platte Broadcasting
Editorial: 809 W Lasalle St, Ville Platte, Louisiana 70586. **T:** 1 337 363-2124
Editorial Profile: KVPI-AM is a commercial station owned by Ville Platte Broadcasting. The format of the station is classic country. KVPI-AM broadcasts to the Ville Platte, LA area at 1050 AM.

KVPI-FM
Owner: Ville Platte Broadcasting
Editorial: 809 W Lasalle St, Ville Platte, Louisiana 70586. **T:** 1 337 363-2124
W: http://www.oldies925.com
Editorial Profile: KVPI-FM is a commercial station owned by Ville Platte Broadcasting. The format of the station is oldies. KVPI-FM broadcasts to the Ville Platte, LA area at 92.5 FM.

KVPR-FM
Owner: White Ash Broadcasting
Editorial: 3437 W Shaw Ave, Ste 101, Fresno, California 93711-3204. **T:** 1 559 275-0764
E: kvpr@kvpr.org **W:** http://www.kvpr.org

KVRC-AM
Owner: Noalmark Broadcasting Corp.
Editorial: 601 S 7th St, Arkadelphia, Arkansas 71923-6209. **T:** 1 870 246-9272
Editorial Profile: KVRC-AM is a commercial station owned by Southwest Arkansas Media, LLC. The format of the station is talk. KVRC-AM broadcasts to the Arkadelphia, AR area at 1240 AM.

KVRD-FM
Owner: Yavapai Broadcasting
Editorial: 3405 E Highway 89A, Cottonwood, Arizona 86326. **T:** 1 928 634-2286
E: kvrd@myradioplace.com
W: http://www.kvrdfm.com
Editorial Profile: KVRD-FM is a commercial station owned by Yavapai Broadcasting. The format of the station is country music. KVRD-FM broadcasts in the Cottonwood, AZ area at 105.7 FM.

KVRE-FM
Owner: Caddo Broadcasting Co.
Editorial: 122 Desoto Center Dr, Hot Springs Village, Arkansas 71909-3168.
T: 1 501 922-5678
Editorial Profile: KVRE-FM is a commercial station owned by Caddo Broadcasting Co. The format of the station is adult standards. KVRE-FM broadcasts to the Hot Springs, AR area at 92.9 FM.

KVRG-FM
Owner: Northeast Broadcasting Co.
Editorial: 3565 Southpark Dr, Jackson, Wyoming 83001. **T.** 1 307 732-0384
W: http://www.1037therange.com
Editorial Profile: KVRG-FM is a commercial station owned by Northeast Broadcasting Co. The format of the station is classic country. KVRG-FM broadcasts to the Jackson, WY area at 103.7 FM.

KVRH-AM
Owner: Headwaters Media LLC
Editorial: 7600 County Road 120, Salida, Colorado 81201. **T:** 1 719 539-0598
Editorial Profile: KVRH-AM is a commercial station owned by Headwaters Media LLC. The format of the station is oldies. KVRH-AM broadcasts to the Salida, CO area at 1340 AM.

KVRH-FM
Owner: Three Eagles Communications Co.
Editorial: 7600 County Road 120, Salida, Colorado 81201. **T:** 1 719 539-2575
W: http://www.kvrh.com
Editorial Profile: KVRH-FM is a commercial station owned by Three Eagles Communications Co. The format of the station is hot adult contemporary. KVRH-FM broadcasts to the Denver area at 92.3 FM.

KVRI-AM
Owner: Multicultural Radio Broadcasting Inc.
Editorial: 4840 Lincoln Rd, Blaine, Washington 98230-9602. **T:** 1 360 371-5500
E: info@radioindialtd.com
W: http://www.radioindialtd.com
Editorial Profile: KVRI-AM is a commercial station owned by Multicultural Radio Broadcasting Inc. The format of the station is multicultural featuring Indian programming. KVRI-AM broadcasts to the northwest Washington State and southwest British Columbia area at 1600 AM.

KVRK-FM
Owner: Research Educational Foundation Inc.
Editorial: 11061 Shady Trl, Dallas, Texas 75229-5603. **T:** 1 214 353-8970
W: http://897powerfm.org
Editorial Profile: KVRK-FM is a non-commercial station owned by the Research Educational Foundation Inc. The format of the station is Christian rock music. KVRK-FM broadcasts to the Dallas area at 89.7 FM.

KVRO-FM
Owner: Mahaffey Enterprises Inc.
Editorial: 408 E Thomas Ave, Stillwater, Oklahoma 74075-2648. **T:** 1 405 372-7800
W: http://www.stillwaterradio.net
Editorial Profile: KVRO-FM is a commercial station owned by Mahaffey Enterprises Inc. The format of the station is classic rock. KVRO-FM's target audience is adults, ages 18 to 64, in the Stillwater, OK and broadcasts at 101.1 FM.

KVRP-AM
Owner: Allied Broadcasting
Editorial: 1406 N 1St St, Haskell, Texas 79521-5436. **T:** 1 940 864-8505
W: http://www.kvrp.com
Editorial Profile: KVRP-AM is a commercial station owned by Allied Broadcasting. The format of the station is contemporary Christian. KVRP-AM broadcasts to the Haskell, TX area at 1400 AM. This station does not accepts press material.

KVRP-FM
Owner: Allied Broadcasting
Editorial: 1406 N 1st St, Haskell, Texas 79521. **T:** 1 940 864-8505
W: http://www.kvrp.com
Editorial Profile: KVRP-FM is a commercial station owned by Allied Broadcasting. The format of the station is contemporary country music. KVRP-FM broadcasts in the Stamford, TX area at 97.1 FM. This station does not accepts press material.

KVRS-FM
Owner: American Family Association
Editorial: 107 Park Gate Dr, Tupelo, Mississippi 38801. **T:** 1 662 844-8888
E: comments@afr.net **W:** http://www.afr.net
Editorial Profile: KVRS-FM is a non-commercial station owned by American Family Association. The format of the station is News Talk KVRS-FM broadcasts to the Lawton, OK area at 90.3 FM.

KVRT-FM
Owner: South Texas Public Broadcasting
Editorial: 4455 S Padre Island Dr, Ste 38, Corpus Christi, Texas 78411.
T: 1 361 855-2213 **W:** http://www.kedt.org
Editorial Profile: KVRT-FM is a non-commercial station owned by South Texas Public Broadcasting. The format of the station is classical, jazz and talk. KVRT-FM broadcasts to the Corpus Christi, TX area at 90.7 FM.

KVRV-FM
Owner: Sonoma Media Group
Editorial: 1410 Neotomas Ave, Santa Rosa, California 95405-7533. **T:** 1 707 543-0100
W: http://www.977theriver.com
Editorial Profile: KVRV-FM is a commercial station owned by Sonoma Media Group. The format of the station is classic rock. KVRV-FM broadcasts locally to the San Francisco, CA area at a frequency of 97.7 FM.

KVRW-FM
Owner: Townsquare Media, LLC
Editorial: 626 SW D Ave, Lawton, Oklahoma 73501-4508. **T:** 1 580 581-3600
E: lawtonpsa@townsquaremedia.com
W: http://www.my1073fm.com
Editorial Profile: KVRW-FM is a commercial station owned by Townsquare Media, LLC. The format of the station is classic hits. KVRW-FM broadcasts to the Lawton, OK area at 107.3 FM.

KVRX-FM
Owner: University of Texas
Editorial: 2500 Whitis Ave, Bldg C, Austin, Texas 78712. **T:** 1 512 471-5106
E: traffic@kvrx.org **W:** http://www.kvrx.org
Editorial Profile: KVRX-FM is a non-commercial station owned by the University of Texas. The format of the station is a variety of music, including world music, hip-hop, blues, jazz, folk, country, techno, and metal. KVRX-FM broadcasts to the University of Texas at Austin and the surrounding area at 91.7 FM.

KVSA-AM
Owner: Southeast Arkansas Broadcasters, Inc.
Editorial: 3453 US Highway 65 South, Dermott, Arkansas 71638. **T:** 1 870 222-4200
E: kvsa1220@yahoo.com

KVSC-FM
Owner: St. Cloud State University
Editorial: SCSU Stewart Hall Room 27, Saint Cloud, Minnesota 56301. **T:** 1 320 308-3066
E: info@kvsc.org **W:** http://www.kvsc.org
Editorial Profile: KVSC-FM is a non-commercial station owned by the St. Cloud State University. The format of the station is college variety. KVSC-FM broadcasts in the St. Cloud, MN area at 88.1 FM.

KVSF-AM
Owner: Hutton Broadcasting, LLC
Editorial: 2502 Camino Entrada Ste C, Santa Fe, New Mexico 87507-4911.
T: 1 505 471-1067
W: http://www.santafe.com/espn
Editorial Profile: KVSF-AM is a commercial station owned by Hutton Broadcasting, LLC. The format of the station is sports. KVSF-AM broadcasts to the Santa Fe, NM area at a frequency of 1400 AM.

KVSF-FM
Owner: Hutton Broadcasting, LLC
Editorial: 2502 Camino Entrada Ste C, Santa Fe, New Mexico 87507-4911.
T: 1 505 471-1067
W: http://www.santafe.com/the-voice
Editorial Profile: KVSF-FM is a commercial station owned by Hutton Broadcasting, LLC. The format of the station is community radio, primarily news and talk, featuring some music programming. KVSF-FM broadcasts to the Santa Fe, NM area at 101.5 FM

KVSH-AM
Owner: Heart City Radio Corp.
Editorial: 126 W 3rd St, Valentine, Nebraska 69201. **T:** 1 402 376-2400
E: kvsh@sandhillswireless.net
Editorial Profile: KVSH-AM is a commercial station owned by Heart City Radio Corp. The format of the station is adult contemporary, country and news. KVSH-AM broadcasts to the Valentine, NE area at 940 AM.

KVSI-AM
Owner: Tri-State Broadcasting Co.
Editorial: 24681 US Highway 89, Montpelier, Idaho 83254-5206. **T:** 1 208 847-1450
E: kvsi@dcdi.net **W:** http://www.kvsi.com
Editorial Profile: KVSI-AM is a commercial station owned by Tri-State Broadcasting Co. The format of the station is classic country. KVSI-AM broadcasts to the Montpelier, ID area at 1450 AM.

KVSL-AM
Owner: New Directions Media, Inc
Editorial: 1838 Commerce Dr Ste A, Lakeside, Arizona 85929-7008. **T:** 1 928 368-8100
E: wmrtraffic@gmail.com
W: http://www.whitemountainradio.com
Editorial Profile: KVSL-AM is a commercial station owned by New Directions Media, Inc. The format of the station is adult standards. KVSL-AM broadcasts to the Show Low, AZ area at 1450 AM.

KVSO-AM
Owner: LKCM Radio Group LP
Editorial: 1205 Northglen St, Ardmore, Oklahoma 73401-1202. **T:** 1 580 226-0421
E: news@sokradio.com
W: http://www.kvso.com
Editorial Profile: KVSO-AM is a commercial station owned by LKCM Radio Group LP. The format of the station is sports and is the ESPN Radio affiliate for the Texoma area. KVSO-AM broadcasts in the Ardmore, OK area at 1240 AM.

KVSP-FM
Owner: Perry Publishing & Broadcasting Inc.
Editorial: 1528 NE 23rd St, Oklahoma City, Oklahoma 73111-3260. **T:** 1 405 427-5877
W: http://www.kvsp.com
Editorial Profile: KVSP-AM is a commercial station owned by Perry Publishing & Broadcasting Inc. The format is urban contemporary music. KVSP-AM broadcasts to the Oklahoma City area at 103.5 FM.

KVSR-FM
Owner: Lake Area Educational Broadcasting Foundation
Editorial: 128 Possom Hollow Dr, Camdenton, Missouri 65020-6755. **T:** 1 573 346-3200
W: http://www.lifechangingradio.org
Editorial Profile: KVSR-FM is a non-commercial station owned by Lake Area Educational Broadcasting Foundation. The format of the station is contemporary Christian. KVSR-FM broadcasts to the Kirksville, MO area at 90.7 FM.

KVSS-FM
Owner: VSS Catholic Communications Inc.
Editorial: 13326 A St, Omaha, Nebraska 68144-3641. **T:** 1 402 571-0200
E: kvss@kvss.com **W:** http://www.kvss.com
Editorial Profile: KVSS-FM is a non-commercial station owned by VSS Catholic Communications Inc. The format of the station is Catholic programming. KVSS-FM broadcasts to the Lincoln, NE area at 102.7 FM.

KVST-FM
Owner: New Wavo Communications Group Inc.
Editorial: 1212 S Frazier St, Conroe, Texas 77301. **T:** 1 936 788-1035
E: news@kstarcountry.com
W: http://www.kstarcountry.com
Editorial Profile: KVST-FM is a commercial station owned by New Wavo Communications Group Inc. The format of the station is country music. KVST-FM broadcasts in the Houston area at 99.7 FM.

KVSV-AM
Owner: McGrath Publishing Company
Editorial: Highway 24 East, Beloit, Kansas 67420. **T:** 1 785 738-2206
E: news@kvsvradio.com
W: http://www.kvsvradio.com
Editorial Profile: KVSV-AM is a commercial station owned by McGrath Publishing Company. The format of the station is adult contemporary music. KVSV-AM broadcasts to the Beloit, KS area at 1190 AM.

KVSV-FM
Owner: McGrath Publishing Company
Editorial: 3185 Us 24 Hwy, Beloit, Kansas 67420-1577. **T:** 1 785 738-2206
E: news@kvsvradio.com
W: http://www.kvsvradio.com
Editorial Profile: KVSV-FM is a commercial station owned by McGrath Publishing Company. The format of the station is easy listening. KVSV-FM broadcasts to the Beloit, KS area at 105.5 FM.

KVTA-AM
Owner: Gold Coast Broadcasting, LLC
Editorial: 2284 S Victoria Ave Ste 2G, Ventura, California 93003-6626. **T:** 1 805 289-1400
E: kvtanews@yahoo.com **W:** http://kvta.com
Editorial Profile: KVTA-AM is a commercial station owned by Gold Coast Broadcasting, LLC. The format of the station is news and talk. KVTA-AM broadcasts to the Ventura, CA area at 1520 AM.

KVTI-FM
Owner: Clover Park Technical College
Editorial: 4500 Steilacoom Blvd SW, Lakewood, Washington 98499-4004.
T: 1 509 335-6500 **E:** nwpr@wsu.edu
W: http://www.nwpr.org
Editorial Profile: KVTI-FM is a non-commercial station owned by Clover Park Technical College and operated by Washington State University. The format of the station is news, talk and classical music. KVTI-FM broadcasts to the Tacoma, WA area at 90.9 FM.

KVTK-AM
Owner: Five Star Communications, Inc.
Editorial: 210 W 3rd St, Yankton, South Dakota 57078-4323. **T:** 1 605 665-2600
E: sports@kvht.com **W:** http://www.kvtk.com
Editorial Profile: KVTK-AM is a commercial station owned by Five Star Communications, Inc. The format of the station is sports. KVTK-AM broadcasts to the Vermillion, SD area at 1570 AM.

KVTO-AM
Owner: YMF Media LLC
Editorial: 55 Hawthorne St Ste 900, San Francisco, California 94105-3967.
T: 1 415 648-7980
E: info@inlanguageradio.com
Editorial Profile: KVTO-AM is a commercial station owned by YMF Media LLC. The format of the station is a variety of Chines language programming. KVTO-AM broadcasts to the San Francisco area at 1400 AM. The station does not have a news department or accept press releases. PSA's are accepted.

KVTY-FM
Owner: Ida-Vend Communications Group
Editorial: 805 Stewart Ave, Lewiston, Idaho 83501. **T:** 1 208 746-5056
E: newsroom@idavend.com
Editorial Profile: KVTY-FM is a commercial station owned by Ida-Vend Communications Group. The format of the station is hot adult contemporary. The station broadcasts to the Lewiston, ID area at 105.1 FM.

KVUU-FM
Owner: Clear Channel Media and Entertainment
Editorial: 2864 S Circle Dr, Ste 150, Colorado Springs, Colorado 80906. **T:** 1 719 540-9200
W: http://www.my999radio.com
Editorial Profile: KVUU-FM is a commercial station owned by Clear Channel Media and Entertainment. The format of the station is Top 40/CHR. KVUU-FM broadcasts to the Colorado Springs, CO area at 99.9 FM.

KVVA-FM
Owner: Entravision Communications Corp.
Editorial: 501 N 44th St, Ste 425, Phoenix, Arizona 85008. **T:** 1 602 776-1400
W: http://www.josephoenix.com
Editorial Profile: KVVA-FM is a commercial station owned by Entravision Communications Corp. The format of the station is Hispanic adult hits. KVVA-FM broadcasts to the Phoenix area at 107.1 FM

KVVF-FM
Owner: Univision Communications Inc.
Editorial: 750 Battery St Ste 200, San Francisco, California 94111-1524.
T: 1 415 733-5765
W: http://hot1057fm.univision.com
Editorial Profile: KVVF-FM is a commercial station owned by Univision Communications Inc. The format of the station is hip hop and R&B. KVVF-FM broadcasts to the San Francisco area at 105.7 FM.

KVVL-FM
Owner: Nodaway Broadcasting Corp
Editorial: 1618 S Main St, Maryville, Missouri 64468. **T:** 1 660 582-2151
E: knim@knimmaryville.com
W: http://www.971thevill.com
Editorial Profile: KVVL-FM is a commercial station owned by Nodaway Broadcasting Corp. The format of the station is rock music. KVVL-FM broadcasts to the Maryville, MO area at 97.1 FM.

KVVN-AM
Owner: YMF Media LLC
Editorial: 55 Hawthorne St Ste 900, San Francisco, California 94105-3967.
T: 1 415 648-7980
E: info@INLANGUAGERADIO.com
Editorial Profile: KVVN-AM is a commercial station owned by YMF Media LLC. The format of the station is a variety of Vietnamese music, news and talk. KVVN-AM broadcasts to the San Jose, CA area at 1430 AM.

KVVP-FM
Owner: Stannard Broadcasting Co.
Editorial: 168 Kvvp Dr, Leesville, Louisiana 71446. **T:** 1 337 537-5887 **E:** kvvp@kvvp.com
W: http://www.kvvp.com
Editorial Profile: KVVP-FM is a commercial station owned by Stannard Broadcasting Co. The format of the station is contemporary country. KVVP-FM broadcasts to the Leesville, LA area at 105.7 FM.

KVVR-FM
Owner: Cherry Creek Radio
Editorial: 20 3rd St N, Ste 231, Great Falls, Montana 59401. **T:** 1 406 761-7600
Editorial Profile: KVVR-FM is a commercial station owned by Cherry Creek Radio. The format of the station is lite rock. KVVR-FM broadcasts to the Great Falls, MT area at 97.9 FM.

KVVS-FM
Owner: Clear Channel Media and Entertainment
Editorial: 3400 W Olive Ave, Ste 550, Burbank, California 91505. **T:** 1 818 559-2252
W: http://www.kiisfm.com
Editorial Profile: KVVS-FM is a commercial station owned by Clear Channel Media and Entertainment. The format of the station is Top 40/CHR. KVVS-FM is a simulcast on KIIS-FM. KVVS-FM broadcasts to the Burbank, CA area on 105.5 FM.

KVVZ-FM
Owner: Univision Communications Inc.
Editorial: 750 Battery St Ste 200, San Francisco, California 94111-1524.
T: 1 415 733-5765
W: http://hot1057fm.univision.com
Editorial Profile: KVVZ-FM is a commercial station owned by Univision Communications Inc. The format of the station is hip hop and R&B. The station airs locally on 100.7 FM and is a simulcast of KVVF-FM in San Jose, CA.

KVWC-AM
Owner: KVWC Inc.
Editorial: 302 Wilbarger St, Vernon, Texas 76384. **T:** 1 940 552-6221 **E:** kvwc@kvwc.com
W: http://www.kvwc.com
Editorial Profile: KVWC-AM is a commercial station owned by KVWC Inc. The format of the station is a variety of music, including country, oldies, and gospel. KVWC-AM broadcasts to the Vernon, TX area at 1490 AM.

KVWC-FM
Owner: KVWC Inc.
Editorial: 302 Wilbarger St, Vernon, Texas 76384. **T:** 1 940 552-6221 **E:** kvwc@kvwc.com
W: http://www.kvwc.com
Editorial Profile: KVWC-FM is a commercial station owned by KVWC Inc. The format of the station is news, country, sports and oldies. KVWC-FM broadcasts to the Vernon, TX area at 93.1 FM.

KVWF-FM
Owner: Connoisseur Media LLC
Editorial: 1938 N Woodlawn St, Ste 138, Wichita, Kansas 67208-1857.
T: 1 316 558-8800
W: http://www.1005thewolfonline.com
Editorial Profile: KVWF-FM is a commercial station owned by Connoisseur Media LLC. The format of the station is contemporary country. KGGG-FM broadcasts to the Wichita, KS area at 100.5 FM.

KVWM-AM
Owner: Petracom
Editorial: 1838 Commerce Dr, Ste A, Lakeside, Arizona 85929. **T:** 1 928 532-3232
E: production@whitemountainradio.com
W: http://www.whitemountainradio.com
Editorial Profile: KVWM-AM is a commercial station owned by Petracom. The format of the station is news and talk. KVWM-AM broadcasts to the Show Low, AZ area at 970 AM.

KVXR-AM
Owner: Real Presence Radio
Editorial: 926 50Th Ave S, Moorhead, Minnesota 56560-7400. **T:** 1 701 795-0122
E: businessmanager@realpresenceradio.com
W: http://yourcatholicradiostation.com
Editorial Profile: KVXR-AM is a non-commercial station owned by Real Presence Radio. The format of the station is religion and talk. KVXR-AM airs in the Moorhead, MN area at 1280 AM.

KVXX-FM
Owner: Huth Broadcasting Inc.
Editorial: 756 Hickory St, Red Bluff, California 96080-3239. **T:** 1 530 527-1490
Editorial Profile: KVXX-FM is a commercial station owned by Huth Broadcasting Inc. The format of the station is alternative rock music. KVXX-FM broadcasts to the Chico, CA area at 101.7 FM

KVYB-FM
Owner: Cumulus Media Inc.
Editorial: 1376 Walter St, Ventura, California 93003-5658. **T:** 1 805 642-8595
W: http://www.1033thevibe.com
Editorial Profile: KVYB-FM is a commercial station owned by Cumulus Media Inc. The format of the station is urban contemporary. KVYB-FM broadcasts to the Ventura, CA area at 103.3 FM.

KVYN-FM
Owner: Wine Country Broadcasting Co.
Editorial: 1124 Foster Rd, Napa, California 94558-6520. **T:** 1 707 258-1111
E: psa@kvyn.com
W: http://www.993thevine.com
Editorial Profile: KVYN-FM is a commercial station owned by Wine Country Broadcasting Co. The format of the station is classic hits. KVYN-FM broadcasts to the Napa, CA area at 99.3 FM.

KWAC-AM
Owner: Lotus Communications Corp.
Editorial: 5100 Commerce Dr, Bakersfield, California 93309-0684. **T:** 1 661 327-9711
Editorial Profile: KWAC-AM is a commercial station owned by Lotus Communications Corp. The format of the station is Hispanic sports. KWAC-FM broadcasts in the Bakersfield, CA area at 1490 AM.

KWAD-AM
Owner: BL Broadcasting Inc.
Editorial: 201 1/2 Jefferson St S, Wadena, Minnesota 56482. T: 1 218 631-1803
W: http://www.superstationk106.com
Editorial Profile: KWAD-AM is a commercial station owned by BL Broadcasting Inc. The format of the station is country music. KWAD-AM broadcasts to the Wadena, MN area at 920 AM.

KWAI-AM
Owner: Radio Hawaii Inc.
Editorial: 100 N Beretania St, Ste 401, Honolulu, Hawaii 96817. T: 1 808 523-3868
E: radiohawaii@inbox.com
Editorial Profile: KWAI-AM is a commercial station owned by Radio Hawaii Inc. The format of the station is talk programming. KWAI-AM broadcasts to the Honolulu area at 1080 AM.

KWAK-AM
Owner: Arkansas County Broadcasters Inc.
Editorial: 1818 S Buerkle St, Stuttgart, Arkansas 72160. T: 1 870 673-1595
E: kdew973@yahoo.com
Editorial Profile: KWAK-AM is a commercial station owned by Arkansas County Broadcasters Inc. The format of the station is sports. KWAK-AM broadcasts to the Stuttgart, AR area at 1240 AM.

KWAK-FM
Owner: Arkansas County Broadcasters Inc.
Editorial: 1818 S Buerkle St, Stuttgart, Arkansas 72160. T: 1 870 673-1595
E: kdew973@yahoo.com
Editorial Profile: KWAK-FM is a commercial station owned by Arkansas County Broadcasters Inc. The format of the station is oldies. KWAK-FM broadcasts to the Stuttgart, AR area at 105.5 FM.

KWAL-AM
Owner: Metals Broadcasting
Editorial: 120 First St, Osburn, Idaho 83849-9999. T: 1 208 752-1141
E: kwalradio@suddenlinkmail.com
Editorial Profile: KWAL-AM is a commercial station owned by Metals Broadcasting. The format of the station is classic country music. KWAL-AM broadcasts to the Spokane, WA area at 620 AM.

KWAM-AM
Owner: Legacy Media Memphis LLC
Editorial: 5495 Murray Rd, Memphis, Tennessee 38119-3703. T: 1 901 261-4200
E: info@kwam990.com
W: http://www.kwam990.com
Editorial Profile: KWAM-AM is commercial station owned by Legacy Media Memphis LLC. The format of the station is news and talk. KWAM-AM broadcasts to the Memphis, TN area at 990 AM.

KWAR-FM
Owner: Wartburg College
Editorial: 100 Wartburg Blvd, Waverly, Iowa 50677-2215. T: 1 319 352-8209
E: yoursound.kwar@gmail.com
W: http://www.kwar.org
Editorial Profile: KWAR-FM is a non-commercial station owned by Wartburg College. The format of the station is variety. KWAR-FM broadcasts to the Waverly, IA area at a frequency of 89.9 FM.

KWAT-AM
Owner: Three Eagles Communications Co.
Editorial: 921 9Th Ave Se, Watertown, South Dakota 57201-4960. T: 1 605 886-8444
E: kwatnews@watertown.threeeagles.com
W: http://www.gowatertown.net
Editorial Profile: KWAT-AM is a commercial station owned by Three Eagles Communications Co. The format of the station is news and talk. KWAT-AM broadcasts to the Watertown, SD area at 950 AM.

KWAV-FM
Owner: Mapleton Communications LLC
Editorial: 5 Harris Ct Bldg C, Monterey, California 93940-5751. T: 1 831 649-0969
E: frontdesk@kwav.com
W: http://www.kwav.com
Editorial Profile: KWAV-FM is a commercial station owned by Mapleton Communications LLC. The format of the station is adult contemporary. KWAV-FM broadcasts to the Monterey, CA area at 96.9FM.

KWAX-FM
Owner: University of Oregon
Editorial: 75 Centennial Loop, Eugene, Oregon 97401. T: 1 541 345-0800
E: inquiry@kwax.com

W: http://www.kwax.com
Editorial Profile: KWAX-FM is a non-commercial station owned by the University of Oregon. The format of the station is classical music. KWAX-FM broadcasts to the Eugene, OR area at 91.1 FM.

KWAY-AM
Owner: Suhr Enterprises(Ael)
Editorial: 110 29th Ave SW, Waverly, Iowa 50677-4301. T: 1 319 352-3550
E: news@kwayradio.com
W: http://www.kwayradio.com
Editorial Profile: KWAY-AM is a commercial station owned by Ael Suhr Enterprises. The format for the station is classic country. KWAY-AM broadcasts to the Cedar Rapids, IA area at 1470 AM.

KWAY-FM
Owner: Suhr Enterprises(Ael)
Editorial: 110 29th Ave SW, Waverly, Iowa 50677. T: 1 319 352-3550
E: news@kwayradio.com
W: http://www.kwayradio.com
Editorial Profile: KWAY-FM is a commercial station owned by Ael Suhr Enterprises. The format for the station is hot adult contemporary. KWAY-FM broadcasts to the Cedar Rapids, IA area at 99.3 FM.

KWBC-AM
Owner: Bryan Broadcasting
Editorial: 303 E Washington Ave, Ste A, Navasota, Texas 77868-3043.
T: 1 936 825-9007
E: news@navasotanews.com
W: http://www.navasotanews.com
Editorial Profile: KWBC-AM is a commercial station owned by Bryan Broadcasting. The format of the station is news and talk. KWBC-AM broadcasts to the Navasota, TX area at 1550 AM.

KWBE-AM
Owner: Siebert Communications Inc.
Editorial: 200 Sherman St, Beatrice, Nebraska 68310. T: 1 402 228-5923
E: kwbe@diodecom.net
W: http://www.kutt995.com
Editorial Profile: KWBE-AM is a commercial station owned by Siebert Communications Inc. The format of the station is classic hits and news. KWBE-AM broadcasts to the Beatrice, NE area at 1450 AM

KWBG-AM
Owner: NRG Media LLC
Editorial: 724 Story St, Ste 201, Boone, Iowa 50036. T: 1 515 432-2046
E: kwbgnews@nrgmedia.com
W: http://www.kwbg.com
Editorial Profile: KWBG-AM is a commercial station owned by NRG Media LLC. The format of the station is news and talk. KWBG-AM broadcasts to the Boone, IA area at 1590 AM.

KWBT-FM
Owner: Kennelwood Broadcasting Company, Inc.
Editorial: 4701 W Waco Dr, Waco, Texas 76710-7015. T: 1 254 399-9450
W: http://www.centraltexasbeat.com/
Editorial Profile: KWBT-FM is a commercial station owned by Kennelwood Broadcasting Company, Inc. The format of the station is rhythmic and urban CHR. KWBT-FM broadcasts to the Waco, TX area at 94.5 FM. The target audience of the station is listeners, ages 18 to 64. KWBT-FM's tagline is "94.5 The Beat." Newscasts air at the top of the hour.

KWBU-FM
Owner: Brazos Valley Public Broadcasting Foundation
Editorial: 1 Bear Pl, Unit 97296, Waco, Texas 76798-7296. T: 1 254 710-3426
W: http://www.kwbu.org
Editorial Profile: KWBU-FM is a non-commercial station owned by Brazos Valley Public Broadcasting Foundation. The format of the station is classical and news. KWBU-FM broadcasts to the Waco, TX area at 103.3 FM.

KWBW-AM
Owner: Eagle Radio Inc.
Editorial: 825 N Main St, Hutchinson, Kansas 67501. T: 1 620 662-4486 E: info@bwradio.biz
W: http://www.bwradio.biz
Editorial Profile: KWBW-AM is a commercial station owned by Eagle Radio Inc. The format of the station is news, sports and talk programming. KWBW-AM broadcasts to the Hutchinson, KS area at 1450 AM.

KWBX-FM
Owner: Corban University

Editorial: 5000 Deer Park Dr SE, Salem, Oregon 97317-9392. T: 1 503 589-8197
E: kwbx@corban.edu W: http://www.air1.com
Editorial Profile: KWRX-FM is a non-commercial station owned by Corban University. The format of the station is contemporary Christian. KWRX-FM broadcasts to the Salem, OR area at 90.1 FM. Programming comes from the Air 1 Network.

KWBY-AM
Owner: Coss (Donald)
Editorial: 1665 James St, Woodburn, Oregon 97071-3475. T: 1 503 981-9400
W: http://www.lapantera940.com
Editorial Profile: KWBY-AM is a commercial station owned by Coss (Donald). The format of the station is regional Mexican music. KWBY-AM broadcasts to Woodburn, OR at 940 AM.

KWBZ-FM
Owner: Prairie Communications LLP
Editorial: 1645 Highway 104 Ste G, Quincy, Illinois 62305-0081. T: 1 217 224-4653
E: wpwq106@adams.net
W: http://www.oldiessuperstation.com

KWCA-FM
Owner: Absolute Communications, LLC
Editorial: 1784 California St, Redding, California 96001-1905. T: 1 530 244-1011
W: http://www.mixredding.com
Editorial Profile: KUSQ-FM is a commercial station owned by Absolute Communications, LLC. The format of the station is Hot AC. KUSQ-FM broadcasts to the Redding, CA area at a frequency of 101.1 FM.

KWCD-FM
Owner: Cherry Creek Radio
Editorial: 2300 E Busby Dr, Sierra Vista, Arizona 85635. T: 1 520 458-4313
E: kwcd@cherrycreekradio.com
Editorial Profile: KWCD-FM is a commercial station owned by Cherry Creek Radio. The format of the station is contemporary country. KWCD-FM broadcasts to the Sierra Vista, AZ area at 92.3 FM.

KWCK-AM
Owner: Crain Media Group LLC
Editorial: 111 N Spring St, Searcy, Arkansas 72143-7712. T: 1 501 268-7123
E: production@crainmedia.com
W: http://www.crainmedia.com
Editorial Profile: KWCK-AM is a commercial station owned by Crain Media Group LLC. The format of the station is news, talk and sports. KWCK-AM broadcasts in the Searcy, AR area at 1300 AM.

KWCK-FM
Owner: Crain Media Group LLC
Editorial: 111 N Spring St, Searcy, Arkansas 72143-7712. T: 1 501 268-7123
E: production@crainmedia.com
W: http://www.crainmedia.com
Editorial Profile: KWCK-FM is a commercial station owned by Crain Media Group LLC. The format of the station is classic country. KWCK-FM broadcasts to the Searcy, AR area at 99.9 FM.

KWCL-FM
Owner: KWCL-FM Broadcasting Company Inc.
Editorial: 230 E Main St, Oak Grove, Louisiana 71263-9346. T: 1 318 428-9670
E: kwcl@bellsouth.net
Editorial Profile: KWCL-FM is a commercial station owned by KWCL-FM Broadcasting Company Inc. The format of the station is classic hits. KWCL-FM broadcasts in the Oak Grove, LA area at 96.7 FM.

KWCO-FM
Owner: Mollman Communications, Inc.
Editorial: 627 W Chickasha Ave, Chickasha, Oklahoma 73018. T: 1 405 224-1560
W: http://www.classichits1055.com
Editorial Profile: KWCO-FM is a commercial station owned by Mollman Communications, Inc. The format of the station is classic hits. KWCO-FM broadcasts to the Oklahoma City area at 105.5 FM.

KWCQ-FM
Owner: Jacobs Radio Programming, LLC
Editorial: 2617 W Falls Ave, Kennewick, Washington 99336-3002. T: 1 509 302-9874
W: http://www.1073thebeat.com/
Editorial Profile: KWCQ-FM is a commercial station owned by Jacobs Radio Programming, LLC. The format of the station is urban contemporary. KWCQ-FM broadcasts to the The Dalles, OR at 106.1 FM.

KWCR-FM
Owner: Weber State University
Editorial: Weber State Univ, Union Bldg, Ste 223, Ogden, Utah 84408-0001.
T: 1 801 626-8450 E: weberfm@gmail.com
W: http://www.weberfm.org
Editorial Profile: KWCR-FM is a non-commercial station owned by Weber State University. The format for the station is variety. KWCR-FM broadcasts to the Salt Lake City area at 88.1 FM.

KWCX-FM
Owner: KZLZ, LLC
Editorial: 900 W Pattie Rd, Willcox, Arizona 85643. T: 1 520 384-4626
W: http://www.xwave1049.com
Editorial Profile: KWCX-FM is a commercial station owned by Lakeshore Media LLC. The format of the station is variety, with a mix of rock, classic rock, top 40, metal, dance and European music. KWCX-FM broadcasts to the Willcox, AZ area at 104.9 FM.

KWDD-FM
Owner: Last Frontier Mediactive, LLC
Editorial: 819 1st Ave Ste A, Fairbanks, Alaska 99701-4449. T: 1 907 451-5910
W: http://www.lfmediactive.com
Editorial Profile: KWDD-FM is a commercial station owned by Last Frontier Mediactive, LLC. The format of the station is contemporary country music. KWDD-FM broadcasts to the Fairbanks, AK area at a frequency of 94.3 FM.

KWDF-AM
Owner: Capital City Radio Corp.
Editorial: 3735 Rigolette Rd, Pineville, Louisiana 71360-7365. T: 1 318 640-4373
E: kwdf@wilkinsradio.com
W: http://www.wilkinsradio.com
Editorial Profile: KWDF-AM is a commercial station owned by Capital City Radio Corp. The format of the station is religious teaching. KWDF-AM broadcasts to the Alexandria, LA area at 840 AM.

KWDM-FM
Owner: West Des Moines Community School District
Editorial: 1140 Valley West Dr, West Des Moines, Iowa 50266. T: 1 515 267-8870
W: http://www.wdm.k12.ia.us/kwdm/
Editorial Profile: KWDM-FM is a non-commercial station owned by West Des Moines Community School District. The format of the station is modern rock music. KWDM-FM broadcasts to the Des Moines, IA area at 88.7 FM.

KWDP-AM
Owner: Reed-Nickerson (Leighton M. & Joan M.)
Editorial: 906 SW Alder St, Newport, Oregon 97365-4712. T: 1 541 265-2266
E: info@kbcham.com
W: http://www.kbcham.com
Editorial Profile: KWDP-AM is a commercial station owned by Reed-Nickerson (Leighton M. & Joan M.). The format of the station is adult standards music, news and talk. KWDP-AM broadcasts to the Waldport, OR area at 820 AM.

KWDQ-FM
Owner: Classic Communications Inc.
Editorial: 1922 22nd St, Woodward, Oklahoma 73801-5307. T: 1 580 254-9102
E: cciradio@sbcglobal.net
W: http://www.woodwardradio.com
Editorial Profile: KWDQ-FM is a commercial station owned by Classic Communications Inc. The format of the station is rock music. KWDQ-FM broadcasts to the Oklahoma City area at 102.3 FM.

KWDS-FM
Owner: Calvary Chapel of Costa Mesa, Inc.
Editorial: 3000 W Macarthur Blvd Ste 500, Santa Ana, California 92704-7947.
T: 1 714 918-6207
Editorial Profile: KWDS-FM is a commercial station owned by Calvary Chapel of Costa Mesa, Inc. The format of the station is Religious. KWDS-FM broadcasts to the Santa Ana, CA area at 89.9 FM.

KWED-AM
Owner: Guadalupe Media, Ltd.
Editorial: 609 E Court St, Seguin, Texas 78155-5713. T: 1 830 379-2234
E: cindy@kwed1580.com
W: http://www.seguintoday.com
Editorial Profile: KWED-AM is a commercial station owned by Guadalupe Media, Ltd. The format of the station is country music. KWED-

AM broadcasts to the Seguin, TX area at 1580 AM.

KWEI-AM
Owner: Treasure Valley Broadcasting
Editorial: 1156 N Orchard St, Boise, Idaho 83706-2234. **T:** 1 208 367-1859
W: http://www.ktrpradio.com
Editorial Profile: KWEI-AM is a commercial station owned by the Treasure Valley Broadcasting. The format of the station is news/talk and Classic Country. KWEI-AM broadcasts to the Boise, ID area at 1260 AM.

KWEL-AM
Owner: CDA Broadcasting Inc.
Editorial: 310 W Wall St, Midland, Texas 79701-5123. **T:** 1 432 620-9393
W: http://www.kwel.com
Editorial Profile: KWEL-AM is a commercial station owned by CDA Broadcasting Inc. The format of the station is talk. KWEL-AM broadcasts to the Midland, TX area at 1070 AM.

KWEN-FM
Owner: Cox Media Group, Inc.
Editorial: 7136 S Yale Ave Ste 500, Tulsa, Oklahoma 74136-6358. **T:** 1 918 494-9500
W: http://www.k955fm.com
Editorial Profile: KWEN-FM is a commercial station owned by Cox Media Group, Inc. The format of the station is contemporary country. KWEN-FM broadcasts to the Tulsa, OK area at 95.5 FM.

KWES-AM
Owner: Walton Stations of New Mexico, Inc.
Editorial: 1096 Mechem Dr Ste 230, Ruidoso, New Mexico 88345-7071. **T:** 1 575 258-2222
E: production@kwes.net
W: http://www.kwes.net
Editorial Profile: KWES-AM is a commercial station owned by Walton Stations of New Mexico, Inc. The format of the station is sports. KWES-AM broadcasts to the Ruidoso, NM area at 1450 AM.

KWES-FM
Owner: Walton Stations of New Mexico, Inc.
Editorial: 1096 Mechem Dr Ste 230, Ruidoso, New Mexico 88345-7071. **T:** 1 575 258-2222
E: production@kwes.net
W: http://www.kwes.net
Editorial Profile: KWES-FM is a commercial station owned by Walton Stations of New Mexico, Inc. The format of the station is country. KWES-FM broadcasts to the Ruidoso, NM area at 93.5 FM.

KWEY-AM
Owner: Wright Broadcasting Systems
Editorial: 10040 Highway 54, Weatherford, Oklahoma 73096-3021. **T:** 1 580 772-5939
E: kwey@wrightwradio.com
W: http://www.kwey.com
Editorial Profile: KWEY-AM is a commercial station owned by Wright Broadcasting Systems. The format of the station is country music. KWEY-AM broadcasts to the Oklahoma City area at 1590 AM.

KWEY-FM
Owner: Wright Broadcasting Systems
Editorial: 10040 Highway 54, Weatherford, Oklahoma 73096-3021. **T:** 1 580 772-5939
E: news@wrightwradio.com
W: http://www.kwey.com
Editorial Profile: KWEY-FM is a commercial station owned by Wright Broadcasting Systems. The format of the station is country music. KWEY-FM broadcasts to the Oklahoma City area at 95.5 FM.

KWFB-FM
Owner: KIXC-FM LLC
Editorial: 719 Scott Ave Ste 1009, Wichita Falls, Texas 76301-2632. **T:** 1 940 322-1009
W: http://www.bobradio.fm
Editorial Profile: KWFB-FM is a commercial station owned by KIXC-FM LLC. The format of the station is Jack FM adult hits. KWFB-FM broadcasts to the Quanah, TX area at 100.9

KWFC-FM
Owner: Baptist Bible College
Editorial: 2316 N Benton Ave, Springfield, Missouri 65803. **T:** 1 417 869-0891
E: news@kwfc.org **W:** http://www.kwfc.org
Editorial Profile: KWFC-FM is a non-commercial station owned by Baptist Bible College. The format of the station is southern gospel music. KWFC-FM broadcasts to the Springfield, MO area at 89.1 FM.

KWFH-FM
Owner: Advance Ministries
Editorial: 510 Acoma Blvd N, Lake Havasu City, Arizona 86403-4838. **T:** 1 928 855-9110
E: info@kwfh.org **W:** http://www.kwfh.org
Editorial Profile: KWFH-FM is a non-commercial station owned by Advance Ministries. The format of the station is contemporary Christian. KWFH-FM broadcasts to the Parker, AZ area at 90.3 FM.

KWFJ-FM
Owner: Bible Broadcasting Network
Editorial: 9010 320th St S, Roy, Washington 98580-8786. **T:** 1 253 843-2738
E: bbn@bbnmedia.org
W: http://www.bbnradio.org
Editorial Profile: KWFJ-FM is a non-commercial station owned by the Bible Broadcasting Network. The format of the station is Christian music and talk. KWFJ-FM broadcasts to the Roy, WA area at 103.6 FM.

KWFL-FM
Owner: Family Life Broadcasting System
Editorial: 300 S Lea Ave, Roswell, New Mexico 88203. **T:** 1 505 296-9100
W: http://www.myflr.org
Editorial Profile: KWFL-FM is a non-commercial station owned by Family Life Broadcasting System. The format of the station is Christian talk and music. KWFL-FM broadcasts to the Albuquerque, NM area at 99.5 FM.

KWFM-AM
Owner: Hudson Communications, Inc.
Editorial: 4433 E Broadway Blvd Ste 210, Tucson, Arizona 85711-3536.
T: 1 520 529-5865 **E:** star1330am@gmail.com
Editorial Profile: KWFM-AM is a commercial station owned by Hudson Communications, Inc. The format of the station is Hot AC. KWFM-AM broadcasts locally to the Tucson, AZ area at 1330 AM.

KWFP-FM
Owner: Wilks Broadcast Group
Editorial: 300 E 2Nd St Ste 1400, Reno, Nevada 89501-1566. **T:** 1 775 333-0123
W: http://www.921thewolf.com
Editorial Profile: KWFP-FM is a commercial station owned by Wilks Broadcast Group. The format of the station is contemporary country. KWFP-FM broadcasts to the Reno, NV area at 92.1 FM.

KWFR-FM
Owner: Foster Communications Co. Inc.
Editorial: 2824 Sherwood Way, San Angelo, Texas 76901. **T:** 1 325 949-2112
W: http://www.kwfrfm.com
Editorial Profile: KWFR-FM is a commercial station owned by Foster Communications Co. Inc. The format of the station is classic rock. KWFR-FM broadcasts to the San Angelo, TX area at 101.9 FM.

KWFS-AM
Owner: Townsquare Media, LLC
Editorial: 2525 Kell Blvd, Ste 200, Wichita Falls, Texas 76308. **T:** 1 940 763-1111
W: http://www.newstalk1290.com
Editorial Profile: KWFS-AM is a commercial station owned by Townsquare Media, LLC. The format of the station is news and talk. KWFS-AM broadcasts to the Wichita Falls, TX area at 1290 AM.

KWFS-FM
Owner: Townsquare Media, LLC
Editorial: 2525 Kell Blvd, Wichita Falls, Texas 76308-1064. **T:** 1 940 763-1111
W: http://1023blakefm.com
Editorial Profile: KWFS-FM is a commercial station owned by Townsquare Media, LLC. The format of the station is contemporary country music. KWFS-FM broadcasts to the Wichita Falls, TX area at 102.3 FM.

KWFX-FM
Owner: Classic Communications Inc.
Editorial: 1922 22nd St, Woodward, Oklahoma 73801. **T:** 1 580 254-9103
E: cciradio@sbcglobal.net
W: http://www.woodwardradio.com
Editorial Profile: KWFX-FM is a commercial station owned by Classic Communications. The format of the station is classic country music. KWFX-FM broadcasts to the Oklahoma City area at 100.1 FM.

KWG-AM
Owner: Immaculate Heart Radio
Editorial: 2280 E Weber Ave, Stockton, California 95205. **T:** 1 209 462-8307
W: http://ihradio.org
Editorial Profile: KWG-AM is a non-commercial station owned by Immaculate Heart Radio. The format of the station is Catholic programming. KWG-AM broadcasts to the Sacramento, CA area at 1230 AM.

KWGB-FM
Owner: Melia Communications Inc.
Editorial: 1065 S Range Ave, Colby, Kansas 67701-3505. **T:** 1 785 899-2309
E: kloe@st-tel.net **W:** http://www.kloe.com
Editorial Profile: KWGB-FM is a commercial station owned by Melia Communications Inc. The format of the station is contemporary country music. KWGB-FM broadcasts to the Goodland, KS area at 97.9 FM.

KWGL-FM
Owner: Western Slope Communications
Editorial: 751 Horizon Ct, Ste 225, Grand Junction, Colorado 81506. **T:** 1 970 241-6460
E: production@wscradio.net
Editorial Profile: KWGL-FM is a commercial station owned by Western Slope Communications. The format for the station is classic country. KWGL-FM broadcasts to the Grand Junction-Montrose, CO area at 105.7 FM.

KWGS-FM
Owner: University of Tulsa
Editorial: 800 Tucker Dr, Tulsa, Oklahoma 74104-9700. **T:** 1 918 631-2577
E: public@publicmediatulsa.org
W: http://www.publicradiotulsa.org
Editorial Profile: KWGS-FM is a non-commercial station owned by the University of Tulsa. The format of the station is news, Folk, Jazz and talk. KWGS-FM broadcasts to the Tulsa, OK area at 89.5 FM.

KWHF-FM
Owner: East Arkansas Broadcasters Inc.
Editorial: 407 W Parker Rd, Jonesboro, Arkansas 72404. **T:** 1 870 932-8400
Editorial Profile: KWHF-FM is a commercial station owned by East Arkansas Broadcasters Inc. The format of the station is classic country. KWHF-FM broadcasts to the Jonesboro, AR area at 95.9 FM.

KWHI-AM
Owner: Whitehead Inc.(Tom S.)
Editorial: 223 E Main St, Brenham, Texas 77833. **T:** 1 979 836-3655 **E:** news@kwhi.com
W: http://www.kwhi.com
Editorial Profile: KWHI-AM is a commercial station owned by Tom S. Whitehead Inc. The format of the station is talk and classic country music. KWHI-AM broadcasts to the Brenham, TX area at 1280 AM.

KWHK-FM
Owner: Ad Astra Per Aspera Broadcasting, Inc.
Editorial: 10 E 5Th Ave, Hutchinson, Kansas 67501-6300. **T:** 1 620 665-5758
E: ksku@adastra.kscoxmail.com
W: http://www.adastraradio.net
Editorial Profile: KWHK-FM is a commercial station owned by Ad Astra Per Aspera Broadcasting, Inc. The format of the station is oldies music. KWHK-FM broadcasts to Wichita-Hutchinson, KS area at 95.9 FM.

KWHL-FM
Owner: Morris Communications
Editorial: 301 Arctic Slope Ave, Ste 200, Anchorage, Alaska 99518. **T:** 1 907 344-9622
W: http://www.kwhl.com
Editorial Profile: KWHL-FM is a commercial station owned by Morris Communications. The format of the station is rock/album-oriented rock. KWHL-FM broadcasts to the Anchorage, AK area at 106.5 FM.

KWHN-AM
Owner: Clear Channel Media and Entertainment
Editorial: 311 Lexington Ave, Fort Smith, Arkansas 72901-3842. **T:** 1 479 782-8888
W: http://www.kwhn.com/main.html
Editorial Profile: KWHN-AM is a commercial station owned by Clear Channel Media and Entertainment. The format of the station is news and talk. KWHN-AM broadcasts to the Fort Smith, AR area at 1320 AM.

KWHQ-FM
Owner: KSRM, Inc.
Editorial: 40960 Kalifornsky Beach Rd, Kenai, Alaska 99611-6445. **T:** 1 907 283-8700
E: rken18@radiokenai.com
W: http://www.radiokenai.com
Editorial Profile: KWHQ-FM is a commercial station owned by Blayde Communications Inc. The format of the station is country. KWHQ-FM broadcasts to the Kenai, AK area at 100.1 FM.

KWHT-FM
Owner: Capps Broadcast Group
Editorial: 2003 NW 56th St, Pendleton, Oregon 97801. **T:** 1 541 276-1511
W: http://www.1035kwheat.com
Editorial Profile: KWHT-FM is a commercial station owned by Capps Broadcasting Group. The format of the station is country music. KWHT-FM broadcasts to the Pendleton, OR area at 103.5 FM.

KWHW-AM
Owner: Monarch Broadcasting
Editorial: 212 W Cypress St, Altus, Oklahoma 73521. **T:** 1 580 482-1450
W: http://www.kwhw.com
Editorial Profile: KWHW-AM is a commercial station owned by Monarch Broadcasting. The format of the station is country. KWHW-AM broadcasts to the Altus, OK area at 1450 AM.

KWHW-FM
Owner: Monarch Broadcasting
Editorial: 212 W Cypress St, Altus, Oklahoma 73521. **T:** 1 580 482-1450
W: http://www.kwhw.com
Editorial Profile: KWHW-FM is a commercial station owned by Monarch Broadcasting. The format of the station is country music. KRKZ-FM broadcasts to the Altus, OK area at 93.5 FM.

KWIC-FM
Owner: Cumulus Media Inc.
Editorial: 825 S Kansas Ave, Ste 100, Topeka, Kansas 66612. **T:** 1 785 272-2122
W: http://www.eagle993.com
Editorial Profile: KWIC-FM is a commercial radio station owned by Cumulus Media. The format of the station is classic hits. KWIC-FM broadcasts to the Topeka, KS area on 99.3 FM.

KWID-FM
Owner: Lotus Communications Corp.
Editorial: 8755 W Flamingo Rd, Las Vegas, Nevada 89147-8667. **T:** 1 702 876-1460
W: http://www.labuenalv.com
Editorial Profile: KWID-FM is a commercial station owned by Lotus Communications Corp. The format of the station is Hispanic oldies. KWID-FM broadcasts to the Las Vegas area at 101.9 FM.

KWIK-AM
Owner: Rich Broadcasting, LLC
Editorial: 259 E Center St, Pocatello, Idaho 83201-6339. **T:** 1 208 233-1133
W: http://www.590kid.com
Editorial Profile: KWIK-AM is a commercial station owned by Rich Broadcasting, LLC. The format of the station is news, sports and talk. KWIK-AM broadcasts to the Pocatello, ID area at 1240 AM.

KWIL-AM
Owner: Extra Mile Media Inc.
Editorial: 34545 Highway 20 SE, Albany, Oregon 97322-9731. **T:** 1 541 926-2233
W: http://www.kwil790.com
Editorial Profile: KWIL-AM is a commercial station owned by Extra Mile Media Inc. The format of the station is religious and Southern gospel. KWIL-AM broadcasts to the Albany, OR area at 790 AM.

KWIM-FM
Owner: Western Indian Ministries
Editorial: Highway 264, 02C Hilltop Drive, HC33 Box 40, Gallup, New Mexico 87301.
T: 1 505 371-5587
E: kwim@westernindian.org
W: http://www.westernindian.net
Editorial Profile: KWIM-FM is a non-commercial station owned by Western Indian Ministries. The format of the station is contemporary Christian. KWIM-FM broadcasts to the Window Rock, AZ area on 104.9 FM.

KWIN-FM
Owner: Cumulus Media Inc
Editorial: 3136 Boeing Way Ste 125, Stockton, California 95206-4989. **T:** 1 209 766-5000
W: http://www.kwin.com
Editorial Profile: KWIN-FM is a commercial station owned by Cumulus Media Inc. The format of the station is urban contemporary. KWIN-FM broadcasts to the Stockton, CA area at 98.3 FM.

KWIP-AM
Owner: Valley Broadcasting

Editorial: 1405 E Ellendale Ave, Dallas, Oregon 97338. **T:** 1 503 623-0245
W: http://www.kwip.com
Editorial Profile: KWIP-AM is a commercial station owned by Valley Broadcasting. The format of the station is regional Mexican. KWIP-FM broadcasts to Dallas, OR, at 880 AM.

KWIQ-AM
Owner: Morris Communications
Editorial: 32 N Mission St Unit B2, Wenatchee, Washington 98801-7210.
T: 1 509 663-5186 **W:** http://www.kkrt.com
Editorial Profile: KWIQ-AM is a commercial station owned by Morris Communications. The format of the station is sports. KWIQ-AM broadcasts to the Moses Lake, WA area at 1020 AM.

KWIQ-FM
Owner: Morris Communications
Editorial: 11768 Kittleson Rd NE, Moses Lake, Washington 98837-9720. **T:** 1 509 765-1761
W: http://www.kwiq.com
Editorial Profile: KWIQ-FM is a commercial station owned by Morris Communications. The format of the station is country music. KWIQ-FM broadcasts to the Spokane, WA area at 100.5 FM.

KWIT-FM
Owner: Western Iowa Tech Community College
Editorial: 4647 Stone Ave, Sioux City, Iowa 51106-1918. **T:** 1 712 274-6406
E: kwitnews@witcc.edu **W:** http://www.kwit.org
Editorial Profile: KWIT-FM is a non-commercial station owned by Western Iowa Tech Community College. The format of the station is news, talk and classical music. KWIT-FM broadcasts to the Sioux City, IA area at 90.3 FM.

KWIX-AM
Owner: Moberly/Macon License Co., LLC
Editorial: 300 W Reed St, Moberly, Missouri 65270. **T:** 1 660 263-1500
E: kresnews@regionalradio.com
W: http://www.centralmoinfo.com
Editorial Profile: KWIX-AM is a commercial station owned by Moberly/Macon License Co., LLC. The format of the station is news and talk. KWIX-AM broadcasts in the Moberly, MO area at 1230 AM.

KWIZ-FM
Owner: Liberman Broadcasting Inc.
Editorial: 3101 W 5th St, Santa Ana, California 92703-1829. **T:** 1 714 554-5000
W: http://www.larockola967.com
Editorial Profile: KWIZ-FM is a commercial station owned by the Liberman Broadcasting Inc. The format of the station is Spanish adult contemporary. KWIZ-FM broadcasts to the Los Angeles area at 96.7 FM.

KWJB-AM
Owner: Butler7Media, LLC
Editorial: 5600 W Lovers Ln Suite 116-255, Dallas, Texas 75209-4330. **T:** 1 214 641-9400
W: http://www.radiokwjb.com
Editorial Profile: KWJB-AM is a commercial station owned by Butler7Media, LLC. The format of the station is News and Talk. KWJB-AM broadcasts to the Canton, TX area at 1510 AM.

KWJC-FM
Owner: William Jewell College
Editorial: 500 College Hl, Liberty, Missouri 64068. **T:** 1 816 415-5091
W: http://www.jewell.edu
Editorial Profile: KWJC-FM is a non-commercial station owned by Willam Jewell College. The format of the station is contemporary Christian, and airs the programming from K-Love network. KWJC-FM broadcasts to the Liberty, MO area at 91.9 FM.

KWJJ-FM
Owner: Entercom Communications Corp.
Editorial: 0700 SW Bancroft St, Portland, Oregon 97239-4226. **T:** 1 503 223-1441
W: http://www.thewolfonline.com
Editorial Profile: KWJJ-FM is a commercial station owned by Entercom Communications Corp. The format of the station is contemporary country music. KWJJ-FM broadcasts to Portland, OR at 99.5 FM.

KWJK-FM
Owner: Billings Broadcasting LLC
Editorial: 1600 Radio Hill Rd, Boonville, Missouri 65233. **T:** 1 660 882-6686
E: kwrt@classicnet.net
W: http://www.931jack.fm

Editorial Profile: KWJK-FM is a commercial station owned by Billings Broadcasting LLC. The format of the station is adult hits music. KWRT-FM broadcasts to the Boonville, MO area at 93.1 FM.

KWKA-AM
Owner: Zia Broadcasting Inc.
Editorial: 710 Cr K, Clovis, New Mexico 88101. **T:** 1 575 762-4411
E: ktqm@plateautel.net

KWKC-AM
Owner: Canfin Enterprises Inc.
Editorial: 402 Cypress St, Ste 510, Abilene, Texas 79601. **T:** 1 325 672-5442
W: http://www.radioabilene.com
Editorial Profile: KWKC-AM is a commercial station owned by Canfin Enterprises Inc. The format of the station is news, talk and sports. KWKC-AM broadcasts to the Abilene, TX area at 1340 AM.

KWKH-AM
Owner: Townsquare Media, LLC
Editorial: 6341 W Port Ave, Shreveport, Louisiana 71129. **T:** 1 318 688-1130
W: http://1130thetiger.com
Editorial Profile: KWKH-AM is a commercial station owned by Townsquare Media, LLC. The format of the station is sports. KWKH-AM broadcasts to the Shreveport, LA area at 1130 AM.

KWKJ-FM
Owner: D & H Media LLC
Editorial: 800 Pca Rd, Warrensburg, Missouri 64093-9275. **T:** 1 660 747-9191
W: http://www.warrensburgradio.com
Editorial Profile: KWKJ-FM is a commercial station owned by D & H Media LLC. The format for the station is contemporary country. KWKJ-FM broadcasts to the Warrensbrug, MO area at 98.5 FM.

KWKK-FM
Owner: East Arkansas Broadcasters Inc.
Editorial: 2705 E Parkway Dr, Russellville, Arkansas 72802-2006. **T:** 1 479 968-6816
E: news@rivervalleyradio.com
W: http://www.riverhitskwkk.com
Editorial Profile: KWKK-FM is a commercial station owned by East Arkansas Broadcasters Inc. The format of the station is hot adult contemporary. KWKK-FM broadcasts to the Russellville, AR area at 100.9 FM.

KWKL-FM
Owner: Educational Media Foundation
Editorial: 7301 Broadway Ext, Ste 131, Oklahoma City, Oklahoma 73116-9038.
T: 1 405 708-5683 **W:** http://www.klove.com
Editorial Profile: KWKL-FM is a non-commercial station owned by Educational Media Foundation. The format of the station is contemporary Christian. KWKL-FM broadcasts to the Grandfield, OK at 89.9 FM.

KWKM-FM
Owner: KM Communications Inc.
Editorial: 1520 E Commerce, Ste B, Show Low, Arizona 85901. **T:** 1 928 532-2949
E: program@kwkm.com
W: http://www.kwkm.com
Editorial Profile: KWKM-FM is a commercial station owned by KM Communications Inc. The format is hot adult contemporary music. KWKM-FM broadcasts to the Show Low, AZ area at 95.7 FM.

KWKQ-FM
Owner: MediaNews Group Inc.
Editorial: 620 Oak St, Graham, Texas 76450-3040. **T:** 1 940 549-1330
E: news@kwkq-kswa.com
Editorial Profile: KWKQ-FM is a commercial station owned by MediaNews Group Inc. The format of the station is heritage rock music. KWKQ-FM broadcasts to the Graham, TX area at 94.7 FM.

KWKR-FM
Owner: Armada Media Corp.
Editorial: 1402 E Kansas Ave, Garden City, Kansas 67846-5806. **T:** 1 620 276-2366
W: http://www.wksradio.com
Editorial Profile: KWKR-FM is a commercial station owned by Armada Media Corp. The format of the station is classic rock. KWKR-FM broadcasts to the Garden City, KS area at 99.9 FM.

KWKU-AM
Owner: Lotus Communications Corp.
Editorial: 3301 Barham Blvd, Ste 201, Los Angeles, California 90068. **T:** 1 323 851-5959

E: kwkw1330@aol.com
W: http://www.espn1330.com
Editorial Profile: KWKU-AM is commercial station owned by the Lotus Communications Corp. The format of the station is Hispanic sports. KWKU-AM broadcasts to the Los Angeles area at 1220 AM and simulcasts on KWKW-AM 1330.

KWKW-AM
Owner: Lotus Communications Corp.
Editorial: 3301 Barham Blvd, Los Angeles, California 90068-1480. **T:** 1 323 851-5959
E: kwkw1330@aol.com
W: http://www.radiodeportes.com
Editorial Profile: KWKW-AM is a commercial station owned by the Lotus Communications Corp. The format of the station is Spanish sports talk. KWKW-AM broadcasts to the Los Angeles area at 1330 AM and simulcasts on KWKU-AM.

KWKZ-FM
Owner: Anderson Broadcasting Inc.
Editorial: 753 Enterprise St, Cape Girardeau, Missouri 63703. **T:** 1 573 334-7800
W: http://www.kwkz.com
Editorial Profile: KWKZ-FM is a commercial station owned by Anderson Broadcasting Inc. The format of the station is classic country. KWKZ-FM broadcasts to the Cape Girardeau, MO area at 106.1 FM.

KWLA-AM
Owner: Baldridge-Dumas Communications Inc.
Editorial: 605 San Antonio Ave, Many, Louisiana 71449-3018. **T:** 1 318 256-5177
Editorial Profile: KWLA-AM is a commercial station owned by Baldridge-Dumas Communications Inc. The format of the station is talk. KWLA-AM broadcasts to the Shreveport, LA area at 1400 AM.

KWLC-AM
Owner: Luther College
Editorial: 700 College Dr, Decorah, Iowa 52101. **T:** 1 563 387-1240
E: kwlcam@luther.edu **W:** http://kwlc.luther.edu
Editorial Profile: KWLC-AM is a non-commercial station owned by Luther College. The format of the station is variety. KWLC-AM broadcasts to the Decorah, IA area at a frequency of 1240 AM.

KWLE-AM
Owner: San Juan Communications Inc
Editorial: 904 32Nd St, Anacortes, Washington 98221-3407. **T:** 1 360 293-3141
E: questions@1340thewhale.com
W: http://www.1340thewhale.com
Editorial Profile: KWLE-AM is a commercial station owned by San Juan Communications Inc. The format of the station is hot adult contemporary. KWLE-AM broadcasts to the Anacortes, WA area at 1340 AM.

KWLF-FM
Owner: Last Frontier Mediactive, LLC
Editorial: 819 1st Ave Ste A, Fairbanks, Alaska 99701-4449. **T:** 1 907 451-5910
W: http://www.kwolf981.com
Editorial Profile: KWLF-FM is a commercial station owned by Last Frontier Mediactive, LLC. The format of the station is Top 40/CHR music. KWLF-FM broadcasts to the Fairbanks, AK area at 98.1 FM.

KWLM-AM
Owner: Lakeland Broadcasting
Editorial: 1340 NW 7th St, Willmar, Minnesota 56201. **T:** 1 320 235-1340
E: askus@kwlm.com
W: http://www.willmarradio.com/kwlm
Editorial Profile: KWLM-AM is a commercial station owned by Lakeland Broadcasting. The format of the station is news and talk. KWLM-AM broadcasts in the Willmar, MN area in the 1340 AM.

KWLN-FM
Owner: Morris Communications
Editorial: 1124 N Miller St, Wenatchee, Washington 98801-1541. **T:** 1 509 663-5186
W: http://www.lanuevaradio.com
Editorial Profile: KWLN-FM is a commercial station owned by Morris Communications. The format of the station is Hispanic Top 40/CHR. KWLN-FM broadcasts to the Seattle area at 103.3 FM.

KWLO-AM
Owner: Woodward Communications, Inc.
Editorial: 514 Jefferson St, Waterloo, Iowa 50701-5422. **T:** 1 319 234-2200
Editorial Profile: KWLO-AM is a commercial station owned by Woodward Communications, Inc. The format for the station is sports.

KWLO-AM broadcasts to the Cedar Rapids, IA area at 1330 AM.

KWLS-FM
Owner: Mid-America AG Network, Inc.
Editorial: 1009 N Rose Hill Rd, Rose Hill, Kansas 67133-9413. **T:** 1 620 262-4378
W: http://www.kwlsradio.com
Editorial Profile: KWLS-FM is a commercial station owned by Mid-America AG Network, Inc. The format of the station is country. KWLS-FM broadcasts to the Wichita, KS area at 107.9 FM.

KWLT-FM
Owner: Ashley County Broadcasters
Editorial: 117 E Wellfield Road, Crossett, Arkansas 71635. **T:** 1 870 364-2181
E: kagh@windstream.net
W: http://www.crossettradio.com
Editorial Profile: KWLT-FM is a commercial station owned by Ashley County Broadcasters. The format of the station is classic rock. KWLT-FM broadcasts to the Crossett, AR area at 102.7 FM.

KWLU-FM
Owner: Educational Media Foundation
Editorial: 5700 W Oaks Blvd, Rocklin, California 95765. **T:** 1 916 251-2142
W: http://www.klove.com
Editorial Profile: KWLU-FM is a non-commercial station owned by the Educational Media Foundation. The format of the station is contemporary Christian. KWLU-FM broadcasts to the Chester, CA area at 98.9 FM.

KWLV-FM
Owner: Baldridge-Dumas Communications Inc.
Editorial: 605 San Antonio Ave, Many, Louisiana 71449-3018. **T:** 1 318 256-5924
W: http://www.bdcradio.com
Editorial Profile: KWLV-FM is a commercial station owned by Baldridge-Dumas Communications Inc. The format of the station is classic country. KWLV-FM broadcasts to the Shreveport, LA area at 107.1 FM.

KWLZ-FM
Owner: Horizon Broadcasting Group
Editorial: 854 Ne 4Th St, Bend, Oregon 97701-4711. **T:** 1 541 383-3825
E: news@horizonbroadcastinggroup.com
W: http://www.newsradiocentraloregon.com
Editorial Profile: KWLZ-FM is a commercial station owned by Horizon Broadcasting Group. The format for the station is news and talk. KWLZ-FM broadcasts to the Warm Springs, OR area at 96.5 FM.

KWMC-AM
Owner: Valdez(Minerva Garza)
Editorial: 903 E Cortinas St, Del Rio, Texas 78840-6756. **T:** 1 830 775-3544
E: kwmc1490@wcsonline.com
W: http://kwmc1490.com
Editorial Profile: KWMC-AM is a commercial station owned by Minerva Garza Valdez. The format of the station is oldies. KWMC-AM broadcasts to the Del Rio, TX area at 1490 AM.

KWME-FM
Owner: Johnson Enterprises Inc.
Editorial: 338 S Kley Dr, Wellington, Kansas 67152-8427. **T:** 1 620 326-3341
E: kley@sutv.com
W: http://www.kleyam.com/kwme.html
Editorial Profile: KWME-FM is a commercial station owned by Johnson Enterprises Inc. The format of the station is oldies. KWME-FM broadcasts to the Wellington, KS area at 92.7 FM.

KWMF-AM
Owner: La Promesa Foundation
Editorial: 1406 Garden Ln, Midland, Texas 79701. **T:** 1 432 682-5476
Editorial Profile: KWMF-AM is a commercial station owned by La Promesa Foundation. The format of the station is Hispanic Catholic religious programming. KWMF-AM broadcasts to the Midland, TX area at 1380 AM.

KWMG-FM
Owner: Clear Channel Media and Entertainment
Editorial: 600 Old Marion Rd NE, Cedar Rapids, Iowa 52402. **T:** 1 319 395-0530
W: http://www.wmtradio.com
Editorial Profile: KWMG-FM is a commercial station owned by Clear Channel Media and Entertainment. The format of the station is news/talk. KWMG-FM broadcasts to the Cedar Rapids, IA area at 95.7 FM.

KWMR-FM
Owner: KWMR
Editorial: 11431 Street, Route 1, Point Reyes Station, California 94956. **T:** 1 415 663-8068
W: http://www.kwmr.org
Editorial Profile: KWMR-FM is a non-commercial station owned by KWMR. The format of the station is variety. KWMR-FM broadcasts to the Point Reyes Station, CA area at 90.5 FM.

KWMT-AM
Owner: Three Eagles Communications Co.
Editorial: 200 N 10th St, Fort Dodge, Iowa 50501-3925. **T:** 1 515 576-7333
W: http://www.kwmt.com
Editorial Profile: KWMT-AM is a commercial station owned by Three Eagles Communications Co. The format of the station is classic country. KWMT-AM broadcasts to the Fort Dodge, IA area at 540 AM.

KWMU-FM
Owner: University of Missouri
Editorial: 1 University Blvd, Saint Louis, Missouri 63121-4400. **T:** 1 314 516-5968
E: news@kwmu.org
W: http://www.news.stlpublicradio.org
Editorial Profile: KWMU-FM is a non-commercial station owned by the University of Missouri. The format of the station is news and talk programming. KWMU-FM broadcasts to the St. Louis area at 90.7 FM.

KWMX-FM
Owner: Grenax Broadcasting
Editorial: 2409 N 4th St, Ste 101, Flagstaff, Arizona 86004-3735. **T:** 1 928 779-1177
W: http://www.967thewolf.com
Editorial Profile: KWMX-FM is a commercial station owned by Grenax Broadcasting. The format of the station is classic rock. KWMX-FM broadcasts to the Phoenix area at 96.7 FM.

KWMY-FM
Owner: Connoisseur Media LLC
Editorial: 2075 Central Ave, Billings, Montana 59102-4956. **T:** 1 406 248-7777
E: my1059@my1059.com
W: http://www.my1059.com
Editorial Profile: KWMY-FM is commercial station owned by Connoisseur Media LLC. The format is classic hits. KWMY-FM broadcasts to the Billings, MT area at a frequency of 105.9 FM.

KWNA-AM
Owner: Buckaroo Broadcasting, LLC
Editorial: 335 W 4th St, Winnemucca, Nevada 89445-3355. **T:** 1 775 623-5203
E: kwnaradio@gmail.com
Editorial Profile: KWNA-AM is a commercial station owned by Buckaroo Broadcasting, LLC. The format of the station is oldies. KWNA-AM broadcasts to the Winnemucca, NV area on 1400 AM.

KWNA-FM
Owner: Buckaroo Broadcasting, LLC
Editorial: 335 W 4th St, Winnemucca, Nevada 89445-3355. **T:** 1 775 623-5203
E: kwnaradio@gmail.com
Editorial Profile: KWNA-FM is a commercial station owned by Buckaroo Broadcasting, LLC. The format of the station is sports. KWNA-FM broadcasts to Winnemucca, NV and the surrounding areas at 92.7 FM.

KWNC-AM
Owner: Cherry Creek Radio
Editorial: 231 N Wenatchee Ave, Wenatchee, Washington 98801-2009. **T:** 1 509 665-6565
W: http://juanradio.co/
Editorial Profile: KWNC-AM is a commercial station owned by Cherry Creek Radio. The format of the station is Spanish Adult Hits. KWNC-AM broadcasts to the Wenatchee, WA area at 1370 AM.

KWND-FM
Owner: Radio Training Network, Inc.
Editorial: 2550 S Campbell Ave, Ste 100, Springfield, Missouri 65807.
T: 1 417 889-0883 **E:** news@88.3thewind.com
W: http://88.3thewind.com
Editorial Profile: KWND-FM is a non-commercial station owned by Radio Training Network, Inc. The format of the station is contemporary Christian programming. KWND-FM broadcasts to the Springfield, MO area at 88.3 FM.

KWNE-FM
Owner: Broadcast Corp. of Mendocino County
Editorial: 1100 Hastings Rd #B, Ukiah, California 95482-7101. **T:** 1 707 462-0945
E: kwine@kwine.com
W: http://www.kwine.com
Editorial Profile: KWNE-FM is a commercial radio station owned by Broadcast Corp. of Mendocino County. The format of the station is hot adult contemporary. KWNE-FM broadcasts to the Ukiah, CA area at 94.5 FM.

KWNG-FM
Owner: Q Media Group, LLC
Editorial: 474 Guernsey Ln, Red Wing, Minnesota 55066-7448. **T:** 1 651 388-7151
E: news@kwng.com **W:** http://www.kwng.com
Editorial Profile: KWNG-FM is a commercial station owned by Q Media Group, LLC. The format of the station is classic hits. KWNG-FM broadcasts to the Red Wing, MN area at 105.9 FM.

KWNJ-FM
Owner: University of Norhtern Iowa
Editorial: University Of Northern Iowa, Cedar Falls, Iowa 50614-0001. **T:** 1 319 273-6400
E: news@iowapublicradio.org
W: http://iowapublicradio.org
Editorial Profile: KWNJ-FM is a non-commercial station owned by the University of Northern Iowa. The format of the station is variety, including music, news and talk. KWNJ-FM broadcasts to the Bettendorf, IA area at 91.1 FM.

KWNN-FM
Owner: Cumulus Media Inc
Editorial: 3136 Boeing Way, Ste 125, Stockton, California 95206. **T:** 1 209 766-5000
W: http://www.kwin.com
Editorial Profile: KWNN-FM is a commercial station owned by Cumulus Media Inc. The format of the station is Top 40/CHR. KWNN-FM broadcasts to the Stockton, CA area at 98.3 FM.

KWNO-AM
Owner: KAGE Inc.
Editorial: 752 Bluffview Cir, Winona, Minnesota 55987. **T:** 1 507 452-4000
W: http://www.winonaradio.com
Editorial Profile: KWNO-AM is a commercial station owned by KAGE Inc. The format of the station is news and talk. KWNO-AM broadcasts to the Winona, MN area at 1380 AM.

KWNO-FM
Owner: KAGE Inc.
Editorial: 752 Bluffview Cir, Winona, Minnesota 55987. **T:** 1 507 452-4000
W: http://www.winonaradio.com
Editorial Profile: KWNO-FM is a commercial station owned by KAGE, Inc. The format of the station is contemporary country. KWNO-FM broadcasts to the Winona, MN area at 99.3 FM.

KWNR-FM
Owner: Clear Channel Media and Entertainment
Editorial: 2880 Meade Ave, Las Vegas, Nevada 89102-0713. **T:** 1 702 238-7300
W: http://www.955thebull.com/main.html
Editorial Profile: KWNR-FM is a commercial station owned by Clear Channel Media and Entertainment. The format of the station is contemporary country. KWNR-FM broadcasts to the Las Vegas area at 95.5 FM.

KWNS-FM
Owner: Foster(Lottie)
Editorial: 215 Market St, Winnsboro, Texas 75494. **T:** 1 903 342-3501
E: kwns-fm@peoplescom.net
Editorial Profile: KWNS-FM is a commercial station owned by Lottie Foster. The format of the station is southern gospel. KWNS-FM broadcasts to the Winnsboro, TX area at 104.7 FM.

KWNW-FM
Owner: Clear Channel Media and Entertainment
Editorial: 2650 Thousand Oaks Blvd Ste 4100, Memphis, Tennessee 38118-2451.
T: 1 901 259-1300
W: http://www.kissfm1019.com/main.html
Editorial Profile: KWNW-FM is a commercial station owned by Clear Channel Media and Entertainment. The format of the station is Top 40/CHR music. KWNW-FM broadcasts to the Memphis, TN area at 101.9 FM.

KWNX-AM
Owner: Genuine Austin Radio
Editorial: 912 S Capital of Texas Hwy Ste 400, West Lake Hills, Texas 78746-6176.
T: 1 512 416-1100 **W:** http://www.hornfm.com
Editorial Profile: KWNX-AM is a commercial station owned by Genuine Austin Radio. The format of the station is sports and classic hits music. KWNX-AM broadcasts to the Austin, TX area at 1260 AM.

KWNZ-FM
Owner: Shamrock Communications, Inc.
Editorial: 510 E Plumb Ln, Reno, Nevada 89502-3565. **T:** 1 775 737-4030
W: http://www.1063popfm.com
Editorial Profile: KWNZ-FM is a commercial station owned by Shamrock Communications, Inc. The format of the station is rhythmic adult contemporary. KWNZ-FM broadcasts to the Reno, NV area at a frequency of 106.3 FM.

KWOA-AM
Owner: Absolute Communications (dba Radio Works)
Editorial: 28779 County Highway 35, Worthington, Minnesota 56187-6322.
T: 1 507 372-4829 **E:** info@myradioworks.net
W: http://kwoa.com
Editorial Profile: KWOA-AM is a commercial station owned by Absolute Communications (dba Radio Works). The format of the station is news/talk. KWOA-AM broadcasts to the Worthington, MN area at 730 AM.

KWOC-AM
Owner: Max Media
Editorial: 1015 W Pine St, Poplar Bluff, Missouri 63901. **T:** 1 573 785-0881
E: kwoc@riverradio.net
W: http://www.riverradio.net/kwoc
Editorial Profile: KWOC-AM is a commercial station owned by Max Media. The format of the station is news and talk. KWOC-AM broadcasts to the Poplar Bluff, MO area at 930 AM.

KWOD-FM
Owner: Entercom Communications Corp.
Editorial: 5345 Madison Ave, Sacramento, California 95841-3141. **T:** 1 916 334-7777
W: http://www.star1065.com
Editorial Profile: KWOD-FM is a commercial station owned by Entercom Communications Corp. The format of the station is Hot AC. KBZC-FM broadcasts to the Sacramento, CA area at 106.5 FM.

KWOF-FM
Owner: Wilks Broadcast Group
Editorial: 720 S Colorado Blvd Ste 1200N, Denver, Colorado 80246. **T:** 1 303 832-5665
W: http://www.925thewolf.com
Editorial Profile: KWOF-FM is a commercial station owned by Wilks Broadcast Group. The format of the station is contemporary country. KWOF-FM broadcasts to the Denver area at 92.5 FM.

KWOI-FM
Owner: Iowa State University
Editorial: 2111 Grand Ave Ste 100, Des Moines, Iowa 50312-5393. **T:** 1 515 725-1700
E: info@iowapublicradio.org
W: http://www.iowapublicradio.org
Editorial Profile: KWOI-FM is a non-commercial station owned by Iowa State University. The format of the station is news and talk. KWOI-FM broadcasts to the Des Moines, IA, area at 90.7 FM.

KWOK-AM
Owner: Morris Communications
Editorial: 1308 Coolidge Rd, Aberdeen, Washington 98520. **T:** 1 360 533-1320
Editorial Profile: KWOK-AM is a commercial station owned by Morris Communications. The format of the station is sports. KWOK-AM broadcasts to the Aberdeen, WA area at 1490 AM.

KWOL-FM
Owner: Rose Communications, Inc.
Editorial: 2432 US Highway 2 E, Kalispell, Montana 59901-2310. **T:** 1 406 755-8700
W: http://www.1051cool.com
Editorial Profile: KWOL-FM is a commercial station owned by Rose Communications, Inc. The format of the station is oldies music. The station airs locally at 105.1 FM.

KWON-AM
Owner: KCD Enterprises Inc.
Editorial: 1200 SE Frank Phillips Blvd, Bartlesville, Oklahoma 74003.
T: 1 918 336-1001
E: radio@bartlesvilleradio.com
W: http://www.bartlesvilleradio.com
Editorial Profile: KWON-AM is a commercial station owned by KCD Enterprises Inc. The format of the station is news and talk. KWON-AM broadcasts to the Bartlesville, OK area at 1400 AM.

KWOR-AM
Owner: Legend Communications
Editorial: 1340 Radio Dr, Worland, Wyoming 82401-8700. **T:** 1 307 347-3231
E: kwor@bhrnwy.com
W: http://www.mybighornbasin.com
Editorial Profile: KWOR-AM is a commercial station owned by Legend Communications. The format of the station is news, talk and sports. KWOR-AM broadcasts to the Casper-Riverton, WY area at 1340 AM.

KWOS-AM
Owner: Zimmer Radio Group
Editorial: 3109 S 10 Mile Dr, Jefferson City, Missouri 65109. **T:** 1 573 893-7857
E: kwos@zrgmail.com
W: http://www.kwos.com
Editorial Profile: KWOS-AM is a commercial station owned by Zimmer Radio Group. The format of the station is news and talk programming. KWOS-AM broadcasts to the Jefferson City, MO area at 950 AM.

KWOU-FM
Owner: University of Oklahoma
Editorial: 860 Van Vleet Oval Rm 300, Norman, Oklahoma 73019-2035.
T: 1 405 325-3388 **W:** http://www.kgou.org/
Editorial Profile: KWOU-FM is a non-commercial station owned by the University of Oklahoma. The format of the station is jazz, news and talk. The station targets listeners, ages 18 to 64. KWOU-FM broadcasts to the Norman, OK area at 88.1FM. KWOU-FM airs KGOU-FM's programming.

KWOW-FM
Owner: Waco Entertainment Group, LLC
Editorial: 6401 Cobbs Dr, Waco, Texas 76710.
T: 1 254 772-6104
W: http://www.laley104.com
Editorial Profile: KWOW-FM is a commercial station owned by Waco Entertainment Group, LLC. The format of the station is regional Mexican music. KWOW-FM broadcasts to the Waco, TX area at 104.1 FM.

KWOX-FM
Owner: Omni Communications Inc.
Editorial: 101 Centre, Williams & Down Ave, Woodward, Oklahoma 73801.
T: 1 580 256-4101 **E:** k101@k101online.com
W: http://www.k101online.com
Editorial Profile: KWOX-FM is a commercial station owned by Omni Communications Inc. The format of the station is country music. KWOX-FM broadcasts to the Oklahoma City area at 101.1 FM.

KWOZ-FM
Owner: WRD Entertainment Inc.
Editorial: 920 Harrison St Ste C, Batesville, Arkansas 72501-6949. **T:** 1 870 793-4196
E: kwozfm@yahoo.com
W: http://www.ar1033.com
Editorial Profile: KWOZ-FM is a commercial station owned by WRD Entertainment Inc. The format of the station is country. KWOZ-FM broadcasts to the Batesville, AR area at 103.3 FM.

KWPC-AM
Owner: Prairie Communications LLP
Editorial: 3218 Mulberry Ave, Muscatine, Iowa 52761. **T:** 1 563 263-2442
E: mail@voiceofmuscatine.com
W: http://www.voiceofmuscatine.com
Editorial Profile: KWPC-AM is a commercial station owned by Prairie Communications LLP. The format of the station is oldies music. KWPC-AM broadcasts to the Muscatine, IA area at 860 AM.

KWPK-FM
Owner: Horizon Broadcasting Group
Editorial: 854 Ne 4Th St, Bend, Oregon 97701-4711. **T:** 1 541 383-3825
E: news@horizonbroadcastinggroup.com
W: http://www.thepeak1041.com
Editorial Profile: KWPK-FM is a commercial station owned by Horizon Broadcasting Group. The format of the station is hot adult contemporary. KWPK-FM broadcasts to the Bend, OR area on 104.1 FM.

KWPM-AM
Owner: Ozark Radio Network Inc.
Editorial: 983 E US Highway 160, West Plains, Missouri 65775. **T:** 1 417 256-3131
W: http://www.ozarknewstalk.com
Editorial Profile: KWPM-AM is a commercial station owned by Ozark Radio Network Inc. The format of the station is news and talk.

KWPM-AM broadcasts to the Springfield, MO area at 1450 AM.

KWPN-AM
Owner: Cumulus Media Inc
Editorial: 4045 NW 64th St, Oklahoma City, Oklahoma 73116-1684. **T:** 1 405 848-0100
Editorial Profile: KWPN-AM is a commercial station owned by Cumulus Media Inc. The format of the station is sports. KWPN-AM broadcasts to the Oklahoma City area at 640 AM.

KWPT-FM
Owner: Lost Coast Communications
Editorial: 1400 Main St, Ste 104, Ferndale, California 95536-9459. **T:** 1 707 786-5104
W: http://kwpt.com
Editorial Profile: KWPT-FM is a commercial station owned by Lost Coast Communications. The format of the station is classic rock. KWPT-FM broadcasts to the Ferndale, CA area at 100.3 FM.

KWPW-FM
Owner: Waco Entertainment Group, LLC
Editorial: 6401 Cobbs Dr, Waco, Texas 76710-2536. **T:** 1 254 772-6104
W: http://power108fm.com
Editorial Profile: KWPW-FM is a commercial station owned by Waco Entertainment Group, LLC. The format is Top 40/CHR. The station broadcasts to the Robinson, TX area at 107.9 FM.

KWPZ-FM
Owner: Crista Ministries
Editorial: 1843 Front St, Ste A, Lynden, Washington 98264-1723. **T:** 1 360 354-5596
E: comments@praise1065.com
W: http://www.praise1065.com
Editorial Profile: KWPZ-FM is a non-commercial station owned by Crista Ministries. The format of the station is contemporary Christian music and talk. KWPZ-FM broadcasts to the Lynden, WA area at 106.5 FM.

KWQW-FM
Owner: Cumulus Media Inc
Editorial: 4143 109th St, Urbandale, Iowa 50322-7925. **T:** 1 515 331-9200
W: http://www.983thetorch.com
Editorial Profile: KWQW-FM is a commercial station owned by Cumulus Media Inc. The format of the station is talk. KWQW-FM broadcasts in the Des Moines, IA area at 98.3 FM.

KWRB-FM
Owner: World Radio Network, Inc.
Editorial: 3320 E Fry Blvd, Sierra Vista, Arizona 85635-2904. **T:** 1 520 452-8022
E: info@sparkfm.com
W: http://www.sparkfm.com
Editorial Profile: KWRB-FM is a non-commercial station owned by the World Radio Network, Inc. The format is contemporary Christian music. KWRB-FM broadcasts to the Sierra Vista, AZ area at 90.9 FM.

KWRD-AM
Owner: Hanszen Broadcast Group
Editorial: 1101 Kilgore Dr, Henderson, Texas 75652-5129. **T:** 1 903 655-1800
E: info@kwrdonline.com
W: http://www.easttexastoday.com
Editorial Profile: KWRD-AM is a commercial station owned by Hanszen Broadcast Group. The format of the station is sports. KWRD-AM broadcasts to the Henderson, TX area at 1470 AM.

KWRD-FM
Owner: Salem Communications
Editorial: 6400 N Belt Line Rd, Ste 110, Irving, Texas 75063-6065. **T:** 1 214 561-9673
W: http://www.thewordfm.com
Editorial Profile: KWRD-FM is a commercial station owned by Salem Communications. The format of the station is Christian talk programming. KWRD-FM broadcasts to the Dallas area at 100.7 FM.

KWRE-AM
Owner: Kaspar Broadcasting Co.
Editorial: 1217 N State Highway 47, Warrenton, Missouri 63383.
T: 1 636 377-2300 **E:** kwrekfav@socket.net
W: http://www.kwre.com
Editorial Profile: KWRE-AM is a commercial station owned by Kaspar Broadcasting Co. The format of the station is classic country. KWRE-AM broadcasts to the Warrentown, MO area at 730 AM.

KWRF-AM
Owner: Pines Broadcasting
Editorial: 1255 N Myrtle St, Warren, Arkansas 71671. **T:** 1 870 226-2653
E: pines.broadcasting@sbcglobal.net
Editorial Profile: KWRF-AM is a commercial station owned by Pines Broadcasting. The format of the station is adult standards music. KWRF-AM broadcasts in the Little Rock, AR area at 860 AM.

KWRF-FM
Owner: Pines Broadcasting
Editorial: 1255 N Myrtle St, Warren, Arkansas 71671. **T:** 1 870 226-2653
E: pines.broadcasting@sbcglobal.net
Editorial Profile: KWRF-FM is commercial station owned by Pines Broadcasting. The format of the station is contemporary country music. KWRF-FM broadcasts in the Warren, AR area at 105.5 FM.

KWRI-FM
Owner: Educational Media Foundation
Editorial: 7301 Broadway Ext, Ste 131, Oklahoma City, Oklahoma 73116-9038.
T: 1 405 708-5683 **W:** http://www.air1.com
Editorial Profile: KWRI-FM is a non-commercial station owned by Educational Media Foundation. The format of the station is contemporary Christian. KWRI-FM broadcasts to the Bartlesville, OK area at 89.1 FM.

KWRK-FM
Owner: Navajo Nation
Editorial: Window Rock Shopping Center, Window Rock, Arizona 86515-9999.
T: 1 928 871-3553
E: webmaster@ktnnonline.com
W: http://www.ktnnonline.com
Editorial Profile: KWRK-FM is a commercial station owned by Navajo Nation. The format of the station is country. KWRK-FM broadcasts to the Albuquerque, NM area at 96.1 FM.

KWRL-FM
Owner: Elkhorn Media Group
Editorial: 1009 Adams Ave, La Grande, Oregon 97850-2667. **T:** 1 541 963-7911
W: http://www.999kwrl.com
Editorial Profile: KWRL-FM is a commercial station owned by Elkhorn Media Group. The format of the station is adult contemporary. KWRL-FM broadcasts to the Portland, OR area at 99.9 FM.

KWRM-AM
Owner: Major Market Stations Inc.
Editorial: 210 Radio Rd, Corona, California 92879-1722. **T:** 1 951 737-1370
E: bella@kwrn1550am.com
W: http://www.kwrm1370am.com
Editorial Profile: KWRM-AM is a commercial station owned by Major Market Stations Inc. The format of the station is multilingual variety programming. KWRM-AM broadcasts to the Corona, CA area at 1370 AM.

KWRN-AM
Owner: Major Market Stations Inc.
Editorial: 15165 7th St Ste D, Victorville, California 92395-3816. **T:** 1 760 955-8722
E: production@lapoderosa1550am.com
W: http://lapoderosa1550am.com
Editorial Profile: KWRN-AM is a commercial station owned by Major Market Stations Inc. The format of the station is regional Mexican. KWRN-AM broadcasts to the Victorville, CA area at 1550 AM.

KWRO-AM
Owner: Bicoastal Media LLC
Editorial: 320 Central Ave, Ste 519, Coos Bay, Oregon 97420. **T:** 1 541 267-2121
E: southcoastpsa@bicoastalmedia.com
W: http://www.kwro.com
Editorial Profile: KWRO-AM is a commercial station owned by Bi-Coastal Media LLC. The format of the station is news and talk. KWRO-AM broadcasts to the Eugene, OR area at 630 AM.

KWRP-AM
Owner: Pueblo Radio Group
Editorial: 3715 Thatcher Ave, Pueblo, Colorado 81005-1255. **T:** 1 719 564-0899
W: http://www.puebloradio.co
Editorial Profile: KWRP-AM is a commercial station owned by Pueblo Radio Group. The format of the station is classic hits. KWRP-AM broadcasts to the Pueblo, CO area at 690 AM.

KWRQ-FM
Owner: McMurray Communications Inc.
Editorial: 3335 W 8th St, Thatcher, Arizona 85552. **T:** 1 928 428-1230
E: traffic@mcmurrayradio.com
W: http://www.mysouthernaz.com
Editorial Profile: KWRQ-FM is a commercial station owned by McMurray Communications Inc. The format of the station is hot adult contemporary music. KWRQ-FM broadcasts to the Safford, AZ area at 102.3 FM.

KWRT-AM
Owner: Billings Broadcasting LLC
Editorial: 1600 Radio Hill Rd, Boonville, Missouri 65233. **T:** 1 660 882-6686
E: kwrt@classicnet.net
W: http://www.1370kwrt.com
Editorial Profile: KWRT-AM is a commercial station owned by Billings Broadcasting LLC. The format of the station is country music. KWRT-AM broadcasts in the Boonville, MO area at 1370 AM.

KWRU-AM
Owner: Multicultural Radio Broadcasting Inc.
Editorial: 2125 N Barton Ave, Fresno, California 93703-2646. **T:** 1 559 454-1300
Editorial Profile: KWRU-AM is a commercial station owned by Multicultural Radio Broadcasting Inc. The format of the station is Hispanic religious. KWRU-AM broadcasts to the Fresno, CA area at 1300 AM.

KWRV-FM
Owner: Minnesota Public Radio
Editorial: 480 Cedar St, Saint Paul, Minnesota 55101. **T:** 1 651 290-1500
E: newsroom@mpr.org **W:** http://www.mpr.org
Editorial Profile: KWRV-FM is a non-commercial station owned by Minnesota Public Radio. The format of the station is classical. KWVR-FM broadcasts to the Saint Paul, MN area at 91.9 FM.

KWRW-FM
Owner: Whitehead Enterprises, Inc.
Editorial: 618 N Main St, Rusk, Texas 75785-1144. **T:** 1 903 683-2258
E: kwrw@mediactr.com
Editorial Profile: KWRW-FM is a commercial station owned by Whitehead Enterprises, Inc. The format of the station is classic rock. KWRW-FM broadcasts to the Rusk, TX area at 97.7 FM.

KWSC-FM
Owner: Wayne State College
Editorial: 1111 Main St, Humanities 409 A, Wayne, Nebraska 68787. **T:** 1 402 375-7424
E: thecat@wsc.edu
W: http://wildcat.wsc.edu/k92
Editorial Profile: KWSC-FM is a non-commercial station owned by Wayne State College. The format of the station is college variety. KWSC-FM broadcasts to the Wayne, NE area at 91.9 FM.

KWSH-AM
Owner: One Ten Broadcasting Group Inc.
Editorial: 1221 N South 358, Seminole, Oklahoma 74868. **T:** 1 405 257-5441
E: onetenbroadcast@onetenbroadcast.com
Editorial Profile: KWSH-AM is a commercial station owned by One Ten Broadcasting Group Inc. The format of the station is country music. KWSH-AM broadcasts to the Oklahoma City area at 1260 AM.

KWSL-AM
Owner: Clear Channel Media and Entertainment
Editorial: 1113 Nebraska St, Sioux City, Iowa 51105-1438. **T:** 1 712 255-1470
W: http://www.247comedy.com
Editorial Profile: KWSL-AM is a commercial station owned by Clear Channel Media and Entertainment. The format of the station is comedy. KWSL-AM broadcasts to the Sioux City, IA area at 1470 AM.

KWSN-AM
Owner: Midwest Communications
Editorial: 500 S Phillips Ave, Sioux Falls, South Dakota 57104-6825. **T:** 1 605 331-5350
E: studio@kwsn.com **W:** http://www.kwsn.com
Editorial Profile: KWSN-AM is a commercial station owned by Midwest Communications. The format of the station is sports. KWSN-AM broadasts to the Sioux Falls, SD area at 1230 AM.

KWSO-FM
Owner: Confederated Tribes of Warm Springs
Editorial: 4174 Hwy 3, Warm Springs, Oregon 97761-9999. **T:** 1 541 553-1968
E: kwsonews@wstribes.org
W: http://www.kwso.org
Editorial Profile: KWSO-FM is a non-commercial station owned by Confederated Tribes of Warm Springs. The format of the station is variety. KWSO-FM broadcasts to the Warm Springs, OR area at 91.9 FM.

KWST-AM
Owner: Entravision Communications Corp.
Editorial: 1803 N Imperial Ave, El Centro, California 92243-1333. **T:** 1 760 482-7777
E: kwst@entravision.com
Editorial Profile: KWST-AM is a commercial station owned by Entravision Communications Corp. The format of the station is Spanish adult hits. KWST-AM broadcasts to the El Centro, CA area at 1430 AM.

KWSU-AM
Owner: Washington State University
Editorial: Murrow Center, Room 382, Pullman, Washington 99164. **T:** 1 509 335-6500
E: nwpr@wsu.edu **W:** http://www.nwpr.org
Editorial Profile: KWSU-AM is a non-commercial station owned by Washington State University. The format of the station is news, talk and classical music. KWSU-AM broadcasts to the Pullman, WA area at 1250 AM.

KWSW-AM
Owner: Eureka Broadcasting Inc.
Editorial: 1101 Marsh Rd, Eureka, California 95501-1574. **T:** 1 707 442-5744
W: http://www.kwsw980.com
Editorial Profile: KWSW-AM is a commercial station owned by Eureka Broadcasting Inc. The format of the station is news and talk. KWSW-AM broadcasts to the Eureka, CA area at 980 AM.

KWSX-AM
Owner: Clear Channel Media and Entertainment
Editorial: 2121 Lancey Dr, Modesto, California 95355-3036. **T:** 1 209 551-1306
E: modestopsa@clearchannel.com
W: http://www.powertalk1280.com/main.html
Editorial Profile: KWSX-AM is a commercial station owned by Clear Channel Media and Entertainment. The format of the station news and talk. KWSX-AM broadcasts to the Sacramento, CA area at 1280 AM.

KWTG-FM
Owner: Radio Group(The)
Editorial: 917 Ee Wallace Blvd S, Ferriday, Louisiana 71334. **T:** 1 318 757-4200
E: kfnv@bellsouth.net
Editorial Profile: KWTG-FM is a commercial station owned the Radio Group. The format of the station is classic country. KWTG-FM broadcasts to the Ferriday, LA area at 104.7 FM.

KWTL-AM
Owner: Real Presence Radio
Editorial: 216 Belmont Rd, Grand Forks, North Dakota 58201-4620. **T:** 1 701 795-0122
E: businessmanager@realpresenceradio.com
W: http://yourcatholicradiostation.com
Editorial Profile: KWTL-AM is a non-commercial station owned by Real Presence Radio. The format of the station is religion and talk.

KWTO-AM
Owner: Meyer Communications
Editorial: 3000 E Chestnut Expy, Springfield, Missouri 65802. **T:** 1 417 862-5600
E: news@radiospringfield.com
W: http://www.newstalk560.com
Editorial Profile: KWTO-AM is a commercial station owned by Meyer Communications. The format of the station is news and talk. KWTO-AM broadcasts to the Springfield, MO area at 560 AM.

KWTO-FM
Owner: Meyer Communications
Editorial: 3000 E Chestnut Expy, Springfield, Missouri 65802. **T:** 1 417 862-5600
E: kwto@radiospringfield.com
W: http://www.jock987.com
Editorial Profile: KWTO-FM is a commercial station owned by Meyer Communications. The format of the station is sports/talk. KWTO-FM broadcasts to the Springfield, MO area at 98.7 FM.

KWTU-FM
Owner: University of Tulsa
Editorial: 800 Tucker Dr, Tulsa, Oklahoma 74104-9700. **T:** 1 918 631-2577
E: public@publicmediatulsa.org
W: http://www.classical887.com
Editorial Profile: KWTU-FM is a non-commercial station owned by University of Tulsa. The format of the station is classical. KWTU-FM broadcasts to the Tulsa, OK area at 88.7 FM.

KWTX-AM

Owner: Clear Channel Media and Entertainment
Editorial: 314 W Highway 6, Waco, Texas 76712. **T:** 1 254 776-3900
W: http://newstalk1230.com
Editorial Profile: KWTX-AM is a commercial station owned by Clear Channel Media and Entertainment. The format of the station is news and talk. KWTX-AM broadcasts to the Waco, TX area at 1230 AM.

KWTX-FM

Owner: Clear Channel Media and Entertainment
Editorial: 314 W Highway 6, Waco, Texas 76712. **T:** 1 254 776-3900
W: http://www.975online.com
Editorial Profile: KWTX-FM is a commercial station owned by Clear Channel Media and Entertainment. The format of the station is Top 40/CHR music. KWTX-FM broadcasts to the Waco, TX area at 97.5 FM.

KWUD-AM

Owner: Rayburn Broadcasting Co.
Editorial: 765 Hemphill St, Jasper, Texas 75951-3104. **T:** 1 409 384-2626
Editorial Profile: KWUD-AM is a commercial station owned by Rayburn Broadcasting Co. The format of the station is country music. KWUD-AM broadcasts to the Woodville, TX area at 1490 AM.

KWUF-AM

Owner: Wolf Creek Broadcasting LLC
Editorial: 702 S 10th St, Pagosa Springs, Colorado 81147. **T:** 1 970 264-5983
E: admin@kwuf.com **W:** http://www.kwuf.com
Editorial Profile: KWUF-AM is a commercial station owned by Wolf Creek Broadcasting LLC. The format of the station is a mix of country music, sports and talk programming. KWUF-AM broadcasts to the Pagosa Springs, CO area at 1400 AM.

KWUF-FM

Owner: Wolf Creek Broadcasting LLC
Editorial: 702 S 10th St, Pagosa Springs, Colorado 81147. **T:** 1 970 264-5983
E: admin@kwuf.com **W:** http://www.kwuf.com
Editorial Profile: KWUF-FM is a commercial station owned by Wolf Creek Broadcasting LLC. The format of the station is adult hits. KWUF-FM broadcasts to the Pagosa Springs, CO area at 106.1 FM.

KWUR-FM

Owner: Washington University Board of Trustees
Editorial: 1 Brookings Dr, Saint Louis, Missouri 63130-4862. **T:** 1 314 935-5952
E: gm@kwur.com **W:** http://www.kwur.com

KWUT-FM

Owner: Mid-Utah Radio Inc.
Editorial: 390 E Annabella Rd, Richfield, Utah 84701-7084. **T:** 1 435 896-4456
E: news@midutahradio.com
W: http://midutahradio.com/kwut
Editorial Profile: KWUT-FM is a commercial station owned by Mid-Utah Radio Inc. The format of the station is contemporary country music. KWUT-FM broadcasts to the Richfield, UT area at 97.7 FM.

KWUZ-FM

Owner: Three Eagles Communications Co.
Editorial: 7600 County Road 120, Salida, Colorado 81201-9423. **T:** 1 719 539-2575
W: http://www.hippieradio975.com
Editorial Profile: KWUZ-FM is a commercial station owned by Three Eagles Communications Co. The format of the station is classic hits. KWUZ-FM broadcasts to the Salida, CO area at 97.5 FM.

KWVA-FM

Owner: University of Oregon
Editorial: University of Oregon Ste M-112, Eugene, Oregon 97403-1274.
T: 1 541 346-4091 **E:** news@kwvaradio.org
Editorial Profile: KWVA-FM is a non-commercial station owned by the University of Oregon. The format of the station is college variety. KWVA-FM broadcasts to the Eugene, OR area at 88.1 FM.

KWVE-FM

Owner: Calvary Chapel of Costa Mesa, Inc.
Editorial: 3000 W Macarthur Blvd, Ste 500, Santa Ana, California 92704.
T: 1 714 918-6207 **W:** http://www.kwve.com
Editorial Profile: KWVE-FM is a commercial station owned by Calvary Chapel of Costa Mesa, Inc. The format of the station is Christian music and talk. KWVE-FM

broadcasts to the Santa Ana, CA area at 107.9 FM.

KWVN-FM

Owner: Capps Broadcast Group
Editorial: 2003 Nw 56Th St, Pendleton, Oregon 97801-4593. **T:** 1 541 276-1511
W: http://www.1077thevine.com
Editorial Profile: KWVN-FM is a commercial station owned by Capps Broadcast Group. The format of the station is adult hits. KWVN-FM broadcasts to the Pendleton, OR area at 107.7 FM

KWVR-AM

Owner: Wallowa Valley Radio LLC
Editorial: 220 W Main St, Enterprise, Oregon 97828. **T:** 1 541 426-4577
E: kwvramfm@eoni.com
W: http://kwvrradio.com
Editorial Profile: KWVR-AM is a commercial station owned by Wallowa Valley Radio LLC. The format of the station is news, talk and sports. KWVR-AM broadcasts in the Enterprise, OR area at 1340 AM.

KWVR-FM

Owner: Wallowa Valley Radio LLC
Editorial: 220 W Main St, Enterprise, Oregon 97828. **T:** 1 541 426-4577
E: kwvramfm@eoni.com
W: http://kwvrradio.com
Editorial Profile: KWVR-FM is a commercial station owned by Wallowa Valley Radio LLC. The format of the station is country music. KWVR-FM broadcasts to the Spokane, WA area at 92.1 FM.

KWVV-FM

Owner: Peninsula Communications Inc.
Editorial: 66060 Diamond Ridge Rd, Homer, Alaska 99603-9229. **T:** 1 907 235-6000
E: kwavefm@xyz.net
Editorial Profile: KWVV-FM is a commercial station owned by Penninsula Communications Inc. The format of the station is adult album alternative. KWVV-FM broadcasts to the Homer, AK area at 103.5 FM.

KWWC-FM

Owner: Stephens College
Editorial: 1405 E Broadway, Columbia, Missouri 65201. **T:** 1 573 876-7297
E: sweet@stephens.edu
Editorial Profile: KWWC-FM is a commercial station owned by Stephens College. The format of the station is jazz music. KWWC-FM broadcasts to the Columbia, MO area at 90.5 FM.

KWWJ-AM

Owner: Salt of the Earth Broadcasting
Editorial: 4638 Decker Dr, Baytown, Texas 77520-1418. **T:** 1 281 837-8777
W: http://www.kwwj.org
Editorial Profile: KWWJ-AM is a commercial station owned by Salt of the Earth Broadcasting. The format of the station is gospel. KWWJ-AM broadcasts to the Baytown, TX area at 1360 AM.

KWWK-FM

Owner: Cumulus Media Inc.
Editorial: 122 4th St SW, Rochester, Minnesota 55902. **T:** 1 507 286-1010
W: http://www.quickcountry.com
Editorial Profile: KWWK-FM is a commercial station owned by Cumulus Media Inc. The format of the station is country music. KWWK-FM broadcasts to the Rochester, MN area at 96.5 FM.

KWWN-AM

Owner: Lotus Communications Corp.
Editorial: 8755 W Flamingo Rd, Las Vegas, Nevada 89147. **T:** 1 702 876-1460
E: espnradio1100@gmail.com
W: http://www.werlv.com
Editorial Profile: KWWN-AM is a commercial station owned by Lotus Communications Corp. The format of the station is sports. KWWN-AM broadcasts to the Las Vegas area at 1100 AM.

KWWR-FM

Owner: Johnson(Anne)
Editorial: 1705 E Liberty St, Mexico, Missouri 65265-3537. **T:** 1 573 581-5500
E: news@radiogetsresults.net
W: http://info.kwwr.com
Editorial Profile: KWWR-FM is a commercial station owned by Anne Johnson. The format of the station is country music. KWWR-FM broadcasts to the Mexico, MO area at 91.9 FM.

KWWS-FM

Owner: Washington State University
Editorial: Murrow Center, Room 382, Pullman, Washington 99164-2530. **T:** 1 509 335-6500
E: nwpr@wsu.edu **W:** http://www.nwpr.org
Editorial Profile: KWWS-FM is a non commercial station owned by Washington State University. The format of the station is news and talk. KWWS-FM broadcasts to the Pullman, WA area at 89.7 FM.

KWWV-FM

Owner: Mapleton Communications LLC
Editorial: 795 Buckley Rd, Ste 2, San Luis Obispo, California 93401. **T:** 1 805 786-2570
W: http://www.wild1061.com
Editorial Profile: KWWV-FM is a commercial station owned by Mapleton Communications LLC. The format of the station is Top 40/CHR. KWWV-FM broadcasts to the San Luis Obispo, CA area at 106.1 FM.

KWWW-FM

Owner: Cherry Creek Radio
Editorial: 231 N Wenatchee Ave, Wenatchee, Washington 98801. **T:** 1 509 665-6565
E: newswenatchee@cherrycreekradio.com
W: http://www.kw3.com
Editorial Profile: KWWW-FM is commercial station owned by Cherry Creek Radio. The format of the station is hot adult contemporary music. KWWW-FM broadcasts to the Wenatchee, WA area at 96.7 FM.

KWWX-FM

Owner: Cherry Creek Radio
Editorial: 231 N Wenatchee Ave, Wenatchee, Washington 98801-2009. **T:** 1 509 665-6565
E: newswenatchee@cherrycreekradio.com
W: http://juanradio.co
Editorial Profile: KWWX-FM is a commercial station owned by Cherry Creek Radio. The format of the station is Spanish Adult Hits. KWWX-FM broadcasts to the Wenatchee, WA area on 106.7 FM.

KWXD-FM

Owner: My Town Media, Inc.
Editorial: 412 N Locust St, Pittsburg, Kansas 66762-4014. **T:** 1 620 232-5993
E: sharon@mytown-media.com
W: http://www.1035x.net
Editorial Profile: KWXD-FM is a commercial station owned by My Town Media, Inc. The format is classic rock. The station airs in the Pittsburg, KS area at 103.5 FM.

KWXI-AM

Owner: DelGiorno (Robert)
Editorial: 180 Highway 70 E, Ste 11, Glenwood, Arkansas 71943-8810.
T: 1 870 356-2151 **E:** info@kwxi.net
W: http://www.kwxi.net
Editorial Profile: KWXI-AM is a commercial station owned by DelGiorno (Robert). The format of the station is news, sports and Christian talk. KWXI-AM broadcasts in the Glenwood, AK area at 670 AM.

KWXS-FM

Owner: Combined Communications, Inc.
Editorial: 63088 Ne 18Th St Ste 200, Bend, Oregon 97701-7102. **T:** 1 541 328-5263
W: http://wild1077.com
Editorial Profile: KWXS-FM is a commercial station owned by Combined Communications, Inc. The format of the station is Top 40 urban contemporary. KXWS-FM broadcasts to the Bend, OR area at a frequency of 107.7 FM.

KWXT-AM

Owner: Domerese(George)
Editorial: 701 E Main St, Ste 4, Russellville, Arkansas 72801. **T:** 1 479 968-1337
E: kwxt1490am@yahoo.com
W: http://www.kwxt1490am.com
Editorial Profile: KWXT-AM is a commercial station owned by George Domerese. The format of the station is Christian programming and Southern gospel music. KWXT-AM broadcasts to the Russellville, AR area at 1490 AM.

KWXX-FM

Owner: New West Broadcasting
Editorial: 1145 Kilauea Ave, Hilo, Hawaii 96720. **T:** 1 808 935-5461
W: http://www.kwxx.com
Editorial Profile: KWXX-FM is a commercial station owned by New West Broadcasting. The format of the station is a variety of Hawaiian music. KWXX-FM broadcasts to Hilo, HI at 94.7 FM.

KWXY-AM

Owner: R & R Radio Corp.

Editorial: 2100 E Tahquitz Canyon Way, Palm Springs, California 92262. **T:** 1 760 325-2580
E: programs@kwxy.com
W: http://www.kwxy.com
Editorial Profile: KWXY-AM is a commercial station owned by R & R Radio Corp. The format of the station is adult standards. KWXY-AM broadcasts to the Palm Springs, CA area at 1340 AM.

KWYD-FM

Owner: Impact Radio
Editorial: 5660 E Franklin Rd Ste 200, Nampa, Idaho 83687-5133. **T:** 1 208 465-9966
E: wild101@impactradiogroup.com
W: http://www.wild101fm.com
Editorial Profile: KWYD-FM is a commercial station owned by Impact Radio. The format of the station is rhythmic Top 40. KWYD-FM broadcasts to the McCall, ID area at 101.1 FM.

KWYE-FM

Owner: Cumulus Media
Editorial: 1071 W Shaw Ave, Fresno, California 93711-3702. **T:** 1 559 490-1011
W: http://www.y101hits.com
Editorial Profile: KWYE-FM is a commercial station owned by Cumulus Media. The format of the station is adult contemporary. KWYE-FM broadcasts in the Fresno, CA area at 101.1 FM.

KWYI-FM

Owner: Naito(Colin H.)
Editorial: 64-1040 Mamalahoa Hwy, Ste 4, Kamuela, Hawaii 96743-8450.
T: 1 808 885-9866
Editorial Profile: KWYI-FM is a commercial station owned by Colin H. Naito. It is located in Kamuela, HI. The station airs locally at 106.9 FM. The format of the station is Top 40/CHR.

KWYK-FM

Owner: Basin Broadcasting Company
Editorial: 1515 W Main St, Farmington, New Mexico 87401-3837. **T:** 1 505 325-1996
W: http://www.kwykradio.com
Editorial Profile: KWYK-FM is a commercial station owned by Basin Broadcasting Company. The format of the station is adult contemporary music. KWYK-FM broadcasts to the Albuquerque, NM area at 94.9 FM.

KWYL-FM

Owner: Cumulus Media Inc
Editorial: 595 E Plumb Ln, Reno, Nevada 89502. **T:** 1 775 789-6700
W: http://www.wild1029.com
Editorial Profile: KWYL-FM is a commercial station owned by Cumulus Media Inc. The format of the station is rhythmic Top 40/CHR. KWYL-FM broadcasts to the Reno, NV are at 102.9 FM.

KWYN-AM

Owner: East Arkansas Broadcasters Inc.
Editorial: 2758 Highway 64, Wynne, Arkansas 72396. **T:** 1 870 238-8141
E: radiokwyn@cablelynx.com
Editorial Profile: KWYN-AM is an commercial station owned by East Arkansas Broadcasters Inc. The format of the station is country music. KWYN-AM broadcasts to the Wynne, AR area at 1400 AM.

KWYN-FM

Owner: East Arkansas Broadcasters Inc.
Editorial: 2758 Highway 64, Wynne, Arkansas 72396-4061. **T:** 1 870 238-8141
E: radiokwyn@cablelynx.com
W: http://www.kwyn.com
Editorial Profile: KWYN-FM is a commercial station owned by East Arkansas Broadcasters Inc. The format of the station is contemporary country. KWYN-FM broadcasts to the Wynne, AR area at 92.5 FM.

KWYO-AM

Owner: Lovcom, Inc.
Editorial: 1716 Kroe Ln, Sheridan, Wyoming 82801-9681. **T:** 1 307 672-7421
E: info@sheridanmedia.com
W: http://www.sheridanmedia.com
Editorial Profile: KWYO-AM is a commercial station owned by Lovcom, Inc. The format of the station is classic country. KWYO-AM broadcasts to the Sheridan, WY area at 1410 AM.

KWYR-AM

Owner: Midwest Radio Corp.
Editorial: 346 Main St, Winner, South Dakota 57580. **T:** 1 605 842-3333
E: kwyrnews@gwtc.net
W: http://www.kwyr.com

Editorial Profile: KWYR-AM is a commercial station owned by the Midwest Radio Corp. The format of the station is country music. KWYR-AM broadcasts to the Winner, SD area at 1260 AM.

KWYR-FM
Owner: Midwest Radio Corp.
Editorial: 346 Main St, Winner, South Dakota 57580. **T:** 1 605 842-3333
E: kwyrnews@gwtc.net
W: http://www.kwyr.com
Editorial Profile: KWYR-FM is a commercial station owned by Midwest Radio Corp. The format of the station is hot adult contemporary. KWYR-FM broadcasts to the Winner, SD area at 93.7 FM.

KWYW-FM
Owner: CarJim LLC
Editorial: 1002 N 8Th St W, Riverton, Wyoming 82501-2427. **T:** 1 307 856-2922
E: ktrztraffic@wyoming.com
Editorial Profile: KWYW-FM is a commercial station owned by CarJim LLC. The format of the station is a mix of modern and classic rock music. KWYW-FM broadcasts to the Riverton, WY, area at 99.1 FM.

KWYY-FM
Owner: Townsquare Media, LLC
Editorial: 150 Nichols Ave, Casper, Wyoming 82601. **T:** 1 307 266-5252
W: http://www.mycountry955.com
Editorial Profile: KWYY-FM is a commercial station owned by Townsquare Media, LLC. The format for the station is country, featuring contemporary and classic hits. KWYY-FM broadcasts to the Casper-Riverton, WY area at 95.5 FM.

KXAA-FM
Owner: Wheeler Broadcasting Inc.
Editorial: 115 N Harris Ave, Cle Elum, Washington 98922. **T:** 1 509 662-3842
E: kxaprod@aol.com
W: http://www.kxa937.com

KXAC-FM
Owner: Radio Mankato
Editorial: 59346 Madison Ave, Mankato, Minnesota 56001-8518. **T:** 1 507 345-4537
E: news@ktoe.com
W: http://www.radiomankato.com
Editorial Profile: KXAC-FM is a commercial station owned by Radio Mankato. The format of the station is oldies music. KXAC-FM broadcasts to the Mankato, MN area at 100.5 FM.

KXAL-FM
Owner: The Church at Lake Cherokee
Editorial: 13618 County Road 2127 N, Henderson, Texas 75652-4808.
T: 1 903 643-7711 **W:** http://www.kxal.org
Editorial Profile: KXAL-FM is a non-commercial station owned by The Church of Lake Cherokee. The format of the station is classical and jazz music. KXAL-FM broadcasts at low power to Henderson, TX area at 104.7 FM.

KXAR-AM
Owner: Sudbury Broadcasting Group
Editorial: 1600 S Elm St, Hope, Arkansas 71801-8106. **T:** 1 870 777-8868
W: http://www.supercountry105.com
Editorial Profile: KXAR-AM is a commercial station owned by Sudbury Broadcasting Group. The format of the station is sports and talk. KXAR-AM broadcasts to the Hope, AR area at 1490 AM.

KXAZ-FM
Owner: Lake Powell Communications
Editorial: 91 7th Ave, Page, Arizona 86040.
T: 1 928 645-8181 **E:** news@kxaz.com
W: http://www.kxaz.com
Editorial Profile: KXAZ-FM is a commercial station owned by Lake Powell Communications. The format of the station is classic Hits. KXAZ-FM broadcasts to the Page, AZ area at 93.3 FM.

KXBA-FM
Owner: Peninsula Communications Inc.
Editorial: 66060 Diamond Ridge Rd, Homer, Alaska 99603-9229. **T:** 1 907 235-6000
E: kwavefm@xyz.net

KXBG-FM
Owner: Clear Channel Media and Entertainment
Editorial: 4270 Byrd Dr, Loveland, Colorado 80538. **T:** 1 970 461-2560
W: http://www.my979.com

Editorial Profile: KXBG-FM is a commercial station owned by Clear Channel Media and Entertainment. The format of the station is country music. KXBG-FM broadcasts to the Fort Collins, CO area at 97.9 FM.

KXBL-FM
Owner: Journal Broadcast Group
Editorial: 4590 E 29th St, Tulsa, Oklahoma 74114-6208. **T:** 1 918 743-7814
E: info@bigcountry995.com
W: http://www.bigcountry995.com
Editorial Profile: KXBL-FM is a commercial station owned by the Journal Broadcast Group. The format of the station is classic country. KXBL-FM broadcasts to the Tulsa, OK area at 99.5 FM.

KXBN-FM
Owner: Cherry Creek Radio
Editorial: 750 Ridgeview Dr, Ste 204, St George, Utah 84770. **T:** 1 435 673-3579
W: http://www.b92fmonline.com
Editorial Profile: KXBN-FM is a commercial station owned by Cherry Creek Radio. The format of the station is Top 40/CHR. KXBN-FM broadcasts to the St. George, UT area at 92.1 FM.

KXBR-FM
Owner: Heartland Christian Broadcasters Inc.
Editorial: 4090 Highway 11, International Falls, Minnesota 56649. **T:** 1 218 285-7398
E: connect@bridge919.com
Editorial Profile: KXBR-FM is a non-commercial station owned by Heartland Christian Broadcasters. The format of the station is Christian rock music. KXBR-FM broadcasts to the International Falls, MN area at 91.9 FM.

KXBT-FM
Owner: University of Texas at Austin
Editorial: 300 W. Dean Keeton (A0704), Austin, Texas 78701-3840. **T:** 1 512 471-1631
Editorial Profile: KXBT-FM is a non-commercial station owned by the University of Texas at Austin. The format of the station is adult album alternative. The station airs locally on 88.1 FM to the Bryan-College Station, TX metro area.

KXBX-AM
Owner: Bicoastal Media LLC
Editorial: 140 N Main St, Lakeport, California 95453-4815. **T:** 1 707 263-6113
W: http://www.kxbx.com
Editorial Profile: KXBX-AM is a commercial station owned by Bicoastal Media LLC. The format of the station is adult standards and sports. KXBX-AM broadcasts to Lakeport, CA at 1270 AM.

KXBX-FM
Owner: Bicoastal Media LLC
Editorial: 140 N Main St, Lakeport, California 95453-4815. **T:** 1 707 263-6113
W: http://www.kxbxfm.com
Editorial Profile: KXBX-FM is a commercial station owned by Bicoastal Media. The format of the station is adult contemporary music. KXBX-FM broadcasts to Lakeport, CA at 98.3 FM.

KXBZ-FM
Owner: Manhattan Broadcasting
Editorial: 2414 Casement Rd, Manhattan, Kansas 66502. **T:** 1 785 776-1350
W: http://www.b1047.com
Editorial Profile: KXBZ-FM is a commercial station owned by Manhattan Broadcasting. The format of the station is contemporary country music. KXBZ-FM broadcasts in the Manhattan, KS area at 104.7 FM.

KXCA-AM
Owner: Perry Publishing & Broadcasting Inc.
Editorial: 1525 SE Flower Mound Rd, Lawton, Oklahoma 73501. **T:** 1 580 355-1050
W: http://www.perry-pub-broadcasting.com/kkrx
Editorial Profile: KXCA-AM is a commercial station owned by Perry Publishing & Broadcasting Inc. The format of the station is R&B oldies. KKRX-AM broadcasts to the Lawton, OK area at 1050 AM.

KXCI-FM
Owner: Foundation for Creative Broadcasting
Editorial: 220 S 4th Ave, Tucson, Arizona 85701. **T:** 1 520 623-1000
W: http://www.kxci.org
Editorial Profile: KXCI-FM is a non-commercial station owned by Foundation for Creative Broadcasting. The format of the station is variety. KXCI-FM broadcasts to the Tucson, AZ area at 91.3 FM.

KXCM-FM
Owner: Copper Mountain Broadcasting
Editorial: 68474 Twentynine Palms Highway, Twentynine Palms, California 92277.
T: 1 760 362-4264
E: coppermountainbroadcasting@yahoo.com
W: http://www.kxcmradio.com
Editorial Profile: KXCM-FM is a commercial station owned by Copper Mountain Broadcasting. The format of the station is contemporary country. KXCM-FM broadcasts to the Los Angeles area at 96.3 FM.

KXCV-FM
Owner: Board of Regents, NWMSU
Editorial: 800 University Dr, Maryville, Missouri 64468. **T:** 1 660 562-1163
E: kxcv@nwmissouri.edu
W: http://www.kxcv.org
Editorial Profile: KXCV-FM is a non-commercial station owned by the Board of Regents, NWMSU. The format for the station is classical, jazz and news. KXCV-FM broadcasts to the Saint Joseph, MO area at 90.5 FM.

KXDD-FM
Owner: New Northwest Broadcasters LLC
Editorial: 1200 Chesterly Dr Ste 160, Yakima, Washington 98902-7345. **T:** 1 509 248-2900
W: http://www.1041kxdd.com
Editorial Profile: KXDD-FM is a commercial station owned by New Northwest Broadcasters LLC. The format of the station is country music. KXDD-FM broadcasts in the Yakima, WA area at 104.1 FM.

KXDG-FM
Owner: Zimmer Radio Inc.
Editorial: 2702 E 32nd St, Joplin, Missouri 64804. **T:** 1 417 624-1025
W: http://www.bigdog979.com
Editorial Profile: KXDG-FM is a commercial station owned by Zimmer Radio Inc. The format of the station is classic rock music. KXDG-FM broadcasts in the Joplin, MO area at 97.9 FM.

KXDL-FM
Owner: Prairie Broadcasting Inc.
Editorial: 221 Central Ave, Long Prairie, Minnesota 56347. **T:** 1 320 732-2164
E: hotrodfm@rea-alp.com
W: http://www.kxdlhotrodradio.com
Editorial Profile: KXDL-FM is a commercial station owned by Prairie Broadcasting Inc. The format of the station is oldies music. KXDL-FM broadcasts in the Long Prairie, MN area at 99.7 FM.

KXDP-FM
Owner: Front Range Sports, LLC
Editorial: 10200 E Girard Ave Bldg B, Denver, Colorado 80231-5500. **T:** 1 720 248-4000
W: http://www.877theticket.com
Editorial Profile: KXDP-FM is a commercial station owned by Front Range Sports Network, LLC. The format for the station is Regional Mexican. KXDP-FM broadcasts to the Denver area at 87.7 FM.

KXDR-FM
Owner: Cherry Creek Radio
Editorial: 1600 North Ave W, Ste 101, Missoula, Montana 59801. **T:** 1 406 728-5000
W: http://www.1067starfm.com
Editorial Profile: KXDR-FM is a commercial station owned by Cherry Creek Radio. The format of the station is Top 40/CHR. KXDR-FM broadcasts to the Missoula, MT area at a frequency of 106.7 FM.

KXDS-FM
Owner: Dixie State College of Utah
Editorial: 225 South 700 East, Jennings Building, #103, Saint George, Utah 84770.
T: 1 435 879-4319 **W:** http://dixie.edu/radio
Editorial Profile: KXDS-FM is a non-commercial college station owned by Dixie State College of Utah. The format of the station is Top 40/CHR. KXDS-FM broadcasts to the St. George, UT area at a frequency of 91.3 FM.

KXDZ-FM
Owner: Mapleton Communications LLC
Editorial: 795 Buckley Rd, Ste 2, San Luis Obispo, California 93401. **T:** 1 805 786-2570
W: http://www.953thebeach.com
Editorial Profile: KXDZ-FM is a commercial station owned by Mapleton Communications LLC. The format of the station is classic hits. KXDZ-FM broadcasts to the San Luis Obispo, CA area at 100.5 FM.

KXEG-AM
Owner: Communicom Broadcasting

Editorial: 2800 N 44th St, Ste 100, Phoenix, Arizona 85008. **T:** 1 602 254-5001
W: http://www.familyvaluesradio.net
Editorial Profile: KXEG-AM is a commercial station owned by Communicom Broadcasting. The format of the station is Christian music and talk programming. KXEG-AM broadcasts to the Phoenix area at 1280 AM.

KXEI-FM
Owner: Hi-Line Radio Fellowship
Editorial: 317 1st St, Havre, Montana 59501.
T: 1 406 265-5845 **E:** info@ynop.org
W: http://www.ynop.org
Editorial Profile: KXEI-FM is a non-commercial station owned by Hi-Line Radio Fellowship. The format for the station is contemporary Christian. KXEI-FM broadcasts to the Havre, MT area at 95.1 FM.

KXEL-AM
Owner: Woodward Communications, Inc.
Editorial: 514 Jefferson St, Waterloo, Iowa 50701-5422. **T:** 1 319 234-2200
E: news@kxel.com **W:** http://www.kxel.com
Editorial Profile: KXEL-AM is a commercial station owned by Woodward Communications, Inc. The format for the station is news and talk. KXEL-AM broadcasts to the Cedar Rapids, IA area at 1540 AM.

KXEN-AM
Owner: Radio Property Ventures, LLC
Editorial: 5615 Pershing Ave Ste 12, Saint Louis, Missouri 63112-1757.
T: 1 314 454-0400 **E:** kxen@aol.com
W: http://www.kxen1010am.com
Editorial Profile: KXEN-AM is a commercial station owned by Radio Property Ventures, LLC. The format of the station is religious. KXEN-AM broadcasts to the St. Louis area at 1010 AM.

KXEO-AM
Owner: Johnson(Anne)
Editorial: 1705 E Liberty St, Mexico, Missouri 65265-3537. **T:** 1 573 581-5500
E: kxeo@radiogetsresults.net
W: http://kxeo.com
Editorial Profile: KXEO-AM is a commercial station owned by Anne Johnson. The format of the station is adult contemporary music. KXEO-AM broadcasts in the Mexico, MO area at 1340 AM.

KXEQ-AM
Owner: Azteca Broadcasting Corp.
Editorial: 225 Linden St, Reno, Nevada 89502-4306. **T:** 1 775 827-1111
Editorial Profile: KXEQ-AM is a commercial station owned by Azteca Broadcasting Corp. The format of the station is regional Mexican music. KXEQ-AM broadcasts to the Reno, NV area at 1340 AM.

KXET-AM
Owner: Bustos Media, LLC
Editorial: 5110 SE Stark St, Portland, Oregon 97215-1751. **T:** 1 503 234-5550
E: contact@bustosmedia.com
Editorial Profile: KXET-AM is a commercial station owned by Bustos Media, LLC. The format of the station is Regional Mexican. KXET-AM broadcasts to the Portland, OR area at 1150 AM.

KXEW-AM
Owner: Clear Channel Media and Entertainment
Editorial: 3202 N Oracle Rd, Tucson, Arizona 85705-3820. **T:** 1 520 618-2100
W: http://www.tejano1600.com/main.html
Editorial Profile: KXEW-AM is a commercial station owned by Clear Channel Media and Entertainment. The format of the station is Tejano music. KXEW-AM broadcasts to the Tucson, AZ, area at 1600 AM.

KXEX-AM
Owner: RAK Communications Inc.
Editorial: 139 W Olive Ave, Fresno, California 93728. **T:** 1 559 233-8803
E: rakradio@comcast.net
Editorial Profile: KXEX-AM is a commercial station owned by RAK Communications Inc. The format of the station is Hispanic religious programming. KXEX-AM broadcasts to the Fresno, CA area at 1550 AM.

KXEZ-FM
Owner: Metro Broadcasters-Texas, Inc.
Editorial: 103 W Main St, Ste B, Allen, Texas 75013. **T:** 1 972 396-1640
W: http://www.kxez.com
Editorial Profile: KXEZ-FM is a commercial station owned by Metro Broadcasters-Texas, Inc. The format of the station is country

music. KXEZ-FM broadcasts to the Allen, TX area at 92.1 FM.

KXFC-FM
Owner: Chickasaw Nation
Editorial: 1019 N Broadway, Ada, Oklahoma 74820-6503. **T:** 1 580 436-1616
E: score@cableone.net
W: http://www.kxfcradio.com
Editorial Profile: KXFC-FM is a commercial station owned by Chickasaw Nation. The format of the station is Top 40/CHR. KXFC-FM broadcasts to the Ada, OK area at 105.5 FM.

KXFE-FM
Owner: Arkansas County Broadcasters Inc.
Editorial: 1818 S Buerkle St, Stuttgart, Arkansas 72160. **T:** 1 870 673-1595
E: kdew973@yahoo.com
Editorial Profile: KXFE-FM is a commercial station owned by Arkansas County Broadcasters Inc. The format of the station is contemporary country music. KXFE-FM broadcasts to the Stuttgart, AR area at 106.9 FM.

KXFF-FM
Owner: Cherry Creek Radio
Editorial: 750 Ridgeview Dr, St George, Utah 84770-2665. **T:** 1 435 673-3579
W: http://www.cherrycreekradio.com
Editorial Profile: KXFF-FM is a commercial station owned by Cherry Creek Radio. The format of the station is sports. KXFF-FM broadcasts to the Salt Lake City, UT area at a frequency of 106.1 FM.

KXFG-FM
Owner: CBS Radio
Editorial: 41593 Winchester Rd, Ste 100, Temecula, California 92590. **T:** 1 951 693-2206
W: http://www.kfrog929.com
Editorial Profile: KXFG-FM is a commercial station owned by CBS Radio. The format of the station is contemporary country. KXFG-FM broadcasts to the Temecula Valley, CA area at 92.9 FM.

KXFM-FM
Owner: El Dorado Broadcasting
Editorial: 2215 Skyway Dr, Santa Maria, California 93455-1118. **T:** 1 805 925-2582
W: http://www.991thefox.com
Editorial Profile: KXFM-FM is a commercial station owned by El Dorado Broadcasting. The format of the station is rock. KXFM-FM broadcasts to the Santa Maria, CA area at 99.1 FM.

KXFN-AM
Owner: Grand Slam Sports, LLC
Editorial: 8045 Big Bend Blvd Ste 200, Saint Louis, Missouri 63119-2714.
T: 1 314 962-0590
Editorial Profile: KXFN-AM is a commercial station owned by Grand Slam Sports, LLC. The format of the station is sports. KXFN-AM broadcasts to the St. Louis area at 1380 AM.

KXFT-FM
Owner: Three Eagles Communications Co.
Editorial: 200 N 10th St, Fort Dodge, Iowa 50501-3925. **T:** 1 515 955-5656
W: http://www.yourfortdodge.com/pages/11104704.php
Editorial Profile: KXFT-FM is a commercial station owned by Three Eagles Communications Co. The format of the station is adult contemporary. KXFT-FM's target audience is adults, ages 18 to 54, in the Fort Dodge, IA area. The station airs locally at 105.9 FM.

KXGE-FM
Owner: Cumulus Media Inc.
Editorial: 5490 Saratoga Rd, Asbury, Iowa 52002-2593. **T:** 1 563 557-1040
W: http://www.eagle102rocks.com
Editorial Profile: KXGE-FM is a commercial station owned by Cumulus Media Inc. The format for the station is classic rock music. KXGE-FM broadcasts to the Cedar Rapids, IA area at 102.3 FM.

KXGF-AM
Owner: Fisher Communications, Inc.
Editorial: 1300 Central Ave W, Great Falls, Montana 59404-3971. **T:** 1 406 761-2800
Editorial Profile: KXGF-AM is a commercial station owned by Fisher Communications, Inc. The format of the station is Hot AC. KXGF-AM broadcasts to the Great Falls, MT area at 1400 AM.

KXGL-FM
Owner: JMJ Broadcasting Company Inc.

Editorial: 3505 Olsen Blvd Ste 120, Amarillo, Texas 79109-3035. **T:** 1 806 351-2345
W: http://www.1009theeagle.com
Editorial Profile: KXGL-FM is a commercial station owned by JMJ Broadcasting Company Inc. The format of the station is classic hits. KXGL-FM broadcasts to the Amarillo, TX area at 100.9 FM.

KXGN-AM
Owner: Glendive Broadcasting Corp.
Editorial: 210 S Douglas St, Glendive, Montana 59330. **T:** 1 406 377-3377
E: kxgnkdzn@midrivers.com
W: http://www.kxgn.com
Editorial Profile: KXGN-AM is a commercial station owned by Glendive Broadcasting Corp. The format for the station is adult contemporary and oldies. KXGN-AM broadcasts to the Glendive, MT area at 1400 AM.

KXGO-FM
Owner: Lost Coast Communications
Editorial: 1400 Main St Ste 104, Ferndale, California 95536-9459. **T:** 1 707 786-5104
W: http://www.kxgo.com
Editorial Profile: KXGO-FM is a commercial station owned by Lost Coast Communications. The format of the station is classic rock. KXGO-FM broadcasts to the Eureka, CA area at 93.1 FM.

KXGR-FM
Owner: Calvary Chapel Aurora
Editorial: 18900 E Hampden Ave, Aurora, Colorado 80013-3609. **T:** 1 303 628-7200
E: studio@897gracefm.com
W: http://www.897gracefm.com
Editorial Profile: KXGR-FM is a non-commercial station owned by Calvary Chapel Aurora. The format of the station is religious. KXGR-FM broadcasts to the Denver area on 89.7 FM.

KXGT-FM
Owner: Two Rivers Broadcasting Inc.
Editorial: 2625 8th Ave SW, Jamestown, North Dakota 58401. **T:** 1 701 252-1400
E: bigdog@daktel.com
W: http://www.newsdakota.com
Editorial Profile: KXGT-FM is a commercial station owned by Two Rivers Broadcasting Inc. The format of the station is adult contemporary music. KXGT-FM broadcasts to the Jamestown, ND area at 98.3 FM.

KXHT-FM
Owner: Flinn Broadcasting Corp.
Editorial: 6080 Mount Moriah Road Ext, Memphis, Tennessee 38115-2645.
T: 1 901 375-9324
W: http://www.hot1071.com
Editorial Profile: KXHT-FM is a commercial station owned by Flinn Broadcasting Corp. The format of the station is urban contemporary. KXHT-FM broadcasts to the Memphis, TN area at 107.1 FM.

KXIA-FM
Owner: Marshalltown Broadcasting Inc.
Editorial: 123 W Main St, Marshalltown, Iowa 50158-5860. **T:** 1 641 753-3361
E: news@marshalltownbroadcasting.com
W: http://www.kixweb.com
Editorial Profile: KXIA-FM is a commercial station owned by Marshalltown Broadcasting Inc. The format of the station is contemporary country music. KXIA-FM broadcasts to the Marshalltown, IA area at 101.1 FM.

KXIC-AM
Owner: Clear Channel Media and Entertainment
Editorial: 1 Stephen Atkins Dr, Iowa City, Iowa 52240-8021. **T:** 1 319 354-9500
E: news@kxic.com **W:** http://www.kxic.com
Editorial Profile: KXIC-AM is a commercial station owned by Clear Channel Media and Entertainment. The format for the station is a news, sports and talk. KXIC-AM broadcasts to the Iowa City, IA area at 800 AM.

KXIO-FM
Owner: Copeland (Jody)
Editorial: 117 S College Ave, Clarksville, Arkansas 72830-3552. **T:** 1 479 705-1069
E: office@kxio-fmradio.com
W: http://www.kxio.nu
Editorial Profile: KXIO-FM is a commercial station owned by Jody Copeland. The format of the station is adult contemporary. KXIO-FM broadcasts to the Clarksville, AR area at 106.9 FM.

KXIT-AM
Owner: Rogco Family I, LLC

Editorial: 323 Denver Ave, Dalhart, Texas 79022-2711. **T:** 1 806 249-2800

KXIT-FM
Owner: Dalhart Radio Inc.
Editorial: 4th and Denver, Dalhart, Texas 79022. **T:** 1 806 249-4747
Editorial Profile: KPPC-FM is a commercial station owned by Dalhart Radio Inc. The format of the station is classic and contemporary country. KPPC-FM broadcasts to the Dalhart, TX area at 96.1 FM.

KXIX-FM
Owner: Bend Radio Group (The)
Editorial: 345 SW Cyber Dr, Ste 101-103, Bend, Oregon 97702-1045. **T:** 1 541 388-3300
W: http://www.power94.fm
Editorial Profile: KXIX-FM is a commercial station owned by Bend Radio Group (The). The format of the station is Top 40/CHR. KXIX-FM broadcasts to the Bend, OR area at a frequency of 94.1 FM.

KXJK-AM
Owner: Forrest City Broadcasting Co.
Editorial: 501 E Broadway St, Forrest City, Arkansas 72335-3801. **T:** 1 870 633-1252
E: radio@arkansas.net
W: http://www.arkradio.com
Editorial Profile: KXJK-AM is a commercial station owned by Forrest City Broadcasting Co. The format of the station is news, sports and talk. KXJK-AM broadcasts to the Forrest City, AR area at 950 AM.

KXJM-FM
Owner: Clear Channel Media and Entertainment
Editorial: 13333 SW 68th Pkwy Ste 310, Tigard, Oregon 97223-8304.
T: 1 503 323-6400
W: http://www.jamn1075.com/main.html
Editorial Profile: KXJM-FM is a commercial station owned by Clear Channel Media and Entertainment. The format of the station is urban and rhythmic contemporary. KXJM-FM broadcasts to Portland, OR at 107.5 FM.

KXJZ-FM
Owner: California State University
Editorial: 7055 Folsom Blvd, Sacramento, California 95826. **T:** 1 916 278-8900
E: news@capradio.org
W: http://www.capradio.org
Editorial Profile: KXJZ-FM is a non-commercial station owned by California State University. The format of the station is news and talk. KXJZ-FM broadcasts to the Sacramento, CA area at 90.9 FM.

KXKC-FM
Owner: Cumulus Media Inc
Editorial: 202 Galbert Rd, Lafayette, Louisiana 70506. **T:** 1 337 232-1311
W: http://www.kxkc.com
Editorial Profile: KXKC-FM is a commercial station owned by Cumulus Media Inc. The format of the station is contemporary country music. KXKC-FM broadcasts to the Lafayette, LA area at 99.1 FM.

KXKL-FM
Owner: Wilks Broadcast Group
Editorial: 720 S Colorado Bvld Ste 1200N, Denver, Colorado 80246. **T:** 1 303 832-5665
W: http://www.kool105.com
Editorial Profile: KXKL-FM is a commercial station owned by Wilks Broadcast Group. The format of the station is classic hits. KXKL-FM broadcasts to the Denver area at 105.1 FM.

KXKQ-FM
Owner: McMurray Communications Inc.
Editorial: 3335 W 8th St, Thatcher, Arizona 85552. **T:** 1 928 428-1230
E: traffic@mcmurrayradio.com
W: http://www.mysouthernaz.com
Editorial Profile: KXKQ-FM is a commercial station owned by McMurray Communications Inc. The format of the station is contemporary country. KXKQ-FM broadcasts to the Safford, AZ area at 94.1 FM.

KXKS-AM
Owner: Wilkins Communications Network Inc.
Editorial: 2000 Randolph Rd SE, Ste 103, Albuquerque, New Mexico 87106.
T: 1 505 244-1190 **E:** kxks@wilkinsradio.com
W: http://www.wilkinsradio.com
Editorial Profile: KXKS-AM is a commercial station owned by Wilkins Communications Inc. The format of the station is religious. KXKS-AM broadcasts to the Albuqueque, NM area at 1190 AM.

KXKS-FM
Owner: Townsquare Media, LLC
Editorial: 6341 W Port Ave, Shreveport, Louisiana 71129. **T:** 1 318 688-1130
W: http://mykisscountry937.com/
Editorial Profile: KXKS-FM is a commercial station owned by Townsquare Media, LLC. The format of the station is contemporary country music. KXKS-FM broadcasts to the Shreveport, LA area at 93.7 FM.

KXKT-FM
Owner: Clear Channel Media and Entertainment
Editorial: 5010 Underwood Ave, Omaha, Nebraska 68132. **T:** 1 402 561-2000
W: http://www.thekat.com
Editorial Profile: KXKT-FM is a commercial station owned by Clear Channel Media and Entertainment. The format of the station is contemporary country. KXKT-FM broadcasts to the Omaha, NE area at 103.3 FM.

KXKU-FM
Owner: Ad Astra Per Aspera Broadcasting, Inc.
Editorial: 10 E 5Th Ave, Hutchinson, Kansas 67501-6300. **T:** 1 620 665-5758
W: http://www.adastraradio.net
Editorial Profile: KXKU-FM is a commercial station owned by Ad Astra Per Aspera Broadcasting, Inc. The format of the station is classic country. KXKU-FM broadcasts to the Hutchinson, KS area at 106.1 FM.

KXKX-FM
Owner: Townsquare Media, LLC
Editorial: 2209 S Limit Ave, Sedalia, Missouri 65301-6950. **T:** 1 660 826-1050
W: http://www.kxkx.com
Editorial Profile: KXKX-FM is a commercial station owned by Townsquare Media, LLC. The format of the station is classic country. KXKX-FM broadcasts to the Sedalia, MO, area at 105.7 FM.

KXKZ-FM
Owner: Red Peach LLC
Editorial: 500 N Monroe St, Ruston, Louisiana 71270-3835. **T:** 1 318 255-5000
E: z1075fm@bayou.com
W: http://www.z1075fm.com
Editorial Profile: KXKZ-FM is a commercial station owned by Red Peach LLC. The format of the station is country music. KXKZ-FM broadcasts to the Ruston, LA area at 107.5 FM.

KXLB-FM
Owner: Townsquare Media, LLC
Editorial: 125 W Mendenhall St, Bozeman, Montana 59715-3586. **T:** 1 406 586-2343
W: http://www.xlcountry.com
Editorial Profile: KXLB-FM is a commercial station owned by Townsquare Media, LLC. The format of the station is classic and contemporary country. KXLB-FM broadcasts to the Bozeman, MT area at 100.7 FM.

KXLE-AM
Owner: KXLE Inc.
Editorial: 1311 Vantage Hwy, Ellensburg, Washington 98926. **T:** 1 509 925-1488
E: kxle@elltel.net
Editorial Profile: KXLE-AM is a commercial station owned by KXLE Inc. The format of the station is news, sports and talk programming. KXLE-AM broadcasts to the Ellensburg, WA area at 1240 AM.

KXLE-FM
Owner: KXLE Inc.
Editorial: 1311 Vantage Hwy, Ellensburg, Washington 98926. **T:** 1 509 925-1488
E: kxle@elltel.net **W:** http://www.kxleradio.com
Editorial Profile: KXLE-FM is a commercial station owned by KXLE Inc. The format of the station is classic country. The station airs locally in the Ellensburg, WA area.

KXL-FM
Owner: Alpha Broadcasting
Editorial: 1211 SW 5th Ave Fl 6, Portland, Oregon 97204-3735. **T:** 1 503 243-7595
E: news@kxl.com **W:** http://kxl.com
Editorial Profile: KXL-FM is a commercial station owned by Alpha Broadcasting. The format of the station is news and talk. KXL-FM broadcasts to the Portland, OR area at 101.1 FM.

KXLG-FM
Owner: Dakota Communications, Ltd.
Editorial: 26 S Broadway, Watertown, South Dakota 57201-3604. **T:** 1 605 753-9910
W: http://www.kxlgradio.com
Editorial Profile: KXLG-FM is a commercial station owned by Dakota Communications, Ltd

and operated under an LMA with TMRG Broadcasting. The format of the station is classic hits. KXLG-FM broadcasts to the Huron, SD area at 99.1 FM.

KXLI-FM

Owner: Radio Activo Broadcasting
Editorial: 2050 S Eastern Ave, Las Vegas, Nevada 89104-4100. **T:** 1 702 444-7777
W: http://www.exafm.com/lasvegas
Editorial Profile: KXLI-FM is a commercial station owned by Radio Activo Broadcasting. The format of the station is Spanish CHR. KXLI-FM broadcasts to the Moapa, NV area at 94.5 FM.

KXLL-FM

Owner: Capital Community Broadcasting Inc.
Editorial: 360 Egan Dr, Juneau, Alaska 99801. **T:** 1 907 463-6499 **E:** news@ktoo.org
W: http://www.kxll.org
Editorial Profile: KXLL-FM is a non-commercial station owned by Capital Community Broadcasting Inc. The format of the station is AAA/modern rock. KXLL-FM broadcasts to the the Juneau, AK area at 100.7 FM.

KXLM-FM

Owner: Lazer Broadcasting Corp.
Editorial: 200 S 8th St., Ste 400, Oxnard, California 93030. **T:** 1 805 240-2070
W: http://www.radiolazer.com/kxlm.php
Editorial Profile: KXLM-FM is a commercial station owned by the Lazer Broadcasting Corp. The format of the station is Regional Mexican music and some talk. KXLM-FM broadcasts to the Santa Barbara, CA area at 101.7 FM.

KXLO-AM

Owner: KXLO Broadcast, Inc.
Editorial: 620 NE Main St, Lewistown, Montana 59457. **T:** 1 406 535-3441
E: traffic@kxlo-klcm.com
W: http://www.kxlo-klcm.com
Editorial Profile: KXLO-AM is a commercial station owned by KXLO Broadcast, Inc. The format for the station is contemporary and classic country. KXLO-AM broadcasts to the Lewistown, MT area at 1230 AM.

KXLP-FM

Owner: Radio Mankato
Editorial: 59346 Madison Ave, Mankato, Minnesota 56001-8518. **T:** 1 507 345-4537
E: news@ktoe.com
W: http://www.kxlp941.com
Editorial Profile: KXLP-FM is a commercial station owned by Radio Mankato. The format of the station is classic rock music. KXLP-FM broadcasts in the Minneapolis area at 94.1 FM.

KXLQ-AM

Owner: Birach Broadcasting
Editorial: 118 W Jefferson St, Osceola, Iowa 50213-1204. **T:** 1 248 557-3500
W: http://www.birach.com
Editorial Profile: KXLQ-AM is a commercial station owned by Birach Broadcasting. The format of the station is sports. KXLQ-AM broadcasts to the Indianola, IA area at a frequency of 1490 AM.

KXLR-FM

Owner: Last Frontier Mediactive, LLC
Editorial: 819 1st Ave Ste A, Fairbanks, Alaska 99701-4449. **T:** 1 907 451-5910
W: http://www.xrock959.com
Editorial Profile: KXLR-FM is a commercial station owned by Last Frontier Mediactive, LLC. The format of the station is classic rock. KXLR-FM broadcasts to the Fairbanks, AK area at 95.9 FM.

KXLS-FM

Owner: Chisholm Trail Broadcasting
Editorial: 316 E Willow Rd, Enid, Oklahoma 73701. **T:** 1 580 237-1390
E: ctbradio@yahoo.com
W: http://www.ctbsports.com
Editorial Profile: KXLS-FM is a commercial station owned by Chisholm Trail Broadcasting. The format of the station is hot adult contemporary music. KXLS-FM broadcasts to Oklahoma City, OK at 95.7 FM.

KXLT-FM

Owner: Townsquare Media, LLC
Editorial: 827 E Park Blvd Ste 100, Boise, Idaho 83712-7783. **T:** 1 208 344-6363
W: http://www.liteonline.com
Editorial Profile: KXLT-FM is a commercial station owned by Townsquare Media, LLC. The format of the station is adult contemporary. KXLT-FM broadcasts to the Boise, ID area at 107.9 FM.

KXLU-FM

Owner: Loyola Marymount University
Editorial: 1 LMU Dr, Los Angeles, California 90045. **T:** 1 310 338-2866
W: http://www.kxlu.com
Editorial Profile: KXLU-FM is a non-commercial station owned by Loyola Marymount University. The format of the station is variety. KXLU-FM broadcasts to the Los Angeles area at 88.9 FM.

KXLW-FM

Owner: Ohana Media Group
Editorial: 833 Gambell St, Anchorage, Alaska 99501-3756. **T:** 1 907 344-4045
W: http://963thewolf.com
Editorial Profile: KXLW-FM is a commercial station owned by Ohana Media Group. The format of the station is country. KXLW-FM broadcasts to the Anchorage, AK area at 96.3 FM.

KXLX-AM

Owner: Queen B Inc.
Editorial: 500 W Boone Ave, Spokane, Washington 99201. **T:** 1 509 324-4200
W: http://www.700espn.com
Editorial Profile: KXLX-AM is a commercial station owned by Queen B Inc. The format of the station is sports. KXLX-AM broadcasts to the Spokane, WA area at 700 AM.

KXLY-AM

Owner: Queen B Inc.
Editorial: 500 W Boone Ave, Spokane, Washington 99201. **T:** 1 509 329-4000
E: news4@kxly.com
W: http://www.kxly920.com
Editorial Profile: KXLY-AM is a commercial station owned by Queen B Inc. The format of the station is news and talk. KXLY-AM broadcasts to the Spokane, WA area at 920 AM.

KXLY-FM

Owner: Queen B Inc.
Editorial: 500 W Boone Ave, Spokane, Washington 99201-2497. **T:** 1 509 324-4000
W: http://www.thebig999coyotecountry.com
Editorial Profile: KXLY-FM is a commercial station owned by Queen B Inc. The format of the station is country music. KXLY-FM broadcasts to the Spokane, WA area at 99.9 FM.

KXMG-FM

Owner: Sunburst Media-Louisiana, LLC
Editorial: 120 Prevost Dr, Houma, Louisiana 70364-2338. **T:** 1 504 832-3555
W: http://www.mega1075fm.com
Editorial Profile: KXMG-FM is a commercial station owned by Sunburst Media-Louisiana, LLC. The format of the station is Spanish Top 40/CHR. KXMG-FM broadcasts to the New Orleans area at 107.5 FM.

KXMO-FM

Owner: Mahaffey Enterprises Inc.
Editorial: 1505 Soest Rd, Rolla, Missouri 65401-3709. **T:** 1 573 364-2525
E: kttrkznn@fidmail.com
W: http://www.resultsradioonline.com
Editorial Profile: KXMO-FM is a commercial station owned by Mahaffey Enterprises Inc. The format of the station is oldies music. KXMO-FM broadcasts to the Cuba, MO area at 95.3 FM.

KXMR-AM

Owner: Clear Channel Media and Entertainment
Editorial: 3500 E Rosser Ave, Bismarck, North Dakota 58501-3376. **T:** 1 701 255-1234
E: kxmr@clearchannel.com
W: http://www.am710thefan.com/main.html
Editorial Profile: KXMR-AM is a commercial station owned by Clear Channel Media and Entertainment. The format of the station is sports. KXMR-AM broadcasts to the Bismarck, ND area at 710 AM.

KXMS-FM

Owner: Missouri Southern State University
Editorial: 3950 Newman Rd, Joplin, Missouri 64801-1512. **T:** 1 417 625-9356
E: kxms@mssu.edu
W: http://www2.mssu.edu/kxms/
Editorial Profile: KXMS-FM is a non-commercial station owned by Missouri Southern State University. The format of the station is classical. KXMS-FM broadcasts to the Joplin, MO area at 88.7 FM.

KXMT-FM

Owner: DMC Broadcasting Inc.
Editorial: 125 Camino De La Merced, A, Taos, New Mexico 87571-5119. **T:** 1 575 758-4491

W: http://www.kxmt.com
Editorial Profile: KXMT-FM is a commercial station owned by DMC Broadcasting Inc. The format of the station is regional Mexican music. KXMT-FM broadcasts in the Taos, NM area at 99.1 FM.

KXMX-FM

Owner: G2 Media Group
Editorial: 333 S Kerr Blvd, Sallisaw, Oklahoma 74955-7212. **T:** 1 91 790-1051
E: themix@kxmx.com
W: http://www.kxmx.com
Editorial Profile: KXMX-FM is a commercial station owned and operated by G2 Media Group. The format of the station is a variety of music and news programming. The station broadcasts to the Sequoyah County, OK area at a frequency of 105.1 FM.

KXNA-FM

Owner: Butler Broadcasting
Editorial: 1780 W Holly St, Fayetteville, Arkansas 72703-1307. **T:** 1 479 582-3776
W: http://www.newrock1049x.com
Editorial Profile: KXNA-FM is a commercial station owned by Butler Broadcasting. The format of the station is rock alternative. KXNA-FM broadcasts to the Fayetteville, AR area at 104.9 FM.

KXNO-AM

Owner: Clear Channel Media and Entertainment
Editorial: 2141 Grand Ave, Des Moines, Iowa 50312-5303. **T:** 1 515 245-8900
W: http://www.kxno.com
Editorial Profile: KXNO-AM is a commercial station owned by Clear Channel Media and Entertainment. The format of the station is sports. KXNO-AM broadcasts to the Des Moines, IA area at 1460 AM.

KXNP-FM

Owner: Armada Media Corp.
Editorial: 305 E 4th St, North Platte, Nebraska 69101. **T:** 1 308 532-3344
W: http://www.tlama.com
Editorial Profile: KXNP-FM is a commercial station owned by Armada Media Corp. The format of the station is contemporary country. KXNP-FM broadcasts to the North Platte, NE area at 103.5 FM.

KXNT-AM

Owner: CBS Radio
Editorial: 7255 South Tenaya Way, Ste 100, Las Vegas, Nevada 89113. **T:** 1 702 889-7300
W: http://lasvegas.cbslocal.com
Editorial Profile: KXNT-AM is a commercial station owned by CBS Radio. The format of the station is news and talk. KXNT-AM broadcasts to the Las Vegas area at 840 AM.

KXNT-FM

Owner: CBS Radio
Editorial: 7255 S Tenaya Way Ste 100, Las Vegas, Nevada 89113-1900.
T: 1 702 889-7300 **W:** http://www.kxnt.com
Editorial Profile: KXNT-FM is a commercial station owned by CBS Radio. The format of the station is news and talk. KXNT-FM broadcasts to the Las Vegas area at 100.5 FM.

KXO-AM

Owner: KXO Inc.
Editorial: 420 Main St, El Centro, California 92243. **T:** 1 760 352-1230
E: kxoamfm@kxoradio.com
W: http://www.kxoradio.com
Editorial Profile: KXO-AM is a commercial station owned by KXO Inc. The format of the station is oldies. KXO-AM broadcasts to the El Centro, CA area at 1230 AM.

KXO-FM

Owner: KXO Inc.
Editorial: 420 Main St, El Centro, California 92243. **T:** 1 760 352-1230
E: kxoamfm@kxoradio.com
W: http://www.kxoradio.com
Editorial Profile: KXO-FM is a commercial station owned by KXO Inc. The format of the station is adult contemporary music. KXO-FM broadcasts to the El Centro, CA area at 107.5 FM.

KXOI-AM

Owner: Hispanic Outreach Ministries Inc.
Editorial: 519 N Lauderdale Ave, Odessa, Texas 79763-4167. **T:** 1 432 333-5061
W: http://www.radioalabanza.info
Editorial Profile: KXOI-AM is a commercial station owned by Hispanic Outreach Ministries Inc. The format of the station is Hispanic contemporary Christian. KXOI-AM broadcasts to the Odessa, TX area at 810 AM.

KXOJ-FM

Owner: Stephens Media Group
Editorial: 2448 E 81st St, Ste 5500, Tulsa, Oklahoma 74137-4201. **T:** 1 918 492-2660
E: kxoj@kxoj.com **W:** http://www.kxoj.com
Editorial Profile: KXOJ-FM is a commercial station owned by Stephens Media Group. The format of the station is contemporary Christian. KXOJ-FM broadcasts to the Tulsa, OK area at 100.9 FM.

KXOL-FM

Owner: Spanish Broadcasting System
Editorial: 10281 W Pico Blvd, Los Angeles, California 90064-2674. **T:** 1 310 203-0900
W: http://www.mega963.com
Editorial Profile: KXOL-FM is a commercial station owned by Spanish Broadcasting System. The format of the station is Spanish CHR/AC. KXOL-FM broadcasts to the Los Angeles area at 96.3 FM.

KXOO-FM

Owner: Paragon Communications Inc.
Editorial: 220 S Pioneer Rd, Elk City, Oklahoma 73644. **T:** 1 580 225-5966
E: kxoo@cableone.net
W: http://www.kxoofm.com
Editorial Profile: KXOO-FM is a commercial station owned by Paragon Communications Inc. The format of the station is contemporary Christian music. KXOO-FM broadcasts in the Elk City, OK, area at 94.3 FM.

KXOQ-FM

Owner: Eagle Bluff Enterprises
Editorial: 700 North Byp, Kennett, Missouri 63857-1343. **T:** 1 573 686-3700
E: frn@tcmax.net
Editorial Profile: KXOQ-FM is a commercial station owned by Eagle Bluff Enterprises. The format of the station is classic rock. KXOQ-FM broadcasts to the Kennett, MO area at 104.3 FM.

KXOR-AM

Owner: Zion Multimedia Oregon Corporation
Editorial: 12145 Woodruff Ave, Downey, California 90241-5605. **T:** 1 562 401-4030
E: contactenos@zionmultimedia.com
W: http://www.radiozion.net
Editorial Profile: KXOR-AM is a commercial station owned by Zion Multimedia Oregon Corporation. The format of the station is Spanish-language Christian programming. KXOR-AM Broadcasts to the Eugene, OR area at a frequency of 660 AM.

KXOR-FM

Owner: Sunburst Media-Louisiana, LLC
Editorial: 120 Prevost Dr, Houma, Louisiana 70364-2338. **T:** 1 985 851-1020
W: http://www.la1063.com
Editorial Profile: KXOR-FM is a commercial station owned by Sunburst Media-Louisiana, LLC. The format of the station is classic and album oriented rock music. KXOR-FM broadcasts to the New Orleans area at 106.3 FM.

KXOS-FM

Owner: 93.9 Holdings, Inc. (Grupo Radio Centro)
Editorial: 2600 W Olive Ave Fl 8, Burbank, California 91505-4553. **T:** 1 818 525-5000
W: http://radiocentro939.com
Editorial Profile: KXOS-FM is a commercial station owned by 93.9 Holdings, Inc. (Grupo Radio Centro). The format of the station is Top 40/CHR. KXOS-FM broadcasts to the Los Angeles area at 93.9 FM.

KXOX-AM

Owner: Stein Broadcasting Co., Inc.
Editorial: 1801 Hoyt St, Sweetwater, Texas 79556-2663. **T:** 1 325 236-6655
E: kxox@att.net **W:** http://www.kxox.net
Editorial Profile: KXOX-AM is a commercial station owned by Stein Broadcasting Co., Inc. The format of the station is country. KXOX-AM broadcasts to the Abilene, TX area at 1240 AM.

KXOX-FM

Owner: Stein Broadcasting Co., Inc.
Editorial: 1801 Hoyt St, Sweetwater, Texas 79556-2663. **T:** 1 325 236-6655
E: kxox@att.net **W:** http://www.kxox.net
Editorial Profile: KXOX-FM is a commercial station owned by Stein Broadcasting Co., Inc. The format of the station is country. KXOX-FM broadcasts to the Sweetwater, TX area at 96.7 FM.

KXPA-AM

Owner: Multicultural Radio Broadcasting Inc.

Editorial: 114 Lakeside Ave, Seattle, Washington 98122-6542. **T:** 1 206 292-7800
E: kxpacontrolroom@gmail.com
W: http://www.kxpa.com
Editorial Profile: KXPA-AM is a commercial station owned by Multicultural Radio Broadcasting Inc. The format of the station is Hispanic. KXPA-AM broadcasts to the Seattle area at 1540 AM.

KXPK-FM
Owner: Entravision Communications Corp.
Editorial: 1907 Mile High Stadium West Cir, Denver, Colorado 80204-1908.
T: 1 303 832-0050
W: http://www.965tricolor.com
Editorial Profile: KXPK-FM is a commercial station owned by Entravision Communications Corp. The format of the station is regional Mexican music. KXPK-FM broadcasts to the Denver area at 96.5 FM.

KXPL-AM
Owner: New Radio System, Inc.
Editorial: 2211 E Missouri Ave, #E237, El Paso, Texas 79903-3807. **T:** 1 915 545-1060
E: kxpl1060am@yahoo.com
Editorial Profile: KXPL-AM is a commercial station owned by New Radio System, Inc. The format is ranchero/regional Mexican. KXPL-AM broadcasts in the El Paso, TX, area at 1060 AM.

KXPN-AM
Owner: Platte River Radio, Inc.
Editorial: 403 E 25th St, Kearney, Nebraska 68847. **T:** 1 308 236-9900
E: generalmanager@espnsuperstation.com
W: http://www.espnsuperstation.com
Editorial Profile: KXPN-AM is a commercial station owned by Platte River Radio, Inc. The format of the station is sports. KXPN-AM broadcasts to the Kearney, NE area at 1460 AM.

KXPO-AM
Owner: Simmons Broadcasting, Inc.
Editorial: 856 W 12th St, Grafton, North Dakota 58237. **T:** 1 701 352-0431
W: http://www.walshcountydailynews.com
Editorial Profile: KXPO-AM is a commercial station owned by Simmons Broadcasting, Inc. The format of the station is classic country. KXPO-AM broadcasts to the Grafton, ND area at 1340 AM.

KXPR-FM
Owner: California State University
Editorial: 7055 Folsom Blvd, Sacramento, California 95826. **T:** 1 916 278-8900
E: news@capradio.org
W: http://www.capradio.org
Editorial Profile: KXPR-FM is a non-commercial station owned by California State University. The format of the station is classical music. KXPR-FM broadcasts in the Sacramento, CA area at 88.9 FM.

KXPS-AM
Owner: CRC Media West, LLC
Editorial: 75-153 Merle Dr Ste D, Palm Desert, California 92211-5197.
T: 1 760 621-0100
W: http://www.1010kxps.com
Editorial Profile: KXPS-AM is a commercial station owned by CRC Media West, LLC. The format of the station is sports. KXPS-AM broadcasts to the Palm Springs, CA area at 1010 AM.

KXPT-FM
Owner: Lotus Communications Corp.
Editorial: 8755 W Flamingo Rd, Las Vegas, Nevada 89147-8667. **T:** 1 702 876-1460
E: lotussignup@yahoo.com
W: http://www.point97.com
Editorial Profile: KXPT-FM is a commercial station owned by Lotus Communications Corp. The format of the station is classic rock music. KXPT-FM broadcasts to the Las Vegas area at 97.1 FM.

KXPZ-FM
Owner: Bravo Mic Communications, LLC
Editorial: 101 Perkins Dr, Las Cruces, New Mexico 88005. **T:** 1 575 527-1111
E: rocket@bravomic.com
W: http://www.rocket995.com
Editorial Profile: KXPZ-FM is a commercial station owned by Bravo Mic Communications, LLC. The format of the station is adult album alternative. KXPZ-FM broadcasts to the Las Cruces, NM area at 99.5 FM.

KXRA-AM
Owner: Paradis Broadcasting
Editorial: 1312 Broadway St, Alexandria, Minnesota 56308. **T:** 1 320 763-3131
E: thefolks@kxra.com **W:** http://www.kxra.com
Editorial Profile: KXRA-AM is a commercial station owned by Paradis Broadcasting. The format of the station is news and talk. KXRA-AM broadcasts to the Alexandria, MN area at 1490 AM.

KXRA-FM
Owner: Paradis Broadcasting
Editorial: 1312 Broadway St, Alexandria, Minnesota 56308. **T:** 1 320 763-3131
E: thefolks@kxra.com **W:** http://www.kxra.com
Editorial Profile: KXRA-FM is a commercial station owned by Paradis Broadcasting. The format of the station is classic rock. KXRA-FM broadcasts to the Alexandria, MN area at 92.3 FM.

KXRB-AM
Owner: Townsquare Media, Inc.
Editorial: 5100 S Tennis Ln, Sioux Falls, South Dakota 57108-2212. **T:** 1 605 361-0300
W: http://www.kxrb.com
Editorial Profile: KXRB-AM is a commercial station owned by Townsquare Media, Inc. The format of the station is classic country music. KXRB-AM broadcasts to the Sioux Falls, SD area at 1000 AM.

KXRC-FM
Owner: KRJ Company
Editorial: 1135 Main Ave, Durango, Colorado 81301-5135. **T:** 1 970 259-1364
E: info@xrock105.com
W: http://www.xrock105.com/
Editorial Profile: KXRC-FM is a commercial station owned and operated by KRJ Company. The format of the station is classic rock. KXRC-FM broadcasts to the Durango, CO area at a frequency of 105.3 FM.

KXRE-AM
Owner: Latino Communications
Editorial: 600 Grant St, Ste 600, Denver, Colorado 80203. **T:** 1 303 733-5266
W: http://www.radioquebueno.com
Editorial Profile: KXRE-AM is a commercial station owned by Latino Communications. The format of the station is regional Mexican. KXRE-AM broadcasts to the the Denver area at 1490 AM.

KXRJ-FM
Owner: Arkansas Tech University
Editorial: 1310 N El Paso, Arkansas Tech University, Russellville, Arkansas 72801.
T: 1 479 964-0806 **E:** kxrj@atu.edu
W: http://www.atu.edu/broadcast/radio.shtml
Editorial Profile: KXRJ-FM is a non-commercial college station owned by Arkansas Tech University. The format of the station is variety. KXRJ-FM broadcasts to the Russellville, AR area at a frequency of 91.9 FM.

KXRK-FM
Owner: Broadway Media
Editorial: 515 S 700 E Ste 1C, Salt Lake City, Utah 84102-2802. **T:** 1 801 524-2600
W: http://www.x96.com
Editorial Profile: KXRK-FM is a commercial station owned by Broadway Media. The format of the station is rock alternative. KXRK-FM broadcasts to the Salt Lake City area at 96.3 FM.

KXRO-AM
Owner: Morris Communications
Editorial: 1308 Coolidge Rd, Aberdeen, Washington 98520-6317. **T:** 1 360 533-1320
W: http://www.kxro.com
Editorial Profile: KXRO-AM is a commercial station owned by Morris Communications. The format of the station is news and talk. KXRO-AM broadcasts in the Aberdeen, WA area at 1320 AM.

KXRQ-FM
Owner: Hall(Charlie)
Editorial: 1420 Weatherby Dr, Ste 200, Vernal, Utah 84078-8045. **T:** 1 435 781-1100
E: news@channelx94.com
W: http://www.channelx94.com
Editorial Profile: KXRQ-FM is a commercial station owned by Charlie Hall. The format of the station is Top 40/CHR and hot AC mix music. KXRQ-FM broadcasts to the Salt Lake City area at 94.3 FM.

KXRR-FM
Owner: Opus Media Partners
Editorial: 1200 N 18th St, Monroe, Louisiana 71201-5459. **T:** 1 318 387-3922
W: http://www.rock106kxrr.com
Editorial Profile: KXRR-FM is a commercial station owned by Opus Media Partners. The format of the station is rock music. KXRR-FM broadcasts to the Monroe, LA area at 106.1 FM.

KXRS-FM
Owner: Lazer Broadcasting Corp.
Editorial: 1950 S Sunwest Ln, Ste 302, San Bernardino, California 92408.
T: 1 909 384-9750 **W:** http://radiolazer.com
Editorial Profile: KXRS-FM is a commercial station owned by the Lazer Broadcasting Corp. The format of the station is Regional Mexican. KXRS-FM broadcasts to the Hemet, CA area at 105.7 FM.

KXRV-FM
Owner: World Radio Link, Inc.
Editorial: 409 N 4Th St, Bismarck, North Dakota 58501-4023. **T:** 1 701 751-4757
E: mojo@mojo1075.com
W: http://www.mojo1075.com
Editorial Profile: KXRV-FM is a commercial station owned by World Radio Link, Inc and operated by Radio Bismark-Mandan (Denver, Bob). The format of the station is classic hits. KXRV-FM broadcasts to the Bismark, ND area at a frequency of 107.5.

KXRX-FM
Owner: Townsquare Media, LLC
Editorial: 2621 W A St, Pasco, Washington 99301. **T:** 1 509 547-9791
W: http://97rockonline.com
Editorial Profile: KXRX-FM is a commercial station owned by Townsquare Media, LLC. The format of the station is rock. KXRX-FM broadcasts to the Pasco, WA area at 97.1 FM.

KXRY-FM
Owner: Common Frequency (Cascade Educational Broadcast System)
Editorial: 5415 N Albina Ave, Portland, Oregon 97217-2345 **W:** http://xray.fm
Editorial Profile: KXRY-FM is a non-commercial station owned by Common Frequency (Cascade Educational Broadcast System). The format of the station is variety. The station broadcasts locally at a frequency of 91.1 FM.

KXRZ-FM
Owner: Paradis Broadcasting
Editorial: 1312 Broadway St, Alexandria, Minnesota 56308. **T:** 1 320 763-3131
E: thefolks@kxra.com
W: http://www.z99radio.com
Editorial Profile: KXRZ-FM is a commercial station owned by Paradis Broadcasting. The format of the station is hot adult contemporary. KXRZ-FM broadcasts to the Alexandria, MN area at 99.3 FM.

KXSA-FM
Owner: Pines Broadcasting
Editorial: 279 Midway Rte, Monticello, Arkansas 71655-8605. **T:** 1 870 367-6854
E: pines.radio@sbcglobal.net
Editorial Profile: KXSA-FM is a commercial station owned by Pines Broadcasting. The format of the station is classic country. KXSA-FM broadcasts to the Monticello, AR area at 103.1 FM.

KXSB-FM
Owner: Lazer Broadcasting Corp.
Editorial: 1950 S Sunwest Ln, Ste 302, San Bernardino, California 92408.
T: 1 909 384-9750
W: http://radiolazer1017.com/
Editorial Profile: KXSB-FM is a commercial station owned by the Lazer Broadcasting Corp. The format for the station is regional Mexican. KXSB-FM broadcasts to the San Bernardino, CA area at 101.7 FM.

KXSC-FM
Owner: University of Southern California
Editorial: 201 3Rd St Suite 1200, San Francisco, California 94103-3143.
T: 1 415 546-8710 **E:** feedback@kdfc.com
W: http://www.kdfc.com
Editorial Profile: KXSC-FM is a non-commercial station owned by University of Southern California. The format of the station is Classical. KXSC-FM broadcasts to the San Francisco Bay area in California locally at 104.9 FM.

KXSE-FM
Owner: Entravision Communications Corp.
Editorial: 1436 Auburn Blvd, Sacramento, California 95815. **T:** 1 916 646-4000
W: http://www.jose1043.com/
Editorial Profile: KXSE-FM is a commercial station owned by Entravision Communications Corp. The format of the station is Hispanic adult hits. KXSE-FM broadcasts to the Sacramento, CA area on 104.3 FM.

KXSM-FM
Owner: Lazer Broadcasting Corp.
Editorial: 600 E Market St, Salinas, California 93905-2109. **T:** 1 831 422-5019
W: http://www.radiolazer.com
Editorial Profile: KXSM-FM is a commercial station owned by Lazer Broadcasting Corp. The format of the station is regional Mexican. KXSM-FM broadcasts to the Monterey, CA area at 93.1 FM.

KXSP-AM
Owner: Journal Broadcast Group
Editorial: 10714 Mockingbird Dr, Omaha, Nebraska 68127-1942. **T:** 1 402 592-5300
W: http://www.am590espnradio.com
Editorial Profile: KXSP-AM is a commercial station owned by Journal Broadcast Group. The format of the station is sports. KXSP-AM broadcasts to the Omaha, NE area at 590 AM.

KXSS-AM
Owner: Townsquare Media, LLC
Editorial: 640 Lincoln Ave SE, Saint Cloud, Minnesota 56304-1024. **T:** 1 320 251-4422
E: thefanman@1390thefan.com
W: http://1390thefan.com
Editorial Profile: KXSS-AM is a commercial station owned by Townsquare Media, LLC. The format of the station is sports. KXSS-AM broadcasts to the Saint Cloud, MN area at 1390 AM.

KXSS-FM
Owner: Townsquare Media, LLC
Editorial: 6214 W 34th Ave, Amarillo, Texas 79109-4006. **T:** 1 806 355-9777
W: http://www.969kmml.com
Editorial Profile: KXSS-FM is a commercial station owned by Townsquare Media, LLC. The format of the station is Top 40/CHR. KXSS-FM broadcasts to the Amarillo, TX area at 96.9 FM.

KXST-AM
Owner: CBS Radio
Editorial: 7255 S Tenaya Way, Las Vegas, Nevada 89113-1900. **T:** 1 702 889-7300
W: http://kydz.radio.com
Editorial Profile: KXST-AM is a commercial station owned by CBS Radio. The format of the station is

KXTC-FM
Owner: Clear Channel Media and Entertainment
Editorial: 1632 S Second St, Gallup, New Mexico 87301-5836. **T:** 1 505 863-9391
W: http://www.999xtc.com
Editorial Profile: KXTC-FM is a commercial station owned by Clear Channel Media and Entertainment. The format of the station is Top 40/CHR music. KXTC-FM broadcasts to the Albuquerque, NM area at 99.9 FM.

KXTD-AM
Owner: Gaytan-Galvan LLC
Editorial: 5807 S Garnett Rd, Ste K, Tulsa, Oklahoma 74146-6824. **T:** 1 918 254-7556
E: kxtdr@tulsacoxmail.com
Editorial Profile: KXTD-AM is a commercial station owned by Gaytan-Galvan LLC. The format of the station is Latin Pop. KXTD-AM broadcasts to the Tulsa, OK area at 1530 AM.

KXTE-FM
Owner: CBS Radio
Editorial: 7255 S Tenaya Way Ste 100, Las Vegas, Nevada 89113-1900.
T: 1 702 257-1075
W: http://www.x1075lasvegas.com
Editorial Profile: KXTE-FM is a commercial station owned by CBS Radio. The format of the station is rock alternative. KXTE-FM broadcasts to the Las Vegas area at 107.5 FM.

KXTG-AM
Owner: Alpha Broadcasting
Editorial: 1211 SW 5th Ave Fl 6, Portland, Oregon 97204-3735. **T:** 1 503 243-7595
W: http://www.750thegame.com
Editorial Profile: KXTG-AM is a commercial station owned by Alpha Broadcasting. The format of the station is sports. KXTG-AM broadcasts to the Portland, OR area at 750 AM.

KXTK-AM
Owner: Pacific Coast Media, LLC
Editorial: 880 Via Esteban, San Luis Obispo, California 93401-7101. **T:** 1 805 547-1280
W: http://www.espnradio1280.com

Editorial Profile: KXTK-AM is a commercial station owned by Pacific Coast Media, LLC. The format of the station is sports. KXTK-AM broadcasts to the San Luis Obispo, CA area at 1280 AM.

KXTL-AM
Owner: Cherry Creek Radio
Editorial: 750 Dewey Blvd, Butte, Montana 59701. **T:** 1 406 494-4442
E: prodbutte@cherrycreekradio.com
W: http://www.kxtl.com
Editorial Profile: KXTL-AM is a commercial station owned by Cherry Creek Radio. The format of the station is talk. KXTL-AM broadcasts to the Butte, MT area at 1370 AM.

KXTN-FM
Owner: Univision Communications Inc.
Editorial: 12451 Network Blvd Ste 140, San Antonio, Texas 78249-3336.
T: 1 210 610-4300 **W:** http://www.kxtn.com
Editorial Profile: KXTN-FM is a commercial station owned by Univision Communications Inc. The format of the station is Hispanic, featuring Tejano music. KXTN-FM broadcasts to the San Antonio area at 107.5 FM.

KXTQ-FM
Owner: Ramar Communications Inc.
Editorial: 9800 University Ave, Lubbock, Texas 79423. **T:** 1 806 745-3434
W: http://magic937.fm
Editorial Profile: KXTQ-FM is a commercial station owned by Ramar Communications II Ltd. The format of the station is Tejano music. KXTQ-FM broadcasts to the Lubbock, TX area at 93.7 FM.

KXTS-FM
Owner: Sinclair Communications
Editorial: 3565 Standish Ave, Santa Rosa, California 95407. **T:** 1 707 588-0707
E: exitos@winecountryradio.net
W: http://www.exitos987.com
Editorial Profile: KXTS-FM is a commercial station owned by Sinclair Communications. The format of the station is regional Mexican. KXTS-FM broadcasts to the Santa Rosa, CA area at 98.7 FM.

KXTZ-FM
Owner: Mapleton Communications LLC
Editorial: 795 Buckley Rd, Ste 2, San Luis Obispo, California 93401. **T:** 1 805 786-2570
W: http://www.953thebeach.com
Editorial Profile: KXTZ-FM is a commercial station owned by Mapleton Communications LLC. The format of the station is classic hits. KXTZ-FM broadcasts to the San Luis Obispo, CA area at 95.3 FM.

KXUL-FM
Owner: University of Louisiana at Monroe
Editorial: 401 Bayou Drive 130 Stubs Hall, Monroe, Louisiana 71209-0001.
T: 1 318 342-5986 **W:** http://kxul.com
Editorial Profile: KXUL-FM is a non-commercial station owned by the University of Louisiana at Monroe. The format of the station is rock alternative music. KXUL-FM broadcasts to the Monroe, LA area at 91.1 FM.

KXUS-FM
Owner: Clear Channel Media and Entertainment
Editorial: 1856 S Glenstone Ave, Springfield, Missouri 65804-2303. **T:** 1 417 890-5555
E: us97@us97.com **W:** http://www.us97.com
Editorial Profile: KXUS-FM is a commercial station owned by Clear Channel Media and Entertainment. The format of the station is classic rock music. KXUS-FM broadcasts to the Springfield, MO area at 97.3 FM.

KXWA-FM
Owner: WAY Media Inc.
Editorial: 1707 Main St Ste 302, Longmont, Colorado 80501-7403. **T:** 1 303 702-9293
W: http://kxwa.wayfm.com
Editorial Profile: KXWA-FM is a commercial station owned by WAY Media Inc. The format of the station is contemporary Christian music. KXWA-FM broadcasts to the Centennial, CO and Denver areas at 101.9 FM.

KXWT-FM
Owner: Matinee Radio, LLC
Editorial: 111 South Highland Ave., Marfa, Texas 79843. **T:** 1 432 729-4578
W: http://www.marfapublicradio.org
Editorial Profile: KXWT-FM is a non-commercial station owned by Matinee Radio, LLC. The format of the station is variety. KXWT-FM broadcasts in the Odessa-Midland, TX area at 91.3 FM. The station airs KRTS-FM's programming.

KXXI-FM
Owner: Millennium Media Inc.
Editorial: 300 W Aztec Ave, Ste 200, Gallup, New Mexico 87301-6304. **T:** 1 505 863-6851
E: mm1@cia-g.com
W: http://www.gallupradio.com
Editorial Profile: KXXI-FM is a commercial station owned by Millennium Media Inc. The format of the station is classic rock music. KXXI-FM broadcasts to the Albuquerque, NM area at 93.7 FM.

KXXJ-AM
Owner: Alaska Broadcast Communications, Inc
Editorial: 3161 Channel Dr, Juneau, Alaska 99801-7865. **T:** 1 907 586-3630
W: http://www.kxjradio.com
Editorial Profile: KXXJ-AM is a commercial station owned by Alaska Broadcast Communications. The format of the station is classic hits. KXXJ-AM broadcasts to the Juneau, AK area at a frequency of 1330 AM.

KXXK-FM
Owner: Morris Communications
Editorial: 1308 Coolidge Rd, Aberdeen, Washington 98520-6317. **T:** 1 360 533-1320
W: http://www.kix953.com
Editorial Profile: KXXK-FM is a commercial station owned by Morris Communications. The format of the station is contemporary country. KXXK-FM broadcasts in the Aberdeen, WA area at 95.3 FM.

KXXL-FM
Owner: Keyhole Broadcasting LLC
Editorial: 305 S Garner Lake Rd, Gillette, Wyoming 82718-8254. **T:** 1 307 687-1003
E: koal1061@koal1061.com
Editorial Profile: KXXL-FM is a commercial station owned by Keyhole Broadcasting LLC. The format of the station is classic rock. KXXL-FM broadcasts to the Gillette, WY area at 106.1 FM.

KXXM-FM
Owner: Clear Channel Media and Entertainment
Editorial: 6222 NW Interstate Highway 10, San Antonio, Texas 78201. **T:** 1 210 736-9700
W: http://www.mix961.com
Editorial Profile: KXXM-FM is a commercial station owned by Clear Channel Media and Entertainment. The format of the station is Top 40/CHR music. KXXM-FM broadcasts to the San Antonio area at 96.1 FM.

KXXN-FM
Owner: Falls Media, LLC
Editorial: 813 8th St Ste 550, Wichita Falls, Texas 76301-3318. **T:** 1 940 488-4963
E: k96@grownfolkjamz.com
W: http://www.grownfolkjamz.com
Editorial Profile: KXXN-FM is a commercial station owned by Falls Media, LLC. The format of the station is Urban AC. The station broadcasts locally at 96.3 in the Wichita Falls, TX area.

KXXO-FM
Owner: Three Cities Inc.
Editorial: 119 Washington St NE, Olympia, Washington 98501. **T:** 1 360 943-9937
E: admin@mixx96.com
W: http://www.mixx96.com
Editorial Profile: KXXO-FM is a commercial station owned by Three Cities Inc. The format of the station is adult contemporary music. KXXO-FM broadcasts in the Seattle area at 96.1 FM.

KXXR-FM
Owner: Cumulus Media Inc
Editorial: 2000 Elm St SE, Minneapolis, Minnesota 55414. **T:** 1 612 617-4000
E: mail@93x.com **W:** http://www.93x.com
Editorial Profile: KXXR-FM is a commercial station owned by Cumulus Media Inc. The format of the station is rock music. KXXR-FM broadcasts to the Minneapolis area at 93.7 FM.

KXXT-AM
Owner: Communicom Broadcasting
Editorial: 2800 N 44th St, Ste 100, Phoenix, Arizona 85008. **T:** 1 602 254-5001
W: http://www.familyvaluesradio.net
Editorial Profile: KXXT-AM is a commercial station owned by Communicom Broadcasting. The format of the station is religious. KXXT-AM broadcasts to the Phoenix area at 1010 AM.

KXXX-AM
Owner: Rocking M Radio
Editorial: 1065 S Range Ave, Colby, Kansas 67701-3505. **T:** 1 785 462-3305
E: kxxxkqlsprod@rockingmradio.com
Editorial Profile: KXXX-AM is a commercial station owned by Rocking M Radio. The format of the station is country. KXXX-AM broadcasts to the Colby, KS area at 790 AM.

KXXY-FM
Owner: Clear Channel Media and Entertainment
Editorial: 1900 NW Expressway, Ste 1000, Oklahoma City, Oklahoma 73118.
T: 1 405 858-1400 **W:** http://www.kxy.com
Editorial Profile: KXXY-FM is a commercial station owned by Clear Channel Media and Entertainment. The format of the station is country music. KXXY-FM broadcasts to the Oklahoma City area at 96.1 FM.

KXXZ-FM
Owner: Dos Costas Communications Corp.
Editorial: 29000 Radio Rd, Barstow, California 92311-1648. **T:** 1 760 256-2121
E: doscostas@yahoo.com
Editorial Profile: KXXZ-FM is a commercial station owned by Dos Costas Communications Corp. The format of the station is regional Mexican. KXXZ-FM broadcasts to the Barstow, CA area at 95.9 FM.

KXYL-AM
Owner: Wendlee Broadcasting
Editorial: 600 Fisk Ave, Brownwood, Texas 76801. **T:** 1 325 646-3535
E: newstalk@wendlee.com
W: http://www.brownwoodradio.com
Editorial Profile: KXYL-AM is a commercial station owned by Wendlee Broadcasting. The format of the station is news and talk. KXYL-AM broadcasts to the Brownwood, TX area at 1240 AM.

KXYL-FM
Owner: Wendlee Broadcasting
Editorial: 600 Fisk Ave, Brownwood, Texas 76801. **T:** 1 325 646-3535
E: newstalk@wendlee.com
W: http://www.wendleebroadcasting.com
Editorial Profile: KXYL-FM is a commercial station owned by Wendlee Broadcasting. The format of the station is news and talk. KXYL-FM broadcasts in the Brownwood, TX area at 102.3 FM.

KXYZ-AM
Owner: Multi Cultural Radio Broadcasting, Inc.
Editorial: 1782 W Sam Houston Pkwy N, Houston, Texas 77043-2723.
T: 1 713 490-2538 **W:** http://kxyzradio.com
Editorial Profile: KXYZ-AM is a commercial station owned by Multi Cultural Radio Broadcasting, Inc. The format of the station is ethnic variety; Mandarin & Hindi. KXYZ-AM broadcasts to the Houston area at 1320 AM.

KXZM-FM
Owner: Lazer Broadcasting Corp.
Editorial: 777 N 1St St Ste 200, San Jose, California 95112-6311. **T:** 1 408 899-6331
E: contactodirecto@radiolazer.com
W: http://www.radiolazer.com
Editorial Profile: KXZM-FM is a commercial station owned by Lazer Broadcasting Corp. The format of the station is Regional Mexican. KXZM-FM broadcasts locally to San Jose, CA and the Greater Bay Area at a frequency of 93.7 FM.

KXZZ-AM
Owner: Cumulus Media Inc.
Editorial: 425 Broad St, Lake Charles, Louisiana 70601-4225. **T:** 1 337 436-7277
W: http://www.kxzz1580am.com
Editorial Profile: KXZZ-AM is a commercial station owned by Cumulus Media Inc. The format of the station is sports talk. KXZZ-AM broadcasts to the Lake Charles, LA area at 1580 AM.

KYAA-AM
Owner: People's Radio Inc.
Editorial: 1680 McKee Rd, San Jose, California 95116-1237. **T:** 1 831 899-1570
E: kyaaradio@yahoo.com
W: http://ihradio.com
Editorial Profile: KYAA-AM is a commercial station owned by People's Radio Inc. The format of the station is religious. KYAA-AM broadcasts to the Hayward, CA area at 1200 AM.

KYAH-AM
Owner: Bushman(Sam)
Editorial: 1259 N 100 W, American Fork, Utah 84003. **T:** 1 435 864-5111
E: kyah@accentradionetwork.com
W: http://www.knakradio.com
Editorial Profile: KYAH-AM is a commercial station owned by Sam Bushman. The format of the station is religious talk. KYAH-AM broadcasts to the Salt Lake City area at 540 AM.

KYAK-AM
Owner: Yakima Christian Broadcasting
Editorial: 706 Butterfield Rd, Yakima, Washington 98901. **T:** 1 509 452-5925
E: kyak@kyak.com **W:** http://www.kyak.com
Editorial Profile: KYAK-AM is a commercial station owned by Yakima Christian Broadcasting. The format of the station is Christian. KYAK-AM broadcasts to the Yakima, WA area at 930 AM.

KYAL-AM
Owner: Stephens Media Group.
Editorial: 2448 E 81st St, Ste 5500, Tulsa, Oklahoma 74137. **T:** 1 918 492-2660
E: studio@sportsanimaltulsa.com
W: http://www.sportsanimaltulsa.com
Editorial Profile: KYAL-AM is a commercial station owned by Stephens Media Group. The format of the station is sports. KYAL-AM broadcasts to the Tulsa, OK area at 1550 AM.

KYAL-FM
Owner: Stephens Media Group.
Editorial: 2448 E 81st St Ste 5500, Tulsa, Oklahoma 74137-4201. **T:** 1 918 492-2660
E: studio@sportsanimalradio.com
W: http://www.sportsanimaltulsa.com
Editorial Profile: KYAL-FM is a commercial station owned by Stephens Media Group. The format of the station is sports. KYAL-FM broadcasts in the Tulsa, OK area at 97.1 FM.

KYAT-FM
Owner: Millennium Media Inc.
Editorial: 300 W Aztec Ave, Gallup, New Mexico 87301-6304. **T:** 1 505 863-6851
E: mm1@cia-g.com
W: http://www.gallupradio.com
Editorial Profile: KYAT-FM is a commercial station owned by Millennium Media Inc. The format of the station features Navajo-language, Native American programming. KYAT-FM broadcasts to the Gallup, NM area at a frequency of 94.5 FM.

KYBA-FM
Owner: Cumulus Media Inc.
Editorial: 122 4th St SW, Rochester, Minnesota 55902-3320. **T:** 1 507 286-1010
E: feedback@y105fm.com
W: http://www.y105fm.com
Editorial Profile: KYBA-FM is a commercial station owned by Cumulus Media Inc. The format of the station is lite rock. KYBA-FM broadcasts to the Rochester, MN, Mason City, IA area at 105.3 FM.

KYBB-FM
Owner: Townsquare Media, Inc.
Editorial: 5100 S Tennis Ln Ste 200, Sioux Falls, South Dakota 57108-2271.
T: 1 605 339-1140 **W:** http://www.b1027.com
Editorial Profile: KYBB-FM is a commercial station owned by Townsquare Media, Inc. The format of the station is classic rock. KYBB-FM broadcasts to the Sioux Falls, SD area at 102.7 FM.

KYBC-AM
Owner: Yavapai Broadcasting
Editorial: 3405 E State Route 89A, Cottonwood, Arizona 86326-5504.
T: 1 928 634-2286
E: news@myradioplace.com
W: http://www.1600kybc.com
Editorial Profile: KYBC-AM is a commercial station owned by Yavapai Broadcasting. The format of the station is adult standards music. KYBC-AM broadcasts to the Cottonwood, AZ area at 1600 AM.

KYBE-FM
Owner: LKCM Radio Group LP
Editorial: 207 W Grand Ave, Frederick, Oklahoma 73542-5229. **T:** 1 580 335-5923
W: http://www.coyotenews.com
Editorial Profile: KYBE-FM is a commercial station owned by LKCM Radio Group LP. The format of the station is contemporary country. KYBE-FM broadcasts to the Frederick, OK area at 95.7 FM.

KYBG-FM
Owner: Acadia Broadcast Partners
Editorial: 320 N Parkerson Ave, Crowley, Louisiana 70526. **T:** 1 337 783-2521
W: http://www.kqis.com
Editorial Profile: KYBG-FM is a commercial station owned by Acadia Broadcast Partners. The format of the station is adult

contemporary music. KYBG-FM broadcasts to the Lafayette, LA area at 102.1 FM.

KYBI-FM
Owner: Pentagon Communications, LLC
Editorial: 121 Cotton Square, Lufkin, Texas 75901. **T:** 1 936 634-6661
E: traffic@yatesmedia.com
W: http://www.kybiradio.com
Editorial Profile: KYBI-FM is a commercial station owned by Yates Media. The format of the station is classic and contemporary country. KYBI-FM broadcasts to the Lufkin, TX area at 100.1 FM.

KYBR-FM
Owner: Rio Chama Broadcasting
Editorial: 403 W Pueblo Dr, Espanola, New Mexico 87532-2530. **T:** 1 505 753-2201
W: http://www.radiooso.com
Editorial Profile: KYBR-FM is a commercial station owned by Rio Chama Broadcasting. The format of the station is regional Mexican and news. KYBR-FM broadcasts to the Albuquerque, NM area at 92.9 FM.

KYCA-AM
Owner: Southwest Broadcasting
Editorial: 500 Henry St, Prescott, Arizona 86301. **T:** 1 928 445-1700
E: prescott@kyca.info **W:** http://www.kyca.info
Editorial Profile: KYCA-AM is a commercial station owned by Southwest Broadcasting. The format of the station is news and talk programming. KYCA-AM broadcasts to the Prescott, AZ, area on 1490 AM.

KYCC-FM
Owner: Your Christian Companion Network
Editorial: 9019 West Ln, Stockton, California 95210-1401. **T:** 1 209 477-3690
E: kycc@kycc.org **W:** http://www.kycc.org
Editorial Profile: KYCC-FM is a non-commercial station owned by Your Christian Companion Network. The format of the station is religious. KYCC-FM broadcasts to the Stockton, CA area at 90.1 FM.

KYCH-FM
Owner: Entercom Communications Corp.
Editorial: 0700 SW Bancroft St, Portland, Oregon 97239-4226. **T:** 1 503 223-1441
W: http://www.charliefm.com
Editorial Profile: KYCH-FM is a commercial station owned by Entercom Communications Corp. The format of the station is adult hits. KYCH-FM broadcasts to the Portland, OR area at 97.1 FM.

KYCK-FM
Owner: Leighton Enterprises Inc.
Editorial: 1185 9th St NE, Thompson, North Dakota 58278. **T:** 1 701 775-4611
E: live@97kyck.com
W: http://www.97kyck.com
Editorial Profile: KYCK-FM is a commercial station owned by Leighton Enterprises Inc. The format of the station is contemporary country music. KYCK-FM broadcasts to the Grand Forks, ND area area at 97.1 FM.

KYCN-AM
Owner: Smith Broadcasting Inc.
Editorial: 450 Cole St, Wheatland, Wyoming 82201-7816. **T:** 1 307 322-5926
E: kycn@communicomm.com
Editorial Profile: KYCN-AM is a commercial station owned by Smith Broadcasting Inc. The format of the station is classic country. KYCN-AM broadcasts to the Wheatland, WY area at 1340 AM.

KYCR-AM
Owner: Salem Communications
Editorial: 2110 Cliff Rd, Eagan, Minnesota 55122-3522. **T:** 1 651 405-8800
W: http://www.business1570.com
Editorial Profile: KYCR-AM is a commercial station owned by Salem Communications. The format of the station is business news and talk. KYCR-AM broadcasts to the Minneapolis-St Paul, MN area at 1280 AM.

KYCS-FM
Owner: Wagonwheel Communications Corp.
Editorial: 40 Shoshone Ave, Green River, Wyoming 82935. **T:** 1 307 362-6746
E: mail@theradionetwork.net
W: http://www.theradionetwork.net
Editorial Profile: KYCS-FM is a commercial station owned by Wagonwheel Communications Corp. The format of the station is hot AC. KYCS-FM broadcasts to the Green River, WY area at 95.1 FM.

KYDN-FM
Owner: San Luis Valley Broadcasting
Editorial: 109 Adams St, Monte Vista, Colorado 81144-1421. **T:** 1 719 852-3581
E: kslv@amigo.net
W: http://www.kslvradio.com
Editorial Profile: KYDN-FM is a commercial station owned by San Luis Valley Broadcasting. The format of the station is contemporary country. KYDN-FM broadcasts to the Monte Vista, CO area at 95.3 FM.

KYDS-FM
Owner: San Juan Unified School District
Editorial: 4300 El Camino Ave, Sacramento, California 95821-6702. **T:** 1 916 971-7453
W: http://www.sanjuan.edu/ElCamino.cfm?subpage=49826
Editorial Profile: KYDS-FM is a non-commercial high school station owned by the San Juan Unified School District. The format of the station is variety. KYDS-FM broadcasts to the Sacramento, CA area at a frequency of 91.5 FM.

KYDT-FM
Owner: Ultimate Caps, Inc.
Editorial: 707 Harding St, Belle Fourche, South Dakota 57717. **T:** 1 605 892-2571
E: kbfs@mato.com **W:** http://www.kydt.com
Editorial Profile: KYDT-FM is a commercial station owned by Ultimate Caps, Inc. The format of the station is country, sports and agricultural programming. KYDT-FM broadcasts to the Belle Fourche, SD area at 103.1 FM.

KYEE-FM
Owner: Burt Broadcasting Inc.
Editorial: 501 S Florida Ave, Alamogordo, New Mexico 88310-6018. **T:** 1 575 434-1414
E: burtbroadcasting@bbiradio.net
W: http://www.94key.net
Editorial Profile: KYEE-FM is a commercial station owned by Burt Broadcasting Inc. The format of the station is adult contemporary music. KYEE-FM broadcasts to the Albuquerque, NM area at 94.3 FM.

KYEL-FM
Owner: KERM Inc.
Editorial: 201 W 2nd St, Russellville, Arkansas 72801. **T:** 1 479 968-1184
Editorial Profile: KYEL-FM is a commercial station owned by KERM Inc. The format of the station is classic country. KYEL-FM broadcasts to the Russellville, AR area at 105.5 FM.

KYEZ-FM
Owner: Morris Communications
Editorial: 131 N Santa Fe Ave, Ste 3, Salina, Kansas 67401-2642. **T:** 1 785 823-1111
W: http://www.y937.com
Editorial Profile: KYEZ-FM is a commercial station owned by Morris Communications. The format of the station is contemporary country. KYEZ-FM broadcasts to the Salina, KS area at 93.7 FM.

KYFB-FM
Owner: Bible Broadcasting Network
Editorial: 4816 S State Highway 91, Denison, Texas 75020. **T:** 1 704 523-5555
W: http://www.bbnradio.org
Editorial Profile: KYFB-FM is a non-commercial station owned by Bible Broadcasting Network. The format is religious. The station broadcasts to the Denison, TX area at 91.5 FM.

KYFG-FM
Owner: Bible Broadcasting Network
Editorial: 5829 N 60th St, Omaha, Nebraska 68104. **T:** 1 704 523-5555
W: http://www.bbnradio.org
Editorial Profile: KYFG-FM is a non-commercial station owned by Bible Broadcasting Network. The format of the station is religious programming. KYFG-FM broadcasts to the Omaha, NE area at 88.9 FM.

KYFM-FM
Owner: KCD Enterprises Inc.
Editorial: 1200 SE Frank Phillips Blvd, Bartlesville, Oklahoma 74003-4332.
T: 1 918 336-1001
E: radio@bartlesvilleradio.com
W: http://www.bartlesvilleradio.com
Editorial Profile: KYFM-FM is a commercial station owned by KCD Enterprises Inc. The format of the station is adult contemporary. KYFM-FM broadcasts to the Bartlesville, OK area at 100.1 FM.

KYFR-AM
Owner: Family Stations Inc.
Editorial: 112 N Elm St, Shenandoah, Iowa 51601. **T:** 1 712 246-5151
E: kyfr@familyradio.org
W: http://www.familyradio.org
Editorial Profile: KYFR-AM is a non-commercial station owned by Family Stations Inc. The format of the station is religious. KYFR-AM broadcasts to the Shenandoah, IA area at 920 AM.

KYFS-FM
Owner: Bible Broadcasting Network
Editorial: 228 Scheutz Dr, Schertz, Texas 78154. **T:** 1 704 523-5555
E: bbn@bbnmedia.org
W: http://www.bbnradio.org
Editorial Profile: KYFS-FM is a non-commercial station owned by Bible Broadcasting Network. The format of the station is religious. KYFS-FM broadcasts to the San Antonio area at 90.9 FM.

KYFW-FM
Owner: Bible Broadcasting Network
Editorial: 11530 Carmel Commons Blvd, Charlotte, North Carolina 28226-3976.
T: 1 800 888-7077 **E:** bbn@bbnmedia.org
W: http://www.bbnradio.org
Editorial Profile: KYFW-FM is a non-commercial station owned by Bible Broadcasting Network. The format of the station is religious programming. KYFW-FM broadcasts to the Derby, KS area at 88.3 FM.

KYGL-FM
Owner: Townsquare Media, LLC
Editorial: 2324 Arkansas Blvd, Texarkana, Arkansas 71854. **T:** 1 870 772-3771
E: eagle1063@gmail.com
W: http://www.kygl.com
Editorial Profile: KYGL-FM is a commercial station owned by Townsquare Media, LLC. The format of the station is classic rock. KYGL-FM broadcasts to the Texarkana, AR area at 106.3 FM.

KYGO-FM
Owner: Lincoln Financial Media
Editorial: 7800 E Orchard Rd, Greenwood Village, Colorado 80111-2583.
T: 1 303 321-0950 **W:** http://www.kygo.com
Editorial Profile: KYGO-FM is a commercial station owned by Lincoln Financial Media. The format of the station is contemporary country music. KYGO-FM broadcasts in the Denver area at 98.5 FM.

KYIS-FM
Owner: Cumulus Media Inc
Editorial: 4045 NW 64th St Ste 600, Oklahoma City, Oklahoma 73116-2607.
T: 1 405 848-0100 **W:** http://www.kyis.com
Editorial Profile: KYIS-FM is a commercial station owned by Cumulus Media Inc. The format of the station is hot adult contemporary music. KYIS-FM broadcasts to the Oklahoma City area at 98.9 FM.

KYIX-FM
Owner: Auel (Carl J.)
Editorial: 1363 Longfellow Ave, Chico, California 95926. **T:** 1 530 894-7325
E: info@air1.com **W:** http://www.air1.com
Editorial Profile: KYIX-FM is a non-commercial station owned by Carl J. Auel. The format of the station is contemporary Christian music. KYIX-FM broadcasts to the residents of Chico, CA at 104.9 FM.

KYIZ-AM
Owner: Kris Bennett Broadcasting Co.
Editorial: 2600 S Jackson St, Seattle, Washington 98144-2402. **T:** 1 206 323-3070
E: ztwins@aol.com
Editorial Profile: KYIZ-AM is a commercial station owned by Kris Bennett Broadcasting Co. The format of the station is urban adult contemporary. KYIZ-AM broadcasts to the Seattle area at 1620 AM.

KYJK-FM
Owner: Spanish Peaks Broadcasting, Inc.
Editorial: 2425 W Central Ave, Ste 203, Missoula, Montana 59801. **T:** 1 406 721-6800
W: http://www.1059jackfm.net
Editorial Profile: KYJK-FM is a commercial station owned by Spanish Peaks Broadcasting, Inc. The format of the station is Jack FM. KYJK-FM broadcasts to the Missoula, MT, area at 105.9 FM.

KYKC-FM
Owner: Chickasaw Nation
Editorial: 1019 N Broadway, Ada, Oklahoma 74820-6503. **T:** 1 580 436-1616
E: kykc@cableone.net **W:** http://www.kykc.net
Editorial Profile: KYKC-FM is a commercial station owned by the Chickasaw Nation. The format of the station is contemporary country. KYKC-FM broadcasts to the South Central Oklahoma area at a frequency of 100.1 FM.

KYKD-FM
Owner: Voice for Christ Ministries Inc.
Editorial: 406 Ptarmigan St, Bethel, Alaska 99559-2428. **T:** 1 907 543-5953
E: kykd@vfcm.org **W:** http://www.vfcm.org
Editorial Profile: KYKD-FM is a commercial station owned by Voice for Christ Ministries Inc. The format of the station is Christian programming. KYKD-FM broadcasts to the Bethel, AK area at 100.1 FM.

KYKK-AM
Owner: Noalmark Broadcasting Corp.
Editorial: 1423 W Bender Blvd, Hobbs, New Mexico 88240-9252. **T:** 1 575 393-1551
W: http://www.hobbsradio.com
Editorial Profile: KYKK-AM is a commercial station owned by Noalmark Broadcasting Corp. The format of the station is news and talk. KYKK-AM broadcasts to the Hobbs, NM area at 1110 AM.

KYKM-FM
Owner: Kremling Enterprises Inc.
Editorial: 111 N Main St, Hallettsville, Texas 77964-2727. **T:** 1 361 798-4333
E: txthunderradio@yahoo.com
W: http://www.texasthunderradio.com
Editorial Profile: KYKM-FM is a commercial radio station owned by Kremling Enterprises Inc. The format of the station is contemporary country music. KYKM-FM broadcasts to the Hallettsville, TX area at 94.3 FM.

KYKN-AM
Owner: Willamette Broadcasting
Editorial: 4205 Cherry Ave NE, Keizer, Oregon 97303. **T:** 1 503 390-3014
W: http://www.kykn.com
Editorial Profile: KYKN-AM is a commercial station owned by Willamette Broadcasting. The format of the station is news and talk. KYKN-AM broadcasts to the Portland, OR area at 1430 AM.

KYKR-FM
Owner: Clear Channel Media and Entertainment
Editorial: 2885 Interstate 10 E, Beaumont, Texas 77702-1001. **T:** 1 409 896-5555
E: kicker951@clearchannel.com
W: http://www.kykr.com
Editorial Profile: KYKR-FM is a commercial station owned by Clear Channel Media and Entertainment. The format of the station is contemporary country music. KYKR-FM broadcasts in the Beaumont, TX area at 95.1 FM.

KYKS-FM
Owner: Townsquare Media, LLC
Editorial: 1216 S 1st St, Lufkin, Texas 75901.
T: 1 936 639-4455
W: http://www.kicks105.com
Editorial Profile: KYKS-FM is a commercial station owned by Townsquare Media, LLC. The format of the station is country music. KYKS-FM broadcasts to the Lufkin, TX area at 105.1 FM.

KYKX-FM
Owner: Access.1 Communications Corp.
Editorial: 4408 N US Highway 259, Longview, Texas 75605-7703. **T:** 1 903 663-9800
E: studio@kykx.com **W:** http://www.kykx.com
Editorial Profile: KYKX-FM is a commercial station owned by Access.1 Communications Corp. The format of the station is contemporary country. KYKX-FM broadcasts to the Longview, TX area at 105.7 FM.

KYKY-FM
Owner: CBS Radio
Editorial: 1220 Olive St Fl 3, Saint Louis, Missouri 63103-2324. **T:** 1 314 621-2345
W: http://y98.radio.com
Editorial Profile: KYKY-FM is a commercial station owned by CBS Radio. The format of the station is hot adult contemporary music. KYKY-FM broadcasts to the St. Louis area at 98.1 FM.

KYKZ-FM
Owner: Cumulus Media Inc.
Editorial: 425 Broad St, Lake Charles, Louisiana 70601. **T:** 1 337 439-3300
W: http://www.kykz.com
Editorial Profile: KYKZ-FM is a commercial station owned by Cumulus Media Inc. The format is country. The station airs in the Lake Charles, LA area at 96.1 FM.

KYLC-FM
Owner: American Family Association
Editorial: 107 Parkgate Dr, Tupelo, Mississippi 38801. **T:** 1 662 844-8888
E: comments@afr.net **W:** http://www.afr.net

KYLD-FM
Owner: Clear Channel Media and Entertainment
Editorial: 340 Townsend St, San Francisco, California 94107-1633. **T:** 1 415 538-1013
W: http://www.wild949.com
Editorial Profile: KYLD-FM is a commercial station owned by Clear Channel Media and Entertainment. The format of the station is rhythmic Top 40/CHR. KYLD-FM broadcasts to the San Francisco area at 94.9 FM.

KYLS-AM
Owner: Dockins Broadcast Group
Editorial: 235 Business Hh, Piedmont, Missouri 63957-9410. **T:** 1 573 223-4518
Editorial Profile: KYLS-AM is a commercial station owned by Dockins Broadcast Group. The format of the station is classic country. KYLS-AM broadcasts to the Farmington, MO area at 1450 AM.

KYLS-FM
Owner: Dockins Broadcast Group
Editorial: 900 E Karsch Blvd, Farmington, Missouri 63640-3405. **T:** 1 573 701-9590
W: http://froggy96online.com
Editorial Profile: KYLS-FM is a commercial station owned by Dockins Broadcast Group. The format of the station is contemporary country music. KYLS-FM broadcasts in the Farmington, MO area at 95.9 FM.

KYLT-AM
Owner: Cherry Creek Radio
Editorial: 1600 North Ave W, Missoula, Montana 59801. **T:** 1 406 728-5000
Editorial Profile: KYLT-AM is a commercial station owned by Cherry Creek Radio. The format for the station is sports. KYLT-AM broadcasts to the Missoula, MT area at 1340 AM.

KYLV-FM
Owner: Educational Media Foundation
Editorial: 7301 Broadway Ext, Ste 131, Oklahoma City, Oklahoma 73116-9038.
T: 1 405 708-5683 **W:** http://www.klove.com
Editorial Profile: KYLV-FM is a non-commercial station owned by Educational Media Foundation. The format of the station is contemporary Christian. KYLV-FM broadcasts to the Oklahoma City, OK at 88.9 FM.

KYLW-AM
Owner: Sun Mountain Inc.
Editorial: RR 1, Hardin, Montana 59034.
T: 1 406 665-2828
W: http://www.bigskyradio.net

KYMG-FM
Owner: Clear Channel Media and Entertainment
Editorial: 800 E Dimond Blvd, Ste 3-370, Anchorage, Alaska 99515-2058.
T: 1 907 522-1515
W: http://www.magic989fm.com
Editorial Profile: KYMG-FM is a commercial station owned by Clear Channel Media and Entertainment. The format of the station is adult contemporary. KYMG-FM broadcasts to the Anchorage, AK area at 98.9 FM.

KYMN-AM
Owner: NorthField Media
Editorial: 200 Division St S Ste 260, Northfield, Minnesota 55057-2079.
T: 1 507 645-5695 **E:** contact@kymnradio.net
W: http://www.kymnradio.net
Editorial Profile: KYMN-AM is a commercial station owned by NorthField Media. The format of the station is adult standards, oldies and classic country. KYMN-AM broadcasts to the Northfield, MN area at 1080 AM.

KYMO-AM
Owner: Usher Broadcasting Inc.
Editorial: 390 S Highway 102, East Prairie, Missouri 63845. **T:** 1 573 649-3597
Editorial Profile: KYMO-AM is a commercial station owned by Usher Broadcasting Inc. The format of the station is gospel music. KYMO-AM broadcasts to the East Prarie, MO area at 1080 AM.

KYMO-FM
Owner: Usher Broadcasting Inc.
Editorial: 390 S Highway 102, East Prairie, Missouri 63845. **T:** 1 573 649-3597

Editorial Profile: KYMO-FM is a commercial station owned by Usher Broadcasting Inc. The format of the station is oldies music. KYMO-FM broadcasts to the East Prairie, MO area at 105.3 FM.

KYMV-FM
Owner: Broadway Media
Editorial: 515 S 700 E Ste 1C, Salt Lake City, Utah 84102-2802. **T:** 1 801 524-2600
W: http://www.rewind1007.com
Editorial Profile: KYMV-FM is a commercial station owned by Broadway Media. The format of the station is adult contemporary. KYMV-FM broadcasts to the Salt Lake City area at 100.7 FM.

KYMX-FM
Owner: CBS Radio
Editorial: 280 Commerce Cir, Sacramento, California 95815-4212. **T:** 1 916 923-6800
W: http://www.kymx.com
Editorial Profile: KYMX-FM is a commercial station owned by CBS Radio. The format of the station is adult contemporary. KYMX-FM broadcasts to the Sacramento, CA area on 96.1 FM.

KYND-AM
Owner: Provenzano(Matt)
Editorial: 16620 Cypress Rosehill Rd, Cypress, Texas 77429. **T:** 1 713 271-7888
Editorial Profile: KYND-AM is a commercial station owned by Matt Provenzano. The format of the station is variety programming. KYND-AM broadcasts to the Cypress, TX area at 1520 AM.

KYNG-AM
Owner: Cumulus Media Inc.
Editorial: 4209 N Frontage Rd, Fayetteville, Arkansas 72703-5002. **T:** 1 479 521-5566
Editorial Profile: KYNG-AM is a commercial station owned by Cumulus Media Inc. The format of the station is Spanish tropical music. KYNG-AM broadcasts to the Fayetteville, AR area at 1590 AM.

KYNO-AM
Owner: Fat Dawgs 7 Broadcasting LLC
Editorial: 351 W Cromwell Ave Ste 108, Fresno, California 93711-6115.
T: 1 559 447-3570
Editorial Profile: KYNO-AM is a commercial station owned by Fat Dawgs 7 Broadcasting LLC. The format of the station is oldies. KYNO-AM broadcasts to the Fresno, CA area at 1430 AM.

KYNR-AM
Owner: Confederated Tribes of the Yakama Nation
Editorial: 711 King Ln, Toppenish, Washington 98948-1170. **T:** 1 509 865-5363
E: kynr@yakama.com
Editorial Profile: KYNR-AM is a non-commercial station owned by Confederated Tribes of the Yakama Nation. The format of the station is variety. KYNR-AM broadcasts to the Yakima, WA area at 1490 AM.

KYNS-AM
Owner: Mapleton Communications LLC
Editorial: 795 Buckley Rd Ste 2, San Luis Obispo, California 93401-8190.
T: 1 805 786-2570
E: sloradiofeedback@gmail.com
W: http://www.b937slo.com
Editorial Profile: KYNS-AM is a commercial station owned by Mapleton Communications LLC. The format of the station is Soft AC. KYNS-AM broadcasts to the San Luis Obispo, CA area at 1340 AM.

KYNT-AM
Owner: Riverfront Broadcasting
Editorial: 202 W 2nd St, Yankton, South Dakota 57078. **T:** 1 605 665-7892
E: news@kynt1450.com
W: http://www.kynt1450.com
Editorial Profile: KYNT-AM is a commercial station owned by Riverfront Broadcasting. The format of the station is variety. KYNT-AM broadcasts to the Yankton, SD area at 1450 AM.

KYNU-FM
Owner: Ingstad Family Media
Editorial: 2625 8th Ave SW, Jamestown, North Dakota 58401. **T:** 1 701 252-1400
E: bigdog@daktel.com
W: http://www.newsdakota.com
Editorial Profile: KYNU-FM is a commercial station owned by Ingstad Family Media. The format of the station is contemporary country music. KYNU-FM broadcasts to the Jamestown, ND area at 95.5 FM.

KYNW-FM
Owner: Clear Channel Media and Entertainment
Editorial: 645 Elliott Ave W Ste 400, Seattle, Washington 98119-3911. **T:** 1 206 494-2000
W: http://www.1029nowhits.com
Editorial Profile: KYNW-FM is a commercial station owned by Clear Channel Media and Entertainment. The format of the station is Hot AC. KYNW-FM broadcasts to the Centralia, WA area at 102.9 FM.

KYNZ-FM
Owner: LKCM Radio Group LP
Editorial: 1205 Northglen St, Ardmore, Oklahoma 73401-1202. **T:** 1 580 226-0421
E: news@sokradio.com
W: http://www.kynz.com
Editorial Profile: KYNZ-FM is a commercial station owned by LKCM Radio Group LP. The format of the station is oldies music. KYNZ-FM broadcasts to the Ardmore, OK area at 107.1 FM.

KYOE-FM
Owner: Del Mar Trust
Editorial: 135 Hay Pkwy, Point Arena, California 95468. **T:** 1 707 882-2323
Editorial Profile: KYOE-FM is a commercial station owned by Del Mar Trust. The format is country music. KYOE-FM broadcasts to the Point Arene, CA area at 102.3 FM.

KYOO-AM
Owner: KYOO Communications
Editorial: 205 N Pike Ave, Bolivar, Missouri 65613. **T:** 1 417 326-5257
E: kyoo@kyooradio.com
W: http://kyooradio.com
Editorial Profile: KYOO-AM is a commercial station owned by KYOO Communications. The format of the station is contemporary country. KYOO-AM broadcasts in the Bolivar, MO area at 1200 AM.

KYOO-FM
Owner: KYOO Communications
Editorial: 205 N Pike Ave, Bolivar, Missouri 65613-1550. **T:** 1 417 326-5257
E: kyoo@kyooradio.com
W: http://kyooradio.com
Editorial Profile: KYOO-FM is a commercial station owned by KYOO Communications. The format of the station is classic rock. KYOO-AM broadcasts in the Bolivar, MO area at 99.1 FM.

KYOS-AM
Owner: Mapleton Radio, LLC
Editorial: 1020 W Main St, Merced, California 95340-4521. **T:** 1 209 723-2192
E: kyos@radiomerced.com
W: http://www.1480kyos.com
Editorial Profile: KYOS-AM is a commercial station owned by Mapleton Radio, LLC. The format of the station is news and talk. KYOS-AM broadcasts to the Merced, CA area at 1480 AM.

KYOT-FM
Owner: Clear Channel Media and Entertainment
Editorial: 4686 E Van Buren St Ste 300, Phoenix, Arizona 85008-6967.
T: 1 602 374-6000
W: http://www.955themountain.com/main.html
Editorial Profile: KYOT-FM is a commercial station owned by Clear Channel Media and Entertainment. The format of the station is adult hits. KYOT-FM broadcasts to the Phoenix area at 95.5 FM.

KYOX-FM
Owner: Cherry Creek Radio
Editorial: 218 N Austin St, Comanche, Texas 76442-2429. **T:** 1 325 356-3090
Editorial Profile: KYOX-FM is a commercial station owned by Cherry Creek Radio. The format of the station is classic rock music. KYOX-FM broadcasts to the Comanche, TX area at 94.3 FM.

KYOY-FM
Owner: Proshop Radio Broadcasting LLC
Editorial: 2232 Dell Range Blvd, Ste 102, Cheyenne, Wyoming 82009-4903.
T: 1 307 637-0301 **W:** http://www.kyoy.net
Editorial Profile: KYOY-FM is a commercial station owned by Proshop Radio Broadcasting LLC. The format for the station is classic hits. KYOY-FM broadcasts to the Kimball, NE area at 92.3 FM.

KYPA-AM
Owner: Multicultural Radio Broadcasting Inc.
Editorial: 747 E Green St, Pasadena, California 91101-2145. **T:** 1 213 487-1300

Editorial Profile: KYPA-AM is a commercial station owned by Multicultural Radio Broadcasting Inc. The format of the station is Korean variety. KYPA-AM broadcasts to the Pasadena, CA area at 1540 AM.

KYPC-FM
Owner: Montana State University-Billings
Editorial: 1500 University Dr, Billings, Montana 59101-0245. **T:** 1 406 657-2941
W: http://www.ypradio.org
Editorial Profile: KYPC-FM is a non-commercial station owned by Montana State University-Billings. The format of the station is public affairs and news and folk, jazz, and classical music. KYPC-FM broadcasts in the Colstrip, MT area at 89.9 FM.

KYPF-FM
Owner: Montana State University-Billings
Editorial: 1500 University Dr, Billings, Montana 59101-0245. **T:** 1 406 657-2941
E: mail@ypradio.org
W: http://www.ypradio.org
Editorial Profile: KYPF-FM is a non-commercial station owned by Montana State University-Billings. The format of the station is news and folk, jazz, and classical music. KYPF-FM broadcasts in the Stanford, MT area at 89.5 FM.

KYPL-FM
Owner: Growing Christian Foundation
Editorial: 606 N Western Ave, Wenatchee, Washington 98801-1204. **T:** 1 509 457-0725
E: kypl@plr.org **W:** http://www.plr.org
Editorial Profile: KYPL-FM is a non-commercial station owned by Growing Christian Foundation. The format of the station is contemporary Christian. KYPL-FM broadcasts to the Yakima, WA area at 91.1 FM.

KYPW-FM
Owner: Montana State University-Billings
Editorial: 1500 University Dr, Billings, Montana 59101-0245. **T:** 1 406 657-2941
E: mail@ypradio.org
W: http://www.ypradio.org
Editorial Profile: KYPW-FM is a non-commercial station owned by Montana State University-Billings. The format of the station is news and folk, jazz, and classical music. KYPW-FM broadcasts in the Stanford, MT area at 88.3 FM.

KYPY-FM
Owner: Guaranty Broadcasting
Editorial: 929B Government St, Baton Rouge, Louisiana 70802-6033. **T:** 1 225 388-9898
W: http://www.1045espn.com
Editorial Profile: KYPY-FM is a commercial station owned by Guaranty Broadcasting. The format of the station is sports. KNXX-FM broadcasts to the Baton Rouge, LA area at 104.9 FM.

KYQQ-FM
Owner: Journal Broadcast Group
Editorial: 4200 N Old Lawrence Rd, Wichita, Kansas 67219. **T:** 1 316 838-9141
E: news@kfdi.com
W: http://www.radiolobo1065.com
Editorial Profile: KYQQ-FM is a commercial station owned by Journal Broadcast Group. The format of the station is regional Mexican. KYQQ-FM broadcasts to the Wichita, KS area on 106.5 FM.

KYQX-FM
Owner: CSSI Non-Profit Educational Broadcasting Corporation
Editorial: 1612 S Main St, Weatherford, Texas 76086. **T:** 1 817 341-8950
E: qxfmnews@yahoo.com
W: http://www.qxfm.com
Editorial Profile: KYQX-FM is a non-commercial station owned by CSSI Non-Profit Educational Broadcasting Corporation. The format of the station is Lite Rock/Lite AC. KYQX-FM broadcasts to the Weatherford, TX area at 89.5 FM.

KYRK-FM
Owner: Withers Family Texas Holdings
Editorial: 4659 Everhart Rd Ste 102, Corpus Christi, Texas 78411-2772. **T:** 1 361 334-4961
W: http://www.1065theshark.com
Editorial Profile: KYRK-FM is a commercial station owned by Withers Family Texas Holdings and operated by Bogey Broadcasting. The format of the station is classic rock, with a focus on the late 1970s - 1990s. KYRK-FM broadcasts to the Corpus Christi, TX area at a frequency of 106.5 FM.

KYRM-FM
Owner: World Radio Network, Inc.
Editorial: 2690 S 3rd Ave, Yuma, Arizona 85364. **T:** 1 928 341-0919
E: manantialyuma@yahoo.com
W: http://www.manantialyuma.org
Editorial Profile: KYRM-FM is a non-commercial station owned by World Radio Network, Inc. The format is Hispanic religious programming. KYRM-FM broadcasts to the Yuma, AZ area at 91.9 FM.

KYRS-FM
Owner: Thin Air Community Radio
Editorial: 35 W Main Ave Ste 340, Spokane, Washington 99201-0119. **T:** 1 509 747-3012
W: http://www.kyrs.org
Editorial Profile: KYRS-FM is a non-commercial community station owned by Thin Air Community Radio. The format of the station is variety, with a mix of news, music and locally produced programs. KYRS-FM broadcasts to the Spokane, WA area at a frequency of 88.1 FM.

KYSC-FM
Owner: Tanana Valley Radio, LLC
Editorial: 3650 Braddock St, Fairbanks, Alaska 99701-7617. **T:** 1 907 452-3697
W: http://www.tvtv.com
Editorial Profile: KYSC-FM is a commercial station owned by Tanana Valley Radio, LLC. The format of the station is classic hits. KYSC-FM broadcasts to the Fairbanks, AK area at 96.9 FM.

KYSE-FM
Owner: Entravision Communications Corp.
Editorial: 5426 N Mesa St, El Paso, Texas 79912-5421. **T:** 1 915 581-1126
W: http://www.elgato947.com
Editorial Profile: KYSE-FM is a commercial station owned by Entravision Communications Corp. The format of the station is regional Mexican. KYSE-FM broadcasts to the El Paso, TX area at 94.7 FM.

KYSJ-FM
Owner: Lighthouse Radio Group
Editorial: 580 Kingwood Ave, Coos Bay, Oregon 97420. **T:** 1 541 266-8531
E: klight1978@live.com
W: http://www.lighthouseradio.com/kysj/
Editorial Profile: KYSJ-FM is a commercial station owned by Lighthouse Radio Group. The format of the station is smooth AC. KYSJ-FM broadcasts to the Coos Bay, OR area at 105.9 FM.

KYSL-FM
Owner: Krystal Broadcasting
Editorial: 701 East Anemone Trail, #203, Dillon, Colorado 80435. **T:** 1 970 513-9393
E: krystalnews@krystal93.com
W: http://www.krystal93.com
Editorial Profile: KYSL-FM is a commercial station owned by Krystal Broadcasting. The format of the station is adult album alternative. KYSL-FM broadcasts to the Dillon, CO area at 93.9 FM.

KYSM-AM
Owner: Radio Mankato
Editorial: 59346 Madison Ave, Mankato, Minnesota 56001-8518. **T:** 1 507 345-4537
E: news@ktoe.com
W: http://www.radiomankato.com
Editorial Profile: KYSM-AM is a commercial station owned by Radio Mankato. The format of the station is sports and news. KYSM-AM broadcasts to the North Mankato, MN area at 1230 AM.

KYSM-FM
Owner: Three Eagles Communications Co.
Editorial: 1807 Lee Blvd, North Mankato, Minnesota 56003. **T:** 1 507 345-4646
W: http://www.country103.com
Editorial Profile: KYSM-FM is a commercial station owned by Three Eagles Communications Co. The format of the station is country. KYSM-FM broadcasts to the North Mankato, MN area at 103.5 FM.

KYSN-FM
Owner: Cherry Creek Radio
Editorial: 231 N Wenatchee Ave, Wenatchee, Washington 98801-2009. **T:** 1 509 665-6565
E: newswenatchee@cherrycreekradio.com
W: http://www.kysn.com
Editorial Profile: KYSN-FM is a commercial station owned by Cherry Creek Radio. The format of the station is country music. KYSN-FM broadcasts in the Seattle area at 97.7 FM.

KYSR-FM
Owner: Clear Channel Media and Entertainment
Editorial: 3400 W Olive Ave, Burbank, California 91505-5538. **T:** 1 818 559-2252
W: http://www.987fm.com
Editorial Profile: KYSR-FM is a commercial station owned by Clear Channel Media and Entertainment. The format of the station is rock alternative. KYSR-FM broadcasts to the Los Angeles area at 98.7 FM.

KYSS-FM
Owner: Townsquare Media, LLC
Editorial: 3250 S Reserve St Ste 200, Missoula, Montana 59801-8236.
T: 1 406 728-9300
E: realcountry@kyssfm.com
W: http://www.kyssfm.com
Editorial Profile: KYSS-FM is a commercial station owned by Townsquare Media, LLC. The format of the station is contemporary country. KYSS-FM broadcasts to the Missoula, MT area at 94.9 FM.

KYST-AM
Owner: Velasquez(Cruz)
Editorial: 7322 Southwest Fwy, Ste 500, Houston, Texas 77074. **T:** 1 713 779-9292
Editorial Profile: KYST-AM is a commercial station owned by Cruz Velasquez. The format of the station is Hispanic talk programming. KYST-AM broadcasts to the Houston area at 920 AM.

KYSX-FM
Owner: BMG Billings
Editorial: 2425 King Ave W Ste B, Billings, Montana 59102-6460. **T:** 1 406 281-8925
E: psa@mojo925.com
Editorial Profile: KYSX-FM is a commercial station owned by BMG Billings. The format of the station is classic country. KYSX-FM broadcasts to the Billings, MT area at 105.1 FM.

KYTC-FM
Owner: Three Eagles Communications Co.
Editorial: 341 S Yorktown Pike, Mason City, Iowa 50401-4533. **T:** 1 641 423-1300
W: http://www.discovernorthiowa.com
Editorial Profile: KYTC-FM is a commercial station owned by Three Eagles Communications Co. The format of the station is classic hits. KYTC-FM broadcasts to the Mason City, IA area at 102.7 FM.

KYTE-FM
Owner: Yaquina Bay Communications Inc.
Editorial: 906 SW Alder St, Newport, Oregon 97365. **T:** 1 541 265-2266
E: news@ybcradio.com
W: http://www.kytefm.com
Editorial Profile: KYTE-FM is a commercial station owned by Yaquina Bay Communications Inc. The format of the station is hot adult contemporary music. KYTE-FM broadcasts to Newport, OR, at 102.7 FM.

KYTI-FM
Owner: Lovcom, Inc.
Editorial: 1716 Kroe Ln, Sheridan, Wyoming 82801-9681. **T:** 1 307 672-7421
E: news@sheridanmedia.com
W: http://www.sheridanmedia.com
Editorial Profile: KYTI-FM is a commercial station owned by Lovcom, Inc. The format of the station is contemporary country. KYTI-FM broadcasts to the Sheridan, WY area at 93.7 FM.

KYTN-FM
Owner: Thunderbolt Broadcasting Co.
Editorial: 223 West Gate Dr, Union City, Tennessee 38261-5044. **T:** 1 731 885-0051
E: newsroom@unioncityradio.com
W: http://www.wcmt.com
Editorial Profile: KYTN-FM is a commercial station owned by Thunderbolt Broadcasting Co. The format of the station is country. KYTN-FM broadcasts to the Union City, TN area at 104.9 FM.

KYTT-FM
Owner: Lighthouse Radio Group
Editorial: 580 Kingwood Ave, Coos Bay, Oregon 97420. **T:** 1 541 269-2022
E: klight1978@live.com
W: http://www.lighthouseradio.com
Editorial Profile: KYTT-FM is a commercial station owned by Lighthouse Radio Group. The format of the station is contemporary Christian music. KYTT-FM broadcasts in the Coos Bay, OR at 98.7 FM.

KYTZ-FM
Owner: Simmons Media Group

Editorial: 1403 3rd St, Langdon, North Dakota 58249-2232. **T:** 1 701 256-1080
W: http://www.thevalleysbiggesthits.com
Editorial Profile: KYTZ-FM is a commercial station owned by Simmons Media Group. The format of the station is hot adult contemporary. KYTZ-FM broadcasts to the Langdon, ND area at 106.7 FM.

KYUK-AM
Owner: Bethel Broadcasting Inc.
Editorial: 640 Radio St, Bethel, Alaska 99559-9999. **T:** 1 907 543-3131
E: webmaster@kyuk.org
W: http://www.kyuk.org
Editorial Profile: KYUK-AM is a non-commercial station owned by Bethel Broadcasting Inc. The format of the station is news and talk programming and a variety of music. KYUK-AM broadcasts to the Bethel, AK area at 640 AM.

KYUN-FM
Owner: Locally Owned Radio, LLC
Editorial: 21361 Highway 30, Twin Falls, Idaho 83301. **T:** 1 208 735-8300
W: http://www.106thecanyon.com
Editorial Profile: KYUN-FM is a commercial station owned by Locally Owned Radio, LLC. The format of the station is country music. KYUN-FM broadcasts to the Twin Falls, ID area at 106.7 FM.

KYUS-FM
Owner: Custer County Broadcasting Inc.
Editorial: 508 Main St, Miles City, Montana 59301. **T:** 1 406 234-5626
W: http://www.kyuskmta.com
Editorial Profile: KYUS-FM is a commercial station owned by Custer County Broadcasting Inc. The format of the station is adult hits. KYUS-FM's broadcasts in the Miles City, MT area at 92.3 FM.

KYVA-AM
Owner: Millennium Media Inc.
Editorial: 300 W Aztec Ave, Gallup, New Mexico 87301-6304. **T:** 1 505 863-6851
E: mm1@cia-g.com
W: http://www.gallupradio.com
Editorial Profile: KYVA-AM is a commercial station owned by Millennium Media Inc. The format of the station is oldies. KYVA-AM broadcasts to the Albuquerque, NM area at 1230 AM.

KYVA-FM
Owner: Millennium Media Inc.
Editorial: 300 W Aztec Ave Ste 200, Gallup, New Mexico 87301-6304. **T:** 1 505 863-6851
E: mm1@cia-g.com
W: http://www.gallupradio.com
Editorial Profile: KYVA-FM is a commercial station owned by Millennium Media Inc. The format of the station is classic hits. KYVA-FM broadcasts to the Gallup, NM area at 103.7 FM.

KYWA-FM
Owner: WAY Media Inc.
Editorial: 110 S Main St, Wichita, Kansas 67202-3700. **T:** 1 316 831-0907
E: impactwichita@wayfm.com
W: http://kywa.wayfm.com
Editorial Profile: KYWA-FM is a non-commercial station owned by WAY Media Inc. The format of the station is contemporary Christian music. KYWA-FM broadcasts to the Wichita, KS area at 90.7 FM.

KYW-AM
Owner: CBS Radio
Editorial: 1555 Hamilton St, Philadelphia, Pennsylvania 19130-4085. **T:** 1 215 238-1060
E: newstips@kyw1060info.com
W: http://philadelphia.cbslocal.com/station/kyw-newsradio
Editorial Profile: KYW-AM is a commercial station owned by CBS Radio. The format of the station is news. KYW-AM broadcasts to the Philadelphia area at 1060 AM.

KYWD-FM
Owner: Clear Channel Media and Entertainment
Editorial: 3202 N Oracle Rd, Tucson, Arizona 85705-3820. **T:** 1 520 618-2100
W: http://www.wildcountry971.com
Editorial Profile: KYWD-FM is a commercial station owned by Clear Channel Media and Entertainment. The format of the station is contemporary country. KYWD-FM broadcasts to the Tucson, AZ area at 97.1 FM.

KYXK-FM
Owner: Southwest Arkansas Media, LLC

Editorial: 601 S 7th St, Arkadelphia, Arkansas 71923-6209. **T:** 1 870 246-9272
W: http://www.arkadelphiaradio.com
Editorial Profile: KYXK-FM is a commercial station owned by Southwest Arkansas Media, LLC. The format of the station is contemporary country. KYXK-FM broadcasts in the Arkadelphia, AR area at 106.9 FM.

KYXX-FM
Owner: Revolution Broadcast Co.
Editorial: 2125 Sidney Baker St, Kerrville, Texas 78028-2551. **T:** 1 830 896-1230
W: http://www.revfmradio.com
Editorial Profile: KYXX-FM is a commercial station owned by Revolution Broadcast Co. The format for the station is classic country. KYXX-FM broadcasts to the Ozona, TX area at 94.3 AM.

KYXY-FM
Owner: CBS Radio
Editorial: 8033 Linda Vista Rd, San Diego, California 92111. **T:** 1 858 571-7600
W: http://www.kyxy.com
Editorial Profile: KYXY-FM is a commercial station owned by CBS Radio. The format of the station is Lite Rock/Lite AC music. KYXY-FM broadcasts to the San Diego area at 96.5 FM.

KYYA-AM
Owner: Connoisseur Media, Inc.
Editorial: 2075 Central Ave, Billings, Montana 59102. **T:** 1 406 652-8400
Editorial Profile: KYYA-AM is a commercial station owned by Connoisseur Media, Inc.. The format of the station is news and talk. KYYA-AM broadcasts in the Billings, MT area at 730 AM.

KYYI-FM
Owner: Cumulus Media Inc.
Editorial: 4302 Call Field Rd, Wichita Falls, Texas 76308. **T:** 1 940 691-2311
W: http://www.bear104.com
Editorial Profile: KYYI-FM is a commercial station owned by Cumulus Media Inc. The format of the station is classic rock music. KYYI-FM broadcasts to the Wichita Falls, TX area at 104.7 FM.

KYYK-FM
Owner: Tomlinson-Leis Communications L.P.
Editorial: 800 W Palestine Ave, Palestine, Texas 75801. **T:** 1 903 729-6077
W: http://www.youreasttexas.com
Editorial Profile: KYYK-FM is a commercial station owned by Tomlinson-Leis Communications L.P. The format of the station is contemporary country. KYYK-FM broadcasts in the Palestine, TX area at 98.3 FM.

KYYO-FM
Owner: KGY Inc.
Editorial: 1700 Marine Dr NE, Olympia, Washington 98501-6908. **T:** 1 253 254-6096
W: http://www.kayo.fm
Editorial Profile: KYYO-FM is a commercial station owned by KGY Inc. The format of the station is country music. KYYO-FM broadcasts to the Seattle area at 96.9 FM.

KYYS-AM
Owner: Entercom Communications Corp.
Editorial: 813 S 7th St, Kansas City, Kansas 66105-2003. **T:** 1 913 788-1255
W: http://www.lasuperx1250.com
Editorial Profile: KYYS-AM is a commercial station owned by Entercom Communications Corp. The format of the station is regional Mexican music. KYYS-AM broadcasts to the Kansas City, MO area at 1250 AM.

KYYT-FM
Owner: Haystack Broadcasting, Inc
Editorial: 620 E 3rd St, The Dalles, Oregon 97058-2506. **T:** 1 541 296-9102
W: http://haystackbroadcasting.com
Editorial Profile: KYYT-FM is a commercial station owned by Haystack Broadcasting, Inc. The format of the station is country. KYYT-FM broadcasts to The Dalles, OR area at 102.3 FM.

KYYW-AM
Owner: Townsquare Media, LLC
Editorial: 3911 S 1st St, Abilene, Texas 79605. **T:** 1 325 676-7711
W: http://1470kyyw.com
Editorial Profile: KYYW-AM is a commercial station owned by Townsquare Media, LLC. The format of the station is news/talk. KYYW-AM broadcasts to the Abilene, TX area at a frequency of 1470 AM.

KYYX-FM

Owner: Clear Channel Media and Entertainment
Editorial: 1000 20th Ave SW, Minot, North Dakota 58701. **T:** 1 701 852-4646
W: http://www.97kicksfm.com
Editorial Profile: KYYX-FM is a commercial station owned by Clear Channel Media and Entertainment. The format of the station is contemporary country. KYYX-FM broadcasts to the Minot-Bismarck, ND area at 97.1 FM.

KYYY-FM

Owner: Clear Channel Media and Entertainment
Editorial: 3500 E Rosser Ave, Bismarck, North Dakota 58501-3376. **T:** 1 701 255-1234
E: y93@y93.fm **W:** http://www.y93.fm
Editorial Profile: KYYY-FM is a commercial station owned by Clear Channel Media and Entertainment. The format of the station is top 40. KYYY-FM broadcasts to the Bismarck, ND area at 92.9 FM.

KYYZ-FM

Owner: Cherry Creek Radio
Editorial: 410 6th St E, Williston, North Dakota 58801. **T:** 1 701 572-5371
W: http://www.kyyzradio.com
Editorial Profile: KYYZ-FM is a commercial station owned by Cherry Creek Radio. The format of the station is contemporary country. KYYZ-FM broadcasts to the Williston, ND area at 96.1 FM.

KYZK-FM

Owner: Rich Broadcasting, LLC.
Editorial: 201 S Main St, Hailey, Idaho 83333-8406. **T:** 1 208 788-7118
E: kech95@cox-internet.com

KYZS-AM

Owner: Gleiser Communications LLC
Editorial: 1001 E Southeast Loop 323, Tyler, Texas 75701-9664. **T:** 1 903 593-2519
E: news@ktbb.com **W:** http://www.ktbb.com
Editorial Profile: KYZS-AM is a commercial station owned by Gleiser Communications LLC. The format of the station is Spanish sports. KYZS-AM broadcasts to the Tyler, TX area at 1490 AM.

KZAL-FM

Owner: Icicle Broadcasting, Inc.
Editorial: 123 E Johnson Ave, Chelan, Washington 98816-9904. **T:** 1 509 682-4033
E: znation@zcountry947.com
W: http://www.zcountry947.com
Editorial Profile: KZAL-FM is a commercial station owned by Icicle Broadcasting, Inc. The format of the station is contemporary country. KZAL-FM broadcasts to the Chelan, WA area at 94.7 FM.

KZAP-AM

Owner: Mapleton of Chico, LLC
Editorial: 1459 Humboldt Rd, Ste D, Chico, California 95928. **T:** 1 530 899-3600
W: http://www.kpig.com
Editorial Profile: KZAP-AM is a commercial station owned by Mapleton of Chico, LLC. The format of the station is adult album alternative. KZAP-AM broadcasts to the San Francisco area at 1510 AM and simulcasts the programming of KPIG-FM in Watsonville, CA.

KZAP-FM

Owner: Mapleton Communications LLC
Editorial: 1459 Humboldt Rd, Ste D, Chico, California 95928. **T:** 1 530 899-3600
Editorial Profile: KZAP-FM is a commercial station owned by Mapleton Communications LLC. The format of the station is classic hits. KZAP-FM broadcasts to the Chico, CA area at 96.7 FM.

KZAR-FM

Owner: Rawhide Radio, LLC
Editorial: 12451 Network Blvd, San Antonio, Texas 78249. **T:** 1 210 610-4141
E: myparty977@gmail.com
Editorial Profile: KZAR-FM is a commercial station owned by Rawhide Radio, LLC. The format of the station is Top 40/CHR. KZAR-FM broadcasts from the San Antonio area at 97.7 FM.

KZAT-FM

Owner: Camrory Broadcasting
Editorial: 205 W 3rd St, Tama, Iowa 52339. **T:** 1 641 484-5958
W: http://www.radioz955fm.com
Editorial Profile: KZAT-FM is a commercial station owned by Camrory Broadcasting. The format for the station is Spanish AC. KZAT-FM broadcasts to the Cedar Rapids, IA area at 95.5 FM.

KZAZ-FM

Owner: Washington State University
Editorial: Murrow Center, Room 382, Pullman, Washington 99164. **T:** 1 509 335-6500
E: nwpr@wsu.edu **W:** http://www.nwpr.org
Editorial Profile: KZAZ-FM is a non-commercial station owned by Washington State University. The format of the station is classical music and news. KZAZ-FM broadcasts to the Bellingham, WA area at 91.7 FM.

KZBB-FM

Owner: Clear Channel Media and Entertainment
Editorial: 311 Lexington Ave, Fort Smith, Arkansas 72901-3842. **T:** 1 479 782-8888
E: b98@kzbb.com **W:** http://www.kzbb.com
Editorial Profile: KZBB-FM is a commercial station owned by Clear Channel Media and Entertainment. The format of the station is Hot AC. KZBB-FM broadcasts to the Fort Smith, AR area at 97.9 FM.

KZBD-FM

Owner: Mapleton Communications LLC
Editorial: 1601 E 57th Ave, Spokane, Washington 99223. **T:** 1 509 448-1000
W: http://www.now1057fm.com
Editorial Profile: KZBD-FM is a commercial station owned by Mapleton Communications LLC. The format of the station is Top 40/CHR. KZBD-FM broadcasts to the Spokane, WA area at 105.7 FM.

KZBE-FM

Owner: North Cascades Broadcasting
Editorial: 320 Emery Dr, Omak, Washington 98841-9237. **T:** 1 509 826-0100
E: news@komw.net **W:** http://www.komw.net
Editorial Profile: KZBE-FM is a commercial station owned by North Cascades Broadcasting. The format of the station is adult contemporary. KZBE-FM broadcasts to the Spokane, WA area at 104.3 FM.

KZBK-FM

Owner: Best Broadcast Group
Editorial: 107 S Main St, Brookfield, Missouri 64628. **T:** 1 660 258-3383
E: kzbk@bestbroadcastgroup.com
W: http://www.kzbkradio.com
Editorial Profile: KZBK-FM is a commercial station owned by Best Broadcast Group. The format of the station is hot adult contemporary music. KZBK-FM broadcasts to the Kansas City, MO area at 96.9 FM.

KZBL-FM

Owner: Baldridge-Dumas Communications Inc.
Editorial: 400 Jefferson St, Natchitoches, Louisiana 71457. **T:** 1 318 352-9696
E: production@bdcradio.com
W: http://www.bdcradio.com
Editorial Profile: KZBL-FM is a commercial station owned by Baldridge-Dumas Communications Inc. The format of the station is oldies music. KZBL-FM broadcasts to the Shreveport, LA area at 100.7 FM.

KZBQ-FM

Owner: Idaho Wireless Corp.
Editorial: 436 N Main St, Pocatello, Idaho 83204. **T:** 1 208 234-1290 **E:** spots@kzbq.com
W: http://www.kzbq.com
Editorial Profile: KZBQ-FM is a commercial station owned by Idaho Wireless Corp. The format of the station is country. KZBQ-FM broadcasts to the Pocatello, ID area at 93.9 FM.

KZBT-FM

Owner: Townsquare Media, LLC
Editorial: 11300 State Highway 191 Bldg 2, Midland, Texas 79707-1367.
T: 1 432 563-9300 **W:** http://www.b93.net
Editorial Profile: KZBT-FM is a commercial station owned by Townsquare Media, LLC. The format of the station is urban contemporary. KZBT-FM broadcasts to the Midland, TX area at 92.3 FM.

KZCD-FM

Owner: Townsquare Media, LLC
Editorial: 626 SW D Ave, Lawton, Oklahoma 73501. **T:** 1 580 581-3600
E: lawtonpsa@townsquaremedia.com
W: http://www.z94.com
Editorial Profile: KZCD-FM is a commercial station owned by Townsquare Media, LLC. The format of the station is new and classic rock music. KZCD-FM broadcasts to the Lawton, OK area at 94.1 FM.

KZCH-FM

Owner: Clear Channel Media and Entertainment
Editorial: 9323 E 37th St N, Wichita, Kansas 67226-2000. **T:** 1 316 494-6600
E: wichitanews@clearchannel.com
W: http://www.channel963.com
Editorial Profile: KZCH-FM is a commercial station owned by Clear Channel Media and Entertainment. The format of the station is Top 40/CHR. KZCH-FM broadcasts to the Wichita, KS area at 96.3 FM.

KZCR-FM

Owner: Results Radio Group
Editorial: 728 Western Ave, Fergus Falls, Minnesota 56537-1095. **T:** 1 218 736-7596
E: contactus@lakesradio.net
W: http://www.lakesradio.net
Editorial Profile: KZCR-FM is a commercial station owned by Results Radio Group. The format of the station is rock music. KZCR-FM broadcasts to the Fergus Falls, MN area at 103.3 FM.

KZDC-AM

Owner: L & L Broadcasting
Editorial: 4050 Eisenhauer Rd, San Antonio, Texas 78218-3409. **T:** 1 210 654-5100
W: http://www.espnsa.com
Editorial Profile: KZDC-AM is a commercial station owned by L & L Broadcasting. The format of the station is sports. KZDC-AM broadcasts to the San Antonio area at 1250 AM.

KZDG-AM

Owner: CBS Radio
Editorial: 40931 Fremont Blvd, Fremont, California 94538-4307. **T:** 1 510 200-4991
E: contact@radiozindagi.com
W: http://www.radiozindagi.com
Editorial Profile: KZDG-AM is a commercial station owned by CBS Radio and managed by CinéMaya Media. The format of the station is South Asian and Indian talk and music programming. KZDG-AM broadcasts to the San Francisco Bay area at 1550 AM.

KZDV-FM

Owner: Payne Radio Group
Editorial: 1600 W Jackson St, Hugo, Oklahoma 74743-5653. **T:** 1 580 326-2555
W: http://payneradiogroup.com/
Editorial Profile: KZDV-FM is a commercial station owned by Payne Radio Group. The format for the station is Contemporary Christian. KZDV-FM broadcasts to the Hugo, OK area at 99.5 FM.

KZDX-FM

Owner: Lee Family Broadcasting
Editorial: 113 Shoshone St N, Twin Falls, Idaho 83301-6150. **T:** 1 208 436-4757
W: http://www.hot100now.com
Editorial Profile: KZDX-FM is a commercial station owned by Lee Family Broadcasting. The format of the station is Top 40/CHR. KZDX-FM broadcasts to the Rupert, ID area at 99.9 FM.

KZDY-FM

Owner: Dierking Communications
Editorial: 1937 Highway 24, Glen Elder, Kansas 67446-9461. **T:** 1 785 545-3220
E: kdnskzdy@nckcn.com
W: http://kdcountry94.com

KZEL-FM

Owner: Cumulus Media Inc.
Editorial: 1200 Executive Pkwy, Ste 440, Eugene, Oregon 97401. **T:** 1 541 284-8500
W: http://www.96kzel.com
Editorial Profile: KZEL-FM is a commercial station owned by Cumulus Media Inc. The format of the station is classic rock music. KZEL-FM broadcasts to the Eugene, OR area at 96.1 FM.

KZEN-FM

Owner: Three Eagles Communications Co.
Editorial: 1418 25th St, Columbus, Nebraska 68601. **T:** 1 402 564-2866
E: newskzen@kzen.threeeagles.com
W: http://www.mycentralnebraska.com
Editorial Profile: KZEN-FM is a commercial station owned by Three Eagles Communications Co. The format of the station is classic and contemporary country music. KZEN-FM broadcasts to the Columbus, NE area at 100.3 FM.

KZEP-FM

Owner: Clear Channel Media and Entertainment
Editorial: 6222 W IH 10, San Antonio, Texas 78201-2013. **T:** 1 210 736-9700
W: http://www.kzep.com
Editorial Profile: KZEP-FM is a commercial station owned by Clear Channel Media and Entertainment. The format of the station is classic rock. KZEP-FM broadcasts to the San Antonio area at 104.5 FM.

KZER-AM

Owner: Lazer Broadcasting Corp.
Editorial: 1330 Cacique St, Santa Barbara, California 93103-3505. **T:** 1 805 240-2070
E: lazerbroadcasting@radiolazer.com
W: http://www.radiolazer.com
Editorial Profile: KZER-AM is a commercial station owned by Lazer Broadcasting Corp. The format of the station is regional Mexican. KZER-AM broadcasts to the Santa Barbara, CA area at 1250 AM.

KZEW-FM

Owner: Smith Broadcasting Inc.
Editorial: 450 Cole St, Wheatland, Wyoming 82201. **T:** 1 307 322-5926
E: kzew@communicomm.com
Editorial Profile: KZEW-FM is a commercial station owned by Smith Broadcasting Inc. The format of the station is adult contemporary. KZEW-FM broadcasts to the Wheatland, WY area at 101.7 FM.

KZFM-FM

Owner: Malkan Interactive Communications
Editorial: 2117 Leopard St, Corpus Christi, Texas 78408. **T:** 1 361 883-3516
E: kzfm@bizstx.rr.com
W: http://www.hotz95.com
Editorial Profile: KZFM-FM is a commercial station owned by Malkan Interactive Communications. The format of the station is hot adult contemporary. KZFM-FM broadcasts to the Corpus Christi, TX area at 95.5 FM.

KZFN-FM

Owner: Ida-Vend Communications Group
Editorial: 1114 N Almon St, Moscow, Idaho 83843. **T:** 1 208 882-2551
Editorial Profile: KZFN-FM is a commercial station owned by Ida-Vend Communications Group. The format for the station is Top 40/CHR. KZFN-FM broadcasts to the Moscow, ID area at 106.1 FM.

KZFR-FM

Owner: Golden Valley Comm. Broadcast
Editorial: 341 Broadway St, Chico, California 95928-5342. **T:** 1 530 895-0706
W: http://kzfr.org
Editorial Profile: KZFR-FM is a non-commercial station owned by Golden Valley Comm. Broadcast. The format of the station is variety. KZFR-FM broadcasts to the Chico, CA area at 90.1 FM.

KZFS-AM

Owner: Clear Channel Media and Entertainment
Editorial: 808 E Sprague Ave, Spokane, Washington 99202-2126. **T:** 1 509 242-2400
W: http://www.1280foxsports.com
Editorial Profile: KZFS-AM is a commercial station owned by Clear Channel Media and Entertainment. The format of the station is sports. KZFS-AM broadcasts to the Spokane, WA area at 590 AM.

KZGF-FM

Owner: Leighton Enterprises Inc.
Editorial: 1185 9th St NE, Thompson, North Dakota 58278. **T:** 1 701 775-4611
E: live@z947.com **W:** http://z947.com
Editorial Profile: KZGF-FM is a commercial station owned by Leighton Enterprises Inc. The format of the station is Top 40/CHR. KZGF-FM broadcasts to the Thompson, ND area at 94.7 FM.

KZGL-FM

Owner: Walker Radio, Inc.
Editorial: 4650 N US Highway 89 Ste A8, Flagstaff, Arizona 86004-2446.
T: 1 928 779-1800
W: http://www.eaglerocksonline.com
Editorial Profile: KZGL-FM is a commercial station owned by Walker Radio, Inc. The format of the station is rock. KZGL-FM broadcasts to the Flagstaff, AZ area at 103.7 FM.

KZGM-FM

Owner: Real Community Radio Network, Inc
Editorial: 1211 Ozark St, Cabool, Missouri 65689-7412. **T:** 1 417 962-4888
E: radio@kz88.org **W:** http://www.kz88.org
Editorial Profile: KZGM-FM is a non-commercial station owned by Real Community Radio Network, Inc. The format of the station is variety. KZGM-FM broadcasts to the Springfield, MO area at 88.1 FM.

KZHE-FM
Owner: A-1 Communications
Editorial: 406 W Union, Magnolia, Arkansas 71753-2747. **T:** 1 870 234-7790
E: kzhe@kzhe.com **W:** http://www.kzhe.com
Editorial Profile: KZHE-FM is a commercial station owned by A-1 Communications. The format of the station is classic and contemporary country. KZHE-FM broadcasts to the Magnolia, AR area at 100.5 FM.

KZHK-FM
Owner: Canyon Media Corporation
Editorial: 619 S. Bluff Tower 1 Ste. 300, Saint George, Utah 84780. **T:** 1 435 628-3643
W: http://www.959thehawk.com
Editorial Profile: KZHK-FM is a commercial station owned by Canyon Media Corporation. The format for the station is classic rock. KZHK-FM broadcasts to the St. George, UT area at 95.9 FM.

KZHN-AM
Owner: Eiffel Tower Broadcasting
Editorial: 402 Munson Place, Ste 111, Rockwall, Texas 75087. **T:** 1 903 784-1234
E: txn1250@gmail.com
W: http://www.txn1250.com
Editorial Profile: KZHN-AM is a commercial station owned by Eiffel Tower Broadcasting. The format of the station is classic country music. KZHN-AM broadcasts to the Paris, TX area at 1250 AM.

KZHR-FM
Owner: Cherry Creek Radio
Editorial: 2823 W Lewis St, Pasco, Washington 99301-6702. **T:** 1 509 547-1618
W: http://www.kzhr.com
Editorial Profile: KZHR-FM is a commercial station owned by Cherry Creek Radio. The format of the station is Hispanic. KZHR-FM broadcasts to the Pasco, WA area at 92.5 FM.

KZHS-AM
Owner: Noalmark Broadcasting Corp.
Editorial: 208 Buena Vista Rd, Hot Springs, Arkansas 71913-8208. **T:** 1 501 525-4600
Editorial Profile: KZHS-AM is a commercial station owned by Noalmark Broadcasting Corp. The format of the station is news and talk. KZHS-AM broadcasts to the Hot Springs, AR area at 590 AM.

KZHT-FM
Owner: Clear Channel Media and Entertainment
Editorial: 2801 Decker Lake Dr, Salt Lake City, Utah 84119-2330. **T:** 1 801 908-1300
W: http://www.971zht.com
Editorial Profile: KZHT-FM is a commercial station owned by Clear Channel Media and Entertainment. The format of the station is Top 40/CHR. KZHT-FM broadcasts to the Salt Lake City area at 97.1 FM.

KZIA-FM
Owner: KZIA Inc.
Editorial: 1110 26th Ave SW, Cedar Rapids, Iowa 52404. **T:** 1 319 363-2061
E: info@kzia.com **W:** http://www.kzia.com
Editorial Profile: KZIA-FM is a commercial station owned by KZIA Inc. The format for the station is Top 40/CHR. KZIA-FM broadcasts to the Cedar Rapids, IA area at 102.9 FM.

KZII-FM
Owner: Townsquare Media, LLC
Editorial: 4413 82nd St, Ste 300, Lubbock, Texas 79424. **T:** 1 806 798-7078
W: http://www.1025kiss.com
Editorial Profile: KZII-FM is a commercial station owned by Townsquare Media, LLC. The format of the station is Top 40/CHR music. KZII-FM broadcasts to the Lubbock, TX area at 102.5 FM.

KZIM-AM
Owner: Max Media
Editorial: 324 Broadway St, Cape Girardeau, Missouri 63701-7331. **T:** 1 573 335-8291
E: kzim@riverradio.net
W: http://www.960kzim.com
Editorial Profile: KZIM-AM is a commercial station owned by Max Media. The format of the station is news and talk programming. KZIM-AM broadcasts to the Cape Girardeau, MO area at 960 AM.

KZIN-FM
Owner: Townsquare Media, LLC
Editorial: 830 Oilfield Ave, Shelby, Montana 59474. **T:** 1 406 434-5241
E: ksen@gapbroadcasting.com
W: http://www.k96fm.com
Editorial Profile: KZIN-FM is a commercial station owned by Townsquare Media, LLC. The format of the station is contemporary country music. KZIN-FM broadcasts in the Shelby, MT area at 96.7 FM.

KZIO-FM
Owner: Red Rock Radio Corp.
Editorial: 501 S Lake Ave, Ste 200, Duluth, Minnesota 55802. **T:** 1 218 728-9500
E: production@redrockradio.org
W: http://www.94xrocks.com
Editorial Profile: KZIO-FM is a commercial station owned by Red Rock Radio Corp. The format of the station is rock. KZIO-FM broadcasts to the Duluth, MN area at 104.3

KZIP-AM
Owner: Tejas Broadcasting
Editorial: 3639 Wolflin Ave, Amarillo, Texas 79102-2119. **T:** 1 806 355-1044
Editorial Profile: KZIP-AM is a commercial station owned by Tejas Broadcasting. The format of the station is agricultural and farming programming. KZIP-AM broadcasts to the Amarillo, TX area at 1310 AM.

KZIQ-FM
Owner: Adelman Broadcasting Inc.
Editorial: 731 Balsam St, Ridgecrest, California 93555-3510. **T:** 1 760 371-1700
E: contact@adelmanbroadcasting.com
W: http://www.927qlite.com
Editorial Profile: KZIQ-FM is a commercial station owned by Adelman Broadcasting Inc.. The format of the station is AC. KZIQ-FM broadcasts to the Ridgecrest, CA area at 92.7 FM.

KZIU-FM
Owner: Alexandra Communications
Editorial: 2823 W Lewis St, Pasco, Washington 99301-6702. **T:** 1 509 547-1618
Editorial Profile: KZIU-FM is a commercial station owned by Alexandra Communications. The format of the station is adult hits radio. KZIU-FM broadcasts to the Walla Walla, WA area at 101.9 FM.

KZIZ-AM
Owner: Kris Bennett Broadcasting Co.
Editorial: 2600 S Jackson St, Seattle, Washington 98144-2402. **T:** 1 206 323-3070
E: ztwins@aol.com
Editorial Profile: KZIZ-AM is a commercial station owned by Kris Bennett Broadcasting Co. The format of the station is jazz. KZIZ-AM broadcasts to the Seattle area at 1560 AM.

KZJF-FM
Owner: Cumulus Media Inc.
Editorial: 1002 Diamond Rdg Ste 400, Jefferson City, Missouri 65109-7902.
T: 1 573 893-5100
W: http://www.sportsradio1041.com
Editorial Profile: KZJF-FM is a commercial station owned by Cumulus Media Inc. The format for the station is sports. KZJF-FM broadcasts to the Jefferson City, MO area at 104.1 FM.

KZJH-FM
Owner: Rich Broadcasting, LLC.
Editorial: 1140 State Highway 22, Jackson, Wyoming 83001-9401. **T:** 1 307 733-2120
E: jacksonholeradio@aol.com
W: http://www.jacksonholeradio.com
Editorial Profile: KZJH-FM is a commercial station owned by Rich Broadcasting, LLC. The format of the station is hot adult contemporary. KZJH-FM is broadcast to the Jackson, WY area at 95.3 FM.

KZJK-FM
Owner: CBS Radio
Editorial: 625 2nd Ave S, Minneapolis, Minnesota 55402. **T:** 1 612 370-0611
W: http://www.1041jackfm.com
Editorial Profile: KZJK-FM is a commercial station owned by CBS Radio. The format of the station is adult hits. KZJK-FM broadcasts to the Minneapolis area at 104.1 FM.

KZKE-FM
Owner: Route 66 Broadcasting LLC
Editorial: 812 E Beale St, Kingman, Arizona 86401-5925. **T:** 1 928 753-9100
W: http://www.kgmn.net/KZKE.htm
Editorial Profile: KZKE-FM is a commercial station owned by Route 66 Broadcasting LLC. The format of the station is rock music. KZKE-FM broadcasts to the Kingman, AZ area at 103.3 FM.

KZKK-FM
Owner: Performance Radio
Editorial: 1726 Dakota Ave S, Huron, South Dakota 57350. **T:** 1 605 352-1933
W: http://www.performance-radio.com
Editorial Profile: KZKK-FM is a commercial station owned by Performance Radio. The format of the station is hot adult contemporary. KZKK-FM broadcasts to the Huron, SD area at 105.1 FM.

KZKR-FM
Owner: First Natchez Radio Group Inc
Editorial: 2 O'Ferrall St, Natchez, Mississippi 39120-3000. **T:** 1 601 442-4895
W: http://www.rock105fm.com
Editorial Profile: KZKR-FM is a commercial station owned by First Natchez Radio Group Inc. The format of the station is classic rock. KZKR-FM broadcasts to the Natchez, MS area at a frequency of 105.1 FM.

KZKS-FM
Owner: Western Slope Communications
Editorial: 751 Horizon Ct, Ste 225, Grand Junction, Colorado 81506. **T:** 1 970 241-6460
E: production@wscradio.net
W: http://www.drive105.net
Editorial Profile: KZKS-FM is a commercial station owned by Western Slopes Communications. The format for the station is classic hits. KZKS-FM broadcasts to the Grand Junction-Montrose, CO area at 105.3 FM.

KZKX-FM
Owner: Three Eagles Communications Co.
Editorial: 3800 Cornhusker Hwy, Lincoln, Nebraska 68504-1533. **T:** 1 402 466-1234
W: http://www.kzkx.com
Editorial Profile: KZKX-FM is a commercial station owned by Three Eagles Communications Co. The format of the station is contemporary country. KZKX-FM broadcasts to the Lincoln, NE area at 96.9 FM.

KZKZ-FM
Owner: Family Communications, Inc.
Editorial: 6420 South Zero St, Fort Smith, Arkansas 72903. **T:** 1 479 646-6700
E: kzkzfm@kzkzfm.com
W: http://www.kzkzfm.com
Editorial Profile: KZKZ-FM is a commercial station owned by Family Communications, Inc. The format of the station is Christian teaching and Contemporary Christian music. KZKZ-FM broadcasts to the Fort Smith, AR area at 106.3 FM.

KZLB-FM
Owner: Three Eagles Communications Co.
Editorial: 200 N 10th St, Fort Dodge, Iowa 50501-3925. **T:** 1 515 955-5656
W: http://www.yourfortdodge.com
Editorial Profile: KZLB-FM is a commercial station owned by Three Eagles Communications Co. The format of the station is rock alternative. KZLB-FM broadcasts to the Fort Dodge, IA area at 92.1 FM.

KZLE-FM
Owner: WRD Entertainment Inc.
Editorial: 920 Harrison St, Ste C, Batesville, Arkansas 72501-6949. **T:** 1 870 793-4196
W: http://www.cr93.com
Editorial Profile: KZLE-FM is a commercial station owned by WRD Entertainment Inc. The format of the station is classic rock. KZLE-FM broadcasts to the Batesville, AR area at 93.1 FM.

KZLI-AM
Owner: Tyler Media, LLC
Editorial: 7777 S Lewis Ave, Tulsa, Oklahoma 74171-0003. **T:** 1 918 629-1380
Editorial Profile: KZLI-AM is a commercial station owned by Tyler Media, LLC. The format is religious talk. KZLI-AM broadcasts to the Tulsa, OK area at 1570 AM.

KZLK-FM
Owner: Duhamel Broadcasting
Editorial: 518 Saint Joseph St, Rapid City, South Dakota 57701. **T:** 1 605 342-2000
W: http://www.maxfmrapidcity.com
Editorial Profile: KZLK-FM is a commercial station owned by Duhamel Broadcasting. The format for the station is hot AC. KZLK-FM broadcasts to the Rapid City, SD area at 106.3. The tagline for the station is "She 106.3".

KZLS-AM
Owner: Champlin Broadcasting
Editorial: 4045 NW 64th St Ste 306, Oklahoma City, Oklahoma 73116-2616.
T: 1 405 633-1099
W: http://radio.securenetsystems.net/v5/KZLS
Editorial Profile: KZLS-AM is a commercial station owned by Champlin Broadcasting. The format of the station is talk. KZLS-AM broadcasts to the Oklahoma City, OK area at 1640 AM.

KZLT-FM
Owner: Leighton Enterprises Inc.
Editorial: 1185 9th St NE, Thompson, North Dakota 58278. **T:** 1 701 775-4611
W: http://literock1043.com
Editorial Profile: KZLT-FM is a commercial station owned by Leighton Enterprises Inc. The format of the station is adult contemporary. KZLT-FM broadcasts to the Thompson, ND area at 104.3 FM.

KZLZ-FM
Owner: CSVJ, LLC
Editorial: 2959 E Grant Rd, Tucson, Arizona 85716-2717. **T:** 1 520 325-3054
Editorial Profile: KZLZ-FM is a commercial station owned by CSVJ, LLC. The format of the station is Hispanic. KZLZ-FM broadcasts to the Tucson, AZ area at 105.3 FM.

KZMA-FM
Owner: Stratemeyer Media
Editorial: 203 Main St, Poplar Bluff, Missouri 63901-5831. **T:** 1 573 778-0142
W: http://www.kzmafm.com
Editorial Profile: KZMA-FM is a commercial station owned by Stratemeyer Media. The format of the station is adult contemporary. KZMA-FM broadcasts to the Poplar Bluff, MO area at 99.9 FM.

KZMC-FM
Owner: GI Family Radio
Editorial: 106 W 8th St, McCook, Nebraska 69001. **T:** 1 308 345-1981
W: http://www.1021kzmc.com
Editorial Profile: KZMC-FM is a commercial station owned by GI Family Radio. The format of the station is rock. KZMC-FM broadcasts to the McCook, NE area at 102.1 FM.

KZMG-FM
Editorial: 5660 E Franklin Rd Ste 200, Nampa, Idaho 83687-5133. **T:** 1 208 465-9966
Editorial Profile: KZMG-FM is a commercial station owned by Impact Radio. The format of the station is Hot Ac. The station broadcasts locally at a frequency of 102.7 FM.

KZMK-FM
Owner: Cherry Creek Radio
Editorial: 2300 E Busby Dr, Sierra Vista, Arizona 85635. **T:** 1 520 458-4313
E: k101@cherrycreekradio.com
W: http://www.allhitskzmk.com
Editorial Profile: KZMK-FM is a commercial station owned by Cherry Creek Radio. The format of the station is hot adult contemporary music. KZMK-FM broadcasts to the Sierra Vista, AZ area at 100.9 FM.

KZML-FM
Owner: Adelante Media Group
Editorial: 706 Butterfield Rd, Yakima, Washington 98901-2021. **T:** 1 509 457-1000
W: http://radiolagrande959.com
Editorial Profile: KZML-FM is a commercial station owned by Adelante Media Group. The format of the station is regional Mexican. KZML-FM broadcasts to the Yakima, WA area at 95.9 FM.

KZMN-FM
Owner: KOFI Inc.
Editorial: 317 1st Ave E, Kalispell, Montana 59901. **T:** 1 406 755-6690
W: http://www.monster1039.com
Editorial Profile: KZMN-FM is a commercial station owned by KOFI Inc. The format of the station is classic rock. KZMN-FM broadcasts to the Missoula, MT, area at 103.9 FM.

KZMP-AM
Owner: Liberman Broadcasting
Editorial: 400 Las Colinas Blvd E, Irving, Texas 75039-5579. **T:** 1 214 258-2800
W: http://espndeportes.espn.go.com/radio/dallas-1540
Editorial Profile: KZMP-AM is a commercial station owned by Liberman Broadcasting and managed by Deportes Media. The format of the station is Hispanic sports. KZMP-AM broadcasts to the Dallas area at 1540 AM.

KZMP-FM
Owner: Liberman Broadcasting Inc.
Editorial: 1210 E Belt Line Rd, Richardson, Texas 75081-3707. **T:** 1 214 675-1754
W: http://www.funasia.net
Editorial Profile: KZMP-FM is a commercial station owned by Liberman Broadcasting Inc. and operated by FunAsia. The format of the station is variety, specializing in Indian/

WORLD NEWS MEDIA

Pakistani programming. KZMP-FM broadcasts to the Dallas area at 104.9 FM.

KZMQ-AM
Owner: Legend Communications
Editorial: 1949 Mountain View Dr, Cody, Wyoming 82414. T: 1 307 578-5000
E: news@bhrnwy.com
W: http://www.mybighornbasin.com
Editorial Profile: KZMQ-AM is a commercial station owned by Legend Communications. The format of the station is classic country. KZMQ-AM broadcasts in the Greybull, WY area at 1140 AM.

KZMQ-FM
Owner: Legend Communications
Editorial: 1949 Mountain View Dr, Cody, Wyoming 82414. T: 1 307 578-5000
E: news@bhrnwy.com
W: http://www.mybighornbasin.com
Editorial Profile: KZMQ-FM is a commercial station owned by Legend Communications. The format of the station is contemporary country music. KZMQ-FM broadcasts to the Cody, WY area at 100.3 FM.

KZMT-FM
Owner: Cherry Creek Radio
Editorial: 110 E Broadway St, Helena, Montana 59601-4232. T: 1 406 442-4490
W: http://www.kzmt.com
Editorial Profile: KZMT-FM is a commercial station owned by Cherry Creek Radio. The format of the station is classic rock music. KZMT-FM broadcasts in the Helena, MT area at 101.1 FM.

KZMU-FM
Owner: Moab Public Radio, Inc.
Editorial: 1734 Rocky Rd, Moab, Utah 84532. T: 1 435 259-8824 E: kzmu@kzmu.org
W: http://www.kzmu.org
Editorial Profile: KZMU-FM is a non-commercial station owned by Moab Public Radio, Inc. The format for the station is variety. KZMU-FM broadcasts to the Salt Lake City area at 90.1 FM.

KZMY-FM
Owner: Townsquare Media, LLC
Editorial: 125 W Mendenhall St Ste 1, Bozeman, Montana 59715-3500.
T: 1 406 586-2343 W: http://my1035.com
Editorial Profile: KZMY-FM is a commercial station owned by Townsquare Media, LLC. The format of the station is hot adult contemporary. KZMY-FM broadcasts to the Bozeman, MT area at 103.5 FM.

KZMZ-FM
Owner: Cenla Broadcasting Inc.
Editorial: 1115 Texas Ave, Alexandria, Louisiana 71301. T: 1 318 445-1234
W: http://www.969rocks.com
Editorial Profile: KZMZ-FM is a commercial station owned by Cenla Broadcasting Inc. The format of the station is classic rock music. KZMZ-FM broadcasts to the Alexandria, LA area at 96.9 FM.

KZNA-FM
Owner: Kanza Society Inc.
Editorial: 210 N 7th St, Garden City, Kansas 67846. T: 1 620 275-7444 E: hppr@hppr.org
W: http://www.hppr.org
Editorial Profile: KZNA-FM is a non-commercial station owned by Kanza Society Inc. The format of the station is news and classical. KZNA-FM broadcasts to the Wichita, KS area at 90.5 FM.

KZND-FM
Owner: Alaska Integrated Media
Editorial: 4700 Business Park Blvd, Anchorage, Alaska 99503-7176.
T: 1 907 522-1018 E: traffic@alaskaim.com
W: http://www.947kznd.com
Editorial Profile: KZND-FM is a commercial station owned by Alaska Integrated Media. The format of the station is active rock. KZND-FM broadcasts to the Anchorage, AK area at a frequency of 94.7 FM.

KZNE-AM
Owner: Bryan Broadcasting
Editorial: 2700 Earl Rudder Fwy S, Ste 5000, College Station, Texas 77845.
T: 1 979 695-9595
E: radio@bryanbroadcasting.com
W: http://www.kzne.com
Editorial Profile: KZNE-AM is a commercial station owned by Bryan Broadcasting. The format of the station is sports. KZNE-AM broadcasts to the College Station, TX area at 1150 AM.

KZNG-AM
Owner: US Stations, LLC
Editorial: 125 Corporate Ter, Hot Springs, Arkansas 71913. T: 1 501 525-9700
W: http://www.myhotsprings.com
Editorial Profile: KZNG-AM is a commercial radio station owned by US Stations LLC. The format of the station is news and talk. KZNG-AM broadcasts to the Little Rock, AR area at 1340 AM.

KZNN-FM
Owner: Mahaffey Enterprises Inc.
Editorial: 1505 Soest Rd, Rolla, Missouri 65401-3709. T: 1 573 364-2525
E: kttrkznn@fidmail.com
W: http://www.resultsradioonline.com
Editorial Profile: KZNN-FM is a commercial station owned by Mahaffey Enterprises Inc. The format of the station is country. KZNN-FM broadcasts in the Rolla, MO area at 105.3 FM.

KZNO-FM
Owner: Lee Family Broadcasting
Editorial: 47 N 100 W, Jerome, Idaho 83338. T: 1 208 324-8181 E: spots@safelink.net
Editorial Profile: KZNO-FM is a commercial station owned by Lee Family Broadcasting. The format of the station is sports and is an ESPN Radio affiliate. KZNO-FM broadcasts to the Jerome, ID area at 102.9 FM.

KZNS-AM
Owner: Miller Group (Larry H.)
Editorial: 301 W South Temple, Salt Lake City, Utah 84101-1216. T: 1 801 537-1414
W: http://www.1280thezone.com
Editorial Profile: KZNS-AM is a commercial station owned by Miller Group (Larry H.). The format of the station is sports. KZNS-AM broadcasts to the Salt Lake City area at 1280 AM.

KZNS-FM
Owner: Miller Broadcasting (Larry H.)
Editorial: 301 W South Temple, Salt Lake City, Utah 84101-1216. T: 1 801 537-1414
W: http://1280thezone.com
Editorial Profile: KZNS-FM is a commercial station owned by Miller Broadcasting (Larry H.). The format of the station is sports. KZNS-FM broadcasts to the Salt Lake City area at 97.5 FM.

KZNT-AM
Owner: Salem Communications
Editorial: 7150 Campus Dr Ste 150, Colorado Springs, Colorado 80920-3157.
T: 1 719 531-5438
W: http://www.newstalk1460.com
Editorial Profile: KZNT-AM is a commercial station owned by Salem Communications. The format of the station is news and talk. KZNT-AM broadcasts to the Colorado Springs, CO area at 1460 AM.

KZNU-AM
Owner: Canyon Media Corporation
Editorial: 619 S. Bluff Tower 1 Ste. 300, Saint George, Utah 84780. T: 1 435 628-3643
W: http://foxnews1450.com
Editorial Profile: KZNU-AM is a commercial station owned by Canyon Media Corporation. The format of the station is news and talk. KZNU-AM broadcasts to the St. George, UT area at 1450 AM.

KZNW-AM
Owner: Cherry Creek Radio
Editorial: 231 N Wenatchee Ave, Wenatchee, Washington 98801. T: 1 509 665-6565
E: newswenatchee@cherrycreekradio.com
Editorial Profile: KZNW-AM is a commercial station owned by Cherry Creek Radio. The format of the station is sports. KZNW-AM broadcasts to the Seattle area at 1340 AM.

KZNX-AM
Owner: American Telecommunications Group, Inc.
Editorial: 912 S Capital of Texas Hwy Ste 400, West Lake Hills, Texas 78746-6176.
T: 1 512 416-1100
W: http://www.espnaustin.com
Editorial Profile: KZNX-AM is a commercial station owned by America Telecommunications Group, Inc. The format of the station is Spanish talk. KZNX-AM broadcasts to the Austin, TX area at 1530 AM.

KZOK-FM
Owner: CBS Radio
Editorial: 1000 Dexter Ave N, Ste 100, Seattle, Washington 98109-3577. T: 1 206 805-1025
W: http://www.kzok.com
Editorial Profile: KZOK-FM is a commercial station owned by CBS Radio. The format of the station is classic rock music. KZOK-FM broadcasts to the Seattle area at 102.5 FM.

KZON-FM
Owner: CBS Radio
Editorial: 840 N Central Ave, Phoenix, Arizona 85004-2003. T: 1 602 452-1000
W: http://live1015phoenix.cbslocal.com/
Editorial Profile: KZON-FM is a commercial station owned by CBS Radio. The format of the station is Top 40/CHR. KZON-FM broadcasts in the Phoenix area at 101.5 FM.

KZOO-AM
Owner: Furuya(David)
Editorial: 2752 Woodlawn Dr, Ste 5-204A, Honolulu, Hawaii 96822. T: 1 808 593-2880
Editorial Profile: KZOO-AM is a commercial station owned by David Furuya. The format of the station is ethnic Japanese, and programming includes music, news, and information. KZOO-AM broadcasts to the Japanese-American community in Honolulu area at 1210 AM.

KZOQ-FM
Owner: Cherry Creek Radio
Editorial: 1600 North Ave W, Ste 101, Missoula, Montana 59801. T: 1 406 728-5000
W: http://www.kzoq.com
Editorial Profile: KZOQ-FM is a commercial station owned by Cherry Creek Radio. The format is classic rock. KZOQ-FM broadcasts to the Missoula, MT area at 100.1 FM.

KZOR-FM
Owner: Noalmark Broadcasting Corp.
Editorial: 619 N Turner St, Hobbs, New Mexico 88240-8232. T: 1 575 397-4969
E: kzor@1radiosquare.com
W: http://www.kzorfm.com
Editorial Profile: KZOR-FM is a commercial station owned by Noalmark Broadcasting Corp. The format of the station is hot adult contemporary. KZOR-FM broadcasts to the Hobbs, NM area at 94.1 FM.

KZOT-AM
Owner: NRG Media LLC
Editorial: 5011 Capitol Ave, Omaha, Nebraska 68132-2921. T: 1 402 342-2000
W: http://1620thezone.com
Editorial Profile: KZOT-AM is a commercial station owned by NRG Media LLC. The format of the station is sports/talk. KZOT-AM broadcasts to the Omaha, NE area at 1180 AM.

KZOY-AM
Owner: Cup O Dirt, LLC
Editorial: 401 E 8Th St Ste 203, Sioux Falls, South Dakota 57103-7033. T: 1 605 582-1985
E: sunny@mysunnyradio.com
W: http://www.mysunnyradio.com
Editorial Profile: KZOY-AM is a commercial station owned by Cup O Dirt, LLC. The format of the station is classic hits of the 80s. KZOY-AM broadcasts to the Brandon and Sioux Falls, SD areas at 1520 AM.

KZOZ-FM
Owner: American General Media
Editorial: 3620 Sacramento Dr Ste 206, San Luis Obispo, California 93401-7215.
T: 1 805 781-2750
E: news@americangeneralmedia.com
W: http://www.kzoz.com
Editorial Profile: KZOZ-FM is a commercial station owned by American General Media. The format of the station is classic rock. KZOZ-FM broadcasts to the San Luis Obispo, CA area at 93.3 FM.

KZPA-AM
Owner: Gwandak Public Broadcasting Inc.
Editorial: 1936 E 3rd Street, Fort Yukon, Alaska 99740. T: 1 907 662-6356
E: kzparadio@hotmail.com
Editorial Profile: KZPA-AM is a commercial station owned by Gwandak Public Broadcasting Inc. The format of the station is variety. KZPA-AM broadcasts to the Fort Yukon, AK area at 900 AM.

KZPK-FM
Owner: Leighton Enterprises Inc.
Editorial: 619 W Saint Germain St, Saint Cloud, Minnesota 56301-3640.
T: 1 320 251-1450
W: http://www.wildcountry99.com
Editorial Profile: KZPK-FM is a commercial station owned by Leighton Enterprises Inc. The format of the station is contemporary country music. KZPK-FM broadcasts in the Saint Cloud, MN area at 98.9 FM. Send any press materials to the station's program director.

KZPO-FM
Owner: Estate of Linda Ware
Editorial: 5119 W Nicholas Ave, Visalia, California 93291-7846. T: 1 559 733-4211
Editorial Profile: KZPO-FM is a commercial station owned by the Estate of Linda Ware. The format of the station is adult standards. KZPO-FM broadcasts to the Visalia, CA area at a frequency of 103.3 FM.

KZPR-FM
Owner: Clear Channel Media and Entertainment
Editorial: 1000 20th Ave SW, Minot, North Dakota 58701. T: 1 701 852-4646
W: http://www.thefox1053.com
Editorial Profile: KZPR-FM is a commercial station owned by Clear Channel Media and Entertainment. The format of the station is classic rock music. KZPR-FM broadcasts to the Minot, ND area at 105.3 FM.

KZPS-FM
Owner: Clear Channel Media and Entertainment
Editorial: 14001 Dallas Pkwy, Ste 300, Dallas, Texas 75240. T: 1 214 866-8000
W: http://www.kzps.com
Editorial Profile: KZPS-FM is a commercial station owned by Clear Channel Media and Entertainment. The format of the station is classic rock. KZPS-FM broadcasts to the Dallas area at 92.5 FM.

KZPT-FM
Owner: Entercom Communications Corp.
Editorial: 7000 Squibb Rd, Mission, Kansas 66202-3233. T: 1 913 576-7997
E: 997ThePoint@gmail.com
W: http://www.997point.com
Editorial Profile: KZPT-FM is a commercial station owned by Entercom Communications Corp. The format of the station is adult contemporary. KZPT-FM broadcasts to the Kansas City, MO area at 99.7 FM.

KZQD-FM
Owner: Loredo(Mario)
Editorial: 322 S Clay Ave, Liberal, Kansas 67901. T: 1 620 626-8282
E: radiolibertad@sbcglobal.net
W: http://www.kzqdradiolibertad.com
Editorial Profile: KZQD-FM is a commercial station owned by Mario Loredo. The format of the station is Hispanic religious programming. KZQD-FM broadcasts to the Liberal, KS area at 105.1 FM.

KZQQ-AM
Owner: Canfin Enterprises Inc.
Editorial: 402 Cypress St, Ste 510, Abilene, Texas 79601. T: 1 325 672-5442
W: http://www.radioabilene.com

KZQX-FM
Owner: Chalkhill Communications, LLC
Editorial: 13618 County Road 2127 N, Henderson, Texas 75652-4808.
T: 1 903 643-7711 E: kzqxfm@aol.com
W: http://www.kzqx.com
Editorial Profile: KZQX-FM is a commercial station owned by Chalkhill Communications, LLC. The format of the station is adult standards. KZQX-FM broadcasts to the Longview, TX, area at 100.3 FM.

KZQZ-AM
Owner: Entertainment Media Trust
Editorial: 6500 W Main St, Ste 315, Belleville, Illinois 62223-3700. T: 1 618 394-9965
E: info@kzqz1430am.com
W: http://www.kzqz1430am.com
Editorial Profile: KZQZ-AM is a commercial station owned by Entertainment Media Trust. The format of the station is oldies. KZQZ-AM broadcasts to the St. Louis area at 1430 AM.

KZRB-FM
Owner: B & H Radio Inc.
Editorial: 710 W Avenue A, Hooks, Texas 75561. T: 1 903 547-3223 E: kzrb@txk.net
W: http://www.kzrb103five.com
Editorial Profile: KZRB-FM is a commercial station owned by B & H Radio Inc. The format of the station is urban contemporary. KZRB-FM broadcasts to the Texarkana, TX area at 103.5 FM.

KZRD-FM
Owner: Rocking M Radio
Editorial: 2601 Central Ave, Dodge City, Kansas 67801-6200. T: 1 620 225-8080
W: http://mykansasradio.com
Editorial Profile: KZRD-FM is a commercial station owned Rocking M Radio. The format of the station is rock. KZRD-FM broadcasts to the Dodge City, KS area at 93.9 FM.

KZRG-AM
Owner: Zimmer Radio Group
Editorial: 2702 E 32Nd St, Joplin, Missouri 64804-4307. **T:** 1 417 624-1025
E: info@zrgmail.com
W: http://www.1310kzrg.com
Editorial Profile: KZRG-AM is a commercial station owned by Zimmer Radio Inc. The format of the station is news and talk. KZRG-AM broadcasts to the Joplin, MO area at 1310 AM.

KZRK-FM
Owner: Cumulus Media Inc.
Editorial: 301 S Polk St, Ste 100, Amarillo, Texas 79101. **T:** 1 806 342-5200
W: http://www.amarillosrockstation.com
Editorial Profile: KZRK-FM is a commercial station owned by Cumulus Media Inc. The format of the station is rock music. KZRK-FM broadcasts in the Amarillo, TX area at 107.9 FM

KZRM-FM
Owner: Chama Broadcasting Corporation
Editorial: 2202 HWY 17, Chama, New Mexico 87520-9711. **T:** 1 575 756-1617
Editorial Profile: KZRM-FM is a commercial station owned by Chama Broadcasting Corporation. The format of the station is contemporary country. KZRM-FM broadcasts to the Albuquerque, NM area at 96.1 FM.

KZRO-FM
Owner: Big Tree Communications
Editorial: 113 E Alma St, Mount Shasta, California 96067. **T:** 1 530 926-1332
E: zmail@zchannelradio.com
W: http://www.zchannelradio.com
Editorial Profile: KZRO-FM is a commercial station owned by Big Tree Communications. The format of the station is classic hits. KZRO-FM broadcasts to the Mount Shasta, CA area at 100.1 FM.

KZRR-FM
Owner: Clear Channel Media and Entertainment
Editorial: 5411 Jefferson St NE, Ste 100, Albuquerque, New Mexico 87109.
T: 1 505 830-6400 **E:** kzrr@94rock.com
W: http://www.94rock.com
Editorial Profile: KZRR-FM is a commercial station owned by Clear Channel Media and Entertainment. The format of the station is rock music. KZRR-FM broadcasts to the Albuquerque, NM area at 94.1 FM.

KZRS-FM
Owner: Rocking M Radio
Editorial: 5501 10th St, Great Bend, Kansas 67530-6319. **T:** 1 620 792-7108
W: http://centralkansasradio.com/old-school-0179
Editorial Profile: KZRS-FM is a commercial station owned by Rocking M Radio. The format of the station is classic hits. KZRS-FM broadcasts to the Great Bend, KS area at 107.9 FM.

KZRV-FM
Owner: Townsquare Media, LLC.
Editorial: 640 Lincoln Ave SE, Saint Cloud, Minnesota 56304. **T:** 1 320 251-4422
W: http://www.rev967.com
Editorial Profile: KZRV-FM is a commercial station owned by Townsquare Media, LLC. The format of the station is rock alternative music. KZRV-FM broadcasts to the Minneapolis area at 96.7 FM.

KZRX-FM
Owner: Clear Channel Media and Entertainment
Editorial: 11291 39th St SW, Dickinson, North Dakota 58601. **T:** 1 701 227-1876
W: http://www.z92fm.net
Editorial Profile: KZRX-FM is a commercial station owned by Clear Channel Media and Entertainment. The format of the station is rock/album oriented rock. KZRX-FM broadcasts to the Dickinson, ND area at 92.1 FM.

KZRZ-FM
Owner: Opus Media Partners
Editorial: 1200 N 18th St, Ste D, Monroe, Louisiana 71201-5449. **T:** 1 318 387-3922
E: sunny983@opusbroadcasting.com
W: http://www.sunny983.com
Editorial Profile: KZRZ-FM is a commercial station owned by Opus Media Partners. The format of the station is adult contemporary music. KZRZ-FM broadcasts in the Monroe, LA area at 98.3 FM.

KZSB-AM
Owner: Santa Barbara Broadcasting
Editorial: 1317 Santa Barbara St, Santa Barbara, California 93101. **T:** 1 805 568-1444
W: http://www.newspress.com
Editorial Profile: KZSB-AM is a commercial station owned by Santa Barbara Broadcasting. The format of the station is talk. KZSB-AM broadcasts to the Santa Barbara, CA area at 1290 AM.

KZSC-FM
Owner: University of California
Editorial: KZSC Santa Cruz, 1156 High Street, Santa Cruz, California 95064-1099.
T: 1 831 459-2811
E: stationmanager@kzsc.org
W: http://www.kzsc.org
Editorial Profile: KZSC-FM is a non-commercial station owned by University of California. The format of the station is college variety. KZSX-FM broadcasts to the Santa Cruz, CA area at 88.1 FM.

KZSE-FM
Owner: Minnesota Public Radio
Editorial: 206 S Broadway, Ste 735, Rochester, Minnesota 55904.
T: 1 507 282-0910 **W:** http://www.mpr.org
Editorial Profile: KZSE-FM is a non-commercial station owned by Minnesota Public Radio. The format of the station is classical music programming. KZSE-FM broadcasts to the Rochester, MN area at 90.7 FM.

KZSJ-AM
Owner: Adelante Media Group
Editorial: 1630 Oakland Rd Ste A109, San Jose, California 95131-2450.
T: 1 408 223-3130 **E:** qhradio@aol.com
W: http://www.quehuongmedia.com
Editorial Profile: KZSJ-AM is a commercial station owned by Adelante Media Group. The format of the station is ethnic and multicultural programming, including Vietnamese variety. KZSJ-AM broadcasts to the San Jose, CA area at 1120 AM.

KZSN-FM
Owner: Clear Channel Media and Entertainment
Editorial: 9323 E 37th St N, Wichita, Kansas 67226-2000. **T:** 1 316 494-6600
E: wichitanews@clearchannel.com
W: http://www.kzsn.com
Editorial Profile: KZSN-FM is a commercial station owned by Clear Channel Media and Entertainment. The format of the station is contemporary country. KZSN-FM broadcasts to the Wichita, KS area at 102.1 FM.

KZSP-FM
Owner: MBM Radio Del Rio, LLC
Editorial: 1201 N Jackson Rd, Ste 900, McAllen, Texas 78501-5764.
T: 1 956 992-8895
W: http://www.valleyjack.com
Editorial Profile: KZSP-FM is a commercial station owned by MBM Radio Del Rio, LLC. The format of the station features Tejano music. KZSP-FM broadcasts to the McAllen, TX area at 95.3.

KZSQ-FM
Owner: Clarke Broadcasting Corp.
Editorial: 342 S Washington St, Sonora, California 95370. **T:** 1 209 533-1450
E: star927@clarkebroadcasting.com
W: http://www.kzsqfm.com
Editorial Profile: KZSQ-FM is a commercial station owned by Clark Broadcasting Corp. The format of the station is adult contemporary. KZSQ-FM broadcasts to the Sonora, CA area at 92.7 FM.

KZST-FM
Owner: Redwood Empire Stereocasters
Editorial: 3392 Mendocino Ave, Santa Rosa, California 95403-3644. **T:** 1 707 528-4434
W: http://www.kzst.com
Editorial Profile: KZST-FM is a commercial station owned by Redwood Empire Stereocasters. The format of the station is adult contemporary. KZST-FM broadcasts to the Santa Rosa, CA, area at 100.1 FM.

KZSU-FM
Owner: Stanford University
Editorial: Memorial Hall, 540 Memorial Way, Stanford, California 44305. **T:** 1 650 725-4868
E: news@kzsu.stanford.edu
W: http://kzsulive.stanford.edu
Editorial Profile: KZSU-FM is a non-commercial station owned by Stanford University. The format of the station is variety. KZSU-FM broadcasts to the Stanford, CA area at 90.1 FM.

KZTA-FM
Owner: Adelante Media Group
Editorial: 706 Butterfield Rd, Yakima, Washington 98901-2021. **T:** 1 509 457-1000
Editorial Profile: KZTA-FM is a commercial station owned by Adelante Media Group. The format of the station is regional Mexican music. KZTA-FM broadcasts to the Yakima, WA area at 96.9 FM.

KZTB-FM
Owner: Adelante Media Group
Editorial: 706 Butterfield Rd, Yakima, Washington 98901-2021. **T:** 1 509 457-1000
Editorial Profile: KZTB-FM is a commercial station owned by Adelante Media Group. The format of the station is regional Mexican music. KZTB-FM broadcasts to the Yakima, WA area at 97.9 FM.

KZTD-AM
Owner: Carrera (Emanuel)
Editorial: 2222 Main St, Little Rock, Arkansas 72206-1530. **T:** 1 501 308-7225
W: http://www.fiestamexicana1350.com
Editorial Profile: KZTD-AM is a commercial station owned by Carrera (Emanuel). The format of the station is Regional Mexican. KZTD-AM broadcasts to the Little Rock, AR area at a frequency of 1350 AM.

KZTH-FM
Owner: Love Station Inc.(The)
Editorial: 6600 W Highway 60, Ponca City, Oklahoma 74601-7926. **T:** 1 580 767-1400
E: mail@thehousefm.com
W: http://www.thehousefm.com
Editorial Profile: KZTH-FM is a non-commercial station owned by The Love Station Inc. The format of the station is contemporary Christian. KZTH-FM broadcasts to the Greater Oklahoma City, OK area (licensed to Piedmont, OK) at 88.5 FM.

KZTK-FM
Owner: Vision Media Inc.
Editorial: 4 N Langer Ave, Casselton, North Dakota 58012. **T:** 1 701 347-5005
E: thetruck1039@yahoo.com
W: http://www.1039thetruck.com
Editorial Profile: KZTK-FM is a commercial station owned by Vision Media Inc. The format of the station is contemporary country. KZTK-FM broadcasts to the Fargo, ND area at 103.9 FM.

KZTL-FM
Owner: Armada Media
Editorial: 305 E 4th St, North Platte, Nebraska 69101-6903. **T:** 1 308 532-3344
W: http://www.newsacrossnebraska.com
Editorial Profile: KZTL-FM is a commercial station owned by Armada Media. The format of the station is adult contemporary. KZTL-FM airs locally at 93.5 FM.

KZTQ-FM
Owner: Scott Communications LLC
Editorial: 961 Matley Ln, Ste 120, Reno, Nevada 89502-2119. **T:** 1 775 829-1964
W: http://www.bob937.com
Editorial Profile: KZTQ-FM is a commercial station owned by Scott Communications LLC. The format of the station is adult hits. KZTQ-FM broadcasts to the Reno, NV area at 93.7 FM.

KZUA-FM
Owner: Petracom
Editorial: 1838 Commerce Dr, Ste A, Lakeside, Arizona 85929-7007. **T:** 1 928 532-3232
E: production@whitemountainradio.com
W: http://www.921kzua.com
Editorial Profile: KZUA-FM is a commercial station owned by Petracom. The format of the station is country music. KZUA-FM broadcasts to the Phoenix area at 92.1 FM.

KZUE-AM
Owner: Galvan(Nancy)
Editorial: 2715 S Radio Rd, El Reno, Oklahoma 73036. **T:** 1 405 262-9184
E: kzue@aol.com
Editorial Profile: KZUE-AM is a commercial station owned by Nancy Galvan. The format of the station is Hispanic. KZUE-AM broadcasts to the Oklahoma City area at 1460 AM.

KZUH-FM
Owner: Rocking M Radio
Editorial: 641 W Cloud St, Salina, Kansas 67401-5618. **T:** 1 785 827-2100
W: http://www.salina-radio.com
Editorial Profile: KZUH-FM is a commercial station owned by Rocking M Radio. The format of the station is Top 40/CHR. KZUH-FM broadcasts to the Salina, KS area at 92.7 FM.

KZUL-FM
Owner: Mad Dog Wireless Inc.
Editorial: 2068 McCulloch Blvd N, Lake Havasu City, Arizona 86403.
T: 1 928 855-1051 **E:** maddog@maddog.net
W: http://www.maddog.net

KZUM-FM
Owner: Sunrise Communications, Inc.
Editorial: 941 O St, Ste 1025, Lincoln, Nebraska 68508. **T:** 1 402 474-5086
W: http://www.kzum.org
Editorial Profile: KZUM-FM is a non-commercial station owned by Sunrise Communications, Inc. The format of the station is variety. KZUM-FM broadcasts to the Lincoln, NE area at 89.3 FM.

KZUS-FM
Owner: Adelante Media Group
Editorial: 910 Basin St SW, Ephrata, Washington 98823-2076. **T:** 1 509 754-4661
W: http://www.adelantemediagroup.com
Editorial Profile: KZUS-FM is a commercial station owned by Adelante Media Group. The format of the station is contemporary country music. KULE-FM broadcasts to the Ephrata, WA area at 92.3 FM.

KZUW-FM
Owner: University of Wyoming
Editorial: 1000 E University Ave, Dept 3984, Laramie, Wyoming 82071-2000.
T: 1 307 766-4240 **E:** wprhelp@uwyo.edu
W: http://www.wyomingpublicradio.net
Editorial Profile: KZUW-FM is a non-commercial station owned by the University of Wyoming. The format of the station is classical music. KZUW-FM broadcasts to the Reliance, WY area at 88.5 FM.

KZUZ-FM
Owner: Petracom
Editorial: 1838 Commerce Dr Ste A, Lakeside, Arizona 85929-7008. **T:** 1 928 368-8100
W: http://www.whitemountainradio.com
Editorial Profile: KZUZ-FM is a commercial station owned by Petracom. The format of the station is classic hits. KZUZ-FM broadcasts at a frequency of 93.5 to the Show Low, AZ area.

KZWA-FM
Owner: B & C Broadcasting Inc.
Editorial: 305 Enterprise Blvd, Lake Charles, Louisiana 70601. **T:** 1 337 491-9955
W: http://www.kzwa.com
Editorial Profile: KZWA-FM is a commercial station owned by B & C Broadcasting Inc. The format of the station is urban contemporary music. KZWA-FM broadcasts to the Lake Charles, LA area at 104.9 FM.

KZWB-FM
Owner: Wagonwheel Communications Corp.
Editorial: 40 Shoshone Ave, Green River, Wyoming 82935. **T:** 1 307 875-6666
E: mail@theradionetwork.net
W: http://www.theradionetwork.net
Editorial Profile: KZWB-FM is a commercial station owned by Wagonwheel Communications Corp. The format of the station is classic hits. KZWB-FM broadcasts to the Green River, WY area at 97.9 FM.

KZWV-FM
Owner: Zimmer Radio Group
Editorial: 1081 Osage Beach Rd, Osage Beach, Missouri 65065-2233.
T: 1 573 746-7873
E: thewave@1019thewave.com
W: http://www.1019thewave.com
Editorial Profile: KZWV-FM is a commercial station owned by Zimmer Radio Group. The format of the station is adult contemporary. KZWV-FM broadcasts to the Osage Beach and Jefferson City areas of Missouri at 101.9 FM.

KZWY-FM
Owner: Lovcom, Inc.
Editorial: 1716 Kroe Ln, Sheridan, Wyoming 82801-9681. **T:** 1 307 672-7421
E: news@sheridanmedia.com
W: http://www.sheridanmedia.com
Editorial Profile: KZWY-FM is a commercial station owned by Lovcom, Inc. The format of the station is classic rock. KZWY-FM broadcasts to the Sheridan, WY area at 94.9 FM.

KZXL-FM
Owner: Pentagon Communications, LLC

Editorial: 121 S Cotton Sq, Lufkin, Texas 75904-2933. **T:** 1 936 634-6661
E: traffic@yatesmedia.com
W: http://www.hot963online.com
Editorial Profile: KZXL-FM is a commercial station owned by Pentagon Communications, LLC. The format of the station is urban adult contemporary. KZXL-FM broadcasts to the Lufkin, TX area at 96.3 FM.

KZXR-AM
Owner: Casa Media Partners, LLC
Editorial: 152101 W County Road 12, Prosser, Washington 99350-7265. **T:** 1 509 786-1310
Editorial Profile: KZXR-AM is a commercial station owned by Casa Media Partners, LLC. The format of the station is Hispanic sports. KZXR-AM broadcasts to the Prosser, WA area at 1310 AM.

KZXY-FM
Owner: El Dorado Broadcasting
Editorial: 12370 Hesperia Rd, Ste 16, Victorville, California 92395.
T: 1 760 241-1313 **W:** http://www.y102fm.com
Editorial Profile: KZXY-FM is a commercial station owned by El Dorado Broadcasting. The format for the station is adult contemporary. KZXY-FM broadcasts to the Victorville, CA area at 102.3 FM.

KZYM-AM
Owner: Zimmer Radio Inc.
Editorial: 2702 E 32nd St, Joplin, Missouri 64804. **T:** 1 417 624-1025
W: http://www.1230thetalker.com
Editorial Profile: KZYM-AM is a commercial station owned by Zimmer Radio Group. The format of the station is talk. KZYM-AM broadcasts to the Joplin, MO area at 1230 AM.

KZYP-AM
Owner: Southwest Arkansas Media, LLC
Editorial: 208 Buena Vista Rd, Hot Springs, Arkansas 71913-8208. **T:** 1 501 525-4600
Editorial Profile: KZYP-AM is a commercial station owned by Southwest Arkansas Media, LLC. The format of the station is classic country. The station broadcasts to the Hot Springs, AR area at a frequency of 1310 AM.

KZYR-FM
Owner: Cool Radio, LLC
Editorial: 275 Main St, Unit 0201, Edwards, Colorado 81632. **T:** 1 970 845-8565
W: http://www.kzyr.com

KZYX-FM
Owner: Mendocino County Public Broadcasting
Editorial: 9300 Highway 128, Philo, California 95466. **T:** 1 707 895-2324 **E:** kzyx@kzyx.org
W: http://www.kzyx.org
Editorial Profile: KZYX-FM is a non-commercial station owned by Mendocino County Public Broadcasting. The format of the station is variety. KZYX-FM broadcasts to the San Francisco area at 90.7 FM.

KZZA-FM
Owner: Liberman Broadcasting Inc.
Editorial: 2410 Gateway Dr, Irving, Texas 75063-2727. **T:** 1 972 652-2900
W: http://www.casa1067.com
Editorial Profile: KZZA-FM is a commercial station owned by Liberman Broadcasting Inc. The format of the station is Latin Urban. KZZA-FM broadcasts to the Dallas area at 106.7 FM.

KZZB-AM
Owner: Martin's Broadcasting Inc.
Editorial: 4638 Decker Dr, Baytown, Texas 77520-1418. **T:** 1 409 833-0990
Editorial Profile: KZZB-AM is a commercial station owned by Martin's Broadcasting Inc. The format of the station is gospel music. KZZB-AM broadcasts to the Beaumont, TX area at 990 AM.

KZZD-AM
Owner: Entercom Communications Corp.
Editorial: 0700 SW Bancroft St, Portland, Oregon 97239-4226. **T:** 1 503 223-1441
Editorial Profile: KZZD-AM is a commercial station owned by Entercom Communications Corp. The format of the station is Spanish language sports. KZZD-AM broadcasts to the Portland, OR area at 1390 AM.

KZZE-FM
Owner: Bicoastal Media LLC
Editorial: 3624 Avion Dr, Medford, Oregon 97504. **T:** 1 541 772-4170
W: http://www.kzze.com

Editorial Profile: KZZE-FM is a commercial station owned by Bicoastal Media LLC. The format of the station is rock music. KZZE-FM broadcasts to the Medford, OR area at 106.3 FM.

KZZI-FM
Owner: Western South Dakota Broadcasting
Editorial: 2827 E Colorado Blvd, Spearfish, South Dakota 57783. **T:** 1 605 642-5747
E: eagle@dberadio.com
W: http://www.myeaglecountry.com
Editorial Profile: KZZI-FM is a commercial station owned by Western South Dakota Broadcasting. The format of the station is country. KZZI-FM broadcasts to the Spearfish, SD area at 95.9 FM.

KZZJ-AM
Owner: Rugby Broadcasters Inc.
Editorial: 230 Highway 2 SE, Rugby, North Dakota 58368. **T:** 1 701 776-5254
E: kzzj@kzzj.com **W:** http://www.kzzj.com
Editorial Profile: KZZJ-AM is a commercial station owned by Rugby Broadcasters Inc. The format of the station is agricultural and classic country music. KZZJ-AM broadcasts to the Rugby, ND area at 1450 AM.

KZZK-FM
Owner: Staradio Corp.
Editorial: 329 Maine St, 1st Fl, Quincy, Illinois 62301. **T:** 1 217 224-4102
E: kzzk@staradio.com **W:** http://www.kzzk.com
Editorial Profile: KZZK-FM is a commercial station owned by Staradio Corp. The format of the station is rock/album-oriented rock. KZZK-FM broadcasts to the Quincy, IL, Hannibal, MO, Keokuk, IA area at 105.9 FM.

KZZL-FM
Owner: Inland Northwest Broadcasting
Editorial: 1114 N Almon St, Moscow, Idaho 83843. **T:** 1 208 882-2551
Editorial Profile: KZZL-FM is commercial station owned by Inland Northwest Broadcasting. The format of the station is contemporary country. KZZL-FM broadcasts to the Moscow, ID area at 99.5 FM.

KZZN-AM
Owner: Cody West
Editorial: 2651 County Road 191, Littlefield, Texas 79339-5846. **T:** 1 806 385-1490
W: http://www.kzznradio.com
Editorial Profile: KZZN-AM is a commercial station owned by Cody West. The format of the station is classic country. KZZN-AM broadcasts to the Littlefield, TX area at 1490 AM.

KZZO-FM
Owner: CBS Radio
Editorial: 280 Commerce Cir, Sacramento, California 95815. **T:** 1 916 923-6800
W: http://www.radiozone.com
Editorial Profile: KZZO-FM is a commercial station owned by CBS Radio. The format of the station is hot adult contemporary. KZZO-FM broadcasts to the Sacramento, CA area at 100.5 FM.

KZZP-FM
Owner: Clear Channel Media and Entertainment
Editorial: 4686 E Van Buren St, Phoenix, Arizona 85008-6959. **T:** 1 602 374-6000
W: http://www.1047kissfm.com
Editorial Profile: KZZP-FM is a commercial station owned by Clear Channel Media and Entertainment. The format of the station is Top 40/CHR. KZZP-FM broadcasts to the Phoenix area at 104.7 FM.

KZZR-FM
Owner: Bustos Media, LLC
Editorial: 5110 SE Stark St, Portland, Oregon 97215-1751. **T:** 1 503 234-5550
W: http://www.bustosmedia.com
Editorial Profile: KZZR-FM is a commercial station owned by Bustos Media, LLC. The format of the station is Hispanic. KZZR-FM broadcasts to the Tillamook, OR area at 94.3 FM.

KZZS-FM
Owner: Legend Communications
Editorial: 1221 Fort St, Buffalo, Wyoming 82834. **T:** 1 307 684-5126 **E:** klgt@vcn.com
Editorial Profile: KZZS-FM is a commercial station owned by Legend Communications. The format for the station is hot adult contemporary. KZZS-FM broadcasts to the Sheridan, WY area at 98.3 FM.

KZZT-FM
Owner: Best Broadcast Group
Editorial: 1037County Rd., suite 2326, Moberly, Missouri 65270. **T:** 1 660 263-9390
E: kzzt@bestbroadcastgroup.com
W: http://www.kzztradio.com
Editorial Profile: KZZT-FM is a commercial station owned by Best Broadcast Group. The format of the station is classic rock music. KZZT-FM broadcasts to the Brookfield, MO, area at 105.5 FM.

KZZU-FM
Owner: Queen B Inc.
Editorial: 500 W Boone Ave, Spokane, Washington 99201-2404. **T:** 1 509 323-9393
E: webmaster@kzzu.com
W: http://www.kzzu.com
Editorial Profile: KZZU-FM is a commercial station owned by Queen B Inc. The format of the station is hot adult contemporary. KZZU-FM broadcasts to the Spokane, WA area at 92.9 FM.

KZZX-FM
Owner: Burt Broadcasting Inc.
Editorial: 501 S Florida Ave, Alamogordo, New Mexico 88310. **T:** 1 575 434-1414
E: burtbroadcasting@bbiradio.net
Editorial Profile: KZZX-FM is a commercial station owned by Burt Broadcasting Inc. The format of the station is contemporary country. KZZX-FM broadcasts to the Alamagordo, NM area at 105.3 FM.

KZZY-FM
Owner: Double Z Broadcasting Inc.
Editorial: 320 Walnut St W, Devils Lake, North Dakota 58301-3506. **T:** 1 701 662-7563
E: kzzyfm@gondtc.com
W: http://www.lrradioworks.com
Editorial Profile: KZZY-FM is a commercial station owned by Double Z Broadcasting Inc. The format of the station is country music. KZZY-FM broadcasts to the Fargo, ND area at 103.5 FM.

KZZZ-AM
Owner: Cameron Broadcasting Inc.
Editorial: 2350 Miracle Mile Ste 300, Bullhead City, Arizona 86442-7505. **T:** 1 928 763-5586
E: news@cameronbroadcasting.com
W: http://www.talkatoz.com
Editorial Profile: KZZZ-AM is a commercial station owned by Cameron Broadcasting. The format of the station is news and talk programming. KZZZ-AM broadcasts to the Bullhead City, AZ area at 1490 AM.

Rádio Disney
Owner: Grupo Estado
Editorial: Av Celestino Bourroul, 100-2M, Sao Paulo 02710-000. **T:** 55 11 2108-6742
W: http://radiodisney.disney.com.br

Rádio Eldorado
Owner: Grupo Estado
Editorial: Av Celestino Bourroul, 100-2M, Sao Paulo 02710-000. **T:** 55 11 2108-6472
W: http://www.territorioeldorado.limao.com.br

Rádio Estadão FM
Owner: Grupo Estado
Editorial: Av Celestino Bourroul, 100-2M, Sao Paulo 02710-000. **T:** 55 11 3856-2122
W: http://radio.estadao.com.br

RAF-STL
Owner: Radio Arts Foundation
Editorial: 7711 Carondelet Ave Ste 302, Saint Louis, Missouri 63105-3313.
T: 1 314 881-3523 **E:** info@rafstl.org
W: http://www.rafstl.org
Editorial Profile: RAF-STL is the station for the Radio Arts Foundation in St. Louis, broadcasting classical music at 107.3 FM or 96.3-HD2. Radio Arts Foundation is a non-profit organization dedicated to filling the void left when longtime St. Louis classical station KFUO Classic 99 FM went off the air. The station includes broadcasts of live performances, interview with conductors, performers and music personalities, and programming that includes orchestral, chamber, jazz, blues, opera and symphonic music.

WAAC-FM
Owner: Rivers Radio Group
Editorial: 2973 US Highway 84 W, Valdosta, Georgia 31601. **T:** 1 229 242-4513
W: http://www.valdostasc93.com
Editorial Profile: WAAC-FM is a commercial station owned by Rivers Radio Group. The format of the station is contemporary country music. WAAC-FM broadcasts to the Valdosta, GA area at 92.9 FM.

WAAF-FM
Owner: Entercom Communications Corp.
Editorial: 20 Guest St, 3rd Fl, Boston, Massachusetts 2135. **T:** 1 617 779-5400
W: http://www.waaf.com
Editorial Profile: WAAF-FM is a commercial station owned by Entercom Communications Corp. The format of the station is rock/album-oriented rock. WAAF-FM broadcasts to the Boston area at 107.3 FM.

WAAG-FM
Owner: Galesburg Broadcasting Co.
Editorial: 154 E Simmons St, Galesburg, Illinois 61401-4658. **T:** 1 309 342-5131
E: fm95@fm95online.com
W: http://www.fm95online.com
Editorial Profile: WAAG-FM is a commercial station owned by Galesburg Broadcasting Co. The format of the station is country. WAAG-FM broadcasts to the Galesburg, IL area at 94.9 FM.

WAAI-FM
Owner: MTS Broadcasting LLC
Editorial: 2 Bay St, Cambridge, Maryland 21613. **T:** 1 410 228-4800
E: waai@mtslive.com
W: http://www.mtslive.com
Editorial Profile: WAAI-FM is a commercial station owned by MTS Broadcasting LLC. The format of the station is country music. WAAI-FM broadcasts to the Cambridge, MD area at 100.9 FM.

WAAJ-FM
Owner: Heartland Ministries, Inc.
Editorial: 219 College St, Hardin, Kentucky 42048. **T:** 1 270 437-4095
E: info@hmiradio.com
W: http://www.hmiradio.com/waaj
Editorial Profile: WAAJ-FM is a non-commercial station owned by Heartland Ministries, Inc. The format of the station is folk and bluegrass music. WAAJ-FM broadcasts to the Hardin, KY, area at 89.7 FM.

WAAL-FM
Owner: Townsquare Media, Inc.
Editorial: 59 Court St, Binghamton, New York 13901-3270. **T:** 1 607 772-8850
W: http://www.991thewhale.com
Editorial Profile: WAAL-FM is a commercial station owned by Townsquare Media, Inc. The format of the station is classic rock. WAAL-FM broadcasts to the Binghampton, NY area on 99.1 FM.

WAAM-AM
Owner: Coolarity A2, LLC
Editorial: 4230 Packard St, Ann Arbor, Michigan 48108-1508. **T:** 1 734 971-1600
W: http://www.waamradio.com
Editorial Profile: WAAM-AM is a commercial station owned by Coolarity A2, LLC. The format of the station is news and talk. WAAM-AM broadcasts to the Ann Arbor, MI area at 1600 AM.

WAAO-FM
Owner: Three Notch Communications, LLC
Editorial: 121 E Three Notch St, Andalusia, Alabama 36420-3120. **T:** 1 334 222-1166
E: waao@waao.com **W:** http://www.waao.com

WAAV-AM
Owner: Cumulus Media Inc.
Editorial: 3233 Burnt Mill Dr, Ste 4, Wilmington, North Carolina 28403.
T: 1 910 763-9977
W: http://www.980waav.com
Editorial Profile: WAAV-AM is a commercial station owned by Cumulus Media Inc. The format of the station is news, talk, and sports. WAAV-AM broadcasts in the Wilmington, NC area at 980 AM.

WAAX-AM
Owner: Clear Channel Media and Entertainment
Editorial: 304 S 4th St, Gadsden, Alabama 35901. **T:** 1 256 543-9229
W: http://www.waax570.com
Editorial Profile: WAAX-AM is a commercial station owned by Clear Channel Media and Entertainment. The format of the station is news, sports and talk. WAAX-AM broadcasts to the Gadsden, AL area at 570 AM.

WAAZ-FM
Owner: Whitaker(James T.)
Editorial: 506 W 1st Ave, Crestview, Florida 32536. **T:** 1 850 682-3040
E: waazwjsb@embarqmail.com
Editorial Profile: WAAZ-FM is a commercial station owned by James T. Whitaker. The format for the station is country. WAAZ-FM

broadcasts to the Mobile, AL, Pensacola, FL area at 104.7 FM.

WABC-AM
Owner: Cumulus Media Inc
Editorial: 2 Penn Plz, New York, New York 10121-0101. **T:** 1 212 613-3800
W: http://www.wabcradio.com
Editorial Profile: WABC-AM is a commercial station owned by Cumulus Media Inc. The format of the station is news and talk. WABC-AM broadcasts to the New York City area at 770 AM. The station does not accept press releases as most of their programming is syndicated.

WABD-FM
Owner: Cumulus Media
Editorial: 2800 Dauphin St Ste 104, Mobile, Alabama 36606-2400. **T:** 1 251 652-2000
W: http://www.975wabd.com
Editorial Profile: WABD-FM is a commercial station owned by Cumulus Media. The format of the station is Top 40/CHR. WABD-FM airs locally at 97.5 FM in Mobile, AL.

WABE-FM
Owner: City of Atlanta Board of Education
Editorial: 740 Bismark Rd NE, Atlanta, Georgia 30324-4102. **T:** 1 678 686-0321
W: http://wabe.org
Editorial Profile: WABE-FM is a non-commercial station owned by City of Atlanta Board of Education. The format of the station is classical music and news. WABE-FM broadcasts to the Atlanta area at 90.1 FM.

WABF-AM
Owner: Gulf Coast Broadcasting Company, Inc.
Editorial: 460 S Section St, Fairhope, Alabama 36532. **T:** 1 251 928-9228
E: wabf1220@bellsouth.net

WABG-AM
Owner: SPB LLC
Editorial: 68233 County Road 518, Greenwood, Mississippi 38930-7358.
T: 1 662 455-1688
W: http://www.awesomeam.com
Editorial Profile: WABG-AM is a commercial station owned by SPB LLC. The format of the station is blues, classic rock and news. WABG-AM broadcasts to the Greenwood, MS area at 960 AM.

WABH-AM
Owner: Pembrook Pines Media Group
Editorial: E Washington St Ext, Bath, New York 14810-9801. **T:** 1 607 776-3326
Editorial Profile: WABH-AM is a commercial station owned by Pembroke Pines Media Group. The format of the station is sports. WABH-AM broadcasts to the Bath, NY area at 1380 AM.

WABJ-AM
Owner: Friends Communications Inc.
Editorial: 121 W Maumee St, Adrian, Michigan 49221. **T:** 1 517 265-1500
E: friends@tc3net.com
Editorial Profile: WABJ-AM is a commercial station owned by Friends Communications Inc. The format of the station is news, sports and talk. WABJ-AM broadcasts to the Adrian, MI area at 1490 AM.

WABK-FM
Owner: Blueberry Broadcasting
Editorial: 125 Community Dr Ste 201, Augusta, Maine 04330-8157.
T: 1 207 623-9000
W: http://www.wabkfm.com
Editorial Profile: WABK-FM is a commercial station owned by Blueberry Broadcasting. The format of the station is classic hits. WABK-FM broadcasts to the Bangor, ME market at 104.3 FM.

WABL-AM
Owner: Spotlight Broadcasting of New Orleans LLC
Editorial: 12515 Bankston Rd, Amite, Louisiana 70422. **T:** 1 985 748-8385
Editorial Profile: WABL-AM is a commercial station owned by Spotlight Broadcasting of New Orleans LLC. The format of the station is country music, news and talk. WABL-AM broadcasts to the Amite, LA area at 1570 AM.

WABN-AM
Owner: Information Communications Corp.
Editorial: 1007A W Main St, Ste 100, Abingdon, Virginia 24210. **T:** 1 276 623-0030
E: wabn@wabn1230.com
W: http://www.wabn1230.com
Editorial Profile: WABN-AM is a commercial station owned by Information Communications Corp. The format of the station is oldies. WABN-AM broadcasts to the Washington, D.C. area at 1230 AM.

WABO-AM
Owner: Martin Broadcasting
Editorial: 6746 Highway 184, Waynesboro, Mississippi 39367-9288. **T:** 1 601 735-4331
E: wabofm@hotmail.com
W: http://www.105wabo.com
Editorial Profile: WABO-AM is a commercial station owned by Martin Broadcasting. The format of the station is classic hits. WABO-AM broadcasts to the Waynesboro, MS area at 990 AM.

WABO-FM
Owner: Martin Broadcasting
Editorial: 6746 Highway 184, Waynesboro, Mississippi 39367-9288. **T:** 1 601 735-4331
E: wabofm@hotmail.com
W: http://www.105wabo.com
Editorial Profile: WABO-FM is a commercial station owned by Martin Broadcasting. The format of the station is classic hits. WABO-FM broadcasts to the Waynesboro, MS area at 105.5 FM.

WABR-FM
Owner: Georgia Public Broadcasting
Editorial: 260 14th St NW, Atlanta, Georgia 30318. **T:** 1 404 685-2548 **E:** ask@gpb.org
W: http://www.gpb.org
Editorial Profile: WABR-FM is a non-commercial station owned by Georgia Public Broadcasting. The format of the station is news and classical and jazz music. WABR-FM broadcasts to the Atlanta area at 91.1 FM.

WABT-FM
Owner: Neversink Radio, LLC
Editorial: 15 Neversink Dr, Port Jervis, New York 12771-3811. **T:** 1 845 856-5185
E: news@pocono967.com
W: http://pocono967.com
Editorial Profile: WABT-FM is commercial station owned by Neversink Radio, LLC. The format of the station is classic hits. WABT-FM broadcasts to Port Jervis, NY and its surrounding area at 96.7 FM.

WABX-FM
Owner: South Central Communications Corp.
Editorial: 1162 Mount Auburn Rd, Evansville, Indiana 47720. **T:** 1 812 424-8284
W: http://www.wabx.net
Editorial Profile: WABX-FM is a commercial station owned by South Central Communications Corp. The format of the station is classic rock. WBAX-FM broadcasts to the Evansville, IN area at 107.5 FM.

WABY-AM
Owner: Empire Broadcasting Corporation
Editorial: 100 Saratoga Village Blvd, Malta, New York 12020-3737. **T:** 1 518 899-3000
E: wabymoon@aol.com
W: http://www.wabyalbany.com
Editorial Profile: WABY-AM is a commercial station owned by Empire Broadcasting Corporation. The format of the station is adult standards music. WABY-AM broadcasts to the Albany, NY area at 1160 AM.

WACA-AM
Owner: AC Aquisitions LLC
Editorial: 11141 Georgia Ave, Ste 310, Wheaton, Maryland 20902. **T:** 1 301 942-3500
W: http://www.radioamerica.net
Editorial Profile: WACA-AM is a commercial station owned by AC Acquisitions LLC. The format of the station is Spanish talk. WACA-AM broadcasts in the Washington, D.C. area at 1540 AM.

WACB-AM
Owner: Apple City Broadcasting Co.
Editorial: 133 E Main Ave, Taylorsville, North Carolina 28681-2514. **T:** 1 828 632-4621
E: news@applecitybroadcasting.com
Editorial Profile: WACB-AM is a commercial station owned by Apple City Broadcasting Co. The format of the station is country. WACB-AM broadcasts to the Charlotte, NC area at 860 AM.

WACC-AM
Owner: Radio Peace Catholic Broadcasting, Inc (Archdiocese of Miami)
Editorial: 1779 NW 28th St, Miami, Florida 33142. **T:** 1 305 638-9729
E: radiopaz830am@gmail.com
W: http://www.paxcc.org/radiopaz
Editorial Profile: WACC-AM is a commercial station owned by Radio Peace Catholic Broadcasting, Inc (Archdiocese of Miami). The format of the station is Spanish religious programming. WACC-AM broadcasts to the Miami area at 830 AM.

WACD-FM
Owner: Results Broadcasting, Inc.
Editorial: N2237 US Highway 45 S, Antigo, Wisconsin 54409. **T:** 1 715 623-4124
E: wacdwatk@yahoo.com
W: http://www.country106.fm
Editorial Profile: WACD-FM is a commercial station owned by Results Broadcasting, Inc. The format of the station is contemporary country music. WACD-FM broadcasts to the Antigo, WI area at 106.1 FM.

WACE-AM
Owner: Carter Broadcasting
Editorial: 326 Chicopee St, Chicopee, Massachusetts 1013. **T:** 1 413 594-6654
W: http://www.waceradio.com
Editorial Profile: WACE-AM is a commercial station owned by Carter Broadcasting. The format of the station is religious talk. WACE-AM broadcasts in the greater Springfield, MA area at 730 AM.

WACG-FM
Owner: Georgia Public Broadcasting
Editorial: 260 14th St NW, Atlanta, Georgia 30318. **T:** 1 404 685-2548 **E:** ask@gpb.org
W: http://www.gpb.org
Editorial Profile: WACG-FM is a non-commercial station owned by Georgia Public Broadcasting. The format of the station is news, jazz and classical music. WACG-FM broadcasts to the Atlanta area at 89.5 FM.

WACK-AM
Owner: Waynco Radio Inc.
Editorial: 187 Vienna Rd, Newark, New York 14513-9124. **T:** 1 315 331-1420
E: 1420wack@rochester.rr.com
W: http://www.1420wack.com
Editorial Profile: WACK-AM is a commercial station owned by Waynco Radio Inc. The format of the station is news and talk programming. WACK-AM broadcasts to the Newark, NY area at 1420 AM.

WACL-FM
Owner: Clear Channel Media and Entertainment
Editorial: 207 University Blvd, Harrisonburg, Virginia 22801-3749. **T:** 1 540 434-1777
W: http://www.98rockme.com
Editorial Profile: WACL-FM is a commercial station owned by Clear Channel Media and Entertainment. The format of the station is rock music. WACL-FM broadcasts to the Harrisonburg, VA area at 98.5 FM.

WACM-AM
Owner: Davidson Media Group
Editorial: 34 Sylvan St, West Springfield, Massachusetts 1089. **T:** 1 413 781-5200
W: http://www.wacmpopular1490.com
Editorial Profile: WACM-AM is a commercial station owned by Davidson Media Group. The format of the station is Hispanic music and news. WACM-AM broadcasts in the West Springfield, MA area at 1490 AM.

WACO-FM
Owner: Clear Channel Media and Entertainment
Editorial: 314 W State Highway 6, Waco, Texas 76712. **T:** 1 254 776-3900
W: http://www.waco100.com
Editorial Profile: WACO-FM is a commercial station owned by Clear Channel Media and Entertainment. The format of the station is country music. WACO-FM broadcasts to the Waco, TX area at 99.9 FM.

WACQ-AM
Owner: Tiger Communications Inc.
Editorial: 320 Barnett Blvd, Tallassee, Alabama 36078-1506. **T:** 1 334 283-6888
E: wacqradio@elmore.rr.com
W: http://www.wacqradio.com
Editorial Profile: WBIL-AM is a commercial station owned by Tiger Communications Inc and operated by Fred Hughey. The format is oldies music. The station airs in the Tuskegee, AL area at 580 AM.

WACR-FM
Owner: URBan Radio Broadcasting, LLC
Editorial: 608 Yellow Jacket Dr, Starkville, Mississippi 39759. **T:** 1 662 338-5424
W: http://www.wacr1053.com
Editorial Profile: WACR-FM is a commercial station owned by URBan Radio Broadcasting, LLC. The format of the station is Urban Adult Contemporary. WACR-FM broadcasts to the Columbus/Starkville, MS area at a frequency of 105.7 FM.

WACT-AM
Owner: Clear Channel Media and Entertainment
Editorial: 3900 11Th Ave, Tuscaloosa, Alabama 35401-7056. **T:** 1 205 344-4589
Editorial Profile: WACT-AM is a commercial station owned by Clear Channel Media and Entertainment. The format of the station is comedy. WACT-AM broadcasts to the Tuscaloosa, AL area at 1420 AM.

WACV-FM
Owner: Bluewater Broadcasting, LLC
Editorial: 4101 Wall St Ste A, Montgomery, Alabama 36106-3724. **T:** 1 334 244-0961
W: http://bluewaterbroadcasting.com
Editorial Profile: WACV-FM is a commercial station owned by Bluewater Broadcasting, LLC. The format of the station is news/talk. WACV-FM broadcasts to the Montgomery, AL area at a frequency of 93.1 FM.

WADB-AM
Owner: Townsquare Media
Editorial: 8 Robbins St, Toms River, New Jersey 08753-7668. **T:** 1 848 221-8000
E: jerseyshorenews@wobmam.com
W: http://wobmam.com
Editorial Profile: WADB-AM is a commercial station owned by Townsquare Media. The format of the station is news and talk. WADB-AM broadcasts in the Ocean, NJ, area at 1310 AM.

WADC-AM
Owner: Burbach of WV, LLC
Editorial: 5 Rosemar Cir, Parkersburg, West Virginia 26104. **T:** 1 304 485-4565
Editorial Profile: WADC-AM is a commercial station owned by Burbach of WV, LLC. The format for the station is adult standards. WADC-AM broadcasts to the Parkersburg, WV area at 1050 AM.

WADE-AM
Owner: Inspirational Deliverance Center Inc
Editorial: 65 Radio Tower Rd, Wadesboro, North Carolina 28170. **T:** 1 704 695-1060
Editorial Profile: WADE-AM is a commercial station owned by Inspirational Deliverance Center Inc. The format of the station is urban gospel with some religious teaching programming. WADE-AM broadcasts in the Wadesboro, NC area at 1340 AM.

WADI-FM
Owner: Power Valley Communications Inc.
Editorial: 121 Front St, Iuka, Mississippi 38852. **T:** 1 662 423-9533
E: wadi@bellsouth.net
Editorial Profile: WADI-FM is a commercial station owned by Power Valley Communications Inc. The format of the station is contemporary country. WADI-FM broadcasts to the Iuka, MS area at 95.3 FM.

WADK-AM
Owner: 3G Broadcasting, Inc.
Editorial: 30 Dagnillo Dr, East Greenwich, Rhode Island 02818-4069. **T:** 1 401 846-1540
Editorial Profile: WADK-AM is a commercial station owned by 3G Broadcasting, Inc. The format of the station is news and talk. WADK-AM broadcasts to the Newport, RI area at 1540 AM.

WADO-AM
Owner: Univision Communications Inc.
Editorial: 485 Madison Ave, Fl 3, New York, New York 10022. **T:** 1 212 310-6000
W: http://www.univision.com/content/channel.jhtml?chid=9486&schid=9722
Editorial Profile: WADO-AM is a commercial station owned by Univision Communications Inc. The format of the station is a variety of Hispanic news and talk. WADO-AM broadcasts to the New York metro area at 1280 AM.

WADS-AM
Owner: Amor II Inc.
Editorial: 261 Portsea St, New Haven, Connecticut 6519. **T:** 1 203 777-7690
E: radioamorwads@sbcglobal.net
Editorial Profile: WADS-AM is a commercial station owned by Amor II Inc. The format of the station is Hispanic religious programming. WADS-AM broadcasts to the Hartford-New Haven, CT area at 690 AM.

WADV-AM
Owner: WADV Radio Inc.
Editorial: 720 E Kercher Ave, Lebanon, Pennsylvania 17046-9230. **T:** 1 717 273-2611

WORLD NEWS MEDIA

Editorial Profile: WADV-AM is a commercial station owned by WADV Radio Inc. The format of the station is gospel music. WADV-AM broadcasts in the Lebanon, PA area in the 940 AM.

WAEB-AM

Owner: Clear Channel Media and Entertainment
Editorial: 1541 Alta Dr, Ste 400, Whitehall, Pennsylvania 18052. **T:** 1 610 434-1742
W: http://www.waeb.com
Editorial Profile: WAEB-AM is a commercial station owned by Clear Channel Media and Entertainment. The format of the station is news, sports and talk. WAEB-AM broadcasts to the Whitehall, PA area at 790 AM.

WAEB-FM

Owner: Clear Channel Media and Entertainment
Editorial: 1541 Alta Dr, Ste 400, Whitehall, Pennsylvania 18052. **T:** 1 610 434-1742
W: http://www.b104.com
Editorial Profile: WAEB-FM is a commercial station owned by Clear Channel Media and Entertainment. The format of the station is Top 40/CHR. WAEB-FM broadcasts to the Whitehall, PA area at 104.1 FM.

WAEC-AM

Owner: Beasley Broadcast Group
Editorial: 1465 Northside Dr NW, Ste 218, Atlanta, Georgia 30318-4239.
T: 1 404 355-8600
W: http://www.love860.com
Editorial Profile: WAEC-AM is a commercial station owned by Beasley Broadcast Group. The format of the station is Christian. WAEC-AM broadcasts to the Atlanta area at 860 AM.

WAEF-FM

Owner: American Family Association
Editorial: 107 Park Gate Dr, Tupelo, Mississippi 38801. **T:** 1 662 844-8888
E: comments@afr.net **W:** http://www.afr.net

WAEG-FM

Owner: Perry Broadcasting Company, Inc.
Editorial: 411 Radio Station Rd, North Augusta, South Carolina 29841.
T: 1 803 279-2330
W: http://923smoothjazz.com
Editorial Profile: WAEG-FM is a commercial station owned by Perry Broadcasting Company, Inc. The format of the station is smooth jazz. WAEG-FM broadcasts to the North Augusta, SC area at 92.3 FM.

WAEI-AM

Owner: Blueberry Broadcasting
Editorial: 184 Target Cir, Bangor, Maine 04401-5718. **T:** 1 207 947-9100
Editorial Profile: WAEI-AM is a commercial station owned by Blueberry Broadcasting. The format of the station is sports. WAEI-AM broadcasts to the Bangor, ME area at 910 AM.

WAER-FM

Owner: Syracuse University
Editorial: 795 Ostrom Ave, Syracuse, New York 13210-2945. **T:** 1 315 443-4021
E: waerfm88@mailbox.syr.edu
W: http://www.waer.org
Editorial Profile: WAER-FM is a non-commercial station owned by Syracuse University. The format of the station is primarily news and talk. WAER-FM broadcasts to the Syracuse, NY area at 88.3 FM.

WAEV-FM

Owner: Clear Channel Media and Entertainment
Editorial: 245 Alfred St, Savannah, Georgia 31408-3205. **T:** 1 912 964-7794
E: programming@973kissfm.com
W: http://www.973kissfm.com
Editorial Profile: WAEV-FM is a commercial station owned by Clear Channel Media and Entertainment. The format of the station is Top 40/CHR. WAEV-FM broadcasts to the Savannah, GA area at 97.3 FM.

WAEW-AM

Owner: Peg Broadcasting Crossville, LLC
Editorial: 961 Miller Ave, Crossville, Tennessee 38555. **T:** 1 931 707-1102
E: production.crossville@pegbroadcasting.com
W: http://www.1330waew.com
Editorial Profile: WAEW-AM is a commercial station owned by Peg Broadcasting Crossville, LLC. The format of the station is talk and oldies. WAEW-AM broadcasts to the Crossville, TN area at 1330 AM.

WAEY-AM

Owner: L & P Broadcasting Inc.
Editorial: 1 Radio Ln, Princeton, West Virginia 24740. **T:** 1 304 425-2151
W: http://www.959wstg.com
Editorial Profile: WAEY-AM is a commercial station owned by L & P Broadcasting Inc. The format of the station is gospel. WAEY-AM broadcasts to the Princeton, WV area at 1490 AM.

WAEZ-FM

Owner: Bristol Broadcasting
Editorial: 901 E Valley Dr, Bristol, Virginia 24201. **T:** 1 276 669-8112
W: http://www.electric949.com
Editorial Profile: WAEZ-FM is a commercial station owned by Bristol Broadcasting. The format of the station is Top 40/CHR. WAEZ-FM broadcasts to the Bristol, VA area at 94.9 FM.

WAFC-AM

Owner: Glades Media Co.
Editorial: 530 E Alverdez Ave, Clewiston, Florida 33440-3901. **T:** 1 863 983-6106
W: http://www.radiofiesta.com
Editorial Profile: WAFC-AM is a commercial station owned by Glades Media Co. The format of the station is oldies. WAFC-AM broadcasts to the Clewiston, FL area at 590 AM.

WAFC-FM

Owner: BMZ Broadcasting, LLC
Editorial: 530 E Alverdez Ave, Clewiston, Florida 33440-3901. **T:** 1 863 983-6106
W: http://www.radiofiesta.com
Editorial Profile: WAFC-FM is a commercial station owned by BMZ Broadcasting, LLC and operated by Glades Media Co. The format of the station is regional Mexican. WAFC-FM broadcasts to the Okeechobee, FL area at 106.1 FM. The station is a simulcast of sister WAFC-AM 590.

WAFD-FM

Owner: Summit Media Broadcasting LLC
Editorial: 180 Main St, Sutton, West Virginia 26601-1317. **T:** 1 304 765-7373
E: production@theboss97fm.com
W: http://www.summitmediawv.com
Editorial Profile: WAFD-FM is a commercial station owned by Summit Media Broadcasting LLC. The format of the station is urban adult contemporary music. WAFD-FM broadcasts to the Sutton, WV area at 100.3 FM.

WAFJ-FM

Owner: Radio Training Network, Inc.
Editorial: 102 Lecompte Ave, North Augusta, South Carolina 29841. **T:** 1 803 819-3125
E: info@wafj.com **W:** http://www.wafj.com
Editorial Profile: WAFJ-FM is a non-commercial station owned by Radio Training Network, Inc. The format of the station is Contemporary Christian. WAFJ-AM broadcasts to the North Augusta, SC area at 88.3 FM.

WAFL-FM

Owner: Delmarva Broadcasting
Editorial: 1666 Blairs Pond Rd, Milford, Delaware 19963-5263. **T:** 1 302 422-7575
E: staff@eagle977.com
W: http://www.eagle977.com
Editorial Profile: WAFL-FM is a commercial station owned by Delmarva Broadcasting. The format of the station is hot AC. WAFL-FM broadcasts to the Milford, DE area at 97.7 FM.

WAFM-FM

Owner: Stanford Communications Inc.
Editorial: 521 Highway 278 W, Amory, Mississippi 38821. **T:** 1 662 256-9726
E: fm95@fm95radio.com
W: http://www.fm95radio.com
Editorial Profile: WAFM-FM is a commercial station owned by Stanford Communications Inc. The format of the station is oldies. WAFM-FM broadcasts to the Amory, MS area at 95.3 FM.

WAFN-FM

Owner: Fun Media Group
Editorial: 981 N Brindlee Mountain Pkwy, Arab, Alabama 35016-1058.
T: 1 256 586-9300 **W:** http://www.fun927.com
Editorial Profile: WAFN-FM is a commercial station owned by Fun Media Group. The format of the station is oldies. WAFM-FM broadcasts to the Arab, AL area at 92.7 FM.

WAFR-FM

Owner: American Family Association
Editorial: 107 Parkgate Dr, Tupelo, Mississippi 38801. **T:** 1 662 844-8888
E: comments@afr.net **W:** http://www.afr.net

WAFS-AM

Owner: Salem Communications
Editorial: 2970 Peachtree Rd NW, Ste 700, Atlanta, Georgia 30305. **T:** 1 404 995-7300
W: http://www.biz1190.com
Editorial Profile: WAFS-AM is a commercial station owned by Salem Communications. The format of the station is business news. WAFS-AM broadcasts to the Atlanta area at 1190 AM.

WAFT-FM

Owner: Christian Radio Fellowship Inc.
Editorial: 215 Waft Hill Ln, Valdosta, Georgia 31602-6512. **T:** 1 229 244-5180
E: mail@waft.org **W:** http://www.waft.org
Editorial Profile: WAFT-FM is a non-commercial station owned by the Christian Radio Fellowship Inc. The format of the station is Christian music and talk. WAFT-FM broadcasts to the Valdosta, GA area at 101.1 FM.

WAFX-FM

Owner: Saga Communications
Editorial: 870 Greenbrier Cir Ste 399, Chesapeake, Virginia 23320-2671.
T: 1 757 366-9900
W: http://www.1069thefox.com
Editorial Profile: WAFX-FM is a commercial station owned by Saga Communications. The format of the station is classic hits. WAFX-FM broadcasts to the Norfolk, VA area at 106.9 FM.

WAFY-FM

Owner: Manning Broadcasting Inc.
Editorial: 5742 Industry Ln, Frederick, Maryland 21704-5191. **T:** 1 301 620-7700
W: http://www.key103radio.com
Editorial Profile: WAFY-FM is a commercial station owned by Manning Broadcasting Inc. The format of the station is Hot AC. WAFY-FM broadcasts to the Frederick, MD area at 103.1 FM.

WAFZ-AM

Owner: Glades Media Co.
Editorial: 2105 Immokalee Dr, Immokalee, Florida 34142-3321. **T:** 1 239 657-9210
E: info@gladesmedia.com
W: http://www.radiofiesta.com
Editorial Profile: WAFZ-AM is a commercial station owned by the Glades Media Co. The format of the station is regional Mexican music. WAFZ-AM broadcasts to the Immokalee, FL area at 1490 AM.

WAFZ-FM

Owner: Glades Media Co.
Editorial: 2105 Immokalee Dr, Immokalee, Florida 34142-3321. **T:** 1 239 657-9210
E: info@gladesmedia.com
W: http://www.wafz.com
Editorial Profile: WAFZ-FM is a commercial station owned by Glades Media Co. The format of the station is Regional Mexican. WAFZ-FM broadcasts to the Immokalee, FL area at 92.1 FM.

WAGF-FM

Owner: Wilson Broadcasting, Inc.
Editorial: 4106 Ross Clark Cir, Dothan, Alabama 36303. **T:** 1 334 671-1753
W: http://www.wjjn.net

WAGG-AM

Owner: Summit Media Broadcasting LLC
Editorial: 2700 Corporate Dr Ste 115, Birmingham, Alabama 35242-2735.
T: 1 205 322-2987
W: http://www.610wagg.com
Editorial Profile: WAGG-AM is a commercial station owned by Summit Media Broadcasting LLC. The format of the station is gospel. WAGG-AM broadcasts to the Birmingham, AL area at 610 AM.

WAGH-FM

Owner: Clear Channel Media and Entertainment
Editorial: 1501 13th Ave, Columbus, Georgia 31901. **T:** 1 706 576-3000
E: info@magic101online.com
W: http://www.mymagic101.com
Editorial Profile: WAGH-FM is a commercial station owned by Clear Channel Media and Entertainment. The format of the station is urban adult contemporary. WAGH-FM broadcasts to the Columbus, GA area at 101.3 FM.

WAGL-AM

Owner: Phillips(Len)
Editorial: 101 S Woodland Dr, Lancaster, South Carolina 29720-2244.
T: 1 803 283-8431

E: waglradio@comporium.net
W: http://www.waglradio.com
Editorial Profile: WAGL-AM is a commercial station owned by Len Phillips. The format of the station is Southern gospel and oldies. WAGL-AM broadcasts to the Lancaster, SC area at 1560 AM.

WAGN-AM

Owner: Radio Plus Bay Cities, LLC
Editorial: 413 10th Ave, Menominee, Michigan 49858-3009. **T:** 1 906 863-5551
E: reception@baycitiesradio.net
W: http://www.baycitiesradio.net
Editorial Profile: WAGN-AM is a commercial station owned by Radio Plus Bay Cities, LLC. The format of the station is talk. WAGN-AM broadcasts to the Menominee, MI area at 1340 AM.

WAGO-FM

Owner: Pathway Christian Academy Inc.
Editorial: 205 N Greene St, Snow Hill, North Carolina 28580. **T:** 1 252 747-8887
E: wago@gomixradio.org
W: http://www.gomixradio.org
Editorial Profile: WAGO-FM is a non-commercial station owned by Pathway Christian Academy Inc. The format of the station is gospel music and religious programming. WAGO-FM broadcasts to the Snow Hill, NC area at 88.7 FM.

WAGP-FM

Owner: Community Broadcasting Corp.
Editorial: 638 Terrace Island Gateway, Beaufort, South Carolina 29906.
T: 1 843 525-1859 **E:** info@wagp.net
W: http://www.wagp.net

WAGR-AM

Owner: Service Media Inc.
Editorial: 5102 Durham Chapel Hill Blvd, Durham, North Carolina 27707.
T: 1 910 486-9438
Editorial Profile: WAGR-AM is a commercial station owned by Service Media Inc. The format of the station is gospel. WAGR-AM broadcasts to the Durham, NC area at 1340 AM.

WAGR-FM

Owner: Sandra U. Cothran, Executrix
Editorial: 100 Radio Road, Lexington, Mississippi 39095. **T:** 1 662 834-1025
Editorial Profile: WAGR-FM is a commercial station owned by Sandra U. Cothran, Executrix. The format of the station is R&B Oldies. WAGR-FM broadcasts to the Lexington, MS area at 102.5 FM.

WAGS-AM

Owner: Beaver Communications
Editorial: 142 Wags Dr, Bishopville, South Carolina 29010. **T:** 1 803 484-5415
E: wagsradio@sc.rr.com
W: http://www.wagsradio.com
Editorial Profile: WAGS-AM is a commercial station owned by Beaver Communications. The format of the station is country. WAGS-AM broadcasts to the Bishopville, SC area at 1380 AM.

WAGY-AM

Owner: Watson & Dobbins Inc.
Editorial: 129 N Powell St, Ste 223, Forest City, North Carolina 28043-3109.
T: 1 828 245-9887
E: wagy1320am@yahoo.com
W: http://www.realcountryonline.com
Editorial Profile: WAGY-AM is a commercial station owned by Watson & Dobbins Inc. The format of the station is classic country. WAGY-AM broadcasts to the Forest City, NC area at 1320 AM.

WAHR-FM

Owner: Black Crow Broadcasting Inc.
Editorial: 1555 The Boardwalk, Ste 1, Huntsville, Alabama 35816-1821.
T: 1 256 536-1568
E: psa@rocketcitybroadcasting.com
W: http://rocketcitynews.com
Editorial Profile: WAHR-FM is a commercial station owned by Black Crow Broadcasting Inc. The format of the station is adult contemporary. WAHR-FM broadcasts to the Huntsville, AL area at 99.1 FM.

WAIC-FM

Owner: American International College
Editorial: 1000 State St, Springfield, Massachusetts 01109-3151.
T: 1 413 205-3941 **W:** http://www.cpbn.org
Editorial Profile: WAIC-FM is a non-commercial station owned by American International College. The format of the station

is news/talk. WAIC-FM broadcasts to the Springfield, MA area at 91.9 FM.

WAID-FM
Owner: Radio Cleveland Inc.
Editorial: 911 S Davis Ave, Cleveland, Mississippi 38732-3941. **T:** 1 662 627-2281
Editorial Profile: WAID-FM is a commercial station owned by Radio Cleveland Inc. The format of the station is urban contemporary music. WAID-FM broadcasts to the Cleveland, MS, area at 106.5 FM.

WAIF-FM
Owner: Stepchild Radio of Cincinnati
Editorial: 1434 E McMillan St, Cincinnati, Ohio 45206-2225. **T:** 1 513 961-8900
E: waifcincinnati@gmail.com
W: http://www.waif883.org
Editorial Profile: WAIF-FM is a non-commercial station owned by Stepchild Radio of Cincinnati. The format of the station is variety. WAIF-FM broadcasts to the Cincinnati area at 88.3 FM.

WAIH-FM
Owner: State University of New York
Editorial: 9050 Barrington Dr, Potsdam, New York 13676. **T:** 1 315 267-4888
E: waih@potsdam.edu
Editorial Profile: WAIH-FM is a non-commercial college station owned by State University of New York. The format of the station is variety. WAIH-FM broadcasts to the Potsdam, NY area at 90.3 FM.

WAIJ-FM
Owner: He's Alive Inc.
Editorial: 34 Springs Road, Grantsville, Maryland 21536. **T:** 1 301 895-3292
E: info@hesalive.net
W: http://www.hesalive.net
Editorial Profile: WAIJ-FM is a non-commercial station owned by He's Alive Inc. The format of the station is contemporary Christian and gospel music. WAIJ-FM broadcasts to the Grantsville, MD area at 90.3 FM.

WAIK-AM
Owner: Prairie Communications LLP
Editorial: 55 Public Sq, Monmouth, Illinois 61462-1755. **T:** 1 309 734-9452
E: wmoi@maplecity.com
W: http://www.1590waik.com
Editorial Profile: WAIK-AM is a commercial station owned by Prairie Communications LLP. The format of the station is news and talk. WAIK-AM broadcasts to the Monmouth, IL area at 1590 AM.

WAIL-FM
Owner: Florida Keys Media, LLC
Editorial: 93351 Overseas Hwy, Tavernier, Florida 33070-2800. **T:** 1 305 852-9085
Editorial Profile: WAIL-FM is a commercial station owned by Florida Keys Media, LLC. The format of the station is classic rock. WAIL-FM broadcasts to the Key West, FL area at 99.5 FM.

WAIM-AM
Owner: Palmetto Broadcasting Inc.
Editorial: 2203 Old Williamston Rd, Anderson, South Carolina 29621-3036.
T: 1 864 226-1511 **E:** info@waim.us
W: http://www.waim.us
Editorial Profile: WAIM-AM is a commercial station owned by Palmetto Broadcasting Inc. The format of the station is news and talk. WAIM-AM broadcasts to the Anderson, SC area at 1230 AM.

WAIN-AM
Owner: Forcht Broadcasting
Editorial: 1521 Liberty Rd, Columbia, Kentucky 42728. **T:** 1 270 384-2135
E: wain@forchtbroadcasting.com
W: http://www.1270wain.com
Editorial Profile: WAIN-AM is a commercial station owned by Forcht Broadcasting. The format of the station is sports. WAIN-AM broadcasts to the Columbia, KY area at 1270 AM.

WAIN-FM
Owner: Forcht Broadcasting
Editorial: 1521 Liberty Rd, Columbia, Kentucky 42728. **T:** 1 270 384-2135
E: wain@forchtbroadcasting.com
W: http://www.935wain.com
Editorial Profile: WAIN-FM is a commercial station owned by Forcht Broadcasting. The format of the station is contemporary country. WAIN-FM broadcasts to the Columbia, KY area at 95.3 FM.

WAIS-AM
Owner: Nelsonville TV Cable Inc.
Editorial: 15751 US Highway 33, Nelsonville, Ohio 45764-9304. **T:** 1 740 753-4094
E: wseo33@nelsonvilletv.com
Editorial Profile: WAIS-AM is a commercial station owned by Nelsonville TV Cable Inc. The format of the station is classic country, news and talk. WAIS-AM broadcasts to the Nelsonville, OH area at 770 AM.

WAIT-AM
Owner: Newsweb Corp.
Editorial: 5625 N Milwaukee Ave, Chicago, Illinois 60646-6221. **T:** 1 773 792-1121
W: http://www.thepromise850.com
Editorial Profile: WAIT-AM is a commercial station owned by Newsweb Corp. The format of the station is bilingual Christian. WAIT-AM broadcasts to the Chicago area at 850 AM. The station airs brokered programming.

WAIV-FM
Owner: Equity Communications LP
Editorial: 8025 Black Horse Pike, Pleasantville, New Jersey 08232-2900. **T:** 1 609 484-8444
W: http://sunny1023.com
Editorial Profile: WAIV-FM is a commercial station owned by Equity Communications LP. The format of the station is classic hits music. WAIV-FM broadcasts to the West Atlantic City, NJ area at 95.1 FM.

WAIZ-AM
Owner: Newton-Conover Communications, Inc.
Editorial: 1666 Radio Station Rd, Newton, North Carolina 28658-9488.
T: 1 828 322-9472
W: http://mytotalradio.com/WAIZ
Editorial Profile: WAIZ-AM is a commercial station owned by Newton-Conover Communications, Inc. The format of the station is oldies music. WAIZ-AM broadcasts to the Charlotte, NC area at 630 AM.

WAJC-FM
Owner: Religious Information Network
Editorial: 2993 Snelling Ave N #M160, Saint Paul, Minnesota 55113-1412.
T: 1 651 307-1507 **W:** http://theremnant.org/
Editorial Profile: WAJC-FM is a non-commercial station owned by Religious Information Network. The format of the station is Christian CHR/Rock music. WAJC-FM broadcasts to the Minneapolis-St. Paul, MN area at a frequency of 88.1 FM.

WAJI-FM
Owner: Sarkes Tarzian Inc.
Editorial: 347 W Berry St Ste 417, Fort Wayne, Indiana 46802-2241.
T: 1 260 423-3676
W: http://www.951bestfm.com
Editorial Profile: WAJI-FM is a commercial station owned by Sarkes Tarzian Inc. The format of the station is adult contemporary. WAJI-FM broadcasts to the Fort Wayne, IN area at 95.1 FM.

WAJK-FM
Owner: LaSalle County Broadcasting Corp.
Editorial: 1 Broadcast Ln, Oglesby, Illinois 61348-9539. **T:** 1 815 223-3100
E: events@993wajk.com
W: http://www.wajk.com
Editorial Profile: WAJK-FM is a commercial station owned by LaSalle County Broadcasting Corp. The format of the station is hot adult contemporary. WAJK-FM broadcasts to the Chicago area at 99.3 FM.

WAJQ-AM
Owner: Blueberry Broadcasting Co.
Editorial: 208 Douglas St, Alma, Georgia 31510. **T:** 1 912 632-1000
Editorial Profile: WAJQ-AM is a commercial station owned by Blueberry Broadcasting Co. The format of the station is gospel. WAJQ-AM broadcasts to the Alma, GA area at 1400 AM.

WAJQ-FM
Owner: Blueberry Broadcasting Co.
Editorial: 208 Douglas St, Alma, Georgia 31510. **T:** 1 912 632-1000
Editorial Profile: WAJQ-FM is a commercial station owned by Blueberry Broadcasting Co. The format of the station is country music. WAJQ-FM broadcasts to the Alma, GA area at 104.3 FM.

WAJR-AM
Owner: West Virginia Radio Corp.
Editorial: 1251 Earl L Core Rd, Morgantown, West Virginia 26505-5881. **T:** 1 304 296-0029
E: wajr@wvradio.com **W:** http://www.wajr.com
Editorial Profile: WAJR-AM is a commercial station owned by West Virginia Radio Corp.

The format of the station is news, talk, and sports. WAJR-AM broadcasts to the Morgantown, WV area at 1440 AM.

WAJR-FM
Owner: West Virginia Radio Corp.
Editorial: 1065 Radio Park Dr, Mount Clare, West Virginia 26408. **T:** 1 304 623-6546
E: wajr@wvradio.com
W: http://www.wajrfm.com
Editorial Profile: WAJR-FM is a commercial station owned by West Virginia Radio Corp. The format of the station is news, sports, and talk. WAJR-FM broadcasts to the Mount Clare, WV area at 103.3 FM.

WAJV-FM
Owner: URBan Radio Broadcasting, LLC
Editorial: 608 Yellow Jacket Dr, Starkville, Mississippi 39759. **T:** 1 662 338-5424
W: http://www.joy989.com
Editorial Profile: WAJV-FM is a commercial station owned by URBan Radio Broadcasting, LLC. The format of the station is gospel. WAJV-FM broadcasts to the Starkville, MS area at 98.9 FM.

WAJZ-FM
Owner: Albany Broadcasting Co.
Editorial: 6 Johnson Rd, Latham, New York 12110. **T:** 1 518 786-6600
W: http://www.jamz963.com
Editorial Profile: WAJZ-FM is a commercial station owned by Albany Broadcasting Co. The format of the station is urban contemporary. WAJZ-FM broadcasts to the Latham, NY area at 96.3 FM.

WAKB-FM
Owner: Perry Broadcasting Company, Inc.
Editorial: 411 Radio Station Rd, North Augusta, South Carolina 29841.
T: 1 803 279-2330
W: http://www.1009magic.com
Editorial Profile: WAKB-FM is a commercial station owned by Perry Broadcasting Company, Inc. The format of the station is urban adult contemporary. WAKB-FM broadcasts to the North Augusta, SC area at 100.9 FM.

WAKE-AM
Owner: Radio One Inc.
Editorial: 2755 Sager Rd, Valparaiso, Indiana 46383-0721. **T:** 1 219 462-6111
E: news@radiooneindiana.com
W: http://www.wakeradio.com
Editorial Profile: WAKE-AM is a commercial station owned by Radio One Inc. The format of the station is oldies. WAKE-AM broadcasts to the Valparaiso, IN area at 1500 AM.

WAKG-FM
Owner: Piedmont Broadcasting Corporation
Editorial: 710 Grove St, Danville, Virginia 24541-1704. **T:** 1 434 797-4290
E: wakg@wakg.com **W:** http://www.wakg.com
Editorial Profile: WAKG-FM is a commercial station owned by Piedmont Broadcasting Corporation. The format of the station is contemporary and classic country. WAKG-FM broadcasts to the Danville, VA area at 103.3 FM.

WAKH-FM
Owner: Southwest Broadcasting
Editorial: 206 N Front St, McComb, Mississippi 39648-3916. **T:** 1 601 684-4116
E: spots@k106.net **W:** http://www.k106.net
Editorial Profile: WAKH-FM is a commercial station owned by Southwest Broadcasting. The format of the station is country. WAKH-FM broadcasts to the McComb, MS area at 105.7 FM.

WAKI-AM
Owner: Peg Broadcasting
Editorial: 230 W Colville St, Mc Minnville, Tennessee 37110-3211. **T:** 1 931 473-9253
E: production.mcminnville@pegbroadcasting. com
Editorial Profile: WAKI-AM is a commercial station owned by Peg Broadcasting. The format of the station is sports. WAKI-AM broadcasts to the McMinnville, TN area at 1230 AM.

WAKK-AM
Owner: Southwest Broadcasting
Editorial: 206 N Front St, McComb, Mississippi 39648-3916. **T:** 1 601 684-4116
E: spots@k106.net
Editorial Profile: WKJN-AM is a commercial station owned by Southwest Broadcasting. The format of the station is gospel. WKJN-AM broadcasts in the McComb, MS area at 980 AM.

WAKM-AM
Owner: Franklin Radio Associates Inc.
Editorial: 222 Mallory Station Rd, Franklin, Tennessee 37067. **T:** 1 615 794-1594
E: wakm950@comcast.net
W: http://wakm950am.tripod.com
Editorial Profile: WAKM-AM is a commercial station owned by Franklin Radio Associates Inc. The format of the station is classic country. WAKM-AM broadcasts to the Franklin, TN area at 950 AM.

WAKO-AM
Owner: Lawrenceville Broadcasting Co. Inc.
Editorial: Business Highway 50 East, Lawrenceville, Illinois 62439.
T: 1 618 943-3354 **E:** wakoradio@yahoo.com
W: http://www.wakoradio.com
Editorial Profile: WAKO-AM is a commercial station owned by the Lawrenceville Broadcasting Co. Inc. The format of the station is adult contemporary, classic country and oldies music. WAKO-AM broadcasts to the Lawrenceville, IL area at 910 AM.

WAKO-FM
Owner: Lawrenceville Broadcasting Co. Inc.
Editorial: Business Highway 50 East, Lawrenceville, Illinois 62439.
T: 1 618 943-3354 **E:** wakoradio@yahoo.com
W: http://www.wakoradio.com
Editorial Profile: WAKO-FM is a commercial station owned by Lawrenceville Broadcasting Co. Inc. The format of the station is adult contemporary, oldies and country music. WAKO-FM broadcasts to the Lawrenceville, IL area at 103.1 FM.

WAKQ-FM
Owner: WENK of Union City, Inc.
Editorial: 206 N Brewer St, Paris, Tennessee 38242-4028. **T:** 1 731 642-7100
W: http://www.kf99kq105.com
Editorial Profile: WAKQ-FM is a commercial station owned by WENK of Union City, Inc. The format of the station is Top 40/CHR music. WAKQ-FM broadcasts to the Paris, TN area at 105.5 FM.

WAKR-AM
Owner: Rubber City Radio Group Inc.
Editorial: 1795 W Market St, Akron, Ohio 44313. **T:** 1 330 869-9800 **E:** news@wakr.net
W: http://www.wakr.net
Editorial Profile: WAKR-AM is a commercial station owned by Rubber City Radio Group Inc. The format of the station is oldies, sports and talk. WAKR-AM broadcasts to the Akron, OH area at 1590 AM.

WAKS-FM
Owner: Clear Channel Media and Entertainment
Editorial: 6200 Oak Tree Blvd, Ste 400, Independence, Ohio 44131-6934.
T: 1 216 520-2600 **E:** feedback@waks.com
W: http://www.kisscleveland.com
Editorial Profile: WAKS-FM is a commercial station owned by Clear Channel Media and Entertainment. The format of the station is Top 40/CHR. WAKS-FM broadcasts to the Independence, OH area at 96.5 FM.

WAKT-FM
Owner: Powell Broadcasting Company, LLC
Editorial: 118 Gwyn Dr, Panama City Beach, Florida 32408-5854. **T:** 1 850 234-8858
W: http://www.1035hankfm.com
Editorial Profile: WKNK-FM is a commercial station owned by Powell Broadcasting Company, LLC. The format of the station is classic and contemporary country music. WKNK-FM broadcasts in the Panama City, FL area at 103.5 FM.

WAKU-FM
Owner: Altrua Investments International Corp.
Editorial: 3225 Hartsfield Rd, Tallahassee, Florida 32303. **T:** 1 850 926-8000
E: mail@wave94.com
W: http://www.wave94.com
Editorial Profile: WAKU-FM is a commercial station owned by Altrua Investments International Corp. The format of the station is contemporary Christian and religious talk. WAKU-FM broadcasts to the Crawfordville, FL area at 94.1 FM.

WAKV-AM
Owner: Vintage Radio Inc.
Editorial: 213 Gilkey St, Plainwell, Michigan 49080-1220. **T:** 1 269 685-2438
E: 980am@net-link.net
W: http://wakv.blogspot.com

WAKW-FM
Owner: Pillar of Fire Inc.

Editorial: 6275 Collegevue Pl, Cincinnati, Ohio 45224-1959. **T:** 1 513 542-9259
W: http://www.mystar933.com
Editorial Profile: WAKW-FM is a commercial station owned by Pillar of Fire Inc. The format of the station is contemporary Christian. WAKW-FM broadcasts to the Cincinnati area at 93.3 FM.

WAKY-FM
Owner: W & B Broadcasting Inc.
Editorial: 519 N Miles St, Elizabethtown, Kentucky 42701-1875. **T:** 1 270 766-1035
W: http://www.waky1035.com
Editorial Profile: WAKY-FM is a commercial station owned by W & B Broadcasting Inc. The format of the station is classic hits. WAKY-FM broadcasts to the Elizabethtown, KY area at 103.5 FM.

WAKZ-FM
Owner: Clear Channel Media and Entertainment
Editorial: 7461 South Ave, Youngstown, Ohio 44512. **T:** 1 330 965-0057
W: http://www.959kiss.com
Editorial Profile: WAKZ-FM is a commercial station owned by Clear Channel Media and Entertainment. The format of the station is Top 40/CHR music. WAKZ-FM broadcasts to the Youngstown, OH area at 95.9 FM.

WALG-AM
Owner: Cumulus Media Inc.
Editorial: 1104 W Broad Ave, Albany, Georgia 31707. **T:** 1 229 436-7233
W: http://www.1590walg.com
Editorial Profile: WALG-AM is a commercial station owned by Cumulus Media Inc. The format of the station is news and talk. WALG-AM's broadcasts to the Albany, GA area at 1590 AM.

WALJ-FM
Owner: Apex Broadcasting, Inc.
Editorial: 534 14th St, Tuscaloosa, Alabama 35401-3434. **T:** 1 205 523-5770
W: http://www.1051jamz.com
Editorial Profile: WALJ-FM is a commercial station owned by Apex Broadcasting, Inc and programmed/ operated by Cox Media Group. The format of the station is urban contemporary. WALJ-FM broadcasts to the Tuscaloosa, AL area at a frequency of 105.1 FM.

WALK-AM
Owner: Connoisseur Media
Editorial: 66 Colonial Dr, Patchogue, New York 11772-5849. **T:** 1 631 475-5200
E: walknews@walkradio.com
W: http://www.1370walk.com
Editorial Profile: WALK-AM is a commercial station owned by Connoisseur Media. The format of the station is adult standards. WALK-AM broadcasts to the Long Island, NY area at 1370 AM.

WALK-FM
Owner: Connoisseur Media
Editorial: 66 Colonial Dr, Patchogue, New York 11772-5849. **T:** 1 631 475-5200
E: walknews@walkradio.com
W: http://www.walkradio.com
Editorial Profile: WALK-FM is a commercial station owned by Connoisseur Media. The format of the station is adult contemporary music. WALK-FM broadcasts throughout the Nassau and Suffolk Counties in New York at 97.5 FM.

WALL-AM
Owner: Townsquare Media
Editorial: 2 Pendell Rd, Poughkeepsie, New York 12601-1513. **T:** 1 845 471-1500
W: http://hudsonvalleytrueoldies.com
Editorial Profile: WALL-AM is a commercial station owned by Townsquare Media. The format of the station is oldies. WALL-FM broadcasts to the Poughkeepsie, NY area at 1340 AM.

WALR-FM
Owner: Cox Media Group, Inc.
Editorial: 1601 W Peachtree St NE, Atlanta, Georgia 30309. **T:** 1 404 897-7500
W: http://www.kiss1041fm.com
Editorial Profile: WALR-FM is a commercial station owned by Cox Media Group, Inc. The format of the station is urban adult contemporary. WALR-FM broadcasts to the Atlanta area at 104.1 FM.

WALS-FM
Owner: Laco Radio, Inc.
Editorial: 3905 Progress Blvd, Peru, Illinois 61354. **T:** 1 815 224-2100

E: walls102@theradiogroup.net
W: http://www.walls102.com
Editorial Profile: WALS-FM is a commercial station owned by Laco Radio, Inc. The format for the station is contemporary country. WALS-FM broadcasts to the Peru, IL area at 102.1 FM.

WALT-AM
Owner: New South Communications Inc.
Editorial: 4307 Highway 39 N, Meridian, Mississippi 39301-1007. **T:** 1 601 693-3434
Editorial Profile: WALT-AM is a commercial station owned by New South Communications Inc. The format for the station is talk. WALT-AM broadcasts to the Meridian, MS area at 910 AM.

WALV-FM
Owner: Brewer Broadcasting Inc.
Editorial: 1305 Carter St, Chattanooga, Tennessee 37402. **T:** 1 423 265-9494
W: http://www.espnchattanooga.com
Editorial Profile: WALV-FM is a commercial station owned by Brewer Broadcasting Inc. The format of the station is sports. WALV-FM broadcasts to the Chattanooga, TN area at 105.1 FM.

WALX-FM
Owner: Scott Communications, Inc.
Editorial: 273 Persimmon Tree Rd, Valley Grande, Alabama 36701. **T:** 1 334 875-9360
Editorial Profile: WALX-FM is a commercial station owned by Scott Communications, Inc. The format of the station is classic hits. WALX-FM broadcasts to the Valley Grande, AL area at 100.9 FM.

WALY-FM
Owner: Forever Broadcasting, LLC.
Editorial: 1 Forever Dr, Hollidaysburg, Pennsylvania 16648. **T:** 1 814 941-9800
W: http://www.waly1039.com
Editorial Profile: WALY-FM is a commercial station owned by Forever Broadcasting, LLC. The format of the station is adult contemporary. WALY-FM broadcasts to the Hollidaysburg, PA area at 103.9 FM.

WALZ-FM
Owner: Machias Valley Broadcasting
Editorial: 637 Main St, Calais, Maine 4619.
T: 1 207 454-7545 **E:** wqdy@wqdy.fm
W: http://www.wqdy.fm
Editorial Profile: WALZ-FM is a commercial station owned by Machias Valley Broadcasting. The format for the station is classic hits. WALZ-FM broadcasts to the Machias, ME area at 95.3 FM.

WAMA-AM
Owner: ZGS Communications
Editorial: 4107 W Spruce St Ste 250, Tampa, Florida 33607-2347. **T:** 1 813 319-4949
W: http://www.laley1550.com
Editorial Profile: WAMA-AM is a commercial station owned by ZGS Communications. The format of the station is Regional Mexican. WAMA-AM broadcasts to the Tampa, FL area at 1550 AM.

WAMB-AM
Owner: Great Southern Broadcasting Co.
Editorial: 1617 Lebanon Pike, Nashville, Tennessee 37210-3217. **T:** 1 615 889-1960
E: wamb@bellsouth.net
W: http://www.wambradio.com
Editorial Profile: WAMB-AM is a commercial station owned by Great Southern Broadcasting Co. The format of the station is Spanish CHR. WAMB-AM broadcasts to the Nashville, TN area at 1200 AM.

WAMC-FM
Owner: WAMC
Editorial: 318 Central Ave, Albany, New York 12206-2522. **T:** 1 518 465-5233
E: mail@wamc.org **W:** http://www.wamc.org
Editorial Profile: WAMC-FM is a non-commercial station owned by WAMC. The format of the station is news and talk. WAMC-FM broadcasts to the Albany, NY area at 90.3 FM.

WAME-AM
Owner: GHB Broadcasting
Editorial: 212 Signal Hill Dr, Statesville, North Carolina 28625. **T:** 1 704 872-0550
W: http://www.wame550.com
Editorial Profile: WAME-AM is a commercial station owned by GHB Broadcasting. The format for the station is classic country. WAME-AM broadcasts to the Charlotte, NC area at 550 AM.

WAMI-FM
Owner: Opp Broadcasting Co. Inc.
Editorial: 1807 N Main St, Opp, Alabama 36467. **T:** 1 334 493-3588
E: wami@oppcatv.com
Editorial Profile: WAMI-FM is a commercial station owned by Opp Broadcasting Co. Inc. The format of the station is classic country. WAMI-FM broadcasts to the Opp, AL area at 102.3 FM.

WAMJ-FM
Owner: Radio One Inc.
Editorial: 101 Marietta St NW, Fl 12, Atlanta, Georgia 30303. **T:** 1 404 765-9750
W: http://majicatl.com
Editorial Profile: WAMJ-FM is a commercial station owned by Radio One Inc. The format of the station is urban AC. WAMJ-FM broadcasts to the Atlanta area at 107.5 FM.

WAMK-FM
Owner: WAMC
Editorial: 318 Central Ave, Albany, New York 12206. **T:** 1 518 465-5233 **E:** mail@wamc.org
W: http://www.wamc.org
Editorial Profile: WAMK-FM is a non-commercial station owned by WAMC. The format of the station is news and talk. WAMK-FM broadcasts to the Kingston, NY area at 90.9 FM.

WAML-AM
Owner: Walking By Faith Ministries
Editorial: 336 Rodenberg Ave, Biloxi, Mississippi 39531-3444. **T:** 1 228 374-9739
E: wqfxradio@bellsouth.net
Editorial Profile: WAML-AM is a commercial station owned by Walking By Faith Ministries. The format of the station is gospel music. WAML-AM broadcasts in Laurel, MS and its surrounding environs at 1340 AM.

WAMN-AM
Owner: Two Virginia's Media
Editorial: 4415 Blue Prince Road, Bluefield, West Virginia 24701. **T:** 1 304 327-9266
W: http://www.mywillie.com
Editorial Profile: WAMN-AM is a commercial station owned by Two Virginia's Media. The format of the station is country. WAMN-AM broadcasts to the Bluefield, WV area at 1050 AM.

WAMO-AM
Owner: Radio Power, Inc.
Editorial: 21 Yost Blvd Ste 505, Pittsburgh, Pennsylvania 15221-5237. **T:** 1 412 829-0100
E: info@wamo100.com
W: http://www.wamo100.com
Editorial Profile: WAMO-AM is a commercial station owned by Langer Broadcasting Group, LLC. The format of the station is urban contemporary. WAMO-AM broadcasts to the Pittsburgh area at 660 AM.

WAMQ-FM
Owner: WAMC
Editorial: 318 Central Ave, Albany, New York 12206-2522. **T:** 1 518 465-5233
E: mail@wamc.org **W:** http://www.wamc.org
Editorial Profile: WAMQ-FM is a non-commercial station owned by WAMC. The format of the station is news and talk. WAMQ-FM broadcasts to the Albany, NY area at 105.1 FM.

WAMR-FM
Owner: Univision Communications Inc.
Editorial: 800 S Douglas Rd, Ste 111, Coral Gables, Florida 33134. **T:** 1 305 447-1140
W: http://amor1075fm.univision.com
Editorial Profile: WAMR-FM is a commercial station owned by Univision Communications Inc. The format of the station is adult contemporary Hispanic music. WAMR-FM broadcasts to the Coral Gables, FL area at 107.5 FM.

WAMS-FM
Owner: Bayshore Media, LLC
Editorial: 7200 Coastal Hwy Ste 101, Ocean City, Maryland 21842-8061.
T: 1 410 524-6862 **W:** http://jack101fm.com
Editorial Profile: WAMS-FM is a commercial station owned by Bayshore Media, LLC. The station airs the Jack FM adult hits music format. WAMS-FM broadcasts to the Salisbury/Ocean City, MD area at 101.1 FM.

WAMT-AM
Owner: Genesis Communications Inc.
Editorial: 1160 S Semoran Blvd, Orlando, Florida 32807-1461. **T:** 1 407 380-9255
E: wamt@radiogenesis.com
W: http://www.newstalkflorida.com

Editorial Profile: WAMT-AM is a commercial station owned by Genesis Communications Inc. The format of the station is news talk. WAMT-AM broadcasts to the Orlando, FL area at 1190 AM. The station airs their WWBA-AM's programming during a portion of the day.

WAMU-FM
Owner: American University
Editorial: 4401 Connecticut Ave NW, Washington, District Of Columbia 20008-2322. **T:** 1 202 885-1200 **E:** news@wamu.org
W: http://wamu.org
Editorial Profile: WAMU-FM is a non-commercial station owned by American University. The format of the station is news and talk programming. WAMU-FM broadcasts to the Washington, D.C. area at 88.5 FM.

WAMV-AM
Owner: Community First Broadcasters
Editorial: 132 School Road, Amherst, Virginia 24521. **T:** 1 434 946-9000
E: wamvradio@aol.com
W: http://www.wamvradio1420.com
Editorial Profile: WAMV-AM is a commercial station owned by Community First Broadcasters. The format of the station is southern gospel and classic country. WAMV-AM broadcasts to the Amherst, VA area at 1420 AM.

WAMW-AM
Owner: DLC Media Inc.
Editorial: 800 W National Hwy, Washington, Indiana 47501. **T:** 1 812 254-6761
W: http://www.fourstarcountry.com
Editorial Profile: WAMW-AM is a commercial station owned by DLC Media Inc. The format of the station is adult standards music. WAMW-AM broadcasts to the Washington, IN area at 1580 AM.

WAMW-FM
Owner: DLC Media Inc.
Editorial: 800 W National Hwy, Washington, Indiana 47501-3326. **T:** 1 812 254-6761
W: http://www.memories1079.com
Editorial Profile: WAMW-FM is a commercial station owned by DLC Media Inc. The format of the station is classic hits. WAMW-FM broadcasts to the Washington, IN, area at 107.9 FM.

WAMX-FM
Owner: Clear Channel Media and Entertainment
Editorial: 134 4th Ave, Huntington, West Virginia 25701-1220. **T:** 1 304 525-7788
W: http://www.1063thebrew.com/main.html
Editorial Profile: WAMX-FM is a commercial station owned by Clear Channel Media and Entertainment. The format of the station is classic rock. WAMX-FM broadcasts to the Huntington, WV area at 106.3 FM.

WAMY-AM
Owner: Stanford Communications Inc.
Editorial: 521 Highway 278 W, Amory, Mississippi 38821. **T:** 1 662 256-9726
E: fm95@fm95radio.com
W: http://www.fm95radio.com
Editorial Profile: WAMY-AM is a commercial station owned by Stanford Communications Inc. The format of the station is news, sports and talk. WAMY-AM broadcasts to the Amory, MS area at 1580 AM.

WAMZ-FM
Owner: Clear Channel Media and Entertainment
Editorial: 4000 Radio Dr, Louisville, Kentucky 40218-4568. **T:** 1 502 479-2222
W: http://www.wamz.com
Editorial Profile: WAMZ-FM is a commercial station owned by Clear Channel Media and Entertainment. The format of the station is contemporary country music. WAMZ-FM broadcasts in the Louisville, KY area at 97.5 FM.

WANB-AM
Owner: Broadcast Communications Inc.
Editorial: 369 Tower Rd, Waynesburg, Pennsylvania 15370. **T:** 1 724 627-5555
E: wanbradio@gmail.com
Editorial Profile: WANB-AM is a commercial station owned by Broadcast Communications Inc. The format of the station is country. WANB-AM broadcasts to the Waynesburg, PA area at 1210 AM.

WANC-FM
Owner: WAMC
Editorial: 318 Central Ave, Albany, New York 12206. **T:** 1 518 465-5233 **E:** mail@wamc.org

W: http://www.wamc.org
Editorial Profile: WANC-FM is a non-commercial station owned by WAMC. The format of the station is news and talk. WANC-FM broadcasts to the Albany, NY area at 103.9 FM.

WANG-AM
Owner: Digity LLC
Editorial: 1361 Colony Dr, New Bern, North Carolina 28562-4129. **T:** 1 252 639-7900
Editorial Profile: WANG-AM is a commercial station owned by Digity LLC. The format of the station is adult standards and middle of the road format. WANG-AM broadcasts to the New Bern, NC area at 1330 AM.

WANI-AM
Owner: Auburn Network, Inc.
Editorial: 197 E University Dr, Auburn, Alabama 36832. **T:** 1 334 826-2929
W: http://www.wani1400.com
Editorial Profile: WANI-AM is a commercial station owned by Auburn Network, Inc. The format of the station is news and talk. WANI-AM broadcasts to the Auburn, AL area at 1400 AM.

WANK-FM
Owner: Red Hills Broadcasting, LLC
Editorial: 3000 Olson Rd, Tallahassee, Florida 32308-3918. **T:** 1 850 386-8004
W: http://www.999hank.fm
Editorial Profile: WANK-FM is a commercial station owned by Red Hills Broadcasting, LLC. The format of the station is adult hits. WANK-FM broadcasts to the Tallahassee, FL area at a frequency of 99.9 FM.

WANM-FM
Owner: Florida A&M University
Editorial: 510 Orr Dr, Ste 3056, Tallahassee, Florida 32307-0001. **T:** 1 850 599-3083
E: psa@wanm.org **W:** http://www.wanm.org
Editorial Profile: WANM-FM is a non-commercial station owned and operated by Florida A&M University. The format of the station is gospel and urban contemporary music. WANM-FM broadcasts to the Tallahassee, FL area at 90.5 FM.

WANO-AM
Owner: Penelope, Inc.
Editorial: 2117 Cumberland Ave, Middlesboro, Kentucky 40965-2876. **T:** 1 606 248-8993
E: wanocountry@gmail.com
W: http://1230wano.com/
Editorial Profile: WANO-AM is a commercial station owned by the Penelope, Inc. The format of the station is contemporary and classic country. WANO-AM broadcasts to the Middlesboro, KY area at 1230 AM.

WANS-AM
Owner: (Bryant) Gary
Editorial: 102 E Shockley Ferry Rd, Anderson, South Carolina 29624-3730.
T: 1 864 224-6733
Editorial Profile: WANS-AM is a commercial station owned by Gary Bryant. The format of the station is sports. WANS-AM broadcasts to the Anderson, SC area at 1280 AM.

WANT-FM
Owner: Bay-Pointe Broadcasting Inc.
Editorial: 510 Trousdale Ferry Pike, Lebanon, Tennessee 37087-4727. **T:** 1 615 449-3699
E: info@wantfm.com
W: http://www.wantfm.com
Editorial Profile: WANT-FM is a commercial station owned by Bay-Pointe Broadcasting Inc. The format of the station is a mix of contemporary and classic country music. WANT-FM broadcasts to the Lebanon, TN area at 98.9 FM.

WANY-AM
Owner: Albany Broadcasting Co.
Editorial: Highway 1590,, Albany, Kentucky 42602. **T:** 1 606 387-5186
E: wanyradio@hotmail.com
Editorial Profile: WANY-AM is a commercial station owned by Albany Broadcasting Co. The format of the station is contemporary and classic country. WANY-AM broadcasts to the Albany, KY area at 1390 AM.

WANY-FM
Owner: Albany Broadcasting Co.
Editorial: Highway 1590,, Albany, Kentucky 42602. **T:** 1 606 387-5186
E: wanyradio@hotmail.com
Editorial Profile: WANY-FM is a commercial station owned by Albany Broadcasting Co. The format of the station is contemporary and classic country. WANY-FM broadcasts to the Albany, KY area at 106.3 FM.

WAOA-FM
Owner: Cumulus Media Inc.
Editorial: 1800 W Hibiscus Blvd Ste 138, Melbourne, Florida 32901-2624.
T: 1 321 984-1000 **W:** http://www.wa1a.com
Editorial Profile: WAOA-FM is a commercial station owned by Cumulus Media Inc. The format of the station is Top 40/CHR music. WAOA-FM broadcasts to the Melbourne, FL area at 107.1 FM.

WAOC-AM
Owner: Phillips Broadcasting, LLC
Editorial: 567 Lewis Point Road Ext, Saint Augustine, Florida 32086-5222.
T: 1 904 797-1955
W: http://www.1420sports.com
Editorial Profile: WAOC-AM is a commercial station owned by Phillips Broadcasting, LLC. The format of the station is sports. WAOC-AM broadcasts to the Saint Augustine, FL area at 1420 AM.

WAOK-AM
Owner: CBS Radio
Editorial: 1201 Peachtree Street, 400 Colony Square, St. 800, Atlanta, Georgia 30361.
T: 1 404 898-8900
W: http://atlanta.cbslocal.com
Editorial Profile: WAOK-AM is a commercial station owned by CBS Radio. The format of the station is news and talk. WAOK-AM broadcasts in the Atlanta area at 1380 AM.

WAOQ-FM
Owner: Alatron Corp. Inc.
Editorial: 1370 N Franklin Rd, Goshen, Alabama 36035-6506. **T:** 1 334 335-2877
E: office@waoq.com

WAOR-FM
Owner: Talking Stick Communications, Inc.
Editorial: 237 W Edison Rd, Mishawaka, Indiana 46545. **T:** 1 574 258-5483
E: feedback@thefanmichiana.com
W: http://www.thefanmichiana.com
Editorial Profile: WAOR-FM is a commercial station owned by Talking Stick Communications, Inc., a division of Federated Media. The format of the station is sports/talk. WAOR-FM broadcasts to the South Bend, IN area at 95.7 FM.

WAOS-AM
Owner: La Favorita Inc.
Editorial: 5815 Westside Rd, Austell, Georgia 30106-3179. **T:** 1 770 944-0900
E: traffic@lamejorestacion.com
W: http://www.lamejorestacion.com
Editorial Profile: WAOS-AM is a commercial station owned by La Favorita Inc. The format of the station is regional Mexican. WAOS-AM broadcasts to the Atlanta area at 1600 AM.

WAOV-AM
Owner: Original Company Inc.(The)
Editorial: 522 Busseron St, Vincennes, Indiana 47591. **T:** 1 812 882-6060
E: waov@originalcompany.com
W: http://www.waovam.com
Editorial Profile: WAOV-AM is a commercial station owned by The Original Company Inc. The format of the station is news, sports, and talk. WAOV-AM broadcasts to the Vincennes, IN area at 1450 AM.

WAOX-FM
Owner: Talley Broadcasting Corp.
Editorial: 6308 Illinois Route 16, Hillsboro, Illinois 62049. **T:** 1 618 635-6000
E: waox@waoxradio.com
W: http://www.waox.com
Editorial Profile: WAOX-FM is a commercial station owned by Talley Broadcasting Corp. The format of the station is hot adult contemporary. WAOX-FM broadcasts to the Hillsboro, IL area at 105.3 FM.

WAOY-FM
Owner: American Family Association
Editorial: 107 Park Gate St., Tupelo, Mississippi 38801. **T:** 1 622 844-8888
E: comments@afr.net **W:** http://www.afr.net

WAPE-FM
Owner: Cox Media Group, Inc.
Editorial: 8000 Belfort Pkwy, Jacksonville, Florida 32256-6934. **T:** 1 904 245-8500
W: http://www.wape.com
Editorial Profile: WAPE-FM is a commercial station owned by Cox Media Group, Inc. The format of the station is Top 40/CHR. WAPE-FM broadcasts to the Jacksonville, FL area at 95.1 FM.

WAPF-AM
Owner: Southwest Broadcasting
Editorial: 206 N Front St, McComb, Mississippi 39648. **T:** 1 601 684-4116
E: spots@k106.net
Editorial Profile: WAPF-AM is a commercial station owned by Southwest Broadcasting. The format of the station is gospel. WAPF-AM broadcasts to the McComb, MS area at 1140 AM.

WAPI-AM
Owner: Cumulus Media Inc
Editorial: 244 Goodwin Crest Dr, Suite 300, Birmingham, Alabama 35209-3716.
T: 1 205 945-4646
W: http://www.1070wapi.com
Editorial Profile: WAPI-AM is a commercial station owned by Cumulus Media Inc. The format of the station is news and talk. WAPI-AM broadcasts to the greater Birmingham, AL area at 1070 AM.

WAPJ-FM
Owner: Torrington Community Radio Foundation, Inc.
Editorial: 40 Water St, Torrington, Connecticut 06790-5318. **T:** 1 860 489-9033
E: info@wapj.org **W:** http://wapjfm.com
Editorial Profile: WAPJ-FM is a non-commercial station owned by Torrington Community Radio Foundation, Inc. The format of the station is variety. WAPJ-FM broadcasts to the Hartford-New Haven, CT area at 89.9 FM.

WAPL-FM
Owner: Woodward Communications, Inc.
Editorial: 2800 E College Ave, Appleton, Wisconsin 54915. **T:** 1 920 734-9226
E: waplstudio@wcinet.com
W: http://www.wapl.com
Editorial Profile: WAPL-FM is a commercial station owned by Woodward Communications Inc. The format is rock. WAPL-FM broadcasts to the Appleton, WI area at 105.7 FM.

WAPN-FM
Owner: Public Radio, Inc.
Editorial: 1508 State Ave, Holly Hill, Florida 32117. **T:** 1 386 677-4272 **E:** wapn@wapn.net
W: http://www.wapn.net
Editorial Profile: WAPN-FM is a non-commercial station owned by Public Radio, Inc. The format of the station is religion. WAPN-FM broadcasts to the Holly Hill, FL area at 91.5 FM.

WAPS-FM
Owner: Board of Ed. Akron City School Dist.
Editorial: 65 Steiner Ave, Akron, Ohio 44301.
T: 1 330 761-3099
W: http://www.913thesummit.com
Editorial Profile: WAPS-FM is a non-commercial station owned by the Board of Ed. Akron City School Dist. The format of the station is adult album alternative music. WAPS-FM broadcasts to the Akron, OH area at 91.3 FM.

WAQE-AM
Owner: T K C Inc.
Editorial: 1859 21st Ave, Rice Lake, Wisconsin 54868-9502. **T:** 1 715 234-9059
E: info@waqe.com
Editorial Profile: WAQE-AM is a commercial station owned by T K C Inc. The format of the station is sports. WAQE-AM broadcasts to the Minneapolis area at 1090 AM.

WAQE-FM
Owner: T K C Inc.
Editorial: 1859 21st Ave, Rice Lake, Wisconsin 54868-9502. **T:** 1 715 234-9059
E: info@waqe.com **W:** http://www.waqe.com
Editorial Profile: WAQE-FM is a commercial station owned by the TKC Inc. The format of the station is hot adult contemporary music. WAQE-FM broadcasts in the Minneapolis area at 97.7 FM.

WAQG-FM
Owner: American Family Association
Editorial: 107 Parkgate Dr, Tupelo, Mississippi 38801. **T:** 1 662 844-8888
E: comments@afr.net **W:** http://www.afr.net

WAQI-AM
Owner: Univision Communications Inc.
Editorial: 800 S Douglas Rd, Coral Gables, Florida 33134-3125. **T:** 1 305 445-4040
W: http://radiomambi710.univision.com
Editorial Profile: WAQI-AM is a commercial station owned by Univision Communications Inc. The format of the station is Hispanic news and talk. WAQI-AM broadcasts to the Coral Gables, FL area at 710 AM.

WAQL-FM
Owner: American Family Association
Editorial: 107 Park Gate Dr, Tupelo, Mississippi 38801-3010. **T:** 1 662 844-8888
E: comments@afr.net **W:** http://www.afr.net
Editorial Profile: WAQL-FM is a commercial station owned by the American Family Association. The format of the station is Adult Contemporary Christian programming. WAQL-FM broadcasts to the McComb, MS area on 90.5 FM.

WAQX-FM
Owner: Cumulus Media Inc
Editorial: 1064 James St, Syracuse, New York 13203. **T:** 1 315 472-0200
W: http://www.95x.com
Editorial Profile: WAQX-FM is a commercial station owned by Cumulus Media Inc. The format of the station is rock music. WAQX-FM broadcasts to the Syracuse, NY area at 95.7 FM.

WAQY-FM
Owner: Saga Communications
Editorial: 45 Fisher Ave, East Longmeadow, Massachusetts 1028. **T:** 1 413 525-4141
W: http://www.rock102.com
Editorial Profile: WAQY-FM is a commercial station owned by Saga Communications. The format of the station is classic rock. WAQY-FM broadcasts to the East Longmeadow, MA area at 102.1 FM.

WARC-FM
Owner: Allegheny College
Editorial: Allegheny College, 520 N Main St WARC Box C, Meadville, Pennsylvania 16335.
T: 1 814 332-3376 **E:** warc@allegheny.edu
W: http://warc.allegheny.edu
Editorial Profile: WARC-FM is a non-commercial station owned by Allegheny College. The format of the station is variety. WARC-FM broadcasts to the Meadville, PA community at 90.3 FM.

WARD-AM
Owner: Henderson(Roy)
Editorial: 13999 S West Bay Shore Dr, Traverse City, Michigan 49684.
T: 1 231 947-3220
Editorial Profile: WARD-AM is a commercial station owned by Roy Henderson The format of the station is contemporary country. WARD-AM broadcasts to the Traverse City, MI area at 750 AM.

WARE-AM
Owner: Success Signal Broadcasting Inc
Editorial: 3 Converse St, Ste 101, Palmer, Massachusetts 01069-1567.
T: 1 413 289-2300
E: bruce.marshall3@verizon.net
W: http://www.realoldies1250.net
Editorial Profile: WARE-AM is a commercial station owned by Success Signal Broadcasting Inc. The format of the station is oldies. WARE-AM broadcasts to the Palmer, MA area at 1250 AM.

WARF-AM
Owner: Clear Channel Media and Entertainment
Editorial: 7755 Freedom Ave NW, North Canton, Ohio 44720. **T:** 1 330 836-4700
W: http://1350sports.com
Editorial Profile: WARF-AM is a commercial station owned by Clear Channel Media and Entertainment. The format of the station is sports. WARF-AM broadcasts to the North Canton, OH area at 1350 AM.

WARG-FM
Owner: Community High School District No. 217
Editorial: 7329 W 63rd St, Summit, Illinois 60501. **T:** 1 708 467-5587
W: http://www.wix.com/filster9000/warg889
Editorial Profile: WARG-FM is a non-commercial station owned by Community High School District No. 217. The format of the station is dance music. WARG-FM broadcasts to the Summit, IL area at 88.9 FM.

WARH-FM
Owner: Hubbard Broadcasting, Inc.
Editorial: 11647 Olive Blvd, Saint Louis, Missouri 63141-7001. **T:** 1 314 983-6000
W: http://www.1065thearch.com
Editorial Profile: WARH-FM is a commercial station owned by Hubbard Broadcasting, Inc. The format of the station is adult hits. WARH-FM broadcasts to the St. Louis area at 106.5 FM.

WARK-AM
Owner: Manning Broadcasting Inc.

Editorial: 880 Commonwealth Ave, Hagerstown, Maryland 21740-6836.
T: 1 301 733-4500
Editorial Profile: WARK-AM is a commercial station owned by Manning Broadcasting Inc. The format of the station is news and talk. WARK-AM broadcasts to the Hagerstown, MD, area at 1490 AM.

WARM-AM
Owner: Cumulus Media Inc
Editorial: 600 Baltimore Dr, Wilkes-Barre, Pennsylvania 18702-7901. **T:** 1 570 824-9000
W: http://www.warm590.com
Editorial Profile: WARM-AM is a commercial station owned by Cumulus Media Inc. The format of the station is oldies music. WARM-AM broadcasts to the Wilkes-Barre, PA area at 590 AM.

WARM-FM
Owner: Cumulus Media Inc.
Editorial: 5989 Susquehanna Plaza Drive, York, Pennsylvania 17406-8910.
T: 1 717 764-1155
W: http://www.warm1033.com
Editorial Profile: WARM-FM is a commercial station owned by Cumulus Media Inc. The format of the station is adult contemporary. WARM-FM broadcasts to the York, PA area at 103.3 FM.

WARO-FM
Owner: Meridian Broadcasting, Inc.
Editorial: 2824 Palm Beach Blvd, Fort Myers, Florida 33916-1503. **T:** 1 239 337-2346
W: http://www.945thearrow.com
Editorial Profile: WARO-FM is a commercial station owned by Meridian Broadcasting, Inc. The format of the station is classic rock. WARO-FM broadcasts to the Fort Myers, FL area at 94.5 FM.

WARQ-FM
Owner: L & L Broadcasting
Editorial: 1900 Pineview Dr, Columbia, South Carolina 29209-5079. **T:** 1 803 695-8600
W: http://q935online.com
Editorial Profile: WARQ-FM is a commercial station owned by L & L Broadcasting. The format of the station is hot AC. WARQ-FM broadcasts to the Columbia, SC area at 93.5 FM.

WARR-AM
Owner: Darensburg Broadcasting
Editorial: 824 US Highway 158 Byp, Warrenton, North Carolina 27589.
T: 1 252 257-5557
Editorial Profile: WARR-AM is a commercial station owned by Darensburg Broadcasting. The format of the station is gospel and R&B oldies. WARR-AM broadcasts to the Warrenton, NC area at 1520 AM.

WARU-AM
Owner: Hoosier AM/FM LLC
Editorial: 1711 E Wabash Rd, Peru, Indiana 46970-8656. **T:** 1 765 473-4448
E: waru@mitunes1019.com
W: http://www.mitunes1019.com
Editorial Profile: WARU-AM is a commercial station owned by Hoosier AM/FM LLC. The format of the station is adult hits. WARU-AM broadcasts to the Peru, IN area at 1600 AM.

WARU-FM
Owner: Hoosier AM/FM LLC
Editorial: 1711 E Wabash Rd, Peru, Indiana 46970-8656. **T:** 1 765 473-4448
E: waru@mitunes1019.com
W: http://www.mitunes1019.com
Editorial Profile: WARU-FM is a commercial station owned by Hoosier AM/FM LLC. The format of the station is adult hits. WARU-FM broadcasts to the Indianapolis area at 101.9 FM.

WARV-AM
Owner: Blount Communications Group
Editorial: 19 Luther Ave, Warwick, Rhode Island 2886. **T:** 1 401 737-0700
E: warv@aol.com **W:** http://www.warv.net
Editorial Profile: WARV-AM is a commercial station owned by Blount Communications Group. The format of the station is religious music. WARV-AM broadcasts to the Providence, RI-New Bedford, MA area at 1590 AM.

WARV-FM
Owner: Main Line Broadcasting
Editorial: 300 Arboretum Place Suite 590, Richmond, Virginia 23236. **T:** 1 804 327-9902
W: http://www.bigoldies1073.com
Editorial Profile: WARV-FM is a commercial station owned by Main Line Broadcasting. The

format of the station is oldies music. WARV-FM broadcasts to the Richmond, VA area at 100.3 FM.

WARY-FM
Owner: Westchester Community College
Editorial: 75 Grasslands Rd, Valhalla, New York 10595-1550. **T:** 1 914 606-6752
W: http://881wary.webs.com
Editorial Profile: WARY-FM is a non-commercial station owned by Westchester Community College. The format of the station is college variety. WARY-FM broadcasts to the New York City area at 88.1 FM.

WASB-AM
Owner: Genesee Media Corp.
Editorial: 20 Office Park Way, Pittsford, New York 14454. **T:** 1 585 335-9369
E: sports@theteam.fm
W: http://team1590.com
Editorial Profile: WASB-AM is a commercial station owned by Genesee Media Corp. The format of the station is sports. WASB-AM broadcasts to the Brockport, NY area at 1590 AM.

WASC-AM
Owner: New South Broadcasting Corporation
Editorial: 840 Wofford St, Spartanburg, South Carolina 29301. **T:** 1 864 585-1530
E: wascradio@bellsouth.net
Editorial Profile: WASC-AM is a commercial station owned by New South Broadcasting Corporation. The format of the station is urban adult contemporary. WASC-AM broadcasts to the Spartanburg, SC area at 1530 AM.

WASG-AM
Owner: Alabama Radio Network
Editorial: 273 Azalea Rd, Two Office Park Rd, Ste. #403, Mobile, Alabama 36609-1970.
T: 1 251 340-0442 **E:** wasg@wilkinsradio.com
W: http://www.wilkinsradio.com
Editorial Profile: WASG-AM is a commercial station owned by Alabama Radio Network. The format of the station is religious talk with a focus on Christian teaching. WASG-AM broadcasts to the Daphne, AL area at a frequency of 540 AM.

WASH-FM
Owner: Clear Channel Media and Entertainment
Editorial: 1801 Rockville Pike Fl 5, Rockville, Maryland 20852-1633. **T:** 1 240 747-2700
W: http://www.washfm.com
Editorial Profile: WASH-FM is a commercial station owned by Clear Channel Media and Entertainment. The format of the station is adult contemporary music. WASH-FM broadcasts to the Washington, D.C. area at 97.1 FM.

WASJ-FM
Owner: Powell Broadcasting Company, LLC
Editorial: 118 Gwyn Dr, Panama City Beach, Florida 32408. **T:** 1 850 234-8858
W: http://bobatthebeach.com
Editorial Profile: WASJ-FM is a commercial station owned by Powell Broadcasting Company, LLC. The format of the station is adult hits. WASJ-FM broadcasts to the Panama City, FL area at 105.1 FM.

WASK-AM
Owner: WASK Inc.
Editorial: 3575 McCarty Ln, Lafayette, Indiana 47905. **T:** 1 765 447-2186
W: http://www.espn1450am.com
Editorial Profile: WASK-AM is a commercial station owned by WASK Inc. The format of the station is sports. WASK-AM broadcasts to the Lafayette, IN area at 1450 AM.

WASK-FM
Owner: WASK Inc.
Editorial: 3575 McCarty Ln, Lafayette, Indiana 47905. **T:** 1 765 447-2186
W: http://www.wask.com
Editorial Profile: WASK-FM is a commercial station owned by WASK Inc. The format for the station is oldies. WASK-FM broadcasts to the Lafayette, IN area at 98.7 FM.

WASL-FM
Owner: Burks(W.E.)
Editorial: 2555 Burks Place, Dyersburg, Tennessee 38024-1793. **T:** 1 731 285-1339
W: http://sl100rocks.com
Editorial Profile: WASL-FM is a commercial station owned by W.E. Burks. The format of the station is rock music. WASL-FM broadcasts to the Dyersburg, TN area at 100.1 FM.

WASN-AM
Owner: Bernard Radio
Editorial: 20 W Federal St Ste T-2, Youngstown, Ohio 44503-1420.
T: 1 330 744-5115
Editorial Profile: WASN-AM is a commercial station owned by Bernard Radio. The format is talk. WASN-AM broadcasts to the Youngstown, OH area at 1500 AM.

WASR-AM
Owner: Hatch(Grant)
Editorial: 73 Varney Rd, Wolfeboro, New Hampshire 03894-4351. **T:** 1 603 569-1420
E: mail@wasr.net **W:** http://www.wasr.net
Editorial Profile: WASR-AM is a commercial station owned by Grant Hatch. The format of the station is talk. WASR-AM broadcasts to the Wolfeboro, NH area at 1420 AM.

WASU-FM
Owner: Appalachian State University
Editorial: Wey Hall, Ste 332, Boone, North Carolina 28608. **T:** 1 828 262-3170
W: http://www.wasurocks.com
Editorial Profile: WASU-FM is a non-commercial station owned by Appalachian State University. The format of the station is rock alternative. WASU-FM broadcasts to the Boone, NC area at 90.5 FM.

WATA-AM
Owner: High Country Adventures, LLC
Editorial: 738 Blowing Rock Rd, Boone, North Carolina 28607-4835. **T:** 1 828 264-2411
E: info@wataradio.com
W: http://goblueridge.net
Editorial Profile: WATA-AM is a commercial station owned by High Country Adventures, LLC, a subsidiary of Curtis Media Group. The format of the station is news and talk. WATA-AM broadcasts to the Boone, NC area at 1450 AM.

WATB-AM
Owner: Multicultural Radio Broadcasting Inc.
Editorial: 3589 N Decatur Rd, Scottdale, Georgia 30079. **T:** 1 404 508-1420
W: http://www.mrbi.net
Editorial Profile: WATB-AM is a commercial station owned by Multicultural Radio Broadcasting Inc. The format of the station is variety, featuring multicultural programming. WATB-AM broadcasts in the Atlanta area at 1420 AM.

WATD-FM
Owner: Perry(Edward & Carol)
Editorial: 130 Enterprise Dr, Marshfield, Massachusetts 2050. **T:** 1 781 837-1166
E: watdnews@gmail.com
W: http://www.959watd.com
Editorial Profile: WATD-FM is a commercial station owned by Carol & Edward Perry. The format of the station is adult contemporary music. WATD-FM broadcasts to the Boston, MA area 95.9 FM.

WATG-FM
Owner: TTA Broadcasting Inc.
Editorial: 2 Mount Alto Rd SW, Rome, Georgia 30165-4142. **T:** 1 706 378-8040
W: http://www.theridge957.com
Editorial Profile: WATG-FM is a commercial station owned by TTA Broadcasting Inc. The format of the station is classic hits. WATG-FM broadcasts to the Chattanooga, TN area at 95.7 FM.

WATH-AM
Owner: WATH Inc.
Editorial: 300 Columbus Rd, Athens, Ohio 45701. **T:** 1 740 593-6651
E: news@970wath.com
W: http://www.970wath.com
Editorial Profile: WATH-AM is a commercial station owned by WATH Inc. The station's format is classic hits. WATH-AM broadcasts to the greater Athens, OH area at 970 AM.

WATK-AM
Owner: Results Broadcasting, Inc.
Editorial: N2237 US Highway 45 S, Antigo, Wisconsin 54409-8889. **T:** 1 715 623-4124
E: country106@gmail.com
W: http://watkantigo.com
Editorial Profile: WATK-AM is a commercial station owned by Results Broadcasting, Inc. The format of the station is adult standards. WATK-AM broadcasts in the Antigo, WI area at 900 AM.

WATN-AM
Owner: Community Broadcasters, LLC
Editorial: 199 Wealtha Ave, Watertown, New York 13601. **T:** 1 315 782-1240

Editorial Profile: WATN-AM is a commercial station owned by Community Broadcasters, LLC. The format of the station is news and talk. WATN-AM broadcasts to the Watertown, NY area at 1240 AM.

WATQ-FM
Owner: Clear Channel Media and Entertainment
Editorial: 619 Cameron St, Eau Claire, Wisconsin 54703. **T:** 1 715 830-4000
W: http://www.moose106.com
Editorial Profile: WATQ-FM is a commercial station owned by Clear Channel Media and Entertainment. The format of the station is country. WATQ-FM broadcasts to the Eau Claire, WI area at 106.7 FM.

WATR-AM
Owner: Gilmore(Mark & Steve)
Editorial: 79 Baldwin Ave, Waterbury, Connecticut 06706-1854. **T:** 1 203 755-1121
E: news@watr.com **W:** http://www.watr.com
Editorial Profile: WATR-AM is a commercial station owned by Mark & Steve Gilmore. The format of the station is news, talk and oldies music. WATR-AM broadcasts to the greater Waterbury, CT area at 1320 AM.

WATS-AM
Owner: WATS Broadcasting Inc.
Editorial: 193 S Keystone Ave, Sayre, Pennsylvania 18840-1330. **T:** 1 570 888-7745
E: wats.wavr@cqservices.com
W: http://www.choice102.com
Editorial Profile: WATS-AM is a commercial station owned by WATS Broadcasting Inc. The format of the station is adult contemporary music. WATS-AM broadcasts to the Sayre, PA area at 960 AM.

WATT-AM
Owner: MacDonald Garber Broadcasting Inc.
Editorial: 7825 Mackinaw Trl, Cadillac, Michigan 49601-9746. **T:** 1 231 775-1263
W: http://www.radiomgb.com
Editorial Profile: WATT-AM is a commercial station owned by MacDonald Garber Broadcasting Inc. The format of the station is news and talk. WATT-AM broadcasts to the Cadillac, MI area at 1240 AM.

WATV-AM
Owner: Sheridan Broadcasting Corp.
Editorial: 3025 Kenley Way, Birmingham, Alabama 35242. **T:** 1 205 780-2014
W: http://www.900goldwatv.com
Editorial Profile: WATV-AM is a commercial station owned by Sheridan Broadcasting Corp. The format of the station is a gospel, R&B and talk. WATV-AM broadcasts to the Birmingham, AL area at 900 AM.

WATW-AM
Owner: Heartland Communications Group, LLC
Editorial: 2320 Ellis Ave, Ashland, Wisconsin 54806. **T:** 1 715 682-2727
E: productionash@charter.net
W: http://www.watwam.com
Editorial Profile: WATW-AM is a commercial station owned by Heartland Communications Group, LLC. The format of the station is talk. WATW-AM broadcasts to the Ashland, WI area at 1400 AM.

WATX-AM
Owner: Stonecom Cookeville LLC
Editorial: 259 S Willow Ave, Cookeville, Tennessee 38501. **T:** 1 931 528-6064
W: http://cookevillesnewstalk.com
Editorial Profile: WATX-AM is a commercial station owned by Stonecom Cookeville LLC. The format of the station is news/talk. WATX-AM broadcasts to the Cookeville, TN area at 1600 AM.

WATY-FM
Owner: Georgia Public Broadcasting
Editorial: 260 14th St NW, Atlanta, Georgia 30318-5360. **T:** 1 404 685-2548
E: news@gpb.org **W:** http://www.gpb.org
Editorial Profile: WATY-FM is a non-commercial station owned by Georgia Public Broadcasting. The format of the station is news, classical and jazz music. WATY-FM broadcasts to the Folkston, GA area at 91.3 FM.

WATZ-AM
Owner: Midwestern Broadcasting Co.
Editorial: 123 Prentiss St, Alpena, Michigan 49707. **T:** 1 989 354-8400
E: watznews@watz.com
W: http://www.watz.com
Editorial Profile: WATZ-AM is a commercial station owned by Midwestern Broadcasting Co. The format for the station is news and

talk. WATZ-AM broadcasts to the Alpena, MI area at 1450 AM.

WATZ-FM
Owner: Midwestern Broadcasting Co.
Editorial: 123 Prentiss St, Alpena, Michigan 49707. **T:** 1 989 354-8400
E: watznews@watz.com
W: http://www.watz.com
Editorial Profile: WATZ-FM is a commercial station owned by Midwestern Broadcasting Co. The format for the station is contemporary country. WATZ-FM broadcasts to the Alpena, MI area at 99.3 FM.

WAUB-AM
Owner: Auburn Broadcasting, Inc.
Editorial: 3568 Lenox Rd, Geneva, New York 14456. **T:** 1 315 781-7000
Editorial Profile: WAUB-AM is a commercial station owned by Auburn Broadcasting, Inc. The format of the station is news, sports and talk programming. WAUB-AM broadcasts to the Geneva, NY area at 1590 AM.

WAUC-AM
Owner: Marvina Enterprises, Inc.
Editorial: 1310 S Florida Ave, Wauchula, Florida 33873-9479. **T:** 1 863 773-9282
E: lagrande1310@gmail.com
Editorial Profile: WAUC-AM is a commercial station owned by Marvina Enterprises, Inc. The format of the station is Regional Mexican. WAUC-AM broadcasts to the Wauchula, FL area on 1310 AM.

WAUD-AM
Owner: Tiger Communications Inc.
Editorial: 2514 S College St, Ste 104, Auburn, Alabama 36832. **T:** 1 334 887-3401
W: http://waudradio.com
Editorial Profile: WAUD-AM is a commercial station owned by Tiger Communications Inc. The format of the station is sports. WAUD-AM broadcasts to the Auburn, AL area at 1230 AM.

WAUG-AM
Owner: St. Augustine's College
Editorial: 1315 Oakwood Ave, Raleigh, North Carolina 27610-2247. **T:** 1 919 516-4750
W: http://www.mywaug.com/
Editorial Profile: WAUG-AM is a commercial station owned by St. Augustine's College. The format of the station is news, talk and sports. WAUG-AM broadcasts to the Raleigh-Durham, NC area at 750 AM.

WAUH-FM
Owner: Hometown Broadcasting LLC
Editorial: W7703 Johnson Ct, Wautoma, Wisconsin 54982. **T:** 1 920 787-7220
E: thebug@wauhradio.com
W: http://www.wauhradio.com
Editorial Profile: WAUH-FM is a commercial station owned by Hometown Broadcasting LLC. The format is oldies music. WAUH-FM broadcasts to the Wautoma, WI area at 102.3 FM.

WAUK-AM
Owner: Good Karma Broadcasting
Editorial: 310 W Wisconsin Ave Unit 100, Milwaukee, Wisconsin 53203-2224.
T: 1 414 273-3776
W: http://espnwisconsin.com
Editorial Profile: WAUK-AM is a commercial station owned by Good Karma Broadcasting. The format of the station is sports. WAUK-AM broadcasts to the Milwaukee area at 540 AM.

WAUN-FM
Owner: Magnum Radio Group
Editorial: 1021 N Superior Ave Ste 5, Tomah, Wisconsin 54660-1192. **T:** 1 920 388-9286
Editorial Profile: WAUN-FM is a commercial station owned by Magnum Radio Group. The format of the station is Regional Mexican music. WAUN-FM broadcasts to the Green Bay, WI, area at 92.7 FM.

WAUO-FM
Owner: American Family Association
Editorial: 107 Park Gate Dr, Tupelo, Mississippi 38801-3010. **T:** 1 662 844-8888
E: comments@afr.net **W:** http://www.afr.net
Editorial Profile: WAUO-FM is a commerical station owned by American Family Association. The format of the station is News Talk. WAUO-FM is a transmitter that broadcasts to the Hohenwald, TN area at 90.7 FM and simulcasts American Family Radio.

WAUR-AM
Owner: Starboard Media Foundation Inc.
Editorial: 1 Broadcast Ctr, Plano, Illinois 60545-2100. **T:** 1 312 467-9755
E: info@relevantradio.com
W: http://www.relevantradio.com
Editorial Profile: WAUR-AM is a non-commercial station owned by Starboard Media Foundation Inc. The format of the station is religious talk programming. WAUR-AM broadcasts to the Plano, IL area at 930 AM.

WAUS-FM
Owner: Andrews Broadcasting Corporation
Editorial: Howard Performing Arts Ctr, Berrien Springs, Michigan 49104. **T:** 1 269 471-3400
E: waus@andrews.edu
W: http://www.waus.org
Editorial Profile: WAUS-FM is a non-commercial station owned by Andrews Broadcasting Corporation. The format of the station is classical music. WAUS-FM broadcasts to the Berrien Springs, MI area at 90.7 FM.

WAVA-AM
Owner: Salem Communications
Editorial: 1901 N Moore St, Ste 200, Arlington, Virginia 22209. **T:** 1 703 807-2266
E: comment@wava.com
W: http://www.wava.com
Editorial Profile: WAVA-AM is a commercial station owned by Salem Communications. The format of the station is Christian talk and music. WAVA-AM broadcasts to the Arlington, VA area at 780 AM.

WAVA-FM
Owner: Salem Communications
Editorial: 1901 N Moore St Ste 200, Arlington, Virginia 22209-1746. **T:** 1 703 807-2266
E: comment@wava.com
W: http://www.wava.com
Editorial Profile: WAVA-FM is a commercial station owned by Salem Communications. The format of the station is Christian music and talk. WAVA-FM broadcasts to the Arlington, VA area at 105.1 FM.

WAVC-FM
Owner: Northern Star Broadcasting LLC
Editorial: 1356 Mackinaw Ave, Cheboygan, Michigan 49721-1003. **T:** 1 231 347-4382
W: http://yourdefendingfathers.us/
Editorial Profile: WAVC-FM is a commercial station owned by Northern Star Broadcasting LLC. The format of the station is Conservative talk. WAVC-FM broadcasts to the Cheboygan, MI area at 93.9 FM.

WAVD-FM
Owner: Delmarva Broadcasting
Editorial: 919 Ellegood St, Salisbury, Maryland 21801. **T:** 1 410 219-3500
W: http://www.971thewave.com
Editorial Profile: WAVD-FM is a commercial station owned by Delmarva Broadcasting. The format of the station is classic hits. WAVD-FM broadcasts to the Salisbury, MD area at a frequency of 97.1 FM.

WAVF-FM
Owner: Apex Broadcasting Inc.
Editorial: 2294 Clements Ferry Rd, Charleston, South Carolina 29492. **T:** 1 843 972-1100
E: frontdesk@apexbroadcasting.com
W: http://www.1017chuckfm.com
Editorial Profile: WAVF-FM is a commercial station owned by Apex Broadcasting Inc. The format of the station is adult hits. WAVF-FM broadcasts to the Charleston, SC area at 101.7 FM.

WAVH-FM
Owner: Bigler Broadcasting, LLC
Editorial: 900 Western America Cir Ste 506, Mobile, Alabama 36609-4105.
T: 1 251 344-1065 **E:** info@fmtalk1065.com
W: http://www.fmtalk1065.com
Editorial Profile: WAVH-FM is a commercial station owned by Bigler Broadcasting, LLC. The format for the station is talk. WAVH-FM broadcasts to the Mobile, AL area at 106.5 FM.

WAVJ-FM
Owner: Commonwealth Broadcasting Corp.
Editorial: 108 W Main St, Princeton, Kentucky 42445. **T:** 1 270 365-2072
E: wavj@commonwealthbroadcasting.com
Editorial Profile: WAVJ-FM is a commercial station owned by Commonwealth Broadcasting Corp. The format of the station is adult contemporary. WAVJ-FM broadcasts to the Princeton, KY area at 104.9 FM.

WAVK-FM
Owner: Gamma Broadcasting LLC
Editorial: 11399 Overseas Hwy, Marathon, Florida 33050-3403. **T:** 1 305 872-9100
Editorial Profile: WAVK-FM is a commercial station owned by Gamma Broadcasting LLC. The format of the station is classic and contemporary country. WAVK-FM broadcasts to the Marathon, FL area at 97.7 FM.

WAVL-AM
Owner: Family-Life Media-Com Inc.
Editorial: 114 S Jefferson St, Kittanning, Pennsylvania 16201-2408. **T:** 1 724 548-8000
Editorial Profile: WAVL-AM is a commercial station owned by Family-Life Media-Com Inc. The format of the station is Christian teaching and music programming. WAVL-AM broadcasts to the Sarver, PA area at 910 AM.

WAVM-FM
Owner: Maynard Public Schools
Editorial: 1 Tiger Dr, Maynard, Massachusetts 1754. **T:** 1 978 897-5179
E: wavmstudio@gmail.com
W: http://www.wavm.org
Editorial Profile: WAVM-FM is a non-commercial station owned by Maynard Public Schools. The format of the station is variety. WAVM-FM broadcasts to the Maynard, MA area at 91.7 FM.

WAVN-AM
Owner: Arlington Broadcasting Compan
Editorial: 6080 Mt. Moriah, Memphis, Tennessee 38115. **T:** 1 662 280-9599
Editorial Profile: WAVN-AM is a commercial station owned by Flinn Broadcasting Corp. The format of the station is gospel. WAVN-AM broadcasts to the Southaven, MS area at 1240 AM.

WAVO-AM
Owner: GHB Broadcasting
Editorial: 5732 N Tryon St, Charlotte, North Carolina 28213. **T:** 1 704 596-4900
W: http://www.1150wavo.com
Editorial Profile: WAVO-AM is a commercial station owned by GHB Broadcasting. The format of the station is adult standards. WAVO-AM broadcasts to the Charlotte, NC area at 1150 AM.

WAVR-FM
Owner: WATS Broadcasting Inc.
Editorial: 193 S Keystone Ave, Sayre, Pennsylvania 18840-1330. **T:** 1 570 888-7745
E: wats.wavr@cqservices.com
W: http://www.choice102.com
Editorial Profile: WAVR-FM is a commercial station owned by WATS Broadcasting Inc. The format of the station is adult contemporary music. WAVR-FM broadcasts to the Sayre, PA area at 102.1 FM.

WAVS-AM
Owner: Alliance Broadcasting Network
Editorial: 6360 SW 41st Pl, Davie, Florida 33314. **T:** 1 954 584-1170
E: info@wavs1170.com
W: http://www.wavs1170.com
Editorial Profile: WAVS-AM is a commercial station owned by Alliance Broadcasting Network. The format of the station is Caribbean music and news programming. WAVS-AM broadcasts to the Davie, FL area at 1170 AM.

WAVT-FM
Owner: Pottsville Broadcasting Company Inc.
Editorial: 212 S Centre St, Pottsville, Pennsylvania 17901-3532. **T:** 1 570 622-1360
W: http://www.t102radio.com
Editorial Profile: WAVT-FM is a commercial station owned by Pottsville Broadcasting Company Inc. The format of the station is hot adult contemporary. WAVT-FM broadcasts to the Pottsville, PA area at 101.9 FM.

WAVU-AM
Owner: Sand Mountain Broadcasting Service
Editorial: 3770 US Highway 431, Albertville, Alabama 35950. **T:** 1 256 878-8575
E: wqsb@aol.com **W:** http://www.wavuam.com
Editorial Profile: WAVU-AM is a commercial station owned by Sand Mountain Broadcasting Service. The format of the station is Southern gospel music. WAVU-AM broadcasts to the Albertville, AL area at 630 AM.

WAVV-FM
Owner: Alpine Broadcasting Corp.
Editorial: 11800 Tamiami Trl E, Naples, Florida 34113. **T:** 1 239 793-1011
W: http://www.wavv101.com
Editorial Profile: WAVV-FM is a commercial station owned by Alpine Broadcasting Corp. The format of the station is easy listening. WAVV-FM broadcasts to the Naples, FL area at 101.1 FM.

WAVW-FM
Owner: Clear Channel Media and Entertainment
Editorial: 3771 SE Jennings Rd, Port Saint Lucie, Florida 34952-7702. **T:** 1 772 335-9300
W: http://www.wavw.com
Editorial Profile: WAVW-FM is a commercial station owned by Clear Channel Media and Entertainment. The format of the station is country. WAVW-FM broadcasts to the West Palm Beach, FL area at 92.7 FM.

WAVZ-AM
Owner: Clear Channel Media and Entertainment
Editorial: 495 Benham St, Hamden, Connecticut 6514. **T:** 1 203 281-9600
W: http://www.espnradio1300.com
Editorial Profile: WAVZ-AM is a commercial station owned by Clear Channel Media and Entertainment. The format for the station is sports. WAVZ-AM broadcasts to the Hartford-New Haven, CT area at 1300 AM.

WAWC-FM
Owner: Talking Stick Communications LLC
Editorial: 216 W Market St, Warsaw, Indiana 46580. **T:** 1 574 372-3064
W: http://www.willie1035.com
Editorial Profile: WAWC-FM is a commercial station owned by Talking Stick Communications LLC. The format for the station is contemporary country music and sports. WAWC-FM broadcasts to the South Bend, IN area at 103.5 FM.

WAWK-AM
Owner: Northeast Indiana Broadcasting Inc.
Editorial: 931 East Ave, Kendallville, Indiana 46755. **T:** 1 260 347-2400
W: http://955fmthehawk.com
Editorial Profile: WAWK-AM is a commercial station owned by Northeast Indiana Broadcasting Inc. The format of the station is classic hits. WAWK-AM broadcasts to the Kendallville, IN area at 1140 AM.

WAWK-FM
Owner: Northeast Indiana Broadcasting Inc.
Editorial: 931 East Ave, Kendallville, Indiana 46755-1148. **T:** 1 260 347-2400
W: http://955fmthehawk.com
Editorial Profile: WAWK-FM is a commercial station owned by Northeast Indiana Broadcasting Inc. The format of the station is classic hits. WAWK-FM's broadcasts to the Kendallville, IN area at 95.5 FM.

WAXL-FM
Owner: DCBroadcasting Inc.
Editorial: 501 Old State Road 231, Huntingburg, Indiana 47542.
T: 1 812 683-1215 **E:** mailbox@waxl.us
W: http://dcbroadcasting.com
Editorial Profile: WAXL-FM is a commercial station owned by DCBroadcasting Inc. The format for the station is adult contemporary music. WAXL-FM broadcasts to the Huntingburg, IN, area at 103.3 FM.

WAXM-FM
Owner: Valley Broadcasting
Editorial: 724 Park Ave NW, Norton, Virginia 24273-1923. **T:** 1 276 679-1901
E: 93.5@waxm.com **W:** http://www.waxm.com
Editorial Profile: WAXM-FM is a commercial station owned by Valley Broadcasting. The format of the station is classic and contemporary country. WAXM-FM broadcasts to the Norton, VA area at 93.5 FM.

WAXO-AM
Owner: Marshall County Radio Corp.
Editorial: 217 W Commerce St, Lewisburg, Tennessee 37091. **T:** 1 931 359-6641
E: waxo@waxo.com **W:** http://www.waxo.com
Editorial Profile: WAXO-AM is a commercial owned by Marshall County Radio Corp. The format of the station is contemporary country. WAXO-AM broadcasts in the greater Lewisburg, TN area at 1220 AM.

WAXO-FM
Owner: Marshall County Radio Corp.
Editorial: 217 W Commerce St, Lewisburg, Tennessee 37091-3337. **T:** 1 931 359-6641
E: waxo@waxo.com **W:** http://www.waxo.com
Editorial Profile: WAXO-FM is a commercial station owned by Marshall County Radio Corp. The format is contemporary country. The station airs in the Lewisburg, TN area at 95.9 FM.

WAXQ-FM
Owner: Clear Channel Media and Entertainment
Editorial: 32 Avenue of the Americas, New York, New York 10013-2473.
T: 1 212 377-7900 **W:** http://www.q1043.com
Editorial Profile: WAXQ-FM is a commercial station owned by Clear Channel Media and Entertainment. The format of the station is classic rock. WAXQ-FM broadcasts to the New York City metro area at 104.3 FM.

WAXR-FM
Owner: American Family Association
Editorial: 3316 Avenue Of The Cities, Moline, Illinois 61265. **T:** 1 602 844-8888
E: comments@afr.net
W: http://www.waxr.afr.net
Editorial Profile: WAXR-FM is a non-commercial station owned by American Family Association. The format of the station is Christian talk. WAXR-FM broadcasts to the Geneseo, IL area at a frequency of 88.1 FM.

WAXS-FM
Owner: Southern Communications Corp.
Editorial: 306 S Kanawha St, Beckley, West Virginia 25801. **T:** 1 304 253-7000
W: http://www.groovy94.com
Editorial Profile: WAXS-FM is a commercial station owned by Southern Communications Corp. The format of the station is classic hits music. WAXS-FM broadcasts to the Beckley, WV area at 94.1 FM.

WAXX-FM
Owner: Mid-West Family Broadcasting
Editorial: 944 Harlem St, Altoona, Wisconsin 54720-1127. **T:** 1 715 832-1530
W: http://www.todayswaxx1045.com
Editorial Profile: WAXX-FM is a commercial station owned by Mid-West Family Broadcasting. The format of the station is contemporary country. WAXX-FM broadcasts to the Eau Claire, WI area at 104.5 FM.

WAXY-AM
Owner: Lincoln Financial Media
Editorial: 20450 NW 2nd Ave, Miami, Florida 33169-2505. **T:** 1 305 521-5100
W: http://www.theticketmiami.com
Editorial Profile: WAXY-AM is a commercial station owned by Lincoln Financial Media. The format of the station is sports. WAXY-AM broadcasts to the Miami area at 790 AM.

WAXY-FM
Owner: Lincoln Financial Media
Editorial: 20450 NW 2nd Ave, Miami, Florida 33169-2505. **T:** 1 305 521-5100
W: http://www.theticketmiami.com
Editorial Profile: WAXY-FM is a commercial station owned by Lincoln Financial Media. The format of the station is sports. WAXY-FM broadcasts to the Miami, FL area at 104.3 FM.

WAYA-FM
Owner: Caswell Capital Partners, LLC
Editorial: 2045 Spaulding Dr, North Charleston, South Carolina 29406-4960.
T: 1 843 529-9293 **E:** wayx@wayfm.com
W: http://wayx.wayfm.com
Editorial Profile: WAYA-FM is a commercial station owned by Caswell Capital Partners, LLC and operated by WAY-FM Media Group, Inc. The format of the station is contemporary Christian. WAYA-FM broadcasts to the Charleston, SC area at 100.9 FM.

WAYC-AM
Owner: Cessna Communications Inc.
Editorial: 134 E Pitt St, 2nd Fl, Bedford, Pennsylvania 15522. **T:** 1 814 623-1000
Editorial Profile: WAYC-AM is a commercial station owned by Cessna Communications Inc. The format of the station is adult standards and religious programming. WAYC-AM broadcasts to the Bedford, PA area at 1600 AM.

WAYC-FM
Owner: Cessna Communications Inc.
Editorial: 134 E Pitt St, 2nd Fl, Bedford, Pennsylvania 15522. **T:** 1 814 623-1000
E: cesscomm@embarqmail.com
W: http://www.hitsandfavorites.com
Editorial Profile: WAYC-FM is a commercial station owned by Cessna Communications Inc. The format of the station is adult contemporary. WAYC-FM broadcasts to the Johnstown-Altoona, PA area at 100.9 FM.

WAYD-FM
Owner: WAY Media Inc.
Editorial: 1945 Scottsville Rd Ste B2 Pmb 363, Bowling Green, Kentucky 42104-5817.
T: 1 888 339-2936 **E:** wayd@wayfm.com

W: http://www.wayfm.com
Editorial Profile: WAYD-FM is a non-commercial station owned by WAY Media Inc. The format of the station is contemporary Christian. WAYD-FM broadcasts to the Bowling Green, KY area on 88.1 FM.

WAYE-AM
Owner: Christian Broadcasting of Birmingham
Editorial: 1449 Spaulding Ishkooda Rd, Birmingham, Alabama 35211-5059.
T: 1 205 942-1776 **E:** info@waye1220.com
W: http://www.waye1220.com
Editorial Profile: WAYE-AM is a commercial station owned by Christian Broadcasting of Birmingham. The format of the station is gospel. WAYE-AM broadcasts to the Birmingham, AL area at 1220 AM.

WAYF-FM
Owner: WAY Media Inc.
Editorial: 800 Northpoint Pkwy, Ste 881, West Palm Beach, Florida 33407-1978.
T: 1 561 881-1929 **E:** wayf@wayfm.com
W: http://www.wayfm.com
Editorial Profile: WAYF-FM is a non-commercial station owned by WAY Media Inc. The format of the station is contemporary Christian. WAYF-FM broadcasts to the West Palm Beach, FL area at 88.1 FM.

WAY-FM
Owner: WAY Media Inc.
Editorial: 1707 N. Main St, Ste 302, Longmont, Colorado 80501.
T: 1 303 702-9293 **W:** http://www.wayfm.com
Editorial Profile: WAY-FM is a commerical station owned by WAY Media Inc. The format of the station is contemporary Christian. WAY-FM broadcasts to the Longmont, CO area on 90.9 FM.

WAYG-FM
Owner: WAY Media Inc.
Editorial: 3211 Grant Line Rd Ste 1, New Albany, Indiana 47150-2175.
T: 1 888 929-1059 **W:** http://wayi.wayfm.com
Editorial Profile: WAYG-FM is a commercial station owned by WAY Media Inc. The format of the station is Contemporary Christian. WLUE-FM broadcasts to the Charlestown, IN area at 104.3 FM.

WAYH-FM
Owner: WAY Media Inc.
Editorial: 9582 Madison Blvd, Madison, Alabama 35758-9107. **T:** 1 256 837-9293
E: contact@wayfm.com
W: http://wayh.wayfm.com
Editorial Profile: WAYH-FM is a non-commercial station owned by WAY Media Inc. The format of the station is contemporary Christian. WAYH-FM broadcasts to the Madison, AL area at 88.1 FM.

WAYJ-FM
Owner: Way Media, Inc.
Editorial: 1860 Boy Scout Dr Ste 202, Fort Myers, Florida 33907-2119. **T:** 1 239 936-1929
W: http://wayj.wayfm.com
Editorial Profile: WAYJ-FM is a non-commercial station owned by FWay Media, Inc. The format of the station is contemporary Christian. WAYJ-FM broadcasts to the Southwest Florida area at 89.5 FM.

WAYL-FM
Owner: Delmarva Educational Association
Editorial: 4190 Belfort Rd, Ste 450, Jacksonville, Florida 32216-1405.
T: 1 904 470-4615 **W:** http://www.fm88.org
Editorial Profile: WAYL-FM is a non-commercial station owned by Delmarva Educational Association. The format of the station is religious and contemporary Christian music and talk. WAYL-FM broadcasts to the St. Augustine, FL area at 91.9 FM.

WAYM-FM
Owner: WAY Media Inc.
Editorial: 1095 McEwen Dr, Franklin, Tennessee 37067-1611. **T:** 1 615 261-9293
W: http://waym.wayfm.com
Editorial Profile: WAYM-FM is a non-commercial station owned by WAY Media Inc. The format of the station is contemporary Christian music. WAYM-FM broadcasts to the Franklin, TN area on 90.5 FM.

WAYN-AM
Owner: WAYN Inc.
Editorial: 1223 Rockingham Rd, Rockingham, North Carolina 28379. **T:** 1 910 895-4041
E: wayninc@aol.com **W:** http://www.wayn.us
Editorial Profile: WAYN-AM is a commercial station owned by WAYN Inc. The format for the station is adult contemporary. WAYN-AM

broadcasts to the Charlotte, NC area at 900 AM.

WAYP-FM
Owner: WAY Media Inc.
Editorial: 2199 N Monroe St, Tallahassee, Florida 32303-4763. **T:** 1 850 422-1929
W: http://wayp.wayfm.com
Editorial Profile: WAYP-FM is a non-commercial station owned by WAY Media Inc. The format of the station is contemporary Christian music and talk. WAYP-FM broadcasts to Marianna, FL at 91.1 FM.

WAYQ-FM
Owner: WAY Media Inc.
Editorial: 2277 C Wilma Rudolph Blvd., Box 103, Clarksville, Tennessee 37040.
T: 1 931 647-8883 **W:** http://wayq.wayfm.com
Editorial Profile: WAYQ-FM is a non-commercial station owned by the WAY Media Inc. The format of the station is contemporary Christian music. WAYQ-FM broadcasts to the Nashville, TN area at 88.3 FM.

WAYR-AM
Owner: Good Tidings Trust Inc.
Editorial: 2500 Russell Rd, Green Cove Springs, Florida 32043. **T:** 1 904 284-1111
E: manager@wayradio.org
W: http://www.wayradio.org
Editorial Profile: WAYR-AM is a non-commercial station owned by Good Tidings Trust Inc. The format of the station is religious. WAYR-AM broadcasts to the greater Orange Park, FL area at 550 AM.

WAYR-FM
Owner: Good Tidings Trust Inc.
Editorial: 1426 Newcastle St, Ste 200, Brunswick, Georgia 31520. **T:** 1 912 342-1083
E: manager@wayradio.org
W: http://907.wayradio.org
Editorial Profile: WAYR-FM is a non-commercial station owned by Good Tidings Trust Inc. The format of the station is contemporary Christian. WAYR-FM broadcasts to the Brunswick, GA area at 90.7 FM.

WAYS-AM
Owner: Cumulus Media Inc.
Editorial: 544 Mulberry St, Ste 500, Macon, Georgia 31201. **T:** 1 478 746-6286
Editorial Profile: WAYS-AM is a commercial station owned by Cumulus Media Inc. The format of the station is sports. WAYS-AM broadcasts to the Macon, GA area at 1500 AM.

WAYT-FM
Owner: WAY Media Inc.
Editorial: 2199 N Monroe St, Tallahassee, Florida 32303-4763. **T:** 1 850 422-1929
W: http://www.wayfm.com
Editorial Profile: WAYT-FM is a non-commercial station owned by WAY Media Inc. The format is contemporary Christian. The station airs in the Tallahassee, FL area at 88.1 FM.

WAYU-FM
Owner: WAY Media, Inc
Editorial: 3331 Rainbow Dr Ste E, PMB 107, Rainbow City, Alabama 35906-6264.
T: 1 888 239-2936 **E:** contact@wayfm.com
W: http://wayu.wayfm.com
Editorial Profile: WAYU-FM is a non-commercial station owned by WAY Media, Inc. The format of the station is Christian contemporary music. WAYU-FM broadcasts at a frequency of 91.1 FM to Gadsden, and the northeast Alabama area.

WAYV-FM
Owner: Equity Communications LP
Editorial: 8025 Black Horse Pike, Pleasantville, New Jersey 08232-2900. **T:** 1 609 484-8444
E: 951wayv@gmail.com
W: http://www.951wayv.com
Editorial Profile: WAYV-FM is a commercial station owned by Equity Communications LP. The format of the station is hot adult contemporary. WAYV-FM broadcasts to the West Atlantic City, NJ area at 95.1 FM.

WAYW-FM
Owner: WAY Media Inc.
Editorial: 1012 W Mcewen Dr, Franklin, Tennessee 37067-1721. **T:** 1 615 261-9293
W: http://www.wayfm.com
Editorial Profile: WAYW-FM is a non-commercial station owned by WAY Media Inc. The format of the station is contemporary Christian music. WAYW-FM broadcasts to the New Johnsonville, TN area at 89.9 FM.

WAYX-AM
Owner: Santilla Broadcast Properties, LLC
Editorial: 1766 Memorial Dr, Ste 1, Waycross, Georgia 31501. **T:** 1 912 285-5002
W: http://www.wayx.net
Editorial Profile: WAYX-AM is a commercial station owned by Santilla Broadcast Properties, LLC. The format of the station is news and talk. WAYX-AM broadcasts to the Waycross, GA area at 1230 AM.

WAYY-AM
Owner: Mid-West Family Broadcasting
Editorial: 944 Harlem St, Altoona, Wisconsin 54720-1127. **T:** 1 715 832-1530
W: http://www.wayy790.com
Editorial Profile: WAYY-AM is a commercial station owned by Mid-West Family Broadcasting. The format of the station is sports and news/talk. WAYY-AM broadcasts to the Altoona, WI area at 790 AM.

WAYZ-FM
Owner: VerStandig Broadcasting
Editorial: 10960 John Wayne Dr, Greencastle, Pennsylvania 17225. **T:** 1 717 597-9200
E: info@wayz.com **W:** http://www.wayz.com
Editorial Profile: WAYZ-FM is a commercial station owned by VerStandig Broadcasting. The format of the station is contemporary country music. WAYZ-FM broadcasts to the Greencastle, PA area at 104.7 FM.

WAZA-FM
Owner: Southwest Broadcasting
Editorial: 206 N Front St, McComb, Mississippi 39648-3916. **T:** 1 601 684-4116
Editorial Profile: WAZA-FM is a commercial station owned by Southwest Broadcasting. The format of the station is R&B. WAZA-FM broadcasts to the McComb, MS area at 107.7 FM.

WAZL-AM
Owner: Geos Communications
Editorial: 679 S Church St, Hazleton, Pennsylvania 18201-7611. **T:** 1 570 455-1490
E: contactus@wazlam.com
W: http://www.wazlam.com
Editorial Profile: WAZL-AM is a commercial station owned by Geos Communications. and operated by KMCS Broadcasting LLC. The format of the station is Classic Country. WAZL-AM broadcasts to the Hazelton, PA area at 1490 AM.

WAZN-AM
Owner: Multicultural Radio Broadcasting Inc.
Editorial: 500 W Cummings Park, Ste 2600, Woburn, Massachusetts 1801.
T: 1 781 938-0869 **W:** http://mrbi.net
Editorial Profile: WAZN-AM is a commercial station owned by Multicultural Radio Broadcasting Inc. The format of the station is ethnic brokered programming. WAZN-AM broadcasts to the Woburn, MA area at 1470 AM.

WAZO-FM
Owner: Capitol Broadcasting Company
Editorial: 25 N Kerr Ave, Ste C, Wilmington, North Carolina 28405. **T:** 1 910 791-3088
W: http://www.z1075.com
Editorial Profile: WAZO-FM is a commercial station owned by Capitol Broadcasting Company. The format of the station is Top 40/CHR. WAZO-FM broadcasts to the Wilmington, NC area at 107.5 FM.

WAZR-FM
Owner: Clear Channel Media and Entertainment
Editorial: 207 University Blvd, Harrisonburg, Virginia 22801-3749. **T:** 1 540 434-1777
W: http://www.937kissfm.com
Editorial Profile: WAZR-FM is a commercial station owned by Clear Channel Media and Entertainment. The format for the station is Top 40/CHR. WAZR-FM broadcasts to the Harrisonburg, VA area at 93.7 FM.

WAZS-AM
Owner: Jabar Communications, Inc.
Editorial: 5081 Rivers Ave, North Charleston, South Carolina 29406. **T:** 1 843 554-1063
E: traffic@jabarcommunications.com
W: http://www.jabarcommunications.com
Editorial Profile: WAZS-AM is a commercial station owned by Jabar Communications, Inc. The format of the station is Hispanic and Top 40/CHR music. WAZS-AM broadcasts to the North Charleston, SC area at 980 AM.

WAZU-FM
Owner: Sirius Synocope, Inc
Editorial: 2122 W Kellogg Ave, West Peoria, Illinois 61604-5587. **T:** 1 309 694-5307

E: comments@wazufm.org
W: http://wazufm.org
Editorial Profile: WAZU-FM is a non-commercial station owned by Sirius Synocope, Inc. The station airs at a frequency of 90.7 in Peoria, IL. WAZU-FM is a new concept station with a format of "community radio" where listeners are involved in programming. Listeners will discover music, news reports, opinions and esoterica in an array of styles and languages providing programming to diverse communities and un-served or under-served groups.

WAZY-FM
Owner: Artistic Media Partners Inc.
Editorial: 3824 S 18Th St, Lafayette, Indiana 47909-9102. **T:** 1 765 474-1410
W: http://www.wazy.com
Editorial Profile: WAZY-FM is a commercial station owned by Artistic Media Partners Inc. The format of the station is Top 40/CHR. WAZY-FM broadcasts to Lafayette, IN at 96.5 FM.

WAZZ-AM
Owner: Beasley Broadcast Group
Editorial: 508 Person St, Fayetteville, North Carolina 28301. **T:** 1 910 486-4114·
W: http://www.am1490wazz.com
Editorial Profile: WAZZ-AM is a commercial station owned by the Beasley Broadcast Group. The format of the station is adult standards music. WAZZ-AM broadcasts to the Fayetteville, NC area at 1490 AM.

WBAA-AM
Owner: Purdue University
Editorial: 712 3rd St, West Lafayette, Indiana 47907. **T:** 1 765 494-5920 **E:** news@wbaa.org
W: http://www.purdue.edu/wbaa/
Editorial Profile: WBAA-AM is a non-commercial station owned by Purdue University. The format for the station is jazz and news. WBAA-AM broadcasts to the Lafayette, IN area at 920 AM.

WBAA-FM
Owner: Purdue University
Editorial: 712 3rd St, West Lafayette, Indiana 47907. **T:** 1 765 494-5920 **E:** news@wbaa.org
W: http://www.purdue.edu/wbaa/
Editorial Profile: WBAA-FM is a non-commercial station owned by Purdue University. The format for the station is classical music and news. WBAA-FM broadcasts to the West Lafayette, IN area at 101.3 FM.

WBAB-FM
Owner: Cox Media Group, Inc.
Editorial: 555 Sunrise Hwy, West Babylon, New York 11704-6009. **T:** 1 631 587-1023
E: wbab@wbab.com **W:** http://www.wbab.com
Editorial Profile: WBAB-FM is a commercial station owned by Cox Media Group, Inc. The format of the station is rock/album-oriented rock. WBAB-FM broadcasts to the New York area at 102.3 FM.

WBAC-AM
Owner: East Tennessee Radio Group
Editorial: 2640 Commerce Dr NE, Cleveland, Tennessee 37311. **T:** 1 423 472-4053
Editorial Profile: WBAC-AM is a commercial station owned by East Tennessee Radio Group. The format of the station is talk, news and sports. WBAC-AM broadcasts to the Cleveland, TN area at 1340 AM.

WBAD-FM
Owner: Interchange Communications
Editorial: 126 Seven Oaks Road, Greenville, Mississippi 38704-4426. **T:** 1 662 335-9265
E: wbad.radio@suddenlinkmail.com
Editorial Profile: WBAD-FM is a commercial station owned by Interchange Communications . The format for the station is urban contemporary. WBAD-FM broadcasts to the Greenwood-Greenville, MS area at 94.3 FM.

WBAE-AM
Owner: Saga Communications
Editorial: 420 Western Ave, South Portland, Maine 04106-1704. **T:** 1 207 774-4561
W: http://am1490thebay.com
Editorial Profile: WBAE-AM is a commercial station owned by Saga Communications. The format of the station is adult standards. WBAE-AM broadcasts to the South Portland, ME area at 1490 AM.

WBAF-AM
Owner: Ploener Radio Group
Editorial: 645 Forsyth St, Barnesville, Georgia 30204. **T:** 1 770 358-1090

Editorial Profile: WBAF-AM is a commercial station owned by Ploener Radio Group. The format of the station is classic country. WBAF-AM broadcasts to the Barnesville, GA area at 1090 AM.

WBAG-AM
Owner: Gray Broadcasting Corp.
Editorial: 1745 Burch Bridge Rd, Burlington, North Carolina 27217. **T:** 1 336 226-1150
E: wbag@bellsouth.net
W: http://www.wbag1150.com
Editorial Profile: WBAG-AM is a commercial station owned by Gray Broadcasting Corp. The format of the station is news and talk. WBAG-AM broadcasts to the Burlington, NC area at 1150 AM.

WBAI-FM
Owner: Pacifica Foundation, Inc.
Editorial: 388 Atlantic Ave, Brooklyn, New York 11217-3399. **T:** 1 347 903-2986
W: http://www.wbai.org
Editorial Profile: WBAI-FM is a non-commercial station owned by Pacifica Foundation, Inc. The format of the station is variety. WBAI-FM broadcasts to the New York area at 99.5 FM. The station is not interested in product news, gadget news, sports news, celebrity news, entertainment news or any of the other non-news stories.

WBAK-FM
Owner: Blueberry Broadcasting
Editorial: 184 Target Cir, Bangor, Maine 04401-5718. **T:** 1 207 947-9100
Editorial Profile: WBAK-FM is a commercial station owned by Blueberry Broadcasting. The format of the station is Classic Hits. WBAK-FM broadcasts to the Bangor, ME area at 104.7 FM.

WBAL-AM
Owner: Hearst Television Inc.
Editorial: 3800 Hooper Ave, Baltimore, Maryland 21211-1313. **T:** 1 410 338-6546
E: news@wbal.com **W:** http://www.wbal.com
Editorial Profile: WBAL-AM is a commercial station owned by Hearst Television Inc. The format of the station is news, sports and talk. WBAL-AM broadcasts to the Baltimore area at 1090 AM.

WBAM-FM
Owner: Bluewater Broadcasting Co. LLC
Editorial: 4101A Wall St, Ste A, Montgomery, Alabama 36106. **T:** 1 334 244-0961
W: http://bamacountry.com
Editorial Profile: WBAM-FM is a commercial station owned by Bluewater Broadcasting Co. LLC. The format of the station is contemporary country. WBAM-FM broadcasts to the Montgomery, AL at a frequency of 98.9 FM.

WBAP-AM
Owner: Cumulus Media Inc
Editorial: 3090 Olive St, Dallas, Texas 75219-7640. **T:** 1 214 526-2400 **E:** news@wbap.com
W: http://www.wbap.com
Editorial Profile: WBAP-AM is a commercial station owned by Cumulus Media Inc. The format of the station is news and talk programming. WBAP-AM broadcasts to the Dallas area at 820 AM.

WBAP-FM
Owner: Cumulus Media Inc
Editorial: 3090 Olive St, Dallas, Texas 75219-7640. **T:** 1 817 695-3500
W: http://www.theticket.com/
Editorial Profile: WBAP-FM is a commercial station owned by Cumulus Media Inc. The format of the station is sports. WBAP-FM broadcasts to the Dallas area at 96.7 FM.

WBAR-FM
Owner: Capital Media Corporation
Editorial: 30 Park Ave, Cohoes, New York 12047-3330. **T:** 1 518 237-1330
E: events@aliveradio.com
W: http://www.aliveradionetwork.com
Editorial Profile: WBAR-FM is a commercial station owned by Capital Media Corporation. The format of the station is religious programming. WBAR-FM broadcasts to the Glen Falls, NY area at 94.7 FM.

WBAT-AM
Owner: Hoosier AM/FM, LLC
Editorial: 820 S Pennsylvania St, Marion, Indiana 46953-2407. **T:** 1 765 664-6239
E: news@wbat.com **W:** http://www.wbat.com
Editorial Profile: WBAT-AM is a commercial station owned by Hoosier AM/FM, LLC. The format of the station is talk. WBAT-AM broadcasts to the Marion, IN area at 1400 AM.

WBAV-FM
Owner: CBS Radio
Editorial: 1520 South Blvd, Ste 300, Charlotte, North Carolina 28203-3701.
T: 1 704 522-1103 **W:** http://www.v1019.com
Editorial Profile: WBAV-FM is a commercial station owned by CBS Radio. The format of the station is urban adult contemporary. WBAV-FM broadcasts to the Charlotte, NC area on 101.9 FM.

WBAX-AM
Owner: Shamrock Communications
Editorial: 149 Penn Ave, Scranton, Pennsylvania 18503-2055. **T:** 1 570 346-6555
W: http://www.nepasespnradio.com/
Editorial Profile: WBAX-AM is a commercial station owned by Shamrock Communications. The format of the station is sports. WBAX-AM broadcasts to the Scranton, PA area at 1240 AM.

WBAZ-FM
Owner: Long Island Radio Broadcasting
Editorial: 249 Montauk Highway, Amagansett, New York 11930. **T:** 1 631 267-7800
E: generaloffice@libroadcasting.com
W: http://www.wbaz.com
Editorial Profile: WBAZ-FM is a commercial station owned by Long Island Radio Broadcasting. The format of the station is Lite AC. WBAZ-FM broadcasts to the Bridgehampton, NY area at 102.5 FM. The station only accepts local press releases and PSAs.

WBBA-FM
Owner: DJ Two Rivers Radio
Editorial: 1260 W Washington St, Pittsfield, Illinois 62363. **T:** 1 217 285-5975
E: wbba@wbbaradio.com
W: http://www.wbbaradio.com
Editorial Profile: WBBA-FM is a commercial station owned by DJ Two Rivers Radio. The format of the station is variety. WBBA-FM broadcasts to the Pittsfield, IL area at 97.5 FM.

WBBB-FM
Owner: Curtis Media Group
Editorial: 3012 Highwoods Blvd, Raleigh, North Carolina 27604-1037.
T: 1 919 876-3831
E: wptfnews@curtismedia.com
W: http://radio961.com
Editorial Profile: WBBB-FM is a commercial station owned by Curtis Media Group. The format of the station is rock/album-oriented rock music. WBBB-FM broadcasts to the Raleigh-Durham, NC area at 96.1 FM.

WBBC-FM
Owner: Denbar Communications Inc.
Editorial: 950 Kenbridge Rd, Blackstone, Virginia 23824. **T:** 1 434 292-4146
E: wbbc@bobcatcountryradio.com
W: http://www.bobcatcountryradio.com
Editorial Profile: WBBC-FM is a commercial station owned by Denbar Communications Inc. The format of the station is contemporary country. WBBC-FM broadcasts to the Blackstone, VA area at 93.5 FM.

WBBD-AM
Owner: Clear Channel Media and Entertainment
Editorial: 1015 Main St, Wheeling, West Virginia 26003-2709. **T:** 1 304 232-1170
W: http://www.foxsports1400wheeling.com/main.html
Editorial Profile: WBBD-AM is a commercial station owned by Clear Channel Media and Entertainment. The format of the station is sports. WBBD-AM broadcasts to the Wheeling, WV area at 1400 AM.

WBBE-FM
Owner: Connoisseur Media LLC
Editorial: 520 N Center St, Bloomington, Illinois 61701. **T:** 1 309 834-1100
W: http://www.bob979.com
Editorial Profile: WBBE-FM is a commercial station owned by Connoisseur Media LLC. The format of the station is adult hits. WBBE-FM broadcasts to the Bloomington, IL area at 97.9 FM.

WBBG-FM
Owner: Clear Channel Media and Entertainment
Editorial: 7461 South Ave, Youngstown, Ohio 44512. **T:** 1 330 740-9300
W: http://www.wbbgfm.com
Editorial Profile: WBBG-FM is a commercial station owned by Clear Channel Media and Entertainment. The format of the station is

oldies. WBBG-FM broadcasts to the Youngstown, OH area at 106.1 FM.

WBBI-FM
Owner: Clear Channel Media and Entertainment
Editorial: 320 N Jensen Rd, Vestal, New York 13850-2111. **T:** 1 607 584-5800
W: http://www.b1075country.com/main.html
Editorial Profile: WBBI-FM is a commercial station owned by Clear Channel Media and Entertainment. The format of the station is contemporary country. WBBI-FM broadcasts to the Binghamton, NY area at 107.5 FM.

WBBK-FM
Owner: Alabama Media Investments, LLC
Editorial: 285 N Foster St Fl 8, Dothan, Alabama 36303-4541. **T:** 1 334 792-0047
Editorial Profile: WBBK-FM is a commercial station owned by Alabama Media Investments, LLC and operated by Low Country Radio, LLC. The format of the station is soul music. WBBK-FM broadcasts to the Dothan, AL area at 93.1 FM.

WBBL-FM
Owner: Cumulus Media Inc
Editorial: 60 Monroe Center St NW, Grand Rapids, Michigan 49503-2916.
T: 1 616 774-8461 **W:** http://www.wbbl.com
Editorial Profile: WBBL-FM is a commercial station owned by Cumulus Media Inc. The format of the station is sports. WBBL-FM broadcasts to the Grand Rapids, MI area at 107.3 FM.

WBBM-AM
Owner: CBS Radio
Editorial: 2 Prudential Plaza, Suite 1100, Chicago, Illinois 60601. **T:** 1 312 297-7800
E: wbbmnewsradiotips@cbsradio.com
W: http://chicago.cbslocal.com
Editorial Profile: WBBM-AM is a commercial station owned by CBS Radio. The format of the station is news. WBBM-AM broadcasts to the Chicago area at 780 AM.

WBBM-FM
Owner: CBS Radio
Editorial: 180 N Stetson Ave Ste 963, Chicago, Illinois 60601-6712.
T: 1 312 861-9600 **E:** info@b96.com
W: http://b96.cbslocal.com
Editorial Profile: WBBM-FM is a commercial station owned by CBS Radio. The format of the station is rhythmic Top 40/CHR. WBBM-FM broadcasts to the Chicago area at 96.3 FM.

WBBN-FM
Owner: Blakeney Communications Inc.
Editorial: 4580 Highway 15 N, Laurel, Mississippi 39440. **T:** 1 601 649-0095
E: b95@b95country.com
W: http://www.b95country.com
Editorial Profile: WBBN-FM is a commercial station owned by Blakeney Communications Inc. The format of the station is country. WBBN-FM broadcasts to the Hattiesburg-Laurel, MS area at 95.9 FM.

WBBO-FM
Owner: Press Communications LLC
Editorial: 2355 W Bangs Ave, Neptune, New Jersey 07753-4111. **T:** 1 732 774-4755
W: http://b985radio.com
Editorial Profile: WBBO-FM is a commercial station owned by Press Communications LLC. The format of the station is Top 40/CHR. WKMK-FM broadcasts to the Neptune, NJ area at 98.5 FM.

WBBP-AM
Owner: Bountiful Blessings, Inc.
Editorial: 369 E Ge Patterson Ave, Memphis, Tennessee 38126-3301. **T:** 1 901 278-7878
E: wbbp1@bbless.org
W: http://www.bbless.org/wbbp.home.htm
Editorial Profile: WBBP-AM is a non-commercial station owned by Bountiful Blessings, Inc. The format of the station is gospel music. WBBP-AM broadcasts to the Memphis, TN area at 1480 AM.

WBBQ-FM
Owner: Clear Channel Media and Entertainment
Editorial: 2743 Perimeter Pkwy, Bldg 100, Ste. 300, Augusta, Georgia 30909.
T: 1 706 396-6000 **W:** http://www.wbbq.com
Editorial Profile: WBBQ-FM is a commercial station owned by Clear Channel Media and Entertainment. The format of the station is adult contemporary music. WBBQ-FM broadcasts to the Augusta, GA area at 104.3 FM.

WBBR-AM
Owner: Bloomberg L.P.
Editorial: 731 Lexington Ave, New York, New York 10022-1331. **T:** 1 212 617-2000
E: release@bloomberg.net
W: http://www.bloomberg.com/radio/
Editorial Profile: WBBR-AM is a commercial station owned by Bloomberg L.P. The format of the station is news. WBBR-AM broadcasts to the New York City area at 1130 AM. The assignment desk should ONLY be contacted to notify the department of serious business news stories about publicly traded companies. The station airs programming on WXKS-AM.

WBBS-FM
Owner: Clear Channel Media and Entertainment
Editorial: 500 Plum St, Ste 100, Syracuse, New York 13204-1401. **T:** 1 315 472-9797
W: http://www.b1047.net
Editorial Profile: WBBS-FM is a commercial station owned by Clear Channel Media and Entertainment. The format of the station is country. WBBS-FM broadcasts to the Syracuse, NY area at 104.7 FM.

WBBT-AM
Owner: TCB Broadcasting
Editorial: 473 N Victory Dr, Lyons, Georgia 30436. **T:** 1 912 526-8122
Editorial Profile: WBBT-AM is a commercial station owned by TCB Broadcasting. The format of the station is urban adult contemporary. WBBT-AM broadcasts to the Lyons, GA area at 1340 AM.

WBBT-FM
Owner: Main Line Broadcasting
Editorial: 300 Arboretum Pl, Ste 590, Richmond, Virginia 23236-3481.
T: 1 804 327-9902
W: http://www.bigoldies1073.com
Editorial Profile: WBBT-FM is a commercial station owned by Main Line Broadcasting. The format of the station is oldies. WBBT-FM broadcasts to the Richmond, VA area at 107.3 FM.

WBBV-FM
Owner: Debut Broadcasting Inc.
Editorial: 1601E N Frontage Rd, Vicksburg, Mississippi 39180-5149. **T:** 1 601 636-2340
Editorial Profile: WBBV-FM is a commercial station owned by Debut Broadcasting Inc. The format of the station is country music. WBBV-FM broadcasts to the Vicksburg, MS area at 101.3 FM.

WBBW-AM
Owner: Cumulus Media Inc.
Editorial: 4040 Simon Rd, Youngstown, Ohio 44512-1362. **T:** 1 330 783-1000
E: wbbw@wbbw.com
W: http://www.wbbw.com
Editorial Profile: WBBW-AM is a commercial station owned by Cumulus Media Inc. The format of the station is sports. WBBW-AM broadcasts to the Youngstown, OH area at 1240 AM.

WBBX-AM
Owner: Pilgrims Pathway Inc.
Editorial: 705 Greenwood St, Kingston, Tennessee 37763. **T:** 1 865 376-6954
Editorial Profile: WBBX-AM is a non-commercial station owned by Pilgrims Pathway Inc. The format of the station is gospel and Christian programming. WBBX-AM broadcasts to the Kingston, TN area at 1410 AM.

WBBZ-AM
Owner: Muchmore(Tom)
Editorial: 1601 E Oklahoma Ave, Ponca City, Oklahoma 74604-5215. **T:** 1 580 765-6607
E: wbbz@wbbz.com **W:** http://www.wbbz.com
Editorial Profile: WBBZ-AM is a commercial station owned by Tom Muchmore. The format of the station is classic hits music. WBBZ-AM broadcasts to the Oklahoma City area at 1230 AM.

WBCB-AM
Owner: Progressive Broadcasting
Editorial: 200 Magnolia Dr, Levittown, Pennsylvania 19054-2007. **T:** 1 215 949-1490
W: http://wbcb1490.com
Editorial Profile: WBCB-AM is a commercial station owned by Progressive Broadcasting. The format of the station is variety. WBCB-AM broadcasts to the Levittown, PA area at 1490 AM.

WBCE-AM
Owner: Gray (Wendell)
Editorial: 1136 Barlow Rd, Wickliffe, Kentucky 42087-9288. **T:** 1 270 335-5171
Editorial Profile: WBCE-AM is a commercial station owned by Gray (Wendell). The format of the station is religious featuring Christian talk and music programming. WBCE-AM broadcasts locally to the Wickliffe, KY area at a frequency of 1200 AM.

WBCF-AM
Owner: BCB Incorporated
Editorial: 525 E Tennessee St, Florence, Alabama 35630. **T:** 1 256 764-8170
E: news@wbcf.com **W:** http://www.wbcf.com
Editorial Profile: WBCF-AM is a commercial station owned by BCB Incorporated. The format of the station is news, sports and talk. WBCF-AM broadcasts to the Florence, AL area at 1240 AM.

WBCG-FM
Owner: Clear Channel Media and Entertainment
Editorial: 24100 Tiseo Blvd Unit 10, Port Charlotte, Florida 33980-5223.
T: 1 941 206-1188
W: http://www.989thebeach.com
Editorial Profile: WBCG-FM is a commercial station owned by Clear Channel Media and Entertainment. The format of the station is hot AC. WBCG-FM broadcasts to the Port Charlotte, FL area at a frequency of 98.9 FM.

WBCH-AM
Owner: Barry Broadcasting Co.
Editorial: 119 W State St, Hastings, Michigan 49058. **T:** 1 269 945-3414
E: wbch@wbch.com **W:** http://www.wbch.com
Editorial Profile: WBCH-AM is a commercial station owned by Barry Broadcasting Co. The format of the station is news and talk radio. WBCH-AM broadcasts to the Grand Rapids area at 1220 AM.

WBCH-FM
Owner: Barry Broadcasting Co.
Editorial: 119 W State St, Hastings, Michigan 49058-1843. **T:** 1 269 945-3414
E: wbch@wbch.com **W:** http://www.wbch.com
Editorial Profile: WBCH-FM is a commercial station owned by Barry Broadcasting Co. The format of the station is contemporary country music. WBCH-FM broadcasts in the Hastings, MI area at 100.1 FM.

WBCI-FM
Owner: Blount Communications Group
Editorial: 122 Main St, Topsham, Maine 04086-1248. **T:** 1 207 725-9224
W: http://www.wbci.fm
Editorial Profile: WBCI-FM is a commercial station owned by Blount Communications Group. The format for the station is Christian talk and music. WBCI-FM broadcasts to the Portland, ME area at 105.9 FM.

WBCJ-FM
Owner: Taylor University Broadcasting Inc.
Editorial: 1025 W Rudisill Blvd, Fort Wayne, Indiana 46807-2168. **T:** 1 260 745-0576
E: newspc@wbcl.org **W:** http://www.wbcl.org
Editorial Profile: WBCJ-FM is a non-commercial station owned by Taylor University Broadcasting Inc. The format of the station is contemporary Christian. WBCJ-FM broadcasts to the Fort Wayne, IN area at 88.1 FM.

WBCK-AM
Owner: Current Radio, LLC
Editorial: 390 Golden Ave, Battle Creek, Michigan 49015-4519. **T:** 1 269 963-5555
Editorial Profile: WBCK-AM is a non-commercial station owned by Current Radio, LLC. The format of the station is sports. WBCK-AM broadcasts to the Battle Creek, MI area at 930 AM.

WBCK-FM
Owner: Townsquare Media, LLC
Editorial: 390 Golden Ave, Battle Creek, Michigan 49015-4519. **T:** 1 269 963-5555
W: http://wbckfm.com
Editorial Profile: WBCK-FM is a commercial station owned by Townsquare Media, LLC . The format of the station is news, sports and talk. WBCK-FM broadcasts to the Battle Creek, MI area at 95.3 FM.

WBCL-FM
Owner: Taylor University Broadcasting Inc.
Editorial: 1115 W Rudisill Blvd, Fort Wayne, Indiana 46807-2142. **T:** 1 260 745-0576
E: newspc@wbcl.org **W:** http://www.wbcl.org
Editorial Profile: WBCL-FM is a non-commercial station owned by Taylor University Broadcasting Inc. The format of the station is contemporary Christian. WBCL-FM broadcasts to the Fort Wayne, IN area at 90.3 FM.

WBCM-FM
Owner: Midwestern Broadcasting Co.
Editorial: 314 E Front St, Traverse City, Michigan 49684. **T:** 1 231 947-7675
E: news@wtcmradio.com
W: http://www.wtcmi.com
Editorial Profile: WBCM-FM is a commercial station owned by Midwestern Broadcasting Co. The format of the contemporary country music. WBCM-FM broadcasts to the Traverse City, MI area at 93.5 FM.

WBCN-AM
Owner: CBS Radio
Editorial: 1520 South Blvd, Charlotte, North Carolina 28203-4786. **T:** 1 704 522-1103
W: http://charlotte.cbslocal.com/station/cbs-sports-radio-1660
Editorial Profile: WBCN-AM is a commercial station owned by CBS Radio. The format of the station is sports. WBCN-AM broadcasts to the Charlotte, NC area at 1660 AM.

WBCO-AM
Owner: Saga Communications
Editorial: 403 E Rensselaer St, Bucyrus, Ohio 44820-2438. **T:** 1 419 562-2222
W: http://www.wbco.com
Editorial Profile: WBCO-AM is a commercial station owned by Saga Communications. The format of the station is adult standards. WBCO-AM broadcasts to Bucyrus, OH area at 1540 AM.

WBCP-AM
Owner: Clark and Pirtle Inc.
Editorial: 904 N 4th St, Ste D, Champaign, Illinois 61820. **T:** 1 217 359-1580
E: wbcpradio@sbcglobal.net
W: http://wbcp1580.com
Editorial Profile: WBCP-AM is a commercial station owned by Clark and Pirtle Inc. The format of the station is urban AC and gospel music. WBCP-AM broadcasts in the Champaign, IL area at 1580 AM.

WBCQ-FM
Owner: Weiner (Allan and Barbara)
Editorial: 274 Britton Rd, Monticello, Maine 04760-3110. **T:** 1 207 538-9180
Editorial Profile: WBCQ-FM is a commercial station currently owned by Weiner (Allan and Barbara), dba WBCQ Radio. The format of the station is classic country. WBCQ-FM broadcasts to the Aroostook County area in Maine at 94.7 FM.

WBCR-FM
Owner: Beloit College
Editorial: 700 College St, Box 39, Beloit, Wisconsin 53511-5509. **T:** 1 608 363-2402
E: wbcrmanager@gmail.com
W: http://www.beloit.edu/wbcr
Editorial Profile: WBCR-FM is a non-commercial college station owned by Beloit College. The format of the station is variety. WBCR-FM broadcasts to the Beloit, WI area at 90.3 FM.

WBCT-FM
Owner: Clear Channel Media and Entertainment
Editorial: 77 Monroe Center St NW, Grand Rapids, Michigan 49503-2903.
T: 1 616 459-1919 **W:** http://www.b93.com
Editorial Profile: WBCT-FM is a commercial station owned by Clear Channel Media and Entertainment. The format of the station is country. WBCT-FM broadcasts to the Grand Rapids, MI area at 93.7 FM.

WBCU-AM
Owner: Union Carolina Broadcasting Company Inc.
Editorial: 210 E Main St, Union, South Carolina 29379. **T:** 1 864 427-2411
W: http://www.wbcuradio.com
Editorial Profile: WBCU-AM is a commercial station owned by Union Carolina Broadcasting Company Inc. The format of the station is contemporary country. WBCU-AM broadcasts to the Union, SC area at 1460 AM.

WBCV-FM
Owner: NRG Media LLC
Editorial: 2301 Plover Rd, Plover, Wisconsin 54467. **T:** 1 715 341-8838
E: bigcheese@nrgmedia.com
W: http://www.bigcheese1079.net
Editorial Profile: WBCV-FM is a commercial station owned by NRG Media LLC. The format of the station is rock/album-oriented rock. WBCV-FM broadcasts to the Wausau, WI area at 107.9 FM.

WBCX-FM
Owner: Brenau University
Editorial: 1 Centennial Cir, Gainesville, Georgia 30501-3668. **T:** 1 770 538-4708
E: wbcx@brenau.edu
W: http://www.brenau.edu/wbcx
Editorial Profile: WBCX-FM is a non-commercial college station owned by Brenau University. The format of the station is variety. WBCX-FM broadcasts to the Gainesville, GA area at 89.1 FM.

WBCY-FM
Owner: Taylor University Broadcasting Inc.
Editorial: 1025 W Rudisill Blvd, Fort Wayne, Indiana 46807-2168. **T:** 1 260 745-0576
E: newspc@wbcl.org **W:** http://www.wbcl.org
Editorial Profile: WBCY-FM is a non-commercial station owned by Taylor University Broadcasting Inc. The format of the station is contemporary Christian. WBCY-FM broadcasts to the Fort Wayne, IN area at 89.5 FM.

WBDC-FM
Owner: DCBroadcasting Inc.
Editorial: 511 Newton St, Ste 202, Jasper, Indiana 47546. **T:** 1 812 683-4144
E: news@wbdc.us **W:** http://www.wbdc.us
Editorial Profile: WBDC-FM is a commercial station owned by DCBroadcasting Inc. The format of the station is classic country music. WBDC-FM broadcasts to the Jasper, IN area at 100.9 FM.

WBDG-FM
Owner: Metropolitan School District of Wayne Township
Editorial: 1200 N Girls School Rd, Indianapolis, Indiana 46214.
T: 1 317 988-7122 **E:** wbdgindy@yahoo.com
W: http://www.wayne.k12.in.us/bdwbdg
Editorial Profile: WBDG-FM is a non-commercial high school station owned by the Metropolitan School District of Wayne Township. The format of the station is variety. WBDG-FM broadcasts to the Indianapolis, IN area at a frequency of 90.9 FM.

WBDK-FM
Owner: Nicolet Broadcasting Inc.
Editorial: 30 N 18Th Ave Ste 8, Sturgeon Bay, Wisconsin 54235-3207. **T:** 1 920 746-9430
E: wbdk@doorcountydailynews.com
W: http://www.doorcountydailynews.com
Editorial Profile: WBDK-FM is a commercial station owned by Nicolet Broadcasting. The format of the station is adult standards. WBDK-FM broadcasts to the Sturgeon Bay, WI area at 96.7 FM.

WBDL-FM
Owner: Magnum Radio Group
Editorial: E 5680-A Highway 33 West, Reedsburg, Wisconsin 53959.
T: 1 608 524-1400
E: info@magnumradiogroup.net
W: http://www.wbdlfm.com
Editorial Profile: WBDL-FM is a commercial station owned by Magnum Radio Group. The format of the station is adult contemporary. WBDL-FM broadcasts to the Reedsburg, WI area at 102.9 FM.

WBDR-FM
Owner: Community Broadcasters, LLC
Editorial: 199 Wealtha Ave, Watertown, New York 13601. **T:** 1 315 782-1240
W: http://www.theborder.fm
Editorial Profile: WBDR-FM is a commercial station owned by Community Broadcasters, LLC. The format of the station is Top 40/CHR music. WBDR-FM broadcasts to the Watertown, NY area at 106.7 FM.

WBDX-FM
Owner: Partners For Christian Media, Inc.
Editorial: 5512 Ringgold Rd, Ste 214, Chattanooga, Tennessee 37412.
T: 1 423 892-1200 **E:** jocks@j103.com
W: http://www.j103.com
Editorial Profile: WBDX-FM is a commercial station owned by Partners For Christian Media, Inc. The format of the station is contemporary Christian. WBDX-FM broadcasts to the Chattanooga, TN area at 102.7 FM.

WBEA-FM
Owner: Long Island Radio Broadcasting
Editorial: 760 Montauk Highway, Watermill, New York 11976. **T:** 1 631 267-7800
E: info@beach1017.com
W: http://www.beach1017.com
Editorial Profile: WBEA-FM is a commercial station owned by Long Island Radio Broadcasting. The format of the station is Top 40/CHR. WBEA-FM broadcasts in the Long Island, NY area at 101.7 FM.

WBEB-FM

Owner: Lee(Jerry)
Editorial: 225 E City Ave, Bala Cynwyd, Pennsylvania 19004-1704. **T:** 1 610 667-8400
W: http://www.morefmphilly.com
Editorial Profile: WBEB-FM is a commercial station owned by Jerry Lee. The format is adult contemporary. WBEB-FM broadcasts to the Philadelphia area at 101.1 FM.

WBEC-AM

Owner: Gamma Broadcasting LLC
Editorial: 211 Jason St, Pittsfield, Massachusetts 01201-5907.
T: 1 413 499-3333 **E:** news@wupe.com
W: http://live959.com
Editorial Profile: WBEC-AM is a commercial station owned by the Gamma Broadcasting LLC. The format of the station is news, sports and talk. WBEC-AM broadcasts to the Pittsfield, MA area at 1420 AM.

WBEC-FM

Owner: Gamma Broadcasting LLC
Editorial: 211 Jason St, Pittsfield, Massachusetts 01201-5907.
T: 1 413 499-3333 **E:** news@wupe.com
W: http://live959.com
Editorial Profile: WBEC-FM is a commercial station owned by Gamma Broadcasting LLC. The format of station is adult contemporary. WBEC-FM broadcasts to the Pittsfield, MA area at 95.9 FM.

WBEE-FM

Owner: Entercom Communications Corp.
Editorial: 70 Commercial St, Rochester, New York 14614. **T:** 1 585 423-2900
W: http://www.wbee.com
Editorial Profile: WBEE-FM is a commercial station owned by Entercom Communications Corp. The format of the station is contemporary country. WBEE-FM broadcasts to the Rochester, NY area at 92.5 FM.

WBEI-FM

Owner: Townsquare Media, Inc.
Editorial: 142 Skyland Blvd, Tuscaloosa, Alabama 35405-4015. **T:** 1 205 345-7200
W: http://www.b1017online.com
Editorial Profile: WBEI-FM is a commercial station owned by Townsquare Media, Inc. The format of the station is hot adult contemporary. WBEI-FM broadcasts to the Tuscaloosa, AL, area at 101.7 FM.

WBEJ-AM

Owner: C.B. Radio Inc.
Editorial: 510 Broad St, Elizabethton, Tennessee 37643. **T:** 1 423 542-2184
E: wbej@planetc.com **W:** http://www.wbej.com
Editorial Profile: WBEJ-AM is a commercial station owned by C.B. Radio Inc. The format of the station is country music. WBEJ-AM broadcasts in the Elizabethton, TN area at 1240 AM.

WBEN-AM

Owner: Entercom Communications Corp.
Editorial: 500 Corporate Pkwy, Ste 200, Buffalo, New York 14226-1263.
T: 1 716 843-0600 **E:** newsroom@wben.com
W: http://www.wben.com
Editorial Profile: WBEN-AM is a commercial station owned by Entercom Communications Corp. The format of the station is news and talk. WBEN-AM broadcasts to Buffalo, NY at 930 AM.

WBEN-FM

Owner: Greater Media Inc.
Editorial: 1 Bala Plz Ste 424, Bala Cynwyd, Pennsylvania 19004-1421. **T:** 1 610 771-0957
E: questions@ilikebenfm.com
W: http://www.957benfm.com
Editorial Profile: WBEN-FM is a commercial station owned by Greater Media Inc. The format of the station is Jack FM-Adult Hits. WBEN-FM broadcasts to the Philadelphia area at 95.7 FM.

WBES-AM

Owner: Bristol Broadcasting
Editorial: 4250 Washington St W, Charleston, West Virginia 25313-2424. **T:** 1 304 744-7020
E: news@wqbe.com
Editorial Profile: WBES-AM is a commercial station owned by Bristol Broadcasting. The format of the station is sports. WBES-AM broadcasts to the Charleston, WV area at 1240 AM.

WBET-AM

Owner: Swick Broadcasting
Editorial: 70808 S Nottawa Rd, Sturgis, Michigan 49091. **T:** 1 269 651-2383
E: info@wbetfm.com

W: http://www.espnradio1230online.com
Editorial Profile: WBET-AM is a commercial station owned by Swick Broadcasting. The format of the station is sports. WBET-AM broadcasts to the Sturgis, MI at 1230 AM.

WBET-FM

Owner: Swick Broadcasting
Editorial: 70808 S Nottawa Rd, Sturgis, Michigan 49091. **T:** 1 269 651-2383
E: info@wbetfm.com
W: http://www.trueoldies993.com
Editorial Profile: WBET-FM is a commercial station owned by Swick Broadcasting. The format of the station is oldies music. WBET-FM broadcasts to the Sturgis, MI area at 99.3 FM.

WBEV-AM

Owner: Good Karma Broadcasting
Editorial: 100 Stoddart St, Beaver Dam, Wisconsin 53916-1306. **T:** 1 920 885-4442
W: http://www.wbevradio.com
Editorial Profile: WBEV-AM is a commercial station owned by Good Karma Broadcasting. The format of the station is news and talk. WBEV-AM broadcasts to the Beaver Dam, WI area at 1430 AM.

WBEW-FM

Owner: Chicago Public Media Inc.
Editorial: 848 E Grand Ave, Chicago, Illinois 60611-3509. **T:** 1 312 948-4600
E: info@vocalo.org **W:** http://www.vocalo.org
Editorial Profile: WBEW-FM is a non-commercial station owned by Chicago Public Media Inc. The format of the station is variety. WBEW-FM broadcasts to the Chicago area at 89.5 FM. WBEW-FM airs programming on WRTE-FM.

WBEX-AM

Owner: Clear Channel Media and Entertainment
Editorial: 45 W Main St, Chillicothe, Ohio 45601. **T:** 1 740 773-3000
E: newsroom@wkkj.com
W: http://www.wbex.com
Editorial Profile: WBEX-AM is a commercial station owned by Clear Channel Media and Entertainment. The format of the station is news and talk. WBEX-AM broadcasts to the Chillicothe, OH area at 1490 AM.

WBEY-FM

Owner: Bay Broadcasting
Editorial: 1637 Dun Swamp Rd, Pocomoke City, Maryland 21851. **T:** 1 410 957-6081
E: bay979@gmail.com
W: http://www.easternshoremedia.net
Editorial Profile: WBEY-FM is a commercial station owned by Bay Broadcasting. The format of the station is contemporary country. WBEY-FM broadcasts to the Salisbury, MD area at 97.9 FM.

WBEZ-FM

Owner: Chicago Public Media Inc.
Editorial: 848 E Grand Ave, Chicago, Illinois 60611-3509. **T:** 1 312 948-4600
E: info@wbez.org **W:** http://www.wbez.org
Editorial Profile: WBEZ-FM is a non-commercial station owned by Chicago Public Media Inc. The format of the station is talk and news. WBEZ-FM broadcasts to the Chicago area at 91.5 FM.

WBFA-FM

Owner: Clear Channel Media and Entertainment
Editorial: 1501 13th Ave, Columbus, Georgia 31901. **T:** 1 706 576-3000
W: http://www.thebeatcolumbus.com
Editorial Profile: WBFA-FM is a commercial station owned by Clear Channel Media and Entertainment. The format of the station is urban contemporary. WBFA-FM broadcasts to the Columbus, GA area at 98.3 FM.

WBFB-FM

Owner: Blueberry Broadcasting
Editorial: 184 Target Cir, Bangor, Maine 04401-5718. **T:** 1 207 947-9100
W: http://www.971thebear.com
Editorial Profile: WBFB-FM is a commercial station owned by Blueberry Broadcasting. The format of the station is contemporary country music. WBFB-FM broadcasts to the Bangor, ME area at 97.1 FM.

WBFC-AM

Owner: Combs Broadcasting Inc.
Editorial: 2401 Paint Creek Rd, Stanton, Kentucky 40380. **T:** 1 606 663-6631
W: http://www.wbfcam.com

WBFD-AM

Owner: Cessna Communications Inc.
Editorial: 134 E Pitt St, 2nd Fl, Bedford, Pennsylvania 15522. **T:** 1 814 623-1000
E: cesscomm@embarqmail.com
Editorial Profile: WBFD-AM is a commercial station owned by Cessna Communications Inc. The format of the station is news and talk. WBFD-AM broadcasts to the Bedford, PA area at 1310 AM.

WBFE-FM

Owner: Blueberry Broadcasting
Editorial: 184 Target Cir, Bangor, Maine 04401-5718. **T:** 1 207 947-9100
W: http://www.971thebear.com
Editorial Profile: WBFE-FM is a commercial station owned by Blueberry Broadcasting. The format of the station is contemporary country. WBFE-FM broadcasts to the Ellsworth, ME area at 99.1 FM.

WBFG-FM

Owner: Crossroads Broadcasting, LLC
Editorial: 584 Smith Ave, Lexington, Tennessee 38351. **T:** 1 731 968-3500
E: wbfg965@yahoo.com
Editorial Profile: WBFG-FM is a commercial station owned by Crossroads Broadcasting, LLC. The format of the station is sports. WBFG-FM broadcasts to the Lexington, TN area at 96.5 FM.

WBFH-FM

Owner: Bloomfield Hills School District
Editorial: 4200 Andover Rd, Bloomfield Hills, Michigan 48302-2000. **T:** 1 248 341-5690
E: wbhf@bloomfield.org
W: http://www.bloomfield.org/departments/wbfhfm-the-biff/index.aspx
Editorial Profile: WBFH-FM is a non-commercial high school station owned by Bloomfield Hills School District. The format of the station is AAA. WBFH-FM broadcasts to the Bloomfield Hills, MI community at 88.3 FM.

WBFI-FM

Owner: Bethel Fellowship Church
Editorial: 14457 South Highway 259, Leitchfield, Kentucky 42754.
T: 1 270 257-2689 **E:** wbfiradio@yahoo.com
W: http://bethel-fellowship.org
Editorial Profile: WBFI-FM is a non-commercial station owned by Bethel Fellowship Church. The format of the station is contemporary Christian and religious programming. WBFI-FM broadcasts to the McDaniels, KY area at 91.5 FM.

WBFJ-AM

Owner: Triad Family Network
Editorial: 1249 N Trade St, Winston Salem, North Carolina 27101. **T:** 1 336 721-1560
E: wbfj@wbfj.org
W: http://www.stereo1550.com
Editorial Profile: WBFJ-AM is a commercial station owned by Triad Family Network. The format of the station is Christian talk. WBFJ-AM broadcasts to the Winston Salem, NC area at the 1550 AM.

WBFJ-FM

Owner: Triad Family Network
Editorial: 1249 N Trade St, Winston Salem, North Carolina 27101. **T:** 1 336 721-1560
E: wbfj@wbfj.org **W:** http://www.wbfj.org
Editorial Profile: WBFJ-FM is a non-commercial station owned by the Triad Family Network. The format of the station is contemporary Christian music. WBFJ-FM broadcasts to the Winston Salem, NC area at 89.3 FM.

WBFM-FM

Owner: Midwest Communications Inc.
Editorial: 2100 Washington Ave, Sheboygan, Wisconsin 53081-7042. **T:** 1 920 458-2107
W: http://www.b93radio.com
Editorial Profile: WBFM-FM is a commercial station owned by Midwest Communications Inc. The format of the station is contemporary country music. WBFM-FM broadcasts to the Milwaukee area at 93.7 FM.

WBFN-AM

Owner: Family Life Radio
Editorial: 13799 Donavan Rd, Albion, Michigan 49224-9618. **T:** 1 800 776-1070
W: http://www.myflr.org
Editorial Profile: WBFN-AM is a commercial station owned by Family Life Radio. The format of the station is gospel and religious music. WBFN-AM broadcasts to the Battle Creek, MI area at 1400 AM.

WBFO-FM

Owner: State of New York
Editorial: 140 Lower Terrace Horizons Plaza, Buffalo, New York 14202. **T:** 1 716 845-7040
E: news@wbfo.org **W:** http://www.wbfo.org
Editorial Profile: WBFO-FM is a non-commercial station owned by the State of New York and operated by the University of Buffalo. The format of the station is news and talk, with some jazz music in the evenings. WBFO-FM broadcasts to Buffalo, NY, at 88.7 FM. The station does not accept PSAs.

WBFR-FM

Owner: Family Stations Inc.
Editorial: 244 Goodwin Crest Dr, Ste 118, Birmingham, Alabama 35209.
T: 1 205 942-3530 **E:** info@familyradio.org
W: http://www.familyradio.com

WBFX-FM

Owner: Clear Channel Media and Entertainment
Editorial: 77 Monroe Center St NW, Grand Rapids, Michigan 49503-2903.
T: 1 616 459-1919
W: http://www.1013thebrew.com
Editorial Profile: WBFX-FM is a commercial station owned by Clear Channel Media and Entertainment. The format of the station is classic hits. WBFX-FM broadcasts to the Grand Rapids, MI area at 101.3 FM.

WBFY-FM

Owner: American Family Association
Editorial: 107 Park Gate Dr, Tupelo, Mississippi 38801. **T:** 1 662 844-8888
E: comments@afr.net **W:** http://www.afr.net

WBGA-FM

Owner: Clear Channel Media and Entertainment
Editorial: 3833 US Highway 82, Brunswick, Georgia 31523-7735. **T:** 1 912 267-1025
W: http://b927jams.com
Editorial Profile: WBGA-FM is a commercial station owned by Clear Channel Media and Entertainment. The format of the station is urban contemporary. WBGA-FM broadcasts to the Brunswick, GA area on 92.7 FM.

WBGE-FM

Owner: Flint Media
Editorial: 521 S Scott St, Bainbridge, Georgia 39819-4101. **T:** 1 229 246-7776
W: http://sowegalive.com
Editorial Profile: WBGE-FM is a commercial station owned by Flint Media, Inc. The format of the station is Hot AC. WBGE-FM broadcasts to the Bainbridge, GA area at 101.9 FM.

WBGF-FM

Owner: BGI Broadcasting LP
Editorial: 2001 State Road 715, Belle Glade, Florida 33430-1203. **T:** 1 561 996-2063
Editorial Profile: WBGF-FM is a commercial station owned by BGI Broadcasting LP. The format of the station is regional Mexican. WBGF-FM broadcasts to the West Palm Beach, FL area at 93.5 FM.

WBGG-AM

Owner: Clear Channel Media and Entertainment
Editorial: 200 Fleet St Floor 4, Pittsburgh, Pennsylvania 15220-2908. **T:** 1 412 937-1441
W: http://www.970espn.com/main.html
Editorial Profile: WBGG-AM is a commercial station owned by Clear Channel Media and Entertainment. The format of the station is sports. WBGG-AM broadcasts to the Pittsburgh area at 970 AM.

WBGG-FM

Owner: Clear Channel Media and Entertainment
Editorial: 7601 Riviera Blvd, Miramar, Florida 33023-6574. **T:** 1 954 862-2000
W: http://www.big1059.com
Editorial Profile: WBGG-FM is a commercial station owned by Clear Channel Media and Entertainment. The format of the station is classic rock music. WBGG-FM broadcasts to the Miramar, FL area at 105.9 FM.

WBGI-FM

Owner: Keymarket of Pennsylvania, LLC
Editorial: 56325 High Ridge Rd, Bellaire, Ohio 43906-9707. **T:** 1 740 676-5661
E: abryan@keymarketradio.com
W: http://www.biggiecountry.com
Editorial Profile: WBGI-FM is a commercial station owned by Keymarket of Pennsylvania, LLC. The format of the station is adult hits. WBGI-FM newscasts air on top of the hour throughout the day.

WBGK-FM

Owner: Roser Communications
Editorial: 185 Genesee St, Ste 1601, Utica, New York 13501. **T:** 1 315 734-9245
W: http://www.bugcountry.com
Editorial Profile: WBGK-FM is a commercial station owned by Roser Communications. The format of the station is contemporary country music. WBGK-FM broadcasts to the Utica, NY area at 99.7 FM and simulcasts with WBUG-FM.

WBGL-FM

Owner: Illinois Bible Institute
Editorial: 4101 Fieldstone Rd, Champaign, Illinois 61822-8800. **T:** 1 217 359-8232
E: wbgl@wbgl.org **W:** http://www.wbgl.org
Editorial Profile: WBGL-FM is a non-commercial station owned by the Illinois Bible Institute. The format of the station is contemporary Christian music and talk. WBGL-FM broadcasts to the Champaign, IL area at 91.7 FM.

WBGN-AM

Owner: Forever Communications Inc.
Editorial: 1919 Scottsville Rd, Bowling Green, Kentucky 42104-3303. **T:** 1 270 843-3333
E: production@beaverfm.com
W: http://www.1340wbgn.com
Editorial Profile: WBGN-AM is a commercial station owned by Forever Communications Inc. The format of the station is sports. WBGN-AM broadcasts to the Bowling Green, KY area at 1340 AM.

WBGO-FM

Owner: Newark Public Radio Inc.
Editorial: 54 Park Pl, Newark, New Jersey 07102-4387. **T:** 1 973 624-8880
E: jazz88@wbgo.org **W:** http://www.wbgo.org
Editorial Profile: WBGO-FM is a non-commercial station owned by Newark Public Radio Inc. The format of the station is jazz, blues, and R&B music. WBGO-FM broadcasts in the Newark, NJ area at 88.3 FM.

WBGQ-FM

Owner: Cherokee Broadcasting Co.
Editorial: 448 Highway 25 E, Bean Station, Tennessee 37708-5603. **T:** 1 865 993-3639
W: http://www.wbgqfm.com
Editorial Profile: WBGQ-FM is a commercial station owned by Cherokee Broadcasting Co. The format of the station is Top 40/CHR. WBGQ-FM broadcasts to the Morristown, TN area at 100.7 FM.

WBGS-AM

Owner: Big River Radio Inc.
Editorial: 303 8th St, Point Pleasant, West Virginia 25550-1209. **T:** 1 304 675-2763
E: wbyg@wbyg.com
Editorial Profile: WBGS-AM is a commercial station owned by Big River Radio Inc. The format of the station is Southern Gospel. WBGS-AM broadcasts to Point Pleasant, WV and surrounding communities at 1030 AM.

WBGU-FM

Owner: Bowling Green State University
Editorial: 120 W Hall, Bowling Green, Ohio 43403. **T:** 1 419 372-8657
E: wbgufm@wbgufm.com
W: http://www.wbgufm.com
Editorial Profile: WBGU-FM is a non-commercial station owned by Bowling Green State University. The format of the station is variety. WBGU-FM broadcasts to the Bowling Green, OH area at 88.1 FM.

WBGV-FM

Owner: Sanilac Broadcasting
Editorial: 19 S Elk St, Sandusky, Michigan 48471. **T:** 1 810 648-2700
W: http://www.sanilacbroadcasting.com
Editorial Profile: WBGV-FM is a commercial station owned by Sanilac Broadcasting. The format of the station is country. WBGV-FM broadcasts to the Sandusky, MI area at 92.5 FM.

WBGW-FM

Owner: Music Ministries Inc.
Editorial: 4463 E 1200 S, Haubstadt, Indiana 47639. **T:** 1 812 386-3342
E: mail@thyword.org
W: http://www.thyword.org
Editorial Profile: WBGW-FM is a non-commercial station owned by Music Ministries Inc. The format of the station is Christian. WBGW-FM broadcasts to the Evansville, IN area at 101.5 FM.

WBGX-AM

Owner: Great Lakes Radio Inc.

Editorial: 5956 S Michigan Ave, Chicago, Illinois 60637-2108. **T:** 1 773 752-1570
W: http://www.gospel1570.com
Editorial Profile: WBGX-AM is a commercial station owned by Great Lakes Radio Inc. The format of the station is gospel music and Talk. WBGX-AM broadcasts to the greater Chicago area at 1570 AM.

WBGZ-AM

Owner: Metroplex Communications, Inc.
Editorial: 227 Market St, Alton, Illinois 62002. **T:** 1 618 465-3535 **E:** news@wbgzradio.com
W: http://www.wbgzradio.com
Editorial Profile: WBGZ-AM is a commercial station owned by Metroplex Communications, Inc. The format of the station is talk. WBGZ-AM broadcasts to Alton, IL and the greater St. Louis area at 1570 AM.

WBHB-AM

Owner: Broadcast South, LLC
Editorial: 601 W Roanoke DR, Fitzgerald, Georgia 31750. **T:** 1 912 389-0995
Editorial Profile: WBHB-AM is a commercial station owned by Broadcast South, LLC. The format of the station is talk. WBHB-AM broadcasts to the Fitzgerald, GA area at 1240 AM.

WBHB-FM

Owner: VerStandig Broadcasting
Editorial: 10960 John Wayne Dr, Greencastle, Pennsylvania 17225-9584. **T:** 1 717 597-9200
E: bigbob@1015bobrocks.com
W: http://www.1015bobrocks.com
Editorial Profile: WBHB-FM is a commercial station owned by VerStandig Broadcasting. The station's format is rock/album oriented rock. WBHB-AM broadcasts to the Greencastle, PA area at 101.5 FM.

WBHC-FM

Owner: Bocock Communications
Editorial: 1816 Savannah Hwy, Hampton, South Carolina 29924-6545.
T: 1 803 943-2831
W: http://www.allhits921.blogspot.com
Editorial Profile: WBHC-FM is a commercial station owned by Bocock Communications. The format of the station is adult hits. WBHC-FM broadcasts to the Savannah, GA area at 92.1 FM.

WBHD-FM

Owner: Cumulus Media Inc.
Editorial: 600 Baltimore Drive, 2nd Floor, Wilkes-Barre, Pennsylvania 18702-7901.
T: 1 570 824-9000 **W:** http://www.97bht.com
Editorial Profile: WBHD-FM is a commercial station owned by Cumulus Media Inc. The format of the station is Top 40/CHR. The station broadcasts to the Olyphant/Scranton, PA area at a frequency of 95.7 FM.

WBHF-AM

Owner: Rei-Con Management Inc.
Editorial: 7 N Wall St, Cartersville, Georgia 30120. **T:** 1 770 386-1450
E: news@wbhfradio.org
W: http://www.wbhfradio.org
Editorial Profile: WBHF-AM is a non-commercial station owned by Rei-Con Management Inc. The format of the station is oldies. WBHF-AM broadcasts to the Cartersville, GA area at 1450 AM.

WBHJ-FM

Owner: Summit Media Broadcasting LLC
Editorial: 2700 Corporate Dr Ste 115, Birmingham, Alabama 35242-2735.
T: 1 205 322-2987
W: http://www.957jamz.com
Editorial Profile: WBHJ-FM is a commercial station owned by Summit Media Broadcasting LLC. The format of the station is urban contemporary. WBHJ-FM broadcasts to the Birmingham, AL area at 95.7 FM.

WBHK-FM

Owner: Summit Media Broadcasting LLC
Editorial: 2700 Corporate Dr Ste 115, Birmingham, Alabama 35242-2735.
T: 1 205 322-2987 **W:** http://www.987kiss.com
Editorial Profile: WBHK-FM is a commercial station owned by Summit Media Broadcasting LLC. The format of the station is R&B. WBHK-FM broadcasts to the Birmingham, AL area at 98.7 FM.

WBHM-FM

Owner: UAB at Birmingham
Editorial: 650 11th St S, Birmingham, Alabama 35233-1221. **T:** 1 205 934-2606
E: info@wbhm.org **W:** http://www.wbhm.org
Editorial Profile: WBHM-FM is a non-commercial station owned by UAB at

Birmingham. The format of the station is classical music and news. WBHM-FM broadcasts to Birmingham, AL at 90.3 FM.

WBHN-AM

Owner: Lighthouse Broadcasting, Inc.
Editorial: 75 Winding Way, Bryson City, North Carolina 28713. **T:** 1 828 488-2682
E: info@1590wbhn.com
W: http://www.1590wbhn.com
Editorial Profile: WBHN-AM is a commercial station owned by Lighthouse Broadcasting, Inc. The format of the station is country music. WBHN-AM broadcasts in the Bryson City, NC area at 1590 AM.

WBHP-AM

Owner: Clear Channel Media and Entertainment
Editorial: 26869 Peoples Rd, Madison, Alabama 35756. **T:** 1 256 309-2400
W: http://www.wbhpam.com
Editorial Profile: WBHP-AM is commercial station owned by Clear Channel Media and Entertainment. The format of the station is news, sports and talk. WBHP-AM broadcasts to the Madison, AL area at 1230 AM.

WBHQ-FM

Owner: Flagler County Broadcasting, LLC
Editorial: 2405 E Moody Blvd, Ste 402, Bunnell, Florida 32110-5994.
T: 1 386 437-1992
W: http://www.beach927.com
Editorial Profile: WBHQ-FM is a commercial station owned by Flagler County Broadcasting, LLC. The format of the station is variety hits. WBHQ-FM broadcasts to Bunnell, FL and surrounding areas at 92.7 FM

WBHR-AM

Owner: Tri-County Broadcasting
Editorial: 1010 2Nd St N, Sauk Rapids, Minnesota 56379-2527. **T:** 1 320 252-6200
E: mail@660wbhr.com
W: http://www.660wbhr.com
Editorial Profile: WBHR-AM is a commercial station owned by Tri-County Broadcasting. The format of the station is sports. WBHR-AM broadcasts in the Sauk Rapids, MN area at 660 AM.

WBHT-FM

Owner: Cumulus Media Inc.
Editorial: 600 Baltimore Drive, 2nd Floor, Wilkes-Barre, Pennsylvania 18702-7901.
T: 1 570 824-9000 **W:** http://www.97bht.com
Editorial Profile: WBHT-FM is a commercial station owned by Cumulus Media Inc. The format of the station is Top 40/CHR music. WBHT-FM broadcasts in the Wilkes Barre, PA area at 97.1 FM.

WBHV-FM

Owner: 2510 Associates
Editorial: 160 Clearview Ave, State College, Pennsylvania 16803. **T:** 1 814 238-5085
E: b945live@gmail.com
W: http://www.b945live.com
Editorial Profile: WBHV-FM is a commercial station owned by 2510 Associates. The format of the station is Top 40/CHR. WBHV-FM broadcasts to the State College, PA, area at 94.5 FM.

WBHW-FM

Owner: Music Ministries Inc.
Editorial: 4463 E 1200 S, Haubstadt, Indiana 47639. **T:** 1 800 264-5550
E: mail@thyword.org
W: http://www.thyword.org
Editorial Profile: WBHW-FM is a non-commercial station owned by Music Ministries Inc. The format of the station is Christian. WBHW-FM broadcasts to the Loogootee, IN area at 88.7 FM and is a simulcast of WBJW-FM.

WBHY-AM

Owner: Goforth Media Inc.
Editorial: 6530B Spanish Fort Blvd, Ste B, Spanish Fort, Alabama 36527-5000.
T: 1 251 473-8488 **E:** news@goforth.org
W: http://www.goforth.org
Editorial Profile: WBHY-AM is a commercial station owned by Goforth Media Inc. The format for the station is religious. WBHY-AM broadcasts to the Mobile, AL and Pensacola, FL areas at 840 AM.

WBHY-FM

Owner: Goforth Media Inc.
Editorial: 6530 Spanish Fort Blvd, Ste B, Spanish Fort, Alabama 36527-5014.
T: 1 251 473-8488 **E:** news@goforth.org
W: http://www.goforth.org

Editorial Profile: WBHY-FM is a commercial station owned by Goforth Media Inc. The format for the station is contemporary Christian. WBHY-FM broadcasts to the Mobile, AL, Pensacola, FL area at 88.5 FM.

WBIB-AM

Owner: DeLoach(James)
Editorial: 1075 Dry Hollow Rd, Centreville, Alabama 35042. **T:** 1 205 926-6286
Editorial Profile: WBIB-AM is a commercial station owned by James DeLoach. The format of the station is southern gospel. WBIB-AM broadcasts in the Centreville, AL area at 1110 AM.

WBIE-FM

Owner: American Family Association
Editorial: 107 Parkgate Dr, Tupelo, Mississippi 38801. **T:** 1 662 844-8888
E: comments@afr.net **W:** http://www.afr.net

WBIG-AM

Owner: Big Broadcasting Co.
Editorial: 620 N Eola Rd, Aurora, Illinois 60502. **T:** 1 630 851-5200
E: wbignews@yahoo.com
W: http://www.wbig1280.com
Editorial Profile: WBIG-AM is a commercial station owned by Big Broadcasting Co. The format of the station is news and talk. WBIG-AM broadcasts to the greater Chicago area at 1280 AM.

WBIG-FM

Owner: Clear Channel Media and Entertainment
Editorial: 1801 Rockville Pike Fl 5, Rockville, Maryland 20852-1633. **T:** 1 240 747-2700
W: http://www.thebigdc.com
Editorial Profile: WBIG-FM is a commercial station owned by Clear Channel Media and Entertainment. The format of the station is classic rock. WBIG-FM broadcasts to the Washington, D.C. area at 100.3 FM.

WBIM-FM

Owner: Bridgewater State College
Editorial: 109 Campus Ctr, Bridgewater, Massachusetts 2325. **T:** 1 508 531-1366
E: wbim@bridgew.edu
W: http://www.bridgew.edu/wbim
Editorial Profile: WBIM-FM is a non-commercial station owned by Bridgewater State College. The format of the station is variety. WBIM-FM broadcasts to the Bridgewater, WA area at 91.5 FM.

WBIN-AM

Owner: Sines(John & Jane)
Editorial: 108 Lifestyle Way, Benton, Tennessee 37307. **T:** 1 423 338-2864

WBIO-FM

Owner: Cromwell Group Inc.(The)
Editorial: 1115 Tamarack Rd Ste 500, Owensboro, Kentucky 42301-6988.
T: 1 270 683-5200
W: http://www.owensbororadio.com
Editorial Profile: WBIO-FM is a commercial station owned by The Cromwell Group Inc. The format for the station is classic country. WBIO-FM broadcasts to the Evansville, IN area at 94.7 FM.

WBIP-AM

Owner: Community Broadcasting Services Inc.
Editorial: 1100 S Second St, Booneville, Mississippi 38829. **T:** 1 662 728-0200
E: wbipam@yahoo.com
Editorial Profile: WBIP-AM is a commercial station owned by Community Broadcasting Services Inc. The format of the station is classic country. WBIP-AM broadcasts to the Booneville, MO area at 1400 AM.

WBIW-AM

Owner: Ad-Venture Media Inc.
Editorial: 424 Heltonville Rd W, Bedford, Indiana 47421-9389. **T:** 1 812 275-7555
E: news@wbiw.com **W:** http://www.wbiw.com
Editorial Profile: WBIW-AM is a commercial radio station owned by Ad-Venture Media Inc. The format of the station is news, talk and sports. WBIW-AM broadcasts to the Bedford, IN area at 1340 AM.

WBIY-FM

Owner: Oscar Aguero Ministry Inc.
Editorial: 6050 W 20th Ave, Hialeah, Florida 33016. **T:** 1 305 826-5555
W: http://www.oscaragueroministry.com
Editorial Profile: WBIY-FM is a non-commercial station owned by Oscar Aguero Ministry Inc. The format of the station is

Spanish Christian. WBIY-FM broadcasts to the Hialeah, FL area at 88.3 FM.

WBIZ-AM
Owner: Clear Channel Media and Entertainment
Editorial: 619 Cameron St, Eau Claire, Wisconsin 54703. **T:** 1 715 830-4000
W: http://www.sportsradio1400.com
Editorial Profile: WBIZ-AM is a commercial station owned by Clear Channel Media and Entertainment. The format of the station is sports. WBIZ-AM broadcasts to the Eau Claire, WI area at 1400 AM.

WBIZ-FM
Owner: Clear Channel Media and Entertainment
Editorial: 619 Cameron St, Eau Claire, Wisconsin 54703. **T:** 1 715 830-4000
W: http://www.z100radio.com
Editorial Profile: WBIZ-FM is a commercial station owned by Clear Channel Media and Entertainment. The format of the station is Top 40/CHR. WBIZ-FM broadcasts to the Eau Claire, WI area at 100.7 FM.

WBJB-FM
Owner: Brookdale Community College
Editorial: 765 Newman Springs Rd, Lincroft, New Jersey 07738-1543. **T:** 1 732 224-2492
E: comments@wbjb.org
W: http://www.90.5thenight.org
Editorial Profile: WBJB-FM is a non-commercial station owned by Brookdale Community College. The format of the station is adult album alternative and news. WBJB-FM broadcasts in the Lincroft, NJ area area at 90.5 FM.

WBJC-FM
Owner: Baltimore City Community College
Editorial: 6776 Reisterstown Rd Ste 202, Baltimore, Maryland 21215-2362.
T: 1 410 580-5800 **W:** http://www.wbjc.com
Editorial Profile: WBJC-FM is a non-commercial station owned by the Baltimore City Community College. The format of the station is classical music. WBJC-FM broadcasts to the Baltimore area at 91.5 FM.

WBJI-FM
Owner: R.P. Broadcasting
Editorial: 2115 Washington Ave S, Bemidji, Minnesota 56601-8918. **T:** 1 218 751-7777
W: http://www.wbji.com
Editorial Profile: WBJI-FM is a commercial station owned by R.P. Broadcasting. The format of the station features a mix of classic and contemporary country music. WBJI-FM broadcasts to the Bemidji, MN area at 98.3 FM.

WBJW-FM
Owner: Music Ministries Inc.
Editorial: 4463 E 1200 S, Haubstadt, Indiana 47639. **T:** 1 812 386-3342
E: mail@thyword.org
W: http://www.thyword.org
Editorial Profile: WBJW-FM is a non-commercial station owned by Music Ministries Inc. The format of the station is Christian. WBJW-FM broadcasts to the Haubstadt, IN area at 91.7 FM.

WBJY-FM
Owner: American Family Association
Editorial: 107 Parkgate Dr., Tupelo, Mississippi 38801. **T:** 1 662 844-8888
E: comments@afr.net **W:** http://www.afr.net

WBKA-FM
Owner: Nassau Broadcasting III, LLC
Editorial: 169 Port Rd, Kennebunk, Maine 04043-7737. **T:** 1 207 967-0993
E: psa@wbachradio.com
W: http://www.wbachradio.com
Editorial Profile: WBKA-FM is a commercial station owned by Nassau Broadcasting III, LLC. The format of the station is classic hitsl. WBKA-FM broadcasts to the Kennebunk, ME area at 107.7 FM.

WBKE-FM
Owner: Manchester College
Editorial: 604 E College Ave, Box 19, North Manchester, Indiana 46962. **T:** 1 260 982-5424
E: jelargent@spartans.manchester.edu
W: http://wbke.manchester.edu
Editorial Profile: WBKE-FM is a non-commercial station owned by Manchester College. The format of the station is variety, news, sports and talk. WBKE-FM broadcasts to the Fort Wayne, IN area at 89.5 FM.

WBKN-FM
Owner: Brookhaven Broadcasting, Inc.
Editorial: 225 S Church St, Brookhaven, Mississippi 39601-3231. **T:** 1 601 833-9210
E: brookhavenbroadcasting@yahoo.com
Editorial Profile: WBKN-FM is a commercial station owned by Brookhaven Broadcasting, Inc. The format of the station is contemporary country music. WBKN-FM broadcasts to the Brookhaven, MS area at 92.1 FM.

WBKR-FM
Owner: Townsquare Media, LLC
Editorial: 3301 Frederica St, Owensboro, Kentucky 42301. **T:** 1 270 683-1558
E: spots@wbkr.com **W:** http://www.wbkr.com
Editorial Profile: WBKR-FM is a commercial station owned by Townsquare Media, LLC. The format of the station is contemporary country. WBKR-FM broadcasts to the Owensboro, KY at a frequency of 92.5 FM.

WBKS-FM
Owner: Clear Channel Media and Entertainment
Editorial: 667 W Market St, Lima, Ohio 45801.
T: 1 419 223-2060
W: http://www.939kisslima.com
Editorial Profile: WBKS-FM is a commercial station owned by Clear Channel Media and Entertainment. The format of the station is Top 40/CHR music. WBKS-FM broadcasts to the Lima, OH area at 93.9 FM.

WBKT-FM
Owner: Townsquare Media, LLC
Editorial: 34 Chestnut St, Oneonta, New York 13820. **T:** 1 607 432-1030
E: cnynews@townsquaremedia.com
W: http://www.wbktfm.com
Editorial Profile: WBKT-FM is a commercial station owned by Townsquare Media, LLC. The format of the station is contemporary country music. WBKT-FM broadcasts to the Oneonta, NY area at 95.3 FM.

WBKV-AM
Owner: Bliss Communications Inc.
Editorial: 2410 S Main St, West Bend, Wisconsin 53095-5766. **T:** 1 262 334-2344
E: news@westbendradio.com
W: http://www.wbkvam.com
Editorial Profile: WBKV-AM is a commercial station owned by Bliss Communications Inc. The format of the station is news and talk. WBKV-AM broadcasts to the West Bend, WI area at 1470 AM.

WBKX-FM
Owner: Chadwick Bay Broadcasting Corporation
Editorial: 4561 Willow Rd, Dunkirk, New York 14048. **T:** 1 716 366-1410
W: http://www.wbkxcountry.com
Editorial Profile: WBKX-FM is a commercial station owned by Chadwick Bay Broadcasting Corporation. The format of the station is contemporary country music. WBXX-FM broadcasts to the Dunkirk-Fredonia, NY area at 96.5 FM.

WBKY-FM
Owner: Magnum Radio Group
Editorial: N2349 Wibu Rd, Poynette, Wisconsin 53955-9556. **T:** 1 608 745-0959
W: http://www.buckycountry959.com
Editorial Profile: WBKY-FM is a commercial station owned by Magnum Radio Group. The format for the station is contemporary country. WBKY-FM broadcasts to the Portage, WI area at 95.9 FM.

WBLA-AM
Owner: Baldwin Branch Missionary Baptist Church
Editorial: 4047 Highway 242 South, Elizabethtown, North Carolina 28337.
T: 1 910 645-2396 **E:** bbc1@instrstar.net
W: http://baldwinbranchmbcnc.com
Editorial Profile: WBLA-AM is a commercial station owned by Baldwin Branch Missionary Baptist Church. The format of the station is Christian teaching and Gospel music. WBLA-AM broadcasts to the Elizabethtown, NC area at 1440 AM.

WBLB-AM
Owner: Nipper(Larry)
Editorial: 3570 Robinson Tract Rd, Pulaski, Virginia 24301. **T:** 1 540 980-3411
E: wblb1340am@verizon.net
Editorial Profile: WBLB-AM is a commercial station owned by Larry Nipper. The format of the station is gospel. WBLB-AM broadcasts to the Pulaski, VA area at 1340 AM.

WBLC-AM
Owner: Three Angels Broadcasting Network Inc.
Editorial: 4787 Browder Hollow Rd, Lenoir City, Tennessee 37771. **T:** 1 865 986-5332
E: wblc3abn@bellsouth.net

WBLE-FM
Owner: Batesville Broadcasting Co.
Editorial: 1040 Highway 6 W, Batesville, Mississippi 38606-8104. **T:** 1 662 563-4664
E: country101radio@yahoo.com
W: http://www.wble101.com

WBLF-AM
Owner: Magnum Broadcasting Inc.
Editorial: 315 S Atherton St, State College, Pennsylvania 16801. **T:** 1 814 272-1320
E: wblfproduction@yahoo.com
Editorial Profile: WBLF-AM is a commercial station owned by Magnum Broadcasting Inc. The format of the station is news talk. WBLF-AM broadcasts to the State College, PA area at 970 AM.

WBLI-FM
Owner: Cox Media Group, Inc.
Editorial: 555 Sunrise Hwy, West Babylon, New York 11704. **T:** 1 631 669-9254
E: wbli@wbli.com **W:** http://www.wbli.com
Editorial Profile: WBLI-FM is a commercial station owned by Cox Media Group, Inc. The format of the station is Top 40/CHR. WBLI-FM broadcasts to the New York area at 106.1 FM.

WBLJ-AM
Owner: North Georgia Radio Group
Editorial: 613 Silver Cir, Dalton, Georgia 30721. **T:** 1 706 278-5511
E: news@ngaradio.com
W: http://wblj1230.com
Editorial Profile: WBLJ-AM is a commercial station owned by North Georgia Radio Group. The format of the station is news, sports and talk. WBLJ-AM broadcasts to the Dalton, GA area at 1230 AM.

WBLJ-FM
Owner: Clear Channel Media and Entertainment
Editorial: 1559 W 4th St, Williamsport, Pennsylvania 17701-5650. **T:** 1 570 327-1400
W: http://www.billcountry.com
Editorial Profile: WBLJ-FM is a commercial station owned by Clear Channel Media and Entertainment. The station's format is contemporary country. WBLJ-FM broadcasts to the Williamsport, PA area at 95.3 FM.

WBLK-FM
Owner: Townsquare Media, LLC
Editorial: 14 Lafayette Sq, Ste 1300, Buffalo, New York 14203-1913. **T:** 1 716 852-9393
W: http://www.wblk.com

WBLL-AM
Owner: V-Teck Communications Inc.
Editorial: 1501 Road 235, Bellefontaine, Ohio 43311. **T:** 1 937 592-1045
W: http://www.peakofohio.com
Editorial Profile: WBLL-AM is a commercial station owned by V-Teck Communications Inc. The format of the station is news, talk, and sports. WBLL-AM broadcasts in the Bellefontaine, OH area at 1390 AM.

WBLM-FM
Owner: Townsquare Media, LLC
Editorial: 1 City Ctr, Portland, Maine 04101-6420. **T:** 1 207 774-6364 **E:** wblm@wblm.com
W: http://www.wblm.com
Editorial Profile: WBLM-FM is a commercial station owned by Townsquare Media, LLC. The format of the station is classic rock. WBLM-FM broadcasts to the Portland, ME area at 102.9 FM.

WBLO-AM
Owner: GHB Radio, Inc
Editorial: 4801 E Independence Blvd Ste 815, Charlotte, North Carolina 28212-5490.
T: 1 704 405-3172
Editorial Profile: WBLO-AM is a commercial station owned by GHB Radio, Inc. The format of the station is regional Mexican. WBLO-AM broadcasts to the High Point, NC area at 790 AM.

WBLQ-AM
Owner: Diponti Communications
Editorial: 16 High St, Westerly, Rhode Island 02891-1850. **T:** 1 401 322-9091
W: http://www.wblq.net
Editorial Profile: WBLQ-AM is a commercial station owned by Diponti Communications. The format of the station is full service with talk and Lite AC music. WBLQ-AM broadcasts to the Westerly, RI area at 1230 AM.

WBLR-AM
Owner: Good News Network
Editorial: 2278 Wortham Ln, Grovetown, Georgia 30813. **T:** 1 706 309-9610
W: http://www.gnnradio.org
Editorial Profile: WBLR-AM is a commercial station owned by Good News Network. The format of the station is Hispanic religious. WBLR-AM broadcasts to the Grovetown, GA area on 1430 AM.

WBLS-FM
Owner: Emmis Communications Corp.
Editorial: 395 Hudson St Fl 7, New York, New York 10014-7452. **T:** 1 212 447-1000
E: info@wbls.com **W:** http://www.wbls.com
Editorial Profile: WBLS-FM is a commercial station owned by Emmis Communications Corp. The format of the station is urban adult contemporary. WBLS-FM broadcasts to the New York area at 107.5 FM.

WBLT-AM
Owner: 3 Daughters Media, Inc.
Editorial: 1035 Avalon Dr, Forest, Virginia 24551-2970. **T:** 1 434 534-6100
E: wblt@inbox.com
W: http://www.espninva.com
Editorial Profile: WBLT-AM is a commercial station owned by 3 Daughters Media, Inc. The format of the station is sports. WBLT-AM broadcasts to the Bedford, VA area at 1350 AM.

WBLU-FM
Owner: Blue Lake Fine Arts Camp
Editorial: 300 E Crystal Lake Rd, Twin Lake, Michigan 49457-9499. **T:** 1 231 894-5656
W: http://www.bluelake.org/radio.html
Editorial Profile: WBLU-FM is a non-commerical stationed owned by Blue Lake Fine Arts Camp. The format of the station is variety of news and arts programming, jazz, classical and folk music. WBLU-FM broadcasts to the Twin Lake, MI and surrounding areas at 90.3 FM.

WBLV-FM
Owner: Blue Lake Fine Arts Camp
Editorial: 300 E Crystal Lake Rd, Twin Lake, Michigan 49457-9499. **T:** 1 231 894-5656
W: http://www.bluelake.org/radio.html
Editorial Profile: WBLV-FM is a non-commerical stationed owned by Blue Lake Fine Arts Camp. The format of the station is variety of news and arts programming, jazz, classical and folk music. WBLV-FM broadcasts to the Twin Lake, MI and surrounding areas at 90.3 FM.

WBLX-FM
Owner: Cumulus Media Inc.
Editorial: 2800 Dauphin St Ste 104, Mobile, Alabama 36606-2400. **T:** 1 251 652-2000
W: http://www.thebigstation93blx.com
Editorial Profile: WBLX-FM is a commercial station owned by Cumulus Media Inc. The format for the station is urban contemporary. WBLX-FM broadcasts to the Mobile, AL area at 92.9 FM.

WBMC-AM
Owner: Peg Broadcasting
Editorial: 230 W Colville St, Mc Minnville, Tennessee 37110-3211. **T:** 1 931 473-9253
E: production.mcminnville@pegbroadcasting.com
Editorial Profile: WBMC-AM is a commercial station owned by Peg Broadcasting. The format of the station is talk. WBMC-AM broadcasts to the McMinnville, TN area at 960 AM. The target audience of the station is adults, ages 18 to 64.

WBMD-AM
Owner: Family Stations Inc.
Editorial: 918 Chesapeake Ave, Annapolis, Maryland 21403-3132. **T:** 1 410 821-9000
E: office@wfsi.net
W: http://www.familyradio.com
Editorial Profile: WBMD-AM is a non-commercial station owned by Family Stations Inc. The format of the station is religious programming. WBMD-AM broadcasts to the Baltimore area at 750 AM and simulcasts with WBGR-AM and WFSI-FM.

WBMH-FM
Owner: Capital Assets, Inc.
Editorial: 4428 N College Ave, Hwy 43, Jackson, Alabama 36545-2017.
T: 1 251 246-4431 **E:** info@bamadixie.com
W: http://bamadixie.com/bama106

WORLD NEWS MEDIA

Editorial Profile: WBMH-FM is a commercial station owned by Capital Assets, Inc. The format for the station is classic country. WBMH-FM broadcasts to the Jackson, AL area at 106.1 FM.

WBMI-FM

Owner: Peggy R. Warner
Editorial: 3275 W M 76, Ste D, West Branch, Michigan 48661-9180. **T:** 1 989 345-4269
E: wbmi@sbcglobal.net
Editorial Profile: WBMI-FM is a commercial station owned by Peggy R. Warner. The format of the station is classic country. WBMI-FM broadcasts to the Flint, MI area at 105.5 FM.

WBMK-FM

Owner: American Family Association
Editorial: 107 Parkgate Dr, Tupelo, Mississippi 38801. **T:** 1 662 844-8888
E: comments@afr.net **W:** http://www.afr.net

WBML-AM

Owner: Sun Broadcasting, Inc.
Editorial: 1023 Ball St, Perry, Georgia 31069-3307. **T:** 1 478 224-9265
Editorial Profile: WBML-AM is a commercial station owned by Sun Broadcasting, Inc. The format of the station is country, featuring classic and contemporary genres. WBML-AM broadcasts to the Macon, GA area at 900 AM.

WBMQ-AM

Owner: Cumulus Media Inc.
Editorial: 214 Television Cir, Savannah, Georgia 31406. **T:** 1 912 961-9000
W: http://www.wbmq.net
Editorial Profile: WBMQ-AM is a commercial station owned by Cumulus Media Inc. The format for the station is news and talk. WBMQ-AM broadcasts to the Savannah, GA area at 630 AM.

WBMT-FM

Owner: Masconomet Regional High School
Editorial: 20 Endicott Rd, Topsfield, Massachusetts 1983. **T:** 1 978 887-2323
W: http://www.masconomet.org/wbmt/
Editorial Profile: WBMT-FM is a non-commercial station owned by Masconomet Regional High School. The format of the station is classic rock and rock/album-oriented rock. WBMT-FM broadcasts to the Topsfield, MA area at 88.3 FM.

WBMV-FM

Owner: Illinois Bible Institute
Editorial: 17387 Cottonwood Lane, Carlinville, Illinois 62626. **T:** 1 217 854-4800
E: wibi@wibi.org **W:** http://www.wibi.org
Editorial Profile: WBMV-FM is a non-commercial station owned by the Illinois Bible Institute. The format of the station is contemporary Christian music. WBMV-FM broadcasts in the Carlinville, IL area at 89.7 FM.

WBMW-FM

Owner: Red Wolf Broadcasting
Editorial: 758 Colonel Ledyard Hwy, Ledyard, Connecticut 06339-1541. **T:** 1 860 464-1065
E: wbmw@aol.com **W:** http://www.wbmw.com
Editorial Profile: WBMW-FM is a commercial station owned by Red Wolf Broadcasting. The format of the station is Lite Rock/Lite AC music. WBMW-FM broadcasts to the Hartford-New Haven, CT area at 106.5 FM.

WBMX-FM

Owner: CBS Radio
Editorial: 83 Leo M Birmingham Pkwy, Boston, Massachusetts 02135-1101.
T: 1 617 746-1300
W: http://mix1041.radio.com
Editorial Profile: WBMX-FM is a commercial station owned by CBS Radio. The format of the station is hot adult contemporary music. WBMX-FM broadcasts to the Boston area at 104.1 FM.

WBMZ-FM

Owner: Radio Metter Inc.
Editorial: 1075 E Lillian St, Metter, Georgia 30439-3909. **T:** 1 912 685-2136
E: wbmz@pineland.net
Editorial Profile: WBMZ-FM is a commercial station owned by Radio Metter Inc. The format of the station is classic rock. WBMZ-FM broadcasts to the Metter, GA area at 103.7 FM.

WBNE-FM

Owner: Hometown Wilmington Media
Editorial: 122 Cinema Dr, Wilmington, North Carolina 28403-1490. **T:** 1 910 772-6300
W: http://www.1037thebone.com

Editorial Profile: WBNE-FM is a commercial station owned by Hometown Wilmington Media. The format of the station in classic rock. WBNE-FM broadcasts to the Wilmington, NC area at 103.7 FM.

WBNH-FM

Owner: Central Illinois Radio Fellowship
Editorial: 1919 Mayflower Dr, Pekin, Illinois 61554-9205. **T:** 1 309 636-8850
E: wbnh@wbnh.org **W:** http://www.wbnh.org
Editorial Profile: WBNH-FM is a non-commercial station owned by Central Illinois Radio Fellowship. The format of the station is religious programming. WBNH-FM broadcasts to the Pekin, IL area at 88.5 FM.

WBNI-FM

Owner: Indiana Public Broadcasting Systems
Editorial: 3204 Clairmont Ct, Fort Wayne, Indiana 46808-4513. **T:** 1 260 452-1189
W: http://www.nipr.fm
Editorial Profile: WBNI-FM is a non-commercial station owned by Indiana Public Broadcasting Systems. The format of the station is classical music. WBNI-FM broadcasts to the Fort Wayne, IN area at 94.1 FM.

WBNK-FM

Owner: Towers Investment Trust
Editorial: 221 S Front St, New Bern, North Carolina 28560-2135. **T:** 1 252 636-3333
W: http://www.bigfishfm.com
Editorial Profile: WBNK-FM is a commercial station owned by Towers Investment Trust. The format of the station is contemporary Christian music. WBNK-FM broadcasts to the New Bern, NC area at 92.7 FM.

WBNL-AM

Owner: Turpen Communications LLC
Editorial: 2177 N State Route 61, Boonville, Indiana 47601. **T:** 1 812 897-2080
E: rturpen@radio1540.net
W: http://www.radio1540.net
Editorial Profile: WBNL-AM is a commercial station owned by Turpen Communications LLC. The format for the station is easy listening. WBNL-AM broadcasts to the Evansville, IN area at 1540 AM.

WBNM-AM

Owner: Jarrell (Jimmy)
Editorial: 908 Opelika Rd, Auburn, Alabama 36830-4024. **T:** 1 256 215-7296
W: http://wjhofm.com
Editorial Profile: WBNM-AM is a commercial station owned by Jarrell (Jimmy). The format of the station is Southern Gospel. WBNM-AM broadcasts to the Alexander City, AL area at 1050 AM.

WBNN-FM

Owner: Positive Radio Group
Editorial: 18498 N James Madison Hwy, Dillwyn, Virginia 23936. **T:** 1 434 983-6621
E: mail@bigcountry1053.com
W: http://www.bigcountry1053.com

WBNO-FM

Owner: Impact Radio, LLC
Editorial: 12810 State Route 34, Bryan, Ohio 43506. **T:** 1 419 636-3175
E: wbno@wbno-wqct.com
W: http://www.wbno-wqct.com
Editorial Profile: WBNO-FM is a commercial station owned by Impact Radio, LLC. The format of the station is classic hits. WBNO-FM broadcasts to the Bryan, OH area at 100.9 FM.

WBNQ-FM

Owner: Cumulus Media Inc.
Editorial: 236 Greenwood Ave, Bloomington, Illinois 61704-7422. **T:** 1 309 829-1221
W: http://www.wbnq.com
Editorial Profile: WBNQ-FM is a commercial station owned by Cumulus Media Inc. The format of the station is Top 40/CHR music. WBNQ-FM broadcasts to the Bloomington, IL area at 101.5 FM.

WBNR-AM

Owner: Pamal Broadcasting, Ltd.
Editorial: 715 Route 52, Beacon, New York 12508-1047. **T:** 1 845 838-6000
W: http://www.hvradionet.com
Editorial Profile: WBNR-AM is a commercial station owned by Pamal Broadcasting, Ltd. The format of the station is country. WBNR-AM broadcasts to the Beacon, NY area at 1260 AM.

WBNS-AM

Owner: Radio Ohio Inc.

Editorial: 605 S Front St Fl 300, Columbus, Ohio 43215-5777. **T:** 1 614 460-3850
W: http://www.espncolumbus.com
Editorial Profile: WBNS-AM is a commercial station owned by Radio Ohio Inc. The format of the station is sports. WBNS-AM broadcasts to the Columbus, OH area at 1460 AM.

WBNS-FM

Owner: Radio Ohio Inc.
Editorial: 605 S Front St, Columbus, Ohio 43215. **T:** 1 614 460-3850
W: http://www.971thefan.com
Editorial Profile: WBNS-FM is a commercial station owned by Radio Ohio Inc. The format of the station is sports. WBNS-FM broadcasts to the Columbus, OH area at 97.1 FM.

WBNT-FM

Owner: Oneida Broadcasters Inc.
Editorial: 1126 Buffalo Rd, Oneida, Tennessee 37841. **T:** 1 423 569-8598
E: wbnt@highland.net
W: http://www.hive105.com
Editorial Profile: WBNT-FM is a commercial station owned by Oneida Broadcasters Inc. The format of the station is country and adult contemporary music and news. WBNT-FM broadcasts to the Oneida, TN area at 105.5 FM.

WBNV-FM

Owner: AVC Communications Inc.
Editorial: 4988 Skyline Dr, Cambridge, Ohio 43725-9729. **T:** 1 740 432-5605
E: info@yourradioplace.com
W: http://www.yourradioplace.com
Editorial Profile: WBNV-FM is a commercial station owned by AVC Communications Inc. The format of the station is easy listening. WBNV-FM broadcasts to the Cambridge, OH, area at 93.5 FM.

WBNW-AM

Owner: Money Matters Radio Inc.
Editorial: 144 Gould St Ste 710, Needham, Massachusetts 02494-2307.
T: 1 781 474-5180
W: http://www.moneymattersradio.net
Editorial Profile: WBNW-AM is a commercial station owned by Money Matters Radio Inc. The format of the station is talk. WBNW-AM broadcasts to the Boston, MA area at 1120 AM.

WBNW-FM

Owner: Clear Channel Media and Entertainment
Editorial: 320 N Jensen Rd, Vestal, New York 13850-2111. **T:** 1 607 584-5800
W: http://www.radionow1057.com
Editorial Profile: WBNW-FM is a commercial station owned by Clear Channel Media and Entertainment. The format of the station is Top 40/CHR. WBNW-FM broadcasts to the Binghamton, NY area at 105.7 FM.

WBNY-FM

Owner: Buffalo State College
Editorial: 1300 Elmwood Ave, Buffalo, New York 14222-1004. **T:** 1 716 878-3080
W: http://www.buffalostate.edu/wbny
Editorial Profile: WBNY-FM is a non-commercial station owned by Buffalo State College. The format of the station is rock alternative. WBNY-FM broadcasts to the Buffalo, NY area at 91.3 FM. The station is completely student operated. WBNY-FM's target audience is Buffalo State College students and others interested in a variety of music. The station airs locally on 91.3 FM.

WBNZ-FM

Owner: Henderson, Roy E.
Editorial: 1532 Forrester Rd, Frankfort, Michigan 49635-9781. **T:** 1 231 947-3220
W: http://www.wbnz.com

WBOB-AM

Owner: Chesapeake-Portsmouth Broadcasting Corp.
Editorial: 4190 Belfort Rd Ste 450, Jacksonville, Florida 32216-1405.
T: 1 904 470-4615
W: http://www.600wbob.com
Editorial Profile: WBOB-AM is a commercial station owned by Chesapeake-Portsmouth Broadcasting Corp. The format of the station is news and talk. WBOB-AM broadcasts to the Jacksonville, FL area at 600 AM.

WBOG-AM

Owner: Magnum Radio Group
Editorial: 1021 N Superior Ave Ste 5, Tomah, Wisconsin 54660-1192. **T:** 1 608 372-9600
E: news@magnumbroadcasting.com
W: http://www.oldies1460.com

Editorial Profile: WBOG-AM is a commercial station owned by Magnum Radio Group. The format of the station is oldies. WBOG-AM broadcasts to the Tomah, WI area at 1460 AM.

WBOI-FM

Owner: Indiana Public Broadcasting Systems
Editorial: 3204 Clairmont Ct, Fort Wayne, Indiana 46808. **T:** 1 260 452-1189
W: http://www.nipr.fm
Editorial Profile: WBOI-FM is a non-commercial station owned by Indiana Public Broadcasting Systems. The format of the station is news, talk and jazz. WBOI-FM broadcasts to the Fort Wayne, IN area at 91.3 FM.

WBOJ-FM

Owner: The Truth, Inc.
Editorial: 1300 Wynnton Rd Ste 110, Columbus, Georgia 31906-5701.
T: 1 706 256-2985
E: request@885thetruth.com
W: http://www.885thetruth.com

WBOK-AM

Owner: Bakewell Media Co.
Editorial: 1639 Gentilly Blvd, New Orleans, Louisiana 70119-2161. **T:** 1 504 942-0106
E: wbok1230am@gmail.com
W: http://www.wbok1230am.com

WBOL-AM

Owner: Shaw(John & Opal)
Editorial: 123 W Market St, Bolivar, Tennessee 38008. **T:** 1 731 658-3690
W: http://www.wojg.com
Editorial Profile: WBOL-AM is a commercial station owned by John and Opal Shaw. The format of the station is oldies. WBOL-AM broadcasts to the Memphis, TN, market at 1560 AM.

WBON-FM

Owner: JVC Broadasting Inc.
Editorial: 3075 Veterans Memorial Hwy, Ronkonkoma, New York 11779.
T: 1 631 648-2500
W: http://www.lafiestali.com
Editorial Profile: WBON-FM is a commercial station owned by JVC Broadasting Inc. The format of the station is Spanish tropical. WBZB-FM broadcasts to the Ronkonkoma, NY area at 98.5 FM.

WBOP-FM

Owner: Gamma Broadcasting LLC
Editorial: 639 N Main St, Mount Crawford, Virginia 22841-2350. **T:** 1 540 432-1063
Editorial Profile: WBOP-FM is a commercial station owned by Gamma Broadcasting LLC. The format for the station is adult contemporary. WBOP-FM broadcasts to the Harrisonburg, VA area at 95.5 FM.

WBOQ-FM

Owner: Westport Communications
Editorial: 8 Enon St, Beverly, Massachusetts 1915. **T:** 1 978 927-1049
W: http://www.northshore1049.com
Editorial Profile: WBOQ-FM is a commercial station owned by Westport Communications. The format of the station is oldies. WBOQ-FM broadcasts to the Beverly, MA area at 104.9 FM.

WBOS-FM

Owner: Greater Media Inc.
Editorial: 55 William T Morrissey Blvd, Dorchester, Massachusetts 02125-3315.
T: 1 617 822-9600 **W:** http://www.wbos.com
Editorial Profile: WBOS-FM is a commercial station owned by Greater Media Inc. The format of the station is rock alternative. WBOS-FM broadcasts to the Boston area at 92.9 FM.

WBOW-FM

Owner: Midwest Communications Inc.
Editorial: 824 S 3rd St, Terre Haute, Indiana 47807-4609. **T:** 1 812 232-4161
W: http://985wbow.com
Editorial Profile: WBOW-FM is a commercial station owned by Midwest Communications Inc. The format of the station is adult contemporary. WBOW-FM broadcasts to the Terre Haute, IN area at 98.5 FM.

WBOX-AM

Owner: Strickland(Ben)
Editorial: 22037 Highway 436, Bogalusa, Louisiana 70427. **T:** 1 985 732-4288

WBOX-FM

Owner: Strickland(Ben)

Editorial: 22037 Highway 436, Bogalusa, Louisiana 70427. **T:** 1 985 732-4288
E: wboxamfm@bellsouth.net
Editorial Profile: WBOX-FM is a commercial station owned by Ben Strickland. The format of the station is country. WBOX-FM broadcasts to the Bogalusa, LA area at 92.9 FM.

WBOZ-FM
Owner: Salem Communications
Editorial: 312 S Church St, Murfreesboro, Tennessee 37130-3732. **T:** 1 615 890-3233
E: info@salemmusicnetwork.com
W: http://www.94fmthefish.net
Editorial Profile: WBOZ-FM is a commercial station owned by Salem Communications. The format of the station is Contemporary Christian music. WBOZ-FM broadcasts to the Murfreesboro, TN area at 104.9 FM.

WBPC-FM
Owner: Beach Radio, Inc.
Editorial: 3900 Marriott Dr, Panama City Beach, Florida 32408. **T:** 1 850 235-2195
W: http://www.beach951.com
Editorial Profile: WBPC-FM is a commercial station owned by Beach Radio, Inc. The format of the station is classic hits. WBPC-FM broadcasts to the Panama City, FL area at 95.1 FM.

WBPE-FM
Owner: Artistic Media Partners Inc.
Editorial: 3824 S 18th St, Lafayette, Indiana 47909. **T:** 1 765 474-1410
W: http://www.wbpefm.com
Editorial Profile: WBPE-FM is a commercial station owned by Artistic Media Partners Inc. The format for the station is adult hits. WBPE-FM broadcasts to the Lafayette, IN area at 95.3 FM.

WBPM-FM
Owner: Pamal Broadcasting Ltd.
Editorial: 715 Route 52, Beacon, New York 12508. **T:** 1 845 838-6000
W: http://www.wbpmfm.com
Editorial Profile: WBPM-FM is a commercial station owned by Pamal Broadcasting Ltd. The format of the station is classic hits. WBPM-FM broadcasts the Poughkeepsie, NY area at 92.9 FM.

WBPR-FM
Owner: University of Massachusetts
Editorial: 100 William T Morrissey Blvd, Dorchester, Massachusetts 2125.
T: 1 617 287-6900 **E:** wumb@umb.edu
W: http://www.wumb.org
Editorial Profile: WBPR-FM is a non-commercial station owned by University of Massachusetts. The format of the station is folk and educational programming. WUMB-FM broadcasts to the Dorchester, MA area at 91.9 FM.

WBPT-FM
Owner: Summit Media Broadcasting LLC
Editorial: 2700 Corporate Dr Ste 115, Birmingham, Alabama 35242-2735.
T: 1 205 916-1100
W: http://www.birminghamseagle.com
Editorial Profile: WBPT-FM is a commercial station owned by Summit Media Broadcasting LLC. The format of the station is classic hits. WBPT-FM broadcasts to the Birmingham, AL area at 106.9 FM.

WBPW-FM
Owner: Townsquare Media, Inc.
Editorial: 551 Main St, Presque Isle, Maine 04769-2450. **T:** 1 207 769-6600
Editorial Profile: WBPW-FM is a commercial station owned by Townsquare Media, Inc. The format of the station is contemporary country. WBPW-FM broadcasts to the Presque Isle, ME area at 96.9 FM.

WBPZ-AM
Owner: Schlesinger Communications
Editorial: 21 E Main St, Lock Haven, Pennsylvania 17745-1303. **T:** 1 570 748-4038
Editorial Profile: WBPZ-AM is a commercial station owned by Lipez Broadcasting Co. The format of the station is oldies music. WBPZ-AM broadcasts to the Lock Haven, PA area at 1230 AM.

WBQB-FM
Owner: Centennial Broadcasting II, LLC
Editorial: 1914 Mimosa St, Fredericksburg, Virginia 22405-3213. **T.** 1 540 373-7721
E: buzzy@wbqb.com
W: http://www.b1015.com
Editorial Profile: WBQB-FM is a commercial station owned by Centennial Broadcasting II, LLC. The format of the station is hot adult contemporary music. WBQB-FM broadcasts to the Fredericksburg, VA area at 101.5 FM.

WBQH-AM
Owner: Hubbard Broadcasting
Editorial: 3400 Idaho Ave NW, 1st Fl, Washington, District Of Columbia 20016-3046.
T: 1 202 450-1693
Editorial Profile: WBQH-AM is a commercial station owned by Hubbard Broadcasting and operated by United Media. The format of the station is regional Mexican. WBQH-AM broadcasts throughout the Washington, D.C. area at 1050 AM.

WBQK-FM
Owner: Local Voice Media
Editorial: 4732 Longhill Rd Ste 2201, Williamsburg, Virginia 23188-1584.
T: 1 757 565-1079 **E:** music@1079bach.com
W: http://www.wbach.net
Editorial Profile: WBQK-FM is a commercial station owned by Local Voice Media. The format of the station is classical. WBQK-FM broadcasts to the Williamsburg, VA area at 107.9 FM.

WBQQ-FM
Owner: WBIN, Inc.
Editorial: 477 Congress St, Portland, Maine 04101-3427. **T:** 1 207 797-0780
W: http://www.999thewolf.com
Editorial Profile: WBQQ-FM is a commercial station owned by WBIN, Inc. The format of the station is country. WBQQ-FM broadcasts to the Kennebunk, ME area at 99.3 FM.

WBQT-FM
Owner: Greater Media Inc.
Editorial: 55 William T Morrissey Blvd, Dorchester, Massachusetts 02125-3315.
T: 1 617 822-9600
W: http://www.hot969boston.com
Editorial Profile: WBQT-FM is a commercial station owned by Greater Media Inc. The format of the station is rhythmic AC. WBQT-FM broadcasts to the Boston area at 96.9 FM.

WBQX-FM
Owner: WBIN, Inc.
Editorial: 119 Tillson Ave, Rockland, Maine 04841-3453. **T:** 1 207 594-9283
W: http://www.wbachradio.com
Editorial Profile: WBQX-FM is a commercial station owned by WBIN, Inc. The format of the station is classical. WBQX-FM broadcasts to the Portland, ME area at 106.9 FM.

WBRB-FM
Owner: West Virginia Radio Corp.
Editorial: 1065 Radio Park Dr, Mount Clare, West Virginia 26408. **T:** 1 304 623-6546
W: http://www.1013thebear.com
Editorial Profile: WBRB-FM is a commercial station owned by West Virginia Radio Corp. The format of the station is contemporary country music. WBRB-FM broadcasts to the Mt. Clare, WV area at 101.3 FM.

WBRD-AM
Owner: Birach Broadcasting Corp.
Editorial: 3912 US Highway 301 N, Ellenton, Florida 34222. **T.** 1 941 955-1420
E: wbrd1420am@yahoo.com
Editorial Profile: WBRD-AM is a commercial station owned by Birach Broadcasting Corp. The format of the station is Hispanic. WBRD-AM broadcasts to the Oneco, FL, area at 1420 AM.

WBRF-FM
Owner: Blue Ridge Radio Inc.
Editorial: 325 Poplar Knob Rd, Galax, Virginia 24333-4106. **T:** 1 276 236-9273
E: info@blueridgecountry98.com
W: http://www.blueridgecountry98.com
Editorial Profile: WBRF-FM is a commercial station owned by Blue Ridge Radio Inc. The format of the station is classic country. WBRF-FM broadcasts to the Roanoke-Lynchburg, VA area at 98.1 FM.

WBRG-AM
Owner: Tri-County Broadcasting
Editorial: 239 Ragland Rd, Madison Heights, Virginia 24572. **T:** 1 434 401-0230
E: info@wbrgradio.com
W: http://www.wbrgradio.com
Editorial Profile: WBRG-AM is a commercial station owned by Tri-County Broadcasting. The format of the station is news, talk and sports. WBRG-AM broadcasts to the Madison Heights, VA area at 1050 AM.

WBRG-FM
Owner: Tri-County Broadcasting
Editorial: 239 Ragland Rd, Madison Heights, Virginia 24572. **T:** 1 434 401-0230
E: info@wbrgradio.com
W: http://www.wbrgradio.com
Editorial Profile: WBRG-FM is a commercial station owned by Tri-County Broadcasting . The format of the station is news, talk and sports. WBRG-FM broadcasts to the Madison Heights, VA area at 104.5 and 96.9 FM.

WBRH-FM
Owner: East Baton Rouge School Board
Editorial: 2825 Government St, Baton Rouge, Louisiana 70806-5412. **T:** 1 225 388-9030
Editorial Profile: WBRH-FM is a non-commercial station owned by the East Baton Rouge School Board. The format of the station is smooth AC. WBRH-FM broadcasts to the Baton Rouge, LA area at 90.3 FM.

WBRI-AM
Owner: Wilkins Communication Networks Inc.
Editorial: 4802 E 62Nd St, Indianapolis, Indiana 46220-5236. **T:** 1 317 255-5484
E: wbri@wilkinsradio.com
W: http://www.wilkinsradio.com
Editorial Profile: WBRI-AM is a commercial station owned by Wilkins Communication Networks Inc. and licensed by Heritage Christian Radio, Inc. The format of the station is Christian talk and news. WBRI-AM broadcasts to the Indianapolis area at 1500 AM.

WBRK-AM
Owner: WBRK Inc.
Editorial: 100 North St, Pittsfield, Massachusetts 1201. **T:** 1 413 442-1553
E: wbrk1340@aol.com
W: http://www.wbrk.com
Editorial Profile: WBRK-AM is a commercial station owned by WBRK Inc. The format of the station is of news, talk and adult standards. WBRK-AM broadcasts to the Pittsfield, MA area at 1340 AM.

WBRK-FM
Owner: WBRK Inc.
Editorial: 100 North St, Pittsfield, Massachusetts 1201. **T:** 1 413 442-1553
E: wbrk1340@aol.com
W: http://www.wbrk.com
Editorial Profile: WBRK-FM is a commercial station owned by WBRK Inc. The format of the station is hot adult contemporary music. WBRK-FM broadcasts to the Pittsfield, MA area at 101.7 FM.

WBRM-AM
Owner: WBRM Inc.
Editorial: 147 N Garden St, Marion, North Carolina 28752-3709. **T:** 1 828 652-9500
E: wbrmnews@gmail.com
Editorial Profile: WBRM-AM is a commercial station owned by WBRM Inc. The format of the station is classic country. WBRM-AM broadcasts to the Marion, NC area at 1250 AM.

WBRN-AM
Owner: Mentor Partners Inc.
Editorial: 18720 16 Mile Rd, Big Rapids, Michigan 49307. **T:** 1 231 796-7000
E: news@bigrapidsradionetwork.com
W: http://www.wbrn.com
Editorial Profile: WBRN-AM is a commercial station owned by Mentor Partners Inc.. The format of the station is news, sports and talk. WBRN-AM broadcasts to the Big Rapids, MI area at 1460 AM.

WBRN-FM
Owner: Mentor Partners Inc.
Editorial: 18720 16 Mile Rd, Big Rapids, Michigan 49307-9303. **T:** 1 231 796-7000
W: http://www.wbrn.com
Editorial Profile: WBRN-FM is a commercial station owned by Mentor Partners Inc. The format of the station is news, sports and talk. The station broadcasts to the Big Rapids, MI area at 107.7 FM.

WBRP-FM
Owner: Guaranty Broadcasting
Editorial: 929 Government St, Ste B, Baton Rouge, Louisiana 70802. **T:** 1 225 388-9898
W: http://www.talk1073.com
Editorial Profile: WBRP-FM is a commercial station owned by Guaranty Broadcasting. The format of the station is news/talk. WBRP-FM broadcasts to the Baton Rouge, LA area at 107.3 FM.

WBRR-FM
Owner: WESB Inc.
Editorial: 1490 Saint Francis Dr, Bradford, Pennsylvania 16701-3282. **T:** 1 814 368-4141
E: 1490@wesb.com
W: http://www.wbrrfm.com
Editorial Profile: WBRR-FM is a commercial station owned by WESB Inc. The format of the station is rock music. WBRR-FM broadcasts to the Buffalo, NY area at 100.1 FM.

WBRS-FM
Owner: Brandeis University
Editorial: 415 South St, Waltham, Massachusetts 02453-2728.
T: 1 781 736-5277 **E:** gm@wbrs.org
W: http://www.wbrs.org
Editorial Profile: WBRS-FM is a non-commercial station owned by Brandeis University. The format of the station is variety programming. WBRS-FM broadcasts to the Waltham, MA area at 100.1 FM.

WBRT-AM
Owner: Bardstown Radio Team, LLC
Editorial: 106 S 3rd St, Bardstown, Kentucky 40004. **T:** 1 502 348-3943
E: wbrt@wbrtradio.com
W: http://www.wbrtcountry.com
Editorial Profile: WBRT-AM is a commercial station owned by Bardstown Radio Team, LLC. The format of the station is country music. WBRT-AM broadcasts to the Bardstown, KY area at 1320 AM.

WBRU-FM
Owner: Brown Broadcasting Services
Editorial: 88 Benevolent St, Providence, Rhode Island 02906-2046. **T:** 1 401 272-9550
W: http://www.wbru.com
Editorial Profile: WBRU-FM is a commercial station owned by Brown Broadcasting Services. The format of the station is rock alternative music. WBRU-FM broadcasts to the Providence, RI area at 95.5 FM.

WBRV-AM
Owner: Flack Broadcasting Group
Editorial: 7606 N State St, Lowville, New York 13367-1318. **T:** 1 315 376-7500
E: sales@themoose.net
W: http://www.themoose.net
Editorial Profile: WBRV-AM is a commercial station owned by Flack Broadcasting Group. The format of the station is oldies. WBRV-FM broadcasts to the Lowville, NY area at 900 AM.

WBRV-FM
Owner: Flack Broadcasting Group
Editorial: 7606 N State St, Lowville, New York 13367. **T:** 1 315 376-7500
E: sales@themoose.net
W: http://www.themoose.net
Editorial Profile: WBRV-FM is a commercial station owned by Flack Broadcasting Group. The format of the station is country music. WBRV-FM broadcasts to the Rome, NY area at 101.3 FM.

WBRW-FM
Owner: Cumulus Media Inc.
Editorial: 7080 Lee Hwy, Fairlawn, Virginia 24141. **T:** 1 540 731-6000
W: http://www.1053thebear.com
Editorial Profile: WBRW-FM is a commercial station owned by Cumulus Media Inc. The format for the station is rock music. WBRW-FM broadcasts to the Fairlawn, VA area at 105.3 FM.

WBRX-FM
Owner: Sherlock Broadcasting
Editorial: 2513 6th Ave, Altoona, Pennsylvania 16602-2129. **T:** 1 814 224-7501
W: http://www.mymix947.com
Editorial Profile: WBRX-FM is a commercial station owned by Sherlock Broadcasting. The format of the station is adult contemporary music. WBRX-FM broadcasts to the Altoona, PA area at 94.7 FM.

WBRY-AM
Owner: Volunteer Broadcasting
Editorial: 153 Mile Valley Rd, Woodbury, Tennessee 37190. **T:** 1 615 563-2313
W: http://www.wbry.com
Editorial Profile: WBRY-AM is a commercial station owned by Volunteer Broadcasting. The format of the station is classic country. WBRY-AM broadcasts to the Woodbury, TN area at 1540 AM.

WBSA-AM
Owner: Watkins Broadcasting Inc.
Editorial: 1525 Wills Rd, Boaz, Alabama 35957. **T:** 1 256 593-4264
E: 1300@wbsaam.com
W: http://www.wbsaam.com

Editorial Profile: WBSA-AM is a commercial station owned by Watkins Broadcasting Inc. The format of the station is Christian programming. WBSA-AM broadcasts to the Boaz, AL area at 1300 AM.

WBSD-FM
Owner: Burlington Area Schools
Editorial: 400 Mc Canna Pkwy, Burlington, Wisconsin 53105. **T:** 1 262 763-0195
W: http://wbsdfm.com

WBSL-FM
Owner: Berkshire School, Inc.
Editorial: 245 N Undermountain Rd, Sheffield, Massachusetts 01257-9638.
T: 1 413 229-1927 **E:** wbslfm@yahoo.com
W: http://www.bsn.net
Editorial Profile: WBSL-FM is a non-commercial station owned by Berkshire School, Inc. The format of the station is variety during the school year and shares NPR news and talk programming during the summer months. WBSL-FM broadcasts to the Sheffield, MA area at 91.7 FM.

WBSM-AM
Owner: Townsquare Media, Inc.
Editorial: 22 Sconticut Neck Rd, Fairhaven, Massachusetts 02719-1914.
T: 1 508 993-1767 **E:** news@wbsm.com
W: http://www.wbsm.com
Editorial Profile: WBSM-AM is a commercial station owned by Townsquare Media, Inc. The format of the station is news, talk, and sports. WBSM-AM broadcasts to the Providence, RI, and New Bedford, MA, area at 1420 AM.

WBSN-FM
Owner: Providence Educational Foundation
Editorial: 3939 Gentilly Blvd, New Orleans, Louisiana 70126-4858. **T:** 1 504 816-8000
E: onair@lifesongs.com
W: http://www.lifesongs.com
Editorial Profile: WBSN-FM is a non-commercial station owned by Providence Educational Foundation. The format of the station is contemporary Christian music. WBSN-FM broadcasts to the New Orleans area at 89.1 FM.

WBSR-AM
Owner: Easy Media Inc.
Editorial: 1601 N Pace Blvd, Pensacola, Florida 32505-6029. **T:** 1 850 438-4982
Editorial Profile: WBSR-AM is a commercial station owned by Easy Media Inc. The format of the station is sports/talk. WBSR-AM broadcasts to the Pensacola, FL area at 1450 AM.

WBSS-AM
Owner: Longport Media
Editorial: 1601 New Rd, Linwood, New Jersey 08221-1116. **T:** 1 609 653-1400
W: http://www.kool983.com
Editorial Profile: WBSS-AM is a commercial station owned by Longport Media. The format of the station is classic hits. WBSS-AM broadcasts to the Linwood, NJ area at 1490 AM. the station is a simulcast of WTKU-FM 98.3.

WBST-FM
Owner: Ball State University
Editorial: Indiana Public Radio, Ball State University, Muncie, Indiana 47306.
T: 1 765 285-5888 **E:** ipr@bsu.edu
W: http://www.bsu.edu/ipr
Editorial Profile: WBST-FM is a non-commercial station owned by Ball State University. The format of the station is variety. WBST-FM broadcasts to the Muncie, IN area at 92.1 FM.

WBSU-FM
Owner: State University of New York
Editorial: 135 Seymour Union, Brockport, New York 14420. **T:** 1 585 395-2580
W: http://www.891thepoint.com
Editorial Profile: WBSU-FM is a non-commercial station owned by State University of New York. The format of the station is classic rock, Top 40/CHR, and alternative. WBSU-FM broadcasts to the Brockport, NY area at 89.1 FM.

WBSX-FM
Owner: Cumulus Media Inc.
Editorial: 600 Baltimore Drive, Wilkes-Barre, Pennsylvania 18702-7901. **T:** 1 570 824-9000
W: http://www.979x.com
Editorial Profile: WBSX-FM is a commercial station owned by Cumulus Media Inc. The format of the station is rock alternative. WBSX-FM broadcasts to the Wilkes Barre, PA area at 97.9 FM.

WBSZ-FM
Owner: Heartland Communications Group, LLC
Editorial: 2320 Ellis Ave, Ashland, Wisconsin 54806. **T:** 1 715 682-2727
W: http://wbszfm.com

WBTA-AM
Owner: HPL Communications
Editorial: 113 Main St, Batavia, New York 14020. **T:** 1 585 344-1490
E: news@wbta1490.com
W: http://www.wbta1490.com
Editorial Profile: WBTA-AM is a commercial station owned by HPL Communications. The format of the station is adult contemporary, news and talk. WBTA-AM broadcasts to the Batavia, NY area at 1490 AM.

WBT-AM
Owner: Greater Media Inc.
Editorial: 1 Julian Price Pl, Charlotte, North Carolina 28208-5211. **T:** 1 704 374-3500
E: wbtnews@wbt.com **W:** http://www.wbt.com
Editorial Profile: WBT-AM is a commercial station owned by Greater Media Inc. The format of the station is news and talk. WBT-AM broadcasts to the Charlotte, NC area at 1110 AM.

WBTC-AM
Owner: Tuscarawas Broadcasting
Editorial: 125 Johnson Dr, Uhrichsville, Ohio 44683-1017. T: 1 740 922-2700
E: wbtc@tusco.net
W: http://www.wbtclive.com
Editorial Profile: WBTC-AM is a commercial station owned by Tuscarawas Broadcasting. The format of the station is news, talk, and sports. WBTC-AM broadcasts to the Uhrichsville, OH area at 1540 AM.

WBTF-FM
Owner: L.M. Communications Inc.
Editorial: 401 W Main St, Lexington, Kentucky 40507-1640. **T:** 1 859 233-1515
E: info@1079thebeat.com
W: http://www.1079thebeat.com
Editorial Profile: WBTF-FM is a commercial station owned by L.M. Communications Inc. The format of the station is urban contemporary. WBTF-FM broadcasts locally to the Lexington, KY area at a frequency of 107.9 FM.

WBT-FM
Owner: Greater Media Inc.
Editorial: 1 Julian Price Pl, Charlotte, North Carolina 28208. **T:** 1 704 374-3500
E: wbtnews@wbt.com **W:** http://www.wbt.com
Editorial Profile: WBT-FM is a commercial station owned by Greater Media Inc. The format of the station is news and talk. WBT-FM broadcasts to the Charlotte, NC, area at 99.3 FM.

WBTG-AM
Owner: Slatton & Associates Broadcasters Inc.
Editorial: 1605 Gospel Rd, Sheffield, Alabama 35660. **T:** 1 256 381-6800
E: announcements@wbtgradio.com
W: http://www.wbtgradio.com
Editorial Profile: WBTG-AM is a commercial station owned by Slatton & Associates Broadcasters Inc. The format of the station is oldies music. WBTG-AM broadcasts to the Sheffield, AL area at 1290 AM.

WBTG-FM
Owner: Slatton & Associates Broadcasters Inc.
Editorial: 1605 Gospel Rd, Sheffield, Alabama 35660-1823. **T:** 1 256 381-6800
E: announcements@wbtgradio.com
W: http://www.wbtgradio.com
Editorial Profile: WBTG-FM is a commercial station owned by Slatton & Associates Broadcasters Inc. The format of the station is gospel. WBTG-FM broadcasts to the Sheffield, AL area at 106.3 FM.

WBTH-AM
Owner: East Kentucky Radio Network
Editorial: 1240 Radio Dr, Pikeville, Kentucky 41501-4779. **T:** 1 304 235-3600
E: frontdesk@ekbradio.com
W: http://www.900wlsi.com

WBTI-FM
Owner: Radio First
Editorial: 808 Huron Ave, Port Huron, Michigan 48060-3705. **T:** 1 810 982-9000
W: http://www.wbti.com
Editorial Profile: WBTI-FM is a commercial station owned by Radio First. The format of the station is hot adult contemporary music. WBTI-FM broadcasts to the Port Huron, MI area at 96.9 FM.

WBTJ-FM
Owner: Clear Channel Media and Entertainment
Editorial: 3245 Basie Rd, Richmond, Virginia 23228-3404. **T:** 1 804 474-0000
W: http://www.wbtj.com
Editorial Profile: WBTJ-FM is a commercial station owned by Clear Channel Media and Entertainment. The format of the station is urban contemporary. WBTJ-FM broadcasts to the Richmond, VA area at 106.5 FM.

WBTK-AM
Owner: Mount Rich Media LLC
Editorial: 2809 Emerywood Pkwy Ste 540, Richmond, Virginia 23294-3745.
T: 1 804 353-8544 **W:** http://www.wbtk.com
Editorial Profile: WBTK-AM is a commercial station owned by Mount Rich Media LLC. The format of the station is Hispanic religious. WBTK-AM broadcasts to the Richmond, VA area at 1380 AM.

WBTM-AM
Owner: Piedmont Broadcasting Corporation
Editorial: 710 Grove St, Danville, Virginia 24541-1704. **T:** 1 434 793-4411
W: http://www.wbtm1330.com
Editorial Profile: WBTM-AM is a commercial station owned by Piedmont Broadcasting Corporation. The format of the station is classic hits. WBTM-AM broadcasts to the Danville, VA area at 1330 AM.

WBTN-AM
Owner: Shires Media Partnership
Editorial: 407 Harwood Hill Rd, Bennington, Vermont 05201-8806. **T:** 1 802 442-6321
E: info@wbtnam.org
W: http://www.wbtnam.org
Editorial Profile: WBTN-AM is a commercial station owned by Shires Media Partnership. The format of the station is adult contemporary and talk. WBTN-AM broadcasts to the Bennington, VT area at 1370 AM.

WBTN-FM
Owner: Vermont Public Radio
Editorial: 365 Troy Ave, Colchester, Vermont 05446-3126. **T:** 1 802 655-9451
E: news@vpr.net **W:** http://www.vpr.net

WBTO-FM
Owner: Original Company Inc.(The)
Editorial: 3 E Van Trees St, Washington, Indiana 47501. **T:** 1 812 324-2200
E: wwblnews@wwbl.com
W: http://www.originalcompany.com/pages/7817255.php
Editorial Profile: WBTO-FM is a commercial station owned by The Original Company Inc. The format is rock/album oriented rock music. WBTO-FM broadcasts to the Washington, IN area at 102.3 FM.

WBTP-FM
Owner: Clear Channel Media and Entertainment
Editorial: 4002 W Gandy Blvd, Tampa, Florida 33611. **T:** 1 813 832-1000
W: http://www.957thebeat.com
Editorial Profile: WBTP-FM is a commercial station owned by Clear Channel Media and Entertainment. The format of the station is urban contemporary. WBTP-FM broadcasts to the Tampa, FL area at 95.7 FM.

WBTQ-FM
Owner: West Virginia Radio Group
Editorial: Washington & Davis Streets, Elkins, West Virginia 26241. **T:** 1 304 636-1300
E: wdne@wvradio.com
W: http://www.935btq.com
Editorial Profile: WBTQ-FM is a commercial station owned by West Virginia Radio Group. The format of the station is Top 40/CHR music. WBTQ-FM broadcasts to the Elkins, WV area at 93.5 FM.

WBTR-FM
Owner: Gradick Communications LLC
Editorial: 102 Parkwood Cir, Carrollton, Georgia 30117. **T:** 1 770 832-9685
W: http://www.b92country.com
Editorial Profile: WBTR-FM is a commercial station owned by Gradick Communications. The format of the station is contemporary country. WBTR-FM broadcasts to the Carrollton, GA area at 92.1 FM.

WBTT-FM
Owner: Clear Channel Media and Entertainment
Editorial: 13320 Metro Pkwy, Ste 1, Fort Myers, Florida 33966-4804. **T:** 1 239 225-4300
W: http://www.1055thebeat.com
Editorial Profile: WBTT-FM is a commercial station owned by Clear Channel Media and Entertainment. The format of the station is urban contemporary. WBTT-FM broadcasts to the Fort Myers, FL area at 105.5 FM.

WBTU-FM
Owner: Adams Radio Group
Editorial: 9604 Coldwater Rd Ste 201, Fort Wayne, Indiana 46825-2096.
T: 1 260 482-9288
Editorial Profile: WBTU-FM is a commercial station owned by Adams Radio Group. The format of the station is contemporary country. WBTU-FM broadcasts to the Fort Wayne, IN area at 93.3 FM.

WBTX-AM
Owner: Massanutten Broadcasting Co. Inc.
Editorial: 166 Main St, Broadway, Virginia 22815. **T:** 1 540 896-8933
E: wbtx@positive-radio.com
W: http://www.positive-radio.com
Editorial Profile: WBTX-AM is a commercial station owned by Massanutten Broadcasting Co. Inc. The format of the station is gospel and religious. WBTX-AM broadcasts to the Broadway, VA area at 1470 AM.

WBTY-FM
Owner: Strickland (Jim &Nancy)
Editorial: Highway 168 & 37, Homerville, Georgia 31634. **T:** 1 912 487-3412
Editorial Profile: WBTY-FM is a commercial station owned by Jim & Nancy Strickland. The format of the station is classic hits. WBTY-FM broadcasts to the Homerville, GA area at 98.7 FM.

WBTZ-FM
Owner: Hall Communications
Editorial: 255 S Champlain St, Burlington, Vermont 5401. **T:** 1 802 860-2440
E: mailbag@999thebuzz.com
W: http://www.999thebuzz.com
Editorial Profile: WBTZ-FM is a commercial station owned by Hall Communications. The format of the station is rock alternative. WBTZ-FM broadcasts to the Burlington, VT area at 99.9 FM.

WBUA-FM
Owner: Boston University
Editorial: 890 Commonwealth Ave Fl 3, Boston, Massachusetts 02215-1205.
T: 1 617 353-0909 **E:** info@wbur.org
W: http://www.wbur.org
Editorial Profile: WBUA-FM is a commercial station owned by Boston University. The format of the station is news/talk. WBUA-FM broadcasts to the Tisbury, MA area at 92.7 FM.

WBUC-AM
Owner: West Virginia Radio Corp.
Editorial: Washington & Davis Streets, Elkins, West Virginia 26241. **T:** 1 304 636-1300
Editorial Profile: WBUC-AM is a commercial station owned by West Virginia Radio Corp. The format of the station is news/talk. WBUC-AM broadcasts to the Buckhannon, WV area at 1460 AM.

WBUF-FM
Owner: Town Square Media
Editorial: 14 Lafayette Sq, Buffalo, New York 14203-1928. **T:** 1 716 852-9292
W: http://929jackfm.com
Editorial Profile: WBUF-FM is a commercial station owned by Town Square Media. The format of the station is adult hits. WBUF-FM broadcasts to the Buffalo, NY area at 92.9 FM.

WBUG-FM
Owner: Roser Communications
Editorial: 185 Genesee St, Ste 1601, Utica, New York 13501. **T:** 1 315 734-9245
W: http://www.bugcountry.com
Editorial Profile: WBUG-FM is a commercial station owned by Roser Communications. The format of the station is contemporary country music. WBUG-FM broadcasts to the Mohawk Valley, NY region at 101.1 FM and 99.7 FM via a simulcast with WBGK-FM.

WBUK-FM
Owner: Blanchard River Broadcasting, Co.
Editorial: 551 Lake Cascades Pkwy, Findlay, Ohio 45840-1388. **T:** 1 419 422-4545
W: http://www.1063thefox.com
Editorial Profile: WBUK-FM is a commercial station owned by Blanchard River Broadcasting, Co. The format of the station is classic rock. WBUK-FM broadcasts to the Lima, OH area at 106.3 FM.

WBUL-FM
Owner: Clear Channel Media and Entertainment
Editorial: 2601 Nicholasville Rd, Lexington, Kentucky 40503-3307. **T:** 1 859 422-1000
W: http://www.wbul.com
Editorial Profile: WBUL-FM is a commercial station owned by Clear Channel Media and Entertainment. The format of the station is country. WBUL-FM broadcasts to the Lexington, KY area at 98.1 FM.

WBUR-FM
Owner: Boston University
Editorial: 890 Commonwealth Ave Fl 3, Boston, Massachusetts 02215-1205.
T: 1 617 353-0909 **E:** wburnews@wbur.org
W: http://www.wbur.org
Editorial Profile: WBUR-FM is a non-commercial station owned by Boston University. The format of the station is news and talk. WBUR-FM broadcast to the Boston area at 90.9 FM.

WBUS-FM
Owner: Forever Broadcasting
Editorial: 2551 Park Center Blvd, State College, Pennsylvania 16801-3007.
T: 1 814 237-9800 **E:** businfo@thebus.net
W: http://www.thebus.net
Editorial Profile: WBUS-FM is a commercial station owned by Forever Broadcasting. The format of the station is classic rock. The station broadcasts locally at 93.7 FM.

WBUT-AM
Owner: Butler County Radio Network
Editorial: 112 Hollywood Dr, Ste 203, Butler, Pennsylvania 16001. **T:** 1 724 287-5778
E: frontdesk@bcrnetwork.com
W: http://www.wbut.com
Editorial Profile: WBUT-AM is a commercial station owned by Butler County Radio Network. The format of the station is contemporary country. WBUT-AM broadcasts to the Butler, PA area at 1050 AM.

WBUV-FM
Owner: Clear Channel Media and Entertainment
Editorial: 286 Debuys Rd, Biloxi, Mississippi 39531-2611. **T:** 1 228 388-2323
W: http://www.newsradio1049fm.com
Editorial Profile: WBUV-FM is a commercial station owned by Clear Channel Media and Entertainment. The format of the station is news and talk. WBUV-FM broadcasts to the Biloxi-Gulfport, MS area at 104.9 FM.

WBUZ-FM
Owner: Cromwell Group Inc.(The)
Editorial: 1824 Murfreesboro Pike, Nashville, Tennessee 37217. **T.** 1 615 399-1029
W: http://www.1029thebuzz.com
Editorial Profile: WBUZ-FM is a commercial station owned by The Cromwell Group Inc. The format of the station is rock. WBUZ-FM broadcasts in the Nashville, TN area at 102.9 FM.

WBVB-FM
Owner: Clear Channel Media and Entertainment
Editorial: 134 4Th Ave, Huntington, West Virginia 25701-1220. **T:** 1 304 525-7788
W: http://www.oldies971.com
Editorial Profile: WBVB-FM is a commercial station owned by Clear Channel Media and Entertainment. The format of the station is oldies. WBVB-FM broadcasts to the Catlettsburg, KY and Ironton, OH areas at 97.1 FM.

WBVE-FM
Owner: Cessna Communications Inc.
Editorial: 134 E Pitt St, 2nd Fl, Bedford, Pennsylvania 15522-1311. **T:** 1 814 623-1000
E: cesscomm@embarqmail.com
Editorial Profile: WBVE-FM is a commercial station owned by Cessna Communications Inc., Inc. The format of the station is classic rock. WBVE-FM broadcasts to Bedford, PA at 107.5 FM.

WBVI-FM
Owner: Tri-County Broadcasting
Editorial: 101 N Main St, Fostoria, Ohio 44830. **T:** 1 419 422-9284
E: production@wfob.com
W: http://www.wbvi.com
Editorial Profile: WBVI-FM is a commercial station owned by Tri-County Broadcasting. The format of the station is adult contemporary music. WBVI-FM broadcasts to the Fostoria, OH area at 96.7 FM.

WBVM-FM
Owner: Diocese of St. Petersburg
Editorial: 717 S Dale Mabry Hwy, Ste 300, Tampa, Florida 33609-4408.
T: 1 813 289-8040
E: contact@spiritfm905.com
W: http://www.spiritfm905.com
Editorial Profile: WBVM-FM is a non-commercial station owned by Diocese of St. Petersburg. The format of the station is contemporary Christian. WBVM-FM broadcasts to the Tampa, FL area at 90.5 FM.

WBVN-FM
Owner: Anderson(Kenneth)
Editorial: 105 S Market St, Marion, Illinois 62959-2513. **T:** 1 618 997-1500
E: wbvn@shawneelink.net
W: http://www.wbvn.org
Editorial Profile: WBVN-FM is a non-commercial station owned by Kenneth Anderson. The format of the station is contemporary Christian music. WBVN-FM broadcasts to the Marion, IL area at 104.5 FM.

WBVP-AM
Owner: Iorio Broadcasting Inc.
Editorial: 1316 7th Ave, Beaver Falls, Pennsylvania 15010. **T:** 1 724 846-4100
E: 1230@wbvp-wmba.com
W: http://www.wbvp-wmba.com
Editorial Profile: WBVP-AM is a commercial station owned by Iorio Broadcasting Inc. The format of the station is news, talk and sports. WBVP-AM broadcasts to the Beaver Falls, PA area at 1230 AM.

WBVR-FM
Owner: Forever Communications Inc.
Editorial: 1919 Scottsville Rd, Bowling Green, Kentucky 42104. **T:** 1 270 843-3333
E: production@beaverfm.com
W: http://www.beaverfm.com

WBVV-FM
Owner: Clear Channel Media and Entertainment
Editorial: 5026 Cliff Gookin Blvd, Tupelo, Mississippi 38801. **T:** 1 662 842-1067
W: http://www.gospel993.com
Editorial Profile: WBVV-FM is a commercial station owned by URBan Radio Broadcasting, LLC. The format of the station is Southern gospel. WBVV-FM broadcasts to the Tupelo, MS area at 99.3 FM.

WBVX-FM
Owner: L.M. Communications Inc.
Editorial: 401 W Main St, Lexington, Kentucky 40507-1640. **T:** 1 859 233-1515
E: info@b92fm.com **W:** http://www.b92fm.com
Editorial Profile: WBVX-FM is a commercial station owned by L.M. Communications Inc. The format of the station is classic hits. WBVX-FM broadcasts locally to the Lexington, KY area at a frequency of 92.1 FM.

WBWB-FM
Owner: Artistic Media Partners Inc.
Editorial: 304 S State Road 446, Bloomington, Indiana 47401-8837. **T:** 1 812 336-8000
E: wbwb@wbwb.com
W: http://www.wbwb.com
Editorial Profile: WBWB-FM is a commercial station owned by Artistic Media Partners Inc. The format of the station is Top 40/CHR music. WBWB-FM broadcasts to the Bloomington, IN area at 96.7 FM.

WBWC-FM
Owner: Baldwin-Wallace College
Editorial: 275 Eastland Rd, Berea, Ohio 44017. **T:** 1 440 826-2145
E: operations@wbwc.com
W: http://www.wbwc.com
Editorial Profile: WBWC-FM is a non-commercial station owned by Baldwin-Wallace College. The format of the station is rock alternative. WBWC-FM broadcasts to Baldwin-Wallace students and Berea, OH at 88.3 FM.

WBWI-FM
Owner: Bliss Communications Inc.
Editorial: 2410 S Main St, Ste A, West Bend, Wisconsin 53095. **T:** 1 262 334-2344
W: http://www.wbwifm.com
Editorial Profile: WBWI-FM is a commercial station owned by Bliss Communications Inc. The format of the station is country music. WBWI-FM broadcasts to the Milwaukee area at 92.5 FM.

WBWN-FM
Owner: Cumulus Media Inc.
Editorial: 236 Greenwood Ave, Bloomington, Illinois 61704-7422. **T:** 1 309 829-1221
E: news@wjbc.com **W:** http://www.wbwn.com
Editorial Profile: WBWN-FM is a commercial station owned by Cumulus Media Inc. The format of the station is contemporary country music. WBWN-FM broadcasts to the Bloomington, IL area at 104.1 FM.

WBWR-FM
Owner: Clear Channel Media and Entertainment
Editorial: 2323 W 5th Ave Ste 200, Columbus, Ohio 43204-4988. **T:** 1 614 486-6101
W: http://www.thebrew1057.com
Editorial Profile: WBWR-FM is a commercial station owned by Clear Channel Media and Entertainment. The format of the station is rock. WBWR-FM broadcasts to the Columbus, OH area at 105.7 FM.

WBWX-AM
Owner: Bold Gold Media Group
Editorial: 1049 N Sekol Ave, Scranton, Pennsylvania 18504. **T:** 1 570 665-6660
W: http://www.thegame-radio.com
Editorial Profile: WBWX-AM is a commercial station owned by Bold Gold Media Group. The format of the station is sports. WBWX-AM broadcasts to the Scranton, PA area at 1280 AM.

WBWZ-FM
Owner: Clear Channel Media and Entertainment
Editorial: 20 Tucker Dr, Poughkeepsie, New York 12603. **T:** 1 845 471-2300
W: http://www.rock933.com
Editorial Profile: WBWZ-FM is a commercial station owned by Clear Channel Media and Entertainment. The format of the station is rock music. WBWZ-FM broadcasts to the Poughkeepsie, NY area at 93.3 FM.

WBXB-FM
Owner: Willis Broadcasting Co.
Editorial: 1900 Paradise Rd, Edenton, North Carolina 27932. **T:** 1 252 482-1903
E: wbxbradio@ymail.com
Editorial Profile: WBXB-FM is a commercial station owned by Willis Broadcasting Co. The format of the station is gospel music. WBXB-FM broadcasts to the Norfolk, VA area at 100.1 FM.

WBXE-FM
Owner: Stonecom Cookeville LLC
Editorial: 259 S Willow Ave, Cookeville, Tennessee 38501. **T:** 1 931 528-6064
W: http://rock937online.com
Editorial Profile: WBXE-FM is a commercial station owned by Stonecom Cookeville LLC. The format of the station is rock music. WBXE-FM broadcasts to the Cookeville, TN area at 93.7 FM.

WBXQ-FM
Owner: Sounds Good Inc.
Editorial: 2513 6th Ave, Altoona, Pennsylvania 16602-2129. **T:** 1 814 224-7501
W: http://www.truecountry943.com
Editorial Profile: WBXQ-FM is a commercial station owned by Sounds Good Inc. The format for the station is classic country. WBXQ-FM broadcasts to the Altoona, PA area at 94.3 FM.

WBXR-AM
Owner: Wilkins Communication Networks Inc.
Editorial: 2926 Huntsville Hwy, Ste D, Fayetteville, Tennessee 37334-7341.
T: 1 931 433-7017 **E:** wbxr@wilkinsradio.com
W: http://www.wilkinsradio.com

WBXX-FM
Owner: Townsquare Media, LLC
Editorial: 390 Golden Ave, Battle Creek, Michigan 49015-4519. **T:** 1 269 660-1049
E: vip.support@townsquaremedia.com
W: http://mix1049online.com
Editorial Profile: WBXX-FM is a commercial station owned by Townsquare Media, LLC. The format of the station is adult contemporary music. WBXX-FM broadcasts to the Battle Creek, MI area at 104.9 FM.

WBXY-FM
Owner: RDA Broadcast Holdings, LLC
Editorial: 1306 E Silver Springs Blvd, Ocala, Florida 34470-6800. **T:** 1 352 414-5230
E: info@gold99fm.com
W: http://www.gold99fm.com
Editorial Profile: WBXY-FM is a commercial station owned by RDA Broadcast Holdings, LLC. The format of the station is adult standards. WBXY-FM broadcasts to the Gainesville, FL area at 99.5 FM.

WBYA-FM
Owner: WBIN, Inc.
Editorial: 477 Congress St Ste 3, Portland, Maine 04101-3417. **T:** 1 207 797-0780
W: http://www.1055frankfm.com
Editorial Profile: WBYA-FM is a commercial station owned by WBIN, Inc. The format of the station is classic hits. WBYA-FM broadcasts to the Portland, ME area at 105.5 FM.

WBYB-FM
Owner: Colonial Radio Group
Editorial: 1 Bluebird Sq, Olean, New York 14760-2552. **T:** 1 866 454-9564
E: news@colonialme.com
W: http://www.colonialme.com
Editorial Profile: WBYB-FM is a commercial station owned by Colonial Radio Group. The format of the station is contemporary country. WBYB-FM broadcasts to the Kane, PA area at 103.9 FM.

WBYE-AM
Owner: Progressive United Communications Inc.
Editorial: 9170 Highway 25, Calera, Alabama 35040. **T:** 1 205 668-6430

WBYG-FM
Owner: Big River Radio Inc.
Editorial: 303 8th St, Point Pleasant, West Virginia 25550-1209. **T:** 1 304 675-2763
E: wbyg@wbyg.com **W:** http://www.wbyg.com
Editorial Profile: WBYG-FM is a commercial station owned by Big River Radio Inc. The format of the station is country music. WBYG-FM broadcasts to Point Pleasant, WV and surrounding communities at 99.5 FM.

WBYL-FM
Owner: Clear Channel Media and Entertainment
Editorial: 1559 W 4th St, Williamsport, Pennsylvania 17701-5650. **T:** 1 570 327-1400
W: http://www.bill95.com/main.html
Editorial Profile: WBYL-FM is a commercial station owned by Clear Channel Media and Entertainment. The format of the station is contemporary country music. WBYL-FM broadcasts to the Williamsport, PA area at 95.5 FM.

WBYN-AM
Owner: Connoisseur Media
Editorial: 619 Alexander Rd, Princeton, New Jersey 08540-6000. **T:** 1 609 419-0300
W: http://www.thelightradio.com
Editorial Profile: WBYN-AM is a commercial station owned by Connoisseur Media. The format of the station is religious programming. WBYN-AM broadcasts to the Boyertown, PA area at 1160 AM.

WBYN-FM
Owner: WDAC Radio Co.
Editorial: 280 Mill St, Boyertown, Pennsylvania 19512. **T:** 1 610 369-7777
W: http://www.wdac.com
Editorial Profile: WBYN-FM is a commercial station owned by WDAC Radio Co. The format of the station is religious and Christian music. WBYN-FM broadcasts to the Boyertown, PA area at 107.5 FM.

WBYO-FM
Owner: Four Rivers Community Broadcasting Corp
Editorial: 746 Route 113, Souderton, Pennsylvania 18964-1004. **T:** 1 215 721-2141
E: wordfm@wordfm.org
W: http://www.wordfm.org
Editorial Profile: WBYO-FM is a non-commercial station owned by Four Rivers Community Broadcasting Corp. The format of the station is contemporary Christian music and talk. WBYO-FM broadcasts to the Boyertown, PA area at 88.9 FM.

WBYP-FM
Owner: Zoo-Bel Broadcasting LLC
Editorial: 611 Center Park Ln, Yazoo City, Mississippi 39194-9073. **T:** 1 662 746-7676
E: power107@power107.org
W: http://www.power107.org
Editorial Profile: WBYP-FM is a commercial station owned by Zoo-Bel Broadcasting LLC. The format of the station is country and gospel. WBYP-FM broadcasts to the Yazoo City, MS area at 107.1 FM.

WBYR-FM
Owner: Pathfinder Communications Corp.
Editorial: 1005 Production Rd, Fort Wayne, Indiana 46808-4107. **T:** 1 260 471-5100
W: http://www.989thebear.com
Editorial Profile: WBYR-FM is a commercial station owned by Pathfinder Communications

Corp. The format of the station is rock. WBYR-FM broadcasts to the Fort Wayne, IN area at 98.9 FM.

WBYS-AM
Owner: Prairie Communications LLP
Editorial: 1000 E Linn St, Canton, Illinois 61520-9401. **T:** 1 309 647-1560
E: wbysnews@yahoo.com
W: http://www.1560wbys.com
Editorial Profile: WBYS-AM is a commercial station owned by Prairie Communications LLP. The format of the station is talk and classic hits music. WBYS-AM broadcasts in the Canton, IL area at 1560 AM.

WBYT-FM
Owner: Pathfinder Communications Corporation
Editorial: 237 W Edison Rd, Mishawaka, Indiana 46545-3103. **T:** 1 574 258-5483
W: http://www.b100.com
Editorial Profile: WBYT-FM is a commercial station owned by Pathfinder Communications Corporation, a division of Federated Media. The format for the station is country. WBYT-FM broadcasts to the South Bend, IN area at 100.7 FM.

WBYY-FM
Owner: Garrison City Broadcasting
Editorial: 101 Back Rd, Dover, New Hampshire 3820. **T:** 1 603 742-0987
E: thebay@987thebay.com
W: http://www.987thebay.com/
Editorial Profile: WBYY-FM is a commercial station owned by Garrison City Broadcasting. The format of the station is Lite Rock/Lite AC music. WBYY-FM broadcasts to the Dover, NH area at 98.7 FM.

WBYZ-FM
Owner: South Georgia Broadcasters Inc.
Editorial: 4005 Golden Isles Parkway, Baxley, Georgia 31513. **T:** 1 912 367-3000
E: peggy@wbyz94.com
W: http://www.wbyz94.com
Editorial Profile: WBYZ-FM is a commercial station owned by South Georgia Broadcasters Inc. The format for the station is country. WBYZ-FM broadcasts to the Baxley, GA area at 94.5 FM.

WBZA-FM
Owner: Entercom Communications Corp.
Editorial: 70 Commercial St, Rochester, New York 14614-1010. **T:** 1 585 423-2900
W: http://www.rochesterbuzz.com
Editorial Profile: WBZA-FM is a commercial station owned by Entercom Communications Corp. The format of the station is classic hits. WBZA-FM broadcasts to the Rochester, NY area at 98.9 FM.

WBZ-AM
Owner: CBS Radio
Editorial: 1170 Soldiers Field Rd, Boston, Massachusetts 02134-1004.
T: 1 617 787-7000 **E:** wbzradionews@wbz.com
W: http://boston.cbslocal.com/station/wbz-news-radio
Editorial Profile: WBZ-AM is a commercial station owned by CBS Radio. The format of the station is news and talk. WBZ-AM broadcasts to the Boston area at 1030 AM.

WBZC-FM
Owner: Burlington County College
Editorial: 601 Pemberton Browns Mills Rd, Pemberton, New Jersey 08068-1536.
T: 1 609 894-9311 1181
W: http://www.z889.org
Editorial Profile: WBZC-FM is a non-commercial college station owned by the Burlington County College. The format of the station is Top 40/CHR. WBZC-FM broadcasts to the Pemberton, NJ area at 88.9 FM. The station is run by students.

WBZD-FM
Owner: Backyard Broadcasting
Editorial: 1685 Four Mile Dr, Williamsport, Pennsylvania 17701-1975. **T:** 1 570 323-8200
W: http://www.wbzd.com
Editorial Profile: WBZD-FM is a commercial station owned by Backyard Broadcasting. The format of the station is oldies music. WBZD-FM broadcasts to the Susquehanna Valley, PA area at 93.3 FM.

WBZE-FM
Owner: Cumulus Media Inc.
Editorial: 3411 W Tharpe St, Tallahassee, Florida 32303. **T:** 1 850 201-3000
W: http://www.mystar98.com

WBZF-FM
Owner: Cumulus Media Inc.
Editorial: 2014 N Irby St, Florence, South Carolina 29501. **T:** 1 843 661-5000
W: http://www.glory985.com
Editorial Profile: WBZF-FM is a commercial station owned by Cumulus Media Inc. The format of the station is gospel music. WBZF-FM broadcasts to the Florence, SC area at 98.5 FM.

WBZ-FM
Owner: CBS Radio
Editorial: 83 Leo M Birmingham Pkwy, Boston, Massachusetts 2135.
T: 1 617 746-1300
W: http://boston.cbslocal.com/category/sports
Editorial Profile: WBZ-FM is a commercial station owned by CBS Radio. The format of the station is sports. WBZ-FM broadcasts to the Boston area at 98.5 FM.

WBZG-FM
Owner: Mendota Broadcasting
Editorial: 3905 Progress Blvd, Peru, Illinois 61354. **T:** 1 815 224-2100
E: wbzg@theradiogroup.net
W: http://www.wbzg.net
Editorial Profile: WBZG-FM is a commercial station owned by Mendota Broadcasting. The format for the station is classic rock. WBZG-FM broadcasts to the Peru, IL area at 100.9 FM.

WBZI-AM
Owner: Town and Country Broadcasting, Inc.
Editorial: 23 E 2nd St, Xenia, Ohio 45385-3415. **T:** 1 937 372-3531
E: myclassiccountry@myclassiccountry.com
W: http://www.myclassiccountry.com
Editorial Profile: WBZI-AM is a commercial station owned by Town and Country Broadcasting, Inc. The format of the station is classic country. WBZI-AM broadcasts to the Xenia, OH area at 1500 AM.

WBZI-FM
Owner: Town and Country Broadcasting, Inc.
Editorial: 23 E 2nd St, Xenia, Ohio 45385-3415. **T:** 1 937 372-3531
E: myclassiccountry@myclassiccountry.com
W: http://www.myclassiccountry.com
Editorial Profile: WBZI-FM is a commercial station owned by Town and Country Broadcasting, Inc. The format of the station is classic country. WBZI-FM broadcasts to the Xenia, OH area at 100.3 FM.

WBZJ-FM
Owner: Curtis Media Group
Editorial: 3012 Highwoods Blvd, Raleigh, North Carolina 27604-1037.
T: 1 919 790-9392
E: new969@curtismedia.com
Editorial Profile: WBZJ-FM is a commercial station owned by Curtis Media Group. The format of the station is Urban AC. WYMY-FM broadcasts to the Raleigh, NC area at 96.9 FM.

WBZN-FM
Owner: Townsquare Media, Inc.
Editorial: 49 Acme Rd, Brewer, Maine 04412-1545. **T:** 1 207 989-5631
E: z1073@midmaine.com
W: http://www.wbzn-fm.com
Editorial Profile: WBZN-FM is a commercial station owned by Townsquare Media, Inc. The format of the station is Top 40/CHR. WBZN-FM broadcasts to the Brewer, ME area at 107.3 FM.

WBZO-FM
Owner: Connoisseur Media
Editorial: 234 Airport Plaza Blvd, Farmingdale, New York 11735-3917. **T:** 1 631 770-4200
E: webmaster@liradiogroup.com
W: http://www.b103.com
Editorial Profile: WBZO-FM is a commercial station owned by Connoisseur Media. The format of the station is oldies music. WBZO-FM broadcasts to the Farmingdale, NY area at 103.1 FM.

WBZR-FM
Owner: 21st Century Broadcasting Inc.
Editorial: 18674 Fairground Rd, Robertsdale, Alabama 36567-3801. **T:** 1 251 923-0993
W: http://www.atmore1059FMRadio.com
Editorial Profile: WBZR-FM is a commercial station owned by 21st Century Broadcasting Inc. The format of the station is classic country. WBZR-FM broadcasts to the Atmore, AL area at 105.9 FM.

WBZS-FM
Owner: 3 Daughters Media, Inc.

Editorial: 1035 Avalon Dr, Forest, Virginia 24551-2970. **T:** 1 434 534-6100
W: http://www.wiqoradio.com
Editorial Profile: WBZS-FM is a commercial station owned by 3 Daughters Media, Inc. The format of the station is news/talk. WBZS-FM broadcasts to the Shawsville, VA area at a frequency of 102.5 FM.

WBZT-AM
Owner: Clear Channel Media and Entertainment
Editorial: 3071 Continental Dr, West Palm Beach, Florida 33407. **T:** 1 561 616-6600
W: http://www.wbzt.com
Editorial Profile: WBZT-AM is a commercial station owned by Clear Channel Media and Entertainment. The format of the station is news and talk. WBZT-AM broadcasts to the West Palm Beach, FL area at 1230 AM.

WBZU-AM
Owner: Entercom Communications Corp.
Editorial: 305 Route 315 Hwy, Pittston, Pennsylvania 18640-3907. **T:** 1 570 883-9800
W: http://www.wilknetwork.com
Editorial Profile: WBZU-AM is a commercial station owned by Entercom Communications Corp. The format of the station is news, sports and talk. WBZU-AM broadcasts to the Pittston, PA area at 910 AM.

WBZV-FM
Owner: Friends Communications Inc.
Editorial: 121 W Maumee St, Adrian, Michigan 49221-2019. **T:** 1 517 265-1500
E: friends@tc3net.com
Editorial Profile: WBZV-FM is a commercial station owned by Friends Communications Inc. The format of the station is classic rock. WBZV-FM broadcasts to the Hillsdale, MI area at 102.5 FM.

WBZW-AM
Owner: Salem Communications
Editorial: 1188 Lake View Dr, Altamonte Springs, Florida 32714-2713.
T: 1 407 682-9494
W: http://www.1520whim.com
Editorial Profile: WBZW-AM is a commercial station owned by Salem Communications. The format of the station is business talk. WBZW-AM broadcasts to the Altamonte Springs, FL area at 1520 AM.

WBZY-FM
Owner: Clear Channel Media and Entertainment
Editorial: 1819 Peachtree Rd NE, Ste 700, Atlanta, Georgia 30309. **T:** 1 404 607-1336
W: http://www.1053elpatron.com
Editorial Profile: WBZY-FM is a commercial station owned by Clear Channel Media and Entertainment. The format of the station is regional Mexican. WBZY-FM broadcasts to the Atlanta area at 105.3 FM.

WBZZ-FM
Owner: CBS Radio
Editorial: 651 Holiday Dr, 2nd Flr, Pittsburgh, Pennsylvania 15220-2740. **T:** 1 412 920-9400
W: http://starpittsburgh.cbslocal.com
Editorial Profile: WBZZ-FM is a commercial station owned by CBS Radio. The format of the station is hot adult contemporary. WBZZ-FM broadcasts to the Pittsburgh area at 100.7 FM.

WCAB-AM
Owner: Bishop (Jim)
Editorial: 191 Whiteside Rd, Rutherfordton, North Carolina 28139. **T:** 1 828 287-3356
E: wcabam59@nctv.com
W: http://www.wcab59.com
Editorial Profile: WCAB-AM is a commercial station owned by Jim Bishop. The format of the station is classic country, news and talk. WCAB-AM broadcasts to the Rutherfordton, NC area at 590 AM.

WCAI-FM
Owner: WGBH Educational Foundation
Editorial: 3 Water St, Woods Hole, Massachusetts 2543. **T:** 1 508 548-9600
E: cainan@wgbh.org
W: http://www.capeandislands.org
Editorial Profile: WCAI-FM is a non-commercial station owned by the WGBH Educational Foundation. The format of the station is news and talk. WCAI-FM broadcasts to the Woods Hole, MA area at 90.1 FM.

WCAL-FM
Owner: Student Association Inc.
Editorial: 428 Hickory St, California, Pennsylvania 15419-1341. **T:** 1 724 938-5823
W: http://wcal.calu.edu

Editorial Profile: WCAL-FM is a non-commercial station owned by Student Association Inc. The format of the station is rock alternative music. WCAL-FM broadcasts to the California, PA at 91.9 FM.

WCAM-AM
Owner: Kershaw Radio Corp.
Editorial: 5 The Commons, Lugoff, South Carolina 29078. **T:** 1 803 438-9002
E: wpubradio@bellsouth.net
W: http://www.kool1027.com
Editorial Profile: WCAM-AM is a commercial station owned by Kershaw Radio Corp. The format of the station is adult standards. WCAM-AM broadcasts to the Lugoff, SC area at 1590 AM.

WCAN-FM
Owner: WAMC
Editorial: 318 Central Ave, Albany, New York 12206-2522. **T:** 1 518 465-5233
E: mail@wamc.org **W:** http://www.wamc.org
Editorial Profile: WCAN-FM is a non-commercial station owned by WAMC. The format of the station is news and talk. WCAN-FM broadcasts to the Canajoharie, NY area at 93.3 FM.

WCAO-AM
Owner: Clear Channel Media and Entertainment
Editorial: 711 W 40th St Ste 350, Baltimore, Maryland 21211-2190. **T:** 1 410 366-7600
W: http://www.heaven600.com
Editorial Profile: WCAO-AM is a commercial station owned by Clear Channel Media and Entertainment. The format of the station is gospel music. WCAO-FM broadcasts to the Baltimore area at 600 AM.

WCAP-AM
Owner: Merrimack Valley Radio LLC
Editorial: 243 Central St, Lowell, Massachusetts 1852. **T:** 1 978 454-0404
W: http://www.980wcap.com
Editorial Profile: WCAP-AM is a commercial station owned by Merrimack Valley Radio LLC. The format of the station is news, talk, and sports. WCAP-AM broadcasts to Lowell, MA, and its surrounding areas at 980 AM.

WCAR-AM
Owner: Birach Broadcasting Corp.
Editorial: 32500 Parklane St, Garden City, Michigan 48135-1527. **T:** 1 734 525-1111
Editorial Profile: WCAR-AM is a commercial station owned by Birach Broadcasting Corp. The format of the station is sports talk. WCAR-AM is the Yahoo! Sports Radio affiliate for the Greater Detroit area. The station broadcasts locally at 1090 AM.

WCAT-AM
Owner: Radio Broadcasting Services, Inc.
Editorial: 372 Dorset St, South Burlington, Vermont 5403. **T:** 1 802 863-1010
W: http://www.cruisin937.com
Editorial Profile: WCAT-AM is a commercial station owned by Radio Broadcasting Services, Inc. The format of the station is oldies music. WCAT-AM broadcasts to the South Burlington, VT area at 1390 AM.

WCAT-FM
Owner: Radio Carlisle
Editorial: 515 S 32Nd St, Camp Hill, Pennsylvania 17011-5106. **T:** 1 717 635-7000
W: http://www.red1023.com
Editorial Profile: WCAT-FM is a commercial station owned by Radio Carlisle. The format of the station is contemporary country music. WCAT-FM broadcasts to the Camp Hill, PA area at 102.3 FM.

WCAZ-AM
Owner: Ralla Broadcasting Inc.
Editorial: 86 S Madison St, Carthage, Illinois 62321. **T:** 1 217 357-3128
E: wcaz@wcazam990.com
W: http://www.wcazam990.com
Editorial Profile: WCAZ-AM is a commercial station owned by Ralla Broadcasting Inc. The format of the station is news and talk programming. WCAZ-AM broadcasts to the Quincy, IL area at 990 AM.

WCBA-AM
Owner: Great Radio, LLC
Editorial: 33 E Market St, Corning, New York 14830-2614. **T:** 1 607 962-4646
Editorial Profile: WCBA-AM is a commercial station owned by Great Radio, LLC. The format of the station is sports talk. WCBA-AM broadcasts to the Corning, NY area at 1350 AM.

WCBC-AM
Owner: Cumberland Broadcasting Co.
Editorial: 35 Baltimore St, Cumberland, Maryland 21502-3024. **T:** 1 301 724-5000
E: newsroom@wcbcradio.com
W: http://www.wcbcradio.com
Editorial Profile: WCBC-AM is a commercial station owned by Cumberland Broadcasting Co. The format of the station is news and talk. WCBC-AM broadcasts in the Cumberland, MD, area at 1270 AM.

WCBC-FM
Owner: Cumberland Broadcasting Co.
Editorial: 35 Baltimore St, Cumberland, Maryland 21502-3024. **T:** 1 301 724-5000
E: newsroom@wcbcradio.com
W: http://www.wcbcradio.com
Editorial Profile: WCBC-FM is a commercial station owned by Cumberland Broadcasting Co. The format of the station is oldies. WCBC-FM broadcasts to the Cumberland, MD area at 107.1 FM.

WCBE-FM
Owner: Columbus Public Schools
Editorial: 540 Jack Gibbs Blvd, Columbus, Ohio 43215. **T:** 1 614 365-5555
E: wcbe-news@wcbe.org
W: http://www.wcbe.org
Editorial Profile: WCBE-FM is a non-commercial station owned by Columbus Public Schools. The format of the station is news and adult album alternative music. WCBE-FM broadcasts to the Columbus, OH area at 90.5 FM.

WCBG-AM
Owner: VerStandig Broadcasting
Editorial: 10960 John Wayne Dr, Greencastle, Pennsylvania 17225-9584. **T:** 1 717 597-9200
E: info@wayz.com
Editorial Profile: WCBG-AM is a commercial station owned by VerStandig Broadcasting. The format of the station is sports. WCBG-AM broadcasts to the Greencastle, PA area at 1360 AM.

WCBH-FM
Owner: Cromwell Group Inc.(The)
Editorial: 209 Lakeland Blvd, Mattoon, Illinois 61938-3904. **T:** 1 217 235-5624
W: http://www.radiomattoon.com
Editorial Profile: WCBH-FM is a commercial station owned by The Cromwell Group Inc. The format of the station is Top 40/CHR. WCBH-FM broadcasts to the Mattoon, IL area at 104.3 FM.

WCBJ-FM
Owner: Morgan County Industries Inc.
Editorial: 129 College St, West Liberty, Kentucky 41472-1156. **T:** 1 606 668-9225
E: radio41472@yahoo.com
Editorial Profile: WCBJ-FM is a commercial station owned by Morgan County Industries Inc. The format of the station is adult contemporary WCBJ-FM broadcasts to the West Liberty, KY area at 103.7 FM.

WCBK-FM
Owner: Mid-America Radio Group
Editorial: 1639 Burton Ln, Martinsville, Indiana 46151-3004. **T:** 1 765 342-3394
E: wcbk@wcbk.com **W:** http://www.wcbk.com
Editorial Profile: WCBK-FM is a commercial station owned by Mid-America Radio Group. The format of the station is contemporary country music. WCBK-FM broadcasts to the Martinsville, IN area at 102.3 FM.

WCBL-AM
Owner: Freeland Broadcasting
Editorial: 1039 Egner's Ferry Road, Benton, Kentucky 42025. **T:** 1 270 527-3102
E: wcbl@bellsouth.net
W: http://www.wcblradio.com

WCBL-FM
Owner: Freeland Broadcasting
Editorial: 1039 Egner's Ferry Road, Benton, Kentucky 42025. **T:** 1 270 527-3102
E: wcbl@bellsouth.net
W: http://www.wcblradio.com

WCBM-AM
Owner: M-10 Broadcasting Inc.
Editorial: 1726 Reisterstown Rd, Ste 117, Pikesville, Maryland 21208. **T:** 1 410 580-6800
E: am680@wcbm.com
W: http://www.wcbm.com
Editorial Profile: WCBM-AM is a commercial station owned by M-10 Broadcasting Inc. The format of the station is news and talk. WCBM-AM broadcasts in the greater Baltimore area at 680 AM.

WCBN-FM
Owner: University of Michigan
Editorial: 530 Student Activ Bldg U of MI, Ann Arbor, Michigan 48109-1316.
T: 1 734 647-4122 **E:** mclancy@umich.edu
W: http://www.wcbn.org
Editorial Profile: WCBN-FM is a non-commercial station owned by the University of Michigan. The format of the station is news, music and talk. WCBN-FM broadcasts to the student, faculty and surrounding community of University of Michigan at 88.3 FM.

WCBQ-AM
Owner: Paradise Network
Editorial: 601 Henderson St, Oxford, North Carolina 27565. **T:** 1 919 693-3540
E: alvin@dralvin.com
Editorial Profile: WCBQ-AM is a commercial station owned by Paradise Network. The format of the station is R&B, gospel, and oldies music. WCBQ-AM broadcasts to the Oxford, NC area at 1340 AM.

WCBR-AM
Owner: WCBR Inc.
Editorial: 509 Leighway Dr, Richmond, Kentucky 40475. **T:** 1 859 623-1235
E: wcbrradio@bellsouth.net
W: http://www.wcbr1110.com
Editorial Profile: WCBR-AM is a commercial station owned by WCBR Inc. The format of the station is religious talk and gospel music. WCBR-AM broadcasts to the Richmond, KY area at 1110 AM.

WCBS-AM
Owner: CBS Radio
Editorial: 524 W 57th St, New York, New York 10019-2930. **T:** 1 212 975-2127
E: desk@wcbs880.com
W: http://newyork.cbslocal.com/station/wcbs-880
Editorial Profile: WCBS-AM is a commercial station owned by CBS Radio. The format of the station is news programming. WCBS-AM broadcasts to the New York area at 880 AM.

WCBS-FM
Owner: CBS Radio
Editorial: 345 Hudson St, New York, New York 10014-4502. **T:** 1 212 314-9200
E: webmaster@wcbsfm.com
W: http://wcbsfm.radio.com
Editorial Profile: WCBS-FM is a commercial station owned by CBS Radio. The format of the station is classic hits. WCBS-FM broadcasts throughout the New York area at 101.1 FM.

WCBT-AM
Owner: Johnson Broadcast Ventures
Editorial: 1406 Saint Andrew St, Tarboro, North Carolina 27886-2532.
T: 1 252 824-7878
Editorial Profile: WCBT-AM is a commercial station owned by Johnson Broadcast Ventures, Ltd. The format of the station is urban inspirational. WCBT-AM broadcasts to the Roanoke Rapids, NC area at 1230 AM.

WCBU-FM
Owner: Bradley University
Editorial: 1501 W Bradley Ave, Peoria, Illinois 61625. **T:** 1 309 677-3690
E: wcbu@bradley.edu
W: http://www.wcbufm.org
Editorial Profile: WCBU-FM is a non-commercial station owned by Bradley University. The format of the station is news. WCBU-FM broadcasts to the Peoria, IL area at 89.9 FM.

WCBX-AM
Owner: Positive Radio Group
Editorial: 1675 Grandview Rd, Martinsville, Virginia 24112-2319. **T:** 1 276 638-5235
E: office@joyfm.org **W:** http://www.joyfm.org
Editorial Profile: WCBX-AM is a commercial station owned by Positive Radio Group. The format of the station is Southern Gospel. WCBX-AM broadcasts to the Martinsville, VA area at 900 AM.

WCBY-AM
Owner: Northern Star Broadcasting LLC
Editorial: 1356 Mackinaw Ave, Cheboygan, Michigan 49721. **T:** 1 231 627-2341
Editorial Profile: WCBY-AM is a commercial station owned by Northern Star Broadcasting LLC. The format of the station is classic country. WCBY-AM broadcasts to the Cheboygan, MI area at 1240 AM.

WCCC-AM
Owner: Marlin Broadcasting

Editorial: 1039 Asylum Ave, Hartford, Connecticut 06105-2400. **T:** 1 860 525-1069
E: request@beethoven.com
W: http://www.beethoven.com
Editorial Profile: WCCC-AM is a commercial station owned by Marlin Broadcasting. The format of the station is classical. WCCC-AM broadcasts in the Hartford, CT area at 1290 AM.

WCCC-FM
Owner: Marlin Broadcasting
Editorial: 1039 Asylum Ave, Hartford, Connecticut 06105-2400. **T:** 1 860 525-1069
W: http://www.wccc.com
Editorial Profile: WCCC-FM is a commercial station owned by Marlin Broadcasting. The format of the station is classic rock music. WCCC-FM broadcasts to the Hartford-New Haven, CT area at 106.9 FM.

WCCD-AM
Owner: New Spirit Revival Center Ministries Inc.
Editorial: 3130 Mayfield Rd, Cleveland Heights, Ohio 44118-1768. **T:** 1 216 320-0000
W: http://www.radio1000.org
Editorial Profile: WCCD-AM is a commercial station owned by New Spirit Revival Center Ministries Inc. The format of the station is religion. WCCD-AM's broadcasts the Cleveland, OH area at 1000 AM.

WCCE-FM
Owner: Radio Training Network, Inc.
Editorial: 7610 Falls Of Neuse Rd, Ste 155, Raleigh, North Carolina 27615.
T: 1 919 256-9787
E: management@hisradiowrtp.com
W: http://www.hisradiowrtp.com
Editorial Profile: WCCE-FM is a non-commercial station owned by Radio Training Network, Inc. The format is contemporary Christian. WCCE-FM broadcasts to the Raleigh, NC area at 90.1 FM.

WCCF-AM
Owner: Clear Channel Media and Entertainment
Editorial: 24100 Tiseo Blvd, Unit 10, Port Charlotte, Florida 33980. **T:** 1 941 206-1188
W: http://www.wccfam.com
Editorial Profile: WCCF-AM is a commerical station owned by Clear Channel Media and Entertainment. The format of the station is news and talk programming. WCCF-AM broadcasts to the Port Charlotte, FL area at 1580 AM.

WCCG-FM
Owner: Carson Communications
Editorial: 115 Gillespie St, Fayetteville, North Carolina 28301-5643. **T:** 1 910 484-4932
W: http://www.wccg1045fm.com
Editorial Profile: WCCG-FM is a commercial station owned by Carson Communications. The format of the station is urban contemporary. WCCG-FM broadcasts to the Fayetteville, NC area at 104.5 FM.

WCCH-FM
Owner: Holyoke Community College
Editorial: 303 Homestead Ave, Holyoke, Massachusetts 01040-1091.
T: 1 413 552-2488
Editorial Profile: WCCH-FM is a college station owned by Holyoke Community College. The format for the station is variety. WCCH-FM broadcasts to the Holyoke, MA area at 103.5 FM.

WCCI-FM
Owner: Carroll County Communications
Editorial: 316 Main St, Savanna, Illinois 61074-1630. **T:** 1 815 273-7757
E: newssports@wcciradio.com
W: http://www.wcciradio.com
Editorial Profile: WCCI-FM is a commercial station owned by Carroll County Communications. The format of the station is country. WCCI-FM broadcasts to the Savanna, IL area on 100.3 FM.

WCCK-FM
Owner: Freeland Broadcasting
Editorial: 7 Aspen St, Calvert City, Kentucky 42029. **T:** 1 270 395-5133
E: wcck@freelandbroadcasting.com

WCCL-FM
Owner: Forever Broadcasting
Editorial: 970 Tripoli St, Johnstown, Pennsylvania 15902-1119. **T:** 1 814 534-8975
W: http://www.cool101online.com
Editorial Profile: WCCL-FM is a commercial station owned by Forever Broadcasting. The format of the station is oldies music. WCCL-

FM broadcasts to the Johnstown, PA area at 101.7 FM.

WCCM-AM
Owner: Costa Eagle Radio Ventures
Editorial: 462 Merrimack St, Methuen, Massachusetts 01844-5804.
T: 1 978 683-7171 **E:** info@1110wccmam.com
W: http://www.1110wccmam.com
Editorial Profile: WCCM-AM is a commercial station owned by Costa Eagle Radio Ventures. The format of the station is news/talk. WCCM-AM broadcasts to the Methuen, MA area at 1110 AM.

WCCN-AM
Owner: Central Wisconsin Broadcasting
Editorial: 1201 E Division St, Neillsville, Wisconsin 54456. **T:** 1 715 743-3333
E: 1075therock@tds.net
W: http://www.cwbradio.com
Editorial Profile: WCCN-AM is a commercial station owned by Central Wisconsin Broadcasting. The format of the station is adult standards. WCCN-AM broadcasts to the Clark County, WI area at a frequency of 1370 AM.

WCCN-FM
Owner: Central Wisconsin Broadcasting
Editorial: 1201 E Division St, Neillsville, Wisconsin 54456. **T:** 1 715 743-3333
E: 1075therock@tds.net
W: http://www.cwbradio.com
Editorial Profile: WCCN-FM is a commercial station owned by Central Wisconsin Broadcasting. The format of the station is classic rock. WCCN-FM broadcasts to the Neillsville, WI area at 107.5 FM.

WCCO-AM
Owner: CBS Radio
Editorial: 625 2Nd Ave S Ste 200, Minneapolis, Minnesota 55402-1908.
T: 1 612 370-0698
E: newstips@wccoradio.com
W: http://minnesota.cbslocal.com
Editorial Profile: WCCO-AM is a commercial station owned by CBS Radio. The format of the station is news, talk and sports. WCCO-AM broadcasts to the Minneapolis area at 830 AM.

WCCP-FM
Owner: Golden Corners Broadcasting
Editorial: 202 Lawrence Rd, Clemson, South Carolina 29631. **T:** 1 864 654-4004
W: http://www.wccpfm.com
Editorial Profile: WCCP-FM is a commercial station owned by Golden Corners Broadcasting and under LMA with Byrne Acquisition Group. The format of the station is sports. WCCP-FM broadcasts to the Clemson, SC area at 104.9 FM.

WCCQ-FM
Owner: Digity LLC
Editorial: 2410 Caton Farm Rd Unit B, Crest Hill, Illinois 60403-1374. **T:** 1 815 556-0100
W: http://www.wccq.com
Editorial Profile: WCCQ-FM is a commercial station owned by Digity LLC. The format of the station is contemporary country. WCCQ-FM broadcasts to the Crest Hill, IL area at 98.3 FM.

WCCR-FM
Owner: Clarion County Broadcasting Corp.
Editorial: 1168 Greenville Pike, Clarion, Pennsylvania 16214-6146. **T:** 1 814 226-4500
E: clarionradio@comcast.net
W: http://clarioncountydailynews.com
Editorial Profile: WCCR-FM is a commercial station owned by Clarion County Broadcasting Corp. The format of the station is adult contemporary. WCCR-FM broadcasts to the Clarion, PA area at 92.7 FM.

WCCS-AM
Owner: Renda Broadcasting
Editorial: 840 Philadelphia St Ste 100, Indiana, Pennsylvania 15701-3922.
T: 1 724 465-4700
W: http://www.1160wccs.com
Editorial Profile: WCCS-AM is a commercial station owned by Renda Broadcasting. The format of the station is sports. WCCS-AM broadcasts in the Indiana, PA area at 1160 AM.

WCCV-FM
Owner: Immanuel Broadcasting Network
Editorial: 779 S Erwin St, Cartersville, Georgia 30120. **T:** 1 770 387-0917 **E:** onair@ibn.org
W: http://www.ibn.org
Editorial Profile: WCCV-FM is a non-commercial station owned by Immanuel

Broadcasting Network. The format of the station is religious. WCCV-FM broadcasts to the Cartersville, GA area at 91.7 FM.

WCCW-AM
Owner: Midwestern Broadcasting Co.
Editorial: 300 E Front St Ste 450, Traverse City, Michigan 49684-5720. **T:** 1 231 946-6211
Editorial Profile: WCCW-AM is a commercial station owned by Midwestern Broadcasting Co. The format of the station is sports. WCCW-AM broadcasts to the Traverse City, MI area at 1310 AM. To contact the station or send press materials e-mail Brian Hale at brianh@wccw.fm.

WCCW-FM
Owner: Midwestern Broadcasting Co.
Editorial: 300 E Front St, Ste 450, Traverse City, Michigan 49684. **T:** 1 231 946-6211
E: prod@wccw.fm **W:** http://www.wccwi.com
Editorial Profile: WCCW-FM is a commerical station owned by Midwestern Broadcasting Co. The format of the station is oldies. The station airs in the Traverse City, MI area at 107.5 FM. Contact the station at the main e-mail address or contact Dave Gauthier at davegauthier@wccw.fm.

WCCX-FM
Owner: Carroll University
Editorial: 100 N East Ave, Waukesha, Wisconsin 53186-3103. **T:** 1 262 524-7355
E: wccx@carrollu.edu
W: http://wccx.carroll.edu
Editorial Profile: WCCX-FM is a non-commercial station owned by Carroll University. The format of the station is variety. WCCX-FM broadcasts to the Waukesha, WI area at 104.5 FM.

WCCY-AM
Owner: Houghton Community Broadcasting Corporation
Editorial: 313 E Montezuma Ave, Houghton, Michigan 49931-2112. **T:** 1 906 482-7700
E: houghtonradio@up.net
W: http://www.wccy.com
Editorial Profile: WCCY-AM is a commercial station owned by Houghton Community Broadcasting Corporation. The format for the station is adult standards and sports. WCCY-AM broadcasts to the Marquette, MI area at 1400 AM.

WCDA-FM
Owner: L.M. Communications Inc.
Editorial: 401 W Main St, Lexington, Kentucky 40507-1640. **T:** 1 859 233-1515
W: http://www.cd1063.com
Editorial Profile: WCDA-FM is a commercial station owned by L.M. Communications Inc. The format of the station is hot adult contemporary. WCDA-FM broadcasts to the Lexington, KY area at 106.3 FM.

WCDB-FM
Owner: State University of New York
Editorial: 1400 Washington Ave Campus Ctr, Campus Center #316, Albany, New York 12222-0001. **T:** 1 518 442-5234
E: news@wcdbfm.com
W: http://www.wcdbfm.com
Editorial Profile: WCDB-FM is a non-commercial station owned by State University of New York. The format of the station is college variety. WCDB-FM broadcasts to the Albany, NY area at 90.9 FM.

WCDD-FM
Owner: Prairie Communications LLP
Editorial: 1000 E Linn St, Canton, Illinois 61520. **T:** 1 309 647-1560
E: wbysnews@yahoo.com
W: http://www.cd1079.net
Editorial Profile: WCDD-FM is a commercial station owned by Prairie Communications LLP. The format of the station is country. WCDD-FM broadcasts to the Peoria, IL area at a frequency of 107.9 FM.

WCDE-FM
Owner: Davis and Elkins College
Editorial: 100 Campus Dr, Elkins, West Virginia 26241-3971. **T:** 1 304 637-1352
Editorial Profile: WCDE-FM is a non-commercial station owned by Davis and Elkins College. The format of the station is Contemporary Christian music. WCDE-FM broadcasts to the Elkins, WV area at 90.3 FM.

WCDK-FM
Owner: Priority Communications
Editorial: 2307 Pennsylvania Ave, Weirton, West Virginia 26062. **T:** 1 304 723-1444
W: http://www.1063theriver.com

Editorial Profile: WCDK-FM is a commercial station owned by Priority Communications. The format of the station is classic hits. WCDK-FM broadcasts to the Wheeling, WV, Steubenville, WV, area at 106.3 FM.

WCDL-AM
Owner: Bold Gold Media Group
Editorial: 1049 N Sekol Ave, Scranton, Pennsylvania 18504-1040. **T:** 1 570 344-1221
E: foxsportsnepa@gmail.com
W: http://boldgoldradionepa.com
Editorial Profile: WCDL-AM is a commercial station owned by Bold Gold Media Group. The format of the station is sports. WCDL-AM broadcasts to the Carbondale, PA area at 1440 AM.

WCDO-AM
Owner: CDO Broadcasting, Inc.
Editorial: 75 Main St, Sidney, New York 13838. **T:** 1 607 563-3588
E: wcdo@wcdofm.com
W: http://www.wcdoradio.com
Editorial Profile: WCDO-AM is a commercial station owned by CDO Broadcasting, Inc. The format of the station is adult contemporary. WCDO-AM broadcasts to the Sidney, NY area at 1490 AM.

WCDO-FM
Owner: CDO Broadcasting, Inc.
Editorial: 75 Main St, Sidney, New York 13838. **T:** 1 607 563-3588
E: wcdo@wcdofm.com
W: http://www.wcdoradio.com
Editorial Profile: WCDO-FM is a commercial station owned by CDO Broadcasting, Inc. The format of the station is adult contemporary music. WCDO-FM broadcasts to the Binghamton, NY area at 100.9 FM. The station simulcasts at WCDO-AM.

WCDQ-FM
Owner: Forcht Broadcasting
Editorial: 1757 N 175 W, Crawfordsville, Indiana 47933-6107. **T:** 1 765 362-8200
W: http://wcdqfm.com
Editorial Profile: WCDQ-FM is a commercial station owned by Forcht Broadcasting. The format of the station is a mix of classic and contemporary country music. WCDQ-FM broadcasts to the Crawfordsville, IN area at 106.3 FM.

WCDS-AM
Owner: Commonwealth Broadcasting Corp.
Editorial: 113 W Public Sq, Ste 400, Glasgow, Kentucky 42141. **T:** 1 270 651-6050
W: http://www.espn1450.net
Editorial Profile: WCDS-AM is a commercial station owned by Commonwealth Broadcasting Corp. The format of the station is sports. WCDS-AM broadcasts to the Glasgow, KY area at 1230 AM.

WCDT-AM
Owner: Yarbrough(Tommy)
Editorial: 1201 S College St, Winchester, Tennessee 37398. **T:** 1 931 967-2201
E: wcdtfeedback@bellsouth.net
W: http://www.wcdt1340.com
Editorial Profile: WCDT-AM is a commercial station owned by Tommy Yarbrough. The format of the station is country music. WCDT-AM broadcasts in the Winchester, TN area at 1340 AM.

WCDX-FM
Owner: Radio One Inc.
Editorial: 2809 Emerywood Pkwy, Ste 300, Richmond, Virginia 23294. **T:** 1 804 672-9299
W: http://www.ipowerrichmond.com
Editorial Profile: WCDX-FM is a commercial station owned by Radio One Inc. The format of the station is urban contemporary. WCDX-FM broadcasts to the Richmond, VA area at 92.1 FM.

WCDY-FM
Owner: Up North Radio, LLC
Editorial: 9052 E 13th St Unit E, Cadillac, Michigan 49601-8258. **T:** 1 231 876-1079
E: 1079cdy@gmail.com
W: http://www.1079cdy.com
Editorial Profile: WCDY-FM is a commercial station owned by Up North Radio, LLC. The format of the station is Hot AC. WCDY-FM broadcasts to the Cadillac, MI area at a frequency of 107.9 FM.

WCDZ-FM
Owner: Thunderbolt Broadcasting Co.
Editorial: 1410 N Lindell St, Martin, Tennessee 38237-5819. **T:** 1 731 364-9595
E: newsroom@wcmt.com
W: http://www.wcmt.com

Editorial Profile: WCDZ-FM is a commercial station owned by Thunderbolt Broadcasting Co. The format of the station is oldies. WCDZ-FM broadcasts to the Martin, TN area at 95.1 FM.

WCEC-AM
Owner: Costa Eagle Radio Ventures
Editorial: 462 Merrimack St, Methuen, Massachusetts 1844. **T:** 1 978 686-9966
W: http://www.1490wcecam.com
Editorial Profile: WCEC-AM is a commercial station owned by Costa Eagle Radio Ventures. The format of the station is sports talk. WCEC-AM broadcasts to the Methuen, MA area at 1490 AM. They do not have any local news content and will not accept pitches. The station does accept PSAs.

WCED-AM
Owner: Priority Communications
Editorial: 12 W Long Ave, Du Bois, Pennsylvania 15801-2100. **T:** 1 814 375-5260
E: news@sunny106.fm
W: http://www.1420wced.com
Editorial Profile: WCED-AM is a commercial station owned by Priority Communications. The format of the station is sports and talk. WCED-AM broadcasts to the Du Bois, PA area at 1420 AM.

WCEF-FM
Owner: Big River Radio Inc.
Editorial: 98 Cedar Lakes Road, Ripley, West Virginia 25271. **T:** 1 304 372-9800
W: http://www.c98.com
Editorial Profile: WCEF-FM is a commercial station owned by Big River Radio Inc. The format of the station is comtemporary country music. WCEF-FM broadcasts to the Ripley, WV area at 98.3 FM.

WCEH-AM
Owner: Georgia Eagle Broadcasting Inc.
Editorial: 218 Eastman Hwy, Hawkinsville, Georgia 31036-5936. **T:** 1 478 892-9061
E: georgiaeagleproduction@gmail.com
Editorial Profile: WCEH-AM is a commercial station owned by Georgia Eagle Broadcasting Inc. The format of the station is Classic Country. WCEH-AM broadcasts to the Hawkinsville, GA area at 610 AM.

WCEI-FM
Owner: First Media Radio LLC
Editorial: 306 Port St, Easton, Maryland 21601-4101. **T:** 1 410 822-3301
E: studio@wceiradio.com
W: http://www.wceiradio.com
Editorial Profile: WCEI-FM is a commercial station owned by First Media Radio LLC. The format of the station is adult contemporary. WCEI-FM broadcasts to Easton, MD at 96.7 FM.

WCEL-FM
Owner: WAMC
Editorial: 318 Central Ave, Albany, New York 12206. **T:** 1 518 465-5233 **E:** mail@wamc.org
W: http://www.wamc.org
Editorial Profile: WCEL-FM is a non-commercial station owned by WAMC. The format of the station is news and talk. WCEL-FM broadcasts to the Albany, NY area at 91.9 FM.

WCEM-AM
Owner: MTS Broadcasting LLC
Editorial: 2 Bay St, Cambridge, Maryland 21613-1257. **T:** 1 410 228-4800
W: http://www.mtslive.com
Editorial Profile: WCEM-AM is a commercial station owned by MTS Broadcasting LLC. The format of the station is adult standards. WCEM-AM broadcasts to the Cambridge, MD area at 1240 AM.

WCEM-FM
Owner: MTS Broadcasting LLC
Editorial: 2 Bay St, Cambridge, Maryland 21613-1257. **T:** 1 410 228-4800
E: theheat@mtslive.com
W: http://www.mtslive.com
Editorial Profile: WCEM-FM is a commercial station owned by MTS Broadcasting LLC. The format of the station is hot adult contemporary music. WCEM-FM broadcasts to Cambridge, MD at 106.3 FM.

WCEN-FM
Owner: Digity LLC
Editorial: 1795 Tittabawassee Rd, Saginaw, Michigan 48604-9431. **T:** 1 989 752-3456
E: themoose@945themoose.com
W: http://www.945themoose.com
Editorial Profile: WCEN-FM is a commercial station owned by Digity LLC. The format for

---

the station is country. WCEN-FM broadcasts to the Flint, MI area at 94.5 FM.

WCEO-AM
Owner: Norsan Group
Editorial: 108 Columbia Northeast Dr, Ste F, Columbia, South Carolina 29223. **T:** 1 803 223-9265
W: http://larazalaraza.com/columbia
Editorial Profile: WCEO-AM is a commercial station owned by Norsan Group. The format of the station is regional Mexican. WCEO-AM broadcasts to the Columbia, SC area on 840 AM.

WCEV-AM
Owner: Migala Communications Corp.
Editorial: 5356 W Belmont Ave, Chicago, Illinois 60641. **T:** 1 773 282-6700
E: wcev@wcev1450.com
W: http://www.wcev1450.com
Editorial Profile: WCEV-AM is a commercial station owned by Migala Communications Corp. The format of the station is ethnic music and programming. WCEV-AM broadcasts to the Chicago area at 1450 AM.

WCEZ-FM
Owner: Withers Broadcasting Co.
Editorial: 108 Washington St, Keokuk, Iowa 52632. **T:** 1 319 524-5410
W: http://keokukradio.com
Editorial Profile: WCEZ-FM is a commercial station owned by Withers Broadcasting Co. The format of the station is adult contemporary. WCEZ-FM broadcasts to the Carthage, IL area at a frequency of 93.9 FM.

WCFB-FM
Owner: Cox Media Group, Inc.
Editorial: 4192 N John Young Pkwy, Orlando, Florida 32804-2620. **T:** 1 321 281-2000
W: http://www.star945.com
Editorial Profile: WCFB-FM is a commercial station owned by Cox Media Group, Inc. The format of the station is urban adult contemporary. WCFB-FM broadcasts to the Orlando, FL area at 94.5 FM.

WCFF-FM
Owner: Saga Communications
Editorial: 2603 W Bradley Ave, Champaign, Illinois 61821-1823. **T:** 1 217 352-4141
E: request@925thechief.com
W: http://www.925thechief.com
Editorial Profile: WCFF-FM is a commercial station owned by Saga Communications. The format of the station is adult hits. WCFF-FM broadcasts to the Champaign, IL area at 92.5 FM.

WCFJ-AM
Owner: Newsweb Corp.
Editorial: 5625 N Milwaukee Ave, Chicago, Illinois 60646-6221. **T:** 1 773 792-1121
W: http://www.accessradiochicago.com
Editorial Profile: WCFJ-AM is a commercial station owned by Newsweb Corp. The format of the station is variety. WCFJ-AM broadcasts to the Chicago area at 1470 AM. The station is a brokered station.

WCFL-FM
Owner: Illinois Bible Institute
Editorial: 4101 Fieldstone Rd, Champaign, Illinois 61822-8800. **T:** 1 217 359-8232
E: wbgl@wbgl.org **W:** http://www.wbgl.org
Editorial Profile: WCFL-FM is a non-commercial station owned by the Illinois Bible Institute. The format of the station is contemporary Christian. WCFL-FM broadcasts to the Chicago area at 104.7 FM.

WCFO-AM
Owner: JW Broadcasting
Editorial: 1100 Spring St NW, Atlanta, Georgia 30309-2846. **T:** 1 404 681-9307
W: http://www.newstalk1160.com
Editorial Profile: WCFO-AM is a commercial station owned by JW Broadcasting. The format of the station is talk. WCFO-AM broadcasts to the Atlanta area at 1160 AM.

WCFR-AM
Owner: Koor Communications
Editorial: 18 Park St, Springfield, Vermont 05156-3023. **T:** 1 802 885-1480
W: http://www.wcfram.com
Editorial Profile: WCFR-AM is a commercial station owned by Koor Communications. The format of the station is adult contemporary. WCFR-AM broadcasts to the Springfield, VT area at 1480 AM.

WCFS-FM
Owner: CBS Radio

Editorial: 2 Prudential Plaza, Ste 1059, Chicago, Illinois 60601. **T:** 1 312 649-0099
W: http://chicago.cbslocal.com
Editorial Profile: WCFS-FM is a commercial station owned by CBS Radio. The format of the station is news talk. WCFS-FM broadcasts to the Chicago area at 105.9 FM. The station airs WBBM-AM's programming.

WCFW-FM
Owner: Bushland Radio Specialties
Editorial: 318 Well St, Chippewa Falls, Wisconsin 54729-1563. **T:** 1 715 723-2257
E: wcfwradio@clearwire.net
W: http://www.chippewavalleyradio.com
Editorial Profile: WCFW-FM is a commercial station owned by Bushland Radio Specialties. The format of the station is adult contemporary. WCFW-FM broadcasts to the Chippewa Falls, WI area at 105.7 FM.

WCFX-FM
Owner: Grenax Broadcasting
Editorial: 5847 Venture Way, Mount Pleasant, Michigan 48858. **T:** 1 989 772-4173
E: hits@wcfx.com **W:** http://www.wcfx.com
Editorial Profile: WCFX-FM is a commercial station owned by Grenax Broadcasting. The format of the station is Hot AC. WCFX-FM broadcasts in the Mt. Pleasant, WI area at 95.3 FM.

WCFY-FM
Owner: Christian Fellowship Church Inc
Editorial: 4100 Millersburg Rd, Evansville, Indiana 47725-7361. **T:** 1 812 867-6464
W: http://www.99thebridge.org
Editorial Profile: WCFY-FM is a low-power commercial station owned by Christian Fellowship Church Inc. The format of the station is Christian music and programming. The station airs in the Evansville, IN area on 99.1 FM.

WCGC-AM
Owner: GHB Broadcasting
Editorial: 6021 W Wilkinson Blvd, Belmont, North Carolina 28012. **T:** 1 704 825-2812
Editorial Profile: WCGC-AM is a commercial station owned by GHB Broadcasting. The format of the station is religious and Christian programming. WCGC-AM broadcasts to the Belmont, NC area at 1270 AM.

WCGL-AM
Owner: JBD Communications
Editorial: 3890 Dunn Ave, Ste 804, Jacksonville, Florida 32218-6429.
T: 1 904 766-9955 **E:** wcgl@aol.com
W: http://www.wcgl1360.com
Editorial Profile: WCGL-AM is a commercial station owned by JBD Communications. The format of the station is religious and gospel music. WCGL-AM broadcasts to the Jacksonville, FL area at 1360 AM.

WCGO-AM
Owner: Kovas Communications
Editorial: 2100 Lee St, Evanston, Illinois 60202. **T:** 1 847 475-1590
W: http://www.1590wcgo.com
Editorial Profile: WCGO-AM is a commercial station owned by Kovas Communications. The format of the station is variety programming. WCGO-AM broadcasts to the Chicago area at 1590 AM.

WCGQ-FM
Owner: PMB Broadcasting, LLC
Editorial: 1820 Wynnton Rd, Columbus, Georgia 31906-2930. **T:** 1 706 327-1217
W: http://www.q1073.com
Editorial Profile: WCGQ-FM is a commercial station owned by PMB Broadcasting, LLC. The format of the station is Top 40/CHR music. WCGQ-FM broadcasts in the Columbus, GA area at 107.3 FM.

WCGR-AM
Owner: The Radio Group
Editorial: 3568 Lenox Rd, Geneva, New York 14456. **T:** 1 315 781-7000
W: http://www.cuchicago.edu/experience/organizations/student-activity-1111111
Editorial Profile: WCGR-AM is a commercial station owned by The Radio Group. The format of the station is Country. WCGR-AM broadcasts to the Geneva, NY area at 1550 AM.

WCGW-AM
Owner: Christian Broadcasting System
Editorial: 501 Darby Creek Rd, Ste 62, Lexington, Kentucky 40509.
T: 1 859 264-9700 **E:** 770am@ckcradio.com
W: http://www.wcgwam.com
Editorial Profile: WCGW-AM is a commercial station owned by Christian Broadcasting System. The format of the station is Southern gospel. WCGW-AM broadcasts to the Lexington, KY area at 770 AM.

WCGX-FM
Owner: Clear Channel Media and Entertainment
Editorial: 2323 W 5th Ave Ste 200, Columbus, Ohio 43204-4988. **T:** 1 614 486-6101
W: http://www.genxcolumbus.com
Editorial Profile: WCGX-FM a commercial station owned by Clear Channel Media and Entertainment. The format of the station is modern adult contemporary with a mix of alternative rock and pop. WCGX-FM broadcasts to the Dublin, OH area at 106.7 FM.

WCHA-AM
Owner: Main Line Broadcasting
Editorial: 25 Penncraft Ave Fl 4, Chambersburg, Pennsylvania 17201-5600.
T: 1 717 263-0813
W: http://www.thenewfm963.com
Editorial Profile: WCHA-AM is a commercial station owned by Main Line Broadcasting. The format of the station is oldies. WCHA-AM broadcasts to the Chambersburg, PA area at 800 AM.

WCHB-AM
Owner: Radio One Inc.
Editorial: 3250 Franklin St, Detroit, Michigan 48207-4219. **T:** 1 313 259-2000
W: http://wchbnewsdetroit.com
Editorial Profile: WCHB-AM is a commercial station owned by Radio One Inc. The format of the station is talk and gospel. WCHB-AM broadcasts to the Detroit area at 1200 AM.

WCHC-FM
Owner: College of the Holy Cross
Editorial: 1 College St, Box G, Worcester, Massachusetts 1610. **T:** 1 508 793-2475
E: wchc@g.holycross.edu
W: http://college.holycross.edu/wchc/
Editorial Profile: WCHC-FM is a non-commercial college station owned by the College of the Holy Cross. The format of the station is variety. WCHC-FM broadcasts to the Worcester, MA area at 88.1 FM.

WCHD-FM
Owner: Clear Channel Media and Entertainment
Editorial: 101 Pine St, Dayton, Ohio 45402-2948. **T:** 1 937 224-1137
W: http://www.channeldayton.com
Editorial Profile: WCHDF-FM is a commercial station owned by Clear Channel Media and Entertainment. The format of the station is Top 40/CHR. WCHD-FM broadcasts to the Dayton, OH area at 99.9 FM.

WCHE-AM
Owner: Chester County Radio Inc.
Editorial: 105 W Gay St, West Chester, Pennsylvania 19380-2923. **T:** 1 610 692-3131
W: http://www.wche1520.com
Editorial Profile: WCHE-AM is a commercial station owned by Chester County Radio Inc. The format of the station is rock music and talk. WCHE-AM broadcasts to the West Chester, PA area on 1520 AM.

WCHG-FM
Owner: Pocahontas Communications Cooperative Corp.
Editorial: 171 Charger Ln, Hot Springs, Virginia 24445-2809. **T:** 1 540 839-5400
E: wchg@tds.net
W: http://www.alleghenymountainradio.org
Editorial Profile: WCHG-FM is a non-commercial community station owned by Pocahontas Communications Cooperative Corp. The format of the station is variety. WCHG-FM broadcasts to the Hot Springs, VA area at a frequency of 107.1 FM.

WCHI-AM
Owner: Clear Channel Media and Entertainment
Editorial: 45 W Main St, Chillicothe, Ohio 45601-3104. **T:** 1 740 773-3000
Editorial Profile: WCHI-AM is a commercial station owned by Clear Channel Media and Entertainment. The format of the station is soft AC. WCHI-AM broadcasts to the Chillicothe, OH area at 1350 AM.

WCHJ-AM
Owner: Tillman Broadcasting Network Inc.
Editorial: 983 Sawmill Ln NE, Brookhaven, Mississippi 39601. **T:** 1 601 823-9006
E: victory1470wchj@birch.net
W: http://victory1470wchj.com
Editorial Profile: WCHJ-AM is a commercial station owned by Tillman Broadcasting Network Inc. The format of the station is gospel. WCHJ-AM broadcasts to the Brookhaven, MS area at 1470 AM.

WCHL-AM
Owner: Vilcom Communications
Editorial: 88 Vilcom Center Dr Ste 130, Chapel Hill, North Carolina 27514-1660.
T: 1 919 933-4165 **E:** info@chapelboro.com
W: http://www.chapelboro.com
Editorial Profile: WCHL-AM is a commercial station owned by Vilcom Communications. The format of the station is news, talk and sports. WCHL-AM broadcasts to the Chapel Hill, NC area at 1360 AM.

WCHM-AM
Owner: Jeffrey T. Batten's WCHM Radio, LLC
Editorial: 583 Grant St Ste J9, Clarkesville, Georgia 30523-5440. **T:** 1 706 839-1490
W: http://www.wchmradio.com
Editorial Profile: WCHM-AM is a commercial station owned by Jeffrey T. Batten's WCHM Radio, LLC. The format of the station is news and talk. WCHM-AM broadcasts to the Atlanta area at 1490 AM.

WCHN-AM
Owner: Townsquare Media, LLC
Editorial: 34 Chestnut St, Oneonta, New York 13820-2466. **T:** 1 607 432-1030
W: http://cnynews.com
Editorial Profile: WCHN-AM is a commercial station owned by Townsquare Media, LLC. The format of the station is news, sports and talk. WCHN-AM broadcasts to the Oneonta, NY area at 970 AM.

WCHO-AM
Owner: Clear Channel Media and Entertainment
Editorial: 1535 N North St, Washington Court House, Ohio 43160-1111. **T:** 1 740 335-0941
E: news@buckeyecountry105.com
W: http://www.wchoam.com
Editorial Profile: WCHO-AM is a commercial station owned by Clear Channel Media and Entertainment. The format of the station is classic hits. WCHO-AM broadcasts to the Washington Court House, OH area at 1250 AM.

WCHO-FM
Owner: Clear Channel Media and Entertainment
Editorial: 1535 N North St, Washington Court House, Ohio 43160. **T:** 1 740 335-0941
E: news@buckeyecountry105.com
W: http://www.buckeyecountry105.com
Editorial Profile: WCHO-FM is a commercial station owned by Clear Channel Media and Entertainment. The format of the station is contemporary country music. WCHO-FM broadcasts to the Washington Courthouse, OH area at 105.5 FM.

WCHP-AM
Owner: Champlain Radio Inc.
Editorial: 137 Rapids Rd, Champlain, New York 12919. **T:** 1 518 298-2800
E: wchp@primelink1.net
W: http://www.wchp.com
Editorial Profile: WCHP-AM is a commercial station owned by Champlain Radio Inc. The format of the station is Christian and religious programming. WCHP-AM broadcasts to the Champlain, NY area at 760 AM.

WCHR-AM
Owner: NB Broadcasting, LLC
Editorial: 619 Alexander Rd Fl 3, Princeton, New Jersey 08540-6000. **T:** 1 609 924-1515
W: http://www.wchram.net
Editorial Profile: WCHR-AM is a commercial station owned by Connoisseur Media. The format of the station is Christian programming. WCHR-AM broadcasts to the Flemington, NJ area at 1040 AM.

WCHR-FM
Owner: Townsquare Media, LLC
Editorial: 8 Robbins St, Toms River, New Jersey 08753-7668. **T:** 1 848 221-8000
W: http://www.1057thehawk.com
Editorial Profile: WCHR-FM is a commercial station owned by Townsquare Media, LLC. The format of the station is classic rock. WCHR-FM broadcasts to the Ocean, NJ area at 105.7 FM.

WCHS-AM
Owner: West Virginia Radio Corp.
Editorial: 1111 Virginia St E, Charleston, West Virginia 25301-2406. **T:** 1 304 342-8131
W: http://www.58wchs.com
Editorial Profile: WCHS-AM is a commercial station owned by West Virginia Radio Corp. The format of the station is news, talk and sports. WCHS-AM broadcasts to the Charleston, WV area at 580 AM.

WCHT-AM
Owner: Radio Results Network
Editorial: 524 Ludington St, Ste 300, Escanaba, Michigan 49829. **T:** 1 906 789-0600
E: rrnnews@radioresultsnetwork.com
W: http://www.wchtradio.com
Editorial Profile: WCHT-AM is a commercial station owned by Radio Results Network. The format of the station is news, sports and talk. WCHT-AM braodcasts to the Escanaba, MI area at 600 AM.

WCHV-AM
Owner: Monticello Media LLC
Editorial: 1150 Pepsi Pl, Ste 300, Charlottesville, Virginia 22901.
T: 1 434 978-4408 **W:** http://www.wchv.com
Editorial Profile: WCHV-AM is a commercial station owned by Monticello Media LLC. The format of the station is news and talk. WCHV-AM broadcasts in the Charlottesville, VA area at 1200 AM.

WCHX-FM
Owner: Mifflin County Communications
Editorial: 114 N Logan Blvd, Burnham, Pennsylvania 17009. **T:** 1 717 242-1055
E: wchx@chx105.com
W: http://www.chx105.com
Editorial Profile: WCHX-FM is a commercial station owned by Mifflin County Communications. The format of the station is classic rock. WCHX-FM broadcasts to the Burnham, PA area at 105.5 FM.

WCHY-FM
Owner: Northern Star Broadcasting LLC
Editorial: 1356 Mackinaw Ave, Cheboygan, Michigan 49721-1003. **T:** 1 231 922-4981
W: http://www.classicrockthebear.com
Editorial Profile: WCHY-FM is a commercial station owned by Northern Star Broadcasting LLC. The format of the station is active rock, a mix of classic and album oriented. WCHY-FM broadcasts to Traverse, MI area at 97.7 FM.

WCHZ-AM
Owner: Beasley Broadcast Group
Editorial: 4051 Jimmie Dyess Pkwy, Augusta, Georgia 30909. **T:** 1 706 396-7000
W: http://95rock.com
Editorial Profile: WCHZ-AM is a commercial station owned by Beasley Broadcast Group. The format of the station is active rock. WCHZ-AM broadcasts to the Augusta, GA areat at 1480 AM.

WCHZ-FM
Owner: Beasley Broadcast Group
Editorial: 4051 Jimmie Dyess Pkwy, Augusta, Georgia 30909. **T:** 1 706 396-7000
W: http://www.95rock.com
Editorial Profile: WCHZ-FM is a commercial station owned by Beasley Broadcast Group. The format of the station is rock. WCHZ-FM broadcasts to the Augusta, GA area at 93.1 FM.

WCIB-FM
Owner: Clear Channel Media and Entertainment
Editorial: 154 Barnstable Rd, Hyannis, Massachusetts 02601-2930.
T: 1 508 778-2888 **E:** news@95wxtk.com
W: http://www.cool102.com
Editorial Profile: WCIB-FM is a commercial station owned by Clear Channel Media and Entertainment. The format of the station is classic hits. WCIB-FM broadcasts to the Hyannis, MA area at 101.9 FM.

WCIC-FM
Owner: Illinois Bible Institute
Editorial: 3902 Barring Trce, Peoria, Illinois 61615-2500. **T:** 1 309 692-9242
E: wcic@wcicfm.org **W:** http://www.wcicfm.org
Editorial Profile: WCIC-FM is a non-commercial station owned by the Illinois Bible Institute. The format of the station is contemporary Christian music and talk. WCIC-FM broadcasts in the Peoria, IL area at 91.5 FM.

WCID-FM
Owner: Family Life Ministries Inc.
Editorial: 7634 County Route 14, Bath, New York 14810-7612. **T:** 1 607 776-4151
E: mail@fln.org **W:** http://www.fln.org
Editorial Profile: WCID-FM is a non-commercial station owned by Family Life

Ministries Inc. The format of the station is contemporary Christian. WCID-FM broadcasts to the Bath, NY area at 89.1 FM.

WCIE-FM
Owner: Radio Training Network, Inc.
Editorial: 6214 Springer Dr, Port Richey, Florida 34668-5339. **T:** 1 727 848-9150
E: thejoyfm@thejoyfm.com
W: http://florida.thejoyfm.com
Editorial Profile: WCIE-FM is a non-commercial station owned by Radio Training Network, Inc. The format of the station is contemporary Christian. WCIE-FM broadcasts to the Port Richey, FL area at 91.5 FM.

WCIF-FM
Owner: First Baptist Church-Melbourne
Editorial: 3301 Dairy Rd, Melbourne, Florida 32904. **T:** 1 321 725-9243 **E:** info@wcif.com
W: http://www.wcif.com
Editorial Profile: WCIF-FM is a commercial station owned by First Baptist Church-Melbourne. The format of the station is religious. WCIF-FM broadcasts to the Melbourne, FL area at 106.3 FM.

WCIG-FM
Owner: Family Life Ministries Inc.
Editorial: 7634 County Route 14, Bath, New York 14810-7612. **T:** 1 607 776-4151
W: http://www.fln.org
Editorial Profile: WCIG-FM is a non-commercial station owned by Family Life Ministries Inc. The format for the station is contemporary Christian. WCIG-FM broadcasts to the Tunkhannock, PA area at 107.7 FM.

WCIH-FM
Owner: Family Life Ministries Inc.
Editorial: 7634 Campbell Road, Bath, New York 14810. **T:** 1 607 776-4151
E: news@fln.org **W:** http://www.fln.org
Editorial Profile: WCIH-FM is a non-commercial station owned by Family Life Ministries Inc. The format of the station is contemporary Christian. WCIH-FM broadcasts to the Bath, NY area at 90.3 FM.

WCII-FM
Owner: Family Life Ministries Inc.
Editorial: 7634 Campbell Road, Bath, New York 14810. **T:** 1 607 776-4151
E: news@fln.org **W:** http://www.fln.org
Editorial Profile: WCII-FM is a non-commercial station owned by Family Life Ministries Inc. The format of the station is contemporary Christian. WCII-FM broadcasts to the Bath, NY area at 88.5 FM.

WCIJ-FM
Owner: Family Life Ministries Inc.
Editorial: 7634 Campbell Road, Bath, New York 14810. **T:** 1 607 776-4151
E: news@fln.org **W:** http://www.fln.org
Editorial Profile: WCIJ-FM is a non-commercial station owned by Family Life Ministries Inc. The format of the station is contemporary Christian. WCIJ-FM broadcasts to the Bath, NY area at 88.9 FM.

WCIK-FM
Owner: Family Life Ministries Inc.
Editorial: 7634 Campbell Creek Rd, Bath, New York 14810-7612. **T:** 1 607 776-4151
E: news@fln.org **W:** http://www.fln.org
Editorial Profile: WCIK-FM is a non-commercial station owned by Family Life Ministries Inc. The format of the station is contemporary Christian. WCIK-FM broadcasts to the Bath, NY area at 103.1 FM.

WCIL-AM
Owner: Max Media
Editorial: 1431 Country Aire Dr, Carterville, Illinois 62918. **T:** 1 618 985-4843
W: http://www.wjpf.com
Editorial Profile: WCIL-AM is a commercial station owned by Max Media. The format of the station is news and talk. WCIL-AM broadcasts to the Harrisburg, IL area at 1020 AM.

WCIL-FM
Owner: Max Media
Editorial: 1431 Country Aire Dr, Carterville, Illinois 62918-5118. **T:** 1 618 985-4843
E: publicservice@riverradio.net
W: http://www.cilfm.com
Editorial Profile: WCIL-FM is a commercial station owned by Max Media. The format of the station is Top 40/CHR. WCIL-FM broadcasts to the Carterville, IL area at 101.5 FM. Send PSAs to publicservice@riverradio.net.

WCIR-FM
Owner: Southern Communications Corp.
Editorial: 306 S Kanawha St, Beckley, West Virginia 25801. **T:** 1 304 253-7000
W: http://www.103cir.com
Editorial Profile: WCIR-FM is a commercial station owned by Southern Communications Corp. The format of the station is Top 40/CHR. WCIR-FM broadcasts to the Beckley, WV area at 103.7 FM.

WCIS-AM
Owner: WFM Inc.
Editorial: 2828 Nc 126, Morganton, North Carolina 28655-8264. **T:** 1 828 584-3176
W: http://www.am760thecross.com
Editorial Profile: WCIS-AM is a commercial station owned by WFM Inc. The format of the station is gospel and religious programming. WCIS-AM broadcasts to the Morganton, NC area at 760 AM.

WCIT-AM
Owner: Childers Media Group, LLC
Editorial: 57 Town Sq, Lima, Ohio 45801-4950. **T:** 1 419 331-1600
W: http://www.940wcit.com
Editorial Profile: WCIT-AM is a commercial station owned by Childers Media Group, LLC. The format of the station is sports. WCIT-AM broadcasts to the Lima, OH area at 940 AM.

WCIT-FM
Owner: Family Life Ministries Inc.
Editorial: 7634 County Route 14, Bath, New York 14810. **T:** 1 607 776-4151
E: news@fln.org **W:** http://www.fln.org
Editorial Profile: WCIT-FM is a non-commercial station owned by Family Life Ministries Inc. The format of the station is contemporary Christian. WCIT-FM broadcasts to the Bath, NY area at 90.1 FM.

WCIY-FM
Owner: Family Life Ministries Inc.
Editorial: 7634 Campbell Creek Rd, Bath, New York 14810. **T:** 1 607 776-4151
E: news@fln.org **W:** http://www.fln.org
Editorial Profile: WCIY-FM is a non-commercial station owned by Family Life Ministries Inc. The format of the station is contemporary Christian. WCIY-FM broadcasts to the Bath, NY area at 88.9 FM.

WCIZ-FM
Owner: Stephens Media Group
Editorial: 134 Mullin St, Watertown, New York 13601. **T:** 1 315 788-0790
W: http://www.z93.fm
Editorial Profile: WCIZ-FM is a commercial station owned by Stephens Media Group. The format of the station is classic rock music. WCIZ-FM broadcasts to the Watertown, NY area at 93.3 FM.

WCJC-FM
Owner: Hoosier AM/FM LLC
Editorial: 820 S Pennsylvania St, Marion, Indiana 46953-2407. **T:** 1 765 664-6239
E: wcjc@comteck.com
W: http://www.wcjc.com
Editorial Profile: WCJC-FM is a commercial station owned by Hoosier AM/FM LLC. The format of the station is contemporary country music. WCJC-FM broadcasts to the Marion, IN area at 99.3 FM.

WCJK-FM
Owner: South Central Media
Editorial: 504 Rosedale Ave, Nashville, Tennessee 37211-2028. **T:** 1 615 259-4567
W: http://www.963jackfm.com
Editorial Profile: WCJK-FM is a commercial station owned by South Central Media. The format of the station is adult hits. WCJK-FM broadcasts to the Nashville, TN area at 96.3 FM.

WCJM-FM
Owner: Clear Channel Media and Entertainment
Editorial: 705 4th Ave, West Point, Georgia 31833-1506. **T:** 1 706 645-2991
W: http://www.wcjmthebull.com
Editorial Profile: WCJM-FM is a commercial station owned by Clear Channel Media and Entertainment. The format of the station is contemporary country music. WCJM-FM broadcasts to the West Point, GA area at 100.9 FM.

WCJO-FM
Owner: Jackson County Broadcasting Inc.
Editorial: 295 E Main St, Jackson, Ohio 45640. **T:** 1 740 286-3023
Editorial Profile: WCJO-FM is a commercial station owned by Jackson County Broadcasting Inc. The format of the station is contemporary country music. WCJO-FM broadcasts to the Jackson, OH area at 97.7 FM.

WCJU-AM
Owner: McDaniel(Thomas)
Editorial: 37 S High School Ave, Columbia, Mississippi 39429. **T:** 1 601 736-2616
E: wcju@wcjufm.com
W: http://www.wcjuam.com
Editorial Profile: WCJU-AM is a commercial station owned by Thomas McDaniel. The format of the station is news and talk. WCJU-AM broadcasts to the Columbia, MS area at 1450 AM.

WCJU-FM
Owner: McDaniel(Thomas)
Editorial: 37 S High School Ave, Columbia, Mississippi 39429. **T:** 1 601 736-8889
E: wcju@wcjufm.com
W: http://www.wcjufm.com
Editorial Profile: WCJU-FM is a commercial station owned by Thomas McDaniel. The format of the station is classic hits. WCJU-FM broadcasts to the Columbia, MS area at 104.9 FM.

WCJW-AM
Owner: Lloyd Lane Inc.
Editorial: 3258 Merchant Rd, Warsaw, New York 14569. **T:** 1 585 786-8131
E: news@wcjw.com **W:** http://www.wcjw.com
Editorial Profile: WCJW-AM is a commercial station owned by Lloyd Lane Inc. The format of the station is country. WCJW-AM broadcasts to the Warsaw, NY area at 1140 AM.

WCJX-FM
Owner: Black Crow Broadcasting Inc.
Editorial: 5348 NW US Highway 41, Lake City, Florida 32055. **T:** 1 386 755-9259
W: http://northflatoday.com
Editorial Profile: WCJX-FM is a commercial station owned by Black Crow Broadcasting Inc. The format of the station is classic hits. WCJX-FM broadcasts to the Lake City, FL area at 106.5 FM.

WCKA-AM
Owner: L.E. Gradick
Editorial: 188 Broadcast Blvd, Jacksonville, Alabama 36265-6659. **T:** 1 877 237-0810
W: http://www.ala810.com
Editorial Profile: WCKA-AM is a commercial station owned by L.E. Gradick. The format of the station is classic country. WCKA-AM broadcasts to the Jacksonville, AL area at 810 AM.

WCKB-AM
Owner: North Carolina Central Broadcasters
Editorial: 17336 US Highway 421 S, Dunn, North Carolina 28334-5580.
T: 1 910 892-3133 **E:** wckb@wckb780.com
W: http://www.wckb780.com
Editorial Profile: WCKB-AM is a commercial station owned by North Carolina Central Broadcasters. The format of the station is Southern gospel music. WCKB-AM broadcasts to the Dunn, NC-area at 780 AM.

WCKC-FM
Owner: Northern Star Broadcasting LLC
Editorial: 1356 Mackinaw Ave, Cheboygan, Michigan 49721-1003. **T:** 1 231 627-2341
E: thebear@classicrockthebear.com
W: http://www.classicrockthebear.com
Editorial Profile: WCKC-FM is a commercial station owned by Northern Star Broadcasting LLC. The format of the station is classic rock. WCKC-FM broadcasts to the Cheboygan, MI area at 107.1 FM.

WCKF-FM
Owner: L.E. Gradick
Editorial: 518 Mountain View Rd, Ashland, Alabama 36251-5060. **T:** 1 256 354-1444
E: alabama1007@aol.com
W: http://wckf100.com
Editorial Profile: WCKF-FM is a commercial station owned by L.E. Gradick. The format of the station is country. WCKF-FM broadcasts to the Anniston, AL area at 100.7 FM.

WCKG-AM
Owner: Gentile(Joseph J.)
Editorial: 5629 Saint Charles Rd Ste 208, Berkeley, Illinois 60163-1139.
T: 1 708 493-1530
W: http://www.wckgchicago.com
Editorial Profile: WCKG-AM is a commercial station owned by Joseph J. Gentile. The format of the station is talk radio. WCKG-AM broadcasts in the suburbs of Chicago at AM 760.

WCKI-AM
Owner: Mediatrix
Editorial: 2 Beeco Rd, Greer, South Carolina 29650. **T:** 1 864 877-8458
E: info@catholicradioinsc.com
W: http://www.catholicradioinsc.com
Editorial Profile: WCKI-AM is a commercial station owned by Mediatrix. The format of the station is Christian talk. WCKI-AM broadcasts to Greer, SC and its surrounding environs at 1300 AM.

WCKJ-FM
Owner: Christian Ministries Inc.
Editorial: 140 Main St, Essex Junction, Vermont 5452. **T:** 1 866 878-8885
E: mailroom@thelightradio.net
W: http://www.thelightradio.net
Editorial Profile: WCKJ-FM is a non-commercial station owned by Christian Ministries Inc. The format of the station is contemporary Christian music and religious programming. WCKJ-FM broadcasts to the Essex Junction, VT area at 90.5 FM.

WCKM-FM
Owner: Regional Radio Group
Editorial: 238 Bay Rd, Queensbury, New York 12804-2006. **T:** 1 518 761-9890
E: news@radiowins.com
W: http://www.radiowins.com/wckm
Editorial Profile: WCKM-FM is a commercial station owned by Regional Radio Group. The format of the station is classic hits. WCKM-FM broadcasts to the Glens Falls, NY area at 98.5 FM.

WCKN-FM
Owner: Apex Broadcasting Inc.
Editorial: 2294 Clements Ferry Rd, Charleston, South Carolina 29492. **T:** 1 843 972-1100
E: frontdesk@apexbroadcasting.com
W: http://www.kickin925.com
Editorial Profile: WCKN-FM is a commercial station owned by Apex Broadcasting Inc. The format of the station is country. WCKN-FM broadcasts to the Charleston, SC area at 92.5 FM.

WCKQ-FM
Owner: Commonwealth Broadcasting Corp.
Editorial: 50 Friendship Pike Rd, Campbellsville, Kentucky 42718-2537.
T: 1 270 789-2401
E: wckq@commonwealthbroadcasting.com
W: http://www.myq104.com
Editorial Profile: WCKQ-FM is a commercial station owned by Commonwealth Broadcasting Corp. The format of the station is hot adult contemporary. WCKQ-FM broadcasts to the Campbellsville, KY area at 104.1 FM.

WCKR-FM
Owner: Canisteo Valley Broadcasting
Editorial: 5942 County Route 64, Hornell, New York 14843-9730. **T:** 1 607 324-1480
E: wleawckr@infoblvd.net
W: http://www.canisteovalleynews.com
Editorial Profile: WCKR-FM is a commercial station owned by Canisteo Valley Broadcasting. The format of the station is country music. WCKR-FM broadcasts to the Hornell, NY area at 92.1 FM.

WCKS-FM
Owner: Gradick Communications LLC
Editorial: 102 Parkwood Cir, Carrollton, Georgia 30117-8353. **T:** 1 770 834-5477
W: http://www.gradickcommunications.com
Editorial Profile: WCKS-FM is a commercial station owned by Gradick Communications LLC. The format of the station is hot adult contemporary. WCKS-FM broadcasts to the Carrollton, GA area at 102.7 FM.

WCKT-FM
Owner: Clear Channel Media and Entertainment
Editorial: 13320 Metro Pkwy, Ste 1, Fort Myers, Florida 33966. **T:** 1 239 225-4300
W: http://www.catcountry1071.com
Editorial Profile: WCKT-FM is a commercial station owned by Clear Channel Media and Entertainment. The format of the station is country music. WCKT-FM broadcasts to the Ft. Myers, FL area at 107.1 FM.

WCKW-AM
Owner: Covenant Network
Editorial: 1908 Short St, Kenner, Louisiana 70062. **T:** 1 314 752-7000
W: http://covenantnet.net
Editorial Profile: WCKW-AM is a commercial station owned by Covenant Network. The

format of the station is religious talk programming. WCKW-AM broadcasts to the Garyville, LA area at 1010 AM.

WCKX-FM
Owner: Radio One Inc.
Editorial: 350 E 1st Ave, Ste 100, Columbus, Ohio 43201. **T:** 1 614 487-1444
W: http://www.mycolumbuspower.com
Editorial Profile: WCKX-FM is a commercial station owned by Radio One Inc. The format of the station is urban contemporary music. WCKX-FM broadcasts in the Columbus, OH area at 107.5 FM.

WCKY-AM
Owner: Clear Channel Media and Entertainment
Editorial: 8044 Montgomery Rd, Cincinnati, Ohio 45236-2919. **T:** 1 513 686-8300
W: http://www.espn1530.com
Editorial Profile: WCKY-AM is a commercial station owned by Clear Channel Media and Entertainment. The format of the station is sports. WCKY-AM broadcasts to the Cincinnati area at 1530 AM.

WCKY-FM
Owner: Clear Channel Media and Entertainment
Editorial: 125 S Superior St, Toledo, Ohio 43604-8747. **T:** 1 419 244-8321
W: http://www.1037wcky.com
Editorial Profile: WCKY-FM is a commercial station owned by Clear Channel Media and Entertainment. The format of the station is contemporary country music. WCKY-FM broadcasts to the Findlay, OH area at 103.7 FM.

WCKZ-FM
Owner: Star Educational Media Network
Editorial: 6000 N Clinton St, Fort Wayne, Indiana 46825-4904. **T:** 1 260 483-8236
W: http://www.star883.com
Editorial Profile: WCKZ-FM is a non-commercial station owned by Star Educational Media Network. The format of the station is Christian music. WCKZ-FM broadcasts to the Fort Wayne, IN area at 91.3 FM.

WCLA-AM
Owner: W. Danny Swain
Editorial: 316 N River St, Claxton, Georgia 30417. **T:** 1 912 739-9252
W: http://www.wclaradio.net
Editorial Profile: WCLA-AM is a commercial station owned by W. Danny Swain. The format for the station is oldies. WCLA-AM broadcasts to the Savannah, GA area at 1470 AM.

WCLB-AM
Owner: RBH Enterprises Inc.
Editorial: 254 Winnebago Dr, Fond du Lac, Wisconsin 54935-2447. **T:** 1 920 921-1071
E: info@wisconsinespn.com
W: http://www.950thegame.com
Editorial Profile: WCLB-AM is a commercial station owned by RBH Enterprises Inc. The format of the station is sports. WCLB-AM broadcasts to the Fond Du Lac, WI area at 950 AM.

WCLC-AM
Owner: Bible Believers Network
Editorial: 224 W Central Ave, Jamestown, Tennessee 38556-3405. **T:** 1 931 879-8188
E: news@newlife105.com
W: http://www.newlife105.com
Editorial Profile: WCLC-AM is a commercial station owned by the Bible Believers Network. The format of the station is southern gospel and religious programming. WCLC-AM broadcasts to the Jamestown, TN area at 1260 AM.

WCLC-FM
Owner: Bible Believers Network
Editorial: 224 W Central Ave, Jamestown, Tennessee 38556-3405. **T:** 1 931 879-8188
E: info@newlife105.com
W: http://www.newlife105.com
Editorial Profile: WCLC-FM is a commercial station owned by the Bible Believers Network. The format of the station is southern gospel and religious programming. WCLC-FM broadcasts to the Jamestown, TN area at 105.1 FM.

WCLD-AM
Owner: Radio Cleveland Inc.
Editorial: 911 S Davis Ave, Cleveland, Mississippi 38732. **T:** 1 662 843-4091
Editorial Profile: WCLD-AM is a commercial station owned by Radio Cleveland, Inc. The format of the station is gospel music. WCLD-AM broadcasts to the Cleveland, MS area at 1490 AM.

WCLD-FM
Owner: Radio Cleveland Inc.
Editorial: 911 S Davis Ave, Cleveland, Mississippi 38732-3941. **T:** 1 662 843-4091
Editorial Profile: WCLD-FM is a commercial station owned by Radio Cleveland, Inc. The format of the station is urban contemporary music. WCLD-FM broadcasts in the Cleveland, MS at 103.9 FM.

WCLE-AM
Owner: Williams Communications Inc.
Editorial: 1860 Executive Park NW, Ste E, Cleveland, Tennessee 37312.
T: 1 423 472-6700 **E:** info@mymix1041.com
W: http://www.1570wcle.com
Editorial Profile: WCLE-AM is a commercial station owned by Williams Communications Inc. The format for the station is news, sports and talk. WCLE-AM broadcasts to the Cleveland, TN area at 1570 AM.

WCLE-FM
Owner: Hartline, LLC
Editorial: 1860 Executive Park NW, Cleveland, Tennessee 37312-2752. **T:** 1 423 472-6700
E: info@mymix1041.com **W:** http://mix104.info
Editorial Profile: WCLE-FM is a commercial station owned by Hartline, LLC. The format for the station is adult contemporary. WCLE-FM broadcasts to the Cleveland, TN area at 104.1 FM.

WCLG-AM
Owner: Bowers Broadcasting
Editorial: 343 High St, Morgantown, West Virginia 26505-5515. **T:** 1 304 292-2222
E: psa@wclg.com
Editorial Profile: WCLG-AM is a commercial station owned by Bowers Broadcasting. The format of the station is oldies. WCLG-AM broadcasts to the Morgantown, WV area at 1300 AM.

WCLG-FM
Owner: Bowers Broadcasting
Editorial: 343 High St, Morgantown, West Virginia 26505-5515. **T:** 1 304 292-2222
E: psa@wclg.com **W:** http://www.wclg.com
Editorial Profile: WCLG-FM is a commercial station owned by Bowers Broadcasting. The format of the station is rock. WCLG-AM broadcasts to the Morgantown, WV area at 100.1 FM.

WCLH-FM
Owner: Wilkes University
Editorial: 84 W South St, Wilkes-Barre, Pennsylvania 18766-0998. **T:** 1 570 408-5907
E: wclhpd@gmail.com **W:** http://www.wclh.org
Editorial Profile: WCLH-FM is a non-commercial station owned by Wilkes University. The format of the station is college variety. WCLH-FM broadcasts to the Wilkes-Barre, PA area at 90.7 FM.

WCLI-FM
Owner: Main Line Broadcasting
Editorial: 717 E David Rd, Kettering, Ohio 45429-5218. **T:** 1 937 294-5858
W: http://www.click1015.com
Editorial Profile: WCLI-FM is a commercial station owned by Main Line Broadcasting. The format of the station is modern AC. WCLI-FM broadcasts to the Springfield, OH area at 101.5 FM.

WCLK-FM
Owner: Clark Atlanta University
Editorial: 111 James P Brawley Dr SW, Atlanta, Georgia 30314-4207.
T: 1 404 880-8284 **E:** wclkfm@cau.edu
W: http://www.wclk.com
Editorial Profile: WCLK-FM is a non-commercial station owned by Clark Atlanta University. The format of the station is jazz. WCLK-FM broadcasts to Atlanta area at 91.9 FM.

WCLM-AM
Owner: World Media Broadcast
Editorial: 3165 Hull St, Richmond, Virginia 23224-3576. **T:** 1 804 231-2186
W: http://www.wclmradioonline.com/
Editorial Profile: WCLM-AM is a commercial station owned by World Media Broadcast. The format of the station is R&B oldies, talk and gospel. WCLM-AM broadcasts to the Richmond, VA area at 1450 AM.

WCLN-AM
Owner: Clinton Sampson Radio Company, Inc.
Editorial: 118 E Main St, Clinton, North Carolina 28328-4029. **T:** 1 910 592-8949
W: http://www.oldies1170.com

WCLN-FM
Owner: Christian Listening Network Inc.
Editorial: 996 Helen St, Fayetteville, North Carolina 28303. **T:** 1 910 864-5028
E: comments@christian107.com
W: http://www.christian107.com
Editorial Profile: WCLN-FM is a commercial station owned by the Christian Listening Network Inc. The format of the station is religious. WCLN-FM broadcasts to the Charlotte, NC area at 107.3 FM.

WCLO-AM
Owner: Bliss Communications Inc.
Editorial: 1 S Parker Dr, Janesville, Wisconsin 53545. **T:** 1 608 752-7895 **E:** news@wclo.com
W: http://www.wclo.com
Editorial Profile: WCLO-AM is a commercial station owned by Bliss Communications Inc. The format of the station is news, sports and talk. WCLO-AM broadcasts to the Janesville, WI area at 1230 AM.

WCLQ-FM
Owner: Christian Life Communications Inc.
Editorial: 4111 Schofield Ave, Ste 10, Schofield, Wisconsin 54476.
T: 1 715 355-5151 **E:** 89q@89q.org
W: http://www.89q.org
Editorial Profile: WCLQ-FM is a non-commercial station owned by Christian Life Communications Inc. The format of the station is contemporary Christian music and talk. WCLQ-FM broadcasts in Schofield, WI area at 89.5 FM.

WCLS-FM
Owner: Mid-America Radio Group
Editorial: 5858 W State Road 46, Bloomington, Indiana 47404-9359.
T: 1 812 935-7400 **E:** wclsfm@smithville.net
W: http://www.wclsclassichits.com
Editorial Profile: WCLS-FM is a commercial station owned by Mid-America Radio Group. The format for the station is classic hits. WCLS-FM broadcasts to the Indianapolis area at 97.7 FM.

WCLT-AM
Owner: WCLT Radio Inc.
Editorial: 674 Jacksontown Rd, Heath, Ohio 43056-9376. **T:** 1 740 345-4004
E: news@wclt.com **W:** http://www.wclt.com
Editorial Profile: WCLT-AM is a commercial station owned by WCLT Radio Inc. The format of the station is sports. WCLT-AM broadcasts to the Newark, OH area at 1430 AM.

WCLT-FM
Owner: WCLT Radio Inc.
Editorial: 674 Jacksontown Rd, Heath, Ohio 43056. **T:** 1 740 345-4004 **E:** news@wclt.com
W: http://www.wclt.com
Editorial Profile: WCLT-FM is a commercial station owned by WCLT Radio Inc. The format of the station is contemporary country. WCLT-FM broadcasts to the Heath, OH area at 100.3 FM.

WCLU-AM
Owner: Royse Radio Inc.
Editorial: 229 W Main St, Glasgow, Kentucky 42141-1707. **T:** 1 270 651-9149
E: news@wcluradio.com
W: http://www.wcluradio.com
Editorial Profile: WCLU-FM is a commercial station owned by Royse Radio Inc. The format of the station is variety. WCLU-FM broadcasts to the Glasgow, KY area on 1490 AM.

WCLU-FM
Owner: Royse Radio Inc.
Editorial: 229 W Main St, Glasgow, Kentucky 42141. **T:** 1 270 651-9149
E: news@wcluradio.com
W: http://www.wcluradio.com
Editorial Profile: WCLU-FM is a commercial station owned by Royse Radio Inc. The format of the station is Lite Rock/Lite AC. WCLU-FM broadcasts to the Glasgow, KY area at 102.3 FM.

WCLV-FM
Owner: WCLV Foundation, Inc.
Editorial: Idea Center, 1375 Euclid Ave, Cleveland, Ohio 44115. **T:** 1 216 916-7140
E: wclv@ideastream.org
W: http://www.wclv.com
Editorial Profile: WCLV-FM is a non-commercial station owned by WCLV Foundation, Inc. The format of the station is classical. WCLV-FM broadcasts to the Cleveland area at 104.9 FM.

WCLW-AM
Owner: Reidsville Baptist Church
Editorial: 116 S Franklin St, Reidsville, North Carolina 27320. **T:** 1 336 634-1774
Editorial Profile: WCLW-AM is a non-commercial station owned by Reidsville Baptist Church. The format of the station is Southern gospel. WCLW-AM broadcasts to the Reidsville, NC area at 1130 AM.

WCLY-AM
Owner: Capitol Broadcasting Company
Editorial: 3100 Highwoods Blvd, Raleigh, North Carolina 27604-1033.
T: 1 919 890-6101
Editorial Profile: WCLY-AM is a commercial station owned by Capitol Broadcasting Company. The format of the station Spanish sports. WCLY-AM broadcasts to the greater Raleigh, NC area at 1550 AM.

WCLZ-FM
Owner: Saga Communications
Editorial: 420 Western Ave, South Portland, Maine 4106. **T:** 1 207 774-4561
W: http://www.989wclz.com
Editorial Profile: WCLZ-FM is a commercial station owned by Saga Communications. The format of the station is adult album alternative. WCLZ-FM broadcasts to the Portland, ME area at 98.9 FM.

WCMC-AM
Owner: Equity Communications LP
Editorial: 8025 Black Horse Pike, Pleasantville, New Jersey 08232-2900. **T:** 1 609 484-8444
W: http://www.classicoldieswmid.com
Editorial Profile: WCMC-AM is a commercial station owned by Equity Communications LP. The format of the station is adult standards. WCMC-AM broadcasts to the Wildwood, NJ area at 1230 AM.

WCMC-FM
Owner: Capitol Broadcasting Company
Editorial: 3100 Highwoods Blvd Ste 140, Raleigh, North Carolina 27604-1065.
T: 1 919 890-6299
W: http://www.espntriangle.com
Editorial Profile: WCMC-FM is a commercial station owned by Capitol Broadcasting Company. The format of the station is sports. WCMC-FM broadcasts to the Raleigh-Durham, NC, area at 99.9 FM.

WCMD-AM
Owner: West Virgina Radio Corporation of the Alleganies
Editorial: 15 Industrial Blvd E, Cumberland, Maryland 21502-4106. **T:** 1 301 759-1005
W: http://www.1230espnam.com
Editorial Profile: WCMD-AM is a commercial station owned by West Virgina Radio Corporation of the Alleganies. The format of the station is sports. WCMD-AM broadcasts to the Cumberland, MD area at 1230 AM.

WCME-AM
Owner: Bleikamp (James)
Editorial: 14 Maine St, Brunswick, Maine 04011-2049. **T:** 1 207 798-9094
W: http://www.radio9wcme.com
Editorial Profile: WCME-AM is a commercial station owned by James Bleikamp. The format of the station is local news, weather and sports. WCME-AM broadcasts to the Midcoast area of Maine at 900 AM.

WCMF-FM
Owner: Entercom Communications Corp.
Editorial: 70 Commercial St, Rochester, New York 14614-1010. **T:** 1 585 423-2900
W: http://www.wcmf.com
Editorial Profile: WCMF-FM is a commercial station owned by Entercom Communications Corp. The format of the station is classic rock. WCMF-FM broadcasts to the Rochester, NY area at 96.5 FM.

WCMG-FM
Owner: Cumulus Media Inc.
Editorial: 2014 N Irby St, Florence, South Carolina 29501-1504. **T:** 1 843 661-5000
W: http://www.magic943fm.com
Editorial Profile: WCMG-FM is a commercial station owned by Cumulus Media Inc. The format of the station is urban adult contemporary. WCMG-FM broadcasts to the Florence, SC area at 94.3 FM.

WCMI-AM
Owner: Kindred Communications
Editorial: 401 11th St, Ste 200, Huntington, West Virginia 25701. **T:** 1 304 523-8401
E: wrvc@wrvc.com **W:** http://www.wcmi.am
Editorial Profile: WCMI-AM is a commercial station owned by Kindred Communications.

The format of the station is sports. WCMI-AM broadcasts to the Huntington, WV area at 1340 AM.

WCMI-FM

Owner: Kindred Communications
Editorial: 401 11th St, Huntington, West Virginia 25701-2218. **T:** 1 304 523-8401
W: http://www.planet927.com
Editorial Profile: WCMI-FM is a commercial station owned by Kindred Communications. The format of the station is rock. WCMI-FM broadcasts to the Huntington, WV area at 92.7 FM.

WCMJ-FM

Owner: AVC Communications Inc.
Editorial: 4988 Skyline Dr, Cambridge, Ohio 43725. **T:** 1 740 432-5605
E: avcnews@yourradioplace.com
W: http://www.wcmj.com
Editorial Profile: WCMJ-FM is a commercial station owned by AVC Communications Inc. The format of the station is adult contemporary music. WCMJ-FM broadcasts in the Cambridge, OH area at 96.7 FM.

WCMM-FM

Owner: Radio Results Network
Editorial: 524 Ludington St, Ste 300, Escanaba, Michigan 49829. **T:** 1 906 789-9700
E: rrnnews@radioresultsnetwork.com
W: http://www.wcmmradio.com
Editorial Profile: WCMM-FM is a commercial station owned by Radio Results Network. The format of the station is contemporary country. WCMM-FM broadcasts to the Marquette, MI area at 102.5 FM.

WCMO-FM

Owner: Marietta College
Editorial: 215 5th St, Marietta, Ohio 45750-4033. **T:** 1 740 376-4800
W: http://www.marietta.edu/~wcmofm/index.htm
Editorial Profile: WCMO-FM is a non-commercial college station owned by Marietta College. The format of the station is variety. WCMO-FM broadcasts to the Marietta, OH area at 98.5 FM.

WCMP-AM

Owner: Red Rock Radio Corp.
Editorial: 15429 Pokegama Lake Rd, Pine City, Minnesota 55063-4592. **T:** 1 320 629-7575
E: jesselogan@redrockonair.com
W: http://www.radiowcmp.com
Editorial Profile: WCMP-AM is a commercial station owned by Red Rock Radio Corp. The format of the station is adult standards music. WCMP-AM broadcasts to the Minneapolis area at 1350 AM.

WCMP-FM

Owner: Red Rock Radio Corp.
Editorial: 15429 Pokegama Lake Rd, Pine City, Minnesota 55063-4592. **T:** 1 320 629-7575
E: pinemill@ecenet.com
W: http://redrockonair.com
Editorial Profile: WCMP-FM is a commercial station owned by Red Rock Radio Corp. The format of the station is contemporary country music. WCMP-FM broadcasts to the Pine City, MN area at 100.9 FM.

WCMQ-FM

Owner: Spanish Broadcasting System
Editorial: 7007 Nw 77Th Ave, Miami, Florida 33166-2836. **T:** 1 305 447-9595
W: http://www.clasica92fm.com
Editorial Profile: WCMQ-FM is a commercial radio station owned by Spanish Broadcasting System. The format of the station is Spanish salsa music. WCMQ-FM broadcasts to Coral Gables, FL at 92.3 FM.

WCMR-AM

Owner: Progressive Broadcasting
Editorial: 25802 County Road 26, Elkhart, Indiana 46517-9132. **T:** 1 574 875-5166
W: http://solidgospel1270.com
Editorial Profile: WCMR-AM is a commercial station owned by Progressive Broadcasting. The format for the station is gospel and religious teaching. WCMR-AM broadcasts to the South Bend, IN area at 1270 AM.

WCMS-FM

Owner: Max Radio of the Carolinas
Editorial: 103 W Wood Hill Dr Ste D-E, Nags Head, North Carolina 27959-9395.
T: 1 252 480-4655 **W:** http://www.wcms.com
Editorial Profile: WCMS-FM is a commercial station owned by Max Radio of the Carolinas. The format of the station is contemporary country. WCMS-FM broadcasts to the Nags Head, NC area at 94.5 FM.

WCMT-AM

Owner: Thunderbolt Broadcasting Co.
Editorial: 1410 N Lindell St, Martin, Tennessee 38237-5819. **T:** 1 731 587-9526
E: newsroom@wcmt.com
W: http://www.wcmt.com
Editorial Profile: WCMT-AM is a commercial station owned by the Thunderbolt Broadcasting Co. The format of the station is oldies, news and talk. WCMT-AM broadcasts to the Paducah, KY; Cape Girardeau, MO; Harrisburg, IL areas at 1410 AM.

WCMT-FM

Owner: Thunderbolt Broadcasting Co.
Editorial: 1410 N Lindell St, Martin, Tennessee 38237-5819. **T:** 1 731 587-9526
E: newsroom@wcmt.com
W: http://www.wcmt.com
Editorial Profile: WCMT-FM is a commercial station owned by Thunderbolt Broadcasting Co. The format of the station is adult contemporary. WCMT-FM broadcasts to the Martin, TN area at 101.3 FM.

WCMU-FM

Owner: Central Michigan University
Editorial: 1999 E Campus Dr, Mount Pleasant, Michigan 48859-0001. **T:** 1 989 774-3105
W: http://www.wcmu.org
Editorial Profile: WCMU-FM is a non-commercial station owned by Central Michigan University. The format for the station is news and classical music. WCMU-FM broadcasts to the Flint, MI area at 89.5 FM.

WCMX-AM

Owner: Twin City Baptist Temple
Editorial: 194 Electric Ave, Lunenburg, Massachusetts 1462. **T:** 1 978 582-4901
W: http://www.hope1000.com
Editorial Profile: WCMX-AM is a non-commercial station owned by Twin City Baptist Temple. The format of the station is religious programming and contemporary Christian. WCMX-AM broadcasts to the Lunenburg, MA area at 1000 AM.

WCMY-AM

Owner: NRG Media LLC
Editorial: 216 W Lafayette St, Ottawa, Illinois 61350. **T:** 1 815 434-6050
E: info@ottawaradio.net
W: http://www.ottawaradio.net
Editorial Profile: WCMY-AM is commercial station owned by NRG Media LLC. The format of the station is news and talk. WCMY-AM broadcasts to the Chicago area at 1430 AM.

WCNA-FM

Owner: Air South Radio Inc.
Editorial: 1241 Cliff Gookin Blvd, Tupelo, Mississippi 38801-6749. **T:** 1 662 842-1019
Editorial Profile: WCNA-FM is a commercial station owned by Air South Radio Inc. and operated by SnyderMedia. The format of the station is Smooth AC. WCNA-FM broadcasts to the Tupelo, MS area at a frequency of 95.9 FM.

WCNC-AM

Owner: East Carolina Radio Group
Editorial: 911 Parsonage St, Elizabeth City, North Carolina 27909. **T:** 1 252 335-4379
E: psa@ecri.net
Editorial Profile: WCNC-AM is a commercial station owned by East Carolina Radio Group. The format of the station is Hispanic. WCNC-AM broadcasts to Elizabeth City, NC at 1240 AM.

WCNG-FM

Owner: Cherokee Broadcasting Co.
Editorial: 195 Hampton Church Rd, Murphy, North Carolina 28906. **T:** 1 828 837-9264
E: murphyradio@mail.com
Editorial Profile: WCNG-FM is a commercial station owned by Cherokee Broadcasting Co. The format of the station is Lite Rock/Lite AC music. WCNG-FM broadcasts to the Chattanooga, TN area at 102.7 FM.

WCNI-FM

Owner: Connecticut College Community Radio, Inc.
Editorial: Connecticut College, 270 Mohegan Ave., New London, Connecticut 6320.
T: 1 860 439-2853 **E:** wcni@conncoll.edu
W: http://www.wcniradio.org
Editorial Profile: WCNI-FM is a non-commercial station owned by Connecticut College Community Radio, Inc. The format of the station is college variety. WCNI-FM broadcasts to the New London, CT area at 90.9 FM.

WCNK-FM

Owner: Gamma Broadcasting LLC
Editorial: 30336 Overseas Hwy, Big Pine Key, Florida 33043-3352. **T:** 1 305 872-9100
W: http://www.conchcountry.com
Editorial Profile: WCNK-FM is a commercial station owned by Gamma Broadcasting LLC. The format of the station is country music. WCNK-FM broadcasts to the Big Pine Key, FL, area at 98.7 FM.

WCNL-AM

Owner: Koor Communications
Editorial: 11 Main St, Newport, New Hampshire 3773. **T:** 1 603 448-0500
E: studio@wntk.com
W: http://www.country1010.com
Editorial Profile: WCNL-AM is a commercial station owned by Koor Communications. The format of the station is country. WCNL-AM broadcasts to the Newport, NH, area at 1010 AM.

WCNN-AM

Owner: Dickey Broadcasting
Editorial: 780 Johnson Ferry Rd NE Ste 500, Atlanta, Georgia 30342-1436.
T: 1 404 688-0068
W: http://www.680thefan.com
Editorial Profile: WCNN-AM is a commercial station owned by Dickey Broadcasting. The format of the station is sports. WCNN-AM broadcasts to the Atlanta area at 680 AM.

WCNO-FM

Owner: National Christian Network
Editorial: 2960 SW Mapp Rd, Palm City, Florida 34990-2737. **T:** 1 772 221-1100
E: wcno@wcno.com **W:** http://www.wcno.com
Editorial Profile: WCNO-FM is a non-commercial station owned by the National Christian Network. The format of the station is contemporary Christian music and religious programming. WCNO-FM broadcasts to the Palm City, FL area at 89.9 FM.

WCNR-FM

Owner: Saga Communications
Editorial: 1140 Rose Hill Dr, Charlottesville, Virginia 22903-5128. **T:** 1 434 220-2300
W: http://www.1061thecorner.com
Editorial Profile: WCNR-FM is a commercial station owned by Saga Communications. The format of the station is adult album alternative music. WCNR-FM broadcasts to the Harrisonburg, VA area at 106.1 FM.

WCNS-AM

Owner: Longo Media Group
Editorial: 400 Unity St, Latrobe, Pennsylvania 15650-1341. **T:** 1 724 537-3338
E: mailbox@wcnsradio.com
W: http://www.1480wcns.com
Editorial Profile: WCNS-AM is a commercial station owned by Longo Media Group. The format of the station is adult standards. WCNS-AM broadcasts to the Latrobe, PA area at 1480 AM.

WCNV-FM

Owner: Commonwealth Public Broadcasting
Editorial: 4016 Dodlyt Rd, Heathsville, Virginia 22473. **T:** 1 804 320-1301
E: webmaster@ideastations.org
W: http://www.ideastations.org/radio
Editorial Profile: WCNV-FM is a non-commercial station owned by Commonwealth Public Broadcasting. The format of the station is classical, jazz music and news. WCNV-FM broadcasts to the Richmond, VA area at 89.1 FM. This station does not accept PSAs.

WCNW-AM

Owner: Vernon R. Baldwin Inc.
Editorial: 8686 Michael Ln, Fairfield, Ohio 45014. **T:** 1 513 829-7700
Editorial Profile: WCNW-AM is a commercial station owned by Vernon R. Baldwin Inc. The format of the station is religious and gospel music. WCNW-AM broadcasts to the Fairfield, OH area at 1560 AM.

WCNY-FM

Owner: Public Broadcasting Council of Central New York
Editorial: 506 Old Liverpool Rd, Liverpool, New York 13088-6223. **T:** 1 315 453-2424
E: wcny-fm@wcny.org
W: http://www.wcny.org
Editorial Profile: WCNY-FM is a non-commercial station owned by the Public Broadcasting Council of Central New York. The format of the station is classical and jazz. WCNY-FM broadcasts to the Syracuse, NY area at 91.3 FM.

WCNZ-AM

Owner: J & B, LLC
Editorial: 5043 Tamiami Trl E, Naples, Florida 34113-4127. **T:** 1 239 732-9369
W: http://twangme.net
Editorial Profile: WCNZ-AM is a commercial station owned by J & B, LLC. The format of the station is classic country music. WCNZ-AM broadcasts to the Marco Island, FL area at 1660 AM.

WCOA-AM

Owner: Cumulus Media Inc.
Editorial: 6565 N W St Ste 270, Pensacola, Florida 32505-1797. **T:** 1 850 478-6011
E: wcoa@cumulus.com
W: http://www.wcoapensacola.com
Editorial Profile: WCOA-AM is a commercial station owned by Cumulus Media Inc. The format of the station is news and talk. WCOA-AM broadcasts to the Pensacola, FL area at 1370 AM.

WCOD-FM

Owner: Clear Channel Media and Entertainment
Editorial: 154 Barnstable Rd, Hyannis, Massachusetts 02601-2930.
T: 1 508 778-2888 **E:** studio@106wcod.com
W: http://www.106wcod.com
Editorial Profile: WCOD-FM is a commercial station owned by Clear Channel Media and Entertainment. The format of the station is hot adult contemporary. WCOD-FM broadcasts to the Hyannis, MA area at 106.1 FM.

WCOE-FM

Owner: La Porte County Broadcasting Co. Inc.
Editorial: 1700 Lincolnway Pl, Ste 8, La Porte, Indiana 46350. **T:** 1 219 362-5290
W: http://wcoefm.com
Editorial Profile: WCOE-FM is a commercial station owned by La Porte County Broadcasting Co. Inc. The format for the station is country. WCOE-FM broadcasts to the La Porte, IN area at 96.7 FM.

WCOG-AM

Owner: Radio Disney Group
Editorial: 875 W 5Th St, Winston Salem, North Carolina 27101-2505.
T: 1 336 885-2191
W: http://www.triadsports.com
Editorial Profile: WCOG-AM is a commercial station owned by Radio Disney Group. The format of the station is sports. WCOG-AM broadcasts to the Winston Salem, NC area at 1320 AM.

WCOG-FM

Owner: Family Life Ministries Inc.
Editorial: 7634 Campbell Creek Rd, Bath, New York 14810. **T:** 1 607 776-4151
E: mail@fln.org **W:** http://www.fln.org
Editorial Profile: WCOG-FM is a non-commercial station owned by Family Life Ministries Inc. The format of the station is contemporary Christian. WCOG-FM broadcasts to the Bath, NY area at 100.7 FM.

WCOH-AM

Owner: Clear Channel Media and Entertainment
Editorial: 154 Boone Dr, Newnan, Georgia 30263. **T:** 1 770 683-7234
W: http://www.wcoh.com
Editorial Profile: WCOH-AM is a commercial station owned by Clear Channel Media and Entertainment. The format of the station is sports. WCOH-AM broadcasts to the Atlanta area at 1400 AM.

WCOH-FM

Owner: Family Life Ministries Inc.
Editorial: 7634 Campbell Creek Rd, Bath, New York 14810-7612. **T:** 1 607 776-4151
E: news@fln.org **W:** http://www.fln.org
Editorial Profile: WCOH-FM is a non-commercial station owned by Family Life Ministries Inc. The format of the station is contemporary Christian. WCOH-FM broadcasts to the Du Bois, PA area on 107.3 FM.

WCOJ-AM

Owner: Holy Spirit Radio Foundation, Inc.
Editorial: 40 Rickert Rd, Doylestown, Pennsylvania 18901-2326. **T:** 1 215 345-1570
E: 1570am@HOLYSPIRITRADIO.org
W: http://www.holyspiritradio.org
Editorial Profile: WCOJ-AM is a commercial station owned by Holy Spirit Radio Foundation, Inc. The format of the station is Catholic programming. WCOJ-AM broadcasts to the West Chester, PA area at 1420 AM.

WCOL-FM
Owner: Clear Channel Media and Entertainment
Editorial: 2323 W 5th Ave, Columbus, Ohio 43204-4899. **T:** 1 614 486-6101
W: http://www.wcol.com
Editorial Profile: WCOL-FM is a commercial station owned by Clear Channel Media and Entertainment. The format of the station is contemporary country music. WCOL-FM broadcasts to the Columbus, OH area at 92.3 FM.

WCOM-FM
Owner: Public Gallery of Carrboro, Inc.
Editorial: 208 E Main St, Carrboro, North Carolina 27510-2310. **T:** 1 919 929-9601
W: http://www.wcomfm.org
Editorial Profile: WCOM-FM is a non-commercial station owned by Public Gallery of Carrboro, Inc. The format of the station is eclectic talk and news. WCOM-FM broadcasts to the Carrboro, NC area at 103.5 FM.

WCON-AM
Owner: Habersham Broadcasting Co.
Editorial: 540 N Main St, Cornelia, Georgia 30531-2322. **T:** 1 706 778-2241
E: wcon@windstream.net
W: http://www.wconfm.com
Editorial Profile: WCON-AM is a commercial station owned by the Habersham Broadcasting Co. The format of the station is adult standard and gospel music. WCON-AM broadcasts to the Atlanta area at 1450 AM.

WCON-FM
Owner: Habersham Broadcasting Co.
Editorial: 540 Main St N, Cornelia, Georgia 30531. **T:** 1 706 778-2241
E: wcon@windstream.net
W: http://www.wconfm.com
Editorial Profile: WCON-FM is a commercial station owned by Habersham Broadcasting Co. The format of the station is country music. WCON-FM broadcasts to the Atlanta area at 99.3 FM.

WCOO-FM
Owner: L.M. Communications Inc.
Editorial: 59 Windermere Blvd, Charleston, South Carolina 29407-7411.
T: 1 843 769-4799
W: http://www.1055thebridge.com
Editorial Profile: WCOO-FM is a commercial station owned by L.M. Communications. The format of the station is AAA-adult album alternative. WCOO-FM broadcasts to the Charleston, SC area at 105.5 FM.

WCOR-AM
Owner: Bay-Pointe Broadcasting Inc.
Editorial: 510 Trousdale Ferry Pike, Lebanon, Tennessee 37087. **T:** 1 615 449-3699
E: info@wantfm.com
W: http://www.wantfm.com
Editorial Profile: WCOR-AM is a commercial station owned by Bay-Pointe Broadcasting Inc. The format of the station is a mix of contemporary and classic country music. WCOR-AM broadcasts to the Nashville, TN area at 1490 AM.

WCOS-AM
Owner: Clear Channel Media and Entertainment
Editorial: 316 Greystone Blvd, Columbia, South Carolina 29210. **T:** 1 803 343-1100
W: http://www.hallelujah1400.com
Editorial Profile: WCOS-AM is a commercial station owned by Clear Channel Media and Entertainment. The format of the station is gospel. WCOS-AM broadcasts to the Columbia, SC area at 1400 AM.

WCOS-FM
Owner: Clear Channel Media and Entertainment
Editorial: 316 Greystone Blvd, Columbia, South Carolina 29210. **T:** 1 803 343-1100
W: http://www.975wcos.com
Editorial Profile: WCOS-FM is a commercial station owned by Clear Channel Media and Entertainment. The format of the station is contemporary country. WCOS-FM broadcasts to the Columbia, SC area at 97.5 FM.

WCOT-FM
Owner: Family Life Ministries Inc.
Editorial: 7634 Campbell Creek Rd, Bath, New York 14810. **T:** 1 607 776-4151
E: mail@fln.org **W:** http://www.fln.org
Editorial Profile: WCOT-FM is a non-commercial station owned by Family Life Ministries Inc. The format of the station is contemporary Christian. WCOT-FM broadcasts to the Bath, NY area at 90.9 FM.

WCOU-FM
Owner: Family Life Ministries Inc.
Editorial: 7634 Campbell Creek Rd, Bath, New York 14810-7612. **T:** 1 607 776-4151
E: mail@fln.org **W:** http://www.fln.org
Editorial Profile: WCOU-FM is a non-commercial station owned by Family Life Ministries Inc. The format of the station is contemporary Christian. WCOU-FM broadcasts to the Bath, NY area at 88.3 FM.

WCOV-FM
Owner: Family Life Ministries Inc.
Editorial: 7634 Campbell Creek Rd, Bath, New York 14810. **T:** 1 607 776-4151
E: news@fln.org **W:** http://www.fln.org
Editorial Profile: WCOV-FM is a non-commercial station owned by Family Life Ministries Inc. The format of the station is contemporary Christian. WCOV-FM broadcasts to the Bath, NY area at 93.7 FM.

WCOW-FM
Owner: Sparta-Tomah Broadcasting Co.
Editorial: 113 W Oak St, Sparta, Wisconsin 54656. **T:** 1 608 269-3100
E: newsdirector@cow97.com
W: http://www.cow97.com
Editorial Profile: WCOW-FM is a commercial station owned by Sparta-Tomah Broadcasting Co. The format of the station is contemporary country. WCOW-FM broadcasts in the Sparta, WI area at 97.1 FM.

WCOY-FM
Owner: Staradio Corp.
Editorial: 329 Maine St, 1st Fl, Quincy, Illinois 62301. **T:** 1 217 224-4102
E: wcoy@staradio.com
W: http://www.wcoy.com

WCPA-AM
Owner: First Media Radio LLC
Editorial: 801 E Dubois Ave, Du Bois, Pennsylvania 15801. **T:** 1 814 371-8300
E: q102radio@comcast.net
Editorial Profile: WCPA-AM is a commercial station owned by First Media Radio LLC. The format of the station is oldies music. WCPA-AM broadcasts to the Clearfield, PA area at 900 AM.

WCPC-AM
Owner: Wilkins Communication Networks Inc.
Editorial: 1189 N Jackson St, Houston, Mississippi 38851-8273. **T:** 1 662 456-3071
E: wcpc@wilkinsradio.com
W: http://www.wilkinsradio.com
Editorial Profile: WCPC-AM is a commercial station owned by Wilkins Communication Networks Inc. and licensed to Cajun Radio Corporation. The format of the station is religious, gospel and talk. WCPC-AM broadcasts to the Houston, MS area at 940 AM.

WCPE-FM
Owner: Educational Information Corp.
Editorial: 1928 Chalk Rd, Wake Forest, North Carolina 27587-9164. **T:** 1 919 556-5178
E: wcpe@theclassicalstation.org
W: http://www.theclassicalstation.org
Editorial Profile: WCPE-FM is a non-commercial station owned by Educational Information Corp. The format of the station is classical. WCPE-FM broadcasts to the Wake Forest, NC area at 89.7 FM.

WCPH-AM
Owner: George C. Hudson, III
Editorial: 202 9th St, Etowah, Tennessee 37331-1343. **T:** 1 423 263-5555
E: wcphradio@yahoo.com
Editorial Profile: WCPH-AM is a commercial station owned by George C. Hudson, III. The format of the station is oldies. WCPH-AM broadcasts to the Chattanooga, TN area at 1220 AM.

WCPI-FM
Owner: Warren County Educational Foundation Inc.
Editorial: 110 S Court Sq, Mc Minnville, Tennessee 37110. **T:** 1 931 506-9274
E: wcpi@blomand.net
Editorial Profile: WCPI-FM is non-commercial station owned by the Warren County Educational Foundation Inc. The format of the station is variety. WCPI-FM broadcasts to the McMinnville, TN area at 91.3 FM.

WCPK-AM
Owner: Willis Broadcasting Co.
Editorial: 645 Church St Ste 400, Norfolk, Virginia 23510-1712. **T:** 1 757 622-4600
E: willisbroadcasting@yahoo.com
Editorial Profile: WCPK-FM is a commercial station owned by Willis Broadcasting Co. The format of the station is gospel and religion. WCPK-FM broadcasts to the Norfolk, VA area at 1600 AM.

WCPM-AM
Owner: Cumberland City Broadcasting, Inc.
Editorial: 101 Keller St, Cumberland, Kentucky 40823. **T:** 1 606 589-4623
W: http://www.wcpmradio.com
Editorial Profile: WCPM-AM is a commercial station owned by Cumberland City Broadcasting, Inc. The format of the station is contemporary country music. WCPM-AM broadcasts to the Cumberland, KY area at 1280 AM.

WCPN-FM
Owner: ideastream
Editorial: 1375 Euclid Ave, Cleveland, Ohio 44115-1844. **T:** 1 216 916-6100
E: comments@wcpn.org
W: http://www.wcpn.org
Editorial Profile: WCPN-FM is a non-commercial station owned by ideastream. The format of the station is news, talk and jazz music. WCPN-FM broadcasts to the Cleveland area at 90.3 FM.

WCPQ-FM
Owner: Newsweb Corp.
Editorial: 6012 S Pulaski Rd, Chicago, Illinois 60629. **T:** 1 773 767-1000
E: web@newswebradio.net
W: http://www.chicagoprogressivetalk.com
Editorial Profile: WCPQ-FM is a commercial station owned by Newsweb Corp. The format of the station is liberal talk and dance music. WCPQ-FM broadcasts to the southern section of the Chicago metro area at 99.9 FM.

WCPR-FM
Owner: L & L Radio
Editorial: 1909 E Pass Rd, Gulfport, Mississippi 39507-3779. **T:** 1 228 388-2001
W: http://www.979cprrocks.com
Editorial Profile: WCPR-FM is a commercial station owned by L & L Radio. The format of the station is rock. WCPR-FM broadcasts to the Biloxi-Gulfport, MS area at 97.9 FM.

WCPS-AM
Owner: Johnson Broadcast Ventures
Editorial: 1406 Saint Andrew St, Tarboro, North Carolina 27886. **T:** 1 252 824-7878
W: http://www.wcpsam760.com
Editorial Profile: WCPS-AM is a commercial station owned by Johnson Broadcast Ventures. The format of the station is gospel and urban oldies music. WCPS-AM broadcasts to the Rocky Mount, NC area at 760 AM.

WCPT-AM
Owner: Newsweb Corp.
Editorial: 5475 N Milwaukee Ave, Chicago, Illinois 60630-1249. **T:** 1 773 792-0400
E: web@newswebradio.net
W: http://www.chicagoprogressivetalk.com
Editorial Profile: WCPT-AM is a commercial station owned by Newsweb Corp. The format of the station is talk. WCPT-AM broadcasts during daytime hours only to Crystal Lake, IL and the northern sections of the Chicago metro area at 820 AM.

WCPT-FM
Owner: Newsweb Corp.
Editorial: 6012 S Pulaski Rd, Chicago, Illinois 60629-4538. **T:** 1 773 767-1000
E: web@newswebradio.net
W: http://www.chicagoprogressivetalk.com
Editorial Profile: WCPT-FM is a commercial station owned by Newsweb Corp. The format of the station is liberal talk and dance music. WCPT-FM broadcasts to the Chicago area at 92.5 FM.

WCPV-FM
Owner: Vox Communications
Editorial: 265 Hegeman Ave, Colchester, Vermont 5446. **T:** 1 802 655-0093
W: http://www.champrocks.com
Editorial Profile: WCPV-FM is a commercial station owned by Vox Communications. The format is classic rock. The station broadcasts to the Colchester, VT area at 101.3 FM.

WCPY-FM
Owner: Newsweb Corp.
Editorial: 5475 N Milwaukee Ave, Chicago, Illinois 60630-1249. **T:** 1 773 792-0400
W: http://www.chicagoprogressivetalk.com
Editorial Profile: WCPY-FM is a commercial station owned by Newsweb Corp. The format of the station is liberal talk and dance music. WCPY-FM broadcasts to the Arlington Heights, IL area and northwest suburbs of Chicago at 106.3 FM.

WCPZ-FM
Owner: BAS Broadcasting
Editorial: 1640 Cleveland Rd, Sandusky, Ohio 44870. **T:** 1 419 625-1010
W: http://www.wcpz.com
Editorial Profile: WCPZ-FM is a commercial station owned by BAS Broadcasting. The format of the station is hot adult contemporary music. WCPZ-FM broadcasts to the Cleveland area at 102.7 FM.

WCQL-FM
Owner: Regional Radio Group
Editorial: 238 Bay Rd, Queensbury, New York 12804-2006. **T:** 1 518 761-9890
W: http://www.radiowins.com
Editorial Profile: WCQL-FM is a commercial station owned by Regional Radio Group. The format of the station is hot adult contemporary. WCQL-FM broadcasts to the Glens Falls, NY area at 95.9 FM.

WCQM-FM
Owner: Heartland Communications Group, LLC
Editorial: 1329 4th Ave S, Park Falls, Wisconsin 54552. **T:** 1 715 762-3221
E: wcqm@pctcnet.net
W: http://www.wcqm.com
Editorial Profile: WCQM-FM is a commercial station owned by Heartland Communications Group, LLC. The format of the station is contemporary country music. WCQM-FM broadcasts in the Park Falls, WI area at 98.3 FM.

WCQR-FM
Owner: Positive Alternative Radio
Editorial: 2312 Oak St, Gray, Tennessee 37615. **T:** 1 423 477-5676 **E:** office@wcqr.org
W: http://www.wcqr.org
Editorial Profile: WCQR-FM is a non-commercial station owned by Positive Alternative Radio. The format of the station is Christian programming. WCQR-FM broadcasts to the Gray, TN area at 88.3 FM.

WCQS-FM
Owner: Western North Carolina Public Radio Inc.
Editorial: 73 Broadway St, Asheville, North Carolina 28801-2919. **T:** 1 828 210-4800
E: info@wcqs.org **W:** http://www.wcqs.org
Editorial Profile: WCQS-FM is a non-commercial station owned by Western North Carolina Public Radio Inc. The format of the station is talk and classical and jazz music. WCQS-FM broadcasts to the Asheville, NC area at 88.1 FM.

WCRA-AM
Owner: Cromwell Group Inc.(The)
Editorial: 405 S Banker St, Ste 201, Effingham, Illinois 62401. **T:** 1 217 342-4141
E: wcrc@wcrc957.com
W: http://www.wcra1090.com
Editorial Profile: WCRA-AM is a commercial station owned by The Cromwell Group Inc. The format of the station is news and talk. WCRA-AM broadcasts in the Effingham, IL area at 1090 AM.

WCRB-FM
Owner: WGBH Educational Foundation
Editorial: 1 Guest St, Boston, Massachusetts 02135-2016. **T:** 1 617 300-2000
E: wgbhradio@wgbh.org
W: http://www.wgbh.org/995/
Editorial Profile: WCRB-FM is a commercial station owned by WGBH Educational Foundation. The format of the station is classical. WCRB-FM broadcasts to the Brighton, MA area at 99.5 FM.

WCRC-FM
Owner: Cromwell Group Inc.(The)
Editorial: 405 S Banker St, Ste 201, Effingham, Illinois 62401. **T:** 1 217 342-4141
E: wcrc@wcrc957.com
W: http://www.wcrc957.com
Editorial Profile: WCRC-FM is a commercial station owned by The Cromwell Group Inc. The format of the station is country music. WCRC-FM broadcasts to the Effingham, IL area at 95.7 FM.

WCRE-AM
Owner: Pee Dee Broadcasting LLC
Editorial: 541 Highway 1 S, Cheraw, South Carolina 29520-3811. **T:** 1 843 537-7887
Editorial Profile: WCRE-AM is a commercial station owned by Pee Dee Broadcasting LLC. The format for the station is oldies. WCRE-AM broadcasts to the Charlotte, NC area at 1420 AM.

WCRF-FM
Owner: Moody Bible Institute
Editorial: 9756 Barr Rd, Cleveland, Ohio 44141. **T:** 1 440 526-1111 **E:** wcrf@moody.edu
W: http://www.moodyradiocleveland.fm
Editorial Profile: WCRF-FM is a commercial station owned by Moody Bible Institute. The format of the station is religious. WCRF-FM broadcasts in the Cleveland area at 103.3 FM.

WCRH-FM
Owner: Cedar Ridge Children's Home & School
Editorial: 12146 Cedar Ridge Rd, Williamsport, Maryland 21795-3031.
T: 1 301 582-0285 **E:** wcrh@wcrh.org
W: http://www.wcrh.org
Editorial Profile: WCRH-FM is a non-commercial station owned by the Cedar Ridge Children's Home & School. The format of the station is contemporary Christian music. WCRH-FM broadcasts to the Williamsport, MD area at 90.5 FM.

WCRI-AM
Owner: The Judson Group, Inc
Editorial: 400 South County Trl Ste A105, Exeter, Rhode Island 02822-3539.
T: 1 401 294-9274 **E:** wcri@classical959.com
W: http://classical959.com
Editorial Profile: WCRI-AM is a commercial station owned by The Judson Group, Inc. The format of the station is Classical. WCRIAM broadcasts to the Providence, RI area at 1180 AM.

WCRI-FM
Owner: Judson Group, Inc.
Editorial: 400 S County Trl Ste A105, Exeter, Rhode Island 02822-3539. **T:** 1 401 294-9274
E: wcri@classical959.com
W: http://classical959.com
Editorial Profile: WCRI-FM is a commercial station owned by Judson Group, Inc.. The format of the station is classical. WCRI-FM broadcasts to the Providence, RI area at 95.9 FM.

WCRJ-FM
Owner: Delmarva Educational Association
Editorial: 4190 Belfort Rd, Ste 450, Jacksonville, Florida 32216-1405.
T: 1 904 641-9626 **W:** http://www.klove.com
Editorial Profile: WCRJ-FM is a non-commercial station owned by Delmarva Educational Association. The format of the station is contemporary Christian music. WCRJ-FM broadcasts to the Jacksonville, FL area at 88.1 FM.

WCRK-AM
Owner: Radio Acquisition Corp.
Editorial: 510 Economy Road, Morristown, Tennessee 37814. **T:** 1 423 586-9101
E: wcrk@lcs.net **W:** http://www.wcrk.com
Editorial Profile: WCRK-AM is commercial station owned by the Radio Acquisition Corp. The format of the station is classic hits. WCRK-AM broadcasts to the Morristown, TN area at 1150 AM.

WCRL-AM
Owner: Blount County Broadcasting
Editorial: 908 2nd Ave E, Oneonta, Alabama 35121-2506 **W:** http://www.wcrlradio.com
Editorial Profile: WCRL-AM is a commercial station owned by Blount County Broadcasting. The format of the station is adult standards music. WCRL-AM broadcasts to the Birmingham, Al area at 1570 AM.

WCRN-AM
Owner: Carter Broadcasting
Editorial: 82 Franklin St, Worcester, Massachusetts 01608-1982.
T: 1 508 792-5803
W: http://www.wcrnradio.com
Editorial Profile: WCRN-AM is a commercial station owned by Carter Broadcasting. The format of the station is talk. WCRN-AM broadcasts to the Boston area at 830 AM.

WCRO-AM
Owner: Greater Johnstown School District
Editorial: 1091 Broad St, Johnstown, Pennsylvania 15906-2437. **T:** 1 814 241-3668
Editorial Profile: WCRO-AM is a commercial station owned by Greater Johnstown School District. The format of the station is adult standards. WCRO-AM broadcasts to the Johnstown, PA area at 1230 AM.

WCRQ-FM
Owner: WQDY Inc.
Editorial: 637 Main St, Calais, Maine 4619.
T: 1 207 454-7545 **E:** wqdy@wqdy.fm
W: http://www.wcrqfm.com
Editorial Profile: WCRQ-FM is a commercial station owned by WQDY Inc. The format for the station is hot adult contemporary. WCRQ-FM broadcasts to the Calais, ME area at 102.9 FM.

WCRS-AM
Owner: Anne's Entertainment Vision, Inc.
Editorial: 1220 Bypass 72 NE, Greenwood, South Carolina 29649-2205.
T: 1 864 229-7984
W: http://wlmawcrsradio.com
Editorial Profile: WCRS-AM is a commercial station owned by Anne's Entertainment Vision, Inc. The format of the station is variety and talk. WCRS-AM broadcasts to the Greenwood, SC area at 1450 AM.

WCRT-AM
Owner: Bott Broadcasting Co.
Editorial: 15 Century Blvd, Ste 101, Nashville, Tennessee 37214-3692. **T:** 1 615 871-1160
E: comments@bottradionetwork.com
W: http://www.bottradionetwork.com
Editorial Profile: WCRT-AM is a commercial station owned by Bott Broadcasting Co. The format of the station is Christian talk. WCRT-AM broadcasts to the Nashville, TN, area at 1160 AM.

WCRU-AM
Owner: Truth Broadcasting
Editorial: 407 Robinson Clemmer Rd, Dallas, North Carolina 28034. **T:** 1 704 922-5960
E: info@wtru.com **W:** http://wtru.com
Editorial Profile: WCRU-AM is a commercial station owned by Truth Broadcasting. The format of the station is religion. WCRU-AM broadcasts to Charlotte-Gastonia, NC area at 960 AM.

WCRV-AM
Owner: Bott Broadcasting Co.
Editorial: 6401 Poplar Ave, Ste 640, Memphis, Tennessee 38119. **T:** 1 901 763-4640
E: comments@bottradionetwork.com
W: http://www.bottradionetwork.com/stations/tennessee/memphis
Editorial Profile: WCRV-AM is a commercial station owned by Bott Broadcasting Co. The format of the station is religious and Christian programming. WCRV-AM broadcasts to the Memphis, TN area at 640 AM.

WCRX-FM
Owner: Columbia College
Editorial: 33 E Congress Pkwy, Ste 700, Chicago, Illinois 60605. **T:** 1 312 663-1693
E: WCRXDJ@colum.edu
W: http://www.wcrx.net
Editorial Profile: WCRX-FM is a non-commercial college station owned by Columbia College. The format of the station is variety programming. WCRX-FM broadcasts to the Chicago area at 88.1 FM.

WCRZ-FM
Owner: Townsquare Media, LLC
Editorial: 3338 E Bristol Rd, Burton, Michigan 48529-1408. **T:** 1 810 743-1080
W: http://www.wcrz.com
Editorial Profile: WCRZ-FM is a commercial station owned by Townsquare Media, LLC. The format of the station is adult contemporary. WCRZ-FM broadcasts to the Burton, MI area at 107.9 FM.

WCSB-FM
Owner: Cleveland State University
Editorial: 2121 Euclid Ave, Rhodes Tower 956, Cleveland, Ohio 44115-2214.
T: 1 216 687-3523 **W:** http://www.wcsb.org
Editorial Profile: WCSB-FM is a non-commercial college station owned by Cleveland State University. The format of the station is variety. WCSB-FM broadcasts to the Cleveland area at 89.3 FM.

WCSF-FM
Owner: College of St. Francis
Editorial: 500 Wilcox St, Joliet, Illinois 60435.
T: 1 815 740-3697 **E:** wcsf@stfrancis.edu
W: http://www.stfrancis.edu/theedge
Editorial Profile: WCSF-FM is a non-commercial station college station owned by the College of St. Francis. The format of the station is rock alternative. WCSF-FM broadcasts to the Joliet, IL area at 88.7 FM.

WCSG-FM
Owner: Cornerstone Communications
Editorial: 1159 E Beltline Ave NE, Grand Rapids, Michigan 49525-5805.
T: 1 616 942-1500 **W:** http://www.wcsg.org
Editorial Profile: WCSG-FM is a non-commercial station owned by Cornerstone Communications. The format of the station is contemporary Christian. WCSG-FM broadcasts to the Grand Rapids, MI area at 91.3 FM.

WCSI-AM
Owner: White River Broadcasting Co., Inc.
Editorial: 3212 Washington St, Columbus, Indiana 47203-1505. **T:** 1 812 372-4448
E: news@wcsiradio.com
W: http://wcsi.whiterivernews.com
Editorial Profile: WCSI-AM is a commercial station owned by White River Broadcasting Co., Inc. The format of the station is news, sports and talk. WCSI-AM broadcasts to the Columbus, IN area at 1010 AM.

WCSJ-AM
Owner: Nelson Multimedia
Editorial: 219 W Washington St, Morris, Illinois 60450-2146. **T:** 1 815 941-1000
E: wcsj-production@nelsonmultimedia.net
W: http://www.wcsjfm.com
Editorial Profile: WCSJ-AM is a commercial station owned by Nelson Multimedia. The format of the station is classic hits. WCSJ-AM broadcasts to the Morris, IL area at 1550 AM.

WCSJ-FM
Owner: Nelson Multimedia
Editorial: 219 W Washington St, Morris, Illinois 60450-2146. **T:** 1 815 941-1000
E: wcsj-production@nelsonmultimedia.net
W: http://www.wcsjfm.com
Editorial Profile: WCSJ-FM is a commercial station owned by Nelson Multimedia. The format of the station is classic hits. WCSJ-FM broadcasts in the Morris, IL area at 103.1 FM.

WCSL-AM
Owner: HRN Broadcasting Inc.
Editorial: 1366 Startown Rd, Lincolnton, North Carolina 28092. **T:** 1 704 735-8071
E: info@hrnb.com **W:** http://www.hrnb.com
Editorial Profile: WCSL-AM is a commercial station owned by HRN Broadcasting Inc. The format of the station is southern gospel. WCSL-AM broadcasts to the Charlotte, NC area at 1590 AM.

WCSM-AM
Owner: Hayco Broadcasting
Editorial: 6458 Meyer Rd, Celina, Ohio 45822.
T: 1 419 586-5134 **E:** wcsm@bright.net
W: http://www.wcsmradio.com
Editorial Profile: WCSM-AM is a commercial station owned by Hayco Broadcasting. The format of the station is news, talk and adult standards. WCSM-AM broadcasts to the Celina, OH area at 1350 AM.

WCSM-FM
Owner: Hayco Broadcasting
Editorial: 6458 Meyer Rd, Celina, Ohio 45822.
T: 1 419 586-5134 **E:** wcsm@bright.net
W: http://www.wcsmradio.com
Editorial Profile: WCSM-FM is a commercial station owned by Hayco Broadcasting. The format of the station is adult contemporary. WCSM-FM broadcasts in the Celina, OH area at 96.7 FM.

WCSN-FM
Owner: Gulf Coast Broadcasting Company, Inc.
Editorial: 2421 E 2nd St, Gulf Shores, Alabama 36542-3177. **T:** 1 251 967-1057
E: sunny105@gulftel.com
W: http://www.sunny105.com
Editorial Profile: WCSN-FM is a commercial station owned by Gulf Coast Broadcasting Company, Inc. The format for the station is adult contemporary. WCSN-FM broadcasts to the Mobile, AL area at 105.7 FM.

WCSP-FM
Owner: C-SPAN
Editorial: 400 N Capitol St NW, Ste 650, Washington, District Of Columbia 20001.
T: 1 202 737-3220 **E:** radio@c-span.org
W: http://www.c-span.org
Editorial Profile: WCSP-FM is a non-commercial station owned by C-SPAN. The format of the stataion is news and talk. WSCP-FM broadcasts to the Washington area at 90.1 FM.

WCSR-AM
Owner: WCSR Inc.
Editorial: 170 N West St, Hillsdale, Michigan 49242-1224. **T:** 1 517 437-4444
E: wcsrinc@comcast.net
W: http://www.radiohillsdale.com
Editorial Profile: WCSR-AM is a commercial station owned by WCSR Inc. The format of the station is adult contemporary. WCSR-AM broadcasts to the Hillsdale, MI area at 1340 AM.

WCSR-FM
Owner: WCSR Inc.
Editorial: 170 N West St, Hillsdale, Michigan 49242. **T:** 1 517 437-4444
E: wcsrinc@comcast.net
W: http://www.radiohillsdale.com
Editorial Profile: WCSR-FM is a commercial station owned by WCSR Inc. The format of the station is adult contemporary music. WCSR-FM broadcasts to the Hillsdale, MI area at 92.1 FM

WCSS-AM
Owner: Cranesville Block
Editorial: 1250 Riverfront Ctr, Amsterdam, New York 12010-4602. **T:** 1 518 684-6000
E: wcss@cranesville.com
W: http://www.wcss1490.com
Editorial Profile: WCSS-AM is a commercial station owned by Cranesville Block. The format of the station is adult contemporary. WCSS-AM broadcasts to the Amsterdam, NY area at 1490 AM.

WCST-AM
Owner: Capper Broadcasting Company
Editorial: 440 Radio Station Ln, Berkeley Springs, West Virginia 25411-4273.
T: 1 304 258-1010 **E:** c929@comcast.net
Editorial Profile: WCST-AM is a commercial station owned by Capper Broadcasting Company. The format of the station is news and talk. WCST-AM broadcasts in the Berkeley Springs, WV area at 1010 AM.

WCSU-FM
Owner: Central State University
Editorial: Cosby Center Central State U, Wilberforce, Ohio 45384-1004.
T: 1 937 376-9278 **W:** http://www.wcsufm.org
Editorial Profile: WCSU-FM is a non-commercial station owned by Central State University. The format of the station is jazz amd urban contemporary. WCSU-FM broadcasts to the Wilberforce, OH area at 88.9 FM.

WCSV-AM
Owner: Peg Broadcasting Crossville, LLC
Editorial: 961 Miller Ave, Crossville, Tennessee 38555. **T:** 1 931 707-1102
E: production.crossville@pegbroadcasting.com
W: http://www.1490wcsv.com
Editorial Profile: WCSV-AM is a commercial station owned by Peg Broadcasting Crossville, LLC. The format of the station is sports. WCSV-AM broadcasts to the Crossville, TN area at 1490 AM.

WCSW-AM
Owner: Zoe Communications Inc.
Editorial: 345 Highway 63 S, Shell Lake, Wisconsin 54871. **T:** 1 715 468-9500
W: http://www.wcsw.com
Editorial Profile: WCSW-AM is a commercial station owned by Zoe Communications Inc. The format of the station is talk. WCSW-AM broadcasts in the Shell Lake, WI area at 940 AM.

WCSX-FM
Owner: Greater Media Inc.
Editorial: 1 Radio Plaza St, Ferndale, Michigan 48220-2140. **T:** 1 248 398-9470
E: feedback@wcsx.com
W: http://www.wcsx.com
Editorial Profile: WCSX-FM is a commercial station owned by Greater Media Inc. The format of the station is classic rock. WCSX-FM broadcasts to the Detroit area at 94.7 FM.

WCSY-FM
Owner: Midwest Family Stations
Editorial: 602 Broadway St, South Haven, Michigan 49090-1926. **T:** 1 269 925-1111
E: wsjm@wsjm.com **W:** http://www.wcsy.com
Editorial Profile: WCSY-FM is a commercial station owned by Midwest Family Stations. The format of the station is oldies. WCSY-FM broadcasts to the Benton Harbor, MI area at 103.7 FM.

WCTB-FM
Owner: Mountain Wireless Corp.
Editorial: 208 Middle Rd, Skowhegan, Maine 4976. **T:** 1 207 474-5171
E: mix1079@gmail.com
W: http://www.935trueoldies.com
Editorial Profile: WCTB-FM is a commercial station owned by Mountain Wireless Corp. The format of the station is oldies. WCTB-FM broadcasts to the Skowhegan, ME area at 93.5 FM.

WCTC-AM
Owner: Greater Media Inc.

Editorial: 78 Veronica Ave, Somerset, New Jersey 8873. **T:** 1 732 249-2600
W: http://www.wctcam.com
Editorial Profile: WCTC-AM is a commercial station owned by Greater Media Inc. The format of the station is Talk. WCTC-AM broadcasts throughout the central New Jersey area at 1450 AM.

WCTF-AM
Owner: Family Stations Inc.
Editorial: 45 1/2 East St, Vernon, Connecticut .06066-3847. **T:** 1 860 871-2526
W: http://www.familyradio.com

WCTG-FM
Owner: Sebago Broadcasting
Editorial: 6324 Maddox Blvd, Chincoteague, Virginia 23336-2614. **T:** 1 757 336-1118
E: studio@965ctg.com **W:** http://965ctg.com
Editorial Profile: WCTG-FM is a commercial station owned by Sebago Broadcasting. The format for the station is adult hits. WCTG-FM broadcasts to the Norfolk, VA area at 96.5 FM.

WCTH-FM
Owner: Florida Keys Media, LLC
Editorial: 93351 Overseas Hwy Ste 2, Tavernier, Florida 33070-2800.
T: 1 305 852-9085
Editorial Profile: WCTH-FM is a commercial station owned by Florida Keys Media, LLC. The format of the station is contemporary country. WCTH-FM broadcasts to the Tavernier, FL area at 100.3 FM.

WCTK-FM
Owner: Hall Communications
Editorial: 75 Oxford St, Providence, Rhode Island 02905-4722. **T:** 1 401 467-4366
E: mail@wctk.com **W:** http://www.wctk.com
Editorial Profile: WCTK-FM is a commercial station owned by Hall Communications. The format of the station is contemporary country music. WCTK-FM broadcasts to the Providence, RI-New Bedford, MA area at 98.1 FM.

WCTL-FM
Owner: Inspiration Time Inc.
Editorial: 10912 Route 19 N, Waterford, Pennsylvania 16441-5108. **T:** 1 814 796-6000
E: wctl@wctl.org **W:** http://www.wctl.org
Editorial Profile: WCTL-FM is a commercial station owned by Inspiration Time Inc. The format of the station is contemporary Christian music. WCTL-FM broadcasts to the Erie, PA area at 106.3 FM.

WCTO-FM
Owner: Cumulus Media Inc.
Editorial: 2158 Avenue C, Ste 100, Bethlehem, Pennsylvania 18017-2148. **T:** 1 610 266-7600
E: cat.studio@cumulus.com
W: http://www.catcountry96.fm
Editorial Profile: WCTO-FM is a commercial station owned by Cumulus Media Inc. The format of the station is country. WCTO-FM broadcasts to the Bethlehem, PA area at 96.1 FM.

WCTQ-FM
Owner: Clear Channel Media and Entertainment
Editorial: 1779 Independence Blvd, Sarasota, Florida 34234-2106. **T:** 1 941 552-4800
W: http://www.1065ctq.com
Editorial Profile: WCTQ-FM is a commercial station owned by Clear Channel Media and Entertainment. The format of the station is contemporary country. WCTQ-FM broadcasts in the Venice, FL area at 106.5 FM.

WCTR-AM
Owner: WCTR Broadcasting, LLC
Editorial: 231 Flatland Rd, Chestertown, Maryland 21620-3359. **T:** 1 410 778-1530
E: info@wctr.com **W:** http://www.wctr.com
Editorial Profile: WCTR-AM is a commercial station owned by WCTR Broadcasting, LLC. The format of the station is talk. WCTR-AM broadcasts in the Chestertown, MD area at 1530 AM.

WCTS-AM
Owner: Central Baptist Theological Seminary
Editorial: 900 Forestview Ln N, Minneapolis, Minnesota 55441-5934. **T:** 1 763 417-8270
E: wcts@centralseminary.edu
W: http://www.wctsradio.com
Editorial Profile: WCTS-AM is a non-commercial station owned by Central Baptist Theological Seminary. The format of the station is Christian music and talk. WCTS-AM broadcasts in the Plymouth, MN area at 1030 AM.

WCTT-AM
Owner: Eubanks Broadcasting Inc.
Editorial: 821 Adams Rd, Corbin, Kentucky 40701-4708. **T:** 1 606 528-4717
E: traffic@wctt.com **W:** http://www.wctt.com
Editorial Profile: WCTT-AM is a commercial station owned by Eubanks Broadcasting Inc. The format of the station is adult standards music and talk programming. WCTT-AM broadcasts to the Lexington, KY area at 680 AM.

WCTT-FM
Owner: Encore Communications, Inc
Editorial: 821 Adams Rd, Corbin, Kentucky 40701-4708. **T:** 1 606 528-4717
E: traffic@wctt.com
Editorial Profile: WCTT-FM is a commercial station owned by Encore Communications, Inc. The format of the station is rock music. WCTT-FM broadcasts to the Corbin, KY area at 107.3 FM.

WCTW-FM
Owner: Clear Channel Media and Entertainment
Editorial: 5620 State Route 9G, Hudson, New York 12534-4127. **T:** 1 518 828-5006
W: http://www.985thecat.com
Editorial Profile: WCTW-FM is a commercial station owned by Clear Channel Media and Entertainment. The format of the station is hot AC. WCTW-FM broadcasts to the Hudson, NY area at 98.5 FM.

WCTY-FM
Owner: Hall Communications
Editorial: 40 Cuprak Rd, Norwich, Connecticut 6360. **T:** 1 860 887-3511
W: http://www.wcty.com
Editorial Profile: WCTY-FM is a commercial station owned by Hall Communications. The format of the station is country music. WCTY-FM broadcasts to the Hartford-New Haven, CT area at 97.7 FM.

WCUB-AM
Owner: Cub Radio Inc.
Editorial: 1915 Mirro Dr, Manitowoc, Wisconsin 54220. **T:** 1 920 683-6800
W: http://www.cubradio.com
Editorial Profile: WCUB-AM is a commercial station owned by Cub Radio Inc. The format of the station is country music. WCUB-AM broadcasts to the Manitowoc, WI area at 980 AM.

WCUE-AM
Owner: Family Stations Inc.
Editorial: 4075 Bellaire Ln, Peninsula, Ohio 44264. **T:** 1 330 920-1150
E: familyradio@familyradio.org
W: http://www.familyradio.com
Editorial Profile: WCUE-AM is a non-commercial station owned by Family Stations Inc. The format of the station is religious. WCUE-AM broadcasts to the Cleveland area at 1150 AM.

WCUM-AM
Owner: Radio Cumbre Broadcasting Inc.
Editorial: 240 Fairfield Ave Floor 2, Bridgeport, Connecticut 06604-4256. **T:** 1 203 335-1450
E: info@radiocumbre.am
W: http://www.radiocumbre.am
Editorial Profile: WCUM-AM is a commercial station owned by Radio Cumbre Broadcasting Inc. The format of the station is Hispanic programming. WCUM-AM broadcasts to the Bridgeport, CT area at 1450 AM.

WCUP-FM
Owner: Keweenaw Bay Indian Community
Editorial: 805 US41 South, Ste B, Baraga, Michigan 49908. **T:** 1 906 353-9287
E: eagleadmin@up.net
W: http://www.keepitintheup.com
Editorial Profile: WCUP-FM is a commercial station owned and operated by the Keweenaw Bay Indian Community. The format of the station is contemporary country. WCUP-FM broadcasts to the L'Anse, Michigan area at a frequency of 105.7 FM.

WCUW-FM
Owner: WCUW Inc.
Editorial: 910 Main St, Worcester, Massachusetts 01610-1433.
T: 1 508 753-1012 **E:** wcuw@wcuw.org
W: http://www.wcuw.org
Editorial Profile: WCUW-FM is a non-commercial station owned by WCUW Inc. The format of the station is variety. WCUW-FM broadcasts to the Worcester, MA area at 91.3 FM.

WCUZ-FM
Owner: Henderson, Roy E.
Editorial: 1532 Forrester Rd, Frankfort, Michigan 49635. **T:** 1 231 352-6374
W: http://www.wouffm.com
Editorial Profile: WCUZ-FM is a commercial station owned by Roy E. Henderson. The format of the station is rock/album oriented rock. WCUZ-FM broadcasts to the Frankfort, MI area at 100.1 FM.

WCVA-AM
Owner: Piedmont Communications Inc.
Editorial: 207 Spicers Mill Rd, Orange, Virginia 22960. **T:** 1 540 825-3900
E: traffic@wjmafm.com
Editorial Profile: WCVA-AM is a commercial station owned by Piedmont Communications Inc. The format of the station is adult standards music. WCVA-AM broadcasts to the Orange, VA at 1490 AM.

WCVC-AM
Owner: WCVC, Inc.
Editorial: 117 1/2 Henderson Rd, Tallahassee, Florida 32312-2337. **T:** 1 850 438-7667
W: http://www.divinewordradio.com
Editorial Profile: WCVC-AM is a commercial station owned by WCVC, Inc. The format of the station is Catholic programming. WCVC-AM broadcasts to the Tallahassee, FL area at 1330 AM.

WCVE-FM
Owner: Commonwealth Public Broadcasting
Editorial: 23 Sesame St, Richmond, Virginia 23235. **T:** 1 804 320-1301
E: webmaster@ideastations.org
W: http://www.ideastations.org
Editorial Profile: WCVE-FM is a non-commercial station owned by Commonwealth Public Broadcasting. The format of the station is classical and jazz music and news. WCVE-FM broadcasts to the Richmond, VA area at 88.9 FM. This station does not accept PSAs.

WCVG-AM
Owner: Great Lakes Radio LLC
Editorial: 135 W 38th St, Covington, Kentucky 41015-1421. **T:** 1 859 291-2255
W: http://www.gospel1320.com
Editorial Profile: WCVG-AM is a commercial station owned by Great Lakes Radio LLC. The format of the station is gospel. WCVG-AM broadcasts to the Covington, KY area at 1320 AM.

WCVH-FM
Owner: Hunterdon Historical Society Board of Education
Editorial: 84 State Route 31, Flemington, New Jersey 8822. **T:** 1 908 782-9595
E: WCVH@hcrhs.org
W: http://central.hcrhs.k12.nj.us/wcvhfm
Editorial Profile: WCVH-FM is a non-commercial station owned by the Hunterdon Historical Society Board of Education. The format of the station is classic and contemporary country. WCVH-FM broadcasts in the Flemington, NJ area at 90.5 FM.

WCVK-FM
Owner: Bowling Green Community Broadcasting
Editorial: 1407 Scottsville Rd, Bowling Green, Kentucky 42104. **T:** 1 270 781-7326
E: wcvk@christianfamilyradio.com
W: http://www.christianfamilyradio.com
Editorial Profile: WCVK-FM is a non-commercial station owned by Bowling Green Community Broadcasting. The format of the station is contemporary Christian. WCVK-FM broadcasts to the Bowling Green, KY area at 90.7 FM.

WCVL-AM
Owner: Forcht Broadcasting
Editorial: 1757 N 175 W, Crawfordsville, Indiana 47933. **T:** 1 765 362-8200
W: http://www.crawfordsvilleradio.com
Editorial Profile: WCVL-AM is a commercial station owned by Forcht Broadcasting. The format of the station is oldies. WCVL-AM broadcasts to the Crawfordsville, IN area at 1550 AM.

WCVM-FM
Owner: Taylor University Broadcasting Inc.
Editorial: 1025 W Rudisill Blvd, Fort Wayne, Indiana 46807-2168. **T:** 1 260 745-0576
E: newspc@wbcl.org **W:** http://www.wbcl.org
Editorial Profile: WCVM-FM is a commercial station owned by Taylor University Broadcasting Inc. The format of the station is contemporary Christian music. WCVM-FM broadcasts to the Bronson, MI area at 94.7 FM.

WCVO-FM
Owner: One Connection Media Group
Editorial: 881 E Johnstown Rd, Gahanna, Ohio 43230-1851. **T:** 1 614 855-9171
E: theriver@1049theriver.com
W: http://www.1049theriver.com
Editorial Profile: WCVO-FM is a non-commercial station owned by One Connection Media Group. The format of the station is contemporary Christian music. WCVO-FM broadcasts to the Columbus, OH area at 104.9 FM.

WCVP-AM
Owner: Cherokee Broadcasting Co.
Editorial: 195 Hampton Church Rd, Murphy, North Carolina 28906. **T:** 1 828 837-2151
Editorial Profile: WCVP-AM is a commercial station owned by Cherokee Broadcasting Co. The format of the station is talk, gospel and country music. WCVP-AM broadcasts to the Chattanooga, TN area at 600 AM.

WCVQ-FM
Owner: Saga Communications
Editorial: 1640 Old Russellville Pike, Clarksville, Tennessee 37043-1709.
T: 1 931 648-7720 **W:** http://www.q108.com
Editorial Profile: WCVQ-FM is a commercial station owned by Saga Communications (dba 5 Star Radio Group). The format of the station is hot adult contemporary music. WCVQ-FM broadcasts to the Nashville, TN area at 107.9 FM.

WCVR-AM
Owner: Koor Communications
Editorial: 62 Radio Dr, Randolph, Vermont 5060. **T:** 1 802 728-4411
W: http://www.realcountry1320.com
Editorial Profile: WCVR-AM is a commercial station owned by Koor Communications. The format of the station is country. WCVR-AM broadcasts to the Randolph, VT area at 1320 AM.

WCVS-FM
Owner: Neuhoff Family Limited Partnership
Editorial: 3055 S 4th St, Springfield, Illinois 62703. **T:** 1 217 528-3033
W: http://www.wcvs.com
Editorial Profile: WCVS-FM is a commercial station owned by Neuhoff Family Limited Partnership. The format of the station is classic rock. WCVS-FM broadcasts in the Springfield, IL area at 96.7 FM.

WCVT-FM
Owner: Radio Vermont Group Inc.
Editorial: 9 Stowe St, Waterbury, Vermont 05676-1820. **T:** 1 802 244-7321
Editorial Profile: WCVT-FM is a commercial station owned by Radio Vermont Group Inc. The format of the station is classical music. WCVT-FM broadcasts to the Stowe-Burlington, VT area at a frequency of 101.7 FM.

WCVU-FM
Owner: Clear Channel Media and Entertainment
Editorial: 24100 Tiseo Blvd, Unit 10, Port Charlotte, Florida 33980-5223.
T: 1 941 206-1188 **W:** http://www.wcvu.com
Editorial Profile: WCVU-FM is a commercial station owned by Clear Channel Media and Entertainment. The format of the station is easy listening music. WCVU-FM broadcasts in the Port Charlotte, FL area at 104.9 FM.

WCVV-FM
Owner: Belpre Educational Broadcasting Foundation
Editorial: 200 First Lane, Belpre, Ohio 45714. **T:** 1 740 423-5895
W: http://wcvv.thecalvarycommunitychurch.com
Editorial Profile: WCVV-FM is a non-commercial station owned by Belpre Educational Broadcasting Foundation. The format of the station is religious. WCVV-FM broadcasts to the Parkersburg, WV area at 89.5 FM.

WCVX-AM
Owner: Christian Broadcasting System, Ltd
Editorial: 635 W 7th St Ste 400, Cincinnati, Ohio 45203-1549. **T:** 1 513 533-2500
E: info@cbslradio.com
W: http://christiantalk1160.com
Editorial Profile: WCVX-AM is a commercial station owned by Christian Broadcasting System, Ltd. The format of the station is will become Christian Talk on February 1, 2013. WCVX-AM broadcasts to the Cincinnati area at 1160 AM.

WCVZ-FM

Owner: Southeastern Ohio Broadcasting, Inc.
Editorial: 629 Downard Rd, Zanesville, Ohio 43701. **T:** 1 740 452-5431
E: webmaster@whizamfmtv.com
W: http://www.whiznews.com/fm
Editorial Profile: WCVZ-FM is a commercial station owned by Southeastern Ohio Broadcasting. The format of the station is contemporary country. WCVZ-FM broadcasts to the Baltimore, OH and surrounding areas at 102.5 FM.

WCWA-AM

Owner: Clear Channel Media and Entertainment
Editorial: 125 S Superior St, Toledo, Ohio 43604. **T:** 1 419 244-8321
E: wcwa@clearchannel.com
W: http://www.wcwa.com
Editorial Profile: WCWA-AM is a commercial station owned by Clear Channel Media and Entertainment. The format of the station is sports. WCWA-AM broadcasts to the Toledo, OH area at 1230 AM.

WCWC-AM

Owner: Whitley County Board of Education
Editorial: 116 N 4th St, Williamsburg, Kentucky 40769-1115. **T:** 1 606 549-7000
E: news1@bellsouth.net
Editorial Profile: WCWC-AM is a non-commercial station owned by the Whitley County Board of Education. The format of the station is variety. WCWC-AM broadcasts to the Williamsburg, KY area at 1440 AM.

WCWM-FM

Owner: College of William & Mary
Editorial: WCWM 90.9 FM, College of William & Mary, Williamsburg, Virginia 23185.
T: 1 757 221-3287 **E:** wcwmxx@wm.edu
W: http://www.wm.edu/so/wcwm
Editorial Profile: WCWM-FM is a non-commercial station owned by College of William & Mary. The format of the station is college variety. WCWM-FM broadcasts to the Williamsburg, VA area at 90.9 FM.

WCWP-FM

Owner: Long Island University
Editorial: 720 Northern Blvd Long Island U, Brookville, New York 11548-1319.
T: 1 516 299-2683
W: http://www.mywcwp.com
Editorial Profile: WCWP-FM is a non-commercial station owned by Long Island University. The format of the station is variety. WCWP-FM broadcasts in the Long Island, NY at 88.1 FM.

WCWS-FM

Owner: College of Wooster(The)
Editorial: 1189 Beall Ave, the College of Wooster, Wishart Hall, Wooster, Ohio 44691-2393. **T:** 1 330 263-2240
E: wcws@wooster.edu
W: http://woo91.wooster.edu
Editorial Profile: WCWS-FM is a non-commercial station owned by The College of Wooster. The format of the station is music and talk. WCWS-FM broadcasts to the students of the College of Wooster and the residents of Wooster, OH area at 90.0 FM.

WCWV-FM

Owner: R&S Broadcasting Co., Inc.
Editorial: 713 Main St, Summersville, West Virginia 26651-1431. **T:** 1 304 872-5202
E: wcwv@wcwv929.com
W: http://www.wcwv929.com
Editorial Profile: WCWV-FM is a commercial station owned by R&S Broadcasting Co., Inc. The format of the station is Southern gospel, positive country and bluegrass music. WCWV-FM broadcasts to the Summersville, WV area at 92.9 FM. Use the main email address for PSAs.

WCXG-FM

Owner: Cornerstone University
Editorial: 1159 E Beltline Ave NE, Grand Rapids, Michigan 49525-5805.
T: 1 269 383-3600 **W:** http://www.wcsg.org
Editorial Profile: WCXG-FM is a commercial station owned by Cornerstone University. The format of the station is Christian AC music. WCXG-FM broadcasts to the Grand Rapids, MI area at 89.9 FM.

WCXI-AM

Owner: Birach Broadcasting Corp.
Editorial: 15130 North Rd, Fenton, Michigan 48430-1380. **T:** 1 810 750-1911
W: http://wcxiradio.com
Editorial Profile: WCXI-AM is a commercial station owned by Birach Broadcasting Corp.

The format for the station is oldies. WCXI-AM broadcasts to the Fenton, MI area at 1160 AM.

WCXK-FM

Owner: Cornerstone University
Editorial: 1159 E Beltline Ave NE, Grand Rapids, Michigan 49525-5805.
T: 1 269 383-3600 **W:** http://www.wcsg.org
Editorial Profile: WCXK-FM is a non-commercial station owned by Cornerstone University. The format of the station is contemporary Christian. WCXK-FM broadcasts to the Grand Rapids, MI area at 88.3 FM.

WCXL-FM

Owner: Max Radio of the Carolinas
Editorial: 103 W Wood Hill Dr, Ste D-E, Nags Head, North Carolina 27959.
T: 1 252 480-4655 **E:** info@beach104.com
W: http://www.beach104.com
Editorial Profile: WCXL-FM is a commercial station owned by Max Radio of the Carolinas. The format of the station is hot adult contemporary. WXCL-FM broadcasts to the Nags Head, NC area at 104.1 FM.

WCXN-AM

Owner: Birach Broadcasting Corp.
Editorial: 21700 Northwestern Hwy Ste 1190, Southfield, Michigan 48075-4923.
T: 1 248 557-3500 **W:** http://www.birach.com
Editorial Profile: WCXN-AM is a commercial station owned by Birach Broadcasting Corp. The format of the station is Hispanic. WCXN-AM broadcasts to the Hickory, NC area at 1170 AM.

WCXO-FM

Owner: Clinton County Broadcasting, Inc.
Editorial: 1611 County Farm Rd, Carlyle, Illinois 62231-6325. **T:** 1 618 594-2490
W: http://www.wcxo967.com
Editorial Profile: WCXO-FM is a commercial station owned by Clinton County Broadcasting, Inc. The format of the station is adult hits music. WCXO-FM broadcasts to the Carlyle, IL area at 96.7 FM.

WCXR-FM

Owner: Backyard Broadcasting
Editorial: 1685 Four Mile Dr, Williamsport, Pennsylvania 17701. **T:** 1 570 323-8200
W: http://www.wzxr.com
Editorial Profile: WCXR-FM is a commercial station owned by Backyard Broadcasting. The station's format is classic rock music. WCXR-FM broadcasts to the Susquehanna Valley, PA area at 103.7 FM.

WCXT-FM

Owner: Midwest Family Stations
Editorial: 580 E Napier Ave, Benton Harbor, Michigan 49022-5816. **T:** 1 269 925-1111
W: http://www.thecoast.fm
Editorial Profile: WCXT-FM is a commercial station owned by Midwest Family Stations. The format of the station is hot adult contemporary. WCXT-FM broadcasts to the South Haven, MI area at 98.3 FM.

WCXU-FM

Owner: Canxus Broadcasting Corp.
Editorial: 152 E Green Ridge Rd, Caribou, Maine 4736. **T:** 1 207 473-7513
E: channelxradio@yahoo.com
W: http://www.channelxradio.com
Editorial Profile: WCXU-FM is a commercial station owned by Canxus Broadcasting Corp. The format for the station is adult contemporary. WCXU-FM broadcasts to the Caribou, ME area at 97.7 FM.

WCXX-FM

Owner: Canxus Broadcasting Corp.
Editorial: 152 E Green Ridge Rd, Caribou, Maine 4736. **T:** 1 207 473-7513
E: channelxradio@yahoo.com
W: http://www.channelxradio.com
Editorial Profile: WCXX-FM is a commercial station owned by Canxus Broadcasting Corp. The format for the station is adult contemporary. WCXX-FM broadcasts to the Caribou, ME area at 102.3 FM.

WCXZ-AM

Owner: Lincoln Memorial University
Editorial: 6965 Cumberland Gap Pkwy, Harrogate, Tennessee 37752.
T: 1 423 869-7400 **W:** http://www.74wcxz.com
Editorial Profile: WCXZ-AM is a commercial station owned by Lincoln Memorial University. The format of the station is country. WCXZ-AM broadcasts to the Harrogate, TN area at 740 AM.

WCYE-FM

Owner: Results Broadcasting, Inc.
Editorial: 38 W Davenport St, Rhinelander, Wisconsin 54501. **T:** 1 715 369-9575
W: http://mycoyoteradio.com
Editorial Profile: WCYE-FM is a commercial station owned by Results Broadcasting, Inc. The format of the station is features classic and contemporary country music. WCYE-FM broadcasts to the Rhinelander, WI area at a frequency of 93.7 FM.

WCYK-FM

Owner: Monticello Media LLC
Editorial: 1150 Pepsi Pl Ste 300, Charlottesville, Virginia 22901-2890.
T: 1 434 978-4408
W: http://www.hitkicker997.com
Editorial Profile: WCYK-FM is a commercial station owned by Monticello Media LLC. The format of the station is classic country music. WCYK-FM broadcasts in the Charlottesville, VA area at 99.7 FM.

WCYN-AM

Owner: WCYN Broadcasting Inc.
Editorial: 117 N Main St Ste 3, Cynthiana, Kentucky 41031-2237. **T:** 1 859 234-1400
W: http://www.wcyn.com
Editorial Profile: WCYN-AM is a commercial station owned by WCYN Broadcasting Inc. The format of the station is country. WCYN-AM broadcasts to the Lexington, KY area at 1400 AM.

WCYN-FM

Owner: Cumulus Media Inc.
Editorial: 300 W Vine St, Lexington, Kentucky 40507. **T:** 1 859 253-5900
W: http://www.wvlkfm.net
Editorial Profile: WCYN-FM is a commercial station owned by Cumulus Media Inc. The format of the station is news/talk. WCYN-FM broadcasts to the Lexington, KY area at 102.3 FM.

WCYO-FM

Owner: Wallingford Broadcasting LLC
Editorial: 128 Big Hill Ave, Richmond, Kentucky 40475-2008. **T:** 1 606 723-5138
W: http://www.wcyofm.com
Editorial Profile: WCYO-FM is a commercial station owned by Wallingford Broadcasting LLC. The format for the station features classic and contemporary country music. WCYO-FM broadcasts to the Lexington, KY area at 100.7 FM.

WCYQ-FM

Owner: Journal Broadcast Group
Editorial: 1533 Amherst Rd, Knoxville, Tennessee 37909-1204. **T:** 1 865 824-1021
W: http://www.q100country.com
Editorial Profile: WCYQ-FM is a commercial station owned by Journal Broadcast Group. The format of the station is contemporary country. WCYQ-FM broadcasts to the Knoxville, TN area at 100.3 FM.

WCYY-FM

Owner: Townsquare Media, LLC
Editorial: 1 City Ctr, Portland, Maine 04101-6420. **T:** 1 207 774-6364
W: http://www.wcyy.com
Editorial Profile: WCYY-FM is a commercial station owned by Townsquare Media, LLC. The format of the station is rock alternative. WCYY-FM broadcasts to the Portland, ME area at 94.3 FM.

WCZQ-FM

Owner: Neuhoff Communications
Editorial: 250 N Water St, Ste 100, Decatur, Illinois 62523. **T:** 1 217 423-9744
W: http://www.hot1055.com
Editorial Profile: WCZQ-FM is a commercial station owned by Neuhoff Communications. The format of the station is urban contemporary and R&B. WCZQ-FM broadcasts to the Decatur, IL area at 105.5 FM.

WCZR-FM

Owner: Clear Channel Media and Entertainment
Editorial: 3771 SE Jennings Rd, Port Saint Lucie, Florida 34952-7702. **T:** 1 772 335-9300
W: http://www.wzzr.com
Editorial Profile: WCZR-FM is a commercial station owned by Clear Channel Media and Entertainment. The format of the station is talk. WCZR-FM broadcasts to the West Palm Beach, FL area at 101.7 FM.

WCZT-FM

Owner: Coastal Broadcasting Systems, Inc.
Editorial: 1602 Route 47 Floor 2, Rio Grande, New Jersey 08242-1404. **T:** 1 609 522-1987

W: http://www.987thecoast.com
Editorial Profile: WCZT-FM is a commercial station owned by Coastal Broadcasting Systems, Inc. The format of the station is adult contemporary. WCZT-FM broadcasts to the Wildwood, NJ area at 98.7 FM.

WCZW-FM

Owner: Midwestern Broadcasting Co.
Editorial: 300 E Front St, Ste 450, Traverse City, Michigan 49684. **T:** 1 231 946-6211
W: http://www.wccwi.com
Editorial Profile: WCZW-FM is a commercial station owned by Midwestern Broadcasting Co. The format of the station is classic hits. The station airs in the Traverse City, MI area at 107.9 FM.

WCZX-FM

Owner: Townsquare Media
Editorial: 2 Pendell Rd, Poughkeepsie, New York 12601-1513. **T:** 1 845 471-1500
W: http://www.mix97fm.com
Editorial Profile: WCZX-FM is a commercial station owned by Townsquare Media. The format of the station is adult contemporary. WCZX-FM broadcasts throughout Poughkeepsie, New York at 97.7 FM. Do NOT send information not pertaining to the Poughkeepsie local area.

WCZY-FM

Owner: Central Michigan Communications Inc.
Editorial: 4895 E Wing Rd, Mount Pleasant, Michigan 48858. **T:** 1 989 772-9664
E: wczy@wczy.net **W:** http://wczy.net
Editorial Profile: WCZY-FM is a commercial station owned by Central Michigan Communications Inc. The format for the station is adult contemporary. WCZY-FM broadcasts to the Flint, MI area at 104.3 FM.

WCZZ-AM

Owner: Broomfield Broadcasting LLC
Editorial: 210 Montague Ave, Greenwood, South Carolina 29649-1935.
T: 1 864 223-4300
Editorial Profile: WCZZ-AM is a commercial station owned by Broomfield Broadcasting LLC. The format of the station is Christian talk and music, and gospel. WCZZ-AM broadcasts to the Greenwood, SC area at 1090 AM.

WDAC-FM

Owner: WDAC Radio Co.
Editorial: 683 Lancaster Pike, New Providence, Pennsylvania 17560-9756.
T: 1 717 284-4123 **E:** postmaster@wdac.com
W: http://www.wdac.com
Editorial Profile: WDAC-FM is a commercial station owned by WDAC Radio Co. The format of the station is religious. The station broadcasts to the Lancaster, PA area at 94.5 FM.

WDAD-AM

Owner: Renda Broadcasting
Editorial: 840 Philadelphia St, Indiana, Pennsylvania 15701-3922. **T:** 1 724 465-4700
W: http://www.wdadradio.com
Editorial Profile: WDAD-AM is a commercial station owned by Renda Broadcasting. The format of the station is oldies music. WDAD-AM broadcasts to the Indiana, PA area at 1450 AM.

WDAE-AM

Owner: Clear Channel Media and Entertainment
Editorial: 4002 W Gandy Blvd, Tampa, Florida 33611-3410. **T:** 1 813 839-9393
E: wdaestudio@clearchannel.com
W: http://www.620wdae.com
Editorial Profile: WDAE-AM is a commercial station owned by Clear Channel Media and Entertainment. The format of the station is sports. WDAE-AM broadcasts to the Tampa, FL area at 620 AM.

WDAF-FM

Owner: Entercom Communications Corp.
Editorial: 7000 Squibb Rd, Mission, Kansas 66202-3233. **T:** 1 913 744-3600
W: http://www.1065thewolf.com
Editorial Profile: WDAF-FM is a commercial station owned by Entercom Communications Corp. The format of the station is contemporary country. WDAF-FM broadcasts to the Greater Kansas City, MO area at 106.5 FM.

WDAI-FM

Owner: Cumulus Media Inc.
Editorial: 11640 Highway 17 Byp, Murrells Inlet, South Carolina 29576-9332.
T: 1 843 651-7869
W: http://www.985kissfm.net

Editorial Profile: WDAI-FM is a commercial station owned by Cumulus Media Inc. The format of the station is urban contemporary music. WDAI-FM broadcasts to the Murrells Inlet, SC area at 98.5 FM.

WDAK-AM
Owner: Clear Channel Media and Entertainment
Editorial: 1501 13th Ave, Columbus, Georgia 31901-1908. **T:** 1 706 576-3000
W: http://www.newsradio540.com
Editorial Profile: WDAK-AM is a commercial station owned by Clear Channel Media and Entertainment. The format of the station is news and talk. WDAK-AM broadcasts to the Columbus, GA area at 540 AM.

WDAL-AM
Owner: North Georgia Radio Group
Editorial: 613 Silver Cir, Dalton, Georgia 30721. **T:** 1 706 278-5511
Editorial Profile: WDAL-AM is a commercial station owned by North Georgia Radio Group. The format of the station is Spanish sports. WDAL-AM broadcasts to Dalton, GA at 1430 AM.

WDAN-AM
Owner: Neuhoff Family Limited Partnership
Editorial: 1501 N Washington Ave, Danville, Illinois 61832-2463. **T:** 1 217 442-1700
W: http://www.vermilioncountyfirst.com/pages/10639776.php
Editorial Profile: WDAN-AM is a commercial station owned by Neuhoff Family Limited Partnership. The format of the station is news, sports and talk. WDAN-AN broadcasts to the Danville, IL area at 1490 AM.

WDAO-AM
Owner: Johnson Communications
Editorial: 1012 W 3rd St, Dayton, Ohio 45402. **T:** 1 937 222-9326 **E:** wdaoam1210@aol.com
W: http://www.wdaoradio.com
Editorial Profile: WDAO-AM is a commercial station owned by Johnson Communications. The format of the station is urban adult contemporary. WDAO-AM broadcasts to the Dayton, OH area at 1210 AM.

WDAQ-FM
Owner: Berkshire Broadcasting Corp
Editorial: 198 Main St, Danbury, Connecticut 6810. **T:** 1 203 744-4800
W: http://www.98q.com
Editorial Profile: WDAQ-FM is a commercial station owned by Berkshire Broadcasting Corp. The format of the station is hot adult contemporary. WDAQ-FM broadcasts to the Danbury, CT area at 98.3 FM.

WDAR-FM
Owner: Clear Channel Media and Entertainment
Editorial: 181 E Evans St Ste 311, Florence, South Carolina 29506-5505.
T: 1 843 667-4600
W: http://sunny1055online.com
Editorial Profile: WDAR-FM is a commercial station owned by Clear Channel Media and Entertainment. The format of the station is Contemporary Christian. WDAR-FM broadcasts to the Florence, SC area at 105.5 FM.

WDAS-AM
Owner: Clear Channel Media and Entertainment
Editorial: 111 Presidential Blvd, Bala Cynwyd, Pennsylvania 19004-1008. **T:** 1 610 784-3333
W: http://www.wjjz.com
Editorial Profile: WDAS-AM is a commercial station owned by Clear Channel Media and Entertainment. The format of the station is smooth jazz. WDAS-AM broadcasts to the Philadelphia area at 1480 AM.

WDAS-FM
Owner: Clear Channel Media and Entertainment
Editorial: 111 Presidential Blvd Ste 100, Bala Cynwyd, Pennsylvania 19004-1009.
T: 1 610 784-3333
W: http://www.wdasfm.com
Editorial Profile: WDAS-FM is a commercial station owned by Clear Channel Media and Entertainment. The format of the station is urban contemporary and R&B. WDAS-FM broadcasts to the Philadelphia area at 105.3 FM.

WDAV-FM
Owner: Trustees of Davidson College
Editorial: 423 N Main St, Davidson, North Carolina 28036-9405. **T:** 1 704 894-8900
E: wdav@wdav.org **W:** http://www.wdav.org
Editorial Profile: WDAV-FM is a non-commercial station owned by Trustees of Davidson College. The format of the station is classical music. WDAV-FM broadcasts in the Charlotte, NC area at 89.9 FM.

WDAY-AM
Owner: Forum Communications Co.
Editorial: 301 8th St S Fl 2, 2nd Fl, Fargo, North Dakota 58103-1826. **T:** 1 701 237-6500
E: wday@wday.com **W:** http://www.wday.com
Editorial Profile: WDAY-AM is a commercial station owned by Forum Communications Co. The format of the station is news, sports and talk. WDAY-AM broadcasts to the Fargo, ND area at 970 AM.

WDAY-FM
Owner: Midwest Communications
Editorial: 1020 25th St S, Fargo, North Dakota 58103-2312. **T:** 1 701 237-5346
E: studio@y94.com **W:** http://www.y94.com
Editorial Profile: WDAY-FM is a commercial station owned by Midwest Communications. The format of the station is Top 40/CHR music. WDAY-FM broadcasts to the Fargo, ND area at 93.7 FM.

WDBC-AM
Owner: KMB Broadcasting Inc.
Editorial: 604 Ludington St, Escanaba, Michigan 49829. **T:** 1 906 786-3800
E: wykxinfo@yahoo.com
W: http://www.kmbbroadcasting.com/wdbc/index.php
Editorial Profile: WDBC-AM is a commercial station owned by KMB Broadcasting Inc. The format of the station is adult standards music, sports and talk programming. WDBC-AM broadcasts to the Marquette, MI, area at 680 AM.

WDBL-AM
Owner: Lightning Broadcasting, LLC
Editorial: 200 Wdbl Rd, Springfield, Tennessee 37172. **T:** 1 615 384-9744
E: wsgi1100@yahoo.com
W: http://wsgi1100.com
Editorial Profile: WDBL-AM is a commercial station owned by Lightning Broadcasting, LLC. The format of the station is news and talk. WDBL-AM broadcasts to the Nashville, TN area at 1590 AM.

WDBM-FM
Owner: Michigan State University
Editorial: G4 E Holden Hall, East Lansing, Michigan 48825. **T:** 1 517 353-4414
E: manager@impact89fm.org
W: http://www.impact89fm.org
Editorial Profile: WDBM-FM is a non-commercial college station owned by Michigan State University. The format of the station is college variety. WDBM-FM broadcasts to the East Lansing, MI area at a frequency of 88.9 FM.

WDBN-FM
Owner: Dowdy Broadcasting, Inc.
Editorial: 807 Bellevue Ave, Dublin, Georgia 31021-4847. **T:** 1 478 272-8896
W: http://www.wdbn-fm.com
Editorial Profile: WDBN-FM is a commercial station owned by Dowdy Broadcasting, Inc. The format of the station is rock music. WDBN-FM broadcasts to the Dublin, GA area at 107.9 FM.

WDBO-AM
Owner: Cox Media Group, Inc.
Editorial: 4192 N John Young Pkwy, Orlando, Florida 32804-2620. **T:** 1 407 295-5858
W: http://www.espn580orlando.com
Editorial Profile: WDBO-AM is a commercial station owned by Cox Media Group, Inc. The format of the station is sports. WDBO-AM broadcasts to the Orlando, FL area at 580 AM. WDBO-AM airs its programming on WHTO-FM.

WDBO-FM
Owner: Cox Media Group, Inc.
Editorial: 4192 N John Young Pkwy, Orlando, Florida 32804-2620. **T:** 1 407 295-5858
E: news@wdbo.com **W:** http://www.wdbo.com
Editorial Profile: WDBO-FM is a commercial station owned by Cox Media Group, Inc. The format of the station is news and talk. WHTQ-FM broadcasts to the Orlando, FL area at 96.5 FM. WDBO-FM airs WDBO-AM's programming.

WDBQ-AM
Owner: Cumulus Media Inc.
Editorial: 5490 Saratoga Rd, Asbury, Iowa 52002-2502. **T:** 1 563 557-1040
W: http://www.wdbqam.com
Editorial Profile: WDBQ-AM is a commercial station owned by Cumulus Media Inc. The format for the station is news, sports and talk. WDBQ-AM broadcasts to the Cedar Rapids, IA area at 1490 AM.

WDBQ-FM
Owner: Cumulus Media Inc.
Editorial: 5490 Saratoga Rd, Dubuque, Iowa 52002-2502. **T:** 1 563 557-1040
W: http://www.myq1075.com
Editorial Profile: WDBQ-FM is a commercial station owned by Cumulus Media Inc. The format of the station is classic hits. WDBQ-FM broadcasts to Dubuque, IA and surrounding communities at 107.5 FM.

WDBR-FM
Owner: Saga Communications
Editorial: 3501 E Sangamon Ave, Springfield, Illinois 62707-9777. **T:** 1 217 753-5400
W: http://www.wdbr.com
Editorial Profile: WDBR-FM is a commercial station owned by Saga Communications. The format of the station is Top 40/CHR. WDBR-FM broadcasts to the Springfield, IL area at a frequency of 103.7 FM.

WDBS-FM
Owner: Summit Media Broadcasting LLC
Editorial: 180 Main St, Sutton, West Virginia 26601-1317. **T:** 1 304 765-7373
E: info@theboss97fm.com
W: http://www.theboss97fm.com
Editorial Profile: WDBS-FM is a commercial station owned by Summit Media Broadcasting LLC. The format of the station is country music. WDBS-FM broadcasts to the Sutton, WV area at 97.1 FM.

WDBT-FM
Owner: Gulf South Communications Inc.
Editorial: 3245 Montgomery Hwy Ste 1, Dothan, Alabama 36303-2150.
T: 1 334 712-9233
Editorial Profile: WDBT-FM is a commercial station owned by Gulf South Communications Inc. The format of the station is news/talk. WDBT-FM broadcasts to the Ozark, AL area at 93.7 FM.

WDBX-FM
Owner: Heterodyne Broadcasting
Editorial: 224 N Washington St, Carbondale, Illinois 62901. **T:** 1 618 529-5900
E: wdbx911@yahoo.com
W: http://www.wdbx.org
Editorial Profile: WDBX-FM is a non-commercial station owned by Heterodyne Broadcasting. The format of the station is a variety of music and talk. WDBX-FM broadcasts to the Paducah, KY, Cape Girardeau, MO and Harrisburg, IL areas at 91.1 FM.

WDBY-FM
Owner: Townsquare Media, LLC
Editorial: 1004 Federal Rd, Brookfield, Connecticut 06804-1123. **T:** 1 203 775-1212
W: http://kicks1055.com
Editorial Profile: WDBY-FM is a commercial station owned by Townsquare Media, LLC. The format of the station is contemporary country. WDBY-FM broadcasts to the Danbury, CT area at 105.5 FM.

WDBZ-AM
Owner: Radio One Inc.
Editorial: 705 Central Ave Ste 200, 1 Centennial Plaza, Cincinnati, Ohio 45202-1900.
T: 1 513 749-1230 **W:** http://thebuzzcincy.com
Editorial Profile: WDBZ-AM is a commercial station owned by Radio One Inc. The format of the station is urban talk. WDBZ-AM broadcasts to the Cincinnati area at 1230 AM.

WDCB-FM
Owner: College of DuPage
Editorial: 425 Fawell Blvd, Glen Ellyn, Illinois 60137-6708. **T:** 1 630 942-4200
E: wdcbmktg@cod.edu
W: http://www.wdcb.org
Editorial Profile: WDCB-FM is a non-commercial station owned by the College of DuPage. The format of the station is news, jazz and blues music. WDCB-FM broadcasts to the Glen Ellyn, IL area at 90.9 FM.

WDCC-FM
Owner: Central Carolina Community College
Editorial: 1105 Kelly Dr, Sanford, North Carolina 27330. **T:** 1 919 718-7382
E: wdcc@cccc.edu
W: http://www.wdccfm.com
Editorial Profile: WDCC-FM is a non-commercial station owned by Central Carolina Community College. The format of the station is top 40/CHR. WDCC-FM broadcasts to the Sanford, NC area at 90.5 FM.

WDCD-FM
Owner: DJRA Broadcasting
Editorial: 4243 Albany St, Albany, New York 12205-4609. **T:** 1 518 862-1540
W: http://www.newlight967.com
Editorial Profile: WDCD-FM is a commercial station owned by DJRA Broadcasting. The format of the station features Christian programming. WDCD-FM broadcasts to the Albany, NY area at 96.7 FM.

WDCF-AM
Owner: Wagenvoord Advertising Group
Editorial: 706 N Myrtle Ave, Clearwater, Florida 33755-4219. **T:** 1 727 424-4991
E: lola@tantalk1340.com
W: http://www.tantalk1340.com
Editorial Profile: WDCF-AM is a commercial station owned by Wagenvoord Advertising Group. The format of the station is adult standards music and talk. WDCF-AM broadcasts to the Dade City, FL area on 1350 AM.

WDCG-FM
Owner: Clear Channel Media and Entertainment
Editorial: 3100 Smoketree Ct Ste 700, Raleigh, North Carolina 27604-1052.
T: 1 919 878-1500 **W:** http://www.g105.com
Editorial Profile: WDCG-FM is a commercial station owned by Clear Channel Media and Entertainment. The format of the station is Top 40/CHR. WDCG-FM broadcasts to the Raleigh, NC area at 105.1 FM.

WDCR-AM
Owner: Dartmouth College
Editorial: 6176 Robinson Hall Fl 3RDDARTMOU, Hanover, New Hampshire 03755-3507. **T:** 1 603 646-3313
E: 99Rock@wfrd.com
W: http://www.webdcr.com
Editorial Profile: WDCR-AM is a non-commercial college station owned by Dartmouth College. The format of the station is college variety, and classic rock during the day. WDCR-AM broadcasts to the Hanover, NH area at 1340 AM.

WDCR-FM
Owner: St. Mary's Hospital (Decatur)
Editorial: 1800 E Lake Shore Dr, Decatur, Illinois 62521-3810. **T:** 1 217 464-2966
Editorial Profile: WDCR-FM is a non-commercial station owned by St. Mary's Hospital (Decatur). The format of the station features Catholic talk radio programming. WDCR-FM broadcasts locally to the Decatur, IL area at a frequency of 88.9 FM.

WDCT-AM
Owner: Family Radio Ltd.
Editorial: 3251 Old Lee Hwy Ste 506, Fairfax, Virginia 22030-1504. **T:** 1 703 273-4000
Editorial Profile: WDCT-AM is a commercial station owned by Family Radio Ltd. The format of the station is religious Korean programming. WDCT-AM broadcasts to the Fairfax, VA area at 1310 AM.

WDCX-AM
Owner: Crawford Broadcasting Co.
Editorial: 2494 Browncroft Blvd, Rochester, New York 14625-1410. **T:** 1 716 883-3010
E: info@wdcxradio.com
W: http://www.wdcxfm.com
Editorial Profile: WDCX-AM is a commercial station owned by Crawford Broadcasting Co. The format of the station is religious talk. WDCX-AM broadcasts to the Rochester, NY area at 990 AM. The station does not accept PSAs.

WDCX-FM
Owner: Crawford Broadcasting Co.
Editorial: 625 Delaware Ave, Buffalo, New York 14202-1009. **T:** 1 716 883-3010
E: info@wdcxradio.com
W: http://www.wdcxfm.com
Editorial Profile: WDCX-FM is a commercial station owned by Crawford Broadcasting Co. The format of the station is contemporary Christian music. WDCX-FM broadcasts to the Buffalo, NY area at 99.5 FM. The station does not accept PSAs.

WDCY-AM
Owner: Word Christian Broadcasting Inc.
Editorial: 8451 S Cherokee Blvd, Ste B, Douglasville, Georgia 30134.
T: 1 770 920-1520 **E:** wordchr@bellsouth.net
W: http://www.wordchristianbroadcasting.com

Editorial Profile: WDCY-AM is a commercial station owned by Word Christian Broadcasting Inc. The format of the station is religious programming and gospel music. WDCY-AM broadcasts to the Douglasville, GA area at 1520 AM.

WDCZ-AM
Owner: Kimtron, Inc.
Editorial: 625 Delaware Ave Ste 308, Buffalo, New York 14202-1007. **T:** 1 716 883-3010
E: info@wdcxradio.com
W: http://www.wdcxfm.com
Editorial Profile: WDCZ-AM is a commercial station owned by Kimtron, Inc. The format of the station is Christian talk. WDCZ-AM broadcasts to the Buffalo-Niagara Falls, NY area at 970 AM area.

WDDC-FM
Owner: Zoe Communications Inc.
Editorial: N6912 US Highway 51, Portage, Wisconsin 53901. **T:** 1 608 742-1001
W: http://www.thunder100fm.com
Editorial Profile: WDDC-FM is a commercial station owned by Zoe Communications Inc. The format for the station is contemporary country. WDDC-FM broadcasts to the Madison, WI area at 100.1 FM.

WDDD-AM
Owner: Withers Broadcasting Co.
Editorial: 1822 N Court St, Marion, Illinois 62959. **T:** 1 618 997-8123
W: http://www.sportstalk810.com
Editorial Profile: WDDD-AM is a commercial station owned by Withers Broadcasting of Southern Illinois. The format of the station is sports. WDDD-AM broadcasts to the Marion, IL area at 810 AM.

WDDD-FM
Owner: Withers Broadcasting of Southern Illinois
Editorial: 1822 N Court St, Marion, Illinois 62959. **T:** 1 618 997-8123
W: http://www.mywithersradio.com
Editorial Profile: WDDD-FM is a commercial station owned by Withers Broadcasting of Southern Illinois. The format of the station is contemporary country music. WDDD-FM broadcasts to the Marion, IL areas at 107.3 FM.

WDDE-FM
Owner: Delaware First Media Corporation
Editorial: 1200 N Dupont Hwy, Dover, Delaware 19901-2202. **T:** 1 302 857-7096
E: news@delawarefirst.org
W: http://www.wdde.org
Editorial Profile: WDDE-FM is a non-commercial station owned by Delaware First Media Corporation. The format of the station is talk and news. WDDE-FM broadcasts to the Dover, DE area at 91.1 FM.

WDDH-FM
Owner: Laurel Media Inc.
Editorial: 14902 Boot Jack Rd, Ridgway, Pennsylvania 15853-6128. **T:** 1 814 772-9700
E: spots@houndcountry.com
W: http://www.houndcountry.com
Editorial Profile: WDDH-FM is a commercial station owned by Laurel Media Inc. The format of the station is classic country. WDDH-FM broadcasts to the Ridgway, PA area at 97.5 FM.

WDDJ-FM
Owner: Bristol Broadcasting
Editorial: 6000 Bristol Dr, Paducah, Kentucky 42003-9213. **T:** 1 270 534-9690
E: news@wkyq.com
W: http://www.electric969.com
Editorial Profile: WDDJ-FM is a commercial station owned by Bristol Broadcasting. The format of the station is Top 40/CHR. WDDJ-FM broadcasts to the Paducah, KY area at 96.9 FM.

WDDK-FM
Owner: Briar Patch Radio Inc
Editorial: 1271B E Broad St, Greensboro, Georgia 30642-2335. **T:** 1 706 453-4140
W: http://www.dock1039.com
Editorial Profile: WDDK-FM is a commercial station owned by Briar Patch Radio Inc. The format of the station is oldies, news and talk. WDDK-FM broadcasts to the Greensboro, GA area at 103.9 FM.

WDDO-AM
Owner: Cumulus Media Inc.
Editorial: 544 Mulberry St, Ste 500, Macon, Georgia 31201. **T:** 1 478 746-6286
W: http://www.wddoam.com

Editorial Profile: WDDO-AM is a commercial station owned by Cumulus Broadcasting. The format of the station is gospel music. WDDO-AM broadcasts to the Macon, GA area at 1240 AM.

WDDQ-FM
Owner: Small Town Broadcasting
Editorial: 118 N Patterson St, Valdosta, Georgia 31601-5570. **T:** 1 229 259-9301
W: http://www.talk921.com
Editorial Profile: WDDQ-FM is a commercial station owned by Small Town Broadcasting. The format of the station is talk. WDDQ-FM broadcasts to the Valdosta, GA area at 92.1 FM.

WDDV-AM
Owner: Clear Channel Media and Entertainment
Editorial: 1779 Independence Blvd, Sarasota, Florida 34234-2106. **T:** 1 941 552-4800
W: http://www.sunnyradioam.com/main.html
Editorial Profile: WDDV-AM is a commercial station owned by Clear Channel Media and Entertainment. The format of the station is adult standards. WDDV-AM broadcasts to the Sarasota, FL area at 1320 AM.

WDDW-FM
Owner: Adelante Media Group
Editorial: 1138 S 108th St, West Allis, Wisconsin 53214-2433. **T:** 1 414 325-1800
W: http://www.adelantemediagroup.com
Editorial Profile: WDDW-FM is a commercial station owned by Adelante Media Group. The format of the station is regional Mexican. WDDW-FM broadcasts to the Milwaukee area at 104.7 FM.

WDDZ-AM
Owner: Walt Disney Co.
Editorial: 400 Ardmore Blvd, Pittsburgh, Pennsylvania 15221
W: http://sports.espn.go.com/stations/espnradio1250
Editorial Profile: WDDZ-AM is a commercial station owned by Walt Disney Co. The format of the station is children's programming. WDDZ-AM broadcasts to the Pittsburgh at 1250 AM.

WDEA-AM
Owner: Townsquare Media, Inc.
Editorial: 49 Acme Rd, Brewer, Maine 04412-1545. **T:** 1 207 989-5631
E: cumuluspublicservice@midmaine.com
W: http://am1370wdea.com
Editorial Profile: WDEA-AM is a commercial station owned by Townsquare Media, Inc. The format of the station is adult standards. WDEA-AM broadcasts to the Brewer, ME area at 1370 AM.

WDEB-AM
Owner: BAZ Broadcasting Inc.
Editorial: 403 Livingston Ave, Jamestown, Tennessee 38556. **T:** 1 931 879-8164
E: wdeb@twlakes.net
Editorial Profile: WDEB-AM is a commercial station owned by BAZ Broadcasting Inc. The format of the station is oldies. WDEB-AM broadcasts to the Jamestown, TN area at 1500 AM.

WDEB-FM
Owner: BAZ Broadcasting Inc.
Editorial: 403 Livingston Ave, Jamestown, Tennessee 38556. **T:** 1 931 879-8164
E: wdebaudio@twlakes.net
Editorial Profile: WDEB-FM is a commercial station owned by BAZ Broadcasting Inc. The format of the station is country. WDEB-FM broadcasts to the Jamestown, TN area at 103.9 FM.

WDEC-FM
Owner: Sumter Broadcasting
Editorial: 214 Georgia Hwy 30 W., Americus, Georgia 31719. **T:** 1 229 924-6500
E: wiskwdec@mchsi.com
W: http://www.americusradio.com
Editorial Profile: WDEC-FM is a commercial station owned by Sumter Broadcasting. The format of the station is adult contemporary. WDEC-FM broadcasts to the Americus, GA area at 94.7 FM.

WDEF-AM
Owner: Bahakel Communications
Editorial: 2615 Broad St, Chattanooga, Tennessee 37408-3100. **T:** 1 423 321-6200
W: http://www.foxsportschattanooga.com
Editorial Profile: WDEF-AM is a commercial station owned by Bahakel Communications. The format of the station is sports. WDEF-AM

broadcasts to the Chattanooga, TN area at 1370 AM.

WDEF-FM
Owner: Bahakel Communications
Editorial: 2615 Broad St, Chattanooga, Tennessee 37408. **T:** 1 423 321-6200
W: http://www.sunny923.com
Editorial Profile: WDEF-FM is a commercial station owned by Bahakel Communications. The format of the station is adult contemporary. WDEF-FM broadcasts to the Chattanooga, TN area at 92.3 FM.

WDEK-AM
Owner: Broomfield Broadcasting, Inc
Editorial: 109 Old Chapin Rd Ste Q, Lexington, South Carolina 29072-2065. **T:** 1 803 785-9335 **E:** wdek@pbtcomm.net
W: http://www.wdek1170am.com
Editorial Profile: WDEKAM is a commercial station owned by Broomfield Broadcasting, Inc. The format for the station is oldies. WDEK-AM broadcasts to the Lexington, SC area at 1170 AM.

WDEL-AM
Owner: Delmarva Broadcasting
Editorial: 2727 Shipley Rd, Wilmington, Delaware 19810-3210. **T:** 1 302 478-2700
E: wdelnews@wdel.com
W: http://www.wdel.com
Editorial Profile: WDEL-AM is a commercial station owned by Delmarva Broadcasting. The format of the station is news and talk. WDEL-AM broadcasts to the Philadelphia area at 1150 AM.

WDEN-FM
Owner: Cumulus Media Inc.
Editorial: 544 Mulberry St, Ste 500, Macon, Georgia 31201. **T:** 1 478 746-6286
E: wdencrew@yahoo.com
W: http://www.wden.com
Editorial Profile: WDEN-FM is a commercial station owned by Cumulus Media Inc. The format of the station is contemporary country music. WDEN-FM broadcasts to the Macon, GA area at 99.1 FM.

WDEO-AM
Owner: Ave Maria Communications
Editorial: 24 Frank Lloyd Wright Dr, Ann Arbor, Michigan 48105-9484.
T: 1 734 930-5200
W: http://www.avemariaradio.net
Editorial Profile: WDEO-AM is a non-commercial station owned by Ave Maria Communications. The format of the station is religious talk. WDEO-AM broadcasts to the Ann Arbor, MI area at 990 AM.

WDER-AM
Owner: Blount Communications Group
Editorial: 8 Lawrence Rd, Derry, New Hampshire 3038. **T:** 1 603 437-9337
E: wderam1320@aol.com
W: http://www.lifechangingradio.com
Editorial Profile: WDER-AM is a commercial station owned by Blount Communications Group. The format of the station is religious programming. WDER-AM broadcasts to the Derry, NH area at 1320 AM.

WDER-FM
Owner: Blount Communications Group
Editorial: 8 Lawrence Rd, Derry, New Hampshire 03038-4191. **T:** 1 603 437-9337
W: http://www.wder.com
Editorial Profile: WDER-FM is a commercial station owned by Blount Communications Group. The format of the station is religious programming. WDER-FM broadcasts to the Peterborough, NH area at a frequency of 92.1 FM.

WDET-FM
Owner: Wayne State University
Editorial: 4600 Cass Ave, Detroit, Michigan 48201-1200. **T:** 1 313 577-4146
E: news@wdetfm.org
W: http://www.wdetfm.org
Editorial Profile: WDET-FM is a non-commercial station owned by Wayne State University. The format of the station is news and talk. WDET-FM broadcasts to the Detroit area at 101.9 FM.

WDEV-AM
Owner: Radio Vermont Group Inc.
Editorial: 9 Stowe St, Waterbury, Vermont 5676. **T:** 1 802 244-7321
E: wdev@radiovermont.com
W: http://www.wdevradio.com
Editorial Profile: WDEV-AM is a commercial station owned by Radio Vermont Group Inc. The format of the station is news, sports, and

talk, with an occasional variety of music. WDEV-AM broadcasts to the Waterbury, VT, area at 550 AM.

WDEV-FM
Owner: Radio Vermont Group Inc.
Editorial: 9 Stowe St, Waterbury, Vermont 5676. **T:** 1 802 244-1764
E: wdev@radiovermont.com
W: http://www.wdevradio.com
Editorial Profile: WDEV-FM is a commercial station owned by Radio Vermont Group Inc. The format of the station is news, sports, and talk, with an occasional variety of music. WDEV-FM broadcasts to the Waterbury, VT area at 96.1 FM.

WDEX-AM
Owner: New Life Broadcasting
Editorial: 3109 Weddington Rd, Monroe, North Carolina 28110-8932.
T: 1 704 289-9339
Editorial Profile: WDEX-AM is a commercial station owned by New Life Broadcasting. The format of the station is gospel music. WDEX-AM broadcasts to the Charlotte, NC area at 1430 AM.

WDEZ-FM
Owner: Midwest Communications Inc.
Editorial: 557 Scott St, Wausau, Wisconsin 54403-4829. **T:** 1 715 842-1672
W: http://www.wdez.com
Editorial Profile: WDEZ-FM is a commercial station owned by Midwest Communications. The format of the station is contemporary country music. WDEZ-FM broadcasts to the Wausau, WI area at 101.9 FM.

WDFB-AM
Owner: Alum Springs Vision & Outreach Corp.
Editorial: 3596 Alum Springs Rd, Danville, Kentucky 40422-9607. **T:** 1 859 236-9333
E: wdfb@wdfb.org **W:** http://www.wdfb.com

WDFB-FM
Owner: Alum Springs Vision & Outreach Corp.
Editorial: 3596 Alum Springs Rd, Danville, Kentucky 40422-9607. **T:** 1 859 236-9333
W: http://www.wdfb.com

WDFH-FM
Owner: Hudson Valley Community Radio, Inc.
Editorial: 21 Brookside Ln, Dobbs Ferry, New York 10522-2010 **W:** http://www.wdfh.org
Editorial Profile: WDFH-FM is a non-commercial station owned by Hudson Valley Community Radio, Inc. The format of the station is variety. WDFH-FM broadcasts to the Dobbs Ferry, NY area at 90.3 FM. The station is NOT accepting any press releases or public service announcements. Do not contact the station via phone or e-mail. The station may only be contacted through its Web site. Any PR professionals wanting to contact the station need to look over the Web site to consider the content covered at the station.

WDFM-FM
Owner: Clear Channel Media and Entertainment
Editorial: 2110 Radio Dr, Defiance, Ohio 43512-1977. **T:** 1 419 782-9336
W: http://www.981mix.com
Editorial Profile: WDFM-FM is a commercial station owned by Clear Channel Media and Entertainment. The format of the station is hot adult contemporary. WDFM-FM broadcasts to the Defiance, OH area at 98.1 FM.

WDFN-AM
Owner: Clear Channel Media and Entertainment
Editorial: 27675 Halsted Rd, Farmington Hills, Michigan 48331-3511. **T:** 1 248 324-5800
W: http://www.wdfn.com
Editorial Profile: WDFN-AM is a commercial station owned by Clear Channel Media and Entertainment. The format of the station is sports. WDFN-AM broadcasts to the Detroit area at 1130 AM.

WDGC-FM
Owner: Community High School District #99
Editorial: 4436 Main St, Downers Grove, Illinois 60515. **T:** 1 630 795-8490
W: http://wdgc.blogspot.com
Editorial Profile: WDGC-FM is a non-commercial high school station owned by Community High School District #99. The format of the station is variety. WDGC-FM broadcasts to the Downers Grove, IL area at a frequency of 88.3 FM.

WDGG-FM
Owner: Kindred Communications

Editorial: 401 11th St Ste 200, Huntington, West Virginia 25701-2226. **T:** 1 304 523-8401
E: studio@937thedawg.com
W: http://www.937thedawg.com
Editorial Profile: WDGG-FM is a commercial station owned by Kindred Communications. The format of the station is country music. WDGG-FM broadcasts to the greater Huntington, WV region at 93.7 FM.

WDGL-FM
Owner: Guaranty Broadcasting
Editorial: 929 Government St, Baton Rouge, Louisiana 70802. **T:** 1 225 388-9898
W: http://www.eagle981.com
Editorial Profile: WDGL-FM is a commercial station owned by Guaranty Broadcasting. The format of the station is classic rock. WDGL-FM broadcasts to the Baton Rouge, LA area at 98.1 FM.

WDGM-FM
Owner: Townsquare Media, Inc.
Editorial: 142 Skyland Blvd E, Tuscaloosa, Alabama 35405-4027. **T:** 1 205 345-7200
W: http://991wdgm.com
Editorial Profile: WDGM-FM is a commercial station owned by Townsquare Media, Inc. The format of the station is sports. WDGM-FM broadcasts to the Tuscaloosa, AL area at 99.1 FM.

WDHA-FM
Owner: Greater Media Inc.
Editorial: 55 Horsehill Rd, Cedar Knolls, New Jersey 07927-2003. **T:** 1 973 538-1250
E: rock@wdhafm.com
W: http://www.wdhafm.com
Editorial Profile: WDHA-FM is a commercial station owned by Greater Media Inc. The format of the station is rock music. WDHA-FM broadcasts in the Cedar Knolls, NJ area at 105.5 FM.

WDHC-FM
Owner: Capper Broadcasting Company
Editorial: 440 Radio Station Ln, Berkeley Springs, West Virginia 25411.
T: 1 304 258-1010 **E:** c929@comcast.net
W: http://www.wdhc.com
Editorial Profile: WDHC-FM is a commercial station owned by Capper Broadcasting Company. The format of the station is classic country and contemporary country music. WDHC-FM broadcasts in the Berkeley Springs, WV area at 92.9 FM.

WDHI-FM
Owner: Townsquare Media, LLC
Editorial: 34 Chestnut St, Oneonta, New York 13820-2466. **T:** 1 607 865-4321
W: http://www.wdhifm.com
Editorial Profile: WDHI-FM is a commercial station owned by Townsquare Media, LLC. The format of the station is oldies. WDHI-FM broadcasts to the Oneonta, NY area at a frequency of 100.3 FM.

WDHR-FM
Owner: East Kentucky Radio Network
Editorial: 1240 Radio Dr, Pikeville, Kentucky 41501-4779. **T:** 1 606 437-4051
E: info@ekbradio.com
W: http://www.wdhr.com
Editorial Profile: WDHR-FM is a commercial station owned by East Kentucky Radio Network. The format of the station is contemporary country music. WDHR-FM broadcasts to the Pikeville, KY area at 93.1 FM.

WDHT-FM
Owner: Main Line Broadcasting
Editorial: 717 E David Rd, Dayton, Ohio 45429-5218. **T:** 1 937 294-5858
W: http://www.hot1029.com
Editorial Profile: WDHT-FM is a commercial station owned by Main Line Broadcasting. The format of the station is urban contemporary music. WDHT-FM broadcasts to the Dayton, OH area at 102.9 FM.

WDIA-AM
Owner: Clear Channel Media and Entertainment
Editorial: 2650 Thousand Oaks Blvd Ste 4100, Memphis, Tennessee 38118-2451.
T: 1 901 259-1300
W: http://www.am1070wdia.com
Editorial Profile: WDIA-AM is a commercial station owned by Clear Channel Media and Entertainment. The format of the station is R&B music. WDIA-AMbroadcasts to the Memphis, TN area at 1070 AM.

WDIC-AM
Owner: Virginia Radio Network
Editorial: 2298 Rose Rdg, Clintwood, Virginia 24228. **T:** 1 276 835-8626
E: wdic@wdicradio.com
W: http://www.wdicradio.com
Editorial Profile: WDIC-AM is a commercial station owned by Virginia Radio Network. The format of the station is classic country. WDIC-AM broadcasts to the Clintwood, VA area at 1430 AM.

WDIC-FM
Owner: Dickenson County Broadcasting
Editorial: 2298 Rose Rdg, Clintwood, Virginia 24228. **T:** 1 276 835-8626
E: wdic@wdicradio.com
W: http://www.wdicradio.com
Editorial Profile: WDIC-FM is a commercial station owned by Dickenson County Broadcasting. The format of the station is classic hits. WDIC-FM broadcasts to the Clintwood, VA area at 92.1 FM.

WDIG-AM
Owner: WWC Inc.
Editorial: 4039 Sunset Blvd, Steubenville, Ohio 43952. **T:** 1 740 264-1760

WDIS-AM
Owner: Discussion Radio Inc.
Editorial: 100 Pond St, Norfolk, Massachusetts 2056. **T:** 1 508 384-8255
E: wdismgmt@aol.com **W:** http://wdisam.com
Editorial Profile: WDIS-AM is a commercial station owned by Discussion Radio Inc. The format of the station is talk. WDIS-AM broadcasts to the Norfolk, MA area at 1170 AM.

WDIY-FM
Owner: Lehigh Valley Community Broadcasters Association Inc.
Editorial: 301 Broadway, Bethlehem, Pennsylvania 18015. **T:** 1 610 694-8100
E: news@wdiy.org **W:** http://www.wdiy.org
Editorial Profile: WDIY-FM is a non-commercial station owned by Lehigh Valley Community Broadcasters Association Inc. The format of the station is AAA-adult album alternative, news and classical. WDIY-FM broadcasts to the Bethlehem, PA area at 88.1 FM.

WDIZ-AM
Owner: Clear Channel Media and Entertainment
Editorial: 1834 Lisenby Ave, Panama City, Florida 32405. **T:** 1 850 769-1408
W: http://www.espn590.com
Editorial Profile: WDIZ-AM is a commercial station owned by Clear Channel Media and Entertainment. The format of the station is sports. WDIZ-AM broadcasts to the Panama City, FL area at 590 AM.

WDJA-AM
Owner: Radio Christo Mi Redentor Universo 1420AM Inc.
Editorial: 2710 W Atlantic Ave, Delray Beach, Florida 33445. **T:** 1 561 278-1420
E: info@universo1420.com
W: http://www.universo1420.com
Editorial Profile: WDJA-AM is a commercial station owned by Radio Christo Mi Redentor Universo 1420AM Inc. The format of the station is Spanish Contemporary Christian. WDJA-AM broadcasts to the Miami area at 1420 AM.

WDJC-FM
Owner: Crawford Broadcasting Co.
Editorial: 120 Summit Pkwy, Ste 200, Birmingham, Alabama 35209.
T: 1 205 879-3324
W: http://www.wdjconline.com
Editorial Profile: WDJC-FM is a commercial station owned by Crawford Broadcasting Co. The format of the station is contemporary Christian. WDJC-FM broadcasts to the Birmingham, AL area at 93.7 FM.

WDJL-AM
Owner: Fifth Avenue Broadcasting
Editorial: 3400 Blue Spring Rd NW Ste A3, Huntsville, Alabama 35810-3446.
T: 1 256 852-1223
Editorial Profile: WDJL-AM is a commercial station owned by Fifth Avenue Broadcasting. The format of the station is gospel. WDJL-AM broadcasts to the Huntsville, AL area at 1000 AM.

WDJM-FM
Owner: Framingham State College
Editorial: 100 State St, #516, Framingham, Massachusetts 01702-2499.
T: 1 508 626-4622 **E:** wdjmfm@gmail.com
W: http://www.wdjm913.org
Editorial Profile: WDJM-FM is a non-commercial college station owned by Framingham State College. The format of the station features a variety of music and talk shows. WDJM-FM broadcasts in the Framingham, MA area at 91.3 FM.

WDJO-AM
Owner: Alchemy Broadcasting
Editorial: 635 W 7Th St, Cincinnati, Ohio 45203-1513. **T:** 1 513 421-1480
W: http://www.oldies1480.net
Editorial Profile: WDJO-AM is a commercial station owned by Alchemy Broadcasting. The format of the station is oldies. WDJO-AM broadcasts to the Cincinnati area at 1480 AM.

WDJQ-FM
Owner: D.A. Peterson Inc.
Editorial: 393 Smyth Ave, Alliance, Ohio 44601-1562. **T:** 1 330 450-9250
W: http://www.q92radio.com
Editorial Profile: WDJQ-FM is a commercial station owned by D.A. Peterson Inc. The format of the station is Top 40/CHR. WZKL-FM broadcasts to the Canton, OH area at 92.5 FM.

WDJR-FM
Owner: Gulf South Communications Inc.
Editorial: 3245 Montgomery Hwy, Ste 1, Dothan, Alabama 36303. **T:** 1 334 712-9233
W: http://www.wdjr.com
Editorial Profile: WDJR-FM is a commercial station owned by Gulf South Communications Inc. The format of the station is Adult Contemporary music. WDJR-FM broadcasts to the Dothan, AL area at 96.9 FM.

WDJS-AM
Owner: Mount Olive Broadcasting Co.
Editorial: 990 N Center St, Mount Olive, North Carolina 28365. **T:** 1 919 658-9751
Editorial Profile: WDJS-AM is a commercial station owned by Mount Olive Broadcasting Co. The format of the station is religious. WDJS-AM broadcasts to the Mount Olive, NC area at 1430 AM.

WDJX-FM
Owner: Main Line Broadcasting
Editorial: 520 S 4th St Ste 200, Louisville, Kentucky 40202-2577. **T:** 1 502 625-1220
W: http://www.wdjx.com
Editorial Profile: WDJX-FM is a commercial station owned by Main Line Broadcasting. The format of the station is Top 40/CHR music. WDJX-FM broadcasts in the Louisville, KY area at 99.7 FM.

WDJZ-AM
Owner: Peoples Broadcast Network LLC
Editorial: 177 State St, Bridgeport, Connecticut 06604-4872. **T:** 1 203 368-4392
W: http://www.wdjzradio.com
Editorial Profile: WDJZ-AM is a commercial station owned by Peoples Broadcast Network LLC. The format of the station is gospel. WDJZ-AM broadcasts to the Bridgeport, CT area at 1530 AM.

WDKB-FM
Owner: DeKalb County Radio Ltd.
Editorial: 2201 N 1st St, #95, Dekalb, Illinois 60115. **T:** 1 815 758-0950
W: http://www.b95fm.com
Editorial Profile: WDKB-FM is a commercial station owned by DeKalb County Radio Ltd. The format of the station is adult contemporary. WDKB-FM broadcasts to the Dekalb, IL area at 94.9 FM.

WDKC-FM
Owner: Mid-Atlantic Broadcasting Inc.
Editorial: 8767 Route 414, Liberty, Pennsylvania 16930. **T:** 1 570 662-9000
E: kc101@frontier.com
Editorial Profile: WDKC-FM is a commercial station owned by Mid-Atlantic Broadcasting Inc. The format of the station is contemporary country. WDKC-FM broadcasts to the Mansfield, PA area at 101.5 FM.

WDKD-AM
Owner: Miller Communications Inc.
Editorial: 593 N Williamsburg County Hwy, Kingstree, South Carolina 29556-6242.
T: 1 803 775-2321 **W:** http://www.miller.fm
Editorial Profile: WDKD-AM is a commercial station owned by Miller Communications Inc. The format of the station is sports. WDKD-AM broadcasts to the Kingstree, SC and surrounding areas at 1310 AM.

WDKM-FM
Owner: Casper Communications, LLC
Editorial: 1040 W Center St, Adams, Wisconsin 53910-9818. **T:** 1 608 339-3221
Editorial Profile: WDKM-FM is a commercial station owned by Casper Communications, LLC. The format of the station is adult contemporary music. WDKM-FM broadcasts to the Adams, WI area at 106.1 FM.

WDKN-AM
Owner: R & F Communications, Inc.
Editorial: 106 E College St, Dickson, Tennessee 37055-1828. **T:** 1 615 446-0752
E: wdkn@bellsouth.net
W: http://www.wdkn1260am.com/
Editorial Profile: WDKN-AM is a commercial station owned by R & F Communications, Inc. The format of the station is country and gospel. WDKN-AM broadcasts to the Dickson, TN area at 1260 AM.

WDKR-FM
Owner: WDKR, Inc.
Editorial: 120 W Wildwood Dr, Mount Zion, Illinois 62549. **T:** 1 217 864-4141
E: wxfmwdkr@comcast.net
Editorial Profile: WDKR-FM is a commercial station owned by WDKR, Inc. The format of the station is oldies music. WDKR-FM broadcasts in the Decatur, IL area at 107.3 FM.

WDKS-FM
Owner: Townsquare Media, LLC
Editorial: 117 SE 5th St, Evansville, Indiana 47708-1639. **T:** 1 812 425-4226
W: http://www.kissfmevansville.com
Editorial Profile: WDKS-FM is a commercial station owned by Townsquare Media, LLC. The format for the station is Top 40/CHR. WDKS-FM broadcasts to the Evansville, IN area at 106.1 FM.

WDKX-FM
Owner: Monroe County Broadcasting Co.
Editorial: 683 E Main St, Rochester, New York 14605. **T:** 1 585 262-2050 **E:** wdkx@wdkx.com
W: http://www.wdkx.com
Editorial Profile: WDKX-FM is a commercial station owned by Monroe County Broadcasting Co. The format of the station is urban contemporary. WDKX-FM broadcasts to the Rochester, NY area at 103.9 FM.

WDKZ-FM
Owner: Clear Channel Media and Entertainment
Editorial: Gateway Crossing, 351 Tilghman Road, Salisbury, Maryland 21804-1920.
T: 1 410 742-1923
W: http://www.kiss1055.com
Editorial Profile: WDKZ-FM is a commercial station owned by Clear Channel Media and Entertainment. The format of the station is Top 40/CHR music. WDKZ-FM broadcasts in the Salisbury, MD area at 105.5 FM.

WDLA-AM
Owner: Townsquare Media, LLC
Editorial: 34 Chestnut St, Oneonta, New York 13820-2466. **T:** 1 607 865-4321
W: http://cnynews.com
Editorial Profile: WDLA-AM is a commercial station owned by Townsquare Media, LLC. The format of the station is news, sports and talk. WDLA-AM broadcasts to the Oneonta, NY area at 1270 AM.

WDLA-FM
Owner: Townsquare Media, LLC
Editorial: 34 Chestnut St, Oneonta, New York 13820-2466. **T:** 1 607 865-4321
W: http://www.wdlafm.com
Editorial Profile: WDLA-FM is a commercial station owned by Townsquare Media, LLC. The format of the station is contemporary country music. WDLA-FM broadcasts to the Oneonta, NY area at 92.1 FM.

WDLB-AM
Owner: Seehafer Broadcasting Corp.
Editorial: 1714 N Central Ave, Marshfield, Wisconsin 54449-1514. **T:** 1 715 384-2191
W: http://www.wdlbam.com
Editorial Profile: WDLB-AM is a commercial station owned by Seehafer Broadcasting Corp. The format of the station is news, talk and oldies music. WDLB-AM broadcasts to the Marshfield, WI area at 1450 AM.

WDLD-FM
Owner: Main Line Broadcasting
Editorial: 25 Penncraft Ave, Chambersburg, Pennsylvania 17201-5600. **T:** 1 717 263-0813
E: wild@wild967.fm **W:** http://www.wild967.fm
Editorial Profile: WDLD-FM is a commercial station owned by Main Line Broadcasting. The format of the station is urban contemporary.

WDLD-FM broadcasts to the Chambersburg, PA area at 96.7 FM.

WDLJ-FM
Owner: KM Communications Inc.
Editorial: 16808 Old US Highway 50, Carlyle, Illinois 62231-2420. **T:** 1 618 594-2620
W: http://www.wdlj.com
Editorial Profile: WDLJ-FM is a commercial station owned by KM Communications Inc. The format of the station is classic rock music. WDLJ-FM broadcasts to the Carlyle, IL area at 97.5 FM.

WDLM-AM
Owner: Moody Bible Institute
Editorial: 18239 E 200Th St, Coal Valley, Illinois 61240-9295. **T:** 1 309 234-5111
E: wdlm@moody.edu
W: http://www.moodyradioqc.fm
Editorial Profile: WDLM-AM is a non-commercial station owned by Moody Bible Institute. The format of the station is religious. WDLM-AM broadcasts in the Moline, IL area at 960 AM.

WDLM-FM
Owner: Moody Bible Institute
Editorial: 18239 E 200th St, Coal Valley, Illinois 61240-9295. **T:** 1 309 234-5111
E: wdlm@moody.edu
W: http://www.moodyradioqc.fm
Editorial Profile: WDLM-FM is a non-commercial station owned by Moody Bible Institute. The format of the station is religion and music. WDLM-FM broadcasts to the Coal Valley, IL area at 89.3 FM.

WDLR-AM
Owner: ICS Holdings, Inc.
Editorial: 1630 Strathshire Hall Pl, Powell, Ohio 43065-9436. **T:** 1 740 549-7002
W: http://1550wdlr.com
Editorial Profile: WDLR-AM is a commercial station owned by ICS Holdings, Inc. The format for the station is regional Mexican music. WDLR-AM broadcasts to the Columbus, OH area at 1550 AM.

WDLS-AM
Owner: Magnum Radio Group
Editorial: N2349 Wibu Rd, Poynette, Wisconsin 53955-9556. **T:** 1 608 745-0959
E: info@magnumradiogroup.net
W: http://www.wdlsam.com
Editorial Profile: WDLS-AM a commercial station owned by Magnum Radio Group. The format of the station is classic country. WDLS-AM broadcasts in the Portage, WI area at 900 AM.

WDLT-FM
Owner: Cumulus Media Inc.
Editorial: 2800 Dauphin St Ste 104, Mobile, Alabama 36606-2400. **T:** 1 251 652-2000
W: http://www.1041wdlt.com
Editorial Profile: WDLT-FM is a commercial station owned by Cumulus Media Inc. The format of the station is Urban AC. WDLT-FM broadcasts to the Mobile, AL, area at 104.1 FM.

WDLW-AM
Owner: WOBL Radio Inc.
Editorial: 45624 US Highway 20, Oberlin, Ohio 44074. **T:** 1 440 774-1320
E: woblwdlw@yahoo.com
W: http://www.koolkatwdlw.com
Editorial Profile: WDLW-AM is a commercial station owned by WOBL Radio Inc. The format of the station is oldies. WDLW-AM broadcasts to the Oberlin, OH area at 1380 AM.

WDLX-AM
Owner: Pirate Media Group LLC
Editorial: 525 Evans St, Greenville, North Carolina 27858. **T:** 1 252 317-1250
W: http://www.pirateradio930.com
Editorial Profile: WDLX-AM is a commercial station owned by Pirate Media Group LLC. The format of the station is talk and sports. WDLX-AM broadcasts to the Greenville, NC area at 930 AM.

WDLZ-FM
Owner: First Media Radio LLC
Editorial: 1714 W Main St, Murfreesboro, North Carolina 27855. **T:** 1 252 398-4111
Editorial Profile: WDLZ-FM is a commercial station owned by First Media Radio LLC. The format of the station is Lite Rock/Lite AC. WDLZ-FM broadcasts to the Murfreesboro, VA area at 98.3 FM.

WDMC-AM
Owner: Divine Mercy Communications, Inc

Editorial: 1800 Turtle Mound Rd, Melbourne, Florida 32934-8105. **T:** 1 321 757-7717
E: info@wdmc920.org
W: http://www.wdmc920.org
Editorial Profile: WDMC-AM is a non-commercial station owned by Divine Mercy Communications, Inc. The format of the station is Catholic talk. WDMC-AM broadcasts to the Melbourne, FL area at 920 AM.

WDMG-AM
Owner: Broadcast South, LLC
Editorial: 1931 Ga Highway 32 E, Douglas, Georgia 31533. **T:** 1 912 389-0995
E: bstraffic@windstream.net
Editorial Profile: WDMG-AM is a commercial station owned by Broadcast South, LLC. The format of the station is news and talk. WDMG-AM broadcasts to the Douglas, GA area at 860 AM.

WDMG-FM
Owner: Broadcast South, LLC
Editorial: 1931 Ga Highway 32 E, Douglas, Georgia 31533. **T:** 1 912 389-0995
E: bstraffic@windstream.net
W: http://979thebigdog.com
Editorial Profile: WDMG-FM is a commercial station owned by Broadcast South, LLC. The format of the station is adult contemporary. WDMG-FM broadcasts to the Albany, GA area at 97.9 FM.

WDMJ-AM
Owner: Sovereign Communications LLC
Editorial: 1009 W Ridge St, Ste A, Marquette, Michigan 49855. **T:** 1 906 225-1313
E: wjpd@wjpd.com **W:** http://www.wjpd.com
Editorial Profile: WDMJ-AM is a commercial station owned by Sovereign Communications LLC. The format of the station is news, sports and talk. WDMJ-AM broadcasts to the Marquette, MI area at 1320 AM.

WDMK-FM
Owner: Radio One Inc.
Editorial: 3250 Franklin St, Detroit, Michigan 48207. **T:** 1 313 259-2000
W: http://www.kissdetroit.com
Editorial Profile: WDMK-FM is a commercial station owned by Radio One Inc. The format of the station is urban adult contemporary. WDMK-FM broadcasts to the Detroit area at 105.9 FM.

WDML-FM
Owner: Volunteer Broadcasting of Illinois, Inc.
Editorial: 3501 Broadway St, Mount Vernon, Illinois 62864. **T:** 1 618 242-3333
E: wdml@mvn.net **W:** http://www.wdml.com
Editorial Profile: WDML-FM is a commercial station owned by Volunteer Broadcasting of Illinois, Inc. The format of the station is classic rock music. WDML-FM broadcasts to the Mount Vernon, IL area at 106.9 FM.

WDMO-FM
Owner: Zoe Communications Inc.
Editorial: 125 E 3Rd St Ste, New Richmond, Wisconsin 54017-1891. **T:** 1 715 246-2254
W: http://www.95gmo.com
Editorial Profile: WDMO-FM is a commercial station owned by Zoe Communications Inc. The format of the stations is country. WDMO-FM broadcasts to the Menomonie, WI area at 95.9 FM.

WDMP-AM
Owner: Dodge Point Broadcasting Co.
Editorial: 2163 State Road 23-151, Dodgeville, Wisconsin 53533. **T:** 1 608 935-2302
E: wdmp@mhtc.net
W: http://www.d99point3.com
Editorial Profile: WDMP-AM is a commercial station owned by Dodge Point Broadcasting Co. The format for the station is contemporary country. WDMP-AM broadcasts to the Madison, WI area at 810 AM.

WDMP-FM
Owner: Dodge Point Broadcasting Co.
Editorial: 2163 State Road 23-151, Dodgeville, Wisconsin 53533-9215. **T:** 1 608 935-2302
E: wdmp@mhtc.net
W: http://www.d99point3.com
Editorial Profile: WDMP-FM is a commercial station owned by Dodge Point Broadcasting Co. The format for the station is contemporary country. WDMP-FM broadcasts to the Madison, WI area at 99.3 FM.

WDMS-FM
Owner: WDMS, Inc.
Editorial: 1383 Pickett St, Greenville, Mississippi 38703. **T:** 1 662 334-4559
E: wdms@bellsouth.net

WDMX-FM
Owner: Clear Channel Media and Entertainment
Editorial: 6006 Grand Central Ave, Parkersburg, West Virginia 26105.
T: 1 304 295-6070 **W:** http://www.wdmx.com
Editorial Profile: WDMX-FM is a commercial station owned by Clear Channel Media and Entertainment. The format for the station is classic hits. WDMX-FM broadcasts to the Parkersburg, WV area at 100.1 FM.

WDNA-FM
Owner: Bascomb Memorial Foundation
Editorial: 2921 Coral Way, Coral Gables, Florida 33145-3205. **T:** 1 305 662-8889
E: info@wdna.org **W:** http://www.wdna.org
Editorial Profile: WDNA-FM is a non-commercial station owned by Bascomb Memorial Foundation. The format of the station is jazz and news. WDNA-FM broadcasts to the Miami area at 88.9 FM.

WDNB-FM
Owner: Bold Gold Media Group
Editorial: 1987 State Route 52, Liberty, New York 12754-8316. **T:** 1 845 292-7535
W: http://www.thunder102.com
Editorial Profile: WDNB-FM is a commercial station owned by Bold Gold Media Group. The format of the station in contemporary country. WDNB-FM broadcasts locally to the Liberty, NY area at 102.1 FM.

WDNC-AM
Owner: Capitol Broadcasting Company
Editorial: 3100 Highwoods Blvd, Raleigh, North Carolina 27604-1033.
T: 1 919 890-6101
W: http://www.espntriangle.com
Editorial Profile: WDNC-AM is a commercial station owned by Capitol Broadcasting Company. The format of the station is sports. WDNC-AM broadcasts to the Raleigh, NC area at 620 AM.

WDND-AM
Owner: Artistic Media Partners Inc.
Editorial: 3371 Cleveland Road Ext, South Bend, Indiana 46628-9780. **T:** 1 574 273-9300
W: http://www.u93.com
Editorial Profile: WDND-AM is a commercial station owned by Artistic Media Partners Inc. The format of the station is Hot AC. WDND-AM broadcasts to the South Bend, IN area at 1620 AM.

WDNE-AM
Owner: West Virginia Radio Corp.
Editorial: Washington & Davis Streets, Elkins, West Virginia 26241. **T:** 1 304 636-1300
E: wdne@wvradio.com
Editorial Profile: WDNE-AM is a commercial station owned by West Virginia Radio Corp. The format of the station is adult standards music. WDNE-AM broadcasts in the Elkins, WV area at 1240 AM.

WDNE-FM
Owner: West Virginia Radio Corp.
Editorial: Washington & Davis Streets, Elkins, West Virginia 26241. **T:** 1 304 636-1300
E: wdne@wvradio.com
W: http://www.wdnefm.com
Editorial Profile: WDNE-FM is a commercial station owned by West Virginia Radio Corp. The format of the station is country music. WDNE-FM broadcasts to the Elkins, WV area at 98.9 FM.

WDNG-AM
Owner: WDNG Inc.
Editorial: 1115 Leighton Ave, Anniston, Alabama 36207-4610. **T:** 1 256 236-8291
W: http://www.wdng.net
Editorial Profile: WDNG-AM is a commercial station owned by WDNG Inc. The format of the station is news and talk. WDNG-AM broadcasts to the Birmingham, AL area at 1450 AM.

WDNH-FM
Owner: Bold Gold Media Group
Editorial: 575 Grove St, Honesdale, Pennsylvania 18431. **T:** 1 570 253-1616
E: jhohman@boldgoldmedia.com
W: http://www.953dnh.com
Editorial Profile: WDNH-FM is a commercial station owned by Bold Gold Media Group. The format of the station is hot adult contemporary/Top 40. WDNH-FM broadcasts to the Honesdale, PA area at 95.3 FM.

WDNL-FM
Owner: Neuhoff Family Limited Partnership
Editorial: 1501 N Washington Ave, Danville, Illinois 61832-2463. **T:** 1 217 442-1700

W: http://www.wdnlfm.com
Editorial Profile: WDNL-FM is a commercial station owned by Neuhoff Family Limited Partnership. The format of the station is adult contemporary. WDNL-FM broadcasts to the Danville, IL area at 102.1 FM.

WDNR-FM
Owner: Widener University
Editorial: 1 University Pl, Chester, Pennsylvania 19013. **T:** 1 610 499-4439
E: wdnr895@mail.widener.edu
W: http://www2.widener.edu/WDNR-895-Radio
Editorial Profile: WDNR-FM is a non-commercial station owned by Widener University. The format of the station is college variety. WDNR-FM broadcasts to the Chester, PA area at 89.5 FM.

WDNS-FM
Owner: Daily News Broadcasting Co.
Editorial: 804 College St, Bowling Green, Kentucky 42101. **T:** 1 270 781-2121
E: 93news@wdnsfm.com
W: http://www.wdnsfm.com
Editorial Profile: WDNS-FM is a commercial station owned by Daily News Broadcasting Co. The format for the station is classic rock. WDNS-FM broadcasts to the Bowling Green, KY area at 93.3 FM.

WDNX-FM
Owner: Rural Life Foundation Inc.
Editorial: 3575 Lonesome Pine Rd, Savannah, Tennessee 38372. **T:** 1 731 925-9236
W: http://www.harberthills.org
Editorial Profile: WDNX-FM is a non-commercial station owned by Rural Life Foundation Inc. The format of the station is religious and Christian programming. WDNX-FM broadcasts to the Savannah, TN area at 89.1 FM.

WDNY-AM
Owner: Genesee Media Corp.
Editorial: 195 Main St, Dansville, New York 14437-1315. **T:** 1 585 335-9369
W: http://geneseenow.com
Editorial Profile: WDNY-AM is a commercial station owned by Genesee Media Corp. The format of the station is classic hits music. WDNY-AM broadcasts to the Dansville, NY at 1400 AM.

WDOC-AM
Owner: WDOC Inc.
Editorial: 95 Jackson St, Prestonsburg, Kentucky 41653-1010. **T:** 1 606 886-8409
E: q95fm@eastky.net **W:** http://www.wdoc.net
Editorial Profile: WDOC-AM is a commercial station owned by WDOC Inc. The format of the station is gospel. WDOC-AM broadcasts to Prestonburg, KY area at 1310 AM.

WDOD-AM
Owner: Bahakel Communications
Editorial: 2615 Broad St, Chattanooga, Tennessee 37408-3100. **T:** 1 423 321-6200
W: http://www.foxsportschattanooga.com
Editorial Profile: WDOD-AM is a commercial station owned by Bahakel Communications. The format of the station is sports. WDOD-AM broadcasts to the Chattanooga, TN area on 1310 AM.

WDOD-FM
Owner: Bahakel Communications
Editorial: 2615 Broad St, Chattanooga, Tennessee 37408. **T:** 1 423 321-6200
W: http://www.965themountain.com
Editorial Profile: WDOD-FM is a commercial station owned by Bahakel Communications. The format of the station is Top 40/CHR. WDOD-FM broadcasts to the Chattanooga, TN area at 96.5 FM.

WDOE-AM
Owner: Chadwick Bay Broadcasting Corporation
Editorial: 4561 Willow Rd, Dunkirk, New York 14048-9644. **T:** 1 716 366-1410
E: community@wdoe1410.com
W: http://www.chautauquatoday.com
Editorial Profile: WDOE-AM is a commercial station owned by Chadwick Bay Broadcasting Corporation. The format of the station is news, sports, and classic hits music. WDOE-AM's broadcasts to the Dunkirk-Fredonia, NY area at 1410 AM.

WDOG-AM
Owner: Good-Radio Broadcast Co.
Editorial: 2447 Augusta Hwy, Allendale, South Carolina 29810. **T:** 1 803 584-3500
E: wdog935@aol.com
W: http://www.bigdogradio.com

Editorial Profile: WDOG-AM is a commercial station owned by Good-Radio Broadcast Co. The format of the station is classic country. WDOG-AM broadcasts to the Allendale, SC area at 1460 AM.

WDOG-FM
Owner: Good-Radio Broadcast Co.
Editorial: 2447 Augusta Hwy, Allendale, South Carolina 29810. **T:** 1 803 584-3500
E: wdog935@aol.com
W: http://www.bigdogradio.com
Editorial Profile: WDOG-FM is a commercial station owned by Good-Radio Broadcast Co. The format of the station is country. WDOG-FM broadcasts to the Allendale, SC area at 93.5 FM.

WDOH-FM
Owner: Childers Media Group, LLC
Editorial: 57 Town Sq, Lima, Ohio 45801-4950. **T:** 1 419 331-1600
E: literock1071@aol.com
W: http://www.literock1071.com
Editorial Profile: WDOH-FM is a commercial station owned by Childers Media Group, LLC. The format of the station is Lite Rock/Lite AC. WDOH-FM broadcasts to the Delphos, OH area at 107.1 FM.

WDOK-FM
Owner: CBS Radio
Editorial: 2644 Saint Clair Ave NE, Cleveland, Ohio 44114-4015. **T:** 1 216 696-0123
W: http://new102.cbslocal.com
Editorial Profile: WDOK-FM is a commercial station owned by CBS Radio. The format of the station is adult contemporary. WDOK-FM broadcasts to the Cleveland area at 102.1 FM.

WDOM-FM
Owner: Corporation of Providence College
Editorial: 549 River Ave, Providence, Rhode Island 02918-7000. **T:** 1 401 865-2460
E: wdomdj@yahoo.com
Editorial Profile: WDOM-FM is a non-commercial station owned by the Corporation of Providence College. The format of the station is college variety. WDOM-FM broadcasts to the Providence, RI area at 91.3 FM. The station closes operations during the summer months, beginning in May.

WDOR-AM
Owner: Door County Broadcasting Co.
Editorial: 800 S 15th Ave, Sturgeon Bay, Wisconsin 54235. **T:** 1 920 743-4411
E: email@wdor.com **W:** http://www.wdor.com
Editorial Profile: WDOR-AM is a commercial station owned by Door County Broadcasting Co. The format of the station is adult contemporary. WDOR-AM broadcasts to the Door County, WI area at 910 AM.

WDOR-FM
Owner: Door County Broadcasting Co.
Editorial: 800 S 15th Ave, Sturgeon Bay, Wisconsin 54235. **T:** 1 920 743-4411
E: email@wdor.com **W:** http://www.wdor.com
Editorial Profile: WDOR-FM is a commercial station owned by Door County Broadcasting Co. The format of the station is adult contemporary music. WDOR-FM broadcasts to the Sturgeon Bay, WI area at 93.9 FM.

WDOS-AM
Owner: Townsquare Media, LLC
Editorial: 34 Chestnut St, Oneonta, New York 13820-2466. **T:** 1 607 432-1030
W: http://cnynews.com
Editorial Profile: WDOS-AM is a commercial station owned by Townsquare Media, LLC. The format of the station is news, sports and talk. WDOS-AM broadcasts to the Oneonta, NY area at 730 AM.

WDOT-FM
Owner: Northeast Broadcasting Co.
Editorial: 169 River St, Montpelier, Vermont 5602. **T:** 1 802 223-2396
E: feedback@pointfm.com
W: http://www.pointfm.com
Editorial Profile: WDOT-FM is a commercial station owned by Northeast Broadcasting Co. The format of the station is adult album alternative music. The station is a simulcast of WNCS-FM. WDOT-FM broadcasts to the Montpelier, VA area at 95.7 FM.

WDOV-AM
Owner: Clear Channel Media and Entertainment
Editorial: 1575 McKee Rd, Ste 206, Dover, Delaware 19904. **T:** 1 302 674-1410
W: http://www.wdov.com
Editorial Profile: WDOV-AM is a commercial station owned by Clear Channel Media and Entertainment. The format of the station is news and talk. WDOV-AM broadcasts in the Dover, DE area at 1410 AM.

WDPC-AM
Owner: Word Christian Broadcasting Inc.
Editorial: 8451 S Cherokee Blvd, Ste B, Douglasville, Georgia 30134.
T: 1 770 920-1520 **E:** wordchr@bellsouth.net
W: http://www.wordchristianbroadcasting.com
Editorial Profile: WDPC-AM is a commercial station owned by Word Christian Broadcasting Inc. The format of station is Christian and religious programming and gospel music. WDPC-AM broadcasts to the Douglasville, GA area at 1500 AM.

WDPG-FM
Owner: Dayton Public Radio Inc.
Editorial: 126 N Main St, Ste 110, Dayton, Ohio 45402. **T:** 1 937 496-3850
E: dpr@dpr.org **W:** http://www.dpr.org
Editorial Profile: WDPG-FM is a non-commercial station owned by Dayton Public Radio Inc. The format of the station is classical music. WDPG-FM broadcasts to the Dayton, OH area at 89.9 FM.

WDPN-AM
Owner: Peterson(Donald A.)
Editorial: 393 Smyth Ave, Alliance, Ohio 44601. **T:** 1 330 821-1111
E: news@q92radio.com
Editorial Profile: WDPN-AM is a commercial station owned by Donald A. Peterson. The format of the station is easy listening. WDPN-AM broadcasts to the Cleveland-Canton, OH area at 1310 AM.

WDPR-FM
Owner: Dayton Public Radio Inc.
Editorial: 126 N Main St, Ste 110, Dayton, Ohio 45402. **T:** 1 937 496-3850
E: dpr@dpr.org **W:** http://www.dpr.org
Editorial Profile: WDPR-FM is a non-commercial station owned by Dayton Public Radio Inc. The format of the station is classical music. WDPR-FM broadcasts to the Dayton, OH area at 88.1 FM.

WDPS-FM
Owner: Dayton Public Schools
Editorial: 741 Washington St Ste 1200, Dayton, Ohio 45402-8446. **T:** 1 937 542-7182
W: http://home.dps.k12.oh.us/departments/PIO/wdps-fm.html
Editorial Profile: WDPS-FM is a non-commercial station owned by Dayton Public Schools. The format of the station is jazz and news. WDPS-FM broadcasts to the Dayton, OH area at 89.5 FM.

WDQN-AM
Owner: Du Quoin Broadcasting Co.
Editorial: US Route 51 North, Du Quoin, Illinois 62832. **T:** 1 618 542-3894
E: wdqnradio@onecliq.net
Editorial Profile: WDQN-AM is a commercial station owned by Du Quoin Broadcasting Co. The format of station is country. WDQN-AM broadcasts to the Du Quoin, IL area at 1580 AM.

WDQN-FM
Owner: Three Angels Broadcasting Network Inc.
Editorial: 2337 US Route 51, Du Quoin, Illinois 62832-4404. **T:** 1 618 627-4651
E: 95.9fm@3abnradio.org
W: http://www.3abnradio.org
Editorial Profile: WDQN-FM is a commercial station owned by Three Angels Broadcasting Network Inc. The format of the station is religious programming. WDQN-FM broadcasts to the Du Quoin, IL area at 95.9 FM.

WDQX-FM
Owner: L & L Radio
Editorial: 331 Fulton St, Peoria, Illinois 61602-1486. **T:** 1 309 637-3700
W: http://www.1023maxfm.com
Editorial Profile: WDQX-FM is a commercial station owned by L & L Radio. The format of the station is rock. WDQX-FM broadcasts to the Peoria, IL, area at 102.3 FM.

WDRC-AM
Owner: Connoisseur Media
Editorial: 869 Blue Hills Ave, Bloomfield, Connecticut 06002-3710. **T:** 1 860 243-1115
W: http://www.talkofconnecticut.com
Editorial Profile: WDRC-AM is a commercial station owned by Connoisseur Media. The format of the station is talk. WDRC-AM broadcasts to the Bloomfield, CT area at 1360 AM.

WDRC-FM
Owner: Connoisseur Media
Editorial: 869 Blue Hills Ave, Bloomfield, Connecticut 06002-3710. **T:** 1 860 243-1115
W: http://www.drcfm.com
Editorial Profile: WDRC-FM is a commercial station owned by Connoisseur Media. The format of the station is oldies. WDRC-FM broadcasts in the Bloomfield, CT area at 102.9 FM.

WDRE-FM
Owner: Equinox Broadcasting Corp.
Editorial: 101 Main St, Johnson City, New York 13790-2426. **T:** 1 607 772-1005
E: info@equinoxbroadcasting.com
Editorial Profile: WDRE-FM is a commercial station owned by Equinox Broadcasting Corp. The format of the station is alternative rock music. WDRE-FM broadcasts to the Johnson City, NY area at 100.5 FM.

WDRJ-AM
Owner: Communicom Broadcasting
Editorial: 2994 E Grand Blvd, Detroit, Michigan 48202-3134. **T:** 1 313 871-1440
W: http://www.1440wdrj.com
Editorial Profile: WDRJ-AM is a commercial station owned by Communicom Broadcasting. The format of the station is gospel. WDRJ-AM broadcasts to the Detroit area at 1440 AM.

WDRK-FM
Owner: Mid-West Family Broadcasting
Editorial: 944 Harlem St, Altoona, Wisconsin 54720-1127. **T:** 1 715 832-1530
W: http://www.bobfm999.com
Editorial Profile: WDRK-FM is a commercial station owned by Mid-West Family Broadcasting. The format of the station is adult hits. WDRK-FM broadcasts in the Altoona, WI area at 99.9 FM.

WDRM-FM
Owner: Clear Channel Media and Entertainment
Editorial: 26869 Peoples Rd, Madison, Alabama 35756. **T:** 1 256 309-2400
W: http://www.wdrm.com
Editorial Profile: WDRM-FM is a commercial station owned by Clear Channel Media and Entertainment. The format of the station is contemporary country. WDRM-FM broadcasts to the Madison, AL area at 102.1 FM.

WDRQ-FM
Owner: Cumulus Media Inc.
Editorial: 3011 W Grand Blvd Ste 800, Detroit, Michigan 48202-3086. **T:** 1 313 871-9300
W: http://www.nashfm931.com
Editorial Profile: WDRQ-FM is a commercial station owned by Cumulus Media Inc. The format of the station is contemporary country. WDRQ-FM broadcasts to the Detroit area at 93.1 FM.

WDRR-FM
Owner: Beasley Broadcast Group
Editorial: 4051 Jimmie Dyess Pkwy, Augusta, Georgia 30909. **T:** 1 706 396-7000
W: http://ilovebobfm.com
Editorial Profile: WDRR-FM is a commercial station owned by Beasley Broadcast Group. The format of the station is adult hits. WDRR-FM broadcasts to the Augusta, GA area on 93.9 FM.

WDRU-AM
Owner: Truth Broadcasting
Editorial: 4405 Providence Ln, Ste D, Winston Salem, North Carolina 27106.
T: 1 336 759-0363 **E:** info@wtru.com
W: http://www.wtru.com
Editorial Profile: WDRU-AM is a commercial station owned by Truth Broadcasting. The format of the station is Christian talk. WDRU-AM broadcasts to the Winston Salem, NC area at 1030 AM.

WDRV-FM
Owner: Hubbard Radio, LLC
Editorial: 875 N Michigan Ave, Ste 1510, Chicago, Illinois 60611-1874.
T: 1 312 274-9710 **W:** http://www.wdrv.com
Editorial Profile: WDRV-FM is a commercial station owned by Hubbard Radio, LLC. The format of the station is classic rock. WDRV-FM broadcasts to the entire Chicago metro area at 97.1 FM.

WDSC-AM
Owner: Clear Channel Media and Entertainment
Editorial: 181 E Evans St Ste 311, Florence, South Carolina 29506-5505.
T: 1 843 667-4600
Editorial Profile: WDSC-AM is a commercial station owned by Clear Channel Media and Entertainment. The format of the station is gospel. WDSC-AM broadcasts to the Florence, SC area at 800 AM.

WDSD-FM
Owner: Clear Channel Media and Entertainment
Editorial: 1575 McKee Rd, Dover, Delaware 19904-1382. **T:** 1 302 674-1410
W: http://www.wdsd.com
Editorial Profile: WDSD-FM is a commercial station owned by Clear Channel Media and Entertainment. The format of the station is classic and contemporary country. WDSD-FM broadcasts to the Dover, DE area at 94.7 FM.

WDSJ-FM
Owner: Clear Channel Media and Entertainment
Editorial: 101 Pine St, Dayton, Ohio 45402.
T: 1 937 224-1137
W: http://www.big1065.com
Editorial Profile: WDSJ-FM is a commercial station owned by Clear Channel Media and Entertainment. The format of the station is classic hits. WDSJ-FM broadcasts in the Dayton, OH area at 106.5 FM.

WDSL-AM
Owner: Shoaf, Farren
Editorial: 431 Eaton Rd, Mocksville, North Carolina 27028-8653. **T:** 1 704 902-9640
E: wdsl1520am@yahoo.com
W: http://www.wdsl1520.com
Editorial Profile: WSDL-AM is a commercial station owned by Farren Soaf. The format of the station is gospel and talk radio. WSDL-AM broadcasts to the Mocksville, NC area at 1520 AM.

WDSM-AM
Owner: Midwest Communications Inc.
Editorial: 715 E Central Entrance, Duluth, Minnesota 55811. **T:** 1 218 722-4321
E: info@wdsm710.com
W: http://www.wdsm710.com
Editorial Profile: WDSM-AM is a commercial station owned by Midwest Communications Inc. The format of the station is news and talk. WDSM-AM broadcasts to the Duluth, MN area at 710 AM.

WDSN-FM
Owner: Priority Communications
Editorial: 12 W Long Ave, Du Bois, Pennsylvania 15801-2100. **T:** 1 814 375-5260
E: news@sunny1065.fm
W: http://www.sunny1065.fm
Editorial Profile: WDSN-FM is a commercial station owned by Priority Communications. The format of the station is adult contemporary music. WDSN-FM broadcasts to the Du Bois, PA area at 106.5 FM.

WDSO-FM
Owner: Duneland School Corp.
Editorial: 2125 S 11th St, Chesterton, Indiana 46304. **T:** 1 219 983-3777
W: http://www.wdso.org
Editorial Profile: WDSO-FM is a commercial station owned by Duneland School Corp. The format of the station is variety. WDSO-FM broadcasts to students and faculty in the Chesterton High School area at 88.3 FM. The station only airs during the school year and ceases operations during June, July and August.

WDSR-AM
Owner: Newman Media Inc.
Editorial: 2485 S Marion Ave, Lake City, Florida 32025-0051. **T:** 1 386 961-9494
W: http://northfloridanow.com
Editorial Profile: WDSR-AM is a commercial station owned by Newman Media Inc. The format of the station is country music. WDSR-AM broadcasts to the Lake City, FL area at 1340 AM.

WDST-FM
Owner: Regional Radio Group
Editorial: 293 Tinker St, Woodstock, New York 12498-1132. **T:** 1 845 679-7600
E: live@wdst.com **W:** http://www.wdst.com
Editorial Profile: WDST-FM is a commercial station owned by Regional Radio Group. The format of the station is adult album alternative music. WDST-FM broadcasts to the Woodstock, NY, area at 100.1 FM.

WDSY-FM
Owner: CBS Radio
Editorial: 651 Holiday Dr, Pittsburgh, Pennsylvania 15220-2740. **T:** 1 412 920-9400
W: http://y108.cbslocal.com

Editorial Profile: WDSY-FM is a commercial station owned by CBS Radio. The format of the station is contemporary country. WDSY-FM broadcasts to the Pittsburgh area at 107.9 FM.

WDTK-AM

Owner: Salem Communications
Editorial: 2 Radio Plaza St, Ferndale, Michigan 48220-2129. **T:** 1 248 581-1234
W: http://www.wdtkam.com
Editorial Profile: WDTK-AM is a commercial station owned by Salem Communications. The format of the station is news and talk. WDTK-AM broadcasts to the Detroit area at 1400 AM.

WDTR-FM

Owner: Superior Communications
Editorial: 148 E Grand River Rd, Williamston, Michigan 48895-9411. **T:** 1 888 887-7139
E: 411@smile.fm **W:** http://www.smile.fm

WDTW-FM

Owner: Clear Channel Media and Entertainment
Editorial: 27675 Halsted Rd, Farmington Hills, Michigan 48331. **T:** 1 248 324-5800
W: http://www.thedrocks.com/main.html
Editorial Profile: WDTW-FM is a commercial station owned by Clear Channel Media and Entertainment. The format of the station is classic rock. WDTW-FM broadcasts to the Detroit area at 106.7 FM.

WDTX-FM

Owner: Sunrise Broadcasting, LLC
Editorial: 1110 E Wausau Ave, Wausau, Wisconsin 54403-3149. **T:** 1 715 845-8218
W: http://www.espn1005.com
Editorial Profile: WDTX-FM is a commercial station owned by Sunrise Broadcating, LLC. The format of the station is sports. WDTX-FM broadcasts to Rothschild and Wausau, WI areas at 100.5 FM.

WDUB-FM

Owner: Denison University
Editorial: Denison University, Slaytor Hall, Granville, Ohio 43023. **T:** 1 740 587-6382
W: http://doobieradio.ning.com
Editorial Profile: WDUB-FM is a non-commercial station owned by Denison University. The format of the station is adult album alternative. WDUB-FM broadcasts to the Granville, OH area at 91.1 FM.

WDUK-FM

Owner: Stimpson(Edwin)
Editorial: 901 N Promenade St, Havana, Illinois 62644. **T:** 1 309 543-3331
Editorial Profile: WDUK-FM is a commercial station owned by Edwin Stimpson. The format of the station is country music and news. WDUK-FM broadcasts to the Havana, IL area at 99.3.

WDUN-AM

Owner: Jacobs Media Corp.
Editorial: 1102 Thompson Bridge Rd, Gainesville, Georgia 30501. **T:** 1 770 532-9921
E: info@jacobsmedia.net
W: http://www.wdun.com
Editorial Profile: WDUN-AM is a commercial station owned by Jacobs Media Corp. The format of the station is news, talk and sports. WDUN-AM broadcasts to the Atlanta area at 550 AM.

WDUN-FM

Owner: Jacobs Media Corp.
Editorial: 1102 Thompson Bridge Rd, Gainesville, Georgia 30501. **T:** 1 770 532-9921
E: info@jacobsmedia.net
W: http://www.wdun.com
Editorial Profile: WDUN-FM is a commercial station owned by Jacobs Media. The format of the station is news/talk. WDUN-FM broadcasts to the Atlanta area at 102.9 FM.

WDUV-FM

Owner: Cox Media Group, Inc.
Editorial: 11300 4th St N, Ste 300, Saint Petersburg, Florida 33716. **T:** 1 727 579-2000
E: 1055comments@coxtampa.com
W: http://www.wduv.com
Editorial Profile: WDUV-FM is a commercial station owned by Cox Media Group, Inc. The format of the station is Lite Rock/Lite AC. WDUV-FM broadcasts to the Tampa, FL area at 105.5 FM.

WDUX-AM

Owner: Laird Broadcasting
Editorial: 200 Tower Rd, Waupaca, Wisconsin 54981. **T:** 1 715 258-5528 **E:** mail@wdux.net
W: http://www.wduxradio.com

Editorial Profile: WDUX-AM is a commercial station owned by Laird Broadcasting. The format of the station is classic country. WDUX-AM broadcasts to the Waupaca, WI area at 800 AM.

WDUX-FM

Owner: Laird Broadcasting
Editorial: 200 Tower Rd, Waupaca, Wisconsin 54981. **T:** 1 715 258-5528 **E:** news@wdux.net
W: http://www.wduxradio.com
Editorial Profile: WDUX-FM is a commercial station owned by Laird Broadcasting. The format of the station is adult contemporary. WDUX-FM broadcasts to the Waupaca, WI area at 92.7 FM.

WDUZ-AM

Owner: Cumulus Media Inc.
Editorial: 810 Victoria St, Green Bay, Wisconsin 54302-2465. **T:** 1 920 468-4100
E: thefan@cumulus.com
W: http://www.thefan1075.com
Editorial Profile: WDUZ-AM is a commercial station owned by Cumulus Media Inc. The format of the station is sports. WDUZ-AM broadcasts to the Green Bay, WI area at 1400 AM.

WDUZ-FM

Owner: Cumulus Media Inc.
Editorial: 810 Victoria St, Green Bay, Wisconsin 54302-2465. **T:** 1 920 468-4100
E: thefan@cumulus.com
W: http://www.thefan1075.com
Editorial Profile: WDUZ-FM is a commercial station owned by Cumulus Media Inc. The format of the station is sports. WDUZ-FM broadcasts to the Green Bay, WI area at 107.5 FM.

WDVA-AM

Owner: Mitchell Communications
Editorial: 1 Radio Ln, Danville, Virginia 24541-5235. **T:** 1 434 797-1250
E: wdvaradio@gmail.com
Editorial Profile: WDVA-AM is a commercial station that is owned by Mitchell Communications. The format of the station is gospel. WDVA-AM broadcasts to the Danville, VA area at 1250 AM.

WDVD-FM

Owner: Cumulus Media Inc.
Editorial: 3011 W Grand Blvd, Ste 800, Detroit, Michigan 48202-3086.
T: 1 313 871-3030
W: http://www.963wdvd.com
Editorial Profile: WDVD-FM is a commercial station owned by Cumulus Media Inc. The format of the station is hot adult contemporary music. WDVD-FM broadcasts to the Detroit area at 96.3 FM.

WDVE-FM

Owner: Clear Channel Media and Entertainment
Editorial: 200 Fleet St, Pittsburgh, Pennsylvania 15220-2910. **T:** 1 412 937-1441
E: feedback@dve.com **W:** http://www.dve.com
Editorial Profile: WDVE-FM is a commercial station owned by Clear Channel Media and Entertainment. The format for the station is classic rock. WDVE-FM broadcasts to the Pittsburgh area at 102.5 FM.

WDVH-AM

Owner: Marc Radio Group, LLC
Editorial: 100 Nw 76Th Dr Ste 2, Gainesville, Florida 32607-6659. **T:** 1 352 313-3150
W: http://www.flafnr.com
Editorial Profile: WDVH-AM is a commercial station owned by Marc Radio Group, LLC. The format of the station is news/talk. WDVH-AM broadcasts to the Gainesville, FL area at 980 AM. WDVH-AM airs WRZN-AM's programming.

WDVH-FM

Owner: Marc Radio Group, LLC
Editorial: 100 NW 76th Dr Ste 2, Gainesville, Florida 32607-6659. **T:** 1 352 463-1345
W: http://www.1017hankfm.com
Editorial Profile: WDVH-FM is a commercial station owned by Marc Radio Group, LLC. The format of the station is classic country. WDVH-FM broadcasts to the Gainesville, FL area at 101.7 FM.

WDVI-FM

Owner: Clear Channel Media and Entertainment
Editorial: 100 Chestnut St Ste 1700, Rochester, New York 14604-2418.
T: 1 585 454-4884
W: http://www.mydrivefm.com

Editorial Profile: WDVI-FM is a commercial station owned by Clear Channel Media and Entertainment. The format of the station is adult contemporary. WDVI-FM broadcasts to the Rochester, NY area at 100.5 FM.

WDVM-AM

Owner: Starboard Media Foundation Inc.
Editorial: 1752 Brackett Ave, Eau Claire, Wisconsin 54701. **T:** 1 715 855-1439
E: info@relevantradio.com
W: http://www.relevantradio.com
Editorial Profile: WDVM-AM is a commercial station owned by Starboard Media Foundation Inc. The format of the station is religious. WDVM-AM broadcasts to the Eau Claire, WI area at 1050 AM.

WDVR-FM

Owner: Penn-Jersey Educational Radio Corp.
Editorial: 604 Route 604, Sergeantsville, New Jersey 08557-0191. **T:** 1 609 397-1620
E: webmaster@wdvrfm.org
W: http://wdvrfm.org
Editorial Profile: WDVR-FM is a non-commercial station owned by the Penn-Jersey Educational Radio Corp. The format of the station is variety. WDVR-FM broadcasts to the New York area at 89.7 FM.

WDVT-FM

Owner: Pamal Broadcasting Ltd.
Editorial: 67 Merchants Row, Rutland, Vermont 5701. **T:** 1 802 775-7500
E: thedrive@catamountradio.com
W: http://www.945thedrive.com
Editorial Profile: WDVT-FM is a commercial station owned by Pamal Broadcasting Ltd. The format of the station is classic hits. WDVT-FM broadcasts to the Rutland, VT area at 94.5 FM.

WDVW-FM

Owner: Grace Broadcasting Services, Inc.
Editorial: 25 Stonebrook Pl Ste G #322, Jackson, Tennessee 38305-3686.
T: 1 731 663-2327
W: http://www.gracebroadcasting.com
Editorial Profile: WDVW-FM is a commercial station owned by Grace Broadcasting Services, Inc. The format of the station is Christian AC. WDVW-FM broadcasts to the Memphis, TN area at 105.3 FM.

WDVX-FM

Owner: Cumberland Communities Communications Corp.
Editorial: 2415 Andersonville Hwy, Clinton, Tennessee 37716. **T:** 1 865 494-2020
E: studio@wdvx.com **W:** http://www.wdvx.com
Editorial Profile: WDVX-FM is a non-commercial station owned by Cumberland Communities Communications Corp. The format of the station is variety. WDVX-FM broadcasts to the Clinton, TN area at a frequency of 89.9.

WDWD-AM

Owner: Walt Disney Co.
Editorial: 900 Circle 75, Ste 1320, Atlanta, Georgia 30339-3095. **T:** 1 770 541-7472
W: http://radiodisney.com/atlanta
Editorial Profile: WDWD-AM is a commercial station owned by Walt Disney Co. The format of the station is children's programming. WDWD-AM broadcasts to the Atlanta area at 590 AM.

WDWG-FM

Owner: First Media Radio LLC
Editorial: 12714 E State Highway 97, Rocky Mount, North Carolina 27803-4626.
T: 1 252 442-8092
E: wecare@firstmedianc.com
W: http://www.bigdawg985.com
Editorial Profile: WDWG-FM is a commercial station owned by First Media Radio LLC. The format of the station is contemporary country. WDWG-FM broadcasts to the Rocky Mount, NC area at 98.5 FM.

WDWN-FM

Owner: Cayuga Community College
Editorial: 197 Franklin St, Auburn, New York 13021. **T:** 1 315 255-1743 2284
E: wdwn@hotmail.com
W: http://www.wdwn.fm
Editorial Profile: WDWN-FM is a non-commercial station owned by Cayuga Community College. The format of the station is rock alternative. WDWN-FM broadcasts to the Auburn, NY area at 89.1 FM.

WDWQ-FM

Owner: Midwest Communications Inc.
Editorial: 824 S 3Rd St, Terre Haute, Indiana 47807-4609. **T:** 1 812 232-4161
W: http://q1027.com

Editorial Profile: WDWQ-FM is a commercial station owned by Midwest Communications Inc.. The format of the station is contemporary country. WDWQ-FM broadcasts to the Terre Haute, IN area at 102.7 FM.

WDWR-AM

Owner: Divine Word Communications
Editorial: 2 Portofino Dr, Ste 1704, Gulf Breeze, Florida 32561-2489.
T: 1 850 777-1568
E: info@divinewordradio.com
W: http://www.divinewordradio.com
Editorial Profile: WDWR-AM is a non-commercial station owned by Divine Word Communications. The format of the station is religious. WDWR-AM broadcasts to the Pensacola, FL area at 1230 AM.

WDWS-AM

Owner: D.W.S. Inc.
Editorial: 2301 S Neil St, Champaign, Illinois 61820. **T:** 1 217 351-5300
E: newsroom@wdws.com
W: http://www.wdws.com
Editorial Profile: WDWS-AM is a commercial station owned by D.W.S. Inc. The format of the station is news and talk programming. WDWS-AM broadcasts to the Champaign, IL area at 1400 AM.

WDXB-FM

Owner: Clear Channel Media and Entertainment
Editorial: 600 Beacon Pkwy W, Birmingham, Alabama 35209-3120. **T:** 1 205 439-9600
W: http://www.1025thebull.com
Editorial Profile: WDXB-FM is a commercial station owned by Clear Channel Media and Entertainment. The format of the station is country music. WDXB-FM broadcasts to the Birmingham, AL area at 102.5 FM.

WDXC-FM

Owner: Cornett (Jackie&Howard)
Editorial: 12548 Orby Cantrell Hwy, Pound, Virginia 24279-4812. **T:** 1 276 796-5411
E: wdxc@wdxcfm.com **W:** http://wdxcfm.com
Editorial Profile: WDXC-FM is a commercial station owned by Jackie & Howard Cornett. The format of the station is contemporary country. WDXC-FM broadcasts to the Pound, VA area at 102.3 FM.

WDXE-AM

Owner: Lakewood Communications LLC
Editorial: 29 Public Sq, Lawrenceburg, Tennessee 38464. **T:** 1 931 762-4411
E: wdxe@wdxe.com **W:** http://www.wdxe.com
Editorial Profile: WDXE-AM is a commercial station owned by Lakewood Communications LLC. The format of the station is classic country. WDXE-AM broadcasts to the Lawrenceburg, TN area at 1370 AM.

WDXE-FM

Owner: Lakewood Communications LLC
Editorial: 29 Public Sq, Lawrenceburg, Tennessee 38464-3351. **T:** 1 931 762-4411
E: wdxe@wdxeradio.com
W: http://www.wdxe.com
Editorial Profile: WDXE-FM is a commercial station owned by Lakewood Communications LLC. The format of the station is adult contemporary music. WDXE-FM broadcasts to the Lawrenceburg, TN area at 106.7 FM.

WDXI-AM

Owner: Hunt(Gerald W.)
Editorial: 1 WDXI Drive, Jackson, Tennessee 38305-4124. **T:** 1 731 427-9611
E: kool103fm@yahoo.com
Editorial Profile: WDXI-AM is a commercial station owned by Gerald W. Hunt. The format of the station is news and talk. WDXI-AM broadcasts to the Jackson, TN area at 1310 AM.

WDXO-FM

Owner: TeleSouth Communications Inc.
Editorial: 110 W Monticello St, Brookhaven, Mississippi 39601. **T:** 1 601 835-5005
E: supertalk1021@yahoo.com
Editorial Profile: WDXO-FM is a commercial station owned by TeleSouth Communications Inc. The format of the station is sports. WDXO-FM broadcasts to the Brookhaven, MS area at 92.9 FM.

WDXQ-AM

Owner: Georgia Eagle Broadcasting Inc.
Editorial: 218 Eastman Hwy, Hawkinsville, Georgia 31036-5936. **T:** 1 478 892-9061
Editorial Profile: WDXQ-AM is a commercial station owned by Georgia Eagle Broadcasting Inc. The format of the station is classic hits.

WDXQ-AM broadcasts to Cochran, GA at 1440 AM.

WDXR-AM
Owner: Bristol Broadcasting
Editorial: 6000 Bristol Dr, Paducah, Kentucky 42003-9213. **T:** 1 270 554-8255
E: news@wkyx.com **W:** http://www.wkyx.com
Editorial Profile: WDXR-AM is a commercial station owned by Bristol Broadcasting. The format of the station is talk. WDXR-AM broadcasts to the Paducah, KY area at 1430 AM.

WDXX-FM
Owner: Broadsouth Communications
Editorial: 505 Lauderdale St, Selma, Alabama 36701-4528. **T:** 1 334 875-3350
W: http://www.fuzion100.com
Editorial Profile: WDXX-FM is a commercial station owned by Broadsouth Communications. The format of the station is country. WDXX-FM broadcasts to the Selma, AL area at 100.1 FM. The station airs WINL-FM's programming.

WDXY-AM
Owner: Miller Communications Inc.
Editorial: 51 Commerce St, Sumter, South Carolina 29150. **T:** 1 803 775-2321
E: production@miller.fm
W: http://www.miller.fm
Editorial Profile: WDXY-AM is a commercial station owned by Miller Communications Inc. The format of the station is news, talk and sports. WDXY-AM broadcasts to the Sumter, SC area at 1240 AM.

WDXZ-AM
Owner: Gulf Coast Broadcasting Company, Inc.
Editorial: 2421 E 2nd St, Gulf Shores, Alabama 36542-3177. **T:** 1 251 967-1057
Editorial Profile: WDXZ-AM is a commercial station owned by Gulf Coast Broadcasting Company, Inc. The format of the station is Southern Gospel. WDXZ-AM broadcasts to the Robertsdale, AL area at 1000 AM.

WDYK-FM
Owner: West Virgina Radio Corporation of the Alleganies
Editorial: 15 Industrial Blvd E, Cumberland, Maryland 21502. **T:** 1 301 759-1005
W: http://www.cumberlandsmagic.com
Editorial Profile: WDYK-FM is a commercial station owned by West Virgina Radio Corporation of the Alleganies. The format of the station is adult contemporary. WDYK-FM broadcasts to the Cumberland, MD area at 100.5 FM.

WDYN-AM
Owner: Tennessee Temple University
Editorial: 1815 Union Ave, Chattanooga, Tennessee 37404-3530. **T:** 1 423 493-4382
E: wdyn@wdyn.com **W:** http://www.wdyn.com
Editorial Profile: WDYN-AM is a commercial station owned by Tennessee Temple University. The format of the station is religious. WDYN–AM broadcasts to the Chattanooga, TN area at 980 AM.

WDYZ-AM
Owner: Walt Disney Co.
Editorial: 610 Sycamore St, Ste 220, Celebration, Florida 34747-4996.
T: 1 407 566-2033
W: http://radio.disney.go.com/music/yourstation/orlando/index.html
Editorial Profile: WDYZ-AM is a commercial station owned by Walt Disney Co. The format of the station is children and family programming. WDYZ-AM broadcasts to the Celebration, FL area at 990 AM.

WDZ-AM
Owner: Neuhoff Communications
Editorial: 250 N Water St, Ste 100, Decatur, Illinois 62523-1300. **T:** 1 217 423-9744
W: http://www.espndecatur.com
Editorial Profile: WDZ-AM is a commercial station owned by Neuhoff Communications. The format of the station is sports. WDZ-AM broadcasts to the Decatur, IL area at 1050 AM.

WDZH-FM
Owner: CBS Radio
Editorial: 26495 American Dr, Southfield, Michigan 48034-6114. **T:** 1 248 327-2900
W: http://987ampradio.cbslocal.com
Editorial Profile: WDZH-FM is a commercial station owned by CBS Radio. The format of the station is Top 40/CHR. WDZH-FM broadcasts to the Detroit area at 98.7 FM.

WDZN-FM
Owner: West Virginia Radio Corporation of the Alleghenies
Editorial: 15 Industrial Blvd E, Cumberland, Maryland 21502-4106. **T:** 1 301 759-1005
W: http://www.tristateswolf.com
Editorial Profile: WVMD-FM is a commercial station owned by West Virginia Radio Corporation of the Alleghenies. The format of the station is contemporary country. WVMD-FM broadcasts to the Romney, WV/ Cumberland, MD area at 100.1 FM.

WDZQ-FM
Owner: Neuhoff Communications
Editorial: 250 N Water St, Ste 100, Decatur, Illinois 62523-1300. **T:** 1 217 423-9744
W: http://www.95q.com
Editorial Profile: WDZQ-FM is a commercial station owned by Neuhoff Communications. The format of the station is contemporary country music. WDZQ-FM broadcasts to the Decatur, IL at 95.1 FM.

WDZZ-FM
Owner: Cumulus Media Inc.
Editorial: 6317 Taylor Dr, Flint, Michigan 48507. **T:** 1 810 238-7300
W: http://www.wdzz.com
Editorial Profile: WDZZ-FM is a commercial station owned by Cumulus Media Inc. The format of the station is urban adult contemporary. WDZZ-FM broadcasts to the Flint, MI area at 92.7 FM.

WEAA-FM
Owner: Morgan State University
Editorial: 1700 E Cold Spring Ln, Baltimore, Maryland 21251-0001. **T:** 1 443 885-3564
E: info@weaa.org **W:** http://www.weaa.org
Editorial Profile: WEAA-FM is a non-commercial station owned by Morgan State University. The format of the station is news, talk and jazz music. WEAA-FM broadcasts to the students and faculty of Morgan State College at 88.9 FM.

WEAF-AM
Owner: Glory Communications Inc.
Editorial: 1709 Lyndhurst Dr, Camden, South Carolina 29020-3339. **T:** 1 803 432-8717
Editorial Profile: WREA-AM is a commercial station owned by Glory Communications Inc. The format of the station is black gospel music. WREA-AM broadcasts to the Camden, SC area at 1130 AM.

WEAG-AM
Owner: Dickerson Broadcasting
Editorial: 1421 S Water St, Starke, Florida 32091. **T:** 1 904 964-5001
Editorial Profile: WEAG-AM is a commercial station owned by Dickerson Broadcasting. The format of the station is contemporary country. WEAG-AM broadcasts to the Starke, FL area at 1490 AM.

WEAG-FM
Owner: Dickerson Broadcasting
Editorial: 1421 S Water St, Starke, Florida 32091-4508. **T:** 1 904 964-5001

WEAI-FM
Owner: Jacksonville Area Radio Broadcasters, Inc.
Editorial: 2161 Old State Rd, Jacksonville, Illinois 62650. **T:** 1 217 245-7171
W: http://wlds.com
Editorial Profile: WEAI-FM is a commercial station owned by the Jacksonville Area Radio Broadcasters, Inc. The format of the station is hot adult contemporary. WEAI-FM broadcasts in the Jacksonville, IL area at 107.1 FM.

WEAL-AM
Owner: Entercom Communications Corp.
Editorial: 7819 National Service Rd, Ste 401, Greensboro, North Carolina 27409.
T: 1 336 605-5200
W: http://www.1510weal.com
Editorial Profile: WEAL-AM is a commercial station owned by Entercom Communications Corp. The format of the station is gospel music. WEAL-AM broadcasts to the Greensboro-Winston Salem, NC area at 1510 AM.

WEAM-FM
Owner: Davis Broadcasting
Editorial: 2203 Wynnton Rd, Columbus, Georgia 31906. **T:** 1 706 576-3565
Editorial Profile: WEAM-FM is a commercial station owned by Davis Broadcasting. The format of the station is gospel music. WEAM-FM broadcasts to the Columbus, GA area at 100.7 FM.

WEAN-FM
Owner: Cumulus Media Inc.
Editorial: 1502 Wampanoag Trl, Riverside, Rhode Island 02915-1018. **T:** 1 401 433-4200
W: http://www.630wpro.com
Editorial Profile: WEAN-FM is a commercial station owned by Cumulus Media Inc. The format of the station is news and talk. WEAN-FM broadcasts to the Riverside, RI area at 99.7 FM.

WEAQ-AM
Owner: Mid-West Family Broadcasting
Editorial: 944 Harlem St, Altoona, Wisconsin 54720-1127. **T:** 1 715 832-1530
W: http://www.oldies1150am.com
Editorial Profile: WEAQ-AM is a commericial station owned by Mid-West Family Broadcasting. The format of the station is oldies. WEAQ-AM broadcasts to the Altoona, WI area at 1150 AM.

WEAS-FM
Owner: Cumulus Media Inc.
Editorial: 214 Television Cir, Savannah, Georgia 31406-4519. **T:** 1 912 961-9000
W: http://www.e93fm.com
Editorial Profile: WEAS-FM is a commercial station owned by Cumulus Media Inc. The format of the station is urban contemporary. WEAS-FM broadcasts to the Savannah, GA area at 93.1 FM.

WEAT-FM
Owner: Palm Beach Broadcasting, LLC
Editorial: 701 Northpoint Pkwy Ste 500, West Palm Beach, Florida 33407-1960.
T: 1 561 616-4777
W: http://www.sunny1079.com
Editorial Profile: WEAT-FM is a commercial station owned by Palm Beach Broadcasting, LLC. The format of the station is adult contemporary. WPBZ-FM broadcasts to the West Palm Beach, FL area at 107.9 FM.

WEAV-AM
Owner: Vox Communications
Editorial: 265 Hegeman Ave, Colchester, Vermont 05446-3174. **T:** 1 802 655-0093
W: http://www.thezone960am.com
Editorial Profile: WEAV-AM is a commercial station owned by Vox Communications. The format of the station is sports. WEAV-AM broadcasts to the Burlington, VT area at 960 AM.

WEAX-FM
Owner: Trine University
Editorial: 1 University Ave, Angola, Indiana 46703. **T:** 1 260 665-4883
W: http://88xradio.com

WEBB-FM
Owner: Townsquare Media, Inc.
Editorial: 56 Western Ave Ste 13, Augusta, Maine 04330-6348. **T:** 1 207 623-4735
W: http://www.b985.fm
Editorial Profile: WEBB-FM is a commercial station owned by Townsquare Media, Inc. The format of the station is classic country. WEBB-FM broadcasts to the Augusta, Maine area at 98.5 FM.

WEBC-AM
Owner: Townsquare Media, LLC
Editorial: 14 E Central Entrance, Duluth, Minnesota 55811. **T:** 1 218 727-4500
E: info@560webc.com **W:** http://webc560.com
Editorial Profile: WEBC-AM is a commercial station owned by Townsquare Media, LLC. The format of the station is sports. WEBC-AM broadcasts to the Duluth, MN area at 560 AM.

WEBE-FM
Owner: Cumulus Media Inc.
Editorial: 350 Fairfield Ave Fl 7, Bridgeport, Connecticut 06604-6014. **T:** 1 203 333-9108
W: http://www.webe108.com
Editorial Profile: WEBE-FM is a commercial station owned by Cumulus Media Inc. The format of the station is adult contemporary. WEBE-FM broadcasts to the Bridgeport, CT area at 107.9 FM.

WEBJ-AM
Owner: Brewton Broadcasting
Editorial: 301 Downing St, Brewton, Alabama 36426. **T:** 1 251 867-5717

WEBL-FM
Owner: Mighty Media Group, LP (Memphis First Ventures LP)
Editorial: 230 Goodman Rd E Ste 2, Southaven, Mississippi 38671-8889.
T: 1 662 349-0826 **E:** studio@rebel953.com
W: http://www.rebel953.com
Editorial Profile: WEBL-FM is a commercial station owned by Mighty Media Group, LP (Memphis First Ventures LP). The format of the station is contemporary country. WEBL-FM broadcasts to the Memphis, TN area at 95.3 FM.

WEBN-FM
Owner: Clear Channel Media and Entertainment
Editorial: 8044 Montgomery Rd, Ste 650, Cincinnati, Ohio 45236. **T:** 1 513 686-8300
W: http://www.webn.com
Editorial Profile: WEBN-FM is a commercial station owned by Clear Channel Media and Entertainment. The format of the station is rock. WEBN-FM broadcasts to the Cincinnati area at 102.7 FM.

WEBO-AM
Owner: Radigan Broadcasting LLC
Editorial: 60 North Ave, Owego, New York 13827-1325. **T:** 1 607 687-9933
E: news@newsradiowebo.com
W: http://www.newsradiowebo.com
Editorial Profile: WEBO-AM is a commercial station owned by Radigan Broadcasting LLC. The format of the station is news, sports and adult contemporary. WEBO-AM broadcasts to the Owego, NY area at 1330 AM.

WEBQ-AM
Owner: Withers Broadcasting Co.
Editorial: 701 S Commercial St, Harrisburg, Illinois 62946. **T:** 1 618 252-6307
E: webq@yourclearwave.com
W: http://webqradio.com
Editorial Profile: WEBQ-AM is a commercial station owned by Withers Broadcasting Co. The format of the station is classic country and talk. WEBQ-AM broadcasts to the Paducah, KY; Cape Girardeau, MO; and Harrisburg, IL areas at 1240 AM.

WEBQ-FM
Owner: Withers Broadcasting Co.
Editorial: 701 S Commercial St, Harrisburg, Illinois 62946. **T:** 1 618 252-6307
E: webq@yourclearwave.com
W: http://www.webqradio.com
Editorial Profile: WEBQ-FM is a commercial station owned by Withers Broadcasting Co. The format of the station is adult contemporary. WEBQ-FM broadcasts to the Harrisburg, IL area at 102.3 FM.

WEBS-AM
Owner: Radio WEBS Inc.
Editorial: 427 S Wall St, Calhoun, Georgia 30701. **T:** 1 706 629-1110
W: http://www.webscalhoun.com
Editorial Profile: WEBS-AM is a commercial station owned by Radio WEBS Inc. The format of the station is oldies music. WEBS-AM broadcasts to the Calhoun, GA area at 1030 AM.

WEBY-AM
Owner: Spinnaker Communications
Editorial: 7179 Printers Aly, Milton, Florida 32583. **T:** 1 850 983-2242
E: weby@1330weby.com
W: http://www.1330weby.com
Editorial Profile: WEBY-AM is a commercial station owned by Spinnaker Communications. The format of the station is news and talk. WEBY-AM broadcasts to the Pensacola, FL area at 1330 AM.

WEBZ-FM
Owner: Clear Channel Media and Entertainment
Editorial: 1834 Lisenby Ave, Panama City, Florida 32405. **T:** 1 850 769-6161
W: http://www.993thebeat.com
Editorial Profile: WEBZ-FM is a commercial station owned by Clear Channel Media and Entertainment. The format of the station is urban contemporary music. WEBZ-FM broadcasts to the Panama City, FL area at 99.3 FM.

WECB-FM
Owner: Southeast Alabama Broadcasters, LLC
Editorial: 3245 Montgomery Hwy, Dothan, Alabama 36303-2172. **T:** 1 334 712-9233
Editorial Profile: WECB-FM is a commercial station owned by Southeast Alabama Broadcasters, LLC and operated by Low Country Radio, LLC. The format of the station is classic country. WECB-FM broadcasts in the Dothan, AL area at 105.3 FM.

WECC-FM
Owner: Lighthouse Christian Broadcasting
Editorial: 5465 Ga Highway 40 E, Saint Marys, Georgia 31558-4036. **T:** 1 912 882-8930

E: mail@thelighthousefm.org
W: http://www.thelighthousefm.org
Editorial Profile: WECC-FM is a non-commercial station owned by Lighthouse Christian Broadcasting. The format of the station is contemporary Christian and religious programming. WECC-FM broadcasts to the Saint Marys, GA area at 89.3 FM.

WECI-FM

Owner: Earlham College
Editorial: 801 National Rd W, Richmond, Indiana 47374. **T:** 1 765 983-1246
W: http://www.weciradio.org
Editorial Profile: WECI-FM is a non-commercial station owned by Earlham College. The format of the station is variety, including music, news, and talk. WECI-FM broadcasts in the Richmond, IN area at 91.5 FM.

WECK-AM

Owner: Culver Communications
Editorial: 2900 Genesee St, Cheektowaga, New York 14225-3102. **T:** 1716 783 9120
W: http://www.timelessweck.com
Editorial Profile: WECK-AM is a commercial station owned by Culver Communications. The format of the station is adult standards. WECK-AM broadcasts to the Buffalo/ Cheektowaga, NY area at 1230 AM.

WECL-FM

Owner: Mid-West Family Broadcasting
Editorial: 944 Harlem St, Altoona, Wisconsin 54720-1127. **T:** 1 715 832-1530
W: http://www.929thex.com
Editorial Profile: WECL-FM is a commercial station owned by Mid-West Family Broadcasting. The format of the station is rock. WECL-FM broadcasts to the Altoona, WI area at 92.9 FM.

WECO-AM

Owner: Morgan County Broadcasting Co., Inc.
Editorial: 305 N Church St, Wartburg, Tennessee 37887-3164. **T:** 1 423 346-3900
E: wecoradio@highland.net
W: http://www.wecoradio.com
Editorial Profile: WECO-AM is a commercial station owned by Morgan County Broadcasting Co., Inc. The format of the station is gospel. WECO-AM broadcasts to the Wartburg, TN area at 940 AM.

WECO-FM

Owner: Morgan County Broadcasting Co., Inc.
Editorial: 305 N Church St, Wartburg, Tennessee 37887. **T:** 1 423 346-3900
E: wecoradio@highland.net
W: http://www.wecoradio.com
Editorial Profile: WECO-FM is a commercial station owned by Morgan County Broadcasting Co., Inc. The format of the station is classic and contemporary country. WECO-FM broadcasts to the Wartburg, TN area at 101.3 FM.

WECQ-FM

Owner: Apex Broadcasting, Inc.
Editorial: 34 Harbor Blvd Ste 202, Destin, Florida 32541-7365. **T:** 1 850 654-1000
W: http://www.fly921.com
Editorial Profile: WECQ-FM is a commercial station owned by Apex Broadcasting, Inc. The format of the station is Top 40/CHR music. WECQ-FM broadcasts to Destin, FL area at 92.1 FM.

WECR-AM

Owner: High Country Adventures, LLC
Editorial: 1281 Newland Hwy, Newland, North Carolina 28657. **T:** 1 828 733-0188
E: wecr@bellsouth.net
W: http://www.wecr1130am.com
Editorial Profile: WECR-AM is a commercial station owned by High Country Adventures, LLC. The format for the station is Christian and gospel music. WECR-AM broadcasts to the Charlotte, NC area at 1130 AM.

WECR-FM

Owner: High Country Adventures, LLC
Editorial: 738 Blowing Rock Rd, Boone, North Carolina 28607-4835. **T:** 1 828 264-2411
W: http://www.highway1061fm.com
Editorial Profile: WECR-FM is a commercial station owned by High Country Adventures, LLC, a subsidiary of Curtis Media Group. The format of the station is contemporary country. WECR-FM broadcasts to the Boone, NC area at 102.3 FM.

WECS-FM

Owner: Eastern Connecticut State University
Editorial: 83 Windham St, Willimantic, Connecticut 6226. **T:** 1 860 465-5354
E: wecs@easternct.edu

W: http://www.easternct.edu/wecs/
Editorial Profile: WECS-FM is a non-commercial station owned by Eastern Connecticut State University. The format of the station is variety. WECS-FM broadcasts to the Hartford-New Haven, CT area at 90.1 FM.

WECU-AM

Owner: True Venture Media Group
Editorial: 1413 Evans St, Ste D, Greenville, North Carolina 27834-4100.
T: 1 252 931-9328 **E:** info@wecu1570.com
W: http://www.wecu1570.com
Editorial Profile: WECU-AM is a commercial station owned by True Venture Media Group. The format of the station is gospel music. WECU-AM broadcasts to the Winterville, NC area at 1570 AM.

WECZ-AM

Owner: Renda Broadcasting
Editorial: 904 N Main St, Punxsutawney, Pennsylvania 15767. **T:** 1 814 938-6000
E: rendaprod1@comcast.net
W: http://www.weczam1540.com
Editorial Profile: WECZ-AM is a commercial station owned by Renda Broadcasting. The format of the station is news and talk. WECZ-AM broadcasts to the Punxsutawney, PA area at 1540 AM.

WEDB-FM

Owner: RadioJones LLC
Editorial: 211 S Monroe St, Dublin, Georgia 31021-5235. **T:** 1 478 237-1590
W: http://www.magic98wedb.com
Editorial Profile: WEDB-FM is a commercial station owned by RadioJones LLC. The format of the station is hot adult contemporary. WEDB-FM broadcasts to the Augusta, GA area at 98.1 FM.

WEDG-FM

Owner: Cumulus Media Inc.
Editorial: 50 James E Casey Dr, Buffalo, New York 14206. **T:** 1 716 881-4555
W: http://www.wedg.com
Editorial Profile: WEDG-FM is a commercial station owned by Cumulus Media Inc. The format of the station is rock alternative music. WEDG-FM broadcasts to the Buffalo, NY area at 103.3 FM.

WEDI-AM

Owner: Town and Country Broadcasting, Inc.
Editorial: 23 E 2nd St, Xenia, Ohio 45385-3415. **T:** 1 937 372-3531
E: myclassiccountry@myclassiccountry.com
W: http://www.myclassiccountry.com
Editorial Profile: WEDI-AM is a commercial station owned by Town and Country Broadcasting, Inc. The format of the station is classic country. WEDI-AM broadcasts to the Xenia, OH area at 1130 AM.

WEDJ-FM

Owner: Continental Broadcast Group LLC
Editorial: 1800 N Meridian St, Ste 603, Indianapolis, Indiana 46202-1433.
T: 1 317 924-1071 **W:** http://www.wedjfm.com
Editorial Profile: WEDJ-FM is a commercial station owned by Continental Broadcast Group LLC. The format of the station is regional Mexican music. WEDJ-FM broadcasts to the greater Indianapolis area at 107.1 FM.

WEDM-FM

Owner: Metropolitan S.D. of Warren Township
Editorial: 9651 E 21st St, Indianapolis, Indiana 46229-1706. **T:** 1 317 532-6301
Editorial Profile: WEDM-FM is a non-commercial station owned by Metropolitan S.D. of Warren Township. The format of the station is educational variety. WEDM-FM broadcasts to the Indianapolis area at 91.1 FM.

WEDO-AM

Owner: 810 Inc.
Editorial: 1985 Lincoln Way, McKeesport, Pennsylvania 15131. **T:** 1 412 664-4431
E: wedoradio@comcast.net
W: http://www.wedo810.com
Editorial Profile: WEDO-AM is a commercial station owned by 810 Inc. The format of the station is variety. WEDO-AM broadcasts to the McKeesport, PA area at 810 AM.

WEDR-FM

Owner: Cox Media Group, Inc.
Editorial: 2741 N 29th Ave, Hollywood, Florida 33020. **T:** 1 305 444-4404
W: http://www.wedr.com
Editorial Profile: WEDR-FM is a commercial station owned by Cox Media Group, Inc. The format of the station is urban contemporary.

WEDR-FM broadcasts to the Hollywood, FL area at 99.1 FM.

WEDW-FM

Owner: Connecticut Public Broadcasting Inc.
Editorial: 1049 Asylum Ave, Hartford, Connecticut 06105-2432. **T:** 1 860 278-5310
E: info@wnpr.org **W:** http://www.wnpr.org
Editorial Profile: WEDW-FM is a non-commercial station owned by Connecticut Public Broadcasting Inc. The format of the station is news and talk. WEDW-FM broadcasts to the Hartford, CT area at 88.5 FM.

WEDX-FM

Owner: Clear Channel Media and Entertainment
Editorial: 10 Cabot Rd Ste 302, Medford, Massachusetts 02155-5173.
T: 1 781 663-2500
W: http://www.evolution1017.com
Editorial Profile: WEDX-FM is a commercial station owned by Clear Channel Media and Entertainment. The format of the station is dance/electronic music. WEDX-FM broadcasts to Boston area at 101.7 FM.

WEEB-AM

Owner: Pinehurst Broadcasting
Editorial: 1650 Midland Rd, Southern Pines, North Carolina 28387-2111.
T: 1 910 692-7440
W: http://www.weeb990.com
Editorial Profile: WEEB-AM is a commercial station owned by Pinehurst Broadcasting. The format of the station is news and talk. WEEB-AM broadcasts to the Southern Pines, NC area at 990 AM.

WEEC-FM

Owner: World Evangelistic Enterprise
Editorial: 2265 Troy Rd, Springfield, Ohio 45504-4229. **T:** 1 937 399-7837
E: info@weec.org **W:** http://www.weec.org
Editorial Profile: WEEC-FM is a non-commercial station owned by The World Evangelistic Enterprise Corporation (WEEC). The format of the station is gospel music and religious. WEEC-FM broadcasts to the Springfield, OH area at 100.7 FM.

WEED-AM

Owner: North Star Broadcasting
Editorial: 115 N Church St, Rocky Mount, North Carolina 27804-5402.
T: 1 252 443-5976
Editorial Profile: WEED-AM is a commercial station owned by North Star Broadcasting. The format of the station is Black Gospel. WEED-AM broadcasts to the Rocky Mount, NC area at 1390 AM.

WEEF-AM

Owner: Polnet Communications
Editorial: 4320 Dundee Rd, Northbrook, Illinois 60062-1703. **T:** 1 847 498-3350
E: polnetradio@gmail.com
W: http://www.weefam.com

WEEI-AM

Owner: Entercom Communications Corp.
Editorial: 20 Guest St Fl 3, Brighton, Massachusetts 02135-2040.
T: 1 617 779-3500
W: http://espn.go.com/boston
Editorial Profile: WEEI-AM is a commercial station owned by Entercom Communications Corp. The format of the station is sports. WEEI-AM broadcasts to the Brighton, MA area at 850 AM.

WEEI-FM

Owner: Entercom Communications Corp.
Editorial: 20 Guest St Fl 3, Brighton, Massachusetts 02135-2040.
T: 1 617 779-3500 **W:** http://www.weei.com
Editorial Profile: WEEI-FM is a commercial station owned by Entercom Communications Corp. The format of the station is sports. WEEI-FM broadcasts to the Providence, RI area at 93.7 FM.

WEEM-FM

Owner: South Madison Community School Corp.
Editorial: 1 Arabian Dr, Pendleton, Indiana 46064. **T:** 1 765 778-2161
W: http://www.917weem.org
Editorial Profile: WEEM-FM is a non-commercial station owned by South Madison Community School Corp. The format of the station is Top 40/CHR. The station broadcasts to the Indianapolis area at 91.7 FM.

WEEN-AM

Owner: Lafayette Broadcasting Inc.
Editorial: 231 Chaffin Rd, Lafayette, Tennessee 37083. **T:** 1 615 666-2169
E: wlct@nctc.com **W:** http://www.wlct.com
Editorial Profile: WEEN-AM is a commercial station owned by Lafayette Broadcasting Inc. The format of the station is gospel music. The station broadcasts to Lafayette, TN at 1460 AM.

WEEO-AM

Owner: Shippensburg Broadcasting, Inc.
Editorial: 180 York Rd, Carlisle, Pennsylvania 17013. **T:** 1 717 243-1200 **E:** wioo@pa.net
W: http://www.wioo.com
Editorial Profile: WEEO-AM is a commercial station owned by Shippensburg Broadcasting, Inc. The format of the station is country. WEEO-AM broadcasts to the Carlisle, PA area at 1480 AM.

WEEO-FM

Owner: Magnum Broadcasting Inc.
Editorial: 37 S Main St, Chambersburg, Pennsylvania 17201-2200. **T:** 1 717 709-0801
E: joefmprod@yahoo.com
W: http://www.fmtalk1037.com
Editorial Profile: WEEO-FM is a commercial station owned by Magnum Broadcasting Inc. The format of the station is news talk. WEEO-FM broadcasts to the Chambersburg, PA area at 103.7 FM.

WEEU-AM

Owner: WEEU Broadcasting Co.
Editorial: 34 N 4th St, Reading, Pennsylvania 19601. **T:** 1 610 376-7335 **E:** weeu@weeu.com
W: http://www.weeu.com
Editorial Profile: WEEU-AM is a commercial station owned by WEEU Broadcasting Co. The format of the station is news and talk. WEEU-AM broadcasts to the Reading, PA area at 830 AM.

WEEX-AM

Owner: Connoisseur Media
Editorial: 107 Paxinosa Rd W, Easton, Pennsylvania 18040-1344. **T:** 1 610 829-5500
W: http://www.espnlv.com
Editorial Profile: WEEX-AM is a commercial station owned by Connoisseur Media. The format of the station is sports. WEEX-AM broadcasts to the Easton, PA area at 1230 AM.

WEEY-FM

Owner: Great Eastern Radio, LLC
Editorial: 99 Main St, Keene, New Hampshire 03431-3770. **T:** 1 603 283-1090
Editorial Profile: WEEY-FM is a commercial station owned by Great Eastern Radio, LLC. The format of the station is sports. WEEY-FM broadcasts to the Lebanon, NH area at 93.5 FM.

WEEZ-AM

Owner: Clear Channel Media and Entertainment
Editorial: 6555 U S Highway 98 W, Ste 8, Hattiesburg, Mississippi 39402.
T: 1 601 296-9800
Editorial Profile: WEEZ-AM is a commercial station owned by Clear Channel Media and Entertainment. The format for the station is blues music. WHJA-AM broadcasts to the Hattiesburg, MS, area at 890 AM.

WEFL-AM

Owner: Good Karma Broadcasting
Editorial: 2090 Palm Beach Lakes Blvd Ste 801, West Palm Beach, Florida 33409-6508.
T: 1 561 697-8353
W: http://www.espnwestpalm.com
Editorial Profile: WEFL-AM is a commercial station owned by Good Karma Broadcasting. The format of the station is Spanish sports. WEFL-AM broadcasts to the West Palm Beach, FL area at 760 AM.

WEFM-FM

Owner: Michigan City FM Broadcasters
Editorial: 1903 Springland Ave, Michigan City, Indiana 46360. **T:** 1 219 879-8201
E: wefmr@yahoo.com
Editorial Profile: WEFM-FM is a commercial station owned by Michigan City FM Broadcasters. The format of the station is adult contemporary and oldies. WEFM-FM broadcasts to the Michigan City, IN area at 95.9 FM.

WEFT-FM

Owner: Prairie Air Inc.
Editorial: 113 N Market St, Champaign, Illinois 61820-4004. **T:** 1 217 359-9338
E: weft@weft.org **W:** http://www.weft.org

Editorial Profile: WEFT-FM is a non-commercial station owned by Prairie Air Inc. The format of the station is variety. WEFT-FM broadcasts in the Champaign, IL area at 90.1 FM.

WEFX-FM
Owner: Community Broadcasters, LLC
Editorial: 199 Wealtha Ave, Watertown, New York 13601-1837. **T:** 1 315 786-9552
Editorial Profile: WEFX-FM is a commercial station owned by Community Broadcasters, LLC. The format of the station is contemporary country. WEFX-FM broadcasts to the Watertown, NY area at 100.7 FM.

WEGB-FM
Owner: Community Bible Church
Editorial: 2837 Noyac Rd, Sag Harbor, New York 11963-1916. **T:** 1 631 725-4155
E: faithfm@eastgatebroadcasting.com
W: http://eastgatebroadcasting.com
Editorial Profile: WEGB-FM is a non-commercial station owned by Community Bible Church. The format of the station is Christian talk and Bible teaching. WEGB-FM broadcasts to the Long Island, NY area at a frequency of 90.7 FM.

WEGC-FM
Owner: Cumulus Media Inc.
Editorial: 1104 W Broad Ave, Albany, Georgia 31707. **T:** 1 229 888-5000
W: http://www.mix1077albany.com
Editorial Profile: WEGC-FM is a commercial station owned by Cumulus Media Inc. The format of the station is adult contemporary music. WEGC-FM broadcasts in the Albany, GA area at 107.7 FM.

WEGE-FM
Owner: Childers Media Group, LLC
Editorial: 57 Town Sq, Lima, Ohio 45801-4950. **T:** 1 419 331-1600
W: http://www.1049theeagle.com
Editorial Profile: WEGE-FM is a commercial station owned by Childers Media Group, LLC. The format of the station is classic rock. WEGE-FM broadcasts to the Lima, OH area at 104.9 FM.

WEGG-AM
Owner: Conner Media Corp.
Editorial: Highway 117, Rose Hill, North Carolina 28458. **T:** 1 252 633-2143
E: Office@yourchristianradio.com
W: http://yourchristianradio.com/default.aspx
Editorial Profile: WEGG-AM is a commercial station owned by Conner Media Corp. The format of the station is gospel music. WEGG-AM broadcasts to the Rose Hill, NC area at 710 AM.

WEGH-FM
Owner: Sunbury Broadcasting Corp.
Editorial: 1227 County Line Rd, Selinsgrove, Pennsylvania 17870. **T:** 1 570 286-5838
E: sales@wqkx.com
W: http://www.eagle107.com
Editorial Profile: WEGH-FM is a commercial station owned by Sunbury Broadcasting Corp. The format of the station is classic rock music. WEGH-FM broadcasts to the Sunbury, PA area at 107.3 FM.

WEGL-FM
Owner: Auburn University
Editorial: 255 Duncan Dr, Ste 1105 AU Student Center, Auburn, Alabama 36849-0001. **T:** 1 334 844-4114 **W:** http://wegl.auburn.edu

WEGO-AM
Owner: Truth Broadcasting
Editorial: 4405 Providence Ln Ste D, Winston Salem, North Carolina 27106-3226.
T: 1 336 759-0363 **E:** info@eagle980.com
W: http://www.eagle980.com
Editorial Profile: WEGO-AM is a commercial station owned by Truth Broadcasting. The format of the station is Conservative talk. WEGO-AM broadcasts to the High Point, NC area at 980 AM.

WEGP-AM
Owner: Decelles-Smith Media, Inc.
Editorial: 28 Houlton Rd, Presque Isle, Maine 4769. **T:** 1 207 762-6700
W: http://www.wegp.net
Editorial Profile: WEGP-AM is a commercial station owned by Decelles-Smith Media, Inc.. The format for the station is talk. WEGP-AM broadcasts to the Presque Isle, ME area at 1390 AM.

WEGR-FM
Owner: Clear Channel Media and Entertainment
Editorial: 2650 Thousand Oaks Blvd, Ste 4100, Memphis, Tennessee 38118-2451.
T: 1 901 259-1300
W: http://www.rock103.com
Editorial Profile: WEGR-FM is a commercial station owned by Clear Channel Media and Entertainment. The format of the station is classic rock music. WEGR-FM broadcasts to the Memphis, TN area at 102.7 FM.

WEGS-FM
Owner: Florida Public Radio, Inc.
Editorial: 1836 E Olive Rd, Pensacola, Florida 32514. **T:** 1 321 267-3000
W: http://www.wegs917.com

WEGW-FM
Owner: Clear Channel Media and Entertainment
Editorial: 1015 Main St, Wheeling, West Virginia 26003. **T:** 1 304 232-1170
W: http://www.wegw.com
Editorial Profile: WEGW-FM is a commercial station owned by Clear Channel Media and Entertainment. The format of the station is rock/album-oriented rock. WEGW-FM broadcasts to the Wheeling, WV area at 107.5 FM.

WEGX-FM
Owner: Clear Channel Media and Entertainment
Editorial: 181 E Evans St Ste 311, Florence, South Carolina 29506-5505.
T: 1 843 667-4600
W: http://eagle929online.com/#&panel1-1
Editorial Profile: WEGX-FM is a commercial station owned by Clear Channel Media and Entertainment. The format of the station is contemporary country music. WEGX-FM broadcasts to the Florence, SC area at 92.9 FM.

WEGZ-FM
Owner: VCY America Inc.
Editorial: 3434 W Kilbourn Ave, Milwaukee, Wisconsin 53208. **T:** 1 414 935-3000
E: wegz@vcyamerica.org
W: http://www.vcyamerica.org
Editorial Profile: WEGZ-FM is a non-commercial station owned by VCY America Inc. The format of the station is religious. WEGZ-FM broadcasts to the Milwaukee area at 105.9 FM.

WEHH-AM
Owner: Pembrook Pines Media Group
Editorial: 1705 Lake St, Elmira, New York 14901. **T:** 1 607 733-5626
E: ppinesmedia1@stny.rr.com
Editorial Profile: WEHH-AM is a commercial station owned by Pembrook Pines Media Group. The format of the station is adult standards. WEHH-AM broadcasts to the Elmira, NY area at 1600 AM.

WEHM-FM
Owner: Long Island Radio Broadcasting
Editorial: 760 Montauk Highway, Watermill, New York 11976. **T:** 1 631 267-7800
E: info@wehm.com **W:** http://www.wehm.com
Editorial Profile: WEHM-FM is a commercial station owned by Long Island Radio Broadcasting. The format of the station is adult album alternative. WEHM-FM broadcasts to the Amagansett, NY area at 92.9 FM.

WEHN-FM
Owner: Long Island Radio Broadcasting
Editorial: 760 Montauk Highway, Watermill, New York 11976. **T:** 1 631 267-7800
E: info@wehm.com **W:** http://www.wehm.com
Editorial Profile: WEHN-FM is a commercial station owned by Long Island Radio Broadcasting. The format of the station is adult album alternative. WEHN-FM broadcasts to the East Hampton, NY, region at 96.9 FM.

WEHP-FM
Editorial: 1229 State St, Erie, Pennsylvania 16501-1913. **T:** 1 814 836-1111
Editorial Profile: WEHP-FM is a commercial station owned by The Erie Radio Company, LLC. The format of the station is Top 40/CHR. WEHP-FM broadcasts to the Erie, PA area at a frequency of 92.7 FM.

WEIB-FM
Owner: Cutting Edge Broadcasting Inc.
Editorial: 8 N King St, Northampton, Massachusetts 01060-2489.
T: 1 413 585-1112 **E:** info@weibfm.com
W: http://www.weibfm.com

WEII-FM
Owner: Clear Channel Media and Entertainment
Editorial: 154 Barnstable Rd, Hyannis, Massachusetts 02601-2930.
T: 1 508 778-2888 **W:** http://www.weei.com
Editorial Profile: WEII-FM is a commercial station owned by Clear Channel Media and Entertainment. The format of the station is sports. WEII-FM broadcasts to the Cape Cod, MA area at 96.3 FM.

WEIO-FM
Owner: Freeland Broadcasting
Editorial: 215 Baker Rd, Huntingdon, Tennessee 38344-7703. **T:** 1 731 986-0242
W: http://www.thefarmradio.com
Editorial Profile: WEIO-FM is a commercial station owned by Freeland Broadcasting. The format of the station is contemporary country. WEIO-FM broadcasts to the Huntingdon, TN area at 100.9 FM.

WEIR-AM
Owner: Priority Communications
Editorial: 2307 Pennsylvania Ave, Weirton, West Virginia 26062. **T:** 1 304 723-1444
E: news@weir1430.com
W: http://www.weir1430.com
Editorial Profile: WEIR-AM is a commercial station owned by Priority Communications. The format of the station is sports. WEIR-AM broadcasts to the Wheeling, WV area at 1430 AM.

WEIS-AM
Owner: Baker Enterprises Inc.
Editorial: 477 S Pratt St, Centre, Alabama 35960. **T:** 1 256 927-4232
E: weisradio@tds.net
W: http://www.weis990am.com
Editorial Profile: WEIS-AM is a commercial station owned by Baker Enterprises Inc. The format of the station is country, gospel, news and sports. WEIS-AM broadcasts to the Centre, AL area at 990 AM.

WEIU-FM
Owner: Eastern Illinois University
Editorial: Radio & TV Center 1521 Buzzard Hall, Charleston, Illinois 61920.
T: 1 217 581-5956 **E:** hitmix@weiu.net
W: http://www.weiuhitmix.net
Editorial Profile: WEIU-FM is a non-commercial station owned by Eastern Illinois University. The format of the station is variety of music hits. WEIU-FM broadcasts in the Charleston, IL area at 88.9 FM.

WEJF-FM
Owner: Florida Public Radio, Inc.
Editorial: 2824B Palm Bay Rd Ne, Palm Bay, Florida 32905-3535. **T:** 1 321 722-9998
W: http://www.ggrn.info
Editorial Profile: WEJF-FM is a non-commercial station owned by Florida Public Radio, Inc. The format of the station is Christian and variety. WEJF-FM broadcasts to the Palm Bay, FL area at 90.3 FM.

WEJK-FM
Owner: South Central Communications Corp.
Editorial: 1162 Mount Auburn Rd, Evansville, Indiana 47720. **T:** 1 812 424-8284
W: http://www.1071jackfm.com
Editorial Profile: WEJK-FM is a commercial station owned by South Central Communications Corp. The format of the station is adult hits. WEJK-FM broadcasts to the Evansville, IN area at 107.1 FM.

WEJL-AM
Owner: Shamrock Communications
Editorial: 149 Penn Ave, Scranton, Pennsylvania 18503. **T:** 1 570 346-6555
W: http://wejl-wbax.com
Editorial Profile: WEJL-AM is a commercial station owned by Shamrock Communications. The format of the station is sports. WEJL-AM broadcasts to the Scranton, PA area at 1240 WBAX-AM.

WEJL-FM
Owner: Shamrock Communications
Editorial: 149 Penn Ave, Scranton, Pennsylvania 18503-2055. **T:** 1 570 346-6555
W: http://www.nepasespnradio.com
Editorial Profile: WEJL-FM is a commercial station owned by Shamrock Communications. The format of the station is sports. WEJL-FM broadcasts to the Scranton, PA area at 100.1 FM.

WEJT-FM
Owner: Cromwell Group Inc.(The)
Editorial: 410 N Water St, Ste B, Decatur, Illinois 62523-2371. **T:** 1 217 428-4487
W: http://www.wejt.com
Editorial Profile: WEJT-FM is a commercial station owned by the Cromwell Group Inc. The format of the station is adult hits. WEJT-FM broadcasts in the Decatur, IL area at 105.1 FM.

WEJZ-FM
Owner: Renda Broadcasting
Editorial: 6440 Atlantic Blvd, Jacksonville, Florida 32211. **T:** 1 904 727-9696
W: http://www.wejz.com
Editorial Profile: WEJZ-FM is a commercial station owned by Renda Broadcasting. The format of the station is adult contemporary music. WEJZ-FM broadcasts to the Jacksonville, FL area at 96.1 FM.

WEKB-AM
Owner: East Kentucky Radio Network
Editorial: 1240 Radio Dr, Pikeville, Kentucky 41501-4779. **T:** 1 606 437-4051
E: frontdesk@ekbradio.com
W: http://www.myoldiesradio.com
Editorial Profile: WEKB-AM is a commercial station owned by East Kentucky Radio Network. The format of the station is oldies music. WEKB-AM broadcasts to the Pikeville, KY area at 1460 AM.

WEKC-AM
Owner: Parks(Gerald)
Editorial: 402 Main St, Williamsburg, Kentucky 40769-1126. **T:** 1 606 549-3000
W: http://www.wekc.net
Editorial Profile: WEKC-AM is a commercial station owned by Gerald Parks. The format of the station is gospel. WEKC-AM broadcasts to the Williamsburg, KY area at 710 AM.

WEKF-FM
Owner: Eastern Kentucky University
Editorial: 521 Lancaster Ave, Bldg 102, Richmond, Kentucky 40475-3100.
T: 1 859 622-1660 **E:** weku@eku.edu
W: http://www.weku.fm
Editorial Profile: WEKF-FM is a non-commercial station owned by Eastern Kentucky University. The format of the station is classical music and news. WEKF-FM broadcasts in the Richmond, KY area at 88.5 FM.

WEKG-AM
Owner: Intermountain Broadcasting
Editorial: 1501 Hargis Ln, Jackson, Kentucky 41339-1102. **T:** 1 606 666-7531
Editorial Profile: WEKG-AM is a commercial station owned by Intermountain Broadcasting. The format of the station is gospel. WEKG-AM broadcasts to the Lexington, KY area at 810 AM.

WEKH-FM
Owner: Eastern Kentucky University
Editorial: 521 Lancaster Ave102 Perkins Bldg, Richmond, Kentucky 40475-3127.
T: 1 859 622-1660 **E:** weku@eku.edu
W: http://www.weku.fm
Editorial Profile: WEKH-FM is a non-commercial station owned by Eastern Kentucky University. The format of the station is news and classical. WEKH-FM broadcasts to the Richmond, KY area at 90.9 FM.

WEKR-AM
Owner: Elk River Broadcasting
Editorial: 7 Old Boonshill Road, Fayetteville, Tennessee 37334. **T:** 1 931 433-3545
Editorial Profile: WEKR-AM is a commercial station owned by Elk River Broadcasting. The format of the station is country. WEKR-AM broadcasts to the Fayetteville, TN area at 1240 AM.

WEKS-FM
Owner: Legacy Media of South Atlanta, LLC.
Editorial: 42 Main St, Senoia, Georgia 30276-1889. **T:** 1 770 599-1923
E: info@925fmthebear.com
W: http://www.925fmthebear.com
Editorial Profile: WEKS-FM is a commercial station owned by Legacy Media of South Atlanta, LLC. The format of the station is classic and contemporary country. WEKS-FM broadcasts to the Senoia, GA area at 92.5 FM.

WEKT-AM
Owner: M & R Broadcasting Inc.
Editorial: 214A Marion St, Elkton, Kentucky 42220. **T:** 1 270 265-5636
E: wektam1070@yahoo.com
W: http://www.wektgospelradio.com
Editorial Profile: WEKT-AM is a commercial station owned by M & R Broadcasting Inc. The format of the station is gospel music.

WEKT-AM broadcasts to the Nashville, TN area at 1070 AM.

WEKU-FM

Owner: Eastern Kentucky University
Editorial: 521 Lancaster Ave, Bldg 102, Richmond, Kentucky 40475-3100.
T: 1 859 622-1660 **E:** wekunews@eku.edu
W: http://www.weku.fm
Editorial Profile: WEKU-FM is a non-commercial station owned by Eastern Kentucky University. The format of the station is classical music and news. WEKU-FM broadcasts to the Richmond, KY area at 88.9 FM.

WEKX-FM

Owner: Whitley Broadcasting
Editorial: 522 Main St, Williamsburg, Kentucky 40769-1127. **T:** 1 606 549-2285
E: wekx@bellsouth.net
W: http://www.werock1027.com
Editorial Profile: WEKX-FM is a commercial station owned by Whitley Broadcasting. The format of the station is classic rock. WEKX-FM broadcasts to the Lexington, KY area at 102.7 FM.

WEKY-AM

Owner: Wallingford Broadcasting LLC
Editorial: 1030 Winchester Rd, Irvine, Kentucky 40336. **T:** 1 606 723-5138
Editorial Profile: WEKY-AM is a commercial station owned by Wallingford Broadcasting LLC. The format of the station is oldies and talk. WEKY-AM broadcasts to the Lexington, KY area at 1340 AM.

WEKZ-AM

Owner: Big Radio
Editorial: W4765 Radio Ln, Monroe, Wisconsin 53566. **T:** 1 608 325-2161
E: wekz@wekz.com **W:** http://www.wekz.com
Editorial Profile: WEKZ-AM is a commercial station owned by Big Radio. The format of the station is country music. WEKZ-AM broadcasts to the Monroe, WI area at 1260 AM. All staff should be contact via fax.

WEKZ-FM

Owner: Big Radio
Editorial: W4765 Radio Ln, Monroe, Wisconsin 53566-9405. **T:** 1 608 325-2161
E: wekz@wekz.com **W:** http://www.wekz.com
Editorial Profile: WEKZ-FM is a commercial station owned by Big Radio. The format of the station is oldies. WEKZ-FM broadcasts to the Monroe, WI area at 93.7 FM. All staff should be contact via fax.

WELB-AM

Owner: Elba Radio Company
Editorial: 20334 Highway 87, Elba, Alabama 36323. **T:** 1 334 897-2216
E: welbam1350@yahoo.com
Editorial Profile: WELB-AM is a commercial station owned by Elba Radio Company. The format of the station is southern gospel. WELB-AM broadcasts to the Elba, AL area at 1350 AM.

WELC-AM

Owner: West Virginia-Virginia Holding Co, LLC
Editorial: 18385 Coal Heritage Rd, Welch, West Virginia 24801-9773. **T:** 1 304 436-2131
E: mail@welcamfm.com
W: http://www.welcamfm.com
Editorial Profile: WELC-AM is a commercial station owned by the West Virginia-Virginia Holding Co, LLC. The format of the station is adult contemporary music. WELC-AM broadcasts to the Welch, WV area at 1150 AM.

WELD-AM

Owner: Thunder Associates LLC
Editorial: 126 Kessel Rd, Fisher, West Virginia 26818-4012. **T:** 1 304 538-6062
E: weld@hardynet.com
W: http://www.weldamfmradio.com
Editorial Profile: WELD-AM is a commercial station owned by Thunder Associates LLC. The format of the station is classic hits. WELD-AM broadcasts in the Fisher, WV area at 690 AM.

WELD-FM

Owner: Thunder Associates LLC
Editorial: 126 Kessel Rd, Fisher, West Virginia 26818-4012. **T:** 1 304 538-6062
E: weld@hardynet.com
Editorial Profile: WELD-FM is a commercial station owned by Thunder Associates LLC. The format of the station is country music. WELD-FM broadcasts to the Fisher, WV area at 101.7 FM.

WELE-AM

Owner: Wings Communications- LMA Goliath Radio
Editorial: 432 S Nova Rd, Ormond Beach, Florida 32174-6121. **T:** 1 386 523-1870
E: big@big1380.com
W: http://www.big1380.com
Editorial Profile: WELE-AM is a commercial station owned by Wings Communications. The format of the station is news, talk and sports. WELE-AM broadcasts to the Ormond Beach, FL area at 1380 AM.

WELH-FM

Owner: The Wheeler School
Editorial: 216 Hope St, Providence, Rhode Island 02906-2214. **T:** 1 401 421-8100
E: news@ripr.org **W:** http://ripr.org
Editorial Profile: WELH-FM is a non-commercial station owned by Wheeler School (The). The format of the station is news/talk. WELH-FM broadcasts to Northern Rhode Island at a frequency of 88.1 FM. The station is part of Rhode Island Public Radio.

WELI-AM

Owner: Clear Channel Media and Entertainment
Editorial: 495 Benham St, Hamden, Connecticut 06514-2009. **T:** 1 203 281-9600
W: http://www.960weli.com
Editorial Profile: WELI-AM is a commercial station owned by Clear Channel Media and Entertainment. The format of the station is news, sports and talk. WELI-AM broadcasts in the greater New Haven, CT area at 960 AM.

WELJ-FM

Owner: Cumulus Media Inc.
Editorial: 7 Governor Winthrop Blvd, New London, Connecticut 6320. **T:** 1 860 443-1980
W: http://www.1047welj.com
Editorial Profile: WELJ-FM is a commercial station owned by Cumulus Media Inc. The format for the station is hot adult contemporary. WELJ-FM broadcasts to the New Haven, CT area at 104.7 FM.

WELK-FM

Owner: West Virginia Radio Corp.
Editorial: Washington & Davis Streets, Elkins, West Virginia 26241. **T:** 1 304 636-1300
E: wdne@wvradio.com
Editorial Profile: WELK-FM is a commercial station owned by West Virginia Radio Corp. The format of station is Hot AC. WELK-FM broadcasts in the Elkins, WV area at 94.7 FM.

WELL-FM

Owner: Alabama Christian Radio, Inc.
Editorial: 658 Horseshoe Bend Rd, Dadeville, Alabama 36853-2756. **T:** 1 334 705-8004
W: http://www.praise887.com
Editorial Profile: WELL-FM is a non-commercial station owned by Alabama Christian Radio, Inc.. The format of the station is contemporary Christian music. WELL-FM broadcasts to the Dadeville, AL area at 88.7 FM.

WELM-AM

Owner: Pembrook Pines Media Group
Editorial: 1705 Lake St, Elmira, New York 14901-1220. **T:** 1 607 733-5626
E: ppinesmedia1@stny.rr.com
W: http://www.welmradio.com
Editorial Profile: WELM-AM is a commercial station owned by Pembrook Pines Media Group. The format of the station is sports. WELM-AM broadcasts to the Elmira, NY area at 1410 AM.

WELO-AM

Owner: Mississippi Radio Group
Editorial: 2214 S Gloster St, Tupelo, Mississippi 38801. **T:** 1 662 842-7658
Editorial Profile: WELO-AM is a commercial station owned by Mississippi Radio Group. The format of the station is classic country. WELO-AM broadcasts to the Tupelo, MS area at 580 AM.

WELP-AM

Owner: Wilkins Communication Networks Inc.
Editorial: 100 Cross Hill Rd, Easley, South Carolina 29640-8854. **T:** 1 864 855-9300
E: welp@wilkinsradio.com
W: http://www.wilkinsradio.com
Editorial Profile: WELP-AM is a commercial station owned by Wilkins Communications Networks Inc. The format of the station is Christian talk. WELP-AM broadcasts to the Easley, SC area at 1360 AM.

WELR-FM

Owner: Eagle's Nest Inc.

Editorial: 6855 Highway 431, Roanoke, Alabama 36274-4614. **T:** 1 334 863-4139
E: welr@eagle1023.com
W: http://www.eagle1023.com
Editorial Profile: WELR-FM is a commercial station owned by Eagle's Nest Inc. The format of the station is country music. WELR-FM broadcasts to the Atlanta area at 102.3 FM.

WELS-AM

Owner: Eastern Airwaves, LLC
Editorial: 2581 US Highway 70 W, Goldsboro, North Carolina 27530-9553.
T: 1 919 736-1150
Editorial Profile: WELS-AM is a commercial station owned by Eastern Airwaves, LLC (a division of Curtis Media Group). The format of the station is black gospel. WELS-AM broadcasts to the Kinston, NC area at 1010 AM.

WELS-FM

Owner: Eastern Airwaves, LLC
Editorial: 2581 US Highway 70 W, Goldsboro, North Carolina 27530-9553.
T: 1 919 736-1150
Editorial Profile: WELS-FM is a commercial station owned by Eastern Airwaves, LLC (a division of Curtis Media Group). The format of the station is gospel. WELS-FM broadcasts to the Kinston, NC area at 102.9 FM.

WELW-AM

Owner: Spirit Broadcasting Corp.
Editorial: 36913 Stevens Blvd, Willoughby, Ohio 44094. **T:** 1 440 946-1330
E: email@welw.com **W:** http://www.welw.com
Editorial Profile: WELW-AM is a commercial station owned by Spirit Broadcasting Corp. The format of the station is talk. WELW-AM broadcasts to the Willoughby, OH area at 1330 AM.

WELY-AM

Owner: Fortune Bay Bois Forte
Editorial: 133 E Chapman St, Ely, Minnesota 55731-1229. **T:** 1 218 365-4444
E: welydj@wely.com **W:** http://www.wely.com
Editorial Profile: WELY-AM is a commercial station owned by Fortune Bay Bois Forte. The format of the station is news and sports talk. WELY-AM broadcasts in the Ely, MN area at 1450 AM.

WELY-FM

Owner: Bois Forte Brand
Editorial: 133 E Chapman St, Ely, Minnesota 55731-1229. **T:** 1 218 365-4444
E: news@wely.com **W:** http://www.wely.com
Editorial Profile: WELY-FM is a commercial station owned by Bois Forte Brand. The format of the station is variety. WELY-FM broadcasts in the Ely, MN area at 94.5 FM.

WELZ-AM

Owner: Zoo-Bel Broadcasting LLC
Editorial: 204 Church St, Belzoni, Mississippi 39038. **T:** 1 662 746-7676
E: power107@power107.org
W: http://www.power107.org
Editorial Profile: WELZ-AM is a commercial station owned by Zoo-Bel Broadcasting LLC. The format of the station is gospel and blues music. WELZ-AM broadcasts to the Belzoni, MS area at 1460 AM.

WEMB-AM

Owner: WEMB Inc.
Editorial: 101 Riverview Rd, Erwin, Tennessee 37650-8722. **T:** 1 423 743-6123
W: http://www.wemb.com
Editorial Profile: WEMB-AM is a commercial station owned by WEMB Inc. The format for the station is country. WEMB-AM broadcasts to the Tri-Cities, TN area at 1420 AM.

WEMC-FM

Owner: Eastern Mennonite University
Editorial: 983 Reservoir St, Harrisonburg, Virginia 22801. **T:** 1 540 568-3812
E: wemc@emu.edu **W:** http://www.wmra.org
Editorial Profile: WEMC-FM is a non-commerical station owned by Eastern Mennonite University. The format for the station is classical music. The station broadcasts to the Harrisonburg, VA area at 91.7 FM. The station does not accept any press releases.

WEMD-AM

Owner: First Media Radio LLC
Editorial: 306 Port St, Easton, Maryland 21601. **T:** 1 410 822-3301
E: studio@wceiradio.com
W: http://www.wceiradio.com
Editorial Profile: WEMD-AM is a commercial station owned by First Media Radio LLC. The

format of the station is adult standards. WEMD-AM broadcasts to Easton, MD at 1460 AM.

WEMG-AM

Owner: Davidson Media Group
Editorial: 1341 N Delaware Ave, Philadelphia, Pennsylvania 19125-4300. **T:** 1 215 426-1900
W: http://www.mega1310am.com
Editorial Profile: WEMG-AM is a commercial station owned by Davidson Media Group. The format of the station is Hispanic programming. WEMG-AM broadcasts to the Philadelphia area at 1310 AM.

WEMI-FM

Owner: Evangel Ministries, Inc.
Editorial: 1909 W 2nd St, Appleton, Wisconsin 54914. **T:** 1 920 749-9456
E: wemi@thefamily.net
W: http://www.thefamily.net
Editorial Profile: WEMI-FM is a non-commercial station owned by Evangel Ministries, Inc. The format of station is contemporary Christian and news. WEMI-FM broadcasts to the Appleton, WI area at 91.9 FM.

WEMJ-AM

Owner: WBIN, Inc.
Editorial: 2 Capital Plz Ste 105, Concord, New Hampshire 03301-4911. **T:** 1 603 224-8486
W: http://www.1490wemj.com
Editorial Profile: WEMJ-AM is a commercial station owned by WBIN, Inc. The format of the station is news and talk. WEMJ-AM broadcasts to the Laconia, NH area on 1490 AM.

WEMM-AM

Owner: Mortenson Broadcasting Co.
Editorial: 703 3rd Ave, Huntington, West Virginia 25701-1421. **T:** 1 304 525-5141
E: audiowemm@hotmail.com
W: http://wemmam.com
Editorial Profile: WEMM-AM is a commercial station owned by Mortenson Broadcasting Co. The format of the station is easy listening and classic hits. WEMM-AM broadcasts to the Huntington, WV area at 1200 AM.

WEMM-FM

Owner: Mortenson Broadcasting Co.
Editorial: 703 3rd Ave, Huntington, West Virginia 25701. **T:** 1 304 525-5141
E: audiowemm@hotmail.com
W: http://www.wemmfm.com
Editorial Profile: WEMM-FM is a commercial station owned by Mortenson Broadcasting Co. The format of the station is religion with a focus on Christian teaching and Southern gospel. WEMM-FM broadcasts to the Huntington, WV area at a frequency of 107.9 FM.

WEMR-FM

Owner: 2510 Associates
Editorial: 160 Clearview Ave, State College, Pennsylvania 16803. **T:** 1 814 238-5085
W: http://eagle987.com
Editorial Profile: WEMR-FM is a commercial station owned by 2510 Associates. The format of the station is active rock. WEMR-FM broadcasts to the Hollidaysburg, PA area at 98.7 FM.

WEMU-FM

Owner: Eastern Michigan University
Editorial: 426 King Hall, Ypsilanti, Michigan 48197. **T:** 1 734 487-2229
E: wemu@wemu.org **W:** http://www.wemu.org
Editorial Profile: WEMU-FM is a non-commercial station owned by Eastern Michigan University. The format of the station is news and jazz. WEMU-FM broadcasts to the Ypsilanti, MI area at 89.1 FM.

WEMX-FM

Owner: Cumulus Media Inc.
Editorial: 650 Wooddale Blvd, Baton Rouge, Louisiana 70806-2930. **T:** 1 225 926-1106
W: http://www.max94one.com
Editorial Profile: WEMX-FM is a commercial station that is owned by Cumulus Media Inc. The format of the station is urban contemporary music. WEMX-FM broadcasts to the Baton Rouge, LA area at 94.1 FM. Please fax any press material.

WEMY-FM

Owner: Evangel Ministries, Inc.
Editorial: 1909 W 2nd St, Appleton, Wisconsin 54914. **T:** 1 920 499-9957
E: wemy@thefamily.net
W: http://www.thefamily.net
Editorial Profile: WEMY-FM is a non-commercial station owned by Evangel

Ministries, Inc. The format of the station is contemporary Christian. WEMY-FM broadcasts to the Appleton, WI area at 91.5 FM.

WENC-AM
Owner: Godwin(J.L.)
Editorial: 108 Radio Station Rd, Whiteville, North Carolina 28472. **T:** 1 910 642-2133
E: wenc@zoomshare.com
Editorial Profile: WENC-AM is a commercial station owned by J.L. Godwin. The format of the station is gospel and R&B Oldies. WENC-AM broadcasts to the Whiteville, NC area at 1220 AM.

WEND-FM
Owner: Clear Channel Media and Entertainment
Editorial: 801 Woodrdg Ctr Dr, Charlotte, North Carolina 28217-1908.
T: 1 704 714-9444 **W:** http://www.1065.com
Editorial Profile: WEND-FM is a commercial station owned by Clear Channel Media and Entertainment. The format of the station is rock alternative. WEND-FM broadcasts to the Charlotte, NC area at 106.5 FM.

WENE-AM
Owner: Clear Channel Media and Entertainment
Editorial: 320 N Jensen Rd, Vestal, New York 13850. **T:** 1 607 584-5800
W: http://www.1430theteam.com
Editorial Profile: WENE-AM is a commercial station owned by Clear Channel Media and Entertainment. The format of the station is sports. WENE-AM broadcasts to the Vestal, NY area at 1430 AM.

WENG-AM
Owner: Viper Communications Inc.
Editorial: 1355 S River Rd, Englewood, Florida 34223-3913. **T:** 1 941 474-3231
E: news@wengradio.com
W: http://www.wengradio.com
Editorial Profile: WENG-AM is a commercial station owned by Viper Communications Inc. The format of the station is news, sports and talk. WENG-AM broadcasts to the Tampa, FL area at 1530 AM.

WENI-AM
Owner: WS2K Media
Editorial: 21 E Market St Ste 101, Corning, New York 14830-2650. **T:** 1 607 937-8181
E: audioonly@stny.rr.com
W: http://www.newstalkweny.com
Editorial Profile: WENI-AM is a commercial station owned by WS2K Media. The format of the station is talk. WENI-AM broadcasts to the Corning, NY area at 1450 AM.

WENI-FM
Owner: WS2K Media
Editorial: 21 E Market St Ste 101, Corning, New York 14830-2650. **T:** 1 607 937-8181
E: audioonly@stny.rr.com
W: http://www.magic927977.com
Editorial Profile: WENI-FM is a commercial station owned by WS2K Media. The format of the station is adult contemporary music. WENI-FM broadcasts to the Corning, NY area at 97.7 FM.

WENJ-FM
Owner: Townsquare Media, LLC
Editorial: 950 Tilton Rd, Ste 200, Northfield, New Jersey 08225-1235. **T:** 1 609 645-9797
W: http://www.973espn.com
Editorial Profile: WENJ-FM is a commercial station owned by the Townsquare Media, LLC. The format of the station is sports. WENJ-FM broadcasts to the Atlantic City, NJ area at 97.3 FM.

WENK-AM
Owner: WENK of Union City, Inc.
Editorial: 1729 Nailling Dr, Union City, Tennessee 38261. **T:** 1 731 885-1240
W: http://www.wenkwtpr.com
Editorial Profile: WENK-AM is a commercial station owned by WENK of Union City, Inc. The format of the station is oldies. WENK-AM broadcasts to the Paducah, KY; Cape Girardeau, MO; Harrisburg, IL areas at 1240 AM.

WENN-AM
Owner: Summit Media Broadcasting LLC
Editorial: 2700 Corporate Dr Ste 115, Birmingham, Alabama 35242-2735.
T: 1 205 322-2987
W: http://www.1021yall.com
Editorial Profile: WENN-AM is a commercial station owned by Summit Media Broadcasting LLC. The format of the station is adult hits. WENN-AM is an ESPN Radio affiliate for the Birmingham, AL area and broadcasts at 1320 AM.

WENO-AM
Owner: Broady Media Group, LLC
Editorial: 2214 Rosa L Parks Blvd Ste 106, Nashville, Tennessee 37228-1341.
T: 1 615 742-6506 22
E: info@760thegospel.com
W: http://www.760thegospel.com
Editorial Profile: WENO-AM is a commercial station owned by Broady Media Group, LLC. The format of the station is gospel. WENO-AM broadcasts in the Nashville, TN area at 760 AM.

WENR-AM
Owner: George C. Hudson, III
Editorial: 202 9th St, Etowah, Tennessee 37331-1343. **T:** 1 423 263-5555
E: wcphradio@yahoo.com
Editorial Profile: WENR-AM is a commercial station owned by George C. Hudson, III. The format of the station is gospel. WENR-AM broadcasts to the Chattanooga, TN area at 1090 AM.

WENT-AM
Owner: Whitney Radio Broadcasting Inc.
Editorial: 138 Harrison St, Gloversville, New York 12078. **T:** 1 518 725-7175
E: went@capital.net
W: http://www.am1340went.com
Editorial Profile: WENT-AM is a commercial station owned by Whitney Radio Broadcasting Inc. The format of the station is news, talk, sports and adult contemporary music. WENT-AM broadcasts to the Gloversville, NY area at 1340 AM.

WENU-AM
Owner: Pamal Broadcasting Ltd.
Editorial: 89 Everts Ave, Queensbury, New York 12804-2040. **T:** 1 518 793-7733
E: production@adirondackbroadcasting.com
Editorial Profile: WENU-AM is a commercial station owned by Pamal Broadcasting Ltd. The format of the station is sports. WENU-AM broadcasts locally to Warren County, NY at 1410 AM.

WENY-AM
Owner: WS2K Media
Editorial: 21 E Market St Ste 101, Corning, New York 14830-2650. **T:** 1 607 937-8181
E: audioonly@stny.rr.com
W: http://www.newstalkweny.com
Editorial Profile: WENY-AM is a commercial station owned by WS2K Media. The format of the station is talk. WENY-AM broadcasts to the Corning, NY area at 1230 AM.

WENY-FM
Owner: WS2K Media
Editorial: 21 E Market St Ste 101, Corning, New York 14830-2650. **T:** 1 607 937-8181
E: audioonly@stny.rr.com
W: http://www.magic927977.com
Editorial Profile: WENY-FM is a commercial station owned by WS2K Media. The format of the station is adult contemporary. WENY-FM broadcasts to the Corning, NY area at 92.7 FM.

WENZ-FM
Owner: Radio One Inc.
Editorial: 2510 Saint Clair Ave NE, Cleveland, Ohio 44114. **T:** 1 216 579-1111
W: http://www.zhiphopcleveland.com
Editorial Profile: WENZ-FM is a commercial station owned by Radio One Inc. The format of the station is urban contemporary. WENZ-FM broadcasts to the Cleveland area at 107.9 FM.

WEOA-AM
Owner: BLS Entertainment, Inc.
Editorial: 915 Main St Ste 1, Evansville, Indiana 47708-1857. **T:** 1 812 424-8864
E: weoa_1@yahoo.com
Editorial Profile: WEOA-AM is a commercial station owned by BLS Entertainment, Inc.. The format for the station is urban adult contemporary. WEOA-AM broadcasts to the Evansville, IN area at 1400 AM.

WEOK-AM
Owner: Townsquare Media
Editorial: 2 Pendell Rd, Poughkeepsie, New York 12601-1513. **T:** 1 845 471-1500
W: http://hudsonvalleytrueoldies.com
Editorial Profile: WEOK-AM is a commercial station owned by Townsquare Media. The format of the station is oldies. WEOK-AM broadcasts to the Poughkeepsie, NY area at 1390 AM.

WEOL-AM
Owner: Elyria-Lorain Broadcasting
Editorial: 538 Broad St Fl 4, Elyria, Ohio 44035-5508. **T:** 1 440 322-3761
E: psa@weol.com
W: http://weol.northcoastnow.com
Editorial Profile: WEOL-AM is a commercial station owned by Elyria-Lorain Broadcasting. The format of the station is news, talk and sports. WEOL-AM broadcasts to the Elyria, OH area at 930 AM.

WEOS-FM
Owner: Hobart & William Smith Colleges
Editorial: 300 Pulteney St, Geneva, New York 14456-3304. **T:** 1 315 781-3456
W: http://www.weos.org
Editorial Profile: WEOS-FM is a non-commercial station owned by Hobart & William Smith Colleges. The format of the station is adult album alternative, news and talk. WEOS-FM broadcasts to the Geneva, NY area 89.5 FM.

WEOW-FM
Owner: Florida Keys Media, LLC
Editorial: 93351 Overseas Hwy, Tavernier, Florida 33070-2800. **T:** 1 305 852-9085
Editorial Profile: WEOW-FM is a commercial station owned by Florida Keys Media, LLC. The format of the station is top 40/CHR. WEOW-FM broadcasts to the Key West, FL area at 92.7 FM.

WEPC-FM
Owner: Toccoa Falls College
Editorial: 292 Old Clarksville Rd, Toccoa, Georgia 30577-6973. **T:** 1 706 282-6030
E: radio@myfavoritestation.net
W: http://www.toccoafallsradio.org/
Editorial Profile: WBMZ-FM is a non-commercial station owned by Toccoa Falls College. The format of the station is religious. WBMZ-FM airs locally in the Toccoa, GA area 88.5 FM.

WEPG-AM
Owner: Rodgers(Charles)
Editorial: 105 N Ash Ave, South Pittsburg, Tennessee 37380-1565. **T:** 1 423 837-8001
E: wepg@att.net
W: http://www.wepgradio.com
Editorial Profile: WEPG-AM is a commercial station owned by Charles Rodgers. The format of the station is classic country. WEPG-AM broadcasts to the Chattanooga, TN area at 910 AM.

WEPM-AM
Owner: Prettyman Broadcasting Co.
Editorial: 1606 W King St, Martinsburg, West Virginia 25401. **T:** 1 304 263-8868
E: wepm@wepm.com
W: http://www.wepm.com
Editorial Profile: WEMP-AM is a commercial station owned by Prettyman Broadcasting Co. The format of the station is news, talk, and sports. WEPM-AM broadcasts in the Martinsburg, WV, area at 1340 AM.

WEPN-AM
Owner: Walt Disney Co.
Editorial: 125 W End Ave Fl 6, New York, New York 10023-6387. **T:** 1 646 699-6800
W: http://espndeportes.espn.go.com/espndeportesradio
Editorial Profile: WEPN-AM is a commercial station owned by Walt Disney Co. The format of the station is Spanish sports programming. WEPN-AM broadcasts to the New York area at 1050 AM.

WEPN-FM
Owner: Emmis Communications Corp.
Editorial: 125 W End Ave Fl 6, New York, New York 10023-6387. **T:** 1 646 699-6800
W: http://espn.go.com/newyork/radio
Editorial Profile: WEPN-FM is a commercial station owned by Emmis Communications Corp., and managed under LMA with ESPN, Inc. (Walt Disney Co.). The format of the station is sports. WEPN-FM broadcasts to the New York City metro area at 98.7 FM.

WEPR-FM
Owner: South Carolina Educational Television Commission
Editorial: 1101 George Rogers Blvd, Columbia, South Carolina 29201-4761.
T: 1 803 737-3200 **W:** http://www.etvradio.org
Editorial Profile: WEPR-FM is a non-commercial station owned by the South Carolina Educational Television Commission. The format of the station is news and classical music. WEPR-FM broadcasts to the Columbia, SC area at 90.1 FM. The station does not accept PSAs.

WEPS-FM
Owner: School Dist. U-46, Elgin, IL
Editorial: 355 E Chicago St, Elgin, Illinois 60120. **T:** 1 847 888-5040
Editorial Profile: WEPS-FM is a non-commercial station owned by School Dist. U-46, Elgin, IL. The format of the station is variety. WEPS-FM broadcasts to the Elgin, IL area at 88.9 FM.

WEQR-FM
Owner: Curtis Media Group
Editorial: 2581 US Highway 70 W, Goldsboro, North Carolina 27530-9553.
T: 1 919 587-0977
W: http://www.curtismedia.com
Editorial Profile: WEQR-FM is a commercial station owned by Curtis Media Group. The format of the station is Top 40/CHR. WEQR-FM broadcasts to the Raleigh, NC area at 97.7 FM.

WEQX-FM
Owner: Northshire Communications Inc.
Editorial: 161 Elm St, Manchester Center, Vermont 05255-9641. **T:** 1 802 362-4800
W: http://www.weqx.com
Editorial Profile: WEQX-FM is a commercial station owned by Northshire Communications Inc. The format of the station is rock alternative music. WEQX-FM broadcasts to the Manchester, VT area at 102.7 FM.

WERC-AM
Owner: Clear Channel Media and Entertainment
Editorial: 600 Beacon Pkwy W, Birmingham, Alabama 35209-3120. **T:** 1 205 439-9600
W: http://www.wercfm.com
Editorial Profile: WERC-AM is a commercial station owned by Clear Channel Media and Entertainment. The format of the station is news/talk. WERC-AM broadcasts to the Birmingham, AL, area at 960 AM.

WERC-FM
Owner: Clear Channel Media and Entertainment
Editorial: 600 Beacon Pkwy W, Birmingham, Alabama 35209-3120. **T:** 1 205 439-9600
W: http://www.talkradio1055.com
Editorial Profile: WERC-FM is a commercial station owned by Clear Channel Media and Entertainment. The format of the station is news/talk. WERC-FM broadcasts to the Birmingham, AL area at 105.5 FM.

WERE-AM
Owner: Radio One Inc.
Editorial: 2510 Saint Clair Ave Ne, Cleveland, Ohio 44114-4013. **T:** 1 216 579-1111
W: http://newstalkcleveland.com
Editorial Profile: WERE-AM is a commercial station owned by Radio One Inc. The format of the station is news and talk. WERE-AM broadcasts in the Cleveland area at 1490 AM.

WERG-FM
Owner: Gannon University
Editorial: 705 Peach Street, Erie, Pennsylvania 16507. **T:** 1 814 871-5841
E: werg@gannon.edu
W: http://www.wergfm.com
Editorial Profile: WERG-FM is a non-commercial station owned by Gannon University. The format of the station is rock alternative. WERG-FM broadcasts to the Erie, PA area at 90.5 FM.

WERH-AM
Owner: Fowler(Martha) and Burleson(Susan)
Editorial: 1597 Military St S, Hamilton, Alabama 35570-5026. **T:** 1 205 921-3481
E: werh@sonet.net
Editorial Profile: WERH-AM is a commercial station owned by Martha Fowler and Susan Burleson. The format of the station is classic country and gospel music. WERH-FM broadcasts to the Hamilton, AL area at 970 AM.

WERH-FM
Owner: Fowler(Martha) and Burleson(Susan)
Editorial: 1597 Military St S, Hamilton, Alabama 35570. **T:** 1 205 921-3481
E: werh@sonet.net
Editorial Profile: WERH-FM is a commercial station owned by Martha Fowler and Susan Burleson. The format of the station is classic rock music. WERH-FM broadcasts to the Hamilton, AL area at 92.1 FM.

WERK-FM
Owner: Backyard Broadcasting
Editorial: 800 E 29th St, Muncie, Indiana 47302-5765. **T:** 1 765 288-4403
E: wlbcstudio@comcast.net

W: http://www.werkradio.com
Editorial Profile: WERK-FM is a commercial station owned by Backyard Broadcasting. The format of the station is oldies music. WERK-FM broadcasts to the Indianapolis area at 104.9 FM.

WERL-AM
Owner: Heartland Communications Group, LLC
Editorial: 909 N Railroad St, Eagle River, Wisconsin 54521-8623. **T:** 1 715 479-4451
Editorial Profile: WERL-AM is a commercial station owned by Heartland Communications Group, LLC. The format of the station is talk. WERL-AM broadcasts to Eagle River, WI area at 950 AM.

WERN-FM
Owner: University of Wisconsin
Editorial: 821 University Ave, Madison, Wisconsin 53706. **T:** 1 608 263-3970
E: listener@wpr.org **W:** http://www.wpr.org
Editorial Profile: WERN-FM is a non-commercial station owned by the University of Wisconsin. The format of the station is news and classical. WERN-FM broadcasts to the Madison, WI area at 88.7 FM.

WERO-FM
Owner: Digity LLC
Editorial: 1361 Colony Dr, New Bern, North Carolina 28562-4129. **T:** 1 252 639-7900
W: http://www.bob933.com
Editorial Profile: WERO-FM is a commercial station owned by Digity LLC. The format of the station is Top 40/CHR music. WERO-FM broadcasts to the Greenville, NC area at 93.3 FM.

WERQ-FM
Owner: Radio One Inc.
Editorial: 1705 Whitehead Rd, Baltimore, Maryland 21207. **T:** 1 410 332-8200
W: http://www.92q.com
Editorial Profile: WERQ-FM is a commercial station owned by Radio One Inc. The format of the station is urban contemporary music. WERQ-FM broadcasts to the Baltimore area at 92.3 FM.

WERS-FM
Owner: Emerson College
Editorial: 180 Tremont St, Boston, Massachusetts 02111-1014.
T: 1 617 824-8891 **E:** news@wers.org
W: http://www.wers.org
Editorial Profile: WERS-FM is a non-commercial station owned by Emerson College. The format of the station is AAA-Adult Album Alternative. WERS-FM broadcasts to the Boston area at 88.9 FM.

WERT-AM
Owner: First Family Broadcasting Inc.
Editorial: 9070 Mendon Rd, Van Wert, Ohio 45891. **T:** 1 419 238-1220 **E:** wert@bright.net
W: http://www.vanwert.com/wert
Editorial Profile: WERT-AM is a commercial station owned by First Family Broadcasting Inc. The format of the station is adult standards. WERT-AM broadcasts to the Van Wert, OH area at 1220 AM.

WERU-FM
Owner: Salt Pond Community Broadcasting
Editorial: 1186 Acadia Highway, East Orland, Maine 4431. **T:** 1 207 469-6600
E: news@weru.org **W:** http://www.weru.org
Editorial Profile: WERU-FM is a non-commercial station owned by Salt Pond Community Broadcasting. The format of the station is variety. WERU-FM broadcasts to the East Orland, ME area at 89.9 FM.

WERV-FM
Owner: Digity LLC
Editorial: 1884 Plain Ave, Aurora, Illinois 60502-8560. **T:** 1 630 898-1580
W: http://www.959theriver.com
Editorial Profile: WERV-FM is a commercial station owned by Digity LLC. The format of the station is classic hits music. WERV-FM broadcasts to the Aurora, IL area at 95.9 FM.

WERX-FM
Owner: East Carolina Radio Group
Editorial: 2422 S Wrightsville Ave, Nags Head, North Carolina 27959-9323.
T: 1 252 441-1024 **E:** psa@ecri.net
W: http://www.1025theshark.com
Editorial Profile: WERX-FM is a commercial station owned by East Carolina Radio Group. The format of the station is classic hits. WERX-FM broadcasts to Nags Head, NC at 102.5 FM.

WERZ-FM
Owner: Clear Channel Media and Entertainment
Editorial: 815 Lafayette Rd, Portsmouth, New Hampshire 03801-5406. **T:** 1 603 436-7300
W: http://www.z107fm.com
Editorial Profile: WERZ-FM is a commercial station owned by Clear Channel Media and Entertainment. The format of the station is top 40/CHR. WERZ-FM broadcasts to the Portsmouth, NH area at 107.1 FM.

WESA-FM
Owner: Pittsburgh Community Broadcasting Corp.
Editorial: 67 Bedford Sq, Pittsburgh, Pennsylvania 15203-1152. **T:** 1 412 381-9131
E: news@wesa.fm **W:** http://wesa.fm
Editorial Profile: WESA-FM is a non-commercial station owned by Pittsburgh Community Broadcasting Corp. The format of the station is news talk. WESA-FM broadcasts in the Pittsburgh area at 90.5 FM.

WESB-AM
Owner: WESB Inc.
Editorial: 1490 Saint Francis Dr, Bradford, Pennsylvania 16701. **T:** 1 814 368-4141
E: news@wesb.com **W:** http://www.wesb.com
Editorial Profile: WESB-AM is a commercial station owned by WESB Inc. The format of the station is hot adult contemporary, news and talk. WESB-AM broadcasts to the Buffalo, NY area at 1490 AM.

WESC-FM
Owner: Clear Channel Media and Entertainment
Editorial: 101 N Main St Ste 1000, Greenville, South Carolina 29601-4852.
T: 1 864 242-4660 **E:** raydioguy@aol.com
W: http://www.wescfm.com
Editorial Profile: WESC-FM is a commercial station owned by Clear Channel Media and Entertainment. The format of the station is contemporary country. WESC-FM broadcasts to the Greenville, SC area at 92.5 FM.

WESE-FM
Owner: URBan Radio Broadcasting, LLC
Editorial: 5026 Cliff Gookin Blvd, Tupelo, Mississippi 38801. **T:** 1 662 842-1067
W: http://www.power925jamz.com
Editorial Profile: WESE-FM is a commercial station owned by URBan Radio Broadcasting, LLC. The format of the station is urban contemporary. WESE-FM broadcasts to the Tupelo, MS area at 92.5 FM.

WESI-FM
Owner: Main Line Broadcasting
Editorial: 520 S 4th St Fl 2, Louisville, Kentucky 40202-2500. **T:** 1 502 625-1220
E: easyrock1051@gmail.com
W: http://www.easyrock1051.com
Editorial Profile: WESI-FM is a commercial station owned by Main Line Broadcasting. The format of the station soft adult contemporary. WESI-FM broadcasts to the Louisville, KY area at 105.1 FM.

WESM-FM
Owner: University of Maryland-Eastern Shore
Editorial: University of Maryland Eastern Shore, WESM-FM, Princess Anne, Maryland 21853. **T:** 1 410 651-8001
E: wesm913@umes.edu
W: http://www.wesm913.org
Editorial Profile: WESM-FM is a non-commercial station owned by the University of Maryland-Eastern Shore. The format of the station is news, blues and jazz music. WESM-FM broadcasts to the Princess Anne, MD area at 91.3 FM.

WESN-FM
Owner: Illinois Wesleyan University
Editorial: 1207 N Main St, Bloomington, Illinois 61701. **T:** 1 309 556-2638
E: wesn@iwu.edu **W:** http://www.wesn.org
Editorial Profile: WESN-FM is a non-commercial station owned by Illinois Wesleyan University. The format of the station is college variety. WESN-FM broadcasts to the Bloomington, IL area at 88.1 FM.

WESO-AM
Owner: Money Matters Radio Inc.
Editorial: 100 Foster St, Southbridge, Massachusetts 01550-2595.
T: 1 508 909-0970
W: http://www.weso970.com
Editorial Profile: WESO-AM is a commercial station owned by Money Matters Radio Inc. The format of the station is business talk. WESO-AM broadcasts to the Southbridge, MA area at 970 AM.

WESP-FM
Owner: Southeast Alabama Broadcasters, LLC
Editorial: 3245 Montgomery Hwy Ste 1, Dothan, Alabama 36303-2150.
T: 1 334 712-9233
W: http://www.q102dothan.com
Editorial Profile: WESP-FM is a commercial station owned by Southeast Alabama Broadcasters, LLC and operated by Low Country Radio, LLC. The format of the station is classic hits. WESP-AM broadcasts to the Dothan, AL area at 102.5 FM.

WESR-AM
Owner: Eastern Shore Radio, Inc.
Editorial: 22479 Front St, Accomac, Virginia 23301-1641. **T:** 1 757 787-3200
W: http://www.shoredailynews.com
Editorial Profile: WESR-AM is a commercial station owned by Eastern Shore Radio, Inc. The format of the station is classic hits and talk. WESR-AM broadcasts to the Norfolk, VA area at 1330 AM.

WESR-FM
Owner: Eastern Shore Radio, Inc.
Editorial: 22479 Front St, Accomac, Virginia 23301-1641. **T:** 1 757 787-3200
W: http://www.shoredailynews.com
Editorial Profile: WESR-FM is a commercial station owned by Eastern Shore Radio, Inc. The format of the station is oldies, adult contemporary, news and talk. WESR-FM broadcasts to the Norfolk, VA area at 103.3 FM.

WESS-FM
Owner: East Stroudsburg University
Editorial: 200 Prospect St, 200, East Stroudsburg, Pennsylvania 18301.
T: 1 570 422-3512 **E:** Wess@esu.com
W: http://www.esu.edu/wess
Editorial Profile: WESS-FM is a non-commercial, educational station owned by East Stroudsburg University. The format of the station is variety. WESS-FM broadcasts to the East Stroudsburg, PA area at 90.3 FM.

WEST-AM
Owner: Grey Matter Broadcasting
Editorial: 1125 Colorado St, Allentown, Pennsylvania 18103-3118. **T:** 1 610 434-4801
W: http://www.holaenturadio.com
Editorial Profile: WEST-AM is a commercial station owned by Grey Matter Broadcasting. The format of the station is Spanish tropical music. WEST-AM broadcasts to the Allentown, PA area at 1400 AM.

WESU-FM
Owner: Wesleyan University
Editorial: 45 Broad St, Middletown, Connecticut 6457. **T:** 1 860 685-7703
E: publicrelations@wesufm.org
W: http://www.wesufm.org
Editorial Profile: WESU-FM is a non-commercial station owned by Wesleyan University. The format of the station is variety. WESU-FM broadcasts to the Middletown, CT area at 88.1 FM.

WESX-AM
Owner: Principle Broadcasting
Editorial: 90 Everett Ave, Chelsea, Massachusetts 02150-2311.
T: 1 617 884-4500
W: http://www.wesx1230am.com
Editorial Profile: WESX-AM is a commercial station owned by Principle Broadcasting. The format of the station is Hispanic variety. WESX-AM broadcasts to the Marblehead, MA area at 1230 AM.

WESY-AM
Owner: Interchange Communications
Editorial: 126 Seven Oaks Road, Greenville, Mississippi 38704-4426. **T:** 1 662 378-9405
Editorial Profile: WESY-AM is a commercial station owned by Interchange Communications. The format of the station is gospel. WESY-AM broadcasts in the Greenville, MS area at 1580 AM.

WETA-FM
Owner: Greater Washington Education & Television Assn.
Editorial: 3939 Campbell Ave, Arlington, Virginia 22206-3440. **T:** 1 703 998-2600
E: fmlistener@weta.com
W: http://www.weta.org
Editorial Profile: WETA-FM is a non-commercial station owned by the Greater Washington Education & Television Assn. The format of the station is classical. WETA-FM broadcasts to Arlington, VA area at 90.9 FM.

WETB-AM
Owner: Mountain Signals Inc.
Editorial: 231 Brandonwood Dr, Johnson City, Tennessee 37604-2156. **T:** 1 423 928-7131
Editorial Profile: WETB-AM is a non-commercial station owned by Mountain Signals Inc. The format of the station is gospel. WETB-AM broadcasts to the Johnson City, TN area at 790 AM.

WETC-AM
Owner: Sanchez Broadcasting Corporation
Editorial: 2164 Southeast Blvd, Clinton, North Carolina 28328-4758. **T:** 1 919 592-1285
Editorial Profile: WETC-AM is a commercial station owned by Sanchez Broadcasting Corporation. The format of the station is Spanish CHR. WETC-AM broadcasts to the Raleigh, NC area at 540 AM.

WETL-FM
Owner: South Bend Community School Corp.
Editorial: 1902 Fellows St, South Bend, Indiana 46613. **T:** 1 574 283-8432

WETN-FM
Owner: Trustees of Wheaton College
Editorial: 501 College Ave, Wheaton, Illinois 60187-5501. **T:** 1 630 752-5074
E: wetn@wheaton.edu
W: http://www.wheaton.edu/wetn
Editorial Profile: WETN-FM is a non-commercial station owned by Trustees of Wheaton College. The format of the station is religious, classical and jazz music. WETN-FM broadcasts to the Wheaton, IL area at 88.1 FM.

WETR-AM
Owner: Moffit Media Inc.
Editorial: 1621 E Magnolia Ave, Knoxville, Tennessee 37917-7825. **T:** 1 865 525-0620
W: http://www.talkradio760.com
Editorial Profile: WETR-AM is a commercial station owned by Moffit Media Inc. The format of the station is news and talk. WETR-AM broadcasts to the Knoxville, TN area at 760 AM.

WETT-FM
Owner: Withers Broadcasting Co.
Editorial: 5 Television Dr, Bridgeport, West Virginia 26330-2621. **T:** 1 304 848-5000
Editorial Profile: WETT-FM is a commercial station owned by Withers Broadcasting Co. The format of the station is adult contemporary music. WETT-FM broadcasts to the Bridgeport, WV area at 104.1 FM.

WETZ-AM
Owner: Dailey Corp.
Editorial: 1130 4Th St, New Martinsville, West Virginia 26155-2110. **T:** 1 304 455-1111
E: wetz@suddenlinkmail.com
Editorial Profile: WETZ-AM is a commercial station owned by Dailey Corp. The format of the station is classic hits. WETZ-AM broadcasts to the New Martinsville, WV area at 1330 AM.

WEUL-FM
Owner: Gospel Opportunities Inc.
Editorial: 130 Carmen Dr, Marquette, Michigan 49855. **T:** 1 906 249-1423 **E:** whwl@whwl.net
W: http://www.whwl.net
Editorial Profile: WEUL-FM is a non-commercial station owned by Gospel Opportunities Inc. The format for the station is religious programming. WEUL-FM broadcasts to the Marquette, MI area at 98.1 FM.

WEUP-AM
Owner: Broadcast One
Editorial: 2609 Jordan Ln NW, Huntsville, Alabama 35816-1030. **T:** 1 256 837-9387
E: promotions@103weup.com
W: http://www.weupam.com
Editorial Profile: WEUP-AM is a commercial station owned by Broadcast One. The format of the station is gospel and talk. WEUP-AM broadcasts to the Huntsville, AL area at 1700 AM.

WEUP-FM
Owner: Broadcast One
Editorial: 2609 Jordan Ln NW, Huntsville, Alabama 35816-1030. **T:** 1 256 837-9387
E: promotions@103weup.com
W: http://www.103weup.com
Editorial Profile: WEUP-FM is a commercial station owned by Broadcast One. The format of the station is urban contemporary music. WEUP-FM broadcasts in the Huntsville, AL area at 103.1 FM.

WEUV-AM
Owner: Broadcast One
Editorial: 2609 Jordan Ln NW, Huntsville, Alabama 35816-1013. **T:** 1 256 837-9387
W: http://www.103weup.com
Editorial Profile: WEUV-AM is a commercial station owned by Broadcast One. The format of the station is urban contemporary music. WEUV-AM broadcasts to the Huntsville, AL area at 1190 AM.

WEUZ-FM
Owner: Broadcast One
Editorial: 2609 Jordan Ln NW, Huntsville, Alabama 35816-1013. **T:** 1 256 837-9387
E: promotions@103weup.com
W: http://www.103weup.com
Editorial Profile: WEUZ-FM is a commerical station owned by Broadcast One. The format of the station is urban contemporary music. WEUZ-FM broadcasts to the Huntsville, AL area at 92.1 FM.

WEVA-AM
Owner: Colonial Media Corp.
Editorial: 705 Washington St, Emporia, Virginia 23847. **T:** 1 434 634-2133
W: http://www.wevaradio.com
Editorial Profile: WEVA-AM is a commercial station owned by Colonial Media Corp. The format of the station is adult contemporary music. WEVA-AM broadcasts to the Emporia, VA area at 860 AM.

WEVE-FM
Owner: Iron Range Broadcasting, Inc.
Editorial: 906 Old Highway 53 & Cemetery Road, Eveleth, Minnesota 55734-8632.
T: 1 218 741-5922 **E:** weve@wevefm.com
Editorial Profile: WEVE-FM is a commercial station owned by Iron Range Broadcasting, Inc. The format of the station is adult contemporary music. WEVE-FM broadcasts in the Eveleth, MN area at 1340 AM.

WEVJ-FM
Owner: New Hampshire Public Radio, Inc.
Editorial: 2 Pillsbury Street, Concord, New Hampshire 3301. **T:** 1 603 228-8910
W: http://www.nhpr.org
Editorial Profile: WEVJ-FM is a non-commercial station owned by New Hampshire Public Radio, Inc. The format of the station is news and talk. WEVJ-FM broadcasts to the Jackson, NH area at 99.5 FM. The station does not accept PSAs.

WEVL-FM
Owner: Southern Communication Volunteers
Editorial: 518 S Main St, Memphis, Tennessee 38103-4443. **T:** 1 901 528-0560
E: wevl@wevl.org **W:** http://www.wevl.org
Editorial Profile: WEVL-FM is a non-commercial station owned by Southern Communication Volunteers. The format of the station is variety. WEVL-FM broadcasts to the Memphis area at 89.9 FM.

WEVN-FM
Owner: New Hampshire Public Radio, Inc.
Editorial: 2 Pillsbury St Fl 6, Concord, New Hampshire 03301-3523. **T:** 1 603 228-8910
W: http://www.nhpr.org
Editorial Profile: WEVN-FM is a non-commercial station owned by New Hampshire Public Radio, Inc. The station airs in the Concord, NH area at 90.7 FM and plays a talk and news format.

WEVO-FM
Owner: New Hampshire Public Radio, Inc.
Editorial: 2 Pillsbury St, Concord, New Hampshire 03301-3523. **T:** 1 603 228-8910
W: http://www.nhpr.org
Editorial Profile: WEVO-FM is a non-commercial station owned by New Hampshire Public Radio, Inc. The format of the station is news and talk. WEVO-FM broadcasts to the Concord, NH area at 89.1 FM.

WEVR-AM
Owner: Hanten Broadcasting Co. Inc.
Editorial: 178 Radio Rd, River Falls, Wisconsin 54022-8255. **T:** 1 715 425-1111
E: wevr.am.fm@gmail.com
Editorial Profile: WEVR-AM is a commercial station owned by Hanten Broadcasting Co. Inc. The format of the station is Lite Rock/Lite AC. WEVR-AM broadcasts in the River Falls, WI area at 1550 AM.

WEVR-FM
Owner: Hanten Broadcasting Co. Inc.
Editorial: 178 Radio Rd, River Falls, Wisconsin 54022-8255. **T:** 1 715 381-1111
E: wevr.am.fm@gmail.com
Editorial Profile: WEVR-FM is a commercial station owned by Hanten Broadcasting Co. Inc. The format of the station is Lite Rock/Lite AC music. WEVR-FM broadcasts to the River Falls, WI area at 106.3 FM.

WEW-AM
Owner: Birach Broadcasting Corp.
Editorial: 2740 Hampton Ave, Saint Louis, Missouri 63139. **T:** 1 314 781-9397
E: wewradio@aol.com
W: http://www.wewradio.com
Editorial Profile: WEW-AM is a commercial station owned by Birach Broadcasting Corp. The format of the station is a variety of adult standards music, talk and ethnic programming. WEW-AM broadcasts to the St. Louis area at 770 AM.

WEWO-AM
Owner: Service Media Inc.
Editorial: 1338 Bragg Blvd, Fayetteville, North Carolina 28301. **T:** 1 910 486-9438
Editorial Profile: WEWO-AM is a commercial station owned by Service Media Inc. The format of the station is gospel. WEWO-AM broadcasts to the Fayetteville, NC area at 1460 AM.

WEXL-AM
Owner: Crawford Broadcasting Co.
Editorial: 12300 Radio Pl, Detroit, Michigan 48228. **T:** 1 313 272-1340
E: station@wmuz.com
W: http://www.wexl1340.com
Editorial Profile: WEXL-AM is a commercial station owned by Crawford Broadcasting Co. The format of the station is gospel. WEXL-AM broadcasts to the Detroit area at 1340 AM.

WEXP-FM
Owner: Woodchuck Radio, LLC
Editorial: 9 Stowe St, Waterbury, Vermont 05676-1820. **T:** 1 802 244-7321
E: wdev@radiovermont.com
Editorial Profile: WEXP-FM is a commercial station owned by Woodchuck Radio, LLC (part of Radio Vermont Group). The format of the station is rock. WEXP-FM broadcasts to the Rutland, VT area at a frequency of 101.5 FM.

WEXR-FM
Owner: Meridian Community College Foundation
Editorial: 910 Highway 19 N, Meridian, Mississippi 39307-5801. **T:** 1 601 484-8789
E: wexrfm@wexrfm.com **W:** http://wexr.us
Editorial Profile: WEXR-FM is a non-commercial station owned by Meridian Community College Foundation. The format of the station is adult standards. WEXR-FM broadcasts to the Meridian, MS area at 106.9 FM.

WEXT-FM
Owner: WMHT Educational Telecommunications
Editorial: 4 Global Vw, Troy, New York 12180.
T: 1 518 880-3400 **E:** email@wmht.org
W: http://exit977.org
Editorial Profile: WEXT-FM is a non-commercial station owned by WMHT Educational Telecommunications. The format of the station is adult album alternative. WEXT-FM broadcasts to the Schenectady, NY area at 97.7 FM.

WEXY-AM
Owner: Multicultural Radio Broadcasting Inc.
Editorial: 412 W Oakland Park Blvd, Wilton Manors, Florida 33311. **T:** 1 954 561-1520
Editorial Profile: WEXY-AM is a commercial station owned by Multicultural Radio Broadcasting Inc. The format of the station is gospel. WEXY-AM broadcasts to the Wilton Manors, FL at 1520 AM.

WEYY-FM
Owner: Barnes Evangelistic Ministries
Editorial: 7550 W Carroll Rd, Carrollton, Georgia 30116-5900. **T:** 1 540 459-7646
W: http://www.barnesministries.com/Radio.htm
Editorial Profile: WEYY-FM is a non-commercial station owned by Barnes Evangelistic Ministries. The format of the station is Southern gospel music. WEYY-FM is licensed to Tallapoosa, GA and broadcasts to the West Atlanta Metro and East Alabama areas at a frequency of 88.7 FM.

WEZB-FM
Owner: Entercom Communications Corp.
Editorial: 400 Poydras St Ste 800, New Orleans, Louisiana 70130-3789.
T: 1 504 593-6376
E: wwlnewsroom@yahoo.com
W: http://www.b97.com
Editorial Profile: WEZB-FM is a commercial station owned by Entercom Communications Corp. The format of the station is Top 40/CHR. WEZB-FM broadcasts to the New Orleans area on 97.1 FM.

WEZC-FM
Owner: Kaskaskia Broadcasting, Inc.
Editorial: 2980 US Highway 51, Clinton, Illinois 61727-9479. **T:** 1 217 935-9590
E: whow@randyradio.com
Editorial Profile: WEZC-FM is a commercial station owned by Kaskaskia Broadcasting, Inc. The format of the station is easy listening. WEZC-FM broadcasts to the Clinton, IL area at 95.9 FM.

WEZE-AM
Owner: Salem Communications
Editorial: 500 Victory Rd, Ste 2, North Quincy, Massachusetts 2171. **T:** 1 617 328-0880
E: contactus@salemradioboston.com
W: http://www.wezeradio.com
Editorial Profile: WEZE-AM is a commercial station owned by Salem Communication. The format of the station is religious news and talk. WEZE-AM broadcasts to the Quincy, MA area at 590 AM.

WEZF-FM
Owner: Vox Communications
Editorial: 265 Hegeman Ave, Colchester, Vermont 5446. **T:** 1 802 655-0093
E: star@star929.com
W: http://www.star929.com
Editorial Profile: WEZF-FM is a commercial station owned by Vox Communications. The format of the station is adult contemporary. WEZF-FM broadcasts to the Burlington, VT area at 92.9 FM.

WEZJ-FM
Owner: Whitley Broadcasting
Editorial: 522 Main St, Williamsburg, Kentucky 40769-1127. **T:** 1 606 549-2285
E: wekx@bellsouth.net
Editorial Profile: WEZJ-FM is a commercial station owned by Whitley Broadcasting. The format of the station is country. WEZJ-FM broadcasts to the Lexington, KY area at 104.3 FM.

WEZL-FM
Owner: Clear Channel Media and Entertainment
Editorial: 950 Houston Northcutt Blvd, Ste 201, Mount Pleasant, South Carolina 29464.
T: 1 843 884-2534
E: generalwezl@clearchannel.com
W: http://www.wezl.com
Editorial Profile: WEZL-FM is a commercial station owned by Clear Channel Media and Entertainment. The format of the station is country music. WEZL-FM broadcasts to the Mount Pleasant, SC area at 103.5 FM.

WEZN-FM
Owner: Connoisseur Media
Editorial: 440 Wheelers Farms Rd, Milford, Connecticut 06461-9133. **T:** 1 203 783-8200
W: http://star999.com
Editorial Profile: WEZN-FM is a commercial station owned by Connoisseur Media. The format of the station is adult contemporary. WEZN-FM broadcasts to the Milford, CT area at 99.9 FM.

WEZO-AM
Owner: Medici Media, Inc.
Editorial: 1802 Killingsworth Rd, Augusta, Georgia 30904-5596. **T:** 1 706 364-9361
W: http://www.italkus.com
Editorial Profile: WEZO-AM is a commercial station owned by Medici Media, Inc. The format of the station is Conservative talk. WEZO-AM broadcasts to the Augusta, GA area at 1230 AM.

WEZQ-FM
Owner: Townsquare Media, Inc.
Editorial: 49 Acme Rd, Brewer, Maine 04412-1545. **T:** 1 207 989-5631
E: wezq@midmaine.com
W: http://www.wezq-fm.com
Editorial Profile: WEQZ-FM is a commercial station owned by Townsquare Media, Inc. The format of the station is Lite Rock/Lite AC. WEQZ-FM broadcasts to the Brewer, ME area at 92.9 FM.

WEZR-AM
Owner: Gleason Radio Group
Editorial: 555 Center St, Auburn, Maine 4210.
T: 1 207 784-5868
E: news@gleasonmedia.com
W: http://www.ez1240.com
Editorial Profile: WEZR-AM is a commercial station owned by Gleason Radio Group. The format of the station is soft adult contemporary. WEZR-AM broadcasts to the Auburn, ME area at 1240 AM.

WEZS-AM
Owner: Hammond(Gary W.)
Editorial: 277 Union Ave, Laconia, New Hampshire 03246-3114. **T:** 1 603 524-6288
E: staff@wezs.com **W:** http://www.wezs.com
Editorial Profile: WEZS-AM is a commercial station owned by Gary W. Hammond. The format of the station is news/talk. WEZS-AM broadcasts to the Boston area at 1350 AM.

WEZV-FM
Owner: Fidelity Broadcasting Inc.
Editorial: 3926 Wesley St, Ste 301, Myrtle Beach, South Carolina 29579.
T: 1 843 903-9962 **E:** staff@wezv.com
W: http://www.wezv.com
Editorial Profile: WEZV-FM is a commercial station owned by Fidelity Broadcasting Inc. The format of the station is easy listening. WEZV-FM broadcasts to the Myrtle Beach, SC area at 105.9 FM.

WEZW-FM
Owner: Equity Communications LP
Editorial: 8025 Black Horse Pike, Ste 100, Pleasantville, New Jersey 8232.
T: 1 609 484-8444 **E:** easy931@gmail.com
W: http://easy931.com
Editorial Profile: WEZW-FM is a commercial station owned by Equity Communications LP. The format of the station is adult hits. WEZW-FM broadcasts to the Atlantic City, NJ area at 93.1 FM.

WEZX-FM
Owner: Shamrock Communications
Editorial: 149 Penn Ave, Scranton, Pennsylvania 18503. **T:** 1 570 346-6555
W: http://www.rock107.com
Editorial Profile: WEZX-FM is a commercial station owned by Shamrock Communications. The format of the station is classic rock. WEZX-FM broadcasts to the Scranton, PA area at 107.3 FM.

WEZY-FM
Owner: Bliss Communications Inc.
Editorial: 4201 Victory Ave, Racine, Wisconsin 53405-3277. **T:** 1 262 634-3311
E: news@racineradio.com
W: http://www.literock921.com
Editorial Profile: WEZY-FM is a commercial station owned by Bliss Communications Inc. The format of the station is Lite Rock/Lite AC music. WEZY-FM broadcasts to the Milwaukee area at 92.1 FM.

WFAE-FM
Owner: University Radio Foundation
Editorial: 8801 J M Keynes Dr, Ste 91, Charlotte, North Carolina 28262.
T: 1 704 549-9323 **E:** news@wfae.org
W: http://www.wfae.org
Editorial Profile: WFAE-FM is a non-commercial station owned by the University Radio Foundation. The format of the station is news and talk. WFAE-FM broadcasts to the Charlotte, NC area at 90.7 FM.

WFAI-AM
Owner: QC Communications Inc.
Editorial: 704 N King St, Ste 604, Wilmington, Delaware 19801. **T:** 1 302 622-8895
W: http://www.faith1510.com
Editorial Profile: WFAI-AM is a commercial station owned by QC Communications Inc. The format of the station is gospel music. WFAI-AM broadcasts to the Wilmington, DE area at 1510 AM.

WFAM-AM
Owner: Wilkins Communications Network Inc.
Editorial: 552 Laney-Walker Ext, Augusta, Georgia 30901. **T:** 1 864 585-1885
E: wfam@wilkinsradio.com
W: http://www.wilkinsradio.com
Editorial Profile: WFAM-AM is a commercial station owned by the Wilkins Communications Network Inc. The format of the station is religious talk. WFAM-AM broadcasts to the Augusta, GA area at 1050 AM.

WFAN-AM
Owner: CBS Radio
Editorial: 345 Hudson St 10th Fl, New York, New York 10014-4502. **T:** 1 212 315-7000
E: fanmail@wfan.com
W: http://newyork.cbslocal.com/station/wfan/
Editorial Profile: WFAN-AM is a commercial station owned by CBS Radio. The format of

the station is sports. WFAN-AM broadcasts to the New York area at 660 AM.

WFAN-FM
Owner: CBS Radio
Editorial: 345 Hudson Street 10th Floor, New York, New York 10014-4502.
T: 1 212 315-7000
W: http://newyork.cbslocal.com/station/wfan
Editorial Profile: WFAN-FM is commercial station owned by CBS Radio. The format of the station is sports. WFAN-FM broadcasts to the New York area at 101.9 FM.

WFAR-FM
Owner: Danbury Community Radio Inc.
Editorial: 25 Chestnut St, Danbury, Connecticut 06810-6816. **T:** 1 203 748-0001
E: wfar@radiofamilia.com
W: http://www.radiofamilia.com
Editorial Profile: WFAR-FM is a non-commercial station owned by Danbury Community Radio Inc. The format of the station is religious programming and Christian music. WFAR-FM broadcasts to the Danbury, CT area at 93.3 FM.

WFAS-AM
Owner: Cumulus Media Inc.
Editorial: 365 Secor Rd, Hartsdale, New York 10530-1229. **T:** 1 914 693-2400
W: http://wfasam.com
Editorial Profile: WFAS-AM is a commercial station owned by Cumulus Media Inc. The format of the station is talk. WFAS-AM broadcasts throughout Westchester County and surrounding areas at 1230 AM.

WFAS-FM
Owner: Cumulus Media Inc.
Editorial: 365 Secor Rd, Hartsdale, New York 10530-1229. **T:** 1 914 693-2400
W: http://www.wfasfm.com
Editorial Profile: WFAS-FM is a commercial station owned by Cumulus Media Inc. The format of the station is adult contemporary music. WFAS-FM broadcasts to the Hartsdale, NY area at 103.9 FM.

WFAU-AM
Owner: Blueberry Broadcasting
Editorial: 125 Community Dr Ste 201, Augusta, Maine 04330-8157.
T: 1 207 623-9000
W: http://www.foxsportsmaine.com
Editorial Profile: WFAU-AM is a commercial station owned by Blueberry Broadcasting. The format of the station is sports. WFAU-AM broadcasts to the Augusta, ME area at 1280 AM.

WFAV-FM
Owner: Milner Broadcasting Co.
Editorial: 292 N Convent St, Bourbonnais, Illinois 60914-2014. **T:** 1 815 933-9287
E: wvlifm@comcast.net
W: http://www.rivervalleyradio.net
Editorial Profile: WFAV-FM is a commercial station owned by Milner Broadcasting Co. The format of the station is Top 40/CHR. WFAV-FM broadcasts to the Bourbonnais, IL area at 95.1 FM.

WFAW-AM
Owner: NRG Media LLC
Editorial: W6355 Eastern Ave, Fort Atkinson, Wisconsin 53538-9335. **T:** 1 920 563-9329
E: ftareception@nrgmedia.com
W: http://www.940wfaw.com
Editorial Profile: WFAW-AM is a commercial station owned by NRG Media LLC. The format of the station is news, talk and sports. WFAW-AM broadcasts to the Fort Atkinson, WI area at 940 AM.

WFAX-AM
Owner: Newcomb Broadcasting Corp.
Editorial: 161 Hillwood Ave Ste B, Falls Church, Virginia 22046-2983.
T: 1 703 532-1220 **E:** wfax@wfax.com
W: http://www.wfax.com
Editorial Profile: WFAX-AM is a commercial station owned by Newcomb Broadcasting Corp. The format of the station is talk and religious. WFAX-AM broadcasts to the Falls Church, VA, area on 1220 AM.

WFAY-AM
Owner: WCIE-AM, Inc.
Editorial: 126 Haith St, Ste 2801, Fayetteville, North Carolina 28303. **T:** 1 910 867-4148
E: wfayespnradio@gmail.com
W: http://www.espn1230radio.com
Editorial Profile: WFAY-AM is a commercial station owned by WCIE-AM, Inc. The format of the station is sports. WFAY-AM broadcasts to the Fayetteville, NC area at 1230 AM.

WFBC-FM
Owner: Entercom Communications Corp.
Editorial: 25 Garlington Rd, Greenville, South Carolina 29615-4613. **T:** 1 864 271-9200
W: http://www.b937online.com
Editorial Profile: WFBC-FM is a commercial station owned by Entercom Communications Corp. The format of the station is Top 40/CHR. WFBC-FM broadcasts to the Greenville, SC area at 93.7 FM.

WFBE-FM
Owner: Cumulus Media Inc.
Editorial: G 4511 Miller Rd, Flint, Michigan 48507-1107. **T:** 1 810 720-9510
W: http://www.nashfm951.com
Editorial Profile: WFBE-FM is a commercial station owned by Cumulus Media Inc. The format for the station is country. WFBE-FM broadcasts to the Flint, MI area at 95.1 FM.

WFBG-AM
Owner: Forever Broadcasting
Editorial: 1 Forever Dr, Hollidaysburg, Pennsylvania 16648. **T:** 1 814 941-9800
W: http://www.wfbg.com
Editorial Profile: WFBG-AM is a commercial station owned by Forever Broadcasting. The format of the station is news and talk. WFBG-AM broadcasts to the Hollidaysburg, PA area at 1290 AM.

WFBL-AM
Owner: Leatherstocking Media Group Inc.
Editorial: 8456 Smokey Hollow Rd, Baldwinsville, New York 13027-8222.
T: 1 315 635-3971 **E:** webmaster@wfbl.com
W: http://www.cnytalkradio.com
Editorial Profile: WFBL-AM is a commercial station owned by Leatherstocking Media Group Inc. The format of the station is talk. WFBL-AM broadcasts to the Baldwinsville, NY area at 1390 AM.

WFBQ-FM
Owner: Clear Channel Media and Entertainment
Editorial: 6161 Fall Creek Rd, Indianapolis, Indiana 46220-5032. **T:** 1 317 257-7565
W: http://www.q95.com
Editorial Profile: WFBQ-FM is a commercial station owned by Clear Channel Media and Entertainment. The format of the station is rock music. WFBQ-FM broadcasts to the Indianapolis area at 94.7 FM.

WFBR-AM
Owner: Multicultural Radio Broadcasting Inc.
Editorial: 159 8th Ave NW, Glen Burnie, Maryland 21061. **T:** 1 410 761-1590
Editorial Profile: WFBR-AM is commercial station owned by Multicultural Radio Broadcasting Inc. The format of the station is urban oldies music. WFBR-AM broadcasts in the greater Baltimore area at 1590 AM.

WFBX-AM
Owner: CRS RADIO HOLDINGS INC
Editorial: 126 Hay Street, Fayetteville, North Carolina 28301. **T:** 1 910 223-1452
Editorial Profile: WFBX-AM is a commercial station owned by CRS RADIO HOLDINGS INC. The format of the station is sports. WFBX-AM broadcasts to the Fayetteville, NC area on 1450 AM.

WFBY-FM
Owner: West Virginia Radio Corp.
Editorial: 1065 Radio Park Dr, Mount Clare, West Virginia 26408-9516. **T:** 1 304 623-6546
W: http://www.wfby.com
Editorial Profile: WFBY-FM is a commercial station owned by West Virginia Radio Corp. The format of the station is classic rock. WFBY-FM broadcasts to the Mount Clare, VA area at 102.3 FM.

WFBZ-FM
Owner: Sparta-Tomah Broadcasting Co.
Editorial: 113 W Oak St, Sparta, Wisconsin 54656. **T:** 1 608 269-3100
W: http://www.espnlacrosse.com
Editorial Profile: WFBZ-FM is a commercial station owned by Sparta-Tomah Broadcasting Co. The format of the station is sports. WFBZ-FM broadcasts to the Sparta, WI area at 105.5 FM.

WFCA-FM
Owner: French Camp Radio Inc.
Editorial: 40 Mecklin Ave, French Camp, Mississippi 39745. **T:** 1 662 547-6414
E: events@wfcafm108.com
W: http://www.wfcafm108.com

WFCC-FM
Owner: Cape Cod Broadcasting
Editorial: 737 W Main St, Hyannis, Massachusetts 2601. **T:** 1 508 771-1224
E: wfcc@capecodbroadcasting.com
W: http://www.wfcc.com
Editorial Profile: WFCC-FM is a commercial station owned by Cape Cod Broadcasting. The format of the station is classical. WFCC-FM broadcasts to the Hyannis, MA area at 107.5 FM.

WFCF-FM
Owner: Flagler College
Editorial: 74 King St, Saint Augustine, Florida 32084-4342. **T:** 1 904 819-6313
E: wfcf@flagler.edu
W: http://www.flagler.edu/campus-life/campus-facilities/wfcf.html
Editorial Profile: WFCF-FM is a non-commercial station owned by Flagler College. The format of the station is college variety. WFCF-FM broadcasts to the Saint Augustine, FL area at 88.5 FM.

WFCI-FM
Owner: Franklin College
Editorial: 101 Branigin Blvd, Franklin, Indiana 46131. **T:** 1 317 738-8205
Editorial Profile: WFCI-FM is a non-commercial station owned by Franklin College. The format of the station is classic rock during the evening, and simulcasts NPR during the day when school is in session. In the summer, WFCI-FM simulcasts NPR all day and night. WFCI-FM broadcasts to the Franklin, IN area at 89.5 FM.

WFCJ-FM
Owner: Strong Tower Christian Media
Editorial: 7333 Manning Rd, Miamisburg, Ohio 45342-1531. **T:** 1 937 866-2471
W: http://www.wfcj.com
Editorial Profile: WFCJ-FM is a non-commercial station owned by Strong Tower Christian Media. The format of the station is religious talk and music. WFCJ-FM broadcasts in the Dayton, OH area at 93.7 FM.

WFCL-FM
Owner: Vanderbilt Student Communications
Editorial: 630 Mainstream Dr, Nashville, Tennessee 37228-1204. **T:** 1 615 760-2903
W: http://www.wpln.org
Editorial Profile: WFCL-FM is a non-commercial station owned by Vanderbilt Student Communications. The format of the station is classical music. WFCL-FM broadcasts to the Nashville, TN area at 91.1 FM.

WFCM-AM
Owner: Moody Bible Institute
Editorial: 1920 E 24th Street Pl, Chattanooga, Tennessee 37404. **T:** 1 423 629-8900
E: wfcm@moody.edu
W: http://www.moodyradiomidsouth.fm
Editorial Profile: WFCM-AM is a non-commercial station owned by Moody Bible Institute. The format of the station is religious. WFCM-AM broadcasts to the Chattanooga, TN area at 710 AM.

WFCO-FM
Owner: Lancaster Educational Broadcasting Foundation
Editorial: 201 S Broad St, Ste 303, Lancaster, Ohio 43130. **T:** 1 740 689-0909
E: wfconews@wfcofm.com
W: http://www.wfcofm.com
Editorial Profile: WFCO-FM is a non-commercial station owned by Lancaster Educational Broadcasting Foundation. The format of the station is religious programming. WFCO-FM broadcasts to the Lancaster, OH area at 90.9 FM.

WFCR-FM
Owner: University of Massachusetts
Editorial: 131 County Cir, Amherst, Massachusetts 01003-9257.
T: 1 413 545-0100 **E:** news@wfcr.org
W: http://nepr.net
Editorial Profile: WFCR-FM is a non-commercial station owned by the University of Massachusetts. The format of the station is news, jazz and classical music. WFCR-FM broadcasts in the Amherst, MA area at 88.5 FM.

WFCS-FM
Owner: Central Connecticut State University
Editorial: 1615 Stanley St, New Britain, Connecticut 6050. **T:** 1 860 832-1883
W: http://clubs.ccsu.edu/wfcs
Editorial Profile: WFCS-FM is a non-commercial station owned by Central Connecticut State University. The format of the station is variety. WFCS-FM broadcasts to the New Britain, CT area at 107.7 FM.

WFCV-AM
Owner: Bott Radio Network
Editorial: 3737 Lake Ave, Fort Wayne, Indiana 46805. **T:** 1 260 423-2337
E: wfcv@bottradionetwork.com
W: http://www.bottradionetwork.com
Editorial Profile: WFCV-AM is a commercial station owned by Bott Radio Network. The format of the station is Christian music and talk. WFCV-AM broadcasts to the Fort Wayne, IN area at 1090 AM.

WFCV-FM
Owner: Bott Radio Network
Editorial: 3737 Lake Ave, Fort Wayne, Indiana 46805-5554. **T:** 1 260 423-2337
E: wfcv@bottradionetwork.com
W: http://www.bottradionetwork.com/stations/indiana/fort-wayne
Editorial Profile: WFCV-FM is a commercial station owned by Bott Radio Network. The format of the station is Christian talk. WFCV-FM broadcasts to the Fort Wayne and Greater Northeastern Indiana area at 100.1 FM.

WFCX-FM
Owner: Northern Broadcast Inc.
Editorial: 1020 Hastings St, Traverse City, Michigan 49686. **T:** 1 231 947-0003
W: http://www.943thefoxfm.com
Editorial Profile: WFCX-FM is a commercial station owned by Northern Broadcast Inc. The format of the station is classic hits. WFCX-FM broadcasts to the Traverse City, MI area at 94.3 FM.

WFDD-FM
Owner: Wake Forest University
Editorial: 56 Wake Forest Road, Winston-Salem, North Carolina 27109.
T: 1 336 758-8850 **E:** wfdd@wfu.edu
W: http://www.wfdd.org
Editorial Profile: WFDD-FM is a non-commercial station owned by Wake Forest University. The format of the station is variety. WFDD-FM broadcasts to the Greensboro-Winston Salem, NC area at 88.5 FM.

WFDF-AM
Owner: ABC Radio Inc.
Editorial: 1000 Town Ctr, Ste 2810, Southfield, Michigan 48075-1183. **T:** 1 248 304-4381
W: http://radio.disney.go.com/music/yourstation/detroit/index.html
Editorial Profile: WFDF-AM is a commercial station owned by ABC Radio Inc. The format of the station is children's programming. WFDF-AM is the Radio Disney affiliate for the Southeastern Michigan and Southwestern Ontario, Canada areas broadcasting locally at 910 AM.

WFDL-AM
Owner: Radio Plus Inc.
Editorial: 609 Home Ave, Waupun, Wisconsin 53963. **T:** 1 920 324-4441 **E:** news@wfdl.com
W: http://www.am1170radio.com
Editorial Profile: WFDL-AM is a commercial station owned by Radio Plus Inc. The format of the station is adult standards. WFDL-AM broadcasts to the Waupun, WI area at 1170 AM.

WFDL-FM
Owner: Radio Plus Inc.
Editorial: 210 S Main St, Fond du Lac, Wisconsin 54935. **T:** 1 920 924-9697
W: http://www.sunny977.com
Editorial Profile: WFDL-FM is a commercial station owned by Radio Plus Inc. The format of the station is adult contemporary. WFDL-FM broadcasts to the Green Bay, WI area at 97.7 FM.

WFDM-AM
Owner: Omni Broadcasting, LLC
Editorial: 21 Miracle Strip Pkwy SE, Fort Walton Beach, Florida 32548.
T: 1 850 244-1400
E: omnibroadcastinginc@gmail.com
W: http://www.freedom945.com
Editorial Profile: WFDM-AM is a commercial station owned by Omni Broadcasting, LLC. The format of the station is news and talk. WFDM-AM broadcasts to the Fort Walton Beach, FL area at 1400 AM.

WFDM-FM
Owner: Pilgrim Communications Inc.
Editorial: 645 Industrial Dr, Franklin, Indiana 46131-9617. **T:** 1 317 736-4040
E: production@freedom959.com
W: http://www.freedom959.com

Editorial Profile: WFDM-FM is a commercial station owned by Pilgrim Communications Inc. The format of the station is talk. WFDM-FM broadcasts to the Franklin, IN area at 95.9 FM.

WFDR-AM
Owner: Ploener Radio Group
Editorial: 129 W Main St, Manchester, Georgia 31816. T: 1 706 846-3016
Editorial Profile: WFDR-AM is a commerical station owned by Ploener Radio Group. The format of the station is talk. WFDR-AM broadcasts to Manchester, GA at 1370 AM.

WFDU-FM
Owner: Fairleigh Dickinson University
Editorial: 1000 River Rd, Teaneck, New Jersey 07666-1914. T: 1 201 692-2806
W: http://www.wfdu.fm
Editorial Profile: WFDU-FM is a non-commercial station owned by Fairleigh Dickinson University. The format of the station is variety. WFDU-FM broadcasts in the Teaneck, NJ, area at 89.1 FM.

WFDX-FM
Owner: Northern Broadcast Inc.
Editorial: 1020 Hastings St, Traverse City, Michigan 49686. T: 1 231 947-0003
W: http://www.943thefoxfm.com
Editorial Profile: WFDX-FM is a commercial station owned by Northern Broadcast Inc. The format of the station is classic hits. WFDX-FM broadcasts to the Traverse City, MI area at 92.5 FM.

WFEA-AM
Owner: Saga Communications
Editorial: 500 N Commercial St, Manchester, New Hampshire 03101-1151.
T: 1 603 669-5777
W: http://www.wfea1370.com
Editorial Profile: WFEA-AM is a commercial station owned by Saga Communications. The format of the station is adult standards. WFEA-AM broadcasts to the Manchester, NH area at 1370 AM.

WFEB-AM
Owner: Powers Broadcasting Company, LLC
Editorial: 1209 Millerville Highway, Sylacauga, Alabama 35150. T: 1 256 245-3144
E: wfeb1340@mysylacauga.com
Editorial Profile: WFEB-AM is a commercial station owned by Powers Broadcasting Company, LLC. The format of the station is news, talk and sports. WFEB-AM broadcasts to the Birmingham, AL area at 1340 AM.

WFED-AM
Owner: Hubbard Radio, LLC
Editorial: 3400 Idaho Ave NW, Washington, District Of Columbia 20016-3046.
T: 1 202 895-5000
W: http://www.federalnewsradio.com
Editorial Profile: WFED-AM is a commercial station owned by Hubbard Radio, LLC. The format of the station is news and talk. WFED-AM broadcasts to the Washington, D.C. area at 1500 AM.

WFEN-FM
Owner: Faith Center Church
Editorial: 4721 S Main St, Rockford, Illinois 61102-5035. T: 1 815 964-9336
E: sky@wfen.org **W:** http://www.wfen.org
Editorial Profile: WFEN-FM is a non-commercial station owned by Faith Center Church. The format of the station is Christian music and talk. WFEN-FM broadcasts to the Rockford, IL area at 88.3 FM.

WFER-AM
Owner: Heartland Communications Group, LLC
Editorial: 809 W Genesee St, Iron River, Michigan 49935. T: 1 906 265-5104
W: http://www.wfer.com
Editorial Profile: WFER-AM is a commercial station owned by Heartland Communications Group, LLC. The format for the station is news and talk. WFER-AM broadcasts to the Marquette, MI, area at 1230 AM.

WFEZ-FM
Owner: Cox Media Group, Inc.
Editorial: 2741 N 29th Ave, Hollywood, Florida 33020-1503. T: 1 305 444-4404
W: http://easy93.com
Editorial Profile: WFEZ-FM is a commercial station owned by Cox Media Group, Inc. The format of the station is Soft AC. WFEZ-FM-FM broadcasts to the Hollywood, FL area at 93.1 FM.

WFFF-AM
Owner: Geiger(Ronald)

Editorial: Gardner Shopping Center, Suite 11, Columbia, Mississippi 39429.
T: 1 601 736-1360 **E:** wfffradio@yahoo.com
Editorial Profile: WFFF-AM is a commercial station owned by Ronald Geiger. The format of the station is classic country. WFFF-AM broadcasts to the Columbia, MS area at 1360 AM.

WFFF-FM
Owner: Geiger(Ronald)
Editorial: Gardner Shopping Center, Suite 11, Columbia, Mississippi 39429.
T: 1 601 736-1360 **E:** wfffradio@yahoo.com
Editorial Profile: WFFF-FM is a commercial station owned by Ronald Geiger. The format of the station is adult contemporary. WFFF-FM broadcasts to the Hattiesburg-Laurel, MS area at 96.7 FM.

WFFG-AM
Owner: Keys Radio Group
Editorial: 109 2Nd Ln, Key Largo, Florida 33037-4647. T: 1 305 394-3736
E: info@themixtrueoldies.com
W: http://www.themixtrueoldies.com
Editorial Profile: WFFG-AM is a commercial station owned by Keys Radio Group. The format of the station is news and talk programming. WFFG-AM broadcasts to the Marathon, FL area at 1300 AM.

WFFG-FM
Owner: Pamal Broadcasting Ltd.
Editorial: 89 Everts Ave, Queensbury, New York 12804-2040. T: 1 518 793-7733
Editorial Profile: WFFG-FM is a commercial station owned by Pamal Broadcasting Ltd. The format of the station is Modern AC. WFFG-FM broadcasts to the Queensbury, NY area at 107.1 FM.

WFFH-FM
Owner: Salem Communications
Editorial: 402 Bna Dr, Nashville, Tennessee 37217-2519. T: 1 615 367-2210
W: http://www.94fmthefish.net
Editorial Profile: WFFH-FM is a commercial station owned by Salem Communications. The format of the station is contemporary Christian music. WFFH-FM broadcasts to the Nashville, TN area at 94.1 FM.

WFFI-FM
Owner: Salem Communications
Editorial: 402 Bna Dr, Nashville, Tennessee 37217-2519. T: 1 615 367-2210
W: http://www.94fmthefish.net
Editorial Profile: WFFI-FM is a commercial station owned by Salem Communications. The format of the station is contemporary Christian music. WFFI-FM broadcasts in the Nashville, TN area at 93.7 FM.

WFFM-FM
Owner: Three Trees Communications
Editorial: 601 2nd St W, Tifton, Georgia 31794-4257. T: 1 229 382-1340
E: contact@hookfmonline.com
W: http://www.hookfmonline.com/Hook_FM/HOME.html
Editorial Profile: WFFM-FM is a commercial station owned by Three Trees Communications. The format of the station is contemporary Christian. WFFM-FM broadcasts to the Albany, GA area at 105.7 FM.

WFFN-FM
Owner: Townsquare Media, Inc.
Editorial: 142 Skyland Blvd E, Tuscaloosa, Alabama 35405-4027. T: 1 205 345-7200
W: http://www.953thebear.com
Editorial Profile: WFFN-FM is a commercial station owned by Townsquare Media, Inc. The format of the station is contemporary country. WFFN-FM broadcasts to the Tuscaloosa, AL area at 95.3 FM.

WFFX-FM
Owner: Clear Channel Media and Entertainment
Editorial: 6555 U S Highway 98 W, Ste 8, Hattiesburg, Mississippi 39402.
T: 1 601 296-9800
E: contact@thefoxrocks1037.com
W: http://www.thefoxrocks1037.com
Editorial Profile: WFFX-FM is a commercial station owned by Clear Channel Media and Entertainment. The format is rock. The station airs in the Hattiesburg, MS area at 103.7 FM.

WFGA-FM
Owner: Talking Stick Communications, Inc.
Editorial: 1005 Production Rd, Fort Wayne, Indiana 46808-4107. T: 1 260 471-5100
E: feedback@thefanfortwayne.com
W: http://thefanfortwayne.com

Editorial Profile: WFGA-FM is a commercial station owned by Talking Stick Communications, Inc., a division of Federated Media. The format of the station is sports. WFGA-FM broadcasts to the Fort Wayne, IN area at 106.7 FM.

WFGB-FM
Owner: Sound of Life Inc.
Editorial: 199 Tuytenbridge Rd, Lake Katrine, New York 12449-5417. T: 1 845 336-6199
W: http://www.soundoflife.org
Editorial Profile: WFGB-FM is a non-commercial station owned by Sound of Life Inc. The format of the station is Christian music and talk. WFGB-FM broadcasts to the Lake Katrine, NY area at 89.7 FM.

WFGE-FM
Owner: Forever Broadcasting
Editorial: 2551 Park Center Blvd, State College, Pennsylvania 16801-3007.
T: 1 814 237-9800
W: http://www.froggy101fm.com
Editorial Profile: WFGE-FM is a commercial station owned by Forever Broadcasting. The format of the station is contemporary country. WFGE-FM broadcasts in the Altoona, PA at 101.1 FM.

WFGF-FM
Owner: Childers Media Group, LLC
Editorial: 57 Town Sq, Lima, Ohio 45801-4950. T: 1 419 331-1600
Editorial Profile: WFGF-FM is a commercial station owned by Childers Media Group, LLC. The format for the station is contemporary country. WFGF-FM broadcasts to the Lima, OH area at 92.1 FM.

WFGH-FM
Owner: Wayne County Board of Education
Editorial: 1 Rebel Dr, Fort Gay, West Virginia 25514-9677. T: 1 304 648-5752
E: hbdamron@gmail.com
W: http://www.tolsiarebels.org/Tech/broadcasting.htm
Editorial Profile: WFGH-FM is a non-commercial station owned by the Wayne County Board of Education. The format of the station is variety programming. WFGH-FM broadcasts to the Fort Gay, WV area at 90.7 FM.

WFGI-AM
Owner: Keymarket of Pennsylvania, LLC
Editorial: 123 Blaine Rd, Brownsville, Pennsylvania 15417-9330. T: 1 724 938-2000
W: http://www.froggyland.com
Editorial Profile: WFGI-AM is a commercial station owned by Keymarket of Pennsylvania, LLC. The format of the station is contemporary country. WFGI-AM broadcasts to the Brownsville, PA area at 940 AM.

WFGI-FM
Owner: Forever Broadcasting
Editorial: 109 Plaza Dr, Johnstown, Pennsylvania 15905-1212. T: 1 814 255-4186
W: http://www.myfroggy95.com
Editorial Profile: WFGI-FM is a commercial station owned by Forever Broadcasting. The format of the station is contemporary country. WFGI-FM broadcasts to the Johnstown, PA area at 95.5 FM.

WFGL-AM
Owner: Horizon Christian Fellowship
Editorial: 356 Broad St, Fitchburg, Massachusetts 1420. T: 1 978 665-9111
W: http://www.horizonfitchburg.org/radio
Editorial Profile: WFGL-AM is a commercial station owned by Horizon Christian Fellowship. The format of the station features Christian teaching programs and contemporary Praise and Worship music. WFGL-AM broadcasts to the Fitchburg, MA at 960 AM.

WFGM-FM
Owner: AJG Broadcasting Co.
Editorial: 1251 Earl L Core Rd, Morgantown, West Virginia 26505-5881. T: 1 304 296-0029
W: http://www.931wfgm.com
Editorial Profile: WFGM-FM is a commercial station owned by AJG Broadcasting Co. The format of the station is classic hits. WFGM-FM broadcasts to the Buckhannon, WV area at 93.1 FM.

WFGN-AM
Owner: Hope Broadcasting Inc.
Editorial: 470 Leadmine Rd, Gaffney, South Carolina 29340. T: 1 864 489-9430
Editorial Profile: WFGN-AM is a commercial station owned by Hope Broadcasting Inc. The format of the station is gospel music. WFGN-

AM broadcasts to the Gaffney, SC area at 1180 AM.

WFGR-FM
Owner: Townsquare Media, LLC
Editorial: 50 Monroe Ave NW, Ste 500, Grand Rapids, Michigan 49503. T: 1 616 451-4800
W: http://www.wfgr.com
Editorial Profile: WFGR-FM is a commercial station owned by Townsquare Media, LLC. The format of the station is classic hits. WFGR-FM broadcasts to the Grand Rapids, MI area at 98.7 FM.

WFGS-FM
Owner: Forever Communications Inc.
Editorial: 1500 Diuguid Dr, Murray, Kentucky 42071. T: 1 270 753-2400
W: http://www.froggy103.com
Editorial Profile: WFGS-FM is a commercial station owned by Forever Communications Inc. The format of the station is country. WFGS-FM broadcasts to the Greater Murray, KY area at a frequency of 103.7 FM.

WFGW-FM
Owner: Blue Ridge Broadcasting Co.
Editorial: 3 Porters Cove Rd, Asheville, North Carolina 28805-2834. T: 1 828 285-8477
W: http://www.1069thelight.org
Editorial Profile: WFGW-FM is a commercial station owned by Blue Ridge Broadcasting Co. The format of the station is Contemporary Christian music.WFGW-FM broadcasts in the Knoxville, TN area at 106.7 FM.

WFGY-FM
Owner: Forever Broadcasting
Editorial: 1 Forever Dr, Hollidaysburg, Pennsylvania 16648-3029. T: 1 814 941-9800
W: http://www.froggyradio.com
Editorial Profile: WFGY-FM is a commercial station owned by Forever Broadcasting. The format of the station is contemporary country. WFGY-FM broadcasts to the Hollidaysburg, PA area at 98.1 FM.

WFHB-FM
Owner: Bloomington Community Radio Inc.
Editorial: 108 W 4th St, Bloomington, Indiana 47404-5100. T: 1 812 323-1200
E: wfhb@wfhb.org **W:** http://www.wfhb.org
Editorial Profile: WFHB-FM is a non-commercial station owned by Bloomington Community Radio Inc. The format of the station is variety. WFHB-FM broadcasts to the Indianapolis area at 91.3 FM.

WFHE-FM
Owner: University Radio Foundation
Editorial: 8801 J M Keynes Dr, Ste 91, Charlotte, North Carolina 28262.
T: 1 704 549-9323 **E:** news@wfae.org
W: http://www.wfae.org
Editorial Profile: WFHE-FM is a non-commercial station owned by the University Radio Foundation. The format of the station is news and talk. WFHE-FM broadcasts to the Hickory, NC area at 90.3 FM.

WFHG-AM
Owner: Bristol Broadcasting
Editorial: 901 E Valley Dr, Bristol, Virginia 24201-4913. T: 1 276 669-8112
Editorial Profile: WFHG-AM is a commercial station owned by Bristol Broadcasting. The format of the station is sports. WFHG-AM broadcasts to the Bristol, VA area at 980 AM.

WFHG-FM
Owner: Bristol Broadcasting
Editorial: 901 E Valley Dr, Bristol, Virginia 24201. T: 1 276 669-8112
W: http://www.supertalkwfhg.com
Editorial Profile: WFHG-FM is a commercial station owned by Bristol Broadcasting. The format of the station is news and talk. WFHG-FM broadcasts to the Bristol, VA area at 92.9 FM.

WFHK-AM
Owner: Stocks Broadcasting Inc.
Editorial: 22 Cogswell Ave, Pell City, Alabama 35125. T: 1 205 338-1430
W: http://www.wfhkradio.com
Editorial Profile: WFHK-AM is a commercial station owned by Stocks Broadcasting Inc. The format of the station is classic country. WFHK-AM broadcasts to the Pell City, AL area at 1430 AM.

WFHM-FM
Owner: Salem Communications
Editorial: 4 Summit Park Dr, Ste 150, Cleveland, Ohio 44131. T: 1 216 901-0921
W: http://www.955thefish.com

Editorial Profile: WFHM-FM is a commercial station owned by Salem Communications. The format of the station is contemporary Christian. WFHM-FM broadcasts to the Cleveland area at 95.5 FM.

WFHN-FM
Owner: Townsquare Media, Inc.
Editorial: 22 Sconticut Neck Rd, Fairhaven, Massachusetts 02719-1914.
T: 1 508 999-6690 **W:** http://fun107.com
Editorial Profile: WFHN-FM is a commercial station owned by Townsquare Media, Inc. The format of the station is Top 40/CHR. WFHN-FM broadcasts to the Providence, RI and Bedford, MA area at 107.1 FM.

WFHR-AM
Owner: Seehafer Broadcasting Corp.
Editorial: 645 25th Ave N, Wisconsin Rapids, Wisconsin 54495. **T:** 1 715 424-1300
E: info@wfhr.com **W:** http://www.wfhr.com
Editorial Profile: WFHR-AM is a commercial station owned by Seehafer Broadcasting Corp. The format for the station is news, sports and talk. WFHR-AM broadcasts to the Wausau, WI, area at 1320 AM.

WFHU-FM
Owner: Freed-Hardeman University
Editorial: 158 E Main St, Henderson, Tennessee 38340-2306. **T:** 1 731 989-6749
E: wfhu@fhu.edu **W:** http://www.fhu.edu/radio
Editorial Profile: WFHU-FM is a non-commercial station owned by Freed-Hardeman University. The format of the station is college variety and adult contemporary. WFHU-FM broadcasts to the Henderson, TN area at 91.5 FM.

WFIA-AM
Owner: Salem Communications
Editorial: 9960 Corporate Campus Dr, Ste 3600, Louisville, Kentucky 40223.
T: 1 502 339-9470 **W:** http://www.wfia-fm.com
Editorial Profile: WFIA-AM is a commercial station owned by Salem Communications. The format of the station is Christian music and talk. WFIA-AM broadcasts in the Louisville, KY area at 900 AM.

WFIA-FM
Owner: Salem Communications
Editorial: 9960 Corporate Campus Dr Ste 3600, Louisville, Kentucky 40223-4070.
T: 1 502 339-9470 **W:** http://www.wfia-fm.com
Editorial Profile: WFIA-FM is a commercial station owned by Salem Communicatons. The format of the station is Christian talk and gospel music. WFIA-FM broadcasts in the Louisville, KY area at 94.7 FM.

WFIC-AM
Owner: Positive Radio Group
Editorial: 1675 Grandview Rd, Martinsville, Virginia 24112-2319. **T:** 1 276 638-5235
Editorial Profile: WFIC-AM is a commercial station owned by Positive Radio Group. The format of the station is Religious teaching. WFIC-AM broadcasts to the Martinsville, VA area at 1530 AM.

WFIF-AM
Owner: Blount Communications Group
Editorial: 90 Kay Ave, Milford, Connecticut 06460-5421. **T:** 1 203 878-5915
E: info@wfif.net
W: http://lifechangingradio.com
Editorial Profile: WFIF-AM is a commercial station owned by Blount Communications Group. The format for the station is religious talk. WFIF-AM broadcasts to the Hartford-New Haven, CT area at 1500 AM.

WFIL-AM
Owner: Salem Communications
Editorial: 117 Ridge Pike, Lafayette Hill, Pennsylvania 19444-1901. **T:** 1 610 828-6965
E: wfil@wfil.com **W:** http://www.wfil.com
Editorial Profile: WFIL-AM is a commercial station owned by Salem Communications. The format of the station is religious and Christian talk. WFIL-AM broadcasts to the Lafayette Hill, PA area at 560 AM.

WFIN-AM
Owner: Blanchard River Broadcasting, Co.
Editorial: 551 Lake Cascade Pkwy, Findlay, Ohio 45840. **T:** 1 419 422-4545
E: wfin@wfin.com **W:** http://www.wfin.com
Editorial Profile: WFIN-AM is a commercial station owned by Blanchard River Broadcasting, Co. The format of the station is news, sports and talk. WFIN-AM broadcasts in the Findlay, OH area at 1330 AM.

WFIR-AM
Owner: Wheeler Inc.(Mel)
Editorial: 3934 Electric Rd, Roanoke, Virginia 24018. **T:** 1 540 345-1511
W: http://www.wfir960.com
Editorial Profile: WFIR-AM is a commercial station owned by Mel Wheeler Inc. The format of the station is news and talk. WFIR-AM broadcasts to the Roanoke, VA area at 960 AM.

WFIS-AM
Owner: Timeless Media, Inc.
Editorial: 1318 N Main St, Fountain Inn, South Carolina 29644-1332. **T:** 1 864 963-5991
W: http://wfisradio.webs.com
Editorial Profile: WFIS-AM is a commercial station owned by Timeless Media, Inc.. The format of the station is news, talk and sports. WFIS-AM broadcasts to the Fountain Inn-Simpsonville, SC at 1600 AM.

WFIT-FM
Owner: Florida Institute of Technology
Editorial: 150 W University Blvd, Melbourne, Florida 32901-6982. **T:** 1 321 674-8140
E: wfit@fit.edu **W:** http://www.wfit.org
Editorial Profile: WFIT-FM is a non-commercial station owned by Florida Institute of Technology. The format of the station is AAA-Adult album alternative and news. WFIT-FM broadcasts to the Melbourne, FL area at 89.5 FM.

WFIU-FM
Owner: Indiana University
Editorial: 1229 E 7th St, Bloomington, Indiana 47405-5501. **T:** 1 812 855-1357
E: wfiu@indiana.edu **W:** http://www.wfiu.org
Editorial Profile: WFIU-FM is a non-commercial station owned by Indiana University. The format of the station is variety. WFIU-FM broadcasts to the Indianapolis area at 103.7 FM.

WFIV-FM
Owner: Horne Radio LLC
Editorial: 517 N Watt Rd, Knoxville, Tennessee 37934-1110. **T:** 1 865 675-4105
W: http://www.wfiv.com
Editorial Profile: WFIV-FM is a commercial station owned by Horne Radio LLC. The format of the station is adult album alternative. WFIV-FM broadcasts to the Knoxville, TN area at 105.3 FM.

WFIX-FM
Owner: Tri-State Inspirational Broadcasting
Editorial: 113 N Seminary St, Florence, Alabama 35630. **T:** 1 256 764-9964
E: wfix@fixfm.net **W:** http://www.wfix.net
Editorial Profile: WFIX-FM is a non-commercial station owned by Tri-State Inspirational Broadcasting. The format of the station is contemporary Christian music and talk programming. WFIX-FM broadcasts to the Florence, AL area at 91.3 FM.

WFIZ-FM
Owner: ROI Broadcasting
Editorial: 950 Danby Rd Ste 230, Ithaca, New York 14850-5714. **T:** 1 607 330-4848
W: http://www.z955.net
Editorial Profile: WFIZ-FM is a commercial station owned by ROI Broadcasting. The format of the station is Top 40/CHR. WFIZ-FM broadcasts to the Dundee, NY area at 95.5 FM.

WFJA-FM
Owner: WWGP Broadcasting Corporation
Editorial: 2201 Jefferson Davis Hwy, Sanford, North Carolina 27330-8973.
T: 1 919 775-3525
E: production@wfjaradio.com
W: http://www.classichitsandoldies.com/v2
Editorial Profile: WFJA-FM is a commercial station owned by WWGP Broadcasting Corporation. The format of the station is oldies music. WFJA-FM broadcasts to the Sanford, NC area at 105.5 FM.

WFJO-FM
Owner: River City Broadcasting, LLC
Editorial: 9090 Hogan Rd, Jacksonville, Florida 32216-4648. **T:** 1 904 641-1011
W: http://www.1010xl.com
Editorial Profile: WJXL-FM is a commercial station owned by River City Broadcasting, LLC. The format of the station sports. WJXL-FM broadcasts to the Jacksonville, FL area on 92.5 FM.

WFJX-AM
Owner: Perception Media Group, Inc.
Editorial: 1848 Clay St SE, Roanoke, Virginia 24013. **T:** 1 540 343-7109
W: http://www.foxradioroanoke.com
Editorial Profile: WFJX-AM is a commercial station owned by Perception Media Group, Inc. The format of the station is news, talk and sports. WFJX-AM broadcasts to the Roanoke, VA area at 910 AM.

WFKL-FM
Owner: Stephens Media Group
Editorial: 28 E Main Street, 8th Floor, Rochester, New York 14614.
T: 1 585 399-5700
W: http://www.fickle933.com
Editorial Profile: WFKL-FM is a commercial station owned by Stephens Media Group. The format of the station is adult hits. WFKL-FM broadcasts to the Rochester, NY area at a frequency of 93.3 FM.

WFKN-AM
Owner: Paxton Media Group
Editorial: 103 N High St, Franklin, Kentucky 42134. **T:** 1 270 586-4481
E: wfkn@franklinfavorite.com
W: http://www.franklinfavorite.com
Editorial Profile: WFKN-AM is a commerial station owned by Paxton Media Group. The format of the station is talk, sports and classic country. WFKN-AM broadcasts to the Franklin, TN area at 1220 AM.

WFKS-FM
Owner: Clear Channel Media and Entertainment
Editorial: One Radio Center, 1388 S Babcock St, Melbourne, Florida 32901-3009.
T: 1 321 733-1000
W: http://www.mykiss951.com
Editorial Profile: WFKS-FM is a commercial station owned by Clear Channel Media and Entertainment. The format of the station is Top 40/CHR. WFKS-FM broadcasts to the Melbourne, FL, area at 95.1 FM.

WFKX-FM
Owner: Southern Stone Communications, LLC
Editorial: 111 W Main St, Jackson, Tennessee 38301. **T:** 1 731 427-9616
W: http://www.96kix.fm
Editorial Profile: WFKX-FM is a commercial station owned by Southern Stone Communications, LLC. The format of the station is urban contemporary. WFKX-FM broadcasts to the Jackson, TN area at 95.7 FM.

WFKY-FM
Owner: CapCity Communications LLC
Editorial: 115 W Main St, Frankfort, Kentucky 40601. **T:** 1 502 875-1130
W: http://www.myfroggy1049.com
Editorial Profile: WFKY-FM is a commercial station owned by CapCity Communications LLC. The format for the station is country. WFKY-FM broadcasts to the Lexington, KY area at 104.9 FM.

WFKZ-FM
Owner: Florida Keys Media, LLC
Editorial: 93351 Overseas Hwy Ste 2, Tavernier, Florida 33070-2800.
T: 1 305 852-9085
Editorial Profile: WFKZ-FM is a commercial station owned by Florida Keys Media, LLC. The format of the station is classic rock. WFKZ-FM broadcasts to the Miami, FL area at 103.1 FM.

WFLA-AM
Owner: Clear Channel Media and Entertainment
Editorial: 4002A W Gandy Blvd, Tampa, Florida 33611. **T:** 1 813 839-9393
W: http://www.970wfla.com
Editorial Profile: WFLA-AM is a commercial station owned by Clear Channel Media and Entertainment. The format of the station is news and talk. WFLA-AM broadcasts to the Tampa, FL area at 970 AM.

WFLA-FM
Owner: Clear Channel Media and Entertainment
Editorial: 325 John Knox Rd, Bldg G, Tallahassee, Florida 32303. **T:** 1 850 422-3107
W: http://www.wflafm.com
Editorial Profile: WBWT-FM is a commercial station owned by Clear Channel Media and Entertainment. The format of the station is talk. WBWT-FM broadcasts to the Tallahassee, FL area at 100.7 FM.

WFLB-FM
Owner: Beasley Broadcast Group
Editorial: 508 Person St, Fayetteville, North Carolina 28301-5841. **T:** 1 910 486-4114
W: http://965bobfm.com
Editorial Profile: WFLB-FM is a commercial station owned by Beasley Broadcast Group. The format of the station is classic hits music. WFLB-FM broadcasts to the Fayetteville, NC area at 96.5 FM.

WFLC-FM
Owner: Cox Media Group, Inc.
Editorial: 2741 N 29th Ave, Hollywood, Florida 33020-1503. **T:** 1 305 444-4404
W: http://www.hits973.com
Editorial Profile: WFLC-FM is a commercial station owned by Cox Media Group, Inc. The format of the station is Top 40. WFLC-FM broadcasts to the Hollywood, FL area at 97.3 FM.

WFLE-AM
Owner: DreamCatcher Communications Inc.
Editorial: 334 Recreation Park Rd, Flemingsburg, Kentucky 41041.
T: 1 606 849-4433
Editorial Profile: WFLE-AM is a commercial station owned by DreamCatcher Communications Inc. The format for the station is country. WFLE-AM broadcasts to the Lexington, KY area at 1060 AM.

WFLE-FM
Owner: DreamCatcher Communications Inc.
Editorial: 334 Recreation Park Rd, Flemingsburg, Kentucky 41041-8915.
T: 1 606 849-4433
Editorial Profile: WFLE-FM is a commercial station owned by DreamCatcher Communications Inc. The format of the station is contemporary country music. WFLE-FM broadcasts to the Flemingsburg, KY area at 95.1 FM.

WFLF-AM
Owner: Clear Channel Media and Entertainment
Editorial: 2500 Maitland Center Pkwy, Ste 401, Maitland, Florida 32751.
T: 1 407 916-7800 **E:** news@540wfla.com
W: http://www.540wfla.com
Editorial Profile: WFLF-AM is a commercial station owned by Clear Channel Media and Entertainment. The format of the station is news and talk. WFLF-AM broadcasts to the Maitland, FL area at 540 AM.

WFLF-FM
Owner: Clear Channel Media and Entertainment
Editorial: 1834 Lisenby Ave, Panama City, Florida 32405-3713. **T:** 1 850 769-1408
W: http://www.945wfla.com/main.html
Editorial Profile: WFLF-FM is a commercial station owned by Clear Channel Media and Entertainment. The format of the station is news and talk. WFLF-FM broadcasts to the Panama City, FL area at 94.5 FM.

WFLI-AM
Owner: WFLI Inc.
Editorial: 621 Ogrady Dr, Chattanooga, Tennessee 37419-1305. **T:** 1 423 821-3555
E: wfliradio@gmail.com
Editorial Profile: WFLI-AM is a commercial station owned by WFLI Inc. The format for the station is southern gospel music and religious programming. WFLI-AM broadcasts to the Chattanooga, TN area at 1070 AM.

WFLK-FM
Owner: Finger Lakes Daily News
Editorial: 3568 Lenox Rd, Geneva, New York 14456-2058. **T:** 1 315 781-7000
W: http://www.fingerlakesdailynews.com
Editorial Profile: WFLK-FM is a commercial station owned Finger Lakes Daily News. The format of the station is contemporary country music. WFLK-FM broadcasts to the Geneva, NY area at 101.7 FM.

WFLL-AM
Owner: JCE Licenses, LLC
Editorial: 2100 Park Central Blvd N Ste 100, Pompano Beach, Florida 33064-2219.
T: 1 954 315-1515 **E:** news@jamescrystal.com
Editorial Profile: WFLL-AM is a commercial station owned by JCE Licenses, LLC. The format of the station is Brazilian Portuguese Pop Music. WFLL-AM broadcasts to the Fort Lauderdale, FL area at 1400 AM.

WFLM-FM
Owner: Midway Broadcasting Corp.
Editorial: 6803 S US Highway 1, Port Saint Lucie, Florida 34952. **T:** 1 772 460-9356
E: production@wflm.cc **W:** http://www.wflm.cc
Editorial Profile: WFLM-FM is a commercial station owned by Midway Broadcasting Corp. The format of the station is urban adult

contemporary. WFLM-FM broadcasts to the Port St. Lucie, FL area at 104.7 FM.

WFLN-AM
Owner: Integrity Radio of FL LLC
Editorial: 201 Asbury St, Arcadia, Florida 34266-8830. T: 1 863 993-1480
E: wflnradio@aol.com W: http://wflnradio.com
Editorial Profile: WFLN-AM is a commercial station owned by Integrity Radio of FL LLC. The format of the station is news and talk. WFLN-AM broadcasts to the Arcadia, FL area 1480 AM.

WFLO-AM
Owner: Colonial Broadcasting Co. Inc.
Editorial: 1582 Cumberland Rd, Farmville, Virginia 23901-4034. T: 1 434 392-4195
E: communitycalendar@wflo.net
W: http://www.wflo.net
Editorial Profile: WFLO-AM is a commercial station owned by Colonial Broadcasting Co. Inc. The format of the station is country music and talk. WFLO-AM broadcasts to the Farmville, VA area at 870 AM.

WFLO-FM
Owner: Colonial Broadcasting Co. Inc.
Editorial: 1582 Cumberland Rd, Farmville, Virginia 23901-4034. T: 1 434 392-4195
E: communitycalendar@wflo.net
W: http://www.wflo.net
Editorial Profile: WFLO-FM is a commercial station owned by Colonial Broadcasting Co. Inc. The format of the station is adult contemporary. WFLO-FM broadcasts to the Farmville, VA area at 95.7 FM.

WFLQ-FM
Owner: Willtronics Broadcasting
Editorial: 2593 N County Road 810 W, West Baden Springs, Indiana 47469-9624. T: 1 812 936-9100 E: wflqfm@smithville.net
W: http://www.wflq.com
Editorial Profile: WFLQ-FM is a commercial station owned by Willtronics Broadcasting. The format of the station is country music. WFLQ-FM broadcasts in the French Lick, IN area at 100.1 FM.

WFLR-AM
Owner: Finger Lakes Radio Group
Editorial: 30 Main St, Dundee, New York 14837. T: 1 607 243-7158
E: wflr@flradiogroup.com
W: http://www.fingerlakesdailynews.com
Editorial Profile: WFLR-AM is a commercial station owned by Finger Lakes Radio Group. The format of the station is contemporary country. WFLR-AM broadcasts to the Dundee, NY area at 1570 AM.

WFLR-FM
Owner: Finger Lakes Radio Group
Editorial: 30 Main St, Dundee, New York 14837-1007. T: 1 607 243-7158
E: wflr@flradiogroup.com
W: http://www.fingerlakesdailynews.com
Editorial Profile: WFLR-FM is a commercial station owned by Finger Lakes Radio Group. The format of the station is contemporary country. WFLR-FM broadcasts to the Dundee, NY area at 96.9 FM.

WFLS-FM
Owner: Free Lance-Star Publishing Company
Editorial: 616 Amelia St, Fredericksburg, Virginia 22401-3887. T: 1 540 373-1500
W: http://www.wfls.com
Editorial Profile: WFLS-FM is a commercial station owned by the Free Lance-Star Publishing Company. The format of the station is classic country. WFLS-FM broadcasts to the Fredericksburg, VA area at 93.3 FM.

WFLT-AM
Owner: C.E.B.A
Editorial: 317 S Averill Ave, Flint, Michigan 48506. T: 1 810 239-5733
E: wflt1420am@aol.com
Editorial Profile: WFLT-AM is a commercial station owned by C.E.B.A. The format of the station is gospel music. WFLT-AM broadcasts in the Flint, MI area at 1420 AM.

WFLW-AM
Owner: Staples Jr.(Stephen)
Editorial: 150 Worsham Ln, Monticello, Kentucky 42633-1610. T: 1 606 348-8427
E: news@wkym.com
W: http://www.wkym.com

WFLY-FM
Owner: Albany Broadcasting Co.
Editorial: 6 Johnson Rd, Latham, New York 12110. T: 1 518 786-6600

W: http://www.fly92.com
Editorial Profile: WFLY-FM is a commercial station owned by Albany Broadcasting Co. The format of the station is Top 40/CHR music. WFLY-FM broadcasts to the Albany, NY area at 92.3 FM.

WFLZ-FM
Owner: Clear Channel Media and Entertainment
Editorial: 4002A W Gandy Blvd, Tampa, Florida 33611. T: 1 813 839-9393
W: http://www.933flz.com
Editorial Profile: WFLZ-FM is a commercial station is owned by Clear Channel Media and Entertainment. The format of the station is Top 40/CHR music. WFLZ-FM broadcasts to the Tampa Bay, FL area at 93.3 FM.

WFMB-AM
Owner: Neuhoff Family Limited Partnership
Editorial: 3055 S 4th St, Springfield, Illinois 62703-4009. T: 1 217 528-3033
W: http://www.sportsradio1450.com
Editorial Profile: WFMB-AM is a commercial station owned by Neuhoff Family Limited Partnership. The format of the station is sports and talk. WFMB-AM broadcasts to the Springfield, IL area at 1450 AM.

WFMB-FM
Owner: Neuhoff Family Limited Partnership
Editorial: 3055 S 4th St, Springfield, Illinois 62703-4009. T: 1 217 528-3033
E: 1045@wfmb.com W: http://www.wfmb.com
Editorial Profile: WFMB-FM is a commercial station owned by Neuhoff Family Limited Partnership. The format of the station is country music. WFMB-FM broadcasts to the Springfield, IL area at 104.5 FM.

WFMC-AM
Owner: Curtis Media Group
Editorial: 2581 US Highway 70 W, Goldsboro, North Carolina 27530. T: 1 919 734-4211
W: http://www.730wfmc.com
Editorial Profile: WFMC-AM is a commercial station owned by Curtis Media Group. The format of the station is gospel music. WFMC-AM broadcasts to the greater Raleigh, NC area at 730 AM.

WFMD-AM
Owner: Clear Channel Media and Entertainment
Editorial: 5966 Grove Hill Rd, Frederick, Maryland 21703-6012. T: 1 301 663-4181
E: news@wfmd.com
W: http://www.wfmd.com/main.html
Editorial Profile: WFMD-AM is a commercial station owned by Clear Channel Media and Entertainment. The format of the station is news, talk and sports. WFMD-AM broadcasts in the Frederick, MD area at 930 AM.

WFME-FM
Owner: Family Stations Inc.
Editorial: 289 Mount Pleasant Ave, West Orange, New Jersey 07052-4107. T: 1 973 736-3600 E: info@wfme.net
W: http://www.wfme.net
Editorial Profile: WFME-FM is a commercial station owned by Family Stations Inc. The format of the station is Christian music and teaching. WDVY-FM broadcasts to the New York City market at 106.3 FM.

WFMF-FM
Owner: Clear Channel Media and Entertainment
Editorial: 5555 Hilton Ave, Ste 500, Baton Rouge, Louisiana 70808. T: 1 225 231-1860
W: http://www.wfmf.com
Editorial Profile: WFMF-FM is a commercial station owned by Clear Channel Media and Entertainment. The format of the station is Top 40/CHR. WFMF-FM broadcasts to the Baton Rouge, LA area at 102.5 FM.

WFMG-FM
Owner: Whitewater Broadcasting
Editorial: 2301 W Main St, Richmond, Indiana 47374-3829. T: 1 765 962-6533
E: news@g1013.com
W: http://www.g1013.com
Editorial Profile: WFMG-FM is a commercial station owned by Whitewater Broadcasting. The format of the station is hot adult contemporary music. WFMG-FM broadcasts to the Richmond, IN area at 101.3 FM.

WFMH-AM
Owner: Jimmy Dale Media, LLC
Editorial: 1707 Warnke Rd NW, Cullman, Alabama 35055-2231. T: 1 256 734-3271
Editorial Profile: WFMH-AM is a commercial station owned by Jimmy Dale Media, LLC. The

format of the station is sports talk. WFMH-AM broadcasts to the Cullman, AL area at 1340 AM.

WFMH-FM
Owner: TNT Inc.
Editorial: 16800 S Hwy 126, Brilliant, Alabama 35548. T: 1 256 810-0613
Editorial Profile: WFMH-FM is a commercial station owned by TNT Inc. The format of the station is country music. WFMH-FM broadcasts to the Cullman, AL area at 95.5 FM.

WFMI-FM
Owner: Communication Systems Inc.
Editorial: 4801 Columbus St Ste 202, Virginia Beach, Virginia 23462-6751.
T: 1 757 490-9364
W: http://www.musicalsoulfood.com
Editorial Profile: WFMI-FM is a commercial station owned by Communication Systems Inc. The format of the station is gospel. WFMI-FM broadcasts to the Norfolk, VA area at 100.9 FM.

WFMK-FM
Owner: Townsquare Media, LLC
Editorial: 3420 Pinetree Rd, Lansing, Michigan 48911-4207. T: 1 517 394-7272
W: http://www.99wfmk.com
Editorial Profile: WFMK-FM is a commercial station owned by Townsquare Media, LLC. The format of the station is lite rock. WFMK-FM broadcasts to the Lansing, MI area at 99.1 FM.

WFML-FM
Owner: Vincennes University Foundation
Editorial: 1200 N 2nd St, Vincennes, Indiana 47591. T: 1 812 254-6761 E: max@wfml.net
W: http://www.wfml.net
Editorial Profile: WFML-FM is a commercial station owned by Vincennes University Foundation. The format of the station is variety. WFML-FM broadcasts to the Vincennes, IN area at 96.7 FM.

WFMM-FM
Owner: TeleSouth Communications Inc.
Editorial: 5266 Old Highway 11 Ste 120, Hattiesburg, Mississippi 39402-7818.
T: 1 601 264-5185
W: http://www.supertalkms.com
Editorial Profile: WFMM-FM is a commercial station owned by TeleSouth Communications Inc. The format of the station is talk. WFMM-FM broadcasts to the Hattiesburg, MS area on 97.3 FM.

WFMN-FM
Owner: TeleSouth Communications Inc.
Editorial: 6311 Ridgewood Rd, Jackson, Mississippi 39211. T: 1 601 957-1700
W: http://www.supertalk.fm
Editorial Profile: WFMN-FM is a commercial station owned by TeleSouth Communications Inc. The format of the station is news, talk and sports. WFMN-FM broadcasts to the Jackson, MS area at 97.3 FM.

WFMO-AM
Owner: Davidson Media Group
Editorial: 5448 Hwy 41 S, Fairmont, North Carolina 28340. T: 1 910 628-6781
Editorial Profile: WFMO-AM is a commercial station owned by Davidson Media Group. The format of the station is Hispanic and tropical music. WFMO-AM broadcasts to the Fayatteville, NC area at 860 AM.

WFMS-FM
Owner: Cumulus Media Inc.
Editorial: 6810 N Shadeland Ave, Indianapolis, Indiana 46220-4236. T: 1 317 842-9550
E: info@wfms.com W: http://www.wfms.com
Editorial Profile: WFMS-FM is a commercial station owned by Cumulus Media Inc. The format of the station is country music. WFMS-FM broadcasts to the Indianapolis area at 95.5 FM.

WFMT-FM
Owner: Window to the World Communications, Inc.
Editorial: 5400 N Saint Louis Ave, Chicago, Illinois 60625-4623. T: 1 773 279-2000
W: http://www.wfmt.com
Editorial Profile: WFMT-FM is a commercial station owned by Window to the World Communications, Inc. The format of the station is classical music. WFMT-FM broadcasts to the Chicago area at 98.7 FM.

WFMU-FM
Owner: Auricle Communications

Editorial: 43 Montgomery St, 4th Fl, Jersey City, New Jersey 7302. T: 1 201 521-1416
E: wfmu@wfmu.org W: http://www.wfmu.org
Editorial Profile: WFMU-FM is a non-commercial station owned by the Auricle Communications. The format of the station is freeform radio. WFMU-FM broadcasts in the Jersey City, NJ area at 91.1 FM.

WFMV-FM
Owner: Glory Communications Inc.
Editorial: 2440 Millwood Ave, Columbia, South Carolina 29205-1128.
T: 1 803 939-9530
E: communitycalendar@wfmv.com
W: http://www.wfmv.com
Editorial Profile: WFMV-FM is a commercial station owned by Glory Communications Inc. The format of the station is gospel. WFMV-FM broadcasts to the Columbia, SC area at 95.3 FM.

WFMW-AM
Owner: Sound Broadcasters Inc.
Editorial: 2380 N Main St, Madisonville, Kentucky 42431. T: 1 270 821-4096
E: news@wfmw.net W: http://www.wfmw.net

WFMX-FM
Owner: Mountain Wireless Corp.
Editorial: 208 Middle Rd, Skowhegan, Maine 4976. T: 1 207 474-5171
E: mix1079@gmail.com
W: http://www.mixmaine.com
Editorial Profile: WFMX-FM is a commercial station owned by Mountain Wireless Corp. The format of the station is adult contemporary. WFMX-FM broadcasts to the Skowhegan, ME area at 107.9 FM.

WFMZ-FM
Owner: CapSan Media, LLC
Editorial: 637 Harbor Rd, Wanchese, North Carolina 27981-9589. T: 1 252 475-1888
W: http://www.classichits1049.com
Editorial Profile: WFMZ-FM is a commercial station owned by CapSan Media, LLC. The format of the station is classic rock. WFMZ-FM broadcasts to the Wanchese, NC area at 104.9 FM.

WFNB-FM
Owner: Emmis Communications
Editorial: 1301 Ohio St, Terre Haute, Indiana 47807-3925. T: 1 812 234-9770
W: http://www.927bob.com
Editorial Profile: WFNB-FM is a commercial station owned by Emmis Communications. The format of the station is adult hits. WFNB-FM broadcasts to the Terre Haute, IN, area at 92.7 FM.

WFNC-AM
Owner: Cumulus Media Inc.
Editorial: 1009 Drayton Rd, Fayetteville, North Carolina 28303-3887. T: 1 910 864-5222
W: http://www.wfnc640am.com
Editorial Profile: WFNC-AM is a commercial station owned by Cumulus Media Inc. The format of the station is news and talk. WFNC-AM broadcasts to the Fayetteville, NC area at 640 AM.

WFNF-AM
Owner: Emmis Communications
Editorial: 1301 Ohio St, Terre Haute, Indiana 47807-3925. T: 1 812 234-9770
W: http://www.1130thefan.com
Editorial Profile: WFNF-AM is a commercial station owned by Emmis Communications. The format of the station is sports. WFNF-AM broadcasts to the Terre Haute, IN area at 1130 AM.

WFNI-AM
Owner: Emmis Communications Corp.
Editorial: 40 Monument Cir, Indianapolis, Indiana 46204-3019. T: 1 317 266-9422
W: http://1070thefan.com
Editorial Profile: WFNI-AM is a commercial station owned by Emmis Communications Corp. The format of the station is sports. WFNI-AM broadcasts to the Indianapolis area at 1070 AM.

WFNK-FM
Owner: WBIN, Inc.
Editorial: 477 Congress St Ste 3, Portland, Maine 04101-3427. T: 1 207 797-0780
W: http://www.1075frank.com
Editorial Profile: WFNK-FM is a commercial station owned by WBIN, Inc. The format of station is classic hits. WFNK-FM broadcasts to the Portland, ME area at 107.5 FM.

WFNL-AM
Owner: Curtis Media Group
Editorial: 3012 Highwoods Blvd, Suite 201, Raleigh, North Carolina 27604-1037.
T: 1 919 790-9392 **E:** wfnl@curtismedia.com
W: http://curtismedia.com/wfnl
Editorial Profile: WFNL-AM is a commercial station owned by Curtis Media Group. The format of the station is comedy. WFNL-AM broadcasts to the Raleigh-Durham, NC area at 570 AM.

WFNN-AM
Owner: Connoisseur Media LLC
Editorial: 1 Boston Store Pl, Erie, Pennsylvania 16501. **T:** 1 814 461-1000
Editorial Profile: WFNN-AM is a commercial station owned by Connoisseur Media LLC. The format of the station is sports. WFNN-AM broadcasts to the Erie, PA area at 1330 AM.

WFNO-AM
Owner: Sunburst Media-Louisiana, LLC
Editorial: 120 Prevost Dr, Houma, Louisiana 70364-2338. **T:** 1 504 832-3555
W: http://www.laraza830.com
Editorial Profile: WFNO-AM is a commercial station owned by Sunburst Media-Louisiana, LLC. The format of the station is Spanish hits. WFNO-AM broadcasts to the New Orleans area at 830 AM.

WFNP-FM
Owner: State University of New York
Editorial: 1 Hawk Dr, New Paltz, New York 12561-2447. **T:** 1 845 257-3094
E: wnpctv@gmail.com **W:** http://www.wfnp.org
Editorial Profile: WFNP-FM is a non-commercial station owned by the State University of New York. The format of the station is rock alternative. WFNP-FM broadcasts to the New Paltz, NY area at 88.7 FM.

WFNQ-FM
Owner: WBIN, Inc.
Editorial: 20 Industrial Park Dr Ste 1, Nashua, New Hampshire 03062-3178.
T: 1 603 889-1063
W: http://www.1063frankfm.com
Editorial Profile: WFNQ-FM is a commercial station owned by WBIN, Inc. The format of the station is classic hits. WFNQ-FM broadcasts to the Hooksett, NH area at 106.3 FM.

WFNR-AM
Owner: Cumulus Media Inc.
Editorial: 7080 Lee Hwy, Fairlawn, Virginia 24141-8416. **T:** 1 540 731-6000
Editorial Profile: WFNR-AM is a commercial station owned by Cumulus Media Inc. The format of the station is news, talk and sports. WFNR-AM broadcasts to the Fairlawn, VA area at 710 AM.

WFNS-AM
Owner: MarMac Communications, LLC
Editorial: 436 Mall Blvd, Brunswick, Georgia 31525-1819. **T:** 1 912 342-7184
E: thefansportsradio@yahoo.com
W: http://www.thefansportsradio.com
Editorial Profile: WFNS-AM is a commercial station owned by MarMac Communications, LLC. The format of the station is sports. WFNS-AM broadcasts to the Waycross, GA area at 1350 AM.

WFNT-AM
Owner: Townsquare Media, LLC
Editorial: 3338 E Bristol Rd, Burton, Michigan 48529-1408. **T:** 1 810 743-1080
W: http://www.wfnt.com
Editorial Profile: WFTN-AM is a commercial station owned by Townsquare Media, LLC. The format of the station is news and talk. WFTN-AM broadcasts to the Burton, MI area at 1470 AM.

WFNX-FM
Owner: Northeast Broadcasting Co.
Editorial: 362 Green St, Gardner, Massachusetts 01440-1348.
T: 1 978 374-4733
Editorial Profile: WFNX-FM is a commercial station owned by Northeast Broadcasting Co. The format of the station is adult hits. WFNX-FM broadcasts to the Gardner, MA area at 99.9 FM.

WFNY-AM
Owner: Sleezer(Michael)
Editorial: 101 S Main St, Gloversville, New York 12078-3820. **T:** 1 518 725-1108
Editorial Profile: WFNY-AM is a commercial station owned by Michael Sleezer. The format of the station is oldies. WFNY-AM broadcasts to the Gloversville, NY area at 1440 AM.

WFNZ-AM
Owner: CBS Radio
Editorial: 1520 South Blvd Ste 300, Charlotte, North Carolina 28203-3701.
T: 1 704 319-9369
W: http://charlotte.cbslocal.com
Editorial Profile: WFNZ-AM is a commercial station owned by CBS Radio. The format of the station is sports. WFNZ-AM broadcasts to the Charlotte, NC area at 610 AM.

WFOB-AM
Owner: Tri-County Broadcasting
Editorial: 101 N Main St, Fostoria, Ohio 44830-2215. **T:** 1 419 435-1430
E: production@wfob.com
W: http://www.wfob.com
Editorial Profile: WFOB-AM is a commercial station owned by Tri-County Broadcasting. The format of the station is sports. WFOB-AM broadcasts to the Fostoria, OH area at 1430 AM.

WFOF-FM
Owner: Moody Bible Institute
Editorial: 1920 W 53rd St, Anderson, Indiana 46013-1110. **T:** 1 888 877-9467
W: http://www.moodyradioindiana.fm/
Editorial Profile: WFOF-FM is a non-commercial station owned by Moody Bible Institute. The format of the station is religious. WFOF-FM broadcasts to the Anderson, IN area at 90.3 FM.

WFOM-AM
Owner: Dickey Broadcasting
Editorial: 780 Johnson Ferry Rd NE Ste 500, Atlanta, Georgia 30342-1436.
T: 1 404 688-0068
W: http://www.1230thefan2.com
Editorial Profile: WFOM-AM is a commercial station owned by Dickey Broadcasting. The format of the station is sports. WFOM-AM broadcasts in the Atlanta area at 1230 AM.

WFON-FM
Owner: RBH Enterprises Inc.
Editorial: 254 Winnebago Dr, Fond du Lac, Wisconsin 54935. **T:** 1 920 921-1071
E: info@k107.com **W:** http://www.k107.com
Editorial Profile: WFON-FM is a commercial station owned by RBH Enterprises Inc. The format of the station is adult contemporary. WFON-FM broadcasts to the Fond du Lac, WI area at 107.1 FM.

WFOR-AM
Owner: Clear Channel Media and Entertainment
Editorial: 6555 U S Highway 98, Ste 8, Hattiesburg, Mississippi 39402.
T: 1 601 296-9800
Editorial Profile: WFOR-AM is a commercial station owned by Clear Channel Media and Entertainment. The format of the station is sports and talk. WFOR-AM broadcasts to the Hattiesburg, MS area at 1400 AM.

WFOS-FM
Owner: Chesapeake Public Schools
Editorial: 1617 Cedar Rd, Chesapeake, Virginia 23322. **T:** 1 757 547-0134
Editorial Profile: WFOS-FM is a non-commercial station owned by Chesapeake Public Schools. The format of the station is variety. WFOS-FM broadcasts to the Chesapeake, VA area at 88.7 FM.

WFOX-FM
Owner: Connoisseur Media
Editorial: 440 Wheelers Farms Rd Ste 302, Milford, Connecticut 06461-9133.
T: 1 203 783-4200
W: http://www.959thefox.com
Editorial Profile: WFOX-FM is a commercial station owned by Connoisseur Media. The format of the station is classic rock. WFOX-FM broadcasts to the Norwalk, CT area at 95.9 FM.

WFOY-AM
Owner: Phillips Broadcasting, LLC
Editorial: 567 Lewis Point Road Ext, Saint Augustine, Florida 32086-5222.
T: 1 904 797-1955
W: http://www.1240news.com
Editorial Profile: WFOY-AM is a commercial station owned by Phillips Broadcasting, LLC. The format of the station is news and talk. WFOY-AM broadcasts to the Jacksonville, FL area at 1240 AM.

WFPB-AM
Owner: University of Massachusetts
Editorial: 100 William T Morrissey Blvd, Dorchester, Massachusetts 02125-3300.
T: 1 617 287-6900 **E:** wumb@umb.edu
W: http://www.wumb.org
Editorial Profile: WFPB-AM is a non-commercial station owned by the University of Massachusetts. The format of the station is folk. WFPB-AM broadcasts to the Dorchester, MA area at 1170 AM.

WFPB-FM
Owner: University of Massachusetts
Editorial: 100 William T Morrissey Blvd, Dorchester, Massachusetts 02125-3300.
T: 1 617 287-6900 **E:** wumb@umb.edu
W: http://www.wumb.org
Editorial Profile: WFPB-FM is a non-commercial station owned by University of Massachusetts. The format of the station is folk, blues and educational. WFPB-FM broadcasts to the Boston area at 91.9 FM.

WFPG-FM
Owner: Townsquare Media, LLC
Editorial: 950 Tilton Rd, Ste 200, Northfield, New Jersey 8225. **T:** 1 609 645-9797
E: lite@literock969.com
W: http://www.literock969.com
Editorial Profile: WFPG-FM is a commercial station owned by the Townsquare Media, LLC. The format of the station is Lite Rock/Lite AC. WFPG-FM broadcasts to the Northfield, NJ area at 96.9 FM.

WFPK-FM
Owner: Louisville Public Media
Editorial: 619 S 4th St, Louisville, Kentucky 40202-2403. **T:** 1 502 814-6500
E: info@louisvillepublicmedia.org
W: http://www.wspl.org
Editorial Profile: WFPK-FM is a non-commercial station owned by Louisville Public Media. The format of the station is adult album alternative. WFPK-FM broadcasts in the Louisville, KY area at 91.9 FM.

WFPL-FM
Owner: Louisville Public Media
Editorial: 619 S 4th St, Louisville, Kentucky 40202-2403. **T:** 1 502 814-6500
E: info@louisvillepublicmedia.org
W: http://www.wfpl.org
Editorial Profile: WFPL-AM is a non-commercial station owned by Louisville Public Media. The format of the station is news and talk. WFPL-AM broadcasts to the Louisville, KY area at 89.3 FM.

WFPR-AM
Owner: Northshore Broadcasting Inc.
Editorial: 200 E Thomas St, Hammond, Louisiana 70401. **T:** 1 985 345-0060
Editorial Profile: WFPR-AM is a commercial station owned by Northshore Broadcasting Inc. The format of the station is country. WFPR-AM broadcasts to the Hammond, LA area at 1400 AM.

WFPS-FM
Owner: Big Radio
Editorial: 834 N Tower Rd, Freeport, Illinois 61032. **T:** 1 815 235-7191
W: http://www.bigradio.fm
Editorial Profile: WFPS-FM is a commercial station owned by Big Radio. The format of the station is contemporary country music. WFPS-FM broadcasts to the Freeport, IL area at 92.1 FM. All staff should be contact via fax.

WFQX-FM
Owner: Clear Channel Media and Entertainment
Editorial: 510 Pegasus Ct, Winchester, Virginia 22602-4596. **T:** 1 540 662-5101
E: winchesterproductions@clearchannel.com
W: http://www.993thefox.com
Editorial Profile: WFQX-FM is a commercial station owned by Clear Channel Media and Entertainment. The format of the station is rock alternative. WFQX-FM broadcasts to the Washington, D.C. area at 99.3 FM.

WFQY-AM
Owner: Titan Broadcasting, LLC
Editorial: 209 Commerce Dr Ste D, Brandon, Mississippi 39042-2756. **T:** 1 601 706-4040
Editorial Profile: WFQY-AM is a commercial station owned by Titan Broadcasting, LLC. The format of the station is classic hip hop. The station broadcasts to the Brandon, MS area at 970 AM.

WFRA-AM
Owner: Forever Broadcasting
Editorial: 900 Water St, Meadville, Pennsylvania 16335. **T:** 1 814 724-1111
E: wmgwboss@yahoo.com
W: http://www.myantsnetwork.com
Editorial Profile: WFRA-AM is a commercial station owned by Forever Broadcasting. The format of the station is news, talk and sports. WFRA-AM broadcasts to the Franklin, PA area at 1450 AM.

WFRB-AM
Owner: Dix Communications
Editorial: 242 Finzel Rd, Frostburg, Maryland 21532-4009. **T:** 1 301 689-8871
W: http://www.talkradio560.com
Editorial Profile: WFRB-AM is a commercial station owned by Dix Communications. The format of the station is talk. WFRB-AM broadcasts in the Frostburg, MD area at 560 AM.

WFRB-FM
Owner: Dix Communications
Editorial: 242 Finzel Rd, Frostburg, Maryland 21532-4009. **T:** 1 301 689-8871
W: http://www.wfrb.com
Editorial Profile: WFRB-FM is a commercial station owned by Dix Communications. The format of the station is classic and contemporary country music. WFRB-FM broadcasts to the Frostburg, MD area at 105.3 FM.

WFRC-FM
Owner: Family Stations Inc.
Editorial: 1010 7th Pl, Phenix City, Alabama 36867. **T:** 1 334 291-0399
E: info@familyradio.org
W: http://www.familyradio.com

WFRE-FM
Owner: Clear Channel Media and Entertainment
Editorial: 5966 Grove Hill Rd, Frederick, Maryland 21703-6012. **T:** 1 301 663-4181
E: news@wfmd.com **W:** http://www.wfre.com
Editorial Profile: WFRE-FM is a commercial station owned by Clear Channel Media and Entertainment. The format of the station is classic and contemporary country music. WFRE-FM broadcasts in the Frederick, MD area at 99.9 FM.

WFRF-AM
Owner: Faith Radio Network
Editorial: 4015 N Monroe St, Tallahassee, Florida 32303. **T:** 1 850 201-1070
E: mailbox@faithradio.us
W: http://www.faithradio.us
Editorial Profile: WFRF-AM is a non-commercial station owned by Faith Radio Network. The format of the station is contemporary Christian, southern gospel, and religious talk. WFRF-AM broadcasts to the Tallahassee, FL area at 1070 AM.

WFRF-FM
Owner: Faith Radio Network
Editorial: 4015 N Monroe St, Tallahassee, Florida 32303. **T:** 1 850 201-1070
E: mailbox@faithradio.us
W: http://www.faithradio.us
Editorial Profile: WFRF-FM is a non-commercial station owned by Faith Radio Network. The format of the station is Christian and religious talk. The station airs locally at 105.7 FM.

WFRG-FM
Owner: Townsquare Media, LLC
Editorial: 9418 River Rd, Marcy, New York 13403-2071. **T:** 1 315 768-9500
W: http://www.bigfrog104.com
Editorial Profile: WFRG-FM is a commercial station owned by Townsquare Media, LLC. The format of the station is country music. WFRG-FM broadcasts to the Utica, NY area at 104.3 FM.

WFRH-FM
Owner: Family Stations Inc.
Editorial: 786 Murray Rd, Kingston, New York 12401-7144. **T:** 1 845 336-0234
E: office@wfsi.net
W: http://www.familyradio.com
Editorial Profile: WFRH-FM is a non-commercial station owned by Family Stations Inc. The format of the station is religious. WFRH-FM broadcasts to the West Shokan, NY area at 81.7 FM.

WFRJ-FM
Owner: Family Stations Inc.
Editorial: 1322 Seanor Rd, Windber, Pennsylvania 15963. **T:** 1 814 467-9466
E: wfrj44@gmail.com
W: http://www.familyradio.com
Editorial Profile: WFRJ-FM is a non-commercial station owned by Family Stations Inc. The format of the station is religious. WFRJ-FM broadcasts to the Windber, PA area at 88.9 FM.

WFRL-AM
Owner: Big Radio
Editorial: 834 N Tower Rd, Freeport, Illinois 61032. **T:** 1 815 235-7191
W: http://www.bigradio.fm
Editorial Profile: WFRL-AM is a commercial station owned by Big Radio. The format of the station is oldies. WFRL-AM broadcasts to the Freeport, IL area at 1570 AM. All staff should be contact via fax.

WFRM-AM
Owner: L-Com Inc.
Editorial: 9 S Main St, Coudersport, Pennsylvania 16915-1301. **T:** 1 814 274-8600
E: whks@verizon.net
Editorial Profile: WFRM-AM is a commercial station owned by L-Com Inc. The format of the station is adult standards. WFRM-AM broadcasts to the Coudersport, PA area at 600 AM.

WFRN-FM
Owner: Progressive Broadcasting
Editorial: 25802 County Road 26, Elkhart, Indiana 46517-9132. **T:** 1 574 875-5166
E: comments@wfrn.com
W: http://www.wfrn.com
Editorial Profile: WFRN-FM is a commercial station owned by Progressive Broadcasting. The format for the station is contemporary Christian. WFRN-FM broadcasts to the South Bend, IN area at 104.7 FM.

WFRO-FM
Owner: BAS Broadcasting
Editorial: 1281 N River Rd, Fremont, Ohio 43420. **T:** 1 419 332-8218
W: http://www.wfroradio.com
Editorial Profile: WFRO-FM is a commercial station owned by BAS Broadcasting. The format of the station is adult contemporary. WFRO-FM broadcasts to the Fremont, OH area at 99.1 FM.

WFRQ-FM
Owner: Codcomm Inc.
Editorial: 243 South St, Hyannis, Massachusetts 02601-3926.
T: 1 508 775-5678
W: http://www.frankplaysitall.com
Editorial Profile: WFRQ-FM is a commercial station owned by Codcomm Inc. The format of the station is Jack FM-Adult Hits. WFRQ-FM broadcasts to the Wast Yarmouth, MA area at 93.5 FM.

WFRS-FM
Owner: Family Stations Inc.
Editorial: 289 Mount Pleasant Ave, West Orange, New Jersey 7052. **T:** 1 973 736-3600
E: info@familyradio.org
W: http://www.familyradio.com
Editorial Profile: WFRS-FM is a non-commercial station owned by Family Stations Inc. The format for the station is religious. WFRS-FM broadcasts to the West Orange, NJ area at 88.9 FM.

WFRX-AM
Owner: Withers Broadcasting of Southern Illinois LLC
Editorial: 1822 N Court St, Marion, Illinois 62959-4558. **T:** 1 618 997-8123
W: http://www.mywithersradio.com
Editorial Profile: WFRX-AM is a commercial station owned by Withers Broadcasting of Southern Illinois LLC. The format of the station is sports. WFRX-AM broadcasts to the Marion, IL areas at 1300 AM.

WFRY-FM
Owner: Stephens Media Group
Editorial: 134 Mullin St, Watertown, New York 13601. **T:** 1 315 788-0790
W: http://www.froggy97.com

WFSC-AM
Owner: Georgia-Carolina Radiocasting Companies LLC
Editorial: 180 Radio Hill Rd, Franklin, North Carolina 28734. **T:** 1 828 524-4418
E: newsradio@gacaradio.com
W: http://www.1050wfsc.com
Editorial Profile: WFSC-AM is a commercial station owned by Georgia-Carolina Radiocasting Companies LLC. The format of the station is oldies. WFSC-AM broadcasts to the Franklin, NC area at 1050 AM.

WFSE-FM
Owner: Edinboro University of Pennsylvania
Editorial: Faculty Anx, Edinboro, Pennsylvania 16444. **T:** 1 814 732-2641

WFSH-FM
Owner: Salem Communications
Editorial: 2970 Peachtree Rd NW, Ste 700, Atlanta, Georgia 30305. **T:** 1 404 995-7300
W: http://www.thefishatlanta.com
Editorial Profile: WFSH-FM is a commercial station owned by Salem Communications. The format of the station is contemporary Christian. WFSH-FM broadcasts to the Atlanta area at 104.7 FM.

WFSI-AM
Owner: Family Stations Inc.
Editorial: 918 Chesapeake Ave, Annapolis, Maryland 21403-3132. **T:** 1 410 825-7700
E: office@wfsi.net
W: http://www.familyradio.com
Editorial Profile: WFSI-AM is a non-commercial station owned by the Family Stations Inc. The format of the station is religious programming. WFSI-AM broadcasts to the Baltimore area at 860 AM.

WFSK-FM
Owner: Fisk University
Editorial: 1000 17th Ave N, Nashville, Tennessee 37208-3045. **T:** 1 615 329-8754
E: info@wfsk.org
W: http://www.fisk.edu/campuslife/wfsk.aspx
Editorial Profile: WFSK-FM is a non-commercial station owned by Fisk University. The format of the station is smooth AC, jazz, and talk. WFSK-FM broadcasts to the Nashville, TN area at 88.1 FM.

WFSO-FM
Owner: Redeemer Broadcasting
Editorial: 314 Acorn Hill Rd, Olivebridge, New York 12461-5439. **T:** 1 888 724-4427
W: http://www.redeemerbroadcasting.org
Editorial Profile: WFSO-FM is a non-commercial station owned by Redeemer Broadcasting. The format of the station is Christian programming. WFSO-FM broadcasts to the Olivebridge, NY area at 88.3 FM. The station requested that its e-mail not be listed.

WFSP-AM
Owner: WFSP Inc.
Editorial: Route 7 West, Kingwood, West Virginia 26537. **T:** 1 304 329-1780
W: http://www.prestoncounty.com/wfsp
Editorial Profile: WFSP-AM is a commercial station owned by WFSP Inc. The format of the station is talk. WFSP-AM broadcasts to the Kingwood, WV area at 1560 AM.

WFSP-FM
Owner: WFSP Inc.
Editorial: Route 7 West, Kingwood, West Virginia 26537. **T:** 1 304 329-1780
E: wfsp@wvdsl.net
W: http://www.prestoncounty.com/wfsp
Editorial Profile: WFSP-FM is a commercial station owned by WFSP Inc. The format of the station is oldies. WFSP-FM broadcasts to the Kingwood, WV area at 107.7 FM.

WFSQ-FM
Owner: Florida State University
Editorial: 1600 Red Barber Plz, Tallahassee, Florida 32310. **T:** 1 850 487-3086
E: wfsufm@wfsu.org **W:** http://www.wfsu.org
Editorial Profile: WFSQ-FM is a non-commercial station owned by Florida State University. The format of the station is jazz and classical music. WFSQ-FM broadcasts to the Tallahassee, FL area at 91.5 FM.

WFSR-AM
Owner: Eastern Broadcasting Co.
Editorial: 125 S Main St, Harlan, Kentucky 40831-2109. **T:** 1 606 573-1470
E: wtuk-wfsr@harlanonline.net
Editorial Profile: WFSR-AM is a commercial station owned by Eastern Broadcasting Co. The format of the station is gospel. WFSR-AM broadcasts to the Harlan, KY area at 970 AM.

WFSS-FM
Owner: Fayetteville State University
Editorial: 1200 Murchison Rd, Fayetteville, North Carolina 28301-4252.
T: 1 910 672-1381 **E:** wfss@uncfsu.edu
W: http://www.wfss.org
Editorial Profile: WFSS-FM is a non-commercial station owned by Fayetteville State University. The format of the station is news, talk, and jazz. WFSS-FM broadcasts to the Fayetteville, NC area at 91.9 FM.

WFST-AM
Owner: Northern Broadcast Ministries Inc.
Editorial: 670 New Sweden Rd, Caribou, Maine 4736. **T:** 1 207 492-6000
E: wfst@maine.rr.com **W:** http://www.wfst.net
Editorial Profile: WFST-AM is a non-commercial station owned by Northern Broadcast Ministries Inc. The format of the station is gospel music. WFST-AM broadcasts to the Caribou, ME area at 600 AM.

WFSU-FM
Owner: Florida State University
Editorial: 1600 Red Barber Plz, Tallahassee, Florida 32310. **T:** 1 850 487-3086
E: wfsufm@wfsu.org **W:** http://www.wfsu.org
Editorial Profile: WFSU-FM is a non-commercial station owned by the Florida State University. The format of the station is classical music, news and talk. WFSU-FM broadcasts to the Tallahassee, FL area at 88.9 FM.

WFSX-FM
Owner: Sun Broadcasting, Inc.
Editorial: 2824 Palm Beach Blvd, Fort Myers, Florida 33916. **T:** 1 239 334-1111
W: http://www.925foxnews.com
Editorial Profile: WFSX-FM is a commercial station owned by Sun Broadcasting, Inc. The format of the station is news and talk. WFSX-FM broadcasts to the Fort Myers, FL area at 92.5 FM.

WFSY-FM
Owner: Clear Channel Media and Entertainment
Editorial: 1834 Lisenby Ave, Panama City, Florida 32405. **T:** 1 850 769-6161
W: http://www.sunny98.com
Editorial Profile: WFSY-FM is a commercial station owned by Clear Channel Media and Entertainment. The format of the station is adult contemporary music. WFSY-FM broadcasts to the Panama City, FL area at 98.5 FM.

WFTA-FM
Owner: Air South Radio Inc.
Editorial: 1241 Cliff Gookin Blvd, Tupelo, Mississippi 38801. **T:** 1 662 842-1019

WFTD-AM
Owner: Prieto Broadcasting, Inc.
Editorial: 2865 Amwiler Rd Ste 650, Doraville, Georgia 30360-2828. **T:** 1 770 825-0090
Editorial Profile: WFTD-AM is a commercial station owned by Prieto Broadcasting, Inc. The format of the station is Spanish news and talk. WFTD-AM broadcasts to the Doraville, GA area at 1080 AM.

WFTF-FM
Owner: Christian Ministries Inc
Editorial: 140 Main St, Essex Junction, Vermont 05452-3208. **T:** 1 802 878-8885
W: http://thelightradio.net
Editorial Profile: WFTF-FM is a non-commercial station owned by Christian Ministries Inc. The format of the station is contemporary Christian music. WFTF-FM broadcasts to the Rutland, VT area at 90.5 FM.

WFTG-AM
Owner: Forcht Broadcasting
Editorial: 534 Tobacco Rd, London, Kentucky 40741. **T:** 1 606 864-2148
Editorial Profile: WFTG-AM is a commercial station owned by Forcht Broadcasting. The format for the station is country. WFTG-AM broadcasts to the Lexington, KY area at 1440 AM.

WFTH-AM
Owner: Tri-City Christian Radio Inc.
Editorial: 227 E Belt Blvd, Richmond, Virginia 23224. **T:** 1 804 233-0765
E: faithradio1590am@yahoo.com
W: http://faith1590.ning.com
Editorial Profile: WFTH-AM is a commercial station owned by Tri-City Christian Radio Inc. The format of the station is black gospel. WFTH-AM broadcasts to the Richmond, VA area at 1590 AM.

WFTI-FM
Owner: Radio Training Network, Inc.
Editorial: 6469 Parkland Dr, Sarasota, Florida 34243-4091. **T:** 1 941 753-2963
E: thejoyfm@thejoyfm.com
W: http://florida.thejoyfm.com
Editorial Profile: WFTI-FM is a non-commercial station owned by Radio Training Network, Inc. The format of the station is Contemporary Christian music. WFTI-FM broadcasts to the Saint Petersburg, FL area at 91.7 FM.

WFTK-FM
Owner: Cumulus Media Inc.
Editorial: 4805 Montgomery Rd, Ste 300, Cincinnati, Ohio 45212-2280.
T: 1 513 241-9898
E: feedback@cincyradio.com
W: http://www.purerock965.com
Editorial Profile: WFTK-FM is a commercial station owned by Cumulus Media Inc. The format of the station is rock. WFTK-FM broadcasts to the Cincinnati area at 96.5 FM.

WFTL-AM
Owner: JCE Licenses, LLC
Editorial: 6600 N Andrews Ave Ste 160, Fort Lauderdale, Florida 33309-2188.
T: 1 954 315-1515 **E:** news@jamescrystal.com
W: http://www.850wftl.com
Editorial Profile: WFTL-AM is a commercial station owned by JCE Licenses, LLC. The format of the station is news and talk programming. WFTL-AM broadcasts to the Fort Lauderdale, FL area at 850 AM.

WFTM-AM
Owner: Standard Tobacco Co.
Editorial: 626 Forest Ave, Maysville, Kentucky 41056-1412. **T:** 1 606 564-3361
E: wftmnews@maysvilleky.net
W: http://www.wftm.net
Editorial Profile: WFTM-AM is a commercial station owned by Standard Tobacco Co. The format of the station is classic hits. WFTM-AM broadcasts to the Maysville, KY area at 1240 AM.

WFTM-FM
Owner: Standard Tobacco Co.
Editorial: 626 Forest Ave, Maysville, Kentucky 41056-1412. **T:** 1 606 564-3361
E: wftmnews@maysvilleky.net
W: http://www.wftm.net
Editorial Profile: WFTM-FM is a commercial station owned by Standard Tobacco Co. The format of the station is adult contemporary music. WFTM-FM broadcasts to the Cincinnati area at 95.9 FM.

WFTN-AM
Owner: Northeast Communications Corp.
Editorial: 110 Babbitt Rd, Franklin, New Hampshire 3235. **T:** 1 603 934-2500
W: http://www.mix941fm.com
Editorial Profile: WFTN-AM is a commercial station owned by Northeast Communications Corp. The format of the station is adult standards. WFTN-AM broadcasts to the Boston area at 1240 AM.

WFTN-FM
Owner: Northeast Communications Corp.
Editorial: 110 Babbitt Rd, Franklin, New Hampshire 3235. **T:** 1 603 253-8080
W: http://www.mix941fm.com
Editorial Profile: WFTN-FM is a commercial station owned by Northeast Communications Corp. The format of the station is hot adult contemporary. WFTN-FM broadcasts to the Boston area at 94.1 FM.

WFTR-AM
Owner: Royal Broadcasting Inc.
Editorial: 1106 Elm St, Front Royal, Virginia 22630-3736. **T:** 1 540 635-4121
Editorial Profile: WFTR-AM is a commercial station owned by Royal Broadcasting Inc. The format of the station is classic country. WFTR-AM broadcasts to the Front Royal, VA area at 1450 AM.

WFTU-AM
Owner: Five Towns College
Editorial: 305 N Service Rd, Dix Hills, New York 11746-5857
W: http://www.ftc.edu/Student%20Life/stu_wftu.html
Editorial Profile: WFTU-AM is a non-commercial college station owned by Five Towns College. The format of the station is college variety. WFTU-AM broadcasts to the Long Island, NY area at a frequency of 1570 AM.

WFTW-AM
Owner: Cumulus Media Inc.
Editorial: 225 Hollywood Blvd NW, Fort Walton Beach, Florida 32548.
T: 1 850 243-7676 **W:** http://www.wftw.com
Editorial Profile: WFTW-AM is a commercial station owned by Cumulus Media Inc. The format of the station is talk, news and sports. WFTW-AM broadcasts to the Fort Walton Beach, FL area at 1260 AM.

WFTZ-FM
Owner: Phase Two Communications
Editorial: 1025 Hillsboro Blvd, Manchester, Tennessee 37355-2029. **T:** 1 931 728-3458
W: http://www.fantasyradio.com

Editorial Profile: WFTZ-FM is a commercial station owned by Phase Two Communications. The format of the station is adult contemporary. WFTZ-FM broadcasts to the Manchester, TN area at 101.5 FM.

WFUM-FM
Owner: University of Michigan
Editorial: 535 W William St Ste 110, Ann Arbor, Michigan 48103-4978.
T: 1 734 764-9210 **E:** newsroom@umich.edu
W: http://www.michiganradio.org
Editorial Profile: WFUM-FM is a non-commercial station owned by University of Michigan. The format of the station is news and talk. WFUM-FM broadcasts to the Flint, MI area at 91.1 FM.

WFUN-AM
Owner: Media One Group
Editorial: 3226 Jefferson Rd, Ashtabula, Ohio 44004-9112. **T:** 1 440 993-2126
W: http://www.espn970wfun.com
Editorial Profile: WFUN-AM is a commercial station owned by Media One Group. The format of the station is sports. WFUN-AM broadcasts to the Ashtabula, OH area at 970 AM.

WFUN-FM
Owner: Radio One Inc.
Editorial: 9666 Olive Blvd, Saint Louis, Missouri 63132-3013. **T:** 1 314 989-9550
W: http://oldschool955.com
Editorial Profile: WFUN-FM is a commercial station owned by Radio One Inc. The format of the station is urban adult contemporary music. WFUN-FM broadcasts in the St. Louis area at 95.5 FM.

WFUR-AM
Owner: Furniture City Broadcasting
Editorial: 399 Garfield Ave SW, Grand Rapids, Michigan 49504. **T:** 1 616 451-9387
E: wfuramfm@sbcglobal.net
W: http://www.wfuramfm.com
Editorial Profile: WFUR-AM is a commercial station owned by Furniture City Broadcasting. The format of the station is religious music and talk. WFUR-AM broadcasts to the Grand Rapids, MI area at 1570 AM. The station does not produce their own news.

WFUR-FM
Owner: Furniture City Broadcasting
Editorial: 399 Garfield Ave SW, Grand Rapids, Michigan 49504-6167. **T:** 1 616 451-9387
E: wfuramfm@sbcglobal.net
W: http://www.wfuramfm.com
Editorial Profile: WFUR-FM is a commercial station owned by Furniture City Broadcasting. The format of the station is religious programming. WFUR-FM broadcasts to Grand Rapids, MI at 102.9 FM. The station does not accept press releases as they don't produce their own news.

WFUS-FM
Owner: Clear Channel Media and Entertainment
Editorial: 4002 W Gandy Blvd, Tampa, Florida 33611-3410. **T:** 1 813 832-1000
W: http://www.us1035.com
Editorial Profile: WFUS-FM is a commercial station owned by Clear Channel Media and Entertainment. The format of the station is country. WFUS-FM broadcasts to the Tampa, FL area at 103.5 FM.

WFUV-FM
Owner: Fordham University
Editorial: Fordham University, Keating Hall-B12, Bronx, New York 10458-5149.
T: 1 718 817-4550 **E:** thefolks@wfuv.org
W: http://www.wfuv.org
Editorial Profile: WFUV-FM is a non-commercial station owned by Fordham University. The format of the station is adult album alternative. WFUV-FM broadcasts to the New York area at 90.7 FM.

WFUZ-FM
Owner: Shamrock Communications
Editorial: 149 Penn Ave Fl 5, Scranton, Pennsylvania 18503-2055. **T:** 1 570 346-6555
W: http://www.radiofm921.com
Editorial Profile: WFUZ-FM is a commercial station owned by Shamrock Communications. The format of the station is modern rock. WFUZ-FM broadcasts to the Scranton, PA area at 92.1 FM.

WFVA-AM
Owner: Centennial Broadcasting
Editorial: 1914 Mimosa St, Fredericksburg, Virginia 22405-3213. **T:** 1 540 373-7721
W: http://www.newstalk1230.net
Editorial Profile: WFVA-AM is a commercial station owned by the Centennial Broadcasting. The format of the station is news and talk. WFVA-AM broadcasts to the Fredericksburg, VA area at 1230 AM.

WFVL-FM
Owner: Cumulus Media Inc.
Editorial: 1009 Drayton Rd, Fayetteville, North Carolina 28303-3887. **T:** 1 910 864-5222
W: http://www.oldiesradionc.com
Editorial Profile: WFVL-FM is a commercial station owned by Cumulus Media Inc. The format of the station is Contemporary Christian. WFVL-FM broadcasts to the Fayetteville, NC area at 102.3 FM.

WFWI-FM
Owner: Federated Media
Editorial: 2915 Maples Rd, Fort Wayne, Indiana 46816-3335. **T:** 1 260 447-5511
W: http://www.wowo.com
Editorial Profile: WFWI-FM is a commercial station owned by Federated Media. The format of the station is News/Talk. WFWI-FM broadcasts to the Fort Wayne, IN area at 92.3 FM.

WFWL-AM
Owner: Community Broadcasting Services Inc.
Editorial: 117 Vicksburg Ave, Camden, Tennessee 38320-1613. **T:** 1 731 584-7570
E: wfwlwrjb@bellsouth.net
Editorial Profile: WFWL-AM is a commercial station owned by Community Broadcasting Services Inc. The format of the station is contemporary country. WFWL-AM broadcasts to the Camden, TN area at 1220 AM.

WFWM-FM
Owner: Frostburg State University
Editorial: Stangle Bldg, Frostburg State University, Frostburg, Maryland 21532.
T: 1 301 687-4143 **E:** wfwm2@frostburg.edu
W: http://www.wfwm.org
Editorial Profile: WFWM-FM is a non-commercial station owned by Frostburg State University. The format of the station is a variety of news, talk and music. WFWM-FM broadcasts to the Frostburg, MD area at 91.9 FM.

WFWN-AM
Owner: Sun Broadcasting, Inc.
Editorial: 2824 Palm Beach Blvd, Fort Myers, Florida 33916-1503. **T:** 1 239 337-2346
Editorial Profile: WFWN-AM is a commercial station owned by Sun Broadcasting, Inc. The format of the station is sports. The station airs locally at 1240 AM.

WFXA-FM
Owner: Perry Broadcasting Company, Inc.
Editorial: 411 Radio Station Rd, North Augusta, South Carolina 29841.
T: 1 803 279-2330
W: http://www.103jamzthefox.com/
Editorial Profile: WFXA-FM is a commercial station owned by Perry Broadcasting Company, Inc. The format of the station is urban contemporary. WFXA-FM broadcasts to the North Augusta, SC area at 103.1 FM.

WFXC-FM
Owner: Radio One Inc.
Editorial: 8001 Creedmoor Rd, Ste 101, Raleigh, North Carolina 27613.
T: 1 919 848-9736
W: http://www.foxyhits.com
Editorial Profile: WFXC-FM is a commercial station owned by Radio One Inc. The format of the station is urban adult contemporary music. WFXC-FM broadcasts to the Raleigh-Durham, NC area at 107.1 FM.

WFXD-FM
Owner: Great Lakes Radio Inc.
Editorial: 3060 US Highway 41 W, Marquette, Michigan 49855-2293. **T:** 1 906 228-6800
E: contact@broadcasteverywhere.com
W: http://www.wfxd.com
Editorial Profile: WFXD-FM is a commercial station owned by Great Lakes Radio Inc. The format for the station is contemporary country music. WFXD-FM broadcasts to the Marquette, MI area at 103.3 FM.

WFXE-FM
Owner: Davis Broadcasting
Editorial: 2203 Wynnton Rd, Columbus, Georgia 31906. **T:** 1 706 576-3565
W: http://www.foxie105fm.com
Editorial Profile: WFXE-FM is a commercial station owned by Davis Broadcasting. The format of the station is urban contemporary music. WFXE-FM broadcasts to the Columbus, GA area at 104.9 FM.

WFXF-FM
Owner: Matrix Broadcasting
Editorial: 8800 US Highway 14, Crystal Lake, Illinois 60012-2740. **T:** 1 815 459-7000
W: http://www.1039thefox
Editorial Profile: WFXF-FM is a commercial station owned by Matrix Broadcasting. The format of the station is classic rock. WFXF-FM broadcasts to the Crystal Lake, IL area at 103.9 FM.

WFXH-FM
Owner: L & L Radio
Editorial: 401 Mall Blvd, Savannah, Georgia 31406-4878. **T:** 1 912 351-9830
W: http://rock1061.com
Editorial Profile: WFXH-FM is a commercial station owned by L & L Radio. The format for the station is rock music. WFXH-FM broadcasts to the Savannah, GA area at 106.1 FM.

WFXJ-AM
Owner: Clear Channel Media and Entertainment
Editorial: 11700 Central Pkwy, Jacksonville, Florida 32224-2600. **T:** 1 904 636-0507
W: http://www.sportsradiojax.com
Editorial Profile: WFXJ-AM is a commercial station owned by Clear Channel Media and Entertainment. The format of the station is sports. WFXJ-AM broadcasts to the Jacksonville, FL area at 930 AM.

WFXJ-FM
Owner: Media One Group
Editorial: 3226 Jefferson Rd, Ashtabula, Ohio 44004-9112. **T:** 1 440 993-2126
W: http://www.thefox1075.com
Editorial Profile: WFXJ-FM is a commercial station owned by Media One Group. The format of the station is classic rock music. WFXJ-FM broadcasts in the Cleveland area at 107.5 FM.

WFXK-FM
Owner: Radio One Inc.
Editorial: 8001 Creedmoor Rd, Ste 101, Raleigh, North Carolina 27613-4396.
T: 1 919 848-9736 **W:** http://foxync.com
Editorial Profile: WFXK-FM is a commercial station owned by Radio One Inc. The format of the station is adult contemporary and urban contemporary. WFKX-FM broadcasts to the Raleigh, NC area at 104.3 FM.

WFXM-FM
Owner: Murray Communications
Editorial: 6174 Ga Highway 57, Macon, Georgia 31217-3405. **T:** 1 478 745-3301
W: http://www.mypower1071.com
Editorial Profile: WFXM-FM is a commercial station owned by Murray Communications. The format of the station is urban contemporary music. WFXM-FM broadcasts to the Macon, GA area at 107.1 FM.

WFXN-AM
Owner: Clear Channel Media and Entertainment
Editorial: 3535 E Kimberly Rd, Davenport, Iowa 52807-2583. **T:** 1 563 344-7000
W: http://www.wfxn.net
Editorial Profile: WFXN-AM is a commercial station owned by Clear Channel Media and Entertainment. The format of the station is sports. WFXN-AM broadcasts to the Davenport, IA area at 1230 AM.

WFXN-FM
Owner: Clear Channel Media and Entertainment
Editorial: 1400 Radio Ln, Mansfield, Ohio 44906-2525. **T:** 1 419 529-2211
W: http://www.foxclassicrock.com
Editorial Profile: WFXN-FM is a commercial station owned by Clear Channel Media and Entertainment. The format of the station is classic rock music. WFXN-FM broadcasts to the Mansfield, OH area at 102.3 FM.

WFXO-FM
Owner: Williams Communications Inc.
Editorial: 801 Noble St Ste 30, Anniston, Alabama 36201-0503. **T:** 1 256 453-9898
Editorial Profile: WFXO-FM is a commercial station owned by Williams Communications Inc. The format of the station is urban AC. WFXO-FM broadcasts to the Anniston, AL area at 98.3 FM.

WFXX-FM
Owner: Haynes Broadcasting
Editorial: 1406 River Falls St, Andalusia, Alabama 36421-2029. **T:** 1 334 222-2222
E: wfxx@alaweb.com
W: http://www.fox107.com

WFXY-AM
Owner: Penelope, Inc.
Editorial: 2117 Cumberland Ave, Middlesboro, Kentucky 40965-2876. **T:** 1 606 248-8993
E: wanocountry@gmail.com
W: http://www.1490wfxy.com
Editorial Profile: WFXY-AM is a commercial station owned by Penelope, Inc. The format of the station is classic hits. WFXY-AM broadcasts to the Middlesboro, KY and surrounding communities at 1490 AM.

WFYB-FM
Owner: Light of Life Ministries, Inc.
Editorial: 160 Riverside Dr, Augusta, Maine 04330-4162. **T:** 1 207 622-1340
Editorial Profile: WFYB-FM is a non-commercial station owned by Light of Life Ministries Inc. The format of the station is Christian talk and music.WFYB-FM broadcasts to the Fryeburg, ME, area at 91.5 FM. This station is simulcasting WWWA-FM 95.3 Winslow/Augusta, ME.

WFYC-AM
Owner: Jacom Inc.
Editorial: 5310 N State Rd, Alma, Michigan 48801-9713. **T:** 1 989 463-3175
E: wqbxfm@gmail.com
Editorial Profile: WFYC-AM is a commercial station owned by Jacom Inc. The format of the station is sports. WFYC-AM broadcasts to the Alma, MI area at 1280 AM.

WFYI-FM
Owner: Metropolitan Indianapolis Public Broadcasting
Editorial: 1630 N Meridian St, Indianapolis, Indiana 46202-1429. **T:** 1 317 636-2020
W: http://www.wfyi.org
Editorial Profile: WFYI-FM is a non-commercial station owned by Indiana Public Broadcasting Systems. The format of the station is news and information. WFYI-FM broadcasts to the Indianapolis area at 90.1 FM.

WFYR-FM
Owner: Cumulus Media Inc.
Editorial: 120 Eaton St, Peoria, Illinois 61603-4217. **T:** 1 309 676-5000
W: http://www.973rivercountry.com
Editorial Profile: WFYR-FM is a commercial station owned by Cumulus Media Inc. The format of the station is country music. WFYR-FM broadcasts to the Peoria, IL area at 97.3 FM.

WFYX-FM
Owner: Great Eastern Radio, LLC
Editorial: 106 N Main St, West Lebanon, New Hampshire 03784-1136. **T:** 1 603 298-0332
Editorial Profile: WFYX-FM is a commercial station owned by Great Eastern Radio, LLC. The format of the station is classic hits. WFYX-FM broadcasts to the Walpole, NH area at 96.3 FM.

WFYY-FM
Owner: Max Media
Editorial: 450 Route 204, Selinsgrove, Pennsylvania 17870-7975. **T:** 1 570 374-5711
W: http://y106.fm

WFZX-AM
Owner: Jacobs Broadcast Group
Editorial: 1913 Barry St, Ste B, Oxford, Alabama 36203. **T:** 1 256 741-6000
Editorial Profile: WFZX-AM is a commercial station owned by Jacobs Broadcast Group. The format of the station is classic hits. WFZX-AM broadcasts to the Anniston/Oxford, AL area at 1490 AM.

WFZX-FM
Owner: Jacobs Broadcast Group, Inc
Editorial: 1913 Barry St, Oxford, Alabama 36203-2319. **T:** 1 256 741-6000
Editorial Profile: WFZX-FM is a commercial station owned by Jacobs Broadcast Group, Inc. The format of the station is classic rock. WFZX-FM broadcasts to the Anniston, AL area airing on WSYA-AM's translator at 104.3 FM.

WGAA-AM
Owner: Burgess Broadcasting Corp.
Editorial: 413 Lakeview Dr, Cedartown, Georgia 30125-2020. **T:** 1 770 748-1340
E: wgaaradio@wgaaradio.com
W: http://www.wgaaradio.com
Editorial Profile: WGAA-AM is a commercial station owned by Burgess Broadcasting Corp. The format is classic hits music. WGAA-AM broadcasts to the Cedartown, GA area at 1340 AM.

WGAB-AM
Owner: Faith Broadcasting Company
Editorial: 2601 S Boeke Rd, Evansville, Indiana 47714. **T:** 1 812 479-5342
E: sales@faith1180.com
W: http://www.faith1180.com
Editorial Profile: WGAB-AM is a commercial station owned by Faith Broadcasting Company. The format of the station is gospel music. WGAB-AM broadcasts to the Evansville, IN area at 1180 AM.

WGAC-AM
Owner: Beasley Broadcast Group
Editorial: 4051 Jimmie Dyess Pkwy, Augusta, Georgia 30909. **T:** 1 706 396-7000
E: news@wgac.com **W:** http://www.wgac.com
Editorial Profile: WGAC-AM is a commercial station owned by Beasley Broadcast Group. The format of the station is news and talk. WGAC-AM broadcasts to the Augusta, GA area at 580 AM.

WGAC-FM
Owner: Beasley Broadcast Group
Editorial: 4051 Jimmie Dyess Pkwy, Augusta, Georgia 30909. **T:** 1 706 396-7000
W: http://www.wgac.com
Editorial Profile: WGAC-FM is a commercial station owned by Beasley Broadcast Group. The format of the station is rock. WGAC-FM broadcasts to the Augusta, GA area at 95.1 FM.

WGAD-AM
Owner: Gadsden Radio Media, LLC
Editorial: 301 N 12th St, Gadsden, Alabama 35901-7200. **T:** 1 256 570-1350
Editorial Profile: WGAD-AM is a commercial station owned by Gadsden Radio Media, LLC. The format of the station is Adult Contemporary. WGAD-AM broadcasts to the Rainbow City, AL at 930 AM.

WGAI-AM
Owner: Max Media
Editorial: 103 W Wood Hill Dr, Ste D-E, Nags Head, North Carolina 27959.
T: 1 252 480-4655
W: http://www.newsradio560.com
Editorial Profile: WGAI-AM is a commercial station owned by Max Media. The format of the station is news and talk. WGAI-AM broadcasts to the Norfolk, VA area at 560 AM.

WGAM-AM
Owner: Absolute Broadcasting, LLC
Editorial: 149 Main St, Nashua, New Hampshire 03060-2725. **T:** 1 603 880-9001
E: info@wgamradio.com
W: http://www.wgamradio.com
Editorial Profile: WGAM-AM is a commercial station owned by Absolute Broadcasting, LLC. The format of the station is sports. WGAM-AM broadcasts to the Nashua, NH area at 1250 AM.

WGAN-AM
Owner: Saga Communications
Editorial: 420 Western Ave, South Portland, Maine 04106-1704. **T:** 1 207 774-4561
E: news@560wgan.com
W: http://www.560wgan.com
Editorial Profile: WGAN-AM is a commercial station owned by Saga Communications. The format of the station is news and talk. WGAN-AM broadcasts to the Portland, ME area at 560 AM.

WGAO-FM
Owner: Dean College
Editorial: 99 Main St, Franklin, Massachusetts 02038-1941. **T:** 1 508 541-1623
Editorial Profile: WGAO-FM is a non-commercial station owned by Dean College. The format of the station is rock. WGAO-FM broadcasts to the Franklin, MA area at 88.3 FM.

WGAP-AM
Owner: Clinton Broadcasters
Editorial: 111 Hillcrest Dr, Clinton, Tennessee 37716-2024. **T:** 1 865 675-4105
Editorial Profile: WGAP-AM is a commercial station owned by Clinton Broadcasters. The format of the station is country. WGAP-AM broadcasts to the Knoxville, TN area at 1400 AM.

WGAR-FM
Owner: Clear Channel Media and Entertainment
Editorial: 6200 Oak Tree Blvd, Cleveland, Ohio 44131-6933. **T:** 1 216 520-2600
W: http://www.wgar.com
Editorial Profile: WGAR-FM is a commercial station owned by Clear Channel Media and Entertainment. The format of the station is country music. WGAR-FM broadcasts to the Cleveland area at 99.5 FM.

WGAS-AM
Owner: Victory Christian Center
Editorial: 1501 Carrier Dr, Charlotte, North Carolina 28216. **T:** 1 704 393-1540
E: info@wordnet.org
W: http://www.wordnet.org
Editorial Profile: WGAS-AM is a non-commercial station owned by Victory Christian Center. The format of the station is black gospel music. WGAS-AM broadcasts to the Charlotte, NC area at 1420 AM.

WGAT-AM
Owner: Tri-Cities Broadcasting Corporation
Editorial: 173 West Jackson St, Ste 203, Gate City, Virginia 24251. **T:** 1 276 386-7025
Editorial Profile: WGAT-AM is a commercial station owned by Tri-Cities Broadcasting Corporation. The format of the station is gospel. WGAT-AM broadcasts to the Gate City, VA area at 1050 AM.

WGAU-AM
Owner: Cox Media Group, Inc.
Editorial: 850 Bobbin Mill Rd, Athens, Georgia 30606. **T:** 1 706 549-1340
E: wgau@southernbroadcasting.com
W: http://www.1340wgau.com
Editorial Profile: WGAU-AM is a commercial station owned by Cox Media Group, Inc. The format of the station is news and talk. WGAU-AM broadcasts to the Athens, GA area at 1340 AM.

WGAW-AM
Owner: Steven Wendell
Editorial: 362 Green St, Gardner, Massachusetts 1440. **T:** 1 978 632-1340
E: mail@wgaw1340.com
W: http://www.wgaw1340.com
Editorial Profile: WGAW-AM is a commercial station owned by Steven Wendell. The format of the station is news and talk. WGAW-AM broadcasts to the Gardener, MA area at 1340 AM.

WGBB-AM
Owner: WGBB-AM, Inc
Editorial: 404 Route 109, West Babylon, New York 11704-6214. **T:** 1 516 623-1240
E: am1240wgbb@yahoo.com
W: http://www.am1240wgbb.com/home.htm
Editorial Profile: WGBB-AM is a commercial station owned by WGBB-AM, Inc. The format of the station is variety. WGBB-AM broadcasts to the West Babylon, NY area at 1240 AM.

WGBF-AM
Owner: Townsquare Media, LLC
Editorial: 117 SE 5th St, Evansville, Indiana 47708-1605. **T:** 1 812 425-4226
W: http://www.newstalk1280.com
Editorial Profile: WGBF-AM is a commercial station owned by Townsquare Media, LLC. The format for the station is news, sports and talk. WGBF-AM broadcasts to the Evansville, IN area at 1280 AM.

WGBF-FM
Owner: Townsquare Media, LLC
Editorial: 117 SE 5th St, Evansville, Indiana 47708-1605. **T:** 1 812 425-4226
W: http://www.103gbfrocks.com
Editorial Profile: WGBF-FM is a commercial station owned by Townsquare Media, LLC. The format for the station is rock/album-oriented rock. WGBF-FM broadcasts to the Evansville, IN area at 103.1 AM.

WGBG-FM
Owner: Great Scott Broadcasting
Editorial: 20200 Dupont Blvd, Georgetown, Delaware 19947. **T:** 1 302 856-2567
E: wgbg@bigclassicrock.com
W: http://www.bigclassicrock.com
Editorial Profile: WGBG-FM is a commercial station owned by Great Scott Broadcasting. The format of the station is classic rock. WGBG-FM broadcasts to the Georgetown, DE area at 98.5 FM.

WGBH-FM
Owner: WGBH Educational Foundation
Editorial: 1 Guest St, Boston, Massachusetts 02135-2016. **T:** 1 617 300-2000
E: wgbhradio@wgbh.org
W: http://www.wgbh.org
Editorial Profile: WGBH-FM is a non-commercial station owned by WGBH Educational Foundation. The format of the station is news and jazz. WGBH-FM broadcasts to the Allston, MA area at 89.7 FM. The station does not accept PSAs.

WGBJ-FM
Owner: Three Amigos Broadcasting
Editorial: 4534 Parnell Ave, Fort Wayne, Indiana 46825-5800. **T:** 1 260 482-4444
E: info@radiounica1023.com
W: http://www.radiounica1023.com/
Editorial Profile: WGBJ-FM is a commercial station owned by Three Amigos Broadcasting. The format of the station is Regional Mexican. WGBJ-FM broadcasts to the Fort Wayne, IN area at 102.3 FM.

WGBK-FM
Owner: Glenbrook School District 225
Editorial: 4000 W Lake Ave, Glenview, Illinois 60026. **T:** 1 847 486-4487
E: musicwgbk@gmail.com
W: http://www.gbsradio.com

WGBN-AM
Owner: Pentecostal Temple Development Corp.
Editorial: 560 7th St, New Kensington, Pennsylvania 15068-6527. **T:** 1 724 337-3588
W: http://www.wgbn.net
Editorial Profile: WGBN-AM is a commercial station owned by Pentecostal Temple Development Corp. The format of the station is gospel. WGBN-AM broadcasts to the New Kensington, PA area at 1150 AM.

WGBR-AM
Owner: Curtis Media Group
Editorial: 2581 US Highway 70 W, Goldsboro, North Carolina 27530. **T:** 1 919 736-1150
W: http://www.wgbr.com
Editorial Profile: WGBR-AM is a commercial station owned by Curtis Media Group. The format of the station is news and talk. WGBR-AM broadcasts to the greater Raleigh, NC area at 1150 AM.

WGBW-AM
Owner: WTRW, Inc.
Editorial: 1414 16th St, Two Rivers, Wisconsin 54241-3031. **T:** 1 920 863-1234
Editorial Profile: WGBW-AM is a commercial station owned by WTRW, Inc. The format of the station is oldies. WGBW-AM broadcasts to the Green Bay, WI area at 1590 AM.

WGCA-FM
Owner: Great Commission Broadcasting Corp.
Editorial: 535 Maine St, Ste 10, Quincy, Illinois 62301. **T:** 1 217 224-9422
E: themix@wgca.org **W:** http://www.wgca.org
Editorial Profile: WGCA-FM is a non-commercial station owned by Great Commission Broadcasting Corp. The format of the station is contemporary Christian. WGCA-FM broadcasts to the Quincy, IL, Hannibal, MO, Keokuk, IA area at 88.5 FM.

WGCH-AM
Owner: BTR Greenwich, Inc.
Editorial: 71 Lewis St, Greenwich, Connecticut 6830. **T:** 1 203 869-1490
W: http://www.wgch.com
Editorial Profile: WGCH-AM is a commercial station owned by BTR Greenwich, Inc. The format of the station is business news and talk. WGCH-AM broadcasts to Greenwich, CT, and its surrounding areas at 1490 AM.

WGCI-FM
Owner: Clear Channel Media and Entertainment
Editorial: 233 N Michigan Ave Ste 2700, Chicago, Illinois 60601-5704.
T: 1 312 540-2000 **W:** http://www.wgci.com
Editorial Profile: WGCI-FM is a commercial station owned by Clear Channel Media and Entertainment. The format of the station is urban contemporary. WGCI-FM broadcasts to the Chicago area at 107.5 FM.

WGCL-AM
Owner: Sarkes Tarzian Inc.
Editorial: 400 One City Ctr, Bloomington, Indiana 47404. **T:** 1 812 332-3366
E: comments@wgclradio.com
W: http://www.wgclradio.com
Editorial Profile: WGCL-AM is a commercial station owned by Sarkes Tarzian Inc. The format of the station is news, sports and talk. WGCL-AM broadcasts to the Bloomington, IN area at 1370 AM.

WGCM-AM
Owner: Dowdy Broadcasting, Inc.
Editorial: 10250 Lorraine Rd, Gulfport, Mississippi 39503. **T:** 1 228 896-5500
Editorial Profile: WGCM-AM is a commercial station owned by Dowdy Broadcasting, Inc. The format of the station is country music. WGCM-AM broadcasts to the Gulfport, MS area at 1240 AM.

WGCM-FM
Owner: Dowdy Broadcasting, Inc.
Editorial: 10250 Lorraine Rd, Gulfport, Mississippi 39503. **T:** 1 228 896-5500
W: http://www.coast102.com
Editorial Profile: WGCM-FM is a commercial station owned by Dowdy Broadcasting, Inc. The format of the station is classic hits. WGCM-FM broadcasts to the Biloxi-Gulfport, MS area at 102.3 FM.

WGCO-FM
Owner: L & L Radio
Editorial: 401 Mall Blvd Ste 101D, Savannah, Georgia 31406-4863. **T:** 1 912 351-9830
W: http://983hankfm.com
Editorial Profile: WGCO-FM is a commercial station owned by L & L Radio. The format of the station is classic country. WGCO-FM broadcasts to the Savannah, GA area at 98.3 FM.

WGCR-AM
Owner: Anchor Baptist Church
Editorial: 3232 Hendersonville Hwy, Pisgah Forest, North Carolina 28768-7806.
T: 1 828 884-9427 **E:** admin@wgcr.net
W: http://wgcr.net
Editorial Profile: WGCR-AM is a non-commercial station owned by Anchor Baptist Church. The format of the station is gospel and religious programming. WGCR-AM broadcasts to the Pisgah Forest, NC area at 720 AM.

WGCS-FM
Owner: Goshen College Broadcasting
Editorial: 1700 S Main St, Goshen, Indiana 46526-4724. **T:** 1 574 535-7488
E: globe@goshen.edu
W: http://www.globeradio.org
Editorial Profile: WGCS-FM is a non-commercial college station owned by Goshen College Broadcasting. The format for the station is adult album alternative. WGCS-FM broadcasts to the South Bend, IN area at 91.1 FM.

WGCU-FM
Owner: Florida Gulf Coast University
Editorial: 10501 Fgcu Blvd S, Fort Myers, Florida 33965. **T:** 1 239 590-2300
E: wgcunews@wgcu.org
W: http://www.wgcu.org
Editorial Profile: WGCU-FM is a non-commercial station owned by Florida Gulf Coast University. The format of the station is news, talk and jazz. WGCU-FM broadcasts to the Ft. Myers, FL area at 90.1 FM.

WGCV-AM
Owner: Glory Communications Inc.
Editorial: 2440 Millwood Ave, Columbia, South Carolina 29205. **T:** 1 803 796-9533
E: traffic@wfmv.com **W:** http://www.wgcv.net
Editorial Profile: WGCV-AM is a commercial station owned by Glory Communications Inc. The format of the station is gospel and talk. WGCV-AM broadcasts to the Columbia, SC area at 620 AM.

WGCY-FM
Owner: F & G Broadcasting Inc.
Editorial: 607 S Sangamon Ave, Gibson City, Illinois 60936-1720. **T:** 1 217 784-8661
E: wgcyproduction@hotmail.com
W: http://www.wgcyradio.com
Editorial Profile: WGCY-FM is a commercial station owned by F&G Broadcasting Inc. The format of the station is easy listening. WGCY-FM broadcasts in the Gibson City, IL area at 106.3 FM.

WGDJ-AM
Owner: Capital Broadcasting
Editorial: 51 S Pearl St, Box 13, Albany, New York 12207-1500. **T:** 1 518 813-4975
E: talk@talk1300.com
W: http://www.talk1300.com
Editorial Profile: WGDJ-AM is a commercial station owned by Capital Broadcasting. The format of the station is talk. WGDJ-AM broadcasts to the Albany, NY area at 1300 AM.

WGDN-AM
Owner: Apple Broadcasting
Editorial: 3601 West Woods Rd, Gladwin, Michigan 48624. **T:** 1 989 426-1031
E: win@103country.com
W: http://www.103country.com
Editorial Profile: WGDN-AM is a commercial station owned by Apple Broadcasting. The format of the station is religious and Christian talk. WGDN-AM broadcasts to the Flint, MI area at 1350 AM.

WGDN-FM
Owner: Apple Broadcasting
Editorial: 3601 Woods Rd, Gladwin, Michigan 48624-9410. **T:** 1 989 426-1031
E: win@103country.com
W: http://www.103country.com
Editorial Profile: WGDN-FM is a commercial station owned by Apple Broadcasting. The format of the station is country. WGDN-FM broadcasts to the Flint, MI area at 103.1 FM.

WGDR-FM
Owner: Goddard College
Editorial: 123 Pitkin Rd, Plainfield, Vermont 5667. **T:** 1 802 454-7367
E: wgdr@goddard.edu **W:** http://www.wgdr.org
Editorial Profile: WGDR-FM is a non-commercial station owned by Goddard College. The format of the station is variety. WGDR-FM broadcasts to the Plainfield, VT area at a frequency of 91.5 FM.

WGEA-AM
Owner: Shelley Broadcasting CO, Inc.
Editorial: 420 S Riverside Ave, Geneva, Alabama 36340. **T:** 1 334 774-7673
W: http://www.wgea.us

WGEE-AM
Owner: Midwest Communications Inc.
Editorial: 715 E Central Entrance, Duluth, Minnesota 55811-5596. **T:** 1 218 722-4321
Editorial Profile: WGEE-AM is a commercial station owned by Midwest Communications Inc. The format of the station is sports. WGEE-AM broadcasts to the Duluth, MN area at 970 AM.

WGEL-FM
Owner: Bond Broadcasting
Editorial: 309 W Main St, Greenville, Illinois 62246. **T:** 1 618 664-3300
W: http://www.wgel.com
Editorial Profile: WGEL-FM is a commercial station owned by Bond Broadcasting. The format of the station is country music. WGEL-FM broadcasts to Greenville, IL at 101.7 FM.

WGEM-AM
Owner: Quincy Broadcasting Inc.
Editorial: 513 Hampshire St, Quincy, Illinois 62301. **T:** 1 217 228-6600
E: news@wgem.com
W: http://www.wgem.com
Editorial Profile: WGEM-AM is a commercial station owned by Quincy Broadcasting Inc. The format of the station is sports. WGEM-AM broadcasts to the Quincy, IL area at 1440 AM.

WGEM-FM
Owner: Quincy Broadcasting Inc.
Editorial: 513 Hampshire St, Quincy, Illinois 62301. **T:** 1 217 228-6600
E: news@wgem.com
W: http://www.wgem.com
Editorial Profile: WGEM-FM is a commercial station owned by Quincy Broadcasting Inc. The format of the station is news and talk. WGEM-FM broadcasts to the Quincy, IL, Hannibal, MO, Keokuk, IA area at 105.1 FM.

WGER-FM
Owner: Digity LLC
Editorial: 1795 Tittabawassee Rd, Saginaw, Michigan 48604-9431. **T:** 1 989 752-3456
W: http://www.mix1063fm.com
Editorial Profile: WGER-FM is a commercial station owned by Digity LLC. The format for the station is hot adult contemporary. WGER-FM broadcasts to the Flint, MI area at 106.3 FM.

WGES-AM
Owner: ZGS Communications
Editorial: 2005 Pan Am Cir, Ste 250, Tampa, Florida 33607-2359. **T:** 1 813 637-8000
E: info@genesis680.com
W: http://www.genesis680.com
Editorial Profile: WGES-AM is a commercial station owned by ZGS Communications. The format of the station is Hispanic contemporary Christian music. WGES-AM broadcasts to the Tampa, FL area at 680 AM.

WGET-AM
Owner: Times & News Publishing Co.
Editorial: 1560 Fairfield Rd, Gettysburg, Pennsylvania 17325-7252. **T:** 1 717 334-3101
W: http://www.wget.com
Editorial Profile: WGET-AM is a commercial station owned by Times & News Publishing Co. The format of the station is adult contemporary and sports. WGET-AM broadcasts to the Gettysburg, PA area at 1320 AM.

WGEX-FM
Owner: Clear Channel Media and Entertainment
Editorial: 809 S Westover Blvd, Albany, Georgia 31707. **T:** 1 229 436-0112
W: http://www.973hitmusicnow.com
Editorial Profile: WGEX-FM is a commercial station owned by Clear Channel Media and Entertainment. The format of the station is Top 40/CHR. WGEX-FM broadcasts to the Albany, GA area at 97.3 FM.

WGEZ-AM
Owner: Alliance Communications, Inc.
Editorial: 622 Public Ave, Beloit, Wisconsin 53511. **T:** 1 608 365-8865
E: wgezam@hotmail.com
W: http://www.1490trueoldies.com
Editorial Profile: WGEZ-AM is a commercial station owned by Alliance Communications, Inc. The format of the station is oldies music. WGEZ-AM broadcasts to the Madison, WI area at 1490 AM.

WGFA-AM
Owner: Martin(Richard & Margaret)
Editorial: 1973 E 1950 North Rd, Watseka, Illinois 60970. **T:** 1 815 432-4955
E: 941fm@wgfaradio.com
W: http://www.wgfaradio.com
Editorial Profile: WGFA-AM is a commercial station owned by Richard & Margaret Martin. The format of the station is news and talk. WGFA-AM broadcasts to the Watseka, IL area at 1360 AM.

WGFA-FM
Owner: Martin(Richard & Margaret)
Editorial: 1973 E 1950 North Rd, Watseka, Illinois 60970-6009. **T:** 1 815 432-4955
E: 941fm@wgfaradio.com
W: http://www.wgfaradio.com
Editorial Profile: WGFA-FM is a commercial station owned by Richard & Margaret Martin. The format of the station is adult contemporary. WGFA-FM broadcasts in the Watseka, IL area at 94.1 FM.

WGFB-FM
Owner: Mid-West Family Broadcasting
Editorial: 2830 Sandy Hollow Rd, Rockford, Illinois 61109-2369. **T:** 1 815 874-7861
W: http://www.b103fm.com
Editorial Profile: WGFB-FM is a commercial station owned by Mid-West Family Broadcasting. The format of the station is adult contemporary music. WGFB-FM broadcasts in the Rockford, IL area at 103.1 FM.

WGFC-AM
Owner: New Life Christian Communication
Editorial: 401 Shooting Creek Road SE, Floyd, Virginia 24091. **T:** 1 276 730-0708
E: broadcasting@nlcm.net
W: http://www.wgfcradio.com
Editorial Profile: WGFC-AM is a commercial station owned by New Life Christian Communication. The format of the station is gospel with a focus on Southern, Country, and Bluegrass sub-genres. WGFC-AM broadcasts to the Floyd, VA area at a frequency of 1030 AM.

WGFG-FM
Owner: Miller Communications Inc.
Editorial: 200 Regional Pkwy, Bldg C, Orangeburg, South Carolina 29118.
T: 1 803 536-1710 **E:** production@miller.fm
W: http://www.catcountry1053.com
Editorial Profile: WGFG-FM is a commercial station owned by Miller Communications Inc. The format of the station is contemporary country. WGFG-FM broadcasts to the Orangeburg, SC area at 105.3 FM.

WGFJ-FM
Owner: Radio Training Network, Inc.
Editorial: 2420 Wade Hampton Blvd, Greenville, South Carolina 29615-1146.
T: 1 864 292-6040
W: http://www.hisradio.com
Editorial Profile: WGFJ-FM is a commercial station owned by Radio Training Network, Inc. The format of the station is contemporary Christian. WGFJ-FM broadcasts to the Greenwood, SC area at 94.1 FM.

WGFM-FM
Owner: Northern Star Broadcasting LLC
Editorial: 1356 Mackinaw Ave, Cheboygan, Michigan 49721. **T:** 1 231 627-2341
W: http://www.realrockradio.fm
Editorial Profile: WGFM-FM is a commercial station owned by Northern Star Broadcasting LLC. The format of the station is active rock, a mix of album oriented and classic rock. WGFM-FM broadcasts to Sheboygan, MI and surrounding areas at 105.1 FM.

WGFN-FM
Owner: Northern Star Broadcasting LLC
Editorial: 1356 Mackinaw Ave, Cheboygan, Michigan 49721-1003. **T:** 1 231 627-2341
E: thebear@classicrockthebear.com
W: http://www.classicrockthebear.com
Editorial Profile: WGFN-FM is a commercial station owned by Northern Star Broadcasting LLC. The format of the station is classic rock. WGFN-FM broadcasts to the Cheboygan, MI area at 98.1 FM.

WGFP-AM
Owner: Just Because Inc.
Editorial: 27 Douglas Rd, Webster, Massachusetts 1570. **T:** 1 508 943-9400
E: info@coolcountry940.com
W: http://www.coolcountry940.com
Editorial Profile: WGFP-AM is a commercial station owned by Just Because Inc. The format of the station is classic country. WGFP-AM broadcasts to the Worcester, MA area at 940 AM.

WGFR-FM
Owner: Adirondack Community College
Editorial: Adirondack Community College, 640 Bay Road, Queensbury, New York 12804.
T: 1 518 743-2311 **W:** http://www.wgfr.org
Editorial Profile: WGFR-FM is a non-commercial college station owned by Adirondack Community College. The format of the station is college variety. WGFR-FM broadcasts to the Queensbury, NY area at 92.7 FM.

WGFS-AM
Owner: Multicultural Radio Broadcasting Inc.
Editorial: 1151 Hendrick St SW, Covington, Georgia 30014. **T:** 1 770 786-1430
W: http://www.mrbi.net
Editorial Profile: WGFS-AM is a commercial station owned by Multicultural Radio Broadcasting Inc. The format of the station is variety. WGFS-AM broadcasts in the Atlanta area at 1430 AM.

WGFT-AM
Owner: Bernard Radio
Editorial: 20 W Federal St, Ste T2, Youngstown, Ohio 44503. **T:** 1 330 744-5115
W: http://www.1330wgft.com
Editorial Profile: WGFT-AM is a commercial station owned by Bernard Radio. The format of the station is talk. WGFT-AM broadcasts to the Youngstown, OH area at 1330 AM.

WGFX-FM
Owner: Cumulus Media
Editorial: 10 Music Cir E, Nashville, Tennessee 37203-4338. **T:** 1 615 321-1067
W: http://www.1045thezone.com
Editorial Profile: WGFX-FM is a commercial station owned by Cumulus Media. The format of the station is sports. WGFX-FM broadcasts to the Nashville, TN area at 104.5 FM.

WGFY-AM
Owner: Walt Disney Co.
Editorial: 1100 S Tryon St, Ste 210, Charlotte, North Carolina 28203-4297.
T: 1 704 377-2223
W: http://www.radiodisney.com
Editorial Profile: WGFY-AM is a commercial station owned by Walt Disney Co. The format of the station is children's programming. WGFY-AM broadcasts to the Charlotte, NC area at 1480 AM.

WGGA-AM
Owner: Jacobs Media Corp.
Editorial: 1102 Thompson Bridge Rd, Gainesville, Georgia 30501. **T:** 1 770 532-9921
E: news@jacobsmedia.net
W: http://www.wovn.com
Editorial Profile: WGGA-AM is a commercial station owned by Jacobs Media Corp. The format of the station is sports. WGGA-AM broadcasts to the Gainesville, GA area at 1240 AM.

WGGC-FM
Owner: Skytower Communications Inc.
Editorial: 1727 US 31W Byp, Bowling Green, Kentucky 42101. **T:** 1 270 651-2142
W: http://www.wggc.com
Editorial Profile: WGGC-FM is a commercial station owned by Skytower Communications Inc. The format of the station is contemporary country. WGGC-FM broadcasts to the Bowling Green, KY area at 95.1 FM.

WGGE-FM
Owner: Burbach of WV, LLC
Editorial: 5 Rosemar Cir, Parkersburg, West Virginia 26104. **T:** 1 304 485-4565
E: requests@froggy99.net
W: http://www.froggy99.net
Editorial Profile: WGGE-FM is a commercial station owned by Burbach of WV, LLC. The format of the station is classic country. WGGE-FM broadcasts to the Parkersburg, WV area at 99.1 FM.

WGGG-AM
Owner: Florida Sportstalk Inc.
Editorial: 343 NE 1st Ave, Ocala, Florida 34470. **T:** 1 352 732-2010
W: http://www.espngo1.com
Editorial Profile: WGGG-AM is a commercial station owned by Florida Sportstalk Inc. The format of the station is sports. WGGG-AM broadcasts to the Ocala, FL area at 1230 AM.

WGGH-AM
Owner: Fishback Media Inc.
Editorial: 1801 E Main St, Marion, Illinois 62959. **T:** 1 618 993-8102
E: wgghproduction@yahoo.com
W: http://www.wggh.net
Editorial Profile: WGGH-AM is a commercial station owned by Fishback Media Inc. The format of the station is news and talk. WGGH-AM broadcasts to the Marion, IL area at 1150 AM.

WGGI-FM
Owner: Entercom Communications Corp.
Editorial: 305 Highway 315, Pittston, Pennsylvania 18640. **T:** 1 570 883-1111
W: http://www.froggy101.com
Editorial Profile: WGGI-FM is a commercial station owned by Entercom Communications Corp. The format of the station is contemporary county. WGGI-FM broadcasts to the Pittston, PA area at 95.9 FM.

WGGL-FM
Owner: Minnesota Public Radio
Editorial: 207 W Superior St, Ste 224, Duluth, Minnesota 55802. **T:** 1 218 722-9411
W: http://minnesota.publicradio.org/radio/stations/wggl/
Editorial Profile: WGGL-FM is a non-commercial station owned by Minnesota Public Radio. The format for the station is classical. WGGL-FM broadcasts to the Marquette, MI area at 91.1 FM.

WGGN-FM
Owner: Christian Faith Broadcast, Inc.
Editorial: 3809 Maple Ave, Castalia, Ohio 44824. **T:** 1 419 684-5311
E: fm97.7@cfbroadcast.net
W: http://www.fm977.net
Editorial Profile: WGGN-FM is a commercial station owned by Christian Faith Broadcast, Inc. The format of the station is religious and contemporary Christian. WGGN-FM broadcasts to the Castalia, OH area at 97.7 FM.

WGGO-AM
Owner: Pembrook Pines Media Group
Editorial: 231 N Union St, Olean, New York 14760-2663. **T:** 1 716 945-1590
W: http://wggosports.com
Editorial Profile: WGGO-AM is a commercial station owned by Pembrook Pines Media Group. The format of the station is Adult Standards. WGGO-AM broadcasts to the Salamanca, NY area at 1590 AM.

WGGY-FM
Owner: Entercom Communications Corp.
Editorial: 305 Highway 315, Pittston, Pennsylvania 18640. **T:** 1 570 883-1111
W: http://www.froggy101.com
Editorial Profile: WGGY-FM is a commercial station owned by Entercom Communications Corp. The format of the station is contemporary country. WGGY-FM broadcasts to the Pittston, PA area at 101.3 FM.

WGH-AM
Owner: Max Media
Editorial: 5589 Greenwich Rd, Ste 200, Virginia Beach, Virginia 23462.
T: 1 757 671-1000 **E:** theboss@star1310.com
W: http://www.star1310.com
Editorial Profile: WGH-AM is a commercial station owned by Max Media. The format of WGH-AM is gospel, talk and religious programming. WGH-AM broadcasts to the Virginia Beach, VA area at 1310 AM.

WGHB-AM
Owner: Pirate Media Group LLC
Editorial: 525 Evans St, Greenville, North Carolina 27858-2311. **T:** 1 252 317-1250

W: http://www.pirateradio1250.com
Editorial Profile: WGHB-AM is a commercial station owned by Pirate Media Group LLC. The format of the station is talk and sports. WGHB-AM broadcasts to the Greenville, NC area at 1250 AM.

WGHC-AM
Owner: Georgia-Carolina Radiocasting Companies LLC
Editorial: 18 Radio Lane, Clayton, Georgia 30525. **T:** 1 706 782-4251
E: rabunradio@windstream.net
W: http://sky104.com
Editorial Profile: WGHC-AM is a commercial station owned by Georgia-Carolina Radiocasting Companies LLC. The format of the station is adult standards and news and talk. WGHC-AM broadcasts to the Clayton, GA area at 1400 AM.

WGH-FM
Owner: Max Media
Editorial: 5589 Greenwich Rd, Ste 200, Virginia Beach, Virginia 23462.
T: 1 757 671-1000 **W:** http://www.eagle97.com
Editorial Profile: WGH-FM is a commercial station owned by Max Media. The format of the station is contemporary country music. WGH-FM broadcasts to the Virginia Beach, VA area at 97.3 FM.

WGHM-AM
Owner: Absolute Broadcasting, LLC
Editorial: 149 Main St, Ste 210, Nashua, New Hampshire 03060-2725. **T:** 1 603 880-9001
E: info@wgamradio.com
W: http://www.wgamradio.com
Editorial Profile: WGHM-AM is a commercial station owned by Absolute Broadcasting, LLC. The format of the station is sports. WGHM-AM broadcasts to the Nashua, NH at 900 AM.

WGHN-AM
Owner: WGHN Inc.
Editorial: 1 S Harbor Dr, Grand Haven, Michigan 49417. **T:** 1 616 842-8110
E: news@wghn.com
W: http://www.sportsradio1370.com
Editorial Profile: WGHN-AM is a commercial station owned by WGHN Inc. The format of the station is sports. WGHN-AM broadcasts to the Grand Rapids, MI area at 1370 AM.

WGHN-FM
Owner: WGHN Inc.
Editorial: 1 S Harbor Dr, Grand Haven, Michigan 49417. **T:** 1 616 842-8110
E: news@wghn.com **W:** http://www.wghn.com
Editorial Profile: WGHN-FM is a commercial station owned by WGHN Inc. The format of the station is adult contemporary music. WGHN-FM broadcasts to the Grand Rapids, MI area at 92.1 FM.

WGHQ-AM
Owner: Pamal Broadcasting Ltd.
Editorial: 715 Route 52, Beacon, New York 12508. **T:** 1 845 838-6000
W: http://www.hvradionet.com
Editorial Profile: WGHQ-AM is a commercial station owned by the Pamal Broadcasting Ltd. The format of the station is news and talk. WGHQ-AM broadcasts to the Poughkeepsie, NY area at 920 AM.

WGHR-FM
Owner: WGUL-FM, Inc.
Editorial: 13825 US Highway 19, Hudson, Florida 34667-1193. **T:** 1 727 697-1063
E: staff@wjqb.com
W: http://www.trueoldies1063.com
Editorial Profile: WGHR-FM is non-commercial station owned by WGUL-FM, Inc. The format of the station is oldies. WGHR-FM broadcasts to the Palm Harbor, FL area at 106.3 FM.

WGHT-AM
Owner: Mariana Broadcasting Inc.
Editorial: 1878 Lincoln Ave, Pompton Lakes, New Jersey 07442-1611. **T:** 1 973 839-1500
W: http://www.wghtradio.com
Editorial Profile: WGHT-AM is a commercial radio owned by Mariana Broadcasting Inc. The format of the station is oldies music, news and talk. WGHT-AM broadcasts in the Pompton Lakes, NJ, area at 1500 AM.

WGIB-FM
Owner: Glen Iris Baptist School
Editorial: 1137 10th Pl S, Birmingham, Alabama 35205-4682. **T:** 1 205 323-1516
W: http://www.gleniris.net/GIBC/index.php?option=com_content&task=view&id=21&Itemid
Editorial Profile: WGIB-FM is a non-commercial station owned by Glen Iris Baptist School. The format of the station is religious programming. WGIB-FM broadcasts to the Birmingham, AL area at 91.9 FM.

WGIE-FM
Owner: Burbach of WV, LLC
Editorial: 1489 Locust Ave, Fairmont, West Virginia 26554. **T:** 1 304 363-8888
W: http://www.froggycountry.net
Editorial Profile: WGIE-FM is a commercial station owned by Burbach of WV, LLC. The format of the station is contemporary country. WGIE-FM broadcasts to the Fairmont, WV area at a frequency of 92.7 FM.

WGIG-AM
Owner: Clear Channel Media and Entertainment
Editorial: 3833 US Highway 82, Brunswick, Georgia 31523-7735. **T:** 1 912 267-1025
E: scottryfun@gmail.com
W: http://1440wgig.net
Editorial Profile: WGIG-AM is a commercial station owned by Clear Channel Media and Entertainment. The format of the station is news, talk and sports. WGIG-AM broadcasts to the Brunswick, GA region at 1440 AM.

WGIL-AM
Owner: Galesburg Broadcasting Co.
Editorial: 154 E Simmons St, Galesburg, Illinois 61401. **T:** 1 309 342-5131
E: news@wgil.com **W:** http://www.wgil.com
Editorial Profile: WGIL-AM is a commercial station owned by Galesburg Broadcasting Co. The format of the station is news, talk and sports. WGIL-AM broadcasts to the Galesburg, IL area at 1400 AM.

WGIN-AM
Owner: Saga Communications
Editorial: 420 Western Ave, South Portland, Maine 04106-1704. **T:** 1 207 774-4561
W: http://www.560wgan.com
Editorial Profile: WGIN-AM is a commercial station owned by Saga Communications. The format of the station is news and talk. WGIN-AM broadcasts to South Portland, ME area at 1400 AM.

WGIR-AM
Owner: Clear Channel Media and Entertainment
Editorial: 195 McGregor St Ste 810, Manchester, New Hampshire 03102-3755.
T: 1 603 625-6915
W: http://www.nhnewsnetwork610.com/main.html
Editorial Profile: WGIR-AM is a commercial station owned by Clear Channel Media and Entertainment. The format of the station is news and talk. WGIR-AM broadcasts to the Manchester, NH area at 610 AM.

WGIR-FM
Owner: Clear Channel Media and Entertainment
Editorial: 195 McGregor St, Ste 810, Manchester, New Hampshire 3102.
T: 1 603 625-6915
W: http://www.rock101fm.com
Editorial Profile: WGIR-FM is a commercial station owned by Clear Channel Media and Entertainment. The format of the station is rock music. WGIR-FM broadcasts to the Manchester, NH area at 101.1 FM.

WGIV-AM
Owner: Neely(Frank)
Editorial: 9349 China Grove Church Rd, Pineville, North Carolina 28134.
T: 1 980 297-7256 **W:** http://www.wgiv.net
Editorial Profile: WGIV-AM is a commercial station owned by Frank Neely. The format of the station is gospel and inspirational talk. WGIV-AM broadcasts to the Gastonia, NC area at 1370 AM.

WGJK-AM
Owner: Woman's World Broadcasting, Inc.
Editorial: 20 John Davenport Dr Nw, Rome, Georgia 30165-2536. **T:** 1 706 291-9496
E: contactus@magic1360.com
W: http://www.magic1360.com
Editorial Profile: WGJK-AM is a commercial station owned by Woman's World Broadcasting, LLC. The format of the station is urban contemporary. WGJK-AM broadcasts to the Rome, GA area at 1360 AM.

WGJU-FM
Owner: Baraga Broadcasting, Inc.
Editorial: 7119 M 68, Indian River, Michigan 49749-9472. **T:** 1 231 238-0811
W: http://www.baragabroadcasting.com
Editorial Profile: WGJU-FM is a non-commercial station owned by Baraga Broadcasting, Inc.. The format of the station is Catholic programming. WGJU-FM broadcasts to the East Tawas and Oscoda areas in Michigan at 91.3 FM.

WGKA-AM
Owner: Salem Communications
Editorial: 2970 Peachtree Rd NW, Ste 700, Atlanta, Georgia 30305. **T:** 1 404 995-7300
W: http://www.920wgka.com
Editorial Profile: WGKA-AM is a commercial station owned by Salem Communications. The format of the station is news and talk. WGKA-AM broadcasts to the Atlanta area at 920 AM.

WGKC-FM
Owner: S.J. Broadcasting Inc.
Editorial: 2702 Boulder Rd, Urbana, Illinois 61802-6996. **T:** 1 217 367-1195
W: http://www.wgkc.net
Editorial Profile: WGKC-FM is a commercial station owned by S.J. Broadcasting Inc. The format of the station is contemporary country. WGKC-FM broadcasts to the Champaign, IL, area at 105.9 FM.

WGKL-FM
Owner: Radio Results Network
Editorial: 524 Ludington St, Ste 300, Escanaba, Michigan 49829. **T:** 1 906 789-9700
E: rrnnews@radioresultsnetwork.com
W: http://www.radioresultsnetwork.com/wgkl/

WGKS-FM
Owner: L.M. Communications Inc.
Editorial: 401 W Main St, Lexington, Kentucky 40507-1640. **T:** 1 859 233-1515
W: http://www.wgks.com
Editorial Profile: WGKS-FM is a commercial station owned by L.M. Communications Inc. The format of the station is adult contemporary. WGKS-FM broadcasts locally to the Lexington, KY area at a frequency of 96.9 FM.

WGKV-FM
Owner: Educational Media Foundation
Editorial: 5090 Us Route 11, Pulaski, New York 13142-2505. **T:** 1 336 227-5076
W: http://www.klove.com
Editorial Profile: WGKV-FM is a non-commercial station owned by Educational Media Foundation. The format of the station is Contemporary Christian. WGKV-FM broadcasts to the Pulaski, NY area at a frequency of 101.7 FM.

WGKX-FM
Owner: Cumulus Media Inc.
Editorial: 5629 Murray Rd, Memphis, Tennessee 38119. **T:** 1 901 682-1106
W: http://www.kix106.com
Editorial Profile: WGKX-FM is a commercial station owned by Cumulus Media Inc. The station's format is contemporary country music. WGKX-FM broadcasts to the Memphis, TN area at 105.9 FM.

WGKY-FM
Owner: Withers Broadcasting of Paducah, LLC
Editorial: 1700 N 8th St, Paducah, Kentucky 42001-1752. **T:** 1 270 335-3696
W: http://www.959wgky.com
Editorial Profile: WGKY-FM is a commercial station owned by Withers Broadcasting of Paducah, LLC. The format of the station is oldies music. WGKY-FM broadcasts to the Paducah, KY, Cape Girardeau, MO, and Harrisburg, IL communities at 95.9 FM.

WGL-AM
Owner: Adams Radio Group
Editorial: 9604 Coldwater Rd Ste 201, Fort Wayne, Indiana 46825-2096.
T: 1 260 747-1511
Editorial Profile: WGL-AM is a commercial station owned by Adams Radio Group. The format of the station is sports. WGL-AM broadcasts to the Fort Wayne, IN area at 1250 AM.

WGLB-AM
Owner: WGLB LLC
Editorial: 5181 N 35th St, Milwaukee, Wisconsin 53209-5399. **T:** 1 414 527-4365
E: wglb@wglbam1560.com
W: http://www.wglbam1560.com
Editorial Profile: WGLB-AM is a commercial station owned by WGLB LLC. The format of the station is gospel music. WGLB-AM broadcasts to the Milwaukee area at 1560 AM.

WGLC-FM
Owner: Mendota Broadcasting
Editorial: 3905 Progress Blvd, Peru, Illinois 61354. **T:** 1 815 224-2100
E: wglc@theradiogroup.net
W: http://www.wglc.net
Editorial Profile: WGLC-FM is a commercial station owned by Mendota Broadcasting. The format of the station is country. WGLC-FM broadcasts to the Peru, IL area at 100.1 FM.

WGLD-AM
Owner: Cumulus Media Inc.
Editorial: 5989 Susquehanna Plaza Drive, York, Pennsylvania 17406. **T:** 1 717 764-1155
W: http://www.sportsradio1440.com
Editorial Profile: WGLD-AM is a commercial station owned by Cumulus Media Inc. The format of the station is sports. WGLD-AM broadcasts to the York, PA area at 1440 AM.

WGLF-FM
Owner: Cumulus Media Inc.
Editorial: 3411 W Tharpe St, Tallahassee, Florida 32303. **T:** 1 850 201-3000
W: http://www.gulf104.com
Editorial Profile: WGLF-FM is a commercial station owned by Cumulus Media Inc. The format of the station is classic hits. WGLF-FM broadcasts to the Tallahassee, FL area at 104.1 FM.

WGLI-FM
Owner: Keweenaw Bay Indian Community
Editorial: 805 US41 South, Ste B, Baraga, Michigan 49908. **T:** 1 906 353-9287
E: eagleadmin@up.net
W: http://www.keepitintheup.com
Editorial Profile: WGLI-FM is a commercial station owned by the Keweenaw Bay Indian Community. The format of the station is rock music. WGLI-FM broadcasts to the Hancock, MI area at a frequency of 98.7 FM.

WGLM-AM
Owner: Packer Radio Greenville, Inc.
Editorial: 9181 SW Greenville Rd, Greenville, Michigan 48838-9404. **T:** 1 616 754-1063
E: office@m1063.com
W: http://www.m1063.com
Editorial Profile: WGLM-AM is a commercial station owned by Packer Radio Greenville, Inc. The format of the station is classic country music. WGLM-AM broadcasts to the Greenville, MI area at 1380 AM.

WGLM-FM
Owner: Packer Radio Greenville, Inc.
Editorial: 9181 S Greenville Rd, Greenville, Michigan 48838-9404. **T:** 1 616 754-1063
E: office@m1063.com
W: http://www.m1063.com

WGLO-FM
Owner: Cumulus Media Inc.
Editorial: 120 Eaton St, Peoria, Illinois 61603-4217. **T:** 1 309 676-5000
W: http://www.955glo.com
Editorial Profile: WGLO-FM is a commercial station owned by Cumulus Media Inc. The format of the station is classic rock. WGLO-FM broadcasts to the Peoria, IL area at 95.5 FM.

WGLQ-FM
Owner: Radio Results Network
Editorial: 524 Ludington St, Ste 300, Escanaba, Michigan 49829. **T:** 1 906 789-9700
W: http://www.wglqradio.com/

WGLR-AM
Owner: Queen B Radio of Wisconsin
Editorial: 51 Means Dr, Platteville, Wisconsin 53818. **T:** 1 608 349-2000
E: wglrnews@wglr.com
W: http://www.wglr.com
Editorial Profile: WGLR-AM is a commercial station owned by Queen B Radio of Wisconsin. The format for the station is sports. WGLR-AM broadcasts to the Platteville, WI area at 1280 AM.

WGLR-FM
Owner: Queen B Radio of Wisconsin and WISC-TV3
Editorial: 51 Means Dr, Platteville, Wisconsin 53818. **T:** 1 608 349-2000
E: wglrnews@wglr.com
W: http://www.wglr.com
Editorial Profile: WGLR-FM is a commercial station owned by Queen B Radio of Wisconsin. The format for the station is country. WGLR-FM broadcasts to the Madison, WI area at 97.7 FM.

WGLS-FM
Owner: Rowan University

Editorial: 201 Mullica Hill Rd, WGLS-FM, Glassboro, New Jersey 8028.
T: 1 856 863-9457 **E:** wgls@rowan.edu
W: http://wgls.rowan.edu
Editorial Profile: WGLS-FM is a non-commercial station owned by Rowan University. The format of the station is college variety. WGLS-FM broadcasts to the Glassboro, NJ area at 89.7 FM.

WGLT-FM
Owner: Illinois State University
Editorial: 8910 Illinois State Univ, Normal, Illinois 61790. **T:** 1 309 438-2255
E: wglt@ilstu.edu **W:** http://www.wglt.org
Editorial Profile: WGLT-FM is a non-commercial station owned by Illinois State University. The format of the station is news, jazz and blues music. WGLT-FM broadcasts to the Normal, IL area at 89.1 FM.

WGLX-FM
Owner: NRG Media LLC
Editorial: 2301 Plover Rd, Plover, Wisconsin 54467. **T:** 1 866 967-9983
W: http://www.wglx.com
Editorial Profile: WGLX-FM is a commercial station owned by NRG Media LLC. The format of the station is rock music. WGLX-FM broadcasts to the Wausau, WI, area at 103.3 FM.

WGLY-FM
Owner: Christian Ministries Inc.
Editorial: 140 Main St, Essex Junction, Vermont 5452. **T:** 1 866 878-8885
E: mailroom@thelightradio.net
W: http://www.thelightradio.net
Editorial Profile: WGLY-FM is a non-commercial station owned by Christian Ministries Inc. The format of the station is contemporary Christian music and religious programming. WGLY-FM broadcasts to the Essex Junction, VT area at 91.5 FM.

WGMC-FM
Owner: Greece Central School District
Editorial: 1139 Maiden Ln, Rochester, New York 14615-1127. **T:** 1 585 966-2660
E: jazzinfo@jazz901.org
W: http://www.jazz901.org
Editorial Profile: WGMC-FM is a non-commercial station owned by Greece Central School District. The format of the station is jazz music. WGMC-FM broadcasts to the Rochester, NY area at 90.1 FM. The station is music intensive and does not produce local news.

WGMD-FM
Owner: Resort Broadcasting
Editorial: 31549 Dutton Ln, Lewes, Delaware 19958. **T:** 1 302 945-2050
E: news@wgmd.com
W: http://www.wgmd.com
Editorial Profile: WGMD-FM is a commercial station owned by Resort Broadcasting. The format of the station is news and talk programming. WGMD-AM broadcasts to the Lewes, DE area at 92.7 FM.

WGMF-AM
Owner: GEOS Communications
Editorial: 54 Wilmar Dr, Tunkhannock, Pennsylvania 18657-6628. **T:** 1 570 836-4200
Editorial Profile: WGMF-AM is a commercial station owned by GEOS Communications. The format for the station is oldies. WGMF-AM broadcasts to the Tunkhannock, PA area at 1460 AM.

WGMG-FM
Owner: Cox Media Group, Inc.
Editorial: 1010 Tower Pl, Bogart, Georgia 30622. **T:** 1 706 549-6222
W: http://www.magic1021fm.com
Editorial Profile: WGMG-FM is a commercial station owned by Cox Media Group, Inc. The format of the station is hot adult contemporary music. WGMG-FM broadcasts to the Crawford, GA area at 102.1 FM.

WGMI-AM
Owner: Garner Ministries Inc.
Editorial: 613 Tallapoosa St W, Bremen, Georgia 30110-1838. **T:** 1 770 537-0840
E: wgmi1440@yahoo.com
W: http://www.1440thetrain.com
Editorial Profile: WGMI-AM is a commercial station owned by Garner Ministries Inc. The format of the station is classic hits. WGMI-AM broadcasts to the Bremen, GA area at 1440 AM.

WGMK-FM
Owner: Flint Media
Editorial: 521 S Scott St, Bainbridge, Georgia 39819-4101. **T:** 1 229 246-1960
W: http://sowegalive.com
Editorial Profile: WGMK-FM is a commercial station owned by Flint Media. The format of the station is oldies music with a classic rock focus. WGMK-FM broadcasts to the Bainbridge, GA area at 106.3 FM.

WGML-AM
Owner: Powerhouse Deliverance Church Inc.
Editorial: 308 Rolland St, Hinesville, Georgia 31313-3104. **T:** 1 912 368-3399
Editorial Profile: WGML-AM is a non-commercial station owned by Powerhouse Deliverance Church Inc. The format of the station is gospel. WGML-AM broadcasts to the Savannah, GA area at 990 AM.

WGMM-FM
Owner: WS2K Media
Editorial: 21 E Market St Ste 101, Corning, New York 14830-2650. **T:** 1 607 937-8181
E: audioonly@stny.rr.com
W: http://www.987gemfm.com
Editorial Profile: WGMM-FM is a commercial station owned by WS2K Media. The format of the station is oldies music. WGMM-FM broadcasts to the Corning, NY area on 98.7 FM.

WGMN-AM
Owner: 3 Daughters Media, Inc.
Editorial: 1035 Avalon Dr, Forest, Virginia 24551. **T:** 1 434 534-6100 **E:** wblt@inbox.com
W: http://www.espninva.com
Editorial Profile: WGMN-AM is a commercial station owned by 3 Daughters Media, Inc. The format of the station is sports. WGMN-AM broadcasts to the Roanoke, VA area at 1240 AM.

WGMO-FM
Owner: Zoe Communications Inc.
Editorial: 345 Highway 63 S, Shell Lake, Wisconsin 54871. **T:** 1 715 468-9500
E: spots@95gmo.com
W: http://www.95gmo.com
Editorial Profile: WGMO-FM is a commercial station owned by Zoe Communications Inc. The format of the station is classic rock. WGMO-FM broadcasts in the Shell Lake, WI area at 95.3 FM.

WGMP-AM
Owner: Bluewater Broadcasting Co. LLC
Editorial: 4101 Wall St Ste A, Montgomery, Alabama 36106-3724. **T:** 1 334 244-0961
W: http://www.1049thegump.com
Editorial Profile: WGMP-AM is a commercial station owned by Bluewater Broadcasting Co. LLC. The format of the station is rock alternative. WGMP-AM broadcasts in the Montgomery, AL area at 1170 AM.

WGMT-FM
Owner: Vermont Broadcast Associates Inc.
Editorial: 10 Church St, Lyndonville, Vermont 5851. **T:** 1 802 626-9800
E: magic977@gmail.com
W: http://www.magic977.com
Editorial Profile: WGMT-FM is a commercial station owned by Vermont Broadcast Associates Inc. The format of the station is hot adult contemporary music. WGMT-FM broadcasts to the Lyndonville, VT area at 97.7 FM.

WGMX-FM
Owner: The Great Marathon Radio Company
Editorial: #1 Boot Key, Marathon, Florida 33050. **T:** 1 305 743-5563
W: http://www.trueoldieschannel.com
Editorial Profile: WGMX-FM is a commercial station owned by The Great Marathon Radio Company. The format of the station is oldies. WGMX-FM broadcasts to the Marathon, FL area at 94.3 FM.

WGMY-FM
Owner: Clear Channel Media and Entertainment
Editorial: 325 John Knox Rd Bldg G, Tallahassee, Florida 32303-4113.
T: 1 850 422-3107
W: http://www.1071hitmusicnow.com/main.html
Editorial Profile: WGMY-FM is a commercial station owned by Clear Channel Media and Entertainment. The format is contemporary hit radio. The station airs in the Tallahassee, FL area at 107.1.

WGMZ-FM
Owner: Clear Channel Media and Entertainment
Editorial: 304 S 4th St, Gadsden, Alabama 35901. **T:** 1 256 549-0931
E: z931@clearchannel.com
W: http://www.wgmz.com
Editorial Profile: WGMZ-FM is a commercial station owned by Clear Channel Media and Entertainment. The format of the station is classic hits. WGMZ-FM broadcasts to the Birmingham, Al area at 93.1 FM.

WGNA-FM
Owner: Townsquare Media, LLC
Editorial: 1241 Kings Rd, Schenectady, New York 12303-2811. **T:** 1 518 8476-1039
W: http://www.wgna.com
Editorial Profile: WGNA-FM is a commercial station owned by Townsquare Media, LLC. The format of the station is contemporary country. WGNA-FM broadcasts in the Albany, NY area at 107.7 FM.

WGN-AM
Owner: Tribune Broadcasting Co.
Editorial: 435 N Michigan Ave, Chicago, Illinois 60611-4066. **T:** 1 312 222-4700
E: news@wgnradio.com
W: http://www.wgnradio.com
Editorial Profile: WGN-AM is a commercial station owned by Tribune Broadcasting Co. The format of the station is news and talk. WGN-AM broadcasts to the Chicago area at 720 AM.

WGNB-FM
Owner: Moody Bible Institute
Editorial: 3764 84th Ave, Zeeland, Michigan 49464-9706. **T:** 1 616 772-7300
E: wgnb@moody.edu
W: http://www.moodyradiowestmichigan.fm
Editorial Profile: WGNB-FM is a non-commercial station owned by Moody Bible Institute. The format of the station is religious programming and Christian music. WGNB-FM broadcasts to the Zeeland, MI area at 89.3 FM.

WGNC-AM
Owner: Neisler (Scott)
Editorial: 1366 Startown Rd, Lincolnton, North Carolina 28092-8038. **T:** 1 704 868-8222
E: 1450am@gmail.com
W: http://www.wgnc.net
Editorial Profile: WGNC-AM is a commercial station owned by Scott Neisler. The format of the station is news, talk and sports. WGNC-AM broadcasts to the Shelby, NC area at 1450 AM.

WGNE-FM
Owner: Renda Broadcasting
Editorial: 6440 Atlantic Blvd, Jacksonville, Florida 32211. **T:** 1 904 727-9696
W: http://www.999gatorcountry.com
Editorial Profile: WGNE-FM is a commercial station owned by Renda Broadcasting. The format of the station is contemporary country. WGNE-FM broadcasts to the Jacksonville, FL area at 99.9 FM.

WGNG-FM
Owner: Team Broadcasting
Editorial: 503 Ione St, Greenwood, Mississippi 38930-3725. **T:** 1 662 453-1646
E: wgnl@bellsouth.net
W: http://www.gogreenwoodbiz.com/Ads/WGNL-WGNG.htm
Editorial Profile: WGNG-FM is a commercial station owned by Team Broadcasting. The format of the station is urban contemporary. WGNG-FM broadcasts to the Greenwood, MS area at 106.3 FM.

WGNI-FM
Owner: Cumulus Media Inc.
Editorial: 3233 Burnt Mill Dr, Ste 4, Wilmington, North Carolina 28403.
T: 1 910 763-9977 **E:** gmail@wgni.com
W: http://www.wgni.com
Editorial Profile: WGNI-FM is a commercial station owned by Cumulus Media Inc. The format of the station is adult contemporary. WGNI-FM broadcasts to the Wilmington, NC area at 102.7 FM.

WGNJ-FM
Owner: Great News Radio Inc.
Editorial: 2421 N 1450 East Rd, White Heath, Illinois 61884. **T:** 1 217 897-6333
E: staff@greatnewsradio.org
W: http://www.greatnewsradio.org
Editorial Profile: WGNJ-FM is a commercial station owned by Great News Radio Inc. The format of the station is religious programming. WGNJ-FM broadcasts to the White Heath, IL area at 89.3 FM.

WGNK-FM
Owner: Genesis Broadcasting Network Corp.
Editorial: 19620 Pines Blvd Ste 114, Pembroke Pines, Florida 33029-1303.
T: 1 954 885-7200 **E:** info@lanuevafm.net
W: http://lanuevafm.net
Editorial Profile: WGNK-FM is a non-commercial station owned by Genesis Broadcasting Network Corp. The format of the station is Spanish Contemporary Christian music programming. WGNK-FM broadcasts to the Miami, FL area at 88.3 FM.

WGNL-FM
Owner: Team Broadcasting
Editorial: 503 Ione St, Greenwood, Mississippi 38930. **T:** 1 662 453-1646
E: wgnl@bellsouth.net
W: http://www.gogreenwoodbiz.com/Ads/WGNL-WGNG.htm
Editorial Profile: WGNL-FM is a commercial station owned by Team Broadcasting. The format of the station is urban adult contemporary music. WGNL-FM broadcasts to the Greenwood, MS area at 104.3 FM.

WGNQ-AM
Owner: MG Media, Inc.
Editorial: 414 Giles Ave, Bridgeport, Alabama 35740. **T:** 1 877 237-6259
E: manager@wgnq.net
W: http://www.wgnq.net
Editorial Profile: WGNQ-AM is a commercial station owned by MG Media, Inc. The format for the station is religious talk and news. WGNQ-AM broadcasts to the Bridgeport, AL area at 1480 AM.

WGNR-AM
Owner: Moody Bible Institute
Editorial: 1920 W 53rd St, Anderson, Indiana 46013-1110. **T:** 1 765 642-2750
E: wgnr@moody.edu
W: http://www.moodyradioindiana.fm
Editorial Profile: WGNR-AM is a non-commercial station owned by Moody Bible Institute. The format of the station is religious. WGNR-AM broadcasts to the Indianapolis, IN area at 1470 AM.

WGNR-FM
Owner: Moody Bible Institute
Editorial: 1920 W 53rd St, Anderson, Indiana 46013-1110. **T:** 1 765 642-2750
E: wgnrnews@moody.edu
W: http://www.moodyradioindiana.fm
Editorial Profile: WGNR-FM is a commercial radio station owned by Moody Bible Institute. The format of the station is religious. WGNR-FM broadcasts to the Indianapolis area at 97.9 FM.

WGNS-AM
Owner: Rutherford Group Inc.
Editorial: 306 S Church St, Murfreesboro, Tennessee 37130-3732. **T:** 1 615 893-5373
W: http://www.wgnsradio.com
Editorial Profile: WGNS-AM is a commercial station owned by Rutherford Group Inc. The format of the station is news, sports and talk. WGNS-AM broadcasts in the Murfreesboro, TN area at 1450 AM.

WGNU-AM
Owner: Radio Property Ventures, LLC
Editorial: 5615 Pershing Ave Ste 12, Saint Louis, Missouri 63112-1757.
T: 1 314 454-0400 **W:** http://wgnu920am.com/
Editorial Profile: WGNU-AM is a commercial station owned by Radio Property Ventures, LLC. The format of the station is sports and talk. WGNU-AM broadcasts to the St. Louis area at 920 AM.

WGNV-FM
Owner: Evangel Ministries, Inc.
Editorial: 10945 Country Highway N, Milladore, Wisconsin 54454.
T: 1 715 457-2988
E: wgnv@thefamilyradio.net
W: http://www.thefamily.net
Editorial Profile: WGNV-FM is a non-commercial station owned by Evangel Ministries, Inc. The format of the station is adult contemporary. WGNV-FM broadcasts to the Milladore, WI area at 88.5 FM.

WGNY-AM
Owner: Sunrise Broadcasting
Editorial: 661 Little Britain Rd, New Windsor, New York 12553-6150. **T:** 1 845 561-2131
W: http://www.foxradio.net
Editorial Profile: WGNY-AM is a commercial station owned by Sunrise Broadcasting. The format of the station is oldies. WGNY-AM broadcasts to the New Windsor, NY area at 1220 AM.

WGNZ-AM
Owner: L & D Broadcasting Inc.
Editorial: 8010 N Main St, Dayton, Ohio 45415. **T:** 1 937 454-9000
W: http://www.wgnz.com
Editorial Profile: WGNZ-AM is a commercial station owned by L & D Broadcasting Inc. The format of the station is religious programming and gospel music. WGNZ-AM broadcasts to the Dayton, OH area at 1110 AM.

WGOC-AM
Owner: Cumulus Media Inc.
Editorial: 162 Free Hill Rd, Gray, Tennessee 37615. **T:** 1 423 477-1000
W: http://www.wgoc.com
Editorial Profile: WGOC-AM is a commercial station owned by Cumulus Media Inc. The format of the station is business talk. WGOC-AM broadcasts to the Gray, TN area at 1320 AM.

WGOG-FM
Owner: Georgia-Carolina Radiocasting Companies LLC
Editorial: 2058 Westminster Hwy, Walhalla, South Carolina 29691. **T:** 1 864 638-3616
W: http://www.wgog.com
Editorial Profile: WGOG-FM is a commercial station owned by Georgia-Carolina Radiocasting Companies LLC. The format of the station is classic country. WGOG-FM broadcasts to the Walhalla, SC area at 96.3 FM.

WGOH-AM
Owner: Carter County Broadcasting Co.
Editorial: 150 Radio Tower Rd, Grayson, Kentucky 41143. **T:** 1 606 474-5144
E: mail@wgohwugo.com
W: http://www.wgohwugo.com
Editorial Profile: WGOH-AM is a commercial station owned by Carter County Broadcasting Co. The format of the station is country music. WGOH-AM broadcasts to the Grayson, KY area at 1370 AM.

WGOJ-FM
Owner: Bible Broadcasting, Inc.
Editorial: 253 Mill St, Conneaut, Ohio 44030. **T:** 1 440 593-1055 **E:** wgoj@suite224.net
W: http://www.wgojradio.com
Editorial Profile: WGOJ-FM is a non-commercial station owned by Bible Broadcasting, Inc. The format of the station is religious. WGOJ-FM broadcasts to the Conneaut, OH area at 105.5 FM.

WGOK-AM
Owner: Cumulus Media Inc.
Editorial: 2800 Dauphin St, Ste 104, Mobile, Alabama 36606. **T:** 1 251 652-2000
W: http://www.wgokgospel900am.com

WGOL-AM
Owner: Pilati Investments Corporation
Editorial: 113 Washington Ave NW, Russellville, Alabama 35653-2652.
T: 1 256 332-0214 **E:** wgolam@yahoo.com
W: http://www.wgolam.com
Editorial Profile: WGOL-AM is a commercial station owned by Pilati Investments Corporation. The format of the station is country. WGOL-AM broadcasts to the Russellville, AL area at a frequency of 920 AM.

WGOP-AM
Owner: Bay Broadcasting
Editorial: 1637 Dun Swamp Rd, Pocomoke City, Maryland 21851. **T:** 1 410 957-6081
Editorial Profile: WGOP-AM is a commercial station owned by Bay Broadcasting. The format of the station is oldies music. WGOP-AM broadcasts to the Pocomoke City, MD area at 540 AM.

WGOS-AM
Owner: Iglesia Nueva Vida of High Point, Inc.
Editorial: 6223 Old Mendenhall Rd, High Point, North Carolina 27261.
T: 1 336 434-5024
W: http://www.cadenaradialnuevavida.com
Editorial Profile: WGOS-AM is a non-commercial station owned by Iglesia Nueva Vida of High Point, Inc. The format of the station is Christian talk, and Hispanic programming. WGOS-AM broadcasts to the Greensboro-Winston Salem, NC area at 1070 AM.

WGOV-FM
Owner: W.G.O.V., Inc.
Editorial: 2973 US Highway 84 W, Valdosta, Georgia 31601-0305. **T:** 1 229 242-4513
Editorial Profile: WGOV-FM is a commercial station owned by W.G.O.V., Inc. (dba Magic 95 Entertainment). The format of the station is urban contemporary music. WGOV-FM broadcasts to Valdosta, GA at 96.7 FM.

WGOW-AM
Owner: Cumulus Media Inc.
Editorial: 821 Pineville Rd, Chattanooga, Tennessee 37405-2633. **T:** 1 423 756-6141
E: wgow@wgow.com **W:** http://wgowam.com
Editorial Profile: WGOW-AM is a commercial station owned by Cumulus Media Inc. The format of the station is news and talk. WGOW-AM broadcasts to the Chattanooga, TN area at 1150 AM.

WGOW-FM
Owner: Cumulus Media Inc.
Editorial: 821 Pineville Rd, Chattanooga, Tennessee 37405. **T:** 1 423 756-6141
E: wgow@wgow.com
W: http://www.wgow.com/home.asp
Editorial Profile: WGOW-FM is a commercial station owned by Cumulus Media Inc. The format for the station is talk. WGOW-FM broadcasts to the Chattanooga, TN area at 102.3 FM.

WGPA-AM
Owner: Timmer Broadcasting Company
Editorial: 528 N New St, Bethlehem, Pennsylvania 18018-5752. **T:** 1 610 866-8074
E: wgpasunny1100@yahoo.com
W: http://wgpasunny1100.com
Editorial Profile: WGPA-AM is a commercial station owned by Timmer Broadcasting Company. The format of the station is variety. WGPA-AM broadcasts to the Bethlehem, PA area at 1100 AM.

WGPB-FM
Owner: Georgia Public Broadcasting
Editorial: 260 14th St NW, Atlanta, Georgia 30318. **T:** 1 404 685-2548 **E:** ask@gpb.org
W: http://www.gpb.org
Editorial Profile: WGPB-FM is a non-commercial station owned by Georgia Public Broadcasting. The format of the station is news and classical music. WGPB-FM broadcasts to the Rome, GA area at 97.7 FM.

WGPC-AM
Owner: Cumulus Media Inc.
Editorial: 1104 W Broad Ave, Albany, Georgia 31707. **T:** 1 229 888-5000
Editorial Profile: WGPC-AM is a commercial station owned by Cumulus Media Inc. The format of the station is sports. WGPC-AM broacasts to the Albany, GA area at 1450 AM.

WGPL-AM
Owner: Willis Broadcasting Co.
Editorial: 645 Church St Ste 400, Norfolk, Virginia 23510-1712. **T:** 1 757 622-4600
E: willisbroadcasting@yahoo.com
Editorial Profile: WGPL-AM is a commercial station owned by Willis Broadcasting Co. The format of the station is urban oldies. WGPL-AM broadcasts to the Norfolk, VA area at 1350 AM.

WGPO-FM
Owner: Cook County Community Radio
Editorial: 1712 W Highway 61, Grand Marais, Minnesota 55604-7507. **T:** 1 218 387-1070
E: wtip@boreal.org **W:** http://www.wtip.org
Editorial Profile: WGPO-FM is a non-commercial station owned by Cook County Community Radio. The format of the station is variety. WGPO-FM broadcasts to the Grand Portage, MN area at 90.1 FM.

WGPR-FM
Owner: WGPR Inc.
Editorial: 3146 E Jefferson Ave, Detroit, Michigan 48207-5034. **T:** 1 313 259-2000
W: http://hothiphopdetroit.com
Editorial Profile: WGPR-FM is a commercial station owned by WGPR Inc. The format of the station is urban contemporary. WGPR-FM broadcasts to the Detroit area at 107.5 FM.

WGQR-FM
Owner: Christian Listening Network Inc.
Editorial: 996 Helen St, Fayetteville, North Carolina 28303. **T:** 1 910 864-5028
W: http://www.wgqr1057.com

WGR-AM
Owner: Entercom Communications Corp.
Editorial: 500 Corporate Pkwy, Ste 200, Buffalo, New York 14226. **T:** 1 716 843-0600
W: http://www.wgr550.com
Editorial Profile: WGR-AM is a commercial station owned by Entercom Communications Corp. The format of the station is sports. WGR-AM broadcasts to the Buffalo, NY area at 550 AM.

WGRB-AM
Owner: Clear Channel Media and Entertainment
Editorial: 233 N Michigan Ave, Chicago, Illinois 60601-5519. **T:** 1 312 540-2000
W: http://www.inspiration1390.com
Editorial Profile: WGRB-AM is a commercial station owned by Clear Channel Media and Entertainment. The format of the station is gospel. WGRB-AM broadcasts to the Chicago area at 1390 AM.

WGRC-FM
Owner: Salt & Light Media Ministries
Editorial: 101 Armory Blvd, Lewisburg, Pennsylvania 17837-9504. **T:** 1 570 523-1190
E: email@wgrc.com **W:** http://www.wgrc.com
Editorial Profile: WGRC-FM is a non-commercial station owned by Salt & Light Media Ministries. The format of the station is contemporary Christian music and news. WGRC-FM broadcasts to the Lewisburg, PA area at 91.3 FM.

WGRD-FM
Owner: Townsquare Media, LLC
Editorial: 50 Monroe Ave NW, Ste 500, Grand Rapids, Michigan 49503. **T:** 1 616 451-4800
W: http://www.wgrd.com
Editorial Profile: WGRD-FM is a commercial station owned by Townsquare Media, LLC. The format of the station is rock alternative. WGRD-FM broadcasts to the Grand Rapids, MI area at 97.9 FM.

WGRE-FM
Owner: DePauw University
Editorial: 609 S Locust St, Greencastle, Indiana 46135-2047. **T:** 1 765 658-4643
E: wgre@depauw.edu
W: http://www.depauw.edu/univ/wgre/index.asp
Editorial Profile: WGRE-FM is a non-commercial station owned by DePauw University. The format of the station is adult album alternative music. WGRE-FM broadcasts to the Greencastle, IN area at 91.5 FM.

WGRF-FM
Owner: Cumulus Media Inc.
Editorial: 50 James E Casey Dr, Buffalo, New York 14206-2367. **T:** 1 716 881-4555
W: http://www.97rock.com
Editorial Profile: WGRF-FM is a commercial station owned by Cumulus Media Inc. The format of the station is classic rock. WGRF-FM broadcasts to the Buffalo, NY area at 96.9 FM.

WGRG-FM
Owner: Geneseo Community Radio Group, Inc.
Editorial: 700 N State St, Geneseo, Illinois 61254-1068. **T:** 1 309 945-0346
Editorial Profile: WGRG-FM is a commercial station owned by Geneseo Community Radio Group, Inc. The format of the station is adult hits. WGRG-FM broadcasts to the Geneseo, Il area at 100.5 FM.

WGRI-AM
Owner: Christian Broadcasting System
Editorial: 635 W 7th St, Cincinnati, Ohio 45203-1513. **T:** 1 513 533-2500
E: calendar@cbslradio.com
W: http://inspiration1050.com
Editorial Profile: WGRI-AM is a commercial station owned by Christian Broadcasting System.The format of the station is Urban Gospel. WGRI-AM broadcasts to the Cincinnati area at 1050 AM.

WGRK-AM
Owner: Commonwealth Broadcasting Corp.
Editorial: 50 Friendship Pike Rd, Campbellsville, Kentucky 42718.
T: 1 270 789-1464
E: wgrk@commonwealthbroadcasting.com
W: http://www.kcountry1057.com
Editorial Profile: WGRK-AM is a commercial station owned by Commonwealth Broadcasting Corp. The format of the station is contemporary country. WGRK-AM broadcasts to the Campbellsville, KY area at a frequency of 1540 AM.

WGRK-FM
Owner: Commonwealth Broadcasting Corp.
Editorial: 50 Friendship Pike Rd, Campbellsville, Kentucky 42718-2537.
T: 1 270 789-1464
E: wgrk@commonwealthbroadcasting.com
W: http://www.kcountry1057.com
Editorial Profile: WGRK-FM is a commercial station owned by Commonwealth Broadcasting Corp. The format of the station is classic and contemporary country. WGRK-FM broadcasts to the Campbellsville, KY area at 105.7 FM.

WGRM-AM
Owner: Christian Broadcasting of Greenwood, Inc.
Editorial: 1110 Wright St, Greenwood, Mississippi 38930-2237. **T:** 1 757 903-4981
E: sales@christiannetcast.com
W: http://www.christiannetcast.com
Editorial Profile: WGRM-AM is a commercial station owned by Christian Broadcasting of Greenwood, Inc. The format of the station is gospel music. WGRM-AM broadcasts to the Greenwood-Greenville, MS area at 1240 AM.

WGRM-FM
Owner: Christian Broadcasting of Greenwood, Inc.
Editorial: 1110 Wright St, Greenwood, Mississippi 38930-2237. **T:** 1 757 903-4981
W: http://www.christiannetcast.com
Editorial Profile: WGRM-FM is a commercial station owned by Christian Broadcasting of Greenwood, Inc. The format of the station is gospel music. WGRM-FM broadcasts to the Greenwood, MS area at 93.9 FM.

WGRN-FM
Owner: Greenville College
Editorial: 315 E College Ave, Greenville, Illinois 62246-1145. **T:** 1 618 664-6792
E: wgrnbusinessdirector@greenville.edu
W: http://www.wgrn.net
Editorial Profile: WGRN-FM a non-commercial station owned by Greenville College. The format of the station is contemporary Christian. WGRN-FM broadcasts to Greenville, IL at 89.5 FM.

WGRO-AM
Owner: Taylor County Broadcasting, Inc.
Editorial: 9206 W US Highway 90, Lake City, Florida 32055-7502. **T:** 1 386 752-0960
Editorial Profile: WGRO-AM is a commercial station owned by Taylor County Broadcasting, Inc. The format of the station is gospel music. WGRO-FM broadcasts to the Lake City, FL area at 960 AM.

WGRQ-FM
Owner: Telemedia Broadcasting
Editorial: 4414 Lafayette Blvd, Ste 100, Fredericksburg, Virginia 22408-4271.
T: 1 540 891-9696
W: http://www.959wgrq.com
Editorial Profile: WGRQ-FM is a commercial station owned by Telemedia Broadcasting. The format of the station is classic hits. WGRQ-FM broadcasts to the Fredericksburg, VA area at 95.9.

WGRR-FM
Owner: Cumulus Media Inc.
Editorial: 4805 Montgomery Rd Ste 300, Cincinnati, Ohio 45212-2280.
T: 1 513 241-9898
E: feedback@cincyradio.com
W: http://www.wgrr.com
Editorial Profile: WGRR-FM is a commercial station owned by Cumulus Media Inc. The format of the station is classic hits. WGRR-FM broadcasts to the Cincinnati area at 103.5 FM.

WGRT-FM
Owner: Port Huron Family Radio Inc.
Editorial: 624 Grand River Ave, Port Huron, Michigan 48060-3817. **T:** 1 810 987-3200
E: news@wgrt.com **W:** http://wgrt.com
Editorial Profile: WGRT-FM is a commercial station owned by Port Huron Family Radio Inc. The format for the station is adult contemporary. WGRT-FM broadcasts to the Port Huron, MI area at 102.3 FM.

WGRV-AM
Owner: Radio Greeneville Inc.
Editorial: 1004 Arnold Rd, Greeneville, Tennessee 37743. **T:** 1 423 638-4147
E: wgrv@greeneville.com
W: http://www.greeneville.com/wgrv
Editorial Profile: WGRV-AM is a commercial station owned by Radio Greeneville Inc. The format of the station is classic country music and talk. WGRV-AM broadcasts to the Greeneville, TN area at 1340 AM.

WGRW-FM
Owner: Word Works Inc.
Editorial: 4265 Hill St, Anniston, Alabama 36206. **T:** 1 256 238-9990
W: http://www.graceradio.com

WGRX-FM
Owner: Telemedia Broadcasting

Editorial: 4414 Lafayette Blvd, Ste 100, Fredericksburg, Virginia 22408-4271.
T: 1 540 891-9696
W: http://www.thunder1045.com
Editorial Profile: WGRX-FM is a commercial station owned by Telemedia Broadcasting. The format of the station is contemporary country and classic rock music. WGRX-FM's broadcasts to the Fredericksburg, VA area at 104.5 FM.

WGRY-AM
Owner: Blarney Stone Broadcasting, Inc.
Editorial: 6514 Old Lake Rd, Grayling, Michigan 49738-7348. **T:** 1 989 348-6171
Editorial Profile: WGRY-AM is a commercial station owned by Blarney Stone Broadcasting, Inc. The format of the station is adult standards. WGRY-AM broadcasts to the Traverse City, MI area at 1230 AM.

WGRY-FM
Owner: Blarney Stone Broadcasting, Inc.
Editorial: 6514 Old Lake Rd, Grayling, Michigan 49738-7348. **T:** 1 989 348-6171
Editorial Profile: WGRY-FM is a commercial station owned by Blarney Stone Broadcasting, Inc. The format of the station is adult contemporary. WGRY-FM broadcasts to the Grayling, MI area at 101.1 FM.

WGSF-AM
Owner: Flinn Broadcasting Corp.
Editorial: 3654 Park Ave, Memphis, Tennessee 38111-5626. **T:** 1 901 454-9948
E: wgsfoffice@bellsouth.net
W: http://www.radioambiente1030am.com
Editorial Profile: WGSF-AM is a commercial station owned by Flinn Broadcasting Corp. The format of the station is regional Mexican music. WGSF-AM broadcasts to the Memphis, TN area on 1030 AM.

WGSG-FM
Owner: Son First Broadcasting, Inc.
Editorial: 331 SE Leola Dr., Mayo, Florida 32066-9802. **T:** 1 386 294-2525
E: wgsg@windstream.net
Editorial Profile: WGSG-FM is a commercial station owned by Son First Broadcasting, Inc. The format of the station is gospel and religious talk programming. WGSG-FM broadcasts to the Mayo, FL area at 89.5 FM.

WGSL-FM
Owner: Educational Media Foundation
Editorial: 5375 Pebble Creek Trl, Loves Park, Illinois 61111. **T:** 1 815 654-1200
W: http://www.klove.com
Editorial Profile: WGSL-FM is a non-commercial station owned byEducational Media Foundation. The format of the station is Christian Contemporary. WGSL-FM broadcasts to the Rockford, IL area at 91.1 FM.

WGSO-AM
Owner: Northshore Radio, LLC
Editorial: 330 Carondelet St, New Orleans, Louisiana 70130-3144. **T:** 1 504 525-3314
E: info@wgso.com **W:** http://www.wgso.com
Editorial Profile: WGSO-AM is a commercial station owned by Northshore Radio, LLC. The format of the station is news talk. WGSO-AM broadcasts to the Metairie, LA area at 990 AM.

WGSP-AM
Owner: Norsan Group
Editorial: 4801 E Independence Blvd, Ste 815, Charlotte, North Carolina 28212-5490.
T: 1 704 442-7277
W: http://pepecharlotte.com
Editorial Profile: WGSP-AM is a commercial station owned by Norsan Group. The format of the station is classic hits. WGSP-AM broadcasts to the Charlotte, NC area at 1310 AM.

WGSP-FM
Owner: Norsan Group
Editorial: 4801 E Independence Blvd, Ste 815, Charlotte, North Carolina 28212-5490.
T: 1 704 442-7277
W: http://www.latina1023.com
Editorial Profile: WGSP-FM is a commercial station owned by Norsan Group. The format of the station is Hispanic tropical music. WGSP-FM broadcasts to the Charlotte, NC area at 102.3 FM.

WGSQ-FM
Owner: Cookeville Communications, LLC
Editorial: 698 S Willow Ave, Cookeville, Tennessee 38501-3802. **T:** 1 931 526-7144
W: http://www.countrygiant.com
Editorial Profile: WGSQ-FM is a commercial station owned by Cookeville Communications, LLC and operated by Great Plains Media. The

format of the station is contemporary country. WGSQ-FM broadcasts to the Cookeville, TN area at 94.7 FM.

WGST-AM
Owner: Clear Channel Media and Entertainment
Editorial: 1819 Peachtree Rd NE Ste 700, Atlanta, Georgia 30309-1849.
T: 1 404 875-8080
W: http://www.640wgst.com
Editorial Profile: WGST-AM is a commercial station owned by Clear Channel Media and Entertainment. The format of the station is news talk. WGST-AM broadcasts to the Atlanta area at 640 AM.

WGSU-FM
Owner: State University of New York
Editorial: 1 College Cir B04, Geneseo, New York 14454-1401. **T:** 1 585 245-5229
W: http://www.geneseo.edu/~wgsu/
Editorial Profile: WGSU-FM is a non-commercial station owned by the State University of New York. The format of the station is rock alternative, sports and news. WGSU-FM broadcasts to the Geneseo, NY area at 89.3 FM.

WGSV-AM
Owner: Guntersville Broadcasting Co.
Editorial: 2301 Thomas Ave, Guntersville, Alabama 35976-2233. **T:** 1 256 582-8131
E: wgsv@wgsv.com **W:** http://www.wgsv.com
Editorial Profile: WGSV-AM is a commercial station owned by Guntersville Broadcasting Co. The format of the station is talk. WGSV-AM broadcasts to the Guntersville, AL at 1270 AM.

WGSY-FM
Owner: Clear Channel Media and Entertainment
Editorial: 1501 13th Ave, Columbus, Georgia 31901-1908. **T:** 1 706 576-3000
W: http://www.sunny100columbus.com
Editorial Profile: WGSY-FM is a commercial station owned by Clear Channel Media and Entertainment. The format of the station is adult contemporary. WGSY-FM broadcasts to the Columbus, GA area at 100.1 FM.

WGTD-FM
Owner: Gateway Technical College
Editorial: 3520 30th Ave, Kenosha, Wisconsin 53144-1619. **T:** 1 262 564-3800
W: http://www.wgtd.org
Editorial Profile: WGTD-FM is a non-commercial station owned by Gateway Technical College. The format of the station is news and talk. WGTD-FM broadcasts to the Kenosha, WI, area at 91.1 FM.

WGTE-FM
Owner: Public Broadcasting Foundation of Northwest Ohio
Editorial: 1270 S Detroit Ave, Toledo, Ohio 43614. **T:** 1 419 380-4600 **E:** fm@wgte.org
W: http://www.wgte.org
Editorial Profile: WGTE-FM is a non-commercial station owned by Public Broadcasting Foundation of Northwest Ohio. The format of the station is classical, jazz and news. WGTE-FM broadcasts to the Toledo, OH area at 91.3 FM.

WGTF-FM
Owner: Dothan Community Educ. Radio
Editorial: 107 Wanda Ct, Dothan, Alabama 36303-3045. **T:** 1 334 794-4770
E: wgtf@bbnmedia.org
Editorial Profile: WGTF-FM is a non-commercial station owned by Dothan Community Educ. Radio. The format of the station is religious. WGTF-FM broadcasts to the Dothan, AL area at 89.5 FM.

WGTH-AM
Owner: High Knob Broadcasters, Inc.
Editorial: 394 Edgewater Dr, Cedar Bluff, Virginia 24609-8825. **T:** 1 276 964-2502
E: wgth@wgth.net **W:** http://www.wgth.net
Editorial Profile: WGTH-AM is a commercial station owned by High Knob Broadcasters, Inc. The format of the station is gospel. WGTH-AM broadcasts to the Cedar Bluff, VA area at 540 AM.

WGTH-FM
Owner: High Knob Broadcasters, Inc.
Editorial: 394 Edgewater Dr, Cedar Bluff, Virginia 24609. **T:** 1 276 964-2502
E: wgth@wgth.net **W:** http://www.wgth.net
Editorial Profile: WGTH-FM is a commercial station owned by High Knob Broadcasters, Inc. The format of the station is southern

gospel. WGTH-FM broadcasts to the Cedar Bluff, VA area at 105.5 FM.

WGTJ-AM
Owner: Vision Communications Inc.
Editorial: 1716 Cleveland Hwy, Gainesville, Georgia 30501. **T:** 1 770 297-7485
E: news@glory1330.com
W: http://www.glory1330.com
Editorial Profile: WGTJ-AM is a commercial station owned by Vision Communications Inc. The format of the station is contemporary Christian and gospel. WGTJ-AM broadcasts to the Gainesville, GA area at 1330 AM.

WGTK-AM
Owner: Salem Communications
Editorial: 9960 Corporate Campus Dr Ste 3600, Louisville, Kentucky 40223-4070.
T: 1 502 339-9470
W: http://www.970wgtk.com
Editorial Profile: WGTK-AM is a commercial station owned by Salem Communications. The format of the station is news and talk. WGTK-AM broadcasts in the Louisville, KY area at 970 AM.

WGTK-FM
Owner: Salem Communications' Caron Broadcasting, Inc.
Editorial: 920 Wade Hampton Blvd, Greenville, South Carolina 29609-4944.
T: 1 864 242-6240
W: http://www.conservativetalk945.com
Editorial Profile: WGTK-FM is a commercial station owned by the Salem Communications' Caron Broadcasting, Inc. The format of the station is Conservative Talk. WGTK-FM broadcasts to Greenville, SC at 94.5 FM.

WGTN-AM
Owner: Stalvey Communications
Editorial: 1217 Mcdonald Rd, Georgetown, South Carolina 29440-4555.
T: 1 843 546-1400 **E:** wgtnradio@aol.com
W: http://www.wgtnradio.com
Editorial Profile: WGTN-AM is a commercial station owned by Stalvey Communications. The format of the station is news, sports and talk. WGTN-AM broadcasts to the Georgetown, SC area at 1400 AM.

WGTN-FM
Owner: Fidelity Broadcasting Inc.
Editorial: 3926 Wesley St, Ste 301, Myrtle Beach, South Carolina 29579.
T: 1 843 903-9962 **W:** http://www.wezv.com

WGTO-AM
Owner: Langford Broadcasting
Editorial: 26914 Marcellus Hwy, Dowagiac, Michigan 49047. **T:** 1 269 782-5106
E: info@wgtoradio.com
W: http://www.wgtoradio.com
Editorial Profile: WGTO-AM is a commercial station owned by Langford Broadcasting. The format of the station is classic hits. WGTO-AM broadcasts to the Dowagiac, MI area at 910 AM.

WGTR-FM
Owner: Clear Channel Media and Entertainment
Editorial: 4841 Highway 17 Byp S, Myrtle Beach, South Carolina 29577-6683.
T: 1 843 293-0107
W: http://www.gator1079.com
Editorial Profile: WGTR-FM is a commercial station owned by Clear Channel Media and Entertainment. The format of the station is country. WGTR-FM broadcasts to the Myrtle Beach, SC area at 107.9 FM.

WGTS-FM
Owner: Columbia Union College Broadcasting Inc.
Editorial: 7600 Flower Ave, Takoma Park, Maryland 20912. **T:** 1 301 891-4200
E: wgts@wgts919.com
W: http://www.wgts919.com
Editorial Profile: WGTS-FM is a non-commercial station owned by Columbia Union College Broadcasting Inc. The format of the station is contemporary Christian music. WGTS-FM broadcasts to the Washington, D.C. area at 91.9 FM.

WGTX-FM
Owner: Dunes 102FM LLC
Editorial: 352 Route 6, Unit 7, Truro, Massachusetts 2652. **T:** 1 508 487-1002
E: info@dunes102.com
W: http://www.dunes102.com
Editorial Profile: WGTX-FM is a commercial station owned by Dunes 102FM LLC. The format of the station is classic hits. WGTX-FM

broadcasts to the Provincetown, MA area at 102.3 FM.

WGTY-FM
Owner: Times & News Publishing Co.
Editorial: 1560 Fairfield Rd, Gettysburg, Pennsylvania 17325-7252. **T:** 1 717 334-3101
E: info@wgty.com **W:** http://www.wgty.com
Editorial Profile: WGTY-FM is a commercial station owned by Times & News Publishing Co. The format of the station is country. WGTY-FM broadcasts to the Gettysburg, PA area at 107.7 FM.

WGTZ-FM
Owner: Main Line Broadcasting
Editorial: 717 E David Rd, Dayton, Ohio 45429-5218. **T:** 1 937 294-5858
E: communitycalendar@mainlinedayton.com
W: http://www.fly929.com
Editorial Profile: WGTZ-FM is a commercial station owned by Main Line Broadcasting. The format of the station is adult hits. WGTZ-FM broadcasts to the Dayton, OH area at 92.9 FM.

WGUC-FM
Owner: Cincinnati Public Radio Inc.
Editorial: 1223 Central Pkwy, Cincinnati, Ohio 45214-2812. **T:** 1 513 241-8282
E: wguc@wguc.org **W:** http://www.wguc.org
Editorial Profile: WGUC-FM is a non-commercial station owned by Cincinnati Public Radio Inc. The format of the station is classical music. WGUC-FM broadcasts to the Cincinnati area at 90.9 FM.

WGUE-AM
Owner: Mighty Media Group, LP (Memphis First Ventures LP)
Editorial: 230 Goodman Rd E Ste 2, Southaven, Mississippi 38671-8889.
T: 1 662 349-0826
Editorial Profile: WGUE-AM is a commercial station owned by Mighty Media Group, LP (Memphis First Ventures LP). The format of the station is adult hits. WGUE-AM broadcasts to the Memphis, TN area at 830 AM.

WGUF-FM
Owner: Renda Broadcasting
Editorial: 10915 K Nine Dr, 2nd Fl, Bonita Springs, Florida 34135. **T:** 1 239 495-8383
W: http://www.wguf989.com
Editorial Profile: WGUF-FM is a commercial station owned by Renda Broadcasting. The format of the station is talk. WGUF-FM broadcasts to the Naples, FL area at 98.9 FM.

WGUL-AM
Owner: Salem Communications
Editorial: 5211 W Laurel St Ste A, Tampa, Florida 33607-1736. **T:** 1 813 639-1903
W: http://www.860wgul.com
Editorial Profile: WGUL-AM is a commercial station owned by Salem Communications. The format of the station is news and talk. WGUL-AM broadcasts to the Tampa, FL area at 860 AM.

WGUN-AM
Owner: W.G.O.V., Inc.
Editorial: 2973 US Highway 84 W, Valdosta, Georgia 31601-0305. **T:** 1 229 242-4513
Editorial Profile: WGUN-AM is a commercial station owned by W.G.O.V., Inc.The format of the station is urban adult contemporary. WGOV-AM broadcasts to the Valdosta, GA area at 950 AM.

WGUO-FM
Owner: Southeast Broadcasting, Inc.
Editorial: 3500 N Causeway Blvd Ste 400, Metairie, Louisiana 70002-3533.
T: 1 504 834-7095
W: http://www.praisefm949.com
Editorial Profile: WGUO-FM is a commercial station owned by Southeast Broadcasting, Inc. The format for the station is gospel. WGUO-FM broadcasts to the Metairie, LA area at 94.9 FM.

WGUR-FM
Owner: Georgia College & State University
Editorial: 231 W Hancock St, Milledgeville, Georgia 31061-3375. **T:** 1 478 445-4102

WGUS-FM
Owner: Beasley Broadcast Group
Editorial: 4051 Jimmie Dyess Pkwy, Augusta, Georgia 30909. **T:** 1 706 396-7000
W: http://www.1027wgus.com
Editorial Profile: WGUS-FM is a commercial station owned by Beasley Broadcast Group. The format of the station is Southern gospel music. WGUS-FM broadcasts to the Augusta, GA area at 102.7 FM.

WGVA-AM

Owner: Finger Lakes Radio Group
Editorial: 3568 Lenox Rd, Geneva, New York 14456. T: 1 315 781-7000
E: news@flradiogroup.com
W: http://flradiogroup.com
Editorial Profile: WGVA-AM is a commercial station owned by Finger Lakes Radio Group. The format of the station is news, sports and talk. WGVA-AM broadcasts to the Geneva, NY area at 1240 AM.

WGVE-FM

Owner: Gary Community School Corp.
Editorial: 1800 E 35th Ave, Gary, Indiana 46409. T: 1 219 962-9483
Editorial Profile: WGVE-FM is a non-commercial station owned by Gary Community School Corp. The format of the station is variety. WGVE-FM broadcasts to the Gary, IN area at 88.7 FM.

WGVL-AM

Owner: Clear Channel Media and Entertainment
Editorial: 101 N Main St, Ste 1000, Greenville, South Carolina 29601-4852.
T: 1 864 991-8203 **W:** http://sports.yahoo.com
Editorial Profile: WGVL-AM is a commercial station owned by Clear Channel Communcations and in an LMA with Greenville Radio Group, LLC. The format of the station is sports. WGVL-AM broadcasts to the Greenville, SC area at 1440 AM.

WGVM-AM

Owner: WDMS, Inc.
Editorial: 1383 Pickett St, Greenville, Mississippi 38703. T: 1 662 334-4559
E: wdms@bellsouth.net
Editorial Profile: WGVM-AM is a commercial station owned by WDMS, Inc. The format of the station is classic rock. WGVM-AM broadcasts to the Greenville, MS area at 1260 AM.

WGVS-AM

Owner: Grand Valley State University
Editorial: 301 Fulton St W, Grand Rapids, Michigan 49504-6430. T: 1 616 331-6666
E: realoldies@wgvu.org
W: http://www.wgvu.org/realoldies

WGVS-FM

Owner: Grand Valley State University
Editorial: 301 Fulton St W, Grand Rapids, Michigan 49504-6430. T: 1 616 331-6666
E: feedback@wgvu.org
W: http://www.wgvu.org
Editorial Profile: WGVS-FM is a commercial station owned by Grand Valley State University. The format of the station is talk and jazz. The station broadcasts to the Whitehall, MI area at a frequency of 95.3 FM.

WGVU-AM

Owner: Grand Valley State University
Editorial: 301 Fulton St W, Grand Rapids, Michigan 49504-6430. T: 1 616 331-6666
E: realoldies@wgvu.org
W: http://www.wgvu.org/realoldies
Editorial Profile: WGVU-AM is a non-commercial station owned by Grand Valley State University. The format of the station is oldies. WGVU-AM broadcasts to the Grand Rapids, MI area at 1480 AM.

WGVU-FM

Owner: Grand Valley State University
Editorial: 301 Fulton St W, Grand Rapids, Michigan 49504-6430. T: 1 616 331-6666
E: feedback@wgvu.org
W: http://www.wgvu.org
Editorial Profile: WGVU-FM is a non-commercial station owned by Grand Valley State University. The format of the station features jazz and news/talk programming. WGVU-FM broadcasts to the Grand Rapids, MI area at a frequency of 88.5-FM.

WGVX-FM

Owner: Cumulus Media Inc.
Editorial: 2000 Elm St SE, Minneapolis, Minnesota 55414-2531. T: 1 612 617-4000
E: info@105theticket.com
W: http://www.105theticket.com
Editorial Profile: WGVX-FM is a commercial station owned by Cumulus Media Inc. The format of the station is sports. WGVX-FM broadcasts to the Greater Minneapolis area at 105.1 FM. WGVX-FM airs programming on WGVY-FM and WVGZ-FM.

WGVZ-FM

Owner: Cumulus Media Inc.
Editorial: 2000 Elm St SE, Minneapolis, Minnesota 55414-2531. T: 1 612 617-4000
E: info@105theticket.com
W: http://www.105theticket.com
Editorial Profile: WGVZ-FM is a commercial station owned by Cumulus Media Inc. The format of the station is sports. WGVZ-FM broadcasts to the Minneapolis area at 105.7 FM. The station is a simulcast of WGVX-FM

WGWM-AM

Owner: WGWM Broadcasting Inc.
Editorial: 948 Moriah Church Rd, London, Kentucky 40741. T: 1 606 878-0980
Editorial Profile: WGWM-AM is a commercial station owned by WGWM Broadcasting Inc. The format of the station is gospel. WGWM-AM broadcasts to the London, KY area at 980 AM.

WGXL-FM

Owner: Great Eastern Radio, LLC
Editorial: 31 Hanover St, Ste 4, Lebanon, New Hampshire 3766. T: 1 603 448-1400
Editorial Profile: WGLX-FM is a commercial station owned by Great Eastern Radio, LLC. The format of the station is Hot AC. WGLX-FM broadcasts to the Lebanon, NH area at a frequency of 92.3 FM.

WGY-AM

Owner: Clear Channel Media and Entertainment
Editorial: 1203 Troy Schenectady Rd, Latham, New York 12110-1046. T: 1 518 452-4800
E: news@wgy.com **W:** http://www.wgy.com
Editorial Profile: WGY-AM is a commercial station owned by Clear Channel Media and Entertainment. The format of the station is news and talk. WGY-AM broadcasts in the Albany, NY, area at 810 AM. WGY-AM airs programing on WGY-FM.

WGYE-FM

Owner: Burbach of WV, LLC
Editorial: 1489 Locust Ave, Ste C, Fairmont, West Virginia 26554. T: 1 304 363-8888
W: http://www.froggycountry.net
Editorial Profile: WGYE-FM is a commercial station owned by Burbach of WV, LLC. The format of the station is contemporary country music. WTUS-FM broadcasts to the Fairmont, WV area at 102.7 FM.

WGY-FM

Owner: Clear Channel Media and Entertainment
Editorial: 1203 Troy Schenectady Rd, Latham, New York 12110-1046. T: 1 518 452-4800
W: http://www.wgy.com
Editorial Profile: WGY-FM is a commercial station owned by Clear Channel Media and Entertainment. The format of the station is news talk. WGY-FM airs WGY-AM's programing. WGY-FM broadcasts to the Albany, NY area at 103.1.

WGYI-FM

Owner: Forever Broadcasting
Editorial: 900 Water St, Meadville, Pennsylvania 16335. T: 1 814 724-1111
E: radio@zoominternet.net
W: http://www.froggyfun.com
Editorial Profile: WGYI-FM is a commercial station owned by Forever Broadcasting. The format of the station is country music. WGYI-FM broadcasts to the Meadville, PA area at 98.5 FM.

WGYL-FM

Owner: Treasure & Space Coast Radio
Editorial: 1235 16th St, Vero Beach, Florida 32960. T: 1 772 567-0937
W: http://thebreeze.fm
Editorial Profile: WGYL-FM is a commercial station owned by Treasure & Space Coast Radio. The format of the station is Lite Rock/ Lite AC. WGYL-FM broadcasts to the Vero Beach, FL area at 93.7 FM.

WGYM-AM

Owner: Atlantic Broadcasting Group
Editorial: 1601 New Rd, Linwood, New Jersey 08221-1116. T: 1 609 653-1400
W: http://www.wondradio.com
Editorial Profile: WGYM-AM is a commercial station owned by Atlantic Broadcasting Group. The format of the station is news and talk. WGYM-AM broadcasts to the Atlantic City, NJ area at 1580 AM.

WGYV-AM

Owner: Williamson Broadcasting
Editorial: 1604 E Commerce St, Greenville, Alabama 36037-3400. T: 1 334 382-5444
Editorial Profile: WGYV-AM is a commercial station owned by Williamson Broadcasting. The format of the station is oldies and talk.

WGYV-AM broadcasts to the Greenville, AL area at 1380 AM.

WGYY-FM

Owner: Forever Broadcasting
Editorial: 900 Water St, Meadville, Pennsylvania 16335. T: 1 814 724-1111
E: radio@zoominternet.net
W: http://www.froggyfun.com
Editorial Profile: WGYY-FM is a commercial station owned by Forever Broadcasting. The format of the station is country music. WGYY-FM broadcasts to the Meadville, PA area at 100.3 FM.

WGZB-FM

Owner: Main Line Broadcasting
Editorial: 520 S 4th St Ste 200, Louisville, Kentucky 40202-2577. T: 1 502 625-1220
W: http://www.hiphopb965.com
Editorial Profile: WGZB-FM is a commercial station owned by Main Line Broadcasting. The format of the station is urban contemporary. WGZB-FM broadcasts to the Louisville, KY area at 96.5 FM.

WGZO-FM

Owner: L & L Radio
Editorial: 2 Corpus Christie Pl Ste 100A, Hilton Head, South Carolina 29928-1720. T: 1 843 363-9956
W: http://www.sc103radio.com
Editorial Profile: WGZO-FM is a commercial station owned by L & L Radio. The format of the station is classic hits. WGZO-FM broadcasts to the Hilton Head, SC area at 106.1 FM.

WGZZ-FM

Owner: Auburn Network, Inc.
Editorial: 197 E University Dr, Auburn, Alabama 36832. T: 1 334 826-2929
W: http://www.wingsfm.com
Editorial Profile: WGZZ-FM is a commercial station owned by Auburn Network, Inc. The format of the station is classic hits. WGZZ-FM broadcasts to the Tallapoosa, AL area at 100.3 FM.

WHAA-FM

Owner: University of Wisconsin
Editorial: 821 University Ave, Madison, Wisconsin 53706. T: 1 608 263-3970
E: listener@wpr.org **W:** http://www.wpr.org
Editorial Profile: WHAA-FM is a non-commercial station owned by University of Wisconsin. The format of the station is news, talk and classical music. WHAA-FM broadcasts to the Madison, WI area at 89.1 FM.

WHA-AM

Owner: University of Wisconsin
Editorial: 821 University Ave, Madison, Wisconsin 53706-1412. T: 1 608 263-3970
E: listener@wpr.org **W:** http://www.wpr.org
Editorial Profile: WHA-AM is a non-commercial station owned by University of Wisconsin. The format of the station is talk. WHA-AM broadcasts to the Madison, WI area at 970 AM.

WHAD-FM

Owner: University of Wisconsin
Editorial: 310 W Wisconsin Ave Ste 750E, Milwaukee, Wisconsin 53203-2271. T: 1 414 227-2040 E: listener@wpr.org
W: http://www.wpr.org
Editorial Profile: WHAD-FM is a non-commercial station owned by the University of Wisconsin. The format of the station is news and talk. WHAD-FM broadcasts to the Milwaukee area at 90.7 FM.

WHAG-AM

Owner: Main Line Broadcasting
Editorial: 1250 Maryland Ave, Hagerstown, Maryland 21740-7244. T: 1 301 797-7300
W: http://www.thenewfm963.com
Editorial Profile: WHAG-AM is a commercial station owned by Main Line Broadcasting. The format of the station is oldies music. WHAG-AM broadcasts to the Hagerstown, MD area at 1410 AM.

WHAI-FM

Owner: Saga Communications
Editorial: 81 Woodard Rd, Greenfield, Massachusetts 1301. T: 1 413 774-4301
W: http://www.whai.com
Editorial Profile: WHAI-FM is a commercial station owned Saga Communications. The format of the station is adult contemporary music. WHAI-FM broadcasts to the Greenfield, MA area at 98.3 FM.

WHAJ-FM

Owner: L & L Broadcasting
Editorial: 900 Bluefield Ave, Bluefield, West Virginia 24701-2744. T: 1 304 327-7114
W: http://www.j1045.com
Editorial Profile: WHAJ-FM is a commercial station owned by L & L Broadcasting. The format of the station is hot adult contemporary music. WHAJ-FM broadcasts to the Bluefield, WV area at 104.5 FM.

WHAK-AM

Owner: Edwards Communications LLC
Editorial: 1491 M 32 W, Alpena, Michigan 49707-8194. T: 1 989 354-4611
E: sales@truenorthradionetwork.com
W: http://www.alpenanow.com
Editorial Profile: WHAK-AM is a commercial station owned by Edwards Communications LLC. The format for the station is oldies. WHAK-AM broadcasts to the Alpena, MI area at 960 AM.

WHAK-FM

Owner: Edwards Communications LLC
Editorial: 1491 M 32 W, Alpena, Michigan 49707. T: 1 989 354-4611
E: news@truenorthradionetwork.com
W: http://www.alpenanow.com
Editorial Profile: WHAK-FM is a commercial station owned by Edwards Communications LLC. The format of the station is oldies. WHAK-FM broadcasts to the Alpena, MI area at 99.9 FM.

WHAL-AM

Owner: Clear Channel Media and Entertainment
Editorial: 1501 13th Ave, Columbus, Georgia 31901-1908. T: 1 706 576-3000
W: http://www.247comedy.com
Editorial Profile: WHAL-AM is a commercial station owned by Clear Channel Media and Entertainment. The format of the station is comedy. WHAL-AM broadcasts to the Columbus, GA area at 1460 AM.

WHAL-FM

Owner: Clear Channel Media and Entertainment
Editorial: 2650 Thousand Oaks Blvd Ste 4100, Memphis, Tennessee 38118-2451. T: 1 901 259-1300
W: http://www.hallelujahfm.com
Editorial Profile: WHAL-FM is a commercial station owned by Clear Channel Media and Entertainment. The format of the station is gospel. WHAL-FM broadcasts to the Memphis, TN area at 95.7 FM.

WHAM-AM

Owner: Clear Channel Media and Entertainment
Editorial: 100 Chestnut St Ste 1700, 100 Chestnut St, Rochester, New York 14604-2418. T: 1 585 454-4884
E: whamnews@clearchannel.com
W: http://www.wham1180.com
Editorial Profile: WHAM-AM is a commercial staion owned by Clear Channel Media and Entertainment. The format of the station is news and talk. WHAM-AM broadcasts to the Rochester, NY area at 1180 AM.

WHAN-AM

Owner: Fifth Estate Broadcasting, LLC
Editorial: 11337 Ashcake Rd, Ashland, Virginia 23005-7633. T: 1 804 798-1010
E: info@whanradio.com
W: http://www.whanradio.com
Editorial Profile: WHAN-AM is a commercial station owned by Fifth Estate Broadcasting, LLC. The format of the station is news and talk programming. WHAN-AM broadcasts to the Ashland, VA area at 1430 AM.

WHAP-AM

Owner: Nugent(Steve) and Hios(David)
Editorial: 150 S Mesa Dr, Hopewell, Virginia 23860. T: 1 804 458-9427
W: http://www.1340whap.com
Editorial Profile: WHAP-AM is a commercial station owned by Steve Nugent and David Hios. The format of the station is news, sports and talk. WHAP-AM broadcasts to the Hopewell, VA area at 1340 AM.

WHAS-AM

Owner: Clear Channel Media and Entertainment
Editorial: 4000 Radio Dr, Louisville, Kentucky 40218-4568. T: 1 502 479-2222
E: whasnews@clearchannel.com
W: http://www.whas.com
Editorial Profile: WHAS-AM is a commercial station owned by Clear Channel Media and Entertainment. The format of the station is

news and talk. WHAS-AM broadcasts to the Louisville, KY area at 840 AM.

WHAT-AM
Owner: Aztec Capital Partners, Inc.
Editorial: 25 Bala Ave, Ste 202, Bala Cynwyd, Pennsylvania 19004-3215. **T:** 1 484 562-0510
W: http://www.elzolphilly.com
Editorial Profile: WHAT-AM is a commercial station owned by Aztec Capital Partners, Inc. The format of the station is Hispanic tropical. WHAT-AM broadcasts to the Philadelphia area at 1340 AM.

WHAT-FM
Owner: Withers Broadcasting of Southern Illinois, LLC
Editorial: 1822 N Court St, Marion, Illinois 62959. **T:** 1 618 997-8123
W: http://www.mywithersradio.com/bear
Editorial Profile: WHAT-FM is a commercial station owned by Withers Broadcasting of Southern Illinois, LLC. The format of the station is classic rock music. WQUL-FM broadcasts to Marion, IL at 97.7 FM.

WHAW-AM
Owner: DJ Broadcasting
Editorial: 300 Harrison Ave, Weston, West Virginia 26452. **T:** 1 304 269-5555
E: info@whawradio.com
W: http://www.whawradio.com
Editorial Profile: WHAW-AM is a commercial station owned by DJ Broadcasting. The format of the station is country. WHAW-AM broadcasts to the Weston, WV area on 980 AM.

WHAY-FM
Owner: Lavender(Tim)
Editorial: 69 Courthouse Ave, Whitley City, Kentucky 42653. **T:** 1 606 376-2218
E: whayradio@highland.net
W: http://www.hay98.com
Editorial Profile: WHAY-FM is a commercial station owned by Tim Lavender. The primary format of the station is Americana, but also features classic country, bluegrass, blues, and some rock. WHAY-FM broadcasts to the Whitley City, KY and surrounding communities at 98.3 FM.

WHAZ-AM
Owner: Capital Media Corporation
Editorial: 30 Park Ave, Cohoes, New York 12047-3330. **T:** 1 518 237-1330
W: http://www.aliveradionetwork.com
Editorial Profile: WHAZ-AM is a commercial station owned by Capital Media Corporation. The format of the station is religious. WHAZ-AM broadcasts to the Cohoes, NY area at 1330 AM.

WHAZ-FM
Owner: Capital Media Corporation
Editorial: 30 Park Ave, Cohoes, New York 12047-3330. **T:** 1 518 237-1330
E: events@aliveradio.com
W: http://www.aliveradionetwork.com
Editorial Profile: WHAZ-FM is a commercial station owned by Capital Media Corporation. The format of the station is religious programming. WHAZ-FM broadcasts to the Cohoes, NY area at 97.5.

WHB-AM
Owner: Union Broadcasting Inc.
Editorial: 6721 W 121st St, Overland Park, Kansas 66209-2003. **T:** 1 913 344-1500
E: info@810whb.com
W: http://www.810whb.com
Editorial Profile: WHB-AM is a commercial station owned by Union Broadcasting Inc. The format of the station is sports. WHB-AM broadcasts to the Kansas City, MO area at 810 AM.

WHBB-AM
Owner: Broadsouth Communications
Editorial: 505 Lauderdale St, Selma, Alabama 36701-4528. **T:** 1 334 875-3350
Editorial Profile: WHBB-AM is a commercial station owned by Broadsouth Communications. The format of the station is talk. WHBB-AM broadcasts to the Selma, AL area at 1490 AM.

WHBC-AM
Owner: Digity LLC
Editorial: 550 Market Ave S, Canton, Ohio 44702-2112. **T:** 1 330 456-7166
E: newstip@whbc.com
W: http://www.whbc.com
Editorial Profile: WHBC-AM is a commercial station owned by Digity LLC. The format of the station is news, talk and sports. WHBC-

AM broadcasts to the Canton, OH area at 1480.

WHBC-FM
Owner: Digity LLC
Editorial: 550 Market Ave S, Canton, Ohio 44702-2112. **T:** 1 330 456-7166
W: http://www.mix941.com
Editorial Profile: WHBC-FM is a commercial station owned by Digity LLC. The format of the station is adult contemporary. WHBC-FM broadcasts to the Canton, OH area at 94.1 FM.

WHBE-AM
Owner: UB Louisville, LLC
Editorial: 11700 Commonwealth Dr, Louisville, Kentucky 40299-6303. **T:** 1 502 240-0602
W: http://espnlouisville.com
Editorial Profile: WHBE-AM is a commercial station owned by UB Louisville, LLC. The format of the station is sports. WHBE-AM broadcasts to the Louisville, KY area at 680 AM.

WHBG-AM
Owner: VerStandig Broadcasting
Editorial: 1820 Heritage Center Way, Harrisonburg, Virginia 22801.
T: 1 540 434-0331
Editorial Profile: WHBG-AM is a commercial station owned by VerStandig Broadcasting. The format for the station is sports. WHBG-AM broadcasts to the Harrisonburg, VA area at 1360 AM. The station does not accept unsolicited faxes. Do NOT e-mail any staff members. Any press information should be sent to WSVA-AM.

WHBK-AM
Owner: Southern Broadcasting, Inc.
Editorial: 1055 Skyway Dr, Marshall, North Carolina 28753. **T:** 1 828 649-3914
E: 1460whbk@gmail.com
W: http://www.1460whbk.com
Editorial Profile: WHBK-AM is a commercial station owned by Southern Broadcasting, Inc. The format of the station is gospel. WHBK-AM broadcasts to the Marshall, NC area at 1460 AM.

WHBL-AM
Owner: Midwest Communications Inc.
Editorial: 2100 Washington Ave, Sheboygan, Wisconsin 53081-7042. **T:** 1 920 458-2107
E: whblnews@whbl.com
W: http://www.whbl.com
Editorial Profile: WHBL-AM is a commercial station owned by Midwest Communications Inc. The format of the station is news, talk and sports. WHBL-AM broadcasts to the Sheboygan, WI area at 1330 AM.

WHBM-FM
Owner: Wisconsin Educational Communications Board
Editorial: 625 Stewart Ave, Wausau, Wisconsin 54401-4563. **T:** 1 715 261-6298
E: listener@wpr.org
W: http://www.wpr.org/whbm
Editorial Profile: WHBM-FM is a non-commercial station owned by Wisconsin Educational Communications Board. The format for the station is news and talk. WHBM-FM broadcasts to the Wausau, WI area at 90.3 FM. Staff can be contacted at their Madison, WI offices at 608-263-3970.

WHBN-AM
Owner: Hometown Broadcasting, Inc.
Editorial: 2063 Shakertown Rd, Danville, Kentucky 40422. **T:** 1 859 236-2711
E: hometownradio@bellsouth.net
Editorial Profile: WHBN-AM is a commercial station owned by Hometown Broadcasting, Inc. The format for the station is country and gospel. WHBN-AM broadcasts to the Lexington, KY area at 1420 AM.

WHBO-AM
Owner: Genesis Communications Inc.
Editorial: 800 8th Ave SE, Largo, Florida 33771-2162. **T:** 1 813 281-1040
E: sportstalkflorida@radiogenesis.com
W: http://www.sportstalkflorida.com
Editorial Profile: WHBO-AM is a commercial station owned by Genesis Communications Inc. The format of the station is sports. WHBO-AM broadcasts to the Tampa, FL area at 1040 AM.

WHBQ-AM
Owner: Flinn Broadcasting Corp.
Editorial: 6080 Mount Moriah Road Ext, Memphis, Tennessee 38115-2645.
T: 1 901 375-9324
W: http://www.sports56whbq.com

Editorial Profile: WHBQ-AM is a commercial station owned by Flinn Broadcasting Corp. The format of the station is sports. WHBQ-AM broadcasts to the Memphis, TN, market at 560 AM.

WHBQ-FM
Owner: Flinn Broadcasting Corp.
Editorial: 6080 Mount Moriah Road Ext, Memphis, Tennessee 38115-2645.
T: 1 901 375-9324 **E:** mail@q1075.com
W: http://www.q1075.com
Editorial Profile: WHBQ-FM is a commercial station owned by Flinn Broadcasting Corp. The format of the station is Top 40/CHR. WHBQ-FM broadcasts to the Memphis, TN area at 107.5 FM.

WHBR-FM
Owner: Burbach of WV, LLC
Editorial: 5 Rosemar Cir, Parkersburg, West Virginia 26104. **T:** 1 304 485-4565
W: http://1031thebear.net/
Editorial Profile: WHBR-FM is a commercial station owned by Burbach of WV, LLC. The format of the station is rock alternative. WHBR-FM broadcasts to the Parkersburg, WV area at 103.1 FM.

WHBS-FM
Owner: Entercom Communications Corp.
Editorial: 305 Route 315 Hwy, Pittston, Pennsylvania 18640-3907. **T:** 1 570 883-9850
W: http://www.sportshub102.com
Editorial Profile: WHBS-FM is a commercial station owned by Entercom Communications Corp. The format of the station is sports. WDMT-FM broadcasts to the Wilkes-Barre, PA area at 102.3 FM.

WHBT-AM
Owner: Cumulus Media Inc.
Editorial: 3411 W Tharpe St, Tallahassee, Florida 32303. **T:** 1 850 201-3000
W: http://www.heaven1410.com
Editorial Profile: WHBT-AM is a commercial station owned by Cumulus Media Inc. The format of the station is gospel. WHBT-AM broadcasts to the Tallahassee, FL area at 1410 AM.

WHBU-AM
Owner: Backyard Broadcasting
Editorial: 800 E 29th St, Muncie, Indiana 47302-5765. **T:** 1 765 288-4403
W: http://www.1240whbu.com
Editorial Profile: WHBU-AM is a commercial station owned by Backyard Broadcasting. The format of the station is news, talk and sports. WHBU-AM broadcasts to the Muncie, IN area at 1240 AM.

WHBX-FM
Owner: Cumulus Media Inc.
Editorial: 3411 W Tharpe St, Tallahassee, Florida 32303. **T:** 1 850 201-3000
W: http://www.961jamz.com
Editorial Profile: WHBX-FM is a commercial station owned by Cumulus Media Inc. The format of the station is urban adult contemporary. WHBX-FM broadcasts to the Tallahassee, FL area at 96.1 FM.

WHBY-AM
Owner: Woodward Communications, Inc.
Editorial: 2800 E College Ave, Appleton, Wisconsin 54915. **T:** 1 920 733-6639
E: whbynews@wcinet.com
W: http://www.whby.com
Editorial Profile: WHBY-AM is a commercial station owned by Woodward Communications, Inc. The format of the station is news, sports and talk programming. WHBY-AM broadcasts to Appleton, WI area at 1150 AM.

WHBZ-FM
Owner: Midwest Communications Inc.
Editorial: 2100 Washington Ave, Sheboygan, Wisconsin 53081-7042. **T:** 1 920 458-2107
E: buzz.studio@whbz.fm
W: http://www.1065thebuzz.com
Editorial Profile: WHBZ-FM is a commercial station owned by Midwest Communications Inc. The format of the station is rock music. WHBZ-FM broadcasts to the Milwaukee area at 106.5 FM.

WHCB-FM
Owner: Appalachian Educational Communication Corp.
Editorial: 340 MLK Jr Blvd, Ste 100, Bristol, Tennessee 37620. **T:** 1 423 878-6279
E: whcb@aecc.org
W: http://www.whcbradio.org
Editorial Profile: WHCB-FM is a non-commercial station owned by the Appalachian Educational Communications Corp. The format

of the station is religious and talk. WHCB-FM broadcasts to the Bristol, TN area at 91.5 FM.

WHCC-FM
Owner: Artistic Media Partners Inc.
Editorial: 304 State Road 446, Bloomington, Indiana 47401-8837. **T:** 1 812 336-8000
E: whcc105@whcc105.com
W: http://www.whcc105.com
Editorial Profile: WHCC-FM is a commercial station owned by Artistic Media Partners Inc. The format of the station is country music. WHCC-FM broadcasts to the Bloomington, IN area at 105.1 FM.

WHCE-FM
Owner: Henrico County Schools
Editorial: 100 Tech Dr, Highland Springs, Virginia 23075. **T:** 1 804 328-4078
W: http://www.mix91.com

WHCF-FM
Owner: Lighthouse Radio Network, Inc.
Editorial: 1476 Broadway, Bangor, Maine 04401-2404. **T:** 1 207 947-2751
E: contact@whcffm.com
W: http://www.whcffm.com
Editorial Profile: WHCF-FM is a non-commercial station owned by the Lighthouse Radio Network, Inc. The format of the station is religious talk and contemporary christian music. WHCF-FM broadcasts to the Bangor, ME area at 88.5 FM.

WHCG-AM
Owner: Radio Metter Inc.
Editorial: 1075 E Lillian St, Metter, Georgia 30439. **T:** 1 912 685-2136
Editorial Profile: WHCG-AM is a commercial station owned by Radio Metter Inc. The format of the station is southern gospel. WHCG-AM broadcasts to the Metter, GA area at 1360 AM.

WHCJ-FM
Owner: Savannah State University
Editorial: 3219 College St, Savannah, Georgia 31404-5254. **T:** 1 912 358-4236
E: whcj@savannahstate.edu
W: http://www.savannahstate.edu/whcj
Editorial Profile: WHCJ-FM is a non-commercial station owned by Savannah State University. The format of the station is college variety. WHCJ-FM broadcasts to the Savannah, GA area at 90.3 FM.

WHCL-FM
Owner: Hamilton College
Editorial: 198 College Hill Rd, Clinton, New York 13323-1218. **T:** 1 315 859-4200
E: mngrwhcl@hamilton.edu
W: http://www.whcl.org
Editorial Profile: WHCL-FM is a non-commercial station owned by Hamilton College. The format of the station is college variety. WHCL-FM broadcasts to the Clinton, NY area at 88.7 FM.

WHCN-FM
Owner: Clear Channel Media and Entertainment
Editorial: 10 Columbus Blvd, Hartford, Connecticut 6106. **T:** 1 860 723-6000
W: http://www.theriver1059.com
Editorial Profile: WHCN-FM is a commercial station owned by Clear Channel Media and Entertainment. The format of the station is classic hits music. WHCN-FM broadcasts to the Hartford, CT area at 105.9 FM.

WHCO-AM
Owner: Hirsch Communications
Editorial: 1230 W Broadway St, Sparta, Illinois 62286. **T:** 1 618 443-2121
E: news@realcountry1230.com
W: http://realcountry1230.com
Editorial Profile: WHCO-AM is a commercial station owned by Hirsch Communications. The format of the station is classic country. WHCO-AM broadcasts to Sparta, IL at 1230 AM.

WHCR-FM
Owner: City College of New York
Editorial: City College 138th St & Covenant Ave, Room 11513, New York, New York 10031-9198. **T:** 1 212 650-7481
E: whcr903fm@whcr.org
W: http://www.whcr.org
Editorial Profile: WHCR-FM is a non-commercial station owned by the City College of New York. The format of the station is college variety. WHCR-FM broadcasts to the New York City metro area at 90.3 FM.

WHCU-AM
Owner: Saga Communications

Editorial: 1751 Hanshaw Rd, Ithaca, New York 14850. **T:** 1 607 257-6400
W: http://www.whcu870.com
Editorial Profile: WHCU-AM is a commercial station owned by Saga Communications. The format of the station is news and talk. WHCU-AM broadcasts to the Ithaca, NY area at 870 AM.

WHCY-FM
Owner: Clear Channel Media and Entertainment
Editorial: 45 Ed Mitchell Ave, Franklin, New Jersey 07416-1588. **T:** 1 973 827-2525
E: webmasternewton@clearchannel.com
W: http://www.max1063.com
Editorial Profile: WHCY-FM is a commercial station owned by Clear Channel Media and Entertainment. The format of the station is Hot AC music. WHCY-FM broadcasts in the Newton, NJ area at 106.3 FM.

WHDD-AM
Owner: Tri-State Public Communications, Inc
Editorial: 67 Main St, Sharon, Connecticut 6069. **T:** 1 860 364-4640
W: http://www.am1020whdd.com
Editorial Profile: WHDD-AM is a commercial station owned by Tri-State Public Communications, Inc. The format of the station is news and talk. WHDD-AM broadcasts to the Sharon, CT area at 1020 AM.

WHDD-FM
Owner: Tri-State Public Communications, Inc
Editorial: 67 Main St, Sharon, Connecticut 6069. **T:** 1 860 364-4640
W: http://www.whddfm.com
Editorial Profile: WHDD-FM is a non-commercial station owned by Tri-State Public Communications, Inc. The format of the station is news and talk. WHDD-FM broadcasts to the Sharon, CT area at 91.9 FM.

WHDG-FM
Owner: NRG Media LLC
Editorial: 3616 Highway 47, Rhinelander, Wisconsin 54501-8819. **T:** 1 715 362-1975
W: http://www.whdg.com
Editorial Profile: WHDG-FM is a commercial station owned by NRG Media LLC. The format of the station is contemporary country music. WHDG-FM broadcasts to the Rhinelander, WI area at 97.3 FM.

WHDI-FM
Owner: Wisconsin Educational Communications Board
Editorial: 2420 Nicolet Dr, Green Bay, Wisconsin 54311. **T:** 1 920 465-2444
E: listener@wpr.org **W:** http://www.wpr.org
Editorial Profile: WHDI-FM is a non-commercial station owned by Wisconsin Educational Communications Board. The format of the station is news and talk. WHDI-FM broadcasts locally to the Sister Bay, WI area at 91.9 FM.

WHDL-AM
Owner: Community Broadcasters, LLC
Editorial: 3163 Nys Route 417, Olean, New York 14760-1853. **T:** 1 716 372-0161
Editorial Profile: WHDL-AM is a commercial station owned by Community Broadcasters, LLC. The format of the station is oldies. WHDL-AM broadcasts to the Olean, NY area at 1450 AM.

WHDM-AM
Owner: WHDM Broadcasting, Inc.
Editorial: 110 India Rd, Paris, Tennessee 38242. **T:** 1 731 644-9455
E: radionews@bellsouth.net
W: http://www.whdmradio.com
Editorial Profile: WHDM-AM is a commercial station owned by WHDM Broadcasting, Inc. of Tennessee. The format of the station is oldies. WHDM-AM broadcasts to the Paris, TN area at 1440 AM.

WHDQ-FM
Owner: Great Eastern Radio, LLC
Editorial: 106 N Main St, West Lebanon, New Hampshire 03784-1136. **T:** 1 603 298-0332
W: http://www.theqrocks.com
Editorial Profile: WHDQ-FM is a commercial station owned by Great Eastern Radio, LLC. The format of the station is classic rock music. WHDQ-FM broadcasts to the West Lebanon, NH area at 106.1 FM.

WHEB-FM
Owner: Clear Channel Media and Entertainment
Editorial: 815 Lafayette Rd, Portsmouth, New Hampshire 03801-7411. **T:** 1 603 436-7300
W: http://www.wheb.com
Editorial Profile: WHEB-FM is a commercial station owned by Clear Channel Media and Entertainment. The format of the station is rock. WHEB-FM broadcasts to the Boston area at 100.3 FM.

WHEE-AM
Owner: Martinsville Media, Inc.
Editorial: 1129 Chatham Rd, Martinsville, Virginia 24112-2149. **T:** 1 276 632-9811
E: news@martinsvilledaily.com
W: http://www.wheeradio.com
Editorial Profile: WHEE-AM is a commercial station owned by Martinsville Media, Inc. The format of the station is news and talk. WHEE-AM broadcasts to the Martinsville, VA area at 1370 AM.

WHEM-FM
Owner: Fourth Dimension Inc.
Editorial: 228 E Lowes Creek Rd, Eau Claire, Wisconsin 54701-7250. **T:** 1 715 838-9595
E: whem@whem.com
W: http://www.whem.com
Editorial Profile: WHEM-FM is a non-commercial station owned by Fourth Dimension Inc. The format of the station is contemporary Christian programming. WHEM-FM broadcasts to the Eau Claire, WI area at 91.3 FM.

WHEN-AM
Owner: Clear Channel Media and Entertainment
Editorial: 500 Plum St, Ste 100, Syracuse, New York 13204. **T:** 1 315 472-9797
W: http://www.wphrfm.com
Editorial Profile: WHEN-AM is a commercial station owned by Clear Channel Media and Entertainment. The format of the station is Urban AC. WHEN-AM broadcasts to the Syracuse, NY area at 620 AM.

WHEO-AM
Owner: Patrick County Communications, Inc.
Editorial: 3824 Wayside Rd, Stuart, Virginia 24171-2506. **T:** 1 276 694-3114
E: 1270am@wheo.info
W: http://www.wheo.info
Editorial Profile: WHEO-AM is a commercial station owned by Patrick County Communications, Inc. The format of the station is classic and contemporary country music. WHEO-AM broadcasts in the Stuart, VA area at 1270 AM.

WHEP-AM
Owner: Stewart Broadcasting Co. Inc.
Editorial: 20109 Whep Ln, Foley, Alabama 36535. **T:** 1 251 943-7131
E: whepnews@yahoo.com
W: http://www.whep1310.com
Editorial Profile: WHEP-AM is a commercial station owned by Stewart Broadcasting Co. Inc. The format for the station is news, talk and adult standards. WHEP-AM broadcasts to the Mobile, AL and Pensacola, FL areas at 1310 AM.

WHET-FM
Owner: Withers Broadcasting Co.
Editorial: 1822 N Court St, Marion, Illinois 62959-4558. **T:** 1 618 997-8123
W: http://www.mywithersradio.com
Editorial Profile: WHET-FM is a commercial station owned by Withers Broadcasting Co. The format of the station is classic country. WHET-FM broadcasts to the Cape Girardeau, MO area at 97.7 FM.

WHEW-AM
Owner: S.G. Communications
Editorial: 1811 Carters Creek Pike, Franklin, Tennessee 37064-6823. **T:** 1 615 599-1384
W: http://www.bonita1380radio.com
Editorial Profile: WHEW-AM is a commercial station owned by S.G. Communications. The format of the station is Hispanic. WHEW-AM broadcasts to the Franklin, TN area at 1380 AM.

WHFA-AM
Owner: Starboard Media Foundation Inc.
Editorial: 702 S High Point Rd, Madison, Wisconsin 53719-3522. **T:** 1 608 833-7888
E: info@relevantradio.com
W: http://www.relevantradio.com
Editorial Profile: WHFA-AM is a non-commercial station owned by Starboard Media Foundation Inc. The format of the station is religious music. WHFA-FM broadcasts to the Madison, WI area at 1240 AM.

WHFB-AM
Owner: Gerard Media LLC
Editorial: 685 East 1675 North, Michigan City, Indiana 46360. **T:** 1 219 879-9810
Editorial Profile: WHFB-AM is a commercial station owned by Gerard Media LLC. The format for the station is Conservative talk. WHFB-AM broadcasts to the Benton Harbor, MI area at 1060 AM.

WHFB-FM
Owner: Douglas Road Radio, Inc.
Editorial: 1301 E Douglas Rd, Mishawaka, Indiana 46545-1732. **T:** 1 574 233-3141
W: http://www.radiomichiana.com
Editorial Profile: WHFB-FM is a commercial station owned by Douglas Road Radio, Inc. The format of the station is contemporary country. WHFB-FM broadcasts to the South Bend, IN area at 99.9 FM.

WHFC-FM
Owner: Harford Community College
Editorial: 401 Thomas Run Rd, Bel Air, Maryland 21015-1627. **T:** 1 443 412-2151
E: whfc@harford.edu
W: http://www.whfc911.org
Editorial Profile: WHFC-FM is a non-commercial station owned by Harford Community College. The format of the station is college variety. WHFC-FM broadcasts to the Bel Air, MD area at 91.1 FM.

WHFH-FM
Owner: Homewood-Flossmoor High School
Editorial: 999 Kedzie Ave, Flossmoor, Illinois 60422-2248. **T:** 1 708 798-9434
Editorial Profile: WHFH-FM is a commercial station owned by Homewood-Flossmoor High School. The format of the station is album oriented rock music. WHFH-FM broadcasts to the Flossmoor, IL area at 88.5 FM.

WHFM-FM
Owner: Cox Media Group, Inc.
Editorial: 555 Sunrise Hwy, West Babylon, New York 11704. **T:** 1 631 587-1023
E: wbab@wbab.com **W:** http://www.wbab.com
Editorial Profile: WHFM-FM is a commercial station owned by Cox Media Group, Inc. The format of the station is rock/album-oriented rock. WHFM-FM broadcasts to the West Babylon, NY area at 95.3 FM.

WHFR-FM
Owner: Henry Ford Community College
Editorial: 5101 Evergreen Road Henry Ford CC, Dearborn, Michigan 48128-1495.
T: 1 313 845-9676 **E:** whfr@hfcc.edu
W: http://www.whfr.fm
Editorial Profile: WHFR-FM is a non-commercial station owned by Henry Ford Community College. The format of the station is a variety of music including blues, jazz, folk, metal rock, classic rock and urban music. WHFR-FM broadcasts to Dearborn, MI at 89.3 FM.

WHFS-AM
Owner: CBS Radio
Editorial: 9721 Executive Center Dr N Ste 200, Saint Petersburg, Florida 33702-2439.
T: 1 727 579-1925
W: http://tampa.cbslocal.com/category/sports
Editorial Profile: WHFS-AM is a commercial station owned by CBS Radio. The format of the station is sports. WHFS-AM broadcasts to the Tampa, FL area at 1010 AM.

WHFS-FM
Owner: CBS Radio
Editorial: 9721 Executive Center Dr N Ste 200, Saint Petersburg, Florida 33702-2439.
T: 1 727 568-0941
W: http://tampa.cbslocal.com/station/98-7-the-fan
Editorial Profile: WHFS-FM is a commercial station owned by CBS Radio. The format of the station is sports talk. WHFS-FM broadcasts to the Tampa, FL area at 98.7 FM.

WHFX-FM
Owner: Clear Channel Media and Entertainment
Editorial: 3833 US Highway 82, Brunswick, Georgia 31523-7735. **T:** 1 912 267-1025
E: scottryfun@gmail.com
W: http://1077thefox.net
Editorial Profile: WHFX-FM is a commercial station owned by Clear Channel Media and Entertainment. The format of the station is rock. WHFX-FM broadcasts to the Brunswick, GA area at 107.7 FM.

WHGB-AM
Owner: Cumulus Media Inc.
Editorial: 2300 Vartan Way, Harrisburg, Pennsylvania 17110-9720. **T:** 1 717 238-1041
W: http://www.sportsradio953.com
Editorial Profile: WHGB-AM is a commercial station owned by Cumulus Media Inc. The format of the station is sports. WHGB-AM broadcasts to the Harrisburg, PA area at 1400 AM.

WHGG-AM
Owner: Information Communications Corp.
Editorial: 340 Martin Luther King Jr Blvd Ste 100, Bristol, Tennessee 37620-4080.
T: 1 423 878-6279
Editorial Profile: WHGG-AM is a commercial station owned by Information Communications Corp. The format of the station is Contemporary Christian. WHGG-AM broadcasts to the Bristol, TN area at 1090 AM.

WHGH-AM
Owner: Gross(Moses)
Editorial: US 19 South 221 Pallbearer Road, Thomasville, Georgia 31792.
T: 1 229 228-4124
Editorial Profile: WHGH-AM is a commercial station owned by Moses Gross. The format of the station is urban contemporary music. WHGH-AM broadcasts to the Thomasville, GA area at 840 AM.

WHGL-FM
Owner: Cantroair Communications Co.
Editorial: 170 Redington Ave, Troy, Pennsylvania 16947. **T:** 1 570 297-0100
E: whgl100@gmail.com
W: http://www.wiggle100.com
Editorial Profile: WHGL-FM is a commercial station owned by Cantroair Communications Co. The format is contemporary country music. WHGL-FM broadcasts to the Troy, PA area at 100.3 FM.

WHHB-FM
Owner: Holliston High School Broadcast Corp.
Editorial: 370 Hollis St, Holliston, Massachusetts 01746-1135.
T: 1 508 429-0681 5109
E: whhbfm@whhbfm.com

WHHD-FM
Owner: Beasley Broadcast Group
Editorial: 4051 Jimmie Dyess Pkwy, Augusta, Georgia 30909. **T:** 1 706 396-7000
W: http://www.hd983.com
Editorial Profile: WHHD-FM is a commercial station owned by Beasley Broadcast Group. The format of the station is Top 40/CHR. WHHD-FM broadcasts to the Augusta, SC area at 98.3 FM.

WHHH-FM
Owner: Radio One Inc.
Editorial: 21 E Saint Joseph St, Indianapolis, Indiana 46204-1025. **T:** 1 317 266-9600
W: http://indyhiphop.com
Editorial Profile: WHHH-FM is a commercial station owned by Radio One Inc. The format of the station is rhythmic Top 40/CHR music. WHHH-FM broadcasts to the Indianapolis area at 96.3 FM.

WHHI-FM
Owner: University of Wisconsin
Editorial: 821 University Ave, Madison, Wisconsin 53706. **T:** 1 608 263-3970
E: listener@wpr.org **W:** http://www.wpr.org
Editorial Profile: WHHI-FM is non-commercial station owned by University of Wisconsin. The format of the station is classical music, news and talk. WHHI-FM broadcasts to the Madison, WI area at 91.3 FM.

WHHL-FM
Owner: Radio One Inc.
Editorial: 9666 Olive Blvd, Suite 610, Saint Louis, Missouri 63132. **T:** 1 314 989-9550
W: http://www.hot1041stl.com
Editorial Profile: WHHL-FM is a commercial station owned by Radio One Inc. The format of the station is urban contemporary. WHHL-FM broadcasts to the St. Louis area at 104.1 FM.

WHHM-FM
Owner: Southern Stone Communications, LLC
Editorial: 111 W Main St, Jackson, Tennessee 38301. **T:** 1 731 427-9616
W: http://www.star1077.fm
Editorial Profile: WHHM-FM is a commercial station owned by Southern Stone Communications, LLC. The format of the station is adult contemporary. WHHM-FM broadcasts to the Jackson, TN area at 107.7 FM.

WHHT-FM
Owner: Commonwealth Broadcasting Corp.

Editorial: 113 W Public Sq Ste 400, Glasgow, Kentucky 42141-2438. **T:** 1 270 651-6050
W: http://www.1037thepoint.net
Editorial Profile: WHHT-FM is a commercial station owned by Commonwealth Broadcasting Corp. The format of the station is country. WHHT-FM broadcasts to the Glasgow, KY area at 103.7 FM.

WHHV-AM
Owner: New Life Christian Communication
Editorial: 343 Virginia Ave, Hillsville, Virginia 24343. **T:** 1 276 728-9114
E: whhv@whhvradio.com
W: http://www.whhvradio.com
Editorial Profile: WHHV-AM is a commercial station owned by New Life Christian Communication. The format of the station is gospel music. WHHV-AM broadcasts to the Hillsville, VA area at 1400 AM.

WHHW-AM
Owner: L & L Radio
Editorial: 1 Augustine Place, Hilton Head, South Carolina. **T:** 1 843 785-9569
W: http://am1130theisland.com
Editorial Profile: WHHW-AM is a commercial station owned by Adventure Radio Group LLC. The format of the station is adult standards. WHHW-AM broadcasts to the Hilton Head, SC area at 1130 AM.

WHHY-FM
Owner: Cumulus Media Inc.
Editorial: 1 Commerce St, Montgomery, Alabama 36104-3510. **T:** 1 334 240-9274
W: http://www.y102montgomery.com
Editorial Profile: WHHY-FM is a commercial station owned by Cumulus Media Inc. The format of the station is Top 40/CHR. WHHY-FM broadcasts to the Montgomery, AL area at 101.9 FM.

WHHZ-FM
Owner: Marc Radio Group, LLC
Editorial: 100 Nw 76Th Dr Ste 2, Gainesville, Florida 32607-6659. **T:** 1 352 313-3150
W: http://www.1005thebuzz.com
Editorial Profile: WHHZ-FM is a commercial station owned by Marc Radio Group, LLC. The format of the station is rock alternative. WHHZ-FM broadcasts to the Gainesville, FL area at 100.5 FM.

WHIC-AM
Owner: Holy Family Communications
Editorial: 1545 East Ave, Rochester, New York 14610-1614. **T:** 1 585 271-0530
E: info@thestationofthecross.com
W: http://www.whicradio.com
Editorial Profile: WHIC-AM is a commercial station owned by Holy Family Communications. The format of the station is religious. WHIC-AM broadcasts to the Rochester, NY area at 1460 AM.

WHID-FM
Owner: University of Wisconsin
Editorial: 2420 Nicolet Dr, Green Bay, Wisconsin 54311-7003. **T:** 1 920 465-2444
E: listener@wpr.org **W:** http://www.wpr.org
Editorial Profile: WHID-FM is a non-commercial station owned by University of Wisconsin. The format of the station is news and talk. WHID-FM broadcasts to the Green Bay, WI, area at 88.1 FM.

WHIE-AM
Owner: Chappell Communications LLC
Editorial: 1000 Memorial Dr, Griffin, Georgia 30223-4446. **T:** 1 770 227-9451
Editorial Profile: WHIE-AM is a commercial station owned by Chappell Communictions LLC. The format of the station is country music. WHIE-AM broadcasts to the Griffin, GA area at 1320 AM.

WHIF-FM
Owner: Putnam Radio Ministries Inc.
Editorial: 201 S Palm Ave, Palatka, Florida 32177-4141. **T:** 1 386 325-3334
E: info@whif.org **W:** http://www.whif.org
Editorial Profile: WHIF-FM is a non-commercial station owned by Putnam Radio Ministries Inc. The format of the station is contemporary Christian. WHIF-FM broadcasts to the Palatka, FL area at 91.3 FM.

WHIJ-FM
Owner: Radio Training Network, Inc.
Editorial: 2131 Nw 40Th Ter Ste E, Gainesville, Florida 32605-5800.
T: 1 352 373-9553 **E:** thejoyfm@thejoyfm.com
W: http://www.thejoyfm.com

WHIL-FM
Owner: Spring Hill College
Editorial: 4000 Dauphin St, Mobile, Alabama 36608. **T:** 1 205 348-6644 **E:** news@whil.org
W: http://www.apr.org
Editorial Profile: WHIL-FM is a non-commercial station owned by Spring Hill College. The format for the station is classical, news and talk. WHIL-FM broadcasts to the Mobile, AL, Pensacola, FL area at 91.3 FM. They do not accept pre-recorded PSAs.

WHIM-AM
Owner: Salem Communications
Editorial: 2828 W Flagler St, Miami, Florida 33135. **T:** 1 305 644-0800
W: http://www.1080wmcu.com
Editorial Profile: WHIM-AM is a commercial station owned by Salem Communications. The format of the station is Christian talk and religious. WHIM-AM broadcasts to the Miami area at 1080 AM.

WHIN-AM
Owner: WHIN Inc.
Editorial: 1625 Highway 109 N, Gallatin, Tennessee 37066. **T:** 1 615 451-0450
E: whinam@comcast.net
W: http://www.whinradio.com
Editorial Profile: WHIN-AM is a commercial station owned by WHIN Inc. The format of the station is classic country. WHIN-AM broadcasts in the Gallatin, TN area at 1010 AM.

WHIO-AM
Owner: Cox Media Group, Inc.
Editorial: 1611 S Main St, Dayton, Ohio 45409-2547. **T:** 1 937 259-2111
W: http://www.newstalkradiowhio.com
Editorial Profile: WHIO-AM is a commercial station owned by Cox Media Group, Inc. The format of the station is news and talk. WHIO-AM broadcasts to the Dayton, OH area at 1290 AM.

WHIO-FM
Owner: Cox Media Group, Inc.
Editorial: 1611 S. Main Street, Dayton, Ohio 45409. **T:** 1 937 259-2111
W: http://newstalkradiowhio.com
Editorial Profile: WHIO-FM is a commercial station owned by Cox Media Group, Inc. The format of the station is news and talk. WDPT-FM broadcasts to the Dayton, OH area at 95.7 FM.

WHIP-AM
Owner: Hamrick(Glenn)
Editorial: 2432 Statesville Hwy, Mooresville, North Carolina 28115-7968.
T: 1 704 664-9447
W: http://carolinascene.com/w/whip/index.htm
Editorial Profile: WHIP-AM is a commercial station owned by Glenn Hamrick. The format of the station is oldies music. WHIP-AM broadcasts to the Mooresville, NC, at 1350 AM.

WHIR-AM
Owner: Hometown Broadcasting
Editorial: 2063 Shakertown Rd, Danville, Kentucky 40422. **T:** 1 859 236-2711
E: hometownradio@bellsouth.net
Editorial Profile: WHIR-AM is a commercial station owned by Hometown Broadcasting. The format for the station is news, sports and talk. WHIR-AM broadcasts to the Lexington, KY area at 1230 AM.

WHIS-AM
Owner: L & L Broadcasting
Editorial: 900 Bluefield Ave, Bluefield, West Virginia 24701-2744. **T:** 1 304 327-7114
W: http://www.whistalkradio.com
Editorial Profile: WHIS-AM is a commercial station owned by L & L Broadcasting. The format of the station is news and talk. WHIS-AM broadcasts to the Bluefield, WV area at 1440 AM.

WHIT-AM
Owner: Midwest Family Broadcasting
Editorial: 730 Ray O Vac Dr, Madison, Wisconsin 53711. **T:** 1 608 273-1000
W: http://www.hitradio1550.com

WHIZ-AM
Owner: Southeastern Ohio Broadcasting, Inc.
Editorial: 629 Downard Rd, Zanesville, Ohio 43701-5108. **T:** 1 740 452-5431
W: http://www.whiznews.com
Editorial Profile: WHIZ-AM is a commercial station owned by Southeastern Ohio Broadcasting, Inc. The format of the station is talk. WHIZ-AM broadcasts locally to the Zanesville, OH area at a frequency of 1240 AM.

WHIZ-FM
Owner: Southeastern Ohio Broadcastng, Inc.
Editorial: 629 Downard Rd, Zanesville, Ohio 43701-5108. **T:** 1 740 452-5431
E: webmaster@whizamfmtv.com
W: http://www.whiznews.com/fm
Editorial Profile: WHIZ-FM is a non-commercial station owned by Southeastern Ohio Broadcastng, Inc. The format of the station is hot adult contemporary. WHIZ-FM broadcasts to the Zanesville, OH area at 92.7 FM.

WHJB-FM
Owner: Renda Broadcasting
Editorial: 2000 Tower Way, Ste 2040, Greensburg, Pennsylvania 15601.
T: 1 724 216-1200 **W:** http://www.whjbfm.com
Editorial Profile: WHJB-FM is a commercial station owned by Renda Broadcasting. The format of the station is classic hits. WHJB-FM broadcasts to the Greensburg area at 107.1 FM.

WHJD-AM
Owner: Broadcast South, LLC
Editorial: 546 Baxley Hwy, Hazlehurst, Georgia 31539-5917. **T:** 1 912 375-4511
Editorial Profile: WHJD-AM is a commercial station owned by Broadcast South, LLC. The format for the station is classic country. WHJD-AM broadcasts to the Savannah, GA area at 920 AM.

WHJE-FM
Owner: Carmel Clay Schools
Editorial: 520 E Main St, Carmel, Indiana 46032. **T:** 1 317 846-7721 **E:** news@whje.com
W: http://www.whje.com
Editorial Profile: WHJE-FM is a non-commercial station owned by Carmel Clay Schools. The format of the station is classic rock and alternative rock music. WHJE-FM broadcasts to the Carmel, IN area at 91.3 FM.

WHJJ-AM
Owner: Clear Channel Media and Entertainment
Editorial: 75 Oxford St, Providence, Rhode Island 02905-4722. **T:** 1 401 781-9979
W: http://www.920whjj.com
Editorial Profile: WHJJ-AM is a commercial station owned by Clear Channel Media and Entertainment. The format of the station is news and talk. WHJJ-AM broadcasts to the Providence, RI area at 920 AM.

WHJT-FM
Owner: Mississippi College
Editorial: 100 S Jefferson, Clinton, Mississippi 39056-4236. **T:** 1 601 925-3458
E: psas@star93fm.com
W: http://www.star93fm.com
Editorial Profile: WHJT-FM is a commercial station owned by Mississippi College. The format of the station is contemporary Christian. WHJT-FM broadcasts to the Clinton, MS area at 93.5 FM.

WHJX-FM
Owner: Cox Media Group, Inc.
Editorial: 8000 Belfort Pkwy, Jacksonville, Florida 32256-6934. **T:** 1 904 245-8500
W: http://www.myhot1065.com
Editorial Profile: WHJX-FM is a commercial station owned by Cox Media Group, Inc. The format of the station is urban oldies. WHJX-FM broadcasts to the Jacksonville, FL area at 106.5 FM.

WHJY-FM
Owner: Clear Channel Media and Entertainment
Editorial: 75 Oxford St, Providence, Rhode Island 2905. **T:** 1 401 781-9979
E: jocks@whjy.com **W:** http://www.whjy.com
Editorial Profile: WHJY-FM is a commercial station owned by Clear Channel Media and Entertainment. The format of the station is rock music. WHJY-FM broadcasts to the Providence, RI area at 94.1 FM.

WHK-AM
Owner: Salem Communications
Editorial: 4 Summit Park Dr Ste 150, Independence, Ohio 44131-6921.
T: 1 216 901-0921
E: youropinioncounts@whkradio.com
W: http://www.whkradio.com
Editorial Profile: WHK-AM is a commercial station owned by Salem Communications. The format of the station is Conservative talk. WHK-AM broadcasts to the Independence, OH area at 1420 AM.

WHKB-FM
Owner: Houghton Community Broadcasting Corporation
Editorial: 313 E Montezuma Ave, Houghton, Michigan 49931-2112. **T:** 1 906 482-7700
E: houghtonradio@up.net
W: http://www.kbear102.com
Editorial Profile: WHKB-FM is a commercial station owned by Houghton Community Broadcasting Corporation. The format of the station is contemporary country music. WHKB-FM broadcasts to the Houghton, MI area at 102.3 FM.

WHKF-FM
Owner: Clear Channel Media and Entertainment
Editorial: 600 Corporate Cir, Harrisburg, Pennsylvania 17110. **T:** 1 717 540-8800
W: http://www.993kissfm.com
Editorial Profile: WHKF-FM is a commercial station owned by Clear Channel Media and Entertainment. The format of the station is Top 40/CHR. WHKF-FM broadcasts to the Harrisburg, PA area at 99.3 FM.

WHKL-FM
Owner: Batesville Broadcasting Co.
Editorial: 1040 Highway 6 W, Batesville, Mississippi 38606-8104. **T:** 1 662 563-4664
E: country101radio@yahoo.com
Editorial Profile: WHKL-FM is owned by Batesville Broadcasting Co. The format of the station is oldies music. WHKL-FM's broadcasts to the Memphis, TN area at 106.9 FM.

WHKN-FM
Owner: Georgia Eagle Broadcasting Inc.
Editorial: 561 E Olliff St, Statesboro, Georgia 30458-4663. **T:** 1 912 764-5446
E: wwnswmcd@yahoo.com
Editorial Profile: WHKN-FM is a commercial station owned by Georgia Eagle Broadcasting Inc. The format of the station is classic and contemporary country. WHKN-FM broadcasts to the Savannah, GA area at 94.9 FM.

WHKO-FM
Owner: Cox Media Group, Inc.
Editorial: 1611 S Main St, Dayton, Ohio 45409-2547. **T:** 1 937 259-2111
W: http://www.k99online.com
Editorial Profile: WHKO-FM is a commercial station owned by Cox Media Group, Inc. The format of the station is country. WHKO-FM broadcasts to the Dayton, OH area at 99.1 FM.

WHKP-AM
Owner: Radio Hendersonville Inc.
Editorial: 1450 7th Ave E, Hendersonville, North Carolina 28792-2860.
T: 1 828 693-9061 **E:** 1450@whkp.com
W: http://www.whkp.com
Editorial Profile: WHKP-AM is a commercial station owned by Radio Hendersonville Inc. The format of the station is talk and variety programming. WHKP-AM broadcasts to the Hendersonville, NC area at 1450 AM.

WHKQ-FM
Owner: Gross Communications Co.
Editorial: 2301 Lucien Way Ste 180, Maitland, Florida 32751-7034. **T:** 1 407 647-5557
W: http://kq103.com
Editorial Profile: WHKQ-FM is a commercial station owned by Gross Communications Co. The format of the station is Spanish Top 40/CHR. WHKQ-FM broadcasts to the Orlando, FL area at 103.1 FM.

WHKR-FM
Owner: Cumulus Media Inc.
Editorial: 1800 W Hibiscus Blvd Ste 138, Melbourne, Florida 32901-2624.
T: 1 321 984-1000
W: http://www.thehitkicker.com
Editorial Profile: WHKR-FM is a commercial station owned by Cumulus Broadcasting. The format of the station is classic and contemporary country music. WHKR-FM broadcasts to the Melbourne, FL area at 102.7 AM.

WHKS-FM
Owner: L-Com Inc.
Editorial: 42 N Main St, Port Allegany, Pennsylvania 16743. **T:** 1 814 642-7004
E: whks@verizon.net
Editorial Profile: WHKS-FM is a commercial station owned by L-Com Inc. The format of the station is adult contemporary music. WHKS-FM broadcasts to the Port Allegany, NY area at 94.9 FM.

WHKT-AM
Owner: Chesapeake-Portsmouth Broadcasting Corp.
Editorial: 2202 Jolliff Rd, Chesapeake, Virginia 23321-1416. **T:** 1 757 488-1010
E: info@1650whkt.com
W: http://1650whkt.com
Editorial Profile: WHKT-AM is owned by Chesapeake-Portsmouth Broadcasting Corporation. The format is conservative talk. The station broadcasts to the Hampton Roads, VA area at a frequency of 1650 AM.

WHKU-FM
Owner: Educational Media Foundation
Editorial: 1365 Wiley Rd Ste 151, Schaumburg, Illinois 60173-4357.
T: 1 847 991-9400 **W:** http://www.klove.com
Editorial Profile: WHKU-FM is an non-commercial station owned by Educational Media Foundation. The format of the station is Christian music. WHKU-FM broadcasts to the Proctorville, OH area at 91.9 FM.

WHKW-AM
Owner: Salem Communications
Editorial: 4 Summit Park Dr, Ste 150, Cleveland, Ohio 44131-6921.
T: 1 216 901-0921
W: http://www.whkwradio.com
Editorial Profile: WHKW-AM is a commercial station owned by Salem Communications. The format of the station is religion. WHKW-AM broadcasts to the Cleveland area at 1220 AM.

WHKX-FM
Owner: L & L Broadcasting
Editorial: 900 Bluefield Ave, Bluefield, West Virginia 24701-2744. **T:** 1 304 327-7114
W: http://www.kickscountry.com
Editorial Profile: WHKX-FM is a commercial station owned by L & L Broadcasting. The format of the station is classic and contemporary country music. WHKX-FM broadcasts to the Bluefield, WV area at 106.3 FM.

WHKY-AM
Owner: Long Communications
Editorial: 526 Main Ave SE, Hickory, North Carolina 28602. **T:** 1 828 322-1290
E: news@whky.com **W:** http://www.whky.com
Editorial Profile: WHKY-AM is a commercial station owned by Long Communications. The format of the station is news, sports and talk. WHKY-AM broadcasts to the Hickory, NC area at 1290 AM.

WHKZ-AM
Owner: Salem Communications
Editorial: 4 Summit Park Dr, Ste 150, Independence, Ohio 44131. **T:** 1 216 901-0921
W: http://www.whkwradio.com
Editorial Profile: WHKZ-AM is a commercial station owned by Salem Communications. The format of the station is religious. WHKZ-AM broadcasts to the Warrenville, OH area at 1220 AM.

WHLA-FM
Owner: Wisconsin Educational Communications Board
Editorial: Whitney Center UW-LaCrosse, 515 N 15th St, La Crosse, Wisconsin 54601.
T: 1 608 785-8380 **E:** wlsuwhla@uwlax.edu
W: http://www.wpr.org/whla
Editorial Profile: WHLA-FM is a non-commercial station owned by Wisconsin Educational Communications Board. The format of the station is news and talk. WHLA-FM broadcasts to the LaCrosse, WI area at 90.3 FM.

WHLC-FM
Owner: Charisma Radio Corp.
Editorial: 2420 Highway 64 East, Highlands, North Carolina 28741. **T:** 1 828 526-1045
E: info@whlc.com **W:** http://www.whlc.com
Editorial Profile: WHLC-FM is a commercial station owned by Charisma Radio Corp. The format of the station is easy listening music. WHLC-FM broadcasts locally to the Greenville, SC and Asheville, NC areas at 104.5 FM.

WHLD-AM
Owner: Cumulus Media Inc.
Editorial: 50 James E Casey Dr, Buffalo, New York 14206-2367. **T:** 1 716 8814555
W: http://www.sportsradio1270.com
Editorial Profile: WHLD-AM is a commercial station owned by Cumulus Media Inc. The format of the station is sports. WHLD-AM broadcasts to the Buffalo, NY area at 1270 AM.

WHLF-FM
Owner: Lakes Media LLC
Editorial: 1210 Porter Ln, South Boston, Virginia 24592-5324. **T:** 1 434 572-2988
E: news@whlf.com **W:** http://www.953hlf.com
Editorial Profile: WHLF-FM is a commercial station owned by Lakes Media LLC. The format of the station is adult contemporary music. WHLF-FM broadcasts to the Roanoke-Lynchburg, VA area at 95.3 FM.

WHLG-FM
Owner: Horton Broadcasting Company, Inc.
Editorial: 1670 NW Federal Hwy, Stuart, Florida 34994. **T:** 1 772 692-9454
E: info@coast1013.com
W: http://www.coast1013.com
Editorial Profile: WHLG-FM is a commercial station owned by Horton Broadcasting Company, Inc. The format of the station is adult contemporary. WHLG-FM broadcasts to the Stuart, FL area at 101.3 FM.

WHLH-FM
Owner: Clear Channel Media and Entertainment
Editorial: 1375 Beasley Rd, Jackson, Mississippi 39206-2018. **T:** 1 601 982-1062
W: http://www.hallelujah955.com
Editorial Profile: WHLH-FM is a commercial station owned by Clear Channel Media and Entertainment. The format of the station is gospel. WHLH-FM broadcasts to the Jackson, MS area at 95.5 FM.

WHLI-AM
Owner: Connoisseur Media, Inc.
Editorial: 234 Airport Plaza Blvd Ste 5, Farmingdale, New York 11735-3938.
T: 1 631 770-4200
E: webmaster@liradiogroup.com
W: http://www.whli.com
Editorial Profile: WHLI-AM is a commercial station owned by Connoisseur Media, Inc. The format of the station is adult standards. WHLI-AM broadcasts to the Farmingdale, NY, area at 1100 AM.

WHLJ-FM
Owner: LaTaurus Productions Inc.
Editorial: 5852 US Highway 84 E, Naylor, Georgia 31641. **T:** 1 229 242-9997
E: whlj@bellsouth.net
Editorial Profile: WHLJ-FM is a commercial station owned by LaTaurus Productions Inc. The format of the station is urban adult contemporary and gospel. WHLJ-FM broadcasts to the Valdosta, GA area at 97.5 FM.

WHLK-FM
Owner: Clear Channel Media and Entertainment
Editorial: 6200 Oak Tree Blvd, Ste 400, Independence, Ohio 44131. **T:** 1 216 520-2600
E: feedback@1065thelake.com
W: http://www.1065thelake.com/main.html
Editorial Profile: WHLK-FM is a commercial station owned by Clear Channel Media and Entertainment. The format of the station is adult hits. WHLK-FM broadcasts in the Cleveland area at 106.5 FM.

WHLL-AM
Owner: Cumulus Media Inc.
Editorial: 1000 Hall of Fame Ave, Springfield, Massachusetts 01105-2538.
T: 1 413 737-1414
W: http://www.1450thehall.com
Editorial Profile: WHLL-AM is a commercial station owned by Cumulus Media Inc. The format of the station is sports. WHLL-AM broadcasts to the Springfield, MA area at 1450 AM.

WHLM-AM
Owner: Columbia Broadcasting Co.
Editorial: 124 E Main St, Bloomsburg, Pennsylvania 17815. **T:** 1 570 784-1200
E: whlmam@aol.com
W: http://www.whlmam.com
Editorial Profile: WHLM-AM is a commercial station owned by Columbia Broadcasting Co. The format of the station is news, talk and sports. WHLM-AM broadcasts to the Bloomsburg, PA area at 930 AM.

WHLM-FM
Owner: Columbia Broadcasting Co.
Editorial: 124 E Main St, Bloomsburg, Pennsylvania 17815-1807. **T:** 1 570 784-1200
E: whlmam@aol.com
W: http://www.whlmfm.com
Editorial Profile: WHLM-FM is a commercial station owned by Columbia Broadcasting Co. The format for the station is adult contemporary. WHLM-FM broadcasts to the Bloomsburg, Pa. area at 103.5 FM.

WHLN-AM
Owner: Radio Harlan Inc.
Editorial: 100 Eversole St, Ste 1, Harlan, Kentucky 40831. **T:** 1 606 573-2540
E: whln@harlanonline.net
Editorial Profile: WHLN-AM is a commercial station owned by Radio Harlan Inc. The format of the station is adult contemporary music. WHLN-AM broadcasts to the Harlan, KY area at 1410 AM.

WHLO-AM
Owner: Clear Channel Media and Entertainment
Editorial: 7755 Freedom Ave NW, North Canton, Ohio 44720. **T:** 1 330 836-4700
W: http://www.640whlo.com
Editorial Profile: WHLO-AM is a commercial station owned by Clear Channel Media and Entertainment. The format of the station is news and talk. WHLO-AM broadcasts in the Cleveland area at 640 AM.

WHLP-FM
Owner: Calvary Radio Network
Editorial: 150 Lincolnway, Ste 2001, Valparaiso, Indiana 46383. **T:** 1 219 548-5800
E: info@calvaryradionet.com
W: http://www.calvaryradionetwork.com
Editorial Profile: WHLP-FM is a non-commercial station owned by Calvary Radio Network. The format of the station is Christian music and religious programming. WHLP-FM broadcasts to the Hanna, IN area at 89.9 FM.

WHLS-AM
Owner: Radio First
Editorial: 808 Huron Ave, Port Huron, Michigan 48060-3705. **T:** 1 810 982-9000
W: http://www.whls.net
Editorial Profile: WHLS-AM is a commercial station owned by Radio First. The format of the station is classic hits. WHLS-AM broadcasts to the Port Huron, MI area at 1450 AM.

WHLW-FM
Owner: Clear Channel Media and Entertainment
Editorial: 203 Gunn Rd, Montgomery, Alabama 36117. **T:** 1 334 274-6464
W: http://www.1043hallelujahfm.com
Editorial Profile: WHLW-FM is a commercial station owned by Clear Channel Media and Entertainment. The format of the station is urban contemporary gospel. WHLW-FM broadcasts to the Montgomery, AL area at 104.3 FM.

WHLX-AM
Owner: Radio First
Editorial: 808 Huron Ave, Port Huron, Michigan 48060-3705. **T:** 1 810 982-9000
W: http://www.whls.net
Editorial Profile: WHLX-AM is a commercial station owned by Radio First. The format of the station is classic hits. WHLX-AM broadcasts to the Port Huron, MI area at 1590 AM.

WHLY-AM
Owner: Times Communications, Inc.
Editorial: 342 Lincoln Way W, South Bend, Indiana 46601-1114. **T:** 1 574 288-1581
E: laraza1580@yahoo.com
W: http://www.laraza1580.com
Editorial Profile: WHLY-AM is a commercial station owned by Times Communications, Inc. The format of the station is Regional Mexican. WHLY-AM broadcasts to the South Bend, IL area at a frequency of 1580 AM.

WHMA-AM
Owner: Williams Communications Inc.
Editorial: 801 Noble St, Ste 30, Anniston, Alabama 36201. **T:** 1 256 236-1880
E: prod983@cableone.net
Editorial Profile: WHMA-AM is a commercial station owned by Williams Communications Inc. The format of the station is gospel. WHMA-AM broadcasts to the Birmingham, AL area at 1390 AM.

WHMA-FM
Owner: Williams Communications Inc.
Editorial: 801 Noble St, Ste 30, Anniston, Alabama 36201-0503. **T:** 1 256 236-1880
E: whmabig95@cableone.net
W: http://www.whmabig95.com
Editorial Profile: WHMA-FM is a commercial station owned by Williams Communications Inc. The format of the station is classic country. WHMA-FM broadcasts to the Anniston, AL area at 95.5 FM.

WHMC-FM
Owner: South Carolina Educational Television Commission
Editorial: 1101 George Rogers Blvd, Columbia, South Carolina 29201.
T: 1 803 737-3200 **E:** gasque@scetv.org
W: http://www.etvradio.org
Editorial Profile: WHMC-FM is a non-commercial station owned by the South Carolina Educational Television Commission. The format of the station is news. WHMC-FM broadcasts to the Conway and Myrtle Beach, SC areas at 90.1 FM.

WHMD-FM
Owner: Northshore Broadcasting Inc.
Editorial: 200 E Thomas St, Hammond, Louisiana 70401-3316. **T:** 1 985 345-0060
W: http://kajun107.com/
Editorial Profile: WHMD-FM is a commercial station owned by Northshore Broadcasting Inc. The format of the station is country music. WHMD-FM broadcasts to the New Orleans area at 107.1 FM.

WHME-FM
Owner: LeSEA Broadcasting
Editorial: 61300 Ironwood Rd, South Bend, Indiana 46614. **T:** 1 574 291-8200
E: whmefm@lesea.com
W: http://www.whmefm.com
Editorial Profile: WHME-FM is a commercial station owned by LeSEA Broadcasting. The format for the station is contemporary Christian. WHME-FM broadcasts to the South Bend, IN area at 103.1 FM.

WHMH-FM
Owner: Tri-County Broadcasting
Editorial: 1010 2nd St N, Sauk Rapids, Minnesota 56379. **T:** 1 320 252-6200
E: mail@rockin101.com
W: http://www.rockin101.com
Editorial Profile: WHMH-FM is a commercial station owned by Tri-County Broadcasting. The format of the station is rock music. WHMH-FM broadcasts in the Sauk Rapids, MN area at 101.7 FM.

WHMI-FM
Owner: Livingston Radio Company
Editorial: 1277 Parkway Dr, Howell, Michigan 48843. **T:** 1 517 546-0860
E: news@whmi.com **W:** http://www.whmi.com
Editorial Profile: WHMI-FM is a commercial station owned by Livingston Radio Company. The format of the station is classic hits. WHMI-FM broadcasts to the Howell, MI area at 93.5 FM.

WHMJ-FM
Owner: Forever Broadcasting
Editorial: 900 Water St, Meadville, Pennsylvania 16335. **T:** 1 814 724-1111
W: http://www.mymajicspace.com
Editorial Profile: WHMJ-FM is a commercial station owned by Forever Broadcasting. The format of the station is hot adult contemporary. WHMJ-FM broadcasts to the Meadville, PA area at 99.3 FM.

WHMP-AM
Owner: Saga Communications
Editorial: 15 Hampton Ave, Northampton, Massachusetts 1060. **T:** 1 413 586-7400
W: http://www.whmp.com
Editorial Profile: WHMP-AM is a commercial station owned by Saga Communications. The format of the station is news and talk. WHMP-AM broadcasts to the Northampton, MA area at 1400 AM.

WHMQ-AM
Owner: Saga Communications
Editorial: 81 Woodard Rd, Greenfield, Massachusetts 1301. **T:** 1 413 774-4301
W: http://www.whmp.com
Editorial Profile: WHMQ-AM is a commercial station owned by Saga Communications. The format of the station is news, sports and talk. WHMQ-AM broadcasts to the Greenfield, MA area at 1240 AM.

WHMS-FM
Owner: D.W.S. Inc.
Editorial: 2301 S Neil St, Champaign, Illinois 61820-7507. **T:** 1 217 351-5300
E: 975@whms.com **W:** http://www.whms.com
Editorial Profile: WHMS-FM is a commercial station owned by D.W.S. Inc. The format of the station is Lite Rock/Lite AC music. WHMS-FM broadcasts to the Champaign, IL area at 97.5 FM.

WHMT-AM
Owner: Coffee County Broadcasting, Inc

Editorial: 1030 Oakdale St, Manchester, Tennessee 37355-5618. **T:** 1 931 728-3526
E: whmtradio@yahoo.com
W: http://tullahomaradio.com
Editorial Profile: WHMT-AM is a commercial station owned by Coffee County Broadcasting, Inc. The format of the station is adult contemporary. WHMT-AM broadcasts to the Tullahoma, TN area at 740 AM.

WHMX-FM
Owner: Lighthouse Radio Network, Inc.
Editorial: 1476 Broadway, Bangor, Maine 04401-2404. **T:** 1 207 262-1057
E: contact@solutionfm.com
W: http://www.solutionfm.com
Editorial Profile: WHMX-FM is a non-commercial station owned by Lighthouse Radio Network, Inc. The format of the station is contemporary Christian music. WHMX-FM broadcasts to the Bangor, ME area at 105.7 FM.

WHNC-AM
Owner: Paradise Radio Network
Editorial: 601 Henderson St, Oxford, North Carolina 27565. **T:** 1 919 693-1340
E: alvin@dralvin.com
Editorial Profile: WHNC-AM is a commercial station owned by Paradise Radio Network. The format of the station is R&B, gospel and oldies music. WHNC-AM broadcasts to the Durham, NC area at 1340 AM.

WHND-FM
Owner: Wisconsin Educational Communications Board
Editorial: 2420 Nicolet Dr, Green Bay, Wisconsin 54311. **T:** 1 920 465-2444
E: listener@wpr.org **W:** http://www.wpr.org
Editorial Profile: WHND-FM is a non-commercial station owned by Wisconsin Educational Communications Board. The format of the station is news and classical music. WHND-FM broadcasts to the Green Bay, WI area at 89.7 FM.

WHNK-AM
Owner: Clear Channel Media and Entertainment
Editorial: 6006 Grand Central Ave, Vienna, West Virginia 26105. **T:** 1 304 295-9441
W: http://hank1450.com
Editorial Profile: WHNK-AM is a commercial station owned by Clear Channel Media and Entertainment. The format of the station is classic country. WHNK-AM broadcasts to the Vienna, WV area at 1450.

WHNN-FM
Owner: Cumulus Media Inc.
Editorial: 1740 Champagne Dr N, Saginaw, Michigan 48604-9239. **T:** 1 989 776-2100
W: http://www.whnn.com
Editorial Profile: WHNN-FM is a commercial station owned by Cumulus Media Inc. The format of the station is classic hits. WHNN-FM broadcasts to the Saginaw, MI area at 96.1 FM.

WHNP-AM
Owner: Saga Communications
Editorial: 15 Hampton Ave, Northampton, Massachusetts 1060. **T:** 1 413 586-7400
W: http://www.whmp.com

WHNR-AM
Owner: Reed, George R.
Editorial: 1505 Dundee Rd, Winter Haven, Florida 33884-1013. **T:** 1 863 299-1141
W: http://www.laley1360.com
Editorial Profile: WHNR-AM is a commercial station owned by Reed, George R. The format of the station is Regional Mexican music. WHNR-AM broadcasts in the Greater Lakeland, FL area at 1360 AM.

WHNY-AM
Owner: CWH Broadcasting
Editorial: 63 Braswell Rd, Hattiesburg, Mississippi 39401-9730. **T:** 1 601 582-7078
E: whsy950@yahoo.com
Editorial Profile: WHNY-AM is a commercial station owned by CWH Broadcasting. The format of the station is news, talk and sports. WHNY-AM broadcasts to the McComb, MS area at 1250 AM.

WHNZ-AM
Owner: Clear Channel Media and Entertainment
Editorial: 4002 W Gandy Blvd, Tampa, Florida 33611-3410. **T:** 1 813 839-9393
W: http://www.whnz.com
Editorial Profile: WHNZ-AM is a commercial station owned by Clear Channel Media and Entertainment. The format of the station is

Sports and talk. WHNZ-AM broadcasts to the Tampa, FL area at 1250 AM.

WHO-AM
Owner: Clear Channel Media and Entertainment
Editorial: 2141 Grand Ave, Des Moines, Iowa 50312. **T:** 1 515 245-8900
W: http://www.whoradio.com
Editorial Profile: WHO-AM is a commercial station owned by Clear Channel Media and Entertainment. The format of the station is news and talk. WHO-AM broadcasts to the Des Moines, IA area at 1040 AM.

WHOC-AM
Owner: WHOC, Inc.
Editorial: 1016 W Beacon St, Philadelphia, Mississippi 39350. **T:** 1 601 656-1490
E: wwslfm@bellsouth.net
Editorial Profile: WHOC-AM is a commercial station owned by WHOC, Inc. The format of the station is talk. WHOC-AM broadcasts to the Philadelphia, MS area at 1490 AM.

WHOD-FM
Owner: Capital Assets, Inc.
Editorial: 4428 N College Ave, Hwy 43, Jackson, Alabama 36545-2017.
T: 1 251 246-4431 **E:** info@bamadixie.com
W: http://bamadixie.com/dixie945
Editorial Profile: WHOD-FM is a commercial station owned by Capital Assets, Inc. The format of the station is classic rock. WHOD-FM broadcasts to the Jackson, AL area at 94.5 FM.

WHOF-FM
Owner: Clear Channel Media and Entertainment
Editorial: 7755 Freedom Ave NW, North Canton, Ohio 44720. **T:** 1 330 836-4700
W: http://www.my1017.com
Editorial Profile: WHOF-FM is a commercial station owned by Clear Channel Media and Entertainment. The format of the station is adult contemporary. WHOF-FM broadcasts to the North Canton, OH area at 107.7 FM.

WHOG-AM
Owner: Hobson City Broadcasting Co.
Editorial: 1330 Noble St, Ste 25, Anniston, Alabama 36201. **T:** 1 256 236-6484
E: hog1120@aol.com
Editorial Profile: WHOG-AM is a commercial station owned by Hobson City Broadcasting Co. The format of the station is urban contemporary. WHOG-AM broadcasts to the Anniston, AL area on 1120 AM.

WHOG-FM
Owner: Black Crow Radio, LLC
Editorial: 126 W International Speedway Blvd, Daytona Beach, Florida 32114-4322.
T: 1 386 239-9506
E: newsdaytonabeach@gmail.com
W: http://www.whog957.com
Editorial Profile: WHOG-FM is a commercial station owned by Black Crow Radio, LLC. The format of the station is classic rock music. WHOG-FM broadcasts to the Daytona Beach, FL area at 95.7 FM.

WHOK-FM
Owner: Wilks Broadcast Group
Editorial: 2400 Corporate Exchange Dr Ste 200, Columbus, Ohio 43231-7669.
T: 1 614 225-9465
W: http://www.classiccountryk1071.com
Editorial Profile: WHOK-FM is a commercial station owned by Wilks Broadcast Group. The format of the station is classic country. WHOK-FM broadcasts to the Columbus, OH area at 107.1 FM.

WHOL-AM
Owner: Grey Matter Broadcasting
Editorial: 1125 Colorado St, Allentown, Pennsylvania 18103-3118. **T:** 1 610 434-4801
W: http://www.holaenturadio.com
Editorial Profile: WHOL-AM is a commercial station owned by Grey Matter Broadcasting. The format of the station is Spanish tropical. WHOL-AM broadcasts to the Allentown, PA area at 1600 AM.

WHOM-FM
Owner: Townsquare Media, LLC
Editorial: 1 City Ctr, Portland, Maine 04101-6420. **T:** 1 207 774-6364
E: 94.9whom@cumulus.com
W: http://www.949whom.com
Editorial Profile: WHOM-FM is a commercial station owned by Townsquare Media, LLC. The format of the station is adult contemporary. WHOM-FM broadcasts to the Portland, ME area at 94.9 FM.

WHON-AM
Owner: Brewer Broadcasting Inc.
Editorial: 2626 Tingler Rd W, Richmond, Indiana 47374. **T:** 1 765 962-1595
W: http://www.1017thepoint.com
Editorial Profile: WHON-AM is a commercial station owned by Brewer Broadcasting Inc. The format of the station is adult contemporary. WHON-AM broadcasts to the Richmond, IN area at 930 AM.

WHOO-AM
Owner: Genesis Communications Inc.
Editorial: 1160 S Semoran Blvd Ste A, Orlando, Florida 32807-1461.
T: 1 407 380-9255
E: sportstalkflorida@radiogenesis.com
W: http://www.sportstalkflorida.com
Editorial Profile: WHOO-AM is a commercial station owned by Genesis Communications Inc. The format of the station is sports. WHOO-AM broadcasts to the Orlando, FL area at 1080 AM.

WHOP-AM
Owner: Forcht Broadcasting Inc.
Editorial: 220 Dink Embrys Buttermilk Rd, Hopkinsville, Kentucky 42240.
T: 1 270 885-5331
E: whop@forchtbroadcasting.com
W: http://www.lite987whop.com
Editorial Profile: WHOP-AM is a commercial station owned by Forcht Broadcasting Inc. The format of the station is news and talk. WHOP-AM broadcasts to the Hopkinsville, KY area at 1230 AM.

WHOP-FM
Owner: HOP Broadcasting Inc.
Editorial: 220 Dink Embry's Buttermilk Road, Hopkinsville, Kentucky 42241.
T: 1 270 885-5331
E: whopamfm@bellsouth.net
W: http://www.lite987whop.com
Editorial Profile: WHOP-FM is a commercial station owned by HOP Broadcasting Inc. The format of the station is adult contemporary. WHOP-FM broadcasts to the Hopkinsville, KY area at 98.7 FM.

WHOS-AM
Owner: Clear Channel Media and Entertainment
Editorial: 26869 Peoples Rd, Madison, Alabama 35756-4632. **T:** 1 256 353-1750
W: http://www.wbhpam.com
Editorial Profile: WHOS-AM is a commercial station owned by Clear Channel Media and Entertainment. The format of the station is news, sports and talk. WHOS-AM broadcasts to the Madison, AL area at 800 AM. WHOS-AM is a simulcast of WBHP-AM in Huntsville.

WHOT-FM
Owner: Cumulus Media Inc.
Editorial: 4040 Simon Rd, Youngstown, Ohio 44512. **T:** 1 330 783-1000
W: http://www.hot101.com
Editorial Profile: WHOT-FM is a commercial station owned by Cumulus Media Inc. The format of the station is Top 40/CHR. WHOT-FM broadcasts to the Youngstown, OH area at 101.1 FM.

WHOU-FM
Owner: Northern Maine Media
Editorial: 39 Court St Ste 215, Houlton, Maine 04730-2055. **T:** 1 207 532-3600
E: production@whoufm.com
W: http://www.whoufm.com
Editorial Profile: WHOU-FM is a commercial station WBCQ-FM is a commercial station currently owned by County Communications Inc, but operated by Northern Maine Media (Grant, Fred). The format of the station is adult contemporary. WHOU-FM broadcasts to the Houlton, ME area at 100.1 FM.

WHOV-FM
Owner: Hampton University
Editorial: Whov-Fm Hampton University H, Hampton, Virginia 23668. **T:** 1 757 727-5670
W: http://whov.hamptonu.edu
Editorial Profile: WHOV-FM is a non-commercial station owned by Hampton University. The format of the station is college variety. WHOV-FM broadcasts to the Hampton, VA area at 88.1 FM.

WHOW-AM
Owner: Kaskaskia Broadcasting, Inc.
Editorial: 2980 US Highway 51, Clinton, Illinois 61727-9479. **T:** 1 217 935-9590
E: whow@randyradio.com
W: http://www.dewittdailynews.com/
Editorial Profile: WHOW-AM is a commercial station owned by Kaskaskia Broadcasting, Inc.

The format of the station is news, talk and agricultural programming. WHOW-AM broadcasts to the Clinton, IL area at 1520 AM.

WHP-AM
Owner: Clear Channel Media and Entertainment
Editorial: 600 Corporate Cir, Harrisburg, Pennsylvania 17110-9787. **T:** 1 717 540-8800
E: news@whp580.com
W: http://www.whp580.com
Editorial Profile: WHP-AM is a commercial station owned by Clear Channel Media and Entertainment. The format of the station is news and talk. WHP-AM broadcasts to the greater Harrisburg, PA area at 580 AM.

WHPC-FM
Owner: Nassau Community College
Editorial: 1 Education Dr, Garden City, New York 11530-6719. **T:** 1 516 572-7438
E: whpc@ncc.edu
W: http://www.ncc.edu/studentlife/whpcradiostation/default.shtml
Editorial Profile: WHPC-FM is a non-commercial college station owned by Nassau Community College. The format of the station is variety. WHPC-FM broadcasts to the Garden City, NY area at 90.3 FM.

WHPD-FM
Owner: LeSEA Broadcasting
Editorial: 61300 Ironwood Rd, South Bend, Indiana 46614-9019. **T:** 1 574 291-8200
E: pulse@lesea.com
W: http://www.pulsefm.com
Editorial Profile: WHPD-FM is a commercial station owned by LeSEA Broadcasting. The format for the station is contemporary Christian music. WHPD-FM broadcasts to the Dowagiac, MI area at 92.1 FM and is a simulcast of WHPZ-FM.

WHPE-FM
Owner: Bible Broadcasting Network
Editorial: 11530 Carmel Commons Blvd, Charlotte, North Carolina 28226-3976.
T: 1 704 523-5555 **E:** bbn@bbnmedia.org
W: http://www.bbnradio.org
Editorial Profile: WHPE-FM is a non-commercial station owned by Bible Broadcasting Network. The format of the station is religious programming. WHPE-FM broadcasts to the High Point, NC area at 95.5 FM.

WHPF-FM
Owner: Light of Life Ministries, Inc.
Editorial: 160 Bangor St, Augusta, Maine 04330-4162. **T:** 1 207 622-1340
E: info@worshipradionetwork.org
W: http://www.worshipradionetwork.org
Editorial Profile: WHPF-FM is a non-commercial station owned by Light of Life Ministries, Inc. The format of the station features Contemporary Christian music. WHPF-FM broadcasts to the Pittston Farm, ME area at a frequency of 88.1 FM.

WHPH-FM
Owner: Great South Wireless, LLC
Editorial: 20747 Alabama Highway 22 West, Clanton, Alabama 35045-8273.
T: 1 205 755-0966
E: thepeach977@yahoo.com
W: http://977thepeach.com/
Editorial Profile: WHPH-FM is a commercial station owned by Great South Wireless, LLC. The format of the station is oldies music. WHPH-FM broadcasts to the Clanton, AL area at 97.7 FM.

WHPI-FM
Owner: Advanced Media Partners LLC
Editorial: 2006 W Altorfer Dr, Peoria, Illinois 61615-1864. **T:** 1 309 691-0101
W: http://www.jack1011.com
Editorial Profile: WHPI-FM is a commercial station owned by Advanced Media Partners LLC. The format of the station is adult hits. WHPI-FM broadcasts to the Peoria, IL area at 101.1 FM.

WHPK-FM
Owner: University of Chicago
Editorial: 5706 S University Ave, Chicago, Illinois 60637-1514. **T:** 1 773 702-8289
E: contact@whpk.org
W: http://whpk.uchicago.edu
Editorial Profile: WHPK-FM is a non-commercial station owned by the University of Chicago. The format of the station is college variety. WHPK-FM broadcasts to the greater Chicago area at 88.5 FM.

WHPO-FM
Owner: Hooterville Broadcasting Inc.

Editorial: 912 S Dixie Hwy, Hoopeston, Illinois 60942-1965. **T:** 1 217 283-7744
E: whpo@whporadio.com
W: http://www.whporadio.com
Editorial Profile: WHPO-FM is a commercial station owned by Hooterville Broadcasting Inc. The format of the station is country. WHPO-FM broadcasts to the Hoopeston, IL area at a frequency of 100.9 FM.

WHPP-FM
Owner: Adams Radio Group
Editorial: 9604 Coldwater Rd Ste 201, Fort Wayne, Indiana 46825-2096.
T: 1 260 436-9598
E: info@redeemerradio.com
W: http://www.redeemerradio.com
Editorial Profile: WHPP-FM is a commercial station owned by Adams Radio Group. The format of the station is Catholic radio. WHPP-FM broadcasts to the Fort Wayne, IN area at 106.3 FM.

WHPR-FM
Owner: R. J.'s Late Night Entertainment Corporation
Editorial: 160 Victor St, Highland Park, Michigan 48203-3130. **T:** 1 313 868-6612
W: http://fm881whpr.com
Editorial Profile: WHPR-FM is a non-commercial station owned by R. J.'s Late Night Entertainment Corporation. The format of the station is oldies and talk. WHPR-FM broadcasts to the Highland Park, MI area at 88.1 FM.

WHPT-FM
Owner: Cox Media Group, Inc.
Editorial: 11300 4th St N Ste 300, Saint Petersburg, Florida 33716-2941.
T: 1 727 579-2000
W: http://www.theboneonline.com
Editorial Profile: WHPT-FM is a commercial station owned by Cox Media Group, Inc. The format of the station is talk. WHPT-FM broadcasts to the Saint Petersburg, FL area at 102.5 FM.

WHPY-FM
Owner: Kensington Digital Media
Editorial: 49 Music Sq W Fl 3, Nashville, Tennessee 37203-3213. **T:** 1 877 393-1555
E: info@hippieradio945.com
W: http://www.hippieradio945.com
Editorial Profile: WHPY-FM is a commercial station owned by Kensington Digital Media. The format of the station is classic hits. WHPY-FM broadcasts to the Greater Nashville, TN area at 94.5 FM.

WHPZ-FM
Owner: LeSEA Broadcasting
Editorial: 61300 Ironwood Rd, South Bend, Indiana 46614. **T:** 1 574 291-8200
E: pulse@lesea.com
W: http://www.pulsefm.com
Editorial Profile: WHPZ-FM is a commercial station owned by LeSEA Broadcasting. The format of the station is contemporary Christian. WHPZ-FM broadcasts to the South Bend, IN area at 96.9 FM.

WHQC-FM
Owner: Clear Channel Media and Entertainment
Editorial: 801 Woodridge Center Dr, Charlotte, North Carolina 28217-1908.
T: 1 704 714-9444
W: http://www.channel961.com
Editorial Profile: WHQC-FM is a commercial station owned by Clear Channel Media and Entertainment. The format of the station is Top 40/CHR. WHQC-FM broadcasts in the Charlotte, NC area at 96.1 FM

WHQG-FM
Owner: Saga Communications
Editorial: 5407 W McKinley Ave, Milwaukee, Wisconsin 53208. **T:** 1 414 978-9000
E: headhog@1029thehog.com
W: http://www.1029thehog.com
Editorial Profile: WHQG-FM is a commercial station owned by Saga Communications. The format of the station is rock music. WHQG-FM broadcasts to the Milwaukee area at 102.9 FM.

WHQQ-FM
Owner: Cromwell Group Inc.(The)
Editorial: 405 S Banker St Ste 201, Effingham, Illinois 62401-2591. **T:** 1 217 342-4141
W: http://www.989thegame.com
Editorial Profile: WHQQ-FM is a commercial station owned by the Cromwell Group Inc. The format of the station is sports. WHQQ-FM broadcasts in the Mattoon, IL area at 98.9 FM.

WHQR-FM
Owner: Friends of Public Radio
Editorial: 254 N Front St, Ste 300, Wilmington, North Carolina 28401.
T: 1 910 343-1640 **E:** news@whqr.org
W: http://www.whqr.org
Editorial Profile: WHQR-FM is a non-commercial station owned by Friends of Public Radio. The format of the station is news and classical music. WHQR-FM broadcasts in the Wilmington, NC area at 91.3 FM.

WHQT-FM
Owner: Cox Media Group, Inc.
Editorial: 2741 N 29th Ave, 3rd Fl, Hollywood, Florida 33020-1503. **T:** 1 305 444-4404
W: http://www.hot105fm.com
Editorial Profile: WHQT-FM is a commercial station owned by Cox Media Group, Inc. The format of the station is urban adult contemporary. WHQT-FM broadcasts to the Hollywood, FL area at 105.1 FM.

WHQX-FM
Owner: L & L Broadcasting
Editorial: 900 Bluefield Ave, Bluefield, West Virginia 24701-2744. **T:** 1 304 327-7114
W: http://www.kickscountry.com
Editorial Profile: WHQX-FM is a commercial station owned by L & L Broadcasting. The format of the station is country music. WHQX-FM broadcasts to the Bluefield, WV area at 107.7 FM.

WHRB-FM
Owner: Harvard Radio Broadcasting Co. Inc.
Editorial: 389 Harvard St, Cambridge, Massachusetts 2138. **T:** 1 617 495-4818
E: news@whrb.org **W:** http://www.whrb.org
Editorial Profile: WHRB-FM is a commercial station owned by Harvard Radio Broadcasting Co. Inc. The format of the station is variety. WHRB-FM broadcasts to the Cambridge, MA area at 95.3 FM.

WHRJ-FM
Owner: Hampton Roads Educational Telecommunications
Editorial: 5200 Hampton Blvd, Norfolk, Virginia 23508-1507. **T:** 1 757 889-6400
Editorial Profile: WHJR-FM is a non-commercial station owned by Hampton Roads Educational Telecommunications. The format of the station is classical music. WHRJ-FM broadcasts to Norfolk, VA area at 89.9 FM.

WHRK-FM
Owner: Clear Channel Media and Entertainment
Editorial: 2650 Thousand Oaks Blvd Ste 4100, Memphis, Tennessee 38118-2451.
T: 1 901 259-1300 **W:** http://www.k97fm.com
Editorial Profile: WHRK-FM is a commercial station owned by Clear Channel Media and Entertainment. The format of the station is urban contemporary music. WHRK-FM broadcasts to the Memphis, TN area at 97.1 FM.

WHRM-FM
Owner: University of Wisconsin
Editorial: 625 Stewart Ave, Wausau, Wisconsin 54401-4563. **T:** 1 715 261-6298
E: listener@wpr.org
W: http://www.wpr.org/whrm
Editorial Profile: WHRM-FM is a non-commercial station owned by the University of Wisconsin. The format of the station is news and classical music. WHRM-FM broadcasts in the Wausau, WI area at 90.9 FM.

WHRO-FM
Owner: Hampton Roads Educational Telecommunications
Editorial: 5200 Hampton Blvd, Norfolk, Virginia 23508-1507. **T:** 1 757 889-9400
E: info@whro.org **W:** http://www.whro.org
Editorial Profile: WHRO-FM is a non-commercial station owned by Hampton Roads Educational Telecommunications. The format of the station is classical music. WHRO-FM broadcasts to Norfolk, VA area at 90.3 FM.

WHRP-FM
Owner: Cumulus Media Inc.
Editorial: 1717 US Highway 72 E, Athens, Alabama 35611-4413. **T:** 1 256 830-8300
W: http://www.whrpfm.com
Editorial Profile: WHRP-FM is a commercial station owned by Cumulus Media Inc. The format of the station is urban adult contemporary music. WHRP-FM broadcasts to the Huntsville, AL area at 94.1 FM.

WHRV-FM
Owner: Hampton Roads Educational Telecommunications
Editorial: 5200 Hampton Blvd, Norfolk, Virginia 23508-1507. **T:** 1 757 889-9400
E: info@whro.org **W:** http://www.whrv.org
Editorial Profile: WHRV-FM is a commercial station owned by Hampton Roads Educational Telecommunications. The format of the station is variety. WHRV-FM broadcasts to the Norfolk, VA area at 89.5 FM.

WHRW-FM
Owner: Binghamton University
Editorial: 4400 Vestal Pkwy East, Vestal, New York 13908. **T:** 1 607 777-2139
W: http://www.whrwfm.org
Editorial Profile: WHRW-FM is a non-commercial station owned by Binghamton University. The format of the station is college variety. WHRW-FM broadcasts to the Binghamton, NY area at 90.5 FM.

WHRY-AM
Owner: Big G Little O Inc.
Editorial: 209 Harrison St, Ironwood, Michigan 49938. **T:** 1 906 932-5234
E: wupm@wupm-whry.com
W: http://www.wupm-whry.com
Editorial Profile: WHRY-AM is a commercial station owned by Big G Little O Inc. The format of the station is oldies music. WHRY-AM broadcasts in the Ironwood, MI area at 1450 AM.

WHSA-FM
Owner: Wisconsin Educational Communications Board
Editorial: 1805 Catlin Ave, Superior, Wisconsin 54880-2873. **T:** 1 715 394-8530
E: listener@wpr.org **W:** http://www.wpr.org
Editorial Profile: WHSA-FM is a non-commercial station owned by the Wisconsin Educational Communications Board. The format of the station is news and classical music. WHSA-FM broadcasts to the Superior, WI area at 89.9 FM.

WHSB-FM
Owner: Edwards Communications LLC
Editorial: 1491 M 32 W, Alpena, Michigan 49707. **T:** 1 989 354-4611
E: thebay@truenorthradionetwork.com
W: http://www.alpenanow.com/
Editorial Profile: WHSB-FM is a commercial station owned by Edwards Communications LLC. The format for the station is hot adult contemporary. WHSB-FM broadcasts to the Alpena, MI area at 107.7 FM.

WHSC-AM
Owner: Cumulus Media Inc.
Editorial: 11640 Highway 17 Byp, Murrells Inlet, South Carolina 29576-9332.
T: 1 843 651-7869
Editorial Profile: WHSC-AM is a commercial station owned by Cumulus Media Inc. The format of the station is sports. WHSC-AM broadcasts to the Murrells Inlet, SC area at 1050 AM.

WHSF-FM
Owner: University of Wisconsin
Editorial: 625 Stewart Ave, Wausau, Wisconsin 54401-4563. **T:** 1 715 261-6298
W: http://wpr.org
Editorial Profile: WHSF-FM is a non-commercial station owned by the University of Wisconsin. The format of the station is public radio news and talk. WHSF-FM broadcasts to the Rhinelander, WI area at a frequency of 89.9 FM.

WHSM-AM
Owner: Red Rock Radio Corp.
Editorial: 16880 W US Highway 63, Hayward, Wisconsin 54843. **T:** 1 715 634-4836
E: news@whsm.com
W: http://www.whsm.com
Editorial Profile: WHSM-AM is a commercial station owned by Red Rock Radio Corp. The format of the station is adult standards music. WHSM-AM broadcasts in the Hayward, WI area at 910 AM.

WHSM-FM
Owner: Red Rock Radio Corp.
Editorial: 16880 W Us Highway 63, Hayward, Wisconsin 54843-7186. **T:** 1 715 634-4836
E: news@whsm.com
W: http://www.whsm.com
Editorial Profile: WHSM-FM is a commercial station owned by Red Rock Radio Corp. The format of the station is adult contemporary. WHSM-FM broadcasts in the Hayward, WI area at 101.1 FM.

WHSN-FM
Owner: Husson University
Editorial: 1 College Cir, Bangor, Maine 4401.
T: 1 207 941-7116 **E:** whsn@nescom.edu
W: http://www.whsn-fm.com
Editorial Profile: WHSN-FM is a non-commercial station owned by Husson University. The format of the station is rock music and news. WHSN-FM broadcasts to the Bangor, ME area at 89.3 FM.

WHSR-AM
Owner: Beasley Broadcast Group
Editorial: 6699 N Federal Hwy Ste 200, Boca Raton, Florida 33487-1660. **T:** 1 561 997-0074
W: http://www.whsrradio.com
Editorial Profile: WHRS-AM is a commercial station owned by Beasley Broadcast Group. The format of the station is ethnic and international talk and entertainment. WHSR-AM broadcasts to the Boca Raton, FL area at 980 AM.

WHST-FM
Owner: Northern Christian Radio
Editorial: 1511 E M 32, Gaylord, Michigan 49735-9702. **T:** 1 989 732-6274
E: studio@thepromisefm.com
W: http://www.thepromisefm.com
Editorial Profile: WHST-FM is a non-commercial station owned by Northern Christian Radio. The format of the station is religious and contemporary Christian programming. WHST-FM broadcasts to the Gaylord, MI area at 106.1 FM.

WHSX-FM
Owner: Forbis Communications Inc.
Editorial: 1130 S Dixie St, Horse Cave, Kentucky 42749-1462. **T:** 1 270 786-1000
E: 991@scrtc.com **W:** http://www.thehoss.com
Editorial Profile: WHSX-FM is a commercial station owned by Forbis Communications Inc. The format of the station is contemporary country music. WHSX-FM broadcasts to the Horse Cave, KY area at 99.1 FM.

WHSY-AM
Owner: Gulf South Communications LLC.
Editorial: 63 Braswell Rd, Hattiesburg, Mississippi 39401. **T:** 1 601 582-7078
E: whsy950@yahoo.com
Editorial Profile: WHSY-AM is a commercial station owned by Gulf South Communications LLC. The format of the station is news, talk and sports. WHSY-AM broadcasts to the Hattiesburg, MS area at 950 AM.

WHTA-FM
Owner: Radio One Inc.
Editorial: 101 Marietta St Nw, Atlanta, Georgia 30303-2720. **T:** 1 404 765-9750
W: http://hotspotatl.com
Editorial Profile: WHTA-FM is a commercial station owned by Radio One Inc. The format of the station is urban contemporary music. WHTA-FM broadcasts to the Atlanta area at 107.9 FM.

WHTB-AM
Owner: Karam(Robert & James)
Editorial: 1 Home St, Somerset, Massachusetts 2725. **T:** 1 508 678-9727
W: http://www.radiovozdoemigrante.com
Editorial Profile: WHTB-AM is a commercial station owned by Robert and James Karam. The format of the station is Portuguese talk programming. WHTB-AM broadcasts to the Somerset, MA area at 1400 AM.

WHTC-AM
Owner: Midwest Communications Inc.
Editorial: 87 Central Ave, Holland, Michigan 49423-2829. **T:** 1 616 392-3121
W: http://www.whtc.com
Editorial Profile: WHTC-AM is a commercial station owned by Midwest Communications Inc. The format of the station is and talk. WHTC-AM broadcasts to the Holland, MI area at 1450 AM.

WHTE-FM
Owner: Monticello Media LLC
Editorial: 1150 Pepsi Pl, Charlottesville, Virginia 22901. **T:** 1 434 978-4408
W: http://www.1019hot.com
Editorial Profile: WHTE-FM is a commercial station owned by Monticello Media LLC. The format of the station is Top 40/CHR music. WHTE-FM broadcasts to the Charlottesville, VA area at 101.9 FM.

WHTF-FM
Owner: Red Hills Broadcasting, LLC
Editorial: 3000 Olson Rd, Tallahassee, Florida 32308-3918. **T:** 1 850 386-8004
W: http://www.hot1049.com
Editorial Profile: WHTF-FM is a commercial station owned by Red Hills Broadcasting, LLC.

The format of the station is Top 40/CHR. WHTF-FM broadcasts to the Tallahassee, FL area at 104.9 FM.

WHTG-AM
Owner: Press Communications LLC
Editorial: 2355 W Bangs Ave, Neptune, New Jersey 07753-4111. **T:** 1 732 774-4755
W: http://www.1410amradio.com
Editorial Profile: WHTG-AM is a commercial station owned by Press Communications LLC. The format of the station is oldies music. WHTG-AM broadcasts in the Neptune, NJ area at 1410 AM.

WHTH-AM
Owner: Runnymede Inc.
Editorial: 1000 N 40th St, Newark, Ohio 43055. **T:** 1 740 522-8171
E: news@wnko.com **W:** http://www.wnko.com
Editorial Profile: WHTH-AM is a commercial station owned by Runnymede Inc. The format of the station is talk. WHTH-AM broadcasts to the Newark, OH area at 790 AM.

WHTI-FM
Owner: Summit Media Broadcasting LLC
Editorial: 812 Moorefield Park Dr, #300, Richmond, Virginia 23236. **T:** 1 804 330-5700
W: http://www.easy1009.com
Editorial Profile: WHTI-FM is a commercial station owned by Summit Media Broadcasting LLC. The format of the station is soft AC. WHTI-FM broadcasts to the Richmond, VA area at 100.9 FM.

WHTK-AM
Owner: Clear Channel Media and Entertainment
Editorial: 1700 HSBC Plaza, 100 Chestnut St., Rochester, New York 14604-2016.
T: 1 585 454-4884 **W:** http://www.whtk.com
Editorial Profile: WHTK-AM is a commercial station owned by Clear Channel Media and Entertainment. The format of the station is sports and talk. WHTK-AM broadcasts to the Rochester, NY area at 1280 AM.

WHTL-FM
Owner: WHTL Group LLC
Editorial: N35609 Highway 53, Whitehall, Wisconsin 54773. **T:** 1 715 538-4341
W: http://whtlradio.com
Editorial Profile: WHTL-FM is a commercial station owned by WHTL Group LLC. The format of the station is oldies. WHTL-FM broadcasts to the Whitehall, WI area at 102.3 FM.

WHTO-FM
Owner: Results Broadcasting
Editorial: 212 W J St, Iron Mountain, Michigan 49801-4646. **T:** 1 906 774-5731
W: http://www.1067themountain.com
Editorial Profile: WHTO-FM is a commercial station owned by Results Broadcasting. The format of the station is oldies. WHTO-FM broadcasts to the Marquette, MI area at 106.7 FM.

WHTP-FM
Owner: Mainestream Media
Editorial: 89 Mussey Rd Suite 100, Scarborough, Maine 04074-5900.
T: 1 207 883-0615
E: hot1047@mainestreamonline.com
W: http://www.hot1047maine.com
Editorial Profile: WHTP-FM is a commercial station owned by Mainestream Media. The format of the station is Top 40/CHR. WHTP-FM broadcasts to the Portland, ME area at 104.7 FM.

WHTQ-FM
Owner: NRG Media LLC
Editorial: 2301 Plover Rd, Plover, Wisconsin 54467. **T:** 1 715 341-8838
W: http://www.hot967fm.com
Editorial Profile: WHTQ-FM is a commercial station owned by NRG Media LLC. The format of the station is Top 40/CHR. WHTQ-FM broadcasts to the Plover, WI area at 96.7 FM.

WHTS-FM
Owner: Cumulus Media Inc.
Editorial: 60 Monroe Ctr NW, Grand Rapids, Michigan 49502-0001. **T:** 1 616 774-8461
W: http://www.1053hotfm.com
Editorial Profile: WHTS-FM is a commercial station owned by Cumulus Media Inc. The format of the station is Top 40/CHR. WHTS-FM broadcasts to the Grand Rapids, MI, area at 105.3 FM.

WHTT-FM
Owner: Cumulus Media Inc.
Editorial: 50 James E Casey Dr, Buffalo, New York 14206. **T:** 1 716 881-4555
E: whtt@whtt.com **W:** http://www.whtt.com
Editorial Profile: WHTT-FM is a commercial station owned by Cumulus Media Inc. The format of the station is classic hits. WHTT-FM broadcasts to the Buffalo, NY area at 104.1 FM.

WHTU-FM
Owner: Todd P. Robinson, Inc.
Editorial: 508 W Oak St, Covington, Virginia 24426-1942. **T:** 1 540 962-1133
Editorial Profile: WHTU-FM is a commercial station owned by Todd P. Robinson, Inc. The format of the station is urban adult contemporary music. WHTU-FM broadcasts to the Covington, VA area at 103.9 FM.

WHTX-AM
Owner: Sagittarius Communications, LLC
Editorial: 5380 Webb Road, Mineral Ridge, Ohio 44515. **T:** 1 330 394-7700
Editorial Profile: WHTX-AM is a commercial station owned by Sagittarius Communications, LLC. The format of the station is urban/rhythmic oldies. WHTX-AM broadcasts to the Warren, OH area at 1570 AM.

WHTY-AM
Owner: Travis Media LLC
Editorial: 2475 Mercer Ave Ste 104, West Palm Beach, Florida 33401-7447.
T: 1 561 242-8155
W: http://www.radiovisionnouvelle.com
Editorial Profile: WHTY-AM is a commercial station owned by Travis Media LLC. The format of the station is Haitian ethnic programming. WHTY-AM broadcasts to the West Palm Beach area at 1600 AM.

WHTZ-FM
Owner: Clear Channel Media and Entertainment
Editorial: 32 Avenue of the Americas Fl 3, New York, New York 10013-2473.
T: 1 212 377-7900 **W:** http://www.z100.com
Editorial Profile: WHTZ-FM is a commercial station owned by Clear Channel Media and Entertainment. The format of the station is Top 40/CHR format. WHTZ-FM broadcasts to the New York City area at 100.3 FM.

WHUB-AM
Owner: Cookeville Communications, LLC
Editorial: 698 S Willow Ave, Cookeville, Tennessee 38501-3802. **T:** 1 931 526-7144
W: http://www.1400thehub.com
Editorial Profile: WHUB-AM is a commercial station owned by Cookeville Communications, LLC. The format of the station is news and talk. WHUB-AM broadcasts to the Cookeville, TN area at 1400 AM.

WHUC-AM
Owner: Clear Channel Media and Entertainment
Editorial: 5620 State Route 9G, Hudson, New York 12534-4127. **T:** 1 518 828-5006
W: http://www.1230whuc.com
Editorial Profile: WHUC-AM is a commercial station owned by Clear Channel Media and Entertainment. The format of the station is adult standards music. WHUC-AM broadcasts to the Hudson, NY area at 1230 AM. Address all mail to Bill Williams, Program Director.

WHUD-FM
Owner: Pamal Broadcasting Ltd.
Editorial: 715 Route 52, Beacon, New York 12508-1047. **T:** 1 845 838-6000
W: http://www.whud.com
Editorial Profile: WHUD-FM is a commercial station owned by Pamal Broadcasting Ltd. The format of the station is adult contemporary music. WHUD-FM broadcasts throughout Hudson Valley and Westchester County in New York at 100.7 FM.

WHUG-FM
Owner: Media One Group, LLC
Editorial: 2 Orchard Rd, Jamestown, New York 14701. **T:** 1 716 487-1151
E: news@whug.com **W:** http://www.whug.com
Editorial Profile: WHUG-FM is a commercial station owned by Media One Group, LLC. The format of the station is country music. WHUG-FM broadcasts in the Jamestown, NY area at 101.9 FM.

WHUN-AM
Owner: Megahertz LLC
Editorial: 10773 William Penn Hwy, Huntingdon, Pennsylvania 16652-6806.
T: 1 814 643-9620
Editorial Profile: WHUN-AM is a commercial station owned by Forever Communications and operated Megahertz LLC. The format of the station is sports. WLLI-AM broadcasts to the Huntingdon, PA area at 1150.

WHUN-FM
Owner: Forever Broadcasting
Editorial: 10773 William Penn Hwy, Huntingdon, Pennsylvania 16652-6806.
T: 1 814 643-9620
W: http://www.hunny106.com
Editorial Profile: WHUN-FM is a commercial station owned by Forever Broadcasting. The format of the station is oldies. WHUN-FM broadcasts to the Huntingdon, PA area at 106.3.

WHUR-FM
Owner: Howard University
Editorial: 529 Bryant St NW, Washington, District Of Columbia 20059-1005.
T: 1 202 806-3500 **E:** publicaffairs@whur.com
W: http://www.whur.com
Editorial Profile: WHUR-FM is a commercial station owned by Howard University. The format of the station is urban adult contemporary music. WHUR-FM broadcasts to the Washington D.C. area at 96.3 FM.

WHUS-FM
Owner: University of Connecticut
Editorial: 2110 Hillside Rd, Unit 3008R, Storrs Mansfield, Connecticut 06269-9093.
T: 1 860 486-4007 **E:** info@whus.org
W: http://www.whus.org
Editorial Profile: WHUS-FM is a non-commercial station owned by University of Connecticut. The format of the station is variety. WHUS-FM broadcasts to the Norwich, CT area at 91.7 FM.

WHVE-FM
Owner: Shoreline Communications Inc.
Editorial: 7955 Russell Springs Rd, Russell Springs, Kentucky 42642. **T:** 1 270 866-7979
E: thewave@ridingthewave.com
W: http://www.ridingthewave.com
Editorial Profile: WHVE-FM is a commercial station owned by Shoreline Communications Inc. The format of the station is adult contemporary. WHVE-FM broadcasts to the Russell Springs, KY area at 92.7 FM.

WHVN-AM
Owner: GHB Broadcasting
Editorial: 5732 N Tryon St, Charlotte, North Carolina 28213. **T:** 1 704 596-4900
W: http://www.heavenradio.org
Editorial Profile: WHVN-AM is a commercial station owned by GHB Broadcasting. The format of the station is religious and Christian programming. WHVN-AM broadcasts to the Charlotte, NC area at 1240 AM.

WHVO-AM
Owner: Ham Broadcasting Co. Inc.
Editorial: 19 Wooldridge Rd, Cadiz, Kentucky 42211. **T:** 1 270 886-1480
E: wkdz@wkdzradio.com
W: http://www.oldies1480.com
Editorial Profile: WHVO-AM is a commercial station owned by Ham Broadcasting Co. Inc. The format of the station is oldies. WHVO-AM broadcasts to the Cadiz, KY area at 1480 AM.

WHVR-AM
Owner: Radio Hanover Inc.
Editorial: 275 Radio Rd, Hanover, Pennsylvania 17331-1140. **T:** 1 717 637-3831
E: info@thepeak985.com
W: http://realcountry1280whvr.com/
Editorial Profile: WHVR-AM is a commercial station owned by Radio Hanover Inc. The format of the station is country music. WHVR-AM broadcasts to the Hanover, PA area at 1280 AM.

WHVT-FM
Owner: Clyde Educational Broadcast Foundation
Editorial: 1022 S Main St, Clyde, Ohio 43410-2039. **T:** 1 419 547-8254
W: http://www.cleanair.fm
Editorial Profile: WHVT-FM is a non-commercial station owned by the Clyde Educational Broadcast Foundation. The format of the station is Christian talk and music. WHVT-FM broadcasts to Clyde, OH, at 90.5 FM.

WHVW-AM
Owner: Ferraro(J.P.)
Editorial: 316 Main St, Poughkeepsie, New York 12601. **T:** 1 845 471-9500
E: whvw@whvw.net **W:** http://www.whvw.net
Editorial Profile: WHVW-FM is a commercial station owned by J.P. Ferraro. The format of the station is oldies. WHVW-FM broadcasts to the Poughkeepsie, NY area at 950 AM.

WHWC-FM
Owner: University of Wisconsin
Editorial: 1221 W Clairemont Ave, Eau Claire, Wisconsin 54701. **T:** 1 715 839-3868
E: listener@wpr.org **W:** http://www.wpr.org
Editorial Profile: WHWC-FM is a non-commercial station owned by the University of Wisconsin. The format of the station is news and talk. WHWC-FM broadcasts in the Eau Claire, WI area at 88.3 FM.

WHWG-FM
Owner: Gospel Opportunities Inc.
Editorial: 130 Carmen Dr, Marquette, Michigan 49855. **T:** 1 906 249-1423 **E:** whwl@whwl.net
W: http://www.whwl.net
Editorial Profile: WHWG-FM is a non-commercial station owned by Gospel Opportunities Inc. The format for the station is religious. WHWG-FM broadcasts to the Marquette, MI area at 89.9 FM.

WHWH-AM
Owner: Multicultural Radio Broadcasting Inc.
Editorial: 3573 Bristol Pike Ste 102&103, Bensalem, Pennsylvania 19020-4666.
T: 1 609 333-9432
W: http://www.radiowttm1680.com
Editorial Profile: WHWH-AM is a commercial station owned by Multicultural Radio Broadcasting Inc. The format of the station is Hispanic programming. WHWH-AM broadcasts to the Princeton, NJ area at 1350 AM.

WHWK-FM
Owner: Townsquare Media, Inc.
Editorial: 59 Court St, Binghamton, New York 13901-3270. **T:** 1 607 772-8400
W: http://www.981thehawk.com
Editorial Profile: WHWK-FM is a commercial station owned by Townsquare Media, Inc. The format of the station is contemporary country. WHWK-FM broadcasts to the Binghamton, NY area at 98.1 FM.

WHWL-FM
Owner: Gospel Opportunities Inc.
Editorial: 130 Carmen Dr, Marquette, Michigan 49855. **T:** 1 906 249-1423 **E:** whwl@whwl.net
W: http://www.whwl.net
Editorial Profile: WHWL-FM is a non-commercial station owned by Gospel Opportunities Inc. The format for the station is religious. WHWL-FM broadcasts to the Marquette, MI area at 95.7 FM.

WHWY-FM
Owner: Apex Broadcasting, Inc.
Editorial: 34 Harbor Blvd Ste 202, Destin, Florida 32541-7365. **T:** 1 850 654-1000
W: http://www.highway98country.com
Editorial Profile: WHWY-FM is a commercial station ownedy by Apex Broadcasting, Inc. The format is contemporary country. The station broadcasts at 98.1 FM in Fort Walton Beach, FL and surrounding areas.

WHXR-FM
Owner: WBIN, Inc.
Editorial: 477 Congress St Ste 3, Portland, Maine 04101-3427. **T:** 1 207 797-0780
W: http://www.boneradio.com
Editorial Profile: WHXR-FM is a commercial station owned by WBIN, Inc. The format of the station is rock. WHXR-FM broadcasts to the Portland, ME area at 106.3 FM.

WHXT-FM
Owner: L & L Broadcasting
Editorial: 1900 Pineview Dr, Columbia, South Carolina 29209-5079. **T:** 1 803 695-8600
W: http://www.hot1039fm.com
Editorial Profile: WHXT-FM is a commercial station owned by L & L Broadcasting. The format of the station is urban contemporary. WHXT-FM broadcasts to the Columbia, SC area at a frequency of 103.9 FM.

WHYA-FM
Owner: Codcomm Inc.
Editorial: 243 South St, Hyannis, Massachusetts 02601-3926.
T: 1 508 778-6000 **W:** http://www.y101.cc
Editorial Profile: WHYA-FM is a commercial station owned by Codcomm Inc. The format of the station is Top 40/CHR. WHYA-FM broadcasts to the Cape Cod, MA area at 101.1 FM.

WHYB-FM
Owner: Radio Plus Bay Cities, LLC

Editorial: 413 10th Ave, Menominee, Michigan 49858-3009. **T:** 1 906 863-5551
E: reception@baycitiesradio.net
W: http://www.baycitiesradio.net
Editorial Profile: WHYB-FM is a commercial station owned by Radio Plus Bay Cities, LLC. The format of the station is oldies. WHYB-FM broadcasts to the Menominee, MI area at 103.7 FM.

WHYC-FM
Owner: Hyde County Board of Education
Editorial: 20472 US Highway 264, Swanquarter, North Carolina 27885.
T: 1 252 926-7201
Editorial Profile: WHYC-FM is a non-commercial station owned by Hyde County Board of Education. The format of the station is variety. WHYC-FM broadcasts to the Swanquarter, NC area at 88.5 FM.

WHYF-AM
Owner: Holy Family Radio, Inc
Editorial: 8 W Main St, Shiremanstown, Pennsylvania 17011-6326. **T:** 1 717 525-8110
E: contact@yourholyfamilyradio.com
W: http://www.yourholyfamilyradio.com
Editorial Profile: WHYF-AM is a commercial station owned by Holy Family Radio, Inc. The format of the station is Catholic programming. WHYF-AM broadcasts to the Shiremanstown, PA area at 720 AM.

WHYI-FM
Owner: Clear Channel Media and Entertainment
Editorial: 7601 Riviera Blvd, Miramar, Florida 33023-6574. **T:** 1 954 862-2000
W: http://www.y100.com
Editorial Profile: WHYI-FM is a commercial station owned by Clear Channel Media and Entertainment. The format of the station is Top 40/CHR music. WHYI-FM broadcasts to the Miami area at 100.7 FM.

WHYM-AM
Owner: Miller Communications Inc.
Editorial: 2423 Walker Swinton Rd, Timmonsville, South Carolina 29161-9351.
T: 1 843 678-9393 **E:** production@miller.fm
W: http://www.miller.fm
Editorial Profile: WHYM-AM is a commercial station owned by Miller Communications Inc. The format of the station is sports. WHYM-AM broadcasts to the Lake City, SC area at 1260 AM.

WHYN-AM
Owner: Clear Channel Media and Entertainment
Editorial: 1331 Main St Ste 4, Springfield, Massachusetts 01103-1621.
T: 1 413 781-1011 **W:** http://www.whyn.com
Editorial Profile: WHYN-AM is a commercial station owned by Clear Channel Media and Entertainment. The format of the station is news and talk. WHYN-AM broadcasts in the Springfield, MA area at 560 AM.

WHYN-FM
Owner: Clear Channel Media and Entertainment
Editorial: 1331 Main St Ste 4, Springfield, Massachusetts 01103-1621.
T: 1 413 781-1011 **W:** http://www.mix931.com
Editorial Profile: WHYN-FM is a commercial station owned by Clear Channel Media and Entertainment. The format of the station is hot adult contemporary. WHYN-FM broadcasts to the Springfield, MA area at 93.1 FM.

WHYP-AM
Owner: Corry Communications Corp.
Editorial: 122 N Center St, Corry, Pennsylvania 16407-1625. **T:** 1 814 664-8694
W: http://www.cool1370online.com
Editorial Profile: WHYP-AM is a commercial station owned by Corry Communications Corp. The format of the station is classic rock and oldies. WHYP-AM broadcasts to the Corry, PA area at 1370 AM.

WHYY-FM
Owner: WHYY Inc.
Editorial: Independence Mall West, 150 N. 6th Street, Philadelphia, Pennsylvania 19106-1521.
T: 1 215 351-1200 **E:** newsroom@whyy.org
W: http://www.whyy.org
Editorial Profile: WHYY-FM is a non-commercial station owned by WHYY Inc. The format of the station is news and talk. WHYY-FM broadcasts to the Philadelphia area at 90.9 FM, and in New Jersey.

WHYZ-FM
Owner: Central Florida Educational Foundation, Inc.
Editorial: 1065 Rainer Dr, Altamonte Springs, Florida 32714-3847. **T:** 1 407 869-8000
E: zcrew@zradio.org **W:** http://www.zradio.org
Editorial Profile: WHYZ-FM is a non-commercial station owned by Central Florida Educational Foundation, Inc. The format of the station is contemporary Christian. WHYZ-FM broadcasts to the Palm Coast, FL area at 91.1 FM. WHYZ-FM is a simulcast of WPOZ-FM.

WHZR-FM
Owner: Mid-America Radio Group
Editorial: 425 2nd St, Logansport, Indiana 46947-3410. **T:** 1 574 732-1037
E: whzr@midamericaradio.net
W: http://indianasbestradio.com
Editorial Profile: WHZR-FM is a commercial station owned by Mid-America Radio Group. The format of the station is country. WHZR-FM broadcasts to the Logansport, IN, area at 103.7 FM.

WHZT-FM
Owner: Summit Media Broadcasting LLC
Editorial: 220 N Main St Ste 402, Greenville, South Carolina 29601-2151.
T: 1 864 232-9810 **W:** http://www.hot981.com
Editorial Profile: WHZT-FM is a commercial station owned by Summit Media Broadcasting LLC. The format of the station is rhythmic Top 40/CHR. WHZT-FM broadcasts to the Greenville, SC area at 98.1 FM.

WHZZ-FM
Owner: MacDonald Broadcasting Co.
Editorial: 600 W Cavanaugh Rd, Lansing, Michigan 48910. **T:** 1 517 393-1320
E: 1017mikefmweb@gmail.com
W: http://www.1017mikefm.com
Editorial Profile: WHZZ-FM is a commercial station owned by the MacDonald Broadcasting Co. The format of the station is adult hits music. WHZZ-FM broadcasts to the Lansing, MI area at 101.7 FM.

WIAA-FM
Owner: Interlochen Center for Arts
Editorial: 4000 M 137, Interlochen, Michigan 49643-8427. **T:** 1 231 276-4400
E: ipr@interlochen.org
W: http://www.interlochen.org/ipr/

WIAD-FM
Owner: CBS Radio
Editorial: 4200 Parliament Pl Ste 300, Lanham, Maryland 20706-1881.
T: 1 301 683-0947
W: http://www.947freshfm.com
Editorial Profile: WIAD-FM is a commercial station owned by CBS Radio. The format of the station is adult contemporary. WIAD-FM broadcasts to the Washington, D.C. area at 94.7 FM.

WIAL-FM
Owner: Mid-West Family Broadcasting
Editorial: 944 Harlem St, Altoona, Wisconsin 54720-1127. **T:** 1 715 832-1530
W: http://www.i94online.com
Editorial Profile: WIAL-FM is a commercial station owned by Mid-West Family Broadcasting. The format of the station is Hot AC. WIAL-FM broadcasts to the Altoona, WI area at 94.1 FM.

WIAM-AM
Owner: Lifeline Ministries, Inc.
Editorial: 1012 East Blvd, Williamston, North Carolina 27892. **T:** 1 252 792-4161
W: http://opendoorradio.com
Editorial Profile: WIAM-AM is a commercial station owned by Lifeline Ministries, Inc. The format of the station is rock alternative. WIAM-AM broadcasts to the Williamston, NC area at 900 AM.

WIAN-AM
Owner: Sovereign Communications LLC
Editorial: 1009 W Ridge St, Ste A, Marquette, Michigan 49855. **T:** 1 906 225-1313
E: wjpd@wjpd.com
W: http://www.nsbroadcasting.com

WIBA-AM
Owner: Clear Channel Media and Entertainment
Editorial: 2651 S Fish Hatchery Rd, Fitchburg, Wisconsin 53711. **T:** 1 608 274-5450
E: wibanews@yahoo.com
W: http://www.wiba.com
Editorial Profile: WIBA-AM is a commercial station owned by Clear Channel Media and Entertainment. The format of the station is news and talk. WIBA-AM broadcasts to the Madison, WI area at 1310 AM.

WIBA-FM
Owner: Clear Channel Media and Entertainment
Editorial: 2651 S Fish Hatchery Rd, Fitchburg, Wisconsin 53711. **T:** 1 608 274-5450
W: http://www.wibafm.com
Editorial Profile: WIBA-FM is a commercial station owned by Clear Channel Media and Entertainment. The format for the station is classic rock. WIBA-FM broadcasts to the Madison, WI, area at 101.5 FM.

WIBB-AM
Owner: Clear Channel Media and Entertainment
Editorial: 7080 Industrial Hwy, Macon, Georgia 31216-7538. **T:** 1 478 781-1063
W: http://www.247comedy.com
Editorial Profile: WIBB-AM is a commercial station owned by Clear Channel Media and Entertainment. The format of the station is comedy. WIBB-AM broadcasts to the Macon, GA area at 1280 AM.

WIBB-FM
Owner: Clear Channel Media and Entertainment
Editorial: 7080 Industrial Hwy, Macon, Georgia 31216. **T:** 1 478 781-1063
W: http://www.wibb.com
Editorial Profile: WIBB-FM is a commercial station owned by Clear Channel Media and Entertainment. The format of the station is urban contemporary. WIBB-FM broadcasts to the Macon, GA area at 97.9 FM.

WIBC-FM
Owner: Emmis Communications Corp.
Editorial: 40 Monument Cir, Ste 400, Indianapolis, Indiana 46204.
T: 1 317 266-9422 **E:** news@wibc.com
W: http://www.wibc.com
Editorial Profile: WIBC-FM is a commercial station owned by Emmis Communications Corp. The format is news and talk. WIBC-FM broadcasts to the Indianapolis area at 93.1 FM.

WIBG-AM
Owner: Brancadora(Enrico S.)
Editorial: 3328 Simpson Ave, Ocean City, New Jersey 08226-2044. **T:** 1 609 398-7575
W: http://www.envivoradio.com
Editorial Profile: WIBG-AM is a commercial station owned by Enrico S. Brancadora. The format of the station is Spanish CHR. WIBG-AM broadcasts to the Atlantic City, NJ area at 1020 AM.

WIBG-FM
Owner: WIBG Limited Liability Company
Editorial: 3328 Simpson Ave, Ocean City, New Jersey 08226-2044. **T:** 1 609 391-0943
W: http://wibg.fm
Editorial Profile: WIBG-FM is a commercial station owned by WIBG Limited Liability Company. The format of the station is oldies. WIBG-FM broadcasts to the Philadelphia area at 94.3 FM.

WIBH-AM
Owner: Ellis(Bass Moury & Ronald)
Editorial: 330 S Main St, Anna, Illinois 62906.
T: 1 618 833-9424 **E:** wibh@ajinternet.net
W: http://www.wibhradio.com
Editorial Profile: WIBH-AM is a commercial station owned by Bass Moury and Ronald Ellis. The format of the station is country music. WIBH-AM broadcasts to the Anna, IL, area at 1440 AM.

WIBI-FM
Owner: Illinois Bible Institute
Editorial: 4101 Fieldstone Rd, Champaign, Illinois 61822-8800. **T:** 1 800 475-9245
W: http://www.wbgl.org
Editorial Profile: WIBI-FM is a non-commercial station owned by the Illinois Bible Institute. The format of the station is contemporary Christian music. WIBI-FM broadcasts to Carlinville, IL area at 91.1 FM.

WIBL-FM
Owner: Great Plains Media
Editorial: 108 Boeykens Pl, Normal, Illinois 61761. **T:** 1 309 888-4496
W: http://www.1077thebull.com
Editorial Profile: WIBL-FM is a commercial station owned by Great Plains Media. The format of the station is contemporary country. WIBL-FM broadcasts to the Peoria, IL area at 107.7 FM.

WIBM-AM
Owner: Jackson Radio Works Inc.
Editorial: 1700 Glenshire Dr, Jackson, Michigan 49201. **T:** 1 517 787-9546
W: http://www.espnradio1450.com
Editorial Profile: WIBM-AM is a commercial station owned by Jackson Radio Works Inc. The format of the station is sports. WIBM-AM broadcasts to the Jackson, MI area at 1450 AM.

WIBN-FM
Owner: Brothers Broadcasting Corp.
Editorial: 130 E McConnell St, Oxford, Indiana 47971. **T:** 1 765 385-2373
E: 98goldproduction@gmail.com
W: http://www.981wibn.com
Editorial Profile: WIBN-FM is a commercial station owned by Brothers Broadcasting Corp. The format of the station is classic hits. WIBM-FM broadcasts to the Oxford, IN area at 98.1 FM.

WIBR-AM
Owner: Cumulus Media
Editorial: 650 Wooddale Blvd, Baton Rouge, Louisiana 70806-2930. **T:** 1 225 926-1106
Editorial Profile: WIBR-AM is a commercial station owned by Cumulus Media. The format of the station is smooth jazz. WIBR-AM broadcasts in the Baton Rouge, LA area at 1300 AM.

WIBT-FM
Owner: Delta Radio Network, LLC.
Editorial: 44 Highway 448, Indianola, Mississippi 38751. **T:** 1 662 887-1380
E: info@deltaradio.net
W: http://www.1055thebeat.net
Editorial Profile: WIBT-FM is a commercial station owned by Delta Radio Network, LLC. The format of the station is urban contemporary. WIBT-FM broadcasts locally in the Indianola, MS area at a frequency of 105.5 FM.

WIBV-FM
Owner: Stratemeyer Media
Editorial: 498 Brink Road, Richview, Illinois 62877. **T:** 1 618 249-6025
E: wibv@wibv102.com
W: http://www.wibv102.com
Editorial Profile: WIBV-FM is a commercial station owned by Stratemeyer Media. The format of the station is contemporary country. WIBV-FM broadcasts to the Irvington, IL area at 102.1 FM.

WIBW-AM
Owner: Morris Communications
Editorial: 1210 SW Executive Dr, Topeka, Kansas 66615-3850. **T:** 1 785 272-3456
E: news@wibw.com
W: http://www.580wibw.com
Editorial Profile: WIBW-AM is a commercial station owned by Morris Communications. The format of the station is news, talk and sports. WIBW-AM broadcasts to the Topeka, KS area at 580 AM.

WIBW-FM
Owner: Morris Communications
Editorial: 1210 SW Executive Dr, Topeka, Kansas 66615-3850. **T:** 1 785 272-3456
E: news@wibw.com
W: http://www.94country.com
Editorial Profile: WIBW-FM is a commercial station owned by Morris Communications. The format of the station is contemporary country music. WIBW-FM broadcasts to the Topeka, KS area at 97.3 FM.

WIBX-AM
Owner: Townsquare Media, LLC
Editorial: 9418 River Rd, Marcy, New York 13403-2071. **T:** 1 315 768-9500
E: news@wibx950.com
W: http://www.wibx950.com
Editorial Profile: WIBX-AM is a commercial station owned by Townsquare Media, LLC. The format of the station is news, sports and talk programming. WIBX-AM broadcasts to the Utica, NY area at 950 AM.

WIBZ-FM
Owner: Miller Communications Inc.
Editorial: 51 Commerce St, Sumter, South Carolina 29150. **T:** 1 803 775-2321
E: production@miller.fm
W: http://www.miller.fm
Editorial Profile: WIBZ-FM is a commercial station owned Miller Communications Inc. The format of the station is adult hits. WIBZ-FM broadcasts to the Columbia, SC area at 95.5 FM.

WICB-FM
Owner: Ithaca College
Editorial: 118 Park Hall Ithaca College, Ithaca, New York 14850. **T:** 1 607 274-1040
E: news@wicb.org **W:** http://www.wicb.org

Editorial Profile: WICB-FM is a non-commercial station owned by Ithaca College. The format of the station is college variety. WICB-FM broadcasts to the Ithaca, NY area at 91.7 FM.

WICC-AM
Owner: Cumulus Media Inc.
Editorial: 2 Lafayette Sq, Bridgeport, Connecticut 06604-6014. **T:** 1 203 366-6000
W: http://www.wicc600.com
Editorial Profile: WICC-AM is a commercial station owned by Cumulus Media Inc. The format of the station is news and talk programming. WICC-AM broadcasts in Bridgeport, CT area at 600 AM.

WICH-AM
Owner: Hall Communications
Editorial: 40 Cuprak Rd, Norwich, Connecticut 6360. **T:** 1 860 887-3511 **E:** news@wich.com
W: http://www.wich.com
Editorial Profile: WICH-AM is a commercial station owned by Hall Communications. The format of the station is adult standards music. WICH-AM broadcasts to the Norwich, CT area at 1310 AM.

WICK-AM
Owner: Bold Gold Media Group
Editorial: 1049 N Sekol Ave, Scranton, Pennsylvania 18504-1040. **T:** 1 570 344-1221
W: http://www.boldgoldradionepa.com/
Editorial Profile: WICK-AM is a commercial station owned by Bold Gold Media Group. The format of the station is sports. WICK-AM broadcasts to the Scranton, PA area at 1400 AM.

WICL-FM
Owner: Prettyman Broadcasting Co.
Editorial: 1606 W King St, Martinsburg, West Virginia 25401-2077. **T:** 1 304 263-8868
Editorial Profile: WICL-FM is a commercial station owned by Prettyman Broadcasting Co. The format of the station is country music. WICL-FM broadcasts to the Martinsburg, MD area at 95.9.

WICN-FM
Owner: WICN Public Radio Inc.
Editorial: 50 Portland St, Worcester, Massachusetts 01608-2013.
T: 1 508 752-0700 **E:** webmaster@wicn.org
W: http://www.wicn.org
Editorial Profile: WICN-FM is a non-commercial station owned by WICN Public Radio Inc. The format of the station is jazz. WICN-FM broadcasts to the Worcester, MA area ar 90.5 FM. The station accepts PSAs as long as they are music event related.

WICO-AM
Owner: Delmarva Broadcasting
Editorial: 919 Ellegood St, Salisbury, Maryland 21801. **T:** 1 410 219-3500
E: wico@wicoam.com
W: http://www.wicoam.com
Editorial Profile: WICO-AM is a commercial station owned by Delmarva Broadcasting. The format of the station is news, talk and sports. WICO-AM broadcasts in the Salisbury, MD area at 1320 AM.

WICO-FM
Owner: Delmarva Broadcasting
Editorial: 919 Ellegood St, Salisbury, Maryland 21801. **T:** 1 410 219-3500
E: wico@wicoam.com
W: http://www.wicotalk.com
Editorial Profile: WICO-FM is a commercial station owned by Delmarva Broadcasting. The format of the station is news and talk. WICO-FM broadcasts in the Salisbury, MD area at 92.5 FM.

WICR-FM
Owner: University of Indianapolis
Editorial: 1400 E Hanna Ave, Indianapolis, Indiana 46227-3630. **T:** 1 317 788-3280
E: wicr@uindy.edu **W:** http://wicr.uindy.edu
Editorial Profile: WICR-FM is a non-commercial station owned by the University of Indianapolis. The format of the station is jazz and classical music. WICR-FM' broadcasts to the Indianapolis area at 88.7 FM.

WICY-AM
Owner: Martz Communications
Editorial: 86 Porter Rd, Malone, New York 12953-3701. **T:** 1 518 483-1100
E: news@country965.com
W: http://www.oldiesradioonline.com
Editorial Profile: WICY-AM is a commercial station owned by Martz Communications. The format of the station is oldies. WICY-AM broadcasts to the Malone, NY area at 1490 AM.

WIDG-AM
Owner: Baraga Broadcasting, Inc.
Editorial: 7078 M 68, Indian River, Michigan 49749-9472. **T:** 1 231 238-0811
W: http://www.baragabroadcasting.com
Editorial Profile: WIDG-AM is a commercial station owned by Baraga Broadcasting, Inc. The format of the station is Catholic programming and music. WIDG-AM broadcasts to the St. Ignace, MI area at 940 AM.

WIDL-FM
Owner: Edwards Communications LLC
Editorial: 1521 W Caro Rd, Caro, Michigan 48723. **T:** 1 989 672-1360
E: production@mix921.com
W: http://www.tuscolatoday.com
Editorial Profile: WIDL-FM is a commercial station owned by Edwards Communications LLC. The format for the station is hot adult contemporary. WDIL-FM broadcasts to the Flint, MI area at 92.1 FM.

WIDR-FM
Owner: Western Michigan University
Editorial: 1501 Faunce Student Services, Western Michigan Univ, Kalamazoo, Michigan 49008. **T:** 1 269 387-6301
E: widr.gm@gmail.com **W:** http://www.widr.org
Editorial Profile: WIDR-FM is a non-commercial station owned by Western Michigan University. The format of the station is a variety. WIDR-FM broadcasts to the Kalamazoo, MI area at 89.1 FM.

WIDS-AM
Owner: Hammond Broadcasting Inc.
Editorial: 4942 US Highway 27 N, Butler, Kentucky 41006-8653. **T:** 1 859 472-1075
E: wids@fuse.net **W:** http://www.wiok.com
Editorial Profile: WIDS-AM is a commercial station owned by Hammond Broadcasting Inc. The format of the station is Christian programming and Southern gospel music. WIDS-AM broadcasts in the Butler, KY area at 570 AM.

WIDU-AM
Owner: WIDU Broadcasting Inc.
Editorial: 1338 Bragg Blvd, Fayetteville, North Carolina 28301. **T:** 1 910 486-9438
E: widu1600@aol.com
W: http://www.lightstreamers.com/widu.htm
Editorial Profile: WIDU-AM is a commercial station owned by WIDU Broadcasting Inc. The format of the station is gospel, news and talk. WIDU-AM broadcasts to the Fayetteville, NC area at 1600 AM.

WIEZ-AM
Owner: First Media Radio LLC
Editorial: 12 E Market St, 2nd Fl, Lewistown, Pennsylvania 17044. **T:** 1 717 248-6757
W: http://www.wiez.com
Editorial Profile: WIEZ-AM is a commercial station owned by First Media Radio LLC. The format of the station is news and talk. WIEZ-AM broadcasts to the Lewistown, PA area at 670 AM.

WIFA-AM
Owner: Progressive Media, Inc.
Editorial: 818 N Cedar Bluff Rd Ste 102, Knoxville, Tennessee 37923-2201.
T: 1 865 531-2005 **E:** wifa.wijv@gmail.com
Editorial Profile: WIFA-FM is a non-commercial station owned by Progressive Media, Inc. The format of the station is contemporary Christian music. WIFA-FM broadcasts to the Knoxville, TN area at 1240 AM.

WIFC-FM
Owner: Midwest Communications Inc.
Editorial: 557 Scott St, Wausau, Wisconsin 54403. **T:** 1 715 842-1672
W: http://www.wifc.com
Editorial Profile: WIFC-FM is a commercial station owned by Midwest Communications Inc. The format of the station is Top 40/CHR music. WIFC-FM broadcasts in the Wausau, WI area at 95.5 FM.

WIFE-FM
Owner: White Water Broadcasting
Editorial: 406 1/2 N Central Ave, Connersville, Indiana 47331-1926. **T:** 1 765 825-6411
E: news@wifefm.com
W: http://www.wifefm.com
Editorial Profile: WIFE-FM is a commercial station owned by White Water Broadcasting. The format for the station is contemporary country music. WIFE-FM broadcasts to the Indianapolis area at 94.3 FM.

WIFI-AM
Owner: Forsyth (John)
Editorial: 123 Egg Harbor Rd, Sewell, New Jersey 08080-9406. **T:** 1 609 472-3524
E: amradiowifi@gmail.com
W: http://wifi1460am.com
Editorial Profile: WIFI-AM is a commercial station owned by John Forsyth. The format of the station is block time. WIFI-AM broadcasts to the Burlington, NJ area at 1460 AM. Send PSAs via the USPS.

WIFM-FM
Owner: Yadkin Valley Broadcasting
Editorial: 813 N Bridge St, Elkin, North Carolina 28621. **T:** 1 336 835-2511
E: wifm@wifmradio.com
W: http://www.wifmradio.com
Editorial Profile: WIFM-FM is a commercial station owned by Yadkin Valley Broadcasting. The format of the station is adult contemporary. WIFM-FM broadcasts to the Elkin, NC area at 100.9 FM.

WIFN-AM
Owner: Dickey Broadcasting
Editorial: 780 Johnson Ferry Rd Ne Ste 500, Atlanta, Georgia 30342-1436.
T: 1 404 688-0068 **W:** http://1230thefan2.com
Editorial Profile: WIFN-AM is a commercial station owned by Dickey Broadcasting. The format of the station is sports. WIFN-AM broadcasts to the Atlanta area at 1340 AM.

WIFO-FM
Owner: Jesup Broadcasting Corp.
Editorial: 2420 Waycross Hwy, Jesup, Georgia 31545. **T:** 1 912 427-3712
E: bigdogstaff@bellsouth.net
Editorial Profile: WIFO-FM is a commercial station owned by Jesup Broadcasting Corp. The format for the station is country. WIFO-FM broadcasts to the Savannah, GA area at 105.5 FM.

WIFY-FM
Owner: Northeast Broadcasting Co.
Editorial: 372 Dorset St, South Burlington, Vermont 05403-6212. **T:** 1 802 863-1010
W: http://www.cruisin937.com
Editorial Profile: WIFY-FM is a commercial station owned by Northeast Broadcasting Co. The format of the station is oldies. WIFY-FM broadcasts to the South Burlington, VT area at 93.7 FM.

WIGL-FM
Owner: Miller Communications Inc.
Editorial: 200 Regional Pkwy, Bldg C, Orangeburg, South Carolina 29118.
T: 1 803 536-1710 **E:** production@miller.fm
W: http://www.miller.fm
Editorial Profile: WIGL-FM is a commercial station owned by Miller Communications Inc. The format of the station is classic rock. WIGL-FM broadcasts to the Winnsboro, SC area at 93.9 FM.

WIGM-AM
Owner: WIGM Inc.
Editorial: 630 S 8th St, Medford, Wisconsin 54451. **T:** 1 715 748-2566
E: k99@k99wigm.com
W: http://www.k99wigm.com
Editorial Profile: WIGM-AM is a commercial station owned by WIGM Inc. The format of the station is sports. WIGM-AM broadcasts to the Medford, WI area at 1490 AM.

WIGN-AM
Owner: Mountain Music Ministries, LLC
Editorial: 2042 Euclid Ave, Bristol, Virginia 24201-3610. **T:** 1 276 591-5800
E: manager@wignam.com
W: http://www.wignam.com

WIGO-AM
Owner: MCL/MCM Georgia, LLC
Editorial: 2424 Old Rex Morrow Rd, Ellenwood, Georgia 30294-3901.
T: 1 404 361-8843
W: http://www.wigoam.com
Editorial Profile: WIGO-AM is a commercial station owned by MCL/MCM Georgia, LLC. The format of the station is gospel and blues. WIGO-AM broadcasts to the Ellenwood, GA area at 1570 AM.

WIGO-FM
Owner: Two Rivers Communications Inc.
Editorial: 101 Radio Rd, Kilmarnock, Virginia 22482-3881. **T:** 1 804 435-1414
W: http://middleneckneews.com
Editorial Profile: WIGO-FM is a commercial station owned by Two Rivers Communications Inc. The format of the station is contemporary country. WIGO-FM broadcasts to the Richmond, VA area at 104.9 FM.

WIGY-FM
Owner: Blueberry Broadcasting
Editorial: 125 Community Dr Ste 201, Augusta, Maine 04330-8010.
T: 1 207 623-9000
W: http://www.foxsportsmaine.com
Editorial Profile: WIGY-FM is a commercial station owned by Blueberry Broadcasting. The format of the station is sports. WIGY-FM broadcasts to the Augusta, ME area at 97.5 FM.

WIHG-FM
Owner: Crossville Radio, Inc.
Editorial: 37 South Dr, Crossville, Tennessee 38555. **T:** 1 931 484-1057
E: studio@1057thehog.com
W: http://www.1057thehog.com
Editorial Profile: WIHG-FM is a commercial station owned by Crossville Radio, Inc. The format of the station is classic hits. WIHG-FM broadcasts to the Crossville, TN area at 105.7 FM.

WIHM-AM
Owner: Covenant Network
Editorial: 4424 Hampton Ave, Saint Louis, Missouri 63109-2232. **T:** 1 314 752-7000
E: covenantnetwork@juno.com
W: http://www.covenantnet.net
Editorial Profile: WIHM-AM is a non-commercial station owned by the Covenant Network. The format of the station is religious music and talk. WIHM-AM broadcasts to the St. Louis area at 1410 AM.

WIHN-FM
Owner: Connoisseur Media LLC
Editorial: 520 N Center St, Bloomington, Illinois 61701. **T:** 1 309 834-1100
W: http://www.967irock.com
Editorial Profile: WIHN-FM is a commercial station owned by Connoisseur Media LLC. The format of the station is rock music. WIHN-FM broadcasts to the Bloomington, IL area at 96.7 FM.

WIHS-FM
Owner: Connecticut Radio Fellowship
Editorial: 1933 S Main St, Middletown, Connecticut 06457-6150. **T:** 1 860 346-1049
E: wihs@comcast.net
W: http://www.wihsradio.org
Editorial Profile: WIHS-FM is a non-commercial station owned by Connecticut Radio Fellowship. The format of the station is religious and contemporary Christian programming. WIHS-FM broadcasts to the Hartford-New Haven, CT area at 104.9 FM.

WIHT-FM
Owner: Clear Channel Media and Entertainment
Editorial: 1801 Rockville Pike Fl 5, Rockville, Maryland 20852-1633. **T:** 1 240 747-2700
W: http://www.hot995.com
Editorial Profile: WIHT-FM is a commercial station owned by Clear Channel Media and Entertainment. The format of the station is Pop Top 40/CHR music. WIHT-FM broadcasts to the Washington, D.C. area at 99.5 FM.

WIII-FM
Owner: Saga Communications
Editorial: 1751 Hanshaw Rd, Ithaca, New York 14850. **T:** 1 607 257-6400
W: http://www.wiii.com
Editorial Profile: WIII-FM is a commercial station owned by Saga Communications. The format of the station is classic rock. WIII-FM broadcasts to the Ithaca, NY area at 100.3 FM.

WIIL-FM
Owner: Digity LLC
Editorial: 8500 Green Bay Rd, Pleasant Prairie, Wisconsin 53158-2721.
T: 1 262 694-7800 **W:** http://95wiilrock.com
Editorial Profile: WIIL-FM is a commercial station owned by Digity LLC. The format of the station is rock music. WIIL-FM broadcasts to the Milwaukee area at 95.1 FM.

WIIN-AM
Owner: New South Communications Inc.
Editorial: 265 Highpoint Dr, Ridgeland, Mississippi 39157. **T:** 1 601 956-0102
W: http://www.us963.com
Editorial Profile: WIIN-AM is a commercial station owned by New South Communications Inc. The format of the station is country. WIIN-AM broadcasts to the Ridgeland, MS,

area at 780 AM. The station airs WUSJ-AM's programming.

WIIS-FM
Owner: Keyed Up Communications Co.
Editorial: 1075 Duval St, Ste C17, Key West, Florida 33040-3195. **T:** 1 305 292-1133
E: mail@island107.com
W: http://island107.com
Editorial Profile: WIIS-FM is a commercial station owned by Keyed Up Communications Co. The format of the station is rock alternative. WIIS-FM broadcasts to the Key West, FL area at 107.1 FM.

WIIT-FM
Owner: Illinois Institute of Technology
Editorial: 3201 S State St, Chicago, Illinois 60616. **T:** 1 312 567-3087
W: http://radio.iit.edu
Editorial Profile: WIIT-FM is a non-commercial station owned by the Illinois Institute of Technology. The format of the station is variety. WIIT-FM broadcasts to the Chicago area at 88.9 FM.

WIIZ-FM
Owner: NicWild Communications Inc.
Editorial: 8968 Marlboro Ave, Barnwell, South Carolina 29812. **T:** 1 803 259-9797
E: thewiz@wiiz979.com
W: http://www.wiizfm.com
Editorial Profile: WIIZ-FM is a commercial station owned by NicWild Communications Inc. The format of the station is urban contemporary. WIIZ-FM broadcasts to the Barnwell, SC area at 97.9 FM.

WIJR-AM
Owner: Birach Broadcasting Corp.
Editorial: 13063 Winu Dr, Highland, Illinois 62249-4800. **T:** 1 618 654-7521
E: info@latremenda880.com
W: http://www.birach.com/wijr.htm
Editorial Profile: WIJR-AM is a commercial station owned by Birach Broadcasting Corp. The format of the station is regional Mexican. WIJR-AM broadcasts to the Highland, IL area at 880 AM.

WIJV-FM
Owner: Progressive Media, Inc.
Editorial: 818 N Cedar Bluff Rd Ste 102, Knoxville, Tennessee 37923-2201.
T: 1 865 531-2005 **E:** wifa.wijv@gmail.com
Editorial Profile: WIJV-FM is a non-commercial station owned by Progressive Media, Inc. The format of the station is contemporary Christian music. WIJV-FM broadcasts to the Knoxville, TN area at 92.7 FM.

WIKB-FM
Owner: Heartland Communications Group, LLC
Editorial: 809 W Genesee St, Iron River, Michigan 49935. **T:** 1 906 265-5104
E: wikb@sbcglobal.net
W: http://www.wikb.com
Editorial Profile: WIKB-FM is a commercial station owned by Heartland Communications Group, LLC. The format of the station is classic and contemporary country music. WIKB-FM broadcasts to the Marquette, MI, area at 99.1 FM.

WIKE-AM
Owner: Great Eastern Radio, LLC
Editorial: 3422 Us Route 5, Derby, Vermont 05829-4430. **T:** 1 802 766-9236
W: http://1490wike.com
Editorial Profile: WIKE-AM is a commercial station owned by Great Eastern Radio, LLC. The format of the station is contemporary country music. WIKE-AM broadcasts to the Derby Center, VT area at 1490 AM.

WIKI-FM
Owner: Wagon Wheel Broadcasting LLC
Editorial: 2604 Michigan Rd, Madison, Indiana 47250. **T:** 1 812 273-2879
E: info@953wiki.com **W:** http://953wiki.com
Editorial Profile: WIKI-FM is a commercial station owned by Wagon Wheel Broadcasting LLC. The format of the station is country music. WIKI-FM broadcasts in the Madison, IN area at 95.3 FM.

WIKK-FM
Owner: Forcht Broadcasting
Editorial: 4667 E Radio Tower Ln, Olney, Illinois 62450. **T:** 1 618 393-2156
W: http://www.1035theeagle.com
Editorial Profile: WIKK-FM is a commercial station owned by Forcht Broadcasting. The format of the station is classic hits during the day and classic rock in the evening. WIKK-FM broadcasts to the Olney, IL area at 103.5 FM.

WIKQ-FM
Owner: Radio Greeneville Inc.
Editorial: 1004 Arnold Rd, Greeneville, Tennessee 37743. **T:** 1 423 639-1831
E: wgrv@greeneville.com
W: http://greeneville.com/wikq
Editorial Profile: WIKQ-FM is a commercial station owned by Radio Greeneville Inc. The format of the station is country. WIKQ-FM broadcasts to the Greenville, TN area at 103.1 FM.

WIKS-FM
Owner: Beasley Broadcast Group
Editorial: 207 Glenburnie Dr, New Bern, North Carolina 28560-2815. **T:** 1 252 633-1500
E: comments@kiss102.com
W: http://www.1019online.com
Editorial Profile: WIKS-FM is a commercial station owned by the Beasley Broadcast Group. The format of the station is urban adult contemporary music. WIKS-FM broadcasts to the New Bern, NC area at 101.9 FM.

WIKX-FM
Owner: Clear Channel Media and Entertainment
Editorial: 24100 Tiseo Blvd Unit 10, Port Charlotte, Florida 33980-5223.
T: 1 941 206-1188
W: http://www.kixcountry929.com/main.html
Editorial Profile: WIKX-FM is a commercial station owned by Clear Channel Media and Entertainment. The format of the station is contemporary country. WIKX-FM broadcasts to the Punta Gorda, FL area at 92.9 FM.

WIKY-FM
Owner: Midwest Communiations, Inc.
Editorial: 1162 Mount Auburn Rd, Evansville, Indiana 47720-5428. **T:** 1 812 424-8284
E: news@wiky.com **W:** http://www.wiky.com
Editorial Profile: WIKY-FM is a commercial station owned by Midwest Communiations, Inc. The format of the station is adult contemporary. WIKY-FM broadcasts to the Evansville, IN area at 104.1 FM.

WIKZ-FM
Owner: Main Line Broadcasting
Editorial: 25 Penncraft Ave, Chambersburg, Pennsylvania 17201-5600. **T:** 1 717 263-0813
E: mix95.1@mix95.com
W: http://www.mix95.com
Editorial Profile: WIKZ-FM is a commercial station owned by Main Line Broadcasting. The format of the station is hot adult contemporary. WIKZ-FM broadcasts to the Chambersburg, PA area at 95.1 FM.

WILB-AM
Owner: Living Bread Radio, Inc.
Editorial: 4365 Fulton Dr NW, Canton, Ohio 44718. **T:** 1 330 966-2903
W: http://www.livingbreadradio.com
Editorial Profile: WILB-AM is a non-commercial station owned by Living Bread Radio, Inc. The format of the station is Catholic news and talk programming. WILB-AM broadcasts to the Canton, OH area at 1060 AM.

WILB-FM
Owner: Living Bread Radio, Inc.
Editorial: 4365 Fulton Dr Nw, Canton, Ohio 44718-2823. **T:** 1 330 966-2903
E: info@livingbreadradio.com
W: http://www.livingbreadradio.com
Editorial Profile: WILB-FM is a non-commercial station owned by Living Bread Radio, Inc. The format of the station is Catholic news and talk programming. The station airs locally at 89.5 FM to the Boardman and Youngstown areas in Ohio.

WILD-AM
Owner: Radio One Inc.
Editorial: 500 Victory Rd, Ste 2, Quincy, Massachusetts 02171-3132.
T: 1 617 931-1090
Editorial Profile: WILD-AM is commercial station owned by Radio One Inc. The format of the station is variety featuring China Radio International programming the majority of the day. WILD-AM broadcasts to the greater Boston area at 1090 AM.

WILE-AM
Owner: AVC Communications Inc.
Editorial: 4988 Skyline Dr, Cambridge, Ohio 43725. **T:** 1 740 432-5605
E: avcnews@yourradioplace.com
W: http://www.yourradioplace.com/wile/am/index.htm
Editorial Profile: WILE-AM is a commercial station owned by AVC Communications Inc. The format of the station is sports. WILE-AM broadcasts to the Cambridge, OH area at 1270 AM.

WILE-FM
Owner: AVC Communications Inc.
Editorial: 4988 Skyline Dr, Cambridge, Ohio 43725. **T:** 1 740 432-5605
E: avcnews@yourradioplace.com
W: http://www.yourradioplace.com
Editorial Profile: WILE-FM is a commercial station owned by AVC Communications Inc. The format of the station is adult standards. WILE-FM broadcasts to the Wheeling, WV, Steubenville, OH, area at 97.7 FM.

WILF-FM
Owner: The Power Foundation
Editorial: 42676 Highway 31, Brewton, Alabama 36426-3386. **T:** 1 251 809-1915
W: http://wilffm.com
Editorial Profile: WILF-FM is a non-commercial station owned by The Power Foundation. The format of the station is Christian talk. WILF-FM broadcasts to the Brewton, AL area at a frequency of 88.9 FM.

WIL-FM
Owner: Hubbard Broadcasting, Inc.
Editorial: 11647 Olive Blvd, Saint Louis, Missouri 63141-7001. **T:** 1 314 983-6000
W: http://www.wil92.com
Editorial Profile: WIL-FM is a commercial station owned by Hubbard Broadcasting, Inc. The format of the station is contemporary country music. WIL-FM broadcasts to the St. Louis area at 92.3 FM.

WILI-AM
Owner: Hall Communications
Editorial: 720 Main St, Willimantic, Connecticut 06226-2648. **T:** 1 860 456-1111
E: wayne@wili.com **W:** http://www.wili.com/am
Editorial Profile: WILI-AM is a commercial station owned by Hall Communications. The format of the station is talk and adult contemporary music. WILI-AM broadcasts to the Hartford-New Haven, CT area at 1400 AM.

WILI-FM
Owner: Hall Communications
Editorial: 720 Main St, Willimantic, Connecticut 06226-2648. **T:** 1 860 456-1111
W: http://www.hitmusici983.com
Editorial Profile: WILI-FM is a commercial station owned by Hall Communications. The format of the station is Top 40/CHR music. WILI-FM broadcasts to the Hartford-New Haven, CT area at 98.3 FM.

WILK-AM
Owner: Entercom Communications Corp.
Editorial: 305 Route 315 Hwy, Pittston, Pennsylvania 18640-3907. **T:** 1 570 883-9800
W: http://www.wilknewsradio.com
Editorial Profile: WILK-AM is a commercial station owned by Entercom Communications Corp. The format of the station is news, sports and talk. WILK-AM broadcasts to the Pittson, PA area at 980 AM.

WILK-FM
Owner: Entercom Communications Corp.
Editorial: 305 Route 315 Hwy, Pittston, Pennsylvania 18640-3907. **T:** 1 570 883-9850
W: http://www.wilknetwork.com
Editorial Profile: WILK-FM is a commercial station owned by Entercom Communications Corp. The format of the station is news and talk. The station is broadcast to the Pittston, PA area at 103.1 FM.

WILL-AM
Owner: University of Illinois
Editorial: 300 N Goodwin Ave, Urbana, Illinois 61801-2316 **E:** willamfm@uiuc.edu
W: http://www.will.illinois.edu
Editorial Profile: WILL-AM is a non-commercial station owned by the University of Illinois. The format of the station is news and talk. WILL-AM broadcasts to the Urbana-Champaign, IL area at 580 AM.

WILL-FM
Owner: University of Illinois
Editorial: 300 N Goodwin Ave, Urbana, Illinois 61801. **T:** 1 217 333-0850
W: http://www.will.illinois.edu
Editorial Profile: WILL-FM is a non-commercial station owned by the University of Illinois. The format of the station is classical and jazz. WILL-FM broadcasts in the Urbana-Champaign, IL area at 90.9 FM.

WILM-AM
Owner: Clear Channel Media and Entertainment
Editorial: 920 W Basin Rd Ste 400, New Castle, Delaware 19720-1013.
T: 1 302 395-9800 **E:** newsroom@wilm.com
W: http://www.wilm.com
Editorial Profile: WILM-AM is a commercial station owned by Clear Channel Media and Entertainment. The format of the station is news and talk. WILM-AM broadcasts to the New Castle, DE, area at 1450 AM.

WILN-FM
Owner: Magic Broadcasting, LLC
Editorial: 7106 Laird St, Ste 102, Panama City, Florida 32408. **T:** 1 850 230-5855
W: http://www.island106.com
Editorial Profile: WILN-FM is a commercial station owned by Magic Broadcasting, LLC. The format of the station is Top 40/CHR music. WILN-FM broadcasts to the Panama City, FL area at 105.9 FM.

WILO-AM
Owner: Kaspar Broadcasting Co.
Editorial: 1401 W Barner St, Frankfort, Indiana 46041. **T:** 1 765 659-3339
W: http://www.wilo.us
Editorial Profile: WILO-AM is a commercial station owned by the Kaspar Broadcasting Co. The format of the station is oldies. WILO-AM broadcasts to the Frankfort, IN, area at 1570 AM.

WILQ-FM
Owner: Backyard Broadcasting
Editorial: 1685 Four Mile Dr, Williamsport, Pennsylvania 17701-1975. **T:** 1 570 323-8200
W: http://www.wilq.com
Editorial Profile: WILQ-FM is a commercial station owned by Backyard Broadcasting. The format of the station is country music. WILQ-FM broadcasts to the Susquehanna Valley, PA area at 105.1 FM.

WILS-AM
Owner: MacDonald Broadcasting Co.
Editorial: 600 W Cavanaugh Rd, Lansing, Michigan 48910. **T:** 1 517 393-1320
E: wilsradio@gmail.com
W: http://www.1320wils.com
Editorial Profile: WILS-AM is a commercial station owned by MacDonald Broadcasting Co. The format of the station is news and talk. WILS-AM broadcasts to the Lansing, MI area at 1320 AM.

WILT-FM
Owner: Capitol Broadcasting Company
Editorial: 25 N Kerr Ave, Ste C, Wilmington, North Carolina 28405. **T:** 1 910 791-3088
W: http://www.1045sunnyfm.com
Editorial Profile: WILT-FM is a commercial station owned by Capitol Broadcasting Company. The format of the station is adult contemporary. WILT-FM broadcasts in the Wilmington, NC area 104.5 FM.

WILV-FM
Owner: Hubbard Radio, LLC
Editorial: 130 E Randolph St Ste 2780, One Prudential Plaza, Chicago, Illinois 60601-6305.
T: 1 312 297-5100 **W:** http://www.wilv.com
Editorial Profile: WILV-FM is a commercial station owned by Hubbard Radio, LLC. The format of the station is adult hits. WILV-FM broadcasts to the Chicago area at 100.3 FM.

WILY-AM
Owner: Withers Broadcasting Co.
Editorial: 302 S Poplar St, Centralia, Illinois 62801-3922. **T:** 1 618 533-5700
E: wilynews@mywithersradio.com
W: http://mywithersradio.com/centralia
Editorial Profile: WILY-AM is a commercial station owned by Withers Broadcasting Co. The format of the station is oldies. WILY-AM broadcasts to the Centralia, IL area at 1210 AM.

WILZ-FM
Owner: Cumulus Media Inc.
Editorial: 1740 Champagne Dr N, Saginaw, Michigan 48604. **T:** 1 877 943-3591
W: http://www.wheelz.fm
Editorial Profile: WILZ-FM is a commercial station owned by Cumulus Media Inc. The format of the station is classic rock. WILZ-FM broadcasts to the Saginaw, MI area at 104.5 FM.

WIMA-AM
Owner: Clear Channel Media and Entertainment
Editorial: 667 W Market St, Lima, Ohio 45801.
T: 1 419 223-2060
W: http://www.1150wima.com
Editorial Profile: WIMA-AM is a commercial station owned by Clear Channel Media and

Entertainment. The format of the station is news and talk. WIMA-AM broadcasts to the Lima, OH area at 1150 AM.

WIMC-FM
Owner: Forcht Broadcasting
Editorial: 1757 N 175 W, Crawfordsville, Indiana 47933. **T:** 1 765 362-8200
W: http://www.crawfordsvilleradio.com
Editorial Profile: WIMC-FM is a commercial station owned by Forcht Broadcasting. The format of the station is classic hits. WIMC-FM broadcasts to the Crawfordsville, IN area at 103.9 FM.

WIMG-AM
Owner: Morris Broadcasting Co.
Editorial: 1842 S Broad St, Trenton, New Jersey 8610. **T:** 1 609 695-1300
W: http://www.wimg1300.com
Editorial Profile: WIMG-AM is a commercial station owned by Morris Broadcasting Co. The format of the station is urban gospel. WIMG-FM broadcasts to the Trenton, NJ area at 1300 AM.

WIMI-FM
Owner: J & J Broadcasting
Editorial: 222 S Lawrence St, Ironwood, Michigan 49938. **T:** 1 906 932-2411
E: wjmswimi@chartermi.net
W: http://www.wimifm.com
Editorial Profile: WIMI-FM is commercial station owned by J & J Broadcasting. The format of the station is adult contemporary music. WIMI-FM broadcasts to the Ironwood, MI area at 99.7 FM.

WIMK-FM
Owner: Northern Star Broadcasting LLC
Editorial: 101 Kent St, Iron Mountain, Michigan 49801-1507. **T:** 1 906 774-4321
E: prodguy@uplogon.com
W: http://www.rockthebear.com
Editorial Profile: WIMK-FM is a commercial station owned by Northern Star Broadcasting LLC. The format for the station is rock music. WIMK-FM broadcasts to the Iron Mountain, MI area at 93.1 FM.

WIMS-AM
Owner: Gerard Media LLC
Editorial: 685 E 1675 N, Michigan City, Indiana 46360-9503. **T:** 1 219 879-9810
E: news@wimsradio.com
W: http://www.wimsradio.com
Editorial Profile: WIMS-AM is a commercial station owned by Gerard Media LLC. The format of the station is sports, news and talk. WIMS-AM broadcasts to the southern Chicago area at 1420 AM.

WIMT-FM
Owner: Clear Channel Media and Entertainment
Editorial: 667 W Market St, Lima, Ohio 45801. **T:** 1 419 223-2060 **W:** http://www.t102.com
Editorial Profile: WIMT-FM is a local, commercial station owned by Clear Channel Media and Entertainment. The format of the station is country music. WIMT-FM broadcasts in the Lima, OH area at 102.1 FM.

WIMX-FM
Owner: URBan Radio Broadcasting, LLC
Editorial: 720 Water St, Fl 4, Toledo, Ohio 43604-1883. **T:** 1 419 244-6354
E: info@urbanradio.fm
W: http://www.mix957.net
Editorial Profile: WIMX-FM is a commercial station owned by URBan Radio Broadcasting, LLC. The format of the station is urban adult contemporary. WIMX-FM broadcasts to the Toledo, OH area at 97.5 FM.

WIMZ-FM
Owner: South Central Communications Corp.
Editorial: 1100 Sharps Ridge Road, Knoxville, Tennessee 37917. **T:** 1 865 525-6000
W: http://www.wimz.com

WINA-AM
Owner: Saga Communications
Editorial: 1140 Rose Hill Dr, Charlottesville, Virginia 22903. **T:** 1 434 220-2300
E: news@wina.com **W:** http://www.wina.com
Editorial Profile: WINA-AM is a commercial station owned by Saga Communications. The format of the station is news and talk. WINA-AM broadcasts to the Charlottesville, VA area at 1070 AM.

WINC-AM
Owner: Centennial Broadcasting
Editorial: 520 N Pleasant Valley Rd, Winchester, Virginia 22601-5654.

T: 1 540 667-2224 **E:** comments@winc.fm
W: http://www.newstalk1400winc.com
Editorial Profile: WINC-AM is a commercial station owned by Centennial Broadcasting. The format of the station is news, sports and talk. WINC-AM broadcasts to the Winchester, VA area at 1400 AM.

WINC-FM
Owner: Centennial Broadcasting
Editorial: 520 N Pleasant Valley Rd, Winchester, Virginia 22601-5654.
T: 1 540 667-2224 **E:** comments@winc.fm
W: http://www.winc.fm
Editorial Profile: WINC-FM is a commercial station owned by Centennial Broadcasting. The format of the station is hot adult contemporary. WINC-FM broadcasts to the Winchester, VA area at 92.5 FM.

WIND-AM
Owner: Salem Communications
Editorial: 25 NW Point Blvd, Elk Grove Village, Illinois 60007-1056. **T:** 1 847 437-5200
W: http://www.560wind.com
Editorial Profile: WIND-AM is a commercial station owned by Salem Communications. The format of the station is talk. WIND-AM broadcasts to the Chicago area at 560 AM.

WINE-AM
Owner: Townsquare Media, LLC
Editorial: 1004 Federal Rd, Brookfield, Connecticut 06804-1123. **T:** 1 203 775-1212
W: http://www.940sportsradio.com
Editorial Profile: WINE-AM is a commercial station owned by Townsquare Media, LLC. The format of the station is sports. WINE-AM broadcasts to the Brookfield, CT area at 940 AM.

WING-AM
Owner: Main Line Broadcasting
Editorial: 717 E David Rd, Dayton, Ohio 45429-5218. **T:** 1 937 294-5858
E: daytonsports@yahoo.com
W: http://www.wingam.com
Editorial Profile: WING-AM is a commercial station owned by Main Line Broadcasting. The format of the station is sports. WING-AM broadcasts to the Dayton, OH area at 1410.

WINI-AM
Owner: Radio Station WINI Partnership
Editorial: 1230 W Broadway St, Sparta, Illinois 62286-1664. **T:** 1 618 684-2128
E: info@winiradio.com
W: http://www.newstalk1420wini.com
Editorial Profile: WINI-AM is a commercial station owned by Radio Station WINI Partnership. The format of the station is news talk. WINI-AM broadcasts to Murphysboro, IL, and its surrounding areas at 1840 AM.

WINK-AM
Owner: Fort Myers Broadcasting Company
Editorial: 2824 Palm Beach Blvd, Fort Myers, Florida 33916-1503. **T:** 1 239 337-2346
W: http://www.winknewsradio.com
Editorial Profile: WINK-AM is a commercial station owned by Fort Myers Broadcasting Company. The format of the station is news and talk. WINK-AM broadcasts to the Fort Myers, FL area at 1200 AM.

WINK-FM
Owner: Meridian Broadcasting, Inc.
Editorial: 2824 Palm Beach Blvd, Fort Myers, Florida 33916-1503. **T:** 1 239 337-2346
W: http://www.969morefm.com
Editorial Profile: WINK-FM is a commercial station owned by Meridian Broadcasting, Inc. The format of the station is adult contemporary music. WINK-FM broadcasts to the Fort Myers, FL area at 96.9 FM.

WINL-FM
Owner: Westburg Broadcasting Alabama, LLC.
Editorial: 1226 Jefferson Rd, Demopolis, Alabama 36732-6205. **T:** 1 334 289-9850
E: sales@mywin98.com
W: http://www.dixiecountry.net
Editorial Profile: WINL-FM is a commercial station owned by Westburg Broadcasting Alabama, LLC. The format of the station is classic country music. WINL-FM broadcasts to the Demopolis, AL area at 98.5 FM.

WINN-FM
Owner: White River Broadcasting Co., Inc.
Editorial: 3212 Washington St, Columbus, Indiana 47203-1505. **T:** 1 812 372-4448
W: http://www.win1049.com
Editorial Profile: WINN-FM is a commercial station owned by White River Broadcasting Co., Inc. The format of the station is Adult

CHR. WINN-FM broadcasts to the Columbus, IN area at 104.9 FM.

WINQ-FM
Owner: Saga Communications
Editorial: 69 Stanhope Ave, Keene, New Hampshire 03431-1577. **T:** 1 603 352-9230
W: http://www.wink987.com
Editorial Profile: WINQ-FM is a commercial station owned by Saga Communications. The format of the station is country. WINQ-FM broadcasts to the Boston area at 98.7.

WINR-AM
Owner: Clear Channel Media and Entertainment
Editorial: 320 N Jensen Rd, Vestal, New York 13850. **T:** 1 607 584-5800
W: http://www.680winr.com
Editorial Profile: WINR-AM is a commercial station owned by Clear Channel Media and Entertainment. The format of the station is Oldies. WINR-AM broadcasts to the Binghamton, NY area at 680 AM.

WINS-AM
Owner: CBS Radio
Editorial: 345 Hudson St, New York, New York 10014-4502. **T:** 1 212 315-7000
E: info@1010winsmail.com
W: http://newyork.cbslocal.com/station/1010-wins
Editorial Profile: WINS-AM is a commercial station owned by CBS Radio. The format of the station is news. WINS-AM broadcasts to the New York area at 1010 AM.

WINX-FM
Owner: First Media Radio LLC
Editorial: 306 Port St, Easton, Maryland 21601-4101. **T:** 1 410 822-3301
W: http://www.winxfm.com
Editorial Profile: WINX-FM is a commercial station owned by First Media Radio LLC. The format of the station is contemporary country. WINX-FM's tagline is "Shore Country 94.3 FM." The target audience of the station is adults, ages 18 to 54. WINX-FM broadcasts to the Easton, MD area at 94.3 FM.

WINY-AM
Owner: Osbrey Broadcasting
Editorial: 45 Pomfret St, Putnam, Connecticut 6260. **T:** 1 860 928-1350
E: news@winyradio.com
W: http://www.winyradio.com
Editorial Profile: WINY-AM is a commercial station owned by Osbrey Broadcasting. The format of the station is adult contemporary. WINY-AM broadcasts to Putnam, CT at 1350 AM.

WINZ-AM
Owner: Clear Channel Media and Entertainment
Editorial: 7601 Riviera Blvd, Miramar, Florida 33023-6574. **T:** 1 954 862-2000
W: http://www.940winz.com/main.html
Editorial Profile: WINZ-AM is a commercial station owned by Clear Channel Media and Entertainment. The format of the station is sports. WINZ-AM broadcasts to the Miami area at 940 AM.

WIOD-AM
Owner: Clear Channel Media and Entertainment
Editorial: 7601 Riviera Blvd, Miramar, Florida 33023-6574. **T:** 1 954 862-2000
E: news@wiod.com **W:** http://www.wiod.com
Editorial Profile: WIOD-AM is a commercial station owned by Clear Channel Media and Entertainment. The format of the station is news and talk. WIOD-AM broadcasts to the Miami area at 610 AM.

WIOG-FM
Owner: Cumulus Media Inc.
Editorial: 1740 Champagne Dr N, Saginaw, Michigan 48604. **T:** 1 989 776-2100
W: http://www.wiog.com
Editorial Profile: WIOG-FM is a commercial station owned by Cumulus Media Inc. The format of the station is Top 40/CHR music. WIOG-FM broadcasts to the Saginaw, MI area at 102.5 FM.

WIOI-AM
Owner: Maillet Media Inc.
Editorial: 1010 Coles Blvd, Portsmouth, Ohio 45662. **T:** 1 606 932-4796
E: 1010am@wioiradio.com
W: http://www.wioiradio.com
Editorial Profile: WIOI-AM is a commercial station owned by Maillet Media Inc. The format of the station is adult standards. WIOI-

AM broadcasts to Portsmouth, OH and surrounding communities at 1010 AM.

WIOK-FM
Owner: Hammond Broadcasting Inc.
Editorial: 4942 US Highway 27 N, Butler, Kentucky 41006-8653. **T:** 1 859 472-1075
E: wiok@fuse.net **W:** http://www.wiok.com
Editorial Profile: WIOK-FM is a commercial station owned by Hammond Broadcasting Inc. The format of the station is gospel. WIOK-FM broadcasts to Butler, KY area at 107.5 FM.

WIOL-FM
Owner: Davis Broadcasting
Editorial: 2203 Wynnton Rd, Columbus, Georgia 31906-2531. **T:** 1 706 576-3565
W: http://www.1580thezone.com
Editorial Profile: WIOL-FM is a commercial station owned by Davis Broadcasting. The format of the station is sports. WIOL-FM broadcasts to the Columbus, GA area at 95.7 FM.

WION-AM
Owner: Packer Radio WION LLC
Editorial: 1150 Haynor Rd, Ionia, Michigan 48846-8532. **T:** 1 616 527-9466
E: office@i1430.com **W:** http://www.i1430.com
Editorial Profile: WION-AM is a commercial station owned by Packer Radio WION LLC. The format of the station is full service. WION-AM broadcasts to the Ionia, MI area on 1430 AM.

WIOO-AM
Owner: WIOO Inc.
Editorial: 180 York Rd, Carlisle, Pennsylvania 17013-3149. **T:** 1 717 243-1200
E: wioo@pa.net **W:** http://www.wioo.com
Editorial Profile: WIOO-AM is a commercial station owned by WIOO Inc. The format of the station is classic country. WIOO-AM broadcasts to the Carlisle, PA area at 1000 AM.

WIOQ-FM
Owner: Clear Channel Media and Entertainment
Editorial: 111 Presidential Blvd, Bala Cynwyd, Pennsylvania 19004-1008. **T:** 1 610 784-3333
W: http://www.q102.com/main.html
Editorial Profile: WIOQ-FM is a commercial station owned by Clear Channel Media and Entertainment. The format of the station is Top 40/CHR. WIOQ-FM broadcasts to the Philadelphia area at 102.1 FM.

WIOS-AM
Owner: Carroll Broadcasting Co.
Editorial: 523 Meadow Rd, Tawas City, Michigan 48763-9189. **T:** 1 989 362-3417
E: wkjc@wkjc.com
Editorial Profile: WIOS-AM is a commercial station owned by Carroll Broadcasting Co. The format of the station is adult standards and talk. WIOS-AM broadcasts to the Tawas City, MI area at 1480 AM.

WIOT-FM
Owner: Clear Channel Media and Entertainment
Editorial: 125 S Superior St, Toledo, Ohio 43604-8747. **T:** 1 419 244-8321
W: http://www.wiot.com
Editorial Profile: WIOT-FM is a commercial station owned by Clear Channel Media and Entertainment. The format of the station is rock. WIOT-FM broadcasts to the Toledo, OH area at 104.7 FM.

WIOU-AM
Owner: Hoosier AM/FM LLC
Editorial: 671 E 400 S, Kokomo, Indiana 46902-8101. **T:** 1 765 453-1212
W: http://www.ihigh.com/wiousports
Editorial Profile: WIOU-AM is a commercial station owned by Hoosier AM/FM LLC. The format of the station is news, sports and talk. WIOU-AM broadcasts to the Kokomo, IN area at 1350 AM.

WIOV-AM
Owner: Cumulus Media Inc.
Editorial: 44 Bethany Rd, Ephrata, Pennsylvania 17522-2416. **T:** 1 717 738-1191
W: http://www.wiov985.com
Editorial Profile: WIOV-AM is a commercial station owned by Cumulus Media Inc. The format of the station is sports. WIOV-AM broadcasts to the Reading, PA area at 1240 AM.

WIOV-FM
Owner: Cumulus Media Inc.

Editorial: 44 Bethany Rd, Ephrata, Pennsylvania 17522. **T:** 1 717 738-1191
W: http://www.wiov.com
Editorial Profile: WIOV-FM is a commercial station owned by Cumulus Media Inc. The format of the station is classic country. WIOV-FM broadcasts to the Ephrata, PA area at 105.1 FM.

WIOZ-AM
Owner: Muirfield Broadcasting
Editorial: 200 Short Rd, Southern Pines, North Carolina 28387. **T:** 1 910 692-2107
W: http://www.wioz.com
Editorial Profile: WIOZ-AM is a commercial station owned by Muirfield Broadcasting. The format of the station is adult standards. WIOZ-AM broadcasts to the Southern Pines, NC at 550 AM.

WIOZ-FM
Owner: Muirfield Broadcasting
Editorial: 200 Short Rd, Southern Pines, North Carolina 28387-6289.
T: 1 910 692-2107
W: http://www.star1025fm.com
Editorial Profile: WIOZ-FM is a commercial station owned by Muirfield Broadcasting. The format of the station is adult contemporary. WIOZ-FM broadcasts to Southern Pines, NC area at 102.5 FM.

WIPA-FM
Owner: University of Illinois
Editorial: 1 University Plz, Rm 130, Springfield, Illinois 62703-5497.
T: 1 217 206-9847 **E:** wuis@uis.edu
W: http://www.wuis.org
Editorial Profile: WIPA-FM is a non-commercial, college station in Springfield, IL. The station airs a simulcast of WUIS-FM, which features classical music, jazz and news. WIPA-FM airs at 89.3 FM.

WIP-AM
Owner: CBS Radio
Editorial: 400 Market St Fl 9, Philadelphia, Pennsylvania 19106-2530. **T:** 1 610 949-7800
W: http://www.cbsphilly.com
Editorial Profile: WIP-AM is a commercial station owned by CBS Radio. The format of the station is sports. WIP-AM broadcasts to the Philadelphia area at 610 AM.

WIPC-AM
Owner: Super W Media Group Inc.
Editorial: 630A Mountain Lake Cutoff Rd, Lake Wales, Florida 33859-7854. **T:** 1 863 679-7178
E: wipc1280@yahoo.com
W: http://www.radio esperanza1280.com
Editorial Profile: WIPC-AM is a commercial station owned by Super W Media Group Inc. The format of the station is Hispanic religious programming. WIPC-AM broadcasts to the Lake Wales, FL area at 1280 AM.

WIP-FM
Owner: CBS Radio
Editorial: 400 Market St Fl 9, Philadelphia, Pennsylvania 19106-2530. **T:** 1 610 949-7800
E: wippromotions@cbsradio.com
W: http://philadelphia.cbslocal.com
Editorial Profile: WIP-FM is a commercial station owned by CBS Radio. The format of the station is sports talk. WIP-FM broadcasts to the Philadelphia area at 94.1 FM. The stations airs WIP-AM's programming.

WIQO-FM
Owner: 3 Daughters Media, Inc.
Editorial: 1035 Avalon Dr, Forest, Virginia 24551-2970. **T:** 1 434 534-6100
W: http://www.wiqoradio.com
Editorial Profile: WIQO-FM is a commercial station owned by 3 Daughters Media, Inc. The format of the station is talk. WIQO-FM broadcasts to the Lynchburg, VA area at 100.9 FM.

WIQQ-FM
Owner: Delta Radio, LLC
Editorial: 1399 E Reed Rd, Greenville, Mississippi 38703. **T:** 1 662 378-2617
W: http://www.q102greenville.com/
Editorial Profile: WIQQ-FM is a commercial station owned by Delta Radio, LLC. The format of the station is hot adult contemporary. WIQQ-FM broadcasts to the Greenville, MS area at 102.3 FM.

WIQR-AM
Owner: Star Power Communications
Editorial: 800 County Road 4 E, Prattville, Alabama 36067-6610. **T:** 1 334 358-0410
W: http://www.wiqr.net
Editorial Profile: WIQR-AM is a commercial station owned by Star Power Communications. The format of the station is sports. WIQR-AM broadcasts to the Prattville, AL area at 1410 AM.

WIRA-AM
Owner: Team One Media, LLC
Editorial: 6803 S US Highway 1, Port Saint Lucie, Florida 34952-1434. **T:** 1 772 460-9356
Editorial Profile: WIRA-AM is a commercial station owned by Team One Media, LLC. The format of the station is jazz music. WIRA-AM broadcasts to the Port St. Lucie, FL area at 1400 AM.

WIRD-AM
Owner: Mountain Communications
Editorial: 159 Santanoni Ave, Saranac Lake, New York 12983-2478. **T:** 1 518 891-1544
E: news@wnbz.com
Editorial Profile: WIRD-AM is a commercial station owned by Mountain Communications. The format of the station is adult standards. WIRD-AM broadcasts to the Saranac Lake, NY area at 920 AM.

WIRE-FM
Owner: Hoosier Broadcasting Corporation
Editorial: 107 N Meridian St Ste 2022, Lebanon, Indiana 46052-2384.
T: 1 765 482-4427
W: http://www.radiomom.fm
Editorial Profile: WIRE-FM is a non-commercial station owned by Hoosier Broadcasting Corporation. The format of the station is adult hits. WIRE-FM broadcasts to the Indianapolis, IN area at 91.1 FM.

WIRK-FM
Owner: Palm Beach Broadcasting, LLC
Editorial: 701 Northpoint Pkwy Ste 500, West Palm Beach, Florida 33407-1960.
T: 1 561 868-1100 **W:** http://www.wirk.com
Editorial Profile: WIRK-FM is a commercial station owned by Palm Beach Broadcasting, LLC. The format of the station is contemporary country. WIRK-FM broadcasts to the West Palm Beach, FL area at 103.1 FM.

WIRL-AM
Owner: L & L Radio
Editorial: 331 Fulton St Ste 1200, Peoria, Illinois 61602-1422. **T:** 1 309 637-3700
E: news@1470wmbd.com
W: http://www.1290wirl.com
Editorial Profile: WIRL-AM is a commercial station owned by L & L Radio. The format of the station is oldies music. WIRL-AM broadcasts to the Peoria, IL area at 1290 AM.

WIRN-FM
Owner: Minnesota Public Radio
Editorial: 207 W Superior St, Ste 224, Duluth, Minnesota 55802. **T:** 1 218 722-9411
E: newsroom@mpr.org **W:** http://www.mpr.org
Editorial Profile: WIRN-FM is a non-commercial station owned by Minnesota Public Radio. The format of the station is news and talk. WIRN-FM broadcasts to the Duluth, MN area at 92.5 FM.

WIRO-AM
Owner: Clear Channel Media and Entertainment
Editorial: 134 4th Ave, Huntington, West Virginia 25701. **T:** 1 304 525-7788
W: http://www.800wvhu.com
Editorial Profile: WIRO-AM is a commercial station owned by Clear Channel Media and Entertainment. The format of the station is sports. WIRO-AM broadcasts to Huntington, WV at 1230 AM.

WIRR-FM
Owner: Minnesota Public Radio
Editorial: 207 W Superior St Ste 224, Duluth, Minnesota 55802-4041. **T:** 1 218 722-9411
E: newsroom@mpr.org
W: http://minnesota.publicradio.org/radio/stations/wirnwirr/
Editorial Profile: WIRR-FM is a non-commercial station owned by Minnesota Public Radio. The format of the station is classical music. WIRR-FM broadcasts to the Duluth, MN area at 90.9 FM.

WIRV-AM
Owner: Wallingford Broadcasting LLC
Editorial: 1030 Winchester Rd, Irvine, Kentucky 40336. **T:** 1 606 723-5138
E: coyote@wcyofm.com
Editorial Profile: WIRV-AM is a commercial station owned by Wallingford Broadcasting LLC. The format for the station is oldies and talk. WIRV-AM broadcasts to the Lexington, KY area at 1550 AM.

WIRX-FM
Owner: Midwest Family Stations
Editorial: 580 E Napier Ave, Benton Harbor, Michigan 49022-5816. **T:** 1 269 925-1111
E: wirx@wirx.com **W:** http://www.wirx.com
Editorial Profile: WIRX-FM is a commercial station owned by Midwest Family Stations. The format of the station is rock music. WIRX-AM broadcasts in the Benton Harbor, MI area at 107.1 FM.

WIRY-AM
Owner: Hometown Radio Inc.
Editorial: 4712 State Route 9, Plattsburgh, New York 12901-6035. **T:** 1 518 563-1340
E: wiry@wiry.com **W:** http://www.wiry.com
Editorial Profile: WIRY-AM is a commercial station owned by Hometown Radio Inc. The format of the station is adult contemporary, oldies and contemporary country music. WIRY-AM broadcasts to the Plattsburgh, NY area at 1340 AM.

WISE-AM
Owner: Saga Communications
Editorial: 1190 Patton Ave, Asheville, North Carolina 28806-2706. **T:** 1 828 259-9695
W: http://espnasheville.com
Editorial Profile: WISE-AM is a commercial station owned by Saga Communications. The format of the station is sports. WISE-AM broadcasts to the Asheville, NC area at 1310 AM.

WISH-FM
Owner: Dana Communications Corp.
Editorial: 303 N Main St, Benton, Illinois 62812-1314. **T:** 1 618 435-4392
W: http://www.wqrlradio.com
Editorial Profile: WISH-FM is a commercial station owned by Dana Communications Corp. located in McLeansboro, Illinois. The station is a sister station to WMCL-AM and WQRL-FM. WISH-FM is broadcast locally on 98.9 FM. The format of the station is adult contemporary music.

WISK-AM
Owner: Sumter Broadcasting
Editorial: 215 Georgia Hwy 30 W., Americus, Georgia 31719. **T:** 1 229 924-6500
E: wiskwdec@mchsi.com
W: http://www.americusradio.com
Editorial Profile: WISK-AM is a commercial station owned by Sumter Broadcasting. The format of the station is oldies. WISK-AM broadcasts in the Americus, GA area at 1390 AM.

WISK-FM
Owner: Sumter Broadcasting
Editorial: 215 Georgia Hwy 30 W, Americus, Georgia 31719. **T:** 1 229 924-6500
E: wiskwdec@mchsi.com
W: http://www.americusradio.com
Editorial Profile: WISK-FM is a commercial station owned by Sumter Broadcasting. The format of the station is country music. WISK-FM broadcasts to the Americus, GA area at 98.7 FM.

WISM-FM
Owner: Clear Channel Media and Entertainment
Editorial: 619 Cameron St, Eau Claire, Wisconsin 54703. **T:** 1 715 830-4000
W: http://www.themix981.com
Editorial Profile: WISM-FM is a commercial station owned by Clear Channel Media and Entertainment. The format of the station is adult contemporary music. WISM-FM broadcasts to the Eau Claire, WI area at 98.1 FM.

WISN-AM
Owner: Clear Channel Media and Entertainment
Editorial: 12100 W Howard Ave, Greenfield, Wisconsin 53228-1851. **T:** 1 414 545-8900
W: http://www.newstalk1130.com
Editorial Profile: WISN-AM is a commercial station owned by Clear Channel Media and Entertainment. The format of the station is news and talk. WISN-AM broadcasts to the Greenfield, WI, area at 1130 AM.

WISP-AM
Owner: Holy Spirit Radio Foundation, Inc.
Editorial: 40 Rickert Rd, Doylestown, Pennsylvania 18901. **T:** 1 215 345-1570
E: 1570am@holyspiritradio.org
W: http://www.holyspiritradio.org
Editorial Profile: WISP-AM is a non-commercial station owned by Holy Spirit Radio Foundation, Inc. The format of the station is religious programming. WISP-AM broadcasts to the Doylestown, PA area at 1570 AM.

WISR-AM
Owner: Butler County Radio Network
Editorial: 112 Hollywood Dr, Butler, Pennsylvania 16001-5691. **T:** 1 724 283-1500
E: frontdesk@bcrnetwork.com
W: http://www.wisr680.com
Editorial Profile: WISR-AM is a commercial station owned by the Butler County Radio Network. The format of the station is news and talk. WISR-AM broadcasts to the Butler, PA area at 680 AM.

WISS-AM
Owner: Hometown Broadcasting LLC
Editorial: 112 N Pearl St, Berlin, Wisconsin 54923. **T:** 1 920 361-3551
W: http://www.wissradio.com
Editorial Profile: WISS-AM is a commercial station owned by Hometown Broadcasting LLC. The format of the station is talk. WISS-AM broadcasts to the Berlin, WI area at 1100 AM.

WIST-AM
Owner: Catholic Community Radio, Inc.
Editorial: 8230 Summa Ave Ste A, Baton Rouge, Louisiana 70809-3421.
T: 1 225 448-3754
W: http://catholiccommunityradio.org/neworleans
Editorial Profile: WIST-AM is a commercial station owned by Catholic Community Radio, Inc.. The format of the station is Catholic radio programming. WIST-AM broadcasts to the New Orleans area at 690 AM.

WIST-FM
Owner: Norsan Group
Editorial: 4801 E Independence Blvd Ste 815, Charlotte, North Carolina 28212-5490.
T: 1 704 405-3172
Editorial Profile: WIST-FM is a commercial station owned by Norsan Group. The format of the station is regional Mexican. WIST-FM broadcasts in the High Point, NC area at 98.3 FM.

WISU-FM
Owner: Indiana State University
Editorial: 217 Dreiser Hall, Terre Haute, Indiana 47809. **T:** 1 812 237-3690
E: wisufm@indstate.edu
W: http://wisu.indstate.edu
Editorial Profile: WISU-FM is a non-commercial station owned by Indiana State University. The format of the station is college variety. WISU-FM broadcasts in the Terre Haute, IN area at 89.7 FM.

WISW-AM
Owner: Cumulus Media Inc.
Editorial: 1801 Charleston Hwy Ste J, Cayce, South Carolina 29033-2019.
T: 1 803 796-7600
W: http://www.1320thefan.com
Editorial Profile: WISW-AM is a commercial station owned by Cumulus Media Inc. The format of the station is sports. WISW-AM broadcasts to the Columbia, SC area at a frequency of 1320 AM.

WISX-FM
Owner: Clear Channel Media and Entertainment
Editorial: 111 Presidential Blvd Ste 100, Bala Cynwyd, Pennsylvania 19004-1009.
T: 1 610 784-3333
W: http://www.mixphiladelphia.com
Editorial Profile: WISX-FM is a commercial station owned by Clear Channel Media and Entertainment. The format of the station is hot adult contemporary. WISX-FM broadcasts to the Philadelphia area at 106.1 FM.

WITA-AM
Owner: F.W. Robbert Broadcasting, Inc.
Editorial: 2914 Sanderson Rd, Knoxville, Tennessee 37921-1625. **T:** 1 865 588-2974
W: http://www.wita1490.com
Editorial Profile: WITA-AM is a commercial station owned by F.W. Robbert Broadcasting, Inc. The format of the station is religious and gospel music. WITA-AM broadcasts to the Knoxville, TN area at 1490 AM.

WITF-FM
Owner: WITF Inc.
Editorial: 4801 Lindle Rd, Harrisburg, Pennsylvania 17111-2444. **T:** 1 717 704-3000
E: news@witf.org **W:** http://www.witf.org
Editorial Profile: WITF-FM is a non-commercial station owned by WITF Inc. The format of the station is news and talk. WITF-

FM broadcasts to the Harrisburg, PA area at 89.5 FM.

WITL-FM

Owner: Townsquare Media, LLC
Editorial: 3420 Pinetree Rd, Lansing, Michigan 48911-4207. **T:** 1 517 394-7272
W: http://www.witl.com
Editorial Profile: WITL-FM is a commercial station owned by Townsquare Media, LLC. The format of the station is contemporary country music. WITL-FM broadcasts to the Lansing, MI area at 100.7 FM.

WITR-FM

Owner: Rochester Institute of Technology
Editorial: 32 Lomb Memorial Dr, Rochester, New York 14623. **T:** 1 585 475-2000
E: feedback@witr.rit.edu **W:** http://witr.rit.edu
Editorial Profile: WITR-FM is a non-commercial college station owned by Rochester Institute of Technology. The format of the station is college variety. WITR-FM broadcasts to the Rochester, NY area at 89.7 FM.

WITS-AM

Owner: Cohan Radio Group Inc.
Editorial: 3750 US Highway 27 N, Ste 1, Sebring, Florida 33870. **T:** 1 863 382-9999
E: cohanradiogroup@htn.net
W: http://www.cohanradiogroup.com
Editorial Profile: WITS-AM is a commercial station owned by Cohan Radio Group Inc. The format of the station is adult standards. WITS-AM broadcasts to the Sebring, FL area at 1340 AM.

WITY-AM

Owner: David Brown
Editorial: 399 Spelter Ave, Tilton, Illinois 61833. **T:** 1 217 446-1312 **E:** wityradio@att.net
W: http://www.wityradio.com
Editorial Profile: WITY-AM is commercial station owned by David Brown. The station's format is adult standards. WITY-AM broadcasts to Vermilion County, IL at 980 AM.

WITZ-AM

Owner: Jasper on the Air Inc.
Editorial: 1978 S Witz Rd, Jasper, Indiana 47546-2672. **T:** 1 812 482-2131
E: news@witzamfm.com
W: http://www.witzamfm.com
Editorial Profile: WITZ-AM is a commercial station owned by Jasper on the Air Inc. The format of the station is adult contemporary music. WITZ-FM broadcasts to the Jasper, IN area at 990 AM.

WITZ-FM

Owner: Jasper on the Air Inc.
Editorial: 1978 S Witz Rd, Jasper, Indiana 47546-2672. **T:** 1 812 482-2131
E: news@witzamfm.com
W: http://www.witzamfm.com
Editorial Profile: WITZ-FM is a commercial station owned by Jasper on the Air Inc. The format of the station is adult contemporary music. WITZ-FM broadcasts to the Jasper, IN area at 104.7 FM.

WIUM-FM

Owner: Western Illinois University
Editorial: 1 University Cir, Macomb, Illinois 61455. **T:** 1 309 298-1873
E: publicradio@wiu.edu
W: http://www.tristatesradio.com
Editorial Profile: WIUM-FM is a non-commercial station owned by Western Illinois University. The format of the station is classical, news and talk. WIUM-FM broadcasts to the Macomb, IL area at 91.3 FM.

WIUP-FM

Owner: Indiana University of Pennsylvania
Editorial: 121 Stouffer Hall Iup, Indiana, Pennsylvania 15705. **T:** 1 724 357-7971
W: http://www.coe.iup.edu/wiupfm/
Editorial Profile: WIUP-FM is a non-commercial station owned by Indiana University of Pennsylvania. The format of the station is college variety. WIUP-FM broadcasts to the Indiana, PA area at 90.1 FM.

WIUS-FM

Owner: Western Illinois University
Editorial: Western Illinois University, 326 Salle Hall, Macomb, Illinois 61455-1390.
T: 1 309 298-3217 **E:** 883thedog@gmail.com
W: http://www.wiu.edu/thedog
Editorial Profile: WIUS-FM is a non-commercial station owned by Western Illinois University. The format of the station is urban contemporary music. WIUS-FM broadcasts to the Macomb, IL area at 88.3 FM.

WIVG-FM

Owner: Flinn Broadcasting Corp.
Editorial: 6080 Mount Moriah Road Ext, Memphis, Tennessee 38115-2645.
T: 1 901 375-9324 **W:** http://96xmemphis.com
Editorial Profile: WIVG-FM is a commercial station owned by Flinn Broadcasting Corp. The format of the station is alternative rock. WIVG-FM broadcasts to the Memphis, TN area at 96.1 FM.

WIVK-FM

Owner: Cumulus Media Inc.
Editorial: 4711 Old Kingston Pike, Knoxville, Tennessee 37919-5207. **T:** 1 865 588-6511
W: http://www.wivk.com
Editorial Profile: WIVK-FM is a commercial station owned by Cumulus Media Inc. The format of the station is contemporary country. WIVK-FM broadcasts to the Knoxville, TN area at 107.7 FM.

WIVQ-FM

Owner: Mendota Broadcasting
Editorial: 3905 Progress Blvd, Peru, Illinois 61354-1121. **T:** 1 815 224-2100
E: q@studstillmedia.com
W: http://www.qhitmusic.com
Editorial Profile: WIVQ-FM is a commercial station owned by Mendota Broadcasting. The format of the station is Top 40/CHR. WIVQ-FM broadcasts to the Peru, IL area at 103.3 FM.

WIVR-FM

Owner: Milner Broadcasting Co.
Editorial: 202 E Walnut St, Watseka, Illinois 60970-1356. **T:** 1 815 933-9287
E: wivrfm@comcast.net
W: http://www.rivervalleyradio.net
Editorial Profile: WIVR-FM is a commercial station owned by Milner Broadcasting Co. The format of the station is contemporary country music. WIVR-FM broadcasts to the Bourbonnais, IL area at 101.7 FM.

WIVY-FM

Owner: Gateway Radio Works Inc.
Editorial: 123 E 1st St, Morehead, Kentucky 40351. **T:** 1 606 784-9966
Editorial Profile: WIVY-FM is a commercial station owned by Gateway Radio Works Inc. The format for the station is adult contemporary. WIVY-FM broadcasts to the Lexington, KY area at 96.3 FM.

WIWA-AM

Owner: Church Capital Florida Holdings, LLC.
Editorial: 12538 Village Park Drive, Orlando, Florida 32812-8214. **T:** 1 407 506-1270
E: 1270am@gmail.com
W: http://www.laestaciondelpueblo.com
Editorial Profile: WIWA-FM is a commercial station owned by Church Capital Florida Holdings, LLC. The format of the station is Spanish News Talk, with a secondary format of Spanish Contemporary Christian. The station broadcasts to the Orlando, FL area at a frequency of 1160 AM.

WIWF-FM

Owner: Cumulus Media Inc.
Editorial: 4230 Faber Place Dr Ste 100, North Charleston, South Carolina 29405-8512.
T: 1 843 277-1200
W: http://www.nashfm969.com
Editorial Profile: WIWF-FM is a commercial station owned by Cumulus Media Inc. The format of the station is classic and contemporary country music. WIWF-FM broadcasts to the Charleston, SC area at 96.9 FM.

WIWS-AM

Owner: Southern Communications Corp.
Editorial: 306 S Kanawha St, Beckley, West Virginia 25801-5619. **T:** 1 304 252-6452
Editorial Profile: WBKW-AM is a commercial station owned by Southern Communications Corp. The format of the station is religious Catholic. WBKW-AM broadcasts locally in the Beckley, WV area at 1070 AM.

WIXC-AM

Owner: Genesis Communications Inc.
Editorial: 6305 State Road 46, Mims, Florida 32754. **T:** 1 813 281-1040
E: info@radiogenesis.com
W: http://www.newstalkflorida.com
Editorial Profile: WIXC-AM is a commercial station owned by Genesis Communications Inc. The format of the station is news and talk. WIXC-AM broadcasts to the Mims, FL area at 1060 AM.

WIXE-AM

Owner: Monroe Broadcasting

Editorial: 1700 Buena Vista Rd, Monroe, North Carolina 28112-6306.
T: 1 704 289-2525 **W:** http://www.wixe.com
Editorial Profile: WIXE-AM is a commercial station owned by Monroe Broadcasting. The format of the station is classic country and talk. WIXE-AM broadcasts in the Charlotte, NC area at 1190 AM.

WIXI-AM

Owner: Rivera Communications
Editorial: 100 Yeager Pkwy, Pelham, Alabama 35124-1859. **T:** 1 205 358-1100
W: http://www.aquimandalajefa.com
Editorial Profile: WIXI-AM is a commercial station owned by Rivera Communications. The format of the station is Regional Mexican. WIXI-AM broadcasts to the Birmingham, AL area at a frequency of 1360 AM.

WIXK-AM

Owner: WIXK-AM, LLC
Editorial: 125 E 3rd St Ste, New Richmond, Wisconsin 54017-1800. **T:** 1 715 246-2254
Editorial Profile: WIXK-AM is a commercial station owned by WIXK-AM, LLC and under an LMA with Zoe Communications, Inc. The format of the station is classic country. WIXK-AM broadcasts to the St. Paul, MN area at 1590 AM.

WIXM-FM

Owner: Northeast Broadcasting Co.
Editorial: 372 Dorset St, South Burlington, Vermont 05403-6212. **T:** 1 802 863-1010
W: http://themix1023.com
Editorial Profile: WIXM-FM is a commercial station owned by Northeast Broadcasting Co. The format of the station is adult contemporary. WIXM-FM broadcasts to the Saint Albans, VT area at 102.3 FM.

WIXN-AM

Owner: NRG Media LLC
Editorial: 1460 S College Ave, Dixon, Illinois 61021. **T:** 1 815 288-3341
W: http://www.am1460wixn.com
Editorial Profile: WIXN-AM is a commercial station owned by NRG Media LLC. The format of the station is adult standards music. WIXN-AM broadcasts to the Dixon, IL area at 1460 AM.

WIXO-FM

Owner: Cumulus Media Inc.
Editorial: 120 Eaton St, Peoria, Illinois 61603-4217. **T:** 1 309 676-5000
W: http://www.1057thexrocks.com
Editorial Profile: WIXO-FM is a commercial station owned by Cumulus Media Inc. The format of the station is rock/album-oriented rock. WIXO-FM broadcasts to the Peoria, IL area at 105.7 FM.

WIXQ-FM

Owner: Millersville University
Editorial: Student Memorial Center, Millersville University, Millersville, Pennsylvania 17551.
T: 1 717 872-3518
E: stationmanager@wixq.com
W: http://www.wixq.com
Editorial Profile: WIXQ-FM in a non-commercial station owned by Millersville University. The format of the station is college variety. WIXQ-FM broadcasts in the Millersville, PA area at 91.7 FM.

WIXT-AM

Owner: Galaxy Communications LP
Editorial: 39 Kellogg Rd, New Hartford, New York 13413. **T:** 1 315 797-1330
Editorial Profile: WIXT-AM is a commercial station owned by Galaxy Communications LP. The format of the station is sports. WLFH-AM broadcasts to the Utica, NY area at 1230 AM.

WIXV-FM

Owner: Cumulus Media Inc.
Editorial: 214 Television Cir, Savannah, Georgia 31406-4519. **T:** 1 912 961-9000
W: http://www.rockofsavannah.net
Editorial Profile: WIXV-FM is a commercial station owned by Cumulus Media Inc. The format of the station is classic rock. WIXV-FM broadcasts to the Savannah, GA area at 95.5 FM.

WIXX-FM

Owner: Midwest Communications Inc.
Editorial: 1420 Bellevue St, Green Bay, Wisconsin 54311. **T:** 1 920 435-3771
W: http://www.wixx.com
Editorial Profile: WIXX-FM is a commercial station owned by Midwest Communications Inc. The format of the station is Top 40/CHR. WIXX-FM broadcasts to the Green Bay, WI area at 101.1 FM.

WIXY-FM

Owner: Saga Communications
Editorial: 2603 W Bradley Ave, Champaign, Illinois 61821. **T:** 1 217 352-4141
W: http://www.wixy.com
Editorial Profile: WIXY-FM is a commercial station owned by Saga Communications. The format of the station is contemporary country. WIXY-FM broadcasts to the Champaign, IL area at 100.3 FM.

WIYD-AM

Owner: Natkim
Editorial: 1428 Saint Johns Ave, Palatka, Florida 32177-4542. **T:** 1 386 325-4556
E: wiyd@wiydradio.com
W: http://wiydradio.com
Editorial Profile: WIYD-AM is a commercial station owned by Hall Broadcasting Co. The format of station is classic country. WIYD-AM broadcasts to the Palatka, FL area at 1260 AM.

WIYN-FM

Owner: Double O Radio
Editorial: 34 Chestnut St, Oneonta, New York 13820. **T:** 1 607 432-1030
E: wdla@frontiernet.net **W:** http://wdhifm.com
Editorial Profile: WIYN-FM is a commercial station owned by Double O Radio. The format of the station is oldies music. WIYN-FM broadcasts to the Oneonta, NY area at 94.7 FM.

WIYY-FM

Owner: Hearst Radio, Inc.
Editorial: 3800 Hooper Ave, Baltimore, Maryland 21211-1313. **T:** 1 410 338-6596
W: http://www.98online.com
Editorial Profile: WIYY-FM is a commercial station owned by the Hearst Radio, Inc. The format of the station is rock music. WIYY-FM broadcasts to the Baltimore area at 97.9 FM.

WIZB-FM

Owner: Radio Training Network, Inc.
Editorial: 2563 Montgomery Hwy Ste 1, Dothan, Alabama 36303-2603.
T: 1 334 699-5672
W: http://alabama.thejoyfm.com
Editorial Profile: WIZB-FM is a non-commercial station owned by Radio Training Network, Inc. The format of the station is adult contemporary Christian programming. WIZB-FM broadcasts in the Dothan, AL area at 94.3 FM.

WIZD-AM

Owner: Letcher County Broadcasting Inc.
Editorial: 486 Lakeside Dr, Jenkins, Kentucky 41537-8917. **T:** 1 606 832-1035
Editorial Profile: WIZD-AM is a commercial station owned by Letcher County Broadcasting. The format of the station is oldies. WIZD-AM broadcasts to the Whitesburg, KY area at 1480 AM.

WIZE-AM

Owner: Clear Channel Media and Entertainment
Editorial: 101 Pine St, Dayton, Ohio 45402.
T: 1 937 224-1137 **W:** http://wizeam.com
Editorial Profile: WIZE-AM is a commercial station owned by Clear Channel Media and Entertainment. The format of the station is classic country. WIZE-AM broadcasts to the Dayton, OH area at 1340 AM.

WIZF-FM

Owner: Radio One Inc.
Editorial: One Centennial Plaza, 705 Central Ave Suite 200, Suite 200705, Cincinnati, Ohio 45202. **T:** 1 513 679-6000
W: http://www.wiznation.com
Editorial Profile: WIZF-FM is a commercial station owned by Radio One Inc. The format of the station is urban contemporary music. WIZF-FM broadcasts in the Cincinnati area at 101.1 FM.

WIZM-AM

Owner: Midwest Family Broadcasting
Editorial: 201 State St, La Crosse, Wisconsin 54601-3246. **T:** 1 608 782-1230
E: news@1410wizm.com
W: http://www.1410wizm.com

WIZM-FM

Owner: Midwest Family Broadcasting
Editorial: 201 State St, La Crosse, Wisconsin 54601-3246. **T:** 1 608 782-1300
E: news@familyradioinc.com
W: http://www.z933.com
Editorial Profile: WIZM-FM is a commercial station owned by Midwest Family Broadcasting. The format of the station is

adult contemporary. WIZM-FM broadcasts to the La Crosse, WI area at 93.3 FM.

WIZN-FM
Owner: Hall Communications
Editorial: 255 S Champlain St, Burlington, Vermont 05401-4881. **T:** 1 802 860-2440
E: wizn@wizn.com **W:** http://www.wizn.com
Editorial Profile: WIZN-FM is a commercial station owned by Hall Communications. The format of the station is rock/album oriented rock. WIZN-FM broadcasts in the Burlington, VT area at 106.7 FM.

WIZS-AM
Owner: Rose Farm & Rentals Inc.
Editorial: 535 Radio Ln, Henderson, North Carolina 27536-2505. **T:** 1 252 492-3001
E: wizs@vance.net **W:** http://www.wizs.com
Editorial Profile: WIZS-AM is a commercial station owned by Rose Farm & Rentals Inc. The format of the station is country. WIZS-AM broadcasts to the Henderson, NC area at 1450 AM.

WJAA-FM
Owner: Midland Media Inc.
Editorial: 1531 W Tipton St, Seymour, Indiana 47274. **T:** 1 812 523-3343 **E:** radio@wjaa.net
W: http://www.wjaa.net
Editorial Profile: WJAA-FM is a commercial station owned by Midland Media Inc. The format of the station is adult album alternative. WJAA-FM broadcasts to the Seymour, IN area at 93.3 FM.

WJAB-FM
Owner: Alabama A&M University
Editorial: 3409 Meridian St N, Huntsville, Alabama 35811-1544. **T:** 1 256 372-5795
W: http://www2.aamu.edu/wjab/
Editorial Profile: WJAB-FM is a non-commercial station owned by Alabama A&M University. The format of the station is jazz and blues. WJAB-FM broadcasts to the Huntsville, AL area at 90.9 FM.

WJAD-FM
Owner: Cumulus Media Inc.
Editorial: 1104 W Broad Ave, Albany, Georgia 31707. **T:** 1 229 888-5000
W: http://www.rock103albany.com
Editorial Profile: WJAD-FM is a commercial station owned by Cumulus Media Inc. The format of the station is rock music. WJAD-FM broadcasts to the Albany, GA area at 103.5 FM.

WJAG-AM
Owner: WJAG Inc.
Editorial: 309 Braasch Ave, Norfolk, Nebraska 68701-4113. **T:** 1 402 371-0780
W: http://www.wjag.com
Editorial Profile: WJAG-AM is a commercial station owned by WJAG Inc. The format of the station is news and talk with an emphasis on agricultural news and information. WJAG-AM broadcasts to the Norfolk, NE area at 780 AM.

WJAG-FM
Owner: WJAG Inc.
Editorial: 309 Braasch Ave, Norfolk, Nebraska 68701-4113. **T:** 1 402 371-0780
W: http://www.wjag.com
Editorial Profile: WJAG-FM is a commercial station owned by WJAG Inc. The format of the station is news. WJAG-FM broadcasts to the Norfolk, NE area at 105.9 FM.

WJAK-AM
Owner: Southern Stone Communications, LLC
Editorial: 111 W Main St, Jackson, Tennessee 38301. **T:** 1 731 427-9616
W: http://jacksonnewsnow.com/sports
Editorial Profile: WJAK-AM is a commercial station owned by Southern Stone Communications, LLC. The format of the station is sports. WJAK-AM broadcasts to the Jackson, TN area at 1460 AM.

WJAM-AM
Owner: Bluewater Broadcasting, LLC (Scott Communications, Inc.)
Editorial: 273 Persimmon Tree Rd, Valley Grande, Alabama 36701. **T:** 1 334 875-9360
Editorial Profile: WJAM-AM is a commercial station licensed under Scott Communications, Inc, but owned and operated under Bluewater Broadcasting, LLC. The format of the station is urban adult contemporary and gospel. WJAM-AM broadcasts to the Selma, AL area at 1340 AM.

WJAQ-FM
Owner: MFR Inc.

Editorial: 4376 Lafayette St, Marianna, Florida 32446-3364. **T:** 1 850 482-3046
E: wjaqfm@gmail.com
Editorial Profile: WJAQ-FM is a commercial station owned by MFR Inc. The format of the station is classic country music. WJAQ-FM broadcasts to the Marianna, FL area at 100.9 FM.

WJAS-AM
Owner: Renda Broadcasting
Editorial: 900 Parish St, 3rd Fl, Pittsburgh, Pennsylvania 15220. **T:** 1 412 875-4800
W: http://www.1320wjas.com
Editorial Profile: WJAS-AM is a commercial station owned by Renda Broadcasting. The format of the station is adult standards. WJAS-AM broadcasts to the Pittsburgh area at 1320 AM.

WJAT-AM
Owner: RadioJones LLC
Editorial: 2 Radio Loop, Swainsboro, Georgia 30401. **T:** 1 478 237-1590
Editorial Profile: WJAT-AM is a commerical station owned by RadioJones LLC. The format of the station is talk. WJAT-AM broadcasts to the Swainsboro, GA area at 800 AM.

WJAW-AM
Owner: JAWCO Inc.
Editorial: 925 Lancaster St, Marietta, Ohio 45750. **T:** 1 740 373-1490
W: http://www.espnwjaw.com
Editorial Profile: WJAW-AM is a commercial station owned by JAWCO Inc. The format of the station is sports. WJAW-AM broadcasts to the Marietta, OH area at 630 AM.

WJAW-FM
Owner: JAWCO Inc.
Editorial: 925 Lancaster St, Marietta, Ohio 45750. **T:** 1 740 373-1490
W: http://www.wmoa1490.com
Editorial Profile: WJAW-FM is a commercial station owned by JAWCO Inc. The format for the station is sports. WJAW-FM broadcasts to the Marietta, OH area at 100.9 FM.

WJAX-AM
Owner: Jones College
Editorial: 5353 Arlington Expy, Jacksonville, Florida 32211. **T:** 1 904 680-1220
W: http://www.wjaxradio.com
Editorial Profile: WJAX-AM is a commercial station owned by Jones College. The format of the station is adult standards. WJAX-AM broadcasts to the Jacksonville, FL area at 1220 AM.

WJAY-AM
Owner: Greater Highway Church of Christ
Editorial: 3004 E Highway 76, Mullins, South Carolina 29574. **T:** 1 843 423-1140
Editorial Profile: WJAY-AM is a commercial station owned by Greater Highway Church of Christ. The format of the station is gospel music. WJAY-AM broadcasts to the Marion, SC area at 1280 AM.

WJBB-AM
Owner: Jeffrey T. Batten's Barrow Radio Broadcasting LLC
Editorial: 850 Arch Tanner Rd, Bethlehem, Georgia 30620-2703. **T:** 1 770 867-1300
W: http://www.wjbbradio.com
Editorial Profile: WJBB-AM is a commercial station owned by Jeffrey T. Batten's Barrow Radio Broadcasting LLC. The format of the station is news and talk, local sports, and oldies rock music. WWJBB-AM broadcasts to the Bethlehem, GA area at 1300 AM.

WJBC-AM
Owner: Cumulus Media Inc.
Editorial: 236 Greenwood Ave, Bloomington, Illinois 61704-7422. **T:** 1 309 829-1221
E: news@wjbc.com **W:** http://www.wjbc.com
Editorial Profile: WJBC-AM is commercial station owned by Cumulus Media Inc. The format of the station is news and talk. WJBC-AM broadcasts to the Bloomington, IL area at 1230 AM.

WJBC-FM
Owner: Cumulus Media Inc.
Editorial: 236 Greenwood Ave, Bloomington, Illinois 61704-7422. **T:** 1 309 829-1221
E: news@wjbc.com **W:** http://www.wjbc.com
Editorial Profile: WJBC-FM is a commercial station owned by Cumulus Media Inc. The format of the station is news and talk. WJBC-FM broadcasts to the Pontiac, IL area at 93.7 FM.

WJBD-AM
Owner: NRG Media LLC
Editorial: 310 W McMackin St, Salem, Illinois 62881. **T:** 1 618 548-2000
E: news@wjbdradio.com
W: http://www.wjbdradio.com
Editorial Profile: WJBD-AM is commercial station owned by NRG Media LLC. The format of the station is country music. WJBD-AM broadcasts to the Salem, IL area at 1350 AM.

WJBD-FM
Owner: NRG Media LLC
Editorial: 310 W McMackin St, Salem, Illinois 62881. **T:** 1 618 548-2000
E: news@wjbdradio.com
W: http://www.wjbdradio.com
Editorial Profile: WJBD-FM is a commercial station owned by NRG Media LLC. The format of the station is Lite Rock/Lite AC music. WJBD-FM broadcasts to Salem, IL at 100.1 FM.

WJBE-AM
Owner: Arm & Rage Broadcasting
Editorial: 2340 Martin Luther King Jr Ave, Knoxville, Tennessee 37915-1625.
T: 1 865 247-6928 **W:** http://www.wjbe.am
Editorial Profile: WJBE-AM is a commercial station owned by Arm & Rage Broadcasting. The format of the station is R&B. WJBE-AM broadcasts to the Knoxville, TN area at 1040 AM.

WJBE-FM
Owner: Big South Community Broadcasting
Editorial: 310 Highway 195 Ste 4, Jasper, Alabama 35503-6513. **T:** 1 205 221-2222
Editorial Profile: WJBE-FM is a non-commercial station owned by Big South Community Broadcasting. The format of the station is classic country. WJBE-FM broadcasts to the Jasper, AL area at a frequency of 88.5 FM.

WJBI-AM
Owner: Batesville Broadcasting Co.
Editorial: 1040 Highway 6 W, Batesville, Mississippi 38606. **T:** 1 662 563-4664
E: country101radio@yahoo.com
W: http://www.wble101.com
Editorial Profile: WJBI-AM is a commercial station owned by Batesville Broadcasting Co. The format of the station is adult standards music. WJBI-AM broadcasts in the Batesville, MS area at 1290 AM.

WJBL-FM
Owner: Flambeau Broadcasting Co., Inc.
Editorial: 4083 S Wilshire Ct, New Berlin, Wisconsin 53151-6210. **T:** 1 715 532-5588
Editorial Profile: WJBL-FM is a commercial station owned by Flambeau Broadcasting Co., Inc. The format of the station is oldies. WJBL-FM broadcasts to the Ladysmith, WI area at 93.1 FM.

WJBM-AM
Owner: DJ Two Rivers Radio
Editorial: 1010 State Highway 16, Jerseyville, Illinois 62052. **T:** 1 618 498-8255
E: wjbm@wjbmradio.com
W: http://www.wjbmradio.com
Editorial Profile: WJBM-AM is a commercial station owned by DJ Two Rivers Radio. The format of the station is news and talk. WJBM-AM broadcasts to Jerseyville, IL at 1480 AM.

WJBO-AM
Owner: Clear Channel Media and Entertainment
Editorial: 5555 Hilton Ave, Ste 500, Baton Rouge, Louisiana 70808. **T:** 1 225 231-1860
W: http://www.wjbo.com
Editorial Profile: WJBO-AM is a commercial station owned by Clear Channel Media and Entertainment. The format of the station is news, talk, and sports. WJBO-AM broadcasts to the Baton Rouge, LA area at 1150 AM.

WJBP-FM
Owner: Family Life Broadcasting, Inc.
Editorial: 7355 N Oracle Rd, Tucson, Arizona 85704-6325. **T:** 1 800 776-1070
W: http://myflr.org
Editorial Profile: WJBP-FM is a non-commercial station owned by Family Life Broadcasting, Inc. The format of the station is contemporary Christian music programming. WJBP-FM broadcasts to the Tucson, AZ area at 91.5 FM.

WJBQ-FM
Owner: Townsquare Media, LLC
Editorial: 1 City Ctr, Portland, Maine 04101-6420. **T:** 1 207 774-6364
W: http://www.wjbq.com

Editorial Profile: WJBQ-FM is a commercial station owned by Townsquare Media, LLC. The format of the station is Top 40/CHR. WJBQ-FM broadcasts to the Portland, ME area at 97.9 FM.

WJBR-FM
Owner: Beasley Broadcast Group
Editorial: 812 Philadelphia Pike, Wilmington, Delaware 19809-2372. **T:** 1 302 765-1160
E: info@wjbr.com **W:** http://www.wjbr.com
Editorial Profile: WJBR-FM is a commercial station owned by Beasley Broadcast Group. The format of the station is adult contemporary. WJBR broadcasts to the Wilmington, DE area at 99.5 FM.

WJBS-AM
Owner: Govan(Harry)
Editorial: 760 Bunch Ford Rd, Holly Hill, South Carolina 29059. **T:** 1 803 496-5352
E: wjbsam@yahoo.com
Editorial Profile: WJBS-AM is a commercial station owned by Harry Govan. The format of the station is gospel. WJBS-AM broadcasts to the Holly Hill, SC area at 1000 AM.

WJBT-FM
Owner: Clear Channel Media and Entertainment
Editorial: 11700 Central Pkwy, Jacksonville, Florida 32224. **T:** 1 904 636-0507
W: http://www.wjbt.com
Editorial Profile: WJBT-FM is a commercial station owned by Clear Channel Media and Entertainment. The format of the station is urban contemporary music. WJBT-FM broadcasts to the Jacksonville, FL area at 93.3 FM.

WJBW-AM
Owner: Jupiter Planet Radio LLC
Editorial: 1235 16th St, Vero Beach, Florida 32960-3620. **T:** 1 772 567-0937
W: http://www.radioazure.com
Editorial Profile: WJBW-AM is a commercial station owned by Jupiter Planet Radio LLC. The format of the station is folk. WJBW-AM broadcasts to the Jupiter and surrounding areas at 1000 AM.

WJBX-AM
Owner: Beasley Broadcast Group
Editorial: 20125 S Tamiami Trl, Estero, Florida 33928-2117. **T:** 1 239 495-2100
Editorial Profile: WJBX-AM is a commercial station owned by Beasley Broadcast Group. The format of the station is sports and talk. WJBX-AM broadcasts to the Estero, FL area at 770 AM.

WJBZ-FM
Owner: CD Broadcast LLC
Editorial: 7101 Chapman Hwy, Knoxville, Tennessee 37920. **T:** 1 865 577-4885
E: inforequest@praise963.com
W: http://www.praise963.com
Editorial Profile: WJBZ-FM is a commercial station owned by CD Broadcast LLC. The format of the station is gospel. WJBZ-FM broadcasts to the Knoxville, TN area at 96.3 FM.

WJCF-FM
Owner: Indiana Community Radio
Editorial: 15 Wood St, Greenfield, Indiana 46140-2162. **T:** 1 317 467-1064
E: wjcfradio@aol.com
W: http://www.wjcfradio.com
Editorial Profile: WJCF-FM is a non-commercial station owned by the Indiana Community Radio Corporation. The format of the station is Top 40 Pop and Contemporary Christian music. WJCF-FM broadcasts to the Indianapolis area at a frequency of 88.1.

WJCH-FM
Owner: Family Stations Inc.
Editorial: 13 Fairlane Dr, Joliet, Illinois 60435-6483. **T:** 1 815 725-1331
E: familyradio@familyradio.com
W: http://www.familyradio.com
Editorial Profile: WJCH-FM is a non-commercial station owned by Family Stations Inc. The format of the station is religious. WJCH-FM broadcasts to the Joliet, IL area at 91.9 FM.

WJCK-FM
Owner: Immanuel Broadcasting Network
Editorial: 9423 Alabama Hwy 21 N, Piedmont, Alabama 36272. **T:** 1 800 387-0917
E: onair@ibn.org **W:** http://www.ibn.org
Editorial Profile: WJCK-FM is a non-commercial station owned by Immanuel Broadcasting Network. The format of the station is contemporary Christian

programming. WJCK-FM broadcasts to the Piedmont, AL area at 88.3 FM.

WJCL-FM
Owner: Cumulus Media Inc.
Editorial: 214 Television Cir, Savannah, Georgia 31406-4519. **T:** 1 912 961-9000
W: http://www.kix96.com
Editorial Profile: WJCL-FM is a commercial station owned by Cumulus Media Inc. The format of the station is contemporary country. WJCL-FM broadcasts to the Savannah, GA area at 96.5 FM.

WJCM-AM
Owner: Cohan Radio Group Inc.
Editorial: 3750 US Highway 27 N, Ste 1, Sebring, Florida 33870. **T:** 1 863 382-9999
E: cohanradiogroup@htn.net
W: http://www.cohanradiogroup.com
Editorial Profile: WJCM-AM is a commercial station owned by Cohan Radio Group Inc. The format of the station is oldies. WJCM-AM broadcasts in the Sebring, FL area at 1050 AM.

WJCO-FM
Owner: Calvary Chapel of Costa Mesa, Inc.
Editorial: 150 Lincolnway, Ste 2001, Valparaiso, Indiana 46383-5556.
T: 1 219 548-5800
E: info@calvaryradionet.com
W: http://www.calvaryradionetwork.com
Editorial Profile: WJCO-FM is a non-commercial station owned by Calvary Chapel of Costa Mesa, Inc. The format of the station is Christian music and religious programming. WJCO-FM broadcasts to the Montpelier, IN area at 91.3 FM.

WJCP-AM
Owner: Taylor (Tom)
Editorial: 2470 N State Highway 7, North Vernon, Indiana 47265-7184.
T: 1 812 346-9527 **E:** wjcp927@yahoo.com
W: http://www.wjcpradio.com
Editorial Profile: WJCP-AM is a commercial station owned by Tom Taylor. The format of the station is classic hits. WJCP-AM broadcasts to the Indianapolis area at 1460 AM.

WJCR-FM
Owner: Powell(Don Jr. & Lauree)
Editorial: 13101 Raider Hollow Rd, Upton, Kentucky 42784-9220. **T:** 1 270 369-8614
E: wjcrfm@yahoo.com **W:** http://www.wjcr.org
Editorial Profile: WJCR-FM is a non-commercial station owned by Don Jr. & Laurie Powell. The format of the station is southern gospel music and religious programming. WJCR-FM broadcasts to the Upton, KY area at 90.1 FM.

WJCS-FM
Owner: Beacon Broadcasting Corp.
Editorial: 300 E Rock Rd, Allentown, Pennsylvania 18103. **T:** 1 610 791-7262
E: wjcs@wjcs.org **W:** http://www.wjcs.org
Editorial Profile: WJCS-FM is a non-commercial station owned by Beacon Broadcasting Corp. The format of the station is religious programming. WJCS-FM broadcasts to the Allentown, PA area at 89.3 FM.

WJCT-FM
Owner: WJCT Inc.
Editorial: 100 Festival Park Ave, Jacksonville, Florida 32202-1309. **T:** 1 904 353-7770
E: news@wjct.org **W:** http://www.wjct.org
Editorial Profile: WJCT-FM is non-commercial station owned by WJCT Inc. The format of the station is news and talk with classical music. WJCT-FM broadcasts to the residents of Jacksonville, FL at 89.9 FM.

WJCU-FM
Owner: John Carroll University
Editorial: 20700 N Park Blvd, University Heights, Ohio 44118. **T:** 1 216 397-4437
E: wjcu.info@gmail.com
W: http://www.wjcu.org
Editorial Profile: WJCU-FM is a non-commercial station owned by John Carroll University. The format of the station is adult album alternative. WJCU-FM broadcasts to the University Heights, OH area at 88.7 FM.

WJCV-AM
Owner: Down East Broadcasting Co.
Editorial: 123A Arnold Road Ext, Jacksonville, North Carolina 28546-6541.
T: 1 910 347-6141 **W:** http://www.wjcv.com
Editorial Profile: WJCV-AM is a commercial station owned by Down East Broadcasting Co. The format of the station is religious

programming and Southern gospel. WJCV-AM broadcasts to the Jacksonville, NC area at 1290 AM.

WJCW-AM
Owner: Cumulus Media Inc.
Editorial: 162 Free Hill Rd, Gray, Tennessee 37615-3144. **T:** 1 423 477-1000
W: http://www.wjcw.com
Editorial Profile: WJCW-AM is a commercial station owned by Cumulus Media Inc. The format of the station is news and talk. WJCW-AM broadcasts to the Gray, TN area at 910 AM.

WJCX-FM
Owner: Calvary Chapel of Costa Mesa, Inc.
Editorial: 154 River Rd, Orrington, Maine 04474-3058. **T:** 1 207 991-9555
E: wjcx@calvarychapel.com
W: http://www.calvaryradionetwork.com
Editorial Profile: WJCX-FM is a commercial station owned by Calvary Chapel of Costa Mesa, Inc. The format of the station is Christian music and religious programming. WJCX-FM broadcasts to the Pittsfield, ME area at 99.5 FM.

WJCY-FM
Owner: Calvary Chapel of Costa Mesa, Inc.
Editorial: 150 Lincolnway, Ste 2001, Valparaiso, Indiana 46383-5556.
T: 1 219 548-5800
E: info@calvaryradionet.com
W: http://www.calvaryradionetwork.com
Editorial Profile: WJCY-FM is a non-commercial station owned by Calvary Chapel of Costa Mesa, Inc. The format of the station is Christian music, religious programming, and sports. WJCY-FM broadcasts to the Cicero, IN area at 91.5 FM.

WJCZ-FM
Owner: Calvary Radio Network
Editorial: 150 Lincolnway, Ste 2001, Valparaiso, Indiana 46383-5556.
T: 1 219 548-5800
E: info@calvaryradionet.com
W: http://www.calvaryradionetwork.com
Editorial Profile: WJCZ-FM is a non-commerical station owned by Calvary Radio Network. The format of the station is Christian music, religious programming and sports. WJCZ-FM broadcasts to the Milford, IL area at 91.3 FM.

WJDA-AM
Owner: Principle Broadcasting
Editorial: 90 Everett Ave, Chelsea, Massachusetts 02150-2311.
T: 1 617 884-4500
W: http://www.wjda1300am.com
Editorial Profile: WJDA-AM is a commercial station owned by Principle Broadcasting. The format of the station is Hispanic gospel programming. WJDA-AM broadcasts to the Chelsea, MA area at 1300 AM.

WJDB-AM
Owner: Griffin Broadcasting Corp.
Editorial: 30280 Highway 43, Thomasville, Alabama 36784. **T:** 1 334 636-4438

WJDB-FM
Owner: Griffin Broadcasting Corp.
Editorial: 30280 Highway 43, Thomasville, Alabama 36784-5740. **T:** 1 334 636-4438
W: http://www.wjdb955.com/index.php

WJDF-FM
Owner: Deane Brothers Broadcasting Corp.
Editorial: 9 S Main St Ste 101, Orange, Massachusetts 01364-1226.
T: 1 978 544-5335 **E:** info@wjdf.com
W: http://www.wjdf.com
Editorial Profile: WJDF-AM is a local, commercial station owned by Deane Brothers Broadcasting Corp. The format of the station is Adult Contemporary. The station airs locally in the Orange, MA area on 97.3 FM.

WJDK-FM
Owner: Nelson Multimedia
Editorial: 219 W Washington St, Morris, Illinois 60450-2146. **T:** 1 815 941-1000
E: wcsj-production@nelsonmultimedia.net
W: http://wjdkfm.com
Editorial Profile: WJDK-FM is a commercial station owned by Nelson Multimedia. The format of the station is adult contemporary. WJDK-FM broadcasts to the Morris, IL area at 95.7 FM.

WJDM-AM
Owner: Multicultural Radio Broadcasting Inc.

Editorial: 449 Broadway Fl 2, New York, New York 10013-2549. **T:** 1 212 966-1059
W: http://www.mrbi.net
Editorial Profile: WJDM-AM is a commercial station owned by Multicultural Radio Broadcasting Inc. The format is Spanish, talk, and contemporary Christian. WJDM-AM broadcasts to the New York City area at 1530 AM.

WJDQ-FM
Owner: Mississippi Broadcasters, LLC
Editorial: 3436 Highway 45 N, Meridian, Mississippi 39301-1509. **T:** 1 601 693-2661
W: http://www.q101radio.net
Editorial Profile: WJDQ-FM is a commercial station owned by Mississippi Broadcasters, LLC. The format of the station is Top 40/CHR. WJDQ-FM broadcasts to the Meridian, MS, area at 101.3 FM.

WJDR-FM
Owner: McDaniel(Thomas)
Editorial: 37 S High School Ave, Columbia, Mississippi 39429-8246. **T:** 1 601 731-2298
E: wjdr2057@windstream.net
W: http://www.wjdrfm.com/
Editorial Profile: WJDR-FM is a commercial station owned by Thomas McDaniel. The format of the station is country. WJDR-FM broadcasts to the Prentiss, MS area at 98.3 FM.

WJDS-FM
Owner: Good News Network
Editorial: 2278 Wortham Ln, Grovetown, Georgia 30813. **T:** 1 706 309-9610
W: http://www.gnnradio.org
Editorial Profile: WJDS-FM is a commercial station owned by Good News Network. The format of the station is Hispanic religious programming. WJDS-FM broadcasts to the Sparta, GA area at 88.7 FM.

WJDT-FM
Owner: Cherokee Broadcasting Co.
Editorial: 448 Highway 25 E, Bean Station, Tennessee 37708-5603. **T:** 1 865 993-3639
E: wjdtradio@gmail.com
W: http://www.wjdtfm.com
Editorial Profile: WJDT-FM is a commercial station owned by Cherokee Broadcasting Co. The format of the station is country. WJDT-FM broadcasts to the Morristown, TN area at 106.5 FM.

WJDV-FM
Owner: VerStandig Broadcasting
Editorial: 1820 Heritage Center Way, Harrisonburg, Virginia 22801.
T: 1 540 434-0331
W: http://www.fresh961.com
Editorial Profile: WJDV-FM is a commercial station owned by VerStandig Broadcasting. The format of the station is Lite Rock/Lite AC. WJDV-FM broadcasts to the Harrisonburg, VA area at 96.1 FM. The station does not accept unsolicited faxes. Do NOT e-mail any staff members. Any press information should be sent to WSVA-AM.

WJDX-AM
Owner: Clear Channel Media and Entertainment
Editorial: 1375 Beasley Rd, Jackson, Mississippi 39206-2018. **T:** 1 601 982-1062
W: http://www.wjdx.com
Editorial Profile: WJDX-AM is a commercial station owned by Clear Channel Communictions. The format of the station is news/talk. WJDX-AM broadcasts to the Jackson, MS area at 620 AM.

WJDX-FM
Owner: Clear Channel Media and Entertainment
Editorial: 1375 Beasley Rd, Jackson, Mississippi 39206. **T:** 1 601 982-1062
W: http://www.1051theriver.com/main.html
Editorial Profile: WJDX-FM is a commercial station owned by Clear Channel Media and Entertainment. The format of the station is variety. WJDX-FM broadcasts to the Jackson, MS area at 105.1 FM.

WJDY-AM
Owner: Clear Channel Media and Entertainment
Editorial: Gateway Crossing, 351 Tilghman Road, Salisbury, Maryland 21804-1920.
T: 1 410 742-1923
Editorial Profile: WJDY-AM is a commercial station owned by Clear Channel Media and Entertainment. The format of the station is comedy. WJDY-AM broadcasts to the Salisbury, MD area at 1470 AM.

WJEC-FM
Owner: Lamar County Broadcasting
Editorial: 47650 Hwy 17 N, Vernon, Alabama 35592. **T:** 1 205 695-9191
E: wjec1065@yahoo.com
W: http://www.wjec1065.com
Editorial Profile: WJEC-FM is a commercial station owned by Lamar County Broadcasting. The format of the station is gospel. WJEC-FM broadcasts locally to the Vernon, AL area at a frequency of 106.5FM.

WJED-FM
Owner: Bethany Bible College
Editorial: 2573 Hodgesville Rd, Dothan, Alabama 36301. **T:** 1 850 547-9405
E: wjed911fm@bethanybc.edu
W: http://www.bethanybc.edu/radio
Editorial Profile: WJED-FM is a non-commercial station owned by Bethany Bible College. The format of the station is Southern gospel music. WJED-FM broadcasts to the Dothan, FL area at 91.1 FM.

WJEE-FM
Owner: Hazen Ministries, Inc (Denny and Marge)
Editorial: 5716 Louisville St, Louisville, Ohio 44641-9483. **T:** 1 330 875-7181
E: dennymarge@aol.com
W: http://faithministryradio.com
Editorial Profile: WJEE-FM is a non-commercial station owned by Hazen Ministries, Inc (Denny and Marge). The format of the station is religion with a focus on Christian teaching. WJEE-FM broadcasts to the Bolivar, OH area at a frequency of 90.1 FM.

WJEH-AM
Owner: Sunny Broadcasting LLC
Editorial: 117 Portsmouth Rd, Gallipolis, Ohio 45631-1047. **T:** 1 740 446-3543
W: http://www.sunny93.net
Editorial Profile: WJEH-AM is a commercial station owned by Sunny Broadcasting LLC. The format of the station is adult standards. WJEH-AM broadcasts to the Gallipolis, OH area at 990 AM.

WJEJ-AM
Owner: Hagerstown Broadcasting Co. Inc.
Editorial: 1135 Haven Rd, Hagerstown, Maryland 21742. **T:** 1 301 739-2323
E: wjej@myactv.net
W: http://www.wjejradio.com
Editorial Profile: WJEJ-AM is a commercial station owned by Hagerstown Broadcasting Co. Inc. The format of the station is easy listening music. WJEJ-AM broadcasts to the Hagerstown, MD area at 1240 AM.

WJEK-FM
Owner: S.J. Broadcasting Inc.
Editorial: 2702 Boulder Rd, Urbana, Illinois 61802-6996. **T:** 1 217 365-1195
W: http://sunnycu.com
Editorial Profile: WJEK-FM is a commercial station owned by S.J. Broadcasting Inc. The format of the station is adult contemporary. WJEK-FM broadcasts to the Champaign, IL area at 95.3 FM.

WJEL-FM
Owner: Metropolitan School District of Washington Township
Editorial: 1901 E 86th St, Indianapolis, Indiana 46240. **T:** 1 317 259-5278
E: thindman@msdwt.k12.in.us
W: http://website.msdwt.k12.in.us/wjelftp
Editorial Profile: WJEL-FM is a non-commercial station owned by the Metropolitan School District of Washington Township. The format of the station is variety. WJEL-AM broadcasts to the Indianapolis area at 89.3 FM.

WJEM-AM
Owner: WJEM Inc.
Editorial: 118 N Patterson St, Valdosta, Georgia 31601-5570. **T:** 1 229 2599301
W: http://www.thejock1150.com
Editorial Profile: WJEM-AM is a commercial station owned by WJEM Inc. The format of the station is sports. WJEM-AM broadcasts to the Valdosta, GA area at 1150 AM.

WJEN-FM
Owner: Pamal Broadcasting Ltd.
Editorial: 67 Merchants Row, Rutland, Vermont 5701. **T:** 1 802 775-7500
E: catcountry@catamountradio.com
W: http://www.catcountryvermont.com
Editorial Profile: WJEN-FM is a commercial station owned by Pamal Broadcasting Ltd. The format of the station is contemporary country. WJEN-FM broadcasts to the Rutland, VT area at 105.3 FM.

WJEQ-FM
Owner: Prestige Communications
Editorial: 31 E Side Sq, Macomb, Illinois 61455. **T:** 1 309 833-2121
E: radio@prestigeradio.com
W: http://www.prestigeradio.com
Editorial Profile: WJEQ-FM is a commercial station owned by Prestige Communications. The format of the station is classic rock. WJEQ-FM broadcasts to the Macomb, IL area at 102.7 FM.

WJER-AM
Owner: Gary Petricola
Editorial: 646 Boulevard St, Dover, Ohio 44622. **T:** 1 330 343-7755 **E:** wjer@wjer.com
W: http://www.wjer.com
Editorial Profile: WJER-AM is a commercial station owned by Gary Petricola. The format of the station is adult contemporary. WJER-AM broadcasts to the Dover, OH area at 1450 AM.

WJET-AM
Owner: Connoisseur Media LLC
Editorial: 1 Boston Store Pl, Erie, Pennsylvania 16501. **T:** 1 814 461-1000
W: http://www.jetradio1400.com
Editorial Profile: WJET-AM is a commercial station owned by Connoisseur Media LLC. The format of the station is news and talk. WJET-AM broadcasts to the Erie, PA area at 1400 AM.

WJEZ-FM
Owner: Cumulus Media Inc.
Editorial: 315 N Mill St, Pontiac, Illinois 61764-1823. **T:** 1 815 844-6101
E: requests@wjez.com
W: http://www.wjez.com
Editorial Profile: WJEZ-FM is a commercial station owned by Cumulus Media Inc.. The format of the station is classic hits music. WJEZ-FM broadcasts to the Pontiac, IL area at 98.9 FM.

WJFC-AM
Owner: Lakeway Broadcasting LLC
Editorial: 1181 N Highway 92, Jefferson City, Tennessee 37760. **T:** 1 865 475-3825
E: wjfc@radiowjfc.com **W:** http://wjfcradio.com
Editorial Profile: WJFC-AM is a commercial station owned by Lakeway Broadcasting LLC. The format of the station is classic country, gospel and bluegrass. WJFC-AM broadcasts to the Knoxville, TN area at 1480 AM.

WJFD-FM
Owner: Henry Arruda
Editorial: 651 Orchard St #300, New Bedford, Massachusetts 02744-1008.
T: 1 508 997-2929 **W:** http://www.wjfd.com
Editorial Profile: WJFD-FM is a commercial station owned by Henry Arruda. The format of the station is Portuguese-language Top 40/ CHR music. WJFD-FM broadcasts to the New Bedford, MA area at 97.3 FM.

WJFF-FM
Owner: Radio Catskill
Editorial: 4765 State Route 52, Jeffersonville, New York 12748. **T:** 1 845 482-4141
E: wjff@wjffradio.org
W: http://www.wjffradio.org
Editorial Profile: WJFF-FM is a non-commercial station owned by Radio Catskill. The format of the station is a variety. WJFF-FM broadcasts to the Catskill, NY area at 90.5 FM.

WJFK-AM
Owner: CBS Radio
Editorial: 4200 Parliament Pl Ste 300, Lanham, Maryland 20706-1881.
T: 1 301 731-1580
W: http://washington.cbslocal.com/station/cbs-sports-radio-1580-am/
Editorial Profile: WJFK-AM is a commercial station owned by CBS Radio. The format of the station is sports. WJFK-AM broadcasts to the Washington, D.C. area at 1580 AM.

WJFK-FM
Owner: CBS Radio
Editorial: 10800 Main St, Fairfax, Virginia 22030. **T:** 1 703 691-1900
W: http://washington.cbslocal.com/station/106-7-the-fan
Editorial Profile: WJFK-FM is a commercial station owned by CBS Radio. The format of the station is sports. WJFK-FM broadcasts to the Washington, D.C. area at 106.7 FM.

WJFL-FM
Owner: Middle Georgia Broadcasting
Editorial: 5440 Tennille Oconee Rd, Tennille, Georgia 31089. **T:** 1 478 553-1019
E: wjfl@wjfl.com **W:** http://www.wjfl.com
Editorial Profile: WJFL-FM is a commercial station owned by Middle Georgia Broadcasting. The format of the station is adult contemporary music. WJFL-FM broadcasts to the Tennille, GA area at 101.9 FM.

WJFM-FM
Owner: Family Worship Center Church, Inc.
Editorial: 8919 World Ministry Ave, Baton Rouge, Louisiana 70810-9006.
T: 1 225 768-8300 **E:** info@jsm.org
W: http://www.jsm.org
Editorial Profile: WJFM-FM is a non-commercial station owned by Family Worship Center Church, Inc. The format of the station is religious music and programming. WJFM-FM broadcasts to the Baton Rouge, LA area at 88.5 FM.

WJFP-FM
Owner: Black Media Works Inc.
Editorial: 2284 N US HWY 1, Fort Pierce, Florida 34946. **T:** 1 772 467-2400
W: http://www.wjfp.com
Editorial Profile: WJFP-FM is a non-commercial station owned by Black Media Works Inc. The format is gospel and urban contemporary music. The station airs in the Fort Pierce, FL area at 91.1 FM.

WJFX-FM
Owner: Adams Radio Group
Editorial: 9604 Coldwater Rd Ste 201, Fort Wayne, Indiana 46825-2096.
T: 1 260 482-9288
W: http://www.hot1079online.com
Editorial Profile: WJFX-FM is a commercial station owned by Adams Radio Group. The format of the station is rhythmic Top 40/CHR music. WJFX-FM broadcasts to the Fort Wayne, IN area at 107.9 FM.

WJGA-FM
Owner: Earnhart Broadcast Co. Inc.
Editorial: 940 Brownlee Rd, Jackson, Georgia 30233. **T:** 1 770 775-3151
Editorial Profile: WJGA-FM is a commercial music station owned by Earnhart Broadcast Co. Inc. The format of the station is adult contemporary music. WJGA-FM broadcasts to the Atlanta area at 92.1 FM.

WJGK-FM
Owner: Sunrise Broadcasting
Editorial: 661 Little Britain Rd, New Windsor, New York 12553-6150. **T:** 1 845 561-2131
W: http://www.foxradio.net
Editorial Profile: WJGK-FM is a commercial station owned by Sunrise Broadcasting. The format of the station is adult contemporary. WJGK-FM broadcasts to the New York area at 103.1 FM.

WJGL-FM
Owner: Cox Media Group, Inc.
Editorial: 8000 Belfort Pkwy, Ste 100, Jacksonville, Florida 32256. **T:** 1 904 245-8500
W: http://www.969theeagle.com
Editorial Profile: WJGL-FM is a commercial station owned by Cox Media Group, Inc. The format of the station is classic hits. WJGL-FM broadcasts to the Jacksonville, FL area at 96.9 FM.

WJGM-FM
Owner: West Jacksonville Baptist Church, Inc.
Editorial: 5634 Normandy Blvd, Jacksonville, Florida 32205-6249. **T:** 1 904 781-4321
W: http://www.westjaxbaptist.org
Editorial Profile: WJGM-FM is a commercial station owned by West Jacksonville Baptist Church, Inc. The format of the station is southern gospel music. WJGM-FM broadcasts to the Jacksonville, FL area at 105.7 FM.

WJGO-FM
Owner: Renda Broadcasting
Editorial: 10915 K Nine Dr, 2nd Fl, Bonita Springs, Florida 34135-6802.
T: 1 239 495-8383
W: http://www.1029bobfm.com
Editorial Profile: WJGO-FM is a commercial station owned by Renda Broadcasting. The format of the station is adult hits. WJGO-FM broadcasts to the Fort Myers, FL area at 102.9 FM.

WJHD-FM
Owner: Portsmouth Abbey School
Editorial: 285 Corys Ln, Portsmouth, Rhode Island 2871. **T:** 1 401 683-2000

WJHM-FM
Owner: CBS Radio
Editorial: 1800 Pembrook Dr Ste 400, Orlando, Florida 32810-6375.
T: 1 407 919-1000
W: http://1019ampradio.cbslocal.com
Editorial Profile: WJHM-FM is a commercial station owned by CBS Radio. The format of the station is CHR. WJHM-FM broadcasts to the Orlando, FL area at 101.9 FM.

WJHO-FM
Owner: Alabama Christian Radio Inc.
Editorial: 908 Opelika Rd, Auburn, Alabama 36830-4024. **T:** 1 334 705-8004
W: http://wjhofm.com
Editorial Profile: WJHO-FM is a non-commercial station owned by Alabama Christian Radio Inc. The format of the station is Contemporary Christian music. WJHO-FM broadcasts to the Alexander City, AL area at a frequency of 89.7 FM.

WJHS-FM
Owner: Whitley Cnty Cons. Schools
Editorial: 600 N Whitley St, Columbia City, Indiana 46725. **T:** 1 260 248-8915
W: http://www.wjhs915.org
Editorial Profile: WJHS-FM is a non-commercial station owned by Whitley Cnty Cons. Schools. The format of the station is adult album alternative music. WJHS-FM broadcasts to the Fort Wayne, IN area at 91.5 FM.

WJHT-FM
Owner: Forever Broadcasting
Editorial: 109 Plaza Dr, Ste 2, Johnstown, Pennsylvania 15905. **T:** 1 814 255-4186
W: http://www.hot92and100.com
Editorial Profile: WJHT-FM is a commercial station owned by Forever Broadcasting. The format of the station is Top 40/CHR. WJHT-FM broadcasts to the Johnstown, PA area at 92.1 FM.

WJHX-AM
Owner: Rivera Communications
Editorial: 100 Yeager Pkwy, Pelham, Alabama 35124-1859. **T:** 1 205 358-1100
Editorial Profile: WJHX-AM is commercial station owned by Rivera Communications. The format of the station is regional Mexican and tropical music. The station airs locally on 620 AM. Newscasts air at the top of the hour.

WJIA-FM
Owner: Lake City Educational Broadcasting
Editorial: 5025 Spring Creek Dr, Guntersville, Alabama 35976. **T:** 1 256 505-0885
W: http://www.wjia885.com
Editorial Profile: WJIA-FM is a non-commercial station owned by Lake City Educational Broadcasting. The format of the station is contemporary Christian. WJIA-FM broadcasts to the Guntersville, AL area at 88.5 FM.

WJIB-AM
Owner: Bob Bittner Broadcasting, Inc.
Editorial: 443 Concord Ave, Cambridge, Massachusetts 2138. **T:** 1 617 868-7400
Editorial Profile: WJIB-AM is a commercial station owned by Bob Bittner Broadcasting, Inc. The format of the station is adult standards. WJIB-AM broadcasts to the Cambridge, MA area at 740 AM.

WJIE-FM
Owner: Evangel Schools, Inc.
Editorial: 5400 Minor Ln, Louisville, Kentucky 40219-3019. **T:** 1 502 968-1220
E: wjie@wjie.org **W:** http://www.wjie.org
Editorial Profile: WJIE-FM is non-commercial station owned by Evangel Schools, Inc. The format of the station is contemporary Christian music, news and talk. WJIE-FM broadcasts to the Louisville, KY area at 88.5 FM.

WJIL-AM
Owner: Morgan County Broadcasting Co., Inc.
Editorial: 1251 E Morton Ave, Jacksonville, Illinois 62650. **T:** 1 217 245-5119
E: 1029wjil@gmail.com
W: http://www.wjvofm.com
Editorial Profile: WJIL-AM is a commercial station owned by Morgan County Broadcasting Co., Inc. The format of the station is adult contemporary. WJIL-AM broadcasts in the Jacksonville, IL area at 1550 AM.

WJIM-AM
Owner: Townsquare Media, LLC
Editorial: 3420 Pinetree Rd, Lansing, Michigan 48911-4207. **T:** 1 517 394-7272
W: http://www.wjimam.com
Editorial Profile: WJIM-AM is a commercial station owned by Townsquare Media, LLC. The format of the station is news and talk. WJIM-AM broadcasts to the Lansing, MI area at 1240 AM.

WJIM-FM
Owner: Townsquare Media, LLC
Editorial: 3420 Pinetree Rd, Lansing, Michigan 48911-4207. **T:** 1 517 394-7272
W: http://975now.com
Editorial Profile: WJIM-FM is a commercial station owned by Townsquare Media, LLC. The format of the station is Top 40/CHR. WJIM-FM broadcasts to the Lansing, MI area at 97.5 FM.

WJIP-AM
Owner: Clear Channel Media and Entertainment
Editorial: 20 Tucker Dr, Poughkeepsie, New York 12603-1644. **T:** 1 845 471-2300
W: http://www.247comedy.com
Editorial Profile: WJIP-AM is a commercial station owned by Clear Channel Media and Entertainment. The format of the station is comedy. WJIP-AM broadcasts to the Ulster County area in New York locally at 1370 AM.

WJIR-FM
Owner: Glad Tidings Tabernacle Church
Editorial: 1209 United St, Key West, Florida 33040-3409. **T:** 1 305 296-4306
Editorial Profile: WJIR-FM is a non-commercial station owned by Glad Tidings Tabernacle Church. The format of the station is Christian music and programming. WJIR-FM broadcasts to the Key West, FL area at 90.9 FM.

WJIS-FM
Owner: Radio Training Network, Inc.
Editorial: 6469 Parkland Dr, Sarasota, Florida 34243-4091. **T:** 1 941 753-0401
E: thejoyfm@thejoyfm.com
W: http://florida.thejoyfm.com
Editorial Profile: WJIS-FM is a non-commercial station owned by Radio Training Network, Inc. The format of the station is contemporary Christian music. WJIS-FM broadcasts to the Tampa, FL area at 88.1 FM.

WJIV-FM
Owner: Christian Broadcasting System
Editorial: 1668 County Highway 50, Cherry Valley, New York 13320. **T:** 1 607 264-3062
E: wjiv@hughes.net
W: http://www.wjivradio.com
Editorial Profile: WJIV-FM is a commercial station owned by Christian Broadcasting System. The format of the station is Christian programming. WJIV-FM broadcasts to the Utica, NY area at 101.9 FM.

WJIW-FM
Owner: Mandy Burke Broadcasting Network
Editorial: 830 Main St, Greenville, Mississippi 38701-4102. **T:** 1 870 338-2700
E: news@lordradio.com
W: http://www.wjiwfm.com
Editorial Profile: WJIW-FM is a commercial station owned by Mandy Burke Broadcasting Network. The format is gospel music. WJIW-FM airs to the Helena, AR area at 104.7 FM.

WJIZ-FM
Owner: Clear Channel Media and Entertainment
Editorial: 809 S Westover Blvd, Albany, Georgia 31707. **T:** 1 229 439-9704
W: http://www.wjiz.com
Editorial Profile: WJIZ-FM is a commercial station owned by Clear Channel Media and Entertainment. The format of the station is urban contemporary. WJIZ-FM broadcasts to the Albany, NY area at 96.3 FM.

WJJB-FM
Owner: Atlantic Coast Radio LLC
Editorial: 779 Warren Ave, Portland, Maine 4103. **T:** 1 207 773-9695
W: http://www.thebigjab.com
Editorial Profile: WJJB-FM is a commercial station owned by Atlantic Coast Radio LLC. The format of the station is sports. WJJB-FM broadcasts to the Portland, ME area at 96.3 FM.

WJJC-AM
Owner: Side Communications Inc.
Editorial: 1801 N Elm St, Commerce, Georgia 30529. **T:** 1 706 335-3155
E: wjjc@windstream.net
W: http://www.wjjc.net
Editorial Profile: WJJC-AM is a commercial station owned by Side Communications Inc. The format of the station is talk. WJJC-AM broadcasts to the Commerce, GA area at 1270 AM.

WJJF-FM

Owner: Full Power Radio
Editorial: 758 Colonel Ledyard Hwy, Ledyard, Connecticut 06339-1541. **T:** 1 860 464-9490
W: http://www.949newsnow.com
Editorial Profile: WJJF-FM is a commercial station owned by Full Power Radio. The format of the station is news/talk. WJJF-FM broadcasts to the Connecticut and Eastern Long Island, NY areas at a frequency of 94.9 FM.

WJJH-FM

Owner: Heartland Communications Group, LLC
Editorial: 2320 Ellis Ave, Ashland, Wisconsin 54806. **T:** 1 715 682-2727
W: http://www.wjjhfm.com
Editorial Profile: WJJH-FM is a commercial station owned by Heartland Communications Group, LLC. The format of the station is classic rock. WJJH-FM broadcasts to the Ashland, WI area at 96.7 FM.

WJJK-FM

Owner: Cumulus Media Inc.
Editorial: 6810 N Shadeland Ave, Indianapolis, Indiana 46220-4236. **T:** 1 317 842-9550
E: info@1045wjjk.com
W: http://www.1045wjjk.com
Editorial Profile: WJJK-FM is a commercial station owned by Cumulus Media Inc. The format of the station is classic hits. WJJK-FM broadcasts to the Indianapolis area at 104.5 FM.

WJJL-AM

Owner: Phillips Corp.(M. John)
Editorial: 976 Union Rd #B, West Seneca, New York 14224-3438. **T:** 1 716 674-9555
E: radio1440@roadrunner.com

WJJM-AM

Owner: Haislip(Michelle W.)
Editorial: 344 E Church St, Lewisburg, Tennessee 37091-2837. **T:** 1 931 359-4511
E: wjjm@wjjm.com **W:** http://www.wjjm.com
Editorial Profile: WJJM-AM is a commercial station owned by Michelle W. Haislip. The format of the station is oldies music. WJJM-AM broadcasts to the Lewisburg, TN area at 1490 AM.

WJJM-FM

Owner: Haislip(Michelle W.)
Editorial: 344 E Church St, Lewisburg, Tennessee 37091-2837. **T:** 1 931 359-4511
E: wjjm@wjjm.com **W:** http://www.wjjm.com
Editorial Profile: WJJM-FM is a commercial station owned by Michelle W. Haislip. The format of the station is classic and contemporary country music. WJJM-FM broadcasts to the Lewisburg, TN area at 94.3 FM.

WJJN-FM

Owner: Wilson Broadcasting, Inc.
Editorial: 4106 Ross Clark Cir, Dothan, Alabama 36303-5741. **T:** 1 334 671-1753
W: http://www.wjjn.net
Editorial Profile: WJJN-FM is a commercial station owned by Wilson Broadcasting, Inc. The format of the station is urban contemporary music. WJJN-FM broadcasts to the Dothan, AL area at 92.1 FM.

WJJO-FM

Owner: Midwest Family Stations
Editorial: 730 Rayovac Dr, Madison, Wisconsin 53711-2472. **T:** 1 608 273-1000
W: http://www.wjjo.com
Editorial Profile: WJJO-FM is a commercial station owned by Midwest Family Stations. The format of the station is rock. WJJO-FM broadcasts to the Madison, WI area at 94.1 FM.

WJJQ-AM

Owner: Albert Broadcasting Inc.
Editorial: 81 E Mohawk Dr, Tomahawk, Wisconsin 54487. **T:** 1 715 453-4482
E: wjjq@wjjq.com **W:** http://www.wjjq.com
Editorial Profile: WJJQ-AM is a commercial station owned by Albert Broadcasting Inc. The format of the station is sports talk. WJJQ-AM broadcasts in the Tomahawk, WI area at 810 AM.

WJJQ-FM

Owner: Albert Broadcasting Inc.
Editorial: 81 E Mohawk Dr, Tomahawk, Wisconsin 54487. **T:** 1 715 453-4482
E: wjjq@wjjq.com **W:** http://www.wjjq.com
Editorial Profile: WJJQ-FM is a commercial station owned by Albert Broadcasting Inc. The format of the station is oldies, Lite Rock/Lite AC music, news, and talk. WJJQ-FM

broadcasts to the Tomahawk, WI area at 92.5 FM.

WJJR-FM

Owner: Pamal Broadcasting Ltd.
Editorial: 67 Merchants Row, Rutland, Vermont 05701-5910. **T:** 1 802 775-7500
E: wjjr@catamountradio.com
W: http://www.wjjr.net
Editorial Profile: WJJR-FM is a commercial station owned by Pamal Broadcasting Ltd. The format of the station is adult contemporary music. WJJR-FM broadcasts to the Rutland, VT area at 98.1 FM.

WJJS-FM

Owner: Clear Channel Media and Entertainment
Editorial: 3807 Brandon Ave SW, Ste 2350, Roanoke, Virginia 24018. **T:** 1 540 725-1220
W: http://www.wjjs.com
Editorial Profile: WJJS-FM is a commercial station owned by Clear Channel Media and Entertainment. The format of the station is Top 40/CHR music. WJJS-FM broadcasts to the Roanoke, VA area at 104.9 FM.

WJJX-FM

Owner: Clear Channel Media and Entertainment
Editorial: 3807 Brandon Ave SW, Ste 2350, Roanoke, Virginia 24018. **T:** 1 540 725-1220
W: http://www.wjjs.com
Editorial Profile: WJJX-FM is a commercial station owned by Clear Channel Media and Entertainment. The format of the station is Top 40/CHR music. WJJX-FM broadcasts to the Roanoke, VA area at 102.7 FM.

WJJY-FM

Owner: BL Broadcasting Inc.
Editorial: 13225 Dogwood Dr, Baxter, Minnesota 56425. **T:** 1 218 828-1244
E: wjjy@1067wjjy.com
W: http://www.1067wjjy.com
Editorial Profile: WJJY-FM is a commercial station owned by BL Broadcasting Inc. The format of the station is adult contemporary music. WJJY-FM broadcasts in the St. Paul, MN area at 106.7 FM.

WJKB-AM

Owner: Kirkman Broadcasting
Editorial: 60 Markfield Dr, Charleston, South Carolina 29407-7907. **T:** 1 843 763-6631
E: 950@kirkmanbroadcasting.com
W: http://www.am950.net
Editorial Profile: WJKB-AM is a commercial station owned by Kirkman Broadcasting. The format of the station is talk. WJKB-AM broadcasts to the Charleston, SC, area at 950 AM.

WJKD-FM

Owner: Treasure & Space Coast Radio
Editorial: 1235 16th St, Vero Beach, Florida 32960-3620. **T:** 1 772 567-0937
E: jack@997jackfm.com
W: http://www.997jackfm.com
Editorial Profile: WJKD-FM is a commercial station owned by Treasure & Space Coast Radio. The format of the station adult hits. WJKD-FM broadcasts to the West Palm Beach, FL area at 99.7 FM.

WJKE-FM

Owner: Empire Broadcasting Corporation
Editorial: 100 Saratoga Village Blvd Ste 21, Malta, New York 12020-3703.
T: 1 518 899-3000
E: 1013thejockey@empirebroadcasting.net
W: http://www.1013thejockey.com
Editorial Profile: WJKE-FM is a commercial station owned by Empire Broadcasting Corporation. The format of the station is adult contemporary. WJKE-FM broadcasts to the Albany, NY area at 101.3 FM.

WJKI-FM

Owner: Great Scott Broadcasting
Editorial: 20200 Dupont Blvd, Georgetown, Delaware 19947. **T:** 1 302 856-2567
E: wgbg@bigclassicrock.com
W: http://www.bigclassicrock.com
Editorial Profile: WJKI-FM is a commercial station owned by Great Scott Broadcasting. The format of the station is classic rock music. WJKI-FM broadcasts to the Salisbury, MD area at 103.5 FM.

WJKK-FM

Owner: New South Communications Inc.
Editorial: 265 Highpoint Dr, Ridgeland, Mississippi 39157-6018. **T:** 1 601 956-0102
W: http://www.mix987.com
Editorial Profile: WJKK-FM is a commercial station owned by New South Communications

Inc. The format of the station is adult contemporary music. WJKK-FM broadcasts to the Ridgeland, MS area at 98.7 FM.

WJKN-FM

Owner: Spring Arbor University
Editorial: 106 E Main St, Spring Arbor, Michigan 49283-9701. **T:** 1 517 750-6540
E: info@home.fm **W:** http://www.home.fm
Editorial Profile: WJKN-FM is a non-commercial station owned by Spring Arbor University. The format of the station is Christian music and religious teaching. WJKN-FM broadcasts to the Spring Arbor, MI area at 89.3 FM.

WJKS-FM

Owner: QC Communications Inc.
Editorial: 704 N King St, Ste 604, Wilmington, Delaware 19801. **T:** 1 302 622-8895
W: http://www.wjks1017.com
Editorial Profile: WJKS-FM is a commercial station owned by QC Communications Inc. The format of the station is urban contemporary. WJKS-FM broadcasts to the Wilmington, DE area at 101.7 FM.

WJKW-FM

Owner: Christian Faith Broadcast, Inc.
Editorial: 3809 Maple Ave, Castalia, Ohio 44824-9484. **T:** 1 419 684-5311
E: wjkw@cfbroadcast.net
W: http://www.wjkw.net
Editorial Profile: WJKW-FM is a commercial station owned by Christian Faith Broadcast, Inc. The format of the station is contemporary Christian music. WJKW-FM broadcasts to the Castalia, OH area at 97.7 FM.

WJKX-FM

Owner: Clear Channel Media and Entertainment
Editorial: 6555 U S Highway 98 W, Ste 8, Hattiesburg, Mississippi 39402.
T: 1 601 296-9800 **E:** contact@102jkx.com
W: http://www.102jkx.com
Editorial Profile: WJKX-FM is a commercial station owned by Clear Channel Media and Entertainment. The format of the station is urban adult contemporary. WJKX-FM broadcasts to the Hattiesburg, MS, area at 102.5 FM.

WJKY-AM

Owner: Lake Cumberland Broadcasters
Editorial: 2804 S Highway 127, Russell Springs, Kentucky 42642. **T:** 1 270 866-3487
E: wjrs1049@duo-county.com
W: http://www.lakercountry.com
Editorial Profile: WJKY-AM is a commercial station owned by Lake Cumberland Broadcasters. The format of the station is sports. WJKY-AM broadcasts to the Russell Springs, KY area at 1060 AM.

WJLB-FM

Owner: Clear Channel Media and Entertainment
Editorial: 27675 Halsted Rd, Farmington Hills, Michigan 48331-3511. **T:** 1 248 324-5800
E: wjlb@fm98wjlb.com
W: http://www.fm98wjlb.com
Editorial Profile: WJLB-FM is a commercial station owned by Clear Channel Media and Entertainment. The format of the station is urban contemporary. WJLB-FM broadcasts to the Detroit area at 97.9 FM.

WJLD-AM

Owner: Richardson Broadcasting Company
Editorial: 1449 Spaulding Ishkooda Rd, Birmingham, Alabama 35211-5059.
T: 1 205 942-1776 **W:** http://www.wjldfm.com
Editorial Profile: WJLD-AM is a commercial station owned by Richardson Broadcasting Company. The format of the station is talk, blues, R&B music and religious programming. WJLD-AM broadcasts to the Birmingham, AL area at 1400 AM.

WJLE-AM

Owner: Stribling (Leon)
Editorial: 2606 McMinnville Hwy, Smithville, Tennessee 37166-5071. **T:** 1 615 597-4265
E: wjle@dtccom.net **W:** http://www.wjle.com
Editorial Profile: WJLE-AM is a commercial station owned by Leon Stribling. The format of the station is country and gospel music. WJLE-AM broadcasts to Smithville, TN area at 1480 AM.

WJLE-FM

Owner: Stribling(Leon)
Editorial: 2606 McMinnville Hwy, Smithville, Tennessee 37166-5071. **T:** 1 615 597-4265
E: wjle@dtccom.net **W:** http://www.wjle.com

Editorial Profile: WJLE-FM is a commercial station owned by Leon Stribling. The format of the station is country and gospel music. WJLE-FM broadcasts to the Smithville, TN area at 101.7 FM.

WJLF-FM

Owner: Radio Training Network, Inc.
Editorial: 2131 Nw 40Th Ter Ste E, Gainesville, Florida 32605-5800.
T: 1 352 373-9553 **E:** thejoyfm@thejoyfm.com
W: http://www.thejoyfm.com
Editorial Profile: WJLF-FM is a non-commercial station owned by Radio Training Network, Inc. The format of the station is contemporary Christian music. WJLF-FM broadcasts to the Gainesville, FL area at 91.7 FM.

WJLG-AM

Owner: Cumulus Media Inc.
Editorial: 214 Television Cir, Savannah, Georgia 31406-4519. **T:** 1 912 961-9000
W: http://www.900theticket.com
Editorial Profile: WJLG-AM is a commercial station owned by Cumulus Media Inc. The format of the station is sports. WJLG-AM broadcasts to the Savannah, GA area at 900 AM.

WJLH-FM

Owner: Cornerstone Broadcasting Corp.
Editorial: 4295 S Ridgewood Ave, Port Orange, Florida 32127. **T:** 1 386 756-9000
E: wjlu@wjlu.org **W:** http://www.wjlu.org
Editorial Profile: WJLH-FM is a non-commercial station owned by Cornerstone Broadcasting Corp. The format of the station is Christian educational talk, news and music. WJLH-FM broadcasts to the Port Orange, FL area at 90.3 FM.

WJLI-FM

Owner: Stratemeyer Media
Editorial: 6120 Waldo Church Rd, Metropolis, Illinois 62960-4903. **T:** 1 270 444-0098
W: http://www.radiojelli.com
Editorial Profile: WJLI-FM is a commercial station owned by Stratemeyer Media. The format of the station is classic rock. WJLI-FM broadcasts to the Metropolis, IL area at 98.3 FM.

WJLK-FM

Owner: Townsquare Media, LLC
Editorial: 8 Robbins St Ste 201, Toms River, New Jersey 08753-7668. **T:** 1 848 221-8000
W: http://www.943thepoint.com
Editorial Profile: WJLK-FM is a commercial station owned by Townsquare Media, LLC. The format of the station is hot adult contemporary music. WJLK-FM broadcasts to the Ocean, NJ area at 94.3 FM.

WJLS-AM

Owner: West Virginia Radio Corp.
Editorial: 102 N Kanawha St, Beckley, West Virginia 25801-4715. **T:** 1 304 253-7311
W: http://www.wjls.com
Editorial Profile: WJLS-AM is a commercial station owned by West Virginia Radio Corp. The format of the station is Southern gospel music. WJLS-AM broadcasts to the Beckley, WV area at 560 AM.

WJLS-FM

Owner: West Virginia Radio Corp.
Editorial: 102 N Kanawha St, Beckley, West Virginia 25801-4715. **T:** 1 304 253-7311
W: http://www.wjls.com
Editorial Profile: WJLS-FM is a commercial station owned by West Virginia Radio Corp. The format of the station is country music, featuring contemporary and classic hits. WJLS-FM broadcasts to the Beckley, WV area at 99.5 FM.

WJLT-FM

Owner: Townsquare Media, LLC
Editorial: 117 Se 5Th St, Evansville, Indiana 47708-1639. **T:** 1 812 425-4226
W: http://wjltevansville.com/
Editorial Profile: WJLT-FM is a commercial station owned by Townsquare Media, LLC. The format of the station is classic hits. WJLT-FM broadcasts to the Evansville, IN area at 105.3 FM.

WJLU-FM

Owner: Cornerstone Broadcasting Corp.
Editorial: 4295 S Ridgewood Ave, Port Orange, Florida 32127. **T:** 1 386 756-9000
E: wjlu@wjlu.org **W:** http://www.wjlu.org
Editorial Profile: WJLU-FM is a non-commercial station owned by Cornerstone Broadcasting Corp. The format of the station is Christian educational talk, news, and music.

WJLU-FM broadcasts to the Port Orange, FL area at 89.7 FM.

WJLX-AM
Owner: Wal Win, LLC
Editorial: 310 Highway 195, Jasper, Alabama 35503-6512. **T:** 1 205 221-2222
Editorial Profile: WJLX-AM is a commercial station owned by Wal Win, LLC. The format of the station is oldies music. WJLX-AM broadcasts to the Jasper, AL area at a frequency of 1240 AM.

WJLY-FM
Owner: Countryside Broadcasting
Editorial: RR 2 Box 51A, Ramsey, Illinois 62080-9345. **T:** 1 618 423-2082
E: wjly@frontiernet.net **W:** http://www.wjly.org
Editorial Profile: WJLY-FM is a non-commercial station owned by Countryside Broadcasting. The format of the station is religious programming. WJLY-FM broadcasts to the St. Louis area at 88.3 FM.

WJLZ-FM
Owner: Virginia Beach Educational Broadcasting Inc.
Editorial: 3500 Virginia Beach Blvd, Ste 201, Virginia Beach, Virginia 23452.
T: 1 757 498-9632 **E:** info@currentfm.com
W: http://www.currentfm.com
Editorial Profile: WJLZ-FM is a non-commercial station owned by the Virginia Beach Educational Broadcasting Inc. The format of the station is contemporary Christian music and talk. WJLZ-FM broadcasts to Virginia Beach, VA at 88.5 FM.

WJMA-FM
Owner: Piedmont Communications Inc.
Editorial: 207 Spicers Mill Rd, Orange, Virginia 22960. **T:** 1 540 672-1000
E: advertising@wjmafm.com
W: http://www.wjmafm.com
Editorial Profile: WJMA-FM is a commercial station owned by Piedmont Communications Inc. The format of the station is country music. WJMA-FM broadcasts to the Orange, VA area at 103.1 FM.

WJMC-AM
Owner: TKC Inc.
Editorial: 1859 21st Ave, Rice Lake, Wisconsin 54868-9502. **T:** 1 715 234-2131
E: wjmc@chibardun.net
W: http://www.wjmcradio.com
Editorial Profile: WJMC-AM is a commercial station owned by TKC Inc. The format of the station is news, talk and adult standards music. WJMC-AM broadcasts to the Minneapolis area at 1240 AM.

WJMC-FM
Owner: T K C Inc.
Editorial: 1859 21st Ave, Rice Lake, Wisconsin 54868-9502. **T:** 1 715 234-2131
E: wjmc@chibardun.net
W: http://www.wjmcradio.com
Editorial Profile: WJMC-FM is a commercial station owned by T K C Inc. The format of the station is country music. WJMC-FM broadcasts in the Ricelake, WI area at 96.1 FM.

WJMD-FM
Owner: Hazard Broadcasting Inc.
Editorial: 516 Main St, Hazard, Kentucky 41701-1775. **T:** 1 606 439-3358
E: wjmd@windstream.net
W: http://www.wjmd104.com
Editorial Profile: WJMD-FM is a commercial station owned by Hazard Broadcasting Services. The format of the station is gospel. WJMD-FM broadcasts to the Hazard, KY, area at 104.7 FM.

WJMG-FM
Owner: Circuit Broadcasting of Hattiesburg
Editorial: 1204 Kinnard St, Hattiesburg, Mississippi 39401-1372. **T:** 1 601 544-1941
Editorial Profile: WJMG-FM is a commercial station owned by Circuit Broadcasting of Hattiesburg. The format of the station is urban contemporary. WJMG-FM broadcasts to the Hattiesburg, MS area at 92.1 FM.

WJMH-FM
Owner: Entercom Communications Corp.
Editorial: 7819 National Service Rd, Ste 401, Greensboro, North Carolina 27409.
T: 1 336 605-5200
W: http://www.102jamz.com
Editorial Profile: WJMH-FM is a commercial station owned by Entercom Communications Corp. The format of the station urban contemporary. WJMH-FM broadcasts to the Greensboro, NC area at 102.1 FM.

WJMI-FM
Owner: L & L Radio
Editorial: 731 S Pear Orchard Rd Ste 27, Ridgeland, Mississippi 39157-4839.
T: 1 601 957-1300 **E:** production@wjmi.com
W: http://www.wjmi.com
Editorial Profile: WJMI-FM is a commercial station owned by L & L Radio. The format of the station is urban contemporary music. WJMI-FM broadcasts to the Jackson, MS area at 99.7 FM.

WJMJ-FM
Owner: Archdiocese of Hartford
Editorial: 15 Peach Orchard Rd, Prospect, Connecticut 06712-1052. **T:** 1 860 242-8800
E: studio@wjmj.org **W:** http://www.wjmj.org
Editorial Profile: WJMJ-FM is a non-commercial station owned by the Archdiocese of Hartford. The format of the station is religious programming and easy listening music. WJMJ-FM broadcasts to the Bloomfield, CT area at 88.9 FM.

WJMK-FM
Owner: CBS Radio
Editorial: 180 N Stetson Ave, Ste 900, Chicago, Illinois 60601-6728.
T: 1 312 870-6400
E: promotions@khitschicago.com
W: http://khitschicago.radio.com/
Editorial Profile: WJMK-FM is a commercial station owned by CBS Radio. The format of the station is classic hits. WJMK-FM broadcasts to the Chicago area at 104.3 FM.

WJML-AM
Owner: Stone Communications, Inc.
Editorial: 2175 Click Rd, Petoskey, Michigan 49770-8818. **T:** 1 231 348-5000
E: talk@wjml.com **W:** http://www.wjml.com
Editorial Profile: WJML-AM is a commercial station owned by Stone Communications, Inc. The format of the station is news and talk. WJML-AM broadcasts to the Petoskey, MI area at 1110 AM.

WJMM-FM
Owner: Christian Broadcasting System
Editorial: 501 Darby Creek Rd, Ste 62, Lexington, Kentucky 40509.
T: 1 859 264-9700 **E:** wjmm@ckcradio.com
W: http://www.wjmm.com
Editorial Profile: WJMM-FM is a commercial station owned by Christian Broadcasting System. The format of the station is Christian programming. WJMM-FM broadcasts to the Lexington, KY area at 99.1 FM.

WJMN-FM
Owner: Clear Channel Media and Entertainment
Editorial: 10 Cabot Rd Ste 302, Medford, Massachusetts 02155-5173.
T: 1 781 663-2500
E: webmaster@jamn945.com
W: http://www.jamn945.com
Editorial Profile: WJMN-FM is a commercial station owned by Clear Channel Media and Entertainment. The format of the station is urban contemporary. WJMN-FM broadcasts to the Medford, MA area at 94.5 FM.

WJMO-AM
Owner: Radio One Inc.
Editorial: 2510 Saint Clair Ave NE, Cleveland, Ohio 44114. **T:** 1 216 579-1111
W: http://www.1490wjmo.com
Editorial Profile: WJMO-AM is a commercial station owned by Radio One Inc. The format of the station is gospel music. WJMO-AM broadcasts to the Cleveland area at 1300 AM.

WJMP-AM
Owner: Media-Com Inc.
Editorial: 2449 State Route 59, Kent, Ohio 44240. **T:** 1 330 673-2323 **E:** news@wnir.com
W: http://www.wnir.com
Editorial Profile: WJMP-AM is a commercial station owned by Media-Com Inc. The format of the station is news and talk. WJMP-AM broadcasts to the Kent, OH area at 1520 AM.

WJMQ-FM
Owner: Results Broadcasting, Inc.
Editorial: 1456 E Green Bay St, Shawano, Wisconsin 54166-2258. **T:** 1 715 524-2194
E: resultsbroadcasting@gmail.com
W: http://www.frogcountry923.com
Editorial Profile: WJMQ-FM is a commercial station owned by Results Broadcasting, Inc. The format of the station is contemporary country. WJMQ-FM broadcasts to the Shawano, WI area at 92.3 FM.

WJMR-FM
Owner: Saga Communications
Editorial: 5407 W McKinley Ave, Milwaukee, Wisconsin 53208. **T:** 1 414 978-9000
W: http://www.jammin983.com
Editorial Profile: WJMR-FM is a commercial station owned by Saga Communications. The format of the station is urban adult contemporary music. WJMR-FM broadcasts to the Milwaukee area at 98.3 FM.

WJMS-AM
Owner: J & J Broadcasting
Editorial: 222 S Lawrence St, Ironwood, Michigan 49938. **T:** 1 906 932-2411
E: wjmswimi@chartermi.net
W: http://www.wjmsam.com
Editorial Profile: WJMS-AM is a commercial station owned by J & J Broadcasting. The format of the station is country music. WJMS-AM broadcasts to the Ironwood, MI area at 590 AM.

WJMT-AM
Owner: Quicksilver Broadcasting, LLC
Editorial: 120 S Mill St, Merrill, Wisconsin 54452. **T:** 1 715 536-6262
E: news@z104rocks.com
W: http://www.wjmt.com
Editorial Profile: WJMT-AM is a commercial station owned by Quicksilver Broadcasting, LLC. The format of the station is country music. WJMT-AM broadcasts in the Merrill, WI area at 730 AM.

WJMU-FM
Owner: Millikin University
Editorial: 1184 W Main St, Decatur, Illinois 62522. **T:** 1 217 424-6377
E: wjmu@mail.millikin.edu
W: http://www.millikin.edu/wjmu
Editorial Profile: WJMU-FM is a non-commercial college station owned by Millikin University. The format of the station is variety. WJMU-FM broadcasts to the Decatur, IL area at 89.5 FM.

WJMX-AM
Owner: Clear Channel Media and Entertainment
Editorial: 181 E Evans St Ste 311, Florence, South Carolina 29506-5505.
T: 1 843 667-4600
W: http://newstalk1400online.com
Editorial Profile: WJMX-AM is a commercial station owned by Clear Channel Media and Entertainment. The format of the station is news and talk. WJMX-AM broadcasts to the Florence, SC area at 1400 AM.

WJMX-FM
Owner: Clear Channel Media and Entertainment
Editorial: 181 E Evans St Ste 311, Florence, South Carolina 29506-5505.
T: 1 843 667-4600
W: http://www.103xonline.com
Editorial Profile: WJMX-FM is a commercial station owned by Clear Channel Media and Entertainment. The format of the station is Hot Adult Contemporary. WJMX-FM broadcasts to the Florence, SC area at 103.3 FM.

WJMZ-FM
Owner: Summit Media Broadcasting LLC
Editorial: 220 N Main St Ste 402, Greenville, South Carolina 29601-2151.
T: 1 864 235-1073
W: http://www.1073jamz.com
Editorial Profile: WJMZ-FM is a commercial station owned by Summit Media Broadcasting LLC. The format of the station is urban adult contemporary. WJMZ-FM broadcasts to the Greenville, SC area at 107.3 FM.

WJNC-AM
Owner: Atlantic Ridge Telecasters Inc.
Editorial: 4206 Bridges Street Ext. Suit B, Morehead City, North Carolina 28557.
T: 1 252 247-6343
E: news@thetalkstation.com
W: http://www.thetalkstation.com
Editorial Profile: WJNC-AM is a commercial station owned by Atlantic Ridge Telecasters Inc. The format of the station is talk, news and sports. WJNC-AM broadcasts to the Newport, NC area at 1240 AM.

WJNG-FM
Owner: Strattan Broadcasting Inc.
Editorial: 517 1/2 Market St, Johnsonburg, Pennsylvania 15845. **T:** 1 814 849-8100
E: megarockradio@windstream.net
W: http://www.megarock.fm
Editorial Profile: WJNG-FM is a commercial station owned by Strattan Broadcasting Inc. The format of the station is classic hits. WJNG-FM broadcasts to the Johnsonburg, PA area at 100.5 FM.

WJNI-FM
Owner: Kirkman Broadcasting
Editorial: 5081 Rivers Ave, North Charleston, South Carolina 29406. **T:** 1 843 763-6631
E: wjni@kirkmanbroadcasting.com
W: http://wjnifm.com
Editorial Profile: WJNI-FM is a commercial station owned by Kirkman Broadcasting. The format of the station is gospel music. WJNI-FM broadcasts to the North Charleston, SC area at 106.3 FM.

WJNJ-AM
Owner: New Covenant Ministries, Inc
Editorial: 2360 Saint Johns Bluff Rd S #1, Jacksonville, Florida 32246-2310.
T: 1 904 301-9565 **E:** mail@pureradiojax.org
W: http://www.pureradiojax.org
Editorial Profile: WJNJ-AM is a commercial station owned by New Covenant Ministries, Inc. The format of the station features Gospel programming. WJNJ-AM broadcasts to the Jacksonville, FL area at 1320 AM.

WJNL-AM
Owner: Stone Communications, Inc.
Editorial: 310 W Front St Ste 411, Traverse City, Michigan 49684-2273. **T:** 1 231 947-1210
W: http://www.wjml.com/1210
Editorial Profile: WJNL-AM is a commercial station owned by Stone Communications, Inc. The format of the station is talk. WJNL-AM broadcasts to the Traverse City, MI area at 1210 AM.

WJNO-AM
Owner: Clear Channel Media and Entertainment
Editorial: 3071 Continental Dr, West Palm Beach, Florida 33407-3274. **T:** 1 561 616-6600
W: http://www.wjno.com
Editorial Profile: WJNO-AM is commercial station owned by Clear Channel Media and Entertainment. The format of the station is news and talk. WJNO-AM broadcasts to the West Palm Beach, FL area at 1290 AM.

WJNR-FM
Owner: Results Broadcasting
Editorial: 212 W J St, Iron Mountain, Michigan 49801. **T:** 1 906 774-5731
E: resultsproduction@gmail.com
W: http://www.frogcountry.com
Editorial Profile: WJNR-FM is a commercial station owned by Results Broadcasting. The format for the station is contemporary country. WJNR-FM broadcasts to the Marquette, MI area at 101.5 FM.

WJNT-AM
Owner: L & L Radio
Editorial: 731 S Pear Orchard Rd Ste 27, Ridgeland, Mississippi 39157-4839.
T: 1 601 957-1300 **E:** contactus@wjnt.com
W: http://www.wjnt.com
Editorial Profile: WJNT-AM is a commercial station owned by L & L Radio. The format of the station is news and talk. WJNT-AM broadcasts to the Jackson, MS area at 1180 AM.

WJNX-AM
Owner: Port St. Lucie Broadcasters
Editorial: 4100 Metzger Rd, Fort Pierce, Florida 34947-1712. **T:** 1 772 340-1590
E: lagigante@lagigante1330.com
W: http://www.lagigante1330.com
Editorial Profile: WJNX-AM is a commercial station owned by Port St. Lucie Broadcasters. The format of the station is Spanish language sports and tallk. WJNX-AM broadcasts to West Palm Beach and Fort Pierce, FL area at 1330 AM.

WJOB-AM
Owner: Vazquez Development LLC
Editorial: Purdue University Calumet, Commercialization Center, 7116 Indianapolis Blvd, Hammond, Indiana. **T:** 1 219 844-1230
W: http://www.wjob1230.com
Editorial Profile: WJOB-AM is a commercial station owned by Vasquez Development LLC. The format is news and talk. WJOB-AM broadcasts to the Hammond, IN area at 1230 AM.

WJOC-AM
Owner: Fryar(Sarah Margarett)
Editorial: 805 Chickamauga Ave, Rossville, Georgia 30741. **T:** 1 706 861-0800
W: http://www.joy1490.com
Editorial Profile: WJOC-AM is a commercial station owned by Sarah Margarett Fryar. The format of the station is Christian talk. WJOC-AM broadcasts to the Rossville, GA area at 1490 AM.

WJOD-FM
Owner: Cumulus Media Inc.
Editorial: 5490 Saratoga Rd, Dubuque, Iowa 52002-2593. **T:** 1 563 557-1040
W: http://www.103wjod.com
Editorial Profile: WJOD-FM is a commercial station owned by Cumulus Media Inc. The format of the station is contemporary country. WJOD-FM broadcasts to the Dubuque, IA area at 103.3 FM.

WJOI-AM
Owner: Saga Communications
Editorial: 870 Greenbrier Cir Ste 399, Chesapeake, Virginia 23320-2671.
T: 1 757 366-9900
W: http://www.1230wjoi.com
Editorial Profile: WJOI-AM is a commercial station owned by Saga Communications. The format of the station is adult standards. WJOI-AM broadcasts to the Chesapeake, VA area at 1230 AM.

WJOK-AM
Owner: Starboard Media Foundation Inc.
Editorial: 2470 Crooks Ave, Kaukauna, Wisconsin 54130. **T:** 1 920 406-7332
E: info@relevantradio.com
W: http://www.relevantradio.com
Editorial Profile: WJOK-AM is a non-commercial station owned by Starboard Media Foundation Inc. The format of the station is religious talk. WJOK-AM broadcasts to the Green Bay, WI area at 1050 AM.

WJOL-AM
Owner: Digity LLC
Editorial: 2410 Caton Farm Rd Unit B, Crest Hill, Illinois 60403-1374. **T:** 1 815 556-0100
E: news@wjol.com **W:** http://www.wjol.com
Editorial Profile: WJOL-AM is a commercial station owned by Digity LLC. The format of the station is talk. WJOL-AM broadcasts to the Joliet, IL area at 1300 AM.

WJON-AM
Owner: Townsquare Media, LLC
Editorial: 640 Lincoln Ave SE, Saint Cloud, Minnesota 56304-1024. **T:** 1 320 251-4422
W: http://www.wjon.com
Editorial Profile: WJON-AM is a commercial station owned by Townsquare Media, LLC. The format of the station is news and talk. WJON-AM broadcasts to the Minneapolis area at 1240 AM.

WJOT-AM
Owner: Hoosier AM/FM LLC
Editorial: 1360 S Wabash St, Wabash, Indiana 46992-4112. **T:** 1 260 563-1161
W: http://www.1059thebash.com
Editorial Profile: WJOT-AM is a commercial station owned by Hoosier AM/FM LLC. The format of the station is oldies. WJOT-AM broadcasts to the Fort Wayne, IN area at 1510 AM.

WJOT-FM
Owner: Hoosier AM/FM LLC
Editorial: 1360 S Wabash St, Wabash, Indiana 46992-4112. **T:** 1 260 563-1161
W: http://1059thebash.com
Editorial Profile: WJOT-FM is a commercial station owned by Hoosier AM/FM LLC. The format of the station is oldies. WJOT-FM broadcasts to the Fort Wayne, IN area at 105.9 FM.

WJOU-FM
Owner: Oakwood College
Editorial: 7000 Adventist Blvd NW, Huntsville, Alabama 35896-0001. **T:** 1 256 726-7420
E: wjou@oakwood.edu **W:** http://www.wjou.org
Editorial Profile: WJOU-FM is a non-commercial station owned by Oakwood College. The format of the station is religious programming. The station broadcasts to the Huntsville, AL area at 90.1 FM.

WJOX-AM
Owner: Cumulus Media Inc.
Editorial: 244 Goodwin Crest Dr, Birmingham, Alabama 35209-3716. **T:** 1 205 945-4646
Editorial Profile: WJOX-AM is a commercial owned by Cumulus Media Inc. The format of the station is sports. WJOX-AM broadcasts to the Birmingham, AL area at 690 AM.

WJOX-FM
Owner: Cumulus Media Inc.
Editorial: 244 Goodwin Crest Dr, Birmingham, Alabama 35209-3716. **T:** 1 205 945-4646
W: http://www.joxfm.com
Editorial Profile: WJOX-FM is a commercial station owned by Cumulus Media Inc. The format of the station is sports. WJOX-FM broadcasts to the Birmingham, AL area at 94.5 FM.

WJOY-AM
Owner: Hall Communications
Editorial: 70 Joy Dr, South Burlington, Vermont 5403. **T:** 1 802 658-1230
E: wjoy@hallradio.com
W: http://www.wjoy.com
Editorial Profile: WJOY-AM is a commercial station owned by Hall Communications. The format of the station is easy listening music. WJOY-AM broadcasts to the South Burlington, VT area at 1230 AM.

WJPA-AM
Owner: Washington Broadcasting
Editorial: 98 S Main St, Washington, Pennsylvania 15301. **T:** 1 724 222-2110
E: email@wjpa.com **W:** http://www.wjpa.com
Editorial Profile: WJPA-AM is a commercial station owned by Washington Broadcasting. The format of the station is oldies. WJPA-AM broadcasts to the Washington, PA area at 1450 AM.

WJPA-FM
Owner: Washington Broadcasting
Editorial: 98 S Main St, Washington, Pennsylvania 15301-6810. **T:** 1 724 222-2110
E: email@wjpa.com **W:** http://www.wjpa.com
Editorial Profile: WJPA-FM is a commercial station owned by Washington Broadcasting. The format of the station oldies. WJPA-FM broadcasts to the Washington, PA area at 95.3 FM.

WJPD-FM
Owner: Sovereign Communications LLC
Editorial: 1009 W Ridge St, Ste A, Marquette, Michigan 49855. **T:** 1 906 225-1313
E: news@wjpd.com **W:** http://www.wjpd.com
Editorial Profile: WJPD-FM is a commercial station owned by Sovereign Communications LLC. The format for the station is country. WJPD-FM broadcasts to the Marquette, MI area at 92.3 FM.

WJPF-AM
Owner: Max Media
Editorial: 1431 Country Aire Dr, Carterville, Illinois 62918. **T:** 1 618 985-4843
W: http://www.wjpf.com
Editorial Profile: WJPF-AM is a commercial station owned by Max Media. The format of the station is news and talk. WJPF-AM broadcasts to the Carterville, IL area at 1340 AM.

WJPH-FM
Owner: Maranatha Ministries
Editorial: 950 Tilton Rd, Ste 101, Northfield, New Jersey 8225. **T:** 1 609 646-0057
E: letters@praise899.org
W: http://www.praise899.org
Editorial Profile: WJPH-FM is a non-commercial station owned by Maranatha Ministries. The format of the station is religious. WJPH-FM broadcasts to the Woodbine, NJ area at 89.9 FM.

WJPI-AM
Owner: 24-7 Communications, LLC
Editorial: 126 Water Street, Plymouth, North Carolina 27962. **T:** 1 252 793-4970
W: http://www.wjpi1470am.com
Editorial Profile: WJPI-AM is a commercial station owned by 24-7 Communications, LLC. The format of the station is gospel. WJPI-AM broadcasts to the Plymouth, NC area at 1470 AM.

WJPT-FM
Owner: Beasley Broadcast Group
Editorial: 20125 S Tamiami Trl, Estero, Florida 33928-2117. **T:** 1 239 495-2100
W: http://www.sunny1063.com
Editorial Profile: WJPT-FM is a commercial station owned by Beasley Broadcasat Group. The format of the station is adult contemporary. WJPT-FM broadcasts to the Fort Myers, FL area at 106.3 FM.

WJPZ-FM
Owner: WJPZ Inc.
Editorial: 316 Waverly Ave, Syracuse, New York 13210-2437. **T:** 1 315 443-4689
E: z89radio@gmail.com
W: http://www.z89online.com
Editorial Profile: WJPZ-FM is a non-commercial college station owned by WJPZ Inc. The format of the station is Top 40/CHR. WJPZ-FM broadcasts to the Syracuse, NY area at 89.1 FM.

WJQK-FM
Owner: Lanser Broadcasting Corp.
Editorial: 425 Centerstone Ct, Zeeland, Michigan 49464-2247. **T:** 1 616 931-9930
E: traffic@jq99.com **W:** http://www.jq99.com
Editorial Profile: WJQK-FM is a commercial station owned by Lanser Broadcasting Corp. The format of the station is contemporary Christian. WJQK-FM broadcasts to the Holland, MI area at 99.3 FM.

WJQM-FM
Owner: Midwest Family Stations
Editorial: 730 Rayovac Dr, Madison, Wisconsin 53711-2472. **T:** 1 608 273-1000
E: info@madtownjamz.com
W: http://www.madisonjams.com
Editorial Profile: WJQM-FM is a commercial station owned by Midwest Family Stations. The format of the station is rhythmic Top 40/CHR. WJQM-FM broadcasts to the Madison, WI area at 93.1 FM.

WJQS-AM
Owner: L & L Radio
Editorial: 840 E River Pl Ste 503, Jackson, Mississippi 39202-3487. **T:** 1 601 965-2001
Editorial Profile: WJQS-AM is a commercial station owned by L & L Radio. The format of the station is oldies. WJQS-AM broadcasts to the Jackson, MS area at 1400 AM.

WJQX-FM
Owner: Cumulus Media Inc
Editorial: 244 Goodwin Crest Dr, Birmingham, Alabama 35209-3716. **T:** 1 205 945-4646
Editorial Profile: WJQX-FM is a commercial station owned by Cumulus Media Inc. The format of the station is sports. WAPI-FM broadcasts to the Birmingham, AL area at 100.5 FM.

WJQZ-FM
Owner: DBM Communications
Editorial: 82 Railroad Ave, Wellsville, New York 14895-1143. **T:** 1 585 593-6070
E: oldiesz103@yahoo.com
W: http://www.wjqz.com
Editorial Profile: WJQZ-FM is a commercial station owned by DBM Communications. The format of the station is oldies. WJQZ-FM broadcasts to the Wellsville, NY area at 103.5 FM.

WJR-AM
Owner: Cumulus Media Inc.
Editorial: 3011 W Grand Blvd, Ste 800, Detroit, Michigan 48202. **T:** 1 313 875-4440
W: http://www.wjr.com
Editorial Profile: WJR-AM is a commercial station owned Cumulus Media Inc. The format of the station is news and talk. WJR-AM broadcasts to the Detroit area at 760 AM.

WJRB-FM
Owner: Jeffrey T. Batten's WJUL Radio, LLC
Editorial: 1352 Main St, Young Harris, Georgia 30582-4314. **T:** 1 706 435-7864
Editorial Profile: WJRB-FM is a commercial station owned by Jeffrey T. Batten's WJUL Radio, LLC. The format of the station is classic country. WJRB-FM broadcasts to the Young Harris, GA area at a frequency of 95.1.

WJRE-FM
Owner: Virden Broadcasting Corporation
Editorial: 133 E Division St, Kewanee, Illinois 61443. **T:** 1 309 853-4471
E: regionalradionews@wkei.com
W: http://www.1025wjre.com
Editorial Profile: WJRE-FM is a commercial station owned by Virden Broadcasting Corporation. The format of the station is country music. WJRE-FM broadcasts to the Kewanee, IL area at 102.5 FM.

WJRF-FM
Owner: Refuge Media Group
Editorial: 4604 Airpark Blvd, Duluth, Minnesota 55811-5751. **T:** 1 218 722-3017
E: airstaff@refugeradio.com
W: http://www.refugeradio.com
Editorial Profile: WJRF-FM is a non-commercial station owned by Refuge Media Group. The format of the station is contemporary Christian music. WJRF-FM broadcasts in the Duluth, MN area at 89.5 FM.

WJRH-FM
Owner: Lafayette College
Editorial: 111 Quad Dr, Easton, Pennsylvania 18042-1707. **T:** 1 610 330-5316
E: wjrh@lafayette.edu **W:** http://www.wjrh.org
Editorial Profile: WJRH-FM is a commercial station owned by Lafayette College. The format of the station is college variety. WJRH-FM broadcasts to the Philadelphia area at 104.9 FM.

WJRI-AM
Owner: Foothills Radio Group, LLC
Editorial: 827 Fairview Dr SW, Lenoir, North Carolina 28645. **T:** 1 828 758-1033
W: http://www.foothillsradio.com
Editorial Profile: WJRI-AM is a commercial station owned by Foothills Radio Group, LLC. The format of the station is news and talk. WJRI-AM broadcasts to the Charlotte, NC area at 1340 AM.

WJRM-AM
Owner: Family Worship Ministries Inc.
Editorial: 1066 Glenn Rd, Troy, North Carolina 27371. **T:** 1 910 576-1390
W: http://www.wjrm.com
Editorial Profile: WJRM-AM is a non-commercial station owned by Family Worship Ministries Inc. The format of the station is Southern gospel and contemporary Christian. WJRM-AM broadcasts to the Troy, NC area at 1390 AM.

WJRR-FM
Owner: Clear Channel Media and Entertainment
Editorial: 2500 Maitland Center Pkwy, Ste 401, Maitland, Florida 32751.
T: 1 407 916-7800
E: programdirector@wjrr.com
W: http://www.wjrr.com
Editorial Profile: WJRR-FM is a commercial station owned by Clear Channel Media and Entertainment. The format of the station is rock alternative music. WJRR-FM broadcasts to the Orlando, FL area at 101.1 FM.

WJRS-FM
Owner: Lake Cumberland Broadcasters
Editorial: 2804 S Highway 127, Russell Springs, Kentucky 42642. **T:** 1 270 343-4444
E: wjrs1049@duo-county.com
W: http://www.lakercountry.com
Editorial Profile: WJRS-FM is a commercial station owned by Lake Cumberland Broadcasters. The format for the station is country. WJRS-FM broadcasts to the Russell Springs, KY area at 104.9 FM.

WJRV-FM
Owner: Momentum Broadcasting
Editorial: 408 N Cedar Bluff Rd, Ste 252, Knoxville, Tennessee 37923-3641.
T: 1 865 246-3848 **E:** spots@river106.com
W: http://www.river106.com
Editorial Profile: WJRV-FM is a commercial station owned by Momentum Broadcasting. The format of the station is hot adult contemporary. The station airs locally at 106.1 FM. WJRV-FM's tagline is "80s 90s and Now."

WJRW-AM
Owner: Cumulus Media Inc.
Editorial: 60 Monroe Center St NW Fl 3, Grand Rapids, Michigan 49503-2916.
T: 1 616 456-5461
W: http://www.wjrwam.com
Editorial Profile: WJRW-AM is a commercial station owned by Cumulus Media Inc. The format of the station is news and talk. WJRW-AM broadcasts to the Grand Rapids, MI area at 1340 AM.

WJRZ-FM
Owner: Greater Media Inc.
Editorial: 1001 Beach Ave, Manahawkin, New Jersey 08050-3218. **T:** 1 609 597-1100
W: http://wp.jerseysgreatest.net
Editorial Profile: WJRZ-FM is a commercial station owned by Greater Media Inc. The format of the station is classic hits. WJRZ-FM broadcasts to the Manahawkin, NJ area at 100.1 FM.

WJSA-AM
Owner: Covenant Broadcasting Co.
Editorial: 262 Allegheny St, Jersey Shore, Pennsylvania 17740-1442. **T:** 1 570 327-1300
W: http://espnwilliamsport.com
Editorial Profile: WJSA-AM is a non-commercial station owned by Covenant Broadcasting Co. The format of the station is sports. WJSA-AM broadcasts to the Scranton, PA area at 1600 AM.

WJSA-FM
Owner: Covenant Broadcasting Co.
Editorial: 262 Allegheny St, Jersey Shore, Pennsylvania 17740-1442. **T:** 1 570 398-7200
E: news@wjsaradio.com
W: http://www.wjsaradio.com
Editorial Profile: WJSA-FM is a non-commercial station owned by Covenant Broadcasting Co. The format of the station is

Christian music and news. WJSA-FM broadcasts to the Jersey Shore, PA area at 96.3 FM.

WJSB-AM
Owner: Whitaker(James T.)
Editorial: 506 W 1st Ave, Crestview, Florida 32536. **T:** 1 850 682-3040
E: waazwjsb@embarqmail.com
Editorial Profile: WJSB-AM is a commercial station owned by James T. Whitaker. The format of the station is classic country. WJSB-AM broadcasts to the Mobile, AL and Pensacola, FL areas at 1050 AM.

WJSC-FM
Owner: Johnson State College
Editorial: 337 College Hl, Johnson, Vermont 5656. **T:** 1 802 635-1355
W: http://www.jsc.edu/StudentLife/WJSCFM/default.aspx
Editorial Profile: WJSC-FM is a non-commercial station owned by Johnson State College. The format of the station is variety. WJSC-FM broadcasts to the Burlington, VT and Plattsburgh, NY areas at 90.7 FM.

WJSE-FM
Owner: Coastal Broadcasting Systems, Inc.
Editorial: 1602 Route 47 Floor 2, Rio Grande, New Jersey 08242-1404. **T:** 1 609 522-1987
W: http://www.wjserocks.com
Editorial Profile: WJSE-FM is a commercial station owned by Coastal Broadcasting Systems, Inc. The format of the station is alternative rock. WJSE-FM broadcasts to the Wildwood, NJ area at 106.7 FM.

WJSG-FM
Owner: Jackson Broadcasting Co.
Editorial: 180 Airport Rd, Rockingham, North Carolina 28379-4251. **T:** 1 910 895-3787
E: g104fm@g104fm.com
W: http://www.g104fm.com
Editorial Profile: WJSG-FM is a commercial station owned by Jackson Broadcasting Co. The format of the station is Christian music. WJSG-FM broadcasts to the Rockingham, NC area at 104.3 FM.

WJSH-FM
Owner: Northshore Broadcasting Inc.
Editorial: 200 E Thomas St, Hammond, Louisiana 70401-3316. **T:** 1 985 345-0060
Editorial Profile: WJSH-FM is a commercial station owned by Northshore Broadcasting Inc. The format of the station is oldies. WJSH-FM broadcasts to the New Orleans area on 104.7 FM.

WJSJ-FM
Owner: Broadast Partners
Editorial: 9090 Hogan Rd, Jacksonville, Florida 32216-4648. **T:** 1 904 638-2965
Editorial Profile: WJSJ-FM is a commercial station owned by Broadcast Partners. The format of the station is Top 40/CHR. WJSJ-FM broadcasts to the Jacksonville, FL area at 105.3 FM.

WJSM-FM
Owner: Martinsburg Broadcasting Inc.
Editorial: 724 Rebecca Furnace Road, Martinsburg, Pennsylvania 16662.
T: 1 814 793-2188 **E:** wjsmradio@gmail.com
W: http://www.wjsm.com
Editorial Profile: WJSM-FM is a commercial station owned by Martinsburg Broadcasting Inc. The format of the station is gospel music and Christian programming. WJSM-FM broadcasts to the Martinsburg, PA area at 92.7 FM.

WJSN-FM
Owner: Intermountain Broadcasting
Editorial: 1501 Hargis Ln, Jackson, Kentucky 41339-1102. **T:** 1 606 666-7531
W: http://www.wjsnfm.com
Editorial Profile: WJSN-FM is a commercial station owned by Intermountain Broadcasting. The format of the station is country music. WJSN-FM broadcasts in the Jackson, KY area at 106.5 FM.

WJSP-FM
Owner: Georgia Public Broadcasting
Editorial: 260 14th St NW, Atlanta, Georgia 30318. **T:** 1 404 685-2548 **E:** ask@gpb.org
W: http://www.gpb.org
Editorial Profile: WJSP-FM is a non-commercial station owned by Georgia Public Broadcasting. The format of the station is news, classical and jazz music. WJSP-FM broadcasts to the Atlanta area at 88.1 FM.

WJSQ-FM
Owner: Sliger Enterprises
Editorial: 2110 Oxnard Rd, Athens, Tennessee 37303. **T:** 1 423 745-1000
E: 1017wlar@bellsouth.net
Editorial Profile: WJSQ-FM is a commercial station owned by Sliger Enterprises. The format of the station is contemporary country. WSJQ-FM broadcasts to the Athens, TN area at 101.7 FM.

WJSR-FM
Owner: Jefferson State Community College
Editorial: 2601 Carson Rd, Birmingham, Alabama 35215. **T:** 1 205 856-6095
Editorial Profile: WJSR-FM is a non-commercial station owned by Jefferson State Community College. The format of the station is classic rock. WJSR-FM broadcasts to the Birmingham, AL area at 91.1 FM.

WJST-AM
Owner: Forever Broadcasting
Editorial: 219 Savannah Gardner Rd, New Castle, Pennsylvania 16101.
T: 1 724 346-5070 **E:** wtsutton@yahoo.com
Editorial Profile: WJST-AM is a commercial station owned by Forever Broadcasting. The format of the station is sports. WJST-AM broadcasts to the New Castle, PA area at 1280 AM.

WJSU-FM
Owner: Jackson State University
Editorial: 1325 Hattiesburg St, Jackson, Mississippi 39204-2335. **T:** 1 601 979-2285
E: wjsufm@jsums.edu **W:** http://www.wjsu.org
Editorial Profile: WJSU-FM is a non-commercial station owned by Jackson State University. The format for the station is jazz music. WJSU-FM broadcasts to the Jackson, MS area at 88.5 FM.

WJSZ-FM
Owner: Krol Communications
Editorial: 103 N Washington St, Owosso, Michigan 48867. **T:** 1 989 725-1925
W: http://www.z925.com

WJTA-FM
Owner: Holy Family Communications, Inc
Editorial: 6048 Road 8E, Leipsic, Ohio 45856-9408. **T:** 1 419 943-1511
W: http://www.wjta889.org/
Editorial Profile: WJTA-FM is a non-commercial station owned by Holy Family Communications, Inc (Tom and Mary Ann Deitering). The station airs on 88.9FM. It broadcasts out of the Deitering home in Leipsic, OH. The station is currently a simulcast of EWTN/ Ave Maria Catholic Radio. Local programming is planned for the future. The station's first broadcast was in June 2010.

WJTB-AM
Owner: Taylor Broadcasting
Editorial: 105 Lake Ave, Elyria, Ohio 44035.
T: 1 440 327-1844
Editorial Profile: WJTB-AM is a commercial station owned by Taylor Broadcasting. The format of the station is gospel. WJTB-AM broadcasts to the Elyria, OH area at 1040 AM.

WJTF-FM
Owner: Family Life Radio
Editorial: 835A S Berthe Ave, Panama City, Florida 32404. **T:** 1 850 874-9900
W: http://www.myflr.org

WJTG-FM
Owner: Family Life Radio
Editorial: 1110 Richardson Mill Rd., Macon, Georgia 31030. **T:** 1 520 742-6976
W: http://www.myflr.org
Editorial Profile: WJTG-FM is a commercial station owned by Family Life Radio. The format of the station is Contemporary Christian music. WJTG-FM broadcasts to the Fort Valley, GA area at 91.3 FM.

WJTH-AM
Owner: Cherokee Broadcasting Co.
Editorial: 329 Richardson Rd SE, Calhoun, Georgia 30701. **T:** 1 706 629-6397
E: am900@wjth.com **W:** http://www.wjth.com
Editorial Profile: WJTH-AM is a commercial station owned by Cherokee Broadcasting Co. The format of the station is country music. WJTH-AM broadcasts to the Atlanta area at 900 AM.

WJTI-AM
Owner: El Sol Broadcasting, LLC
Editorial: 611 W National Ave, Ste 201, Milwaukee, Wisconsin 53204.
T: 1 414 384-1460 **E:** uniyes@aol.com
W: http://lanuevaritmo.com
Editorial Profile: WJTI-AM is a commercial station owned by El Sol Broadcasting, LLC. The format of the station is regional Mexican. WJTI-AM broadcasts to the Milwaukee area at 1460 AM.

WJTK-FM
Owner: Newman Broadcasting Inc.
Editorial: 229 SW Main Blvd, Lake City, Florida 32025-7049. **T:** 1 386 758-9696
W: http://northfloridanow.com/index92.htm
Editorial Profile: WJTK-FM is a commercial station owned by Newman Broadcasting Inc. The format of the station is news talk. WJTK-FM broadcasts to the Lake City, FL area at 96.5 FM.

WJTL-FM
Owner: Creative Ministries Inc.
Editorial: 1875 Junction Rd, Manheim, Pennsylvania 17545-8853. **T:** 1 717 392-3690
E: contact@wjtl.com **W:** http://www.wjtl.com
Editorial Profile: WJTL-FM is a non-commercial station owned by Creative Ministries Inc. The format of the station is contemporary Christian music. WJTL-FM broadcasts to the Lancaster, PA area at 90.3 FM.

WJTN-AM
Owner: Media One Group, LLC
Editorial: 2 Orchard Rd, Jamestown, New York 14701. **T:** 1 716 487-1151
W: http://www.wjtn.com
Editorial Profile: WJTN-AM is a commercial station owned by Media One Group, LLC. The format of the station is news, talk and sports. WJTN-AM broadcasts to the Jamestown, NY area at 1240 AM.

WJTQ-FM
Owner: Cumulus Media Inc.
Editorial: 6565 N W St Ste 270, Pensacola, Florida 32505-1797. **T:** 1 850 478-6011
W: http://wjtq-fm.pro.cumulus.tritonflex.com
Editorial Profile: WJTQ-FM is a commercial station owned by Cumulus Media Inc. The format of the station is classic hits. WJTQ-FM broadcasts to the Mobile, AL/Pensacola, FL area at 100.7 FM.

WJTT-FM
Owner: Brewer Broadcasting Inc.
Editorial: 1305 Carter St, Chattanooga, Tennessee 37402. **T:** 1 423 265-9494
W: http://www.power94.com
Editorial Profile: WJTT-FM is a commercial station owned by Brewer Broadcasting Inc. The format of the station is urban contemporary. WJTT-FM broadcasts to the Chattanooga, TN area at 94.3 FM.

WJTY-FM
Owner: Family Life Radio
Editorial: 341 S Washington St, Lancaster, Wisconsin 53813. **T:** 1 608 723-7888
W: http://www.myflr.org
Editorial Profile: WJTY-FM is a non-commmercial station owned by Family Life Radio. The format is contemporary Christian. WJTY-FM broadcasts to Lancaster, WI area at 88.1 FM.

WJUB-AM
Owner: Jubilation Ministries
Editorial: N5569 State Road 57, Plymouth, Wisconsin 53073-4236. **T:** 1 920 893-2661
E: 1420thebreeze@jmiradio.org
W: http://www.1420thebreeze.com
Editorial Profile: WJUB-AM is a commercial station owned by Jubilation Ministries. The format of the station is adult standards. WJUB-AM broadcasts to the Milwaukee area at 1420 AM.

WJUC-FM
Owner: Welch Communications
Editorial: 5902 Southwyck Blvd, Toledo, Ohio 43614. **T:** 1 419 861-9582 **E:** wjuc@aol.com
W: http://www.thejuice1073.com
Editorial Profile: WJUC-FM is a commercial station owned by Welch Communications. The format of the station is urban contemporary. WJUC-FM broadcasts to the Toledo, OH area at 107.3 FM.

WJUF-FM
Owner: University of Florida
Editorial: 2206-C Weimer Hall Univ Of Florida, Gainesville, Florida 32611-8405.
T: 1 352 392-5551 **E:** radio@wuft.org
W: http://www.wuft.org
Editorial Profile: WJUF-FM is a non-commercial station owned by the University of Florida. The format of the station is news and talk. WJUF-FM broadcasts to the Gainesville, FL area at 90.1 FM.

WJUN-AM
Owner: Starview Media Inc.
Editorial: Old Route 22 East, Mexico, Pennsylvania 17056-9999. **T:** 1 717 436-2135
W: http://wjun925.com
Editorial Profile: WJUN-AM is a commercial station owned by Starview Media Inc. The format of the station is sports. WJUN-AM broadcasts to the Mexico, PA area at station at 1220 AM.

WJUN-FM
Owner: Starview Media Inc.
Editorial: Old Route 22 East, Mexico, Pennsylvania 17056-9999. **T:** 1 717 436-2135
E: wjun@nmax.net
W: http://www.wjun925.com
Editorial Profile: WJUN-FM is a commercial station owned by Starview Media Inc. The format of the station is country music. WJUN-FM broadcasts to the Mexico, PA area at 92.5 FM.

WJUS-AM
Owner: Grace Baptist Temple Church
Editorial: Highway 14, Marion, Alabama 36756. **T:** 1 334 683-2043
E: wjus@bellsouth.net

WJUX-FM
Owner: Bridgelight Corp.
Editorial: 127 White Oak Ln, Old Bridge, New Jersey 08857-1945. **T:** 1 732 901-9953
E: info@bridgefm.org
W: http://www.bridgefm.org
Editorial Profile: WJUX-FM is a non-commercial station owned by Bridgelight Corp. The format for the station is religious talk and music. WJUX-FM broadcasts to the New York area at 99.7 FM.

WJVC-FM
Owner: JVC MEDIA, LLC
Editorial: 3075 Veterans Memorial Hwy Ste 201, Ronkonkoma, New York 11779-7600.
T: 1 631 648-2500 **W:** http://licountry.com
Editorial Profile: WJVC-FM is a commercial station, owned by JVC MEDIA, LLC. The format of the station is country. WJVC-FM broadcasts in the Medford, NY area at 96.1 FM.

WJVL-FM
Owner: Bliss Communications Inc.
Editorial: 1 S Parker Dr, Janesville, Wisconsin 53545. **T:** 1 608 752-7895 **E:** news@wclo.com
W: http://www.wjvl.com
Editorial Profile: WJVL-FM is a commercial station owned by Bliss Communications Inc. The format of the station is country. WJVL-FM broadcasts to the Madison, WI area at 99.9 FM.

WJVO-FM
Owner: Morgan County Broadcasting Co., Inc.
Editorial: 1251 E Morton Ave, Jacksonville, Illinois 62650. **T:** 1 217 245-5119
W: http://wjvofm.com
Editorial Profile: WJVO-FM is a commercial station owned by Morgan County Broadcasting Co., Inc. The format of the station is classic and contemporary country music. WJVO-FM broadcasts in the Jacksonville, IL at 105.5 FM.

WJVR-FM
Owner: United States CP, LLC
Editorial: 508 W Oak St, Covington, Virginia 24426-1942. **T:** 1 540 962-1133
W: http://www.1019theriver.com
Editorial Profile: WJVR-FM is a commercial station owned by United States CP, LLC. The format of the station is light adult contemporary. WJVR-FM broadcasts to the Allegheny County, VA area at a frequency of 101.9 FM.

WJWD-FM
Owner: Calvary Chapel of Costa Mesa, Inc.
Editorial: 150 Lincolnway Ste 2001, Valparaiso, Indiana 46383-5556.
T: 1 219 548-5800 **E:** wjwdradio@yahoo.com
Editorial Profile: WJWD-FM is a non-commercial station owned by Calvary Chapel of Costa Mesa, Inc. The format of the station is Christian music and religious programming. WJWD-FM broadcasts to the Marshall, WI area at 90.3 FM.

WJWF-AM
Owner: Cumulus Media Inc.
Editorial: 200 6th St N, Columbus, Mississippi 39701-4567. **T:** 1 662 327-1183
W: http://www.1031theteam.com

Editorial Profile: WJWF-AM is a commercial station owned by Cumulus Media Inc. The format of the station is sports. WJWF-AM broadcasts to the Columbus, MS area at 1400 AM.

WJWJ-FM
Owner: South Carolina Educational Television Commission
Editorial: 1101 George Rogers Blvd, Columbia, South Carolina 29201.
T: 1 803 737-3200 **W:** http://www.etvradio.org
Editorial Profile: WJWJ-FM is a non-commercial station owned by the South Carolina Educational Television Commission. The format of the station is news. WJWJ-FM broadcasts to the Beaufort and Hilton Head, SC areas at 89.9 FM.

WJWK-AM
Owner: Great Scott Broadcasting
Editorial: 20200 Dupont Blvd, Georgetown, Delaware 19947. **T:** 1 302 856-2567
Editorial Profile: WJWK-AM is a commercial station owned by Great Scott Broadcasting. The format of the station is adult hits. WJWK-AM broadcasts to the Georgetown, DE area at 1280 AM.

WJWL-AM
Owner: Great Scott Broadcasting
Editorial: 20200 Dupont Blvd, Georgetown, Delaware 19947. **T:** 1 302 422-2600
E: radio@maxima900.com
W: http://www.maxima90zero.com
Editorial Profile: WJWL-AM is a commercial station owned by Great Scott Broadcasting (under LMA with Hola Media Network, LLC). The format of the station is Spanish Top 40/ CHR music. WJWK-AM broadcasts to the Georgetown, DE area at 900 AM.

WJWT-FM
Owner: Horizon Christian Fellowship
Editorial: 356 Broad St, Fitchburg, Massachusetts 01420-3030.
T: 1 978 665-9111 **W:** http://renewfm.org
Editorial Profile: WJWT-FM is a commerical station owned by Horizon Christian Fellowship. The format of the station is Christian music and religious programming. WJWT-FM broadcasts to the Gardner, MA area at 91.7 FM.

WJWV-FM
Owner: Georgia Public Broadcasting
Editorial: 260 14th St NW, Atlanta, Georgia 30318. **T:** 1 404 685-2548 **E:** ask@gpb.org
W: http://www.gpb.org
Editorial Profile: WJWV-FM is a non-commercial station owned by Georgia Public Broadcasting. The format of the station is news, jazz and classical music. WJWV-FM broadcasts to the Atlanta area at 90.9 FM.

WJWZ-FM
Owner: Bluewater Broadcasting Co. LLC
Editorial: 4101 Wall St, Ste A, Montgomery, Alabama 36106. **T:** 1 334 244-0961
W: http://www.979jamz.com
Editorial Profile: WJWZ-FM is a commercial station owned by Bluewater Broadcasting Co. LLC. The format of the station is urban contemporary. WJWZ-FM broadcasts to the Montgomery, AL area at 97.9 FM.

WJXA-FM
Owner: Midwest Communications Inc.
Editorial: 504 Rosedale Ave, Nashville, Tennessee 37211-2028. **T:** 1 615 259-0929
W: http://www.mix929.com
Editorial Profile: WJXA-FM is a commercial station owned by Midwest Communications Inc.. The format of the station is contemporary. WJXA-FM broadcasts in the Nashville, TN area at 92.9 FM.

WJXB-FM
Owner: Midwest Communications, Inc.
Editorial: 1100 Sharps Ridge Mem Park Dr, Knoxville, Tennessee 37917-3000.
T: 1 865 525-6000 **W:** http://www.b975.com
Editorial Profile: WJXB-FM is a commercial station owned by Midwest Communications, Inc. The format of the station is adult contemporary. WJXB-FM broadcasts to the Knoxville, TN area at 97.5 FM.

WJXL-AM
Owner: Seven Bridges Radio, LLC
Editorial: 9090 Hogan Rd, Jacksonville, Florida 32216. **T:** 1 904 641-1011
W: http://www.1010xl.com
Editorial Profile: WJXL-AM is a commercial station owned by Seven Bridges Radio, LLC. The format of the station is sports. WJXL-AM broadcasts to the Jacksonville, FL area at 1010 AM.

WJXM-FM
Owner: Mississippi Broadcasters, LLC
Editorial: 3436 Highway 45 N, Meridian, Mississippi 39301. **T:** 1 601 693-2661
W: http://www.1057thebeat.com
Editorial Profile: WJXM-FM is a commercial station owned by Mississippi Broadcasters, LLC. The format of the station is urban contemporary. WJXM-FM broadcasts to the Meridian, MS area at 107.5 FM.

WJXP-FM
Owner: Horizon Christian Fellowship
Editorial: 356 Broad St, Fitchburg, Massachusetts 01420-3030.
T: 1 978 665-9111
W: http://horizonfitchburg.org
Editorial Profile: WJXP-FM is a non-commercial station owned by Horizon Christian Fellowship. The format of the station is Contemporary Christian. WJXP-FM broadcasts to the Fitchburg, MA area at a frequency of 90.1 FM.

WJXQ-FM
Owner: Midwest Communiations, Inc.
Editorial: 2495 Cedar St, Holt, Michigan 48842-7400. **T:** 1 517 699-0111
W: http://www.z93hits.com
Editorial Profile: WJXQ-FM is a commercial station owned by Midwest Communiations, Inc. The format of the station is rock. WJXQ-FM broadcasts to the Lansing, MI area at 106.1 FM.

WJXR-FM
Owner: Perich(Greg & Sarah)
Editorial: 28 W Macclenny Ave, Ste 9, Macclenny, Florida 32063-2078.
T: 1 904 314-9749 **E:** wjxr@aol.com
W: http://www.wjxr.com
Editorial Profile: WJXR-FM is a commercial station owned by Greg & Sarah Perich. The format of the station is talk. WJXR-FM broadcasts to the Jacksonville, FL area at 92.1 FM.

WJXY-FM
Owner: Cumulus Media Inc.
Editorial: 11640 Highway 17 Byp, Murrells Inlet, South Carolina 29576-9332.
T: 1 843 651-7869
W: http://939theoutlaw.com
Editorial Profile: WJXY-FM is a commercial station owned by Cumulus Media Inc. The format of the station is Southern Rock and Contemporary Country. WJXY-FM broadcasts to the Myrtle Beach, SC area at 93.9 FM.

WJYA-FM
Owner: Positive Alternative Radio
Editorial: 22226 Timberlake Rd., Lynchburg, Virginia 24502. **T:** 1 434 237-9798
E: office@spiritfm.com
W: http://www.spiritfm.com

WJYE-FM
Owner: Townsquare Media, LLC
Editorial: 1200 Rand Bldg, Buffalo, New York 14203-7505. **T:** 1 716 856-3550
W: http://961joyfm.com
Editorial Profile: WJYE-FM is a commercial station owned by Townsquare Media, LLC. The format of the station is adult contemporary. WJYE-FM broadcasts to the Buffalo, NY area on 96.1 FM.

WJYI-AM
Owner: Saga Communications
Editorial: 5407 W McKinley Ave, Milwaukee, Wisconsin 53208-2540. **T:** 1 414 978-9000
W: http://www.joy1340.com
Editorial Profile: WJYI-AM is a commercial station owned by Saga Communications. The format of the station is Christian programming and gospel music. WJYI-AM broadcasts to the Milwaukee area at 1340 AM.

WJYJ-FM
Owner: Positive Alternative Radio
Editorial: 6546 Lovers Ln, Warrenton, Virginia 20186. **T:** 1 540 347-4825
E: info@positivehits.org
W: http://www.positivehits.org
Editorial Profile: WJYJ-FM is a non-commercial station owned by Positive Alternative Radio. The format of the station is contemporary Christian music. WJYJ-FM broadcasts to the Warrenton, VA area at 90.5 FM.

WJYK-AM
Owner: Battaglia(Stephen and Janis)
Editorial: 1612 Milo Rd, Richmond, Virginia 23225-7416. **T:** 1 804 276-2060
W: http://www.joyam980.com
Editorial Profile: WJKY-AM is a commercial station owned by Stephen and Janice Battaglia. The format of the station is contemporary Christian music and religious. WJKY-AM broadcasts to the Chase City, VA area at 980 AM.

WJYO-FM
Owner: Airwaves for Jesus
Editorial: 6211 Briarcliff Rd, Fort Myers, Florida 33912. **T:** 1 239 274-9150
E: info@kingdom.fm
W: http://www.kingdom.fm
Editorial Profile: WJYO-FM is a non-commercial station owned by Airwaves for Jesus. The format of the station is gospel. WJYO-FM broadcasts to the Ft. Myers, FL area at 91.5 FM.

WJYP-AM
Owner: LM Communications, Inc.
Editorial: 100 Kanawha Ter, Saint Albans, West Virginia 25177-2771. **T:** 1 304 722-3308
E: wjypnet@gmail.com **W:** http://wjypam.com
Editorial Profile: WJYP-AM is a commercial station owned by LM Communications, Inc. The format of the station is sports. WJYP-AM broadcasts to the Saint Albans, WV area at 1300 AM.

WJYW-FM
Owner: Positive Alternative Radio
Editorial: 505 S Division St, Union City, Ohio 45390. **T:** 1 937 968-5633
E: office@889joyfm.com
W: http://www.889joyfm.com
Editorial Profile: WJYW-FM is a commercial station owned by Positive Alternative Radio. The format of the station is contemporary Christian. WJYW-FM broadcasts to the Union City, OH area at 88.9 FM.

WJYY-FM
Owner: WBIN, Inc.
Editorial: 2 Capital Plz Ste 105, Concord, New Hampshire 03301-4911. **T:** 1 603 224-8486
W: http://www.wjyy.com
Editorial Profile: WJYY-FM is a commercial station owned by WBIN, Inc. The format of the station is Top 40/CHR music. WJYY-FM broadcasts to the Concord, NH area at 105.5 FM.

WJYZ-AM
Owner: Clear Channel Media and Entertainment
Editorial: 809 S Westover Blvd, Albany, Georgia 31707. **T:** 1 229 439-9704
W: http://www.wjyz.com
Editorial Profile: WJYZ-AM is a commercial station owned by Clear Channel Media and Entertainment. The format of the station is gospel music. WJYZ-AM broadcasts to the Albany, GA area at 960 AM.

WJZ-AM
Owner: CBS Radio
Editorial: 1423 Clarkview Rd Ste 1000, Baltimore, Maryland 21209-2134.
T: 1 410 825-1000
W: http://baltimore.cbslocal.com/station/cbs-sports-radio-1300/
Editorial Profile: WJZ-AM is a commercial station owned by CBS Radio. The format of the station is sports. WJZ-AM broadcasts to the Baltimore area at 1300 AM.

WJZD-FM
Owner: WJZD Inc.
Editorial: 10211 Southpark Dr, Gulfport, Mississippi 39503. **T:** 1 228 896-5307
E: info@wjzd.com **W:** http://www.wjzd.com
Editorial Profile: WJZD-FM is a commercial station owned by WJZD Inc. The format of the station is urban contemporary music. WJZD-FM broadcasts in the Gulfport, MS area at 94.5 FM.

WJZE-FM
Owner: URBan Radio Broadcasting, LLC
Editorial: 720 Water St, Fl 4, Toledo, Ohio 43604. **T:** 1 419 244-6354
W: http://www.hot973.net
Editorial Profile: WFZE-FM is a commercial station owned by URBan Radio Broadcasting, LLC. The format of the station is urban contemporary. WFZE-FM broadcasts to the Toledo, OH area at 97.3 FM.

WJZ-FM
Owner: CBS Radio
Editorial: 1423 Clarkview Rd, Ste 100, Baltimore, Maryland 21209-2190.
T: 1 410 828-7722
W: http://baltimore.cbslocal.com/category/sports/
Editorial Profile: WJZ-FM is a commercial station owned by CBS Radio. The format of the station is sports programming. WJZ-FM broadcasts to the Baltimore area at 105.7 FM.

WJZM-AM
Owner: Cumberland Radio Partners Inc.
Editorial: 925 Martin St, Clarksville, Tennessee 37040-4090. **T:** 1 931 645-6414
E: 14jzm@wjzm.com **W:** http://www.wjzm.com
Editorial Profile: WJZM-AM is a commercial station owned by Cumberland Radio Partners Inc. The format of the station is sports with some news and talk in the morning. WJZM-AM broadcasts to the Clarksville, TN area at 1400 AM.

WJZN-AM
Owner: Townsquare Media, Inc.
Editorial: 56 Western Ave Ste 13, Augusta, Maine 04330-6348. **T:** 1 207 623-4735
W: http://www.1400and1490.com
Editorial Profile: WJZN-AM is a commercial station owned by Townsquare Media, Inc. The format of the station is adult standards. WJZN-AM broadcasts to the Waterville, ME area at 1400 AM.

WJZQ-FM
Owner: Midwestern Broadcasting Co.
Editorial: 314 E Front St, Traverse City, Michigan 49684. **T:** 1 231 947-7675
W: http://www.z93hits.com
Editorial Profile: WJZQ-FM is a commercial station owned by Midwestern Broadcasting Co. The format of the station is top 40/CHR. WJZQ-FM broadcasts to the Traverse City, MI area at 92.9 FM.

WJZR-FM
Owner: North Coast Radio Inc.
Editorial: 1237 E Main St, Rochester, New York 14609. **T:** 1 585 288-5020
Editorial Profile: WJZR-FM is a commercial station owned by North Coast Radio Inc. The format of the station is jazz and blues music. WJZR-FM broadcasts to the Rochester, NY area at 105.9 FM.

WKAA-FM
Owner: Black Crow Broadcasting Inc.
Editorial: 1711 Ellis Dr, Valdosta, Georgia 31601. **T:** 1 229 244-8642
W: http://valdostatoday.com/995KixCountry.html
Editorial Profile: WKAA-FM is a commercial station owned by Black Crow Broadcasting Inc. The format of the station is contemporary country . WKAA-FM broadcasts to the Valdosta, GA area at 92.5 FM.

WKAC-AM
Owner: Casey(Kenneth)
Editorial: 19245 Al Highway 127, Athens, Alabama 35614. **T:** 1 256 232-6827
E: wkac@wkac1080.com
W: http://www.wkac1080.com
Editorial Profile: WKAC-AM is a commercial station owned by Kenneth Casey. The format of the station is oldies. WKAC-AM broadcasts to the Athens, AL area at 1080 AM.

WKAD-FM
Owner: MacDonald Garber Broadcasting Inc.
Editorial: 7825 Mackinaw Trl, Cadillac, Michigan 49601. **T:** 1 231 775-1263
Editorial Profile: WKAD-FM is a commercial station owned by MacDonald Garber Broadcasting Inc. The format of the station is sports. WKAD-FM broadcasts to the Cadillac, MI area at a frequency of 93.7 FM.

WKAF-FM
Owner: Entercom Communications Corp.
Editorial: 20 Guest St, 3rd Fl, Boston, Massachusetts 2135. **T:** 1 617 779-5400
W: http://www.waaf.com
Editorial Profile: WKAF-FM is a commercial station owned by Entercom Communications Corp. The format of the station is rock. WKAF-FM broadcasts to the Quincy, MA area at 97.7 FM.

WKAI-FM
Owner: Prestige Communications
Editorial: 1034 W Jackson St, Macomb, Illinois 61455-1924. **T:** 1 309 833-2121
E: news@prestigeradio.com
W: http://www.macombradio.com
Editorial Profile: WKAI-FM is a commercial station owned by Prestige Communications. The format of the station is hot adult contemporary. WKAI-FM broadcasts to the Macomb, IL area at 100.1 FM.

WKAK-FM
Owner: Cumulus Media Inc.
Editorial: 1104 W Broad Ave, Albany, Georgia 31707. **T:** 1 229 888-5000
W: http://www.kcountry104.com
Editorial Profile: WKAK-FM is a commercial station owned by Cumulus Media Inc. The format of the station is contemporary country music. WKAK-FM broadcasts to the Albany, GA area at 104.5 FM.

WKAM-AM
Owner: I.B. Communications
Editorial: 930 E Lincoln Ave, Goshen, Indiana 46528-3504. **T:** 1 574 533-3330
E: nzepedav13@hotmail.com
W: http://lamejor1460am.com
Editorial Profile: WKAM-AM is a commercial station owned by I.B. Communications. The format of the station is regional Mexican music. WKAM-AM broadcasts to the South Bend, IN area at 1460 AM.

WKAN-AM
Owner: Staradio Corp.
Editorial: 70 Meadowview Ctr, Ste 400, Kankakee, Illinois 60901. **T:** 1 815 935-9555
E: wkannews@staradio.com
W: http://www.wkan.com
Editorial Profile: WKAN-AM is a commercial station owned by Staradio Corp. The format of the station is news and talk. WKAN-AM broadcasts to the Chicago area at 1320 AM.

WKAR-AM
Owner: Michigan State University
Editorial: 404 Wilson Rd Rm 283, East Lansing, Michigan 48824-6423.
T: 1 517 432-9527 **E:** mail@wkar.org
W: http://www.wkar.org
Editorial Profile: WKAR-AM is a non-commercial station owned by Michigan State University. The format of the station is news and talk. WKAR-AM broadcasts to the East Lansing, MI area at 870 AM.

WKAR-FM
Owner: Michigan State University
Editorial: 404 Wilson Rd Rm 283, East Lansing, Michigan 48824-6423.
T: 1 517 432-9527 **E:** newsinfo@wkar.org
W: http://www.wkar.org
Editorial Profile: WKAR-FM is a non-commercial station owned by Michigan State University. The format of the station is news and classical music. WKAR-FM broadcasts to the East Lansing, MI area at 90.5 FM.

WKAT-AM
Owner: Salem Communications
Editorial: 2828 W Flagler St, Miami, Florida 33135-1337. **T:** 1 305 503-1340
W: http://www.1360wkat.com
Editorial Profile: WKAT-AM is a commercial station owned by Salem Communications. The format of the station is religious Hispanic. WKAT-AM broadcasts to the Miami area at 1360 AM.

WKAV-AM
Owner: Monticello Media LLC
Editorial: 1150 Pepsi Pl, Ste 300, Charlottesville, Virginia 22901.
T: 1 434 978-4408 **W:** http://www.wkav.com
Editorial Profile: WKAV-AM is a commercial station owned by Monticello Media LLC. The format of the station is sports. WKAV-AM broadcasts to the Charlottesville, VA area at 1400 AM.

WKAX-AM
Owner: Pilati Investments Corporation
Editorial: 113 Washington Ave NW, Russellville, Alabama 35653-2244.
T: 1 256 332-6103
W: http://www.wkaxam.com/
Editorial Profile: WKAX-AM is a commercial station owned by Pilati Investments Corporation. The format of the station is Regional Mexican. WKAX-AM broadcasts to the Russellville, AL area at 1500 AM.

WKAY-FM
Owner: Galesburg Broadcasting Co.
Editorial: 154 E Simmons St, Galesburg, Illinois 61401. **T:** 1 309 342-5131
E: kfm@1053kfm.com
W: http://www.1053kfm.com
Editorial Profile: WKAY-FM is a commercial station owned by Galesburg Broadcasting Co. The format of the station is adult contemporary. WKAY-FM broadcasts to the Galesburg, IL area at 105.3 FM.

WKAZ-AM
Owner: West Virginia Radio Corp.
Editorial: 1111 Virginia St E, Charleston, West Virginia 25301-2406. **T:** 1 304 342-8131
Editorial Profile: WKAZ-AM is a commercial station owned by West Virginia Radio Corp. The format of the station is oldies. The station broadcasts to the Charleston, WV area at 680 AM.

WKAZ-FM
Owner: West Virginia Radio Corp.
Editorial: 1111 Virginia St E, Charleston, West Virginia 25301-2406. **T:** 1 304 342-8131
W: http://www.1073krock.com
Editorial Profile: WKAZ-FM is a commercial station owned by the West Virginia Radio Corp. The format of the station is classic rock. WKAZ-FM broadcasts to Charleston, WV and surrounding communities at 107.3 FM.

WKBA-AM
Owner: Moran (David)
Editorial: 2043 10th St NE, Roanoke, Virginia 24012. **T:** 1 540 343-5597 **E:** wkba@cox.net
W: http://www.wkbaradio.com
Editorial Profile: WKBA-AM is a commercial station owned by David Moran. The format of the station is religious and gospel. WKBA-AM broadcasts to the Roanoke, VA area at 1550 AM.

WKBB-FM
Owner: TeleSouth Communications Inc.
Editorial: 201 Academy Rd, Ste 4, Starkville, Mississippi 39759. **T:** 1 662 494-1450
W: http://www.supertalkms.com
Editorial Profile: WKBB-FM is a commercial station owned by TeleSouth Communications Inc. The format of the station is talk. WKBB-FM broadcasts in the Starkville, MS area at 100.9 FM.

WKBC-AM
Owner: Wilkes Broadcasting
Editorial: 400 C St, North Wilkesboro, North Carolina 28659-4326. **T:** 1 336 667-2221
E: wkbcam@charter.net
Editorial Profile: WKBC-AM is a commercial station owned by Wilkes Broadcasting. The format of the station is classic country. WKBC-AM broadcasts to the Greensboro-Winston Salem, NC area at 800 AM.

WKBC-FM
Owner: Wilkes Broadcasting
Editorial: 400 C St, North Wilkesboro, North Carolina 28659-4326. **T:** 1 336 667-2221
E: myhitsongs@gmail.com
Editorial Profile: WKBC-FM is a commercial station owned by Wilkes Broadcasting. The format of the station is hot adult contemporary. WKBC-FM broadcasts to the North Wilkesboro, NC area at 97.3 FM.

WKBE-FM
Owner: Pamal Broadcasting Ltd.
Editorial: 89 Everts Ave, Queensbury, New York 12804-2040. **T:** 1 518 793-7733
W: http://www.froggy107.com/
Editorial Profile: WKBE-FM is a commercial station owned by Pamal Broadcasting Ltd. The format of the station is Hot AC. WKBE-FM broadcasts to the Glens Falls, NY area at 100.3 FM.

WKBF-AM
Owner: La Jefa Latino Broadcasting
Editorial: 1035 Lincoln Rd, Ste 205, Bettendorf, Iowa 52722-4149.
T: 1 563 355-7974
E: latinobroadcasting@live.com
W: http://www.lajefa1270.com/
Editorial Profile: WKBF-AM is a commercial station owned by La Jefa Latino Broadcasting. The format of the station is regional Mexican. WKBF-AM broadcasts to the Davenport, IA area at 1270 AM.

WKBH-AM
Owner: Starboard Media Foundation Inc.
Editorial: 701 S High Point Rd, Madison, Wisconsin 53719-3523. **T:** 1 608 779-4418
E: info@relevantradio.com
W: http://www.relevantradio.com
Editorial Profile: WKBH-AM is a non-commercial station owned by Starboard Media Foundation Inc. The format of the station is religious. WKBH-AM broadcasts to the Onalaska, WI area at 1570 AM.

WKBH-FM
Owner: Mississippi Valley Broadcasters LLC
Editorial: 1407 2nd Ave N, Onalaska, Wisconsin 54650. **T:** 1 608 782-8335
E: news@lacrosseradiogroup.net
W: http://www.classicrock1001.com
Editorial Profile: WKBH-FM is a commercial station owned by Mississippi Valley Broadcasters LLC. The format of the station is classic rock. WKBH-FM broadcasts to the Onalaska, WI area at 100.1 FM.

WKBI-AM
Owner: Allegheny Mountain Network
Editorial: 14902 Boot Jack Road, Ridgway, Pennsylvania 15853. **T:** 1 814 834-2821
E: info@wkbiradio.com
W: http://www.wkbiradio.com/
Editorial Profile: WKBI-AM is a commercial station owned by Allegheny Mountain Network. The format of the station is oldies music. WKBI-AM broadcasts to the Saint Marys, PA area at 93.9 FM.

WKBI-FM
Owner: Allegheny Mountain Network
Editorial: 137 Melody Rd, Saint Marys, Pennsylvania 15857-2607. **T:** 1 814 834-2821
E: info@wkbiradio.com
W: http://www.wkbiradio.com
Editorial Profile: WKBI-FM is a commercial station owned by Allegheny Mountain Network. The format of the station is hot adult contemporary music. WKBI-FM broadcasts to the Saint Marys, PA area at 93.9 FM.

WKBK-AM
Owner: Saga Communications
Editorial: 69 Stanhope Ave, Keene, New Hampshire 3431. **T:** 1 603 352-9230
W: http://www.wkbkam.com
Editorial Profile: WKBK-AM is a commercial station owned by Saga Communications. The format of the station is news and talk. WKBK-AM broadcasts to the Boston area at 1290 AM.

WKBL-AM
Owner: Covington Broadcasting Inc.
Editorial: 101 Wkbl Dr, Covington, Tennessee 38019. **T:** 1 901 476-7129
W: http://www.us51country.com
Editorial Profile: WKBL-AM is commercial station owned by Covington Broadcasting Inc. The format of the station is classic country. WKBL-AM broadcasts to the Covington, TN area at 1250 AM.

WKBN-AM
Owner: Clear Channel Media and Entertainment
Editorial: 7461 South Ave, Youngstown, Ohio 44512. **T:** 1 330 965-0057
W: http://www.570wkbn.com
Editorial Profile: WKBN-AM is a commercial station owned by Clear Channel Media and Entertainment. The format of the station is news, sports, and talk. WKBN-AM broadcasts to the Youngstown, OH area at 570 AM.

WKBO-AM
Owner: One Heart Ministries
Editorial: 600 Corporate Cir, Harrisburg, Pennsylvania 17110. **T:** 1 717 697-6463
E: oneheartministries@verizon.net
W: http://www.oneheartministries.com
Editorial Profile: WKBO-AM is a commercial station owned by One Heart Ministries. The format of the station is contemporary Christian. WKBO-AM broadcasts to the greater Harrisburg, PA area at 1230 AM.

WKBQ-FM
Owner: Covington Broadcasting Inc.
Editorial: 101 Wkbl Dr, Covington, Tennessee 38019-1581. **T:** 1 901 476-7129
W: http://www.us51country.com
Editorial Profile: WKBQ-FM is a commercial station owned by Covington Broadcasting Inc. The format of the station is contemporary and classic country. WKBQ-FM broadcasts to the Covington, TN area at 93.5 FM.

WKBU-FM
Owner: Entercom Communications Corp.
Editorial: 400 Poydras St, Ste 800, New Orleans, Louisiana 70130. **T:** 1 504 593-6376
W: http://www.bayou957.com
Editorial Profile: WKBU-FM is a commercial station owned by Entercom Communications Corp. The format of the station is classic rock music. WKBU-FM broadcasts to the New Orleans m area at 95.7 FM.

WKBV-AM
Owner: Whitewater Broadcasting
Editorial: 2301 W Main St, Richmond, Indiana 47374-3829. **T:** 1 765 962-6533
E: psa@g1013.com **W:** http://g1013.com
Editorial Profile: WKBV-AM is a commercial station owned by Whitewater Broadcasting. The format of the station is news, talk and sports. WKBV-AM broadcasts to the Richmond, IN area at 1490 AM.

WKBX-FM
Owner: Neal Ardman
Editorial: 111 N Grove Blvd, Kingsland, Georgia 31548-6347. **T:** 1 912 729-6000
E: wkbx@k-bay106.com
W: http://kbay1063.com
Editorial Profile: WKBX-FM is a commercial station owned by Neal Ardman. The format of the station is country music. WKBX-FM broadcasts to the Jacksonville, FL area at 106.3 FM.

WKBY-AM
Owner: Lawrence G. Campbell Se.
Editorial: 12932 US Highway 29, Chatham, Virginia 24531. **T:** 1 434 432-8108
E: wkby@gamewood.net
Editorial Profile: WKBY-AM is a commercial station owned by Lawrence G. Campbell Se.. The format of the station is gospel. WKBY-AM broadcasts to the Chatham, VA area at 1080 AM.

WKBZ-AM
Owner: Clear Channel Media and Entertainment
Editorial: 3565 Green St, Muskegon, Michigan 49444. **T:** 1 231 733-2600
W: http://www.newstalk1090.com
Editorial Profile: WKBZ-AM is a commercial station owned by Clear Channel Media and Entertainment. The format of the station is news and talk. WKBZ-AM broadcasts to the Muskegon, MI area at 1090 AM.

WKCA-FM
Owner: Gateway Radio Works Inc.
Editorial: 123 E 1St St, Morehead, Kentucky 40351-1701. **T:** 1 606 674-2266
Editorial Profile: WKCA-FM is a commercial station owned by Gateway Radio Works Inc. The format of the station is country. WKCA-FM broadcasts to the Georgetown, OH area at 97.7 FM.

WKCB-AM
Owner: Hindman Broadcasting
Editorial: 1517 Highway 550 W, Hindman, Kentucky 41822. **T:** 1 606 785-3129
W: http://www.wkcb.com
Editorial Profile: WKCB-AM is a commercial station owned by Hindman Broadcasting. The format of the station is Christian talk and music. WKCB-AM broadcasts in the Hindman, KY area at 1340 AM.

WKCB-FM
Owner: Hindman Broadcasting
Editorial: 1570 Highway 550 W, Hindman, Kentucky 41822-8830. **T:** 1 606 785-3129
W: http://www.wkcb.com
Editorial Profile: WKCB-FM is a commercial station owned by Hindman Broadcasting. The format of the station is classic rock and adult contemporary music. WKCB-FM broadcasts to the Lexington, KY area at 107.1 FM.

WKCC-FM
Owner: Kankakee Community College
Editorial: 100 College Dr, Kankakee, Illinois 60901-6505. **T:** 1 815 802-8232
E: wkcc@kcc.edu
W: http://www.wkccradio.org
Editorial Profile: WKCC-FM is a non-commercial station owned by Kankakee Community College. The format of the station is classical and jazz music, news and talk. WKCC-FM broadcasts to the Kankakee, IL area at 91.1 FM.

WKCE-AM
Owner: Kirkland Wireless Broadcasters Inc.
Editorial: 9040 Executive Park Dr Ste 303, Knoxville, Tennessee 37923-4639.
T: 1 865 243-2877
Editorial Profile: WKCE-AM is a commercial station owned by Kirkland Wireless Broadcasters Inc. The format of the station is Spanish sports. WKCE-AM broadcasts to the Knoxville, TN area at 1120 AM.

WKCH-FM
Owner: NRG Media LLC
Editorial: W6355 Eastern Ave, Fort Atkinson, Wisconsin 53538-9335. **T:** 1 920 563-9329
Editorial Profile: WKCH-FM is a commercial station owned by NRG Media LLC. The format of the station is oldies. WKCH-FM broadcasts to the Milwaukee area at 106.5 FM.

WKCI-AM
Owner: Clear Channel Media and Entertainment
Editorial: 207 University Blvd, Harrisonburg, Virginia 22801-3749. **T:** 1 540 434-1777
W: http://www.wkcyam.com

Editorial Profile: WKCI-AM is a commercial station owned by Clear Channel Media and Entertainment. The format of the station is talk. WKCI-AM broadcasts to the Harrisonburg, VA area at 970 AM.

WKCI-FM
Owner: Clear Channel Media and Entertainment
Editorial: 495 Benham St, Hamden, Connecticut 06514-2009. **T:** 1 203 281-9600
W: http://www.kc101.com
Editorial Profile: WKCI-FM is a commercial station owned by Clear Channel Media and Entertainment. The format of the station is Top 40/CHR music. WCKI-FM broadcasts to the Hartford-New Haven, CT area at 101.3 FM.

WKCL-FM
Owner: Chapel of the Holy Spirit Church and Bible College
Editorial: 528 College Park Rd, Ladson, South Carolina 29456-3328. **T:** 1 843 553-1525
E: info@wkclradio.com
W: http://www.wkclradio.com
Editorial Profile: WKCL-FM is a non-commercial station owned by Chapel of the Holy Spirit Church and Bible College. The format of the station is religious programming. WKCL-FM broadcasts to the Charleston, SC area at 91.5 FM.

WKCM-AM
Owner: Cromwell Group Inc.(The)
Editorial: 1115 Tamarack Rd, Owensboro, Kentucky 42301-6984. **T:** 1 270 683-5200
E: kyproduction@cromwellradio.com
W: http://www.owensbororadio.com
Editorial Profile: WKCM-AM is a commercial station owned by the Cromwell Group Inc. The format of the station is country music. WKCM-AM broadcasts to the Owensboro, KY area at 1160 AM.

WKCN-FM
Owner: PMB Broadcasting, LLC
Editorial: 1820 Wynnton Rd, Columbus, Georgia 31906-2930. **T:** 1 706 327-1217
W: http://www.ilovekissin.com
Editorial Profile: WKCN-FM is a commercial station owned by PMB Broadcasting, LLC. The format of the station is country. WKCN-FM broadcasts to the Columbus, GA area at 99.3 FM.

WKCO-FM
Owner: Kenyon College
Editorial: Kenyon College, Farr Hall Basement, Gambier, Ohio 43022. **T:** 1 740 427-5412
E: wkco@kenyon.edu
W: http://wkco.kenyon.edu
Editorial Profile: WKCO-FM is a non-commercial station owned by Kenyon College. The format of the station is college variety. WKCO-FM broadcasts to the Gambier, OH area at 91.9 FM.

WKCP-FM
Owner: American Public Media Group
Editorial: 330 Himmarshee St, Ste 207, Fort Lauderdale, Florida 33312-1712.
T: 1 954 522-8755
W: http://www.classicalsouthflorida.org
Editorial Profile: WKCP-FM is a non-commercial station owned by American Public Media Group. The format of the station is classical music. WKCP-FM broadcasts to the Pompano Beach, FL area at 89.7 FM.

WKCQ-FM
Owner: MacDonald Broadcasting Co.
Editorial: 2000 Whittier St, Saginaw, Michigan 48601-2271. **T:** 1 989 752-8161
W: http://www.98fmkcq.com
Editorial Profile: WKCQ-FM is a commercial station owned by MacDonald Broadcasting Co. The format for the station is country. WKCQ-FM broadcasts to the Flint, MI area at 98.1 FM.

WKCR-FM
Owner: Columbia University
Editorial: 2920 Broadway, New York, New York 10027-7164. **T:** 1 212 854-9920
E: news@wkcr.org
W: http://www.studentaffairs.columbia.edu/wkcr
Editorial Profile: WKCR-FM is a non-commercial station owned by Columbia University. The format of the station is college variety. WKCR-FM broadcasts in the New York metro area at 89.9 FM.

WKCS-FM
Owner: Fulton High School
Editorial: 2509 N Broadway St, Knoxville, Tennessee 37917. **T:** 1 865 594-1259
E: wkcs@knoxschools.org
W: http://www.wkcsradio.org

WKCT-AM
Owner: Daily News Broadcasting Co.
Editorial: 804 College St, Bowling Green, Kentucky 42101-2133. **T:** 1 270 781-2121
E: 93news@wdnsfm.com
W: http://www.93wkct.com
Editorial Profile: WKCT-AM is a commercial station owned by Daily News Broadcasting Co. The format for the station is news and talk. WKCT-AM broadcasts to the Bowling Green, KY area at 930 AM.

WKCU-AM
Owner: TeleSouth Communications Inc.
Editorial: 1608 S Johns St, Corinth, Mississippi 38834-6547. **T:** 1 662 286-8451
Editorial Profile: WKCU-AM is a commercial station owned by TeleSouth Communications Inc. The format of the station is sports. WKCU-AM broadcasts to the Corinth, MS area at a frequency of 1350 AM.

WKCW-AM
Owner: Metro Radio, Inc
Editorial: 9540 Godwin Dr, Manassas, Virginia 20110-4165. **T:** 1 703 330-8224
W: http://www.1420wkcw.com
Editorial Profile: WKCW-AM is a commercial station owned by Metro Radio, Inc. The format of the station is adult hits. WKCW-AM broadcasts to the Washington, D.C. area at 1420 AM.

WKCY-AM
Owner: Clear Channel Media and Entertainment
Editorial: 207 University Blvd, Harrisonburg, Virginia 22801-3749. **T:** 1 540 434-1777
W: http://www.wkcyam.com
Editorial Profile: WKCY-AM is a commercial station owned by Clear Channel Media and Entertainment. The format for the station is talk. WACL-FM broadcasts to the Harrisonburg, VA area at 1300 AM.

WKCY-FM
Owner: Clear Channel Media and Entertainment
Editorial: 207 University Blvd, Harrisonburg, Virginia 22801-3749. **T:** 1 540 434-1777
W: http://www.countrykcy.com
Editorial Profile: WKCY-FM is a commercial station owned by Clear Channel Media and Entertainment. The format for the station is country. WKCY-FM broadcasts to the Harrisonburg, VA area at 104.3 FM.

WKDB-FM
Owner: Great Scott Broadcasting
Editorial: 20200 Dupont Blvd, Georgetown, Delaware 19947. **T:** 1 302 856-2567
W: http://www.musicontheb.com
Editorial Profile: WKDB-FM is a commercial station owned by Great Scott Broadcasting. The format of the station is hot AC/modern AC. WKDB-FM broadcasts to the Salisbury, MD area at 95.3 FM.

WKDD-FM
Owner: Clear Channel Media and Entertainment
Editorial: 7755 Freedom Ave NW, North Canton, Ohio 44720. **T:** 1 330 836-4700
W: http://www.wkdd.com
Editorial Profile: WKDD-FM is a commercial station owned by Clear Channel Media and Entertainment. The format of the station is hot adult contemporary music. WKKD-FM broadcasts to the North Canton, OH area at 98.1 FM.

WKDE-AM
Owner: D.J. Broadcasting Corp.
Editorial: 200 Frazier Rd, Altavista, Virginia 24517. **T:** 1 434 369-5588
E: info@kdcountry.com
W: http://www.kdcountry.com
Editorial Profile: WKDE-AM is a commercial station owned by D.J. Broadcasting Corp. The format of the station is talk. WKDE-AM broadcasts to the Altavista, VA area at 1000 AM.

WKDE-FM
Owner: D.J. Broadcasting Corp.
Editorial: 200 Frazier Rd, Altavista, Virginia 24517-1021. **T:** 1 434 369-5588
E: info@kdcountry.com
W: http://www.kdcountry.com
Editorial Profile: WKDE-FM is a commercial station owned by D.J. Broadcasting Corp. The format of the station is country. WKDE-FM broadcasts to the Altavista, VA area at 105.5 FM.

WKDF-FM
Owner: Cumulus Media Inc.
Editorial: 10 Music Cir E, Nashville, Tennessee 37203-4338. **T:** 1 615 321-1067
E: promotions@103wkdf.com
W: http://www.103wkdf.com
Editorial Profile: WKDF-FM is a commercial station owned by Cumulus Media Inc. The format of the station is country music. WKDF-FM broadcasts to the Nashville, TN area at 103.3 FM.

WKDI-AM
Owner: Positive Radio Group
Editorial: 24580 Station Rd, Denton, Maryland 21629-1943. **T:** 1 410 479-2288
E: wkdi@verizon.net
W: http://www.wkdiam840.com
Editorial Profile: WKDI-AM is a commercial station owned by Positive Radio Group. The format of the station is Christian news and talk. WKDI-AM is licensed to Denton, MD and broadcasts to the Delmarva Peninsula area at 840 AM.

WKDJ-FM
Owner: Radio Cleveland Inc.
Editorial: 911 S Davis Ave, Cleveland, Mississippi 38732-3941. **T:** 1 662 627-2281
Editorial Profile: WKDJ-FM is a commercial station owned by Radio Cleveland Inc. The format of the station is hot adult contemporary music. WKDJ-FM broadcasts to the Cleveland, MS, area at 96.5 FM.

WKDK-AM
Owner: Newberry Broadcasting Co.
Editorial: 3000 Hazel St, Newberry, South Carolina 29108-2140. **T:** 1 803 276-2957
E: contactus@wkdk.com
W: http://www.wkdk.com
Editorial Profile: WKDK-AM is a commercial station owned by Newberry Broadcasting Co. The format of the station is adult contemporary and country. WKDK-AM broadcasts to the Newberry, SC area at 1240 AM.

WKDL-AM
Owner: Metro Radio, Inc.
Editorial: 9540 Godwin Dr, Manassas, Virginia 20110. **T:** 1 703 330-8244
E: metroradioinc@msn.com
W: http://www.metroradioinc.com
Editorial Profile: WKDL-AM is a commercial station owned by Metro Radio, Inc. The format of the station is talk. WKDL-AM broadcasts to the Washington, D.C. area at 1250 AM.

WKDM-AM
Owner: Multicultural Radio Broadcasting Inc.
Editorial: 27 Exchange Pl Fl 11, New York, New York 10005-2701. **T:** 1 212 966-1059
W: http://www.mrbi.net/wkdm.htm
Editorial Profile: WKDM-AM is a commercial station owned by Multicultural Radio Broadcasting Inc. The format of the station is variety. The station's programming is broadcast in Chinese Mandarin Monday through Friday and in Spanish on Saturdays and Sundays. WJDM-AM broadcasts to the New York City area at 1380 AM.

WKDO-AM
Owner: Wesley(Carlos)
Editorial: 988 Highway 1649, Liberty, Kentucky 42539. **T:** 1 606 787-7331
Editorial Profile: WKDO-AM is a commercial station owned by Carlos Wesley. The format of the station is classic country. WKDO-AM broadcasts in the Liberty, KY area at 1560 AM.

WKDO-FM
Owner: Wesley(Carlos)
Editorial: 988 Highway 1649, Liberty, Kentucky 42539. **T:** 1 606 787-7331
Editorial Profile: WKDO-FM is a commercial station owned by Carlos Wesley. The format for the station is country. WKDO-FM broadcasts to the Lexington, KY area at 98.7 FM.

WKDP-AM
Owner: Eubanks Broadcasting Inc.
Editorial: 821 Adams Rd, Corbin, Kentucky 40701-4708. **T:** 1 606 528-6617
E: news@wkdp.com
Editorial Profile: WKDP-AM is a commercial station owned by Eubanks Broadcasting Inc. The format of the station is news and talk programming. WKDP-AM broadcasts to the Corbin, KY area at 1330 AM.

WKDP-FM
Owner: Eubanks Broadcasting Inc.
Editorial: 821 Adams Rd, Corbin, Kentucky 40701-4708. **T:** 1 606 528-6617

W: http://www.kdcountry995.com
Editorial Profile: WKDP-FM is a commercial station owned by Eubanks Broadcasting Inc. The format for the station is country. WKDP-FM broadcasts to the Corbin, KY area at 99.5 FM. Submit PSAs via their website.

WKDQ-FM
Owner: Townsquare Media, LLC
Editorial: 117 SE 5th St, Evansville, Indiana 47708-1605. **T:** 1 812 425-4226
W: http://www.wkdq.com
Editorial Profile: WKDQ-FM is a commercial station owned by Townsquare Media, LLC. The format of the station is country music. WKDQ-FM broadcasts to the Evansville, IN area at 99.5 FM.

WKDR-AM
Owner: Lunderville(Barry)
Editorial: 195 Main St, Lancaster, New Hampshire 03584-3035. **T:** 1 603 788-3636
E: kiss102@together.net
Editorial Profile: WKDR-AM is a commercial station owned by Barry Lunderville. The format of the station is classic rock. WKDR-AM broadcasts to the Berlin, NH area at 1490 AM.

WKDU-FM
Owner: Drexel University
Editorial: 3210 Chestnut St, Philadelphia, Pennsylvania 19104-5407. **T:** 1 215 895-5920
W: http://www.wkdu.org
Editorial Profile: WKDU-FM is a non-commercial station owned by Drexel University. The format of the station is college variety. WKDU-FM broadcasts to the Philadelphia area at 91.7 FM.

WKDV-AM
Owner: Metro Radio, Inc.
Editorial: 9540 Godwin Dr, Manassas, Virginia 20110. **T:** 1 703 330-8022
W: http://www.metroradioinc.com
Editorial Profile: WKDV-AM is commercial station owned by Metro Radio, Inc. The format of the station is Regional Mexican. WKDV-AM broadcasts to the Manassas, VA area at 1460 AM.

WKDW-AM
Owner: Clear Channel Media and Entertainment
Editorial: 207 University Blvd, Harrisonburg, Virginia 22801-3749. **T:** 1 540 434-1777
W: http://www.wkdwam.com
Editorial Profile: WKDW-AM is a commercial station owned by Clear Channel Media and Entertainment. The format for the station is classic country. WKDW-AM broadcasts to the Harrisonburg, VA area at 900 AM.

WKDX-AM
Owner: McLaurin Group(The)
Editorial: 310 5th St, Hamlet, North Carolina 28345. **T:** 1 910 582-1997
E: wkdxthespirit@yahoo.com
W: http://www.wkdx.net
Editorial Profile: WKDX-AM is a commercial station owned by The McLaurin Group. The format of the station is religious and gospel music. WKDX-AM broadcasts to the Hamlet, NC area at 1250 AM.

WKDZ-AM
Owner: Ham Broadcasting Co. Inc.
Editorial: 19 Wooldridge Rd, Cadiz, Kentucky 42211-6734. **T:** 1 270 522-3232
E: wkdz@wkdzradio.com
W: http://www.oldies1480.com
Editorial Profile: WKDZ-AM is a commercial station owned by Ham Broadcasting Co. Inc. The format of the station is oldies. WKDZ-AM broadcasts to the Cadiz, KY area at 1110 AM.

WKDZ-FM
Owner: Ham Broadcasting Co. Inc.
Editorial: 19 Wooldridge Rd, Cadiz, Kentucky 42211-6734. **T:** 1 270 522-3232
E: wkdz@wkdzradio.com
W: http://www.wkdzradio.com
Editorial Profile: WKDZ-FM is a commercial station owned by Ham Broadcasting Co. Inc. The format of the station is country music. WKDZ-FM broadcasts to the Cadiz, KY area at 106.5 FM.

WKEA-FM
Owner: KEA Radio Inc.
Editorial: 19784 John T Reid Pkwy, Scottsboro, Alabama 35768-7909.
T: 1 256 259-2341 **W:** http://www.wkeafm.com
Editorial Profile: WKEA-FM is a commercial station owned by KEA Radio Inc. The format of the station is comtemporary country.

WKEA-FM broadcasts to the Scottsboro, AL area at 98.3 FM.

WKEB-FM
Owner: WIGM Inc.
Editorial: 630 S 8th St, Medford, Wisconsin 54451-2017. **T:** 1 715 748-2566
E: k99@k99wigm.com
W: http://www.k99wigm.com
Editorial Profile: WKEB-FM is a commercial station owned by WIGM Inc. The format of the station is classic hits music. WKEB-FM broadcasts to the Medford, WI area at 99.3 FM.

WKEE-FM
Owner: Clear Channel Media and Entertainment
Editorial: 134 4th Ave, Huntington, West Virginia 25701. **T:** 1 304 525-7788
E: 100keefm@clearchannel.com
W: http://www.wkee.com
Editorial Profile: WKEE-FM is a commercial station owned by Clear Channel Media and Entertainment. The format of the station is Top 40/CHR. WKEE-FM broadcasts to Huntington, WV and surrounding communities at 100.5 FM.

WKEI-AM
Owner: Virden Broadcasting Corporation
Editorial: 133 E Division St, Kewanee, Illinois 61443. **T:** 1 309 853-4471
E: regionalradionews@wkei.com
W: http://www.wkei.com
Editorial Profile: WKEI-AM is a commercial station owned by Virden Broadcasting Corp. The format of the station is news and talk. WKEI-AM broadcasts to the Kewanee, IL area at 1450 AM.

WKEK-FM
Owner: Cook County Community Radio
Editorial: 1712 W Highway 61, Grand Marais, Minnesota 55604-7507. **T:** 1 218 387-1070
W: http://www.wtip.org

WKEQ-FM
Owner: Clear Channel Media and Entertainment
Editorial: 101 1st Radio Ln, Somerset, Kentucky 42503-4639. **T:** 1 606 678-5153
E: wsek@clearchannel.com
W: http://www.q97rock.com/main.html
Editorial Profile: WKEQ-FM is a commercial station owned by Clear Channel Media and Entertainment. The format for the station is classic rock. WKEQ-FM broadcasts to the Somerset, KY area at 97.1 FM.

WKES-FM
Owner: Moody Bible Institute
Editorial: 5800 100th Way N, Saint Petersburg, Florida 33708. **T:** 1 727 391-9994
W: http://www.wkes.fm
Editorial Profile: WKES-FM is a non-commercial station owned by Moody Bible Institute. The format of the station is contemporary Christian music and religious talk. WKES-FM broadcasts to the St. Petersburg, FL area at 91.1 FM. Press releases can be sent by fax.

WKET-FM
Owner: Kettering City School District
Editorial: 3301 Shroyer Rd, Kettering, Ohio 45429. **T:** 1 937 499-1688
E: wket@ketteringschools.org
Editorial Profile: WKET-FM is a non-commercial station owned by Kettering City School District. The format of the station is rock alternative. WKET-FM broadcasts to the Kettering, OH area at 98.3 FM.

WKEU-AM
Owner: WLT & Associates
Editorial: 1000 Memorial Dr, Griffin, Georgia 30223. **T:** 1 770 227-5507 **E:** wkeu@aol.com
W: http://www.wkeuradio.com
Editorial Profile: WKEU-AM is a commercial station owned by WLT & Associates. The format of the station is news, sports and oldies music. WKEU-AM broadcasts to the Griffin, GA area at 1450 AM.

WKEU-FM
Owner: WLT & Associates
Editorial: 1000 Memorial Dr, Griffin, Georgia 30223-4446. **T:** 1 770 227-5507
E: info@wkeuradio.com
W: http://www.wkeuradio.com
Editorial Profile: WKEU-FM is a non-commercial station owned by WLT & Associates. The format of the station is news, talk, and sports. WKEU-FM broadcasts to the Atlanta area at 88.9 FM.

WKEW-AM
Owner: Truth Broadcasting
Editorial: 4405 Providence Ln, Winston Salem, North Carolina 27106-3226.
T: 1 336 759-0363
W: http://www.1340thelight.com

WKEX-AM
Owner: Positive Radio Group
Editorial: 145 Jackson St NE, Blacksburg, Virginia 24060. **T:** 1 540 951-9791
E: wkexam@yahoo.com
W: http://www.espnblacksburg.com
Editorial Profile: WKEX-AM is a commercial station owned by Positive Radio Group. The format of the station is sports. WKEX-AM broadcasts to the Blacksburg, VA area at 1430 AM.

WKEY-AM
Owner: Todd P. Robinson, Inc.
Editorial: 508 W Oak St, Covington, Virginia 24426-1942. **T:** 1 540 962-1133
E: wkeywiqo@aol.com
Editorial Profile: WKEY-AM is a commercial station owned by Todd P. Robinson, Inc. The format of the station is countryl. WKEY-AM broadcasts to the Covington, VA area at 1340 AM.

WKEY-FM
Owner: Clear Channel Media and Entertainment
Editorial: 5450 MacDonald Ave Ste 110, Key West, Florida 33040-5903. **T:** 1 305 296-7511
W: http://www.iheart.com/
Editorial Profile: WKEY-FM is a commercial station owned by Clear Channel Media and Entertainment. The format of the station is adult contemporary. WKEY-FM broadcasts to the Key West, FL area at 93.7 FM.

WKEZ-AM
Owner: L & L Broadcasting
Editorial: 900 Bluefield Ave, Bluefield, West Virginia 24701-2744. **T:** 1 304 327-7114
W: http://www.roosterclassiccountry.com
Editorial Profile: WKEZ-AM is a commercial station owned by L & L Broadcasting. The format of the station is classic country. WKEZ-AM broadcasts to the Bluefield, WV area at 1240 AM.

WKEZ-FM
Owner: Clear Channel Media and Entertainment
Editorial: 93351 Overseas Hwy, Ste 2, Tavernier, Florida 33070-2800.
T: 1 305 852-9085 **W:** http://www.iheart.com/
Editorial Profile: WKEZ-FM is a commercial station owned by Clear Channel Media and Entertainment. The format of the station is adult contemporary. WKEZ-FM broadcasts to the Florida Keys, FL area at 96.9 FM.

WKFB-AM
Owner: Broadcast Communications Inc.
Editorial: 1918 Lincoln Hwy, North Versailles, Pennsylvania 15137. **T:** 1 412 823-7000
Editorial Profile: WKFB-AM is a commercial station owned by Broadcast Communications Inc. The format of the station is classic hits music and talk. WKFB-AM broadcasts to the North Versailles, PA area at 770 AM.

WKFC-FM
Owner: Lincoln-Garrard County Broadcasting
Editorial: 222 Daniel Boone Dr, Barbourville, Kentucky 40906-1104. **T:** 1 606 878-1600
W: http://www.wkfcfm.com
Editorial Profile: WKFC-FM is a commercial station owned by Lincoln-Garrard County Broadcasting. The format for the station is variety including classic country, contemporary Christian, classic rock and oldies. WKFC-FM broadcasts to the London, KY area at 101.9 FM.

WKFI-AM
Owner: Town and Country Broadcasting, Inc.
Editorial: 23 E 2nd St, Xenia, Ohio 45385-3415. **T:** 1 937 374-3636
E: myclassiccountry@myclassiccountry.com
W: http://www.wkfi.com
Editorial Profile: WKFI-AM is a commercial station owned by Town and Country Broadcasting, Inc. The format of the station is classic country. WKFI-AM broadcasts to the Wilmington, OH area at 1090 AM.

WKFM-FM
Owner: Elyria-Lorain Broadcasting
Editorial: 10327 US Highway 250 N, Milan, Ohio 44846. **T:** 1 419 609-5961
E: k96@wkfm.com **W:** http://www.wkfm.com
Editorial Profile: WKFM-FM is a commercial station owned by Elyria-Lorain Broadcasting.

The format of the station is country music. WKFM-FM broadcasts to the Milan, OH area at 96.1 FM.

WKFN-AM
Owner: Saga Communications
Editorial: 1640 Old Russellville Pike, Clarksville, Tennessee 37043-1709.
T: 1 931 648-7720
Editorial Profile: WKFN-AM is a commercial station owned by Saga Communications (dba 5 Star Radio Group). The format of the station is sports. WKFN-AM broadcasts to the Nashville, TN area at 540 AM.

WKFP-FM
Owner: Educational Media Foundation
Editorial: 2070 N Palafox St, Pensacola, Florida 32501-2145. **T:** 1 225 612-4927
W: http://www.klove.com
Editorial Profile: WKFP-FM is a non-commercial station owned by Educational Media Foundation. The station's format is contemporary Christian music. WKFP-FM airs in the Pensacola, FL area at 95.7 FM.

WKFR-FM
Owner: Townsquare Media, LLC
Editorial: 4154 Jennings Dr, Kalamazoo, Michigan 49048-1087. **T:** 1 269 344-0111
E: vip.support@townsquaremedia.com
W: http://www.wkfr.com
Editorial Profile: WKFR-FM is a commercial station owned by Townsquare Media, LLC. The format of the station is Top 40/CHR. WKFR-FM broadcasts to the Kalamazoo, MI area at 103.3 FM.

WKFS-FM
Owner: Clear Channel Media and Entertainment
Editorial: 8044 Montgomery Rd, Ste 650, Cincinnati, Ohio 45236. **T:** 1 513 686-8300
W: http://www.kiss107.com
Editorial Profile: WKFS-FM is a commercial station owned by Clear Channel Media and Entertainment. The format of the station is Top 40/CHR. WKFS-FM broadcasts to the Cincinnati area at 107.1 FM.

WKFX-FM
Owner: T K C Inc.
Editorial: 1859 21st Ave, Rice Lake, Wisconsin 54868-9502. **T:** 1 715 736-0991
E: news@fox99.com **W:** http://www.fox99.com
Editorial Profile: WKFX-FM is a commercial station owned by T K C Inc. The format of the station is classic hits. The station broadcasts to the Rice Lake, WI area at 99.1 FM.

WKGA-FM
Owner: Lake Broadcasting, Inc.
Editorial: 1009 Cherokee Rd, Alexander City, Alabama 35010-3918. **T:** 1 256 234-6977
E: wkgaproduction@gmail.com
W: http://www.wkga975.com
Editorial Profile: WKGA-FM is a commercial station owned by Lake Broadcasting, Inc. The format of the station is country. WKGA-FM broadcasts to the Alexander City, AL area at 97.5 FM.

WKGB-FM
Owner: Clear Channel Media and Entertainment
Editorial: 320 N Jensen Rd, Vestal, New York 13850-2111. **T:** 1 607 584-5800
W: http://www.925kgb.com
Editorial Profile: WKGB-FM is a commercial station owned by Clear Channel Media and Entertainment. The format of the station is rock alternative. WKGB-FM broadcasts to the Binghamton, NY area at 92.5 FM.

WKGC-AM
Owner: Gulf Coast Community College
Editorial: 5230 W Highway 98, Panama City, Florida 32401. **T:** 1 850 873-3500
W: http://www.wkgc.org
Editorial Profile: WKGC-AM is a non-commercial station owned by Gulf Coast Community College. The format of the station is classical, news and talk. WKGC-AM broadcasts to the Panama City, FL area at 1480 AM.

WKGC-FM
Owner: Gulf Coast Community College
Editorial: 5230 W Highway 98, Panama City, Florida 32401. **T:** 1 850 873-3500
W: http://www.wkgc.org
Editorial Profile: WKGC-FM is a non-commercial station owned by Gulf Coast Community College. The target audience is listeners, ages 18 to 64. The format of the station is music, talk and news. The station

broadcasts to the Panama City, FL area at 1480 AM and on 90.7 FM.

WKGL-FM
Owner: Cumulus Media Inc.
Editorial: 3901 Brendenwood Rd, Rockford, Illinois 61107. **T:** 1 815 399-2233
W: http://www.967theeagle.net
Editorial Profile: WKGL-FM is a commercial station owned by Cumulus Media Inc. The format for the station is classic rock. WKGL-FM broadcasts to the Rockford, IL area at 96.7 FM.

WKGM-AM
Owner: Positive Radio Group
Editorial: 13379 Great Spring Rd, Smithfield, Virginia 23430. **T:** 1 757 357-9546
E: wkgm940@yahoo.com
Editorial Profile: WKGM-AM is a commercial station owned by Positive Radio Group. The format of the station is religious. WKGM-AM broadcasts to the Smithfield, VA area at 940 AM.

WKGN-AM
Owner: Norsan Group
Editorial: 1017 Cox St, Knoxville, Tennessee 37919. **T:** 1 865 546-7900

WKGO-FM
Owner: Dix Communications
Editorial: 350 Byrd Ave, Cumberland, Maryland 21502-3219. **T:** 1 301 722-6666
E: mail@go106.com **W:** http://www.go106.com
Editorial Profile: WKGO-FM is a commercial station owned by Dix Communications. The format of the station is rock. WKGO-FM broadcasts to the Cumberland, MD area at 106.1 FM.

WKGR-FM
Owner: Clear Channel Media and Entertainment
Editorial: 3071 Continental Dr, West Palm Beach, Florida 33407-3274. **T:** 1 561 616-6600
W: http://www.gater.com
Editorial Profile: WKGR-FM is a commercial station owned by Clear Channel Media and Entertainment. The format of the station is classic rock music. WKGR-FM broadcasts to the West Palm Beach, FL area at 98.7 FM.

WKGS-FM
Owner: Clear Channel Media and Entertainment
Editorial: 100 Chestnut St Ste 1700, Rochester, New York 14604-2418.
T: 1 585 454-4884
W: http://www.1067kissfm.com
Editorial Profile: WKGS-FM is a commercial station owned by Clear Channel Media and Entertainment. The format of the station is Top 40. WKGS-FM broadcasts to the Rochester, NY area at a frequency of 106.7 FM.

WKGX-AM
Owner: Foothills Radio Group, LLC
Editorial: 827 Fairview Dr SW, Lenoir, North Carolina 28645-6023. **T:** 1 828 758-1033
W: http://www.foothillsradio.com
Editorial Profile: WKGX-AM is commercial station owned by Foothills Radio Group, LLC. The format of the station is folk and bluegrass. WKGX-AM broadcasts to the Lenoir, NC area at 1080 AM.

WKHB-AM
Owner: Broadcast Communications Inc.
Editorial: 1918 Lincoln Hwy, North Versailles, Pennsylvania 15137. **T:** 1 412 823-7000
Editorial Profile: WKHB-AM is a commercial station owned by Broadcast Communications Inc. The format of the station is oldies music and talk. WKHB-AM broadcasts to the North Versailles, PA area at 620 AM.

WKHF-FM
Owner: United States CP, LLP
Editorial: 828 Main St Floor, 16th Floor, Ste 1601, Lynchburg, Virginia 24504-1500.
T: 1 434 455-4321 **E:** 937KHF@gmail.com
W: http://www.937khf.com
Editorial Profile: WKHF-FM is a commercial station owned by United States CP, LLP and operated by Radiowerks Broadcasting. The format of the station is Hot AC. WKHF-FM broadcasts to the Lynchburg, VA area at a frequency of 93.7 FM.

WKHG-FM
Owner: Heritage Media of Kentucky Inc
Editorial: 2160 Brandenburg Rd, Leitchfield, Kentucky 42754-7503. **T:** 1 270 259-5692
E: info@k105.com **W:** http://www.k105.com

WKHI-FM

Owner: Great Scott Broadcasting
Editorial: 20200 Dupont Blvd, Georgetown, Delaware 19947-3105. **T:** 1 302 856-2567
E: hotcountry1077@gmail.com
W: http://www.hotcountry1077.com
Editorial Profile: WKHI-FM is a commercial station owned by Great Scott Broadcasting. The format of the station is contemporary country. WKHI-FM broadcasts to the Georgetown, DE area at 107.7 FM.

WKHJ-FM

Owner: Radiowerks, Inc.
Editorial: 407 Lothian St, Mountain Lake Park, Maryland 21550-2909. **T:** 1 301 334-4272
E: office@wkhj.com **W:** http://www.wkhj.com
Editorial Profile: WKHJ-FM is a commercial station owned by Radiowerks, Inc. The format of the station is adult contemporary. WKHJ-FM broadcasts to the Mountain Lake Park, MD area at 104.5 FM.

WKHK-FM

Owner: Summit Media Broadcasting LLC
Editorial: 812 Moorefield Park Dr, Ste 300, Richmond, Virginia 23236. **T:** 1 804 330-5700
W: http://k95country.com
Editorial Profile: WKHK-FM is a commercial station owned by Summit Media Broadcasting LLC. The format of the station is country. WKHK-FM broadcasts to the Richmond, VA area at 95.3 FM.

WKHM-AM

Owner: Jackson Radio Works Inc.
Editorial: 1700 Glenshire Dr, Jackson, Michigan 49201. **T:** 1 517 787-9546
E: news@wkhm.com
W: http://www.wkhm.com
Editorial Profile: WKHM-AM is a commercial station owned by Jackson Radio Works Inc. The format of the station is news and talk. WKHM-AM broadcasts to the Jackson, MI area at 970 AM.

WKHM-FM

Owner: Jackson Radio Works Inc.
Editorial: 1700 Glenshire Dr, Jackson, Michigan 49201. **T:** 1 517 787-9546
E: news@wkhm.com
W: http://www.k1053.com
Editorial Profile: WKHM-FM is a commercial station owned by Jackson Radio Works Inc. The format of the station is adult contemporary. WKHM-FM broadcasts to the Jackson, MI area at 105.3 FM.

WKHQ-FM

Owner: MacDonald Garber Broadcasting Inc.
Editorial: 2095 S US Highway 131, Petoskey, Michigan 49770-9216. **T:** 1 231 347-8713
E: programming@106khq.com
W: http://www.106khq.com
Editorial Profile: WKHQ-FM is a commercial station owned by MacDonald Garber Broadcasting Inc. The format of the station is Top 40/CHR. WKHQ-FM broadcasts to the Petoskey, MI area at 105.9 FM.

WKHR-FM

Owner: Kenston Local School District
Editorial: 17425 Snyder Rd, Chagrin Falls, Ohio 44023-2730. **T:** 1 440 543-9646
E: info@wkhr.org **W:** http://www.wkhr.org
Editorial Profile: WKHR-FM is a non-commercial station owned by Kenston Local School District. The format of the station is adult standards. WKHR-FM broadcasts to the Chagrin Falls, OH area at 91.5 FM.

WKHS-FM

Owner: Kent County School Board
Editorial: 25301 Lambs Meadow Rd, Worton, Maryland 21678-1924. **T:** 1 410 778-4249
E: wkhsradio@gmail.com
W: http://wkhsradio.org
Editorial Profile: WKHS-FM is a non-commercial station owned by Kent County School Board. The format of the station is variety. WKHS-FM broadcasts to the Worton, MD area at 90.5 FM.

WKHT-FM

Owner: Journal Broadcast Group
Editorial: 1533 Amherst Rd, Knoxville, Tennessee 37909. **T:** 1 865 693-1020
W: http://www.hot1045.net
Editorial Profile: WKHT-FM is a commercial station owned by Journal Broadcast Group. The format of the station is urban contemporary. WKHT-FM broadcasts to the Knoxville, TN area at 104.5 FM.

WKHX-FM

Owner: Cumulus Media Inc.
Editorial: 780 Johnson Ferry Rd Fl 5, Atlanta, Georgia 30342-1434. **T:** 1 404 497-4701
W: http://www.kicks1015.com
Editorial Profile: WKHX-FM is a commercial station owned by Cumulus Media Inc. The format of the station is contemporary country. WKHX-FM broadcasts to the Atlanta area at 101.5 FM.

WKHY-FM

Owner: WASK Inc.
Editorial: 3575 McCarty Ln, Lafayette, Indiana 47905-4985. **T:** 1 765 448-1566
W: http://www.wkhy.com
Editorial Profile: WKHY-FM is a commercial station owned by WASK Inc. The format of the station is rock music. WKHY-FM broadcasts to the Lafayette, IN area at 93.5 FM.

WKHZ-AM

Owner: Epcot Broadcasting
Editorial: 306 Port St, Easton, Maryland 21601-4101. **T:** 1 410 723-9100
Editorial Profile: WKHZ-AM is a commercial station owned by Epcot Broadcasting. The format for the station is contemporary playing a variety of music from the 1980s. WKHZ-AM broadcasts to the Ocean City, MD area at 1590 AM.

WKIB-FM

Owner: W. Russell Withers
Editorial: 901 S Kingshighway St, Cape Girardeau, Missouri 63703. **T:** 1 573 339-7000
E: news@withersradio.net
W: http://www.mix965.net
Editorial Profile: WKIB-FM is a commercial station owned by W. Russell Withers. The format of the station is Top 40/CHR. WKIB-FM broadcasts to the Cape Girardeau, MO area at 96.5 FM.

WKIC-FM

Owner: Leslie County Broadcasting
Editorial: 516 Main St, Hazard, Kentucky 41701-1775. **T:** 1 606 436-9898
E: wsgs@windstream.net
W: http://www.wsgs.com
Editorial Profile: WKIC-FM is a commercial station owned by Leslie County Broadcasting. The format for the station is mix of adult contemporary and adult hits. WKIC-FM broadcasts to the Lexington, KY area at 97.9 FM.

WKID-FM

Owner: Dial Broadcasting Inc.
Editorial: 315 Ferry St Ste A, Vevay, Indiana 47043-1189. **T:** 1 812 427-9590
W: http://froggy959.com
Editorial Profile: WKID-FM is a commercial station owned by Dial Broadcasting Inc. The format of the station is country music. WKID-FM broadcasts to the Vevay, IN area at 95.9 FM.

WKII-AM

Owner: Clear Channel Media and Entertainment
Editorial: 24100 Tiseo Blvd, Unit 10, Port Charlotte, Florida 33980-5223.
T: 1 941 206-1188 **W:** http://www.wkiiam.com
Editorial Profile: WKII-AM is a commercial station owned by Clear Channel Media and Entertainment. The format of the station is Classic Country. The station airs locally on 1070 AM.

WKIK-AM

Owner: Somar Communications Inc.
Editorial: 28095 Three Notch Rd, Ste 2B, Mechanicsville, Maryland 20659.
T: 1 301 870-5550 **E:** wkikfm@aol.com
W: http://www.country1029wkik.com
Editorial Profile: WKIK-AM is a commercial station owned by Somar Communications Inc. The format of the station is country music. WKIK-AM broadcasts to the Mechanicsville, MD area at 1560 AM.

WKIK-FM

Owner: Somar Communications Inc.
Editorial: 28095 Three Notch Rd, Ste 2B, Mechanicsville, Maryland 20659.
T: 1 301 870-5550 **E:** wkikfm@aol.com
W: http://www.country1029wkik.com
Editorial Profile: WKIK-FM is a commercial station owned by Somar Communications Inc. The format of the station is contemporary country. WKIK-FM broadcasts to the Mechanicsville, MD area at 102.9 FM.

WKIM-FM

Owner: Cumulus Media Inc.
Editorial: 5629 Murray Rd, Memphis, Tennessee 38119. **T:** 1 901 682-1106
W: http://newstalkfm989.com

Editorial Profile: WKIM-FM is a commercial station owned by Cumulus Media Inc. The format of the station is news/talk. WKIM-FM broadcasts to the Memphis, TN area at 98.9 FM.

WKIO-FM

Owner: D.W.S. Inc.
Editorial: 2301 S Neil St, Champaign, Illinois 61820-7507. **T:** 1 217 351-5300
W: http://www.1079wkio.com
Editorial Profile: WKIO-FM is a commercial station owned by D.W.S. Inc. The format of the station is rock and classic hits. WKIO-FM broadcasts to the Champaign, IL area at 107.9 FM.

WKIP-AM

Owner: Clear Channel Media and Entertainment
Editorial: 20 Tucker Dr, Poughkeepsie, New York 12603-1644. **T:** 1 845 471-2300
W: http://www.newstalkwkip.com
Editorial Profile: WKIP-AM is a commercial station owned by Clear Channel Media and Entertainment. The format of the station is talk. WKIP-AM broadcasts to the Poughkeepsie, NY area at 1450 AM.

WKIQ-AM

Owner: Rama Communications
Editorial: 3765 N John Young Pkwy, Orlando, Florida 32804-3213. **T:** 1 352 483-1090
W: http://www.lagiganteradio.net
Editorial Profile: WKIQ-AM is a commercial radio station that is owned by Rama Communications. The format of the station is Regional Mexican. WKIQ-AM airs locally in Eustis, FL on 1240 AM.

WKIS-FM

Owner: Beasley Broadcast Group
Editorial: 194 Nw 187Th St, Miami, Florida 33169-4050. **T:** 1 305 654-1700
W: http://www.wkis.com
Editorial Profile: WKIS-FM is a commercial station owned by the Beasley Broadcast Group. The format of the station is country music. WKIS-FM broadcasts to the Miami area at 99.9 FM.

WKIT-FM

Owner: Zone Corporation(The)
Editorial: 861 Broadway, Bangor, Maine 04401-2916. **T:** 1 207 990-2800
E: wkit@zoneradio.com
W: http://www.zoneradio.com/wkit
Editorial Profile: WKIT-FM is a commercial station owned by The Zone Corporation. The format of the station is classic rock. WKIT-FM broadcasts to the Bangor, ME area at 100.3 FM.

WKIW-FM

Owner: Educational Media Foundation
Editorial: 1365 Wiley Rd Ste 151, Schaumburg, Illinois 60173-4357.
T: 1 847 991-9400 **W:** http://www.klove.com
Editorial Profile: WKIW-FM is a non-commercial station owned by Educational Media Foundation. The format of the station is Christian contemporary music. WKIW-FM broadcasts locally to the Ironwood, MI area at a frequency of 88.3 FM.

WKIX-FM

Owner: McClatchey Broadcasting Company
Editorial: 4601 Six Forks Rd Ste 520, Raleigh, North Carolina 27609-5210.
T: 1 919 875-9100
W: http://www.kix1029.com

WKIZ-AM

Owner: Seattle Streaming Radio LLC
Editorial: 5016 5th Ave, Key West, Florida 33040. **T:** 1 305 947-8979
E: gerencia@almavision.tv
W: http://www.almavision.tv
Editorial Profile: WKIZ-AM is a commercial station owned by Seattle Streaming Radio LLC. The format of the station is Hispanic religious. WKIZ-AM broadcasts to the Miami and Ft. Lauderdale, FL areas at 1500 AM.

WKJC-FM

Owner: Carroll Broadcasting Co.
Editorial: 523 Meadow Rd, Tawas City, Michigan 48763-9189. **T:** 1 989 362-3417
E: wkjc@wkjc.com **W:** http://www.wkjc.com
Editorial Profile: WKJC-FM is a commercial station owned by Carroll Broadcasting Co. The format of the station is contemporary country music. WKJC-FM broadcasts to the Flint, MI area at 104.7 FM.

WKJG-AM

Owner: Pathfinder Communications Corporation
Editorial: 2915 Maples Rd, Fort Wayne, Indiana 46816. **T:** 1 260 447-5511
E: news@wowo.com
W: http://www.espnfortwayne.com
Editorial Profile: WKJC-AM is a commercial station owned by Pathfinder Communications Corporation, a division of Federated Media. The format of the station is sports. WKJC-AM broadcasts to the Fort Wayne, IN area at 1380 AM.

WKJK-AM

Owner: Clear Channel Media and Entertainment
Editorial: 4000 Radio Dr Ste 1, Louisville, Kentucky 40218-4568 **E:** psa@cclouisville.com
W: http://www.talkradio1080.com
Editorial Profile: WKJK-AM is a commercial station owned by Clear Channel Media and Entertainment. The format of the station is talk. WKJK-AM broadcasts to the Louisville, KY area at 1080 AM.

WKJQ-AM

Owner: Clenney Broadcasting Corp.
Editorial: 109 Iron Hill Rd, Parsons, Tennessee 38363. **T:** 1 731 847-3011
Editorial Profile: WKJQ-AM is a commercial station owned by Clenney Broadcasting Corp. The format of the station is gospel. WKJQ-AM broadcasts to the Parsons, TN area at 1550 AM.

WKJQ-FM

Owner: Clenney Broadcasting Corp.
Editorial: 109 Iron Hill Rd, Parsons, Tennessee 38363-2901. **T:** 1 731 847-3011
W: http://www.q973fm.com
Editorial Profile: WKJQ-FM is a commercial station owned by Clenney Broadcasting Corp. The format of the station is contemporary country music. WKJQ-FM broadcasts to the Parsons, TN area at 97.3 FM.

WKJR-AM

Owner: Ruben's Productions, Inc.
Editorial: 129 N Garrard St, Rantoul, Illinois 61866. **T:** 1 217 893-1460
E: mrgto@quepasanetwork.com
W: http://www.quepasanetwork.com
Editorial Profile: WKJR-AM is a commercial station owned by Ruben's Productions, Inc. The format of the station is Hispanic. WKJR-AM broadcasts to the Rantoul, IL area on 1460 AM.

WKJS-FM

Owner: Radio One Inc.
Editorial: 2809 Emerywood Pkwy Ste 300, Richmond, Virginia 23294-3743.
T: 1 804 672-9299
W: http://kissrichmond.com/
Editorial Profile: WKJS-FM is a commercial station owned by Radio One Inc. The format of the station is urban adult contemporary. WKJS-FM broadcasts to the Richmond, VA area at 105.7 FM.

WKJT-FM

Owner: Premier Broadcasting, Inc
Editorial: 206 S Willow St, Effingham, Illinois 62401-3637. **T:** 1 217 347-5518
E: info@thexradio.com
W: http://www.kjcountry.com
Editorial Profile: WKJT-FM is a commercial station owned by Premier Broadcasting, Inc. The format of the station is country music. WKJT-FM broadcasts to the Effingham, IL area at 102.3 FM.

WKJV-AM

Owner: International Baptist Outreach Mission Inc.
Editorial: 70 Adams Hill Rd, Asheville, North Carolina 28806-3841. **T:** 1 828 252-1380
E: wkjvradio@cleaninter.net
W: http://www.wkjv.com
Editorial Profile: WKJV-AM is a commercial station owned by International Baptist Outreach Mission Inc. The format of the station is gospel. WKJV-AM broadcasts to the Asheville, NC area at 1380 AM.

WKJX-FM

Owner: East Carolina Radio Group
Editorial: 911 Pasonage St Ext, Elizabeth City, North Carolina 27909. **T:** 1 252 335-4379
E: psa@ecri.net
W: http://www.967theblock.com
Editorial Profile: WKJX-FM is a commercial station owned by East Carolina Radio Group. The format of the station is urban contemporary and R & B. WKJX-FM

broadcasts to the Elizabeth City, NC area at 96.7 FM.

WKJY-FM
Owner: Connoisseur Media
Editorial: 234 Airport Plaza Blvd, Farmingdale, New York 11735-3917. **T:** 1 631 770-4200
E: webmaster@liradiogroup.com
W: http://www.kjoy.com
Editorial Profile: WKJY-FM is a commercial station owned by Connoisseur Media. The format of the station is adult contemporary. WKJY-FM broadcasts to the Garden City, NY area 98.3 FM.

WKJZ-FM
Owner: Carroll Broadcasting Co.
Editorial: 523 Meadow Rd, Tawas City, Michigan 48763-9189. **T:** 1 989 362-3417
E: hitsfm@speednetllc.com
W: http://www.hitsfm.net
Editorial Profile: WKJZ-FM is a commercial station owned by Carroll Broadcasting Co. The format of the station is classic hits. WKJZ-FM broadcasts to the Flint, MI area at 94.9 FM.

WKKB-FM
Owner: Davidson Media Group
Editorial: 75 Oxford St Ste 302, Providence, Rhode Island 02905-4722. **T:** 1 401 331-1003
W: http://www.latina1003fm.com
Editorial Profile: WKKB-FM is a commercial station owned by Davidson Media Group. The format of the station is Hispanic. WKKB-FM broadcasts to the Providence, RI area at 100.3 FM.

WKKC-FM
Owner: City Colleges of Chicago
Editorial: 6301 S Halsted St, Chicago, Illinois 60621. **T:** 1 773 602-5544
W: http://www.wkkc.fm
Editorial Profile: WKKC-FM is a non-commercial college station owned by The City Colleges of Chicago. The format of the station is urban contemporary. The station airs in the Chicago area at 89.3 FM.

WKKF-FM
Owner: Clear Channel Media and Entertainment
Editorial: 1203 Troy Schenectady Rd, Latham, New York 12110-1046. **T:** 1 518 452-4800
W: http://www.1023kissfm.com
Editorial Profile: WKKF-FM is a commercial station owned by Clear Channel Media and Entertainment. The format of the station is Top 40. WKKF-FM broadcasts to the Latham, NY area on 102.3 FM.

WKKG-FM
Owner: White River Broadcasting Co., Inc.
Editorial: 3212 Washington St, Columbus, Indiana 47203. **T:** 1 812 372-4448
E: wkkg@wkkg.com **W:** http://www.wkkg.com
Editorial Profile: WKKG-FM is a commercial station owned by White River Broadcasting Co., Inc. The format of the station is country music. WKKG-FM broadcasts to the Columbus, IN area at 101.5 FM.

WKKI-FM
Owner: Schmitmeyer (Paul)
Editorial: 126 W Fayette St, Celina, Ohio 45822. **T:** 1 419 586-7715 **E:** k94@bright.net
W: http://www.k943.com
Editorial Profile: WKKI-FM is a commercial station owned by Paul Schmitmeyer. The format of the station is classic hits music. WKKI-FM broadcasts to the Dayton, OH area at 94.3 FM.

WKKJ-FM
Owner: Clear Channel Media and Entertainment
Editorial: 45 W Main St, Chillicothe, Ohio 45601-3104. **T:** 1 740 773-3000
E: newsroom@wkkj.com
W: http://www.wkkj.com
Editorial Profile: WKKJ-FM is a commercial station owned by Clear Channel Media and Entertainment. The format of the station is country music. WKKJ-FM broadcasts in the Columbus, OH area at 94.3 FM.

WKKL-FM
Owner: Cape Cod Community College
Editorial: 2240 Iyannough Rd, West Barnstable, Massachusetts 02668-1532.
T: 1 508 375-4030 **E:** wkkl247@yahoo.com
W: http://www.capecod.edu/web/wkkl-90.7
Editorial Profile: WKKL is a non-commercial station owned by Cape Cod Community College. The format of the station is variety. WKKL-FM broadcasts to Cape Cod, MA area at 90.7 FM.

WKKN-FM
Owner: Great Eastern Radio, LLC
Editorial: 99 Main St, Keene, New Hampshire 03431-3770. **T:** 1 603 283-1090
W: http://www.kixx.com
Editorial Profile: WKKN-FM is a commercial station owned by Great Eastern Radio, LLC. The format of the station is contemporary country. WKKN-FM broadcasts to the Lebanon, NH area at 101.7 FM.

WKKO-FM
Owner: Cumulus Media Inc.
Editorial: 3225 Arlington Ave, Toledo, Ohio 43614. **T:** 1 419 725-5700
E: k100@k100country.com
W: http://www.k100country.com
Editorial Profile: WKKO-FM is a commercial station owned by Cumulus Media Inc. The format of the station is contemporary country. WKKO-FM broadcasts to the Toledo, OH area at 99.9 FM.

WKKP-AM
Owner: Earnhart Broadcast Co. Inc.
Editorial: 940 Brownlee Rd, Jackson, Georgia 30233. **T:** 1 770 775-3151
Editorial Profile: WKKP-AM is a commercial station owned by the Earnhart Broadcast Co. Inc. The format of the station is classic country. WKKP-AM broadcasts to the Jackson, GA area at 1410 AM.

WKKQ-FM
Owner: Barbourville Community Broadcasting
Editorial: 222 Daniel Boone Dr, Barbourville, Kentucky 40906-1104. **T:** 1 606 546-4128
E: production@wkkqfm.com
W: http://www.wkkqfm.com

WKKR-FM
Owner: Clear Channel Media and Entertainment
Editorial: 915 Veterans Pkwy, Opelika, Alabama 36801-3367. **T:** 1 334 745-4656
W: http://www.kickerfm.com
Editorial Profile: WKKR-FM is a commercial station owned by Clear Channel Media and Entertainment. The format of the station is contemporary country music. WKKR-FM broadcasts to the Opelika, AL area at 97.7 FM.

WKKS-AM
Owner: Brown Communications Inc.
Editorial: 1074 Fairlane Dr, Vanceburg, Kentucky 41179-5403. **T:** 1 606 796-3031
Editorial Profile: WKKS-AM is a commercial station owned by Brown Communications Inc. The format of the station is country music. WKKS-AM broadcasts to the Vanceburg, KY area at 1570 AM.

WKKS-FM
Owner: Brown Communications Inc.
Editorial: 1074 Fairlane Dr, Vanceburg, Kentucky 41179-5403. **T:** 1 606 796-3031
Editorial Profile: WKKS-FM is a commercial station owned by Brown Communications Inc. The format of the station is country music and gospel. WKKS-FM broadcasts to the Vanceburg, KY area at 104.9 FM.

WKKT-FM
Owner: Clear Channel Media and Entertainment
Editorial: 801 Woodridge Center Dr, Charlotte, North Carolina 28217-1908.
T: 1 704 714-9444 **W:** http://www.wkktfm.com
Editorial Profile: WKKT-FM is a commercial station owned by Clear Channel Media and Entertainment. The format of the station is country music. WKKT-FM broadcasts to the Charlotte, NC area at 96.9 FM.

WKKV-FM
Owner: Clear Channel Media and Entertainment
Editorial: 12100 W Howard Ave, Greenfield, Wisconsin 53228. **T:** 1 414 545-8900
W: http://www.v100.com
Editorial Profile: WKKV-FM is a commercial station owned by Clear Channel Media and Entertainment. The format of the station is urban contemporary music. WKKV-FM broadcasts in the greater Milwaukee area at 100.7 FM.

WKKW-FM
Owner: West Virginia Radio Corp.
Editorial: 1251 Earl L Core Rd, Morgantown, West Virginia 26505-5881. **T:** 1 304 296-0029
W: http://www.wkkwfm.com
Editorial Profile: WKKW-FM is a commercial station owned by West Virginia Radio Corp. The format of the station is classic country. WKKW-FM broadcasts in the Morgantown, WV area at 97.9 FM.

WKKX-AM
Owner: RCK 1 Group, LLC
Editorial: 1201 Main St, Wheeling, West Virginia 26003-2850. **T:** 1 304 214-1610
W: http://wkkx.com
Editorial Profile: WKKX-AM is a commercial station owned by RCK 1 Group, LLC. The format of the station is news and talk. WKKX-AM broadcasts to the Wheeling, WV area at 1600 AM.

WKKY-FM
Owner: Music Express Broadcasting
Editorial: 95 W Main St, Geneva, Ohio 44041-1225. **T:** 1 440 466-9559 **E:** wkky@wkky.com
W: http://www.wkky.com
Editorial Profile: WKKY-FM is a commercial station owned by Music Express Broadcasting. The format of the station is contemporary country. WKKY-FM broadcasts to the Geneva, OH are at 104.7 FM.

WKKZ-FM
Owner: Kirby Broadcasting
Editorial: 1006 Martin Luther King Jr Dr, Dublin, Georgia 31021-5065.
T: 1 478 272-9270 **E:** prod927@bellsouth.net
W: http://www.wkkz927.com
Editorial Profile: WKKZ-FM is a commercial station owned by Kirby Broadcasting Co. The format of the station is adult contemporary music. WKKZ-FM broadcasts to the Dublin, GA area at 92.7 FM.

WKLA-AM
Owner: Lake Michigan Broadcasting Inc.
Editorial: 5941 W US Highway 10, Ludington, Michigan 49431-2447. **T:** 1 231 843-3438
Editorial Profile: WKLA-AM is a commercial station owned by Lake Michigan Broadcasting Inc, operated by Synergy Media under LMA. The format of the station is adult contemporary. The station airs locally at 1450 AM.

WKLA-FM
Owner: Lake Michigan Broadcasting Inc.
Editorial: 5941 W US Highway 10, Ludington, Michigan 49431-2447. **T:** 1 231 843-3438
Editorial Profile: WKLA-FM is a commercial station owned by Lake Michigan Broadcasting Inc, operated by Synergy Media under LMA. The format of the station is adult contemporary. WKLA-FM broadcasts to the Ludington, MI area at 106.3 FM.

WKLB-AM
Owner: Barker(Larry)
Editorial: 80 & 421 South, Manchester, Kentucky 40962. **T:** 1 606 598-2445
Editorial Profile: WKLB-AM is a commercial station owned by Larry Barker. The format of the station is country. WKLB-AM broadcasts to the Manchester, KY area at 1290 AM.

WKLB-FM
Owner: Greater Media Inc.
Editorial: 55 William T Morrissey Blvd, Dorchester, Massachusetts 02125-3315.
T: 1 617 822-6200 **W:** http://www.wklb.com
Editorial Profile: WKLB-FM is a commercial station owned by Greater Media Inc. The format of the station is contemporary country music. WKLB-FM broadcasts to the Boston area at 102.5 FM.

WKLC-FM
Owner: WKLC Inc.
Editorial: 100 Kanawha Ter, Saint Albans, West Virginia 25177-2771. **T:** 1 304 722-3308
E: traffic@wklc.com **W:** http://www.wklc.com
Editorial Profile: WKLC-FM is a commercial station owned by WKLC Inc. The format of the station is modern rock music. WKLC-FM broadcasts to Saint Albans, WV and surrounding communities at 105.1 FM.

WKLG-FM
Owner: WKLG Inc.
Editorial: 1460 Jefferson Dr Apt F, Homestead, Florida 33034-2681.
T: 1 305 246-1123 **E:** cs@wklginc.com
W: http://www.wklginc.com
Editorial Profile: WKLG-FM is a commercial station owned by WKLG Inc. The format of the station is adult contemporary. WKLG-FM broadcasts to the Florida City, FL area at 102.1 FM.

WKLH-FM
Owner: Saga Communications
Editorial: 5407 W McKinley Ave, Milwaukee, Wisconsin 53208-2540. **T:** 1 414 978-9000
E: klhstudio@wklh.com
W: http://www.wklh.com
Editorial Profile: WKLH-FM is a commercial station owned by Saga Communications. The format of the station is classic rock. WKLH-FM broadcasts to the Milwaukee area at 96.5 FM.

WKLI-FM
Owner: Albany Broadcasting Co.
Editorial: 6 Johnson Rd, Latham, New York 12110-5641. **T:** 1 518 786-6600
W: http://www.1009thecat.com
Editorial Profile: WKLI-FM is a commercial station owned by Albany Broadcasting Co. The format of the station is contemporary country. WKLI-FM broadcasts to the Latham, NY area at 100.9 FM.

WKLJ-AM
Owner: Sparta-Tomah Broadcasting Co.
Editorial: 113 W Oak St, Sparta, Wisconsin 54656. **T:** 1 608 269-3100
W: http://www.espnlacrosse.com
Editorial Profile: WKLJ-AM is a commercial station owned by Sparta-Tomah Broadcasting Co. The format of the station is sports. WKLJ-AM broadcasts to the Sparta, WI area at 1290 AM.

WKLK-AM
Owner: Quarnstrom Media Group LLC
Editorial: 1104 Cloquet Ave, Cloquet, Minnesota 55720. **T:** 1 218 879-4534
E: wklk@aol.com
Editorial Profile: WKLK-AM is a commercial station owned by Quarnstrom Media Group LLC. The format of the station is adult standards music. WKLK-AM broadcasts to the Cloquet, MN area at 1230 AM.

WKLK-FM
Owner: Quarnstrom Media Group LLC
Editorial: 1104 Cloquet Ave, Cloquet, Minnesota 55720. **T:** 1 218 879-4534
E: wklk@aol.com
Editorial Profile: WKLK-FM is a commercial station owned by Quarnstrom Media Group LLC. The format of the station is classic rock music. WKLK-FM broadcasts in the Cloquet, MN area at 96.5 FM.

WKLL-FM
Owner: Galaxy Communications LP
Editorial: 39 Kellogg Rd, New Hartford, New York 13413-2849. **T:** 1 315 797-1330
W: http://www.krock.com
Editorial Profile: WKLL-FM is a commercial station owned by Galaxy Communications LP. The format of the station is rock music. WKLL-FM broadcasts to the Utica, NY area at 94.9 FM.

WKLM-FM
Owner: WKLM Radio Inc.
Editorial: 7409 Private Road 341, Millersburg, Ohio 44654-9270. **T:** 1 330 674-1953
Editorial Profile: WKLM-FM is a commercial station owned by WKLM Radio Inc. The format of the station is country music. WKLM-FM broadcasts to the Millersburg, OH area at 95.3 FM.

WKLP-AM
Owner: West Virgina Radio Corporation of the Alleganies
Editorial: 15 Industrial Blvd E, Cumberland, Maryland 21502-4106. **T:** 1 301 759-1005
W: http://www.1230espnam.com
Editorial Profile: WKLP-AM is a commercial station owned by West Virgina Radio Corporation of the Alleganies. The format of the station is sports. WKLP-AM broadcasts to the Cumberland, MD area at 1390 AM.

WKLQ-AM
Owner: Cumulus Media Inc.
Editorial: 3375 Merriam St Ste 201, Muskegon, Michigan 49444-3173.
T: 1 231 830-0176 **W:** http://bigtalk1490.com
Editorial Profile: WKQL-AM is a commercial station owned by Cumulus Media Inc. The format of the station is news/talk. WKQL-AM broadcasts to the Muskegon, MI area at 1490 AM.

WKLR-FM
Owner: Summit Media Broadcasting LLC
Editorial: 812 Moorefield Park Dr, Ste 300, Richmond, Virginia 23236. **T:** 1 804 330-5700
W: http://www.classicrock965.com
Editorial Profile: WKLR-FM is a commercial station owned by Summit Media Broadcasting LLC. The format of the station is classic rock. WKLR-FM broadcasts to the Richmond, VA area at 96.5 FM.

WKLS-FM
Owner: Williams Communications Inc.

Editorial: 801 Noble St Ste 30, Anniston, Alabama 36201-0503. **T:** 1 256 453-9898
W: http://www.rock1059.net
Editorial Profile: WKLS-FM is a commercial station owned by Williams Communications Inc. The format of the station is rock. WKLS-FM broadcasts to the Anniston, AL area at 105.9 FM.

WKLT-FM
Owner: Northern Broadcast Inc.
Editorial: 1020 Hastings St Ste 102, Traverse City, Michigan 49686-3457. **T:** 1 231 947-0003
W: http://www.wklt.com
Editorial Profile: WKLT-FM is a commercial station owned by Northern Broadcast Inc. The format of the station is classic rock music. WKLT-FM broadcasts to the Traverse City, MI area at a frequency of 97.5 FM.

WKLV-AM
Owner: Denbar Communications Inc.
Editorial: 950 Kenbridge Rd, Blackstone, Virginia 23824. **T:** 1 434 292-4146
E: wbbc@bobcatcountryradio.com
Editorial Profile: WKLV-AM is a commercial station owned by Denbar Communications Inc. The format of the station is sports. WKLV-AM broadcasts to the Blackstone, VA area at 1400 AM.

WKLW-FM
Owner: B & G Broadcasting Inc.
Editorial: Route 321, Ste 6 Woodland Place, Paintsville, Kentucky 41240-5407.
T: 1 606 789-6664 **E:** news@wklw.com
W: http://www.wklw.com
Editorial Profile: WKLW-FM is a commercial station owned by B&G Broadcasting Inc. The format of the station is hot adult contemporary music. WKLW-FM broadcasts to the Paintsville, KY area at 94.7 FM.

WKLX-FM
Owner: Commonwealth Broadcasting Corp.
Editorial: 1823 McIntosh St, Ste 107, Bowling Green, Kentucky 42104. **T:** 1 270 846-0222
E: bgsamevents@yahoo.com
W: http://www.bowlinggreensam.com
Editorial Profile: WKLX-FM is a commercial station owned by Commonwealth Broadcasting Corp. The format of the station is adult hits. WKLX-FM broadcasts to the Bowling Green, KY area at 100.7 FM.

WKLY-AM
Owner: WKLY Broadcasting Company
Editorial: 2235 Bowersville Highway, Hartwell, Georgia 30643. **T:** 1 706 376-2233
E: wklyradio@hartcom.net
W: http://www.wklyradio.com
Editorial Profile: WKLY-AM is a commercial station owned by WKLY Broadcasting Corp. The format of the station is country music and gospel. WKLY-AM broadcasts to the Hartwell, GA area at 980 AM.

WKLZ-FM
Owner: Northern Broadcast Inc.
Editorial: 1020 Hastings St, Traverse City, Michigan 49686-3457. **T:** 1 231 947-0003
W: http://www.wklt.com
Editorial Profile: WKLZ-FM is a commercial station owned by Northern Broadcast Inc. The format of the station is rock music. The station broadcasts in the Traverse City, MI area at 98.9 FM.

WKMB-AM
Owner: World Harvest Communications, Inc.
Editorial: 120 W 7th St, Ste 201, Plainfield, New Jersey 7060. **T:** 1 908 822-1515
E: harvestproductions1070@gmail.com
W: http://www.harvestradio.net
Editorial Profile: WKMB-AM is a commercial station owned by World Harvest Communications, Inc. The format of the station is gospel music. WKMB-AM broadcasts to the Plainfield, NJ area at 1070 AM.

WKMC-AM
Owner: Handsome Brothers Inc.
Editorial: 2513 6th Ave, Altoona, Pennsylvania 16602-2129. **T:** 1 814 224-7501
W: http://www.1370wkmc.com
Editorial Profile: WKMC-AM is a commercial station owned by Handsome Brothers Inc. The format of the station is oldies music. WKMC-AM broadcasts to the Altoona, PA area at 1370 AM.

WKMD-FM
Owner: Murray State University
Editorial: 2018 University Sta, Murray, Kentucky 42071-3301. **T:** 1 270 809-4359
E: msu.wkms@murraystate.edu
W: http://www.wkms.org

WKMG-AM
Owner: Blakely(Cornell)
Editorial: 1840 Glenn Street Ext, Newberry, South Carolina 29108. **T:** 1 803 405-0111
Editorial Profile: WKMG-AM is a commercial station owned by Cornell Blakely. The format of the station is oldies music. WKMG-AM broadcasts to the Newberry, SC area at 1520 AM.

WKMI-AM
Owner: Townsquare Media, LLC
Editorial: 4154 Jennings Dr, Kalamazoo, Michigan 49048-1087. **T:** 1 269 344-0111
E: vip.support@townsquaremedia.com
W: http://www.wkmi.com
Editorial Profile: WKMI-AM is a commercial station owned by Townsquare Media, LLC. The format of the station is news and talk. WKMI-AM broadcasts to the Kalamazoo, MI area at 1360 AM.

WKMJ-FM
Owner: J&J Broadcasting
Editorial: 326 Quincy St, Hancock, Michigan 49930. **T:** 1 906 482-3700
E: wmplprod@themix93.com
W: http://www.themix93.com
Editorial Profile: WKMJ-FM is a commercial station owned by J&J Broadcasting. The format of the station is hot adult contemporary. WKMJ-FM broadcasts to the Hancock, MI area at 93.5 FM.

WKMK-FM
Owner: Press Communications LLC
Editorial: 2355 W Bangs Ave, Neptune, New Jersey 7753. **T:** 1 732 774-4755
E: news@breezeradio.com
W: http://thunder106.com
Editorial Profile: WKMK-FM is a commercial station owned by Press Communications LLC. The format of the station is country. WKMK-FM broadcasts to the Neptune, NJ area at 106.3 FM.

WKML-FM
Owner: Beasley Broadcast Group
Editorial: 508 Person St, Fayetteville, North Carolina 28301. **T:** 1 910 483-9565
E: production@wkml.com
W: http://www.wkml.com
Editorial Profile: WKML-FM is a commercial station owned by Beasley Broadcast Group. The format of the station is contemporary country music. WKML-FM broadcasts to the Fayetteville, NC area at 95.7 FM.

WKMM-FM
Owner: Mar Pat Corporation
Editorial: 106 E Main St, Kingwood, West Virginia 26537. **T:** 1 304 329-0967
E: wkmmfm@yahoo.com
W: http://www.wkmmfm.com
Editorial Profile: WKMM-FM is a commercial station owned by Mar Pat Corporation. The format of the station is contemporary country music. WKMM-FM broadcasts in the Kingwood, WV area at 96.7 FM.

WKMO-FM
Owner: Commonwealth Broadcasting Corp.
Editorial: 611 W Poplar St Ste C2, Elizabethtown, Kentucky 42701-2483.
T: 1 270 763-0800
E: news@commonwealthbroadcasting.com
W: http://www.kmocountry.com
Editorial Profile: WKMO-FM is a commercial station owned by Commonwealth Broadcasting Corp. The format of the station is adult contemporary. WKMO-FM broadcasts to the Louisville, KY area at 99.3 FM.

WKMQ-AM
Owner: URBan Radio Broadcasting, LLC
Editorial: 5026 Cliff Gookin Blvd, Tupelo, Mississippi 38801. **T:** 1 662 842-1067
W: http://www.wkmqonline.com
Editorial Profile: WKMQ-AM is a commercial station owned by URBan Radio Broadcasting, LLC. The format of the station is news and talk. WKMQ-AM broadcasts to the Tupelo, MS area at 1060 AM.

WKMS-FM
Owner: Murray State University
Editorial: 2018 University Sta, Murray, Kentucky 42071. **T:** 1 270 809-4359
E: msu.wkms@murraystate.edu
W: http://www.wkms.org
Editorial Profile: WKMS-FM is a non-commercial station owned by Murray State University. The format of the station is variety. WMKS-FM broadcasts to the Murray, KY area at 91.3 FM.

WKMT-FM
Owner: Murray State University
Editorial: 2018 University Station, Murray, Kentucky 42071. **T:** 1 270 809-4359
E: msu.wkms@murraystate.edu
W: http://www.wkms.org
Editorial Profile: WKMT-FM is a non-commercial station owned by Murray State University. The format of the station is variety. WMKT-FM broadcasts to the Murray, KY area at 89.5 FM.

WKMX-FM
Owner: Gulf South Communications, Inc.
Editorial: 285 N Foster St Fl 8, Dothan, Alabama 36303-4541. **T:** 1 334 792-0047
W: http://www.wkmx.com
Editorial Profile: WKMX-FM is a commercial station owned by Gulf South Communications, Inc. The format for the station is Top 40/CHR. WKMX-FM broadcasts to the Dothan, AL area at 106.7 FM.

WKNA-FM
Owner: WLGN, LLC
Editorial: 1 Radio Ln, Logan, Ohio 43138-8762. **T:** 1 740 385-2151
W: http://983samfm.com
Editorial Profile: WKNA-FM is a commercial station owned by WLGN, LLC. The format of the station is classic hits. WKNA-FM broadcasts to the Hocking County, OH area at 98.3 FM.

WKNB-FM
Owner: Radio Partners LLC
Editorial: 310 2nd Ave, Warren, Pennsylvania 16365. **T:** 1 814 723-1310
E: info@kibcoradio.com
W: http://www.kibcoradio.com
Editorial Profile: WKNB-FM is a commercial station owned by Radio Partners LLC. The format of the station is country music. WKNB-FM broadcasts to the Warren, PA area at 104.3 FM.

WKNC-FM
Owner: North Carolina State University
Editorial: 343 Witherspoon, Raleigh, North Carolina 27695. **T:** 1 919 515-2401
E: gm@wknc.org **W:** http://www.wknc.org
Editorial Profile: WKNC-FM is a non-commercial station owned by North Carolina State University. The format of the station is variety. WKNC-FM broadcasts to the Raleigh, NC area at 88.1 FM.

WKND-AM
Owner: Gois Broadcasting
Editorial: 135 Burnside Ave, East Hartford, Connecticut 06108-3466. **T:** 1 860 524-0001
W: http://www.goisradio.com/power-1480
Editorial Profile: WKND-AM is a commercial station owned by Gois Broadcasting. The format of the station is urban adult contemporary music and talk. WKND-AM broadcasts to the Hartford, CT area at 1480 AM.

WKNE-FM
Owner: Saga Communications
Editorial: 69 Stanhope Ave, Keene, New Hampshire 03431-1584. **T:** 1 603 352-9230
E: frontdesk@monadnockradiogroup.com
W: http://www.wknefm.com
Editorial Profile: WKNE-FM is a commercial station owned by Saga Communications. The format of the station is hot adult contemporary. WKNE-FM broadcasts to the Boston area at 103.7 FM.

WKNG-AM
Owner: Gradick Communications LLC
Editorial: 1 Golf Course Rd, Tallapoosa, Georgia 30176-3677. **T:** 1 770 574-1060
W: http://www.gradickcommunications.com
Editorial Profile: WKNG-AM is a commercial station owned by Gradick Communications LLC. The format of the station is country music. WKNG-AM broadcasts to the Tallapoosa, GA area at 1000 AM.

WKNH-FM
Owner: Keene State College
Editorial: 229 Main St, Keene, New Hampshire 03435-0001. **T:** 1 603 358-2734
W: http://www.wknh.org
Editorial Profile: WKNH-FM is a non-commercial station owned by Keene State College. The format of the station is college variety. WKNH-FM broadcasts to the Keene, NH area at 91.3 FM.

WKNJ-FM
Owner: Kean University Board of Trustees
Editorial: Kean University, WKNJ Radio, Union, New Jersey 07083-7133.
T: 1 908 737-0450 **E:** wknjfm@gmail.com
W: http://www.wknj903.com
Editorial Profile: WKNJ-FM is a non-commercial station owned by Kean University Board of Trustees. The format of the station is college variety and weekend Spanish music programming. WKNJ-FM broadcasts to the Union, NJ area at 90.3 FM.

WKNL-FM
Owner: Hall Communications
Editorial: 40 Cuprak Rd, Norwich, Connecticut 06360-2008. **T:** 1 860 887-3511
W: http://www.radioroxy.com
Editorial Profile: WKNL-FM is a commercial station owned by Hall Communications. The format for the station is Hot AC. WKNL-FM broadcasts to the Hartford-New Haven, CT area at 100.9 FM.

WKNN-FM
Owner: Clear Channel Media and Entertainment
Editorial: 286 Debuys Rd, Biloxi, Mississippi 39531-2611. **T:** 1 228 388-2323
W: http://www.k99fm.com
Editorial Profile: WKNN-FM is a commercial station owned by WKNN-FM. The format is classic country. The station airs in the Biloxi, MS area at 99.1FM.

WKNO-FM
Owner: Mid-South Public Communications Foundation
Editorial: 7151 Cherry Farms Road, Cordova, Tennessee 38016. **T:** 1 901 325-6544
E: radio@wkno.org **W:** http://www.wknofm.org
Editorial Profile: WKNO-FM is a non-commercial station owned by Mid-South Public Communications Foundation. The format of the station is news, talk and classical music. WKNO-FM broadcasts to the Memphis, TN area at 91.1 FM.

WKNR-AM
Owner: Good Karma Broadcasting
Editorial: 1301 E 9th St, Cleveland, Ohio 44114-1804. **T:** 1 216 583-9901
W: http://www.espncleveland.com
Editorial Profile: WKNR-AM is a commercial station owned by Good Karma Broadcasting. The format of the station is sports. WKNR-AM broadcasts to the Cleveland area at 850 AM.

WKNS-FM
Owner: Craven Community College
Editorial: 800 College Ct, New Bern, North Carolina 28562. **T:** 1 252 638-3434
W: http://www.publicradioeast.org
Editorial Profile: WKNS-FM is a non-commercial station owned by Craven Community College. The format of the station is news and talk. WKNS-FM broadcasts to the New Bern, NC area at 90.3 FM.

WKNU-FM
Owner: WKNU Radio Inc.
Editorial: 2832 Ridge Rd, Brewton, Alabama 36426. **T:** 1 251 867-4824
E: wknubroadcasting@bellsouth.net
W: http://www.wnku.org
Editorial Profile: WKNU-FM is a commercial station owned by WKNU Radio Inc. The format of the station is country music. WKNU-FM broadcasts in the Mobile, AL area at 106.3 FM.

WKNV-AM
Owner: Positive Radio Group
Editorial: 145 Jackson St NE, Blacksburg, Virginia 24060. **T:** 1 540 951-9791
E: wknv@yahoo.com
Editorial Profile: WKNV-AM is a commercial station owned by Positive Radio Group. The format of the station is gospel and religious programming. WKNV-AM broadcasts to the Blacksburg, VA area at 890 AM.

WKNW-AM
Owner: Sovereign Communications LLC
Editorial: 1402 Ashmun St, Sault Sainte Marie, Michigan 49783-2864.
T: 1 906 635-0995
W: http://tunein.com/radio/WKNW-1400-s30319
Editorial Profile: WKNW-AM is a commercial station owned by Sovereign Communications LLC. The format of the station is news and talk. WKNW-AM broadcasts to the Sault Sainte Marie, MI area at 1400 AM.

WKNY-AM
Owner: Townsquare Media
Editorial: 718 Broadway, Kingston, New York 12401-3450. **T:** 1 845 331-1490
E: vip.support@townsquaremedia.com
W: http://1490wkny.com

Editorial Profile: WKNY-AM is a commercial station owned by Townsquare Media. The format of the station is adult contemporary music. WKNY-AM broadcasts in the Kingston, NY area at 1490 AM.

WKNZ-FM
Owner: Eagle's Nest Fellowship Church
Editorial: 9078 Appels Rd, Lincoln, Delaware 19960-3417. **T:** 1 302 422-6909
E: info@887thebridge.com
W: http://www.887thebridge.com
Editorial Profile: WKNZ-FM is a non-commercial station owned by Eagle's Nest Fellowship Church. The format of the station is contemporary Christian programming. WKNZ-FM broadcasts to the Salisbury, MD market at 88.7 FM.

WKOA-FM
Owner: WASK Inc.
Editorial: 3575 McCarty Ln, Lafayette, Indiana 47905-4985. **T:** 1 765 447-2186
W: http://www.wkoa.com
Editorial Profile: WKOA-FM is a commercial station owned by WASK Inc. The format of the station is country. WKOA-FM broadcasts to the Lafayette, IN area at 105.3 FM.

WKOK-AM
Owner: Sunbury Broadcasting Corp.
Editorial: 1227 County Line Rd, Selinsgrove, Pennsylvania 17870-8188. **T:** 1 570 286-5838
E: newsroom@wkok.com
W: http://www.wkok.com
Editorial Profile: WKOK-AM is a commercial station owned by Sunbury Broadcasting Corp. The format of the station is news and sports. WKOK-AM broadcasts to the Sunbury, PA area at 1070 AM.

WKOL-FM
Owner: Hall Communications
Editorial: 70 Joy Dr, South Burlington, Vermont 05403-6118. **T:** 1 802 658-1230
E: kool105@hallradio.com
W: http://www.wkol.com
Editorial Profile: WKOL-FM is a commercial station owned by Hall Communications. The format of the station is classic hits music. WKOL-FM broadcasts to the Burlington, VT area at 105.1 FM.

WKOM-FM
Owner: Middle Tennessee Broadcasting Co. Inc.
Editorial: 315 W 7th St, Columbia, Tennessee 38401. **T:** 1 931 388-3636
E: radio1340@bellsouth.net
Editorial Profile: WKOM-FM is a commercial station owned by Middle Tennessee Broadcasting Co. Inc. The format of the station is oldies. WKOM-FM broadcasts to the Columbia, TN area at 101.7 FM.

WKOR-AM
Owner: Cumulus Media Inc.
Editorial: 200 6th St N, Ste 205, Columbus, Mississippi 39701. **T:** 1 662 327-1183
Editorial Profile: WKOR-AM is a commercial station owned by Cumulus Media Inc. The format of the station is sports. WKOR-AM broadcasts to the Columbus, MS area at 980 AM.

WKOR-FM
Owner: Cumulus Media Inc.
Editorial: 200 6th St N Ste 205, Columbus, Mississippi 39701-4552. **T:** 1 662 327-1183
W: http://www.k949.net
Editorial Profile: WKOR-FM is a commercial station owned by Cumulus Media Inc. The format of the station is country. The station broadcasts to the Columbus, MS area at a frequency of 94.9 FM.

WKOS-FM
Owner: Cumulus Media Inc.
Editorial: 162 Free Hill Rd, Johnson City, Tennessee 37615-3144. **T:** 1 423 477-1000
E: greatcountry@greatcountry1049.com
W: http://channel1049.net
Editorial Profile: WKOS-FM is a commercial station owned by Cumulus Media Inc. The format of the station is Country. WKOS-FM broadcasts to the Johnson City, TN area at 104.9 FM.

WKOV-FM
Owner: Jackson County Broadcasting Inc.
Editorial: 295 E Main St, Jackson, Ohio 45640-1744. **T:** 1 740 286-3023
Editorial Profile: WKOV-FM is a commercial station owned by Jackson County Broadcasting Inc. The format of the station is hot adult contemporary. WKOV-FM broadcasts to the Jackson, OH area at 96.7 FM.

WKOX-AM
Owner: Clear Channel Media and Entertainment
Editorial: 10 Cabot Rd, Ste 302, Medford, Massachusetts 02155-5173.
T: 1 781 663-2500
W: http://www.mia1430.com
Editorial Profile: WKOX-AM is a commercial station owned by Clear Channel Media and Entertainment. The format of the station is Spanish hits. WKOX-AM broadcasts to the Medford, MA area at 1430 AM.

WKOY-FM
Owner: L & L Broadcasting
Editorial: 900 Bluefield Ave, Bluefield, West Virginia 24701-2744. **T:** 1 304 327-7114
W: http://www.theeaglefm.com
Editorial Profile: WKOY-FM is a commercial station owned by L & L Broadcasting. The format of the station is classic rock music. WKOY-FM broadcasts to the Bluefield, WV area at 100.9 FM.

WKOZ-AM
Owner: Boswell Media LLC
Editorial: 1 Golf Course Rd, Kosciusko, Mississippi 39090. **T:** 1 662 289-1050
E: breezy@boswellmedia.net
W: http://www.breezynews.com
Editorial Profile: WKOZ-AM is a commercial station owned by Boswell Media LLC. The format of the station is R&B oldies and classic soul. WKOZ-AM broadcasts to the Kosciusko, MO area at 1340 AM.

WKOZ-FM
Owner: Boswell Media LLC
Editorial: 1 Golf Course Rd, Kosciusko, Mississippi 39090-3267. **T:** 1 601 289-1050
E: submit@boswellmedia.net
W: http://www.kicks98.com
Editorial Profile: WKOZ-FM is a commercial station owned by Boswell Media LLC. The format of the station is country. WKOZ-FM broadcasts to the Kosciusko, MO area at 98.3 FM.

WKPA-AM
Owner: Moran (David)
Editorial: 2043 10th St NE, Roanoke, Virginia 24012. **T:** 1 540 343-5597 **E:** wkba@cox.net
W: http://www.wkbaradio.com
Editorial Profile: WKPA-AM is a commercial station owned by David Moran. The format of the station is religious talk. The station airs locally at 1390 AM.

WKPE-FM
Owner: Cape Cod Broadcasting
Editorial: 737 W Main St, Hyannis, Massachusetts 02601-3422.
T: 1 508 771-1224
E: news@capecodbroadcasting.com
W: http://www.capecountry104.com
Editorial Profile: WKPE-FM is a commercial station owned by Cape Cod Broadcasting. The format of the station is country. WKPE-FM broadcasts to the Cape Cod and Hyannis, MA area at 104.7 FM.

WKPL-FM
Owner: Keymarket of Pennsylvania, LLC
Editorial: 131 Pleasant Dr, Ste 5U, Aliquippa, Pennsylvania 15001. **T:** 1 724 378-1271
W: http://www.picklefm.com
Editorial Profile: WKPL-FM is a commercial station owned by Keymarket of Pennsylvania, LLC. The format of the station is classic hits and classic rock. WKPL-FM broadcasts to the Aliquippa, PA area at 104.3 FM.

WKPO-FM
Owner: Robinson Corporation
Editorial: E7601a County Road Ss, Viroqua, Wisconsin 54665-8502. **T:** 1 608 637-7200
E: wkpo@wkporadio.com
Editorial Profile: WKPO-FM is a commercial station owned by Robinson Corporation. The format of the station is variety hits. WKPO-FM broadcasts to the Viroqua, WI area at 105.9 FM.

WKPQ-FM
Owner: Sound Communications, LLC
Editorial: 1484 Beech St, Hornell, New York 14843. **T:** 1 607 324-1596
Editorial Profile: WKPQ-FM is a commercial station owned by Sound Communications, LLC. The format of the station is country. WKPQ-FM broadcasts to the Hornell, NY area at 105.3 FM.

WKPR-AM
Owner: Kalamazoo Broadcasting Company, Inc.
Editorial: 2244 Ravine Rd, Kalamazoo, Michigan 49004-3506. **T:** 1 616 451-9387
E: wkprradio@sbcglobal.net
Editorial Profile: WKPR-AM is a commercial station owned by Kalamazoo Broadcasting Company, Inc. The format of the station is religious. WKPR-AM broadcasts to the Kalamzoo, MI area at 1440 AM.

WKPS-FM
Owner: Board of Regents of Pennsylvania State University
Editorial: 125 HUB-Robeson Center, University Park, Pennsylvania 16802. **T:** 1 814 865-7983
E: lion-officers@psu.edu
W: http://www.thelion.fm
Editorial Profile: WKPS-FM is a non-commercial station owned by the Board of Regents of Pennsylvania State University. The format of the station includes music, news, talk, and sports. WKPS-FM broadcasts to the students of Penn State University at 90.7 FM.

WKPT-AM
Owner: Holston Valley Broadcasting Corp.
Editorial: 222 Commerce St, Kingsport, Tennessee 37660-4319. **T:** 1 423 246-9578
W: http://www.wkptam.com
Editorial Profile: WKPT-AM is a commercial station owned by Holston Valley Broadcasting Corp. The format of the station is sports. WKPT-AM broadcasts to the Kingsport, TN area at 1400 AM.

WKPW-FM
Owner: State of Indiana/Eder Vocational Center
Editorial: 8149 W U.S. 40, Knightstown, Indiana 46148. **T:** 1 765 345-9070
E: wkpw@wkpwfm.com
W: http://www.wkpw.net
Editorial Profile: WKPW-FM is a non-commercial station owned by State of Indiana/ Eder Vocational Center. The format of the station is classic hits. WKPW-FM broadcasts to the Knightstown, IN area at 90.7 FM.

WKPX-FM
Owner: Broward County School Board
Editorial: 8000 NW 44th St, Lauderhill, Florida 33351. **T:** 1 754 322-1700
W: http://www.wkpx.freeservers.com
Editorial Profile: WKPX-FM is a non-commercial station owned by Broward County School Board. The format of the station is rock alternative. WKPX-FM broadcasts to the Lauderhill, FL area at 88.5 FM.

WKQA-AM
Owner: Word Broadcasting Network, Inc.
Editorial: 700 Monticello Ave, Norfolk, Virginia 23510-2517. **T:** 1 757 622-9256
Editorial Profile: WKQA-AM is a commericial station owned by Word Broadcasting Network, Inc. The format of the station is Christian talk and religious. WKQA-AM broadcasts to the Norfolk, VA area at 1110 AM.

WKQB-FM
Owner: West Virginia-Virginia Holding Co, LLC
Editorial: 18385 Coal Heritage Rd, Welch, West Virginia 24801-9773. **T:** 1 304 436-2131
W: http://www.kissfmnow.com
Editorial Profile: WKQB-FM is a commercial station owned by West Virginia-Virginia Holding Co, LLC. The format of the station is Top 40/CHR. WKQB-FM broadcasts to the Welch, WV area at 102.9 FM.

WKQC-FM
Owner: CBS Radio
Editorial: 1520 South Blvd, Ste 300, Charlotte, North Carolina 28203-3701.
T: 1 704 522-1103 **W:** http://www.k1047.com
Editorial Profile: WKQC-FM is a commercial station owned by CBS Radio. The format of the station is adult contemporary. WKQC-FM broadcasts to the Charlotte, NC area at 104.7 FM.

WKQH-FM
Owner: Muzzy Broadcasting
Editorial: 500 Division St, Stevens Point, Wisconsin 54481. **T:** 1 715 341-9800
W: http://www.b1049.com
Editorial Profile: WKQH-FM is a commercial station owned by Muzzy Broadcasting. The format of the station is country music. WKQH-FM broadcasts to the Wausau, WI area at 104.9 FM.

WKQI-FM
Owner: Clear Channel Media and Entertainment
Editorial: 27675 Halsted Rd, Farmington Hills, Michigan 48331-3511. **T:** 1 248 324-5800
W: http://www.channel955.com
Editorial Profile: WKQI-FM is a commercial station owned by Clear Channel Media and Entertainment. The format of the station is Top 40/CHR. WKQI-FM broadcasts to the Detroit area at 95.5 FM.

WKQK-FM
Owner: Entercom Communications Corp.
Editorial: 1835 Moriah Woods Blvd., Building 1, Memphis, Tennessee 38117.
T: 1 901 384-5900 **W:** http://www.941kqk.com
Editorial Profile: WKQK-FM is a commercial station owned by Entercom Communications Corp. The format of the station is classic hits. WKQK-FM broadcasts to the Memphis, TN area at 94.1 FM.

WKQL-FM
Owner: Renda Broadcasting
Editorial: 904 N Main St, Punxsutawney, Pennsylvania 15767. **T:** 1 814 938-6000
W: http://www.kool1033fm.com
Editorial Profile: WKQL-FM is a commercial station owned by Renda Broadcasting. The format of the station is classic rock. WKQL-FM broadcasts to the Punxsutawney, PA area at 103.3 FM.

WKQQ-FM
Owner: Clear Channel Media and Entertainment
Editorial: 2601 Nicholasville Rd, Lexington, Kentucky 40503-3307. **T:** 1 859 422-1000
W: http://www.wkqq.com
Editorial Profile: WKQQ-FM is a commercial station owned by Clear Channel Media and Entertainment. The format of the station is rock. WKQQ-FM broadcasts to the Lexington, KY area at 100.1 FM.

WKQR-FM
Owner: West Virginia-Virginia Holding Co, LLC
Editorial: 213A Howard Ave, Mullens, West Virginia 25882-1420. **T:** 1 304 294-4405
W: http://www.kissfmnow.com
Editorial Profile: WKQR-FM is a commercial station owned by West Virginia-Virginia Holding Co, LLC. The format of the station is Top 40/CHR. WKQR-FM broadcasts in the Bluefeld, WV area at 92.7 FM.

WKQS-FM
Owner: Great Lakes Radio Inc.
Editorial: 3060 Us Highway 41 W, Marquette, Michigan 49855-2293. **T:** 1 906 228-6800
E: contact@broadcasteverywhere.com
W: http://www.wkqsfm.com
Editorial Profile: WKQS-FM-FM is a commercial station owned by Great Lakes Radio Inc. The format for the station is easy listening music. WKQS-FM broadcasts to the Marquette, MI area at 101.9 FM.

WKQV-FM
Owner: Summit Media Broadcasting LLC
Editorial: 180 Main St, Sutton, West Virginia 26601. **T:** 1 304 765-7373
E: mail@105kqv.com
W: http://www.105kqv.com
Editorial Profile: WKQV-FM is a commercial station owned by Summit Media Broadcasting LLC. The format of the station is rock and classic rock. WKQV-FM broadcasts to the Sutton, WV area at 105.5 FM.

WKQW-AM
Owner: Clarion County Broadcasting Corp.
Editorial: 806C Grandview Road, Oil City, Pennsylvania 16301-1321. **T:** 1 814 676-8254
E: info@kqw.com
W: http://www.venangocountydailynews.com
Editorial Profile: WKQW-AM is a commercial station owned by Clarion County Broadcasting Corp. The format of the station is sports. WKQW-AM broadcasts to the Oil City, PA area at 1120 AM.

WKQW-FM
Owner: Clarion County Broadcasting Corp.
Editorial: 806C Grandview Road, Oil City, Pennsylvania 16301-1337. **T:** 1 814 676-8254
E: kqwtraffic@usachoice.net
W: http://www.venangocountydailynews.com
Editorial Profile: WKQW-FM is a commercial station owned by Clarion County Broadcasting Corp. The format of the station is adult contemporary. WKQW-FM broadcasts to the Oil City, PA area at 96.3 FM.

WKQX-FM
Owner: Cumulus Media
Editorial: 222 Merchandise Mart Plz Ste 230, Chicago, Illinois 60654-1008.
T: 1 312 527-8348
W: http://www.101WKQX.com
Editorial Profile: WKQX-FM is a commercial station owned by Cumulus Media. The station

airs an alternative rock format. WKQX-FM broadcasts to the Chicago area at 101.1 FM.

WKQY-FM
Owner: L & L Broadcasting
Editorial: 900 Bluefield Ave, Bluefield, West Virginia 24701-2744. **T:** 1 304 327-7114
W: http://www.theeaglefm.com
Editorial Profile: WKQY-FM is a commercial station owned by L & L Broadcasting. The format of the station is classic rock music. WKQY-FM broadcasts to the Bluefield, WV area at 100.1 FM.

WKQZ-FM
Owner: Cumulus Media Inc.
Editorial: 1740 Champagne Dr N, Saginaw, Michigan 48604. **T:** 1 989 776-2100
W: http://www.z93kqz.fm
Editorial Profile: WKQZ-FM is a commercial station owned by Cumulus Media Inc. The format of the station is rock/album-oriented rock. WKQZ-FM broadcasts to the Saginaw, MI area at 93.3 FM.

WKRA-AM
Owner: Autry(Billy)
Editorial: 1400 Highway 4 E Ste C, Holly Springs, Mississippi 38635-2140.
T: 1 662 252-1810
Editorial Profile: WKRA-AM is a commercial station owned Independently by Billy Autry. The format of the station is News, Music and Gospel. WKRA-AM broadcasts at a frequency of 1110 AM to the Holly Springs, MS area.

WKRA-FM
Owner: Autry(Billy)
Editorial: 1400 Highway 4 E, Ste C, Holly Springs, Mississippi 38635.
T: 1 662 252-1810 **E:** power927@gmail.com

WKRB-FM
Owner: Kingsborough Community College
Editorial: 2001 Oriental Blvd, Brooklyn, New York 11235-2333. **T:** 1 718 368-4572
E: wkrb903@gmail.com
W: http://www.wkrb.org
Editorial Profile: WKRB-FM is a non-commercial station owned by Kingsborough Community College. The format of the station is Top 40/CHR. WKRB-FM broadcasts to the Brooklyn, NY area at 90.3 FM.

WKRC-AM
Owner: Clear Channel Media and Entertainment
Editorial: 8044 Montgomery Rd, Ste 650, Cincinnati, Ohio 45236. **T:** 1 513 686-8300
W: http://www.55krc.com
Editorial Profile: WKRC-AM is a commercial station owned by Clear Channel Media and Entertainment. The format of the station is news and talk. WKRC-AM broadcasts to the Cincinnati area at 550 AM.

WKRD-AM
Owner: Clear Channel Media and Entertainment
Editorial: 4000 Radio Dr, Louisville, Kentucky 40218-4568. **T:** 1 502 479-2222
W: http://www.790krd.com
Editorial Profile: WKRD-AM is a commercial station owned by Clear Channel Media and Entertainment. The format of the station is sports. WKRD-AM broadcasts to the Louisville, KY area at 790 AM.

WKRD-FM
Owner: Southern Belle, LLC
Editorial: 115 W Main St, Frankfort, Kentucky 40601-2807. **T:** 1 502 875-1130
W: http://www.myfroggy1049.com
Editorial Profile: WKRD-FM is a commercial station owned by Southern Belle, LLC. The format of the station is contemporary country. WKRD-FM broadcasts to the Louisville, KY area on 101.7 FM.

WKRF-FM
Owner: Entercom Communications Corp.
Editorial: 305 Highway 315, Pittston, Pennsylvania 18640. **T:** 1 570 883-9850
W: http://www.wkrz.com
Editorial Profile: WKRF-FM is a commercial station owned by Entercom Communications Corp. The format of the station is Top 40/CHR. WKRF-FM broadcasts to the Pittston, PA area at 107.9 FM.

WKRH-FM
Owner: Galaxy Communications LP
Editorial: 235 Walton St, Syracuse, New York 13202-1533. **T:** 1 315 472-9111
W: http://www.krock.com
Editorial Profile: WKRH-AM is a commercial station owned by Galaxy Communications LP. The format of the station is rock music. WKRH-AM broadcasts to the Syracuse, NY area at 106.5 FM.

WKRK-AM
Owner: Radford Communications, Inc.
Editorial: 427 Hill St, Murphy, North Carolina 28906. **T:** 1 828 837-4332
W: http://www.1320am.com
Editorial Profile: WKRK-AM is a commercial station owned by Radford Communications, Inc. The format of the station is classic country and gospel. WKRK-AM broadcasts to the Murphy, NC area at 1320 AM.

WKRK-FM
Owner: CBS Radio
Editorial: 1041 Huron Rd E, Cleveland, Ohio 44115-1706. **T:** 1 216 861-0100
W: http://www.923thefan.com
Editorial Profile: WKRK-FM is a commercial station owned by CBS Radio. The format of the station is sports news and talk. WKRK-FM broadcasts to the Cleveland area at 92.3 FM. The station does not do interviews since it does not have DJs.

WKRL-FM
Owner: Galaxy Communications LP
Editorial: 235 Walton St, Syracuse, New York 13202. **T:** 1 315 472-9111
W: http://www.krock.com
Editorial Profile: WKRL-FM is a commercial station owned by Galaxy Communications LP. The format of the station is rock alternative music. WKRL-FM broadcasts to the Syracuse, NY area at 100.9 FM.

WKRM-AM
Owner: Middle Tennessee Broadcasting Co. Inc.
Editorial: 315 W 7th St, Columbia, Tennessee 38401. **T:** 1 931 388-3636
E: radio1340@bellsouth.net
Editorial Profile: WKRM-AM is a commercial station owned by Middle Tennessee Broadcasting Co. Inc. The format of the station is adult contemporary music and talk. WKRM-AM broadcasts to the Columbia, TN area at 1340 AM.

WKRO-AM
Owner: Stratemeyer(Benjamin)
Editorial: 1 Mile North on Highway 37, Cairo, Illinois 62914. **T:** 1 618 734-1490
E: info@stratemeyermedia.com
W: http://www.stratemeyermedia.com
Editorial Profile: WKRO-AM is a commercial station owned by Benjamin Stratemeyer. The format of the station is urban adult contemporary. WKRO-AM broadcasts to the Cairo, IL area at 1490 AM.

WKRO-FM
Owner: Black Crow Radio, LLC
Editorial: 126 W International Speedway Blvd, Daytona Beach, Florida 32114-4322.
T: 1 386 255-9300
E: newsdaytonabeach@gmail.com
W: http://wkro931.com
Editorial Profile: WKRO-FM is a commercial station owned by Black Crow Radio, LLC. The format of the station is contemporary country music. WKRO-FM broadcasts to the Daytona Beach, FL area at 93.1 FM.

WKRQ-FM
Owner: Hubbard Broadcasting, Inc.
Editorial: 2060 Reading Rd, Cincinnati, Ohio 45202. **T:** 1 513 699-5102
W: http://www.wkrq.com
Editorial Profile: WKRQ-FM is a commercial station owned by Hubbard Broadcasting, Inc. The format of the station is hot adult contemporary. WKRQ-FM broadcasts to the Cincinnati area at 101.9 FM.

WKRR-FM
Owner: Dick Jr.(James A.)
Editorial: 192 E Lewis St, Greensboro, North Carolina 27406-1459. **T:** 1 336 274-8042
W: http://www.rock92.com
Editorial Profile: WKRR-FM is a commercial station owned by James A. Dick Jr. The format of the station is classic rock. WKRR-FM broadcasts to the Greensboro, NC area at 92.3 FM.

WKRS-AM
Owner: Digity LLC
Editorial: 3250 Belvidere Rd, Waukegan, Illinois 60085-6041. **T:** 1 847 336-7900
W: http://espndeportes1220.com
Editorial Profile: WKRS-AM is a commercial station owned by Digity LLC. The format of the station is Spanish sports talk. WKRS-AM is the ESPN Desportes affiliate for the Waukegan and Lake County areas in Illinois and broadcasts locally at 1220 AM.

WKRU-FM
Owner: Cumulus Media Inc.
Editorial: 810 Victoria St, Green Bay, Wisconsin 54302. **T:** 1 920 468-4100
W: http://www.wkrufm.com
Editorial Profile: WKRU-FM is a commercial station owned by Cumulus Media Inc. The format for the station is adult album alternative. WKRU-FM broadcasts to the Green Bay, WI area at 106.7 FM.

WKRV-FM
Owner: Cromwell Group Inc.(The)
Editorial: 232 S 4th St, Vandalia, Illinois 62471. **T:** 1 618 283-2325
E: wkrv@sbcglobal.net
W: http://vandaliaradio.com
Editorial Profile: WKRV-FM is a commercial station owned by The Cromwell Group Inc. The format of the station is classic hits. WKRV-FM broadcasts to the Vandalia, IL area at 107.1 FM.

WKRX-FM
Owner: Roxboro Broadcasting Co.
Editorial: 2070 Hurdle Mills Road, Roxboro, North Carolina 27573. **T:** 1 336 599-0266
E: wkrx@radioroxboro.com
W: http://www.radioroxboro.com
Editorial Profile: WKRX-FM is a commercial station owned by Roxboro Broadcasting Co. The format of the station is country. WKRX-FM broadcasts to the Roxboro, NC area at 96.7 FM.

WKRZ-FM
Owner: Entercom Communications Corp.
Editorial: 305 Route 315 Hwy, Pittston, Pennsylvania 18640-3907. **T:** 1 570 883-9850
W: http://www.985krz.com
Editorial Profile: WKRZ-FM is a commercial station owned by Entercom Communications Corp. The format of the station is Top 40/CHR. WKRZ-FM broadcasts to the Pittston, PA area at 98.5 FM.

WKSA-FM
Owner: Clear Channel Media and Entertainment
Editorial: 1003 Norfolk Sq, Norfolk, Virginia 23502-3234. **T:** 1 757 466-0009
W: http://www.kissfmvirginia.com
Editorial Profile: WKSA-FM is a commercial station owned by Clear Channel Media and Entertainment. The format of the station is urban AC. WKSA-FM is licensed to Moyock, NC and broadcasts to the Norfolk/Virgina Beach, VA area at 92.1 FM.

WKSB-FM
Owner: Clear Channel Media and Entertainment
Editorial: 1559 W 4Th St, Williamsport, Pennsylvania 17701-5650. **T:** 1 570 327-1400
W: http://www.wksb.com
Editorial Profile: WKSB-FM is a commercial station owned by Clear Channel Media and Entertainment. The format of the station is hot adult contemporary music. WKSB-FM broadcasts to the Williamsport, PA area at 102.7 FM.

WKSC-FM
Owner: Clear Channel Media and Entertainment
Editorial: 233 N Michigan Ave, Ste 2800, Chicago, Illinois 60601. **T:** 1 312 540-2000
W: http://www.kiss1035.com
Editorial Profile: WKSC-FM is commercial station owned by Clear Channel Media and Entertainment. The format of the station is Top 40/CHR. WKSC-FM broadcasts to the Chicago area at 103.5 FM.

WKSD-FM
Owner: First Family Broadcasting Inc.
Editorial: 9070 Mendon Rd, Van Wert, Ohio 45891. **T:** 1 419 238-1220 **E:** wert@bright.net
W: http://www.vanwert.com/wert/
Editorial Profile: WKSD-FM is a commercial station owned by First Family Broadcasting Inc. The format of the station is sports and oldies. WKSD-FM broadcasts to the Van Wert, OH area at 99.7 FM.

WKSE-FM
Owner: Entercom Communications Corp.
Editorial: 500 Corporate Pkwy, Ste 200, Buffalo, New York 14226. **T:** 1 716 843-0600
W: http://www.kiss985.com
Editorial Profile: WKSE-FM is a commercial station owned by Entercom Communications Corp. The format of the station is Top 40/CHR. WKSE-FM broadcasts to the Buffalo, NY area at 98.5 FM.

WKSF-FM
Owner: Clear Channel Media and Entertainment
Editorial: 13 Summerlin Dr, Asheville, North Carolina 28806-2800. **T:** 1 828 257-2700
E: ashevillepsa@clearchannel.com
W: http://www.99kisscountry.com
Editorial Profile: WKSF-FM is a commercial station owned by Clear Channel Media and Entertainment. The format of the station is country. WKSF-FM broadcasts to the Asheville, NC area at 99.9 FM.

WKSG-FM
Owner: Daystar Public Radio Inc.
Editorial: 7 E Silver Springs Blvd Ste 102, Ocala, Florida 34470-6663. **T:** 1 352 369-8950
Editorial Profile: WKSG-FM is a non-commercial station owned by Daystar Public Radio Inc. The format of the station is adult standards. WKSG-FM broadcasts to the Ocala, FL area at 89.5 FM.

WKSI-FM
Owner: Clear Channel Media and Entertainment
Editorial: 510 Pegasus Ct, Winchester, Virginia 22602. **T:** 1 540 662-5101
E: winchesterproductions@clearchannel.com
W: http://www.983kissfm.com
Editorial Profile: WKSI-FM is a commercial station owned by Clear Channel Media and Entertainment. The format of the station is Top 40/CHR music. WKSI-FM broadcasts to Winchester, VA and surrounding areas at 98.3 FM.

WKSJ-FM
Owner: Clear Channel Media and Entertainment
Editorial: 555 Broadcast Dr, 3rd Fl, Mobile, Alabama 36606-2936. **T:** 1 251 450-0100
W: http://www.95ksj.com
Editorial Profile: WKSJ-FM is a commercial station owned by Clear Channel Media and Entertainment. The format of the station is country music. WKSJ-AM broadcasts to the Mobile, AL area at 94.9 FM.

WKSK-AM
Owner: Caddell Broadcasting Inc.
Editorial: 240 Radio Road, West Jefferson, North Carolina 28694. **T:** 1 336 246-6001
E: wksk@skybest.com
W: http://www.580wksk.com
Editorial Profile: WKSK-AM is a commercial station owned by Caddell Broadcasting Inc. The format of the station is country. WKSK-AM broadcasts to the West Jefferson, NC area at 580 AM.

WKSK-FM
Owner: Lakes Media, LLC
Editorial: 16256 Highway 47, South Hill, Virginia 23970. **T:** 1 434 447-4007
W: http://www.rewind1019.com
Editorial Profile: WKSK-FM is a commercial station owned by Lakes Media, LLC. The format of the station is classic hits with a mixture of oldies and rock. WKSK-FM broadcasts to the South Hill, VA area at a frequency of 101.9 FM.

WKSL-FM
Owner: Clear Channel Media and Entertainment
Editorial: 3100 Smoketree Ct Ste 700, Raleigh, North Carolina 27604-1052.
T: 1 919 878-1500
W: http://www.b939online.com
Editorial Profile: WKSL-FM is a commercial station owned by Clear Channel Media and Entertainment. The format of the station is contemporary country. WKSL-FM broadcasts to the Raleigh, NC area at 93.9 FM.

WKSM-FM
Owner: Cumulus Media Inc.
Editorial: 225 Hollywood Blvd NW, Fort Walton Beach, Florida 32548-4725.
T: 1 850 243-7676 **W:** http://www.wksm.com
Editorial Profile: WKSM-FM is a commercial station targeting adults ages 18 to 35. Aired locally on 99.9 FM, the format of the station is rock music and features news, weather, and sports updates on the hour throughout the morning.

WKSN-AM
Owner: Media One Group, LLC
Editorial: 2 Orchard Rd, Jamestown, New York 14701. **T:** 1 716 487-1151
W: http://www.wksn.com

Editorial Profile: WKSN-AM is a commercial station owned by Media One Group, LLC. The format of the station is oldies. WKSN-AM broadcasts to the Jamestown, NY area at 1340 AM.

WKSO-FM
Owner: First Natchez Corp.
Editorial: 2 Oferrall St, Natchez, Mississippi 39120. **T:** 1 601 442-4895
W: http://www.kiss973fm.com

WKSP-FM
Owner: Clear Channel Media and Entertainment
Editorial: 2743 Perimeter Pkwy, Ste 300, Augusta, Georgia 30909-6429.
T: 1 706 396-6000
W: http://www.963kissfm.com
Editorial Profile: WKSP-FM is a commercial station owned by Clear Channel Media and Entertainment. The format of the station is urban adult contemporary. WKSP-FM broadcasts to the Augusta, GA area at 96.3 FM.

WKSQ-FM
Owner: Blueberry Broadcasting
Editorial: 184 Target Cir, Bangor, Maine 4401.
T: 1 207 947-9100
W: http://www.wksqfm.com
Editorial Profile: WKSQ-FM is a commercial station owned by Blueberry Broadcasting. The format of the station is hot adult contemporary. WKSQ-FM broadcasts to the Bangor, ME area at 94.5 FM.

WKSR-AM
Owner: Pulaski Broadcasting
Editorial: 104 S 2nd St, Pulaski, Tennessee 38478-3219. **T:** 1 931 363-2505
E: wksr@igiles.net **W:** http://www.wksr.com
Editorial Profile: WKSR-AM is a commercial station owned by Pulaski Broadcasting. The format of the station is classic country. WKSR-AM broadcasts in the Pulaski, TN area at 1420 AM.

WKSR-FM
Owner: Pulaski Broadcasting
Editorial: 104 S 2nd St, Pulaski, Tennessee 38478. **T:** 1 931 363-2505 **E:** wksr@wksr.com
W: http://www.wksr.com
Editorial Profile: WKSR-FM is a commercial station owned by Pulaski Broadcasting. The format of the station is classic and contemporary country music. WKSR-FM broadcasts to the Pulaski, TN area at 98.3 FM.

WKSS-FM
Owner: Clear Channel Media and Entertainment
Editorial: 10 Columbus Blvd Ste 1, Hartford, Connecticut 06106-1976. **T:** 1 860 723-6000
W: http://www.kiss957.com
Editorial Profile: WKSS-FM is a commercial station owned by Clear Channel Media and Entertainment. The format of the station is Top 40/CHR. WKSS-FM broadcasts to the Hartford, CT area at 95.7 FM.

WKST-AM
Owner: Forever Broadcasting
Editorial: 219 Savannah Gardner Rd, New Castle, Pennsylvania 16101.
T: 1 724 346-5070 **E:** wtsutton@yahoo.com
W: http://www.wkst.com
Editorial Profile: WKST-AM is a commercial station owned by Forever Broadcasting. The format of the station is news, talk and sports. WKST-AM broadcasts to the New Castle, PA area at 1200 AM.

WKST-FM
Owner: Clear Channel Media and Entertainment
Editorial: 200 Fleet St Floor 4, Pittsburgh, Pennsylvania 15220-2908. **T:** 1 412 937-1441
E: feedback@961kissfm.net
W: http://www.kissfm961.com
Editorial Profile: WKST-FM is a commercial station owned by Clear Channel Media and Entertainment. The format of the station is Top 40/CHR. WKST-FM broadcasts to the Pittsburgh area at 96.1 FM.

WKSU-FM
Owner: Kent State University
Editorial: 1613 E Summit St, Kent, Ohio 44242. **T:** 1 330 672-3114 **E:** letters@wksu.org
W: http://www.wksu.org
Editorial Profile: WKSU-FM is a non-commercial station owned by Kent State University. The format of the station is news, classical music and folk music. WKSU-FM broadcasts to the Kent, OH area at 89.7 FM.

WKSW-FM
Owner: Cookeville Communications, LLC
Editorial: 698 S Willow Ave, Cookeville, Tennessee 38501-3802. **T:** 1 931 526-7144
W: http://www.kissfm985.com
Editorial Profile: WKSW-FM is a commercial station owned by Cookeville Communications, LLC. The format of station is Top 40/CHR. WKSW-FM broadcasts to the Cookeville, TN area at 98.5 FM.

WKSX-FM
Owner: Edgefield-Saluda Radio Co. Inc.
Editorial: 102 Slide Hill Rd, Johnston, South Carolina 29832. **T:** 1 803 275-4444
Editorial Profile: WKSX-FM is a commercial station owned by Edgefield-Saluda Radio Co. Inc. The format of the station is oldies. WKSX-FM broadcasts to the Johnston, SC area at 92.7 FM.

WKSZ-FM
Owner: Woodward Communications, Inc.
Editorial: 2800 E College Ave, Appleton, Wisconsin 54915. **T:** 1 920 734-9226
E: kissfm@wcinet.com
W: http://www.959kissfm.com
Editorial Profile: WKSZ-FM is a commercial station owned by Woodward Communications, Inc. The format is Top 40/CHR music. WKSZ-FM broadcasts to the Green Bay, WI area at 95.9 FM.

WKTA-AM
Owner: Polnet Communications
Editorial: 4320 Dundee Rd, Northbrook, Illinois 60062-1703. **T:** 1 847 498-3350
E: polnetradio@gmail.com
Editorial Profile: WKTA-AM is a commercial station owned by Polnet Communications. The format of the station is variety ethnic. WKTA-AM broadcasts to the Chicago area at 1330 AM.

WKTE-AM
Owner: Booth-Newsome Broadcasting
Editorial: 117 WKTE Drive, King, North Carolina 27021. **T:** 1 336 983-3111
Editorial Profile: WKTE-AM is a commercial station owned by Booth-Newsome Broadcasting. The format of the station is oldies music. WKTE-AM broadcasts to the King, NC area at 1090 AM.

WKTG-FM
Owner: Sound Broadcasters Inc.
Editorial: 2380 N Main St, Madisonville, Kentucky 42431. **T:** 1 270 821-1156
E: wktg@wktg.com **W:** http://www.wktg.com
Editorial Profile: WKTG-FM is a commercial station owned by Sound Broadcasters Inc. The format of the station is rock. WKTG-FM broadcasts to the Madisonville, KY area at 93.9 FM.

WKTJ-FM
Owner: Clearwater Communications LLC
Editorial: 121 Broadway, Farmington, Maine 4938. **T:** 1 207 778-3400 **E:** wktj@wktj.com
W: http://www.wktj.com
Editorial Profile: WKTJ-FM is a commercial station owned by Clearwater Communications LLC. The format of the station is variety. WKTJ-FM broadcasts to the Farmington, ME area at 99.3 FM.

WKTK-FM
Owner: Entercom Communications Corp.
Editorial: 3600 NW 43rd St, Ste B, Gainesville, Florida 32606. **T:** 1 352 377-0985
W: http://www.ktk985.com
Editorial Profile: WKTK-FM is a commercial station owned by Entercom Communications Corp. The format of the station is adult contemporary. WKTK-FM broadcasts to the Gainesville, FL area at 98.5 FM.

WKTM-FM
Owner: Good News Network
Editorial: 2278 Wortham Ln, Grovetown, Georgia 30813. **T:** 1 706 309-9610
W: http://www.gnnradio.org
Editorial Profile: WKTM-FM is a non-commercial station owned by Good News Network. The format of the station is Spanish religious. WKTM-FM broadcasts locally at 106.1 FM to the Soperton, GA area.

WKTN-FM
Owner: Radio General Ltd.
Editorial: 112 N Detroit St, Kenton, Ohio 43326-1558. **T:** 1 419 675-2355
E: wktn@kenton.com **W:** http://www.wktn.com
Editorial Profile: WKTN-FM is a commercial station owned by Radio General Ltd. The format of the station is adult contemporary. WKTN-FM broadcasts locally to Columbus, OH at 95.3 FM.

WKTO-FM
Owner: Mims Community Radio Inc.
Editorial: 900 Old Mission Rd, New Smyrna Beach, Florida 32168-8562. **T:** 1 386 427-1095
E: info@wkto.net **W:** http://www.wkto.net
Editorial Profile: WKTO-FM is a non-commercial station owned by Mims Community Radio Inc. The format of the station is religous. WKTO-FM broadcasts to New Smyrna Beach, FL area at 88.9 FM.

WKTP-AM
Owner: Holston Valley Broadcasting Corp.
Editorial: 222 Commerce St, Kingsport, Tennessee 37660-4319. **T:** 1 423 246-9578
W: http://www.wkptam.com
Editorial Profile: WKTP-AM is a commercial station owned by Holston Valley Broadcasting Corp. The format of the station is sports. WKTP-AM broadcasts to the Johnson City, TN area at 1590 AM.

WKTQ-AM
Owner: Gleason Radio Group
Editorial: 243 Main St, Norway, Maine 4268.
T: 1 207 743-5911 **E:** info@woxo.com
W: http://www.wtme.com
Editorial Profile: WKTQ-AM is a commercial station owned by the Gleason Radio Group. The format of the station is contemporary Christian and religious programming. WKTQ-AM broadcasts to the Norway, ME area at 1450 AM.

WKTR-AM
Owner: Positive Radio Group
Editorial: 100 Spotswood Bus Pk Cir, Quinque, Virginia 22965. **T:** 1 434 985-8585
Editorial Profile: WKTR-AM is a commercial station owned by Positive Radio Group. The format of the station is southern gospel. WKTR-AM broadcasts to the Charlottesville, VA area at 840 AM.

WKTT-FM
Owner: Delmarva Broadcasting
Editorial: 919 Ellegood St, Salisbury, Maryland 21801-8433. **T:** 1 410 219-3500
E: catcountry@catcountryradio.com
W: http://www.catcountryradio.com
Editorial Profile: WKTT-FM is a commercial station owned by Delmarva Broadcasting. The format of the station is contemporary country music. WKTT-FM broadcasts to the Salisbury, MD area at 97.5 FM.

WKTU-FM
Owner: Clear Channel Media and Entertainment
Editorial: 32 Avenue of the Americas Fl 3, New York, New York 10013-2473.
T: 1 212 377-7900 **W:** http://www.ktu.com
Editorial Profile: WKTU-FM is a commercial station owned by Clear Channel Media and Entertainment. The format of the station is dance music. WKTU-FM broadcasts to the New York area at 103.5 FM.

WKTX-AM
Owner: Kossanyi (Maria)
Editorial: 11906 Madison Ave, Lakewood, Ohio 44107. **T:** 1 216 221-0330
Editorial Profile: WKTX-FM is a commercial station owned by Nicholas Kossanyi. The format or the station is ethnic. WKTX-FM broadcasts to the Lakewood, OH area at 830 AM.

WKTY-AM
Owner: Midwest Family Broadcasting
Editorial: 201 State St, La Crosse, Wisconsin 54601. **T:** 1 608 782-1230
W: http://www.580wkty.com
Editorial Profile: WKTY-AM is a commercial station owned by Midwest Family Broadcasting. The format of the station is sports. WKTY-AM broadcasts in the La Crosse, WI area at 580 AM.

WKTZ-FM
Owner: Jones College
Editorial: 5353 Arlington Expy, Jacksonville, Florida 32211-5540. **T:** 1 904 371-1184
W: http://wktz.jones.edu
Editorial Profile: WKTZ-FM is a non-commercial station owned by Jones College. WKTZ-FM's format is easy listening music. WKTZ-FM broadcasts to the Jacksonville, FL area at 90.9 FM.

WKUA-FM
Owner: TBTA Ministries
Editorial: 1900 Crestwood Blvd Ste 111, Irondale, Alabama 35210-2060.
T: 1 205 402-4266
W: http://www.myrevradio.com
Editorial Profile: WKUA-FM is a non-commercial station owned by TBTA Ministries. The format of the station features Christian rock and pop music. WKUA-FM broadcasts to the Birmingham, AL area at a frequency of 88.5 FM.

WKUB-FM
Owner: Mattox Broadcasting Inc.
Editorial: 2132 US Highway 84, Blackshear, Georgia 31516. **T:** 1 912 449-3391
E: wkub@almatel.net
Editorial Profile: WKUB-FM is a commercial station owned by Mattox Broadcasting Inc. The format of the station is country. WKUB-FM broadcasts to the Blackshear, GA area at 105.1 FM.

WKUL-FM
Owner: Jonathan Christian Corp.
Editorial: 214 1st Ave SE, Cullman, Alabama 35055. **T:** 1 256 734-0183
E: wkulfm@excite.com
W: http://www.wkul.com
Editorial Profile: WKUL-FM is a commercial station owned by Jonathan Christian Corp. The format of the station is country music, sports and talk. WKUL-FM broadcasts to the Cullman, AL area at 92.1 FM.

WKUN-AM
Owner: Anderson(B.R.)
Editorial: 1610 Launius Rd, Good Hope, Georgia 30641. **T:** 1 770 267-0923
W: http://www.wmoqfm.com
Editorial Profile: WKUN-AM is a commercial station owned by B.R. Anderson. The format of the station is gospel music. WKUN-AM broadcasts to the Bostwick, GA area at 1580 AM.

WKUZ-FM
Owner: Brothers Broadcasting Corp.
Editorial: 1864 S Wabash St, Wabash, Indiana 46992-4120. **T:** 1 260 563-4111
E: news@wkuz.com
Editorial Profile: WKUZ-FM is a commercial station owned by Brothers Broadcasting Corp. The format of the station is adult contemporary. WKUZ-FM broadcasts to the Wabash, IN area at 95.9 FM.

WKVA-AM
Owner: WVNW Inc.
Editorial: 114 N Logan Blvd, Burnham, Pennsylvania 17009. **T:** 1 717 242-1493
E: kvatoday@wkva920.com
W: http://www.wkva920.com
Editorial Profile: WKVA-AM is a commercial station owned by WVNW Inc. The format of the station is oldies. WKVA-AM broadcasts to the Burnham, PA area at 920 AM.

WKVB-FM
Owner: 2510 Associates
Editorial: 970 Tripoli St, Johnstown, Pennsylvania 15902. **T:** 1 814 534-8975
W: http://www.klove.com

WKVE-FM
Owner: Broadcast Communications Inc.
Editorial: 1918 Lincoln Hwy, North Versailles, Pennsylvania 15137-2706. **T:** 1 412 823-1301
W: http://kve.fm
Editorial Profile: WKVE-FM is a commercial station owned by Broadcast Communications Inc. The format of the station is classic rock. WKVE-FM broadcasts to the Greater Pittsburgh, PA area at 103.1 FM.

WKVG-AM
Owner: Martin's and Associates Inc.
Editorial: 20 Main St, Jenkins, Kentucky 41537-9614. **T:** 1 606 832-4655
E: wkvgradio@windstream.net
Editorial Profile: WKVG-AM is a commercial station owned by Martin's and Associates Inc. The format of the station is religious programming and gospel music. WKVG-AM broadcasts to the Jenkins, KY area at 1000 AM.

WKVI-AM
Owner: Kankakee Valley Broadcasting Inc.
Editorial: 400 W Culver Rd, Knox, Indiana 46534. **T:** 1 574 772-6241 **E:** spots@wkvi.com
W: http://www.wkvi.com
Editorial Profile: WKVI-AM is a commercial station owned by Kankakee Valley Broadcasting Inc. The format of the station is hot adult contemporary. WKVI-AM broadcasts to the South Bend, IN area at 1520 AM.

WKVI-FM

Owner: Kankakee Valley Broadcasting Inc.
Editorial: 400 W Culver Rd, Knox, Indiana 46534. **T:** 1 574 772-6241 **E:** spots@wkvi.com
W: http://www.wkvi.com
Editorial Profile: WKVI-FM is a commercial station owned by Kankakee Valley Broadcasting Inc. The format of the station is hot adult contemporary. WKVI-FM broadcasts to the South Bend, IN area at 99.3 FM.

WKVL-AM

Owner: Blount Broadcasting Corp.
Editorial: 517 N Watt Rd, Knoxville, Tennessee 37934. **T:** 1 865 984-0729 **E:** info@wkvl.com
Editorial Profile: WKVL-AM is a commercial station owned by Horne Radio LLC. The format of the station is country. WKVL-AM broadcasts to the Knoxville, TN area at 850 AM.

WKVN-FM

Owner: Educational Media Foundation
Editorial: 1339 US Highway 60 W, Morganfield, Kentucky 42437.
T: 1 916 251-1600 **E:** info@klove.com
W: http://www.klove.com

WKVQ-AM

Owner: Baker(Craig)
Editorial: 869 Church St, Eatonton, Georgia 31024. **T:** 1 706 485-8792
Editorial Profile: WKVQ-AM is a commercial station owned by Craig Baker. The format of the station is adult standards. WKVQ-AM broadcasts to the Eatonton, GA area at 1520 AM.

WKVS-FM

Owner: Foothills Radio Group, LLC
Editorial: 827 Fairview Dr SW, Lenoir, North Carolina 28645-6023. **T:** 1 828 758-1033
W: http://www.foothillsradio.com
Editorial Profile: WKVS-FM is a commercial station owned by Foothills Radio Group, LLC. The format of the station is contemporary country music. WKVS-FM broadcasts to the Charlotte, NC area at 103.3 FM.

WKVT-AM

Owner: Saga Communications
Editorial: 458 Williams St, Brattleboro, Vermont 5301. **T:** 1 802 254-2343
E: production@wkvt.com
W: http://www.1490wkvt.com
Editorial Profile: WKVT-AM is a commercial station owned by Saga Communications. The format of the station is progressive talk and news. WKVT-AM broadcasts to the Brattleboro, VT area at 1490 AM.

WKVT-FM

Owner: Saga Communications
Editorial: 458 Williams St, Brattleboro, Vermont 05301-6235. **T:** 1 802 254-2343
E: production@wkvt.com
W: http://www.wkvt.com
Editorial Profile: WKVT-FM is a commercial station owned by Saga Communications. The format of the station is classic hits. WKVT-FM broadcasts to the Brattleboro, VT area at 92.7 FM.

WKVX-AM

Owner: WWST Corporation
Editorial: 186 S Hillcrest Dr, Wooster, Ohio 44691. **T:** 1 330 264-5122
E: contact@wqkt.com
W: http://www.wqkt.com
Editorial Profile: WKVX-AM is a commercial station owned by WWST Corporation. The format of the station is oldies music. WKVX-AM broadcasts to the Cleveland area at 960 AM.

WKWC-FM

Owner: Kentucky Wesleyan College
Editorial: 3000 Frederica St, Owensboro, Kentucky 42301. **T:** 1 270 852-3601
E: pantherradio@kwc.edu
W: http://radio.owensboroky.net/PantherRadio/

WKWF-AM

Owner: Spottswood & Co.
Editorial: 5450 MacDonald Ave, Key West, Florida 33040-5903. **T:** 1 305 296-2523
W: http://www.sportsradio1600.com
Editorial Profile: WKWF-AM is a commercial station owned by Spottswood & Co and operated by Clear Channel Media and Entertainment. The format of the station is sports. WKWF-AM broadcasts to the Key West, FL area at 1600 AM.

WKWI-FM

Owner: Two Rivers Communications Inc.

Editorial: 101 Radio Rd, Kilmarnock, Virginia 22482-3881. **T:** 1 804 435-1414
E: onair@1017bayfm.com
Editorial Profile: WKWI-FM is a commercial station owned by Two Rivers Communications Inc. The format of the station is adult contemporary. WKWI-FM broadcasts to the Kilmarnock, VA area at 101.7 FM.

WKWK-FM

Owner: Clear Channel Media and Entertainment
Editorial: 1015 Main St, Wheeling, West Virginia 26003-2709. **T:** 1 304 232-1170
W: http://www.mix973wheeling.com
Editorial Profile: WKWK-FM is a commercial station owned by Clear Channel Media and Entertainment. The format of the station is adult contemporary. WKWK-FM broadcasts to the Wheeling, WV area at 97.3 FM.

WKWM-FM

Owner: Dade County School Board
Editorial: 172 NE 15th St, Miami, Florida 33132-1348. **T:** 1 305 995-1717
E: info@wlrn.org **W:** http://www.wlrn.org/web
Editorial Profile: WKWM-FM is a non-commercial station owned by the Dade County School Board. The format of the station is jazz, news and talk. WKWM-FM broadcasts to the Miami area at 91.5 FM.

WKWN-AM

Owner: Dade County Broadcasting
Editorial: 12544 N Main St, Trenton, Georgia 30752. **T:** 1 706 657-7594
W: http://www.discoverdade.com/newsradio.htm
Editorial Profile: WKWN-AM is a commercial station owned by Dade County Broadcasting. The format of the station is news and talk. WKWN-AM broadcasts to the Trenton, GA area at 1420 AM.

WKWS-FM

Owner: West Virginia Radio Corp.
Editorial: 1111 Virginia St E, Charleston, West Virginia 25301-2406. **T:** 1 304 342-8131
W: http://www.961thewolf.com
Editorial Profile: WKWS-FM is a commercial station owned by West Virgina Radio Corp. The format of the station is contemporary country music. WKWS-FM broadcasts to the Charleston, WV area at 96.1 FM.

WKWX-FM

Owner: Melco Inc.
Editorial: 695 Wayne Rd, Box 40, Savannah, Tennessee 38372. **T:** 1 731 925-9600
E: wkwx@bellsouth.net
Editorial Profile: WKWX-FM is a commercial station owned by Melco Inc. The format of the station is contemporary country. WKWX-FM broadcasts to the Savannah, TN area at 93.5 FM.

WKWY-FM

Owner: Whittimore Enterprises
Editorial: 341 Radio Station Rd, Tompkinsville, Kentucky 42167-8572. **T:** 1 270 487-6119
E: kixcountry@windstream.net

WKXA-FM

Owner: Blanchard River Broadcasting, Co.
Editorial: 551 Lake Cascade Pkwy, Findlay, Ohio 45840. **T:** 1 419 422-4545
E: wkxa@wkxa.com **W:** http://www.wkxa.com
Editorial Profile: WKXA-FM is a commercial station owned by Blanchard River Broadcasting, Co. The format of the station is country. WKXA-FM broadcasts to the Findlay, OH area at 100.5 FM.

WKXB-FM

Owner: Capitol Broadcasting Company
Editorial: 25 N Kerr Ave, Ste C, Wilmington, North Carolina 28405. **T:** 1 910 791-3088
W: http://www.jammin999fm.com
Editorial Profile: WKXB-FM is a commercial station owned by Capitol Broadcasting Company. The format of the station is R&B oldies. WKXB-FM broadcasts to the Wilmington, NC area at 99.9 FM.

WKXC-FM

Owner: Beasley Broadcast Group
Editorial: 4051 Jimmie Dyess Pkwy, Augusta, Georgia 30909-9469. **T:** 1 706 855-9494
W: http://www.kicks99.com
Editorial Profile: WKXC-FM is a commercial station owned by the Beasley Broadcast Group. The format of the station is classic country. WKXC-FM broadcasts to the Augusta, GA area at 99.5 FM.

WKXD-FM

Owner: Stonecom Cookeville LLC
Editorial: 259 S Willow Ave, Cookeville, Tennessee 38501-3140. **T:** 1 931 528-6064
W: http://www.1069kicksfm.com
Editorial Profile: WKXD-FM is a commercial station owned by Stonecom Cookeville LLC. The format of the station is country. WKXD-FM broadcasts to the Cookeville, TN area at 106.9 FM.

WKXH-FM

Owner: Vermont Broadcast Associates Inc.
Editorial: 1303 Concord Ave, Saint Johnsbury, Vermont 5819. **T:** 1 802 748-2362
E: kix105@kix1055.com
W: http://www.kix1055.com
Editorial Profile: WKXH-FM is a commercial station owned by Vermont Broadcast Associates Inc. The format of the station contemporary country music. WKXH-FM broadcasts to the St. Johnsbury, VT area at 105.5 FM.

WKXI-FM

Owner: L & L Radio
Editorial: 731 S Pear Orchard Rd Ste 27, Ridgeland, Mississippi 39157-4839.
T: 1 601 957-1300 **E:** production@wjmi.com
W: http://www.kixie107.com
Editorial Profile: WKXI-FM is a commercial station owned by L & L Radio. The format of the station is urban contemporary. WKXI-FM broadcasts to the Jackson, MS area at 107.5 FM.

WKXJ-FM

Owner: Clear Channel Media and Entertainment
Editorial: 7413 Old Lee Hwy, Chattanooga, Tennessee 37421-1142. **T:** 1 423 892-3333
W: http://www.kisschattanooga.com
Editorial Profile: WKXJ-FM is a commercial station owned by Clear Channel Media and Entertainment. The format of the station is Top 40/CHR. WKXJ-FM broadcasts to the Chattanooga, TN area at 103.7 FM.

WKXK-FM

Owner: Autaugaville Radio Inc.
Editorial: 563 Manningham Rd, Greenville, Alabama 36037. **T:** 1 334 382-6555
E: wkxn@wkxn.com **W:** http://www.wkxn.com
Editorial Profile: WKXK-FM is a commercial station owned by Autaugaville Radio Inc. The format of the station is gospel, urban contemporary and oldies. WKXK-FM broadcasts to the Pine Hill, AL area at 96.7 FM.

WKXL-AM

Owner: New Hampshire Family Radio LLC
Editorial: 37 Redington Rd, Concord, New Hampshire 03301-2440. **T:** 1 603 224-4094
E: news@wkxl1450.com
W: http://www.wkxl1450.com
Editorial Profile: WKXL-AM is a commercial station owned by New Hampshire Family Radio LLC. The format of the station is news, talk and sports. WKXL-AM broadcasts to the Concord, NH area at 1450 AM..

WKXM-FM

Owner: Ad-Media Management Corp
Editorial: 655 Fairview Rd, Winfield, Alabama 35594-4755. **T:** 1 205 487-3261
Editorial Profile: WKXM-FM is a commercial station owned by Ad-Media Management Corp. The format of the station is classic hits. WKXM-FM's broadcasts to the Birmingham, AL at 97.7 FM.

WKXN-FM

Owner: Autaugaville Radio Inc.
Editorial: 563 Manningham Rd, Greenville, Alabama 36037. **T:** 1 334 382-6555
E: wkxn@wkxn.com **W:** http://www.wkxn.com
Editorial Profile: WKXN-FM is a commercial station owned by Autaugaville Radio Inc. The format of the station is gospel and urban contemporary. WKXN-FM broadcasts to the Greenville, AL area at 95.9 FM.

WKXP-FM

Owner: Townsquare Media
Editorial: 2 Pendell Rd, Poughkeepsie, New York 12601-1513. **T:** 1 845 471-1500
W: http://hudsonvalleycountry.com
Editorial Profile: WKXP-FM is a commercial station owned by Townsquare Media. The format of the station is country. WKPX-FM broadcasts to the Poughkeepsie, NY area on 94.3 FM.

WKXQ-FM

Owner: LB Sports Production, LLC

Editorial: 108 E Main St, Beardstown, Illinois 62618-1241. **T:** 1 217 323-1790
W: http://www.wkxqfm.com
Editorial Profile: WKXQ-FM is a commercial station owned by LB Sports Production, LLC. The format of the station is adult standards. WKXQ-FM broadcasts in the Rushville, IL area at 92.5 FM.

WKXR-AM

Owner: Randolph Broadcasting Inc.
Editorial: 1119 Eastview Dr, Asheboro, North Carolina 27203. **T:** 1 336 625-2187
E: wkxr@atomic.net **W:** http://www.wkxr.com
Editorial Profile: WKXR-AM is a commercial station owned by Randolph Broadcasting Inc. The format of the station is country. WKXR-AM broadcasts to the Asheboro, NC area at 1260 AM.

WKXS-FM

Owner: Cumulus Media Inc.
Editorial: 3233 Burnt Mill Dr, Ste 4, Wilmington, North Carolina 28403.
T: 1 910 763-9977
W: http://www.945thehawkradio.com
Editorial Profile: WKXS-FM is a commercial station owned by Cumulus Media Inc. The format of the station is classic hits. WKXS-FM broadcasts to the Wilmington, NC area at 94.5 FM.

WKXV-AM

Owner: Ra-Tel Broadcasting Company Inc.
Editorial: 5106 Middlebrook Pike, Knoxville, Tennessee 37921. **T:** 1 865 558-0900
E: wkxv@bellsouth.net
Editorial Profile: WKXV-AM is a commercial station owned by Ra-Tel Broadcasting Company Inc. The format of the station is religious programming and Southern gospel music. WKXV-AM broadcasts to the Knoxville, TN area at 900 AM.

WKXW-FM

Owner: Townsquare Media, LLC
Editorial: 109 Walters Ave, Ewing, New Jersey 08638-1829. **T:** 1 609 882-4600
W: http://nj1015.com
Editorial Profile: WKXW-FM is a commercial station owned by Townsquare Media, LLC. The format of the station is news and talk. WKXW-FM broadcasts to the greater Philadelphia, PA area at 101.5 FM.

WKXX-FM

Owner: Broadcast Media LLC
Editorial: 100 Spurlock St, Rainbow City, Alabama 35906-5864. **T:** 1 256 442-3944
W: http://www.wkxx.com
Editorial Profile: WKXX-FM is a commercial station owned by Broadcast Media LLC. The format for the station is hot adult contemporary. WKXX-FM broadcasts to the Rainbow City, AL area at 102.9 FM.

WKXY-FM

Owner: Delta Radio, LLC
Editorial: 201 E Sunflower Rd, Cleveland, Mississippi 38732-2715. **T:** 1 662 843-3392
E: info@deltaradio.net
W: http://www.kix921.com
Editorial Profile: WKXY-FM is a commercial station owned by Delta Radio, LLC. The format of the station is a mix of contemporary and classic country. WKXY-FM broadcasts to the Cleveland, MS area at 92.1 FM.

WKXZ-FM

Owner: Townsquare Media, LLC
Editorial: 34 Chestnut St., Oneonta, New York 13820. **T:** 1 607 432-1030
E: cnynews@townsquaremedia.com
W: http://www.wkxzfm.com
Editorial Profile: WKXZ-FM is a commercial station owned by Townsquare Media, LLC. The format of the station is hot adult contemporary music. WKXZ-FM broadcasts to the Oneonta, NY area at 93.9 FM.

WKYA-FM

Owner: Starlight Broadcasting Co.
Editorial: 464 State Route 189 S, Greenville, Kentucky 42345. **T:** 1 270 338-6655

WKY-AM

Owner: Cumulus Media Inc.
Editorial: 4045 NW 64th St, Ste 600, Oklahoma City, Oklahoma 73116.
T: 1 405 848-0100
W: http://www.laindomable.com
Editorial Profile: WKY-AM is a commercial station owned by Cumulus Media Inc. The format of the station is Regional Mexican. WKY-AM broadcasts to Oklahoma City at 930 AM.

WKYE-FM
Owner: Forever Broadcasting
Editorial: 109 Plaza Dr, Ste 2, Johnstown, Pennsylvania 15905-1212. **T:** 1 814 255-4186
W: http://www.96key.com
Editorial Profile: WKYE-FM is a commercial station owned by Forever Broadcasting. The format of the station is adult contemporary. WKYE-FM broadcasts to the Johnstown, PA area at 96.5 FM.

WKYK-AM
Owner: Mark Media Inc.
Editorial: 749 Saw Mill Hollow Rd, Burnsville, North Carolina 28714-9789.
T: 1 828 682-3510 **E:** 940@wkyk.com
W: http://www.ourlocalcommunityonline.com
Editorial Profile: WKYK-AM is a commercial station owned by Mark Media Inc. The format of the station is classic country. WKYK-AM broadcasts to the Burnsville, NC area at 940 AM.

WKYL-FM
Owner: Davenport Broadcasting Inc.
Editorial: 88 C Michael Davenport Blvd, Ste 2, Frankfort, Kentucky 40601-4389.
T: 1 502 839-1021 **E:** classic1021@wkyl.org
W: http://www.weku.fm/post/classic-1021-wkyl
Editorial Profile: WKYL-FM is a non-commercial station owned by Davenport Broadcasting and programmed by Eastern Kentucky University. The format of the station is primarily classical music programming. WKYL-FM broadcasts to the Greater Lexington and Lawrenceburg area in Kentucky.

WKYM-FM
Owner: Staples Jr.(Stephen)
Editorial: 150 Worsham Ln, Monticello, Kentucky 42633-1610. **T:** 1 606 348-7083
E: news@wkym.com
W: http://www.wkym.com

WKYN-FM
Owner: Gateway Radio Works Inc.
Editorial: 22 West Main Street, Mount Sterling, Kentucky 40353. **T:** 1 859 498-1077
Editorial Profile: WKYN-FM is a commercial station owned by Gateway Radio Works Inc. The format for the station is country. WKYN-FM broadcasts to the Lexington, KY area at 107.7 FM.

WKYO-AM
Owner: Edwards Communications LLC
Editorial: 1521 W Caro Rd, Caro, Michigan 48723. **T:** 1 989 672-1360
E: news@mix921.com
W: http://www.tuscolatoday.com
Editorial Profile: WKYO-AM is a commercial station owned by Edwards Communications LLC. The format of the station is oldies music. WKYO-AM broadcasts to the Caro, MI area at 1360 AM.

WKYQ-FM
Owner: Bristol Broadcasting
Editorial: 6000 Bristol Dr, Paducah, Kentucky 42003-9213. **T:** 1 270 554-0093
E: news@wkyq.com **W:** http://www.wkyq.com
Editorial Profile: WKYQ-FM is a commercial station owned by Bristol Broadcasting. The format of the station is contemporary country. WKYQ-FM broadcasts to the Paducah, KY area at 93.3 FM.

WKYR-FM
Owner: WKYR Inc.
Editorial: 1089 S Main St, Burkesville, Kentucky 42717-9402. **T:** 1 270 433-7191
E: wkyr@mchsi.com

WKYS-FM
Owner: Radio One Inc.
Editorial: 5900 Princess Garden Pkwy Fl 8, Lanham, Maryland 20706-2925.
T: 1 301 306-1111 **W:** http://kysdc.com
Editorial Profile: WKYS-FM is a commercial station owned by Radio One. The format of the station is urban contemporary music. WKYS-FM broadcasts to the Washington, D.C. area at 93.9 FM.

WKYU-FM
Owner: Western Kentucky University
Editorial: 1906 College Heights Blvd, #11035, Bowling Green, Kentucky 42101.
T: 1 270 745-5489 **E:** wkyufm@wku.edu
W: http://www.wku.edu/wkyu-fm/
Editorial Profile: WKYU-FM is a non-commercial station owned by Western Kentucky University. The format for the station is classical music, news and talk. WKYU-FM broadcasts to the Bowling Green, KY area at 88.9 FM.

WKYW-AM
Owner: Capcity Communications Inc.
Editorial: 115 W Main St, Frankfort, Kentucky 40601. **T:** 1 502 875-1130
Editorial Profile: WKYW-AM is a commercial station owned by Forever Communication Inc. The format is smooth AC. The station airs in the Frankfort, KY area at 1490 AM.

WKYX-AM
Owner: Bristol Broadcasting
Editorial: 6000 Bristol Dr, Paducah, Kentucky 42003-9213. **T:** 1 270 554-8255
E: news@wkyx.com **W:** http://www.wkyx.com
Editorial Profile: WKYX-AM is a commercial station owned by Bristol Broadcasting. The format of the station is news and talk. WKYX-AM broadcasts in the Paducah, KY area at 570 AM.

WKYX-FM
Owner: Bristol Broadcasting
Editorial: 6000 Bristol Dr, Paducah, Kentucky 42003-9213. **T:** 1 270 554-8255
E: news@wkyx.com **W:** http://www.wkyx.com
Editorial Profile: WKYX-FM is a commercial station owned by Bristol Broadcasting. The format of the station is news and talk. WKYX-FM broadcasts to the Paducah, KY area at 94.3 FM.

WKYZ-FM
Owner: Keys Media Company, Inc
Editorial: 5555 College Rd, Key West, Florida 33040-4307. **T:** 1 305 294-1017
W: http://www.pirateradiokeywest.com
Editorial Profile: WKYZ-FM is a commercial station owned by Keys Media Company, Inc. The format of the station is adult rock with a mixture of classic and alternative music. WKYZ-FM broadcasts to the Marathon, FL area at 101.7 FM.

WKZC-FM
Owner: Lake Michigan Broadcasting Inc.
Editorial: 5941 W US Highway 10, Ludington, Michigan 49431-2447. **T:** 1 231 843-3438
W: http://www.yourcountryz95.com
Editorial Profile: WKZC-FM is a commercial station owned by Lake Michigan Broadcasting Inc, operated by Synergy Media under LMA. The format of the station is contemporary country music. WKZC-FM broadcasts to the Ludington, MI area at 94.9 FM.

WKZD-AM
Owner: Abercrombie Broadcasting, Inc.
Editorial: 219 Chestnut St Ne, Hartselle, Alabama 35640-1903. **T:** 1 256 773-4114
Editorial Profile: WKZD-AM is a commercial station owned by Abercrombie Broadcasting, Inc. The format of the station is oldies. WKZD-AM broadcasts to the Hartselle, AL area at 1310 AM.

WKZE-FM
Owner: Willpower Radio LLC
Editorial: 7392 S Broadway, Red Hook, New York 12571-1785. **T:** 1 845 758-9810
E: info@wkze.com **W:** http://www.wkze.com
Editorial Profile: WKZE-FM is a commercial station owned by Willpower Radio LLC. The format of the station is adult album alternative music. WKZE-FM broadcasts to the Redhook, NY area at 98.1 FM.

WKZF-FM
Owner: Hall Communications
Editorial: 1996 Auction Rd, Manheim, Pennsylvania 17545-9159. **T:** 1 717 653-0800
W: http://www.927kzf.com
Editorial Profile: WKZF-FM is a commercial station owned by Hall Communications. The format of the station is classic rock. WKZF-FM broadcasts to the Manheim, PA area at 92.7 FM.

WKZG-FM
Owner: Woodward Communications, Inc.
Editorial: 2800 E College Ave, Appleton, Wisconsin 54915-3255. **T:** 1 920 733-6639
W: http://www.kz1043.com
Editorial Profile: WKZG-FM is a commercial station owned by Woodward Communications, Inc. The station's format is Hot AC. WKZG-FM broadcasts to the Appleton, WI area at 104.3 FM.

WKZI-AM
Owner: Word Power Inc.
Editorial: 18889 N 2350th St, Dennison, Illinois 62423. **T:** 1 217 826-9673
E: wkzi@rr1.net **W:** http://www.wordpower.us
Editorial Profile: WKZI-AM is a commercial station owned by World Power Inc. The format of the station is religious music and talk. WKZI-AM broadcasts to the Dennison, IL area at 800 AM.

WKZJ-FM
Owner: Davis Broadcasting
Editorial: 2203 Wynnton Rd, Columbus, Georgia 31906. **T:** 1 706 576-3565
W: http://www.k927.com
Editorial Profile: WKZJ-FM is a commercial station owned by David Broadcasting. The format of the station is adult contemporary. WKZJ-FM broadcasts to the Columbus, GA area at 92.7 FM.

WKZK-AM
Owner: Gospel Radio Inc.
Editorial: 2 Milledge Rd, Augusta, Georgia 30904. **T:** 1 706 738-9191
W: http://www.wkzk.net
Editorial Profile: WKZK-AM is a commercial station owned by Gospel Radio Inc. The format of the station is gospel. WKZK-AM broadcasts to the Augusta, GA area at 1600 AM.

WKZL-FM
Owner: Dick Jr.(James A.)
Editorial: 192 E Lewis St, Greensboro, North Carolina 27406. **T:** 1 336 274-8042
W: http://www.1075kzl.com
Editorial Profile: WKZL-FM is a commercial station owned by James A. Dick Jr. The format of the station is Top 40/CHR. WKZL-FM broadcasts to the Greensboro-Winston Salem, NC area at 107.5 FM.

WKZN-AM
Owner: Entercom Communications Corp.
Editorial: 305 Route 315 Hwy, Pittston, Pennsylvania 18640-3907. **T:** 1 570 883-9850
W: http://www.wilknetwork.com
Editorial Profile: WKZN-AM is a commercial station owned by Entercom Communications Corp. The format of the station is news, sports and talk. WKZN-AM broadcasts to the Wilkes Barre-Scranton, PA area at 1300 AM.

WKZO-AM
Owner: Midwest Communications Inc.
Editorial: 4200 W Main St, Kalamazoo, Michigan 49006. **T:** 1 269 345-7121
E: wkzonews@wkzo.com
W: http://www.wkzo.com
Editorial Profile: WKZO-AM is a commercial station owned by Midwest Communications Inc. The format of the station is news and talk. WKZO-AM broadcasts to the Kalamazoo, MI area at 590 AM.

WKZO-FM
Owner: Midwest Communications Inc.
Editorial: 4200 W Main St, Kalamazoo, Michigan 49006-2749. **T:** 1 269 345-7121
E: wkzonews@wkzo.com
W: http://www.wkzo.com
Editorial Profile: WKZO-FM is a commercial station owned by Midwest Communications Inc. The format of the station is modern rock. WKZO-FM broadcasts to the Grand Rapids, MI area at 96.5 FM.

WKZP-FM
Owner: Clear Channel Media and Entertainment
Editorial: Gateway Crossing, 351 Tilghman Road, Salisbury, Maryland 21804.
T: 1 410 742-1923
W: http://www.kiss959fm.com
Editorial Profile: WKZP-FM is a commercial station owned by Clear Channel Media and Entertainment. The format of the station is Top 40/CHR. WKZP-FM broadcasts to the Salisbury, MD area. area at 95.9 FM.

WKZQ-FM
Owner: Digity LLC
Editorial: 1016 Ocala St, Myrtle Beach, South Carolina 29577-8007. **T:** 1 843 448-1041
W: http://www.wkzq.net
Editorial Profile: WKZQ-FM is a commercial station owned by Digity LLC. The format of the station is rock. WKZQ-FM broadcasts to the Myrtle Beach, SC area at 96.1 FM.

WKZR-FM
Owner: Beasley(W.R.)
Editorial: 1250 W Charlton St, Milledgeville, Georgia 31061. **T:** 1 478 452-0587
E: mail@country102fm.com
W: http://www.country102fm.com
Editorial Profile: WKZR-FM is a commercial station owned by W.R. Beasley. The format of the station is country music. WKZR-FM broadcasts to the Milledgeville, GA area at 102.3 FM.

WKZS-FM
Owner: Benton-Weatherford Broadcasting Inc. of Tennessee
Editorial: 820 Railroad St, Covington, Indiana 47932-1357. **T:** 1 765 793-4823
E: info@kisscountryradio.com
W: http://www.kisscountryradio.com
Editorial Profile: WKZS-FM is a commercial station owned by Benton-Weatherford Broadcasting Inc. of Tennessee. The format of the station is contemporary country. WKZS-FM broadcasts to the Covington, IN area at 103.1 FM.

WKZU-FM
Owner: Kudzu Communications Inc
Editorial: 107 Spring Street, Ripley, Mississippi 38663. **T:** 1 662 837-1023
E: classicradiofm@aol.com
W: http://www.classicradiofm.com
Editorial Profile: WKZU-FM is a commercial station owned by Kudzu Communications Inc. The format of the station is country. WKZU-FM broadcasts to the Ripley, MS area at 104.9 FM.

WKZW-FM
Owner: Blakeney Communications Inc.
Editorial: 4580 Highway 15 N, Laurel, Mississippi 39440. **T:** 1 601 649-0095
E: kz943@kz943.com **W:** http://www.kz94.com
Editorial Profile: WKZW-FM is a commercial station owned by Blakeney Communications Inc. The format of the station is adult contemporary music. WKZW-FM broadcasts to the Laurel, MS area at 94.3 FM.

WKZX-FM
Owner: BP Broadcasters
Editorial: 406 E Broadway St, Lenoir City, Tennessee 37771. **T:** 1 865 986-9850
E: wkzx@aol.com
Editorial Profile: WKZX-FM is a commercial station owned by BP Broadcasters. The format of the station is regional Mexican programming. WKZX-FM broadcasts to the Lenoir City, TN area at 93.5 FM.

WKZY-FM
Owner: Woodward Communications, Inc.
Editorial: 2800 E College Ave, Appleton, Wisconsin 54915-3255. **T:** 1 920 734-9226
W: http://www.kz1043.com
Editorial Profile: WKZY-FM is a commercial station owned by Woodward Communications, Inc. The format of the station is adult contemporary. WKZY-FM broadcasts to the Chilton, WI area at a frequency of 92.9 FM.

WKZZ-FM
Owner: Broadcast South, LLC
Editorial: 1931 Ga Highway 32 E, Douglas, Georgia 31533. **T:** 1 912 389-0995
Editorial Profile: WKZZ-FM is a commercial station owned by Broadcast South, LLC. The format of the station is adult contemporary. WKZZ-FM broadcasts to the Douglas, GA area at 92.5 FM.

WLAA-AM
Owner: Rama Communications Inc.
Editorial: 3765 N John Young Pkwy, Orlando, Florida 32804-3213. **T:** 1 407 293-9652
W: http://www.ramacomm.com
Editorial Profile: WLAA-AM is a commercial station owned by Rama Communications Inc. The format of the station is regional Mexican. WLAA-AM broadcasts to the Orlando, FL area at 1680 AM.

WLAB-FM
Owner: Star Educational Media Network
Editorial: 6600 N Clinton St, Fort Wayne, Indiana 46825. **T:** 1 260 483-8236
W: http://www.star883.com
Editorial Profile: WLAB-FM is a commercial station owned by Star Educational Media Network. The format of the station is contemporary Christian. WLAB-FM broadcasts to the Fort Wayne, IN area at 88.3 FM.

WLAC-AM
Owner: Clear Channel Media and Entertainment
Editorial: 55 Music Sq W, Nashville, Tennessee 37203-3207. **T:** 1 615 664-2400
E: programming@wlac.com
W: http://www.wlac.com
Editorial Profile: WLAC-AM is a commercial station owned by Clear Channel Media and Entertainment. The format of the station is news and talk. WLAC-AM broadcasts to the Nashville, TN area at 1510 AM. To send a PSA, email nashvillepsa@clearchannel.com.

WLAD-AM
Owner: Berkshire Broadcasting Corp

Editorial: 198 Main St, Danbury, Connecticut 06810-6662. **T:** 1 203 744-4800
E: news@wlad.com **W:** http://www.wlad.com
Editorial Profile: WLAD-AM is a commercial station owned by Berkshire Broadcasting Corp. The format of the station is news, talk and sports. WLAD-AM broadcasts to the Danbury, CT area at 800 AM.

WLAF-AM
Owner: Stair Company
Editorial: 210 N 5th St, La Follette, Tennessee 37766. **T:** 1 423 562-3557
E: wlaf@bellsouth.net
Editorial Profile: WLAF-AM is a commercial station owned by Stair Company. The format of the station is Southern gospel. WLAF-AM broadcasts to the La Follette, TN area at 1450 AM.

WLAG-AM
Owner: Eagle's Nest Inc.
Editorial: 304 Broome St, Lagrange, Georgia 30240. **T:** 1 706 845-1023
E: welr@eagle1023.com
W: http://www.eagle1023.com
Editorial Profile: WLAG-AM is a commercial station owned by Eagle's Nest Inc. The format of the station is sports. WLAG-AM broadcasts to the Lagrange, GA area at 1240 AM.

WLAM-AM
Owner: WBIN, Inc.
Editorial: 477 Congress St Ste 3, Portland, Maine 04101-3417. **T:** 1 207 797-0780
Editorial Profile: WLAM-AM is a commercial station owned by WBIN, Inc. The format of the station is oldies. WLAM-AM broadcasts to the Portland, ME area at 1470 AM.

WLAN-AM
Owner: Clear Channel Media and Entertainment
Editorial: 1685 Crown Ave, Ste 100, Lancaster, Pennsylvania 17601.
T: 1 717 295-9700
W: http://www.whp580.com
Editorial Profile: WLAN-AM is a commercial station owned by Clear Channel Media and Entertainment. The format of the station is Conservative news and talk. WLAN-AM broadcasts to the Lancaster, PA area at 1390 AM.

WLAN-FM
Owner: Clear Channel Media and Entertainment
Editorial: 1685 Crown Ave, Ste 100, Lancaster, Pennsylvania 17601-6310.
T: 1 717 295-9700 **E:** webmaster@fm97.com
W: http://www.fm97.com
Editorial Profile: WLAN-FM is a commercial station owned by Clear Channel Media and Entertainment. The format of the station is Top 40/CHR. WLAN-FM broadcasts to the Lancaster, PA area at 96.9 FM.

WLAP-AM
Owner: Clear Channel Media and Entertainment
Editorial: 2601 Nicholasville Rd, Lexington, Kentucky 40503-3307. **T:** 1 859 422-1000
E: news@wlap.com **W:** http://www.wlap.com
Editorial Profile: WLAP-AM is a commercial station owned by Clear Channel Media and Entertainment. The format of the station is news and talk. WLAP-AM broadcasts to the Lexington, KY area at 630 AM.

WLAQ-AM
Owner: Cripple Creek Broadcasting
Editorial: 2 Mount Alto Rd SW, Rome, Georgia 30165. **T:** 1 706 232-7767
E: wlaq@comcast.net
W: http://www.wlaq1410.com
Editorial Profile: WLAQ-AM is a commercial station owned by Cripple Creek Broadcasting. The format of the station is news, sports and talk. WLAQ-AM broadcasts to the Rome, GA area 1410 AM.

WLAR-AM
Owner: Sliger Enterprises
Editorial: 2110 Oxnard Rd, Athens, Tennessee 37303. **T:** 1 423 745-1000
E: 1017wlar@bellsouth.net
Editorial Profile: WLAR-AM is a commercial station owned by Sliger Enterprises. The format for the station is contemporary country. WLAR-AM broadcasts to the Chattanooga, TN area at 1450 AM.

WLAT-AM
Owner: Gois Broadcasting
Editorial: 135 Burnside Ave Fl 2, East Hartford, Connecticut 06108-3466.
T: 1 860 524-0001
Editorial Profile: WLAT-AM is a commercial station owned by Gois Broadcasting. The format for the station is tropical Hispanic music. WLAT-AM broadcasts to the Hartford-New Haven, CT area at 910 AM.

WLAU-FM
Owner: TeleSouth Communications, Inc.
Editorial: 6311 Ridgewood Rd, Jackson, Mississippi 39211-2035. **T:** 1 601 957-1700
E: newsms@supertalk.fm
W: http://www.supertalk.fm
Editorial Profile: WLAU-FM is a commercial station owned by TeleSouth Communications, Inc. The format of the station is talk. WLAU-FM broadcasts to the Hattiesburg, MS area at 99.3 FM.

WLAV-FM
Owner: Cumulus Media Inc.
Editorial: 60 Monroe Center St NW Fl 3, Grand Rapids, Michigan 49503-2916.
T: 1 616 456-5461 **W:** http://www.wlav.com
Editorial Profile: WLAV-FM is a commercial station owned by Cumulus Media Inc. The format of the station is classic rock. WLAV-FM broadcasts to the Grand Rapids, MI area at 96.9 FM.

WLAW-FM
Owner: Cumulus Media Inc.
Editorial: 3375 Merriam St, Ste 201, Muskegon, Michigan 49444.
T: 1 231 830-0176
W: http://www.925fmtheoutlaw.com
Editorial Profile: WLAW-FM is a commercial station owned by Cumulus Media Inc.. The format of the station is classic country. WLAW-FM broadcasts to the Muskegon, MI, area at 92.5 FM.

WLAY-AM
Owner: URBan Radio Broadcasting, LLC
Editorial: 509 N Main St, Tuscumbia, Alabama 35674. **T:** 1 256 383-2525
W: http://www.wlaythesound.com
Editorial Profile: WLAY-AM is a commercial station owned by Urban Radio Broadcasting, LLC. The format of the station is variety. WLAY-AM broadcasts to the Muscle Shoals, AL area at 1450 AM.

WLAY-FM
Owner: URBan Radio Broadcasting, LLC
Editorial: 509 N Main St, Tuscumbia, Alabama 35674-2048. **T:** 1 256 383-2525
E: info@urbanradio.fm
W: http://www.wlay1035.com
Editorial Profile: WLAY-FM is a commercial station owned by URBan Radio Broadcasting, LLC. The format of the station is classic country music. WLAY-FM broadcasts to the Tuscumbia, AL area at 103.5 FM.

WLAZ-FM
Owner: Font (Otoniel)
Editorial: 972 E Osceola Pkwy, Kissimmee, Florida 34744-1615. **T:** 1 407 518-7150
E: contacto@laestaciondelafamilia.com
W: http://www.laestaciondelafamilia.com
Editorial Profile: WLAZ-FM is a commercial station owned by Otoniel Font. The format of the station is Christian programming. WLAZ-FM broadcasts to the Kissimmee, FL area at 89.1 FM.

WLBA-AM
Owner: La Favorita Inc.
Editorial: 5815 Westside Rd, Austell, Georgia 30106-3179. **T:** 1 770 944-0900
E: traffic@lamejorestacion.com
W: http://www.lamejorestacion.com
Editorial Profile: WLBA-AM is a commercial station owned by La Favorita Inc. The format of the station is regional Mexican. WLBA-AM broadcasts to the Atlanta area at 1130 AM.

WLBB-AM
Owner: Gradick Communications LLC
Editorial: 808 Newnan Rd, Carrollton, Georgia 30117. **T:** 1 678 601-1330
E: news@newstalk1330.com
W: http://www.newstalk1330.com
Editorial Profile: WLBB-AM is a commercial station owned by Gradick Communications LLC. The format of the station is news and talk. WLBB-AM broadcasts to the Carrollton, GA area at 1330 AM.

WLBC-FM
Owner: Backyard Broadcasting
Editorial: 800 E 29th St, Muncie, Indiana 47302-5765. **T:** 1 765 288-4403
W: http://www.wlbc.com
Editorial Profile: WLBC-FM is a commercial station owned by Backyard Broadcasting. The format of the station is hot adult contemporary music. WLBC-FM broadcasts to the Indianapolis area at 101.4 FM.

WLBE-AM
Owner: WLBE 790 Inc.
Editorial: 32900 Radio Rd, Leesburg, Florida 34788-3903. **T:** 1 352 787-7900
W: http://my790am.com
Editorial Profile: WLBE-AM is a commercial station owned by WLBE 790 Inc. The format of the station is oldies and talk. WLBE-AM broadcasts to the Leesburg, FL area at 790 AM.

WLBF-FM
Owner: Faith Broadcasting
Editorial: 381 Mendel Pkwy E, Montgomery, Alabama 36117. **T:** 1 334 271-8900
E: mail@faithradio.org
W: http://www.faithradio.org
Editorial Profile: WLBF-FM is a non-commercial station owned by Faith Broadcasting. The format of the station is Christian religious programming. WLBF-FM broadcasts to the Montgomery, AL area at 89.1 FM.

WLBG-AM
Owner: Southeastern Broadcast Assocs. Inc.
Editorial: 405 Hillcrest Dr, Laurens, South Carolina 29360-2345. **T:** 1 864 984-3544
E: mail@wlbg.com **W:** http://www.wlbg.com
Editorial Profile: WLBG-AM is a commercial station owned by Southeastern Broadcast Associates Inc. The format of the station is news, sports, talk and gospel. WLBG-AM broadcasts to the Laurens, SC area at 860 AM.

WLBK-AM
Owner: Dekalb County Broadcasters, Inc.
Editorial: 2410 Sycamore Rd Ste C, Dekalb, Illinois 60115-2091. **T:** 1 815 748-1000
W: http://www.1360wlbk.com
Editorial Profile: WLBK-AM is a commercial station owned by Dekalb County Broadcasters, Inc. The format of the station is news and talk programming. WLBK-AM broadcasts to the De Kalb, IL area at 1360 AM.

WLBL-AM
Owner: Wisconsin Educational Communications Board
Editorial: 625 Stewart Ave, Wausau, Wisconsin 54401-4563. **T:** 1 715 261-6298
E: listener@wpr.org **W:** http://www.wpr.org
Editorial Profile: WLBL-AM is a non-commercial station owned by Wisconsin Educational Communications Board. The format of the station is news and talk. WLBL-AM broadcasts in the Wassau, WI area at 91.9 FM.

WLBN-AM
Owner: Choice Radio Corporation
Editorial: 253 W Main St, Lebanon, Kentucky 40033-1240. **T:** 1 270 692-3126
W: http://www.1590wlbn.com
Editorial Profile: WLBN-AM is a commercial station owned by Choice Radio Corporation. The format of the station is oldies. WLBN-AM broadcasts in the Lebanon, KY area at 1590 AM.

WLBQ-AM
Owner: Beech Tree Publishing
Editorial: 107 West Ohio Street, Morgantown, Kentucky 42261. **T:** 1 270 526-5393
E: info@beechtreenews.com
W: http://www.beechtreenews.com
Editorial Profile: WLBQ-AM is a commercial station owned by Beech Tree Publishing. The format of the station is news and country. WLBQ-AM broadcasts to the Morgantown, KY area at 1570 AM.

WLBR-AM
Owner: Lebanon Broadcasting Co.
Editorial: 440 Rebecca Ln, Lebanon, Pennsylvania 17046-1734. **T:** 1 717 272-7651
Editorial Profile: WLBR-AM is a commercial station owned by Lebanon Broadcasting Co. The format of the station is variety. WLBR-AM broadcasts to the Lebanon, PA area at 1270 AM.

WLBS-FM
Owner: Bux-Mont Educational Association
Editorial: 126 S York Rd, Hatboro, Pennsylvania 19040-3327. **T:** 1 215 674-8002
E: info@wrdv.com **W:** http://www.wrdv.org
Editorial Profile: WLBS-FM is a non-commercial station owned by the Bux-Mont Educational Association. The format of the station is adult standards. WLBS-FM broadcasts to the Hatboro, PA, area at 91.7 FM.

WLBW-FM
Owner: Clear Channel Media and Entertainment
Editorial: Gateway Crossing, 351 Tilghman Road, Salisbury, Maryland 21804-1920.
T: 1 410 742-1923
W: http://www.isurfthewave.com
Editorial Profile: WLBW-FM is a commercial station owned by Clear Channel Media and Entertainment. The format of the station is oldies music. WLBW-FM broadcasts to the Salisbury, MD area at 92.1 FM.

WLBY-AM
Owner: Cumulus Media Inc.
Editorial: 1100 Victors Way, Ann Arbor, Michigan 48108-5220. **T:** 1 734 302-8100
E: programming@1290wlby.com
W: http://www.1290wlby.com
Editorial Profile: WLBY-AM is a commercial station owned by Cumulus Media Inc. The format of the station is business talk. WLBY-AM broadcasts to the Ann Arbor, MI area at 1290 AM.

WLCA-FM
Owner: Lewis & Clark Community College
Editorial: 5800 Godfrey Rd, Godfrey, Illinois 62035. **T:** 1 618 466-8936 **E:** wlca@lc.edu
W: http://www.wlcafm.com
Editorial Profile: WLCA-FM is a non-commercial station owned by Lewis & Clark Community College. The format of the station is alternative and new rock music. WLCA-FM broadcasts to the Godfrey, IL area at 89.9 FM.

WLCC-AM
Owner: Salem Communications
Editorial: 5211 W Laurel St Ste 101, Tampa, Florida 33607-1725. **T:** 1 813 639-1903
W: http://760radioluz.com
Editorial Profile: WLCC-AM is a commercial station owned by Salem Communications. The format of the station is Spanish Christian. WLCC-AM broadcasts to the Tampa Bay, FL area at 760 AM.

WLCE-FM
Owner: Midwest Family Stations
Editorial: 1510 N Third St, Riverton, Illinois 62561. **T:** 1 217 629-7077 **E:** alice@alice.fm
W: http://www.alice.fm
Editorial Profile: WLCE-FM is a commercial station owned by Midwest Family Stations. The format of the station is adult album alternative. WLCE-FM broadcasts to the Riverton, IL area at 97.7 FM.

WLCH-FM
Owner: SACA Spanish-American Civic Association
Editorial: 30 N Ann St, Lancaster, Pennsylvania 17602-3063. **T:** 1 717 295-7996
W: http://wlchradio.org
Editorial Profile: WLCH-FM is a non-commercial station owned by SACA Spanish-American Civic Association. The format of the station is Hispanic talk. WLCH-FM broadcasts in the Lancaster, PA area at 91.3 FM.

WLCK-AM
Owner: Skytower Communications Inc.
Editorial: 104 1/2 W Public Sq, Scottsville, Kentucky 42164-1175. **T:** 1 270 237-3148
E: newswatch@wvle.net

WLCM-AM
Owner: Christian Broadcasting System
Editorial: 1613 Lawrence Hwy, Charlotte, Michigan 48813. **T:** 1 517 543-8200
W: http://www.wlcmradio.com
Editorial Profile: WLCM-AM is a commercial station owned by Christian Broadcasting System. The format of the station is religious programming. WLCM-AM broadcasts to the Charlotte, MI area at 1500 AM.

WLCN-FM
Owner: KM Communications Inc.
Editorial: 1779 2250th St, Atlanta, Illinois 61723. **T:** 1 217 648-5510
E: lincolncountry@yahoo.com
W: http://www.wlcnonline.com
Editorial Profile: WLCN-FM is a commercial station owned by KM Communications Inc. The format of the station is contemporary country and classic rock. WLCN-FM broadcasts to the Atlanta, IL area at 96.3 FM.

WLCO-AM
Owner: Townsquare Media, LLC
Editorial: 3338 E Bristol Rd, Burton, Michigan 48529-1408. **T:** 1 810 743-1080
Editorial Profile: WLCO-AM is a commercial station owned by Townsquare Media, LLC. The format for the station is classic country.

WLCO-AM broadcasts to the Burton, MI area at 1530 AM.

WLCQ-FM
Owner: Lighthouse Christian Center
Editorial: 522 Springfield St, Feeding Hills, Massachusetts 01030-2104.
T: 1 413 821-0997 **E:** contact@wlcq.com
W: http://www.theq997.com
Editorial Profile: WLCQ-FM is a non-commercial station owned by Lighthouse Christian Center. The format of the station is contemporary Christian. WLCQ broadcasts to the Springfield, MA area at 99.7 FM.

WLCR-AM
Owner: LCR Partners LP
Editorial: 3600 Goldsmith Ln, Louisville, Kentucky 40220-2326. **T:** 1 502 451-9527
W: http://www.wlcr.org
Editorial Profile: WLCR-AM is a commercial station owned by LCR Partners LP. The format of the station is religious programming. WLCR-AM broadcasts to the Louisville, KY area at 1040 AM.

WLCS-FM
Owner: Cumulus Media Inc.
Editorial: 3375 Merriam St, Ste 201, Muskegon, Michigan 49444.
T: 1 231 830-0176
W: http://www.983wlcs.com
Editorial Profile: WLCS-FM is a commercial station owned by Cumulus Media Inc. The format of the station is classic hits music. WLCS-FM broadcasts to Muskegon, MI at 98.3 FM.

WLCT-FM
Owner: Lafayette Broadcasting Inc.
Editorial: 231 Chaffin Rd, Lafayette, Tennessee 37083-5004. **T:** 1 615 666-2169
E: wlct@nctc.com **W:** http://www.wlct.com
Editorial Profile: WLCT-FM is a commercial station owned by Lafayette Broadcasting Inc. The format of the station is country. WLCT-FM broadcasts to the Lafayette, TN area at 102.1 FM.

WLCU-FM
Owner: Campbellsville University
Editorial: 203 W Broadway St, Campbellsville, Kentucky 42718-2779. **T:** 1 270 789-5000
W: http://www.campbellsville.edu/wlcu
Editorial Profile: WLCU-FM is a non-commercial college station owned by Campbellsville University. The format of the station is Contemporary Christian. WLCU-FM broadcasts to the Campbellsville, KY area at a frequency of 88.7 FM.

WLCY-FM
Owner: Renda Broadcasting
Editorial: 840 Philadelphia St, Ste 100, Indiana, Pennsylvania 15701.
T: 1 724 465-4700
W: http://www.catcountry1063.com
Editorial Profile: WLCY-FM is a commercial station owned by Renda Broadcasting. The format of the station is contemporary country music. WLCY-FM broadcasts in the Indiana, PA area at 106.3 FM.

WLDA-FM
Owner: Alabama Media, LLC
Editorial: 285 N Foster St, Dothan, Alabama 36303-4541. **T:** 1 334 792-0047
Editorial Profile: WLDA-FM is a commercial station owned by Alabama Media, LLC. The format of the station is rock. WLDA-FM broadcasts to the Slocomb, AL area at 100.5 FM.

WLDB-FM
Owner: Milwaukee Radio Alliance
Editorial: N72W12922 Good Hope Rd, Menomonee Falls, Wisconsin 53051-4441.
T: 1 414 771-1021 **E:** info@b933fm.com
W: http://www.b933fm.com
Editorial Profile: WLDB-FM is a commercial station owned by Milwaukee Radio Alliance. The format of the station is adult contemporary. WLDB-FM broadcasts to the Milwaukee area at 93.3 FM.

WLDE-FM
Owner: Sarkes Tarzian Inc.
Editorial: 347 W Berry St Ste 600, Fort Wayne, Indiana 46802-2241.
T: 1 260 423-3676 **W:** http://www.wlde.com
Editorial Profile: WLDE-FM is a commercial station owned by Sarkes Tarzian Inc. The format of the station is classic hits. WLDE-FM broadcasts to the Fort Wayne, IN area at 101.7 FM.

WLDI-FM
Owner: Clear Channel Media and Entertainment
Editorial: 3071 Continental Dr, West Palm Beach, Florida 33407. **T:** 1 561 616-6600
W: http://www.wild955.com
Editorial Profile: WLDI-FM is a commercial station owned by Clear Channel Media and Entertainment. The format of the station is Top 40/CHR music. WLDI-FM broadcasts to the West Palm Beach, FL area at 95.5 FM.

WLDR-FM
Owner: Henderson, Roy E.
Editorial: 13999 S West Bay Shore Dr, Traverse City, Michigan 49684-5712.
T: 1 231 947-3220 **E:** wldrnews@gmail.com
W: http://www.wldrradio.com

WLDS-AM
Owner: Jacksonville Area Radio Broadcasters, Inc.
Editorial: 2161 Old State Rd, Jacksonville, Illinois 62650. **T:** 1 217 245-7171
E: wlds@wlds.com **W:** http://www.weai.com
Editorial Profile: WLDS-AM is a commercial station owned by Jacksonville Area Radio Broadcasters, Inc. The format of the station is news, talk and adult contemporary music. WLDS-AM broadcasts in the Jacksonville, IL area at 1180 AM.

WLDX-AM
Owner: Dean Broadcasting, Inc.
Editorial: 733 Columbus St E, Fayette, Alabama 35555. **T:** 1 205 932-9539
E: wldx@wldx.com **W:** http://www.wldx.com
Editorial Profile: WLDX-AM is a commercial station owned by Thomley Broadcasting Co. The format of the station is country music. WLDX-AM broadcasts to the Fayette, AL area at 990 AM.

WLDY-AM
Owner: Flambeau Broadcasting Co., Inc.
Editorial: W8746 US Highway 8, Ladysmith, Wisconsin 54848-9565. **T:** 1 715 532-5588
E: wldywjbl@yahoo.com
W: http://wldtwjbl.com
Editorial Profile: WLDY-AM is a commercial station owned by Flambeau Broadcasting Co., Inc. The format of the station is sports. WLDY-AM broadcasts to the Ladysmith, WI area at 1340 AM.

WLEA-AM
Owner: Canisteo Valley Broadcasting
Editorial: 5942 County Route 64, Hornell, New York 14843-9730. **T:** 1 607 324-1480
E: newsroom@am1480wlea.com
W: http://www.am1480wlea.com
Editorial Profile: WLEA-AM is a commercial station owned by Canisteo Valley Broadcasting. The format of the station is news. WLEA-AM broadcasts to the Hornell, NY area at 1480 AM.

WLEC-AM
Owner: BAS Broadcasting
Editorial: 1640 Cleveland Rd, Sandusky, Ohio 44870. **T:** 1 419 625-1010
W: http://www.wlec.com
Editorial Profile: WLEC-AM is a commercial station owned by BAS Broadcasting. The format of the station is adult standards. WLEC-AM broadcasts to the Sandusky, OH area at 1450 AM.

WLEE-AM
Owner: Davidson Media Group
Editorial: 308 W Broad St, Richmond, Virginia 23220. **T:** 1 804 643-0990
W: http://www.wlee990.am
Editorial Profile: WLEE-AM is a commercial station owned by Davidson Media Group. The format of the station is news and talk. WLEE-AM broadcasts to the Richmond, VA area at 990 AM.

WLEG-FM
Owner: Pathfinder Communications Corporation
Editorial: 216 W Market St, Warsaw, Indiana 46580-2800. **T:** 1 574 372-3064
W: http://www.1027thefan.com
Editorial Profile: WLEG-FM is a commercial station owned by Pathfinder Communications Corporation, a division of Federated Media. The format of the station is sports. WLEG-FM broadcasts to the Ligonier, Elkhart and Goshen areas in areas at a frequency of 102.7 FM.

WLEL-FM
Owner: Summer Rose Broadcasting
Editorial: 109 E Oglethorpe St, Ellaville, Georgia 31806. **T:** 1 229 937-9967
W: http://www.wlelclassichits.com
Editorial Profile: WLEL-FM is a commerical station in Americus, GA owned by Summer Rose Broadcasting. The format is classic hits and airs locally on 94.3 FM.

WLEM-AM
Owner: Salter Communications
Editorial: 241 West 4th St, Emporium, Pennsylvania 15834. **T:** 1 814 486-3712
E: wlemwqky@yahoo.com
W: http://www.theriver989.com
Editorial Profile: WLEM-AM is a commercial station owned by Salter Communications. The format of the station is adult hits. WLEM-AM broadcasts to the Emporium, PA area at 1250 AM.

WLEN-FM
Owner: Lenawee Broadcasting
Editorial: 242 W Maumee St, Adrian, Michigan 49221. **T:** 1 517 263-1039 **E:** news@wlen.com
W: http://www.wlen.com
Editorial Profile: WLEN-FM is a commercial station owned by Lenawee Broadcasting. The format of the station is adult contemporary. WLEN-FM broadcasts to the Adrian, MI area at 103.9 FM.

WLER-FM
Owner: Butler County Radio Network
Editorial: 112 Hollywood Dr, Ste 203, Butler, Pennsylvania 16001. **T:** 1 724 287-5778
E: frontdesk@bcrnetwork.com
W: http://www.977rocks.com
Editorial Profile: WLER-FM is a commercial station owned by Butler County Radio Network. The format of the station is active rock music. WLER-FM broadcasts to the Butler, PA area at 97.7 FM.

WLES-AM
Owner: Truth Broadcasting
Editorial: 2162 Lawrenceville Plank Rd, Lawrenceville, Virginia 23868.
T: 1 336 759-0363 **E:** info@wtru.com
W: http://www.wtru.com
Editorial Profile: WLES-AM is a commercial station owned by Truth Broadcasting. The format of the station is religious programming. WLES-AM broadcasts to the Lawrenceville, VA area at 590 AM.

WLEV-FM
Owner: Cumulus Media Inc.
Editorial: 2158 Avenue C, Ste 100, Bethlehem, Pennsylvania 18017. **T:** 1 610 266-7600
W: http://www.wlevradio.com
Editorial Profile: WLEV-FM is a commercial station owned by Cumulus Media Inc. The format of the station is adult contemporary. WLEV-FM broadcasts to the Bethlehem, PA area at 100.7 FM.

WLEW-AM
Owner: Thumb Broadcasting Inc.
Editorial: 935 S Van Dyke Rd, Bad Axe, Michigan 48413. **T:** 1 989 269-9931
E: wlew@avci.net **W:** http://www.thumbnet.net
Editorial Profile: WLEW-AM is a commercial station owned by Thumb Broadcasting Inc. The format of the station is classic country. WLEW-AM broadcasts to the Bad Axe, MI area at 1340 AM.

WLEW-FM
Owner: Thumb Broadcasting Inc.
Editorial: 935 S Van Dyke Rd, Bad Axe, Michigan 48413. **T:** 1 989 269-9931
E: wlew@avci.net **W:** http://www.thumbnet.net
Editorial Profile: WLEW-FM is a commercial station owned by Thumb Broadcasting Inc. The format of the station is classic hits. WLEW-FM broadcasts to the Flint, MI area at 102.1 FM.

WLEY-FM
Owner: Spanish Broadcasting System
Editorial: 150 N Michigan Ave Ste 1040, Chicago, Illinois 60601-7570.
T: 1 312 920-9500 **E:** info@laley1079.com
W: http://www.laley1079.com
Editorial Profile: WLEY-FM is a commercial station owned by the Spanish Broadcasting System. The format of the station is regional Mexican music. The station offers a digital Podcast. WLEY-FM broadcasts to the Chicago area at 107.9 FM

WLFA-FM
Owner: Radio Training Network, Inc.
Editorial: 2420 Wade Hampton Blvd, Greenville, South Carolina 29615.
T: 1 864 292-6040
E: comments@hisradio.com
W: http://www.hisradio.com
Editorial Profile: WLFA-FM is a non-commercial station owned by Radio Training Network, Inc. The format of the station is contemporary Christian. WLFA-FM broadcasts to the Greenville, SC area at 91.3 FM.

WLFC-FM
Owner: University of Findlay
Editorial: 1000 N Main St, Findlay, Ohio 45840. **T:** 1 419 434-6921
E: wlfc883@findlay.edu
Editorial Profile: WLFC-FM is a non-commercial station owned by University of Findlay. The format of the station is Indie Rock music. WLFC-FM broadcasts to the Findlay, OH, area at 88.3 FM.

WLFF-FM
Owner: Cumulus Media Inc.
Editorial: 11640 Hwy 17 Byp South, Murrells Inlet, South Carolina 29576.
T: 1 843 651-7869
W: http://1065thecoyote.com
Editorial Profile: WLFF-FM is a commercial station owned by Cumulus Media Inc. The format of the station is contemporary and classic country. WLFF-FM broadcasts to the Charleston, SC area at 106.5 FM.

WLFJ-AM
Owner: Radio Training Network, Inc.
Editorial: 2420 Wade Hampton Blvd, Greenville, South Carolina 29615-1146.
T: 1 864 292-6040
W: http://www.christiantalk660.com
Editorial Profile: WLFJ-AM is a commercial station owned by Radio Training Network, Inc. The format of the station is christian talk. WLFJ-AM broadcasts in the Greenville, SC area at 660 AM.

WLFJ-FM
Owner: Radio Training Network, Inc.
Editorial: 2420 Wade Hampton Blvd, Greenville, South Carolina 29615-1146.
T: 1 864 292-6040
E: comments@hisradio.com
W: http://www.hisradio.com
Editorial Profile: WLFJ-FM is a non-commercial station owned by Radio Training Network, Inc. The format of the station is contemporary Christian. WLFJ-FM broadcasts to the Greenville, SC area at 89.3 FM.

WLFK-FM
Owner: Community Broadcasters, LLC
Editorial: 199 Wealtha Ave, Watertown, New York 13601-1837. **T:** 1 315 393-1100
Editorial Profile: WLFK-FM is a commercial station owned by Community Broadcasters, LLC. The format of the station is country. WLFK-FM broadcasts to the Ogdensburg, NY area at 95.3 FM.

WLFN-AM
Owner: Mississippi Valley Broadcasters LLC
Editorial: 1407 2Nd Ave N, Onalaska, Wisconsin 54650-9166. **T:** 1 608 782-8335
E: news@lacrosseradiogroup.net
W: http://www.1490wlfn.com
Editorial Profile: WLFN-AM is a commercial station owned by Mississippi Valley Broadcasters LLC. The format of the station is talk. WLFN-AM broadcasts to the Onalaska, WI area at 1490 AM.

WLFR-FM
Owner: Richard Stockton College of New Jersey
Editorial: Richard Stockton College of NJ, 101 Vera King Farris Drive, Galloway, New Jersey 8205. **T:** 1 609 652-4781
E: wlfroffice@aim.com **W:** http://wlfr.fm
Editorial Profile: WLFR-FM is a non commercial station owned by Richard Stockton College of New Jersey. The format of the station is variety. WLFR-FM boradcasts to the Pomona, NJ area at 91.7 FM.

WLFS-FM
Owner: RadioTraining Network Inc.
Editorial: 5859 Abercorn St, Ste 3, Savannah, Georgia 31405-5530. **T:** 1 912 353-9226
W: http://www.hisradio.com
Editorial Profile: WLFS-FM is a non-commercial station owned by RadioTraining Network Inc. The format of the station is contemporary Christian. WLFS-FM broadcasts to the Savannah, GA area at 91.9 FM.

WLFV-FM
Owner: Main Line Broadcasting
Editorial: 300 Arboretum Pl, Ste 590, Richmond, Virginia 23236-3473.
T: 1 804 327-9902
W: http://www.931thewolf.com
Editorial Profile: WLFV-FM is a commercial station owned by Main Line Broadcasting. The format of the station is country. WLFV-FM

broadcasts to the Richmond, VA area at 93.1 FM.

WLFW-FM
Owner: South Central Communications Corp.
Editorial: 1162 Mount Auburn Rd, Evansville, Indiana 47720. **T:** 1 812 424-8284
W: http://www.935thewolf.com
Editorial Profile: WLFW-FM is a commercial station owned by South Central Communications Corp. The format of the station is classic country. WJPS-FM broadcasts to the Evansville, IN area at 93.5 FM.

WLFX-FM
Owner: Wallingford Broadcasting LLC
Editorial: 128 Big Hill Ave, Richmond, Kentucky 40475-2008. **T:** 1 606 723-5138
W: http://www.wlfxfm.com
Editorial Profile: WLFX-FM is a commercial station owned by Wallingford Broadcasting LLC. The format for the station is Top 40/CHR. WLFX-FM broadcasts to the Lexington, KY area at 106.7 FM.

WLFZ-AM
Owner: Saga Communications
Editorial: 1640 Old Russellville Pike, Clarksville, Tennessee 37043-1709.
T: 1 931 648-7720
W: http://www.eagle943.com
Editorial Profile: WLFZ-AM is a commercial station owned by Saga Communications (dba 5 Star Radio Group). The format is classic hits. WLFZ-AM broadcasts to the Nashville, TN area at 1370 AM.

WLFZ-FM
Owner: Saga Communications
Editorial: 3501 E Sangamon Ave, Springfield, Illinois 62707-9777. **T:** 1 217 753-5400
W: http://capitolwolf.com
Editorial Profile: WLFZ-FM is a commercial station owned by Saga Communications. The format of the station is contemporary country. WQQL-FM broadcasts to the Springfield, IL area at a frequency of 101.9 FM.

WLGC-FM
Owner: Greenup County Broadcasting, Inc.
Editorial: 1401 Winchester Ave, Ashland, Kentucky 41101-7587. **T:** 1 606 920-9565
E: production@wlgcradio.com
W: http://koolhits1057.com/
Editorial Profile: WLGC-FM is a commercial station owned by Greenup County Broadcasting, Inc. The format of the station is classic hits. WLGC-FM broadcasts to the Ashland, KY area at 105.7 FM.

WLGE-FM
Owner: Mesic (Michael J.)
Editorial: 10331 North Water Street, Ephraim, Wisconsin 54211. **T:** 1 920 854-3400
E: contact@fm1069thelodge.com
W: http://www.fm1069thelodge.com
Editorial Profile: WLGE-FM is a commercial station owned by Michael J. Mesic. The format of the station is adult album alternative. WLGE-FM broadcasts to the Ephraim, WI area at 106.9 FM.

WLGH-FM
Owner: Superior Communications
Editorial: 148 E Grand River Ave, Williamston, Michigan 48895. **T:** 1 517 381-0573
E: 411@smile.fm **W:** http://www.smile.fm
Editorial Profile: WLGH-FM is a non-commercial station owned by Superior Communications. The format of the station is contemporary Christian music and inspirational talk. WLGH-FM broadcasts to the Williamston, MI area at 88.1 FM.

WLGI-FM
Owner: Regional Baha'i Council of The Southern States
Editorial: 1272 Williams Hill Rd, Hemingway, South Carolina 29554-4039.
T: 1 866 501-9544 **E:** wlgi@usbnc.org
Editorial Profile: WLGI-FM is a non-commercial station owned by Regional Baha'i Council of The Southern States. The format of the station is religious music. WLGI-FM broadcasts to the Hemingway, SC area at 90.9 FM.

WLGN-AM
Owner: WLGN, LLC
Editorial: 1 Radio Ln, Logan, Ohio 43138.
T: 1 740 385-2151
Editorial Profile: WLGN-AM is a commercial station owned by WLGN, LLC. The format of the station is oldies. WLGN-AM broadcasts to the Hocking County, OH area at 1510 AM.

WLGP-FM
Owner: Good News Network
Editorial: 2278 Wortham Ln, Grovetown, Georgia 30813. **T:** 1 706 309-9610
W: http://www.gnnradio.org
Editorial Profile: WLGP-FM is a non-commercial station owned by Good News Network. The format of the station is religious. WLGP-FM broadcasts locally at 100.3 FM to the Harker's Island, NC area.

WLGT-FM
Owner: Media East, LLC
Editorial: 408 W Arlington Blvd Ste 101C, Greenville, North Carolina 27834-5706.
T: 1 252 446-9262
Editorial Profile: WLGT-FM is a commercial station owned by Media East, LLC. The format of the station is Contemporary Christian. WLGT-FM broadcasts to the New Bern, NC area at 98.3 FM.

WLGX-FM
Owner: Clear Channel Media and Entertainment
Editorial: 4000 Radio Dr, Ste 1, Louisville, Kentucky 40218-4568. **T:** 1 502 479-2222
W: http://www.genxlouisville.com
Editorial Profile: WLGX-FM is a commercial station owned by Clear Channel Media and Entertainment. The format of the station is adult contemporary and features music from the 1980s and 1990s. WLGX-FM broadcasts to the Louisville, KY area at 100.5 FM.

WLGZ-FM
Owner: DJRA Broadcasting
Editorial: 2494 Browncroft Blvd, Rochester, New York 14625. **T:** 1 585 264-1027
E: info@legends1027.com
W: http://www.legends1027.com
Editorial Profile: WLGZ-FM is a commercial station owned by DJRA Broadcasting. The format of the station is classic hits and oldies. WLGZ-FM broadcasts to the Rochester, NY area at 102.7 FM.

WLHC-FM
Owner: Woolstone Corporation
Editorial: 102 S Steele St, Ste 301, Sanford, North Carolina 27330-4288.
T: 1 919 775-1031 **E:** wlhc@life1031.com
W: http://www.life1031.com
Editorial Profile: WLHC-FM is a commercial station owned by Woolstone Corporation. The format of the station is oldies and adult standards. WLHC-FM broadcasts to the Sanford, NC area at 103.1 FM.

WLHH-FM
Owner: Low Country Radio, LLC
Editorial: 2 Corpus Christie Pl Ste 100A, Hilton Head Island, South Carolina 29928-1720. **T:** 1 843 363-9956
W: http://www.1049thesurf.com
Editorial Profile: WLHH-FM is a commercial station owned by Low Country Radio, LLC. The format for the station is classic hits. WLHH-FM broadcasts to the Hilton Head Island, SC area at 104.9 FM.

WLHK-FM
Owner: Emmis Communications Corp.
Editorial: 40 Monument Cir, Indianapolis, Indiana 46204-3019. **T:** 1 317 266-9700
W: http://www.971hankfm.com
Editorial Profile: WLHK-FM is a commercial station owned by Emmis Communications Corp. The format of the station is classic and contemporary country. WLHK-FM broadcasts to the Indianapolis area at 97.1 FM.

WLHM-FM
Owner: Mid-America Radio Group
Editorial: 425 2nd St, Logansport, Indiana 46947-3410. **T:** 1 574 722-4000
E: mix102wlhm@gmail.com
W: http://indianasbestradio.com/index-mix.php
Editorial Profile: WLHM-FM is a commercial station owned by Mid-America Radio Group. The format of the station is classic hits. WLHM-FM broadcasts to the Indianapolis area at 102.3 FM.

WLHR-FM
Owner: Georgia-Carolina Radiocasting Companies LLC
Editorial: 122715 Augusta Rd., Lavonia, Georgia 30553. **T:** 1 706 356-0921
E: wlhrpro@gmail.com
W: http://www.921wlhr.com
Editorial Profile: WLHR-FM is a commercial station owned by Georgia-Carolina Radiocasting Companies LLC. The format of the station is a mix of contemporary and classic country. WLHR-FM broadcasts to the Lavonia, GA area at 92.1 FM.

WLHT-FM
Owner: Townsquare Media, LLC
Editorial: 50 Monroe Ave NW, Ste 500, Grand Rapids, Michigan 49503. **T:** 1 616 451-4800
W: http://www.mychannel957.com
Editorial Profile: WLHT-FM is a commercial station owned by Townsquare Media, LLC. The format of the station is modern adult contemporary. WLHT-FM broadcasts to the Grand Rapids, MI area at 95.7 FM.

WLIB-AM
Owner: Emmis Communications Corp.
Editorial: 395 Hudson St Fl 7, New York, New York 10014-7452. **T:** 1 212 447-1000
E: info@wlib.com **W:** http://www.wlib.com
Editorial Profile: WLIB-AM is a commercial station owned by Emmis Communications Corp. The format of the station is gospel. WLIB-AM broadcasts to the New York area at 1190 AM.

WLIC-FM
Owner: He's Alive Inc.
Editorial: 34 Springs Road, Grantsville, Maryland 21536. **T:** 1 301 895-3292
W: http://www.hesalive.net
Editorial Profile: WLIC-FM is a non-commercial station owned by He's Alive Inc. The format of the station is contemporary Christian and gospel music. WLIC-FM broadcasts to the Grantsville, MD area at 97.1 FM.

WLIE-AM
Owner: Principle Broadcasting
Editorial: 2395 Ocean Ave, Ronkonkoma, New York 11779-5670. **T:** 1 631 580-0540
W: http://www.wlie540am.com
Editorial Profile: WLIE-AM is a commercial station owned by Principle Broadcasting. The format of the station is Hispanic Christian. WLIE-AM broadcasts in the New York City area at 540 AM.

WLIF-FM
Owner: CBS Radio
Editorial: 1423 Clarkview Rd Ste 100, Baltimore, Maryland 21209-2190.
T: 1 410 296-1019
W: http://todays1019.cbslocal.com/
Editorial Profile: WLIF-FM is a commercial station owned by CBS Radio. The format of the station is Lite Rock/Lite AC music. WLIF-FM broadcasts to the Baltimore area at 101.9 FM.

WLIH-FM
Owner: Good Christian Radio Broadcasting Inc.
Editorial: 2352 Charleston Rd, Wellsboro, Pennsylvania 16901. **T:** 1 570 724-4272
E: info@wlih.com **W:** http://www.wlih.com
Editorial Profile: WLIH-FM is a non-commercial station owned by Good Christian Radio Broadcasting Inc. The format of the station is Christian. WLIH-FM broadcasts to the Wellsboro, PA area at 107.1 FM.

WLIJ-AM
Owner: Jax Broadcasting, LLC
Editorial: 236 Woodland Dr, Shelbyville, Tennessee 37160-6759. **T:** 1 931 684-1514
E: wlijradio@gmail.com
Editorial Profile: WLIJ-AM is a commercial station owned by Jax Broadcasting, LLC. The format of the station is classic country. WLIJ-AM broadcasts to the Nashville, TN area at 1580 AM.

WLIK-AM
Owner: WLIK Inc.
Editorial: 640 W Highway 25 70, Newport, Tennessee 37821-8068. **T:** 1 423 623-3095
E: wlik@wilk.net **W:** http://www.wlik.net
Editorial Profile: WLIK-AM is a commercial station owned by WLIK Inc. The format of the station is oldies and religious talk. WLIK-AM broadcasts to Newport, TN and surrounding areas at 1270 AM.

WLIL-AM
Owner: Fowler's Holdings Inc.
Editorial: 14542 El Camino Ln, Lenoir City, Tennessee 37771. **T:** 1 865 986-7536
E: wlilcountry@aol.com
W: http://wlilcountry.com
Editorial Profile: WLIL-AM is a commercial station owned by Fowler's Holdings Inc. The format of the station is classic country and sports. WLIL-AM broadcasts to the Knoxville, TN area at 730 AM.

WLIM-AM
Owner: Polnet Communications
Editorial: 41 Pennsylvania Ave, Medford, New York 11763. **T:** 1 631 475-1580

E: radioadonai1580@hotmail.com
W: http://www.ministeriodiosestaaqui.com
Editorial Profile: WLIM-AM is a commercial station owned by Polnet Communications. The format of the station is Spanish Christian. WLIM-AM broadcasts to the Medford, NY area at 1580 AM.

WLIN-FM
Owner: Boswell Media LLC
Editorial: 1 Golf Course Rd, Kosciusko, Mississippi 39090. **T:** 1 662 289-1050
E: breezy@boswellmedia.net
W: http://www.breezynews.com
Editorial Profile: WLIN-FM is a commercial station owned by Boswell Media LLC. The format of the station is adult contemporary. WLIN-FM broadcasts to the Kosciusko, MO area at 101.1 FM.

WLIP-AM
Owner: Digity LLC
Editorial: 8500 Green Bay Rd, Pleasant Prairie, Wisconsin 53158-2721.
T: 1 262 694-7800 **W:** http://www.wlip.com
Editorial Profile: WLIP-AM is a commercial station owned by Digity LLC. The format of the station is talk. WLIP-AM broadcasts to the Milwaukee area at 1050 AM.

WLIQ-AM
Owner: Double O Radio
Editorial: 408 N 24th St, Quincy, Illinois 62301-3254. **T:** 1 573 221-3450
W: http://wliqlite1530.com
Editorial Profile: WLIQ-AM is a commercial station owned by Double O Radio. The format of the station is Lite Rock/Lite AC. WLIQ-AM broadcasts to the Quincy, IL area at 1530 AM.

WLIS-AM
Owner: Crossroads Communications LLC
Editorial: 777 River Rd, Middletown, Connecticut 06457-3922. **T:** 1 860 388-1420
E: radio@wliswmrd.net
W: http://www.wliswmrd.net
Editorial Profile: WLIS-AM is a commercial station owned by Crossroads Communications LLC. The format for the station is talk. WLIS-AM broadcasts to the Middletown, CT area at 1420 AM.

WLIT-FM
Owner: Clear Channel Media and Entertainment
Editorial: 233 N Michigan Ave Ste 2800, Chicago, Illinois 60601-5704.
T: 1 312 540-2000
W: http://www.939myfm.com
Editorial Profile: WLIT-FM is a commercial station owned by Clear Channel Media and Entertainment. The format of the station is Hot AC. WLIT-FM broadcasts to the entire Chicago metro area at 93.9 FM.

WLIV-AM
Owner: Sunny Broadcasting LLC
Editorial: 1130 W Main St, Livingston, Tennessee 38570-2206. **T:** 1 931 823-1226
W: http://wlivradio.com
Editorial Profile: WLIV-AM is a commercial station owned by Sunny Broadcasting LLC. The format of the station is classic country. WLIV-AM broadcasts to the Nashville, TN area at 920 AM.

WLIV-FM
Owner: Sunny Broadcasting LLC
Editorial: 1130 W Main St, Livingston, Tennessee 38570. **T:** 1 931 823-1226
Editorial Profile: WLIV-FM is a commercial station owned by Sunny Broadcasting LLC. The format of the station is contemporary country music. WLIV-FM broadcasts to the Livingston, TN area at 104.7 FM.

WLJA-FM
Owner: Tri-State Communications, Inc.
Editorial: 134 S Main St, Jasper, Georgia 30143-1702. **T:** 1 678 454-9350
W: http://wljaradio.com
Editorial Profile: WLJA-FM is a commercial station owned by Tri-State Communications, Inc. The format for the station is classic country, southern gospel, and sports. WLJA-FM broadcasts to the Atlanta area at 101.1 FM.

WLJC-FM
Owner: Hour of Harvest, Inc.
Editorial: 219 WLJC Dr., Beattyville, Kentucky 41311-9043. **T:** 1 606 464-3600
E: wljc@wljc.com **W:** http://www.wljc.com
Editorial Profile: WLJC-FM is a non-commercial station owned by Hour of Harvest, Inc. The format for the station is religious.

WLJC-FM broadcasts to the Beattyville, KY area at 102.1 FM.

WLJE-FM
Owner: Radio One Inc.
Editorial: 2755 Sager Rd, Valparaiso, Indiana 46383. **T:** 1 219 462-6111
W: http://www.indiana105.com
Editorial Profile: WLJE-FM is a commercial station owned by Radio One Inc. The format of the station is country. WLJE-FM broadcasts to the Valparaiso, IN area at 105.5 FM.

WLJK-FM
Owner: South Carolina Educational Television Commission
Editorial: 1101 George Rogers Blvd, Columbia, South Carolina 29201.
T: 1 803 737-3200 **W:** http://www.etvradio.org
Editorial Profile: WLJK-FM is a non-commercial station owned by South Carolina Educational Television Commission. The format of the station is news. WLJK-FM broadcasts to the Aiken and Augusta, SC areas at 89.1 FM. The station does not accept PSAs.

WLJN-AM
Owner: Good News Media Inc.
Editorial: 1101 Cass St, Traverse City, Michigan 49684-3235. **T:** 1 231 946-1400
E: info@wljn.com **W:** http://www.wljn.com
Editorial Profile: WLJN-AM is a non-commercial station owned by Good News Media Inc. The format of the station is Christian talk. WLJN-AM broadcasts to the Traverse City, MI area at 1400 AM.

WLJN-FM
Owner: Good News Media Inc.
Editorial: 1101 Cass St, Traverse City, Michigan 49684. **T:** 1 231 946-1400
E: info@wljn.com **W:** http://www.wljn.com
Editorial Profile: WLJN-FM is a non-commercial station owned by Good News Media Inc. The format of the station is Christian programming. WLJN-FM broadcasts to the Traverse City, MI area at 89.9 FM.

WLJR-FM
Owner: Briarwood Presbyterian Church
Editorial: 2200 Briarwood Way, Birmingham, Alabama 35243. **T:** 1 205 776-5232
E: info@briarwood.org
W: http://www.briarwood.org/wljr
Editorial Profile: WLJR-FM is a non-commercial station owned by the Briarwood Presbyterian Church. The format of the station is gospel music and religious talk. WLJR-FM broadcasts to the Birmingham, AL area at 88.5 FM.

WLJS-FM
Owner: Jacksonville State University
Editorial: 700 Pelham Rd N, Jacksonville, Alabama 36265. **T:** 1 256 782-5572
W: http://www.jsu.edu/92j
Editorial Profile: WLJS-FM is a commercial station owned by Jacksonville State University. The format of the station is jazz, news and album-oriented rock. WLJS-FM broadcasts to the Jacksonville, AL area at 91.9 FM.

WLJY-FM
Owner: Seehafer Broadcasting Corp.
Editorial: 645 25th Ave N, Wisconsin Rapids, Wisconsin 54495-2223. **T:** 1 715 424-1300
E: info@wfhr.com **W:** http://www.wrcwfm.com
Editorial Profile: WLJY-FM is a commercial station owned by Seehafer Broadcasting Corp. The format of the station is adult contemporary. WLJY-FM broadcasts to the Wisconsin Rapids, WI area at 105.5 FM.

WLKC-FM
Owner: Northeast Broadcasting Co.
Editorial: 30 How St, Haverhill, Massachusetts 01830-6131. **T:** 1 978 374-4733
W: http://www.wxrv.com
Editorial Profile: WLKC-FM is a commercial station owned by Northeast Broadcasting Co. The format of the station is adult album alternative. WLKC-FM broadcasts to Plymouth, MA at 105.7 FM.

WLKD-AM
Owner: NRG Media LLC
Editorial: 3616 State Highway 47 N, Rhinelander, Wisconsin 54501-8819.
T: 1 715 362-1975
W: http://www.am1570wlkd.com
Editorial Profile: WLKD-AM is a commercial station, owned by NRG Media LLC. The format of the station is soft AC. WLKD-AM broadcasts in the Minocqua, WI area at 1570 AM.

WLKE-FM
Owner: Radio Partners LLC
Editorial: 104 S Center St, Ebensburg, Pennsylvania 15931-1656. **T:** 1 814 472-4060
W: http://www.klove.com
Editorial Profile: WLKE-FM is a commercial station owned by Radio Partners LLC. The format of the station is Contemporary Christian. WLKE-FM broadcasts to the Altoona, PA area at 93.5 FM.

WLKF-AM
Owner: Hall Communications
Editorial: 404 W Lime St, Lakeland, Florida 33815-4651. **T:** 1 863 682-8184
W: http://www.wlkf.com
Editorial Profile: WLKF-AM is a commercial station owned by Hall Communications. The format of the station is talk. WLKF-AM broadcasts in the Tampa, FL, area at 1430 AM.

WLKG-FM
Owner: CTJ Communications Ltd.
Editorial: 500 Interchange N, Lake Geneva, Wisconsin 53147-8900. **T:** 1 262 249-9600
W: http://www.lake961.com
Editorial Profile: WLKG-FM is a commercial station owned by CTJ Communications Ltd. The format of the station is adult contemporary. WLKG-FM broadcasts to the Lake Geneva, WI area at 96.1 FM.

WLKH-FM
Owner: 2510 Associates
Editorial: 970 Tripoli St, Johnstown, Pennsylvania 15902. **T:** 1 814 534-8975
W: http://www.klove.com

WLKI-FM
Owner: Swick Broadcasting
Editorial: 2655 N State Road 127, Angola, Indiana 46703. **T:** 1 260 665-9554
E: wlki@wlki.com **W:** http://www.wlki.com
Editorial Profile: WLKI-FM is a commercial station owned by Swick Broadcasting. The format of the station is Hot AC. WLKI-FM broadcasts to the Angola, IN area at 100.3 FM.

WLKJ-FM
Owner: 2510 Associates
Editorial: 970 Tripoli St, Johnstown, Pennsylvania 15902. **T:** 1 800 434-8400
W: http://www.klove.com
Editorial Profile: WLKJ-FM is a commercial station owned by 2510 Associates in an LMA agreement with Educational Media Foundation. The format is contemporary Christian. The station airs in the Johnstown, PA area at 105.7 FM.

WLKK-FM
Owner: Entercom Communications Corp.
Editorial: 500 Corporate Pkwy Ste 200, Buffalo, New York 14226-1263.
T: 1 716 843-0600
W: http://www.alternativebuffalo.com
Editorial Profile: WLKK-FM is a commercial station owned by Entercom Communications Corp. The format of the station is alternative rock. WLKK-FM broadcasts to the Buffalo, NY area at 107.7 FM.

WLKL-FM
Owner: Lake Land College
Editorial: 5001 Lake Land Blvd, Mattoon, Illinois 61938. **T:** 1 217 234-5373
E: 899themax@lakelandcollege.edu
W: http://www.899themax.com
Editorial Profile: WLKL-FM is a non-commercial station owned by Lake Land College. The format of the station is variety. WLKL-FM broadcasts to the Mattoon, IL area at 89.9 FM.

WLKM-FM
Owner: Impact Radio, LLC
Editorial: 59750 Constantine Rd, Three Rivers, Michigan 49093-9303. **T:** 1 269 278-1815
E: info@wlkm.com **W:** http://www.wlkm.com
Editorial Profile: WLKM-FM is a commercial station owned by Impact Radio, LLC. The format of the station is adult contemporary. WLKM-FM broadcasts to the Grand Rapids, MI area at 95.9 FM.

WLKN-FM
Owner: Seehafer Broadcasting Corp.
Editorial: 1050 Linden St, Cleveland, Wisconsin 53015-1469. **T:** 1 920 693-3103
E: wlkn@wlkn.com **W:** http://www.wlkn.com
Editorial Profile: WLKN-FM is a commercial station owned by Seehafer Broadcasting Corp. The format of the station is adult contemporary. WLKN-FM broadcasts to the Cleveland, WI area at 98.1 FM.

WLKO-FM
Owner: Clear Channel Media and Entertainment
Editorial: 801 Woodrdg Ctr Dr, Charlotte, North Carolina 28217-1908.
T: 1 704 714-9444
W: http://www.1029thelake.com/main.html
Editorial Profile: WLKO-FM is a commercial station owned by Clear Channel Media and Entertainment. The format of the station is adult hits. WLKO-FM broadcasts to the Charlotte, NC area at 102.9 FM.

WLKQ-FM
Owner: Davis Broadcasting
Editorial: 1176 Satellite Blvd, Ste 200, Suwanee, Georgia 30024. **T:** 1 770 945-9953
E: laraza1023@hotmail.com
W: http://www.laraza1023.com
Editorial Profile: WLKQ-FM is a commercial station owned by Davis Broadcasting. The format of the station is Hispanic. WLKQ-FM broadcasts to the Atlanta area at 102.3 FM.

WLKR-AM
Owner: Elyria-Lorain Broadcasting
Editorial: 10327 US Highway 250 N, Milan, Ohio 44846. **T:** 1 419 668-8151
E: wlkr@wlkrradio.com
W: http://www.wlkrradio.com
Editorial Profile: WLKR-AM is a commercial station owned by Elyria-Lorain Broadcasting. The format of the station is classic hits. WLKR-AM broadcasts to the Milan, OH area at 95.3 FM.

WLKR-FM
Owner: Elyria-Lorain Broadcasting
Editorial: 10327 US Highway 250 N, Milan, Ohio 44846. **T:** 1 419 609-5961
E: wlkr@wlkrradio.com
W: http://www.wlkrradio.com
Editorial Profile: WLKR-FM is a commercial station owned by Elyria-Lorain Broadcasting. The format of the station is adult album alternative. WLKR-FM broadcasts to the Milan, OH area at 95.3 FM.

WLKS-AM
Owner: Morgan County Industries Inc.
Editorial: 129 College St, West Liberty, Kentucky 41472. **T:** 1 606 784-4141
E: radio41472@yahoo.com
Editorial Profile: WLKS-AM is a commercial station owned by Morgan County Industries Inc. The format of the station is oldies. WLKS-AM broadcasts to the West Liberty, KY area at 1450 AM.

WLKS-FM
Owner: Morgan County Industries Inc.
Editorial: 129 College St, West Liberty, Kentucky 41472. **T:** 1 606 743-1029
E: radio41472@yahoo.com
Editorial Profile: WLKS-FM is a commercial station owned by Morgan County Industries Inc. The format of the station is classic country music. WLKS-FM broadcasts to the West Liberty, KY, area at 102.9 FM.

WLKT-FM
Owner: Clear Channel Media and Entertainment
Editorial: 2601 Nicholasville Rd, Lexington, Kentucky 40503-3307. **T:** 1 859 422-1000
W: http://www.1045thecat.com
Editorial Profile: WLKT-FM is a commercial station owned by Clear Channel Media and Entertainment. The format of the station is Top 40/CHR. WLKT-FM broadcasts to the Lexington, KY area at 104.5 FM.

WLKW-AM
Owner: Hall Communications
Editorial: 75 Oxford St, Providence, Rhode Island 2905. **T:** 1 401 467-4366
Editorial Profile: WLKW-AM is a commercial station owned by Hall Communications. The format of the station is sports. WLKW-AM broadcasts to the Providence, RI area at 1450 AM.

WLKX-FM
Owner: Lakes Broadcasting Company, Inc.
Editorial: 14443 Armstrong Blvd NW, Ramsey, Minnesota 55303-7284. **T:** 1 763 450-7777
Editorial Profile: WLKX-FM is a commercial station owned by Lakes Broadcasting Company, Inc. The format of the station is Spanish Religious. The station broadcasts to the Forest Lake, MN area at 95.9 FM.

WLKZ-FM
Owner: Great Eastern Radio, LLC
Editorial: 25 Country Club Rd Bldg One, Gilford, New Hampshire 03249-6972.
T: 1 603 225-1160
W: http://www.thehawkrocks.com
Editorial Profile: WLKZ-FM is a commercial station owned by Great Eastern Radio, LLC. The format of the station is classic rock. WLKZ-FM broadcasts to the Gilford, NH area on 104.9 FM.

WLLD-FM
Owner: CBS Radio
Editorial: 9721 Executive Center Dr N, Ste 200, Saint Petersburg, Florida 33702.
T: 1 727 579-1925
W: http://www.wild941.com
Editorial Profile: WLLD-FM is a commercial station owned by CBS Radio. The format of the station is urban contemporary. WLLD-FM broadcasts to the Saint Petersburg, FL area at 94.1 FM.

WLLE-FM
Owner: Bristol Broadcasting
Editorial: 6000 Bristol Dr, Paducah, Kentucky 42003-9213. **T:** 1 270 554-0093
E: news@wkyq.com
W: http://www.willieradio.com
Editorial Profile: WLLE-FM is a commercial station owned by Bristol Broadcasting. The format of the station is country. WLLE-FM broadcasts to the Paducah, KY area at 102.1 FM.

WLLF-FM
Owner: Cumulus Media Inc.
Editorial: 2030 Pine Hollow Blvd, Hermitage, Pennsylvania 16148-2520. **T:** 1 724 346-4113
W: http://www.sportsradio967.com
Editorial Profile: WLLF-FM is a commercial station owned by Cumulus Media Inc. The format of the station is sports. WLLF-FM broadcasts to the Youngstown, OH area at 96.7 FM.

WLLG-FM
Owner: Flack Broadcasting Group
Editorial: 7606 N State St, Lowville, New York 13367. **T:** 1 315 376-7500
E: sales@themoose.net
W: http://www.themoose.net

WLLH-AM
Owner: Gois Broadcasting
Editorial: 122 Green St, Worcester, Massachusetts 01604-4138.
T: 1 508 791-2111
W: http://www.goisbroadcasting.com
Editorial Profile: WLLH-AM is a commercial station owned by Gois Broadcasting. The format of the station is Spanish variety. WLLH-AM broadcasts to Charlestown, MA at 1400 AM.

WLLI-AM
Owner: Forever Broadcasting
Editorial: 109 Plaza Dr, Johnstown, Pennsylvania 15905-1212. **T:** 1 814 255-4186
W: http://www.ntjnetwork.com
Editorial Profile: WLLI-AM is a commercial station owned by Forever Broadcasting. The format of the station is sports, news and talk. WLLI-AM broadcasts to the Johnstown, PA area at 990 AM.

WLLJ-FM
Owner: Friendship Broadcasting, LLC
Editorial: 5512 Ringgold Rd, Ste 214, Chattanooga, Tennessee 37412.
T: 1 423 892-1200 **E:** jocks@j103.com
W: http://www.j103.com
Editorial Profile: WLLJ-FM is a commercial station owned by Friendship Broadcasting, LLC. The format of the station is contemporary Christian. WLLJ-FM broadcasts to the Chattanooga, TN area at 103.1 FM.

WLLK-FM
Owner: Clear Channel Media and Entertainment
Editorial: 101 1st Radio Ln, Somerset, Kentucky 42503-4639. **T:** 1 606 678-5151
W: http://www.lake1023.com
Editorial Profile: WLLK-FM is a commercial station owned by Clear Channel Media and Entertainment. The format for the station is Top 40/CHR. WLLK-FM broadcasts to the Somerset, KY area at 102.3 FM.

WLLM-AM
Owner: Cornerstone Community Radio Inc.
Editorial: 800 S Postville Dr, Lincoln, Illinois 62656-1287. **T:** 1 217 735-9735
E: wllmam@juno.com
W: http://www.wllmradio.com
Editorial Profile: WLLM-AM is a non-commercial station owned by Cornerstone Community Radio Inc. The format of the station is easy listening and Christian. WLLM-AM broadcasts to the Lincoln, IL area at 1370

AM. The station is temporarily off-air due to technical problems resulting from an electrical fire.

WLLQ-AM
Owner: Davidson Media Group
Editorial: 3025 Waughtown St Ste G, Winston Salem, North Carolina 27107-1679.
T: 1 336 784-9004
W: http://www.quepasamedia.com
Editorial Profile: WLLQ-AM is a commercial station owned by Davidson Media Group. The format of the station is Regional Mexican. WLLQ-AM broadcasts to the Raleigh, NC area at 1530 AM.

WLLR-FM
Owner: Clear Channel Media and Entertainment
Editorial: 3535 E Kimberly Rd, Davenport, Iowa 52807-2583. **T:** 1 563 344-7000
W: http://www.1037wllr.com
Editorial Profile: WLLR-FM is a commercial station owned by Clear Channel Media and Entertainment. The format of the station is contemporary country. WLLR-FM broadcasts to the Davenport, IA area at 103.7 FM.

WLLT-FM
Owner: Sauk Valley Broadcasting Company
Editorial: 260 Il Route 2, Dixon, Illinois 61021. **T:** 1 815 284-1077
E: wllt@comcast.net
Editorial Profile: WLLT-FM is a commercial station owned by Sauk Valley Broadcasting Company. The format of the station is oldies music. WLLT-FM broadcasts to the Dixon, IL area at 107.7 FM.

WLLV-AM
Owner: Golden Door Broadcasting, LLC
Editorial: 2001 W Broadway, Ste 13, Louisville, Kentucky 40203. **T:** 1 502 776-1240
E: wlouwllv@aol.com
Editorial Profile: WLLV-AM is a commercial station owned by Golden Door Broadcasting, LLC. The format of the station is religous programming and teaching. WLLV-AM broadcasts in the Louisville, KY area at 1240 AM.

WLLW-FM
Owner: Finger Lakes Radio Group
Editorial: 3568 Lenox Rd, Geneva, New York 14456. **T:** 1 315 781-7000
E: news@flradiogroup.com
W: http://www.fingerlakesdailynews.com
Editorial Profile: WLLW-FM is a commercial station owned by Auburn Broadcasting, Inc. The format of the station is classic rock music. WLLW-FM broadcasts to the Geneva, NY area at 99.3 FM.

WLLX-FM
Owner: Prospect Communications
Editorial: 1212 N Locust Ave, Lawrenceburg, Tennessee 38464. **T:** 1 931 363-9997
E: wlxnews@bellsouth.net
W: http://www.wlxonline.com
Editorial Profile: WLLX-FM is a commercial station owned by Prospect Communications. The format of the station is contemporary country music. WLLX-FM broadcasts to the Nashville, TN area at 97.5 FM.

WLLY-FM
Owner: Glades Media Co.
Editorial: 530 E Alverdez Ave, Clewiston, Florida 33440-3901. **T:** 1 863 902-0995
W: http://www.radiofiesta.com
Editorial Profile: WLLY-FM is a commercial station owned by Glades Media Co. The format of the station is regional Mexican. WLLY-FM broadcasts to the Clewiston, FL area at 100.5 FM.

WLMA-AM
Owner: Anne's Entertainment Vision, Inc
Editorial: 1220 Bypass 72 NE, Greenwood, South Carolina 29649-2205.
T: 1 864 229-7984 **E:** wcrs@wcrs1450am.net
W: http://wlmawcrsradio.com
Editorial Profile: WLMA-AM is a commercial station owned by Anne's Entertainment Vision, Inc. The format of the station is news, sports and talk. WLMA-AM broadcasts to the Greenwood, SC area at 1350 AM.

WLMC-AM
Owner: Stalvey Communications
Editorial: 1217 Mcdonald Rd, Georgetown, South Carolina 29440-4555.
T: 1 843 546-1400 **E:** wlmcradio@aol.com
W: http://www.wlmcradio.com
Editorial Profile: WLMC-AM is a commercial station owned by Stalvey Communications. The format of the station is gospel music. WLMC-AM broadcasts to the Georgetown, SC area at 1470 AM.

WLMD-FM
Owner: Prestige Communications
Editorial: 31 E Side Sq, Macomb, Illinois 61455-2248. **T:** 1 309 833-2121
E: news@prestigeradio.com
W: http://www.prestigeradio.com
Editorial Profile: WLMD-FM is a commercial station owned by Prestige Communications. The format of the station is contemporary country. WLMD-FM broadcasts to the Macomb, IL area at 104.7 FM.

WLME-FM
Owner: Cromwell Group Inc.(The)
Editorial: 1115 Tamarack Rd, Owensboro, Kentucky 42301-6984. **T:** 1 270 683-5200
W: http://www.owensbororadio.com
Editorial Profile: WLME-FM is a commercial station owned by The Cromwell Group Inc. The format of the station is sports. WLME-FM broadcasts to the Owensboro, KY area at 102.9 FM.

WLMG-FM
Owner: Entercom Communications Corp.
Editorial: 400 Poydras St, Ste 800, New Orleans, Louisiana 70130. **T:** 1 504 593-6376
W: http://www.magic1019.com
Editorial Profile: WLMG-FM is a commercial station owned by Entercom Communications Corp. The format of the station is adult contemporary music. WLMG-FM broadcasts to the New Orleans area at 101.9 FM.

WLMI-FM
Owner: Midwest Communications, Inc.
Editorial: 2495 Cedar St, Holt, Michigan 48842. **T:** 1 517 699-0111
W: http://www.929wlmi.com
Editorial Profile: WLMI-FM is a commercial station owned by Midwest Communications, Inc. The format of the station is classic hits. WLMI-FM broadcasts to the Lansing, MI area at 92.7 FM.

WLML-FM
Owner: Robinson Entertainment, LLC
Editorial: 100 Lakeshore Dr Apt 2051, North Palm Beach, Florida 33408-3650.
T: 1 860 409-7297
Editorial Profile: WLML-FM is a commercial station owned by Robinson Entertainment, LLC. The format of the station is adult standards. WLML-FM broadcasts to the Palm Beach County, FL area at a frequency of 100.3 FM. Station will debut in November 2013.

WLMR-AM
Owner: Wilkins Communication Networks Inc.
Editorial: 3809 Ringgold Rd, Chattanooga, Tennessee 37412-1639. **T:** 1 423 624-4200
E: wlmr@wilkinsradio.com
W: http://www.wilkinsradio.com
Editorial Profile: WLMR-AM is a commercial station owned by Wilkins Communication Networks Inc. The format of the station is religious talk. WLMR-AM broadcasts to the Chattanooga, TN area at 1450 AM.

WLMU-FM
Owner: Lincoln Memorial University
Editorial: 6965 Cumberland Gap Pkwy, Harrogate, Tennessee 37752-8245.
T: 1 423 869-6331
W: http://www.913thegap.com
Editorial Profile: WLMU-FM is a non-commercial station owned by Lincoln Memorial University. The format of the station is a Top 40/CHR. WLMU-FM broadcasts to the Harrogate, TN and surrounding communities at 91.3 FM.

WLMV-AM
Owner: Midwest Family Stations
Editorial: 730 Rayovac Dr, Madison, Wisconsin 53711. **T:** 1 608 273-1000
W: http://www.lamovidaradio.com
Editorial Profile: WLMV-AM is a commercial station owned by Midwest Family Stations. The format of the station is Hispanic. WLMV-AM broadcasts to the Madison, Wi area at a frequency of 1480 AM.

WLMX-FM
Owner: Red Rock Radio Corp.
Editorial: 328 100Th St, Amery, Wisconsin 54001-4024. **T:** 1 715 268-7185
E: info@radio715.com **W:** http://radio715.com
Editorial Profile: WLMX-FM is a commercial station owned by Red Rock Radio Corp. The format of the station is adult variety hits. WLMX-FM broadcasts to the Amery, WI area at 104.9 FM.

WLMY-FM
Owner: Backyard Broadcasting
Editorial: 1685 Four Mile Dr, Williamsport, Pennsylvania 17701-1975. **T:** 1 570 323-8200
Editorial Profile: WLMY-FM is a commercial station owned by Backyard Broadcasting. The format of the station is Lite Rock/Lite AC. WLMY-FM broadcasts to the Williamsport, PA area at 107.9 FM.

WLNA-AM
Owner: Pamal Broadcasting Ltd.
Editorial: 715 Route 52, Beacon, New York 12508-1047. **T:** 1 845 838-6000
E: newsroom@pamal.com
W: http://www.hvradionet.com
Editorial Profile: WLNA-AM is a commercial station owned by Pamal Broadcasting Ltd. The format of the station is classic country. WLNA-AM broadcasts to the Beacon, NY area at 1420 AM.

WLNC-AM
Owner: Scotland Broadcasting Company, Inc.
Editorial: 1011 Lila Dr, Laurinburg, North Carolina 28352-3221. **T:** 1 910 276-1300
E: wlnc@wlncradio.com
W: http://www.wlncradio.com
Editorial Profile: WLNC-AM is a commercial station owned by Scotland Broadcasting Company, Inc. The format of the station is adult contemporary and oldies. WLNC-AM broadcasts to the Laurinburg, NC area at 1300 AM.

WLND-FM
Owner: Clear Channel Media and Entertainment
Editorial: 7413 Old Lee Hwy, Chattanooga, Tennessee 37421. **T:** 1 423 892-3333
W: http://www.981thelake.com
Editorial Profile: WNLD-FM is a commercial station owned by Clear Channel Media and Entertainment. The format of the station is adult hits. WLND-FM broadcasts to the Chattanooga, TN area at 98.1 FM.

WLNG-FM
Owner: Main Street Broadcasting Co., Inc.
Editorial: 23 Redwood Rd, Sag Harbor, New York 11963-2639. **T:** 1 631 725-2300
E: info@wlng.com **W:** http://www.wlng.com
Editorial Profile: WLNG-FM is a commercial station owned by Main Street Broadcasting Co., Inc. The The format of the station is oldies music. WLNG-FM broadcasts in the Sag Harbor, NY area at 92.1 FM area.

WLNH-FM
Owner: WBIN, Inc.
Editorial: 2 Capital Plz Ste 105, Concord, New Hampshire 03301-4911. **T:** 1 603 224-8486
W: http://www.wlnh.com
Editorial Profile: WLNH-FM is a commercial station owned by WBIN, Inc. The format of the station is adult contemporary. WLNH-FM broadcasts to the Gilford, NH area at 98.3 FM.

WLNI-FM
Owner: Wheeler Inc.(Mel)
Editorial: 3934 Electric Rd, Roanoke, Virginia 24018-4513. **T:** 1 434 845-5463
E: comments@wlni.com
W: http://www.wlni.com
Editorial Profile: WLNI-FM is a commercial station owned by Wheeler Inc.(Mel). The format of the station is news and talk. WLNI-FM broadcasts to the Lynchburg, VA area at 105.9 FM.

WLNK-FM
Owner: Greater Media Inc.
Editorial: 1 Julian Price Pl, Charlotte, North Carolina 28208. **T:** 1 704 374-3500
W: http://www.1079thelink.com
Editorial Profile: WLNK-FM is a commercial station owned by Greater Media Inc. The format of the station is hot adult contemporary music and talk. WLNK-FM broadcasts to the Charlotte, NC area at 107.9 FM.

WLNL-AM
Owner: Trinity Media Ltd.
Editorial: 3134 Lake Rd, Horseheads, New York 14845. **T:** 1 607 330-0223
Editorial Profile: WLNL-AM is a commercial station owned by Trinity Media Ltd. The format of the station is contemporary Christian music and religious talk programming. WLNL-AM broadcasts to the Horseheads, NY area at 1000 AM.

WLNX-FM
Owner: Lincoln University
Editorial: 300 Keokuk St, Lincoln, Illinois 62656-1630. **T:** 1 217 732-3155
W: http://www.wlnxradio.com
Editorial Profile: WLNX-FM is a non-commercial college station owned by Lincoln University. The format of the station is alternative rock. WLNX-FM broadcasts to the Lincoln, IL area at a frequency of 88.9 FM.

WLNZ-FM
Owner: Lansing Community College
Editorial: 400 N Capitol Ave, Ste 001, Lansing, Michigan 48933. **T:** 1 517 483-1710
E: wlnzinfo@yahoo.com
W: http://www.lcc.edu/radio
Editorial Profile: WLNZ-FM is a non-commercial station owned by Lansing Community College. The format of the station is adult album alternative, jazz and blues. WLNZ-FM broadcasts to the Lansing, MI area at 89.7 FM.

WLOB-AM
Owner: Atlantic Coast Radio LLC
Editorial: 779 Warren Ave, Portland, Maine 04103-1007. **T:** 1 207 773-9695
E: newstalkwlob@yahoo.com
W: http://www.wlobradio.com
Editorial Profile: WLOB-AM is a commercial station owned by Atlantic Coast Radio LLC. The format of the station is news talk. WLOB-AM broadcasts to the Portland, ME area at 1310 AM.

WLOC-AM
Owner: Forbis Communications Inc.
Editorial: 1130 S Dixie St, Horse Cave, Kentucky 42749-1462. **T:** 1 270 786-1000
E: wloc@scrtc.com
W: http://www.wloconline.com
Editorial Profile: WLOC-AM is a commercial station owned by Forbis Communications Inc. The format of the station is news, talk, and sports with a focus on Reds Baseball. WLOC-AM broadcasts to the Horse Cave, KY area at 1150 AM.

WLOE-AM
Owner: Mayo Broadcasting Corporation
Editorial: 1203 Harris St, Eden, North Carolina 27288-6321. **T:** 1 336 627-9563
W: http://www.wloewmyn.com
Editorial Profile: WLOE-AM is commercial station owned by Mayo Broadcasting Corporation. The format of the station is religious programming, news and talk. WLOE-AM broadcasts to the Greensboro-Winston Salem, NC area at 1490 AM.

WLOF-FM
Owner: Holy Family Communications
Editorial: 6325 Sheridan Dr, Williamsville, New York 14221. **T:** 1 716 839-6117
E: info@wlof.net **W:** http://www.wlof.net
Editorial Profile: WLOF-FM is a non-commercial station owned by Holy Family Communications. The format of the station is religious. WLOF-FM broadcasts to the Williamsville, NY area at 101.7 FM.

WLOH-AM
Owner: Bohach(Mark & Arlene)
Editorial: 2686 N Columbus St, Ste 101, Lancaster, Ohio 43130. **T:** 1 740 653-4373
E: news@wloh.net **W:** http://www.wloh.net
Editorial Profile: WLOH-AM is a commercial station owned by Mark and Arlene Bohach. The format of the station is news, talk and sports. WLOH-AM broadcasts to Lancaster, OH at 1320 AM.

WLOI-AM
Owner: La Porte County Broadcasting Co. Inc.
Editorial: 1700 Lincolnway Pl, Ste 8, La Porte, Indiana 46350. **T:** 1 219 362-6144
Editorial Profile: WLOI-AM is a commercial station owned by the La Porte County Broadcasting Co. Inc. The format of the station is adult standards. WLOI-AM broadcasts to the La Porte, IN area at 1540 AM.

WLOK-AM
Owner: Gilliam Communications Inc.
Editorial: 363 S 2nd St, Memphis, Tennessee 38103. **T:** 1 901 527-9565
E: wlokradio@aol.com
W: http://www.wlok.com
Editorial Profile: WLOK-AM is a commercial station owned by Gilliam Communications Inc. The format of the station is gospel music. WLOK-AM broadcasts to the Memphis, TN area at 1340 AM.

WLOL-AM
Owner: Starboard Media Foundation Inc.
Editorial: 7575 Golden Valley Rd Ste 310, Golden Valley, Minnesota 55427-4596.
T: 1 612 643-4110 **E:** info@relevantradio.com

W: http://www.relevantradio.com
Editorial Profile: WLOL-AM is a commercial station owned by Starboard Media Foundation Inc. The format of the station is religious programming. WLOL-AM broadcasts to the Golden Valley, MN area at 1330 AM.

WLOL-FM
Owner: Light of Life Community, Inc
Editorial: 132 Carubia Dr, Core, West Virginia 26541-7137. **T:** 1 304 598-0026
E: info@lolradio.org **W:** http://lolradio.org
Editorial Profile: WLOL-FM is a non-commercial station owned by Light of Life Community, Inc. The format of the station is religious featuring a focus on Catholicism. WLOL-FM broadcasts to the Star City, Morgantown, Granville, Westover areas in West Virginia at a frequency of 89.7 FM.

WLON-AM
Owner: HRN Broadcasting Inc.
Editorial: 1366 Startown Rd, Lincolnton, North Carolina 28092. **T:** 1 704 735-8071
E: info@hrnb.com
W: http://www.hrnb.com/wlon_index.html
Editorial Profile: WLON-AM is a commercial station owned by HRN Broadcasting Inc. The format of the station is oldies and sports. WLON-AM broadcasts to the Lincolnton, NC area at 1050 AM.

WLOP-AM
Owner: Jesup Broadcasting Corp.
Editorial: 2420 Waycross Hwy, Jesup, Georgia 31545-2332. **T:** 1 912 427-3711
E: comments@wlop1370.com
Editorial Profile: WLOP-AM is a commercial station owned by Jesup Broadcasting Corp. The format for the station is sports. WLOP-AM broadcasts to the Savannah, GA area at 1370 AM.

WLOR-AM
Owner: Black Crow Broadcasting Inc.
Editorial: 1555 the Boardwalk Ste 1, Huntsville, Alabama 35816-1821.
T: 1 256 536-1568
W: http://rocketcitynews.com
Editorial Profile: WLOR-AM is a commercial station owned by Black Crow Broadcasting Inc. The format of the station is R&B oldies. WLOR-AM broadcasts to the Huntsville, AL area at 1550 AM.

WLOU-AM
Owner: Golden Door Broadcasting, LLC
Editorial: 2001 W Broadway Ste 13, Louisville, Kentucky 40203-3584. **T:** 1 502 776-1240
E: wlouwllv@aol.com
Editorial Profile: WLOU-AM is a commercial station owned by Golden Door Broadcasting, LLC. The format of the station is gospel music. WLOU-AM broadcasts to the Louisville, KY area at 1350 AM.

WLOV-FM
Owner: Hall, Susan
Editorial: 3889 S Atlantic Ave, Daytona Beach, Florida 32118-7701. **T:** 1 386 255-9300
Editorial Profile: WLOV-FM is a commercial station owned by Susan Hall and operated by Black Crow Radio. The format of the station is soft adult contemporary. WLOV-FM broadcasts to the Daytona Beach, FL area at a frequency of 99.5 FM.

WLOY-AM
Owner: Three Rivers Media Corp.
Editorial: 110 W Spiller St, Wytheville, Virginia 24382. **T:** 1 276 228-3185
E: office@threeriversmedia.net
W: http://www.wxbx.com

WLPA-AM
Owner: Hall Communications
Editorial: 1996 Auction Rd, Manheim, Pennsylvania 17545-9159. **T:** 1 717 653-0800
W: http://www.wlpa.com
Editorial Profile: WLPA-AM is a commercial station owned by Hall Communications. The format of the station is sports, news and talk. WLPA-AM broadcasts to the Manheim, PA area at 1490 AM.

WLPE-FM
Owner: Good News Network
Editorial: 2278 Wortham Ln, Grovetown, Georgia 30813. **T:** 1 706 309-9610
W: http://www.gnnradio.org
Editorial Profile: WLPE-FM is a non-commercial station owned by Good News Network. The format of the station is

WLPK-AM
Owner: Rodgers Broadcasting Corp.
Editorial: 406 1/2 N Central Ave, Connersville, Indiana 47331-1926. **T:** 1 765 825-6411
W: http://superoldies1580.com
Editorial Profile: WLPK-AM is a commercial station owned by Rodgers Broadcasting Corp. The format of the station is oldies music. WLPK-AM broadcasts to the Connersville, IN area at 1580 AM.

WLPO-AM
Owner: LaSalle County Broadcasting Corp.
Editorial: 1 Broadcast Ln, Oglesby, Illinois 61348-9539. **T:** 1 815 223-3100
W: http://wlpoamandfm.com
Editorial Profile: WLPO-AM is a commercial station owned by LaSalle County Broadcasting Corp. The format of the station is classic hits. WLPO-AM broadcasts to the Chicago area at 1220 AM.

WLPR-AM
Owner: Goforth Media Inc.
Editorial: 6530-B Spanish Fort Blvd, Spanish Fort, Alabama 36527-5014. **T:** 1 251 473-8488
E: news@goforth.org
W: http://www.goforth.org
Editorial Profile: WLPR-AM is a commercial station owned by Goforth Media Inc. The format of the station is Southern gospel. WLPR-AM broadcasts in the Mobile, AL area at 960 AM.

WLPR-FM
Owner: Northwest Indiana Public Broadcasting, Inc.
Editorial: 8625 Indiana Pl, Merrillville, Indiana 46410-6369. **T:** 1 219 756-5656
E: news@lakeshorepublicmedia.org
W: http://www.thelakeshorefm.com
Editorial Profile: WLPR-FM is a non-commercial station owned by Northwest Indiana Public Broadcasting, Inc. The format of the station is news and talk. WLPR-FM broadcasts to the Merrillville, IN area at 89.1 FM.

WLPW-FM
Owner: Mountain Communications
Editorial: 159 Santanoni Ave, Saranac Lake, New York 12983. **T:** 1 518 891-1544
E: news@wnbz.com
W: http://www.theclassicrock105.com
Editorial Profile: WLPW-FM is a commercial station owned by Mountain Communications. The format of the station is classic rock. WLPW-FM broadcasts to the Saranac Lake, NY area at 105.5 FM.

WLQB-FM
Owner: Clear Channel Media and Entertainment
Editorial: 4841 Highway 17 Byp S, Myrtle Beach, South Carolina 29577-6683.
T: 1 843 293-0107
Editorial Profile: WLQB-FM is a commercial station owned by Clear Channel Media and Entertainment. The format of the station is adult contemporary. WLQB-FM broadcasts to the Ocean Isle, NC area at 93.5 FM.

WLQH-AM
Owner: Dix Communications
Editorial: 2830 Nw Old Fannin Rd, Chiefland, Florida 32626-9172. **T:** 1 352 493-4940
W: http://www.trueoldies.com
Editorial Profile: WLQH-AM is a commercial station owned by Dix Communications. The format of the station is oldies. WLQH-AM broadcasts to the Chiefland, FL area at 940 AM.

WLQI-FM
Owner: Brothers Broadcasting Corp.
Editorial: 560 W Amsler Rd, Rensselaer, Indiana 47978. **T:** 1 219 866-4104
E: wrin@ffni.com
Editorial Profile: WLQI-FM is a commercial station owned by Brothers Broadcasting Corporation. The format of the station is classic hits. WLQI-FM broadcasts to the Rensselaer, IN area at 97.7 FM.

WLQK-FM
Owner: Stonecom Cookeville LLC
Editorial: 259 S Willow Ave, Cookeville, Tennessee 38501. **T:** 1 931 528-6064
W: http://www.literock959.com
Editorial Profile: WLQK-FM is a commercial station owned by Stonecom Cookeville LLC. The format of the station is Lite Rock/Lite AC. WLQK-FM broadcasts to the Cookeville, TN area at 95.9 FM.

WLQM-AM
Owner: Franklin Broadcasting Corp.
Editorial: 320 N Franklin St, Franklin, Virginia 23851. **T:** 1 757 562-3135
E: wlqm@wlqmradio.com
W: http://www.wlqmradio.com
Editorial Profile: WLQM-AM is a commercial station owned by Franklin Broadcasting Corp. The format of the station is gospel music. WLQM-AM broadcasts to the Franklin, VA area at 1250 AM.

WLQM-FM
Owner: Franklin Broadcasting Corp.
Editorial: 320 N Franklin St, Franklin, Virginia 23851. **T:** 1 757 562-3135
E: wlqm@wlqmradio.com
W: http://www.wlqmradio.com
Editorial Profile: WLQM-FM is a commercial station owned by Franklin Broadcasting Corp. The format of the station is a mix of contemporary and classic country. WLQM-FM broadcasts to the Franklin, VA area at 101.7 FM.

WLQR-AM
Owner: Cumulus Media Inc.
Editorial: 3225 Arlington Ave, Toledo, Ohio 43614-2427. **T:** 1 419 725-5700
W: http://talkradio1470.com
Editorial Profile: WLQR-AM is a commercial station owned by Cumulus Media Inc. The format of the station is news/talk. WLQR-AM broadcasts to the Toledo, OH area at 1470 AM.

WLQR-FM
Owner: Cumulus Media Inc.
Editorial: 3225 Arlington Ave, Toledo, Ohio 43614-2427. **T:** 1 419 725-5700
W: http://www.1065theticket.com
Editorial Profile: WLQR-FM is a commercial station owned by Cumulus Media Inc. The format of the station is sports. WLQR-FM-FM broadcasts to the Toledo, OH area at 106.5 FM.

WLQT-FM
Owner: Clear Channel Media and Entertainment
Editorial: 101 Pine St, Dayton, Ohio 45402.
T: 1 937 224-1137
W: http://www.945litefm.com
Editorial Profile: WLQT-FM is a commercial station owned by Clear Channel Media and Entertainment. The format of the station is Soft AC. WDKF-FM broadcasts to the Dayton, OH area at 94.5 FM.

WLQV-AM
Owner: Salem Communications
Editorial: 2 Radio Plaza St, Ferndale, Michigan 48220-2129. **T:** 1 248 581-1234
W: http://www.faithtalk1500.com
Editorial Profile: WLQV-AM is a commercial station owned by Salem Communications. The format of the station is Christian programming. WLQV-AM broadcasts to the Ferndale, MI area at 1500 AM.

WLQY-AM
Owner: Entravision Communications Corp.
Editorial: 10800 Biscayne Blvd, Ste 810, Miami, Florida 33161. **T:** 1 305 891-1729
E: wlqy@bellsouth.net
Editorial Profile: WLQY-AM is a commercial station owned by Entravision Communications Corp. The format of the station is variety programming. WLQY-AM broadcasts to the Miami area at 1320 AM.

WLRA-FM
Owner: Lewis University
Editorial: 1 University Pkwy, Box 11, Romeoville, Illinois 60446. **T:** 1 815 836-5214
E: wlraradio@lewisu.edu
W: http://www.wlraradio.com
Editorial Profile: WLRA-FM is a non-commercial station owned by Lewis University. The format of the station is variety. WLRA-FM broadcasts to the Romeoville, IL area at 88.1 FM.

WLRB-AM
Owner: Colchester Radio, Inc.
Editorial: 31 E Side Sq, Macomb, Illinois 61455-2248. **T:** 1 309 833-2121
E: news@prestigeradio.com
W: http://www.prestigeradio.com
Editorial Profile: WLRB-AM is a commercial station owned by Colchester Radio, Inc. The format of the station is talk. WLRB-AM broadcasts to the Macomb, IL area at 1510 AM.

WLRC-AM
Owner: Clayton(B.R. & Martha)
Editorial: Po Box 37, 7760 Highway 72 East, Walnut, Mississippi 38683-0037.
T: 1 662 223-4071
W: http://www.wlrcradio.com
Editorial Profile: WLRC-AM is a commercial station owned by B.R. & Martha Clayton. The format of the station is southern gospel and religious. WLRC-AM broadcasts to the Walnut, MS area at 850 AM.

WLRD-FM
Owner: Christian Faith Broadcast, Inc.
Editorial: 3809 Maple Ave, Castalia, Ohio 44824-9484. **T:** 1 419 684-5311
E: fm97.7@cfbroadcast.net
W: http://www.wlrd.net
Editorial Profile: WLRD-FM is a commercial station owned by Christian Faith Broadcast, Inc. The format of the station is Southern gospel. WRLD-FM broadcasts to the Castalia, OH area at 96.9 FM.

WLRH-FM
Owner: Alabama Educational Television Commission
Editorial: U A H Campus John Wright Dr, Huntsville, Alabama 35899-0001.
T: 1 256 895-9574 **W:** http://www.wlrh.org
Editorial Profile: WLRH-FM is a non-commercial station owned by Alabama Educational Television Commission. The format of the station is news, classical and jazz. WLRH-FM broadcasts to the Huntsville, AL area at 89.3 FM.

WLRM-AM
Owner: CPT & T RADIO STATION, INC.
Editorial: 6960 Bucknell Rd, Millington, Tennessee 38053-7502. **T:** 1 901 872-8861
W: http://www.wlrm1380.com
Editorial Profile: WLRM-AM is a non-commercial station owned by CPT & T RADIO STATION, INC. The format of the station is Spanish Contemporary Christian. WLRM-AM broadcasts to the Millington, TN area.

WLRN-FM
Owner: Miami-Dade County School Board
Editorial: 172 NE 15th St, Miami, Florida 33132-1348. **T:** 1 305 995-1717
E: info@wlrn.org **W:** http://www.wlrn.org
Editorial Profile: WLRN-FM is a non-commercial station owned by the Miami-Dade County School Board. The format of the station is jazz, news and talk. WLRN-FM broadcasts to the Miami at 91.3 FM.

WLRO-AM
Owner: Clear Channel Media and Entertainment
Editorial: 5555 Hilton Ave Ste 500, Baton Rouge, Louisiana 70808-2564.
T: 1 225 231-1860
W: http://www.247comedy.com
Editorial Profile: WLRO-AM is a commercial station owned by Clear Channel Media and Entertainment. The format of the station is comedy. WLRO-AM broadcasts to the Baton Rouge, LA area at 1210 AM.

WLRQ-FM
Owner: Clear Channel Media and Entertainment
Editorial: One Radio Center, 1388 S Babcock St, Melbourne, Florida 32901-3009.
T: 1 321 733-1000 **E:** literock@wlrq.com
W: http://www.wlrq.com
Editorial Profile: WLRQ-FM is a commercial station owned by Clear Channel Media and Entertainment. The format of the station is easy listening. WLRQ-FM broadcasts to the Melbourne, FL area at 99.3 FM.

WLRS-AM
Owner: New Albany Broadcasting, Inc.
Editorial: 220 Potters Ln, Clarksville, Indiana 47129-1020. **T:** 1 812 949-1570
W: http://www.newstalk1570.com
Editorial Profile: WLRS-AM is a commercial station owned by New Albany Broadcasting, Inc. The format of the station is news talk. WLRS-AM broadcasts to the Eminence, KY and surrounding areas at 1600 AM.

WLRT-AM
Owner: Christian Broadcasting System
Editorial: 501 Darby Creek Rd, Ste 62, Lexington, Kentucky 40509.
T: 1 859 264-9700
W: http://www.wlrtradio.com
Editorial Profile: WLRT-AM is a commercial station owned by Christian Broadcasting System. The format of the station is news and talk programming. WLRT-AM broadcasts to the Lexington, KY area at 1250 AM.

WLRV-AM
Owner: Ward Broadcasting Corp.(Gary W.)
Editorial: 484 W Main St, Lebanon, Virginia 24266. **T:** 1 276 889-1380 **E:** radio@wlrv.com
W: http://www.wlrv.com

Editorial Profile: WLRV-AM is a commercial station owned by Gary W. Ward Broadcasting Corp. The format of the station is country, classic rock, bluegrass and southern gospel music. WLRV-AM broadcasts to the Lebanon, VA area at 1380 AM.

WLRW-FM
Owner: Saga Communications
Editorial: 2603 W Bradley Ave, Champaign, Illinois 61821-1823. **T:** 1 217 352-4141
E: production@mix945.com
W: http://www.mix945.com
Editorial Profile: WLRW-FM is a commercial station owned by Saga Communications. The format is hot adult contemporary. The station airs at 94.5 FM in the Champaign, IL area.

WLRX-FM
Owner: Clear Channel Media and Entertainment
Editorial: 134 4th Ave, Huntington, West Virginia 25701-1220. **T:** 1 304 525-7788
W: http://www.1071thebear.com/main.html
Editorial Profile: WLRX-FM is a commercial station owned by Clear Channel Media and Entertainment. The format of the station is classic country. WLRX-FM broadcasts to Huntington, WV and surrounding communities at 107.1 FM.

WLRY-FM
Owner: Archangel Broadcasting Foundation
Editorial: 4244 Logan Thornville Rd NE, Rushville, Ohio 43150. **T:** 1 740 536-0885
W: http://www.wlry.org
Editorial Profile: WLRY-FM is a non-commercial station owned by Archangel Broadcasting Foundation. The format of the station is Christian music and talk programming. WLRY-FM broadcasts to the Rushville, OH area at 88.5 FM.

WLS-AM
Owner: Cumulus Media Inc.
Editorial: 190 N State St, Chicago, Illinois 60601-3302. **T:** 1 312 984-0890
W: http://www.wlsam.com
Editorial Profile: WLS-AM is a commercial station owned by Cumulus Media Inc. The format of the station is news and talk. WLS-AM broadcasts to the Chicago area at 890 AM.

WLSC-AM
Owner: Banana Jack Productions, LLC
Editorial: 4164 Main St, Loris, South Carolina 29569. **T:** 1 843 756-5225
E: info@wlscradio.com
W: http://www.tigerradio.com
Editorial Profile: WLSC-AM is a commercial station owned by Banana Jack Productions, LLC. The format of the station is oldies. WLSC-AM broadcasts to the Loris, SC area at 1240 AM.

WLSD-AM
Owner: Valley Broadcasting
Editorial: 1748 Holton Ave E, Big Stone Gap, Virginia 24219-3346. **T:** 1 276 523-1700
Editorial Profile: WLSD-AM is a commercial station owned by Valley Broadcasting. The format of the station is Southern gospel and religious programming. WLSD-AM broadcasts to the Big Stone Gap, VA area at 1220 AM.

WLS-FM
Owner: Cumulus Media Inc.
Editorial: 190 N State St, Chicago, Illinois 60601-3302. **T:** 1 312 984-9923
W: http://www.947wls.com
Editorial Profile: WLS-FM is a commercial station owned by Cumulus Media Inc. The format of the station is classic hits. WLS-FM broadcasts to the Chicago area at 94.7 FM.

WLSH-AM
Owner: J-Systems Franchising Corp.
Editorial: 2147 Market St, Nesquehoning, Pennsylvania 18240-1422. **T:** 1 570 645-3123
E: wmgh@ptd.net **W:** http://www.wmgh.com
Editorial Profile: WLSH-AM is a commercial station owned by J-Systems Franchising Corp. The format of the station is Easy Listening. WLSH-AM broadcasts to the Lansford, PA area at 1410 AM.

WLSI-AM
Owner: East Kentucky Radio Network
Editorial: 1240 Radio Dr, Pikeville, Kentucky 41501-4779. **T:** 1 304 235-3600
E: frontdesk@ekbradio.com
W: http://www.900wlsi.com
Editorial Profile: WLSI-AM is a commercial station owned by East Kentucky Radio Network. The format of the station is talk. WLSI-AM broadcasts to the Charleston - Huntington, WV area at 900 AM.

WLSK-FM
Owner: Choice Radio Corporation
Editorial: 253 W Main St, Lebanon, Kentucky 40033-1240. **T:** 1 270 692-3126
W: http://www.lebanonmike.com
Editorial Profile: WLSK-FM is a commercial station owned by Choice Radio Corporation. The format of the stations is contemporary country. WLSK-FM broadcasts in the Lebanon, KY area at 100.9 FM.

WLSM-FM
Owner: Harrison Communications
Editorial: 2142 Highway 14 E, Louisville, Mississippi 39339-7665. **T:** 1 662 773-3481
E: magic107.1@gmail.com
Editorial Profile: WLSM-FM is a commercial station owned by Harrison Communications. The format of the station is adult contemporary music. WLSM-FM broadcasts to the Louisville, MS area at 107.1 FM.

WLSN-FM
Owner: Minnesota Public Radio
Editorial: 207 W Superior St, Ste 224, Duluth, Minnesota 55802. **T:** 1 218 722-9411
E: newsroom@mpr.org
W: http://minnesota.publicradio.org
Editorial Profile: WLSN-FM is a non-commercial station owned by Minnesota Public Radio. The format of the station is news and talk. WLSN-FM broadcasts to the Duluth, MN area at 89.7 FM.

WLSO-FM
Owner: Lake Superior State University
Editorial: 650 W Easterday Ave, Sault Sainte Marie, Michigan 49783. **T:** 1 906 635-7504
E: station_manager@lssu.edu
W: http://wlso.lssu.edu
Editorial Profile: WLSO-FM is a non-commercial station owned by Lake Superior State University. The format of the station is a college variety. WLSO-FM broadcasts to the Sault Sainte Marie, MI area at 90.1 FM.

WLSR-FM
Owner: Galesburg Broadcasting Co.
Editorial: 154 E Simmons St, Galesburg, Illinois 61401. **T:** 1 309 342-5131
E: news@wgil.com
W: http://www.thelaseronline.com
Editorial Profile: WLSR-FM is a commercial station owned by Galesburg Broadcasting Co. The format of the station is rock music. WLSR-FM broadcasts to the Galesburg, IL area at 92.7 FM.

WLSS-AM
Owner: Salem Communications
Editorial: 5211 W Laurel St Ste A, Tampa, Florida 33607-1736. **T:** 1 941 363-0930
W: http://www.wlssradio.com
Editorial Profile: WLSS-AM is a commercial station owned by Salem Communications. The format of the station is talk. WLSS-AM broadcasts to the Sarasota, FL, area at 930 AM.

WLST-FM
Owner: Radio Plus Bay Cities, LLC
Editorial: 413 10th Ave, Menominee, Michigan 49858-3009. **T:** 1 906 863-5551
E: reception@baycitiesradio.net
W: http://catcountry951online.com
Editorial Profile: WLST-FM is a commercial station owned by Radio Plus Bay Cities, LLC. The format of the station is contemporary country music. WLST-FM broadcasts to the Menominee, MI area at 95.1 FM.

WLSU-FM
Owner: University of Wisconsin
Editorial: Whitney Center UW-La Crosse, 515 N 15th St, La Crosse, Wisconsin 54601.
T: 1 608 785-8380 **E:** wlsuwhla@uwlax.edu
W: http://www.wpr.org/wlsu
Editorial Profile: WLSU-FM is a non-commercial station owned by University of Wisconsin. The format of the station is news, classical and jazz music. WLSU-FM broadcasts in the La Crosse, WI area at 88.9 FM. Staff should be contacted at their Madison, WI offices at (608)263-3970.

WLSV-AM
Owner: DBM Communications
Editorial: 82 Railroad Ave, Wellsville, New York 14895-1143. **T:** 1 585 593-6070
E: oldiesz103@yahoo.com
W: http://www.wlsv.com
Editorial Profile: WLSV-AM is a commercial station owned by DBM Communications. The format of the station is country. WLSV-AM broadcasts to the Wellsville, NY area at 790 AM.

WLSW-FM
Owner: Wall(L. Stanley)
Editorial: 2532 Springfield Pike, Connellsville, Pennsylvania 15425. **T:** 1 724 628-2800
E: wlswproduction@hotmail.com
Editorial Profile: WLSW-FM is a commercial station owned by L. Stanley Wall. The format of the station is classic hits. WLSW-FM broadcasts to the Connellsville, PA area at 103.9 FM.

WLTA-AM
Owner: Salem Communications
Editorial: 2970 Peachtree Rd NW, Ste 700, Atlanta, Georgia 30305. **T:** 1 404 995-7300
W: http://www.wniv.com
Editorial Profile: WLTA-AM is a commercial station owned by Salem Communications. The format of the station is Christian talk. WLTA-AM broadcasts to the Atlanta area at 1400 AM.

WLTB-FM
Owner: GM Broadcasting
Editorial: 3215 E Main St, Ste 2, Endwell, New York 13760-5905. **T:** 1 607 748-9131
E: info@magic1017fm.com
W: http://www.magic1017fm.com
Editorial Profile: WLBT-FM is a commercial station owned by GM Broadcasting. The format of the station is Hot Adult Contemporary and Adult Contemporary. WLBT-FM broadcasts to the Vestal, NY area at 101.7 FM.

WLTC-FM
Owner: PMB Broadcasting, LLC
Editorial: 1820 Wynnton Rd, Columbus, Georgia 31906-2930. **T:** 1 706 327-1217
W: http://www.1037lite.fm
Editorial Profile: WLTC-FM is a commercial station owned by PMB Broadcasting, LLC. It features adult contemporary music. The station airs on 103.7 FM in the Columbus, GA area.

WLTF-FM
Owner: Prettyman Broadcasting Co.
Editorial: 1606 W King St, Martinsburg, West Virginia 25401. **T:** 1 304 263-8868
W: http://www.lite975.com
Editorial Profile: WLTF-FM is a commercial station owned by Prettyman Broadcasting Co. The format of the station is AC. WLTF-FM broadcasts in the Martinsburg, MD area at 97.5.

WLTG-AM
Owner: Hour Group Broadcasting Inc.
Editorial: 3100 E 15th St, Panama City, Florida 32405. **T:** 1 850 784-9873
E: wltg@bellsouth.net
Editorial Profile: WLTG-AM is a commercial station owned by Hour Group Broadcasting Inc. The format of the station is news, sports, and talk. WLTG-AM broadcasts to the Panama City, FL area at 1430 AM.

WLTH-AM
Owner: WLTH Radio Inc.
Editorial: 1563 E 85th Ave, Merrillville, Indiana 46410. **T:** 1 219 794-1370
E: wlth1370@yahoo.com
W: http://www.wlth1370.com
Editorial Profile: WLTH-AM is a commercial station owned by WLTH Radio Inc. The format of the station is talk. WLTH-AM broadcasts to the greater Chicago area at 1370 AM.

WLTI-AM
Owner: Cumulus Media Inc.
Editorial: 1134 W State Road 38, New Castle, Indiana 47362-9781. **T:** 1 765 529-2600
Editorial Profile: WLTI-AM is a commercial station owned by Cumulus Media Inc. The format of the station is classic country. WLTI-AM broadcasts to the Indianapolis area at 1550 AM.

WLTJ-FM
Owner: Steel City Media
Editorial: 650 Smithfield St, Ste 2200, Pittsburgh, Pennsylvania 15222.
T: 1 412 316-3342 **W:** http://q929fm.com
Editorial Profile: WLTJ-FM is a commercial station owned by Steel City Media. The format of the station is hot AC. WLTJ-FM broadcasts to the Pittsburgh area at 92.9 FM.

WLTK-FM
Owner: Massanutten Broadcasting Co. Inc.
Editorial: 166 Main St, Broadway, Virginia 22815. **T:** 1 540 896-9585
W: http://www.klove.com
Editorial Profile: WLTK-FM is a commercial station owned by Massanutten Broadcasting Co. Inc. The format for the station is contemporary Christian, coming from the K-Love network. WLTK-FM broadcasts to the New Market VA area at 102.9 FM.

WLTL-FM
Owner: Lyons Township High School
Editorial: 100 S Brainard Ave, La Grange, Illinois 60525-2101. **T:** 1 708 482-9585
W: http://www.wltl.net
Editorial Profile: WLTL-FM is non-commercial high school station owned by Lyons Township High School. The format of the station is rock alternative music and news. WLTL-FM broadcasts to the students and faculty of Lyons Township High School at 88.1 FM.

WLTM-FM
Owner: Delta Radio, LLC
Editorial: 1399 E Reed Rd, Greenville, Mississippi 38703-7234. **T:** 1 662 378-2617
W: http://www.lite979.com
Editorial Profile: WLTM-FM is a commercial station owned by Delta Radio, LLC. The format of the station is Lite Rock/Lite AC. WLTM-FM broadcasts to the Greenville, MS area at 97.9 FM.

WLTN-AM
Owner: Lunderville(Barry)
Editorial: 15 Main St, Littleton, New Hampshire 3561. **T:** 1 603 444-3911
E: kiss102@together.net
Editorial Profile: WLTN-AM is a commercial station owned by Barry Lunderville. The format of the station is oldies music. WLTN-AM broadcasts to the Littleton, NH area at 1400 AM.

WLTN-FM
Owner: Lunderville(Barry)
Editorial: 15 Main St, Littleton, New Hampshire 3561. **T:** 1 603 444-3911
E: mix967@roadrunner.com
Editorial Profile: WLTN-FM is a commercial station owned by Barry Lunderville. The format of the station is adult contemporary music. WLTN-FM broadcasts to the Littleton, NH area at 96.7 FM.

WLTO-FM
Owner: Cumulus Media Inc.
Editorial: 300 W Vine St Ste 3, Lexington, Kentucky 40507-1806. **T:** 1 859 253-5900
W: http://www.hot102.net
Editorial Profile: WLTO-FM is a commercial station owned by Cumulus Media Inc. The format of the station is rhythmic Top 40/CHR music. WLTO-FM broadcasts to the Lexington, KY area at 102.5 FM.

WLTP-AM
Owner: Clear Channel Media and Entertainment
Editorial: 6006 Grand Central Ave, Parkersburg, West Virginia 26105.
T: 1 304 295-6070 **W:** http://www.wltp.com
Editorial Profile: WLTP-AM is a commercial station owned by Clear Channel Media and Entertainment. The format for the station is news and talk. WLTP-AM broadcasts to the Parkersburg, WV area at 910 AM.

WLTQ-AM
Owner: Mediatrix SC, Inc.
Editorial: 143 Calhoun St, Charleston, South Carolina 29401-3514. **T:** 1 866 263-1700
W: http://catholicradioinsc.com
Editorial Profile: WLTQ-AM is a non-commercial station owned by Mediatrix SC, Inc. The format of the station is Catholic radio music and teaching programming. WLTQ-AM broadcasts to the Mount Pleasant, SC area at 730 AM.

WLTQ-FM
Owner: Clear Channel Media and Entertainment
Editorial: 1779 Independence Blvd, Sarasota, Florida 34234-2106. **T:** 1 941 552-4800
W: http://www.921thecoast.com
Editorial Profile: WLTQ-FM is a commercial station owned by Clear Channel Media and Entertainment. The format of the station is AC. WLTQ-FM broadcasts to the Sarasota, FL area at 92.1 FM.

WLTR-FM
Owner: South Carolina Educational Television Commission
Editorial: 1101 George Rogers Blvd, Columbia, South Carolina 29201.
T: 1 803 737-3200 **W:** http://www.etvradio.org
Editorial Profile: WLTR-FM is a non-commercial station owned by the South Carolina Educational Television Commission. The format of the station is news and classical music. WLTR-FM broadcasts to the Columbia,

SC area at 91.3 FM. The station only accepts written PSAs involving the fine arts.

WLTT-AM
Owner: Hometown Wilmington Media
Editorial: 122 Cinema Dr, Wilmington, North Carolina 28403-1490. **T:** 1 910 772-6300
W: http://portcityradio.com
Editorial Profile: WLTT-AM is a commercial station owned by Hometown Wilmington Media. The format of the station news/talk. WSFM-AM broadcasts in the Wilmington, NC area at 1180 AM.

WLTU-FM
Owner: Cub Radio Inc.
Editorial: 1915 Mirro Dr, Manitowoc, Wisconsin 54220. **T:** 1 920 683-6800
W: http://www.cubradio.com
Editorial Profile: WLTU-FM is a commercial station owned by Cub Radio Inc. The format of the station is oldies music. WLTU-FM broadcasts to the Manitowoc, WI area at 92.1 FM.

WLTW-FM
Owner: Clear Channel Media and Entertainment
Editorial: 32 Avenue of the Americas, New York, New York 10013-2473.
T: 1 212 377-7900
W: http://www.1067litefm.com
Editorial Profile: WLTW-FM is a commercial station owned by Clear Channel Media and Entertainment. The format of the station is adult contemporary. WLTW-FM broadcasts to the New York City area at 106.7 FM.

WLTY-FM
Owner: Clear Channel Media and Entertainment
Editorial: 316 Greystone Blvd, Columbia, South Carolina 29210. **T:** 1 803 343-1100
W: http://www.967stevefm.com
Editorial Profile: WLTY-FM is a commercial station owned by Clear Channel Media and Entertainment. The format of the station is adult hits. WLTY-FM broadcasts to the Columbia, SC area at 96.7 FM.

WLUJ-FM
Owner: Cornerstone Community Radio Inc.
Editorial: 600 W Mason St, Springfield, Illinois 62702-5025. **T:** 1 217 528-2300
E: comments@wluj.org **W:** http://www.wluj.org
Editorial Profile: WLUJ-FM is a non-commercial station owned by Cornerstone Community Radio Inc. The format of the station is contemporary Christian music and talk. WLUJ-FM broadcasts in Springfield, IL at 89.7 FM and simulcasts in Lincoln, IL at 1370 AM.

WLUM-FM
Owner: Milwaukee Radio Alliance
Editorial: N72W12922 Good Hope Rd, Menomonee Falls, Wisconsin 53051-4441.
T: 1 414 771-1021
E: info@milwaukeeradio.com
W: http://www.fm1021milwaukee.com
Editorial Profile: WLUM-FM is a commercial station owned by Milwaukee Radio Alliance. The format of the station is alternative music. WLUM-FM broadcasts to the Milwaukee area at 102.1 FM.

WLUN-FM
Owner: Michigan Radio Communications & Great Lakes Loons(The)
Editorial: 825 E Main St, Midland, Michigan 48640. **T:** 1 989 837-2255
W: http://www.espn1009.com
Editorial Profile: WLUN-FM is a commercial station owned by Michigan Radio Communications and Great Lakes Loons(The). The format of the station is sports. WLUN-FM broadcasts to the Saginaw, MI area at 100.9 FM.

WLUP-FM
Owner: Cumulus Media
Editorial: 222 Merchandise Mart Plz, Chicago, Illinois 60654-1103. **T:** 1 312 245-1200
W: http://www.wlup.com
Editorial Profile: WLUP-FM is a commercial station owned by Cumulus Media. The format of the station is classic rock music. WLUP-FM broadcasts to the Chicago area at 97.9 FM. The station does not air PSAs.

WLUR-FM
Owner: Washington & Lee University
Editorial: WLUR/John W. Elrod University Commons, 204 West Washington St., Lexington, Virginia 24450. **T:** 1 540 458-4017
E: wlur915@wlu.edu
W: http://www.wlu.edu/x37490.xml
Editorial Profile: WLUR-FM is a non-commercial college station owned by Washington & Lee University. The format of the station is variety. WLUR-FM broadcasts to the Lexington, VA area at a frequency of 91.5 FM.

WLUS-FM
Owner: Lakes Media LLC
Editorial: 109 Hillsboro St, Oxford, North Carolina 27565. **T:** 1 919 693-7900
E: studio@us983.com
W: http://www.us983.com
Editorial Profile: WLUS-FM is a commercial station owned by the Lakes Media LLC. The format of the station is country music. WLUS-FM broadcasts to the Oxford, NC area at 98.3 FM.

WLUV-AM
Owner: Loves Park Broadcasting Co.
Editorial: 2272 Elmwood Rd, Rockford, Illinois 61103. **T:** 1 815 877-9588
Editorial Profile: WLUV-AM is a commercial station owned by Loves Park Broadcasting Co. The format of the station is country music. WLUV-AM broadcasts in the Rockford, IL area at 1520 AM.

WLUW-FM
Owner: Loyola University Chicago
Editorial: 6525 N Sheridan Rd, Chicago, Illinois 60626-5761. **T:** 1 773 508-8080
E: wluwnews@luc.edu **W:** http://www.wluw.org
Editorial Profile: WLUW-FM is a non-commercial station owned by Loyola University Chicago. The format of the station is variety programming. WLUW-FM broadcasts to the Chicago area at 88.7 FM.

WLVA-AM
Owner: Chesapeake-Portsmouth Broadcasting Corp.
Editorial: 230 Chelsea Dr, Forest, Virginia 24551-3142. **T:** 1 434 534-0400
Editorial Profile: WLVA-AM is a commercial station owned by Chesapeake-Portsmouth Broadcasting Corp. The format of the station is talk. WLVA-AM broadcasts to the Lynchburg, VA area at a frequency of 580 AM.

WLVB-FM
Owner: Radio Vermont Group Inc.
Editorial: Route 15, Morrisville, Vermont 5661. **T:** 1 802 888-4294
E: wlvb@radiovermont.com
Editorial Profile: WLVB-FM is a commercial station owned by Radio Vermont Group Inc. The format of the station is country. WLVB-FM broadcasts to the Morrisville, VT area at 93.9 FM.

WLVF-AM
Owner: Landmark Baptist Church Inc.
Editorial: 810 E Hinson Ave, Haines City, Florida 33844. **T:** 1 863 422-5175
E: info@gospel903.com
W: http://www.gospel903.com
Editorial Profile: WLVF-AM is a non-commercial station owned by Landmark Baptist Church Inc. The format of the station is southern gospel and religious programming. WLVF-AM broadcasts to the Haines City, FL area at 930 AM.

WLVF-FM
Owner: Landmark Baptist Church Inc.
Editorial: 810 E Hinson Ave, Haines City, Florida 33844. **T:** 1 863 422-5175
E: info@gospel903.com
W: http://www.gospel903.com
Editorial Profile: WLVF-FM is a non-commercial station owned by Landmark Baptist Church Inc. The format is of the station is southern gospel and religious programming. WLVF-FM broadcasts to the Haines City, FL at 90.3 FM.

WLVG-FM
Owner: Educational Media Foundation
Editorial: 5700 W Oaks Blvd, Rocklin, California 95765-3719. **T:** 1 916 251-1600
W: http://www.klove.com
Editorial Profile: WLVG-FM is a commercial station owned by Educational Media Foundation. The format for the station is adult standards. WLVG-FM broadcasts to the New Bern, NC area at 105.1 FM.

WLVH-FM
Owner: Clear Channel Media and Entertainment
Editorial: 245 Alfred St, Savannah, Georgia 31408-3205. **T:** 1 912 964-7794
E: community@love1011.com
W: http://www.love1011.com
Editorial Profile: WLVH-FM is a commercial station owned by Clear Channel Media and Entertainment. The format of the station is urban adult contemporary. WLVH-FM broadcasts to the Savannah, GA area at 101.1 FM.

WLVJ-AM
Owner: Actualidad 1040 AM, LLC
Editorial: 2555 Ponce De Leon Blvd Ste 225, Coral Gables, Florida 33134-6033.
T: 1 786 388-3855
W: http://actualidadradio.com
Editorial Profile: WLVJ-AM is a commercial station owned by Actualidad 1040 AM, LLC. The format of the station is Spanish language news. WLVJ-AM broadcasts to the Miami area at 1040 AM.

WLVL-AM
Owner: Culver Communications
Editorial: 320 Michigan St, Lockport, New York 14094. **T:** 1 716 433-5944
E: news@wlvl.com **W:** http://www.wlvl.com
Editorial Profile: WLVL-AM is a commercial station owned by Culver Communications. The format of the station is news, talk, and sports. WLVL-AM broadcasts to the Lockport, NY area at 1340 AM.

WLVP-AM
Owner: WBIN, Inc.
Editorial: 477 Congress St Ste 3, Portland, Maine 04101-3417. **T:** 1 207 797-0780
Editorial Profile: WLVP-AM is a commercial station owned by WBIN, Inc. The format of the station is oldies. WLVP-AM broadcasts to the Portland, ME area at 870 AM.

WLVQ-FM
Owner: Wilks Broadcast Group
Editorial: 2400 Corporate Exchange Dr Ste 200, Columbus, Ohio 43231-7669.
T: 1 614 227-9696 **W:** http://www.qfm96.com
Editorial Profile: WLVQ-FM is a commercial station owned by Wilks Broadcast Group. The format of the station is rock music. WLVQ-FM broadcasts to the Columbus, OH area on 96.3 FM.

WLVS-FM
Owner: Gold Coast Broadcasting
Editorial: 624 Sam Phillips St, Florence, Alabama 35630. **T:** 1 256 764-8121
W: http://www.wxfl.com
Editorial Profile: WLVS-FM is a commercial station owned by Gold Coast Broadcasting. The format of the station is country. WLVS-FM broadcasts to the Florence, AL area at a frequency of 106.5 FM.

WLVU-FM
Owner: Cumulus Media Inc.
Editorial: 10 Music Cir E, Nashville, Tennessee 37203-4338. **T:** 1 615 321-1067
W: http://www.971rqq.com
Editorial Profile: WLVU-FM is a commercial station owned by Cumulus Media Inc. The format of the station is Contemporary Christian. WLVU-FM broadcasts to the Nashville, TN area at 97.1 FM.

WLVX-FM
Owner: Educational Media Foundation
Editorial: 44 McCracken Rd, Greenville, Pennsylvania 16125-8605. **T:** 1 916 251-1600
W: http://www.air1.com
Editorial Profile: WLVX-FM is a commercial station owned by Educational Media Foundation. The format of the station is Christian CHR/Rock. WLVX-FM broadcasts to the Greenville, PA area at 107.1 FM.

WLVY-FM
Owner: Pembrook Pines Media Group
Editorial: 1705 Lake St, Elmira, New York 14901. **T:** 1 607 733-5626
E: ppinesmedia1@stny.rr.com
W: http://www.94rockfm.com
Editorial Profile: WLVY-FM is a commercial station owned by Pembrook Pines Media Group. The format of the station is Top 40/ CHR music. WLVY-FM broadcasts to the Elmira, NY area at 94.3 FM.

WLW-AM
Owner: Clear Channel Media and Entertainment
Editorial: 8044 Montgomery Rd, Cincinnati, Ohio 45236-2919. **T:** 1 513 686-8300
E: news@700wlw.com
W: http://www.700wlw.com
Editorial Profile: WLW-AM is a commercial station owned by Clear Channel Media and Entertainment. The format of the station is news, sports and talk. WLW-AM broadcasts to the Cincinnati area at 700 AM.

WLWE-AM
Owner: Eagle's Nest Inc.
Editorial: 6855 Highway 431, Roanoke, Alabama 36274-4614. **T:** 1 334 863-6692
W: http://www.eagle1023.com
Editorial Profile: WLWE-AM is a commercial station owned by Eagle's Nest Inc. The format of the station is sports. WLWE-AM broadcasts to the Roanoke, AL area at 1360 AM.

WLWF-FM
Owner: LaSalle County Broadcasting Corp.
Editorial: 1 Broadcast Ln, Oglesby, Illinois 61348. **T:** 1 815 223-3100
W: http://20inarowcountry.com
Editorial Profile: WLWF-FM is a commercial station owned by Lasalle County Broadcasting Corp. The format of the station is contemporary country. WLWF-FM broadcasts to Ottawa, LaSalle and Peru, IL areas at 96.5 FM.

WLWI-AM
Owner: Cumulus Media Inc.
Editorial: 1 Commerce St, Ste 300, Montgomery, Alabama 36104-3549.
T: 1 334 240-9274
W: http://www.newsradio1440.com
Editorial Profile: WLWI-AM is a commercial station owned by Cumulus Media Inc. The format of the station is news and talk. WLWI-AM broadcasts to the Montgomery, AL area at 1440 AM.

WLWI-FM
Owner: Cumulus Media Inc.
Editorial: 1 Commerce St Ste 300, Montgomery, Alabama 36104-3542.
T: 1 334 240-9274 **W:** http://www.wlwi.com
Editorial Profile: WLWI-FM is a commercial station owned by Cumulus Media Inc. The format of the station is country music. WLWI-FM broadcasts to the Montgomery, AL area at 92.3 FM.

WLWK-FM
Owner: Journal Broadcast Group
Editorial: 720 E Capitol Dr, Milwaukee, Wisconsin 53212-1308. **T:** 1 414 332-9611
W: http://www.945lakefm.com
Editorial Profile: WLWK-FM is a commercial station owned by Journal Broadcast Group. The format of the station is adult hits. WLWK-FM broadcasts to the Milwaukee area at 94.5 FM.

WLWL-AM
Owner: MarCam Broadcasting
Editorial: 275 River Rd, Rockingham, North Carolina 28379. **T:** 1 910 895-9595
Editorial Profile: WLWL-AM is a commercial station owned by MarCam Broadcasting. The format of the station is R&B oldies. WLWL-AM broadcasts to the Rockingham, NC area at 770 AM.

WLXC-FM
Owner: Cumulus Media Inc.
Editorial: 1801 Charleston Hwy Ste J, Cayce, South Carolina 29033-2019.
T: 1 803 796-9975
W: http://www.kiss-1031.com
Editorial Profile: WLXC-FM is a commercial station owned by Cumulus Media Inc. The format of the station is urban adult contemporary. WLXC-FM broadcasts to the Columbia, SC area at 103.1 FM.

WLXE-AM
Owner: Multicultural Radio Broadcasting Inc.
Editorial: 13321 New Hampshire Ave Ste 207, Silver Spring, Maryland 20904-3450.
T: 1 301 424-9292 **E:** rbcstudios@aol.com
Editorial Profile: WLXE-AM is a commercial station owned by Multicultural Radio. The format of the station is Hispanic news and talk. WLXE-AM broadcasts to the Rockville, MD area at 1600 AM.

WLXG-AM
Owner: L.M. Communications Inc.
Editorial: 401 W Main St, Lexington, Kentucky 40507-1640. **T:** 1 859 233-1515
W: http://www.wlxg.com
Editorial Profile: WLXG-AM is a commercial station owned by L.M. Communications Inc. The format of the station is sports. WLXG-AM broadcasts in the Lexington, KY area at 1300 AM.

WLXN-AM
Owner: Davidson County Broadcasting
Editorial: 200 Radio Dr, Lexington, North Carolina 27292-8010. **T:** 1 336 248-2716
E: info@wlxn.com **W:** http://www.wlxn.com
Editorial Profile: WLXN-AM is a commercial station owned by Davidson County

Broadcasting. The format of the station is oldies. WLXN-AM broadcasts to the Lexington, NC area at 1440 AM.

WLXO-FM
Owner: Clarity Communications Inc
Editorial: 401 W Main St, Lexington, Kentucky 40507-1640. **T:** 1 859 294-0961
E: comments@hank961.com
W: http://www.hank961.com
Editorial Profile: WLXO-FM is a commercial station owned by Clarity Communications Inc and managed by LM Communications. The format of the station is classic country. WLXO-FM broadcasts to the Lexington, KY area at 96.1 FM.

WLXR-FM
Owner: Mississippi Valley Broadcasters LLC
Editorial: 1407 2nd Ave N, Onalaska, Wisconsin 54650. **T:** 1 608 782-8335
E: news@lacrosseradiogroup.net
W: http://www.wlxr.com
Editorial Profile: WLXR-FM is a commercial station owned by Mississippi Valley Broadcasters LLC. The format of the station is adult contemporary. WLXR-FM broadcasts to the La Crosse, WI area at 104.9 FM.

WLXT-FM
Owner: MacDonald-Garber Broadcasting Inc.
Editorial: 2095 S US Highway 131, Petoskey, Michigan 49770. **T:** 1 231 347-8713
E: mail@lite96.com **W:** http://www.lite96.com
Editorial Profile: WLXT-FM is a commercial station owned by MacDonald-Garber Broadcasting Inc. The format for the station is Lite Rock/Lite AC. WLXT-FM broadcasts to the Petoskey, MI area at 96.3 FM.

WLXV-FM
Owner: MacDonald Garber Broadcasting Inc.
Editorial: 7825 Mackinaw Trl, Cadillac, Michigan 49601-9746. **T:** 1 231 775-1263
W: http://www.mix96cadillac.com
Editorial Profile: WLXV-FM is a commercial station owned by MacDonald Garber Broadcasting Inc. The format of the station is adult contemporary. WLXV-FM broadcasts to the Cadillac, MI area at a frequency of 96.7 FM.

WLXX-FM
Owner: Cumulus Media Inc.
Editorial: 300 W Vine St Ste 3, Lexington, Kentucky 40507-1806. **T:** 1 859 253-5900
W: http://www.929wlxx.com
Editorial Profile: WLXX-FM is a commercial station owned by Cumulus Media Inc. The format for the station is contemporary country. WLXX-FM broadcasts to the Lexington, KY area at 92.9 FM.

WLYC-AM
Owner: Colonial Radio Group of Williamsport, LLC
Editorial: 210 Market St, Ste 207, Williamsport, Pennsylvania 17701-6638.
T: 1 570 327-1300
W: http://www.espnwilliamsport.com

WLYE-FM
Owner: Forever Communications Inc.
Editorial: 227 W Main St, Glasgow, Kentucky 42141-1707. **T:** 1 270 651-5290
W: http://www.willie941.com
Editorial Profile: WLYE-FM is a commercial station owned by Forever Communications Inc. The format of the station is classic and contemporary country music. WLYE-FM broadcasts to the Glasgow, KY area at a frequency of 94.1 FM.

WLYF-FM
Owner: Lincoln Financial Media
Editorial: 20450 NW 2nd Ave, Miami, Florida 33169. **T:** 1 305 521-5100
E: litefm@litemiami.com
W: http://www.litemiami.com
Editorial Profile: WLYF-FM is a commercial station owned by Lincoln Financial Media. The format of the station is Lite Rock/Lite AC music. WLYF-FM broadcasts to the Miami area at 101.5 FM.

WLYN-AM
Owner: Multicultural Radio Broadcasting Inc.
Editorial: 500 W Cummings Park, Ste 2600, Woburn, Massachusetts 1801.
T: 1 781 938-0869 **W:** http://mrbi.net
Editorial Profile: WLYN-AM is a commercial station owned by Multicultural Radio Broadcasting Inc. The format of the station is ethnic brokered programming. WLYN-AM broadcasts to the Cambridge, MA area at 1360 AM.

WLYU-FM
Owner: TCB Broadcasting
Editorial: 473 N Victory Dr, Lyons, Georgia 30436-1947. **T:** 1 912 526-8122
Editorial Profile: WLYU-FM is a commercial station owned by TCB Broadcasting. The format for the station is contemporary country. WYLU-FM broadcasts to the Savannah, GA area at 100.9 FM.

WLYV-AM
Owner: Fort Wayne Catholic Radio Group, Inc.
Editorial: 4618 E State Blvd Ste 200, Fort Wayne, Indiana 46815-6966.
T: 1 260 436-9598
E: info@redeemerradio.com
W: http://www.redeemerradio.com
Editorial Profile: WLYV-AM is a commercial station owned by Fort Wayne Catholic Radio Group, Inc. The format of the station is religious programming. WLYV-AM broadcasts to the Fort Wayne, IN area at 1450 AM.

WLZA-FM
Owner: Metro Radio Inc.
Editorial: 1105A Stark Rd, Starkville, Mississippi 39759. **T:** 1 662 324-9601
E: wlza@961wlza.com
W: http://www.961wlza.com
Editorial Profile: WLZA-FM is a commercial station owned by Metro Radio Inc. The format of the station is adult contemporary. WLZA-FM broadcasts to the Starkville and East-Central Mississippi area at a frequency of 96.1 FM.

WLZK-FM
Owner: Benton-Weatherford Broadcasting Inc. of Tennessee
Editorial: 110 India Rd, Paris, Tennessee 38242-7565. **T:** 1 731 644-9455
E: wlzk@bellsouth.net
W: http://www.wmufradio.com/WLZK.html
Editorial Profile: WLZK-FM is a commercial station owned by Benton-Weatherford Broadcasting Inc. of Tennessee. The format of the station is hot AC. WLZK-FM broadcasts to the Paris, TN area at 94.1 FM.

WLZL-FM
Owner: CBS Radio
Editorial: 4200 Parliament Pl Ste 300, Lanham, Maryland 20706-1881.
T: 1 301 918-0955
W: http://elzolradio.radio.com
Editorial Profile: WLZL-FM is a non-commercial station owned by CBS Radio. The format of the station is Latin Urban and Pop music. WLZL-FM is licensed to the Annapolis, MD area and broadcasts to the DMV area (Baltimore, MD and Washington, DC) at 107.9 FM.

WLZN-FM
Owner: Cumulus Media Inc.
Editorial: 544 Mulberry St, Ste 500, Macon, Georgia 31201. **T:** 1 478 746-6286
W: http://www.blazin923.com
Editorial Profile: WLZN-FM is a commercial station owned by Cumulus Media Inc. The format of the station is urban contemporary. WLZN-FM broadcasts to the Macon, GA area on 92.3 FM.

WLZS-FM
Owner: Starview Media Inc.
Editorial: Old Route 22 East, Mexico, Pennsylvania 17056-9999. **T:** 1 717 436-2135
E: wjun@nmax.net
W: http://www.wheels1061.com
Editorial Profile: WLZS-FM is a commercial station owned by Starview Media Inc. The format of the station is oldies music. WLZS-FM broadcasts to the Harrisburg, PA area at 106.1 FM.

WLZT-FM
Owner: Clear Channel Media and Entertainment
Editorial: 2323 W 5th Ave Ste 200, Columbus, Ohio 43204-4988. **T:** 1 614 486-6101
E: newsroom@wkkj.com
W: http://www.oldies933fm.com
Editorial Profile: WODC-FM is a commercial station owned by Clear Channel Media and Entertainment. The format for the station is oldies. WODC-FM broadcasts to the Columbus, OH area at 93.3 FM.

WLZW-FM
Owner: Townsquare Media, LLC
Editorial: 9418 River Rd, Marcy, New York 13403. **T:** 1 315 768-9500
W: http://www.lite987.com
Editorial Profile: WLZW-FM is a commercial station owned by Townsquare Media, LLC. The format of the station is adult contemporary. WLZW-FM broadcasts to the Utica, NY area at 98.7 FM.

WLZX-FM
Owner: Saga Communications
Editorial: 45 Fisher Ave, East Longmeadow, Massachusetts 1028. **T:** 1 413 525-4141
W: http://www.lazer993.com
Editorial Profile: WLZX-FM is a commercial station owned by Saga Communications. The format of the station is rock. WLZX-FM broadcasts to Springfield, MA at 99.3 FM.

WLZZ-FM
Owner: Swick Broadcasting
Editorial: 05691 State Route 15 Suite B, Bryan, Ohio 43506-8879. **T:** 1 419 633-1045
E: wlzz@wlzzradio.com
W: http://www.wlzzradio.com
Editorial Profile: WLZZ-FM is a commercial station owned by Swick Broadcasting. The format of the station is country, news and talk. WLZZ-FM broadcasts to the Montpelier, OH area at 104.5 FM.

WMAC-AM
Owner: Cumulus Media Inc.
Editorial: 544 Mulberry St, Ste 500, Macon, Georgia 31201. **T:** 1 478 746-6286
W: http://www.wmac-am.com
Editorial Profile: WMAC-AM is a commercial station owned by Cumulus Media Inc. The format of the station is news, talk and sports. WMAC-AM broadcasts in the Macon, GA area at 940 AM.

WMAD-FM
Owner: Clear Channel Media and Entertainment
Editorial: 2651 S Fish Hatchery Rd, Fitchburg, Wisconsin 53711. **T:** 1 608 274-1070
W: http://www.963starcountry.com
Editorial Profile: WMAD-FM is a commercial station owned by Clear Channel Media and Entertainment. The format for the station is contemporary country. WMAD-FM broadcasts to the Madison, WI area at 96.3 FM.

WMAF-AM
Owner: Walker(Geneva)
Editorial: 574 SW Captain Brown Rd, Madison, Florida 32340. **T:** 1 850 973-3233
E: countrywmaf@embarqmail.com
W: http://www.wmafcountry.com
Editorial Profile: WMAF-AM is a commercial station owned by Geneva Walker. The format of the station is classic country and gospel music. WMAF-AM broadcasts to the Madison, FL area at 1230 AM.

WMAG-FM
Owner: Clear Channel Media and Entertainment
Editorial: 2B Pai Park Floor 2, Greensboro, North Carolina 27409-9428.
T: 1 336 822-2000
W: http://www.995wmag.com
Editorial Profile: WMAG-FM is a commercial station owned by Clear Channel Media and Entertainment. The format of the station is adult contemporary. WMAG-FM broadcasts to the Greensboro, NC area at 99.5 FM.

WMAJ-FM
Owner: Forever Broadcasting
Editorial: 2551 Park Center Blvd, State College, Pennsylvania 16801.
T: 1 814 237-9800 **E:** majic99fm@gmail.com
W: http://www.majic99.com
Editorial Profile: WMAJ-FM is a commercial station owned by Forever Broadcasting. The format of the station is adult hits. WMAJ-FM broadcasts to the State College, PA area at 99.5 FM.

WMAK-AM
Owner: Last Of A Dying Breed Broadcasting
Editorial: 100 E Main St, Linden, Tennessee 37096-3006. **T:** 1 724 516-8885
W: http://www.1013hankfm.com
Editorial Profile: WMAK-AM is commercial station owned by Last Of A Dying Breed Broadcasting. The format for the station is bluegrass WNKX-AM broadcasts to the Perry County, TN area at 1570 AM.

WMAL-AM
Owner: Cumulus Media
Editorial: 4400 Jenifer St NW Fl 4, Washington, District Of Columbia 20015-2134.
T: 1 202 686-3100 **E:** news@wmal.com
W: http://www.wmal.com
Editorial Profile: WMAL-AM is a commercial station owned by Cumulus Media. The format of the station is news and talk. WMAL-AM broadcasts in the Washington area at 630 AM.

WMAL-FM
Owner: Cumulus Media Inc.
Editorial: 4400 Jenifer St NW, Ste 4, Washington, District Of Columbia 20015.
T: 1 202 686-3100 **W:** http://www.wmal.com
Editorial Profile: WMAL-FM is a commercial station owned by Cumulus Media Inc. The format of the station is news/talk. WMAL-FM broadcasts to Washington, D.C. area at 105.9 FM.

WMAM-AM
Owner: Radio Plus Bay Cities, LLC
Editorial: 413 10th St, Menominee, Michigan 49858. **T:** 1 906 863-5551
E: reception@baycitiesradio.net
W: http://www.baycitiesradio.net
Editorial Profile: WMAM-AM is a commercial station owned by Radio Plus Bay Cities, LLC. The format of the station is sports. WMAM-AM broadcasts to the Menominee, MI area at 570 AM.

WMAN-AM
Owner: Clear Channel Media and Entertainment
Editorial: 1400 Radio Ln, Mansfield, Ohio 44906. **T:** 1 419 529-2211
W: http://www.wmanfm.com
Editorial Profile: WMAN-AM is a commercial station owned by Clear Channel Media and Entertainment. The format of the station is news and talk. WMAN-AM broadcasts to the Mansfield, OH area at 1400 AM.

WMAS-FM
Owner: Cumulus Media Inc.
Editorial: 1000 Hall Of Fame Ave, Springfield, Massachusetts 01105-2538.
T: 1 413 737-1414
W: http://www.947wmas.com
Editorial Profile: WMAS-FM is a commercial station owned by Cumulus Media Inc. The format of the station is adult contemporary music. WMAS-FM broadcasts to the Springfield, MA area at 94.7 FM.

WMAX-AM
Owner: Ave Maria Communications
Editorial: 3535 Bay Rd, Saginaw, Michigan 48603-2464. **T:** 1 734 930-5200
E: amrcomments@avemariaradio.net
W: http://www.avemariaradio.net
Editorial Profile: WMAX-AM is a commercial station owned by Ave Maria Communications. The format of the station is religious talk. WMAX-AM broadcasts to the Saginaw, MI area at 1440 AM.

WMAX-FM
Owner: Clear Channel Media and Entertainment
Editorial: 77 Monroe Center St Nw, Grand Rapids, Michigan 49503-2903.
T: 1 616 459-1919
W: http://www.espn961.com
Editorial Profile: WMAX-FM is a commercial station owned by Clear Channel Media and Entertainment. The format of the station is sports. WMAX-FM broadcasts to the Grand Rapids, MI area at 96.1 FM.

WMAY-AM
Owner: Midwest Family Stations
Editorial: 1510 N Third St, Riverton, Illinois 62561. **T:** 1 217 629-7077
E: wmay@wmay.com
W: http://www.wmay.com
Editorial Profile: WMAY-AM is a commercial station owned by Midwest Family Stations. The format of the station is news and talk. WMAY-AM broadcasts to the Riverton, IL area at 970 AM.

WMBA-AM
Owner: Iorio Broadcasting Inc.
Editorial: 1316 7th Ave, Beaver Falls, Pennsylvania 15010. **T:** 1 724 846-4100
E: 1230@wbvp-wmba.com
W: http://www.wbvp-wmba.com
Editorial Profile: WMBA-AM is a commercial station owned by Iorio Broadcasting Inc. The format of the station is news, sports and talk. WMBA-AM broadcasts to the Beaver Falls, PA area at 1460 AM.

WMBD-AM
Owner: L & L Radio
Editorial: 331 Fulton St Ste 1200, Peoria, Illinois 61602-1422. **T:** 1 309 637-3700
E: news@1470wmbd.com
W: http://centralillinoisag.com
Editorial Profile: WMBD-AM is a commercial station owned by L & L Radio. The format of the station is news and talk. WMBD-AM broadcasts to the Peoria, IL, area at 1470 AM.

WMBG-AM
Owner: Williamsburg's Radio Stations Inc.
Editorial: 1005 Richmond Rd, Williamsburg, Virginia 23185. **T:** 1 757 229-7400
E: info@wmbgradio.com
W: http://www.wmbgradio.com
Editorial Profile: WMBG-AM is a commercial station owned by Williamsburg's Radio Stations Inc. The format of the station is adult standards. WMBG-AM broadcasts to the Norfolk, VA at 740 AM.

WMBI-AM
Owner: Moody Bible Institute
Editorial: 820 N La Salle Dr, Chicago, Illinois 60610-3214 **E:** radiomoody@moody.edu
W: http://www.radiomoody.org
Editorial Profile: WMBI-AM is a non-commercial station owned by Moody Bible Institute. The format of the station is Spanish-language Christian talk and music. WMBI-AM broadcasts to the Chicago area at 1110 AM.

WMBI-FM
Owner: Moody Bible Institute
Editorial: 820 N La Salle Blvd, 8th Fl, Chicago, Illinois 60610. **T:** 1 312 329-4300
E: wmbi@moody.edu
W: http://www.moodyradiochicago.fm
Editorial Profile: WMBI-FM is a non-commercial station owned by the Moody Bible Institute. The format of the station is religious programming. WMBI-FM broadcasts to the Chicago area at 90.1 FM.

WMBJ-FM
Owner: Radio Training Network, Inc.
Editorial: 2420 Wade Hampton Blvd, Greenville, South Carolina 29615.
T: 1 864 292-6040
E: comments@hisradio.com
W: http://www.hisradio.com
Editorial Profile: WMBJ-FM is a non-commercial station owned by Radio Training Network, Inc. The format of the station is contemporary Christian. WMBJ-FM broadcasts to the Greenville, SC area at 88.3 FM.

WMBM-AM
Owner: New Birth Broadcasting
Editorial: 13242 NW 7th Ave, North Miami, Florida 33168. **T:** 1 305 769-1100
E: wmbm@wmbm.com
W: http://www.wmbm.com
Editorial Profile: WMBM-AM is a commercial station owned by New Birth Broadcasting. The format of the station is gospel. WMBM-AM broadcasts to the Miami area at 1490 AM.

WMBN-AM
Owner: MacDonald Garber Broadcasting Inc.
Editorial: 2095 S US Highway 131, Petoskey, Michigan 49770. **T:** 1 231 347-8713
E: info@1340amwmbn.com
Editorial Profile: WMBN-AM is a commercial station owned by MacDonald Garber Broadcasting Inc. The format of the station is sports. WMBN-AM broadcasts to the Petoskey, MI area at 1340 AM.

WMBO-AM
Owner: Wolf Radio, Inc.
Editorial: 401 W Kirkpatrick St, Syracuse, New York 13204-1305. **T:** 1 315 472-0222
E: wolfdisn@twcny.rr.com
Editorial Profile: WMBO-AM is a commercial station owned by Wolf Radio, Inc. The format of the station is children's programming. WMBO-AM broadcasts to the Syracuse, NY area at 1340 AM.

WMBR-FM
Owner: Technology Broadcasting Corp.
Editorial: 3 Ames St, Cambridge, Massachusetts 02142-1305.
T: 1 617 253-4000 **E:** psa@wmbr.org
W: http://wmbr.mit.edu
Editorial Profile: WMBR-FM is a non-commercial station owned by Technology Broadcasting Corp. The format of the station is variety. WMBR-FM broadcasts to the Cambridge, MA area at 88.1 FM.

WMBS-AM
Owner: Fayette Broadcasting Corporation
Editorial: 44 S Mount Vernon Ave, Uniontown, Pennsylvania 15401. **T:** 1 724 438-3900
W: http://www.wmbs590.com
Editorial Profile: WMBS-AM is a commercial station owned by Fayette Broadcasting Corporation. The format of the station is adult standards. WMBS-AM broadcasts to the Uniontown, PA area at 590 AM.

WMBU-FM
Owner: Moody Bible Institute
Editorial: 5189 Lake Norris Rd, Lake, Mississippi 39092-8505. **T:** 1 601 775-3100
E: wmft@moody.edu
W: http://www.moodyradiosouth.fm
Editorial Profile: WMBU-FM is a non-commercial radio station owned by the Moody Bible Institute. The format of the station is religious. WMBU-FM broadcasts to the Lake, MS area at 89.1 FM.

WMBV-FM
Owner: Moody Bible Institute
Editorial: 5710 Watermelon Rd Ste 316, Northport, Alabama 35473-7694.
T: 1 205 758-7900
E: moodyradiosouth@moody.edu
W: http://www.moodyradiosouth.fm
Editorial Profile: WMBV-FM is a non-commercial station owned by Moody Bible Institute. The format of the station is gospel music and religious talk. WMBV-FM broadcasts to the Dixons Mills, AL area at 91.9 FM.

WMBW-FM
Owner: Moody Bible Institute
Editorial: 1920 E 24th Street Pl, Chattanooga, Tennessee 37404-5810. **T:** 1 423 629-8900
E: wmbw@moody.edu
W: http://wmbw.mbn.org
Editorial Profile: WMBW-FM is a non-commercial station owned by Moody Bible Institute. The format is religious music and talk. WMBW-FM broadcasts to the Chattanooga, TN area at 88.9 FM.

WMBX-FM
Owner: Palm Beach Broadcasting, LLC
Editorial: 701 Northpoint Pkwy Ste 500, West Palm Beach, Florida 33407-1960.
T: 1 561 686-9505 **W:** http://thex1023.com
Editorial Profile: WMBX-FM is a commercial station owned by Palm Beach Broadcasting, LLC. The format of the station is urban contemporary. WMBX-FM broadcasts to the West Palm Beach, FL area at 102.3 FM.

WMCA-AM
Owner: Salem Communications
Editorial: 111 Broadway Fl 3, New York, New York 10006-1992. **T:** 1 212 372-0097
E: contact@nycradio.com
W: http://www.wmca.com
Editorial Profile: WMCA-AM is commercial station owned by Salem Communications. The format of the station is religious talk. WMCA-AM broadcasts to the New York City area at 570 AM.

WMC-AM
Owner: Entercom Communications Corp.
Editorial: 1835 Moriah Woods Blvd, Memphis, Tennessee 38117-7122. **T:** 1 901 767-0104
Editorial Profile: WMC-AM is a commercial station owned by Entercom Communications Corp. The format of the station is sports. WMC-AM broadcasts to the Memphis, TN area at 790 AM.

WMCD-FM
Owner: Georgia Eagle Broadcasting Inc.
Editorial: 561 E Olliff St, Statesboro, Georgia 30458-4663. **T:** 1 912 764-5446
E: wwnswmcd@yahoo.com
Editorial Profile: WMCD-FM is a commercial station owned by Georgia Eagle Broadcasting Inc. The format of the station is talk. WMCD-FM broadcasts to the Savannah, GA area at 107.3 FM.

WMCE-AM
Owner: Mercyhurst College
Editorial: 16 W Division St, North East, Pennsylvania 16428-1008. **T:** 1 814 725-9963
W: http://wmce.mercyhurst.edu
Editorial Profile: WMCE-AM is a commercial station owned by Mercyhurst College. The format of the station is oldies music. WMCE-AM broadcasts to the Northeast, PA area at 1530 AM.

WMCE-FM
Owner: Mercyhurst University
Editorial: 501 E 38th St, Erie, Pennsylvania 16546-0002. **T:** 1 814 824-2294
W: http://wmce.mercyhurst.edu
Editorial Profile: WMCE-FM is a non-commercial station owned by Mercyhurst College. The format for the station is oldies and classic hits. WMCE-FM broadcasts to the Erie, PA area at 88.5 FM.

WMC-FM
Owner: Entercom Communications Corp.
Editorial: 1835 Moriah Woods Blvd, Building 1, Memphis, Tennessee 38117-7122.
T: 1 901 767-0104
W: http://www.fm100memphis.com
Editorial Profile: WMC-FM is a commercial station owned by Entercom Communications Corp. The format of the station is hot adult contemporary. WMC-FM broadcasts to the Memphis, TN area at 99.7 FM.

WMCG-FM
Owner: Dowdy Broadcasting, Inc.
Editorial: 807 Bellevue Ave, Dublin, Georgia 31021. **T:** 1 478 272-4422
W: http://www.1049wmcg.com
Editorial Profile: WMCG-FM is a commercial station owned by Dowdy Broadcasting, Inc. The format of the station is classic country. WMCG-FM broadcasts to the Dublin, GA area at 104.9 FM.

WMCH-AM
Owner: Media Link, Inc.
Editorial: 439 Richmond St, Church Hill, Tennessee 37642. **T:** 1 423 357-5601
E: wmchradio@yahoo.com
W: http://www.wmchradio.com
Editorial Profile: WMCH-AM is a commercial station owned by Media Link, Inc. The format of the station is religious talk. WMCH-AM broadcasts in the Church Hill, TN area at 1260 AM.

WMCI-FM
Owner: Cromwell Group Inc.(The)
Editorial: 209 Lake Land Blvd, Mattoon, Illinois 61938-3904. **T:** 1 217 235-5624
W: http://www.radiomattoon.com
Editorial Profile: WMCI-FM is a commercial station owned by The Cromwell Group Inc. The format of the station features classic and contemporary country music. WMCI-FM broadcasts in the Mattoon, IL area at 101.3 FM.

WMCJ-AM
Owner: Jimmy Dale Media, LLC
Editorial: 1707 Warnke Rd NW, Cullman, Alabama 35055-2231. **T:** 1 256 734-3271
Editorial Profile: WMCJ-AM is a commercial station owned by Jimmy Dale Media, LLC. The format of the station is sports. WMCJ-AM broadcasts to the Cullman, AL area at 1340 AM.

WMCL-AM
Owner: Dana Communications Corp.
Editorial: 303 N Main St, Benton, Illinois 62812-1314. **T:** 1 618 435-4346
E: wmcl1060@gmail.com
W: http://www.wmcl1060.com
Editorial Profile: WMCL-AM is a commercial station owned by Dana Communications Corp. The format of the station is classic country. WMCL-AM broadcasts to the McLeansboro, IL area at 1060 AM.

WMCO-FM
Owner: Muskingum University
Editorial: 163 Stormont St, New Concord, Ohio 43762-1118. **T:** 1 740 826-8379
E: wmco@muskingum.edu
W: http://www.orbitmediaonline.com
Editorial Profile: WMCO-FM is a non-commercial station owned by Muskingum University. The format for the station is college variety. WMCO-FM broadcasts to the New Concord, OH area at 90.7 FM.

WMCP-AM
Owner: Maury County Boosters Corp.
Editorial: 886 Mount Olivet Rd, Columbia, Tennessee 38401-8031. **T:** 1 931 388-3241
Editorial Profile: WMCP-AM is a commercial station owned by Maury County Boosters Corp. The format of the station is country music. WMCP-AM broadcasts to the Columbia, TN area at 1280 AM.

WMCR-AM
Owner: Leatherstocking Media Group Inc.
Editorial: 237 Genesee St, Oneida, New York 13421-2701. **T:** 1 315 363-6050
E: wmcrradio@aol.com
W: http://www.wmcronline.com
Editorial Profile: WMCR-AM is a commercial station owned by Leatherstocking Media Group Inc. The format of the station is talk. WMCR-AM broadcasts to the Oneida, NY area at 1600 AM.

WMCR-FM
Owner: Leatherstocking Media Group Inc
Editorial: 237 Genesee St, Oneida, New York 13421. **T:** 1 315 363-6050
E: wmcrradio@aol.com
W: http://www.wmcronline.com
Editorial Profile: WMCR-FM is a non-commercial station owned by Leatherstocking Media Group Inc. The format of the station is adult contemporary music. WMCR-FM broadcasts to Oneida, NY and the surrounding areas at 106.3 FM.

WMCT-AM
Owner: Johnson County Broadcasting Co.
Editorial: 1211 N Church St, Mountain City, Tennessee 37683. **T:** 1 423 727-6701
E: wmct@wmctradio.net
W: http://www.wmctradio.net
Editorial Profile: WMCT-AM is a commercial station owned by Johnson County Broadcasting Co. The format of the station is country and gospel. WMCT-AM broadcasts to the Mountain City, TN area at 1390 AM.

WMCX-FM
Owner: Monmouth University
Editorial: 400 Cedar Ave, West Long Branch, New Jersey 7764. **T:** 1 732 571-3482
E: wmcxradio@monmouth.edu
W: http://www.wmcx.com
Editorial Profile: WMCX-FM is a non-commercial station owned by Monmouth University. The format of the station is rock alternative music. WMCX-FM broadcasts to the West Long Branch, NJ area at 88.9 FM.

WMDB-AM
Owner: TBLC Media, LLC
Editorial: 209 10th Ave S Ste 342, Nashville, Tennessee 37203-0758. **T:** 1 615 242-1411
E: spanishmc@activa1240.com
W: http://www.elsol880.com
Editorial Profile: WMDB-AM is a commercial station owned by TBLC Media, LLC. The format of the station is Spanish AC. WMDB-AM broadcasts to the Nashville, TN area at 880 AM.

WMDC-FM
Owner: Radio Plus Inc.
Editorial: 132 N Main St Ste 1, Mayville, Wisconsin 53050-1638. **T:** 1 920 387-0000
E: bigsky@great98.net
W: http://www.great98.net
Editorial Profile: WMDC-FM is a commercial station owned by Radio Plus Inc. The format of the station is classic rock. WMDC-FM broadcasts to the Mayville, WI area at 98.7 FM.

WMDH-FM
Owner: Cumulus Media Inc.
Editorial: 1134 W State Road 38, New Castle, Indiana 47362-9781. **T:** 1 765 529-2600
W: http://www.wmdh.com
Editorial Profile: WMDH-FM is a commercial station owned by Cumulus Media Inc. The format of the station is contemporary country music. WMDH-FM broadcasts to the Indianapolis area at 102.5 FM.

WMDJ-FM
Owner: Floyd County Broadcasting Inc.
Editorial: 9030 Ky Route 1428, Allen, Kentucky 41601-9478. **T:** 1 606 874-8005
E: fm100wmdj@mikrotec.com
W: http://www.wmdjfm.com
Editorial Profile: WMDJ-FM is a commercial station owned by Floyd County Broadcasting Inc. The format of the station is classic country. WMDJ-FM broadcasts to the Martin, KY area at 100.1 FM.

WMDM-FM
Owner: Somar Communications Inc.
Editorial: 28095 Three Notch Rd Ste 2B, Mechanicsville, Maryland 20659-3373.
T: 1 301 870-5550
W: http://www.977therocket.com
Editorial Profile: WMDM-FM is a commercial station owned by Somar Communications Inc. The format of the station is classic rock. WMDM-FM broadcasts to the Mechanicsville, MD area at 97.7 FM.

WMDR-AM
Owner: Light of Life Ministries Inc.
Editorial: 160 Riverside Dr, Augusta, Maine 4330. **T:** 1 207 622-1340
E: wmdr@adelphia.net
W: http://www.wmdr.org
Editorial Profile: WMDR-AM is a non-commercial station owned by Light of Life Ministries Inc. The format of the station is Christian rock. WMDR-AM broadcasts to the Augusta, ME area at 1340 AM.

WMDR-FM
Owner: Light of Life Ministries Inc.
Editorial: 160 Riverside Dr, Augusta, Maine 4330. **T:** 1 207 622-1340
E: info@worshipradionetwork.org
W: http://www.godscountry889.com
Editorial Profile: WMDR-FM is a non-commercial station owned by Light of Life

Ministries Inc. The format of the station is Christian Country and Southern Gospel. WMDR-FM broadcasts to the Augusta, ME area on 88.9 FM.

WMEA-FM
Owner: Maine Public Broadcasting Network
Editorial: 63 Texas Ave, Bangor, Maine 04401-4324. **T:** 1 207 941-1010
E: comments@mpbn.net
W: http://www.mpbn.net
Editorial Profile: WMEA-FM is a non-commercial station owned by Maine Public Broadcasting Network. The format for the station is classical, news and talk. WMEA-FM broadcasts to the Bangor, ME area at 90.1 FM.

WMEB-FM
Owner: University of Maine
Editorial: 5748 Memorial Un, Orono, Maine 04469-5748. **T:** 1 207 581-4340
E: wmeb_feedback@umit.maine.edu
W: http://wmebsports.com
Editorial Profile: WMEB-FM is a non-commercial station owned by University of Maine. The format of the station is rock alternative. WMEB-FM broadcasts to the Orono, ME area at 91.9 FM.

WMED-FM
Owner: Maine Public Broadcasting Network
Editorial: 63 Texas Ave, Bangor, Maine 04401-4324. **T:** 1 207 941-1010
E: comments@mpbn.net
W: http://www.mpbn.net
Editorial Profile: WMED-FM is a non-commercial station owned by Maine Public Broadcasting Network. The format of the station is classical, news and talk. WMED-FM broadcasts to the Bangor, ME area at 89.7 FM.

WMEE-FM
Owner: Federated Media
Editorial: 2915 Maples Rd, Fort Wayne, Indiana 46816. **T:** 1 260 447-5511
W: http://www.wmee.com
Editorial Profile: WMEE-FM is a commercial station owned by Federated Media. The format of the station is hot adult contemporary. WMEE-FM broadcasts to the Fort Wayne, IN area at 97.3 FM.

WMEF-FM
Owner: Maine Public Broadcasting Network
Editorial: 63 Texas Ave, Bangor, Maine 04401-4324. **T:** 1 207 941-1010
E: contactus@mpbn.net
W: http://www.mpbn.net
Editorial Profile: WMEF-FM is a non-commercial station owned by Maine Public Broadcasting Network. The format of the station is classical, news and talk. WMEF-FM broadcasts to the Bangor, ME area at 106.5 FM.

WMEH-FM
Owner: Maine Public Broadcasting Network
Editorial: 63 Texas Ave, Bangor, Maine 04401-4324. **T:** 1 207 941-1010
E: comments@mpbn.net
W: http://www.mpbn.net
Editorial Profile: WMEH-FM is a non-commercial station owned by Maine Public Broadcasting Network. The format of the station is classical, news and talk. WMEH-FM broadcasts to the Bangor, ME area at 90.9 FM.

WMEJ-AM
Owner: Hancock Broadcasting
Editorial: 1190 Hollywood Blvd, Bay Saint Louis, Mississippi 39520-1662.
T: 1 228 467-1190
Editorial Profile: WMEJ-AM is a commercial station owned by Hancock Broadcasting. The format of the station is Gospel. WMEJ-AM broadcasts to the Bay Saint Louis, MS area at 1190 AM.

WMEL-AM
Owner: Harper [John]
Editorial: 2355 Pluckebaum Rd, Cocoa, Florida 32926-5179. **T:** 1 321 631-1300
W: http://www.1300wmel.com
Editorial Profile: WMEL-AM is a commercial station owned by John Harper. The format of the station is talk. WMEL-AM broadcasts to the Melbourne, FL area at 1300 AM.

WMEM-FM
Owner: Maine Public Broadcasting Network
Editorial: 63 Texas Ave, Bangor, Maine 04401-4324. **T:** 1 207 941-1010
E: comments@mpbn.net
W: http://www.mpbn.net
Editorial Profile: WMEM-FM is a non-commercial station owned by Maine Public Broadcasting Network. The format of the station is classical, talk and news. WMEME-FM broadcasts to the Bangor, ME area at 106.1 FM.

WMEN-AM
Owner: JCE Licenses, LLC
Editorial: 2100 Park Central Blvd N Ste 100, Pompano Beach, Florida 33064-2219.
T: 1 954 315-1515 **W:** http://wftlsports.com
Editorial Profile: WMEN-AM is a commercial radio station owned by JCE Licenses, LLC. The format of the station is sports. WMEN-AM broadcasts to the West Palm Beach, FL at 640 AM.

WMEP-FM
Owner: Maine Public Broadcasting Network
Editorial: 65 Texas Ave, Bangor, Maine 4401.
T: 1 207 941-1010 **E:** contactus@mpbn.net
W: http://www.mpbn.net
Editorial Profile: WMEP-FM is a commercial station owned by Maine Public Broadcasting Network. The format of the station is classical, jazz and news. WMEP-FM broadcasts to the Camden, ME area at 90.5 FM.

WMEQ-AM
Owner: Clear Channel Media and Entertainment
Editorial: 619 Cameron St, Eau Claire, Wisconsin 54703-4708. **T:** 1 715 830-4000
W: http://www.wmeq.com
Editorial Profile: WMEQ-AM is a commercial station owned by Clear Channel Media and Entertainment. The format of the station is news and talk. WMEQ-AM broadcasts to the Eau Claire, WI area at 880 AM.

WMEQ-FM
Owner: Clear Channel Media and Entertainment
Editorial: 619 Cameron St, Eau Claire, Wisconsin 54703. **T:** 1 715 830-4000
W: http://www.rock921.com
Editorial Profile: WMEQ-FM is a commercial station owned by Clear Channel Media and Entertainment. The format of the station is classic rock. WMEQ-FM broadcasts to the Eau Claire, WI area at 92.1 FM.

WMER-AM
Owner: Carter, Jr. (N. Brad)
Editorial: 315 A St, Meridian, Mississippi 39301-4512. **T:** 1 601 207-1391
W: http://wmerworldwide.com
Editorial Profile: WMER-AM is a non-commercial station owned by Carter, Jr. (N. Brad). The format of the station is gospel. WMER-AM broadcasts to the Meridian, MS area at a frequency of 1390 AM.

WMET-AM
Owner: Guadalupe Radio Network
Editorial: 8121 Georgia Ave Ste 806, Silver Spring, Maryland 20910-4945.
T: 1 301 585-1305
W: http://www.grnonline.com
Editorial Profile: WMET-AM is a commercial station owned by Guadalupe Radio Network. The format of the station is religious. WMET-AM broadcasts to the Washington, D.C. area at 1160 AM.

WMEV-AM
Owner: Holston Valley Broadcasting Corp.
Editorial: 1041 Radio Hill Rd, Marion, Virginia 24354-6597. **T:** 1 276 783-3151
E: fm94@fm94.com **W:** http://www.fm94.com
Editorial Profile: WMEV-AM is a commercial station owned by Holston Valley Broadcasting Corp. The format of the station is Southern gospel music. WMEV-AM broadcasts to the Marion, VA area at 1010 AM.

WMEV-FM
Owner: Holston Valley Broadcasting Corp.
Editorial: 1041 Radio Hill Rd, Marion, Virginia 24354-6597. **T:** 1 276 783-3151
E: fm94@fm94.com **W:** http://www.fm94.com
Editorial Profile: WMEV-FM is a commercial station owned by Holston Valley Broadcasting Corp. The format of the station is country music. WMEV-FM broadcasts to the Tri-Cities, TN area at 93.9 FM.

WMEW-FM
Owner: Maine Public Broadcasting Network
Editorial: 65 Texas Ave, Bangor, Maine 4401.
T: 1 207 941-1010 **E:** contactus@mpbn.net
W: http://www.mpbn.net
Editorial Profile: WMEW-FM is a non-commercial station owned by Maine Public Broadcasting Network. The format of the station is classical, jazz, news and talk. WMEW-FM broadcasts to the Waterville, ME area at 91.3 FM.

WMEZ-FM
Owner: Cumulus Media Inc.
Editorial: 6085 Quintette Rd, Pace, Florida 32571-6759. **T:** 1 850 994-5357
W: http://www.softrock941.com
Editorial Profile: WMEZ-FM is a commercial station owned by Cumulus Media Inc. The format of the station is Lite Rock/Lite AC. WMEZ-FM broadcasts to the Pensacola, FL area at 94.1 FM.

WMFA-AM
Owner: W & V Broadcasting Enterprises Inc.
Editorial: 1085 E Central Ave, Raeford, North Carolina 28376. **T:** 1 910 875-6225
E: wmfa1400@yahoo.com
Editorial Profile: WMFA-AM is a commercial station owned by W & V Broadcasting Enterprises Inc. The format of the station is gospel music. WMFA-AM broadcasts to the Raeford, NC area at 1400 AM.

WMFC-AM
Owner: Monroe Broadcasting Co., Inc.
Editorial: 961 Pineville Rd, Monroeville, Alabama 36460. **T:** 1 251 575-3281
E: wmfc@frontiernet.net
Editorial Profile: WMFC-AM is a commercial station owned by Monroe Broadcasting Co., Inc. The format of the station is oldies. WMFC-AM broadcasts to the Monroeville, AL area at 1360 AM.

WMFC-FM
Owner: Monroe Broadcasting Co., Inc.
Editorial: 961 Pineville Rd, Monroeville, Alabama 36460. **T:** 1 251 575-3281
E: wmfc@frontiernet.net
Editorial Profile: WMFC-FM is a commercial station owned by Monroe Broadcasting Co., Inc. The format of the station is oldies music. WMFC-FM broadcasts to the Monroeville, AL area at 99.3 FM.

WMFD-AM
Owner: Capitol Broadcasting Company
Editorial: 25 N Kerr Ave, Ste C, Wilmington, North Carolina 28405. **T:** 1 910 791-3088
E: am630@live.com **W:** http://www.am630.net
Editorial Profile: WMFD-AM is a commercial station owned by Capitol Broadcasting Company. The format of the station is sports talk. WMFD-AM broadcasts in the Wilmington, NC area at 630 AM.

WMFE-FM
Owner: Community Communications
Editorial: 11510 E Colonial Dr, Orlando, Florida 32817. **T:** 1 407 273-2300
E: wmfenews@wmfe.org
W: http://www.wmfe.org
Editorial Profile: WMFE-FM is a non-commercial station owned by Community Communications. The format of the station is news and talk. WMFE-FM broadcasts to the Orlando, FL area at 90.7 FM. The station does not accept PSAs.

WMFG-AM
Owner: Midwest Communications Inc.
Editorial: 807 W 37th St, Hibbing, Minnesota 55746. **T:** 1 218 263-7531
W: http://www.wmfgam.com
Editorial Profile: WMFG-AM is a commercial station owned by Midwest Communications Inc. The format of the station is adult standards. WMFG-AM broadcasts to the Hibbing, MN area at 1240 AM.

WMFG-FM
Owner: Midwest Communications Inc.
Editorial: 807 W 37th St, Hibbing, Minnesota 55746. **T:** 1 218 263-7531
W: http://mwcradio.com
Editorial Profile: WMFG-FM is a commercial station owned by Midwest Communications Inc. The format of the station is classic hits. WMFG-FM broadcasts to the Hibbing, MN area at 106.3 FM.

WMFJ-AM
Owner: Cornerstone Broadcasting Corp.
Editorial: 4295 S Ridgewood Ave, Port Orange, Florida 32127. **T:** 1 386 756-9094
E: wjlu@wjlu.org **W:** http://www.wjlu.org
Editorial Profile: WMFJ-AM is a non-commercial station owned by Cornerstone Broadcasting Corp. The format of the station is religion and contemporary Christian. WMFJ-AM broadcasts to the Port Orange, FL area at 1450 AM.

WMFM-FM
Owner: South Broadcasting System, Inc.
Editorial: 7007 NW 77th Ave, Miami, Florida 33166-2836. **T:** 1 305 447-9595
Editorial Profile: WMFM-FM is a commercial station owned by South Broadcasting System, Inc. The station airs a Spanish tropical format in the Coral Gables, FL are at 107.9 FM. The station is a simulcast of WXDJ-FM.

WMFN-AM
Owner: Birach Broadcasting Corp.
Editorial: 2422 Burton St SE, Grand Rapids, Michigan 49546-4806. **T:** 1 616 451-0551
W: http://www.lapoderosaradio.net
Editorial Profile: WMFN-AM is a commercial station owned by Birach Broadcasting Corp. The format of the station is regional Mexican. WMFN-AM broadcasts to the Grand Rapids, MI area at 640 AM.

WMFO-FM
Owner: Tufts University
Editorial: 474 Boston Ave, Medford, Massachusetts 02155-5584.
T: 1 617 627-3800 **E:** wmfo@wmfo.org
W: http://www.wmfo.org
Editorial Profile: WMFO-FM is a non-commercial station owned by Tufts University. The format of the station is college variety. WMFO-FM broadcasts to the Medford, MA area at 91.5 FM.

WMFQ-FM
Owner: JVC Broadcasting Inc.
Editorial: 3357 SW 7th St, Ocala, Florida 34474-1956. **T:** 1 352 732-0079
E: info@radio92q.com
W: http://www.radio92q.com
Editorial Profile: WMFQ-FM is a commercial station owned by JVC Broadcasting Inc. The format of the station is hot adult contemporary. WMFQ-FM broadcasts to the Ocala, FL area at 92.9 FM.

WMFR-AM
Owner: Curtis Media Group
Editorial: 875 W 5th St, Winston Salem, North Carolina 27101. **T:** 1 336 885-2191
W: http://www.triadsports.com
Editorial Profile: WMFR-AM is a commercial station owned by Curtis Media Group. The format of the station is sports. WMFR-AM broadcasts to the Greensboro, NC area on 1230 AM.

WMFS-AM
Owner: Entercom Communications Corp.
Editorial: 1835 Moriah Woods Blvd., Building 1, Memphis, Tennessee 38117.
T: 1 901 767-0104
W: http://www.680wsmb.com
Editorial Profile: WMFS-AM is a commercial station owned by Entercom Communications Corp. The format of the station is sports. WMFS-AM broadcasts to the Memphis, TN area at 680 AM.

WMFS-FM
Owner: Entercom Communications Corp.
Editorial: 1835 Moriah Woods Blvd, Building 1, Memphis, Tennessee 38117-7122.
T: 1 901 384-5900
W: http://www.680wsmb.com
Editorial Profile: WMFS-FM is a commercial station owned by Entercom Communications Corp. The format of the station sports. WMFS-FM broadcasts to the Memphis, TN area at 92.9 FM.

WMFU-FM
Owner: Auricle Communications
Editorial: 43 Montgomery St, 4th Fl, Jersey City, New Jersey 7302. **T:** 1 201 521-1416
E: wfmu@wfmu.org **W:** http://www.wfmu.org
Editorial Profile: WMFU-FM is a non-commercial station owned by Auricle Communications. The format of the station is freeform radio. WMFU-FM broadcasts to the Mount Hope, NY area at 90.1 FM.

WMFX-FM
Owner: L & L Broadcasting
Editorial: 1900 Pineview Dr, Columbia, South Carolina 29209-5079. **T:** 1 803 695-8600
W: http://fox1023.com
Editorial Profile: WMFX-FM is a commercial station owned by L & L Broadcasting. The format of the station is rock. WMFX-FM broadcasts to the Columbia, SC area at 102.3 FM.

WMGA-FM
Owner: Fifth Avenue Broadcasting Company
Editorial: 919 5th Ave Ste 210, Huntington, West Virginia 25701-2003. **T:** 1 304 399-9603
W: http://hits979.com
Editorial Profile: WMGA-FM is a commercial station owned by Fifth Avenue Broadcasting Company. The format of the station is Hot AC.

WMGA-FM broadcasts to Huntington, WV and surrounding communities at 97.9 FM.

WMGB-FM

Owner: Cumulus Media Inc.
Editorial: 544 Mulberry St, Fl 5, Macon, Georgia 31201-2770. **T:** 1 478 746-6286
W: http://www.allthehitsb951.com
Editorial Profile: WMGB-FM is a commercial station owned by Cumulus Media Inc. The format of the station is Top 40/CHR music. WMGB-FM broadcasts in the Macon, GA area at 95.1 FM.

WMGC-AM

Owner: Silva Entertainment
Editorial: 2514 Eugenia Ave, Nashville, Tennessee 37211-2117. **T:** 1 615 251-1222
E: sabrosa810@aol.com
W: http://www.lasabrosita810am.net
Editorial Profile: WMGC-AM is a commercial station owned by Silva Entertainment. The format of the station is regional Mexican music. WMGC-AM broadcasts to the Nashville, TN area at 810 AM.

WMGC-FM

Owner: Greater Media Inc.
Editorial: 1 Radio Plaza St, Ferndale, Michigan 48220-2140. **T:** 1 248 414-5600
W: http://www.detroitsports1051.com/
Editorial Profile: WMGC-FM is a commercial station owned by Greater Media Inc. The format of the station is sports. WMGC-FM broadcasts to the Detroit area at 105.1 FM.

WMGE-FM

Owner: Clear Channel Media and Entertainment
Editorial: 7601 Riviera Blvd, Miramar, Florida 33023. **T:** 1 305 503-0069
W: http://www.mega949.com
Editorial Profile: WMGE-FM is a commercial station owned by Clear Channel Media and Entertainment. The format of the station is Hispanic Top 40/CHR music. WMGE-FM broadcasts to the Miramar, FL area at 94.9 FM.

WMGF-FM

Owner: Clear Channel Media and Entertainment
Editorial: 2500 Maitland Center Pkwy Ste 401, Maitland, Florida 32751-4179.
T: 1 407 916-7800
W: http://www.magic107.com
Editorial Profile: WMGF-FM is a commercial station owned by Clear Channel Media and Entertainment. The format of the station is adult contemporary. WMGF-FM broadcasts to the Maitland, FL area at 107.7 FM.

WMGG-AM

Owner: Genesis Communications Inc.
Editorial: 800 8th Ave SE, Largo, Florida 33771-2162. **T:** 1 813 281-1040
E: contactus@radiogenesis.com
W: http://www.newstalkflorida.com/noti-america-1470-am
Editorial Profile: WMGG-AM is a commercial station owned by Genesis Communications Inc. The format of the station is Spanish news/talk. WMGG-AM broadcasts to the Tampa, FL area at 1470 AM.

WMGH-FM

Owner: J-Systems Franchising Corp.
Editorial: 2147 Market St, Nesquehoning, Pennsylvania 18240-1422. **T:** 1 570 645-2105
E: wmgh@ptd.net **W:** http://www.wmgh.com
Editorial Profile: WMGH-FM is a commercial station owned by owned by J-Systems Franchising Corp. The format of the station is adult contemporary music. WMGH-FM broadcasts to the Lansford, PA area at 105.5 FM.

WMGI-FM

Owner: Midwest Communications Inc.
Editorial: 824 S 3rd St, Terre Haute, Indiana 47807-4609. **T:** 1 812 232-4161
E: mixfm@1007mixfm.com
W: http://www.1007mixfm.com
Editorial Profile: WMGI-FM is a commercial station owned by Midwest Communications Inc. The format of the station is Top 40/CHR. WMGI-FM broadcasts to the Terre Haute, IN area at 100.7 FM.

WMGJ-AM

Owner: Donald(Floyd)
Editorial: 815 Tuscaloosa Ave, Gadsden, Alabama 35901. **T:** 1 256 546-4434
E: wmgj@wmgj.com **W:** http://www.wmgj.com

WMGK-FM

Owner: Greater Media Inc.
Editorial: 1 Bala Plz Ste 339, Bala Cynwyd, Pennsylvania 19004-1424. **T:** 1 610 667-8500
E: theoffice@wmgk.com
W: http://www.wmgk.com
Editorial Profile: WMGK-FM is a commercial station owned by Greater Media Inc. The format of the station is classic rock. WMGK-FM broadcasts to the Philadelphia area at 102.9 FM.

WMGL-FM

Owner: Cumulus Media Inc.
Editorial: 4230 Faber Place Dr, Ste 100, North Charleston, South Carolina 29405.
T: 1 843 277-1200
W: http://www.magic1017.com
Editorial Profile: WMGL-FM is a commercial station owned by Cumulus Media Inc. The format of the station is urban adult contemporary music. WMGL-FM broadcasts to the North Charleston, SC area at 107.3 FM.

WMGM-FM

Owner: Longport Media
Editorial: 1601 New Rd, Linwood, New Jersey 08221-1116. **T:** 1 609 653-1400
W: http://1037wmgm.com
Editorial Profile: WMGM-FM is a commercial station owned by Longport Media. The format of the station is active rock. WMGM-FM broadcasts to the Atlantic City, NJ area at 103.7 FM.

WMGN-FM

Owner: Midwest Family Stations
Editorial: 730 Rayovac Dr, Madison, Wisconsin 53711-2472. **T:** 1 608 273-1000
E: info@magic98.com
W: http://www.magic98.com
Editorial Profile: WMGN-FM is a commercial station owned by Midwest Family Stations. The format of the station is adult contemporary. WMGN-FM broadcasts to the Madison, WI area at 98.1 FM.

WMGO-AM

Owner: WMGO Broadcasting Corp.
Editorial: 107 W Peace St, Canton, Mississippi 39046. **T:** 1 601 859-2373
E: admin@wmgoradio.com
W: http://www.wmgoradio.com

WMGP-FM

Owner: Clear Channel Media and Entertainment
Editorial: 154 Boone Dr, Newnan, Georgia 30263-2801. **T:** 1 770 683-7234
W: http://www.magic981.com
Editorial Profile: WMGP-FM is a commercial station owned by Clear Channel Media and Entertainment. The format of the station is classic hits. WMGP-FM broadcasts to the Newnan, GA area at 98.1 FM.

WMGQ-FM

Owner: Greater Media Inc.
Editorial: 78 Veronica Ave, Somerset, New Jersey 8873. **T:** 1 732 249-2600
W: http://www.wmgqfm.com
Editorial Profile: WMGQ-FM is a commercial station owned by Greater Media Inc. The format of the station is adult contemporary. WMGQ-FM broadcasts in the Somerset, NJ area at 98.3 FM.

WMGR-AM

Owner: Flint Media
Editorial: 521 S Scott St, Bainbridge, Georgia 39819-4101. **T:** 1 229 246-7776
Editorial Profile: WMGR-AM is a commercial station owned by Flint Media, Inc. The format of the station is sports. WMGR-AM broadcasts to the Bainbridge, GA area at 930 AM.

WMGS-FM

Owner: Cumulus Media Inc.
Editorial: 600 Baltimore Drive, Wilkes-Barre, Pennsylvania 18702-7901. **T:** 1 570 824-9000
W: http://www.magic93fm.com
Editorial Profile: WMGS-FM is a commercial station owned by Cumulus Media Inc. The format is Lite Rock/Lite AC. WMGS-FM broadcasts to the Wilkes Barre, PA area at 92.9 FM.

WMGU-FM

Owner: Cumulus Media Inc.
Editorial: 1009 Drayton Rd, Fayetteville, North Carolina 28303-3887. **T:** 1 910 864-5222
W: http://www.magic1069.com
Editorial Profile: WMGU-FM is a commercial station owned by Cumulus Media Inc. The format of the station is urban adult contemporary. WMGU-FM broadcasts to the Fayetteville, NC area at 106.9 FM.

WMGV-FM

Owner: Beasley Broadcast Group
Editorial: 207 Glenburnie Dr, New Bern, North Carolina 28560. **T:** 1 252 633-1500
E: webmaster@v1033.com
W: http://www.v1033.com
Editorial Profile: WMGV-FM is a commercial station owned by Beasley Broadcast Group. The format of the station is adult contemporary. WMGV-FM broadcasts to the New Bern, NC area at 103.3 FM.

WMGW-AM

Owner: Forever Broadcasting
Editorial: 900 Water St, Meadville, Pennsylvania 16335. **T:** 1 814 724-1111
Editorial Profile: WMGW-AM is a commercial station owned by Forever Broadcasting. The format of the station is news, talk and sports. WMGW-AM broadcasts to the Meadville, PA area at 1490 AM.

WMGX-FM

Owner: Saga Communications
Editorial: 420 Western Ave, South Portland, Maine 04106-1704. **T:** 1 207 774-4561
W: http://www.coast931.com
Editorial Profile: WMGX-FM is a commercial station owned by Saga Communications. The format of the station is hot adult contemporary music. WMGX-FM broadcasts to the Portland, ME, area at 93.1 FM.

WMGY-AM

Owner: GHB Broadcasting
Editorial: 2305 Upper Wetumpka Rd, Montgomery, Alabama 36107.
T: 1 334 834-3710 **E:** admin@wmgyradio.com
W: http://www.wmgyradio.com
Editorial Profile: WMGY-AM is a commercial station owned by GHB Broadcasting. The format of the station is southern gospel and religious programming. WMGY-AM broadcasts to the Montgomery, AL area at 800 AM.

WMGZ-FM

Owner: Southern Stone Broadcasting
Editorial: 156 Lake Laurel Rd NE, Milledgeville, Georgia 31061-9007.
T: 1 478 453-9406 **E:** wmgz.z97@gmail.com
W: http://www.z97.fm
Editorial Profile: WMGZ-FM is a commercial station owned by Southern Stone Broadcasting. The format of the station is hot adult contemporary. WMGZ-FM broadcasts to the Milledgeville, GA area at 97.7 FM.

WMHB-FM

Owner: Mayflower Hill Broadcasting Corp.
Editorial: 4000 Mayflower Hill Drive, Waterville, Maine 4901. **T:** 1 207 859-5454
E: info@wmhb.org **W:** http://www.wmhb.org
Editorial Profile: WMHB-FM is a non-commercial college station owned by Mayflower Hill Broadcasting Corp. The format of the station is variety. WMHB-FM broadcasts in the Waterville, ME area at 89.7 FM.

WMHD-FM

Owner: Rose Hulman Institute of Technology
Editorial: 5500 Wabash Ave, Terre Haute, Indiana 47803. **T:** 1 812 872-6923
E: manager@wmhdradio.org
W: http://www.wmhdradio.org
Editorial Profile: WMHD-FM is a non-commercial station owned by Rose Hulman Institute of Technology. The format of the station is rock alternative. WMHD-FM broadcasts to the Terre Haute, IN area at 90.7 FM.

WMHK-FM

Owner: Columbia International University
Editorial: 7435 Monticello Rd, Columbia, South Carolina 29203. **T:** 1 803 754-5400
E: wmhk@wmhk.com
W: http://www.wmhk.com
Editorial Profile: WMHK-FM is a non-commercial station owned by Columbia International University. The format of the station is contemporary Christian. WMHK-FM broadcasts to the Columbia, SC area at 89.7 FM.

WMHQ-FM

Owner: Mars Hill Broadcasting Co Inc.
Editorial: 4044 Makyes Rd, Syracuse, New York 13215. **T:** 1 315 469-5051
E: mhn@marshillnetwork.org
W: http://www.marshillnetwork.org
Editorial Profile: WMHQ-FM is a non-commercial station owned by Mars Hill Broadcasting. The format of the station is Christian programming with a focus on teaching and music. The station broadcasts locally to the Malone/Massena, NY and Cornwall, Ontario areas at 90.1 FM.

WMHR-FM

Owner: Mars Hill Broadcasting Co Inc.
Editorial: 4044 Makyes Rd, Syracuse, New York 13215-9797. **T:** 1 315 469-5051
E: mhn@marshillnetwork.org
W: http://www.marshillnetwork.org
Editorial Profile: WMHR-FM is a non-commercial station owned by Mars Hill Broadcasting. The format of the station is Christian programming with a focus on teaching and music. WMHR-FM broadcasts to the Syracuse, NY area at 102.9 FM.

WMHT-FM

Owner: WMHT Educational Telecommunications
Editorial: 4 Global Vw, Troy, New York 12180-8368. **T:** 1 518 880-3400 **E:** email@wmht.org
W: http://www.wmht.org
Editorial Profile: WMHT-FM is a non-commercial station owned by WMHT Educational Telecommunications. The format of the station is classical. WMHT-FM broadcasts in Eastern New York and Western New England area at 89.1 FM.

WMHW-FM

Owner: Central Michigan University
Editorial: Central Michigan University, 180 Moore Hall, Mount Pleasant, Michigan 48859.
T: 1 989 774-7764 **E:** wmhw@cmich.edu
W: http://www.wmhw.org
Editorial Profile: WMHW-FM is a non-commercial station college owned by Central Michigan University. The format of the station is rock alternative. WMHW-FM broadcasts to the Mount Pleasant, MI area at 91.5 FM.

WMHX-FM

Owner: Entercom Communications Corp.
Editorial: 7601 Ganser Way, Madison, Wisconsin 53719-2074. **T:** 1 608 826-0077
W: http://mix1051fm.com
Editorial Profile: WMHX-FM is a commercial station owned by Entercom Communications Corp. The format of the station is hot AC. WMHX-FM broadcasts to Madison, WI at 105.1 FM.

WMIA-FM

Owner: Clear Channel Media and Entertainment
Editorial: 7601 Riviera Blvd, Miramar, Florida 33023. **T:** 1 954 862-2000
W: http://www.939mia.com
Editorial Profile: WMIA-FM is a commercial station owned by Clear Channel Media and Entertainment. The format of the station is rhythmic AC. WMIA-FM broadcasts to the Miami area at 93.9 FM.

WMIB-FM

Owner: Clear Channel Media and Entertainment
Editorial: 7601 Riviera Blvd, Miramar, Florida 33023-6574. **T:** 1 954 862-2000
W: http://www.1035thebeat.com
Editorial Profile: WMIB-FM is a commercial station owned by Clear Channel Media and Entertainment. The format of the station is urban contemporary. WMIB-FM broadcasts to the Miramar, FL area at 103.5 FM.

WMIC-AM

Owner: Sanilac Broadcasting
Editorial: 19 S Elk St, Sandusky, Michigan 48471. **T:** 1 810 648-2700
W: http://www.sanilacbroadcasting.com
Editorial Profile: WMIC-AM is a commercial station owned by Sanilac Broadcasting. The format of the station is country, news and talk. WMIC-AM broadcasts to the Sandusky, MI area at 660 AM.

WMID-AM

Owner: Equity Communications LP
Editorial: 8025 Black Horse Pike Ste 100, Pleasantville, New Jersey 08232-2959.
T: 1 609 484-8444
W: http://www.classicoldieswmid.com
Editorial Profile: WMID-AM is a commercial station owned by Equity Communications LP. The format of the station is oldies music. WMID-AM broadcasts to the West Atlantic City, NJ area at 1340 AM.

WMIE-FM

Owner: National Christian Network
Editorial: 1150 King St, Cocoa, Florida 32922.
T: 1 321 632-1000
W: http://www.wmiefm.com
Editorial Profile: WMIE-FM is a non-commercial station owned by the National Christian Network. The format of the station is contemporary Christian. WMIE-FM broadcasts to the Cocoa, FL area at 91.5 FM.

WMIL-FM
Owner: Clear Channel Media and Entertainment
Editorial: 12100 W Howard Ave, Greenfield, Wisconsin 53228-1851. **T:** 1 414 545-8900
E: eteam@fm106.com
W: http://www.fm106.com
Editorial Profile: WMIL-FM is a commercial station owned by Clear Channel Media and Entertainment. The format of the station is contemporary country. WMIL-FM broadcasts to the greater Milwaukee area at 106.1 FM.

WMIM-FM
Owner: Cumulus Media Inc.
Editorial: 14 S Monroe St, Monroe, Michigan 48161-2231. **T:** 1 734 242-6600
W: http://www.my983.com
Editorial Profile: WMIM-FM is a commercial station owned by Cumulus Media Inc. The format of the station is adult contemporary. WMIM-FM broadcasts to the Monroe, MI area on 98.3 FM.

WMIN-AM
Owner: Tri-County Broadcasting
Editorial: 1010 2nd St N, Sauk Rapids, Minnesota 56379-2527. **T:** 1 320 252-6200
E: tcbi.redhouse@gmail.com
W: http://www.1010wmin.com
Editorial Profile: WMIN-AM is a commercial station owned by Tri-County Broadcasting. The format of the station is adult standards and nostalgia. WMIN-AM broadcasts in the Sauk Rapids, MN area at 1010 AM.

WMIQ-AM
Owner: Sovereign Communications
Editorial: 101 Kent St, Iron Mountain, Michigan 49801-1507. **T:** 1 906 774-4321
E: talk1450wmiq@uplogon.com
W: http://wmiq.net
Editorial Profile: WMIQ-AM is a commercial station owned by Sovereign Communications. The format of the station is news, sports and talk programming. WMIQ-AM broadcasts in the Iron Mountain, MI area at 1450 AM.

WMIR-AM
Owner: Atlantic Beach Radio
Editorial: 4337 Big Barn Dr, Little River, South Carolina 29566. **T:** 1 843 399-2653
Editorial Profile: WMIR-AM is a commercial station owned by Atlantic Beach Radio. The format of the station is gospel. WMIR-AM broadcasts to the Little River, SC area at 1200 AM.

WMIS-AM
Owner: Natchez Communications
Editorial: 20 E Franklin St, Natchez, Mississippi 39120. **T:** 1 601 442-2522
E: wmiswtyj@bellsouth.net
Editorial Profile: WMIS-AM is a commercial station owned by Natchez Communications. The format of the station is urban contemporary music. WMIS-AM broadcasts in the Natchez, MS area at 1240 AM.

WMIS-FM
Owner: Paskvan Media, Inc.
Editorial: 2115 Washington Ave S, Bemidji, Minnesota 56601-8918. **T:** 1 218 751-7777
W: http://www.wmisfm.com
Editorial Profile: WMIS-FM is a commercial station owned by Paskvan Media, Inc. The format of the station is adult contemporary. WMIS-FM broadcasts locally to the Blackduck, MN area at 92.1 FM.

WMIT-FM
Owner: Blue Ridge Broadcasting Corp.
Editorial: 3 Porters Cove Rd, Asheville, North Carolina 28805-2834. **T:** 1 828 285-8477
E: thankyou@brb.org
W: http://www.1069thelight.org
Editorial Profile: WMIT-FM is a non-commercial station owned by Blue Ridge Broadcasting Corp. The format of the station is contemporary Christian. WMIT-FM broadcasts to the Asheville, NC area at 106.9 FM.

WMIX-AM
Owner: Withers Broadcasting Co.
Editorial: 3501 Broadway St, Mount Vernon, Illinois 62864-2202. **T:** 1 618 242-3500
W: http://www.withersradio.com/wmix
Editorial Profile: WMIX-AM is a commercial station owned by Withers Broadcasting Co. The format of the station is adult standards, and news and talk. WMIX-AM broadcasts to the Mt. Vernon, IL area at 940 AM.

WMIX-FM
Owner: Withers Broadcasting Co.
Editorial: 3501 Broadway St, Mount Vernon, Illinois 62864-2202. **T:** 1 618 242-3500
W: http://www.mywithersradio.com/wmix
Editorial Profile: WMIX-FM is a commercial station owned by Withers Broadcasting Co. The format of the station is contemporary country music. WMIX-FM broadcasts to the Mt. Vernon, IL area at 94.1 FM.

WMIZ-AM
Owner: Clear Communications Inc.
Editorial: 632 Maurice River Pkwy, Vineland, New Jersey 8360. **T:** 1 856 692-8888
W: http://www.wmizradio.com
Editorial Profile: WMIZ-AM is a commercial station owned by Clear Communications Inc. The format of the station is adult contemporary and Hispanic programming. WMIZ-AM broadcasts to Vineland, NJ area at 1270 AM.

WMJD-FM
Owner: Peggy Sue Broadcasting Media Inc.
Editorial: 1011 Radio Dr, Grundy, Virginia 24614. **T:** 1 276 935-7227
E: wmjd.fm@gmail.com
Editorial Profile: WMJD-FM is a commercial station owned by Peggy Sue Broadcasting Media, Inc. The format of the station is classic country music. WMJD-FM broadcasts to the Grundy, VA area at 100.7 FM.

WMJH-AM
Owner: Canto's Broadcasting
Editorial: 21700 Northwestern Hwy, Ste 1190, Southfield, Michigan 48075-4923.
T: 1 616 451-0551
E: comments@hottalk640.com
Editorial Profile: WMJH-AM is a commercial station owned by Canto's Broadcasting. The format of the station is regional Mexican music. WMJH-AM broadcasts to the Grand Rapids, MI area at 810 AM.

WMJI-FM
Owner: Clear Channel Media and Entertainment
Editorial: 6200 Oak Tree Blvd, Ste 400, Independence, Ohio 44131. **T:** 1 216 520-2600
E: feedback@wmji.com
W: http://www.wmji.com
Editorial Profile: WMJI-FM is a commercial station owned by Clear Channel Media and Entertainment. The format of the station is Oldies, classic hits and talk. WMJI-FM broadcasts to the Independence, OH area at 105.7 FM.

WMJJ-FM
Owner: Clear Channel Media and Entertainment
Editorial: 600 Beacon Pkwy W Ste 400, Birmingham, Alabama 35209-3118.
T: 1 205 439-9600
W: http://www.magic96.com
Editorial Profile: WMJJ-FM is a commercial station owned by Clear Channel Media and Entertainment. The format of the station is adult contemporary. WMJJ-FM broadcasts to the Birmingham, Al area at 96.5 FM.

WMJK-FM
Owner: BAS Broadcasting
Editorial: 1640 Cleveland Rd, Sandusky, Ohio 44870. **T:** 1 419 625-1010
W: http://www.wmjkradio.com
Editorial Profile: WMJK-FM is a commercial station owned by BAS Broadcasting. The format of the station is a mix of contemporary and classic country. WMJK-FM broadcasts to the Sandusky, OH area at 100.9 FM.

WMJL-FM
Owner: Joemyers Productions Inc.
Editorial: 251 Club Dr, Marion, Kentucky 42064-1244. **T:** 1 270 965-2271
Editorial Profile: WMJL-FM is a commercial station owned by Joemyers Productions Inc. The format of the station is oldies. WMJL-FM broadcasts to the Marion, KY area at a frequency of 102.7 FM.

WMJM-FM
Owner: Main Line Broadcasting
Editorial: 520 S 4th St Fl 2, Louisville, Kentucky 40202-2500. **T:** 1 502 625-1220
W: http://www.1013online.com
Editorial Profile: WMJM-FM is a commercial station owned by Main Line Broadcasting. The format of the station is urban adult contemporary. WMJM-FM broadcasts to the Louisville, KY area on 101.3 FM.

WMJO-FM
Owner: MacDonald Broadcasting Co.
Editorial: 2000 Whittier St, Saginaw, Michigan 48601-2271. **T:** 1 989 752-8161
W: http://www.973joefm.com
Editorial Profile: WMJO-FM is a commercial station owned by MacDonald Broadcasting Co. The format of the station is hot adult contemporary. WMJO-FM broadcasts to the Saginaw, MI area at 97.3 FM.

WMJR-AM
Owner: Thy Kingdom Come Network Inc.
Editorial: 195 Moore Dr, Lexington, Kentucky 40503-2918. **T:** 1 859 278-0894
E: info@realliferadio.com
W: http://www.realliferadio.com

WMJU-FM
Owner: Brookhaven Broadcasting, Inc.
Editorial: 911 Highway 550, Brookhaven, Mississippi 39601-4447. **T:** 1 601 833-9210
E: brookhavenbroadcasting@yahoo.com
Editorial Profile: WMJU-FM is a commercial station owned by Brookhaven Broadcasting, Inc. The format for the station is hot adult contemporary. WMJU-FM broadcasts to the Bude, MS area at 104.3 FM.

WMJW-FM
Owner: Radio Cleveland Inc.
Editorial: 911 S Davis Ave, Cleveland, Mississippi 38732-3941. **T:** 1 662 843-4091
Editorial Profile: WMJW-FM is a commercial station owned by Radio Cleveland Inc. The format for the station is country. WMJW-FM broadcasts to the Greenwood-Greenville, MS area at 107.5 FM.

WMJX-FM
Owner: Greater Media Inc.
Editorial: 55 William T Morrissey Blvd, Dorchester, Massachusetts 02125-3315.
T: 1 617 822-9600
W: http://www.magic1067.com
Editorial Profile: WMJX-FM is a commercial station owned by Greater Media Inc. The format of the station is Soft adult contemporary. WMJX-FM broadcasts to the Dorchester, MA area at 106.7 FM.

WMJY-FM
Owner: Clear Channel Media and Entertainment
Editorial: 286 Debuys Rd, Biloxi, Mississippi 39531. **T:** 1 228 388-2323
W: http://www.magic937.com
Editorial Profile: WMJY-FM is a commercial station owned by Clear Channel Media and Entertainment. The format of the station is adult contemporary. WMJY-FM broadcasts to the Biloxi, MS at 93.7 FM.

WMJZ-FM
Owner: Darby Advertising Inc.
Editorial: 3687 Old US Highway 27 S, Gaylord, Michigan 49735. **T:** 1 989 732-2341
W: http://www.radioeaglegaylord.com
Editorial Profile: WMJZ-FM is a commercial station owned by Darby Advertising Inc. The format of the station is adult hits. WMJZ-FM broadcasts to the Gaylord, MI, area at 101.5 FM.

WMKB-FM
Owner: KM Communications Inc.
Editorial: 4756 E 4th Rd, Mendota, Illinois 61342-9544. **T:** 1 815 538-7500
E: info@wmkbradio.com
W: http://www.wmkbradio.com/
Editorial Profile: WMKB-FM is a commercial station owned by KM Communications Inc. The format of the station is Regional Mexican music from the 1980s to now. The station broadcasts to the Mendota, IL area on 102.9 FM.

WMKC-FM
Owner: Northern Star Broadcasting LLC
Editorial: 1356 Mackinaw Ave, Cheboygan, Michigan 49721. **T:** 1 231 627-2341
W: http://www.1029bigcountry.com
Editorial Profile: WMKC-FM is a commercial station owned by Northern Star Broadcasting LLC. The format of the station is contemporary country. WMKC-FM broadcasts to the Cheboygan, MI area at 102.9 FM.

WMKD-FM
Owner: Sovereign Communications LLC
Editorial: 1411 Ashmun St, Sault Sainte Marie, Michigan 49783-2871.
T: 1 906 635-0995
Editorial Profile: WMKD-FM is a commercial station owned by Sovereign Communications LLC. The format for the station is contemporary country. WMKD-FM broadcasts to the Sault Sainte Marie, MI, area at 105.5 FM.

WMKI-AM
Owner: Walt Disney Co.
Editorial: 309 Waverley Oaks Rd, Waltham, Massachusetts 02452-8403.
T: 1 781 472-7920
W: http://www.radiodisney.com/boston
Editorial Profile: WMKI-AM is a commercial station owned by Walt Disney Co. The format of the station is children's programming. WMKI-AM is the Radio Disney affiliate for the Boston, MA area broadcasting locally at 1260 AM.

WMKL-FM
Owner: Call Communications Group, Inc.
Editorial: 8900 SW 168th St, Bldg 4000, Village of Palmetto Bay, Florida 33157-4569.
T: 1 305 662-7736 **E:** md@callfm.com
W: http://www.callfm.com
Editorial Profile: WMKL-FM is a commercial station owned by Call Communications Group, Inc. The format of the station is contemporary Christian. WMKL-FM broadcasts to the Miami area at 91.9 FM.

WMKR-FM
Owner: Miller Communications Inc.
Editorial: 918 E Park St, Taylorville, Illinois 62568-1916. **T:** 1 217 824-3395
W: http://www.taylorvilledailynews.com
Editorial Profile: WMKR-FM is a commercial station owned by Miller Communications Inc. The format of the station is country music. WMKR-FM broadcasts in the Taylorville, IL, area at 94.3 FM.

WMKS-FM
Owner: Clear Channel Media and Entertainment
Editorial: 2B Pai Park, Greensboro, North Carolina 27409-9428. **T:** 1 336 822-2000
W: http://www.1003kissfm.com/main.html
Editorial Profile: WMKS-FM is a commercial station owned by Clear Channel Media and Entertainment. The format of the station is rock. WMKS-FM broadcasts to the Greensboro, NC area at 100.3 FM.

WMKT-AM
Owner: MacDonald Garber Broadcasting Inc.
Editorial: 2095 S US Highway 131, Petoskey, Michigan 49770-9216. **T:** 1 231 347-8713
W: http://www.wmktthetalkstation.com
Editorial Profile: WMKT-AM is a commercial station owned by MacDonald Garber Broadcasting Inc. The format of the station is news/talk. WMKT-AM broadcasts to the Traverse City, MI area at a frequency of 1270 AM.

WMKV-FM
Owner: Maple Knoll Communities
Editorial: 11100 Springfield Pike, Cincinnati, Ohio 45246. **T:** 1 513 782-2427
E: wmkvfm@mkcommunities.org
W: http://www.wmkvfm.org
Editorial Profile: WMKV-FM is a non-commercial station owned by Maple Knoll Communities. The format of the station is adult standards. WMKV-FM broadcasts to the Cincinnati area at 89.3 FM.

WMKW-FM
Owner: Moody Bible Institute
Editorial: 1920 E 24th Street Pl, Chattanooga, Tennessee 37404. **T:** 1 423 629-8900
E: wmbw@moody.edu
W: http://www.moodyradiosoutheast.fm
Editorial Profile: WMKW-FM is a non-commercial station owned by Moody Bible Institute. The format of the station is religious programming. WSJQ-FM broadcasts to the Chattanooga, TN area at 89.3 FM.

WMKX-FM
Owner: Strattan Broadcasting Inc.
Editorial: 517 1/2 Market St, Johnsonburg, Pennsylvania 15845. **T:** 1 814 849-8100
E: megarockstudio@windstream.net
W: http://www.megarock.fm
Editorial Profile: WMKX-FM is a commercial station owned by Strattan Broadcasting Inc. The format of the station is rock. WMKX-FM broadcasts to the Johnsonburg, PA area at 105.5 FM.

WMKY-FM
Owner: Morehead State University
Editorial: 132 Breckinridge Hall, Morehead, Kentucky 40351-1689. **T:** 1 606 783-2001
E: wmky@morehead-st.edu
W: http://www.moreheadstate.edu/wmky
Editorial Profile: WMKY-FM is a non-commercial station owned by Morehead State University. The format for the station is news and variety. WMKY-FM broadcasts to the Lexington, KY area at 90.3 FM.

WMKZ-FM
Owner: Monticello Wayne County Media Inc.
Editorial: 105 Highway 3106, Monticello, Kentucky 42633-6801. **T:** 1 606 348-3393
E: studio@z93country.com
W: http://www.wmkz.com
Editorial Profile: WMKZ-FM is a commercial station owned by Monticello Wayne County Media Inc. The format for the station is contemporary country. WMKZ-FM broadcasts to the Lexington, KY area at 93.1 FM.

WMLB-AM
Owner: JW Broadcasting
Editorial: 1100 Spring St NW Ste 610, Atlanta, Georgia 30309-2828. **T:** 1 404 681-9307
W: http://www.1690wmlb.com
Editorial Profile: WMLB-AM is a commercial station owned by JW Broadcasting. The format of the station is talk and variety. WMLB-AM broadcasts to the Atlanta area at 1690 AM.

WMLC-AM
Owner: Walking By Faith Ministries
Editorial: 336 Rodenberg Ave, Biloxi, Mississippi 39531. **T:** 1 228 374-9739
E: wqfxradio@bellsouth.net
Editorial Profile: WMLC-AM is a commercial station owned by Walking By Faith Ministries. The format is sports and gosepl. WMLC-AM broadcasts to the Biloxi, MS area at 1270 AM.

WMLL-FM
Owner: Saga Communications
Editorial: 500 North Commercial St, Manchester, New Hampshire 3101.
T: 1 603 669-5777
W: http://www.965themill.com
Editorial Profile: WMLL-FM is a commercial station owned by Saga Communications. The format of the station is classic hits. WMLL-FM broadcasts to the Manchester, NH area at 96.5 FM.

WMLM-AM
Owner: Krol Communications
Editorial: 4170 N State Rd, Alma, Michigan 48801-9316. **T:** 1 989 463-4013
Editorial Profile: WMLM-AM is a commercial station owned by Krol Communications. The format of the station is country. WMLM-AM broadcasts to the Alma, MI area at 1520 AM.

WMLN-FM
Owner: Curry College
Editorial: 1071 Blue Hill Ave, Milton, Massachusetts 2186. **T:** 1 617 333-0311
W: http://www.curry.edu/about-curry/news-and-events/curry-radio.html
Editorial Profile: WMLN-FM is a non-commercial college station owned by Curry College. The format of the station is variety. WMLN-FM broadcasts to the Milton, MA area at 91.5 FM.

WMLP-AM
Owner: Sunbury Broadcasting Corp.
Editorial: 1227 County Line Rd, Selinsgrove, Pennsylvania 17870-8188. **T:** 1 570 286-5838
E: newsroom@wkok.com
W: http://www.1380wmlp.com
Editorial Profile: WMLP-AM is a commercial station owned by Sunbury Broadcasting Corp. The format of the station is talk. WMLP-AM broadcasts to the Lewisburg, PA area at 1380 AM.

WMLQ-FM
Owner: Synergy Media
Editorial: 5399 W Wallace Ln, Ludington, Michigan 49431-2439. **T:** 1 231 843-0941
W: http://www.westmicoastfm.com
Editorial Profile: WMLQ-FM is a commercial station owned by Synergy Media. The format of the station is Lite Rock/Lite AC. WMLQ-FM broadcasts to the Ludington, MI area at 97.7 FM.

WMLR-AM
Owner: 2 Brothers Broadcasting.
Editorial: 184 Switzerland Rd, Hohenwald, Tennessee 38462. **T:** 1 931 796-5966
E: wmlr1230am@bellsouth.net
Editorial Profile: WMLR-AM is a commercial station owned by 2 Brothers Broadcasting. The format of the station is oldies. WMLR-AM broadcasts to the Hohenwald, TN area at 1230 AM.

WMLS-FM
Owner: Minnesota Public Radio
Editorial: 207 W Superior St, Ste 224, Duluth, Minnesota 55802. **T:** 1 218 722-9411
E: newsroom@mpr.org
W: http://minnesota.publicradio.org/radio/stations/wlsnwmls/

Editorial Profile: WMLS-FM is a non-commercial station owned by Minnesota Public Radio. The format of the station is classical music. WMLS-FM broadcasts to the Duluth, MN area at 88.7 FM.

WMLT-AM
Owner: State Broadcasting, Inc.
Editorial: 807 Bellevue Ave, Dublin, Georgia 31021. **T:** 1 478 272-4422
W: http://www.1330wmlt.com
Editorial Profile: WMLT-AM is a commercial station owned by State Broadcasting, Inc. The format of the station is urban contemporary featuring R&B and Old School music. WMLT-AM broadcasts to the Dublin, GA area at 1330 AM.

WMLU-FM
Owner: Longwood Radio Associates
Editorial: 201 High St, Farmville, Virginia 23909-1800. **T:** 1 434 395-2792
E: wmlu@wmlu.org **W:** http://www.wmlu.org
Editorial Profile: WMLU-FM is a non-commercial station owned by Longwood Radio Assoicates. The format of the station is college variety. WMLU-FM broadcasts to the Farmville, VA area at 91.3 FM.

WMLX-FM
Owner: Clear Channel Media and Entertainment
Editorial: 667 W Market St, Lima, Ohio 45801.
T: 1 419 223-2060
W: http://www.mix1033.com
Editorial Profile: WMLX-FM is a commercial station owned by Clear Channel Media and Entertainment. The format of the station is adult contemporary. WMLX-FM broadcasts to the Lima, OH area at 103.3 FM.

WMMA-FM
Owner: Starboard Media Foundation Inc.
Editorial: 321 Market St, Wisconsin Rapids, Wisconsin 54494. **T:** 1 715 424-5050
E: info@relevantradio.com
W: http://www.relevantradio.com
Editorial Profile: WMMA-FM is a non-commercial station owned by Starboard Media Foundation Inc. The format of the station is religious. WMMA-FM broadcasts to the Wisconsin Rapids, WI area at 93.9 FM.

WMMB-AM
Owner: Clear Channel Media and Entertainment
Editorial: 1388 S Babcock St, Melbourne, Florida 32901-3009. **T:** 1 321 733-1000
W: http://www.wmmbam.com
Editorial Profile: WMMB-AM is a commercial station owned by Clear Channel Media and Entertainment. The format of the station is news and talk. WMMB-AM broadcasts to the Melbourne, FL area at 1240 AM.

WMMC-FM
Owner: JDL Broadcasting Inc.
Editorial: 627 1/2 Archer Ave, Marshall, Illinois 62441-1267. **T:** 1 217 826-8017
E: wmmc106@aol.com
W: http://www.wmmcradio.com
Editorial Profile: WMMC-FM is a commercial station owned by JDL Broadcasting Inc. The format of the station is classic hits music. WMMC-FM broadcasts to the Marshall, IL area at 105.9 FM.

WMME-FM
Owner: Townsquare Media, Inc.
Editorial: 56 Western Ave Ste 13, Augusta, Maine 04330-6348. **T:** 1 207 623-4735
W: http://www.92moose.fm
Editorial Profile: WMME-FM is a commercial station owned by Townsquare Media, Inc. The format of the station is Top 40/CHR. WMME-FM broadcasts to the Augusta, ME area at 92.3 FM.

WMMG-AM
Owner: Meade County Communications Inc.
Editorial: 1715 Bypass Rd, Brandenburg, Kentucky 40108-1623. **T:** 1 270 422-3961
E: wmmg935@bbtel.com
W: http://www.wmmgradio.com
Editorial Profile: WMMG-AM is a commercial station owned by Meade County Communications Inc. The format of the station is classic country. WMMG-AM broadcasts to the Brandenburg, KY area at 1140 AM.

WMMG-FM
Owner: Meade County Communications Inc.
Editorial: 1715 Bypass Rd, Brandenburg, Kentucky 40108. **T:** 1 270 422-3961
E: wmmg935@bbtel.com
W: http://www.wmmgradio.com

Editorial Profile: WMMG-FM is a commercial station owned by Meade County Communications Inc. The format of the station is country music. WMMG-FM broadcasts to the Brandenburg, KY area at 93.5 FM.

WMMI-AM
Owner: Central Michigan Communications Inc.
Editorial: 4895 E Wing Rd, Mount Pleasant, Michigan 48858-7057. **T:** 1 989 772-9664
E: wczy@wczy.net **W:** http://wczy.net
Editorial Profile: WMMI-AM is a commercial station owned by Central Michigan Communications Inc. The format for the station is talk. WMMI-AM broadcasts to the Flint, MI area at 830 AM.

WMMJ-FM
Owner: Radio One Inc.
Editorial: 5900 Princess Garden Pkwy, Fl 8, Lanham, Maryland 20706. **T:** 1 301 306-1111
W: http://mymajicdc.com
Editorial Profile: WMMJ-FM is a commercial station owned by Radio One Inc. The format of the station is urban adult contemporary. WMMJ-FM broadcasts to the Washington, D.C. area at 102.3 FM.

WMML-AM
Owner: Pamal Broadcasting Ltd.
Editorial: 89 Everts Ave, Queensbury, New York 12804-2040. **T:** 1 518 793-7733
E: production@adirondackbroadcasting.com
Editorial Profile: WMML-AM is a commercial station owned by Pamal Broadcasting Ltd. The format of the station is sports. The station airs locally at 1230 AM.

WMMM-FM
Owner: Entercom Communications Corp.
Editorial: 7601 Ganser Way, Madison, Wisconsin 53719-2074. **T:** 1 608 826-0077
E: 1055triplem@entercom.com
W: http://www.1055triplem.com
Editorial Profile: WMMM-FM is a commercial station owned by Entercom Communications Corp. The format for the station is adult album alternative. WMMM-FM broadcasts to the Madison, WI area at 105.5 FM.

WMMO-FM
Owner: Cox Media Group, Inc.
Editorial: 4192 N John Young Pkwy, Orlando, Florida 32804-2620. **T:** 1 321 281-2000
W: http://www.wmmo.com
Editorial Profile: WMMO-FM is a commercial station owned by Cox Media Group, Inc. The format of the station is Lite Rock/Lite AC. WMMO-FM broadcasts to the Orlando, FL area at 98.9 FM.

WMMQ-FM
Owner: Townsquare Media, LLC
Editorial: 3420 Pinetree Rd, Lansing, Michigan 48911-4207. **T:** 1 517 394-7272
W: http://www.wmmq.com
Editorial Profile: WMMQ-FM is a commercial station owned by Townsquare Media, LLC. The format of the station is classic rock. WMMQ-FM broadcasts to the Lansing, MI area at 94.9 FM.

WMMR-FM
Owner: Greater Media Inc.
Editorial: 1 Bala Plz, Ste 424, Bala Cynwyd, Pennsylvania 19004. **T:** 1 610 771-0933
W: http://www.wmmr.com
Editorial Profile: WMMR-FM is a commercial station owned by Greater Media Inc. The format of the station is rock/album-oriented rock. WMMR-FM broadcasts to the Philadelphia area at 93.3 FM.

WMMS-FM
Owner: Clear Channel Media and Entertainment
Editorial: 6200 Oak Tree Blvd, Independence, Ohio 44131-6933. **T:** 1 216 520-2600
W: http://www.wmms.com
Editorial Profile: WMMS-FM is a commercial station owned by Clear Channel Media and Entertainment. The format of the station is rock. WMMS-FM broadcasts to the Cleveland area at 100.7 FM.

WMMT-FM
Owner: Appalshop Inc.
Editorial: 91 Madison Ave, Whitesburg, Kentucky 41858-9317. **T:** 1 606 633-0108
W: http://www.wmmt.org
Editorial Profile: WMMT-FM is a non-commercial station owned by Appalshop Inc. The format of the station is variety. WMMT-FM broadcasts to the Whitesburg, KY, area at 88.7 FM.

WMMV-AM
Owner: Clear Channel Media and Entertainment
Editorial: 1388 S Babcock St, Melbourne, Florida 32901. **T:** 1 321 733-1000
W: http://www.wmmbam.com
Editorial Profile: WMMV-AM is a commercial station owned by Clear Channel Media and Entertainment. The format of station is news and talk. WMMV-AM broadcasts to the Melbourne, FL area at 1350 AM.

WMMW-AM
Owner: Connoisseur Media
Editorial: 869 Blue Hills Ave, Bloomfield, Connecticut 06002-3710. **T:** 1 860 243-1115
W: http://www.talkofconnecticut.com
Editorial Profile: WMMW-AM is a commercial station owned by Connoisseur Media. The format of the station is talk. WMMW-AM broadcasts to the Bloomfield, CT area at 1470 AM.

WMMX-FM
Owner: Clear Channel Media and Entertainment
Editorial: 101 Pine St, Dayton, Ohio 45402-2925. **T:** 1 937 224-1137
W: http://www.wmmx.com
Editorial Profile: WMMX-FM is a commercial station owned by Clear Channel Media and Entertainment. The format of the station is hot adult contemporary music. WMMX-FM broadcasts to the Dayton, OH area at 107.7 FM.

WMMY-FM
Owner: High Country Adventures, LLC
Editorial: 738 Blowing Rock Rd, Boone, North Carolina 28607-4835. **T:** 1 828 264-2411
W: http://www.highway1061fm.com
Editorial Profile: WMMY-FM is a commercial station owned by High Country Adventures, LLC, a subsidiary of Curtis Media Group. The format of the station is contemporary country. WMMY-FM broadcasts to the Boone, NC area at 106.1 FM.

WMNA-FM
Owner: 3 Daughters Media, Inc.
Editorial: 677 Zion Road, Gretna, Virginia 24557-0730. **T:** 1 434 534-6100
E: wblt@inbox.com
W: http://www.wiqoradio.com
Editorial Profile: WMNA-FM is a commercial station owned by 3 Daughters Media, Inc. The format of the station is talk. WMNA-FM broadcasts to the Roanoke, VA area at 106.3 FM.

WMNC-AM
Owner: Cooper Broadcasting Corp.
Editorial: 1103 N Green St, Morganton, North Carolina 28655. **T:** 1 828 437-0521
E: wmnc@bellsouth.net
Editorial Profile: WMNC-AM is a commercial station owned by Cooper Broadcasting Corp. The format of the station is classic country. WMNC-AM broadcasts to the Morganton, NC area at 1430 AM.

WMNC-FM
Owner: Cooper Broadcasting Corp.
Editorial: 1103 N Green St, Morganton, North Carolina 28655. **T:** 1 828 437-0521
E: wmnc@bellsouth.net
W: http://www.bigdawg92fm.com
Editorial Profile: WMNC-FM is a commercial station owned by Cooper Broadcasting Corp. The format of the station is contemporary country. WMNC-FM broadcasts to the Morganton, NC area at 92.1 FM.

WMNF-FM
Owner: Stubblefield Foundation(Nathan)
Editorial: 1210 E Dr Martin Luther King Jr Blvd, Tampa, Florida 33603-4417.
T: 1 813 238-8001 **E:** newsroom@wmnf.org
W: http://www.wmnf.org
Editorial Profile: WMNF-FM is a non-commercial station owned by Nathan Stubblefield Foundation. The format of the station is variety. WMNF-FM broadcasts to the Tampa, FL area at 88.5 FM.

WMNI-AM
Owner: North American Broadcasting
Editorial: 1458 Dublin Rd, Columbus, Ohio 43215-1010. **T:** 1 614 481-7800
W: http://www.wmni.com
Editorial Profile: WMNI-AM is a commercial station owned by North American Broadcasting. The format of the station is adult standards. WMNI-AM broadcasts to the Columbus, OH area at 920 AM. Slogan is "Playing America's Best Music."

WMNI-FM

Owner: North American Broadcasting
Editorial: 1458 Dublin Rd, Columbus, Ohio 43215-1010. **T:** 1 614 481-7800
E: mail@nabco-inc.com
W: http://news.wmni.com/
Editorial Profile: WMNI-FM is a commercial station owned by North American Broadcasting. The format of the station is Classic Hits. WMNI-FM broadcasts to the Columbus, OH area at 103.9 FM.

WMNP-FM

Owner: 3G Broadcasting, Inc.
Editorial: 30 Dagnillo Dr, East Greenwich, Rhode Island 02818-4069. **T:** 1 401 846-1540
Editorial Profile: WMNP-FM is a commercial station owned by 3G Broadcasting, Inc. The format of the station is Top 40/CHR. WMNP-FM broadcasts to the Newport, RI area at 99.3 FM.

WMNR-FM

Owner: Town of Monroe, CT
Editorial: 731 Main St, Monroe, Connecticut 06468-2872. **T:** 1 203 268-9667
E: info@wmnr.org **W:** http://www.wmnr.org
Editorial Profile: WMNR-FM is a non-commercial station owned by the Town of Monroe, CT. The format of the station is classical. WMNR-FM broadcasts to the Monroe, CT area at 88.1 FM.

WMNV-FM

Owner: Capital Media Corporation
Editorial: 30 Park Ave, Cohoes, New York 12047-3330. **T:** 1 518 237-1330
E: events@aliveradio.com
W: http://www.aliveradionetwork.com
Editorial Profile: WMNV-FM is a commercial station owned by Capital Media Corporation. The format of the station is religious programming. WMNV-FM broadcasts to the Cohoes, NY area at 104.1 FM. Address all mail to Paul Lotters.

WMNX-FM

Owner: Cumulus Media Inc.
Editorial: 3233 Burnt Mill Dr, Ste 4, Wilmington, North Carolina 28403.
T: 1 910 763-9977
W: http://www.coast973.com
Editorial Profile: WMNX-FM is a commercial station owned by Cumulus Media Inc. The format of the station is urban contemporary. WMNX-FM broadcasts to the Wilmington, NC area at 97.3 FM.

WMNZ-AM

Owner: Macon County Broadcasting Co.
Editorial: 115 1/2 Cherry St, Montezuma, Georgia 31063. **T:** 1 478 472-8386
E: wmnz1050am@yahoo.com
Editorial Profile: WMNZ-AM is a commercial owned by Macon County Broadcasting Co. The format of the station is contemporary country. WMNZ-AM broadcasts to the Montezuma, GA area at 1050 AM.

WMOA-AM

Owner: JAWCO Inc.
Editorial: 925 Lancaster St, Marietta, Ohio 45750-2531. **T:** 1 740 373-1490
E: news@wmoa1490.com
W: http://www.wmoa1490.com
Editorial Profile: WMOA-AM is a commercial station owned by JAWCO Inc. The format for the station is Lite Rock/Lite AC. WMOA-AM broadcasts to the Marietta, OH area at 1490 AM.

WMOB-AM

Owner: Buddy Tucker Association, Inc.
Editorial: 2500 Battleship Pkwy, Mobile, Alabama 36652. **T:** 1 251 432-1360

WMOC-FM

Owner: Full Gospel Church of God Written
Editorial: 414 Renwick St, Lumber City, Georgia 31549. **T:** 1 912 363-2203
E: wmoc887@yahoo.com
W: http://www.wmoc887fm.com
Editorial Profile: WMOC-FM is a non-commercial station owned by Full Gospel Church of God Written. The format of the station is gospel. WMOC-FM broadcasts to the Lumber City, GA area at a frequency of 88.7 FM.

WMOD-FM

Owner: WMOD Inc.
Editorial: 200 E Market St, Bolivar, Tennessee 38008-2362. **T:** 1 731 658-7328
E: wmod@wmodradio.com
W: http://wmodradio.com
Editorial Profile: WMOD-FM is a commercial station owned by WMOD Inc. The format of

the station is primarily classic country music. WMOD-FM broadcasts to the Bolivar, TN area at 96.7 FM.

WMOG-AM

Owner: Clear Channel Media and Entertainment
Editorial: 3833 US Highway 82, Brunswick, Georgia 31523-7735. **T:** 1 912 267-1025
Editorial Profile: WMOG-AM is a commercial station owned by Clear Channel Media and Entertainment. The format of the station is classic hits. WMOG-AM broadcasts to the Brunswick, GA area at 1490 AM.

WMOH-AM

Owner: Vernon Baldwin Broadcasting
Editorial: 2081 Fairgrove Ave, Hamilton, Ohio 45011-1967. **T:** 1 513 863-1111
W: http://www.wmoh.com
Editorial Profile: WMOH-AM is a commercial station owned by Vernon Baldwin Broadcasting. The format of the station is news, talk and sports. WMOH-AM broadcasts to the Hamilton, OH area at 1450 AM.

WMOI-FM

Owner: Prairie Communications LLP
Editorial: 55 Public Sq, Monmouth, Illinois 61462. **T:** 1 309 734-9452
E: wmoi@maplecity.com
W: http://www.977wmoi.com
Editorial Profile: WMOI-FM is a commercial station owned by Prairie Communications LLP. The format of the station is adult contemporary. WMOI-FM broadcasts to the Monmouth, IL area at 97.7 FM.

WMOK-AM

Owner: Withers Broadcasting Co.
Editorial: 339 Fairgrounds Rd, Metropolis, Illinois 62960. **T:** 1 618 524-9209
E: wmok920@frontier.com
W: http://www.920wmok.com

WMOM-FM

Owner: Bay View Broadcasting
Editorial: 206 E Ludington Ave, Ludington, Michigan 49431. **T:** 1 231 845-9666
E: news@wmom.fm **W:** http://www.wmom.fm
Editorial Profile: WMOM-FM is a commercial station owned by Bay View Broadcasting. The format of the station is Top 40/CHR. WMOM-FM broadcasts to the Ludington, MI area at 102.7 FM.

WMON-AM

Owner: LM Communications, Inc.
Editorial: 100 Kanawha Ter, Saint Albans, West Virginia 25177-2771. **T:** 1 304 722-3308
E: wjypnet@gmail.com **W:** http://wjypam.com/
Editorial Profile: WMON-AM is a commercial station owned by LM Communications, Inc. The format of the station is sports. WMON-AM broadcasts to the Montgomery, WV area at 1340.

WMOO-FM

Owner: Great Eastern Radio, LLC
Editorial: 3422 US Route 5, Derby, Vermont 05829-4430. **T:** 1 802 766-9236
E: wmooproduction.vba@gmail.com
W: http://www.moo92.com
Editorial Profile: WMOO-FM is a commercial station owned by Great Eastern Radio, LLC. The format of the station is hot adult contemporary music. WMOO-FM broadcasts to the Derby, VT area at 92.1 FM.

WMOP-AM

Owner: Florida Sportstalk Inc.
Editorial: 2320 Ne 2Nd St, Ocala, Florida 34470-8228. **T:** 1 352 732-2010
Editorial Profile: WMOP-AM is a commercial station owned by Florida Sportstalk Inc. The format of the station is sports. WMOP-AM broadcasts to the Ocala, FL area at 900 AM.

WMOQ-FM

Owner: Bostwick Broadcasting Group
Editorial: 1610 Launius Rd, Good Hope, Georgia 30641-2639. **T:** 1 770 267-0923
W: http://www.wmoqfm.com
Editorial Profile: WMOQ-FM is a commercial station owned by Bostwick Broadcasting Group. The format of the station is classic country. WMOQ-FM broadcasts to the Good Hope, GA area at 92.3 FM.

WMOR-AM

Owner: Morgan County Industries Inc.
Editorial: 129 College St, West Liberty, Kentucky 41472. **T:** 1 606 784-4141
E: radio41472@yahoo.com
Editorial Profile: WMOR-AM is a commercial station owned by Morgan County Industries

Inc. The format of the station is oldies. WMOR-AM broadcasts to the West Liberty, KY area at 1330 AM.

WMOR-FM

Owner: Morgan County Industries Inc.
Editorial: 129 College St, West Liberty, Kentucky 41472-1156. **T:** 1 606 784-4141
Editorial Profile: WMOR-FM is a commercial station owned by Morgan County Industries Inc. The format of the station is adult hits. WMOR-FM broadcasts to the West Liberty, KY area at 106.1 FM.

WMOS-FM

Owner: Cumulus Media Inc.
Editorial: 7 Governor Winthrop Blvd, New London, Connecticut 06320-6428.
T: 1 860 443-1980
W: http://www.1023thewolf.com
Editorial Profile: WMOS-FM is a commercial station owned by Cumulus Media Inc. The format of the station is classic rock. WMOS-FM broadcasts to the Hartford-New Haven, CT area at 102.3 FM.

WMOT-FM

Owner: Middle Tennessee State University
Editorial: 1301 E Main St, Murfreesboro, Tennessee 37132-0002. **T:** 1 615 898-2800
W: http://www.wmot.org
Editorial Profile: WMOT-FM is a non-commercial station owned by Middle Tennessee State University. The format of the station is news, talk, classical and jazz music. WMOT-FM broadcasts to the Murfreesboro, TN area at 89.5 FM.

WMOU-AM

Owner: Lunderville(Barry)
Editorial: 15 Main St, Littleton, New Hampshire 03561-4037. **T:** 1 603 752-1230
E: kiss102@together.net
Editorial Profile: WMOU-AM is a commercial station owned by Barry Lunderville. The format of the station is Hot AC. WMOU-AM broadcasts to the Berlin, NH area at 1230 AM.

WMOV-AM

Owner: Vandalia Media Partners
Editorial: 527 Gibbs St, Ravenswood, West Virginia 26164-1011. **T:** 1 304 273-2544
Editorial Profile: WMOV-AM is a commercial station owned by Vandalia Media Partners. The format of the station is classic hits. WMOV-AM broadcasts to the Ravenswood, WV area at 1360 AM.

WMOV-FM

Owner: Clear Channel Media and Entertainment
Editorial: 1003 Norfolk Sq, Norfolk, Virginia 23502-3234. **T:** 1 757 466-0009
W: http://www.movin1077fm.com
Editorial Profile: WMOV-FM is a commercial station owned by Clear Channel Media and Entertainment. The format of the station is rhythmic adult contemporary. WMOV-FM broadcasts to the Norfolk, VA area at 107.7 FM.

WMOX-AM

Owner: Magnolia State Broadcasting
Editorial: 451 Highway 11/80, Meridian, Mississippi 39301-2779. **T:** 1 601 693-1891
E: wmoxradio@wmox.net
W: http://www.wmox.net
Editorial Profile: WMOX-AM is a commercial station owned by Magnolia State Broadcasting. The format of the station is talk. WMOX-AM broadcasts to the Meridian, MS area at 1010 AM.

WMOZ-FM

Owner: Quarnstrom Media Group LLC
Editorial: 1104 Cloquet Ave, Cloquet, Minnesota 55720. **T:** 1 218 879-4534
E: wklk@aol.com
Editorial Profile: WMOZ-FM is a commercial station owned by Quarnstrom Media Group LLC. The format of the station is oldies music. WMOZ-FM broadcasts to the Duluth, MN area at 106.9 FM.

WMPC-AM

Owner: Calvary Bible Church of Lapeer
Editorial: 1800 N Lapeer Rd, Lapeer, Michigan 48446-7794. **T:** 1 810 664-6211
W: http://www.wmpc.org
Editorial Profile: WMPC-AM is a non-commercial station owned by the Calvary Bible Church of Lapeer. The format of the station is Christian music and talk programming. WMPC-AM broadcasts to the Lapeer, MI, area at 1230 AM.

WMPG-FM

Owner: University of Southern Maine
Editorial: 96 Falmouth St, Portland, Maine 04103-4864. **T:** 1 207 780-4943
W: http://www.wmpg.org
Editorial Profile: WMPG-FM is a non-commercial station owned by University of Southern Maine. The format for the station is college variety and news. WMPG-FM broadcasts to the Portland, ME area at 90.9 FM.

WMPI-FM

Owner: Rice Broadcasting Inc.(D.R.)
Editorial: 22 E McClain Ave, Scottsburg, Indiana 47170-1844. **T:** 1 812 752-5612
W: http://www.i1053online.com
Editorial Profile: WMPI-FM is a commercial station owned by D.R. Rice Broadcasting Inc. The format of the station is contemporary country music. WMPI-FM broadcasts in the Scottsburg, IN area at 105.3 FM.

WMPL-AM

Owner: J&J Broadcasting
Editorial: 326 Quincy St, Hancock, Michigan 49930. **T:** 1 906 482-3700
E: wmplprod@themix93.com
W: http://www.wmpl920.com
Editorial Profile: WMPL-AM is a commercial station owned by J&J Broadcasting. The format of the station is news, sports and talk. WMPL-AM broadcasts to the Hancock, MI area at 920 AM.

WMPM-AM

Owner: Family Media Group, LLC
Editorial: 1270 Buffalo Rd, Smithfield, North Carolina 27577. **T:** 1 919 934-2434
E: churchnews@1270wmpm.com
W: http://www.1270wmpm.com
Editorial Profile: WMPM-AM is a commercial station owned by Family Media Group, LLC. The format of the station is contemporary Christian. WMPM-AM broadcasts to the Smithfield, NC area at 1270 AM.

WMPN-FM

Owner: Mississippi Authority For Educational Television
Editorial: 3825 Ridgewood Rd, Jackson, Mississippi 39211. **T:** 1 601 432-6565
E: psa@mpbonline.org
W: http://www.mpbonline.org
Editorial Profile: WMPN-FM is a non-commercial station owned by Mississippi Authority For Educational Television. The format of the station is news, talk and classical music. WMPN-FM broadcasts to the Jackson, MS area at 91.3 FM.

WMPO-AM

Owner: Positive Radio Group
Editorial: 39540 Bradbury Rd, Middleport, Ohio 45760. **T:** 1 740 992-6485
E: office@wyvk.com **W:** http://www.wyvk.com
Editorial Profile: WMPO-AM is a commercial station owned by the Positive Radio Group. The format of the station is sports news and talk. WMPO-AM broadcasts to Middleport, OH and surrounding communities at 1390 AM.

WMPR-FM

Owner: Maxwell Broadcasting Inc.(J.C.)
Editorial: 1018 Pecan Park Cir, Jackson, Mississippi 39209-6913. **T:** 1 601 948-5835
W: http://www.wmpr901.com
Editorial Profile: WMPR-FM is a commercial station owned by J.C. Maxwell Broadcasting Inc. The format of the station is blues and gospel. WMPR-FM broadcasts to Jackson, MS and its surrounding environs at 90.1 FM.

WMPS-AM

Owner: Flinn Broadcasting Corp.
Editorial: 6080 Mount Moriah Road Ext, Memphis, Tennessee 38115-2645.
T: 1 901 756-7356 **E:** mail@flinn.com
W: http://www.wmpsthepoint.com
Editorial Profile: WMPS-AM is a commercial station owned by Flinn Broadcasting Corp. The format of the station is conservative news/talk. WMPS-AM broadcasts to the Memphis, TN market at AM 1210.

WMPX-AM

Owner: Steel Broadcasting
Editorial: 1510 Bayliss St, Midland, Michigan 48640. **T:** 1 989 631-1490
E: admin@wmpxwmrx.com
W: http://www.wmpxwmrx.com
Editorial Profile: WMPX-AM is a commercial station owned by Steel Broadcasting. The format for the station is adult standards. WMPX-AM broadcasts to the Flint, MI area at 1490 AM.

WMPZ-FM
Owner: Brewer Broadcasting Inc.
Editorial: 1305 Carter St, Chattanooga, Tennessee 37402. **T:** 1 423 265-9494
W: http://www.groove93.com
Editorial Profile: WMPZ-FM is a commercial station owned by Brewer Broadcasting Inc. The format of the station is urban adult contemporary. WMPZ-FM broadcasts to the Chattanooga, TN area at 93.5 FM.

WMQA-FM
Owner: NRG Media LLC
Editorial: 3616 State Highway 47 N, Rhinelander, Wisconsin 54501.
T: 1 715 362-1975
E: wmqa@nrgnorthwoods.com
W: http://www.wmqa.com
Editorial Profile: WMQA-FM is a commercial station owned by NRG Media LLC. The format of the station is classic hits. WMQA-FM broadcasts in the Minocqua, WI, area at 95.9 FM.

WMQM-AM
Owner: Robbert Broadcasting Co.(F.W.)
Editorial: 3704 Whittier Rd, Memphis, Tennessee 38108. **T:** 1 901 327-2500
W: http://www.1600wmqm.com
Editorial Profile: WMQM-AM is a commercial station owned by F.W. Robbert Broadcasting Co. The format of the station is religious and talk. WMQM-AM broadcasts to the Memphis, TN area at 1600 AM.

WMQT-FM
Owner: Taconite Broadcasting
Editorial: 121 N Front St, Ste A, Marquette, Michigan 49855. **T:** 1 906 225-9100
E: newswmqt@wmqt.com
W: http://www.wmqt.com
Editorial Profile: WMQT-FM is a commercial station owned by Taconite Broadcasting. The format of the station is hot adult contemporary music. WMQT-FM broadcasts to the Marquette, MI area at 107.7 FM.

WMQX-FM
Owner: Backyard Broadcasting
Editorial: 800 E 29th St, Muncie, Indiana 47302-5765. **T:** 1 765 378-2080
W: http://www.maxrocks.net
Editorial Profile: WMQX-FM is a commercial station owned by Backyard Broadcasting. The format of the station is classic rock music. WMQX-FM broadcasts to the Muncie, IN area at 96.7 FM.

WMQZ-FM
Owner: Prestige Communications
Editorial: 31 E Side Sq, Macomb, Illinois 61455-2248. **T:** 1 309 833-2121
E: news@prestigeradio.com
W: http://www.prestigeradio.com
Editorial Profile: WMQZ-FM is a commercial station owned by Prestige Communications. The format of the station is oldies. WMQZ-FM broadcasts to the Macomb, IL area at 104.1 FM.

WMRA-FM
Owner: James Madison University
Editorial: 983 Reservoir St, Harrisonburg, Virginia 22801. **T:** 1 540 568-6221
E: wmra@jmu.edu **W:** http://www.wmra.org
Editorial Profile: WMRA-FM is a non-commercial station owned by James Madison University. The format for the station is news and talk. WMRA-FM broadcasts to the Harrisonburg, VA area at 90.7 FM. The station does not accept press releases.

WMRC-AM
Owner: Tom McAuliffe II
Editorial: 258 Main St, Milford, Massachusetts 01757-2525. **T:** 1 508 473-1490
E: news@wmrcdailynews.com
W: http://www.wmrcradio.com
Editorial Profile: WMRC-AM is a commercial station owned by Tom McAuliffe II. The format of the station is adult contemporary. WMRC-AM broadcasts the Milford, MA area at 1490 AM.

WMRD-AM
Owner: Crossroads Communications LLC
Editorial: 777 River Rd, Middletown, Connecticut 6457. **T:** 1 860 347-9673
E: radio@wliswmrd.net
W: http://www.wliswmrd.net
Editorial Profile: WMRD-AM is a commercial station owned by Crossroads Communications LLC. The format for the station is talk. WMRD-AM broadcasts to the Middletown, CT area at 1150 AM.

WMRE-AM
Owner: Clear Channel Media and Entertainment
Editorial: 510 Pegasus Ct, Winchester, Virginia 22602-4596. **T:** 1 540 662-5101
E: winchesterproductions@clearchannel.com
W: http://www.sportstalk1550.com
Editorial Profile: WMRE-AM is a commercial station owned by Clear Channel Media and Entertainment. The format of the station is sports. WMRE-AM broadcasts in the Winchester, VA area at 1550 AM.

WMRF-FM
Owner: First Media Radio LLC
Editorial: 12 E Market St Fl 2, Lewistown, Pennsylvania 17044-2123. **T:** 1 717 248-6757
E: news@merfradio.com
W: http://new.merfradio.com
Editorial Profile: WMRF-FM is a commercial station owned by First Media Radio LLC. The format of the station is hot adult contemporary music. WMRF-FM broadcasts to the Lewistown, PA area at 95.7 FM.

WMRI-AM
Owner: Hoosier AM/FM LLC
Editorial: 820 S Pennsylvania St, Marion, Indiana 46953-2407. **T:** 1 765 664-7396
E: production@wmri.com
W: http://www.wmri.com
Editorial Profile: WMRI-AM is a commercial station owned by Hoosier AM/FM LLC. The format of the station is sports. WMRI-AM broadcasts in the Marion, IN area at 860 AM.

WMRK-FM
Owner: Alexander Broadcasting Company, LLC
Editorial: 4101 Wall St Ste A, Montgomery, Alabama 36106-3724. **T:** 1 334 244-0961
W: http://www.klove.com
Editorial Profile: WMRK-FM is a commercial station owned by Alexander Broadcasting Company, LLC. The format of the station is Contemporary Christian. WMRK-FM is the K-LOVE affiliate for the Montgomery, AL area and broadcasts at 107.9 FM.

WMRN-AM
Owner: Clear Channel Media and Entertainment
Editorial: 1330 N Main St, Marion, Ohio 43302-1525. **T:** 1 740 383-1131
W: http://www.wmrn.com
Editorial Profile: WMRN-AM is a commercial station owned by Clear Channel Media and Entertainment. The format of the station is news, sports and talk. WMRN-AM broadcasts to the Marion, OH area at 1490 AM.

WMRN-FM
Owner: Clear Channel Media and Entertainment
Editorial: 1330 N Main St, Marion, Ohio 43302. **T:** 1 740 383-1131
W: http://www.buckeyecountry943.com
Editorial Profile: WMRN-FM is a commercial station owned by Clear Channel Media and Entertainment. The format of the station is contemporary country. WMRN-FM broadcasts to the Marion, OH area at 94.3 FM.

WMRQ2-FM
Owner: Red Wolf Broadcasting
Editorial: 131 New London Tpke Ste 101, Glastonbury, Connecticut 06033-2246.
T: 1 860 657-1041
W: http://www.bomba971.com
Editorial Profile: WMRQ2-FM is owned by Red Wolf Broadcasting. The format for the station is Hispanic music. WMRQ2-FM broadcasts to the Hartford, CT on 97.1 FM. Digital radio technology is used by AM and FM radio stations, via a digital signal embedded in their analog signal, to transmit audio and data.

WMRQ-FM
Owner: Red Wolf Broadcasting
Editorial: 131 New London Tpke Ste 101, Glastonbury, Connecticut 06033-2246.
T: 1 860 657-1041 **E:** requests@radio1041.fm
W: http://www.radio1041.fm
Editorial Profile: WMRQ-FM is a commercial station owned by Red Wolf Broadcasting. The format for the station is rock alternative. WMRQ-FM broadcasts to the Hartford, CT area at 104.1 FM.

WMRR-FM
Owner: Clear Channel Media and Entertainment
Editorial: 3565 Green St, Muskegon, Michigan 49444. **T:** 1 231 733-2600
W: http://www.wmrr.com
Editorial Profile: WMRR-FM is a commercial station owned by Clear Channel Media and Entertainment. The format of the station is classic rock music. WMRR-FM broadcasts to the Muskegon, MI and surrounding communities at 101.7 FM.

WMRS-FM
Owner: Monticello Community Radio
Editorial: 132 N Main St, Monticello, Indiana 47960. **T:** 1 574 583-8933
W: http://www.wmrsradio.com
Editorial Profile: WMRS-FM is a commercial station owned by Monticello Community Radio. The format of the station is adult contemporary. WMRS-FM broadcasts to the Indianapolis area at 107.7 FM.

WMRT-FM
Owner: Marietta College
Editorial: McKinney Media Center, 508 Putnam St, Marietta, Ohio 45750-3032.
T: 1 740 376-4800 **E:** wmrt@marietta.edu
W: http://www.wmrtfm.com
Editorial Profile: WMRT-FM is a non-commercial station owned by Marietta College. The format for the station is classical and jazz. WMRT-FM broadcasts to the Marietta, OH area at 88.3 FM.

WMRV-FM
Owner: Genesee Media Corp.
Editorial: 195 Main St, Dansville, New York 14437-1315. **T:** 1 585 335-9369
W: http://geneseenow.com
Editorial Profile: WMRV-FM is a commercial station owned by Genesee Media Corp. The format of the station is adult contemporary music. WMRV-FM broadcasts to the Dansville, NY area at 93.9 FM.

WMRX-FM
Owner: Steel Broadcasting
Editorial: 1510 Bayliss St, Midland, Michigan 48640-5507. **T:** 1 989 631-1490
E: admin@wmpxwmrx.com
W: http://www.wmpxwmrx.com
Editorial Profile: WMRX-FM is a commercial station owned by Steel Broadcasting. The format for the station is adult standards music. WMRX-FM broadcasts to the Flint, MI area at 97.7 FM.

WMRZ-FM
Owner: Clear Channel Media and Entertainment
Editorial: 809 S Westover Blvd, Albany, Georgia 31707. **T:** 1 229 883-5397
W: http://www.kissalbany.com
Editorial Profile: WMRZ-FM is a commercial station owned by Clear Channel Media and Entertainment. The format of the station is urban adult contemporary music. WMRZ-FM broadcasts to the Albany, GA area at 98.1 FM.

WMSA-AM
Owner: Stephens Media Group Massena, LLC
Editorial: 2155 State Highway 420, Massena, New York 13662-3351. **T:** 1 315 769-3333
E: news@1340wmsa.com
W: http://www.1340wmsa.com
Editorial Profile: WMSA-AM is a commercial station owned by Stephens Media Group Massena, LLC. The format of the station is news, talk, sports and oldies. WMSA-AM broadcasts to the Massena, NY area at 1340 AM.

WMSC-FM
Owner: Montclair State University
Editorial: Student Ctr Annex Montclair SU, Room 110, Upper Montclair, New Jersey 07043-1624. **T:** 1 973 655-4257
E: aa@wmscradio.com
W: http://www.wmscradio.com
Editorial Profile: WMSC-FM is a non-commercial station owned by Montclair State University. The station's format is college variety. WMSC-FM broadcasts to the Upper Montclair, NJ area on 90.3 FM.

WMSE-FM
Owner: Milwaukee School of Engineering
Editorial: 820 N Milwaukee St, Milwaukee, Wisconsin 53202. **T:** 1 414 277-7247
E: wmse@msoe.edu **W:** http://www.wmse.org
Editorial Profile: WMSE-FM is a non-commercial station owned by the Milwaukee School of Engineering. The format of the station is college variety. WMSE-FM broadcasts to the Milwaukee area on 91.7 FM.

WMSG-AM
Owner: Radiowerks, Inc.
Editorial: 407 Lothian St, Mountain Lake Park, Maryland 21550-2909. **T:** 1 301 334-4272
E: office@wkhj.com **W:** http://www.wmsg.com
Editorial Profile: WMSG-AM is a commercial station owned by Radiowerks, Inc. The format of the station is oldies. WMSG-AM broadcasts

to the Mountain Lake Park, MD area at 1050 AM.

WMSI-FM
Owner: Clear Channel Media and Entertainment
Editorial: 1375 Beasley Rd, Jackson, Mississippi 39206-2018. **T:** 1 601 982-1062
W: http://www.miss103.com
Editorial Profile: WMSI-FM is a commercial station owned by Clear Channel Media and Entertainment. The format of the station is contemporary country. WMSI-FM broadcasts to Jackson, MS area at 102.9 FM.

WMSJ-FM
Owner: The Positive Radio Network Inc.
Editorial: 1456 US Route 1, Freeport, Maine 4032. **T:** 1 207 865-3448
W: http://www.positive.fm
Editorial Profile: WMSJ-FM is a non-commercial station owned by The Positive Radio Network Inc. The format of the station is contemporary Christian. WMSJ-FM broadcasts to the Freeport, ME area at 89.3 FM.

WMSK-AM
Owner: Henson Media of Union Co. LLC
Editorial: 1339 US Highway 60 W, Morganfield, Kentucky 42437.
T: 1 270 389-1550 **E:** wmsk@bellsouth.net
W: http://www.wmskamfm.com
Editorial Profile: WMSK-AM is a commercial station owned by Henson Media of Union Co LLC. The format of the station is country. WMSK-AM broadcasts to the Morganfield, KY area at 1550 AM.

WMSK-FM
Owner: Henson Media, Inc.
Editorial: 1339 US Highway 60 W, Morganfield, Kentucky 42437.
T: 1 270 389-1550 **E:** wmsk@bellsouth.net
W: http://www.wmskamfm.com

WMSL-FM
Owner: Prince Avenue Christian School
Editorial: 2121 Ruth Jackson Rd, Bogart, Georgia 30622. **T:** 1 770 725-8890
W: http://www.wmsl.fm
Editorial Profile: WMSL-FM is a non-commercial station owned by Prince Avenue Christian School. The format of the station is contemporary Christian. WMSL-FM broadcasts to the Athens, GA area at 88.9 FM.

WMSP-AM
Owner: Cumulus Media Inc.
Editorial: 1 Commerce St, Montgomery, Alabama 36104-3510. **T:** 1 334 240-9274
W: http://www.sportsradio740.com
Editorial Profile: WMSP-AM is commercial station owned by Cumulus Media Inc. The format of the station is sports. WMSP-AM broadcasts to the Montgomery, AL area at 740 AM.

WMSR-AM
Owner: Clutter(Rob)
Editorial: 1030 Oakdale St, Manchester, Tennessee 37355. **T:** 1 931 728-3526
E: wmsr@thunder1320.com
W: http://www.thunder1320.com
Editorial Profile: WMSR-AM is a commercial station owned by Rob Clutter. The format of the station is talk. WMSR-AM broadcasts to the Manchester, TN area at 1320 AM.

WMST-AM
Owner: Gateway Radio Works Inc.
Editorial: 22 W Main St, Mount Sterling, Kentucky 40353-1314. **T:** 1 859 498-1150
W: http://www.wmstradio.com
Editorial Profile: WMST-AM is a commercial station owned by Gateway Radio Works Inc. The format of the station is adult standards. WMST-AM broadcasts to the Lexington, KY area at 1150 AM.

WMSU-FM
Owner: URBan Radio Broadcasting, LLC
Editorial: 608 Yellow Jacket Dr, Starkville, Mississippi 39759. **T:** 1 662 338-5424
W: http://www.power92jamz.net
Editorial Profile: WMSU-FM is a commercial station owned by URBan Radio Broadcasting, LLC. The format of the station is urban contemporary. WMSU-FM broadcasts to the Starkville, MS area at a frequency of 92.1 FM.

WMSV-FM
Owner: Mississippi State University
Editorial: Student Media Center MSU, Mississippi State, Mississippi 39762.
T: 1 662 325-8034 **E:** wmsv@msstate.edu

W: http://www.wmsv.msstate.edu
Editorial Profile: WMSV-FM is a non-commercial college station owned by Mississippi State University. The format of the station is adult album contemporary. WMSV-FM broadcasts to the Mississippi State campus and surrounding areas at a frequency of 91.1 FM.

WMTA-AM
Owner: Faith Broadcasting Company
Editorial: 1 WMTA Drive, Central City, Kentucky 42330. **T:** 1 270 754-1380
E: sales@faithmusicmissions.org
W: http://www.faith1180.com
Editorial Profile: WMTA-AM is a non-commercial station owned by Faith Broadcasting Company. The format of the station is gospel music. WMTA-AM broadcasts to the Central City, KY area at 1380 AM.

WMT-AM
Owner: Clear Channel Media and Entertainment
Editorial: 600 Old Marion Rd NE, Cedar Rapids, Iowa 52402. **T:** 1 319 395-0530
E: newsroom@wmtradio.com
W: http://www.wmtradio.com
Editorial Profile: WMT-AM is a commercial station owned by Clear Channel Media and Entertainment. The format of the station is news and talk. WMT-AM broadcasts to the Cedar Rapids, IA area at 600 AM.

WMTB-FM
Owner: Mount St. Mary's University
Editorial: 16300 Old Emmitsburg Rd, Emmitsburg, Maryland 21727.
T: 1 301 447-5240 **E:** wmtb@msmary.edu
W: http://www.msmary.edu/wmtb
Editorial Profile: WMTB-FM is a non-commercial station owned by Mount St. Mary's College. The format of the station is college variety. WMTB-FM broadcasts to the Emmitsburg, MD area on 89.9 FM.

WMTC-AM
Owner: Kentucky Mountain Holiness Assoc.
Editorial: 1036 Highway 541, Jackson, Kentucky 41339. **T:** 1 606 666-5006
E: studio@mountaingospel.org
W: http://www.mountaingospel.org
Editorial Profile: WMTC-AM is a commercial station owned by Kentucky Mountain Holiness Assoc. The format of the station is gospel. WMTC-AM broadcasts to the Lexington, KY area at 730 AM.

WMTC-FM
Owner: Kentucky Mountain Holiness Assoc.
Editorial: 1036 Highway 541, Jackson, Kentucky 41339-9434. **T:** 1 606 666-5006
E: studio@mountaingospel.org
W: http://www.mountaingospel.org
Editorial Profile: WMTC-FM is a commercial station owned by Kentucky Mountain Holiness Assoc. The format of the station is gospel music. WMTC-FM broadcasts to the Lexington, KY area at 99.9 FM.

WMTD-AM
Owner: Southern Communications Corp.
Editorial: 306 S Kanawha St, Beckley, West Virginia 25801. **T:** 1 304 252-6452
Editorial Profile: WMTD-AM is a commercial station owned by Southern Communications Corp. The format of the station is classic hits music. WMTD-AM broadcasts to the Beaver, WV area at 1070 AM.

WMTD-FM
Owner: Southern Communications Corp.
Editorial: 306 S Kanawha St, Beckley, West Virginia 25801. **T:** 1 304 253-7000
W: http://www.theticket102.com
Editorial Profile: WMTD-FM is a commercial station owned by Southern Communications Corp. The format of the station is sports. WMTD-FM broadcasts to the Beckley, WV area at 102.3 FM.

WMTI-FM
Owner: Cumulus Media Inc.
Editorial: 201 Saint Charles Ave Ste 201, New Orleans, Louisiana 70170-1017.
T: 1 504 581-7002
W: http://www.1061neworleans.com
Editorial Profile: WMTI-FM is a commercial station owned by Cumulus Media Inc. The format of the station is sports. WMTI-FM broadcasts to the New Orleans area at 106.1 FM.

WMTL-AM
Owner: Heritage Media of Kentucky Inc
Editorial: 2160 Brandenburg Rd, Leitchfield, Kentucky 42754. **T:** 1 270 259-5692
E: info@k105.com **W:** http://www.k105.com
Editorial Profile: WMTL-AM is a commercial station owned by Heritage Media of Kentucky Inc. The station broadcasts at a frequency of 870 AM to the Leitchfield, KY area. The format of the station is country.

WMTM-AM
Owner: Colquitt Broadcasting Co., LLC
Editorial: 100 Wmtm Rd, Moultrie, Georgia 31788. **T:** 1 229 985-1300
Editorial Profile: WMTM-AM is a commercial station owned by Colquitt Broadcasting Co., LLC. The format of the station is news and talk. WMTM-AM broadcasts to the Moultrie, GA, area at 1300 AM.

WMTM-FM
Owner: Colquitt Broadcasting Co., LLC
Editorial: 100 Wmtm Rd, Moultrie, Georgia 31788. **T:** 1 229 985-1300
W: http://www.cruisin94.com
Editorial Profile: WMTM-FM is a commercial station owned by Colquitt Broadcasting Co., LLC. The format of the station is classic hits. WMTM-FM broadcasts to the Moultrie, GA area at 93.9 FM.

WMTN-AM
Owner: Radio Acquisition Corp.
Editorial: 510 W Economy Rd, Morristown, Tennessee 37814-3223. **T:** 1 423 586-9101
W: http://www.wmtnradio.com
Editorial Profile: WMTN-AM is a commercial station owned by Radio Acquisition Corp. The format of the station is classic country music. WMTN-AM broadcasts to the Morristown, TN area at 1300 AM.

WMTR-AM
Owner: Greater Media Inc.
Editorial: 55 Horsehill Rd, Cedar Knolls, New Jersey 07927-2003. **T:** 1 973 538-1250
W: http://www.wmtram.com
Editorial Profile: WMTR-AM is a commercial station owned by Greater Media Inc. The format of the station is oldies. WMTR-AM broadcasts to the Cedar Knolls, NJ area at 1250 AM.

WMTR-FM
Owner: Nobco Inc.
Editorial: 303 1/2 N Defiance St, Archbold, Ohio 43502-1193. **T:** 1 419 445-9050
E: wmtr@rtecexpress.net
W: http://www.961wmtr.com
Editorial Profile: WMTR-FM is a commercial station owned by Nobco Inc. The format of the station is classic rock. WMTR-FM broadcasts to the Archbold, OH area at 96.1 FM.

WMTS-FM
Owner: Middle Tennessee State University
Editorial: 1301 E Main St #1558, Murfreesboro, Tennessee 37132-0001.
T: 1 615 898-2636 **E:** manager@wmts.org
W: http://www.mtsu.edu/~wmts
Editorial Profile: WMTS-FM is a non-commercial station owned by Middle Tennessee State University. The format of the station is variety. WMTS-FM broadcasts to the Nashville, TN area at 88.3 FM.

WMTT-FM
Owner: Europa Communications, Inc.
Editorial: 734 Chemung St, Horseheads, New York 14845. **T:** 1 607 795-0795
E: info@equinoxbroadcasting.com
W: http://www.themetrocks.com
Editorial Profile: WMTT-FM is a commercial station owned by Europa Communications, Inc. The format of the station is classic rock. WMTT-FM broadcasts to the Horseheads, NY area at 94.7 FM.

WMTX-FM
Owner: Clear Channel Media and Entertainment
Editorial: 4002 W Gandy Blvd, Tampa, Florida 33611. **T:** 1 813 839-9393
W: http://www.tampabaysmix.com
Editorial Profile: WMTX-FM is a commercial station owned by Clear Channel Media and Entertainment. The format of the station is hot adult contemporary. WMTX-FM broadcasts to the Tampa and St. Petersburg, FL areas at 100.7 FM.

WMTY-AM
Owner: Horne Radio LLC
Editorial: 517 N Watt Rd, Knoxville, Tennessee 37934. **T:** 1 865 675-4105
Editorial Profile: WMTY-AM is a commercial station owned by Horne Radio LLC. The format of the station is oldies. WMTY-AM broadcasts to Knoxville, TN at 670 AM.

WMUA-FM
Owner: University of Massachusetts
Editorial: 105 Campus Center, Amherst, Massachusetts 1003. **T:** 1 413 545-2876
E: news@wmua.org **W:** http://www.wmua.org
Editorial Profile: WMUA-FM is a non-commercial station owned by the University of Massachusetts. The format of the station is variety. WMUA-FM broadcasts to the Amherst, MA area on 91.1 FM.

WMUB-FM
Owner: Cincinnati Public Radio Inc.
Editorial: 1223 Central Pkwy, Cincinnati, Ohio 45214-2812. **T:** 1 513 352-9185
E: wmub@cinradio.org
W: http://www.wmub.org
Editorial Profile: WMUB-FM is a non-commercial station owned by Cincinnati Public Radio Inc. The format of the station is news and talk. WMUB-FM broadcasts to the Cincinnati area at 88.5 FM.

WMUF-FM
Owner: Benton-Weatherford Broadcasting Inc. of Tennessee
Editorial: 110 India Rd, Paris, Tennessee 38242. **T:** 1 731 644-9455
E: radionews@bellsouth.net
W: http://www.wmufradio.com/wmuf-fm.html
Editorial Profile: WMUF-FM is a commercial station owned by Benton-Weatherford Broadcasting Inc. of Tennessee. The format of the station is classic and contemporary country music. WMUF-FM broadcasts to the Nashville, TN area at 104.7 FM.

WMUH-FM
Owner: Muhlenberg College
Editorial: 2400 Chew St, Allentown, Pennsylvania 18104-5564. **T:** 1 484 664-3239
E: wmuh@muhlenberg.edu
W: http://www.muhlenberg.edu/wmuh
Editorial Profile: WMUH-FM is a non-commercial college station owned by Muhlenberg College. The format of the station is variety. WMUH-FM broadcasts to the Allentown, PA area at 91.7 FM.

WMUK-FM
Owner: Western Michigan University
Editorial: 1903 W Michigan Ave, Kalamazoo, Michigan 49008-5200. **T:** 1 269 387-5715
W: http://www.wmuk.org
Editorial Profile: WMUK-FM is a non-commercial station owned by Western Michigan University. The format of the station is news and classical music. WMUK-FM broadcasts in the Kalamazoo, MI area at 102.1 FM.

WMUL-FM
Owner: Marshall University Board of Governors
Editorial: 1 John Marshall Dr, Huntington, West Virginia 25755. **T:** 1 304 696-2295
E: wmul@marshall.edu
W: http://www.marshall.edu/wmul
Editorial Profile: WMUL-FM is a non-commercial station owned by the Marshall University Board of Governors. The format of the station is college variety. WMUL-FM broadcasts to the Huntington, WV area on 88.1 FM.

WMUM-FM
Owner: Georgia Public Broadcasting
Editorial: 260 14th St NW, Atlanta, Georgia 30318. **T:** 1 404 685-2548 **E:** ask@gpb.org
W: http://www.gpb.org
Editorial Profile: WMUM-FM is a non-commercial station owned by Georgia Public Broadcasting. The format of the station is news, classical and jazz music. WMUM-FM broadcasts to the Atlanta area at 89.7 FM.

WMUS-FM
Owner: Clear Channel Media and Entertainment
Editorial: 3565 Green St, Muskegon, Michigan 49444-3875. **T:** 1 231 733-2600
W: http://www.107mus.com
Editorial Profile: WMUS-FM is a commercial station owned by Clear Channel Media and Entertainment. The format of the station is classic country. WMUS-FM broadcasts to the Muskegon, MI area at 107.9 FM.

WMUT-FM
Owner: Flinn Broadcasting Corp.
Editorial: 157 Dowdle Rd, Grenada, Mississippi 38901. **T:** 1 901 375-9324
W: http://theradiophantom.com
Editorial Profile: WMUT-FM is a commercial station owned by Flinn Broadcasting Corp. The format of the station is adult hits. WMUT-FM broadcasts to the Grenada, MS area at 101.3 FM.

WMUV-FM
Owner: Renda Broadcasting
Editorial: 6440 Atlantic Blvd, Jacksonville, Florida 32211-8724. **T:** 1 904 727-9696
W: http://www.bull1007.com
Editorial Profile: WMUV-FM is a commercial station owned by Renda Broadcasting. The format of the station is country. WMUV-FM broadcasts to the Jacksonville, FL and Southern Georgia areas at 100.7 FM.

WMUZ-FM
Owner: Crawford Broadcasting Co.
Editorial: 12300 Radio Pl, Detroit, Michigan 48228. **T:** 1 313 272-3434
E: station@wmuz.com
W: http://www.wmuz.com
Editorial Profile: WMUZ-FM is a commercial station owned by Crawford Broadcasting Co. The format of the station is religious/Christian talk. WMUZ-FM broadcasts to the Detroit area at 103.5 FM.

WMVA-AM
Owner: Martinsville Media, Inc.
Editorial: 1129 Chatham Rd, Martinsville, Virginia 24112. **T:** 1 276 632-2152
W: http://martinsvillemedia.com
Editorial Profile: WMVA-AM is a commercial station owned by Martinsville Media, Inc. The format of the station is news and talk. WMVA-AM broadcasts to the Martinsville, VA area at 1450 AM.

WMVB-AM
Owner: Quinn Broadcasting Inc.
Editorial: 4369 S Lincoln Ave, Vineland, New Jersey 08361-7757. **T:** 1 856 765-9033
W: http://www.wsnjam.com
Editorial Profile: WMVB-AM is a commercial station owned by Quinn Broadcasting Inc.. The format of the station is news talk. WMVB-AM broadcasts to the Millville, NJ area at 1440 AM.

WMVE-FM
Owner: Commonwealth Public Broadcasting
Editorial: 23 Sesame St, Richmond, Virginia 23235. **T:** 1 804 320-1301
E: webmaster@ideastations.org
W: http://www.ideastations.org/radio
Editorial Profile: WMVE-FM is a non-commerical station owned by Commonwealth Public Broadcasting. The format for the station is news, classical and jazz. WMVE-FM broadcasts to the Richmond, VA, area at 90.1 FM. This station does not accept PSAs.

WMVG-AM
Owner: Beasley(W.R.)
Editorial: 1250 W Charlton St, Milledgeville, Georgia 31061. **T:** 1 478 452-0586
E: mail@country102fm.com
W: http://www.country102fm.com
Editorial Profile: WMVG-AM is a commercial station owned by W.R. Beasley. The format of the station is sports, news and talk. WMVG-AM broadcasts to the Milledgeville, GA area at 1450 AM.

WMVL-FM
Owner: Vilkie Communications Inc.
Editorial: 16271 Conneaut Lake Rd, Ste 102, Meadville, Pennsylvania 16335.
T: 1 814 337-8440 **E:** wmvl@zoominternet.net
W: http://www.cool1017online.com
Editorial Profile: WMVL-FM is a commercial station owned by Vilkie Communications Inc. The format of the station is classic hits. WMVL-FM broadcasts to the Meadville, PA area at 101.7 FM.

WMVN-FM
Owner: Wolf Radio, Inc.
Editorial: 401 W Kirkpatrick St, Syracuse, New York 13204. **T:** 1 315 472-0222
E: programming@movin100.com
W: http://www.movin100.com
Editorial Profile: WMVN-FM is a commercial station owned by Wolf Radio, Inc. The format of the station is rhythmic contemporary/R&B. WMVN-FM broadcasts to the Syracuse, NY area at 100.3 FM.

WMVO-AM
Owner: BAS Broadcasting
Editorial: 17421 Coshocton Rd, Mount Vernon, Ohio 43050-9256. **T:** 1 740 397-1000
W: http://www.wmvo.com
Editorial Profile: WMVO-AM is a commercial station owned by BAS Broadcasting. The format of the station is talk and Oldies. WMVO-AM broadcasts to the Mount Vernon, OH, area at 1300 AM.

WMVP-AM
Owner: Walt Disney Co.
Editorial: 190 N State St Fl 7, Chicago, Illinois 60601-3310. T: 1 312 980-1000
W: http://espn.go.com/chicago/radio/index
Editorial Profile: WMVP-AM is a commercial station owned by Walt Disney Co. The format of the station is sports. WMVP-AM broadcasts to the Chicago area at 1000 AM.

WMVR-FM
Owner: Dean Miller Broadcasting Corp.
Editorial: 2929 W Russell Rd, Sidney, Ohio 45365. T: 1 937 492-1270
E: onair@hits1055.com
W: http://www.hits1055.com
Editorial Profile: WMVR-FM is a commercial station owned by Dean Miller Broadcasting Corp. The format of the station is hot adult contemporary music. WMVR-FM broadcasts to the Sidney, OH area at 105.5 FM.

WMVV-FM
Owner: Life Radio Ministries Inc.
Editorial: 100 S Hill St, Ste 100, Griffin, Georgia 30223. T: 1 770 229-2020
E: contactus@newlife.fm
W: http://www.wmvv.com
Editorial Profile: WMVV-FM is a non-commercial station owned by Life Radio Ministries Inc. The format of the station is religious programming. WMVV-FM broadcasts to the Griffin, GA area at 90.7 FM.

WMVW-FM
Editorial: 100 S Hill St Ste 100, Griffin, Georgia 30223-3400. T: 1 770 229-2020
W: http://www.wmvv.com
Editorial Profile: WMVW-FM is a non-commercial station owned by Life Radio Ministries Inc. The format of the station is religious programming. WMVW-FM broadcasts to the Peachtree City, GA area at 90.7 FM.

WMVX-AM
Owner: Willow Farm Inc.
Editorial: 31 Woodbury St, South Hamilton, Massachusetts 01982-2324.
T: 1 508 954-1282
W: http://www.power800am.com
Editorial Profile: WMVX-AM is a commercial station owned by Willow Farm Inc. The format of the station is Hispanic. WMVX-AM broadcasts to the Hamilton, MA area at 1570 AM.

WMWK-FM
Owner: Family Stations Inc.
Editorial: 13 Fairlane Dr, Joliet, Illinois 60435-6483. T: 1 414 964-9794
E: wmwkfm@aol.com
W: http://www.familyradio.com
Editorial Profile: WMWK-FM is a non-commercial station owned by Family Stations Inc. The format of the station is religious programming. WMWK-FM broadcasts to the Milwaukee area at 88.1 FM.

WMWM-FM
Owner: Salem State College
Editorial: 352 Lafayette St, Salem, Massachusetts 1970. T: 1 978 542-8501
E: wmwmsalem@gmail.com
W: http://www.wmwmsalem.com
Editorial Profile: WMWM-FM is a non-commercial station owned by Salem State College. The format of the station is variety. WMWM-FM broadcasts to the Salem, MA area at 91.7 FM.

WMWV-FM
Owner: Mt. Washington Radio & Gramophone LLC
Editorial: 2 Common Ct Unit A30, North Conway, New Hampshire 03860-5400.
T: 1 603 356-8870 E: news@wmwv.com
W: http://www.wmwv.com
Editorial Profile: WMWV-FM is a commercial station owned by Mt. Washington Radio & Gramophone LLC. The format of the station is adult album alternative. WMWV-FM broadcasts to the North Conway, NH area at 93.5 FM.

WMWX-FM
Owner: Spryex Communications Inc.
Editorial: 5114 Princeton-Glendale Road, Hamilton, Ohio 45011. T: 1 513 481-8890
E: classx@classxradio.com
W: http://classxradio.com
Editorial Profile: WMWX-FM is a non-commercial station owned by Spryex Communications Inc. The format of the station is classic rock and adult album alternative. WMWX-FM broadcasts to the Hamilton, OH area on 88.9 FM.

WMXA-FM
Owner: Clear Channel Media and Entertainment
Editorial: 915 Veterans Pkwy, Opelika, Alabama 36801-3367. T: 1 334 745-4656
W: http://www.mix967online.com
Editorial Profile: WMXA-FM is a commercial station owned by Clear Channel Media and Entertainment. The format of the station is hot adult contemporary. WMXA-FM broadcasts to the Opelika, AL area at 96.7 FM.

WMXB-AM
Owner: Lawson of Tuscaloosa, Inc.
Editorial: 601 Greensboro Ave, Tuscaloosa, Alabama 35401-1749. T: 1 205 345-4787
Editorial Profile: WMXB-AM is a commercial station owned by Lawson of Tuscaloosa, Inc. The format of the station is urban AC. WMXB-AM broadcasts to the Tuscaloosa, AL area at 1280 AM.

WMXC-FM
Owner: Clear Channel Media and Entertainment
Editorial: 555 Broadcast Dr, 3rd Fl, Mobile, Alabama 36606-2936. T: 1 251 450-0100
E: news@ccmobile.com
W: http://www.litemix.com
Editorial Profile: WMXC-FM is a commercial station owned by Clear Channel Media and Entertainment. The format for the station is adult contemporary. WMXC-FM broadcasts to the Mobile, AL area at 99.9 FM.

WMXD-FM
Owner: Clear Channel Media and Entertainment
Editorial: 27675 Halsted Rd, Farmington Hills, Michigan 48331-3511. T: 1 248 324-5800
W: http://www.mix923fm.com
Editorial Profile: WMXD-FM is a commercial station owned by Clear Channel Media and Entertainment. The format of the station is urban adult contemporary. WMXD-FM broadcasts to the Detroit area at 92.3 FM.

WMXE-FM
Owner: LM Communications, Inc.
Editorial: 100 Kanawha Ter, Saint Albans, West Virginia 25177. T: 1 304 722-3308
E: mixstudio@wmxe.net
W: http://www.wmxe.net
Editorial Profile: WMXE-FM is a commercial station owned by LM Communications, Inc. The format of the station is classic hits. WMXE-FM broadcasts to South Charleston, WV and surrounding communities at 100.9 FM.

WMXF-AM
Owner: Clear Channel Media and Entertainment
Editorial: 13 Summerlin Dr, Asheville, North Carolina 28806-2800. T: 1 828 257-2700
W: http://www.am1400thepeak.com
Editorial Profile: WMXF-AM is a commercial station owned by Clear Channel Media and Entertainment. The format of the station is news and talk. WMXF-AM broadcasts to the Asheville, NC area at 1400 AM.

WMXH-FM
Owner: Hayden Hamilton Media Strategies
Editorial: 1057 US Highway 211 W, Luray, Virginia 22835-5245. T: 1 540 743-5167
Editorial Profile: WMXH-FM is a commercial station owned by Hayden Hamilton Media Strategies. The format for the station is adult standards. WMXH-FM broadcasts to the Harrisonburg, VA area at 105.7 FM.

WMXI-FM
Owner: Rainey Broadcasting Inc.
Editorial: 7501 U S Highway 49, Hattiesburg, Mississippi 39402. T: 1 601 261-0898
E: zoo107@bellsouth.net
W: http://www.wmxi.net

WMXJ-FM
Owner: Lincoln Financial Media
Editorial: 20450 Nw 2Nd Ave, Miami, Florida 33169-2505. T: 1 305 521-5100
W: http://www.magicmiami.com
Editorial Profile: WMXJ-FM is a commercial station owned by Lincoln Financial Media. The format of the station is classic hits. WMXJ-FM broadcasts to the Miami area at 102.7 FM.

WMXL-FM
Owner: Clear Channel Media and Entertainment
Editorial: 2601 Nicholasville Rd, Lexington, Kentucky 40503-3307. T: 1 859 422-1000
W: http://www.wmxl.com
Editorial Profile: WMXL-FM is a commercial station owned by Clear Channel Media and Entertainment. The format of the station is hot adult contemporary. WMXL-FM broadcasts to the Lexington, KY area at 94.5 FM.

WMXM-FM
Owner: Lake Forest College
Editorial: 555 N Sheridan Rd, Lake Forest, Illinois 60045. T: 1 847 735-5220
E: wmxmgm@lfc.edu
W: http://www.wmxm.org
Editorial Profile: WMXM-FM is a non-commercial station owned by Lake Forest College. The format of the station is variety. WMXM-FM broadcasts to the Lake Forest, IL area at 88.9 FM.

WMXN-FM
Owner: KEA Radio Inc.
Editorial: 19784 John T Reid Pkwy, Scottsboro, Alabama 35768-7909.
T: 1 256 259-2341
W: http://www.1017thestorm.com
Editorial Profile: WMXN-FM is a commercial station owned by KEA Radio Inc. The format of the station is classic hits. WMXN-FM broadcasts to the Scottsboro, AL area at 101.7 FM.

WMXO-FM
Owner: Pembrook Pines Media Group
Editorial: 231 N Union St, Olean, New York 14760-2663. T: 1 716 375-1015
E: mixtraffic@roadrunner.com
W: http://www.themixwmxo.com
Editorial Profile: WMXO-FM is a commercial station owned by Pembrook Pines Media Group. The format of the station is hot adult contemporary music. WMXO-FM broadcasts to the Olean, NY area at 101.5 FM.

WMXQ-FM
Owner: Backyard Broadcasting
Editorial: 800 E 29th St, Muncie, Indiana 47302-5765. T: 1 765 378-2080
W: http://www.maxrocks.net
Editorial Profile: WMXQ-FM is a commercial station owned by Backyard Broadcasting. The format of the station is classic rock. WMXQ-FM broadcasts to the Muncie, IN area on 93.5 FM.

WMXS-FM
Owner: Cumulus Media Inc.
Editorial: 1 Commerce St, Montgomery, Alabama 36104-3510. T: 1 334 240-9274
W: http://www.mix103.com
Editorial Profile: WMXS-FM is a commercial station owned by Cumulus Media Inc. The format of the station is Lite Rock/Lite AC. WMXS-FM broadcasts to the Montgomery, AL area at 103.3 FM.

WMXT-FM
Owner: Cumulus Media Inc.
Editorial: 2014 N Irby St, Florence, South Carolina 29501. T: 1 843 661-5000
W: http://www.1021thefox.com
Editorial Profile: WMXT-FM is a commercial station owned by Cumulus Media Inc. The format of the station is classic rock music. WMXT-FM broadcasts to the Florence, SC area at 102.1 FM.

WMXU-FM
Owner: Cumulus Media Inc.
Editorial: 200 6th St N Court Square Towers, Ste 205, Columbus, Mississippi 39701.
T: 1 662 327-1183
W: http://www.mymix1061.com
Editorial Profile: WMXU-FM is a commercial station owned by Cumulus Media Inc. The format is adult contemporary and urban contemporary music. The station airs in the Columbus, MS area.

WMXV-FM
Owner: URBan Radio Broadcasting, LLC
Editorial: 509 N Main St, Tuscumbia, Alabama 35674. T: 1 256 383-2525
E: info@urbanradio.fm
W: http://www.wmxv1015.com
Editorial Profile: WMXV-FM is a commercial station owned by URBan Radio Broadcasting, LLC. The format of the station is urban contemporary. WMXV-FM broadcasts to the St. Joseph, TN area at 101.5 FM.

WMXW-FM
Owner: Clear Channel Media and Entertainment
Editorial: 320 N Jensen Rd, Vestal, New York 13850. T: 1 607 584-5800
W: http://www.mix1033fm.com
Editorial Profile: WMXW-FM is a commercial station owned by Clear Channel Media and Entertainment. The format of the station is adult contemporary. WMXW-FM broadcasts to the Binghamton, NY area at 103.3 FM.

WMXX-FM
Owner: Hunt(Gerald W.)
Editorial: 1 WDXI Dr, Jackson, Tennessee 38305-4124. T: 1 731 427-9611
E: kool103fm@yahoo.com
W: http://www.kool103.com
Editorial Profile: WMXX-FM is a commercial station owned by Gerald W. Hunt. The format of the station is oldies. WMXX-FM broadcasts to the Jackson, TN area at 103.1 FM.

WMXY-FM
Owner: Clear Channel Media and Entertainment
Editorial: 7461 South Ave, Youngstown, Ohio 44512. T: 1 330 965-0057
W: http://www.mix989.com
Editorial Profile: WMXY-FM is a commercial station owned by Clear Channel Media and Entertainment. The format of the station is hot adult contemporary music. WKBN-FM broadcasts in the Youngstown, OH area at 98.9 FM.

WMXZ-FM
Owner: Apex Broadcasting Inc.
Editorial: 2294 Clements Ferry Rd, Charleston, South Carolina 29492-7729.
T: 1 843 972-1100
E: production@apexbroadcasting.com
W: http://www.mix959.com
Editorial Profile: WMXZ-FM is a commercial station owned by Apex Broadcasting Inc. The format of the station is Hot AC. WMXZ-FM broadcasts to the Charleston, SC area at 95.9 FM.

WMYB-FM
Owner: Digity LLC
Editorial: 1016 Ocala St, Myrtle Beach, South Carolina 29577-8007. T: 1 843 448-1041
W: http://www.star921.net
Editorial Profile: WMYB-FM is a commercial station owned by Digity LLC. The format for the station is hot adult contemporary. WMYB-FM broadcasts to the Myrtle Beach, SC area at 92.1 FM.

WMYF-AM
Owner: Clear Channel Media and Entertainment
Editorial: 815 Lafayette Rd, Portsmouth, New Hampshire 03801-5406. T: 1 603 436-7300
W: http://www.wmyf.com
Editorial Profile: WMYF-AM is a commercial station owned by Clear Channel Media and Entertainment. The format of the station is adult standards. WMYF-AM broadcasts to the Portsmouth, NH area at 1380 AM.

WMYI-FM
Owner: Clear Channel Media and Entertainment
Editorial: 101 N Main St, Ste 1000, Greenville, South Carolina 29601. T: 1 864 242-4660
W: http://www.wmyi.com
Editorial Profile: WMYI-FM is a commercial station owned by Clear Channel Media and Entertainment. The format of the station is adult contemporary music. WMYI-FM broadcasts to Greenville, SC at 102.5 FM.

WMYJ-AM
Owner: Hoosier AM/FM LLC
Editorial: 1639 Burton Ln, Martinsville, Indiana 46151-3004. T: 1 765 342-3394
E: webmaster@wcbk.com
Editorial Profile: WMYJ-AM is a commercial station owned by Hoosier AM/FM LLC. The format of the station is solid gospel. WMYJ-AM broadcasts to the Bloomington, IN area at 1540 AM.

WMYK-FM
Owner: Hoosier AM/FM LLC
Editorial: 671 E 400 S, Kokomo, Indiana 46902. T: 1 765 455-9850
E: kokomoradiotraffic@att.net
W: http://www.rock985.com
Editorial Profile: WMYK-FM is a commercial station owned by Hoosier AM/FM LLC. The format of the station is rock music. WMYK-FM broadcasts to the Kokomo, IN area at 98.5 FM.

WMYL-FM
Owner: Clinton Broadcasters
Editorial: 119 Pine Rd, Clinton, Tennessee 37716-2025. T: 1 865 457-1380
E: office@merlefm.com
W: http://www.merlefm.com
Editorial Profile: WMYL-FM is a commercial station owned by Clinton Broadcasters. The format of the station is classic country.

WMYL-FM broadcasts to the Clinton, TN area at 96.7 FM.

WMYM-AM
Owner: Walt Disney Co.
Editorial: 2150 W 68th St, Ste 202, Hialeah, Florida 33016. **T:** 1 305 823-0990
W: http://www.radiodisney.com/miami/
Editorial Profile: WMYM-AM is a commercial station owned by Walt Disney Co. The format of the station is children's programming. WMYM-AM broadcasts to the Miami area at AM 990.

WMYN-AM
Owner: Mayo Broadcasting Corporation
Editorial: 1203 Harris St, Eden, North Carolina 27288-6321. **T:** 1 336 427-9696
W: http://www.wloewmyn.com
Editorial Profile: WMYN-AM is owned by Mayo Broadcasting Corporation. The format of the station is religious programming, news and talk. WMYN-AM broadcasts to the Greensboro-Winston Salem, NC area at 1420 AM.

WMYR-AM
Owner: J & B, LLC
Editorial: 5043 Tamiami Trl E, Naples, Florida 34113-4127. **T:** 1 239 732-9369
W: http://twangme.net
Editorial Profile: WMYR-AM is a commercial station owned by J & B, LLC. The format of the station is classic country music. WMYR-AM broadcasts to the Fort Myers, FL area area at 1410 AM.

WMYX-FM
Owner: Entercom Communications Corp.
Editorial: 11800 W Grange Ave, Hales Corners, Wisconsin 53130. **T:** 1 414 529-1250
W: http://www.991wmyx.com
Editorial Profile: WMYX-FM is a commercial station owned by Entercom Communications Corp. The format of the station is hot adult contemporary music. WMYX-FM broadcasts to the Milwaukee area at 99.1 FM.

WMYY-FM
Owner: Capital Media Corporation
Editorial: 30 Park Ave, Cohoes, New York 12047. **T:** 1 518 237-1330
W: http://www.aliveradionetwork.com
Editorial Profile: WMYY-FM is a commercial station owned by Capital Media Corporation. The format of the station is religious programming. WMYY-FM broadcasts to the Schenectady, NY area at 97.3 FM.

WMYZ-FM
Owner: Central Florida Educational Foundation, Inc.
Editorial: 1065 Rainer Dr, Altamonte Springs, Florida 32714-3847. **T:** 1 407 869-8000
E: zcrew@zradio.com **W:** http://www.zradio.org
Editorial Profile: WMYZ-FM is a non-commercial station owned by Central Florida Educational Foundation, Inc. The format of the station is contemporary Christian and religious programming. WMYZ-FM broadcasts to the Altamonte Springs, FL area at 88.7 FM.

WMZK-FM
Owner: Quicksilver Broadcasting, LLC
Editorial: 120 S Mill St, Merrill, Wisconsin 54452. **T:** 1 715 536-6262
E: news@z104rocks.com
W: http://www.z104rocks.com
Editorial Profile: WMZK-FM is a commercial station owned by Quicksilver Broadcasting, LLC. The format of the station is rock. WMZK-FM broadcasts to the Merrill, WI area at 104.1.

WMZQ-FM
Owner: Clear Channel Media and Entertainment
Editorial: 1801 Rockville Pike, 5th Fl, Rockville, Maryland 20852-1633.
T: 1 240 747-2700 **W:** http://www.wmzq.com
Editorial Profile: WMZQ-FM is a commercial station owned by Clear Channel Media and Entertainment. The format of the station is country. WMZQ-FM broadcasts to the Washington, D.C. area at 98.7 FM.

WNAA-FM
Owner: North Carolina A&T State University
Editorial: 200 Price Hall Nc A & T Universi, Greensboro, North Carolina 27411.
T: 1 336 334-7936 **E:** wnaafm@ncat.edu
W: http://wnaa-online.ncat.edu
Editorial Profile: WNAA-FM is a non-commercial station owned by North Carolina A&T State University. The format of the station is college variety. WNAA-FM broadcasts to the Greensboro, NC area at 90.1 FM.

WNAE-AM
Owner: Radio Partners LLC
Editorial: 310 2nd Ave, Warren, Pennsylvania 16365. **T:** 1 814 723-1310
E: newsroom@kibcoradio.com
W: http://www.kibcoradio.com
Editorial Profile: WNAE-AM is a commercial station owned by Radio Partners LLC. The format of the station is news, talk and sports. WNAE-AM broadcasts to the Warren, PA area at 1310 AM.

WNAH-AM
Owner: Hermitage Broadcasting Corp.
Editorial: 44 Music Sq E, Nashville, Tennessee 37203-4309. **T:** 1 615 254-7611
W: http://www.wnah.com/
Editorial Profile: WNAH-AM is a commercial station owned by Hermitage Broadcasting Corp. The format of the station is Christian and religious talk. WNAH-AM broadcasts to the Nashville, TN area at 1360 AM.

WNAM-AM
Owner: Cumulus Media Inc.
Editorial: 491 S Washburn St, Ste 400, Oshkosh, Wisconsin 54904.
T: 1 920 426-3239
W: http://www.1280wnam.com
Editorial Profile: WNAM-AM is a commercial station owned by Cumulus Media Inc. The format of the station is adult standards. WNAM-AM broadcasts to the Oshkosh, WI area at 1280 AM.

WNAN-FM
Owner: WGBH Educational Foundation
Editorial: 3 Water St, Woods Hole, Massachusetts 2543. **T:** 1 508 548-9600
E: cainan@wgbh.org **W:** http://www.cainan.org
Editorial Profile: WNAN-FM is a commercial station owned by WGBH Educational Foundation. The format of the station is news and talk. WNAN-FM broadcasts to the Woods Hole, MA area at 91.1 FM.

WNAP-AM
Owner: GHB Broadcasting
Editorial: 2311 Old Arch Rd, Norristown, Pennsylvania 19401-2013. **T:** 1 610 272-7600
E: gospel@wnap1110am.com
W: http://www.mygospelhighway11.com
Editorial Profile: WNAP-AM is a commercial station owned by GHB Broadcasting. The format of the station is gospel music. WNAP-AM broadcasts to the Norristown, PA area at 1110 AM.

WNAS-FM
Owner: New Albany School Board
Editorial: 1020 Vincennes St, New Albany, Indiana 47150-3148. **T:** 1 812 542-8506
W: http://www.wnas.org

WNAT-AM
Owner: First Natchez Corp.
Editorial: 2 O'Ferrall St, Natchez, Mississippi 39120-3000. **T:** 1 601 442-4895
W: http://www.1450amwnat.com
Editorial Profile: WNAT-AM is a commercial station owned by First Natchez Corp. The format of the station is news, talk and sports. WNAT-AM broadcasts to the Natchez, MS area at 1450 AM.

WNAU-AM
Owner: MPM Investment Group
Editorial: 204 Moss Hill Dr, New Albany, Mississippi 38652-3400. **T:** 1 662 534-8133
E: info@wnau1470.com
W: http://wnau1470.com
Editorial Profile: WNAU-AM is a commercial station owned by MPM Investment Group. The format of the station is oldies. WNAU-AM broadcasts to the New Albany, MS area at 1470 AM.

WNAV-AM
Owner: Sajak Broadcasting Corp.
Editorial: 236 Admiral Dr, Annapolis, Maryland 21401-3123. **T:** 1 410 263-1430
E: news@wnav.com **W:** http://www.wnav.com
Editorial Profile: WNAV-AM is a commercial station owned by Sajak Broadcasting Corp. The format of the station is news, talk and adult contemporary music. WNAV-AM broadcasts to the Annapolis, MD area at 1430 AM.

WNAW-AM
Owner: Gamma Broadcasting LLC
Editorial: 466 Curran Hwy, North Adams, Massachusetts 01247-3919.
T: 1 413 663-6567 **E:** news@wnaw.com
W: http://www.wnaw.com
Editorial Profile: WNAW-AM is a commercial station owned by Gamma Broadcasting LLC.

The format of the station is adult contemporary. WNAW-AM broadcasts to the North Adams, MA area at 1230 AM.

WNAX-AM
Owner: Saga Communications
Editorial: 1609 E Highway 50, Yankton, South Dakota 57078. **T:** 1 605 665-7442
E: wnax@wnax.com **W:** http://www.wnax.com
Editorial Profile: WNAX-AM is a commercial station owned by Saga Communications. The format of the station is news, talk and sports. WNAX broadcasts in the Sioux Falls, SD area at 570 AM.

WNAX-FM
Owner: Saga Communications
Editorial: 1609 E Highway 50, Yankton, South Dakota 57078. **T:** 1 605 665-7442
E: wnax@wnax.com
W: http://www.bigcountry1041.com
Editorial Profile: WNAX-FM is a commercial station owned by Saga Communications. The format of the station is contemporary country. WNAX-FM broadcasts to the Sioux Falls, SD area at 104.1 FM.

WNBF-AM
Owner: Townsquare Media, Inc.
Editorial: 59 Court St, Binghamton, New York 13901-3270. **T:** 1 607 772-8400
Editorial Profile: WNBF-AM is a commercial station owned by Townsquare Media, Inc. The format of the station is news and talk programming. WNBF-AM broadcasts to the Binghamton, NY area at 1290 AM.

WNBH-AM
Owner: Hall Communications
Editorial: 888 Purchase St, Unit 221, New Bedford, Massachusetts 2740.
T: 1 401 467-4366
Editorial Profile: WNBH-AM is a commercial station owned by Hall Communications. The format of the station is sports. WNBH-AM broadcasts to the Boston area at 1340 AM.

WNBK-FM
Owner: Richburg Educational Broadcasters Inc.
Editorial: 3451 Armenia Rd, Chester, South Carolina 29706-6185. **T:** 1 803 581-9030
E: wrbk@truvista.net
Editorial Profile: WNBK-FM is a commercial station owned by Richburg Educational Broadcasters Inc. The format of the station is oldies music.

WNBP-AM
Owner: Port Broadcasting, LLC
Editorial: 6 Federal St Fl 2, Newburyport, Massachusetts 01950-2804.
T: 1 978 462-1450 **W:** http://www.wnbp.com
Editorial Profile: WNBP-AM is a commercial station owned by Port Broadcasting, LLC. The format of the station is oldies. WNBP-AM broadcasts to the Newburyport, MA area at 1450 AM.

WNBS-AM
Owner: Forever Communications Inc.
Editorial: 1500 Diuguid Dr, Murray, Kentucky 42071. **T:** 1 270 753-2400
E: wnbsnews@gmail.com
W: http://www.1340wnbs.com
Editorial Profile: WNBS-AM is a commercial station owned by Forever Communications Inc. The format of the station is news, talk and sports. WNBS-AM broadcasts in the Murray, KY area at 1340 AM.

WNBT-AM
Owner: Allegheny Mountain Network
Editorial: 12385 Route 6, Wellsboro, Pennsylvania 16901. **T:** 1 570 724-1490
E: wnbt@ptd.net **W:** http://www.wnbt.net
Editorial Profile: WNBT-AM is a commercial station owned by Allegheny Mountain Network. The format of the station is adult standards. WNBT-AM broadcasts to the Wellsboro, PA area at 1490 AM.

WNBU-FM
Owner: Inner Banks Media, LLC
Editorial: 1848 W Arlington Blvd Ste 101B, Greenville, North Carolina 27834-5704.
T: 1 252 672-5900 **E:** prod@ibxmedia.com
W: http://www.wnbufm.com
Editorial Profile: WNBU-FM is a commercial station owned by Inner Banks Media, LLC. The format of the station is talk. WNBU-FM broadcasts to the New Bern, NC area at 94.1 FM.

WNBY-AM
Owner: Sovereign Communications LLC

Editorial: Michigan State Hwy 123 South, Newberry, Michigan 49868. **T:** 1 906 293-3221
W: http://www.1450wnby.com
Editorial Profile: WNBY-AM is a commercial owned by Sovereign Communications LLC. The format of the station is country. WNBY-AM broadcasts to the Newberry, MI area at 1450 AM.

WNBY-FM
Owner: Sovereign Communications LLC
Editorial: Michigan State Highway 123 South, Newberry, Michigan 49868. **T:** 1 906 293-3221
E: info@oldies93fm.com
W: http://www.oldies93fm.com
Editorial Profile: WNBY-FM is a commercial station owned by Sovereign Communications LLC. The format of the station is oldies. WNBY-FM broadcasts to the Newberry, MI area at 93.9 FM.

WNBZ-AM
Owner: Mountain Communications
Editorial: 159 Santanoni Ave, Saranac Lake, New York 12983-2478. **T:** 1 518 891-1544
E: news@wnbz.com **W:** http://www.wnbz.com
Editorial Profile: WNBZ-AM is a commercial station owned by Mountain Communications. The format of the station is adult standards music. WNBZ-AM broadcasts to the Saranac Lake, NY area at 1240 AM.

WNCA-AM
Owner: Chatham Broadcasting Co. Inc.
Editorial: 17890 US Highway 64 W, Siler City, North Carolina 27344-1631.
T: 1 919 742-2135
Editorial Profile: WNCA-AM is a commercial station owned by Chatham Broadcasting Co. Inc. The format of the station is full service, featuring music, news and talk. WNCA-AM broadcasts to the Siler City, NC area at 1570 AM.

WNCC-FM
Owner: Georgia-Carolina Radiocasting Companies LLC
Editorial: 180 Radio Hill Rd, Franklin, North Carolina 28734. **T:** 1 828 524-4418
E: franklinradio@gacaradio.com
W: http://www.967wncc.com
Editorial Profile: WNCC-FM is a commercial station owned by Georgia-Carolina Radiocasting Companies LLC. The format of the station is country. WNCC-FM broadcasts to the Franklin, NC area at 96.7 FM.

WNCD-FM
Owner: Clear Channel Media and Entertainment
Editorial: 7461 South Ave, Youngstown, Ohio 44512. **T:** 1 330 965-0057
W: http://www.cd933.com
Editorial Profile: WNCD-FM is a commercial station owned by Clear Channel Media and Entertainment. The format of the station is rock/album-oriented rock. WNCD-FM broadcasts to the Youngstown, OH area at 93.3 FM.

WNCH-FM
Owner: Vermont Public Radio
Editorial: 365 Troy Ave, Colchester, Vermont 5446. **T:** 1 802 655-9451 **E:** news@vpr.net
W: http://www.vpr.net
Editorial Profile: WNCH-FM is a non-commercial station owned by Vermont Public Radio. The format is classical music. The station airs at 88.1 FM in the Colcester, VT area.

WNCI-FM
Owner: Clear Channel Media and Entertainment
Editorial: 2323 W 5th Ave Ste 200, Columbus, Ohio 43204-4988. **T:** 1 614 486-6101
E: webmaster@wnci.com
W: http://www.wnci.com
Editorial Profile: WNCI-FM is a commercial station owned by Clear Channel Media and Entertainment. The format of the station is Top 40/CHR music. WNCI-FM broadcasts in the Columbus, OH area at 97.9 FM.

WNCL-FM
Owner: Delmarva Broadcasting
Editorial: 1666 Blairs Pond Rd, Milford, Delaware 19963. **T:** 1 302 422-7575
W: http://www.cool1013.com
Editorial Profile: WNCL-FM is a commercial station owned by Delmarva Broadcasting. The format of the station is oldies. WNCL-FM broadcasts to the Milford, DE area at 101.3 FM.

WNCO-AM

Owner: Clear Channel Media and Entertainment
Editorial: 1400 Radio Ln, Mansfield, Ohio 44906-2525. **T:** 1 419 529-2211
W: http://www.wncoam.com
Editorial Profile: WNCO-AM is a commercial station owned by Clear Channel Media and Entertainment. The format of the station is sports. WNCO-AM broadcasts to the Mansfield, OH area at 1340 AM.

WNCO-FM

Owner: Clear Channel Media and Entertainment
Editorial: 1400 Radio Ln, Mansfield, Ohio 44906-2525. **T:** 1 419 529-2211
W: http://www.wncofm.com
Editorial Profile: WNCO-FM is a commercial station owned by Clear Channel Media and Entertainment. The format of the station is contemporary country. WNCO-FM broadcasts to the Mansfield, OH area at 101.3 FM.

WNCQ-FM

Owner: Stephens Media Group LLC
Editorial: 1 Bridge Plz, Ste 204, Ogdensburg, New York 13669. **T:** 1 315 393-1220
W: http://www.q1029.com
Editorial Profile: WNCQ-FM is a commercial station owned by Stephens Media Group LLC. The format of the station is contemporary country music. WNCQ-FM broadcasts to the Ogdensburg, NY area at 102.9 FM.

WNCS-FM

Owner: Northeast Broadcasting Co.
Editorial: 169 River St, Montpelier, Vermont 5602. **T:** 1 802 223-2396
E: feedback@pointfm.com
W: http://www.pointfm.com
Editorial Profile: WNCS-FM is a commercial station owned by Northeast Broadcasting Co. The format of the station is adult album alternative music. WNCS-FM broadcasts to the Montpelier, VT area at 104.7 FM.

WNCT-AM

Owner: Beasley Broadcast Group
Editorial: 2929 Radio Station Rd, Greenville, North Carolina 27834. **T:** 1 252 757-0011
E: live@1079wnct.com
W: http://www.1070wnct.com
Editorial Profile: WNCT-FM is a commercial station owned by Beasley Broadcast Group. The format of the station is rhythmic oldies and blues. WNCT-FM broadcasts to the Greenville, NC area at 1070 AM.

WNCT-FM

Owner: Beasley Broadcast Group
Editorial: 2929 Radio Station Rd, Greenville, North Carolina 27834. **T:** 1 252 757-0011
E: live@1079wnct.com
W: http://www.oldies1079.com
Editorial Profile: WNCT-FM is a commercial station owned by Beasley Broadcast Group. The format of the station is classic hits. WNCT-FM broadcasts to the Greenville, NC area at 107.9 FM.

WNCU-FM

Owner: North Carolina Central University
Editorial: 1801 Fayetteville St, Durham, North Carolina 27707-3129. **T:** 1 919 530-7445
W: http://wncu.org
Editorial Profile: WNCU-FM is a non-commercial station owned by North Carolina Central University. The format of the station is jazz and news. WNCU-FM broadcasts to the Raleigh-Durham, NC area at 90.7 FM.

WNCV-FM

Owner: Cumulus Media Inc.
Editorial: 225 Hollywood Blvd NW, Fort Walton Beach, Florida 32548-4725.
T: 1 850 243-2323 **W:** http://www.wncv.com

WNCW-FM

Owner: Isothermal Community College
Editorial: 286 ICC Loop Road, Spindale, North Carolina 28160. **T:** 1 828 287-8000
E: info@wncw.org **W:** http://www.wncw.org
Editorial Profile: WNCW-FM is a non-commercial station owned by Isothermal Community College. The format of the station is adult album alternative. WNCW-FM broadcasts to the Greenville, SC area at 88.7 FM.

WNCX-FM

Owner: CBS Radio
Editorial: 1041 Huron Rd E, Cleveland, Ohio 44115-1706. **T:** 1 216 861-0100
W: http://www.wncx.com
Editorial Profile: WNCX-FM is a commercial station owned by CBS Radio. The format of

the station is classic rock. WNCX-FM broadcasts to the Cleveland area at 98.5 FM.

WNCY-FM

Owner: Midwest Communications Inc.
Editorial: 1420 Bellevue St, Green Bay, Wisconsin 54311-5649. **T:** 1 920 435-3771
W: http://www.wncy.com
Editorial Profile: WNCY-FM is a commercial station owned by Midwest Communications Inc. The format of the station is contemporary country music. WNCY-FM broadcasts to the Green Bay, WI area at 100.3 FM.

WNDA-AM

Owner: New Albany Broadcasting Co. Inc.
Editorial: 220 Potters Ln, Clarksville, Indiana 47129-1020. **T:** 1 812 949-1570
W: http://www.newstalk1570.com
Editorial Profile: WNDA-AM is a commercial station owned by New Albany Broadcasting Co. Inc. The format of the station is news/talk. WNDA-AM broadcasts to the Clarksville, IN area at 1570 AM.

WNDB-AM

Owner: Black Crow Radio, LLC
Editorial: 126 W International Speedway Blvd, Daytona Beach, Florida 32114.
T: 1 386 257-1150
E: newsdaytonabeach@gmail.com
W: http://www.newsdaytonabeach.com
Editorial Profile: WNDB-AM is a commercial station owned by Black Crow Radio, LLC. The format of the station is news/talk. WNDB-AM broadcasts to the Daytona Beach, FL area at 1150 AM.

WNDD-FM

Owner: Ocala Broadcasting Corp. LLC
Editorial: 3602 NE 20th Pl, Ocala, Florida 34470. **T:** 1 352 622-9500
W: http://www.windfm.com
Editorial Profile: WNDD-FM is a commercial station owned by Ocala Broadcasting Corp. LLC. The format of the station is classic rock. WNDD-FM broadcasts to the Ocala, FL area at 95.5 FM.

WNDE-AM

Owner: Clear Channel Media and Entertainment
Editorial: 6161 Fall Creek Rd, Indianapolis, Indiana 46220-5032. **T:** 1 317 257-7565
W: http://www.sportsradio1260.com
Editorial Profile: WNDE-AM is a commercial station owned by Clear Channel Media and Entertainment. The format for the station is sports. WNDE-AM broadcasts to the Indianapolis area at 1260 AM.

WNDH-FM

Owner: Clear Channel Media and Entertainment
Editorial: 709 N Perry St, Napoleon, Ohio 43545. **T:** 1 419 592-8060
E: wndh@clearchannel.com
W: http://www.wndh1031.com
Editorial Profile: WNDH-FM is a commercial station owned by Clear Channel Media and Entertainment. The format of the station is adult contemporary. WNDH-FM broadcasts to the Napoleon, OH area at 103.1 FM.

WNDI-AM

Owner: JTM Broadcasting Corp.
Editorial: 556 E State Road 54, Sullivan, Indiana 47882. **T:** 1 812 268-6322
Editorial Profile: WNDI-AM is a commercial station owned by JTM Broadcasting Corp. The format of the station is contemporary country music. WNDI-AM broadcasts to the Sullivan, IN area at 1550 AM.

WNDI-FM

Owner: JTM Broadcasting Corp.
Editorial: 556 E State Road 54, Sullivan, Indiana 47882. **T:** 1 812 268-6322
Editorial Profile: WNDI-FM is a commercial station owned by JTM Broadcasting Corp. The format of the station is country music. WNDI-FM broadcasts to the Sullivan, IN area at 95.3 FM.

WNDN-FM

Owner: Ocala Broadcasting Corp. LLC
Editorial: 3602 NE 20th Pl, Ocala, Florida 34470. **T:** 1 352 622-9500
W: http://www.windfm.com
Editorial Profile: WNDN-FM is a commercial station owned by Ocala Broadcasting Corp. LLC. The format of the station is classic rock. WNDN-FM broadcasts to the Ocala, FL area at 107.9 FM.

WNDR-FM

Owner: C R A M Communications LLC
Editorial: 7095 Myers Rd, East Syracuse, New York 13057-9748. **T:** 1 315 656-2231
Editorial Profile: WNDR-FM is a commercial station owned by C R A M Communications LLC. The station is currently stunting formats and broadcasts to the East Syracuse, NY area at 103.9 FM.

WNDT-FM

Owner: Ocala Broadcasting Corp. LLC
Editorial: 4020 W Newberry Rd, Ste 100, Gainesville, Florida 32607. **T:** 1 352 373-6644
E: windfm@windfm.com
W: http://www.windfm.com
Editorial Profile: WNDT-FM is a commercial station owned by Ocala Broadcasting Corp. LLC. The format of the station is classic rock. WNDT-FM broadcasts to the Gainesville, FL area at 92.5 FM.

WNDV-FM

Owner: Artistic Media Partners Inc.
Editorial: 3371 New Cleveland Road, Suite 300, South Bend, Indiana 46628.
T: 1 574 273-9300 **W:** http://www.u93.com
Editorial Profile: WNDV-FM is a commercial station owned by Artistic Media Partners Inc. The format for the station is Hot AC. WNDV-FM broadcasts to the South Bend, IN area at 92.9 FM.

WNDZ-AM

Owner: Newsweb Corp.
Editorial: 5625 N Milwaukee Ave, Chicago, Illinois 60646-6221. **T:** 1 773 792-1121
W: http://www.accessradiochicago.com
Editorial Profile: WNDZ-AM is a commercial station owned by Newsweb Corp. The format of the station is a variety of ethnic programming. WNDZ-AM broadcasts to the Chicago area at 750 AM. The station airs brokered programming.

WNEA-AM

Owner: Word Christian Broadcasting Inc.
Editorial: 8451 S Cherokee Blvd, Ste B, Douglasville, Georgia 30134.
T: 1 770 920-1520 **E:** wordchr@bellsouth.net
W: http://www.wordchristianbroadcasting.com
Editorial Profile: WNEA-AM is a commercial station owned by Word Christian Broadcasting Inc. The format of the station is religious programming and gospel music. WNEA-AM broadcasts to the Douglasville, GA area at 1300 AM.

WNED-FM

Owner: Western New York Public Broadcasting Association
Editorial: 140 Lower Terrace St, Buffalo, New York 14202-4330. **T:** 1 716 845-7000
E: news@wned.org **W:** http://www.wned.org
Editorial Profile: WNED-FM is a non-commercial station owned by Western New York Public Broadcasting Association. The format of the station is classical. WNED-FM broadcasts to the Buffalo, NY area at 94.5 FM.

WNEG-AM

Owner: Georgia-Carolina Radiocasting Companies LLC
Editorial: 145 N Alexander St, Toccoa, Georgia 30577. **T:** 1 706 886-2191
E: wneg@windstream.net
W: http://www.wnegradio.com
Editorial Profile: WNEG-AM is a commercial station owned by Georgia-Carolina Radiocasting Companies LLC. The format of the station is oldies. WNEG-AM broadcasts to the Toccoa, GA area at 1120 AM.

WNEK-FM

Owner: Western New England College
Editorial: 1215 Wilbraham Rd, Springfield, Massachusetts 1119. **T:** 1 413 782-1582
W: http://www.wnekradio.org
Editorial Profile: WNEK-FM is a non-commercial station owned by Western New England College. The format for the station is college variety. WNEK-FM broadcasts to the Springfield, MA area at 105.1 FM.

WNER-AM

Owner: Stephens Media Group
Editorial: 134 Mullin St, Watertown, New York 13601. **T:** 1 315 788-0790
W: http://www.wner1410.com
Editorial Profile: WNER-AM is a commercial station owned by Stephens Media Group. The format of the station is sports. WNER-AM broadcasts to the Watertown, NY area at 1410 AM.

WNES-AM

Owner: Starlight Broadcasting Co.

Editorial: 314 S Main St, Hartford, Kentucky 42347-1129. **T:** 1 270 298-3268

WNEV-FM

Owner: Delta Force II Radio
Editorial: 700 W Martin Luther King Jr Dr Ste 2, West Helena, Arkansas 72390-3526.
T: 1 870 572-9506
W: http://www.force2radio.com
Editorial Profile: WNEV-FM is a commercial station owned by Delta Force II Radio. The format of the station is urban contemporary, blues and gospel. WNEV-FM broadcasts to the Friars Point, MS area at 98.7 FM.

WNEW-FM

Owner: CBS Radio
Editorial: 4200 Parliament Pl, Ste 300, Lanham, Maryland 20706. **T:** 1 301 306-0991
E: desk@wnew.com
W: http://washington.cbslocal.com
Editorial Profile: WNEW-FM is a commercial station owned by CBS Radio. The format of the station is news/talk. WNEW-FM broadcasts to the Washington, D.C. area at 99.1 FM.

WNEX-AM

Owner: Register Communications
Editorial: 1691 Forsyth St, Macon, Georgia 31201. **T:** 1 478 745-5858
Editorial Profile: WNEX-AM is a commercial station owned by Register Communications. The format of the station is gospel music. WNEX-AM broadcasts to the Macon, GA area at 1400 AM.

WNEZ-AM

Owner: Gois Broadcasting
Editorial: 135 Burnside Ave Floor 2, East Hartford, Connecticut 06108-3466.
T: 1 860 524-0001
W: http://www.latina1230.com
Editorial Profile: WNEZ-AM is a commercial station owned by Gois Broadcasting. The format of the station is Hispanic music and romantica. WNEZ-AM broadcasts in the Harford, CT area at 1230 AM.

WNFA-FM

Owner: Ross Bible Church
Editorial: 2865 Maywood Dr, Port Huron, Michigan 48060. **T:** 1 810 985-3260
E: info@wnradio.com
W: http://www.power883.com
Editorial Profile: WNFA-FM is a non-commercial station owned by the Ross Bible Church. The format of the station is contemporary Christian music. WNFA-FM broadcasts to the Port Huron, MI area at 88.3 FM.

WNFB-FM

Owner: Newman Media Inc.
Editorial: 2485 S Marion Ave, Lake City, Florida 32025-0051. **T:** 1 386 961-9494
Editorial Profile: WNFB-FM is a commercial station owned by Newman Media Inc. The format of the station is adult contemporary. WNFB-FM broadcasts to the Lake City, FL area at 94.3 FM.

WNFK-FM

Owner: Taylor County Broadcasting, Inc.
Editorial: 5450 E US 27 Hwy, Perry, Florida 32347-0643. **T:** 1 850 584-9210
Editorial Profile: WNFK-FM is a commercial station owned by Taylor County Broadcasting, Inc. The format for the station is contemporary country. WNFK-FM broadcasts to the Perry, FL area at 92.1 FM.

WNFL-AM

Owner: Midwest Communications Inc.
Editorial: 1420 Bellevue St, Green Bay, Wisconsin 54311. **T:** 1 920 435-3771
W: http://www.wnflam.com
Editorial Profile: WNFL-AM is a commercial station owned by Midwest Communications Inc. The format of the station is sports. WNFL-AM broadcasts to the Green Bay, WI area at 1440 AM.

WNFM-FM

Owner: Magnum Broadcasting
Editorial: E 5680-A Highway 33 West, Reedsburg, Wisconsin 53959.
T: 1 608 524-1400
E: info@magnumbroadcasting.com
W: http://www.wnfmcountry.com
Editorial Profile: WNFM-FM is a commercial station owned by Magnum Broadcasting. The format of the station is country. WNFM-FM broadcasts to the Reedsburg, WI, area at 104.9 FM.

WNFN-FM
Owner: Cumulus Media Inc.
Editorial: 10 Music Cir E, Nashville, Tennessee 37203-4338. **T:** 1 615 321-1067
W: http://www.i106hits.com
Editorial Profile: WNFN-FM is a commercial station owned by Cumulus Media Inc. The format of the station is Top 40/CHR. WNFN-FM broadcasts to the Nashville, TN area at 106.7 FM.

WNFR-FM
Owner: Ross Bible Church
Editorial: 2865 Maywood Dr, Port Huron, Michigan 48060. **T:** 1 810 985-3260
E: info@wnradio.com
W: http://www.wnradio.com
Editorial Profile: WNFR-FM is a non-commercial station owned by Ross Bible Church. The format of the station is contemporary Christian music and religious programming. WNFR-FM broadcasts to the Port Huron, MI area at 90.7 FM.

WNFZ-FM
Owner: Oak Ridge FM
Editorial: 1100 Sharps Ridge Road, Knoxville, Tennessee 37917. **T:** 1 865 525-6000
Editorial Profile: WNFZ-FM is a commercial station owned by Oak Ridge FM. The format of the station is news/talk. WNFZ-FM broadcasts to the Knoxville, TN area at 94.3 FM.

WNGA-FM
Owner: Tugart Properties
Editorial: 705 Brucken Strasse, Helen, Georgia 30545-3606. **T:** 1 706 878-1051
E: wngaradio@gmail.com
Editorial Profile: WNGA-FM is a commercial station owned by Tugart Properties, and under LMA with Cox Media Group. The format of the station is a mix of classic country and classic rock. WNGA-FM broadcasts to the Clermont, GA area at 105.1 FM.

WNGC-FM
Owner: Cox Media Group, Inc.
Editorial: 850 Bobbin Mill Rd, Athens, Georgia 30606-4208. **T:** 1 706 549-6222
W: http://www.1061wngc.com
Editorial Profile: WNGC-FM is a commercial station owned by Cox Media Group, Inc. The format of the station is country music. WNGC-FM broadcasts to the Bogart, GA area at 106.1 FM.

WNGE-FM
Owner: Sovereign Communications LLC
Editorial: 1009 W Ridge St, Ste A, Marquette, Michigan 49855. **T:** 1 906 225-1313
E: wjpd@wjpd.com
Editorial Profile: WNGE-FM is a commercial station owned by Sovereign Communications LLC. The format of the station is oldies music. WNGE-FM broadcasts to the Marquette, MI area at 99.5 FM.

WNGH-FM
Owner: Georgia Public Broadcasting
Editorial: 260 14th St NW, Atlanta, Georgia 30318-5360. **T:** 1 404 685-2548
E: ask@gpb.org **W:** http://www.gpb.org
Editorial Profile: WNGH-FM is a non-commercial station owned by Georgia Public Broadcasting. The format of the station is jazz, classical and news. WNGH-FM broadcasts to the Dalton, GA area at 98.9 FM.

WNGL-AM
Owner: Archangel Communications, Inc.
Editorial: 370 S Section St, Fairhope, Alabama 36532-1769. **T:** 1 251 928-2111
E: office@archangelradio.com
W: http://www.wngl1410am.com
Editorial Profile: WNGL-AM is a commercial station owned by Archangel Communications, Inc. The format for the station is religious. WNGL-AM broadcasts to the Mobile, AL area at 1410 AM.

WNGN-FM
Owner: Northeast Gospel Broadcasting Inc.
Editorial: 65 Kings Rd, Buskirk, New York 12028. **T:** 1 518 686-0975
W: http://www.wngn.org

WNGO-AM
Owner: Bristol Broadcasting
Editorial: 6000 Bristol Dr, Paducah, Kentucky 42003-9213. **T:** 1 270 554-8255
E: news@wkyx.com **W:** http://www.wkyx.com
Editorial Profile: WNGO-AM is a commercial station owned by Bristol Broadcasting. The format of the station is news and talk. WNGO-AM broadcasts to the Paducah, KY area at 1320 AM.

WNGU-FM
Owner: Georgia Public Broadcasting
Editorial: 260 14th St NW, Atlanta, Georgia 30318. **T:** 1 404 685-2548 **E:** ask@gpb.org
W: http://www.gpb.org
Editorial Profile: WNGU-FM is a non-commercial station owned by Georgia Public Broadcasting. The format of the station is news, jazz and classical music. WNGU-FM broadcasts to the Atlanta area at 89.5 FM.

WNGZ-FM
Owner: Community Broadcasters, LLC
Editorial: 2205 College Ave, Elmira, New York 14903-1201. **T:** 1 607 732-4400
W: http://www.wngz.com
Editorial Profile: WNGZ-FM is a commercial station owned by Community Broadcasters, LLC. The format of the station is classic rock. WNGZ-FM broadcasts to the Elmira, NY area at 104.9 FM.

WNHU-FM
Owner: University of New Haven
Editorial: 300 Boston Post Rd, West Haven, Connecticut 06516-1916. **T:** 1 203 479-8800
W: http://www.wnhu.net
Editorial Profile: WNHU-FM is a non-commercial station owned by the University of New Haven. The format of the station is variety. WNHU-FM broadcasts to the New Haven, CT area on 88.7 FM.

WNHW-FM
Owner: WBIN, Inc.
Editorial: 2 Capital Plz Ste 105, Concord, New Hampshire 03301-4911. **T:** 1 603 224-8486
W: http://www.933thewolf.com
Editorial Profile: WNHW-FM is a commercial station owned by WBIN, Inc. The format of the station is country. WNHW-FM broadcasts to the Hooksett, NH area at 93.3 FM.

WNIC-FM
Owner: Clear Channel Media and Entertainment
Editorial: 27675 Halsted Rd, Farmington Hills, Michigan 48331-3511. **T:** 1 248 324-5800
W: http://www.wnic.com
Editorial Profile: WNIC-FM is a commercial station owned by Clear Channel Media and Entertainment. The format of the station is adult contemporary. WNIC-FM broadcasts to the Detroit area at 100.3 FM.

WNIJ-FM
Owner: Northern Illinois University
Editorial: 801 N 1st St, Dekalb, Illinois 60115-2366. **T:** 1 815 753-9000 **E:** nprnews@niu.edu
W: http://www.wnij.org
Editorial Profile: WNIJ-FM is a non-commercial station owned by Northern Illinois University. The format of the station is news and talk programming. WNIJ-FM broadcasts to the De Kalb, IL area at 89.5 FM.

WNIL-AM
Owner: Williams (Marion R.)
Editorial: 237 W Edison Rd Ste 200, Mishawaka, Indiana 46545-3103.
T: 1 574 258-5483
W: http://www.thefanmichiana.com/
Editorial Profile: WNIL-AM is a commercial station owned by Williams (Marion R.). The format for the station is sports/talk. WNIL-AM broadcasts to the Niles, MI area at 1290 AM.

WNIN-FM
Owner: Tri-State Media
Editorial: 405 Carpenter St, Evansville, Indiana 47708. **T:** 1 812 423-2973
W: http://www.wnin.org
Editorial Profile: WNIN-FM is a non-commercial radio station owned by Tri-State Media. The format of the station is classical music and news. WNIN-FM broadcasts to the Evansville, IN area at 88.3 FM.

WNIO-AM
Owner: Clear Channel Media and Entertainment
Editorial: 7461 South Ave, Youngstown, Ohio 44512. **T:** 1 330 965-0057
W: http://www.sportsradio1390.com
Editorial Profile: WNIO-AM is a commercial station owned by Clear Channel Media and Entertainment. The format of the station is sports. WNIO-AM broadcasts to the Youngstown, OH area at 1390 AM.

WNIR-FM
Owner: Media-Com Inc.
Editorial: 2449 State Route 59, Ravenna, Ohio 44266-1641. **T:** 1 330 673-2323
E: news@wnir.com **W:** http://www.wnir.com
Editorial Profile: WNIR-FM is a commercial station owned by Media-Com Inc. The format of the station is news and talk. WNIR-FM broadcasts in the Kent, OH area at 100.1 FM.

WNIS-AM
Owner: Sinclair Telecable Inc.
Editorial: 999 Waterside Dr, Ste 500, Norfolk, Virginia 23510. **T:** 1 757 640-8500
W: http://www.wnis.com
Editorial Profile: WNIS-AM is a commercial station owned by Sinclair Telecable Inc. The format of the station is news and talk. WNIS-AM broadcasts to the Norfolk, VA area at 790 AM.

WNIU-FM
Owner: Northern Illinois University
Editorial: 801 N 1st St, Dekalb, Illinois 60115-2366. **T:** 1 815 753-9000 **E:** nprnews@niu.edu
W: http://northernpublicradio.org
Editorial Profile: WNIU-FM is a non-commercial station owned by Northern Illinois University. The format of the station is classical music. WNIU-FM broadcasts to the De Kalb, IL area at 90.5 FM.

WNIV-AM
Owner: Salem Communications
Editorial: 2970 Peachtree Rd NW, Ste 700, Atlanta, Georgia 30305. **T:** 1 404 995-7300
W: http://www.wniv.com
Editorial Profile: WNIV-AM is a commercial station owned by Salem Communications. The format of the station is Christian talk. WNIV-AM broadcasts to the Atlanta area at 970 AM.

WNIX-AM
Owner: Delta Radio, LLC
Editorial: 1399 E Reed Rd, Greenville, Mississippi 38703-7234. **T:** 1 662 378-2617
E: info@deltaradio.net
W: http://www.wnixradio.com
Editorial Profile: WNIX-AM is a commercial station owned by Delta Radio, LLC. The format of the station is news/talk. WNIX-AM broadcasts to the Greenville, MS area at 1330 AM.

WNJA-FM
Owner: Western New York Public Broadcasting Association
Editorial: 140 Lower Terrace St, Buffalo, New York 14202. **T:** 1 716 845-7000
E: classical@wned.org
W: http://www.wned.org
Editorial Profile: WNJA-FM is a non-commercial station owned by the Western New York Public Broadcasting Association. The format of the station is classical music programming. WNJA-FM broadcasts locally to the Jamestown, NY area at 89.7 FM.

WNJC-AM
Owner: Forsythe Broadcasting Inc.
Editorial: 123 Egg Harbor Rd Ste 302, Sewell, New Jersey 08080-9406. **T:** 1 856 227-1360
W: http://www.wnjc1360.com
Editorial Profile: WNJC-AM is a commercial station owned by Forsythe Broadcasting Inc. The format of the station is variety. WNJC-AM broadcasts to the Sewell, NJ area at 1360 AM.

WNJE-AM
Owner: NB Broadcasting, LLC
Editorial: 619 Alexander Rd Fl 3, Princeton, New Jersey 08540-6000. **T:** 1 609 419-0300
W: http://www.920thevoice.com
Editorial Profile: WNJE-AM is a commercial station owned by NB Broadcasting, LLC. The format of the station is talk. WNJE-AM broadcasts in the Boyertown, PA area at 920 AM.

WNJM-FM
Owner: New Jersey Public Broadcasting Authority
Editorial: 25 S Stockton St, Trenton, New Jersey 08608-1832. **T:** 1 609 777-5000
E: talkback@whyy.org **W:** http://www.whyy.org
Editorial Profile: WNJM-FM is a non-commercial station owned by New Jersey Public Broadcasting Authority. The format of the station is news/talk. WNJM-FM broadcasts to New Jersey families at 89.9 FM.

WNJT-FM
Owner: New Jersey Public Broadcasting Authority
Editorial: 25 S Stockton St, Trenton, New Jersey 8608. **T:** 1 609 777-5000
E: publicity@nypublicradio.org
W: http://www.njpublicradio.org
Editorial Profile: WNJT-FM is a non-commercial station owned by New Jersey Public Broadcasting Authority. The format of the station is news/talk WNJT-FM broadcasts to the Trenton, NJ area at 88.1 FM.

WNJY-FM
Owner: New Jersey Public Broadcasting Authority
Editorial: 25 Stockton St, Trenton, New Jersey 08619-1950. **T:** 1 609 777-5000
E: publicity@nypublicradio.org
W: http://www.njpublicradio.org
Editorial Profile: WNJY-FM is a non-commercial station owned by New Jersey Public Broadcasting Authority. The format of the station is news/talk. WNJY-FM broadcasts to the Netcong, NJ area at 89.3 FM.

WNKE-FM
Owner: Northern Kentucky University
Editorial: 301 Landrum Academic Center, Highland Heights, Kentucky 41099-0001.
T: 1 859 5726500 **E:** radio@wnku.org
W: http://www.wnku.org
Editorial Profile: WNKE-FM is a non-commercial station managed by Northern Kentucky University. The format of the station is adult album alternative music and news. WNKE-FM broadcasts to the Highland Heights, KY, area at 104.1 FM.

WNKI-FM
Owner: Community Broadcasters, LLC
Editorial: 2205 College Ave, Elmira, New York 14903-1201. **T:** 1 607 732-4400
W: http://www.wink106.com
Editorial Profile: WNKI-FM is a commercial station owned by Community Broadcasters, LLC. The format of the station is hot adult contemporary music. WNKI-FM broadcasts to the Elmira, NY area at 106.1 FM.

WNKJ-FM
Owner: Pennyrile Christian Comm. Inc.
Editorial: 1100 E 18th St, Hopkinsville, Kentucky 42240. **T:** 1 270 886-9655
E: wnkj@wnkj.org **W:** http://www.wnkj.org
Editorial Profile: WNKJ-FM is a non-commercial station owned by Pennyrile Christian Comm. Inc. The format of the station is religious, and gospel and contemporary Christian music. WNKJ-FM broadcasts to the Hopkinsville, KY area at 89.3 FM.

WNKN-FM
Owner: Northern Kentucky University
Editorial: 301 Landrum Academic Center, Highland Heights, Kentucky 41099-0001.
T: 1 859 572-6500 **E:** radio@wnku.edu
W: http://www.wnku.org
Editorial Profile: WNKN-FM is a non-commercial station owned by Northern Kentucky University. The format of the station is adult album alternative music and news. WNKN-FM broadcasts to the Highland Heights, KY, area at 89.7 FM.

WNKO-FM
Owner: Runnymede Inc.
Editorial: 1000 N 40th St, Newark, Ohio 43055-1467. **T:** 1 740 522-8171
E: studio@wnko.com **W:** http://www.wnko.com
Editorial Profile: WNKO-FM is a commercial station owned by Runnymede Inc. The format of the station is classic hits music. WNKO-FM broadcasts to the Newark, OH, area at 101.7 FM.

WNKR-FM
Owner: Grant Co. Broadcasters, Inc.
Editorial: 118 S Main St, Dry Ridge, Kentucky 41035. **T:** 1 859 824-9106
W: http://www.1067wnkr.com
Editorial Profile: WNKR-FM is a commercial station owned by Grant Co. Broadcasters, Inc. The format of the station is classic country. WNKR-FM broadcasts to the Dry Ridge, KY area at 106.7 FM.

WNKS-FM
Owner: CBS Radio
Editorial: 1520 South Blvd, Charlotte, North Carolina 28203-4786. **T:** 1 704 522-1103
W: http://kiss951.cbslocal.com
Editorial Profile: WNKS-FM is commercial station owned by CBS Radio. The format of the station is Top 40/CHR music. WNKS-FM broadcasts to the Charlotte, NC area at 95.1 FM.

WNKT-FM
Owner: Cumulus Media Inc
Editorial: 1801 Charleston Hwy, Cayce, South Carolina 29033-2019. **T:** 1 803 796-7600
W: http://www.1075thegame.com
Editorial Profile: WNKT-FM is a commercial station owned by Cumulus Media Inc. The format of the station is sports. WNKT-FM broadcasts to the Columbia, SC area at 107.5 FM.

WNKU-FM
Owner: Northern Kentucky University
Editorial: 301 Landrum Academic Center, Highland Heights, Kentucky 41099-5999. **T:** 1 859 572-6500 **E:** radio@wnku.org
W: http://www.wnku.org
Editorial Profile: WNKU-FM is a non-commercial station owned by Northern Kentucky University. The format of the station is adult album alternative music and news. WNKU-FM broadcasts to the Highland Heights, KY, area at 89.7 FM.

WNKX-FM
Owner: Hickman County Broadcasting Co.
Editorial: 150 Highway 50 E, Centerville, Tennessee 37033-5273. **T:** 1 931 729-5191
E: wnkx@countrykix96.com
W: http://www.countrykix96.com
Editorial Profile: WNKX-FM is a commercial station owned by the Hickman County Broadcasting Co. The format of the station is country music. WNKX-FM broadcasts to the Nashville, TN area at 96.7.

WNLA-AM
Owner: Delta Radio
Editorial: Highway 448, Indianola, Mississippi 38751. **T:** 1 662 887-1380
E: wnlaamfm@bellsouth.net
W: http://www.wnlafm.com
Editorial Profile: WNLA-AM is a commercial station owned by Delta Radio. The format of the station is gospel music. WNLA-AM broadcasts in the Indianola, MS area at 1380 AM.

WNLC-FM
Owner: Hall Communications
Editorial: 40 Cuprak Rd, Norwich, Connecticut 06360-2008. **T:** 1 860 887-3511
E: feedback@wnlc.com
W: http://www.wnlc.com
Editorial Profile: WNLC-FM is a commercial station owned by Hall Communications. The format of the station is classic hits. WNLC-FM broadcasts to the Norwich, CT area at 98.7 FM.

WNLD-FM
Owner: Illinois Bible Institute
Editorial: 4101 Fieldstone Rd, Champaign, Illinois 61822-8800. **T:** 1 217 359-8232
E: wbgl@wbgl.org **W:** http://www.wbgl.org
Editorial Profile: WNLD-FM is a non-commercial station owned by the Illinois Bible Institute. The format of the station is Christian. WNLD-FM broadcasts to the Decatur, IL area at 88.1 FM.

WNLF-FM
Owner: Prestige Communications
Editorial: 31 E Side Sq, Macomb, Illinois 61455-2248. **T:** 1 309 833-2121
E: news@prestigeradio.com
W: http://www.prestigeradio.com
Editorial Profile: WNLF-FM is a commercial station owned by Prestige Communications. The format of the station is rock alternative. WNLF-FM broadcasts to the Macomb, IL area at 95.9 FM.

WNLR-AM
Owner: New Life Ministries Inc.
Editorial: 35 Eagle Rock Lane, Churchville, Virginia 24421. **T:** 1 540 885-8600
E: wnlr@nlministries.org
W: http://www.nlministries.org
Editorial Profile: WNLR-AM is a commercial station owned by New Life Ministries Inc. The format of the station is contemporary Christian programming. WNLR-AM broadcasts to the Churchville, VA area at 1150 AM.

WNLS-AM
Owner: Clear Channel Media and Entertainment
Editorial: 325 John Knox Rd, Bldg G, Tallahassee, Florida 32303. **T:** 1 850 422-3107
E: wnls-am@clearchannel.com
W: http://www.wnls.com
Editorial Profile: WNLS-AM is a commercial station owned by Clear Channel Media and Entertainment. The format of the station is sports. WNLS-AM broadcasts to the Tallahassee, FL area at 1270 AM.

WNLT-FM
Owner: Baldwin Broadcasting
Editorial: 8686 Michael Ln, Fairfield, Ohio 45014. **T:** 1 513 829-7700
W: http://www.klove.com
Editorial Profile: WNLT-FM is a non-commercial station owned by Baldwin Broadcasting but programming is leased by Educational Media Foundation and carries K-Love programming. WNLT-FM broadcasts to the Harrison, OH area at 104.3 FM.

WNMA-AM
Owner: Multicultural Radio Broadcasting Inc.
Editorial: 2 Alhambra Plz Fl 9, Coral Gables, Florida 33134-5202. **T:** 1 305 759-7280
W: http://espndeportesmiami.com
Editorial Profile: WNMA-AM is a commercial station owned by Multicultural Radio Broadcasting Inc and under LMA with Deportes Media LLC. The format of the station is Spanish sports. WNMA-AM broadcasts to the Spanish speaking adults in the Miami area at 1210 AM.

WNMB-AM
Owner: Norman Communications Inc.
Editorial: 429 Pine St, North Myrtle Beach, South Carolina 29582. **T:** 1 843 249-6662
E: wnmb@sc.rr.com **W:** http://www.wnmb.net
Editorial Profile: WNMB-AM is a commercial station owned by Norman Communications Inc. The format of the station is oldies music. WNMB-AM broadcasts in the North Myrtle Beach, SC area at 900 AM.

WNMC-FM
Owner: Northwestern Michigan College
Editorial: 1701 E Front St, Traverse City, Michigan 49686. **T:** 1 231 995-1090
E: wnmc@nmc.edu **W:** http://www.wnmc.org
Editorial Profile: WNMC-FM is a non-commercial station owned by Northwestern Michigan College. The format of the station is a variety. WNMC-FM broadcasts to the Traverse City, MI area at 90.7 FM.

WNMH-FM
Owner: Northfield Mt. Hermon School
Editorial: 206 Main St, Northfield, Massachusetts 1360. **T:** 1 413 498-3915
W: http://wnmh.nmhschool.org

WNML-AM
Owner: Cumulus Media Inc.
Editorial: 4711 Old Kingston Pike, Knoxville, Tennessee 37919-5207. **T:** 1 865 588-6511
W: http://www.sportsanimal99.com
Editorial Profile: WNML-AM is a commercial station owned by Cumulus Media Inc. The format of the station is sports. WNML-AM broadcasts to the Knoxville, TN area at 990 AM.

WNML-FM
Owner: Cumulus Media Inc.
Editorial: 4711 Old Kingston Pike, Knoxville, Tennessee 37919-5207. **T:** 1 865 588-6511
W: http://www.sportsanimal99.com
Editorial Profile: WNML-FM is a commercial station owned by Cumulus Media Inc. The format of the station is sports. WNML-FM broadcasts to the Knoxville, TN area at 99.1 FM.

WNMQ-FM
Owner: Cumulus Media Inc.
Editorial: 200 6th St N Court Square Towers, Ste 205, Columbus, Mississippi 39701.
T: 1 662 327-1183

WNMT-AM
Owner: Midwest Communications Inc.
Editorial: 807 W. 37th St., Hibbing, Minnesota 55746. **T:** 1 218 263-7531
W: http://www.wnmtradio.com
Editorial Profile: WNMT-AM is commercial station owned by Midwest Communications Inc. The format of the station is news, talk and sports. WNMT-AM broadcasts in the Duluth, MN area at 650 AM.

WNMU-FM
Owner: Board of Trustees of Northern Michigan University(The)
Editorial: 1401 Presque Isle Ave, Marquette, Michigan 49855. **T:** 1 906 227-2600
E: pr90@nmu.edu **W:** http://wnmufm.org
Editorial Profile: WNMU-FM is a non-commercial station owned by the Board of Trustees of Northern Michigan University. The format of the station is jazz, classical and news programming. WNMU-FM broadcasts to the Marquette, MI area at 90.1 FM.

WNMX-FM
Owner: Cumulus Media Inc.
Editorial: 7080 Lee Hwy, Radford, Virginia 24141-8416. **T:** 1 540 731-6000
W: http://www.mix100fm.com
Editorial Profile: WNMX-FM is a commercial station owned by Cumulus Media Inc. The format of the station is hot adult contemporary. WNMX-FM broadcasts to the Fairlawn, VA area at 100.7 FM.

WNNC-AM
Owner: Newton-Conover Communications, Inc.
Editorial: 1666 Radio Station Rd, Newton, North Carolina 28658-9488.
T: 1 828 464-4041
Editorial Profile: WNNC-AM is a commercial station owned by Newton-Conover Communications, Inc. The format of the station is adult contemporary music and talk. WNNC-AM broadcast to the Newton, NC area at 1230 AM.

WNND-FM
Owner: Saga Communications
Editorial: 4401 Carriage Hill Ln, Columbus, Ohio 43220. **T:** 1 614 451-2191
W: http://www.rewindcolumbus.com
Editorial Profile: WNND-FM is a commercial station owned by Saga Communications. The format of the station is classic hits. WNND-FM broadcasts to the Columbus, OH, area at 103.5 FM.

WNNF-FM
Owner: Cumulus Media Inc.
Editorial: 4805 Montgomery Rd Ste 300, Cincinnati, Ohio 45212-2280.
T: 1 513 241-9898
E: feedback@cincyradio.com
W: http://www.nashfm941.com
Editorial Profile: WNNF-FM is a commercial station owned by Cumulus Media Inc. The station's format is contemporary country. WNNF-FM broadcasts to the Cincinnati area at 94.1 FM.

WNNG-FM
Owner: Georgia Eagle Broadcasting Inc.
Editorial: 1350 Radio Loop, Warner Robins, Georgia 31088-3626. **T:** 1 478 923-3416
E: georgiaeagleproduction@gmail.com
W: http://www.warnerrobinspatriot.com
Editorial Profile: WNNG-FM is a commercial station owned by Georgia Eagle Broadcasting Inc. The format for the station is news/talk. WNNG-FM broadcasts to the Warner Robins, GA area at 99.9 FM.

WNNH-FM
Owner: WBIN, Inc.
Editorial: 169 Port Rd, Kennebunk, Maine 04043-7737. **T:** 1 207 967-0993
W: http://991frankfm.com
Editorial Profile: WNNH-FM is a commercial station owned by WBIN, Inc. The format of the station is classic hits. WNNH-FM broadcasts to the Gilford, NH area at 99.1 FM.

WNNJ-FM
Owner: Clear Channel Media and Entertainment
Editorial: 45 Ed Mitchell Ave, Franklin, New Jersey 07416-1588. **T:** 1 973 827-2525
W: http://www.wnnj.com
Editorial Profile: WNNJ-FM is a commercial station owned by Clear Channel Media and Entertainment. The format of the station is classic rock. WNNJ-FM broadcasts to the Franklin, NJ area at 103.7 FM.

WNNK-FM
Owner: Cumulus Media Inc.
Editorial: 2300 Vartan Way, Harrisburg, Pennsylvania 17110-9720. **T:** 1 717 238-1041
W: http://www.wink104.com
Editorial Profile: WNNK-FM is a commercial station owned by Cumulus Media Inc. The format of the station is hot adult contemporary. WNNK-FM broadcasts to the Harrisburg, PA area at 104.1 FM.

WNNL-FM
Owner: Radio One Inc.
Editorial: 8001 Creedmoor Rd, Ste 101, Raleigh, North Carolina 27613.
T: 1 919 848-9736 **W:** http://thelightnc.com
Editorial Profile: WNNL-FM is a commercial station owned by Radio One Inc. The format of the station is gospel. WNNL-FM broadcasts to the Raleigh-Durham, NC area at 103.9 FM.

WNNO-FM
Owner: Magnum Radio Group
Editorial: N2349 Wibu Rd, Poynette, Wisconsin 53955-9556. **T:** 1 608 745-0959
E: magnumprod@magnumradiogroup.net
W: http://www.mix106wnno.com
Editorial Profile: WNNO-FM is a commercial station owned by Magnum Radio Group. The format for the station is hot adult contemporary. WNNO-FM broadcasts to the Portage, WI area at 106.9 FM.

WNNP-FM
Owner: Saga Communications
Editorial: 4401 Carriage Hill Ln, Columbus, Ohio 43220. **T:** 1 614 451-2191
W: http://www.rewindcolumbus.com
Editorial Profile: WNNP-FM is a commercial station owned by Saga Communications. The format of the station is classic hits. WNNP-FM broadcasts to the Columbus, OH area at 104.3 FM.

WNNR-AM
Owner: Norsan Broadcasting System
Editorial: 9831 Beach Blvd Ste 7, Jacksonville, Florida 32246-4703. **T:** 1 904 361-3150
W: http://larazalaraza.com/jacksonville
Editorial Profile: WNNR-AM is a commercial station owned by Norsan Broadcasting System. The format of the station is regional Mexican. WNNR-AM broadcasts to the Jacksonville, FL area at 970 AM.

WNNS-FM
Owner: Midwest Family Stations
Editorial: 1510 N Third St, Riverton, Illinois 62561. **T:** 1 217 629-7077
E: wnns@wnns.com **W:** http://www.wnns.com
Editorial Profile: WNNS-FM is a commercial station owned by Midwest Family Stations. The format of the station is Lite Rock/Lite AC music. WNNS-FM broadcasts to the Springfield, IL area at 98.7 FM.

WNNT-FM
Owner: Real Media, Inc.
Editorial: 156 Prince street, Tappahannock, Virginia 22560. **T:** 1 804 333-4900
E: rivercountry1009@verizon.net
W: http://realradio804.com
Editorial Profile: WNNT-FM is a commercial station owned by Real Media, Inc. The format of the station is country. WNNT-FM broadcasts to the Warsaw, VA area at 107.5 FM.

WNNW-AM
Owner: Costa Eagle Radio Ventures
Editorial: 462 Merrimack St, Methuen, Massachusetts 01844-5804.
T: 1 978 686-9966 **W:** http://power800am.com
Editorial Profile: WNNW-AM is a commercial station owned by Costa Eagle Radio Ventures. The format of the station is Hispanic programming. WNNW-AM broadcasts to the Methuen, MA area at 800 AM.

WNNW-FM
Owner: Costa Eagle Radio Ventures
Editorial: 462 Merrimack St, Methuen, Massachusetts 01844-5804.
T: 1 978 686-9966
W: http://www.power800am.com
Editorial Profile: WNNW-FM is a commercial station owned by Costa Eagle Radio Ventures. The format of the station is Hispanic programming. WNNW-FM broadcasts to the Methuen, MA area at 92.1 FM.

WNNX-FM
Owner: Cumulus Media Inc.
Editorial: 780 Johnson Ferry Rd NE, Fl 5, Atlanta, Georgia 30342. **T:** 1 404 497-4700
W: http://www.atlantasrockstation.com
Editorial Profile: WNNX-FM is a commercial station owned by Cumulus Media Inc. The format of the station is classic rock. WNNX-FM broadcasts to the Atlanta area at 100.5 FM.

WNNZ-AM
Owner: Clear Channel Media and Entertainment
Editorial: 1331 Main St, Ste 4, Springfield, Massachusetts 1103. **T:** 1 413 781-1011
E: news@wfcr.org **W:** http://www.wfcr.org
Editorial Profile: WNNZ-AM is a commercial station owned by Clear Channel Media and Entertainment. The format of the station is news and talk. WNNZ-AM broadcasts to the Springfield, MA area at 640 AM and 91.7 FM.

WNOB-FM
Owner: Sinclair Telecable Inc.
Editorial: 999 Waterside Dr, Ste 500, Norfolk, Virginia 23510. **T:** 1 757 640-8500
W: http://www.937bobfm.com
Editorial Profile: WNOB-FM is a commercial station owned by Sinclair Telecable Inc. The format of the station is adult hits. WNOB-FM broadcasts to the Norfolk, VA area at 93.7 FM.

WNOE-FM
Owner: Clear Channel Media and Entertainment
Editorial: 929 Howard Ave, New Orleans, Louisiana 70113-1148. **T:** 1 504 679-7300
W: http://www.wnoe.com
Editorial Profile: WNOE-FM is a commercial station owned by Clear Channel Media and Entertainment. The format of the station is contemporary country music. WNOE-FM

broadcasts to the New Orleans area at 101.1 FM.

WNOG-AM

Owner: Sun Broadcasting, Inc.
Editorial: 2824 Palm Beach Blvd, Fort Myers, Florida 33916-1503. **T:** 1 239 337-2346
Editorial Profile: WNOG-AM is a commercial station owned by Sun Broadcasting, Inc. The format of the station is sports. WNOG-AM broadcasts to the Ft. Myers, FL area at 1270 AM.

WNOH-FM

Owner: Clear Channel Media and Entertainment
Editorial: 1003 Norfolk Sq, Norfolk, Virginia 23502-3234. **T:** 1 757 466-0009
W: http://www.now105.com
Editorial Profile: WNOH-FM is a commercial station owned by Clear Channel Media and Entertainment. The format of the station is Top 40/CHR. WNOH-FM broadcasts to the Norfolk, VA area at 105.3 FM.

WNOI-FM

Owner: H & R Communications
Editorial: 1001 N Olive Road, Flora, Illinois 62839. **T:** 1 618 662-8331 **E:** info@wnoi.com
W: http://www.wnoi.com
Editorial Profile: WNOI-FM is a commercial station owned by H & R Communications. The format of the station is adult contemporary music. WNOI-FM broadcasts to the Flora, IL area at 103.9 FM.

WNOK-FM

Owner: Clear Channel Media and Entertainment
Editorial: 316 Greystone Blvd, Columbia, South Carolina 29210. **T:** 1 803 343-1100
W: http://www.wnok.com
Editorial Profile: WNOK-FM is a commercial station owned by Clear Channel Media and Entertainment. The format for the station is Top 40/CHR. WNOK-FM broadcasts to the Columbia, SC area at 104.7 FM.

WNOO-AM

Owner: Clear Media LLC
Editorial: 1108 Hendricks St, Chattanooga, Tennessee 37406. **T:** 1 423 698-8617
E: wnoo@epbinternet.com
W: http://www.wnooradio.com
Editorial Profile: WNOO-AM is a commercial station owned by Clear Media LLC. The format of the station is gospel music. WNOO-AM broadcasts to the Chattanooga, TN area at 1260 AM.

WNOP-AM

Owner: Sacred Heart Radio
Editorial: 5440 Moeller Ave, Cincinnati, Ohio 45212-1211. **T:** 1 513 731-7740
E: info@sacredheartradio.com
W: http://www.sacredheartradio.com
Editorial Profile: WNOP-AM is a non-commercial station owned by Sacred Heart Radio. The format of the station is religious talk programming. WNOP-AM broadcasts to the Cincinnati area at 740 AM.

WNOR-FM

Owner: Saga Communications
Editorial: 870 Greenbrier Cir Ste 399, Chesapeake, Virginia 23320-2671.
T: 1 757 366-9900 **W:** http://www.fm99.com
Editorial Profile: WNOR-FM is a commercial station owned by Saga Communications. The format of the station is rock. WNOR-FM broadcasts to the Norfolk, VA area at 98.7 FM.

WNOS-AM

Owner: CTC Media Group
Editorial: 1202 Pollock St, New Bern, North Carolina 28560-5538. **T:** 1 252 638-8888
W: http://www.rfenc.com
Editorial Profile: WNOS-AM is a commercial station owned by the CTC Media Group. The format of the station is sports and some talk. WNOS-AM broadcasts to New Bern, NC at 1450 AM.

WNOU-FM

Owner: Radio One Inc.
Editorial: 21 E Saint Joseph St, Indianapolis, Indiana 46204-1025. **T:** 1 317 266-9600
W: http://www.radionowindy.com
Editorial Profile: WNOU-FM is a commercial station owned by Radio One Inc. The format of the station is Top 40/CHR music. WNOU-FM broadcasts to the Indianapolis area at 100.9 FM.

WNOW-AM

Owner: Davidson Media/Gabo Broadcasting Group/
Editorial: 4321 Stuart Andrew Blvd, Ste E, Charlotte, North Carolina 28217-1588.
T: 1 704 6659355
W: http://poderpurasbuenas.com
Editorial Profile: WNOW-AM is a commercial station owned by Davidson Media Group. The station is the ESPN Deportes affiliate in the area. The format of the station is sports in Spanish. WNOW-AM broadcasts to the Charlotte, NC area at 1030 AM.

WNOW-FM

Owner: CBS Radio
Editorial: 345 Hudson St, New York, New York 10014-4502. **T:** 1 212 314-9200
W: http://923amp.cbslocal.com
Editorial Profile: WNOW-FM is a commercial station owned by CBS Radio. The format of the station is Top 40/CHR. WNOW-FM broadcasts to the New York area at 92.3 FM.

WNOX-FM

Owner: Journal Broadcast Group
Editorial: 1533 Amherst Rd, Knoxville, Tennessee 37909-1204. **T:** 1 865 824-1021
W: http://www.931wnox.com
Editorial Profile: WNOX-FM is a commercial station owned by Journal Broadcast Group. The format of the station is classic hits. WNOX-FM broadcasts to the Knoxville, TN area at 93.1 FM.

WNPC-AM

Owner: Bristol Broadcasting
Editorial: 377 Graham St, Newport, Tennessee 37821-2712. **T:** 1 423 623-8744
Editorial Profile: WNPC-AM is a commercial station owned by Bristol Broadcasting. The format of the station is country. WNPC-AM broadcasts to the Newport, TN area at 1060 AM.

WNPC-FM

Owner: Bristol Broadcasting
Editorial: 377 Graham St, Newport, Tennessee 37821-2712. **T:** 1 423 623-8744
W: http://www.923wnpc.com
Editorial Profile: WNPC-FM is a commercial station owned by Bristol Broadcasting. The format of the station is classic country. WNPC-FM broadcasts to the Newport, TN area at 92.9 FM.

WNPL-AM

Owner: Fort Myers Broadcasting Co.
Editorial: 2824 Palm Beach Blvd, Fort Myers, Florida 33916-1503. **T:** 1 239 337-2346
W: http://www.winknewsradio.com
Editorial Profile: WNPL-AM is a commercial station owned by Fort Myers Broadcasting Co. The format of the station is news and talk. WNPL-AM broadcasts to the Fort Myers, FL area at 1460 AM.

WNPQ-FM

Owner: Tuscarawas Broadcasting
Editorial: 3969 Convenience Cir NW, Ste 205, Canton, Ohio 44718. **T:** 1 330 492-9590
E: office@thelight959.com
W: http://www.thelight959.com
Editorial Profile: WNPQ-FM is a commercial owned by Tuscarawas Broadcasting. The format of the station is Christian Contemporary. WNPQ-FM broadcasts to the Canton, OH area at 95.9 FM.

WNPR-FM

Owner: Connecticut Public Broadcasting Inc.
Editorial: 1049 Asylum Ave, Hartford, Connecticut 06105-2432. **T:** 1 860 278-5310
E: info@wnpr.org **W:** http://www.cpbn.org
Editorial Profile: WNPR-FM is a non-commercial station owned by Connecticut Public Broadcasting Inc. The format of the station is news and talk. WNPR-FM broadcasts to the Hartford, CT area at 90.5 FM.

WNPS-FM

Owner: American Public Media Group
Editorial: 330 Himmarshee St Ste 207, Fort Lauderdale, Florida 33312-1712.
T: 1 855 444-5355
E: info@classicalsouthflorida.org
W: http://classicalsouthflorida.publicradio.org
Editorial Profile: WNPS-FM is a non-commercial station owned by American Public Media Group, specifically Classical South Florida, Inc. The format of the station is classical music programming. WNPS-FM broadcasts to the Fort Myers, FL area at 88.7 FM.

WNPT-FM

Owner: John Sisty Enterprises Inc.
Editorial: 2110 McFarland Blvd E, Ste C, Tuscaloosa, Alabama 35404-5820.
T: 1 205 758-5523 **E:** wtbc1@wtbc1230.com
Editorial Profile: WNPT-FM is a commercial station owned by John Sisty Enterprises Inc. The format of the station is country. WNPT-FM broadcasts to the Linden, AL and surrounding communities at 102.9 FM.

WNPV-AM

Owner: WNPV Inc.
Editorial: 1210 Snyder Rd, Lansdale, Pennsylvania 19446. **T:** 1 215 855-8211
W: http://www.wnpv1440.com
Editorial Profile: WNPV-AM is a commercial station owned by WNPV Inc. The format of the station is news, talk and sports. WNPV-AM broadcasts to the Lansdale, PA area at 1440 AM.

WNPZ-AM

Owner: Metropolitan Management Corporation of Tennessee
Editorial: 804 N Broadway St, Knoxville, Tennessee 37917-7203. **T:** 1 865 525-5756
W: http://www.rejoice1580.com
Editorial Profile: WNPZ-AM is a commercial station owned by Metropolitan Management Corporation of Tennessee. The format of the station is black gospel. WNPZ-AM broadcasts to the Knoxville, TN area at a frequency of 1570 AM.

WNQM-AM

Owner: Robbert Broadcasting Co.(F.W.)
Editorial: 1300 Wwcr Ave, Nashville, Tennessee 37218. **T:** 1 615 255-1300
E: askwwcr@wwcr.com
W: http://www.1300wnqm.com
Editorial Profile: WNQM-AM is a commercial station owned by F.W. Robbert Broadcasting Co. The format of the station is religious. WNQM-AM broadcasts to the Nashville, TN area at 1300 AM.

WNRG-AM

Owner: Peggy Sue Broadcasting Media Inc.
Editorial: 1011 Radio Dr, Grundy, Virginia 24614. **T:** 1 276 935-7227
E: wmjd.fm@gmail.com
Editorial Profile: WNRG-AM is a commercial station owned by Peggy Sue Broadcasting Media Inc. The format of the station is gospel. WNRG-AM broadcasts to the Grundy, VA area at 940 AM.

WNRG-FM

Owner: Saga Communications
Editorial: 5407 W McKinley Ave, Milwaukee, Wisconsin 53208-2540. **T:** 1 414 978-9000
W: http://www.energy1069.com
Editorial Profile: WNRG-FM is a commercial station owned by Saga Communications. The format of the station is rhythmic contemporary. WNRG-FM broadcasts to the Milwaukee area at 106.9.

WNRI-AM

Owner: Bouchard Broadcasting Inc.
Editorial: 786 Diamond Hill Rd, Woonsocket, Rhode Island 02895-1476. **T:** 1 401 769-6925
W: http://www.wnri.com
Editorial Profile: WNRI-AM is a commercial station owned by Bouchard Broadcasting Inc. The format of the station is news and talk. WRNI-AM broadcasts to the Woonsocket, RI area at 1380 AM.

WNRJ-FM

Owner: Dailey Corp.
Editorial: 1601 Grand Central Ave, Vienna, West Virginia 26105-1082. **T:** 1 304 916-1884
E: wnrj@suddenlinkmail.com
Editorial Profile: WNRJ-FM is a commercial station owned by Dailey Corp. The format of the station is Hot AC. WNRJ-FM broadcasts to the New Martinsville, WV area at 103.9 FM.

WNRN-FM

Owner: Stu-Comm Inc.
Editorial: 2250 Old Ivy Rd, Ste 2, Charlottesville, Virginia 22903.
T: 1 434 971-4096 **E:** info@wnrn.org
W: http://www.wnrn.org
Editorial Profile: WNRN-FM is a commercial station owned by Stu-Comm Inc. The format of the station is adult album alternative and rock alternative. WNRN-FM broadcasts to the Charlottesville, VA area at 91.9 FM.

WNRP-AM

Owner: ADX Communications
Editorial: 7251 Plantation Rd, Pensacola, Florida 32504. **T:** 1 850 494-2800
E: news@newsradio1620.com

W: http://www.newsradio1620.com
Editorial Profile: WNRP-AM is a commercial station owned by ADX Communications. The format of the station is news and talk. WNRP-AM broadcasts to the Pensacola, FL area at 1620 AM.

WNRQ-FM

Owner: Clear Channel Media and Entertainment
Editorial: 55 Music Sq W, Nashville, Tennessee 37203-3207. **T:** 1 615 664-2400
E: nashvillepsa@clearchannel.com
W: http://www.1059therock.com/main.html
Editorial Profile: WNRQ-FM is a commercial station owned by Clear Channel Media and Entertainment. The format of the station is classic rock music. WNRQ-FM broadcasts to the Nashville, TN area at 105.9 FM. To send a PSA, email nashvillepsa@clearchannel.com.

WNRS-AM

Owner: Arjuna Broadcasting Corp.
Editorial: 11 Crescent St, Ilion, New York 13357-2309. **T:** 1 315 866-9200
E: wxur@hotmail.com
Editorial Profile: WNRS-AM is a commercial station owned by Arjuna Broadcasting Corp. The format of the station is oldies. WNRS-AM broadcasts to the Ilion, NY area at 1420 AM.

WNRW-FM

Owner: Clear Channel Media and Entertainment
Editorial: 4000 Radio Dr, Louisville, Kentucky 40218-4568. **T:** 1 502 479-2222
W: http://www.989radionow.com/main.html
Editorial Profile: WNRW-FM is a commercial station owned by Clear Channel Media and Entertainment. The format of the station is Top 40/CHR music. WNRW-FM broadcasts to the Louisville, KY area at 98.9 FM.

WNSC-FM

Owner: South Carolina Educational Television Commission
Editorial: ETV Radio 1101 George Rogers Blvd, Columbia, South Carolina 29201.
T: 1 803 737-3200 **W:** http://www.etvradio.org
Editorial Profile: WNSC-FM is a non-commercial station owned by South Carolina Educational Television Commission. The format of the station is news and talk. WNSC-FM broadcasts to the Columbia, SC area at 88.9 FM.

WNSH-FM

Owner: Cumulus Media Inc.
Editorial: 2 Penn Plz Fl 17, New York, New York 10121-1701. **T:** 1 212 613-8900
W: http://www.nashfm947.com
Editorial Profile: WNSH-FM is a commercial station owned by Cumulus Media. The format of the station is contemporary country. WNSH-FM broadcasts to the Newark, NJ area at 94.7 FM.

WNSL-FM

Owner: Clear Channel Media and Entertainment
Editorial: 6555 U S Highway 98, Ste 8, Hattiesburg, Mississippi 39402.
T: 1 601 296-9800 **E:** contact@sl100.com
W: http://www.sl100.com
Editorial Profile: WNSL-FM is a commercial station owned by Clear Channel Media and Entertainment. The format of the station is top 40 contemporary hit radio.

WNSN-FM

Owner: Schurz Communications Inc.
Editorial: 1301 E Douglas Rd, Mishawaka, Indiana 46545-1732. **T:** 1 574 233-3141
E: communitycalendar@wsbt.com
W: http://www.sunny1015.com
Editorial Profile: WNSN-FM is a commercial station owned by Schurz Communications Inc. The format of the station is adult contemporary. WNSN-FM broadcast to South Bend, IN at 101.5 FM.

WNSP-FM

Owner: Dot Com Plus, LLC
Editorial: 1100 Dauphin St, Mobile, Alabama 36604-2571. **T:** 1 251 438-5460
E: wnsp@wnsp.com **W:** http://www.wnsp.com
Editorial Profile: WNSP-FM is a commercial station owned by Dot Com Plus, LLC. The format of the station is sports. WNSP-FM's broadcasts to the Mobile, AL area on 105.5 FM.

WNSR-AM

Owner: Southern Wabash Communications Corp.
Editorial: 1815 Division St, Ste 110, Nashville, Tennessee 37203. **T:** 1 615 844-1039

E: info@wnsr.com **W:** http://www.wnsr.com
Editorial Profile: WNSR-AM is a commercial station owned by Southern Wabash Communications Corp. The format of the station is sports. WNSR-AM broadcasts to the Nashville, TN area at 560 AM.

WNSS-FM
Owner: Hammock Educational and Environmental Community Services
Editorial: 4 Ocean Ridge Blvd S, Palm Coast, Florida 32137-3377. **T:** 1 386 447-7108
E: wnssfm@aol.com
W: http://www.wnssfm.com
Editorial Profile: WNSS-FM is a non-commercial station owned by Hammock Educational and Environmental Community Services. The format of the station is Christian music and religious talk. WNSS-FM broadcasts to the Palm Coast, FL area at a frequency of 89.3 FM.

WNST-AM
Owner: Nasty 1570 Sports LLC
Editorial: 1550 Hart Rd, Towson, Maryland 21286-1635. **T:** 1 410 821-9678
W: http://www.wnst.net
Editorial Profile: WNST-AM is a commercial station owned by Nasty 1570 Sports LLC. The format of the station is sports. WNST-AM broadcasts to the Baltimore area at 1570 AM.

WNSV-FM
Owner: Dana Communications Corp.
Editorial: 186 E Saint Louis St, Nashville, Illinois 62263-1714. **T:** 1 618 327-4444
Editorial Profile: WNSV-FM is a commercial station owned by Dana Communications Corp. The format of the station is adult contemporary music. WNSV-FM broadcasts to the Nashville, IL area at 104.7 FM.

WNSW-AM
Owner: Multicultural Radio Broadcasting Inc.
Editorial: 27 William St, New York, New York 10005-2701. **T:** 1 212 966-1059
W: http://www.mrbi.net
Editorial Profile: WNSW-AM is a commercial station owned by Multicultural Radio Broadcasting Inc. The format of the station is Hispanic contemporary Christian. WNSW-AM broadcasts to the New York area at 1430 AM.

WNSX-FM
Owner: Stony Creek Broadcasting
Editorial: 409 High St, Ellsworth, Maine 04605-2505. **T:** 1 207 667-0002
W: http://wnsxradio.com
Editorial Profile: WNSX-FM is a commercial station owned by Stony Creek Broadcasting. The format of the station is adult contemporary. WNSX-FM broadcasts to the Bangor, ME area at 97.7 FM.

WNSY-FM
Owner: Davis Broadcasting
Editorial: 1176 Satellite Blvd Bldg., Suwanee, Georgia 30024-2868. **T:** 1 770 623-8772
E: laraza1023@hotmail.com
Editorial Profile: WNSY-FM is a commercial station owned by Davis Broadcasting. The format of the station is Hispanic Top 40/CHR. WNSY-FM broadcasts to the Suwanee, GA area at 100.1 FM.

WNTA-AM
Owner: Mid-West Family Broadcasting
Editorial: 2830 Sandy Hollow Rd, Rockford, Illinois 61109-2369. **T:** 1 815 874-7861
W: http://www.lamovidaradiorockford.com
Editorial Profile: WNTA-AM is a commercial station owned by Mid-West Family Broadcasting. The format of the station is Spanish Variety. WNTA-AM broadcasts to the Rockford, IL area at 1330 AM.

WNTB-FM
Owner: Hometown Wilmington Media
Editorial: 122 Cinema Dr, Wilmington, North Carolina 28403-1490. **T:** 1 910 772-6300
E: newsroom@sea-comm.com
W: http://gottalovethedude.com/home
Editorial Profile: WNTB-FM is a commercial station owned by Hometown Wilmington Media. The format of the station is contemporary country. WNTB-FM broadcasts to the Wilmington, NC area at 106.3 FM.

WNTC-FM
Owner: Southern Wabash Communications Corp.
Editorial: 1815 Division St, Ste 110, Nashville, Tennessee 37203. **T:** 1 615 844-1039
E: info@wnsr.com **W:** http://www.wnsr.com
Editorial Profile: WNTC-FM is a commercial station owned by Southern Wabash Communications Corp. The format of the station is sports. WNTC-FM broadcasts to the Nashville, TN area at 103.9 FM.

WNTD-AM
Owner: M&S WNTD, LLC
Editorial: 1496 Bellevue St, Green Bay, Wisconsin 54311-4205. **T:** 1 312 467-9755
E: info@relevantradio.com
W: http://www.relevantradio.com
Editorial Profile: WNTD-AM is a commercial station owned by M&S WNTD, LLC. The format of the station is Catholic talk during the day and jazz at night. WNTD-AM broadcasts to the Chicago area at 950 AM.

WNTE-FM
Owner: Mansfield University of Pennsylvania
Editorial: 85 Hemlock Dr, Mansfield, Pennsylvania 16933. **T:** 1 570 662-4653
W: http://www.wnte.com
Editorial Profile: WNTE-FM is a non-commercial station owned by Mansfield University of Pennsylvania. The format of the station is college variety. WNTE-FM broadcasts to the Mansfield, PA area at 89.5 FM.

WNTF-AM
Owner: Rama Communications Inc.
Editorial: 3765 N John Young Pkwy, Orlando, Florida 32804-3213. **T:** 1 407 293-9652
E: info@latina1580.net
W: http://www.latina1580.net
Editorial Profile: WNTF-AM is a commercial station owned by Rama Communications Inc. The format of the station is Hispanic women's talk. WNTF-AM broadcasts to the Orlando, FL area at 1580 AM.

WNTH-FM
Owner: New Trier Board of Education
Editorial: 385 Winnetka Ave, Ste 504, Winnetka, Illinois 60093. **T:** 1 847 446-7000
E: wnth@newtrier.k12.il.us
W: http://www.wnth.org
Editorial Profile: WNTH-FM is a non-commercial station owned by New Trier Board of Education. The format of the station is variety. WNTH-FM broadcasts to the Winnetka, IL area at 88.1 FM.

WNTI-FM
Owner: Centenary College
Editorial: 400 Jefferson St, Hackettstown, New Jersey 07840-2184. **T:** 1 908 979-4355
W: http://www.wnti.org
Editorial Profile: WNTI-FM is a non-commercial station owned by the Centenary College. The format of the station is a variety. WNTI-FM broadcasts in Northeast PA, and Southwest NY area at 91.9 FM.

WNTJ-AM
Owner: Forever Broadcasting
Editorial: 109 Plaza Dr, Johnstown, Pennsylvania 15905. **T:** 1 814 255-4186
W: http://www.ntjnetwork.com
Editorial Profile: WNTJ-AM is a commercial station owned by Forever Broadcasting. The format of the station is sports, news and talk. WNTJ-AM broadcasts in the Johnstown, PA area at 1490 AM.

WNTK-FM
Owner: Koor Communications
Editorial: 25 Newport Rd, New London, New Hampshire 3257. **T:** 1 603 448-0500
E: studio@wntk.com **W:** http://www.wntk.com
Editorial Profile: WNTK-FM is a commercial station owned by Koor Communications. The format of the station is news and talk. WNTK-FM broadcasts to the New London, NH area at 99.7 FM.

WNTM-AM
Owner: Clear Channel Media and Entertainment
Editorial: 555 Broadcast Dr, 3rd Fl, Mobile, Alabama 36606. **T:** 1 251 450-0100
W: http://www.newsradio710.com
Editorial Profile: WNTM-AM is a commercial station owned by Clear Channel Media and Entertainment. The format of the station is news and talk. WNTM-AM broadcasts to the Mobile, AL area at 710 AM.

WNTN-AM
Owner: Colt Communications LLC
Editorial: 143 Rumford Ave, Auburndale, Massachusetts 2466. **T:** 1 617 969-1550
W: http://www.wntn.com
Editorial Profile: WNTN-AM is a commercial station owned by Colt Communications LLC. The format of the station is variety. WNTN-AM broadcasts to the Auburndale, MA area at 1550 AM.

WNTO-FM
Owner: Sunny Broadcasting LLC
Editorial: 117 Portsmouth Rd, Gallipolis, Ohio 45631-1047. **T:** 1 740 446-3543
W: http://www.sunny93.net
Editorial Profile: WNTO-FM is a commercial station owned by Sunny Broadcasting LLC. The format of the station is hot adult contemporary. WNTO-FM broadcasts to the Gallipolis, OH, area at 93.1 FM.

WNTP-AM
Owner: Salem Communications
Editorial: 117 Ridge Pike, Lafayette Hill, Pennsylvania 19444-1901. **T:** 1 610 940-0990
E: wntp@wntp.com **W:** http://www.wntp.com
Editorial Profile: WNTP-AM is a commercial station owned by Salem Communications. The format of the station is news and talk. WNTP-AM broadcasts to the Lafayette Hill, PA area at 990 AM.

WNTQ-FM
Owner: Cumulus Media Inc.
Editorial: 1064 James St, Syracuse, New York 13203. **T:** 1 315 472-0200
W: http://www.93q.com
Editorial Profile: WNTQ-FM is a commercial station owned by Cumulus Media Inc. The format of the station is Top 40/CHR. WNTQ-FM broadcasts to the Syracuse, NY area at 93.1 FM.

WNTR-FM
Owner: Entercom Communications Corp.
Editorial: 9245 N Meridian St Ste 300, Indianapolis, Indiana 46260-1832.
T: 1 317 816-4000 **E:** indypsa@entercom.com
W: http://www.indysmix.com
Editorial Profile: WNTR-FM is a commercial station owned by Entercom Communications Corp. The format of the station is Hot AC. WNTR-FM broadcasts to the Indianapolis area at 107.9 FM.

WNTS-AM
Owner: Davidson Media Group
Editorial: 3745 W Washington St Ste 5, Indianapolis, Indiana 46241-1510.
T: 1 317 924-1071
Editorial Profile: WNTS-AM is a commercial station owned by Davidson Media Group with an LMA from Continental Broadcast Group LLC. The format of the station is regional Mexican. WNTS-AM broadcasts to the Davidson, NC area at 1590 AM.

WNTT-AM
Owner: Craft(Aileen)
Editorial: 115 Blue Top Rd, Tazewell, Tennessee 37879. **T:** 1 423 626-4203
W: http://www.wntt1250am.com
Editorial Profile: WNTT-AM is a commercial station owned by Aileen Craft. The format of the station is classic country. WNTT-AM broadcasts to the Tazewell, TN and surrounding areas at 1250 AM.

WNTW-AM
Owner: Delmarva Educational Association
Editorial: 4301 W Hundred Rd, Chester, Virginia 23831-1959. **T:** 1 804 717-2000
W: http://www.820theanswer.com
Editorial Profile: WGGM-AM is a commercial station owned by Delmarva Educational Association. The format for the station is Conservative talk. WGGM-AM broadcasts to the Chester, VA area at 820 AM.

WNTX-AM
Owner: Free Lance-Star Publishing Company
Editorial: 616 Amelia St, Fredericksburg, Virginia 22401. **T:** 1 540 374-5500
E: lapositiva1350@gmail.com
Editorial Profile: WNTX-AM is a commercial station owned by Free Lance-Star Publishing Company. The format of the station is regional Mexican and Top 40/CHR. WNTX-AM broadcasts to the Fredericksburg, VA area at 1350 AM.

WNUA-FM
Owner: Clear Channel Media and Entertainment
Editorial: 233 N Michigan Ave, Chicago, Illinois 60601-5519. **T:** 1 312 540-2000
W: http://www.955elpatron.com
Editorial Profile: WNUA-FM is a commercial station owned by Clear Channel Media and Entertainment. The format of the station is Regional Mexican music. WNUA-FM broadcasts in the Chicago area at 95.5 FM.

WNUB-FM
Owner: Norwich University
Editorial: 158 Harmon Dr, Northfield, Vermont 5663. **T:** 1 802 485-2483
E: wnub@norwich.edu
Editorial Profile: WNUB-FM is a non-commercial station owned by Norwich University. The format of the station is variety. WNUB-FM broadcasts to the Northfield, VT area on 88.3 FM.

WNUQ-FM
Owner: Cumulus Media Inc.
Editorial: 1104 W Broad Ave, Albany, Georgia 31707. **T:** 1 229 888-5000
W: http://www.q102albany.com
Editorial Profile: WNUQ-FM is a commercial station owned by Cumulus Media Inc. The format of the station is Top 40/CHR music. WNUQ-FM broadcasts to the Albany, GA area at 102.1 FM.

WNUR-FM
Owner: Northwestern University
Editorial: 1877 Campus Dr, Evanston, Illinois 60208-0887. **T:** 1 847 491-7101
W: http://www.wnur.org
Editorial Profile: WNUR-FM is a non-commercial station owned by Northwestern University. The format of the station is college variety. WNUR-FM broadcasts to the Evanston, IL area at 89.3 FM.

WNUS-FM
Owner: Clear Channel Media and Entertainment
Editorial: 6006 Grand Central Ave, Parkersburg, West Virginia 26105.
T: 1 304 295-6070 **W:** http://www.wnus.com
Editorial Profile: WNUS-FM is a commercial station owned by Clear Channel. The format of the station is contemporary country. WNUS-FM broadcasts to the Vienna, WV area at 107.1 FM.

WNVA-AM
Owner: Radio Wise, Inc.
Editorial: 214 Walnut Dr SE Gaydawn Acres, Wise, Virginia 24293-5322. **T:** 1 276 328-2244
W: http://www.wnva.net
Editorial Profile: WNVA-AM is a commercial station owned by Radio Wise, Inc. The format of the station is sports. WNVA-AM broadcasts to the Tri-Cities, TN area at 1350 AM.

WNVA-FM
Owner: Radio Wise, Inc.
Editorial: 214 Walnut Dr SE, Wise, Virginia 24293-5322. **T:** 1 276 328-2244
W: http://www.wnva.net
Editorial Profile: WNVA-FM is a commercial station owned by Radio Wise, Inc. The format of the station is adult contemporary. WNVA-FM broadcasts to the Tri-Cities, TN area at 106.3 FM.

WNVL-AM
Owner: TBLC Media, LLC
Editorial: 209 10th Ave S Ste 342, Nashville, Tennessee 37203-0758. **T:** 1 615 242-1411
E: spanishmc@activa1240.com
W: http://www.activa1240.com
Editorial Profile: WNVL-AM is a commercial station owned by TBLC Media, LLC. The format of the station is Regional Mexican music. WNVL-AM broadcasts in the Nashville, TN area at 1240 AM.

WNVR-AM
Owner: Polnet Communications
Editorial: 3656 W Belmont Ave, Chicago, Illinois 60618-5328. **T:** 1 773 588-6300
E: polskieradio@polskieradio.com
W: http://www.polskieradio.com
Editorial Profile: WNVR-AM is a commercial station owned by Polnet Communications. The format of the station is variety. WNVR-AM broadcasts to the Chicago area at 1030 AM.

WNVY-AM
Owner: Wilkins Communications Network Inc.
Editorial: 2070 N Palafox St, Pensacola, Florida 32501-2145. **T:** 1 850 432-3658
E: wnvy@wilkinsradio.com
W: http://www.wilkinsradio.com
Editorial Profile: WNVY-AM is a commercial station owned by the Wilkins Communications Network Inc. The format for the station is gospel. WNVY-AM broadcasts to the Pensacola, FL area at 1070 AM.

WNVZ-FM
Owner: Entercom Communications Corp.
Editorial: 236 Clearfield Ave, Ste 206, Virginia Beach, Virginia 23462-1893.
T: 1 757 497-2000 **W:** http://www.z104.com
Editorial Profile: WNVZ-FM is a commercial station owned by Entercom Communications Corp. The format of the station is rhythmic Top 40/CHR. WNVZ-FM broadcasts to Virginia Beach, VA at 104.5 FM.

WNWC-AM
Owner: Northwestern College
Editorial: 5606 Medical Cir, Madison, Wisconsin 53719-1204. **T:** 1 608 271-1025
E: wnwc@unwsp.edu
W: http://wnwc.nwc.edu/page.php
Editorial Profile: WNWC-AM is a non-commercial station owned by Northwestern College. The format for the station is religious. WNWC-AM broadcasts to the Madison, WI area at 1190 AM.

WNWC-FM
Owner: Northwestern College
Editorial: 5606 Medical Cir, Madison, Wisconsin 53719-1204. **T:** 1 608 271-1025
E: wnwc@unwsp.edu
W: http://wnwc.nwc.edu/page.php
Editorial Profile: WNWC-FM is a non-commercial station owned by Northwestern College. The format for the station is Christian music. WNWC-FM broadcasts to the Madison, WI area at 102.5 FM.

WNWF-AM
Owner: Andala Enterprises, Inc.
Editorial: 215 Mountain Dr Ste 104, Destin, Florida 32541-2346. **T:** 1 850 654-1718
E: wnwf@destin1120am.com
W: http://www.destin1120am.com
Editorial Profile: WNWF-AM is a commercial station owned by Andala Enterprises, Inc. The format of the station is news and talk. WNWF-AM broadcasts to the Destin, FL area at 1120 AM.

WNWI-AM
Owner: Birach Broadcasting Corp.
Editorial: 934 W 138th St, Riverdale, Illinois 60827. **T:** 1 708 201-9600
E: sima@birach.com
W: http://www.birach.com/wnwi.html
Editorial Profile: WNWI-AM is a commercial station owned by Birach Broadcasting Corp. The format of the station is a variety of ethnic programming, mostly Polish. WNWI-AM broadcasts in the greater Chicago area at 1080 AM.

WNWK-AM
Owner: EKO Media Group Inc.
Editorial: 1076 S Chapel St, Newark, Delaware 19702-1304. **T:** 1 240 481-8242
W: http://www.sabrosaradio.com
Editorial Profile: WNWK-AM is a commercial station owned by EKO Media Group Inc. The format of the station is regional Mexican. WNWK-AM broadcasts to the Dover, DE area at 1260 AM.

WNWN-AM
Owner: Midwest Communications Inc.
Editorial: 4200 W Main St, Kalamazoo, Michigan 49006-2749. **T:** 1 269 345-7121
E: amy.burrow@mwcradio.com
W: http://go955.com
Editorial Profile: WNWN-AM is a commercial station owned by the Midwest Communications Inc. The format of the station is urban contemporary. WNWN-AM broadcasts to the Kalamazoo, MI area at 1560 AM.

WNWN-FM
Owner: Midwest Communications Inc.
Editorial: 25 Michigan Ave W, Battle Creek, Michigan 49017-3610. **T:** 1 269 968-1991
E: pj.lacey@mwcradio.com
W: http://wincountry.com
Editorial Profile: WNWN-FM is a commercial station owned by the Midwest Communications Inc. The format of the station is contemporary country music. WNWN-FM broadcasts to the Battle Creek, MI area at 98.5 FM.

WNWR-AM
Owner: Global Radio LLC
Editorial: 200 Monument Rd Ste 6, Bala Cynwyd, Pennsylvania 19004-1726
W: http://www.wnwr.com
Editorial Profile: WNWR-AM is a commercial station owned by Global Radio LLC. The format of the station is variety. WNWR-AM broadcasts to the Philadelphia area at 1540 AM.

WNWS-FM
Owner: Wireless Group Inc.(The)
Editorial: 207 W Lafayette St, Jackson, Tennessee 38301-6110. **T:** 1 731 423-8316
W: http://wnws.point5digital.com:8080/p5d/servlet/contentpage?3,92, WNWS+Home
Editorial Profile: WNWS-FM is a commercial station owned by The Wireless Group Inc. The format of the station is news and talk. WNWS-FM broadcasts to the Jackson, TN area at 101.5 FM.

WNWV-FM
Owner: Rubber City Radio Group, Inc.
Editorial: 6133 Rockside Rd, Independence, Ohio 44131-2223. **T:** 1 330 869-9800
W: http://1073thewave.net
Editorial Profile: WNWV-FM is a commercial station owned by Rubber City Radio Group, Inc. The format of the station is smooth AC. WNWV-FM broadcasts to the Elyria, OH area at 107.3 FM.

WNWW-FM
Owner: Clear Channel Media and Entertainment
Editorial: 11700 Central Pkwy, Jacksonville, Florida 32224-2600. **T:** 1 904 636-0507
W: http://www.979kissfm.com/main.html
Editorial Profile: WNWW-FM is a commercial station owned by Clear Channel Media and Entertainment. The format of the station is Hot AC. WNWW-FM broadcasts to the Jacksonville, FL area at 97.9 FM.

WNWZ-AM
Owner: Townsquare Media, LLC
Editorial: 50 Monroe Ave NW Ste 500, Grand Rapids, Michigan 49503-2656.
T: 1 616 451-4800
E: vip.support@townsquaremedia.com
W: http://touch1410.com/
Editorial Profile: WNWZ-AM is a commercial station owned by Townsquare Media, LLC. The format of the station is Urban AC. WNWZ-AM broadcasts to the Grand Rapids, MI area at 1410 AM.

WNXR-FM
Owner: Heartland Communications Group, LLC
Editorial: 2320 Ellis Ave, Ashland, Wisconsin 54806. **T:** 1 715 682-2727
W: http://www.wnxrfm.com
Editorial Profile: WNXR-FM is a commercial station owned by Heartland Communications Group, LLC. The format of the station is oldies. WNXR-FM broadcasts to the Ashland, WI area at 107.3 FM.

WNXT-AM
Owner: Hometown Broadcasting
Editorial: 405 Masonic Bldg, Portsmouth, Ohio 45662. **T:** 1 740 353-1161
E: wnxtradio@yahoo.com
W: http://www.wnxtradio.com
Editorial Profile: WNXT-AM is a commercial station owned by Hometown Broadcasting. The format of the station is news, sports and talk. WNXT-AM broadcasts to Portsmouth, OH and surrounding communities at 1260 AM.

WNXT-FM
Owner: Hometown Broadcasting
Editorial: 405 Masonic Bldg, Portsmouth, Ohio 45662. **T:** 1 740 353-1161
E: wnxtnews@yahoo.com
W: http://www.wnxtradio.com
Editorial Profile: WNXT-FM is a commercial station owned by Hometown Broadcasting. The format of the station is adult contemporary. WNXT-FM broadcasts to Portsmouth, OH and surrounding communities at 99.3 FM.

WNXX-FM
Owner: Guaranty Broadcasting Company of Baton Rouge, LLC.
Editorial: 929 Government St B, Baton Rouge, Louisiana 70802-6034. **T:** 1 225 388-9898
W: http://www.1045espn.com
Editorial Profile: WNXX-FM is a commercial station owned by Guaranty Broadcasting Company of Baton Rouge, LLC. The format of the station is sports. WNXX-FM broadcasts in the Jackson, LA area at 104.5 FM.

WNYC-AM
Owner: New York Public Radio
Editorial: 160 Varick St, New York, New York 10013-1220. **T:** 1 646 829-4400
E: newsroom@wnyc.org
W: http://www.wnyc.org
Editorial Profile: WNYC-AM is a non-commercial station owned by New York Public Radio. The format of the station is news and talk. WNYC-AM broadcasts in the New York City area at 820 AM.

WNYC-FM
Owner: New York Public Radio
Editorial: 160 Varick St, New York, New York 10013-1220. **T:** 1 646 829-4400
E: newsroom@wnyc.org
W: http://www.wnyc.org
Editorial Profile: WNYC-FM is a non-commercial station owned by New York Public Radio. The format of the station is classical music, news and talk. WNYC-FM broadcasts to the New York City area at 93.9 FM.

WNYE-FM
Owner: NYC Media Group
Editorial: 112 Tillary St, Brooklyn, New York 11201. **T:** 1 212 669-7400
W: http://www.nyc.gov/radio
Editorial Profile: WNYE-FM is a non-commercial station owned by NYC Media Group. The format of the station is talk, music, news and educational programming. WNYE-FM broadcasts to New York City at 91.5 FM.

WNYG-AM
Owner: Radio Cantico Nuevo Inc.
Editorial: 449 Broadway Fl 2, New York, New York 10013-2549. **T:** 1 845 3542000
W: http://www.radiocanticonuevo.com/
Editorial Profile: WNYG-AM is a commercial station owned by Radio Cantico Nuevo Inc. The format of the station is Hispanic contemporary Christian. WNYG-AM broadcasts to the Medford, NY area at 1440 AM.

WNYM-AM
Owner: Salem Communications
Editorial: 777 Terrace Ave, Hasbrouck Heights, New Jersey 07604-3110. **T:** 1 201 298-9700
E: contact@nycradio.com
W: http://www.am970theanswer.com
Editorial Profile: WNYM-AM is a commercial station owned by Salem Communications. The format of the station is news and talk. WNYM-AM broadcasts to the New York City area at 970 AM.

WNYN-FM
Owner: Devon Broadcasting Company, Inc
Editorial: 288 S River Rd, Bedford, New Hampshire 3110. **T:** 1 603 668-6400
Editorial Profile: WNYN-FM is a commercial station owned by Devon Broadcasting Company, Inc. The format is adult contemporary. The station airs in the Bedford, NH area at 99.1 FM.

WNYO-FM
Owner: State University of New York
Editorial: 101 Campus Center, Oswego, New York 13126. **T:** 1 315 312-2101
E: wnyo@wnyo.org **W:** http://www.wnyo.org
Editorial Profile: WNYO-FM is a non-commercial station owned by the State University of New York. The format of the station is variety. WNYO-FM broadcasts to the Oswego, NY area at 88.9 FM.

WNYQ-FM
Owner: Pamal Broadcasting Ltd.
Editorial: 89 Everts Ave, Queensbury, New York 12804-2040. **T:** 1 518 793-7733
E: production@adirondackbroadcasting.com
W: http://www.classichitswnyq.com
Editorial Profile: WNYQ-FM is a commercial station owned by Pamal Broadcasting Ltd. The format of the station is classic hits. WNYQ-FM broadcasts to the Albany-Schenectady-Troy, NY area at 101.7 FM.

WNYR-FM
Owner: Lake Country Broadcasting, Inc.
Editorial: 3568 Lenox Rd, Geneva, New York 14456. **T:** 1 315 781-7000
E: wnyr@flradiogroup.com
W: http://fingerlakesdailynews.com/webpages/view/WNYR/
Editorial Profile: WNYR-FM is a commercial station owned by Lake Country Broadcasting, Inc. The format of the station is adult contemporary music. WNYR-FM broadcasts to the Geneva, NY area at 98.5 FM.

WNYU-FM
Owner: New York University
Editorial: 5 University Pl #11, New York, New York 10003-4534. **T:** 1 212 998-1660
E: general.manager@wnyu.org
W: http://www.wnyu.org
Editorial Profile: WNYU-FM is a non-commercial station owned by New York University. The format of the station is college variety. WNYU-FM broadcasts to the entire New York metro area at 89.1 FM.

WNYV-FM
Owner: Pine Tree Broadcasting Company
Editorial: 1214 Vermont Route 30 S, Poultney, Vermont 5764. **T:** 1 802 287-9031
E: wvnrwnyv@yahoo.com
Editorial Profile: WNYV-FM is a commercial station owned by Pine Tree Broadcasting Company. The format of the station is adult contemporary. WNYV-FM broadcasts to the Poultney, VT area at 94.1 FM.

WNYY-AM
Owner: Saga Communications
Editorial: 1751 Hanshaw Rd, Ithaca, New York 14850-9105. **T:** 1 607 257-6400
W: http://www.1470wnyy.com
Editorial Profile: WNYY-AM is a commercial station owned by Saga Communications. The format of the station is progressive talk. WNYY-AM broadcasts to the Ithaca, NY area at 1470 AM.

WNZF-AM
Owner: Flagler County Broadcasting, LLC
Editorial: 2405 E Moody Blvd, Ste 402, Bunnell, Florida 32110-5994.
T: 1 386 437-1992 **E:** newsradio@wnzf.com
W: http://www.wnzf.com/index.asp
Editorial Profile: WBHQ-FM is a commercial station owned by Flagler County Broadcasting, LLC. The format of the stations is news and talk. WBHQ-FM broadcasts to the Bunnell, FL area at 1550 AM.

WNZK-AM
Owner: Birach Broadcasting Corp.
Editorial: 21700 Northwestern Hwy, Ste 1190, Southfield, Michigan 48075.
T: 1 248 557-3500 **W:** http://www.birach.com
Editorial Profile: WNZK-AM is a commercial station owned by Birach Broadcasting Corp. The format of the station is variety. WNZK-AM broadcasts to the Southfield, MI area at 690 AM.

WNZN-FM
Owner: Velazquez(Milton)
Editorial: 511 W 26th St, Lorain, Ohio 44052.
T: 1 419 588-3700

WNZR-FM
Owner: Mount Vernon Nazarene University
Editorial: 800 Martinsburg Rd, Mount Vernon, Ohio 43050-9509. **T:** 1 740 392-9090
E: wnzr@mvnu.edu **W:** http://www.wnzr.fm
Editorial Profile: WNZR-FM is a non-commerical station owned by Mount Vernon Nazarene University. The format of the station is contemporary Christian music. WNZR-FM broadcasts to the Mt. Vernon, OH, area at 90.9 FM.

WNZS-AM
Owner: Waterfront Communications Inc
Editorial: 379 Riverside Dr, Eddington, Maine 04428-3115. **T:** 1 207 947-9697
E: wnzproduction@aol.com
Editorial Profile: WNZS-AM is a commercial station owned by Waterfront Communications Inc. The format of the station is News/Talk. WNZS-AM broadcasts to the Bangor, ME area at 1340 AM.

WNZZ-AM
Owner: Cumulus Media Inc.
Editorial: 1 Commerce St Ste 300, Montgomery, Alabama 36104-3542.
T: 1 334 240-9274
W: http://www.wnzz950.com
Editorial Profile: WNZZ-AM is a commercial station owned by Cumulus Media Inc. The format of the station is adult standards. WNZZ-AM broadcasts to the Montgomery, AL area at 950 AM.

WOAB-AM
Owner: Saint Joseph Missions
Editorial: 3660 State Route 30 Ste D, Latrobe, Pennsylvania 15650-4309. **T:** 1 724 640-0361
Editorial Profile: WAOB-AM is a commercial station owned by Saint Joseph Missions. The format of the station is Catholic programming. WAOB-AM broadcasts to the Pittsburgh area at 860 AM.

WOAB-FM
Owner: Ozark Broadcasting Corporation
Editorial: 982 W Highway 27, Ozark, Alabama 36360-4859. **T:** 1 334 774-5600
W: http://www.woab1049.net
Editorial Profile: WOAB-FM is a commercial station owned by Ozark Broadcasting Corporation. The format of the station is oldies music. WOAB-FM broadcasts to the Ozark, AL area at 104.9 FM.

WOAD-AM
Owner: L & L Radio
Editorial: 731 S Pear Orchard Rd Ste 27, Ridgeland, Mississippi 39157-4839.
T: 1 601 957-1300 **E:** production@wjmi.com
W: http://www.woad.com
Editorial Profile: WOAD-AM is a commercial station owned by L & L Radio. The format of the station is gospel. WOAD-AM broadcasts to the Jackson, MS area at 1300 AM.

WOAH-FM
Owner: Broadcast Executives

Editorial: 832 Elma G Miles Pkwy, Hinesville, Georgia 31313-4554. **T:** 1 912 408-1063
Editorial Profile: WOAH-FM is a commercial station owned by Broadcast Executives. The format of the station is urban contemporary. WOAH-FM broadcasts to the Hinesville, GA area at 106.3 FM.

WOAI-AM
Owner: Clear Channel Media and Entertainment
Editorial: 6222 W Interstate 10, San Antonio, Texas 78201-2013. **T:** 1 210 736-9700
E: woai@clearchannel.com
W: http://radio.woai.com/main.html
Editorial Profile: WOAI-AM is a commercial station owned by Clear Channel Media and Entertainment. The format of the station is news and talk. WOAI-AM broadcasts to the San Antonio area at 1200 AM.

WOAK-FM
Owner: Oakside Christian School
Editorial: 1921 Hamilton Rd, Lagrange, Georgia 30241-6015. **T:** 1 706 884-2950
E: woak@woak.org **W:** http://www.woak.org
Editorial Profile: WOAK-FM is a non-commercial station owned by the Oakside Christian School. The format of the station is Christian music and talk programming. WOAK-FM broadcasts to the LaGrange, GA area at 90.9 FM.

WOAM-AM
Owner: Kelly Communications Inc.
Editorial: 1 Broadcast Ctr, Plano, Illinois 60545-2100. **T:** 1 309 693-5531
Editorial Profile: WOAM-AM is a commercial station owned by Kelly Communications Inc. The format of the station is adult standards. WOAM-AM broadcasts to the Peoria, IL area at 1350 AM.

WOAP-AM
Owner: Cano's Broadcasting
Editorial: 2301 N M 52, Owosso, Michigan 48867-1142. **T:** 1 989 472-4104
W: http://www.thebig1080.com
Editorial Profile: WOAP-AM is a commercial station owned by Cano's Broadcasting. The format of the station is oldies. WOAP-AM broadcasts to the Owosso, MI area at 1080 AM.

WOAS-FM
Owner: Ontonagon Area School District
Editorial: 701 Parker Ave, Ontonagon, Michigan 49953. **T:** 1 906 884-4433
W: http://www.woas-fm.org
Editorial Profile: WOAS-FM is a non-commercial station owned by Ontonagon Area School District. The format for the station is variety. WOAS-FM broadcasts to the Marquette, MI area at 88.5 FM.

WOAY-AM
Owner: Mountaineer Media, Inc.
Editorial: 240 Central Ave, Oak Hill, West Virginia 25901. **T:** 1 304 465-0534
E: info@woayradio.com
W: http://www.woayradio.com
Editorial Profile: WOAY-AM is a commercial station owned by Mountaineer Media, Inc. The format of the station is religious and talk. WOAY-AM broadcasts to the Oak Hill, WV area at 860 AM.

WOBB-FM
Owner: Clear Channel Media and Entertainment
Editorial: 809 S Westover Blvd, Albany, Georgia 31707-4953. **T:** 1 229 439-9704
W: http://www.b100wobb.com
Editorial Profile: WOBB-FM is a commercial station owned by Clear Channel Media and Entertainment. The format of the station is country music. WOBB-FM broadcasts to the Albany, GA area at 100.3 FM.

WOBC-FM
Owner: Oberlin College
Editorial: Wilder 319, 135 W Lorain St, Oberlin, Ohio 44074. **T:** 1 440 775-8107
E: wobc@oberlin.edu **W:** http://www.wobc.org
Editorial Profile: WOBC-FM is a non-commercial station owned by Oberlin College. The format of the station is variety. WOBC-FM broadcasts to the Cleveland, OH area at 91.5 FM.

WOBE-FM
Owner: Results Broadcasting
Editorial: 212 W J St, Iron Mountain, Michigan 49801-4646. **T:** 1 906 774-5731
E: resultsproduction@gmail.com
W: http://www.classichitsb100fm.com
Editorial Profile: WOBE-FM is a commercial station owned by Results Broadcasting. The format of the station is Top 40/CHR. WOBE-FM broadcasts to the Marquette, MI area at 100.7 FM.

WOBG-FM
Owner: Burbach of WV, LLC
Editorial: 1489 Locust Ave, Fairmont, West Virginia 26554-1393. **T:** 1 304 363-8888
E: comments@rock1057.com
W: http://www.rock1057.com
Editorial Profile: WOBG-FM is a commercial station owned by Burbach of WV, LLC. The format of the station features rock music programming. WOBG-FM broadcasts to the Fairmont, WV area at 105.7 FM.

WOBL-AM
Owner: WOBL Radio Inc.
Editorial: 45624 Us Highway 20, Oberlin, Ohio 44074-9486. **T:** 1 440 774-1320
E: woblwdlw@yahoo.com
W: http://www.woblwdlw.com
Editorial Profile: WOBL-AM is a commercial station owned by WOBL Radio Inc. The format of the station is country music. WOBL-AM broadcasts in the Oberlin, OH area at 1320 AM.

WOBM-AM
Owner: Townsquare Media, LLC
Editorial: 8 Robbins St, Toms River, New Jersey 08753-7668. **T:** 1 848 221-8000
E: jerseyshorenews@wobmam.com
W: http://wobmam.com
Editorial Profile: WOBM-AM is a commercial station owned by Townsquare Media, LLC. The format of the station is news and talk. WOBM-AM broadcasts in the New York area at 1160 AM.

WOBM-FM
Owner: Townsquare Media, LLC
Editorial: 1015 Atlantic City Blvd, Bayville, New Jersey 8721. **T:** 1 732 269-0927
W: http://www.wobm.com
Editorial Profile: WOBM-FM is a commercial station owned by Townsquare Media, LLC. The format of the station features smooth adult contemporary. WOBM-FM broadcasts in the Bayville, NJ area at 92.7 FM.

WOBN-FM
Owner: Otterbein College
Editorial: Otterbein College, Westerville, Ohio 43081-2006. **T:** 1 614 823-1557
W: http://www.wobn.net
Editorial Profile: WOBN-FM is a non-commercial station owned by Otterbein College. The format of the station is adult album alternative. WOBN-FM broadcasts to the Westerville, OH area at 97.5 FM.

WOBO-FM
Owner: Educational Community Radio Inc.
Editorial: 4156 Half Acre Rd, Batavia, Ohio 45103-3250. **T:** 1 513 724-3999
W: http://www.wobofm.com
Editorial Profile: WOBO-FM is a non-commercial station owned by Educational Community Radio Inc. The format of the station is variety. WOBO-FM broadcasts to the Owensville, OH community at 88.7 FM.

WOBR-FM
Owner: East Carolina Radio Group
Editorial: 2422 S Wrightsville Ave, Nags Head, North Carolina 27959-9323.
T: 1 252 441-1024 **E:** admin@ecri.net
W: http://www.wobr.com
Editorial Profile: WOBR-FM is a commercial station owned by East Carolina Radio Group. The format of the station is rock music. WOBR-FM broadcasts to the Nags Head, NC area at 95.3 FM.

WOBT-AM
Owner: NRG Media LLC
Editorial: 3616 Highway 47, Rhinelander, Wisconsin 54501-8819. **T:** 1 715 362-1975
Editorial Profile: WOBT-AM is a commercial station owned by NRG Media LLC. The format of the station is country. WOBT-AM broadcasts to the Rhinelander, WI area at 1240 AM.

WOBX-AM
Owner: East Carolina Radio Group
Editorial: 3855 Mills Landing Road, Wanchese, North Carolina 27981.
T: 1 252 441-1024
Editorial Profile: WOBX-AM is a commercial station owned by East Carolina Radio Group. The format of the station is Southern Gospel. WOBX-AM broadcasts to Wanchese, NC at 1530 AM.

WOBX-FM
Owner: East Carolina Radio Group
Editorial: 2422 S Wrightsville Ave, Nags Head, North Carolina 27959-9323.
T: 1 252 441-1024
Editorial Profile: WOBX-FM is a commercial station owned by East Carolina Radio Group. The format of the station is variety. WOBX-FM broadcasts to the Nags Head, NC area at 98.1 FM.

WOCA-AM
Owner: Westshore Broadcasting Inc.
Editorial: 1515 E Silver Springs Blvd Ste 134, Ocala, Florida 34470-6830. **T:** 1 352 732-8000
W: http://thesource1370.com
Editorial Profile: WOCA-AM is a commercial station owned by Westshore Broadcasting Inc. The format of the station is news and talk. WOCA-AM broadcasts to the Ocala, FL area at 1370 AM.

WOC-AM
Owner: Clear Channel Media and Entertainment
Editorial: 3535 E Kimberly Rd, Davenport, Iowa 52807. **T:** 1 563 344-7000
W: http://www.woc1420.com
Editorial Profile: WOC-AM is a commercial station owned by Clear Channel Media and Entertainment. The format of the station is news and talk. WOC-AM broadcasts to the Davenport, IA area at 1420 AM.

WOCC-AM
Owner: Brabandt(Richard)
Editorial: 211 N Capitol Ave, Corydon, Indiana 47112-1142. **T:** 1 812 738-9622
W: http://www.woccradio.com
Editorial Profile: WOCC-AM is a commercial station owned by Richard Brabandt. The format of the station is oldies music. WOCC-AM broadcasts to the Corydon, IN area at 1550 AM.

WOCE-FM
Owner: North Georgia Radio Group
Editorial: 613 Silver Cir, Dalton, Georgia 30721-4551. **T:** 1 706 278-5511
E: quebuena@ngaradio.com
W: http://www.quebuena1019.com
Editorial Profile: WOCE-FM is a commercial station owned by North Georgia Radio Group. The format of the station is Hispanic programming. WOCE-FM broadcasts to the Dalton, GA area at 101.9 FM.

WOCL-FM
Owner: CBS Radio
Editorial: 1800 Pembrook Dr, Ste 400, Orlando, Florida 32810. **T:** 1 407 919-1000
W: http://www.sunny1059.com
Editorial Profile: WOCL-FM is a commercial station owned by CBS Radio. The format of the station is classic hits. WOCL-FM broadcasts to the Orlando, FL area at 105.9 FM.

WOCM-FM
Owner: More(Leighton)
Editorial: 117 49th St, Ocean City, Maryland 21842. **T:** 1 410 723-3683
W: http://www.irieradio.com
Editorial Profile: WOCM-FM is a commercial station owned by Leighton More. The format of the station is adult album alternative music. WOCM-FM broadcasts to the Ocean City, MD area at 98.1 FM.

WOCN-AM
Owner: DM FL Licensee, LLC
Editorial: 350 NE 71st St, Miami, Florida 33138. **T:** 1 305 759-7280
Editorial Profile: WOCN-AM is a commercial station owned by DM FL Licensee, LLC. The format of the station is Hispanic talk and tropical music. WOCN-AM broadcasts to the Miami area at 1450 AM.

WOCN-FM
Owner: Cape Cod Broadcasting
Editorial: 737 W Main St, Hyannis, Massachusetts 02601-3422.
T: 1 508 771-1224
E: news@capecodbroadcasting.com
W: http://www.ocean1047.com
Editorial Profile: WOCN-FM is a commercial station owned by Cape Cod Broadcasting. The format of the station is Lite Rock/Lite AC. WOCN-FM broadcasts to the Hyannis, MA area at 104.7 FM.

WOCO-AM
Owner: Lamardo Inc.
Editorial: 3829 State Highway 22, Oconto, Wisconsin 54153. **T:** 1 920 834-3540
E: woco@centurytel.net
Editorial Profile: WOCO-AM is a commercial station owned by Larmardo Inc. The format of the station is classic country. WOCO-AM broadcasts to the Oconto, WI area at 1260 AM.

WOCO-FM
Owner: Lamardo Inc.
Editorial: 3829 State Highway 22, Oconto, Wisconsin 54153. **T:** 1 920 834-3540
E: woco@centurytel.net
Editorial Profile: WOCO-FM is a commercial station owned by Larmardo Inc. The format of the station is oldies and lite AC. WOCO-FM broadcasts to the Oconto, WI area at 107.1 AM.

WOCQ-FM
Owner: Great Scott Broadcasting
Editorial: 20200 Dupont Blvd, Georgetown, Delaware 19947. **T:** 1 302 856-2567
W: http://www.oc104.com
Editorial Profile: WOCQ-FM is a commercial station owned by Great Scott Broadcasting. The format of the station is urban contemporary music. WOCQ-FM broadcasts to the Salisbury, MD area at 103.9 FM.

WOCV-AM
Owner: Oneida Broadcasters Inc.
Editorial: 1126 Buffalo Rd, Oneida, Tennessee 37841. **T:** 1 423 569-8598
E: wbnt@highland.net
W: http://www.hive105.com
Editorial Profile: WOCV-AM is a commercial station owned by Oneida Broadcasters Inc. The format of the station is country and adult contemporary music and news. WOCV-AM broadcasts to the Oneida, TN area at 1310 AM.

WOCY-FM
Owner: 3G Broadcasting, Inc.
Editorial: 200-B Reid Avenue, Port St. Joe, Florida 32456. **T:** 1 850 705-1065
Editorial Profile: WOCY-FM is a commercial station owned by 3G Broadcasting, Inc. The format of the station is sports. WOCY-FM is licensed to Carrabelle, FL and broadcasts locally at 106.5 FM.

WODE-FM
Owner: Connoisseur Media
Editorial: 107 Paxinosa Rd W, Easton, Pennsylvania 18040-1344. **T:** 1 610 258-6155
W: http://www.999thehawk.com
Editorial Profile: WODE-FM is a commercial station owned by Connoisseur Media. The format of the station is classic hits. WODE-FM broadcasts to the Easton, PA area at 99.9 FM.

WODI-AM
Owner: JKC Media Ventures, LLC
Editorial: 1230 Radio Rd, Brookneal, Virginia 24528-3141. **T:** 1 434 376-1230
W: http://1230thefan.newstalk.fm
Editorial Profile: WODI-AM is a commercial station owned by JKC Media Ventures, LLC and programmed by Dot FM Group, LLC. The format of the station is sports talk. WODI-AM broadcasts to the Brookneal, VA area at 1230 AM.

WODR-FM
Owner: Padner Group, LLC
Editorial: 126 Memory Plz, Whiteville, North Carolina 28472-2640. **T:** 1 910 642-2005
W: http://www.coolbeach1053.com
Editorial Profile: WODR-FM is a commercial station owned by Padner Group, LLC. The format of the station is oldies and music focusing on beaches and beach lifestyle. WODR-FM broadcasts to the Wilmington, NC area at 105.3 FM.

WODS-FM
Owner: CBS Radio
Editorial: 83 Leo M Birmingham Pkwy, Boston, Massachusetts 02135-1101.
T: 1 617 787-7500
W: http://1033ampradio.cbslocal.com
Editorial Profile: WODS-FM is a commercial station owned by CBS Radio. The format of the station is Top 40. WODS-FM broadcasts to the Boston area at 103.3 FM.

WODT-AM
Owner: Clear Channel Media and Entertainment
Editorial: 929 Howard Ave, New Orleans, Louisiana 70113-1148. **T:** 1 504 679-7300
Editorial Profile: WODT-AM is a commercial station owned by Clear Channel Media and Entertainment. The format of the station is gospel. WODT-AM broadcasts to the New Orleans area at 1280 AM.

WODX-FM
Owner: Clear Channel Media and Entertainment
Editorial: 1700 HSBC Plaza, 100 Chestnut St., Rochester, New York 14604.
T: 1 585 454-4884
W: http://www.oldiesrochester.com
Editorial Profile: WODX-FM is a commercial station owned by Clear Channel Media and Entertainment. The format of the station is oldies music. WODX-FM broadcasts to the Rochester, NY area at 107.3 FM.

WODY-AM
Owner: Base Communications, Inc.
Editorial: 1675 Grandview Rd, Martinsville, Virginia 24112-2319. **T:** 1 276 638-5235
W: http://www.southsidesportsmedia.com
Editorial Profile: WODY-AM is a commercial station owned by Base Communications, Inc. The format of the station is sports. WODY-AM broadcasts to the Martinsville, VA area at 1160 AM.

WODZ-FM
Owner: Townsquare Media, LLC.
Editorial: 9418 River Rd, Marcy, New York 13403-2071. **T:** 1 315 768-9500
W: http://961wodz.com
Editorial Profile: WODZ-FM is a commercial station owned by Townsquare Media, LLC. The format of the station is oldies. WODZ-FM broadcasts to the Utica, NY area at 96.1 FM.

WOEG-AM
Owner: TeleSouth Communications Inc.
Editorial: 110 W Monticello St, Brookhaven, Mississippi 39601. **T:** 1 601 587-9363
Editorial Profile: WOEG-AM is a commercial station owned by TeleSouth Communications Inc. The format of the station is gospel. WOEG-AM broadcasts to the Brookhaven, MS area at 1220 AM.

WOEL-FM
Owner: Maryland Baptist Bible College & Acad.
Editorial: 3141 Old Elk Neck Rd, Elkton, Maryland 21921. **T:** 1 410 392-3225
W: http://www.mbcmin.org/woel/

WOEN-AM
Owner: Pembrook Pines Media Group
Editorial: 231 N Union St, Olean, New York 14760-2663. **T:** 1 716 375-1015
E: mixtraffic@roadrunner.com
W: http://www.newstalkwoen.com
Editorial Profile: WOEN-AM is a commercial station owned by Pembrook Pines Media Group. The format of the station is Adult Standards. WOEN-AM broadcasts to the Olean, NY area at 1360 AM.

WOEZ-FM
Editorial: 1356 Mackinaw Ave, Cheboygan, Michigan 49721-1003. **T:** 1 231 627-2341
W: http://www.wqez.fm
Editorial Profile: WOEZ-FM is a commercial station owned by Northern Star Broadcasting LLC. The format of the station is soft adult contemporary. WOEZ-FM broadcasts to Cheboygan, MI area at 106.3 FM.

WOFC-AM
Owner: Forever Communications Inc.
Editorial: 1500 Diuguid Dr, Murray, Kentucky 42071. **T:** 1 270 753-2400
W: http://www.1130theoffice.com
Editorial Profile: WOFC-AM is a commercial station owned by Forever Communications Inc. The format of the station is sports. WOFC-AM broadcasts to the Murray, KY area at 1130 AM.

WOFX-AM
Owner: Clear Channel Media and Entertainment
Editorial: 1203 Troy Schenectady Rd, Latham, New York 12110-1046. **T:** 1 518 452-4800
E: wofx@clearchannel.com
W: http://www.foxsports980.com
Editorial Profile: WOFX-AM is a commercial station owned by Clear Channel Media and Entertainment. The format of the station is sports. WOFX-AM broadcasts to the Latham, NY area at 980 AM.

WOFX-FM
Owner: Cumulus Media Inc.
Editorial: 4805 Montgomery Rd Ste 300, Cincinnati, Ohio 45212-2280.
T: 1 513 241-9898
E: feedback@cincyradio.com
W: http://www.foxcincinnati.com
Editorial Profile: WOFX-FM is a commercial station owned by Cumulus Media Inc. The format of the station is classic rock music. WOFX-FM broadcasts to the Cincinnati area at 92.5 FM.

WOGB-FM
Owner: Cumulus Media Inc.
Editorial: 810 Victoria St, Green Bay, Wisconsin 54302. **T:** 1 920 468-4100
E: wogb@cumulus.com **W:** http://wogb.fm
Editorial Profile: WOGB-FM is a commercial station owned by Cumulus Media. Inc. The format of the station is classic hits. WOGB-FM broadcasts to the Green Bay, WI area at 103.1 FM.

WOGG-FM
Owner: Keymarket of Pennsylvania, LLC
Editorial: 123 Blaine Rd, Brownsville, Pennsylvania 15417-9330. **T:** 1 724 938-2000
W: http://www.froggyland.com
Editorial Profile: WOGG-FM is a commercial station owned by Keymarket of Pennsylvania, LLC. The format of the station is contemporary country. WOGG-FM broadcasts to the Brownsville, PA area at 94.9 FM.

WOGH-FM
Owner: Keymarket of Ohio, LLC
Editorial: 320 Market St, Steubenville, Ohio 43952. **T:** 1 740 283-4747
W: http://www.froggyland.com
Editorial Profile: WOGH-FM is a commercial station owned by Keymarket of Ohio, LLC. The format of the station is contemporary country. WOGH-FM broadcasts to the Wheeling, WV and Steubenville, OH areas at 103.5 FM.

WOGI-FM
Owner: Keymarket of Pennsylvania, LLC
Editorial: 131 Pleasant Dr Ste 5U, Aliquippa, Pennsylvania 15001-1300. **T:** 1 724 3781271
W: http://www.froggyland.com
Editorial Profile: WOGI-FM is a commercial station owned by Keymarket of Pennsylvania, LLC. The format of the station is contemporary country. WOGI-FM broadcasts to the Pittsburgh area at 104.3 FM.

WOGK-FM
Owner: Ocala Broadcasting Corp. LLC
Editorial: 3602 NE 20th Pl, Ocala, Florida 34470-4957. **T:** 1 352 622-5600
E: kcountrynews@aol.com
W: http://www.937kcountry.com
Editorial Profile: WOGK-FM is a commercial station owned by Ocala Broadcasting Corp. LLC. The format of the station is country. WOGK-FM broadcasts to the Ocala, FL area at 93.7 FM.

WOGL-FM
Owner: CBS Radio
Editorial: 2 Bala Plz Ste 800, Bala Cynwyd, Pennsylvania 19004-1515. **T:** 1 610 668-5900
E: questions@wogl.com
W: http://wogl.cbslocal.com
Editorial Profile: WOGL-FM is commercial station owned by CBS Radio. The format of the station is classic hits music. WOGL-FM broadcasts to the Philadelphia area at 98.1 FM.

WOGO-AM
Owner: Stewards of Sound Inc.
Editorial: 2396 Hallie Rd, Ste 1, Chippewa Falls, Wisconsin 54729-7519.
T: 1 715 723-1037 **E:** wogo@wogo.com
W: http://www.wogo.com
Editorial Profile: WOGO-AM is a commercial station owned by Stewards of Sound Inc. The format of the station is news, sports and talk. WOGO-AM broadcasts to the Chippewa Falls, WI area at 680 AM.

WOGR-AM
Owner: Victory Christian Center
Editorial: 1501 Carrier Dr, Charlotte, North Carolina 28216. **T:** 1 704 393-1540
E: info@wordnet.org
W: http://www.wordnet.org
Editorial Profile: WOGR-AM is a non-commercial station owned by the Victory Christian Center. The format of the station is urban contemporary gospel music. WOGR-AM broadcasts to the Charlotte, NC area at 1540 AM.

WOGR-FM
Owner: Victory Christian Center
Editorial: 1501 Carrier Dr, Charlotte, North Carolina 28216. **T:** 1 704 393-1540
E: info@wordnet.org
W: http://www.wordnet.org
Editorial Profile: WOGR-FM is a non-commercial station owned by Victory Christian Center. The format of the station is gospel music. WOGR-FM broadcasts to the Charlotte, NC area at 93.3 FM.

WOGT-FM
Owner: Cumulus Media Inc.
Editorial: 821 Pineville Rd, Chattanooga, Tennessee 37405-2601. **T:** 1 423 756-6141
W: http://1079bigfm.com
Editorial Profile: WOGT-FM is a commercial station owned by Cumulus Media Inc. The format of the station is oldies. WOGT-FM broadcasts to the Chattanooga, TN area at 107.9 FM.

WOGY-FM
Owner: Forever Communications Inc.
Editorial: 122 Radio Rd, Jackson, Tennessee 38301. **T:** 1 731 427-3316
W: http://www.froggy1041.com
Editorial Profile: WOGY-FM is a commercial station owned by Forever Communications Inc. The format of the station is classic and contemporary country music. WOGY-FM broadcasts to the Jackson, TN area at 104.1 FM.

WOHF-FM
Owner: BAS Broadcasting
Editorial: 1281 N River Rd, Fremont, Ohio 43420. **T:** 1 419 332-8218
W: http://www.wohfradio.com
Editorial Profile: WOHF-FM is a commercial station owned by BAS Broadcasting. The format of the station is oldies. WOHF-FM broadcasts to the Toledo, OH area at 92.1 FM.

WOHI-AM
Owner: Keymarket of Pennsylvania, LLC
Editorial: 131 Pleasant Dr, Ste 5U, Aliquippa, Pennsylvania 15001. **T:** 1 866 586-2338
Editorial Profile: WOHI-AM is a commercial station owned by Keymarket of Pennsylvania, LLC. The format of the station is classic rock. WOHI-AM broadcasts to the Aliquippa, PA area at 1490 AM.

WOHS-AM
Owner: HRN Broadcasting Inc.
Editorial: 1511 W Dixon Blvd, Shelby, North Carolina 28152-5033. **T:** 1 704 482-1390
E: info@realcountry1390.com
W: http://www.hrnb.com
Editorial Profile: WOHS-AM is a commercial station owned by HRN Broadcasting Inc. The format of the station is classic and contemporary country. WOHS-AM broadcasts to the Lincolnton, NC area at 1390 AM.

WOHT-FM
Owner: Century Broadcasting
Editorial: 157 Dowdle Rd, Grenada, Mississippi 38901. **T:** 1 662 294-1448
E: star92@cableone.net

WOI-AM
Owner: Iowa State University
Editorial: 2111 Grand Ave Ste 100, Des Moines, Iowa 50312-5393. **T:** 1 515 725-1700
E: info@iowapublicradio.org
W: http://www.iowapublicradio.org
Editorial Profile: WOI-AM is a non-commercial station owned by Iowa State University. The format of the station is news and talk. WOI-AM broadcasts to the greater Des Moines, IA area at 640 AM.

WOIC-AM
Owner: L & L Broadcasting
Editorial: 1900 Pineview Dr, Columbia, South Carolina 29209-5079. **T:** 1 803 695-8600
W: http://www.espncolumbia.com
Editorial Profile: WOIC-AM is a commercial station owned by L & L Broadcasting. The format of the station is sports. WOIC-AM broadcasts to the Columbia, SC area at 1230 AM.

WOI-FM
Owner: Iowa State University
Editorial: 2111 Grand Ave Ste 100, Des Moines, Iowa 50312-5393. **T:** 1 515 725-1700
E: info@iowapublicradio.org
W: http://www.iowapublicradio.org
Editorial Profile: WOI-FM is a non-commercial station owned by Iowa State University. The format of the station is classical and jazz music. WOI-FM broadcasts to the greater Ames, IA area at 90.1 FM.

WOJB-FM
Owner: Lac Courte Oreilles Ojibwe Reservation
Editorial: 13386 W Trepania Rd, Hayward, Wisconsin 54843-2186. **T:** 1 715 634-2100
E: wojbfm@wojb.org **W:** http://www.wojb.org
Editorial Profile: WOJB-FM is a non-commercial station owned by the Lac Courte Oreilles Ojibwe Community College. The format of the station is variety. WOJB-FM broadcasts in the Hayward, WI area at 88.9 FM.

WOJC-FM
Owner: Calvary Chapel of Costa Mesa, Inc.
Editorial: 150 Lincolnway, Ste 2001, Valparaiso, Indiana 46383-5556.
T: 1 219 548-5800
E: info@calvaryradionet.com
W: http://www.calvaryradionetwork.com
Editorial Profile: WOJC-FM is a non-commercial station owned by Calvary Chapel of Costa Mesa, Inc. The format of the station is Christian music and religious programming. WOJC-FM broadcasts to the Crothersville, IN area at 89.7 FM.

WOJG-FM
Owner: Shaw's Broadcasting
Editorial: 123 W Market St, Bolivar, Tennessee 38008-2325. **T:** 1 731 658-3690
W: http://www.wojg.com
Editorial Profile: WOJG-FM is a commercial station owned by Shaw's Broadcasting. The format of the station is gospel. WOJG-FM broadcasts to the Bolivar, TN, area at 94.7 FM.

WOJL-FM
Owner: Piedmont Communications Inc.
Editorial: 207 Spicers Mill Rd, Orange, Virginia 22960. **T:** 1 540 967-1142
W: http://1055samfm.com
Editorial Profile: WOJL-FM is a commercial station owned by Piedmont Communications Inc. The format of the station is adult hits music. WOJL-FM broadcasts to the Orange, VA area at 105.5 FM.

WOJO-FM
Owner: Univision Communications Inc.
Editorial: 625 N Michigan Ave Ste 300, Chicago, Illinois 60611-3110.
T: 1 312 981-1800
W: http://quebuenachicago.univision.com
Editorial Profile: WOJO-FM is a commercial station owned by Univision Communications Inc. The format of the station is regional Mexican music. WOJO-FM broadcasts to the Chicago area at 105.1 FM.

WOKA-AM
Owner: Coffee County Broadcasters
Editorial: 1310 Walker St W, Douglas, Georgia 31533-7952. **T:** 1 912 384-8153
E: production1067@gmail.com

WOKA-FM
Owner: Coffee County Broadcasters
Editorial: 1310 Walker St W, Douglas, Georgia 31533-7952. **T:** 1 912 384-8153
W: http://www.dixiecountry.com
Editorial Profile: WOKA-FM is a commercial station owned by Coffee County Broadcasters. The format of the station is classic country. WOKA-FM broadcasts to the Douglas, GA area at 106.7 FM.

WOKB-AM
Owner: Rama Communications Inc.
Editorial: 3765 N John Young Pkwy, Orlando, Florida 32804. **T:** 1 407 293-9652
E: info@wokbradio.com
W: http://www.wokbradio.com
Editorial Profile: WOKB-AM is a commercial station owned by Rama Communications Inc. The format of the station is gospel. WOKB-AM broadcasts to the Orlando, FL area at 1600 AM.

WOKC-AM
Owner: Glades Media Co.
Editorial: 210 W. North Park St, Ste 102, Okeechobee, Florida 34972.
T: 1 863 467-1570 **E:** wokc@gladesmedia.com
W: http://www.wokc.com
Editorial Profile: WOKC-AM is a commercial station owned by Glades Media Co. The format of the station is classic and contemporary country. WOKC-AM broadcasts to the area of Okeechobee, FL area at 1570 AM.

WOKD-FM
Owner: Positive Alternative Radio
Editorial: 22226 Timberlake Rd, Lynchburg, Virginia 24502. **T:** 1 540 774-9798
E: office@spiritfm.com
W: http://www.spiritfm.com

WOKE-FM
Owner: Big River Radio, Inc.
Editorial: 303 8th St, Point Pleasant, West Virginia 25550-1209. **T:** 1 304 675-2763
Editorial Profile: WOKE-FM is a commercial station owned by Big River Radio, Inc. The format of the station is Contemporary Christian music. WOKE-FM broadcasts to the Huntington, WV area at a frequency of 98.3 FM.

WOKH-FM

Owner: Choice Radio Corporation
Editorial: 253 W Main St, Lebanon, Kentucky 40033-1240. **T:** 1 502 348-1027
W: http://www.1027wysb.com
Editorial Profile: WOKH-FM is a commercial station owned by Choice Radio Corporation. The format of the station is Lite Rock/Lite AC. WOKH-FM broadcasts to the Bardstown, KY area at 102.7 FM.

WOKI-FM

Owner: Cumulus Media Inc.
Editorial: 4711 Old Kingston Pike, Knoxville, Tennessee 37919. **T:** 1 865 588-6511
W: http://987newstalk.com
Editorial Profile: WOKI-FM is a commercial station owned by Cumulus Media Inc. The format of the station is news/talk. WOKI-FM broadcasts to the Knoxville, TN area at 98.7 FM.

WOKK-FM

Owner: Mississippi Broadcasters, LLC
Editorial: 3436 Highway 45 N, Meridian, Mississippi 39301-1509. **T:** 1 601 693-2661
E: onair@wokk.com **W:** http://www.wokk.com
Editorial Profile: WOKK-FM is a commercial station owned by Mississippi Broadcasters, LLC. The format for the station is contemporary country. WOKK-FM broadcasts to the Meridian, MS area at 97.1 FM.

WOKN-FM

Owner: Pembrook Pines Media Group
Editorial: 1705 Lake St, Elmira, New York 14901-1220. **T:** 1 607 733-5626
E: ppinesmedia1@stny.rr.com
W: http://995woknelmira.com
Editorial Profile: WOKN-FM is a commercial station owned by Pembrook Pines Media Group. The format of the station is contemporary country music. WOKN-FM broadcasts to the Elmira, NY area at 99.5 FM.

WOKO-FM

Owner: Hall Communications
Editorial: 70 Joy Dr, South Burlington, Vermont 5403. **T:** 1 802 658-1230
E: woko@hallradio.com
W: http://www.woko.com
Editorial Profile: WOKO-FM is a commercial station owned by Hall Communications. The format of the station is Contemporary Country music. WOKO-FM broadcasts to the South Burlington, VT area at 98.9 FM.

WOKQ-FM

Owner: Townsquare Media
Editorial: 292 Middle Rd, Dover, New Hampshire 03820-4901. **T:** 1 603 749-9750
E: news@wokq.com **W:** http://www.wokq.com
Editorial Profile: WOKQ-FM is a commercial station owned by Townsquare Media. The format of the station is contemporary country music. WOKQ-FM broadcasts to the Dover, NH area at 97.5 FM.

WOKR-FM

Owner: Educational Media Foundation
Editorial: 1701 Westchester Dr Ste 350, High Point, North Carolina 27262-7248.
T: 1 888 937-2471 **W:** http://www.klove.com
Editorial Profile: WOKR-FM is a commercial station owned by Educational Media Foundation. The format of the station is Christian rock music. WOKR-FM broadcasts to the Remsen, NY area at 93.5 FM.

WOKS-AM

Owner: Davis Broadcasting
Editorial: 2203 Wynnton Rd, Columbus, Georgia 31906. **T:** 1 706 576-3565
W: http://www.1340woks.com
Editorial Profile: WOKS-AM is a commercial station owned by Davis Broadcasting. The format of the station is gospel and oldies. WOKS-AM broadcasts to the Columbus, GA area at 1340 AM.

WOKV-AM

Owner: Cox Media Group, Inc.
Editorial: 8000 Belfort Pkwy, Jacksonville, Florida 32256. **T:** 1 904 245-8500
W: http://wokv.com
Editorial Profile: WOKV-AM is a commercial station owned by Cox Media Group, Inc. The format of the station is news, sports and talk. WOKV-AM broadcasts to the Jacksonville, FL area at 690 AM.

WOKV-FM

Owner: Cox Media Group, Inc.
Editorial: 8000 Belfort Pkwy, Jacksonville, Florida 32256-6934. **T:** 1 904 245-8500
W: http://www.wokv.com

Editorial Profile: WOKV-FM-FM is a commercial station owned by Cox Media Group, Inc. The station's format is news/talk. WOKV-FM broadcasts to the Jacksonville, FL area at 104.5 FM.

WOKW-FM

Owner: Harley(Mark E.)
Editorial: 712 River Rd, Clearfield, Pennsylvania 16830. **T:** 1 814 765-4955
E: news@wokw.com **W:** http://www.wokw.com
Editorial Profile: WOKW-FM is a commercial station owned by Mark E. Harley. The format of the station is adult contemporary music. WOWK-FM broadcasts to the Clearfield, PA area at 102.9 FM.

WOKY-AM

Owner: Clear Channel Media and Entertainment
Editorial: 12100 W Howard Ave, Greenfield, Wisconsin 53228-1851. **T:** 1 414 545-8900
W: http://www.thebig920.com
Editorial Profile: WOKY-AM is a commercial station owned by Clear Channel Media and Entertainment. The format of the station is classic country. WOKY-AM broadcasts to the Milwaukee area at 920 AM.

WOL-AM

Owner: Radio One Inc.
Editorial: 5900 Princess Garden Pkwy, 8th Fl, Lanham, Maryland 20706. **T:** 1 301 306-1111
W: http://woldcnews.com/
Editorial Profile: WOL-AM is a commercial station owned by Radio One Inc. The format of the station is African-American news, business, and general interest talk. WOL-AM broadcasts to the Washington D.C. area at 1450 AM.

WOLB-AM

Owner: Radio One Inc.
Editorial: 1705 Whitehead Rd, Baltimore, Maryland 21207-4033. **T:** 1 410 332-8200
W: http://www.wolb1010.com
Editorial Profile: WOLB-AM is a commercial station owned by Radio One Inc. The format of the station is news and talk. WOLB-AM broadcasts in the Baltimore area at 1010 AM.

WOLC-FM

Owner: Marantha, Inc.
Editorial: 11890 Crisfield Lane, Princess Anne, Maryland 21853-2114. **T:** 1 410 543-9652
E: wolc@wolc.org **W:** http://www.wolc.org
Editorial Profile: WOLC-FM is a non-commercial station owned by Maranatha, Inc. The format of the station is Christian talk and music. WOLC-FM broadcasts in the Princess Anne, MD area at 102.5 FM.

WOLD-FM

Owner: T.E.C. 2 Broadcasting, Inc.
Editorial: 114 W Main St, Marion, Virginia 24354-2514. **T:** 1 276 783-4042
W: http://www.1025therenegade.com
Editorial Profile: WOLD-FM is a commercial station owned by T.E.C. 2 Broadcasting, Inc. The format for the station is adult contemporary. WOLD-FM broadcasts to the Marion, VA area at 102.5 FM.

WOLF-FM

Owner: Foxfur Communications
Editorial: 401 W Kirkpatrick St, Syracuse, New York 13204. **T:** 1 315 472-0222
W: http://www.wolf1051.com
Editorial Profile: WOLF-FM is a commercial station owned by Foxfur Communications. The format is contemporary country. WOLF-FM broadcasts to the Syracuse, NY area at 105.1 FM.

WOLG-FM

Owner: Covenant Network
Editorial: 4424 Hampton Ave, Saint Louis, Missouri 63109. **T:** 1 314 752-7000
E: covenantnetwork@juno.com
W: http://www.covenantnet.net
Editorial Profile: WOLG-FM is a non-commercial station owned by the Covenant Network. The format of the station is religious music and talk. WOLG-FM broadcasts in the St. Louis area at 95.9 FM.

WOLH-AM

Owner: Miller Communications Inc.
Editorial: 2423 Walker Swinton Rd, Timmonsville, South Carolina 29161-9351.
T: 1 843 678-9393 **E:** production@miller.fm
W: http://www.miller.fm
Editorial Profile: WOLH-AM is a commercial station owned by Miller Communications Inc. The format of the station is sports. WOLH-AM broadcasts to the Florence, SC area at 1230 AM.

WOLI-AM

Owner: Davidson Media Group
Editorial: 225 S Pleasantburg Dr, Greenville, South Carolina 29607-2544.
T: 1 864 751-0113
W: http://www.woli-am.com
Editorial Profile: WOLI-AM is a commercial station owned by Davidson Media Group. The format for the station is oldies and local sports. WOLI-AM broadcasts to the Greenville/Spartanburg, SC areas at 910 AM.

WOLL-FM

Owner: Clear Channel Media and Entertainment
Editorial: 3071 Continental Dr, West Palm Beach, Florida 33407-3274. **T:** 1 561 616-6600
W: http://www.kool1055.com
Editorial Profile: WOLL-FM is a commercial station owned by Clear Channel Media and Entertainment. The format of the station is oldies. WOLL-FM broadcasts to the West Palm Beach, FL area at 105.5 FM.

WOLS-FM

Owner: Norsan Group
Editorial: 4801 E Independence Blvd, Ste 815, Charlotte, North Carolina 28212-5490.
T: 1 704 405-3172
W: http://www.larazalaraza.com
Editorial Profile: WNMX-FM is a commercial station owned by Norsan Group. The format of the station is regional Mexican WNMX-FM broadcasts to the Charlotte, NC area at 106.1 FM.

WOLT-FM

Owner: Caron Broadcasting, LLC
Editorial: 225 S Pleasantburg Dr, Greenville, South Carolina 29607-2544.
T: 1 864 751-0113
W: http://www.wolt-fm.com/wolt-fm.html
Editorial Profile: WOLT-FM is a commercial station owned by Caron Broadcasting, LLC. The format of the station is classic hits. WOLT-FM broadcasts to the Greenville, SC area at 103.3 FM.

WOLV-FM

Owner: Houghton Community Broadcasting Corporation
Editorial: 313 E Montezuma Ave, Houghton, Michigan 49931-2112. **T:** 1 906 482-7700
E: houghtonradio@up.net
W: http://www.thewolf.com
Editorial Profile: WOLV-FM is a commercial station owned by Houghton Community Broadcasting Corporation. The format of the station is classic hits. WOLV-FM broadcasts to the Houghton, MI area at 97.7 FM.

WOLW-FM

Owner: Northern Christian Radio
Editorial: 1511 E M 32, Gaylord, Michigan 49735-9702. **T:** 1 989 732-6274
E: studio@ncradio.org
W: http://www.ncradio.org
Editorial Profile: WOLW-FM is a non-commercial station owned by Northern Christian Radio. The format of the station is contemporary Christian and religious programming. WOLW-FM broadcasts to the Gaylord, MI area at 91.1 FM.

WOLX-FM

Owner: Entercom Communications Corp.
Editorial: 7601 Ganser Way, Madison, Wisconsin 53719-2074. **T:** 1 608 826-0077
E: wolx@entercom.com
W: http://www.wolx.com
Editorial Profile: WOLX-FM is a commercial station owned by Entercom Communications Corp. The format of the station is oldies. WOLX-FM broadcasts to the Madison, WI area at 94.9 FM.

WOLZ-FM

Owner: Clear Channel Media and Entertainment
Editorial: 13320 Metro Pkwy, Ste 1, Fort Myers, Florida 33966-4703. **T:** 1 239 225-4300
E: wolz@clearchannel.com
W: http://www.wolz.com
Editorial Profile: WOLZ-FM is a commercial station owned by Clear Channel Media and Entertainment. The format of the station is classic hits. WOLZ-FM broadcasts to the Fort Myers, FL area at 95.3 FM.

WOMB-FM

Owner: Mary's Children, Inc
Editorial: 8212 W Hendricks Rd, Bloomington, Indiana 47403-9618. **T:** 1 812 8254742
E: fitheotokos@bluemarble.net
W: http://airmaria.com
Editorial Profile: WOMB-FM is a non-commercial station ownedy by Mary's

---

Children, Inc. The format of the station features Catholic programming. WOMB-FM broadcasts to the Ellettsville and Bloomington, IN area at a frequency of 89.9 FM.

WOMC-FM

Owner: CBS Radio
Editorial: 2201 Woodward Hts, Ferndale, Michigan 48220. **T:** 1 248 546-9600
W: http://womc.radio.com
Editorial Profile: WOMC-FM is a commercial station owned by CBS Radio. The format of the station is classic hits. WOMC-FM broadcasts to the Detroit area at 104.3 FM.

WOMG-FM

Owner: Cumulus Media Inc.
Editorial: 1801 Charleston Hwy Ste J, Cayce, South Carolina 29033-2019.
T: 1 803 796-9975
W: http://www.nashfm985.com
Editorial Profile: WOMG-FM is a commercial station owned by Cumulus Media Inc. The format of the station is country. WOMG-FM broadcasts to the Columbia, SC area at 98.5 FM.

WOMI-AM

Owner: Townsquare Media, LLC
Editorial: 3301 Frederica St, Owensboro, Kentucky 42301. **T:** 1 270 683-1558
E: spots@wbkr.com
W: http://www.1490womi.com
Editorial Profile: WOMI-AM is a commercial station owned by Townsquare Media, LLC. The format of the station is news and talk. WOMI-AM broadcasts to the Owensboro, KY area at 1490 AM.

WOMN-AM

Owner: Pittman Broadcast Services LLC
Editorial: 2200 N Highway 190 Ste D, Covington, Louisiana 70433-9067.
T: 1 985 624-9452
W: http://www.catcountry989.com
Editorial Profile: WOMN-AM is a commercial station owned by Pittman Broadcast Services LLC. The format of the station is contemporary country. WOMN-AM broadcasts to the Franklinton, LA area at 1110 AM.

WOMP-AM

Owner: Keymarket Communications LLC
Editorial: 56325 High Ridge Rd, Bellaire, Ohio 43906. **T:** 1 740 676-5661
E: froggy103prod@keymarketradio.com
Editorial Profile: WOMP-AM is a commercial station owned by Keymarket Communications LLC. The format for the station is classic country. WOMP-AM broadcasts to the Wheeling, WV area at 1290 AM.

WOMR-FM

Owner: Lower Cape Communications
Editorial: 494 Commercial St, 2nd Fl, Provincetown, Massachusetts 02657-2414.
T: 1 508 487-2619 **E:** info@womr.org
W: http://www.womr.org
Editorial Profile: WOMR-FM is a non-commercial station owned by Lower Cape Communications. The format of the station is variety. WOMR-FM broadcasts to the Provincetown, MA area at 92.1 FM.

WOMT-AM

Owner: Seehafer Broadcasting Corp.
Editorial: 3730 Mangin St, Manitowoc, Wisconsin 54220. **T:** 1 920 682-0351
E: news@womtradio.com
W: http://www.womtradio.com
Editorial Profile: WOMT-AM is a commercial station owned by Seehafer Broadcasting Corp. The format of the station is adult contemporary music and sports. WOMT-AM broadcasts to the Manitowoc, WI area at 1240 AM.

WOMX-FM

Owner: CBS Radio
Editorial: 1800 Pembrook Dr, Ste 400, Orlando, Florida 32810-6375.
T: 1 407 919-1000
W: http://www.mix1051.com
Editorial Profile: WOMX-FM is a commercial station owned by CBS Radio. The format of the station is hot adult contemporary music. WOMX-FM broadcasts to the Orlando, FL area at 105.1 FM.

WONA-FM

Owner: Southern Electronics Inc.
Editorial: 1006 S Applegate St, Winona, Mississippi 38967. **T:** 1 662 283-1570
E: wonafm@gmail.com
W: http://www.hawg95.com
Editorial Profile: WONA-FM is a commercial station owned by Southern Electronics Inc.

The format of the station is country music. WONA-FM broadcasts to the Winona, MS area at 95.1 FM.

WONB-FM
Owner: Ohio Northern University
Editorial: 525 S Main St, Ada, Ohio 45810-6000. **T:** 1 419 772-1194 **E:** wonb@onu.edu
W: http://www.wonbradio.net
Editorial Profile: WONB-FM is a non-commercial station owned by Ohio Northern University. The format of the station is Top 40/ CHR. WONB-FM broadcasts the Ada, OH area at 94.9 FM.

WONC-FM
Owner: North Central College
Editorial: 232 E Chicago Ave, Naperville, Illinois 60540. **T:** 1 630 637-8989
W: http://www.wonc.org
Editorial Profile: WONC-FM is a non-commercial station owned by North Central College. The format of the station is rock/ album oriented rock. WONC-FM broadcasts to the Naperville, IL area at 89.1 FM.

WOND-AM
Owner: Longport Media
Editorial: 1601 New Rd, Linwood, New Jersey 08221-1116. **T:** 1 609 653-1400
W: http://www.wondradio.com
Editorial Profile: WOND-AM is a commercial station owned by Longport Media. The format of the station is news and talk. WOND-AM broadcasts to the Linwood, NJ area at 1400 AM.

WONE-AM
Owner: Clear Channel Media and Entertainment
Editorial: 101 Pine St, Dayton, Ohio 45402. **T:** 1 937 224-1137 **W:** http://www.wone.com
Editorial Profile: WONE-AM is a commercial station owned by Clear Channel Media and Entertainment. The format of the station is sports. WONE-AM broadcasts in the Dayton, OH area at 980 AM.

WONE-FM
Owner: Rubber City Radio Group Inc.
Editorial: 1795 W Market St, Akron, Ohio 44313-7001. **T:** 1 330 869-9800
E: news@wakr.net **W:** http://www.wone.net
Editorial Profile: WONE-FM is a commercial station owned by the Rubber City Radio Group Inc. The format of the station is classic rock music. WONE-FM broadcasts to the Akron, OH area at 97.5 FM.

WONG-AM
Owner: Williams (Marion R.)
Editorial: 126 E Sowell Rd, Canton, Mississippi 39046-9251. **T:** 1 601 855-2035
W: http://www.wong1150.com

WONN-AM
Owner: Hall Communications
Editorial: 404 W Lime St, Lakeland, Florida 33815-4651. **T:** 1 863 682-8184
W: http://www.wonn.com
Editorial Profile: WONN-AM is a commercial station owned by Hall Communications. The format of the station is adult standards music. WONN-AM broadcasts to the Lakeland, FL area at 1230 AM.

WONQ-AM
Owner: Florida Broadcasters
Editorial: 1355 E Altamonte Dr, Altamonte Springs, Florida 32701. **T:** 1 407 830-0800
W: http://www.lagrande1030am.com
Editorial Profile: WONQ-AM is a commercial station owned by Florida Broadcasters. The format of the station is Spanish language news talk. WONQ-AM broadcasts to the Altamonte Springs, FL area at 1030 AM.

WONU-FM
Owner: Olivet Nazarene University
Editorial: 1 University Ave, Bourbonnais, Illinois 60914-2345. **T:** 1 815 939-5330
E: shine@olivet.edu **W:** http://chicago.shine.fm
Editorial Profile: WONU-FM is a non-commercial station owned by Olivet Nazarene University. The format of the station is contemporary Christian. WONU-FM broadcasts to the Kankakee, Bourbonnais and the south suburbs of Chicago at 89.7 FM.

WONW-AM
Owner: Clear Channel Media and Entertainment
Editorial: 2110 Radio Dr, Defiance, Ohio 43512. **T:** 1 419 782-8126
W: http://www.wonw1280.com
Editorial Profile: WONW-AM is a commercial station owned by Clear Channel Media and Entertainment. The format of the station is news, sports and talk. WONW-AM broadcasts to the Defiance, OH area at 1280 AM.

WONY-FM
Owner: State University of New York
Editorial: 116 Alumni Hall Suny-Oneonta,, Oneonta, New York 13820. **T:** 1 607 436-2712
E: wony@oneonta.edu
W: http://organizations.oneonta.edu/wony/main.html
Editorial Profile: WONY-FM is a non-commercial station owned by the State University of New York. The format of the station is college variety. WONY-FM broadcasts to the Oneonta, NY area at 90.9 FM.

WOOD-AM
Owner: Clear Channel Media and Entertainment
Editorial: 77 Monroe Center St NW, Ste 1000, Grand Rapids, Michigan 49503.
T: 1 616 459-1919 **E:** news@woodradio.com
W: http://www.woodradio.com
Editorial Profile: WOOD-AM is a commercial station owned by Clear Channel Media and Entertainment. The format of the station is news, sports and talk. WOOD-AM broadcasts to the Grand Rapids, MI area at 1300 AM.

WOOD-FM
Owner: Clear Channel Media and Entertainment
Editorial: 77 Monroe Center St Nw Ste 1000, Grand Rapids, Michigan 49503-2912.
T: 1 616 459-1919
W: http://www.woodradio.com
Editorial Profile: WOOD-FM is a commercial station owned by Clear Channel Media and Entertainment. The format of the station is news/talk. WOOD-FM broadcasts to the Grand Rapids, MI at a frequency of 106.9 FM.

WOOF-AM
Owner: Woof Inc.
Editorial: 2518 Columbia Hwy, Dothan, Alabama 36303. **T:** 1 334 792-1149
E: woof@ala.net **W:** http://www.woofradio.com
Editorial Profile: WOOF-AM is a commercial station owned by Woof Inc. The format of the station is sports. WOOF-AM broadcasts in the Dothan, AL area at 560 AM.

WOOF-FM
Owner: Woof Inc.
Editorial: 2518 Columbia Hwy, Dothan, Alabama 36303. **T:** 1 334 792-1149
E: general@997wooffm.com
W: http://www.997wooffm.com
Editorial Profile: WOOF-FM is a commercial station owned by Woof Inc. The format of the station is adult contemporary music. WOOF-FM broadcasts in the Dothan, AL area at 99.7 FM.

WOON-AM
Owner: O-N Radio Inc.
Editorial: 985 Park Ave, Woonsocket, Rhode Island 02895-6332. **T:** 1 401 762-1240
E: email@onworldwide.com
W: http://www.on-radio.com
Editorial Profile: WOON-AM is a commercial station owned by O-N Radio Inc. The format of the station is variety. WOON-AM broadcasts to the Woonsocket, RI area at 1240 AM.

WOOW-AM
Owner: Rouse(James)
Editorial: 405 Evans St, Greenville, North Carolina 27858. **T:** 1 252 757-0365
E: mvoicenews@yahoo.com
W: http://www.jimrousecommunications.com
Editorial Profile: WOOW-AM is a commercial station owned by James Rouse. The format of the station is gospel and talk. WOOW-AM broadcasts to the Greenville, NC area at 1340 AM.

WOOZ-FM
Owner: Max Media
Editorial: 1431 Country Aire Dr, Carterville, Illinois 62918-5118. **T:** 1 618 985-4843
E: publicservice@riverradio.net
W: http://www.z100fm.com
Editorial Profile: WOOZ-FM is a commercial station which is owned by Max Media. The format of the station is contemporary country. WOOZ-FM broadcasts to the Carterville, IL area on 99.9 FM. Send PSAs to publicservice@riverradio.net.

WOPC-FM
Owner: Last Of A Dying Breed Broadcasting
Editorial: 100 E Main St, Linden, Tennessee 37096-3006. **T:** 1 724 516-8885
W: http://www.1013hankfm.com
Editorial Profile: WOPC-FM is a commercial station owned by Last Of A Dying Breed Broadcasting. The format of the station is classic country. WOPC-FM broadcasts to the Linden, TN area at a frequency of 101.3 FM.

WOPP-AM
Owner: E & R Broadcasting Inc.
Editorial: 1101 Cameron Rd, Opp, Alabama 36467-2407. **T:** 1 334 493-4545
E: wopp@wopp.com **W:** http://www.wopp.com
Editorial Profile: WOPP-AM is a commercial station owned by E & R Broadcasting Inc. The format of the station is classic country and oldies. WOPP-AM broadcasts to the Opp, AL area at 1290 AM.

WOR-AM
Owner: Clear Channel Media and Entertainment
Editorial: 32 Avenue of the Americas, New York, New York 10013-2473.
T: 1 212 642-4500 **W:** http://www.wor710.com
Editorial Profile: WOR-AM is a commercial station owned by Clear Channel Media and Entertainment. The format of the station is news and talk. WOR-AM broadcasts to the New York area at 710 AM.

WORC-AM
Owner: Gois Broadcasting
Editorial: 122 Green St, Ste 2R, Worcester, Massachusetts 1604. **T:** 1 508 791-2111
E: admin@power1310.com
W: http://www.megaworcester.com/
Editorial Profile: WORC-AM is a commercial station owned by Gois Broadcasting. The format of the station is Hispanic programming. WORC-AM broadcasts to the Worcester, MA area at 1310 AM.

WORC-FM
Owner: Cumulus Media Inc.
Editorial: 250 Commercial St Ste 530, Worcester, Massachusetts 01608-1726.
T: 1 508 752-1045 **W:** http://www.orcfm.com
Editorial Profile: WORC-FM is a commercial station owned by Cumulus Media Inc. The format of the station is oldies. WORC-FM broadcasts to the Worcester, MA area at 98.9 FM.

WORD-AM
Owner: Entercom Communications Corp.
Editorial: 25 Garlington Rd, Greenville, South Carolina 29615-4613. **T:** 1 864 271-9200
W: http://www.espnupstate.com
Editorial Profile: WORD-AM is a commercial station owned by Entercom Communications Corp. The format of the station is sports talk. WORD-AM broadcasts to the Greenville, SC area at 950 AM.

WORD-FM
Owner: Salem Communications
Editorial: 7 Parkway Ctr, Ste 625, Pittsburgh, Pennsylvania 15220. **T:** 1 412 937-1500
E: word@wordfm.com
W: http://www.wordfm.com
Editorial Profile: WORD-FM is a commercial station owned by Salem Communications. The format of the station is contemporary Christian music and religious talk. WORD-FM broadcasts to the Pittsburgh area at 101.5 FM.

WORG-FM
Owner: Garris Communications Inc.
Editorial: 1675 Chestnut St, Orangeburg, South Carolina 29115-3327.
T: 1 803 516-8400 **E:** worg@worg.com
W: http://www.worg.com
Editorial Profile: WORG-FM is a commercial station owned by Garris Communications Inc. The format of the station is adult contemporary. WORG-FM broadcasts to the Orangeburg, SC area at 100.3 FM.

WORL-AM
Owner: Salem Communications
Editorial: 1188 Lake View Dr, Altamonte Springs, Florida 32714. **T:** 1 407 682-9494
E: worl@salemorlando.com
W: http://www.worl660.com
Editorial Profile: WORL-AM is a commercial station owned by Salem Communications. The format of the station is news and talk. WORL-AM broadcasts to the Orlando, FL area at 660 AM.

WORM-AM
Owner: Hunt(Gerald W.)
Editorial: 165 Bowen Dr, Savannah, Tennessee 38372. **T:** 1 731 925-7102
Editorial Profile: WORM-AM is a commercial station owned by Gerald W. Hunt. The format of the station is oldies. WORM-AM broadcasts to the Savannah, TN area at 1010 AM.

WORM-FM
Owner: Hunt(Gerald W.)
Editorial: 165 Bowen Dr, Savannah, Tennessee 38372. **T:** 1 731 925-7102
E: thewormq105@yahoo.com
Editorial Profile: WORM-FM is a commercial station owned by Gerald W. Hunt. The format of the station is country. WORM-FM broadcasts to the Savannah, TN area at 101.7 FM.

WORQ-FM
Owner: Lakeshore Communications
Editorial: 1253 Schering Rd Unit B, De Pere, Wisconsin 54115-1003. **T:** 1 920 494-9010
E: mail@q90fm.com
W: http://www.q90fm.com
Editorial Profile: WORQ-FM is a non-commercial station owned by Lakeshore Communications. The format of the station is contemporary Christian. WORQ-FM broadcasts to the Green Bay, WI area at 90.1 FM.

WORT-FM
Owner: Back Porch Radio Broadcasting
Editorial: 118 S Bedford St, Madison, Wisconsin 53703-2626. **T:** 1 608 256-2695
E: news@wortfm.org
W: http://www.wort-fm.org
Editorial Profile: WORT-FM is a non-commercial station owned by Back Porch Radio Broadcasting. The format for the station is variety. WORT-FM broadcasts to the Madison, WI area at 89.9 FM.

WORV-AM
Owner: Circuit Broadcasting of Hattiesburg
Editorial: 1204 Kinnard St, Hattiesburg, Mississippi 39401. **T:** 1 601 544-1941

WORW-FM
Owner: Port Huron Area School District
Editorial: 1799 Krafft Rd, Port Huron, Michigan 48060. **T:** 1 810 984-2672
Editorial Profile: WORW-FM is a non-commercial station owned by the Port Huron School District. The format of the station is Top 40/CHR. WORW-FM broadcasts to the Port Huron, MI area at 91.9 FM.

WORX-FM
Owner: DCBroadcasting Inc.
Editorial: 1224 E Telegraph Hill Rd, Madison, Indiana 47250-9273. **T:** 1 812 265-3322
E: thebestmusic@worxradio.com
W: http://www.worxradio.com
Editorial Profile: WORX-FM is a commercial station owned by DCBroadcasting Inc. The format of the station is adult contemporary music. WORX-FM broadcasts to the Madison, IN area at 96.7 FM.

WOSA-FM
Owner: WOSU Public Media
Editorial: 2400 Olentangy River Rd, Columbus, Ohio 43210-1027.
T: 1 614 292-9678 **E:** wosu@osu.edu
W: http://www.wosu.org
Editorial Profile: WOSA-FM is a non-commercial station owned by WOSU Public Media. The format of the station is classical. The station broadcasts to the Columbus, OH area at a frequency of 101.1 FM.

WOSB-FM
Owner: Ohio State University
Editorial: 2400 Olentangy River Rd, Columbus, Ohio 43210-1027.
T: 1 614 292-9678 **E:** wosu@osu.edu
W: http://www.wosu.org
Editorial Profile: WOSE-FM is a non-commercial station owned by Ohio State University. The format of the station is classical music. WOSE-FM broadcasts to the Coshocton, OH area at a frequency of 101.1 FM.

WOSE-FM
Owner: Ohio State University
Editorial: 2400 Olentangy River Rd, Columbus, Ohio 43210-1027.
T: 1 614 292-9678 **E:** wosu@osu.edu
W: http://www.wosu.org
Editorial Profile: WOSE-FM is a non-commercial station owned by Ohio State University. The format of the station is classical music. WOSE-FM broadcasts to the Coshocton, OH area at a frequency of 89.7 FM.

WOSF-FM
Owner: Radio One Inc.
Editorial: 8809 Lenox Pointe Dr Unit A, Charlotte, North Carolina 28273-3377.
T: 1 704 548-7800
W: http://oldschool1053.com
Editorial Profile: WOSF-FM is a commercial station owned by Radio One Inc. The format of the station is R&B oldies featuring hits from the 70s and 80s. WOSF-FM broadcasts to the Charlotte, NC area at 105.3 FM.

WOSH-AM
Owner: Cumulus Media Inc.
Editorial: 491 S Washburn St, Ste 400, Oshkosh, Wisconsin 54904.
T: 1 920 426-3239
E: wosh.news@cumulus.com
W: http://www.1490wosh.com
Editorial Profile: WOSH-AM is a commercial station owned by Cumulus Media Inc. The format of the station is news, talk and sports. WOSH-AM broadcasts in the Oshkosh, WI area at 1490 AM.

WOSL-FM
Owner: Radio One Inc.
Editorial: One Centennial Plaza, 705 Central Ave Suite 200, Cincinnati, Ohio 45202-1900.
T: 1 513 679-6000
W: http://oldschoolcincy.com
Editorial Profile: WOSL-FM is a commercial station owned by Radio One Inc. The format of the station is rhythmic contemporary music. WOSL-FM broadcasts to the Cincinnati area at 100.3 FM.

WOSM-FM
Owner: Telesouth Communications Inc.
Editorial: 4720 Radio Rd, Ocean Springs, Mississippi 39564-7509. **T:** 1 228 875-9031
W: http://www.supertalkms.com
Editorial Profile: WOSM-FM is a commercial station owned by Telesouth Communications Inc. The format of the station is talk. WOSM-FM broadcasts in the Ocean Springs, MS area at 103.1 FM.

WOSN-FM
Owner: Treasure & Space Coast Radio
Editorial: 1235 16th St, Vero Beach, Florida 32960-3620. **T:** 1 772 567-0937
W: http://www.wosnfm.com

WOSQ-FM
Owner: Seehafer Broadcasting Corp.
Editorial: 1714 N Central Ave, Marshfield, Wisconsin 54449. **T:** 1 715 384-2191
W: http://wosqfm.com
Editorial Profile: WOSQ-FM is a commercial station owned by Seehafer Broadcasting Corp. The format for the station is sports. WOSQ-FM broadcasts to the Wausau, WI, area at 92.3 FM.

WOSR-FM
Owner: WAMC
Editorial: 318 Central Ave, Albany, New York 12206. **T:** 1 518 465-5233 **E:** mail@wamc.org
W: http://www.wamc.org
Editorial Profile: WOSR-FM is a non-commercial station owned by WAMC. The format of the station is news and talk. WOSR-FM broadcasts to the Albany, NY area at 91.7 FM.

WOSU-FM
Owner: Ohio State University
Editorial: 2400 Olentangy River Rd, Columbus, Ohio 43210-1027.
T: 1 614 292-9678 **E:** news@wosu.org
W: http://www.wosu.org
Editorial Profile: WOSU-FM is a non-commercial station owned by Ohio State University. The format of the station is news. WOSU-AM broadcasts to the Columbus, OH area at 89.7 FM.

WOSW-AM
Owner: Cram Communications, LLC
Editorial: 401 W Kirkpatrick St, Syracuse, New York 13204-1305. **T:** 1 315 472-0222
Editorial Profile: WOSW-AM is a commercial station owned by Cram Communications, LLC. The format of the station is gospel. WOSW-AM broadcasts to the Fulton, NY area at 1300 AM.

WOTB-FM
Owner: New Horizon Christian Fellowship
Editorial: 3401 Pontchartrain Dr, Slidell, Louisiana 70458-4849. **T:** 1 985 781-3174
W: http://thebridge.fm/
Editorial Profile: WOTB-FM is a non-commercial station owned by New Horizon Christian Fellowship. The format of the station is Contemporary Christian music. WOTB-FM broadcasts to the Greater New Orleans area at a frequency of 88.7 FM.

WOTC-FM
Owner: Valley Baptist Church
Editorial: 146 Parsons Point Ln, Edinburg, Virginia 22824-3635. **T:** 1 540 984-8998
E: wotcfm@shentel.net
W: http://www.valleybaptistchurch.net

WOTE-AM
Owner: Results Broadcasting, Inc.
Editorial: 1456 E Green Bay St, Shawano, Wisconsin 54166. **T:** 1 715 524-2194
E: wtchwown@yahoo.com
W: http://www.oldies1380.com
Editorial Profile: WOTE-AM is a commercial station owned by Results Broadcasting, Inc. The format of the station is adult standards. WOTE-AM broadcasts to the Shawano, WI area at 1380 AM.

WOTJ-FM
Owner: Grace Missionary Baptist Church
Editorial: 520 Roberts Rd, Newport, North Carolina 28570-8616. **T:** 1 252 223-4600
E: fbn@fbnradio.com
W: http://www.fbnradio.com
Editorial Profile: WOTJ-FM is a non-commercial station owned by Grace Missionary Baptist Church. The format of the station is religious programming. WOTJ-FM broadcasts to the Newport, NC area at 90.7 FM.

WOTL-FM
Owner: Family Stations Inc.
Editorial: 716 N Westwood Ave, A, Toledo, Ohio 43607-3558. **T:** 1 815 725-1331
E: info@familyradio.org
W: http://www.familyradio.com
Editorial Profile: WOTL-FM is a commercial station owned by Family Stations Inc. The format of the station is religious programming. WOTL-FM broadcasts to the Toledo, OH area at 90.3 FM.

WOTS-AM
Owner: J & V Communications Inc.
Editorial: 222 Hazard St, Orlando, Florida 32804-3030. **T:** 1 407 841-8282
E: wprd1440@gmail.com
W: http://www.wots1220.com
Editorial Profile: WOTS-AM is a commercial station owned by J & V Communications Inc. The format of the station is Hispanic religious programming. WOTS-AM broadcasts to the Orlando, FL area at 1220 AM.

WOTT-FM
Owner: Community Broadcasters, LLC
Editorial: 199 Wealtha Ave, Watertown, New York 13601-1837. **T:** 1 315 786-9552
W: http://www.allrockwott.com
Editorial Profile: WOTT-FM is a commercial station owned by Community Broadcasters, LLC. The format of the station is rock/album-oriented rock. WOTT-FM broadcasts to the Watertown, NY area at 94.1 FM.

WOUB-AM
Owner: Ohio University
Editorial: 9 S College St, Athens, Ohio 45701-2905. **T:** 1 740 593-4554 **E:** news@woub.org
W: http://www.woub.org
Editorial Profile: WOUB-AM is a non-commercial station owned by Ohio University. The format of the station is news. WOUB-AM broadcasts to the Athens, OH area at 1340 AM.

WOUB-FM
Owner: Ohio University
Editorial: 9 S College St, Athens, Ohio 45701-2905. **T:** 1 740 593-4554 **E:** news@woub.org
W: http://www.woub.org
Editorial Profile: WOUB-FM is a non-commercial station owned by Ohio University. The format of the station is adult album alternative, news and talk. WOUB-FM broadcasts to the Athens, OH area at 91.3 FM.

WOUF-FM
Owner: Henderson, Roy E.
Editorial: 1532 Forrester Rd, Frankfort, Michigan 49635. **T:** 1 231 352-6374
W: http://www.wouffm.com
Editorial Profile: WOUF-FM is a commercial station owned by Roy E. Henderson. The format of the station is rock/album oriented rock. WOUF-FM broadcasts to the Frankfort, MI area at 99.3 FM.

WOUR-FM
Owner: Galaxy Communications LP
Editorial: 39 Kellogg Rd, New Hartford, New York 13413. **T:** 1 315 797-1330
E: askwour@wour.com
W: http://www.wour.com
Editorial Profile: WOUR-FM is a commercial station owned by Galaxy Communications LP. The format of the station is classic rock. WOUR-FM broadcasts to the Utica, NY area at 96.9 FM.

WOVK-FM
Owner: Clear Channel Media and Entertainment
Editorial: 1015 Main St, Wheeling, West Virginia 26003. **T:** 1 304 232-1170
E: wovk987fm@yahoo.com
W: http://www.wovk.com
Editorial Profile: WOVK-FM is a commercial station owned by Clear Channel Media and Entertainment. The format of the station is contemporary country. WOVK-FM broadcasts to the Wheeling, WV area at 98.7 FM.

WOVM-FM
Owner: Music that Matters, Inc
Editorial: 2300 Riverside Dr, Green Bay, Wisconsin 54301. **T:** 1 920 271-2700
E: web@theavenue91.com
W: http://www.theavenue91.com
Editorial Profile: WOVM-FM is a non-commercial station owned by Music that Matters, Inc. The format of the station is jazz. WOVM-FM broadcasts to the Green Bay, WI area at 91.1 FM.

WOWB-FM
Owner: Agape Educational Media, Inc.
Editorial: 42676 Highway 31, Brewton, Alabama 36426. **T:** 1 251 809-1915
E: info@wowradio.org
W: http://www.weljfm.com

WOWC-FM
Owner: Peg Broadcasting
Editorial: 230 W Colville St, Mc Minnville, Tennessee 37110-3211. **T:** 1 931 473-9253
E: production.mcminnville@pegbroadcasting.com **W:** http://www.1053wowcountry.com
Editorial Profile: WOWC-FM is a commercial station owned by Peg Broadcasting. The format of the station is country. WOWC-FM broadcasts to the McMinnville, TN area at 105.3 FM.

WOWE-FM
Owner: Praestantia Broadcasting
Editorial: 444 Church St, Flint, Michigan 48502. **T:** 1 810 234-4335
E: wowe98.9@sbcglobal.net
Editorial Profile: WOWE-FM is a commercial station owned by Praestantia Broadcasting. The format of the station is R&B oldies. WOWE-FM broadcasts to the Flint, MI area at 98.9 FM.

WOWF-FM
Owner: Peg Broadcasting Crossville, LLC
Editorial: 961 Miller Ave, Crossville, Tennessee 38555. **T:** 1 931 707-1102
E: news@1025wowcountry.com
W: http://www.1025wowcountry.com
Editorial Profile: WOWF-FM is a commercial station owned by Peg Broadcasting Crossville, LLC. The format of the station is country. WOWF-FM broadcasts to the Crossville, TN area at 102.5 FM.

WOWI-FM
Owner: Clear Channel Media and Entertainment
Editorial: 1003 Norfolk Sq, Norfolk, Virginia 23502-3234. **T:** 1 757 466-0009
E: 103jamz@clearchannel.com
W: http://www.103jamz.com
Editorial Profile: WOWI-FM is a commercial station owned by Clear Channel Media and Entertainment. The format of the station is urban contemporary music. WOWI-FM broadcasts to the Norfolk, VA area at 102.9 FM.

WOWN-FM
Owner: Results Broadcasting, Inc.
Editorial: 1456 E Green Bay St, Shawano, Wisconsin 54166. **T:** 1 715 524-2194
E: wtchwown@yahoo.com
W: http://www.b993.com
Editorial Profile: WOWN-FM is a commercial station owned by Results Broadcasting, Inc. The format of the station is classic hits. WOWN-FM broadcasts to the Shawano, WI area at 99.3 FM.

WOWO-AM
Owner: Federated Media
Editorial: 2915 Maples Rd, Fort Wayne, Indiana 46816. **T:** 1 260 447-5511
E: news@wowo.com
W: http://www.wowo.com
Editorial Profile: WOWO-AM is a commercial station owned by Federated Media. The format of the station is news and talk. WOWO-AM broadcasts to the Fort Wayne, IN area at 1190 AM.

WOWQ-FM
Owner: First Media Radio LLC
Editorial: 801 E Dubois Ave, Du Bois, Pennsylvania 15801-3643. **T:** 1 814 371-8300
E: q102radio@comcast.net
W: http://www.q102radio.fm
Editorial Profile: WOWQ-FM is a commercial station owned by First Media Radio LLC. The format of the station is contemporary country. WOWQ-FM broadcasts to the Du Bois, PA area at 91.1 FM.

WOWW-AM
Owner: Flinn Broadcasting Corp.
Editorial: 230 Goodman Rd E Ste 202, Southaven, Mississippi 38671-5151.
T: 1 901 272-0008 **W:** http://rebel953.com/
Editorial Profile: WOWW-AM is a commercial station owned by Flinn Broadcasting Corp. and operated by Mighty Media Group LP. The format of the station is country. WOWW-AM broadcasts to the Memphis, TN area at 1430 AM.

WOWY-FM
Owner: 2510 Associates
Editorial: 160 W Clearview Ave, State College, Pennsylvania 16803-1617. **T:** 1 814 238-5085
W: http://www.wowyonline.com
Editorial Profile: WOWY-FM is a commercial station owned by 2510 Associates. The format of the station is oldies. WOWY-FM broadcasts to the State College, PA area on 97.1 FM.

WOXD-FM
Owner: Taylor Communications, Inc.
Editorial: 302 Highway 7 S, Oxford, Mississippi 38655. **T:** 1 662 234-9631
E: production@bullseye955.com
W: http://www.bullseye955.com
Editorial Profile: WOXD-FM is a comercial station owned by Taylor Communications, Inc. The format of the station is classic hits. WOXD-FM broadcasts in the Oxford, MS area at 95.5 FM.

WOXL-FM
Owner: Saga Communications
Editorial: 1190 Patton Ave, Asheville, North Carolina 28806-2706. **T:** 1 828 259-9695
W: http://www.965woxl.com
Editorial Profile: WOXL-FM is a commercial station owned by Saga Communications. The format of the station is Lite Rock/Lite AC. WOXL-FM broadcasts to the Asheville, NC area at 98.1 FM.

WOXM-FM
Owner: Vermont Public Radio
Editorial: 365 Troy Ave, Colchester, Vermont 05446-3126. **T:** 1 802 655-9451
Editorial Profile: WOXM-FM is a non-commercial station owned by Vermont Public Radio. The format is classical music. WOXM-FM broadcasts to the Middleburg, VT area at 90.1 FM.

WOXO-FM
Owner: Gleason Radio Group
Editorial: 243 Main St, Norway, Maine 4268.
T: 1 207 743-5911 **E:** woxo@woxo.com
W: http://www.woxo.com
Editorial Profile: WOXO-FM is a commercial station owned by Gleason Radio Group. The format of the station is classic country. WOXO-FM broadcasts to the Norway, ME area at 92.7 FM.

WOXR-FM
Owner: Vermont Public Radio
Editorial: 365 Troy Ave, Colchester, Vermont 05446-3126. **T:** 1 802 655-9451
E: news@vpr.net **W:** http://www.vpr.net
Editorial Profile: WOXR-FM is a non-commercial station owned by Vermont Public Radio. The format of the station is classical. WOXR-FM broadcasts to the Burlington, VT area at 90.9 FM. The station does not accept PSAs.

WOYK-AM
Owner: WOYK Inc.
Editorial: 1051 Dairy Ln, Elizabethtown, Pennsylvania 17022-9547. **T:** 1 717 840-0355
W: http://www.woyk1350.com/
Editorial Profile: WOYK-AM is a commercial station owned by WOYK Inc. The format of the station is sports. WOYK-AM broadcasts to the Elizabethtown, PA area at 1350 AM.

WOYS-FM
Owner: PD Michael Allen's East Bay Broadcasting
Editorial: 35 Island Dr Ste 16, Eastpoint, Florida 32328-3264. **T:** 1 850 670-8450
W: http://www.oysterradio.com
Editorial Profile: WOYS-FM is a commercial station owned by PD Michael Allen's East Bay Broadcasting. The format of the station is classic hits music. The station broadcasts in Eastpoint, FL at 100.5 FM.

WOZI-FM
Owner: Townsquare Media, Inc.
Editorial: 551 Main St, Presque Isle, Maine 04769-2450. **T:** 1 207 769-6600
W: http://www.102therock.com
Editorial Profile: WOZI-FM is a commercial station owned by Townsquare Media, Inc. The format of the station is classic rock. WOZI-FM broadcasts to the Presque Isle, ME area at 101.9 FM.

WOZK-AM
Owner: Ozark Broadcasting Corporation
Editorial: 982 W Highway 27, Ozark, Alabama 36360-4859. **T:** 1 334 774-5600
Editorial Profile: WOZK-AM is a commercial station owned by Ozark Broadcasting Corporation. The format of the station is adult standards. WOZK-AM broadcasts to the Ozark, AL area at 900 AM.

WOZN-AM
Owner: Midwest Family Stations
Editorial: 730 Rayovac Dr., Madison, Wisconsin 53711. **T:** 1 608 273-1000
W: http://www.madcitysportszone.com
Editorial Profile: WOZN-AM is a commercial station owned by Midwest Family Stations. The station is sports. WOZN-AM broadcasts to the Madison, WI area at 1670 AM.

WOZN-FM
Owner: Midwest Family Stations
Editorial: 730 Rayovac Dr, Madison, Wisconsin 53711. **T:** 1 608 273-1000
W: http://www.madcitysportszone.com
Editorial Profile: WOZN-FM is a commercial station owned by Midwest Family Stations. The station is sports. WOZN-FM broadcasts to the Madison, WI area at 106.7 FM.

WOZQ-FM
Owner: Smith College
Editorial: 100 Elm St, Northampton, Massachusetts 01063-6334.
T: 1 413 585-4956 **E:** wozq@smith.edu
W: http://sophia.smith.edu/org/wozq
Editorial Profile: WOZQ-FM is a non-commercial station owned by Smith College. The format of the station is college variety. WOZQ-FM broadcasts to the Northampton, MA area at 91.9 FM.

WOZZ-FM
Owner: Midwest Communications Inc.
Editorial: 557 Scott St, Wausau, Wisconsin 54403. **T:** 1 715 842-1672
E: the.studio@rock947.com
W: http://www.rock947.com
Editorial Profile: WOZZ-FM is a commercial station owned by Midwest Communications Inc. The format of the station is classic rock. WOZZ-FM broadcasts to the Wausau, WI area at 94.7 FM.

WPAD-AM
Owner: Bristol Broadcasting
Editorial: 6000 Bristol Dr, Paducah, Kentucky 42003-9213. **T:** 1 270 554-8255
E: pd@995thefanpaducah.com
W: http://www.995thefanpaducah.com/
Editorial Profile: WPAD-AM is a commercial station owned by Bristol Broadcasting. The format of the station is sports. WPAD-AM broadcasts to the Paducah, KY area at 1560 AM.

WPAE-FM
Owner: Port Allen Educ. Broadcasting Found.
Editorial: 122 E Main St, Centreville, Mississippi 39631. **T:** 1 601 645-6515
E: wpaefm@telepak.net
W: http://www.soundradio.org
Editorial Profile: WPAE-FM is a non-commercial station owned by Port Allen Educ. Broadcasting Found. The format of the station is religious. WPAE-FM broadcasts to the Centreville, MS area at 89.7 FM.

WPAK-AM
Owner: Great Virginia Ventures, Inc
Editorial: 446 Plank Rd, Farmville, Virginia 23901-4015. **T:** 1 804 392-8114
W: http://www.crosscountryfm.com
Editorial Profile: WPAK-AM is a non-commercial station owned by Great Virginia Ventures, Inc. The format of the station is Christian country music. WPAK-AM broadcasts to the Farmville, VA area at 1490 AM.

WPAP-FM
Owner: Clear Channel Media and Entertainment
Editorial: 1834 Lisenby Ave, Panama City, Florida 32405. **T:** 1 850 769-1408
W: http://www.wpapfm.com
Editorial Profile: WPAP-FM is a commercial station owned by Clear Channel Media and Entertainment. The format of the station is country music. WPAP-FM broadcasts to the Panama City, FL area at 92.5 FM.

WPAQ-AM
Owner: WPAQ Radio, Inc.
Editorial: 2147 Springs Rd, Mount Airy, North Carolina 27030. **T:** 1 336 786-6111
E: info@wpaq740.com
W: http://www.wpaq740.com
Editorial Profile: WPAQ-AM is a commercial station owned by WPAQ Radio, Inc. The format of the station is bluegrass and old time music. WPAQ-AM broadcasts to the Mount Airy, NC area at 740 AM.

WPAR-FM
Owner: Positive Alternative Radio
Editorial: 22226 Timberlake Rd, Lynchburg, Virginia 24502-7214. **T:** 1 434 237-9798
E: office@spiritfm.com
W: http://www.spiritfm.com
Editorial Profile: WPAR-FM is a non-commercial station owned by Positive Alternative Radio. The format of the station is contemporary Christian music. WPAR-FM broadcasts to the Lynchburg, VA area at 91.3 FM.

WPAT-AM
Owner: Multicultural Radio Broadcasting Inc.
Editorial: 449 Broadway Fl 2, New York, New York 10013-2549. **T:** 1 212 966-1059
W: http://mrbi.net
Editorial Profile: WPAT-AM is a commercial station owned by Multicultural Radio Broadcasting Inc. The format of the station is variety. WPAT-AM broadcasts to the New York area at 930 AM.

WPAT-FM
Owner: Spanish Broadcasting System
Editorial: 26 W 56th St, New York, New York 10019-3801. **T:** 1 212 541-9200
E: info@931amor.com
W: http://www.931amor.com
Editorial Profile: WPAT-FM a commercial station owned by the Spanish Broadcasting System. The format of the station is Hispanic adult hits. WPAT-FM broadcasts to the New York City area at 93.1 FM.

WPAW-FM
Owner: Entercom Communications Corp.
Editorial: 7819 National Service Rd, Ste 401, Greensboro, North Carolina 27409.
T: 1 336 605-5200
W: http://www.931wolfcountry.com
Editorial Profile: WPAW-FM is a commercial station owned by Entercom Communications Corp. The format of the station is contemporary country. WPAW-FM broadcasts to the Greensboro, NC area at 93.1 FM.

WPAX-AM
Owner: Lenrob Enterprises Inc.
Editorial: 117 Remington Ave, Thomasville, Georgia 31792. **T:** 1 229 226-1240
W: http://www.wpaxradio.com
Editorial Profile: WPAX-AM is a commercial station owned by Lenrob Enterprises Inc. The format of the station is adult standards and variety. WPAX-AM broadcasts to the Thomasville, GA area at 1240 AM.

WPBC-AM
Owner: Hanmi Broadcasting, Inc (Chang, Kim)
Editorial: 3684 Stewart Rd Ste A3, Atlanta, Georgia 30340-2760. **T:** 1 770 986-9500
Editorial Profile: WPBC-AM is a commercial station owned by Hanmi Broadcasting, Inc. The format of the station is gospel. WPBC-AM broadcasts to Decatur, GA and its surrounding areas at 1310 AM.

WPBG-FM
Owner: L & L Radio
Editorial: 331 Fulton St, Peoria, Illinois 61602-1486. **T:** 1 309 637-3700
E: news@1470wmbd.com
W: http://www.933thedrive.com
Editorial Profile: WPGB-FM is a commercial station owned by L & L Radio. The format of the station is classic hits. WPGB-FM broadcasts to the Peoria, IL area at 93.3 FM.

WPBQ-AM
Owner: TalkQ Corporation
Editorial: 1985 Lakeland Dr, Ste 108, Jackson, Mississippi 39216. **T:** 1 601 832-8023
W: http://www.rebsportsradio.com
Editorial Profile: WPBQ-AM is a commercial station owned by TalkQ Corporation. The format of the station is sports. WPBQ-AM broadcasts locally to the Jackson, MS area at a frequency of 1240 AM.

WPBR-AM
Owner: Omni-Lingual Broadcasting Corp
Editorial: 1776 Lake Worth Rd Ste 201, Lake Worth, Florida 33460-3692. **T:** 1 561 641-8882
Editorial Profile: WPBR-AM is a commercial station owned by Omni-Lingual Broadcasting Corp. The format of the station is ethnic programming WPBR-AM broadcasts to the West Palm Beach, FL, area at 1340 AM.

WPBS-AM
Owner: Pacific Star Broadcasting
Editorial: 3230 Steve Reynolds Blvd Ste 219, Duluth, Georgia 30096-8833.
T: 1 770 813-0307
E: info@atlantaradiokorea.com
W: http://www.atlantaradiokorea.com
Editorial Profile: WPBS-AM is an commercial station owned by Pacific Star Broadcasting. The format of the station is Korean talk and music programming. WPBS-AM broadcasts to the Atlanta area at 1040 AM.

WPBX-FM
Owner: Peg Broadcasting Crossville, LLC
Editorial: 961 Miller Ave, Crossville, Tennessee 38555. **T:** 1 931 707-1102
W: http://www.mix993.net
Editorial Profile: WPBX-FM is a commercial station owned by Peg Broadcasting Crossville, LLC. The format of the station is adult contemporary. WPBX-FM broadcasts to the Crossville, TN area at 99.3 FM.

WPCD-FM
Owner: Parkland College
Editorial: 2400 W Bradley Ave, Champaign, Illinois 61821. **T:** 1 217 351-2450
E: wpcdradio@parkland.edu
W: http://www.parkland.edu/wpcd
Editorial Profile: WPCD-FM is a non-commercial station owned by Parkland College. The format of the station is urban AC and rock alternative music. WPCD-FM broadcasts in Champaign, IL at 88.7 FM.

WPCE-AM
Owner: Willis Broadcasting Co.
Editorial: 645 Church St, Norfolk, Virginia 23510-1712. **T:** 1 757 622-4600
E: willisbroadcasting@yahoo.com
W: http://www.wpceradio.com
Editorial Profile: WPCE-AM is a commercial station owned by Willis Broadcasting Co. (dba Christian Broadcasting of Portsmouth, Inc.) The format of the station is gospel and religious programming. WPCE-AM broadcasts in the Norfolk, VA area at 1400 AM.

WPCF-AM
Owner: Magic Broadcasting, LLC
Editorial: 7106 Laird St Ste 102, Panama City Beach, Florida 32408-7622. **T:** 1 850 230-5855
W: http://939playfm.com/
Editorial Profile: WPCF-AM is a commercial station owned by Magic Broadcasting, LLC. The format of the station is dance. WPCF-AM broadcasts to Panama City Beach, FL at 1290 AM.

WPCH-FM
Owner: Clear Channel Media and Entertainment
Editorial: 7080 Industrial Hwy, Macon, Georgia 31216-7538. **T:** 1 478 781-1063
W: http://www.newcountry965.com
Editorial Profile: WPCH-FM is a commercial station owned by Clear Channel Media and Entertainment. The format of the station is contemporary country. WPCH-FM broadcasts to the Macon, GA area at 96.5 FM.

WPCK-FM
Owner: Cumulus Media Inc.
Editorial: 810 Victoria St, Green Bay, Wisconsin 54302-2465. **T:** 1 920 468-4100
W: http://www.thewolf.fm
Editorial Profile: WPCK-FM is a commercial station owned by Cumulus Media Inc. The format of the station is contemporary country. WPCK-FM broadcasts to the Green Bay, WI area at 104.9 FM.

WPCL-FM
Owner: He's Alive Inc.
Editorial: 34 Springs Road, Grantsville, Maryland 21536. **T:** 1 301 895-3292
W: http://www.hesalive.net
Editorial Profile: WPCL-FM is a non-commercial station owned by He's Alive Inc. The format of the station is contemporary Christian and gospel music. WPCL-FM broadcasts to the Grantsville, MD area at 97.3 FM.

WPCM-AM
Owner: Curtis Media Group
Editorial: 1109 Tower Dr, Burlington, North Carolina 27215-4425. **T:** 1 336 584-0126
E: wpcm@curtismedia.com
W: http://www.920wpcm.com
Editorial Profile: WPCM-AM is a commercial station owned by Curtis Media Group. The format of the station is oldies music. WPCM-AM broadcasts to the Burlington, NC area at 920 AM.

WPCR-FM
Owner: Plymouth State University
Editorial: 17 High St, Plymouth, New Hampshire 3264. **T:** 1 603 535-2242
Editorial Profile: WPCR-FM is a non-commercial station owned by Plymouth State University. The format of the station is variety. WPCR-FM broadcasts to the Plymouth, NH area at 91.7 FM.

WPCS-FM
Owner: Pensacola Christian College
Editorial: 250 Brent Ln, Pensacola, Florida 32503-2267. **T:** 1 850 479-6570
E: rbn@rejoice.org **W:** http://www.rejoice.org
Editorial Profile: WPCS-FM is a non-commercial station owned by Pensacola Christian College. The format of the station is religious programming. WPCS-FM broadcasts to the Pensacola, FL area at 89.5 FM. The station does not do interviews.

WPCV-FM
Owner: Hall Communications
Editorial: 404 W Lime St, Lakeland, Florida 33815-4651. **T:** 1 863 682-8184
W: http://www.wpcv.com
Editorial Profile: WPCV-FM is a commercial station owned by Hall Communications. The format of the station is contemporary country music. WPCV-FM broadcasts to the Lakeland, FL area at 97.5 FM.

WPDA-FM
Owner: Townsquare Media
Editorial: 2 Pendell Rd, Poughkeepsie, New York 12601-1513. **T:** 1 845 471-1500
W: http://www.wpdh.com
Editorial Profile: WPDA-FM is a commercial station owned by Townsquare Media. The format of the station is rock music. WPDA-FM broadcasts to the Poughkeepsie, NY area at 106.1 FM.

WPDC-AM
Owner: JVJ Communications
Editorial: 1051 Dairy Ln, Elizabethtown, Pennsylvania 17022-9547. **T:** 1 717 367-1600
E: espn1600@att.net
Editorial Profile: WPDC-AM is a commercial station owned by JVJ Communications. The format of the station is sports. WPDC-AM broadcasts to the Harrisburg, PA area at 1600 AM.

WPDH-FM
Owner: Townsquare Media
Editorial: 2 Pendell Rd, Poughkeepsie, New York 12601-1513. **T:** 1 845 471-1500
W: http://www.wpdh.com
Editorial Profile: WPDH-FM is a commercial station owned by Townsquare Media. The format of the station is rock/album-oriented rock music. WPDH-FM broadcasts in the Poughkeepsie, NY area at 101.5 FM.

WPDM-AM
Owner: Waters Communications Inc.
Editorial: 7064 US Highway 11, Potsdam, New York 13676-3197. **T:** 1 315 265-5510
E: scott@b993.fm **W:** http://www.99hits.com
Editorial Profile: WPDM-AM is a commercial station owned by Waters Communications Inc. The format of the station is country music. WPDM-AM broadcasts to the Potsdam, NY area on 99.3 FM.

WPDR-AM
Owner: Magnum Radio Group

Editorial: N6912 US Highway 51, Portage, Wisconsin 53901. **T:** 1 608 742-1001
W: http://www.wpdr.com
Editorial Profile: WPDR-AM is a commercial station owned by Magnum Radio Group. The format for the station is oldies. WPDR-AM broadcasts to the Madison, WI area at 1350 AM.

WPDT-FM
Owner: Glory Communications Inc.
Editorial: 2440 Millwood Ave, Columbia, South Carolina 29205. **T:** 1 843 374-5255
W: http://www.wpdt.net
Editorial Profile: WPDT-FM is a commercial station owned by Glory Communications Inc. The format of the station is gospel. WPDT-FM broadcasts to the Columbia, SC area at 105.1 FM.

WPDX-AM
Owner: Tschudy Broadcasting
Editorial: 59 Mountain Park Dr., Whitehall, West Virginia 26554. **T:** 1 304 363-3851
W: http://www.wpdxcountry.com
Editorial Profile: WPDX-AM is a commercial station owned by Tschudy Broadcasting. The format of the station is classic country. WPDX-AM broadcasts to the Clarksburg-Weston, WV area at 750 AM.

WPDX-FM
Owner: Tschudy Broadcasting
Editorial: 59 Mountain Park Dr, Fairmont, West Virginia 26554-8993. **T:** 1 304 624-6425
E: wpdx@wpdxcountry.com
W: http://www.wpdxcountry.com
Editorial Profile: WDPX-FM is a commercial station owned by Tschudy Broadcasting. The format of the station is country music. WDPX-FM broadcasts to the Clarksburg-Weston, WV area at 104.9 FM.

WPEG-FM
Owner: CBS Radio
Editorial: 1520 South Blvd, Ste 300, Charlotte, North Carolina 28203-3701.
T: 1 704 522-1103
W: http://power98fm.radio.com
Editorial Profile: WPEG-FM is a commercial station owned by CBS Radio. The format of the station is urban contemporary. WPEG-FM broadcasts to the greater Charlotte, NC area at 97.9 FM.

WPEH-AM
Owner: Peach Broadcasting
Editorial: 5442 Middleground Road, Louisville, Georgia 30434. **T:** 1 478 625-7248
Editorial Profile: WPEH-AM is a commercial station owned by Peach Broadcasting. The format of the station is country and oldies. WPEH-AM broadcasts to the Louisville, GA area at 1420 AM.

WPEH-FM
Owner: Peach Broadcasting
Editorial: 5442 Middleground Road, Louisville, Georgia 30434. **T:** 1 478 625-7248
Editorial Profile: WPEH-FM is a commercial station owned by Peach Broadcasting. The format of the station is country and oldies. WPEH-FM broadcasts to the Louisville, GA area at 92.1 FM.

WPEI-FM
Owner: Atlantic Coast Radio LLC
Editorial: 779 Warren Ave, Portland, Maine 4103. **T:** 1 207 773-9695
W: http://www.weei.com
Editorial Profile: WPEI-FM is a commercial station owned by Atlantic Coast Radio LLC. The format of the station is sports. WPEI-FM broadcasts to the Portland, ME area at 95.9 FM.

WPEK-AM
Owner: Clear Channel Media and Entertainment
Editorial: 13 Summerlin Rd, Asheville, North Carolina 28806-2800. **T:** 1 828 257-2700
E: ashevillepsa@clearchannel.com
W: http://www.880therevolution.com
Editorial Profile: WPEK-AM is a commercial station owned by Clear Channel Media and Entertainment. The format of the station is talk. WPEK-AM broadcasts to the Asheville, NC area at 880 AM.

WPEL-AM
Owner: Montrose Broadcasting Corp.
Editorial: 251 High St, Montrose, Pennsylvania 18801-1444. **T:** 1 570 278-2811
E: mail@wpel.org **W:** http://www.wpel.org
Editorial Profile: WPEL-AM is a non-commercial station owned by Montrose Broadcasting Corp. The format of the station

is Southern gospel. WPEL-AM broadcasts to the Montrose, PA area at 800 AM.

WPEL-FM
Owner: Montrose Broadcasting Corp.
Editorial: 251 High St, Montrose, Pennsylvania 18801-1444. **T:** 1 570 278-2811
E: mail@wpel.org **W:** http://www.wpel.org
Editorial Profile: WPEL-FM is a non-commercial station owned by Montrose Broadcasting Corp. The format of the station is religious programming with easy listening and classical music. WPEL-FM broadcasts to the Montrose, PA area at 96.5 FM.

WPEN-FM
Owner: Greater Media Inc.
Editorial: 1 Bala Plz, Bala Cynwyd, Pennsylvania 19004-1409. **T:** 1 610 771-9750
W: http://www.975thefanatic.com
Editorial Profile: WPEN-FM is a commercial station owned by Greater Media Inc. The format of the station is sports and talk. WPEN-FM broadcasts to the Philadelphia area at 97.5 FM.

WPEO-AM
Owner: Pinebrook Foundation Inc.
Editorial: 1708 Highview Rd, East Peoria, Illinois 61611. **T:** 1 309 698-9736
E: wpeo@wpeo.com **W:** http://www.wpeo.com
Editorial Profile: WPEO-AM is a commercial station owned by Pinebrook Foundation Inc. The format of the station is religious talk. WPEO-AM broadcasts to the East Peoria, IL area at 1020 AM.

WPER-FM
Owner: Positive Alternative Radio
Editorial: 6546 Lovers Ln, Warrenton, Virginia 20186. **T:** 1 540 347-4825
E: info@positivehits.org
W: http://www.positivehits.org
Editorial Profile: WPER-FM is a non-commercial station owned by Positive Alternative Radio. The format of the station is contemporary Christian music. WPER-FM broadcasts in the Warrenton, VA area at 89.9 FM.

WPET-AM
Owner: Entercom Communications Corp.
Editorial: 7819 National Service Rd, Ste 401, Greensboro, North Carolina 27409.
T: 1 336 275-9738 **E:** tradio@entercom.com
W: http://www.wpetam950.com
Editorial Profile: WPET-AM is a commercial station owned by Entercom Communications Corp. The format of the station is gospel music. WPET-AM broadcasts to the Greensboro, NC area at 950 AM.

WPEZ-FM
Owner: Cumulus Media Inc.
Editorial: 544 Mulberry St, Ste 500, Macon, Georgia 31201. **T:** 1 478 746-6286
W: http://www.z937.com
Editorial Profile: WPEZ-FM is a commercial station owned by Cumulus Media Inc. The format of the station is adult contemporary music. WPEZ-FM broadcasts to the Macon, GA area at 93.7 FM.

WPFC-AM
Owner: Victory & Power Ministries Inc.
Editorial: 6943 Titian Ave, Baton Rouge, Louisiana 70806. **T:** 1 225 926-6550
E: wpfc1550am@gmail.com
Editorial Profile: WPFC-AM is a commercial station owned by Victory & Power Ministries Inc. The format of the station is gospel. WPFC-AM broadcasts to the Baton Rouge, LA area at 1550 AM.

WPFG-FM
Owner: Cumberland Valley Christian Radio
Editorial: 14 Stover Dr, Carlisle, Pennsylvania 17015-9782. **T:** 1 717 241-9734
E: wpfgmail@wpfgfm.org **W:** http://wpfgfm.org
Editorial Profile: WPFG-FM is a non-commercial station owned by Cumberland Valley Christian Radio. The format of the station is Christian music and talk programming. WPFG-FM broadcasts to the Carlisle, PA area at a frequency of 91.3 FM.

WPFJ-AM
Owner: Toccoa Falls College
Editorial: 185 Franklin Plaza Dr, Franklin, North Carolina 28734-3249.
T: 1 800 251-8326
E: radio@myfavoritestation.net
W: http://www.toccoafallsradio.org
Editorial Profile: WPFJ-AM is a commercial station owned by Toccoa Falls College. The format of the station is religious featuring Christian teaching and music. WPFJ-AM

broadcasts to the Franklin, NC area at 1480 AM.

WPFL-FM
Owner: Tri-County Broadcasting
Editorial: 20630 Highway 31, Flomaton, Alabama 36441-5210. **T:** 1 251 296-1051
E: wpflradio@bellsouth.net
Editorial Profile: WPFL-FM is a commercial station owned by Tri-County Broadcasting. The format of the station is primarily classic country with some contemporary country hits. WPFL-FM broadcasts to the Flomaton, AL area on 105.1 FM.

WPFM-FM
Owner: Powell Broadcasting Company, LLC
Editorial: 118 Gwyn Dr, Panama City Beach, Florida 32408-5854. **T:** 1 850 234-8858
W: http://hot1079pc.com
Editorial Profile: WPFM-FM is a commercial station owned by Powell Broadcasting Company, LLC. The format of the station is Top 40/CHR. WPFM-FM's broadcasts to the Panama City, FL area at 107.9 FM.

WPFP-AM
Owner: Heartland Communications Group, LLC
Editorial: 1329 4th Ave S, Park Falls, Wisconsin 54552-1926. **T:** 1 715 762-3221
E: wcqm@pctcnet.net

WPFR-AM
Owner: Word Power Inc.
Editorial: 18889 N 2350th St, Dennison, Illinois 62423-2523. **T:** 1 217 826-9673
E: wpfr@joink.com
W: http://www.wordpower.us
Editorial Profile: WPFR-AM is a commercial station owned by Word Power Inc. The format of the station is Christian programming. WPFR-AM broadcasts to the Dennison, IL area at 1480 AM.

WPFR-FM
Owner: Word Power Inc.
Editorial: 18889 N 2350th St, Dennison, Illinois 62423-2523. **T:** 1 217 826-9673
E: wpfr@joink.com
W: http://www.wordpower.us
Editorial Profile: WPFR-FM is a commercial station owned by Word Power Inc. The format of the station is Christian. WPFR-FM broadcasts to the Dennison, IL area at 93.9 FM.

WPFT-FM
Owner: East Tennessee Radio Group
Editorial: 196 W Dumplin Valley Rd, Kodak, Tennessee 37764-1934. **T:** 1 865 932-6002
Editorial Profile: WPFT-FM is a commercial station owned by East Tennessee Radio Group. The format of the station is sports. WPFT-FM broadcasts to the Kodak, TN area at 106.3 FM.

WPFW-FM
Owner: Pacifica Foundation, Inc.
Editorial: 1819 L St NW Fl 7, Washington, District Of Columbia 20036-3807.
T: 1 202 588-0999 344
W: http://www.wpfwfm.org
Editorial Profile: WPFW-FM is a non-commercial station owned by Pacifica Foundation, Inc. The format of the station is news/talk and music. WPFW-FM broadcasts to the Washington area at 89.3 FM.

WPFX-FM
Owner: Toledo Radio LLC
Editorial: 720 Water Street, 4th Floor, Toledo, Ohio 43604. **T:** 1 419 255-0107
W: http://1077wolf.com
Editorial Profile: WPFX-FM is a commercial station owned by Toledo Radio LLC. The format of the station is contemporary country. WPFX-FM broadcasts to the Toledo, OH area at 107.7 FM.

WPGA-AM
Owner: Register Communications
Editorial: 1691 Forsyth St, Macon, Georgia 31201. **T:** 1 478 745-5858
W: http://www.macon.tv
Editorial Profile: WPGA-AM is a commercial station owned by Register Communications. The format of the station is gospel music. WPGA-AM broadcasts to the Macon, GA area at 980 AM.

WPGA-FM
Owner: Register Communications
Editorial: 1691 Forsyth St, Macon, Georgia 31201. **T:** 1 478 745-5858 **E:** mix@macon.tv
W: http://www.macon.tv

Editorial Profile: WPGA-FM is a commercial station owned by Register Communications. The format of the station is adult contemporary. WPGA-FM broadcasts to the Macon, GA area at 100.9 FM.

WPGB-FM
Owner: Clear Channel Media and Entertainment
Editorial: 200 Fleet St Floor 4, Pittsburgh, Pennsylvania 15220-2908. **T:** 1 412 937-1441
E: feedback@wpgb.com
W: http://www.wpgb.com
Editorial Profile: WPGB-FM is a commercial station owned by Clear Channel Media and Entertainment. The format of the station is news, talk and sports. WPGB-FM broadcasts to the Pittsburgh area at 104.7 FM.

WPGC-FM
Owner: CBS Radio
Editorial: 4200 Parliament Pl Ste 300, Lanham, Maryland 20706-1881.
T: 1 301 918-0955 **W:** http://www.wpgc.com
Editorial Profile: WPGC-FM is a commercial station owned by CBS Radio. The format of the station is urban contemporary. WPGC-FM broadcasts to the Washington, D.C. area at 95.5 FM.

WPGG-AM
Owner: Townsquare Media, LLC
Editorial: 950 Tilton Rd Ste 200, Northfield, New Jersey 08225-1235. **T:** 1 609 645-9797
W: http://wpg1450.com
Editorial Profile: WPGG-AM is a commercial station owned by Townsquare Media, LLC. The format of the station is talk. WENJ-AM broadcasts to the Atlantic City, NJ area at 1450 AM.

WPGI-FM
Owner: Community Broadcasters, LLC
Editorial: 2205 College Ave, Elmira, New York 14903-1201. **T:** 1 607 732-4400
W: http://www.bigpigfm.com
Editorial Profile: WPGI-FM is a commercial station owned by Community Broadcasters, LLC. The format of the station is contemporary country music. WPGI-FM broadcasts to the Elmira, NY area at 100.9 FM.

WPGM-AM
Owner: Montrose Broadcasting Corp.
Editorial: 8 E Market St, Danville, Pennsylvania 17821. **T:** 1 570 275-1570
W: http://www.wpgmfm.org
Editorial Profile: WPGM-AM is a non-commercial station owned by the Montrose Broadcasting Corp. The format of the station is contemporary Christian music and religious programming. WPGM-AM broadcasts to the Danville, PA area at 1500 AM.

WPGM-FM
Owner: Montrose Broadcasting Corp.
Editorial: 8 E Market St, Danville, Pennsylvania 17821. **T:** 1 570 275-1570
W: http://www.wpgmfm.org
Editorial Profile: WPGM-FM is a non-commercial station owned by the Montrose Broadcasting Corp. The format of the station is gospel music and religion. WPGM-FM broadcasts to the Danville, PA area at 96.7 FM.

WPGR-AM
Owner: Saint Joseph Missions
Editorial: 3660 State Route 30 Ste D, Latrobe, Pennsylvania 15650-4309. **T:** 1 724 640-0361
Editorial Profile: WPGR-AM is a commercial station owned by Saint Joseph Missions. The format of the station is Catholic programming. WPGR-AM broadcasts to the Pittsburgh area at 1510 AM.

WPGS-AM
Owner: WPGS Inc.
Editorial: 805 N Dixie Ave, Titusville, Florida 32796-2018. **T:** 1 321 383-1000
E: WPGS840@aol.com **W:** http://local840.com
Editorial Profile: WPGS-AM is a commercial station owned by WPGS Inc. The format of the station is classic country. WPGS-AM broadcasts to the Titusville, FL area at 840 AM.

WPGU-FM
Owner: Illini Media Company
Editorial: 512 E Green St, Ste 107, Champaign, Illinois 61820. **T:** 1 217 337-3100
E: wpgu@wpgu.com
W: http://www.the217.com/wpgu/
Editorial Profile: WPGU-FM is a commercial station owned by the Illini Media Co. The format of the station is rock alternative music.

WPGU-FM broadcasts in the Champaign, IL area at 107.1 FM.

WPGW-AM
Owner: WPGW Inc.
Editorial: 1891 W State Road 67, Portland, Indiana 47371. **T:** 1 260 726-8729
E: wpgw@jayco.net **W:** http://wpgwradio.com
Editorial Profile: WPGW-AM is a commercial station owned by WPGW Inc. The format of the station is adult contemporary music. WPGW-AM broadcasts to the Portland, IN area at 1440 AM.

WPGW-FM
Owner: WPGW Inc.
Editorial: 1891 W State Road 67, Portland, Indiana 47371. **T:** 1 260 726-8729
W: http://wpgwradio.com
Editorial Profile: WPGW-FM is a commercial station owned by WPGW Inc. The format of the station is contemporary country music. WPGW-FM broadcasts in the Portland, IN area at 100.9 FM.

WPGY-AM
Owner: Tri-State Communications, Inc.
Editorial: 134 S Main St, Jasper, Georgia 30143. **T:** 1 678 454-9350
W: http://www.wljaradio.com
Editorial Profile: WPGY-AM is a commercial station owned by Tri-State Communications, Inc. The format for the station is oldies. WPGY-AM broadcasts to the Atlanta area at 1560 AM.

WPHB-AM
Owner: Magnum Broadcasting Inc.
Editorial: 1884 Port Matilda Hwy, Philipsburg, Pennsylvania 16866. **T:** 1 814 342-2300
E: wphb1260@gmail.com
Editorial Profile: WPHB-AM is a commercial station owned by Magnum Broadcasting Inc. The format for the station is country and talk. WPHB-AM broadcasts to the State College, PA, area at 1260 AM.

WPHE-AM
Owner: Radio Salvacion Inc.
Editorial: 321 W Sedgley Ave, Philadelphia, Pennsylvania 19140-4541. **T:** 1 215 739-3083
W: http://www.radiosalvacion.com
Editorial Profile: WPHE-AM is a commercial station owned by Radio Salvacion Inc. The format of the station is Hispanic religious. WPHE-AM broadcasts to the Philadelphia area at 690 AM.

WPHI-FM
Owner: Radio One Inc.
Editorial: 333 E City Ave Ste 700, Bala Cynwyd, Pennsylvania 19004-1521.
T: 1 610 538-1100
W: http://hot1079philly.com
Editorial Profile: WPHI-FM is a commercial station owned by Radio One Inc. The format of the station is rhythmic Top 40/CHR. WPHI-FM broadcasts to the Philadelphia area at 107.9 FM.

WPHK-FM
Owner: Blountstown Communications
Editorial: 20872 NE Kelley Ave, Blountstown, Florida 32424. **T:** 1 850 674-5101
Editorial Profile: WPHK-FM is a commercial station owned by Blountstown Communications. The format of the station is country music. WPHK-FM broadcasts in the Blountstown, FL area at 102.7 FM.

WPHM-AM
Owner: Radio First
Editorial: 808 Huron Ave, Port Huron, Michigan 48060-3705. **T:** 1 810 982-9000
E: newsroom@bluewaternews.net
W: http://www.wphm.net
Editorial Profile: WPHM-AM is a commercial station owned by Radio First. The format of the station is news, sports and talk. WPHM-AM broadcasts to the Port Huron, MI area at 1380 AM.

WPHN-FM
Owner: Northern Christian Radio
Editorial: 1511 E M 32, Gaylord, Michigan 49735-9702. **T:** 1 989 732-6274
E: studio@ncradio.org
W: http://www.ncradio.org
Editorial Profile: WPHN-FM is a non-commercial station owned by Northern Christian Radio. The format of the station is religious and contemporary Christian programming. WPHN-FM broadcasts to the Traverse City, MI area at 90.5 FM.

WPHP-FM
Owner: Ohio County Board of Education
Editorial: 1976 Park View Rd, Wheeling, West Virginia 26003. **T:** 1 304 243-0400

WPHR-FM
Owner: Clear Channel Media and Entertainment
Editorial: 3071 Continental Dr, West Palm Beach, Florida 33407-3274. **T:** 1 561 616-6600
W: http://www.RushRadio947.com
Editorial Profile: WPHR-FM is a commercial station owned by Clear Channel Media and Entertainment. The station's format is country. WPHR-FM broadcasts to the greater Fort Pierce, FL area at 94.7 FM and is based out of its West Palm Beach, FL offices.

WPHS-FM
Owner: Warren Cousino High School
Editorial: 30333 Hoover Rd, Warren, Michigan 48093. **T:** 1 586 698-4501
E: jermack@yahoo.com
W: http://www.wphs.com
Editorial Profile: WPHS-FM is a non-commercial station owned by Warren Cousino High School. The format of the station is variety. WPHS-FM broadcasts to the Warren, MI area at 89.1 FM.

WPHT-AM
Owner: CBS Radio
Editorial: 2 Bala Plz, Bala Cynwyd, Pennsylvania 19004-1501. **T:** 1 610 668-5800
E: thebigtalker1210@cbsradio.com
W: http://philadelphia.cbslocal.com/station/talk-radio-1210
Editorial Profile: WPHT-AM is a commercial station owned by CBS Radio. The format of the station is talk. WPHT-AM broadcasts to the Philadelphia area at 1210 AM.

WPHZ-FM
Owner: Mitchell Community Broadcasting
Editorial: 424 Heltonville Rd W, Bedford, Indiana 47421-9389. **T:** 1 812 275-7555
E: comments@wphz.com
W: http://www.wphz.com
Editorial Profile: WPHZ-FM is a commercial station owned by Mitchell Community Broadcasting. The format of the station is adult contemporary. WPHZ-FM broadcasts to the Bedford, IN area at 102.5 FM.

WPIA-FM
Owner: Advanced Media Partners LLC
Editorial: 2006 W Altorfer Dr, Peoria, Illinois 61615-1864. **T:** 1 309 691-0101
W: http://www.kissfmpeoria.com
Editorial Profile: WPIA-FM is a commercial station owned by Advanced Media Partners LLC. The format of the station is Top 40/CHR music. WPIA-FM broadcasts to the Peoria, IL area at 98.5 FM.

WPIB-FM
Owner: Positive Alternative Radio
Editorial: 22226 Timberlake Rd., Lynchburg, Virginia 24502-7214. **T:** 1 434 237-9798
E: office@spiritfm.com
W: http://www.spiritfm.com
Editorial Profile: WPIB-FM is a non-commercial station owned by Positive Alternative Radio. The format of the station is contemporary Christian and religion. WPIB-FM broadcasts to the Blacksburg, VA area at 91.1 FM.

WPIC-AM
Owner: Cumulus Media Inc.
Editorial: 2030 Pine Hollow Blvd, Hermitage, Pennsylvania 16148. **T:** 1 724 346-4113
W: http://790wpic.com
Editorial Profile: WPIC-AM is a commercial station owned by Cumulus Media Inc. The format of the station is news and talk. WPIC-AM broadcasts to the Hermitage, PA area at 790 AM.

WPID-AM
Owner: Piedmont Radio Company
Editorial: 412 Cedartown Hwy, Piedmont, Alabama 36272. **T:** 1 256 447-9096

WPIE-AM
Owner: Taughannock Media, LLC
Editorial: 3100 N Triphammer Rd Ste 100, Lansing, New York 14882-8983.
T: 1 607 533-0057 **W:** http://1160espn.com
Editorial Profile: WPIE-AM is a commercial station owned by Taughannock Media, LLC. The format of the station is sports. WPIE-AM broadcasts to the Elmira, NY area at 1160 AM.

WPIG-FM
Owner: Community Broadcasters, LLC

Editorial: 3163 Nys Route 417, Olean, New York 14760-1853. **T:** 1 716 372-0161
W: http://www.cbolean.com/pig
Editorial Profile: WPIG-FM is a commercial station owned by Community Broadcasters, LLC. The format of the station is country, featuring contemporary and classic hits. WPIG-FM broadcasts to the Olean, NY area at 95.7 FM.

WPIK-FM
Owner: Summerland Media, LLC
Editorial: 22500 Pieces of Eight Rd, Cudjoe Key, Florida 33042-4256. **T:** 1 305 745-4162
W: http://www.radioritmolafabulosa.com
Editorial Profile: WPIK-FM is a commercial station owned by Summerland Media, LLC. The format of the station is Hispanic. WPIK-FM broadcasts to the Summerland Key, FL area at 102.5 FM.

WPIL-FM
Owner: Jarrell(Jimmy)
Editorial: 256 Brockford Rd, Heflin, Alabama 36264-1608. **T:** 1 256 463-4226
E: wpil@wpilfm.com
W: http://www.wpilfm.com
Editorial Profile: WPIL-FM is a non-commercial station owned by Jimmy Jarrell. The format of the station is variety, featuring a mix of classic country, gospel and bluegrass with a Christian base. WPIL-FM broadcasts to the Heflin, AL area at 91.7 FM.

WPIM-FM
Owner: Positive Alternative Radio
Editorial: 22226 Timberlake Rd., Lynchburg, Virginia 24502-7214. **T:** 1 434 237-9798
E: office@spiritfm.com
W: http://www.spiritfm.com

WPIN-AM
Owner: Positive Radio Group
Editorial: 145 Jackson St NE, Blacksburg, Virginia 24060. **T:** 1 540 951-9791
E: wpin810@yahoo.com
W: http://www.810wpin.com
Editorial Profile: WPIN-AM is a commercial station owned by Positive Radio Group. The format of the station is country. WPIN-AM broadcasts to the Blacksburg, VA area at 810 AM.

WPIN-FM
Owner: Positive Alternative Radio
Editorial: 22226 Timberlake Rd., Lynchburg, Virginia 24502-7214. **T:** 1 800 774-9798
E: office@spiritfm.com
W: http://www.spiritfm.com
Editorial Profile: WPIN-FM is a non-commercial station owned by Positive Alternative Radio. The format of the station is contemporary Christian and religion. WPIN-FM broadcasts to the Blacksburg, VA area at 91.5 FM.

WPIO-FM
Owner: Florida Public Radio, Inc.
Editorial: 505 Josephine St, Titusville, Florida 32796. **T:** 1 321 267-3000 **E:** wpio@gate.net
W: http://www.noncomradio.net
Editorial Profile: WPIO-FM is a non-commercial station owned by Florida Public Radio, Inc. The format of the station is religious. WPOI-FM broadcasts to the Titusville, FL area at 89.3 FM.

WPIP-AM
Owner: Berean Baptist Church
Editorial: 4135 Thomasville Rd, Winston Salem, North Carolina 27107-4427.
T: 1 336 785-0527
E: wpip880am@triad.rr.com
W: http://www.wpipbereanradio.org
Editorial Profile: WPIP-AM is is a non-commercial station owned by Berean Baptist Church. The format of the station is religious. WPIP-AM broadcasts to the Winston-Salem, NC area at 880 AM.

WPIR-FM
Owner: Positive Alternative Radio
Editorial: 3289 WCXN Radio Rd, Claremont, North Carolina 28610-9715.
T: 1 828 459-9803 **E:** shelley@bellsouth.net
W: http://www.joyfm.org/pages/wpir/
Editorial Profile: WPIR-FM is a non-commercial station owned by Positive Alternative Radio. The format of the station is southern gospel music and religious talk. WPIR-FM broadcasts in the Claremont, NC area at 88.1 FM.

WPIT-AM
Owner: Salem Communications
Editorial: 7 Parkway Ctr, Ste 625, Pittsburgh, Pennsylvania 15220-3707. **T:** 1 412 937-1500

E: word@wordfm.com
W: http://www.wpitam.com
Editorial Profile: WPIT-AM is a commercial station owned by Salem Communications. The format of the station is religious talk. WPIT-AM broadcasts to the Pittsburgh, PA area at 730 AM.

WPJC-FM
Owner: WPRR, Inc.
Editorial: 3777 44th St SE, Grand Rapids, Michigan 49512-3945. **T:** 1 616 656-2619
E: info@publicrealityradio.org
W: http://www.publicrealityradio.org
Editorial Profile: WPJC-FM is a non-commerical station owned by WPRR, Inc. The format of the station is variety. WPJC-FM broadcasts to the Pontiac, IL area at 88.3 FM.

WPJL-AM
Owner: WPJL Inc.
Editorial: 515 Bart St, Raleigh, North Carolina 27610. **T:** 1 919 834-6401 **E:** wpjl@nc.rr.com
W: http://www.wpjlradio.com
Editorial Profile: WPJL-AM is a commercial station owned by WPJL Inc. The format of the station is religious programming. WPJL-AM broadcasts in the Raleigh, NC area at 1240 AM.

WPJM-AM
Owner: Full Gospel WPJM 800 AM Radio Inc.
Editorial: 305 N. Tryon St, Greer, South Carolina 29651. **T:** 1 864 877-1112
E: wpjesusmusic@bellsouth.net
W: http://800wpjm.com
Editorial Profile: WPJM-AM is a commercial station owned by Full Gospel WPJM 800 AM Radio Inc. The format of the station is gospel. WPJM-AM broadcasts to the Greenville, SC and Asheville, NC area at 800 AM.

WPJS-AM
Owner: WPJS Broadcasting Inc.
Editorial: 1516 B 4th Ave, Conway, South Carolina 29526. **T:** 1 843 248-6365
W: http://www.gospel1330.com
Editorial Profile: WPJS-AM is a commercial station owned by WPJS Broadcasting Inc. The format of the station is gospel music. WPJS-AM broadcasts to the Conway, SC area at 1330 AM.

WPJX-AM
Owner: Polnet Communications
Editorial: 4320 Dundee Rd, Northbrook, Illinois 60062-1703. **T:** 1 847 498-3350
E: polnetradio@gmail.com
Editorial Profile: WPJX-AM is a commercial station owned by Polnet Communications. The format of the station is Spanish. WPJX-AM broadcasts to the Northbrook, IL area at 1500 AM.

WPJY-FM
Owner: Positive Alternative Radio
Editorial: 3501 Emerson Ave Ste 8B, Parkersburg, West Virginia 26104-1854.
T: 1 877 456-9361 **E:** office@walkfm.org
W: http://walkfm.org
Editorial Profile: WPJY-FM is a non-commercial station owned by Positive Alternative Radio. The format of the station is Contemporary Christian. WPJY-FM broadcasts to the Parkersburg, WV area at 88.7 FM.

WPKE-AM
Owner: East Kentucky Radio Network
Editorial: 1240 Radio Dr, Pikeville, Kentucky 41501-4779. **T:** 1 606 432-8103
E: frontdesk@ekbradio.com
W: http://www.myoldiesradio.com
Editorial Profile: WPKE-AM is a commercial station owned by East Kentucky Radio Network. The format of the station is oldies music. WPKE-AM broadcasts to the Pikeville, KY area at 1240 AM.

WPKE-FM
Owner: East Kentucky Radio Network
Editorial: 1240 Radio Dr, Pikeville, Kentucky 41501-4779. **T:** 1 606 437-4051
E: frontdesk@ekbradio.com
W: http://www.wpke.com
Editorial Profile: WPKE-FM is a commercial station owned by East Kentucky Radio Network. The format of the station is classic rock. WPKE-FM target broadcasts to Pikeville, KY and surrounding communities at 103.1 FM.

WPKF-FM
Owner: Clear Channel Media and Entertainment
Editorial: 20 Tucker Dr, Poughkeepsie, New York 12603-1644. **T:** 1 845 471-2300
W: http://www.kissfmhv.com

Editorial Profile: WPKF-FM is a commercial station owned by Clear Channel Media and Entertainment. The format of the station is rhythmic Top 40/CHR music. WPKF-FM broadcasts to the Poughkeepsie, NY area at 96.1 FM.

WPKG-FM
Owner: Central Wisconsin Broadcasting
Editorial: 1201 E Division St, Neillsville, Wisconsin 54456. **T:** 1 715 743-3333
E: 1075therock@tds.net
W: http://www.cbwradio.com
Editorial Profile: WPKG-FM is a commercial station owned by Central Wisconsin Broadcasting. The format of the station is Hot AC. WPKG-FM broadcasts to the Clarks County, Wisconsin area at a frequency of 92.7 FM.

WPKL-FM
Owner: Keymarket of Pennsylvania, LLC
Editorial: 123 Blaine Rd, Brownsville, Pennsylvania 15417-9330. **T:** 1 724 938-2000
W: http://www.picklefm.com
Editorial Profile: WPKL-FM is a commercial station owned by Keymarket of Pennsylvania, LLC. The format of the station is classic hits music. WPKL-FM broadcasts in the Brownsville, PA area on 99.3 FM.

WPKN-FM
Owner: WPKN Inc.
Editorial: 244 University Ave, Bridgeport, Connecticut 06604-7775. **T:** 1 203 331-9756
E: press@wpkn.org **W:** http://www.wpkn.org
Editorial Profile: WPKN-FM is a non-commercial station owned by WPKN Inc. The format of the station is variety. WPKN-FM broadcasts in the Bridgeport, CT area at 89.5 FM.

WPKO-FM
Owner: V-Teck Communications Inc.
Editorial: 1501 Road 235, Bellefontaine, Ohio 43311. **T:** 1 937 592-1045
W: http://www.peakofohio.com
Editorial Profile: WPKO-FM is a commercial station owned by V-Tech Communications Inc. The format of the station is adult contemporary music. WPKO-FM's target audience is adult contemporary music listeners, ages 18 to 64, in the Dayton, OH area. The station's tagline is "Mix 98.3"

WPKQ-FM
Owner: Townsquare Media
Editorial: 2617 White Mountain Hwy, North Conway, New Hampshire 03860-5120.
T: 1 603 356-7500 **E:** news@wokq.com
W: http://www.wokq.com
Editorial Profile: WPKQ-FM is a commercial station owned by Townsquare Media. The format of the station is contemporary country. WPKQ-FM broadcasts to the North Conway, NH area at 103.7 FM.

WPKR-FM
Owner: Cumulus Media Inc.
Editorial: 491 S Washburn St, Oshkosh, Wisconsin 54904-6733. **T:** 1 920 426-3239
W: http://www.thewolf.fm
Editorial Profile: WPKR-FM is a commercial station owned by Cumulus Media Inc. The format of the station is contemporary country. WPKR-FM broadcasts to the Green Bay, WI area at 99.5 FM.

WPKT-FM
Owner: Connecticut Public Broadcasting Inc.
Editorial: 1049 Asylum Ave, Hartford, Connecticut 06105-2432. **T:** 1 860 278-5310
E: wherewelive@wnpr.org
W: http://www.cpbn.org
Editorial Profile: WPKT-FM is a non-commercial station owned by Connecticut Public Broadcasting Inc. The format of the station is news and talk. WPKT-FM broadcasts to the Hartford, CT area at 89.1 FM. WPKT-FM airs WNPR-FM's programming.

WPKX-AM
Owner: Clear Channel Media and Entertainment
Editorial: 195 McGregor St Ste 810, Manchester, New Hampshire 03102-3755.
T: 1 603 625-6915
W: http://www.foxsports930.com/main.html
Editorial Profile: WPKX-AM is a commercial station owned by Clear Channel Media and Entertainment. The format of the station is sports talk. WPKX-AM broadcasts to the Manchester, NH area at 930 AM.

WPKY-AM
Owner: Commonwealth Broadcasting Corp.

Editorial: 108 W Main St, Princeton, Kentucky 42445. **T:** 1 270 365-2072
E: wavj@commonwealthbroadcasting.com
Editorial Profile: WPKY-AM is a commercial station owned by Commonwealth Broadcasting Corp. The format of the station is sports. WPKY-AM broadcasts to the Princeton, KY area at 1580 AM.

WPKZ-AM
Owner: Central Broadcasting Company LLC
Editorial: 762 Water St, Fitchburg, Massachusetts 01420-6497.
T: 1 978 343-3766 **E:** info@wpkz.net
W: http://wpkz.net
Editorial Profile: WPKZ-AM is a commercial station owned by Central Broadcasting Company LLC. The format of the station is sports and news talk. WPKZ-AM broadcasts to the Fitchburg, MA area at 1280 AM.

WPLA-AM
Owner: Clear Channel Media and Entertainment
Editorial: 7080 Industrial Hwy, Macon, Georgia 31216-7538. **T:** 1 478 781-1063
W: http://www.foxsports1670.com
Editorial Profile: WPLA-AM is a commercial station owned by Clear Channel Media and Entertainment. The format of the station is sports. WPLA-AM broadcasts to the Macon, GA area at 1670 AM.

WPLJ-FM
Owner: Cumulus Media Inc
Editorial: 2 Penn Plz, New York, New York 10121-0101. **T:** 1 212 613-8900
W: http://www.plj.com
Editorial Profile: WPLJ-FM is a commercial station owned by Cumulus Media Inc. The format of the station is hot adult contemporary music. WPLJ-FM broadcasts throughout the New York City area at 95.5 FM.

WPLK-AM
Owner: Bullock (Wayne)
Editorial: 1428 Saint Johns Ave, Palatka, Florida 32177-4542. **T:** 1 386 325-5800
E: wplk@wplk.com **W:** http://www.wplk.com
Editorial Profile: WPLK-AM is a commercial station owned by Wayne Bullock. The format of the station is adult standards. WPLK-AM broadcasts to the Palatka, FL area at 800 AM.

WPLL-FM
Owner: Marc Radio Group, LLC
Editorial: 100 NW 76th Dr Ste 2, Gainesville, Florida 32607-6659. **T:** 1 352 313-3150
W: http://www.1069pulsefm.com
Editorial Profile: WPLL-FM is a commercial station owned by Marc Radio Group, LLC. The format of the station is Contemporary Christian. WPLL-FM broadcasts to the Gainesville, FL area at 106.9 FM.

WPLM-AM
Owner: Plymouth Rock Broadcasting
Editorial: 17 Columbus Rd, Plymouth, Massachusetts 02360-4810.
T: 1 508 746-1390
W: http://www.easy991.com
Editorial Profile: WPLM-AM is a commercial station owned by Plymouth Rock Broadcasting. The format of the station is classic soft hits. WPLM-AM broadcasts to the Plymouth, MA area at 1390 AM.

WPLM-FM
Owner: Plymouth Rock Broadcasting
Editorial: 17 Columbus Rd, Plymouth, Massachusetts 02360-4810.
T: 1 508 746-1390
W: http://www.easy991.com
Editorial Profile: WPLM-FM is a commercial station owned by Plymouth Rock Broadcasting. The format of the station is classic soft hits. WPLM-FM broadcasts to the Plymouth, MA area at 99.1 FM.

WPLN-AM
Owner: Nashville Public Radio
Editorial: 630 Mainstream Dr, Nashville, Tennessee 37228-1204. **T:** 1 615 760-2903
E: wpln@wpln.org **W:** http://www.wpln.org
Editorial Profile: WPLN-AM is a non-commercial station owned by Nashville Public Radio. The format of the station is news and talk. WPLN-AM broadcasts to the Nashville, TN area at at 1430 AM.

WPLN-FM
Owner: Nashville Public Radio
Editorial: 630 Mainstream Dr, Nashville, Tennessee 37228-1204. **T:** 1 615 760-2903
E: wpln@wpln.org **W:** http://www.wpln.org
Editorial Profile: WPLN-FM is a non-commercial station owned by Nashville Public

Radio. The format of the station is news and talk. WPLN-FM broadcasts to the Nashville, TN area at 90.3 FM.

WPLO-AM
Owner: Prieto Communications
Editorial: 239 Ezzard St, Lawrenceville, Georgia 30046-5936. **T:** 1 770 237-9897
Editorial Profile: WPLO-AM is a commercial station owned by Prieto Communications. The format of the station is Hispanic. WPLO-AM broadcasts to the Lawrenceville, GA area at 610 AM.

WPLR-FM
Owner: Connoisseur Media
Editorial: 440 Wheelers Farms Rd, Milford, Connecticut 06461-9133. **T:** 1 203 783-8200
W: http://www.wplr.com
Editorial Profile: WPLR-FM is a commercial station owned by Connoisseur Media. The format of the station is classic rock. WPLR-FM broadcasts to the Milford, CT area at 99.1 FM.

WPLS-FM
Owner: Furman University
Editorial: 3300 Poinsett Hwy, Greenville, South Carolina 29613-0002.
T: 1 864 294-3054
W: http://www.furman.edu/orgs/wpls
Editorial Profile: WPLS-FM is a non-commercial station owned by Furman University. The format for the station is rock alternative. WPLS-FM broadcasts to the Greenville, SC; Asheville, NC area at 95.9 FM.

WPLV-AM
Owner: Clear Channel Media and Entertainment
Editorial: 705 4th Ave, West Point, Georgia 31833-1506. **T:** 1 706 645-2991
W: http://www.intouch910am.com/default.asp
Editorial Profile: WPLV-AM is a commercial station owned by Clear Channel Media and Entertainment. The format of the station is urban contemporary and R & B oldies. WPLV-AM broadcasts to the Atlanta area at 1310 AM.

WPLW-FM
Owner: Curtis Media Group
Editorial: 3012 Highwoods Blvd Ste 201, Raleigh, North Carolina 27604-1031.
T: 1 919 790-9392 **E:** info@curtismedia.com
W: http://www.pulse102.com
Editorial Profile: WPLW-FM is a commercial station owned by Curtis Media Group. The format of the station is Top 40. WPLW-FM broadcasts to the greater Raleigh, NC area at 102.5 FM.

WPLZ-FM
Owner: Brewer Broadcasting Inc.
Editorial: 1305 Carter St, Chattanooga, Tennessee 37402. **T:** 1 423 265-9494
W: http://www.catcountry953.com
Editorial Profile: WPLZ-FM is a commercial station owned by Brewer Broadcasting Inc. The format of the station is contemporary country. WPLZ-FM broadcasts to the Cleveland, TN area at 95.3 FM.

WPMB-AM
Owner: Cromwell Group Inc.(The)
Editorial: 232 S 4th St, Vandalia, Illinois 62471. **T:** 1 618 283-2325
E: wkrv@sbcglobal.net
W: http://www.vandaliaradio.com
Editorial Profile: WPMB-AM is a commercial station owned by the Cromwell Group Inc. The format of the station is adult standards. WPMB-AM broadcasts to Vandalia, IL at 1500 AM.

WPMH-AM
Owner: Chesapeake-Portsmouth Broadcasting Corp.
Editorial: 2202 Jolliff Rd, Chesapeake, Virginia 23321-1416. **T:** 1 757 488-1010
E: info@wwip.org
W: http://www.wpmh1010.com
Editorial Profile: WPMH-AM is a commercial station owned by Chesapeake-Portsmouth Broadcasting Corp. The format of the station is religious talk. WPMH-AM broadcasts to the Chesapeake, VA area at 1010 AM.

WPMO-AM
Owner: JDL Corporation
Editorial: 3276 Highway 198 W, Lucedale, Mississippi 39452-7914. **T:** 1 601 947-8151
W: http://www.talkradio1580.com
Editorial Profile: WPMO-AM is a commercial station owned by JDL Corporation. The format of the station is news, sports and talk.

WPMO-AM broadcasts at a frequency of 1580 AM to the Pascagoula, MS area.

WPMX-FM
Owner: Georgia Eagle Broadcasting Inc.
Editorial: 561 E Olliff St, Statesboro, Georgia 30458-4663. **T:** 1 912 764-5446
E: wwnswmcd@yahoo.com
Editorial Profile: WPMX-FM is a commercial station owned by Georgia Eagle Broadcasting Inc. The format for the station is adult contemporary. WPMX-FM broadcasts to the Savannah, GA area at 102.9 FM.

WPMZ-AM
Owner: Video Mundo Broadcasting Co.
Editorial: 1270 Mineral Spring Ave, North Providence, Rhode Island 02904-4637.
T: 1 401 726-8413 **E:** info@poder1110.com
W: http://www.poder1110.com

WPNA-AM
Owner: Alliance Communications, Inc.
Editorial: 408 S Oak Park Ave, Oak Park, Illinois 60302-3876. **T:** 1 708 848-8980
E: email@wpna1490am.com
W: http://www.wpna1490am.com
Editorial Profile: WPNA-AM is a commercial station owned by Alliance Communications, Inc. The format of the station is talk programming spoken in the native dialect of Poland. WPNA-AM broadcasts to the Oak Park, IL area at 1490 AM.

WPNC-FM
Owner: Durlyn Broadcasting Inc.
Editorial: 930 NC Highway 32 S, Plymouth, North Carolina 27962-9354.
T: 1 252 793-9995 **E:** magic959@mchsi.com
W: http://magic959online.com
Editorial Profile: WPNC-FM is a commercial station owned by Durlyn Broadcasting Inc. The format of the station is adult contemporary. WPNC-FM broadcasts to the Plymouth, NC area at 95.9 FM.

WPNE-FM
Owner: University of Wisconsin
Editorial: 2420 Nicolet Dr, Green Bay, Wisconsin 54311. **T:** 1 920 465-2444
E: listener@wpr.org **W:** http://www.wpr.org
Editorial Profile: WPNE-FM is a non-commercial station owned by the University of Wisconsin. The format of the station is classical. WPNE-FM broadcasts to the Green Bay, WI area at 89.3 FM.

WPNG-FM
Owner: Broadcast South, LLC
Editorial: 1931Highway 32 E, Douglas, Georgia 31533-9074. **T:** 1 912 422-6122
Editorial Profile: WPNG-FM is a commercial station owned by Broadcast South, LLC. The format of the station is Top 40/CHR. WPNG-FM broadcasts to the Pearson, GA area at 101.9 FM.

WPNH-AM
Owner: Northeast Communications Corp.
Editorial: 110 Babbitt Rd, Franklin, New Hampshire 03235-2105. **T:** 1 888 941-1069
Editorial Profile: WPNH-AM is a commercial station owned by Northeast Communications Corp. The format of the station is adult standards music. WPNH-AM broadcasts to the Boston area at 1300 AM.

WPNH-FM
Owner: Northeast Communications Corp.
Editorial: 110 Babbitt Rd, Franklin, New Hampshire 03235-2105. **T:** 1 603 536-2500
E: annie@wpnhfm.com
W: http://www.wpnhfm.com
Editorial Profile: WPNH-FM is a commercial station owned by Northeast Communications Corp. The format of the station is rock alternative music. WPNH-FM broadcasts to the Boston area at 100.1 FM.

WPNN-AM
Owner: Schroeder(Don)
Editorial: 3801 N Pace Blvd, Pensacola, Florida 32505. **T:** 1 850 433-1141
W: http://www.wpnnradio.com
Editorial Profile: WPNN-AM is a commercial station owned by Don Schroeder. The format of the station is news and talk programming. WPNN-AM broadcasts to the Pensacola, FL area at 790 AM.

WPNW-AM
Owner: Lanser Broadcasting Corp.
Editorial: 425 Centerstone Ct, Zeeland, Michigan 49464-2247. **T:** 1 616 931-9930
E: news@1260thepledge.com
W: http://1260thepledge.com

Editorial Profile: WPNW-AM is a commercial station owned by Lanser Broadcasting Corp. The format of the station is talk. WPNW-AM broadcasts to the Holland, MI area at 1260 AM.

WPOC-FM

Owner: Clear Channel Media and Entertainment
Editorial: 711 W 40th St Ste 350, Baltimore, Maryland 21211-2190. **T:** 1 410 366-7600
W: http://www.wpoc.com
Editorial Profile: WPOC-FM is a commercial station owned by Clear Channel Media and Entertainments. The format of the station is country music. WPOC-FM broadcasts to the Baltimore area at 93.1 FM.

WPOG-AM

Owner: Grace Baptist Church of Orangeburg
Editorial: 4305 Columbia Rd, Orangeburg, South Carolina 29118-1268.
T: 1 803 536-4300
Editorial Profile: WPOG-FM is a commercial station owned by Grace Baptist Church of Orangeburg. The format of the station is religious. WPOG-FM broadcasts to the Saint Matthews, SC area at 710 AM.

WPOI-FM

Owner: Cox Media Group, Inc.
Editorial: 11300 4th St N Ste 300, Saint Petersburg, Florida 33716-2941.
T: 1 727 579-2000
W: http://www.hot1015tampabay.com
Editorial Profile: WPOI-FM is a commercial station owned by Cox Media Group, Inc. The format of the station is Hot AC. WPOI-FM broadcasts to the Saint Petersburg, FL area at 101.5 FM.

WPOL-AM

Owner: Truth Broadcasting
Editorial: 4405 Providence Ln, Winston Salem, North Carolina 27106-3226.
T: 1 336 759-0363
W: http://www.1340thelight.com
Editorial Profile: WPOL-AM is a commercial station owned by Truth Broadcasting. The format of the station is gospel. WPOL-AM broadcasts to the Winston Salem, NC area at 1340 AM.

WPOP-AM

Owner: Clear Channel Media and Entertainment
Editorial: 10 Columbus Blvd Ste 1, Hartford, Connecticut 06106-1976. **T:** 1 860 723-6000
W: http://www.foxsportsradio1410.com
Editorial Profile: WPOP-AM is a commercial station owned by Clear Channel Media and Entertainment. The format of the station is sports. WPOP-AM broadcasts to the Hartford, CT area at 1410 AM.

WPOR-FM

Owner: Saga Communications
Editorial: 420 Western Ave, South Portland, Maine 04106-1704. **T:** 1 207 774-4561
E: wpor@wpor.com **W:** http://www.wpor.com
Editorial Profile: WPOR-FM is a commercial station owned by Saga Communications. The format of the station is contemporary country. WPOR-FM broadcasts to the Portland, ME area at 101.9 FM.

WPOS-FM

Owner: Maumee Valley Broadcasting Association
Editorial: 7112 Angola Rd, Holland, Ohio 43528-9631. **T:** 1 419 865-5551
E: office@wposfm.com
W: http://www.wposfm.com
Editorial Profile: WPOS-FM is a non-commercial station owned by Maumee Valley Broadcasting Association. The format of the station is Christian AC. WPOS-FM broadcasts to the Holland, OH area at 102.3 FM.

WPOW-FM

Owner: Beasley Broadcast Group
Editorial: 194 NW 187th St, Miami, Florida 33169-4050. **T:** 1 305 654-1700
W: http://www.power96.com
Editorial Profile: WPOW-FM is a commercial station owned by the Beasley Broadcast Group. The format of the station is rhythmic Top 40/CHR. WPOW-FM broadcasts to the Miami area at 96.5 FM.

WPOZ-FM

Owner: Central Florida Educational Foundation, Inc.
Editorial: 1065 Rainer Dr, Altamonte Springs, Florida 32714. **T:** 1 407 869-8000
E: zcrew@zradio.org **W:** http://www.zradio.org

Editorial Profile: WPOZ-FM is a non-commercial station owned by Central Florida Educational Foundation, Inc. The format of the station is contemporary Christian. WPOZ-FM broadcasts to the Tampa and St. Petersburg, FL areas at 88.3 FM.

WPPA-AM

Owner: Pottsville Broadcasting Company Inc.
Editorial: 212 S Centre St, Pottsville, Pennsylvania 17901-3532. **T:** 1 570 622-1360
E: news@pbcradio.com
W: http://www.wpparadio.com
Editorial Profile: WPPA-AM is a commercial station owned by Pottsville Broadcasting Company Inc. The format of the station is talk. WPPA-AM broadcasts to the Pottsville, PA area at 1360 AM.

WPPB-FM

Owner: Peconic Public Broadcasting, Inc.
Editorial: 71 Hill St, Southampton, New York 11968-5319. **T:** 1 631 591-7000
W: http://www.peconicpublicbroadcasting.org
Editorial Profile: WPPB-FM is a non-commercial station owned by Peconic Public Broadcasting, Inc. The format of the station is jazz and news. WPPB-FM broadcasts in the Southhampton, NY, area at 88.3 FM.

WPPG-FM

Owner: Wolff Broadcasting Corporation.
Editorial: Highway 31 South, Evergreen, Alabama 36401. **T:** 1 251 578-3121
E: wppg@att.net
Editorial Profile: WPPG-FM is a commercial station owned by Wolff Broadcasting Corporation. The format of the station is country music. WPPG-FM broadcasts to the Evergreen, AL area at 101.1 FM.

WPPI-FM

Owner: Atlantic Coast Radio LLC
Editorial: 779 Warren Ave, Portland, Maine 04103-1007. **T:** 1 617 779-3500
W: http://www.weei.com
Editorial Profile: WPPI-FM is a commercial station owned by Atlantic Coast Radio LLC. The format of the station is sports. WPPI-FM broadcasts to the Portland, ME area at 95.5 FM. WPPI-FM airs WEEI-AM's programming.

WPPL-FM

Owner: White(James Timothy)
Editorial: 333 E Highland St, Blue Ridge, Georgia 30513-4544. **T:** 1 706 632-9775
E: wppl@tds.net
W: http://www.mountaincountryradio.com
Editorial Profile: WPPL-FM is a commercial station owned by James Timothy White. The format for the station is contemporary country. WPPL-FM broadcasts to the Chattanooga, TN area at 103.9 FM.

WPPN-FM

Owner: Univision Communications Inc.
Editorial: 625 N Michigan Ave Ste 300, Chicago, Illinois 60611-3110.
T: 1 312 981-1800
W: http://amor1067.univision.com
Editorial Profile: WPPN-FM is a commercial station owned by Univision Communications Inc. The format of the station is Spanish AC. WPPN-FM broadcasts to the Chicago area at 106.7 FM.

WPPR-FM

Owner: Georgia Public Broadcasting
Editorial: 260 14th St NW, Atlanta, Georgia 30318. **T:** 1 404 685-2548 **E:** news@gpb.org
W: http://www.gpb.org
Editorial Profile: WPPR-FM is a non-commercial station owned by Georgia Public Broadcasting. The format of the station is news, classical and jazz music. WPPR-FM broadcasts to the Atlanta area at 88.3 FM.

WPPT-FM

Owner: VerStandig Broadcasting
Editorial: 10960 John Wayne Dr, Greencastle, Pennsylvania 17225. **T:** 1 717 597-9200
W: http://now921.com
Editorial Profile: WPPT-FM is a commercial station owned by VerStandig Broadcasting. The format of the station is Top 40/CHR. WPPT-FM broadcasts to the Greencastle, PA area at 92.1 FM.

WPPZ-FM

Owner: Radio One Inc.
Editorial: 333 E City Ave Ste 700, Bala Cynwyd, Pennsylvania 19004-1521.
T: 1 610 538-1100 **W:** http://praisephilly.com
Editorial Profile: WPPZ-FM is a commercial station owned by Radio One Inc. The format of the station is gospel. WPPZ-FM broadcasts to the Philadelphia area at 103.9 FM.

WPRB-FM

Owner: Princeton Broadcasting Service
Editorial: 030 Bloomberg Hall Princeton Uni, Princeton, New Jersey 8544.
T: 1 609 258-3655 **E:** news@wprb.com
W: http://www.wprb.com
Editorial Profile: WPRB-FM is a commercial station owned by Princeton Broadcasting Service. The format for the station is variety. WPRB-FM broadcasts to the Princeton, NJ area at 103.3 FM.

WPRD-AM

Owner: J & V Communications Inc.
Editorial: 222 Hazard St, Orlando, Florida 32804-3030. **T:** 1 407 841-8282
E: wprd1440@gmail.com
W: http://www.wprd.com
Editorial Profile: WPRD-AM is a commercial station owned by J&V Communications Inc. The format of the station is Hispanic variety. WPRD-AM broadcasts to the Orlando, FL area at 1440 AM.

WPRE-AM

Owner: Robinson Corporation
Editorial: 640 N Villa Louis Rd, Prairie du Chien, Wisconsin 53821. **T:** 1 608 326-2411
E: wqpcwpre@mwt.net
W: http://www.wpreradio.com
Editorial Profile: WPRE-AM is a commercial station owned by Robinson Corporation. The format of the station is oldies. WPRE-AM broadcasts to the Prairie Du Chien, WI area at 980 AM.

WPRK-FM

Owner: Rollins College
Editorial: 1000 Holt Ave, Winter Park, Florida 32789-4499. **T:** 1 407 646-2241
E: wprkfm@rollins.edu **W:** http://wprk.org
Editorial Profile: WPRK-FM is a non-commercial station owned by Rollins College. The format of the station is Variety. WPRK-FM broadcasts to the Winter Park, FL area at 91.5 FM.

WPRL-FM

Owner: Alcorn State University
Editorial: 1000 Alcorn Dr, Box 269, Lorman, Mississippi 39096. **T:** 1 601 877-6290
W: http://www.wprl.org

WPRO-AM

Owner: Cumulus Media Inc.
Editorial: 1502 Wampanoag Trl, Riverside, Rhode Island 02915-1018. **T:** 1 401 433-4200
W: http://www.630wpro.com
Editorial Profile: WPRO-AM is a commercial station owned by Cumulus Media Inc. The format of the station is news, sports and talk. WPRO-AM broadcasts to the Riverside, RI area at 630 AM.

WPRO-FM

Owner: Cumulus Media Inc.
Editorial: 1502 Wampanoag Trl, Riverside, Rhode Island 2915. **T:** 1 401 433-4200
W: http://www.92profm.com
Editorial Profile: WPRO-FM is a commercial station owned by Cumulus Media Inc. The format of the station is Top 40/CHR. WPRO-FM broadcasts to the Riverside, RI area at 92.3 FM.

WPRR-AM

Owner: WPRR, Inc.
Editorial: 3777 44th St SE, Grand Rapids, Michigan 49512-3945. **T:** 1 616 656-2619
E: info@publicrealityradio.org
W: http://www.publicrealityradio.org
Editorial Profile: WPRR-AM is a non-commercial station owned by WPRR, Inc. The format of the station is talk. WPRR-AM broadcasts to the Grand Rapids, MI area at 1680 AM.

WPRS-AM

Owner: Midwest Communications Inc.
Editorial: 12861 Il Highway 133, Paris, Illinois 61944-6753. **T:** 1 812 232-4161
W: http://www.wprsam.com
Editorial Profile: WPRS-AM is a commercial station owned by Midwest Communications Inc. The format of the station is country. WPRS-AM broadcasts to the Terre Haute, IN area at 1440 AM.

WPRS-FM

Owner: Radio One Inc.
Editorial: 5900 Princess Garden Pkwy, 8th Fl, Lanham, Maryland 20706-2925.
T: 1 301 306-1111 **W:** http://praisedc.com
Editorial Profile: WPRS-FM is a commercial station owned by Radio One Inc. The format of the station is gospel. WPRS-FM broadcasts to the Washington, D.C. area at 104.1 FM.

WPRT-AM

Owner: East Kentucky Radio Network
Editorial: 1240 Radio Dr, Pikeville, Kentucky 41501-4779. **T:** 1 304 235-3600
E: frontdesk@ekbradio.com
W: http://www.900wlsi.com
Editorial Profile: WPRT-AM is a commercial station owned by East Kentucky Radio Network. The format of the station is talk. WPRT-AM broadcasts to the Pikeville, KY area at 960 AM.

WPRT-FM

Owner: Cromwell Group Inc.(The)
Editorial: 1824 Murfreesboro Pike, Nashville, Tennessee 37217. **T:** 1 615 399-1029
W: http://www.1025thegame.com
Editorial Profile: WPRT-FM is a commercial station owned by The Cromwell Group Inc. The format of the station is sports. WPRT-FM broadcasts to the Nashville, TN area at 102.5 FM.

WPRV-AM

Owner: Cumulus Media Inc.
Editorial: 1502 Wampanoag Trl, Riverside, Rhode Island 2915. **T:** 1 401 433-4200
W: http://www.790business.com
Editorial Profile: WPRV-AM is a commercial station owned by Cumulus Media Inc. The format of the station is business talk. WPRV-AM broadcasts to the Riverside, RI area at 790 AM.

WPRW-FM

Owner: Clear Channel Media and Entertainment
Editorial: 2743 Perimeter Pkwy, Ste 300, Augusta, Georgia 30909-6429.
T: 1 706 396-6000
W: http://www.power107.net
Editorial Profile: WPRW-FM is a commercial station owned by Clear Channel Media and Entertainment. The format of the station is urban contemporary. WPRW-FM broadcasts to the Augusta, GA area at 107.7 FM.

WPRX-AM

Owner: Nievezquez Productions
Editorial: 1253 Berlin Tpke, Floor 2, Berlin, Connecticut 06037-3228. **T:** 1 860 348-0667
E: wprx1120@comcast.net
W: http://www.wprx1120.net
Editorial Profile: WPRX-AM is a commercial station owned by Nievezquez Productions. The format of the station is Hispanic and tropical music. WPRX-AM broadcasts to the New Britain, CT area at 1120 AM.

WPRY-AM

Owner: Dockins Broadcast Group
Editorial: 872 E Highway 27, Perry, Florida 32347. **T:** 1 850 223-1400
Editorial Profile: WPRY-AM is a commercial station owned by Dockins Broadcast Group. The format of the station is oldies. WPRY-AM airs in the Perry, FL area at 1400 AM.

WPSC-FM

Owner: William Paterson University
Editorial: 300 Pompton Rd, Wayne, New Jersey 07470-2103. **T:** 1 973 720-3319
E: wpsc@wpunj.edu **W:** http://wpsc.wpunj.edu
Editorial Profile: WPSC-FM is a non-commercial station owned by William Paterson University. The format of the station is rock alternative. WPSC-FM broadcasts to the Wayne, NJ area at 88.7 FM.

WPSE-AM

Owner: The Board of Regents of Pennsylvania State University
Editorial: 4071 College Dr, Erie, Pennsylvania 16563. **T:** 1 814 898-6495
W: http://www.pserie.psu.edu/newscal/wpseradio.htm
Editorial Profile: WPSE-AM is a commercial station owned by the Board of Regents of Pennsylvania State University. The format of the station is news and talk. WPSE-AM broadcasts to the Erie, PA area at 1450 AM.

WPSF-FM

Owner: Call Communications Group, Inc.
Editorial: 8900 SW 168th St, Bldg 4000, Village of Palmetto Bay, Florida 33157-4569.
T: 1 305 662-7736 **E:** md@callfm.com
W: http://www.callfm.com
Editorial Profile: WPSF-FM is a commercial station owned by Call Communications Group, Inc. The format of the station is contemporary Christian and rock. WPSF-FM broadcasts to the Clewiston, FL area at 91.5 FM.

WPSK-FM

Owner: Cumulus Media Inc.

Editorial: 7080 Lee Hwy, Fairlawn, Virginia 24141-8416. **T:** 1 540 731-6000
W: http://www.wpsk107.com
Editorial Profile: WPSK-FM is a commercial station owned by Cumulus Media Inc. The format of the station is classic and contemporary country music. WPSK-FM broadcasts to the Lynchburg, VA area at 107.1 FM.

WPSL-AM
Owner: Port St. Lucie Broadcasters
Editorial: 4100 Metzger Rd, Fort Pierce, Florida 34947. **T:** 1 772 340-1590
E: wpsl@wpsl.com **W:** http://www.wpsl.com
Editorial Profile: WPSL-AM is a commercial station owned by Port St. Lucie Broadcasters. The format of the station is news, sports and talk. WPSL-AM broadcasts to the Port Saint Lucie, FL area at 1590 AM.

WPSM-FM
Owner: Ft. Walton Beach Educational Broadcasting Foundation
Editorial: 233 Hill Ave NW, Fort Walton Beach, Florida 32548-3850. **T:** 1 850 244-7667
E: contact@wpsm.com
W: http://www.wpsm.com
Editorial Profile: WPSM-FM is non-commercial station owned by Ft. Walton Beach Educational Broadcasting Foundation. The format of the station is contemporary Christian. WPSM-FM broadcasts to the Fort Walton Beach, FL area at 91.1 FM.

WPSN-AM
Owner: Bold Gold Media Group
Editorial: 575 Grove St, Honesdale, Pennsylvania 18431. **T:** 1 570 253-1616
W: http://www.waynepikenews.com
Editorial Profile: WPSN-AM is a commercial station owned by Bold Gold Media Group. The format of the station is news talk. WPSN-AM broadcasts to the Honesdale, PA area at 1590 AM.

WPSO-AM
Owner: ASA Broadcasting Network
Editorial: 109 S Bayview Blvd Ste A, Oldsmar, Florida 34677-3124. **T:** 1 813 814-7575
E: wzra48@yahoo.com
W: http://www.wpso.com
Editorial Profile: WPSO-AM is a commercial station owned by ASA Broadcasting Network. The format of the station is variety. WPSO-AM broadcasts to the Oldsmar, FL area at 1500 AM.

WPSP-AM
Owner: Q Broadcasting
Editorial: 5730 Corporate Way, Ste 210, West Palm Beach, Florida 33407. **T:** 1 561 681-9777
W: http://www.wpspradio.com
Editorial Profile: WPSP-AM is a commercial radio station owned by Q Broadcasting. The format of the station is Hispanic adult contemporary. WPSP-AM broadcasts to the West Palm Beach, FL area at 1190 AM.

WPSR-FM
Owner: Evansville Vanderburgh School Corporation
Editorial: 1901 Lynch Rd, Evansville, Indiana 47711. **T:** 1 812 435-8241
E: wpsr@evsc.k12.in.us
Editorial Profile: WPSR-FM is a non-commercial station owned by Evansville Vanderburgh School Corporation. The format for the station is variety. WPSR-FM broadcasts to the Evansville, IN area at 90.7 FM.

WPST-FM
Owner: Connoisseur Media
Editorial: 619 Alexander Rd, Princeton, New Jersey 08540-6000. **T:** 1 609 419-0300
W: http://www.wpst.com
Editorial Profile: WPST-FM is a commercial station owned by Connoisseur Media. The format of the station is Top 40/CHR. WPST-FM broadcasts to the Princeton, NJ area at 94.5 FM.

WPSU-FM
Owner: Board of Trustees of Pennsylvania State University
Editorial: 174 Outreach Bldg, University Park, Pennsylvania 16802. **T:** 1 814 865-1877
E: wpsu@psu.edu **W:** http://www.wpsu.org
Editorial Profile: WPSU-FM is a non-commercial station owned by the Board of Trustees of Pennsylvania State University. The format of the station is classical music and news. WPSU-FM broadcasts to the Central Pennsylvania area at 91.5 FM.

WPSX-FM
Owner: Board of Trustees of Pennsylvania State University
Editorial: 174 Outreach Bldg, University Park, Pennsylvania 16802-7012. **T:** 1 814 865-1877
E: radionews@psu.edu **W:** http://wpsu.psu.edu
Editorial Profile: WPSX-FM is a non-commercial station owned by Board of Trustees of Pennsylvania State University. The format of the station is news and classical music. WPSX-FM broadcasts to the University Park, PA area at 90.1 FM.

WPTB-AM
Owner: Georgia Eagle Media, Inc.
Editorial: 561 E Olliff St, Statesboro, Georgia 30458-4663. **T:** 1 912 764-5446
E: wwnswmcd@yahoo.com
Editorial Profile: WPTB-AM is a commercial station owned by Georgia Eagle Media, Inc. The format of the station is sports. WPTB-AM broadcasts to the Atlanta area at 850 AM.

WPTC-FM
Owner: Lycoming Broadcast Foundation
Editorial: 1 College Ave, Williamsport, Pennsylvania 17701-5778.
T: 1 570 320-2400 7548 **E:** wptc@pct.edu
W: http://www.pct.edu/wptc
Editorial Profile: WPTC-FM is a non-commercial college station owned by Lycoming Broadcast Foundation. The format of the station is modern rock (weekdays) and jazz (weekends). WPTC-FM broadcasts to the Pennsylvania College of Technology community and surrounding areas at a frequency of 88.1 FM.

WPTE-FM
Owner: Entercom Communications Corp.
Editorial: 236 Clearfield Ave Ste 206, Virginia Beach, Virginia 23462-1893.
T: 1 757 497-2000
W: http://www.pointradio.com
Editorial Profile: WPTE-FM is a commercial station owned by Entercom Communications Corp. The format of the station is hot adult contemporary. WPTE-FM broadcasts to the Norfolk, VA area at 94.9 FM.

WPTF-AM
Owner: Curtis Media Group
Editorial: 3012 Highwoods Blvd Ste 201, Raleigh, North Carolina 27604-1031.
T: 1 919 790-9392
E: wptfnews@curtismedia.com
W: http://www.wptf.com
Editorial Profile: WPTF-AM is a commercial station owned by the Curtis Media Group. The format of the station is news and talk. WPTF-AM broadcasts to the Raleigh-Durham, NC area at 680 AM.

WPTH-FM
Owner: VCY America, Inc.
Editorial: 3434 W Kilbourn Ave, Milwaukee, Wisconsin 53208-3313. **T:** 1 414 935-3000
E: wpth@vcyamerica.org
W: http://vcyamerica.org
Editorial Profile: WPTH-FM is a non-commercial station owned by VCY America, Inc. The format of the station is religious. WPTH-FM broadcasts to the Olney, IL area at 88.1 FM.

WPTI-FM
Owner: Clear Channel Media and Entertainment
Editorial: 2B Pai Park Fl 2, Greensboro, North Carolina 27409-9428. **T:** 1 336 822-2000
W: http://www.rushradio945.com
Editorial Profile: WPTI-FM is a commercial station owned by Clear Channel Media and Entertainment. The format of the station is news and talk. WPTI-FM broadcasts to the Greensboro, NC area at 94.5 FM.

WPTJ-FM
Owner: Lay Witness Outreach, Inc.
Editorial: 1811 Millersburg Cynthiana Rd, Paris, Kentucky 40361-9354.
T: 1 859 484-9691 **W:** http://www.wptj.org
Editorial Profile: WPTJ-FM is a non-commercial station owned by Lay Witness Outreach, Inc. The format of the station is contemporary Christian music. WPTJ-FM broadcasts to the Paris, KY area at 90.7 FM.

WPTK-AM
Owner: Curtis Media Group
Editorial: 4601 Six Forks Rd Ste 520, Raleigh, North Carolina 27609-5210.
T: 1 919 875-9100 **W:** http://www.wptf.com
Editorial Profile: WPTK-AM is a commercial station owned by Curtis Media Group. The format of the station is news/talk. WPTK-AM broadcasts to the Raleigh-Durham, NC area at 850 AM.

WPTL-AM
Owner: Skycountry Broadcasting Inc.
Editorial: 133 Pisgah Dr, Canton, North Carolina 28716. **T:** 1 828 648-3576
E: admin@wptlradio.net **W:** http://wptlradio.net
Editorial Profile: WPTL-AM is a commercial station owned by Skycountry Broadcasting Inc. The format for the station is classic country. WPTL-AM broadcasts to the Canton, NC area at 920 AM.

WPTM-FM
Owner: First Media Radio LLC
Editorial: 3 E 1st St, Weldon, North Carolina 27890. **T:** 1 252 536-3115
W: http://www.1023wptm.com
Editorial Profile: WPTM-FM is a commercial station owned by First Media Radio LLC. The format of the station is classic country. WPTM-FM broadcasts to the Roanoke Rapids, NC area at 102.3 FM.

WPTN-AM
Owner: Cookeville Communications, LLC
Editorial: 698 S Willow Ave, Cookeville, Tennessee 38501-3802. **T:** 1 931 526-7144
W: http://www.foxsportsradio1061theeagle.com/
Editorial Profile: WPTN-AM is a commercial station owned by Cookeville Communications, LLC. The format of the station is sports. WPTN-AM broadcasts to the Cookeville, TN area at 780 AM.

WPTQ-FM
Owner: Commonwealth Broadcasting Corp.
Editorial: 113 W Public Sq Ste 400, Glasgow, Kentucky 42141-2438. **T:** 1 270 651-6050
W: http://www.1053thepoint.com/
Editorial Profile: WPTQ-FM is a commercial station owned by Commonwealth Broadcasting Corp. The format of the station is mainstream rock. WPTQ-FM broadcasts to the Glasgow, KY area on 105.3 FM.

WPTR-AM
Owner: Empire Broadcasting Corporation
Editorial: 100 Saratoga Village Blvd Ste 21, Malta, New York 12020-3703.
T: 1 518 899-3000
W: http://www.sporty1240.com
Editorial Profile: WPTR-AM is a commercial station owned by Empire Broadcasting Corporation. The format of the station is sports. WPTR-AM broadcasts to the Albany, NY area at 1240 AM.

WPTS-FM
Owner: University of Pittsburgh
Editorial: 411 William Pitt Un, Pittsburgh, Pennsylvania 15260. **T:** 1 412 648-7990
E: wpts@pitt.edu **W:** http://www.wpts.pitt.edu
Editorial Profile: WPTS-FM is a non-commercial station owned by the University of Pittsburgh. The format of the station is college variety. WPTS-FM broadcasts to the University of Pittsburgh community at 92.1 FM.

WPTX-AM
Owner: Somar Communications Inc.
Editorial: 28095 Three Notch Rd, Ste 2B, Mechanicsville, Maryland 20659.
T: 1 301 870-5550 **E:** wptxam@aol.com
Editorial Profile: WPTX-AM is a commercial station owned by Somar Communications Inc. The format of the station is news, talk and sports. WPTX-AM broadcasts to the Mechanicsville, MD area at 1690 AM.

WPTY-FM
Owner: JVC Broadcasting Inc.
Editorial: 3075 Veterans Memorial Hwy, Ronkonkoma, New York 11779-7667.
T: 1 631 648-2500
W: http://www.partymusicleader.com
Editorial Profile: WPTY-FM is a commercial station owned by JVC Broadcasting Inc. The format of the station is Top 40/CHR. WPTY-FM broadcasts to the Long Island, NY area at 105.3 FM.

WPUB-FM
Owner: Kershaw Radio Corp.
Editorial: 5 The Commons, Lugoff, South Carolina 29078-8949. **T:** 1 803 438-9002
E: wpubradio@bellsouth.net
W: http://www.kool1027.com
Editorial Profile: WPUB-FM is a commercial station owned by the Kershaw Radio Corp. The format of the station is oldies. WPUB-FM broadcasts to the Lugoff, SC area at 102.7 FM.

WPUL-AM
Owner: PSI Communications Inc
Editorial: 427 S Dr Martin Luther King Jr Blvd, Daytona Beach, Florida 32114-4856.
T: 1 386 492-2908
W: http://www.wpul1590.com
Editorial Profile: WPUL-AM is a commercial station owned by PSI Communications Inc. The format of the station is news and talk. WPUL-AM broadcasts to the Daytona Beach, FL area on 1590 AM.

WPUP-FM
Owner: Cox Media Group, Inc.
Editorial: 1010 Tower Pl, Bogart, Georgia 30622. **T:** 1 706 549-6222
W: http://www.powerathens.com
Editorial Profile: WPUP-FM is a commercial station owned by Cox Media Group, Inc. The format of the station is Top 40/CHR. WPUP-FM broadcasts to the Athens, GA area at 100.1 FM.

WPUR-FM
Owner: Townsquare Media, LLC
Editorial: 950 Tilton Rd, Ste 200, Northfield, New Jersey 8225. **T:** 1 609 645-9797
W: http://www.catcountry1073.com
Editorial Profile: WPUR-FM is a commercial station owned by the Townsquare Media, LLC. The format for the station is country music. WPUR-FM broadcasts to the Northfield, NJ area at 107.3 FM.

WPUT-AM
Owner: Townsquare Media, LLC
Editorial: 1004 Federal Rd, Brookfield, Connecticut 06804-1123. **T:** 1 203 775-1212
W: http://www.940sportsradio.com
Editorial Profile: WPUT-AM is a commercial station owned by Townsquare Media, LLC. The format of the station is sports. WPUT-AM broadcasts to the Brewster, NY area at 1510 AM.

WPVA-FM
Owner: Positive Alternative Radio
Editorial: 22226 Timberlake Rd, Lynchburg, Virginia 24502. **T:** 1 434 237-9798
E: office@spiritfm.com
W: http://www.spiritfm.com
Editorial Profile: WPVA-FM is a non-commercial station owned by Positive Alternative Radio The format for the station is contemporary Christian. WPVA-FM broadcasts to the Roanoke-Lynchburg, VA area at 90.1 FM.

WPVL-AM
Owner: Queen B Radio of Wisconsin
Editorial: 51 Means Dr, Platteville, Wisconsin 53818. **T:** 1 608 349-2000
E: wpvl@queenbradio.com
Editorial Profile: WPVL-AM is a commercial station owned by Queen B Radio of Wisconsin. The format of the station is sports. WPVL-AM broadcasts to the Platteville, WI area at 1590 AM.

WPVL-FM
Owner: Queen B Radio of Wisconsin
Editorial: 51 Means Dr, Platteville, Wisconsin 53818. **T:** 1 608 349-2000
E: wpvl@queenbradio.com
W: http://www.wpvl.com
Editorial Profile: WPVL-FM is a commercial station owned by Queen B Radio of Wisconsin. The format for the station is top 40/CHR. WPVL-FM broadcasts to the Platteville, WI area at 107.1 FM.

WPVM-FM
Owner: Mountain Area Information Network
Editorial: 34 Wall St Ste 107, Asheville, North Carolina 28801-2725. **T:** 1 828 258-0085
E: info@wpvm.org **W:** http://www.wpvm.org
Editorial Profile: WPVM-FM is a non-commercial station owned by Mountain Area Information Network. The format of the station is variety. WPVM-FM broadcasts to the Asheville, NC, area at 103.5 FM.

WPVQ-FM
Owner: Saga Communications
Editorial: 81 Woodard Rd, Greenfield, Massachusetts 1301. **T:** 1 413 774-4301
W: http://www.bear953.com
Editorial Profile: WPVQ-FM is a commercial station owned by Saga Communications. The format of the station is classic country. WPVQ-FM broadcasts in the Northampton, MA area at 95.3 FM.

WPWA-AM
Owner: Mount Ocean Media LLC
Editorial: 12 Kent Rd, Aston, Pennsylvania 19014. **T:** 1 610 358-1400

E: poder1590@wpwa.net
W: http://www.wpwa.net
Editorial Profile: WPWA-AM is a commercial station owned by Mount Ocean Media LLC. The format of the station is Hispanic religious. WPWA-AM broadcasts to the Aston, PA area at 1590 AM.

WPWC-AM
Owner: JMK Communications Inc.
Editorial: 1918 Martin Luther King Jr Ave SE, Washington, District Of Columbia 20020-7006. **T:** 1 202 413-6160
W: http://www.weactradio.com
Editorial Profile: WPWC-AM is a commercial station owned by JMK Communications Inc. The format of the station is news talk. WPWC-AM broadcasts to the Woodbridge, VA area at 1480 AM. The station accepts PSA's from members and supporters only.

WPWQ-FM
Owner: Prairie Communications LLP
Editorial: 1645 Highway 104, Ste G, Quincy, Illinois 62305. **T:** 1 217 885-3222
E: wpwq106@adams.net
W: http://www.oldiessuperstation.com

WPWT-AM
Owner: Information Communications Corp.
Editorial: 340 Martin Luther King Jr Blvd, Ste 100, Bristol, Tennessee 37620.
T: 1 423 878-6279
W: http://www.powertalk870.com
Editorial Profile: WPWT-AM is a commercial station owned by Information Communications Corp. The format of the station is classic country. WPWT-AM broadcasts to the Bristol, TN area at 870 AM.

WPWX-FM
Owner: Crawford Broadcasting Co.
Editorial: 6336 Calumet Ave, Hammond, Indiana 46324. **T:** 1 219 933-4455
E: power92feedback@crawfordbroadcasting.com **W:** http://www.power92chicago.com
Editorial Profile: WPWX-FM is a commercial station owned by Crawford Broadcasting Co. The format of the station is urban contemporary music. WPWX-FM broadcasts to the Chicago area at 92.3 FM.

WPWZ-FM
Owner: First Media Radio LLC
Editorial: 12714 E NC 97, Rocky Mount, North Carolina 27803. **T:** 1 252 442-8092
E: wecare@firstmedianc.com
W: http://www.powerhits95.com
Editorial Profile: WPWZ-FM is a commercial station owned by First Media Radio LLC. The format of the station is urban contemporary. WPWZ-FM broadcasts to the Rocky Mount, NC area at 95.5 FM.

WPXC-FM
Owner: Codcomm Inc.
Editorial: 243 South St, Hyannis, Massachusetts 02601-3926.
T: 1 508 778-6000
W: http://www.pixy103.com
Editorial Profile: WPXC-FM is a commercial station owned by Codcomm Inc.. The format of the station is rock/album-oriented rock. WPXC-FM broadcasts to the West Yarmouth, MA area at 102.9 FM.

WPXN-FM
Owner: Paxton Broadcasting Corp.
Editorial: 361 N Railroad Ave, Paxton, Illinois 60957. **T:** 1 217 379-9796
W: http://www.wpxnradio.com
Editorial Profile: WPXN-FM is a commercial station owned by the Paxton Broadcasting Corp. The format of the station is classic hits. WPXN-FM broadcasts to the Paxton, IL area at 104.9 FM.

WPXY-FM
Owner: Entercom Communications Corp.
Editorial: 70 Commercial St, Rochester, New York 14614. **T:** 1 585 423-2900
W: http://www.wpxy.com
Editorial Profile: WPXY-FM is a commercial station owned by Entercom Communications Corp. The format of the station is Top 40/CHR. WPXY-FM broadcasts to the Rochester, NY area at 97.9 FM.

WPXZ-FM
Owner: Renda Broadcasting
Editorial: 904 N Main St, Punxsutawney, Pennsylvania 15767. **T:** 1 814 938-6000
E: rendaprod1@comcast.net
W: http://www.wpxz1041fm.com
Editorial Profile: WPXZ-FM is a commercial station owned by Renda Broadcasting. The format of the station is adult contemporary. WPXZ-FM broadcasts to the Punxsutawney, PA area at 104.1 FM.

WPYB-AM
Owner: Benson-Dunn Broadcasting Inc.
Editorial: 2234 Hodges Chapel Road, Benson, North Carolina 27504. **T:** 1 919 894-1130
W: http://www.wpyb1130am.com
Editorial Profile: WPYB-AM is a commercial station owned by Benson-Dunn Broadcasting Inc. The format of the station is gospel, classic and contemporary country music. WPYB-AM broadcasts to the Benson, NC area at 1130 AM.

WPYO-FM
Owner: Cox Media Group, Inc.
Editorial: 4192 N John Young Pkwy, Orlando, Florida 32804-2620. **T:** 1 407 299-9595
W: http://www.power953.com
Editorial Profile: WPYO-FM is a commercial station owned by Cox Media Group, Inc. The format of the station is urban contemporary. WPYO-FM broadcasts to the Orlando, FL area at 95.3 FM.

WPYR-AM
Owner: Catholic Community Radio, Inc.
Editorial: 8230 Summa Ave, Baton Rouge, Louisiana 70809-3421. **T:** 1 225 448-3754
W: http://www.brcatholicradio.com
Editorial Profile: WPYR-AM is a commercial station owned by Catholic Community Radio, Inc. The format of the station is religious Catholic programming. WPYR-AM broadcasts to the Baton Rouge, LA area at 1380 AM.

WPYX-FM
Owner: Clear Channel Media and Entertainment
Editorial: 1203 Troy Schenectady Rd, Latham, New York 12110. **T:** 1 518 452-4800
E: feedback@pyx106.com
W: http://www.pyx106.com
Editorial Profile: WPYX-FM is a commercial station owned by Clear Channel Media and Entertainment. The format of the station is classic rock. WPYX-FM broadcasts to the Albany, NY area at 106.5 FM.

WPZE-FM
Owner: Radio One Inc.
Editorial: 101 Marietta St Nw, Atlanta, Georgia 30303-2720. **T:** 1 404 765-9750
W: http://mypraiseatl.com
Editorial Profile: WPZE-FM is a commercial station owned by Radio One Inc. The format of the station is gospel music. WPZE-FM broadcasts to the Atlanta area at 102.5 FM.

WPZR-FM
Owner: Radio One Inc.
Editorial: 3250 Franklin St, Detroit, Michigan 48207. **T:** 1 313 259-2000
Editorial Profile: WPZR-FM is a commercial station owned by Radio One Inc. The format of the station is black gospel. WPZR-FM broadcasts to the Detroit area at 102.7 FM.

WPZS-FM
Owner: Radio One Inc.
Editorial: 8809 Lenox Pointe Dr Unit A, Charlotte, North Carolina 28273-3377.
T: 1 704 548-7800
W: http://www.praise1009fm.com
Editorial Profile: WPZS-FM is a commercial station owned by Radio One Inc. The format of the station is gospel. WPZS-FM broadcasts to the Charlotte, NC area at 100.9 FM.

WPZZ-FM
Owner: Radio One Inc.
Editorial: 2809 Emerywood Pkwy, Ste 300, Richmond, Virginia 23294. **T:** 1 804 672-9299
W: http://www.praise1047.com
Editorial Profile: WPZZ-FM is a commercial station owned by Radio One Inc. The format of the station is gospel. WPZZ-FM broadcasts to the Richmond, VA area at 104.7 FM.

WQAC-FM
Owner: Alma College
Editorial: 614 W Superior St, Alma, Michigan 48801. **T:** 1 989 463-7095
W: http://www.wqac.org
Editorial Profile: WQAC-FM is a commercial station owned by Alma College. The format of the station is variety. WQAC-FM broadcasts to the Flint, MI area at 90.9 FM.

WQAH-FM
Owner: Abercrombie Broadcasting, Inc.
Editorial: 219 Chestnut St, Hartselle, Alabama 35640. **T:** 1 256 773-4114 **E:** info@WQAH.com
W: http://www.wqah.com
Editorial Profile: WQAH-FM is a commercial station owned by Abercrombie Broadcasting, Inc. The format of the station is country. WQAH-FM broadcasts to the Hartselle, AL area at 105.7 FM.

WQAK-FM
Owner: Thunderbolt Broadcasting Co.
Editorial: 223 Westgate Dr, Union City, Tennessee 38261-3058. **T:** 1 731 885-0051
E: newsroom@unioncityradio.com
Editorial Profile: WQAK-FM is a commercial station owned by Thunderbolt Broadcasting Co. The format of the station is alternative. WQAK-FM broadcasts to the Union City, TN at 105.7 FM.

WQAL-FM
Owner: CBS Radio
Editorial: 2644 Saint Clair Ave NE, Cleveland, Ohio 44114-4015. **T:** 1 216 696-0123
W: http://q104.radio.com
Editorial Profile: WQAL-FM is a commercial station owned by CBS Radio. The format of the station is hot adult contemporary. WQAL-FM broadcasts to the Cleveland area at 104.1 FM.

WQAM-AM
Owner: Beasley Broadcast Group
Editorial: 194 Nw 187Th St, Miami, Florida 33169-4050. **T:** 1 305 654-1700
W: http://www.wqam.com
Editorial Profile: WQAM-AM is a commercial station owned by Beasley Broadcast Group. The format of the station is sports. WQAM-AM broadcasts to the Miami area at 560 AM.

WQBA-AM
Owner: Univision Communications Inc.
Editorial: 800 S Douglas Rd Ste 111, Coral Gables, Florida 33134-3187.
T: 1 305 447-1140
W: http://univisionamerica.com
Editorial Profile: WQBA-AM is a commercial station owned by Univision Communications Inc. The format of the station is Spanish news and talk. WQBA-AM broadcasts to the Miami, FL area at 1140 AM.

WQBB-FM
Owner: L & L Radio
Editorial: 1909 E Pass Rd, Gulfport, Mississippi 39507-3779. **T:** 1 228 388-2001
W: http://www.bob1059.com
Editorial Profile: WQBB-FM is a commercial station owned by L & L Radio. The format of the station is adult hits. WHGO-FM broadcasts to the Biloxi-Gulfport, MS area at 105.9 FM.

WQBE-FM
Owner: Bristol Broadcasting
Editorial: 817 Suncrest Pl, Charleston, West Virginia 25303-2302. **T:** 1 304 342-3136
E: news@wqbe.com **W:** http://www.wqbe.com
Editorial Profile: WQBE-FM is a commercial station owned by Bristol Broadcasting. The format of the station is contemporary country music. WQBE-FM broadcasts to Charleston, WV and surrounding communities at 97.5 FM.

WQBJ-FM
Owner: Townsquare Media, LLC
Editorial: 1241 Kings Rd, Schenectady, New York 12303-2811. **T:** 1 518 476-1039
W: http://www.q103albany.com
Editorial Profile: WQBJ-FM is a commercial station owned by Townsquare Media, LLC. The format of the station is rock music. WQBJ-FM broadcasts to the Albany, NY area 103.5 FM.

WQBK-FM
Owner: Townsquare Media, LLC
Editorial: 1241 Kings Rd, Schenectady, New York 12303-2811. **T:** 1 518 476-1077
W: http://www.q103albany.com
Editorial Profile: WQBK-FM is a commercial station owned by Townsquare Media, LLC. The format of the station is rock music. WQBK-FM broadcasts to the Schenectady, NY area at 103.9 FM.

WQBN-AM
Owner: Radio Tropical, Inc.
Editorial: 4023 N Armenia Ave Ste 400, Tampa, Florida 33607-1053.
T: 1 813 871-1333 **E:** wqbnradio@gmail.com
W: http://www.q1300.com
Editorial Profile: WQBN-AM is a commercial station owned by Radio Tropical, Inc. The format of the station is Hispanic. WQBN-AM broadcasts to the Tampa, FL area at 1300 AM.

WQBQ-AM
Owner: Rama Communications Inc.
Editorial: 203 N 3rd St, Leesburg, Florida 34748-5105. **T:** 1 352 326-9742
Editorial Profile: WQBQ-AM is a commercial station owned by Rama Communications Inc. and under LMA with All-N-One Media Group. The format of the station is black gospel/urban inspirational. WQBQ-AM broadcasts to the Leesburg, FL area at 1410 AM.

WQBR-FM
Owner: Maximum Impact Comm. Inc.
Editorial: 330 McElhattan Drive, McElhattan, Pennsylvania 17748. **T:** 1 570 769-2327
E: bear@cub.kcnet.org
W: http://www.bear999.com
Editorial Profile: WQBR-FM is a commercial station owned by Maximum Impact Comm. Inc. format of the station is contemporary country. WQBR-FM broadcasts to the Avis, PA area at 99.9 FM.

WQBT-FM
Owner: Clear Channel Media and Entertainment
Editorial: 245 Alfred St, Savannah, Georgia 31408-3205. **T:** 1 912 964-7794
E: info@941thebeat.com
W: http://www.941thebeat.com
Editorial Profile: WQBT-FM is a commercial station owned by Clear Channel Media and Entertainment. The format for the station is urban contemporary. WQBT-FM broadcasts to the Savannah, GA area at 94.1 FM.

WQBU-FM
Owner: Univision Communications Inc.
Editorial: 485 Madison Ave Fl 3, New York, New York 10022-5869. **T:** 1 212 310-6000
W: http://univisionamerica.univision.com
Editorial Profile: WQBU-FM is a commercial station owned by Univision Communications Inc. The format of the station is Spanish news/talk. WQBU-FM broadcasts to the New York area at 92.7 FM.

WQBW-FM
Owner: Clear Channel Media and Entertainment
Editorial: 100 Chestnut St Ste 1700, Rochester, New York 14604-2418.
T: 1 585 454-4884
W: http://www.951thebrew.com
Editorial Profile: WQBW-FM is a commercial station owned by Clear Channel Media and Entertainment. The format of the station is classic rock. WQBW-FM broadcasts to the Rochester, NY area at 95.1 FM.

WQBX-FM
Owner: Jacom Inc.
Editorial: 5310 N State Rd, Alma, Michigan 48801. **T:** 1 989 463-3175
E: wqbxfm@gmail.com
Editorial Profile: WQBX-FM is a commercial station owned by Jacom Inc. The format of the station is hot adult contemporary music. WQBX-FM broadcasts to the Alma, MI area at 104.9 FM.

WQBZ-FM
Owner: Clear Channel Media and Entertainment
Editorial: 7080 Industrial Hwy, Macon, Georgia 31216. **T:** 1 478 781-1063
W: http://www.q106.fm
Editorial Profile: WQBZ-FM is a commercial station owned by Clear Channel Media and Entertainment. The format of the station is rock music. WQBZ-FM broadcasts to the Macon, GA area at 106.3 FM.

WQCB-FM
Owner: Townsquare Media, Inc.
Editorial: 49 Acme Rd, Brewer, Maine 04412-1545. **T:** 1 207 989-5631
E: cumulusnews@midmaine.com
W: http://www.wqcb-fm.com
Editorial Profile: WQCB-FM is a commercial station owned by Townsquare Media, Inc. The format of the station is contemporary country. WQCB-FM broadcasts to the Brewer, ME area at 106.5 FM.

WQCC-FM
Owner: Mississippi Valley Broadcasters LLC
Editorial: 1407 2nd Ave N, Onalaska, Wisconsin 54650-9166. **T:** 1 608 782-8335
E: news@lacrosseradiogroup.net
W: http://www.cc1063.com
Editorial Profile: WQCC-FM is a commercial station owned by Mississippi Valley Broadcasters LLC. The format of the station is contemporary country. WQCC-FM broadcasts to the Onalaska, WI area at 106.3 FM.

WQCH-AM
Owner: Radix Broadcasting Inc.

Editorial: 130 Rodeo Dr, La Fayette, Georgia 30728-9201. **T:** 1 706 638-3276
W: http://www.wqch.net
Editorial Profile: WQCH-AM is a commercial station owned by Radix Broadcasting Inc. The format of the station is contemporary and classic country. WQCH-AM broadcasts to the Chattanooga, TN area at 1590 AM.

WQCK-FM
Owner: Magnum Broadcasting Inc.
Editorial: 315 S Atherton St, State College, Pennsylvania 16801-4045. **T:** 1 814 272-1320
E: magnumprod1059@gmail.com
W: http://www.1059qwikrock.com
Editorial Profile: WQCK-FM is a commercial station owned by Magnum Broadcasting Inc. The format of the station is rock and classic rock. WQCK-FM broadcasts to the Philipsburg, PA, area at 105.9 FM.

WQCM-FM
Owner: Main Line Broadcasting
Editorial: 25 Penncraft Ave, Chambersburg, Pennsylvania 17201-5600. **T:** 1 717 263-0813
W: http://www.wqcmfm.com
Editorial Profile: WQCM-FM is a commercial station owned by Main Line Broadcasting. The format of the station is classic rock. WQCM-FM broadcasts to the Hagerstown, MD area at 94.3 FM.

WQCR-AM
Owner: Rivera Communications
Editorial: 100 Yeager Pkwy, Pelham, Alabama 35124-1859. **T:** 1 205 358-1100
Editorial Profile: WQCR-AM is commercial station owned by Rivera Communications. The format of the station is regional Mexican and tropical music. The station airs locally on 1500 AM. Newscasts air at the top of the hour.

WQCS-FM
Owner: Indian River Community College
Editorial: 3209 Virginia Ave, Fort Pierce, Florida 34981-5541. **T:** 1 772 465-8989
E: info@wqcs.org **W:** http://www.wqcs.org
Editorial Profile: WQCS-FM is a non-commercial station owned by Indian River Community College. The format of the station is news, public affairs, and classical music. WQCS-FM broadcasts to the Melbourne, FL area at 88.9 FM.

WQCT-AM
Owner: Impact Radio, LLC
Editorial: 12810 State Route 34, Bryan, Ohio 43506-8809. **T:** 1 419 636-3175
E: wbno@wbnowqct.com
W: http://www.wbnowqct.com
Editorial Profile: WQCT-AM is a commercial station owned by Impact Radio, LLC. The format of the station is oldies. WQCT-AM broadcasts to the Bryan, OH area at 1520 AM.

WQCY-FM
Owner: Staradio Corp.
Editorial: 329 Maine St, Quincy, Illinois 62301. **T:** 1 217 224-4102
W: http://www.1039thefox.com
Editorial Profile: WQCY-FM is a commercial station owned by Staradio Corp. The format of the station is classic rock. WQCY-FM broadcasts to the Quincy, IL area at 103.9 FM.

WQDK-FM
Owner: Max Media
Editorial: 443 Hwy 42 W, Ahoskie, North Carolina 27910-9712. **T:** 1 252 332-7993
E: wqdk@yahoo.com
Editorial Profile: WQDK-FM is a commercial station owned by Max Media. The format of the station is country. WQDK-FM broadcasts to the Ahoskie, NC area at 99.3 FM.

WQDR-FM
Owner: Curtis Media Group
Editorial: 3012 Highwoods Blvd, Raleigh, North Carolina 27604-1037.
T: 1 919 790-9392
E: wptfnews@curtismedia.com
W: http://www.947qdr.com
Editorial Profile: WQDR-FM is a commercial station owned by Curtis Media Group. The format of the station is contemporary country music. WQDR-FM broadcasts to the Raleigh-Durham, NC area at 94.7 FM.

WQDY-FM
Owner: WQDY Inc.
Editorial: 637 Main St, Calais, Maine 4619. **T:** 1 207 454-7545 **E:** wqdy@wqdy.fm
W: http://www.wqdy.fm
Editorial Profile: WQDY-FM is a commercial station owned by WQDY Inc. The format for the station is classic hits. WQDY-FM broadcasts to the Calais, ME area at 92.7 FM.

WQED-FM
Owner: WQED Multimedia
Editorial: 4802 5th Ave, Pittsburgh, Pennsylvania 15213. **T:** 1 412 622-1436
E: wqed@wqed.org
W: http://www.wqed.org/fm
Editorial Profile: WQED-FM is a non-commercial station owned by WQED Multimedia. The format is classical music and news. WQED-FM broadcasts to the Pittsburgh area at 89.3 FM.

WQEJ-FM
Owner: WQED Multimedia
Editorial: 4802 5th Ave, Pittsburgh, Pennsylvania 15213. **T:** 1 412 622-1436
E: wqed@wqed.org
W: http://www.wqed.org/fm
Editorial Profile: WQEJ-FM is a non-commercial station owned by WQED Multimedia. The format is classical music. WQEJ-FM broadcasts to the Pittsburgh area at 89.7 FM.

WQEL-FM
Owner: Franklin Communications, Inc.
Editorial: 403 E Rensselaer St, Bucyrus, Ohio 44820. **T:** 1 419 562-2222
W: http://www.wqel.com
Editorial Profile: WQEL-FM is a commercial station owned by Franklin Communications, Inc. The format of the station is classic hits. WQEL-FM broadcasts to the Columbus, OH area at 92.7 FM.

WQEM-FM
Owner: Glen Iris Baptist School
Editorial: 1137 10th Pl S, Birmingham, Alabama 35205. **T:** 1 205 323-1516
W: http://www.gleniris.net/GIBC/index.php?option=com_content&task=view&id=21&Itemid
Editorial Profile: WQEM-FM is a non-commercial station owned by Glen Iris Baptist School. The format of the station is religious programming. WQEM-FM broadcasts to the Birmingham, AL area at 101.5 FM.

WQEN-FM
Owner: Clear Channel Media and Entertainment
Editorial: 600 Beacon Pkwy W Ste 400, Birmingham, Alabama 35209-3118.
T: 1 205 439-9600
W: http://www.1037theq.com
Editorial Profile: WQEN-FM is a commercial station owned by Clear Channel Media and Entertainment. The format of the station is adult contemporary music. WQEN-FM broadcasts to the Birmingham, AL area at 103.7 FM.

WQEW-AM
Owner: Walt Disney Co.
Editorial: 2 Penn Plz, Fl 17, New York, New York 10121-0085. **T:** 1 212 615-3250
W: http://www.radiodisney.com
Editorial Profile: WQEW-AM is a commercial station owned by Walt Disney Co. The format of the station is top 40. WQEW-AM broadcasts to the New York area at 1560 AM.

WQEZ-FM
Owner: Northern Star Broadcasting LLC
Editorial: 1356 Mackinaw Ave, Cheboygan, Michigan 49721-1003. **T:** 1 231 627-2341
W: http://www.wqez.fm
Editorial Profile: WQEZ-FM is a commercial station owned by Northern Star Broadcasting LLC. The format of the station is soft adult contemporary. WJZJ-FM broadcasts to Traverse, MI area at 95.5 FM.

WQFL-FM
Owner: Educational Media Foundation
Editorial: 5375 Pebble Creek Trl, Loves Park, Illinois 61111. **T:** 1 815 654-1200
E: positive@101qfl.com
W: http://www.101qfl.com
Editorial Profile: WQFL-FM is a non-commercial station owned by Educational Media Foundation. The format of the station is contemporary Christian music. WQFL-FM broadcasts to the Rockford, IL area at 101.1 FM

WQFS-FM
Owner: Guilford College
Editorial: 17714 Founders Hall, Greensboro, North Carolina 27410-4126.
T: 1 336 316-2352 **E:** wqfs@guilford.edu
W: http://www.guilford.edu/wqfs
Editorial Profile: WQFS-FM is a non-commercial station owned by Guilford College. The format of the station is college variety. WQFS-FM broadcasts to the Greensboro, NC area at 90.9 FM.

WQFX-AM
Owner: Walking By Faith Ministries
Editorial: 336 Rodenberg Ave, Biloxi, Mississippi 39531. **T:** 1 228 374-9739
E: wqfxradio@bellsouth.net
W: http://www.wqfxonline.net
Editorial Profile: WQFX-AM is a commercial station owned by Walking By Faith Ministries. The format of the station is gospel. WQFX-AM broadcasts to the Biloxi, MS area at 1130 AM.

WQFX-FM
Owner: Media One Group, LLC
Editorial: 2 Orchard Rd, Jamestown, New York 14701. **T:** 1 716 487-1151
E: news@whug.com
W: http://www.wqfx1031.com

WQGA-FM
Owner: Clear Channel Media and Entertainment
Editorial: 3833 US Highway 82, Brunswick, Georgia 31523-7735. **T:** 1 912 267-1025
W: http://my103q.com
Editorial Profile: WQGA-FM is a commercial station owned by Clear Channel Media and Entertainment. The format of the station is Top 40/CHR. WQGA-FM broadcasts to the Brunswick, GA area at 103.3 FM.

WQGN-FM
Owner: Cumulus Media Inc.
Editorial: 7 Governor Winthrop Blvd, New London, Connecticut 6320. **T:** 1 860 443-1980
W: http://www.q105.fm
Editorial Profile: WQGN-FM is a commercial station owned by Cumulus Media Inc. The format of the station is Top 40/CHR. WQGN-FM broadcasts to the New London, CT area at 105.5 FM.

WQGR-FM
Owner: Media One Group
Editorial: 9179 Mentor Ave, Mentor, Ohio 44060-6398. **T:** 1 440 974-5900
W: http://www.cougar937.com/
Editorial Profile: WQGR-FM is a commercial station owned by Media One Group. The format of the station is Hot AC. The station broadcasts locally at 93.7 FM to Lake County, OH.

WQHH-FM
Owner: MacDonald Broadcasting Co.
Editorial: 600 W Cavanaugh Rd, Lansing, Michigan 48910. **T:** 1 517 393-1320
W: http://www.power965fm.com
Editorial Profile: WQHH-FM is a commercial station owned by MacDonald Broadcasting Co. The format of the station is urban contemporary. WQHH-FM broadcasts to the Lansing, MI area at 96.5 FM.

WQHK-FM
Owner: Federated Media
Editorial: 2915 Maples Rd, Fort Wayne, Indiana 46816-3335. **T:** 1 260 447-5511
W: http://www.k105fm.com
Editorial Profile: WQHK-FM is a commercial station owned by Federated Media. The format of the station is country music. WQHK-FM broadcasts to the Fort Wayne, IN area at 105.1 FM.

WQHL-AM
Owner: Black Crow Broadcasting Inc.
Editorial: 1305 Helvenston St SE, Live Oak, Florida 32064. **T:** 1 386 362-1250
Editorial Profile: WQHL-AM is a commercial station owned by Black Crow Broadcasting Inc. The format of the station is oldies music. WQHL-AM broadcasts in the Orlando, FL area at 1250 AM.

WQHL-FM
Owner: Black Crow Broadcasting Inc.
Editorial: 1305 Helvenston St SE, Live Oak, Florida 32064. **T:** 1 386 362-1250
E: audio@wqhl981.com
W: http://www.wqhl981.com
Editorial Profile: WQHL-FM is a commercial station owned by Black Crow Broadcasting Inc. The format of the station is contemporary country music. WQHL-FM broadcasts to the Live Oak, FL area at 98.1 FM.

WQHQ-FM
Owner: Clear Channel Media and Entertainment
Editorial: Gateway Crossing, 351 Tilghman Road, Salisbury, Maryland 21804-1920.
T: 1 410 742-1923
E: delmarvapsa@clearchannel.com
W: http://www.q105fm.com
Editorial Profile: WQHQ-FM is a commercial station owned by Clear Channel Media and Entertainment. The format of the station is adult contemporary music. WQHQ-FM broadcasts to the Salisbury, MD area at 104.7 FM.

WQHR-FM
Owner: Townsquare Media, Inc.
Editorial: 551 Main St, Presque Isle, Maine 04769-2450. **T:** 1 207 769-6600
Editorial Profile: WQHR-FM is a commercial station owned by Townsquare Media, Inc. The format for the station is hot adult contemporary. WQHR-FM broadcasts to the Presque Isle, ME area at 96.1 FM.

WQHT-FM
Owner: Emmis Communications Corp.
Editorial: 395 Hudson St, New York, New York 10014-3669. **T:** 1 212 229-9797
W: http://www.hot97.com
Editorial Profile: WQHT-FM is a commercial station owned by Emmis Communications Corp. The format of the station is urban contemporary. WQHT-FM broadcasts to the New York City metro area at 97.1 FM.

WQHU-FM
Owner: Huntington University
Editorial: 2303 College Ave, Huntington, Indiana 46750. **T:** 1 260 359-4281
W: http://www.wqhu.net
Editorial Profile: WQHU-FM is a commercial station owned by Huntington University. The format of the station is rock alternative. WQHU-FM broadcasts to the Huntington, IN area at 105.5 FM.

WQHY-FM
Owner: WDOC Inc.
Editorial: 95 Jackson St, Prestonsburg, Kentucky 41653. **T:** 1 606 886-8409
E: q95fm@eastky.net **W:** http://www.q95fm.net
Editorial Profile: WQHY-FM is a commercial station owned by WDOC Inc. The format of the station is hot adult contemporary. WQHY-FM broadcasts to the Prestonsburg, KY area at 95.5 FM.

WQHZ-FM
Owner: Cumulus Media Inc.
Editorial: 471 Robison Rd, Erie, Pennsylvania 16509-5425. **T:** 1 814 868-5355
W: http://www.z1023online.com
Editorial Profile: WQHZ-FM is a commercial station owned by Cumulus Media Inc. The format of the station is classic rock. WQHZ-FM broadcasts to the Erie, PA area at 102.3 FM.

WQIC-FM
Owner: Lebanon Broadcasting Co.
Editorial: 440 Rebecca Street, Lebanon, Pennsylvania 17046-1734. **T:** 1 717 272-7651
Editorial Profile: WQIC-FM is a commercial station owned by Lebanon Broadcasting Co. The format of the station is adult contemporary music. WQIC-FM broadcasts to the Lebanon, PA area at 100.1 FM.

WQIK-FM
Owner: Clear Channel Media and Entertainment
Editorial: 11700 Central Pkwy, Jacksonville, Florida 32224. **T:** 1 904 636-0507
W: http://www.wqik.com
Editorial Profile: WQIK-FM is a commercial station owned by Clear Channel Media and Entertainment. The format of the station is classic country. WQIK-FM broadcasts to the Jacksonville, FL area at 99.1 FM.

WQIL-FM
Owner: GSW, Inc.
Editorial: 807 Bellevue Ave, Dublin, Georgia 31021. **T:** 1 478 272-4422
W: http://www.1013wqil.com
Editorial Profile: WQIL-FM is a commercial station owned by GSW, Inc. The format of the station is contemporary Christian. WQIL-FM broadcasts to the Dublin, GA area at 101.3 FM.

WQIO-FM
Owner: BAS Broadcasting
Editorial: 17421 Coshocton Rd, Mount Vernon, Ohio 43050-9256. **T:** 1 740 397-1000
E: wqio@basbroadcasting.com
W: http://www.wqioradio.com
Editorial Profile: WQIO-FM is a commercial station owned by BAS Broadcasting. The format of the station is adult contemporary music. WQIO-FM broadcasts in the Mount Vernon, OH, area at 93.7 FM.

WQIZ-AM
Owner: Mediatrix SC, LLC

Editorial: 715 Hampton St, Walterboro, South Carolina 29488-4125. **T:** 1 866 263-1700
W: http://catholicradioinsc.com
Editorial Profile: WQIZ-AM is a non-commercial station owned by Mediatrix SC, LLC. The format of the station is religious with a focus on Catholicism. WQIZ-AM broadcasts to the Walterboro, SC area at a frequency of 810 AM.

WQJQ-FM
Owner: Vermont Broadcast Associates Inc.
Editorial: 1303 Concord Ave, Saint Johnsbury, Vermont 05819-8423. **T:** 1 802 748-2362
E: Magic977@gmail.com
W: http://www.magic977.com
Editorial Profile: WQJQ-FM is a commercial station owned by Vermont Broadcast Associates Inc. The format of the station is bluegrass. WQJQ-FM is licensed to Barton, VT and broadcasts locally at 100.3 FM.

WQKC-AM
Owner: Dugan (Ryan)
Editorial: 213 Magnolia Ave, Jeffersonville, Indiana 47130-6446. **T:** 1 502 992-0939
Editorial Profile: WQKC-AM is a commercial station owned by Dugan (Ryan). The format of the station is sports/talk. WQKC-AM broadcasts to the Louisville, KY area at 1450 AM.

WQKE-FM
Owner: State University of New York
Editorial: 110 Angell College Center, Plattsburgh, New York 12901-2637.
T: 1 518 564-2727
E: thequakeradio@gmail.com
W: http://www.plattsburgh.edu/about/tour/wqke.php
Editorial Profile: WQKE-FM is a non-commercial station owned by the State University of New York. The format of the station is college variety. WQKE-FM broadcasts to the Plattsburgh, NY area on 93.9 FM.

WQKI-FM
Owner: Miller Communications Inc.
Editorial: 200 Regional Pkwy, Bldg C Ste 200, Orangeburg, South Carolina 29118-9700.
T: 1 803 536-1710 **E:** wqki@miller.fm
W: http://www.miller.fm
Editorial Profile: WQKI-FM is a commercial station owned by Miller Communications Inc. The format of the station is R&B oldies. WQKI-FM broadcasts to the Orangeburg, SC area at 102.9 FM.

WQKK-FM
Owner: Magnum Broadcasting Inc.
Editorial: 315 S Atherton St, State College, Pennsylvania 16801-4045. **T:** 1 814 272-1320
W: http://y106fm.com
Editorial Profile: WQKK-FM is a commercial station owned by Magnum Broadcasting Inc. The format of the station is hot AC. WQKK-FM broadcasts to the Wilkes Barre-Scranton, PA area at 106.9 FM.

WQKL-FM
Owner: Cumulus Media Inc.
Editorial: 1100 Victors Way, Ste 100, Ann Arbor, Michigan 48108. **T:** 1 734 302-8100
E: programming@annarbors107one.com
W: http://www.annarbors107one.com
Editorial Profile: WQKL-FM is a commercial station owned by Cumulus Media Inc. The format of the station is adult album alternative. WQKL-FM broadcasts to the Ann Arbor, MI area at 107.1 FM.

WQKQ-FM
Owner: Pritchard Broadcasting Co.
Editorial: 1610 N. 4th Street, Ste. 300, Burlington, Iowa 52601. **T:** 1 319 752-5402
E: news@burlingtonradio.com
W: http://www.kq92rocks.com
Editorial Profile: WQKQ-FM is a commercial station owned by Pritchard Broadcasting Co. The format of the station is rock. WQKQ-FM broadcasts to the Burlington, IA area at 92.1 FM.

WQKR-AM
Owner: Venture Broadcasting
Editorial: 100 Main St, Ste 201, Portland, Tennessee 37148. **T:** 1 615 325-3250
E: wqkr@comcast.net **W:** http://www.wqkr.com
Editorial Profile: WQKR-AM is a commercial station owned by Venture Broadcasting. The format of the station is classic hits music. WQKR-AM broadcasts to the Portland, TN area at 1270 AM. The station also has a simulcast on 95.9 FM.

WQKS-FM
Owner: Bluewater Broadcasting Co. LLC
Editorial: 4101A Wall St, Ste A, Montgomery, Alabama 36106. **T:** 1 334 244-0961
W: http://q961fm.com
Editorial Profile: WQKS-FM is a commercial station owned by Bluewater Broadcasting Co. LLC. The format of the station is classic hits. WQKS-FM broadcasts to the Montgomery, AL area at 96.1 FM.

WQKT-FM
Owner: WWST Corporation
Editorial: 186 S Hillcrest Dr, Wooster, Ohio 44691-3727. **T:** 1 330 264-5122
E: contact@wqkt.com
W: http://www.wqkt.com
Editorial Profile: WQKT-FM is a commercial station owned by WWST Corporation. The format of the station is classic and contemporary country. WQKT-FM broadcasts to the Cleveland area at 104.5 FM.

WQKX-FM
Owner: Sunbury Broadcasting Corp.
Editorial: 1227 County Line Rd, Selinsgrove, Pennsylvania 17870-8188. **T:** 1 570 286-5838
E: equest@wqkx.com **W:** http://www.wqkx.net
Editorial Profile: WQKX-FM is a commercial station owned by Sunbury Broadcasting Corp. The format of the station is hot adult contemporary music. WQKX-FM broadcasts to the Wilkes Barre-Scranton area at 107.3 FM.

WQKY-FM
Owner: Salter Communications
Editorial: 241 West 4th St, Emporium, Pennsylvania 15834. **T:** 1 814 486-3712
E: theriver989@yahoo.com
W: http://www.theriver989.com
Editorial Profile: WQKY-FM is a commercial station owned by Salter Communications. The format of the station is classic hits. WQKY-FM broadcasts to the Emporium, PA area on 98.9 FM.

WQKZ-FM
Owner: GEM Communications
Editorial: 1978 S Witz Rd, Jasper, Indiana 47546-2672. **T:** 1 812 367-1884
E: wqkz@psci.net
W: http://www.witzamfm.com
Editorial Profile: WQKZ-FM is a commercial station owned by GEM Communications. The format of the station is contemporary country music. WQKZ-FM broadcasts to the Jasper, IN, area at 98.5 FM.

WQLB-FM
Owner: Carroll Broadcasting Co.
Editorial: 523 Meadow Rd, Tawas City, Michigan 48763. **T:** 1 989 362-3417
E: hitsfm@speednetllc.com
W: http://www.hitsfm.net
Editorial Profile: WQLB-FM is a commercial station owned by Carroll Broadcasting Co. The format of the station is classic rock music. WQLB-FM broadcasts to the Tawas City, MI area at 103.3 FM.

WQLC-FM
Owner: Taylor County Broadcasting, Inc.
Editorial: 9206 W US Highway 90, Lake City, Florida 32055-7502. **T:** 1 386 755-4102
W: http://www.powercountry102.com
Editorial Profile: WQLC-FM is a commercial station owned by Taylor County Broadcasting, Inc. The format of the station is contemporary country music. WQLC-FM broadcasts to the Lake City, FL at 102.1 FM.

WQLF-FM
Owner: Big Radio
Editorial: 834 N Tower Rd, Freeport, Illinois 61032-8650. **T:** 1 815 235-7191
W: http://www.wekz.com
Editorial Profile: WQLF-FM is a commercial station owned by Big Radio. The format of the station is classic rock. WQLF-FM broadcasts to the Monroe, WI area at 102.1 FM. All staff should be contact via fax.

WQLH-FM
Owner: Cumulus Media Inc.
Editorial: 810 Victoria St, Green Bay, Wisconsin 54302. **T:** 1 920 468-4100
W: http://www.star98.net
Editorial Profile: WQLH-FM is a commercial station owned by Cumulus Media Inc. The format of the station is hot adult contemporary. WQLH-FM broadcasts to the Green Bay, WI area at 98.5 FM.

WQLI-FM
Owner: Flint Media
Editorial: 521 S Scott St, Bainbridge, Georgia 39819-4101. **T:** 1 229 246-7776
W: http://sowegalive.com
Editorial Profile: WQLI-FM is a commercial station owned by Flint Media. The format of the station is AC. WQLI-FM broadcasts to the Pelham, GA area at a frequency of 92.3 FM.

WQLJ-FM
Owner: TeleSouth Communications Inc.
Editorial: 461 Highway 6 W, Oxford, Mississippi 38655-9073. **T:** 1 662 236-0093
E: q937@telesouth.com
W: http://www.q937.com
Editorial Profile: WQLJ-FM is a commercial station owned by TeleSouth Communications Inc. The format of the station is hot adult contemporary music. WQLJ-FM broadcasts to the Oxford, MS area at 93.7 FM.

WQLK-FM
Owner: Brewer Broadcasting Inc.
Editorial: 2626 Tingler Rd W, Richmond, Indiana 47374-9273. **T:** 1 765 962-1595
E: news@kicks96.com
W: http://www.kicks96.com
Editorial Profile: WQLK-FM is a commercial station owned by Brewer Broadcasting Inc. The format of the station is country music. WQLK-FM broadcasts to the Richmond, IN area at 96.1 FM.

WQLL-AM
Owner: M-10 Broadcasting Inc.
Editorial: 1726 Reisterstown Rd Ste 117, Baltimore, Maryland 21208-2986.
T: 1 410 580-6800 **W:** http://www.q1370.com
Editorial Profile: WQLL-AM is a commercial station owned by M-10 Broadcasting Inc. The format of the station is classic hits. WQLL-AM broadcasts to Baltimore area at 1370 AM.

WQLN-FM
Owner: Public Broadcasting of Northwest Pennsylvania
Editorial: 8425 Peach St, Erie, Pennsylvania 16509. **T:** 1 814 864-3001 **E:** wqln@wqln.org
W: http://www.wqln.org
Editorial Profile: WQLN-FM is a non-commercial station owned by Public Broadcasting of Northwest Pennsylvania. The format of the station is news and classical music. WQLN-FM broadcasts to the Erie, PA area at 91.3 FM.

WQLR-AM
Owner: Midwest Communications Inc.
Editorial: 4200 W Main St, Kalamazoo, Michigan 49006-2749. **T:** 1 269 345-7121
E: wkzonews@wkzo.com
W: http://www.1660thefan.com
Editorial Profile: WQLR-AM is a commercial station owned by Midwest Communications Inc. The format of the station is sports. WQLR-AM broadcasts to the Kalamazoo, MI area at 1660 AM.

WQLT-FM
Owner: Big River Broadcasting Corp.
Editorial: 624 Sam Phillips St, Florence, Alabama 35630-5859. **T:** 1 256 764-8121
W: http://www.wqlt.com
Editorial Profile: WQLT-FM is a commercial station owned by Big River Broadcasting Corp. The format for the station is adult contemporary. WQLT-FM broadcasts to the Huntsville, AL area at 107.3 FM.

WQLV-FM
Owner: Cooper(Richard L.)
Editorial: 234 Union St, Millersburg, Pennsylvania 17061-1607. **T:** 1 717 362-1099
E: info@wqlvfm.com
W: http://www.wqlvfm.com
Editorial Profile: WQLV-FM is a commercial station owned by Richard L. Cooper. The format of the station is hot adult contemporary music. WQLV-FM broadcasts to the Millersburg, PA area at 98.9 FM.

WQLX-FM
Owner: Clear Channel Media and Entertainment
Editorial: 45 W Main St, Chillicothe, Ohio 45601-3104. **T:** 1 740 773-3000
E: newsroom@wkkj.com
W: http://www.wqlx1065.com
Editorial Profile: WQLX-FM is a commercial station owned by Clear Channel Media and Entertainment. The format of the station is hot adult contemporary. WQLX-FM broadcasts to the Hillsboro, OH area at 106.5 FM.

WQLZ-FM
Owner: Midwest Family Broadcasting
Editorial: 1510 N 3rd St, Riverton, Illinois 62561-9594. **T:** 1 217 629-7077
E: webmaster@wqlz.com
W: http://www.wqlz.com
Editorial Profile: WQLZ-FM is a commercial station owned by Midwest Family Stations. The format of the station is rock. WQLZ-FM broadcasts to the Springfield, IL area at 92.7 FM.

WQME-FM
Owner: Anderson University Inc.
Editorial: 1102 E 6th St, Anderson, Indiana 46012. **T:** 1 765 641-4349
E: news@wqme.com
W: http://www.wqme.com
Editorial Profile: WQME-FM is a commercial station owned by Anderson University Inc. The format of the station is contemporary Christian music. WQME-FM broadcasts to the Indianapolis area at 98.7 FM.

WQMF-FM
Owner: Clear Channel Media and Entertainment
Editorial: 4000 Radio Dr, Louisville, Kentucky 40218-4568. **T:** 1 502 479-2222
W: http://www.wqmf.com
Editorial Profile: WQMF-FM is a commercial station owned by Clear Channel Media and Entertainment. The format of the station is classic rock music. WQMF-FM broadcasts in the Louisville, KY area at 95.7 FM.

WQMG-FM
Owner: Entercom Communications Corp.
Editorial: 7819 National Service Rd, Ste 401, Greensboro, North Carolina 27409.
T: 1 336 605-5200 **W:** http://www.wqmg.com
Editorial Profile: WQMG-FM is a commercial station owned by Entercom Communications Corp. The format of the station is urban adult contemporary. WQMG-FM broadcasts to the Greensboro-Winston Salem, NC at 97.1 FM.

WQMJ-FM
Owner: Roberts Communications
Editorial: 6174 Georgia Highway 57, Macon, Georgia 31217. **T:** 1 478 745-3301
Editorial Profile: WQMJ-FM is a commercial station owned by Roberts Communications. The format of the station is R&B oldies. WQMJ-FM broadcasts to the Macon, GA area at 100.1 FM.

WQMS-AM
Owner: Matadors, LLC
Editorial: 311 County Road 140, Quitman, Mississippi 39355. **T:** 1 601 557-4710
E: info@wqmsradio.com
W: http://www.wqmsradio.com
Editorial Profile: WQMS-AM is a commercial radio station owned by Matadors, LLC. The format of the station is classic country music. The station airs locally in the Quitman, MS area at 1500 AM.

WQMU-FM
Owner: Renda Broadcasting
Editorial: 840 Philadelphia St, Ste 100, Indiana, Pennsylvania 15701.
T: 1 724 465-4700
W: http://www.u92radio.com
Editorial Profile: WQMU-FM is a commercial station owned by Renda Broadcasting. The format of the station is hot adult contemporary music. WQMU-FM broadcasts in the Indiana, PA area at 92.5 FM.

WQMX-FM
Owner: Rubber City Radio Group Inc.
Editorial: 1795 W Market St, Akron, Ohio 44313-7001. **T:** 1 330 869-9800
E: news@rcrg.net **W:** http://www.wqmx.com
Editorial Profile: WQMX-FM is a commercial station owned by Rubber City Radio Group Inc. The format of the station is country music. WQMX-FM broadcasts to the Akron, OH area at 94.9 FM.

WQMZ-FM
Owner: Saga Communications
Editorial: 1140 Rose Hill Dr, Charlottesville, Virginia 22903-5128. **T:** 1 434 220-2300
E: mail@literockz951.com
W: http://www.literockz951.com
Editorial Profile: WQMZ-FM is a commercial station owned by Saga Communications. The station's format is adult contemporary. WQMZ-FM broadcasts to the Charlottesville, VA area on 95.1 FM.

WQNA-FM
Owner: Capital Area Career Center
Editorial: 2201 Toronto Rd, Springfield, Illinois 62712-3802. **T:** 1 217 529-5431
E: info@wqna.org **W:** http://www.wqna.org
Editorial Profile: WQNA-FM is a non-commercial station owned by Capital Area Career Center. The format of the station is

college variety. WQNA-FM broadcasts to the Springfield, IL area at 88.3 FM.

WQNC-FM
Owner: Radio One Inc.
Editorial: 8809 Lenox Pointe Dr Unit A, Charlotte, North Carolina 28273-3377.
T: 1 704 548-7800
W: http://praisecharlotte.com
Editorial Profile: WQNC-FM is a commercial station owned by Radio One Inc. The format of the station is urban gospel. WQNC-FM broadcasts to the Charlotte, NC area at 92.7 FM. The station airs WPZS-FM's programming.

WQNQ-FM
Owner: Clear Channel Media and Entertainment
Editorial: 13 Summerlin Rd, Asheville, North Carolina 28806. **T:** 1 828 257-2700
E: ashevillepsa@clearchannel.com
W: http://www.star1043.com
Editorial Profile: WQNQ-FM is a commercial station owned by Clear Channel Media and Entertainment. The format of the station is Top 40. WQNQ-FM broadcasts to the Asheville, NC area at 104.3 FM.

WQNR-FM
Owner: Tiger Communications Inc.
Editorial: 2514 S College St, Ste 104, Auburn, Alabama 36832. **T:** 1 334 887-9999
E: info@katefm.net **W:** http://www.katefm.net
Editorial Profile: WQNR-FM is a commercial station owned by Tiger Communications Inc. The format of the station is adult hits. WQNR-FM broadcasts to the Auburn, AL area at 99.9 FM.

WQNS-FM
Owner: Clear Channel Media and Entertainment
Editorial: 13 Summerlin Dr, Asheville, North Carolina 28806-2800. **T:** 1 828 257-2700
E: ashevillepsa@clearchannel.com
W: http://www.1051rocks.com/main.html
Editorial Profile: WQNS-FM is a commercial station owned by Clear Channel Media and Entertainment. The format for the station is rock. WQNS-FM broadcasts to the Asheville, NC area at 105.1 FM.

WQNT-AM
Owner: Kirkman Broadcasting
Editorial: 60 Markfield Dr, Ste 4, Charleston, South Carolina 29407. **T:** 1 843 763-6631
W: http://www.foxsports1450.net
Editorial Profile: WQNT-AM is a commercial station owned by Kirkman Broadcasting. The format of the station is sports and talk. WQNT-AM broadcasts to the Charleston, SC area at 1450 AM.

WQNU-FM
Owner: Summit Media Broadcasting LLC
Editorial: 612 S 4th St, Louisville, Kentucky 40202-2460. **T:** 1 502 589-4800
W: http://newcountryq1031.com
Editorial Profile: WQNU-FM is a commercial station owned by Summit Media Broadcasting LLC. The format of the station is contemporary country. WQNU-FM broadcasts to the Louisville, KY area at 103.1 FM.

WQNY-FM
Owner: Saga Communications
Editorial: 1751 Hanshaw Rd, Ithaca, New York 14850. **T:** 1 607 257-6400
W: http://www.qcountry1037.com
Editorial Profile: WQNY-FM is a commercial station owned by Saga Communications. The format of the station is contemporary country. WQNY-FM broadcasts to the Ithaca, NY area at 103.7 FM.

WQNZ-FM
Owner: First Natchez Corp.
Editorial: 2 Oferrall St, Natchez, Mississippi 39120. **T:** 1 601 442-4895
E: wqnzfm@bellsouth.net
W: http://www.95country.com
Editorial Profile: WQNZ-FM is a commercial station owned by First Natchez Corp. The format of the station is country. WQNZ-FM broadcasts to the Natchez, MS area on 95.1 FM.

WQOK-FM
Owner: Radio One Inc.
Editorial: 8001 Creedmoor Rd Ste 101, Raleigh, North Carolina 27613-4396.
T: 1 919 848-9736 **W:** http://hiphopnc.com/
Editorial Profile: WQOK-FM is a commercial station owned by Radio One Inc. The format of the station is urban contemporary music. WQOK-FM broadcasts to the Raleigh-Durham, NC area at 97.5 FM.

WQOL-FM
Owner: Clear Channel Media and Entertainment
Editorial: 3771 SE Jennings Rd, Port Saint Lucie, Florida 34952. **T:** 1 772 335-9300
W: http://www.oldiesradio1037.com
Editorial Profile: WQOL-FM is a commercial station owned by Clear Channel Media and Entertainment. The station's format is classic hits. WQOL-FM broadcasts to the Fort Pierce, FL area at 103.7 FM.

WQOM-AM
Owner: Holy Family Communications
Editorial: 100 Mount Wayte Ave, Ste 400, Framingham, Massachusetts 1702.
T: 1 716 839-6117
W: http://www.wqom.org/index.php
Editorial Profile: WQOM-AM is a non-commercial station owned by Holy Family Communications. The format of the station is religious, specifically Catholic. WQOM-AM broadcasts to the Framingham, MA area at 1060 AM.

WQON-FM
Owner: Blarney Stone Broadcasting, Inc.
Editorial: 6514 Old Lake Rd, Grayling, Michigan 49738-7348. **T:** 1 989 348-6171
Editorial Profile: WQON-FM is a commercial station owned by Blarney Stone Broadcasting, Inc. The format of the station is classic rock. WQON-FM broadcasts in the Traverse City, MI area at 100.3 FM.

WQOP-AM
Owner: Queen of Peace Radio, Inc.
Editorial: 1611 Atlantic Blvd, Atlantic Beach, Florida 32233-2516. **T:** 1 904 241-3311
E: queenofpeaceradio@yahoo.com
W: http://www.qopradio.com
Editorial Profile: WQOP-AM is a commercial station owned by Queen of Peace Radio, Inc. The format of the station is religious talk and music. WQOP-AM broadcasts to the Jacksonville, FL area at 1460 AM.

WQOX-FM
Owner: Memphis Board of Education
Editorial: 2485 Union Ave, Memphis, Tennessee 38112-4319. **T:** 1 901 416-3460
W: http://www.mcsk12.net/aboutmcs_88.5.asp
Editorial Profile: WQOX-FM is a non-commercial station owned by Memphis Board of Education. The format of the station is urban adult contemporary. WQOX-FM broadcasts to the Memphis, TN area at 88.5 FM.

WQPC-FM
Owner: Robinson Corporation
Editorial: 640 N Villa Louis Rd, Prairie du Chien, Wisconsin 53821-1338.
T: 1 608 326-2411 **E:** wqpcwpre@mwt.net
W: http://www.wqpcradio.com
Editorial Profile: WQPC-FM is an independent and commercial station owned by Robinson Corporation. The format of the station is country music. WQPC-FM broadcasts to the Prairie du Chien, WI area at 94.3 FM.

WQPO-FM
Owner: VerStandig Broadcasting
Editorial: 1820 Heritage Center Way, Harrisonburg, Virginia 22801-8451.
T: 1 540 434-0331
W: http://www.q101online.com
Editorial Profile: WQPO-FM is a commercial station owned by VerStandig Broadcasting. The format for the station is Top 40/CHR music. WQPO-FM broadcasts to the Harrisonburg, VA area at 100.7 FM. The station does not accept unsolicited faxes. Do NOT e-mail any staff members. Any press information should be sent to WSVA-AM.

WQPR-FM
Owner: University of Alabama
Editorial: 905 University Blvd, Tuscaloosa, Alabama 35487-0001. **T:** 1 205 348-6644
E: aprnews@apr.org **W:** http://www.apr.org
Editorial Profile: WQPR-FM is a non-commercial station owned by the University of Alabama. The format of the station is variety. WQPR-FM broadcasts to the Shoals, AL area at 88.7 FM.

WQPW-FM
Owner: Black Crow Broadcasting Inc.
Editorial: 1711 Ellis Dr, Valdosta, Georgia 31601. **T:** 1 229 244-8642
W: http://www.957themix.fm
Editorial Profile: WQPW-FM is a commercial station owned by Black Crow Broadcasting Inc. The format of the station is adult contemporary music. WQPW-FM broadcasts to the Valdosta, GA area at 95.7 FM.

WQQB-FM
Owner: S.J. Broadcasting Inc.
Editorial: 2702 Boulder Rd, Urbana, Illinois 61802-6996. **T:** 1 217 367-1195
W: http://www.wqqb.com
Editorial Profile: WQQB-FM is a commercial station owned by S.J. Broadcasting Inc. The format of the station is Top 40/CHR music. WQQB-FM broadcasts to the Champaign, IL area at 96.1 FM.

WQQK-FM
Owner: Cumulus Media Inc.
Editorial: 506 2nd Ave S, Nashville, Tennessee 37210-2002. **T:** 1 615 321-1067
W: http://www.92qnashville.com
Editorial Profile: WQQK-FM is a commercial station owned by Cumulus Media Inc. The format of the station is urban adult contemporary music. WQQK-FM broadcasts to the Nashville, TN area at 92.1 FM.

WQQL-FM
Owner: Saga Communications
Editorial: 3501 E Sangamon Ave, Springfield, Illinois 62707-9777. **T:** 1 217 753-5400
Editorial Profile: WQQL-FM is a commercial radio station owned by the Saga Communications Network. The format of the station is oldies. WQQL-FM broadcasts to Springfield, IL at 93.9 FM and on an FM-translator at 107.5 FM.

WQQQ-FM
Owner: Ridgefield Broadcasting (Jackson, Dennis)
Editorial: 5151 Park Ave, Fairfield, Connecticut 06825-1090. **T:** 1 203 365-6604
E: news@wshu.org **W:** http://www.wshu.org
Editorial Profile: WQQQ-FM is a non-commercial public radio station owned by Ridgefield Broadcasting (Jackson, Dennis) and operated by Sacred Heart University. The format of the station is news/talk. WQQQ-FM at 103.3 FM, broadcasting to Noyack, NY and surrounding areas, is a simulcast of WSHU-FM in the Fairfield, CT.

WQQR-FM
Owner: Bristol Broadcasting
Editorial: 6000 Bristol Dr, Paducah, Kentucky 42003-9213. **T:** 1 270 554-0093
E: news@wkyx.com **W:** http://www.wqqr.com
Editorial Profile: WQQR-FM is a commercial station owned by Bristol Broadcasting. The station's current format is adult contemporary. and broadcasts to the Paducah, KY area on 94.7 FM.

WQQW-AM
Owner: Entertainment Media Trust
Editorial: 6500 W Main St Ste 315, Belleville, Illinois 62223-3700. **T:** 1 618 394-9965
Editorial Profile: WQQW-AM is a commercial station owned by Entertainment Media Trust. The format of the station is Spanish. WQQW-AM broadcasts to the St. Louis area at 1510 AM.

WQQX-AM
Owner: Entertainment Media Trust
Editorial: 6500 W Main St, Belleville, Illinois 62223-3700. **T:** 1 618 394-9965
Editorial Profile: WQQX-AM is a commercial station owned by Entertainment Media Trust. The format of the station is Sports. WQQX-AM broadcasts to the St. Louis area at 1490 AM.

WQRB-FM
Owner: Clear Channel Media and Entertainment
Editorial: 619 Cameron St, Eau Claire, Wisconsin 54703. **T:** 1 715 830-4000
W: http://www.b95radio.com
Editorial Profile: WQRB-FM is a commercial station owned by Clear Channel Media and Entertainment. The format of the station is contemporary country. WQRB-FM broadcasts to the Eau Claire, WI area at 95.1 FM.

WQRC-FM
Owner: Cape Cod Broadcasting
Editorial: 737 W Main St, Hyannis, Massachusetts 02601-3422.
T: 1 508 771-1224
E: wqrc@capecodbroadcasting.com
W: http://www.wqrc.com
Editorial Profile: WQRC-FM is a commercial station owned by Cape Cod Broadcasting. The format of the station is hot adult contemporary. WQRC-FM broadcasts to the Hyannis, MA area at 99.9 FM.

WQRK-FM
Owner: Ad-Venture Media Inc.
Editorial: 424 Heltonville Rd W, Bedford, Indiana 47421-9389. **T:** 1 812 275-7555

E: tips@superoldies.net
W: http://www.wqrk.com
Editorial Profile: WQRK-FM is a commercial station owned by Ad-Venture Media Inc. The format for the station is oldies music. WQRK-AM broadcasts to the Indianapolis area at 105.5 FM.

WQRL-FM
Owner: Dana Communications Corp.
Editorial: 303 N Main St, Benton, Illinois 62812-1314. **T:** 1 618 435-8100
E: wqrlfm@shawneelink.net
W: http://www.wqrlradio.com
Editorial Profile: WQRL-FM is a commercial station owned by Dana Communications Corp. The format of the station is oldies music. WRQL-FM broadcasts to the Benton, IL at 106.3 FM.

WQRP-FM
Owner: Educational Media Foundation
Editorial: 1365 Wiley Rd Ste 151, Schaumburg, Illinois 60173-4357.
T: 1 847 991-9400 **W:** http://www.air1.com
Editorial Profile: WQRP-FM is a non-commercial station owned by Educational Media Foundations. This station is a transmitter of Air1 in Rocklin, CA. There is no physical station with local staff or programming. The station broadcasts to the Dayton, OH area at 89.5.

WQRS-FM
Owner: Pembrook Pines Media Group
Editorial: 4104 Killbuck Rd, Salamanca, New York 14779-9612. **T:** 1 716 375-1015
W: http://98rockswqrs.com
Editorial Profile: WQRS-FM is a commercial station owned by Pembrook Pines Media Group. The format of the station is classic rock. WQRS-FM broadcasts to the Buffalo, NY area at 98.3 FM.

WQRV-FM
Owner: Clear Channel Media and Entertainment
Editorial: 26869 Peoples Rd, Madison, Alabama 35756-4632. **T:** 1 256 353-1750
W: http://www.wqrv.com
Editorial Profile: WQRV-FM is a commercial station owned by Clear Channel Media and Entertainment. The format of the station is classic hits. WQRV-FM broadcasts to the Huntsville, AL, area at 100.3 FM.

WQRW-FM
Owner: Pembrook Pines Media Group
Editorial: 74 Main St, Hornell, New York 14843. **T:** 1 585 593-9553
E: wqrw93radio@yahoo.com
Editorial Profile: WQRW-FM is a commercial station owned by Pembrook Pines Media Group. The format of the station is adult contemporary music. WQRW-FM broadcasts to the Hornell, NY area at 93.5 FM.

WQRX-AM
Owner: Good News Network
Editorial: 2278 Wortham Ln, Grovetown, Georgia 30813. **T:** 1 706 309-9610 3
W: http://www.gnnradio.org
Editorial Profile: WQRX-AM is a commercial station owned by Good News Network. The format of the station is Hispanic religious programming. WQRX-AM broadcsats to the Valley Head, AL area at a frequency of 870 AM.

WQSB-FM
Owner: Sand Mountain Broadcasting Service
Editorial: 3770 US Highway 431, Albertville, Alabama 35950. **T:** 1 256 878-8575
E: wqsb@aol.com **W:** http://www.wqsb.com
Editorial Profile: WQSB-FM is a commercial station owned by Sand Mountain Broadcasting Service. The format for the station is country. WQSB-FM broadcasts to the Albertville, AL area at 105.1 FM.

WQSC-AM
Owner: Kirkman Broadcasting
Editorial: 60 Markfield Dr Ste 4, Charleston, South Carolina 29407-7907.
T: 1 843 763-6631 **E:** info@wqsc1340.com
W: http://www.wqsc1340.com
Editorial Profile: WQSC-AM is a commercial station owned by Kirkman Broadcasting. The format of the station is news/talk. WQSC-AM broadcasts to the Charleston, SC area at 1340 AM.

WQSE-AM
Owner: JWL Communications, LLC.
Editorial: 201 Hall Ln, White Bluff, Tennessee 37187-9057. **T:** 1 615 797-9785
W: http://www.gracebroadcasting.com

Editorial Profile: WQSE-AM is a commercial station owned by JWL Communications, LLC. The format of the station is gospel music. WQSE-AM broadcasts in the White Bluff, TN area at 1030 AM.

WQSH-FM
Owner: Townsquare Media, LLC
Editorial: 1241 Kings Rd, Schenectady, New York 12303-2811. **T:** 1 518 476-1039
W: http://www.popcrush1057.com
Editorial Profile: WQSH-FM is a commercial station owned by Townsquare Media, LLC. The format of the station is Adult CHR. WQSH-FM broadcasts to the Albany, NY area at 105.7 FM. Please address all mail to Tom Jacobsen, Operations Manager.

WQSI-FM
Owner: Tiger Communications Inc.
Editorial: 2514 S College St, Ste 104, Auburn, Alabama 36832. **T:** 1 334 887-9999
W: http://www.wqsifm.com

WQSL-FM
Owner: Digity LLC
Editorial: 1361 Colony Dr, New Bern, North Carolina 28562-4129. **T:** 1 252 639-7900
W: http://www.wqsl.com
Editorial Profile: WQSL-FM is a commercial station owned by Digity LLC. The format of the station is country. WQSL-FM broadcasts to the New Bern, NC area at 92.3 FM.

WQSM-FM
Owner: Cumulus Media Inc.
Editorial: 1009 Drayton Rd, Fayetteville, North Carolina 28303-3887. **T:** 1 910 864-5222
W: http://www.q98fm.com
Editorial Profile: WQSM-FM is a commercial station owned by Cumulus Media Inc. The format of the station is hot adult contemporary music. WQSM-FM broadcasts to the Fayetteville, NC area at 98.1 FM.

WQSO-FM
Owner: Clear Channel Media and Entertainment
Editorial: 815 Lafayette Rd, Portsmouth, New Hampshire 03801-5406. **T:** 1 603 436-7300
W: http://www.967thewave.com
Editorial Profile: WQSO-FM is a commercial station owned by Clear Channel Media and Entertainment. The format of the station is talk. WQSO-FM broadcasts to the Portsmouth, NH area at 96.7 FM.

WQSR-FM
Owner: Clear Channel Media and Entertainment
Editorial: 711 W 40th St, Ste 350, Baltimore, Maryland 21211-2190. **T:** 1 410 366-7600
W: http://www.1027jackfm.com
Editorial Profile: WQSR-FM is a commercial station owned by Clear Channel Media and Entertainment. The format of the station is adult hits. WQSR-FM broadcasts to the Baltimore area at 102.7 FM.

WQSS-FM
Owner: Blueberry Broadcasting
Editorial: 125 Community Dr Ste 201, Augusta, Maine 04330-8157.
T: 1 207 623-9000
Editorial Profile: WQSS-FM is a commercial station owned by Blueberry Broadcasting. The format of the station is adult contemporary. WQSS-FM broadcasts to the Rockland, ME area at 102.5 FM.

WQST-AM
Owner: Ace Broadcasting Inc.
Editorial: 18844 Highway 80, Forest, Mississippi 39074. **T:** 1 601 469-1960
W: http://www.850amwqst.com
Editorial Profile: WQST-AM is a commercial station owned by Ace Broadcasting Inc. The format for the station is southern gospel. WQST-AM broadcasts to the Jackson, MS area at 850 AM.

WQST-FM
Owner: American Family Association
Editorial: 107 Park Gate Dr, Tupelo, Mississippi 38801-3010. **T:** 1 662 844-8888
E: comments@afr.net **W:** http://www.afr.net
Editorial Profile: WQST-FM is a non-commercial station owned by American Family Association. The format of the station is contemporary Christian. WQST-FM broadcasts to the Jackson, MS area at 92.5 FM.

WQSU-FM
Owner: Susquehanna University
Editorial: 514 University Ave, Selinsgrove, Pennsylvania 17870-1164. **T:** 1 570 372-4030
W: http://www.wqsu.com
Editorial Profile: WQSU-FM is a non-commercial station owned by Susquehanna University. The format of the station is alternative rock. WQSU-FM broadcasts to the Selinsgrove, PA area at 88.9 AM.

WQTC-FM
Owner: Seehafer Broadcasting Corp.
Editorial: 3730 Mangin St, Manitowoc, Wisconsin 54220. **T:** 1 920 682-0351
E: news@womtradio.com
W: http://www.womtradio.com
Editorial Profile: WQTC-FM is a commercial station owned by Seehafer Broadcasting Corp. The format of the station is classic hits. WQTC-FM broadcasts to the Manitowoc, WI area at 102.3 FM.

WQTE-FM
Owner: Friends Communications Inc.
Editorial: 121 W Maumee St, Adrian, Michigan 49221-2019. **T:** 1 517 265-1500
E: friends@tc3net.com
Editorial Profile: WQTE-FM is a commercial station owned by Friends Communications Inc. The format of the station is contemporary country music. WQTE-FM broadcasts to the Adrian, MI area at 95.3 FM.

WQTK-FM
Owner: Community Broadcasters, LLC
Editorial: 199 Wealtha Ave, Watertown, New York 13601-1837. **T:** 1 315 393-1100
E: burgproduction@commbroadcasters.com
Editorial Profile: WQTK-FM is a commercial station owned by Community Broadcasters, LLC. The format of the station is news and talk. WQTK-FM broadcasts to the Ogdensburg, NY area at 92.7 FM.

WQTL-FM
Owner: Red Hills Broadcasting, LLC
Editorial: 3000 Olson Rd, Tallahassee, Florida 32308-3918. **T:** 1 850 386-8004
W: http://www.1061thepath.com
Editorial Profile: WQTL-FM is a commercial station owned by Red Hills Broadcasting, LLC. The format of the station is a mix of classic rock and adult album alternative. WQTL-FM broadcasts to the Tallahassee, FL area at 106.1 FM.

WQTT-AM
Owner: ICS Communications, Inc
Editorial: 113 S Main St, Marysville, Ohio 43040-1551. **T:** 1 614 754-4850
E: news@icsohio.com
W: http://www.qt1270.com
Editorial Profile: WQTT-AM is a commercial station owned by ICS Communications, Inc. The format of the station is oldies. WQTT-AM broadcasts to the Marysville, OH area at a frequency of 1570 AM.

WQTU-FM
Owner: Rome Radio Partners
Editorial: 20 John Davenport Dr NW, Rome, Georgia 30165-2536. **T:** 1 706 291-9496
W: http://www.q102rome.com
Editorial Profile: WQTU-FM is a commercial station owned by Rome Radio Partners. The format of the station is adult contemporary. WQTU-FM broadcasts to the Atlanta area at 102.3 FM.

WQTW-AM
Owner: Wall(L. Stanley)
Editorial: 2532 Springfield Pike, Connellsville, Pennsylvania 15425. **T:** 1 724 532-1778
E: wlswproduction@hotmail.com
Editorial Profile: WQTW-AM is a commercial station owned by L. Stanley Wall. The format of the station is classic hits. WQTW-AM broadcasts to the Latrobe, PA area at 1570 AM.

WQTX-FM
Owner: Midwest Communications, Inc.
Editorial: 2495 Cedar St, Ste 106, Holt, Michigan 48842. **T:** 1 517 699-0111
W: http://www.wqtx.net
Editorial Profile: WQTX-FM is a commercial station owned by Midwest Communications, Inc. The format of the station is Coutry. WQTX-FM broadcasts to the Holt, MI area at 92.1 FM.

WQTY-FM
Owner: Original Company Inc.(The)
Editorial: 522 Busseron St, Vincennes, Indiana 47591-2030. **T:** 1 812 882-6060
W: http://www.wqtyradio.com
Editorial Profile: WQTY-FM is a commercial station owned by The Original Company Inc. The format of the station is classic hits. WQTY-FM broadcasts to the Vincennes, IN area at 93.3 FM.

WQUB-FM
Owner: Quincy University Corporation
Editorial: 1800 College Ave, Quincy, Illinois 62301-2670. **T:** 1 217 228-5410
E: info@wqub.org
W: http://www.news.stlpublicradio.org
Editorial Profile: WQUB-FM is a non-commercial station owned by Quincy University Corporation. The format of the station is a variety of classical, jazz, news and rock alternative. WQUB-FM broadcasts to the Quincy, IL area at 90.3 FM.

WQUE-FM
Owner: Clear Channel Media and Entertainment
Editorial: 929 Howard Ave, New Orleans, Louisiana 70113-1148. **T:** 1 504 679-7300
W: http://www.q93.com
Editorial Profile: WQUE-FM is a commercial station owned by Clear Channel Media and Entertainment. The format of the station is urban contemporary music. WQUE-FM broadcasts to the New Orleans area at 93.3 FM.

WQUL-AM
Owner: BJL Broadcasting Inc
Editorial: 360 Sloan Rd, Woodruff, South Carolina 29388. **T:** 1 864 476-7184
Editorial Profile: WQUL-AM is a commercial station owned by BJL Broadcasting Inc. The format of the station is country. WQUL-AM broadcasts to the Woodruff, SC area at 1510 AM.

WQUN-AM
Owner: Quinnipiac University
Editorial: 3085 Whitney Ave, Hamden, Connecticut 06518-2318. **T:** 1 203 582-8984
E: wqun@quinnipiac.edu
W: http://www.quinnipiac.edu/news-and-events/wqun
Editorial Profile: WQUN-AM is a commercial station owned by Quinnipac University. The format of the station is adult standards. WQUN-AM broadcasts to the Hartford-New Haven, CT area at 1220 AM.

WQUS-FM
Owner: Townsquare Media, LLC
Editorial: 3338 E Bristol Rd, Burton, Michigan 48529. **T:** 1 810 742-1470
W: http://us103.com
Editorial Profile: WQUS-FM is a commercial station owned by Townsquare Media, LLC. The format of the station is classic rock. WQUS-FM broadcasts to the Burton, MI area at 103.1 FM.

WQUT-FM
Owner: Cumulus Media Inc.
Editorial: 162 Free Hill Rd, Gray, Tennessee 37615-3144. **T:** 1 423 477-1000
E: classicrock@wqut.com
W: http://www.wqut.com
Editorial Profile: WQUT-FM is a commercial station owned by Cumulus Media Inc. The format of the station is classic rock. WQUT-FM broadcasts to the Gray, TN area at 101.5 FM.

WQVE-FM
Owner: Cumulus Media Inc.
Editorial: 1104 W Broad Ave, Albany, Georgia 31707. **T:** 1 229 888-5000
W: http://www.wqvealbany.com
Editorial Profile: WQVE-FM is a commercial station owned by Cumulus Media Inc. The format of the station is urban adult contemporary. WQVE-FM broadcasts to the Albany, GA area at 101.7 FM.

WQWK-AM
Owner: Forever Broadcasting
Editorial: 2551 Park Center Blvd, State College, Pennsylvania 16801.
T: 1 814 237-9800
W: http://www.1450espnradio.com
Editorial Profile: WQWK-AM is a commercial station owned by Forever Boradcasting. The format of the station is sports. WQWK-AM broadcasts to the State College, PA area at 1450 AM.

WQWV-FM
Owner: McGuire Broadcasting LLC
Editorial: 2 Alt Ave, Petersburg, West Virginia 26847-1758. **T:** 1 304 257-4432
E: v103@newcountryv103.com
W: http://www.newcountryv103.com
Editorial Profile: WQWV-FM is a commercial station owned by McGuire Broadcasting LLC. The format of the station is contemporary country music. WQWV-FM broadcasts to the Petersburg, WV area at 103.7 FM.

WQXA-FM
Owner: Cumulus Media Inc.
Editorial: 515 S 32nd St, Camp Hill, Pennsylvania 17011. **T:** 1 717 635-7000
W: http://www.1057thex.com
Editorial Profile: WQXA-FM is a commercial station owned by Cumulus Media Inc. The format of the station is rock alternative. WQXA-FM broadcasts to Elizabethtown, PA area at 105.7 FM.

WQXB-FM
Owner: THE RAYANNA CORP
Editorial: 1348 Sunset Dr, Grenada, Mississippi 38901-4000. **T:** 1 662 226-1400
E: b100@bellsouth.net
W: http://www.myb100.com

WQXC-FM
Owner: Forum Communications Co.
Editorial: 706 E Allegan St, Otsego, Michigan 49078. **T:** 1 269 343-1717 **E:** news@wqxc.com
W: http://www.wqxc.com
Editorial Profile: WQXC-FM is a commercial station owned by Forum Communications Co. The format of the station is oldies music. WQXC-FM broadcasts to the Ostego, MI area at 100.9 FM.

WQXE-FM
Owner: Skytower Communications Inc.
Editorial: 233 W Dixie Ave, Elizabethtown, Kentucky 42701-1560. **T:** 1 270 736-9830
E: quicksie@wqxe.com
W: http://www.wqxe.com
Editorial Profile: WQXE-FM is a commercial station owned by Skytower Communications Inc. The format is adult contemporary. WQXE-FM broadcasts to the Elizabethtown, KY area at 98.3 FM.

WQXI-AM
Owner: Big League Broadcasting
Editorial: 210 Interstate North Cir SE, Atlanta, Georgia 30339-2206. **T:** 1 404 237-0079
E: zonewebmaster@790thezone.com
W: http://www.790thezone.com
Editorial Profile: WQXI-AM is a commercial station owned by Big League Broadcasting. The format of the station is sports. WQXI-AM broadcasts to the Atlanta area at 790 AM.

WQXJ-FM
Owner: Omni Broadcasting Co.
Editorial: 502 Beltrami Ave NW, Bemidji, Minnesota 56601. **T:** 1 218 444-1500
Editorial Profile: WQXJ-FM is a commercial station owned by Omni Broadcasting Co. The format of the station is oldies. WQXJ-FM broadcasts to the Minneapolis area at 104.5 FM.

WQXK-FM
Owner: Cumulus Media Inc.
Editorial: 4040 Simon Rd, Youngstown, Ohio 44512. **T:** 1 330 783-1000
W: http://www.k105country.com
Editorial Profile: WQXK-FM is a commercial station owned by Cumulus Media Inc. The format for the station is country music. WQXK-FM broadcasts to the Youngstown, OH area at 105.1 FM.

WQXL-AM
Owner: Glory Communications Inc.
Editorial: 2440 Millwood Ave, Columbia, South Carolina 29205-1128.
T: 1 803 563-8558
E: info@makethepointradio.com
W: http://makethepointradio.com
Editorial Profile: WQXL-AM is a commercial station owned by Glory Communications Inc. and operated by Capital City Media, LLC. The format of the station is talk. WQXL-AM broadcasts to the Columbia, SC area at 1470 AM.

WQXM-AM
Owner: Osvaldo Vega
Editorial: 1355 N Maple Ave, Bartow, Florida 33830-3024. **T:** 1 305 345-7177
E: programacion@lax1460.com
W: http://lax1460.com
Editorial Profile: WQXM-AM is a commercial station owned by Osvaldo Vega. The format of the station is Hispanic news talk and entertainment, and regional Mexican music. WQXM-AM broadcasts to the Tampa, FL area at 1460 AM.

WQXO-AM
Owner: Great Lakes Radio Inc.

Editorial: 3060 Us Highway 41 W, Marquette, Michigan 49855-2293. **T:** 1 906 228-6800
E: contact@broadcasteverywhere.com
W: http://www.greatlakesradio.org
Editorial Profile: WQXO-AM is a commercial station owned by Great Lakes Radio Inc. The format for the station is oldies music. WQXO-AM broadcasts to the Marquette, MI area at 1400 AM.

WQXQ-FM
Owner: Starlight Broadcasting Co.
Editorial: 314 S Main St, Hartford, Kentucky 42347-1129. **T:** 1 270 685-1235
Editorial Profile: WQXQ-FM is a commercial station owned by Starlight Broadcasting Co. The format of the station is sports. WQXQ-FM's broadcasts to the Owensboro, KY area.

WQXR-FM
Owner: New York Public Radio
Editorial: 160 Varick St, New York, New York 10013-1220. **T:** 1 646 829-4400
W: http://www.wqxr.org
Editorial Profile: WQXR-FM is a non-commercial station owned by the New York Public Radio. The format of the station is classical music. WQXR-FM broadcasts to the New York City area at 105.9 FM.

WQXZ-FM
Owner: Georgia Eagle Broadcasting Inc.
Editorial: 218 Eastman Highway, Hawkinsville, Georgia 31036. **T:** 1 478 892-9061
E: gebhawk@gmail.com
Editorial Profile: WQXZ-FM is a commercial station owned by Georgia Eagle Broadcasting Inc. The format of the station is oldies. WQXZ-FM broadcasts to the Hawkinsville, GA area at 103.9 FM.

WQYK-FM
Owner: CBS Radio
Editorial: 9721 Executive Center Dr N, Saint Petersburg, Florida 33702-2449.
T: 1 727 579-1925 **W:** http://www.wqyk.com
Editorial Profile: WQYK-FM is a commercial station owned by CBS Radio. The format of the station is classic country. WQYK-FM broadcasts to the St. Petersburg, FL area at 99.5 FM.

WQYX-FM
Owner: First Media Radio LLC
Editorial: 801 E Dubois Ave, Du Bois, Pennsylvania 15801. **T:** 1 814 371-8300
E: fmclearfield@yahoo.com
W: http://www.qyxfm.com
Editorial Profile: WQYX-FM is a commercial station owned by First Media Radio LLC. The format of the station is Top 40 music. WQYX-FM broadcasts to the Clearfield, PA, area at 93.1 FM.

WQYZ-FM
Owner: Clear Channel Media and Entertainment
Editorial: 286 Debuys Rd, Biloxi, Mississippi 39531. **T:** 1 228 388-2323
W: http://www.92fmthebeat.com
Editorial Profile: WQYZ-FM is a commercial station owned by Clear Channel Media and Entertainment. The format of the station is adult contemporary. WQYZ-FM broadcasts to the Biloxi, MS area at 92.5 FM.

WQZK-FM
Owner: West Virgina Radio Corporation of the Alleganies
Editorial: 15 Industrial Blvd E, Cumberland, Maryland 21502. **T:** 1 301 759-1005
W: http://www.941qzk.com
Editorial Profile: WQZK-FM is a commercial station owned by West Virgina Radio Corporation of the Alleganies. The format of the station is Top 40/CHR. WQZK-FM broadcasts to Keyser, WV area at 94.1 FM.

WQZL-FM
Owner: Digity LLC
Editorial: 1361 Colony Dr, New Bern, North Carolina 28562-4129. **T:** 1 252 639-7900
W: http://www.wqsl.com
Editorial Profile: WQZL-FM is a commercial station owned by Digity LLC. The format of the station is country. WQZL-FM broadcasts to the New Bern, NC area at 101.1 FM.

WQZQ-AM
Owner: Cromwell Group Inc.(The)
Editorial: 1824 Murfreesboro Pike, Nashville, Tennessee 37217-3208. **T:** 1 931 645-1550
W: http://sportstalk830.com
Editorial Profile: WQZQ-AM is commercial station owned by The Cromwell Group. The format of the station is sports talk. WQZQ-AM broadcasts in the Nashville, TN area at 830 AM.

WQZS-FM
Owner: Wahl(Roger)
Editorial: 128 Hunsrick Rd, Meyersdale, Pennsylvania 15552. **T:** 1 814 634-9111
Editorial Profile: WQZS-FM is a commercial station owned by Roger Wahl. The station format of the station is oldies music. WQZS-FM broadcasts to the Meyersdale, PA area at 93.3 FM.

WQZX-FM
Owner: Haynes Broadcasting
Editorial: 205 W Commerce St, Greenville, Alabama 36037. **T:** 1 334 382-6633
W: http://www.q94.net
Editorial Profile: WQZX-FM is a commercial station owned by Haynes Broadcasting. The format of the station is contemporary country. WQZX-FM broadcasts to the Greenville, AL area at 94.3 FM.

WQZY-FM
Owner: State Broadcasting, Inc.
Editorial: 807 Bellevue Ave, Dublin, Georgia 31021. **T:** 1 478 272-4422
W: http://www.wqzy.com
Editorial Profile: WQZY-FM is a commercial station owned by State Broadcasting, Inc. The format of the station is country music. WQZY-FM broadcasts to the Dublin, GA area at 95.9 FM.

WRAA-AM
Owner: Hayden Hamilton Media Strategies
Editorial: 1057 US Highway 211 W, Luray, Virginia 22835-5245. **T:** 1 540 743-5167
Editorial Profile: WRAA-AM is a commercial station owned by Hayden Hamilton Media Strategies. The format of the station is country music. WRAA-AM broadcasts to the Harrisonburg, VA area at 1330 AM.

WRAB-AM
Owner: Reed Broadcasting LLC
Editorial: 619 S Brindlee Mountain Pkwy, Arab, Alabama 35016. **T:** 1 256 586-4123
E: wrab@otelco.net **W:** http://www.wrab.net
Editorial Profile: WRAB-AM is a commercial station owned by Reed Broadcasting LLC. The format for the station is country and gospel. WRAB-AM broadcasts to the Huntsville, AL area at 1380 AM.

WRAC-FM
Owner: DreamCatcher Communications Inc.
Editorial: 114 S Manchester St, West Union, Ohio 45693-1221. **T:** 1 937 544-9722
E: c103country@yahoo.com
W: http://www.c103.fm
Editorial Profile: WRAC-FM is a commercial station owned by DreamCatcher Communications Inc. The format of the station is contemporary country. WRAC-FM broadcasts to the West Union, OH area at 103.1 FM.

WRAD-AM
Owner: Cumulus Media Inc.
Editorial: 7080 Lee Hwy, Fairlawn, Virginia 24141-8416. **T:** 1 540 731-6000
Editorial Profile: WRAD-AM is a commercial station owned by Cumulus Media Inc. The format of the station is oldies. WRAD-AM broadcasts to the Fairlawn, VA area at 1460 AM.

WRAF-FM
Owner: Toccoa Falls College
Editorial: 292 Old Clarksville Rd, Toccoa, Georgia 30577-6973. **T:** 1 706 282-6030
W: http://www.toccoafallsradio.org
Editorial Profile: WRAF-FM is a non-commercial station owned by Toccoa Falls College. The format of the station is religious programming. WRAF-FM broadcasts to the Toccoa, GA area at 90.9 FM.

WRAK-AM
Owner: Clear Channel Media and Entertainment
Editorial: 1559 W 4th St, Williamsport, Pennsylvania 17701. **T:** 1 570 327-1400
E: wrak@clearchannel.com
W: http://www.wrak.com
Editorial Profile: WRAK-AM is a commercial station owned by Clear Channel Media and Entertainment. The format of the station is news, sports and talk. WRAK-AM broadcasts to the Williamsport, PA area at 1400 AM.

WRAL-FM
Owner: Capitol Broadcasting Company
Editorial: 3100 Highwoods Blvd, Ste 140, Raleigh, North Carolina 27604-1033.
T: 1 919 890-6101 **W:** http://www.wralfm.com
Editorial Profile: WRAL-FM is a commercial station owned by Capitol Broadcasting Company. The format of the station is adult contemporary. WRAL-FM broadcasts to the Raleigh, NC area at 101.5 FM.

WRAM-AM
Owner: Prairie Communications LLP
Editorial: 55 Public Sq, Monmouth, Illinois 61462. **T:** 1 309 734-9452
E: wmoi@maplecity.com
W: http://www.1330wram.com
Editorial Profile: WRAM-AM is a commercial station owned by Prairie Communications LLP. The format of the station is classic country. WRAM-AM broadcasts to the Monmouth, IL area at 1330 AM.

WRAN-FM
Owner: Miller Communications Inc.
Editorial: 918 E Park St, Taylorville, Illinois 62568. **T:** 1 217 824-3395
E: wran983@randyradio.com
W: http://www.wranradio.com
Editorial Profile: WRAN-FM is a commercial station owned by Miller Communications Inc. The format of the station is oldies and classic hits music from the 60s, 70s and 80s. WRAN-FM broadcasts to the Taylorville, IL area at a frequency of 98.3 FM.

WRAR-FM
Owner: Real Media, Inc.
Editorial: 156 Prince St, Tappahannock, Virginia 22560. **T:** 1 804 443-4321
W: http://www.wrarfm.com
Editorial Profile: WRAR-FM is a commercial station owned by Real Media, Inc. The format of the station is adult contemporary. WRAR-FM broadcasts to the Tappahannock, VA area at 105.5 FM.

WRAS-FM
Owner: Georgia State University
Editorial: 33 Gilmer St SE #280, Atlanta, Georgia 30303-3044. **T:** 1 404 413-1630
W: http://www.gsu.edu/wras
Editorial Profile: WRAS-FM is a non-commercial station owned by Georgia State University. The format of the station is college variety. WRAS-FM broadcasts in the Atlanta area at 88.5 FM.

WRAT-FM
Owner: Greater Media Inc.
Editorial: 1731 Main St, Belmar, New Jersey 07719-3051. **T:** 1 732 681-3800
W: http://www.wrat.com
Editorial Profile: WRAT-FM is a commercial station owned by Greater Media Inc. The format of the station is rock music. WRAT-FM broadcasts to the Belmar, NJ area at 95.5 FM.

WRAU-FM
Owner: American University
Editorial: 4000 Brandywine St Nw, Washington, District Of Columbia 20016-1844.
T: 1 202 885-1200 **W:** http://www.wamu.org
Editorial Profile: WRAU-FM is a non-commercial station owned by American University. The format of the station is news and talk programming. The target audience of the station is listeners, ages 18 to 64. WRAU-FM broadcasts to the Ocean City, MD area at 88.3 FM.

WRAW-AM
Owner: Clear Channel Media and Entertainment
Editorial: 1265 Perkiomen Ave, Reading, Pennsylvania 19602-1366. **T:** 1 610 376-6671
E: webmaster@wrfy.com
W: http://www.1340wraw.com
Editorial Profile: WRAW-AM is a commercial station owned by Clear Channel Media and Entertainment. The format of the station is oldies. WRAW-AM broadcasts to the Reading, PA area at 1340 AM.

WRAY-AM
Owner: Princeton Broadcasting Co.
Editorial: 1900 W Broadway St, Princeton, Indiana 47670. **T:** 1 812 386-1250
E: wray@wrayradio.com
W: http://www.wrayradio.com
Editorial Profile: WRAY-AM is a commercial station owned by Princeton Broadcasting Co. The format of the station is news, talk, and sports. WRAY-AM broadcasts to the Princeton, IN area at 1250 AM.

WRAY-FM
Owner: Princeton Broadcasting Co.
Editorial: 1900 W Broadway St, Princeton, Indiana 47670. **T:** 1 812 386-1250
E: wray@wrayradio.com
W: http://www.wrayradio.com
Editorial Profile: WRAY-FM is a commercial station owned by Princeton Broadcasting Co. The format of the station is contemporary country music. WRAY-FM broadcasts to the Princeton, IN area at 98.1 FM.

WRBA-FM
Owner: Powell Broadcasting Company, LLC
Editorial: 118 Gwyn Dr, Panama City Beach, Florida 32408. **T:** 1 850 234-8858
W: http://www.959online.com
Editorial Profile: WRBA-FM is a commercial station owned by Powell Broadcasting Company, LLC. The format of the station is classic rock music. The station broadcasts to the Panama City, FL area at 95.9 FM.

WRBB-FM
Owner: Northeastern University
Editorial: 360 Huntington Ave, Boston, Massachusetts 02115-5005.
T: 1 617 373-4338 **E:** manager@wrbbradio.org
W: http://www.wrbbradio.org
Editorial Profile: WRBB-FM is a non-commercial station owned by Northeastern University. The format of the station is college variety. WRBB-FM broadcasts to the Boston area at 104.9 FM.

WRBE-FM
Owner: JDL Corporation
Editorial: 3276 Highway 198 W, Lucedale, Mississippi 39452-7914. **T:** 1 601 947-8151
W: http://wrbeamfm.com
Editorial Profile: WRBE-FM is a commercial station owned by JDL Corporation. The format for the station is gospel and country. WRBE-FM broadcasts to the Lucedale, MS area at 106.9 FM.

WRBF-FM
Owner: Toole (Howard C.)
Editorial: 20 John Davenport Dr Nw, Rome, Georgia 30165-2536. **T:** 1 706 291-9496
W: http://www.1049therebel.com
Editorial Profile: WRBF-FM is a commercial station owned by Toole (Howard C.). The format of the station is classic rock. WRBF-FM broadcasts to the Rome, GA area at a frequency of 104.9 FM.

WRBH-FM
Owner: Radio for the Blind and Print Handicapped
Editorial: 3606 Magazine St, New Orleans, Louisiana 70115-2545. **T:** 1 504 899-1144
E: wrbh883@gmail.com
W: http://www.wrbh.org
Editorial Profile: WRBH-FM is a non-commercial station owned by Radio for the Blind and Print Handicapped. The format of the station is news and talk. WRBH-FM broadcasts to the New Orleans area at 88.3 FM.

WRBI-FM
Owner: Lesson Media, LLC
Editorial: 133 S Main St, Batesville, Indiana 47006-1344. **T:** 1 812 934-5111
E: wrbi@wrbiradio.com
W: http://www.wrbiradio.com
Editorial Profile: WRBI-FM is a commercial station owned by Lesson Media, LLC. The format of the station is country music. WRBI-FM broadcasts to the Batesville, IN area at 103.9 FM.

WRBJ-FM
Owner: Roberts Broadcasting Co.
Editorial: 745 N State St, Jackson, Mississippi 39202-3006. **T:** 1 601 974-5700
Editorial Profile: WRBJ-FM is a commercial station owned by Roberts Broadcasting Co. The format of the station is urban contemporary. WRBJ-FM broadcasts to the Jackson, MS area at 97.7 FM.

WRBK-FM
Owner: Richburg Educational Broadcasters Inc.
Editorial: 3451 Armenia Rd, Chester, South Carolina 29706. **T:** 1 803 581-9030
E: wrbk@truvista.net
Editorial Profile: WRBK-FM is a commercial station owned by Richburg Educational Broadcasters Inc. The format of the station is oldies music. WNKX-FM broadcasts to the Richburg, SC area at 90.3 FM.

WRBN-FM
Owner: Georgia-Carolina Radiocasting Companies LLC

Editorial: 18 Radio Lane, Clayton, Georgia 30525. **T:** 1 706 782-4251
E: sky104wrbn@gmail.com
W: http://www.sky104.com
Editorial Profile: WRBN-FM is a commercial station owned by Georgia-Carolina Radiocasting Companies LLC. The format of the station is adult contemporary. WRBN-FM broadcasts to the Clayton, GA area at 104.1 FM.

WRBO-FM
Owner: Cumulus Media Inc.
Editorial: 5629 Murray Ave, Memphis, Tennessee 38119-3831. **T:** 1 901 682-1106
W: http://www.soulclassics.com
Editorial Profile: WRBO-FM is a commercial station owned by Cumulus Media Inc. The format of the station is R&B oldies. WRBO-FM broadcasts to the Memphis, TN area at 103.5 FM.

WRBQ-FM
Owner: CBS Radio
Editorial: 9721 Executive Center Dr N, Ste 200, Saint Petersburg, Florida 33702-2439.
T: 1 727 579-1925
W: http://www.tampabaysq105.com
Editorial Profile: WRBQ-FM is a commercial station owned by CBS Radio. The format of the station is classic hits music. WRBQ-FM broadcasts throughout the Tampa Bay, FL area at 104.7 FM.

WRBR-FM
Owner: Talking Stick Communications
Editorial: 237 W Edison Rd Ste 200, Mishawaka, Indiana 46545-3103.
T: 1 574 258-5483 **W:** http://www.wrbr.com
Editorial Profile: WRBR-FM is a commercial station owned by Talking Stick Communications. The format for the station is rock. WRBR-FM broadcasts to the South Bend, IN area at 103.9 FM.

WRBS-AM
Owner: Peter and John Radio Fellowship, Inc.
Editorial: 3500 Commerce Dr, Baltimore, Maryland 21227-1670. **T:** 1 410 247-4100
W: http://www.wrbs.com
Editorial Profile: WRBS-AM is a commercial station owned by Peter and John Radio Fellowship, Inc. The format of the station is religious programming and talk. WRBS-AM broadcasts to the Baltimore area at 1230 AM.

WRBS-FM
Owner: Peter and John Radio Fellowship, Inc.
Editorial: 3500 Commerce Drive, Baltimore, Maryland 21227. **T:** 1 410 247-4100
W: http://www.wrbs.com
Editorial Profile: WRBS-FM is a commercial station owned by Peter and John Radio Fellowship, Inc. The format of the station is contemporary Christian music and religious talk. WRBS-FM broadcasts to Baltimore area at 95.1 FM.

WRBT-FM
Owner: Clear Channel Media and Entertainment
Editorial: 600 Corporate Cir, Harrisburg, Pennsylvania 17110. **T:** 1 717 540-8800
W: http://www.bobradio.com
Editorial Profile: WRBT-FM is a commercial station owned by Clear Channel Media and Entertainment. The format of the station is contemporary country. WRBT-FM broadcasts to the Harrisburg, PA area at 94.9 FM.

WRBV-FM
Owner: Clear Channel Media and Entertainment
Editorial: 7080 Industrial Hwy, Macon, Georgia 31216. **T:** 1 478 781-1063
W: http://www.v1017.com
Editorial Profile: WRBV-FM is a commercial station owned by Clear Channel Media and Entertainment. The format of the station is urban adult contemporary. WRBV-FM broadcasts to the Macon, GA area at 101.7 FM.

WRBX-FM
Owner: Register(William Keith)
Editorial: 125 Friar Tuck Circle, Reidsville, Georgia 30453. **T:** 1 912 557-4140
E: wrbxwtnl@windstream.net
W: http://www.wrbx.org
Editorial Profile: WRBX-FM is a commercial station owned by William Keith Register. The format for the station is Christian talk and Southern gospel. WRBX-FM broadcasts to the Reidsville, GA area at 104.1 FM.

WRBZ-AM
Owner: Contemporary Media, Inc.
Editorial: 2821 US Highway 231, Wetumpka, Alabama 36093. **T:** 1 334 567-9279
W: http://www.koolclassichits.com
Editorial Profile: WRBZ-AM is a commercial station owned by Contemporary Media, Inc. The format of the station is classic hits. WRBZ-AM broadcasts to the Wetumpka, AL area at 1250 AM.

WRCA-AM
Owner: Beasley Broadcast Group
Editorial: 552 Massachusetts Ave, Ste 201, Cambridge, Massachusetts 02139-4088.
T: 1 617 492-3300 **E:** wrca1330@aol.com
W: http://www.1330wrca.com
Editorial Profile: WRCA-AM is a commercial station owned by Beasley Broadcast Group. The format of the station is Hispanic variety. WRCA-AM broadcasts to the Cambridge, MA area at 1330 AM.

WRCD-FM
Owner: Stephens Media Group Massena, LLC
Editorial: 2155 State Highway 420, Massena, New York 13662. **T:** 1 315 769-3333
W: http://www.1015thefox.com
Editorial Profile: WRCD-FM is a commercial station owned by Stephens Media Group Massena, LLC. The format of the station is classic rock. WRCD-FM broadcasts to the Massena, NY area at 101.5 FM.

WRCE-AM
Owner: Community Broadcasters, LLC
Editorial: 2205 College Ave, Elmira, New York 14903-1201. **T:** 1 607 732-4400
Editorial Profile: WRCE-AM is a commercial station owned by Community Broadcasters, LLC. The format of the station is sports. WRCE-AM broadcasts to the Elmira, NY area at 1490 AM.

WRCG-AM
Owner: PMB Broadcasting, LLC
Editorial: 1820 Wynnton Rd, Columbus, Georgia 31906. **T:** 1 706 327-1217
W: http://www.1069rocks.com
Editorial Profile: WRCG-AM is a commercial station owned by PMB Broadcasting, LLC. The format of the station is modern rock. WRCG-AM broadcasts to the Columbus, GA in the 1420 AM.

WRCG-FM
Owner: PMB Broadcasting, LLC
Editorial: 1820 Wynnton Rd, Columbus, Georgia 31906-2930. **T:** 1 706 327-1217
W: http://www.1069rocks.com
Editorial Profile: WRCG-FM (W295AY) is a broadcast translator owned by PMB Broadcasting, LLC. The format of the station is modern rock. WRCG-FM broadcasts to the Columbus, GA area at a frequency of 106.9 FM.

WRCH-FM
Owner: CBS Radio
Editorial: 10 Executive Dr, Farmington, Connecticut 06032-2841. **T:** 1 860 677-6700
W: http://wrch.cbslocal.com
Editorial Profile: WRCH-FM is a commercial station owned by CBS Radio. The format of the station is Lite Rock/Lite AC music. WRCH-FM broadcasts to the Hartford-New Haven, CT area at 100.5 FM.

WRCI-AM
Owner: Impact Radio, LLC
Editorial: 59750 Constantine Rd, Three Rivers, Michigan 49093. **T:** 1 269 278-1815
E: info@wlkm.com **W:** http://www.wlkm.com
Editorial Profile: WRCI-AM is a commercial station owned by Impact Radio, LLC. The format of the station is classic country hits. WRCI-AM broadcasts to the Grand Rapids, MI area at 1510 AM.

WRCJ-FM
Owner: Detroit Board of Education
Editorial: 123 Selden St, Detroit, Michigan 48201. **T:** 1 313 494-6400 **E:** 90.9@dptv.org
W: http://www.wrcj909fm.org
Editorial Profile: WRCJ-FM is a non-commercial station owned by Detroit Board of Education. The format of the station is classical and jazz. WRCJ-FM broadcasts to the Detroit area at 90.9 FM.

WRCK-AM
Owner: Good Guys Broadcasting
Editorial: 185 Genesee St Ste 1601, Utica, New York 13501-2110. **T:** 1 315 734-9245
W: http://www.1550wutq.com
Editorial Profile: WRCK-AM is a commercial station owned by Good Guys Broadcasting. The format of the station is sports. WRCK-AM broadcasts to the Utica, NY area at 1480 AM.

WRCL-FM
Owner: Townsquare Media, LLC
Editorial: 3338 E Bristol Rd, Burton, Michigan 48529. **T:** 1 810 743-1080
W: http://www.club937.com
Editorial Profile: WRCL-FM is a commercial station owned by Townsquare Media, LLC. The format of the station is urban contemporary. WRCL-FM broadcasts to the Bristol, MI area at 93.7 FM.

WRCM-FM
Owner: Columbia International University
Editorial: 1092 Radio Rd, Indian Trail, North Carolina 28079. **T:** 1 704 821-9293
E: info@newlife919.com
W: http://www.newlife919.com
Editorial Profile: WRCM-FM is a non-commercial station owned by the Columbia International University. The format of the station is contemporary Christian music. WRCM-FM broadcasts to the Charlotte, NC area at 91.9 FM.

WRCN-FM
Owner: JVC Broadcasting Inc.
Editorial: 3075 Veterans Memorial Hwy, Ronkonkoma, New York 11779-7667.
T: 1 631 648-2500 **W:** http://linewsradio.com
Editorial Profile: WRCN-FM is a commercial station owned by JVC Broadcasting Inc. The format of the station is news and talk. WRCN-FM broadcasts to the Medford, NY area at 103.9 FM.

WRCO-AM
Owner: Fruit Broadcasting LLC
Editorial: 2111 Bohmann Dr, Richland Center, Wisconsin 53581. **T:** 1 608 647-2111
E: wrco@wrco.com **W:** http://www.wrco.com
Editorial Profile: WRCO-AM is a commercial station owned by Fruit Broadcasting LLC. The format for the station is adult standards. WRCO-AM broadcasts to the Madison, WI area at 1450 AM.

WRCO-FM
Owner: Fruit Broadcasting LLC
Editorial: 2111 Bohmann Dr, Richland Center, Wisconsin 53581. **T:** 1 608 647-2111
E: wrconews@wrco.com
W: http://www.wrco.com
Editorial Profile: WRCO-FM is a commercial station owned by Fruit Broadcasting LLC. The format for the station is country. WRCO-FM broadcasts to the Madison, WI area at 100.9 FM.

WRCQ-FM
Owner: Cumulus Media Inc.
Editorial: 1009 Drayton Rd, Fayetteville, North Carolina 28303. **T:** 1 910 864-5222
W: http://www.rock103rocks.com
Editorial Profile: WRCQ-FM is a commercial station owned by Cumulus Media Inc. The format of the station is rock music. WRCQ-FM broadcasts to the Fayetteville, NC area at 103.5 FM.

WRCS-AM
Owner: WRCS 970 AM Inc.
Editorial: 443 Nc Highway 42 W, Ahoskie, North Carolina 27910. **T:** 1 252 332-3101
E: wrcs@embarqmail.com
Editorial Profile: WRCS-AM is a commercial station owned by WRCS 970 AM Inc. The format of the station is gospel music. WRCS-AM broadcasts to Ahoskie, NC at 970 AM.

WRCT-FM
Owner: WRCT Radio, Inc.
Editorial: 1 WRCT Plaza, 5000 Forbes Ave, Pittsburgh, Pennsylvania 15213.
T: 1 412 621-0728 **E:** info@wrct.org
W: http://www.wrct.org
Editorial Profile: WRCT-FM is a non-commercial station owned by WRCT Radio, Inc. The format of the station is a college variety. WRCT-FM broadcasts to the Pittsburgh area at 88.3 FM.

WRCU-FM
Owner: Colgate University
Editorial: 13 Oak Dr, Hamilton, New York 13346-1338. **T:** 1 315 228-7901
E: wrcu@mail.colgate.edu
W: http://wrcufm.com
Editorial Profile: WRCU-FM is a non-commercial station owned by Colgate University. The format of the station is variety. WRCU-FM broadcasts to the Hamilton, NY area at 90.1 FM.

WRCV-FM
Owner: NRG Media LLC
Editorial: 1460 S College Ave, Dixon, Illinois 61021. **T:** 1 815 288-3341
W: http://www.rivercountry1017.com
Editorial Profile: WRCV-FM is a commercial station owned by NRG Media LLC. The format of the station is country music. WRCV-FM broadcasts to Dixon, IL at 101.7 FM.

WRCY-AM
Owner: Original Company Inc.(The)
Editorial: 7109 Upton Rd, Mount Vernon, Indiana 47620. **T:** 1 812 838-4484
E: wyfx@originalcompany.com
W: http://wrcyam.com
Editorial Profile: WRCY-AM is a commercial station owned by The Original Company Inc. The format of the station is country music. WRCY-AM broadcasts to the Mount Vernon, IN area at 1590 AM.

WRDA-FM
Owner: Clear Channel Media and Entertainment
Editorial: 1819 Peachtree Rd NE, Atlanta, Georgia 30309-1848. **T:** 1 404 607-1336
W: http://www.radio1057.com
Editorial Profile: WRDA-FM is a commercial station owned by Clear Channel Media and Entertainment. The format of the station is alternative rock. WRDA-FM broadcasts to the greater Atlanta area at 105.7 FM.

WRDB-AM
Owner: Magnum Radio Group
Editorial: E 5680-A Highway 33 West, Reedsburg, Wisconsin 53959.
T: 1 608 524-1400
E: info@magnumradiogroup.net
W: http://www.wrdb.com
Editorial Profile: WRDB-AM is a commercial station owned by Magnum Radio Group. The format of the station is adult standards. WRDB-AM broadcasts to the Reedsburg, WI area at 1400 AM.

WRDL-FM
Owner: Ashland College
Editorial: 401 College Ave, Ashland, Ohio 44805-3702. **T:** 1 419 289-5157
W: http://www.ashland.edu/clubs-and-organizations/wrdl-889fm
Editorial Profile: WRDL-FM is a non-commercial college station owned by Ashland College. The format of the station is Top 40/CHR. WRDL-FM broadcasts to the Ashland, OH area at 88.9 FM.

WRDO-FM
Owner: Broadcast South, LLC
Editorial: South 601 W Roanoke Dr., Fitzgerald, Georgia 31750. **T:** 1 229 423-2077
W: http://www.realradio969.com
Editorial Profile: WRDO-FM is a commercial station owned by Broadcast South, LLC. The format of the station is Lite Rock/Lite AC music. WRDO-FM broadcasts to the Douglas, GA area at 96.9 FM.

WRDR-FM
Owner: Bridgelight Corp.
Editorial: 127 White Oak Ln, Old Bridge, New Jersey 08857-1945. **T:** 1 732 901-9953
E: info@bridgefm.org
W: http://www.bridgefm.org
Editorial Profile: WRDR-FM is a non-commercial station owned by Bridgelight Corp. The format of the station is religious talk and music. WRDR-FM broadcasts to the Howell, NJ area at 89.7 FM.

WRDT-AM
Owner: Crawford Broadcasting Co.
Editorial: 12300 Radio Pl, Detroit, Michigan 48228-1029. **T:** 1 313 272-3434
E: station@wmuz.com
W: http://www.wrdt560.com
Editorial Profile: WRDT-AM is commercial station owned by Crawford Broadcasting Co. The format of the station is Christian programming. WRDT-AM broadcasts to the Detroit area at 560 AM.

WRDU-FM
Owner: Clear Channel Media and Entertainment
Editorial: 3100 Smoketree Ct, Raleigh, North Carolina 27604-1086. **T:** 1 919 878-1500
W: http://www.wrdu.com/main.html
Editorial Profile: WRDU-FM is a commercial station owned by Clear Channel Media and Entertainment. The format of the station is classic rock. WRDU-FM broadcasts to the Raleigh, NC area at 100.7 FM.

WRDV-FM
Owner: Bux-Mont Educational Association
Editorial: 126 S York Rd, Hatboro, Pennsylvania 19040. **T:** 1 215 674-8002
E: wrdv@verizon.net **W:** http://www.wrdv.org

Editorial Profile: WRDV-FM is a non-commercial station owned by Bux-Mont Educational Association. The format of the station is variety. WRDV-FM broadcasts to the Hatboro, PA area at 89.3 FM.

WRDW-AM
Owner: Beasley Broadcast Group
Editorial: 4051 Jimmie Dyess Pkwy, Augusta, Georgia 30909. **T:** 1 706 396-7000
E: ab@wrdwam.com
W: http://www.wrdwam.com
Editorial Profile: WRDW-AM is a commercial station owned by Beasley Broadcast Group. The format of the station is news, talk, and sports. WRDW-AM broadcasts to the Martinez, GA area at 1630 AM.

WRDW-FM
Owner: Beasley Broadcast Group
Editorial: 555 E City Ave Ste 330, Bala Cynwyd, Pennsylvania 19004-1137.
T: 1 610 667-9000
W: http://www.wired965.com
Editorial Profile: WRDW-FM is a commercial station owned by Beasley Broadcast Group. The format of the station is rhythmic Top 40/CHR. WRDW-FM broadcasts to the Philadelphia area at 96.5 FM.

WRDX-FM
Owner: Clear Channel Media and Entertainment
Editorial: 920 W Basin Rd, New Castle, Delaware 19720. **T:** 1 302 395-9800
W: http://www.929tomfm.com
Editorial Profile: WRDX-FM is a commercial station owned by Clear Channel Media and Entertainment. The format of the station is adult hits. WRDX-FM broadcasts to the Dover, DE area at 92.9 FM.

WRDZ-AM
Owner: Walt Disney Co.
Editorial: 401 N Michigan Ave, Ste 2010, Chicago, Illinois 60611. **T:** 1 312 683-1300
W: http://www.radiodisney.com/chicago
Editorial Profile: WRDZ-AM is a commercial station owned by Walt Disney Co. The format of the station is children's programming. WRDZ-AM broadcasts to the Chicago area at 1300 AM.

WRDZ-FM
Owner: Walt Disney Co.
Editorial: 630 W Carmel Dr, Ste 160, Carmel, Indiana 46032. **T:** 1 317 574-2000
W: http://radio.disney.go.com/music/yourstation/indianapolis/index.html
Editorial Profile: WRDZ-FM is a commercial station owned by Walt Disney Co. The format of the station is Top 40/CHR for children. WRDZ-FM broadcasts to the Indianapolis area at 98.3 FM.

WREB-FM
Owner: Original Company Inc.(The)
Editorial: 2468 W County Road 25 N, Greencastle, Indiana 46135.
T: 1 765 653-9717
E: wreb@originalcompany.com
W: http://www.wrebfm.com
Editorial Profile: WREB-FM is a commercial station owned by The Original Company Inc. The format of the station is adult contemporary. WREB-FM broadcasts to the Indianapolis area at 94.3 FM.

WREC-AM
Owner: Clear Channel Media and Entertainment
Editorial: 2650 Thousand Oaks Blvd Ste 4100, Memphis, Tennessee 38118-2451.
T: 1 901 259-1300 **E:** news@600wrec.com
W: http://www.600wrec.com
Editorial Profile: WREC-AM is a commercial station owned by Clear Channel Media and Entertainment. The format of the station is news, sports and talk. WREC-AM broadcasts to the Memphis, TN, area at 600 AM.

WRED-AM
Owner: Atlantic Coast Radio LLC
Editorial: 779 Warren Ave, Portland, Maine 04103-1007. **T:** 1 207 773-9695
W: http://www.thebigjab.com
Editorial Profile: WRED-AM is a commercial station owned by Atlantic Coast Radio LLC. The format of the station is sports. WRED-AM broadcasts to the Portland, ME area at 1440 AM.

WREF-AM
Owner: Berkshire Broadcasting Corp
Editorial: 198 Main St, Danbury, Connecticut 6810. **T:** 1 203 744-4800
E: feedback@b1073fm.com
W: http://www.b1073fm.com
Editorial Profile: WREF-AM is a commercial station owned by Berkshire Broadcasting. The format of the station is oldies music. WREF-AM broadcasts to the Danbury, CT area at 850 AM.

WREJ-AM
Owner: Davidson Media Group
Editorial: 308 W Broad St, Richmond, Virginia 23220-4240. **T:** 1 804 643-0990
W: http://www.rejoice1540.com
Editorial Profile: WREJ-AM is a commercial station owned by Davidson Media Group. The format of the station is urban gospel. WREJ-AM broadcasts to the Richmond, VA area at 1540 AM.

WREK-FM
Owner: Georgia Institute of Technology
Editorial: 350 Ferst Dr. NW, Suite 2224, Atlanta, Georgia 30332-0630.
T: 1 404 894-2468
E: general.manager@wrek.org
W: http://www.wrek.org
Editorial Profile: WREK-FM is a non-commercial station owned by the Georgia Institute of Technology. The format of the station is college variety. WREK-FM broadcasts in the Atlanta area at 91.1 FM.

WREL-AM
Owner: First Media Radio LLC
Editorial: 392 E Midland Trl, Lexington, Virginia 24450-5703. **T:** 1 540 463-2161
E: news@wrel.com **W:** http://www.wrel.com
Editorial Profile: WREL-AM is a commercial station owned by First Media Radio LLC. The format of the station is news, sports and talk. WREL-AM broadcasts to the Lexington, VA area at 1450 AM.

WREO-FM
Owner: Media One Group
Editorial: 9179 Mentor Ave, Mentor, Ohio 44060-6398. **T:** 1 440 993-2126
W: http://www.mix971fm.com
Editorial Profile: WREO-FM is a commercial station owned by Media One Group. The format of the station is adult contemporary music. WREO-FM broadcasts to the Cleveland area at 97. 1 FM.

WRES-FM
Owner: Empowerment Resource Center of Asheville/Buncombe County
Editorial: 91 Patton Ave, Asheville, North Carolina 28801. **T:** 1 828 281-3065
E: shoutout@wresfm.com
W: http://www.wresfm.com
Editorial Profile: WRES-FM is a non-commercial station owned by Empowerment Resource Center of Asheville/Buncombe County. The format of the station is urban contemporary. WRES-FM broadcasts to the Asheville, NC area at 100.7 FM.

WREV-AM
Owner: Que Pasa Media
Editorial: 3025 Waughtown St, Winston Salem, North Carolina 27107.
T: 1 336 714-2892
W: http://www.quepasamedia.com
Editorial Profile: WREV-AM is a commercial station owned by Que Pasa Media. The format of the station is Hispanic music. WREV-AM broadcasts to the Greensboro, NC area at 1590 AM.

WREW-FM
Owner: Hubbard Broadcasting, Inc.
Editorial: 2060 Reading Rd, Cincinnati, Ohio 45202-1454. **T:** 1 513 699-5959
W: http://www.949cincinnati.com
Editorial Profile: WREW-FM is a commercial station owned by Hubbard Broadcasting, Inc. The format of the station is adult hits. WREW-FM broadcasts to the Cincinnati area at 94.9 FM.

WREY-AM
Owner: Guadalupe Gonzalez
Editorial: 2619 E Lake St, Minneapolis, Minnesota 55406-1925. **T:** 1 612 729-3776
W: http://www.radiorey630am.com
Editorial Profile: WREY-AM is a commercial station owned by Guadalupe Gonzalez. The format of the station is regional Mexican. WREY-AM broadcasts to the Minneapolis area at 630 AM.

WREZ-FM
Owner: Withers Broadcasting of Paducah, LLC
Editorial: 1700 N 8th St, Paducah, Kentucky 42001-1752. **T:** 1 270 538-5251
W: http://www.1055thecat.com
Editorial Profile: WREZ-FM is a commercial station owned by Withers Broadcasting of Paducah, LLC. The format of the station is Top 40/CHR. WREZ-FM broadcasts to the Paducah, KY area at 105.5 FM.

WRFA-FM
Owner: Arts Council for Chautauqua County, Inc.
Editorial: 116 E 3rd St, Jamestown, New York 14701-5402. **T:** 1 716 664-2465
E: wrfa@artscouncil.com
W: http://www.wrfalp.com
Editorial Profile: WRFA-FM is a non-commercial station owned by Arts Council for Chautauqua County, Inc. The format of the station is variety. WRFA-FM broadcasts to the Jamestown, NY area at 107.9 FM.

WRFC-AM
Owner: Cox Media Group, Inc.
Editorial: 1010 Tower Pl, Bogart, Georgia 30622-3052. **T:** 1 706 549-6222
E: theref@southernbroadcasting.com
W: http://www.960theref.com
Editorial Profile: WRFC-AM is a commercial station owned by Cox Media Group, Inc. The format of the station is sports. WRFC-AM broadcasts to the Athens, GA area at 960 AM.

WRFD-AM
Owner: Salem Communications
Editorial: 8101 N High St Ste 360, Columbus, Ohio 43235-1442. **T:** 1 614 885-0880
E: mail@wrfd.com **W:** http://www.wrfd.com
Editorial Profile: WRFD-AM is a commercial station owned by Salem Communications. The format of the station is religious, talk and agricultural programming. WRFD-AM broadcasts to the Columbus, OH area at 880 AM.

WRFF-FM
Owner: Clear Channel Media and Entertainment
Editorial: 111 Presidential Blvd, Ste 100, Bala Cynwyd, Pennsylvania 19004-1009.
T: 1 610 784-3333
E: radio1045fm@gmail.com
W: http://www.radio1045.com
Editorial Profile: WRFF-FM is a commercial station owned by Clear Channel Media and Entertainment. The format of the station is rock alternative. WRFF-FM broadcasts to the Philadelphia area at 104.5 FM.

WRFG-FM
Owner: Radio Free Georgia Broadcasting Foundation
Editorial: 1083 Austin Ave NE, Atlanta, Georgia 30307-1940. **T:** 1 404 523-3471
E: info@wrfg.org **W:** http://www.wrfg.org
Editorial Profile: WRFG-FM is a non-commercial station owned by the Radio Free Georgia Broadcasting Foundation. The format of the station is variety. WRFG-FM broadcasts to the Atlanta area at 89.3 FM.

WRFK-FM
Owner: Great Eastern Radio, LLC
Editorial: 41 Jacques St, Barre, Vermont 05641-5320. **T:** 1 802 476-4168
W: http://www.1071frankfm.com
Editorial Profile: WRFK-FM is a commercial station owned by Great Eastern Radio, LLC. The format of the station is adult hits. WRFK-FM broadcasts to the Barre, VT area at 107.1 FM.

WRFL-FM
Owner: University of Kentucky
Editorial: 777 University Sta, Lexington, Kentucky 40506. **T:** 1 859 257-4636
W: http://www.wrfl.fm
Editorial Profile: WRFL-FM is a non-commercial station owned by the University of Kentucky. The format of the station is college variety. WRFL-FM broadcasts to the Lexington, KY area at 88.1 FM.

WRFM-AM
Owner: Indiana Community Radio
Editorial: 15 Wood St, Greenfield, Indiana 46140-2162. **T:** 1 317 467-1064
E: wjcfradio@aol.com

WRFM-FM
Owner: Hoosier Public Radio
Editorial: 15 Wood St, Greenfield, Indiana 46140-2162. **T:** 1 317 467-1064
E: wjcfradio@aol.com

WRFQ-FM
Owner: Clear Channel Media and Entertainment
Editorial: 950 Houston Northcutt Blvd, Ste 201, Mount Pleasant, South Carolina 29464.
T: 1 843 884-2534 **W:** http://www.q1045.com
Editorial Profile: WPRFQ-FM is a commercial station owned by Clear Channel Media and Entertainment. The format of the station is classic rock. WRFQ-FM broadcasts to the Charleston, SC area at 104.5 FM.

WRFW-FM
Owner: University of Wisconsin at River Falls
Editorial: 410 S 3rd St, Rm 306, River Falls, Wisconsin 54022. **T:** 1 715 425-3886
W: http://www.pureradio887.com
Editorial Profile: WRFW-FM is a non-commercial station owned by University of Wisconsin at River Falls. The format of the station is college variety. WRFW-FM broadcasts to the River Falls, WI area at 88.7 FM.

WRFX-FM
Owner: Clear Channel Media and Entertainment
Editorial: 801 Woodrdg Ctr Dr, Charlotte, North Carolina 28217-1908.
T: 1 704 714-9444 **W:** http://www.wrfx.com
Editorial Profile: WRFX-FM is a commercial station owned by Clear Channel Media and Entertainment. The format of the station is classic rock. WRFX-FM broadcasts to the Charlotte, NC area at 99.7 FM.

WRFY-FM
Owner: Clear Channel Media and Entertainment
Editorial: 1265 Perkiomen Ave, Reading, Pennsylvania 19602-1366. **T:** 1 610 376-6671
W: http://www.y102reading.com
Editorial Profile: WRFY-FM is a commercial station owned by Clear Channel Media and Entertainment. The format of the station is rock. WRFY-FM broadcasts to the Reading, PA area at 102.5 FM.

WRGA-AM
Owner: Rome Radio Partners
Editorial: 20 John Davenport Dr NW, Rome, Georgia 30165-2536. **T:** 1 706 291-9496
E: news@wrgarome.com
W: http://www.wrgarome.com
Editorial Profile: WRGA-AM is a commercial station owned by Rome Radio Partners. The format of the station is news and talk. WRGA-AM broadcasts to the Atlanta area at 1470 AM.

WRGC-AM
Owner: Five Forty Broadcasting Company LLC
Editorial: 1846 Skyland Dr, Sylva, North Carolina 28779-8008. **T:** 1 828 586-2221
E: info@wrgc.com **W:** http://wrgc.com
Editorial Profile: WRGC-AM is a commercial station owned by Five Forty Broadcasting Company LLC. The format for the station is a variety of soft rock, adult contemporary and country. WRGC-AM broadcasts to the Sylva, NC area at 540 AM.

WRGC-FM
Owner: Georgia College & State University
Editorial: 231 W Hancock St, Milledgeville, Georgia 31061-3375. **T:** 1 478 445-5579
W: http://www.gcsu.edu/communications/radio.htm
Editorial Profile: WRGC-FM is a non-commercial station owned by Georgia College & State University. The format of the station features news, classical and jazz music. WRGC-FM is licensed to Milledgeville, GA and broadcasts to the Georgia counties of Baldwin, Putnam, Morgan, Jones, Wilkinson and parts of Jasper at a frequency of 88.3 FM.

WRGF-FM
Owner: Greenfield Central School District
Editorial: 110 W North St., Greenfield, Indiana 46140. **T:** 1 317 462-9211
W: http://www.gcsc.k12.in.us/~gchs/WRGF/
Editorial Profile: WRGF-FM is a non-commercial station owned by Greenfield Central School District. The format of the station is classic rock and oldies. The station airs locally at 89.7 FM.

WRGM-AM
Owner: Johnny Appleseed Broadcasting Co. Inc.
Editorial: 2900 Park Ave W, Mansfield, Ohio 44906. **T:** 1 419 529-5900
E: newsroom@wmfd.com
W: http://www.wrgm.com
Editorial Profile: WRGM-AM is a commercial station owned by Johnny Appleseed Broadcasting Co. Inc. The format of the station is sports. WRGM-AM broadcasts to the Cleveland area at 1440 AM.

WRGN-FM
Owner: Updyke(Burl)
Editorial: 2457 State Route 118, Hunlock Creek, Pennsylvania 18621. **T:** 1 570 477-3688
E: wrgn@epix.net **W:** http://www.wrgn.com
Editorial Profile: WRGN-FM is a non-commercial station owned by Burl Updyke. The format of the station is Christian and religious music. WRGN-FM broadcasts to the Hunlock Creek, PA area at 88.1 FM.

WRGO-FM
Owner: WRGO Radio LLC
Editorial: 63 Ramsgate Rd, Savannah, Georgia 31419-3274. **T:** 1 855 2761027
E: info@wrgoradio.com
W: http://www.wrgoradio.com
Editorial Profile: WRGO-FM is a commercial station owned by WRGO Radio LLC. The format of the station is classic hits. WRGO-FM broadcasts to the Tampa, FL area at 102.7 FM.

WRGP-FM
Owner: Florida International University
Editorial: 11200 SW 8th St 11200 St SW SW, Miami, Florida 33199. **T:** 1 305 348-3071
E: wrgp@fiu.edu **W:** http://www.wrgp.org
Editorial Profile: WRGP-FM is a non-commercial station owned by Florida International University. The format of the station is variety. WRGP-FM broadcasts to the Miami area at 88.1 FM.

WRGR-FM
Owner: Mountain Communications
Editorial: 159 Santanoni Ave, Saranac Lake, New York 12983-2478. **T:** 1 518 891-1544
E: news@wnbz.com
W: http://www.theclassicrock105.com
Editorial Profile: WRGR-FM is a commercial station owned by Mountain Communications. The format of the station is classic rock music. WRGR-FM broadcasts to the Tupper Lake, NY area at 102.1 FM.

WRGS-AM
Owner: Debbie Beal
Editorial: 211 Burem Rd, Rogersville, Tennessee 37857. **T:** 1 423 272-2628
E: stationmanager@wrgsradio.com
W: http://www.wrgsradio.com
Editorial Profile: WRGS-AM is a commercial station owned by Philip Beal. The format of the station is country and gospel music. WRGS-AM broadcasts to the Rogersville, TN area at 1370 AM.

WRGV-FM
Owner: Clear Channel Media and Entertainment
Editorial: 6485 Pensacola Blvd, Pensacola, Florida 32505-1701. **T:** 1 850 473-0400
E: pensacolapromotions@clearchannel.com
W: http://www.1073now.com
Editorial Profile: WRGV-FM is a commercial station owned by Clear Channel Media and Entertainment. The format for the station is Top 40/CHR. WRGV-FM broadcasts to Pensacola, FL area at 103.7 FM.

WRGZ-FM
Owner: Midwestern Broadcasting Co.
Editorial: 123 Prentiss St, Alpena, Michigan 49707. **T:** 1 989 354-8400 **E:** watz@watz.com
W: http://www.watz.com
Editorial Profile: WRGZ-FM is a commercial station owned by Midwest Broadcasting Co. The format of the station is contemporary country. WRGZ-FM broadcasts to the Alpena, MI area at 96.7 FM.

WRHC-AM
Owner: Fenix Broadcasting Corp.
Editorial: 330 SW 27th Ave Ste 207, Miami, Florida 33135-2957. **T:** 1 305 541-3300
W: http://cadenaazul.com
Editorial Profile: WRHC-AM is a commercial station is owned by Fenix Broadcasting Corp. The format of the station is Hispanic. WRHC-AM broadcasts to the Miami area at 1550 AM.

WRHD-FM
Owner: Inner Banks Media, LLC
Editorial: 1848 W Arlington Blvd Ste 101C, Greenville, North Carolina 27834-5704.
T: 1 252 672-5900 **E:** prod@ibxmedia.com
W: http://www.star943.com
Editorial Profile: WRHD-FM is a commercial station owned by Inner Banks Media, LLC. The format of the station is hot AC. WRHD-FM broadcasts to the Greenville, NC area at 94.3 FM.

WRHI-AM
Owner: Our Three Sons Broadcasting
Editorial: 142 N Confederate Ave, Rock Hill, South Carolina 29730-5314.
T: 1 803 324-1340 **E:** newsroom@wrhi.com
W: http://www.wrhi.com
Editorial Profile: WRHI-AM is a commercial station owned by Our Three Sons Broadcasting. The format for the station is news and talk. WRHI-AM broadcasts to the Rock Hill, SC area at 1340 AM.

WRHK-FM
Owner: Neuhoff Family Limited Partnership
Editorial: 1501 N Washington Ave, Danville, Illinois 61832-2463. **T:** 1 217 442-1700
W: http://www.949krock.com
Editorial Profile: WRHK-FM is a commercial station owned by Neuhoff Family Limited Partnership. The format of the station is classic rock. WRHK-FM broadcasts to the Danville, IL area at 94.9 FM.

WRHL-AM
Owner: Rochelle Broadcasting Co.
Editorial: 400 May Mart Dr, Rochelle, Illinois 61068-1720. **T:** 1 815 562-7001
W: http://www.wrhl.net
Editorial Profile: WRHL-AM is a commercial station owned by the Rochelle Broadcasting Company. The format of the station is news and talk. WRHL-AM broadcasts to the Rochelle, IL area at 1060 AM.

WRHL-FM
Owner: Rochelle Broadcasting Co.
Editorial: 400 May Mart Dr, Rochelle, Illinois 61068-1836. **T:** 1 815 562-7001
E: sam@wrhl.net
W: http://www.1023thecoyote.com
Editorial Profile: WRHL-FM is a commercial station owned by the Rochelle Broadcasting Co. The format of the station is adult hits. WRHL-FM broadcasts in the Rochelle, IL area at 102.3 FM.

WRHM-FM
Owner: Our Three Sons Broadcasting
Editorial: 142 N Confederate Ave, Rock Hill, South Carolina 29730. **T:** 1 803 324-1071
E: newsroom@wrhi.com
W: http://www.fm107.com
Editorial Profile: WRHM-FM is a commercial station owned by Our Three Sons Broadcasting. The format of the station is contemporary country. WRHM-FM broadcast to the Rock Hill, SC area at 101.7 FM.

WRHN-FM
Owner: NRG Media LLC
Editorial: 3616 Highway 47, Rhinelander, Wisconsin 54501-8819. **T:** 1 715 362-1975
W: http://www.wrhn.com
Editorial Profile: WRHN-FM is a commercial radio station owned by NRG Media LLC. The format of the station is adult hits. WRHN-FM broadcasts to the Wausau, WI, area at 97.5 FM.

WRHQ-FM
Owner: Thoroughbred Communications
Editorial: 1102 E 52nd St, Savannah, Georgia 31404-4216. **T:** 1 912 234-1053
E: qualityrock@wrhq.com
W: http://www.wrhq.com
Editorial Profile: WRHQ-FM is a commercial station owned by Thoroughbred Communications. The format for the station is adult contemporary. WRHQ-FM broadcasts to the Savannah, GA area at 105.3 FM.

WRHT-FM
Owner: Inner Banks Media, LLC
Editorial: 408 W Arlington Blvd Ste 101C, Greenville, North Carolina 27834-5706.
T: 1 252 355-1037
W: http://www.thundercountryonline.com
Editorial Profile: WRHT-FM is a commercial station owned by Inner Banks Media, LLC. The format of the station is contemporary country music. WRHT-FM broadcasts in the Greenville, NC area at 96.3 FM.

WRHU-FM
Owner: Hofstra University
Editorial: 111 Hofstra University, Rm 127, Hempstead, New York 11549-1110.
T: 1 516 463-5667 **E:** wrhunews@wrhu.org
W: http://www.wrhu.org
Editorial Profile: WRHU-FM is a non-commercial station owned by Hofstra University. The format of the station is a variety of music and news. WRHU-FM broadcasts to Hofstra University and surrounding communities at 88.7 FM.

WRHV-FM
Owner: WMHT Educational Telecommunications
Editorial: 4 Global Vw, Troy, New York 12180.
T: 1 518 880-3400 **E:** email@wmht.org
W: http://www.wmht.org
Editorial Profile: WRHV-FM is a non-commercial station owned by WMHT Educational Telecommunications. The format of the station is classical music. WRHV-FM broadcasts in the Western New England area at 88.7 FM.

WRIC-FM
Owner: RR & WT Broadcasting
Editorial: 201 Suffolk Ave, Ste 210, Richlands, Virginia 24641. **T:** 1 304 425-2151
W: http://www.star95.com
Editorial Profile: WRIC-FM is a commercial station owned by RR & WT Broadcasting. The format of the station is adult contemporary. WRIC-FM broadcasts to the Richlands, VA area at 97.7 FM.

WRIE-AM
Owner: Cumulus Media Inc.
Editorial: 471 Robison Rd, Erie, Pennsylvania 16509-5425. **T:** 1 814 868-5355
W: http://am1260thescore.com
Editorial Profile: WRIE-AM is a commercial station owned by Cumulus Media Inc. The format of the station is sports. WRIE-AM broadcasts to the Erie, PA area at 1260 AM.

WRIF-FM
Owner: Greater Media Inc.
Editorial: 1 Radio Plaza St, Ferndale, Michigan 48220-2140. **T:** 1 248 547-0101
W: http://www.wrif.com
Editorial Profile: WRIF-FM is a commercial station owned by Greater Media Inc. The format of the station is rock/album-oriented rock. WRIF-FM broadcasts to the Detroit area at 101.1 FM.

WRIG-AM
Owner: Midwest Communications Inc.
Editorial: 557 Scott St, Wausau, Wisconsin 54403. **T:** 1 715 842-1672
W: http://foxsports1390.com
Editorial Profile: WRIG-AM is a commercial station owned by Midwest Communications Inc. The format of the station is sports. WOFM-FM broadcasts to the Wausau, WI area at 1390 AM.

WRIJ-FM
Owner: He's Alive Inc.
Editorial: 34 Springs Road, Grantsville, Maryland 21536. **T:** 1 301 895-3292
W: http://www.hesalive.net
Editorial Profile: WRIJ-FM is a non-commercial station owned by He's Alive Inc. The format of the station is contemporary Christian and gospel music. WRIJ-FM broadcasts to the Grantsville, MD area at 106.9 FM.

WRIK-AM
Owner: Stratemeyer Media
Editorial: 6120 Waldo Church Rd, Metropolis, Illinois 62960-4903. **T:** 1 618 564-9836
W: http://www.stratemeyermedia.com/wthqprofile.html
Editorial Profile: WRIK-AM is a commercial station owned by Stratemeyer Media. The format of the station is contemporary country. WRIK-AM broadcasts to the Metropolis, IL area at 750 AM.

WRIN-AM
Owner: Brothers Broadcasting Corp.
Editorial: 560 W Amsler Rd, Rensselaer, Indiana 47978. **T:** 1 219 866-4104
E: wrin@ffni.com
Editorial Profile: WRIN-AM is a commercial station owned by Brothers Broadcasting Corp. The format of the station is adult standards. WRIN-AM broadcasts to the Rensselaer, IN area at 1560 AM.

WRIP-FM
Owner: RIP Radio, LLC (Jackson, Dennis)
Editorial: 134 County Route 12, Windham, New York 12496-5510. **T:** 1 518 734-4747
W: http://www.wrip979.com
Editorial Profile: WRIP-FM is a commercial station owned by RIP Radio, LLC (Jackson, Dennis). The format of the station is adult contemporary and variety on the weekends. WRIP-FM broadcasts to the Windham, NY area at 97.9 FM.

WRIT-FM
Owner: Clear Channel Media and Entertainment
Editorial: 12100 W Howard Ave, Greenfield, Wisconsin 53228-1851. **T:** 1 414 545-8900
W: http://www.milwaukeeoldies.com
Editorial Profile: WRIT-FM is a commercial station owned by Clear Channel Media and Entertainment. The format of the station is oldies. WRIT-FM broadcasts to the Milwaukee area at 95.7 FM.

WRIU-FM
Owner: University of Rhode Island
Editorial: 326 Memorial Union, Kingston, Rhode Island 2881. **T:** 1 401 874-4949
E: news@wriu.org **W:** http://www.wriu.org
Editorial Profile: WRIU-FM is a non-commercial station owned by the University of Rhode Island. The station has a format of variety programming. WRIU-FM broadcasts to the Kingston, RI area at 90.3 FM.

WRIV-AM
Owner: Crystal Coast Communications
Editorial: 40 W Main St, Riverhead, New York 11901. **T:** 1 631 727-1390
E: 1390wriv@gmail.com
W: http://www.1390wriv.com
Editorial Profile: WRIV-AM is a commercial station owned by Crystal Coast Communications. The format of the station is adult standards music. WRIV-AM broadcasts to the New York City area at 1390 AM.

WRIX-AM
Owner: (Bryant) Gary
Editorial: 102 E Shockley Ferry Rd, Anderson, South Carolina 29624-3730.
T: 1 864 224-6733
E: productions@wrixfm.com
Editorial Profile: WRIX-AM is a commercial station owned by Gary Bryant. The format of the station is gospel and religous programming. WRIX-AM broadcasts to the Anderson, SC area at 1020 AM.

WRIX-FM
Owner: (Bryant) Gary
Editorial: 102 E Shockley Ferry Rd, Anderson, South Carolina 29624-3746.
T: 1 864 224-6733
E: productions@wrixfm.com
W: http://wrixfm.com
Editorial Profile: WRIX-FM is a commercial station owned by Gary Bryant. The format for the station is adult contemporary. WRIX-FM broadcasts to the Anderson, SC area at 103.1 FM.

WRJA-FM
Owner: South Carolina Educational Television Commission
Editorial: 1101 George Rogers Blvd, Columbia, South Carolina 29201.
T: 1 803 737-3200 **W:** http://www.etvradio.org
Editorial Profile: WRJA-FM is a non-commercial station owned by the South Carolina Educational Television Commission. The format of the station is news and jazz. WRJA-FM broadcasts to the Sumter and Columbia, SC areas at 88.1 FM.

WRJB-FM
Owner: Magic Valley Publishing Co., Inc
Editorial: 117 Vicksburg Ave, Camden, Tennessee 38320. **T:** 1 731 584-4444
E: wfwlwrjb@bellsouth.net
W: http://www.wrjbradio.com
Editorial Profile: WRJB-FM is a commercial station owned by Magic Valley Publishing Co., Inc. The format of the station is hot adult contemporary music. WRJB-FM broadcasts to the Camden, TN area at 95.9 FM.

WRJC-AM
Owner: WRJC Inc.
Editorial: N5240 Fairway Ln, Mauston, Wisconsin 53948-9357. **T:** 1 608 847-6565
E: info@wrjc.com **W:** http://www.wrjc.com
Editorial Profile: WRJC-AM is a commercial station owned by WRJC Inc. The format of the station is country. WRJC-AM broadcasts to the Madison, WI area at 1270 AM.

WRJC-FM
Owner: WRJC Inc.
Editorial: N5240 Fairway Ln, Mauston, Wisconsin 53948-9357. **T:** 1 608 847-6565
E: info@wrjc.com **W:** http://www.wrjc.com
Editorial Profile: WRJC-FM is a commercial station owned by WRJC Inc. The format for the station is country. WRJC-FM broadcasts to the Madison, WI area at 92.1 FM.

WRJE-AM
Owner: K-5 Communications, LLC
Editorial: 400 Walker Rd, Dover, Delaware 19904. **T:** 1 302 730-4200
W: http://www.sabrosaradio.com
Editorial Profile: WRJE-AM is a commercial station owned by K-5 Communications, LLC. The format of the station is Regional Mexican music. WRJE-AM broadcasts to the Dover, DE area at a frequency of 1600 AM.

WRJL-FM
Owner: Rojo Inc.
Editorial: 5610 Highway 55 E, Eva, Alabama 35621-7927. **T:** 1 256 796-8000
Editorial Profile: WRJL-FM is a commercial station owned by Rojo Inc. The format for the station is Southern gospel. WRJL-FM broadcasts to the Huntsville, AL area at 99.9 FM.

WRJN-AM
Owner: Bliss Communications Inc.
Editorial: 4201 Victory Ave, Racine, Wisconsin 53405-3277. **T:** 1 262 634-3311
E: news@racineradio.com
W: http://www.wrjn.com
Editorial Profile: WRJN-AM is a commercial station owned by Bliss Communications Inc. The format of the station is talk, news and sports. WRJN-AM broadcasts to the Milwaukee area at 1400 AM.

WRJO-FM
Owner: Heartland Communications Group, LLC
Editorial: 909 N Railroad St, Eagle River, Wisconsin 54521-8623. **T:** 1 715 479-4451
E: frontdesk@wrjo.com
W: http://www.wrjo.com
Editorial Profile: WRJO-FM is a commercial station owned by Heartland Communications Group, LLC. The format of the station is oldies music. WRJO-FM broadcasts in the Eagle River, WI area at 94.5 FM.

WRJT-FM
Owner: Northeast Broadcasting Co.
Editorial: 169 River St, Montpelier, Vermont 5602. **T:** 1 802 223-2396
E: feedback@pointfm.com
W: http://www.pointfm.com
Editorial Profile: WRJT-FM is a commercial station owned by Northeast Broadcasting Co. The format of the station is adult album alternative music. The station is a simulcast of WNCS-FM. Sister stations include WNCS-FM, WSKI-AM, and WDOT-FM.

WRJW-AM
Owner: Pearl River Communications Inc.
Editorial: 2438 Highway 43 S, Picayune, Mississippi 39466-8278. **T:** 1 601 798-4835
E: wrjw@charter.net
W: http://www.wrjwradio.com
Editorial Profile: WRJW-AM is a commercial station owned by Pearl River Communications Inc. The format of the station is classic country. WRJW-AM broadcasts to the Picayune, MS area at 1320 AM.

WRJX-AM
Owner: Capital Assets, Inc.
Editorial: 4428 N College Ave, Hwy 43, Jackson, Alabama 36545-2017.
T: 1 251 246-4431 **E:** info@bamadixie.com
W: http://bamadixie.com
Editorial Profile: WRJX-AM is a commercial station owned by Capital Assets, Inc. The format of the station is classic country. WRJX-AM broadcasts to the Jackson, AL area at 1230 AM.

WRJY-FM
Owner: Golden Isles Broadcasting LLC
Editorial: 185 Benedict Rd, Brunswick, Georgia 31520-2938. **T:** 1 912 261-1000
E: info@goldenislesbroadcasting.com
W: http://www.thewave1041.com
Editorial Profile: WRJY-FM is a commercial station owned by Golden Isles Broadcasting LLC. The format of the station is country. WRJY-FM broadcasts to the Brunswick, GA area at 104.1 FM.

WRJZ-AM
Owner: Moffit Media Inc.
Editorial: 1621 E Magnolia Ave, Knoxville, Tennessee 37917-7825. **T:** 1 865 525-0620
E: joy62@wrjz.com **W:** http://www.wrjz.com
Editorial Profile: WRJZ-AM is a commercial station owned by Moffit Media Inc. The format of the station is religious talk. WRJZ-AM broadcasts to the Knoxville, TN area at 620 AM.

WRKA-FM
Owner: Summit Media Broadcasting LLC
Editorial: 612 S 4th St, Louisville, Kentucky 40202-2460. **T:** 1 502 589-4800
W: http://www.hawklouisville.com
Editorial Profile: WRKA-FM is a commercial station owned by Summit Media Broadcasting LLC. The format of the station is classic country. WRKA-FM broadcasts to the Louisville, KY area at 103.9 FM.

WRKB-AM
Owner: Ford Broadcasting
Editorial: 910 Fairview St, Kannapolis, North Carolina 28083-5206. **T:** 1 704 857-1101
W: http://www.fordbroadcasting.com
Editorial Profile: WRKB-AM is a commercial station owned by Ford Broadcasting. The format of the station is Southern gospel. WRKB-AM broadcasts to the Kannapolis, NC area at 1460 AM.

WRKC-FM
Owner: King's College
Editorial: 133 N Franklin St, Wilkes-Barre, Pennsylvania 18701-1401. **T:** 1 570 208-5931
E: wrkc@kings.edu
W: http://departments.kings.edu/wrkc/about.htm
Editorial Profile: WRKC-FM is a non-commercial station owned by King's College. The format of the station is college variety. WRKC-FM broadcasts to the Wilkes-Barre, PA area on 88.5 FM.

WRKD-AM
Owner: Blueberry Broadcasting
Editorial: 15 Payne Ave Route 1 South, Rockland, Maine 04841-2117.
T: 1 207 623-9000
Editorial Profile: WRKD-AM is a commercial station owned by Blueberry Broadcasting. The format of the station is sports. WRKD-AM broadcasts to the Rockland, ME area at 1000 AM.

WRKF-FM
Owner: Public Radio International
Editorial: 3050 Valley Creek Dr, Baton Rouge, Louisiana 70808-3170. **T:** 1 225 926-3050
W: http://www.wrkf.org
Editorial Profile: WRKF-FM is a non-commercial station owned by Public Radio International. The format of the station is classical and news. WRKF-FM broadcasts to the Baton Rouge, LA area at 89.3 FM.

WRKH-FM
Owner: Clear Channel Media and Entertainment
Editorial: 555 Broadcast Dr, 3rd Fl, Mobile, Alabama 36606-2936. **T:** 1 251 450-0100
W: http://www.961therocket.com
Editorial Profile: WRKH-FM is owned by Clear Channel Media and Entertainment. The format of the station is classic rock music. WRKH-FM broadcasts to the Mobile, Alabama area at 96.1 FM.

WRKI-FM
Owner: Townsquare Media, LLC
Editorial: 1004 Federal Rd, Brookfield, Connecticut 06804-1123. **T:** 1 203 775-1212
W: http://www.i95rock.com
Editorial Profile: WRKI-FM is a commercial station owned by Townsquare Media, LLC. The format of the station is rock. WRKI-FM broadcasts to the Brookfield, CT area at 95.1 FM.

WRKK-AM
Owner: Clear Channel Media and Entertainment
Editorial: 1559 W 4th St, Williamsport, Pennsylvania 17701. **T:** 1 570 327-1400
W: http://www.wrak.cc
Editorial Profile: WRKK-AM is a commercial station owned by Clear Channel Media and Entertainment. The format of the station is news and talk. WRKK-AM broadcasts to the Williamsport, PA area at 1200 AM.

WRKL-AM
Owner: Polnet Communications
Editorial: 449 Broadway Fl 2, New York, New York 10013-2549. **T:** 1 908 558-1430
W: http://www.radiocanticonuevo.com
Editorial Profile: WRKL-AM is a commercial station owned by Polnet Communications and is under local management agreement with Radio Cantico Nuevo. The format of the station is Spanish language Christian music. WRKL-AM broadcasts to the Pomona, NY area at 910 AM.

WRKM-AM
Owner: Banka (Dennis and Tracy)
Editorial: 104 Z Country Ln, Carthage, Tennessee 37030. **T:** 1 615 735-1350
E: info@1041theranch.net
W: http://www.1041theranch.net
Editorial Profile: WRKM-AM is a commercial station owned by Dennis and Tracy Banka. The format of the station is sports. WRKM-AM broadcasts to the Nashville, TN area at 1350 AM.

WRKN-FM
Owner: Cumulus Media Inc.
Editorial: 201 Saint Charles Ave Ste 201, New Orleans, Louisiana 70170-1017.
T: 1 504 581-7002
W: http://www.nashfm923.com
Editorial Profile: WRKN-FM is a commercial station owned by Cumulus Media Inc. The format of the station is country. WRKN-FM broadcasts to the New Orleans area at 92.3 FM.

WRKO-AM
Owner: Entercom Communications Corp.
Editorial: 20 Guest St, 3rd Fl, Boston, Massachusetts 2135. **T:** 1 617 779-3400
W: http://www.wrko.com
Editorial Profile: WRKO-AM is a commercial station owned by Entercom Communications Corp. The format of the station is news and talk. WRKO-AM broadcasts to the Boston area at 680 AM.

WRKQ-AM
Owner: Beverly Broadcasting Company, LLC
Editorial: 880 Englewood Rd, Madisonville, Tennessee 37354. **T:** 1 423 442-1446
W: http://www.wrkq.net
Editorial Profile: WRKQ-AM is a commercial station owned by Beverly Broadcasting Company, LLC. The format of the station is oldies. WRKQ-AM broadcasts to the Madisonville, TN area at 1250 AM.

WRKR-FM
Owner: Townsquare Media, LLC
Editorial: 4154 Jennings Dr, Kalamazoo, Michigan 49048-1087. **T:** 1 269 344-0111
E: vip.support@townsquaremedia.com
W: http://www.wrkr.com
Editorial Profile: WRKR-FM is a commercial station owned by Townsquare Media, LLC. The format of the station is rock. WRKR-FM broadcasts to the Kalamazoo, MI area at 107.7 FM.

WRKS-FM
Owner: L & L Radio
Editorial: 731 S Pear Orchard Rd Ste 27, Ridgeland, Mississippi 39157-4839.
T: 1 601 957-1300 **E:** info@thezone1059.com
W: http://www.thezone1059.com
Editorial Profile: WRKS-FM is a commercial station owned by L & L Radio. The format of the station is sports. WRKS-FM broadcasts in the Jackson, MS area at 105.9 FM

WRKT-FM
Owner: Connoisseur Media LLC
Editorial: 1 Boston Store Pl, Erie, Pennsylvania 16501. **T:** 1 814 461-1000
E: rocket101@rocket101.com
Editorial Profile: WRKT-FM is a commercial station owned by Connoisseur Media LLC. The format of the station is classic rock music. WRKT-FM broadcasts to the Erie, PA area at 100.9 FM.

WRKU-FM
Owner: Nicolet Broadcasting Inc.
Editorial: 30 N 18Th Ave Ste 8, Sturgeon Bay, Wisconsin 54235-3207. **T:** 1 920 746-9430
E: wbdk@doorcountydailynews.com
W: http://www.doorcountydailynews.com
Editorial Profile: WRKU-FM is a commercial station owned by Nicolet Broadcasting Inc. The format of the station is classic hits. WRKU-FM broadcasts to the Sturgeon Bay, WI area at 102.1 FM.

WRKW-FM
Owner: Forever Broadcasting
Editorial: 109 Plaza Dr, Johnstown, Pennsylvania 15905-1212. **T:** 1 814 255-4186
W: http://www.rocky99.com
Editorial Profile: WRKW-FM is a commercial station owned by Forever Broadcasting. The format of the station is rock. WRKW-FM broadcasts to the Johnstown, PA area at 99.1 FM.

WRKX-FM
Owner: NRG Media LLC
Editorial: 216 W Lafayette St, Ottawa, Illinois 61350. **T:** 1 815 434-6050
W: http://www.ottawaradio.net
Editorial Profile: WRKX-FM is a commercial station owned by NRG Media LLC. The format of the station is adult hits. WRKX-FM broadcasts to the Chicago area at 95.3 FM.

WRKY-FM
Owner: Forever Broadcasting
Editorial: 1 Forever Dr, Hollidaysburg, Pennsylvania 16648-3029. **T:** 1 814 941-9800
W: http://www.rocky1049.com
Editorial Profile: WRKY-FM is a commercial station owned by Forever Broadcasting. The format of the station is rock. WRKY-FM broadcasts to the Hollidaysburg, PA area at 104.9 FM.

WRKZ-FM
Owner: North American Broadcasting
Editorial: 1458 Dublin Rd, Columbus, Ohio 43215-1010. **T:** 1 614 481-7800
E: mail@nabco-inc.com
W: http://www.theblitz.com
Editorial Profile: WRKZ-FM is a commercial station owned by North American Broadcasting. The format of the station is rock. WRKZ-FM broadcasts to the Columbus, OH area at 99.7 FM.

WRLA-AM
Owner: Tiger Communications Inc.
Editorial: 503 W 8th St, West Point, Georgia 31833-1570. **T:** 1 706 645-1490
E: wrla1490@gmail.com
Editorial Profile: WRLA-AM is a commercial station owned by Tiger Communications Inc. The format of the station is oldies. WRLA-AM broadcasts to the Auburn, GA area at 1490 AM.

WRLB-FM
Owner: Radio Greenbriar, LLC
Editorial: 276 Seneca Trl, Ronceverte, West Virginia 24970-1343. **T:** 1 304 645-1400
E: radio@wron.net
W: http://radiogreenbrier.com
Editorial Profile: WRLB-FM is a commercial station owned by Radio Greenbriar, LLC. The format of the station is Hot AC. WRLB-FM broadcasts to the Lewisburg, WV area at 95.3 FM.

WRLC-FM
Owner: Lycoming College
Editorial: 700 College Pl, Williamsport, Pennsylvania 17701. **T:** 1 570 321-4340
E: wrlc@lycoming.edu
W: http://www.lycoming.edu/orgs/wrlc/

WRLD-FM
Owner: PMB Broadcasting, LLC
Editorial: 1820 Wynnton Rd, Columbus, Georgia 31906-2930. **T:** 1 706 327-1217
W: http://www.953theride.com
Editorial Profile: WRLD-FM is a commercial station owned by PMB Broadcasting, LLC. The format of the station is classic hits. WRLD-FM broadcasts to the Columbus, GA area at 95.3 FM.

WRLI-FM
Owner: Connecticut Public Broadcasting Inc.
Editorial: 1049 Asylum Ave, Hartford, Connecticut 6105. **T:** 1 860 278-5310
E: info@wnpr.org **W:** http://www.wnpr.org
Editorial Profile: WRLI-FM is a non-commercial station owned by Connecticut Public Broadcasting Inc. The format of the station is news and talk. WRLI-FM broadcasts to the Hartford, CT area at 91.3 FM.

WRLL-AM
Owner: Midway Broadcasting Corp.
Editorial: 1000 E 87th St, Chicago, Illinois 60619-6397. **T:** 1 773 247-6200
W: http://wrll1450.com/english
Editorial Profile: WRLL-AM is a commercial station owned by Midway Broadcasting Corp. The format of the station is Hispanic. WRLL-AM broadcasts to the Chicago area at 1450 AM.

WRLO-FM
Owner: NRG Media LLC
Editorial: 3616 Highway 47, Rhinelander, Wisconsin 54501-8819. **T:** 1 715 362-6140
W: http://www.wrlo.com
Editorial Profile: WRLO-FM is a commercial station owned by NRG Media LLC. The format of the station is classic rock. WRLO-FM broadcasts to the Rhinelander, WI, area at 105.3 FM.

WRLR-FM
Owner: Rondaradio Inc.
Editorial: 629 Pontiac Ct, Round Lake Heights, Illinois 60073-1328. **T:** 1 847 546-9757
E: studio@wrlr.fm **W:** http://www.wrlr.fm
Editorial Profile: WRLR-FM is a commercial station owned by Rondaradio Inc. The format of the station is variety programming. WRLR-FM broadcasts to the Round Lake Heights, IL area at 98.3 FM.

WRLS-FM
Owner: Vacationland Broadcasting Inc.
Editorial: 16344 West Radio Hill Road, Hayward, Wisconsin 54843.
T: 1 715 634-4871 **E:** wrls@cheqnet.net
W: http://www.wrlsfm.com

WORLD NEWS MEDIA

Editorial Profile: WRLS-FM is a commercial station owned by Vacationland Broadcasting Inc. The format of the station is adult contemporary. WRLS-FM broadcasts in the Hayward, WI area at 92.3 FM.

WRLT-FM
Owner: Tuned-In Broadcasting
Editorial: 1310 Clinton St Ste 200, Nashville, Tennessee 37203-2888. **T:** 1 615 242-5600
E: psa@lightning100.com
W: http://www.lightning100.com
Editorial Profile: WRLT-FM is a commercial station owned by Tuned-In Broadcasting. The format of the station is adult album alternative. WRLT-FM broadcasts to the Nashville, TN area at 100.1 FM.

WRLU-FM
Owner: Nicolet Broadcasting Inc.
Editorial: 30 N 18Th Ave Ste 8, Sturgeon Bay, Wisconsin 54235-3207. **T:** 1 920 746-9430
E: wbdk@doorcountydailynews.com
W: http://www.doorcountydailynews.com
Editorial Profile: WRLU-FM is a commercial station owned by Nicolet Broadcasting Inc. The format of the station is country. WRLU-FM broadcasts to the Sturgeon Bay, WI area at 104.1 FM.

WRLX-FM
Owner: Clear Channel Media and Entertainment
Editorial: 3071 Continental Dr, West Palm Beach, Florida 33407. **T:** 1 561 616-6600
W: http://www.mia921.com
Editorial Profile: WRLX-FM is a commercial station owned by Clear Channel Media and Entertainment. The format of the station is Spanish adult contemporary music. WRLX-FM broadcasts to the West Palm Beach, FL area at 92.1 FM.

WRMA-FM
Owner: Spanish Broadcasting System
Editorial: 7007 NW 77th Ave, Miami, Florida 33166-2836. **T:** 1 305 447-9595
W: http://www.elzol.com
Editorial Profile: WRMA-FM is a commercial station owned by the Spanish Broadcasting System. The format of the station features Spanish CHR music. WRMA-FM broadcasts in the greater Miami area at 95.7 FM.

WRMB-FM
Owner: Moody Bible Institute
Editorial: 1511 W Boynton Beach Blvd, Boynton Beach, Florida 33436-4601.
T: 1 561 737-9762 **E:** wrmb@moody.edu
W: http://www.moodyradiosouthflorida.fm
Editorial Profile: WRMB-FM is a non-commercial station owned by Moody Bible Institute. The format of the station is religious and christian talk. WRMB-FM broadcasts to the West Palm Beach, FL area at 89.3 FM.

WRMC-FM
Owner: Middlebury College
Editorial: Campus Activities, Middlebury College, Middlebury, Vermont 05753-0029.
T: 1 802 443-6324 **E:** wrmc911@gmail.com
W: http://wrmc.middlebury.edu
Editorial Profile: WRMC-FM is a non-commercial station owned by Middlebury College. The format of the station is college variety. WRMC-FM broadcasts to the Middlebury, VT area at 91.1 FM.

WRMF-FM
Owner: Palm Beach Broadcasting, LLC
Editorial: 701 Northpoint Pkwy Ste 500, West Palm Beach, Florida 33407-1960.
T: 1 561 868-1100 **W:** http://www.wrmf.com
Editorial Profile: WRMF-FM is a commercial station owned by Palm Beach Broadcasting, LLC. The format of the station is hot adult contemporary music. WRMF-FM broadcasts to the West Palm Beach area at 97.9 FM.

WRMG-AM
Owner: Ivy Broadcasting
Editorial: 621 4th St., Red Bay, Alabama 35582. **T:** 1 256 356-4458
W: http://www.wrmgradio.com
Editorial Profile: WRMG-AM is commercial station owned by Ivy Broadcasting. The format of the station is country. WRMG-AM broadcasts to the Red Bay, AL area at 1430 AM.

WRMJ-FM
Owner: Western Illinois Broadcasting
Editorial: 2104 SE 3rd St, Aledo, Illinois 61231. **T:** 1 309 582-5666
E: contactus@wrmj.com
W: http://www.wrmj.com

Editorial Profile: WRMJ-FM is a commercial station owned by Western Illinois Broadcasting. The format of the station is contemporary country music. WRMJ-FM broadcasts to the Aledo, IL area at 102.3 FM.

WRMK-FM
Owner: Good News Church (The)
Editorial: 400 Warren Rd, Augusta, Georgia 30907-3782. **T:** 1 706 739-0022
E: wrmk@goodnewsaugusta.com
W: http://newstalk1079.com
Editorial Profile: WRMK-FM is a low-powered, non-commercial station owned by Good News Church (The). The format of the station is religious programming. WRMK-FM broadcasts in the Montgomery, AL area at 100.3 FM.

WRMM-FM
Owner: Stephens Media Group
Editorial: 28 E Main St, Fl 8, Rochester, New York 14614-1915. **T:** 1 585 399-5700
E: info@warm1013.com
W: http://www.warm1013.com
Editorial Profile: WRMM-FM is a commercial station owned by Stephens Media Group. The format of the station is Lite Rock/Lite AC. WRMM-FM broadcasts to the Rochester, NY area at 101.3 FM. Public service announcements should be faxed.

WRMN-AM
Owner: Fox Valley Broadcasting.
Editorial: 14 Douglas Ave, Elgin, Illinois 60120-5546. **T:** 1 847 741-7700
W: http://www.wrmn1410.com
Editorial Profile: WRMN-AM is a commercial station owned by Fox Valley Broadcasting Inc. The format of the station is news and talk. WRMN-AM broadcasts to the Elgin, IL area at 1410 AM.

WRMQ-AM
Owner: Florida Broadcasters
Editorial: 1355 E Altamonte Dr, Altamonte Springs, Florida 32701-5011.
T: 1 407 830-0800
W: http://www.rejoice1140.com
Editorial Profile: WRMQ-AM is a commercial station owned by Florida Broadcasters. The format of the station is gospel. WRMQ-AM broadcasts to the Orlando, FL area at 1140 AM.

WRMR-FM
Owner: Capitol Broadcasting Company
Editorial: 25 N Kerr Ave, Ste C, Wilmington, North Carolina 28405-3403.
T: 1 910 791-3088
W: http://www.modernrock987.com
Editorial Profile: WRMR-FM is a commercial station owned by Capitol Broadcasting Company. The format of the station is modern rock. WRMR-FM broadcasts to the New Bern, NC area at 98.7 FM.

WRMS-FM
Owner: LB Sports Productions, LLC
Editorial: 108 E Main St, Beardstown, Illinois 62618. **T:** 1 217 323-1790
E: wrms943@yahoo.com
W: http://www.wrmsfm.com
Editorial Profile: WRMS-FM is a commercial station owned by LB Sports Productions, LLC. The format of the station is contemporary country. WRMS-FM broadcasts to the Beardstown, IL area at 94.3 FM.

WRMT-AM
Owner: First Media Radio LLC
Editorial: 12714 E State Highway 97, Rocky Mount, North Carolina 27803-4626.
T: 1 252 442-8092
Editorial Profile: WRMT-AM is a commercial station owned by First Media Radio LLC. The format of the station is Gospel. WRMT-AM broadcasts to the greater Rocky Mount, NC area at 1490 AM.

WRMU-FM
Owner: University of Mount Union
Editorial: 1972 Clark Ave, Alliance, Ohio 44601-3929. **T:** 1 330 823-2414
E: wrmu@mountunion.edu
W: http://www.mountunion.edu/WRMU
Editorial Profile: WRMU-FM is a non-commercial station owned by Mount Union College. The format of the station is variety. WRMU-FM broadcasts to the Alliance, OH area at 91.1 FM.

WRNA-AM
Owner: Ford Broadcasting
Editorial: 633 Patterson St, China Grove, North Carolina 28023-2041.
T: 1 704 857-1101
W: http://www.fordbroadcasting.com

Editorial Profile: WRNA-AM is a commercial station owned by Ford Broadcasting. The format of the station is southern gospel. WRNA-AM broadcasts to the China Grove, NC area at 1140 AM.

WRNB-FM
Owner: Radio One Inc.
Editorial: 333 E City Ave Ste 700, Bala Cynwyd, Pennsylvania 19004-1521.
T: 1 610 538-1100
W: http://www.rnbphilly.com
Editorial Profile: WRNB-FM is a commercial station owned by Radio One Inc. The format of the station is R&B with a focus on the 1970s and 1980s. WRNB-FM broadcasts to the Philadelphia area at 100.3 FM.

WRND-FM
Owner: Saga Communications
Editorial: 1640 Old Russellville Pike, Clarksville, Tennessee 37043-1709.
T: 1 931 648-7720 **W:** http://rewind943.com
Editorial Profile: WRND-FM is a commercial station owned by Saga Communications (dba 5 Star Radio Group). The format of the station is adult hits. WRND-FM broadcasts to the Nashville, TN area at 94.3 FM.

WRNE-AM
Owner: Media One Group
Editorial: 312 E Nine Mile Rd, Ste 29D, Pensacola, Florida 32514. **T:** 1 850 478-6000
Editorial Profile: WRNE-AM is a commercial station owned by Media One Group. The format of the station is a unique blend of R&B, urban, gospel, news and talk. WRNE-AM broadcasts to the Mobile, AL and Pensacola, FL area at 980 AM.

WRNI-AM
Owner: Rhode Island Public Radio
Editorial: 1 Union Sta, Providence, Rhode Island 02903-1758. **T:** 1 401 942-3881
E: news@lprri.org
W: http://www.lprri.org/inicio/
Editorial Profile: WRNI-AM is a non-commercial station owned by Rhode Island Public Radio. The format of the station is Spanish news and talk, carrying Latino Public Radio programming. WRNI-AM broadcasts to the Providence, RI area at 1290 AM.

WRNI-FM
Owner: Rhode Island Public Radio
Editorial: 1 Union Sta, Providence, Rhode Island 02903-1758. **T:** 1 401 351-2800
E: news@ripr.org **W:** http://ripr.org
Editorial Profile: WRNI-FM is a non-commercial station owned by Rhode Island Public Radio. The format of the station is news and talk. WRNI-FM broadcasts to the Providence, RI area at 102.7 FM.

WRNJ-AM
Owner: WRNJ Radio Inc.
Editorial: 100 US Route 46 W, Hackettstown, New Jersey 07840-4932. **T:** 1 908 850-1000
E: info@wrnj.com
W: http://www.wrnjradio.com
Editorial Profile: WRNJ-AM is a commercial station owned by WRNJ Radio Inc. The format of the station is oldies. WRNJ-AM broadcasts to the Hackettstown, NJ area at 1510 AM.

WRNL-AM
Owner: Clear Channel Media and Entertainment
Editorial: 3245 Basie Rd, Richmond, Virginia 23228. **T:** 1 804 474-0000
W: http://www.sportsradio910.com
Editorial Profile: WRNL-AM is a commercial station owned by Clear Channel Media and Entertainment. The format of the station is sports. WRNL-AM broadcasts to the Richmond, VA area on 910 AM.

WRNN-AM
Owner: Digity LLC
Editorial: 1016 Ocala St, Myrtle Beach, South Carolina 29577-8007. **T:** 1 843 448-1041
Editorial Profile: WRNN-AM is a commercial station owned by Digity LLC. The format of the station is sports. WRNN-AM broadcasts to the Myrtle Beach, SC area at 1450 AM.

WRNN-FM
Owner: Digity LLC
Editorial: 1016 Ocala St, Myrtle Beach, South Carolina 29577-8007. **T:** 1 843 448-1041
W: http://www.wrnn.net
Editorial Profile: WRNN-FM is a commercial station owned by Digity LLC . The format of the station is news and talk. WRNN-FM broadcasts to the Myrtle Beach, SC area at 99.5 FM.

WRNO-FM
Owner: Clear Channel Media and Entertainment
Editorial: 929 Howard Ave, New Orleans, Louisiana 70113-1148. **T:** 1 504 679-7300
E: news@wrno.com **W:** http://www.wrno.com
Editorial Profile: WRNO-FM is a commercial station owned by Clear Channel Media and Entertainment. The format of the station is news and talk. WRNO-FM broadcasts to the New Orleans area at 99.5 FM.

WRNP-AM
Owner: The ADD Radio Group Inc.
Editorial: 127 Dorrance St Ste 5, Providence, Rhode Island 02903-2828. **T:** 1 401 521-5945
W: http://www.1320warlradio.com
Editorial Profile: WRNP-AM is a commercial station owned by The ADD Radio Group Inc. The format of the station is adult contemporary. WRNP-AM broadcasts to the Providence, RI area at 1320 AM.

WRNQ-FM
Owner: Clear Channel Media and Entertainment
Editorial: 20 Tucker Dr, Poughkeepsie, New York 12603-1644. **T:** 1 845 471-2300
W: http://www.921litefm.com
Editorial Profile: WRNQ-FM is a commercial station owned by Clear Channel Media and Entertainment. The format of the station is Lite Rock/Lite AC music. WRNQ-FM broadcasts to the Poughkeepsie, NY area at 92.1 FM.

WRNR-AM
Owner: Shenandoah Communications
Editorial: 1762 Eagle School Rd, Martinsburg, West Virginia 25404-0709. **T:** 1 304 263-6540
E: news@talkradiowrnr.com
W: http://www.talkradiowrnr.com
Editorial Profile: WRNR-AM is a commercial station owned by Shenandoah Communications. The format of the station is news, talk and sports. WRNR-AM broadcasts to the Martinsburg, WV area at 740 AM.

WRNR-FM
Owner: Empire Broadcasting
Editorial: 112 Main St, Floor 3, Annapolis, Maryland 21401-2026. **T:** 1 410 626-0103
W: http://www.wrnr.com
Editorial Profile: WRNR-FM is a commercial station owned by Empire Broadcasting. The format of the station is adult album alternative. WRNR-FM broadcasts to the Annapolis area at 103.1 FM.

WRNS-AM
Owner: Digity LLC
Editorial: 1361 Colony Dr, New Bern, North Carolina 28562-4129. **T:** 1 252 639-7900
W: http://www.wrns.com
Editorial Profile: WRNS-AM is a commercial station owned by Digity LLC . The format of the station is country music. WRNS-AM broadcasts to the New Bern, NC area at 960 AM.

WRNS-FM
Owner: Digity LLC
Editorial: 1361 Colony Dr, New Bern, North Carolina 28562-4129. **T:** 1 252 639-7900
W: http://www.wrns.com
Editorial Profile: WRNS-FM is a commercial station owned by Digity LLC . The format of the station is country music. WRNS-FM broadcasts to the New Bern, NC area at 95.1 FM.

WRNW-FM
Owner: Clear Channel Media and Entertainment
Editorial: 12100 W Howard Ave, Greenfield, Wisconsin 53228-1851. **T:** 1 414 545-8900
E: clearupdatemke@clearchannel.com
W: http://www.973radionow.com
Editorial Profile: WRNW-FM is a commercial station owned by Clear Channel Media and Entertainment. The format of station is Top 40/CHR. WRNW-FM broadcasts to the Milwaukee area at 97.3 FM.

WRNX-FM
Owner: Clear Channel Media and Entertainment
Editorial: 1331 Main St Ste 4, Springfield, Massachusetts 01103-1621.
T: 1 413 536-1105 **E:** advertising@kix979.com
W: http://www.mykix1009.com
Editorial Profile: WRNX-FM is a commercial station owned by Clear Channel Media and Entertainment. The format of the station is contemporary country. WRNX-FM broadcasts to the Springfield, MA area at 100.9 FM.

WRNY-AM
Owner: Galaxy Communications LP
Editorial: 39 Kellogg Rd, New Hartford, New York 13413-2849. **T:** 1 315 797-1330
Editorial Profile: WRNY-FM is a commercial station owned by Galaxy Communications LP. The format of the station is sports. WRNY-FM broadcasts to the New Hartford, NY area at 1350 AM.

WRNZ-FM
Owner: Hometown Broadcasting
Editorial: 2063 Shakertown Rd, Danville, Kentucky 40422. **T:** 1 859 236-2711
E: hometownradio@bellsouth.net
Editorial Profile: WRNZ-FM is a commercial station owned by Hometown Broadcasting. The format of the station is hot adult contemporary. WRNZ-FM broadcasts to the Danville, KY area at 105.1 FM.

WROA-AM
Owner: Dowdy Broadcasting, Inc.
Editorial: 10250 Lorraine Rd, Gulfport, Mississippi 39503. **T:** 1 228 896-5500

WROC-AM
Owner: Entercom Communications Corp.
Editorial: 70 Commercial St, Rochester, New York 14614. **T:** 1 585 423-2900
W: http://www.sportsradioespn950.com
Editorial Profile: WROC-AM is a commercial station owned by Entercom Communications Corp. The format of the station is sports. WROC-AM broadcasts to the Rochester, NY area at 950 AM.

WROD-AM
Owner: Volusia Broadcasting Co.
Editorial: 100 Marina Point Dr, Daytona Beach, Florida 32114-5059. **T:** 1 386 253-0000
E: spots@wrodam.com
W: http://www.wrodradio.com
Editorial Profile: WROD-AM is a commercial station owned by Volusia Broadcasting Co. The format of the station is adult standards music. WROD-AM broadcasts to the Daytona Beach, FL area at 1340 AM.

WROI-FM
Owner: Bair Communications Inc.
Editorial: 110 E 8th St, Rochester, Indiana 46975. **T:** 1 574 223-6059 **E:** wroi@rtcol.com
W: http://www.wroifm.com
Editorial Profile: WROI-FM is a commercial station owned by Bair Communications Inc. The format of the station is oldies. WROI-FM broadcasts to the South Bend, IN area at 92.1 FM.

WROK-AM
Owner: Cumulus Media Inc.
Editorial: 3901 Brendenwood Rd, Rockford, Illinois 61107-2246. **T:** 1 815 399-2233
E: news@1440wrok.com
W: http://www.1440wrok.com
Editorial Profile: WROK-AM is a commercial station owned by Cumulus Media Inc. The format of the station is news and talk. WROK-AM broadcasts in the Rockford, IL area at 1440 AM.

WROK-FM
Owner: Cumulus Media Inc.
Editorial: 544 Mulberry St, Ste 500, Macon, Georgia 31201. **T:** 1 478 746-6286
W: http://www.rock1055online.com
Editorial Profile: WROK-FM is a commercial station owned by Cumulus Media Inc. The format of the station is rock. WROK-FM broadcasts to the Macon, GA area at 105.5 FM.

WROL-AM
Owner: Salem Communications
Editorial: 500 Victory Rd, North Quincy, Massachusetts 02171-3139.
T: 1 617 328-0880
E: contactus@salemradioboston.com
W: http://www.wrolradio.com
Editorial Profile: WROL-AM is a commercial station owned by Salem Communications. The format of the station is contemporary Christian music and talk. WROL-AM broadcasts to the Boston area at 950 AM.

WROM-AM
Owner: LGV Broadcasting Inc.
Editorial: 725 Calloway Dr, Rockmart, Georgia 30153-5403. **T:** 1 706 234-7171
E: radio@joychristian.com
W: http://joychristian.com
Editorial Profile: WROM-AM is a commercial station owned by LGV Broadcasting Inc. The format of the station is southern gospel. WROM-AM broadcasts to the Rome, GA area at 710 AM.

WRON-AM
Owner: Radio Greenbrier, LLC
Editorial: 276 Seneca Trl, Ronceverte, West Virginia 24970. **T:** 1 304 645-1400
E: radio@wron.net **W:** http://www.wron.com
Editorial Profile: WRON-AM is a commercial station owned by Radio Greenbrier, LLC. The format of the station is news and talk. WRON-AM broadcasts to the Ronceverte, KS area at 1400 AM.

WRON-FM
Owner: Radio Greenbrier, LCC
Editorial: 276 Seneca Trl, Ronceverte, West Virginia 24970. **T:** 1 304 645-1400
E: radio@wron.net **W:** http://www.wron.com
Editorial Profile: WRON-FM is a commercial station owned by Radio Greenbrier, LCC. The format of the station is contemporary country music. WRON-FM broadcasts to the Ronceverte, WV area at 103.1 FM.

WROO-FM
Owner: Clear Channel Media and Entertainment
Editorial: 101 N Main St Ste 1000, Greenville, South Carolina 29601-4852.
T: 1 864 242-1005
W: http://www.shine967.com
Editorial Profile: WROO-FM is a commercial station owned by Clear Channel Media and Entertainment. The format is classic rock music. WROO-FM broadcasts to the Greenville, SC area at 96.7 FM.

WROQ-FM
Owner: Entercom Communications Corp.
Editorial: 25 Garlington Rd, Greenville, South Carolina 29615-4613. **T:** 1 864 271-9200
W: http://www.classicrock1011.com
Editorial Profile: WROQ-FM is a commercial station owned by Entercom Communications Corp. The format of the station is classic rock music. WROQ-FM broadcasts to the Greenville, SC area at 101.1 FM.

WROR-FM
Owner: Greater Media Inc.
Editorial: 55 William T Morrissey Blvd, Dorchester, Massachusetts 02125-3315.
T: 1 617 822-9600 **W:** http://www.wror.com
Editorial Profile: WROR-FM is a commercial station owned by Greater Media Inc. The format of the station is classic hits music. WROR-FM broadcasts to the Boston area at 105.7 FM.

WROS-AM
Owner: Hall(Elwyn)
Editorial: 5590 Rio Grande Ave, Jacksonville, Florida 32254-1354. **T:** 1 904 353-1050
E: wros@bellsouth.net **W:** http://www.wros.net
Editorial Profile: WROS-AM is a commercial station owned by Elwyn Hall. The format of the station is religious. WROS-AM broadcasts to the Jacksonville, FL area at 1050 AM.

WROU-FM
Owner: Main Line Broadcasting
Editorial: 717 E David Rd, Dayton, Ohio 45429-5218. **T:** 1 937 294-5858
W: http://www.921wrou.com
Editorial Profile: WROU-FM is a commercial station owned by Main Line Broadcasting. The format of the station is urban adult contemporary. WROU-FM broadcasts in the Dayton, OH area at 92.1 FM.

WROV-FM
Owner: Clear Channel Media and Entertainment
Editorial: 3807 Brandon Ave SW, Ste 2350, Roanoke, Virginia 24018. **T:** 1 540 725-1220
W: http://www.rovrocks.com/main.html
Editorial Profile: WROV-FM is a commercial station owned by Clear Channel Media and Entertainment. The format of the station is album-oriented rock music. WROV-FM broadcasts to the Roanoke, VA area at 96.3 FM.

WROW-AM
Owner: Albany Broadcasting Co.
Editorial: 6 Johnson Rd, Latham, New York 12110. **T:** 1 518 786-6600
W: http://www.albanymagic.com
Editorial Profile: WROW-AM is a commercial station owned by Albany Broadcasting Co. The format of the station is easy listening. WROW-AM broadcasts to the Latham, NY area at 590 AM.

WROX-AM
Owner: LL James Media, LLC
Editorial: 628 Desoto Ave, Clarksdale, Mississippi 38614-5219. **T:** 1 662 627-1450
W: http://www.wroxradio.com

Editorial Profile: WROX-AM is a commercial station owned by LL James Media, LLC. The format of the station is oldies. WROX-AM broadcasts to the Clarksdale, MS area at 1450 AM.

WROX-FM
Owner: Sinclair Telecable Inc.
Editorial: 999 Waterside Dr Ste 500, Norfolk, Virginia 23510-3300. **T:** 1 757 640-8500
W: http://www.96x.fm
Editorial Profile: WROX-FM is a commercial station owned by Sinclair Telecable Inc. The format of the station is rock alternative music. WROX-FM broadcasts in the Norfolk, VA area at 96.1 FM.

WROY-AM
Owner: Withers Broadcasting Co.
Editorial: 101 N Church St, Carmi, Illinois 62821. **T:** 1 618 382-4161
W: http://www.wrul.com
Editorial Profile: WROY-AM is a commercial station owned by Withers Broadcasting Co. The format of the station is oldies. WROY-AM broadcasts to the Carmi, IN area at 1460 AM.

WROZ-FM
Owner: Hall Communications
Editorial: 1996 Auction Rd, Manheim, Pennsylvania 17545-9159. **T:** 1 717 653-0800
E: wroz@hallradio.com
W: http://www.roseradio.com
Editorial Profile: WROZ-FM is a commercial station owned by Hall Communications. The format of the station is hot adult contemporary. WROZ-FM broadcasts to the Manheim, PA area at 101.3 FM.

WRPI-FM
Owner: Rensselaer Polytechnic Institute
Editorial: 1 Wrpi Plz, Troy, New York 12180. **T:** 1 518 276-6248 **E:** wrpi-bm@rpi.edu
W: http://www.wrpi.org
Editorial Profile: WRPI-FM is a commercial station owned by Rensselaer Polytechnic Institute. The format of the station is college variety. WRPI-FM broadcasts in the Troy, NY area at 91.5 FM. The station does not accept pitching.

WRPN-AM
Owner: Radio One Communications, LLC
Editorial: N7502 Radio Rd, Ripon, Wisconsin 54971-9231. **T:** 1 920 748-5111
E: wrpn@wrpnam.com
W: http://www.wrpnam.com
Editorial Profile: WRPN-AM is a commercial station owned by Radio One Communications, LLC. The format of the station is news, talk and sports. WRPN-AM broadcasts to the Ripon, WI area at 1600 AM.

WRPN-FM
Owner: Ripon College Board of Trustees
Editorial: 300 W Seward St, Ripon, Wisconsin 54971. **T:** 1 920 748-8717
E: wrpn.fm@gmail.com
W: http://www.ripon.edu/studentlife/clubs_orgs/media_pubs/wrpn
Editorial Profile: WRPN-FM is a non-commercial station owned by Ripon College Board of Trustees. The format of the station is variety. WRPN-FM broadcasts to the Ripon, WI area at 90.1 FM.

WRPP-FM
Owner: Great Lakes Radio Inc.
Editorial: 3060 US Highway 41 W, Marquette, Michigan 49855-2293. **T:** 1 906 228-6800
W: http://wrup.com
Editorial Profile: WRPP-FM is a commercial station owned by Great Lakes Radio Inc. The format of the station is classic rock. WRPP-FM broadcasts to the Marquette, MI area at a frequency of 92.7 FM.

WRPQ-AM
Owner: Baraboo Broadcasting Co.
Editorial: 407 Oak St, Baraboo, Wisconsin 53913-2415. **T:** 1 608 356-3974
E: wrpqtv43@wrpq.com
W: http://www.wrpq.com
Editorial Profile: WRPQ-AM is a commercial station owned by Baraboo Broadcasting Co. The format of the station is Lite AC. WRPQ-AM broadcasts to the Madison, WI area at 740 AM.

WRPR-FM
Owner: Ramapo College
Editorial: 501 Ramapo Valley Rd, Mahwah, New Jersey 7430. **T:** 1 201 684-7998
W: http://ww2.ramapo.edu/studentmedia/wrpr

WRPW-FM
Owner: Great Plains Media
Editorial: 108 Boeykens Pl, Normal, Illinois 61761. **T:** 1 309 888-4496
E: mail@cities929.com
W: http://www.cities929.com
Editorial Profile: WRPW-FM is a commercial station owned by Great Plains Media. The format of the station is talk and news. WRPW-FM broadcasts to the Normal, IL area at 92.9 FM.

WRQE-FM
Owner: Midwest Communications Inc.
Editorial: 1420 Bellevue St, Green Bay, Wisconsin 54311-5649. **T:** 1 920 435-3771
W: http://93rockon.com
Editorial Profile: WRQE-FM is a commercial station owned by Midwest Communications Inc. The format of the station is rock. WRQE-FM broadcasts to the Appleton, WI area at 93.5 FM.

WRQK-FM
Owner: Clear Channel Media and Entertainment
Editorial: 7755 Freedom Ave NW, North Canton, Ohio 44720. **T:** 1 330 492-4700
W: http://www.akroncantonrocks.com
Editorial Profile: WRQK-FM is a commercial station owned by Clear Channel Media and Entertainment. The format of the station is rock. WRQK-FM broadcasts to the Cleveland area at 106.9 FM.

WRQM-FM
Owner: University of North Carolina
Editorial: 120 Friday Center Dr, Chapel Hill, North Carolina 27517-9495.
T: 1 919 455-9150 **E:** wunc@wunc.org
W: http://www.wunc.org
Editorial Profile: WRQM-FM is a non-commercial station owned by University of North Carolina. The format of the station is news and talk. WRQM-FM broadcasts to the Raleigh-Durham, NC area at 90.9 FM. WUNC-FM and WRQM-FM are not accepting PSAs for the remainder of 2013.

WRQN-FM
Owner: Cumulus Media Inc.
Editorial: 3225 Arlington Ave, Toledo, Ohio 43614-2427. **T:** 1 419 725-5700
W: http://www.935wrqn.com
Editorial Profile: WRQN-FM is a commercial station owned by Cumulus Media Inc. The format of the station is oldies. WRQN-FM broadcasts to the Toledo, OH area at 93.5 FM.

WRQO-FM
Owner: TeleSouth Communications Inc.
Editorial: 110 W Monticello St, Brookhaven, Mississippi 39601. **T:** 1 601 835-5005
E: supertalk1021@yahoo.com
W: http://www.supertalkms.com
Editorial Profile: WRQO-FM is a commercial station owned by TeleSouth Communications Inc. The format of the station is talk. WRQO-FM broadcasts to the Jackson, MS, area at 102.1 FM.

WRQQ-FM
Owner: Cumulus Media Inc.
Editorial: 650 Wooddale Blvd, Baton Rouge, Louisiana 70806-2930. **T:** 1 225 926-1106
W: http://www.classichits1033.com
Editorial Profile: WRQQ-FM is a commercial station owned by Cumulus Media Inc. The format of the station is classic hits. WCDV-FM broadcasts to the Baton Rouge, LA area at 103.3 FM.

WRQR-AM
Owner: Benton-Weatherford Broadcasting Inc. of Tennessee
Editorial: 110 India Rd, Paris, Tennessee 38242-7565. **T:** 1 731 644-9455
E: radionews@bellsouth.net
Editorial Profile: WRQR-AM is a commercial station owned by Benton-Weatherford Broadcasting Inc. of Tennessee. The format of the station is country music. WRQR-AM broadcasts to the Nashville, TN area at 1000 AM.

WRQT-FM
Owner: Midwest Family Broadcasting
Editorial: 201 State St, La Crosse, Wisconsin 54601. **T:** 1 608 782-1230
W: http://www.957therock.com
Editorial Profile: WRQT-FM is a commercial station owned by Midwest Family Broadcasting. The format of the station is rock. WRQT-FM broadcasts to the La Crosse, WI area at 95.7 FM.

WRQX-FM

Owner: Cumulus Media
Editorial: 4400 Jenifer St NW Fl 4, Washington, District Of Columbia 20015-2134. **T:** 1 202 686-3100
W: http://www.mix1073fm.com
Editorial Profile: WRQX-FM is a commercial station owned by Cumulus Media. The format of the station is Top 40/CHR. WRQX-FM broadcasts in the Washington, D.C. area at 107.3. The station does not air news.

WRRB-FM

Owner: Townsquare Media
Editorial: 2 Pendell Rd, Poughkeepsie, New York 12601-1513. **T:** 1 845 471-1500
W: http://www.wrrv.com
Editorial Profile: WRRB-FM is a commercial station owned by Townsquare Media. The format of the station is rock alternative music. WRRB-FM broadcasts to the Poughkeepsie, NY area at 96.9 FM.

WRRD-AM

Owner: Good Karma Broadcasting
Editorial: 310 W Wisconsin Ave Unit 100, Milwaukee, Wisconsin 53203-2224.
T: 1 414 273-3776
E: deportes@espnmilwaukee.com
W: http://espnmilwaukee.com/
Editorial Profile: WRRD-AM is a commercial station owned by Good Karma Broadcasting. The format of the station is Hispanic sports. WRRD-AM broadcasts to the Milwaukee area at 1510 AM.

WRR-FM

Owner: City of Dallas Municipality
Editorial: 1516 First Ave, Dallas, Texas 75210. **T:** 1 214 670-8888 **E:** info@wrr101.com
W: http://www.wrr101.com
Editorial Profile: WRR-FM is a commercial station owned by the City of Dallas Municipality. The format of the station is classical music. WRR-FM broadcasts to the Dallas area at 101.1 FM.

WRRG-FM

Owner: Triton College
Editorial: 2000 5Th Ave, River Grove, Illinois 60171-1907. **T:** 1 708 456-0300 3462
E: wrrg@hotmail.com
Editorial Profile: WRRG-FM is a non-commercial station owned by Triton College. The format of the station is college variety. WRRG-FM broadcasts to the River Grove, IL area at 88.9 FM.

WRRK-FM

Owner: Steel City Media
Editorial: 650 Smithfield St, Ste 2200, Pittsburgh, Pennsylvania 15222-3925.
T: 1 412 316-3342
E: feedback@bobfm969.com
W: http://www.bobfm969.com
Editorial Profile: WRRK-FM is a commercial station owned by Steel City Media. The format of the station is adult hits. WRRK-FM broadcasts to the Pittsburgh area at 96.9 FM.

WRRM-FM

Owner: Cumulus Media Inc.
Editorial: 4805 Montgomery Rd, Ste 300, Cincinnati, Ohio 45212-2280.
T: 1 513 241-9898
E: feedback@cincyradio.com
W: http://www.warm98.com
Editorial Profile: WRRM-FM is a commercial station owned by Cumulus Media Inc. The format of the station is adult contemporary. WRRM-FM broadcasts to the Cincinnati area at 98.5 FM.

WRRN-FM

Owner: Radio Partners LLC
Editorial: 310 2nd Ave, Warren, Pennsylvania 16365. **T:** 1 814 723-1310
E: newsroom@kibcoradio.com
W: http://www.kibcoradio.com
Editorial Profile: WRRN-FM is a commercial station owned by Radio Partners LLC. The format of the station is oldies music. WRRN-FM broadcasts to the Warren, PA area at 92.3 FM.

WRRQ-FM

Owner: Equinox Broadcasting Corp.
Editorial: 101 Main St, Johnson City, New York 13790-2426. **T:** 1 607 772-1005
W: http://www.cool100.coolesthits.com
Editorial Profile: WRRQ-FM is a commercial station owned by Equinox Broadcasting Corp. The format for the station is classic hits. WRRQ-FM broadcasts to the Binghamton, NY area at 106.7 FM.

WRRR-FM

Owner: Seven Ranges Radio Company Inc.
Editorial: Greens Run Road, Saint Marys, West Virginia 26170. **T:** 1 304 684-3400
W: http://www.literock93r.com
Editorial Profile: WRRR-FM is a commercial station owned by Seven Ranges Radio Company Inc. The format of the station is adult contemporary. WRRR-FM broadcasts to the Saint Marys, WV area at 93.9 FM.

WRRV-FM

Owner: Townsquare Media
Editorial: 2 Pendell Rd, Poughkeepsie, New York 12601-1513. **T:** 1 845 471-1500
E: wrrv@wrrv.com **W:** http://www.wrrv.com
Editorial Profile: WRRV-FM is a commercial station owned byTownsquare Media. The format of the station is rock alternative music. WRRV-FM broadcasts to the Poughkeepsie, NY area at 92.7 FM.

WRRX-FM

Owner: Cumulus Media Inc.
Editorial: 6565 N W St, Ste 270, Pensacola, Florida 32505. **T:** 1 850 478-6011
E: wcoa@cumulus.com
W: http://www.mymagic106.com
Editorial Profile: WRRX-FM is a commercial station owned by Cumulus Media Inc. The format of the station is urban adult contemporary. WRRX-FM broadcasts to the Pensacola, FL area at 106.1 FM.

WRRZ-AM

Owner: Sanchez Broadcasting Corporation
Editorial: 2164 Southeast Blvd, Clinton, North Carolina 28328-4758. **T:** 1 910 592-1285
W: http://www.radionuevavida880.com
Editorial Profile: WRRZ-AM is a commercial station owned by Sanchez Broadcasting Corporation. The format of the station is Spanish Christian music and talk. WRRZ-AM broadcast to the Clinton, NC area at 880 AM.

WRSA-FM

Owner: NCA Inc.
Editorial: 8402 Memorial Pkwy SW, Huntsville, Alabama 35802-3033. **T:** 1 256 885-9797
E: wrsa@wrsa.com **W:** http://www.lite969.com
Editorial Profile: WRSA-FM is a commercial station owned by NCA Inc. The format of the station is Lite Rock/Lite AC music. WRSA-FM broadcasts to the Huntsville, AL area at 96.9 FM.

WRSB-AM

Owner: Genesee Media Corp.
Editorial: 20 Office Park Way, Pittsford, New York 14534. **T:** 1 585 919-1482
E: sports@theteam.fm **W:** http://theteam.fm
Editorial Profile: WRSB-AM is a commercial station owned by Genesee Media Corp. The format of the station is sports talk. WRSB-AM broadcasts to the Brockport, NY area at 1310 AM.

WRSC-AM

Owner: Forever Broadcasting
Editorial: 2551 Park Center Blvd, State College, Pennsylvania 16801.
T: 1 814 237-9800 **E:** wmaj@comcast.net
Editorial Profile: WRSC-AM is a commercial station owned by Forever Broadcasting. The format of the station is sports. WRSC-AM broadcasts to State College, PA at 1390 AM.

WRSC-FM

Owner: Forever Broadcasting
Editorial: 2551 Park Center Blvd, State College, Pennsylvania 16801.
T: 1 814 237-9800 **W:** http://www.wrscfm.com
Editorial Profile: WRSC-FM is a commercial station owned by Forever Broadcasting. The format of the station is news and talk. WRSC-FM broadcasts to the State College, PA area at 103.1 FM.

WRSF-FM

Owner: East Carolina Radio Group
Editorial: 2422 S Wrightsville Ave, Nags Head, North Carolina 27959. **T:** 1 252 441-1024
W: http://www.dixie1057.com
Editorial Profile: WRSF-FM is a commercial station owned by East Carolina Radio Group. The format of the station is contemporary country. WRSF-FM broadcasts to the Nags Head, NC area at 93.3 FM.

WRSH-FM

Owner: Richmond County Schools
Editorial: 838 Highway #1 North, Rockingham, North Carolina 28379.
T: 1 910 997-9812
Editorial Profile: WRSH-FM is a non-commercial station owned by Richmond County Schools. The format of the station is educational and variety. WRSH-FM broadcasts to the Rockingham, NC area at 91.1 FM.

WRSI-FM

Owner: Saga Communications
Editorial: 15 Hampton Ave, Northampton, Massachusetts 1060. **T:** 1 413 586-7400
W: http://www.wrsi.com
Editorial Profile: WRSI-FM is a commercial station owned by Saga Communications. The format of the station is adult album alternative music. WRSI-FM broadcasts to the Northampton, MA area at 93.9 FM.

WRSO-AM

Owner: Star Over Orlando, Inc.
Editorial: 999 Douglas Ave Ste 3318, Altamonte Springs, Florida 32714-2063.
T: 1 407 774-8810 **E:** info@810cbssports.com
W: http://810cbssports.com
Editorial Profile: WRSO-AM is a commercial station owned and operated by Star Over Orlando, Inc. The format of the station is sports talk. WRSO-AM broadcasts to the Orlando, FL area at 810 AM.

WRSR-FM

Owner: Krol Communications
Editorial: 103 N Washington St, Owosso, Michigan 48867-2819. **T:** 1 989 725-1925
W: http://www.classicfox.com
Editorial Profile: WRSR-FM is a commercial station owned by Krol Communications. The format of the station is classic rock. WRSR-FM broadcasts to the Flint, MI area at 103.9 FM.

WRST-FM

Owner: University of Wisconsin
Editorial: 800 Algoma Blvd, Oshkosh, Wisconsin 54901-3551. **T:** 1 920 424-3113
E: wrstfm@uwosh.edu
W: http://www.uwosh.edu/wrst
Editorial Profile: WRST-FM is a commercial station owned by the University of Wisconsin. The format of the station is variety. WRST-FM broadcasts to the Oshkosh, WI area at 90.3 FM.

WRSU-FM

Owner: Rutgers University
Editorial: 126 College Ave, New Brunswick, New Jersey 08901-1166. **T:** 1 732 932-7800
E: news@wrsu.org
W: http://wrsu.rutgers.edu/index.php
Editorial Profile: WRSU-FM is a commercial station owned by Rutgers University. The format of the station is college variety. WRSU-FM broadcasts to the student body and faculty of Rutgers University in the New Brunswick, NJ area at 88.7 FM.

WRSV-FM

Owner: North Star Broadcasting
Editorial: 115 N Church St, Rocky Mount, North Carolina 27804-5402.
T: 1 252 937-6111
E: soul92_2000@yahoo.com
W: http://www.soul92jams.com
Editorial Profile: WRSV-FM is a commercial station owned by North Star Broadcasting. The format of the station is urban contemporary and gospel. WRSV-FM broadcasts to the Rocky Mount, NC area at 92.1 FM.

WRSW-AM

Owner: Talking Stick Communications LLC
Editorial: 216 W Market St, Warsaw, Indiana 46580-2800. **T:** 1 574 372-3064
W: http://1480newsnow.com
Editorial Profile: WRSW-AM is a commercial station owned by Talking Stick Communications LLC. The format of the station is news/talk. WRSW-AM broadcasts to the Warsaw, IN area at 1480 AM.

WRSW-FM

Owner: Talking Stick Communications LLC
Editorial: 216 W Market St, Warsaw, Indiana 46580. **T:** 1 574 372-3064
W: http://www.wrsw.net
Editorial Profile: WRSW-FM is a commercial station owned by Talking Stick Communications LLC. The format for the station is classic rock. WRSW-FM broadcasts to the South Bend, IN area at 107.3 FM.

WRSY-FM

Owner: Saga Communications
Editorial: 15 Hampton Ave, Northampton, Massachusetts 1060. **T:** 1 413 586-7400
W: http://www.wrsi.com

WRTA-AM

Owner: Handsome Brothers Inc.
Editorial: 2513 6th Ave, Altoona, Pennsylvania 16602. **T:** 1 814 943-6112
W: http://www.wrta.com
Editorial Profile: WRTA-AM is a commercial station owned by Handsome Brothers Inc. The format of the station is news and talk. WRTA-AM broadcasts to the Altoona, PA area at 1240 AM.

WRTB-FM

Owner: Mid-West Family Broadcasting
Editorial: 2830 Sandy Hollow Rd, Rockford, Illinois 61109-2369. **T:** 1 815 874-7861
W: http://www.953thebull.com
Editorial Profile: WRTB-FM is a commercial station owned by Mid-West Family Broadcasting. The format of the station is contemporary country. The station airs locally at 95.3 FM.

WRTE-FM

Owner: Chicago Public Media Inc.
Editorial: 1401 W 18th St, Chicago, Illinois 60608-3003. **T:** 1 312 455-9455
W: http://vocalo.org
Editorial Profile: WRTE-FM is a non-commercial station owned by Chicago Public Media Inc. The format of the station is community radio, featuring a variety of news, talk, public affairs and music programming. WRTE-FM broadcasts to the Greater Chicago area at 90.7 FM. WRTE-FM airs WBEW-FM's programming.

WRTG-AM

Owner: Isasi (Jose)
Editorial: 4600 New Bern Ave Ste 101, Raleigh, North Carolina 27610-1881.
T: 1 919 645-1680
W: http://www.quepasamedia.com
Editorial Profile: WRTG-AM is a commercial station owned by Jose Isasi. The format of the station is Regional Maxican music. WRTG-AM broadcasts to the Raleigh-Durham, NC area at 1000 AM.

WRTI-FM

Owner: Temple University
Editorial: 1509 Cecil B Moore Ave, 3rd Fl, Philadelphia, Pennsylvania 19121-3410.
T: 1 215 204-8405 **E:** comments@wrti.org
W: http://www.wrti.org
Editorial Profile: WRTI-FM is a non-commercial station owned by Temple University. The format of the station is classical, jazz and news. WRTI-FM broadcasts to the Philadelphia area at 90.1 FM.

WRTJ-FM

Owner: Temple University
Editorial: 1509 Cecil B Moore Ave Fl 3, Philadelphia, Pennsylvania 19121-3410.
T: 1 215 204-8405 **E:** programming@wrti.org
W: http://www.wrti.org
Editorial Profile: WRTJ-FM is a non-commercial station owned by Temple University. The format of the station is classical, jazz and news. WRTJ-FM broadcasts to the Coatsville, PA and surrounding areas at 89.3 FM.

WRTM-FM

Owner: Commander Communications Corp.
Editorial: 1901 N Frontage Rd, Vicksburg, Mississippi 39180-5184. **T:** 1 601 956-1932
E: wrtmfm@bellsouth.net
W: http://www.smoothsoul1005.com
Editorial Profile: WRTM-FM is a commercial station owned by Commander Communications Corp. The formt for the station is R&B. WRTM-FM broadcasts to the Jackson, Miss. area at 1005. FM.

WRTO-AM

Owner: Univision Communications Inc.
Editorial: 625 N Michigan Ave Ste 300, Chicago, Illinois 60611-3110.
T: 1 312 981-1800
W: http://univisionamerica.com
Editorial Profile: WRTO-AM is a commercial station owned by Univision Communications Inc. The format of the station is Spanish news and talk. WRTO-AM broadcasts in the greater Chicago area at 1200 AM.

WRTO-FM

Owner: Univision Communications Inc.
Editorial: 800 S Douglas Rd, Ste 111, Coral Gables, Florida 33134. **T:** 1 305 447-1140
W: http://mix983.univision.com
Editorial Profile: WRTO-FM is a commercial station owned by Univision Communications Inc. The format of the station is Hispanic Top 40/CHR. WRTO-FM broadcasts to the Coral Gables, FL area at 98.3 FM.

WRTP-FM
Owner: Radio Training Network, Inc.
Editorial: 7610 Falls Of Neuse Rd, Ste 155, Raleigh, North Carolina 27615.
T: 1 919 256-9787
E: management@hisradiowrtp.com
W: http://www.hisradiowrtp.com
Editorial Profile: WRTP-FM is a non-commercial station owned by Radio Training Network, Inc. The format is contemporary Christian. WRTP-FM broadcasts to the Raleigh, NC area at 88.5 FM.

WRTR-FM
Owner: Clear Channel Media and Entertainment
Editorial: 3900 11Th Ave, Tuscaloosa, Alabama 35401-7056. **T:** 1 205 344-4589
W: http://www.news1420.com
Editorial Profile: WRTR-FM is a commercial station owned by Clear Channel Media and Entertainment. The format of the station is talk. WRTR-FM broadcasts to the Tuscaloosa, AL area at 105.9 FM.

WRTS-FM
Owner: Connoisseur Media LLC
Editorial: 1 Boston Store Pl, Erie, Pennsylvania 16501. **T:** 1 814 461-1000
W: http://www.star104.com
Editorial Profile: WRTS-FM is a commercial station owned by Connoisseur Media LLC. The format of the station is Top 40/CHR music. WRTS-FM broadcasts to the Erie, PA area at 103.7 FM.

WRTT-FM
Owner: Black Crow Broadcasting Inc.
Editorial: 1555 The Boardwalk, Ste 1, Huntsville, Alabama 35816-1821.
T: 1 256 536-1568
W: http://www.rocket951.fm
Editorial Profile: WRTT-FM is a commercial station owned by Black Crow Broadcasting Inc. The format of the station is rock music. WRTT-FM broadcasts to the Huntsville, AL area at 95.1 FM.

WRTW-FM
Owner: Hyles-Anderson College
Editorial: 507 State St, Hammond, Indiana 46320-1533. **T:** 1 219 228-2995
E: info@thekeyfm.com **W:** http://thekeyfm.com
Editorial Profile: WRTW-FM is a non-commercial station owned by Hyles-Anderson College. The format of the station features Christian talk programming. WRTW-FM broadcasts locally to the Crown Point, IN area at a frequency of 90.5 FM.

WRTX-FM
Owner: Temple University
Editorial: 1509 Cecil B Moore Ave Fl 3, Philadelphia, Pennsylvania 19121-3410.
T: 1 215 204-8405 **E:** comments@wrti.org
W: http://www.wrti.org
Editorial Profile: WRTX-FM is a non-commerical station owned by Temple University. The format for the station is classical, jazz and news. WRTX-FM broadcasts to the Philadelphia area at 91.7 FM.

WRUC-FM
Owner: Union College
Editorial: WRUC Union College, Reamar Campus Center, Schenectady, New York 12308. **T:** 1 518 388-6154
E: wruc897@gmail.com
W: http://wruc.union.edu

WRUF-AM
Owner: University of Florida
Editorial: 3200 Weimer Hall, Gainesville, Florida 32611-0001. **T:** 1 352 392-0771
E: cc@wruf.com **W:** http://www.wruf.com
Editorial Profile: WRUF-AM is a commercial station owned by the University of Florida. The format of the station is sports and talk. WRUF-AM broadcasts in the Gainesville, FL area at 850 AM.

WRUF-FM
Owner: University of Florida
Editorial: 3200 Weimer Hall, Gainesville, Florida 32611-2084. **T:** 1 352 392-0771
W: http://www.country1037thegator.com
Editorial Profile: WRUF-FM is a commercial station owned by the University of Florida. The format of the station is country. WRUF-AM broadcasts to the Gaineville, FL area at 103.7 FM.

WRUL-FM
Owner: Withers Broadcasting Co.
Editorial: 101 N Church St, Carmi, Illinois 62821-1468. **T:** 1 618 382-4161
E: wrul973@frontier.com
W: http://www.wrul.com
Editorial Profile: WRUL-FM is a commercial station owned by Withers Broadcasting Co. The format of the station is contemporary country music. WRUL-FM broadcasts to the Carmi, IL area at 97.3 FM.

WRUM-FM
Owner: Clear Channel Media and Entertainment
Editorial: 2500 Maitland Center Pkwy, Ste 401, Maitland, Florida 32751-4179.
T: 1 407 916-7800
W: http://www.rumba1003.com
Editorial Profile: WRUM-FM is a commercial station owned by Clear Channel Media and Entertainment. The format of the station is Hurban, featuring urban Spanish music and tropical music. WRUM-FM broadcasts to the Orlando, FL, area at 100.3 FM.

WRUN-FM
Owner: WAMC
Editorial: 318 Central Ave, Albany, New York 12206-2522. **T:** 1 518 465-5233
E: news@wamc.org **W:** http://www.wamc.org
Editorial Profile: WRUN-FM is a non-commercial station owned by WAMC. The format of the station is news and talk. WRUN-FM broadcasts to the Remsen, NY area at 90.3 FM.

WRUP-FM
Owner: Great Lakes Radio Inc.
Editorial: 3060 US Highway 41 W, Marquette, Michigan 49855-2293. **T:** 1 906 228-6800
E: contact@broadcasteverywhere.com
W: http://www.wrup.com
Editorial Profile: WRUP-FM is a commercial station owned by Great Lakes Radio Inc. The format of the station is classic rock. The station broadcasts to Marquette, MI on 98.3 FM.

WRUR-FM
Owner: University of Rochester Broadcasting Corporation
Editorial: 280 State St, Rochester, New York 14614-1033. **T:** 1 585 325-7500
E: newsroom@wxxi.org **W:** http://wrur.org
Editorial Profile: WRUR-FM is a non-commercial station owned by University of Rochester Broadcasting Corporation. The format of the station is variety. WRUR-FM broadcasts to the Rochester, NY area at a frequency of 88.5 FM.

WRUS-AM
Owner: Logan Radio Inc.
Editorial: 1601 Nashville St, Russellville, Kentucky 42276. **T:** 1 270 726-2471
E: wrus@bellsouth.net
W: http://www.wrusam.com
Editorial Profile: WRUS-AM is a commercial station owned by Logan Radio Inc. The format of the station is variety. WRUS-AM broadcasts in the Russellville, KY area at 610 AM.

WRUV-FM
Owner: University of Vermont
Editorial: Davis Student Center, Burlington, Vermont 5405. **T:** 1 802 656-0796
E: wruv@wruv.org **W:** http://www.wruv.org
Editorial Profile: WRUV-FM is a non-commercial station owned by the University of Vermont. The format of the station is variety. WRUV-FM broadcasts to the Burlington, VT area at 90.1 FM.

WRUW-FM
Owner: Case Western Reserve University
Editorial: 11220 Bellflower Rd, Cleveland, Ohio 44106-3933. **T:** 1 216 368-2207
E: pr@wruw.org **W:** http://www.wruw.org
Editorial Profile: WRUW-FM is a non-commercial college station owned by Case Western Reserve University. The format of the station is variety. WRUW-FM broadcasts to the Cleveland area at 91.1 FM.

WRVA-AM
Owner: Clear Channel Media and Entertainment
Editorial: 3245 Basie Rd, Richmond, Virginia 23228-3404. **T:** 1 804 474-0000
W: http://www.1140wrva.com
Editorial Profile: WRVA-AM is a commercial station owned by Clear Channel Media and Entertainment. The format of the station is news and talk. WRVA-AM broadcasts to the Richmond, VA area at 1140 AM.

WRVB-FM
Owner: Clear Channel Media and Entertainment
Editorial: 6006 Grand Central Ave, Parkersburg, West Virginia 26105.
T: 1 304 295-6070
W: http://www.102theriver.com
Editorial Profile: WRVB-Fm is a commercial station owned by Clear Channel Media and Entertainment. The format of the station is Top 40/CHR. WRVB-FM broadcasts to the Vienna, WV area at 102.1 FM.

WRVC-AM
Owner: Kindred Communications
Editorial: 401 11Th St Ste 200, Huntington, West Virginia 25701-2235. **T:** 1 304 523-8401
E: wrvc@wrvc.com
W: http://www.supertalk941.com
Editorial Profile: WRVC-AM is a commercial station owned by Kindred Communications. The format of the station is news, talk and sports. WRVC-AM broadcasts to the Huntington, WV area at 930 AM.

WRVE-FM
Owner: Clear Channel Media and Entertainment
Editorial: 1203 Troy Schenectady Rd, Latham, New York 12110-1046. **T:** 1 518 452-4800
W: http://www.995theriver.com
Editorial Profile: WRVE-FM is a commercial station owned by Clear Channel Media and Entertainment. The format of the station is hot adult contemporary. WRVE-FM broadcasts to the Latham, NY area at 99.5 FM.

WRVF-FM
Owner: Clear Channel Media and Entertainment
Editorial: 125 S Superior St, Toledo, Ohio 43604. **T:** 1 419 244-8321
E: 1015theriver@1015theriver.com
W: http://www.1015theriver.com
Editorial Profile: WRVF-FM is a commercial station owned by Clear Channel Media and Entertainment. The format of the station is Lite Rock/Lite AC music. WRVF-FM broadcasts to the Toledo, OH area at 101.5 FM.

WRVK-AM
Owner: Saylor Broadcasting Inc.
Editorial: 235 Red Foley Rd, Renfro Valley, Kentucky 40473. **T:** 1 606 256-2146
E: manager@wrvk1460.com
W: http://www.wrvk1460.com
Editorial Profile: WRVK-AM is a commercial station owned by Saylor Broadcasting Inc. The format of the station is classic country and news. WRVK-AM broadcasts to the Renfro Valley, KY area at 1460 AM.

WRVL-FM
Owner: Liberty University
Editorial: 1971 University Blvd, Lynchburg, Virginia 24502-2269. **T:** 1 434 582-3688
E: wrvl@liberty.edu **W:** http://www.wrvlfm.com
Editorial Profile: WRVL-FM is a non-commercial station owned by Liberty University. The format of the station is religious. WRVL-FM broadcasts to the Lynchburg, VA area at 88.3 FM.

WRVM-FM
Owner: WRVM Inc.
Editorial: Highway 32 North, Suring, Wisconsin 54174. **T:** 1 920 842-2839
E: wrvm@wrvm.org **W:** http://www.wrvm.org
Editorial Profile: WRVM-FM is a non-commercial station owned by WRVM Inc. The format of the station is religious. WRVM-FM broadcasts to the Green Bay, WI, area at 102.7 FM.

WRVO-FM
Owner: State University of New York
Editorial: 7060 State Route 104, Oswego, New York 13126. **T:** 1 315 312-3690
E: feedback@wrvo.fm **W:** http://www.wrvo.fm
Editorial Profile: WRVO-FM is a non-commercial station owned by State University of New York. The format of the station is news and talk programming. WRVO-FM broadcasts to the Oswego, NY area at 89.9 FM.

WRVP-AM
Owner: Radio Vision Christiana Management Corp.
Editorial: 419 Broadway, Paterson, New Jersey 07501-2104. **T:** 1 973 881-8700
W: http://www.radiovision.net
Editorial Profile: WRVP-AM is a non-commercial station owned by the Radio Vision Christiana Management Corp. The format of the station is Hispanic religious. WRVP-AM broadcasts to the New York metro at 1310 AM.

WRVQ-FM
Owner: Clear Channel Media and Entertainment
Editorial: 3245 Basie Rd, Richmond, Virginia 23228-3404. **T:** 1 804 474-0000
W: http://q94radio.com
Editorial Profile: WRVQ-FM is a commercial station owned by Clear Channel Media and Entertainment. The format of the station is Top 40/CHR. WRVQ-FM broadcasts to the Richmond, VA area at 94.5 FM.

WRVR-FM
Owner: Entercom Communications Corp.
Editorial: 1835 Moriah Woods Blvd, Ste 1, Memphis, Tennessee 38117-7122.
T: 1 901 767-0104 **E:** river104@wrvr.com
W: http://www.wrvr.com
Editorial Profile: WRVR-FM is a commercial station owned by Entercom Communications Corp. The format of the station is adult contemporary music. WRVR-FM broadcasts to the Memphis, TN, area at 104.5 FM.

WRVS-FM
Owner: Elizabeth City State Univ.
Editorial: 1704 Weeksville Rd, Elizabeth City, North Carolina 27909-7977.
T: 1 252 335-3517
W: http://www.ecsu.edu/wrvs
Editorial Profile: WRVS-FM is a non-commercial station owned by Elizabeth City State Univ. The format of the station is variety. WRVS-FM broadcasts to the Elizabeth City, NC area at 89.9 FM.

WRVT-FM
Owner: Vermont Public Radio
Editorial: 365 Troy Ave, Colchester, Vermont 05446-3126. **T:** 1 802 655-9451
E: news@vpr.net **W:** http://www.vpr.net
Editorial Profile: WRVT-FM is a non-commercial station owned by Vermont Public Radio. The format of the station is news and talk. WRVT-FM broadcasts to the Colchester, VT area at 88.7 FM. The station does not accept PSAs.

WRVV-FM
Owner: Clear Channel Media and Entertainment
Editorial: 600 Corporate Cir, Harrisburg, Pennsylvania 17110-9787. **T:** 1 717 540-8800
E: wrvv@river973.com
W: http://www.river973.com
Editorial Profile: WRVV-FM is a commercial station owned by Clear Channel Media and Entertainment. The format of the station is classic hits. WRVV-FM broadcasts to the Harrisburg, PA area at 97.3 FM.

WRVW-FM
Owner: Clear Channel Media and Entertainment
Editorial: 55 Music Sq W, Nashville, Tennessee 37203-3207. **T:** 1 615 664-2400
E: nashvillepsa@clearchannel.com
W: http://www.1075theriver.com
Editorial Profile: WRVW-FM is a commercial station owned by Clear Channel Media and Entertainment. The format of the station is Top 40/CHR music. WRVW-FM broadcasts to the Nashville, TN area at 107.5 FM. To send a PSA, email nashvillepsa@clearchannel.com.

WRVY-FM
Owner: WZOE Inc.
Editorial: 2209 S Main St, Princeton, Illinois 61356-9179. **T:** 1 815 875-8014
E: newsroom@wzoe.com
W: http://www.wzoe.com
Editorial Profile: WRVY-FM is a commercial station owned by WZOE Inc. The format of the station is country music. WRVY-FM broadcasts to the Henry, IL area at 100.5 FM.

WRVZ-FM
Owner: West Virginia Radio Corp.
Editorial: 1111 Virginia St E, Charleston, West Virginia 25301. **T:** 1 304 342-8131
W: http://www.987thebeat.com
Editorial Profile: WRVZ-FM is a commercial station owned by the West Virginia Radio Corp. The format of the station is urban contemporary. WRVZ-FM broadcasts to Charleston, WV and surrounding communities at 98.7 FM.

WRWA-FM
Owner: Troy University
Editorial: Troy University Wallace Hall, Troy, Alabama 36082. **T:** 1 334 670-3268
E: publicradio@troy.edu
W: http://wtsu.troy.edu
Editorial Profile: WRWA-FM is a non-commercial station owned by Troy University. The format of the station is variety programming including classical music. WRWA-FM broadcasts to the Troy, AL area at 88.7 FM.

WRWB-FM
Owner: Clear Channel Media and Entertainment
Editorial: 20 Tucker Dr, Poughkeepsie, New York 12603-1644. **T:** 1 845 471-2300
W: http://www.wrwdfm.com
Editorial Profile: WRWB-FM is a commercial station owned by Clear Channel Media and Entertainment. The format of the station is contemporary country. WRWB-FM airs locally on 99.3.

WRWD-FM
Owner: Clear Channel Media and Entertainment
Editorial: 20 Tucker Dr, Poughkeepsie, New York 12603-1644. **T:** 1 845 471-2300
W: http://www.wrwdcountry.com
Editorial Profile: WRWD-FM is a commercial station owned by Clear Channel Media and Entertainment. The format of the station is country. WRWD-FM broadcasts to the Poughkeepsie, NY area at 107.3 FM.

WRWH-AM
Owner: White County Media LLC
Editorial: 681 Hood St, Cleveland, Georgia 30528-1452. **T:** 1 706 865-3181
E: info@wrwh.com **W:** http://www.wrwh.com
Editorial Profile: WRWH-AM is a commercial station owned by White County Media LLC. The format of the station is news and talk. WRWH-AM broadcasts to the Atlanta area at 1350 AM.

WRWJ-FM
Owner: He's Alive Inc.
Editorial: 34 Springs Road, Grantsville, Maryland 21536. **T:** 1 301 895-3292
W: http://www.hesalive.net
Editorial Profile: WRWJ-FM is a non-commercial station owned by He's Alive Inc. The format of the station is religious programming. WRWJ-FM broadcasts to the Grantsville, MD area at 88.1 FM.

WRWM-FM
Owner: Cumulus Media Inc.
Editorial: 6810 N Shadeland Ave, Indianapolis, Indiana 46220. **T:** 1 317 842-9550
W: http://www.i94hits.com
Editorial Profile: WRWM-FM is a commercial station owned by Cumulus Media Inc. The format of the station is Top 40/CHR. WRWM-FM broadcasts to the Indianapolis area at 93.9 FM.

WRWN-FM
Owner: L & L Radio
Editorial: 1 Saint Augustine Pl, Hilton Head Island, South Carolina 29928-4717.
T: 1 843 785-9569 **W:** http://y1079online.com
Editorial Profile: WRWN-FM is a commercial station owned by L & L Radio. The format of the station is classic hits. WRWN-FM broadcasts to the Savannah, GA, area at 107.9 FM.

WRWR-AM
Owner: Murray (Christopher L.)
Editorial: 6174 Hwy 57, Macon, Georgia 31217. **T:** 1 404 307-8079
Editorial Profile: WRWR-AM is a commercial station owned by Christopher L. Murray, dba WRWR-AM RADIO LLC. The format of the station is news and sports. WRWR-AM broadcasts to the Macon, GA area at 1350.

WRXB-AM
Owner: Polnet Communications
Editorial: 3551 42nd Avenue South, Suite B-106, Saint Petersburg, Florida 33711.
T: 1 727 865-1591 **W:** http://www.wrxb.us
Editorial Profile: WRXB-AM is a commercial station owned by Polnet Communications. The station's format is gospel music. WRXB-AM broadcasts to the St. Petersburg, FL area at 1590 AM.

WRXK-FM
Owner: Beasley Broadcast Group
Editorial: 20125 S Tamiami Trl, Estero, Florida 33928-2117. **T:** 1 239 495-2100
W: http://www.96krock.com
Editorial Profile: WRXK-FM is a commercial station owned by Beasley Broadcast Group. The format of the station is rock. WRXK-FM broadcasts to the Naples, FL area at 96.1 FM.

WRXL-FM
Owner: Clear Channel Media and Entertainment
Editorial: 3245 Basie Rd, Richmond, Virginia 23228-3404. **T:** 1 804 474-0000
W: http://www.wrxl.com
Editorial Profile: WRXL-FM is a commercial station owned by Clear Channel Media and Entertainment. The format of the station is rock alternative. WRXL-FM broadcasts to the Richmond, VA area at 102.1 FM.

WRXO-AM
Owner: Roxboro Broadcasting Co.
Editorial: 2070 Hurdle Mills Road, Roxboro, North Carolina 27573. **T:** 1 336 599-0266
E: radiod@aol.com
W: http://www.radioroxboro.com
Editorial Profile: WRXO-AM is a commercial station owned by Roxboro Broadcasting Co. The format of the station is country. WRXO-AM broadcasts to the Roxboro, NC area at 1430 AM.

WRXP-FM
Owner: Cumulus Media Inc.
Editorial: 2000 Elm St SE, Minneapolis, Minnesota 55414-2531. **T:** 1 612 617-4000
E: info@105theticket.com
W: http://www.105theticket.com
Editorial Profile: WRXP-FM is a commercial station owned by Cumulus Media Inc. The format of the station is sports. WRXP-FM broadcasts to the Greater Minneapolis area at 105.3 FM. The station is a simulcast of WGVX-FM.

WRXQ-FM
Owner: Digity LLC
Editorial: 2410 Caton Farm Rd Unit B, Crest Hill, Illinois 60403-1374. **T:** 1 815 556-0100
E: news@wjol.com **W:** http://www.wrxq.com
Editorial Profile: WRXQ-FM is a commercial station owned by Digity LLC . The format of the station is classic rock music. WRXQ-FM broadcasts to the Crest Hill, IL area at 100.7 FM.

WRXR-FM
Owner: Clear Channel Media and Entertainment
Editorial: 7413 Old Lee Hwy, Chattanooga, Tennessee 37421-1142. **T:** 1 423 892-3333
W: http://www.rock105.net
Editorial Profile: WRXR-FM is a commercial station owned by Clear Channel Media and Entertainment. The format of the station is rock music. WRXR-FM broadcasts to the Chattanooga, TN area at 105.5 FM.

WRXT-FM
Owner: Positive Alternative Radio
Editorial: 22226 Timberlake Rd, Lynchburg, Virginia 24502-7214. **T:** 1 800 774-9798
E: office@spiritfm.com
W: http://www.spiritfm.com
Editorial Profile: WRXT-FM is a non-commercial station owned by Positive Alternative Radio. The format of the station is contemporary Christian. WRXT-FM broadcasts to the Lynchburg, VA area at 90.3 FM.

WRXV-FM
Owner: Invisible Allies Ministries
Editorial: 925 Houserville Rd, State College, Pennsylvania 16801-7163. **T:** 1 814 867-3836
E: info@revfm.net **W:** http://revfm.net
Editorial Profile: WRXV-FM is a non-commercial station owned by Invisible Allies Ministries. The format of the station is Contemporary Christian. WRXV-FM broadcasts to the State College, Altoona Philipsburg and Huntingdon areas in Pennsylvania at 89.1 FM.

WRXX-FM
Owner: Withers Broadcasting Co.
Editorial: 302 S Poplar St, Centralia, Illinois 62801-3922. **T:** 1 618 533-5700
E: wilynews@mywithersradio.com
W: http://www.mywithersradio.com/centralia
Editorial Profile: WRXX-FM is a commercial station owned by Withers Broadcasting Co. The format of the station is hot adult contemporary. WRXX-FM broadcasts to the Centralia, IL area at 95.3 FM.

WRXZ-FM
Owner: Clear Channel Media and Entertainment
Editorial: 4841 Highway 17 Byp S, Myrtle Beach, South Carolina 29577-6683.
T: 1 843 293-0107 **W:** http://rock107mb.com
Editorial Profile: WRXZ-FM is an commercial station owned by Clear Channel Media and Entertainment. The format of the station is rock/album-oriented rock. WRXZ-FM broadcasts to the Myrtle Beach, SC area at 107.1 FM.

WRYM-AM
Owner: Eight Forty Broadcasting
Editorial: 1056 Willard Ave, Newington, Connecticut 6111. **T:** 1 860 666-5646
E: radio@wrym840.com
W: http://www.wrymradio.com
Editorial Profile: WRYM-AM is a commercial station owned by Eight Forty Broadcasting. The format of the station is Hispanic music. WRYM-AM broadcasts to the Newington, CT area at 840 AM.

WRYP-FM
Owner: Horizon Christian Fellowship
Editorial: 356 Broad St, Fitchburg, Massachusetts 1420. **T:** 1 888 310-7729
W: http://www.renewfm.org
Editorial Profile: WRYP-FM is a non-commercial station owned by Horizon Christian Fellowship. The format of the station is contemporary Christian. WRYP-FM broadcasts to the Fitchburg, MA area at 90.1 FM.

WRYT-AM
Owner: Covenant Network
Editorial: 4424 Hampton Ave, Saint Louis, Missouri 63109. **T:** 1 314 752-7000
E: covenantnetwork@juno.com
W: http://www.covenantnet.net
Editorial Profile: WRYT-AM is a non-commercial station owned by the Covenant Network. The format of the station is contemporary Christian and talk. WRYT-AM broadcasts to the St. Louis area at 1080 AM.

WRZE-FM
Owner: Qantum Communications Inc.
Editorial: 181 E Evans St Ste 311, Florence, South Carolina 29506-5505.
T: 1 843 667-4600
W: http://swagga941.com/#&panel1-1
Editorial Profile: WRZE-FM is a commercial station owned by Qantum Communications Inc. The format of the station is urban contemporary. WRZE-FM broadcasts to the Florence, SC area at 94.1 FM.

WRZI-FM
Owner: Commonwealth Broadcasting Corp.
Editorial: 611 W Poplar St Ste C2, Elizabethtown, Kentucky 42701-2483.
T: 1 270 763-0800
E: lhaggard@commonwealthbroadcasting.com
W: http://www.1073thepoint.com
Editorial Profile: WRZI-FM is a commercial station owned by Commonwealth Broadcasting Corp. The format of the station is classic rock. WRZI-FM airs at 107.3 FM in the Elizabethtown, KY area.

WRZK-FM
Owner: Holston Valley Broadcasting Corp.
Editorial: 222 Commerce St, Kingsport, Tennessee 37660-4319. **T:** 1 423 246-9578
E: news@wtfm.com **W:** http://www.wrzk.com
Editorial Profile: WRZK-FM is a commercial station owned by Holston Valley Broadcasting Corp. The format of the station is rock/album-oriented rock. WRZK-FM broadcasts to the Kingsport, TN area at 95.9 FM.

WRZM-FM
Owner: Columbia International University
Editorial: 106 Emily Lane, Boiling Springs, North Carolina 28017. **T:** 1 704 406-3525
E: info@wgwg.org **W:** http://www.wgwg.org
Editorial Profile: WRZM-FM is a non-commercial college station owned by Columbia International University. The format of the station is variety. WRZM-FM broadcasts to the Boiling Springs, NC area at 88.3 FM.

WRZN-AM
Owner: Marc Radio Group, LLC
Editorial: 100 Nw 76Th Dr Ste 2, Gainesville, Florida 32607-6659. **T:** 1 352 313-3150
W: http://www.flafnr.com
Editorial Profile: WRZN-AM is a commercial station owned by Marc Radio Group, LLC. The format of the station is news talk. WRZN-AM broadcasts to the Hernando, FL area at 720 AM. The station airs programming on WDVH-AM.

WRZQ-FM
Owner: Reising Radio Partners Inc.
Editorial: 825 Washington St, Columbus, Indiana 47201-6265. **T:** 1 812 379-1077
E: qmix@qmix.com **W:** http://www.qmix.com
Editorial Profile: WRZQ-FM is a commercial station owned by Reising Radio Partners Inc. The format of the station is adult contemporary music. WRZQ-FM broadcasts to the Indianapolis area at 107.3 FM.

WRZR-FM
Owner: Hembree Communications Inc.
Editorial: 514 N John F Kennedy Ave, Loogootee, Indiana 47553. **T:** 1 812 295-9480
E: wrzr@psci.net
Editorial Profile: WRZR-FM is a commercial station owned by Hembree Communications Inc. The format of the station is classic rock music. WRZR-FM broadcasts to the Loogootee, IN area at 94.5 FM.

WRZX-FM
Owner: Clear Channel Media and Entertainment
Editorial: 6161 Fall Creek Rd, Indianapolis, Indiana 46220-5032. **T:** 1 317 257-7565
E: airstaff@x103.com **W:** http://www.x103.com
Editorial Profile: WRZX-FM is a commercial station owned by Clear Channel Media and Entertainment. The format for the station is rock alternative music. WRZX-FM broadcasts to the Indianapolis area at 103.3 FM.

WRZZ-FM
Owner: Burbach of WV, LLC
Editorial: 5 Rosemar Cir, Parkersburg, West Virginia 26104. **T:** 1 304 485-4565
W: http://www.z106.net
Editorial Profile: WRZZ-FM is a commercial station owned by Burbach of WV, LLC. The format of the station is classic rock. WRZZ-FM broadcasts to the Parkersburg, WV area at 106.1 FM.

WSAA-FM
Owner: WSAA, LLC
Editorial: 2640 Commerce Dr NE, Cleveland, Tennessee 37311-1451. **T:** 1 706 278-5511
W: http://www.air1.com
Editorial Profile: WSAA-FM is a commercial station owned by WSAA, LLC. The format of the station is Christian rock music programming. WSAA-FM broadcasts to the Cleveland, TN area at 93.1 FM.

WSAE-FM
Owner: Spring Arbor University
Editorial: 106 E Main St, Spring Arbor, Michigan 49283. **T:** 1 517 750-6540
E: info@home.fm **W:** http://www.home.fm
Editorial Profile: WSAE-FM is a non-commercial station owned by Spring Arbor University. The format of the station is contemporary Christian. WSAE-FM broadcasts to the Spring Arbor, MI area at 106.9 FM.

WSAG-FM
Owner: MacDonald Broadcasting Co.
Editorial: 2000 Whittier St, Saginaw, Michigan 48601. **T:** 1 989 752-8161
W: http://www.thebay104fm.com
Editorial Profile: WSAG-FM is a commercial station owned by MacDonald Broadcasting Co. The format of the station is Lite Rock/Lite AC. WSAG-FM broadcasts to the Saginaw, MI area at 104.1 FM.

WSAI-AM
Owner: Clear Channel Media and Entertainment
Editorial: 8044 Montgomery Rd, Ste 650, Cincinnati, Ohio 45236. **T:** 1 513 686-8300
W: http://www.foxsports1360.com
Editorial Profile: WSAI-AM is a commercial station owned by Clear Channel Media and Entertainment. The format of the station is sports. WSAI-AM broadcasts to the Cincinnati area at 1360 AM.

WSAK-FM
Owner: Cumulus Media Inc.
Editorial: 292 Middle Rd, Dover, New Hampshire 03820-4901. **T:** 1 603 749-9750
W: http://www.shark1053.com
Editorial Profile: WSAK-FM is a commercial station owned by Cumulus Media Inc. The format of the station is classic hits. WSAK-FM broadcasts to the Dover, NH area at 102.1 FM.

WSAL-AM
Owner: Hoosier AM/FM LLC
Editorial: 425 2nd St, Logansport, Indiana 46947-3410. **T:** 1 574 722-4000
E: 1230wsal@gmail.com
W: http://indianasbestradio.com
Editorial Profile: WSAL-AM is a commercial station owned by Hoosier AM/FM LLC. The format of the station is oldies and talk. WSAL-AM broadcasts to the Indianapolis area at 1230 AM.

WSAM-AM
Owner: MacDonald Broadcasting Co.
Editorial: 2000 Whittier St, Saginaw, Michigan 48601. **T:** 1 989 752-8161
W: http://thebay104fm.com
Editorial Profile: WSAM-AM is a commercial station owned by MacDonald Broadcasting Co. The format of the station is Lite Rock/Lite AC music. WSAM-AM broadcasts to the Saginaw, MI area at 1400 AM.

WSAN-AM

Owner: Clear Channel Media and Entertainment
Editorial: 1541 Alta Dr Ste 400, Whitehall, Pennsylvania 18052-5632. **T:** 1 610 434-1742
W: http://www.fox1470.com/main.html
Editorial Profile: WSAN-AM is a commercial station owned by Clear Channel Media and Entertainment. The format of the station is sports. WSAN-AM broadcasts to the Whitehall, PA area at 1470 AM.

WSAO-AM

Owner: Ross & Ross Communications
Editorial: 15763 Hwy 4 E, Senatobia, Mississippi 38668. **T:** 1 662 562-4445
Editorial Profile: WSAO-AM is a commercial station owned by Ross & Ross Communications. The format of the station is Christian talk and gospel music. WSAO-AM broadcasts to the Memphis, TN area at 1140 AM.

WSAQ-FM

Owner: Radio First
Editorial: 808 Huron Ave, Port Huron, Michigan 48060-3705. **T:** 1 810 982-9000
W: http://www.wsaq.com
Editorial Profile: WSAQ-FM is a commercial station owned by Radio First. The format of the station is country. WSAQ-FM broadcasts to the Port Huron, MI area at 107.1 FM.

WSAR-AM

Owner: Karam(Robert & James)
Editorial: 1 Home St, Somerset, Massachusetts 02725-1002.
T: 1 508 678-9727 **E:** news@wsar.com
W: http://www.wsar.com
Editorial Profile: WSAR-AM is a commercial station owned by Robert & James Karam. The format of the station is talk. WSAR-AM broadcasts to the south coast of Massachusetts and the Providence, RI area at 1480 AM.

WSAT-AM

Owner: Cap Communications
Editorial: 1525 Jake Alexander Blvd W, Salisbury, North Carolina 28147.
T: 1 704 633-0621
W: http://www.1280wsat.com
Editorial Profile: WSAT-AM is a commercial station owned by Cap Communications. The format of the station is adult standards. WSAT-AM broadcasts to the Charlotte, NC area at 1280 AM.

WSAU-AM

Owner: Midwest Communications Inc.
Editorial: 557 Scott St, Wausau, Wisconsin 54403. **T:** 1 715 842-1672
W: http://www.wsau.com
Editorial Profile: WSAU-AM is a commercial station owned by Midwest Communications Inc. The format of the station is news, talk and sports. WSAU-AM broadcasts in the Wausau, WI area at 550 AM.

WSAU-FM

Owner: Midwest Communications Inc.
Editorial: 557 Scott St, Wausau, Wisconsin 54403-4829. **T:** 1 715 842-1672
W: http://www.wsau.com
Editorial Profile: WSAU-FM is a commercial station owned by Midwest Communications Inc. The format of the station is news, talk and sports. WSAU-FM broadcasts to the Plover, WI area at 99.9 FM.

WSBA-AM

Owner: Cumulus Media Inc.
Editorial: 5989 Susquehanna Plaza Dr, York, Pennsylvania 17406-0910. **T:** 1 717 764-1155
E: info@wsba910.com
W: http://www.wsba910.com
Editorial Profile: WSBA-AM is a commercial station owned by Cumulus Media Inc. The format of the station is news and talk. WSBA-AM broadcasts to the York, PA area at 910 AM.

WSB-AM

Owner: Cox Media Group, Inc.
Editorial: 1601 W Peachtree St NE, Atlanta, Georgia 30309-2641. **T:** 1 404 897-7500
E: newstips@wsbradio.com
W: http://wsbradio.com
Editorial Profile: WSB-AM is a commercial station owned by Cox Media Group, Inc. The format of the station is news and talk. WSB-AM broadcasts to the Atlanta area at 750 AM.

WSBB-AM

Owner: Diegel Communications LLC
Editorial: 229 Canal St, New Smyrna Beach, Florida 32168-7005. **T:** 1 386 428-9091

Editorial Profile: WSBB-AM is a commercial station owned by Diegel Communications LLC. The format of the station is adult contemporary. WSBB-AM broadcasts to the Orlando, FL, area at 1230 AM.

WSBB-FM

Owner: Cox Media Group, Inc.
Editorial: 1601 W Peachtree St NE, Atlanta, Georgia 30309-2641. **T:** 1 404 897-7500
E: newstips@wsbradio.com
W: http://www.wsbradio.com
Editorial Profile: WSBB-FM is a commercial station owned by Cox Media Group, Inc. The format of the station is news and talk. WSBB-FM broadcasts to the Atlanta area at 95.5 FM.

WSBF-FM

Owner: Clemson University- Board of Trustees
Editorial: 315 Hendrix Ctr, Clemson, South Carolina 29634-0001. **T:** 1 864 656-4010
W: http://wsbf.clemson.edu
Editorial Profile: WSBF-FM is a non-commercial station owned by Clemson University-Board of Trustees. The format of the station is college variety. WSBF-FM broadcasts to the Clemson, SC area at 88.1 FM.

WSB-FM

Owner: Cox Media Group, Inc.
Editorial: 1601 W Peachtree St NE, Atlanta, Georgia 30309. **T:** 1 404 897-7500
E: newstips@wsbradio.com
W: http://www.b985.com
Editorial Profile: WSB-FM is a commercial station owned by Cox Media Group, Inc. The format of the station is adult contemporary. WSB-FM broadcasts to the Atlanta area at 98.5 FM.

WSBG-FM

Owner: Connoisseur Media
Editorial: 22 S 6th St, Stroudsburg, Pennsylvania 18360-2002. **T:** 1 570 421-2100
W: http://www.935sbg.com
Editorial Profile: WSBG-FM is a commercial station owned by Connoisseur Media. The format of the station is Hot AC. WSBG-FM broadcasts to the Stroudsburg, PA area at 93.5 FM.

WSBH-FM

Owner: Horizon Broadcasting Co, LLC
Editorial: 380 N Wickham Rd, Melbourne, Florida 32935-8646. **T:** 1 321 752-9850
W: http://www.beach985.com
Editorial Profile: WSBH-FM is a commercial station owned by Horizon Broadcasting Co, LLC. The format of the station is classic hits. WSBH-FM broadcasts to the Stuart, FL area at 98.5 FM.

WSBI-AM

Owner: Cox (Donnie)
Editorial: 1079 E Trinity Ln, Nashville, Tennessee 37216-3043. **T:** 1 606 387-6625
W: http://www.wsbiam.com
Editorial Profile: WSBI-AM is a commercial station owned by Donnie Cox. The format of the station is classic country music. WSBI-AM broadcasts to the Nashville, TN area at 1210 AM.

WSBM-AM

Owner: Big River Broadcasting Corp.
Editorial: 624 Sam Phillips St, Florence, Alabama 35630-5859. **T:** 1 256 764-8121
W: http://www.wsbm.com
Editorial Profile: WSBM-AM is a commercial station owned by Big River Broadcasting Corp. The format of the station is sports. WSBM-AM broadcasts to the Florence, AL area at 1340 AM.

WSBR-AM

Owner: Beasley Broadcast Group
Editorial: 1650 S Dixie Hwy Floor 5, Boca Raton, Florida 33432-7462. **T:** 1 561 997-0074
W: http://www.wsbrradio.com
Editorial Profile: WSBR-AM is a commercial station owned by Beasley Broadcast Group. The format of the station is financial business news and talk. WSBR-AM broadcasts to the Boca Raton, FL area at 740 AM.

WSBS-AM

Owner: Gamma Broadcasting LLC
Editorial: 425 Stockbridge Rd, Great Barrington, Massachusetts 01230-1233.
T: 1 413 528-0860 **E:** fun@wsbs.com
W: http://www.wsbs.com
Editorial Profile: WSBS-AM is a commercial station owned by Gamma Broadcasting LLC. The format of the station is adult contemporary. WSBS-AM broadcasts to the Great Barrington, MA area at 860 AM.

WSBT-AM

Owner: Schurz Communications Inc.
Editorial: 1301 E Douglas Rd, Mishawaka, Indiana 46545-1732. **T:** 1 574 233-3141
E: communitycalendar@wsbt.com
W: http://www.wsbtradio.com
Editorial Profile: WSBT-AM is a commercial station owned by WSBT Inc. The format of the station is news, sports, and talk. WSBT-AM broadcasts to South Bend, IN at 960 AM.

WSBU-FM

Owner: St. Bonaventure University
Editorial: Reilly Center #210, Saint Bonaventure, New York 14778-9999.
T: 1 716 375-2307 **E:** wsbufm@sbu.edu
W: http://www.wsbufm.net
Editorial Profile: WSBU-FM is a non-commercial college station owned by St. Bonaventure University. The format of the station is adult album alternative music. WSBU-FM broadcasts in the St. Bonaventure University, NY area at 88.3 FM.

WSBV-AM

Owner: Waller-Barton (Linda)
Editorial: 1180 Plywood Trail, South Boston, Virginia 24592. **T:** 1 434 572-4418
E: wsbvgm@wsbvsouthboston.com
W: http://www.wsbvsouthboston.com
Editorial Profile: WSBV-AM is a commercial station owned by Linda Waller-Barton. The format of the station is gospel music. WSBV-AM broadcasts to the South Boston, VA area at 1560 AM.

WSBW-FM

Owner: Nicolet Broadcasting Inc.
Editorial: 30 N 18Th Ave Ste 8, Sturgeon Bay, Wisconsin 54235-3207. **T:** 1 920 746-9430
E: wbdk@doorcountydailynews.com
W: http://www.doorcountydailynews.com
Editorial Profile: WSBW-FM is a commercial station owned by Nicolet Broadcasting Inc. The format of the station is adult standards. WSBW-FM broadcasts to the Sturgeon Bay, WI area at 105.1 FM.

WSBY-FM

Owner: Clear Channel Media and Entertainment
Editorial: Gateway Crossing, 351 Tilghman Road, Salisbury, Maryland 21804-1920.
T: 1 410 742-1923 **W:** http://www.wsby.com
Editorial Profile: WSBY-FM is a commercial station owned by Clear Channel Media and Entertainment. The format of the station is urban adult contemporary music. WSBY-FM broadcasts to the Salisbury, MD area at 98.9 FM.

WSBZ-FM

Owner: Carter Broadcasting
Editorial: 1306 Bay Dr, Santa Rosa Beach, Florida 32459-5587. **T:** 1 850 267-3279
E: office@wsbz.com
W: http://www.seabreeze.fm
Editorial Profile: WSBZ-FM is a commercial station owned by Carter Broadcasting. The format of the station is smooth jazz. WSBZ-FM broadcasts to the Destin, FL area at 106.3 FM.

WSCC-FM

Owner: Clear Channel Media and Entertainment
Editorial: 950 Houston Northcutt Blvd, Ste 201, Mount Pleasant, South Carolina 29464-5645. **T:** 1 843 884-2534
W: http://www.943wsc.com
Editorial Profile: WSCC-FM is a commercial station owned by Clear Channel Media and Entertainment. The format of the station is news and talk. WSCC-FM broadcasts to the Charleston, SC area at 94.3 FM.

WSCD-FM

Owner: Minnesota Public Radio
Editorial: 207 W Superior St, Ste 224, Duluth, Minnesota 55802. **T:** 1 218 722-9411
E: newsroom@mpr.org
W: http://access.mpr.org/stations/wscnwscd
Editorial Profile: WSCD-FM is a non-commercial station owned by Minnesota Public Radio. The format of the station is classical music. WSCD-FM broadcasts to the Duluth, MN area at 92.9 FM.

WSCF-FM

Owner: Central Educational Broadcasting Inc.
Editorial: 6767 20th St, Vero Beach, Florida 32966-7904. **T:** 1 800 780-0919
E: comments@wscf.com
W: http://www.christianfm.com
Editorial Profile: WSCF-FM is a non-commercial station owned by Central Educational Broadcasting Inc. The format of the station is contemporary Christian music.

WSCF-FM broadcasts to the Vero Beach, FL area at 91.9 FM.

WSCG-FM

Owner: Clear Channel Media and Entertainment
Editorial: 2743 Perimeter Pkwy Ste 300, Augusta, Georgia 30909-6429.
T: 1 706 396-6000
W: http://www.g1057.com/main.html
Editorial Profile: WSCG-FM is a commercial station owned by Clear Channel Media and Entertainment. The format of the station is contemporary country. WSCG-FM broadcasts to the Augusta, GA area at 105.7 FM.

WSCH-FM

Owner: Wagon Wheel Broadcasting LLC
Editorial: 20 E High St, Lawrenceburg, Indiana 47025-1820. **T:** 1 812 537-0944
E: info@eaglecountryonline.com
W: http://www.eaglecountryonline.com
Editorial Profile: WSCH-FM is a commercial station owned by Wagon Wheel Broadcasting LLC. The format of the station is contemporary country music. WSCH-FM broadcasts to the Lawrenceburg, IN area at 99.3 FM.

WSCI-FM

Owner: South Carolina Educational Television Commission
Editorial: 1101 George Rogers Blvd, Columbia, South Carolina 29201.
T: 1 803 737-3200 **W:** http://www.etvradio.org
Editorial Profile: WSCI-FM is a non-commercial station owned by the South Carolina Educational Television Commission. The format of the station is news and classical music. WSCI-FM broadcasts to the Charleston, SC area at 89.3 FM. The station does not accept PSAs.

WSCL-FM

Owner: Salisbury University Foundation Inc.
Editorial: Salisbury Univ Route 13, Caruthers Hall, Salisbury, Maryland 21801.
T: 1 410 543-6895 **E:** prd@salisbury.edu
W: http://publicradiodelmarva.net
Editorial Profile: WSCL-FM is a non-commercial station owned by Salisbury University Foundation Inc. The format of the station is classical music and news. WSCL-FM broadcasts to the Salisbury, MD area at 89.5 FM.

WSCN-FM

Owner: Minnesota Public Radio
Editorial: 207 W Superior St, Ste 224, Duluth, Minnesota 55802. **T:** 1 218 722-9411
E: newsroom@mpr.org **W:** http://www.mpr.org
Editorial Profile: WSCN-FM is a non-commercial station owned by Minnesota Public Radio. The format of the station is news and talk. WSCN-FM broadcasts to the Duluth, MN area at 100.5 FM.

WSCO-AM

Owner: Woodward Communications, Inc.
Editorial: 2800 E College Ave, Appleton, Wisconsin 54915. **T:** 1 920 733-6639
E: thescore@wcinet.com
W: http://www.am1570thescore.com
Editorial Profile: WSCO-AM is a commercial station owned by Woodward Communications, Inc. The format of the station is sports. WSCO-AM broadcasts to the Appleton, WI area at 1570 AM.

WSCR-AM

Owner: CBS Radio
Editorial: 180 N Stetson Ave Ste 1250, Chicago, Illinois 60601-6732.
T: 1 312 729-3967
W: http://chicago.cbslocal.com/category/sports
Editorial Profile: WSCR-AM is a commercial station owned by CBS Radio. The format of the station is sports. WSCR-AM broadcasts to the Chicago area at 670 AM.

WSCS-FM

Owner: Colby-Sawyer College
Editorial: 541 Main St, New London, New Hampshire 3257. **T:** 1 603 526-3493
E: wscs@colby-sawyer.edu
W: http://www.colby-sawyer.edu/wscs
Editorial Profile: WSCS-FM is a non-commercial station owned by Colby-Sawyer College. The format of the station is college variety. WSCS-FM broadcasts to the New London, NH area at 90.9 FM.

WSCW-AM

Owner: LM Communications, Inc.
Editorial: 100 Kanawha Ter, Saint Albans, West Virginia 25177-2771. **T:** 1 304 722-3308
E: wjypnet@gmail.com

W: http://www.wscwam.com/
Editorial Profile: WSCW-AM is a commercial station owned by LM Communications, Inc. The format of the station is Christian teaching. WSCW-AM broadcasts to the South Charleston, WV area at 1410 AM.

WSCY-FM
Owner: Northeast Communications Corp.
Editorial: 110 Babbitt Rd, Franklin, New Hampshire 03235-2105. **T:** 1 603 934-2500
W: http://www.wscy.com
Editorial Profile: WSCY-FM is a commercial station owned by Northeast Communications Corp. The format of the station is classic country. WSCY-FM broadcasts to the Boston area at 106.9 FM.

WSDE-AM
Owner: Schoharie County Broadcasting, LLC
Editorial: 813 E Main St Ste 5, Cobleskill, New York 12043-5011. **T:** 1 518 234-3400
W: http://www.1190wsde.com
Editorial Profile: WSDE-AM is a commercial station owned by Schoharie County Broadcasting, LLC. The format of the station is adult standards. WSDE-AM broadcasts in the Cobleskill, NY area at 1190 AM.

WSDK-AM
Owner: Blount Masscom, Inc
Editorial: 160 Chapel Rd Ste 106, Manchester, Connecticut 06042-8929. **T:** 1 860 432-9735
E: info@wsdk1550.com
W: http://lifechangingradio.com/wsdk
Editorial Profile: WSDK-AM is a commercial stationed owned by Blount Masscom, Inc. The format of the station is Christian talk. WSDK-AM broadcasts to the Hartford, CT area at a frequency of 1550 AM.

WSDL-FM
Owner: Salisbury University Foundation Inc.
Editorial: Salisbury Univ Route 13, Caruthers Hall, Salisbury, Maryland 21801.
T: 1 410 543-6895 **E:** prd@salisbury.edu
W: http://publicradiodelmarva.net
Editorial Profile: WSDL-FM is a non-commercial station owned by Salisbury University Foundation Inc. The format of the station is news and talk. WSDL-FM broadcasts to the Salisbury, MD area at 90.7 FM.

WSDM-FM
Owner: Innovation Center, Inc.
Editorial: 15 Wood St, Greenfield, Indiana 46140-2162. **T:** 1 317 467-1062
E: wjcfradio@aol.com
Editorial Profile: WSDM-FM is a non-commercial station owned by the Innovation Center, Inc. and operated Indiana Community Radio Corporation. The format of the station is Top 40 Pop and Contemporary Christian music. WSDM-FM broadcasts to the Indianapolis area at a frequency of 90.1 FM.

WSDO-AM
Owner: J & V Communications Inc.
Editorial: 222 Hazard St, Orlando, Florida 32804. **T:** 1 407 841-8282
E: wprd1440@gmail.com
W: http://www.wprd.com
Editorial Profile: WSDO-AM is commercial station owned by J & V Communications Inc. The format of the station is Hispanic religious talk. WSDO-AM broadcasts to the Orlando, FL area at 1400 AM.

WSDP-FM
Owner: Plymouth Canton Community Schools
Editorial: 46181 Joy Rd, Canton, Michigan 48187-1316. **T:** 1 734 416-7732
E: 881thepark@gmail.com
W: http://www.881thepark.com
Editorial Profile: WSDP-FM is a non-commercial station owned by Plymouth Canton Community Schools. The format of the station is Hot AC. WSDP-FM broadcasts to the Canton, MI area at 88.1 FM.

WSDQ-AM
Owner: Rodgson Inc.
Editorial: 1446 Main St, Dunlap, Tennessee 37327-3704. **T:** 1 423 949-5805
E: wsdq1190@gmail.com
W: http://www.wsdq1190.com
Editorial Profile: WJDQ-AM is a commercial station owned by Rodgson Inc. The format of the station is classic country. WSDQ-AM broadcasts to the Dunlap, TN area at 1190 AM.

WSDR-AM
Owner: Withers Broadcasting Co.
Editorial: 3101 Freeport Rd, Sterling, Illinois 61081-8612. **T:** 1 815 625-3400
E: wsdr1240@theramp.net
Editorial Profile: WSDR-AM is a commercial station owned by Withers Broadcasting Co. The format of the station is news and talk. WSDR-AM broadcasts to the Sterling, IL area at 1240 AM.

WSDS-AM
Owner: Birach Broadcasting Corp.
Editorial: 580 W Clark Rd, Ypsilanti, Michigan 48198. **T:** 1 734 484-0078
E: wsds@explosiva1480.com
W: http://www.explosiva1480.com
Editorial Profile: WSDS-AM is a commercial station owned by Birach Broadcasting Corp. The format of the station is Hispanic. WSDS-AM broadcasts to the Ypsilanti, MI area at 1480 AM.

WSDV-AM
Owner: Clear Channel Media and Entertainment
Editorial: 1779 Independence Blvd, Sarasota, Florida 34234-2106. **T:** 1 941 552-4800
W: http://www.sunnyradioam.com/main.html
Editorial Profile: WSDV-AM is a commercial station owned by Clear Channel Media and Entertainment. The format of the station is adult standards. WSDV-AM broadcasts to the Sarasota, FL, area at 1450 AM.

WSDZ-AM
Owner: Walt Disney Co.
Editorial: 1978 Innerbelt Business Center Dr, Saint Louis, Missouri 63114-5760.
T: 1 314 428-4023
W: http://www.radiodisney.com/stlouis
Editorial Profile: WSDZ-AM is a commercial station owned by Walt Disney Co. The format of the station is pre-teen music. WSDZ-AM broadcasts to the St. Louis area at 1260 AM.

WSEA-FM
Owner: Cumulus Media Inc.
Editorial: 11640 Highway 17 Byp, Murrells Inlet, South Carolina 29576-9332.
T: 1 843 651-7869
W: http://www.teammyrtlebeach.com
Editorial Profile: WSEA-FM is a commercial station owned by Cumulus Media Inc. The format of the station is sports. WSEA-FM broadcasts in the Murrells Inlet, SC area at 100.3 FM.

WSEB-FM
Owner: Suncoast Educational Broadcasting Corp.
Editorial: 135 W Dearborn St, Englewood, Florida 34223-3236. **T:** 1 941 475-9732
E: comments@wsebfm.com
W: http://www.wsebfm.com
Editorial Profile: WSEB-FM is a non-commercial station owned by Suncoast Educational Broadcasting Corp. The format of the station is southern gospel. WSEB-FM broadcasts to the Englewood, FL area at 91.3 FM.

WSEI-FM
Owner: Forcht Broadcasting
Editorial: 4667 E Radio Tower Ln, Olney, Illinois 62450. **T:** 1 618 393-2156
E: freedom929@forchtbroadcasting.com
W: http://www.freedom929.com
Editorial Profile: WSEI-FM is a commercial station owned by Forcht Broadcasting. The format of the station is contemporary country. WSEI-FM broadcasts to the Olney, IL area at 92.9 FM.

WSEK-FM
Owner: Clear Channel Media and Entertainment
Editorial: 101 1st Radio Ln, Somerset, Kentucky 42503-4639. **T:** 1 606 678-5151
W: http://www.k93country.com

WSEL-AM
Owner: Collins Jr.(Ollie)
Editorial: Highway 6 West, Pontotoc, Mississippi 38863. **T:** 1 662 489-0297

WSEL-FM
Owner: Collins Jr.(Ollie)
Editorial: Highway 6 East, Pontotoc, Mississippi 38863. **T:** 1 662 489-0297

WSEM-AM
Owner: Flint Media
Editorial: 521 S Scott St, Bainbridge, Georgia 39819-4101. **T:** 1 229 246-1960
Editorial Profile: WSEM-AM is a commercial station owned by Flint Media. The format of the station is news, sports. WSEM-AM broadcasts to the Donalsonville, GA area at 1500 AM.

WSEN-AM
Owner: Leatherstocking Media Group Inc.
Editorial: 8456 Smokey Hollow Rd, Baldwinsville, New York 13027.
T: 1 315 635-3971
E: webmaster@wsenfm.com
W: http://www.oldiesradio1050.com
Editorial Profile: WSEN-AM is a commercial station owned by Leatherstocking Media Group Inc. The format of the station is oldies music. WSEN-AM broadcasts to the Syracuse, NY area at 1050 AM.

WSEN-FM
Owner: Leatherstocking Media Group Inc.
Editorial: 8456 Smokey Hollow Rd, Baldwinsville, New York 13027.
T: 1 315 635-3971
E: webmaster@wsenfm.com
W: http://www.wsenfm.com
Editorial Profile: WSEN-FM is a commercial station owned by Leatherstocking Media Group Inc. The format of the station is classic hits. WSEN-FM broadcasts to the Baldwinsville, NY area at 92.1 FM.

WSEO-FM
Owner: Nelsonville TV Cable Inc.
Editorial: 15751 US Highway 33, Nelsonville, Ohio 45764. **T:** 1 740 753-4094
E: wseo33@nelsonvilletv.com
Editorial Profile: WSEO-FM is a commercial station owned by Nelsonville TV Cable Inc. The format for the station is country. WSEO-FM broadcasts to the Charleston-Huntington, WV area at 107.7 FM.

WSEV-FM
Owner: East Tennessee Radio Group
Editorial: 196 W Dumplin Valley Rd, Kodak, Tennessee 37764-1934. **T:** 1 865 932-6002
W: http://www.mixx1055.com
Editorial Profile: WSEV-FM is a commercial station owned by East Tennessee Radio Group. The format of the station is adult contemporary. WSEV-FM broadcasts to Kodak, TN and surrounding areas at 105.5 FM.

WSEY-FM
Owner: NRG Media LLC
Editorial: 1460 S College Ave, Dixon, Illinois 61021. **T:** 1 815 288-3341
W: http://www.koolfm957.com
Editorial Profile: WSEY-FM is a commercial station owned by NRG Media LLC. The format of the station is oldies music. WSEY-FM broadcasts to the Dixon, IL area at 95.7 FM.

WSEZ-AM
Owner: Diamond Shores Broadcasting LLC
Editorial: 192 S Court St, Paoli, Indiana 47454-1322. **T:** 1 812 723-4484
E: wume@blueriver.net
Editorial Profile: WSEZ-AM is a commercial station owned by Diamond Shores Broadcasting LLC. The format of the station is oldies music. WSEZ-AM broadcasts to the Paoli, IN area at 1560 AM.

WSFB-AM
Owner: Small Town Broadcasting
Editorial: 118 N Patterson St, Valdosta, Georgia 31601-5570. **T:** 1 229 259-9301
Editorial Profile: WSFB-AM is a commercial station owned by Small Town Broadcasting. The format of the station is Talk. WSFB-AM broadcasts to the Quitman, GA area at 1490 AM.

WSFC-AM
Owner: Clear Channel Media and Entertainment
Editorial: 101 1st Radio Ln, Somerset, Kentucky 42503. **T:** 1 606 678-5151
E: wsek@clearchannel.com
W: http://www.wsfcam.com
Editorial Profile: WSFC-AM is a commercial station owned by Clear Channel Media and Entertainment. The format of the station is news and talk. WSFC-AM broadcasts to the Somerset, KY area at 1240 AM.

WSFE-AM
Owner: Clear Channel Media and Entertainment
Editorial: 101 1st Radio Ln, Somerset, Kentucky 42503. **T:** 1 606 678-5151
E: wsek@clearchannel.com
W: http://www.wsfeam.com
Editorial Profile: WSFE-AM is a commercial station owned by Clear Channel Media and Entertainment. The format of the station is news and talk. WSFE-AM broadcasts to the Somerset, KY area at 910 AM.

WSFF-FM
Owner: Clear Channel Media and Entertainment
Editorial: 3807 Brandon Ave SW, Ste 2350, Roanoke, Virginia 24018. **T:** 1 540 725-1220
W: http://www.1061stevefm.com
Editorial Profile: WSFF-FM is a commercial station owned by Clear Channel Media and Entertainment. The format of the station is Jack FM-Adult Hits. WSFF-FM broadcasts in the Roanoke, VA area at 106.1 FM.

WSFL-FM
Owner: Beasley Broadcast Group
Editorial: 207 Glenburnie Dr, New Bern, North Carolina 28560-2815. **T:** 1 252 633-1500
W: http://www.wsfl.com

WSFN-AM
Owner: MarMac Communications, LLC
Editorial: 436 Mall Blvd, Brunswick, Georgia 31525-1819. **T:** 1 912 264-6251
E: thefansportsradio@yahoo.com
W: http://www.thefansportsradio.com
Editorial Profile: WSFN-AM is a commercial station owned by MarMac Communications, LLC. The format of the station is sports. WSFN-AM broadcasts to the Brunswick, GA area at 790 AM.

WSFP-FM
Owner: Superior Communications
Editorial: 148 E Grand River Rd, Williamston, Michigan 48895-9411. **T:** 1 517 381-0573
E: 411@smile.fm **W:** http://www.smile.fm
Editorial Profile: WSFP-FM is a commercial station owned by Superior Communications. The format of the station is contemporary Christian music and inspirational talk. WSFP-FM broadcasts to the Rust Township, MI area at 88.1 FM.

WSFQ-FM
Owner: Radio Plus Bay Cities, LLC
Editorial: 413 10th Ave, Menominee, Michigan 49858-3009. **T:** 1 906 863-5551
E: reception@baycitiesradio.net
W: http://www.hits96online.com
Editorial Profile: WSFQ-FM is a commercial station owned by Radio Plus Bay Cities, LLC. The format of the station is adult contemporary. WSFQ-FM broadcasts to the Menominee, MI area at 96.3 FM.

WSFR-FM
Owner: Summit Media Broadcasting LLC
Editorial: 612 S 4th St, Louisville, Kentucky 40202-2460. **T:** 1 502 589-4800
W: http://1077theeagle.com
Editorial Profile: WSFR-FM is a commercial station owned by Summit Media Broadcasting LLC. The format of the station is classic hits. WSFR-FM broadcasts to the Louisville, KY area at 107.7 FM.

WSFW-AM
Owner: Calvary Chapel Twin Falls
Editorial: 4002 N 3300 E, Twin Falls, Idaho 83301-0354. **T:** 1 208 734-4357
W: http://www.csnradio.com
Editorial Profile: WSFW-AM is a non-commercial station owned by Calvary Chapel Twin Falls. The format of the station is religious. WSFW-AM broadcasts to the Senecca Falls, NY area at 1110 AM.

WSFZ-AM
Owner: Sportsrad, Inc.
Editorial: 571 Highway 51, Ste H, Ridgeland, Mississippi 39157-2597. **T:** 1 601 675-8255
E: info@supersport930.com
W: http://www.supersport930.com
Editorial Profile: WSFZ-AM is a commercial station owned by Sportsrad, Inc. The format of the station is sports programming. WSFZ-AM broadcasts to the Jackson, MS area at 930 AM.

WSGA-FM
Owner: WRGO Radio LLC
Editorial: 6605 Abercorn St Ste 213, Savannah, Georgia 31405-5892.
T: 1 912 691-1934
E: office@923classiccountry.com
W: http://www.923classiccountry.com
Editorial Profile: WSGA-FM is a commercial station owned by WRGO Radio LLC (dba Savannah Radio Group). The format of the station is country. WSGA-FM broadcasts to the Hinesville, GA area at 92.3 FM.

WSGB-AM
Owner: Summit Media Broadcasting LLC
Editorial: 180 Main St, Sutton, West Virginia 26601-1317. **T:** 1 304 765-7373
W: http://www.summitmediawv.com

Editorial Profile: WSGB-AM is a commercial station owned by Summit Media Broadcasting LLC. The format of the station is classic hits. WSGB-AM broadcasts to the Sutton, WV area at 1490 AM.

WSGC-AM
Owner: Georgia-Carolina Radiocasting Companies LLC
Editorial: 562 Jones St, Elberton, Georgia 30635. **T:** 1 706 283-1400
E: wsgc@elbertonradio.com
Editorial Profile: WSGC-AM is a commercial station owned by Georgia-Carolina Radiocasting Companies LLC. The format of the station is oldies. WSGC-AM broadcasts to the Elberton, GA area at 1400 AM.

WSGC-FM
Owner: Georgia-Carolina Radiocasting Companies LLC
Editorial: 562 Jones St, Elberton, Georgia 30635-1957. **T:** 1 706 283-1400
E: wsgc@elbertonradio.com
W: http://www.wsgcradio.com
Editorial Profile: WSGC-FM is a commercial station owned by Georgia-Carolina Radiocasting Companies LLC. The format of the station is country music. WSGC-FM broadcasts to the Elberton, GA area at 96.7 FM.

WSGE-FM
Owner: Board of Trustees, Gaston College
Editorial: 201 Highway 321 S, Dallas, North Carolina 28034-1402. **T:** 1 704 922-6552
W: http://www.wsge.org
Editorial Profile: WSGE-FM is a non-commercial station owned by Board of Trustees, Gaston College. The format of the station is adult album alternative. WSGE-FM broadcasts to the Charlotte-Gastonia, NC area at 91.7 FM.

WSGH-AM
Owner: Golden Door Broadcasting, LLC
Editorial: 4015 Brownsboro Rd, Winston Salem, North Carolina 27106-3380.
T: 1 336 714-7504
W: http://www.quepasamedia.com

WSGI-AM
Owner: Lightning Broadcasting, LLC
Editorial: 200 Wdbl Rd, Springfield, Tennessee 37172. **T:** 1 615 384-9744
E: wsgi1100@yahoo.com
W: http://www.wsgi1100.com
Editorial Profile: WSGI-AM is a commercial station owned by Lightning Broadcasting, LLC. The format of the station is oldies and country. WSGI-AM broadcasts to the Springfield, TN area at 1100 AM.

WSGL-FM
Owner: Renda Broadcasting
Editorial: 10915 K Nine Dr, 2nd Fl, Bonita Springs, Florida 34135-6802.
T: 1 239 495-8383
W: http://www.1047mixfm.com

WSGM-FM
Owner: Cumberland Communications Corporations
Editorial: Firetower Road, Tracy City, Tennessee 37387. **T:** 1 931 592-7777
E: wsgmfm@hotmail.com

WSGO-AM
Owner: Galaxy Communications LP
Editorial: 235 Walton St, Syracuse, New York 13202. **T:** 1 315 472-9111
W: http://galaxycommunications.com
Editorial Profile: WSGO-AM is a commercial station owned by Galaxy Communications LP. The format of the station is sports. WSGO-AM broadcasts to the Syracuse, NY area at 1440 AM.

WSGR-FM
Owner: St. Clair County Comm. College
Editorial: 323 Erie St, Port Huron, Michigan 48060-3812. **T:** 1 810 989-5564
E: wsgr@sc4.edu
Editorial Profile: WSGR-FM is a non-commercial college station owned by St. Clair County Comm. College. The format of the station is alternative rock and free form radio. WSGR-FM broadcasts to the Port Huron, MI area at a frequency of 91.3 FM.

WSGS-FM
Owner: Mountain Broadcasting Service
Editorial: 516 Main St, Hazard, Kentucky 41701-1775. **T:** 1 606 436-2121
E: wsgs@windstream.net
W: http://www.wsgs.com

WSGT-FM
Owner: Mattox Broadcasting, Inc.
Editorial: 2132 Us Highway 84, Blackshear, Georgia 31516-1160. **T:** 1 912 449-3391
Editorial Profile: WSGT-FM is a commercial station owned by Mattox Broadcasting, Inc. The format of the station is classic hits. WSGT-FM broadcasts locally to the Patterson, GA area at a frequency of 107.1 FM.

WSGW-AM
Owner: Digity LLC
Editorial: 1795 Tittabawassee Rd, Saginaw, Michigan 48604-9431. **T:** 1 989 752-3456
E: news@wsgw.com **W:** http://www.wsgw.com
Editorial Profile: WSGW-AM is a commercial station owned by Digity LLC . The format of the station is news, talk and sports. WSGW-AM broadcasts to the Saginaw, MI area at 790 AM.

WSGW-FM
Owner: Digity LLC
Editorial: 1795 Tittabawassee Rd, Saginaw, Michigan 48604-9431. **T:** 1 989 752-3456
E: wsgw@wsgw.com
W: http://www.fmtalk1005.com
Editorial Profile: WSGW-FM is a commercial station owned by Digity LLC . The format of the station is talk and sports. WSGW-FM broadcasts to the Saginaw, MI area at 100.5 FM.

WSHA-FM
Owner: Shaw University
Editorial: 118 E South St, Raleigh, North Carolina 27601-2341. **T:** 1 919 546-8430
E: wsha@shawu.edu
W: http://www.wshafm.org
Editorial Profile: WSHA-FM is a non-commercial owned by Shaw University. The format of the station is jazz music. WSHA-FM broadcasts to the Raleigh, NC area at 88.9 FM.

WSHC-FM
Owner: Shepherd University
Editorial: 301 N. King St., Shepherdstown, West Virginia 25443. **T:** 1 304 876-5134
E: wshc@shepherd.edu
W: http://www.897wshc.org

WSHE-AM
Owner: THE TRUTH, INC.
Editorial: 1501 13th Ave, Columbus, Georgia 31901-1908. **T:** 1 706 576-3000
W: http://www.am1270radio.com
Editorial Profile: WSHE-AM is a commercial station owned by THE TRUTH, INC,. The format of the station is Southern gospel. WSHE-AM broadcasts to the Columbus, GA area at 1270 AM.

WSHH-FM
Owner: Renda Broadcasting
Editorial: 900 Parish St, 3rd Fl, Pittsburgh, Pennsylvania 15220. **T:** 1 412 875-9500
W: http://www.wshh.com
Editorial Profile: WSHH-FM is a commercial station owned by Renda Broadcasting. The format of the station is Lite Rock/Lite AC. WSHH-FM broadcasts to the Pittsburgh area at 99.7 FM.

WSHK-FM
Owner: Cumulus Media Inc.
Editorial: 292 Middle Rd, Dover, New Hampshire 03820-4901. **T:** 1 603 749-9750
W: http://www.shark1053.com
Editorial Profile: WSHK-FM is a commercial station owned by Cumulus Media Inc. The format of the station is classic hits. WSHK-FM broadcasts to the Dover, NH area at 105.3 FM.

WSHO-AM
Owner: Shadowlands Communications LLC
Editorial: 365 Canal St Ste 1175, New Orleans, Louisiana 70130-1182.
T: 1 504 527-0800
E: wsho@cisocompuserve.com
W: http://www.wsho.com
Editorial Profile: WSHO-AM is a commercial station owned by Shadowlands Communications LLC. The format of the station is religious. WSHO-AM broadcasts to the New Orleans market area at 800 AM.

WSHS-FM
Owner: Sheboygan Area School District
Editorial: 1042 School Ave, Sheboygan, Wisconsin 53083-4053. **T:** 1 920 459-3610
E: 91.7wshs@gmail.com
W: http://www.sheboygan.k12.wi.us/news/wshs.html
Editorial Profile: WSHS-FM is a non-commercial station owned by Sheboygan Area School District. The format of the station is variety. WSHS-FM broadcasts to the Sheboygan, WI, area at 91.7 FM.

WSHU-AM
Owner: Sacred Heart University
Editorial: 5151 Park Ave, Fairfield, Connecticut 06825-1090. **T:** 1 203 365-6604
E: news@wshu.org **W:** http://wshu.org
Editorial Profile: WSHU-AM is a non-commercial station owned by Sacred Heart University. The format of the station is news and talk. WSHU-AM broadcasts to the Fairfield, CT, area at 1260 AM.

WSHU-FM
Owner: Sacred Heart University
Editorial: 5151 Park Ave, Fairfield, Connecticut 6825. **T:** 1 203 365-6604 **E:** news@wshu.org
W: http://www.wshu.org
Editorial Profile: WSHU-FM is a non-commercial station owned by Sacred Heart University. The format of the station is classical music and news. WSHU-FM broadcasts to the Fairfield, CT area at 91.1 FM.

WSHV-AM
Owner: Lakes Media LLC
Editorial: Highway 47 North, South Hill, Virginia 23970. **T:** 1 434 447-8997
E: wshvam@yahoo.com
Editorial Profile: WSHV-AM is a commercial station owned by Lakes Media LLC. The format of the station is urban contemporary music. WSHV-AM broadcasts to the South Hill, VA area at 1370 AM.

WSHW-FM
Owner: Kaspar Broadcasting Co.
Editorial: 1401 W Barner St, Frankfort, Indiana 46041. **T:** 1 765 659-3339
E: newsroom@kasparradio.com
W: http://www.wshw.com
Editorial Profile: WSHW-FM is a commercial station owned by Kaspar Broadcasting Co. The format of the station is Lite Rock/Lite AC music. WSHW-FM broadcasts to the Indianapolis area at 99.7 FM.

WSHY-AM
Owner: Artistic Media Partners Inc.
Editorial: 3824 S 18th St, Lafayette, Indiana 47909-9102. **T:** 1 765 474-1410
Editorial Profile: WSHY-AM is a commercial station owned by Artistic Media Partners Inc. The format of the station is sports talk. WSHY-AM broadcasts to the Lafayette, IN area at 1410 AM.

WSIA-FM
Owner: College of Staten Island(The)
Editorial: 2800 Victory Blvd, Staten Island, New York 10314-6609. **T:** 1 718 982-3050
W: http://www.wsia.fm
Editorial Profile: WSIA-FM is a non-commercial, college station owned by The College of Staten Island. The format of the station is adult alternative. WSIA-FM broadcasts to the Staten Island, NY area at 88.9 FM.

WSIB-FM
Owner: Grace Broadcasting Services Inc.
Editorial: 25 Stonebrook Pl Ste G322, Jackson, Tennessee 38305-3686.
T: 1 731 855-0098
W: http://gracebroadcasting.com/wsib
Editorial Profile: WSIB-FM is a commercial station owned by Grace Broadcasting Services Inc. The format of the station is adult contemporary. WSIB-FM broadcasts to the Selmer, TN area at 93.9 FM.

WSIC-AM
Owner: Iredell Broadcasting Inc.
Editorial: 1117 Radio Rd, Statesville, North Carolina 28677-3350. **T:** 1 704 872-6345
E: news@wsicweb.com
W: http://www.wsicweb.com
Editorial Profile: WSIC-AM is a commercial station owned by Iredell Broadcasting Inc. The format of the station is news, talk and sports. WSIC-AM broadcasts to the Charlotte, NC, area at 1400 AM.

WSIE-FM
Owner: Southern Illinois University
Editorial: outhern Illinois University Edwardsville, 0141 Dunham Hall, Edwardsville, Illinois 62026. **T:** 1 618 650-2228
E: wsie-887@siue.edu
W: http://www.wsie.com
Editorial Profile: WSIE-FM is a non-commercial station owned by Southern Illinois University. The format of the station is jazz music. WSIE-FM broadcasts to the Edwardsville, IL and St. Louis metropolitan area at 88.7 FM.

WSIG-FM
Owner: Gamma Broadcasting LLC
Editorial: 639 N Main St, Mount Crawford, Virginia 22841-2350. **T:** 1 540 432-1063
W: http://www.969wsig.com
Editorial Profile: WSIG-FM is a commercial station owned by Gamma Broadcasting LLC. The format for the station is country. WSIG-FM broadcasts to the Harrisonburg, VA area at 96.9 FM.

WSIM-FM
Owner: Miller Communications Inc.
Editorial: 2425 Walker Swinton Rd, Timmonsville, South Carolina 29161-9351.
T: 1 843 678-9393 **E:** production@miller.fm
W: http://www.miller.fm
Editorial Profile: WSIM-FM is a commercial station owned by Miller Communications Inc. The format of the station is Hot AC. WSIM-FM broadcasts to the Florence, SC at 93.7 FM.

WSIP-AM
Owner: Forcht Broadcasting
Editorial: 127 Main St, Paintsville, Kentucky 41240. **T:** 1 606 789-5311
E: wsipprod@keybroadcasting.net
W: http://www.wsipfm.com
Editorial Profile: WSIP-AM is a commercial station owned by Forcht Broadcasting. The format of the station is oldies. WSIP-AM broadcasts to the Paintsville, KY area at 1490 AM

WSIP-FM
Owner: Forcht Broadcasting
Editorial: 124 Main St, Paintsville, Kentucky 41240. **T:** 1 606 789-5311
E: wsipprod@keybroadcasting.net
W: http://www.wsipfm.com
Editorial Profile: WSIP-FM is a commercial station owned by Forcht Broadcasting. The format for the station is country. WSIP-FM broadcasts to the Charleston-Huntington, WV area at 98.9 FM.

WSIR-AM
Owner: Anscombe Broadcasting Group Ltd.
Editorial: 665 Lake Howard Dr SW, Winter Haven, Florida 33880-2577. **T:** 1 863 295-9411
W: http://www.rejoice1490.com
Editorial Profile: WSIR-AM is a commercial station owned by Anscombe Broadcasting Group Ltd. The format of the station is gospel and urban AC music. WSIR-AM broadcasts to the Tampa Bay, FL area at 1490 AM.

WSIU-FM
Owner: WSIU Public Broadcasting
Editorial: 1100 Lincoln Dr, Carbondale, Illinois 62901-4306. **T:** 1 618 453-4343
E: wsiuradio@wsiu.org
W: http://www.wsiu.org
Editorial Profile: WSIU-FM is a non-commercial station owned by WSIU Public Broadcasting. The format of the station is news and classical music. WSIU-FM broadcasts to the Paducah, KY-Cape Girardeau, MO-Harrisburg, IL areas at 91.9 FM.

WSIV-AM
Owner: C R A M Communications LLC
Editorial: 7095 Myers Rd, East Syracuse, New York 13057. **T:** 1 315 656-2231
W: http://www.wsiv1540.com
Editorial Profile: WSIV-AM is a commercial radio station owned by C R AM Communications LLC. The format of the station is gospel music. The station airs to the East Syracuse area at 1540 AM.

WSIX-FM
Owner: Clear Channel Media and Entertainment
Editorial: 55 Music Sq W, Nashville, Tennessee 37203-3207. **T:** 1 615 664-2400
W: http://www.wsix.com
Editorial Profile: WSIX-FM is a commercial station owned by Clear Channel Media and Entertainment. The format of the station is country music. WSIX-FM broadcasts to the Nashville, TN area at 97.9 FM. To send a PSA, email nashvillepsa@clearchannel.com.

WSJD-FM
Owner: WSJD Inc.
Editorial: 328 N Market St, Mount Carmel, Illinois 62863-1519. **T:** 1 618 263-4300
E: wsjd@live.com

WSJK-FM
Owner: S.J. Broadcasting Inc.
Editorial: 2702 Boulder Rd, Urbana, Illinois 61802-6996. **T:** 1 217 367-1195
W: http://www.espncu.com

Editorial Profile: WSJK-FM is a commercial station owned by S.J. Broadcasting Inc. The format of the station is sports/talk. WSJK-FM broadcasts to the Champaign, IL area at 93.5 FM.

WSJL-FM
Owner: Elijah Radio, Inc.
Editorial: 9233 S Main St, Wilsonville, Alabama 35186-7219. **T:** 1 205 585-6706
Editorial Profile: WSJL-FM is a non-commercial station owned by Elijah Radio, Inc. The format of the station is religious. WSJL-FM broadcasts to the Bessemer, AL area at a frequency of 88.1 FM.

WSJM-AM
Owner: Midwest Family Stations
Editorial: 580 E Napier Ave, Benton Harbor, Michigan 49022. **T:** 1 269 925-1111
E: news@wsjm.com **W:** http://www.wsjm.com
Editorial Profile: WSJM-AM is a commercial station owned by Midwest Family Stations. The format of the station is news, talk and sports. WSJM-AM airs locally on 1400 AM to the Benton Harbor, MI area.

WSJM-FM
Owner: Midwest Family Stations
Editorial: 580 E Napier Ave, Benton Harbor, Michigan 49022. **T:** 1 269 925-1111
E: news@wsjm.com **W:** http://www.wsjm.com
Editorial Profile: WSJM-FM is a commercial station owned by Midwest Family Stations. The format of the station is news, talk and sports. WSJM-FM broadcasts in the Benton Harbor, MI area at 94.9 FM.

WSJO-FM
Owner: Townsquare Media, LLC
Editorial: 950 Tilton Rd Ste 200, Northfield, New Jersey 08225-1235. **T:** 1 609 645-9797
W: http://www.sojo1049.com
Editorial Profile: WSJO-FM is a commercial station owned by the Townsquare Media, LLC. The format is hot adult contemporary. WSJO-FM broadcasts to the Princeton, NJ area at 104.9 FM.

WSJR-FM
Owner: Cumulus Media Inc.
Editorial: 600 Baltimore Drive, Wilkes-Barre, Pennsylvania 18702-7901. **T:** 1 570 824-9000
W: http://www.greatcountry937.com
Editorial Profile: WSJR-FM is a commercial station owned by Cumulus Media Inc. The format of the station is contemporary country. WSJR-FM broadcasts to the Wilkes-Barre, PA area at 93.7 FM.

WSJS-AM
Owner: Curtis Media Group
Editorial: 875 W 5th St, Winston Salem, North Carolina 27101-2505. **T:** 1 336 777-3900
W: http://www.wsjs.com
Editorial Profile: WSJS-AM is a commercial station owned by Curtis Media Group. The format of the station is news and talk. WSJS-AM broadcasts to the Greensboro-Winston Salem, NC area at 600 AM.

WSJY-FM
Owner: NRG Media LLC
Editorial: W6355 Eastern Ave, Fort Atkinson, Wisconsin 53538. **T:** 1 920 563-9329
W: http://www.lite1073.com
Editorial Profile: WSJY-FM is a commercial station owned by NRG Media LLC. The format of the station is Lite Rock/Lite AC. WSJY-FM broadcasts to the Milwaukee area at 107.3 FM.

WSJZ-FM
Owner: Cumulus Media Inc.
Editorial: 1800 W Hibiscus Blvd, Melbourne, Florida 32901-2629. **T:** 1 321 984-1000
W: http://www.sportsradio959.com
Editorial Profile: WSJZ-FM is a commercial station owned by Cumulus Media Inc. The format of the station is sports. WSJZ-FM broadcasts to the Melbourne, FL area at 95.9 FM.

WSKB-FM
Owner: Westfield State College
Editorial: Ely Hall, 577 Western Ave., Westfield, Massachusetts 1086.
T: 1 413 572-5579 **W:** http://wsc.ma.edu/wskb
Editorial Profile: WSKB-FM is a non-commercial station owned by Westfield State College. The format of the station is college variety. WSKB-FM broadcasts to the Westfield, MA area at 89.5 FM.

WSKE-FM
Owner: New Millennium Communications Group
Editorial: 151 E 1St Ave, Everett, Pennsylvania 15537-1351. **T:** 1 814 652-2600
E: wske@penn.com
Editorial Profile: WSKE-FM is a commercial station owned by New Millennium Communications Group. The format of the station is country music. WSKE-FM broadcasts to the Everett, PA area at 104.3 FM.

WSKG-FM
Owner: WSKG Public Telecommunications
Editorial: 601 Gates Rd, Vestal, New York 13850. **T:** 1 607 729-0100
W: http://www.wskg.com
Editorial Profile: WSKG-FM is a non-commercial station owned by WSKG Public Telecommunications. The format of the station is classical, jazz and news. WSKG-FM broadcasts to the Vestal, NY area at 89.3 FM.

WSKI-AM
Owner: Northeast Broadcasting Co.
Editorial: 169 River St, Montpelier, Vermont 5602. **T:** 1 802 223-2396
E: feedback@pointfm.com
W: http://www.pointfm.com
Editorial Profile: WSKI-AM is a commercial station owned by Northeast Broadcasting Co. The format of the station is sports talk. WSKI-AM broadcasts to the Montpelier, VT area at 1240 AM.

WSKK-FM
Owner: Kudzu Communications, Inc.
Editorial: 107 E Spring St, Ripley, Mississippi 38663-2043. **T:** 1 662 837-1023
E: classicradiofm@aol.com
W: http://www.classicradiofm.com
Editorial Profile: WSKK-FM is a commercial station owned by Kudzu Communications. The format of the station is classic hits. WSKK-FM broadcasts to the Ripley, MS area at 102.3 FM.

WSKL-FM
Owner: Zona Communications, Inc.
Editorial: 820 Railroad St, Covington, Indiana 47932-1357. **T:** 1 765 793-4823
E: fmkool929@aol.com
W: http://www.koololdies.net
Editorial Profile: WSKL-FM is a commercial station owned by Zona Communications, Inc. The format of the station is oldies music. WSKL-FM broadcasts to the Covington, IL area at 92.9 FM.

WSKO-AM
Owner: Cumulus Media Inc.
Editorial: 1064 James St, Syracuse, New York 13203-2704. **T:** 1 315 472-0200
W: http://www.thescore1260.com
Editorial Profile: WSKO-AM is a commercial station owned by Cumulus Media Inc. The format of the station is sports. WSKO-AM broadcasts to Syracuse, NY at 1260 AM.

WSKP-FM
Owner: Red Wolf Broadcasting
Editorial: 758 Colonel Ledyard Hwy, Ledyard, Connecticut 06339-1541. **T:** 1 860 464-1065
W: http://www.jammin1077.com
Editorial Profile: WSKP-FM is a commercial station owned by Red Wolf Broadcasting. The format of the station is urban contemporary music. WSKP-FM broadcasts to the Hartford-New Haven, CT area at 107.7 FM.

WSKQ-FM
Owner: Spanish Broadcasting System
Editorial: 26 W 56th St, New York, New York 10019. **T:** 1 212 541-9200
W: http://lamega.lamusica.com
Editorial Profile: WSKQ-FM is a commercial station owned by Spanish Broadcasting System. The format of the station is tropical Hispanic music. WSKQ-FM broadcasts to the New York City area at 97.9 FM.

WSKS-FM
Owner: Roser Communications
Editorial: 185 Genesee St, Ste 1601, Utica, New York 13501. **T:** 1 315 734-9245
E: audio@rosergroup.com
W: http://www.cnykiss.com
Editorial Profile: WSKS-FM is a commercial station owned by Roser Communications. The format of the station is Top 40/CHR. WSKS-FM broadcasts to the Utica, NY area at 97.9 FM.

WSKU-FM
Owner: Roser Communications
Editorial: 185 Genesee St Ste 1601, Utica, New York 13501-2110. **T:** 1 315 734-9245
W: http://www.cnykiss.com
Editorial Profile: WSKU-FM is a commercial station owned by Roser Communications. The format of the station is Top 40/CHR. WSKU-FM broadcasts to the Utica, NY area at 105.5.

WSKV-FM
Owner: Moore Country 104, LLC
Editorial: 28 W Halls Rd, Stanton, Kentucky 40380. **T:** 1 606 663-2811
E: wskv@wskvfm.com
W: http://www.wskvfm.com
Editorial Profile: WSKV-FM is a commercial station owned by Moore Country 104, LLC. The format of the station is country and bluegrass. WSKV-FM broadcasts to the Lexington, KY area at 104.9 FM.

WSKW-AM
Owner: Mountain Wireless Corp.
Editorial: 208 Middle Rd, Skowhegan, Maine 4976. **T:** 1 207 474-5171
E: mix1079@gmail.com
Editorial Profile: WSKW-AM is a commercial station owned by Mountain Wireless Corp. The format of the station is sports. WSKW-AM broadcasts to the Skowhegan, ME area at 1160 AM.

WSKX-FM
Owner: Clear Channel Media and Entertainment
Editorial: 815 Lafayette Rd, Portsmouth, New Hampshire 03801-5406. **T:** 1 603 436-7300
W: http://www.953thecoast.com
Editorial Profile: WSKX-FM is a commercial station owned by Clear Channel Media and Entertainment. The station format of the station is adult hits. WSKX-FM broadcasts to the Portsmouth, NH area at 95.3 FM.

WSKY-AM
Owner: Wilkins Communication Networks Inc.
Editorial: 40 Westgate Pkwy Ste F, Asheville, North Carolina 28806-3886.
T: 1 828 251-2000 **E:** wsky@wilkinsradio.com
W: http://www.wilkinsradio.com
Editorial Profile: WSKY-AM is a commercial station owned by Wilkins Communication Networks Inc.and licensed by Macon Media, Inc. The format of the station is religious. WSKY-AM broadcasts to the Asheville, NC area at a frequency of 1230 AM.

WSKY-FM
Owner: Entercom Communications Corp.
Editorial: 3600 NW 43rd St, Ste B, Gainesville, Florida 32606. **T:** 1 352 337-9729
W: http://www.thesky973.com
Editorial Profile: WSKY-FM is a commercial radio station owned by Entercom Communications Corp. The format of the station is news, talk, and information. The station airs locally on 97.3 FM. The tagline is, "The Sky." Newscasts air at the top and bottom of every hour, ET.

WSKZ-FM
Owner: Cumulus Media Inc.
Editorial: 821 Pineville Rd, Chattanooga, Tennessee 37405-2601. **T:** 1 423 756-6141
W: http://www.wskz.com
Editorial Profile: WSKZ-FM is a commercial station owned by Cumulus Media Inc. The format of the station is classic rock. WSKZ-FM broadcasts to the Chattanooga, TN area at 106.5 FM.

WSLA-AM
Owner: Mapa Broadcasting, L.L.C
Editorial: 38230 Coast Blvd, Slidell, Louisiana 70458-8644. **T:** 1 985 643-1560
E: wsla1560@bellsouth.net
W: http://wslaradio.com
Editorial Profile: WSLA-AM is a commercial station owned by Mapa Broadcasting, L.L.C. The format of the station is sports talk. WSLA-AM broadcasts to the Slidell, LA area at 1560 AM.

WSLB-AM
Owner: Community Broadcasters, LLC
Editorial: 199 Wealtha Ave, Watertown, New York 13601-1837. **T:** 1 315 393-1100
Editorial Profile: WSLB-AM is a commercial station owned by Community Broadcasters, LLC. The format of the station sports. WSLB-AM broadcasts to the Ogdensburg, NY area at 1400 AM.

WSLC-FM
Owner: Wheeler Inc.(Mel)
Editorial: 3934 Electric Rd, Roanoke, Virginia 24018-4513. **T:** 1 540 772-0102
W: http://www.949starcountry.com
Editorial Profile: WSLC-FM is a commercial station owned by Mel Wheeler, Inc. The format of the station is contemporary country. WSLC-FM broadcasts to the Roanoke, VA area at 94.9 FM.

WSLD-FM
Owner: Prairie Communications LLP
Editorial: 6534 Highway 89 North, Whitewater, Wisconsin 53190-4190. **T:** 1 608 883-6677
E: wsld@prariecommunications.net
W: http://www.1045wsld.com
Editorial Profile: WSLD-FM is a commercial station owned by Prairie Communications LLP. The format of the station is contemporary country. WSLD-FM broadcasts to the Milwaukee area at 104.5 FM.

WSLJ-FM
Owner: St. Lawrence University
Editorial: EJ Medical Bldg. Rm 201, 80 E Main St, Canton, New York 13617.
T: 1 315 229-5356 **E:** radio@ncpr.org
W: http://www.ncpr.org
Editorial Profile: WSLJ-FM is a non-commercial station owned by St. Lawrence University. The format of the station is variety, news and talk. WSLJ-FM broadcasts to the Canton, NY area at 88.9 FM.

WSLK-AM
Owner: Smile Broadcasting LLC
Editorial: 1126 Hendricks Store Rd, Ste B, Moneta, Virginia 24121-3337.
T: 1 540 297-7880 **E:** info@wslk880.com
W: http://www.wslk880.com
Editorial Profile: WSLK-AM is a commercial station owned by Smile Broadcasting LLC. The format of the station is oldies. WSLK-AM broadcasts to Moneta, VA and surrounding areas at 880 AM.

WSLL-FM
Owner: St. Lawrence University
Editorial: EJ Medical Bldg. Rm 201, 80 E Main ST, Canton, New York 13617.
T: 1 315 229-5356 **E:** radio@ncpr.org
W: http://www.ncpr.org
Editorial Profile: WSLL-FM is a non-commercial station owned by St. Lawrence University. The format of the station is variety, news and talk. WSLL-FM broadcasts to the Canton, NY area at 90.5 FM.

WSLM-AM
Owner: White (Becky)
Editorial: 1308 E Hackberry St, Salem, Indiana 47167-9604. **T:** 1 812 883-3401
E: wslmradio@gmail.com
W: http://wslmradio.com

WSLM-FM
Owner: White (Becky)
Editorial: 1308 E Hackberry St, Salem, Indiana 47167-9604. **T:** 1 812 883-5750
E: wslmradio@gmail.com
W: http://wslmradio.com
Editorial Profile: WSLM-FM is a commercial station owned by Beck White. The format of the station is classic hits and sports. WSLM-FM broadcasts to the Salem, IN area at 97.9 FM.

WSLO-FM
Owner: St. Lawrence University
Editorial: EJ Medical Bldg. Rm 201, 80 E Main St, Canton, New York 13617.
T: 1 315 229-5356 **E:** radio@ncpr.org
W: http://www.ncpr.org
Editorial Profile: WSLO-FM is a non-commercial station owned by St. Lawrence University. The format of the station is variety, news and talk. WSLO-FM broadcasts to the Canton, NY area at 90.9 FM.

WSLQ-FM
Owner: Mel Wheeler Broadcasting Inc.
Editorial: 3934 Electric Rd, Roanoke, Virginia 24018. **T:** 1 540 387-0234
W: http://www.q99fm.com
Editorial Profile: WSLQ-FM is a commercial station owned by Mel Wheeler Broadcasting Inc. The format of the station is adult contemporary. WSLQ-FM broadcasts to the Roanoke, VA area at 99.1 FM.

WSLU-FM
Owner: St. Lawrence University
Editorial: North Country Public Radio, St Lawrence University, Canton, New York 13617-1475. **T:** 1 315 229-5356
E: radio@ncpr.org
W: http://www.northcountrypublicradio.org
Editorial Profile: WSLU-FM is a non-commercial station owned by St. Lawrence University. The format of the station is variety. WSLU-FM broadcasts to the Canton, NY area at 89.5 FM.

WSLV-AM
Owner: B & E Broadcasting Inc.
Editorial: 25995 State Line Rd, Ardmore, Tennessee 38449-3199. **T:** 1 931 427-2178
E: wslv@ardmore.net
W: http://www.wslvradio.com
Editorial Profile: WSLV-AM is a commercial station owned by B & E Broadcasting Inc. The format of the station is classic and contemporary country. WSLV-AM broadcasts to the Ardmore, TN area at 1110 AM.

WSLW-AM
Owner: Radio Greenbrier
Editorial: 276 Seneca Trl, Ronceverte, West Virginia 24970. **T:** 1 304 645-1327
E: radio@wron.net **W:** http://www.wron.com
Editorial Profile: WSLW-AM is a commercial station owned by Radio Greenbrier. The format of the station is sports. WSLW-AM broadcasts to the White Sulphur Springs, WV area at 1310 AM.

WSLY-FM
Owner: Grantell Broadcasting Co.
Editorial: 11474 Hwy 11, York, Alabama 36925. **T:** 1 205 392-5234
Editorial Profile: WSLY-FM is a commercial station owned by Grantell Broadcasting Co. The format of the station is sports. WSLY-FM broadcasts to the York, AL area at 104.9 FM.

WSM-AM
Owner: Grand Ole Opry, LLC
Editorial: 2644 McGavock Pike, Nashville, Tennessee 37214-1202. **T:** 1 615 458-4650
E: email@wsmonline.com
W: http://www.wsmonline.com
Editorial Profile: WSM-AM is a commercial station owned by Grand Ole Opry, LLC. The format of the station is country music. WSM-AM broadcasts to the Nashville, TN at 650 AM.

WSMC-FM
Owner: Southern Adventist University
Editorial: 5077 Industrial Dr?, Collegedale, Tennessee 37315. **T:** 1 423 236-2905
E: wsmc@southern.edu
W: http://www.wsmc.org
Editorial Profile: WSMC-FM is a non-commercial station owned by Southern Adventist University. The format for the station is classical and news. WSMC-FM broadcasts to the Collegedale, TN area at 90.5 FM.

WSMD-FM
Owner: Somar Communications Inc.
Editorial: 28095 Three Notch Rd, Ste 2B, Mechanicsville, Maryland 20659.
T: 1 301 870-5550 **E:** wsmdfm@aol.com
W: http://www.star983.com
Editorial Profile: WSMD-FM is a commercial station owned by Somar Communications Inc. The format of the station is classic hits music. WSMD-FM broadcasts to the Mechanicsville, MD area at 98.3 FM.

WSME-AM
Owner: B&M Broadcasting LLC
Editorial: 410 New Bridge St Ste 3B, Jacksonville, North Carolina 28540-4759.
T: 1 910 346-2248 **E:** wsme1120@yahoo.com
W: http://www.ctc-media.com
Editorial Profile: WSME-AM is a commercial station owned by B&M Broadcasting LLC. The format of the station is oldies. WSME-AM broadcasts to the New Bern, NC area at a frequency of 1120 AM.

WSM-FM
Owner: Cumulus Media Inc.
Editorial: 506 2nd Ave S, Nashville, Tennessee 37210-2002. **T:** 1 615 321-1067
W: http://www.955thewolf.com
Editorial Profile: WSM-FM is a commercial station owned by Cumulus Media Inc. The format of the station is contemporary country music. WSM-FM broadcasts to the Nashville, TN area at 95.5 FM.

WSMG-AM
Owner: Radio Greeneville Inc.
Editorial: 1004 Arnold Rd, Greeneville, Tennessee 37743. **T:** 1 423 638-3188
E: wsmg@greeneville.com
W: http://www.greeneville.com/wsmg
Editorial Profile: WSMG-AM is a commercial station owned by Radio Greeneville Inc. The format of the station is oldies music. WSMG-AM broadcasts to the Greenville, TN area at 1450 AM.

WSMI-AM
Owner: Talley Broadcasting Corp.
Editorial: 6308 Illinois Route 16, Hillsboro, Illinois 62049. **T:** 1 217 324-5921
E: news@wsmiradio.com
W: http://www.wsmiradio.com
Editorial Profile: WSMI-AM is a commercial station owned by Talley Broadcasting Corp. The format of the station is classic country and talk. WSMI-AM broadcasts to the Litchfield, IL area at 1540 AM.

WSMI-FM
Owner: Talley Broadcasting Corp.
Editorial: 6308 Illinois Route 16, Hillsboro, Illinois 62049-3419. **T:** 1 217 324-5921
E: wsmi@wsmiradio.com
W: http://www.wsmiradio.com
Editorial Profile: WSMI-FM is a commercial station owned by Talley Broadcasting Corp. The format of the station is contemporary country. WSMI-FM broadcasts in the Litchfield, IL area at 106.1 FM.

WSMK-FM
Owner: Williams (Marion R.)
Editorial: 925 N 5th St, Niles, Michigan 49120. **T:** 1 269 683-4343
Editorial Profile: WSMK-FM is a commercial station owned by Marion R. Williams. The format of the station is rhythmic adult contemporary music. WSMK-FM broadcasts to the South Bend, IN area at 99.1 FM.

WSML-AM
Owner: Curtis Media Group
Editorial: 875 W 5th St, Winston Salem, North Carolina 27101-2505. **T:** 1 336 777-3900
W: http://www.triadsports.com
Editorial Profile: WSML-AM is a commercial station owned by Curtis Media Group. The format of the station is sports. WSML-AM broadcasts to the Greensboro-Winston Salem, NC area at 600 AM.

WSMM-FM
Owner: Artistic Media Partners Inc.
Editorial: 3371 W Cleveland Road Ext, Ste 300, South Bend, Indiana 46628.
T: 1 574 273-9300
W: http://www.stream1023.com
Editorial Profile: WSMM-FM is a commercial station owned by Artistic Media Partners Inc. The format of the station is oldies. WSMM-FM broadcasts to South Bend, IN area at 102.3 FM.

WSMN-AM
Owner: Absolute Broadcasting, LLC
Editorial: 149 Main St, Ste 210, Nashua, New Hampshire 03060-2725. **T:** 1 603 880-9001
E: info@wsmnradio.com
W: http://www.wsmnradio.com
Editorial Profile: WSMN-AM is a commercial station owned by Absolute Broadcasting, LLC. The format of the station is talk. WSMN-AM broadcasts to the Nashua, NH area at 1590 AM.

WSMO-FM
Owner: Smile FM
Editorial: 148 E Grand River Rd, Williamston, Michigan 48895-8400. **T:** 1 888 887-7139
E: 411@smile.fm **W:** http://www.smile.fm
Editorial Profile: WSMO-FM is a non-commercial station owned by Smile FM. The format of the station is contemporary Christian music. WSMO-FM broadcasts to the Mount Forest, MI area at 91.9 FM.

WSMS-FM
Owner: Cumulus Media Inc.
Editorial: 200 6th St N, Ste 205, Columbus, Mississippi 39701. **T:** 1 662 327-1183
W: http://www.999thefoxrocks.com

WSMT-AM
Owner: Peg Broadcasting, LLC
Editorial: 520 N Spring St, Sparta, Tennessee 38583-1305. **T:** 1 931 836-1055
W: http://www.1050wsmt.com
Editorial Profile: WSMT-AM is a commercial station owned by Peg Broadcasting, LLC. The format of the station is gospel music. WSMT-AM broadcasts to the Sparta, TN area at 1050 AM.

WSMW-FM
Owner: Entercom Communications Corp.
Editorial: 7819 National Service Rd, Ste 401, Greensboro, North Carolina 27409.
T: 1 336 605-5200
W: http://www.987simon.com
Editorial Profile: WSMW-FM is a commercial station owned by Entercom Communications Corp. The format of the station is adult hits. WSMW-FM broadcasts to the Greensboro-Winston Salem, NC area at 98.7 FM.

WSMX-AM
Owner: Truth Broadcasting
Editorial: 4405 Providence Ln, Winston Salem, North Carolina 27106.
T: 1 336 768-0050
W: http://www.radiolamovidita.com
Editorial Profile: WSMX-AM is owned by Truth Broadcasting in local marketing agreement with La Movidita Inc.

WSMY-AM
Owner: First Media Radio LLC
Editorial: 3 E 1st St, Weldon, North Carolina 27890-1560. **T:** 1 252 536-3115
Editorial Profile: WSMY-AM is a commercial station owned by First Media Radio LLC. The format of the station is sports talk. WSMY-AM broadcasts to the Weldon, NC area at 1400 AM.

WSNC-FM
Owner: Winston-Salem State University
Editorial: 601 S Martin Luther King Jr Dr, Winston Salem, North Carolina 27110-0003.
T: 1 336 750-2321
W: http://www.wsncradio.org
Editorial Profile: WSNC-FM is a non-commercial station owned by Winston-Salem State University. The format of WSNC-FM is jazz music and talk. WSNC-FM broadcasts to the Greensboro-Winston Salem, NC area at 90.5 FM.

WSND-FM
Owner: University of Notre Dame
Editorial: 315 Lafortune Student Ctr, Notre Dame, Indiana 46556. **T:** 1 574 631-4069
E: wsnd@nd.edu **W:** http://www.nd.edu/~wsnd
Editorial Profile: WSND-FM is a non-commercial station owned by University of Notre Dame. The format for the station is classical and college variety. WSND-FM broadcasts to the South Bend, IN area at 88.9 FM.

WSNE-FM
Owner: Clear Channel Media and Entertainment
Editorial: 75 Oxford St, Providence, Rhode Island 02905-4722. **T:** 1 401 781-9979
E: feedback@coast933.com
W: http://www.coast933.com
Editorial Profile: WSNE-FM is a commercial station owned by Clear Channel Media and Entertainment. The format of the station is hot adult contemporary. WSNE-FM broadcasts to the Providence, RI area at 93.3 FM.

WSNG-AM
Owner: Connoisseur Media
Editorial: 869 Blue Hills Ave, Bloomfield, Connecticut 06002-3710. **T:** 1 860 243-1115
W: http://www.talkofconnecticut.com
Editorial Profile: WSNG-AM is a commercial station owned by Connoisseur Media. The format of the station is talk. WSNG-AM broadcasts to the Bloomfield, CT area at 610 AM.

WSNI-FM
Owner: Saga Communications
Editorial: 69 Stanhope Ave, Keene, New Hampshire 03431-1577. **T:** 1 603 352-9230
W: http://www.sunnykeene.com
Editorial Profile: WSNI-FM is a commercial station owned by Saga Communications. The format of the station is adult contemporary. WSNI-FM broadcasts to the Keene, NH area at 97.7 FM.

WSNJ-AM
Owner: Quinn Communications and Marketing, LLC
Editorial: 1771 S Burlington Rd, Bridgeton, New Jersey 08302-4303. **T:** 1 856 327-8800
E: information@wsnjam.com
W: http://www.wsnjam.com
Editorial Profile: WSNJ-AM is a commercial station owned by Quinn Communications and Marketing, LLC. The format of the station is variety. WSNJ-AM broadcasts to the Bridgeton, NJ area at 1240 AM.

WSNL-AM
Owner: Christian Broadcasting System
Editorial: 5210 S Saginaw Rd, Flint, Michigan 48507. **T:** 1 810 694-4146
E: info@cbslradio.com
W: http://www.cbslradio.com
Editorial Profile: WSNL-AM is a commercial station owned by Christian Broadcasting System. The format of the station is contemporary Christian music and religious programming. WSNL-AM broadcasts to the Grand Blanc, MI area at 1500 AM.

WSNN-FM
Owner: Martz Communications
Editorial: 7064 US Highway 11, Potsdam, New York 13676-3197. **T:** 1 315 265-5510
E: hits@99hits.com **W:** http://www.99hits.com
Editorial Profile: WSNN-FM is a commercial station owned by Martz Communications. The format of the station is country music. WSNN-FM broadcasts to the Potsdam, NY area at 99.3 FM.

WSNO-AM
Owner: Great Eastern Radio, LLC
Editorial: 41 Jacques St, Barre, Vermont 05641-5320. **T:** 1 802 476-4168
W: http://www.wsno1450.com
Editorial Profile: WSNO-AM is a commercial station owned by Great Eastern Radio, LLC. The format of the station is news, talk and sports. WSNO-AM broadcasts to the Barre, VT area at 1450 AM.

WSNQ-FM
Owner: Equity Communications LP
Editorial: 8025 Black Horse Pike, Pleasantville, New Jersey 08232-2900. **T:** 1 609 484-8444
W: http://www.951wayv.com/
Editorial Profile: WSNQ-FM is a commercial station owned by Equity Communications LP. The format of the station is Top 40/CHR. WSNQ-FM broadcasts to the Ocean City, NJ area at 105.5 FM.

WSNR-AM
Owner: Blackstrap Broadcasting LLC
Editorial: 2508 Coney Island Ave Floor 2, Brooklyn, New York 11223-5026.
T: 1 516 431-6662
Editorial Profile: WSNR-AM is a commercial station owned by Blackstrap Broadcasting LLC. The format of the station is variety. WSNR-AM broadcasts to the New York City area at 620 AM.

WSNT-AM
Owner: WSNT Inc.
Editorial: 312 Morningside Dr, Sandersville, Georgia 31082. **T:** 1 478 552-5182
E: sales@waco100fm.com
W: http://www.waco100fm.com
Editorial Profile: WSNT-AM in a commercial station owned by WSNT Inc. The format of the station is classic country. WSNT-AM broadcasts to the Atlanta area at 1490 AM.

WSNT-FM
Owner: WSNT Inc.
Editorial: 312 Morningside Dr, Sandersville, Georgia 31082. **T:** 1 478 552-5182
W: http://www.realcountryonline.com
Editorial Profile: WSNT-FM is a commercial station owned by WSNT Inc. The format of the station is country. WNST-FM broadcasts to the Sandersville, GA area at 99.9 FM.

WSNU-FM
Owner: Schlesinger Communications
Editorial: 21 E Main St, Lock Haven, Pennsylvania 17745-1303. **T:** 1 570 748-4038
E: wbpz@kcnet.org
Editorial Profile: WSNU-FM is a commercial station owned by Lipez Broadcasting Co. The format of the station is adult contemporary music. WSNU-FM broadcasts to the Lock Haven, PA area at 92.1 FM.

WSNV-FM
Owner: Clear Channel Media and Entertainment
Editorial: 3807 Brandon Ave SW, Ste 2350, Roanoke, Virginia 24018. **T:** 1 540 725-1220
W: http://www.mysunnyfm.com
Editorial Profile: WSNV-FM is a commercial station owned by Clear Channel Media and Entertainment. The format of the station is classic hits. WSNV-FM broadcasts to the Roanoke, VA area at 93.5 FM.

WSNW-AM
Owner: Georgia-Carolina Radiocasting Companies LLC
Editorial: 103 Ram Cat Aly, Seneca, South Carolina 29678-3243. **T:** 1 864 882-9769
W: http://wsnwradio.com
Editorial Profile: WSNW-AM is a commercial station owned by Georgia-Carolina Radiocasting Companies LLC. The format of the station is adult contemporary. WSNW-AM broadcasts to the Seneca, SC area at 1150 AM.

WSNX-FM
Owner: Clear Channel Media and Entertainment
Editorial: 77 Monroe Center St NW, Grand Rapids, Michigan 49503-2903.
T: 1 616 459-1919

W: http://www.1045snx.com/main.html
Editorial Profile: WSNX-FM is a commercial station owned by Clear Channel Media and Entertainment. The format of the station is Top 40/CHR. WSNX-FM broadcasts to the Grand Rapids, MI area at 104.5 FM.

WSNY-FM
Owner: Saga Communications
Editorial: 4401 Carriage Hill Ln, Columbus, Ohio 43220. **T:** 1 614 451-2191
W: http://www.sunny95.com
Editorial Profile: WSNY-FM is a commercial station owned by Saga Communications. The format of the station is adult contemporary music. WSNY-FM broadcasts to the Columbus, OH area at 94.7 FM.

WSNZ-FM
Owner: Clear Channel Media and Entertainment
Editorial: 3807 Brandon Ave Sw Ste 2350, Roanoke, Virginia 24018-1477.
T: 1 540 725-1220
W: http://www.1061stevefm.com
Editorial Profile: WSNZ-FM is a commercial station owned by Clear Channel Media and Entertainment. The format of the station is adult hits. WSNZ-FM broadcasts to the Lynchburg, VA area at 101.7 FM.

WSOC-FM
Owner: CBS Radio
Editorial: 1520 South Blvd, Charlotte, North Carolina 28203-4786. **T:** 1 704 522-1103
W: http://thenew1037.cbslocal.com
Editorial Profile: WSOC-FM is a commercial station owned by CBS Radio. The format of the station is country. WSOC-FM broadcasts to the Charlotte, NC area at 103.7 FM.

WSOF-FM
Owner: Madisonville Christian Schools
Editorial: 1415 Island Ford Rd, Madisonville, Kentucky 42431. **T:** 1 270 825-3004
E: comments@wsof.org
W: http://www.wsof.org
Editorial Profile: WSOF-FM is a non-commercial station owned by Madisonville Christian Schools. The format of the station is Southern gospel music and religious programming. WSOF-FM broadcasts to the Madisonville, KY area at 89.9 FM.

WSOK-AM
Owner: Clear Channel Media and Entertainment
Editorial: 245 Alfred St, Savannah, Georgia 31408. **T:** 1 912 964-7794
W: http://www.1230wsok.com
Editorial Profile: WSOK-AM is a commercial station owned by Clear Channel Media and Entertainment. The format of the station is gospel. WSOK-AM broadcasts to the Savannah, GA area at 1230 AM.

WSOL-FM
Owner: Clear Channel Media and Entertainment
Editorial: 11700 Central Pkwy, Jacksonville, Florida 32224. **T:** 1 904 636-0507
W: http://www.v1015.com
Editorial Profile: WSOL-FM is a commercial station owned by Clear Channel Media and Entertainment. The format of the station is urban adult contemporary music. WSOL-FM broadcasts to the Jacksonville, FL area at 101.5 FM.

WSOM-AM
Owner: Cumulus Media Inc.
Editorial: 4040 Simon Rd, Youngstown, Ohio 44512. **T:** 1 330 783-1000
W: http://www.600wsom.com
Editorial Profile: WSOM-AM is a commercial station owned by Cumulus Media Inc. The format of the station is news/talk. WSOM-AM broadcasts to the Youngstown, OH area at 600 AM.

WSON-AM
Owner: Henson Media of Henderson County, LLC
Editorial: 230 2nd St, Henderson, Kentucky 42420. **T:** 1 270 826-3923
E: wson@insightbb.com

WSOO-AM
Owner: Sovereign Communications LLC
Editorial: 1411 Ashmun St, Sault Sainte Marie, Michigan 49783. **T:** 1 906 632-2231
E: info@rock101.net
W: http://www.1230wsoo.com

WSOS-AM
Owner: Geddings, Kevin
Editorial: 3000 N Ponce De Leon Blvd, Saint Augustine, Florida 32084-8602.
T: 1 904 495-1370
W: http://staugustineradio.com
Editorial Profile: WSOS-AM is a commercial station owned by Geddings, Kevin. The format of the station is oldies. WSOS-AM broadcasts to the St. Augustine, FL area at 1170 AM.

WSOS-FM
Owner: Renda Broadcasting
Editorial: 6440 Atlantic Blvd, Jacksonville, Florida 32211. **T:** 1 904 824-0833
W: http://www.classicrock941.com
Editorial Profile: WSOS-FM is a commercial station owned by Renda Broadcasting. The format of the station is classic rock. WSOS-FM broadcasts to the Jacksonville, FL area at 94.1 FM.

WSOU-FM
Owner: Seton Hall University
Editorial: 400 S Orange Ave, South Orange, New Jersey 7079. **T:** 1 973 761-9768
E: wsounews@gmail.com
W: http://www.wsou.net
Editorial Profile: WSOU-FM is non-commercial station owned by Seton Hall University. The format of the station is modern active rock music. WSOU-FM broadcasts to the South Orange, NJ area at 89.5 FM.

WSOX-FM
Owner: Cumulus Media Inc.
Editorial: 5989 Susquehanna Plaza Drive, York, Pennsylvania 17406-8910.
T: 1 717 764-1155
W: http://www.961wsox.com
Editorial Profile: WSOX-FM is a commercial station owned by Cumulus Media Inc. The format of the station is classic hits. WSOX-FM broadcasts to the York, PA area at 96.1 FM.

WSOY-AM
Owner: Neuhoff Communications
Editorial: 250 N Water St, Ste 100, Decatur, Illinois 62523. **T:** 1 217 877-5371
E: news@wsoyam.com
W: http://www.wsoyam.com
Editorial Profile: WSOY-AM a commercial station owned by Neuhoff Communications. The format of the station is news and talk. WSOY-AM broadcasts to the Decatur, IL area at 1340 AM.

WSOY-FM
Owner: Neuhoff Communications
Editorial: 250 N Water St, Ste 100, Decatur, Illinois 62523. **T:** 1 217 877-5371
E: news@wsoyam.com
W: http://www.y103.com
Editorial Profile: WSOY-FM is a commercial station owned by Neuhoff Communications. The format of the station is Top 40/CHR music. WSOY-FM broadcasts to Decatur, IL at 102.9 FM.

WSPA-FM
Owner: Entercom Communications Corp.
Editorial: 25 Garlington Rd, Greenville, South Carolina 29615-4613. **T:** 1 864 271-9200
W: http://www.magic989online.com
Editorial Profile: WSPA-FM is a commercial station owned by Entercom Communications Corp. The format for the station is adult contemporary. WSPA-FM broadcasts to the Greenville, SC area at 98.9 FM.

WSPC-AM
Owner: Stanly Communications Inc.
Editorial: 1234 Magnolia St, Albemarle, North Carolina 28001. **T:** 1 704 983-1580
E: wspc@ctc.net
W: http://www.1010wspc.com
Editorial Profile: WSPC-AM is a commercial station owned by Stanly Communications Inc. The format of the station is news and talk. WSPC-AM broadcasts to the Albemarle, NC area at 1010 AM.

WSPD-AM
Owner: Clear Channel Media and Entertainment
Editorial: 125 S Superior St, Toledo, Ohio 43604-8790. **T:** 1 419 244-8321
E: toledonewsroom@clearchannel.com
W: http://www.wspd.com
Editorial Profile: WSPD-AM is a commercial station owned by Clear Channel Media and Entertainment. The format of the station is news and talk. WSPD-AM broadcasts to the Toledo, OH area at 1370 AM.

WSPK-FM
Owner: Pamal Broadcasting Ltd.
Editorial: 715 Route 52, Beacon, New York 12508-1047. **T:** 1 845 838-6000
W: http://www.k104online.com
Editorial Profile: WSPK-FM is a commercial station owned by Pamal Broadcasting Ltd. The format of the station is Top 40/CHR. WSPK-FM broadcasts to the Beacon, NY area on 104.7 FM.

WSPL-AM
Owner: Mendota Broadcasting
Editorial: Highway 23 North, Streator, Illinois 61364. **T:** 1 815 672-2947
E: news@theradiogroup.net
W: http://www.am1250wspl.com
Editorial Profile: WSPL-AM is a commercial station owned by Mendota Broadcasting. The format of the station is news, talk and sports programming. WSPL-AM broadcasts to the Streator, IL area at 1250 AM.

WSPM-FM
Owner: Inter Mifica, Inc.
Editorial: 3500 Depauw Blvd Ste 2085, Indianapolis, Indiana 46268-6103.
T: 1 317 870-8400 21
E: info@catholicradioindy.org
W: http://www.catholicradioindy.org
Editorial Profile: WSPM-FM is a non-commercial station owned by Inter Mifica, Inc. The format of the station is Catholic teaching programming. WSPM-FM broadcasts to the Indianapolis, IN area at 89.1 FM.

WSPN-FM
Owner: Skidmore College
Editorial: 815 N Broadway, Saratoga Springs, New York 12866. **T:** 1 518 580-5787
E: wspn@skidmore.edu
W: http://www.skidmore.edu/studentorgs/wspn/

WSPO-AM
Owner: Apex Broadcasting Inc.
Editorial: 2294 Clements Ferry Rd, Charleston, South Carolina 29492-7729.
T: 1 843 972-1100
E: cvi@apexbroadcasting.com
W: http://www.charlestonvisitorinfo.com
Editorial Profile: WSPO-AM is a commercial station owned by Apex Broadcasting Inc. The format of the station is travel information. WSPO-AM broadcasts to the Charleston, SC area at 1390 AM.

WSPQ-AM
Owner: Hawk Communications Ltd.
Editorial: 51 Franklin St, Springville, New York 14141-1340. **T:** 1 716 592-1330
E: wspq1330@yahoo.com
W: http://wspq1330.com
Editorial Profile: WSPQ-AM is a commercial station owned by Hawk Communications Ltd. The format of the station is classic hits music. WSPQ-AM broadcasts to the Springville, NY area at 1330 AM.

WSPR-AM
Owner: Davidson Media Group
Editorial: 34 Sylvan St, West Springfield, Massachusetts 1089. **T:** 1 413 781-5200
W: http://www.wsprpower1270.com
Editorial Profile: WSPR-AM is a commercial station owned by Davidson Media Group. The format of the station is Hispanic tropical. WSPR-AM broadcasts to the West Springfield, MA area at 1270 AM.

WSPS-FM
Owner: St. Paul's School
Editorial: 325 Pleasant St, Concord, New Hampshire 3301. **T:** 1 603 230-5810
E: wsps@sps.edu **W:** http://wsps.sps.edu

WSPT-AM
Owner: Muzzy Broadcasting
Editorial: 500 Division St, Stevens Point, Wisconsin 54481. **T:** 1 715 342-1010
W: http://www.1010wspt.com
Editorial Profile: WSPT-AM is a commercial station owned by Muzzy Broadcasting. The format of the station is news, talk and oldies. WSPT-AM broadcasts to the Stevens Point, WI area at 1010 AM.

WSPT-FM
Owner: Muzzy Broadcasting
Editorial: 500 Division St, Stevens Point, Wisconsin 54481. **T:** 1 715 341-1300
W: http://www.979wspt.com
Editorial Profile: WSPT-FM is a commercial station owned by Muzzy Broadcasting. The format of the station is oldies. WSPT-FM broadcasts in the Stevens Point, WI area at 97.9 FM.

WSPX-FM
Owner: Glory Communications Inc.
Editorial: 1236 Five Chop Rd, Orangeburg, South Carolina 29115. **T:** 1 803 539-9450
E: wspx@sc.rr.com **W:** http://www.wfmv.com
Editorial Profile: WSPX-FM is a commercial station owned by Glory Communications Inc. The format of the station is gospel. WSPX-FM broadcasts to the Orangeburg, SC area at 97.5 FM.

WSPY-AM
Owner: Nelson Enterprises Inc.
Editorial: 1 Broadcast Ctr, Plano, Illinois 60545-2100. **T:** 1 630 552-1000
W: http://www.wspyfm.com/nelson/index.html
Editorial Profile: WSPY-AM is a commercial station owned by Nelson Enterprises Inc. The format of the station is classic hits. WSPY-AM broadcasts to the Plano, IL area at 1480 FM.

WSPY-FM
Owner: Nelson Enterprises Inc.
Editorial: 1 Broadcast Ctr, Plano, Illinois 60545-2100. **T:** 1 630 552-1000
W: http://wspyfm.com
Editorial Profile: WSPY-FM is a commercial station owned by Nelson Enterprises Inc. The format of the station is Lite Rock/Lite AC. WSPY-FM broadcasts to the Plano, IL area at 107.1 FM.

WSPZ-AM
Owner: Red Zebra Broadcasting
Editorial: 1801 Rockville Pike, Ste 405, Rockville, Maryland 20852. **T:** 1 301 230-3500
W: http://www.sportstalk570.com
Editorial Profile: WSPZ-AM is a commercial station owned by Red Zebra Broadcasting. The format of the station is sports/talk. WSPZ-AM broadcasts to the Silver Spring, MD area at 570 AM. The station is affiliated with ESPN Radio.

WSQL-AM
Owner: Go Nuts Media
Editorial: 62 W Main St, Brevard, North Carolina 28712. **T:** 1 828 877-5252
E: info@wsqlradio.com
W: http://www.wsqlradio.com
Editorial Profile: WSQL-AM is a commercial station owned by Go Nuts Media. The format for the station is variety. WSQL-AM broadcasts to the Brevard, NC area at 1240 AM.

WSQR-AM
Owner: DeKalb County Broadcasters Inc.
Editorial: 1 Broadcast Ctr, Plano, Illinois 60545-2100. **T:** 1 815 899-1000
W: http://www.wspyfm.com/nelson
Editorial Profile: WSQR-AM is a commercial station owned by DeKalb County Broadcasters Inc. The format of the station is classic hits. WSQR-AM broadcasts to the Sycamore, IL area at 1180 AM.

WSQX-FM
Owner: WSKG Public Telecommunications
Editorial: 601 Gates Rd, Vestal, New York 13850. **T:** 1 607 729-0100 **E:** mail@wskg.org
W: http://www.wskg.com
Editorial Profile: WSQX-FM is a non-commercial station owned by WSKG Public Telecommunications. The format of the station is educational and news. WSQX-FM broadcasts to the Binghamton, NY area at 91.5 FM.

WSRA-AM
Owner: Fulton (Livingston)
Editorial: 2804 N Jefferson St, Albany, Georgia 31701. **T:** 1 229 228-5051
W: http://www.wsraradio.com
Editorial Profile: WSRA-AM is a commercial station owned by Livingston Fulton. The format of the station is sports. WSRA-AM broadcasts to the Albany, GA area at 1250 AM.

WSRB-FM
Owner: Crawford Broadcasting Co.
Editorial: 6336 Calumet Ave, Hammond, Indiana 46324-1243. **T:** 1 219 933-4455
W: http://www.soul1063radio.com
Editorial Profile: WSRB-FM is a commercial station owned by Crawford Broadcasting Co. The format of the station is urban contemporary and R&B. WSRB-FM broadcasts to the Chicago area at 106.3 FM.

WSRF-AM
Owner: Niche Radio Inc.
Editorial: 1510 NE 162nd St, North Miami Beach, Florida 33162. **T:** 1 305 940-1580
E: info@wsrf.com **W:** http://www.wsrf.com
Editorial Profile: WSRF-AM is a commercial station owned by Niche Radio Inc. The station

follows an ethnic brokered format. WSRF-AM broadcasts to the Miami area at 1580 AM.

WSRG-FM
Owner: Al Johnson Broadcasting LLC
Editorial: 1009 Egg Harbor Rd, Sturgeon Bay, Wisconsin 54235-1200. **T:** 1 920 743-6677
E: buzz@977thebigdawg.com
W: http://www.977thebigdawg.com
Editorial Profile: WSRG-AM is a commercial station owned by Al Johnson Broadcasting LLC. The format of the station is contemporary country. WSRG-FM broadcasts to the Sturgeon Bay, WI area at 97.7 FM.

WSRJ-FM
Owner: Northern Broadcast Inc.
Editorial: 1020 Hastings St Ste 102, Traverse City, Michigan 49686-3457. **T:** 1 231 947-0003
W: http://www.espnradionorthernmichigan.com
Editorial Profile: WSRJ-FM is a commercial station owned by Northern Broadcast Inc. The format of the station is sports. WSRJ-FM broadcasts to the Traverse City, MI area on 105.5 FM.

WSRK-FM
Owner: Townsquare Media, LLC
Editorial: 34 Chestnut St, Oneonta, New York 13820-2466. **T:** 1 607 432-1030
E: cnynews@townsquaremedia.com
W: http://wsrkfm.com
Editorial Profile: WSRK-FM is a commercial station owned by Townsquare Media, LLC. The format of the station is adult contemporary music. WSRK-FM broadcasts to the Oneonta, NY area at 103.9 FM.

WSRM-FM
Owner: Rome Radio Partners
Editorial: 20 John Davenport Dr NW, Rome, Georgia 30165-2536. **T:** 1 706 291-9496
W: http://southern935.com
Editorial Profile: WSRM-FM is a commercial station owned by Rome Radio Partners. The format of the station is classic country. WSRM-FM broadcasts to the Rome, GA area at 93.5 FM.

WSRN-FM
Owner: Swarthmore College
Editorial: 500 College Ave, Swarthmore, Pennsylvania 19081-1306. **T:** 1 610 328-8335
W: http://www.wsrnfm.org
Editorial Profile: WSRN-FM is a non-commercial station owned by Swarthmore College. The format of the station is college variety. WSRN-FM broadcasts in the Swarthmore, PA area at 91.5 FM.

WSRO-AM
Owner: Langer Broadcasting Group, LLC
Editorial: 100 Mount Wayte Ave, Framingham, Massachusetts 1702. **T:** 1 508 424-2568
W: http://www.wsro.com
Editorial Profile: WSRO-AM is a commercial station owned by Langer Broadcasting Group, LLC. The format of the station features community, religious, news, music and entertainment programming all in Portuguese. WSRO-AM broadcasts to the Framingham, MA area at 650 AM.

WSRQ-AM
Owner: Florida Talk Radio, LLC
Editorial: 3679 Webber St, Sarasota, Florida 34232-4412. **T:** 1 941 952-1220
E: traffic@sarasotatalkradio.com
W: http://www.sarasotatalkradio.com
Editorial Profile: WSRQ-AM is a commercial station owned by Florida Talk Radio, LLC. The format of the station is talk. WSRQ-AM broadcasts to the Sarasota, FL area at 1220 AM.

WSRS-FM
Owner: Clear Channel Media and Entertainment
Editorial: 96 Stereo Ln, Paxton, Massachusetts 01612-1376.
T: 1 508 757-9696 **W:** http://www.wsrs.com
Editorial Profile: WSRS-FM is a commercial station owned by Clear Channel Media and Entertainment. The format of the station is adult contemporary. WSRS-FM broadcasts to the Paxton, MA area at 96.1 FM.

WSRT-FM
Owner: Northern Broadcast Inc.
Editorial: 1020 Hastings St Ste 102, Traverse City, Michigan 49686-3457. **T:** 1 231 947-0003
W: http://www.espnradionorthernmichigan.com
Editorial Profile: WSRT-FM is a commercial station owned by Northern Broadcast Inc. The format of the station is sports. WSRT-FM broadcasts to the Traverse City, MI area at 106.7 FM.

WSRV-FM
Owner: Cox Media Group, Inc.
Editorial: 1601 W Peachtree St NE, Atlanta, Georgia 30309-2641. **T:** 1 404 897-7500
W: http://www.971theriver.com
Editorial Profile: WSRV-FM is a commercial station owned by Cox Media Group, Inc. The format of the station is classic hits. WSRV-FM broadcasts to the Atlanta area at 97.1 FM.

WSRW-AM
Owner: Clear Channel Media and Entertainment
Editorial: 5675 State Route 247, Hillsboro, Ohio 45133-7328. **T:** 1 937 393-1590
W: http://www.buckeyecountry105.com/main.html
Editorial Profile: WSRW-AM is a commercial station owned by Clear Channel Media and Entertainment. The format of the station is contemporary country. WSRW-AM broadcasts to the Hillsboro, OH area at 1590 AM.

WSRW-FM
Owner: Clear Channel Media and Entertainment
Editorial: 77 Monroe Center St NW, Ste 1000, Grand Rapids, Michigan 49503-2912.
T: 1 616 459-1919
W: http://www.star1057online.com
Editorial Profile: WSRW-FM is a commercial station owned by Clear Channel Media and Entertainment. The format of the station is adult contemporary. WSRW-FM broadcasts to the Grand Rapids, MI area 105.7 FM.

WSRY-AM
Owner: Priority Radio, Inc.
Editorial: 179 Stanton Christiana Rd, Newark, Delaware 19702-1619. **T:** 1 302 731-0690
Editorial Profile: WSRY-AM is a commercial station owned by World Revivals Inc. The format of the station is sports talk. WSRY-AM broadcasts to the Newark, DE area at 1550 AM.

WSRZ-FM
Owner: Clear Channel Media and Entertainment
Editorial: 1779 Independence Blvd, Sarasota, Florida 34234-2106. **T:** 1 941 552-4800
W: http://www.oldies108.com
Editorial Profile: WSRZ-FM is a commercial station owned by Clear Channel Media and Entertainment. The format of the station is Classic Hits. WSRZ-FM broadcasts in the Tampa Bay, FL area at 107.9 FM.

WSSB-FM
Owner: South Carolina State University
Editorial: 300 College Ave, Orangeburg, South Carolina 29115-4427. **T:** 1 803 536-8196
E: wssb@scsu.edu
W: http://www.wssb903fm.org
Editorial Profile: WSSB-FM is a non-commercial station owned by South Carolina State University. The forma of the station is Jazz and R&B. WSSB-FM broadcasts to the Orangeburg, SC area on 90.3 FM.

WSSC-AM
Owner: Sumter Baptist Temple Inc.
Editorial: 201 Oswego Road, Sumter, South Carolina 29150-4431. **T:** 1 803 469-0288
Editorial Profile: WSSC-AM is a commercial station owned by Sumter Baptist Temple Inc. The format of the station is Christian programming. WSSC-AM broadcasts to the Sumter, SC area at 1340 AM.

WSSD-FM
Owner: Lakeside Telecommunications
Editorial: 515 W 111th St, Chicago, Illinois 60628. **T:** 1 773 928-8800
E: wssdthemusicstation@yahoo.com
Editorial Profile: WSSD-FM is a non-commercial station owned by Lakeside Telecommunications. The station's format is variety. WSSD-FM broadcasts to the Chicago area at 88.1 FM.

WSSG-AM
Owner: Curtis Media Group
Editorial: 2581 US Highway 70 W, Goldsboro, North Carolina 27530-9553.
T: 1 919 736-1150
W: http://goldsborodailynews.com
Editorial Profile: WSSG-AM is a commercial station owned by Curtis Media Group, dba Eastern Airwaves LLC. The format of the station is gospel. WSSG-AM broadcasts to the Goldsboro, NC area at 1300 AM.

WSSL-FM
Owner: Clear Channel Media and Entertainment
Editorial: 101 N Main St, Ste 1000, Greenville, South Carolina 29601. **T:** 1 864 242-1005
W: http://www.wsslfm.com
Editorial Profile: WSSL-FM is a commercial station owned by Clear Channel Media and Entertainment. The format for the station is contemporary country. WSSL-FM broadcasts to the Greenville, SC area at 100.5 FM.

WSSO-AM
Owner: Cumulus Media Inc.
Editorial: 200 6th St N, Ste 205, Columbus, Mississippi 39701. **T:** 1 662 327-1183
Editorial Profile: WSSO-AM is a commercial station owned by Cumulus Media Inc. The format of the station is news, sports and talk. WSSO-AM broadcasts to the Columbus, MS area at 1230 AM.

WSSP-AM
Owner: Entercom Communications Corp.
Editorial: 11800 W Grange Ave, Hales Corners, Wisconsin 53130-1035.
T: 1 414 529-1250
E: live@sportsradio1250.com
W: http://www.sportsradio1250.com
Editorial Profile: WSSP-AM is a commercial station owned by Entercom Communications Corp. The format of the station is sports. WSSP-AM broadcasts to the Milwaukee area at 1250 AM.

WSSQ-FM
Owner: Withers Broadcasting Co.
Editorial: 3101 Freeport Rd, Sterling, Illinois 61081-8612. **T:** 1 815 625-3400
E: wsdr1240@theramp.net
Editorial Profile: WSSQ-FM is a commercial station owned by Withers Broadcasting Co. The format of the station is adult contemporary. WSSQ-FM broadcasts to the Sterling, IL area at 94.3 FM.

WSSR-FM
Owner: Digity LLC
Editorial: 2410 Caton Farm Rd Unit B, Crest Hill, Illinois 60403-1374. **T:** 1 815 556-0100
W: http://www.star967.net
Editorial Profile: WSSR-FM is a commercial station owned by Digity LLC . The format of the station is adult contemporary music. WSSR-FM broadcasts to the Crest Hill, IL area at 96.7 FM.

WSSX-FM
Owner: Cumulus Media Inc.
Editorial: 4230 Faber Place Dr Ste 100, North Charleston, South Carolina 29405-8512.
T: 1 843 277-1200 **W:** http://www.95sx.com
Editorial Profile: WSSX-FM is a commercial station owned by Cumulus Media Inc. The format of the station is top 40/CHR. WSSX-FM broadcasts to the Charleston, SC area at 95.1 FM.

WSSY-FM
Owner: Georgia Eagle Broadcasting Inc.
Editorial: 218 Eastman Highway, Hawkinsville, Georgia 31036. **T:** 1 478 892-9061
Editorial Profile: WSSY-FM is a commercial station owned by Georgia Eagle Broadcasting Inc. The format of the station is adult standards. WSSY-FM broadcasts to the Cordele, GA area at 98.3 FM.

WSTG-FM
Owner: L & P Broadcasting Inc.
Editorial: 1 Radio Ln, Princeton, West Virginia 24740-2886. **T:** 1 304 425-2152
W: http://www.star95.com
Editorial Profile: WSTG-FM is a commercial station owned and operated by L & P Broadcasting Inc. The format of the station is adult contemporary music. WSTG-FM broadcasts to the Princeton, WV area at 95.9 FM.

WSTH-FM
Owner: Premier Radio Networks
Editorial: 1501 13th Ave, Columbus, Georgia 31901. **T:** 1 706 576-3000
W: http://www.mysouth1061.com
Editorial Profile: WSTH-FM is a commercial station owned by Premier Radio Networks. The format of the station is country. WSTH-FM broadcasts to the Columbus, GA area at 106.1 FM.

WSTI-FM
Owner: Black Crow Broadcasting Inc.
Editorial: 1711 Ellis Dr, Valdosta, Georgia 31601. **T:** 1 229 244-8642
W: http://valdostatoday.com/Star1053.html
Editorial Profile: WSTI-FM is a commercial station owned by Black Crow Broadcasting Inc. The format of the station is urban contemporary music. WSTI-FM broadcasts to Valdosta, GA area at 105.3 FM.

WSTJ-AM
Owner: Vermont Broadcast Associates Inc.
Editorial: 1303 Concord Ave, Saint Johnsbury, Vermont 5819. **T:** 1 802 748-1340
E: wstjstudio@gmail.com
Editorial Profile: WSTJ-AM is a commercial station owned by Vermont Broadcast Associates Inc. The format of the station is adult standards. WSTJ-AM broadcasts to the St. Johnsbury, VT area at 1340 AM.

WSTL-AM
Owner: New England Christian Media Inc.
Editorial: 95 Sagamore Rd, Seekonk, Massachusetts 2771. **T:** 1 508 336-4233
E: info@wstl.us **W:** http://www.wstl.us
Editorial Profile: WSTL-AM is a non-commercial station owned by New England Christian Media Inc. The format of the station is Christian music and talk. WSTL-AM broadcasts to the Seekonk, MA area at 1220 AM.

WSTM-FM
Owner: Jubilation Ministries
Editorial: N 5569 State Highway 57, Plymouth, Wisconsin 53073-4236.
T: 1 920 893-2661 **E:** wstm@jmiradio.org
W: http://www.wstmfm.org
Editorial Profile: WSTM-FM is a non-commercial station owned by Jubliation Ministries. The format of the station is contemporary Christian. WSTM-FM broadcasts to the Plymouth, WI area at 91.3 FM.

WSTO-FM
Owner: South Central Communications Corp.
Editorial: 1162 Mount Auburn Rd, Evansville, Indiana 47720-5428. **T:** 1 812 424-8284
W: http://www.hot96.com
Editorial Profile: WSTO-FM is a commercial station owned by South Central Communications Corp. The format of the station is Top 40/CHR music. WSTO-FM broadcasts to the Evansville, IN area 96.1 FM.

WSTP-AM
Owner: Rowan Media
Editorial: 1105 Statesville Blvd, Salisbury, North Carolina 28144-2232.
T: 1 704 636-3811
E: newsradio1490@yahoo.com
W: http://www.1490wstp.com
Editorial Profile: WSTP-AM is a commercial station owned by Rowan Media. The format of the station is news and talk. WSTP-AM broadcasts to the Salisbury, NC area at 1490 AM.

WSTQ-FM
Owner: Mendota Broadcasting
Editorial: 3905 Progress Blvd, Peru, Illinois 61354-1121. **T:** 1 815 224-2100
E: q@studstillmedia.com
W: http://www.qhitmusic.com
Editorial Profile: WSTQ-FM is a commercial station owned by Mendota Broadcasting. The format of the station is Top 40/CHR. WSTQ-FM broadcasts to the Peru, IL area at 97.7 FM.

WSTR-FM
Owner: Lincoln Financial Media
Editorial: 210 Interstate North Cir SE, Atlanta, Georgia 30339-2206. **T:** 1 404 261-2970
W: http://www.star94.com
Editorial Profile: WSTR-FM is a commercial station owned by Lincoln Financial Media. The format of the station is Top 40/CHR. WSTR-FM broadcasts to the Atlanta area at 94.1 FM.

WSTS-FM
Owner: Davidson Media Group
Editorial: 5448 Hwy 41 S, Fairmont, North Carolina 28340. **T:** 1 910 628-6781
W: http://www.wstsfm.com
Editorial Profile: WSTS-FM is a commercial station owned by Davidson Media Group. The format of the station is Southern gospel. WSTS-FM broadcasts to the Fairmont, NC area at 100.9 FM.

WSTT-AM
Owner: Williams (Marion)
Editorial: 2194 US Highway 319 S, Thomasville, Georgia 31792.
T: 1 229 377-2337 **W:** http://wstt730.com
Editorial Profile: WSTT-AM is a non-commercial station owned by Marion Williams. The format of the station is gospel. WSTT-AM

broadcasts to the Thomasville, GA area at 730 AM.

WSTU-AM

Owner: Treasure Coast Broadcasters
Editorial: 4100 Metzger Rd, Fort Pierce, Florida 34947. **T:** 1 772 340-1590
E: wpsl@wpsl.com
W: http://www.wstu1450.com
Editorial Profile: WSTU-AM is a commercial station owned by Treasure Coast Broadcasters. The format of the station is news, sports and talk. WSTU-AM broadcasts to the Port St. Lucie, FL area at 1450 AM.

WSTV-FM

Owner: Capacity Communications Inc.
Editorial: 115 W Main St, Frankfort, Kentucky 40601. **T:** 1 502 875-1130
W: http://www.star1037.com
Editorial Profile: WSTV-FM is a commercial station owned by Capacity Communications Inc. The format for the station is hot adult contemporary. WSTV-FM broadcasts to the Lexington, KY area at 103.7 FM.

WSTW-FM

Owner: Delmarva Broadcasting
Editorial: 2727 Shipley Rd, Wilmington, Delaware 19810-3299. **T:** 1 302 478-2700
E: wdelnews@wdel.com
W: http://www.wstw.com
Editorial Profile: WSTW-FM is a commercial station owned by Delmarva Broadcasting. The format of the station is Top 40/CHR. WSTW-FM broadcasts to the Wilmington, DE area at 93.7 FM.

WSTZ-FM

Owner: Clear Channel Media and Entertainment
Editorial: 1375 Beasley Rd, Jackson, Mississippi 39206-2018. **T:** 1 601 982-1062
W: http://www.z106.com
Editorial Profile: WSTZ-FM is a commercial station owned by Clear Channel Media and Entertainment. The format of the station is classic rock. WSTZ-FM broadcasts to the Jackson, MS area at 106.7 FM.

WSUA-AM

Owner: Groupo Latino De Ratio (GLR) Networks
Editorial: 2100 Coral Way, Coral Gables, Florida 33145-2635. **T:** 1 305 285-1260
W: http://www.caracol1260.com
Editorial Profile: WSUA-AM is a commercial station owned by Groupo Latino De Ratio (GLR) Networks. The format of the station is Spanish language news talk. WSUA-AM broadcasts to the Miami area at 1260 AM.

WSUE-FM

Owner: Sovereign Communications LLC
Editorial: 1411 Ashmun St, Sault Sainte Marie, Michigan 49783. **T:** 1 906 632-2231
E: webmaster@rock101.net
W: http://www.rock101.net

WSUF-FM

Owner: Sacred Heart University
Editorial: 5151 Park Ave, Fairfield, Connecticut 6825. **T:** 1 203 365-6604 **E:** news@wshu.org
W: http://www.wshu.org
Editorial Profile: WSUF-FM is a non-commercial station owned by Sacred Heart University. The format of the station is news and talk. WSUF-FM broadcasts to the Fairfield, CT area at 89.9 FM.

WSUI-AM

Owner: University of Iowa
Editorial: 710 S Clinton St, Iowa City, Iowa 52240-4214. **T:** 1 319 335-5730
E: news@iowapublicradio.org
W: http://iowapublicradio.org
Editorial Profile: WSUI-AM is a non-commercial station owned by the University of Iowa. The format of the station is news and talk. WSUI-AM broadcasts to the Iowa City, IA area at 910 AM.

WSUL-FM

Owner: Watermark Communications
Editorial: 198 Bridgeville Rd, Monticello, New York 12701. **T:** 1 845 794-9898
W: http://www.wsul.com
Editorial Profile: WSUL-FM is a commercial station owned by Watermark Communications. The format of the station is hot adult contemporary. WSUL-FM broadcasts to the Monticello, NY area at 98.3 FM.

WSUM-FM

Owner: University of Wisconsin

Editorial: 333 East Campus Mall, Ste 4100, Madison, Wisconsin 53715-1365.
T: 1 608 262-1864 **E:** news@wsum.wisc.edu
W: http://www.wsum.org
Editorial Profile: WSUM-FM is a non-commercial station owned by University of Wisconsin. The format of the station is college variety. WSUM-FM broadcasts to the Madison, WI area at 91.7 FM.

WSUN-FM

Owner: Cox Media Group, Inc.
Editorial: 11300 4th St N, Saint Petersburg, Florida 33716-2918. **T:** 1 727 579-2000
E: 97xcomments@97xonline.com
W: http://www.97xonline.com
Editorial Profile: WSUN-FM is a commercial station owned by Cox Media Group, Inc. The format of the station is user generated rock alternative. WSUN-FM broadcasts to the Tampa, FL area at 97.1 FM.

WSUP-FM

Owner: University of Wisconsin
Editorial: 42 Pioneer Tower, 1 University Plaza, Platteville, Wisconsin 53818.
T: 1 608 342-1165
W: http://www.uwplatt.edu/org/wsup/
Editorial Profile: WSUP-FM is a non-commercial college station owned by the University of Wisconsin. The format of the station is AAA. WSUP-FM broadcasts to the Platteville, WI area at 90.5 FM.

WSUS-FM

Owner: Clear Channel Media and Entertainment
Editorial: 45 Ed Mitchell Ave, Franklin, New Jersey 07416-1588. **T:** 1 973 827-2525
W: http://www.wsus1023.com
Editorial Profile: WSUS-FM is a commercial station owned by Clear Channel Media and Entertainment. The format of the station is adult contemporary. WSUS-FM broadcasts to the Franklin, NJ area at 102.3 FM.

WSUW-FM

Owner: University of Wisconsin
Editorial: 800 W Main St, Whitewater, Wisconsin 53190-1705. **T:** 1 262 472-1323
W: http://www.wsuw.org

WSVA-AM

Owner: VerStandig Broadcasting
Editorial: 1820 Heritage Center Way, Harrisonburg, Virginia 22801-8451.
T: 1 540 434-0331 **E:** news@valleyradio.com
W: http://www.wsvaonline.com
Editorial Profile: WSVA-AM is a commercial station owned by VerStandig Broadcasting. The format of the station is news and talk. WVSA-AM broadcasts to the Harrisonburg, VA area at 550 AM. The station does not accept unsolicited faxes. WSVA-AM prefers to receive press inquiries via phone. Do NOT e-mail any staff members.

WSVH-FM

Owner: Georgia Public Broadcasting
Editorial: 13040 Abercorn St Ste 8, Savannah, Georgia 31419-1967. **T:** 1 912 344-3565
E: publicradio@wsvh.org
W: http://www.wsvh.org
Editorial Profile: WSVH-FM is a non-commercial station owned by Georgia Public Broadcasting. The format of the station is classical, jazz and news. WSVH-FM broadcasts to the Savannah, GA area at 91.1 FM.

WSVM-AM

Owner: GHB Broadcasting
Editorial: 1117 Praley St SW, Valdese, North Carolina 28690. **T:** 1 828 874-0000
Editorial Profile: WSVM-AM is a commercial station owned by GHB Broadcasting. The format of the station is adult standards. WSVM-AM broadcasts to the Valdese, NC area at 1490 AM.

WSVO-FM

Owner: Clear Channel Media and Entertainment
Editorial: 207 University Blvd, Harrisonburg, Virginia 22801. **T:** 1 540 434-1777
W: http://www.mixradioonline.com
Editorial Profile: WSVO-FM is a commercial station owned by Clear Channel Media and Entertainment. The format for the station is Lite Rock/Lite AC. WSVO-FM broadcasts to the Harrisonburg, VA area at 93.1 FM.

WSVS-AM

Owner: Gee Communications Inc.
Editorial: 1032 Melody Lane, Crewe, Virginia 23930. **T:** 1 434 645-7734
W: http://www.wsvsam.com

Editorial Profile: WSVS-AM is a commercial station owned by Gee Communications Inc. The format of the station is classic country. WSVS-AM broadcasts to the Crewe, VA area at 800 AM.

WSVU-AM

Owner: North Palm Beach Broadcasting Inc.
Editorial: 8895 N Military Trl Ste 206C, West Palm Beach, Florida 33410-6279.
T: 1 561 627-9966
W: http://www.seaviewam960.com
Editorial Profile: WSVU-AM is a commercial station owned by North Palm Beach Broadcasting Inc. The format of the station is adult standards. WSVU-AM broadcasts to the West Palm Beach, FL area at 960 AM.

WSVX-AM

Owner: 3 Towers Broadcasting LLC
Editorial: 2356 N Morristown Rd, Shelbyville, Indiana 46176-9172. **T:** 1 317 398-2200
W: http://www.wsvx.com
Editorial Profile: WSVX-AM is a commercial station owned by 3 Towers Broadcasting LLC. The format of the station is Top 40/CHR. WSVX-AM broadcasts to the Indianapolis area at 1520 AM.

WSWI-AM

Owner: University of Southern Indiana
Editorial: 8600 University Blvd, Evansville, Indiana 47712-3534. **T:** 1 812 465-1665
W: http://www.820theedge.com

WSWN-AM

Owner: BGI Broadcasting LP
Editorial: 2001 State Road 715, Belle Glade, Florida 33430-1203. **T:** 1 561 996-2063
E: sold935900@yahoo.com
W: http://www.sugar900am.com
Editorial Profile: WSWN-AM is a commercial station owned by BGI Broadcasting LP. The format of the station is gospel music. WSWN-AM broadcasts to the West Palm Beach, FL area at 900 AM.

WSWR-FM

Owner: Clear Channel Media and Entertainment
Editorial: 1400 Radio Ln, Mansfield, Ohio 44906. **T:** 1 419 529-2211
E: cruisin100@clearchannel.com
W: http://www.my1001fm.com
Editorial Profile: WSWR-FM is a commercial station owned by Clear Channel Media and Entertainment. The format of the station is classic hits. WSWR-FM broadcasts to the Mansfield, OH area at 100.1 FM.

WSWT-FM

Owner: L & L Radio
Editorial: 331 Fulton St, Peoria, Illinois 61602-1486. **T:** 1 309 637-3700
E: news@1470wmbd.com
W: http://www.literock107.com
Editorial Profile: WSWT-FM is a commercial station owned by L & L Radio. The format of the station is adult contemporary. WSWT-FM broadcasts to the Peoria, IL area at 106.9 FM.

WSWV-AM

Owner: BC Broadcasting Co. Inc.
Editorial: 282 Westgate Mall Cir, Pennington Gap, Virginia 24277-2879. **T:** 1 276 546-2520
E: sales@wswv.net **W:** http://www.wswv.net
Editorial Profile: WSWV-AM is a commercial station owned by BC Broadcasting Co. Inc. The format of the station is southern gospel music. WSWV-FM broadcasts to the Pennington Gap, VA area at 1570 AM.

WSWV-FM

Owner: BC Broadcasting Co. Inc.
Editorial: 282 Westgate Mall Cir, Pennington Gap, Virginia 24277-2879. **T:** 1 276 546-2520
E: sales@wswv.net **W:** http://www.wswv.net
Editorial Profile: WSWV-FM is a commercial station owned by BC Broadcasting Co. Inc. The format of the station is country music. WSWV-FM broadcasts to the Pennington Gap, VA area at 105.5 FM.

WSWW-AM

Owner: West Virginia Radio Corp.
Editorial: 1111 Virginia St E, Charleston, West Virginia 25301. **T:** 1 304 342-8131
W: http://www.wvradioadvertising.com
Editorial Profile: WSWW-AM is a commercial station owned by West Virginia Radio Corp. The format for the station is sports. WSWW-AM broadcasts to the Charleston-Huntington, WV area at 1490 AM.

WSYB-AM

Owner: Pamal Broadcasting Ltd.

Editorial: 67 Merchants Row, Rutland, Vermont 05701-5910. **T:** 1 802 775-7500
W: http://www.wsyb1380am.com
Editorial Profile: WSYB-AM is a commercial station owned by Pamal Broadcasting Ltd. The format of the station is news, talk and sports. WSYB-AM broadcasts to the Rutland, VT area at 1380 AM.

WSYC-FM

Owner: Shippensburg University
Editorial: 1871 Old Main Dr, Cumberland Union Bldg 2nd Floor, Shippensburg, Pennsylvania 17257-2200. **T:** 1 717 532-6006
E: wsycgm@ship.edu
W: http://clubs.ship.edu/WSYC
Editorial Profile: WSYC-FM is a non-commercial radio station owned by Shippensburg University. The format of the station is college variety. WSYC broadcasts to the Harrisburg, PA are at 88.7-FM.

WSYD-AM

Owner: Granite City Broadcasting Inc.
Editorial: 2147 Springs Rd, Mount Airy, North Carolina 27030-2447. **T:** 1 336 786-2147
W: http://www.wsyd1300.com
Editorial Profile: WSYD-AM is a commercial station owned by Granite City Broadcasting Inc. The format of the station is country and gospel music. WSYD-AM broadcasts to the Greensboro-Winston Salem, NC area at 1300 AM.

WSYE-FM

Owner: Mississippi Radio Group
Editorial: 2214 S Gloster St, Tupelo, Mississippi 38801-6814. **T:** 1 662 842-7658
W: http://www.sunny933fm.com

WSYL-AM

Owner: Georgia Eagle Broadcasting Inc.
Editorial: 561 E Olliff St, Statesboro, Georgia 30458-4663. **T:** 1 912 764-5446
E: wwnswmcd@yahoo.com
Editorial Profile: WSYL-AM is a commercial station owned by Georgia Eagle Broadcasting Inc. The format for the station is oldies. WSYL-AM broadcasts to the Savannah, GA area at 1490 AM.

WSYN-FM

Owner: Cumulus Media Inc.
Editorial: 11640 Highway 17 Byp, Murrells Inlet, South Carolina 29576-9332.
T: 1 843 651-7869 **W:** http://sunny1031.com
Editorial Profile: WSYN-FM is a commercial station owned by Cumulus Media Inc. The format of the station is oldies music. WSYN-FM broadcasts to the Murrells Inlet, SC area at 103.1 FM.

WSYR-AM

Owner: Clear Channel Media and Entertainment
Editorial: 500 Plum St, Syracuse, New York 13204-1496. **T:** 1 315 472-9797
E: wsyrnews@clearchannel.com
W: http://www.570wsyr.com
Editorial Profile: WSYR-AM is a commercial station owned by Clear Channel Media and Entertainment. The format of the station is news and talk. WSYR-AM broadcasts to the Syracuse, NY area at 570 AM. The station airs its programming on WSYR-FM.

WSYR-FM

Owner: Clear Channel Media and Entertainment
Editorial: 500 Plum St, Ste 100, Syracuse, New York 13204. **T:** 1 315 472-9797
E: wsyrnews@clearchannel.com
W: http://www.wsyr.com/main.html
Editorial Profile: WSYR-FM is a commercial station owned by Clear Channel Media and Entertainment. The format of the station is news talk. WSYR-FM broadcasts to the Syracuse, NY area at 106.9 FM. The station airs WSYR-AM's programming.

WSYW-AM

Owner: Continental Broadcast Group LLC
Editorial: 1800 N Meridian St Ste 603, Indianapolis, Indiana 46202-1433.
T: 1 317 924-1071
W: http://www.lajoya810.com
Editorial Profile: WSYW-AM is a commercial station owned by Continental Broadcast Group LLC. The format of the station is Hispanic contemporary Christian music. WSYW-AM broadcasts to the Indianapolis area at 810 AM.

WSYY-AM

Owner: Katahdin Communications
Editorial: Lake Road, Millinocket, Maine 4462.
T: 1 207 723-9657
E: spots@themountain949.com

W: http://www.themountain949.com
Editorial Profile: WSYY-AM is a commercial station owned by Katahdin Communications. The format of the station is sports. WSYY-AM broadcasts to the Millinocket, ME area at 1240 AM.

WSYY-FM
Owner: Katahdin Communications
Editorial: Lake Road, Millinocket, Maine 4462. **T:** 1 207 723-9657
E: spots@themountain949.com
W: http://www.themountain949.com
Editorial Profile: WSYY-FM is a commercial station owned by Katahdin Communications. The format of the station is Jack FM/adult hits. WSYY-FM broadcasts to the Millinocket, ME area at 94.9 FM.

WTAB-AM
Owner: WTAB Inc.
Editorial: 210 Avon St, Tabor City, North Carolina 28463. **T:** 1 910 653-2131
E: wtab@wtabradio.com
W: http://www.wtabradio.com
Editorial Profile: WTAB-AM is a commercial station owned by WTAB Inc. The format of the station is country and Southern gospel music. WTAB-AM broadcasts to the Tabor City, NC area at 1370 AM.

WTAD-AM
Owner: Staradio Corp.
Editorial: 329 Maine St, 1st Fl, Quincy, Illinois 62301. **T:** 1 217 224-4102
E: wtad@staradio.com
W: http://www.wtad.com
Editorial Profile: WTAD-AM is a commercial station owned by Staradio Corp. The format of the station is news and talk. WTAD-AM broadcasts to the Quincy, IL area at 930 AM.

WTAG-AM
Owner: Clear Channel Media and Entertainment
Editorial: 96 Stereo Ln, Paxton, Massachusetts 01612-1376.
T: 1 508 795-0580 **W:** http://www.wtag.com
Editorial Profile: WTAG-AM is a commercial station owned by Clear Channel Media and Entertainment. The format of the station is news, sports and talk. WTAG-AM broadcasts to the Paxton, MA area at 580 AM.

WTAK-FM
Owner: Clear Channel Media and Entertainment
Editorial: 26869 Peoples Rd, Madison, Alabama 35756. **T:** 1 256 309-2400
W: http://www.wtak.com
Editorial Profile: WTAK-FM is a commercial station owned by Clear Channel Media and Entertainment. The format for the station is classic rock. WTAK-FM broadcasts to the Huntsville, AL area at 106.1 FM.

WTAL-AM
Owner: Live Communications
Editorial: 1363 E Tennessee St, Tallahassee, Florida 32308-5107. **T:** 1 850 877-0105
E: wtal@wtal1450.com
W: http://www.wtal1450.com
Editorial Profile: WTAL-AM is a commercial station owned by Live Communications. The format of the station features Gospel and talk programming. WTAL-AM broadcasts to the Tallahassee, FL area at a frequency of 1450 AM.

WTAM-AM
Owner: Clear Channel Media and Entertainment
Editorial: 6200 Oak Tree Blvd, 4th Fl, Independence, Ohio 44131. **T:** 1 216 520-2600
E: news@wtam.com **W:** http://www.wtam.com
Editorial Profile: WTAM-AM is a commercial station owned by Clear Channel Media and Entertainment. The format of the station is news and talk. WTAM-AM broadcasts in the Cleveland area at 1100 AM.

WTAN-AM
Owner: Wagenvoord Advertising Group
Editorial: 706 N Myrtle Ave, Clearwater, Florida 33755-4219. **T:** 1 727 424-4991
W: http://www.tantalk1340.com
Editorial Profile: WTAN-AM is a commercial station owned by Wagenvoord Advertising Group. The format of the station is adult standards music and talk. WTAN-AM broadcasts to the Clearwater, FL area at 1340 AM.

WTAO-FM
Owner: Withers Broadcasting of Southern Illinois LLC
Editorial: 1822 N Court St, Marion, Illinois 62959. **T:** 1 618 997-8123
W: http://www.taorocks.com
Editorial Profile: WTAO-FM is a commercial station owned by Withers Broadcasting of Southern Illinois LLC. The format of the station is rock/album oriented rock. WTAO-FM broadcasts to the Carbondale, IL area at 92.7 FM.

WTAQ-AM
Owner: Midwest Communications Inc.
Editorial: 1420 Bellevue St, Green Bay, Wisconsin 54311-5649. **T:** 1 920 435-3771
E: wtaq.news@wtaq.com
W: http://www.wtaq.com
Editorial Profile: WTAQ-AM is a commercial station owned by Midwest Communications Inc. The format of the station is news and talk. WTAQ-AM broadcasts to the Green Bay, WI area at 1360 AM.

WTAQ-FM
Owner: Midwest Communications Inc.
Editorial: 1420 Bellevue St, Green Bay, Wisconsin 54311-5649. **T:** 1 920 435-3771
E: wtaq.news@wtaq.com
W: http://www.wtaq.com
Editorial Profile: WTAQ-FM is a commercial station owned by Midwest Communications Inc. The format of the station is news and talk. WTAQ-FM broadcasts to the Green Bay, WI area at 97.5 FM.

WTAR-AM
Owner: Sinclair Telecable Inc.
Editorial: 999 Waterside Dr, Norfolk, Virginia 23510-3300. **T:** 1 757 640-8500
E: amproduction@wtar.com
W: http://www.wtar.com
Editorial Profile: WTAR-AM is a commercial station owned by Sinclair Telecable Inc. The format of the station is talk and sports. WTAR-AM broadcasts to Norfolk, VA, at 850 AM.

WTAW-AM
Owner: Bryan Broadcasting
Editorial: 2700 Earl Rudder Fwy S, College Station, Texas 77845-5010. **T:** 1 979 695-9595
E: news@bryanbroadcasting.com
W: http://www.wtaw.com
Editorial Profile: WTAW-AM is a commercial station owned by Bryan Broadcasting. The format of the station is news, talk, and sports. WTAW-AM broadcasts in the College Station, TX area at 1620 AM.

WTAX-AM
Owner: Saga Communications
Editorial: 3501 E Sangamon Ave, Springfield, Illinois 62707-9777. **T:** 1 217 753-5400
E: wtaxnews@wtax.com
W: http://www.wtax.com
Editorial Profile: WTAX-AM is a commercial station owned by Saga Communications. The format of the station is news and talk. WTAX-AM broadcasts to the Springfield, IL area at 1470 AM.

WTAY-AM
Owner: The Original Company Inc
Editorial: Route 33 West, Robinson, Illinois 62454. **T:** 1 618 544-2191
W: http://www.wtyefm.com
Editorial Profile: WTAY-AM is a commercial station owned by The Original Company Inc. The format of the station is sports news. WTAY-AM broadcasts to the Robinson, IL area at 1570 AM.

WTBC-AM
Owner: John Sisty Enterprises Inc.
Editorial: 2110 McFarland Blvd E, Tuscaloosa, Alabama 35404-5857. **T:** 1 205 758-5523
E: wtbc1@wtbc1230.com
W: http://www.wtbc1230.com
Editorial Profile: WTBC-AM is a commercial station owned by John Sisty Enterprises Inc. The format of the station is classic country music. WTBC-AM broadcasts to the Tuscaloosa, AL, area at 1230 AM.

WTBF-AM
Owner: Troy Broadcasting Corp.
Editorial: 67 Court Square, Troy, Alabama 36081. **T:** 1 334 566-0300
W: http://www.wtbf.com
Editorial Profile: WTBF-AM is a commercial station owned by Troy Broadcasting Corp. The format of the station is sports and talk. WTBF-AM broadcasts to the Troy, AL area at 970 AM.

WTBF-FM
Owner: Troy Broadcasting Corp.
Editorial: 67 Court Square, Troy, Alabama 36081. **T:** 1 334 566-0300
W: http://www.wtbf.com
Editorial Profile: WTBF-FM is a commercial station owned by Troy Broadcasting Corp. The format of the station is a oldies. WTBF-FM broadcasts to the Troy, AL area at 94.7 FM.

WTBG-FM
Owner: Wireless Group Inc.(The)
Editorial: 42 S Washington Ave, Brownsville, Tennessee 38012-3032. **T:** 1 731 772-3700
W: http://www.brownsvilleradio.com
Editorial Profile: WTBG-FM is a commercial station owned by The Wireless Group Inc. The format of the station is country and gospel. WTBG-FM broadcasts to the Brownsville, TN area at 95.3 FM.

WTBH-FM
Owner: Long Pond Baptist Church
Editorial: 8950 Nw 75Th Ave, Chiefland, Florida 32626-5139. **T:** 1 352 493-2650
W: http://www.wtbhradio.com
Editorial Profile: WTBH-FM is a non-commercial station owned by Long Pond Baptist Church. The format of the station is gospel music and religious programming. WTBH-FM broadcasts to the Gainesville, FL area at 91.5 FM.

WTBI-AM
Owner: Tabernacle Baptist Church
Editorial: 3931 White Horse Rd, Greenville, South Carolina 29611-5546.
T: 1 864 295-2145
E: wtbi@tabernacleministries.org
W: http://www.tbc.sc
Editorial Profile: WTBI-AM is a non-commercial station owned by Tabernacle Baptist Church. The format of the station is religious. WTBI-AM broadcasts to the Greenville, SC area at 1540 AM.

WTBI-FM
Owner: Tabernacle Baptist Church
Editorial: 3931 White Horse Rd, Greenville, South Carolina 29611. **T:** 1 864 295-2145
E: wtbi@tabernacleministries.org
W: http://www.tbc.sc
Editorial Profile: WTBI-FM is a non-commercial college station owned by Tabernacle Baptist Church. The format of the station is Christian programming. WTBI-FM broadcasts to the Greenville, SC area at 91.5 FM.

WTBK-FM
Owner: Choice Radio Corporation
Editorial: 107 Dickenson St, Manchester, Kentucky 40962-1254. **T:** 1 606 598-7588
E: wtbkradio@yahoo.com
W: http://www.wtbkfm.com
Editorial Profile: WTBK-FM is a commercial station owned by Choice Radio Corporation. The format of the station is contemporary country. WTBK-FM broadcasts to the Lexington, KY area at 105.7 FM.

WTBM-FM
Owner: Gleason Radio Group
Editorial: 243 Main St, Norway, Maine 4268.
T: 1 207 743-5911
E: news@gleasonmedia.com
W: http://www.woxo.com
Editorial Profile: WTBM-FM is a commercial station owned by Gleason Radio Group. The format of the station is classic country. WTBM-FM broadcasts to the Norway, ME area at 100.7 FM.

WTBN-AM
Owner: Salem Communications
Editorial: 5211 W Laurel St Ste A, Tampa, Florida 33607-1736. **T:** 1 813 349-8231
W: http://www.letstalkfaith.com
Editorial Profile: WTBN-AM is a commercial station owned by Salem Communications. The format of the station is religious talk. WTBN-AM broadcasts in the Tampa, FL area at 570 AM.

WTBO-AM
Owner: Dix Communications
Editorial: 350 Byrd Ave, Cumberland, Maryland 21502. **T:** 1 301 722-6666
E: mail@go106.com
W: http://www.foxsportsradio1450.com
Editorial Profile: WTBO-AM is a commercial station owned by Dix Communications. The format of the station is oldies and sports. WTBO-AM broadcasts in the Cumberland, MD area at 1450 AM.

WTBQ-AM
Owner: FST Broadcasting Corp.
Editorial: 179 Sanfordville Rd, Warwick, New York 10990-2849. **T:** 1 845 651-1110
E: wtbq@optonline.net
W: http://www.wtbq.com
Editorial Profile: WTBQ-AM is a commercial station owned by the FST Broadcasting Corp. The format of the station is talk. WTBQ-AM broadcasts to Florida, NY area at 1110 AM. Also operates on 93.5 FM

WTBU-AM
Owner: Boston University
Editorial: 640 Commonwealth Ave, Boston, Massachusetts 02215-2422.
T: 1 617 353-6401
W: http://www.wtburadio.org
Editorial Profile: WTBU-AM is a non-commercial station owned by Boston University. The format for the station is variety. WTBU-AM broadcasts to the Boston, MA area at 640 AM and 89.3 FM.

WTBX-FM
Owner: Midwest Communications Inc.
Editorial: 807 W 37th St, Hibbing, Minnesota 55746. **T:** 1 218 263-7531
W: http://www.wtbx.com

WTCA-AM
Owner: Community Service Broadcasters
Editorial: 112 W Washington St, Plymouth, Indiana 46563. **T:** 1 574 936-4096
E: wtca@am1050.com
W: http://www.am1050.com
Editorial Profile: WTCA-AM is a commercial station owned by Community Service Broadcasters. The format of the station is classic hits. WTCA-AM broadcasts to the Plymouth, IN area at 1050 AM.

WTCB-FM
Owner: Cumulus Media Inc.
Editorial: 1801 Charleston Hwy, Cayce, South Carolina 29033-2019. **T:** 1 803 796-7600
E: wtcb@b1067fm.com
W: http://www.b106fm.com
Editorial Profile: WTCB-FM is a commercial station owned by Cumulus Media Inc. The format of the station is hot adult contemporary. WTCB-FM broadcasts to the Columbia, SC area at a frequency of 106.7 FM.

WTCC-FM
Owner: Springfield Tech Comm. College
Editorial: 1 Armory Sq, Springfield, Massachusetts 01105-1700.
T: 1 413 746-9822 **W:** http://www.wtccfm.org
Editorial Profile: WTCC-FM is a non-commercial station owned by Springfield Technical Community College. The format of the station is college variety. WTCC-FM broadcasts in the Springfield, MA area at 90.7 FM.

WTCD-FM
Owner: TeleSouth Communications Inc.
Editorial: 3192 Browning Road 520, Greenwood, Mississippi 38930-3830.
T: 1 662 453-2174
W: http://www.supertalkms.com

WTCH-AM
Owner: Results Broadcasting, Inc.
Editorial: 1456 E Green Bay St, Shawano, Wisconsin 54166-2258. **T:** 1 715 524-2194
E: resultsbroadcasting@gmail.com
W: http://www.wtcham960.com
Editorial Profile: WTCH-AM is a commercial station owned by Results Broadcasting, Inc. The format of the station is classic country. WTCH-AM broadcasts to the Shawano, WI area at 960 AM.

WTCJ-AM
Owner: Cromwell Group Inc.(The)
Editorial: 1115 Tamarack Rd, Ste 500, Owensboro, Kentucky 42301.
T: 1 270 683-5200
E: kyproduction@cromwellradio.com
W: http://www.tellcityradio.com
Editorial Profile: WTCJ-AM is a commercial station owned by The Cromwell Group Inc. The format of the station is classic hits. WTCJ-AM broadcasts to the Owensboro, KY area at 1230 AM.

WTCJ-FM
Owner: Cromwell Group Inc.(The)
Editorial: 1115 Tamarack Rd, Owensboro, Kentucky 42301-6984. **T:** 1 270 683-5200
W: http://www.owensbororadio.com
Editorial Profile: WTCJ-FM is a commercial station owned by The Cromwell Group Inc. The format of the station is classic rock. WTCJ-FM broadcasts to the Owensboro, KY area at 105.7 FM.

WTCM-AM
Owner: Midwestern Broadcasting Co.

Editorial: 314 E Front St, Traverse City, Michigan 49684. **T:** 1 231 947-7675
E: wtcm@wtcmradio.com
W: http://www.wtcmradio.com
Editorial Profile: WTCM-AM is a commercial station owned by Midwestern Broadcasting Co. The format of the station is news and talk. WTCM-AM broadcasts to the Traverse City, MI area at 580 AM.

WTCM-FM
Owner: Midwestern Broadcasting Co.
Editorial: 314 E Front St, Traverse City, Michigan 49684. **T:** 1 231 947-7675
E: wtcm@wtcmradio.com
W: http://www.wtcmi.com
Editorial Profile: WTCM-FM is a commercial station owned by Midwestern Broadcasting Co. The format of the station is contemporary country music. WTCM-FM broadcasts to the Traverse City, MI area at 103.5 FM.

WTCO-AM
Owner: Commonwealth Broadcasting Corp.
Editorial: 50 Friendship Pike Rd, Campbellsville, Kentucky 42718-2537.
T: 1 270 789-2401
E: wckq@commonwealthbroadcasting.com
W: http://www.wtcosports.com

WTCQ-FM
Owner: Vidalia Communications Group
Editorial: 1501 Mount Vernon Rd, Vidalia, Georgia 30474-3031. **T:** 1 912 537-9202
W: http://www.southeastgeorgiatoday.com
Editorial Profile: WTCQ-FM is a commercial station owned by Vidalia Communications Group. The format of the station is adult contemporary. WTCQ-FM broadcasts to the Savannah, GA area at 97.7 FM.

WTCR-AM
Owner: Clear Channel Media and Entertainment
Editorial: 134 4Th Ave, Huntington, West Virginia 25701-1220. **T:** 1 304 525-7788
W: http://www.foxsports1420.com
Editorial Profile: WTCR-AM is a commercial station owned by Clear Channel Media and Entertainment. The format of the station sports. WTCR-AM broadcasts to the Huntington, WV area on 1420 AM.

WTCR-FM
Owner: Clear Channel Media and Entertainment
Editorial: 134 4th Ave, Huntington, West Virginia 25701. **T:** 1 304 525-7788
E: wtcr@clearchannel.com
W: http://www.wtcr.com
Editorial Profile: WTCR-FM is a commercial station owned by Clear Channel Media and Entertainment. The format of the station is classic country. WTCR-FM broadcasts to the Huntington, WV area at 103.3 FM.

WTCW-AM
Owner: Forcht Broadcasting
Editorial: 1149 Hwy 1862, Mayking, Kentucky 41837. **T:** 1 606 633-4434
E: wxkq@yahoo.com
W: http://www.1039thebulldog.com
Editorial Profile: WTCW-AM is a commercial station owned by Forcht Broadcasting. The format of the station is classic country music. WTCW-AM broadcasts to the Mayking, KY area at 920 AM.

WTCX-FM
Owner: Radio Plus Inc.
Editorial: 210 S Main St, Fond du Lac, Wisconsin 54935. **T:** 1 920 924-9697
W: http://www.wtcx.com
Editorial Profile: WTCX-FM is a commercial station owned by Radio Plus Inc. The format of the station is classic hits. WTCX-FM broadcasts to the Green Bay, WI area at 96.1 FM.

WTDK-FM
Owner: MTS Broadcasting LLC
Editorial: 2 Bay St, Cambridge, Maryland 21613-1257. **T:** 1 410 228-4800
E: theduck@mtslive.com
W: http://www.mtslive.com
Editorial Profile: WTDK-FM is a commercial station owned by MTS Broadcasting LLC. The format of the station is oldies. WTDK-FM broadcasts to the Cambridge, MD area at 107.1 FM.

WTDR-AM
Owner: Rainbow City Media, LLC
Editorial: 750 Walnut St, Gadsden, Alabama 35901-4139. **T:** 1 256 546-1611
W: http://www.wgad.com
Editorial Profile: WTDR-AM is a commercial station owned by Rainbow City Media, LLC. The format of the station is country. WTDR-AM broadcasts to the Gadsden, AL area at 1350 AM.

WTDR-FM
Owner: Jacobs Broadcast Group
Editorial: 1913 Barry St, Ste B, Oxford, Alabama 36203. **T:** 1 256 741-6000
E: news@thunder927.com
W: http://www.wtdrthunder.com
Editorial Profile: WTDR-FM is a commercial station owned by Jacobs Broadcast Group. The format of the station is country. WTDR-FM broadcasts to the Oxford, AL area at 92.7 FM.

WTEB-FM
Owner: Craven Community College
Editorial: 800 College Ct, New Bern, North Carolina 28562. **T:** 1 252 638-3434
W: http://www.publicradioeast.org
Editorial Profile: WTEB-FM is a non-commercial station owned by Craven Community College. The format of the station is classical music and news. WTEB-FM broadcasts to the New Bern, NC area at 89.3 FM.

WTEM-AM
Owner: Red Zebra Broadcasting
Editorial: 1801 Rockville Pike, Ste 405, Rockville, Maryland 20852. **T:** 1 301 230-3500
W: http://www.espn980.com
Editorial Profile: WTEM-AM is a commercial station owned by Red Zebra Broadcasting. The format of the station is sports. WTEM-AM broadcasts to the Washington, D.C. area at 980 AM.

WTFM-FM
Owner: Holston Valley Broadcasting Corp.
Editorial: 222 Commerce St, Kingsport, Tennessee 37660-4319. **T:** 1 423 246-9578
E: news@wtfm.com **W:** http://www.wtfm.com
Editorial Profile: WTFM-FM is owned by Holston Valley Broadcasting Corp. The format of the station is adult contemporary. WTFM-FM broadcasts to the Kingsport, TN area at 98.5 FM.

WTFX-FM
Owner: Clear Channel Media and Entertainment
Editorial: 4000 Radio Dr, Louisville, Kentucky 40218-4568. **T:** 1 502 479-2222
W: http://www.foxrocks.com
Editorial Profile: WTFX-FM is a commercial station owned by Clear Channel Media and Entertainment. The format of the station is rock music. WTFX-FM broadcasts to Louisville, KY at 93.1 FM.

WTGA-AM
Owner: Radio Georgia Inc.
Editorial: 208 S Center St, Thomaston, Georgia 30286. **T:** 1 706 647-7121
E: wtga@fun101fm.com
W: http://www.fun101fm.com
Editorial Profile: WTGA-AM is a commercial station owned by Radio Georgia Inc. The format of the station is Lite Rock/Lite AC and talk. WTGA-AM broadcasts to the Atlanta area at 1590 AM.

WTGA-FM
Owner: Radio Georgia Inc.
Editorial: 208 S Center St, Thomaston, Georgia 30286. **T:** 1 706 647-7121
E: wtga@fun101fm.com
W: http://www.fun101fm.com
Editorial Profile: WTGA-FM is commercial station owned by Radio Georgia Inc. The format of the station is adult contemporary. WTGA-FM broadcasts to the Thomaston, GA area at 101.1 FM.

WTGD-FM
Owner: VerStandig Broadcasting
Editorial: 1820 Heritage Center Way, Harrisonburg, Virginia 22801.
T: 1 540 434-0331
W: http://www.1051bobrocks.com
Editorial Profile: WTGD-FM is a commercial station owned by VerStandig Broadcasting. The format of the station is rock. WTGD-FM broadcasts to the Harrisonburg, VA area at 105.1 FM. The station does not accept unsolicited faxes. Do NOT e-mail any staff members. Any press information should be sent to WSVA-AM.

WTGE-FM
Owner: Guaranty Broadcasting
Editorial: 929 Government St, Ste B, Baton Rouge, Louisiana 70802. **T:** 1 225 388-9898
W: http://www.1007thetiger.com
Editorial Profile: WTGE-FM is a commercial station owned by Guaranty Broadcasting. The format of the station is contemporary country. WTGE-FM broadcasts to the Baton Rouge, LA area at 100.7 FM.

WTGF-FM
Owner: Faith Bible College
Editorial: 4670 Highway 90, Milton, Florida 32571-1411. **T:** 1 850 994-3747
E: wtgf@bellsouth.net
W: http://www.truthradiofm.org
Editorial Profile: WTGF-FM is a non-commercial station owned by Faith Bible College. The format for the station is religious and Southern gospel. WTGF-FM broadcasts to the Pace, FL area at 90.5 FM.

WTGG-FM
Owner: Northshore Broadcasting Inc.
Editorial: 200 E Thomas St, Hammond, Louisiana 70401-3316. **T:** 1 985 345-0060
W: http://www.tangiradio.net/
Editorial Profile: WTGG-FM is commercial station owned by Northshore Broadcasting Inc. The format of the station is oldies. WTGG-FM broadcasts to the Hammond, LA area at 96.5 FM.

WTGM-AM
Owner: Clear Channel Media and Entertainment
Editorial: Gateway Crossing, 351 Tilghman Road, Salisbury, Maryland 21804-1920.
T: 1 410 742-1923
W: http://www.sportstalk960.com
Editorial Profile: WTGM-AM is a commercial station owned by Clear Channel Media and Entertainment. The format of the station is sports. WTGM-AM broadcasts to the Salisbury, MD area at 960 AM.

WTGN-FM
Owner: Associated Christian Broadcasters
Editorial: 1600 Elida Rd, Lima, Ohio 45805.
T: 1 419 227-2525 **E:** info@wtgn.org
W: http://www.wtgn.org
Editorial Profile: WTGN-FM is a non-commercial station owned by Associated Christin Broadcasters. The format for the station is religious. WTGN-FM broadcasts to the Lima, OH area at 97.7 FM.

WTGR-FM
Owner: Positive Radio Group
Editorial: 514 Martin St, Greenville, Ohio 45331. **T:** 1 937 548-5085
W: http://www.wtgr.com
Editorial Profile: WTGR-FM is a commercial station owned by Positive Radio Group. The format of the station is country music. WTGR-FM broadcasts in the Dayton, OH area at 97.5.

WTGV-FM
Owner: Sanilac Broadcasting
Editorial: 19 S Elk St, Sandusky, Michigan 48471. **T:** 1 810 648-2700
W: http://www.sanilacbroadcasting.com
Editorial Profile: WTGV-FM is a commercial station owned by Sanilac Broadcasting. The format of the station is Lite Rock/Lite AC. WTGV-FM broadcasts to the Sandusky, MI area at 97.7 FM.

WTGZ-FM
Owner: Tiger Communications Inc.
Editorial: 2514 S College St Ste 104, Auburn, Alabama 36832-6925. **T:** 1 334 887-9999
W: http://www.thetiger.fm
Editorial Profile: WTGZ-FM is a commercial station owned by Tiger Communications Inc. The format of the station is alternative rock music. WTGZ-FM broadcasts to the Auburn, AL area at 93.9 FM.

WTHB-AM
Owner: Perry Broadcasting Company, Inc.
Editorial: 411 Radio Station Rd, North Augusta, South Carolina 29841.
T: 1 803 279-2330
Editorial Profile: WTHB-AM is a commercial station owned by Perry Broadcasting Company, Inc. The format of the station is gospel and talk. WTHB-AM broadcasts to the North Augusta, SC area at 1550 AM.

WTHB-FM
Owner: Perry Broadcasting Company, Inc.
Editorial: 411 Radio Station Rd, North Augusta, South Carolina 29841.
T: 1 803 279-2330
Editorial Profile: WTHB-FM is a commercial station owned by Perry Broadcasting Company, Inc. The format of the station is gospel. WTHB-FM broadcasts to the North Augusta, GA area at 96.9 FM.

WTHD-FM
Owner: Swick Broadcasting
Editorial: 206 S High St, Lagrange, Indiana 46761. **T:** 1 260 463-8500 **E:** wthd@wthd.net
W: http://www.wthd.net
Editorial Profile: WTHD-FM is a commercial station owned by Swick Broadcasting. The format for the station is country music. WTHD-FM broadcasts to the South Bend, IN area at 105.5 FM.

WTHE-AM
Owner: Universal Broadcasting
Editorial: 260 E 2nd St, Mineola, New York 11501. **T:** 1 516 742-1520
E: nygospelradio@aol.com
W: http://www.wthe1520am.com
Editorial Profile: WTHE-AM is a commercial station owned by Universal Broadcasting. The format of the station is gospel music. WTHE-AM broadcasts to the Mineola, NY at 1520 AM.

WTHG-FM
Owner: Savannah Radio (WRGO Radio, LLC)
Editorial: 63 Ramsgate Rd, Savannah, Georgia 31419-3274. **T:** 1 214 282-0844
W: http://www.1047thehawk.com
Editorial Profile: WTHG-FM is a commercial station owned by WRGO Radio, LLC dba Savannah Radio. The format of the station is classic hits. WTHG-FM broadcasts to the Savannah, GA area at 104.7 FM.

WTHI-FM
Owner: Emmis Communications Corp.
Editorial: 918 Ohio St, Terre Haute, Indiana 47807-3733. **T:** 1 812 917-3901
W: http://www.hi99.com
Editorial Profile: WTHI-FM is a commercial station owned by Emmis Communications Corp. The format of the station is contemporary country music. WTHI-FM broadcasts to the Terre Haute, IN area at 98.7 FM.

WTHL-FM
Owner: Somerset Educational Broadcasting
Editorial: 93 Rainbow Ter, Somerset, Kentucky 42503-4653. **T:** 1 606 679-6300
W: http://www.kingofkingsradio.net

WTHN-FM
Owner: Northern Christian Radio
Editorial: 1511 E M 32, Gaylord, Michigan 49735-9702. **T:** 1 989 732-6274
E: studio@ncradio.org
W: http://www.thepromisefm.com

WTHO-FM
Owner: Camellia City Communications
Editorial: 788 Cedar Rock Rd, Thomson, Georgia 30824-7642. **T:** 1 706 595-5122
W: http://www.wtho.com
Editorial Profile: WTHO-FM is commercial station owned by Camellia City Communications. The format of the station is country. WTHO-FM broadcasts to the Thomson, GA area at 101.7 FM.

WTHP-FM
Owner: Good News Network
Editorial: 2278 Wortham Ln, Grovetown, Georgia 30813. **T:** 1 706 309-9610
W: http://www.gnnradio.org
Editorial Profile: WTHP-FM is a commercial station owned by Good News Network. The format of the station is religious. WTHP-FM broadcasts to the Augusta, GA area at 94.3 FM.

WTHS-FM
Owner: Hope College
Editorial: 257 Columbia Ave, Martha Miller Center 156, Holland, Michigan 49423-3615.
T: 1 616 395-7878 **E:** wthsnews@hope.edu
W: http://wths.hope.edu
Editorial Profile: WTHS-FM is a non-commercial station owned by Hope College. The format of the station is adult album alternative and variety. WTHS-FM broadcasts to the Holland, MI area at 89.9 FM.

WTHT-FM
Owner: WBIN, Inc.
Editorial: 477 Congress St Ste 3, Portland, Maine 04101-3427. **T:** 1 207 797-0780
W: http://www.999thewolf.com
Editorial Profile: WTHT-FM is a commercial station owned by WBIN, Inc. The format of the station is classic country. WTHT-FM broadcasts to the Portland, ME area at 99.9 FM.

WTHU-AM
Owner: Christian Radio Coalition, Inc.

Editorial: 10 Radio Ln, Thurmont, Maryland 21788. **T:** 1 301 637-6736 **W:** http://wthu.org
Editorial Profile: WTHU-AM is a commercial station owned by Christian Radio Coalition, Inc. The format of the station is talk, Sports and news. WTHU-AM broadcasts in the Thurmont, MD area at 1450 AM.

WTHV-AM
Owner: Eternal Life Ministries Inc.
Editorial: 2352 Jaycee Shack Rd, Valdosta, Georgia 31602-6475. **T:** 1 229 245-9848
E: wthv810am@yahoo.com
W: http://wthvradio.com
Editorial Profile: WTHV-AM is a commercial station owned by Eternal Life Ministries Inc. The format of the station is Southern gospel. WTHV-AM broadcasts to the Valdosta, GA area at 810 AM.

WTHX-FM
Owner: Commonwealth Broadcasting Corp.
Editorial: 611 W Poplar St Ste C2, Elizabethtown, Kentucky 42701-2483.
T: 1 270 763-0800
E: news@commonwealthbroadcasting.com
W: http://www.titansradio.com
Editorial Profile: WTHX-FM is a commercial station owned by Commonwealth Broadcasting Corp. The format of the station is sports. WTHX-FM broadcasts to the Elizabethtown, KY area at 101.5 FM.

WTIB-FM
Owner: Inner Banks Media, LLC
Editorial: 408 W Arlington Blvd Ste 101C, Greenville, North Carolina 27834-5706.
T: 1 252 355-1037 **W:** http://www.wtibfm.com
Editorial Profile: WTIB-FM is a commercial station owned by Inner Banks Media, LLC. The format of the station is news, talk and sports. WTIB-FM broadcasts to the Greenville, NC area at 103.7 FM.

WTIC-AM
Owner: CBS Radio
Editorial: 10 Executive Dr, Farmington, Connecticut 06032-2841. **T:** 1 860 677-6700
E: wticnews@cbs.com
W: http://connecticut.cbslocal.com/station/wtic-news-talk-1080
Editorial Profile: WTIC-AM is a commercial station owned by CBS Radio. The format for the station is news and talk. WTIC-AM broadcasts to the Hartford-New Haven, CT area at 1080 AM.

WTIC-FM
Owner: CBS Radio
Editorial: 10 Executive Dr, Farmington, Connecticut 06032-2841. **T:** 1 860 677-6700
W: http://965tic.cbslocal.com
Editorial Profile: WTIC-FM is a commercial station owned by CBS Radio. The format of the station is hot adult contemporary. WTIC-FM broadcasts in the Hartford, CT area at 96.5 FM.

WTIF-AM
Owner: Three Trees Communications
Editorial: 601 2nd St W, Tifton, Georgia 31794-4257. **T:** 1 229 382-1340

WTIF-FM
Owner: Three Trees Communications
Editorial: 601 2nd St W, Tifton, Georgia 31794-4257. **T:** 1 229 382-1340
Editorial Profile: WTIF-FM is a commercial station owned by Three Trees Communications. The format of the station is contemporary country. WTIF-FM broadcasts to the Tifton, GA, area at 107.5 FM.

WTIG-AM
Owner: WTIG Inc.
Editorial: 3580 Karen Ave Nw, Massillon, Ohio 44647-9513. **T:** 1 330 837-9900
E: espn990@gmail.com
W: http://www.espn990.com
Editorial Profile: WTIG-AM is a commercial station owned by WTIG Inc. The format of the station is sports. WTIG-AM broadcasts to the Massillon, OH area at 990 AM.

WTIK-AM
Owner: Davidson Media Group
Editorial: 707 Leon St, Durham, North Carolina 27704-4125. **T:** 1 919 236-5337
W: http://www.lameganc.com
Editorial Profile: WTIK-AM is a commercial station owned by Davidson Media Group and operated by Prieto Broadcasting Inc. The format of the station is Hispanic music. WTIK-AM broadcasts to the Durham, NC area at 1310 AM.

WTIM-FM
Owner: Miller Communications Inc.
Editorial: 918 E Park St, Taylorville, Illinois 62568-1916. **T:** 1 217 824-3395
E: news@taylorvilledailynews.com
W: http://www.wtimradio.com
Editorial Profile: WTIM-FM is a commercial station owned by the Miller Communications Inc. The format of the station is news, talk, and public affairs programming. WTIM-FM broadcasts in the Taylorville, IL area at 97.3 FM.

WTIP-FM
Owner: Cook County Community Radio
Editorial: 1712 W Highway 61, Grand Marais, Minnesota 55604-7507. **T:** 1 218 387-1070
E: wtip@boreal.org **W:** http://www.wtip.org
Editorial Profile: WTIP-FM is a non-commercial station owned by Cook County Community Radio. The format of the station is variety. WTIP-FM broadcasts to the Grand Marais, MN area at 90.7 FM.

WTIQ-AM
Owner: Radio Results Network
Editorial: 7876 W County Rd, Ste 442, Manistique, Michigan 49854.
T: 1 906 341-8444
E: wtiq@radioresultsnetwork.com
W: http://www.radioresultsnetwork.com
Editorial Profile: WTIQ-AM is a commercial station owned by Radio Results Network. The format of the station is oldies. WTIQ-AM broadcasts to the Escanaba, MI area at 1490 AM.

WTIS-AM
Owner: WTIS-AM, Inc.
Editorial: 311 112Th Ave Ne, Saint Petersburg, Florida 33716-3334.
T: 1 727 576-2234
E: businessoffice@wtis1110.com
W: http://www.wtis1110.com
Editorial Profile: WTIS-AM is a commercial station owned by WTIS-AM, Inc. The format of the station is Christian talk. WTIS-AM broadcasts to the Saint Petersburg, FL area at 1110 AM.

WTIV-AM
Owner: Forever Broadcasting
Editorial: 900 Water St, Meadville, Pennsylvania 16335-3428. **T:** 1 814 724-1111
E: radio@zoominternet.net
Editorial Profile: WTIV-AM is a commercial station owned by Forever Broadcasting. The format of the station is news, sports and talk. WTIV-AM broadcasts to the Titusville, PA area at 1230 AM.

WTIX-AM
Owner: GHB Broadcasting
Editorial: 212 Signal Hill Dr, Statesville, North Carolina 28625-4327. **T:** 1 704 872-0500
W: http://www.mycountrylegends.com/Statesville_Radio_Station.html
Editorial Profile: WTIX-AM is a commercial station owned by GHB Broadcasting. The format of the station is classic country. WTIX-AM is licensed to Concord, NC and broadcasts to the Charlotte, NC area at 1410 AM.

WTIX-FM
Owner: Fleur de Lis Broadcasting, Inc.
Editorial: 4539 N Interstate 10 Service Rd W, 3rd Fl, Metairie, Louisiana 70006-6575.
T: 1 504 454-9000 **W:** http://www.wtixfm.com
Editorial Profile: WTIX-FM is a commercial station owned by Fleur de Lis Broadcasting, Inc. The format of the station is oldies. WTIX-FM broadcasts to the Metairie, LA area at 94.3 FM.

WTJJ-FM
Owner: Forever Communications Inc.
Editorial: 122 Radio Rd, Jackson, Tennessee 38301-3465. **T:** 1 731 427-3316
W: http://www.wtjs.com
Editorial Profile: WTJJ-FM is a commercial station owned by Forever Communications Inc. The format of the station is news and talk. WTJJ-FM broadcasts to the Humboldt, TN area at 94.3 FM.

WTJK-AM
Owner: Big Radio
Editorial: 1 Parker Pl Ste 485, Janesville, Wisconsin 53545-4078. **T:** 1 608 758-9025
W: http://www.thebigam1380.com
Editorial Profile: WTJK-AM is a commercial station owned by Big Radio. The format of the station is news, talk and sports. WTJK-AM broadcasts to the Janesville, WI area on 1380 AM.

WTJS-AM
Owner: Forever Communications Inc.
Editorial: 122 Radio Rd, Jackson, Tennessee 38301. **T:** 1 731 427-3316 **E:** studio@wtjs.com
W: http://www.wtjs.com
Editorial Profile: WTJS-AM is a commercial station owned by Forever Communications Inc. The format of the station is news, talk and sports programming. WTJS-AM broadcasts to the Jackson, TN area at 1390 AM.

WTJT-FM
Owner: Thompson(Earl)
Editorial: 957 Highway C 4A, Baker, Florida 32531-8743. **T:** 1 850 537-2009
E: wtjtradio@yahoo.com
Editorial Profile: WTJT-FM is a non-commercial station owned by Earl Thompson. The format for the station is religious and Southern gospel. WTJT-FM broadcasts to the Mobile, AL, Pensacola, FL area at 90.1 FM.

WTJU-FM
Owner: University of Virginia
Editorial: Lambeth Commons, 2nd Fl, Charlottesville, Virginia 22904.
T: 1 434 924-0885 **E:** wtjunews@virginia.edu
W: http://wtju.net
Editorial Profile: WTJU-FM is a non-commercial station owned by the University of Virginia. The format for the station is variety. WTJU-FM broadcasts to the Charlottesville, VA area at 91.1 FM.

WTJV-AM
Owner: J & V Communications Inc.
Editorial: 222 Hazard St, Orlando, Florida 32804-3030. **T:** 1 407 841-8282
E: wprd1440@gmail.com
Editorial Profile: WTJV-AM is a commercial station owned by J & V Communications Inc. The format of the station is adult standards. WTJV-AM broadcasts to the Orlando, FL market at 1490 AM.

WTJY-FM
Owner: Positive Alternative Radio
Editorial: 600 W Clemmonsville Rd, Winston Salem, North Carolina 27127-5045.
T: 1 336 788-1155 **E:** office@joyfm.org
W: http://www.joyfm.org
Editorial Profile: WTJY-FM is a non-commercial station owned by Positive Alternative Radio. The format of the station is Southern Gospel. WTJY-FM broadcasts to the Winston-Salem, NC area at 89.5 FM.

WTJZ-AM
Owner: Chesapeake-Portsmouth Broadcasting Corp.
Editorial: 553 Michigan Dr, Hampton, Virginia 23669-3832. **T:** 1 757 488-1010
E: faithbroadcasting@gmail.com
Editorial Profile: WTJZ-AM is a commercial station owned by Chesapeake-Portsmouth Broadcasting Corp. The format of the station is Christian and gospel. WTJZ-AM broadcasts to the Hampton, VA area at 1270 AM.

WTKA-AM
Owner: Cumulus Media Inc.
Editorial: 1100 Victors Way, Ste 100, Ann Arbor, Michigan 48108. **T:** 1 734 302-8100
E: studio@wtka.com **W:** http://www.wtka.com
Editorial Profile: WTKA-AM is a commercial station owned by Cumulus Media Inc. The format of the station is sports. WTKA-AM broadcasts to Ann Arbor, MI, at 1050 AM.

WTKB-FM
Owner: Solid Rock Broadcasting, LLC
Editorial: 2048 South First St, Ste E, Milan, Tennessee 38358. **T:** 1 731 562-9852
W: http://www.victory937.com
Editorial Profile: WTKB-FM is a commercial station owned by Solid Rock Broadcasting, LLC. The format of the station is contemporary Christian and news and talk. WTKB-FM broadcasts to the Milan and Jackson, TN areas at 93.7 FM.

WTKF-FM
Owner: Atlantic Ridge Telecasters Inc.
Editorial: 4206 Bridges Street Ext. Suit B, Morehead City, North Carolina 28557.
T: 1 252 247-6343
E: news@thetalkstation.com
W: http://www.wtkf107.com
Editorial Profile: WTKF-FM is a commercial station owned by Atlantic Ridge Telecaster Inc. The format of the station is news, talk, and sports. WTKF-FM broadcasts in the Newport, NC area at 107.3 FM.

WTKG-AM
Owner: Clear Channel Media and Entertainment
Editorial: 77 Monroe Center St NW, Ste 1000, Grand Rapids, Michigan 49503.
T: 1 616 459-1919 **W:** http://www.wtkg.com
Editorial Profile: WTKG-AM is a commercial station owned by Clear Channel Media and Entertainment. The format of the station is news and talk. WTKG-AM broadcasts to the Grand Rapids, MI area at 1230 AM.

WTKK-FM
Owner: Clear Channel Media and Entertainment
Editorial: 3100 Smoketree Ct, Raleigh, North Carolina 27604-1086. **T:** 1 919 878-1500
W: http://www.1061fmtalk.com/main.html
Editorial Profile: WTKK-FM is a commercial station owned by Clear Channel Media and Entertainment. The format of the station is conservative talk and news. WTKK-FM broadcasts to the Raleigh, NC area at 106.1 FM.

WTKM-AM
Owner: Kettle Moraine Broadcasting
Editorial: 27 N Main St, Hartford, Wisconsin 53027-1531. **T:** 1 262 673-3550
E: wtkmradio@gmail.com
W: http://www.wtkm.com
Editorial Profile: WTKM-AM is a commercial station owned by Kettle Moraine Broadcasting. The format of the station is oldies. WTKM-AM broadcasts to the Hartford, WI area at 1540 AM.

WTKM-FM
Owner: Kettle Moraine Broadcasting
Editorial: 27 N Main St, Hartford, Wisconsin 53027-1531. **T:** 1 262 673-7800
E: wtkmradio@gmail.com
W: http://www.wtkmradio.com
Editorial Profile: WTKM-FM is a commercial station owned by Kettle Moraine Broadcasting. The format of the station is classic country, polka music, and ethnic broadcasting. WTKM-FM broadcasts to the Hartford, WI, area at 104.9 FM.

WTKP-FM
Owner: Omni Broadcasting Co.
Editorial: 1834 Lisenby Ave, Panama City, Florida 32405-3713. **T:** 1 850 244-1400
E: omnibroadcastinginc@gmail.com
W: http://www.theticketsportsnetwork.com
Editorial Profile: WTKP-FM is a commercial station owned by Omni Broadcasting Co. The format of the station is sports talk. WTKP-FM broadcasts to the Panama City, FL area at 93.5 FM. The station is a simulcast of WTKE-FM.

WTKS-AM
Owner: Clear Channel Media and Entertainment
Editorial: 245 Alfred St, Savannah, Georgia 31408. **T:** 1 912 964-7794
W: http://www.newsradio1290wtks.com
Editorial Profile: WTKS-AM is a commercial station owned by Clear Channel Media and Entertainment. The format for the station is news and talk. WTKS-AM broadcasts to the Savannah, GA area at 1290 AM.

WTKS-FM
Owner: Clear Channel Media and Entertainment
Editorial: 2500 Maitland Center Pkwy, Ste 401, Maitland, Florida 32751-4179.
T: 1 407 916-7800 **W:** http://www.realradio.fm
Editorial Profile: WTKS-FM is a commercial station owned by Clear Channel Media and Entertainment. The format of the station is talk. WTKS-FM broadcasts to the Orlando, FL area at 104.1 FM.

WTKT-AM
Owner: Clear Channel Media and Entertainment
Editorial: 600 Corporate Cir, Harrisburg, Pennsylvania 17110-9787. **T:** 1 717 540-8800
E: webmaster@1460theticket.com
W: http://www.wtkt.com
Editorial Profile: WTKT-AM is a commercial station owned by Clear Channel Media and Entertainment. The format of the station is sports. WTKT-AM broadcasts to the Harrisburg, PA area at 1460 AM.

WTKU-FM
Owner: Longport Media
Editorial: 1601 New Rd, Linwood, New Jersey 08221-1116. **T:** 1 609 653-1400
W: http://www.kool983.com
Editorial Profile: WTKU-FM is a commercial station owned by Longport Media. The format of the station is classic hits. WTKU-FM broadcasts to the Atlantic City, NJ area at 98.3 FM.

WTKV-FM
Owner: Galaxy Communications LP
Editorial: 235 Walton St, Syracuse, New York 13202. **T:** 1 315 472-9111 **E:** asktk@tk99.net
W: http://www.tk99.net
Editorial Profile: WTKV-FM is a commercial station owned by Galaxy Communications LP. The format of the station is classic rock. WTKV-FM broadcasts to the Syracuse, NY area at a frequency at 105.5.

WTKW-FM
Owner: Galaxy Communications LP
Editorial: 235 Walton St, Syracuse, New York 13202. **T:** 1 315 472-9111 **E:** asktk@tk99.net
W: http://www.tk99.net
Editorial Profile: WTKW-FM is a commercial station owned by Galaxy Communications LP. The format of the station is classic rock. WTKW-FM broadcasts to the Syracuse, NY area at 99.5 FM.

WTKX-FM
Owner: Clear Channel Media and Entertainment
Editorial: 6485 Pensacola Blvd, Pensacola, Florida 32505-1701. **T:** 1 850 473-0400
E: radio@tk101.com **W:** http://www.tk101.com
Editorial Profile: WTKX-FM is a commercial station owned by Clear Channel Media and Entertainment. The format for the station is rock/album-oriented rock. WTKX-FM broadcasts to the Pensacola, FL area at 101.5 FM.

WTKY-AM
Owner: Whittimore Enterprises
Editorial: 341 Radio Station Rd, Tompkinsville, Kentucky 42167-8572. **T:** 1 270 487-6119
E: kixcountry@windstream.net
Editorial Profile: WTKY-AM is a commercial station owned by Whittimore Enterprises. The format of the station is classic country. WTKY-AM broadcasts to the Tompkinsville, KY area at 1370 AM.

WTKY-FM
Owner: Whittimore Enterprises
Editorial: 341 Radio Station Rd, Tompkinsville, Kentucky 42167-8572. **T:** 1 270 487-6119
E: kixcountry@windstream.net

WTKZ-AM
Owner: NB Broadcasting, LLC
Editorial: 107 Paxinosa Rd W, Easton, Pennsylvania 18040-1344. **T:** 1 610 829-5500
W: http://www.espnlv.com
Editorial Profile: WTKZ-AM is a commercial station owned by NB Broadcasting, LLC. The format of the station is sports. WTKZ-AM broadcasts to the Easton, PA area at 1320 AM.

WTLA-AM
Owner: Galaxy Communications LP
Editorial: 235 Walton St, Syracuse, New York 13202-1533. **T:** 1 315 472-9111
E: community@galaxycommunications.com
W: http://www.galaxycommunications.com
Editorial Profile: WTLA-AM is a commercial station owned by Galaxy Communications LP. The format of the station is sports. WTLA-AM broadcasts to the Syracuse, NY area at 1200 AM.

WTLB-AM
Owner: Galaxy Communications LP
Editorial: 39 Kellogg Rd, New Hartford, New York 13413. **T:** 1 315 797-1330
Editorial Profile: WTLB-AM is a commercial station owned by Galaxy Communications LP. The format of the station is sports. WTLB-AM broadcasts to the Syracuse, NY area at 1310 AM.

WTLC-AM
Owner: Radio One Inc.
Editorial: 21 E Saint Joseph St, Indianapolis, Indiana 46204-1025. **T:** 1 317 266-9600
W: http://praiseindy.com
Editorial Profile: WTLC-AM is a commercial station owned by Radio One Inc. The format of the station is gospel music and talk. WTLC-AM broadcasts in the Indianapolis area at 1310 AM.

WTLC-FM
Owner: Radio One Inc.
Editorial: 21 E Saint Joseph St, Indianapolis, Indiana 46204-1025. **T:** 1 317 266-9600
W: http://www.tlcnaptown.com
Editorial Profile: WTLC-FM is a commercial station owned by Radio One Inc. The format of the station is urban adult contemporary music. WTLC-FM broadcasts to the Indianapolis area at 106.7 FM.

WTLG-FM
Owner: American Family Association
Editorial: 163 W Jefferson St, Starke, Florida 32091. **T:** 1 662 844-5036
W: http://www.afr.net

WTLI-FM
Owner: Superior Communications
Editorial: 148 E Grand River Rd, Williamston, Michigan 48895. **T:** 1 517 381-0573
E: info@smile.fm **W:** http://www.smile.fm

WTLK-AM
Owner: Apple City Broadcasting Co.
Editorial: 133 E Main Ave, Taylorsville, North Carolina 28681-2514. **T:** 1 828 632-4621
E: wacbwtlk@applecitybroadcasting.com
Editorial Profile: WTLK-AM is a commercial station owned by Apple City Broadcasting Co. The format of the station is gospel music. WTLK-AM broadcasts to the greater Taylorsville, NC area at 1570 AM.

WTLM-AM
Owner: Clear Channel Media and Entertainment
Editorial: 915 Veterans Pkwy, Opelika, Alabama 36801-3367. **T:** 1 334 745-4656
Editorial Profile: WTLM-AM is a commercial station owned by Clear Channel Media and Entertainment. The format of the station is adult standards. WTLM-AM broadcasts to the Opelika, AL area at 1520 AM.

WTLN-AM
Owner: Salem Communications
Editorial: 1188 Lake View Dr, Altamonte Springs, Florida 32714-2713.
T: 1 407 682-9494 **E:** wtln@wtln.com
W: http://www.wtln.com
Editorial Profile: WTLN-AM is a commercial station owned by Salem Communications. The format of the station is religious music and talk. WTLN-AM broadcasts to the Altamonte Springs, FL area at 950 AM.

WTLO-AM
Owner: Forcht Broadcasting
Editorial: 290 Wtlo Rd, Somerset, Kentucky 42503. **T:** 1 606 678-8151 **E:** wtlo@usa.com
W: http://www.wtloradio.com
Editorial Profile: WTLO-AM is a commercial station owned by Forcht Broadcasting. The format of the station is adult standards. WTLO-AM broadcasts to the Somerset, KY area at 1480 AM.

WTLP-FM
Owner: Hubbard Broadcasting, Inc.
Editorial: 3400 Idaho Ave NW, Washington, District Of Columbia 20016.
T: 1 202 895-5000
W: http://www.wtopnews.com
Editorial Profile: WTLP-FM is a commercial station owned by Hubbard Broadcasting, Inc. The format of the station is news and talk. WTLP-FM broadcasts to the Braddock Heights, MD area at 103.9 FM.

WTLQ-FM
Owner: Fort Myers Broadcasting Co.
Editorial: 2824 Palm Beach Blvd, Fort Myers, Florida 33916-1503. **T:** 1 239 337-2346
W: http://www.latino977.com/
Editorial Profile: WTLQ-FM is a commercial station owned by Fort Myers Broadcasting Co. The format of the station is Spanish hits. WTLQ-FM broadcasts to the Fort Myers, FL area at 97.7 FM.

WTLR-FM
Owner: Central Pennsylvania Christian Institute
Editorial: 2020 Cato Ave, State College, Pennsylvania 16801. **T:** 1 814 237-9857
E: info@cpci.org **W:** http://cpci.org
Editorial Profile: WTLR-FM is a non-commercial station owned by Central Pennsylvania Christian Institute. The format of the station is religious. WTLR-FM broadcasts to the State College, PA area at 89.9 FM.

WTLS-AM
Owner: Michael Butler Broadcasting, LLC
Editorial: 2045 Alabama Hwy 229, Tallassee, Alabama 36078. **T:** 1 334 283-8200
W: http://www.1300wtls.com
Editorial Profile: WTLS-AM is a commercial station owned by Michael Butler Broadcasting, LLC. The format of the station is sports and talk. WTLS-AM broadcasts to the Atlanta area at 1300 AM.

WTLX-FM
Owner: Good Karma Broadcasting
Editorial: 7025 Raymond Rd, Madison, Wisconsin 53719-5053. **T:** 1 608 245-9859
W: http://www.madisonsportsradio.com
Editorial Profile: WTLX-FM is a commercial station owned by Good Karma Broadcasting. The format of the station is sports programming. WTLX-FM broadcasts to the Beaver Dam, WI area at 100.5 FM.

WTLZ-FM
Owner: Digity LLC
Editorial: 1795 Tittabawassee Rd, Saginaw, Michigan 48604-9431. **T:** 1 989 752-3456
W: http://www.hotwtlz.com
Editorial Profile: WTLZ-FM is a commercial station owned by Digity LLC. The format of the station is urban contemporary music. WTCF-FM broadcasts to the Saginaw, MI area at 100.5 FM.

WTMA-AM
Owner: Cumulus Media Inc.
Editorial: 4230 Faber Place Dr Ste 100, Charleston, South Carolina 29405-8512.
T: 1 843 277-1200 **W:** http://www.wtma.com
Editorial Profile: WTMA-AM is a commercial station owned by Cumulus Media Inc. The format of the station is news and talk. WTMA-AM broadcasts to the Charleston, SC area at 1250 AM.

WTMB-FM
Owner: Magnum Radio Group
Editorial: 1021 N Superior Ave, Ste 5, Tomah, Wisconsin 54660. **T:** 1 608 372-9400
E: news@magnumbroadcasting.com
W: http://www.classicrockwtmb.com
Editorial Profile: WTMB-FM is a commercial station owned by Magnum Radio Group. The format of the station is classic rock music. WTMB-FM broadcasts to the Tomah, WI area at 94.5 FM.

WTMD-FM
Owner: Towson University
Editorial: 8000 York Rd, Towson, Maryland 21252-0001. **T:** 1 410 704-8938
E: wtmd@towson.edu **W:** http://www.wtmd.org
Editorial Profile: WTMD-FM is a non-commercial station owned by Towson University. The format of the station is adult album alternative music. WTMD-FM broadcasts in the Baltimore-Towson, MD area at 89.7 FM.

WTME-AM
Owner: Gleason Radio Group
Editorial: 243 Main St, Norway, Maine 4268.
T: 1 207 743-5911
E: news@gleasonmedia.com
W: http://www.wtme.com
Editorial Profile: WTME-AM is a commercial station owned by Gleason Radio Group. The format of the station is news and religious programming. WTME-AM broadcasts to the Norway, ME area at 780 AM.

WTMG-FM
Owner: Marc Radio Group, LLC
Editorial: 100 NW 76th Dr Ste 2, Gainesville, Florida 32607-6659. **T:** 1 352 313-3110
W: http://www.magic1013.com
Editorial Profile: WTMG-FM is a commercial station owned by Marc Radio Group, LLC. The format of the station is urban contemporary. WTMG-FM broadcasts in the Gainesville, FL area at 101.3 FM.

WTMJ-AM
Owner: Journal Broadcast Group
Editorial: 720 E Capitol Dr, Milwaukee, Wisconsin 53212-1308. **T:** 1 414 332-9611
E: webteam@wtmj.com
W: http://www.620wtmj.com
Editorial Profile: WTMJ-AM is a commercial station owned by Journal Broadcast Group. The format of the station is news, sports and talk. WTMJ-AM broadcasts to the Milwaukee area at 620 AM.

WTMK-FM
Owner: Calvary Chapel of Costa Mesa, Inc.
Editorial: 150 Lincolnway, Ste 2001, Valparaiso, Indiana 46383-5556.
T: 1 219 548-5800
E: info@calvaryradionet.com
W: http://www.calvaryradionetwork.com
Editorial Profile: WTMK-FM is a non-commercial station owned by Calvary Chapel of Costa Mesa, Inc. The format of the station is Christian music and religious programming. WTMK-FM broadcasts to the Lowell, IN area at 88.5 FM.

WTMM-FM
Owner: Townsquare Media, LLC.
Editorial: 1241 Kings Road, Schenectady, New York 12303. **T:** 1 518 881-1515
W: http://1045theteam.com
Editorial Profile: WTMM-FM is a commercial station owned by Townsquare Media, LLC. The format of the station is sports. WTMM-FM broadcasts to the Albany, NY area at 104.5 FM

WTMN-AM
Owner: Marc Radio Group, LLC
Editorial: 100 NW 76th Dr Ste 2, Gainesville, Florida 32607-6659. **T:** 1 352 313-3150
Editorial Profile: WTMN-AM is a station owned by Marc Radio Group, LLC and operated by Sunshine Broadcasting. The format of the station is sports. WTMN-AM broadcasts to the Gainsville, FL area at a frequency of 1430 AM.

WTMP-AM
Owner: West Coast Media Group
Editorial: 407 N Howard Ave Ste 200, Tampa, Florida 33606-1575. **T:** 1 813 259-9867
W: http://www.am1150wtmp.com
Editorial Profile: WTMP-AM is a commercial station owned by West Coast Media Group. The format of the station is urban adult contemporary and talk. WTMP-AM broadcasts to the Tampa area at 1150 AM.

WTMP-FM
Owner: Davidson Media Group
Editorial: 407 N Howard Ave Ste 200, Tampa, Florida 33606-1575. **T:** 1 813 259-9867
W: http://lamexicana961.com
Editorial Profile: WTMP-FM is a commercial station owned by Davidson Media Group. The format of the station is regional Mexican. WTMP-FM broadcasts to the Tampa, FL area at 96.1 FM.

WTMR-AM
Owner: Beasley Broadcast Group
Editorial: 2775 Mount Ephraim Ave, Camden, New Jersey 08104-3211. **T:** 1 856 962-8000
W: http://www.wtmrradio.com
Editorial Profile: WTMR-AM is a commercial station owned by Beasley Broadcast Group. The format of the station is religious. WTMR-AM broadcasts to the Camden, NJ area at 800 AM.

WTMT-FM
Owner: Saga Communications
Editorial: 1190 Patton Ave, Asheville, North Carolina 28806-2706. **T:** 1 828 259-9695
W: http://www.1059themountain.com
Editorial Profile: WTMT-FM is a commercial station owned by Saga Communications. The format of the station is rock. WTMT-FM broadcasts to the Asheville, NC area at 105.9 FM.

WTMX-FM
Owner: Hubbard Radio, LLC
Editorial: 130 E Randolph St Ste 2700, Chicago, Illinois 60601-6307.
T: 1 312 946-1019 **W:** http://www.wtmx.com
Editorial Profile: WTMX-FM is a commercial station owned by Hubbard Radio, LLC. The format of the station is Hot AC. WTMX-FM broadcasts to the Chicago area at 101.9 FM.

WTMY-AM
Owner: Polnet Communications
Editorial: 1956 Main St, Sarasota, Florida 34236-5915. **T:** 1 941 955-9387
E: traffic.wtmy@gmail.com
W: http://www.wtmy.com
Editorial Profile: WTMY-AM is a commercial station owned by Polnet Communications. The format of the station is adult standards. WTMY-AM broadcasts to the Sarasota, FL area at 1280 AM.

WTMZ-AM
Owner: Kirkman Broadcasting
Editorial: 60 Markfield Dr, Charleston, South Carolina 29407-7907. **T:** 1 843 763-6631
W: http://www.charlestonsportsradio.com
Editorial Profile: WTMZ-AM is a commercial station owned by Kirkman Broadcasting. The format of the station is sports. WTMZ-AM broadcasts to the Charleston, SC area at 910 AM.

WTNI-AM
Owner: L & L Radio
Editorial: 1909 E Pass Rd Ste D11, Gulfport, Mississippi 39507-3778. **T:** 1 228 388-2001
Editorial Profile: WTNI-AM is a commercial station owned by L & L Radio. The format of the station is sports. WTNI-AM broadcasts to the Biloxi-Gulfport, MS area at 1640 AM.

WTNJ-FM
Owner: Southern Communications Corp.
Editorial: 306 S Kanawha St, Beckley, West Virginia 25801. **T:** 1 304 252-6452

W: http://www.wtnjfm.com
Editorial Profile: WTNJ-FM is a commercial station owned by Southern Communications Corp. The format of the station is country music. WTNJ-FM broadcasts to the Beckley, WV area at 105.9 FM.

WTNK-AM
Owner: G & L Aircasters Inc.
Editorial: 165 Marlene St, Hartsville, Tennessee 37074. **T:** 1 615 374-2111
E: wtnk@ainweb.net **W:** http://www.wtnk.com
Editorial Profile: WTNK-AM is a commercial station owned by G & L Aircasters Inc. The format of the station is contemporary country. WTNK-AM broadcasts to the Hartsville, TN area at 1090 AM.

WTNL-AM
Owner: Register (William Keith)
Editorial: 125 Friar Tuck Circle, Reidsville, Georgia 30453. **T:** 1 912 557-4140
E: wrbxwtnl@windstream.net
W: http://www.wrbx.org
Editorial Profile: WTNL-AM is a commercial station owned by Register (William Keith). The format of the station is Christian talk and Southern Gospel. WTNL-AM broadcasts to the Reidsville, GA area at a frequency of 1390 AM.

WTNM-FM
Owner: TeleSouth Communications Inc.
Editorial: 461 Highway 6 W, Oxford, Mississippi 38655-9073. **T:** 1 662 236-0093
E: oxford@telesouth.com
W: http://www.supertalk.fm
Editorial Profile: WTNM-FM is a commercial station owned by TeleSouth Communications Inc. The format of the station is talk. WTNM-FM broadcasts to the Oxford, MS area at 105.5 FM.

WTNN-FM
Owner: Impact Radio, INC
Editorial: 4049 Williston Rd Ste 7, South Burlington, Vermont 05403-6048.
T: 1 802 864-9750
W: http://eaglecountry975.com
Editorial Profile: WTNN-FM is a commercial station owned by Impact Radio, INC. The format of the station is country. WTNN-FM broadcasts to the South Burlington, VT area at a frequency of 97.5 FM.

WTNQ-FM
Owner: Momentum Broadcasting
Editorial: 305 E Central Ave, La Follette, Tennessee 37766-3618. **T:** 1 423 566-1310
W: http://wtnqfm.com
Editorial Profile: WTNQ-FM is a commercial station owned by Momentum Broadcasting. The format of the station is country. WTNQ-FM broadcasts to the La Follette, TN area at 104.9 FM.

WTNR-FM
Owner: Cumulus Media Inc.
Editorial: 60 Monroe Center St NW, Grand Rapids, Michigan 49503-2916.
T: 1 616 774-8461
W: http://www.nashfm945.com
Editorial Profile: WTNR-FM is a commercial station owned by Cumulus Media Inc. The format of the station is country. WTNR-FM broadcasts to the Grand Rapids, MI area at 94.5 FM.

WTNS-AM
Owner: Coshocton Broadcasting Company
Editorial: 114 N 6th St, Coshocton, Ohio 43812. **T:** 1 740 622-1560
W: http://www.mywtnsradio.com
Editorial Profile: WTNS-AM is a commercial station owned by Coshocton Broadcasting Company. The format of the station is classic country. WTNS-AM broadcasts to the Coshocton, OH, area at 1560 AM.

WTNS-FM
Owner: Coshocton Broadcasting Company
Editorial: 114 N 6th St, Coshocton, Ohio 43812-1601. **T:** 1 740 622-1560
W: http://www.mywtnsradio.com
Editorial Profile: WTNS-FM is a commercial station owned by Coshocton Broadcasting Company. The station's format is adult contemporary. WTNS-FM broadcasts to the Coschocton, OH area at 99.3 FM.

WTNT-FM
Owner: Clear Channel Media and Entertainment
Editorial: 325 John Knox Rd Bldg G, Tallahassee, Florida 32303-4113.
T: 1 850 422-3107
W: http://www.949tnt.com/main.html
Editorial Profile: WTNT-FM is a commercial station owned by Clear Channel Media and Entertainment. The format of the station is contemporary country music. WTNT-FM broadcasts to the Tallahassee, FL area at 94.9 FM.

WTNV-FM
Owner: Burks(W.E.)
Editorial: 2555 Burks Pl, Dyersburg, Tennessee 38024-1724. **T:** 1 731 285-1339
W: http://www.eagle973.net
Editorial Profile: WTNV-FM is a commercial station owned by W.E. Burks. The format of the station is contemporary country. WTNV-FM broadcasts to the Dyersburg, TN area at 97.3 FM.

WTNW-AM
Owner: Shelton Broadcasting
Editorial: 4896 Main St, Jasper, Tennessee 37347-3681. **T:** 1 423 942-1700
W: http://www.gospel820.com
Editorial Profile: WTNW-AM is a commercial station owned by Shelton Broadcasting. The format of the station is classic country. WTNW-AM broadcasts to the Jasper, TN area at 820 AM.

WTNY-AM
Owner: Stephens Family LP
Editorial: 134 Mullin St, Watertown, New York 13601. **T:** 1 315 788-0790
E: morning@790wtny.com
W: http://www.790wtny.com
Editorial Profile: WTNY-AM is a commercial station owned by Stephens Family LP. The format of the station is news and talk. WTNY-AM broadcasts to the Watertown, NY area at 790 AM.

WTOB-AM
Owner: Davidson Media Group
Editorial: 4015 Brownsboro Rd, Ste 200, Winston Salem, North Carolina 27106-3380.
T: 1 336 714-2831
W: http://www.quepasamedia.com
Editorial Profile: WTOB-AM is a commercial station owned by Davidson Media Group and run by Que Pasa Media Network. The format of the station is regional Mexican. WWBG-AM broadcasts to the Winston Salem, NC area at 1380 AM.

WTOD-AM
Owner: Cumulus Media Inc.
Editorial: 2014 N Irby St, Florence, South Carolina 29501-1504. **T:** 1 843 661-5000
W: http://www.thefanfm.com
Editorial Profile: WTOD-AM is a commercial station owned by Cumulus Media Inc. The format of the station is sports. WTOD-AM broadcasts to the Florence, SC area at 1450 AM.

WTOE-AM
Owner: Mountain Valley Media Inc.
Editorial: 749 Sawmill Road, Burnsville, North Carolina 28714-6749. **T:** 1 828 765-7441
E: 1470@wtoe.com **W:** http://www.wtoe.com
Editorial Profile: WTOE-AM is a commercial station owned by Mountain Valley Media Inc. The format of the station is classic hits. WTOE-AM broadcasts to the Burnsville, NC area at 1470 AM.

WTOF-AM
Owner: Buddy Tucker Association, Inc.
Editorial: 720 S White Ave, Bay Minette, Alabama 36507-7527. **T:** 1 251 947-1000

WTOH-FM
Owner: Salem Communications
Editorial: 8101 N High St Ste 360, Columbus, Ohio 43235-1442. **T:** 1 614 885-0880
W: http://www.989theanswer.com
Editorial Profile: WTOH-FM is a commercial station owned by Salem Communications. The format of the station is talk. WTOH-FM broadcasts to the Columbus, OH area at 98.9 FM.

WTOJ-FM
Owner: Community Broadcasters, LLC
Editorial: 199 Wealtha Ave, Watertown, New York 13601. **T:** 1 315 782-1240
Editorial Profile: WTOJ-FM is a commercial station owned by Community Broadcasters, LLC. The format of the station is adult contemporary. WTOJ-FM broadcasts to the Watertown, NY area at 103.1 FM.

WTON-AM
Owner: High Impact Communications Inc.
Editorial: 304 W Beverley St, Staunton, Virginia 24401-4207. **T:** 1 540 885-5188
E: star94@ntelos.net
Editorial Profile: WTON-AM is a commercial station owned by High Impact Communications Inc. The format of the station is sports. WTON-AM broadcasts to Staunton, VA at 1240 AM.

WTON-FM
Owner: High Impact Communications Inc.
Editorial: 304 W Beverly St, Staunton, Virginia 24401. **T:** 1 540 885-5188
E: star94@ntelos.net
Editorial Profile: WTON-FM is a commercial station owned by High Impact Communications Inc. The format of the station is classic hits music. WTON-FM broadcasts to the Richmond, VA, area at 94.3 FM.

WTOP-FM
Owner: Hubbard Broadcasting
Editorial: 3400 Idaho Ave NW, Washington, District Of Columbia 20016-3046.
T: 1 202 895-5000 **W:** http://www.wtop.com
Editorial Profile: WTOP-FM is a commercial station owned by Hubbard Broadcasting. The format of the station is news. WTOP-FM broadcasts to the Washington, D.C. area at 103.5 FM.

WTOS-FM
Owner: Blueberry Broadcasting
Editorial: 125 Community Dr Ste 201, Augusta, Maine 04330-8157.
T: 1 207 623-9000 **W:** http://www.wtosfm.com
Editorial Profile: WTOS-FM is a commercial station owned by Blueberry Broadcasting. The format of the station is rock music. WTOS-FM broadcasts to the Augusta, ME area at 105.1 FM.

WTOT-AM
Owner: GFR Inc.
Editorial: 4376 Lafayette St Ste A, Marianna, Florida 32446-3300. **T:** 1 850 482-3046
E: wjaqfm@gmail.com
Editorial Profile: WTOT-AM is a commercial station owned by GFR Inc. The format of the station is contemporary Christian music. WTOT-AM broadcasts to the Marianna, FL area at 980 AM.

WTOW-AM
Owner: Rouse(James)
Editorial: 903 Hackney Ave, Washington, North Carolina 27889. **T:** 1 252 975-1320
Editorial Profile: WTOW-AM is a commercial station owned by James Rouse. The format of the station is gospel. WTOW-AM broadcasts to the Washington, NC area at 1320 AM.

WTOX-AM
Owner: Davidson Media Group
Editorial: 308 W Broad St, Richmond, Virginia 23220. **T:** 1 804 643-0990
E: wtox@davidsonmediagroup.com
W: http://www.lagrand1480.com
Editorial Profile: WTOX-AM is a commercial station owned by Davidson Media Group. The format of the station is Regional Mexican. WTOX-AM broadcasts to the Richmond, VA area at 1480 AM.

WTOY-AM
Owner: Ward(Irvin)
Editorial: 504 23rd St NW, Roanoke, Virginia 24017. **T:** 1 540 344-9869
E: wtoyradio@aol.com
Editorial Profile: WTOY-AM is a commercial station owned by Irvin Ward. The format of the station is urban contemporary and gospel. WTOY-AM broadcasts to the Roanoke, VA area at 1480 AM.

WTPA-FM
Owner: Sickafus, Patrick
Editorial: 515 S 32nd St, Camp Hill, Pennsylvania 17011-5106. **T:** 1 717 238-6397
W: http://www.921wtpa.com
Editorial Profile: WTPA-FM is a commercial station owned by Patrick Sickafus. The format of the station is classic rock. WTPA-FM broadcasts to the Harrisburg, PA area at 92.1 FM.

WTPL-FM
Owner: Great Eastern Radio, LLC
Editorial: 501 South St Fl 3, Bow, New Hampshire 03304-3416. **T:** 1 603 545-0777
E: production@wtplfm.com
W: http://www.wtplfm.com
Editorial Profile: WTPL-FM is a commercial station owned by Great Eastern Radio, LLC. The format of the station is news, talk and sports. WTPL-FM broadcasts to the Concord, NH area at 107.7 FM.

WTPR-AM
Owner: WENK of Union City, Inc.
Editorial: 206 N Brewer St, Paris, Tennessee 38242. **T:** 1 731 642-7100
W: http://www.wenkwtpr.com
Editorial Profile: WTPR-AM is a commercial station owned by WENK of Union City, Inc. The format of the station is oldies. WTPR-AM broadcasts to the Paris, TN area at 710 AM.

WTPR-FM
Owner: WENK of Union City, Inc.
Editorial: 206 N Brewer St, Paris, Tennessee 38242. **T:** 1 731 642-7100
W: http://www.wenkwtpr.com
Editorial Profile: WTPR-FM is a commercial station owned by WENK of Union City, Inc. The format of the station is oldies. WTPR-FM broadcasts to the Paris, TN area at 101.7 FM.

WTPS-AM
Owner: Radio One Inc.
Editorial: 2809 Emerywood Pkwy Ste 300, Richmond, Virginia 23294-3743.
T: 1 804 672-9299
W: http://www.newstalk1240wtps.com
Editorial Profile: WTPS-AM is a commercial station owned by Radio One Inc. The format for the station is talk and R&B oldies. WTPS-AM broadcasts to the Richmond VA, area at 1240 AM.

WTPT-FM
Owner: Entercom Communications Corp.
Editorial: 25 Garlington Rd, Greenville, South Carolina 29615-4613. **T:** 1 864 271-9200
W: http://www.newrock933.com
Editorial Profile: WTPT-FM is a commercial station owned by Entercom Communications Corp. The format of the station is active rock. WTPT-FM broadcasts to the Greensville, SC area at 93.3 FM.

WTQR-FM
Owner: Clear Channel Media and Entertainment
Editorial: 2B Pai Park, Greensboro, North Carolina 27409-9428. **T:** 1 336 822-2000
W: http://www.wtqr.com
Editorial Profile: WTQR-FM is a commercial station owned by Clear Channel Media and Entertainment. The format of the station is contemporary country. WTQR-FM broadcasts to the Greensboro, NC area at 104.1 FM.

WTQX-FM
Owner: Blueberry Broadcasting
Editorial: 125 Community Dr Ste 201, Augusta, Maine 04330-8157.
T: 1 207 623-9000 **W:** http://www.wtosfm.com
Editorial Profile: WTQX-FM is a commercial station owned by Blueberry Broadcasting. The format of the station is rock music. WTQX-FM broadcasts to the Augusta, ME area at 96.7 FM.

WTRB-AM
Owner: WTRB, INC.
Editorial: 372 S Jefferson St, Ripley, Tennessee 38063. **T:** 1 731 635-1570
E: wtrb@newwavecomm.net
Editorial Profile: WTRB-AM is a commercial station owned by WTRB, INC. The format of the station is country variety. WTRB-AM broadcasts in the Ripley, TN area at 1570 AM.

WTRC-AM
Owner: Pathfinder Communications Corporation
Editorial: 237 W Edison Rd, Mishawaka, Indiana 46545-3103. **T:** 1 574 258-5483
W: http://www.953mnc.com
Editorial Profile: WTRC-AM is a commercial station owned by Pathfinder Communications Corporation, a division of Federated Media. The format of the station is news and talk. WTRC-AM broadcasts to the Elkhart, IN area at 1340 AM.

WTRC-FM
Owner: Pathfinder Communications Corporation
Editorial: 237 W Edison Rd, Mishawaka, Indiana 46545-3103. **T:** 1 574 258-5483
W: http://www.953mnc.com
Editorial Profile: WTRC-FM is a commercial station owned by Pathfinder Communications Corporation, a division of Federated Media. The format of the station is news and talk. WTRC-FM broadcasts to the South Bend, IN area at 95.3 FM.

WTRE-AM
Owner: WTRE, Inc.
Editorial: 1217 W Park Rd, Greensburg, Indiana 47240-7886. **T:** 1 812 663-3000
E: wtre.wtre@gmail.com

W: http://www.1330wtre.com
Editorial Profile: WTRE-AM is a commercial station owned by WTRE, Inc. The format for the station is country. WTRE-FM broadcasts to the Indianapolis area at 1330 AM.

WTRG-FM
Owner: First Media Radio LLC
Editorial: 3 E 1st St, Weldon, North Carolina 27890-1560. **T:** 1 252 538-9790
W: http://www.thegreat98fm.com
Editorial Profile: WTRG-FM is a commercial station owned by First Media Radio LLC. The format of the station is classic hits. WTRG-FM broadcasts to the Weldon, NC area at 97.9 FM.

WTRH-FM
Owner: Countryside Broadcasting
Editorial: RR 2, Box 51A, Ramsey, Illinois 62080-9345. **T:** 1 618 423-2082
E: wtrh@frontiernet.net
Editorial Profile: WTRH-FM is a commercial station owned by Countryside Broadcasting. The format of the station is oldies, gospel and talk. WTRH-FM broadcasts to the Ramsey, IL area at 93.3 FM.

WTRJ-FM
Owner: Delmarva Educational Association
Editorial: 4190 Belfort Rd Ste 450, Jacksonville, Florida 32216-1405.
T: 1 904 641-9626
W: http://www.ilovethepromise.com
Editorial Profile: WTRJ-FM is a non-commercial station owned by Delmarva Educational Association. The format of the station is Contemporary Christian music. WTRJ-FM broadcasts to the Jacksonville, FL area at 91.7 FM.

WTRM-FM
Owner: American Family Association, Inc.
Editorial: 2045 Valley Ave, Winchester, Virginia 22601-2751. **T:** 1 540 723-0123
E: office@southernlight.us
W: http://www.southernlight.us
Editorial Profile: WTRM-FM is a non-commercial station owned by American Family Association, Inc. The format of the station is gospel music and religious talk. WTRM-FM broadcasts in the Winchester, VA area at 91.3 FM.

WTRN-AM
Owner: Allegheny Mountain Network
Editorial: 5620 E Pleasant Valley Blvd, Tyrone, Pennsylvania 16686-1280. **T:** 1 814 684-3200
E: amnnet@aol.com
Editorial Profile: WTRN-AM is a commercial station owned by Allegheny Mountain Network. The format of the station is adult contemporary music. WTRN-AM broadcasts to the Altoona, PA area at 1340 AM.

WTRO-AM
Owner: Burks(W.E.)
Editorial: 2555 Burks Pl, Dyersburg, Tennessee 38024-1724. **T:** 1 731 285-1339
W: http://www.wtroradio.net
Editorial Profile: WTRO-AM is a commercial station owned by W. E. Burks. The format of the station is oldies. WTRO-AM broadcasts to the Dyersburg, TN area at 1450 AM.

WTRP-AM
Owner: Tiger Communications Inc.
Editorial: 806 New Franklin Rd, Lagrange, Georgia 30240-1844. **T:** 1 706 884-8611
E: wtrp@charter.net
Editorial Profile: WTRP-AM is a commercial station owned by Tiger Communications Inc. The format of the station is classic hits. WTRP-AM broadcasts to the Lagrange, GA area at 620 AM.

WTRS-FM
Owner: JVC Broadcasting Inc.
Editorial: 3357 SW 7th St, Ocala, Florida 34474-1956. **T:** 1 352 867-1023
E: info@mycountryfla.com
W: http://www.mycountryfla.com
Editorial Profile: WTRS-FM is a commercial station owned by JVC Broadcasting Inc. The format is contemporary country music. WTRS-FM broadcasts to the Ocala, FL area at 102.3 FM.

WTRT-FM
Owner: Heartland Ministries, Inc.
Editorial: 219 College St, Hardin, Kentucky 42048. **T:** 1 270 437-4095
E: info@hmiradio.com
W: http://www.hmiradio.com/wtrt
Editorial Profile: WTRT-FM is a commercial station owned by Heartland Ministries, Inc. The format of the station is contemporary Christian. WTRT-FM broadcasts to the Hardin, KY area at 88.1 FM.

WTRU-AM
Owner: Truth Broadcasting
Editorial: 4405 Providence Ln, Winston Salem, North Carolina 27106-3226.
T: 1 336 759-0363 **E:** info@wtru.com
W: http://www.wtru.com
Editorial Profile: WTRU-AM is a commercial station owned by Truth Broadcasting. The format of the station is Christian news and talk. WTRU-AM broadcasts to the Winston Salem, NC area at 830 AM.

WTRV-FM
Owner: Townsquare Media, LLC
Editorial: 50 Monroe Ave NW Ste 500, Grand Rapids, Michigan 49503-2656.
T: 1 616 451-4855
E: vip.support@townsquaremedia.com
W: http://rivergrandrapids.com
Editorial Profile: WTRV-FM is a commercial station owned by Townsquare Media, LLC. The format of the station is Lite Rock/Lite AC. WTRV-FM broadcasts to the Grand Rapids, MI listeners at 100.5 FM.

WTRW-FM
Owner: Bold Gold Media Group
Editorial: 1049 N Sekol Ave, Scranton, Pennsylvania 18504-1040. **T:** 1 570 344-1221
W: http://www.talker943.com
Editorial Profile: WTRW-FM is a commercial station owned by Bold Gold Media Group. The format of the station is news and talk. WTRW-FM broadcasts to the Nanticoke, PA area at 94.3 FM.

WTRX-AM
Owner: Cumulus Media Inc.
Editorial: G 4511 Miller Rd, Flint, Michigan 48507. **T:** 1 810 720-9510
W: http://www.wtrxsports.com
Editorial Profile: WTRX-AM is a commercial station owned by Cumulus Media Inc. The format of the station is sports and talk. WTRX-AM broadcasts to the Flint, MI area at 1330 AM.

WTRY-FM
Owner: Clear Channel Media and Entertainment
Editorial: 1203 Troy Schenectady Rd, Latham, New York 12110. **T:** 1 518 452-4800
W: http://www.wtry.com
Editorial Profile: WTRY-FM is a commercial station owned by Clear Channel Media and Entertainment. The format of the station is oldies. WTRY-FM broadcasts to the Latham, NY area at 98.3 FM.

WTRZ-FM
Owner: Peg Broadcasting
Editorial: 230 W Colville St, Mc Minnville, Tennessee 37110. **T:** 1 931 473-9253
W: http://www.star201fm.net
Editorial Profile: WTRZ-FM is a commercial station owned by Peg Broadcasting. The format of the station is adult contemporary. WTRZ-FM broadcasts to the McMinnville, TN area at 107.3 FM.

WTSA-AM
Owner: Four Seasons Media Inc.
Editorial: 464 Putney Rd, Brattleboro, Vermont 05301-9053. **T:** 1 802 254-4577
E: news@wtsa.net **W:** http://www.wtsa.net
Editorial Profile: WTSA-AM is a commercial station owned by Four Seasons Media Inc. The format of the station is sports. WTSA-AM broadcasts to the Brattleboro, VT, area at 1450 AM.

WTSA-FM
Owner: Four Seasons Media Inc.
Editorial: 464 Putney Rd, Brattleboro, Vermont 05301-9053. **T:** 1 802 254-4577
E: news@wtsa.net **W:** http://www.wtsa.net
Editorial Profile: WTSA-FM is a commercial station owned by Four Seasons Media Inc. The format of the station is adult contemporary. WTSA-FM broadcasts to the Brattleboro, VT area at 96.7 FM.

WTSB-AM
Owner: Lamm Media Group
Editorial: 4001 US Highway 301 S, Four Oaks, North Carolina 27524. **T:** 1 919 934-6789
E: info@wtsbradio.com
W: http://www.wtsbradio.com
Editorial Profile: WTSB-AM is a commercial station owned by Lamm Media Group. The format of the station is news, country and gospel. WTSB-AM broadcasts to the Four Oaks, NC area at 1090 AM.

WTSH-FM
Owner: Woman's World Broadcasting, Inc.
Editorial: 20 John Davenport Dr NW, Rome, Georgia 30165-2536. **T:** 1 706 291-9496
E: south107@aol.com
W: http://www.south107.com
Editorial Profile: WTSH-FM is a commercial station owned by Woman's World Broadcasting, Inc and operated by Cumulus Media.The format of the station is contemporary country. WTSH-FM broadcasts to the Rome, GA and Metro Atlanta areas at 107.1 FM.

WTSK-AM
Owner: Townsquare Media, Inc.
Editorial: 142 Skyland Blvd, Tuscaloosa, Alabama 35405-4015. **T:** 1 205 345-7200
W: http://www.790wtsk.com
Editorial Profile: WTSK-AM is a commercial station owned by Townsquare Media, Inc. The format of the station is gospel. WTSK-AM broadcasts to the Tuscaloosa, AL area at 790 AM.

WTSL-AM
Owner: Great Eastern Radio, LLC
Editorial: 31 Hanover St, Lebanon, New Hampshire 03766-1312. **T:** 1 603 448-1400
W: http://www.wtsl.com
Editorial Profile: WTSL-AM is a commercial station owned by Great Eastern Radio, LLC. The format of the station is news and talk. WTSL-AM broadcasts to the Connecticut River Valley area at 1400 AM.

WTSM-FM
Owner: Woodville Communications Inc.
Editorial: 435 Saint Francis St, Tallahassee, Florida 32301. **T:** 1 850 561-8400
E: studio@979espnradio.com
W: http://www.979espnradio.com/
Editorial Profile: WTSM-FM is a commercial station owned by Woodville Communications Inc. The format of the station is sports. WTSM-FM broadcasts to the Tallahassee, FL area at 97.9 FM.

WTSN-AM
Owner: Garrison City Broadcasting
Editorial: 101 Back Rd, Dover, New Hampshire 03820-5003. **T:** 1 603 742-0987
W: http://www.wtsnam1270.com
Editorial Profile: WTSN-AM is a commercial station owned by Garrison City Broadcasting Inc. The format of the station is sports, news and talk. WTSN-AM broadcasts to the Portsmouth, NH area at 1270 AM.

WTSO-AM
Owner: Clear Channel Media and Entertainment
Editorial: 2651 S Fish Hatchery Rd, Fitchburg, Wisconsin 53711-5410. **T:** 1 608 274-5450
W: http://www.thebig1070.com
Editorial Profile: WTSO-AM is a commercial station owned by Clear Channel Media and Entertainment. The format of the station is sports. WTSO-AM broadcasts to the Madison, WI area at 1070 AM.

WTSR-FM
Owner: The College of New Jersey
Editorial: 2000 Pennington Rd, Ewing, New Jersey 8618. **T:** 1 609 771-3200
E: wtsr@wtsr.org **W:** http://www.wtsr.org
Editorial Profile: WTSR-FM is a non-commercial station owned by The College of New Jersey. The format of the station is college variety. WTSR-FM broadcasts to the Trenton, NJ area at 91.3 FM.

WTSS-FM
Owner: Entercom Communications Corp.
Editorial: 500 Corporate Pkwy, Ste 200, Buffalo, New York 14226. **T:** 1 716 843-0600
W: http://www.mystar1025.com
Editorial Profile: WTSS-FM is a commercial station owned by Entercom Communications Corp. The format of the station is hot adult contemporary music. WTSS-FM broadcasts in the Buffalo, NY area at 102.5 FM.

WTSU-FM
Owner: Troy University
Editorial: Troy University Wallace Hall, Troy, Alabama 36082. **T:** 1 334 670-3268
E: publicradio@troy.edu
W: http://wtsu.troy.edu
Editorial Profile: WTSU-FM is a non-commercial station owned by Troy University. The format of the station is classical music and news. WTSU-FM broadcasts to the Troy, AL area at 89.9 FM.

WTSV-AM
Owner: Great Eastern Radio, LLC
Editorial: 106 N Main St, West Lebanon, New Hampshire 03784-1136. **T:** 1 603 298-0332
W: http://www.wtsl.com
Editorial Profile: WTSV-AM is a commercial station owned by Great Eastern Radio, LLC. The format of the station is news and talk. WTSV-AM broadcasts to the Connecticut River Valley area of New Hampshire and Vermont at 1230 AM.

WTTB-AM
Owner: Treasure & Space Coast Radio
Editorial: 1235 16th St, Vero Beach, Florida 32960. **T:** 1 772 567-0937
E: news@wttbam.com
W: http://www.wttbam.com
Editorial Profile: WTTB-AM is a commercial station owned by Treasure & Space Coast Radio. The format of the station is news and talk programming. WTTB-AM broadcasts to the Vero Beach, FL area at 1490 AM.

WTTC-AM
Owner: Cantroair Communications Co.
Editorial: 170 Redington Ave, Troy, Pennsylvania 16947. **T:** 1 570 297-0100
E: whgl100@gmail.com
W: http://www.wtzn.com
Editorial Profile: WTTC-AM is a commercial station owned by Cantroair Communications Co. The format of the station is sports. WTTC-AM broadcasts to the Troy, PA area at 1550 AM.

WTTC-FM
Owner: Cantroair Communications Co.
Editorial: 170 Redington Ave, Troy, Pennsylvania 16947. **T:** 1 570 297-0100
E: thebridgefm@frontiernet.net
W: http://www.953thebridge.com
Editorial Profile: WTTC-FM is a commercial station owned by Cantroair Communications Co. The format of the station is classic hits. WTTC-FM broadcasts ot the Troy, PA area at 95.3 FM.

WTTF-AM
Owner: BAS Broadcasting
Editorial: 310 E Market St, Tiffin, Ohio 44883-2434. **T:** 1 419 447-2212
W: http://www.wttf.com
Editorial Profile: WTTF-AM is a commercial station owned by Heidelberg College. The format of the station is oldies, news, and sports. WTTF-AM broadcasts to the Toledo, OH area at 1600 AM.

WTTH-FM
Owner: Equity Communications LP
Editorial: 8025 Black Horse Pike, Ste 100, Pleasantville, New Jersey 8232.
T: 1 609 484-8444
W: http://www.961wtth.com
Editorial Profile: WTTH-FM is a commercial station owned by Equity Communications LP. The format of the station is urban contemporary music. WTTH-FM broadcasts to the West Atlantic City, NJ area at 96.1 FM.

WTTI-AM
Owner: Hall Broadcasting (Troy)
Editorial: 562 Deck Dr, Rocky Face, Georgia 30740. **T:** 1 706 673-2222
E: wttiradio1530@yahoo.com
W: http://www.wttiradio.com
Editorial Profile: WTTI-AM is a commercial station owned by Troy Hall Broadcasting. The format of the station is Contemporary Christian. WTTI-AM broadcasts to the Dalton, GA area at 1530 AM.

WTTL-AM
Owner: Commonwealth Broadcasting Corp.
Editorial: 265 S Main St, Madisonville, Kentucky 42431. **T:** 1 270 821-1310
Editorial Profile: WTTL-AM is a commercial radio station owned by Commonwealth Broadcasting Corp. The format of the station is sports talk. The station airs locally on 1310 AM.

WTTM-AM
Owner: Multicultural Radio Broadcasting Inc.
Editorial: 3573 Bristol Pike Suite 102&103, Bensalem, Pennsylvania 19020-4666.
T: 1 267 527-9886 **E:** wttm1680@yahoo.com
W: http://www.radiowttm1680.com
Editorial Profile: WTTM-AM is a commercial station owned by Multicultural Radio Broadcasting Inc. The format of the station is Hispanic music and programming. WTTM-AM's broadcasts to the Philadelphia area at 1680 AM.

WTTN-AM
Owner: Good Karma Broadcasting

Editorial: 100 Stoddart St, Beaver Dam, Wisconsin 53916-1306. **T:** 1 920 885-4442
W: http://espndeportes.espn.go.com
Editorial Profile: WTTN-AM is a commercial station owned by Good Karma Broadcasting. The format of the station is Spanish sports. WTTN-AM broadcasts to the Watertown, WI area at 1580 AM.

WTTR-AM
Owner: Sajak Broadcasting Corp.
Editorial: 101 Wttr Ln, Westminster, Maryland 21158-4269. **T:** 1 410 848-5511
E: news@wttr.com **W:** http://www.wttr.com
Editorial Profile: WTTR-AM is a commercial station owned by Sajak Broadcasting Corp. The format of the station is oldies. WTTR-AM broadcasts to the Westminster, MD area at 1470 AM.

WTTS-FM
Owner: Sarkes Tarzian Inc.
Editorial: 120 W 7th St Ste 400, Bloomington, Indiana 47404-3869. **T:** 1 812 332-3366
E: comments@wttsfm.com
W: http://www.wttsfm.com
Editorial Profile: WTTS-FM is a commercial station owned by Sarkes Tarzian Inc. The format of the station is adult album alternative. WTTS-FM broadcasts to the Indianapolis area at 92.3 FM.

WTTU-FM
Owner: Tennessee Technological University
Editorial: Roaden University Ctr, Room 376, Cookeville, Tennessee 38505.
T: 1 931 372-3169 **E:** davewttu@gmail.com
W: http://www.tntech.edu
Editorial Profile: WTTU-FM is a non-commercial station owned by Tennessee Technological University. The format of the station is Alternative Music. WTTU-FM broadcasts to the Nashville, TN area at 88.5 FM.

WTTX-FM
Owner: Positive Alternative Radio
Editorial: 22226 Timberlake Rd, Lynchburg, Virginia 24502-7305. **T:** 1 434 352-7607
E: joy107fm@yahoo.com
W: http://www.joyfm.org
Editorial Profile: WTTX-FM is a non-commercial station owned by Positive Alternative Radio. The format of the station is Southern gospel. WTTX-FM broadcasts to the Lynchburg, VA area at 107.1 FM.

WTUA-FM
Owner: Snipe(Alex)
Editorial: 4013 Byrnes Dr, Saint Stephen, South Carolina 29479-3988.
T: 1 843 567-2091 **E:** wtua@tds.net
W: http://www.wtuaradio.com
Editorial Profile: WTUA-FM is a commercial station owned by Alex Snipe. The format of the station is gospel. WTUA-FM broadcasts to the Saint Stephen, SC area at 106.1 FM.

WTUE-FM
Owner: Clear Channel Media and Entertainment
Editorial: 101 Pine St, Dayton, Ohio 45402-2925. **T:** 1 937 224-1137
W: http://www.wtue.com
Editorial Profile: WTUE-FM is a commercial station owned by Clear Channel Media and Entertainment. The format of the station is rock/album-oriented rock music. WTUE-FM broadcasts in the Dayton, OH area at 104.7 FM.

WTUF-FM
Owner: Lenrob Enterprises Inc.
Editorial: 117 Remington Ave, Thomasville, Georgia 31792. **T:** 1 229 225-1063
W: http://www.wtufradio.com
Editorial Profile: WTUF-FM is a commercial station owned by Lenrob Enterprises Inc. The format of the station is country music. WTUF-FM broadcasts to the Tallahassee, FL Thomasville, GA area at 106.3 FM.

WTUG-FM
Owner: Townsquare Media, Inc.
Editorial: 142 Skyland Blvd, Tuscaloosa, Alabama 35405-4015. **T:** 1 205 345-7200
W: http://www.wtug.com
Editorial Profile: WTUG-FM is a commercial station owned by Townsquare Media, Inc. The format of the station is urban adult contemporary music. WTUG-FM broadcasts to the Tuscaloosa, AL area at 92.9 FM.

WTUK-FM
Owner: Eastern Broadcasting Co.
Editorial: 125 S Main St, Harlan, Kentucky 40831-2109. **T:** 1 606 573-1470

E: wtuk-wfsr@harlanonline.net
W: http://www.wtuk1051.com
Editorial Profile: WTUK-FM is a commercial station owned by Eastern Broadcasting Co. The format of the station is country. WTUK-FM broadcasts to the Harlan, KY area at 105.1 FM.

WTUP-AM
Owner: URBan Radio Broadcasting, LLC
Editorial: 5026 Cliff Gookin Blvd, Tupelo, Mississippi 38801. **T:** 1 662 842-1067
W: http://www.wtup1490.com

WTUV-AM
Owner: Corona Media Group LLC
Editorial: 1939 Goldsmith Ln Ste 227, Louisville, Kentucky 40218-3178.
T: 1 502 618-4996
E: info@coronamediagroup.com
W: http://lapoderosaky.com
Editorial Profile: WTUV-AM is a commercial station owned by Corona Media Group LLC. The format of the station is regional Mexican. WTUV-AM broadcasts to the Louisville, KY area at 620 AM.

WTUV-FM
Owner: UB Louisville, LLC
Editorial: 11700 Commonwealth Dr, Louisville, Kentucky 40299-6303. **T:** 1 502 240-0602
W: http://www.espnlouisville.com
Editorial Profile: WTUV-FM is a commercial station owned by UB Louisville, LLC. The format of the station is sports talk. WTUV-FM broadcasts to the Louisville, KY area at 105.7 FM.

WTUX-FM
Owner: Blueberry Broadcasting
Editorial: 125 Community Dr Ste 201, Augusta, Maine 04330-8157.
T: 1 207 623-9000 **W:** http://www.wtosfm.com
Editorial Profile: WTUX-FM is a commercial station owned by Blueberry Broadcasting. The format of the station is rock music. WTUX-FM broadcasts to the Gouldsboro, ME area at 101.1 FM.

WTUZ-FM
Owner: WTUZ Radio Inc.
Editorial: 2424 E High Ave, New Philadelphia, Ohio 44663-3341. **T:** 1 330 339-2222
E: news@wtuz.com **W:** http://www.wtuz.com
Editorial Profile: WTUZ-FM is a commercial station owned by WTUZ Radio Inc. The format of the station is classic and contemporary country. WTUZ-FM broadcasts to the New Philadelphia, OH area at 99.9 FM.

WTVB-AM
Owner: Midwest Communications Inc.
Editorial: 182 N Angola Rd, Coldwater, Michigan 49036-9554. **T:** 1 517 279-1590
E: webmaster.wtvb@wtvbam.com
W: http://www.wtvbam.com
Editorial Profile: WTVB-AM is a commercial station owned by Midwest Communications Inc. The format of the station is oldies. WTVB-AM broadcasts to the Coldwater, MI area at 1590 AM.

WTVL-AM
Owner: Townsquare Media, LLC
Editorial: 56 Western Ave Ste 13, Augusta, Maine 04330-6348. **T:** 1 207 623-4735
W: http://www.1400and1490.com
Editorial Profile: WTVL-AM is a commercial station owned by Townsquare Media, LLC. The format of the station is adult standards music. WTVL-AM broadcasts to the Augusta, ME area at 1490 AM.

WTVN-AM
Owner: Clear Channel Media and Entertainment
Editorial: 2323 W 5th Ave Ste 200, Columbus, Ohio 43204-4988. **T:** 1 614 486-6101
E: newsroom@610wtvn.com
W: http://www.610wtvn.com
Editorial Profile: WTVN-AM is a commercial station owned by Clear Channel Media and Entertainment. The format of the station is news and talk. WTVN-AM broadcasts to the Columbus, OH area at 610 AM.

WTVR-FM
Owner: Clear Channel Media and Entertainment
Editorial: 3245 Basie Rd, Richmond, Virginia 23228. **T:** 1 804 474-0000
W: http://www.lite98.com
Editorial Profile: WTVR-FM is a commercial station owned by Clear Channel Media and Entertainment. The format of the station is Lite Rock/Lite AC music. WTVR-FM broadcasts to the Richmond, VA area at 98.1 FM.

WTVY-FM
Owner: Gulf South Communications, Inc.
Editorial: 285 N Foster St Floor 8, Dothan, Alabama 36303-4541. **T:** 1 334 792-0047
W: http://www.955wtvy.com
Editorial Profile: WTVY-FM is a commercial station owned by Gulf South Communications, Inc. The format of the station is country music. WTVY-FM broadcasts to the Dothan, AL area at 95.5 FM.

WTWA-AM
Owner: Camellia City Communications
Editorial: 788 Cedar Rock Rd, Thomson, Georgia 30824-7642. **T:** 1 706 595-1561
E: wtho@classicsouth.net
Editorial Profile: WTWA-AM is a commercial station owned by Camellia City Communications. The format of the station is oldies. WTWA-AM broadcasts to the Thomson, GA area at 1240 AM.

WTWB-AM
Owner: La Raza Media Group
Editorial: 127 Glenn Rd, Auburndale, Florida 33823-2401. **T:** 1 863 968-1100
E: laraza1570@gmail.com
W: http://www.laraza1570.com
Editorial Profile: WTWB-AM is a commercial station owned by La Raza Media Group. The format of the station is regional Mexican. WTWB-AM broadcasts to the Auburndale, FL area at 1570 AM.

WTWD-AM
Owner: Salem Communications
Editorial: 5211 W Laurel St Ste A, Tampa, Florida 33607-1736. **T:** 1 813 349-8231
W: http://www.letstalkfaith.com
Editorial Profile: WTWD-AM is a commercial station owned by Salem Communications. The format of the station is religious talk. WTWD-AM broadcasts to the Tampa, FL area on 910 AM.

WTWF-FM
Owner: Connoisseur Media LLC
Editorial: 1 Boston Store Pl, Erie, Pennsylvania 16501. **T:** 1 814 461-1000
E: production@connoisseurerie.com
W: http://www.939thewolf.com
Editorial Profile: WTWF-FM is a commercial station owned by Connoisseur Media LLC. The format of the station is country. WTWF-FM broadcasts to the Erie, PA area at 93.9 FM.

WTWG-AM
Owner: T & W Communications
Editorial: 1910 14th Ave N, Columbus, Mississippi 39701. **T:** 1 662 328-1050
E: wtwg1050@yahoo.com

WTWK-AM
Owner: Northeast Broadcasting Co.
Editorial: 372 Dorset St, South Burlington, Vermont 05403-6363. **T:** 1 802 863-1010
W: http://www.wtwk1070.com
Editorial Profile: WTWK-AM is a commercial station owned by Northeast Broadcasting Co. The format of the station is business news. WTWK-AM broadcasts to the South Burlington, VT, area at 1070 AM.

WTWN-AM
Owner: Puffer Broadcasting Inc.
Editorial: Route 302, Wells River, Vermont 05081-9742. **T:** 1 802 757-2773
E: studio@wykr.com
W: http://www.wtwnradio.com
Editorial Profile: WTWN-AM is a commercial station owned by Puffer Broadcasting Inc. The format of the station is Christian programming. WTWN-AM broadcasts to the Wells River, VT area at 1100 AM.

WTWS-FM
Owner: Coltrace Communications, Inc.
Editorial: 125 W Houghton Lake Dr, Prudenville, Michigan 48651.
T: 1 989 366-5364 **E:** wupsfm@yahoo.com
W: http://www.ilovethetwister.com
Editorial Profile: WTWS-FM is a commercial station owned by Coltrace Communications, Inc. The format of the station is contemporary country. WTWS-FM broadcasts to the Prudenville, MI market at 92.1 FM.

WTWT-FM
Owner: Calvary Chapel of Russell
Editorial: 8160 Market St, Russell, Pennsylvania 16345-4128. **T:** 1 814 757-8744
W: http://www.wtwtfm.org
Editorial Profile: WTWT-FM is a non-commercial station owned by Calvary Chapel of Russell. The format of the station features Christian programming, including contemporary Christian music. WTWT-FM

broadcasts to the Bradford, PA area at 90.5 FM.

WTWX-FM
Owner: Guntersville Broadcasting Co.
Editorial: 2301 Thomas Ave, Guntersville, Alabama 35976. **T:** 1 256 582-4946
E: wtwx@wtwx.com **W:** http://www.wtwx.com
Editorial Profile: WTWX-FM is a commercial station owned by Guntersville Broadcasting Co. The format for the station is country. WTWX-FM broadcasts to the Huntsville, AL area at 95.9 FM.

WTWZ-AM
Owner: Wood(Terry)
Editorial: 4611 Terry Rd, Ste C, Jackson, Mississippi 39212-5646. **T:** 1 601 346-0074
E: am1120@wtwzradio.com
Editorial Profile: WTWZ-AM is a commercial station owned by Terry Wood. The format of the station is variety with bluegrass music. WTWZ-AM broadcasts to the Jackson, MS area at 1120 AM.

WTXK-AM
Owner: Frontdoor Broadcasting
Editorial: 1359 Carmichael Way, Montgomery, Alabama 36106-3629. **T:** 1 334 239-9750
W: http://www.wtxktheticket.com
Editorial Profile: WTXK-AM is a commercial station owned by Frontdoor Broadcasting. The format of the station is sports. WTXK-AM broadcasts to the Ozark, AL area at 1210 AM.

WTXR-FM
Owner: Toccoa Falls College
Editorial: Toccoa Falls College Falls Road, Toccoa Falls, Georgia 30598.
T: 1 706 886-6831 **E:** wtxr@tfc.edu
W: http://www.wtxr.com
Editorial Profile: WTXR-Fm is a non-commercial station owned by Toccoa Falls College. The format of the station is contemporary Christain. WTXR-FM broadcasts to the Toccoa Falls, GA area at 89.7 FM.

WTXT-FM
Owner: Clear Channel Media and Entertainment
Editorial: 3900 11th Ave, Tuscaloosa, Alabama 35401-7056. **T:** 1 205 344-4589
W: http://www.98txt.com
Editorial Profile: WTXT-FM is a commercial station owned by Clear Channel Media and Entertainment. The station has a music format, airing contemporary country music. WTXT-FM broadcasts to the greater Tuscaloosa, AL area at 98.1 FM.

WTXY-AM
Owner: WTXY Radio LLC
Editorial: 635 Madison St, Whiteville, North Carolina 28472. **T:** 1 910 642-8214
W: http://www.wtxy1540.com
Editorial Profile: WTXY-AM is a commercial station owned by Jason Dozier, Robby Kendall & Rod Sheeks. The format of the station is news, sports, talk and music from the 60s and 70s. WTXY-AM broadcasts to the Whiteville, NC area at 1540 AM.

WTYB-FM
Owner: Cumulus Media Inc.
Editorial: 214 Television Cir, Savannah, Georgia 31406-4519. **T:** 1 912 961-9000
W: http://www.magic1039fm.com
Editorial Profile: WTYB-FM is a commercial station owned by Cumulus Media Inc. The format of the station is urban adult contemporary. WTYB-FM broadcasts to the Savannah, GA area at 103.9 FM.

WTYD-FM
Owner: Local Voice Media
Editorial: 4732 Longhill Rd Ste 2201, Williamsburg, Virginia 23188-1584.
T: 1 757 565-1079 **E:** music@tideradio.com
W: http://www.tideradio.com
Editorial Profile: WTYD-FM is a commercial station owned by Local Voice Media. The format of the station is adult album alternative. WTYD-FM broadcasts to the Northern Neck area of Virginia at 92.3 FM.

WTYE-FM
Owner: Ann Broadcasting Corp.
Editorial: 9016 E 1050th Ave, Robinson, Illinois 62454. **T:** 1 618 544-2191
E: wtaywtye@yahoo.com
W: http://www.wtyefm.com
Editorial Profile: WTYE-FM is a commercial station owned by Ann Broadcasting Corp. The format of the station is adult contemporary music. WTYE-FM broadcasts to the Robinson, IL area at 101.7 FM.

WTYJ-FM
Owner: Natchez Communications
Editorial: 20 E Franklin St, Natchez, Mississippi 39120. **T:** 1 601 442-2522
E: wmiswtyj@bellsouth.net

WTYL-AM
Owner: Tylertown Broadcasting Company Inc.
Editorial: 930 Union Rd, Tylertown, Mississippi 39667-2246. **T:** 1 601 876-2105
Editorial Profile: WTYL-AM is a commercial station owned by Tylertown Broadcasting Company Inc. The format of the station is mainstream country. WTYL-AM broadcasts to the Tylertown, MS area at 1290 AM.

WTYL-FM
Owner: Tylertown Broadcasting Company Inc.
Editorial: 930 Union Rd, Tylertown, Mississippi 39667. **T:** 1 601 876-2105
Editorial Profile: WTYL-FM is a commercial station owned by Tylertown Broadcasting Company Inc. The format of the station is mainstream country. WTYL-FM broadcasts to the Tylertown, MS area at 97.7 FM.

WTYM-AM
Owner: Family-Life Media-Com Inc.
Editorial: 114 S Jefferson St, Kittanning, Pennsylvania 16201-2408. **T:** 1 724 543-1380
W: http://www.wtymradio.com
Editorial Profile: WTYM-AM is a commercial station owned by Family-Life Media-Com Inc. The format of the station is news and talk. WTYM-AM broadcasts to the Kittanning, PA area at 1380 AM.

WTYS-AM
Owner: Adams(James L., Jr.)
Editorial: 2725 Jefferson St, Marianna, Florida 32448. **T:** 1 850 482-2131
E: wtysradio@embarqmail.com
W: http://www.wtys.cc
Editorial Profile: WTYS-AM is a commercial station owned by James L. Adams, Jr. The format of the station is classic country and bluegrass music. WTYS-AM broadcasts to the Marianna, FL area at 1340 AM.

WTYS-FM
Owner: Adams(James L., Jr.)
Editorial: 2725 Jefferson St, Marianna, Florida 32448. **T:** 1 850 482-2131
E: wtysradio@embarqmail.com
W: http://www.wtys.cc
Editorial Profile: WTYS-FM is a commercial station owned by James L. Adams Jr. The format of the station is southern gospel music. WTYS-FM broadcasts to the Marianna, FL area at 94.1 FM.

WTZA-AM
Owner: WGUN, Inc.
Editorial: 2901 Mountain Industrial Blvd, Tucker, Georgia 30084-3011.
T: 1 770 491-7748
W: http://www.oldschool1010.com
Editorial Profile: WTZA-AM is a commercial station owned by WGUN, Inc. The format of the station is R&B oldies. WTZA-AM broadcasts to the Tucker, GA area at 1010 AM.

WTZB-FM
Owner: Clear Channel Media and Entertainment
Editorial: 1779 Independence Blvd, Sarasota, Florida 34234. **T:** 1 941 552-4800
W: http://www.1059thebuzz.com
Editorial Profile: WTZB-FM is a commercial station owned by Clear Channel Media and Entertainment. The format of the station is rock alternative. WTZB-FM broadcasts to the Tampa Bay, FL area at 105.9.

WTZE-AM
Owner: L & L Broadcasting
Editorial: 900 Bluefield Ave, Bluefield, West Virginia 24701-2744. **T:** 1 304 327-7114
W: http://www.whistalkradio.com
Editorial Profile: WTZE-AM is a commercial station owned by L & L Broadcasting. The format of the station is news and talk. WTZE-AM broadcasts to the Bluefield, WV area at 1470 AM.

WTZN-AM
Owner: Cantroair Communications Co.
Editorial: 170 Redington Ave, Troy, Pennsylvania 16947. **T:** 1 570 297-0100
E: trueoldieschannel@wtzn.com
W: http://www.wtzn.com
Editorial Profile: WTZN-AM is a commercial station owned by Cantroair Communications Co. The format of the station is sports. WTZN-AM broadcasts to the Troy, PA area at 1310 AM.

WTZQ-AM
Owner: Timeless Media, Inc.
Editorial: 418 Duncan Rd, Flat Rock, North Carolina 28731-4712. **T:** 1 828 692-1600
E: 1600@wtzq.com **W:** http://www.wtzq.com
Editorial Profile: WTZQ-AM is a commercial station owned by Timeless Media, Inc. The format of the station is adult standards. WTZQ-AM broadcasts to the Hendersonville, NC area at 1600 AM.

WTZR-FM
Owner: Bristol Broadcasting
Editorial: 901 E Valley Dr, Bristol, Virginia 24201. **T:** 1 276 669-8112
W: http://www.zrock993.com
Editorial Profile: WTZR-FM is a commercial station owned by Bristol Broadcasting. The format of the station is rock alternative. WTZR-FM broadcasts to the Bristol, VA area at 99.3 FM.

WTZX-AM
Owner: Peg Broadcasting, LLC
Editorial: 520 N Spring St, Sparta, Tennessee 38583-1305. **T:** 1 931 836-1055
Editorial Profile: WTZX-AM is a commercial station owned by Peg Broadcasting, LLC. The format of the station is oldies. WTZX-AM broadcasts to the Nashville, TN area at 860 AM.

WUAG-FM
Owner: University of North Carolina
Editorial: 1000 Spring Garden St, Greensboro, North Carolina 27412-0001.
T: 1 336 334-4308 **E:** wuag@uncg.edu
W: http://www.wuag.net
Editorial Profile: WUAG-FM is a commercial radio station owned by the University of North Carolina. The format for the station is variety. WUAG-FM broadcasts to the Guilford County area at 103.1 FM.

WUAL-FM
Owner: University of Alabama
Editorial: 905 University Blvd, Tuscaloosa, Alabama 35487-0001. **T:** 1 205 348-6644
E: aprnews@apr.org **W:** http://www.apr.org
Editorial Profile: WUAL-FM is a non-commercial station owned by University of Alabama. The format of the station is variety. WUAL-FM broadcasts to the Tuscaloosa, AL and Birmingham, AL areas at 91.5 FM.

WUAM-AM
Owner: Empire Broadcasting Corporation
Editorial: 100 Saratoga Village Blvd, Malta, New York 12020-3737. **T:** 1 518 899-3000
W: http://albany.twcnews.com
Editorial Profile: WUAM-AM is a commercial station owned by Empire Broadcasting Corporation. The format of the station is news. WUAM-AM broadcasts to the Albany, NY area at 900 AM.

WUAT-AM
Owner: Bownds(Joyce)
Editorial: 101 Main St, Pikeville, Tennessee 37367-4947. **T:** 1 423 447-2906
W: http://www.wuatradio.com
Editorial Profile: WUAT-AM is a commercial station owned by Joyce Bownds. The format for the station is gospel and country. WUAT-AM broadcasts to the Chattanooga, TN area at 1110 AM.

WUAW-FM
Owner: Central Carolina Community College
Editorial: 215 Maynard Lake Rd, Erwin, North Carolina 28339-8507. **T:** 1 910 897-8070
Editorial Profile: WUAW-FM is a non-commercial station owned by Central Carolina Community College. The format of the station is rhythmic Top 40. WUAW-FM broadcasts to the Erwin, NC area at 88.3 FM.

WUBB-FM
Owner: L & L Radio
Editorial: 1 Saint Augustine Pl, Hilton Head Island, South Carolina 29928-4717.
T: 1 843 785-9569 **E:** bob1069shh@gmail.com
W: http://www.bob1069.com
Editorial Profile: WUBB-FM is a commercial station owned by L & L Radio. The format for the station is country music. WUBB-FM broadcasts to the Hilton Head Island, SC area at 106.9 FM.

WUBE-FM
Owner: Hubbard Broadcasting, Inc.
Editorial: 2060 Reading Rd, Cincinnati, Ohio 45202-1454. **T:** 1 513 699-5105
W: http://www.b105.com
Editorial Profile: WUBE-FM is a commercial station owned by Hubbard Broadcasting, Inc. The format of the station is classic country. WUBE-FM broadcasts to the Cincinnati area at 105.1 FM.

WUBL-FM
Owner: Clear Channel Media and Entertainment
Editorial: 1819 Peachtree Rd NE, Ste 700, Atlanta, Georgia 30309. **T:** 1 404 875-8080
W: http://www.949thebull.com
Editorial Profile: WUBL-FM is a commercial station owned by Clear Channel Media and Entertainment. The format of the station is contemporary country. WUBL-FM broadcasts to the Atlanta area at 94.9 FM.

WUBS-FM
Owner: Interfaith Christian Union
Editorial: 702 Lincolnway W, South Bend, Indiana 46616. **T:** 1 574 287-4700
W: http://www.wubs.org
Editorial Profile: WUBS-FM is a non-commercial station owned by the Interfaith Christian Union. The format of the station is gospel and religious music. WUBS-FM broadcasts to the South Bend, IN area at 89.7 FM.

WUBT-FM
Owner: Clear Channel Media and Entertainment
Editorial: 55 Music Sq W, Nashville, Tennessee 37203-3207. **T:** 1 615 664-2400
E: nashvillepsa@clearchannel.com
W: http://www.101thebeat.com
Editorial Profile: WUBT-FM is a commercial station owned by Clear Channel Media and Entertainment. The format of the station is urban contemporary. WUBT-FM broadcasts to the Nashville, TN area at 101.1 FM. To send a PSA, email nashvillepsa@clearchannel.com.

WUBU-FM
Owner: Partnership Radio
Editorial: 401 E Colfax Ave, Ste 300, South Bend, Indiana 46617-2736. **T:** 1 574 233-3505
E: wubustudio@wubufm.com
W: http://www.wubufm.com
Editorial Profile: WUBU-FM is a commercial station owned by Partnership Radio. The format for the station is urban adult contemporary music. WUBU-FM broadcasts to the South Bend, IN, area at 106.3 FM.

WUCF-FM
Owner: University of Central Florida
Editorial: 4000 Central Florida Blvd, Bldg 75, Ste 130, Orlando, Florida 32816.
T: 1 407 823-0899 **W:** http://www.wucf.org
Editorial Profile: WUCF-FM is a non-commercial station owned by the University of Central Florida. The format of the station is jazz music. WUCF-FM broadcasts to the Orlando, FL area at 89.9 FM.

WUCS-FM
Owner: Clear Channel Media and Entertainment
Editorial: 10 Columbus Blvd Ste 1, Hartford, Connecticut 06106-1976. **T:** 1 860 723-6000
W: http://www.979espn.com
Editorial Profile: WUCS-FM is a commercial station owned by Clear Channel Media and Entertainment. The format of the station is sports. WUCS-FM broadcasts to the Hartford, CT area at 97.9 FM.

WUCX-FM
Owner: Central Michigan University
Editorial: 1999 E Campus Dr, Mount Pleasant, Michigan 48859. **T:** 1 989 774-3105
E: wucx@delta.edu
W: http://www.delta.edu/broadcasting
Editorial Profile: WUCX-FM is a non-commercial station owned by Central Michigan University. The format of the station is news and classical music. WUCX-FM broadcasts to the Mount Pleasant, MI area at 90.1 FM.

WUCZ-FM
Owner: Banka (Dennis and Tracy)
Editorial: 104 Z Country Ln, Carthage, Tennessee 37030. **T:** 1 615 735-1350
E: info@1041theranch.net
W: http://www.1041theranch.net
Editorial Profile: WUCZ-FM is a commercial station owned by Dennis and Tracy Banka. The format of the station is contemporary country music. WUCZ-FM broadcasts to the Nashville, TN area at 104.1 FM.

WUDE-FM
Owner: Hometown Wilmington Media
Editorial: 122 Cinema Dr, Wilmington, North Carolina 28403-1490. **T:** 1 910 772-6300
E: music@gottalovethedude.com
W: http://gottalovethedude.com/home
Editorial Profile: WUDE-FM is a commercial station owned by Hometown Wilmington Media. The format of the station is contemporary country. WUDE-FM broadcasts to the Wilmington, NC area at 93.7 FM.

WUEV-FM
Owner: University of Evansville
Editorial: 1800 Lincoln Ave, Evansville, Indiana 47714-1506. **T:** 1 812 488-2022
E: wuev@evansville.edu **W:** http://wuev.org
Editorial Profile: WUEV-FM is a non-commercial station owned by University of Evansville. The format of the station is college variety. WUEV-FM broadcasts to the Evansville, IN area at 91.5 FM.

WUEZ-FM
Owner: Max Media
Editorial: 1431 Country Aire Dr, Carterville, Illinois 62918-5118. **T:** 1 618 985-4843
E: publicservice@riverradio.net
W: http://www.magic951.com
Editorial Profile: WUEZ-FM is a commercial station owned by Max Media. The format of the station is Lite Rock/Lite AC music. WUEZ-FM broadcasts to the Paducah, KY-Cape Girardeau, MO-Harrisburg, IL areas at 95.1 FM. Send PSAs to publicservice@riverradio.net.

WUFC-AM
Owner: Blackstrap Broadcasting LLC
Editorial: 308 Victory Rd, Quincy, Massachusetts 02171-3129.
T: 1 201 288-8200 **E:** info@900wilc.com
W: http://1510wufc.com
Editorial Profile: WUFC-AM is a commercial station owned by Blackstrap Broadcasting LLC and operated by Wallis Communications. The format of the station is talk. WUFC-AM broadcasts to the Burlington, MA area at 1510 AM.

WUFE-AM
Owner: South Georgia Broadcasters Inc.
Editorial: 4005 Golden Isles Parkway, Baxley, Georgia 31513. **T:** 1 912 367-3000
Editorial Profile: WUFE-AM is a commercial station owned by South Georgia Broadcasters Inc. The format for the station is oldies. WUFE-AM broadcasts to the Baxley, GA area at 1260 AM.

WUFF-FM
Owner: Dodge Broadcasting Inc.
Editorial: 855 College St, Eastman, Georgia 31023. **T:** 1 478 374-3437
W: http://www.wolfcountry975.com
Editorial Profile: WUFF-FM is a commercial station owned by Dodge Broadcasting Inc. The format of the station is contemporary country music. WUFF-FM broadcasts to the Eastman, GA area at 97.5 FM.

WUFL-AM
Owner: Family Life Radio
Editorial: 39949 Garfield Rd, Ste B, Clinton Township, Michigan 48038-4301.
T: 1 586 263-1030 **W:** http://www.myflr.org
Editorial Profile: WUFL-AM is a non-commercial station owned by Family Life Radio. The format of the station is contemporary Christian programming. WUFL-AM broadcasts to the Clinton Township, MI area at 1030 AM.

WUFM-FM
Owner: Spirit Communications, Inc.
Editorial: 116 County Line Rd W, Westerville, Ohio 43082. **T:** 1 614 839-7100
E: radiou@radiou.com
W: http://tvulive.com/radiou/
Editorial Profile: WUFM-FM is a non-commercial station owned by Spirit Communications, Inc. The format of the station is alternative. WUFM-FM broadcasts to the Westerville, OH area at 88.7 FM.

WUFO-AM
Owner: Sheridan Broadcasting Corp.
Editorial: 143 Broadway St, Buffalo, New York 14203-1629. **T:** 1 716 834-1080
W: http://www.wufoam.com
Editorial Profile: WUFO-AM is a commercial station owned by Sheridan Broadcasting Corp. The format of the station is gospel, R & B and talk. WUFO-AM broadcasts to the Buffalo, NY area at 1080 AM.

WUFT-FM
Owner: University of Florida
Editorial: 2206-C Weimer Hall Univ of Florida, Gainesville, Florida 32611-2084.
T: 1 352 392-5200 **E:** radio@wuft.org
W: http://www.wuftfm.org

Editorial Profile: WUFT-FM is a non-commercial station owned by the University of Florida. The format of the station is news and talk. WUFT-FM broadcasts in the Gainesville, FL area at 89.1 FM.

WUGA-FM
Owner: Georgia Public Broadcasting
Editorial: University of Georgia, 1197 S Lumpkin St, Athens, Georgia 30602.
T: 1 706 542-9842 **E:** wuga@uga.edu
W: http://www.wuga.org
Editorial Profile: WUGA-FM is a non-commercial station owned by the Georgia Public Broadcasting. The format of the station is classical, jazz and news. WUGA-FM broadcasts to the Athens, GA area at 91.7 FM.

WUGN-FM
Owner: Family Life Radio
Editorial: 510 E Isabella Rd, Midland, Michigan 48640. **T:** 1 989 631-7060
E: 997@997.org **W:** http://www.997flr.org
Editorial Profile: WUGN-FM is a non-commercial station owned by Family Life Radio. The format of the station is religious and contemporary Christian programming. WUGN-FM broadcasts to Midland, MI and the surrounding area at 99.7 FM.

WUGO-FM
Owner: Carter County Broadcasting Co.
Editorial: 150 Radio Tower Rd, Grayson, Kentucky 41143. **T:** 1 606 474-5144
E: mail@wgohwugo.com
W: http://www.wgohwugo.com
Editorial Profile: WUGO-FM is a commercial station owned by Carter County Broadcasting Co. The format of the station is adult contemporary music. WUGO-FM broadcasts to the Grayson, KY area at 102.3 FM.

WUHT-FM
Owner: Cumulus Media Inc.
Editorial: 244 Goodwin Crest Dr, Ste 300, Birmingham, Alabama 35209.
T: 1 205 945-4646
W: http://www.hot1077radio.com
Editorial Profile: WUHT-FM is a commercial station owned by Cumulus Media Inc. The format of the station is urban adult contemporary music. WUHT-FM broadcasts to the Birmingham, AL area at 107.7 FM.

WUHU-FM
Owner: Forever Communications Inc.
Editorial: 1919 Scottsville Rd, Bowling Green, Kentucky 42104. **T:** 1 270 843-3333
E: production@beaverfm.com
W: http://www.allhitwuhu107.com
Editorial Profile: WUHU-FM is a commercial station owned by Forever Communications Inc. The format of the station is hot adult contemporary. WUHU-FM broadcasts to the Bowling Green KY area at 107.1 FM.

WUIN-FM
Owner: Hometown Wilmington Media
Editorial: 122 Cinema Dr, Wilmington, North Carolina 28403-1490. **T:** 1 910 772-6300
E: penguinrequests@hometownwilmington.com **W:** http://983thepenguin.com/home
Editorial Profile: WUIN-FM is a commercial station owned by Hometown Wilmington Media. The format of the station is AAA. WUIN-FM broadcasts in the Wilmington, NC area at 98.3 FM.

WUIS-FM
Owner: University of Illinois
Editorial: 1 University Plz, Rm 130, Springfield, Illinois 62703-5497.
T: 1 217 206-6516 **E:** wuis@uis.edu
W: http://www.wuis.org
Editorial Profile: WUIS-FM is a non-commercial station owned by University of Illinois. The format of the station is news, jazz, and classical music. WUIS-FM broadcasts in the Springfield, IL area at 91.9 FM

WUJM-FM
Owner: L & L Radio
Editorial: 1909 E Pass Rd, Gulfport, Mississippi 39507-3779. **T:** 1 228 388-6000
W: http://www.967thechamp.com
Editorial Profile: WUJM-FM is a commercial station owned by L & L Radio. The format of the station is sports. WUJM-FM broadcasts to the Gulfport, MS area at a frequency of 96.7 FM.

WUKL-FM
Owner: Keymarket Communications LLC
Editorial: 56325 High Ridge Rd, Bellaire, Ohio 43906. **T:** 1 740 676-5661
E: kool105@hotmail.com
W: http://www.mykool105.com
Editorial Profile: WUKL-FM is a commercial station owned by Keymarket Communications LLC. The format of the station is oldies. WUKL-FM broadcasts to the Bellaire, OH area at 105.5 FM.

WUKS-FM
Owner: Beasley Broadcast Group
Editorial: 508 Person St, Fayetteville, North Carolina 28301. **T:** 1 910 486-4114
W: http://www.kiss1077.com
Editorial Profile: WUKS-FM is a commercial station owned by Beasley Broadcast Group. The format of the station is urban adult contemporary music. WUKS-FM broadcasts to the Fayetteville, NC area at 107.7 FM.

WUKY-FM
Owner: University of Kentucky
Editorial: 340 McVey Hall Univ Of Kentucky, Lexington, Kentucky 40506-0001.
T: 1 859 257-3221 **E:** wukynews@hotmail.com
W: http://www.wuky.org
Editorial Profile: WUKY-FM is a commercial station owned by the University of Kentucky. The format of the station is adult album alternative and news. WUKY-FM broadcasts to the Lexington, KY area at 91.3 FM.

WULF-FM
Owner: Skytower Communications Inc.
Editorial: 233 W Dixie Ave, Elizabethtown, Kentucky 42701. **T:** 1 270 765-0943
W: http://www.943wulf.com
Editorial Profile: WULF-FM is a commercial station owned by Skytower Communications Inc. The format of the station is contemporary country music. WULF-FM broadcasts to the Elizabethtown, KY area at 94.3 FM.

WULR-AM
Owner: Iglesia Nueva Vida of High Point, Inc.
Editorial: 6223 Old Mendenhall Rd, High Point, North Carolina 27263-3940.
T: 1 336 471-1839
E: nuevavida980@yahoo.com
W: http://cadenaradialnuevavida.com
Editorial Profile: WULR-AM is a commercial station owned by Iglesia Nueva Vida of High Point, Inc.. The format for the station is Spanish Religious. WULR-AM broadcasts to the Charlotte, NC area at 980 AM.

WULS-FM
Owner: WULS Inc.
Editorial: 702 Madison Ave N, Ste 101, Douglas, Georgia 31533. **T:** 1 912 384-9857
Editorial Profile: WULS-FM is a commercial station owned by WULS Inc. The format of the station is Southern gospel. WULS-FM broadcasts to the Douglas, GA area at 103.7 FM.

WUMB-FM
Owner: University of Massachusetts
Editorial: 100 William T Morrissey Blvd, Dorchester, Massachusetts 02125-3300.
T: 1 617 287-6900 **E:** wumb@umb.edu
W: http://www.wumb.org
Editorial Profile: WUMB-FM is a non-commercial station owned by University of Massachusetts. The format of the station is folk, blues and educational programming. WUMB-FM broadcasts to the Boston area at 91.9 FM.

WUMD-FM
Owner: University of Massachusetts
Editorial: 285 Old Westport Rd, North Dartmouth, Massachusetts 02747-2356.
T: 1 508 999-8149 **E:** wumd@umassd.edu
W: http://www.893wumd.org
Editorial Profile: WUMD-FM is a non-commercial station owned by the University of Massachusetts. The format of the station is variety. WSMU-FM broadcasts to the North Dartmouth, MA area at 89.3 FM.

WUME-FM
Owner: Diamond Shores Broadcasting LLC
Editorial: 192 S Court St, Paoli, Indiana 47454-1322. **T:** 1 812 723-4484
E: wume@blueriver.net
Editorial Profile: WUME-FM is a commercial station owned by Diamond Shores Broadcasting LLC. The format of the station is adult contemporary music. WUME-FM broadcasts to the Paoli, IN area at 95.3 FM.

WUMF-FM
Owner: University of Maine
Editorial: 111 South St, Farmington, Maine 04938-6823. **T:** 1 207 778-7352
E: wumf915@gmail.com
W: http://wumf.umf.maine.edu
Editorial Profile: WUMF-FM is a non-commercial station owned by the University of Maine. The format of the station is variety. WUMF-FM is a college station broadcasting to the Farmington, ME area at a frequency of 91.5.

WUMJ-FM
Owner: Radio One Inc.
Editorial: 101 Marietta St NW, 12th Fl, Atlanta, Georgia 30303. **T:** 1 404 765-9750
W: http://majicatl.com
Editorial Profile: WUMJ-FM is a commercial station owned by Radio One Inc. The format of the station is urban adult contemporary. WUMJ-FM broadcasts to the Atlanta area at 97.5 FM.

WUML-FM
Owner: University of Massachusetts
Editorial: 1 University Ave, Lowell, Massachusetts 1854. **T:** 1 978 934-4975
W: http://www.wuml.org
Editorial Profile: WUML-FM is a non-commercial station owned by University of Massachusetts. The format of the station is college variety. WUML-FM broadcasts to the Lowell, MA area at 91.5 FM.

WUMP-AM
Owner: Cumulus Media Inc.
Editorial: 1717 US Highway 72 E, Athens, Alabama 35611-4413. **T:** 1 256 830-8300
W: http://www.730ump.com
Editorial Profile: WUMP-AM is a commercial station owned by Cumulus Media Inc. The format of the station is sports. WUMP-AM broadcasts to the Huntsville, AL area at 730 AM.

WUMR-FM
Owner: University of Memphis
Editorial: Dept Of Communications Tc 14, Memphis, Tennessee 38152.
T: 1 901 678-2560 **E:** wumrfm@gmail.com
W: http://www.memphis.edu/wumr
Editorial Profile: WUMR-FM is a non-commercial station owned by the University of Memphis. The format of the station is jazz. WUMR-FM broadcasts to the Memphis, TN area at 91.7 FM.

WUMS-FM
Owner: University of Mississippi
Editorial: Student Media Center - 201 Bishop Hall, University, Mississippi 38677-9999.
T: 1 662 915-5503
E: 921rebelradio@gmail.com
W: http://www.myrebelradio.com
Editorial Profile: WUMS-FM is a commercial college station owned by the University of Mississippi. The format of the station is Top 40/CHR. The station broadcasts to the northern Mississippi area at a frequency of 92.1 FM.

WUMX-FM
Owner: Galaxy Communications LP
Editorial: 39 Kellogg Rd, New Hartford, New York 13413. **T:** 1 315 797-1330
E: mix@galaxycommunications.com
W: http://www.mix1025.com
Editorial Profile: WRBY-FM is a commercial station owned by Galaxy Communications LP. The format of the station is hot adult contemporary music. WRBY-FM broadcasts to the Utica, NY area at 102.5 FM.

WUMY-AM
Owner: Pollack Broadcasting Co.
Editorial: 5500 Poplar Ave Ste 1, Memphis, Tennessee 38119-3732. **T:** 1 901 683-3993
E: comments@kxiqradio.com
W: http://www.kxiqradio.com
Editorial Profile: WUMY-AM is a commercial station owned by Pollack Broadcasting Co. The format of the station is classic country. WUMY-AM broadcasts to the Memphis, TN area at a frequency of 1180 AM.

WUNA-AM
Owner: J & V Communications, Inc.
Editorial: 749 S Bluford Ave, Ocoee, Florida 34761-2942. **T:** 1 407 841-8282
E: wprd1440@gmail.com
Editorial Profile: WUNA-AM is a commercial station owned by J & V Communications, Inc. The format of the station is ethnic. WUNA-AM broadcasts to the Orlando, FL area at 1480 AM.

WUNC-FM
Owner: University of North Carolina
Editorial: 120 Friday Center Dr, Chapel Hill, North Carolina 27517-9495.
T: 1 919 445-9150 **E:** news@wunc.org
W: http://www.wunc.org
Editorial Profile: WUNC-FM is a non-commercial station owned by the University of North Carolina. The format of the station is news and talk. WUNC-FM broadcasts to the Raleigh-Durham, NC area at 91.5 FM. WUNC-FM and WRQM-FM are not accepting PSAs for the remainder of 2013.

WUNH-FM
Owner: University of New Hampshire
Editorial: Memorial Union Bldg, Durham, New Hampshire 3824. **T:** 1 603 862-2541
W: http://www.wunh.org
Editorial Profile: WUNH-FM is a non-commercial station owned by the University of New Hampshire. The format of the station is rock alternative and urban contemporary music. WUNH-FM broadcasts to the Durham, NH area at 91.3 FM.

WUNN-AM
Owner: Family Life Radio
Editorial: 13799 Donavan Rd, Albion, Michigan 49224. **T:** 1 800 776-1070
W: http://www.myflr.org
Editorial Profile: WUNN-AM is a non-commercial station owned by Family Life Radio. The format of the station is gospel and religious music. WUNN-AM broadcasts to the Grand Rapids, MI area at 1110 AM.

WUNR-AM
Owner: Champion Broadcasting System
Editorial: 60 Temple Pl, Fl 2, Boston, Massachusetts 02111-1324.
T: 1 617 367-9003 **E:** info@wunr.com
W: http://www.wunr.net
Editorial Profile: WUNR-AM is a commercial station owned by Champion Broadcasting System. The format of the station is Hispanic programming. WUNR-AM broadcasts in the Boston area at 1600 AM.

WUNV-FM
Owner: Georgia Public Broadcasting
Editorial: 260 14th St NW, Atlanta, Georgia 30318. **T:** 1 404 685-2548 **E:** news@gpb.org
W: http://www.gpb.org
Editorial Profile: WUNV-FM is a non-commercial station owned by Georgia Public Broadcasting. The format of the station is classical and jazz music, and news talk. WUNV-FM broadcasts to the Atlanta area at 91.7 FM.

WUOG-FM
Owner: University of Georgia
Editorial: Memorial Hall, Fifth Floor, Athens, Georgia 30602-3401. **T:** 1 706 542-7100
E: info@wuog.org **W:** http://www.wuog.org
Editorial Profile: WUOG-FM is a non-commercial station owned by the University of Georgia. The format of the station is adult alternative. WUOG-FM broadcasts to the Atlanta area at 90.5 FM.

WUOL-FM
Owner: Louisville Public Media
Editorial: 619 S 4th St, Louisville, Kentucky 40202. **T:** 1 502 814-6500 **E:** studio@wuol.org
W: http://www.wuol.org
Editorial Profile: WUOL-FM is a commercial station owned by Louisville Public Media. The format of the station is classical music. WUOL-FM broadcasts to the Louisville, KY area at 90.5 FM.

WUOM-FM
Owner: University of Michigan
Editorial: 535 W William St Ste 110, Ann Arbor, Michigan 48103-4978.
T: 1 734 764-9210
E: michigan.radio@umich.edu
W: http://www.michiganradio.org
Editorial Profile: WUOM-FM is a non-commercial station owned by University of Michigan. The format of the station is news and talk. WUOM-FM broadcasts to the Ann Arbor, MI area at 91.7 FM.

WUOT-FM
Owner: University of Tennessee
Editorial: 209 Communications Bldg, Knoxville, Tennessee 37996.
T: 1 865 974-5375 **E:** newsroom@wuot.org
W: http://www.wuot.org
Editorial Profile: WUOT-FM is a non-commercial station owned by the University of Tennessee. The format of the station is classical, jazz and news. WUOT-FM broadcasts to the Knoxville, TN area at 91.9 FM.

WUPE-AM
Owner: Gamma Broadcasting LLC
Editorial: 211 Jason St, Pittsfield, Massachusetts 01201-5907.
T: 1 413 499-3333 **E:** news@wupe.com
W: http://www.wupe.com

Editorial Profile: WUPE-AM is a commercial station owned by Gamma Broadcasting LLC. The format of the station is oldies. WUPE-AM broadcasts to the Pittsfield, MA area at 1110 AM.

WUPE-FM
Owner: Gamma Broadcasting LLC
Editorial: 211 Jason St, Pittsfield, Massachusetts 01201-5907.
T: 1 413 499-3333 **E:** fun@wupe.com
W: http://www.wupe.com
Editorial Profile: WUPE-FM is a commercial station owned by Gamma Broadcasting LLC. The format of the station is oldies. WUPE-FM broadcasts to the Pittsfield, MA area at 100.1 FM.

WUPG-FM
Owner: Radioactive, LLC
Editorial: 308 Cleveland Ave Ste 302, Ishpeming, Michigan 49849-1845.
T: 1 906 485-4313
W: http://www.radioeaglemarquette.com
Editorial Profile: WUPG-FM (formerly WUPZ-FM) (96.7 FM) is a radio station licensed to Republic, Michigan. The station is currently owned by Radioactive, LLC and was granted its license on April 17, 2008. The station signed on in July 2008 with a Variety Hits format. On March 4th, 2014, changed formats to Classic Country branded as "Yooper Country 96.7".

WUPI-FM
Owner: University of Maine
Editorial: WUPI Radio, 181 Main Street, Presque Isle, Maine 4769. **T:** 1 207 768-9741
E: wupi@maine.edu
W: http://utimes.umpi.edu/wupi-radio
Editorial Profile: WUPI-FM is a non-commercial station owned by University of Maine and operated by the Presque Isle campus. The format of the station is Top 40/CHR. WUPI-FM broadcasts locally to the University of Maine Presque Isle campus and the Presque Isle, ME area at a frequency of 92.1 FM.

WUPK-FM
Owner: Northern Star Broadcasting LLC
Editorial: 1009 W Ridge St Ste A, Marquette, Michigan 49855-3997. **T:** 1 906 225-1313
W: http://www.rockthebear.com
Editorial Profile: WUPK-FM is a commercial station owned by Northern Star Broadcasting LLC. The format of the station is classic rock. WUPK-FM broadcasts to the Marquette, MI area at 94.1 FM.

WUPM-FM
Owner: Big G Little O Inc.
Editorial: 209 Harrison St, Ironwood, Michigan 49938. **T:** 1 906 932-5234
E: wupm@wupm-whry.com
W: http://www.wupm-whry.com
Editorial Profile: WUPM-FM is a commercial station owned by Big G Little O Inc. The format of the station is Hot AC music. WUPM-FM broadcasts in the Ironwood, MI area at 106.9 FM.

WUPS-FM
Owner: Coltrace Communications, Inc.
Editorial: 125 W Houghton Lake Dr, Prudenville, Michigan 48651.
T: 1 989 366-5364 **E:** wupsfm@yahoo.com
W: http://www.wups.com

WUPX-FM
Owner: Northern Michigan University
Editorial: 1204 University Center, Marquette, Michigan 49855. **T:** 1 906 227-1844
W: http://www.wupx.com
Editorial Profile: WUPX-FM is a non-commercial station owned by Northern Michigan University. The format of the station is college variety. WUPX-FM broadcasts to the Marquette, MI area at 91.5 FM.

WUPY-FM
Owner: J & J Broadcasting, Inc.
Editorial: 622 River St, Ontonagon, Michigan 49953. **T:** 1 906 884-9668
E: wupy@jamadots.com
W: http://www.wupy101.com
Editorial Profile: WUPY-FM is a commercial station owned by J & J Broadcasting, Inc. The format of the station is country music. WUPY-FM broadcasts to Ontonagon, MI and the surrounding area on 101.1 FM.

WURC-FM
Owner: Rust College Inc.
Editorial: 150 Rust Ave, Holly Springs, Mississippi 38635. **T:** 1 662 252-5881
W: http://www.wurc.org

WURD-AM
Owner: WURD Radio, LLC
Editorial: 1341 N Delaware Ave Ste 300, Philadelphia, Pennsylvania 19125-4309.
T: 1 215 425-7489
E: 900amwurd@wurdradio.com
W: http://www.900amwurd.com
Editorial Profile: WURD-AM is a commercial station owned by WURD Radio, LLC. The format of the station is news and talk. WURD-AM broadcasts to the Philadelphia area at 900 AM. They only accepts PSAs from non-profits.

WURL-AM
Owner: Bill Davison Evangelistic Association
Editorial: 2999 Radio Park Dr, Moody, Alabama 35004. **T:** 1 205 699-9875
E: wurlradio@aol.com
W: http://www.wurlradio.com
Editorial Profile: WURL-AM is a commercial radio station owned by Bill Davison Evangelistic Association. The format of the station is Southern gospel music. WURL-AM broadcasts to the Moody, AL area at 760 AM.

WURN-AM
Owner: Actualidad 1020 AM, LLC
Editorial: 2555 Ponce De Leon Blvd Ste 225, Coral Gables, Florida 33134-6033.
T: 1 786 388-3855
W: http://actualidadradio.com
Editorial Profile: WURN-AM is a commercial station owned by Actualidad 1020 AM, LLC. The format of the station is Spanish language news and talk. WLVJ-AM broadcasts to the Miami area at 1020 AM.

WURV-FM
Owner: Summit Media Broadcasting LLC
Editorial: 812 Moorefield Park Dr, Ste 300, Richmond, Virginia 23236. **T:** 1 804 330-5700
W: http://www.1037river.com
Editorial Profile: WURV-FM is a commercial station owned by Summit Media Broadcasting LLC. The format of the station is a hot AC. WURV-FM broadcasts to the Richmond, VA area at 103.7 FM.

WUSB-FM
Owner: State University of New York
Editorial: Stony Brook University, WUSB Radio, Union Bldg, 2nd Floor, Stony Brook, New York 11794-0001. **T:** 1 631 632-6500
E: info@wusb.fm **W:** http://www.wusb.fm
Editorial Profile: WUSB-FM is a non commercial college station owned by State University of New York. The format of the station is variety. WUSB-FM broadcasts to the Stony Brook, NY area at 90.1 FM.

WUSC-FM
Owner: University of South Carolina
Editorial: 1400 Greene St 343 Russell House, Columbia, South Carolina 29208.
T: 1 803 777-5468 **E:** wuscpad@sc.edu
W: http://wusc.sc.edu
Editorial Profile: WUSC-FM is a non-commercial station owned by the University of South Carolina. The format of the station is college variety. WUSC-FM broadcasts to the Columbia, SC area at 90.5 FM.

WUSF-FM
Owner: University of South Florida
Editorial: 4202 E Fowler Ave, Tampa, Florida 33620-9951. **T:** 1 813 974-8700
E: news@wusf.org **W:** http://www.wusf.usf.edu
Editorial Profile: WUSF-FM is a non-commercial station owned by University of South Florida. The format of the station is news, public affairs and jazz. WUSF-FM broadcasts to the Tampa, FL area at 89.7 FM.

WUSH-FM
Owner: Sinclair Telecable Inc.
Editorial: 999 Waterside Dr, Ste 500, Norfolk, Virginia 23510. **T:** 1 757 640-8500
W: http://www.us1061.com
Editorial Profile: WUSH-FM is a commercial station owned by Sinclair Telecable Inc. The format of the station is contemporary country. WUSH-FM broadcasts to the Norfolk, VA area at 106.1 FM.

WUSJ-FM
Owner: New South Communications Inc.
Editorial: 265 Highpoint Dr, Ridgeland, Mississippi 39157. **T:** 1 601 956-0102
W: http://www.us963.com
Editorial Profile: WUSJ-FM is a commercial station owned by New South Communications Inc. The format of the station is country. WUSJ-FM broadcasts to the Jackson, MS area at 96.3 FM.

WUSL-FM
Owner: Clear Channel Media and Entertainment
Editorial: 111 Presidential Blvd, Ste 100, Bala Cynwyd, Pennsylvania 19004.
T: 1 610 784-3333
W: http://www.power99.com
Editorial Profile: WUSL-FM is a commercial station owned by Clear Channel Media and Entertainment. The format of the station is urban contemporary. WUSL-FM broadcasts to the Philadelphia area at 98.9 FM.

WUSM-FM
Owner: University of Southern Mississippi
Editorial: 118 College Dr Ste 10045, Hattiesburg, Mississippi 39406-0002.
T: 1 601 266-4287 **E:** wusm@usm.edu
W: http://www.southernmissradio.com
Editorial Profile: WUSM-FM is a non-commercial station owned by University of Southern Mississippi. The format of the station is a variety of music and news. WUSM-FM broadcasts to the Hattiesburg, MS area at 88.5 FM.

WUSN-FM
Owner: CBS Radio
Editorial: 180 N Stetson Ave Ste 1000, Chicago, Illinois 60601-6822.
T: 1 312 649-0099
W: http://us995.cbslocal.com
Editorial Profile: WUSN-FM is a commercial station owned by CBS Radio. The format of the station is contemporary country. WUSN-FM broadcasts to the Chicago area at 99.5 FM.

WUSP-AM
Owner: Good Guys Broadcasting
Editorial: 185 Genesee St Ste 1601, Utica, New York 13501-2110. **T:** 1 315 734-9245
Editorial Profile: WUSP-AM is a commercial station owned by Good Guys Broadcasting. The format of the station is sports. WUSP-AM broadcasts to the Utica, NY area at 1550 AM.

WUSQ-FM
Owner: Clear Channel Media and Entertainment
Editorial: 510 Pegasus Ct, Winchester, Virginia 22602-4596. **T:** 1 540 662-5101
E: yourcommunity@hotmail.com
W: http://www.shenandoahcountryq102.com/main.html
Editorial Profile: WUSQ-FM is a commercial station owned by Clear Channel Media and Entertainment. The format of the station is contemporary country music. WUSQ-FM broadcasts to the Winchester, VA area at 102.5 FM.

WUSR-FM
Owner: University of Scranton
Editorial: University Of Scranton, 800 Linden St, Scranton, Pennsylvania 18510.
T: 1 570 941-7648 **E:** wusrfm@scranton.edu
W: http://www.scranton.edu/wusr
Editorial Profile: WUSR-FM is a commercial station owned by the University of Scranton. The format of the station is college variety. WUSR-FM broadcasts in the Scranton, PA area at 99.5 FM.

WUST-AM
Owner: New World Radio
Editorial: 2131 Crimmins Ln, Falls Church, Virginia 22043-1962. **T:** 1 703 532-0400
E: contactwust@wust1120.com
W: http://www.wust1120.com
Editorial Profile: WUST-AM is a commercial station owned by New World Radio. The format of the station is a variety of ethnic programming. WUST-AM broadcasts to the Washington D.C. area at 1120 AM.

WUSY-FM
Owner: Clear Channel Media and Entertainment
Editorial: 7413 Old Lee Hwy, Chattanooga, Tennessee 37421. **T:** 1 423 892-3333
W: http://www.us101country.com
Editorial Profile: WUSY-FM is a commercial station owned by Clear Channel Media and Entertainment. The format of the station is contemporary country. WUSY-FM broadcasts to the Chattanooga, TN area on 100.7 FM.

WUSZ-FM
Owner: Midwest Communications Inc.
Editorial: 807 W 37th St, Hibbing, Minnesota 55746. **T:** 1 218 263-7531
E: info@radiousa.com
W: http://www.radiousa.com

WUTC-FM
Owner: University of Tennessee at Chattanooga
Editorial: 615 McCallie Ave, Dept 1151, Chattanooga, Tennessee 37403-2504.
T: 1 423 425-4756 **W:** http://www.wutc.org
Editorial Profile: WUTC-FM is a non-commercial station owned by University of Tennessee at Chattanooga. The format for the station is news and adult album alternative. WUTC-FM broadcasts to the Chattanooga, TN area at 88.1 FM.

WUTI-AM
Owner: Leatherstocking Media Group, Inc
Editorial: 8456 Smokey Hollow Rd, Baldwinsville, New York 13027-8222.
T: 1 315 635-3971
W: http://www.cnytalkradio.com
Editorial Profile: WUTI-AM is a non-commercial station owned by Leatherstocking Media Group, Inc. The format of the station is talk. WUTI-AM broadcasts to the Utica, NY area at 1150 AM.

WUTK-FM
Owner: University of Tennessee
Editorial: P-103 Andy Holt Tower, Knoxville, Tennessee 37996. **T:** 1 865 974-1120
E: wutk@utk.edu
W: http://www.wutkradio.com
Editorial Profile: WUTK-FM is a non-commercial college station owned by University of Tennessee. The format of the station is primarily rock. WUTK-FM broadcasts to the Knoxville, TN area at a frequency or 90.3 FM.

WUTM-FM
Owner: University of Tennessee
Editorial: 220 Gooch Hall Ut Martin Ut Mart, Martin, Tennessee 38238. **T:** 1 731 881-7095
E: wutm@utm.edu
W: http://www.utm.edu/~wutm
Editorial Profile: WUTM-FM is a non-commercial station owned by the University of Tennessee. The format of the station is variety. WUTM-FM broadcasts to the Martin, TN area at a frequency of 90.3 FM.

WUUB-FM
Owner: Good Karma Broadcasting
Editorial: 2090 Palm Beach Lakes Blvd Ste 801, West Palm Beach, Florida 33409-6508.
T: 1 561 697-8353
E: management@gkbsports.com
W: http://www.espnwestpalm.com
Editorial Profile: WUUB-FM is a commercial station owned by Good Karma Broadcasting. The format of the station is sports. WUUB-FM broadcasts to the West Palm Beach, FL area at 106.3 FM.

WUUF-FM
Owner: Waynco Radio Inc.
Editorial: 187 Vienna Rd, Newark, New York 14513-9414. **T.** 1 315 331-9667
E: bigdogfm@rochester.rr.com
W: http://www.bigdog1035.com
Editorial Profile: WUUF-FM is a commercial station owned by Waynco Radio Inc. The format of the station is classic country. WUUF-FM broadcasts to the Newark, NY area at 103.5 FM.

WUUQ-FM
Owner: 3 Daughters Media, Inc.
Editorial: 2615 Broad St, Chattanooga, Tennessee 37408-3100. **T:** 1 423 643-2212
W: http://www.wuuqradio.com
Editorial Profile: WUUQ-FM is a commercial station owned by 3 Daughters Media, Inc. The format of the station is classic country. WUUQ-FM broadcasts to the Chattanooga, TN area at 97.3 FM.

WUUU-FM
Owner: Pittman Broadcast Services LLC
Editorial: 23369 E Fairgrounds Rd, Franklinton, Louisiana 70438-5135.
T: 1 985 624-9452
W: http://www.catcountry989.com
Editorial Profile: WUUU-FM is a commercial station owned by Pittman Broadcast Services LLC. The format of the station is comtemporary country. The station broadcasts to the Mandeville, LA area at 98.9 FM.

WUVA-FM
Owner: WUVA Inc.
Editorial: 1928 Arlington Blvd, Ste 312, Charlottesville, Virginia 22903.
T: 1 434 817-6880 **E:** info@92.7kissfm.com
W: http://www.92.7kissfm.com
Editorial Profile: WUVA-FM is a commercial station owned by WUVA Inc. The format of the station is urban adult contemporary. WUVA-

FM broadcasts to the Charlottesville, VA area at 92.7 FM.

WUVT-FM
Owner: Educational Media Company at Virginia Tech, Inc.
Editorial: 350 Squires Student Ctr, Blacksburg, Virginia 24061. **T:** 1 540 231-9880
E: wuvtamfm@vt.edu
W: http://www.wuvt.vt.edu
Editorial Profile: WUVT-FM is a non-commercial station owned by Educational Media Company at Virginia Tech, Inc. The format of the station is variety. WUVT-FM broadcasts to the Blacksburg, VA area at 90.7 FM.

WUWF-FM
Owner: University of West Florida
Editorial: 11000 University Pkwy, Pensacola, Florida 32514. **T:** 1 850 474-2787
E: wuwf@wuwf.org **W:** http://www.wuwf.org
Editorial Profile: WUWF-FM is a non-commercial station owned by the University of West Florida. The format for the station is news and talk. WUWF-FM broadcasts to the Mobile, AL and Pensacola, FL areas at 88.1 FM.

WUWG-FM
Owner: Georgia Public Broadcasting
Editorial: 260 14th St NW, Atlanta, Georgia 30318. **T:** 1 404 685-2548 **E:** news@gpb.org
W: http://www.gpb.org
Editorial Profile: WUWG-FM is a non-commercial station owned by Georgia Public Broadcasting. The format of the station is jazz, classical and news. WUWG-FM broadcasts to the Atlanta area at 90.7 FM.

WUWM-FM
Owner: University of Wisconsin
Editorial: 111 E Wisconsin Ave Ste 700, Milwaukee, Wisconsin 53202-4822.
T: 1 414 227-3355 **E:** wuwmnews@uwm.edu
W: http://www.wuwm.com
Editorial Profile: WUWM-FM is a non-commercial station owned by the University of Wisconsin. The format of the station is variety. WUWM-FM broadcasts to the Milwaukee area at 89.7 FM.

WUZR-FM
Owner: Original Company Inc.(The)
Editorial: 522 Busseron St, Vincennes, Indiana 47591. **T:** 1 812 882-6060
E: wuzr@originalcompany.com
W: http://www.wuzr.com
Editorial Profile: WUZR-FM is a commercial station owned by The Original Company Inc. The format of the station is contemporary country. WUZR-FM broadcasts to the Vincennes, IN area at 105.7 FM.

WUZZ-FM
Owner: Forever Broadcasting
Editorial: 900 Water St, Meadville, Pennsylvania 16335-3428. **T:** 1 814 724-1111
E: radio@zoominternet.net
W: http://www.mywuzz.com
Editorial Profile: WUZZ-FM is a commercial station owned by Forever Broadcasting. The format of the station is classic rock music. WUZZ-FM broadcasts to the Meadville, PA area at 94.3 FM.

WVAF-FM
Owner: West Virginia Radio Corp.
Editorial: 1111 Virginia St E, Charleston, West Virginia 25301-2406. **T:** 1 304 342-8131
W: http://www.v100.fm
Editorial Profile: WVAF-FM is a commercial station owned by West Virginia Radio Corp. The format of the station is adult contemporary music. WVAF-FM broadcasts to the Charleston, WV area at 99.9 FM.

WVAL-AM
Owner: Tri-County Broadcasting
Editorial: 1010 2nd St N, Sauk Rapids, Minnesota 56379. **T:** 1 320 252-6200
W: http://www.800wval.com
Editorial Profile: WVAL-AM is a commercial station owned by Tri-County Broadcasting. The format of the station is classic country. WVAL-AM broadcasts to the Sauk Rapids, MN area at a frequency of 800 AM.

WVAM-AM
Owner: Forever Broadcasting
Editorial: 1 Forever Dr, Hollidaysburg, Pennsylvania 16648. **T:** 1 814 941-9800
W: http://www.wvamam.com
Editorial Profile: WVAM-AM is a commercial station owned by Forever Broadcasting. The format of the station is sports. WVAM-AM broadcasts to the Hollidaysburg, PA area at 1430 AM.

WVAQ-FM
Owner: West Virginia Radio Corp.
Editorial: 1251 Earl L Core Rd, Morgantown, West Virginia 26505-5881. **T:** 1 304 296-0029
W: http://www.wvaq.com
Editorial Profile: WVAQ-FM is a commercial station owned by West Virginia Radio Corp. The format of the station is Top 40/CHR. WVAQ-FM broadcasts to the Morgantown, WV area at 101.9 FM.

WVAR-AM
Owner: Summit Media Broadcasting LLC
Editorial: 713 Main St, Summersville, West Virginia 26651-1431. **T:** 1 304 765-7373
E: info@theboss97fm.com
W: http://www.summitmediawv.com
Editorial Profile: WVAR-AM is a commercial station owned by Summit Media Broadcasting LLC. The format of the station is classic hits. The station is aired in the Sutton, WV area at 600 AM. WVAR-AM is a simulcast of WSGB-AM.

WVAS-FM
Owner: Alabama State University
Editorial: 915 S Jackson St, Montgomery, Alabama 36104-5732. **T:** 1 334 229-4708
W: http://www.wvasfm.org
Editorial Profile: WVAS-FM is a non-commercial station owned by Alabama State University. The primary format of the station is jazz. WVAS-FM broadcasts to the Montgomery, AL area at 90.7 FM.

WVAX-AM
Owner: Saga Communications
Editorial: 1140 Rose Hill Dr, Charlottesville, Virginia 22903-5128. **T:** 1 434 220-2300
E: news@wina.com **W:** http://www.wvax.com
Editorial Profile: WVAX-AM is a commercial station owned by Saga Communications. The format for the station is sports/talk. WVAX-AM broadcasts to the Charlottesville, VA area at 1450 AM.

WVAZ-FM
Owner: Clear Channel Media and Entertainment
Editorial: 233 N Michigan Ave Ste 2700, Chicago, Illinois 60601-5704.
T: 1 312 540-2000 **W:** http://www.v103.com
Editorial Profile: WVAZ-FM is a commercial station owned by Clear Channel Media and Entertainment. The format of the station is urban adult contemporary. WVAZ-FM broadcasts to the Chicago area at 102.7 FM.

WVBB-FM
Owner: Wheeler, Inc. (Mel)
Editorial: 276 Seneca Trl, Ronceverte, West Virginia 24970. **T:** 1 304 645-1327
E: info@vibe100.com
W: http://www.vibe100.com
Editorial Profile: WVBB-FM is a commercial station owned by Mel Wheeler, Inc. The format of the station is R&B. WVBB-FM broadcasts to the Ronceverte, WV area at 97.7 FM.

WVBD-FM
Owner: Summit Media Broadcasting LLC
Editorial: 180 Main St, Sutton, West Virginia 26601-1317. **T:** 1 304 765-7373
Editorial Profile: WVBD-FM is a commercial station owned by Summit Media Broadcasting LLC. The format of the station is classic country music.

WVBE-AM
Owner: Wheeler Inc.(Mel)
Editorial: 3934 Electric Rd, Roanoke, Virginia 24018. **T:** 1 540 989-4591
E: info@vibe100.com
W: http://www.vibe100.com
Editorial Profile: WVBE-AM is a commercial station owned by Mel Wheeler Inc. The format of the station is R&B. WVBE-AM broadcasts in the Roanoke, VA area at 610 AM.

WVBE-FM
Owner: Wheeler Inc.(Mel)
Editorial: 3934 Electric Rd, Roanoke, Virginia 24018. **T:** 1 540 989-4591
E: info@vibe100.com
W: http://www.vibe100.com
Editorial Profile: WVBE-FM is a commercial station owned by Mel Wheeler Inc. The format of the station is urban adult contemporary. WVBE-FM broadcasts to the Roanoke, VA area at 100.1 FM.

WVBG-AM
Owner: Owensville Communication
Editorial: 1102 Newitt Vick Dr, Vicksburg, Mississippi 39183-8755. **T:** 1 601 883-0848
W: http://www.newstalk1490.net
Editorial Profile: WVBG-AM is a commercial station owned by Owensville Communication. The format of the station is talk. WVBG-AM broadcasts to the Vicksburg, MS area at 1490 AM.

WVBG-FM
Owner: Lendsi Radio
Editorial: 1102 Newitt Vick Dr, Vicksburg, Mississippi 39183. **T:** 1 601 883-0848
W: http://www.vicksburgv105.com
Editorial Profile: WVBG-FM is a commercial radio station owned by Lendsi Radio. The format of the station is classic hits. WVBG-FM broadcasts to the Vicksburg, MS area at 105.5 FM.

WVBO-FM
Owner: Cumulus Media Inc.
Editorial: 491 S Washburn St, Ste 400, Oshkosh, Wisconsin 54904.
T: 1 920 426-3239 **E:** wvbo@cumulus.com
W: http://www.1039wvbo.com
Editorial Profile: WVBO-FM is a commercial station owned by Cumulus Media Inc. The format of the station is oldies. WVBO-FM broadcasts to the Oshkosh, WI area at 103.9 FM.

WVBR-FM
Owner: Cornell Radio Guild
Editorial: 957B Mitchell St, Ithaca, New York 14850-4936. **T:** 1 607 273-4000
E: contact@wvbr.com **W:** http://www.wvbr.com
Editorial Profile: WVBR-FM is a commercial station owned by Cornell Radio Guild. The format of the station is rock music. WVBR-FM broadcasts to the Ithaca, NY area at 93.5 FM.

WVBS-AM
Owner: Bible/Grace Missionary Baptist Churches
Editorial: 2190 US Highway 117 S, Burgaw, North Carolina 28425. **T:** 1 910 259-5718
W: http://www.bbcburgaw.com
Editorial Profile: WVBS-AM is a non-commercial station owned by Bible/Grace Missionary Baptist Churches. The format of the station is Christian music and talk. WVBS-AM broadcasts in the Burgaw, NC area at 1470 AM.

WVBU-FM
Owner: Bucknell University
Editorial: Bucknell University, Box C-3956, Lewisburg, Pennsylvania 17837.
T: 1 570 577-1174 **E:** wvbu@bucknell.edu
W: http://www.wvbu.com

WVBW-FM
Owner: Max Media
Editorial: 5589 Greenwich Rd, Ste 200, Virginia Beach, Virginia 23462.
T: 1 757 671-1000
E: thebass@929thewave.com
W: http://www.929thewave.com
Editorial Profile: WVBW-FM is a commercial station owned by Max Media. The format of the station is classic hits. WVBW-FM broadcasts to the Norfolk, VA area at 92.9 FM.

WVBX-FM
Owner: Free Lance-Star Publishing Company
Editorial: 616 Amelia St, Fredericksburg, Virginia 22401. **T:** 1 540 374-5500
W: http://www.993thevibe.com
Editorial Profile: WVBX-FM is a commercial station owned by Free Lance-Star Publishing Company. The format of the station is rhythmic Top 40/CHR music. WVBX-FM broadcasts to the Fredericksburg, VA area at 99.3 FM.

WVBZ-FM
Owner: Clear Channel Media and Entertainment
Editorial: 2B Pai Park Fl 2, Greensboro, North Carolina 27409-9428. **T:** 1 336 822-2000
W: http://www.1057now.com
Editorial Profile: WVBZ-FM is a commercial station owned by Clear Channel Media and Entertainment. The format of the station is Top 40/CHR WVBZ-FM broadcasts to the Greensboro, NC area at 105.7 FM.

WVCC-AM
Owner: Clear Channel Media and Entertainment
Editorial: 154 Boone Dr, Newnan, Georgia 30263-2801. **T:** 1 770 683-7234
W: http://www720thevoice.com
Editorial Profile: WVCC-AM is a commercial station owned by Clear Channel Media and Entertainment. The format of the station is news and talk. WVCC-AM broadcasts to the Newnan, GA area at 720 AM.

WVCH-AM
Owner: WVCH Communications Inc.
Editorial: 308 E Dutton Mill Rd, Brookhaven, Pennsylvania 19015. **T:** 1 610 279-9000
W: http://www.wvch.com
Editorial Profile: WVCH-AM is a commercial station owned by WVCH Communications Inc. The format of the station is religious programming and contemporary Christian. WVCH-AM broadcasts to the Brookhaven, PA area at 740 AM.

WVCO-FM
Owner: CBM Broadcasting Corp.
Editorial: 429 Pine St, North Myrtle Beach, South Carolina 29582. **T:** 1 843 445-9491
E: surf949@yahoo.com
W: http://www.949thesurf.com
Editorial Profile: WVCO-FM is a commercial station owned by CBM Broadcasting Corp. The format of the station is classic hits. WVCO-FM broadcasts to the North Myrtle Beach, SC area at 94.9 FM.

WVCP-FM
Owner: Volunteer State College
Editorial: 1480 Nashville Pike, Ramer Bldg #101, Gallatin, Tennessee 37066-3148.
T: 1 615 230-3618 **E:** wvcp@volstate.edu
W: http://www.wvcp.net
Editorial Profile: WVCP-FM is a non-commercial station owned by Volunteer State College. The format of the station is oldies. WVCP-FM broadcasts to the Gallatin, TN area at 88.5 FM.

WVCR-FM
Owner: Siena College
Editorial: 515 Loudon Rd, Loudonville, New York 12211-1459. **T:** 1 518 782-6750
W: http://www.wvcr.com
Editorial Profile: WVCR-FM is a non-commerical station owned by Siena College. The format of the station is adult hits. WVCR-FM broadcasts to the Albany, NY area at 88.3 FM.

WVCV-AM
Owner: Piedmont Communications Inc.
Editorial: 207 Spicers Mill Rd, Orange, Virginia 22960. **T:** 1 540 825-3900
E: traffic@wjmafm.com
Editorial Profile: WVCV-AM is a commercial station owned by Piedmont Communications. The format of the station is adult standards music. WVCV-AM broadcasts in the Orange, VA area at 1340 AM.

WVCX-FM
Owner: VCY America Inc.
Editorial: 3434 W Kilbourn Ave, Milwaukee, Wisconsin 53208-3313. **T:** 1 414 935-3000
E: wvcx@vcyamerica.org
W: http://www.vcyamerica.org
Editorial Profile: WVCX-FM is a non-commercial station owned by VCY America Inc. The format of the station is religous. WVCX-FM broadcasts to the Milwaukee area at 98.9 FM.

WVCY-AM
Owner: VCY America Inc.
Editorial: 1455 W County Road Y, Oshkosh, Wisconsin 54904. **T:** 1 414 935-3000
E: wvcyam@vcyamerica.org
W: http://www.vcyamerica.org
Editorial Profile: WVCY-AM is a non-commercial station owned by VCY America Inc. The format of the station is gospel and religious talk. WVCY-AM broadcasts to Milwaukee, WI and surrounding communities at 690 AM.

WVCY-FM
Owner: VCY America Inc.
Editorial: 3434 W Kilbourn Ave, Milwaukee, Wisconsin 53208-3313. **T:** 1 414 935-3000
E: wvcyfm@vcyamerica.org
W: http://www.vcyamerica.org
Editorial Profile: WVCY-FM is a non-commercial station owned by VCY America Inc. The format of the station is gospel music and religious talk. WVCY-FM broadcasts to Milwaukee and the surrounding communities at 107.7 FM.

WVEE-FM
Owner: CBS Radio
Editorial: 1201 Peachtree St NE, 400 Colony Square, Atlanta, Georgia 30361-3503.
T: 1 404 898-8900
W: http://v103.cbslocal.com
Editorial Profile: WVEE-FM is a commercial station owned by CBS Radio. The format of

the station is urban contemporary. WVEE-FM broadcasts to the Atlanta area at 103.3 FM.

WVEI-AM
Owner: Entercom Communications Corp.
Editorial: 181 Moreland St, Worcester, Massachusetts 01609-1049.
T: 1 508 752-5611 **W:** http://www.weei.com
Editorial Profile: WVEI-AM is a commercial station owned by Entercom Communications Corp. The format of the station is sports. WVEI-AM broadcasts to the Worcester, MA area at 1440 AM.

WVEI-FM
Owner: Entercom Communications Corp.
Editorial: 20 Guest St, 3rd Fl, Brighton, Massachusetts 2135. **T:** 1 617 779-3500
W: http://www.weei.com
Editorial Profile: WVEI-FM is a commercial station owned by Entercom Communications Corp. The format of the station is sports. WVEI-FM broadcasts to the Brighton, MA area at 105.5 FM.

WVEK-FM
Owner: Holston Valley Broadcasting Corp.
Editorial: 222 Commerce St, Kingsport, Tennessee 37660-4319. **T:** 1 423 246-9578
E: classichits1027@live.com
W: http://www.classichits1027.com

WVEL-AM
Owner: Cumulus Media Inc.
Editorial: 120 Eaton St, Peoria, Illinois 61603-4217. **T:** 1 309 676-5000
W: http://www.wvel.com
Editorial Profile: WVEL-AM is a commercial station owned by Cumulus Media Inc. The format of the station is Christian music. WVEL-AM broadcasts to the Peoria, IL area at AM 1140 AM.

WVES-FM
Owner: Chincoteague Broadcasting Corp.
Editorial: 27214 Mutton Hunk Rd, Parksley, Virginia 23421-3238. **T:** 1 757 665-6500
E: hotcountry993@yahoo.com
W: http://sharecountry.net
Editorial Profile: WVES-FM is a commercial station owned by Chincoteague Broadcasting Corp. The format of the station is contemporary country music. WVES-FM broadcasts to the Parksley, VA area at 99.3 FM.

WVEZ-FM
Owner: Summit Media Broadcasting LLC
Editorial: 612 S 4th St, Louisville, Kentucky 40202-2460. **T:** 1 502 589-4800
W: http://lite1069.com
Editorial Profile: WVEZ-FM is a commercial station owned by Summit Media Broadcasting LLC. The format of the station is adult contemporary. WVEZ-FM broadcasts to the Louisville, KY area at 106.9 FM.

WVFB-FM
Owner: Whittimore Enterprises
Editorial: 341 Radio Station Rd, Tompkinsville, Kentucky 42167-8572. **T:** 1 270 487-6119
E: kixcountry@windstream.net

WVFJ-FM
Owner: Radio Training Network
Editorial: 1175 Senoia Rd, Ste E, Tyrone, Georgia 30290-3608. **T:** 1 770 487-4500
E: info@wvfj.com
W: http://georgia.thejoyfm.com
Editorial Profile: WVFJ-FM is a non-commercial station owned by Radio Training Network. The format of the station is adult contemporary Christian music programming. WVFJ-FM broadcasts to the Greater Atlanta, GA area at 93.3 FM.

WVFM-FM
Owner: Midwest Communications Inc.
Editorial: 4200 W Main St, Kalamazoo, Michigan 49006-2749. **T:** 1 269 345-7121
E: wkzonews@wkzo.com
W: http://www.wvfm.fm
Editorial Profile: WVFM-FM is a commercial station owned by Midwest Communications Inc. The format of the station is adult contemporary music. WVFM-FM broadcasts to the Kalamazoo, MI area at 106.5 FM.

WVFN-AM
Owner: Townsquare Media, LLC
Editorial: 3420 Pinetree Rd, Lansing, Michigan 48911-4207. **T:** 1 517 394-7272
W: http://www.thegame730am.com
Editorial Profile: WVFN-AM is a commercial station owned by Townsquare Media, LLC. The format of the station is sports programming.

WVFN-AM broadcasts to the Lansing, MI area at 730 AM.

WVFS-FM
Owner: Florida State University Board of Trustees
Editorial: FSU 420 Diffenbaugh Building, Tallahassee, Florida 32306. **T:** 1 850 644-9692
W: http://wvfs.fsu.edu
Editorial Profile: WVFS-FM is a non-commercial station owned by Florida State University Board of Trustees. The format of the station is adult album alternative. WVFS-FM broadcasts to the Tallahassee, FL area at 89.7 FM.

WVGA-FM
Owner: Black Crow Broadcasting Inc.
Editorial: 1711 Ellis Dr, Valdosta, Georgia 31601. **T:** 1 229 244-8642
W: http://www.valdostatoday.com
Editorial Profile: WVGA-FM is a commercial station owned by Black Crow Broadcasting Inc. The format of the station is news, talk and sports. WVGA-FM broadcasts to the Valdosta, GA area at 105.9 FM.

WVGB-AM
Owner: Vivian Broadcasting
Editorial: 806 Monson St, Beaufort, South Carolina 29902-4551. **T:** 1 843 524-4700
Editorial Profile: WVGB-AM is a commercial station owned by Vivian Broadcasting. The format of the station is gospel. WVGB-AM broadcasts to the Beaufort, SC area at 1490 AM.

WVGG-AM
Owner: JDL Corporation
Editorial: 3276 Highway 198 W, Lucedale, Mississippi 39452-7914. **T:** 1 601 947-8151
E: wrbe@wrberadio.com
W: http://www.talkradio1580.com
Editorial Profile: WVGG-AM is a commercial station owned by JDL Corporation. The format of the station is news/talk. WVGG-AM broadcasts to the Lucedale, MS area at 1440 AM.

WVGM-AM
Owner: 3 Daughters Media, Inc.
Editorial: 1035 Avalon Dr, Forest, Virginia 24551-2970. **T:** 1 434 534-6100
E: wblt@inbox.com
W: http://www.espninva.com
Editorial Profile: WVGM-AM is a commercial station owned by 3 Daughters Media, Inc. The format of the station is sports. WVGM-AM broadcasts to the Roanoke, VA area at 1320 AM and is simulcast of WGMN-AM.

WVGR-FM
Owner: University of Michigan
Editorial: 535 W William St Ste 110, Ann Arbor, Michigan 48103-4978.
T: 1 734 764-9210 **E:** newsroom@umich.edu
W: http://www.michiganradio.org
Editorial Profile: WVGR-FM is a non-commercial station owned by University of Michigan. The format of the station is news and talk. WVGR-FM broadcasts to the Grand Rapids, MI area at 104.1 FM.

WVGS-FM
Owner: Georgia Southern University
Editorial: Georgia Southern University, Statesboro, Georgia 30460-0001.
T: 1 912 681-0877 **E:** thebuzz919@yahoo.com
W: http://www.919thebuzz.net
Editorial Profile: WVGS-FM is a non-commercial station owned by Georgia Southern University. The format for the station is variety. WVGS-FM broadcasts to the Savannah, GA area at 91.9 FM.

WVHC-FM
Owner: Herkimer County Community College
Editorial: 100 Reservoir Road Technology Ctr, Herkimer, New York 13350-1545.
T: 1 315 866-0300 **E:** wvhc@herkimer.edu
W: http://www.herkimer.edu/wvhc
Editorial Profile: WVHC-FM is a non-commercial station owned by Herkimer County Community College. The format of the station is jazz. WVHC-FM broadcasts to the Herkimer, NY area at 91.5 FM.

WVHF-AM
Owner: Holy Family Radio
Editorial: 2504 Ardmore St Se, Grand Rapids, Michigan 49506-4901. **T:** 1 616 956-1140
E: contact@holyfamilyradio.net
W: http://www.holyfamilyradio.net
Editorial Profile: WVHF-AM is a non-commercial radio station owned by Amicus Management. The format of the station is religious. WVHF-AM broadcasts to the Grand

Rapids, MI and surrounding communities at 1140 AM.

WVHI-AM
Owner: Word Broadcasting Network, Inc.
Editorial: 2207 J E Morgan Avenue, Evansville, Indiana 47415. **T:** 1 812 475-9930
W: http://www.wvhi.com
Editorial Profile: WVHI-AM is a commercial station owned by Word Broadcasting Network, Inc. The format of the station is religious talk and christian music. WVHI-AM broadcasts in the Evansville, IN area at 1330 AM.

WVHL-FM
Owner: Farmville Herald Inc.(The)
Editorial: 116 North St, Farmville, Virginia 23901. **T:** 1 434 392-9393 **E:** v93@wvhl.net
W: http://www.wvhl.net
Editorial Profile: WVHL-FM is a commercial station owned by The Farmville Herald Inc. The format of the station is contemporary country. WVHL-FM broadcasts to the Farmville, VA area at 92.9 FM.

WVHM-FM
Owner: Heartland Ministries, Inc.
Editorial: 219 College St, Hardin, Kentucky 42048. **T:** 1 270 437-4095
E: info@hmiradio.com
W: http://www.hmiradio.com

WVHT-FM
Owner: Max Media
Editorial: 5589 Greenwich Rd, Ste 200, Virginia Beach, Virginia 23462.
T: 1 757 671-1000
W: http://www.hot1005.com
Editorial Profile: WVHT-FM is a commercial station owned by Max Media. The format of the station is top 40/CHR. WVHT-FM broadcasts to the Virginia Beach, VA area at 100.5 FM.

WVHU-AM
Owner: Clear Channel Media and Entertainment
Editorial: 134 4th Ave, Huntington, West Virginia 25701. **T:** 1 304 525-7788
W: http://www.800wvhu.com
Editorial Profile: WVHU-AM is a commercial station owned by Clear Channel Media and Entertainment. The format for the station is news and talk. WVHU-AM broadcasts to the Charleston-Huntington, WV area at 800 AM.

WVIA-FM
Owner: N.E. Pennsylvania Educational TV Assoc.
Editorial: 100 WVIA Way, Pittston, Pennsylvania 18640-6127. **T:** 1 570 826-6144
E: wviafm@wvia.org **W:** http://www.wvia.org
Editorial Profile: WVIA-FM is a non-commercial station owned by N.E. Pennsylvania Educational TV Assoc. The format of the station is a classical, jazz, news and talk. WVIA-FM broadcasts to Pittston, PA area at 89.9 FM.

WVIB-FM
Owner: Cumulus Media Inc
Editorial: 3375 Merriam St, Ste 201, Muskegon, Michigan 49444.
T: 1 231 830-0176 **W:** http://www.v100fm.com
Editorial Profile: WVIB-FM is a commercial station owned by Cumulus Media Inc. The format of the station is urban adult contemporary. WVIB-FM broadcasts to the Muskegon, MI area at 100.1 FM.

WVIC-FM
Owner: Midwest Communications, Inc.
Editorial: 2495 Cedar St, Holt, Michigan 48842. **T:** 1 517 699-0111
W: http://www.941theedge.com
Editorial Profile: WVIC-FM is a commercial station owned by Midwest Communications, Inc. The format of the station is rock alternative. WVIC-FM broadcasts to the Holt, MI area at 94.1 FM.

WVIK-FM
Owner: Augustana College
Editorial: 639 38th St, Rock Island, Illinois 61201-2210. **T:** 1 309 794-7500
E: news@wvik.org **W:** http://www.wvik.org
Editorial Profile: WVIK-FM is a non-commercial station owned by Augustana College. The format of the station is news and classical. WVIK-FM broadcasts to the Rock Island, IL area at 90.3 FM.

WVIL-FM
Owner: LB Sports Productions LLC
Editorial: 108 E Main St, Beardstown, Illinois 62618-1241. **T:** 1 217 3231790

W: http://www.wvilfm.com
Editorial Profile: WVIL-FM is a commercial station owned by LB Sports Productions LLC. The format of the station is sports. WVIL-FM broadcasts in the Jacksonville, IL at 101.3 FM.

WVIN-FM
Owner: Pembrook Pines Media Group
Editorial: E Washington St Ext, Bath, New York 14810-9801. **T:** 1 607 776-3326
E: wvinsales@stny.rr.com
W: http://wvinbath.com
Editorial Profile: WVIN-FM is a commercial station owned by Pembrook Pines Media Group. The format of the station is Hot AC. WVIN-FM broadcasts to the Bath, NY area at 98.3 FM.

WVIP-FM
Owner: Whitney Radio Broadcasting Inc.
Editorial: 411 5th Ave, New Rochelle, New York 10801-2047. **T:** 1 914 636-1460
E: info@wvox.com **W:** http://www.wvipfm.com
Editorial Profile: WVIP-FM is a commercial station owned by Whitney Radio Broadcasting Inc. The format of the station is variety. WVIP-FM broadcasts to the New Rochelle, NY area at 93.5 FM.

WVIV-FM
Owner: Univision Communications Inc.
Editorial: 625 N Michigan Ave Ste 300, Chicago, Illinois 60611-3110.
T: 1 312 981-1800
W: http://maximamusica.univision.com
Editorial Profile: WVIV-FM is a commercial station owned by Univision Communications Inc. The format of the station is Hurban featuring Spanish urban contemporary music. WVIV-FM broadcasts to the Chicago area at 103.1 FM.

WVIX-FM
Owner: Univision Communications Inc.
Editorial: 625 N Michigan Ave Ste 300, Chicago, Illinois 60611-3110.
T: 1 312 981-1800
W: http://maximamusica.univision.com
Editorial Profile: WVIX-FM is a commercial station owned by Univision Communications. The format of the station is Hurban featuring Spanish urban contemporary. WVIX-FM broadcasts to the Chicago area at 93.5 FM.

WVJC-FM
Owner: Illinois Eastern Community Colleges
Editorial: 2200 College Dr, Mount Carmel, Illinois 62863. **T:** 1 618 262-8641
W: http://www.bashradio.com

WVJS-AM
Owner: Cromwell Group Inc.(The)
Editorial: 1115 Tamarack Rd, Ste 500, Owensboro, Kentucky 42301.
T: 1 270 683-5200
E: kyproduction@cromwellradio.com
W: http://www.owensbororadio.com/wvjs/index.html
Editorial Profile: WVJS-AM is a commercial station owned by The Cromwell Group Inc. The format of the station is classic hits. WVJS-AM broadcasts to the Evansville, IN area at 1420 AM.

WVKF-FM
Owner: Clear Channel Media and Entertainment
Editorial: 1015 Main St, Wheeling, West Virginia 26003. **T:** 1 304 232-1170
W: http://www.kisswheeling.com
Editorial Profile: WVKF-FM is a commercial station owned by Clear Channel Media and Entertainment. The format of the station is Top 40/CHR. WVKF-FM broadcasts to the Wheeling, WV area at 95.7 FM.

WVKL-FM
Owner: Entercom Communications Corp.
Editorial: 236 Clearfield Ave, Ste 206, Virginia Beach, Virginia 23462. **T:** 1 757 497-2000
W: http://www.957rnb.com
Editorial Profile: WVKL-FM is a commercial station owned by Entercom Communications Corp. The format of the station is urban adult contemporary and R&B music. WVKL-FM broadcasts to the Virginia Beach, VA area at 95.7 FM.

WVKM-FM
Owner: Hatfield McCoy Communications, Inc.
Editorial: 156 Radio Hill St, McCarr, Kentucky 41544-8553. **T:** 1 606 427-7261
Editorial Profile: WVKM-FM is a commercial station owned by Hatfield McCoy Communications, Inc. The format of the station is classic rock. WVKM-FM broadcasts to the McCarr, KY area at 106.7 FM.

WVKO-AM
Owner: Bernard Ohio LLC
Editorial: 3360 E Livingston Ave Ste 2A, Columbus, Ohio 43227-1961.
T: 1 614 824-2550 **E:** info@1580thepraise.com
W: http://1580thepraise.com
Editorial Profile: WVKO-AM is a commercial station owned by Bernard Ohio LLC. The format of the station is Black Gospel. WVKO-AM broadcasts to the Columbus, OH, area at 1580 AM.

WVKR-FM
Owner: Vassar College
Editorial: 124 Raymond Ave, Box 726 - Vassar College, Poughkeepsie, New York 12604-0001. **T:** 1 845 437-5475
E: newsdirector@wvkr.org
W: http://www.wvkr.org
Editorial Profile: WVKR-FM is a non-commercial station owned by Vassar College. The format of the station is college variety. WVKR-FM broadcasts to the Poughkeepsie, NY area at 91.3 FM.

WVKS-FM
Owner: Clear Channel Media and Entertainment
Editorial: 125 S Superior St, Toledo, Ohio 43602-1747. **T:** 1 419 244-8321
W: http://www.925kissfm.com
Editorial Profile: WVKS-FM is a commercial station owned by Clear Channel Media and Entertainment. The format of the station is Top 40/CHR music. WVKS-FM broadcasts to the Toledo, OH area at 92.5 FM.

WVKX-FM
Owner: Wilkins Communications Network Inc.
Editorial: 104 High Hill St, Irwinton, Georgia 31042. **T:** 1 478 946-3445
Editorial Profile: WVKX-FM is a commercial station owned by Wilkins Communications Network Inc. The format of the station is urban contemporary music. WVKX-FM broadcasts to the Irwinton, GA area at 103.7 FM.

WVLC-FM
Owner: Shoreline Communications Inc.
Editorial: 101 E Main St, Campbellsville, Kentucky 42718-2237. **T:** 1 270 789-0099
E: bigdawg@wvlc.com
W: http://www.wvlc.com
Editorial Profile: WVLC-FM is a commercial station owned by Shoreline Communications Inc. The format of the station is country. WVLC-FM broadcasts to the Campbellsville, KY area at 99.9 FM.

WVLD-AM
Owner: Black Crow Broadcasting Inc.
Editorial: 1711 Ellis Dr, Valdosta, Georgia 31601. **T:** 1 229 242-4821
W: http://www.talkradio1069.fm
Editorial Profile: WVLD-AM is a commercial station owned by Black Crow Broadcasting Inc. The format of the station is sports. WVLD-AM broadcasts to the Valdosta, GA area at 1450 AM.

WVLE-FM
Owner: Skytower Communications Inc.
Editorial: 104 1/2 W Public Sq, Scottsville, Kentucky 42164-1175. **T:** 1 270 237-3148
E: newswatch@wvle.net **W:** http://wvle.net
Editorial Profile: WVLE-FM is a commercial station owned by Skytower Communications Inc. The format of the station is adult contemporary. WVLE-FM broadcasts to the Nashville, TN area at 99.3 FM.

WVLF-FM
Owner: Stephens Media Group Massena, LLC
Editorial: 2155 State Highway 420, Massena, New York 13662. **T:** 1 315 769-3333
E: mikeg@mymix961.com
W: http://www.mymix961.com
Editorial Profile: WVLF-FM is a commercial station owned by Stephens Media Group Massena, LLC. The format of the station is adult contemporary. WVLF-FM broadcasts to the Massena, NY area at 96.1 FM.

WVLG-AM
Owner: Senior Broadcasting Corp.
Editorial: 1161 Main St, The Villages, Florida 32159-7721. **T:** 1 352 753-1119
E: wvlgradio@thevillagesmedia.com
W: http://www.thevillagesdailysun.com
Editorial Profile: WVLG-AM is a commercial station owned by Senior Broadcasting Corp. The format of the station is adult hits. WVLG-AM broadcasts to The Villages, FL area at 640 AM.

WVLI-FM
Owner: Milner Broadcasting Enterprises, LLC
Editorial: 292 N Convent St, Bourbonnais, Illinois 60914-2014. **T:** 1 815 933-9287
W: http://www.rivervalleyradio.net
Editorial Profile: WVLI-FM is a commercial station owned by Newsweb Corp. The format of the station is Top 40/CHR. WVLI-FM broadcasts to the Kankakee, IL area at 92.7 FM.

WVLK-AM
Owner: Cumulus Media Inc.
Editorial: 300 W Vine St Ste 3, Lexington, Kentucky 40507-1806. **T:** 1 859 253-5900
E: news@wvlkam.com
W: http://www.wvlkam.com
Editorial Profile: WVLK-AM is a commercial station owned by Cumulus Media Inc. The format of the station is news, sports and talk. WVLK-AM broadcasts to the Lexington, KY area at 590 AM.

WVLK-FM
Owner: Cumulus Media Inc.
Editorial: 300 W Vine St Ste 3, Lexington, Kentucky 40507-1806. **T:** 1 859 253-5900
W: http://www.wvlkfm.net
Editorial Profile: WVLK-FM is a commercial station owned by Cumulus Media Inc. The format of the station is news/talk. WVLK-FM broadcasts to the Lexington, KY area at 101.5 FM.

WVLN-AM
Owner: Forcht Broadcasting
Editorial: 4667 E Radio Tower Ln, Olney, Illinois 62450-4742. **T:** 1 618 393-2156
W: http://www.wvlnam.com
Editorial Profile: WVLN-AM is a commercial station owned by Forcht Broadcasting. The format of the station is sports. WVLN-AM broadcasts to the Olney, IL area at 740 AM.

WVLS-FM
Owner: Pocahontas Communications Cooperative Corp.
Editorial: 80 East Main Street, Monterey, Virginia 24465. **T:** 1 540 468-1234
W: http://www.alleghenymountainradio.org
Editorial Profile: WVLS-FM is a non-commercial community station owned by Pocahontas Communications Cooperative Corp. The format of the station is variety. WVLS-FM broadcasts to the Monterey, VA area at a frequency of 89.7 FM.

WVLT-FM
Owner: Clear Communications Inc.
Editorial: 632 Maurice River Pkwy, Vineland, New Jersey 08360-2629. **T:** 1 856 692-8888
W: http://www.wvlt.com
Editorial Profile: WVLT-FM is a commercial station owned by Clear Communications Inc. The format of the station is oldies. WVLT-FM broadcasts to the Vineland, NJ area at 92.1 FM.

WVLY-AM
Owner: Monroe Communications
Editorial: 1143 Main St, Wheeling, West Virginia 26003-2743. **T:** 1 304 233-9859
W: http://www.talkradio1370.com
Editorial Profile: WVLY-AM is a commercial station owned by Monroe Communications. The format of the station is talk. WVLY-AM broadcasts to the Wheeling, WV area at 1370 AM.

WVLY-FM
Owner: Sunbury Broadcasting Corp.
Editorial: 1227 County Line Rd, Selinsgrove, Pennsylvania 17870-8188. **T:** 1 570 286-5838
W: http://www.wkok.com/The_Valley/index.html
Editorial Profile: WVLY-FM is a commercial station owned by Sunbury Broadcasting Corp. The format of the station is adult contemporary. WVLY-FM broadcasts to the Scranton, PA area at 100.9 FM.

WVLZ-AM
Owner: Kirkland Wireless Broadcasters Inc.
Editorial: 9040 Executive Park Dr Ste 303, Knoxville, Tennessee 37923-4639.
T: 1 865 243-2877
W: http://www.tnsportsradio.com
Editorial Profile: WVLZ-AM is a commercial station owned by Kirkland Wireless Broadcasters Inc. and co-owned by Action Sports Media. The format of the station is sports. WVLZ-AM broadcasts to the Knoxville, TN area at 1180 AM.

WVMC-FM
Owner: Mansfield Christian School Board
Editorial: 500 Logan Rd, Mansfield, Ohio 44907-2819. **T:** 1 419 756-5651
E: events@wvmcfm.com
W: http://www.wvmcfm.com
Editorial Profile: WVMC-FM is a non-commercial station owned by Mansfield Christian School Board. The format of the station is Christian Music. WVMC-FM broadcasts to the Mansfield, OH area at 90.7 FM.

WVMD-FM
Owner: West Virgina Radio Corporation of the Alleganies
Editorial: 15 Industrial Blvd E, Cumberland, Maryland 21502-4106. **T:** 1 301 759-1005
Editorial Profile: WVMD-FM is a commercial station owned by West Virgina Radio Corporation of the Alleganies. The format of the station is alternative rock music. WVMD-FM broadcasts to the Cumberland, MD, area at 99.5 FM.

WVMJ-FM
Owner: Mt. Washington Radio & Gramophone LLC
Editorial: Settler's Green OVP Route 16, #A30, North Conway, New Hampshire 3860.
T: 1 603 356-8870
E: office@conwaymagic.com
W: http://www.conwaymagic.com
Editorial Profile: WVMJ-FM is a commercial station owned by Mt. Washington Radio & Gramophone LLC. The format of the station is hot adult contemporary. WVMJ-FM broadcasts to the North Conway, NH area at 104.5 FM.

WVMM-FM
Owner: Messiah College
Editorial: 1 College Ave, Messiah College, Mechanicsburg, Pennsylvania 17055-6805.
T: 1 717 691-6081
E: pulsefmmusicmanager@gmail.com
W: http://pulse.messiah.edu/wvmm
Editorial Profile: WVMM-FM is a non-commercial station owned by Messiah College. The format of the station is contemporary Christian. WVMM-FM broadcasts to Grantham, PA at 90.7 FM.

WVMP-FM
Owner: Centennial Broadcasting
Editorial: 210 1st St SW, Ste 240, Roanoke, Virginia 24011-1607. **T:** 1 540 344-2800
E: wvmp@centennialbroadcasting.com
W: http://www.1015themusicplace.com
Editorial Profile: WVMP-FM is a commercial station owned by Centennial Broadcasting. The format of the station is AAA-Adult album alternative. The station also works with local cultural and social organizations in order to elevate interest in those areas. WVMP-FM broadcasts to the Vinton, VA area 101.5 FM.

WVMR-AM
Owner: Pocahontas Communications Cooperative Corp.
Editorial: State Route 28, Dunmore, West Virginia 24934. **T:** 1 304 799-6004
E: amr@frontiernet.net
W: http://www.alleghenymountainradio.org
Editorial Profile: WVMR-AM is a non-commercial station owned by the Pocahontas Communications Cooperative Corp. The format of the station is country music and variety. WVMR-AM broadcasts to Pocahontas County, WV at 1370 AM.

WVMS-FM
Owner: Moody Bible Institute
Editorial: 9756 Barr Rd, Cleveland, Ohio 44141. **T:** 1 440 526-1111 **E:** wcrf@moody.edu
W: http://wcrf.mbn.org
Editorial Profile: WVMS-FM is a non-commercial station owned by the Moody Bible Institute. The format of the station is religious. WVMS-FM broadcasts to the Cleveland area at 103.3 FM.

WVMT-AM
Owner: Sison Broadcasting Inc.
Editorial: 118 Malletts Bay Ave, Colchester, Vermont 5446. **T:** 1 802 655-1620
E: talk@newstalk620wvmt.com
W: http://www.newstalk620wvmt.com
Editorial Profile: WVMT-AM is a commercial station owned by Sison Broadcasting Inc. The format of the station is news, sports and talk. WVMT-AM broadcasts to the Colchester, VT area at 620 AM.

WVMW-FM
Owner: Marywood University
Editorial: 2300 Adams Ave, Scranton, Pennsylvania 18509. **T:** 1 570 348-6202
W: http://www.vmfm917.org
Editorial Profile: WVMW-FM is a non-commercial station owned by Marywood University. The format of the station is rock. WVMW-FM broadcasts to the Scranton, PA area at 91.5 FM.

WVMX-FM
Owner: Saga Communications
Editorial: 4401 Carriage Hill Ln, Columbus, Ohio 43220-3837. **T:** 1 614 451-2191
W: http://www.mymix1079.com
Editorial Profile: WVMX-FM is a commercial station owned by Saga Communications. The format of the station is hot adult contemporary. WVMX-FM broadcasts to the Columbus, OH, area at 107.9 FM.

WVNA-AM
Owner: URBan Radio Broadcasting, LLC
Editorial: 509 N Main St, Tuscumbia, Alabama 35674-2048. **T:** 1 256 383-2525
E: info@urbanradio.fm
W: http://www.newstalkwvna.com
Editorial Profile: WVNA-AM is a commercial station owned by URBan Radio Broadcasting, LLC. The format for the station is news and talk. WVNA-AM broadcasts to the Huntsville, AL area at 1590 AM.

WVNA-FM
Owner: URBan Radio Broadcasting, LLC
Editorial: 509 N Main St, Tuscumbia, Alabama 35674-2048. **T:** 1 256 383-2525
E: info@urbanradio.fm
W: http://www.bigdog1055.com
Editorial Profile: WVNA-FM is a commercial station owned by URBan Radio Broadcasting, LLC. The format of the station is rock. WVNA-FM broadcasts to the Tuscumbia, AL area at 105.5 FM.

WVNE-AM
Owner: Blount Communications Group
Editorial: 70 James St, Ste 201, Worcester, Massachusetts 01603-1045.
T: 1 508 831-9863 **E:** info@wvne.net
W: http://www.wvne.net
Editorial Profile: WVNE-AM is a commercial station owned by Blount Communications Group. The format of the station is Christian programming. WVNE-AM broadcasts to the Worcester, MA area at 760 AM.

WVNH-FM
Owner: New Hampshire Gospel Radio Inc.
Editorial: 37 Redington Road, Concord, New Hampshire 3301. **T:** 1 603 227-0911
E: info@nhgr.org **W:** http://www.nhgr.org
Editorial Profile: WVNH-FM is a non-commercial station owned by New Hampshire Gospel Radio Inc. The format of the station is Christian music and talk. WVNH-FM broadcasts to the Concord, NH area at 91.1 FM.

WVNI-FM
Owner: Mid-America Radio Group
Editorial: 4317 E 3rd St, Bloomington, Indiana 47401-5551. **T:** 1 812 335-9500
E: spirit95@spirit95fm.com
W: http://www.spirit95fm.com
Editorial Profile: WVNI-FM is a commercial station owned by Mid-America Radio Group. The format for the station is contemporary Christian. WVNI-FM broadcasts to the Bloomington, IN area at 95.1 FM.

WVNJ-AM
Owner: Universal Broadcasting
Editorial: 1086 Teaneck Rd, Ste 4F, Teaneck, New Jersey 7666. **T:** 1 201 837-0400
E: wvnj1160am@aol.com
W: http://www.wvnj.com
Editorial Profile: WVNJ-AM is a commercial station owned by Universal Broadcasting. The format of the station is talk. WVNJ-AM broadcasts to the Teaneck, NJ area at 1160 AM. The station does not accept news items as all their news is syndicated.

WVNL-FM
Owner: Illinois Bible Institute
Editorial: 17280 Lakeside Dr, Carlinville, Illinois 62626-2539. **T:** 1 217 854-4800
E: wibi@wibi.org **W:** http://www.wibi.org
Editorial Profile: WVNL-FM is a non-commercial station owned by Illinois Bible Institute. The format of the station is contemporary Christian music. WVNL-FM broadcasts to the Carlinville, IL area at 91.7 FM.

WVNN-AM
Owner: Cumulus Media Inc.
Editorial: 1717 Us Highway 72 E, Athens, Alabama 35611-4413. **T:** 1 256 830-8300
W: http://www.wvnn.com

Editorial Profile: WVNN-FM is a commercial station owned by Cumulus Media Inc. The format of the station is news and talk. WVNN-FM broadcasts to the Huntsville, AL area at 770 AM.

WVNN-FM
Owner: Cumulus Media Inc.
Editorial: 1717 US Highway 72 E, Athens, Alabama 35611-4413. **T:** 1 256 830-8300
W: http://www.wvnn.com
Editorial Profile: WVNN-FM is a commercial station owned by Cumulus Media Inc. The format for the station is news and talk simulcasted from WVNN-AM. WVNN-FM broadcasts to the Huntsville, AL area at 92.5 FM.

WVNO-FM
Owner: Johnny Appleseed Broadcasting Co. Inc.
Editorial: 2900 Park Ave W, Mansfield, Ohio 44906. **T:** 1 419 529-5900
E: comments@wvno.com
W: http://www.wvno.com
Editorial Profile: WVNO-FM is a commercial station owned by Johnny Appleseed Broadcasting Co. Inc. The format of the station is adult contemporary music. WVNO-FM broadcasts to the Mansfield, OH area at 106.1 FM.

WVNR-AM
Owner: Pine Tree Broadcasting Company
Editorial: 1214 Vermont Route 30 S, Poultney, Vermont 5764. **T:** 1 802 287-9031
E: wvnrwnyv@yahoo.com
Editorial Profile: WVNR-AM is a commercial station owned by Pine Tree Broadcasting Company. The format of the station is country, oldies and adult contemporary music. WVNR-AM broadcasts to the Poultney, VT area at 1340 AM.

WVNT-AM
Owner: Burbach of WV, LLC
Editorial: 5 Rosemar Cir, Parkersburg, West Virginia 26104. **T:** 1 304 485-4565
W: http://www.wvnt.net

WVNU-FM
Owner: Southern Ohio Broadcasting Inc.
Editorial: 321 Jefferson St, Greenfield, Ohio 45123. **T:** 1 937 981-5050
E: news@wvnu.com **W:** http://www.wvnu.com
Editorial Profile: WVNU-FM is a commercial station owned by Southern Ohio Broadcasting Inc. The format of the station is adult contemporary music. WVNU-FM broadcasts to the Greenfield, OH area at 97.5 FM.

WVNV-FM
Owner: Martz Communications
Editorial: 86 Porter Rd, Malone, New York 12953-3701. **T:** 1 518 483-1100
E: news@country965.com
W: http://www.country965.com
Editorial Profile: WVNV-FM is a commercial station owned by Martz Communications. The format of the station is contemporary country music. WVNV-FM broadcasts to the Malone, NY area at 96.5 FM.

WVNW-FM
Owner: WVNW Inc.
Editorial: 114 N Logan Blvd, Burnham, Pennsylvania 17009. **T:** 1 717 242-1493
E: wvnw@star967.com
W: http://www.star967.com
Editorial Profile: WVNW-FM is a commercial station owned by WVNW Inc. The format of the station is contemporary country. WVNW-FM broadcasts to the Burnham, PA area at 96.7 FM.

WVNZ-AM
Owner: Davidson Media Group
Editorial: 308 W Broad St, Richmond, Virginia 23220-4240. **T:** 1 804 643-0990
E: wvnz@davidsonmediagroup.com
W: http://www.selecta1320.com
Editorial Profile: WVNZ-AM is a commercial station owned by Davidson Media Group LLC. The format of the station is Spanish Contemporary music. WVNZ-AM broadcasts to the Richmond, VA area at 1320 AM.

WVOB-FM
Owner: Bethany Bible College
Editorial: 2573 Hodgesville Rd, Dothan, Alabama 36301. **T:** 1 334 671-9862
E: wvob913fm@bethanybc.edu
W: http://www.bethanybc.edu/radio
Editorial Profile: WVOB-FM is a non-commercial station owned by Bethany Bible College. The format of the station is Southern gospel music. WVOB-FM broadcasts to the Dothan, AL area at 91.3 FM.

WVOC-FM
Owner: Clear Channel Media and Entertainment
Editorial: 316 Greystone Blvd, Columbia, South Carolina 29210. **T:** 1 803 343-1100
W: http://www.wvoc.com
Editorial Profile: WVOC-FM is a commercial station owned by Clear Channel Media and Entertainment. The format of the station is news/talk/sports. WVOC-FM broadcasts to the Columbia, SC area at 100.1 FM.

WVOD-FM
Owner: CapSan Media, LLC
Editorial: 637 Harbor Rd, Wanchese, North Carolina 27981. **T:** 1 252 475-1888
W: http://www.991thesound.com
Editorial Profile: WVOD-FM is a commercial station owned by CapSan Media, LLC. The format of the station is adult album alternative. WVOD-FM broadcasts to the Wanchese, NC area at 99.1 FM.

WVOE-AM
Owner: Ebony Enterprises Inc.
Editorial: 1528 Old 74 Highway West, Chadbourn, North Carolina 28431.
T: 1 910 654-5621
Editorial Profile: WVOE-AM is a commercial station owned by Ebony Enterprises Inc. The format of the station is gospel, jazz and R&B oldies. WVOE-AM broadcasts to the Chadbourn, NC area at 1590 AM.

WVOF-FM
Owner: Fairfield University
Editorial: 1073 N Benson Rd, Fairfield, Connecticut 06824-5171. **T:** 1 203 254-4144
W: http://www.wvof.org
Editorial Profile: WVOF-FM is a non-commercial station owned by Fairfield University. The format of the station is college variety. WVOF-FM broadcasts to the Fairfield, CT area at 88.5 FM.

WVOG-AM
Owner: Robbert Broadcasting Co.(F.W.)
Editorial: 2730 Loumor Ave, Metairie, Louisiana 70001-5425. **T:** 1 504 831-6941
E: wvog@bellsouth.net
W: http://www.wwcr.com/wvog.html
Editorial Profile: WVOG-AM is a commercial station owned by F.W. Robbert Broadcasting Co. The format of the station is religious talk. WVOG-AM broadcasts to the Metairie, LA area at 600 AM.

WVOH-FM
Owner: Broadcast South, LLC
Editorial: 546 Baxley Hwy, Hazlehurst, Georgia 31539-5917. **T:** 1 912 375-4511
W: http://www.935theeagle.fm/
Editorial Profile: WVOH-FM is a commercial station owned by Broadcast South, LLC. The format of the station is classic hits. WVOH-FM broadcasts to the Savannah, GA area at 93.5 FM.

WVOI-AM
Owner: WCNZ LLC
Editorial: 5043 Tamiami Trl E, Naples, Florida 34113-4127. **T:** 1 239 732-9369
W: http://www.wmyrcountry.com
Editorial Profile: WVOI-AM is a commercial station owned by WCNZ LLC. The format of the station is classic country. WVOI-AM broadcasts to the Naples, FL area at 1480 AM.

WVOK-AM
Owner: Woodard Broadcasting Co.
Editorial: 1215 Church St, Oxford, Alabama 36203. **T:** 1 256 835-1580
E: email@979wvok.com
W: http://www.979wvok.com
Editorial Profile: WVOK-AM is a commercial station owned by Woodard Broadcasting Co. The format of the station is oldies. WOXR-AM broadcasts to the Oxford, AL area at 1580 AM.

WVOK-FM
Owner: Woodard Broadcasting Co.
Editorial: 1215 Church St, Oxford, Alabama 36203-1639. **T:** 1 256 835-1580
E: email@979wvok.com
W: http://www.979wvok.com
Editorial Profile: WVOK-FM is a commercial station owned by Woodard Broadcasting Co. The format for the station is Hot AC. WVOK-FM broadcasts to the Oxford, AL area at 97.9 FM.

WVOL-AM
Owner: Heidelberg Broadcasting LLC
Editorial: 1320 Brick Church Pike, Nashville, Tennessee 37207. **T:** 1 615 226-9510
E: wvol1470@aol.com
W: http://www.wvol1470.com
Editorial Profile: WVOL-AM is a commercial station owned by Heidelberg Broadcasting LLC. The format of the station is R&B oldies and urban contemporary music. WVOL-AM broadcasts to the Nashville, TN area at 1470 AM.

WVOM-FM
Owner: Blueberry Broadcasting
Editorial: 184 Target Cir, Bangor, Maine 4401.
T: 1 207 947-9100
W: http://www.wvomfm.com
Editorial Profile: WVOM-FM is a commercial station owned by Blueberry Broadcasting. The format of the station is news, talk and sports. WVOM-AM broadcasts to the Bangor, ME area at 103.9 FM.

WVON-AM
Owner: Midway Broadcasting Corp.
Editorial: 1000 E 87th St, Chicago, Illinois 60619-6397. **T:** 1 773 247-6200
E: info@wvon.com **W:** http://www.wvon.com
Editorial Profile: WVON-AM is a commercial station owned by Midway Broadcasting Corp. The format of the station is talk. WVON-AM broadcasts to the Chicago area at 1690 AM.

WVOP-AM
Owner: Vidalia Communications Group
Editorial: 1501 Mount Vernon Rd, Vidalia, Georgia 30474-3031. **T:** 1 912 537-9202
W: http://www.southeastgeorgiatoday.com
Editorial Profile: WVOP-AM is a commercial station owned by Vidalia Communications Group. The format of the station is news and talk. WVOP-AM broadcasts to the Vidalia, GA area at 970 AM.

WVOR-FM
Owner: Clear Channel Media and Entertainment
Editorial: 100 Chestnut St, 1700 HSBC Plaza, Rochester, New York 14604-2419.
T: 1 585 454-4884
W: http://www.radiosunny.com
Editorial Profile: WVOR-FM is a commercial station owned by Clear Channel Media and Entertainment. The format of the station is adult contemporary. WVOR-FM broadcasts to the Rochester, NY area at 102.3 FM.

WVOS-AM
Owner: Watermark Communications
Editorial: 198 Bridgeville Rd, Monticello, New York 12701. **T:** 1 845 794-9898
E: mail@wvosfm.com
Editorial Profile: WVOS-AM is a commercial station owned by Watermark Communications. The format of the station is Spanish sports. WVOS-AM broadcasts to the New York area at 1240 AM.

WVOS-FM
Owner: Watermark Communications
Editorial: 198 Bridgeville Rd, Monticello, New York 12701. **T:** 1 845 794-9898
W: http://www.wvosfm.com
Editorial Profile: WVOS-FM is a commercial station owned by Watermark Communications. The format of the station is classic hits. WVOS-FM broadcasts to the New York area at 95.9 FM.

WVOT-AM
Owner: Kingdon Expansion Corp.
Editorial: 2860 Ward Blvd Ste B, Wilson, North Carolina 27893-1749.
T: 1 252 243-1420
Editorial Profile: WVOT-AM is an commercial station owned by Kingdon Expansion Corp. The format of the station is gospel music. WVOT-AM broadcasts to the Wilson, NC area 1420 AM.

WVOW-AM
Owner: Logan Broadcasting
Editorial: 204 Main St, Ste 201, Logan, West Virginia 25601. **T:** 1 304 752-5080
Editorial Profile: WVOW-AM is a commercial station owned by Logan Broadcasting. The format of the station is adult contemporary music and sports. Newscasts air at various times throughout the day.

WVOW-FM
Owner: Logan Broadcasting
Editorial: 204 Main St, Ste 201, Logan, West Virginia 25601. **T:** 1 304 752-5080
Editorial Profile: WVOW-FM is a commercial station owned by Logan Broadcasting. The format of the station is adult contemporary music and sports. WVOW-FM broadcasts to the Logan, WV area at 101.9 FM and is simulcast on WVOW-AM.

WVOX-AM
Owner: Whitney Radio Broadcasting Inc.
Editorial: 1 Broadcast Forum, New Rochelle, New York 10801-2094. **T:** 1 914 636-1460
W: http://www.wvox.com
Editorial Profile: WVOX-AM is a commercial station owned by Whitney Radio Broadcasting Inc. The format of the station is news and talk. WVOX-AM broadcasts to the New Rochelle, NY area at 1460 AM.

WVPA-FM
Owner: Vermont Public Radio
Editorial: 365 Troy Ave, Colchester, Vermont 05446-3126. **T:** 1 802 655-9451
E: news@vpr.net **W:** http://www.vpr.net
Editorial Profile: WVPA-FM is a non-commercial station owned by Vermont Public Radio. The format of the station is news and talk. WVPA-FM broadcasts to the St. Johnsbury, VT area at 88.5 FM. The station does not accept PSAs.

WVPB-FM
Owner: State of West Virginia
Editorial: 600 Capitol St, Charleston, West Virginia 25301-1223. **T:** 1 304 556-4900
E: feedback@wvpubcast.org
W: http://www.wvpubcast.org
Editorial Profile: WVPB-FM is a non-commercial station owned by the State of West Virginia. The format of the station is news and talk as well as classical music. The target audience of the station is listeners, ages 13 to 100. WVPN-FM broadcasts to the Charleston, WV area at 88.5 FM. Send or fax one copy only of press releases to West Virginia Public Radio, not its individual stations. No broadcast tape announcements are accepted.

WVPE-FM
Owner: Elkhart Community Schools
Editorial: 2424 California Rd, Elkhart, Indiana 46514. **T:** 1 574 674-9873 **E:** wvpe@wvpe.org
W: http://www.wvpe.org
Editorial Profile: WVPE-FM is a non-commercial station owned by Elkhart Community Schools. The format for the station is news, blues, folk and jazz.. WVPE-FM broadcasts to the South Bend, IN area at 88.1 FM.

WVPN-FM
Owner: State of West Virginia
Editorial: 600 Capitol St, Charleston, West Virginia 25301-1223. **T:** 1 304 556-4900
E: feedback@wvpubcast.org
W: http://www.wvpubcast.org
Editorial Profile: WVPN-FM is a non-commercial station owned by the State of West Virginia. The format of the station is news and talk as well as classical music. WVPN-FM broadcasts to the Charleston, WV area at 88.5 FM. Send or fax one copy only of press releases to West Virginia Public Radio, not its individual stations. No broadcast tape announcements are accepted.

WVPO-AM
Owner: Connoisseur Media
Editorial: 22 S 6th St, Stroudsburg, Pennsylvania 18360-2002. **T:** 1 570 421-2100
Editorial Profile: WVPO-AM is a commercial station owned by Connoisseur Media. The format of the station is talk. WVPO-AM broadcasts to the Stroudsburg, PA area at 840 AM.

WVPR-FM
Owner: Vermont Public Radio
Editorial: 365 Troy Ave, Colchester, Vermont 05446-3126. **T:** 1 802 655-9451
W: http://www.vpr.net
Editorial Profile: WVPR-FM is a non-commercial station owned by Vermont Public Radio. The format of the station is news and talk. WVPR-FM broadcasts to the Colchester, VT area at 89.5 FM. The station does not accept PSAs.

WVPS-FM
Owner: Vermont Public Radio
Editorial: 365 Troy Ave, Colchester, Vermont 5446. **T:** 1 802 655-9451 **E:** news@vpr.net
W: http://www.vpr.net
Editorial Profile: WVPS-FM is a non-commercial station owned by Vermont Public Radio. The format of the station is news and talk. WVPS-FM broadcasts to the Colchester, VT area at 107.9 FM.

WVQM-FM
Owner: Blueberry Broadcasting

Editorial: 125 Community Dr Ste 201, Augusta, Maine 04330-8157.
T: 1 207 623-9000
W: http://www.wvomfm.com
Editorial Profile: WVQM-FM is a commercial station owned by Blueberry Broadcasting. The format of the station is news and talk. WVQM-FM broadcasts to the Augusta, ME area at 101.3 FM.

WVRA-FM
Owner: Truth Broadcasting Corporation
Editorial: 840 S Wesleyan Blvd, Rocky Mount, North Carolina 27803-2227.
T: 1 252 446-9262
Editorial Profile: WVRA-FM is a commercial station owned by Truth Broadcasting Corporation. The format of the station is religious. WVRA-FM broadcasts to the Rocky Mount, NC area at 107.3 FM.

WVRB-FM
Owner: Baldwin Broadcasting
Editorial: 8686 Michael Ln, Fairfield, Ohio 45014. **T:** 1 513 829-7700
W: http://www.air1.com
Editorial Profile: WVRB-FM is a commercial station owned by Baldwin Broadcasting. The format of the station is Christian rock music. WVRB-FM broadcasts to the Wilmore, KY area at 95.3 FM.

WVRC-AM
Owner: Star Communications, Inc.
Editorial: 106 Radio St, Spencer, West Virginia 25276. **T:** 1 304 927-3760
E: contact@wvrcfm.com
W: http://www.wvrcfm.com
Editorial Profile: WVRC-AM is a commercial station owned by Star Communications, Inc. The format for the station is gospel. WVRC-AM broadcasts to the Spencer, WV area at 1400 AM.

WVRC-FM
Owner: Star Communications, Inc.
Editorial: 106 Radio St, Spencer, West Virginia 25276. **T:** 1 304 927-3760
E: contact@wvrcfm.com
W: http://www.wvrcfm.com
Editorial Profile: WVRC-FM is a commercial station owned by Star Communications, Inc. The format of the station is contemporary country music. WVRC-FM broadcasts to the Spencer, WV area at 104.7 FM.

WVRD-FM
Owner: Liberty University
Editorial: 1971 University Blvd, Lynchburg, Virginia 24502-2269. **T:** 1 434 582-3688
E: wvrl@liberty.edu
W: http://www.victoryfm.net
Editorial Profile: WVRD-FM is a non-commercial station owned by Liberty University. The format of the station is Christian music and religious programming. WVRD-FM broadcasts to the Zebulon, NC area at 90.5 FM.

WVRE-FM
Owner: Radio Dubuque Inc.
Editorial: 346 W 8th St, Dubuque, Iowa 52001. **T:** 1 563 690-0800
W: http://www.1011theriver.com

WVRH-FM
Owner: Liberty University
Editorial: 1971 University Blvd, Lynchburg, Virginia 24502-2269. **T:** 1 434 582-3688
E: wvrl@liberty.edu
W: http://www.victoryfm.net
Editorial Profile: WVRH-FM is a non-commercial station owned by Liberty University. The format of the station is Christian music and religious programming. WVRH-FM broadcasts to the Norlina, NC area at 94.3 FM.

WVRK-FM
Owner: Clear Channel Media and Entertainment
Editorial: 1501 13th Ave, Columbus, Georgia 31901. **T:** 1 706 576-3000
W: http://www.rock103columbus.com
Editorial Profile: WVRK-FM is a commercial station owned by Clear Channel Media and Entertainment. The format of the station is rock. WVRK-FM broadcasts to the Columbus, GA area at 102.9 FM.

WVRL-FM
Owner: Liberty University
Editorial: 905 Halstead Blvd, Elizabeth City, North Carolina 27909-6986.
T: 1 434 582-3688 **E:** wvrl@liberty.edu
W: http://www.victoryfm.net

Editorial Profile: WVRL-FM is a non-commercial station owned by Liberty University. The format of the station is Christian music and religious programming. WVRL-FM broadcasts to the Elizabeth City, NC area at 88.3 FM.

WVRP-FM
Owner: Liberty University
Editorial: 1971 University Blvd, Lynchburg, Virginia 24502-2269. **T:** 1 434 582-3688
E: wvrl@liberty.edu
W: http://www.victoryfm.net
Editorial Profile: WVRP-FM is a non-commercial station owned by Liberty University. The format of the station is Christian music and religious programming. WVRP-FM broadcasts to the Roanoke Rapids, NC area at 91.1 FM.

WVRQ-AM
Owner: Robinson Corporation
Editorial: E7601A County Road SS, Viroqua, Wisconsin 54665. **T:** 1 608 637-7200
E: wvrq@mwt.net **W:** http://www.wvrq.com
Editorial Profile: WVRQ-AM is a commercial station owned by Robinson Corporation. The format of the station is oldies. WVRQ-AM broadcasts to the Viroqua, WI area at 1360 AM.

WVRQ-FM
Owner: Robinson Corporation
Editorial: E7601a County Road Ss, Viroqua, Wisconsin 54665-8502. **T:** 1 608 637-7200
E: wvrq@mwt.net **W:** http://www.wvrq.com
Editorial Profile: WVRQ-FM is a commercial station owned by Robinson Corporation. The format of the station is country music. WVRQ-FM broadcasts to the Viroqua, WI area at 102.3 FM.

WVRR-FM
Owner: Positive Alternative Radio
Editorial: 3027 Lester Ln, Ashland, Kentucky 41102-9642. **T:** 1 877 456-9361
E: office@walkfm.org **W:** http://walkfm.org
Editorial Profile: WVRR-FM is a non-commercial station owned by Positive Alternative Radio. The format of the station is contemporary Christian. WVRR-FM broadcast to the Point Pleasant, WV area at 88.1 FM.

WVRT-FM
Owner: Clear Channel Media and Entertainment
Editorial: 1559 W 4th St, Williamsport, Pennsylvania 17701-5650. **T:** 1 570 327-1400
E: wvrt@variety977.com
W: http://www.variety977.com
Editorial Profile: WVRT-FM is a commercial station owned by Clear Channel Media and Entertainment. The format of the station is Top 40/CHR music. WVRT-FM broadcasts to the Williamsport, PA area at 97.7 FM.

WVRU-FM
Owner: Radford University
Editorial: 801 E Main St, Radford, Virginia 24142-0001. **T:** 1 540 831-6059
E: wvru@radford.edu **W:** http://www.wvru.org
Editorial Profile: WVRU-FM is a non-commercial station owned by Radford University. The format of the station is adult album alternative. WVRU-FM broadcasts to the Radford, VA area at 89.9 FM.

WVRV-FM
Owner: Back Door Broadcasting
Editorial: 1359 Carmichael Way, Montgomery, Alabama 36106-3629. **T:** 1 334 239-9750
W: http://www.wvrvfmtheriver.com
Editorial Profile: WVRV-FM is a commercial station owned by Back Door Broadcasting. The format of the station is Contemporary Christian. WVRV-FM broadcasts to the Montgomery, AL area at a frequency of 97.5 FM.

WVRW-FM
Owner: Marlena Broadcasting
Editorial: 300 Harrison Ave, Weston, West Virginia 26452-2100. **T:** 1 304 269-5555
E: wvrwtrueoldies@aol.com
W: http://www.wvrwfm.com

WVRX-FM
Owner: Midwest Communications Inc.
Editorial: 1100 Sharps Ridge Mem Park Dr, Knoxville, Tennessee 37917-3000.
T: 1 865 525-6000
W: http://www.957thex.com
Editorial Profile: WVRX-FM is a commercial station owned by Midwest Communications Inc. The format of the station is modern rock. WVRX-FM broadcasts in the Knoxville, TN area at 95.7 FM.

WVRY-FM
Owner: JWL Communications, LLC.
Editorial: 201 Hall Ln, White Bluff, Tennessee 37187-9057. **T:** 1 615 797-9785
W: http://www.gracebroadcasting.com
Editorial Profile: WVRY-FM is a commercial station owned by JWL Communications, LLC. The format of the station is gospel music. WVRY-FM broadcasts to the White Bluff, TN area at 105.1 FM.

WVRZ-FM
Owner: Clear Channel Media and Entertainment
Editorial: 1559 W 4th St, Williamsport, Pennsylvania 17701-5650. **T:** 1 570 327-1400
W: http://v97fm.com
Editorial Profile: WVRZ-FM is a commercial station owned by Clear Channel Media and Entertainment. The format of the station is Top 40/CHR music. WVRZ-FM broadcasts in the Shamokin, PA area at 99.7 FM and is a simulcast of WVRT-FM.

WVSA-AM
Owner: Lamar County Broadcasting
Editorial: 47650 Hwy 17 N, Vernon, Alabama 35592. **T:** 1 205 695-9191
E: wjec1065@yahoo.com
Editorial Profile: WVSA-AM is a commercial station owned by Lamar County Broadcasting. The format of the station is sports talk. WVSA-AM broadcasts in the Vernon, AL at 1380 AM.

WVSB-FM
Owner: West Virginia School for the Deaf & Blind
Editorial: 301 E Main St, Romney, West Virginia 26757. **T:** 1 304 822-4838
E: classiccountry104@yahoo.com
W: http://wvsdb2.state.k12.wv.us
Editorial Profile: WVSB-FM is a commercial station owned by West Virginia School for the Deaf & Blind. The format of the station is country. WVSB-FM broadcasts to the Romney, WV area at 104.1 FM.

WVSD-FM
Owner: Mississippi Valley State University
Editorial: 14000 Highway 82 W #7221, Itta Bena, Mississippi 38941-1400.
T: 1 662 254-3611
W: http://www.mvsu.edu/public_broadcasting/
Editorial Profile: WVSD-FM is a non-commercial station owned by Mississippi Valley State University. The format of the station is variety. WVSD-FM broadcasts to the Greenville, MS area at 91.7 FM.

WVSG-AM
Owner: St. Gabriel Radio Inc
Editorial: 4673 Winterset Dr, Columbus, Ohio 43220-8113. **T:** 1 614 459-4820
E: info@stgabrielradio.com
W: http://stgabrielradio.com
Editorial Profile: WVSG-AM is a non-commercial station owned by St. Gabriel Radio Inc. The format of the station is Catholic radio programming. WVSG-AM broadcasts to the Columbus, OH area at 820 AM.

WVSL-AM
Owner: Max Media
Editorial: 450 Route 204, Selinsgrove, Pennsylvania 17870. **T:** 1 570 374-8819
Editorial Profile: WVSL-AM is a commercial station owned by Max Media. The format of the station is sports. WVSL-AM broadcasts to the Selinsgrove, PA area at 1240 AM.

WVSL-FM
Owner: Max Media
Editorial: 450 Route 204, Selinsgrove, Pennsylvania 17870. **T:** 1 570 374-1155
Editorial Profile: WVSL-FM is a commercial radio station owned by Max Media. The format of the station is sports. WVSL-FM broadcasts to the Selinsgrove, PA area at 92.3 FM.

WVSM-AM
Owner: Sand Mountain Advertising Company, Inc.
Editorial: 368 McCurdy Ave N, Rainsville, Alabama 35986. **T:** 1 256 638-2137
E: wvsm@farmerstel.com
W: http://www.wvsm.net
Editorial Profile: WVSM-AM is a commercial station owned by Sand Mountain Advertising Company, Inc. The format for the station is gospel. WVSM-AM broadcasts to the Huntsville, AL area at 1500 AM.

WVSP-FM
Owner: Max Media
Editorial: 5589 Greenwich Rd, Ste 200, Virginia Beach, Virginia 23462.

T: 1 757 671-1000
W: http://www.espnradio941.com
Editorial Profile: WVSP-FM is a commercial station owned by Max Media. The format of the station is sports talk. WVSP-FM broadcasts to the Norfolk, VA area at 94.1 FM.

WVSR-FM
Owner: Bristol Broadcasting
Editorial: 817 Suncrest Pl, Charleston, West Virginia 25303. **T:** 1 304 342-3136
W: http://www.electric102.com
Editorial Profile: WVSR-FM is a commercial station owned by Bristol Broadcasting. The format of the station is Top 40/CHR. WVSR-FM broadcasts to the Charleston-Huntington, WV area at 102.7 FM.

WVST-FM
Owner: Virginia State University
Editorial: Room 130 Harris Hall, Petersburg, Virginia 23806. **T:** 1 804 524-6725
W: http://www.vsu.edu/wvst/
Editorial Profile: WVST-FM is a non-commercial station owned by Virgina State University (VSU). The format of the station is variety. WVST-FM broadcasts to the students, faculty and local community of Virginia State University at 91.3 FM.

WVSU-FM
Owner: Samford University
Editorial: 800 Lakeshore Dr, Birmingham, Alabama 35229. **T:** 1 205 726-2877
E: wvsu@samford.edu
W: http://www.samford.edu/wvsu
Editorial Profile: WVSU-FM is a non-commercial station owned by Samford University. The format of the station is smooth AC. WVSU-FM broadcasts to the Birmingham, AL area at 91.1 FM.

WVSZ-FM
Owner: Our Three Sons Broadcasting
Editorial: 142 N Confederate Ave, Rock Hill, South Carolina 29730. **T:** 1 803 324-1071
E: newsroom@wrhi.com
W: http://www.fm107.com
Editorial Profile: WVSZ-FM is a commercial station owned by Our Three Sons Broadcasting. The format of the station is country music. WVSZ-FM broadcasts to the Rock Hill, SC area at 94.3 FM

WVTF-FM
Owner: Virginia Tech Foundation
Editorial: 3520 Kingsbury Lane, Roanoke, Virginia 24014-1356. **T:** 1 540 989-8900
E: wvtf@vt.edu **W:** http://www.wvtf.org
Editorial Profile: WVTF-FM is a non-commercial station owned by Virginia Tech Foundation. The format of the station is jazz, classical music and news. WVTF-FM broadcasts to the Roanake, VA area at 89.1 FM.

WVTJ-AM
Owner: Wilkins Communications Network Inc.
Editorial: 2070 N Palafox St, Pensacola, Florida 32501. **T:** 1 850 432-3658
E: wvtj@wilkinsradio.com
W: http://www.wilkinsradio.com
Editorial Profile: WVTJ-AM is a commercial station owned by Wilkins Communications Network Inc. The primary format of the station is religious teaching. Its secondary format is gospel. WVTJ-AM broadcasts to the Pensacola, FL area at 610 AM.

WVTK-FM
Owner: WVTK Radio LLC
Editorial: 63 Maple St Ste 9, Middlebury, Vermont 05753-1603. **T:** 1 802 388-2563
W: http://www.921wvtk.com
Editorial Profile: WVTK-FM is a commercial station owned by WVTK Radio LLC. The format of the station is adult contemporary. WVTK-FM broadcasts to the Middlebury, VT area at a frequency of 92.1 FM.

WVTL-AM
Owner: Roser Communications
Editorial: 5816 Route 30, South Amsterdam, New York 12010-8056. **T:** 1 518 843-9284
W: http://www.1570wvtl.com
Editorial Profile: WVTL-AM is a commercial station owned by Roser Communications. The format of the station is Lite AC. WVTL-AM broadcasts to the Utica, NY area at 1570 AM.

WVTQ-FM
Owner: Vermont Public Radio
Editorial: 365 Troy Ave, Colchester, Vermont 5446. **T:** 1 802 655-9451 **E:** news@vpr.net
W: http://www.vpr.net
Editorial Profile: WVTQ-FM is a non-commercial station owned by Vermont Public

Radio. The format of the station is talk and classical music. WVTQ-FM broadcasts to the Burlington, VT area at 95.1 FM.

WVTS-AM
Owner: Bristol Broadcasting
Editorial: 817 Suncrest Pl, Charleston, West Virginia 25303-2302. **T:** 1 304 342-3136
E: news@wqbe.com
W: http://www.wvtsam950.com/newdesign
Editorial Profile: WVTS-AM is a commercial station owned by Bristol Broadcasting. The format of the station is news talk. WVTS-AM broadcasts to the Charleston-Huntington, WV area at 950 AM.

WVTS-FM
Owner: Bristol Broadcasting
Editorial: 817 Suncrest Pl, Charleston, West Virginia 25303-2302. **T:** 1 304 342-3136
W: http://www.wvtsam950.com
Editorial Profile: WVTS-FM is a commercial station owned by Bristol Broadcasting. The format of the station is news and talk. WVTS-FM broadcasts to the Charleston, WV area at 94.5 FM.

WVTT-FM
Owner: Colonial Radio Group
Editorial: 1 Bluebird Sq, Olean, New York 14760-2552. **T:** 1 716 372-9564
E: news@colonialme.com
W: http://www.colonialme.com
Editorial Profile: WVTT-FM is a commercial station owned by Colonial Radio Group. The format of the station is news/talk. WVTT-FM broadcasts to the Coudersport, PA at 96.7 FM.

WVUA-FM
Owner: University of Alabama
Editorial: 297 Phifer Hall, Tuscaloosa, Alabama 35487. **T:** 1 205 348-6061
E: wvua@sa.ua.edu
W: http://www.wvuafm.ua.edu
Editorial Profile: WVUA-FM is a non-commercial station owned by the University of Alabama. The format of the station is rock alternative. WVUA-FM broadcasts to the Tuscaloosa, AL area at 90.7 FM.

WVUB-FM
Owner: Vincennes University
Editorial: 1200 N 2nd St, Vincennes, Indiana 47591. **T:** 1 812 888-4347 **E:** wvub@vinu.edu
W: http://www.wvubhd.com
Editorial Profile: WVUB-FM is a non-commercial station owned by Vincennes University. The format of the station is hot adult contemporary. WVUB-FM broadcasts to the Vincennes, IN area at 91.1 FM.

WVUD-FM
Owner: University of Delaware
Editorial: Perkins Student Center, Newark, Delaware 19716. **T:** 1 302 831-2701
E: ud.wvud@gmail.com
W: http://www.wvud.org
Editorial Profile: WVUD-FM is a commercial station owned by University of Delaware. The format of the station is variety. WVUD-FM broadcasts to the Newark, DE area at 91.3 FM.

WVUM-FM
Owner: WVUM Inc.
Editorial: 1306 Stanford Dr, UC 110, Coral Gables, Florida 33124. **T:** 1 305 284-3131
E: office@wvum.org **W:** http://www.wvum.org
Editorial Profile: WVUM-FM is a non-commercial station owned by WVUM Inc. The format of the station is adult album alternative music. WVUM-FM broadcasts to the Miami area at 90.5 FM.

WVUR-FM
Owner: Valparaiso University
Editorial: 32 Schnabel Hall, Valparaiso, Indiana 43683. **T:** 1 219 464-5383
E: thesource95.1@valpo.edu
W: http://www.valpo.edu/student/wvur/
Editorial Profile: WVUR-FM is a non-commercial station owned by Valparaiso University. The format of the station is variety. WVUR-FM broadcasts to the Valparaiso, IN area at 95.1 FM.

WVUS-AM
Owner: Light of Life Community, Inc
Editorial: 132 Carubia Dr, Core, West Virginia 26541-7137. **T:** 1 304 598-0026
E: info@lolradio.org **W:** http://www.lolradio.org
Editorial Profile: WVUS-AM is a non-commercial station owned by Light of Life Community, Inc. The format of the station is religious, Catholic and music. WVUS-AM broadcasts to the Grafton, WV area at 1190 AM.

WVVC-FM
Owner: Northeast Gospel Broadcasting, Inc.
Editorial: 65 King Rd, Buskirk, New York 12028-2221. **T:** 1 518 686-0975
W: http://www.northeastgospelbroadcasting.com
Editorial Profile: WVVC-FM is a non-commercial station owned by Northeast Gospel Broadcasting, Inc. The format of the station is Christian music and teaching. WVVC-FM broadcasts to the Dolgeville, NY area at 88.1 FM.

WVVE-FM
Owner: Magic Broadcasting, LLC
Editorial: 7106 Laird St, Panama City, Florida 32408-7653. **T:** 1 850 230-5855
W: http://www.getyourgrooveonpc.com
Editorial Profile: WVVE-FM is a commercial station owned by Magic Broadcasting, LLC. The format of the station is rhythmic oldies. WVVE-FM broadcasts to the Panama City, FL area at 100.1.

WVVL-FM
Owner: Boll Weevil Communications, LLC
Editorial: 100 N Main St, Enterprise, Alabama 36330. **T:** 1 334 347-5621
E: wvvl@weevil101.com
W: http://www.weevil101.com
Editorial Profile: WVVL-FM is a commercial station owned by Boll Weevil Communications, LLC. The format of the station is classic country. WVVL-FM broadcasts to the Enterprise, AL area at 101.1 FM.

WVVR-FM
Owner: Saga Communications
Editorial: 1640 Old Russellville Pike, Clarksville, Tennessee 37043-1709.
T: 1 931 648-7720
W: http://www.thebeaverfm.com
Editorial Profile: WVVR-FM is a commercial station owned by Saga Communications (dba 5 Star Radio Group). The format of the station is contemporary country music. WVVR-FM broadcasts to the Nashville, TN area at 100.3 FM.

WVVS-FM
Owner: Valdosta State University
Editorial: 1500 N Patterson St., 2nd Fl, Valdosta, Georgia 31698-0001.
T: 1 229 333-5662
W: http://www.valdosta.edu/wvvs

WVVV-FM
Owner: Seven Ranges Radio Company Inc.
Editorial: 1627 Rosemar Rd, Parkersburg, West Virginia 26105-8128. **T:** 1 304 295-3100
W: http://www.v969radio.net
Editorial Profile: WVVV-FM is a commercial station owned by Seven Ranges Radio Company Inc. The format of the station is adult contemporary music. WVVV-FM broadcasts to the Vienna, WV area at 96.9 FM.

WVWC-FM
Owner: West Virginia Wesleyan College
Editorial: 59 College Ave, Box 167, Buckhannon, West Virginia 26201.
T: 1 304 473-8292 **E:** c92@wvwc.edu
W: http://www.wvwc.edu/c92

WVXG-FM
Owner: ICS Communications, Inc
Editorial: 501 Bowtown Rd, Delaware, Ohio 43015-9410 **W:** http://www.951rocks.com
Editorial Profile: WVXG-FM is a commercial radio station that is owned by ICS Communications, Inc. The format of the station is classic rock. The station airs locally on 95.1 FM.

WVXR-FM
Owner: Vermont Public Radio
Editorial: 365 Troy Ave, Colchester, Vermont 05446-3126. **T:** 1 802 655-9451
W: http://www.vpr.net
Editorial Profile: WVXR-FM is a non-commercial station owned by Vermont Public Radio. The format of the station is classical music. WVXR-FM broadcasts to the Randolph, VT area at 102.1 FM.

WVXU-FM
Owner: Cincinnati Public Radio Inc.
Editorial: 1223 Central Pkwy, Cincinnati, Ohio 45214-2812. **T:** 1 513 352-9170
E: wvxu@wvxu.org **W:** http://www.wvxu.org
Editorial Profile: WVXU-FM is a commercial station owned by Cincinnati Public Radio Inc. The format of the station is news and talk. WVXU-FM broadcasts to the Cincinnati area at 91.7 FM.

WVXX-AM
Owner: Hindlin Broadcasting
Editorial: 740 Duke St Ste 450, Norfolk, Virginia 23510-1544. **T:** 1 757 627-9899
E: andy@selecta1050.com
W: http://www.selecta1050.com
Editorial Profile: WVXX-AM is a commercial station owned by Hindlin Broadcasting. The format of the station is Hispanic music. WVXX-AM broadcasts to the Norfolk, VA area on 1050 AM.

WVYA-FM
Owner: N.E. Pennsylvania Educational TV Assoc.
Editorial: 100 WVIA Way, Pittston, Pennsylvania 18640. **T:** 1 570 826-6144
E: wviafm@wvia.org **W:** http://www.wvia.org
Editorial Profile: WVYA-FM is a non-commercial station owned by N.E. Pennsylvania Educational TV Assoc. The format for the station is classical, jazz and news. WVYA-FM broadcasts to the Wilkes Barre-Scranton, PA area at 89.7 FM.

WVYB-FM
Owner: Black Crow Radio, LLC
Editorial: 126 W International Speedway Blvd, Daytona Beach, Florida 32114.
T: 1 386 257-6900
E: newsdaytonabeach@gmail.com
W: http://www.newsdaytonabeach.com
Editorial Profile: WVYB-FM is a commercial station owned by Black Crow Radio, LLC. The format of the station is Top 40/CHR music. WVYB-FM broadcasts to the Daytona Beach, FL area at 103.3 FM.

WVYC-FM
Owner: York College of Pennsylvania
Editorial: Student Union Bldg York College, 3rd Floor, York, Pennsylvania 17405.
T: 1 717 815-1932 **E:** gm@wvyc.org
W: http://www.wvyc.org
Editorial Profile: WVYC-FM is a non-commercial station owned by York College of Pennsylvania. The format of the station is rock alternative music. WVYC-FM broadcasts to the York College of Pennsylvania area at 88.1 FM.

WVZA-FM
Owner: Withers Broadcasting of Southern Illinois LLC
Editorial: 1822 N Court St, Marion, Illinois 62959. **T:** 1 618 997-8123
W: http://www.mywithersradio.com/vza
Editorial Profile: WVZA-FM is a commercial station owned by Withers Broadcasting of Southern Illinois LLC. The format of the station is adult contemporary. WVZA-FM broadcasts to the Marion, IL area at 105.1 FM.

WWAB-AM
Owner: WWAB Inc.
Editorial: 1203 W Chase St, Lakeland, Florida 33815. **T:** 1 863 682-2998
E: wwab@verizon.net
W: http://www.wwabradio.com
Editorial Profile: WWAB-AM is a commercial station owned by WWAB Inc. The format of the station is gospel music and oldies. WWAB-AM broadcasts to the Tampa Bay, FL area at 1330 AM.

WWAC-FM
Owner: Longport Media
Editorial: 1601 New Rd, Linwood, New Jersey 8221. **T:** 1 609 653-1400
W: http://ac1027.com
Editorial Profile: WWAC-FM is a commercial station owned by Longport Media. The format of the station is Hot AC. WWAC-FM broadcasts to the Linwood, NJ area at 102.7 FM.

WWAG-FM
Owner: Brockman(Dan)
Editorial: 1731 Highway 1071, Tyner, Kentucky 40486-8223. **T:** 1 606 287-9924

WWAV-FM
Owner: Apex Broadcasting, Inc.
Editorial: 34 Harbor Blvd Ste 202, Destin, Florida 32541-7365. **T:** 1 850 654-1000
W: http://www.1021thewave.com
Editorial Profile: WWAV-FM is a commercial station owned by Apex Broadcasting, Inc. The format for the station is classic hits. WWAV-FM broadcasts to the Destin, FL area at 102.1 FM.

WWAX-FM
Owner: Red Rock Radio Corp.
Editorial: 501 S Lake Ave Ste 200, Duluth, Minnesota 55802-2392. **T:** 1 218 728-9500
E: production@redrockradio.org
W: http://nu92.fm
Editorial Profile: WWAX-FM is a commercial station owned by Red Rock Radio Corp. The format of the station is Hot AC. WWAX-FM broadcasts to the Duluth, MN area at 92.1 FM.

WWBA-AM
Owner: Genesis Communications Inc.
Editorial: 4300 W Cypress St, Tampa, Florida 33607-4159. **T:** 1 813 281-1040
W: http://www.newstalkflorida.com/820-news/
Editorial Profile: WWBA-AM is a commercial station owned by Genesis Communications Inc. The format of the station is news and talk. WWBA-AM broadcasts to the Tampa, FL area on 820 AM.

WWBB-FM
Owner: Clear Channel Media and Entertainment
Editorial: 75 Oxford St, Providence, Rhode Island 02905-4722. **T:** 1 401 781-9979
E: feedback@b101.com
W: http://www.b101.com
Editorial Profile: WWBB-FM is a commercial station owned by Clear Channel Media and Entertainment. The format of the station is classic hits. WWBB-FM broadcasts to the Providence, RI area at 101.5 FM.

WWBC-AM
Owner: National Christian Network
Editorial: 1150 King St, Cocoa, Florida 32922.
T: 1 321 632-1510
W: http://www.1510wwbc.com
Editorial Profile: WWBC-AM is a non-commercial station owned by National Christian Network. The format of the station is religious programming. WWBC-AM broadcasts to the Cocoa, FL area at 1510 AM.

WWBD-FM
Owner: Miller Communications Inc.
Editorial: 51 Commerce St, Sumter, South Carolina 29150. **T:** 1 803 775-2321
E: production@miller.fm
W: http://www.miller.fm
Editorial Profile: WWBD-FM is a commercial station owned by Miller Communications Inc. The format of the station is active rock. WWBD-FM broadcasts to the Sumter, SC area at 94.7 FM.

WWBE-FM
Owner: Max Media
Editorial: 450 Route 204, Selinsgrove, Pennsylvania 17870. **T:** 1 570 374-8819
E: bigcountryrequest@hotmail.com
W: http://www.bigcountrynow.com
Editorial Profile: WWBE-FM is a commercial station owned by Max Media. The format of the station is contemporary country music. WWBE-FM broadcasts to the Selinsgrove, PA area at 98.3 FM.

WWBF-AM
Owner: Thornburg Communications Inc.
Editorial: 1130 Radio Rd, Bartow, Florida 33830. **T:** 1 863 533-0744
W: http://www.wwbf.com
Editorial Profile: WWBF-AM is a commercial station owned by Thornburg Communications Inc. The format for the station is oldies. WWBF-AM broadcasts to the Bartow, FL area at 1130 AM.

WWBG-AM
Owner: Davidson Media Group
Editorial: 4015 Brownsboro Rd Ste 200, Winston Salem, North Carolina 27106-3380.
T: 1 336 714-2831
W: http://www.quepasamedia.com
Editorial Profile: WWBG-AM is a commercial station owned by Davidson Media Group and run by Que Pasa Media Network. The format of the station is regional Mexican. WWBG-AM broadcasts to the Greensboro, NC area at a frequency of 1470 AM.

WWBJ-AM
Owner: Martinsburg Broadcasting Inc.
Editorial: 724 Rebecca Furnace Rd, Martinsburg, Pennsylvania 16662-7302.
T: 1 814 793-2188 **E:** wjsmradio@gmail.com
W: http://www.wjsm.com
Editorial Profile: WWBJ-AM is a non-commercial station owned by Martinsburg Broadcasting Inc. The format of the station is Christian programming and music. WWBJ-AM broadcasts to the Martinsburg, PA area at 1110 AM.

WWBL-FM
Owner: Original Company Inc.(The)
Editorial: 3 E Van Trees St, Washington, Indiana 47501. **T:** 1 812 254-4300
E: wwblnews@wwbl.com
W: http://www.wwbl.com

Editorial Profile: WWBL-FM is a commercial station owned by The Original Company Inc. The format of the station is country music. WWBL-FM broadcasts to the Vincennes, IN area at 106.5 FM.

WWBN-FM
Owner: Townsquare Media, LLC
Editorial: 3338 E Bristol Rd, Burton, Michigan 48529. T: 1 810 743-1080
W: http://www.banana1015.com
Editorial Profile: WWBN-FM is a commercial station owned by Townsquare Media, LLC. The format of the station is rock music. WWBN-FM broadcasts to the Flint, MI area at 101.5 FM.

WWBR-FM
Owner: Mentor Partners Inc.
Editorial: 18720 16 Mile Rd, Big Rapids, Michigan 49307-9303. T: 1 231 796-7000
E: news@bigrapidsradionetwork.com
W: http://www.bigcountry1009.com
Editorial Profile: WWBR-FM is a commercial station owned by Mentor Partners Inc. The format of the station is country music. WWBR-FM broadcasts to the Traverse City, MI area at 100.9 FM.

WWBU-FM
Owner: Cumulus Media Inc.
Editorial: 7080 Lee Hwy, Fairlawn, Virginia 24141-8416. T: 1 540 731-6000
W: http://www.supersports1017.com
Editorial Profile: WWBU-FM is a commercial station owned by Cumulus Media Inc. The format for the station is sports. WWBU-FM broadcasts to the Fairlawn, VA area at 101.7 FM.

WWBZ-AM
Owner: County Broadcasting Company, LLC (Northeast Broadcasting Co.)
Editorial: 30 How St, Haverhill, Massachusetts 01830-6131. T: 1 978 374-4733
W: http://www.legends700.com
Editorial Profile: WWBZ-AM is a commercial owned by County Broadcasting Company, LLC (Northeast Broadcasting Co). The format of the station is oldies. WWBZ-AM broadcasts to the Orange-Athol, MA areas at 700 AM.

WWCA-AM
Owner: Starboard Media Foundation Inc.
Editorial: 107 W 78Th Pl, Merrillville, Indiana 46410-5468. T: 1 219 736-7524
W: http://www.relevantradio.com
Editorial Profile: WWCA-AM is a non-commercial station owned by Starboard Media Foundation Inc. The format of the station is religious. WWCA-AM broadcasts to the Merrillville, IN area at 1270 AM.

WWCD-FM
Owner: Fun With Radio Inc.
Editorial: 1036 S Front St, Columbus, Ohio 43206-3402. T: 1 614 221-9923
E: webmaster@cd1025.com
W: http://www.cd1025.com
Editorial Profile: WWCD-FM is a commercial station owned by Fun With Radio Inc. The format of the station is rock alternative music. WWCD-FM broadcasts to the Columbus, OH area at 102.5 FM.

WWCH-AM
Owner: Clarion County Broadcasting Corp.
Editorial: 1168 Greenville Pike, Clarion, Pennsylvania 16214-6146. T: 1 814 226-4500
E: clarionradio@comcast.net
W: http://www.clarioncountydailynews.com
Editorial Profile: WWCH-AM is a commercial station owned by Clarion County Broadcasting Corp. The format of the station is country. WWCH-AM broadcasts to the Clarion, PA area at 1300 AM.

WWCK-AM
Owner: Cumulus Media Inc.
Editorial: 6317 Taylor Dr, Flint, Michigan 48507. T: 1 810 238-7300
W: http://www.supertalk1570.com
Editorial Profile: WWCK-AM is a commercial station owned by Cumulus Media Inc. The format of the station is news and talk programming. WWCK-AM broadcasts to the Flint, MI area at 1570 AM.

WWCK-FM
Owner: Cumulus Media Inc.
Editorial: 6317 Taylor Dr, Flint, Michigan 48507-4683. T: 1 810 238-7300
W: http://www.ck1055.fm
Editorial Profile: WWCK-FM is a commercial station owned by Cumulus Media Inc. The format of the station is Top 40/CHR. WWCK-

FM broadcasts to the Flint, MI area at 105.5 FM.

WWCN-FM
Owner: Beasley Broadcast Group
Editorial: 20125 S Tamiami Trl, Estero, Florida 33928-2117. T: 1 239 495-2100
W: http://993espn.com
Editorial Profile: WWCN-FM is a commercial station owned by Beasley Broadcast Group. The format of the station is sports talk. WWCN-FM broadcasts to the Ft. Myers, FL area at 99.3 FM.

WWCO-AM
Owner: Connoisseur Media
Editorial: 869 Blue Hills Ave, Bloomfield, Connecticut 06002-3710. T: 1 860 243-1115
W: http://www.talkofconnecticut.com
Editorial Profile: WWCO-AM is a commercial station owned by Connoisseur Media. The format of the station is talk. WWCO-AM broadcasts to the Bloomfield, CT area at 1240 AM.

WWCS-AM
Owner: Birach Broadcasting Corp.
Editorial: 400 Ardmore Blvd, Pittsburgh, Pennsylvania 15221. T: 1 412 244-4586
Editorial Profile: WWCS-AM is a commercial station owned by Birach Broadcasting Corp. The format of the station is sports. WWCS-AM broadcasts to Canonsburg, PA at 540 AM.

WWCT-FM
Owner: Advanced Media Partners LLC
Editorial: 2006 W Altorfer Dr, Peoria, Illinois 61615-1864. T: 1 309 691-0101
E: info@ampillinois.com
W: http://www.wwctfm.com
Editorial Profile: WWCT-FM is a commercial station owned by Advanced Media Partners LLC. The format for the station is adult album alternative music. WWCT-FM broadcasts to the Peoria, IL area at 99.9 FM.

WWCU-FM
Owner: Western Carolina University
Editorial: Western Carolina University, 123 Stillwell, Cullowhee, North Carolina 28723. T: 1 828 227-7454 E: psa@wwcufm.com
W: http://www.wwcufm.com
Editorial Profile: WWCU-FM is a non-commercial station owned by the Western Carolina University. The format of the station is classic hits music. WWCU-FM broadcasts to the Cullowhee, NC, area at 90.5.

WWDB-AM
Owner: Beasley Broadcast Group
Editorial: 555 E City Ave, Bala Cynwyd, Pennsylvania 19004-1115. T: 1 610 667-9000
W: http://www.wwdbam.com
Editorial Profile: WWDB-AM is a commercial station owned by Beasley Broadcast Group. The format of the station is variety featuring music, news and talk multicultural programming. WWDB-AM broadcasts to the Philadelphia area at 860 AM.

WWDC-FM
Owner: Clear Channel Media and Entertainment
Editorial: 1801 Rockville Pike Fl 5, Rockville, Maryland 20852-1633. T: 1 240 747-2700
W: http://www.dc101.com
Editorial Profile: WWDC-FM is a commercial station owned by Clear Channel Media and Entertainment. The format of the station is rock alternative. WWDC-FM broadcasts to the Washington, D.C. area at 101.1 FM.

WWDE-FM
Owner: Entercom Communications Corp.
Editorial: 236 Clearfield Ave Ste 206, Virginia Beach, Virginia 23462-1893.
T: 1 757 497-2000
W: http://www.thenew1013.com
Editorial Profile: WWDE-FM is a commercial station owned by Entercom Communications Corp. The format of the station is adult contemporary. WWDE-FM broadcasts to the Virginia Beach, VA area at 101.3 FM.

WWDJ-AM
Owner: Salem Communications
Editorial: 500 Victory Rd, Ste 2, North Quincy, Massachusetts 2171. T: 1 617 328-0880
W: http://radioluzboston.com
Editorial Profile: WWDJ-AM is a commercial station owned by Salem Communications. The format of the station is Hispanic religious programming. WWDJ-AM broadcasts to the Boston area at 1150 AM.

WWDM-FM
Owner: L & L Broadcasting
Editorial: 1900 Pineview Dr, Columbia, South Carolina 29209-5079. T: 1 803 695-8600
W: http://www.thebigdm.com
Editorial Profile: WWDM-FM is a commercial station owned by L & L Broadcasting. The format of the station is urban adult contemporary. WWDM-FM broadcasts to the Columbia, SC area at 101.3 FM.

WWDN-AM
Owner: Lakes Media LLC
Editorial: 1336 Piney Forest Rd, Danville, Virginia 24540-1606. T: 1 434 799-1010
W: http://www.1045thedan.com
Editorial Profile: WWDN-AM is a commercial station owned by Lakes Media LLC. The format of the station is classic hits. WWDN-AM broadcasts to the Danville, VA area at 1580 AM.

WWDR-AM
Owner: First Media Radio LLC
Editorial: 1714 W Main St, Murfreesboro, North Carolina 27855. T: 1 252 398-4111
W: http://bestaround.moonfruit.com
Editorial Profile: WWDR-AM is a commercial station owned by First Media Radio LLC. The format of the station is gospel. WWDR-AM broadcasts to the Murfreesboro, NC area at 1080 AM.

WWDV-FM
Owner: Hubbard Radio, LLC
Editorial: 875 N Michigan Ave Ste 1510, Chicago, Illinois 60611-1874.
T: 1 312 274-9710
Editorial Profile: WWDV-FM is a commercial station owned by Hubbard Radio, LLC. The format of the station is classic rock. WWDV-FM broadcasts to the Zion, IL area at a frequency of 96.9 FM.

WWDW-FM
Owner: First Media Radio LLC
Editorial: 3 E 1st St, Weldon, North Carolina 27890. T: 1 252 536-3115
W: http://www.bestradioaround.com
Editorial Profile: WWDW-FM is a commercial station owned by First Media Radio LLC. The format of the station is adult contemporary. WWDW-FM broadcasts to the Weldon, NC area at 107.7 FM.

WWDX-AM
Owner: Freeland Broadcasting
Editorial: 215 Baker Rd, Huntingdon, Tennessee 38344. T: 1 731 986-0242
W: http://www.thefarmradio.com
Editorial Profile: WWDX-AM is a commercial station owned by Freeland Broadcasting. The format of the station is classic country. WWDX-AM broadcasts to the Huntingdon, TN area at 1530 AM.

WWEB-FM
Owner: Choate Rosemary Hall Foundation
Editorial: 333 Christian St, Wallingford, Connecticut 06492-3818. T: 1 203 697-2252
Editorial Profile: WWEB-FM is a non-commercial station owned by the Choate Rosemary Hall Foundation. The format of the station is college variety. WWEB-FM broadcasts to the Wallingford, CT area at 89.9 FM.

WWEC-FM
Owner: Elizabethtown College
Editorial: 1 Alpha Dr, Elizabethtown, Pennsylvania 17022-2298. T: 1 717 361-1553
E: wwec@etown.edu **W:** http://wwec.fm
Editorial Profile: WWEC-FM is a non-commercial station owned by Elizabethtown College. The format of the station is variety. The station broadcasts to the Elizabethtown, PA area at a frequency of 88.3 FM.

WWED-FM
Owner: Educational Media Corporation
Editorial: 830 Gunnery Hill Rd, Spotsylvania, Virginia 22551-2215. T: 1 540 582-9700
W: http://www.wwedfm.org
Editorial Profile: WWED-FM is a non-commercial station owned by Educational Media Corporation. The format of the station is classical music. WWED-FM broadcasts to Spotsylvania, VA area at 89.5 FM.

WWEG-FM
Owner: Manning Broadcasting Inc.
Editorial: 880 Commonwealth Ave, Hagerstown, Maryland 21740-6836.
T: 1 301 733-4500
W: http://www.1069theeagle.com
Editorial Profile: WWEG-FM is a commercial station owned by Manning Broadcasting Inc.

The format of the station is classic hits. WWEG-FM broadcasts in the Hagerstown, MD area at 106.9 FM.

WWEL-FM
Owner: Forcht Broadcasting
Editorial: 534 Tobacco Rd, London, Kentucky 40741. T: 1 606 864-2148
W: http://www.sam1039.com
Editorial Profile: WWEL-FM is a commercial station owned by Forcht Broadcasting. The format of the station is adult hits. WWEL-FM broadcasts to the London, KY area at 103.9 FM.

WWEM-FM
Owner: Educational Media Corporation
Editorial: 830 Gunnery Hill Rd, Spotsylvania, Virginia 22551-2215. T: 1 540 582-9700
W: http://www.wwedfm.org
Editorial Profile: WWEM-FM is a non-commercial station owned by Educational Media Corporation. The format of the station is classical music. WWEM-FM broadcasts to Rustburg, VA area at 91.7 FM.

WWET-FM
Owner: Georgia Public Broadcasting
Editorial: 260 14th St NW, Atlanta, Georgia 30318. T: 1 404 685-2548 E: news@gpb.org
W: http://www.gpb.org
Editorial Profile: WWET-FM is a commercial station owned by Georgia Public Broadcasting. The format of the station is news, classical and jazz music, and talk. WWET-FM broadcasts to the Hasty, GA area at 91.7 FM.

WWEV-FM
Owner: War Hill Christian Fellowship, Inc.
Editorial: 1705 Sawnee Dr, Cumming, Georgia 30040-4473. T: 1 770 781-9150
E: wwev@wwev.org **W:** http://victory915.com
Editorial Profile: WWEV-FM is a non-commercial station owned by the War Hill Christian Fellowship, Inc. The format of the station is contemporary Christian music. WWEV-FM broadcasts to the Cumming, GA area at 91.5 FM.

WWFD-AM
Owner: Hubbard Broadcasting, Inc.
Editorial: 3400 Idaho Ave NW, Washington, District Of Columbia 20016-3046.
T: 1 202 895-5000
Editorial Profile: WWFD-AM is a commercial station owned by Hubbard Broadcasting, Inc. The format of the station is AAA. WWFD-AM broadcasts to the Frederick, MD area at 820 AM.

WWFE-AM
Owner: Fenix Broadcasting Corp.
Editorial: 330 SW 27th Ave Ste 207, Miami, Florida 33135-2957. T: 1 305 541-3300
E: info@lapoderosa.com
W: http://www.lapoderosa.com
Editorial Profile: WWFE-AM is a commercial station owned by Fenix Broadcasting Corp. The format of the station is Spanish language news and talk. WWFE-AM broadcasts to the Miami area at 670 AM.

WWFF-FM
Owner: Cumulus Media Inc.
Editorial: 1717 US Highway 72 E, Athens, Alabama 35611. T: 1 256 830-8300
W: http://www.journey933.com
Editorial Profile: WWFF-FM is a commercial station owned by Cumulus Media Inc. The format of the station is classic hits and adult contemporary. WWFF-FM broadcasts to the Huntsville, AL area at 93.3 FM.

WWFG-FM
Owner: Clear Channel Media and Entertainment
Editorial: Gateway Crossing, 351 Tilghman Road, Salisbury, Maryland 21804-1920.
T: 1 410 742-1923
E: dickraymond@clearchannel.com
W: http://www.froggy999.com
Editorial Profile: WWFG-FM is a commercial station owned by Clear Channel Media and Entertainment. The format of the station is country music. WWFG-FM broadcasts in the Salisbury, MD area at 99.9 FM.

WWFM-FM
Owner: Mercer County Community College
Editorial: 1200 Old Trenton Rd, Princeton Junction, New Jersey 8550.
T: 1 609 587-8989 E: info@wwfm.org
W: http://www.wwfm.org
Editorial Profile: WWFM-FM is a non-commercial station owned by Mercer County Community College. The format of the station

is classical music. WWFM-FM broadcasts to the Windsor, NJ area at 89.1 FM.

WWFN-FM
Owner: Cumulus Media Inc.
Editorial: 2014 N Irby St, Florence, South Carolina 29501. **T:** 1 843 661-5000
W: http://www.thefanfm.com
Editorial Profile: WWFN-FM is a commercial station owned by Cumulus Media Inc. The format of the station is sports. WWFN-FM broadcasts to the Florence, SC area at 100.1 FM.

WWFS-FM
Owner: CBS Radio
Editorial: 345 Hudson St, New York, New York 10014-4502. **T:** 1 212 315-7000
W: http://www.fresh1027.com
Editorial Profile: WWFS-FM is a commercial station owned by CBS Radio. The format of the station is adult contemporary. WWFS-FM broadcasts to the New York area at 102.7 FM.

WWFW-FM
Owner: Adams Radio Group
Editorial: 9604 Coldwater Rd, Fort Wayne, Indiana 46825-2096. **T:** 1 260 747-1511
Editorial Profile: WWFW-FM is a commercial station owned by Adams Radio Group. The format of the station is soft rock. The station broadcasts in Fort Wayne, IN at 103.9 FM.

WWFX-FM
Owner: Cumulus Media Inc.
Editorial: 250 Commercial St, Ste 530, Worcester, Massachusetts 01608-1726.
T: 1 508 752-1045 **W:** http://thefoxfm.com
Editorial Profile: WWFX-FM is a commercial station owned by Cumulus Media Inc. The format of the station is classic hits. WWFX-FM broadcasts to the Worcester, MA area at 100.1 FM.

WWFY-FM
Owner: Great Eastern Radio, LLC
Editorial: 41 Jacques St, Barre, Vermont 05641-5320. **T:** 1 802 476-4168
W: http://www.froggy1009.com
Editorial Profile: WWFY-FM is a commercial station owned by Great Eastern Radio, LLC. The format of the station is country. WWFY-FM broadcasts to the Barre, VT area at a frequency of 100.9 FM.

WWGB-AM
Owner: Good Body Media
Editorial: 6710 Oxon Hill Rd Ste 100, Oxon Hill, Maryland 20745-1158. **T:** 1 301 899-1444
E: radio@wwgb.com **W:** http://www.wwgb.com
Editorial Profile: WWGB-AM is a commercial station owned by Good Body Media. The format of the station is Hispanic gospel music and religious programming. WWGB-AM broadcasts to the Suitland, MD area at 1030 AM.

WWGF-FM
Owner: Good News Network
Editorial: 2278 Wortham Ln, Grovetown, Georgia 30813. **T:** 1 706 309-9610
W: http://www.gnnradio.org
Editorial Profile: WWGF-FM is a commercial station owned by Good News Network. The format of the station is religious. WWGF-FM broadcasts to the Donalsonville area at a frequency of 107.5 FM.

WWGK-AM
Owner: Good Karma Broadcasting
Editorial: 1301 E 9th St, Ste 252, Cleveland, Ohio 44114. **T:** 1 216 583-9901
W: http://www.espncleveland.com
Editorial Profile: WWGK-AM is a commercial station owned by Good Karma Broadcasting. The format of the station is sports. WWGK-AM broadcasts to the Cleveland area at 1540 AM.

WWGM-FM
Owner: Grace Broadcasting Services Inc.
Editorial: 2263 N Highland Ave, Jackson, Tennessee 38305. **T:** 1 731 664-9497
Editorial Profile: WWGM-FM is a commercial station owned by Grace Broadcasting Services Inc. The format of the station is gospel. WWGM-FM broadcasts to the Jackson, TN area at 93.1 FM.

WWGO-FM
Owner: Cromwell Group Inc.(The)
Editorial: 209 Lake Land Blvd, Mattoon, Illinois 61938-3904. **T:** 1 217 235-5624
W: http://www.radiomattoon.com
Editorial Profile: WWGO-FM is a commercial station owned by Cromwell Group Inc. The format of the station is classic rock music.

WWGO-FM broadcasts to the Mattoon, IL area at 92.1 FM.

WWGP-AM
Owner: WWGP Broadcasting Corporation
Editorial: 2201 Jefferson Davis Hwy, Sanford, North Carolina 27330. **T:** 1 919 775-3525
E: production@wfjaradio.com
Editorial Profile: WWGP-AM is a commercial station owned by WWGP Broadcasting Corp. The format of the station is country music. WWGP-AM broadcasts in the Sanford, NC area at 1050 AM.

WWGR-FM
Owner: Renda Broadcasting
Editorial: 10915 K Nine Dr, Bonita Springs, Florida 34135-6802. **T:** 1 239 495-8383
W: http://www.gatorcountry1019.com

WWGY-FM
Owner: Forever Broadcasting
Editorial: 219 Savannah Gardner Rd, New Castle, Pennsylvania 16101-5546.
T: 1 724 346-5070
W: http://www.froggy95pa.com
Editorial Profile: WWGY-FM is a commercial station owned by Forever Broadcasting. The format of the station is contemporary country music. WWGY-FM broadcasts in the New Castle, PA area at 95.1 FM.

WWHG-FM
Owner: Big Radio
Editorial: 1 Parker Pl Ste 485, Janesville, Wisconsin 53545-4078. **T:** 1 608 758-9025
E: sales@1059thehog.com
W: http://www.1059thehog.com
Editorial Profile: WWHG-FM is a commercial station owned by Good Karma Broadcasting. The format of the station is classic rock. WWHG-FM broadcasts to the Janesville, WI area at 105.9 FM.

WWHM-AM
Owner: Miller Communications Inc.
Editorial: 51 Commerce St, Sumter, South Carolina 29150. **T:** 1 803 775-2321
E: production@miller.fm
W: http://www.miller.fm
Editorial Profile: WWHM-AM is a commercial station owned by Miller Communications Inc. The format of the station is R&B oldies. WWHM-AM's broadcasts to the Sumter, SC area at 1290 AM.

WWHN-AM
Owner: Hawkins Broadcasting
Editorial: 10321 S Halsted St, Chicago, Illinois 60628-2321. **T:** 1 773 239-3100
E: wwhn@sbcglobal.net
Editorial Profile: WWHN-AM is a commercial station owned by Hawkins Broadcasting. The format of the station is gospel. WWHN-AM broadcasts to the Joliet, IL and the south suburbs of Chicago at 1510 AM.

WWHP-FM
Owner: WMS 1 Inc.
Editorial: 407 Main St, Farmer City, Illinois 61842. **T:** 1 309 928-9876
E: wwhp@farmwagon.com
W: http://www.wwhp.com
Editorial Profile: WWHP-FM is a commercial station owned by WMS 1 Inc. The format of the station is adult album alternative music. WWHP-FM broadcasts in the Farmer City, IL at 98.3 FM.

WWHQ-FM
Owner: Radiowerks, Inc.
Editorial: 407 Lothian St, Mountain Lake Park, Maryland 21550-2909. **T:** 1 301 334-4272
E: office@wkhj.com
W: http://www.92wwhq.com
Editorial Profile: WWHC-FM is a commercial station owned by Radiowerks, Inc. The format of the station is contemporary country. WWHC-FM broadcasts to the Mountain Lake Park, MD area at 92.3 FM.

WWHR-FM
Owner: Western Kentucky University
Editorial: 330 Mass Media & Technology Hall, Western Kentucky University, Bowling Green, Kentucky 42101. **T:** 1 270 745-5439
E: info@revolution.fm
W: http://www.revolution.fm
Editorial Profile: WWHR-FM is a non-commercial station owned by Western Kentucky University. The format of the station is adult album alternative. WWHR-FM broadcasts to the Bowling Green, KY area at 91.7 FM.

WWHS-FM
Owner: Hampden Sydney College
Editorial: Hampden Sydney College, 606 Graham Hall, Hampden Sydney, Virginia 23943. **T:** 1 434 223-6009
W: http://www.wwhsfm.org
Editorial Profile: WWHS-FM is a non-commercial station owned by Hampden Sydney College. The format of the station is variety. WWHS-FM broadcasts to the Hampden Sydney, VA area at 92.1 FM.

WWHT-FM
Owner: Clear Channel Media and Entertainment
Editorial: 500 Plum St, Ste 100, Syracuse, New York 13204. **T:** 1 315 472-9797
W: http://www.hot1079.com
Editorial Profile: WWHT-FM is a commercial station owned by Clear Channel Media and Entertainment. The format of the station is hot adult contemporary. WWHT-FM broadcasts to the Syracuse, NY area at 107.9 FM.

WWHX-FM
Owner: Connoisseur Media LLC
Editorial: 520 N Center St, Bloomington, Illinois 61701. **T:** 1 309 834-1100
W: http://www.bloomingtonhits.com
Editorial Profile: WWHX-FM is a commercial station owned by Connoisseur Media LLC. The format of the station is Top 40/CHR. WWHX-FM broadcasts to the Bloomington, IL area at 100.7 FM.

WWIB-FM
Owner: Stewards of Sound Inc.
Editorial: 2396 Hallie Rd Ste 1, Chippewa Falls, Wisconsin 54729-7519.
T: 1 715 723-1037 **E:** wwib@wwib.com
W: http://www.wwib.com
Editorial Profile: WWIB-FM is a commercial station owned by Stewards of Sound Inc. The format of the station is contemporary Christian. WWIB-FM broadcasts to the Chippewa Falls, WI area at 103.7 FM.

WWIC-AM
Owner: Scottsboro Broadcasting Co.
Editorial: 815 W Willow St, Scottsboro, Alabama 35768. **T:** 1 256 259-1050
E: wwic@scottsboro.org
W: http://www.wwicradio.com
Editorial Profile: WWIC-AM is a commercial station owned by Scottsboro Broadcasting Co. The format of the station is country music. WIWC-AM broadcasts to the Huntsville, AL area at 1050 AM.

WWIK-FM
Owner: Kirkman Broadcasting
Editorial: 60 Markfield Dr, Charleston, South Carolina 29407-7907. **T:** 1 843 763-6631
W: http://www.charlestonsportsradio.com
Editorial Profile: WWIK-FM is a commercial station owned by Kirkman Broadcasting. The format of the station is sports. WWIK-FM broadcasts to the North Charleston, SC area at 98.9 FM.

WWIN-AM
Owner: Radio One Inc.
Editorial: 1705 Whitehead Rd, Baltimore, Maryland 21207. **T:** 1 410 332-8200
W: http://www.spirit1400.com
Editorial Profile: WWIN-AM is a commercial station owned by Radio One Inc. The format of the station is gospel music. WWIN-AM broadcasts to the Baltimore area at 1400 AM.

WWIN-FM
Owner: Radio One Inc.
Editorial: 1705 Whitehead Rd, Baltimore, Maryland 21207. **T:** 1 410 332-8200
W: http://www.magic959baltimore.com
Editorial Profile: WWIN-FM is a commercial station owned by Radio One Inc. The format of the station is urban adult contemporary music. WWIN-FM broadcasts to the Baltimore area at 95.9 FM.

WWIP-FM
Owner: Delmarva Educational Association
Editorial: 2202 Jolliff Rd, Chesapeake, Virginia 23321-1416. **T:** 1 757 465-1603
E: info@wwip.org **W:** http://www.wwip.org
Editorial Profile: WWIP-FM is a non-commercial station owned by Delmarva Educational Association. The format of the station is religious teaching and Christian music. WWIP-FM broadcasts to the Chesapeak, VA area at 89.1 FM.

WWIS-AM
Owner: WWIS Radio Inc.
Editorial: W11573 Town Creek Rd, Black River Falls, Wisconsin 54615. **T:** 1 715 284-4391

E: wwis@wwisradio.com
W: http://www.wwisradio.com
Editorial Profile: WWIS-AM is a commercial station owned by WWIS Radio Inc. The format of the station is adult contemporary music. WWIS-AM broadcasts to the Black River Falls, WI area at 1260 AM.

WWIS-FM
Owner: WWIS Radio Inc.
Editorial: W11573 Town Creek Rd, Black River Falls, Wisconsin 54615. **T:** 1 715 284-4391
E: wwis@wwisradio.com
W: http://www.wwisradio.com
Editorial Profile: WWIS-FM is a commercial station owned by WWIS Radio Inc. The format of the station is classic country music. WWIS-FM broadcasts to the Black River Falls, WI area at 99.7 FM.

WWIZ-FM
Owner: Cumulus Media Inc.
Editorial: 4040 Simon Rd, Youngstown, Ohio 44512. **T:** 1 330 783-1000
W: http://www.realrock104.com
Editorial Profile: WWIZ-FM is a commercial station owned by Cumulus Media Inc. The format of the station is rock alternative. WWIZ-FM broadcasts to the Youngstown, OH area at 103.9 FM.

WWJ-AM
Owner: CBS Radio
Editorial: 26495 American Dr, Southfield, Michigan 48034. **T:** 1 248 455-7200
E: wwjnewsroom@cbsradio.com
W: http://detroit.cbslocal.com
Editorial Profile: WWJ-AM is a commercial station owned by CBS Radio. The format of the station is news. WWJ-AM broadcasts to the Detroit area at 950 AM.

WWJB-AM
Owner: Hernando Broadcasting Co.
Editorial: 55 W Fort Dade Ave, Brooksville, Florida 34601. **T:** 1 352 796-7469
E: info@wwjb.com **W:** http://www.wwjb.com
Editorial Profile: WWJB-AM is a commercial station owned by Hernando Broadcasting Co. The format of the station is news and talk. WWJB-AM broadcasts in the Brooksville, FL area at 1450 AM.

WWJC-AM
Owner: VCY America Inc.
Editorial: 3434 W Kilbourn Ave, Milwaukee, Wisconsin 53208-3313. **T:** 1 800 729-9829
E: wwjc@vcyamerica.org
W: http://www.vcyamerica.org
Editorial Profile: WWJC-AM is a non-commercial station owned by VCY America Inc. The format of the station is Christian talk and teaching. WWJC-AM broadcasts to the Duluth, MN area at 850 AM.

WWJD-FM
Owner: Alice Lloyd College
Editorial: 100 Purpose Rd, Pippa Passes, Kentucky 41844-9005. **T:** 1 606 368-6131
E: wwjd@alc.edu **W:** http://www.alc.edu
Editorial Profile: WWJD-FM is a non-commercial station owned by Alice Lloyd College. The format of the station is contemporary Christian. WWJD-FM broadcasts to the Lexington, KY area at 91.7 FM.

WWJK-FM
Owner: Clear Channel Media and Entertainment
Editorial: 11700 Central Pkwy, Jacksonville, Florida 32224-2600. **T:** 1 904 636-0507
W: http://www.1073jack.com
Editorial Profile: WWJK-FM is a commercial station owned by Clear Channel Media and Entertainment. The format of the station is adult hits WWJK-FM broadcasts to Jacksonville, FL at 107.3 FM.

WWJM-FM
Owner: Perry County Broadcasting
Editorial: 247 Market St, Zanesville, Ohio 43701-3428. **T:** 1 740 455-3961
E: wwjmp3@aol.com
W: http://www.wwjm.com
Editorial Profile: WWJM-FM is a commercial station owned by Perry County Broadcasting. The format of the station is adult contemporary music. WWJM-FM broadcasts to the New Lexington, OH area at 105.9 FM.

WWJO-FM
Owner: Townsquare Media, LLC
Editorial: 640 Lincoln Ave SE, Saint Cloud, Minnesota 56304. **T:** 1 320 251-4422
W: http://www.98country.com
Editorial Profile: WWJO-FM is a commercial station owned by Townsquare Media, LLC. The

format of the station is contemporary country music. WWJO-FM broadcasts to the St. Cloud, MN area at 98.1 FM.

WWJZ-AM
Owner: Walt Disney Co.
Editorial: 501 Office Center Dr Ste 190, Fort Washington, Pennsylvania 19034-3268. **T:** 1 215 591-0100
W: http://radio.disney.go.com/music/yourstation/philadelphia/index.html
Editorial Profile: WWJZ-AM is a commercial station owned by Walt Disney Co. The format of the station is children's programming. WWJZ-AM broadcasts to the Philadelphia area at 640 AM.

WWKA-FM
Owner: Cox Media Group, Inc.
Editorial: 4192 N John Young Pkwy, Orlando, Florida 32804-2620. **T:** 1 321 281-2000
E: news@wdbo.com
W: http://www.k923orlando.com
Editorial Profile: WWKA-FM is a commercial station owned by Cox Media Group, Inc. The format of the station is country. WWKA-FM broadcasts to the Orlando, FL area at 92.3 FM.

WWKB-AM
Owner: Entercom Communications Corp.
Editorial: 500 Corporate Pkwy, Buffalo, New York 14226-1263. **T:** 1 716 843-0600
W: http://www.espn1520.com
Editorial Profile: WWKB-AM is a commercial station owned by Entercom Communications Corp. The primary format of the station is sports. WWKB-AM broadcasts to the Buffalo, NY, area at 1520 AM.

WWKC-FM
Owner: AVC Communications Inc.
Editorial: 4988 Skyline Dr, Cambridge, Ohio 43725. **T:** 1 740 732-5777
E: avcnews@yourradioplace.com
W: http://www.yourradioplace.com
Editorial Profile: WWKC-FM is a commercial station owned by AVC Communications Inc. The format of the station is country. WWKC-FM broadcasts to the Cambridge, OH area at 104.9 FM.

WWKF-FM
Owner: WENK of Union City, Inc.
Editorial: 1729 Nailling Dr, Union City, Tennessee 38261. **T:** 1 731 885-1240
W: http://www.kf99kq105.com
Editorial Profile: WWKF-FM is a commercial station owned by WENK of Union City, Inc. The format of the station is Top 40/CHR music. WWKF-FM broadcasts to the Union City, TN area at 99.3 FM.

WWKI-FM
Owner: Cumulus Media Inc.
Editorial: 519 N Main St, Kokomo, Indiana 46901-4619. **T:** 1 765 459-4191
E: wwki@cumulus.com
W: http://www.wwki.com
Editorial Profile: WWKI-FM is a commercial station owned by Cumulus Media Inc. The format of the station is contemporary country music. WWKI-FM broadcasts to the Indianapolis area at 100.5 FM.

WWKL-FM
Owner: Cumulus Media Inc.
Editorial: 2300 Vartan Way, Harrisburg, Pennsylvania 17110-9720. **T:** 1 717 238-1041
W: http://www.hot92.com
Editorial Profile: WWKL-FM is a commercial station owned by Cumulus Media Inc. The format of the station is Uban music. WWKL-FM broadcasts to the Harrisburg, PA area at 93.5 FM.

WWKR-FM
Owner: Synergy Media Inc.
Editorial: 5399 W Wallace Ln, Ludington, Michigan 49431. **T:** 1 231 843-0941
W: http://www.94k-rock.com
Editorial Profile: WWKR-FM is a commercial station owned by Synergy Media Inc. The format of the station is classic rock music. WWKR-FM broadcasts to the Pentwater, MI area at 94.1 FM.

WWKT-FM
Owner: Miller Communications Inc.
Editorial: 51 Commerce St, Sumter, South Carolina 29150. **T:** 1 803 775-2321
E: production@miller.fm
W: http://www.katcountry993.net
Editorial Profile: WWKT-FM is a commercial station owned by Miller Communications Inc. The format of the station is contemporary country. WWKT-FM broadcasts to the Sumter, SC area at 99.3 FM

WWKU-AM
Owner: Commonwealth Broadcasting Corp.
Editorial: 1823 McIntosh St, Ste 107, Bowling Green, Kentucky 42104. **T:** 1 270 846-0222
E: espnradio1450@yahoo.com
W: http://www.espn1450.net
Editorial Profile: WWKU-AM is a commercial station owned by Commonwealth Broadcasting Corp. The format of the station is sports. WWKU-AM broadcasts to the Bowling Green, KY area at 1450 AM.

WWKX-FM
Owner: Cumulus Media Inc.
Editorial: 1502 Wampanoag Trl, Riverside, Rhode Island 2915. **T:** 1 401 433-4200
W: http://www.hot1063.com
Editorial Profile: WWKX-FM is a commercial station owned by Cumulus Media Inc. The format of the rhythmic Top 40/CHR. WWKX-FM broadcasts to the Riverside, RI area at 106.3 FM.

WWKY-FM
Owner: Commonwealth Broadcasting Corp.
Editorial: 265 S Main St, Madisonville, Kentucky 42431. **T:** 1 270 825-9779
Editorial Profile: WWKY-FM is a commercial station owned by Commonwealth Broadcasting Corp. The format of the station is oldies. WWKY-FM broadcasts to the Madisonville, KY area at 97.7 FM.

WWKZ-FM
Owner: URBan Radio Broadcasting, LLC
Editorial: 5026 Cliff Gookin Blvd, Tupelo, Mississippi 38801. **T:** 1 662 842-1067
W: http://www.kz103.com
Editorial Profile: WWKZ-FM is a commercial station owned by URBan Radio Broadcasting, LLC. The format of the station is Top 40/CHR. WWKZ-FM broadcasts to the Tupelo, MS area at 103.9 FM.

WWL-AM
Owner: Entercom Communications Corp.
Editorial: 400 Poydras St, Ste 800, New Orleans, Louisiana 70130. **T:** 1 504 593-6376
E: wwlnewsroom@yahoo.com
W: http://www.wwl.com
Editorial Profile: WWL-AM is a commercial station owned by Entercom Communications Corp. The format of the station is news, sports and talk. WWL-AM broadcasts to the New Orleans area at 870 AM.

WWLB-FM
Owner: Main Line Broadcasting
Editorial: 300 Arboretum Pl Ste 590, Richmond, Virginia 23236. **T:** 1 804 327-9902
E: news@wjmafm.com
W: http://www.989liberty.com
Editorial Profile: WWLB-FM is a commercial station owned by Main Line Broadcasting. The format of the station is Jack FM-Adult Hits. WWLB-FM broadcasts to the Richmond, VA, area at 98.9 FM.

WWLD-FM
Owner: Cumulus Media Inc.
Editorial: 3411 W Tharpe St, Tallahassee, Florida 32303. **T:** 1 850 201-3000
W: http://www.blazin1023.com
Editorial Profile: WWLD-FM is a commercial station owned by Cumulus Media Inc. The format for the station is urban contemporary. WWLD-FM broadcasts to the Tallahassee, FL area at 102.3 FM.

WWLE-AM
Owner: 1170 Broadcast Radio Inc.
Editorial: 343 Broadway, Newburgh, New York 12550-5301. **T:** 1 845 569-7010
E: newsdesk@prodigy.net
Editorial Profile: WWLE-AM is a commercial station owned by 1170 Broadcast Radio Inc. The format of the station is news. WWLE-AM broadcasts in the Newburgh, NY area at 1170 AM.

WWLF-FM
Owner: Wolf Radio, Inc.
Editorial: 401 W Kirkpatrick St, Syracuse, New York 13204. **T:** 1 315 472-0222
E: programming@movin100.com
W: http://www.wolf1051.com
Editorial Profile: WWLF-FM is a commercial station owned by Wolf Radio, Inc. The format of the station is contemporary country. WWLF-FM broadcasts to the Syracuse, NY area at 96.7 FM.

WWL-FM
Owner: Entercom Communications Corp.
Editorial: 400 Poydras St, Ste 800, New Orleans, Louisiana 70130. **T:** 1 504 593-6376
E: wwlnewsroom@yahoo.com
W: http://www.wwl.com
Editorial Profile: WWL-FM is a commercial station owned by Entercom Communications Corp. The format of the station is a news, talk and sports. WWL-FM broadcasts to the New Orleans area at 105.3 FM.

WWLG-FM
Owner: Clear Channel Media and Entertainment
Editorial: 1819 Peachtree Rd NE, Atlanta, Georgia 30309-1848. **T:** 1 404 875-8080
W: http://www.radio1057.com
Editorial Profile: WWLG-FM is a commercial station owned by Clear Channel Media and Entertainment. The format of the station is alternative rock. WWLG-FM broadcasts to the Atlanta area at 96.7 FM.

WWLI-FM
Owner: Cumulus Media Inc.
Editorial: 1502 Wampanoag Trl, Riverside, Rhode Island 2915. **T:** 1 401 433-4200
W: http://www.lite105.com
Editorial Profile: WWLI-FM is a commercial station owned by Cumulus Media Inc. The format of the station is adult contemporary music. WWLI-FM broadcasts to the Riverside, RI area at 105.1 FM.

WWLL-FM
Owner: Cohan Radio Group Inc.
Editorial: 3750 US Highway 27 N, Sebring, Florida 33870. **T:** 1 863 382-9999
E: cohanradiogroup@htn.net
W: http://www.cohanradiogroup.com
Editorial Profile: WWLL-FM is a commercial station owned by Cohan Radio Group Inc. The format of the station is adult contemporary music. WWLL-FM broadcasts in the Sebring, FL area at 105.7 FM.

WWLR-FM
Owner: Lyndon State College
Editorial: 1001 College Rd, Lyndonville, Vermont 5851. **T:** 1 802 626-6214
E: wwlr@lyndonstate.edu
W: http://www.lyndonstate.edu/ProspectiveStudents/AboutLyndon/ProgramsInstitutes/WW

WWLS-FM
Owner: Cumulus Media Inc
Editorial: 4045 NW 64th St, Oklahoma City, Oklahoma 73116-1684. **T:** 1 405 848-0100
W: http://www.thesportsanimal.com
Editorial Profile: WWLS-FM is a commercial station owned by Cumulus Media Inc. The format of the station is sports. WWLS-FM broadcasts to the Oklahoma City area at 98.1 FM.

WWLV-FM
Owner: EMF
Editorial: 200 Radio Dr, Lexington, North Carolina 27292-8010. **T:** 1 336 248-2716
W: http://www.klove.com
Editorial Profile: WWLV-FM is a non-commercial station owned by Davidson County Broadcasting. The format of the station is contemporary Christian. WWLV-FM broadcasts to the Greensboro, High Point, Winston Salem, Charlotte and Lexington, NC area at 94.1 FM. The programming comes from the K-Love network.

WWLW-FM
Owner: West Virginia Radio Corp.
Editorial: 1065 Radio Park Dr, Mount Clare, West Virginia 26408. **T:** 1 304 623-6546
W: http://www.wvmagic.com
Editorial Profile: WWLW-FM is a commercial station owned by West Virginia Radio Corp. The format of the station is adult contemporary. WWLW-FM broadcasts to the Mount Clare, WV area at 106.5 FM.

WWLX-AM
Owner: Prospect Communications
Editorial: 1212 N Locust Ave, Lawrenceburg, Tennessee 38464. **T:** 1 931 762-6200
E: wlxnews@bellsouth.net
W: http://www.wlxonline.com
Editorial Profile: WWLX-AM is a commercial station owned by Prospect Communications. The format of the station is classic hits. WWLX-AM broadcasts to the Lawrenceburg, TN area at 590 AM.

WWLZ-AM
Owner: Community Broadcasters, LLC
Editorial: 2205 College Ave, Elmira, New York 14903-1201. **T:** 1 607 732-4400
W: http://wwlzam820.com/
Editorial Profile: WWLZ-AM is a commercial station owned by Community Broadcasters, LLC. The format of the station is news and talk programming. WWLZ-AM broadcasts to the Elmira, NY area at 820 AM.

WWMC-FM
Owner: Liberty University
Editorial: 1971 University Blvd, Lynchburg, Virginia 24502. **T:** 1 434 582-3691
E: wwmcfm@liberty.edu
W: http://www.thelightonline.com
Editorial Profile: WWMC-FM is a non-commercial station owned by Liberty University. The format of the station is contemporary Christian. WWMC-FM broadcasts to the Lynchburg, VA area at 90.9 FM.

WWMG-FM
Owner: Clear Channel Media and Entertainment
Editorial: 203 Gunn Rd, Montgomery, Alabama 36117. **T:** 1 334 274-6464
W: http://www.mymagic97.com
Editorial Profile: WWMG-FM is a commercial station owned by Clear Channel Media and Entertainment. The format of the station is urban adult contemporary. WWMG-FM broadcasts to the Montgomery, AL area at 97.1 FM.

WWMI-AM
Owner: Walt Disney Co.
Editorial: 11300 4th St N Ste 143, Saint Petersburg, Florida 33716-2939. **T:** 1 727 577-4500
W: http://radio.disney.go.com/music/yourstation/tampa/index.html
Editorial Profile: WWMI-AM is a commercial station owned by Walt Disney Co. The format of the station is children's programming. WWMI-AM broadcasts to the Saint Petersburg, FL area at 1380 AM.

WWMJ-FM
Owner: Townsquare Media, Inc.
Editorial: 49 Acme Rd, Brewer, Maine 04412-1545. **T:** 1 207 989-5631
E: i95@midmaine.com
W: http://www.wwmj-fm.com
Editorial Profile: WWMJ-FM is a commercial station owned by Townsquare Media, Inc. The format of the station is classic hits. WWMJ-FM broadcasts to the Brewer, ME area at 95.7 FM.

WWMK-AM
Owner: Walt Disney Co.
Editorial: 175 Ken Mar Industrial Pkwy, Broadview Heights, Ohio 44147-2950. **T:** 1 440 746-1010
W: http://radio.disney.go.com/music/yourstation/cleveland/index.html
Editorial Profile: WWMK-AM is a commercial station owned by Walt Disney Co. The format of the station is children music and programming. WWMK-AM is the Radio Disney affiliate for the Cleveland, OH area broadcasting locally at 1260 AM.

WWMM-FM
Owner: Clear Channel Media and Entertainment
Editorial: 1400 Radio Ln, Mansfield, Ohio 44906-2525. **T:** 1 419 529-2211
W: http://www.wmanfm.com
Editorial Profile: WWMM-FM is a commercial station owned by Clear Channel Media and Entertainment. The format of the station is news/talk. WWMM-FM broadcasts to the Ashland, OH area at 98.3 FM

WWMP-FM
Owner: Northeast Broadcasting Co.
Editorial: 372 Dorset St, South Burlington, Vermont 5403. **T:** 1 802 863-1010
E: joannad@champlainradio.com
W: http://www.mp103.com
Editorial Profile: WWMP-FM is a commercial station owned by Northeast Broadcasting Co. The format of the station is adult hits. WWMP-FM broadcasts to the South Burlington, VT area at 103.3 FM.

WWMS-FM
Owner: Mississippi Radio Group
Editorial: 2214 S Gloster St, Tupelo, Mississippi 38801-6814. **T:** 1 662 842-7658
W: http://www.miss98.net
Editorial Profile: WWMS-FM is a commercial station owned by Mississippi Radio Group. The format of the station is country music. WWMS-FM broadcasts to the Tupelo, MI area at 97.5 FM.

WWMX-FM
Owner: CBS Radio
Editorial: 1423 Clarkview Rd Ste 100, Baltimore, Maryland 21209-2190.

T: 1 410 825-1065
W: http://mix1065fm.cbslocal.com
Editorial Profile: WWMX-FM is a commercial station owned by CBS Radio. The format of the station is hot adult contemporary music. WWMX-FM broadcasts to the Baltimore area at 106.5 FM.

WWNB-AM
Owner: CTC Media Group
Editorial: 1202 Pollock St, New Bern, North Carolina 28560-5538. **T:** 1 252 633-1490
W: http://www.rfenc.com
Editorial Profile: WWNB-AM is a commercial owned by the CTC Media Group. The format of the station is sports. WWNB-AM broadcasts to the New Bern, NC area at 1490 AM.

WWNC-AM
Owner: Clear Channel Media and Entertainment
Editorial: 13 Summerlin Rd, Asheville, North Carolina 28806. **T:** 1 828 257-2700
E: ashevillepsa@clearchannel.com
W: http://www.wwnc.com
Editorial Profile: WWNC-AM is a commercial station owned by Clear Channel Media and Entertainment. The format for the station is talk. WWNC-AM broadcasts to the Asheville, NC area at 570 AM.

WWNJ-FM
Owner: Mercer County Community College
Editorial: 1200 Old Trenton Rd, Princeton Junction, New Jersey 8550.
T: 1 609 587-8989 **E:** info@wwfm.org
W: http://www.wwfm.org
Editorial Profile: WWNJ-FM is a non-commercial station owned by Mercer County Community College. The format of the station is classical music. WWNJ-FM broadcasts to the Princeton Junction, NJ area at 91.1 FM.

WWNL-AM
Owner: Wilkins Communication Networks Inc.
Editorial: 5316 William Flynn Hwy, Ste 3N, Gibsonia, Pennsylvania 15044.
T: 1 724 443-4844 **E:** wwnl@wilkinsradio.com
W: http://www.wilkinsradio.com
Editorial Profile: WWNL-AM is a commercial station owned by Wilkins Communication Networks Inc. The format for the station is Christian talk. WWNL-AM broadcasts to the Gibsonia, PA area at 1080 AM.

WWNN-AM
Owner: Beasley Broadcast Group
Editorial: 1650 S Dixie Hwy Fl 5, Boca Raton, Florida 33432-7462. **T:** 1 561 997-0074
W: http://www.wwnnradio.com
Editorial Profile: WWNN-AM is a commercial station owned by Beasley Broadcast Group. The format of the station is health talk. WWNN-AM broadcasts to the Boca Raton, FL area at 1470 AM.

WWNO-FM
Owner: University of New Orleans
Editorial: 2000 Lakeshore Dr, University of New Orleans, New Orleans, Louisiana 70148.
T: 1 504 280-7000 **E:** comments@wwno.org
W: http://www.wwno.org
Editorial Profile: WWNO-FM is a non-commercial station owned by the University of New Orleans. The format of the station is news, jazz, and classical music. WWNO-FM broadcasts to the New Orleans area at 89.9 FM.

WWNQ-FM
Owner: Local Voice Media
Editorial: 1010 Gervais St Ste 100, Columbia, South Carolina 29201-3130.
T: 1 803 753-6800
E: country@hometowncolumbia.com
W: http://943thedude.com
Editorial Profile: WWNQ-FM is a commercial station owned by Local Voice Media. The format of the station is contemporary country. WWNQ-FM broadcasts to the Columbia, SC area at 94.3 FM.

WWNR-AM
Owner: Southern Communications Corp.
Editorial: 306 S Kanawha St, Beckley, West Virginia 25801. **T:** 1 304 253-7000
E: wwnr@radiocitywv.com
W: http://www.wwnrnewstalk620.com
Editorial Profile: WWNR-AM is a commercial station owned by Southern Communications Corp. The format of the station is news, sports, and talk. WWNR-AM broadcasts to the Beckley, WV area at 620 AM.

WWNS-AM
Owner: Georgia Eagle Broadcasting Inc.
Editorial: 561 E Olliff St, Statesboro, Georgia 30458-4663. **T:** 1 912 764-5446
E: statonspots@hotmail.com
Editorial Profile: WWNS-AM is a commercial station owned by Georgia Eagle Broadcasting Inc. The format for the station is news. WWNS-AM broadcasts to the Savannah, GA area at 1240 AM.

WWNT-AM
Owner: WWNT LLC
Editorial: 1733 Highway 52 East, Dothan, Alabama 36303-5433. **T:** 1 334 671-0075
E: wwntradio@hotmail.com
W: http://wwntradio.com
Editorial Profile: WWNT-AM is a commercial station owned by WWNT LLC. The format of the station is news and talk. WWNT-AM broadcasts to the Dothan, AL area at 1450 AM.

WWNU-FM
Owner: Local Voice Media
Editorial: 1010 Gervais St Ste 100, Columbia, South Carolina 29201-3130.
T: 1 803 753-6800
E: music@hometowncolumbia.com
W: http://thepalmfm.com
Editorial Profile: WWNU-FM is a commercial station owned by Local Voice Media. The format of the station is AAA. WWNU-FM broadcasts to the Columbia, SC area at 92.1 FM.

WWNW-FM
Owner: Westminster College
Editorial: Westminster College, Box 89, New Wilmington, Pennsylvania 16172.
T: 1 724 946-7242
E: titanradio@westminster.edu
W: http://www.westminster.edu/student/orgs/radio/radio_news.cfm
Editorial Profile: WWNW-FM is non-commercial station owned by Westminster College. The format of the station is hot adult contemporary music. WWNW-FM broadcasts in the Westminster, PA area at 88.9 FM.

WWNZ-AM
Owner: Waterfront Communications Inc.
Editorial: 379 Riverside Dr, Eddington, Maine 4428. **T:** 1 207 947-9697
E: wnzproduction@aol.com
Editorial Profile: WWNZ-AM is a commercial station owned by Waterfront Communications Inc. The format of the station is conservative news and talk. WWNZ-FM broadcasts to Eddington, ME area 1400 AM.

WWOD-FM
Owner: Great Eastern Radio, LLC
Editorial: 31 Hanover St, Lebanon, New Hampshire 03766-1312. **T:** 1 603 448-1400
Editorial Profile: WWOD-FM is a commercial station owned by Great Eastern Radio, LLC. The format of the station is classic hits. WWOD-FM broadcasts to the Lebanon, NH area at a frequency of 93.9 FM.

WWOF-FM
Owner: Red Hills Broadcasting, LLC
Editorial: 3000 Olson Rd, Tallahassee, Florida 32308-3918. **T:** 1 850 386-8004
W: http://www.1031thewolf.com
Editorial Profile: WWOF-FM is a commercial station owned by Red Hills Broadcasting, LLC. The format of the station is contemporary country music. WWOF-FM broadcasts to the Tallahassee, FL area at 103.1 FM.

WWOG-FM
Owner: Somerset Educational Broadcasting
Editorial: 93 Rainbow Ter, Somerset, Kentucky 42503-4653. **T:** 1 606 679-6300
W: http://www.kingofkingsradio.net
Editorial Profile: WWOG-FM is a non-commercial station owned by Somerset Educational Broadcasting. The format of the station is religious. WWOG-FM broadcasts to the Lexington, KY area at 90.9 FM.

WWOJ-FM
Owner: Cohan Radio Group Inc.
Editorial: 3750 US Highway 27 N, Ste 1, Sebring, Florida 33870. **T:** 1 863 382-9999
E: cohanradiogroup@htn.net
W: http://www.cohanradiogroup.com
Editorial Profile: WWOJ-FM is a commercial station owned by Cohan Radio Group Inc. The format of the station is contemporary country. WWOJ-FM broadcasts to the Sebring, FL area at 99.1 FM.

WWOL-AM
Owner: Holly Springs Baptist Church
Editorial: 1381 W Main St, Forest City, North Carolina 28043-2525. **T:** 1 828 245-0078
E: wwol780@yahoo.com
W: http://www.wwol780.com
Editorial Profile: WWOL-AM is a commercial station owned by Holly Springs Baptist Church. The format for the station is gospel. WWOL-AM broadcasts to the Greenville, SC; Asheville, NC area at 780 AM.

WWOT-FM
Owner: Forever Broadcasting
Editorial: 1 Forever Dr, Hollidaysburg, Pennsylvania 16648-3029. **T:** 1 814 941-9800
W: http://www.hot92and100.com
Editorial Profile: WWOT-FM is a commercial station owned by Forever Broadcasting. The format of the station is Top 40/CHR. WWOT-FM broadcasts to the Hollidaysburg, PA area at 100.1 FM.

WWOW-AM
Owner: Cause Plus Marketing, LLC
Editorial: 229 Broad St, Conneaut, Ohio 44030-2616. **T:** 1 440 593-2233
E: wwow1360@aol.com
Editorial Profile: WWOW-AM is a commercial station owned by Cause Plus Marketing, LLC. The format of the station is oldies. WWOW-AM broadcasts to the Conneaut, OH area at 1360 AM.

WWOZ-FM
Owner: Friends of WWOZ Inc.
Editorial: 1008 N Peters St Fl 2, New Orleans, Louisiana 70116-3317. **T:** 1 504 568-1239
E: feedback@wwoz.org
W: http://www.wwoz.org
Editorial Profile: WWOZ-FM is a non-commercial station owned by Friends of WWOZ Inc. The format of the station is jazz and R&B oldies music. WWOZ-FM broadcasts to the New Orleans area at 90.7 FM.

WWPA-AM
Owner: Backyard Broadcasting
Editorial: 1685 Four Mile Dr, Williamsport, Pennsylvania 17701. **T:** 1 570 323-8200
Editorial Profile: WWPA-AM is a commercial station owned by Backyard Broadcasting. The format of the station is news, talk, and sports. WWPA-AM broadcasts to the Williamsport, PA area at 1340 AM.

WWPG-FM
Owner: Lawson Communications(Jim)
Editorial: 601 Greensboro Ave Ste 507, Tuscaloosa, Alabama 35401-1795.
T: 1 205 345-4787
Editorial Profile: WWPG-FM is a commercial station owned by Lawson Communications. The format of the station is black gospel. WWPG-FM broadcasts to the Tuscaloosa, AL area at 104.3 FM.

WWPL-FM
Owner: New Age Communications, Inc
Editorial: 3012 Highwoods Blvd Ste 201, Raleigh, North Carolina 27604-1031.
T: 1 919 8759100 **E:** info@curtismedia.com
W: http://www.pulse102.com
Editorial Profile: WWPL-FM is a commercial station owned by New Age Communications, Inc. The format of the station is Top 40. WWPL-FM broadcasts to the Raleigh, NC area at 102.3 FM.

WWPN-FM
Owner: Santmyire(Ernest F.)
Editorial: 12 N Lavale St, Lavale, Maryland 21502. **T:** 1 301 463-5100
W: http://www.spirit101.com
Editorial Profile: WWPN-FM is a commercial station owned by Ernest F. Santmyire. The format of the station is contemporary Christian. WWPN-FM broadcasts to the Lavale, MD area at 101.1 FM.

WWPR-AM
Owner: Vidify Media Inc.
Editorial: 5910 Cortez Rd W Ste 130, Bradenton, Florida 34210-2707.
T: 1 941 761-8843
W: http://www.1490wwpr.com
Editorial Profile: WWPR-AM is a commercial station owned by Vidify Media Inc. The format of the station is talk. WWPR-AM broadcasts to the Bradenton, FL area at 1490 AM.

WWPR-FM
Owner: Clear Channel Media and Entertainment
Editorial: 32 Avenue of the Americas Fl 3, New York, New York 10013-2473.
T: 1 212 377-7900
W: http://www.power1051fm.com
Editorial Profile: WWPR-FM is a commercial station owned by Clear Channel Media and Entertainment. The format of the station is urban contemporary music. WWPR-FM broadcasts to the entire New York City metro area at 105.1 FM.

WWPV-FM
Owner: St. Michael's College
Editorial: 1 Winooski Park, Colchester, Vermont 05439-1000. **T:** 1 802 651-2334
W: http://www.wwpv.org
Editorial Profile: WWPV-FM is a non-commercial student-run college station owned by St. Michael's College. The format of the station is variety. WWPV-FM broadcasts to the Colchester, VT area at a frequency of 88.7 FM.

WWPW-FM
Owner: Clear Channel Media and Entertainment
Editorial: 1819 Peachtree Rd Ne Ste 700, Atlanta, Georgia 30309-1849.
T: 1 404 875-8080
W: http://www.power961.com
Editorial Profile: WWPW-FM is a commercial station owned by Clear Channel Media and Entertainment. The format of the station is top40/CHR music. WWPW-FM broadcasts to the Atlanta area at 96.1 FM.

WWQM-FM
Owner: Midwest Family Broadcasting
Editorial: 730 Ray O Vac Dr, Madison, Wisconsin 53711. **T:** 1 608 273-1000
W: http://www.q106.com
Editorial Profile: WWQM-FM is a commercial station owned by Midwest Family Broadcasting. The format of the station is country. WWQM-FM broadcasts to the Madison, WI area at 106.3 FM.

WWQQ-FM
Owner: Cumulus Media Inc.
Editorial: 3233 Burnt Mill Dr, Ste 4, Wilmington, North Carolina 28403.
T: 1 910 763-9977
W: http://www.wwqq101.com
Editorial Profile: WWQQ-FM is a commercial station owned by Cumulus Media Inc. The format of the station is country. WWQQ-FM broadcasts to the Wilmington, NC area at 101.3 FM.

WWRC-AM
Owner: Salem Communications
Editorial: 1901 N Moore St Ste 200, Arlington, Virginia 22209-1706. **T:** 1 703 807-2266
E: events@1260wrc.com
W: http://www.1260wrc.com
Editorial Profile: WWRC-AM is a commercial station owned by Salem Communications. The format of the station is talk. WWRC-AM broadcasts to the Washington, D.C. area at 1260 AM.

WWRF-AM
Owner: Radio Fiesta, Inc.
Editorial: 2326 S Congress Ave, Ste 2A, West Palm Beach, Florida 33406. **T:** 1 561 721-9950
W: http://www.radiofiesta.com
Editorial Profile: WWRF-AM is a commercial station owned by Radio Fiesta, Inc. The format of the station is regional Mexican. WWRF-AM broadcasts to the West Palm Beach, FL area at 1380 AM.

WWRK-AM
Owner: Clear Channel Media and Entertainment
Editorial: 181 E Evans St Ste 311, Florence, South Carolina 29506-5505.
T: 1 843 665-0970
W: http://swagga941.com/#&panel1-2
Editorial Profile: WWRK-AM is a commercial station owned by Clear Channel Media and Entertainment. The format of the station is urban contemporary. WWRK-AM broadcasts to the Florence, SC area at 970 AM.

WWRL-AM
Owner: Access.1 Communications Corp.
Editorial: 333 7th Ave, New York, New York 10001-5004. **T:** 1 212 631-0800
W: http://www.lainvasora1600.com
Editorial Profile: WWRL-AM is a commercial station owned by Access.1 Communications Corp. The format of the station is Regional Mexican music. WWRL-AM broadcasts to the New York City area at 1600 AM.

WWRM-FM
Owner: Cox Media Group, Inc.
Editorial: 11300 4th St N Ste 300, Saint Petersburg, Florida 33716-2941.
T: 1 727 579-2000
E: 949comments@coxtampa.com
W: http://www.mymagic949.com
Editorial Profile: WWRM-FM is a commercial station owned by Cox Media Group, Inc. The

format of the station is Lite Rock/Lite AC. WWRM-FM broadcasts to the Saint Petersburg, FL area at 94.9 FM.

WWRQ-FM
Owner: Black Crow Broadcasting Inc.
Editorial: 1711 Ellis Dr, Valdosta, Georgia 31601. **T:** 1 229 244-8642
W: http://www.rock108.fm
Editorial Profile: WWRQ-FM is a commercial station owned by Black Crow Broadcasting Inc. The format of the station is rock music. WWRQ-FM broadcasts to the Valdosta, GA area at 107.9 FM.

WWRR-FM
Owner: Bold Gold Media Group
Editorial: 1049 N Sekol Ave, Scranton, Pennsylvania 18504. **T:** 1 570 344-1221
W: http://www.105theriver.net
Editorial Profile: WWRR-FM is a commercial station owned by Bold Gold Media Group. The format of the station is classic hits. WWRR-FM broadcasts to the Scranton, PA area at 104.9 FM.

WWRU-AM
Owner: Multicultural Radio Broadcasting Inc.
Editorial: 449 Broadway, New York, New York 10013-2549. **T:** 1 718 358-9300
W: http://mrbi.net
Editorial Profile: WWRU-AM is a commercial station owned by Multicultural Radio Broadcasting Inc. The format of the station is variety, featuring brokered Korean-language programming. WWRU-AM broadcasts to the New York City metro area at 1660 AM.

WWRV-AM
Owner: Radio Vision Christiana Management Corp.
Editorial: 419 Broadway, Paterson, New Jersey 7501. **T:** 1 973 881-8700
W: http://www.radiovision.net
Editorial Profile: WWRV-AM is a commercial station owned by Radio Vision Christiana Management Corp. The format of the station is Hispanic religious programming. WWRV-AM broadcasts to the Paterson, NJ area at 1330 AM.

WWRW-FM
Owner: Clear Channel Media and Entertainment
Editorial: 2601 Nicholasville Rd, Lexington, Kentucky 40503-3307. **T:** 1 859 422-1000
W: http://www.rewind1055.com
Editorial Profile: WWRW-FM is a commercial station owned by Clear Channel Media and Entertainment. The format of the station is classic hits. WWRW-FM broadcasts to the Lexington, KY area at 105.5 FM.

WWRZ-FM
Owner: Hall Communications
Editorial: 404 W Lime St, Lakeland, Florida 33815-4651. **T:** 1 863 682-8184
W: http://www.max983fm.com
Editorial Profile: WWRZ-FM is a commercial station owned by Hall Communications. The format of the station is adult hits. WWRZ-FM broadcasts in the Lakeland, FL, area at 98.3 FM.

WWSC-AM
Owner: Regional Radio Group
Editorial: 238 Bay Rd, Queensbury, New York 12804-2006. **T:** 1 518 761-9890
E: news@radiowins.com
W: http://www.radiowins.com
Editorial Profile: WWSC-AM is a commercial station owned by Regional Radio Group. The format of the station is news and talk. WWSC-AM broadcasts in the Glens Falls, NY area at 1450 AM.

WWSE-FM
Owner: Media One Group, LLC
Editorial: 2 Orchard Rd, Jamestown, New York 14701. **T:** 1 716 487-1151
W: http://www.se933.com
Editorial Profile: WWSE-FM is a commercial station owned by Media One Group, LLC. The format of the station is adult contemporary music. WWSE-FM broadcasts to the Jamestown, NY area at 93.3 FM.

WWSF-AM
Owner: Port Broadcasting, LLC
Editorial: 6 Federal St Floor 2, Newburyport, Massachusetts 01950-2804.
T: 1 978 462-1450 **W:** http://www.wnbp.com
Editorial Profile: WWSF-AM is a commercial station owned by Port Broadcasting, LLC. The format of the station is adult standards and modern jazz. WWSF-AM broadcasts to the Sanford, ME area at 1220 AM.

WWSJ-AM
Owner: Harp(Larry and Helen)
Editorial: 1363 W Parks Rd, Saint Johns, Michigan 48879. **T:** 1 989 224-7911
E: joy1580@sbcglobal.net
W: http://www.joy1580.com
Editorial Profile: WWSJ-AM is a commercial station owned by Larry and Helen Harp. The format of the station is urban contemporary gospel. WWSJ-AM broadcasts to the St. Johns, MI area at 1580 AM.

WWSK-FM
Owner: Connoisseur Media
Editorial: 234 Airport Plaza Blvd Ste 5, Farmingdale, New York 11735-3938.
T: 1 631 770-4200
W: http://www.943theshark.com
Editorial Profile: WWSK-FM is a commercial station owned by Connoisseur Media. The format of the station is rock music. WWSK-FM broadcasts in the greater Long Island, NY area at 94.3 FM.

WWSL-FM
Owner: HGC Inc.
Editorial: 1016 W Beacon St, Philadelphia, Mississippi 39350. **T:** 1 601 656-7102
E: wwslfm@bellsouth.net
Editorial Profile: WWSL-FM is a commercial station owned by HGC Inc. The format of the station is hot adult contemporary music. WWSL-FM broadcasts to the Philadelphia, MS area at 102.3 FM.

WWSM-AM
Owner: Sickafus, Patrick
Editorial: 621 Cumberland St, Suite 4, Lebanon, Pennsylvania 17042-8500.
T: 1 717 272-1510 **E:** wwsm2@evenlink.com
W: http://www.wwsm.us
Editorial Profile: WWSM-AM is a commercial station owned by Patrick Sickafus. The format of the station is classic country. WWSM-AM broadcasts to the Harrisburg, PA area at 1510 AM.

WWSN-FM
Owner: Cumulus Media Inc.
Editorial: 3375 Merriam St Ste 201, Muskegon, Michigan 49444-3173.
T: 1 231 830-0176 **W:** http://sunny975.com
Editorial Profile: WWSN-FM is a commercial station owned by Cumulus Media Inc. The format of the station is adult contemporary. WWSN-FM broadcasts to the Muskegon, MI area at 97.5 FM.

WWSP-FM
Owner: University of Wisconsin
Editorial: 105 CAC-UWSP Reserve St, Stevens Point, Wisconsin 54481. **T:** 1 715 346-3755
E: wwsp@uwsp.edu
W: http://www.uwsp.edu/stuorg/wwsp/
Editorial Profile: WWSP-FM is a non-commercial station owned by the University of Wisconsin. The format of the station is variety. WWSP-FM broadcasts in the Stevens Point, WI area at 89.9 FM.

WWSR-FM
Owner: Childers Media Group, LLC
Editorial: 57 Town Sq, Lima, Ohio 45801-4950. **T:** 1 419 331-1600
W: http://www.931thefan.com
Editorial Profile: WWSR-FM is a commercial station owned by Childers Media Group, LLC. The format of the station is sports. WWSR-FM broadcasts to the Lima, OH area at 93.1 FM.

WWST-FM
Owner: Journal Broadcast Group
Editorial: 1533 Amherst Rd, Knoxville, Tennessee 37909-1204. **T:** 1 865 824-1021
W: http://www.star1021fm.com
Editorial Profile: WWST-FM is a commercial station owned by Journal Broadcast Group. The format of the station is Top 40/CHR. WWST-FM broadcasts to the Knoxville, TN area at 102.1 FM.

WWSW-FM
Owner: Clear Channel Media and Entertainment
Editorial: 200 Fleet St Floor 4, Pittsburgh, Pennsylvania 15220-2908. **T:** 1 412 937-1441
E: feedback@3wsradio.com
W: http://www.3wsradio.com
Editorial Profile: WWSW-FM is a commercial station owned by Clear Channel Media and Entertainment. The format of the station is classic hits. WWSW-FM broadcasts to the Pittsburgh area at 94.5 FM.

WWTC-AM
Owner: Salem Communications
Editorial: 2110 Cliff Rd, Eagan, Minnesota 55122-3522. **T:** 1 651 405-8800
E: comments@am1280thepatriot.com
W: http://www.am1280thepatriot.com
Editorial Profile: WWTC-AM is a commercial station owned by Salem Communications. The format of the station is news and talk. WWTC-AM broadcasts to the Minneapolis area at 1280 AM.

WWTF-AM
Owner: Clear Channel Media and Entertainment
Editorial: 2601 Nicholasville Rd, Lexington, Kentucky 40503-3307. **T:** 1 859 422-1000
W: http://www.foxsports1580.com/main.html
Editorial Profile: WWTF-AM is a commercial station owned by Clear Channel Media and Entertainment. The format of the station is sports. WWTF-AM broadcasts to the Lexington, KY area at 1580 AM.

WWTH-FM
Owner: Edwards Communications LLC
Editorial: 1491 M 32 W, Alpena, Michigan 49707. **T:** 1 989 354-4611
E: sales@truenorthradionetwork.com
W: http://www.alpenanow.com
Editorial Profile: WWTH-FM is a commercial station owned by Edwards Communications LLC. The format of the station is contemporary country. WWTH-FM broadcasts to Oscoda, MI at 100.7 FM.

WWTJ-FM
Owner: Monticello Media LLC
Editorial: 1150 Pepsi Pl, Ste 300, Charlottesville, Virginia 22901.
T: 1 434 978-4408
W: http://www.1075tom.com
Editorial Profile: WWTJ-FM is a commercial station owned by Monticello Media LLC. The format of the station is news/talk. WWTJ-FM broadcasts to the Charlottesville, VA area at 107.5 FM.

WWTK-AM
Owner: Cohan Radio Group Inc.
Editorial: 3750 US Highway 27 N, Ste 1, Sebring, Florida 33870. **T:** 1 863 382-9999
E: cohanradiogroup@htn.net
W: http://www.cohanradiogroup.com
Editorial Profile: WWTK-AM is a commercial station owned by Cohan Radio Group Inc. The format of the station is news and talk. WWTK-AM broadcasts to the Sebring, FL area at 730 AM.

WWTM-AM
Owner: R & B Communications Inc.
Editorial: 1209 Danville Rd Sw Ste N, Decatur, Alabama 35601-3853. **T:** 1 256 353-1400
E: feedback@espn1400.info
W: http://www.espn1400.info
Editorial Profile: WWTM-AM is a commercial station owned by R & B Communications. The format of the station is sports. WWTM-AM broadcasts to the Decatur, AL area at 1400 AM.

WWTN-FM
Owner: Cumulus Media Inc.
Editorial: 506 2nd Ave S, Nashville, Tennessee 37210-2002. **T:** 1 615 321-1067
W: http://www.997wtn.com
Editorial Profile: WWTN-FM is a commercial station owned by Cumulus Media Inc. The format of the station is news, talk and sports. WWTN-FM broadcasts in the Nashville, TN area at 99.7 FM.

WWTR-AM
Owner: EBC Music, Inc.
Editorial: 2088 US Highway 130, Monmouth Junction, New Jersey 08852-3094.
T: 1 732 821-6009 **E:** info@ebcmusic.com
W: http://www.ebcmusic.com
Editorial Profile: WWTR-AM is a commercial station owned by EBC Music, Inc. The format of the station is variety music, news and talk; primarily ethnic Indian and South Asian programming. WWTR-AM broadcasts to the Cedar Knolls, NJ area at 1170 AM.

WWTX-AM
Owner: Clear Channel Media and Entertainment
Editorial: 920 W Basin Rd, Ste 400, New Castle, Delaware 19720. **T:** 1 302 395-9800
W: http://www.1290theticket.com
Editorial Profile: WWTX-AM is a commercial station owned by Clear Channel Media and Entertainment. The format of the station is sports talk. WWTX-AM broadcasts to the Claymont, DE area at 1290 AM.

WWUF-FM
Owner: Mattox Broadcasting Inc.
Editorial: 2132 US Highway 84, Blackshear, Georgia 31516. **T:** 1 912 449-3391
E: wkub@almatel.net
Editorial Profile: WWUF-FM is a commercial station owned by Mattox Broadcasting Inc. The format of the station is adult contemporary. WWUF-FM broadcasts to the Blackshear, GA area at 97.7 FM.

WWUH-FM
Owner: University of Hartford
Editorial: 200 Bloomfield Ave, West Hartford, Connecticut 6117. **T:** 1 860 768-4703
E: wwuh@hartford.edu
W: http://www.wwuh.org
Editorial Profile: WWUH-FM is a non-commercial station owned by University of Hartford. The format of the station is variety. WWUH-FM broadcasts to the Hartford-New Haven, CT area at 91.3 FM.

WWUS-FM
Owner: Gamma Broadcasting LLC
Editorial: 30336 Overseas Hwy, Big Pine Key, Florida 33043-3352. **T:** 1 305 872-9100
E: us1radio@us1radio.com
W: http://www.us1radio.com
Editorial Profile: WWUS-FM is a commercial station owned by Gamma Broadcasting LLC. The format of the station is classic hits. WWUS-FM broadcasts to the Big Pine Key, FL area at 104.1 FM.

WWUZ-FM
Owner: Free Lance-Star Publishing Company
Editorial: 616 Amelia St, Fredericksburg, Virginia 22401. **T:** 1 540 374-5500
W: http://www.classicrock969.com
Editorial Profile: WWUZ-FM is a commercial station owned by Free Lance-Star Publishing Company. The format of the station is classic rock music. WWUZ-FM broadcasts to the Fredericksburg, VA area at 96.9 FM.

WWVA-AM
Owner: Clear Channel Media and Entertainment
Editorial: 1015 Main St, Wheeling, West Virginia 26003. **T:** 1 304 232-1170
W: http://www.wwva.com
Editorial Profile: WWVA-AM is a commercial station owned by Clear Channel Media and Entertainment. The format of the station is news, sports and talk. WWVA-AM broadcasts to the Wheeling, WV area at 1170 AM.

WWVO-FM
Owner: Lamad Ministries Inc.
Editorial: 2416 Dawson Rd, Albany, Georgia 31707-2344. **T:** 1 229 439-1100
W: http://www.wwvothevoice.com
Editorial Profile: WWVO-FM is a non-commercial station owned by Lamad Ministries Inc. The format of the station is Christian music featuring a variety of Southern Gospel, Bluegrass and Modern Praise. WWVO-FM broadcasts to the Albany, GA area at a frequency of 90.7 FM.

WWVR-FM
Owner: Emmis Communications Corp.
Editorial: 918 Ohio St, Terre Haute, Indiana 47807-3733. **T:** 1 812 917-3901
W: http://www.1055theriver.com
Editorial Profile: WWVR-FM is a commercial station owned by Emmis Communications Corp. The format of the station is classic rock. WWVR-FM broadcasts to the Terre Haute, IN area at 105.5 FM.

WWVT-AM
Owner: Virginia Tech Foundation
Editorial: 3520 Kingsbury Cir, Roanoke, Virginia 24014. **T:** 1 540 989-8900
W: http://www.wvtf.org
Editorial Profile: WWVT-AM is a non-commercial station owned by the Virginia Tech Foundation. The format of the station is jazz, classical, news and talk. WWVT-AM broacasts to the Roanoke-Lynchburg, VA area at 1260 AM.

WWVU-FM
Owner: West Virginia University Board of Governors
Editorial: Mountain Lair Student Union WVU, Morgantown, West Virginia 26506.
T: 1 304 293-3329
E: news@taylorvilledailynews.com
W: http://u92.wvu.edu
Editorial Profile: WWVU-FM is a non-commercial station owned by West Virginia University Board of Governors. The format of the station is rock alternative music. WWVU-

FM broadcasts in the Morgantown, WV area at 91.7 FM.

WWWA-FM
Owner: Light of Life Ministries Inc.
Editorial: 160 Riverside Dr, Augusta, Maine 04330-4162. **T:** 1 207 622-1340
E: info@worshipradionetwork.org
W: http://worshipradionetwork.org
Editorial Profile: WWWA-FM is a non-commercial station owned by Light of Life Ministries Inc. The format of the station is contemporary Christian music. WWWA-FM broadcasts to the Augusta, ME, area at 95.3 FM. WFYB-FM is simulcasting from WWWA-FM.

WWWC-AM
Owner: Foothills Media, Inc.
Editorial: 413 Wilkesboro Blvd, Wilkesboro, North Carolina 28697. **T:** 1 336 838-1241
E: news@12403wc.com
W: http://www.12403wc.com
Editorial Profile: WWWC-AM is a commercial station owned by Foothills Media, Inc. The format of the station is gospel and religion. WWWC-AM broadcasts to the Wilkesboro, NC area at 1240 AM.

WWWE-AM
Owner: Beasley Broadcast Group
Editorial: 1465 Northside Dr Nw Ste 218, Atlanta, Georgia 30318-4239.
T: 1 404 352-9993
W: http://www.1100espndeportes.com
Editorial Profile: WWWE-AM is a commercial station owned by Beasley Broadcast Group. The format of the station is sports. The station airs ESPN Deportes from 4pm to 7pm. WWWE-AM broadcasts to the Atlanta area at 1100 AM.

WWWH-AM
Owner: AMS Radio LLC
Editorial: 1411 Soaring Trl, Marietta, Georgia 30062-3280. **T:** 1 404 386-9792
Editorial Profile: WWWH-AM is a commercial station owned by AMS Radio LLC. The format of the station is southern gospel music. WJBB-AM broadcasts to the Haleyville, AL area at 1230 AM.

WWWH-FM
Owner: AMS Radio LLC
Editorial: 1411 Soaring Trl, Marietta, Georgia 30062-3280. **T:** 1 404 386-9792
Editorial Profile: WWWH-FM is a commercial station owned by AMS Radio LLC. The format of the station is Hot AC. WWWH-FM broadcasts to the Haleyville, AL area at 92.7 FM.

WWWI-AM
Owner: Tower Broadcasting Corp.
Editorial: 305 W Washington St, Brainerd, Minnesota 56401-2923. **T:** 1 218 828-9994
E: talk@3wiradio.com
W: http://www.3wiradio.com
Editorial Profile: WWWI-AM is a commercial station owned by Tower Broadcasting Corp. The format of the station is news, sports and talk programming. WWWI-AM broadcasts to the Brainerd, MN area at 1270 AM.

WWWI-FM
Owner: Tower Broadcasting Corp.
Editorial: 305 W Washington St, Brainerd, Minnesota 56401-2923. **T:** 1 218 828-9994
E: talk@3wiradio.com
W: http://www.3wiradio.com
Editorial Profile: WWWI-FM is a commercial station owned by Tower Broadcasting Corp. The format of the station is news and talk. WWWI-FM broadcasts to the Brainerd, MN area at 95.9 FM.

WWWJ-AM
Owner: Twin County Broadcasting Corp.
Editorial: 325 Poplar Knob Rd, Galax, Virginia 24333-4106. **T:** 1 276 236-2921
Editorial Profile: WWWJ-AM is a commercial station owned by Twin County Broadcasting Corporation. The format of the station is southern gospel. WWWJ-AM broadcasts to the Galax, VA area at 1360 AM.

WWWL-AM
Owner: Entercom Communications Corp.
Editorial: 400 Poydras St Ste 800, New Orleans, Louisiana 70130-3789.
T: 1 504 593-6376
Editorial Profile: WWWL-AM is a commercial station owned by Entercom Communications Corp. The format of the station is talk and sports. WWWL-AM broadcasts to the New Orleans area at 1350 AM.

WWWM-FM
Owner: Cumulus Media Inc.
Editorial: 3225 Arlington Ave, Toledo, Ohio 43614-2427. **T:** 1 419 725-5700
W: http://www.star105toledo.com
Editorial Profile: WWWM-FM is a commercial station owned by Cumulus Media Inc. The format of the station is Top 40. WWWM-FM broadcasts to the Toledo, OH area at 105.5 FM.

WWWQ-FM
Owner: Cumulus Media Inc.
Editorial: 780 Johnson Ferry Rd NE, Fl 5, Atlanta, Georgia 30342. **T:** 1 404 497-4700
W: http://www.q100atlanta.com
Editorial Profile: WWWQ-FM is a commercial station owned by Cumulus Media Inc. The format of the station is Top 40/CHR. WWWQ-FM broadcasts to the Atlanta area at 99.1 FM.

WWWS-AM
Owner: Entercom Communications Corp.
Editorial: 500 Corporate Pkwy, Ste 200, Buffalo, New York 14226. **T:** 1 716 843-0600
W: http://www.am1400solidgoldsoul.com
Editorial Profile: WWWS-AM is a commercial station owned by Entercom Communications Corp. The format of the station is R&B oldies. WWWS-AM broadcasts to the Buffalo, NY area at 1400 AM.

WWWT-FM
Owner: Hubbard Broadcasting, Inc.
Editorial: 3400 Idaho Ave NW, Washington, District Of Columbia 20016.
T: 1 202 895-5000
W: http://www.wtopnews.com
Editorial Profile: WWWT-FM is a commercial station owned by Hubbard Broadcasting, Inc. The format of the station is news. WWWT-FM broadcasts to the Washington, D.C. area at 107.7 FM.

WWWV-FM
Owner: Saga Communications
Editorial: 1140 Rose Hill Dr, Charlottesville, Virginia 22903. **T:** 1 434 220-2300
W: http://www.3wv.com
Editorial Profile: WWWV-FM is a commercial station owned by the Saga Communications. The format for the station is classic rock. WWWV-FM broadcasts to the Charlottesville, VA area at 97.5 FM.

WWWW-FM
Owner: Cumulus Media Inc.
Editorial: 1100 Victors Way, Ste 100, Ann Arbor, Michigan 48108-5220.
T: 1 734 302-8100
E: programming@w4country.com
W: http://www.w4country.com
Editorial Profile: WWWW-FM is a commercial station owned by Cumulus Media Inc. The format of the station is classic country. WWWW-FM broadcasts to the Ann Arbor, MI area at 102.9 FM.

WWWX-FM
Owner: Cumulus Media Inc.
Editorial: 491 S Washburn St Ste 400, Oshkosh, Wisconsin 54904-6733.
T: 1 920 426-3239 **W:** http://www.fox969.com
Editorial Profile: WWWX-FM is a commercial station owned by Cumulus Media Inc. The format of the station is modern rock. WWWX-FM broadcasts to the Green Bay, WI area at 96.9 FM.

WWWY-FM
Owner: White River Broadcasting Co., Inc.
Editorial: 3212 Washington St, Columbus, Indiana 47203-1505. **T:** 1 812 372-4448
W: http://www.1061theriver.com
Editorial Profile: WWWY-FM is a commercial station owned by White River Broadcasting Co., Inc. The format of the station is classic hits. WWWY-FM broadcasts to the Columbus, IN area at 106.1 FM.

WWWZ-FM
Owner: Cumulus Media Inc.
Editorial: 4230 Faber Place Dr Ste 100, North Charleston, South Carolina 29405-8512.
T: 1 843 277-1200
W: http://www.z93jamz.com
Editorial Profile: WWWZ-FM is a commercial station owned by Cumulus Media Inc. The format of the station is urban contemporary. WWWZ-FM broadcasts to the Charleston, SC area at 93.3 FM.

WWXL-AM
Owner: Nolan (Juanita H.)
Editorial: 103 3rd St, Manchester, Kentucky 40962. **T:** 1 606 598-2319
Editorial Profile: WWXL-AM is a commercial station owned by Juanita H. Nolan. The format of the station is talk, sports and news. WWXL-AM broadcasts to the Manchester, KY area at 1450 AM.

WWXM-FM
Owner: Clear Channel Media and Entertainment
Editorial: 4841 Highway 17 Byp S, Myrtle Beach, South Carolina 29577-6683.
T: 1 843 293-0107
W: http://mix977online.com
Editorial Profile: WWXM-FM is a commercial station owned by Clear Channel Media and Entertainment. The format of the station is Top 40/CHR. WWXM-FM broadcasts to the Myrtle Beach, SC area at 97.7 FM.

WWXT-FM
Owner: Red Zebra Broadcasting
Editorial: 1801 Rockville Pike, Rockville, Maryland 20852-1633. **T:** 1 301 230-3500
E: redskinsradio@redskins.com
W: http://www.espn980.com
Editorial Profile: WWXT-FM is a commercial station owned by Red Zebra Broadcasting. The format of the station is sports. WWXT-FM broadcasts to the Washington, D.C. area at 92.7 FM.

WWXX-FM
Owner: Red Zebra Broadcasting
Editorial: 1801 Rockville Pike Ste 405, Rockville, Maryland 20852-5604.
T: 1 301 230-3500
E: management@espn980.com
W: http://www.espn980.com
Editorial Profile: WWXX-FM is a commercial station owned by Red Zebra Broadcasting. The format of the station is sports. WWXX-FM broadcasts to the Warrenton, VA area at 94.3 FM.

WWYL-FM
Owner: Townsquare Media, Inc.
Editorial: 59 Court St, Binghamton, New York 13901-3270. **T:** 1 607 772-8400
W: http://www.wild104fm.com
Editorial Profile: WWYL-FM is a commercial station owned by Townsquare Media, Inc. The format of the station is Top 40/CHR. WWYL-FM broadcasts to the Binghamton, NY area at a frequency of 104.1 FM.

WWYN-FM
Owner: Southern Stone Communications, LLC
Editorial: 111 W Main St, Jackson, Tennessee 38301-6147. **T:** 1 731 427-9616
W: http://jacksonnewsnow.com
Editorial Profile: WWYN-FM is a commercial station owned by Southern Stone Communications, LLC. The format of the station is classic country. WWYN-FM broadcasts to the Jackson, TN area at 106.9 FM.

WWYO-AM
Owner: Jennings(Rudolph D.)
Editorial: 608 College Ave, Bluefield, West Virginia 24701. **T:** 1 304 327-5651
E: wwyo970am@frontier.com
Editorial Profile: WWYO-AM is a commercial station owned by Rudolph D. Jennings. The format of the station is full service and variety. WWYO-AM broadcasts in the the Bluefield, WV area at 970 AM.

WWYY-FM
Owner: Connoisseur Media
Editorial: 22 S 6th St, Stroudsburg, Pennsylvania 18360-2002. **T:** 1 570 421-2100
W: http://www.107thebone.fm
Editorial Profile: WWYY-FM is a commercial station owned by Connoisseur Media. The format of the station is rock music. WWYY-FM broadcasts to the Stroudsburg, PA area at 107.1 FM.

WWYZ-FM
Owner: Clear Channel Media and Entertainment
Editorial: 10 Columbus Blvd, 1st floor, Hartford, Connecticut 6106.
T: 1 860 723-6000
W: http://www.country925.com
Editorial Profile: WWYZ-FM is a commercial station owned by Clear Channel Media and Entertainment. The format of the station is country music. WWYZ-FM broadcasts to the Hartford, CT area at 92.5 FM.

WWZD-FM
Owner: URBan Radio Broadcasting, LLC
Editorial: 5026 Cliff Gookin Blvd, Tupelo, Mississippi 38801. **T:** 1 662 842-1067
W: http://www.wizard106.com
Editorial Profile: WWZD-FM is a commercial station owned by URBan Radio Broadcasting, LLC. The format of the station is country. WWZD-FM broadcasts to the Tupelo, MS area at 106.7 FM.

WWZQ-AM
Owner: Stanford Communications Inc.
Editorial: 1053 S Meridian St, Aberdeen, Mississippi 39730. **T:** 1 662 369-4561
E: fm95@fm95radio.com
W: http://www.fm95radio.com
Editorial Profile: WWZQ-AM is a commercial station owned by Stanford Communications Inc. The format of the station is news, talk and sports. WWZQ-AM broadcasts to the Aberdeen, MS area at 1240 AM.

WWZW-FM
Owner: First Media Radio LLC
Editorial: 392 E Midland Trl, Lexington, Virginia 24450-5703. **T:** 1 540 463-2161
E: news@wrel.com **W:** http://www.3wzfm.com
Editorial Profile: WWZW-FM is a commercial station owned by First Media Radio LLC. The format of the station is classic hits. WWZW-FM broadcast to the Lexington, VA area at 96.7 FM.

WWZY-FM
Owner: Press Communications LLC
Editorial: 2355 W Bangs Ave, Neptune, New Jersey 07753-4111. **T:** 1 732 774-4755
W: http://www.breezeradio.com
Editorial Profile: WWZY-FM is a commercial station owned by Press Communications LLC. The format of the station is adult contemporary. WWZY-FM broadcasts to the Neptune, NJ area at 107.1 FM.

WXAJ-FM
Owner: Neuhoff Family Limited Partnership
Editorial: 3055 S 4Th St, Springfield, Illinois 62703-4009. **T:** 1 217 528-3033
W: http://www.997kissfm.com
Editorial Profile: WXAJ-FM is a commercial station owned by Neuhoff Family Limited Partnership. The format of the station is Top 40/CHR. WXAJ-FM broadcasts to the Springfield, IL area at 99.7 FM.

WXAM-AM
Owner: Commonwealth Broadcasting Corp.
Editorial: 611 W Poplar St Ste C2, Elizabethtown, Kentucky 42701-2483.
T: 1 270 358-4707
E: news@commonwealthbroadcasting.com
W: http://espnradio1430.net
Editorial Profile: WXAM-AM is a commercial station owned by Commonwealth Broadcasting Corp. The format for the station is sports. WXAM-AM broadcasts to the Elizabethtown, KY area at 1430 AM.

WXAN-FM
Owner: Southern Gospetality LLC
Editorial: 9077 Ava Rd, Ava, Illinois 62907.
T: 1 618 426-3308 **E:** wxangm@yahoo.com
W: http://www.mysoutherngospel.net
Editorial Profile: WXAN-FM is a commercial station owned by Southern Gospetality LLC. The format of the station is Christian programming. WXAN-FM broadcasts to the Ava, IL area at 103.9 FM.

WXBB-FM
Owner: Connoisseur Media LLC
Editorial: 1 Boston Store Pl, Erie, Pennsylvania 16501. **T:** 1 814 461-1000
W: http://www.947bobfm.com
Editorial Profile: WXBB-FM is a commercial station owned by Connoisseur Media LLC. The format of the station is Jack FM - adult hits. WXBB-FM broadcasts to the Erie, PA area at 94.7 FM.

WXBC-FM
Owner: Breckinridge Broadcasting
Editorial: 110 S Main St, Hardinsburg, Kentucky 40143-2653. **T:** 1 270 756-1043
E: wxbc@bbtel.com
W: http://www.wxbc1043.com
Editorial Profile: WXBC-FM is a commercial station owned by Breckinridge Broadcasting, Inc. The format for the station is country. WXBC-FM broadcasts to the Hardinsburg, KY area at 104.3 FM. The target audience of the station is listeners ages 18 to 54.

WXBD-AM
Owner: L & L Radio
Editorial: 1909 E Pass Rd Ste D11, Gulfport, Mississippi 39507-3778. **T:** 1 228 388-2001
Editorial Profile: WXBD-AM is a commercial station owned by L & L Radio. The format for the station is sports. WXBD-AM broadcasts to the Biloxi-Gulfport, MS area at 1490 AM.

WXBM-FM
Owner: Cumulus Media Inc.
Editorial: 6085 Quintette Rd, Pace, Florida 32571-6759. **T:** 1 850 994-5357
E: communityannouncement@wxbm.com
W: http://www.wxbm.com
Editorial Profile: WXBM-FM is a commercial station owned by Cumulus Media Inc. The format for the station is contemporary country. WXBM-FM broadcasts to the Pace, FL area at 102.7 FM.

WXBN-FM
Owner: Centennial Broadcasting
Editorial: 520 N Pleasant Valley Rd, Winchester, Virginia 22601. **T:** 1 540 667-2224
W: http://www.rockthebone.com
Editorial Profile: WXBN-FM is a commercial station owned by Centennial Broadcasting. The format of the station is rock music. WXBN-FM broadcasts in the Winchester, VA area at 105.5 FM.

WXBQ-FM
Owner: Bristol Broadcasting
Editorial: 901 E Valley Dr, Bristol, Virginia 24201-4913. **T:** 1 276 669-8112
E: news@wxbq.com **W:** http://www.wxbq.com
Editorial Profile: WXBQ-FM is a commercial station owned by Bristol Broadcasting. The format of the station is classic country. WXBQ-FM broadcasts to the Bristol, VA area at 96.9 FM.

WXBT-AM
Owner: Clear Channel Media and Entertainment
Editorial: 316 Greystone Blvd, Columbia, South Carolina 29210. **T:** 1 803 343-1100
W: http://www.560theteam.com
Editorial Profile: WXBT-AM is a commercial station owned by Clear Channel Media and Entertainment. The format of the station is sports. WXBT-AM broadcasts to the Columbia, SC area at 560 AM.

WXBW-FM
Owner: Fifth Avenue Broadcasting Company
Editorial: 919 5th Ave, Ste 210, Huntington, West Virginia 25701. **T:** 1 304 399-9603
W: http://www.bigbuck1015.com
Editorial Profile: WXBW-FM is a commercial station owned by Fifth Avenue Broadcasting Company. The format of the station is contemporary country. WXBW-FM broadcasts to Huntington, WV and surrounding communities at 101.5 FM.

WXBX-FM
Owner: Three Rivers Media Corp.
Editorial: 110 W Spiller St, Wytheville, Virginia 24382-1952. **T:** 1 276 228-3185
E: office@threeriversmedia.net
W: http://www.wxbx.com
Editorial Profile: WXBX-FM is a commercial station owned by Three Rivers Media Corp. The format of the station is oldies. WXBX-FM broadcasts to the Wytheville, VA area at 95.3 FM.

WXCC-FM
Owner: East Kentucky Radio Network
Editorial: 1240 Radio Dr, Pikeville, Kentucky 41501-4779. **T:** 1 606 437-4051
E: frontdesk@ekbradio.com
W: http://www.wxccfm.com
Editorial Profile: WXCC-FM is a commercial station owned by East Kentucky Radio Network. The format of the station is country. WXCC-FM broadcasts to the Pikeville, KY area at 96.5 FM.

WXCE-AM
Owner: Red Rock Radio Corp.
Editorial: 328 100Th St, Amery, Wisconsin 54001-4024. **T:** 1 715 268-7185
E: info@radio715.com **W:** http://radio715.com
Editorial Profile: WXCE-AM is a commercial station owned by Red Rock Radio Corp. The format of the station is adult standards. WXCE-AM broadcasts in the Amery, WI area at 1260 AM.

WXCH-FM
Owner: Reising Radio Partners Inc.
Editorial: 825 Washington St, Columbus, Indiana 47201-6265. **T:** 1 812 379-1077
W: http://www.mojo1029.com
Editorial Profile: WXCH-FM is a commercial station owned by Reising Radio Partners Inc. The format of the station is classic hits. WXCH-FM broadcasts to Aurora, IN at 102.9 FM.

WXCI-FM
Owner: Western Connecticut State University
Editorial: 181 White St, Danbury, Connecticut 6810. **T:** 1 203 837-8387
W: http://clubs.wcsu.edu/wxci
Editorial Profile: WXCI-FM is a non-commercial station owned by Western Connecticut State University. The format of the station is rock alternative music. WXCI-FM broadcasts to Western Connecticut State University and the surrounding community at 91.7 FM.

WXCL-FM
Owner: L & L Radio
Editorial: 331 Fulton St, Peoria, Illinois 61602-1486. **T:** 1 309 637-3700
E: news@1470wmbd.com
W: http://www.1049thewolf.com
Editorial Profile: WXCL-FM is a commercial station owned by L & L Radio. The format of the station is contemporary country music. WXCL-FM broadcasts in the Peoria, IL, area at 104.9 FM.

WXCM-FM
Owner: Cromwell Group Inc.(The)
Editorial: 1115 Tamarack Rd, Owensboro, Kentucky 42301-6984. **T:** 1 270 683-5200
W: http://www.owensbororadio.com
Editorial Profile: WXCM-FM is a commercial station owned by The Cromwell Group Inc. The format of the station is rock music. WXCM-FM broadcasts to the Evansville, IN area at 97.1 FM.

WXCO-AM
Owner: Sunrise Broadcasting, LLC
Editorial: 1110 E Wausau Ave, Wausau, Wisconsin 54403-3149. **T:** 1 715 845-8218
W: http://www.1230wxco.com
Editorial Profile: WXCO-AM is a commercial station owned by Sunrise Broadcasting, LLC. The format of the station is adult standards. WXCO-AM broadcasts in the Wausau, WI area at 1230 AM.

WXCR-FM
Owner: Seven Ranges Radio Company Inc.
Editorial: Greens Run Road, Saint Marys, West Virginia 26170. **T:** 1 304 684-3400
W: http://www.literock93r.com
Editorial Profile: WXCR-FM is a commercial station owned by Seven Ranges Radio Company Inc. The format of the station is classic rock. The station broadcasts to the Saint Mary's, VA area at 92.3 FM.

WXCT-AM
Owner: Davidson Media Group
Editorial: 440 Old Turnpike Rd, Southington, Connecticut 6489. **T:** 1 860 621-1754
W: http://wsprpower1270.com
Editorial Profile: WXCT-AM is a commercial station owned by Davidson Media Group. The format of the station is Spanish Tropical music. WXCT-AM broadcasts to the Hartford-New Haven, CT area at 990 AM.

WXCV-FM
Owner: WXOF, Inc.
Editorial: 4554 S Suncoast Blvd, Homosassa, Florida 34446-1103. **T:** 1 352 628-4444
W: http://www.citrus953.com
Editorial Profile: WXCV-FM is a commercial station owned by WXOF, Inc. The format of the station is hot adult contemporary music. WXCV-FM broadcasts in the Homosassa, FL area at 95.3 FM.

WXCX-FM
Owner: Red Rock Radio Corp.
Editorial: 15429 Pokegama Lake Rd, Pine City, Minnesota 55063-4592. **T:** 1 888 629-7575
E: jesselogan@redrockonair.com
W: http://www.redrockonair.com
Editorial Profile: WXCX-FM is a commercial station owned by Red Rock Radio Corp. The format of the station is adult hits. WXCX-FM broadcasts to the Minneapolis area at 105.7 FM.

WXCY-FM
Owner: Delmarva Broadcasting
Editorial: 707 Revolution St, Havre de Grace, Maryland 21078-3321. **T:** 1 410 939-1100
W: http://www.wxcyfm.com
Editorial Profile: WXCY-FM is a commercial station owned by Delmarva Broadcasting. The format of the station is country music. WXCY-FM broadcasts to the Baltimore, MD area at 103.7 FM.

WXDE-FM
Owner: Delmarva Broadcasting
Editorial: 1666 Blairs Pond Rd, Milford, Delaware 19963-5263. **T:** 1 302 422-7575
E: news@delaware1059.com
W: http://www.delaware1059.com
Editorial Profile: WXDE-FM is a commercial station owned by Delmarva Broadcasting. The format of the station is news talk. WXDE-FM broadcasts to the Salisbury, MD area at 105.9 FM.

WXDJ-FM
Owner: Spanish Broadcasting System
Editorial: 7007 NW 77th Ave, Miami, Florida 33166-2836. **T:** 1 305 447-9595
W: http://elzol.com
Editorial Profile: WXDJ-FM is a commercial station owned by Spanish Broadcasting System. The format of the station is Spanish tropical. WXDJ-FM broadcasts to the Miami, FL area at 106.7 FM.

WXDU-FM
Owner: Duke University
Editorial: 101 Bivins Bldg, Durham, North Carolina 27708-0001. **T:** 1 919 684-2957
E: news@wxdu.org **W:** http://www.wxdu.org
Editorial Profile: WXDU-FM is a non-commercial station owned by Duke University. The format of the station is college variety. WXDU-FM broadcasts to the Durham, NC area at 88.7 FM.

WXDX-FM
Owner: Clear Channel Media and Entertainment
Editorial: 200 Fleet St Floor 4, Pittsburgh, Pennsylvania 15220-2908. **T:** 1 412 937-1441
W: http://www.1059thex.com
Editorial Profile: WXDX-FM is a commercial station owned by Clear Channel Media and Entertainment. The format of the station rock alternative. WXDX-FM broadcasts to the Pittsburgh area at 105.9 FM.

WXEF-FM
Owner: Premier Broadcasting
Editorial: 206 S Willow St, Effingham, Illinois 62401-3637. **T:** 1 217 347-5518
E: info@thexradio.com
W: http://www.thexradio.com
Editorial Profile: WXEF-FM is a commercial station owned by Premier Broadcasting. The format of the station is hot adult contemporary music. WXEF-FM broadcasts in the Effingham, IL area at 97.9 FM.

WXEG-FM
Owner: Clear Channel Media and Entertainment
Editorial: 101 Pine St, Dayton, Ohio 45402. **T:** 1 937 224-1137 **W:** http://www.wxeg.com
Editorial Profile: WXEG-FM is a commercial station owned by Clear Channel Media and Entertainment. The format of the station is rock alternative music. WXEG-FM broadcasts to the Dayton, OH area at 103.9 FM.

WXEM-AM
Owner: La Favorita Inc.
Editorial: 5815 Westside Rd, Austell, Georgia 30106-3179. **T:** 1 770 944-0900
E: traffic@lamejorestacion.com
W: http://www.lamejorestacion.com
Editorial Profile: WXEM-AM is a commercial station owned by La Favorita Inc. The format of the station is regional Mexican music. WXEM-AM broadcasts to the Austell, GA area at 1460 AM.

WXER-FM
Owner: Midwest Communications Inc.
Editorial: 2100 Washington Ave, Sheboygan, Wisconsin 53081. **T:** 1 920 458-2107
W: http://www.wxerfm.com
Editorial Profile: WXER-FM is a commercial station owned by Midwest Communications Inc. The format of the station is hot adult contemporary music. WXER-FM broadcasts to the Sheboygan, WI area at 104.5 FM.

WXFL-FM
Owner: Big River Broadcasting Corp.
Editorial: 624 Sam Phillips St, Florence, Alabama 35630. **T:** 1 256 764-8121
W: http://www.kix96country.com/
Editorial Profile: WXFL-FM is a commercial station owned by Big River Broadcasting Corp. The format of the station is country. WXFL-FM broadcasts to the Florence, AL area at 96.1 FM.

WXFM-FM
Owner: Technicom Inc.
Editorial: 120 W Wildwood Dr, Mount Zion, Illinois 62549-1151. **T:** 1 217 864-4141
E: wxfmwdkr@comcast.net
Editorial Profile: WXFM-FM is a commercial station owned by Technicom Inc. The format of the station is hot adult contemporary. WXFM-FM broadcasts to the Mt. Zion, IL area at 99.3 FM.

WXFN-AM
Owner: Backyard Broadcasting
Editorial: 800 E 29th St, Muncie, Indiana 47302. **T:** 1 765 288-4403 **W:** http://wxfn.com
Editorial Profile: WXFN-AM is a commercial station owned by Backyard Broadcasting. The format of the station is sports. WXFN broadcasts in the Muncie, IN area at 1340 AM.

WXFX-FM
Owner: Cumulus Media Inc.
Editorial: 1 Commerce St, Ste 300, Montgomery, Alabama 36104.
T: 1 334 240-9274 **W:** http://www.wxfx.com
Editorial Profile: WXFX-FM is a commercial station owned by Cumulus Media Inc. The format of the station is classic and rock/album-oriented rock. WXFX-FM broadcasts to the Montgomery, AL area at 95.1 FM.

WXGI-AM
Owner: Red Zebra Broadcasting
Editorial: 701 German School Rd, Richmond, Virginia 23225. **T:** 1 804 233-7666
E: espn950am@redskins.com
W: http://www.espn950am.com
Editorial Profile: WXGI-AM is a commercial station owned by Red Zebra Broadcasting. The format of the station is sports. WXGI-AM broadcasts to the Washington, D.C. area at 950 AM.

WXGL-FM
Owner: Cox Media Group, Inc.
Editorial: 11300 4th St N Ste 300, Saint Petersburg, Florida 33716-2941.
T: 1 727 577-7131
E: 1073comments@coxtampa.com
W: http://www.1073theeagle.com
Editorial Profile: WXGL-FM is a commercial station owned by Cox Media Group, Inc. The format of the station is classic hits. WXGL-FM broadcasts to the Saint Petersburg, FL area at 107.3 FM.

WXGM-AM
Owner: WXGM Inc.
Editorial: 6267 Professional Dr, Gloucester, Virginia 23061. **T:** 1 804 693-2105
E: office@xtra99.com
W: http://www.xtra99.com
Editorial Profile: WXGM-AM is a commercial station owned by WXGM Inc. The format of the station is oldies. WXGM-AM broadcasts to the Gloucester, VA area at 1420 AM.

WXGM-FM
Owner: WXGM Inc.
Editorial: 6267 Professional Dr, Gloucester, Virginia 23061-4454. **T:** 1 804 693-2105
E: news@xtra99.com
W: http://www.xtra99.com
Editorial Profile: WXGM-FM is a commercial station owned by WXGM Inc. The format of the station is adult contemporary. WXGM-FM broadcasts to the Gloucester, VA area at 99.1 FM.

WXGO-AM
Owner: DCBroadcasting Inc.
Editorial: 1224 E Telegraph Hill Rd, Madison, Indiana 47250-9273. **T:** 1 812 265-3322
E: thebestmusic@worxradio.com
W: http://www.worxradio.com
Editorial Profile: WXGO-AM is a commercial station owned by DCBroadcasting Inc. The format of the station is oldies. WXGO-AM broadcasts to the Madison, IN area at 1270 AM.

WXHB-FM
Owner: Blakeney Communications Inc.
Editorial: 4580 Highway 15 N, Laurel, Mississippi 39440. **T:** 1 601 544-0095
E: wxhb@wxhbfm.com **W:** http://wxhbfm.com
Editorial Profile: WXHB-FM s a commercial station owned by Blakeney Communications Inc. The format is gospel. The station airs in the Laurel, MS area at 96.5FM.

WXHC-FM
Owner: Eves Broadcasting Inc.
Editorial: 12 S Main St, Homer, New York 13077-1327. **T:** 1 607 749-9942
E: prod@wxhc.com **W:** http://www.wxhc.com
Editorial Profile: WXHC-FM is a commercial station owned by Eves Broadcasting Inc. The format of the station is oldies. WXHC-FM broadcasts to the Homer, NY area at 101.5 FM.

WXHT-FM
Owner: Black Crow Broadcasting Inc.
Editorial: 1711 Ellis Dr, Valdosta, Georgia 31601. **T:** 1 229 249-8200
W: http://www.hot1027.fm

Editorial Profile: WXHT-FM is a commercial station owned by Black Crow Broadcasting Inc. The format of the station is Top 40/CHR. WXHT-FM broadcasts to the Valdosta, GA area at 102.7 FM.

WXIC-AM
Owner: Crystal Communications Corp.
Editorial: 6655 State Route 220, Waverly, Ohio 45690-8987. **T:** 1 740 947-7660
E: wxic@roadrunner.com
W: http://am660-wxic.com
Editorial Profile: WXIC-AM is a commercial station owned by Crystal Communications Corp. The format of the station is Southern gospel and Christian music. WXIC-AM broadcasts to Columbus, OH, at 660 AM.

WXIL-FM
Owner: Burbach of WV, LLC
Editorial: 5 Rosemar Cir, Parkersburg, West Virginia 26104. **T:** 1 304 485-4565
E: productionparkersburg@resultsradiowv.com

WXIS-FM
Owner: WEMB Inc.
Editorial: 101 Riverview Rd, Erwin, Tennessee 37650. **T:** 1 423 743-6123
W: http://923jamzfm.com
Editorial Profile: WXIS-FM is a commercial station owned by WEMB Inc. The format of the station is rhythmic Top 40/CHR. WXIS-FM broadcasts to the Erwin, TN area at 103.9 FM.

WXIT-AM
Owner: High Country Adventures, LLC
Editorial: 738 Blowing Rock Rd, Boone, North Carolina 28607-4835. **T:** 1 828 264-2411
W: http://www.goblueridge.net
Editorial Profile: WXIT-AM is a commercial station owned by High Country Adventures, LLC, a subsidiary of Curtis Media Group. The format of the station is news and talk. WXIT-AM broadcasts to the Boone, NC area at 1200 AM.

WXIZ-FM
Owner: Crystal Communications Corp.
Editorial: 6655 State Route 220, Waverly, Ohio 45690-8987. **T:** 1 740 947-7660
E: wxiz@roadrunner.com
W: http://www.wxiz.com
Editorial Profile: WXIZ-FM is a commercial station owned by Crystal Communications Corp. The format of the station is contemporary country music. WXIZ-FM broadcasts to the Waverly, OH, area at 100.9 FM.

WXJC-AM
Owner: Crawford Broadcasting Co.
Editorial: 120 Summit Pkwy, Ste 200, Homewood, Alabama 35209.
T: 1 205 879-3324 **W:** http://850wxjc.com
Editorial Profile: WXJC-AM is a commercial station owned by Crawford Broadcasting Co. The format of the station is Christian teaching, talk and Southern gospel programming. WXJC-AM broadcasts to the Birmingham, AL area at 850 AM.

WXJC-FM
Owner: Crawford Broadcasting Co.
Editorial: 120 Summit Pkwy, Ste 200, Birmingham, Alabama 35209-4719.
T: 1 205 879-3324 **W:** http://850wxjc.com
Editorial Profile: WXJC-FM is a commercial station owned by Crawford Broadcasting Co. The format of the station is Christian teaching, talk and Southern gospel. WXJC-FM broadcasts to the Birmingham, AL, area at 92.5 FM.

WXJK-FM
Owner: Layne(David)
Editorial: 31 Edgewood Drive Ext, Farmville, Virginia 23901-4044. **T:** 1 434 392-9955

WXJO-AM
Owner: Monte Sinai, Inc.
Editorial: 6174 Ga Highway 57, Macon, Georgia 31217-3405. **T:** 1 770 920-1520
E: wordchr@bellsouth.net
W: http://www.wordchristianbroadcasting.com
Editorial Profile: WXJO-AM will become a non-commercial station owned by Monte Sinai, Inc. in early 2012. The format of the station is Hispanic religious programming. WXJO-AM broadcasts to the Douglasville, GA area at 1120 AM.

WXJY-FM
Owner: Cumulus Media Inc.
Editorial: 11640 Highway 17 Byp, Murrells Inlet, South Carolina 29576-9332.
T: 1 843 651-7869 **W:** http://www.i100fm.com

Editorial Profile: WXJY-FM is a commercial station owned by Cumulus Media Inc. The format of the station is sports. WXJY-FM broadcasts to the Murrells Inlet, SC area at 93.7 FM.

WXJZ-FM
Owner: JVC Broadcasting Inc.
Editorial: 4424 NW 13th St Ste C5, Gainesville, Florida 32609-1881.
T: 1 352 375-1317
W: http://www.floridasparty.com
Editorial Profile: WXJZ-FM is a commercial station owned by JVC Broadcasting Inc. The format of the station is Rhythmic-CHR. WXJZ-FM broadcasts in the Gainesville, FL area at 100.9 FM.

WXKB-FM
Owner: Beasley Broadcast Group
Editorial: 20125 S Tamiami Trl, Estero, Florida 33928-2117. **T:** 1 239 495-2100
W: http://www.b1039.com
Editorial Profile: WXKB-FM is a commercial station owned by Beasley Broadcast Group. The format of the station is Top 40/CHR. WXKB-FM broadcasts to the Fort Meyers, FL area at 103.9 FM.

WXKC-FM
Owner: Cumulus Media Inc.
Editorial: 471 Robison Rd, Erie, Pennsylvania 16509-5425. **T:** 1 814 868-5355
W: http://www.classy100.com
Editorial Profile: WXKC-FM is a commercial station owned by Cumulus Media Inc. The format of the station is adult contemporary. WXKC-FM broadcasts to the Erie, PA area at 99.9 FM.

WXKE-FM
Owner: Adams Radio Group
Editorial: 9604 Coldwater Rd Ste 201, Fort Wayne, Indiana 46825-2096.
T: 1 260 747-1511
Editorial Profile: WXKE-FM is a commercial station owned by Adams Radio Group. The format of the station is classic rock music. WXKE-FM broadcasts to the Fort Wayne, IN area at 96.3 FM.

WXKL-AM
Owner: Thomas(James)
Editorial: 1516 Woodland Ave, Sanford, North Carolina 27330-5652. **T:** 1 919 774-1080
E: wxkl1290radio@yahoo.com
Editorial Profile: WXKL-AM is a commercial station owned by James Thomas. The format of the station is gospel and Hispanic programming. WXKL-AM broadcasts to the Sanford, NC area at 1290 AM.

WXKO-AM
Owner: Sun Broadcasting, Inc.
Editorial: 1023 Ball St, Perry, Georgia 31069-3307. **T:** 1 478 987-1823
Editorial Profile: WXKO-AM is a commercial station owned by Sun Broadcasting, Inc. The format of the station is country. WXKO-AM broadcasts to Fort Valley, GA area at a frequency of 1150 AM.

WXKQ-FM
Owner: Forcht Broadcasting
Editorial: 1149 Hwy 1862, Mayking, Kentucky 41837. **T:** 1 606 633-4434
E: wxkq@yahoo.com
W: http://www.1039thebulldog.com
Editorial Profile: WXKQ-FM is a commercial station owned by Forcht Broadcasting. The format of the station is classic country WXKQ-FM broadcasts to the Mayking, KY area at 103.9 FM.

WXKR-FM
Owner: Cumulus Media Inc.
Editorial: 3225 Arlington Ave, Toledo, Ohio 43614-2427. **T:** 1 419 725-5700
W: http://www.wxkr.com
Editorial Profile: WXKR-FM is a commercial station owned by Cumulus Media Inc. The format of the station is classic rock. WXKR-FM broadcasts to the Toledo, OH area at 94.5 FM.

WXKS-AM
Owner: Clear Channel Media and Entertainment
Editorial: 10 Cabot Rd, Medford, Massachusetts 02155-5177.
T: 1 781 396-1430
W: http://www.bloomberg.com/radio
Editorial Profile: WXKS-AM is a commercial station owned by Clear Channel Media and Entertainment. The format of the station is business news. WXKS-AM broadcasts to the

Medford, MA area at 1200 AM. The station airs WBBR-AM's programming.

WXKS-FM
Owner: Clear Channel Media and Entertainment
Editorial: 10 Cabot Rd Ste 302, Medford, Massachusetts 02155-5173.
T: 1 781 396-1430 **E:** press@kiss108.com
W: http://www.kiss108.com
Editorial Profile: WXKS-FM is a commercial station owned by Clear Channel Media and Entertainment. The format of the station is Top 40/CHR. WXKS-FM broadcasts to the Boston area at 107.9 FM.

WXKT-FM
Owner: Cox Media Group, Inc.
Editorial: 340 Jesse Jewell Pkwy Se Ste 400, Gainesville, Georgia 30501-7701.
T: 1 706 549-6222
W: http://www.1037chuckfm.com
Editorial Profile: WXKT-FM is a commercial station owned by Cox Media Group, Inc. The format of the station is adult hits. WXKT-FM broadcasts to the Washington, GA area at 103.7 FM.

WXKU-FM
Owner: BK Media, LLC
Editorial: 1534 N Ewing St, Seymour, Indiana 47274-1121. **T:** 1 812 522-1390
W: http://www.kix927.com
Editorial Profile: WXKU-FM is a commercial station owned by BK Media, LLC. The format of the station is contemporary country music. WXKU-FM broadcasts to the Seymour, IN area at 92.7 FM.

WXKZ-FM
Owner: Gearheart Broadcasting
Editorial: 98 Church Rd, Harold, Kentucky 41635. **T:** 1 606 478-1200
Editorial Profile: WXKZ-FM is a commercial station owned by Gearheart Broadcasting. The format of the station is oldies. WXKZ-FM broadcasts to the Harold, KY area at 105.3 FM.

WXLA-AM
Owner: MacDonald Broadcasting Co.
Editorial: 600 W Cavanaugh Rd, Lansing, Michigan 48910. **T:** 1 517 393-1320
Editorial Profile: WXLA-AM is a commercial station owned by MacDonald Broadcasting Co. The format of the station is adult standards. WXLA-AM broadcasts to the Lansing, MI area at 1180 AM.

WXLB-FM
Owner: St. Lawrence University
Editorial: EJ Medical Bldg. Rm201, 80 E Main St, Canton, New York 13617.
T: 1 315 229-5356 **E:** radio@ncpr.org
W: http://www.ncpr.org
Editorial Profile: WXLB-FM is a non-commercial station owned by St. Lawrence University and broadcasting to the Canton, NY area at 91.7 FM. The format for the station is Variety, with a focus on News and Talk.

WXLC-FM
Owner: Digity LLC
Editorial: 3250 Belvidere Rd, Waukegan, Illinois 60085-6041. **T:** 1 847 336-7900
W: http://www.1023xlc.com
Editorial Profile: WXLC-FM is a commercial station owned by Digity LLC . The format of the station is hot adult contemporary. The station broadcasts to the Waukegan, IL area at 102.3 FM.

WXLF-FM
Owner: WBIN, Inc.
Editorial: 106 N Main St, West Lebanon, New Hampshire 03784-1136. **T:** 1 603 298-0332
W: http://www.953thewolf.com
Editorial Profile: WXLF-FM is a commercial station owned by WBIN, Inc. The format of the station is country music. WXLF-FM broadcasts to the West Lebanon, NH area at 95.3 FM and simulcasts on WZSH-FM.

WXLI-AM
Owner: Kirby Broadcasting
Editorial: 1006 Martin Luther King Jr Dr, Dublin, Georgia 31021. **T:** 1 478 272-9270
E: prod927@bellsouth.net
Editorial Profile: WXLI-AM is a commercial station owned by Kirby Broadcasting. The format of the station is classic country and gospel. WXLI-AM broadcasts to the Dublin, GA area at 1230 AM.

WXLK-FM
Owner: Wheeler Inc.(Mel)

Editorial: 3934 Electric Rd, Roanoke, Virginia 24018. **T:** 1 540 774-9200
W: http://www.k92radio.com
Editorial Profile: WXLK-FM is a commercial station owned by Mel Wheeler Inc. The format of the station is Top 40/CHR. WXLK-FM broadcasts to the Roanoke, VA area at 92.3 FM.

WXLM-AM
Owner: Cumulus Media Inc.
Editorial: 7 Governor Winthrop Blvd, New London, Connecticut 6320. **T:** 1 860 443-1980
W: http://www.wxlm.fm
Editorial Profile: WXLM-AM is a commercial station owned by Cumulus Media Inc. The format of the station is news/talk/sports. WXLM-AM broadcasts to the New London, CT area at 980 AM.

WXLN-FM
Owner: Bullock's Christian Broadcasting Corporation
Editorial: 670 Southlawn Dr, Shelbyville, Kentucky 40065-8834
E: wxlnradio@insightbb.com
W: http://www.wxlnradio.com
Editorial Profile: WXLN-FM is a non-commercial station owned by Bullock's Christian Broadcasting Corporation. The format of the station is Christian Religious talk programming. WXLN-FM broadcasts to the Shelbyville, KY area at 93.3 FM. WXLN's target audience is residents around Shelbyville, KY ages 13 to 100. The tagline is "Power 93.3".

WXLO-FM
Owner: Cumulus Media Inc.
Editorial: 250 Commercial St, Ste 530, Worcester, Massachusetts 1608.
T: 1 508 752-1045 **W:** http://www.wxlo.com
Editorial Profile: WXLO-FM is a commercial station owned by Cumulus Media Inc. The format of the station is hot adult contemporary. WXLO-FM broadcasts to the Worcester, MA area at 104.5 FM.

WXLP-FM
Owner: Townsquare Media
Editorial: 1229 Brady St, Davenport, Iowa 52803-4616. **T:** 1 563 326-2541
W: http://97x.com
Editorial Profile: WXLP-FM is a commercial station owned by Townsquare Media. The format of the station is classic rock. WXLP-FM broadcasts to the Davenport, IA area at 96.9 FM.

WXLR-FM
Owner: Gearheart Broadcasting
Editorial: 99 Church Rd, Harold, Kentucky 41635. **T:** 1 606 478-1200

WXLS-FM
Owner: St. Lawrence University
Editorial: North Country Public Radio, St Lawrence University, Canton, New York 13617.
T: 1 315 229-5356 **E:** radio@ncpr.org
W: http://www.ncpr.org
Editorial Profile: WXLS-FM is a non-commercial station owned by St. Lawrence University. The format of the station is variety. WXLS-FM broadcasts to the Canton, NY area at 88.3 FM.

WXLT-FM
Owner: Max Media
Editorial: 1431 Country Aire Dr, Carterville, Illinois 62918-5118. **T:** 1 618 985-4843
E: publicservice@riverradio.net
W: http://www.1035espn.com
Editorial Profile: WXLT-FM is a commercial station owned by Max Media. The format of the station is sports. WXLT-FM broadcasts to the Carterville, IL area at 103.5 FM. Send PSAs to publicservice@riverradio.net.

WXLU-FM
Owner: St. Lawrence University
Editorial: EJ Noble Medical Bldg. Rm 201, 80 E Main St, Canton, New York 13617.
T: 1 315 229-5356 **E:** radio@ncpr.org
W: http://www.ncpr.org
Editorial Profile: WXLU-FM is a non-commerical station owned by St. Lawrence University. The format is variety, news and talk. WXLU-FM broadcasts to the Canton, NY area at 88.1 FM.

WXLV-FM
Owner: Lehigh Carbon Community College
Editorial: 4525 Education Park Dr, Schnecksville, Pennsylvania 18078.
T: 1 610 799-1145 **E:** info@wxlvradio.com
W: http://www.wxlvradio.com
Editorial Profile: WXLV-FM is a non-commercial station owned by Lehigh Carbon

Community College. The format of the station is variety. WXLV-FM broadcasts to the Schnecksville, PA area at 90.3 FM.

WXLW-AM
Owner: Pilgrim Communications Inc.
Editorial: 645 Industrial Dr, Franklin, Indiana 46131-9617. **T:** 1 317 736-4040
W: http://www.freedom95.us
Editorial Profile: WXLW-AM is a commercial station owned by Pilgrim Communications Inc. The format of the station is talk. WXLW-AM broadcasts to the Indianapolis area at 950 AM.

WXLY-FM
Owner: Clear Channel Media and Entertainment
Editorial: 950 Houston Northcutt Blvd, Ste 201, Mount Pleasant, South Carolina 29464-5645. **T:** 1 843 884-2534
W: http://www.y1025.com
Editorial Profile: WXLY-FM is a commercial station owned by Clear Channel Media and Entertainment. The format of the station is adult contemporary. WXLY-FM broadcasts to the Mount Pleasant, SC area at 102.5 FM.

WXLZ-AM
Owner: Yeary Broadcasting Inc.
Editorial: 265 WXLZ Dr., Lebanon, Virginia 24266. **T:** 1 276 889-1073
E: wxlz1073@bvu.net **W:** http://www.wxlz.net

WXLZ-FM
Owner: Yeary Broadcasting Inc.
Editorial: 265 WXLZ Dr, Lebanon, Virginia 24266. **T:** 1 276 889-1073
E: wxlz1073@bvu.net **W:** http://www.wxlz.net

WXMA-FM
Owner: Main Line Broadcasting
Editorial: 520 S 4th St Fl 2, Louisville, Kentucky 40202-2500. **T:** 1 502 625-1220
E: themaxfm@gmail.com
W: http://www.themaxfm.com
Editorial Profile: WXMA-FM is a commercial station owned by Main Line Broadcasting. The format of the station is hot adult contemporary music. WXMA-FM broadcasts in the Louisville, KY area at 102.3 FM.

WXME-AM
Owner: Weiner (Allan and Barbara)
Editorial: 274 Britton Rd, Monticello, Maine 04760-3110. **T:** 1 207 538-9180
Editorial Profile: WXME-AM is a commercial station owned by Weiner (Allan and Barbara). The format of the station is classic country. WXME-AM broadcasts to the Aroostook County area in Maine at 780 AM.

WXMG-FM
Owner: Radio One Inc.
Editorial: 350 E 1st Ave, Ste 100, Columbus, Ohio 43201. **T:** 1 614 487-1444
W: http://www.mycolumbusmagic.com
Editorial Profile: WXMG-FM is a commercial station owned by Radio One Inc. The format of the station is urban adult contemporary. WXMG-FM broadcasts to the Columbus, OH area at 106.3 FM.

WXMJ-FM
Owner: Forever Broadcasting
Editorial: 900 Water St, Meadville, Pennsylvania 16335. **T:** 1 814 724-1111
W: http://www.mymajicspace.com
Editorial Profile: WXMJ-FM is a commercial station owned by Forever Broadcasting. The format of the station is hot adult contemporary. WXMJ-FM broadcasts to the Meadville, PA area at 104.5 FM.

WXMK-FM
Owner: Golden Isles Broadcasting LLC
Editorial: 185 Benedict Rd, Brunswick, Georgia 31520-2938. **T:** 1 912 261-1000
W: http://www.magic1059.com
Editorial Profile: WXMK-FM is a commercial station owned by Golden Isles Broadcasting LLC. The format of the station is hot adult contemporary. WXMK-FM broadcasts to the Brunswick, GA area at 105.9 FM.

WXML-FM
Owner: Kayser Broadcast Ministries
Editorial: 1800 E Wyandot Ave, Upper Sandusky, Ohio 43351. **T:** 1 419 294-2900
E: contactus@newvision.fm
W: http://www.newvision.fm
Editorial Profile: WXML-FM is a non-commercial station owned by Kayser Broadcast Ministries. The format of the station is religious programming. WXML-FM broadcasts to the Toledo, OH area at 90.1 FM.

WXMT-FM
Owner: Colonial Radio Group
Editorial: 1 Bluebird Sq, Olean, New York 14760-2552. **T:** 1 814 837-9564
Editorial Profile: WXMT-FM is a commercial station owned by Colonial Radio Group. The format of the station is classic hits. WXMT-FM broadcasts to the Smethport, PA area at 106.3 FM.

WXMW-FM
Owner: Kayser Broadcast Ministries
Editorial: 1800 E Wyandot Ave, Upper Sandusky, Ohio 43351-9652.
T: 1 419 294-2900 **E:** contactus@newvision.fm
W: http://www.newvision.fm
Editorial Profile: WXMW-FM is a non-commercial station owned by Kayser Broadcast Ministries. The format of the station is religious programming. WXMW-FM's broadcasts at a frequency of 89.3 FM in the Sycamore, OH area.

WXMX-FM
Owner: Cumulus Media Inc.
Editorial: 5629 Murray Ave, Memphis, Tennessee 38119-3831. **T:** 1 901 682-1106
W: http://www.981themax.com
Editorial Profile: WXMX-FM is a commercial station owned by Cumulus Media Inc. The format of the station is rock. WXMX-FM broadcasts to the Memphis, TN area at 98.1 FM.

WXMZ-FM
Owner: Starlight Broadcasting Co.
Editorial: 314 S Main St, Hartford, Kentucky 42347. **T:** 1 270 298-3268
Editorial Profile: WXMZ-FM is a commercial station owned by Starlight Broadcasting Co. The format of the station is oldies. WXMZ-FM broadcasts to the Hartford, KY area at 106.3 FM.

WXNC-AM
Owner: Norsan Group
Editorial: 4801 E Independence Blvd, Ste 815, Charlotte, North Carolina 28212.
T: 1 770 442-7277
Editorial Profile: WXNC-AM is a commercial station owned by Norsan Group. The format of the station is Hispanic Christian music. WXNC-AM broadcasts to the Charlotte, NC area at 1060 AM.

WXNR-FM
Owner: Beasley Broadcast Group
Editorial: 207 Glenburnie Dr, New Bern, North Carolina 28560. **T:** 1 252 633-1500
W: http://www.wxnr.com
Editorial Profile: WXNR-FM is a commercial station owned by Beasley Broadcast Group. The format of the station is rock alternative. WXNR-FM broadcasts to the New Bern, NC area at 99.5 FM.

WXNT-AM
Owner: Entercom Communications Corp.
Editorial: 9245 N Meridian St Ste 300, Indianapolis, Indiana 46260-1832.
T: 1 317 816-4000 **E:** indypsa@entercom.com
W: http://www.cbssports1430.com
Editorial Profile: WXNT-AM is a CBS Sports Radio affiliate owned by Entercom Communications Corp. The format for the station is sports. WXNT-AM broadcasts to the Indianapolis area at 1430 AM.

WXNU-FM
Owner: Staradio Corp.
Editorial: 70 Meadowview Ctr, Ste 400, Kankakee, Illinois 60901-2061.
T: 1 815 935-9555 **E:** wxnu@staradio.com
W: http://www.xcountry1065.com
Editorial Profile: WXNU-FM is a commercial station owned by Staradio Corp. The format of the station is contemporary country music. WXNU-FM broadcasts to the Kankakee, IL, area at 106.5 FM.

WXNX-FM
Owner: Meridian Broadcasting, Inc.
Editorial: 2824 Palm Beach Blvd, Fort Myers, Florida 33916-1503. **T:** 1 239 337-2346
W: http://93x.fm
Editorial Profile: WXNX-FM is a commercial station owned by Meridian Broadcasting, Inc. The format of the station is alternative rock. WXNX-FM broadcasts to the Fort Meyers, FL area at a frequency of 93.7 FM.

WXNY-FM
Owner: Univision Communications Inc.
Editorial: 485 Madison Ave, New York, New York 10022-5803. **T:** 1 212 310-6000
W: http://x963fm.univision.com
Editorial Profile: WXNY-FM is a commercial station owned by Univision Communications Inc. The format of the station is English and Spanish rhythmic hits. WXNY-FM broadcasts to the New York area at 96.3 FM.

WXOF-FM
Owner: WXOF, Inc.
Editorial: 4554 S Suncoast Blvd, Homosassa, Florida 34446-1103. **T:** 1 352 628-4444
E: staff@citrus953.com
W: http://www.thefox963.com
Editorial Profile: WXOF-FM is a commercial station owned by WXOF, Inc. The format of the station is classic hits. WXOF-FM broadcasts to the Homosassa, FL area at 96.7 FM.

WXOK-AM
Owner: Cumulus Media Inc.
Editorial: 650 Wooddale Blvd, Baton Rouge, Louisiana 70806. **T:** 1 225 926-1106
W: http://www.heaven1460.com
Editorial Profile: WXOK-AM is a commercial station owned by Cumulus Media Inc. The format of the station is gospel music. WXOK-AM broadcasts to the Baton Rouge, LA area at 1460 AM.

WXOQ-FM
Owner: Hunt(Gerald W.)
Editorial: 165 Bowen Dr, Savannah, Tennessee 38372-1490. **T:** 1 731 925-7102
Editorial Profile: WXOQ-FM is a commercial station owned by Gerald W. Hunt. The format of the station is country. WXOQ-FM broadcasts to the Savannah, TN area at 105.5 FM.

WXOS-FM
Owner: Hubbard Broadcasting, Inc.
Editorial: 11647 Olive Blvd, Saint Louis, Missouri 63141-7001. **T:** 1 314 983-6000
E: webmaster@101sports.com
W: http://www.101espn.com
Editorial Profile: WXOS-FM is a commercial station owned by Hubbard Broadcasting, Inc. The format of the station is sports. WXOS-FM broadcasts to the St. Louis area at 101.1 FM.

WXOU-FM
Owner: Oakland University
Editorial: 69 Oakland Ctr, Rochester Hills, Michigan 48309-4409. **T:** 1 248 370-4273
E: wxou@wxou.org **W:** http://wxou.org
Editorial Profile: WXOU-FM is a non-commercial college station owned by Oakland University. The format of the station is variety, featuring music, news and sports programming. WXOU-FM broadcasts to the Auburn Hills, MI area at a frequency of 88.3.

WXPH-FM
Owner: University of Pennsylvania
Editorial: 3025 Walnut St, Philadelphia, Pennsylvania 19104. **T:** 1 215 898-6677
E: wxpndesk@xpn.org **W:** http://www.xpn.org
Editorial Profile: WXPH-FM is a non-commercial station owned by the University of Pennslyvania. The format of the station is adult album alternative. WXPH-FM broadcasts to the Philadelphia area at 88.7 FM. .

WXPK-FM
Owner: Pamal Broadcasting Ltd.
Editorial: 56 Lafayette Ave, Ste 370, White Plains, New York 10603-1684.
T: 1 914 397-0127
E: studio@1071thepeak.com
W: http://www.1071thepeak.com
Editorial Profile: WXPK-FM is a commercial station owned by Pamal Broadcasting Ltd. The format of the station is adult album alternative. WXPK-FM broadcasts to the White Plains, NY area at 107.1 FM.

WXPN-FM
Owner: University of Pennsylvania
Editorial: 3025 Walnut St, Philadelphia, Pennsylvania 19104. **T:** 1 215 898-6677
E: wxpndesk@xpn.org **W:** http://www.xpn.org
Editorial Profile: WXPN-FM is a non-commercial station owned by University of Pennsylvania. The format of the station is album adult alternative. WXPN-FM broadcasts to the Philadelphia area at 88.5 FM. The station is a trimulcast of WZXM-FM and WXPH-FM.

WXPR-FM
Owner: White Pine Community Broadcasting Inc.
Editorial: 303 W Prospect St, Rhinelander, Wisconsin 54501-3867. **T:** 1 715 362-6000
W: http://www.wxpr.org
Editorial Profile: WXPR-FM is a non-commercial station owned by White Pine Community Broadcasting Inc. The format of the station is variety. WXPR-FM broadcasts in the Rhinelander, WI area at 91.7 FM.

WXPW-FM
Owner: White Pine Community Broadcasting Inc.
Editorial: 303 W Prospect St, Rhinelander, Wisconsin 54501-3867. **T:** 1 715 362-6000
W: http://www.wxpr.org
Editorial Profile: WXPW-FM is a non-commercial station owned by White Pine Community Broadcasting Inc. The format of the station is variety. WXPW-FM broadcasts in the Rhinelander, WI area at 91.9 FM. WXPW-FM will only accept PSAs in a written format.

WXQR-FM
Owner: Digity LLC
Editorial: 1361 Colony Dr, New Bern, North Carolina 28562-4129. **T:** 1 252 639-7900
W: http://www.carolinaspurerock.com
Editorial Profile: WXQR-FM is a commercial station owned by Digity LLC . The format of the station is rock. WXQR-FM broadcasts to the New Bern, NC area at 105.5 FM.

WXQW-AM
Owner: Cumulus Media Inc.
Editorial: 2800 Dauphin St Ste 104, Mobile, Alabama 36606-2400. **T:** 1 251 652-2000
W: http://www.wgokgospel900am.com
Editorial Profile: WXQW-AM is a commercial station owned by Cumulus Media Inc. The format of the station is gospel. WWFF-AM broadcasts to the Mobile, AL area at 660 AM.

WXRC-FM
Owner: Pacific Broadcasting Group Inc.
Editorial: 1666 Radio Station Rd, Newton, North Carolina 28658-9488.
T: 1 704 527-0957
W: http://www.957theride.com
Editorial Profile: WXRC-FM is a commercial station owned by Pacific Broadcasting Group Inc. The format of the station is classic hits. WXRC-FM broadcasts to the Charlotte, NC area at 95.7 FM.

WXRD-FM
Owner: Radio One Inc.
Editorial: 2755 Sager Rd, Valparaiso, Indiana 46383. **T:** 1 219 462-6111
W: http://www.xrock1039.com
Editorial Profile: WXRD-FM is a commercial station owned by Radio One Inc. The format of the station is classic rock. WXRD-FM broadcasts to the Valparaiso, IN area at 103.9 FM.

WXRI-FM
Owner: Positive Alternative Radio
Editorial: 600 W Clemmonsville Rd, Winston Salem, North Carolina 27127-5045.
T: 1 336 788-1155 **E:** office@joyfm.org
W: http://www.joyfm.org
Editorial Profile: WXRI-FM is a non-commercial station owned by Positive Alternative Radio. The format of the station is Southern Gospel. WXRI-FM broadcasts to the Winston Salem, NC area at 91.3 FM.

WXRL-AM
Owner: Dome Broadcasting Inc.
Editorial: 5426 William St, Lancaster, New York 14086-9320. **T:** 1 716 681-1313
E: info@wxrl.com **W:** http://www.wxrl.com
Editorial Profile: WXRL-AM is a commercial station owned by Dome Broadcasting Inc. The format of the station is country. WXRL-AM broadcasts to the Lancaster, NY area at 1300 AM.

WXRO-FM
Owner: Good Karma Broadcasting
Editorial: 100 Stoddart St, Beaver Dam, Wisconsin 53916-1306. **T:** 1 920 885-4442
W: http://www.wxroradio.com
Editorial Profile: WXRO-FM is a commercial station owned by Good Karma Broadcasting. The format of the station is classic country music. WXRO-FM broadcasts to the Milwaukee area at 95.3 FM.

WXRQ-AM
Owner: New Life Community Temple of Faith, Inc.
Editorial: 209 Bond St, Mount Pleasant, Tennessee 38474. **T:** 1 931 379-3119
E: wxrq@yahoo.com
W: http://www.1460wxrq.com
Editorial Profile: WXRQ-AM is a commercial station owned by New Life Community Temple of Faith, Inc. The format of the station is southern gospel music. WXRQ-AM broadcasts to the Nashville, TN area at 1460 AM.

WXRR-FM

Owner: Blakeney Communications Inc.
Editorial: 4580 Highway 15 N, Laurel, Mississippi 39440. **T:** 1 601 649-0095
E: rock104@rock104fm.com
W: http://www.rock104fm.com
Editorial Profile: WXRR-FM is a commercial station owned by Blakeney Communications Inc. The format of the station is classic rock music. WXRR-FM broadcasts to the Laurel, MS area at 104.5 FM.

WXRS-AM

Owner: RadioJones LLC
Editorial: 2 Radio Loop, Swainsboro, Georgia 30401. **T:** 1 478 237-1590
Editorial Profile: WXRS-AM is a commercial station owned by RadioJones LLC. The format of the station is oldies. WXRS-AM broadcasts to the Swainsboro, GA area at 1590 AM.

WXRS-FM

Owner: RadioJones LLC
Editorial: 2 Radio Loop, Swainsboro, Georgia 30401. **T:** 1 478 237-1590
Editorial Profile: WXRS-FM is a commercial station owned by RadioJones LLC. The format of the station is country. WXRS-FM broadcasts to the Swainsboro, GA area at 100.5 FM.

WXRT-FM

Owner: CBS Radio
Editorial: 180 N Stetson Ave Ste 963, Chicago, Illinois 60601-6712.
T: 1 312 649-0099 **E:** xrtcomments@wxrt.com
W: http://wxrt.radio.com
Editorial Profile: WXRT-FM is a commercial station owned by CBS Radio. The format of the station is adult album alternative music. WXRT-FM broadcasts to the Chicago area at 93.1 FM.

WXRV-FM

Owner: Northeast Broadcasting Co.
Editorial: 30 How St, Haverhill, Massachusetts 01830-6131. **T:** 1 978 374-4733
W: http://theriverboston.com
Editorial Profile: WXRV-FM is a commercial station owned by Northeast Broadcasting Co. The format of the station is AAA - Adult Album Alternative. WXRV-FM broadcasts to Haverhill, MA area at 92.5 FM.

WXRX-FM

Owner: Maverick Media
Editorial: 2830 Sandy Hollow Rd, Rockford, Illinois 61109-2369. **T:** 1 815 874-7861
W: http://www.wxrx.com
Editorial Profile: WXRX-FM is a commercial station owned by Mid-West Family Broadcasting. The format of the station is rock music. WXRX-FM broadcasts to the Rockford, IL area at 105.9 FM.

WXRZ-FM

Owner: TeleSouth Communications Inc.
Editorial: 1608 S Johns St, Corinth, Mississippi 38834-6547. **T:** 1 662 286-8451
W: http://www.supertalkms.com
Editorial Profile: WXRZ-FM is a commercial station owned by TeleSouth Communications Inc. The format of the station is talk. WXRZ-FM broadcasts to the Corinth, MS area at 94.3 FM.

WXSH-FM

Owner: Great Scott Broadcasting
Editorial: 20200 Dupont Blvd, Georgetown, Delaware 19947-3105. **T:** 1 302 228-8942
E: radio@maxima900.com
W: http://www.maxima90zero.com
Editorial Profile: WXSH-FM is a commercial station owned by Great Scott Broadcasting. The format of the station is Spanish Top 40/CHR. The station airs locally in the Pocomoke City, MD area at 106.1 FM.

WXSM-AM

Owner: Cumulus Media Inc.
Editorial: 162 Free Hill Rd, Gray, Tennessee 37615-3144. **T:** 1 423 477-1064
E: sportsmonster@640wxsm.com
W: http://www.640wxsm.com
Editorial Profile: WXSM-AM is a commercial station owned by Cumulus Media Inc. The format of the station is sports. WXSM-AM broadcasts to the Johnson City, TN area at 640 AM.

WXSR-FM

Owner: Clear Channel Media and Entertainment
Editorial: 325 John Knox Rd, Bldg G, Tallahassee, Florida 32303. **T:** 1 850 422-3107
W: http://www.x1015.com

Editorial Profile: WXSR-FM is a commercial station owned by Clear Channel Media and Entertainment. The format of the station is rock alternative. WXSR-FM broadcasts to the Tallahassee, FL area at 101.5 FM.

WXSS-FM

Owner: Entercom Communications Corp.
Editorial: 11800 W Grange Ave, Hales Corners, Wisconsin 53130. **T:** 1 414 529-1250
W: http://www.1037kissfm.com
Editorial Profile: WXSS-FM is a commercial station owned by Entercom Communications Corp. The format of the station is Top 40/CHR music. WXSS-FM broadcasts to the Milwaukee area at 103.7 FM.

WXST-FM

Owner: Apex Broadcasting Inc.
Editorial: 2294 Clements Ferry Rd, Charleston, South Carolina 29492. **T:** 1 843 972-1100
E: frontdesk@apexbroadcasting.com
W: http://www.star997.com
Editorial Profile: WXST-FM is a commercial station owned by Apex Broadcasting Inc. The format of the station is urban adult contemporary. WXST-FM broadcasts to the Charleston, SC area at 99.7 FM.

WXTA-FM

Owner: Cumulus Media Inc
Editorial: 471 Robison Rd, Erie, Pennsylvania 16509-5425. **T:** 1 814 868-5355
W: http://www.979nashfm.com
Editorial Profile: WXTA-FM is a commercial station owned by Cumulus Media Inc. The format of the station is contemporary country. WXTA-FM broadcasts to the Erie, PA area at 97.9 FM.

WXTB-FM

Owner: Clear Channel Media and Entertainment
Editorial: 4002 W Gandy Blvd, Tampa, Florida 33611-3410. **T:** 1 813 832-1000
W: http://www.98rock.com
Editorial Profile: WXTB-FM is a commercial station owned by Clear Channel Media and Entertainment. The format of the station is rock music. WXTB-FM broadcasts to the Tampa, FL area at 97.9 FM.

WXTG-AM

Owner: Local Voice Media
Editorial: 4732 Longhill Rd Ste 2201, Williamsburg, Virginia 23188-1584.
T: 1 757 565-1079
Editorial Profile: WXTG-AM is a commercial station owned by Local Voice Media. The format of the station is sports. WXTG-AM broadcasts to the Virginia Beach, VA area at 1490 AM.

WXTG-FM

Owner: Local Voice Media
Editorial: 4732 Longhill Rd Ste 2201, Williamsburg, Virginia 23188-1584.
T: 1 757 565-1079 **E:** music@tideradio.com
W: http://tideradio.com
Editorial Profile: WXTG-FM is a commercial station owned by Local Voice Media. The format of the station is AAA. WXTG-FM broadcasts to the Virginia Beach, VA area at 102.1 FM.

WXTK-FM

Owner: Clear Channel Media and Entertainment
Editorial: 154 Barnstable Rd, Hyannis, Massachusetts 02601-2930.
T: 1 508 778-2888 **E:** psa@95wxtk.com
W: http://www.95wxtk.com
Editorial Profile: WXTK-FM is a commercial station owned by Clear Channel Media and Entertainment. The format of the station is news, talk, and sports. WXTK-FM broadcasts to the Boston area at 95.1 FM.

WXTL-FM

Owner: Cumulus Media Inc
Editorial: 1064 James St, Syracuse, New York 13203. **T:** 1 315 472-0200
W: http://www.1059therebel.com
Editorial Profile: WXTL-FM is a commercial station owned by Cumulus Media Inc. The format of the station is classic rock. WXTL-FM broadcasts to the Syracuse, NY area at 105.9 FM.

WXTN-AM

Owner: Sandra U. Cothran, Executrix
Editorial: 100 Radio Road, Lexington, Mississippi 39095. **T:** 1 662 834-1025
E: class102@cableone.net
Editorial Profile: WXTN-AM is a commercial station owned by Sandra U. Cothran, Executrix. The format of the station is gospel

and news. WXTN-AM broadcasts to the Lexington, MS area at 1000 AM.

WXTQ-FM

Owner: WATH Inc.
Editorial: 300 Columbus Rd, Athens, Ohio 45701-1336. **T:** 1 740 593-6651
E: news@970wath.com
W: http://www.wxtq.com
Editorial Profile: WXTQ-FM is a commercial station owned by WATH Inc. The format for the station is hot adult contemporary. WXTQ-FM broadcasts to the Athen, OH area at 105.5 FM.

WXTS-FM

Owner: Toledo Board of Education
Editorial: 3281 Upton Ave, Toledo, Ohio 43613-5109. **T:** 1 419 244-6875
Editorial Profile: WXTS-FM is a non-commercial station owned by Toledo Board of Education. The format is jazz and blues music. The station airs at 88.3 FM in the Toledo, OH area.

WXTU-FM

Owner: Beasley Broadcast Group
Editorial: 555 E City Ave Ste 330, Bala Cynwyd, Pennsylvania 19004-1137.
T: 1 610 667-9000 **W:** http://925xtu.com
Editorial Profile: WXTU-FM is a commercial station owned by Beasley Broadcast Group. The format of the station is contemporary country. WXTU-FM broadcasts to the Philadelphia area at 92.5 FM.

WXUR-FM

Owner: Arjuna Broadcasting Corp.
Editorial: 566 Baum Rd, Herkimer, New York 13357. **T:** 1 315 266-0250
E: wxur@hotmail.com
W: http://927thedrive.net
Editorial Profile: WXUR-FM is a commercial station owned by Arjuna Broadcasting Corp. The format of the station is adult album alternative. WXUR-FM broadcasts to the Herkimer, NY area at 92.7 FM.

WXUT-FM

Owner: University of Toledo
Editorial: 2801 W Bancroft St, Toledo, Ohio 43606-3328. **T:** 1 419 530-4172
E: 883wxut@gmail.com
W: http://www.wxut.com
Editorial Profile: WXUT-FM is a non-commercial station owned by the University of Toledo. The format for the station is variety. WXUT-FM broadcasts to the Toledo, OH area at 88.3 FM.

WXVI-AM

Owner: New Life Ministries Inc.
Editorial: 912 S Perry St, Montgomery, Alabama 36104. **T:** 1 334 263-4141
Editorial Profile: WXVI-AM is a commercial station owned by New Life Ministries Inc. The format of the station is gospel. WXVI-AM broadcasts to the Montgomery, AL area at 1600 AM.

WXVS-FM

Owner: Georgia Public Broadcasting
Editorial: 260 14th St NW, Atlanta, Georgia 30318. **T:** 1 404 685-2400 **E:** ask@gpb.org
W: http://www.gpb.org
Editorial Profile: WXVS-FM is a non-commercial station owned by Georgia Public Broadcasting. The format of the station is classical music, jazz, news and talk. WXVS-FM broadcasts to the Atlanta area at 90.1 FM.

WXVU-FM

Owner: Villanova University
Editorial: 800 E Lancaster Ave, 210 Dougherty Hall, Villanova, Pennsylvania 19085.
T: 1 610 519-7200
E: villanova.radio@gmail.com
W: http://www.wxvufm.com

WXXB-FM

Owner: WASK Inc.
Editorial: 3575 Mccarty Ln, Lafayette, Indiana 47905-4985. **T:** 1 765 448-1566
W: http://www.b1029.com
Editorial Profile: WXXB-FM is a commercial station owned by WASK Inc. The format of the station is Top 40/CHR. WXXB-FM broadcasts to the Lafayette, IN area at 102.9 FM.

WXXC-FM

Owner: Hoosier AM/FM LLC
Editorial: 820 S Pennsylvania St, Marion, Indiana 46953-2407. **T:** 1 765 664-7396
W: http://www.star1069fm.com
Editorial Profile: WXXC-FM is a commercial station owned by Hoosier AM/FM LLC. The

format for the station is Hot AC. WXXC-FM broadcasts to the Indianapolis area at 106.9 FM.

WXXF-FM

Owner: Clear Channel Media and Entertainment
Editorial: 1400 Radio Ln, Mansfield, Ohio 44906-2525. **T:** 1 419 529-2211
W: http://www.foxclassicrock.com
Editorial Profile: WXXF-FM is a commercial station owned by Clear Channel Media and Entertainment. The format of the station is classic rock. WXXF-FM broadcasts to the Mansfield, OH area at 107.7 FM and simulcasts the programming of WFXN-FM in the Mansfield, OH area.

WXXI-AM

Owner: WXXI Public Broadcast Council
Editorial: 280 State St, Rochester, New York 14614. **T:** 1 585 325-7500 **E:** wxxi@wxxi.org
W: http://interactive.wxxi.org
Editorial Profile: WXXI-AM is a non-commercial station owned by WXXI Public Broadcast Council. The format of the station is news and talk. WXXI-AM broadcasts to the Rochester, NY area at 1370 AM.

WXXI-FM

Owner: WXXI Public Broadcast Council
Editorial: 280 State St, Rochester, New York 14614-1033. **T:** 1 585 325-7500
E: radio@wxxi.org
W: http://interactive.wxxi.org/classical
Editorial Profile: WXXI-FM is a non-commercial station owned by the WXXI Public Broadcasting Council. The format of the station is classical. WXXI-FM broadcasts to the Rochester, NY area at 91.5 FM.

WXXJ-FM

Owner: Cox Media Group, Inc.
Editorial: 8000 Belfort Pkwy, Ste 100, Jacksonville, Florida 32256. **T:** 1 904 245-8500
W: http://www.x1029.com
Editorial Profile: WXXJ-FM is a commercial station owned by Cox Media Group, Inc. The format of the station is rock alternative. WXXJ-FM broadcasts to the Jacksonville, FL area at 102.9 FM.

WXXK-FM

Owner: Great Eastern Radio, LLC
Editorial: 31 Hanover St Ste 4, Lebanon, New Hampshire 03766-1312. **T:** 1 603 448-1400
W: http://www.kixx.com
Editorial Profile: WXXK-FM is a commercial station owned by Great Eastern Radio, LLC. The format of the station is contemporary country. WXXK-FM broadcasts to the Lebanon, NH area at 100.5 FM.

WXXL-FM

Owner: Clear Channel Media and Entertainment
Editorial: 2500 Maitland Center Pkwy, Ste 401, Maitland, Florida 32751.
T: 1 407 916-7800 **W:** http://www.xl1067.com
Editorial Profile: WXXL-FM is a commercial station owned by Clear Channel Media and Entertainment. The format of the station is Top 40/CHR. WXXL-FM broadcasts to the Orlando, FL area at 106.7 FM.

WXXM-FM

Owner: Clear Channel Media and Entertainment
Editorial: 2651 S Fish Hatchery Rd, Fitchburg, Wisconsin 53711. **T:** 1 608 274-1070
W: http://www.themic921.com
Editorial Profile: WXXM-FM is a commercial station owned by Clear Channel Media and Entertainment. The format of the station is progressive talk. WXXM-FM broadcasts to the Madison, WI area at 92.1 FM.

WXXQ-FM

Owner: Cumulus Media Inc.
Editorial: 3901 Brendenwood Rd, Rockford, Illinois 61107. **T:** 1 815 399-2233
W: http://www.q985online.com
Editorial Profile: WXXQ-FM is a commercial station owned by Cumulus Media Inc. The format of the station is country music. WXXQ-FM broadcasts to the Rockford, IL area at 98.5 FM.

WXXR-FM

Owner: Midwest Communications Inc.
Editorial: 824 S 3rd St, Terre Haute, Indiana 47807. **T:** 1 812 232-4161
W: http://x959fm.com
Editorial Profile: WXXR-FM is a commercial station owned by Midwest Communications Inc. The format of the station is modern rock.

WXXR-FM broadcasts to the Terre Haute, IN, area at 95.9 FM.

WXXS-FM
Owner: Lunderville(Barry)
Editorial: 195 Main St, Lancaster, New Hampshire 3584. **T:** 1 603 788-3636
E: kiss102@together.net
Editorial Profile: WXXS-FM is a commercial station owned by Barry Lunderville. The format of the station is Hot AC. WXXS-FM broadcasts to the Portland, ME area at 102.3 FM.

WXXX-FM
Owner: Sison Broadcasting Inc.
Editorial: 118 Malletts Bay Ave, Colchester, Vermont 5446. **T:** 1 802 655-1620
E: 95triplex@95triplex.com
W: http://www.95triplex.com
Editorial Profile: WXXX-FM is a commercial station owned by Sison Broadcasting Inc. The format of the station is Top 40/CHR music. WXXX-FM broadcasts to the Colchester, VT market at 95.5 FM.

WXXY-FM
Owner: WXXI Public Broadcast Council
Editorial: 280 State St, Rochester, New York 14601. **T:** 1 585 325-7500 **E:** wxxi@wxxi.org
W: http://www.wxxi.org
Editorial Profile: WXXY-FM is a non-commercial station owned by WXXI Public Broadcast Council. The format of the station is classical, news, talk and public radio. WXXY-FM broadcasts to the Houghton, NY area at 90.3 FM.

WXYB-AM
Owner: ASA Broadcasting Network
Editorial: 109 S Bayview Blvd Ste A, Oldsmar, Florida 34677-3124. **T:** 1 727 725-5555
E: wzra48@yahoo.com
W: http://www.wpso.com
Editorial Profile: WXYB-AM is a commercial station owned by ASA Broadcasting Network. The format of the station is ethnic programming. WXYB-AM broadcasts to the Oldsmar, FL area at 1520 AM.

WXYC-FM
Owner: Student Educational Broadcasting Inc.
Editorial: 5210 Carolina Un, Chapel Hill, North Carolina 27599-0001. **T:** 1 919 962-7768
E: info@wxyc.org **W:** http://www.wxyc.org
Editorial Profile: WXYC-FM is a non-commercial station owned by Student Educational Broadcasting Inc. The format of the station is variety. WXYC-FM broadcasts to the Chapel Hill, NC area at 89.3 FM.

WXYG-AM
Owner: Tri-County Broadcasting
Editorial: 1010 2nd St N, Sauk Rapids, Minnesota 56379-2527. **T:** 1 320 252-6200
E: tcbi.redhouse@gmail.com
W: http://www.540wxyg.com
Editorial Profile: WXYG-AM is a commercial station owned by Tri-County Broadcasting. The format of the station is rock. WXYG-AM broadcasts in the Sauk Rapids, MN area at 540 AM.

WXYK-FM
Owner: L & L Radio
Editorial: 1909 E Pass Rd, Gulfport, Mississippi 39507-3779. **T:** 1 228 388-2001
W: http://www.1071themonkey.net
Editorial Profile: WXYK-FM is a commercial station owned by L & L Radio. The format of the station is Top 40/CHR music. WXYK-FM broadcasts to the Gulfport, MS area at 107.1 FM.

WXYM-FM
Owner: Magnum Radio Group
Editorial: 1021 N Superior Ave, Ste 5, Tomah, Wisconsin 54660. **T:** 1 608 372-9400
E: news@magnumbroadcasting.com
W: http://www.mix96wxym.com
Editorial Profile: WXYM-FM is a commercial station owned by the Magnum Radio Group. The format of the station is hot adult contemporary. WXYM-FM broadcasts to the Tomah, WI area at 96.1 FM.

WXYT-AM
Owner: CBS Radio
Editorial: 26495 American Dr, Southfield, Michigan 48034-6114. **T:** 1 248 455-7200
W: http://detroit.cbslocal.com/station/talk-radio-1270-am-wxyt/
Editorial Profile: WXYT-AM is a commercial station owned by CBS Radio. The format of the station is sports. WXYT-AM broadcasts to the Detroit area at 1270 AM.

WXYT-FM
Owner: CBS Radio
Editorial: 31555 W 14 Mile Rd, Farmington Hills, Michigan 48334-1239.
T: 1 248 327-2900
W: http://detroit.cbslocal.com/category/sports/
Editorial Profile: WXYT-FM is a commercial station owned by CBS Radio. The format of the station is sports. WXYT-FM broadcasts to the Detroit area at 97.1 FM.

WXYY-FM
Owner: L & L Broadcasting
Editorial: 401 Mall Blvd Ste 101D, Savannah, Georgia 31406-4863. **T:** 1 912 351-9830
W: http://y100.fm
Editorial Profile: WXYY-FM is a commercial station owned by L & L Broadcasting. The format of the station is Hot AC. WXYY-FM airs locally in the Hinesville, GA area at 100.1 FM.

WXZO-FM
Owner: Vox Communications
Editorial: 265 Hegeman Ave, Colchester, Vermont 5446. **T:** 1 802 655-0093
W: http://www.theplanet967.com
Editorial Profile: WXZO-FM is a commercial station owned by Vox Communications. The format of the station is Top 40 CHR. WXZO-FM broadcasts to the Burlington, VT area at 96.7 FM.

WXZQ-FM
Owner: Piketon Communication Corp.
Editorial: 6655 State Route 220, Waverly, Ohio 45690-8987. **T:** 1 740 947-0059
E: wxiz@roadrunner.com
W: http://wxzqfm.com
Editorial Profile: WXZQ-FM is a commercial station owned by Piketon Communications Corp. The format of the station is Top 40/CHR. WXZQ-FM broadcasts to the Waverly, OH area at 100.1 FM.

WXZZ-FM
Owner: Cumulus Media Inc.
Editorial: 300 W Vine St Ste 3, Lexington, Kentucky 40507-1806. **T:** 1 859 253-5900
W: http://www.zrock103.com
Editorial Profile: WXZZ-FM is a commercial station owned by Cumulus Media Inc. The format of the station is rock. WXZZ-FM broadcasts to the Lexington, KY at 103.3 FM.

WYAB-FM
Owner: SSR Communications Inc.
Editorial: 740 Highway 49, Ste R, Flora, Mississippi 39071-9653. **T:** 1 601 879-0093
E: info@wyab.com **W:** http://www.wyab.com
Editorial Profile: WYAB-FM is a commercial station owned by SSR Communications Inc. The format of the station is talk. WYAB-FM broadcasts to the Flora, MS area at 103.9 FM.

WYAL-AM
Owner: Daybreak Broadcasting Company
Editorial: 25539 Highway 125, Scotland Neck, North Carolina 27874. **T:** 1 252 826-3066
Editorial Profile: WYAL-AM is a commercial station owned by Daybreak Broadcasting Company. The format of the station is gospel music. WYAL-AM broadcasts to the Scotland Neck, NC area at 1280 AM.

WYAM-AM
Owner: Decatur Communication Properties, LLC
Editorial: 1301 Central Pkwy Sw, Decatur, Alabama 35601-4817. **T:** 1 256 355-4567
Editorial Profile: WYAM-AM is a commercial station owned by Decatur Communications Properties, LLC. The format of the station is Hispanic music. WYAM-AM broadcasts in the Decatur, AL area at 890 AM.

WYAV-FM
Owner: Digity LLC
Editorial: 1016 Ocala St, Myrtle Beach, South Carolina 29577-8007. **T:** 1 843 448-1041
W: http://www.wave104.net
Editorial Profile: WYAV-FM is a commercial station owned by Digity LLC . The format of the station is classic rock music. WYAV-FM broadcasts to the Myrtle Beach, SC area at 104.1 FM.

WYAY-FM
Owner: Cumulus Media Inc
Editorial: 210 Interstate North Pkwy SE Fl 1, Atlanta, Georgia 30339-2230.
T: 1 404 497-4700
E: newsroom@newsradio1067.com
W: http://www.newsradio1067.com
Editorial Profile: WYAY-FM is a commercial station owned by Cumulus Media Inc. The format of the station is news/talk. WYAY-FM broadcasts to the Atlanta area at 106.7 FM.

WYBA-FM
Owner: Bible Broadcasting Network
Editorial: 385 Airport Rd, Coldwater, Michigan 49036-9313. **T:** 1 704 523-5555
E: bbn@bbnmedia.org
W: http://www.bbnradio.org
Editorial Profile: WYBA-FM is a non-commercial station owned by Bible Broadcasting Networ . The format of the station is religious music and programming. WYBA-FM broadcasts to the Coldwater, MI area at 90.1 FM.

WYBB-FM
Owner: L.M. Communications Inc.
Editorial: 59 Windermere Blvd, Charleston, South Carolina 29407-7411.
T: 1 843 769-4799
W: http://www.98xonline.com
Editorial Profile: WYBB-FM is a commercial station owned by L.M. Communications Inc. The format of the station is rock/album-oriented rock. WYBB-FM broadcasts to the Charleston, SC area at 98.1 FM.

WYBC-AM
Owner: Yale Broadcasting Co.
Editorial: 142 Temple St, Ste 203, New Haven, Connecticut 6510. **T:** 1 203 776-4118
E: news@wshu.org **W:** http://www.wshu.org
Editorial Profile: WYBC-AM is a commercial station owned by Yale Broadcasting Co. The station is being managed by Sacred Heart University. The format of the station is news/talk and classical music. WYBC-AM broadcasts to the Hartford-New Haven, CT area at 1340 AM.

WYBC-FM
Owner: Yale Broadcasting Co.
Editorial: 142 Temple St, New Haven, Connecticut 06510-2600. **T:** 1 203 776-4118
E: music@wybc.com
W: http://www.943wybc.com
Editorial Profile: WYBC-FM is a commercial station owned by Yale Broadcasting Co. and operated by Connoisseur Media. The format of the station is R&B Oldies music. WYBC-FM broadcasts to the Hartford-New Haven, CT area at 94.3 FM.

WYBF-FM
Owner: Cabrini College
Editorial: 610 King Of Prussia Rd, Radnor, Pennsylvania 19087-3623. **T:** 1 610 902-8453
E: wybf891@gmail.com
W: http://www.wybf.com
Editorial Profile: WYBF-FM is a commercial station owned by Cabrini College. The format of the station is college variety. WYBF-FM broadcasts to the Wayne, PA area at 89.1 FM.

WYBG-AM
Owner: Wade Communication Inc.
Editorial: 24 Andrews St, Massena, New York 13662-1804. **T:** 1 315 764-0554
E: wybgradio@nnymail.com
W: http://www.wybg1050.com
Editorial Profile: WYBG-AM is a commercial station owned by Wade Communication Inc. The format of the station is talk. WYBG-AM broadcasts to the Massena, NY area at 1050 AM.

WYBK-FM
Owner: Bible Broadcasting Network, Inc
Editorial: 1815 Union Ave, Chattanooga, Tennessee 37404-3530. **T:** 1 423 493-4382
Editorial Profile: WYBK-FM is a non-commercial station owned by Bible Broadcasting Network, Inc. The format for the station is religious. WYBK-FM broadcasts to the Chattanooga, TN area at 89.7 FM.

WYBL-FM
Owner: Media One Group
Editorial: 3226 Jefferson Rd, Ashtabula, Ohio 44004. **T:** 1 440 993-2126
W: http://www.983thebull.com
Editorial Profile: WYBL-FM is a commercial station owned by Media One Group. The format of the station is classic country. WYBL-FM broadcasts to the Ashtabula, OH area at 98.3 FM.

WYBR-FM
Owner: Mentor Partners Inc.
Editorial: 18720 16 Mile Rd, Big Rapids, Michigan 49307. **T:** 1 231 796-7000
E: news@bigrapidsradionetwork.com
W: http://www.wybr.com
Editorial Profile: WYBR-FM is a commercial station owned by Mentor Partners Inc. The format of the station is hot adult contemporary. WYBR-FM broadcasts to the Big Rapids, MI area at 102.3 FM.

WYBT-AM
Owner: Blountstown Communications
Editorial: 20872 NE Kelley Ave, Blountstown, Florida 32424. **T:** 1 850 674-5101
Editorial Profile: WYBT-AM is a commercial station owned by Blountstown Communications. The format of the station is oldies. WYBT-AM broadcasts to the Blountstown, FL area at 1000 AM.

WYBZ-FM
Owner: Y-Bridge Broadcasting
Editorial: 2895 Maysville Pike, Unit A, Zanesville, Ohio 43701. **T:** 1 740 453-6004
W: http://www.wybz.com
Editorial Profile: WYBZ-FM is a commercial station owned by Y-Bridge Broadcasting. The format of the station is oldies. WYBZ-FM broadcasts to the Zanesville, OH area at 107.3 FM.

WYCA-FM
Owner: Crawford Broadcasting Co.
Editorial: 6336 Calumet Ave, Hammond, Indiana 46324. **T:** 1 219 933-4455
W: http://www.wyca1023.com
Editorial Profile: WYCA-FM is a commercial station owned by Crawford Broadcasting Co. The format of the station is gospel music. WYCA-FM broadcasts to the Chicago area at 102.3 FM.

WYCB-AM
Owner: Radio One Inc.
Editorial: 5900 Princess Garden Pkwy, Ste 800, Lanham, Maryland 20706.
T: 1 301 306-1111
W: http://www.wycb1340.com
Editorial Profile: WYCB-AM is a commercial station owned by Radio One Inc. The format of the station is gospel music. WYCB-AM broadcasts to the Lanham, MD area at 1340 AM.

WYCD-FM
Owner: CBS Radio
Editorial: 26555 Evergreen Rd, Southfield, Michigan 48076-4206. **T:** 1 248 546-9600
W: http://wycd.cbslocal.com
Editorial Profile: WYCD-FM is a commercial station owned by CBS Radio. The format of the station is contemporary country. WYCD-FM broadcasts to the Detroit area at 99.5 FM.

WYCE-FM
Owner: Grand Rapids Cable Access Center Inc.
Editorial: 711 Bridge St NW, Grand Rapids, Michigan 49504-5560. **T:** 1 616 459-4788
E: comment@wyce.org
W: http://www.grcmc.org
Editorial Profile: WYCE-FM is a non-commercial station owned by Grand Rapids Cable Access Center Inc. The format of the station is variety. WYCE-FM broadcasts to the Grand Rapids, MI area at 88.1 FM.

WYCK-AM
Owner: Bold Gold Media Group
Editorial: 1049 N Sekol Ave, Scranton, Pennsylvania 18504-1040. **T:** 1 570 344-1221
E: foxsportsnepa@gmail.com
W: http://www.boldgoldradionepa.com
Editorial Profile: WYCK-AM is a commercial station owned by Bold Gold Media Group. The format of the station is sports. WYCK-AM broadcasts to the Scranton, PA area at 1340 AM.

WYCM-FM
Owner: Artistic Media Partners Inc.
Editorial: 3824 S 18th St, Lafayette, Indiana 47909-9102. **T:** 1 765 474-1410
Editorial Profile: WYCM-FM is a commercial owned by Artistic Media Partners Inc. The format of the station is contemporary country music. WYCM-FM broadcasts in the Lafayette, IN area at 95.7 FM.

WYCR-FM
Owner: McAnall(Joan)
Editorial: 275 Radio Rd, Hanover, Pennsylvania 17331-1140. **T:** 1 717 792-0098
E: info@thepeak985.com
W: http://www.thepeak985.com
Editorial Profile: WYCR-FM is a commercial station owned by Joan McAnall. The format of the station is classic hits. WYCR-FM broadcasts to the Hanover, PA area at 98.5 FM.

WYCT-FM
Owner: ADX Communications
Editorial: 7251 Plantation Rd, Pensacola, Florida 32504. **T:** 1 850 494-2800
E: comments@CatCountry987.com
W: http://www.catcountry987.com

Editorial Profile: WYCT-FM is a commercial station owned by ADX Communications. The format of the station is country. WYCT-FM broadcasts to the Pensacola, FL area at 98.7 FM.

WYCV-AM

Owner: Freedom Broadcasting Corp.
Editorial: 398 S Main St Highway 321-A, Granite Falls, North Carolina 28630.
T: 1 828 396-3361 **E:** wycvradio@charter.net
W: http://www.gospel9.com
Editorial Profile: WYCV-AM is a commercial station owned by Freedom Broadcasting Corp. The format of the station is Southern gospel music. WYCV-AM broadcasts to the Granite Falls, NC area at 900 AM.

WYCY-FM

Owner: Bold Gold Media Group
Editorial: 575 Grove St, Honesdale, Pennsylvania 18431. **T:** 1 570 253-1616
W: http://www.classichits1053.com
Editorial Profile: WYCY-FM is commercial station owned by Bold Gold Media Group. The format of the station is classic hits. WYCY-FM broadcasts to the Honesdale, PA, area at 105.3 FM.

WYDE-AM

Owner: Crawford Broadcasting Co.
Editorial: 120 Summit Pkwy, Birmingham, Alabama 35209-4741. **T:** 1 205 879-3324
W: http://www.101wyde.com
Editorial Profile: WYDE-AM is a commercial station owned by Crawford Broadcasting Co. The format of the station is talk. WYDE-AM broadcasts to the Birmingham, AL area at 1260 AM.

WYDE-FM

Owner: Crawford Broadcasting Co.
Editorial: 120 Summit Pkwy, Birmingham, Alabama 35209-4741. **T:** 1 205 879-3324
W: http://www.101wyde.com
Editorial Profile: WYDE-FM is a commercial station owned by Crawford Broadcasting Co. The format of the station is talk. WYDE-FM broadcasts to Birmingham, AL area at 101.1 FM.

WYDK-FM

Owner: Big Fish Broadcasting LLC
Editorial: 1347 S Eufaula Ave Ste H, Eufaula, Alabama 36027-3000. **T:** 1 334 232-4532
E: info@dock979.com
W: http://www.dock979.com
Editorial Profile: WYDK-FM is a commercial station owned by Big Fish Broadcasting LLC. The format of the station is oldies and classic hits music. The station airs locally at 97.9 FM.

WYDL-FM

Owner: Flinn Broadcasting Corp.
Editorial: 102 N Cass St, Corinth, Mississippi 38834-5726. **T:** 1 662 284-4611
Editorial Profile: WYDL-FM is a commercial station owned by Flinn Broadcasting Corp. The format of the station is classic rock. WYDL-FM is licensed to the Middleton, TN area and broadcasts at a frequency of 100.7 FM.

WYDR-FM

Owner: Midwest Communications Inc.
Editorial: 1420 Bellevue St, Green Bay, Wisconsin 54311. **T:** 1 920 435-3771
E: webmaster.wydr@wydrthedrive.com
W: http://www.wydrthedrive.com
Editorial Profile: WYDR-FM is a commercial station owned by Midwest Communications Inc. The format of the station is classic hits. WYDR-FM broadcasts to the Green Bay, WI area at 94.3 FM.

WYDS-FM

Owner: Cromwell Group Inc.(The)
Editorial: 410 N Water St, Decatur, Illinois 62523-2369. **T:** 1 217 428-4487
E: wydscontests@cromwellradio.com
W: http://www.decaturradio.com
Editorial Profile: WYDS-FM is a commercial station owned by The Cromwell Group Inc. The format of the station is Top 40/CHR. WYDS-FM broadcasts to the Decatur, IL area at 93.1 FM.

WYEA-AM

Owner: Marble City Media, LLC
Editorial: 1 Motes Rd, Sylacauga, Alabama 35150-1731. **T:** 1 256 249-4263
E: info@wyea.net **W:** http://www.wyea.net
Editorial Profile: WYEA-AM is a commercial radio station owned by Marble City Media, LLC. The format of the station is classic hits. WYEA-AM broadcasts to the South Central Alabama area locally at 1290 AM.

WYEC-FM

Owner: Virden Broadcasting Corporation
Editorial: 133 E Division St, Kewanee, Illinois 61443. **T:** 1 309 853-4471 **E:** wyec@wyec.com
W: http://www.wyec.com
Editorial Profile: WYEC-FM is a commercial station owned by Virden Broadcasting Corporation. The format of the station is easy listening. WYEC-FM broadcasts to the Kewanee, IL area at 93.9 FM.

WYEP-FM

Owner: Pittsburgh Community Broadcasting Corp.
Editorial: 67 Bedford Sq, Pittsburgh, Pennsylvania 15203-1152. **T:** 1 412 381-9131
E: info@wyep.org **W:** http://www.wyep.org
Editorial Profile: WYEP-FM is a non-commercial station owned by Pittsburgh Community Broadcasting Corp. The format of the station is adult album alternative. WYEP-FM broadcasts to the Pittsburgh area at 91.3 FM.

WYEZ-FM

Owner: Fidelity Broadcasting Inc.
Editorial: 3926 Wesley St, Ste 301, Myrtle Beach, South Carolina 29579.
T: 1 843 903-9962 **E:** staff@wezv.com
W: http://www.wezv.com
Editorial Profile: WYEZ-FM is a commercial station owned by Fidelity Broadcasting Inc. The format of the station is Rhythmic Contemporary/R&B. WYEZ-FM broadcasts to the Myrtle Beach, SC area at 94.5 FM.

WYFA-FM

Owner: Bible Broadcasting Network
Editorial: 1388 Old Waynesboro Rd, Waynesboro, Georgia 30830.
T: 1 706 523-5555
W: http://www.bbnradio.org
Editorial Profile: WYFA-FM is a non-commercial station owned by Bible Broadcasting Network. The format of the station is religious. WYFA-FM broadcasts to the Waynesboro, GA area at 107.1 FM.

WYFB-FM

Owner: Bible Broadcasting Network
Editorial: 11530 Carmel Commons Blvd, Charlotte, North Carolina 28226-3976.
T: 1 704 523-5555 **E:** bbn@bbnmedia.org
W: http://www.bbnradio.org
Editorial Profile: WYFB-FM is a non-commercial station owned by Bible Broadcasting Network. The format of the station is religious. WYFB-FM broadcasts to the Keystone Heights, FL area at 90.5 FM.

WYFH-FM

Owner: Bible Broadcasting Network
Editorial: 6150 Cannons Campground Rd, Cowpens, South Carolina 29330-9605.
T: 1 800 888-7077 **E:** bbn@bbnmedia.org
W: http://www.bbnradio.org
Editorial Profile: WYFH-FM is a non-commercial station owned by Bible Broadcasting Network. The format of the station is religious talk. WYFH-FM broadcasts to the Cowpens, SC, area at 90.7 FM.

WYFI-FM

Owner: Bible Broadcasting Network
Editorial: 4310 Indian River Rd Ste 5, Chesapeake, Virginia 23325-3100.
T: 1 800 888-7077 **E:** bbn@bbnmedia.org
W: http://www.bbnradio.org
Editorial Profile: WYFI-FM is a non-commercial station owned by Bible Broadcasting Network. The format of the station is Christian programming. WYFI-FM broadcasts to the Norfolk, VA area at 99.7 FM. This station DOES NOT want any PR contact.

WYFJ-FM

Owner: Bible Broadcasting Network
Editorial: 407 S Washington Hwy, Ashland, Virginia 23005. **T:** 1 800 888-7077
W: http://www.bbnradio.org
Editorial Profile: WYFI-FM is a non-commercial station owned by Bible Broadcasting Network. The format of the station is Christian programming. WYFI-FM broadcasts to the Ashland, VA area at 99.9 FM. This station DOES NOT want any PR contact.

WYFL-FM

Owner: Bible Broadcasting Network
Editorial: 11530 Carmel Commons Blvd, Charlotte, North Carolina 28226-3976.
T: 1 704 523-5555 **E:** bbn@bbnmedia.org
W: http://www.bbnradio.org
Editorial Profile: WYFL-FM is a non-commercial station owned by Bible Broadcasting Network. The format of the station is religious programming. WYFL-FM broadcasts to the Wake Forest, NC area at 92.5 FM.

WYFM-FM

Owner: Cumulus Media Inc.
Editorial: 4040 Simon Rd, Youngstown, Ohio 44512. **T:** 1 330 783-1000
W: http://www.y-103.com
Editorial Profile: WYFM-FM is a commercial station owned by Cumulus Media Inc. The format of the station is classic rock. WYFM-FM broadcasts to the Youngstown, OH area at 102.9 FM.

WYFQ-AM

Owner: Bible Broadcasting Network
Editorial: 11530 Carmel Commons Blvd, Charlotte, North Carolina 28226-3976.
T: 1 704 523-5555 **E:** bbn@bbnmedia.org
Editorial Profile: WYFQ-AM is a non-commercial station owned by Bible Broadcasting Network. The format of the station is religious. WYFQ-AM broadcasts to the Charlotte, NC area at 930 AM.

WYFQ-FM

Owner: Bible Broadcasting Network
Editorial: 11530 Carmel Commons Blvd, Charlotte, North Carolina 28226-3976.
T: 1 704 523-5555 **E:** bbn@bbnmedia.org
Editorial Profile: WYFQ-FM is a non-commercial station owned by Bible Broadcasting Network. The format of the station is religious. WYFQ-FM broadcasts to the Charlotte, NC area at 93.5 FM.

WYFX-FM

Owner: Original Company Inc.(The)
Editorial: 7109 Upton Rd, Mount Vernon, Indiana 47620. **T:** 1 812 838-4484
W: http://www.wyfxfm.com

WYGB-FM

Owner: Reising Radio Partners Inc.
Editorial: 825 Washington St, Columbus, Indiana 47201-6265. **T:** 1 812 379-1077
W: http://www.korncountry.com
Editorial Profile: WYGB-FM is a commercial station owned by Reising Radio Partners Inc. The format of the station is contemporary country music. WYGB-FM broadcasts to the Indianapolis area at 102.9 FM.

WYGE-FM

Owner: Ethel Huff Broadcasting
Editorial: 201 E 2nd St, London, Kentucky 40741-1403. **T:** 1 606 877-1326
E: wygeradio@yahoo.com
Editorial Profile: WYGE-FM is a commercial station owned by Ethel Huff Broadcasting. The format for the station is Christian. WYGE-FM broadcasts to the Lexington, KY area at 92.3 FM.

WYGH-AM

Owner: Hammond Broadcasting Inc.
Editorial: 4942 US Highway 27 N, Butler, Kentucky 41006-8653. **T:** 1 859 472-1075
E: wygh@fuse.net **W:** http://www.wiok.com
Editorial Profile: WYGH-AM is a commercial station owned by Hammond Broadcasting Inc. The format of the station is Southern gospel music and Hispanic religious programming. WYGH-AM broadcasts to the Paris, KY, area at 1440 AM.

WYGL-FM

Owner: Max Media
Editorial: 450 Route 204, Selinsgrove, Pennsylvania 17870-7975. **T:** 1 570 374-1155
W: http://983b.com/
Editorial Profile: WYGL-FM is a commercial station owned by Max Media. The format of the station is contemporary country music. WYGL-FM broadcasts to the Central Pennsylvania area at 100.5 FM.

WYGM-AM

Owner: Clear Channel Media and Entertainment
Editorial: 2500 Maitland Center Pkwy, Maitland, Florida 32751-7224.
T: 1 407 916-7800
W: http://www.740thegame.com/main.html
Editorial Profile: WYGM-AM is a commercial station owned by Clear Channel Media and Entertainment. The format is sports. WYGM-AM broadcasts to the Orlando, FL area at 740 AM.

WYGO-FM

Owner: Sliger Enterprises
Editorial: 2110 Oxnard Rd, Athens, Tennessee 37303. **T:** 1 423 745-1000
E: wygo@bellsouth.net
Editorial Profile: WYGO-FM is a commercial station owned by Sliger Enterprises. The format of the station is hot adult contemporary. WYGO-FM broadcasts to the Athens, TN area at 99.5 FM.

WYGR-AM

Owner: WYGR Broadcasting
Editorial: 1303 Chicago Dr SW, Wyoming, Michigan 49509. **T:** 1 616 452-8589
E: wygr1530@yahoo.com
W: http://www.wygr.net
Editorial Profile: WYGR-AM is a commercial station owned by WYGR Broadcasting. The format of the station is urban contemporary. WYGR-AM broadcasts to the Wyoming, MI area at 1530 AM.

WYGS-FM

Owner: Good Shepherd Radio
Editorial: 825 Washington St, Columbus, Indiana 47201-6265. **T:** 1 812 373-9947
W: http://www.wygs.org
Editorial Profile: WYGS-FM is a non-commercial station owned by Good Shepherd Radio. The format of the station is gospel music. WYGS-FM broadcasts to the Columbus, IN area at 91.1 FM.

WYGY-FM

Owner: Hubbard Broadcasting, Inc.
Editorial: 2060 Reading Rd, Cincinnati, Ohio 45202-1454. **T:** 1 513 699-5103
W: http://www.theworldwidewolf.com
Editorial Profile: WYGY-FM is a commercial station owned by Hubbard Broadcasting, Inc. The format of the station is classic country. WYGY-FM broadcasts to the Cincinnati area at 97.3 FM.

WYHL-AM

Owner: URBan Radio Broadcasting, LLC
Editorial: 3436 Highway 45 N, Meridian, Mississippi 39301-1509. **T:** 1 601 693-2661
Editorial Profile: WYHL-AM is a commercial station owned by URBan Radio Broadcasting, LLC. The format of the station is gospel. WYHL-AM broadcasts to the Meridian, MS area at 1450 AM.

WYHM-AM

Owner: The Holler, Inc.
Editorial: 319 W Rockwood St, Rockwood, Tennessee 37854-2245. **T:** 1 865 250-6718
Editorial Profile: WYHM-AM is a commercial station owned by Southern Media Group, Inc. The format of the station is a mix of high energy bluegrass music. WYHM-AM broadcasts to the Knoxville, TN area at 580 AM.

WYHT-FM

Owner: Clear Channel Media and Entertainment
Editorial: 1400 Radio Ln, Mansfield, Ohio 44906-2525. **T:** 1 419 529-2211
W: http://www.wyht.com
Editorial Profile: WYHT-FM is a commercial station owned by Clear Channel Media and Entertainment. The format of the station is hot adult contemporary. WYHT-FM broadcasts to the Mansfield, OH area at 105.3 FM.

WYHY-AM

Owner: Big River Radio Inc.
Editorial: 3027 Lester Ln, Ashland, Kentucky 41102-9642. **T:** 1 606 928-3778
W: http://www.1080wyhy.com
Editorial Profile: WYHY-AM is a commercial station owned by Big River Radio Inc. The format of the station is Southern gospel. WYHY-AM broadcasts to the Ashland, KY area at 1080 AM.

WYJB-FM

Owner: Albany Broadcasting Co.
Editorial: 6 Johnson Rd, Latham, New York 12110-5641. **T:** 1 518 786-6600
W: http://www.b95.com
Editorial Profile: WYJB-FM is a commercial station owned by Albany Broadcasting Co. The format of the station is Lite Rock/Lite AC music. WYJB-FM broadcasts in the Albany, NY area at 95.5 FM.

WYJJ-FM

Owner: Forever Communications Inc.
Editorial: 122 Radio Rd, Jackson, Tennessee 38301-3465. **T:** 1 731 427-3316
W: http://forevercomm.com
Editorial Profile: WYJJ-FM is a commercial station owned by Forever Communications Inc. The format is urban contemporary. WYJJ-FM broadcasts to the Trenton, TN area at 97.7 FM.

WYJK-FM

Owner: Keymarket Communications LLC
Editorial: 56325 High Ridge Rd, Bellaire, Ohio 43906-9707. **T:** 1 740 676-5661
W: http://www.wyjkfm.com
Editorial Profile: WYJK-FM is a commercial station owned by Keymarket Communications LLC. The format of the station is country. WYJK-FM broadcasts to the Wheeling, WV Steubenville, OH area at 100.5 FM.

WYKC-AM

Owner: Chatterbox Communications
Editorial: 1348 Sunset Dr, Grenada, Mississippi 38901. **T:** 1 662 226-1400

WYKE-FM

Owner: Baynet Management, Inc.
Editorial: 5399 W Gulf To Lake Hwy, Lecanto, Florida 34461-8531. **T:** 1 352 527-2341
Editorial Profile: WYKE-FM is a commercial station owned by Baynet Management, Inc. The format of the station is sports. WYKE-FM broadcasts to the Lecanto, FL area at 104.3 FM.

WYKK-FM

Owner: Educational Media Foundation
Editorial: 300 Castlewoods Blvd, Ste 8, Brandon, Mississippi 39047-7654.
T: 1 601 992-6988 **W:** http://www.klove.com
Editorial Profile: WYKK-FM is a commercial station owned by Educational Media Foundation. The format of the station is contemporary christian. WYKK-FM broadcasts in the Quitman, MS area at 98.9 FM.

WYKM-AM

Owner: Mountain States Radio Inc.
Editorial: 714 Nicholas St, Rupert, West Virginia 25984. **T:** 1 304 392-6003
E: wykm@frontiernet.net
Editorial Profile: WYKM-AM is a commercial station owned by Mountain States Radio Inc. The format of the station is classic country. WYKM-FM broadcasts to the Rupert, WV area at 1250 AM.

WYKR-FM

Owner: Puffer Broadcasting Inc.
Editorial: 1047 Route 302, Wells River, Vermont 5081. **T:** 1 802 757-2773
E: studio@wykr.com **W:** http://www.wykr.com
Editorial Profile: WYKR-FM is a commercial station owned by Puffer Broadcasting Inc. The format of the station is country. WYKR-FM broadcasts to the Wells River, VT area at 101.3 FM.

WYKS-FM

Owner: Gillen Broadcasting Corp.
Editorial: 7120 SW 24th Ave, Gainesville, Florida 32607. **T:** 1 352 331-2200
E: kiss1053@aol.com
W: http://www.kiss1053.com
Editorial Profile: WYKS-FM is a commercial station owned by Gillen Broadcasting Corp. The format of the station is Top 40/CHR music. WYKS-FM broadcasts to the Gainesville, FL area at 105.3 FM.

WYKT-FM

Owner: Staradio Corp.
Editorial: 70 Meadowview Ctr, Ste 400, Kankakee, Illinois 60901. **T:** 1 815 935-9555
W: http://www.kat1055.com
Editorial Profile: WYKT-FM is a commercial station owned by Staradio Corp. The format of the station is classic rock. WYKT-FM broadcasts to the Kankakee, IL area at 105.5 FM.

WYKX-FM

Owner: KMB Broadcasting Inc.
Editorial: 604 Ludington St, Escanaba, Michigan 49829. **T:** 1 906 786-3800
E: wykxinfo@yahoo.com
W: http://kmbbroadcasting.com/wykx
Editorial Profile: WYKX-FM is a commercial station owned by KMB Broadcasting Inc. The format for the station is country. WYKX-FM broadcasts to the Escanaba, MI area at 104.7 FM.

WYKY-FM

Owner: Forcht Broadcasting
Editorial: 290 Wtlo Rd, Somerset, Kentucky 42503-3728. **T:** 1 606 678-8151
E: wtlo@usa.com
W: http://www.somerset106.com
Editorial Profile: WYKY-FM is a commercial station owned by Forcht Broadcasting. The format of the station is adult hits. WYKY-FM broadcasts to the Somerset, KY area at 106.1 FM.

WYKZ-FM

Owner: Clear Channel Media and Entertainment
Editorial: 245 Alfred St, Savannah, Georgia 31408. **T:** 1 912 964-7794
E: river@987theriver.com
W: http://www.987theriver.com
Editorial Profile: WYKZ-FM is a commercial station owned by Clear Channel Media and Entertainment. The format of the station is adult contemporary. WYKZ-FM broadcasts to the Savannah, GA area at 98.7 FM.

WYLD-AM

Owner: Clear Channel Media and Entertainment
Editorial: 929 Howard Ave, New Orleans, Louisiana 70113. **T:** 1 504 679-7300
W: http://www.am940.com
Editorial Profile: WYLD-AM is a commercial station owned by Clear Channel Media and Entertainment. The format of the station is gospel music. WYLD-AM broadcasts to the New Orleans area at 940 AM.

WYLD-FM

Owner: Clear Channel Media and Entertainment
Editorial: 929 Howard Ave, New Orleans, Louisiana 70113. **T:** 1 504 679-7300
W: http://www.wyldfm.com
Editorial Profile: WYLD-FM is a commercial station owned by Clear Channel Media and Entertainment. The format of the station is urban adult contemporary music. WYLD-FM broadcasts to the New Orleans area at 98.5 FM.

WYLF-AM

Owner: M.B. Communications
Editorial: 100 Main St, Penn Yan, New York 14527-1233. **T:** 1 315 536-0850
E: admin@wylf.com **W:** http://www.wylf.com
Editorial Profile: WYLF-AM is a commercial station owned by M.B. Communications. The format of the station is adult standards music. WYLF-AM broadcasts to the Penn Yan, NY area at 850 AM.

WYLK-FM

Owner: Northshore Broadcasting Inc.
Editorial: 200 E Thomas St, Hammond, Louisiana 70401-3316. **T:** 1 985 345-0060
W: http://www.lake947.net
Editorial Profile: WYLK-FM is a commercial station owned by Northshore Broadcasting Inc. The format for the station is adult contemporary music. WYLK-FM broadcasts to the Hammond, LA area at 94.7 FM.

WYLL-AM

Owner: Salem Communications
Editorial: 25 Northwest Point Blvd, Ste 400, Elk Grove Village, Illinois 60007.
T: 1 847 956-5030 **W:** http://www.wyll.com
Editorial Profile: WYLL-AM is a commercial station owned by Salem Communications. The format of the station is Christian talk. WYLL-AM broadcasts to the entire Chicago metro area at 1160 AM.

WYLS-AM

Owner: Grantell Broadcasting Co.
Editorial: 11474 U S Highway 11, York, Alabama 36925. **T:** 1 205 392-5234
Editorial Profile: WYLS-AM is a commercial station owned by Grantell Broadcasting Co. The format for the station is blues. WYLS-AM broadcasts to the York, AL area at 670 AM.

WYMB-AM

Owner: Cumulus Media Inc.
Editorial: 2014 N Irby St, Florence, South Carolina 29501-1504. **T:** 1 843 661-5000
Editorial Profile: WYMB-AM is a commercial station owned by Cumulus Media Inc. The format of the station is sports. WYMB-AM broadcasts to the Florence, SC area at 920 AM.

WYMC-AM

Owner: JDM Communications Inc.
Editorial: 197 Wymc Dr, Mayfield, Kentucky 42066-6832. **T:** 1 270 247-1430
E: radio@wymcradio.com
W: http://www.mywymc.com
Editorial Profile: WYMC-AM is a commercial station owned by JDM Communications Inc. The format of the station is oldies music. WYMC-AM broadcasts to the Paducah, KY and Cape Girardeau, MO areas at 1430 AM.

WYMC-FM

Owner: JDM Communications Inc.
Editorial: 197 Wymc Dr, Mayfield, Kentucky 42066-6832. **T:** 1 270 247-1430
E: radio@wymcradio.com

W: http://www.mywymc.com
Editorial Profile: WYMC-FM is a commercial station owned by JDM Communications Inc. The format of the station is oldies. WYMC-FM broadcasts to the Paducah, KY and Cape Girardeau, MO area at 93.9 FM.

WYMG-FM

Owner: Saga Communications
Editorial: 3501 E Sangamon Ave, Springfield, Illinois 62707-9777. **T:** 1 217 753-5400
E: wymg@wymg.com
W: http://www.wymg.com
Editorial Profile: WYMG-FM is a commercial station owned by Saga Communications. The format of the station is classic rock. WYMG-FM broadcasts to the Springfield, IL area at 100.5 FM.

WYMJ-FM

Owner: Dailey Corp.
Editorial: 1130 4th St, New Martinsville, West Virginia 26155. **T:** 1 304 455-1111
E: wetz@suddenlinkmail.com
Editorial Profile: WYMJ-FM is a commercial station owned by Dailey Corp. The format of the station is country. WYMJ-FM broadcasts to the New Martinsville, WV area at 99.5 FM.

WYMM-AM

Owner: Word Broadcasting Network, Inc.
Editorial: 5900 Pickettville Rd, Jacksonville, Florida 32254-1172. **T:** 1 904 786-2400
E: lamasgrande1530@gmail.com
W: http://www.lamasgrande1530.com/
Editorial Profile: WYMM-AM is a commercial station owned by Word Broadcasting Network, Inc. The format of the station is Regional Mexican music. WYMM-AM broadcasts to the Jacksonville, FL area at 1530 AM.

WYMS-FM

Owner: The Milwaukee School Board
Editorial: 5312 W Vliet St, Milwaukee, Wisconsin 53208-2639. **T:** 1 414 475-8900
W: http://www.radiomilwaukee.org
Editorial Profile: WYMS-FM is a non-commercial station owned by the Milwaukee School Board. The format of the station is adult album alternative, urban and rock music. WYMS-FM broadcasts to the Milwaukee area at 88.9 FM.

WYMV-FM

Owner: Commonwealth Broadcasting Corp.
Editorial: 265 S Main St, Madisonville, Kentucky 42431-2557. **T:** 1 270 825-1079
Editorial Profile: WYMV-FM is a commercial station owned by Commonwealth Broadcasting Corp. The format of the station is adult contemporary. WYMV-FM broadcasts to the Madisonville, KY area at 106.9 FM.

WYMX-FM

Owner: TeleSouth Communications Inc.
Editorial: 3192 Browning Road 520, Greenwood, Mississippi 38930.
T: 1 662 453-2174
Editorial Profile: WYMX-FM is a commercial station owned by TeleSouth Communications Inc. The format of the station is oldies music. The station airs in the Greenwood, MS area at 99.1 FM.

WYMY-FM

Owner: Curtis Media Group
Editorial: 1109 Tower Dr, Burlington, North Carolina 27215-4425. **T:** 1 336 584-0126
E: wpcm@curtismedia.com
W: http://www.laleync.com
Editorial Profile: WYMY-FM is a commercial station owned by Curtis Media Group. The station is regional Mexican. WZTK-FM broadcasts to the Burlington, NC, area at 96.9 FM.

WYNA-FM

Owner: Clear Channel Media and Entertainment
Editorial: 4841 Highway 17 Byp S, Myrtle Beach, South Carolina 29577-6683.
T: 1 843 293-0107
W: http://www.1049bobfm.com
Editorial Profile: WYNA-FM is a commercial station owned by Clear Channel Media and Entertainment. The format of the station is adult hits music. WYNA-FM broadcasts to the Myrtle Beach, SC area at 104.9 FM.

WYNC-AM

Owner: Semora Broadcasting
Editorial: 545 Fire Tower Road, Yanceyville, North Carolina 27379. **T:** 1 336 694-7343
E: wync@embarqmail.com
Editorial Profile: WYNC-AM is a commercial station owned by Semora Broadcasting, Inc. The format of the station is gospel music.

WYNC-AM broadcasts in the Greensboro, NC area at 1540 AM.

WYND-AM

Owner: Buddy Tucker Association, Inc.
Editorial: 316 E Taylor Rd, Deland, Florida 32724. **T:** 1 386 734-1310
E: wynd@buddytuckerassociation.org
W: http://www.buddytuckerassociation.org
Editorial Profile: WYND-AM is a commercial station owned by Buddy Tucker Association, Inc. The format of the station is religious. WYND-AM broadcasts to the Deland, FL area at 1310 AM.

WYNF-AM

Owner: Clear Channel Media and Entertainment
Editorial: 2743 Perimeter Pkwy Ste 100-300, Augusta, Georgia 30909-6415.
T: 1 706 396-6000
E: augustapsa@clearchannel.com
W: http://www.espncsra.com
Editorial Profile: WYNF-AM is a commercial station owned by Clear Channel Media and Entertainment. The format of the station is sports. WYNF-AM broadcasts to the Augusta, GA area at 1340 AM.

WYNG-FM

Owner: Withers Broadcasting Co.
Editorial: 127 W 3rd St, Mount Carmel, Illinois 62863. **T:** 1 618 263-3500
E: wyng@wyng949.com
W: http://www.wyng949.com
Editorial Profile: WYNG-FM is a commercial station owned by Withers Broadcasting Co. The format of the station is classic hits. WYNG-FM broadcasts to the Evansville, IN area at 94.9 FM.

WYNK-FM

Owner: Clear Channel Media and Entertainment
Editorial: 5555 Hilton Ave, Ste 500, Baton Rouge, Louisiana 70808. **T:** 1 225 231-1860
W: http://www.wynk.com
Editorial Profile: WYNK-FM is a commercial station owned by Clear Channel Media and Entertainment. The format of the station is country music. WYNK-FM broadcasts to the Baton Rouge, LA area at 101.5 FM.

WYNN-AM

Owner: Cumulus Media Inc.
Editorial: 2014 N Irby St, Florence, South Carolina 29501. **T:** 1 843 661-5000
W: http://www.glory985.com
Editorial Profile: WYNN-AM is a commercial station owned by Cumulus Media Inc. The format of the station is gospel music. WYNN-AM broadcasts to the Florence, SC area at 540 AM.

WYNN-FM

Owner: Cumulus Media Inc.
Editorial: 2014 N Irby St, Florence, South Carolina 29501. **T:** 1 843 661-5000
W: http://www.wynn1063.com
Editorial Profile: WYNN-FM is a commercial station owned by Cumulus Media Inc. The format of the station is urban contemporary music. WYNN-FM broadcasts to the Florence, SC area at 106.3 FM.

WYNR-FM

Owner: Clear Channel Media and Entertainment
Editorial: 3833 US Highway 82, Brunswick, Georgia 31523-7735. **T:** 1 912 267-1025
W: http://1025wynr.net
Editorial Profile: WYNR-FM is a commercial station owned by Clear Channel Media and Entertainment. The format of the station is contemporary country. WYNR-FM broadcasts to the Brunswick, GA area at 102.5 FM.

WYNT-FM

Owner: Clear Channel Media and Entertainment
Editorial: 1330 N Main St, Marion, Ohio 43302. **T:** 1 740 383-1131
W: http://www.majic959.com
Editorial Profile: WYNT-FM is a commercial station owned by Clear Channel Media and Entertainment. The format of the station is Lite Rock/Lite AC. WYNT-FM broadcasts to the Marion, OH area at 95.9 FM.

WYNU-FM

Owner: Forever Communications Inc.
Editorial: 122 Radio Rd, Jackson, Tennessee 38301-3465. **T:** 1 731 427-3316
E: production@forevertn.com
W: http://fmu92.com
Editorial Profile: WYNU-FM is a commercial station owned by Forever Communications

Inc. The format of the station is classic hits. WYNU-FM broadcasts to the Jackson, TN area at 92.3 FM.

WYNW-FM
Owner: Starboard Media Foundation Inc.
Editorial: 645 25Th Ave N, Wisconsin Rapids, Wisconsin 54495-2223. **T:** 1 715 424-1300
E: info@relevantradio.com
W: http://www.relevantradio.com
Editorial Profile: WYNW-FM is a non-commercial station owned by Starboard Media Foundation Inc. The format of the station is religious and talk. WYNW-FM broadcasts to the Wisconsin Rapids, WI area at 92.9 FM.

WYNZ-FM
Owner: Saga Communications
Editorial: 420 Western Ave, South Portland, Maine 04106-1704. **T:** 1 207 774-4561
W: http://rewind1009.com
Editorial Profile: WYNZ-FM is a commercial station owned by Saga Communications. The format of the station is classic hits. WYNZ-FM broadcasts to the South Portland, ME area at 100.9 FM.

WYOO-FM
Owner: Magic Broadcasting, LLC
Editorial: 7106 Laird St, Ste 102, Panama City, Florida 32408. **T:** 1 850 230-5855
W: http://www.talkradio101.com
Editorial Profile: WYOO-FM is a commercial station owned by Magic Broadcasting, LLC. The format for the station is talk. WYOO-FM broadcasts to the Panama City, FL area at 101.1 FM.

WYOS-AM
Owner: Townsquare Media, Inc.
Editorial: 59 Court St, Binghamton, New York 13901-3270. **T:** 1 607 772-8400
Editorial Profile: WYOS-AM is a commercial station owned by Townsquare Media, Inc. The format of the station is sports. WYOS-AM broadcasts to the Binghampton, NY area at 1360 AM.

WYOY-FM
Owner: New South Communications Inc.
Editorial: 265 Highpoint Dr, Ridgeland, Mississippi 39157. **T:** 1 601 956-0102
W: http://www.y101.com
Editorial Profile: WYOY-FM is a commercial station owned by New South Communications Inc. The format of the station is Top 40/CHR music. WYOY-FM broadcasts to the Jackson, MS area at 101.7 FM.

WYPC-AM
Owner: Jackson County Broadcasting Inc.
Editorial: 295 E Main St, Jackson, Ohio 45640-1744. **T:** 1 740 286-3023
Editorial Profile: WYPC-AM is a commercial station owned by Jackson County Broadcasting Inc. The format of the station is sports. WYPC-AM broadcasts to the Jackson, OH area at 1330 AM.

WYPF-FM
Owner: WYPR License Holding LLC
Editorial: 2216 N Charles St, Baltimore, Maryland 21218. **T:** 1 410 235-1660
E: frontdesk@wypr.org
W: http://www.wypr.org
Editorial Profile: WYPF-FM is a non-commercial station owned by WYPR License Holding LLC. The format is news, talk and jazz. WYPF-FM broadcasts to the Baltimore area at 88.1 FM.

WYPL-FM
Owner: Cossitt Library
Editorial: 3030 Poplar Ave, Memphis, Tennessee 38111-3527. **T:** 1 901 415-2752
W: http://www.memphislibrary.org/wypl/index.html
Editorial Profile: WYPL-FM is a variety news, talk, music, children's programming station, which serves the Memphis area. The station is privately owned by the Memphis/Shelby County Public Library and Information Center. Send any information to the station via fax.

WYPM-FM
Owner: WITF Inc.
Editorial: 4801 Lindle Rd, Harrisburg, Pennsylvania 17111-2444. **T:** 1 717 704-3000
E: news@witf.org **W:** http://www.witf.org
Editorial Profile: WYPM-FM is a commercial station owned by WITF Inc. The format of the station is news and talk. WYPM-FM broadcasts to the Chambersburg, MD area at 93.3 FM.

WYPR-FM
Owner: WYPR License Holding LLC
Editorial: 2216 N Charles St, Baltimore, Maryland 21218. **T:** 1 410 235-1660
E: frontdesk@wypr.org
W: http://www.wypr.org
Editorial Profile: WYPR-FM is a non-commercial station owned by WYPR License Holding LLC. The format of the station is talk, news and jazz. WYPR-FM broadcasts to Baltimore area at 88.1 FM.

WYPV-FM
Owner: Northern Star Broadcasting LLC
Editorial: 1356 Mackinaw Ave, Cheboygan, Michigan 49721-1003. **T:** 1 231 627-2341
W: http://yourdefendingfathers.us
Editorial Profile: WYPV-FM is a commercial station owned by Northern Star Broadcasting LLC. The format of the station is Conservative talk. WYPV-FM broadcasts to the Mackinaw City, MI area at 94.5.

WYPZ-FM
Owner: Murray (Christopher L.)
Editorial: 6174 Hwy 57, Macon, Georgia 31217. **T:** 1 404 307-8079
Editorial Profile: WYPZ-FM is a commercial station owned by Christopher L. Murray, dba Praise 107.5 FM Radio LLC. The format of the station is black gospel. WYPZ-FM broadcasts to the Macon, GA area at 107.5 FM.

WYQQ-FM
Owner: Christian Mix Radio, Inc.
Editorial: 29 Trolley Crossing Rd #A, Charlton, Massachusetts 01507-1351.
T: 1 508 248-0049 **E:** info@wycm.com
W: http://www.wycm.com
Editorial Profile: WYQQ-FM is a non-commercial station owned by Christian Mix Radio, Inc. The format of the station is Contemporary Christian music. WYQQ-FM broadcasts to the Greater Worcester, MA area at a frequency of 90.1 FM.

WYQS-FM
Owner: Western North Carolina Public Radio Inc.
Editorial: 73 Broadway St, Asheville, North Carolina 28801-2919. **T:** 1 828 210-4800
E: info@wcqs.org **W:** http://www.wcqs.org
Editorial Profile: WYQS-FM is a non-commercial station owned by Western North Carolina Public Radio Inc. The format of the station is news and talk. WYQS-FM broadcasts to the Madison, NC area at 90.5 FM.

WYRD-AM
Owner: Entercom Communications Corp.
Editorial: 25 Garlington Rd, Greenville, South Carolina 29615-4613. **T:** 1 864 271-9200
W: http://www.espnupstate.com
Editorial Profile: WYRD-AM is a commercial station owned by Entercom Communications Corp. The format of the station is sports talk. WYRD-AM broadcasts to the Greenville, SC area at 1330 AM.

WYRD-FM
Owner: Entercom Communications Corp.
Editorial: 25 Garlington Rd, Greenville, South Carolina 29615-4613. **T:** 1 864 271-9200
W: http://www.word1063.com
Editorial Profile: WYRD-FM is a commercial station owned by Entercom Communications Corp. The format of the station is news and talk. WYRD-FM broadcasts to the Greenville, SC area at 106.3 FM.

WYRE-FM
Owner: Cortona Media, LLC
Editorial: 253 Zygmont Ct, Saint Augustine, Florida 32084-5846. **T:** 1 904 824-5500
W: http://www.wyrefm.com
Editorial Profile: WYRE-FM is a commercial station owned by Cortona Media, LLC. The format of the station is Hot AC. WYRE-FM broadcasts to the Jacksonville, FL area at 105.5 FM.

WYRK-FM
Owner: Townsquare Media, LLC
Editorial: 14 Lafayette Sq, Buffalo, New York 14203-1928. **T:** 1 716 852-7444
W: http://www.wyrk.com
Editorial Profile: WYRK-FM is a commercial station owned by Townsquare Media, LLC. The format of the station is contemporary country. WYRK-FM broadcasts to the Buffalo, NY area at 106.5 FM.

WYRN-AM
Owner: Johnson Broadcast Ventures
Editorial: 495 Building, Highway 561 East, Louisburg, North Carolina 27549.
T: 1 919 496-4071
Editorial Profile: WYRN-AM is a commercial station owned by Johnson Broadcast Ventures. The format of the station is gospel, R&B and oldies. WYRN-AM broadcasts to the greater Raleigh, NC area at 1480 AM.

WYRO-FM
Owner: Davis Broadcasting Media
Editorial: 295 E Main St, Jackson, Ohio 45640-1744. **T:** 1 740 286-3023

WYRQ-FM
Owner: Little Falls Radio Corp.
Editorial: 16405 Haven Rd, Little Falls, Minnesota 56345. **T:** 1 320 632-2992
W: http://www.fallsradio.com
Editorial Profile: WYRQ-FM is a commercial station owned by Little Falls Radio Corp. The format of the station is contemporary country music. WYRQ-FM broadcasts to the Little Falls, MN area at 92.1 FM.

WYRV-AM
Owner: Faith Communications, Inc.
Editorial: 504 Middle Creek Rd, Cedar Bluff, Virginia 24609. **T:** 1 276 964-9619
W: http://wyrvam770.com
Editorial Profile: WYRV-AM is a commercial station owned by Faith Communications, Inc. The format of the station is contemporary Christian music. WYRV-AM broadcasts to the Cedar Bluff, VA area at 770 AM.

WYRY-FM
Owner: Tri-Valley Broadcasting
Editorial: 30 Warwick Rd, Ste 10, Winchester, New Hampshire 3470. **T:** 1 603 239-8200
E: wyry@wyry.com **W:** http://www.wyry.com
Editorial Profile: WYRY-FM is a commercial station owned by Tri-Valley Broadcasting. The format of the station is contemporary country. WYRY-FM broadcasts to the Winchester, NH area at 104.9 FM.

WYSA-FM
Owner: Side By Side Inc.
Editorial: 5115 Glendale Ave, Toledo, Ohio 43614. **T:** 1 419 389-0893
E: yesfm@yeshome.com
W: http://www.yeshome.com

WYSC-FM
Owner: Cinecom Broadcasting Systems Inc.
Editorial: Highway 341 South, McRae, Georgia 31055. **T:** 1 229 868-5611
Editorial Profile: WYSC-FM is a commercial station owned by Cinecom Broadcasting Systems Inc. The format of the station is urban adult contemporary. WYSC-FM broadcasts to the Macon, GA area at 102.7 FM.

WYSE-AM
Owner: Saga Communications
Editorial: 1190 Patton Ave, Asheville, North Carolina 28806. **T:** 1 828 259-9695
W: http://www.1310bigwise.com
Editorial Profile: WYSE-AM is a commercial station owned by Saga Communications. The format of the station is sports. WYSE-AM broadcasts to the Asheville, NC area at 970 AM.

WYSH-AM
Owner: Clinton Broadcasters
Editorial: 111 Hillcrest Dr, Clinton, Tennessee 37716-2024. **T:** 1 865 457-1380
E: wysh@wyshradio.com
W: http://www.wyshradio.com

WYSL-AM
Owner: Radio Livingston Ltd.
Editorial: 5620 S Lima Rd, Avon, New York 14414-9791. **T:** 1 585 346-3000
E: news@wysl1040.com
W: http://www.wysl1040.com
Editorial Profile: WYSL-AM is a commercial station owned by Radio Livingston Ltd. The format of the station is news, talk and sports. WYSL-AM broadcasts to the Avon, NY area at 1040 AM.

WYSO-FM
Owner: Antioch University
Editorial: 800 Livermore St, Yellow Springs, Ohio 45387-1608. **T:** 1 937 767-6420
E: wyso@wyso.org **W:** http://www.wyso.org
Editorial Profile: WYSO-FM is a non-commercial station owned by Antioch University. The format of the station is news and adult album alternative music. WYSO-FM broadcasts to the Yellow Springs, OH area at 91.3 FM.

WYSS-FM
Owner: Sovereign Communications LLC
Editorial: 1402 Ashmun St, Sault Sainte Marie, Michigan 49783. **T:** 1 906 635-0995
W: http://www.yesfm.net
Editorial Profile: WYSS-FM is a commercial station owned by Sovereign Communications LLC. The format of the station is Top 40/CHR music. WYSS-FM broadcasts to the Sault Sainte Marie, MI area at 99.5 FM.

WYSU-FM
Owner: Youngstown State University
Editorial: 1 University Plz, Youngstown, Ohio 44555. **T:** 1 330 941-3363 **E:** info@wysu.org
W: http://www.wysu.org
Editorial Profile: WYSU-FM is a non-commercial station owned by Youngstown State University. The format of the station is classical music. WYSU-FM broadcasts to the Youngstown, OH area at 88.5 FM.

WYSX-FM
Owner: Stephens Media Group LLC
Editorial: 1 Bridge Plz, Ste 204, Ogdensburg, New York 13669. **T:** 1 315 393-1220
W: http://www.yesfm.com
Editorial Profile: WYSX-FM is a commercial station owned by Stephens Media Group LLC. The format of the station is Top 40/CHR. WYSX-FM broadcasts to the Ogdensburg, NY area at 96.7 FM.

WYSZ-FM
Owner: Side By Side Inc.
Editorial: 5105 Glendale Ave, Toledo, Ohio 43614-1850. **T:** 1 419 389-0893
E: yesfm@yeshome.com
W: http://www.yeshome.com
Editorial Profile: WYSZ-FM is a non-commercial station owned by Side By Side Inc. The format of the station is contemporary Christian. WYSZ-FM broadcasts to the Toledo, OH area at 89.3 FM.

WYTE-FM
Owner: NRG Media LLC
Editorial: 2301 Plover Rd, Plover, Wisconsin 54467. **T:** 1 715 341-8838
W: http://www.wyte.com
Editorial Profile: WYTE-FM is a commercial station owned by NRG Media LLC. The format of the station is contemporary country. WYTE-FM broadcasts in the Plover, WI, area at 106.5 FM.

WYTI-AM
Owner: Jefferson(William E.)
Editorial: 275 Glennwood Dr, Rocky Mount, Virginia 24151. **T:** 1 540 483-9955
E: wyti@wytiradio.com
W: http://www.wytiradio.com
Editorial Profile: WYTI-AM is a commercial station owned by William E. Jefferson. The format of the station is classic country, bluegrass and gospel music. WYTI-AM broadcasts to the Rocky Mount, VA area at 1570 AM.

WYTK-FM
Owner: Valley Broadcasting
Editorial: 113 N Seminary St, Florence, Alabama 35630-4701. **T:** 1 256 764-9390
E: thescore@939thescore.com
W: http://www.939thescore.com
Editorial Profile: WYTK-FM is a commercial station owned by Valley Broadcasting. The format of the station is sports. WYTK-FM broadcasts to the Florence, AL area at 93.9 FM.

WYTM-FM
Owner: Time Broadcasting Inc.
Editorial: 76 Molino Rd, Fayetteville, Tennessee 37334-3813. **T:** 1 931 433-1531
Editorial Profile: WYTM-FM is a commercial station owned by Time Broadcasting Inc. The format of the station is country. WYTM-FM broadcasts to the Huntsville, AL area at 105.5 FM.

WYTN-FM
Owner: Family Stations Inc.
Editorial: 3930 Sunset Blvd, Youngstown, Ohio 44512. **T:** 1 815 725-1331
E: info@familyradio.org
W: http://www.familyradio.com
Editorial Profile: WYTN-FM is a commercial station owned by Family Stations Inc. The format of the station is religious programming. WYTN-FM broadcasts to the Youngstown, OH area at 91.7 FM.

WYTS-AM
Owner: Clear Channel Media and Entertainment
Editorial: 2323 W 5th Ave, Ste 200, Columbus, Ohio 43204. **T:** 1 614 486-6101
W: http://www.talk1230wyts.com

Editorial Profile: WYTS-AM is a commercial station owned by Clear Channel Media and Entertainment. The format of the station is sports. WYTS-AM broadcasts to the Columbus, OH area at 1230 AM.

WYTZ-FM

Owner: Midwest Family Stations
Editorial: 580 E Napier Ave, Benton Harbor, Michigan 49022. **T:** 1 269 925-1111
E: wildbill@wytz.com
W: http://975ycountry.com
Editorial Profile: WYTZ-FM is a commercial station owned by Midwest Family Stations. The format of the station is country music. WYTZ-FM broadcasts to the Benton Harbor, MI area at 97.5 FM.

WYUL-FM

Owner: Martz Communications
Editorial: 86 Porter Rd, Malone, New York 12953. **T:** 1 518 483-1100
E: news@country965.com
W: http://www.947hits.com
Editorial Profile: WYUL-FM is a commercial station owned by Martz Communications. The format of the station is Top 40/CHR music. WYUL-FM broadcasts to the Malone, NY and Pointe-Claire, QC area at 94.7 FM.

WYUM-FM

Owner: Vidalia Communications Group
Editorial: 1501 Mount Vernon Rd, Vidalia, Georgia 30474-3031. **T:** 1 912 538-1017
W: http://www.southeastgeorgiatoday.com
Editorial Profile: WYUM-FM is a commercial station owned by Vidalia Communications Group. The format for the station is classic country. WYUM-FM broadcasts to the Savannah, GA area at 101.7 FM.

WYUR-FM

Owner: Milner Broadcasting Co.
Editorial: 202 E Walnut St, Watseka, Illinois 60970-1356. **T:** 1 815 933-9287
E: wvlifm@comcast.net
W: http://www.rivervalleyradio.net
Editorial Profile: WYUR-FM is a commercial station owned by Milner Broadcasting Co. The format of the station is contemporary country. WYUR-FM broadcasts to the Gilman, IL area at 103.7 FM.

WYUS-AM

Owner: Delmarva Broadcasting
Editorial: 1666 Blairs Pond Rd, Milford, Delaware 19963-5263. **T:** 1 302 422-7575
W: http://laexitosa.com
Editorial Profile: WYUS-AM is a commercial station owned by Delmarva Broadcasting. The format of the station is Hispanic music. WYUS-AM broadcasts in the Milford, DE area at 930 AM.

WYUU-FM

Owner: CBS Radio
Editorial: 9721 Executive Center Dr N Ste 200, Saint Petersburg, Florida 33702-2439.
T: 1 727 579-1925
W: http://www.925maxima.com
Editorial Profile: WYUU-FM is a commercial station owned by CBS Radio. The format of the station is Hispanic music. WYUU-FM broadcasts to the Tampa, FL, area at 92.5 FM.

WYVE-AM

Owner: Three Rivers Media Corp.
Editorial: 110 W Spiller St, Wytheville, Virginia 24382. **T:** 1 276 228-3185
E: office@threeriversmedia.net
W: http://www.wyve.com

WYVK-FM

Owner: Positive Radio Group
Editorial: 39540 Bradbury Rd, Middleport, Ohio 45760-9703. **T:** 1 740 992-6485
E: k92thefrog@yahoo.com
W: http://www.wyvk.com
Editorial Profile: WYVK-FM is a commercial station owned by Positive Radio Group. The format for the station is hot adult contemporary. WYVK-FM broadcasts to the Charleston-Huntington, WV area at 92.1 FM.

WYVN-FM

Owner: Midwest Communications Inc.
Editorial: 87 Central Ave, Holland, Michigan 49423-2829. **T:** 1 616 392-3121
E: info@927thevan.com
W: http://www.927thevan.com
Editorial Profile: WYVN-FM is a commercial station owned by Midwest Communications Inc. The format of the station is classic hits. WYVN-FM broadcasts to the Holland, MI area at 92.7 FM.

WYWY-AM

Owner: Barbourville Community Broadcasting
Editorial: 222 Daniel Boone Dr, Barbourville, Kentucky 40906-1104. **T:** 1 606 546-4128
E: production@wkkqfm.com
W: http://www.wywyradio.com
Editorial Profile: WYWY-AM is a commercial station owned by Barbourville Community Broadcasting. The format of the station is gospel. WYWY-AM broadcasts to the Barbourville, KY area at 950 AM.

WYXB-FM

Owner: Emmis Communications Corp.
Editorial: 40 Monument Cir, Ste 600, Indianapolis, Indiana 46204.
T: 1 317 684-1057 **W:** http://www.b1057.com
Editorial Profile: WYXB-FM is a commercial station owned by Emmis Communications Corp. The format for the station is Lite Rock/Lite AC. WYXB-FM broadcasts to the Indianapolis area at 105.7 FM.

WYXC-AM

Owner: Clarion Communication, Inc.
Editorial: 1410 Highway 411 Ne, Cartersville, Georgia 30121-5115. **T:** 1 770 334-8302
E: news@newstalk1270.com
W: http://www.newstalk1270.com
Editorial Profile: WYXC-AM is a commercial station owned by Clarion Communication, Inc. The format of the station is news/talk. WYXC-AM broadcasts to the Cartersville, GA area at a frequency of 1270 AM.

WYXE-AM

Owner: Iglesia de Dios Hispana Pentecostal
Editorial: 1079 E Trinity Ln, Nashville, Tennessee 37216-3043. **T:** 1 615 227-1130
W: http://www.radiovida1130.com
Editorial Profile: WYXE-AM is a commercial station owned by Iglesia de Dios Hispana Pentecostal. The format of the station is Hispanic religious programming. WYXE-AM broadcasts to the Tacoma, WA area at 1130 AM.

WYXI-AM

Owner: Cornerstone Broadcasting Inc.
Editorial: 104 Cherry St, Athens, Tennessee 37303-7401. **T:** 1 423 745-1390
E: wyxi@bellsouth.net **W:** http://www.wyxi.com
Editorial Profile: WYXI-AM is a commercial station owned by Cornerstone Broadcasting Inc. The format for the station is oldies and talk. WYXI-AM broadcasts to the Chattanooga, TN area at 1390 AM.

WYXL-FM

Owner: Saga Communications
Editorial: 1751 Hanshaw Rd, Ithaca, New York 14850-9105. **T:** 1 607 257-6400
W: http://www.lite97fm.com
Editorial Profile: WYXL-FM is a commercial station owned by Saga Communications. The format of the station is adult contemporary. WYXL-FM broadcasts to the Ithaca, NY area at 97.3 FM.

WYXY-FM

Owner: Saga Communications
Editorial: 2603 W Bradley Ave, Champaign, Illinois 61821-1823. **T:** 1 217 352-4141
W: http://www.wixy.com
Editorial Profile: WYXY-FM is a commercial station owned by Saga Communications. The format of the station is country. WYXY-FM broadcasts to the Champaign, IL area at 99.1 FM.

WYYC-AM

Owner: Wilkins Communications Network Inc.
Editorial: 1545 N Queen St, York, Pennsylvania 17404-2129. **T:** 1 717 848-4418
E: wyyc@wilkinsradio.com
W: http://www.wilkinsradio.com
Editorial Profile: WYYC-AM is a commercial station owned by Wilkins Communications Network Inc. The format of the station is Christian programming. WYYC-AM broadcasts to the York, PA area at 1250 AM.

WYYD-FM

Owner: Clear Channel Media and Entertainment
Editorial: 3807 Brandon Ave SW, SW Suite 2350, Roanoke, Virginia 24018-1490.
T: 1 540 725-1220
W: http://www.newcountry1079.com/main.html
Editorial Profile: WYYD-FM is a commercial station owned by Clear Channel Media and Entertainment. The format of the station is country. WYYD-FM broadcasts to the Roanoke, VA area at 107.9 FM.

WYYS-FM

Owner: Mendota Broadcasting
Editorial: 3905 Progress Blvd, Peru, Illinois 61354. **T:** 1 815 224-2100
E: wyys@theradiogroup.net
W: http://www.classichits106.com
Editorial Profile: WYYS-FM is a commercial station owned by Mendota Broadcasating. The format of the station is classic hits. WYYS-FM broadcasts to the Peru, IL area at 106.1 FM.

WYYU-FM

Owner: North Georgia Radio Group
Editorial: 613 Silver Cir, Dalton, Georgia 30721-4551. **T:** 1 706 278-5511
E: mix1045@ngaradio.com
W: http://mixx1045.com
Editorial Profile: WYYU-FM is a commercial station owned by North Georgia Radio Group. The format of the station is adult contemporary. WYYU-FM broadcasts to the Dalton, GA area at 104.5 FM.

WYYX-FM

Owner: Magic Broadcasting, LLC
Editorial: 7106 Laird St, Ste 102, Panama City, Florida 32408. **T:** 1 850 230-5855
W: http://www.wyyx.com
Editorial Profile: WYYX-FM is a commercial station owned by Magic Broadcasting, LLC. The format of the station is rock alternative music. WYYX-FM broadcasts to the Panama City, FL area at 97.7 FM.

WYYY-FM

Owner: Clear Channel Media and Entertainment
Editorial: 500 Plum St Ste 100, Syracuse, New York 13204-1401. **T:** 1 315 472-9797
W: http://www.y94fm.com
Editorial Profile: WYYY-FM is a commercial station owned by Clear Channel Media and Entertainment. The format of the station is adult contemporary. WYYY-FM broadcasts to the Syracuse, NY area at 94.5 FM.

WYYZ-AM

Owner: Enlightment LLC
Editorial: 268 Hood Rd, Jasper, Georgia 30143. **T:** 1 706 692-4100
E: wyyz_1490am@yahoo.com
W: http://www.wyyzradio.net
Editorial Profile: WYYZ-AM is a commercial station owned by Enlightment LLC. The format of the station is classic country, gospel and talk. WYYZ-AM broadcasts in the Jasper, GA area at 1490 AM.

WYZB-FM

Owner: Cumulus Media Inc.
Editorial: 225 Hollywood Blvd NW, Fort Walton Beach, Florida 32548-4725.
T: 1 850 243-2323
W: http://www.nashfm1055.com
Editorial Profile: WYZB-FM is a commercial station owned by Cumulus Media Inc. The format for the station is contemporary country. WYZB-FM broadcasts to the Fort Walton Beach, FL area at 105.5 FM.

WYZD-AM

Owner: Gospel Broadcasting Inc.
Editorial: 121 Atkins St, Dobson, North Carolina 27017. **T:** 1 336 356-1560
E: wyzdradio@yahoo.com
W: http://www.wyzdradio.org
Editorial Profile: WYZD-AM is a non-commercial station owned by Gospel Broadcasting Inc. The format of the station is gospel and religious programming. WYZD-AM broadcasts to the Dobson, NC area at 1560 AM.

WYZE-AM

Owner: GHB Broadcasting
Editorial: 1111 Boulevard SE, Atlanta, Georgia 30312-3810. **T:** 1 404 622-7802
E: wyzepressmail@bellsouth.net
W: http://www.wyzeradio.com
Editorial Profile: WYZE-AM is a non-commercial station owned by GHB Broadcasting. The format of the station is gospel. WYZE-AM broadcasts to the Atlanta area at 1480 AM.

WYZI-AM

Owner: Oconee River Broadcasting
Editorial: 259 Turner St, Royston, Georgia 30662-3920. **T:** 1 706 246-0059
Editorial Profile: WYZI-AM is a commercial station owned by Oconee River Broadcasting. The format of the station is sports. WYZI-AM broadcasts to the Royston, GA area at 810 AM.

WYZY-FM

Owner: Mountain Communications

Editorial: 159 Santanoni Ave, Saranac Lake, New York 12983. **T:** 1 518 891-1544
E: news@wnbz.com
W: http://www.y1063i.com
Editorial Profile: WYZY-FM is a commercial station owned by Mountain Communications. The format of the station is adult contemporary music. WYZY-FM broadcasts to the Saranac Lake, NY area at 106.3 FM.

WZAB-AM

Owner: Salem Communications
Editorial: 2828 W Flagler St, Miami, Florida 33135-1337. **T:** 1 305 644-0800
W: http://www.880thebiz.com
Editorial Profile: WZAB-AM is a commercial station owned by Salem Communications. The format of the station is business news and talk. WZAB-AM broadcasts to the Miami area at 880 AM.

WZAC-FM

Owner: Price Broadcasting
Editorial: 351 Hopkins Ave, Danville, West Virginia 25053. **T:** 1 304 369-5201
E: wzac@kvinet.com
Editorial Profile: WZAC-FM is a commercial station owned by Price Broadcasting. The format of the station is country music. WZAC-FM broadcasts to the Danville, WV area at 92.5 FM.

WZAD-FM

Owner: Townsquare Media
Editorial: 2 Pendell Rd, Poughkeepsie, New York 12601-1513. **T:** 1 845 471-1500
E: newsroom@pendellrd.com
W: http://www.hudsonvalleycountry.com
Editorial Profile: WZAD-FM is a commercial station owned by Townsquare Media. The format of the station is country. WZAD-FM broadcasts to the Poughkeepsie, NY area at 97.3 FM.

WZAE-FM

Owner: Radio Training Network, Inc.
Editorial: 102 Lecompte Ave, North Augusta, South Carolina 29841-3032.
T: 1 803 819-3125 **E:** info@wafj.com
W: http://www.wafj.com
Editorial Profile: WZAE-FM is a non-commercial station owned by Radio Training Network, Inc. The format of the station is Contemporary Christian. WZAE-FM broadcasts to the Wadley, SC area at 93.3 FM.

WZAK-FM

Owner: Radio One Inc.
Editorial: 2510 Saint Clair Ave NE, Cleveland, Ohio 44114-4013. **T:** 1 216 579-1111
Editorial Profile: WZAK-FM is a commercial station owned by Radio One Inc. The format of the station is urban adult contemporary. WZAK-FM broadcasts to the Cleveland area at 93.1 FM.

WZAM-AM

Owner: Taconite Broadcasting
Editorial: 121 N Front St, Ste A, Marquette, Michigan 49855. **T:** 1 906 225-9100
W: http://www.espn970.com
Editorial Profile: WZAM-AM is a commercial station owned by Taconite Broadcasting. The format of the station is sports. WZAM-AM broadcasts to the Marquette, MI area at 970 AM.

WZAN-AM

Owner: Saga Communications
Editorial: 420 Western Ave, South Portland, Maine 04106-1704. **T:** 1 207 774-4561
W: http://www.970wzan.com
Editorial Profile: WZAN-AM is a commercial station owned by Saga Communications. The format of the station is news, sports, and talk. WZAN-AM broadcasts to the Portland, ME area at 970 AM.

WZAP-AM

Owner: RAM Communications Inc.
Editorial: 11373 Wallace Pike, Bristol, Virginia 24202-2743. **T:** 1 276 669-6950
E: wzapradio@aol.com
W: http://www.wzapradio.com
Editorial Profile: WZAP-AM is a commercial station owned by RAM Communications Inc. The format of the station is religious programming. WZAP-AM broadcasts to the Bristol, VA area at 690 AM.

WZAQ-FM

Owner: Expression Production Group
Editorial: 113 E Madison St, Louisa, Kentucky 41230-1324. **T:** 1 606 638-9203
E: info@wzaqfm.com
W: http://www.wzaqfm.com

Editorial Profile: WZAQ-FM is a commercial station owned by Expression Production Group. The format for the station is contemporary Christian. WZAQ-FM broadcasts to the Charleston-Huntington, WV area at 92.3 FM.

WZAT-FM
Owner: Cumulus Media Inc.
Editorial: 214 Television Cir, Savannah, Georgia 31406-4519. **T:** 1 912 961-9000
W: http://www.sportsradio1021.com
Editorial Profile: WZAT-FM is a commercial station owned by Cumulus Media Inc. The format of the station is sports/talk. WZAT-FM broadcasts to the Savannah, GA area at 102.1 FM.

WZAX-FM
Owner: First Media Radio LLC
Editorial: 12714 Hwy 97 E, Rocky Mount, North Carolina 27803. **T:** 1 252 442-8092
E: wecare@firstmedianc.com
W: http://www.jammin993.com
Editorial Profile: WZAX-FM is a commercial station owned by First Media Radio LLC. The format of the station is classic hits. WZAX-FM broadcasts to the Rocky Mount, NC area at 99.3 FM.

WZAZ-AM
Owner: Titus Harvest Dome Spectrum Church Inc
Editorial: 4190 Belfort Rd, Ste 450, Jacksonville, Florida 32216. **T:** 1 904 470-4707
E: programming@wzaz.com
W: http://www.wzaz.com
Editorial Profile: WZAZ-AM is a commercial station owned by Titus Harvest Dome Spectrum Church Inc. The format of the station is gospel. WZAZ-AM broadcasts in the Jacksonville, FL area at 1400 AM.

WZBA-FM
Owner: Shamrock Communications
Editorial: 11350 McCormick Rd, Exec Plaza 3 #701, Hunt Valley, Maryland 21031-1002.
T: 1 410 771-8484
W: http://www.thebayonline.com
Editorial Profile: WZBA-FM is a commercial station owned by Shamrock Communications Inc. The format of the station is classic rock music. WZBA-FM broadcasts to Baltimore area at 100.7 FM.

WZBB-FM
Owner: Brook(Donny)
Editorial: 10899 Virginia Ave, Bassett, Virginia 24055. **T:** 1 276 629-7999
E: traffic@wzbbfm.com
W: http://www.supercountryonline.com
Editorial Profile: WZBB-FM is a commercial station owned by Donny Brook. The format of the station is country. WZBB-FM broadcasts to the Rocky Mount, VA area at 99.9 FM.

WZBC-FM
Owner: Boston College
Editorial: 107 McElroy Commons, Boston College, Chestnut Hill, Massachusetts 2167.
T: 1 617 552-3511 **E:** wzbcfm@gmail.com
W: http://www.wzbc.org
Editorial Profile: WZBC-FM is non-commercial station owned by Boston College. The format of the station is rock alternative. WZBC-FM broadcasts to the Boston area at 90.3 FM.

WZBD-FM
Owner: Adams County Radio Inc.
Editorial: 955 US Highway 27 N, Berne, Indiana 46711. **T:** 1 260 726-8729
E: wzbd@onlyinternet.net
W: http://www.wzbd.com
Editorial Profile: WZBD-FM is a commercial station owned by Adams County Radio Inc. The format of the station is adult contemporary music. WZBD-FM broadcasts to the Berne, IN area at 92.7 FM.

WZBG-FM
Owner: Local Boys and Girls Broadcasting
Editorial: 49 Commons Dr, Litchfield, Connecticut 6759. **T:** 1 860 567-3697
E: info@wzbg.com **W:** http://www.wzbg.com
Editorial Profile: WZBG-FM is a commercial station owned by Local Boys and Girls Broadcasting. The format for the station is adult contemporary music. WZBG-FM broadcasts to the Hartford-New Haven, CT area at 97.3 FM.

WZBH-FM
Owner: Great Scott Broadcasting
Editorial: 20200 Dupont Blvd, Georgetown, Delaware 19947. **T:** 1 302 856-2567
W: http://www.wzbhrocks.com

Editorial Profile: WZBH-FM is a commercial station owned by Great Scott Broadcasting. The format of the station is rock/album oriented rock music. WZBH-FM broadcasts in the Salisbury, MD area at 93.5 FM.

WZBK-AM
Owner: Saga Communications
Editorial: 69 Stanhope Ave, Keene, New Hampshire 3431. **T:** 1 603 352-9230
Editorial Profile: WZBK-AM is a commercial station owned by Saga Communications and is the ESPN Radio affliate for the Keene, NH area. The format of the station is sports. WZBK-AM broadcasts at 1220 AM.

WZBN-FM
Owner: Greater 2nd Mt. Olive Missionary Baptist Church
Editorial: 235 W Roosevelt Ave Ste 203, Albany, Georgia 31701-5110.
T: 1 229 888-3778
E: power1055albany@gmail.com
W: http://www.power105theking.com
Editorial Profile: WZBN-FM is a commercial station owned by Light Media. The format of the station is contemporary gospel music. WZBN-FM broadcasts to the Albany, GA area at 105.5 FM.

WZBO-AM
Owner: East Carolina Radio Group
Editorial: 911 Parsonage St, Elizabeth City, North Carolina 27909. **T:** 1 252 335-4379
Editorial Profile: WZBO-AM is a commercial station owned by East Carolina Radio Group. The format of the station is Hispanic. WZBO-AM broadcasts to the Elizabeth City, NC area at 1260 AM.

WZBQ-FM
Owner: Clear Channel Media and Entertainment
Editorial: 3900 11th Ave, Tuscaloosa, Alabama 35401. **T:** 1 205 344-4589
W: http://www.941zbq.com
Editorial Profile: WZBQ-FM is a commercial station owned by Clear Channel Media and Entertainment. The format of the station is Top 40/CHR music. WZBQ-FM broadcasts to the Tuscaloosa, AL area at 94.1 FM.

WZBX-FM
Owner: Georgia Eagle Broadcasting Inc.
Editorial: 561 E Olliff St, Statesboro, Georgia 30458-4663. **T:** 1 912 764-5446
E: wwnswmcd@yahoo.com
Editorial Profile: WZBX-FM is a commercial station owned Georgia Eagle Broadcasting Inc. The format of the station is classic rock. WZBX-FM broadcasts to the Savannah, GA area at 106.5 FM.

WZBZ-FM
Owner: Equity Communications LP
Editorial: 8025 Black Horse Pike, Pleasantville, New Jersey 08232-2900. **T:** 1 609 484-8444
W: http://993thebuzz.com
Editorial Profile: WZBZ-FM is a commercial station owned by Equity Communications LP. The format of the station is urban contemporary. WZBZ-FM broadcasts to the Atlantic City, NJ area at 99.3 FM.

WZCC-AM
Owner: Sun Coast Radio
Editorial: 174 Ne 351 Hwy, Cross City, Florida 32628-3120. **T:** 1 352 498-0304
W: http://www.suncoastradio.com
Editorial Profile: WZCC-AM is a commercial station owned by Suncoast Radio. The format of the station is oldies music. The station airs locally at 1240 AM.

WZCH-FM
Owner: Clear Channel Media and Entertainment
Editorial: 7080 Industrial Hwy, Macon, Georgia 31216. **T:** 1 478 781-1063
W: http://www.newcountry1025.com
Editorial Profile: WZCH-FM is a commercial station owned by Clear Channel Media and Entertainment and licensed to the Aloha Station Trust, LLC. The format of the station is contemporary country. WZCH-FM broadcasts to the Macon, GA area at 102.5 FM.

WZCP-FM
Owner: One Connection Media Group
Editorial: 881 E Johnstown Rd, Gahanna, Ohio 43230-1851. **T:** 1 614 855-9171
E: theriver@1049theriver.com
W: http://www.riverradio.com
Editorial Profile: WZCP-FM is a non-commercial station owned by One Connection Media Group. The format of the station is

contemporary Christian. WZCP-FM broadcasts to the Chillicothe, OH area at 89.3 FM.

WZCR-FM
Owner: Clear Channel Media and Entertainment
Editorial: 5620 State Route 9G, Hudson, New York 12534. **T:** 1 518 828-5006
W: http://www.cruisin935.com
Editorial Profile: WZCR-FM is a commercial station owned by Clear Channel Media and Entertainment. The format of the station is oldies. WZCR-FM broadcasts to the Hudson, NY area at 93.5 FM.

WZCT-AM
Owner: Bonner/Carlile Enterprises Inc.
Editorial: 1111 E Willow St, Scottsboro, Alabama 35768-2210. **T:** 1 256 574-1330
E: wzct5000watts@scottsboro.org
W: http://www.southerngospelam1330.com

WZCY-FM
Owner: Cumulus Media Inc.
Editorial: 515 S 32nd St, Camp Hill, Pennsylvania 17011-5106. **T:** 1 717 635-7000
W: http://www.nashfm1067.com
Editorial Profile: WZCY-FM is a commercial station owned by Cumulus Media Inc. The format of the station is contemporary country. WZCY-FM broadcasts to the Harrisburg, PA area at 106.7 FM.

WZDB-FM
Owner: First Media Radio LLC
Editorial: 801 E Dubois Ave, Du Bois, Pennsylvania 15801-3643. **T:** 1 814 371-8300
E: q102radio@comcast.net
W: http://www.959zdb.com
Editorial Profile: WZDB-FM is a commercial station owned by First Media Radio LLC. The format of the station is classic rock. WZDB-FM broadcasts to the Du Bois, PA area at 95.9 FM.

WZDM-FM
Owner: Original Company Inc.(The)
Editorial: 522 Busseron St, Vincennes, Indiana 47591. **T:** 1 812 882-6060
E: wzdm@wzdm.com
W: http://www.wzdm.com
Editorial Profile: WZDM-FM is a commercial station owned The Original Company Inc. The format of the station is adult contemporary. WZDM-FM broadcasts to the Vincennes, IN area at 92.1 FM.

WZDQ-FM
Owner: Southern Stone Communications, LLC
Editorial: 111 W Main St, Jackson, Tennessee 38301-6147. **T:** 1 731 427-9616
E: 1023therocket@thomasmedia.fm
W: http://jacksonnewsnow.com
Editorial Profile: WZDQ-FM is a commercial station owned by Southern Stone Communications, LLC. The format of the station is rock/album-oriented rock. WZDQ-FM broadcasts to the Jackson, TN area at 102.3 FM.

WZDR-FM
Owner: Midwest Communications Inc.
Editorial: 1420 Bellevue St, Green Bay, Wisconsin 54311. **T:** 1 920 435-3771
E: webmaster.wydr@wydrthedrive.com
W: http://www.wydrthedrive.com
Editorial Profile: WZDR-FM is a commercial station owned by Midwest Communications Inc. The format of the station is classic hits. WZDR-FM broadcasts to the Green Bay, WI area at 99.7 FM.

WZEB-FM
Owner: Great Scott Broadcasting
Editorial: 20200 Dupont Blvd, Georgetown, Delaware 19947. **T:** 1 302 856-2567
Editorial Profile: WZEB-FM is a commercial station owned by Great Scott Broadcasting. The format of the station is hot adult contemporary music. WZEB-FM broadcasts in the Salisbury, MD area at 101.7 FM.

WZEE-FM
Owner: Clear Channel Media and Entertainment
Editorial: 2651 S Fish Hatchery Rd, Fitchburg, Wisconsin 53711. **T:** 1 608 274-1070
W: http://www.z104fm.com
Editorial Profile: WZEE-FM is a commercial station owned by Clear Channel Media and Entertainment. The format of the station is Top 40/CHR. WZEE-FM broadcasts to the Madison, WI area at 104.1 FM.

WZEP-AM
Owner: Walton County Broadcasting Inc.

Editorial: 449 N 12th St, Defuniak Springs, Florida 32433. **T:** 1 850 892-3158
E: wzep@wzep1460.com
W: http://www.wzep1460.com
Editorial Profile: WZEP-AM is a commercial station owned by Walton County Broadcasting Inc. The format of the station is variety, including country and oldies. WZEP-AM broadcasts to the DeFuniak Springs, FL area at 1460 AM.

WZEW-FM
Owner: Dot Com Plus, LLC
Editorial: 1100 Dauphin St, Ste E, Mobile, Alabama 36604. **T:** 1 251 438-5460
E: 92zew@92zew.net **W:** http://www.92zew.net
Editorial Profile: WZEW-FM is a commercial station owned by Dot Com Plus, LLC . The format for the station is adult album alternative. WZEW-FM broadcasts to the Mobile, AL area at 92.1 FM.

WZFC-FM
Owner: Centennial Broadcasting
Editorial: 520 N Pleasant Valley Rd, Winchester, Virginia 22601. **T:** 1 540 667-2224
Editorial Profile: WZFC-FM is a commercial station owned by Centennial Broadcasting. The format of the station is country. WZFC-FM broadcasts to the Winchester, VA area at 104.9 FM.

WZFG-AM
Owner: SMAHH Communications, LLC
Editorial: 3301 University Dr S, Fargo, North Dakota 58104-6289. **T:** 1 701 356-4220
E: support@am1100theflag.com
W: http://am1100theflag.com
Editorial Profile: WZFG-AM is a commercial station owned by SMAHH Communications, LLC. The format of the station is news and talk. WZFG-AM broadcasts to the Fargo, ND area at 1100 AM.

WZFM-FM
Owner: Positive Radio Group
Editorial: 145 Jackson St NE, Blacksburg, Virginia 24060. **T:** 1 540 951-9791
Editorial Profile: WZFM-FM is a commercial station owned by Positive Radio Group. The format of the station is classic hits. WZFM-FM broadcasts to the Blacksburg, VA area at 101.3 FM.

WZFR-FM
Owner: Faith Radio Network, Inc.
Editorial: 35 Island Dr Ste 16, Eastpoint, Florida 32328-3264. **T:** 1 850 201-1070
W: http://www.faithradio.us
Editorial Profile: WZFR-FM is a commercial station owned by Faith Radio Network, Inc. The format of the station is Christian and religious talk. WZFR-FM broadcasts to the Eastpoint, FL area at 104.5 FM.

WZFT-FM
Owner: Clear Channel Media and Entertainment
Editorial: 711 W 40th St Ste 350, Baltimore, Maryland 21211-2190. **T:** 1 410 366-7600
W: http://www.z1043.com
Editorial Profile: WZFT-FM is a commercial station owned by Clear Channel Media and Entertainment. The format of the station is Top 40/CHR. WZFT-FM broadcasts to Baltimore area at 104.3 FM.

WZFX-FM
Owner: Beasley Broadcast Group
Editorial: 508 Person St, Fayetteville, North Carolina 28301. **T:** 1 910 486-4114
E: wzfx@foxy99.com
W: http://www.foxy99.com
Editorial Profile: WZFX-FM is a commercial station owned by Beasley Broadcasting Group. The format of the station is urban contemporary music. WZFX-FM broadcasts to the Fayetteville, NC area at 99.1 FM.

WZGC-FM
Owner: CBS Radio
Editorial: 1201 Peachtree St Ne Ste 800, Atlanta, Georgia 30361-6318.
T: 1 404 898-8900
W: http://atlanta.cbslocal.com/station/ 92-9-the-game/
Editorial Profile: WZGC-FM is a commercial station owned by the CBS Radio. The format of the station is sports. WZGC-FM broadcasts to the Atlanta area at 92.9 FM.

WZGL-FM
Owner: Illinois Bible Institute
Editorial: 4101 Fieldstone Rd, Champaign, Illinois 61822-8800. **T:** 1 217 359-8232
E: wbgl@wbgl.org **W:** http://www.wbgl.org

Editorial Profile: WZGL-FM is a non-commercial station owned by the Illinois Bible Institute. The format of the station is contemporary Christian music and talk. WZGL-FM broadcasts to the Champaign, IL area at 88.1 FM.

WZGM-AM
Owner: HRN Broadcasting Inc.
Editorial: 101 West St, Black Mountain, North Carolina 28711-3166. T: 1 828 669-6224
Editorial Profile: WZGM-AM is a commercial station owned by HRN Broadcasting Inc and operated by News Talk 50, Inc. The format of the station is talk. WZGM-AM broadcasts to the Asheville, NC area at 1350 AM.

WZGN-FM
Owner: Monticello Media LLC
Editorial: 1150 Pepsi Pl, Ste 300, Charlottesville, Virginia 22901.
T: 1 434 978-4408
W: http://www.generations1023.com
Editorial Profile: WZGN-FM is a commercial station owned by Monticello Media LLC. The format of the station is classic hits. WZGN-FM broadcasts in the Charlottesville, VA area at 102.3 FM.

WZGO-FM
Owner: Pathway Christian Academy Inc.
Editorial: 205 N Greene St, Snow Hill, North Carolina 28580. T: 1 252 747-8887
E: wago@gomixradio.org
W: http://www.gomixradio.org
Editorial Profile: WZGO-FM is a non-commercial station owned by Pathway Christian Academy Inc. The format of the station is Christian programming. WZGO-FM broadcasts to the Snow Hill, NC area at 91.1 FM.

WZGV-AM
Owner: HRN Broadcasting Inc.
Editorial: 1366 Startown Rd, Lincolnton, North Carolina 28092-8038. T: 1 704 732-8011
W: http://www.espn730.com
Editorial Profile: WZGV-AM is a commercial station owned by HRN Broadcasting Inc. The format of the station is sports. The station is affiliated with ESPN Radio. WZGV-AM broadcasts to the Shelby, NC area at 730 AM.

WZGX-AM
Owner: Rivera Communications
Editorial: 100 Yeager Pkwy, Pelham, Alabama 35124-1859. T: 1 205 358-1100
Editorial Profile: WZGX-AM is commercial station owned by Rivera Communications. The format of the station is regional Mexican and tropical music. WZGX-AM broadcasts to the Bessemer, AL area at 1450 AM.

WZHF-AM
Owner: Multicultural Radio Broadcasting Inc.
Editorial: 13321 New Hampshire Ave, Ste 207, Silver Spring, Maryland 20904-3450.
T: 1 301 879-9077
Editorial Profile: WZHF-AM is a commerical station owned by Multicultural Radio Broadcasting Inc. The format of the station is Spanish-language news talk. WZHF-AM broadcasts to Silver Spring, MD at 1390 AM.

WZHR-AM
Owner: Radio World
Editorial: 706 N Myrtle Ave, Clearwater, Florida 33755-4219. T: 1 727 441-3311
Editorial Profile: WZHR-AM is a commercial station owned by Radio World. The format of the station is contemporary Christian. WZHR-AM broadcasts to the Tampa area at 1400 AM.

WZHT-FM
Owner: Clear Channel Media and Entertainment
Editorial: 203 Gunn Rd, Montgomery, Alabama 36117. T: 1 334 274-6464
W: http://www.myhot105.com
Editorial Profile: WZHT-FM is a commercial station owned by Clear Channel Media and Entertainment. The format of the station is urban contemporary. WZHT-FM broadcasts to the Montgomery, AL area at 105.7 FM.

WZID-FM
Owner: Saga Communications
Editorial: 500 N Commercial St, Manchester, New Hampshire 03101-1151.
T: 1 603 669-5777 W: http://www.wzid.com
Editorial Profile: WZID-FM is a commercial station owned by Saga Communications. The format of the station is adult contemporary music. WZID-FM broadcasts to the Manchester, NH area at 95.7 FM.

WZIM-FM
Owner: Great Plains Media
Editorial: 108 Boeykens Pl, Normal, Illinois 61761-2139. T: 1 309 888-4496
W: http://www.magic995fm.com
Editorial Profile: WZIM-FM is a commercial station owned by Great Plains Media. The format of the station is adult contemporary. WZIM-FM broadcasts to the Normal, IL area at 99.5 FM.

WZIP-FM
Owner: University of Akron
Editorial: University Of Akron, Akron, Ohio 44325. T: 1 330 972-7105
E: wzip@uakron.edu W: http://www.wzip.fm
Editorial Profile: WZIP-FM is a commercial station owned by University of Akron. The format of the station is Top 40/CHR and rock at night. WZIP-FM broadcasts to the Akron, OH area at 88.1 FM.

WZJS-FM
Owner: High Country Adventures, LLC
Editorial: 738 Blowing Rock Rd, Boone, North Carolina 28607-4835. T: 1 828 264-2411
E: info@wataradio.com
W: http://goblueridge.net
Editorial Profile: WZJS-FM is a commercial station owned by High Country Adventures, LLC, a subsidiary of Curtis Media Group. The format of the station is classic hits. WZJS-FM broadcasts to the Boone, NC area at 100.7 FM.

WZJY-AM
Owner: Jabar Communications, Inc.
Editorial: 5081 Rivers Ave, North Charleston, South Carolina 29406. T: 1 843 554-1063
W: http://www.jabarcommunications.com
Editorial Profile: WZJY-AM is a commercial station owned by Jabar Communications, Inc. The format of the station is Hispanic Top 40/CHR. WZJY-AM broadcasts to the North Charleston, SC area at 1480 AM.

WZJZ-FM
Owner: Clear Channel Media and Entertainment
Editorial: 13320 Metro Pkwy, Ste 1, Fort Myers, Florida 33966-4703. T: 1 239 225-4300
W: http://www.z100florida.com
Editorial Profile: WZJZ-FM is a commercial station owned by Clear Channel Media and Entertainment. The format of the station is Top 40/CHR. WZJZ-FM broadcasts to the Fort Myers, FL area at 100.1 FM.

WZKB-FM
Owner: Carolina's Christian Broadcasting Inc.
Editorial: 409 Warsaw Rd, Clinton, North Carolina 28328-3550. T: 1 910 592-7601
Editorial Profile: WZKB-FM is a commercial station owned by Carolina's Christian Broadcasting Inc. The format of the station is Hispanic CHR. WZKB-FM broadcasts to the Wallace, NC area at 94.3 FM.

WZKR-FM
Owner: Morning Star Media, LLC
Editorial: 1106 18th Ave, Meridian, Mississippi 39301-4101. T: 1 601 693-1103
E: b103@comcast.net
Editorial Profile: WZKR-FM is a commercial station owned by Morning Star Media, LLC. The format of the station is classic hits. WZKR-FM broadcasts to the Meridian, MS area at 103.3 FM.

WZKS-FM
Owner: URBan Radio Broadcasting, LLC
Editorial: 3436 Highway 45 N, Meridian, Mississippi 39301-1509. T: 1 601 483-5477
E: meridianproduction@urbanradio.fm
W: http://www.1041kissfm.com
Editorial Profile: WZKS-FM is a commercial station owned by URBan Radio Broadcasting, LLC. The format for the station is urban adult contemporary music. WZKS-FM broadcasts to the Meridian, MS area at 104.1 FM.

WZKX-FM
Owner: Dowdy Broadcasting, Inc.
Editorial: 10250 Lorraine Rd, Gulfport, Mississippi 39503. T: 1 228 896-5500
W: http://www.kicker108.com
Editorial Profile: WZKX-FM is a commercial station owned by Dowdy Broadcasting, Inc. The format of the station is contemporary country music. WZKX-FM broadcasts to the Gulfport, MS area at 107.9 FM.

WZKY-AM
Owner: Stanly Communications Inc.
Editorial: 1234 Magnolia St, Albemarle, North Carolina 28001. T: 1 704 983-1580
E: wspc@ctc.net

W: http://www.1010wspc.com
Editorial Profile: WZKY-AM is a commercial station owned by Stanly Communications Inc. The format of the station is oldies. WZKY-AM broadcasts to the Albemarle, NC area at 1580 AM.

WZKZ-FM
Owner: Pembrook Pines Media Group
Editorial: 3012 Eastside Ave, Wellsville, New York 14895. T: 1 585 593-9553
E: wzkz@wny.twcbc.com
W: http://www.kz102fm.com
Editorial Profile: WZKZ-FM is a commercial station owned by Pembrook Pines Media Group. The format of the station is contemporary country. WZKZ-FM broadcasts to the Wellsville, NY area at 101.9 FM.

WZLA-FM
Owner: Rocket 88 Broadcasting, LLP.
Editorial: 112 N Main St, Abbeville, South Carolina 29620. T: 1 864 366-5785
E: z93@wctel.net W: http://www.z93oldies.com
Editorial Profile: WZLA-FM is a commercial station owned by Rocket 88 Broadcasting, LLP. The format of the station is oldies. WZLA-FM broadcasts to the Abbeville, SC area at 92.9 FM.

WZLB-FM
Owner: Apex Broadcasting, Inc
Editorial: 34 Harbor Blvd Ste 202, Destin, Florida 32541-7365. T: 1 850 654-1000
Editorial Profile: WZLB-FM is a commercial station owned by Apex Broadcasting, Inc. The station's format is active rock. WZLB-FM broadcasts to the Mobile, AL, Pensacola, FL area at 103.1 FM.

WZLD-FM
Owner: Clear Channel Media and Entertainment
Editorial: 6555 U S Highway 98, Ste 8, Hattiesburg, Mississippi 39402.
T: 1 601 296-9800 E: contact@wzldfm.com
W: http://www.wzldfm.com
Editorial Profile: WZLD-FM is a commercial station owned by Clear Channel Media and Entertainment. The format of the station is urban contemporary. WZLD-FM broadcasts to the Hattiesburg, MS area at 106.3 FM.

WZLF-FM
Owner: WBIN, Inc.
Editorial: 106 N Main St, West Lebanon, New Hampshire 03784-1136. T: 1 603 298-0332
W: http://www.953thewolf.com
Editorial Profile: WZLF-FM is a commercial station owned by WBIN, Inc. The format of the station is country. WZLF-FM broadcasts to the West Lebanon, NH area at 107.1 FM.

WZLK-FM
Owner: East Kentucky Radio Network
Editorial: 1240 Radio Dr, Pikeville, Kentucky 41501-4779. T: 1 606 437-4051
E: frontdesk@ekbradio.com
W: http://www.1075zrock.com
Editorial Profile: WZLK-FM is a commercial station owned by East Kentucky Radio Network. The format for the station is Top 40/CHR. WZLK-FM broadcasts to the Pikeville, KY area at 107.5 FM.

WZLO-FM
Owner: Zone Corporation(The)
Editorial: 14 E Main St, Dover Foxcroft, Maine 04426-1414. T: 1 207 564-2642
E: wzlo@zoneradio.com
W: http://www.wzlofm.com
Editorial Profile: WZLO-FM is a commercial station owned by The Zone Corporation. WZLO-FM broadcasts to the Dover Foxcroft, ME area at 103.1 FM. The station's format is Adult Alternative music.

WZLQ-FM
Owner: Mississippi Radio Group
Editorial: 2214 S Gloster St, Tupelo, Mississippi 38801-6814. T: 1 662 842-7658
W: http://www.z985.net
Editorial Profile: WZLQ-FM is a commercial station owned by Mississippi Radio Group. The format of the station is rock. WZLQ-FM broadcasts to the Columbus, MS area at 98.5.

WZLR-FM
Owner: Cox Media Group, Inc.
Editorial: 1611 S Main St, Dayton, Ohio 45409-2547. T: 1 937 259-2111
W: http://www.953theeagle.com
Editorial Profile: WZLR-FM is a commercial station owned by Cox Media Group, Inc. The format of the station is classic rock. WZLR-FM broadcasts to the Dayton, OH area at 95.3 FM.

WZLT-FM
Owner: Lexington Broadcasting Service, Inc.
Editorial: 584 Smith Ave, Lexington, Tennessee 38351. T: 1 731 968-9990
E: wzlt993@yahoo.com
W: http://www.wzlt993.com
Editorial Profile: WZLT-FM is a commercial station owned by Lexington Broadcasting Service, Inc. The format of the station is adult contemporary. WZLT-FM broadcasts to the Lexington, TN area at 99.3 FM.

WZLX-FM
Owner: CBS Radio
Editorial: 83 Leo M Birmingham Pkwy, Boston, Massachusetts 2135.
T: 1 617 746-5100 W: http://www.wzlx.com
Editorial Profile: WZLX-FM is a commercial station owned by CBS Radio. The format of the station is classic rock. WZLX-FM broadcasts to the Boston area at 100.7 FM.

WZLY-FM
Owner: Wellesley College
Editorial: 106 Central St, Wellesley, Massachusetts 02481-8203.
T: 1 781 283-2791 E: wzly@wellesley.edu
W: http://www.wzly.net
Editorial Profile: WZLY-FM is a non-commercial college station owned by Wellesley College. The primary format of the station is AAA. WZLY-FM broadcasts to Wellesley, MA at 91.5 FM.

WZMB-FM
Owner: East Carolina University
Editorial: Menden Hall Student Center ECU, Greenville, North Carolina 27858.
T: 1 252 328-4751 E: wzmb@ecu.edu
W: http://www.ecu.edu/wzmb/stream.cfm
Editorial Profile: WZMB-FM is a non-commercial station owned by East Carolina University. The format of the station is college variety. WZMB-FM's broadcasts in the Greenville, NC area at 91.3 FM.

WZMG-AM
Owner: Clear Channel Media and Entertainment
Editorial: 915 Veterans Pkwy, Opelika, Alabama 36801-3367. T: 1 334 745-4656
W: http://www.intouch910am.com
Editorial Profile: WZMG-AM is a commercial station owned by Clear Channel Media and Entertainment. The format of the station is R&B oldies music. WZMG-AM broadcasts to the Opelika, AL area at 910 AM.

WZMJ-FM
Owner: Lake Murray Communications, LLC
Editorial: 109 Old Chapin Rd Ste R, Lexington, South Carolina 29072-2065.
T: 1 803 785-9596
E: lakemurrayradio@comporium.net
W: http://www.lakemurrayradio.com
Editorial Profile: WZMJ-FM is a commercial station owned by Lake Murray Communications, LLC. The format of the station is adult hits. WZMJ-FM broadcasts to Columbia, SC at 93.1 FM.

WZMR-FM
Owner: Albany Broadcasting Co.
Editorial: 6 Johnson Rd, Latham, New York 12110-5641. T: 1 518 786-6600
W: http://www.1049thepeak.com/
Editorial Profile: WZMR-FM is a commercial station owned by Albany Broadcasting Co. The format of the station is Triple A. WZMR-FM broadcasts in the Albany, NY area at 104.9 FM.

WZMX-FM
Owner: CBS Radio
Editorial: 10 Executive Dr, Farmington, Connecticut 6032. T: 1 860 677-6700
W: http://www.hot937.com
Editorial Profile: WZMX-FM is a commercial station owned by CBS Radio. The format of the station is urban contemporary. WZMX-FM broadcasts to the Farmington, CT area at 93.7 FM.

WZNE-FM
Owner: Stephens Media Group
Editorial: 28 E Main St Fl 8, Rochester, New York 14614-1915. T: 1 585 399-5700
E: info@thezone941.com
W: http://www.thezone941.com
Editorial Profile: WZNE-FM is a commercial station owned by Stephens Media Group. The format of the station is rock alternative. WZNE-FM broadcasts to the Rochester, NY area at 94.1 FM.

WZNF-FM
Owner: Dowdy Broadcasting, Inc.

Editorial: 10250 Lorraine Rd, Gulfport, Mississippi 39503. **T:** 1 228 896-5500
W: http://www.z95fm.com
Editorial Profile: WZNF-FM is a commercial station owned by Dowdy Broadcasting, Inc. The format of the station is classic rock music. WZNF-FM broadcasts to the Biloxi and Gulfport, MS area at 95.3 FM.

WZNG-AM
Owner: Jax Broadcasting, LLC
Editorial: 236 Woodland Dr, Shelbyville, Tennessee 37160-6759. **T:** 1 931 680-1214
E: wlijradio@gmail.com
W: http://www.thisisjaxradio.com
Editorial Profile: WZNG-AM is a commercial station owned by Jax Broadcasting, LLC. The format of the station is news, sports, and talk. WZNG-AM broadcasts to the Shelbyville, TN area at 1400 AM.

WZNJ-FM
Owner: Westburg Broadcasting Alabama, LLC.
Editorial: 1226 Jefferson Rd, Demopolis, Alabama 36732. **T:** 1 334 289-1106
W: http://www.znj1065.com
Editorial Profile: WZNJ-FM is a commercial station owned by Westburg Broadcasting Alabama, LLC. The format of the station is classic rock music. WZNJ-FM broadcasts to the Demopolis, AL area at 106.5 FM.

WZNL-FM
Owner: Sovereign Communications, LLC
Editorial: 101 Kent St, Iron Mountain, Michigan 49801. **T:** 1 906 774-4321
Editorial Profile: WZNL-FM is a commercial station owned by Sovereign Communications, LLC. The format of the station is adult contemporary. WZNL-FM broadcasts to the Norway, MI area at a frequency of 94.3 FM.

WZNN-FM
Owner: Summit Media Broadcasting, LLC
Editorial: 2700 Corporate Dr Ste 115, Birmingham, Alabama 35242-2735.
T: 1 205 916-1100
Editorial Profile: WZNN-FM is a commercial station owned by Summit Media Broadcasting LLC. The format of the station is currently stunting formats. WZNN-FM broadcasts to the Birmingham, AL area at 97.3 FM.

WZNP-FM
Owner: One Connection Media Group
Editorial: 41 S Paint St, Ste 3, Chillicothe, Ohio 45601-3254. **T:** 1 614 855-9171
E: theriver@1049theriver.com
W: http://www.riverradio.com
Editorial Profile: WZNP-FM is a non-commercial station owned by One Connection Media Group. The format of the station is contemporary Christian. WZNP-FM broadcasts to the Newark, OH area at 89.3 FM.

WZNS-FM
Owner: Cumulus Media Inc.
Editorial: 225 Hollywood Blvd NW, Fort Walton Beach, Florida 32548-4725.
T: 1 850 243-7676 **W:** http://www.z96.com
Editorial Profile: WZNS-FM is a commercial station owned by Cumulus Media Inc. The format of the station is Top 40 music, consisting of contemporary pop and rock. WZNS-FM's tagline is "Z-96."

WZNX-FM
Owner: Cromwell Group Inc.(The)
Editorial: 410 N Water St, Ste B, Decatur, Illinois 62523-2371. **T:** 1 217 428-4487
W: http://www.1067thefox.com
Editorial Profile: WZNX-FM is a commercial station owned by The Cromwell Group Inc. The format of the station is classic rock. WZNX-FM broadcasts to the Decatur, IL area at 106.7 FM.

WZNY-FM
Owner: Clear Channel Media and Entertainment
Editorial: 2743 Perimeter Pkwy Bldg 100, Suite 300, Augusta, Georgia 30909-6429.
T: 1 706 396-6000
W: http://www.eagle102.com/main.html
Editorial Profile: WZNY-FM is a commercial station owned by Clear Channel Media and Entertainment. The format of the station is classic rock. WZNY-FM broadcasts to the Augusta, GA area at 102.3 FM.

WZNZ-AM
Owner: Queen of Peace Radio, Inc.
Editorial: 4190 Belfort Rd, Jacksonville, Florida 32216-1407. **T:** 1 904 470-4615
E: feedback@1600thebeach.com
W: http://www.1600thebeach.com

Editorial Profile: WZNZ-AM is a commercial station owned by Queen of Peace Radio, Inc. The format of the station is oldies. WZNZ-AM broadcasts to the Jacksonville Beach, FL area at 1600 AM.

WZOB-AM
Owner: Central Broadcasting Inc.
Editorial: 1605 Roland Walls Dr., Fort Payne, Alabama 35967-0748. **T:** 1 256 845-2810
Editorial Profile: WZOB-AM is a commercial station owned by Central Broadcasting Inc. The format of the station is classic country. WZOB-AM broadcasts to the Fort Payne, AL area at 1250 AM.

WZOC-FM
Owner: Douglas Road Radio, Inc.
Editorial: 1301 E Douglas Rd, Mishawaka, Indiana 46545-1732. **T:** 1 574 233-3141
W: http://www.radiomichiana.com/wzoc
Editorial Profile: WZOC-FM is a commercial station owned by Douglas Road Radio, Inc. The format of the station is oldies. WZOC-FM broadcasts to the Plymouth, IN area at 94.3 FM.

WZOE-AM
Owner: WZOE Inc.
Editorial: 2209 S Main St, Princeton, Illinois 61356-9179. **T:** 1 815 875-8014
E: newsroom@wzoe.com
W: http://www.wzoe.com
Editorial Profile: WZOE-AM is a commercial station owned by WZOE Inc. The format of the station is news and talk. WZOE-AM broadcasts to the Princeton, IL area at 1490 AM.

WZOE-FM
Owner: WZOE Inc.
Editorial: 2209 S Main St, Princeton, Illinois 61356-9179. **T:** 1 815 875-8014
E: newsroom@wzoe.com
W: http://www.wzoe.com
Editorial Profile: WZOE-FM is a commercial station owned by WZOE Inc. The format of the station is classic hits. WZOE-FM broadcasts to the Princeton, IL area at 98.1 FM.

WZOH-FM
Owner: Wilks Broadcast Group
Editorial: 2400 Corporate Exchange Dr Ste 200, Columbus, Ohio 43231-7669.
T: 1 614 225-9465
W: http://www.955thegameonline.com
Editorial Profile: WZOH-FM is a commercial station owned by Wilks Broadcast Group. The format of the station is sports talk. WZOH-FM broadcasts to the Columbus, OH area at 95.5 FM.

WZOK-FM
Owner: Cumulus Media Inc.
Editorial: 3901 Brendenwood Rd, Rockford, Illinois 61107. **T:** 1 815 399-2233
W: http://www.97zokonline.com
Editorial Profile: WZOK-FM is a commercial station owned by Cumulus Media Inc. The format of the station is Top 40/CHR music. WZOK-FM broadcasts in the Rockford, IL area at 97.5 FM.

WZOM-FM
Owner: Clear Channel Media and Entertainment
Editorial: 2110 Radio Dr, Defiance, Ohio 43512. **T:** 1 419 782-8126
W: http://www.1057thebull.com
Editorial Profile: WZOM-FM is a commercial station owned by Clear Channel Media and Entertainment. The format of the station is contemporary country. WZOM-FM broadcasts to the Defiance, OH area at 105.7 FM.

WZON-AM
Owner: Zone Corporation(The)
Editorial: 861 Broadway, Bangor, Maine 4401. **T:** 1 207 990-2800 **E:** thepulse@zoneradio.com
W: http://www.zoneradio.com
Editorial Profile: WZON-AM is a commercial station owned by The Zone Corporation. The format of the station is news/talk. WZON-AM broadcasts to the Bangor, ME area at 620 AM.

WZOO-AM
Owner: Faith Enterprises, Inc.
Editorial: 2641 Lazy Pine Rd, Randleman, North Carolina 27317-7542.
T: 1 336 672-0944 **E:** info@wzooradio.com
W: http://www.wzooradio.com
Editorial Profile: WZOO-AM is a commercial station owned by Faith Enterprises, Inc. The format of the station is Southern gospel. WZOO-AM broadcasts to the Randleman, NC area at 710 AM.

WZOO-FM
Owner: Media One Group
Editorial: 3226 Jefferson Rd, Ashtabula, Ohio 44004. **T:** 1 440 993-2126
W: http://www.magicoldies1025.com
Editorial Profile: WZOO-FM is a commercial station owned by Media One Group. The format of the station is oldies. WZOO-FM broadcasts in the Ashtabula, OH area at 102.5 FM.

WZOR-FM
Owner: Woodward Communications, Inc.
Editorial: 2800 E College Ave, Appleton, Wisconsin 54915. **T:** 1 920 734-9226
E: razor@wcinet.com
W: http://www.razor947.com
Editorial Profile: WZOR-FM is a commercial station owned by Woodward Communications, Inc. The format is rock alternative. WZOR-FM broadcasts to the Appleton, WI area at 94.7 FM.

WZOT-AM
Owner: Woman's World Broadcasting, Inc.
Editorial: 602 W Elm St, Rockmart, Georgia 30153. **T:** 1 770 684-7848
Editorial Profile: WZOT-AM is a commercial station owned by Woman's World Broadcasting, Inc. The format of the station is Southern gospel. WZOT-AM broadcasts to the Rockmart, GA area at 1220 AM.

WZOW-FM
Owner: Artistic Media Partners Inc.
Editorial: 3371 Cleveland Road Ext Ste 300, South Bend, Indiana 46628-9780.
T: 1 574 273-9300
W: http://www.stream1023.com
Editorial Profile: WZOW-FM is a commercial station owned by Artistic Media Partners Inc. The format of the station is oldies. WZOW-FM broadcasts to the South Bend, IN area at 97.7 FM.

WZOZ-FM
Owner: Townsquare Media, LLC
Editorial: 34 Chestnut St, Oneonta, New York 13820-2466. **T:** 1 607 432-1030
E: cnynews@townsquaremedia.com
W: http://www.wzozfm.com
Editorial Profile: WZOZ-FM is a commercial station owned by Townsquare Media, LLC. The format of the station is classic hits. WZOZ-FM broadcasts to the Oneonta, NY area at 103.1 FM.

WZPL-FM
Owner: Entercom Communications Corp.
Editorial: 9245 N Meridian St Ste 300, Indianapolis, Indiana 46260-1832.
T: 1 317 816-4000 **E:** indypsa@entercom.com
W: http://www.wzpl.com
Editorial Profile: WZPL-FM is a commercial station owned by Entercom Communications Corp. The format for the station is hot adult contemporary music. WZPL-FM broadcasts to the Indianapolis area at 99.5 FM.

WZPN-FM
Owner: Advanced Media Partners LLC
Editorial: 2006 W Altorfer Dr, Peoria, Illinois 61615-1864. **T:** 1 309 691-0101
W: http://espnpeoria.com
Editorial Profile: WZPN-FM is a commercial station owned by Advanced Media Partners LLC. The format of the station is sports. WZPN-FM broadcasts to the Peoria, IL area at 96.5 FM.

WZPR-FM
Owner: CapSan Media, LLC
Editorial: 637 Harbor Rd, Wanchese, North Carolina 27981-9589. **T:** 1 252 475-1888
W: http://www.classichits1049.com
Editorial Profile: WZPR-FM is a commercial station owned by CapSan Media, LLC. The format of the station is classic rock. WZPR-FM broadcasts to the Wanchese, NC area at 92.3 FM.

WZPW-FM
Owner: Cumulus Media Inc.
Editorial: 120 Eaton St, Peoria, Illinois 61603-4217. **T:** 1 309 676-5000
W: http://www.powerpeoria.com
Editorial Profile: WZPW-FM is a commercial station owned by Cumulus Media Inc. The format of the station is rhythmic Top 40/CHR. WZPW-FM broadcasts to the Peoria, IL area at 92.3 FM.

WZQQ-AM
Owner: Mountain Broadcasting Service
Editorial: 516 Main St, Hazard, Kentucky 41701-1775. **T:** 1 606 436-2121
E: wsgsfm@windstream.net

Editorial Profile: WZQQ-AM is a commercial station owned by Mountain Broadcasting Service. The format of the station is adult standards. WZQQ-AM broadcasts to the Hazard, KY area at 1390 AM.

WZQZ-AM
Owner: HS Production Inc.
Editorial: 10143 Commerce St, Summerville, Georgia 30747-1356. **T:** 1 706 859-1180
E: chattooga1180am@hotmail.com
W: http://www.chattoogainfo.com
Editorial Profile: WZQZ-AM is a commercial station owned by HS Production Inc. The format of the station is classic country. WZQZ-AM broadcasts to the Summerville, GA area at 1180 AM.

WZRC-AM
Owner: Multicultural Radio Broadcasting Inc.
Editorial: 449 Broadway Fl 2, New York, New York 10013-2549. **T:** 1 212 965-1480
W: http://www.mrbi.net
Editorial Profile: WZRC-AM is a commercial station owned by Multicultural Radio Broadcasting Inc. The format of the station is variety. WZRC-AM broadcasts to the New York area at 1480 AM.

WZRD-FM
Owner: Northeastern Illinois University
Editorial: 5500 N Saint Louis Ave, Chicago, Illinois 60625-4625. **T:** 1 773 442-4586
E: info@wzrdchicago.org
W: http://www.wzrdchicago.org
Editorial Profile: WZRD-FM is a non-commercial station owned by Northeastern Illinois University. The format of the station is variety. WZRD-FM broadcasts to the Chicago metro area at 88.3 FM.

WZRN-FM
Owner: Roanoke Valley Communications Inc.
Editorial: 232 Roanoke Ave Ste A, Roanoke Rapids, North Carolina 27870-1916.
T: 1 252 308-0885 **E:** wago@gomixradio.org
W: http://www.wzru.org
Editorial Profile: WZRN-FM is a non-commercial station owned by Roanoke Valley Communications Inc. The format of the station is contemporary christian. WZRN-FM broadcasts to the Roanoke and Norlina, NC areas at 90.5 FM.

WZRR-FM
Owner: Cumulus Media Inc
Editorial: 244 Goodwin Crest Dr, Ste 300, Birmingham, Alabama 35209.
T: 1 205 945-4646 **W:** http://www.wzrr.com
Editorial Profile: WZRR-FM is a commercial station owned by Cumulus Media Inc. The format of the station is Top 40/CHR. WZRR-FM broadcasts to the Birmingham, AL area at 99.5 FM.

WZRT-FM
Owner: Pamal Broadcasting Ltd.
Editorial: 67 Merchants Row, Rutland, Vermont 05701-5910. **T:** 1 802 775-5597
W: http://www.z971.com
Editorial Profile: WZRT-FM is a commercial station owned by Pamal Broadcasting Ltd. The format of the station is Top 40/CHR. WZRT-FM broadcasts to the Rutland, VT area at 97.1 FM.

WZRU-FM
Owner: Roanoke Valley Communications Inc.
Editorial: 232 Roanoke Ave Ste A, Roanoke Rapids, North Carolina 27870-1916.
T: 1 252 308-0885 **E:** wago@gomixradio.org
W: http://www.gomixradio.org
Editorial Profile: WZRU-FM is a non-commercial station owned by Roanoke Valley Communications Inc. The format of the station is contemporary Christian. WZRU-FM broadcasts to the Roanoke, NC area at 90.1 FM.

WZRV-FM
Owner: Royal Broadcasting Inc.
Editorial: 1106 Elm St, Front Royal, Virginia 22630. **T:** 1 540 635-4121
W: http://www.theriver953online.com
Editorial Profile: WZRV-FM is a commercial station owned by Royal Broadcasting Inc. The format of the station is classic hits. WZRV-FM broadcasts in the Front Royal, VA area at 95.3 FM.

WZRX-FM
Owner: Clear Channel Media and Entertainment
Editorial: 667 W Market St, Lima, Ohio 45801-4603. **T:** 1 419 223-2060
W: http://www.wzrxfm.com
Editorial Profile: WZRX-FM is a commercial station owned by Clear Channel Media and

Entertainment. The format of the station is rock music. WZRX-FM broadcasts to the Lima, OH area at a frequency of 107.5 FM.

WZSK-AM

Owner: New Millennium Communications Group
Editorial: 151 E 1st Ave, Everett, Pennsylvania 15537-1351. **T:** 1 814 652-2600
E: wzsk@penn.com
Editorial Profile: WZSK-AM is a commercial station owned by the New Millennium Communications Group. The format of the station is news and talk. WZSK-AM broadcasts to the Everett, PA area at 1040 AM.

WZSN-FM

Owner: Broomfield Broadcasting LLC
Editorial: 210 Montague Ave, Greenwood, South Carolina 29649. **T:** 1 864 223-4300
E: sunny@sunny103-5.com
W: http://www.sunny103-5.com
Editorial Profile: WZSN-FM is a commercial station owned by Broomfield Broadcasting LLC. The format for the station is soft adult contemporary. WZSN-FM broadcasts to the Greenwood, SC area at 103.5 FM.

WZSP-FM

Owner: Heartland Broadcasting
Editorial: 7891 US Highway 17 S, Zolfo Springs, Florida 33890. **T:** 1 863 494-4111
E: info@lazeta.fm **W:** http://www.lazeta.fm
Editorial Profile: WZSP-FM is a commercial station owned by Heartland Broadcasting. The station's format is Hispanic. WZSP-FM broadcasts to the Zolfo Springs, FL area at 105.3 FM.

WZSR-FM

Owner: Matrix Broadcasting
Editorial: 8800 US Highway 14, Crystal Lake, Illinois 60012-2740. **T:** 1 815 459-7000
W: http://www.star105.com
Editorial Profile: WZSR-FM is a commerical station owned by Matrix Broadcasting. The format of the station is adult contemporary music. WZSR-FM broadcasts to Crystal Lake, IL and the far northwest suburbs of Chicago at 105.5 FM.

WZTA-AM

Owner: Clear Channel Media and Entertainment
Editorial: 3771 SE Jennings Rd, Port Saint Lucie, Florida 34952-7702. **T:** 1 772 335-9300
W: http://www.waxe1370.com/main.html
Editorial Profile: WZTA-AM is a commercial station owned by Clear Channel Media and Entertainment. The format of the station is talk. WZTA-AM broadcasts to the Fort Pierce, FL area at 1370 AM.

WZTF-FM

Owner: Clear Channel Media and Entertainment
Editorial: 181 E Evans St Ste 311, Florence, South Carolina 29506-5505.
T: 1 843 667-4600
W: http://theflo1029.com/#&panel1-1
Editorial Profile: WZTF-FM is a commercial station owned by Clear Channel Media and Entertainment. The format of the station is urban adult contemporary. WWRK-FM broadcasts to the Florence, SC, area at 102.9 FM.

WZTI-AM

Owner: Milwaukee Radio Alliance
Editorial: 4222 W Capitol Dr, Milwaukee, Wisconsin 53216-2500. **T:** 1 414 444-1290
W: http://www.1290martiniradio.com
Editorial Profile: WZTI-AM is a commercial station owned by Milwaukee Radio Alliance. The format of the station is adult standards. WZTI-AM broadcasts to the Milwaukee area at 1290 AM.

WZTR-FM

Owner: Ridgeline Communications, LLC
Editorial: 1376 Ben Higgins Rd, Dahlonega, Georgia 30533. **T:** 1 706 867-1043
E: info@thunder1043fm.com
W: http://www.thunder1043fm.com
Editorial Profile: WZTR-FM is a commercial station owned by Ridgeline Communications, LLC. The format of the station is classic rock, with a focus on Americana. WZTR-FM broadcasts to the Dahlonega, GA area at 104.3 FM.

WZUM-AM

Owner: AM Guys, LLC
Editorial: 4736 Penn Ave, Pittsburgh, Pennsylvania 15224-1341. **T:** 1 203 323-7300
Editorial Profile: WZUM-AM is a commercial station owned by AM Guys, LLC. The format

of the station is news talk. WZUM-AM broadcasts to the Greater Pittsburgh area at 1550 AM.

WZUM-AM

Owner: Believe and Achieve Family and Educational Center Inc.
Editorial: 4939 Buttermilk Hollow Rd, West Mifflin, Pennsylvania 15122-1138.
T: 1 757 624-8444
Editorial Profile: WZUM-AM is a non-commercial station owned by Believe and Achieve Family and Educational Center Inc. The format of the station is gospel. WZUM-AM broadcasts to the West Mifflin, PA area at 1590 AM.

WZUN-FM

Owner: Galaxy Communications LP
Editorial: 235 Walton St, Syracuse, New York 13202-1226. **T:** 1 315 472-9111
E: asksunny@thesunnyspot.com
W: http://www.thesunnyspot.com
Editorial Profile: WZUN-FM is a commercial station owned by Galaxy Communications LP. The format of the station is classic hits. WZUN-FM broadcasts to the Syracuse, NY area at 102.1 FM.

WZUP-FM

Owner: Conner Media Corp.
Editorial: 3389 NC 121, Farmville, North Carolina 27828. **T:** 1 252 753-3202
E: lainvasora910@yahoo.com
Editorial Profile: WZUP-FM is a commercial station owned by Conner Media Corp. The format of the station is Regional Mexican music. WZUP-FM broadcasts to the Farmville, NC area at 104.7 FM.

WZUS-FM

Owner: Cromwell Group Inc.(The)
Editorial: 410 N Water St, Ste C, Decatur, Illinois 62523. **T:** 1 217 428-4487
W: http://www.talk101decatur.com
Editorial Profile: WZUS-FM is a commercial radio station owned by Comwell Group Inc. The format of the station is talk. WZUS-FM broadcasts to the Decatur, IL area at 100.9 FM.

WZUU-FM

Owner: Forum Communications Co.
Editorial: 706 E Allegan St, Otsego, Michigan 49078. **T:** 1 269 343-1717
W: http://www.wzuu.com
Editorial Profile: WZUU-FM is a commercial station owned by Forum Communications Co. The format of the station is rock music. WZUU-FM broadcasts to the Otsego, MI area at 92.5 FM.

WZVA-FM

Owner: T.E.C. 2 Broadcasting, Inc.
Editorial: 114 W Main St, Marion, Virginia 24354-2514. **T:** 1 276 783-4042
W: http://www.1035thundercountry.com
Editorial Profile: WZVA-FM is a commercial station owned by T.E.C. 2 Broadcasting, Inc. The format of the station is contemporary country music. WZVA-FM broadcasts to the Marion, VA area at 103.5 FM.

WZVN-FM

Owner: Radio One Inc.
Editorial: 2755 Sager Rd, Valparaiso, Indiana 46383-0721. **T:** 1 219 462-6111
W: http://www.z1071.com
Editorial Profile: WZVN-FM is a commercial station owned by Radio One Inc. The format of the station is adult contemporary. WZVN-FM broadcasts to the Valparaiso, IN area at 107.1 FM.

WZWP-FM

Owner: One Connection Media Group
Editorial: 41 S Paint St, #3, Chillicothe, Ohio 45601-3254. **T:** 1 614 855-9171
E: theriver@1049theriver.com
W: http://www.riverradio.com
Editorial Profile: WZWP-FM is a non-commercial station owned by One Connection Media Group. The format of the station is contemporary Christian. WZWP-FM broadcasts to the West Union, OH area at 89.5 FM.

WZWW-FM

Owner: First Media Radio LLC
Editorial: 863 Benner Pike, Ste 200, State College, Pennsylvania 16801.
T: 1 814 231-0953 **E:** webmaster@3wz.com
W: http://www.3wz.com
Editorial Profile: WZWW-FM is a commercial station owned by First Media Radio LLC. The format for the station is hot adult contemporary. WZWW-FM broadcasts to the Johnstown-Altoona, PA area at 95.3 FM.

WZWZ-FM

Owner: Hoosier AM/FM LLC
Editorial: 671 E 400 S, Kokomo, Indiana 46902. **T:** 1 765 453-1212
E: kokomoradiotraffic@att.net
W: http://www.z925fm.com
Editorial Profile: WZWZ-FM is a commercial station owned by Hoosier AM/FM LLC. The format of the station is adult contemporary. WZWZ-FM broadcasts to the Kokomo, IN area at 92.5 FM.

WZXL-FM

Owner: Equity Communications LP
Editorial: 8025 Black Horse Pike, Ste 100, Pleasantville, New Jersey 8232.
T: 1 609 484-8444 **W:** http://www.wzxl.com
Editorial Profile: WZXL-FM is a commercial station owned by Equity Communications LP. The format of the station is classic rock. WZXL-FM broadcasts to the Pleasantville, NJ area at 100.7 FM.

WZXR-FM

Owner: Backyard Broadcasting
Editorial: 1685 Four Mile Dr, Williamsport, Pennsylvania 17701-1975. **T:** 1 570 323-8200
W: http://www.wzxr.com
Editorial Profile: WZXR-FM is a commercial station owned by Backyard Broadcasting. The station's format is classic rock music. WZXR-FM broadcasts to the Susquehanna Valley at 99.3 FM.

WZXV-FM

Owner: Calvery Chapel of the Finger Lakes
Editorial: 1777 Rochester Rd, Farmington, New York 14425. **T:** 1 585 398-3569
W: http://ccfingerlakes.org/wzxv
Editorial Profile: WZXV-FM is a non-commercial station owned by Calvery Chapel of the Finger Lakes. The format of the station is religion. WZXV-FM broadcasts to the Rochester, NY area at 99.7 FM.

WZYP-FM

Owner: Cumulus Media Inc.
Editorial: 1717 US Highway 72 E, Athens, Alabama 35611. **T:** 1 256 830-8300
W: http://www.wzyp.com
Editorial Profile: WZYP-FM is a commercial station owned by Cumulus Media Inc. The format of the station is Top 40/CHR. WZYP-FM broadcasts to the Huntsville, AL area at 104.3 FM.

WZYX-AM

Owner: Wiseman Media
Editorial: 540 Cumberland St W, Cowan, Tennessee 37318-3115. **T:** 1 931 967-7471
W: http://www.wzyxradio.net
Editorial Profile: WZYX-AM is a commercial station owned by Wiseman Media. The format of the station is adult hits. WZYX-AM broadcasts to the Cowan, TN area at 1440 AM.

WZZA-AM

Owner: Muscle Shoals Broadcasting
Editorial: 1570 Woodmont Dr, Tuscumbia, Alabama 35674-3850. **T:** 1 256 381-1862
E: promotions@wzzaradio.com
W: http://www.wzzaradio.com
Editorial Profile: WZZA-AM is a commercial station owned by Muscle Shoals Broadcasting. The format for the station is gospel and R&B. WZZA-AM broadcasts to the Huntsville, AL area at 1410 AM.

WZZB-AM

Owner: Midnight Hour Broadcasting, LLC
Editorial: 1534 N Ewing St, Seymour, Indiana 47274-1121. **T:** 1 812 522-1390
E: wzzb@comcast.net
Editorial Profile: WZZB-AM is a commercial station owned by Midnight Hour Broadcasting, LLC. The format of the station is adult contemporary. WZZB-AM broadcasts to the Seymour, IN area at 1390 AM.

WZZH-FM

Owner: Four Rivers Community Broadcasting Corp
Editorial: 746 Route 113, Souderton, Pennsylvania 18964-1004. **T:** 1 215 721-2141
E: wordfm@wordfm.org
W: http://www.wordfm.org
Editorial Profile: WZZH-FM is a non-commercial station owned by Four Rivers Community Broadcasting Corp. The format of the station is contemporary Christian music and talk. WZZH-FM broadcasts to the Scranton, PA and surrounding areas at 90.9 FM.

WZZI-FM

Owner: Todd P. Robinson, Inc.

Editorial: 19 Wadsworth St Ste C, Lynchburg, Virginia 24501-2633. **T:** 1 434 845-3698
Editorial Profile: WZZI-FM is a commercial station owned by Todd P. Robinson, Inc. The format of the station is sports talk. WZZI-FM broadcasts to the Lynchburg, VA area at 106.9 FM.

WZZK-FM

Owner: Summit Media Broadcasting LLC
Editorial: 2700 Corporate Dr Ste 115, Birmingham, Alabama 35242-2735.
T: 1 205 916-1100 **W:** http://www.wzzk.com
Editorial Profile: WZZK-FM is a commercial station owned by Summit Media Broadcasting LLC. The format of the station is classic country. WZZK-FM broadcasts to the Birmingham, AL area at 104.7 FM.

WZZL-FM

Owner: Withers Broadcasting of Paducah, LLC
Editorial: 1700 N 8th St, Paducah, Kentucky 42001-1752. **T:** 1 270 538-5272
E: prod@withersradio.net
W: http://www.wzzl.com
Editorial Profile: WZZL-FM is a commercial station owned by Withers Broadcasting of Paducah, LLC. The format of the station is rock. WZZL-FM broadcasts to the Paducah, KY area at 106.7 FM.

WZZN-FM

Owner: Great South Wireless, LLC
Editorial: 108 Woodson St NW, Huntsville, Alabama 35801-5521. **T:** 1 256 382-0724
W: http://www.977thezone.com
Editorial Profile: WZZN-FM is a commercial station owned by Great South Wireless, LLC. The format of the station is sports talk. WZZN-FM broadcasts to the Huntsville, AL area at a frequency of 97.7 FM.

WZZO-FM

Owner: Clear Channel Media and Entertainment
Editorial: 1541 Alta Dr, Ste 400, Whitehall, Pennsylvania 18052. **T:** 1 610 434-1742
E: studio@wzzo.com **W:** http://www.wzzo.com
Editorial Profile: WZZO-FM is a commercial station owned by Clear Channel Media and Entertainment. The format of the station is rock. WZZO-FM broadcasts to the Whitehall, PA area at 95.1 FM.

WZZP-FM

Owner: Saga Communications
Editorial: 1640 Old Russellville Pike, Clarksville, Tennessee 37043-1709.
T: 1 931 648-7720 **W:** http://www.z975.com
Editorial Profile: WZZP-FM is a commercial station owned by Saga Communications (dba 5 Star Radio Group). The format of the station is rock music. WZZP-FM broadcasts to the Nashville, TN area at 97.5 FM.

WZZQ-AM

Owner: Fowler Broadcast Communications, Inc
Editorial: 340 Providence Rd, Gaffney, South Carolina 29341-2006. **T:** 1 864 489-9066
E: feedback@wzzqradio.com
W: http://wzzqradio.com
Editorial Profile: WZZQ-AM is a commercial station owned by Fowler Broadcast Communications, Inc. The format of the station is contemporary country. WZZQ-AM broadcasts to the Gaffney, SC area at 1500 AM.

WZZR-FM

Owner: Clear Channel Media and Entertainment
Editorial: 3071 Continental Dr, West Palm Beach, Florida 33407-3274. **T:** 1 561 616-6600
W: http://www.wzzr.com
Editorial Profile: WZZR-FM is a commercial station owned by Clear Channel Media and Entertainment. The format of the station is talk. WZZR-FM broadcasts to the West Palm Beach, FL, area at 94.3 FM.

WZZS-FM

Owner: Heartland Broadcasting
Editorial: 7891 Us Highway 17 S, Zolfo Springs, Florida 33890-4728.
T: 1 863 494-4111 **E:** info@bull.fm
W: http://www.bull.fm
Editorial Profile: WZZS-FM is a commercial station owned by Heartland Broadcasting. The format of the station is contemporary country music. WZZS-FM broadcasts to the Zolfo Springs, FL area at 106.9 FM.

WZZT-FM

Owner: Withers Broadcasting Co.
Editorial: 3101 Freeport Rd, Sterling, Illinois 61081-8612. **T:** 1 815 625-3400

E: wsdr1240@theramp.net
Editorial Profile: WZZT-FM is a commercial station owned by Withers Broadcasting Co. The format of the station is classic rock. WZZT-FM broadcasts to the Sterling, IL area at 102.7 FM.

WZZU-FM
Owner: Todd P. Robinson, Inc.
Editorial: 19 Wadsworth St Ste C, Lynchburg, Virginia 24501-2633. **T:** 1 434 845-3698
W: http://www.rocktheplanet.fm

WZZW-AM
Owner: Clear Channel Media and Entertainment
Editorial: 134 4th Ave, Huntington, West Virginia 25701. **T:** 1 304 525-7788
W: http://www.800wvhu.com
Editorial Profile: WZZW-AM is a commercial station owned by Clear Channel Media and Entertainment. The format for the station is news and talk. WZZW-AM broadcasts to the Charleston-Huntington, WV area at 1600 AM.

WZZY-FM
Owner: Whitewater Broadcasting
Editorial: 2301 W Main St, Richmond, Indiana 47374. **T:** 1 765 962-6533
E: news@todaysmusicmix.com
W: http://www.todaysmusicmix.com
Editorial Profile: WZZY-FM is a commercial station owned by Whitewater Broadcasting. The format of the station is adult contemporary music. WZZY-FM broadcasts in the Richmond, IN area at 98.3.

XEITE-AM
Owner: Grupo Radio Capital
Editorial: Montes Urales No. 425, 2° Piso, Lomas De Chapultepec, Mexico City, Distrito Federal C.P. 06600. **T:** 52 55 30993000
W: http://gruporadiocapital.mx/xeite
Editorial Profile: Audience: 2,294,740

XEMO-AM
Owner: Uniradio Corp.
Editorial: 5030 Camino De La Siesta, Ste 403, San Diego, California 92108-3120.
T: 1 619 497-0600
W: http://www.uniradio.com
Editorial Profile: XEMO-AM is a commercial station owned by Grupo Uniradio Corp. The format of the station is regional Mexican. XEMO-AM broadcasts to the San Diego area at 860 AM.

XEPE-AM
Owner: Broadcast Company of the Americas
Editorial: 6160 Cornerstone Ct E, Ste 100, San Diego, California 92121-3720.
T: 1 858 535-2500
W: http://www.espnradio1700.com
Editorial Profile: XEPE-AM is a commercial station owned by Broadcast Company of the Americas. The format of the station is sports. XEPE-AM broadcasts in the San Diego area at 1700 AM.

XERCN-AM
Owner: Grupo Uniradio Corp.
Editorial: 5030 Camino De La Siesta, Ste 403, San Diego, California 92108.
T: 1 619 497-0600
W: http://www.radiohispana1470.com
Editorial Profile: XERCN-AM is a commercial station owned by Grupo Uniradio Corp. The format of the station is Hispanic news and talk. XERCN-AM broadcasts to the San Diego area at 1470 AM.

XESPN-AM
Owner: Mario Mayans
Editorial: 1027 10th Ave, Ste C, San Diego, California 92101. **T:** 1 619 696-9902
W: http://www.espnradio800.com
Editorial Profile: XESPN-AM is a commercial station owned by Mario Mayans. The format for the station is Spanish sports. XESPN-AM broadcasts to the San Diego area at 800 AM.

XEWW-AM
Owner: GLR Southern California Inc.
Editorial: 3500 W Olive Ave Ste 250, Burbank, California 91505-5526. **T:** 1 818 972-4200
W: http://www.wradio690.com
Editorial Profile: XEWW-AM is a commercial station owned by GLR Southern California Inc. The format of the station is Hispanic talk. XEWW-AM broadcasts to the Los Angeles area at 690 AM.

XEXX-AM
Owner: Radiorama, S.A. de C.V.
Editorial: 353 3rd Ave, Ste 201, Chula Vista, California 91910. **T:** 1 619 427-1420
Editorial Profile: XEXX-AM is a commercial station owned by Radiorama, S.A. de C.V. The format of the station is Hispanic news, talk and sports. XEXX-AM broadcasts to the San Diego area at 1420 AM.

XHFG-FM
Owner: Grupo Uniradio Corp.
Editorial: 5030 Camino De La Siesta, Ste 403, San Diego, California 92108.
T: 1 619 497-0600
W: http://www.pulsarfm.com
Editorial Profile: XHFG-FM is a commercial station owned by Grupo Uniradio Corp. The format of the station is Spanish and English Top 40/CHR. XHFG-FM broadcasts to the San Diego area at 107.3 FM.

XHNK-FM
Owner: Grupo Radiorama
Editorial: 1510 Calle Del Norte Ste 2, Laredo, Texas 78041-6048. **T:** 1 956 727-3670
E: grupo@radiorama.com.mx
W: http://www.radiorama.com
Editorial Profile: XHNK-FM is a commercial station owned by Grupo Radiorama. The format of the station is Spanish and English Top 40/CHR. XHNK-FM broadcasts to the Laredo, TX and Nuevo Laredo, Tamaulipas, Mexico areas at a frequency of 99.3 FM.

XHPX-FM
Owner: Mvs Radio
Editorial: 5862 Cromo Dr Ste 151, El Paso, Texas 79912-5510. **T:** 1 915 231-5500
W: http://www.exafm.com/elpaso
Editorial Profile: XHPX-FM is a commercial station owned by Mvs Radio. The format is Hispanic adult contemporary. The station airs to the El Paso, TX area at 98.3 FM.

XHRM-FM
Owner: Local Media San Diego
Editorial: 6160 Cornerstone Ct E, Ste 100, San Diego, California 92121-3724.
T: 1 858 535-2500 **W:** http://lmasandiego.com
Editorial Profile: XHRM-FM is a commercial station owned by Local Media San Diego. The format of the station is R&B oldies music. XHRM-FM broadcasts to the San Diego area at 92.5 FM.

XHTY-FM
Owner: Uniradio Corp.
Editorial: 5030 Camino De La Siesta, Ste 403, San Diego, California 92108.
T: 1 619 497-0600 **W:** http://invasora997.com
Editorial Profile: XHTY-FM is a commercial station owned by Uniradio Corp. The format of the station is regional Mexican music. XHTY-FM broadcasts to the San Diego area at 99.7 FM.

XHTZ-FM
Owner: Local Media San Diego
Editorial: 6160 Cornerstone Ct E Ste 100, San Diego, California 92121-3724.
T: 1 858 535-2500 **W:** http://www.z90.com
Editorial Profile: XHTZ-FM is a commercial station owned by Local Media San Diego. The format of the station is rhythmic Top 40/CHR music. XHTZ-FM broadcasts to the San Diego area at 90.3 FM.

XLNC-FM
Owner: XLNC1 Inc.
Editorial: 1690 Frontage Rd, Chula Vista, California 91911. **T:** 1 619 575-9090
E: info@xlnc1.org
W: http://www.hitsforever.org
Editorial Profile: XLNC-FM is a non-commercial station owned by XLNC1 Inc. The format of the station is classical music. XLNC-FM broadcasts at a frequency of 104.9 FM to the San Diego / Baja California region.

XLTN-FM
Owner: Grupo Imagen
Editorial: 2403 Hoover Ave, National City, California 91950-6619. **T:** 1 619 336-7800
W: http://www.1045radiolatina.com
Editorial Profile: XLTN-FM is a commercial station owned by Grupo Imagen. The format of the station is Hispanic adult contemporary music. XLTN-FM broadcasts to the National City, CA area at 104.5 FM.

XMOR-FM
Owner: Cadena Baja California
Editorial: 1027 10th Ave, Ste C, San Diego, California 92101. **T:** 1 619 696-9902
W: http://www.cbc.com.mx/morefm989.html
Editorial Profile: XMOR-FM is a commercial station owned by Cadena Baja California and operated by the MEC Network. The format for the station is Spanish rock music. XMOR-FM broadcasts to the San Diego and Baja California area at 98.9 FM.

XOCL-FM
Owner: MVS Radio
Editorial: 1690 Frontage Rd, Chula Vista, California 91911-3936. **T:** 1 619 429-8702
W: http://www.diego993.com
Editorial Profile: XOCL-FM is a commercial station owned by MVS Radio. The format for the station is Spanish oldies. XOCL-FM broadcasts to the San Diego and Baja California areas at 99.3 FM.

XPRS-AM
Owner: Broadcast Company of the Americas
Editorial: 6160 Cornerstone Ct E, San Diego, California 92121-3720. **T:** 1 858 535-2500
W: http://www.themighty1090.com
Editorial Profile: XPRS-AM is a commercial station owned by Broadcast Company of the Americas. The format for the station is sports. XPRS-AM broadcasts to the San Diego area at 1090 AM.

XPRS-FM
Owner: Broadcast Company of the Americas
Editorial: 6160 Cornerstone Ct E, Ste 100, San Diego, California 92121-3724.
T: 1 858 535-2500 **E:** dmason@bcaradio.com
W: http://www.walrusfm.com
Editorial Profile: XPRS-FM is a commercial station owned by Broadcast Company of the Americas. The format of the station is classic hits. XPRS-FM broadcasts to the San Diego area at 105.7.

XSUR-AM
Owner: Mount Wilson FM Broadcasters
Editorial: 1500 Cotner Ave, Los Angeles, California 90025. **T:** 1 310 478-5540
W: http://www.1260.am
Editorial Profile: XSUR-AM is a commercial station owned by Mount Wilson FM Broadcasters. The format of the station is news and talk. XSUR-AM broadcasts to the Los Angeles area at 540 AM.

XTRA-FM
Owner: Local Media San Diego
Editorial: 6160 Cornerstone Ct E, Ste 100, San Diego, California 92121-3724.
T: 1 858 888-7000 **W:** http://www.91x.com
Editorial Profile: XTRA-FM is a commercial station owned by Local Media San Diego. The format of the station is rock alternative. XTRA-FM broadcasts to the San Diego area at 91.1 FM.

RADIO NETWORKS

3ABN/Three Angels Broadcasting Network
Editorial: 3391 Charley Good Rd, West Frankfort, Illinois 62896-5815.
T: 1 618 627-4651 **E:** mail@3abn.org
W: http://www.3abn.org
Editorial Profile: Round-the-clock Christian lifestyle network presenting news, music and talk programs to a worldwide audience, through traditional broadcasting and over the Internet. Three Angels Broadcasting Network's (3ABN) programming is designed to reach into the hearts and lives of the listeners, addressing their everyday problems and most urgent needs.

ABC News Radio
Editorial: 1717 Desales St NW, Washington, District Of Columbia 20036-4401.
T: 1 202 222-7600
W: http://abcnewsradioonline.com

ABC News Radio
Editorial: 13725 Montfort Dr, Dallas, Texas 75240-4455. **T:** 1 972 991-9200
W: http://abcnewsradioonline.com

ABC News Radio
Editorial: 2 Alhambra Plz, Coral Gables, Florida 33134-5202. **T:** 1 305 448-9036
W: http://abcnewsradioonline.com

ABC News Radio
Editorial: 500 Circle Seven Dr, Glendale, California 91201-2331. **T:** 1 818 553-5500
W: http://abcnewsradioonline.com

ABC News Radio Network
Editorial: 125 W End Ave Fl 6, New York, New York 10023-6387. **T:** 1 212 456-5100
W: http://abcnewsradioonline.com

ABC Sports Radio
Editorial: 125 W End Ave, New York, New York 10023-6387
W: http://abcnewsradioonline.com/sports-news

Advanced Radio Network
Editorial: 6816 Main St, Hialeah, Florida 33014-2051. **T:** 1 305 824-9000
E: advanced@graveline.com
W: http://www.advancedradionetwork.com
Editorial Profile: Distributor of Into Tomorrow with Dave Graveline, the listener interactive network radio show covering the latest in consumer electronics and technology.

Ag Radio Network
T: 1 315 896-4750 **E:** agradionet@aol.com
W: http://www.jlfarmakis.com/Radio/AgRadioNetwork/tabid/94/Default.aspx

Agrinet Farm Radio Network
Editorial: 176 Radio Rd, Powells Point, North Carolina 27966. **T:** 1 252 491-2414
E: info@agrinetradio.com
W: http://www.agrinetradio.com
Editorial Profile: Distributes agriculture and farm reports to 150 stations across the United States. The network provides international, national and regional agricultural news, weather and markets.

Air 1 Radio Network
Owner: Educational Media Foundation
Editorial: 5700 W Oaks Blvd, Rocklin, California 95765-3719. **T:** 1 916 251-1600
E: newstip@air1.com **W:** http://www.air1.com
Editorial Profile: Air 1 Radio is a satellite broadcasting network of radio stations and FM translators owned by Educational Media Foundation. The network provides contemporary Christian music and Bible-inspired news and programming geared toward teenagers and young adults.

American Family Radio
Owner: American Family Association
Editorial: 107 Park Gate Dr, Tupelo, Mississippi 38801. **T:** 1 662 844-8888
E: comments@afr.net
W: http://www.afa.net/radio
Editorial Profile: American Family Radio supplies Christian-oriented radio programming to Southern and Midwestern states. The network has approximately 40 professional broadcasters, news and engineer personnel who combine their knowledge and skills to provide the very finest in Christian radio. PSAs should be directed to the network's main e-mail address.

American Forces Network Broadcast Center
Editorial: 23755 Z St, Riverside, California 92518-2031. **T:** 1 951 413-2351
E: contactus@myafn.net
W: http://myafn.dodmedia.osd.mil
Editorial Profile: American Forces Network Broadcast Center (AFN-BC) operates and provides multi-channel broadcast quality radio and television services and expanded internal information products to all Department of Defense members and their families stationed overseas, on contingency operations, and onboard Navy ships around the world. All entertainment, news, sports and information programming is acquired and distributed by AFN based on the popularity of programs within the specific Department of Defense audience demographics, the unique interests of military audiences and AFN scheduling needs.

American Public Media
Editorial: 480 Cedar St, Saint Paul, Minnesota 55101-2217. **T:** 1 651 290-1500
W: http://americanpublicmedia.publicradio.org
Editorial Profile: American Public Media is the national production and distribution arm of Minnesota Public Radio, one of the nation's premier public radio organizations.

American Urban Radio Networks
Editorial: 960 Penn Ave, 4th floor, Pittsburgh, Pennsylvania 15222. **T:** 1 412 456-4000
E: information@aurn.com
W: http://www.aurn.com
Editorial Profile: AURN is the only African American owned network radio company in the United States. It is the largest network reaching urban America. With more than 300 weekly shows, AURN reaches an estimated 20 million listeners. Through four programming networks and one marketing division, American Urban Radio Networks reaches more African Americans than any other medium in America and produces more urban programming than all other broadcasting

companies combined. American Urban Radio Networks broadcasts news, entertainment, sports and information programming to more than 400 radio stations nationwide. AURN's SPM Urban Network specializes in the creation, implementation and execution of national promotions and fully integrated marketing programs. It is the only African American broadcaster with a bureau in the White House. AURN has offices in New York, Pittsburgh, Atlanta, Chicago, Detroit, Los Angeles and Washington, D.C.

America's Talk Radio Network
W: http://www.americastalkradionetwork.com

Animal Radio Network
Owner: Animal Radio Network LLC
Editorial: 699 Paula St, Morro Bay, California 93442-1773. **T:** 1 805 772-1314
E: root@animalradio.com
W: http://animalradio.com
Editorial Profile: Animal Radio Network brings the world's best pet shows together under one roof. Animal Radio, according to Arbitron radio ratings, provides the most-listened-to animal programming in the United States. Animal Radio attracts the most concentrated radio audience of targeted animal lovers anywhere. Animal Radio's design is to educate humans on being better guardians, reducing surrenders and the ultimate euthanasia of homeless animals. It's truly programming with a purpose. If it's happening in the animal world, it's happening on Animal Radio.

Animal Talk Network
T: 1 586 777-5559
W: http://www.animaltalkradio.com
Editorial Profile: Producer of the Animal Talk radio program.

Associated Press Broadcast
Editorial: 1100 13th St NW, Washington, District Of Columbia 20005-4051.
T: 1 202 641-9710 **E:** info@ap.org
W: http://www.ap.org/products-services/radio
Editorial Profile: AP Broadcast offers coverage of news, sports, business news, political news, technology news, entertainment, and weather. News, analysts and experts should first be pitched to local or regional bureaus before the national network.

Associated Press Broadcast
Editorial: 450 W 33rd St, 14th floor, New York, New York 10001. **T:** 1 212 621-1524
Editorial Profile: Send all pitches by mail. The bureau does not accept faxes.

Associated Press Broadcast
Editorial: 221 S Figueroa St, 3rd Fl, Los Angeles, California 90012. **T:** 1 213 626-1200
E: losangeles@ap.org

Associated Press Broadcast
Editorial: 11 Stanwix St, Ste 1020, Pittsburgh, Pennsylvania 15222. **T:** 1 412 281-3747
E: appittsburgh@ap.org

Associated Press Broadcast
Editorial: 645 Albany Shaker Rd, Albany, New York 12211-1158. **T:** 1 518 458-7821
E: apalbany@ap.org

BARN
Editorial: 51294 WCR 76, Briggsdale, Colorado 80611. **T:** 1 970 656-3489
E: barnmedia@yahoo.com
W: http://www.barnmedia.net
Editorial Profile: The network offers accurate and factual information regarding agriculture and issues concerning producers and the agriculture sector.

BBN/Bible Broadcasting Network
Editorial: 11530 Carmel Commons Blvd, Charlotte, North Carolina 28226-3976.
T: 1 704 523-5555 **E:** bbn@bbnmedia.org
W: http://www.bbnradio.org
Editorial Profile: BBN/Bible Broadcasting Network's mission is to share the Word of God around the world. The network operates AM and FM radio stations in 14 countries that reach over 200 million people in six languages.

BET Radio Network
Editorial: 40 W 57th St, Fl 5, New York, New York 10019. **T:** 1 212 641-2000
W: http://affiliates.westwoodone.com/music/betrn.asp
Editorial Profile: BET Radio Network is a comprehensive network of news and music tailored to contemporary urban stations. BET Radio Network features exclusive access to BET talent, show prep, audio cuts and news and information from BET. Affiliates also get exclusive live interviews and celebrity one-on-ones, BET concerts and live events and live remotes with access to BET studios.

BizTalkRadio
Owner: Center Post Holdings
Editorial: 401 Shippan Ave, Stamford, Connecticut 06902-6075. **T:** 1 817 274-1609
W: http://www.biztalkradioshow.com
Editorial Profile: This business, financial and lifestyle all-talk programming network is delivered via satellite, 24-hours a day. The BizTalkRadio spotlights everything from personal finance to dining and home improvement. Send PSAs to the network via the main e-mail or fax and they will be distributed to the appropriate person. Press releases and guest pitches may also be sent to the network's main e-mail address. Books, videos and samples may be sent to the network by mail.

Black Radio Network
Editorial: 375 5th Ave, New York, New York 10016-3323. **T:** 1 212 686-6850
E: news@blackradionetwork.com
W: http://www.blackradionetwork.com
Editorial Profile: Radio network distributed to affiliates serving black and other minority communities throughout the United States and providing reports and news on issues affecting African-Americans. The network also specializes in news of interest to Hispanics, Asians, Native Americans and women.

Bloomberg Radio Network
Owner: Bloomberg L.P.
Editorial: 731 Lexington Ave, New York, New York 10022-1331. **T:** 1 212 318-2000
E: nydesk@bloomberg.net
W: http://www.bloomberg.com/tvradio/radio
Editorial Profile: Bloomberg Radio provides live updates on world and national news as well as the latest in business news 24 hours a day. The network distributes news and information throughout North America. Bloomberg provides syndicated reports to more than 750 radio stations around the nation. Outside of the United States, the outlet delivers news in the local languages of the countries where they broadcast. Bloomberg Radio currently offers programming in English, French, German, Japanese, Spanish and Portuguese. The assignment desk should ONLY be contacted to notify the department of serious business news stories about publicly traded companies.

Bloomberg Radio Network
Editorial: 1399 New York Ave NW, Fl 11, Washington, District Of Columbia 20005-4749.
T: 1 202 624-1800

Bloomberg Radio Network
Editorial: 100 Summer St, Boston, Massachusetts 02110-2106.
T: 1 617 210-4600

Blue Funk Broadcasting
Editorial: 428 Broadway St, New Haven, Indiana 46774. **T:** 1 260 493-7279
E: comments@bluefunkbroadcasting.com
W: http://www.bluefunkbroadcasting.com
Editorial Profile: Syndicates the Ric Bratton Show, This Week in America with Ric Bratton, and Boomer and Company.

Bott Radio Network
Editorial: 10550 Barkley St, Ste 100, Overland Park, Kansas 66212. **T:** 1 913 642-7770
E: comments@bottradionetwork.com
W: http://www.bottradionetwork.com
Editorial Profile: Bott Radio Network provides a wide range of spiritual and religious programming to affiliates across the United States. The network's stated purpose is to serve the Lord's people and to help strengthen each Christian family in its listening audience. The network encourages each listener to walk more closely with the Lord. Its stations broadcast Bible teachings and Christian news and information programming across America. Do not send PSAs to the network.

CBS Radio Network
Owner: CBS Radio
Editorial: 1271 Avenue of the Americas Fl 44, New York, New York 10020-1401.
T: 1 212 975-4321
W: http://www.cbsradio.com
Editorial Profile: CBS Radio Network provides the latest in news, sports and entertainment programming. The network features a wide variety of news and public affairs programming, including news on the hour, breaking news and feature programs.

CBS Radio Network
Editorial: 2020 M St NW, Washington, District Of Columbia 20036-3304. **T:** 1 202 457-4321
Editorial Profile: The bureau no longer uses faxes at all and does not accept any unsolicited press material.

CBS Radio Network
Editorial: 13816 Valleybrooke Ln, Orlando, Florida 32826-2642. **T:** 1 407 823-8747

CBS Sports Radio Network
Owner: CBS Radio
Editorial: 1271 Avenue of the Americas, New York, New York 10020-1300.
T: 1 212 649-9600
W: http://radio.cbssports.com
Editorial Profile: CBS Sports Radio launched on January 2, 2013. Cumulus Media is the network's exclusive distributor and content is produced by CBS Radio and CBS Sports.

CMT Radio Network
Editorial: 330 Commerce St, Nashville, Tennessee 37201. **T:** 1 615 335-8400
W: http://www.cmt.com/music/radio
Editorial Profile: CMT Radio Network is a comprehensive network of news and music tailored to country music stations. CMT Radio Network features exclusive access to CMT talent, show prep, audio cuts and news and information from CMT. Affiliates also get exclusive live interviews and celebrity one-on-ones, CMT concerts and live events. The network is owned and operated by Westwood One.

CNN en Español Radio
Owner: Time Warner Inc.
Editorial: 1 Cnn Ctr NW, Atlanta, Georgia 30303-2762. **T:** 1 404 827-1220
W: http://www.cnnenespanol.com/radio/
Editorial Profile: Full-service Spanish language radio network providing radio affiliates in the United States and throughout Latin America with the latest information in news, sports, business and entertainment. The network offers a menu of actualities and reports in closed-circuit news feeds, which are produced using the network's own Latin American resources, CNN's nine domestic and 20 international bureaus, and radio and television affiliates.

Compass Media Networks
Editorial: 32 Elm Pl, Ste 3N, Rye, New York 10580-2972. **T:** 1 914 600-5099
W: http://compassmedianetworks.com
Editorial Profile: Debuted in January 2009 with the mission of providing outstanding representation and marketing services to the best brands and programs in national radio.

Cox Radio Inc.
Owner: Cox Enterprises, Inc.
Editorial: 6205 Peachtree Dunwoody Rd NE, Atlanta, Georgia 30328-4524.
T: 1 404 892-8227 **E:** cxr.info@cox.com
W: http://www.coxmediagroup.com
Editorial Profile: Cox Radio Inc. is one of the largest radio broadcasting companies in the United States based on revenues. Cox Radio Inc. owns, operates or provides sales and marketing services to 80 stations in 18 markets. In 15 of its 18 markets, Cox Radio Inc. operates three or more stations.

CRN/Cable Radio Network
Owner: Cable Radio Network, Inc.
Editorial: 10487 Sunland Blvd, Sunland, California 91040-1905. **T:** 1 818 352-7152
E: webmaster@crntalk.net
W: http://www.crntalk.com
Editorial Profile: CRN is a 24-hour nationally syndicated radio network. Launched in 1983, CRN can also be heard worldwide via the Internet at www.crni.net. The network is made up of six digital radio channels: CRN1, CRN2, CRN3, CRN4, CRN5, and CRN6.

Crystal Media Networks
Editorial: 7201 Wisconsin Ave, Ste 780, Bethesda, Maryland 20814-4879.
T: 1 240 223-0850
W: http://www.crystalmedianetworks.com
Editorial Profile: National radio network providing programming to radio stations nationwide in various genres, including sports, nostalgia, entertainment and finance. The network is a leading independent creator, producer and distributor of creative entertainment and music-related radio programs and a supplier of marketing and promotional services to the radio industry. Crystal produces, syndicates and/or reps to more than 2,300 radio station affiliates nationwide.

CSN International Radio Network
Owner: CSN International
Editorial: 4002 N 3300 E, Twin Falls, Idaho 83301. **T:** 1 800 357-4226
E: feedback@csnradio.com
W: http://www.csnradio.com
Editorial Profile: Producer of religious and Christian programming for a national audience. CSN International is a non-profit organization, an outreach of Calvary Chapel of Twin Falls. The network broadcasts programming that faithfully follows sound Biblical teaching and anointed praise and worship music 24 hours a day to communities throughout the United States and the world.

C-SPAN Radio
Editorial: 400 N Capitol St NW, Ste 650, Washington, District Of Columbia 20001.
T: 1 202 737-3220 **E:** radio@c-span.org
W: http://www.c-span.org
Editorial Profile: C-SPAN Radio offers commercial-free public affairs programming 24 hours a day. Listeners hear live coverage from Washington, D.C. of important congressional hearings, key speeches from national leaders, along with archival recordings of presidential tapes, military memoirs and judicial proceedings from both contemporary times and before the advent of television. C-SPAN Radio should not be contacted via fax. General inquiries may be sent via the main e-mail address.

Cumulus Media Networks
Owner: Cumulus Media Inc.
Editorial: 3280 Peachtree Rd NE Ste 2300, Atlanta, Georgia 30305-2455.
T: 1 404 949-0700
W: http://www.cumulusmedianetworks.com
Editorial Profile: Headquartered in Atlanta, G.A., Cumulus Media Networks is a national radio network that broadcasts five full-service news networks, ABC News Radio, Radio Disney, ESPN Radio, music, talk and information programming, 10 ABC Radio 24-Hour formats and daily and weekly long and short form programming.

Cumulus Media Networks en Espanol
Owner: Cumulus Media Inc
Editorial: 2 Alhambra Plz, Coral Gables, Florida 33134-5202. **T:** 1 305 567-2271
W: http://adsales.cumulusmedianetworks.com/tag/Hispanic
Editorial Profile: Cumulus Media Networks en Espanol is a recognized leader in Spanish-language programming. With a presence in 28 of the top 30 Hispanic DMAs and the only two Hispanic RADAR rated networks, Cumulus Media Networks en Espanol reaches more than 10 million Hispanic listeners in an average week across 131 Spanish language radio stations in the United States. Programming includes Latino superstars and megabrands.

Deutsche Welle Radio Washington Bureau
Owner: Deutsche Welle
Editorial: 2000 M St NW, Washington, District Of Columbia 20036-3307. **T:** 1 202 785-5730
W: http://www.dw-world.de
Editorial Profile: Deutsche Welle Radio (DW Radio) is Germany's international news and information broadcaster. DW Radio's Washington bureau produces segments of shows and occasionally an entire show, all of which are then broadcast from the headquarters in Germany.

Entertainment Radio Network
Editorial: 231 SW I St, Grants Pass, Oregon 97526-2814. **T:** 1 541 471-1479
E: info@ernlive.com
W: http://www.ernlive.com
Editorial Profile: Entertainment Radio Network (ERN) is aligned with many popular magazines, including Motor Trend, Hot Rod, Motorcyclist, Popular Science among others, and bringing them to life. Programming is listener interactive and provides more information, insight and content outside of the print/digital publications.

Envision Networks
Editorial: 3733 Park East Dr, Cleveland, Ohio 44122-4338. **T:** 1 216 831-3761
W: http://www.envisionradio.com
Editorial Profile: Independently owned affiliate relations company. It supplies all types of programming and services for radio including

news (www.virtualnewscenter.com) and weather, morning show prep, short-form vignettes, live syndicated morning shows, long-form weekend programming, comedy services, remote broadcasts and event programming, off-air tools and web content, album releases and artist specials.

ESPN Deportes Radio Network
Owner: Walt Disney Co.
Editorial: 2 Alhambra Plz, Coral Gables, Florida 33134-5202. **T:** 1 305 567-2270
W: http://espndeportes.espn.go.com
Editorial Profile: ESPN Deportes is a radio network dedicated to broadcasting sports-related programming 24/7 in the Spanish language. The channel broadcasts transmissions made in different ESPN studios in North America.

ESPN Radio Network
Owner: Walt Disney Co.
Editorial: 545 Middle St, Bristol, Connecticut 06010-8413. **T:** 1 860 766-2000
E: radio@espn.com
W: http://espn.go.com/espnradio
Editorial Profile: The ESPN Radio Network features the latest sports information and personality-driven commentary and talk. The network spotlights the exclusive national radio broadcast rights to Major League baseball, NBA basketball games during the regular season and the playoffs, and the Bowl Championship Series in college football. News, scores and updates are provided in conjunction with the vast resources of the ESPN cable television network.

Family Life Network
Owner: Family Life Ministries Inc.
Editorial: 7634 Campbell Creek Road, Box 506, Bath, New York 14810-7612.
T: 1 607 776-4151
W: http://www.fln.org/radio-network
Editorial Profile: Network features radio programming that shares Christ through music, biblical teaching, and creative communication. Music ranges from inspirational to adult contemporary to southern gospel. Teaching programs that offer instruction from well-respected pastors and teachers. Family Life also has news and public affairs programming that keeps listeners informed from a Biblical perspective.

Family Life Radio
Owner: Family Life Communications, Inc.
Editorial: 7355 N Oracle Rd, Tucson, Arizona 85704-6325. **T:** 1 520 742-6976
W: http://www.myflr.org
Editorial Profile: Family Life Radio delivers inspirational, Christ-centered Christian music with relevant, Bible-based programs all focused on communicating Christ's love and hope. Family Life Radio connects personally with its listeners through live broadcasts and community events, and works in partnership with area churches and ministries.

Family Stations Radio Network
Owner: Family Stations Inc.
Editorial: 290 Hegenberger Rd, Oakland, California 94621-1436. **T:** 1 510 568-6200
E: familyradio@familyradio.com
W: http://www.familyradio.com
Editorial Profile: Family Stations Radio Network is a Christian nonprofit, nondenominational, educational organization that produces and broadcasts Christian programming and music around the world.

Farmhouse Media LLC
Editorial: 2400 E Highland Dr Fl 4, Jonesboro, Arkansas 72401-6213. **T:** 1 870 931-7500
W: http://www.agwatchnetwork.com
Editorial Profile: AgWatch Network provides a daily source for agriculture news updates of regional, national, livestock & poultry, and market reports for Arkansas, Kentucky, Mississippi, Missouri and Tennessee.

FOX News Radio Network
Editorial: 1211 Avenue Of The Americas, New York, New York 10036-8701.
T: 1 212 301-3000
E: foxnewsradio@foxnews.com
W: http://radio.foxnews.com
Editorial Profile: FOX News Radio features news, sports and entertainment actualities produced for radio, along with breaking news coverage from FOX News Channel. Pitch stories to the assignment desk by e-mail. Only call the assignment desk with breaking news of national interest.

FOX News Radio Network
Editorial: 2044 Armacost Ave, Los Angeles, California 90025-6113. **T:** 1 310 571-2000

FOX Sports Radio Network
Owner: Premiere Radio Networks
Editorial: 15260 Ventura Blvd, Ste 400, Sherman Oaks, California 91403-5300.
T: 1 818 377-5300
W: http://www.foxsportsradio.com
Editorial Profile: FOX Sports Radio Network is a 24-hour radio network that provides sports programming to affiliates nationwide. FOX Sports Radio Network is a division of Premiere Radio Networks, in connection with FOX Sports and FOX Sports Net.

GAB Network
Owner: Global American Broadcasting Network
Editorial: 2300 5Th Ave Suite 131, Vero Beach, Florida 32960-5169. **T:** 1 772 770-9000
W: http://gabradionetwork.com
Editorial Profile: GAB Network (Global American Broadcasting) was formed in 2000 to provide satellite and production services to the growing population of program syndicaters. Global American Broadcasting Network Inc was founded by Dr. Gene Hood and Ronald Crider.

GLR Networks
Editorial: 5000 SW 75th Ave Fl 4, Miami, Florida 33155-4488 **E:** info@glrnetworks.com
W: http://glrnetworks.com
Editorial Profile: The network provides Spanish language radio stations in the USA with news services, sports, entertainment and community programming, as well as a variety of musical formats.

Head On Radio Network
Editorial: 1038 N Eisenhower Dr, Pmb 318, Beckley, West Virginia 25801-3116.
T: 1 304 658-3333
W: http://headonradionetwork.com
Editorial Profile: The Head On Radio Network is a national broadcast radio network providing a range of Liberal talk programming.

HIA Radio Network
Editorial: 10540 Marty St Ste 240, Overland Park, Kansas 66212-2596. **T:** 1 913 385-2224
W: http://hiaradio.com

Hispanic Communications Network
Owner: Hispanic Communications Network, Inc.
Editorial: 1126 16th St NW, Washington, District Of Columbia 20036-4804.
T: 1 202 637-8800 **E:** press@hcnmedia.com
W: http://www.hcnmedia.com
Editorial Profile: Hispanic Communications Network (formerly known as the Hispanic Radio Network) produces and syndicates Spanish-language radio programs aimed at educating and informing the Hispanic population. These programs are broadcast throughout the USA on more than 200 popular Spanish language radio stations.

Hodgson Media
Editorial: 28840 County Road R, Brush, Colorado 80723. **T:** 1 970 842-2902
E: office@hodgsonmedia.com
W: http://www.hodgsonmedia.com
Editorial Profile: The network provides comprehensive and frequent reports on the livestock and agricultural markets, in addition to farm and agricultural news and information.

Icon Radio Network
Editorial: 6625 Lenox Park Dr Ste 110, Memphis, Tennessee 38115-4434.
T: 1 888 510-4266
W: http://www.iconradionetwork.com
Editorial Profile: Network syndicates the Ben Ferguson Show, and launched in May 2009.

Indianapolis Motor Speedway Radio Network
Editorial: 4555 W 16th St, Indianapolis, Indiana 46222-2513. **T:** 1 317 492-6596
E: imsradio@brickyard.com
W: http://www.imsproductions.tv
Editorial Profile: Network providing live coverage of the Indy Racing League (IRL) IndyCar Series racing and qualifications, plus a weekly talk show featuring IRL news, as well as interviews with drivers, owners and track officials. The Network covers 16 IRL races each year, including the Indianapolis 500, plus it carries NASCAR's Brickyard 400 and associated programing. The IMS Radio Network is a division of IMS Productions.

Information Radio Network, Inc./ IRN USA News
Editorial: 1010 June Rd Ste 100, Memphis, Tennessee 38119-3726. **T:** 1 901 761-0115
E: info@irnusanews.com
W: http://www.irnnews.com
Editorial Profile: Information Radio Network, Inc./IRN USA News is a nationally distributed radio network airing programs dealing with a range of general and topical issues. The network provides news and programming to radio stations and radio networks, covering national and international news, business news, sports news and Christian interest news. IRN also provides over 30 long form programs to radio stations and delivers news and programs from a platform of 5 satellite channels for radio stations, 6 XM channels and over 3,000 affiliates.

Information Radio Network, Inc./ IRN USA News
Editorial: 3622 Stanford Cir, Falls Church, Virginia 22041. **T:** 1 703 354-6795

Information Radio Network, Inc./ IRN USA News
Editorial: 2290 Springlake Rd, Ste 107, Dallas, Texas 75234. **T:** 1 972 484-3900
Editorial Profile: The Dallas bureau is the original site of the USA Radio Network. This bureau handles IRN/USA Radio Network's business, sports and religion content. All submissions can be directed to the bureau chief via e-mail.

Irish Radio Network
Owner: Flannelly Promotions Ltd.
Editorial: 515 Madison Ave, Fl 11, New York, New York 10022. **T:** 1 212 935-0606
E: info@irishradio.com
W: http://www.irishradio.com
Editorial Profile: The Irish Radio Network is the preeminent broadcast source of topical issues and entertainment, aimed at over 44 million Americans of Irish ancestry.

K-Love
Owner: Educational Media Foundation
Editorial: 5700 W Oaks Blvd, Rocklin, California 95765. **T:** 1 916 251-1600
E: klove@klove.com **W:** http://www.klove.com
Editorial Profile: K-Love is a satellite broadcasting network of radio stations and FM translators. The network provides contemporary Christian music, K-LOVE co-sponsored Christian concerts and Bible-inspired news and programming.

Liberty News Radio Network
Editorial: 1259 N 100 W, American Fork, Utah 84003-2703. **T:** 1 801 350-3990
W: http://libertynewsradio.com

Lifestyle Talk Radio Network
Owner: Lifestyle Talk Radio
Editorial: 401 Shippan Ave, Stamford, Connecticut 6902. **T:** 1 203 323-7300
W: http://www.lifestyletalkradio.com
Editorial Profile: Radio network distributing talk programming 24 hours a day, five days a week. The network offers a potpourri of live listener call-in programming covering a wide array of issues. Lifestyle Talk Radio, formerly known as Liberty Broadcasting, offers stations a new kind of talk radio that is entertaining, informative and engaging. This approach represents a fresh, compelling alternative to some of the combative styles on the radio today that alienate listeners, or lofty, high-minded rhetoric that lacks any real energy.

LifeTalk Radio Network
Owner: Adventist Media Center
Editorial: 101 W Cochran St, Simi Valley, California 93065-6217. **T:** 1 800 775-4673
E: office@lifetalk.net **W:** http://www.lifetalk.net
Editorial Profile: Radio outlet showcasing Christian and religious-themed programming. Aims to improve listeners lives through interactive talk radio, balanced with quality music and a profound faith-based programming philosophy.

MarketWatch.com Radio Network
Owner: News Corporation Ltd.
Editorial: 1025 Connecticut Ave NW, Ste 800, Washington, District Of Columbia 20036-5405.
T: 1 202 862-9200 4
E: radio@marketwatch.com
W: http://www.marketwatch.com
Editorial Profile: Radio outlet for the MarketWatch.com Web site, providing around-the-clock financial market updates to radio stations in major markets across the country. The MarketWatch.com Radio Network offers business reports twice an hour, 24 hours a day, five days a week, plus weekend features and special extended coverage of major business news stories. A team of broadcasters gathers news using the resources of MarketWatch.com's 90 reporters and news analysts in bureaus from London to Tokyo.

MarketWatch.com Radio Network
Owner: News Corporation Ltd.
Editorial: 11 Wall St, New York, New York 10005. **T:** 1 212 363-6836
W: http://www.marketwatch.com

Metro News Network
T: 1 312 878-6420
E: newsdesk@mymetronews.org
W: http://www.mymetronews.org
Editorial Profile: Metro News Network includes news and information for its affiliates.

Midwest Racing Radio Network
Owner: Midwest Racing Radio Network LLC
T: 1 701 219-3273
E: midwestracingradio@gmail.com
Editorial Profile: Motorsports talk network.

Money Matters Financial Network
Editorial: 75 Montebello Rd, Suffern, New York 10901. **T:** 1 800 433-0323
W: http://www.mmfn.net
Editorial Profile: Money Matters Financial Network is the only true interactive financial network where you ask the questions and choose the topics. The network produces the show Money Matters which is syndicated on seven stations in the tristate NY/NJ/CT area.

Motor Sports Radio Network
Owner: PK Communications Co.
Editorial: 518 Hooper Rd #279, Endwell, New York 13760-1960. **T:** 1 607 232-2232
W: http://www.msrpk.com
Editorial Profile: Provides coverage of major series auto racing and testing of American and foreign cars and light trucks.

MRN - Motor Racing Network
Owner: International Speedway Corporation
Editorial: 555 MRN Drive, Concord, North Carolina 28027. **T:** 1 704 262-6700
E: feedback@mrnradio.com
W: http://www.motorracingnetwork.com
Editorial Profile: Network providing live coverage of NASCAR stock car racing plus a weekly telephone talk show and a daily news show. The network also covers over 80 races a year for the NASCAR Winston Cup Series, NASCAR Busch Series, Grand National Division and NASCAR Craftsman Truck Series.

MTV Radio Network
Owner: Viacom Inc.
Editorial: 1515 Broadway, New York, New York 10036-8901. **T:** 1 212 846-8000
W: http://affiliates.westwoodone.com/music/mtvrn.asp
Editorial Profile: The MTV Radio Network gives stations affiliation with one of the most powerful brand names in music. The network has three different formats: Alternative/Rock, CHR/Pop and Urban/Hip-Hop, which provide stations with coverage and exclusive access to the biggest artists and bands on the planet. All guest ideas and press submissions should be addressed to the talent relations director.

NBC Radio Network
Owner: NBC Universal
Editorial: 1166 Avenue of the Americas Fl 10, New York, New York 10036-2743.
T: 1 212 641-2000
W: http://www.dialglobal.com
Editorial Profile: Tapping into its extensive resources across the country and around the world, the NBC Radio Network provides fair, accurate and fast-breaking news coverage when and where it happens. One-minute, hourly news reports air from 6am to 10pm on weekdays. The network is owned by NBC Universal and distributed by Dial Global.

NBC Sports Radio Network
Editorial: 30 Rockefeller Plz, New York, New York 10112-0015. **T:** 1 212 664-4444
E: nbcsportsradio@dialglobal.com
W: http://www.nbcsportsradio.com
Editorial Profile: NBC Sports Radio Network launched in Fall 2012. It is produced by NBC Sports Group and distributed by Dial Global. The network covers all sports 24/7.

New Sky Radio Network
Owner: CBS Radio
Editorial: 2201 Woodward Heights Blvd, Ferndale, Michigan 48220. **T:** 1 248 581-2200

W: http://sky.radio.com
Editorial Profile: Network offers programs for the mind, body and spirit, and includes entertainment, music, horoscopes and shows on enlightenment and the paranormal.

Northern Broadcasting System
Editorial: 600 1St Ave N, Billings, Montana 59101-2654. **T:** 1 406 252-6661
E: newsdesk@northernbroadcasting.com
W: http://www.northernbroadcasting.com
Editorial Profile: Northern Broadcasting System delivers nearly 200 radio programs each week via satellite to listeners in nine states and Canada. It includes the Northern Ag Network which provides farm news and market reports, weather programs and special features, and the Northern News Network, which provides Montana state news programs along with Montana sports, weather and legislative reports.

NPR/National Public Radio
Owner: National Public Radio
Editorial: 1111 N Capitol St NE, Washington, District Of Columbia 20002-7502.
T: 1 202 513-2000 **W:** http://www.npr.org
Editorial Profile: National Public Radio is an internationally acclaimed producer and distributor of non-commercial news, talk and entertainment programming. A privately supported, not-for-profit membership organization, NPR serves a growing audience of more than 34.6 million Americans each week in partnership with more than 849 independently operated, non-commercial public radio stations. NPR also produces content worldwide for satellite radio, the Internet and podcasting.

NPR/National Public Radio
Editorial: 11 W 42nd St, Fl 19, New York, New York 10036-8002. **T:** 1 212 880-3500
Editorial Profile: All faxes should be sent to the network headquarters in Washington, DC.

NPR/National Public Radio
Editorial: 848 E Grand Ave, Chicago, Illinois 60611. **T:** 1 312 948-4600

NPR/National Public Radio
Editorial: 2601 Mariposa St, San Francisco, California 94110-1426. **T:** 1 415 864-2000

NPR/National Public Radio
Editorial: 9909 Jefferson Blvd, Culver City, California 90232-3505. **T:** 1 310 815-4200

NPR/National Public Radio
Editorial: 4107 Medical Pkwy, Austin, Texas 78756-3735. **T:** 1 512 371-7303

NPR/National Public Radio
Editorial: 172 NE 15Th St, Miami, Florida 33132-1348. **T:** 1 305 995-1717

One Radio Network
E: email@oneradionetwork.com
W: http://www.oneradionetwork.com
Editorial Profile: The radio network airs talk show on mostly health, wealth and well being.

Oracle Broadcasting Network
E: staff@oraclebroadcasting.com
W: http://oraclebroadcasting.com
Editorial Profile: Oracle Broadcasting Network streams the best uncensored talk radio, geared to freedom and liberty minded listeners around the globe.

Orion Talk Radio Network
Editorial: 296 Bannard Ave, Tonawanda, New York 14150-6218 **E:** oriontalkradio@gmail.com
W: http://oriontalkradio.com
Editorial Profile: Alternative talk radio network dedicated to getting out the truth.

Pacifica Radio Network
Owner: Pacifica Foundation, Inc.
Editorial: 1925 Martin Luther King Jr Way, Berkeley, California 94704-1037.
T: 1 510 849-2590 **E:** contact@pacifica.org
W: http://pacificanetwork.org
Editorial Profile: Producer and distributor of news features and reports for a national radio audience. The goal of the network is to promote the full distribution of public information and to report news and topics not commonly addressed in the mainstream media.

Performance Racing Network
Owner: Speedway Motorsports, Inc.
Editorial: 5555 Concord Pkwy S, Concord, North Carolina 28027-4600.
T: 1 704 455-3228 **W:** http://www.goprn.com
Editorial Profile: Performance Racing Network broadcasts all NASCAR-sanctioned Sprint Cup and Nationwide Series events held at Speedway Motorsports-controlled tracks which include Atlanta, Bristol, Infineon, Las Vegas, Charlotte Motor Speedway, New Hampshire, Kentucky Speedway and Texas. It also assists the Indianapolis Motor Speedway Radio Network for the Brickyard 400. Performance Racing Network and Motor Racing Network on most occasions share the same radio affiliates.

Premiere Radio Network
Owner: Clear Channel Media and Entertainment
Editorial: 15260 Ventura Blvd, Ste 400, Sherman Oaks, California 91403.
T: 1 818 377-5300
E: webmaster@premiereradio.com
W: http://www.premiereradio.com
Editorial Profile: Premiere Radio Networks, a subsidiary of Clear Channel Media and Entertainment, was founded in 1987. It syndicates more than 100 radio programs and services to more than 7,800 radio affiliations and reaches over 180 million listeners weekly. Premiere Radio is the number one radio network in the country and has featured such personalities as Rush Limbaugh, Jim Rome, Casey Kasem, Blair Garner and Carson Daly. In addition, Premiere acts as the sales representative for several non-owned radio networks such as the WOR Talk Network and XM Satellite Radio.

Premiere Radio Network
Editorial: 777 NE 7th St, Grants Pass, Oregon 97526-1632. **T:** 1 541 955-0100

Premiere Radio Network
Editorial: 1270 Avenue Of The Americas, Fl 9, New York, New York 10020.
T: 1 212 445-3900

PRI/Public Radio International
Editorial: 401 2nd Ave N Ste 500, Minneapolis, Minnesota 55401-2097.
T: 1 612 338-5000 **E:** questions@pri.org
W: http://www.pri.org
Editorial Profile: Public Radio International, an independent, non-profit corporation, is the nation's leading developer and supplier of non-commercial audio content. PRI's 400 hours of weekly programming falls into four general formats: News and information, comedy and variety, classical music and contemporary music. The programming is broadcast and streamed online by its 400+ affiliate stations throughout the United States and Guam and is available internationally through World Radio Network and nationwide via Sirius Satellite Radio.

Pulse of Radio
Editorial: 1065 Avenue Of The Americas, Fl 3, New York, New York 10018.
T: 1 212 536-3600
W: http://www.pulseofradio.com
Editorial Profile: Network providing a wide range of music and general entertainment programming services. Distributes music formats for adult contemporary, new adult contemporary, alternative rock, classical, urban contemporary, talk and country music genres. Talk shows spotlight the music and entertainment industries. Affiliated with United Stations Radio Networks.

Pulse of Radio
Editorial: 1108 17th Ave S, Ste B, Nashville, Tennessee 37212-2291. **T:** 1 615 340-0077
W: http://www.pulseofradio.com

Radio America
Owner: American Studies Center(The)
Editorial: 1100 N Glebe, 9th Fl, Arlington, Virginia 22201. **T:** 1 703 302-1000
E: affiliates@radioamerica.org
W: http://www.radioamerica.org
Editorial Profile: Radio America is a division of The American Studies Center. The network is driven by its commitment to traditional American values, limited government and the free market. The network features news and talk programs on weekdays and a variety of special programs on weekends.

Radio Bilingue
Owner: Radio Bilingüe, Inc.
Editorial: 5005 E Belmont Ave, Fresno, California 93727-2441. **T:** 1 800 509-4772
E: mail@radiobilingue.org
W: http://www.radiobilingue.org
Editorial Profile: The network is a provider and distributor of Latino public radio programming.

Radio Disney
Owner: Walt Disney Co.
Editorial: 3800 W Alameda Ave Fl 17, Burbank, California 91505-4300.
T: 1 818 973-4680
W: http://music.disney.com/radio-disney
Editorial Profile: Radio Disney, created by ABC Radio Network, launched in 1996. Radio Disney targets children, ages 2 to 11, with 24-hour interactive daily programming. Music screened for wholesomeness accounts for 90 percent of the programming, including pop, oldies, kids' songs, and television and movie soundtracks.

Radio Disney
Editorial: 13725 Montfort Dr, Dallas, Texas 75240. **T:** 1 972 448-3335

Radio Free Asia
Editorial: 2025 M St NW, Ste 300, Washington, District Of Columbia 20036.
T: 1 202 530-4900 **E:** contact@rfa.org
W: http://www.rfa.org
Editorial Profile: Radio Free Asia (RFA) is a private, non-profit corporation broadcasting news and information in nine languages to listeners in Asia who do not have access to free news media. The purpose of RFA is to deliver accurate and timely news, information and commentary, and to provide a forum for a variety of opinions and voices from within Asian countries.

Radio Free Europe/Radio Liberty
Editorial: 1201 Connecticut Ave NW, Washington, District Of Columbia 20036-2630.
T: 1 202 457-6900 **W:** http://www.rferl.org
Editorial Profile: The mission of Radio Free Europe/Radio Liberty is to promote democratic values and institutions by disseminating factual information and ideas. From Central Europe to the Pacific, from the Baltic to the Black Sea, from Russia to Central Asia to the Persian Gulf, countries are struggling to overcome autocratic institutions, violations of human rights, centralized economies, ethnic and religious hostilities, regional conflicts, and controlled media. Stability throughout this region, based on democracy and free-market economies, is essential to global peace.

Radio Marti
Editorial: 4201 NW 77th Ave, Doral, Florida 33166. **T:** 1 305 437-7012
W: http://www.martinoticias.com/radio.asp
Editorial Profile: Network broadcasting news from the United States to the island of Cuba, with the goal of presenting democratic ideals and information to its citizens. The network airs an all news format.

Radio One, Inc.
Editorial: 8515 Georgia Ave Fl 9, Silver Spring, Maryland 20910-3403.
T: 1 301 306-1111
W: http://www.radio-one.com
Editorial Profile: Radio One was founded in 1980 and primarily targets African Americans. The network owns and/or operates 69 stations in 22 markets. Many of these stations are in the top 20 African American radio markets. The service also programs one channel on the XM Satellite Radio system. The company's strategy is to expand within existing markets and into new markets that have a significant African American presence.

RAI Corporation - New York Bureau
Editorial: 32 Avenue of the Americas Fl 25, New York, New York 10013-2473.
T: 1 212 468-2500 **W:** http://www.rai.it
Editorial Profile: RAI Corporation is the US subsidiary of Radiotelevisione Italiana. RAI Corporation was established in 1960 as an operational base for the production of segments of RAI programs aired in Italy and for the international distribution of Italian programs. RAI Corporation supplies a variety of services to all departments of RAI, including the production of news and entertainment programs; distribution; acquisition; sales; and marketing research. RAI Corporation's headquarters are located in New York, with affiliate offices in Montevideo, Uruguay and Toronto, Canada.

Republic Broadcasting Network
T: 1 512 246-9549
W: http://republicbroadcasting.org

Salem Music Network
Owner: Salem Communications Corp.
Editorial: 402 Bna Dr, Nashville, Tennessee 37217-2519. **T:** 1 615 367-2210
E: info@salemmusicnetwork.com
W: http://www.salemmusicnetwork.com
Editorial Profile: Salem Music Network provides 24-hour, adult contemporary Christian, praise and southern gospel music and programming vvia digital satellite to more than 250 radio

Salem Radio Network
Owner: Salem Radio Network
Editorial: 6400 N Belt Line Rd, Irving, Texas 75063-6093. **T:** 1 972 831-1920
W: http://www.srnonline.com
Editorial Profile: Broadcast outlet airing a bevy of personality-driven talk shows with viewer call-ins and guests. Also features an hourly news feed spotlighting the latest news and information from around the globe. Salem Radio Network (SRN), created in 1993, serves as a full-service satellite-delivered radio network headquartered in Dallas, TX, serving Christian-formatted and general market news/talk stations, through affiliate partnerships. SRN's central focus is the development and syndication of a broad range of programming specifically targeted to both Christian and general market news and talk radio stations.

Sheridan Gospel Network
Owner: Sheridan Broadcasting Corp.
Editorial: 2424 Old Rex Morrow Rd, Ellenwood, Georgia 30294-3901.
T: 1 404 361-1570
W: http://www.sgnthelight.com
Editorial Profile: Producer and distributor of gospel music and talk programs for a national radio audience. The network's primary service is "The Light," a 24 hour, satellite distributed Gospel radio format.

SIRIUS XM Radio
Owner: SIRIUS XM Radio Inc.
Editorial: 1221 Avenue of the Americas, New York, New York 10020-1001.
T: 1 212 584-5100
W: http://www.siriusxm.com
Editorial Profile: SIRIUS XM Radio provides a wide variety of digital entertainment, broadcast live to cars or trucks with crystal clear reception and outstanding digital sound broadcast coast-to-coast. It broadcasts more than 300 channels of programming, including exclusive radio offerings from Howard Stern, Oprah, Opie & Anthony and Martha Stewart, among others.

SIRIUS XM Radio
Owner: SIRIUS XM Radio Inc.
Editorial: 1500 Eckington Pl NE, Washington, District Of Columbia 20002-2128.
T: 1 202 380-4000
Editorial Profile: SIRIUS XM Radio's offices in Washington, D.C.

Soldiers Radio and Television
Owner: U.S. Army
Editorial: 2530 Crystal Dr Suite 100, Arlington, Virginia 22202-3934.
T: 1 703 602-8009 **E:** dmajointdesk@dma.mil
W: http://www.army.mil/media/srtv
Editorial Profile: Produces radio and television programming that keeps both soldiers and the public informed on what's happening in the Army.

Sound of Hope
Editorial: 333 Kearny St Fl 5, San Francisco, California 94108-3268. **T:** 1 408 320-5888
E: info@sohnetwork.com
W: http://sohnetwork.com
Editorial Profile: This is a non-profit radio network which provides independent around-the-clock reporting about China and China-related issues. Their programs feature Asian news and culture, traditional Chinese stories, Chinese recipes, lessons on the Chinese language, and more.

SRN Broadcasting
Owner: SRN Broadcasting & Marketing Inc.
T: 1 847 735-1995 **E:** mail@internetfm.com
W: http://www.internetfm.com
Editorial Profile: The network focuses on sports programming but also produces and distributes other general interest programming. SRN reporters are at all major sports events, such as the Super Bowl, NBA Finals, World Series, Stanley Cup and NCAA Final Four, providing regular and post-season coverage.

Starboard Network
Editorial: 1496 Bellevue St, Green Bay, Wisconsin 54311-4205. **T:** 1 877 291-0123
E: info@relevantradio.com
W: http://www.relevantradio.com
Editorial Profile: Starboard Network is a leading operator of community Catholic talk radio stations. Starboard Network owns and

operates multiple stations and syndicates programming to many affiliated stations throughout the United States. They also provide live streaming audio via the web. Starboard Network has branded its programming as Relevant Radio, a format of Catholic talk radio designed to bridge the gap between faith and everyday life by providing timely programming relevant to today's world. The majority of the programming day consists of live, listener-interactive shows.

Stardome Radio Networks
Owner: Stardome Media Group
Editorial: 8815 Conroy Windermere Rd, Orlando, Florida 32835-3129.
T: 1 407 674-7991
W: http://stardomemedia.com/sd2/
Editorial Profile: Stardome Radio Networks targets the Hispanic listener market with various programming, including news, talk, sports, music, entertainment and more.

Sun Broadcast Group
Editorial: 101 Plaza Real S Ste 217, Boca Raton, Florida 33432-4856. **T:** 1 800 871-6163
W: http://www.sunbgi.com
Editorial Profile: A new generation national broadcast network that programs and syndicates its own content, and provides targeted content and advertising solutions across America. The network is committed to offering the highest quality programming that not only delivers ratings success for station affiliates, but also marketing success advertisers.

Superadio Latino Network
Owner: Superadio, LLC
Editorial: 112 W 34th St Ste 1401, New York, New York 10120-1517
W: http://www.superadiolatino.com
Editorial Profile: Superadio Latino Networks is a Spanish multi-format producer and distributor of Regional Mexican, Latin Pop, Tropical, Latin Hurban and News/Talk formats.

Syndication One
Editorial: 5900 Princess Garden Pkwy, 7th Fl, Lanham, Maryland 20706. **T:** 1 301 306-1111
W: http://syndication1.com
Editorial Profile: Syndication One offers listeners an engaging lineup of programs that discuss, analyze and dissect ideas and issues targeted to the African-American audience, but appealing to the general market. This network is a forum where all points of view are welcomed regardless of race, politics and religion. Instead of the traditional divisive nature of talk radio, each show will offer listeners timely, relevant, probing and entertainment programming.

Talk Radio Network
Owner: Talk Radio Network
Editorial: 724 E Pine St, Central Point, Oregon 97502-2449. **T:** 1 541 664-8827
W: http://www.trn1.com
Editorial Profile: Talk Radio Network distributes a wide variety of talk programming to radio stations nationwide. It spotlights a range of talk-formatted and viewer call-in shows. Topics covered include sports, science and technology, automobiles, politics and general public affairs issues. Hosts are experts and top radio personalities from all walks of life.

Tiger Financial News Network
Owner: Tiger Financial News Network
Editorial: 601 Cleveland St, Ste 618, Clearwater, Florida 33755. **T:** 1 727 467-9190
W: http://www.tfnn.com
Editorial Profile: The mission of Tiger Financial News Network is to assist its listeners in achieving their financial objectives, thoughtfully and prudently, through education and ongoing communication. Through its interactive call-in radio talk shows, TFNN is able to teach all levels of investors the technical skills needed for trading in today's marketplace.

TKO Radio Network
Editorial: 4141 Office Pkwy, Dallas, Texas 75204-3675
W: http://www.tkoradionetwork.com
Editorial Profile: TKO Radio Network offers radio programming in the formats they label Classic Top 40 and into the 70s. Shows are music-based but occasionally feature guests and interviews.

Total Traffic & Weather Network
Owner: Clear Channel Media and Entertainment

Editorial: 1320 Greenway Dr Ste 900, Irving, Texas 75038-7506. **T:** 1 214 596-2300
W: http://totaltraffic.com
Editorial Profile: Total Traffic & Weather Network (TTWN) is the largest provider of local content of news, sports, traffic, weather, business and entertainment information. It is a division of Clear Channel Media and Entertainment and has over 2000 affiliated radio and television stations.

Total Traffic & Weather Network Midwest
Owner: Clear Channel Media and Entertainment
Editorial: 161 N Clark St, Chicago, Illinois 60601-3206. **T:** 1 312 705-1717
E: info@totaltraffic.com
W: http://totaltraffic.com

Total Traffic & Weather Network Northeast
Editorial: 513 W 57th St Ste 6375, New York, New York 10019-2901. **T:** 1 212 975-3741
Editorial Profile: Total Traffic & Weather Network Northeast: Washington, D.C. (240-747-2700), Philadelphia (610-667-4000), Boston (617-472-0088), NYC (212-975-3741).

Total Traffic & Weather Network Northwest/Mountain
Owner: Clear Channel Media and Entertainment
Editorial: 221 Main St Ste 900, San Francisco, California 94105-1923. **T:** 1 415 901-7900
W: http://totaltraffic.com
Editorial Profile: Total Traffic & Weather Network Northwest/Mountain region.

Total Traffic & Weather Network Southeast
Owner: Clear Channel Media and Entertainment
Editorial: 2970 Clairmont Rd NE, Atlanta, Georgia 30329-1638. **T:** 1 770 290-1300
W: http://totaltraffic.com

Total Traffic & Weather Network Southwest/Pacific
Owner: Clear Channel Media and Entertainment
Editorial: 8965 Lindblade St, Culver City, California 90232-2438. **T:** 1 714 647-0117
E: totaltrafficla@clearchannel.com
W: http://totaltrafficla.com

United Stations Radio Network
Editorial: 1065 Avenue of the Americas, New York, New York 10018-1878.
T: 1 212 869-1111 **E:** info@unitedstations.com
W: http://www.unitedstations.com
Editorial Profile: Radio network providing a variety of personality-driven, caller-intensive talk radio programming all delivered to affiliates via satellite. The network provides a variety of music, comedy and information shows and services delivered to affiliates via CD, satellite and the Internet.

Univision America
Owner: Univision Communications, Inc.
Editorial: 605 3rd Ave Fl 12, New York, New York 10158-1299. **T:** 1 212 455-5200
W: http://univisionamerica.com
Editorial Profile: Talk radio network providing topical Spanish-language broadcasting to a national Hispanic audience on AM stations nationwide.

Univision Radio
Owner: Univision Communications Inc.
Editorial: 605 3rd Ave Fl 12, New York, New York 10158-1299. **T:** 1 212 455-5200
W: http://www.univision.com
Editorial Profile: Network providing a variety of Spanish-language broadcasting to a national Hispanic audience. Univision Radio station formats are composed of a variety of music from throughout the Spanish-speaking world. The network also features a news/talk format that is of particular interest to the audience in the United States.

USDA Radio Network
Editorial: 1400 Independence Ave SW, Rm 1623 C, Washington, District Of Columbia 20783. **T:** 1 202 720-3628
Editorial Profile: Produces agriculture news events and features.

VH1 Radio Network
Editorial: 1515 Broadway, New York, New York 10036-8901
W: http://www.dialglobal.com
Editorial Profile: VH1 Radio Network offers services tailored to two formats: Classic Rock/

Rock and Hot AC. Services include daily prep, audio cuts, exclusive interviews and entertainment news. Special programming includes Behind the Music, Storytellers, simulcasts of VH1 concerts and special events as well as special promotions exclusively for radio. The network is owned and operated by Westwood One.

Voice of America Radio Network
Owner: Government-owned
Editorial: 330 Independence Ave SW, Washington, District Of Columbia 20237-0001.
T: 1 202 203-4959
E: coverage-desk@voanews.com
W: http://www.voanews.com
Editorial Profile: The Voice of America (VOA) is an international news service, supported by the U.S. Government, that serves more than 1,200 affiliate radio and television stations overseas. It provides news about the U.S. and world events in a manner designed to report information accurately.

Voice of America Radio Network
Editorial: 11000 Wilshire Blvd, Ste C300, Los Angeles, California 90024. **T:** 1 310 235-7227
E: la@voanews.com

Voice of America Radio Network
Editorial: 26 Federal Plz, Ste 30-100, New York, New York 10278. **T:** 1 212 264-2345
E: nyc@voanews.com

Voice of America Radio Network
Editorial: 27 Gate Hill Dr, Spring, Texas 77381-3291. **T:** 1 281 465-4170

Voice of Russia
Editorial: 1325 G St NW, Washington, District Of Columbia 20005-3104. **T:** 1 202 942-3310
W: http://voiceofrussia.com/radio_broadcast/ alf_programs
Editorial Profile: Voice of Russia is the U.S.-based arm of the national radio network. It reports on international and U.S. news, from a variety of perspectives not always covered in main-stream media.

The Wall Street Journal Radio Network
Owner: News Corporation Ltd.
Editorial: 4300 Route 1 & Ridge Road, Bldg 1, South Brunswick, New Jersey 8852.
T: 1 609 520-4100
W: http://www.wsjradio.com
Editorial Profile: Network providing hourly business and financial news reports transmitted live via satellite 24 hours daily from the Wall Street Journal's newsroom. Also airs regular programming spotlighting money news and consumer trends. Additionally, the network provides business news script services. All PR submissions should be directed to the news department e-mail address, which sends the information to all the radio editors including the network, Podcast and talk show editors.

The Wall Street Journal Radio Network
Editorial: 2000 Town Center, Ste 750, Detroit, Michigan 48226-3541. **T:** 1 248 204-5500

The Wall Street Journal Radio Network
Editorial: 1211 Avenue Of The Americas, Fl 5, New York, New York 10036-8706.
T: 1 212 416-2000

Washington Radio and Press Service
Editorial: 6702 Pawtucket Rd, Bethesda, Maryland 20817. **T:** 1 301 229-2576
Editorial Profile: Radio news service with domestic and Canadian clients. Focuses on coverage of national affairs and politics from a local angle.

WAY Media Network Services
Owner: WAY Media Inc.
T: 1 719 533-0300
W: http://www.waymedianetwork.com
Editorial Profile: WAY Media Network Services is a division of WAY Media, Inc. based in Colorado Springs, CO. Established in 1997, WAY Media Network Services offers cutting edge, award winning radio programming to more than 100 radio stations nationwide. Markets include; Nashville, Denver, Louisville, Portland, and many more.

The Weather Channel Radio Network
Editorial: 300 Interstate North Pkwy SE, Atlanta, Georgia 30339. **T:** 1 770 226-0000
E: twcrn@weather.com
W: http://www.weather.com/aboutus/radio

Editorial Profile: Network affiliated with The Weather Channel cable television outlet. Provides weather information, forecasts and updates to affiliated stations and satellite radio throughout the United States.

WestwoodOne
Owner: Cumulus Media
Editorial: 220 W 42nd St, New York, New York 10036-7200. **T:** 1 212 419-2926
W: http://www.westwoodone.com
Editorial Profile: WestwoodOne, previously Dial Global, provides over more than 200 news, sports, music, talk and entertainment programs as well as features, live events and 24/7 formats. Through its subsidiaries, Metro Networks/Shadow Broadcast Services, WestwoodOne provides local content to the radio and TV industries including news, sports, weather, traffic, video news services and other information. SmartRoute Systems, also a subsidiary of WestwoodOne, manages traffic information centers for state and local departments of transportation, and markets traffic and travel content to wireless, Internet, in-vehicle navigation systems and voice portal customers. WestwoodOne serves more than 7,700 radio stations. Its networks reach 225 million people a week.

WestwoodOne
Owner: Cumulus Media
Editorial: 8403 Colesville Rd, Silver Spring, Maryland 20910-6331. **T:** 1 301 628-2300

WestwoodOne
Owner: Cumulus Media
Editorial: 8965 Lindblade St, Culver City, California 90232-2438. **T:** 1 310 840-4000

WestwoodOne
Owner: Cumulus Media
Editorial: 25061 Avenue Stanford, Valencia, California 91355-3443. **T:** 1 661 702-9908
Editorial Profile: Entertainment and lifestyle programming.

WestwoodOne
Owner: Cumulus Media
Editorial: 3131 Elliott Ave Ste 770, Seattle, Washington 98121-1044. **T:** 1 206 728-2741

WestwoodOne
Owner: Cumulus Media
Editorial: 701 5th Ave, Seattle, Washington 98104-7097. **T:** 1 206 386-7770

WestwoodOne
Owner: Cumulus Media
Editorial: 220 W 42nd St Fl 4, New York, New York 10036-7200. **T:** 1 212 419-2926

WestwoodOne
Owner: Cumulus Media
Editorial: 2020 M St NW, Washington, District Of Columbia 20036-3304. **T:** 1 202 457-7990

WOR Radio Network
Owner: Clear Channel Media and Entertainment
Editorial: 111 Broadway, New York, New York 10006-1901. **T:** 1 212 642-4533
E: newsda@gmail.com
W: http://www.wor710.com
Editorial Profile: Nationally syndicated world class talk programming distributed via satellite 24 hours a day, seven days a week to nearly 400 stations. All shows include listener phone-ins and topical guest interviews.

Yahoo! Sports Radio
Owner: Gow Broadcasting, LLC
Editorial: 5353 W Alabama St Ste 415, Houston, Texas 77056-5942.
T: 1 800 224-2004
W: http://sports.yahoo.com/radio
Editorial Profile: National network distributing a variety of personality-driven sports talk programming 24 hours a day to over 400 outlets across America. Programming emphasizes listener call-ins, in addition to studio guests, interviews and in-depth analysis of the latest issues in the world of sports.

TELEVISION NETWORKS

ABC Television Network
Owner: Walt Disney Co.
Editorial: 77 W 66th St, New York, New York 10023-6201. **T:** 1 212 456-7777
W: http://abc.go.com
Editorial Profile: ABC Television Network is a national broadcast television network providing a range of general entertainment fare. The network airs numerous original

drama and comedy series, daytime dramas, children's shows, theatrical film airings, news broadcasts, public affairs forums and exclusive sports events programming. It also provides programming to affiliated stations nationwide.

ABC Television Network
Editorial: 190 N State St Fl 3, Chicago, Illinois 60601-3303. **T:** 1 312 899-4015

ABC Television Network
Editorial: 500 Circle Seven Dr, Glendale, California 91201-2331. **T:** 1 818 553-5500
E: deskabcla@gmail.com

ABC Television Network
Editorial: 1717 Desales St NW, Washington, District Of Columbia 20036-4401.
T: 1 202 222-7700

ABC Television Network
Editorial: 3845 Pleasantdale Rd, Atlanta, Georgia 30340. **T:** 1 678 245-7570
Editorial Profile: The newsroom at ABC News in Atlanta prefers to have items faxed to the main fax number.

ABC Television Network
Editorial: 2 Alhambra Plz, Ph 1C, Coral Gables, Florida 33134. **T:** 1 305 448-9036
E: abctv.miami.bureau@abc.com

ABC Television Network
Editorial: 47 W 66th St, Fl 3, New York, New York 10023. **T:** 1 212 456-2700

ABC Television Network
Editorial: 140 4th Ave N, Seattle, Washington 98109-4940. **T:** 1 206 404-9112

ABC Television Network
Editorial: 500 S Buena Vista St, Burbank, California 91521-0001. **T:** 1 818 560-1000

ABC Television Network
Editorial: 900 Front St, San Francisco, California 94111-1427. **T:** 1 415 954-7321

ABC Television Network
T: 86 10 65322671

America One
Owner: USFR Media Group
Editorial: 6125 Airport Fwy, Ste 100, Fort Worth, Texas 76117. **T:** 1 817 546-1400
E: comments@americaone.com
W: http://www.americaone.com
Editorial Profile: General entertainment television network providing family-oriented programming to television stations throughout the United States. It is a full service syndication and distribution television network. The wide variety of programming includes children's shows, sports, nostalgic Hollywood movies, classic television series, time-honored Westerns, outdoor shows, fitness programs, and music presentations.

Azteca
Editorial: 1139 Grand Central Ave, Glendale, California 91201-2423. **T:** 1 310 432-7650
E: info@aztecaamerica.com
W: http://us.azteca.com
Editorial Profile: Azteca is TV Azteca's wholly-owned Spanish language broadcasting network for the U.S. Hispanic market. The network supplies TV Azteca's content, including telenovelas, news, sports, and other entertainment.

Azteca
Editorial: 1430 Broadway Fl 10, New York, New York 10018-3308. **T:** 1 646 360-1788
W: http://us.azteca.com

Bounce TV
Owner: Bounce Media, LLC
Editorial: 600 Galleria Pkwy Se Ste 1900, Atlanta, Georgia 30339-5990
E: info@bouncetv.com **W:** http://bouncetv.com
Editorial Profile: Bounce TV is a television network that features a programming mix of theatrical motion pictures, live sporting events, documentaries, specials, inspirational faith-based programs, off-net series, original programming and more. The network is geared towards African-American audiences. The network launched in fall 2011.

CBS Television Network
Owner: CBS Corporation
Editorial: 524 W 57th St, New York, New York 10019-2930. **T:** 1 212 975-4321
W: http://www.cbs.com
Editorial Profile: Nationally-distributed broadcast television network providing a variety of news, information and entertainment programming to over 200 local affiliates. Assets include an extensive news reporting and public affairs division, exclusive coverage of major sporting events around the globe via CBS Sports, and original first-run comedy and drama series via CBS Entertainment.

CBS Television Network
Editorial: 2020 M St NW, Washington, District Of Columbia 20036-3368. **T:** 1 202 457-4444

CBS Television Network
Editorial: 7800 Beverly Blvd, Los Angeles, California 90036-2112. **T:** 1 323 575-2345
E: cbsla@cbsnews.com

CBS Television Network
Editorial: 855 Battery St, San Francisco, California 94111-1503. **T:** 1 415 362-8177

CBS Television Network
Editorial: 5001 Spring Valley Rd Ste 1060E, Dallas, Texas 75244-3960. **T:** 1 972 869-2000

CBS Television Network
Editorial: 4770 Biscayne Blvd, Ste 1170, Miami, Florida 33137. **T:** 1 305 571-4400

CBS Television Network
Editorial: 817 W Peachtree St Nw Ste 305, Atlanta, Georgia 30308-1168.
T: 1 404 876-8925

CBS Television Network
Editorial: 22 W Washington St, Chicago, Illinois 60602-1606. **T:** 1 312 899-2121

CBS Television Network
Editorial: 524 W 57th St, New York, New York 10019. **T:** 1 212 975-6121

CBS Television Network
T: 44 20 78873020
E: londondesk@cbsnews.com

CBS Television Network
T: 1 813 358-7186

CCTV America
Owner: China Central Television
Editorial: 1100 13th St NW Ste 1188, Washington, District Of Columbia 20005-4289.
T: 1 202 393-1850 **E:** info@cctv-america.com
W: http://cctv.cntv.cn/lm/cctvamerica/01/index.shtml
Editorial Profile: CCTV America is a national news network affiliated with China Central Television News. The network aims to inform, engage, and provide debate on a range of issues of relevance to American and global viewers with a particular interest in China and Asia. Send futures press materials to planning@cctv-america.com.

Cox Broadcasting Corporation
Owner: Cox Media Group, Inc.
Editorial: 400 N Capitol St NW, Ste 750, Washington, District Of Columbia 20001-1536.
T: 1 202 777-7000
W: http://www.coxenterprises.com
Editorial Profile: Cox entered the television industry in 1948 and now owns or operates 15 TV stations in 11 markets reaching 30 million viewers.

Cozi TV
Owner: NBCUniversal Media, LLC
Editorial: 30 Rockefeller Plz, New York, New York 10112-0015. **T:** 1 212 664-4444
W: http://www.cozitv.com
Editorial Profile: Cozi TV is a digital multicast television network bringing viewers America's most beloved and iconic television series, hit movies and original programming brought to you by the NBC Owned Television Stations.

CW Television Network
Owner: CW Network, LLC
Editorial: 3300 W Olive Ave, Burbank, California 91505-4640. **T:** 1 818 977-2500
E: feedback@cwtv.com
W: http://www.cwtv.com
Editorial Profile: The CW Television Network is a joint venture of CBS Corp. and Warner Bros. The network officially launched in September 2006. The CW Network consists of a six night, 13 hour programming lineup, Sunday through Friday, with a Saturday morning animation block. Altogether the network airs 30 hours of programming over seven days.

Daystar Television Network
Editorial: 3901 Highway 121, Bedford, Texas 76021-3009. **T:** 1 817 571-1229
E: contactus@daystar.com
W: http://www.daystar.com
Editorial Profile: The Daystar Television Network is headquartered in the greater Dallas/Fort Worth Metroplex and is a division of Word Of God Fellowship, Inc., a Georgia-based 501(c)3 non-profit organization. The Network owns and/or operates broadcast television stations in: Philadelphia, PA; San Francisco, CA; Boston, MA; Dallas, TX; Atlanta, GA; Houston, TX; Seattle, WA; Tampa, FL; Phoenix, AZ; Denver, CO; Sacramento, CA; Stockton, CA; Modesto, CA; Raleigh, NC; Nashville, TN; San Antonio, TX; Memphis, TN; Buffalo, NY; Las Vegas, NV; Little Rock, AR; Knoxville, TN; Honolulu, HI; Maui, HI; Jackson, MS; Macon, GA; Gainesville, GA; and Apex, NC. Daystar is seen nationwide on DirecTV and Dish Network (in six major metro areas).

Estrella TV
Owner: Liberman Broadcasting Inc.
Editorial: 1845 W Empire Ave, Burbank, California 91504-3402. **T:** 1 818 563-5722
W: http://www.estrellatv.com
Editorial Profile: Estrella TV is a Spanish-language television network owned by Liberman Broadcasting Inc. The network launched on September 14, 2009. KRCA-TV is the flagship affiliate for Estrella TV.

ETTV America
Owner: Eastern Broadcasting Co.
Editorial: 18430 San Jose Ave Ste A, City of Industry, California 91748-1263.
T: 1 626 581-8899
W: http://www.ettvamerica.com
Editorial Profile: ETTV America is a Chinese language news and business network.

Focus TV
Editorial: 229 N Vermont St, Covington, Louisiana 70433-3239. **T:** 1 985 635-0333
W: http://www.focustvonline.com
Editorial Profile: A religious network that features programming consisting of religious, entertaining, informative news and cultural shows to every Catholic.

FOX Broadcasting Company
Owner: News Corporation Ltd.
Editorial: 10201 W Pico Blvd, Los Angeles, California 90064-2606. **T:** 1 310 369-3553
E: askfox@fox.com **W:** http://www.fox.com
Editorial Profile: National broadcast network providing entertainment and feature programming to 185 primary affiliates throughout the United States. Programming fare includes original dramatic and comedy series, theatrical and made-for-tv films, and exclusive broadcast rights to NFL football, Major League baseball, and NASCAR.

Fox Broadcasting Company
Editorial: 55 W Wacker Dr, Chicago, Illinois 60601-1610. **T:** 1 312 494-0428
E: askfox@fox.com

Fox Broadcasting Company
Editorial: 400 N Capitol St NW, Washington, District Of Columbia 20001-1511.
T: 1 202 824-6300 **E:** askfox@fox.com

Fox Broadcasting Company
Editorial: 1211 Avenue of the Americas, New York, New York 10036-8701.
T: 1 212 556-2400 **E:** askfox@fox.com

here!
Owner: Here Media, Inc.
Editorial: 242 W 17th St, Ste 1200, New York, New York 10011-5302. **T:** 1 212 242-8100
E: editor@advocate.com
W: http://www.heretv.com
Editorial Profile: Founded in 2002, here! airs on all major U.S. cable systems as a 24-hour subscription service. here! appears in 96 of the top 100 U.S. markets, including every top 10 market. here! was also the first gay network originating in the U.S. to launch internationally.

Home Shopping Network
Editorial: 1 Hsn Dr, Saint Petersburg, Florida 33729. **T:** 1 727 872-1000
W: http://www.hsn.com
Editorial Profile: This network allows viewer's to shop from home. Network programming includes descriptions of new products on the market that can be ordered by viewers via telephone or online via the network's Web site.

India Waves
T: 1 510 487-4988 **E:** info@indiawaves.com
W: http://www.indiawaves.com
Editorial Profile: Network features programming of the best of Bollywood, Hollywood and youth. It spotlights icons and celebrities from the Indian film industry, and highlights the making of Bollywood films, the latest in Bollywood contemporary music and entertainment news.

ION Media Networks
Owner: ION Media Networks
Editorial: 601 Clearwater Park Rd, West Palm Beach, Florida 33401-6233. **T:** 1 561 659-4122
W: http://www.iontelevision.com
Editorial Profile: ION Television airs programming seven days a week, 24 hours a day and reaches over 260 million Americas in 100 million homes in the U.S. via nationwide broadcast television, cable and satellite distribution systems. The ION Television entertainment line-up features a combination of classic and more recent TV hits, popular movies, sports and special events.

ION Media Networks
Editorial: 1330 Avenue Of The Americas, New York, New York 10019. **T:** 1 212 757-3100

The Jewish Life Television Network
Owner: Phil Blazer Communications
Editorial: 16501 Ventura Blvd, Ste 504, Encino, California 91436. **T:** 1 818 786-4000
E: info@blazermediagroup.com
W: http://www.jltv.tv
Editorial Profile: The Jewish Life Television Network (JLTV) is the first television network featuring Jewish-themed programming for all Americans, both Jewish and non-Jewish. JLTV features news and sports, movies, music videos, documentaries, magazine programs, shows for children and young adults, comedy and more.

Latinoamerica Televisión
E: info@latele.tv
Editorial Profile: Latinoamerica Television is a channel with exclusive content from Latin America to the U.S. Hispanic audience. Programming fare includes movies, sporting events, news and information, current affairs, children's programs, comedy, variety and talk shows and dramatic series.

Link TV
Editorial: 901 Battery St Ste 308, San Francisco, California 94111-1350.
T: 1 415 248-3950 **E:** pr@linktv.org
W: http://www.linktv.org
Editorial Profile: Nationwide television channel dedicated to providing Americans with global perspectives on news, events and culture. The channel was launched in December 1999 on DIRECTV and was later added to EchoStar's DISH Network. The channel is available as a basic service in more than 31 million U.S. homes that receive direct broadcast satellite television. Link TV broadcasts programs that engage, educate and activate viewers to become involved in the world. These programs provide a unique perspective on international news, current events, and diverse cultures, presenting issues not often covered in the U.S. media.

ME TV
Owner: Weigel Broadcasting Co.
Editorial: 26 N Halsted St, Chicago, Illinois 60661-2107. **T:** 1 312 705-2600
W: http://www.metvnetwork.com
Editorial Profile: ME TV is a national television network consisting of classic television programs.

MyNetworkTV
Owner: News Corporation
Editorial: 1211 Avenue of the Americas, New York, New York 10036-8701.
T: 1 212 301-5400
W: http://www.mynetworktv.com
Editorial Profile: MyNetworkTV launched on September 5, 2006. It offers a wide array of entertainment programming. Most of its affiliates are former affiliates of The WB and UPN that did not join the CW Network. MyNetworkTV is a sister network of the FOX Broadcasting Network.

NBC Television Network
Owner: NBC Universal
Editorial: 30 Rockefeller Plz, New York, New York 10112-0015. **T:** 1 212 664-4444
W: http://www.nbc.com
Editorial Profile: The NBC Television Network's strength derives from combining NBC's strong national identity and

programming with the local identity and programming of its affiliates in communities across America. The sale of advertising time enables the NBC Television Network to provide programming to the public free of charge. Affiliated television stations are an integral part of NBC's overall broadcast service. The NBC Television Network broadcasts approximately 5,000 hours of TV programming each year, transmitting to more than 200 affiliated stations across the United States. These independently owned affiliates then broadcast the NBC signal to an estimated 99 percent of all homes in the United States with television sets. In addition to airing NBC's national programming, affiliates serve their communities by producing news, sports, and public affairs programming that addresses local needs.

NBC Television Network
Editorial: 4001 Nebraska Ave NW, Washington, District Of Columbia 20016-2733. **T:** 1 202 885-4200
E: nbcdcpressadvisories@nbc.com

NBC Television Network
Editorial: 454 N Columbus Dr, Chicago, Illinois 60611-5807. **T:** 1 312 836-5566

NBC Television Network
Editorial: 3000 W Alameda Ave, Burbank, California 91523-0002. **T:** 1 818 840-4444

NBC Television Network
Editorial: 1 Monroe Pl Ne, Atlanta, Georgia 30324-4836. **T:** 1 404 881-0154

NBC Television Network
Editorial: 3900 Barnett St, Fort Worth, Texas 76103-1400. **T:** 1 214 871-7373

NBC Television Network
Editorial: 30 Rockefeller Plz, Rm 300, New York, New York 10112-0002.
T: 1 212 664-5900

NBC Television Network
Editorial: 846 Howard Ave, New Orleans, Louisiana 70113-1134. **T:** 1 504 528-8744

NBC Television Network
T: 44 207 843-8700
E: london.newsdesk@nbc.com

NBC Television Network
Editorial: 925 Woodrdg Ctr Dr, Charlotte, North Carolina 28217-1986.
T: 1 704 329-8700
Editorial Profile: NBC Television Network bureau in Charlotte, North Carolina.

New Paradigm Broadcasting Network
Owner: Paradigm Shift Media LLC
Editorial: 1201 W 5Th St Ste M120, Los Angeles, California 90017-1461.
T: 1 866 622-8520 **W:** http://www.npbn.com
Editorial Profile: New Paradigm Broadcasting Network is a television and Internet broadcast network dedicated to delivering entertainment for the nation's ever-changing African-American and Latino audiences. The network focused on entertaining content specifically for these communities.

Pan Desi
Editorial: 1 Ethel Rd, Edison, New Jersey 08817-2838. **T:** 1 732 287-2500
E: team@pandesi.com
W: http://www.pandesi.com
Editorial Profile: Pan Desi (Day-see) is an English language television network for South Asians in America. The network, which launched in 2008, uniquely targets the audience of Americanized people of Indian, Pakistani and similar South Asian descent. Pan Desi's audience of South-Asian Americans represents one of the most affluent and fastest-growing ethnic groups in the United States. The network offers programming for Desi families, women, men, teens and children. The networks programming slate includes entertainment, movies, sports, magazine shows, late night comedy blocks and issues-based, interactive audience participation programs that make use of in-person, telephone and computer technologies. Programming from the Pan Desi Network is available nationwide to more than seventeen million households through an agreement with CoLours TV.

PBS/Public Broadcasting Service
Editorial: 2100 Crystal Dr, Arlington, Virginia 22202-3784. **T:** 1 703 739-5000
E: pressroom@pbs.org **W:** http://www.pbs.org
Editorial Profile: PBS is a media enterprise that serves 355 public non-commercial television stations and reaches nearly 73 million people each week through on-air and online content. Bringing diverse viewpoints to television and the Internet, PBS provides high-quality documentary and dramatic entertainment. PBS is a leading provider of digital learning content for pre-K-12 educators, and offers a broad array of other educational services. The national broadcast entity, founded in 1969, provides quality TV programming and related services to 355 non-commercial stations serving all 50 states, Puerto Rico, the U.S. Virgin Islands, Guam and American Samoa.

Premium Sports Inc.
Editorial: 170 Columbus Ave Ste 201, San Francisco, California 94133-5160.
T: 1 415 400-4869
W: http://www.premiumsportsinc.com
Editorial Profile: Premium Sports Inc. features live broadcasts of popular international soccer, rugby, Gaelic sports and boxing. Past featured sporting events include, the Euro Cup, IRB Rugby World Cup, Barclays Premier League, the UEFA Champions League. Premium Sports is available via a closed-circuit satellite feed.

Qubo Channel
Owner: Ion Media Networks, NBC Universal, Corus Nelvana, Scholastic Media
Editorial: 810 7Th Ave, New York, New York 10019-5818. **T:** 1 212 603-8488
E: pr@qubo.com **W:** http://www.qubo.com
Editorial Profile: Qubo is a groundbreaking bilingual, multi-platform entertainment destination for children that focuses on literacy, values and healthy lifestyles while celebrating the unlimited possibilities of a child's imagination. Most of Qubo's shows are associated with popular children's books, and the network's interstitial programming continues to reinforce messages about early literacy and healthy living.

RTN/Retro Television
Owner: Luken Communications
Editorial: 735 Broad St Ste 1205, Chattanooga, Tennessee 37402-1804.
T: 1 800 294-4800
W: http://www.myretrotv.com
Editorial Profile: RTV/Retro Televison is a broadcast television network that provides retro programming to its affiliates across the country. Most of its programming includes re-runs of classic television shows such as Hogan's Heroes, Family Ties and The Brady Bunch.

Swiss TV - Washington Bureau
Editorial: 2000 M St NW, #370, Washington, District Of Columbia 20036.
T: 1 202 429-9668 **W:** http://www.sf.tv
Editorial Profile: The Washington, D.C. bureau of Swiss TV. Swiss TV's Web site is not available in English. The bureau prefers that press materials be submitted via fax.

Telemundo
Owner: NBC Universal
Editorial: 2290 W 8th Ave, Hialeah, Florida 33010-2017. **T:** 1 305 884-8200
W: http://msnlatino.telemundo.com
Editorial Profile: Spanish-language broadcast network targeting the Hispanic audience in the United States and around the world. Lineup includes motion pictures, comedies, game shows, news and information programming, sporting events, concerts, theater and novelas.

Telemundo
Editorial: 400 N Capitol St NW Ste 850, Washington, District Of Columbia 20001-1555.
T: 1 202 737-7830

Telemundo
Editorial: 3000 W Alameda Ave Fl 4, Burbank, California 91505-4400. **T:** 1 818 840-4444

Telemundo
Editorial: 30 Rockefeller Plz Rm 764E-3, New York, New York 10112-0015.
T: 1 201 969-4247

ThisTV
Owner: Weigel Broadcasting Co.
Editorial: 26 N Halsted St, Chicago, Illinois 60661-2107. **T:** 1 312 705-2600
W: http://www.thistv.com
Editorial Profile: ThisTV offers movies and mini series. ThisTV is owned by Weigel Broadcasting Co.

TV Marti
Editorial: 2200 NW 72nd Ave, Miami, Florida 33152-9001. **T:** 1 305 437-7000
E: info@martinoticias.com
W: http://www.martinoticias.com
Editorial Profile: Television network broadcasting news from the United States to the island of Cuba, with the goal of presenting democratic ideals and information to its citizens.

UniMas
Editorial: 9405 NW 41st St, Doral, Florida 33178-2301. **T:** 1 305 421-2900
W: http://tv.univision.com/unimas
Editorial Profile: Spanish-language network reaching 86% of all Hispanic homes throughout the United States. Broadcasting 24 hours a day, the network includes news, novelas, talk shows, variety shows, movies and sports programming. The network does not accept unsolicited faxes. The network launched in January 2002. On January 7, 2013, the network rebranded from TeleFutura Television Network to UniMas.

Univision Television Network
Owner: Univision Communications Inc.
Editorial: 9405 NW 41st St, Doral, Florida 33178-2301. **T:** 1 305 471-3900
W: http://www.univision.com
Editorial Profile: Univision Television provides an extensive lineup of Spanish language programming produced in the United States and throughout the Hispanic world. Programming fare includes movies, sporting events, news and information, current affairs, children's programs, comedy, variety and talk shows and dramatic series.

Univision Television Network
Editorial: 605 3rd Ave, Fl 12, New York, New York 10158. **T:** 1 212 455-5200
W: http://www.univision.com

Univision Television Network
Editorial: 101 Constitution Ave NW, Ste 810E, Washington, District Of Columbia 20001.
T: 1 202 682-6160

V-me
Owner: V-me Media Inc.
Editorial: 450 W 33rd St Fl 11, New York, New York 10001-2650. **T:** 1 212 273-4800
W: http://www.vmetv.com
Editorial Profile: Spanish-language network featuring programming adapted specifically for American Latinos. Features a diverse range of regular programming and specials focusing on kids, lifestyle, history, public affairs, science, the arts and entertainment.

CABLE

A&E
Owner: A+E Networks
Editorial: 235 E 45th St, New York, New York 10017-3305. **T:** 1 212 210-1400
E: feedback@aetn.com
W: http://www.aetv.com
Editorial Profile: National arts and entertainment network, producing a wide array of original programming from mysteries to award-winning biographies of famous individuals. Features documentaries and series covering everything from crime and justice to transportation and flight.

ABC Family Channel
Editorial: 500 S Buena Vista St, Burbank, California 91521-0001. **T:** 1 818 560-1000
W: http://www.abcfamily.com
Editorial Profile: ABC Family offers fun, light-hearted programming with a twist for kids, teens, and adults. The channel features original series and movies, major theatrical releases, and repurposed programming from the ABC Television Network. ABC Family does not accept any unsolicited pitches or story ideas.

ABC News Now
Editorial: 77 W 66th St Rm, New York, New York 10023-6201. **T:** 1 212 456-4441
W: http://abcnews.go.com
Editorial Profile: ABC News Now is ABC's digital news operation. The 24-hour satellite news channel provides reports from all ABC News broadcasts. The service is currently distributed via On Demand, Comcast, RealNetworks' SuperPass, AOL, BellSouth, Comcast.net and SBC Yahoo!. It is also available on wireless devices through deals with MobiTV, GoTV, and SmartVideo.

ABC NewsOne
Owner: Walt Disney Co.
Editorial: 47 W 66th St, New York, New York 10023-6201. **T:** 1 212 456-4110
W: http://www.abcnews.com
Editorial Profile: ABC NewsOne is a 24-hour syndicated news feed service of the ABC Television Network. Provides repackaged audio and video feeds of developing news, sports and weather events to over 200 affiliates throughout the country, along with foreign news agencies and other ABC News programs.

ABC NewsOne
Editorial: 1717 Desales St NW, Washington, District Of Columbia 20036-4407.
T: 1 202 222-7525

AccentHealth
Owner: AccentHealth, Inc.
Editorial: 5440 Beaumont Center Blvd, Tampa, Florida 33634-5246. **T:** 1 813 349-7127
E: info@accenthealth.com
W: http://www.accenthealth.com
Editorial Profile: AccentHealth provides national coverage in 10,500 waiting rooms of healthcare offices across the United States. Owned by CNN and AccentHealth, the network aims to provide informative programming for patients at the point of care. PR professionals are advised to contact the network's staff by e-mail.

AccentHealth
Editorial: 747 3rd Ave, 14th Fl, New York, New York 10017. **T:** 1 212 763-5100

The Africa Channel
Editorial: 11135 Magnolia Blvd Ste 110, North Hollywood, California 91601-3819.
T: 1 818 655-9977
E: info@theafricachannel.com
W: http://www.theafricachannel.com
Editorial Profile: The Africa Channel is an all-English, high-quality "all Africa" television network. All of the network's programming is filmed, produced, and originally aired in Africa, reformatted for American audiences. Programming is produced in conjunction with Weller/Grossman Productions.

Alhurra
Owner: Middle East Broadcasting Networks
Editorial: 7600 Boston Blvd, Springfield, Virginia 22153-3136. **T:** 1 703 852-9000
E: comments@alhurra.com
W: http://www.alhurra.com
Editorial Profile: This commercial-free channel is devoted to broadcasting news, talk shows and information programs on health, entertainment, sports, fashion, science and technology. The channel is part of the Middle East Broadcasting Networks and financed by the US government.

Alhurra-Iraq
Owner: Middle East Broadcasting Networks
Editorial: 7600 Boston Blvd, Springfield, Virginia 22153-3136. **T:** 1 703 852-9000
E: comments@alhurra.com
W: http://www.alhurra.com
Editorial Profile: Satellite channel broadcasts news from Alhurra, as well as news, talk shows and informational programming specifically dealing with Iraq. The channel is part of the Middle East Broadcasting Networks, Inc. and financed by the US government.

AMC
Owner: AMC Networks Inc.
Editorial: 11 Penn Plz, New York, New York 10001-2006. **T:** 1 516 803-4300
E: info-amc@amc.com
W: http://www.amctv.com
Editorial Profile: Launched in 1984, AMC is a 24-hour, movie-based network, dedicated to the American movie fan. The network, which reaches over 90 million homes, offers a comprehensive library of popular movies and a critically-acclaimed slate of original programming.

American Forces Network Broadcast Center
Editorial: 23755 Z St, Riverside, California 92518-2031. **T:** 1 951 413-2351
E: dmajointdesk@dma.mil
W: http://myafn.dodmedia.osd.mil
Editorial Profile: American Forces Network Broadcast Center (AFN-BC) operates and provides multi-channel broadcast quality radio and television services and expanded internal information products to all Department of Defense members and their families stationed overseas, on contingency operations, and onboard Navy ships around the world. All

entertainment, news, sports and information programming is acquired and distributed by AFN based on the popularity of programs within the specific Department of Defense audience demographics, the unique interests of military audiences and AFN scheduling needs.

American Heroes Channel
Owner: Discovery Communications, Inc.
Editorial: 1 Discovery Pl, Silver Spring, Maryland 20910-3354. **T:** 1 240 662-3709
W: http://www.ahctv.com
Editorial Profile: Formerly known as Discovery Wings Channel and the Military Channel, American Heroes Channel focuses on all aspects of the armed forces, military strategies and personnel throughout the ages. The channel has formed partnerships with the USO, the National D-Day Museum and the Congressional Medal of Honor Foundation to develop programming for the channel as well as educational campaigns and public service announcements.

Animal Planet
Owner: Discovery Communications, Inc.
Editorial: 1 Discovery Pl, Silver Spring, Maryland 20910-3354. **T:** 1 240 662-2000
W: http://animal.discovery.com
Editorial Profile: Launched in October 1996, Animal Planet is the only television network dedicated exclusively to the connection between humans and animals. Animal Planet gives men and women, parents and children a co-viewing experience that inspires them with the wow, whoa and wonders of the animal kingdom. The network's original programming brings together people of all ages by tapping into a fundamental fascination with animals and providing a diverse mix of programming including original movies, adventure series, sports, drama and sitcoms. The network has more than 88 million subscribers.

Animal Planet
Editorial: 850 3Rd Ave Ste 1004, New York, New York 10022-7256. **T:** 1 212 548-5555

Antena 3 Television - New York Bureau
Editorial: 450 W 33rd St, Fl 14, New York, New York 10001-2626. **T:** 1 212 506-6187
W: http://www.antena3tv.es

Al Arabiya TV - New York Bureau
Owner: MBC Group
Editorial: 405 E 42nd St, New York, New York 10017-3507. **T:** 1 212 355-5845
W: http://www.alarabiya.net
Editorial Profile: Arabic language provider of news and current affairs worldwide.

Arise News
Editorial: 401 5th Ave, New York, New York 10016-3317. **T:** 1 212 401-4900
E: info@arise.tv **W:** http://www.arise.tv
Editorial Profile: Arise News is a global media network reflecting the experiences of under-served communities, championing the voices of the African diaspora across all continents and engaging citizens of the world. Available on Sky Channel 519.

ASPiRE
Owner: Magic Johnson Enterprises
Editorial: 2077 Convention Center Concourse, Suite 300, Atlanta, Georgia 30337
E: media@magicjent.com **W:** http://aspiretv.tv
Editorial Profile: ASPiRE is a cable network delivering entertainment and programming catered to African-Americans families. The network will feature a diverse slate of original and acquired programming in the categories of movies, documentaries, short films, music, comedy, visual and performing arts, faith and inspirational programs. The network launched in late June 2012.

Associated Press Broadcast
Editorial: 1100 13th St NW, Washington, District Of Columbia 20005-4051.
T: 1 202 641-9000 **E:** info@ap.org
W: http://www.apbroadcast.com
Editorial Profile: More than 1,000 U.S. media Web sites and 4,300 television and radio stations depend on the Associated Press for text stories, audio, video, graphics, and photo services for building their on-air and online products and services. AP offers coverage of news, sports, business news, political news, technology news, entertainment, and weather. Founded in 1848, AP is the world's oldest and largest newsgathering organization, serving more than one billion people worldwide. Today, AP employs more than 3,500 staffers in 240 bureaus, with its broadcast division based in Washington, D.C.

Associated Press Broadcast
Editorial: 450 W 33rd St, 14th Floor, New York, New York 10001. **T:** 1 212 621-1670

Associated Press Broadcast
Editorial: 221 S Figueroa St, Ste 300, Los Angeles, California 90012-2553.
T: 1 213 626-1200 **E:** losangeles@ap.org

Associated Press Broadcast
Editorial: 303 2nd St, Ste 680N, San Francisco, California 94107-1327.
T: 1 415 495-1708 **E:** sanfrancisco@ap.org

Associated Press Broadcast
Editorial: 10 S Wacker Dr, Ste 2500, Chicago, Illinois 60606-7491. **T:** 1 312 781-0500
E: chifax@ap.org

Associated Press Broadcast
Editorial: 645 Albany Shaker Rd, Albany, New York 12211-1158. **T:** 1 518 458-7821
E: apalbany@ap.org

The Associated Press Broadcast
Editorial: 101 Marietta St Nw Ste 2450, Atlanta, Georgia 30303-2772.
T: 1 404 522-8971

Associated Press Broadcast
Editorial: 4851 Lyndon B Johnson Fwy Ste 300, Dallas, Texas 75244-6047.
T: 1 972 991-2100 **E:** aptexas@ap.org

AWE
Owner: Herring Broadcasting, Inc.
Editorial: 4575 Morena Blvd, San Diego, California 92117-3649. **T:** 1 858 270-6900
E: info@herringbroadcasting.com
W: http://www.awetv.com
Editorial Profile: AWE is a 24/7 high definition cable television network devoted to taking viewers on a journey of how wealth is achieved, used and enjoyed. AWE defines wealth as an abundance of good, not just money.

AXS TV
Owner: AXS TV
Editorial: 320 S Walton St, Dallas, Texas 75226-1972. **T:** 1 214 698-3800
W: http://www.axs.tv
Editorial Profile: AXS TV (formerly HDNet) launched September 2001 by co-founders Mark Cuban, (owner of the Dallas Mavericks), and Philip Garvin of Colorado Studios. The network produces and televises pop culture, music, fashion and more. In July 2012, HDNet rebranded to AXS TV.

AXS TV
Editorial: 8269 E 23Rd Ave, Denver, Colorado 80238-3556. **T:** 1 303 542-5600
Editorial Profile: AXS TV Denver bureau.

BabyFirstTV
Owner: BabyFirstTV, LLC
Editorial: 10390 Santa Monica Blvd, Los Angeles, California 90025-5058.
T: 1 888 251-2229
W: http://www.babyfirsttv.com
Editorial Profile: BabyFirstTV is the first cable and satellite channel in the United States dedicated to providing innovative programming designed to inspire baby's learning in a delightful and engaging way. Programming is developed by child development experts and specifically tailored to meet the needs of babies and toddlers up to three years of age in a safe, positive, commercial-free learning environment. In addition to original children's series, BabyFirstTV offers programming from popular children's DVDs, a series for parents offering tips and advice on various parenting topics and interactive tools to help parents better understand the developmental benefits each program offers their babies.

Back9Network
Editorial: 1 American Row Fl 10, Hartford, Connecticut 06103-2801
W: http://www.back9network.com
Editorial Profile: Back9Network is a multiplatform lifestyle network for golf lovers.

BBC America
Owner: British Broadcasting Corp.
Editorial: 1120 Avenue of the Americas Fl 5, New York, New York 10036-6700.
T: 1 212 705-9300
W: http://www.bbcamerica.com
Editorial Profile: BBC America delivers U.S. audiences high-quality, innovative and intelligent programming. Established in 1998, it has been the launch pad for talent embraced by American mainstream pop culture, including Ricky Gervais, Gordon Ramsay, Graham Norton, and successful programming formats including ground-breaking non-scripted television like Top Gear and top-rated science-fiction like Doctor Who. Owned by BBC Worldwide, the commercial arm of the BBC, BBC America has attracted both critical acclaim and major awards including an Emmy, four Golden Globes and ten Peabody Awards. The channel attracts one of cable's most affluent and educated audiences and is available on digital cable and satellite TV in more than 68 million homes. It broadcasts in both standard and high-definition, with content available On Demand across all major digital platforms. Online, www.bbcamerica.com is the place to go to dig deeper into pop culture with a British twist.

BBC/British Broadcasting Corporation
Owner: British Broadcasting Corp.
Editorial: 450 W 33rd St, New York, New York 10001-2603. **T:** 1 212 501-1540
E: bbcnews24@bbc.co.uk
W: http://www.bbc.com
Editorial Profile: A worldwide leader in program and news production since the 1920s. It provides a wide range of distinctive programs and services for everyone, free of commercial interests and political bias. They include television, radio, national, local, children's, educational, language and other services for key interest groups.

BBC/British Broadcasting Corporation
Editorial: United Nations, Room C-309, New York, New York 10017. **T:** 1 212 688-6266

BBC/British Broadcasting Corporation
Editorial: 2000 M St NW, Washington, District Of Columbia 20036-3307. **T:** 1 202 223-2050

BBC/British Broadcasting Corporation
Editorial: 5775 Blue Lagoon Dr, Ste 220, Miami, Florida 33126. **T:** 1 305 267-8650

BBC/British Broadcasting Corporation
Editorial: 10351 Santa Monica Blvd Ste 250, Los Angeles, California 90025-6952.
T: 1 310 405-8205

The Berns Bureau
Editorial: 50 Constitution Ave NE, Washington, District Of Columbia 20002.
T: 1 202 314-5165
Editorial Profile: Independent news service that reports on Washington news and news makers for radio stations and networks. The bureau primarily focuses on stories regarding agricultural news and issues.

BET/Black Entertainment Television
Owner: Viacom Inc.
Editorial: 1235 W St NE, Washington, District Of Columbia 20018-1101. **T:** 1 202 608-2000
W: http://www.bet.com
Editorial Profile: Network distributed throughout the United States targeting African-Americans and providing a variety of family-oriented programming. Includes regular features and specials in news, public affairs, talk, music, sports, and entertainment.

Big Ten Network
Owner: Big Ten Conference
Editorial: 600 W Chicago Ave Ste 875, Chicago, Illinois 60654-2531.
T: 1 312 665-0700 **W:** http://btn.com
Editorial Profile: The Big Ten Network, launched August 30, 2007, is dedicated to covering the Big Ten Conference and its 11 member institutions. It provides unprecedented access to an extensive schedule of conference sports events and shows; original programs in academics, the arts and sciences; campus activities and associated personalities.

Bio/The Biography Channel
Owner: A+E Networks
Editorial: 235 E 45th St, New York, New York 10017-3305. **T:** 1 212 210-1400
E: feedback@aetn.com **W:** http://www.fyi.tv
Editorial Profile: Bio is a spin-off of the popular television series Biography on A&E. Features in-depth, informative biographies of famous individuals from the world of politics, arts, and entertainment.

Biz Television
Editorial: 810 E Abram St, Arlington, Texas 76010-1277. **T:** 1 817 274-1609
E: info@biztelevision.com
W: http://www.biztelevision.com
Editorial Profile: Biz Television is a national television network that focuses on managing money in all phases of life. The programming is distinctive, educational and entertaining and addresses the broad range of personal planning, finance, money and investment needs of individuals, families, investors and entrepreneurs.

Bloomberg Television
Owner: Bloomberg L.P.
Editorial: 731 Lexington Ave, New York, New York 10022-1331. **T:** 1 212 318-2000
E: release@bloomberg.net
W: http://www.bloomberg.com/tv
Editorial Profile: A 24-hour business and financial news channel delivering tools and information for businesses and investors. Shown via 10 networks in seven languages, Bloomberg Television reaches more than 310 million homes around the world. The network utilizes world-class resources to present up-to-the-minute market coverage, and features anchors and journalists who deliver news with added perspectives and analyses.

Bloomberg Television
Editorial: 1399 New York Ave NW, Fl 11, Washington, District Of Columbia 20005-4749.
T: 1 202 624-1800

Bloomberg Television
Editorial: 111 S Wacker Dr, Ste 4950, Chicago, Illinois 60606-4301.
T: 1 312 443-5900

Bloomberg Television
T: 81 332018900

Bloomberg Television
Editorial: 6500 Wilshire Blvd Ste 2360, Los Angeles, California 90048-4916.
T: 1 323 782-4220
Editorial Profile: Bloomberg Television Los Angeles bureau.

Bloomberg Television
T: 44 20 73307460
E: newsalert@bloomberg.net
Editorial Profile: Bloomberg Television London bureau.

Bloomberg Television
Editorial: Pier 3, Suite 101, San Francisco, California 94111. **T:** 1 415 617-7100

The Boating Channel
Owner: Boating Channel, Inc.(The)
T: 1 631 725-4440
E: contact@webworldtv.com
W: http://www.youtube.com/user/boatingchanneltv
Editorial Profile: Focusing on the world of boating, this network features a wide variety of nautical-based programming including historical documentaries, instructional features, and equipment reviews. Also included is marine news and weather, cruise vacation shows, and general information for recreational and pleasure boaters.

Bravo
Owner: NBC Universal
Editorial: 30 Rockefeller Plz Floor 46, New York, New York 10112-0015.
T: 1 212 664-4444 **E:** bravofeedback@nbc.com
W: http://www.bravotv.com
Editorial Profile: Bravo is an arts and culture network featuring a variety of programs presented in an original and engaging way. Currently seen in more than 76 million homes, Bravo is the television destination for viewers who want creativity, experimentation and innovation. The network offers programming with a unique point of view, featuring original series and specials, feature films (both independent and mainstream) and performance specials and compelling documentary series.

Bravo - Burbank Office
Owner: NBC Universal
Editorial: 3000 W Alameda Ave, Burbank, California 91523-0001. **T:** 1 818 840-4444

Capitol News Service
Editorial: 310 N Monroe St, Tallahassee, Florida 32301-7622. **T:** 1 850 224-5546

W: http://www.flanews.com
Editorial Profile: Capitol News Service provides coverage of Florida's Capitol to state and national news outlets.

The Cartoon Network
Owner: Time Warner Inc.
Editorial: 1050 Techwood Dr NW, Atlanta, Georgia 30318-5604. **T:** 1 404 827-1700
E: cartooncomments@turner.com
W: http://www.cartoonnetwork.com
Editorial Profile: The 24-hour network is devoted to providing cartoon and animation programming. Drawing from the world's largest cartoon library, Cartoon Network showcases unique original cartoon ventures. The network is currently seen in more than 97 million U.S. homes and 166 countries around the world, offering cable service in original, acquired and classic entertainment for youth and families.

Cartoon Network
Owner: Time Warner Inc.
Editorial: 300 N 3Rd St, Burbank, California 91502-1107 **E:** cartooncomments@turner.com
W: http://www.cartoonnetwork.com

Cartoon Network
Owner: Time Warner Inc.
Editorial: 1 Time Warner Ctr Fl 19, New York, New York 10019-8017. **T:** 1 212 2750000
E: cartooncomments@turner.com
W: http://www.cartoonnetwork.com

Catholic TV
Owner: iCatholic Media, Inc.
Editorial: 34 Chestnut St, Watertown, Massachusetts 02472-2339.
T: 1 617 923-0220 **E:** info@catholictv.com
W: http://www.catholictv.com
Editorial Profile: CatholicTV is the largest diocesan Catholic television station in the world and presents a blend of spiritual, educational, and entertaining programming.

CBN/Christian Broadcasting Network
Owner: Christian Broadcasting Network(The)
Editorial: 977 Centerville Tpke, Virginia Beach, Virginia 23463-1001. **T:** 1 757 226-7000
W: http://www.cbn.com
Editorial Profile: CBN's mission is to prepare the United States of America and the nations of the world for the coming of Jesus Christ and the establishment of the kingdom of God on Earth. The network is headquartered in Virginia Beach, VA with bureaus in Washington, D.C. and Jerusalem.

CBN/Christian Broadcasting Network
Editorial: 1919 M St NW, Ste 100, Washington, District Of Columbia 20036.
T: 1 202 833-2707

CBS Newspath
Owner: CBS Corporation
Editorial: 524 W 57th St, New York, New York 10019-2930. **T:** 1 212 975-2881
E: newspath@cbs.com
W: http://cbsnewspath.blogspot.com
Editorial Profile: CBS Newspath is the unit of CBS News that provides a full spectrum of services for local affiliates to use in producing their news broadcasts. CBS Newspath is part of each station's daily editorial process, assisting in the coordination, exchange and distribution of news. It ensures the timely movement of material from CBS News to affiliates and among affiliates nationwide.

CBS Newspath
Editorial: 2020 M St NW, Washington, District Of Columbia 20036-3304. **T:** 1 202 457-4321
Editorial Profile: The bureau mostly covers the White House, Capitol Hill and Federal Government.

CBS Newspath
Editorial: 4200 Radford Ave, Studio City, California 91604. **T:** 1 818 655-2500

CBS Newspath
Editorial: 300 E Royal Ln Ste 125, Irving, Texas 75039-3514. **T:** 1 972 869-2000
E: newspathsouthwestregion@cbs.com

CBS Newspath
Editorial: 1 Julian Price Pl, Charlotte, North Carolina 28208. **T:** 1 704 374-3500

CBS Sports Network
Owner: CBS Corporation
Editorial: 28 E 28th St Fl 15, New York, New York 10016-7939. **T:** 1 212 975-5100
W: http://www.cbssportsnetwork.com

Editorial Profile: CBS Sports Network is the original 24-hour cable network dedicated to capturing the passion of college sports. Available to up to 95 million homes nationwide, we cover 25 men's and women's sports. The network televises more than 250 live events each year, including 50 football games and over 140 basketball games, in HD. In addition, CBS Sports Network is the Home of Armed Forces Football, with exclusive rights to home Army, Navy and Air Force games. Throughout the year, the network also airs a full slate of original programming such as behind-the-scenes series, documentaries and studio coverage featuring expert analysis, predictions, in-depth interviews and more.

Centric
Owner: Viacom Inc.
Editorial: 1235 W St NE, Washington, District Of Columbia 20018-1101. **T:** 1 202 608-2000
E: contactus@bet.com
W: http://www.centrictv.com
Editorial Profile: Centric is a network that mirrors the network BET, but targeted towards a more mature audience. Centric's programming includes a mix of music, lifestyle programming and retro viewing including regular scheduled episodes of Soul Train.

Channel One News
Editorial: 151 W 26th St, Fl 9, New York, New York 10001-6810. **T:** 1 212 329-8377
E: feedback@channelone.com
W: http://www.channelone.com
Editorial Profile: Peabody and Telly Award-winning Channel One News, an Alloy Media + Marketing company, is the leading television news network for teens, reaching nearly six million young people in middle schools and high schools nationwide - broadcast each day to close to 1 in 4 of all teenagers in the U.S. The dynamic, daily broadcast and supplementary educational resources inform, educate, and inspire teens, connecting them with important current events and the world around them. Channel One News has covered fast-breaking global events from regions such as Haiti, Chile, Mexico, Sierra Leone, North Korea, Afghanistan, Sri Lanka, Germany and Qatar.

Chiller Network
Owner: NBC Universal
Editorial: 900 Sylvan Avenue, 1 CNBC Plaza, Englewood Cliffs, New Jersey 7632.
T: 1 818 777-1300 **E:** feedback@chillertv.com
W: http://www.chillertv.com
Editorial Profile: Network is dedicated to the popular horror genre. It features exclusive horror and thriller programming from favorite mainstream series.

Chung T'ien Television
Owner: Want Want China Holdings
Editorial: 1255 Corporate Center Dr Ste 212, Monterey Park, California 91754-7616.
T: 1 323 415-0068 **E:** ctiusa@ctitv.com.tw
W: http://www.ctitv.com.tw
Editorial Profile: Chung T'ien Television (CTi TV), owned by Want Want China Holdings is a Taiwan-based television network featuring Mandarin-language news, lifestyle, entertainment and talk programming. The US office is based in Los Angeles and distributed by Comcast.

Cinemax
Owner: Time Warner Inc.
Editorial: 1100 Avenue of the Americas, New York, New York 10036-6712.
T: 1 212 512-1000
W: http://www.cinemax.com
Editorial Profile: Cinemax offers collection of premium television networks that broadcasts feature films, documentaries and special behind-the-scenes features. It was launched in August 1980 and is sister networks with HBO/ Home Box Office.

Citybuzz
Owner: Vidicom
Editorial: 1775 Broadway, New York, New York 10019-1903. **T:** 1 212 895-8300
W: http://vidicom.com
Editorial Profile: Citybuzz selects the best in upscale restaurants, nightlife, shopping, entertainment, hotels, and exploration activities in every major city in the United States. Citybuzz's content is seen on television, hotel broadcasts, cruise lines, and in-flight programs.

Classic Arts Showcase
T: 1 323 878-0283 **E:** casmail@sbcglobal.net
W: http://www.classicartsshowcase.org
Editorial Profile: Classic Arts Showcase is a non-commercial operation that presents clips of 16 different arts disciplines such as opera, ballet and classical music 24 hours a day, free and unscrambled. Available to all non-commercial broadcasters or individuals in North and South America. The network is a monumental audience development project provided as a public service to stimulate interest and support for the arts. There is no other programming produced at the network.

Cloo
Owner: NBC Universal
Editorial: 30 Rockefeller Center, 21 Floor, New York, New York 10112. **T:** 1 212 664-4444
W: http://www.cloo.com
Editorial Profile: Cloo is a 24-hour entertainment cable channel dedicated to the popular and enduring crime, mystery and suspense genre. The channel features crime and mystery classics from NBC Universal's extensive library of feature films, classic television shows, reality series and documentaries. Programming includes popular and cult television series like Miami Vice, The A-Team, and Knight Rider. Crime, mystery and suspense films like Scarface, The Jackal, Casino, Sneakers and Mercury Rising.

CMT/Country Music Television
Owner: Viacom Inc.
Editorial: 330 Commerce St, Nashville, Tennessee 37201-1821. **T:** 1 615 335-8400
E: viewerservices@cmt.com
W: http://www.cmt.com
Editorial Profile: Country Music Television (CMT), a unit of Viacom's MTV Networks (NYSE: VIA and VIA.B), is the leading television and digital authority on country music and entertainment, reaching more than 90 million homes in the U.S. CMT offers a mix of music, news, live concerts and series and is the top resource for country music on demand. The network's digital platforms include the 24-hour music channel CMT Pure Country, CMT Mobile and CMT VOD. CMT was launched in 1983.

CNBC Cable Network
Owner: NBC Universal
Editorial: 900 Sylvan Ave, Englewood Cliffs, New Jersey 07632-3312. **T:** 1 201 735-2622
E: planning@nbcuni.com
W: http://www.cnbc.com
Editorial Profile: CNBC offers in-depth and breaking news coverage, focusing on politics, business, finance and entertainment. Programming includes live ongoing coverage of daily stock market activity, breaking business news, and in-depth interviews with top business analysts and executives. PR professionals should be aware that CNBC typically covers only publicly-traded companies worth over 500 million dollars, the exception being a smaller company that is somehow directly related to a major national or international news story. Send press releases to the CNBC assignment desk or to the producer of the appropriate CNBC program.

CNBC Cable Network
Editorial: 1 S Wacker Dr, Chicago, Illinois 60606-4614. **T:** 1 312 750-4080

CNBC Cable Network
Editorial: 1025 Connecticut Ave NW, Washington, District Of Columbia 20036-5405.
T: 1 202 776-7418
E: cnbcdcproducers@nbcuni.com

CNBC Cable Network
Editorial: 100 Universal City Plz Ste 260, Universal City, California 91608-1002.
T: 1 818 622-2622

CNBC Cable Network
Editorial: 2450 N 1st St, San Jose, California 95131-1002. **T:** 1 408 432-4520
Editorial Profile: The San Jose, CA bureau for cable network CNBC.

CNBC World
Editorial: 900 Sylvan Ave, Englewood Cliffs, New Jersey 7632. **T:** 1 201 735-2622
W: http://www.cnbc.com
Editorial Profile: CNBC World, a service of CNBC and Dow Jones, is a digital network offering global financial markets in real time, live, worldwide. CNBC World combines the resources CNBC business news from Asia, Europe and the Middle East into a 24-hour a day, global business news network. Designed

with original content and coverage, CNBC World provides in-depth market coverage from around the world, major industry news conferences and one-on-one interviews with business leaders. CNBC World is owned by NBC; their parent company is General Electric.

CNN Airport Network
Owner: Time Warner Inc.
Editorial: 1 CNN Center, Atlanta, Georgia 30303. **T:** 1 404 827-5131
E: airportnetwork2@cnn.com
W: http://www.cnn.com/cnn/programs/airport.network/
Editorial Profile: Launched in 1992, CNN Airport Network is the only live, satellite-delivered television service that provides general news, live breaking news, business and financial reports, sports updates, weather, lifestyle and general interest segments to the traveling public. The network contains no original programming and all content is simulcasted from other CNN and Turner networks. The service is offered in 44 of the busiest airports, covering more than 1,800 gates and other viewing areas and represents more than 800 million enplaning passengers annually.

CNN en Espanol
Editorial: 820 1st St NE, Washington, District Of Columbia 20229-1114. **T:** 1 202 515-2990

CNN en Espanol
Editorial: 1 Time Warner Ctr, New York, New York 10019-6038. **T:** 1 212 275-8091

CNN en Español
Owner: Time Warner Inc.
Editorial: 1 Cnn Ctr NW, Atlanta, Georgia 30303-2762. **T:** 1 404 878-1555
W: http://cnnespanol.cnn.com
Editorial Profile: CNN en Espanol is a 24-hour, Spanish-language news network currently available throughout Latin America and the United States. It is the first 24-hour network in a language other than English produced independently by CNN. CNN en Espanol provides continuous news reports on major world events, live breaking news coverage supported by in-depth analysis, worldwide business and financial news, global weather updates, sports and features.

CNN International
Editorial: 1 Cnn Ctr NW, Atlanta, Georgia 30303-2762. **T:** 1 404 827-1500
W: http://edition.cnn.com
Editorial Profile: CNN International, worldwide cable and satellite distribution arm of the vast Cable News Network, was launched in 1985. It provides round-the-clock breaking news coverage and public affairs programming designed to appeal to audiences around the globe.

CNN International - Tokyo Bureau
T: 81 35 776-2255
W: http://edition.cnn.com/ASIA

CNN Newsource
Owner: Time Warner Inc.
Editorial: 1 Cnn Ctr NW, Atlanta, Georgia 30303-2762. **T:** 1 404 827-2659
W: http://newsource.cnn.com/Login.aspx?ReturnUrl=%2f
Editorial Profile: CNN Newsource is the world's most extensive syndicated news service, comprised of over 700 local news-producing affiliates, including TV stations and cable news channels throughout North America. CNN Newsource is the affiliate wire service division of CNN. The service re-distributes CNN's news and information, and on occasion covers stories of its own. CNN Newsource partners receive everything needed to efficiently produce local newscasts including: multiple daily feeds targeted to key news dayparts, providing regional, national and international news, weather, sports, medical, business, lifestyle and entertainment stories, along with graphics and exclusive Newsource-produced franchise pieces; dependable live opportunities via correspondents on the scene of breaking news and select feature stories; and localized CNN Marketsource reports live from the floor of the NYSE.

CNN Newsource
Editorial: 1620 I St NW Ste 1000, Washington, District Of Columbia 20006-4026.
T: 1 202 777-7266
W: http://newsource.cnn.com

CNN/Cable News Network
Owner: Time Warner Inc.

Editorial: 1 Cnn Ctr NW, Atlanta, Georgia 30303-2762. **T:** 1 404 827-1500
E: cnn.pr@turner.com **W:** http://us.cnn.com
Editorial Profile: Worldwide cable news network providing live, ongoing coverage of news around the globe 24 hours a day. Regular programs spotlight public affairs, news, politics, science, technology, business, food, medicine, fashion, sports and entertainment. Also emphasizes topical and in-depth interviews and discussions with newsmakers, politicians, celebrities and people in the news.

CNN/Cable News Network
Editorial: 820 1st St NE, Washington, District Of Columbia 20229-1114. **T:** 1 202 898-7900
E: dcdesk@turner.com

CNN/Cable News Network
Editorial: 1 Time Warner Ctr Fl 5, New York, New York 10019-6038. **T:** 1 212 275-7800
Editorial Profile: New York bureau of CNN.

CNN/Cable News Network
Editorial: 435 N Michigan Ave Ste 715, Chicago, Illinois 60611-4027.
T: 1 312 645-8555
E: cnnchicagobureau@turner.com

CNN/Cable News Network
Editorial: 6430 W Sunset Blvd, Los Angeles, California 90028-7901. **T:** 1 323 993-5000

CNN/Cable News Network
Editorial: 1201 Main St Ste 1525, Dallas, Texas 75202-3998. **T:** 1 214 747-1440
E: cnndallas@turner.com
Editorial Profile: CNN/Cable News Network bureau in Dallas.

CNN/Cable News Network
Editorial: 50 California St Ste 950, San Francisco, California 94111-4606.
T: 1 415 438-5000

CNN/Cable News Network
Editorial: 12000 Biscayne Blvd Ste 101, North Miami, Florida 33181-2742. **T:** 1 954 635-6860

CNN/Cable News Network
Editorial: 637 Washington St Ste 208, Brookline, Massachusetts 02446-4579.
T: 1 617 264-9905

CNN/Cable News Network
Editorial: 8811 Highway 55, Golden Valley, Minnesota 55427-4762. **T:** 1 763 797-7215
Editorial Profile: CNN's one-person Minneapolis news bureau. An all-platform journalist covering the Twin Cities works out of KARE-TV's newsroom.

CNN/Cable News Network
T: 1 971 240-1245
Editorial Profile: CNN bureau based in Abu Dhabi.

CoLours TV
Owner: Black Star Communications (BSC)
Editorial: 200 Quebec St, Denver, Colorado 80230-7144. **T:** 1 303 326-0088
E: info@colourstv.org **W:** http://colourstv.org
Editorial Profile: The purpose of this network and Web site is to bridge the cultural divide by promoting programming that features positive images of ethnically diverse people. CoLours TV is a multi-media network that provides television programming for a multicultural and multi-ethnic America. The programming offers a unique perspective on entertainment, information, news, lifestyles, community issues and public affairs. CoLours TV is a non-profit organization.

Comedy Central
Owner: Viacom Inc.
Editorial: 345 Hudson St, New York, New York 10014-4502. **T:** 1 212 767-8600
W: http://www.comedycentral.com
Editorial Profile: Comedy Central is a round-the-clock national comedy network featuring 60 percent original programming. Comedy Central presents comedy stars from the past and present along with today's newcomers. Comedy Central's schedule is an eclectic mix of original programming, stand-up comedy, sketch comedy, classic television shows and movies. Comedy Central is a division of Viacom Inc.

Comedy Central
Editorial: 2600 Colorado Ave, Santa Monica, California 90404-3519. **T:** 1 310 752-8000

Cooking Channel
Owner: Scripps Networks, Inc.
Editorial: 9721 Sherrill Blvd, Knoxville, Tennessee 37932-3330. **T:** 1 865 694-2700
W: http://www.cookingchanneltv.com
Editorial Profile: Cooking Channel is a 24-hour network that caters to avid food lovers by focusing on food information and instructional cooking programming. The network launched on May 31, 2010.

Cornerstone TV
Owner: Cornerstone Television, Inc.
Editorial: 1 Signal Hill Dr, Wall, Pennsylvania 15148-1436. **T:** 1 412 824-3930
E: info@ctvn.org **W:** http://www.ctvn.org
Editorial Profile: Cornerstone TV is a viewer-supported ministry absolutely committed to using television as a force for good. The network aims to impact our culture by broadcasting the Gospel and bringing a fresh, positive, Christ-centered outlook.

The Crime Channel
Editorial: 7802 Varner Rd, Suite D131, Palm Desert, California 92211. **T:** 1 760 360-6151
E: crimechannel@dc.rr.com
W: http://www.crimechannel.net
Editorial Profile: Cable network focusing on the world of crime and law enforcement. Focuses programming on public safety, crime prevention and law enforcement through feature films, television series, international news, specials and documentaries. Included are docu-dramas dedicated to informing people on how to prevent their cars, homes, and property from being vandalized.

CRN/Cable Radio Network
Owner: Cable Radio Network, Inc.
Editorial: 10487 Sunland Blvd, Sunland, California 91040-1905. **T:** 1 818 352-7152
E: webmaster@crntalk.net
W: http://www.crntalk.com
Editorial Profile: Round-the-clock talk radio service provided for cable television systems throughout the United States. Programs are a variety of news, information, entertainment, lifestyle and sports-related fare. The network features six channels of talk radio for digital cable and satellite subscribers.

C-SPAN
Owner: National Cable Satellite Corporation
Editorial: 400 N Capitol St Nw Ste 650, Washington, District Of Columbia 20001-1550. **T:** 1 202 737-3220 **E:** DCeditor@c-span.org
W: http://www.c-span.org
Editorial Profile: Cable network broadcasting live gavel-to-gavel coverage of the United States House of Representatives. Also airs public affairs programs, speeches, seminars and government committee meetings of interest to viewers around the nation. Due to the kind of programming the network airs, very few editors are pitchable.

C-SPAN2
Owner: National Cable Satellite Corporation
Editorial: 400 N Capitol St NW, Ste 650, Washington, District Of Columbia 20001.
T: 1 202 737-3220 **E:** events@c-span.org
W: http://www.c-span.org
Editorial Profile: Network providing live gavel-to-gavel coverage of the United States Senate in session. Also features Senate committee hearings and public affairs programming.

C-SPAN3
Owner: National Cable Satellite Corporation
Editorial: 400 N Capitol St NW, Ste 650, Washington, District Of Columbia 20001.
T: 1 202 737-3220 **E:** events@c-span.org
W: http://www.c-span.org
Editorial Profile: C-SPAN3 televises key national events from Washington, D.C., including congressional hearings, press conferences, the best in political seminars and conferences and National Press Club speeches in the unique long-form style that's classic C-SPAN. Late nights and weekends, C-SPAN3 spotlights American history with award-winning original history series such as: The Lincoln-Douglas Debates, Traveling Tocqueville's America, and American Presidents: Life Portraits.

Destination America
Owner: Discovery Communications, Inc.
Editorial: 1 Discovery Pl, Silver Spring, Maryland 20910-3354. **T:** 1 240 662-2000
W: http://america.discovery.com
Editorial Profile: Destination America is a network that celebrates the people, places and stories of the U.S. Original series cover such diverse subjects as American food from Tex Mex to barbecue; American mysteries from Jesse James' lost fortune to Area 51; America's heroes from those who embody the values of our past to those who invent the technology of our future; as well as never before seen footage of America's iconic landmarks, including Yellowstone National Park to the Everglade swamps. On May 26, 2012, Planet Green rebranded to Destination America.

Deutsche Welle TV Washington Bureau
Owner: Deutsche Welle
Editorial: 2000 M St NW, Ste 335, Washington, District Of Columbia 20036-3391.
T: 1 202 785-5730 **W:** http://www.dw-world.de
Editorial Profile: Deutsche Welle TV (DW-TV) is Germany's international satellite television service of news and information. DW-TV's Washington bureau produces segments of shows and occasionally an entire show, all of which are then broadcast from the headquaters in Germany.

Discovery Channel
Owner: Discovery Communications, Inc.
Editorial: 1 Discovery Pl, Silver Spring, Maryland 20910-3354. **T:** 1 240 662-2000
W: http://producers.discovery.com
Editorial Profile: Discovery Channel is a widely distributed educational cable network in the United States, providing a wide array of original science and technology based programs, special and series.

Discovery Channel
Editorial: 10100 Santa Monica Blvd Ste 1500, Los Angeles, California 90067-4117.
T: 1 310 551-1611

Discovery Communications
Owner: Discovery Communications, Inc.
Editorial: 1 Discovery Pl, Silver Spring, Maryland 20910-3354. **T:** 1 240 662-2000
W: http://dsc.discovery.com
Editorial Profile: Family of networks providing a wide array of science and technology-based documentaries, specials, and series. Features original productions of a scientific and investigative nature, in addition to features on nature, wildlife, and human biology and history. ** A vast majority of programming aired on Discovery is developed by producers outside the network. As a result, it is suggested that most shows should be contacted via network headquarters in Silver Spring, MD. **

Discovery en Espanol
Editorial: 6505 Blue Lagoon Dr, Ste 190, Miami, Florida 33126. **T:** 1 786 273-4700
W: http://www.tudiscovery.com
Editorial Profile: Cable network offering quality programming in Spanish for the entire family, including science, technology, health, aviation, nature, history, culture, travel and exploration.

Discovery Familia
Owner: Discovery Communications, Inc.
Editorial: 6505 Blue Lagoon Dr Ste 190, Miami, Florida 33126-6030. **T:** 1 786 273-4700
W: http://www.discoveryfamilia.com/familia
Editorial Profile: Discovery Familia is the premiere Spanish-language network dedicated to bringing the best educational and entertaining, family-oriented programming to kids and families.

Discovery Fit & Health
Editorial: 1 Discovery Pl, Silver Spring, Maryland 20910-3354. **T:** 1 240 662-2000
W: http://health.discovery.com
Editorial Profile: Discovery Fit & Health entertains viewers with gripping, real-life dramas featuring storytelling that chronicles the human experience from the cradle to the grave. Calling on the network's long history of health programming, content will include forensic mysteries, amazing medical stories, emergency room trauma dramas, baby and pregnancy programming, parenting challenges, and stories of extreme life conditions. The network also features fitness and wellness programs for both men and women interested in enhancing their well-being through the following exercise styles, regimens, personal trainers, motivational and nutritional advice. On February 1, 2011, FitTV was rebranded to Discovery Fit & Health.

Disney Channel
Editorial: 3800 W Alameda Ave Ste, Burbank, California 91505-4398. **T:** 1 818 569-7500
W: http://www.disney.go.com
Editorial Profile: Family entertainment channel broadcasting original movies, specials, and children's entertainment programming culled from the vast video library of the Walt Disney Co. Programming is designed for kids and families. Disney Channel is a division of ABC Cable Networks Group, a subsidiary of The Walt Disney Company. It is currently in more than 80 million homes.

Disney Junior
Editorial: 3800 W Alameda Ave, Burbank, California 91505-4300. **T:** 1 818 5697500
W: http://disney.go.com/junior/pre/index.html
Editorial Profile: Disney Junior is aimed at children ages 2 to 7 and features timeless characters and children's programming.

Disney XD
Owner: Walt Disney Co.
Editorial: 3800 W Alameda Ave, Burbank, California 91505. **T:** 1 818 569-7500
W: http://disney.go.com/disneyxd
Editorial Profile: Nationally-distributed cable network featuring the rich array of Disney animation archives from the 1930s to the 1990s. Network airs short features and series with classic Disney characters, in addition to animated Disney theatrical releases and classic character-themed programming.

DIY Network
Owner: Scripps Networks, Inc.
Editorial: 9721 Sherrill Blvd, Knoxville, Tennessee 37932-3330. **T:** 1 865 694-2700
W: http://www.diynetwork.com
Editorial Profile: DIY Network is the go-to destination for rip-up, knock-out home improvement television. DIY Network's programs and experts answer the most sought-after questions and offer creative projects for do-it-yourself enthusiasts. DIY Network's programming covers a broad range of categories, including home improvement and landscaping.

E! Entertainment Television
Owner: Comcast Corporation
Editorial: 5750 Wilshire Blvd, Los Angeles, California 90036-3697. **T:** 1 323 954-2400
W: http://www.eonline.com
Editorial Profile: 24-hour network dedicated to the world of entertainment. The network offers compelling celebrity interviews, talk shows, news, docudramas, behind-the-scenes specials, comedy, movie previews and the most comprehensive coverage of the entertainment industry's awards shows.

E! Entertainment Television
Editorial: 5 Times Sq Fl 10, New York, New York 10036-6531. **T:** 1 212 852-5100

Ebru TV
Owner: Samanyolu Broadcasting Company
Editorial: 300 Franklin Square Dr, Somerset, New Jersey 08873-4187. **T:** 1 732 560-0800
W: http://www.ebru.tv

The Ecology Channel
Owner: Ecology Communications Group, Inc.
Editorial: 9171 Victoria Dr, Ellicott City, Maryland 21042-2564. **T:** 1 410 465-0480
E: community@ecology.com
W: http://www.ecology.com
Editorial Profile: Cable network focusing on the world of environmental and ecological development and preservation. Features news and informational programming related to trends, issues, and ideas in environmental processes and evolution.

El Rey Network
Owner: Comcast
Editorial: 4900 Old Manor Rd, Austin, Texas 78723-4522 **E:** info@elreynetwork.com
W: http://www.elreynetwork.com
Editorial Profile: El Rey Network is an entertainment network targeted towards English-speaking Latinos. Launched on March 11, 2014.

Encore
Owner: Liberty Media Corp.
Editorial: 8900 Liberty Cir, Englewood, Colorado 80112-7057. **T:** 1 720 8527700
W: http://www.starz.com/channels/encore
Editorial Profile: Encore is a premium television channel featuring mainly older and recent blockbuster motion pictures. It launched in April 1991 and the channel's sister network is Starz.

Enlace TBN
Owner: Trinity Broadcasting Network
Editorial: 2823 W Irving Blvd, Irving, Texas 75061-4236. **T:** 1 469 499-0820
E: comments@tbn.org

W: http://www.enlace.org
Editorial Profile: Enlace TBN is a digital cable network for the Hispanic faith community. TBN Enlace is owned and operated by TBN, a nonprofit, nondenominational religious organization. TBN Enlace features a unique combination of inspirational programs from Latin America and the most popular programs from TBN.

ESPN
Owner: Walt Disney Co.
Editorial: 935 Middle St, Bristol, Connecticut 06010-1000. **T:** 1 860 766-2000
W: http://espn.go.com
Editorial Profile: This 24-hour sports programming network provides an extensive package of live and taped sporting events, including NFL football, NBA basketball, NASCAR, NCAA college football and basketball and Major League Baseball.

ESPN
Editorial: 77 W 66th St, Fl 21, New York, New York 10023. **T:** 1 212 916-9200

ESPN Classic-The Classic Sports Network
Editorial: 545 Middle St, Bristol, Connecticut 06010-8413. **T:** 1 860 766-2000
W: http://www.espn.com
Editorial Profile: ESPN Classic focuses on the past glories of modern athletics and sport. The network features replays of classic ball games and championships, historical documentaries, interviews with sports heroes of yesterday, and collectible and merchandising information.

ESPN Deportes
Owner: Walt Disney Co.
Editorial: 77 W 66th St, New York, New York 10023-6201. **T:** 1 860 766-2000
W: http://espndeportes.espn.go.com/
Editorial Profile: This Spanish-language sports programming network provides an extensive Spanish-language package of live and taped sporting events, including NFL football, NHL hockey, NCAA college football and basketball, Major League Baseball, auto racing, boxing, and tennis. It also presents an extensive schedule of sports news programming throughout the day, in addition to special interviews with sports personalities and guest commentary about the sporting world.

ESPN2
Owner: Walt Disney Co.
Editorial: 935 Middle St, Bristol, Connecticut 06010-1099. **T:** 1 860 766-2000
W: http://espn.go.com
Editorial Profile: ESPN2 presents more than 4,800 live and/or original hours of sports programming annually featuring MLB, college football and basketball, and much more.

ESPNEWS
Editorial: 935 Middle St, Bristol, Connecticut 6010. **T:** 1 860 766-2000
W: http://sports.espn.go.com/espntv/espnNetwork?networkID=4
Editorial Profile: The only 24-hour sports news network, ESPNEWS features continuous news, highlights, scores, analysis and live press conferences. Since its inception in 1996, ESPNEWS has established itself as an immediate source of sports news and information, utilizing the vast resources of ESPN and its award-winning SportsCenter. ESPNEWS merges ESPN's on-air and online entities to present the ultimate interactive sports news outlet.

ESPNU
Editorial: 11001 Rushmore Dr, Charlotte, North Carolina 28277-3434.
T: 1 704 973-5000
W: http://espn.go.com/espnu
Editorial Profile: Network devoted entirely to college sports. The network airs over 300 live collegiate sporting events throughout the year and features pregame, halftime, and postgame shows.

Esquire Network
Owner: Comcast Corporation
Editorial: 5750 Wilshire Blvd Fl 4, Los Angeles, California 90036-3697.
T: 1 323 954-2400 **W:** http://tv.esquire.com
Editorial Profile: Esquire Network brings the men's brand to television with programming that explores and celebrates the interests, passions and aspirations of men today. Championing intelligence, wit and style, the network reflects a wide range of pursuits with male appeal, including: gaming, gear,

entertainment, food, fashion, women, humor, travel, competition, danger and more.

Everwell TV
Owner: MediVista Media
Editorial: 1100 Spring St NW, Suite 750, Atlanta, Georgia 30309-2846.
T: 1 404 817-7767 **E:** contact@everwell.com
W: http://www.everwelltv.com
Editorial Profile: Everwell TV informs and entertains consumers with premier health video content in the waiting rooms of physicians.

EWTN Global Catholic Network
Owner: Eternal Word Television Network Inc.
Editorial: 5817 Old Leeds Rd, Irondale, Alabama 35210-2198. **T:** 1 205 271-2900
E: viewer@ewtn.com **W:** http://www.ewtn.com
Editorial Profile: A 24-hour national Catholic cable channel. Provides programming of a family-oriented nature through movies, regular series, documentaries, and talk shows. Includes coverage of daily Mass and prayer services across the country while furthering the teachings of the Catholic faith.

FamilyNet Television
Owner: Comstar Media, LLC
Editorial: 6565 N MacArthur Blvd Ste 400, Irving, Texas 75039-2468. **T:** 1 214 4447100
W: http://www.comstarmedia.com
Editorial Profile: FamilyNet is a 24-hour television network airing more than 50 hours of original, values-based programs weekly providing a reliable, safe viewing destination for today's family. FamilyNet is available to more than 30 million TV households nationwide via cable systems and broadcast stations nationwide. It targets families looking for a wholesome alternative to standard television fare. Appealing family programs include kids' series, original concerts, comedy, crafts, health, and live talk along with movies and inspirational shows.

FEARnet
Owner: Lionsgate Entertainment Corp.
Editorial: 2700 Colorado Ave Ste 200, Santa Monica, California 90404-5502.
T: 1 323 634-6003 **E:** webmaster@fearnet.com
W: http://www.fearnet.com
Editorial Profile: FEARnet is a multi-platform movie network created by Lionsgate, Comcast, and Sony Pictures Entertainment that offers free horror, thriller, and suspense movies.

Feature Story News
Owner: Marks(Simon)
Editorial: 1730 Rhode Island Ave NW, Washington, District Of Columbia 20036-3108.
T: 1 202 296-9012 **E:** info@featurestory.com
W: http://www.featurestory.com
Editorial Profile: Feature Story News, the world's leading independent broadcast agency, offers a unique service in the news industry. The organization provides ready-to-air television and radio news material, tailored to individual on-air styles. Produced and edited to suit a program's on-air style, delivered by deadline, and complete with sign-off. Gives networks an international reach without the sky-high costs of opening and maintaining overseas bureaus.

Feature Story News
Editorial: 1133 Broadway, Ste 1420, New York, New York 10010-7942.
T: 1 212 764-5848
Editorial Profile: Feature Story News, the world's leading independent broadcast agency, offers a unique service in the news industry. The organization provides ready-to-air television and radio news material, tailored to individual on-air styles. Produced and edited to suit a program's on-air style, delivered by deadline, and complete with sign-off. Feature Story News gives networks an international reach without the sky-high costs of opening and maintaining overseas bureaus.

Flix
Owner: Showtime Networks Inc.
Editorial: 1633 Broadway Fl 7, New York, New York 10019-6708. **T:** 1 212 7081600
W: http://www.sho.com/site/schedules/channel.do?channel=FLX
Editorial Profile: Flix is a premium television network owned by Showtime Networks Inc, a subsidiary of CBS Corporation, that features hit movies of the 80s, 90s and 00's. It was launched in 1992 and has the sister network channels of Showtime and The Movie Channel.

Food Network
Owner: Scripps Networks, Inc.

Editorial: 75 9Th Ave Fl 2, New York, New York 10011-7028. **T:** 1 212 398-8836
W: http://www.foodnetwork.com
Editorial Profile: Food Network is a 24-hour cable network dedicated to good food and good times. The network airs a variety of taped and live programs dealing with cooking, health, nutrition, and food. Shows emphasize unique recipes, cooking tips and techniques, and feature famous personalities in the cooking world.

FOX Business Network
Owner: News Corporation Ltd.
Editorial: 1211 Avenue of the Americas Fl 16, New York, New York 10036-8701.
T: 1 212 601-7000 **E:** desk@foxbusiness.com
W: http://www.foxbusiness.com
Editorial Profile: FOX Business Network is a cable and satellite news channel offering in-depth and breaking business and financial news coverage. It launched October 15, 2007 to over 30 million subscribers.

FOX Business Network
Editorial: 20 S Wacker Dr, Chicago, Illinois 60606-7431. **T:** 1 312 494-0428

FOX Business Network
Editorial: 400 N Capitol St NW, Ste 550, Washington, District Of Columbia 20001.
T: 1 202 824-6300

FOX Business Network
Editorial: 2044 Armacost Ave, Los Angeles, California 90025. **T:** 1 310 571-2000

Fox Deportes
Editorial: 1440 S Sepulveda Blvd, Los Angeles, California 90025-3458.
T: 1 310 444-8100
W: http://www.foxdeportes.com
Editorial Profile: Fox Deportes is the premier Spanish-language sports network in the United States. It delivers year round, high-profile quality sports programming that appeals most to the growing, diverse U.S. Hispanic market. The channel reaches more than 7 million cable and satellite households in the U.S. The network combines big event programming with game-day action positioning itself as "Hispanic America's Sports Network." On October 1, 2010 the network was renamed to Fox Deportes from Fox Sports en Espanol.

FOX News Channel
Owner: News Corporation Ltd.
Editorial: 1211 Avenue of the Americas, New York, New York 10036-8701.
T: 1 212 301-3000
E: newsmanager@foxnews.com
W: http://www.foxnews.com
Editorial Profile: FOX News Channel is a basic cable news service covering breaking news as well as political, entertainment and business news. The network offers live updates every 30 minutes, 24 hours a day. The network also features interviews with newsmakers.

FOX News Channel
Editorial: 400 N Capitol St NW, Ste 550, Washington, District Of Columbia 20001-1502.
T: 1 202 824-6300 **E:** dcdesk@foxnews.com

FOX News Channel
Editorial: 55 W Wacker Dr, Ste 500, Chicago, Illinois 60601. **T:** 1 312 494-0428

FOX News Channel
Editorial: 2044 Armacost Ave, Los Angeles, California 90025-6113. **T:** 1 310 571-2000

FOX News Channel
Editorial: 100 E Speer Blvd, Ste 300, Denver, Colorado 80203-3437. **T:** 1 303 861-0460
E: fncdenver@gmail.com

FOX News Channel
Editorial: 1666 79th Street Cswy, Ste 203, North Bay Village, Florida 33141-4134.
T: 1 305 866-8007 **E:** miami@foxnews.com

FOX News Channel
Editorial: 901 Battery St, Ste 210, San Francisco, California 94111.
T: 1 415 951-8550

FOX News Channel
Editorial: 260 14th St NW, Fl 1, Atlanta, Georgia 30318. **T:** 1 404 685-2280

FOX News Channel
Editorial: 1201 Main St, Ste 2444, Dallas, Texas 75202-3916. **T:** 1 214 742-5005

FOX News Channel
Editorial: 50 Hunt St, Watertown, Massachusetts 2472. **T:** 1 617 926-2986

FOX NewsEdge
Owner: News Corporation Ltd.
Editorial: 1211 Avenue Of The Americas, Frnt 1, New York, New York 10036.
T: 1 212 301-3444
E: newsmanager@foxnews.com
W: http://www.foxnews.com
Editorial Profile: News service for the FOX Broadcasting Network, with bureaus around the country. News feeds may include material from the FNC/FOX News Channel.

FOX NewsEdge
Editorial: 2044 Armacost Ave, Los Angeles, California 90025-6113. **T:** 1 310 571-2000

FOX NewsEdge
Editorial: 400 N Capitol St NW, Ste 550, Washington, District Of Columbia 20001-1502.
T: 1 202 824-6481

FOX NewsEdge
Editorial: 999 18th St, Ste 1665, Denver, Colorado 80202. **T:** 1 303 861-0460

FOX NewsEdge
Editorial: 901 Battery St, Ste 210, San Francisco, California 94111.
T: 1 415 951-8550

FOX NewsEdge
Editorial: 1201 Main St, Ste 2444, Dallas, Texas 75202-3916. **T:** 1 214 742-5735

FOX NewsEdge
Editorial: 260 14th St NW, Fl 1, Atlanta, Georgia 30318-5360. **T:** 1 404 685-2280

FOX NewsEdge
Editorial: 1230 Washington St, West Newton, Massachusetts 02465-2146.
T: 1 617 926-2986

FOX Sports 1
Owner: News Corporation Ltd
Editorial: 1220 W W T Harris Blvd, Charlotte, North Carolina 28262-8536.
T: 1 704 501-5700
W: http://msn.foxsports.com/foxsports1
Editorial Profile: FOX Sports 1 is a national, multi-sport network that will launch August 17, 2013. It features live college basketball, college football, Major League Baseball, NASCAR, soccer and UFC contests.

FOX Sports 2
Owner: News Corporation Ltd.
Editorial: 1440 S Sepulveda Blvd, Los Angeles, California 90025-3458.
T: 1 310 369-1000
W: http://msn.foxsports.com
Editorial Profile: FOX Sports 2 is a national, multi-sport network that will launch August 17, 2013. It features live college basketball, college football, Major League Baseball, NASCAR, soccer and UFC contests, including the weigh-ins and pre/post-fight coverage.

Free Speech TV
Owner: Free Speech TV
Editorial: 2900 Welton St Ste 300, Denver, Colorado 80205-3010. **T:** 1 303 442-8445
W: http://www.freespeech.org
Editorial Profile: Free Speech TV provides a nationwide platform for voices traditionally absent from mainstream media. Working with activists and artists, FSTV uses television to expose social and environmental injustices - to help build community, to teach tolerance, to encourage personal creativity and stand for non-violent social action. FSTV is a media conduit to advance progressive social change. FSTV airs primarily social, political, cultural, and environmental documentaries, although some experimental and dramatic work is featured as well. FSTV acquires its programming from independent producers and distributors from all around the world.

FSN/FOX Sports Net
Owner: News Corporation Ltd
Editorial: 10201 W Pico Blvd, Ste 100-4350, Los Angeles, California 90064-2606.
T: 1 310 369-6000
E: feedback@foxsports.com
W: http://msn.foxsports.com
Editorial Profile: FSN is the national cable outlet for FOX Sports. The network provides a variety of sports news, information, and event programming via a combination of eleven owned and operated regional FOX Sports outlets and 10 affiliated regional sports cable

networks located from coast-to-coast. The network holds telecast rights to numerous professional baseball, basketball, and hockey teams. FSN also airs an array of collegiate athletics, boxing, tennis, volleyball, and other sporting events.

Fuji Television
Owner: Fujisankei Communications International, Inc.
Editorial: 150 E 52nd St, New York, New York 10022-6017. **T:** 1 212 753-8100
W: http://www.fujisankei.com
Editorial Profile: Fuji Television gathers news for Fuji TV and Sankei Shimbun. It also produces, distributes, and acquires television programming, explores investment opportunities in film, music, publishing, and culture. Fuji also broadcasts Japanese-language television shows on American television stations and cable channels. Additionally, it strives to help American and European businesses target Japanese consumers.

Fuji Television
Editorial: 529 14th St NW Ste 330, Washington, District Of Columbia 20045-1301. **T:** 1 202 347-6070
W: http://www.fujisankei.com

Fuji Television
Editorial: 10100 Santa Monica Blvd, Los Angeles, California 90067-4003.
T: 1 310 553-5828 **E:** info@fci-ny.com
Editorial Profile: Fuji Television gathers news for Fuji TV and Sankei Shimbun. It also produces, distributes, and acquires television programming, explores investment opportunities in film, music, publishing, and culture. Fuji also broadcasts Japanese-language television shows on American television stations and cable channels. Additionally, it strives to help American and European businesses target Japanese consumers

FUNimation
Owner: Olympusat Media
Editorial: 560 Village Blvd, West Palm Beach, Florida 33409-1945. **T:** 1 561 684-5657
W: http://www.funimation.tv/
Editorial Profile: The 24-hour network is devoted to providing Anime and cartoon. The network offers cable service in original, acquired and classic entertainment for youth and families.

Fuse
Owner: SiTV Media
Editorial: 11 Penn Plz, New York, New York 10001-2006. **T:** 1 212 324-3400
E: info@fuse.tv **W:** http://www.fuse.tv
Editorial Profile: Fuse is the nation's only all-music, viewer-influenced television network, featuring music videos, exclusive artist interviews, live concerts and specials. Formerly known as MuchMusic USA, Fuse officially launched in May 2003.

Fusion
Editorial: 8551 NW 30th Ter, Doral, Florida 33122-1908 **E:** website.services@fusion.net
W: http://www.fusion.net
Editorial Profile: Fusion is a joint 24-hour English cable network between Univision Television Network and ABC News. Editorial coverage will focus on the issues most relevant for U.S. Hispanics, including the economy, entertainment, music, food, immigration, education, politics, health and wellness and more. The cable network launched on October 28, 2013.

FX Movie Channel
Owner: News Corporation Ltd.
Editorial: 10201 W Pico Blvd, Los Angeles, California 90064-2606. **T:** 1 310 369-0949
W: http://www.fxnetworks.com/fxm
Editorial Profile: FX Movie Channel, also known as FXM, features dramas, comedies and horror films, 24 hours a day. The network is distributed via cable and satellite around the world.

FX Networks, Inc.
Owner: News Corporation Ltd.
Editorial: 10201 W Pico Blvd Bldg 103, Los Angeles, California 90064-2606.
T: 1 310 369-0949 **E:** user@fxnetworks.com
W: http://www.fxnetworks.com
Editorial Profile: FX, the flagship general entertainment basic cable network from Fox, is geared toward viewers with a young, savvy mindset. The diverse schedule includes a growing roster of distinctive original series and movies, a roster of acquired hit series, an

established film library with box-office hits from 20th Century Fox and other major studios, with many basic cable television premieres. Marquee sports such as NASCAR and Major League Baseball are also featured.

G4
Owner: Comcast Corporation
Editorial: 5750 Wilshire Blvd, Los Angeles, California 90036-3697. **T:** 1 323 954-2400
W: http://www.g4tv.com
Editorial Profile: Formed by the 2004 Merger of G4 and TEchTV, G4 is the only 24-hour television network that is plugged into every dimension of games, gear, gadgets and gigabytes. G4 airs programming that covers every aspect of the videogame culture. Shows feature breaking industry news, reviews, the hottest games and gear, celebrity interviews, insider opinions and underground trend in sports, animation and technology.

Galavision
Owner: Univision Communications Inc.
Editorial: 9405 NW 41st St, Doral, Florida 33178-2301. **T:** 1 305 471-3900
W: http://www.galavision.com
Editorial Profile: Round-the-clock basic cable channel serving the Hispanic-American community with family-oriented programming including kids shows, sports, movies, music and telenovelas.

GCN/Global Christian Network
Editorial: 4440 Tuck Road, Loganville, Georgia 30052. **T:** 1 770 913-8036 **E:** info@gcntv.org
W: http://www.gcntv.org
Editorial Profile: GCN/Global Christian Network, also called The People Channel, delivers quality, innovative, multilingual television programs with Christian and family values to independent television stations, local networks, and home satellite and cable providers around the world. GCN aims to unite cultures and continents with the life-changing message of Jesus Christ through inspired and unique television that accompanies viewers in their daily lives. The network offers its audiences a diverse collage of colors, cultures, and faces presented through talk, magazines, music, history, news, comedy, entertainment, education, travel, life, youth, animations, teaching, worship, human interest and more.

Golf Channel
Owner: NBCUniversal
Editorial: 7580 Golf Channel Dr, Orlando, Florida 32819-8947. **T:** 1 407 345-4653
W: http://www.golfchannel.com
Editorial Profile: 24-hour cable channel devoted to the world of golf. It features live coverage of men's, women's and senior tour events, educational instruction programs, travel-related shows and interviews and profiles of golf professionals.

Great American Country
Owner: Scripps Networks, Inc.
Editorial: 49 Music Sq W Ste 301, Nashville, Tennessee 37203-3243. **T:** 1 615 327-7525
W: http://www.gactv.com
Editorial Profile: Great American Country is America's main street for the widest variety of country music, its artists and the lifestyles they influence. In addition to country music videos, GAC features original programming, special music performances and live concerts, and is the exclusive television home of the Grand Ole Opry.

GSN
Owner: Liberty Media Corporation
Editorial: 2150 Colorado Ave, Ste 100, Santa Monica, California 90404. **T:** 1 310 255-6800
E: community@gsn.com
W: http://www.gsn.com
Editorial Profile: GSN, the Network for Games, is the only U.S. television network dedicated to game-related programming and interactive game playing. The network features game shows, reality series, documentaries and casino games. As the industry leader in interactivity, GSN features over 133 hours per week of interactive programming, which allows viewers a chance to win prizes by playing along with GSN's televised games via gsn.com. Reaching 60 million Nielsen homes, GSN is distributed in the U.S. through all major cable systems and satellite providers. For further media information, visit GSN's press website at corp.gsn.com.

H2
Owner: A+E Networks
Editorial: 235 E 45th St, New York, New York 10017-3305. **T:** 1 212 210-1400
W: http://www.history.com/h2

Editorial Profile: Spin-off of The History Channel. Broadcasts a range of documentaries, historical re-enactments, documentaries, motion pictures, and mini-series relating to world history and events. Aims to provide audiences with programming of history as seen through the eyes of the rest of the world. In September 2011, the network rebranded History International to H2.

Hallmark Channel
Owner: Crown Media Family Networks
Editorial: 12700 Ventura Blvd Ste 200, Studio City, California 91604-2469.
T: 1 818 755-2400
W: http://www.hallmarkchannel.com
Editorial Profile: The Hallmark Channel is a 24-hour television destination that provides a diverse slate of high-quality entertainment characterized by cinematic excellence and strong stories that are relevant to viewers and their lives. The network, launched in 2001, brings to audiences a brand with a 50-plus-year television legacy that resonates with viewers.

Hallmark Movie Channel
Owner: Crown Media Family Networks
Editorial: 12700 Ventura Blvd Ste 200, Studio City, California 91604-2469. **T:** 1 818 7552400
W: http://www.hallmarkmoviechannel.com
Editorial Profile: Hallmark Movie Channel was launched in April 2008 and offers audiences an unparalleled family-friendly viewing experience. It is the fastest-growing cable TV network in 2009 and 2010 and now in 37 million homes, is a 24-hour digital cable network dedicated to bringing viewers original movies with a mix of classic theatrical films, presentations from the acclaimed Hallmark Hall of Fame library, Hallmark Channel Original Movies and special events.

HBO Family
Owner: Time Warner Inc.
Editorial: 1100 Avenue Of The Americas, New York, New York 10036. **T:** 1 212 512-1000
E: family@hbo.com
W: http://www.hbofamily.com
Editorial Profile: Safe and commercial free, HBO Family programming is suitable for all the children in the family, whatever their ages. In the spirit of HBO, HBO Family offers high-quality, original programming that can't be found anywhere else.

HBO/Home Box Office
Owner: Time Warner Inc.
Editorial: 1100 Avenue Of The Americas, New York, New York 10036. **T:** 1 212 512-1000
W: http://www.hbo.com
Editorial Profile: Premium cable channel that features first-run theatrical motion pictures, original movies, investigative documentaries, drama and comedy series, concert specials, and live sporting events.

HBO/Home Box Office
Editorial: 2500 Broadway, Ste 400, Santa Monica, California 90404. **T:** 1 310 382-3200

HGTV
Owner: Scripps Networks, Inc.
Editorial: 9721 Sherrill Blvd, Knoxville, Tennessee 37932-3330. **T:** 1 865 694-2700
W: http://www.hgtv.com
Editorial Profile: Cable and Satellite Network with national distribution focusing on an array of home, lifestyle, decorating, gardening, hobbies and craft related topics. Broadcasts a potpourri of original and exclusive programming hosted by experts in these various fields. ** A vast majority of programming aired on HGTV is developed by producers outside the network. As a result, it is suggested that most shows should be contacted via network headquarters in Knoxville. ** Additionally, HGTV accepts ideas and information about product resources, potential guests, locations and events, and story ideas via their online resource directory at http://resourcedirectory.hgtv.com.

Hispanic Information & Television Network
Editorial: 63 Flushing Ave Unit 211, Brooklyn, New York 11205-1072. **T:** 1 212 966-5660
E: programacion@hitn.org
W: http://www.hitn.tv
Editorial Profile: The Hispanic Information and Telecommunications Network Inc. was established in 1983 as a private non-profit organization to create a network of non-commercial telecommunications facilities to advance the educational, social, cultural, and economic aspirations of Hispanics.

History
Owner: A+E Networks
Editorial: 235 E 45th St, New York, New York 10017-3305. **T:** 1 212 210-1400
W: http://www.history.com
Editorial Profile: History broadcasts a range of documentaries, historical re-enactments, motion pictures, and mini-series dealing with significant figures, events, and inventions through the years.

History en Español
Owner: A+E Networks
Editorial: 235 E 45Th St Fl 8, New York, New York 10017-3305. **T:** 1 212 210-1400
W: http://www.historyenespanol.com/espanol
Editorial Profile: History en Español is a 24-hour television network dedicated to the Spanish-speaking audience in the United States. It presents a wide range of Spanish-language programming that focuses on great dramatic moments and events as well as the pivotal figures in history.

HLN
Owner: Time Warner Inc.
Editorial: 1 Cnn Ctr NW, Atlanta, Georgia 30303-2762. **T:** 1 404 827-1500
W: http://www.hlntv.com
Editorial Profile: HLN provides viewers with the top stories in national and international news, current weather forecasts, consumer and financial updates, sports scores and highlights, as well as the latest in entertainment, fashion, health and more. Sectioned into four distinct dayparts, the content has been streamlined to focus on news that is most relevant and useful to their viewer's daily lives. In Session, truTV's daytime courtside programming, is produced by HLN.

The Hub Network
Owner: Discovery Communications, Inc.
Editorial: 2950 N Hollywood Way Ste 100, Burbank, California 91505-1069.
T: 1 818 531-3600
W: http://kids.discovery.com
Editorial Profile: The Hub Network is a specialty cable channel that presents programs to help kids explore their world and satisfy their curiosities in an entertaining way. The target audience is children, ages 2 to 14. On October 10, 2010, Discovery Kids Channel relaunched as The Hub. As a joint venture of Discovery Communications and Hasbro, Inc., the network remains children's programming.

ICN TV Network
Owner: Beauty Media
Editorial: 9550 Flair Dr Ste 102, El Monte, California 91731-2917. **T:** 1 626 337-8889
W: http://www.icntv.net
Editorial Profile: ICN TV Network, formally known as International Audio-Visual Communication Inc., was established in 1980. ICN has become the largest Chinese television media entity in the U.S.

The Independent Film Channel
Owner: AMC Networks Inc.
Editorial: 11 Penn Plz, New York, New York 10001-2006. **T:** 1 917 542-6200
E: webmaster@ifc.com **W:** http://www.ifc.com
Editorial Profile: Cable service airing first-run theatrical motion pictures produced by small and independent film companies and producers. Programming includes documentaries, animation, shorts, coverage of all major film festivals, cult classics, and exclusive originals.

INSP
Owner: The Inspirational Networks, Inc.
Editorial: 3000 World Reach Dr, Indian Land, South Carolina 29707-6542.
T: 1 803 578-1000 **E:** info@insp.com
W: http://www.insp.com
Editorial Profile: INSP is a 24-hour, daily network available to more than 70 million U.S. households via cable and satellite television. The network targets over 79 million Baby Boomers, 35 million of whom self-identify as "socially conservative". INSP features original and exclusive music programs and a wide variety of family friendly entertainment, including The Waltons, Little House on the Prairie, Brady Bunch, Happy Days and feature films. INSP is distributed to more than 2,800 cable systems and to DIRECTV and DISH Network.

Investigation Discovery
Owner: Discovery Communications, Inc.
Editorial: 1 Discovery Pl, Silver Spring, Maryland 20910-3354. **T:** 1 240 662-3709
W: http://investigation.discovery.com

Editorial Profile: Investigation Discovery brings viewers provocative, engaging and relevant documentary series and specials about the events and ideas shaping our times. The network has won multiple industry honors for its breakthrough programming, including three Emmys, and Overseas Press Club Award, three National Headliner Awards and a BANFF Rockie Award. In addition, the network has held films premiere at various film festivals, including the Sundance Film Festival, Tribeca Film Festival, San Francisco International Film Festival and the Tokyo Video Festival.

ION Life
Owner: ION Media Networks
Editorial: 601 Clearwater Park Rd, West Palm Beach, Florida 33401-6233. **T:** 1 561 659-4122
W: http://www.ionlife.com
Editorial Profile: ION Life is a digital television network that is carried by ION Television affiliates. The programming includes subjects pertaining to health and wellness, cooking, home decor, travel and fitness. ION Life is available via cable, satellite and telco carriage. The network launched on February 19. 2007.

Iran TV and Radio - New York Bureau
Owner: Islamic Republic Of Iran Broadcasting (IRIB)
Editorial: 60 E 42nd St, Fl 30, New York, New York 10165-0059. **T:** 1 212 867-9220
E: englishradio@irib.ir **W:** http://english.irib.ir

Al Jazeera America
Owner: Al Jazeera Media Network
Editorial: 435 Hudson St, New York, New York 10014-3941. **T:** 1 646 273-8700
E: america@aljazeera.net
W: http://america.aljazeera.com
Editorial Profile: Al Jazeera America is a news, information, lifestyle and investigative journalism television network and online news desk headquartered in New York City . The network broadcasts 24 hours a day, seven days a week from studios around the United States and the world.

Al Jazeera America
Editorial: 555 Pennsylvania Ave NW, Washington, District Of Columbia 20001-2114

Al Jazeera America
Editorial: 875 N Michigan Ave Ste 3740, Chicago, Illinois 60611-1946

Al Jazeera Arabic - New York Bureau
Owner: Al Jazeera Network
Editorial: 405 E 42nd St, New York, New York 10017-3507. **T:** 1 212 207-4742
W: http://www.aljazeera.net
Editorial Profile: Arabic language news and current affairs channel.

Al Jazeera English - Chicago Bureau
Owner: Al Jazeera Network
Editorial: 875 N Michigan Ave, Chicago, Illinois 60611-1779. **T:** 1 202 496-4500
W: http://www.aljazeera.com
Editorial Profile: Al Jazeera English is the 24-hour English-language news and current affairs channel headquartered in Doha, the capital of Qatar with broadcasting centers Kuala Lumpur, Malaysia; London and Washington, D.C. and supporting bureaus worldwide. Al Jazeera English is designed to be the English-language channel of reference for Middle Eastern events, balancing the current typical information flow by reporting from the developing world back to the west and from the southern to the northern hemisphere.

Al Jazeera English - New York Bureau
Owner: Al Jazeera Network
Editorial: 405 E 42nd St Rm C-309, New York, New York 10017-3507. **T:** 1 212 317-8238
W: http://www.aljazeera.com
Editorial Profile: Al Jazeera English is the 24-hour English-language news and current affairs channel headquartered in Doha, the capital of Qatar with broadcasting centers Kuala Lumpur, Malaysia; London and Washington, D.C. and supporting bureaus worldwide. Al Jazeera English is designed to be the English-language channel of reference for Middle Eastern events, balancing the current typical information flow by reporting from the developing world back to the west and from the southern to the northern hemisphere.

Al Jazeera English - Washington D.C. Bureau
Owner: Al Jazeera Network
Editorial: 1627 K St NW, Washington, District Of Columbia 20006-1704. **T:** 1 202 496-4500
W: http://www.aljazeera.com
Editorial Profile: Al Jazeera English is the 24-hour English-language news and current affairs channel headquartered in Doha, the capital of Qatar with broadcasting centers Kuala Lumpur, Malaysia; London and Washington, D.C. and supporting bureaus worldwide. Al Jazeera English is designed to be the English-language channel of reference for Middle Eastern events, balancing the current typical information flow by reporting from the developing world back to the west and from the southern to the northern hemisphere.

LATV
Owner: LATV LLC
Editorial: 2323 Corinth Ave, Los Angeles, California 90064. **T:** 1 310 943-5288
W: http://www.latv.com
Editorial Profile: LATV is the nation's first bilingual music and entertainment network distributed via digital multicast. This network targets Hispanic teenagers and young adults. Programs are mainly focusing on music, lifestyle and entertainment.

Liberty Channel
Editorial: 1971 University Blvd, Lynchburg, Virginia 24502. **T:** 1 800 332-1883
E: wtlu@liberty.edu
W: http://www.libertychannel.com
Editorial Profile: Liberty Channel is a satellite/ cable network offering family-friendly television for every member of the American family, young to old. Liberty Channel is uplifting, inspirational and entertaining with a strong, conservative and moral foundation. The Liberty Channel provides viewers with a connection to America's most exciting university-Liberty University-in Lynchburg, VA.

Lifetime
Owner: A+E Networks
Editorial: 685 3Rd Ave, New York, New York 10017-4024. **T:** 1 212 424-7000
W: http://www.mylifetime.com
Editorial Profile: Lifetime is a national cable network dedicated to providing a wide variety of contemporary women's interest programming. This includes original movies, mini-series, celebrity close-ups, comedies, and lifestyle shows dealing with trends and issues of concern to women.

Lifetime
Owner: A+E Networks
Editorial: 2049 Century Park E, Ste 840, Los Angeles, California 90067-3110.
T: 1 310 556-7500

Lifetime Movie Network
Owner: A+E Networks
Editorial: 685 3Rd Ave, New York, New York 10017-4024. **T:** 1 212 424-7000
W: http://www.lmn.tv
Editorial Profile: The movies on Lifetime Movie Network cover every dimension of a woman's life presented in a way that Lifetime Television viewers have come to know and value. Genres include drama, suspense, family, romance, issue-oriented, comedy and mystery.

Lifetime Real Women
Owner: A+E Networks
Editorial: 685 3Rd Ave, New York, New York 10017-4024. **T:** 1 212 424-7000
W: http://www.lifetimetv.com
Editorial Profile: 24-hour channel relying on original series and movies based on true stories. All programming targets women and aims to provide entertainment that will engage and interest this group of viewers.

Live Well Network
Owner: Walt Disney Co.
Editorial: 77 W 66th St Rm, New York, New York 10023-6201 **E:** lwhd@livewellhd.com
W: http://livewellnetwork.com
Editorial Profile: Live Well Network focuses on home, health and lifestyle programming. The digital subchannel broadcasts at ABC affiliates in New York, Chicago, Los Angeles, Philadelphia, San Francisco, Houston, TX; Raleigh-Durham, NC; Fresno, CA; Flint, MI and Toledo, OH. And also Belo affiliates in Dallas, St. Louis, New Orleans, Hampton-Norfolk, Charlotte and more. The digital subchannel does not have a main office; the personnel are located at different affiliates and are noted in their profiles.

Logo
Owner: Viacom Inc.
Editorial: 1515 Broadway, New York, New York 10036-8901. **T:** 1 212 654-3005
W: http://www.logotv.com
Editorial Profile: This cable network is advertiser-supported and targets primarily gays and lesbians, ages 25 to 49. Logo provides a mix of original and acquired programming that is authentic, smart, inclusive and open-minded.

MAVTV
Owner: Lucas Oil Products Inc.
Editorial: 302 N Sheridan St, Corona, California 92880-2067. **T:** 1 877 475-1711
W: http://www.mavtv.com
Editorial Profile: MAVTV was founded in 2002 by four former Showtime Networks executives and was originally geared towards a male dominated audience. In 2011, MAVTV was purchased by Lucas Oil Products, an automotive lubricant manufacturer with a history in television production.

Mega TV
Owner: Spanish Broadcasting System Inc.
Editorial: 7007 NW 77th Ave, Miami, Florida 33166-2836. **T:** 1 305 644-4800
E: info@mega.tv **W:** http://www.mega.tv
Editorial Profile: Spanish-language news, talk and entertainment network.

MLB Network
Editorial: 40 Hartz Way, Secaucus, New Jersey 07094-2403. **T:** 1 201 520-6400
W: http://www.mlb.com/network/
Editorial Profile: MLB Network airs live games, original programming, highlights, classic games, and coverage of baseball events.

Mnet
Owner: CJ Corporation
Editorial: 11828 Teale St, Culver City, California 90230-6331. **T:** 1 310 313-5194
W: http://www.mnetamerica.com
Editorial Profile: Mnet is the only 24/7 English-language television network in the U.S. devoted to Asian pop culture that serves all American viewers who love music and entertainment.

MSNBC
Owner: NBC Universal
Editorial: 30 Rockefeller Plz Fl 3, New York, New York 10112-0015. **T:** 1 212 664-4444
E: planning@nbcuni.com
W: http://tv.msnbc.com
Editorial Profile: Built on the worldwide resources of NBC, MSNBC defines news for the next generation with world class reporting and a full schedule of live news coverage, political analysis and award-winning documentary programming- 24 hours a day, seven days a week. MSNBC's companion, award-winning Web site, NBCNews.com, boasts the state-of-the art technology of Microsoft and the world-class reporting of NBC News. By developing programming simultaneously for cable and the Internet, MSNBC offers truly integrated television, interactive news and dynamic discussion of topical events.

MSNBC
Editorial: 4001 Nebraska Ave Nw, Washington, District Of Columbia 20016-2733.
T: 1 202 885-4800

MTV
Owner: Viacom Inc.
Editorial: 1515 Broadway, New York, New York 10036-8901. **T:** 1 212 846-8000
W: http://www.mtv.com
Editorial Profile: MTV is a 24-hour music video and entertainment channel that emphasizes the variety of styles and tastes in popular culture today. The network features news and interview programs with music stars and movie celebrities in addition to award shows, concerts, and special musical events.

MTV
Owner: Viacom Inc.
Editorial: 2600 Colorado Ave, Santa Monica, California 90404. **T:** 1 310 752-8000

MTV Latin America
Owner: Viacom Inc.
Editorial: 1111 Lincoln Rd, Fl 6, Miami, Florida 33139-2402. **T:** 1 305 535-3700
W: http://www.mtvla.com
Editorial Profile: MTV Latin America is the world's first 24-hour Spanish-language network specifically for young adults whose roots extend to both U.S. and Latin cultures.

MTV2
Owner: Viacom Inc.
Editorial: 1515 Broadway, New York, New York 10036-8901. **T:** 1 212 846-8000
W: http://www.mtv2.com
Editorial Profile: A spin-off of MTV, MTV2 provides a 24-hour video-intensive brand of music programming to cable outlets throughout the nation, with a playlist made up of a broad group of artists and genres of music. The network's target audience is young males, ages 12 to 24.

mtvU
Owner: Viacom Inc.
Editorial: 770 Broadway, 10th Fl, New York, New York 10003. **T:** 1 212 654-7016
E: feedback@mtvu.com
W: http://www.mtvu.com
Editorial Profile: mtvU is dedicated to every aspect of college life, from music to news to student life and campus events. The channel is designed to reflect the fast pace of students' lifestyles, and to reach them everywhere they hang out, whether they're watching TV in their dorm rooms, surfing the Web, or walking across campus. mtvU takes a three-pronged approach to reaching students: on-air, online and on campus. With music at its heart, mtvU plays a diverse mix of music programming ranging from hip hop to rock to punk to reggae to dance, along with a constant focus on up-and-coming artists creating a buzz on campus.

mun2 Television
Owner: NBC Universal
Editorial: 3000 W Alameda Ave, Burbank, California 91523-0001. **T:** 1 818 622-4080
W: http://www.mun2.tv
Editorial Profile: The network targets 18 to 34-year olds with a fresh, new and authentic programming line-up that includes music video programs, entertainment shows, young dramatic series, an eclectic blend of movies, game and comedy shows. The network aims to reflect an experience that is both Latin and uniquely American, with offerings that reflect common themes yet don't pander to stereotypes. It's committed to the development of original, domestic programming and is motivated cultural relevance more than language. mun2 Television reaches 2.8 million U.S. Hispanic households. It broadcasts to 18 of the top 20 U.S. Hispanic markets through cable, direct to home and low power television.

MundoFOX
Owner: FOX International Channels and RCN Televisión
Editorial: 1440 S Sepulveda Blvd, Los Angeles, California 90025-3458.
T: 1 310 444-8505 **E:** foxtv.info@fox.com
W: http://www.mundofox.com
Editorial Profile: MundoFOX is a Hispanic cable network that premiered on August 13, 2012. The network is a joint venture between Fox International Channels and RCN Television Group.

MundoFOX
Editorial: 1211 Avenue of the Americas, New York, New York 10036-8701
Editorial Profile: New York bureau of MundoFOX.

Music Choice
Owner: Music Choice
Editorial: 328 W 34th St, New York, New York 10001-2401. **T:** 1 646 459-3300
E: comments@musicchoice.com
W: http://www.musicchoice.com
Editorial Profile: With over 45 Music Channels to choose from, there's one for every music taste - from today's hottest music to hits from the past. Our selection of Urban, Pop, Rock, Country, Christian, Kids, Classical and Oldies Channels offer hours of uninterrupted listening, along with fun artist facts. Available in 47 million households across the U.S., the Music Channels reach 44 million monthly viewers.

MUSL TV
Editorial: 14141 Covello St Ste 10A, Van Nuys, California 91405-1448.
T: 1 818 8495447 **W:** http://www.musltv.com
Editorial Profile: MUSL TV (Muscle, Ultra-Sports and Lifestyle Network) is a 24/7 HD linear entertainment network fully devoted to all levels of fitness, training and competitive performance.

My Family TV
Owner: ValCom, Inc.

Editorial: 2113 Gulf Blvd Unit A, Indian Rocks Beach, Florida 33785-3806. **T:** 1 727 375-8200
W: http://www.myfamilytv.tv
Editorial Profile: My Family TV (formerly Faith Television Network) is a network created for America's families. Nearly half of the programming consists of family movies and daily children's programming. The network also includes uplifting spiritual programming designed to enhance family values and build character.

My Life
Owner: National Cable Communications
Editorial: 405 Lexington Ave, Fl 6, New York, New York 10174-0699. **T:** 1 212 548-3300
W: http://www.spotcable.com
Editorial Profile: My Life is a video-on-demand cable channel available to digital cable subscribers across the United States. An on demand channel allows viewers to pick what they watch, when they want to watch it. This channel features advertising-supported educational programming focusing on health and wellness. The channel should only be pitched regarding healthcare-related advertising.

Nat Geo Wild
Owner: National Geographic Ventures & FOX Cable Networks
Editorial: 1145 17th St NW, Washington, District Of Columbia 20036-4707.
T: 1 202 912-6500
E: newsdesk@nationalgeographic.com
W: http://www.natgeowild.com
Editorial Profile: Nat Geo Wild is a cable network that brings audiences extraordinary natural history programming and offers intimate encounters with nature's ferocious fighters and gentle creatures of land, sea and air.

National Geographic Channel
Owner: National Geographic Ventures & FOX Cable Networks
Editorial: 1145 17th St NW, Washington, District Of Columbia 20036-4707.
T: 1 202 912-6500
E: newsdesk@nationalgeographic.com
W: http://channel.nationalgeographic.com
Editorial Profile: National Geographic Channel is the critically acclaimed network for viewers who "Dare to Explore," providing info-rich entertainment that changes the way you see the world. A trusted source for over 100 years, National Geographic provides NGC with unique access to the most respected scientists, journalists and filmmakers, resulting in innovative and contemporary programming of unparalleled quality that pushes boundaries and takes you as far as you can go. NGC has carriage with all of the nation's major cable and satellite television providers, making it currently available to 67 million homes.

NBA TV
Owner: Turner Sports Interactive, Inc.
Editorial: 450 Harmon Meadow Blvd, Secaucus, New Jersey 07094-3618.
T: 1 201 865-1500
W: http://www.nba.com/nba_tv
Editorial Profile: NBA TV, launched in 1999, is the ultimate source for everything basketball. NBA TV provides viewers behind-the-scenes access, authenticity and an insider's perspective. The network shows more than 100 NBA regular season and playoff games, WNBA games, D-League games, major international competitions and weekly Euroleague games.

NBC News Channel
Owner: NBC Universal
Editorial: 925 Woodrdg Ctr Dr, Charlotte, North Carolina 28217-1986.
T: 1 704 329-8700
Editorial Profile: Syndicated news service of the NBC Television Network serving over 200 NBC affiliates throughout the United States. Provides video, reporting, and commentary on late-breaking news, business, sports, and features for use on local television broadcasts.

NBC News Channel
Editorial: 30 Rockefeller Plz, Ste 724E, New York, New York 10112. **T:** 1 212 664-7591

NBC News Channel
Editorial: 400 N Capitol St NW, Ste 850, Washington, District Of Columbia 20001-1555.
T: 1 202 783-2615

NBC Sports Network
Owner: Comcast Corporation
Editorial: 1701 John F Kennedy Blvd, Philadelphia, Pennsylvania 19103-2833.
T: 1 215 286-1700
W: http://www.nbcsports.com
Editorial Profile: NBC Sports Network offers exclusive programming in all major sports categories including NFL, NHL, NBA, MLB, NCAA, Golf, Soccer, Olympics and more. The network is distributed via cable systems and satellite operators throughout the continental United States and Hawaii. On January 2, 2012, the network was rebranded from Versus.

NECN/New England Cable News
Editorial: 100 William Loeb Dr, Manchester, New Hampshire 3109. **T:** 1 603 668-1131

NECN/New England Cable News
Editorial: 10 Columbus Blvd, Hartford, Connecticut 06106-1976. **T:** 1 617 630-4203

NET NY
Editorial: 1712 10th Ave, Brooklyn, New York 11215-6215. **T:** 1 718 499-9705
W: http://netny.net
Editorial Profile: NET NY is a faith-centered network based in Brooklyn, NY. Broadcasts include news, entertainment, children's, and music, as well as religious programs. It serves the young and old, the churched and unchurched, and men and women from different social, ethnic and religious backgrounds, showing how they work together to make the world a better place. Network launched December 8, 2008.

New Tang Dynasty TV
Editorial: 229 W 28th St, New York, New York 10001-5915. **T:** 1 212 736-8535
E: biz@ntdtv.com **W:** http://english.ntdtv.com
Editorial Profile: New Tang Dynasty Television (NTDTV) is an independent, nonprofit television broadcaster established in 2001. Headquartered in New York City, NTDTV currently has reporters and correspondents in over 70 cities worldwide.

New Tang Dynasty TV
Editorial: 10411 Motor City Dr Ste 750, Bethesda, Maryland 20817-1289
Editorial Profile: Provides news and entertainment in Mandarin and Cantonese to Chinese Canadians.

News 12 New Jersey - Trenton Bureau
Editorial: CN021 125 W State St, Trenton, New Jersey 8625. **T:** 1 609 396-2381

NFL Network
Owner: NFL Enterprises, L.P.
Editorial: 10950 Washington Blvd, Culver City, California 90232-4026. **T:** 1 310 840-4635
W: http://www.nfl.com/nflnetwork
Editorial Profile: NFL Network provides millions of football fans with a network to call their own. NFL Network takes 87 years of NFL history and combines it with the latest technology to bring television viewers sports entertainment at its highest level. NFL Network is a destination for all that happens around the league, on and off the field, during the season and throughout the offseason.

NHL Network
Owner: National Hockey League
Editorial: 1185 Avenue of the Americas, New York, New York 10036-2601.
T: 1 212 789-2000 **W:** http://www.nhl.com
Editorial Profile: NHL Network is the first 24-hour network dedicated to the National Hockey League, dedicated to comprehensive hockey coverage, both on and off the ice. The programming includes live games, daily highlight shows, up-to-the-minute hockey news and special events.

Nick Jr.
Owner: Viacom Inc.
Editorial: 1515 Broadway, Fl 37, New York, New York 10036. **T:** 1 212 258-6000
E: press@nickjr.com **W:** http://www.nickjr.com
Editorial Profile: Nick Jr. is the commercial-free, educational preschool network from Nickelodeon. Nick Jr. strives to be a place where preschoolers can engage with characters they love while building their imaginations, gaining key cognitive and social-emotional skills, and learning about the world around them.

Nickelodeon
Owner: Viacom Inc.
Editorial: 1515 Broadway, New York, New York 10036-8901. **T:** 1 212 258-7500
W: http://www.nick.com
Editorial Profile: Nickelodeon is the industry's leading producer of original programming for kids, the network offers an incredible lineup of original animation, known as "Nicktoons," variety and game shows, as well as adventure and news magazine shows. Nickelodeon is a division of Viacom Inc.

Nickelodeon
Editorial: 2600 Colorado Ave, 2nd Fl, Santa Monica, California 90404-3519.
T: 1 310 752-8000

Nippon Television - New York Bureau
Owner: NTV International Corporation
Editorial: 646 5th Ave, Ste 303, New York, New York 10019-6107. **T:** 1 212 660-6900
E: contact@ntvic.com
W: http://www.ntvic.com

nuvoTV
Owner: Independent
Editorial: 700 N Central Ave, Ste 600, Glendale, California 91203-3438.
T: 1 323 256-8900
W: http://www.mynuvotv.com
Editorial Profile: nuvoTV is America's first media company to reach the millions of 18 to 34 year-old Latinos who prefer their content in English and seek it across all platforms, including linear television, the Internet, video-on-demand and wireless devices. nuvoTV offers authentic, relevant content and a 60 percent original programming slate that ranges from outrageous comedy to music, independent movies, lifestyle and talk. The network is available nationwide on Dish Network and in more than 200 cities and communities across America, including New York, Chicago, Dallas, Houston, Detroit, Denver, San Antonio and Las Vegas. nuvoTV's cable and telco affiliates include AT&T, Cox, Comcast, Insight, Qwest, Time Warner Cable and Verizon, among others. On July 4, 2011, nuvoTV was rebranded from Si TV.

Oasis TV
Owner: OTV Media Group, INC.
Editorial: 2029 Century Park E, Ste 1400, Los Angeles, California 90067-2915.
T: 1 310 553-4300 **E:** info@watchotv.com
W: http://watchotv.com
Editorial Profile: Interactive cable/satellite television network spotlighting body, mind, and spirit programming about holistic health, spirituality, metaphysics, environmental issues, visionary art, personal growth and world peace. Oasis TV celebrates the global forces and visionaries transforming our world with live and recorded broadband streaming, TV programming, thought-provoking editorial content and cutting edge news and information.

One America News Network
Owner: Herring Broadcasting, Inc.
Editorial: 4757 Morena Blvd, San Diego, California 92117-3462. **T:** 1 858 270-6900
W: http://www.oann.com
Editorial Profile: The network provides unbiased, substantive national and international news 24/7.

The Outdoor Channel
Owner: Outdoor Channel Holdings Inc.
Editorial: 43445 Business Park Dr, Temecula, California 92590-3669. **T:** 1 951 699-6991
E: info@outdoorchannel.com
W: http://www.outdoorchannel.com
Editorial Profile: The Outdoor Channel is a nationally broadcast cable network featuring programming designed to educate and entertain outdoor enthusiasts of all ages. The channel promotes traditional outdoor activities that are a vital part of America's national heritage including fishing, hunting, bull riding, and shooting sports, with a focus on activities that families can enjoy in the great outdoors.

Outside Television Network
Owner: Mariah Media, Inc.
Editorial: 33 Riverside Ave Fl 4, Westport, Connecticut 06880-4223. **T:** 1 203 221-9240
W: http://www.outsidetelevision.com
Editorial Profile: Outside Television broadcasts in more than 110 prime destination-area markets around the country. Through its affiliated stations, it serves these local resorts by providing relevant local information combined with national entertainment. When visiting resort markets around the country, vacationers shows the best places to eat, what to do with the kids, where to shop, and how to get around.

Ovation - The Arts Network
Owner: Hubbard Media Group
Editorial: 2850 Ocean Park Blvd Ste 225, Santa Monica, California 90405-6217.
T: 1 310 430-7575 **E:** info@ovationtv.com
W: http://www.ovationtv.com
Editorial Profile: Ovation - the Arts Network is a cable television network featuring documentary and performance programs on the arts including theater, dance, opera, jazz, classical music, literature and the visual arts. The network presents tours of great museums and exhibitions, profiles of best-loved and up and coming artists; documentaries on musical styles and artistic movements; performances by preeminent musicians and orchestras, dance, theater and opera companies; behind-the-scenes coverage of important arts events and explorations into the arts of cultures around the world.

OWN: Oprah Winfrey Network
Owner: Discovery Communications, Inc.
Editorial: 5700 Wilshire Blvd Ste 120, Los Angeles, California 90036-3644.
T: 1 323 602-5500 **W:** http://www.own.tv
Editorial Profile: OWN: Oprah Winfrey Show is the network of self-discovery, connecting people to each other and to their greatest potential. The programming includes a mix of nonfiction, short form programming, movies, documentaries and acquisitions. OWN is a joint venture between Oprah Winfrey and Discovery Communications launched on January 1, 2011.

Oxygen Media
Owner: NBC Universal
Editorial: 75 9th Ave Fl 7, New York, New York 10011-7011. **T:** 1 212 651-5000
W: http://www.oxygen.com
Editorial Profile: Oxygen is a cable network that works to combine the best qualities of the Internet and television to serve a female audience. It offers tools to simplify life and programming that match the energy, wit, intelligence and lifestyle of the modern woman.

Pac-12 Network
Owner: Pac-12 Media Enterprises
Editorial: 1350 Treat Blvd Ste 500, Walnut Creek, California 94597-8853.
T: 1 925 932-4411 **W:** http://www.pac-12.org
Editorial Profile: Pac-12 Network is a sports cable television network dedicated to the Pac-12 Conference.

PEN/Persian Entertainment Network
Editorial: 6431 Independence Ave, Woodland Hills, California 91367-2608.
T: 1 818 592-0077 **E:** info@penonline.tv
W: http://www.penonline.tv
Editorial Profile: Middle Eastern satellite channel broadcasts entertainment and educational programming 24 hours a day.

The Pentagon Channel
Owner: Defense Media Activity
Editorial: 601 N Fairfax St, Alexandria, Virginia 22314-2054. **T:** 1 301 222-6780
E: info@pentagonchannel.mil
W: http://www.pentagonchannel.mil
Editorial Profile: The Pentagon Channel broadcasts military news and information for the 2.6 million members of the U.S. Armed Forces through programming including, Department of Defense news briefings, military news, interviews with top Defense officials, short stories about the work of our military.

Pivot
Owner: Participant Media
Editorial: 331 Foothill Rd Fl 3, Beverly Hills, California 90210-3669. **T:** 1 310 550-5100
E: press@pivot.tv **W:** http://www.pivot.tv
Editorial Profile: Pivot is a television network from Participant Media — the people that brought you movies and documentaries like Lincoln, Food, Inc., and An Inconvenient Truth.

QVC
Owner: Liberty Media Corporation
Editorial: 1200 Wilson Dr, West Chester, Pennsylvania 19380-4267. **T:** 1 484 7011000
W: http://www.qvc.com
Editorial Profile: QVC is one of the largest multimedia retailers in the world. QVC provides its customers with thousands of contemporary beauty, fashion, jewelry and home products. Its programming is distributed to approximately 195 million homes worldwide.

RAI Corporation - New York Bureau

Editorial: 32 Avenue of the Americas, 25th FL, New York, New York 10013.
T: 1 212 468-2500 **W:** http://www.raicorp.net
Editorial Profile: RAI Corporation is the US subsidiary of Radiotelevisione Italiana. RAI Corporation was established in 1960 as an operational base for the production of segments of RAI programs aired in Italy and for the international distribution of Italian programs. RAI Corporation supplies a variety of services to all departments of RAI, including the production of news and entertainment programs; distribution; acquisition; sales; and marketing research. RAI Corporation's headquarters are located in New York, with affiliate offices in Montevideo, Uruguay and Toronto.

ReelzChannel

Owner: Hubbard Media Group
Editorial: 5650 University Blvd SE, Albuquerque, New Mexico 87106-9700.
T: 1 505 212-8800 **E:** info@reelzchannel.com
W: http://www.reelzchannel.com
Editorial Profile: Dedicated to entertaining, informing, directing and connecting fans to everything movies. Original programming features movie reviews, celebrity interviews and behind-the-scenes clips.

ReelzChannel

Editorial: 1201 W 5th St Ste 345, Los Angeles, California 90017-2019.
T: 1 213 534-3524

ReelzChannel

Editorial: 122 E 42nd St, Rm 1505, New York, New York 10168-1594. **T:** 1 212 697-2024

Reuters Television

Owner: Thomson Reuters
Editorial: 3 Times Sq, New York, New York 10036-6564. **T:** 1 646 223-4000
E: tvdne@thomsonreuters.com
W: http://www.reuters.com
Editorial Profile: Thomson Reuters is the world's largest news and television agency. It is a news production and broadcast services operation for local television stations and outlets. The network provides an array of national and international news, sports, business news, entertainment, and weather via a network of bureaus and satellites covering the globe.

Reuters Television

Editorial: 1333 H St NW, Ste 500, Washington, District Of Columbia 20005-4707.
T: 1 202 898-0056

Reuters Television

Editorial: 633 W 5Th St Ste 2300, Los Angeles, California 90071-2049.
T: 1 213 380-2014 **W:** http://www.reuters.com

REVOLT TV

Editorial: 1800 N Highland Ave Fl 6, Los Angeles, California 90028-4521
E: contactus@revolt.tv **W:** http://www.revolt.tv
Editorial Profile: REVOLT TV will deliver music content and be a destination for conversations around music, artists, and their creations. It will leverage the power of social media communication tools to fuel the live music dialog and influence music culture and content in real time for the video-centric generation.

RFD-TV

Owner: RFD Communications, Inc.
Editorial: 3201 Dickerson Pike, Nashville, Tennessee 37207-2905. **T:** 1 615 227-9292
E: info@rfdtv.com **W:** http://www.rfdtv.com
Editorial Profile: Launched in December 2000, RFD-TV is the nation's first 24-hour television network dedicated to serving the needs and interests of rural America and agriculture. The channel is produced and uplinked via satellite to all 50 states from Northstar Studios in Nashville, TN. The channel is carried by DISH Network, DIRECTV, Mediacom, and NCTC cable systems, with new cable systems adding the channel most everyday.

RLTV

Editorial: 5525 Research Park Dr, Baltimore, Maryland 21228-4873. **T:** 1 410 402-9600
W: http://www.rl.tv
Editorial Profile: RLTV is television for Americans 55 and older. The network informs viewers on topics including health, lifestyle, finance and politics and provides engaging stories about ordinary people who lead extraordinary lives.

RNN/Regional News Network

Editorial: 721 Broadway, Kingston, New York 12401-3449. **T:** 1 845 339-6200

RTVi

Owner: Overseas Media
Editorial: 304 Hudson St Rm 4, New York, New York 10013-1026. **T:** 1 646 292-0000
E: info@rtvi.com **W:** http://www.rtvi.ru
Editorial Profile: RTVi is a Russian-language television network broadcasting in Europe, North America and Israel, as well as in countries of the Commonwealth of Independent States. The network offers news and culture shows to the Russian-speaking diaspora.

RTVi

Owner: Overseas Media
Editorial: 1001 Pennsylvania Ave NW, Ste 6310, Washington, District Of Columbia 20004-2505. **T:** 1 202 742-6576

Science

Owner: Discovery Communications, Inc.
Editorial: 8516 Georgia Ave, Silver Spring, Maryland 20910-3401. **T:** 1 240 662-2000
W: http://science.discovery.com
Editorial Profile: Specialty cable channel which uncovers the clues to the questions that have eluded us for centuries and reveal life's greatest mysteries and smallest wonders. Content is from the worlds of astronomy, physics, chemistry, earth science and related fields. ** A vast majority of programming aired on Discovery Science is developed by producers outside the network. As a result, it is suggested that most shows should be contacted via network headquarters in Silver Spring, MD. On June 8, 2011, Science Channel rebranded to Science.

Shalom TV

T: 1 201 242-9460 **E:** news@shalomtv.com
W: http://www.shalomtv.com
Editorial Profile: Shalom TV is a mainstream Jewish cable television network covering the panorama of Jewish life. More than 34 million homes nationwide now have access to the free Jewish television service. Programs on Shalom TV reflect and address the diversity and pluralism of the Jewish experience. The service does not represent any specific movement or organization in the Jewish community. Shalom TV is directed to every Jewish person with a sense of Jewish identity, and for members of the Jewish community seeking their roots.

Showtime Networks Inc.

Owner: CBS Corporation
Editorial: 1633 Broadway, New York, New York 10019-6708. **T:** 1 212 708-1600
W: http://www.sho.com
Editorial Profile: Showtime network provides a variety of movies and original programming. The network also markets and distributes sports and entertainment events for exhibition to subscribers on a pay-per-view basis through Showtime Event Television Pay Per View.

Showtime Networks Inc.

Editorial: 10880 Wilshire Blvd, Ste 1600, Los Angeles, California 90024. **T:** 1 310 234-5200

Sinclair News Central

Editorial: 10706 Beaver Dam Rd, Hunt Valley, Maryland 21030. **T:** 1 410 568-1500
W: http://www.sbgi.net
Editorial Profile: Sinclair News Central is a centralized news service located in Maryland which produces and distributes national and regional news, sports and weather to Sinclair owned and operated stations using current technology that allows repetitive efforts to be eliminated or reduced. This structure allows the local station to focus completely on reporting local news stories that affect the community.

The Ski Channel

Owner: Atonal Sports and Entertainment
Editorial: 881 Alma Real Dr, Pacific Palisades, California 90272-3731. **T:** 1 310 230-2050
E: info@theskichannel.com
W: http://www.theskichannel.com
Editorial Profile: The Ski Channel is an original ad supported network delivered via VOD, web, wireless and other means of distribution and the worlds first clearly defined Television 2.0 network. It is the only cable television network devoted to the wide variety of year round mountain activities such as skiing, snowboarding, hiking, biking, backpacking, climbing, etc, along with many off-slope activities. The Ski Channels' content

includes a myriad of movies, events and episodic television shows and well as programming in news, weather, destination travel, equipment, instruction and real estate.

Sky Link TV

Editorial: 500 Montebello Blvd, Rosemead, California 91770-4303. **T:** 1 323 888-0028
E: info@skylinktv.us
W: http://www.skylinktv.us
Editorial Profile: Sky Link TV is a 24-hour Mandarin Chinese general entertainment channel tailor-made for the Chinese audience in North America with a wide variety of programming. The program lineup includes top-rated, most popular Chinese and Korean dramas, immediate news from China and Taiwan, local-produced news that is customized for Chinese American audiences, popular political commentary programs, variety and talk shows from Taiwan and China.

Smile of a Child Network

Owner: Trinity Broadcasting Network
Editorial: 2442 Michelle Dr, Tustin, California 92780. **T:** 1 714 832-2950
W: http://www.smileofachild.org
Editorial Profile: Founded by the Trinity Broadcasting Network, Smile of a Child offers quality Christian children's programming 24 hours per day. It is available in 13 major markets via digital multi-casting. The programming both entertains as well as morally instructs children during their formative years by bringing the best moral and biblical teachings through fun and constructive television.

Smithsonian Channel

Owner: SNI/SI Networks L.L.C.
Editorial: 1633 Broadway Fl 15, New York, New York 10019-6755. **T:** 1 212 708-1601
E: pressinquiries@smithsoniannetworks.com
W: http://www.smithsonianchannel.com
Editorial Profile: Smithsonian Channel showcases scientific, cultural and historical programming based largely upon the assets of the Smithsonian Institution, the world's largest museum complex. Smithsonian Channel features original documentaries, short-subject explorations and innovative groundbreaking programs highlighting America's historical, cultural and scientific heritage.

Smithsonian Channel

Editorial: 1225 19Th St Nw Ste 250, Washington, District Of Columbia 20036-2458.
T: 1 202 261-1700

Soldiers Radio and Television

Owner: U.S. Army
Editorial: 2530 Crystal Dr Suite 100, Arlington, Virginia 22202-3934.
T: 1 703 602-8009 **E:** dmajointdesk@dma.mil
W: http://www.army.mil/media/srtv
Editorial Profile: Produces radio and television programming that keeps both soldiers and the public informed on what's happening in the Army.

Sony Entertainment Television Asia

Owner: Sony Entertainment Television Asia
Editorial: MSM North America Inc., 550 Madison Ave, New York, New York 10022.
T: 1 212 833-7684 **W:** http://www.setasia.tv
Editorial Profile: Features contemporary programming tailored to South Asian tastes and sensibilities. Reaching the upscale, economically active 18 to 49 year-old age group.

Spike TV

Owner: Viacom Inc.
Editorial: 345 Hudson St, New York, New York 10014-4502. **T:** 1 212 767-4001
W: http://www.spike.com
Editorial Profile: Spike TV is dedicated to the things men want. The brand speaks to the bold, adventuresome side of men with action-packed entertainment, including a mix of comedy, blockbuster movies, sports, innovative originals and live events. It is available in 86 million homes and is a division of Viacom Inc.

Spike TV

Editorial: 2600 Colorado Ave, Santa Monica, California 90404-3519. **T:** 1 310 407-1200

Sportsman Channel

Owner: InterMedia Partners VII L.P.
Editorial: 2855 S James Dr, Ste 101, New Berlin, Wisconsin 53151. **T:** 1 262 432-9100
E: sportsman@thesportsmanchannel.com
W: http://www.thesportsmanchannel.com
Editorial Profile: Launched in 2003, Sportsman Channel is the only television and

digital media company fully devoted to the more than 82 million sportsmen in the United States, delivering entertaining and educational programming focused exclusively on hunting, shooting and fishing activities. Sportsman Channel is now available in HD, check with your local cable or satellite provider. In San Antonio, the Sportsman Channel is located on channel 267. Acquired by InterMedia Outdoors Holdings in 2006, Sportsman Channel reaches almost 27 million U.S. television households and is a part of the nation's largest multimedia company targeted exclusively to serving the information and entertainment needs of outdoors enthusiasts. The tagline of the network is "The Leader in Outdoor TV for the American Sportsman ." To learn more, visit www.thesportsmanchannel.com, follow on Twitter, @SPORTSMANchnl, or Fan on Facebook, www.facebook.com/ sportsmanchannel

Sprout

Owner: PBS
T: 1 877 768-8411 **E:** info@sproutonline.com
W: http://www.sproutonline.com
Editorial Profile: Sprout is the first 24-hour preschool destination available on TV, on demand and online for kids ages 2 to 5 and their parents and caregivers.

Starz Entertainment

Owner: Liberty Media Corp.
Editorial: 8900 Liberty Cir, Englewood, Colorado 80112. **T:** 1 720 852-7700
W: http://www.starz.com
Editorial Profile: Starz Entertainment is a premier movie service provider in the United States. It offers various movie channels, including the flagship Starz and Encore channels. Starz Entertainment also airs more than 1,000 movies per month across its pay television channels, including Starz On Demand, the only on-demand pay television subscription service available on cable, satellite and broadband platforms. The network also offers a suite of advanced video offerings, including Starz! HD, Starz! Hi-Res, Sharper Movies HD, and Starz on Demand HD.

Starz InBlack

Owner: Liberty Media Corp.
Editorial: 8900 Liberty Cir, Englewood, Colorado 80112-7057. **T:** 1 720 852-7700
W: http://www.starz.com/channels/starz/ starzinblack
Editorial Profile: Pay movie channel spotlighting the cinematic accomplishments of African-American filmmakers, and providing an audience for up-and-coming filmmakers. Programming includes exclusive first-run theatrical releases, recent popular titles, classic movies, independent films, films from Africa and the African Diaspora, and original productions 24 hours a day, seven days a week.

Sun Sports

Owner: Fox Broadcasting Company
Editorial: 1000 Legion Pl, Ste 1600, Orlando, Florida 32801. **T:** 1 407 648-1150
W: http://www.foxsportsflorida.com
Editorial Profile: Regional sports outlet serving over 6.1 million cable and satellite homes in Florida. Sports programs include live coverage of Orlando Magic and Miami Heat NBA basketball, and Tampa Bay Lightning NHL hockey. Network also broadcasts a wide variety of college athletics, including University of Florida, Florida State University, Acc and SEC events and also originates regional sports shows.

Sun Sports

Editorial: 1550 Sawgrass Corporate Pkwy, Ste 350, Sunrise, Florida 33323-2822.
T: 1 954 845-9994
W: http://www.foxsportsflorida.com
Editorial Profile: Regional sports outlet serving over 6.1 million cable and satellite homes in Florida. Sports programs include live coverage of Orlando Magic and Miami Heat NBA basketball, and Tampa Bay Lightning NHL hockey. Network also broadcasts a wide variety of college athletics, including University of Florida, Florida State University, Acc and SEC events and also originates regional sports shows.

SundanceTV

Owner: AMC Networks Inc.
Editorial: 11 Penn Plz Fl 2, New York, New York 10001-2028. **T:** 1 212 324-8500
W: http://www.sundance.tv
Editorial Profile: Under the creative direction of Robert Redford, Sundance is the television destination for independent-minded viewers

seeking something different. Bold, uncompromising and irreverent, Sundance Channel offers audiences a diverse and engaging selection of films, documentaries and original programs, all uncut and commercial free.

The Surf Channel
Editorial: 881 Alma Real Dr, T8, Pacific Palisades, California 90272-3731.
T: 1 310 230-2050
E: info@thesurfchannel.com
W: http://www.thesurfchannel.com
Editorial Profile: The Surf Channel is an original, free, ad supported VOD television network delivered on cable, satellite and IPTV services, web and wireless.

Syfy
Owner: NBC Universal
Editorial: 30 Rockefeller Plz, New York, New York 10112-0015. **T:** 1 212 664-4444
E: feedback@scifi.com
W: http://www.syfy.com
Editorial Profile: This network focuses on science fiction programming. It features made-for-television and theatrical films, themed specials, horror shows, and vintage science fiction television series like Knight Rider, The Twilight Zone and Star Trek.

Syfy
Editorial: 100 Universal City Plz, Bldg 1440, Universal City, California 91608.
T: 1 818 777-6898

TBN/Trinity Broadcasting Network
Owner: Trinity Broadcasting Network
Editorial: 2442 Michelle Dr, Tustin, California 92780-7091. **T:** 1 714 832-2950
E: comments@tbn.org **W:** http://www.tbn.org
Editorial Profile: Religious cable network with programming of a multi-denominational nature. TBN is the world's largest Christian television network. The network is distributed throughout America and around the world. TBN is seen on over 2,500 television stations, 17 satellites, the Internet and thousands of cable systems around the world. The network produces original Christian programs and gospel music concerts from Nashville and includes live coverage of major Christian events and informative talk shows with exciting guests.

TBS
Owner: Time Warner Inc.
Editorial: 1010 Techwood Dr Nw, Atlanta, Georgia 30318-5604. **T:** 1 404 827-1717
W: http://www.tbs.com
Editorial Profile: TBS, a division of Turner Broadcasting System, Inc., bill itself as television's "Very Funny" network. It serves as home to such contemporary comedies as Sex and the City, Everybody Loves Raymond, Family Guy, Seinfeld and Friends. The network also features original comedy series programming, specials and special events, blockbuster movies and hosted movie showcases.

TBS - Los Angeles Bureau
Editorial: 3500 W Olive Ave, Fl 15, Burbank, California 91505-4630. **T:** 1 818 977-5500

TeenNick
Owner: MTV Networks
Editorial: 1515 Broadway, New York, New York 10036-8901. **T:** 1 212 258-6000
W: http://www.teennick.com
Editorial Profile: TeenNick is a 24 hour network for young adults featuring movies, original series, animated productions and general entertainment fare that focuses on the real life issues teens face every day. In addition to original programming, the network also airs hit series from Nickelodeon. In addition, Emmy winning Web site, www.The-N.com, provides fans with complete access to behind-the-scenes interviews, pictures and videos, plus a robust community of 2 million members who interact with message boards, user profiles and blogs. TeenNick is targeted towards teens between the ages of 13 and 16 and is currently available in over 56 million homes. On September 28, 2009, The N was rebranded to TeenNick.

TeleMiami
Editorial: 2920 NW 7th St, Miami, Florida 33125-4306. **T:** 1 305 642-7777
E: informacion@telemiami.com
W: http://www.telemiami.com
Editorial Profile: TeleMiami is a Spanish language cable network covering the Dade and Broward County areas.

The Tennis Channel
Owner: The Tennis Channel Inc.
Editorial: 2850 Ocean Park Blvd, Santa Monica, California 90405-2955.
T: 1 310 314-9400
W: http://www.thetennischannel.com
Editorial Profile: The Tennis Channel serves up prestigious matches featuring today's most celebrated players. In addition to the major American tournaments such as the ATA and WTA, many other domestic tournaments and a wide array of international events are aired. In addition, World Team Tennis matches, scores of events from the Intercollegiate Tennis Association and top national junior events are shown along with a seasoning of other racket sports including squash, badminton, table tennis and paddle tennis.

TheBlaze
Owner: Mercury Radio Arts
Editorial: 6301 Riverside Dr, Irving, Texas 75039-3531 **W:** http://www.theblaze.com/tv
Editorial Profile: The network provides 24/7 news, opinion and entertainment programming from a libertarian conservative perspective.

TLC
Owner: Discovery Communications, Inc.
Editorial: 8516 Georgia Ave, Silver Spring, Maryland 20910-3401. **T:** 1 240 662-2000
W: http://producers.discovery.com
Editorial Profile: TLC is dedicated to high-quality, intelligent and relatable non-fiction entertainment that inspires, engages, informs and unites the audience in the spirit of life's possibilities. TLC intimately connects more than 94 million homes in North America. Programming includes a variety of documentaries, investigative reports and historic footage. A vast majority of programming aired on Discovery Science is developed by producers outside the network. As a result, it is suggested that most shows should be contacted via network headquarters in Silver Spring, MD.

TLC
Owner: Discovery Communications, Inc.
Editorial: 10100 Santa Monica Blvd, 1050, Los Angeles, California 90067-4003.
T: 1 310 551-1611 **W:** http://tlc.discovery.com

TMC/The Movie Channel
Owner: Showtime Networks Inc.
Editorial: 1633 Broadway Fl 7, New York, New York 10019-6708. **T:** 1 212 7081600
W: http://www.sho.com/site/tmc/home.do
Editorial Profile: TMC/The Movie Channel is a premium channel owned by Showtime Networks Inc., a subsidiary of CBS Corporation. The channel features mostly movies, as well as special behind the scenes features, softcore adult erotica and movie trivia. The channel launched in 1973 as Star Channel and was rebranded in 1979 to The Movie Channel. Sister networks include Showtime and Flix.

TNT/Turner Network Television
Owner: Time Warner Inc.
Editorial: 1050 Techwood Dr NW, Atlanta, Georgia 30318-5604. **T:** 1 404 885-4339
E: tnt@turner.com **W:** http://www.tnt.tv
Editorial Profile: Basic cable channel featuring movies, original series, original motion pictures, mini-series productions, off-net dramas and championship sports all supporting the network's brand as a destination for dramatic entertainment. TNT is available in high-definition.

Total Living Network
Editorial: 2880 Vision Ct, Aurora, Illinois 60506. **T:** 1 630 801-3838 **E:** mail@tln.com
W: http://www.tln.com
Editorial Profile: Network providing a range of specialty programming dealing with health, fitness, spiritual and nutritional topics. TLN is a media provider offering entertaining and inspirational programming that offers practical information for today's lifestyles. TLN distributes programming through broadcast, cable, digital, satellite and the Internet.

Tr3s: MTV, Musica y Mas
Owner: Viacom Inc.
Editorial: 1515 Broadway, Fl 25, New York, New York 10036-8901. **T:** 1 212 846-8000
W: http://www.tr3s.com
Editorial Profile: Tr3s: MTV, Musica y Mas is in 7.4 million Hispanic TV households and 34 million total TV households, making it the most-widely distributed TV network dedicated to superserving today's bicultural Latino youth. Tr3s: MTV, Musica y Mas programming is rooted in the fusion of American and Latino

music, cultures, lifestyles and languages. Music programming is at the core of Tr3's and the channel features hitmakers, emerging artists and new sounds that resonate with young U.S. Latinos. In addition to music programming, the Tr3's programming slate also features lifestyle series, news, documentaries and other long-form programs that celebrate US Latino hybrid identity and culture.

Travel Channel
Owner: Scripps Networks, Inc.
Editorial: 5425 Wisconsin Ave, Chevy Chase, Maryland 20815-3552. **T:** 1 301 244-7500
W: http://www.travelchannel.com
Editorial Profile: Basic cable network devoted exclusively to travel entertainment capturing the fascination, freedom and fun of travel. Travel Channel delivers insightful stories about the world's most popular destinations and inspiring diversions.

Tribune Broadcasting Company
Owner: Tribune Company
Editorial: 435 N Michigan Ave, Chicago, Illinois 60611-4066. **T:** 1 312 222-3342
W: http://www.tribune.com
Editorial Profile: News service serving Tribune-owned television stations throughout the country. Tribune Broadcasting owns and operates 23 major-market television stations including the superstation WGN which can be viewed in more than 50 million homes outside of Chicago via cable and satellite services. Many of the Tribune stations are affiliates of CW Television Network, in which they have an investment. Tribune Broadcasting compiles stories and feeds to be distributed throughout the Tribune family of stations.

truTV
Owner: Time Warner Inc.
Editorial: 1 Time Warner Ctr, New York, New York 10019-6038. **T:** 1 212 275-0700
W: http://www.truTV.com
Editorial Profile: Formerly known as Court TV, a cable network dedicated to crime and justice, truTV now focuses on original documentaries, series and specials, plus popular off-network series dealing with crime and investigation. With the rebranding of the network as truTV, programming is reality-based and unscripted. In Session, truTV's daytime courtside programming, is produced by HLN.

TUFF TV
Owner: TUFF TV Media Group, LLC
Editorial: 3340 Peachtree Rd NE, Atlanta, Georgia 30326-1023. **T:** 1 404 230-9600
E: info@tufftv.com **W:** http://www.tufftv.com
Editorial Profile: TUFF TV is a digital broadcast network offering original programming targeted at men. The network launch in June 2009.

Turner Classic Movies
Owner: Time Warner Inc.
Editorial: 1050 Techwood Dr NW, Atlanta, Georgia 30318. **T:** 1 404 827-1700
W: http://www.tcm.com
Editorial Profile: Airings of classic films from Hollywood's golden era. Commercial-free outlet with occasional themed marathons of individual actors, directors, and studios all culled from the vast film libraries of MGM and Warner Brothers.

TV Asia
Editorial: 76 National Rd, Edison, New Jersey 08817-2809. **T:** 1 732 650-1100
E: info@tvasiausa.com
W: http://www.tvasiausa.com
Editorial Profile: TV Asia is a informational and entertainment channel for the South-Asian and Indian community in North America . The network is based on a wide range of programming from news, local community news and educational programs to dramas, music, movies, in-house programs.

TV Japan
Owner: NHK Cosmomedia America, Inc.
Editorial: 100 Broadway Floor 15, New York, New York 10005-1983. **T:** 1 212 262-3377
E: tvjapan@tvjapan.net
W: http://nhkcosmomedia.com
Editorial Profile: TV Japan is a 24-hour Japanese-language television network offering news, drama, education, music and sports programming to the Japanese diaspora in the United States and Canada. Some of its programming comes from NHK, the Japanese public television network.

TV Japan
Editorial: 3130 Wilshire Blvd Ste 360, Santa Monica, California 90403-2367.
T: 1 310 829-5575

TV Land
Owner: Viacom Inc.
Editorial: 345 Hudson St, New York, New York 10014-4502. **T:** 1 212 258-8000
E: postmaster@tvland.com
W: http://www.tvland.com
Editorial Profile: TV Land features programming from vintage and classic television series of yesterday. The network's eclectic program mixes popular dramas, sitcoms, westerns, retromercials and a television-preferential interstitial audience in mind.

TV One
Owner: Radio One Inc.
Editorial: 1010 Wayne Ave, Ste 1000, Silver Spring, Maryland 20910. **T:** 1 301 755-0400
W: http://www.tvoneonline.com
Editorial Profile: Cable network targeting adult African American and urban viewers. The network includes a broad mix of original and existing programming from all the entertainment genres, including scripted and unscripted dramas, sitcoms, game shows, movies, plays and news magazines.

TV5 MONDE USA
Owner: TV5 MONDE
Editorial: 8733 W Sunset Blvd, West Hollywood, California 90069-2244.
T: 1 800 737-0455
E: toutsavoir@tv5monde.org
W: http://www.tv5.org/usa
Editorial Profile: TV5 MONDE USA is a division of the French television station TV5 MONDE. The network offers programming in films, sports, news and documentaries. The network promotes programming from French-speaking countries including Canada, Belgium, Switzerland and France. All programming originates in the central Paris offices. Story ideas and news tips should be sent to the main e-mail address.

TVG Network/Television Games Network
Owner: Betfair
Editorial: 6701 Center Dr W Ste 160, Los Angeles, California 90045-1558.
T: 1 310 2429400 **E:** pr@tvg.com
W: http://www.tvg.com
Editorial Profile: TVG Network is a specialty channel dedicated to horse racing. TVG Network is an interactive horse racing network that combines live, televised coverage from over 100 of the World's premier racetracks and allows viewers to make wagers from home: online, by phone, mobile phone and, where available, using a set-top remote control. In addition to live horse racing, TVG Network features professional race analysis, interviews, handicapping tips, feature stories on the superstars of horse racing, the horses, personalities and legends of racing other programming.

TVGN
Owner: Lionsgate Entertainment Corp.
Editorial: 1800 N Highland Ave Fl 6, Los Angeles, California 90028-4521.
T: 1 323 856-4000 **E:** press@tvgn.tv
W: http://tvgn.tv
Editorial Profile: Channel provides cable viewers across the country with programming grids and schedules, previews of upcoming shows and inside information on celebrities, television shows and movies. TVGN is seen in more than 80 million homes nationwide and online at TVGN.tv and has more than 23 million unique users per month. In early 2013, the network rebranded from TV Guide Network to TVGN.

TVK 24
Owner: Television Korea24, Inc.
Editorial: 3435 Wilshire Blvd Ste 1900, Los Angeles, California 90010-2005.
T: 1 213 382-9600 **W:** http://www.tvk24.com
Editorial Profile: TVK is a 24 hour leading Korean language network, dedicated to serving Korean-American communities across the United States.

UMTV
Owner: University of Miami
Editorial: 1320 S Dixie Hwy, Coral Gables, Florida 33146-2926 **E:** umtv@miami.edu
W: http://umtv.miami.edu
Editorial Profile: UMTV is the University of Miami's Cable Television Channel, owned and operated by the School of Communication.

Since 1981, UMTV has provided University of Miami students hands-on training in television production with state-of-the-art equipment as well served the Coral Gables community with local and educational programming. UMTV is a place to educate, explore and learn, for students, faculty, and audiences alike.

Universal Sports
Owner: NBC Universal
Editorial: 2 Dole Dr, Westlake Village, California 91362-7300. **T:** 1 818 661-4100
E: info@universalsports.com
W: http://www.universalsports.com
Editorial Profile: Universal Sports, formerly World Championship Sports Network (WCSN), serves as the preeminent multiplatform destination for Olympic and lifestyle sports programming. The network delivers an immersive experience via exclusive live and on-demand coverage of world-class competitions, interaction with top athletes and in-depth access to sports news and information year round. The network also has production facilities at Denver's Comcast Media Center.

Univision Deportes Network
Owner: Univision Communications Inc.
Editorial: 9405 Nw 41St St, Doral, Florida 33178-2301. **T:** 1 305 471-3900
W: http://deportes.univision.com
Editorial Profile: Univision Deportes Network is 24/7 all-sports network from Univision. The UDN difference is access to the top sports content such as the Liga Mexicana de Fútbol, Major League Soccer, CONCACAF Champions League, U.S. National Team, Mexican National Team, World Cup qualifiers and unmatched coverage leading up to World Cup 2014. The network launched in April 2012.

UP
Owner: Humbard (Charles)
Editorial: 1514 Cleveland Ave Ste 240, Atlanta, Georgia 30344-6943. **T:** 1 770 692-8890
W: http://www.uptv.com
Editorial Profile: UP features uplifting music and entertainment, featuring music and inspiring stories the whole family will enjoy. UP is the only TV network with every program certified as family safe by the Parents Television Council. UP is found on DIRECTV channel 338 and DISH Network channel 188 nationally, and many local cable systems.On June 1, 2013, the network was rebranded from GMC to UP.

USA Network
Owner: NBC Universal
Editorial: 30 Rockefeller Plz, New York, New York 10112-0015. **T:** 1 212 664-4444
E: feedback@usanetwork.com
W: http://www.usanetwork.com
Editorial Profile: USA Network is basic cable television's leading provider of original series, feature movies, sporting events, off-net television shows, and blockbuster theatrical films. USA Network is a service of NBC Universal.

USA Network
Editorial: 100 Universal City Plz, Bldg 1440, Universal City, California 91608.
T: 1 818 777-6898

USArmenia TV
Owner: USArmenia Worldwide
Editorial: 18751 Ventura Blvd, Tarzana, California 91356-3360. **T:** 1 818 955-9933
E: info@usarmeniatv.com
W: http://www.usarmeniatv.com
Editorial Profile: USArmenia was established in May 2008 and features programming directly from Armenia and Los Angeles, CA. The programs will vary in content and style. The line-up includes, but is not limited to, reality shows, comedy programs, soap operas and news programs.

Velocity
Owner: Discovery Communiations
Editorial: 1 Discovery Pl, Silver Spring, Maryland 20910-3354
W: http://velocity.discovery.com/videos
Editorial Profile: Velocity, an upscale male lifestyle network, features more than 400 premiere hours of new and returning series and specials showcasing the best of the automotive, sports and leisure, adventure, and travel genres. The cable network premiered in October 2011.

Veria Living
Owner: Asia TV USA Ltd
Editorial: 1 Penn Plz 250 West 34th St, Ste 3501, New York, New York 10119-3601.
T: 1 646 745-9000 **E:** info@veria.com
W: http://www.veria.com/tv
Editorial Profile: Veria Living is a 24/7 TV network dedicated to empowering people in their pursuit of natural wellness. Veria features engaging and entertaining lifestyle shows with an emphasis on healthy cooking, fitness, green living and eco-travel.

VH1
Owner: Viacom Inc.
Editorial: 1515 Broadway, New York, New York 10036-8901. **T:** 1 212 258-7800
W: http://www.vh1.com
Editorial Profile: VH1 is a 24-hour cable network that connects viewers to today's hottest artists and music through series, specials, live events, exclusive online content, public affairs initiatives and other original programming.

VH1
Editorial: 2600 Colorado Ave, Santa Monica, California 90404-3519. **T:** 1 310 752-8000

VH1 Classic
Editorial: 1515 Broadway, New York, New York 10036-8901. **T:** 1 212 846-8000
E: inbox@vh1mail.com
W: http://www.vh1classic.com
Editorial Profile: Digital network of 24-hour music video and performances, concentrating on the music favored by baby boomers.

Voice of America Television Network
Owner: Government-owned
Editorial: 330 Independence Ave SW, Washington, District Of Columbia 20237-0001.
T: 1 202 203-4959 **E:** voanews@voanews.com
W: http://www.voanews.com
Editorial Profile: The Voice of America, which first went on the air in 1942, is a multimedia international broadcasting service funded by the U.S. government through the Broadcasting Board of Governors. VOA broadcasts more than 1,000 hours of news, information, educational, and cultural programming every week.

We TV
Owner: AMC Networks Inc.
Editorial: 11 Penn Plz, New York, New York 10001-2006. **T:** 1 646 273-3500
W: http://www.wetv.com
Editorial Profile: We TV offers compelling, entertaining stories that focus on key life stages of a modern woman, from getting married to having children and raising a family. Available in nearly 77 million homes, the network's original programming includes the critically acclaimed, viewer favorite The Locator (the network's most-watched series ever), the poignant, and often comical, real-life story of a family raising multiple toddlers, Raising Sextuplets, and a robust line-up of wedding series, including the hit show Bridezillas, Amazing Wedding Cakes and My Fair Wedding with David Tutera. WE tv is available in HD and WE tv On Demand is available in more than 30 million homes. The network launched in mid-January 2001.

The Weather Channel
Owner: NBC Universal
Editorial: 300 Interstate North Pkwy SE, Atlanta, Georgia 30339-2403.
T: 1 770 226-0000 **W:** http://www.weather.com
Editorial Profile: 24-hour national weather news and information network. Features continuous, up-to-the-minute reports on weather conditions throughout the world, compelling weather-related feature specials, and regional, local, and national forecasts.

Wedding Central
Owner: AMC Networks Inc.
Editorial: 11 Penn Plz Fl 19, New York, New York 10001-2006. **T:** 1 646 273-3500
E: contactwe@wetvnetworks.com
W: http://www.weddingcentral.com
Editorial Profile: Wedding Central is the ultimate television destination for women to indulge in all things related to dating, relationships and weddings. The network currently offers more than 300 hours of series and specials culled from the unsurpassed library of popular relationship and wedding programming found on WE tv, with plans to offer channel-specific original programming in the upcoming future.

WGN America
Owner: Tribune Broadcasting Co.
Editorial: 2501 W Bradley Pl, Chicago, Illinois 60618-4701. **T:** 1 773 528-2311
E: wgntvinfo@tribune.com
W: http://www.wgnamerica.com
Editorial Profile: Nationally-distributed cable television network which broadcasts the programming of WGN-TV in Chicago. The network airs a variety of first-run and syndicated programs, as well as Chicago Bulls NBA basketball, Chicago Cubs and White Sox baseball to cable subscribers.

The Word Network
Owner: Adell Broadcasting
Editorial: 20733 W 10 Mile Rd, Southfield, Michigan 48075-1086. **T:** 1 248 357-4566
W: http://www.thewordnetwork.org
Editorial Profile: The Word Network has established itself as a mainstream media broadcaster for African American ministries and gospel music. The Word Network offers value positive religious family programming embraced by millions of African Americans in urban and rural markets. The Word Network provides programming that is sensitive to, and touches the fabric of, the urban African American community.

Worship Network
Owner: Christian Network Inc.(The)
Editorial: 320 Billingsly Ct, Franklin, Tennessee 37067-4706. **T:** 1 800 728-8723
W: http://worship.net
Editorial Profile: The Worship Network is a national network that focuses on the Christian religion. Unique and uplifting television programming is featured, providing viewers with music, scripture, interactive fellowship and prayer. The format of the network emphasizes God-directed ministry rather than personality-driven television.

Xinhua News Agency - New York Bureau
Editorial: 1540 Broadway, 44th Floor, New York, New York 10036-4039.
T: 1 718 335-8388
W: http://www.xinhuanet.com/english2010

youtoo
Owner: Comstar Media, LLC
Editorial: 6565 N MacArthur Blvd Ste 400, Irving, Texas 75039-2468. **T:** 1 214 444-7100
W: http://www.youtoo.com
Editorial Profile: The nation's only full-time cable channel dedicated to providing lifestyle, entertainment, and information programming for the baby boomer generation. The network offers vintage sitcoms, dramas, music, entertainment and movies, as well as a variety of original series.

URUGUAY Tel: 598
Standard Time: GMT -3
Continent: The Americas
Capital City: Montevideo

NEWSPAPERS & PUBLICATIONS

NEWSPAPERS

Acción
Editorial: Artigas 352, Mercedes 75000.
T: 598 53 22236
E: diarioaccion@adinet.com.uy
Freq: Daily
Editorial Profile: Accion is a daily newspaper serving Mercedes, Uruguay and the surrounding area. The newspaper circulates in the departments of Soriano, Río Negro and Colonia. The paper is published in Spanish.
Language (s): Spanish
DAILY NEWSPAPER

Actualidad
Editorial: Garibaldi 539, Las Piedras 90200.
T: 598 36 45358 **E:** actualid@adinet.com.uy
Freq: Weekly
Editorial Profile: Semanario con circulación en las localidades de:Las Piedras, La Paz, Progreso, Juanicó, Los Cerrillos, Sauce, Canelones y parte de la Ciudad de la Costa.Edición de 24 páginas color.Director: Sergio Guerrero.Fecha de Aparición: 27368
Language (s): Spanish
DAILY NEWSPAPER

Arequita
Editorial: Minas **E:** arequit@adinet.com.uy
W: http://www.galeon.com/arequita/
Freq: Weekly
Editorial Profile: Semanario Independiente. Minas, Lavalleja, República Oriental del Uruguay. DIRECTOR: Álvaro Rodriguez Díaz. REDACTOR RESPONSABLE: Luis María Rodríguez Bentancour. SECRETARIO DE REDACCIÓN y DISEÑO: Luis Rodríguez Díaz
Language (s): Spanish
DAILY NEWSPAPER

Avisos Clasificados (El País)
Editorial: Av. 18 de Julio 1489, Montevideo 11200. **T:** 598 2 4002141
E: avisos@elpaisclasific.com.uy
W: http://gallito.elpais.com.uy
Freq: Weekly
Editor: Mr./Ms. Editor
Editorial Profile: Semanario de avisos clasificados de oferta y demanda de bienes y servicios. Se publica cada domingo con El País.
Language (s): Spanish
DAILY NEWSPAPER

Batoví
Editorial: Juan Ortiz 300, Tacuarembó 45000.
T: 598 63 23900
E: semanariobatovi@adinet.com.uy
W: http://www.batovi.com.uy
Freq: Daily
Editor: Mr./Ms. Editor
Editorial Profile: Semanario que sale los viernes y circula en las localidades de : Tacuarembó, Paso de los Toros, Achar, Curtina, Ansina, San Gregorio de Polanco yTambores. Fecha de Aparición: 30195
Language (s): Spanish
DAILY NEWSPAPER

Búsqueda
Editorial: Av. Uruguay 1146, Montevideo 11200. **T:** 598 2 9021300
E: busqueda@busqueda.com.uy
W: http://www.busqueda.com.uy
Freq: Weekly
Editor: Mr./Ms. Editor
Editorial Profile: Semanario independiente de gran prestigio e influencia en los ámbitos políticos, económicos y culturales del país. Distribución nacional. Su público objetivo son las clases media alta y alta. Fecha de Aparición: 1972
Language (s): Spanish
DAILY NEWSPAPER

Cambio
Editorial: Salto 50000. **T:** 598 73 35045
E: otlas@adinet.com.uy
W: http://www.diariocambiodigital.com.uy
Freq: Daily
Editorial Profile: Circula en las localidades de : Salto, Bella Unión.Edición de 24 páginas.Director: Carlos F. Artía. Fecha de Aparición: 30834
Language (s): Spanish
DAILY NEWSPAPER

Carta Popular
Editorial: Fernández Crespo 2106, Montevideo. **T:** 598 2 9290410
Freq: Weekly
Editor: Mr./Ms. Editor
Language (s): Spanish
DAILY NEWSPAPER

Centenario
Editorial: Artigas 1324, Cardona 75200.
T: 598 53 69224
W: http://www.centenario.com.uy
Freq: Weekly
Editor: Mr./Ms. Editor
Editorial Profile: Tri semanario que sale los días: lunes miércoles y sábados.Edición de 20 páginas.Circula en las localidades de : Cardona, Florencio Sánchez, Cortinas, Santa Catalina, Ombúes de Lavalle, Miguelete y Rodó. Fecha de Aparición: 11067
Language (s): Spanish
DAILY NEWSPAPER

Crónicas
Editorial: 484 Buenos Aires, Primer Piso, Oficina 4, Montevideo 11000.
T: 598 2 915-6511
E: cronicas@cronicas.com.uy
W: http://www.cronicas.com.uy
Freq: Weekly
Editor: Oscar Cestau
Editorial Profile: Crónicas es un semanario que brinda información sobre la Economía, Política, Agro, Sociedad, Seguros en Uruguay. Crónicas is a weekly publication that provides coverage of Economy, Politics, Agriculture, Society Insurance in Uruguay.
Language (s): Spanish
DAILY NEWSPAPER

Diario Atlas
Editorial: 18 de Julio 664, Melo 37000.
T: 598 64 23726 **E:** atlasmel@adinet.com.uy
Freq: Bi-Monthly

Editorial Profile: Edición de 12 páginas.Director: Zelmar Paggiola. Fecha de Aparición: 31190
Language (s): Spanish
DAILY NEWSPAPER

Diario Correo de Punta del Este
Editorial: Maldonado 2000. **T:** 598 42 235633
E: info@diariocorreo.com
W: http://www.diariocorreo.com
Freq: Weekly
Editor: Mr./Ms. Editor
Language (s): Spanish
DAILY NEWSPAPER

Diario Crónicas
Editorial: Eusebio Giménez 695, Mercedes 75000. **T:** 598 53 25310
E: diariocronicas@adinet.com.uy
W: http://www.diariocronicas.com.uy
Freq: Weekly
Editorial Profile: Edición de 16 páginas, color.Circula en las localidades de : Departamentos de Soriano, Río Negro, Colonia.Director: Ricardo Nolé Laguno. Fecha de Aparición: 30021
Language (s): Spanish
DAILY NEWSPAPER

Diario Helvecia
Editorial: Colón 1117, Nueva Helvecia 70.201. **T:** 598 55 44031 **E:** helvecia@adinet.com.uy
W: http://www.colonia-suiza.com.uy/helvecia.htm
Freq: Weekly
Editorial Profile: Circula en las localidades de : Nueva Helvecia, Colonia Valdense, Rosario, Ecilda Paullier, Cufré y Balnearios.Edición de 16 páginas.Director: Alfredo Stutz. Fecha de Aparición: 5149
Language (s): Spanish
DAILY NEWSPAPER

Diario la Unión
Editorial: Florencio Sánchez 569, Minas 30000. **T:** 598 44 22065
E: decano@chasque.net
W: http://www.lavalleja.com/noticias/marco_news.htm
Freq: Daily
Editorial Profile: Diario vespertino de la capital departamental de Lavalleja.Redactor Responsable: Hugo Vázquez Ortiz.Edición de 16 páginas.
Language (s): Spanish
DAILY NEWSPAPER

Ecos
Editorial: Dr. Pedro E. Ferrer 1644, Castillos. **T:** 598 47 59600
Freq: Daily
Editorial Profile: Circula en las localidades de : Rocha, Castillos, Lascano, Chuy, La Paloma, Cebollatí, La Coronilla, La Pedrera.Edición de 26 páginas. Director:Julio A. Bianchi Coello. Fecha de Aparición: 33229
Language (s): Spanish
DAILY NEWSPAPER

Ecos Regionales de Durazno
Editorial: Fructuoso Rivera 364, Durazno 97000. **T:** 598 36 22146
E: ecossrl@adinet.com.uy
Freq: Daily
Editorial Profile: Circula en las localidades de: Departamentos de Durazno, Flores y Paso de los Toros.Edición de 32 páginas.Director: Ricardo Ariel López. Fecha de Aparición: 34831
Language (s): Spanish
DAILY NEWSPAPER

Ecos Regionales de Trinidad
Editorial: Luis Alberto de Herrera 812, Trinidad 85000. **T:** 598 36 44666
E: ecossrl@adinet.com.uy
Editorial Profile: Bi semanario que sale los martes y viernes.Edición de 32 páginas.Circula en las localidades de : Departamentos de Flores, Durazno y Paso de los Toros.Director: Ricardo Ariel López. Fecha de Aparición: 34831
Language (s): Spanish
DAILY NEWSPAPER

El Acontecer
Editorial: Artigas 374, Durazno 97000. **T:** 598 36 24416 **E:** acontece@adinet.com.uy
Freq: Bi-Monthly
Editorial Profile: Circula en las localidades del departamento de Durazno.Edición de 20 páginas, color.Director: Carlos Román Fernández. Fecha de Aparición: 31427
Language (s): Spanish
DAILY NEWSPAPER

El Avisador
Editorial: Dr. Catalina 181, Tacuarembó 45000. **T:** 598 63 24411 **E:** diario@avisador.com.uy
W: http://www.avisador.com.uy
Freq: Daily
Editorial Profile: Director: Jorge W. Carozo Redactor Responsable:Jorge Carozo Barcelona.Circula en las localidades de : Tacuarembó, Rivera, San Gregorio, Ansina y Curtina. Fecha de Aparición: 31048
Language (s): Spanish
DAILY NEWSPAPER

El Correo
Editorial: Maldonado. **T:** 598 42 235633
E: gallardo@adinet.com.uy
W: http://www.diariocorreo.com
Freq: Weekly
Editorial Profile: Sale de lunes a viernes y circula en el departamento de maldonado.Edición de 12 páginas.Director: María Palmira Rodríguez. Fecha de Aparición: 34043
Language (s): Spanish
DAILY NEWSPAPER

El Diario Médico
Editorial: Antonio María Fernández 765, Florida. **T:** 598 35 23833
E: saludhoy@adinet.com.uy
W: http://www.smu.org.uy/publicaciones/eldiariomedico/
Freq: Monthly
Editorial Profile: Tabloide mensual dedicado al acontecer médico.Redactor Responsable:Prof. Elbio D. Álvarez.
Language (s): Spanish
DAILY NEWSPAPER

El Eco de Colonia
Editorial: Ruta 21 1630, Colonia. **T:** 598 52 21395 **E:** elecosrl@adinet.com.uy
Freq: Monthly
Editorial Profile: Semanario que sale los sábados.Tiene cobertura departamental.Director: Daniel Roselli.Edición de 20 páginas. Fecha de Aparición: 37919
Language (s): Spanish
DAILY NEWSPAPER

El Eco de Palmira
Editorial: Nueva Palmira 70101. **T:** 598 54 46815 **E:** elecosrl@adinet.com.uy
W: http://www.nuevapalmira.net/eleco
Freq: Daily
Editorial Profile: Circula en las localidades de: Nueva Palmira, Carmelo y zona rural de influencia.Edición de 24 páginas.Directora: Nancy Banchero.
Language (s): Spanish
DAILY NEWSPAPER

El Este
Editorial: Zorrilla 70, Rocha. **T:** 598 47 22099
E: info@diarioeleste.com
W: http://www.diarioeleste.com
Freq: Daily
Editorial Profile: Matutino capitalino del departamento de Rocha.Director: José Carlos Cardozo.Edición de 16 páginas.Circula en las localidades de : Rocha, Castillos, Lascano, Chuy, La Paloma, Cebollatí, La Coronilla y La Pedrera. Fecha de Aparición: 16674
Language (s): Spanish
DAILY NEWSPAPER

El Heraldo
Editorial: Independencia 825, Florida 94000. **T:** 598 35 22229 **E:** marino9753@hotmail.com
W: http://www.elheraldo.com.uy
Freq: Daily
Editorial Profile: Edición de 20 páginas, color.Director: Alvaro Riva Rey. Fecha de Aparición: 6974
Language (s): Spanish
DAILY NEWSPAPER

El Mundo y sus Comarcas
Editorial: Héctor Miranda 87, Santa Lucía 90700. **T:** 598 33 46022
E: rlegnani@adinet.com.uy
Freq: Weekly
Editorial Profile: Quincenario que sale los días jueves.Con cobertura en el departamento de Canelones.Edición: 10 páginas. Director:Eduardo Pi. Fecha de Aparición: 34335
Language (s): Spanish
DAILY NEWSPAPER

El Nuevo Rionegrense
Editorial: 25 de agosto 3118, Fray Bentos 65000. **T:** 598 56 22210
E: elrione@adinet.com.uy
Freq: Monthly
Editorial Profile: Bi Semanario (miércoles y sábado), circula en las localidades de : Fray Bentos, Young y Nuevo Berlin.Edición de 8 páginas.Director: Félix Omar Rovelli. Fecha de Aparición: 37469
Language (s): Spanish
DAILY NEWSPAPER

El Observador
Editorial: Cuareim 2052, Montevideo 11800. **T:** 598 2 9247000
W: http://www.observa.com.uy
Freq: Daily
Editor: Mr./Ms. Editor
Editorial Profile: Matutino de alcance nacional.Tendencia liberal. Afín católico. De consumo de clases media, media alta y alta. Fecha de Aparición: 33878
Language (s): Spanish
DAILY NEWSPAPER

El Pueblo
Editorial: Luis A. De Herrera 479, Santa Lucía 90700. **T:** 598 33 46151
E: diarioelpueblo@hotmail.com
Freq: Monthly
Editorial Profile: Semanario que sale los días miércoles.Circula en las localidades de: Santa Lucía, Canelones y zonas cercanas. Edición 8 páginas. Director:Gilda Caputi. Fecha de Aparición: 7868
Language (s): Spanish
DAILY NEWSPAPER

El Pueblo
Editorial: 18 de Julio 151, Salto 50000. **T:** 598 73 34133 **E:** dipueblo@adinet.com.uy
W: http://www.diarioelpueblo.com.uy
Freq: Daily
Editorial Profile: Diario de información local.Circula en las localidades de: Salto, Belén, Constitución, Artigas y Bella Unión.Edición de 32 páginas, color.Director: Walter Martínez. Fecha de Aparición: 20515
Language (s): Spanish
DAILY NEWSPAPER

El Sol
Editorial: Fosalva 614, Colonia 70000. **T:** 598 52 26017 **E:** monteric@adinet.com.uy
Freq: Daily
Editorial Profile: Circula en las localidades de: Colonia y zonas cercanas. Director: Ricardo Montenegro.Edición de 30 páginas. Fecha de Aparición: 30939
Language (s): Spanish
DAILY NEWSPAPER

El Telégrafo
Editorial: 18 de Julio 1027, Paysandú 60000. **T:** 598 72 24605 **E:** correo@eltelegrafo.com
W: http://www.eltelegrafo.com
Freq: Daily
Editorial Profile: Edición de 28 páginas, color.Circula en las localidades de : Paysandú, Salto, Young, Mercedes y Tacuarembó.Director: Fernando Baccaro. Fecha de Aparición: 3835
Language (s): Spanish
DAILY NEWSPAPER

Hechos
Editorial: Buxareo Oribe 2478, San Ramón 90600. **T:** 598 31 22142
E: shechos@adinet.com.uy
Freq: Daily
Editorial Profile: Semanario que sale los ías viernes.Circula en las localidades de : San Ramón, Santa Rosa, San Baustista, Castellanos, Tala, Fray Marcos y Chamizo.Edición: 14 páginas. Director:Jorge Zitto Ferré. Fecha de Aparición: 31321
Language (s): Spanish
DAILY NEWSPAPER

Hoy Canelones
Editorial: Tomás Berreta 207, Canelones 90000. **T:** 598 33 24386
E: hoycanel@adinet.com.uy
W: http://www.hoycanelones.com.uy
Freq: Daily
Editorial Profile: Diario local que cubre el área de de la ciudad de canelones y aledaños en forma diaria. Se dedica a las noticias de orden local y nacional. Cubre el área nacional en la modalidad de sucscripción y envío.Director: Julio Britos Bide.Diario: Lunes a Sábado. Edición: 24 páginas en color. Fecha de Aparición: 29779
Language (s): Spanish
DAILY NEWSPAPER

Irupe
Editorial: Asencio 1341, Dolores 75100. **T:** 598 53 42134 **E:** irupe21@adinet.com.uy
Freq: Daily
Editorial Profile: Circula en las localidades de : Dolores, Cañada Nieto, Villa Soriano y Mercedes.Edición de 12 páginas.Director: Miguel Pose. Fecha de Aparición: 22883
Language (s): Spanish
DAILY NEWSPAPER

Jornada
Editorial: Brasil 1262, Rivera 40000. **T:** 598 62 23991 **E:** jornada@adinet.com.uy
Freq: Daily
Editorial Profile: De circulación departamental.Edición de 12 páginas.Directora: Neiva Zampayo de Gaál. Fecha de Aparición: 31217
Language (s): Spanish
DAILY NEWSPAPER

La Colonia
Editorial: Gral. Flores 317, Colonia 70000. **T:** 598 52 22580
W: http://www.portalcolonia.com
Freq: Daily
Editorial Profile: Bi semanario que circula en las localidades de:Colonia y alrededores, El General, Real de San Carlos y zonas rurales de influencia.Director: Juan Carlos Puppo. Edición de 36 páginas. Fecha de Aparición: 532
Language (s): Spanish
DAILY NEWSPAPER

La Democracia
Editorial: 18 de Julio 25, San Carlos 20000. **T:** 598 42 250321
Freq: Daily
Editorial Profile: Sale de lunes a sábado y circula en las localidades de : San Carlos, Maldonado, Punta del Este, zonas de la costa, Piriápolis y Pan de Azúcar. Edición de 24 páginas.Director: Raúl José Arias. Fecha de Aparición: 8266
Language (s): Spanish
DAILY NEWSPAPER

La Diaria
Editorial: Juan Paullier 1235, Montevideo. **T:** 598 2 4012100 **E:** ladiaria@ladiaria.com.uy
W: http://www.ladiaria.com.uy
Freq: Daily
Editorial Profile: Nuevo periódico joven, que trata temas de actualidad como una mirada seria y renovada. Secciones: política, cultura, internacional, sociedad, economía, deportes y humor. Tiene contenido gratuito a través de su página web. Exite la opción de suscribirse por $220 pesos mensuales, € 15 o US$ 18 para la versión en PDF para el exterior.
Language (s): Spanish
DAILY NEWSPAPER

La Juventud
Editorial: Nueva York 1326, Montevideo
E: juvnetud@chasque.net
W: http://chasque.apc.org/juventud/
Freq: Monthly
Editor: Mr./Ms. Editor
Editorial Profile: Diario de izquierda idetificado con el Frente Amplio.
Language (s): Spanish
DAILY NEWSPAPER

La Noticia
Editorial: Garzón 450, Artigas 55000. **T:** 598 77 25091 **E:** lnoticia@adinet.com.uy
W: http://www.publimatic.com/diariolanoticia
Freq: Daily
Editorial Profile: Circula en las localidades de: Artigas, Bella Unión, Tomás Gomensoro y Baltasar Brum.Edición de 12 páginas, color.Director: Ricardo Pedrón. Fecha de Aparición: 32295
Language (s): Spanish
DAILY NEWSPAPER

La Tribuna
Editorial: Manuel Oribe 452, Paso De Los Toros 45100. **T:** 598 66 42268
E: latribuna@pasodelostoros.com
W: http://www.pasodelostoros.com/latribuna/
Freq: Weekly
Editorial Profile: Circula en las localidades de : Paso de los Toros, Tacuarembó, Achar, San Gregorio de Polanco, Salto, Rivera, Durazno y Centenario.Edición de 20 páginas, color.Director: Iris Andrada de Andrada. Fecha de Aparición: 19977
Language (s): Spanish
DAILY NEWSPAPER

Norte
Editorial: San Martín 711, Rivera 40000. **T:** 598 62 35676 **E:** norte1@adinet.com.uy
Freq: Weekly
Editorial Profile: Circula en las localidades de : Rivera, Tacuarembó, Tranqueras, Minas de Corrales, Vichadero, Cerro Pelado, Paso de los Toros.Edición de 22 páginas.Directora: María del Carmen Pereira Soáres de Araújo. Fecha de Aparición: 19836

Language (s): Spanish
DAILY NEWSPAPER

Opción Veintiuno
Editorial: Ciganda 720, San José.
T: 598 34 29353
Freq: Daily
Editorial Profile: Semanario que sale los viernes.Es de circulaciónen todo el departamento y consta de 20 páginas en color.Director: Gabriel Reyes Montes. Fecha de Aparición: 36588
Language (s): Spanish
DAILY NEWSPAPER

Orejano
Editorial: Dionisio Oribe 1388, Treinta Y Tres 33000. **T:** 598 45 24512
Freq: Weekly
Editorial Profile: Semanario que sale los viernes de cobertura departamental.Edición de 12 páginas.Director: Damián Blanco. Fecha de Aparición: 35156
Language (s): Spanish
DAILY NEWSPAPER

El País
Editorial: Zelmar Michelini (diario), Plaza Cagancha 1162 (administración) 1287, Montevideo. **T:** 598 2 9020115
W: http://www.elpais.com.uy
Freq: Daily
Editor: Mr./Ms. Editor
Language (s): Spanish
DAILY NEWSPAPER

Patria
Editorial: Av. Rivera 2476, 5 1, Montevideo.
T: 598 2 9080250
E: semanariopatria@gmail.com
W: http://www.patria.com.uy
Freq: Weekly
Editor: Mr./Ms. Editor
Editorial Profile: Semanario que publica el Partido Nacional
Language (s): Spanish
DAILY NEWSPAPER

Prensa Rosarina
Editorial: Boulevar José E. Rodó 433, Rosario 70200. **T:** 598 55 22390
E: prensaro@adinet.com.uy
Freq: Daily
Editor: Mr./Ms. Editor
Editorial Profile: Bi semanario.Circula en las localidades de : Rosario, Colonia Valdense, Nueva Helvecia, Cufré, Colonia Española, Balnearios. Fecha de Aparición: 28357
Language (s): Spanish
DAILY NEWSPAPER

Primera Hora
Editorial: 25 de Mayo 488, San José.
T: 598 34 21598 **E:** primerah@adinet.com.uy
Freq: Daily
Editorial Profile: Circula en las localidades de : San José, Ecilda Paullier, Villa Rodríguez, Libertad, Rincón de la Bolsa, Playa Pascual.Director:Wilson Ramírez.Edición de 16 páginas. Fecha de Aparición: 36368
Language (s): Spanish
DAILY NEWSPAPER

Progreso al Día
Editorial: Progreso 9300. **T:** 598 36 89592
E: proaldia@adinet.com.uy
Freq: Weekly
Editorial Profile: Semanario (sábado) con circulación en las localidades de Progreso, Juanicó y Canelón Chico. Edición: 16 páginas. Director:Jorge Javier Peraza Bartora. Fecha de Aparición: 33390
Language (s): Spanish
DAILY NEWSPAPER

Que hacemos hoy
Editorial: Punta Del Este
E: redaccion@quehacemoshoy.com.uy
W: http://www.quehacemoshoy.com.uy
Freq: Weekly
Editor: Mr./Ms. Editor
Editorial Profile: Semanario de Punta del Este.
Language (s): Spanish
DAILY NEWSPAPER

Que Hacemos Hoy
Editorial: Marsella 1234, Punta Del Este.
T: 598 42 489117
Freq: Bi-Monthly
Editor: Mr./Ms. Editor
Language (s): Spanish
DAILY NEWSPAPER

La República
Editorial: Garibaldi 2597, Montevideo.
T: 598 2 4873565 **W:** http://www.lr21.com.uy

Freq: Daily
Editor: Gustavo Carbajal; **Editor:** Mr./Ms. Editor
Language (s): Spanish
DAILY NEWSPAPER

San José Hoy
Editorial: Sarandí 786, San José.
T: 598 34 23189 **E:** sanjose@adinet.com.uy
W: http://www.sanjoseonline.com
Freq: Monthly
Editorial Profile: Tri semanario: lunes miércoles y viernes.De circulación local.Directora: Mirtana López.Edición de 20 páginas. Fecha de Aparición: 33215
Language (s): Spanish
DAILY NEWSPAPER

Santa Clara
Editorial: Santa Clara De Olimar 37007.
T: 598 46 45084
Freq: Weekly
Editorial Profile: Circula en las localidades de : Santa Clara de Olimar y zonas cercanas.Edición de 8 páginas.Director: Ruben Medina. Fecha de Aparición: 22867
Language (s): Spanish
DAILY NEWSPAPER

Semanario Brecha
Editorial: Av.Uruguay 844, Montevideo 11200.
T: 598 2 9000388 **E:** brecha@brecha.com.uy
W: http://www.brecha.com.uy
Freq: Weekly
Editor: Mr./Ms. Editor
Editorial Profile: Semanario de línea editorial de izquierda. Sucesor del legendario semanario Marcha. Fecha de Aparición: 1985
Language (s): Spanish
DAILY NEWSPAPER

Semanario de Acá
Editorial: Roosvelt 730, Mercedes.
T: 598 53 22999
Freq: Daily
Editorial Profile: Semanario que sale los sábados.Circula en las localidades de : Mercedes, Palmitas y Dolores. Edición de 16 páginas.Director: Juan Manuel Delpino. Fecha de Aparición: 37926
Language (s): Spanish
DAILY NEWSPAPER

Semanario Minuano
Editorial: Carabajal 513, Minas 30000.
T: 598 44 23554 **E:** sepe16@hotmail.com
Freq: Daily
Editorial Profile: Semanario que sale los viernes, tiene cobertura departamental.Edición de 16 páginas.Director: Fernando Bonhomme. Fecha de Aparición: 34243
Language (s): Spanish
DAILY NEWSPAPER

Semanario Realidad
Editorial: Punta Del Este. **T:** 598 42 494730
Freq: Daily
Editor: Mr./Ms. Editor
Language (s): Spanish
DAILY NEWSPAPER

Serrano
Editorial: Washington Beltrán 480, Minas 30000. **T:** 598 44 24100
E: serrano@adinet.com.uy
Freq: Daily
Editorial Profile: Diario que sale de lunes a sábado, de alcance departamental.Edición de 20 páginas, color.Director: Juan Caraballo. Fecha de Aparición: 31229
Language (s): Spanish
DAILY NEWSPAPER

Tiempo
Editorial: Treinta y Tres 1080, Pando 91000.
T: 598 29 20222 **E:** diariotiempo@hotmail.com
Freq: Daily
Editorial Profile: Edición de 6 páginas. Cubre la zona este del departamento. Director: Daniel Mesa. Fecha de Aparición: 30724
Language (s): Spanish
DAILY NEWSPAPER

Tri Semanario Profesional
Editorial: 18 de Julio 997, Melo 37000.
T: 598 64 29750
Freq: Daily
Editorial Profile: Trisemanario de 12 páginas.Director: Alejandro Olmedo. Fecha de Aparición: 35632
Language (s): Spanish
DAILY NEWSPAPER

Tribuna Popular
Editorial: El Fanal 410, Río Branco 37100.
T: 598 67 52103 **E:** comtri@adinet.com.uuy

Freq: Daily
Editorial Profile: Semanario que sale los días viernes.Edición de 20 páginas.Circula en las localidades de: Rio Branco y Yaguarón.Director: Claudina González Fecha de Aparición: 31367
Language (s): Spanish
DAILY NEWSPAPER

Últimas Noticias
Editorial: Paysandú 1179, Montevideo.
T: 598 2 9020452
E: redaccion@ultimasnoticias.com.uy
W: http://www.ultimasnoticias.com.uy
Freq: Daily
Editor: Mr./Ms. Editor
Language (s): Spanish
DAILY NEWSPAPER

Vamos
Editorial: Defensa 310, Juan Lacaze 70.001.
T: 598 58 63218 **E:** vamos@adinet.com.uy
Freq: Weekly
Editorial Profile: Circula en las localidades de : Juan Lacaze y zona de influencia. Sale los viernes.Edición de 14 páginas.Director: Juan Cervantes.Edición de 22 páginas.Director: Raúl Collazo. Fecha de Aparición: 30504
Language (s): Spanish
DAILY NEWSPAPER

Verdad
Editorial: José Pedro Varela 2170, Tarariras 70002. **T:** 598 57 43530
E: semanarioverdad@adinet.com.uy
Freq: Weekly
Editorial Profile: Sale los días viernes.Circula en las localidades de : Tarariras, Colonia Miguelete, Semillero, Estanzuela Edición de 24 páginas.Director: Pablo Celedón Vergara.Fecha de Aparición: 20944
Language (s): Spanish
DAILY NEWSPAPER

Visión Ciudadana
Editorial: Treinta y Tres 427, San José 80000.
T: 598 34 30988
E: visionciudadana@adinet.com.uy
Freq: Weekly
Editorial Profile: Tri semanario que sale los días martes, jueves y sábados.Circula en las localidades de : San José, Ecilda Paullier, Villa Rodríguez, Libertad, Peraza, Puntas de Valdez, Capurro.Director: Jorge Scagni Gandini Montes. Edición de 16 páginas. Fecha de Aparición: 37978
Language (s): Spanish
DAILY NEWSPAPER

NEWS SERVICE/SYNDICATE

Agencia Alemana de Prensa (DPA)
Editorial: Av. 18 de Julio 994, Montevideo.
T: 598 2 9022662
Editor: Mr./Ms. Editor
Language (s): Spanish
NEWS SERVICE/SYNDICATE

Agencia EFE
Editorial: Wilson Ferreira 1294, Montevideo.
T: 598 2 9020322 **W:** http://www.efe.es
Editor: Mr./Ms. Editor
Language (s): Spanish
NEWS SERVICE/SYNDICATE

Agencia France Presse
Editorial: Montevideo. **T:** 598 2 71202576
W: http://www.afp.com
Editor: Mr./Ms. Editor
Language (s): Spanish
NEWS SERVICE/SYNDICATE

Agencia noticiosa ANSA
Editorial: Florida 1408, Montevideo.
T: 598 2 90819050
Editor: Mr./Ms. Editor
Language (s): Spanish
NEWS SERVICE/SYNDICATE

Associated Press
T: 598 2 9018291 **W:** http://www.ap.org
Editor: Mr./Ms. Editor
Language (s): Spanish
NEWS SERVICE/SYNDICATE

COMCOSUR
Editorial: Dr. Pablo de María 1435, Montevideo. **T:** 598 2 4081650
E: comcosur@comcosur.com.uy
W: http://comcosur.com.uy
Editor: Mr./Ms. Editor
Language (s): Spanish
NEWS SERVICE/SYNDICATE

Intercomm
Editorial: 25 de mayo 447, Montevideo.
T: 598 2 9168413
Editor: Mr./Ms. Editor
Language (s): Spanish
NEWS SERVICE/SYNDICATE

Interpress Service para América Latina
Editorial: J.C. Gómez 1445, Montevideo.
T: 598 2 9170277
W: http://ipslatam.net/ipslatam
Editor: Mr./Ms. Editor
Language (s): Spanish
NEWS SERVICE/SYNDICATE

Reuters
Editorial: Pza. Independencia 835, Montevideo. **T:** 598 2 9027912
W: http://www.reuters.com
Editor: Mr./Ms. Editor
Language (s): Spanish
NEWS SERVICE/SYNDICATE

Sucesos
Editorial: Cnel. Brandzen 1956, Montevideo.
T: 598 2 4086723
Editor: Mr./Ms. Editor
Language (s): Spanish
NEWS SERVICE/SYNDICATE

BROADCASTING

TELEVISION NETWORKS

Canal 10, Saeta TV
Editorial: Lorenzo Carnelli 1234, Montevideo 11100. **T:** 598 2 4102120
E: subrayado@canal10.com.uy
W: http://www.canal10.com.uy
Editorial Profile: Primer canal de televisión abierta del país. Petenece a las familias De Feo y Fontaina dueños también de Radio Carve de Montevideo y Nuevotiempo (Mont.). Es el medio televisivo que produce la mayor cantidad de programas nacionales; periodísticos y de entetenimiento. Fecha de Aparición: 1957

Canal 4 Montecarlo TV
Editorial: Paraguay 2253, Montevideo 11800.
T: 598 2 9244444
E: secretarias@montecarlotv.com.uy
W: http://www.canal4.com.uy
Editorial Profile: Canal de televisión abierta perteneciente a la familia Romay Salvo que conforma un grupo que posee otros canales de televisión abierta (en el interior) y emisoras de radio. Pantalla orientada a la clase media y sectores populares. Tiene un acuerdo de programación con Telefé de Argentina. Fecha de Aparición: 22372

Televisión Nacional de Uruguay
Editorial: Bvar. Artigas 2552, Montevideo 11600. **T:** 598 2 19595
E: contacto@tnu.com.uy
W: http://www.tnu.com.uy
Editorial Profile: Canal estatal de alcance nacional de alcance nacional a través de repetidoras, de escasa audiencia. Fecha de Aparición: 1965

UZBEKISTAN   Tel: 998

Standard Time: GMT +5
Continent: Asia
Capital City: Tashkent

NEWSPAPERS & PUBLICATIONS

NEWSPAPERS

Narodnoye slovo
Editorial: ul. Matbuotchilar 32, Tashkent.
T: 998 3712 233 15 22
E: info@narodnoeslovo.uz
W: http://www.narodnoeslovo.uz
Freq: Daily
Editorial Profile: National newspaper covering official parliament and president's documentation, legal information, social and cultural issues.
Language (s): Russian
DAILY NEWSPAPER

Pravda Vostoka
Editorial: ul. Matbutchilar 32, Tashkent 700000. **T:** 998 71 133 15 20 **E:** info@pv.uz
W: http://www.pv.uz **Circ:** 10000

Editorial Profile: National weekly covering economical, business, financial, social and cultural issues.
Language (s): Russian
NEWSPAPER

Uzbekistan Ovozi
Owner: Narodnaya Partya Uzbekistana
Editorial: ul. Matbuotchilar 32, Tashkent 700000. **T:** 998 71 13 36 545
E: uzbovozi@sarkor.uz
W: http://www.uzbekistonovozi.uz
Freq: 2 Times/Week; **Circ:** 12000 Publisher's Statement
Editor-in-Chief: Safar Ostanov
Editorial Profile: Newspaper focusing on national and international news, business, politics, culture and sport.
Language (s): Uzbek (Northern)
DAILY NEWSPAPER

NEWS SERVICE/SYNDICATE

INTER-PRESS
Editorial: ul. Navoi 13, Tashkent 100011.
T: 998 97 55 09 55 **E:** book@interpress.uz
W: http://www.interpress.uz
Editorial Profile: Information agency dealing with national news, specializing in newspapers and magazines' national subscription, book trade and library fund formation.
Language (s): Uzbek (Northern)
NEWS SERVICE/SYNDICATE

Press-uz.info
Editorial: ul. Navoi 16, Tashkent.
T: 998 371 14 42 506 **E:** admin@press-uz.info
W: http://www.press-uz.info
Editor In Chief: Akhror Djobbarov
Editorial Profile: Political, socio-economical information on Uzbekistan. The information resources of IA Press-uz.info on the internet are provided in Uzbek, Russian and English.
Language (s): Uzbek (Northern)
NEWS SERVICE/SYNDICATE

Uzbekistan National News Agency
Editorial: ul. Buyuk Turon 41, Tashkent 700047. **T:** 998 71 13 31 622
E: uzauz@inbox.uz **W:** http://uza.uz
Editor: Golib Hasanov; **Editor:** A. Sattarov
Editorial Profile: National Information Agency of Uzbekistan (UzA) is the official source of information and a leading news agency of the country.
Language (s): English, Russian, Uzbek (Northern)
NEWS SERVICE/SYNDICATE

BROADCASTING

RADIO STATIONS

Radio Grand
Editorial: P.O. BOX 5655, ul Druzhby Narodovov 15, 1st floor, Tashkent 100043.
T: 998 71 17 39 248 **E:** radio@grand.uz
W: http://www.grand.uz
Editorial Profile: CHR (Contemporary Hit Radio). 50% of the programmes are in Uzbek language and 50% are in Russian.

TELEVISION STATIONS

Uzbek State TV
Editorial: 69 Navoi St, Tashkent 100098.
T: 998 71 13 38 106 **W:** http://www.mtrk.uz

VANUATU Tel: 678
Standard Time: GMT +11
Continent: Oceania
Capital City: Port Vila

NEWSPAPERS & PUBLICATIONS

NEWSPAPERS

The Ni-Vanuatu
Owner: Moses Stevens
E: thenivanuatu@vanuatu.com.vu
W: http://cometo.vu/news/frontpage.htm
Freq: Daily
Language (s): English
DAILY NEWSPAPER

Vanuatu Daily Post
Owner: Trading Post Ltd
Editorial: PO Box 1292, Port Vila, Vanuatu.
T: 678 23 111 **E:** editor@dailypost.com.vu
W: http://dailypost.com.vu
Freq: Daily; **Circ:** 3000 Publisher's Statement
Editor: Kiery Mannaseh; **Publisher:** Marc Neil-Jones
Editorial Profile: Offers most up-to-date news service, and often id first source of regional breaking news stories.
Language (s): English
DAILY NEWSPAPER

The Vanuatu Independent
Owner: The Independent Foundation
Editorial: BP 1555, Port Vila, Vanuatu.
T: 678 29 999 **E:** editor@independent.vu
W: http://independent.vu
Freq: Weekly
Editor: Bob Makin
Editorial Profile: Provide independent and balanced news & information to citizens and inhabitants of Vanuatu.
Language (s): English
NEWSPAPER

Vanuatu News Online
Owner: Port Vila Presse
Editorial: PO Box 637, Port Vila, Vanuatu.
T: 678 27 676 **E:** publisher@news.vu
W: http://presse.com.vu
Freq: Daily
Editor: Mark Lowen
Editorial Profile: Site provides online news service for Vanuatu.
Language (s): English
DAILY NEWSPAPER

BROADCASTING

RADIO NETWORKS

Radio Vanuatu
Owner: Vanuatu Broadcasting & Television Corporation (VBTC)
Editorial: Port Vila, Vanuatu. **T:** 678 22 999
W: http://vbtc.com.vu
Editorial Profile: Radio station in Vanuatu covering local news.

TELEVISION STATIONS

Television Blong Vanuatu
Owner: Vanuatu Broadcasting & Television Corporation (VBTC)
Editorial: Port Vila, Vanuatu. **T:** 678 22 999
W: http://www.vanuatu2u.com/tv-vanuatu-television.html
Editorial Profile: Television Blong Vanuatu is the television channel in Vanuatu based in Port Vila. Launched in 1993 with the help of Radio France Overseas (RFO).

VATICAN CITY Tel: 39
Standard Time: GMT +1
Continent: Europe
Capital City: Vatican City

NEWSPAPERS & PUBLICATIONS

NEWSPAPERS

L' Osservatore Romano
Owner: Edizioni Tipografia Vaticana
Editorial: Via Del Pellegrino, Rome 120.
T: 39 06 69883461 **E:** ornet@ossrom.va
W: http://www.vatican.va/news_services/or/home_ita.html
Freq: Daily; **Circ:** 60000 Publisher's Statement
Caporedattore: Antonio Chilà; **Redattore:** Piero di Domenicantonio
Editorial Profile: L'Osservatore Romano is a newspaper of the Holy See. It covers all the Pope's public activities, publishes editorials by important churchmen, and runs official documents after being released.
Language (s): English, French, German, Italian, Polish, Portuguese, Spanish
DAILY NEWSPAPER

NEWS SERVICE/SYNDICATE

Agenzia Fides
Editorial: Palazzo "de Propaganda Fide", Citta Del Vaticano 120. **T:** 39 06 69 88 01 15
E: fides@fides.va **W:** http://www.fides.org
Capo redattore: Stefano Lodigiani; **Direttore:** Luca Mata
Editorial Profile: News and photo agency of the Holly See focussing on religion, news and current affairs and health.
Language (s): Chinese
NEWS SERVICE/SYNDICATE

Holy See Press Office
Editorial: Citta Del Vaticano 120.
T: 39 06 698 921 **E:** lombardi@pressva.va
W: http://www.vatican.va/news_services/press/index.htm
Direttore: Miguel Castellvi
Editorial Profile: Official press agency of the Holy See.
Language (s): English
NEWS SERVICE/SYNDICATE

BROADCASTING

TELEVISION STATIONS

Centro Televisivo Vaticano
Editorial: Via del Pellegino, Rome 120.
T: 39 06 69885467 **E:** ctv@ctv.va
W: http://www.vatican.va/news_services/television/index_it.htm
Editorial Profile: Centro Televisivo Vaticano (CTV) produces programmes covering the daily public activities of the Pope and the main events taking place within the Vatican City. The main services of CTV are: live broadcasts, production, archiving, and daily assistance to other broadcasters.

Vatican Radio
Editorial: Palazzo Pio, Piazza Pia 3, Citta Del Vaticano 120. **T:** 39 06 698 832 37
E: sedoc@vatiradio.va
W: http://www.vaticanradio.org
Editorial Profile: Broadcasting station of the Holy See focussing on communication and evangelisation, serving the Pope's ministry.

VENEZUELA Tel: 58
Standard Time: GMT -5
Continent: The Americas
Capital City: Caracas

NEWSPAPERS & PUBLICATIONS

NEWSPAPERS

2001
Owner: Bloque Editorial de Armas
Editorial: Final Avenida San Martín con Avenida La Paz, Edificio Bloque De Armas Piso 6, Caracas. **T:** 58 212 406 41 11
E: 2001@dearmas.com
W: http://www.2001.com.ve
Freq: Daily; **Circ:** 150000 Not Audited
Editor: Jorge Collazo; **Editor:** José Feijoo; **Editor:** Marcos Moreno
Editorial Profile: Tabloid-sized covering national and world news, politics, economics, features, opinion, social issues and sport.
Language (s): Spanish
DAILY NEWSPAPER

Correio de Venezuela
Owner: Editorial Correio C.A.
Editorial: Av. Principal de las Mercedes, referencia Banco Plaza, Edificio Centro Vectorial, piso 3, Caracas. **T:** 58 2129932026
E: correio.prensa@gmail.com
W: http://www.correiodevenezuela.com
Freq: Weekly; **Circ:** 11000 Not Audited
Editorial Profile: Newspaper of the Portuguese community in Venezuela and it is written in Portuguese language.
Language (s): Portuguese
DAILY NEWSPAPER

Diario Vea
Owner: Diario Vea
Editorial: Av. Fuerzas Armadas, Esquina de Cristo Arizmendi, San Agustín del Norte, Edificio Diario Vea, local #98, Caracas.
T: 58 212 578 39 09
W: http://www.diariovea.com.ve
Freq: Daily; **Circ:** 80000 Not Audited
Editor in Chief: Mercedes Ortuño; **Editor in Chief:** Argelio Perez
Language (s): Spanish
DAILY NEWSPAPER

El Informador
Owner: Diario El Informador C.A.
Editorial: Carrera 21 esquina calle 23, Edificio El Informador, Barquisimeto (lara).
T: 58 251 231 18 11
E: informador@elinformador.com.ve
W: http://www.elinformador.com.ve
Freq: Daily; **Circ:** 45000 Not Audited
Editor: Erick Espinoza; **Editor in Chief:** Jeovanny Villamizar
Editorial Profile: Covers regional and national news.
Language (s): Spanish
DAILY NEWSPAPER

El Mundo
Owner: Cadena Capriles C.A.
Editorial: Cadena Capriles, Plaza el Panteón, Torre la Prensa, Caracas. **T:** 58 2125961911
E: cmundo@cadena-capriles.com
W: http://www.elmundo.com.ve
Freq: Daily; **Circ:** 33731 Not Audited
Editor: Maria Lourdes Sandoval; **Editor in Chief:** Gregorio Yepez
Editorial Profile: Newspaper covering national and world news, economics, opinion, community, social, sport, events, country profiles and entertainment.
Language (s): Spanish
DAILY NEWSPAPER

La Nación
Owner: Editorial Torbes
Editorial: Calle 4 entre Carreras 6 y 7, Edificio La Nación, La Concordia, San Cristobal (táchira). **T:** 58 2763462178
E: redaccion@lanacion.com.ve
W: http://www.lanacion.com.ve
Freq: Daily; **Circ:** 30000 Not Audited
Editor: Gustavo Carrillo; **Editor in Chief:** Omaira Labrador; **Editor:** Augusto Medina; **Editor:** Gloria Niño de Cortes; **Editor:** Leidy Zafra
Editorial Profile: Newspaper covering national and world news, politics, economics, features, opinion, social issues and sport.
Language (s): Spanish
DAILY NEWSPAPER

El Nacional
Owner: CA Editoria El National
Editorial: Avenida Principal de los Cortijos de Lourdes con 3ra Transversal, Edificio El Nacional frente a la Coca Cola FEMSA. CP 1071-A, Caracas. **T:** 58 2122033168
E: contactenos@el-nacional.com
W: http://www.el-nacional.com
Freq: Daily; **Circ:** 254000 Not Audited
Editor in Chief: Cenovia Casas; **Editor:** Patricia Espadaro
Editorial Profile: Newspaper covering national and international news, politics, economics, finance, business, culture and sport.
Language (s): Spanish
DAILY NEWSPAPER

El Norte
Owner: Diario El Norte
Editorial: Avenida Intercomunal Jorge Rodríguez, Sector Las Garzas. Grupo UP, Barcelona (anzoategui). **T:** 58 281 286 24 84
E: diarioelnorte@elnorte.com.ve
W: http://www.elnorte.com.ve
Freq: Daily; **Circ:** 60000 Not Audited
Editor: Edgar Alfaro; **Editor:** Gina Mistaje
Language (s): Spanish
DAILY NEWSPAPER

Notitarde
Owner: Editorial Notitarde C.A
Editorial: Avenida Boyacá 98 #107-148, Sector Las Flores, Carabobo.
T: 58 241 850 16 66
E: redaccion@notitarde.com
W: http://www.notitarde.com
Freq: Daily; **Circ:** 80000 Not Audited
Editor in Chief: Luis Borja; **Editor:** María Julia Melendez; **Editor:** Marleni Pina
Editorial Profile: Newspaper covering national and international news, politics, economics, finance, business, culture and sport.
Language (s): Spanish
DAILY NEWSPAPER

El Nuevo País
Owner: El Nuevo País
Editorial: Pinto Santarosalía, Edificio Nuevo País No 44, Caracas. **T:** 58 212 545 73 46
E: elnuevopais1@gmail.com
Freq: Daily; **Circ:** 45000 Not Audited
Editor in Chief: Luis Camacho; **Editor in Chief:** Francisco Orta
Editorial Profile: Newspaper covering national and world news, politics, economics, features, opinion, social issues and sport.
Language (s): Spanish
DAILY NEWSPAPER

Panorama
Owner: CA Diario Panorama
Editorial: Avenida 15 No.95 - 60, Maracaibo.
T: 58 261 721 10 00

E: redaccion@panodi.com
W: http://www.panodi.com
Freq: Daily; Circ: 120000 Not Audited
Editor: Anaida Larreal; Editor: Heilet Morales;
Editor in Chief: Lolimar Suárez
Editorial Profile: Newspaper covering national
and international news, politics, economics,
finance, business, culture and sport.
Language (s): Spanish
DAILY NEWSPAPER

El Periodiquito
Owner: Editorial Mara
Editorial: Calle Páez Este N° 178, Maracay
(aragua). T: 58 243 232 14 22
E: elperiodiquito@gmail.com
W: http://www.elperiodiquito.com
Freq: Daily; Circ: 100000 Not Audited
News Editor: Ana Maria Campos; Editor in
Chief: Yosseline Luna; Editor: Rafael
Rodriguez-Rendon
Editorial Profile: National newspaper.
Language (s): Spanish
DAILY NEWSPAPER

El Progreso
Owner: Diario El Progreso
Editorial: Calle Vidal con Urbina, Sector Negro
Primero, Estado Bolívar, Aptdo 8001, Bolívar.
T: 58 285 654 71 54
E: publiprogres@cantv.net
W: http://www.diarioelprogreso.com
Freq: Daily; Circ: 30000 Not Audited
Editor in Chief: Karen Mejias
Language (s): Spanish
DAILY NEWSPAPER

Quinto Dia
Owner: MC Master Communication CA
Editorial: Avenida principal de los Ruices con
Avenida Romulo Gallegos, Res. Los
Almendros Nivel Mezzanina, Oficina 05, Los
Ruices, Caracas. T: 58 212 237 98 09
E: redaccion@quintodia.com
W: http://www.quintodia.com
Freq: Weekly; Circ: 150000 Not Audited
Editor in Chief: Carlos Croes
Editorial Profile: Newspaper featuring national
and international news, business and
economy, current affairs, sport and culture.
Language (s): Spanish
DAILY NEWSPAPER

La Razón
Owner: CA Diario La Razón
Editorial: Avenida Urdaneta esquina Urapal,
Edificio Valores Sótano A La Candelaria,
Caracas. T: 58 212 578 31 43
E: larazon@cantv.net
Freq: Sun; Circ: 150000 Not Audited
Editor in Chief: Carlos Diaz
Editorial Profile: Broadsheet covering national
and international news, politics, economics,
finance, business, culture and sport.
Language (s): Spanish
DAILY NEWSPAPER

Región
Owner: Editora de Región Oriente
Editorial: Calle Bonpland, Edificio Región,
detrás de la Avenida Gran Mariscal, Cumaná
(sucre). T: 58 293 441 00 71
E: regionoriente@cantv.net
W: http://www.diarioregion.com.ve
Freq: Daily; Circ: 53360 Not Audited
Editor: Luis Marcano Barrios
Editorial Profile: Covers news of the west
region of Venezuela.
Language (s): Spanish
DAILY NEWSPAPER

Tal Cual
Owner: Editorial La Mosca Analfabeta C.A.
Editorial: Rómulo Gallego Edificio Pascal B
Piso 1 Oficina 3, Caracas.
T: 58 212 710 82 53
E: hbecerra@talcualdigital.com
W: http://www.talcualdigital.com
Freq: Daily; Circ: 45000 Not Audited
Editor: Héctor Becerra; Editor in Chief:
Alejandro Botía; Editor: Carmen Mendez
Editorial Profile: National Newspaper.
Language (s): Spanish
DAILY NEWSPAPER

Últimas Noticias
Owner: Cadena Capriles C.A.
Editorial: Ultimas Noticias, Cadena Capriles,
Plaza el Panteón, Torre la Prensa, Caracas
1192. T: 58 212 5961911
E: rnoticias@cadena-capriles.com
W: http://www.ultimasnoticias.com.ve
Freq: Daily; Circ: 142039 Not Audited
Editor in Chief: Erys Wilfredo Alvarado; News
Editor: Hilda Carmona; Editor: Hugo Chávez;
Editor: Jesús Duran; Editor: Hercilia Garnica;
Editor: Desiree Lozano; Editor: Adela Medina

Editorial Profile: Newspaper covering national
and world news, politics, economics, features,
opinion, social issues and sport.
Language (s): Spanish
DAILY NEWSPAPER

El Universal
Owner: Grupo El Universal
Editorial: Avenida Urdaneta Esquina de
Animas, Urbanización La Candelaria, Edif El
Universal, Caracas. T: 58 212 505 22 90
E: erojas@eluniversal.com
W: http://www.eluniversal.com
Freq: Daily; Circ: 86281 Not Audited
Editor: Richard Delgado; Editor: Ernesto
Ecarri; Editor: Pedro García Otero; Editor:
Carmen Rosa Gómez; Editor: Robert Gómez;
Editor: María Angela Lando; Editor: Amalia
LLorca; Editor in Chief: Elides Rojas
Editorial Profile: Newspaper covering national
and international news, economics, politics,
sport, social, culture, travel and classified
advertising.
Language (s): Spanish
DAILY NEWSPAPER

La Verdad
Owner: Sinergia Editorial, Diario La Verdad, CA
Editorial: Avenida 13 con calle 82 y 83,
Maracaibo (zulia). T: 58 261 798 13 59
E: noticias@laverdad.com
W: http://www.laverdad.com
Freq: Daily; Circ: 215000 Not Audited
Editor: Enrique Peña; Editor: Luis Pérez;
Editor: Sheila Urdaneta
Editorial Profile: A metropolitan newspaper in
four parts which includes, economy, sports,
politics and city information.
Language (s): Spanish
DAILY NEWSPAPER

NEWS SERVICE/SYNDICATE

Agencia EFE
Editorial: Quinta Altas Cumbres, Calle Coro
esq. San Cristobal, Urb Las Palmas, Caracas
1050. T: 58 212 793 71 18
W: http://www.efe.com
Editor: Giovana Ferulo; Editor: Aldo Rodriguez;
Editor: Ramón Ruiz
Language (s): Spanish
NEWS SERVICE/SYNDICATE

Associated Press
Editorial: Edificio el Universal Avinida
Urdaneta, Esquina Animas Piso 9 Oficina D,
Caracas 1010. T: 58 212 564-1834
Bureau Chief: Joshua Goodman
NEWS SERVICE/SYNDICATE

Bloomberg News
Editorial: Avda. Francisco de Miranda con
Avenida El Parque, Torre Edicampo, Piso 5
Oficina 51-52, Caracas. T: 58 212 277-3700
NEWS SERVICE/SYNDICATE

Dow Jones Newswires
Editorial: Edificio El Universal, Avenida
Urdaneta Esquina Animas Piso 2 Oficina D,
Caracas 1010. T: 58 25642911
NEWS SERVICE/SYNDICATE

Reuters
Editorial: Ave Eugenio Mendoza Angel Lamas,
Edftorre La Castellane Tiso #4, Caracas
D.F.1060. T: 58 115 5547334
E: caracas.newsroom@thomsonreuters.com
W: http://lta.reuters.com
NEWS SERVICE/SYNDICATE

Reuters
Editorial: Avda. Eugenio Mendoza, Ed. Torre la
Castellana, piso 4°, Urb. La Castella, Caracas.
T: 582 12 277 27 00
E: caracas.newsroom@thomsonreuters.com
W: http://www.lta.reuters.com
Editor: Andy Cawthorne
Language (s): Spanish
NEWS SERVICE/SYNDICATE

BROADCASTING

RADIO NETWORKS

Radio Caracas Radio
Owner: Empresas 1BC
Editorial: Avenida José Antonio Páez, Edificio
RCR El Paraiso, Caracas. T: 58 2124813590
E: rcrinformacion@rcr.com.ve
W: http://www.informercr.blogspot.com
Editorial Profile: Radio Caracas Radio is a
Venezuelan radio network owned by Empresas
1BC. It broadcasts news from Caracas,

Venezuela to regions and communities
throughout the country. Presents also
international news.

TELEVISION NETWORKS

Televen
Editorial: Avenida Rómulo Gallegos con 4ª
Transversal de Horizontes, Edificio Televen,
Urbanización Boleita Norte, Caracas.
T: 58 212 280 00 11
E: pautasprensa@televen.com
W: http://www.televen.com
Editorial Profile: National television
broadcasting news, entertainment, and sport
programs.

Venevisión
Editorial: Final Avenida La Salle Edificio
Venevisión, Colinas de los Caobos. Apartado
66774, Caracas. T: 58 212 708 94 44
E: noticiero@venevision.com.ve
W: http://www.venevision.com.ve
Editorial Profile: Television network
broadcasting news and producing original
soap operas and series for the local and
international market.

VIETNAM   Tel: 84

Standard Time: GMT +7
Continent: Asia
Capital City: Hanoi

NEWSPAPERS & PUBLICATIONS

NEWSPAPERS

Binh Dinh
Editorial: People's Committee of Binh Dinh, 84
Pham Hung, Quy Nhon, Binh Dinh.
T: 84 56 821867
W: http://www.baobinhdinh.com.vn
Freq: 2 Times/Week; Circ: 4001 Not Audited
Editor in Chief: Nguyen Hung Do
Editorial Profile: Covers local and national
news.
Language (s): Vietnamese
DAILY NEWSPAPER

Business Monthly
Editorial: Lien minh Hop tac xa Viet Nam, 77
Nguyen Thai Hoc, Hanoi. T: 84 46 6728543
E: info@baodoanhnghiep.com.vn
W: http://www.baodoanhnghiep.com.vn/
Freq: Monthly; Circ: 20001 Not Audited
Editor in Chief: Pham Le Tan Phong
Editorial Profile: Cover topics related to
business.
Language (s): Vietnamese
DAILY NEWSPAPER

Business Weekly
Editorial: Lien minh Hop tac xa Viet Nam, 77
Nguyen Thai Hoc, Hanoi. T: 84 46 6728543
E: info@bandoanhghiep.com.vn
W: http://www.baodoanhnghiep.com.vn
Freq: Weekly; Circ: 32801 Not Audited
Editor in Chief: Pham Le Tan Phong
Editorial Profile: Covers current affairs and
news.
Language (s): Vietnamese
DAILY NEWSPAPER

Economy And The Urban Areas
Editorial: People's Committee of Hanoi City,
21 Huynh Thuc Khang Street, Dong Da
District, Hanoi. T: 84 043 7732198
E: hanoinet@fpt.vn
W: http://www.ktdt.com.vn
Freq: Weekly; Circ: 10001 Not Audited
Editorial Profile: Covers the economy in
Vietnam's big cities.
Language (s): Vietnamese
DAILY NEWSPAPER

Hai Phong
Editorial: People's Committee of Hai Phong
City, 8 Da Nang st., Ngo Quyen dist., Hai
Phong. T: 84 31 3852806
E: haiphongdientu@vnn.vn
W: http://www.baohaiphong.com.vn
Freq: Daily; Circ: 15001 Not Audited
Editor in Chief: Trong Nghia Le
Editorial Profile: Covers current local, national
and international news topics.
Language (s): Vietnamese
DAILY NEWSPAPER

Lao Dong
Editorial: Lao Dong Newspaper, 15/167 Tay
Son - Dong Da, Hanoi. T: 84 43 5330304

E: webmaster@laodong.vn
W: http://www.laodong.com.vn
Freq: Daily; Circ: 80001 Not Audited
Editorial Profile: Covers all current news
topics nationally, locally and internationally.
Language (s): Vietnamese
DAILY NEWSPAPER

Liberation Saigon
Editorial: Bao Sai Gon Giai Phong, 399 Hong
Bang, Ward 14, Dist. 5, Quan 3, Thanh Pho,
Ho Chi Minh City. T: 84 8 3929409
E: sggponline@sggp.org.vn
W: http://www.sggp.org.vn
Freq: Daily; Circ: 130001 Not Audited
Editor in Chief: The Tuyen Tran
Editorial Profile: Covers a variety of topics
from business to sports and from a local to
international range. Also publishes a Chinese
edition.
Language (s): Mandarin, Vietnamese
DAILY NEWSPAPER

New Hanoi
Editorial: Bao Hanoimoi, 44 Le Thai To Street,
Hoan Kiem, Hanoi. T: 84 43 8253067
W: http://www.hanoimoi.com.vn
Freq: Daily; Circ: 50001 Not Audited
Editor in Chief: To Quang Phan
Editorial Profile: Covers a wide range of news
and business news. Also includes both local
and international topics.
Language (s): Vietnamese
DAILY NEWSPAPER

Nhan Dan Newspaper
Editorial: Nhan Dan Newspaper (Bao Nhan
Dan), 71 Hang Trong Street, Hoan Kiem
District, Hanoi. T: 84 438254231
E: toasoan@nhandan.org.vn
W: http://www.nhandan.org.vn
Freq: Daily; Circ: 180001 Not Audited
Editor in Chief: The Huynh Dinh
Editorial Profile: Covers current issues and
news.
Language (s): Vietnamese
DAILY NEWSPAPER

People's Army
Editorial: People's Army Newspaper, No.7
Phan Dinh Phung Street, Hanoi.
T: 84 43 7471748 E: webmaster@qdnd.vn
W: http://www.qdnd.vn
Freq: Daily; Circ: 25001 Not Audited
Editor in Chief: Le Phuc Nguyen
Editorial Profile: Covers news and politics and
Vietnamese Army affairs.
Language (s): Vietnamese
DAILY NEWSPAPER

People's Army Weekly
Editorial: People's Army Newspaper, No.7
Phan Dinh Phung Street, Hanoi.
T: 84 4 37471748 E: dientubqd@gmail.com
W: http://www.qdnd.vn
Freq: Weekly; Circ: 40003 Not Audited
Editor in Chief: Le Phuc Nguyen
Editorial Profile: Covers a variety of topics
including army news.
Language (s): Vietnamese
DAILY NEWSPAPER

Saigon Times Daily
Editorial: Saigon Times Group, 35 Nam Ky
Khoi Nghia Street, District 1, Ho Chi Minh City.
T: 848 8295936 E: daily@thesaigontimes.vn
W: http://english.thesaigontimes.vn/Home
Freq: Daily; Circ: 20001 Not Audited
Editor in Chief: Tran Thi Ngoc Hue
Editorial Profile: Covers policies and national
issues and the future of the country.
Language (s): English
DAILY NEWSPAPER

Vietnam Economic Times
Editorial: Vietnam Economic Times, 96 Hoang
Quoc Viet, Cau Giay District, Hanoi.
T: 84 43 7552060 E: editor@vneconomy.vn
W: http://vneconomy.vn
Freq: Daily; Circ: 43001 Not Audited
Editor in Chief: Nguyen Cat Dao
Editorial Profile: Covers all things dealing with
Vietnam and it's economy in a Vietnamese and
English edition. Also covers economic and
business trends.
Language (s): English, Vietnamese
DAILY NEWSPAPER

Vietnam Investment Review
Editorial: Ministry of Planning & Investment,
47 Quan Thanh Street, Hanoi.
T: 84 43 8450537 E: vir.hn@vir.com.vn
W: http://www.vir.com.vn
Freq: Weekly; Circ: 25000 Not Audited
Editor in Chief: Anh Tuan Nguyen

Editorial Profile: Covers all financial and investment topics including banking and trading (import-export).
Language (s): English
DAILY NEWSPAPER

Vietnam News

Editorial: Vietnam News Agency, 11 Tran Hung Dao, Hanoi. **T:** 84 43 9332316
E: vnnews@vnagency.com.vn
W: http://vietnamnews.vnagency.com.vn
Freq: Daily; **Circ:** 30001 Not Audited
Editorial Profile: Covers all news in Vietnam and Internationally as well.
Language (s): English
DAILY NEWSPAPER

The Workers Newspaper

Editorial: 14 Cach Mang Thang 8, Ho Chi Minh City, District 1, Ho Chi Minh City.
T: 84 83 9306262 **E:** ng.laodong@nld.com.vn
W: http://www.nld.com.vn
Freq: 2 Times/Week; **Circ:** 60001 Not Audited
Editor in Chief: Danh Phuong Do
Editorial Profile: Covers issues for the working class and union workers of Ho Chi Minh City.
Language (s): Vietnamese
DAILY NEWSPAPER

NEWS SERVICE/SYNDICATE

Associated Press

Editorial: 33 Le Tranh Tong, Hanoi.
T: 84 4 825-0732
NEWS SERVICE/SYNDICATE

Bloomberg News

Editorial: 14 Tran Binh Trong, Hanoi.
T: 84 439366727
Bureau Chief: Oanh Ha
NEWS SERVICE/SYNDICATE

Dow Jones Newswires

Editorial: Rm. 701 Phu Quy Building, 209 Giang Vo, Hanoi. **T:** 84 435123041
NEWS SERVICE/SYNDICATE

Reuters

Editorial: 8 Tran Hung Dao, 4th Floor, Hanoi.
T: 84 48249819
E: hanoi.newsroom@thomsonreuters.com
NEWS SERVICE/SYNDICATE

Vietnam News Agency

Owner: Vietnam News Agency,
Editorial: Vietnam News Agency, 79 Ly Thuong Kiet Str., Hanoi. **T:** 84 438 255443
E: btk@vnanet.vn **W:** http://news.vnanet.vn
Freq: Daily
Editorial Profile: News service covering a range of current issues locally and internationally.
Language (s): English, Vietnamese
NEWS SERVICE/SYNDICATE

BROADCASTING

RADIO STATIONS

The Voice of Ho Chi Minh City's People

Owner: Ho Chi Minh City People's Committee,
Editorial: Ho Chi Minh City People's Committee, #3 Nguyen Dinh Chieu Street, District 1, Ho Chi Minh City. **T:** 84 8 38225933
E: radiohcm@hcm.vnn.vn
W: http://www.voh.com.vn
Editorial Profile: News, Music, etc.

TELEVISION STATIONS

Hanoi TV and Radio

Editorial: 3-5 Huynh Thuc Khang, Hanoi.
T: 84 4 3835670 **E:** baodientu@hanoitv.vn
W: http://www.hanoitv.org.vn
Editorial Profile: Covers current events and news on television and radio outlets.

Ho Chi Minh City TV

Editorial: 14 Dinh Tien Hoang St, Ho Chi Minh City. **T:** 84 8 38291667 **E:** web@htv.com.vn
W: http://www.htv.com.vn
Editorial Profile: Television coverage of all local news topics.

VIRGIN ISLANDS (BRITISH) Tel: 1 284

Standard Time: GMT -4
Continent: The Americas
Capital City: Road Town (Tortola)

NEWSPAPERS & PUBLICATIONS

NEWSPAPERS

The Island Sun

Owner: Sun Enterprises (BVI) Ltd
Editorial: 112 Main St, Tortola 1110.
T: 1 2844942476 **E:** issun@candwbvi.net
W: http://www.islandsun.com
Freq: Sat
Editorial Profile: Island Sun is a weekly newspaper serving the British Virgin Islands. It covers local and Caribbean news, events, sports and features. Deadlines are Mondays at 1pm AST.
Language (s): English
NEWSPAPER

VIRGIN ISLANDS (USA) Tel: 1 340

Standard Time: GMT -4
Continent: The Americas
Capital City: Charlotte Amalie (St Thomas)

NEWSPAPERS & PUBLICATIONS

NEWSPAPERS

St. John Tradewinds Newspaper

Editorial: 4A Estate Enighed, Saint John 831.
T: 1 340 776-6496 **E:** info@tradewinds.vi
W: http://www.tradewinds.vi
Freq: Weekly; **Circ:** 3000 Not Audited
News Editor: Jaime Elliott
Editorial Profile: Weekly newspaper.
Language (s): English
NEWSPAPER

The Virgin Islands Daily News

Owner: Times-Shamrock Communications
Editorial: 9155 Estate Thomas, Saint Thomas 802. **T:** 1 340 774-8772
E: dailynews@vipowernet.net
W: http://www.virginislandsdailynews.com
Freq: Daily
Publisher: Jason Robbins
Editorial Profile: The Virgin Islands Daily News is a source of information for news, sports, entertainment and events in St. Thomas, St. Croix, St. John and the British Islands of Tortola and Virgin Gorda in the Virgin Islands.
Language (s): English
DAILY NEWSPAPER

WALLIS & FUTUNA Tel: 681

Standard Time: GMT +12

BROADCASTING

TELEVISION STATIONS

RFO WALLIS ET FUTUNA

Editorial: Mata Utu - Pointe Matala, Pacifique Sud, Iles De Wallis-Et-Futuna.
T: 681 7 22 02 0 **W:** http://www.rfo.fr
Editorial Profile: Regional TV and radio station focussing on regional interest, news, sport, magazines, music, ethology, history, faith and traditions. Local Translation: Télévision et radio régionales. Journaux d'actualités, sports, émissions diverses : musique, ethnologie, histoire, croyances, traditions...

YEMEN Tel: 967

Standard Time: GMT +3
Continent: Asia
Capital City: Sanaa

NEWSPAPERS & PUBLICATIONS

NEWSPAPERS

14th October

Owner: October Corporation for Press
Editorial: PO Box 5487, Ma'alla, Aden.
T: 967 2 242660 **E:** 14october@14october.com
W: http://www.14october.com
Freq: Daily; **Circ:** 26000 Rate Card
News Editor: Mohamed Abou Ras
Editorial Profile: 14th October is a government-owned, Arabic daily newspaper covering local and international news, business and sport. It was first published in 1968.
Language (s): Arabic
DAILY NEWSPAPER

26-Sep

Owner: Moral Guidance Department for Yemen Armed Forces
Editorial: PO Box 17, Sana'a. **T:** 967 1 262626
E: 26sept@yemen.net.ye
W: http://www.26sep.net
Freq: Thu; **Circ:** 45000 Publisher's Statement
Editor In Chief: Yahya Al Abdullah; **News Editor:** Murshed Al-A'aji
Editorial Profile: 26 September is a weekly Arabic newspaper published by the Moral Guidance Department of the Yemen Armed Forces. The newspaper covers national and international news, currents affairs, military news, politics, business and sport. It launched in 1982 and is published on Thursdays.
Language (s): Arabic
DAILY NEWSPAPER

Akhbar Al-Youm

Owner: Shomoa Foundation for Press & Information
Editorial: PO Box 3347, Taiz Street, Sana'a.
T: 967 1 606711 **E:** info@akhbaralyom.net
W: http://www.akhbaralyom.net
Freq: Daily; **Circ:** 48000 Publisher's Statement
Editor In Chief: Ibrahim Mogahid
Editorial Profile: Akhbar Al-Youm (The Daily News) is a daily Arabic newspaper covering local and international news, business, politics and sport. It was first published in 2003.
Language (s): Arabic
DAILY NEWSPAPER

Al Gomhuryah

Owner: Al Gomhuryah Establishment for Journalism and Publishing
Editorial: PO Box 6604, Taiz. **T:** 967 4 230951
E: info@algomhoriah.net
W: http://www.algomhoriah.net
Freq: Daily; **Circ:** 44900 Rate Card
Editor: Salah Al Dakak; **Editor in Chief:** Sameer Al-Yosofi
Editorial Profile: Al Gomhuryah is a government-owned, daily Arabic newspaper covering news, business, politics and sport. It was first published in 1962.
Language (s): Arabic
DAILY NEWSPAPER

Al Sahwa

Owner: Al Sahwa Est.
Editorial: PO Box 425, Sana'a.
T: 967 1 230317 **E:** aa230317@yahoo.com
W: http://www.alsahwa-yemen.net
Freq: Thu; **Circ:** 20000 Publisher's Statement
Editor In Chief: Mohammed Al-Youssoufi
Editorial Profile: Al Sahwa is a weekly Arabic newspaper covering national and international news, current affairs, politics, business and sport. It launched in 1985 and is published on Thursdays.
Language (s): Arabic
DAILY NEWSPAPER

Al Shomoa

Owner: Shomoa Foundation for Press & Information
Editorial: PO Box 3347, Taiz Street, Sana'a.
T: 967 1 635181 **E:** abast66@hotmail.com
Freq: Sat; **Circ:** 40000 Publisher's Statement
Editor In Chief: Abdelbasit Al Shemeery; **News Editor:** Nazih Nasser
Editorial Profile: Al Shomoa (Candles) is a weekly Arabic newspaper covering national and international news, current affairs, politics, business and sport. It launched in 1997 and is published on Saturdays.

Language (s): Arabic
DAILY NEWSPAPER

Al Thawrah

Owner: Al Thawra Press, Printing & Publishing
Editorial: PO Box 1475, Airport Road, Sana'a.
T: 967 1 321532 **E:** al-thawrah@y.net.ye
W: http://www.althawranews.net
Freq: Daily; **Circ:** 22000 Publisher's Statement
Editorial Profile: Al Thawrah is daily Arabic newspaper covering politics, culture, social and general news. It was first published in 1962.
Language (s): Arabic
DAILY NEWSPAPER

NEWS SERVICE/SYNDICATE

Yemen News Agency

Owner: Yemen News Agency
Editorial: PO Box 881, Sana'a.
T: 967 1 250083 **E:** yemensb98@gmail.com
W: http://www.sabanews.net
Editorial Profile: Official Yemeni news agency - coverage includes government news and issues of national importance.
Language (s): Arabic, English, French
NEWS SERVICE/SYNDICATE

BROADCASTING

RADIO STATIONS

Aden Radio

Owner: Yemen General Corporation For Radio and TV
Editorial: PO Box 1222, Tawahi, Aden.
T: 967 2 203984 **E:** adenradio@yemen.net.ye
W: http://www.adenradio.net
Editorial Profile: Aden Radio is a state-owned, regional radio station broadcasting news, music and entertainment programmes for 18-hrs a day to the Aden region of Yemen. It launched on 7 August 1954 and airs on MW 830 and MW 792.

Sana'a Radio

Owner: Yemen General Corporation For Radio and TV
Editorial: PO Box 2371, Sana'a.
T: 967 1 282061 **E:** sanaaradio@yahoo.com
W: http://www.sanaaradio.net
Editorial Profile: Sana'a Radio is a national radio station broadcasting Arabic entertainment, music, news, analysis and sports for 24-hours a day, including one hour in English. The state-owned station broadcasts on 96.0 FM and MW 787. It was originally launched in January 1946 but closed after two years, resuming in 1955. Between 1976 and 1990, broadcasting in northern Yemen was the responsibility of the Yemeni General Corporation for Radio and Television, while broadcasting in the south was controlled by the Radio and Television Authority. The two bodies merged upon the unification of Yemen in 1990 to form the General Corporation for Radio and Television, which operates under the Ministry of Information.

TELEVISION STATIONS

Aden TV

Owner: Yemen General Corporation For Radio and TV
Editorial: PO Box 1264, Tawahi, Aden.
T: 967 2 202481 **E:** syednet2000@yahoo.com
W: http://www.tvaden.net
Editorial Profile: Aden TV is a state-owned terrestrial television station broadcasting news, drama serials, documentaries, religious shows, business programmes and public announcements. Previously called Yamania TV, the channel launched in 1964.

Yemen TV

Owner: Yemen General Corporation For Radio and TV
Editorial: PO Box 1140, Sana'a.
T: 967 1 226466 **E:** info@yemen-tv.net
W: http://www.yemen-tv.net
Editorial Profile: Yemen TV is a state-owned television station broadcasting news, dramas, entertainment and documentaries. Most programmes are in Arabic, but also includes news broadcasts in English. The channel launched in 1975 and broadcasts terrestrially in Yemen and free-to-air on satellite.

ZAMBIA — Tel: 260

Standard Time: GMT +2
Continent: Africa
Capital City: Lusaka

NEWSPAPERS & PUBLICATIONS

NEWSPAPERS

The Post
Owner: Post Newspapers Ltd
Editorial: 36 Bwinjimfumu Rd. Rhodespark,
Rhodespark, P/bag E 352, Lusaka.
T: 260 211 231092 **E:** editorial@post.co.zm
W: http://www.postzambia.com
Freq: Daily; **Circ:** 45000 Not Audited
Managing Director: Fred M'membe; **Editor in Chief:** Sam Mujuda
Editorial Profile: Newspaper covering national and international news, politics, business, economics, lifestyle and sport.
Language (s): English
DAILY NEWSPAPER

Times of Zambia
Owner: Post Newspapers Ltd
Editorial: P.O. Box 70069, Kabelenga Avenue, Lusaka. **T:** 260 211 227348
E: times@times.co.zm
W: http://www.times.co.zm
Freq: Daily; **Circ:** 14000
Editorial Profile: Newspaper covering national and international news, politics, business, entertainment and sports.
Language (s): English
DAILY NEWSPAPER

Zambia Daily Mail
Owner: Zambia Daily Mail
Editorial: PO Box 31421, Lusaka.
T: 260 211 221364 **E:** editor@daily-mail.co.zm
W: http://www.daily-mail.co.zm
Freq: Daily
Editor in Chief: Sheikh Chifuwe
Editorial Profile: Newspaper focusing on national and international news, politics, business, entertainment and sports.
Language (s): English
DAILY NEWSPAPER

BROADCASTING

RADIO NETWORKS

5fm
Owner: AZoM.com Pty Ltd
Editorial: 9th Floor, Lotti House, Cairo Road, Lusaka. **T:** 260 211 221 515
E: 5fm@zamtel.zm
W: http://www.5fmzambia.com
Editorial Profile: Radio station focussing on local news and entertainment including health, technology, business, sports and world news.

Radio Maria
Owner: AZoM.com Pty Ltd
Editorial: P.O. Box 510307, Chipata 10101.
T: 260 21 6221154
E: administration.zam@radiomaria.org
W: http://www.radiomaria.org
Editorial Profile: Radio station covering religion and society.

Zambia National Radio - ZNBC
Owner: AZoM.com Pty Ltd
Editorial: Mass Media Complex, Alick Nkhata Road, Lusaka. **T:** 260 211 251983
E: znbcnews@yahoo.com
W: http://www.znbc.co.zm
Editorial Profile: National radio station covering national and international news including health, business, entertainment and sports.

TELEVISION STATIONS

Zambia National Television - ZNBC
Owner: AZoM.com Pty Ltd
Editorial: Mass Media Complex, Alick Nkhata Road, Lusaka. **T:** 260 211 251983
E: znbcnews@yahoo.com
W: http://www.znbc.co.zm
Editorial Profile: National television station covering national and international news including health, business, entertainment and sports.

ZIMBABWE — Tel: 263

Standard Time: GMT +2
Continent: Africa
Capital City: Harare

NEWSPAPERS & PUBLICATIONS

NEWSPAPERS

The Herald Zimbabwe
Editorial: PO Box 396, Harare.
T: 263 4 79 57 71
E: theherald@zimpapers.co.zw
W: http://www.herald.co.zw
Freq: Daily; **Circ:** 90000
Editor: Ceasar Zvayi
Editorial Profile: The Herald is Zimbabwe daily newspaper and is the flagship of Zimbabwe Newspapers (1980) Limited.
Language (s): English
DAILY NEWSPAPER

The Sunday Mail (Zimbabwe)
Owner: Zimbabwe Newspapers (1980) Ltd
Editorial: PO Box 396, Harare.
T: 263 4 70 43 76
E: sundaymail@zimpapers.co.zw
W: http://www.sundaymail.co.zw
Freq: Sun
Editor: Edmund Kudzayi; **Editor:** Augustine Moyo
Editorial Profile: The Sunday Mail is Zimbabwe's weekly newspaper published by Zimbabwe Newspapers 1980 Limited.
Language (s): English
DAILY NEWSPAPER

MASTER INDEX

When contacting publications, please mention you found them in Benn's Media

MASTER INDEX

When contacting publications, please mention you found them in Benn's Media

When contacting publications, please mention you found them in Benn's Media

MASTER INDEX

When contacting publications, please mention you found them in Benn's Media

H

MASTER INDEX

When contacting publications, please mention you found them in Benn's Media

MASTER INDEX

When contacting publications, please mention you found them in Benn's Media

MASTER INDEX

When contacting publications, please mention you found them in Benn's Media

MASTER INDEX

MASTER INDEX

When contacting publications, please mention you found them in Benn's Media

MASTER INDEX

When contacting publications, please mention you found them in Benn's Media

MASTER INDEX

MASTER INDEX

P

MASTER INDEX

W

MASTER INDEX

MASTER INDEX

When contacting publications, please mention you found them in Benn's Media

MASTER INDEX

When contacting publications, please mention you found them in Benn's Media

When contacting publications, please mention you found them in Benn's Media

MASTER INDEX

When contacting publications, please mention you found them in Benn's Media

When contacting publications, please mention you found them in Benn's Media

MASTER INDEX

When contacting publications, please mention you found them in Benn's Media

When contacting publications, please mention you found them in Benn's Media